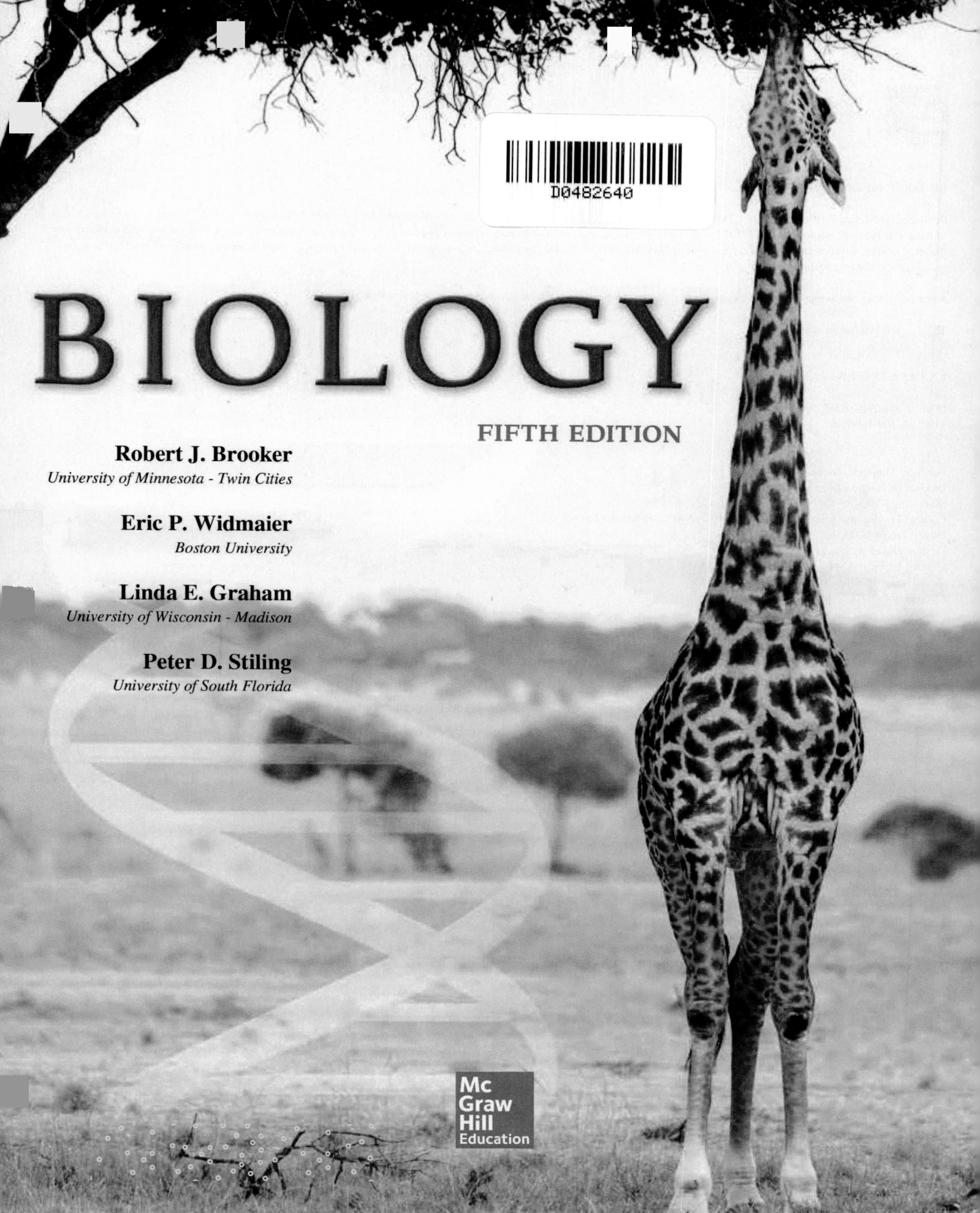

BIOLOGY

FIFTH EDITION

Robert J. Brooker
University of Minnesota - Twin Cities

Eric P. Widmaier
Boston University

Linda E. Graham
University of Wisconsin - Madison

Peter D. Stiling
University of South Florida

D0482640

Mc
Graw
Hill
Education

BIOLOGY, FIFTH EDITION

Published by McGraw-Hill Education, 2 Penn Plaza, New York, NY 10121. Copyright © 2020 by McGraw-Hill Education. All rights reserved. Printed in the United States of America. Previous editions © 2017, 2014, and 2011. No part of this publication may be reproduced or distributed in any form or by any means, or stored in a database or retrieval system, without the prior written consent of McGraw-Hill Education, including, but not limited to, in any network or other electronic storage or transmission, or broadcast for distance learning.

Some ancillaries, including electronic and print components, may not be available to customers outside the United States.

This book is printed on acid-free paper.

1 2 3 4 5 6 7 8 9 LWI 21 20 19

ISBN 978-1-260-16962-1
MHID 1-260-16962-6

Portfolio Manager: *Andrew Urban*
Product Developer: *Elizabeth M. Sievers*
Marketing Manager: *Kelly Brown*
Content Project Managers: *Jessica Portz/Brent Dela Cruz/Sandra Schnee*
Buyer: *Laura M. Fuller*
Design: *David W. Hash*
Content Licensing Specialist: *Lori Hancock*
Cover Image: *©BlueOrange Studio/Shutterstock*
Compositor: *MPS Limited*

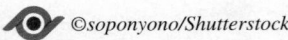 *©soponyono/Shutterstock*

Library of Congress Cataloging-in-Publication Data

Brooker, Robert J., author.
  Biology / Robert J. Brooker, University of Minnesota - Twin Cities,
  Eric P. Widmaier, Boston University, Linda E. Graham, University of
  Wisconsin - Madison, Peter D. Stiling, University of South Florida.
  Fifth edition. | New York, NY : McGraw-Hill Education, [2020] |
  Includes index.
  LCCN 2018023793 | ISBN 9781260169621
  LCSH: Biology—Textbooks.
  LCC QH308.2 .B564445 2020 | DDC 570—dc23 LC record
  available at https://lccn.loc.gov/2018023793

mheducation.com/highered

Brief Contents

About the Authors

Robert J. Brooker

Rob Brooker (Ph.D., Yale University) received his B.A. in biology at Wittenberg University, Springfield, Ohio, in 1978, and studied genetics while a graduate student at Yale. For his postdoctoral work at Harvard, he studied lactose permease, the product of the *lacY* gene of the *lac* operon. He continued working on transporters at the University of Minnesota, where he is a Professor in the Department of Genetics, Cell Biology, and Development and the Department of Biology Teaching and Learning. At the University of Minnesota, Dr. Brooker teaches undergraduate courses in biology, genetics, and cell biology. In addition to many other publications, he has written two undergraduate genetics texts published by McGraw-Hill: *Genetics: Analysis & Principles*, 6th edition, copyright 2018, and *Concepts of Genetics*, 3rd edition, copyright 2019.

Eric P. Widmaier

Eric Widmaier received his B.A. degree in biological sciences at Northwestern University in 1979, where he performed research in animal behavior. In 1984, he earned his Ph.D. in endocrinology from the University of California at San Francisco, where he examined hormonal actions and their mechanisms in mammals. As a postdoctoral fellow at the Worcester Foundation for Experimental Research and later at The Salk Institute, he continued his focus on the cellular and molecular control of hormone secretion and action, with a particular focus on the brain. His current research focuses on the control of body mass and metabolism in mammals, the hormonal correlates of obesity, and the effects of high-fat diets on intestinal cell function. Dr. Widmaier is currently Professor of Biology at Boston University, where he teaches undergraduate human physiology and recently received the university's highest honor for excellence in teaching. Among other publications, he is lead author of *Vander's Human Physiology: The Mechanisms of Body Function*, 15th edition, published by McGraw-Hill, copyright 2019.

Linda E. Graham

Linda Graham earned an undergraduate degree from Washington University (St. Louis), a master's degree from the University of Texas, and Ph.D. from the University of Michigan, Ann Arbor, where she also did postdoctoral research. Presently Professor of Botany at the University of Wisconsin-Madison, her research explores the evolutionary origins of algae and land-adapted plants, focusing on their cell and molecular biology as well as microbial interactions. In recent years Dr. Graham has engaged in research expeditions to remote regions of the world to study algal and plant microbiomes. She teaches undergraduate courses in microbiology and plant biology. She is the coauthor of, among other publications, *Algae*, 3rd edition, copyright 2016, a textbook on algal biology, and *Plant Biology*, 3rd edition, copyright 2015, both published by LJLM Press.

Left to right: Eric Widmaier, Linda Graham, Peter Stiling, and Rob Brooker

The authors are grateful for the help, support, and patience of their families, friends, and students, Deb, Dan, Nate, and Sarah Brooker, Maria, Caroline, and Richard Widmaier, Jim, Michael, Shannon, and Melissa Graham, and Jacqui, Zoe, Leah, and Jenna Stiling.

Peter D. Stiling

Peter Stiling obtained his Ph.D. from University College, Cardiff, United Kingdom. Subsequently, he became a postdoctoral fellow at Florida State University and later spent two years as a lecturer at the University of the West Indies, Trinidad. Dr. Stiling was formerly Chair of the Department of Integrative Biology at the University of South Florida (USF) at Tampa, where he is currently an Assistant Vice Provost for Strategic Initiatives and Professor of Biology. His research interests include plant-animal relationships and invasive species. He currently teaches biology to students in the USF in London summer program which he established in 2015. Dr. Stiling was elected an AAAS Fellow in 2012. He is also the author of *Ecology: Global Insights and Investigations*, 2nd edition, published by McGraw-Hill.

A Message from the Authors

As active teachers and writers, one of the great joys of this process for us is that we have been able to meet many more educators and students during the creation of this textbook. It is humbling to see the level of dedication our peers bring to their teaching. Likewise, it is encouraging to see the energy and enthusiasm so many students bring to their studies. We hope this book and its digital resources will serve to aid both faculty and students in meeting the challenges of this dynamic and exciting course. For us, this remains a work in progress, and we encourage you to let us know what you think of our efforts and what we can do to serve you better.

Rob Brooker, Eric Widmaier, Linda Graham, Peter Stiling

Acknowledgements

The lives of most science-textbook authors do not revolve around an analysis of writing techniques. Instead, we are people who understand science and are inspired by it, and we want to communicate that information to our students. Simply put, we need a lot of help to get it right.

Editors are a key component who help the authors modify the content of this textbook so it is logical, easy to read, and inspiring. The editorial team for this *Biology* textbook has been a catalyst that kept this project rolling. The members played various roles in the editorial process. Andrew Urban and his predecessor Justin Wyatt, Portfolio Managers (Majors Biology), have done an excellent job overseeing the 5th edition. Elizabeth Sievers, Senior Product Developer, has been the master organizer. Liz's success at keeping us on schedule is greatly appreciated. We would also like to acknowledge our copy editor, Jane Hoover, for her thoughtful editing that has contributed to the clarity of this textbook.

Another important aspect of the editorial process is the actual design, presentation, and layout of materials. It's confusing if the text and art aren't on the same page, or if a figure is too large or too small. We are indebted to the tireless efforts of Jessica Portz, Content Project Manager, and David Hash, Senior Designer at McGraw-Hill. Likewise, our production company, MPS Limited, did an excellent job with the paging, revision of existing art, and the creation of new art for the 5th edition. Their artistic talents, ability to size and arrange figures, and attention to the consistency of the figures have been remarkable. We would also like to acknowledge the ongoing efforts of the superb marketing staff at McGraw-Hill. Special thanks to Kelly Brown, Executive Marketing Manager, whose effort intensifies when this edition comes out.

Finally, other staff members at McGraw-Hill Higher Education have ensured that the authors and editors were provided with adequate resources to achieve the goal of producing a superior textbook. These include G. Scott Virkler, Senior Vice President, Products & Markets; Michael Ryan, Vice President, General Manager, Products & Markets; and Betsy Whalen, Vice President, Production and Technology Services.

Reviewers for *Biology*, 5th edition

- Lubna Abu-Niaaj *Central State University*
- Joseph Covi *University of North Carolina at Wilmington*
- Art Frampton *University of North Carolina at Wilmington*
- Brian Gibbens *University of Minnesota*
- Judyth Gulden *Tulsa Community College*
- Alexander Motten *Duke University*
- Melissa Schreiber *Valencia College*
- Madhavi Shah *Raritan Valley Community College*
- Jack Shurley *Idaho State University*
- Om Singh *University of Pittsburgh at Bradford*
- Michelle Turner-Edwards *Suffolk County Community College*
- Ryan Udan *Missouri State University*
- D. Alexander Wait *Missouri State University*
- Kimberly Wallace *Texas A & M University San Antonio*
- Megan Wise de Valdez *Texas A & M University San Antonio*

A Modern Vision for Learning: Emphasizing Core Concepts and Core Skills

Over the course of five editions, the ways in which biology is taught have dramatically changed. We have seen a shift away from the memorization of details, which are easily forgotten, and a movement toward emphasizing core concepts and critical thinking skills. The previous edition of *Biology* strengthened skill development by adding two new features, called CoreSKILLS and BioTIPS (described later), which are aimed at helping students develop effective strategies for solving problems and applying their knowledge in novel situations. In this edition, we have focused our pedagogy on the five core concepts of biology as advocated by "Vision and Change" and introduced at a national conference organized by the American Association for the Advancement of Science (see www.visionandchange.org). These core concepts, which are introduced in Chapter 1 (see Figure 1.4) include the following:

1. *Evolution:* The diversity of life evolved over time by processes of mutation, selection, and genetic exchange.
2. *Structure and function:* Basic units of structure define the function of all living things.
3. *Information flow, exchange, and storage:* The growth and behavior of organisms are activated through the expression of genetic information.
4. *Pathways and transformations of energy and matter:* Biological systems grow and change via processes that are based on chemical transformation pathways and are governed by the laws of thermodynamics.
5. *Systems:* Living systems are interconnected and interacting.

In addition to core concepts, "Vision and Change" has strongly advocated the development of core skills (also called core competencies). Those skills that are emphasized in this textbook are as follows:

- The ability to apply the process of science
- The ability to use quantitative reasoning
- The ability to use models and simulation (each chapter in *Biology, 5e*, contains a new feature called Modeling Challenge that asks students to create their own model or interpret a model provided)
- The ability to tap into the interdisciplinary nature of science
- The ability to communicate and collaborate with professionals in other disciplines
- The ability to understand the relationship between science and society

A key goal of this textbook is to bring to life these five core concepts of biology and the core skills. These concepts and skills are highlighted in each chapter with a "Vision and Change" icon, an icon, which indicates subsections and figures that focus on one or more of them. This approach will serve two purposes. First, the icon will help students to see how the various topics in this textbook are connected to each other by the five core concepts of biology. Second, the icon will allow students to appreciate the important skills they are developing as they progress through the text.

KEY PEDAGOGICAL FEATURES OF THIS EDITION

The author team is dedicated to producing the most engaging and current text available for undergraduate students who are majoring in biology. We have listened to educators and reviewed documents, such as *Vision and Change, A Call to Action*, which includes a summary of recommendations made at a national conference organized by the American Association for the Advancement of Science. We want our textbook to reflect core concepts and skills and provide a more learner-centered approach. To achieve these goals, *Biology*, 5th edition, has the following pedagogical features.

- *NEW!* **Core Concepts:** As mentioned, the five core concepts are introduced in Chapter 1 (see Figure 1.4). Throughout Chapters 2 through 60, these core concepts are emphasized by a Vision and Change icon, an icon, placed next to headings of particular subsections and beneath certain figure legends.

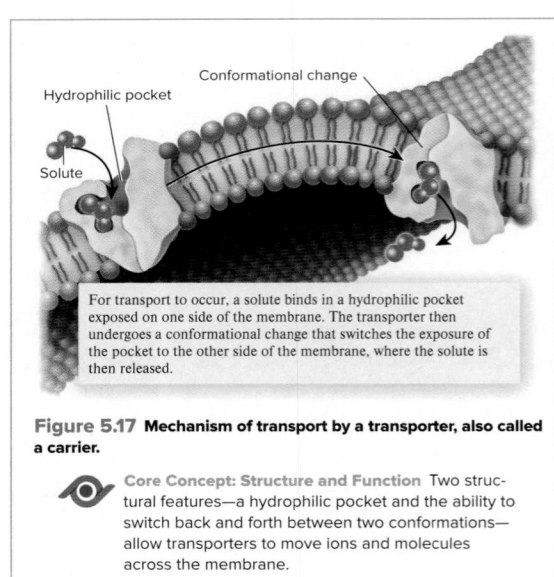

For transport to occur, a solute binds in a hydrophilic pocket exposed on one side of the membrane. The transporter then undergoes a conformational change that switches the exposure of the pocket to the other side of the membrane, where the solute is then released.

Figure 5.17 Mechanism of transport by a transporter, also called a carrier.

Core Concept: Structure and Function Two structural features—a hydrophilic pocket and the ability to switch back and forth between two conformations—allow transporters to move ions and molecules across the membrane.

- *NEW!* Core Skills: Six core skills are also introduced in Chapter 1 (see Section 1.6). In Chapters 2 through 60, these core skills are emphasized by a Vision and Change icon, , placed next to headings of particular subsections, such as Feature Investigations, and beneath certain figure legends. To distinguish them from the Core Concepts, the Core Skills are highlighted in blue type. In addition, the designator CoreSKILLS has been added to certain learning outcomes and end-of-chapter questions that emphasize skills needed in the study of biology.

Genotype	PP	Pp	pp
Amount of functional protein P produced	100%	50%	0%
Phenotype	Purple	Purple	White

Only 50% of the functional protein is needed to produce the purple phenotype

Colorless precursor molecule   Protein P   Purple pigment

Figure 17.16 How genes give rise to traits during simple Mendelian inheritance. In the heterozygote, the amount of protein encoded by a single dominant allele is sufficient to produce the dominant phenotype. In this example, the gene encodes an enzyme that is needed to produce a purple pigment. A plant with one or two copies of the dominant allele makes enough pigment to produce purple flowers. In a *pp* homozygote, the complete lack of the functional protein (enzyme) results in white flowers.

 Core Skill: Quantitative Reasoning In a simple dominant/recessive relationship, even though the heterozygote may produce less of a functional protein compared to the homozygote that has two copies of the dominant allele, the amount made by the heterozygote is sufficient to yield the dominant phenotype.

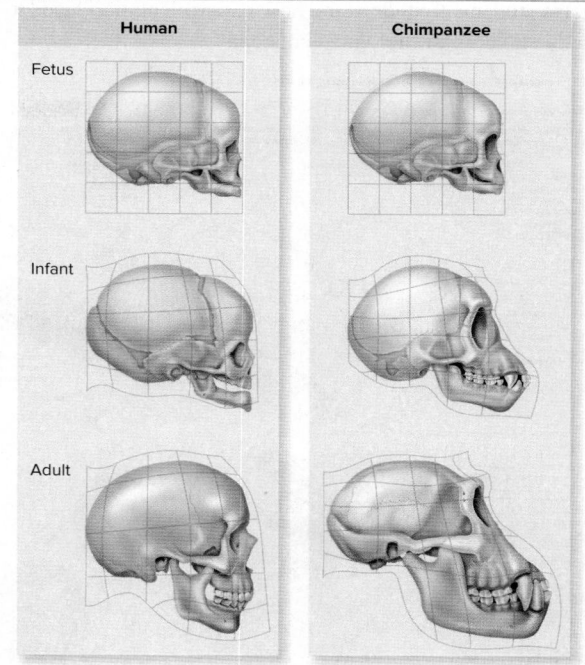

Figure 24.16 Heterochrony. Due to heterochrony, one region of the body may grow faster than another during development in different species. For example, the skulls of adult chimpanzees and humans have different shapes even though their fetal skull shapes are quite similar.

Core Skill: Modeling The goal of this modeling challenge is to make a series of models that show the differences in limb lengths among orangutans, chimpanzees, and humans.

Modeling Challenge: Search the Internet and look at photos of orangutans, chimpanzees, and humans. Even though these species look similar, one noticeable difference is the relative lengths of their limbs. Although the limbs in an early fetus look similar in all three species, the limbs in the adults show significant differences in their relative lengths. Draw models, similar to those in **Figure 24.16**, that show an early fetus, infant, and adult for all three species. Include an explanation of how heterochrony affects limb development.

- *NEW!* Modeling Challenges: A growing trend is the use of models in biology education. Students are asked to interpret models and to create models based on data or a scenario. Furthermore, using models and simulations is one of the core skills that is emphasized by "Vision and Change." The author team has added a new feature called Modeling Challenge that asks students to create a model or to interpret a model they are given. Possible answers to the Modeling Challenges are provided in Connect.

- Feature Investigations: The emphasis on skill development continues in the Feature Investigations, which provide complete descriptions of experiments. These investigations begin with background information in the text that describes the events that led to a particular study. The study is then presented as an illustration that begins with the hypothesis and then describes the experimental protocol at the experimental and conceptual levels. The illustration also includes data and the conclusions that were drawn from the data. This integrated approach helps students to understand how experimentation leads to an understanding of biological concepts.

Figure 5.16 The discovery of water channels (aquaporins) by Agre. (4): Courtesy Dr. Peter Agre

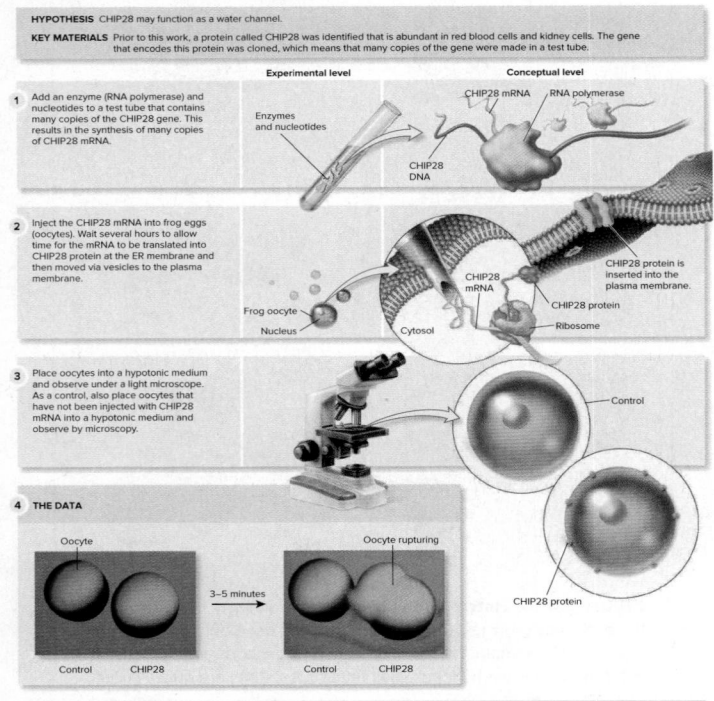

HYPOTHESIS CHIP28 may function as a water channel.

KEY MATERIALS Prior to this work, a protein called CHIP28 was identified that is abundant in red blood cells and kidney cells. The gene that encodes this protein was cloned, which means that many copies of the gene were made in a test tube.

Experimental level	Conceptual level

1 Add an enzyme (RNA polymerase) and nucleotides to a test tube that contains many copies of the CHIP28 gene. This results in the synthesis of many copies of CHIP28 mRNA.

Enzymes and nucleotides

CHIP28 DNA · CHIP28 mRNA · RNA polymerase

2 Inject the CHIP28 mRNA into frog eggs (oocytes). Wait several hours to allow time for the mRNA to be translated into CHIP28 protein at the ER membrane and then moved via vesicles to the plasma membrane.

CHIP28 protein is inserted into the plasma membrane.

Frog oocyte · Nucleus · Cytosol · CHIP28 mRNA · CHIP28 protein · Ribosome

3 Place oocytes into a hypotonic medium and observe under a light microscope. As a control, also place oocytes that have not been injected with CHIP28 mRNA into a hypotonic medium and observe by microscopy.

Control

4 **THE DATA**

Oocyte · Oocyte rupturing · 3–5 minutes

Control · CHIP28 · Control · CHIP28

CHIP28 protein

5 **CONCLUSION** The CHIP28 protein, now called aquaporin, allows the rapid movement of water across the membrane.

6 **SOURCE** Preston, G. M., Carroll, T. P., Guggino, W. B., and Agre, P. 1992. Appearance of water channels in Xenopus oocytes expressing red cell CHIP28 protein. *Science* 256: 385–387.

- **BioTIPS:** A feature that was added to the previous edition is aimed at helping students improve their problem-solving skills. Chapters 2 through 60 contain solved problems called **BioTIPS**, where "TIPS" stands for **T**opic, **I**nformation, and **P**roblem-**S**olving **S**trategy. These solved problems follow a consistent pattern in which students are given advice on how to solve problems in biology using 11 different problem-solving strategies: Make a drawing. Compare and contrast. Relate structure and function. Sort out the steps in a complicated process. Propose a hypothesis. Design an experiment. Predict the outcome. Interpret data. Use statistics. Make a calculation. Search the literature.

BIO TIPS

THE QUESTION *A diploid cell has 12 chromosomes, or 6 pairs. In the following diagram, in what phase of mitosis, meiosis I or meiosis II, is this cell?*

TOPIC *What topic in biology does this question address?* The topic is cell division. More specifically, the question is asking you to be able to look at a drawing and discern which phase of cell division a particular cell is in.

INFORMATION *What information do you know based on the question and your understanding of the topic?* In the question, you are given a diagram of a cell at a particular phase of the cell cycle. This cell is derived from a mother cell with 6 pairs of chromosomes. From your understanding of the topic, you may remember the various phases of mitosis, meiosis I, and meiosis II, which are described in Figures 16.8 and 16.13. If so, you may initially realize that the cell is in metaphase.

PROBLEM-SOLVING **S**TRATEGY *Sort out the steps in a complicated process.* To solve this problem, you may need to describe the steps, starting with a mother cell that has 6 pairs of chromosomes. Keep in mind that a mother cell with 6 pairs of chromosomes has 12 chromosomes during G_1, which then replicate to form 12 pairs of sister chromatids during S phase. Therefore, at the beginning of M phase, this mother cell will have 12 pairs of sister chromatids. During mitosis, the 12 pairs of sister chromatids will align at metaphase. During meiosis I, 6 bivalents will align along the metaphase plate in the mother cell. During meiosis II, 6 pairs of sister chromatids will align along the metaphase plate in the two cells.

ANSWER *The cell is in metaphase of meiosis II. You can tell because the chromosomes are lined up in a single row along the metaphase plate, and the cell has only 6 pairs of sister chromatids. If it were mitosis, the cell would have 12 pairs of sister chromatids. If it were in meiosis I, bivalents would be aligned along the metaphase plate.*

- **Formative Assessment:** A trend in biology education is to spend more class time engaging students in active learning. While this is a positive approach that fosters learning, a drawback is that instructors have less time to explain the material in the textbook. When students are expected to learn textbook material on their own, it is imperative that they are regularly given formative assessment—feedback regarding their state of learning while they are engaging in the learning process. This allows students to gauge whether they are mastering the material. Formative assessment is a major feature of this textbook and is bolstered by Connect—a state-of-the art digital assignment and assessment platform. In *Biology*, 5th edition, formative assessment is provided in multiple ways.

  - First, many figure legends have Concept Check questions that focus on key concepts of a given topic.

  - Second, questions in Assess and Discuss at the end of each chapter explore students' understanding of concepts and mastery of skills. Core Concepts and Core Skills are again addressed under the Conceptual Questions. The answers to the Concept Checks and the end-of-chapter questions are in Appendix B, so students can immediately see if they are mastering the material.

Conceptual Questions

1. The Earth's atmosphere consists of 78% nitrogen. Why is nitrogen a limiting nutrient?

2. Why does maximum sustainable yield occur at the midpoint of the logistic curve and not where the population is at carrying capacity?

3. **Core Skill: Science and Society** In one family, parents, who were born in 1900, have twins at age 20 but then have no more children. Their children, grandchildren, and so on behave in the same way. In another family, parents, who were also born in 1900, delay reproduction until age 33 but have triplets. Their children and grandchildren behave in the same way. Which family has the most descendants by 2000? What can you conclude?

- In Connect, a particularly robust type of formative assessment is SmartBook, which guides a student through the textbook. SmartBook is an adaptive learning tool that is described later in this Preface.

- **Unit openers:** Each unit begins with a unit opener that provides an overview of the chapters within that unit. This overview allows the student to see the big picture of the unit. In addition, the unit openers draw attention to the core concepts and core skills of biology that will be emphasized in each unit.

- **Learning Outcomes:** As advocated in *Vision and Change*, educational materials should have well-defined learning goals. Each section of every chapter begins with a set of Learning Outcomes. These outcomes inform students of the key concepts they will learn and the skills they will acquire in mastering the material. They also provide a tangible indication of how student learning will be assessed. The assessments in Connect were developed using these Learning Outcomes as a guide in formulating online questions, thereby linking the learning goals of the text with the assessments in Connect.

13.1 Overview of Non-coding RNAs

Learning Outcomes:

1. Describe the ability of ncRNAs to bind to other molecules and macromolecules.
2. Outline the general functions of ncRNAs.
3. Define ribozyme.
4. List several examples of ncRNAs, and describe their functions.

UNIT III
GENETICS

Genetics is the branch of biology that deals with inheritance—the transmission of characteristics from parent to offspring. We begin this unit by examining the structure of the genetic material, namely DNA, at the molecular and cellular levels. We will explore the structure and replication of DNA and see how it is packaged into chromosomes (Chapter 11). We will then consider how those genes are expressed at the molecular level to produce mRNA, proteins, and noncoding RNAs (Chapters 12 and 13). In Chapter 14, we will also examine how mutations alter the properties of genes and even lead to diseases such as cancer (Chapter 15).

In Chapter 16, we turn our attention to the mechanisms by which genes are transmitted from parent to offspring, beginning with a discussion of how chromosomes are sorted and transmitted during cell division. Chapters 17 and 18 explore the relationships between the transmission of genes and the outcome of an offspring's traits. We will look at genetic patterns called Mendelian inheritance and more complex patterns that could not have been predicted from Mendel's work.

The remaining chapters of this unit explore additional topics that are of interest to biologists. In Chapter 19, we will examine some of the unique genetic properties of bacteria and viruses. Chapter 20 considers the central role genes play in the development of animals and plants from a fertilized egg to an adult. We end this unit by exploring genetic technologies that are used by researchers, clinicians, and biotechnologists to unlock the mysteries of genes and provide tools and applications that benefit humans (Chapter 21).

The following Core Concepts and Core Skills will be emphasized in this unit:

- *Information: Throughout this unit, we will see how the genetic material carries the information to sustain life.*
- *Structure and Function: In Chapters 11 through 15, we will examine how the structures of DNA, RNA, genes, and chromosomes underlie their functions.*
- *Quantitative Reasoning: In Chapters 17 and 18, we will consider methods used to predict the outcome of genetic crosses.*
- *Science and Society: In Chapter 21, we will examine genetic technologies that have many applications in our society.*
- *Process of Science: Every chapter in this unit has a Feature Investigation that describes a pivotal experiment that provided insights into our understanding of genetics.*

The following Core Concepts and Core Skills will be emphasized in this unit:

- *Information: Throughout this unit, we will see how the genetic material carries the information to sustain life.*
- *Structure and Function: In Chapters 11 through 15, we will examine how the structures of DNA, RNA, genes, and chromosomes underlie their functions.*
- *Quantitative Reasoning: In Chapters 17 and 18, we will consider methods used to predict the outcome of genetic crosses.*
- *Science and Society: In Chapter 21, we will examine genetic technologies that have many applications in our society.*
- *Process of Science: Every chapter in this unit has a Feature Investigation that describes a pivotal experiment that provided insights into our understanding of genetics.*

(11): ©Peter Van De Vijver/Science Photo Library/Science Source; (13): ©Mauro Giacca, Ana Eulalio, Miguel Mano/ Connecticut; (15): ©Yvette Cardozo/Workbook Stock/ Associated/Science Source; (17): ©Radu Sigheti/ (19): ©CAMR/A. Barry Dowsett/Science Source; Photo; (21): ©Fumihiro Sugiyama

USING STUDENT USAGE DATA TO MAKE IMPROVEMENTS

To help guide the revision for the 5th edition, the authors consulted student usage data and input, which were derived from thousands of SmartBook® users of the 4th edition. SmartBook "heat maps" provided a quick visual snapshot of chapter usage data and the relative difficulty students experienced in mastering the content. These data directed the authors to evaluate text content that was particularly challenging for students. These same data were also used to revise the SmartBook probes.

- If the data indicated that the subject was more difficult than other parts of the chapter, as evidenced by a high proportion of students responding incorrectly to the SmartBook questions, the authors revised or reorganized the content to be as clear and illustrative as possible, for example, by rewriting the section or providing additional examples or revised figures to assist visual learners.

- In other cases, one or more of the SmartBook questions for a section was not as clear as it should have been or did not appropriately reflect the content in the chapter. In these cases the question, rather than the text, was edited.

Below is an example of one of the heat maps from Chapter 8. The color-coding of highlighted sections indicates the various levels of difficulty students experienced in learning the material, topics highlighted in red being the most challenging for students.

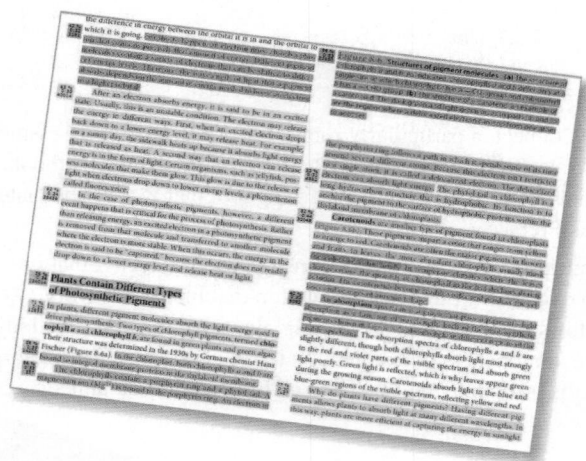

Preparing Students for Careers in Biology with *NEW* Cutting-Edge Content

A key purpose of a majors biology course is to prepare students for biology-related careers, including those in the health professions, teaching, and research. The author team has reflected on the direction of biology and how that direction will affect future careers that students may pursue. We are excited to announce that *Biology,* 5th edition, has four new chapters that reflect current trends in biology research and education. These trends are opening the doors to exciting new career options in biology.

- *Chapter 13. Gene Expression at the Molecular Level II: Non-coding RNAs.* The past decade or so has seen an explosion in the discovery of different types of non-coding RNAs. This work has revealed a variety of roles of non-coding RNAs at the molecular level, as well as roles in human diseases and plant health.

- *Chapter 30. Microbiomes: Microbial Systems On and Around Us.* Recent research has revealed the staggering complexity and biological importance of microbiomes—assemblages of microbes that are associated with a particular host or environment. This new chapter explores how microbiomes are analyzed and describes their interactions with diverse hosts, including humans, protists, and plants.

- *Chapter 53: Integrated Responses of Animal Organ Systems to a Challenge to Homeostasis.* Systems biology has been a recent trend in biological research and education. This chapter takes systems biology to a new level by exploring how multiple organs systems respond in a coordinated way to the same threat—a challenge to homeostasis.

- *Chapter 59: The Age of Humans.* We face a tug-of-war between the undesirable effects of humans on the environment and the efforts of ecologists to prevent such changes. This new chapter surveys the impacts that the growing human population has had on climate change and on the survival of native species. This material may inspire some students to pursue a career as an ecologist or environmental biologist.

With regard to the scientific content in the textbook, the author team has worked with faculty reviewers to refine this new edition and to update the content so that students are exposed to the most current material. In addition to the four new chapters and our new pedagogical additions involving Core Concepts, Core Skills, and Modeling Challenges, every chapter has been extensively edited for clarity, presentation, layout, readability, modifications of artwork, and new and challenging end-of-chapter questions. Examples of some of the key changes are summarized below.

- **Chapter 1. An Introduction to Biology.** Chapter 1 provides a description of the Core Concepts (see Figure 1.4) and the Core Skills (see Section 1.6) that are advocated by *Vision and Change*.

Chemistry Unit

- **Chapter 2. The Chemical Basis of Life I: Atoms, Molecules, and Water.** The topics of pH and buffers have been placed in their own section (see Section 2.4).

Cell Unit

- **Chapter 4. Evolutionary Origin of Cells and Their General Features.** This chapter now begins with a discussion of the evolutionary origin of cells (see Section 4.1). It also discusses a new topic, droplet organelles, which are organelles that are not surrounded by a membrane (see Section 4.3).
- **Chapter 6. An Introduction to Energy, Enzymes, and Metabolism.** For the topic of how cells use ATP as a source of energy, a revised subsection compares the Core Concept: Information to the Core Concept: Energy and Matter.
- **Chapter 7. Cellular Respiration and Fermentation.** A Modeling Challenge asks students to predict the effects of a mutation on the function of ATP synthase (see Figure 7.12).
- **Chapter 10. Multicellularity.** Four figures have been revised to better depict the relative locations of cell junctions between animal cells.

Genetics Unit

- **Chapter 11. Nucleic Acid Structure, DNA Replication, and Chromosome Structure.** Figure 11.8b has a Modeling Challenge that asks students to predict how the methylation of a base would affect the ability of that base to hydrogen bond with a base in the opposite strand.
- **Chapter 13. *NEW!* Gene Expression at the Molecular Level II: Non-coding RNAs.** This new chapter begins with an overview of the general properties of non-coding RNAs and then describes specific examples in which non-coding RNAs are involved with chromatin structure, transcription, translation, protein sorting, and genome defense.
- **Chapter 16. The Eukaryotic Cell Cycle, Mitosis, and Meiosis.** The Core Concept: Evolution is highlighted in a subsection that explains how mitosis in eukaryotes evolved from binary fission in prokaryotic cells (see Figure 16.10).
- **Chapter 17. Mendelian Patterns of Inheritance.** The organization of this chapter has been revised to contain the patterns of inheritance that obey Mendel's laws.
- **Chapter 18. Epigenetics, Linkage, and Extranuclear Inheritance.** This chapter now covers inheritance patterns that violate Mendel's laws. The topic of epigenetics has been expanded from one section in the previous edition to four sections in the 5th edition (see Sections 18.1 through 18.4).
- **Chapter 19. Genetics of Viruses and Bacteria.** Discussion of the Zika virus has been added to this chapter.
- **Chapter 21. Genetic Technologies and Genomics.** The use of CRISPR-Cas technology to alter genes is now discussed (see Figure 21.10).

Evolution Unit

- **Chapter 22. An Introduction to Evolution.** This chapter has been moved so that it is the first chapter in this unit on evolution.
- **Chapter 23. Population Genetics.** After learning about the Hardy-Weinberg equation, students are presented with a Modeling Challenge that asks them to propose a mathematical model that extends the Hardy-Weinberg equation to a gene that exists in three alleles (see Figure 23.2).
- **Chapter 25. Taxonomy and Systematics.** The topic of taxonomy is related to the Core Concept: Evolution through an explanation of how taxonomy is based on the evolutionary relationships among different species.
- **Chapter 26. History of Life on Earth and Human Evolution.** The topic of human evolution has been moved from the unit on diversity to this unit. The expanded version of this topic describes recent examples of human evolution and discusses the amount of genetic variation between different human populations (see Section 26.3).

Diversity Unit

- **Chapter 27. Archaea and Bacteria.** This chapter has been reorganized to provide essential background for new Chapter 30 (an exploration of microbiomes). The Core Skill: Connections is illustrated by linking electromagnetic sensing in bacteria with that in certain animals.
- **Chapter 29. Fungi.** An overview of fungal phylogeny has been updated to reflect new research discoveries. Coverage of plant root-fungal associations (mycorrhizae) and lichens has been moved to new Chapter 30.
- **Chapter 30. *NEW!* Microbiomes: Microbial Systems On and Around Us.** This new chapter integrates information about microbial diversity (Chapters 27 through 29) with material on genetic technologies that is introduced in Chapter 21 to explain the evolutionary, medical, agricultural, and environmental importance of microbial associations.
- **Chapter 31. Plants and the Conquest of Land.** The diagrammatic overview of plant phylogeny has been updated to reveal challenges in understanding the pattern of plant evolution.
- **Chapter 33. An Introduction to Animal Diversity.** Figure 33.3, animal phylogeny, has been redrawn to reflect the idea that ctenophores, rather than sponges, are now considered to be the earliest diverging animals. Section 33.2 on animal classification has been largely revised.
- **Chapter 34. The Invertebrates.** Following the new themes introduced in Chapter 33, this chapter has been reorganized to discuss ctenophores as the earlier evolving animals, followed by sponges, cnidria, jellyfish, and other radially symmetrical animals.

Flowering Plants Unit

- **Chapter 36. An Introduction to Flowering Plant Form and Function.** A new chapter opener links the economic importance of plants, represented by cotton, to the significance of plant structure-function relationships.

- **Chapter 37. Flowering Plants: Behavior.** A **Modeling Challenge** links plant responses to conditions on Earth to those experienced in space.
- **Chapter 38. Flowering Plants: Nutrition.** In a **Modeling Challenge** related to plant-microbe interaction process, students infer how specific mutations might affect an important nutritional feature.
- **Chapter 40. Flowering Plants: Reproduction.** This chapter explores intriguing parallels between the reproductive processes of animals and those of plants.

Animals Unit

- **Chapter 41. Animal Bodies and Homeostasis.** A section entitled "Homeostatic Control of Internal Fluids" (Section 41.4) now follows the section "General Principles of Homeostasis," providing students with an understanding of body fluid compartments, osmolarity, and how animal bodies exchange ions and water with their environments. These concepts are important to students' understanding of subsequent chapters.
- **Chapter 42. Neuroscience I: Cells of the Nervous System.** The **Core Skill: Science and Society** is featured numerous times in the unit on animals, including in Figure 42.18 which describes the use of magnetic resonance imaging in modern medicine.
- **Chapter 43. Neuroscience II: Evolution, Structure, and Function of the Nervous System.** The **Core Skill: Connections** is also featured throughout the unit on animals, including in Figure 43.1 in which students are asked to identify the defining features of animals by referring to Chapter 33.
- **Chapter 44. Neuroscience III: Sensory Systems.** New research demonstrating a correlation between the types of locomotion of vertebrates and the relative sizes of their semicircular canals is described.
- **Chapter 46. Nutrition and Animal Digestive Systems.** A **Modeling Challenge** was added in which students are tasked with creating models of hypothetical alimentary canals of two species with different diets, eating patterns, and teeth.
- **Chapter 47. Control of Energy Balance, Metabolic Rate, and Body Temperature.** The meaning of body mass index and its usefulness and limitations are more fully elucidated, and data on obesity statistics in the United States have been updated to reflect current trends.
- **Chapter 48. Circulatory and Respiratory Systems.** These topics were formerly addressed in two chapters but are now integrated into a single chapter that streamlines the presentation and emphasizes important connections between the two systems.
- **Chapter 49. Excretory Systems.** The chapter has been more narrowly focused on excretory systems by moving the material on osmoregulation and body fluids earlier in the unit, to Chapter 41.
- **Chapter 51. Animal Reproduction and Development.** Formerly two chapters, this material is now covered in one chapter, which eliminated redundancy in coverage. For example, the topic of fertilization (Section 51.2) is now covered in its entirety in the same section as the topic of gametogenesis, rather than being split between two chapters.
- **Chapter 52. Immune Systems.** Exciting new information has been added that describes the evolution of toll-like receptors and the presence of a TLR-domain in bacterial genes associated with immune defenses.
- **Chapter 53. *NEW!* Integrated Responses of Animal Organ Systems to a Challenge to Homeostasis.** This new chapter integrates material from virtually the entire unit on animals, using a classic challenge to homeostasis as an example. It includes a compelling case study of a young athlete that begins and concludes the chapter.

Ecology Unit

- **Chapter 54. An Introduction to Ecology and Biomes.** The section on aquatic biomes as been expanded with a new figure and explanation of the annual cycle of temperate lakes, as well as new information on tide formation and waves.
- **Chapter 57. Species Interactions.** This chapter has been reduced in length by the deletion of four figures and streamlined for easier understanding.
- **Chapter 58. Communities and Ecosystems: Ecological Organization at Large Scales.** This chapter has been reorganized to include both community ecology and ecosystems ecology.
- **Chapter 59. *NEW!* The Age of Humans.** This new chapter synthesizes information concerning the effects of humans on the natural environment. It contains discussions of human population growth (previously covered in Chapter 56), the effect of global warming on climate change (previously covered in Chapter 54), and human effects on biogeochemical cycles and biomagnification (previously covered in Chapter 59), and new information on habitat destruction, overexploitation, and invasive species.
- **Chapter 60. Biodiversity and Conservation Biology.** The coverage of the value of biodiversity to human welfare, detailed in Section 60.3 has been updated and expanded.

Strengthening Problem-Solving Skills and Key Concept Development with Connect®

Detailed Feedback in Connect®

Learning is a process of iterative development, of making mistakes, reflecting, and adjusting over time. The question and test banks in Connect® for *Biology*, 5th edition, are more than direct assessments; they are self-contained learning experiences that systematically build student learning over time.

For many students, choosing the right answer is not necessarily based on applying content correctly; it is more a matter of increasing the statistical odds of guessing. A major fault with this approach is students don't learn how to process the questions correctly, mostly because they are repeating and reinforcing their mistakes rather than reflecting and learning from them. To help students develop problem-solving skills, all higher-level Bloom's questions in Connect are supported with hints, to help students focus on important information needed to answer the questions, and detailed feedback that walks students through the problem-solving process, using Socratic questions in a decision-tree framework to scaffold learning, in which each step models and reinforces the learning process.

The feedback for each higher-level Bloom's question (Apply, Analyze, Evaluate) follows a similar process: Clarify Question, Gather Content, Consider Alternatives, Choose Answer, Reflect on Process.

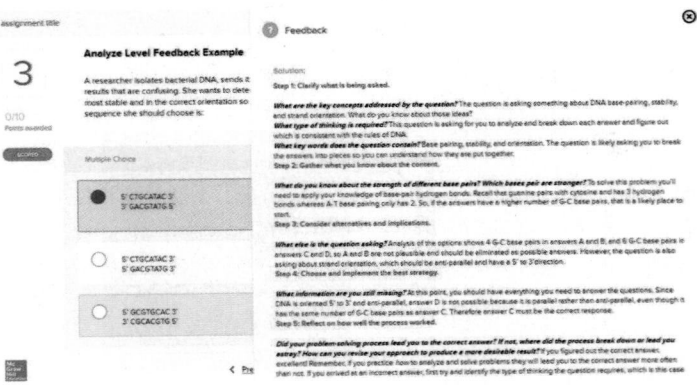

Unpacking the Concepts

We've taken problem solving a step further. In each chapter, two higher-level Bloom's questions in the question and test banks are broken down according to the steps in the detailed feedback.

Rather than leaving it up to the student to work through the detailed feedback, we present a second version of the question in a stepwise format. Following the problem-solving steps, students need to answer questions about the problem-solving process, such as "What is the key concept addressed by the question?" before answering the original question. A professor can choose which version of the question to include in the assignment based on the problem-solving skills of the students.

Graphing Interactives

To help students develop analytical skills, Connect® for *Biology*, 5th edition, is enhanced with interactive graphing questions. Students are presented with a scientific problem and the opportunity to manipulate variables, producing different results on a graph. A series of questions follows the graphing activity to assess if the student understands and is able to interpret the data and results.

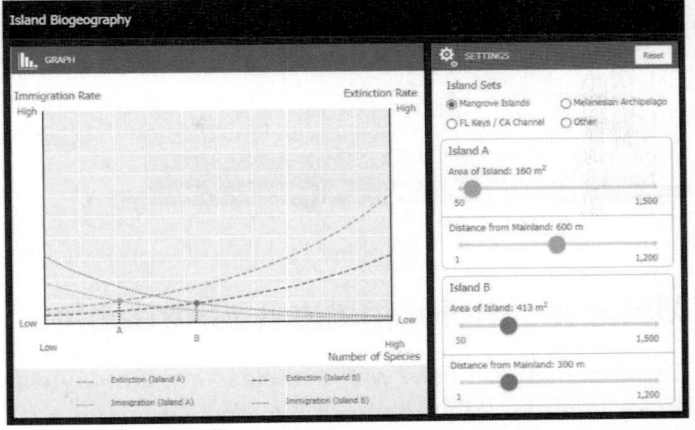

![McGraw Hill Education] **connect®** | Students—study more efficiently, retain more and achieve better outcomes. Instructors—focus on what you love—teaching.

SUCCESSFUL SEMESTERS INCLUDE CONNECT

FOR INSTRUCTORS

You're in the driver's seat.

Want to build your own course? No problem. Prefer to use our turnkey, prebuilt course? Easy. Want to make changes throughout the semester? Sure. And you'll save time with Connect's auto-grading too.

65%
Less Time Grading

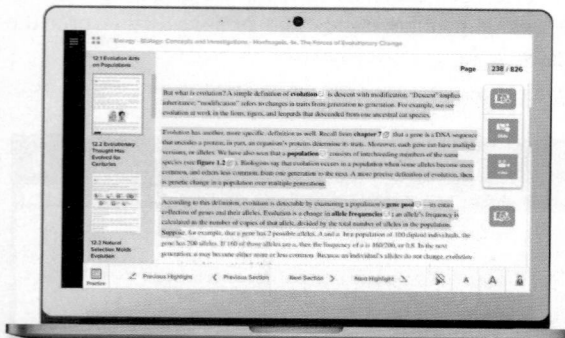

They'll thank you for it.

Adaptive study resources like SmartBook® help your students be better prepared in less time. You can transform your class time from dull definitions to dynamic debates. Hear from your peers about the benefits of Connect at **www.mheducation.com/highered/connect**

Make it simple, make it affordable.

Connect makes it easy with seamless integration using any of the major Learning Management Systems—Blackboard®, Canvas, and D2L, among others—to let you organize your course in one convenient location. Give your students access to digital materials at a discount with our inclusive access program. Ask your McGraw-Hill representative for more information.

©Hill Street Studios/Tobin Rogers/Blend Images LLC

Solutions for your challenges.

A product isn't a solution. Real solutions are affordable, reliable, and come with training and ongoing support when you need it and how you want it. Our Customer Experience Group can also help you troubleshoot tech problems—although Connect's 99% uptime means you might not need to call them. See for yourself at **status.mheducation.com**

FOR STUDENTS

Effective, efficient studying.

Connect helps you be more productive with your study time and get better grades using tools like SmartBook, which highlights key concepts and creates a personalized study plan. Connect sets you up for success, so you walk into class with confidence and walk out with better grades.

©Shutterstock/wavebreakmedia

" I really liked this app—it made it easy to study when you don't have your text-book in front of you. "

- Jordan Cunningham,
Eastern Washington University

Study anytime, anywhere.

Download the free ReadAnywhere app and access your online eBook when it's convenient, even if you're offline. And since the app automatically syncs with your eBook in Connect, all of your notes are available every time you open it. Find out more at **www.mheducation.com/readanywhere**

No surprises.

The Connect Calendar and Reports tools keep you on track with the work you need to get done and your assignment scores. Life gets busy; Connect tools help you keep learning through it all.

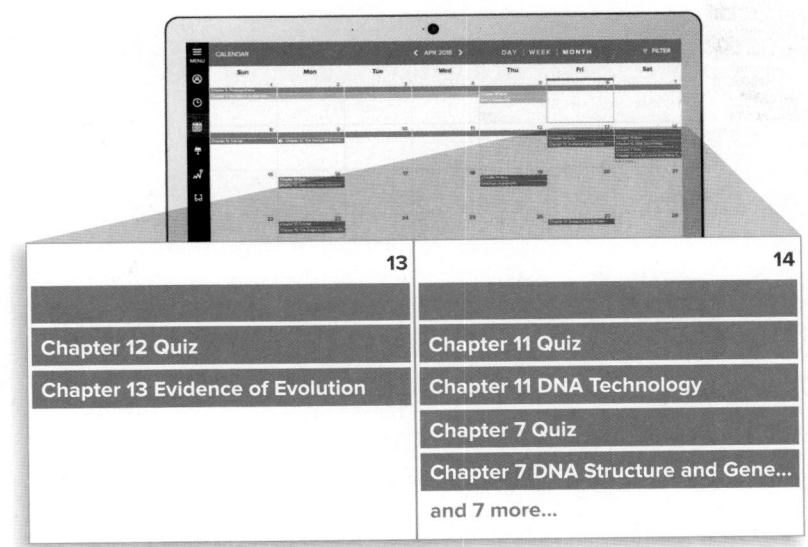

13	14
Chapter 12 Quiz	Chapter 11 Quiz
Chapter 13 Evidence of Evolution	Chapter 11 DNA Technology
	Chapter 7 Quiz
	Chapter 7 DNA Structure and Gene...
	and 7 more...

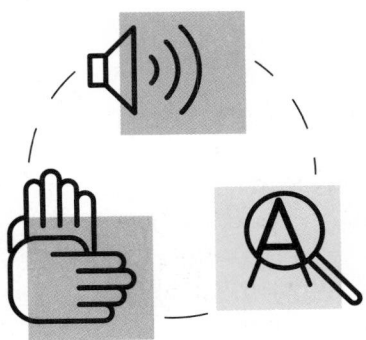

Learning for everyone.

McGraw-Hill works directly with Accessibility Services Departments and faculty to meet the learning needs of all students. Please contact your Accessibility Services office and ask them to email accessibility@mheducation.com, or visit **www.mheducation.com/about/accessibility.html** for more information.

Contents

UNIT I   Chemistry

©Dr. Parvinder Sethi

UNIT II   Cell

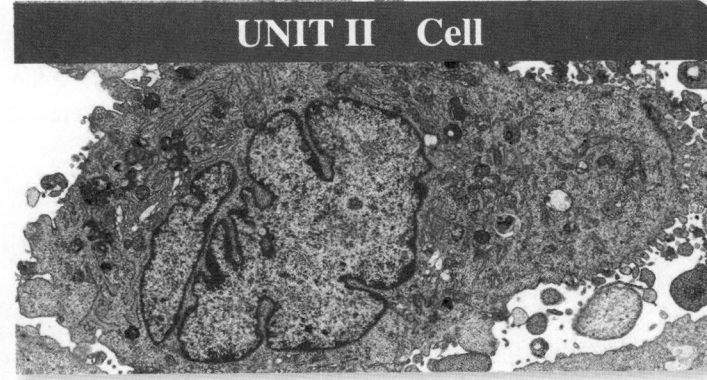

©Steve Gschmeissner/Science Source

Chapter 6

An Introduction to Energy, Enzymes, and Metabolism 127

Chapter 7

Cellular Respiration and Fermentation 145

Chapter 8

Photosynthesis 164

Chapter 9

Cell Communication 183

Chapter 10

Multicellularity 202

UNIT III   Genetics

©Pieter Van De Vijverl/Science Photo Library/Corbis

Chapter 11

Nucleic Acid Structure, DNA Replication, and Chromosome Structure 220

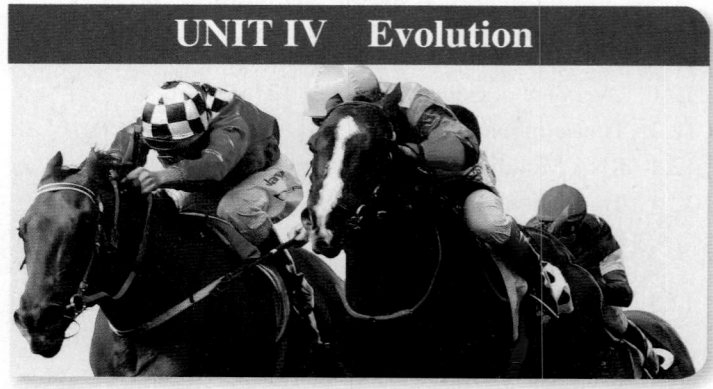

UNIT IV   Evolution

©Mark Dadswell/Getty Images

Chapter 25

Taxonomy and Systematics   516

Chapter 26

History of Life on Earth and Human Evolution   535

UNIT V   Diversity

©Dr. Jeremy Burgess/SPL/Science Source

Chapter 27

Archaea and Bacteria   561

Chapter 28

Protists   581

Chapter 29

Fungi   605

Chapter 30

Microbiomes: Microbial Systems On and Around Us   622

Chapter 31

Plants and the Conquest of Land   641

UNIT VI Flowering Plants

©Linda Graham

Chapter 36

An Introduction to Flowering Plant Form and Function 760

©John Rowley/Getty Images

UNIT VIII   Ecology

©Dante Fenolio/Science Source

Chapter 54

An Introduction to Ecology and Biomes   1149

An Introduction to Biology

1

The giraffe, genus *Giraffa*. Giraffes, which are found in Africa, are the tallest living terrestrial animals. They are members of the genus *Giraffa*. Until recently, biologists thought that all giraffes belonged to a single species. As discussed later in this chapter, that view may be changing as a result of analyses of genetic features of giraffes from different regions of Africa. ©Robert Muckley/Getty Images

Biology is the study of life. The diverse forms of life found on Earth provide biologists with an amazing array of organisms to study. In many cases, the investigation of living things leads to discoveries that no one would have imagined. For example, researchers determined that the venom from certain poisonous snakes contains a chemical that lowers blood pressure in humans. By analyzing that chemical, scientists developed drugs to treat high blood pressure (**Figure 1.1**).

Biologists have discovered that plants can communicate with each other. For example, the beautiful umbrella thorn acacia (*Vachellia tortillis*), shown in **Figure 1.2**, emits volatile organic molecules when it is attacked by herbivores. These molecules warn other nearby acacia trees that herbivores are in the area, and those trees release toxins to protect themselves.

Another interesting example of a biological discovery is a seemingly bizarre phenomenon known as **zombie parasites**. As you may know, zombies are fictional creatures featured in some horror and fantasy novels and movies, where they appear as dead

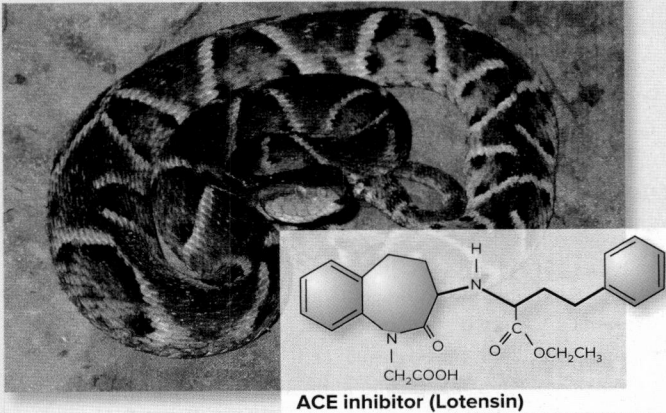

ACE inhibitor (Lotensin)

Figure 1.1 The Brazilian arrowhead viper and an inhibitor of high blood pressure. Derivatives of a chemical, called an angiotensin-converting enzyme (ACE) inhibitor, are found in the venom of the Brazilian arrowhead viper and are commonly used to treat high blood pressure. ©Francois Gohier/Science Source

Figure 1.2 Plant communication. If attacked by herbivores, this acacia tree will emit molecules that will warn other acacia trees in the area. ©Mark Snodgrass/Getty Images

Table 1.1	Examples of Zombie Parasites	
Host	**Parasite**	**Description**
House cricket (*Acheta domesticus*)	Horsehair worm (*Paragordius varius*)	A horsehair worm larva infects a cricket and grows inside it. The cricket is terrestrial, but the adult stage of the horsehair worm is aquatic. When the larva matures into an adult, it alters the behavior of the cricket, causing it to jump into the nearest body of water! As the cricket drowns, an adult horsehair worm emerges.
Spider (*Plesiometa argyra*)	Wasp (*Hymenoepimecis argyraphaga*)	A female wasp glues an egg onto a spider's body. After the egg develops into a larva, the larva pokes a few holes in the spider's abdomen, which allows it to suck the spider's blood and also to transfer chemicals into the spider, which control its behavior. The spider stops building its normal orb-shaped web and starts building a web whose geometry is strikingly different: The new web is designed to suspend the larva's cocoon in the air, where it will be protected from predators.
Various vertebrates, including mice and rats	Protozoan (*Toxoplasma gondii*)	*Toxoplasma gondii* is a parasite whose life cycle involves more than one vertebrate host. The definitive host is the cat, which is where *T. gondii* becomes mature and reproduces sexually. An intermediate host can be any of a variety of vertebrates, including mice and rats, which can ingest the parasite from cat feces. In the intermediate host, the parasite develops and reproduces asexually. To escape an intermediate host, such as a mouse or rat, and move to the definitive host, *T. gondii* dramatically alters the host's behavior. The infected animal becomes attracted to the smell of cat urine! This makes it more likely to be eaten by a cat and thereby allows *T. gondii* to enter its definitive host and mature.

creatures that are able to move because of some magical force. A zombie parasite is a parasite that infects its host and is then able to control the host's behavior. A relatively small group of researchers have begun to investigate this phenomenon, and their work has spawned a new field called **neuroparasitology**—the study of how parasites control the nervous systems of their hosts. During the past few decades, researchers have discovered many examples of zombie parasites. A few are described in Table 1.1.

These are but a few of the many discoveries that make biology an intriguing discipline. The study of life not only reveals the fascinating characteristics of living species but also leads to the development of medicines and research tools that benefit the lives of people.

To make new discoveries, biologists view life from many different perspectives: What is the composition of living things? How is life organized? How do organisms reproduce? Sometimes the questions posed by biologists are fundamental and even philosophical in nature: How did living organisms originate? Can we live forever? What is the physical basis for memory? Can we save endangered species?

Future biologists will continue to make important advances. Biologists are scientific explorers looking for answers to some of life's most enduring mysteries. Unraveling these mysteries presents exciting challenges to the best and brightest minds. The rewards of a career in biology include the excitement of forging into uncharted territory, the thrill of making discoveries that can improve the health and lives of people, and the satisfaction of trying to preserve the environment and protect endangered species. For these and many other compelling reasons, students seeking challenging and rewarding careers may wish to choose biology as a lifelong pursuit.

In this chapter, we will begin by examining the levels of biology and the core concepts that are common to all forms of life. One of those core concepts is evolution, which is discussed in greater depth in Section 1.3. We then explore the general approaches that scientists follow when making new discoveries. Finally, we will consider the skills that students need to develop as they pursue careers in this exciting discipline and the ways in which this textbook fosters those skills.

1.1 Levels of Biology

Learning Outcome:

1. Explain how life can be viewed at different levels of biological complexity.

Let's begin our journey through the wonderful world of biology by considering how life is organized. The term **organism** can be applied to all forms of life. Organisms maintain an internal order that is separated from the environment. The complexity of living organisms can be analyzed at different levels, starting with the smallest level of organization and progressing to levels that are physically much larger and more complex. **Figure 1.3** depicts a biologist's view of the levels of biological organization.

1. *Atoms.* An **atom** is the smallest unit of an element that has the chemical properties of the element. All matter is composed of atoms.

2. *Molecules and macromolecules.* As discussed in Unit I, atoms bond with each other to form **molecules**. A polymer such as a polypeptide is formed of many molecules bonded together and is called a **macromolecule**. Carbohydrates, proteins, and nucleic acids (DNA and RNA) are important macromolecules found in living organisms.

3. *Cells.* The simplest unit of life is the **cell**, which we will examine in Unit II. A cell is surrounded by a membrane and contains a variety of molecules and macromolecules. Unicellular organisms are composed of one cell, whereas multicellular organisms, such as plants and animals, contain many cells.

4. *Tissues.* In multicellular organisms, many cells of the same type associate with each other to form **tissues**. An example is muscle tissue.

5. *Organs.* In complex multicellular organisms, an **organ** is composed of two or more types of tissue. For example, the heart is composed of several types of tissues, including muscle, nervous, and connective tissue.

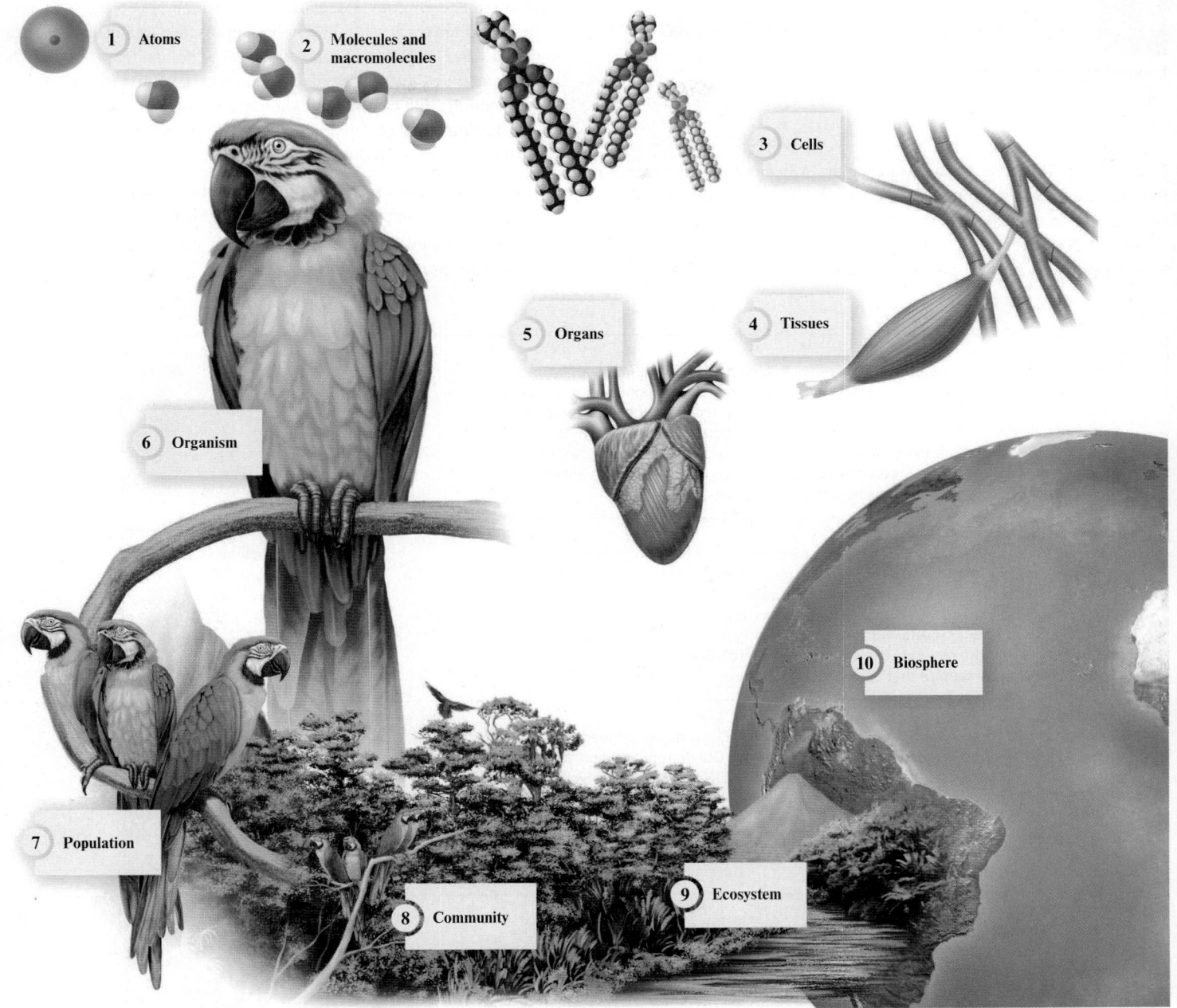

Figure 1.3 The levels of biological organization.

Concept Check: *At which level of biological organization would you place a herd of buffalo?*

6. *Organism.* All living things can be called **organisms**.
Biologists classify organisms as belonging to a particular
species, which is a related group of organisms that share a
distinctive form and set of attributes in nature. The members
of the same species are closely related genetically. In Units VI
and VII, we will examine plants and animals at the level of
cells, tissues, organs, and complete organisms.

7. *Population.* A group of organisms of the same species that
occupy the same environment is called a **population**.

8. *Community.* A biological **community** is an assemblage of
populations of different species. The types of species found in

a community are determined by the environment and by the
interactions of species with each other.

9. *Ecosystem.* Researchers may extend their work beyond living
organisms and also study the physical environment. Ecologists
analyze **ecosystems**, which are formed by interactions of a
community of organisms with their physical environment.
Unit VIII considers biological organization from populations
to ecosystems.

10. *Biosphere.* The **biosphere** includes all of the places on the
Earth where living organisms exist. Life is found in the air, in
bodies of water, on the land, and in the soil.

1.2 Core Concepts of Biology

Learning Outcome:

1. Describe the core concepts of biology as advocated by "Vision and Change."

In 2007, the American Association for the Advancement of Science initiated a series of regional conversations with more than 200 biology faculty to discuss how to improve undergraduate biology education. In 2009, using the findings of these regional conversations, the organization held a conference called "Vision and Change in Undergraduate Biology Education." More than 500 biology faculty, college and university administrators, representatives of professional societies, and students and postdoctoral scholars from around the country attended the conference. The proceedings led to various recommendations that can be found at http://visionandchange.org.

A key outcome of "Vision and Change" was the identification of five core concepts of biology (**Figure 1.4**):

1. *Evolution:* The diversity of life evolved over time by processes of mutation, natural selection, and genetic exchange.

2. *Structure and function:* Basic units of structure define the function of all living things.

(a) Evolution: Biological evolution, or simply evolution, refers to a heritable change in a population of organisms from generation to generation. As a result of evolution, populations become better adapted to the environment in which they live. For example, the long snout of an anteater is an adaptation that enhances its ability to obtain food, namely ants, from hard-to-reach places. Over the course of many generations, the fossil record indicates that the long snout occurred via biological evolution in which modern anteaters evolved from populations of organisms with shorter snouts.	
(b) Structure and function: Biologists often say "structure determines function." This core concept pertains to very tiny biological molecules and to very large biological structures. The feet of different birds provide a striking example. Aquatic birds have webbed feet that function as paddles for swimming. By comparison, the feet of nonaquatic birds are not webbed and are better adapted for grasping food, perching on branches, and running along the ground. The structure of a bird's feet, webbed versus non-webbed, is a critical feature that affects their function.	
(c) Information: Genetic material composed of DNA (deoxyribonucleic acid) provides a blueprint for the organization, development, and function of living things. During reproduction, a copy of this blueprint is transmitted from parents to offspring. DNA is heritable, which means that offspring inherit DNA from their parents. A key feature of reproduction is that offspring tend to have characteristics that greatly resemble those of their parent(s). As seen here, this mother dolphin and her offspring have strikingly similar features.	
(d) Energy and matter: All living organisms acquire energy and matter from the environment and use them to synthesize essential molecules and maintain the organization of their cells and bodies. These sunflower plants carry out photosynthesis in which they capture light energy and acquire carbon dioxide and water, thereby allowing them to make carbohydrates. This process provides energy and organic molecules so the plants can grow and produce beautiful flowers.	
(e) Systems: When the parts of an organism interact with each other or with the external environment to create novel structures and functions, the resulting characteristics are called emergent properties. For example, the human eye is composed of many different types of cells that are organized to sense incoming light and transmit signals to the brain. Our ability to see is an emergent property of this complex arrangement of different cell types. Biologists use the term systems biology to describe the study of how new properties of life arise by complex interactions of its individual parts.	

 Figure 1.4 Core concepts of biology, as advocated by "Vision and Change." These core concepts will be emphasized throughout this textbook. a: ©Lucas Leuzinger/Shutterstock; b: ©G.K. & Vikki Hart/Getty Images; c: ©Image Source/Getty Images; d: Source: Photo by Bruce Fritz, USDA-ARS; e: ©Maria Teijeiro/Getty Images

3. ***Information flow, exchange, and storage:*** The growth and behavior of organisms are activated through the expression of genetic information.

4. ***Pathways and transformations of energy and matter:*** Biological systems grow and change via processes that are based on chemical transformation pathways and are governed by the laws of thermodynamics.

5. ***Systems:*** Living systems are interconnected and interacting.

A key goal of this textbook is to bring to life these five core concepts of biology. These concepts will be highlighted in each chapter with a "Vision and Change" icon, , which indicates subsections and figures that focus on one or more of these five core concepts.

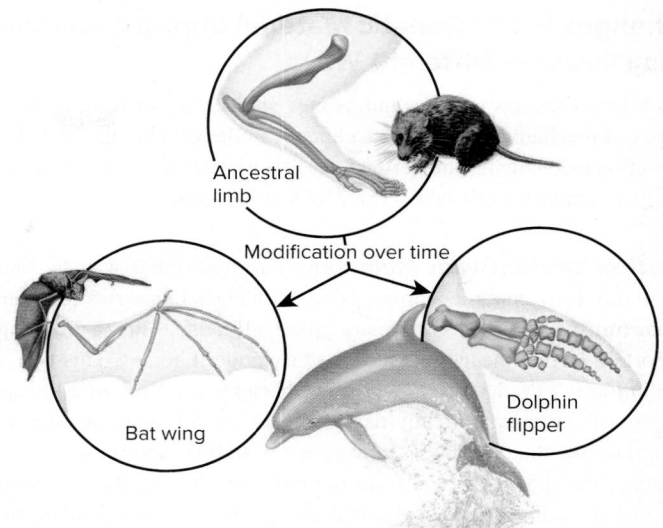

Figure 1.5 **An example of a modification that has occurred as a result of biological evolution.** The wing of a bat and the flipper of a dolphin are modifications of a limb that was used for walking in a pre-existing ancestor.

Core Concepts: Evolution, Structure and Function Via evolution, the different structures of the front limbs seen here result in functions that are best suited for these organisms.

1.3 Biological Evolution

Learning Outcomes:

1. Explain two mechanisms by which evolutionary change occurs: vertical descent with mutation and horizontal gene transfer.

2. Describe how changes in genomes and proteomes underlie evolutionary changes.

Unity and diversity are two words that often are used to describe the living world. All modern forms of life display a common set of characteristics that distinguish them from nonliving objects. In this section, we will explore how this unity of common traits is rooted in the phenomenon of **biological evolution**, or simply **evolution**, which is a heritable change in a population of organisms from one generation to the next. Life on Earth is united by an evolutionary past in which modern organisms have evolved from populations of pre-existing organisms. This unity is a core concept of biology.

However, evolutionary unity does not mean that organisms are exactly alike. The Earth has many different types of environments, ranging from tropical rain forests to salty oceans, hot and dry deserts, and cold mountaintops. Diverse forms of life have evolved in ways that help them prosper in the different environments the Earth has to offer. In this and the following section, we will begin to examine the unity and diversity that exists within the biological world.

Modern Forms of Life Are Connected by an Evolutionary History

Life began on Earth as primitive cells about 3.5–4 billion years ago (bya). Since that time, populations of living organisms have undergone evolutionary changes that ultimately gave rise to the species we see today. Understanding the evolutionary history of species can provide key insights into the structure and function of an organism's body, because evolutionary change frequently involves modifications of characteristics in pre-existing populations. Over long periods of time, populations may change so that structures with a particular function become modified to serve a new function. For example, the wing of a bat is used for flying, and the flipper of a dolphin is used for swimming. Evidence from

the fossil record indicates that both structures were modified from a front limb that was used for walking in a pre-existing ancestor (**Figure 1.5**).

Evolutionary Change Involves Changes in the Genetic Material

The example shown in Figure 1.5 represents evolution at the macroscopic level. At the molecular level, evolution involves changes in the genetic material, which is composed of **DNA (deoxyribonucleic acid)**. DNA provides a blueprint for the organization, development, and function of living things. During reproduction, a copy of this blueprint is transmitted from parent to offspring. DNA is **heritable**, which means that offspring inherit DNA from their parents.

As discussed in Unit III, **genes**, which are segments of DNA, govern the characteristics, or traits, of organisms. Most genes are transcribed into a type of **RNA (ribonucleic acid)** molecule called messenger RNA (mRNA), which is then translated into a **polypeptide** with a specific amino acid sequence. A **protein** is composed of one or more polypeptides. The structures and functions of proteins play a key role in determining the traits of organisms.

On relatively rare occasions, changes may occur in DNA. A **mutation** is a heritable change in the genetic material—one that can be passed from cell to cell or from parent to offspring. Mutations can alter the properties of genes and thereby affect the characteristics of the offspring that inherit them. With regard to survival, mutations can be beneficial, detrimental, or neutral. As described next, changes in the genetic material underlie the process of evolution.

Changes to the Genetic Material during Evolution May Occur in Different Ways

As a given species evolves and as new species are formed, different types of mechanisms may cause changes in the genetic material. Two common mechanisms are vertical descent with mutation and horizontal gene transfer. Let's take a brief look at each one.

Vertical Descent with Mutation   The traditional way to study evolution is to examine a progression of changes in a series of related ancestral species. Such a series is called a **lineage**. **Figure 1.6** shows a portion of the lineage that gave rise to modern horses. This type of evolution is called **vertical evolution** because it occurs in a lineage. Biologists have traditionally depicted such evolutionary change in a diagram like the one shown in Figure 1.6. In this mechanism of evolution, new species evolve from pre-existing ones by the accumulation of mutations. But why would some mutations accumulate in a population and eventually change the characteristics of an entire species? One reason is that a mutation may alter the traits of organisms

in a way that increases their chances of survival and reproduction. When a mutation causes such a beneficial change, the frequency of the mutation may increase in a population from one generation to the next, a process called **natural selection**. This topic is discussed in Units IV and V. Evolution also involves the accumulation of neutral changes that do not benefit or harm a species, and evolution sometimes involves rare changes that may be harmful.

With regard to the horses shown in Figure 1.6, the fossil record has revealed adaptive changes in various traits such as size and tooth morphology. The first horses were the size of dogs, whereas modern horses typically weigh more than a half ton. The teeth of *Hyracotherium* were relatively small compared with those of modern horses. Over the course of millions of years, horses' teeth have increased in size, and a complex pattern of ridges has developed on the molars. How do evolutionary biologists explain these changes in horse characteristics? They can be attributed to natural selection, in which changing global climates favored the survival and reproduction of horses with certain types of traits. Over North America, where much of horse evolution occurred, large areas changed from dense forests to grasslands.

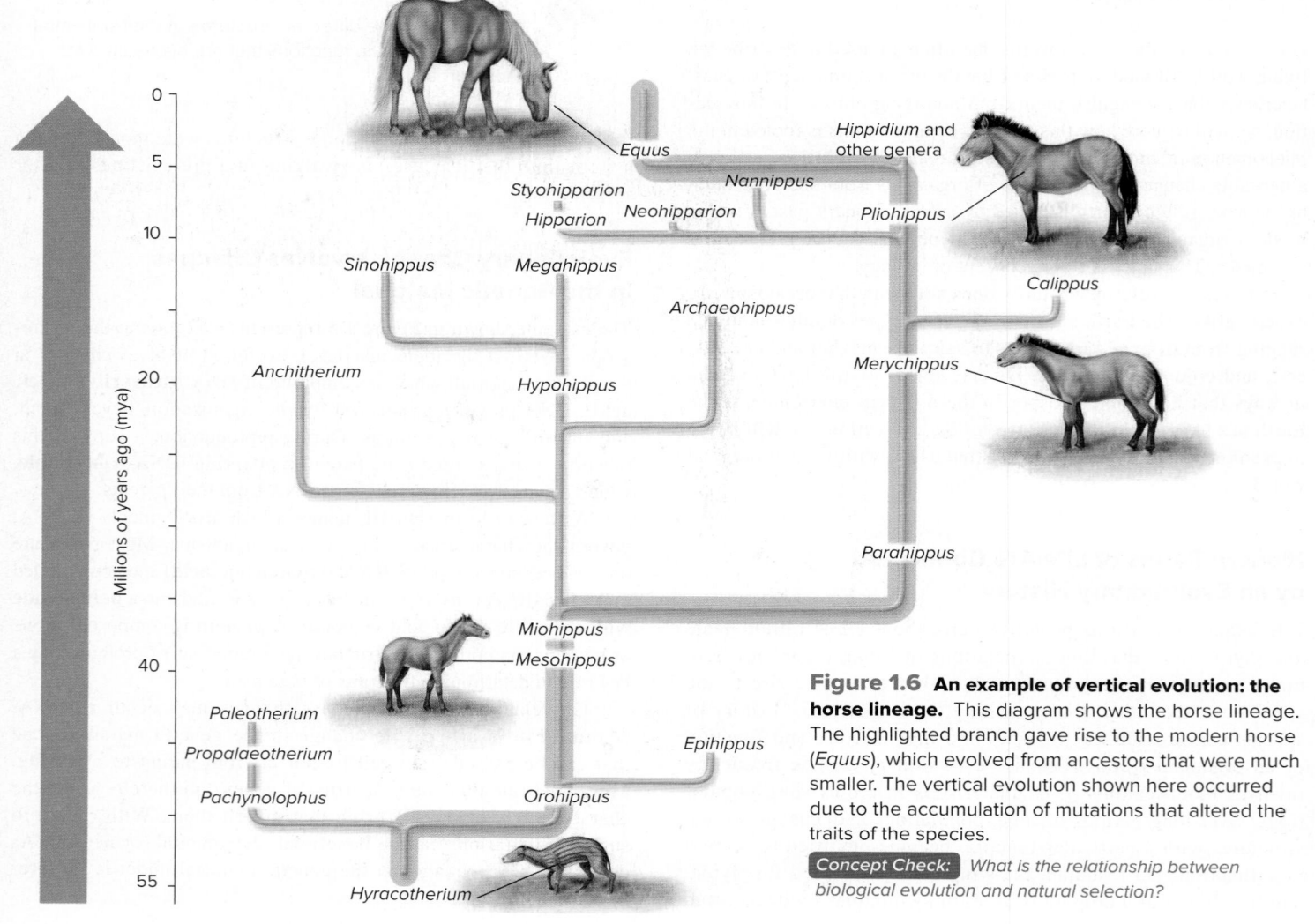

Figure 1.6 An example of vertical evolution: the horse lineage. This diagram shows the horse lineage. The highlighted branch gave rise to the modern horse (*Equus*), which evolved from ancestors that were much smaller. The vertical evolution shown here occurred due to the accumulation of mutations that altered the traits of the species.

Concept Check: *What is the relationship between biological evolution and natural selection?*

Horses with genetic variation that made them larger were more likely to escape predators and to be able to travel greater distances in search of food. The changes seen in horses' teeth are consistent with a dietary shift from eating tender leaves to eating grasses and other types of vegetation that are more abrasive and require more chewing.

Horizontal Gene Transfer   The most common way for genes to be transferred is in a vertical manner. This can involve the transfer of genetic material from a mother cell to daughter cells, or it can occur via gametes—sperm and egg—that unite to form a new organism. However, as discussed in later chapters, genes are sometimes transferred between organisms by other mechanisms. These other mechanisms are collectively known as **horizontal gene transfer**, which is the transfer of genetic material from one organism to another organism that is not its offspring. In some cases, horizontal gene transfer can occur between members of different species. For example, you may have heard in the news media that resistance to antibiotics among bacteria is a growing medical problem. As discussed in Chapter 19, genes that confer antibiotic resistance are sometimes transferred between different bacterial species (**Figure 1.7**).

Genes transferred horizontally may be subject to natural selection and promote changes in an entire species. This has been an important mechanism of evolutionary change, particularly among bacterial species. In addition, during the early stages of evolution, which occurred a few billion years ago, horizontal gene transfer was an important part of the process that gave rise to all modern species.

Traditionally, biologists have described evolution using diagrams that depict the vertical evolution of species on a long time scale. This type of evolutionary tree was shown earlier in Figure 1.6. For many decades, a simplistic view held that all living organisms evolved from a common ancestor, resulting in a "tree of life" that depicted the vertical evolution that gave rise to all modern species. Now that we understand the great importance of horizontal gene transfer in the evolution of life on Earth, biologists have re-evaluated the way evolution has occurred over time. Rather than a tree of life, a more appropriate way

to view the unity of living organisms is as a "web of life," as shown in **Figure 1.8**, which accounts for both vertical descent and horizontal gene transfer. In a lineage in which the time scale is depicted on a vertical axis, horizontal gene transfer between different species is shown as a horizontal line.

Core Concept: Evolution

The Study of Genomes and Proteomes Provides an Evolutionary Foundation for Our Understanding of Biology

As we have seen, evolutionary unity is a core concept of biology. We can understand the unity of modern organisms by realizing that all living species evolved from an interrelated group of ancestors. However, from an experimental perspective, this realization presents a dilemma—we cannot take a time machine back over the course of 4 billion years to carefully study the characteristics of extinct organisms and fully appreciate the series of changes that have led to modern species. Fortunately, though, evolution has given biologists some wonderful puzzles to study, including the fossil record and the genomes of modern species.

The term **genome** refers to the complete genetic composition of an organism or species (**Figure 1.9a**). The genomes of bacteria and archaea usually contain a few thousand genes, whereas those of eukaryotes may contain tens of thousands. A genome is critical to life because it performs these functions:

- *Stores information in a stable form:* The genome of every organism stores information that provides a blueprint for producing that organism's characteristics.

- *Provides continuity from generation to generation:* The genome is copied and transmitted from generation to generation.

- *Acts as an instrument of evolutionary change:* Every now and then, the genome undergoes a mutation that may alter the characteristics of an organism. In addition, a genome may acquire new genes by horizontal gene transfer. The accumulation of genome changes from generation to generation produces the evolutionary changes that alter species and produce new species.

An exciting advance in biology over the past couple of decades has been the ability to analyze the DNA sequence of genomes, a technology called **genomics**. For example, a researcher can compare the genomes of a frog, a giraffe, and a petunia and discover intriguing similarities and differences. These comparisons help us to understand how new traits evolved. All three types of organisms have the same kinds of genes needed for the breakdown of nutrients such as sugars. In contrast, only the petunia has genes that allow it to carry out photosynthesis. Also, genomics helps us to understand evolutionary relationships. As discussed later in this chapter, researchers analyzed the genomes of giraffes across Africa and concluded that they constitute four distinct species.

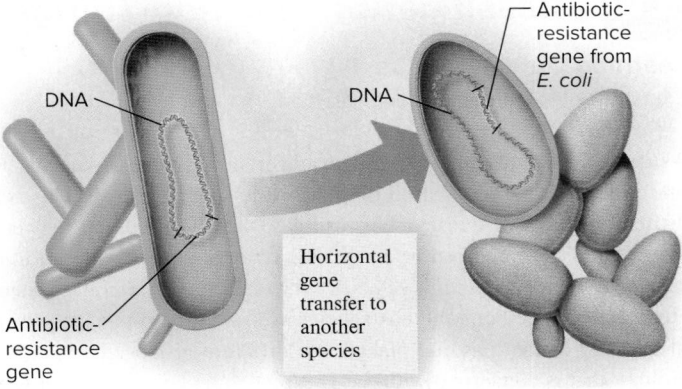

Figure 1.7 An example of horizontal gene transfer: antibiotic resistance. One bacterial species may transfer a gene, such as a gene that confers resistance to an antibiotic, to another bacterial species.

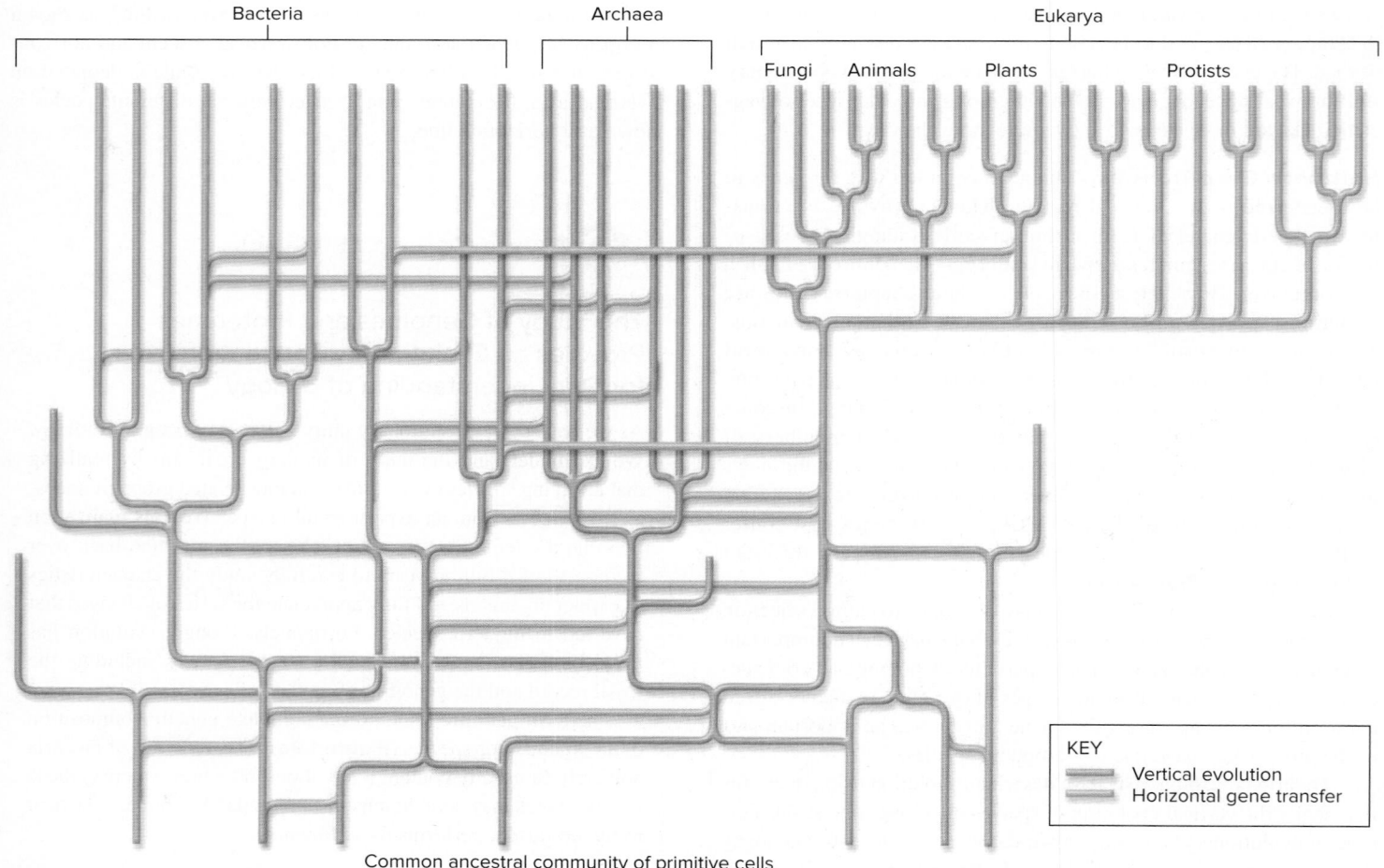

Bacteria   Archaea   Eukarya

Fungi   Animals   Plants   Protists

KEY
— Vertical evolution
— Horizontal gene transfer

Common ancestral community of primitive cells

Figure 1.8   The web of life, showing both vertical descent and horizontal gene transfer.   This diagram includes both of these important mechanisms in the evolution of life on Earth. Note: Archaea are unicellular species that are similar in cell structure to bacteria.

Concept Check: *How does the concept of a tree of life differ from that of a web of life?*

An extension of genome analysis is the study of the **proteome**, which refers to all of the proteins that a cell or organism makes. The function of most genes is to encode polypeptides that become units in proteins. As shown in **Figure 1.9b**, these include proteins that form a cytoskeleton and proteins that function in cell organization and as enzymes, transport proteins, cell-signaling proteins, and extracellular proteins. The genome of each species carries the information to make its proteome—the hundreds or thousands of proteins that each cell of that species makes. Proteins are largely responsible for the structures and functions of cells and organisms. The set of techniques known as **proteomics** allows researchers to analyze the proteome of a single species and compare the proteomes of different species. Proteomics helps us understand how the various levels of biology are related to one another, from the molecular level—at the level of protein molecules—to higher levels, such as how the functioning of proteins produces the characteristics of cells and organisms and affects the ability of populations of organisms to survive in their natural environments.

1.4   Classification of Living Things

Learning Outcome:

1. Outline how organisms are classified.

As biologists study species and discover new species, they try to place them into groups based on their evolutionary history. This is a difficult task because researchers estimate that the Earth has between 5 and 50 million different species! The rationale for classification is based on vertical descent. Species with a recent common ancestor are grouped together, whereas species whose common ancestor was in the very distant past are placed into different groups. The field of biology that is concerned with the grouping and classification of species is termed **taxonomy**.

Why is taxonomy useful? First, taxonomy allows use to appreciate the amazing diversity of life on Earth. Also, because taxonomy is based on evolution, it provides a view of the evolutionary relationships among living species, and between living and extinct species.

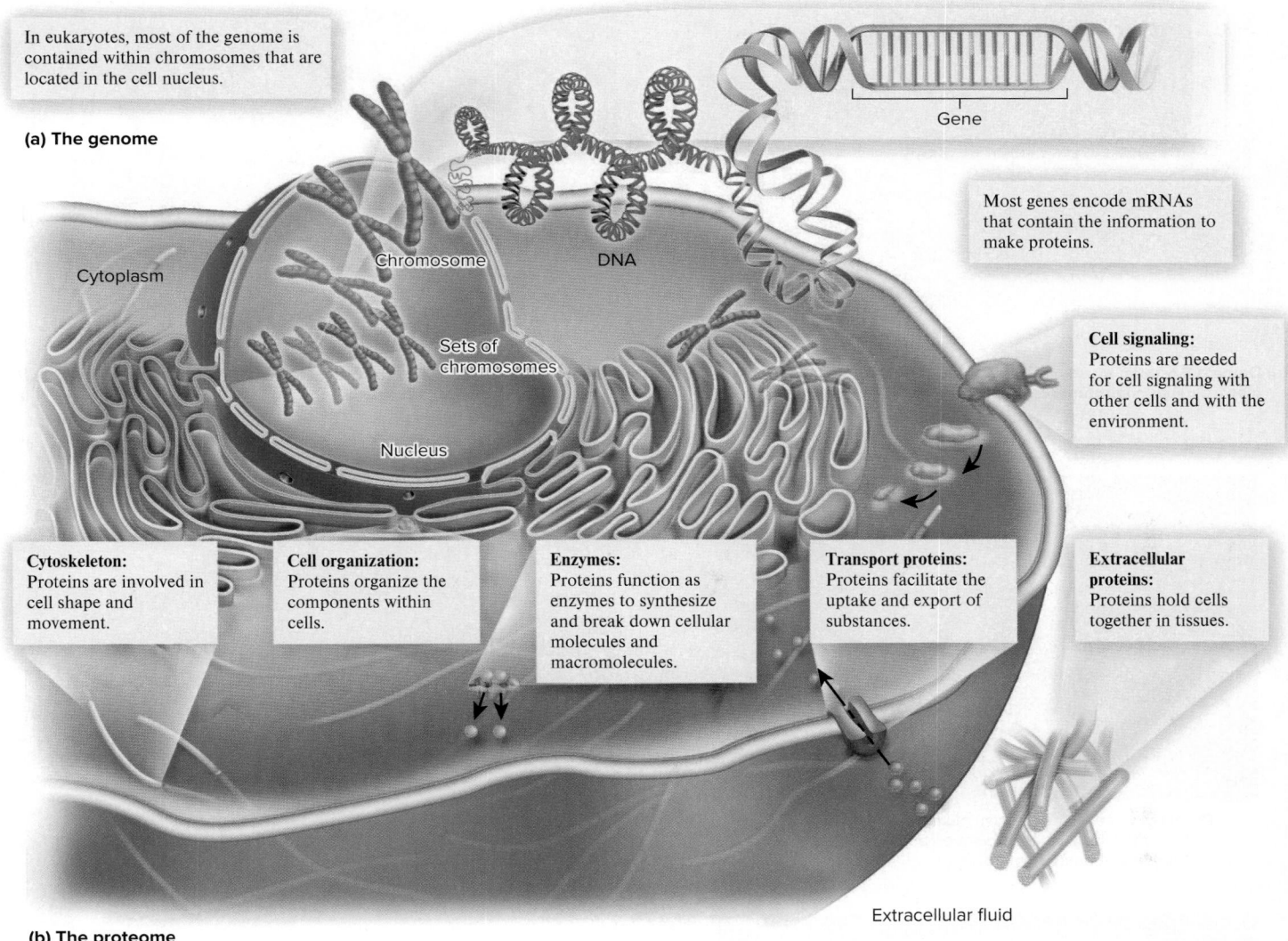

In eukaryotes, most of the genome is contained within chromosomes that are located in the cell nucleus.

(a) The genome

Gene

Most genes encode mRNAs that contain the information to make proteins.

Cytoplasm

Chromosome   DNA

Sets of chromosomes

Nucleus

Cell signaling: Proteins are needed for cell signaling with other cells and with the environment.

Cytoskeleton: Proteins are involved in cell shape and movement.

Cell organization: Proteins organize the components within cells.

Enzymes: Proteins function as enzymes to synthesize and break down cellular molecules and macromolecules.

Transport proteins: Proteins facilitate the uptake and export of substances.

Extracellular proteins: Proteins hold cells together in tissues.

Extracellular fluid

(b) The proteome

Figure 1.9 Genomes and proteomes. (a) The genome, which is composed of DNA, is the entire genetic composition of an organism. Most of the genetic material in eukaryotic cells is found in the cell nucleus. The primary function of the genome is to encode the proteome **(b)**, which is the entire protein complement of a cell or organism. Six general categories of proteins are illustrated. Proteins are largely responsible for the structure and function of cells and organisms.

Concept Check: *Biologists sometimes say that the genome is the storage unit of life, whereas the proteome is largely the functional unit of life. Explain this statement.*

The Classification of Living Organisms Allows Biologists to Appreciate the Unity and Diversity of Life

Let's first consider taxonomy on a broad scale. You may have noticed that Figure 1.8 showed three main groups of organisms. From an evolutionary perspective, all forms of life can be placed into those three large categories, or domains, called **Bacteria**, **Archaea**, and **Eukarya** (**Figure 1.10**). Bacteria and archaea are microorganisms that are also termed **prokaryotic** because their cell structure is relatively simple. At the molecular level, bacterial and archaeal cells show significant differences in their compositions. By comparison, organisms in the domain Eukarya are **eukaryotic** and have cells with internal compartments that

serve various functions. A defining distinction between prokaryotic and eukaryotic cells is that eukaryotic cells have a **cell nucleus** in which the genetic material is surrounded by a membrane.

The organisms in domain Eukarya were once subdivided into four major categories, or kingdoms, called Protista (protists), Plantae (plants), Fungi, and Animalia (animals). However, as discussed in Chapter 25 and Unit V, this traditional view became invalid as biologists gathered new information regarding the evolutionary relationships of these organisms. We now know that the protists do not form a single kingdom but instead are divided into several broad categories called supergroups.

Taxonomy involves multiple levels in which particular species are placed into progressively smaller and smaller groups whose

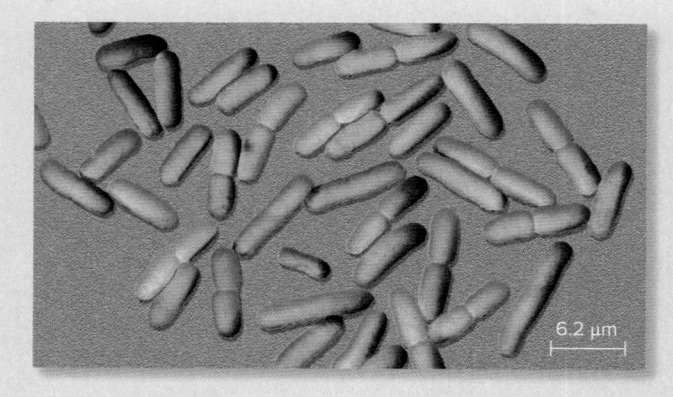

6.2 μm

(a) Domain Bacteria: Mostly unicellular prokaryotes that inhabit many diverse environments on Earth.

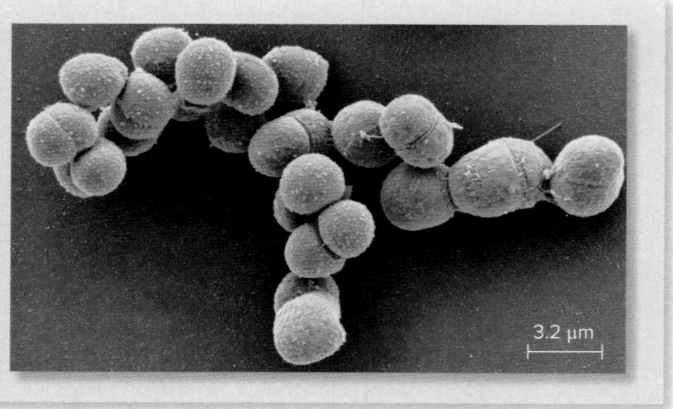

3.2 μm

(b) Domain Archaea: Unicellular prokaryotes that often live in extreme environments, such as hot springs.

375.2 μm

Protists: Unicellular and small multicellular organisms that are now subdivided into seven broad groups based on their evolutionary relationships.

Plants: Multicellular organisms that can carry out photosynthesis.

Fungi: Unicellular and multicellular organisms that have a cell wall but cannot carry out photosynthesis. Fungi usually survive on decaying organic material.

Animals: Multicellular organisms that usually have a nervous system and are capable of locomotion. They must eat other organisms or the products of other organisms to live.

(c) Domain Eukarya: Unicellular and multicellular organisms having cells with internal compartments that serve various functions.

Figure 1.10 The three domains of life. Two of these domains, **(a)** Bacteria and **(b)** Archaea, consist of species with prokaryotic cells. The third domain, **(c)** Eukarya, comprises species that are eukaryotes. a: ©BSIP/age fotostock; b: ©Eye of Science/Science Source; c (protists): ©Jan Hinsch/Getty Images; c (plants): ©Kent Foster/Science Source; c (fungi): ©Carl Schmidt-Luchs/Science Source; c (animals): ©Ingram Publishing/age fotostock

  Core Skill: Connections Look ahead to Figure 25.1. Are fungi more closely related to plants or animals?

Taxonomic group	The ocellaris clownfish is found in	Approximate time when the common ancestor for this group arose	Approximate number of modern species in this group	Examples
Domain	Eukarya	2,000 mya	> 5,000,000	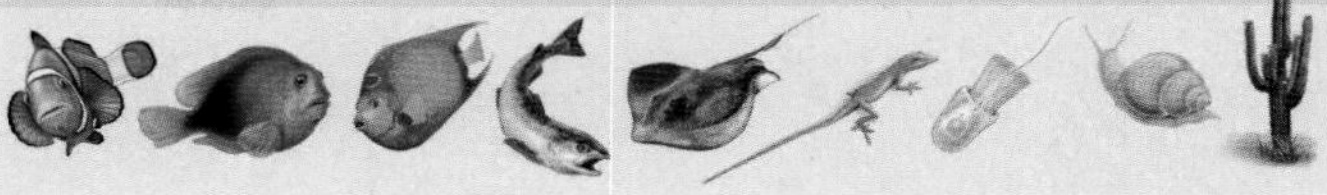
Supergroup	Opisthokonta	2,000 mya	> 1,000,000	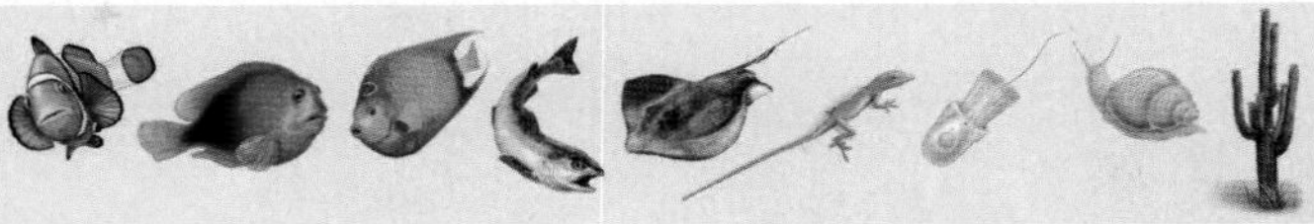
Kingdom	Animalia	600 mya	> 1,000,000	
Phylum	Chordata	525 mya	50,000	
Class	Actinopterygii	420 mya	30,000	
Order	Perciformes	80 mya	7,000	
Family	Pomacentridae	~ 40 mya	360	
Genus	*Amphiprion*	~ 9 mya	28	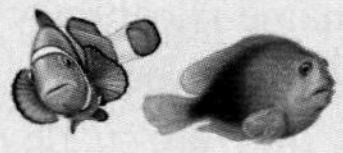
Species	*ocellaris*	< 3 mya	1	

Figure 1.11 Taxonomic classification of the ocellaris clownfish.

Concept Check: *Why is it useful to place organisms into taxonomic groupings?*

members are more closely related to each other evolutionarily. Such an approach emphasizes the unity and diversity of different species. As an example, let's consider the clownfish, a popular saltwater aquarium fish (**Figure 1.11**). Several species of clownfish have been identified.

One species of clownfish, which is orange with white stripes, has several common names, including ocellaris clownfish. The broadest grouping for this clownfish is the domain, namely, Eukarya, followed by progressively smaller divisions, from supergroup (Opisthokonta), to kingdom (Animalia), and eventually to species. In the animal kingdom, clownfish are part of a phylum, Chordata, the chordates, which is subdivided into classes. Clownfish are in a class called Actinopterygii, which includes all ray-finned fishes.

The common ancestor that gave rise to ray-finned fishes arose about 420 million years ago (mya). Actinopterygii is subdivided into several smaller orders. The clownfish are in the order Perciformes (bony fish). The order is, in turn, divided into families; the clownfish belong to the family of marine fish called Pomacentridae, which are often brightly colored. Families are divided into genera (singular, genus). The genus *Amphiprion* is composed of 28 different species; these are various types of clownfish. Therefore, the genus contains species that are very similar to each other in form and have evolved from a common (extinct) ancestor that lived relatively recently on an evolutionary time scale.

Biologists use a two-part description, called **binomial nomenclature**, to provide each species with a unique scientific name. The

Figure 1.12 A proposal that giraffes constitute four distinct species. Each species has its own distinctive coat pattern. From left to right: northern giraffe (*Giraffa camelopardalis*), reticulated giraffe (*G. reticulata*), Masai giraffe (*G. tippelskirchi*), and southern giraffe (*G. giraffa*).
(northern giraffe): ©NSP-RF/Alamy Stock Photo; (reticulated giraffe): ©McGraw-Hill Education; (Masai giraffe): ©iStock/Getty Images; (southern giraffe): ©Egmont Strigl/Westend61/ Getty Images

 Core Skill: Process of Science The gathering and analysis of new data suggest that giraffes, which were once thought to be a single species, constitute four different species.

scientific name of the ocellaris clownfish is *Amphiprion ocellaris*. The first word is the genus, and the second word is the specific epithet, or species descriptor. By convention, the genus name is capitalized, whereas the specific epithet is not. Both names are italicized. Scientific names are usually Latinized, which means they are made similar in appearance to Latin words. The origins of scientific names are typically Latin or Greek, but they can come from a variety of sources, including a person's name.

Taxonomy Changes as Researchers Gather Evidence Regarding the Characteristics and Genetic Composition of Organisms Located in Different Places

How do we judge if a gray squirrel living in Minnesota and another one living in California are members of the same species? As discussed in Chapter 24, biologists use different criteria to decide if similar organisms living in different places are the same species or different species. For example, they may analyze morphological features or study DNA samples. Science is a work in progress. As biologists gather new information and conduct experiments, their views often change. An interesting example involves the classification of giraffes, shown on the cover of this textbook.

Giraffes are currently classified as a single species, *Giraffa camelopardalis,* but recent studies are challenging that conclusion. In 2016, a study by Axel Janke and colleagues suggested that there are four distinct species of giraffes. This work was based on a genetic analysis of DNA samples taken from 190 giraffes across Africa. By comparing these DNA samples, the researchers concluded that giraffes should be classified as four distinct species (**Figure 1.12**).

While not all experts agree on this conclusion, this work illustrates how our perception of biological diversity can change as we gather more information.

1.5 Biology as a Scientific Discipline

Learning Outcomes:

1. Explain how researchers study biology at different levels, ranging from molecules to ecosystems.

2. **CoreSKILL »** Distinguish between discovery-based science and hypothesis testing, and describe the steps of the scientific method.

What is science? Surprisingly, the definition of science is not easy to state. Most people have an idea of what science is, but actually articulating that idea proves difficult. In biology, we can define **science** as the observation, identification, experimental investigation, and theoretical explanation of natural phenomena.

Science is conducted in different ways and at different levels. Some biologists study the molecules that compose life, and others try to understand how organisms survive in their natural environments. Experimentally, researchers often focus their efforts on **model organisms**—organisms studied by many different researchers so they can compare their results and determine scientific principles that apply more broadly to other species. Examples of model organisms include *Escherichia coli* (a bacterium), *Saccharomyces cerevisiae* (a yeast), *Drosophila melanogaster* (fruit fly), *Caenorhabditis elegans* (a nematode worm), *Mus musculus* (mouse), and *Arabidopsis thaliana* (a flowering plant). Model organisms offer experimental advantages over other species. For example, *E. coli* is a very simple organism that can be easily grown in the laboratory. By limiting their work to a few model organisms, researchers can gain a deeper understanding of these species. Importantly, the discoveries made using model organisms help us to understand how biological processes work in other species, including humans.

In this section, we will examine how biologists follow a standard approach, called the **scientific method**, to test their ideas. We will explore how scientific knowledge makes predictions that can be experimentally tested. However, not all discoveries are the result of researchers following the scientific method. Some discoveries are made simply by gathering new information. For example, as illustrated earlier, in Figure 1.1 the characterization of many living organisms has led to the development of important medicines. In this section, we will also consider how researchers often set out on "fact-finding missions" aimed at uncovering new information that may eventually lead to important discoveries in biology.

Biologists Investigate Life at Different Levels of Organization

In Figure 1.3, we examined the various levels of biological organization. The study of these different levels depends not only on the scientific interests of biologists but also on the tools available to them. The study of organisms in their natural environments is a branch of biology called **ecology**, which considers populations, communities, and ecosystems (**Figure 1.13a**). Some researchers examine the structures and functions of plants and animals; these subjects form the disciplines called **anatomy** and **physiology** (**Figure 1.13b**). With the advent of microscopy, **cell biology**, which is the study of cells and their interactions, became an important branch of biology in the early 1900s and remains so today (**Figure 1.13c**). In the 1970s, genetic tools became available for studying single genes and the proteins they encode. This genetic technology enabled researchers to study individual molecules, such as proteins, in living cells and thereby spawned the field of **molecular biology**. Together with biochemists and biophysicists, molecular biologists focus their efforts on the structure and function of the molecules of life (**Figure 1.13d**). Such researchers want to understand how biology works at the molecular and even atomic levels. Overall, the 20th century saw a progressive increase in the number of biologists who used an approach to understanding biology called **reductionism**—reducing complex systems to simpler components as a way to understand how the system works. In biology, reductionists study the parts of a cell or organism as individual units.

In the 1990s, the pendulum began to swing in the other direction. Scientists have invented new tools that allow them to study groups of genes (genomic techniques) and groups of proteins (proteomic techniques). Biologists now use the term **systems biology** to describe research aimed at understanding how emergent properties arise. This term is often applied to the study of cells. In this context, systems biology may involve the investigation of groups of genes that encode proteins with a common purpose (**Figure 1.13e**). For example, a systems biologist may conduct experiments that try to characterize an entire cellular process, which is driven by dozens of different proteins. However, systems biology is not new. Animal

Ecologists study species in their native environments.

(a) Ecology—population/ community/ecosystem levels

Anatomists and physiologists study how the structures of organisms are related to their functions.

(b) Anatomy and physiology— tissue/organ/organism levels

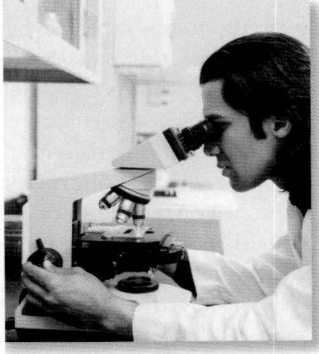

Cell biologists often use microscopes to learn how cells function.

(c) Cell biology—cellular levels

Molecular biologists and biochemists study the molecules and macromolecules that make up cells.

(d) Molecular biology— atomic/molecular levels

Systems biologists may study groups of molecules. The microarray shown in the inset determines the expression of many genes simultaneously.

(e) Systems biology—all levels, shown here at the molecular level

Figure 1.13 Biological investigation at different levels of organization. a: ©Diane Nelson; b: ©Purestock/SuperStock; c: ©Erik Isakson/Blend Images; d: ©Northwestern, Shu-Ling Zhou/AP Images; e: ©Andrew Brookes/Corbis/ Getty Images; e (inset): ©Alfred Pasieka/Science Source

and plant physiologists have been studying the functions of complex organ systems for centuries. Likewise, ecologists have been characterizing ecosystems for a very long time. The excitement surrounding systems biology in recent years has been the result of new experimental tools that allow biologists to study complex interactions at the molecular level.

A Hypothesis Is a Proposed Idea, Whereas a Theory Is a Broad Explanation Backed by Extensive Evidence

Let's now consider the process of science. In biology, a **hypothesis** is a proposed explanation for a natural phenomenon. It is a proposition based on previous observations or experimental studies. For example, with knowledge of seasonal changes, you might hypothesize that maple trees drop their leaves in the autumn because of the shortened amount of daylight. An alternative hypothesis might be that the trees drop their leaves because of lower temperatures. In biology, a hypothesis requires more work by researchers to evaluate its validity.

A useful hypothesis must make **predictions**—expected outcomes that can be shown to be correct or incorrect. In other words, a useful hypothesis is **testable**. If a hypothesis is incorrect, it should be **falsifiable**, which means that it can be shown to be incorrect by additional observations or experimentation. Alternatively, a hypothesis may be correct, so further work will not disprove it. In such cases, we say that the researchers have failed to reject the hypothesis. Even so, in science, a hypothesis is never really proven but rather always remains provisional. Researchers accept the possibility that perhaps they have not yet conceived of the correct hypothesis. After many experiments, biologists may conclude that a hypothesis is consistent with known data, but they should never say the hypothesis is proven.

By comparison, the term **theory**, as it is used in biology, is a broad explanation of some aspect of the natural world that is substantiated by a large body of evidence. Biological theories incorporate observations, hypothesis testing, and the laws of other disciplines such as chemistry and physics. Theories are powerful because they allow us to make many predictions about the properties of living organisms. As an example, let's consider the theory that DNA is the genetic material and that it is organized into units called genes. An overwhelming body of evidence has substantiated this theory. Thousands of living species have been analyzed at the molecular level. All of them have been found to use DNA as their genetic material and to express genes that produce the proteins that lead to their characteristics. This theory makes many valid predictions. For example, certain types of mutations in genes are expected to affect the traits of organisms. This prediction has been confirmed experimentally. Similarly, this theory predicts that genetic material is copied and transmitted from parents to offspring. By comparing the DNA of parents and offspring, this prediction has also been confirmed. Furthermore, the theory explains the observation that offspring resemble their parents. Overall, two key attributes of a scientific theory are (1) consistency with a vast amount of known data and (2) the ability to make many correct predictions.

The meaning of "theory" is sometimes muddled because the word is used in different situations. In everyday language, a theory is often viewed as little more than a guess. For example, a person might say, "My theory is that Professor Simpson did not come to class today because he went to the beach." However, in biology, a theory is much more than a guess. A theory is an established set of ideas that explains a vast amount of data and offers valid predictions that can be tested. Like a hypothesis, a theory can never be proven to be true. Scientists acknowledge that they do not know everything. Even so, biologists would say that theories are extremely likely to be true, based on all known information. In this regard, theories are viewed as **knowledge**, which is the awareness and understanding of information.

Discovery-Based Science and Hypothesis Testing Are Scientific Approaches That Help Us Understand Biology

The path that leads to an important discovery is rarely a straight line. Rather, scientists ask questions, make observations, ask modified questions, and may eventually conduct experiments to test their hypotheses. The first attempts at experimentation may fail, and new experimental approaches may be needed. To suggest that scientists follow a rigid scientific method is an oversimplification of the process of science. Scientific advances often occur as scientists dig deeper and deeper into a topic that interests them. Curiosity is the key phenomenon that sparks scientific inquiry. How is biology actually conducted? As discussed next, researchers typically follow two general types of approaches: discovery-based science and hypothesis testing.

Discovery-Based Science   The collection and analysis of data without the need for a preconceived hypothesis is called **discovery-based science**, or simply **discovery science**. Why is discovery-based science carried out? The information gained from discovery-based science may lead to the formation of new hypotheses and, in the long run, may have practical applications that benefit people. Researchers, for example, have identified and begun to investigate previously unknown genes within the human genome without already knowing the function of those genes. The goal is to gather additional clues that may eventually allow them to propose a hypothesis that explains a gene's function. Discovery-based science often leads to hypothesis testing.

Hypothesis Testing   In biological science, the scientific method, also known as **hypothesis testing**, is usually followed to formulate and test the validity of a hypothesis. This strategy may be described as a five-step method:

1. Observations are made regarding natural phenomena.
2. These observations lead to a hypothesis that tries to explain the phenomena. A useful hypothesis is one that is testable because it makes specific predictions.
3. Experimentation is conducted to determine if the predictions are correct.
4. The data from the experiment are analyzed.
5. The hypothesis is considered to be consistent with the data, or it is rejected.

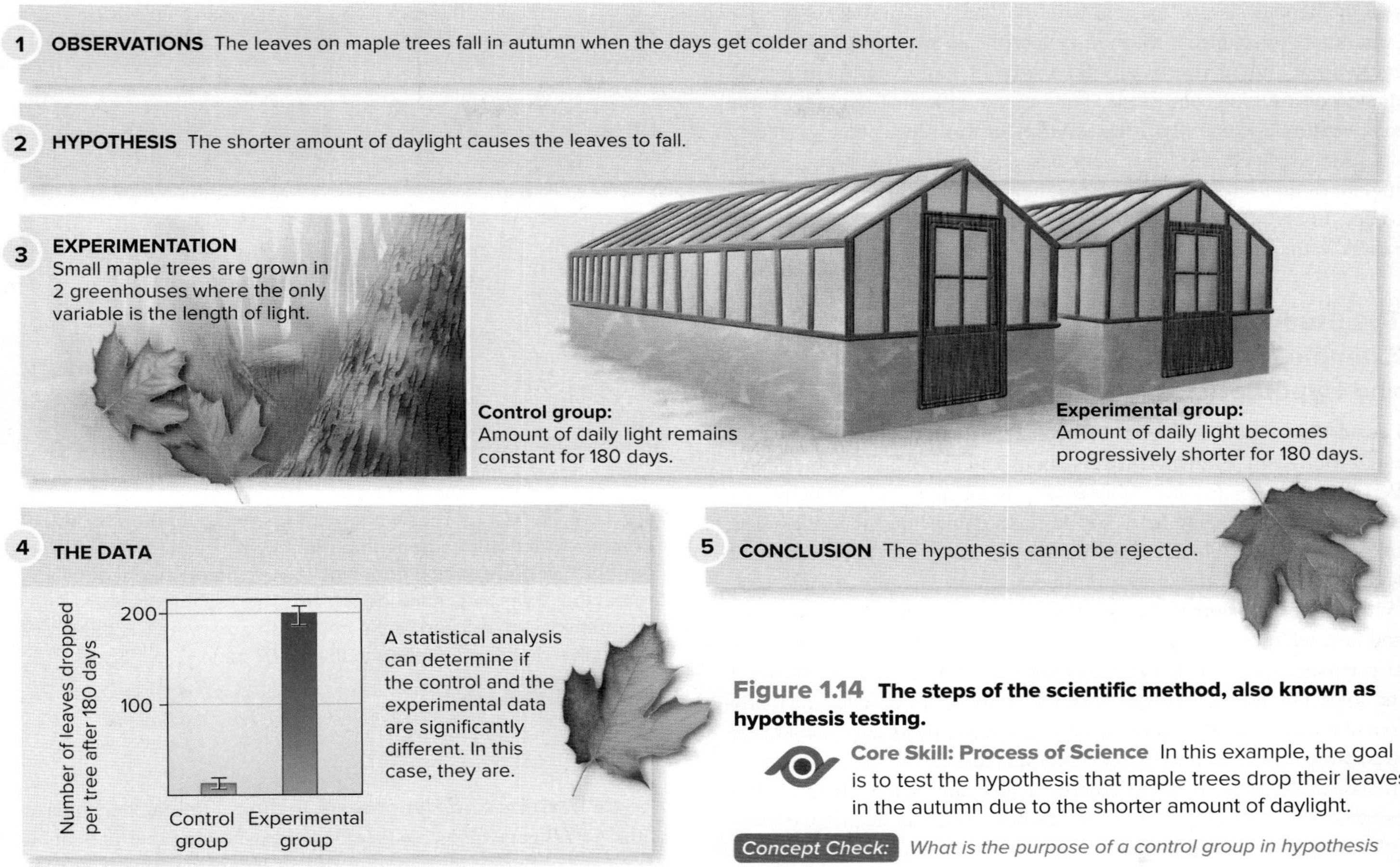

1 **OBSERVATIONS** The leaves on maple trees fall in autumn when the days get colder and shorter.

2 **HYPOTHESIS** The shorter amount of daylight causes the leaves to fall.

3 **EXPERIMENTATION**
Small maple trees are grown in 2 greenhouses where the only variable is the length of light.

Control group:
Amount of daily light remains constant for 180 days.

Experimental group:
Amount of daily light becomes progressively shorter for 180 days.

4 **THE DATA**

A statistical analysis can determine if the control and the experimental data are significantly different. In this case, they are.

5 **CONCLUSION** The hypothesis cannot be rejected.

Figure 1.14 The steps of the scientific method, also known as hypothesis testing.

Core Skill: Process of Science In this example, the goal is to test the hypothesis that maple trees drop their leaves in the autumn due to the shorter amount of daylight.

Concept Check: *What is the purpose of a control group in hypothesis testing?*

The scientific method is intended to be an objective way to gather knowledge. As an example, let's return to the question of why maple trees drop their leaves in autumn. By observing the length of daylight throughout the year and comparing that data with the time of the year when leaves fall, one hypothesis might be that leaves fall in response to a shorter amount of daylight (**Figure 1.14**). This hypothesis makes a prediction—exposure of maple trees to shorter periods of daylight will cause their leaves to fall. To test this prediction, researchers would design and conduct an experiment.

How is hypothesis testing conducted? Although hypothesis testing may follow many paths, certain experimental features are common to this approach. First, data are often collected in two parallel ways. One set of experiments is done on the **control group**, while another set is conducted on the **experimental group**. In an ideal experiment, the control and experimental groups differ by only one factor. For example, an experiment could be conducted in which two groups of trees are observed, and the only difference between their environments is the length of light each day. To conduct such an experiment, researchers would grow small trees in a greenhouse where they could keep other factors such as temperature, water, and nutrients the same between the control and experimental groups, while providing the two groups with different amounts of light via artificial lighting. In the control group, the number of hours of light

provided is kept constant each day, whereas in the experimental group, the amount of light provided each day becomes progressively shorter to mimic seasonal light changes. The researchers would then record the number of leaves dropped by the two groups of trees over a certain period of time.

Another key feature of hypothesis testing is data analysis. The result of experimentation is a set of data from which a biologist tries to draw conclusions. Biology is a quantitative science. When experimentation involves control and experimental groups, a common form of analysis is to determine if the data collected from the two groups are truly different. Biologists apply statistical analyses to their data to determine if the outcomes from the control and experimental groups are likely to differ because of the single variable that is different between the two groups. When differences between the control and experimental data are statistically significant, they are not likely to have occurred as a matter of random chance.

In our example in Figure 1.14, the trees in the control group dropped far fewer leaves than did those in the experimental group. A statistical analysis could determine if the data collected from the two greenhouses are significantly different from each other. If the two sets of data are found not to be significantly different, the hypothesis will be rejected. Alternatively, if the differences between the two sets of data are significant, as shown in Figure 1.14, biologists can conclude that the hypothesis is consistent with the data, though it is not proven. A hallmark of science is that valid experiments are **repeatable**, which means that similar results are obtained when an experiment is conducted on multiple occasions. For our example in Figure 1.14, the data would be valid only if the experiment was repeatable.

As described next, discovery-based science and hypothesis testing are often used together to learn more about a particular scientific topic. As an example, let's look at how both approaches led to successes in the study of the disease called cystic fibrosis.

The Study of Cystic Fibrosis Provides Examples of Discovery-Based Science and Hypothesis Testing

Let's consider how biologists made discoveries related to the disease cystic fibrosis (CF), which affects about 1 in every 3,500 Americans. Persons with CF produce abnormally thick and sticky mucus that obstructs the lungs and leads to life-threatening lung infections. The thick mucus also blocks ducts in the pancreas, which prevents the digestive enzymes this organ produces from reaching the intestine. Without these enzymes, the intestine cannot fully absorb amino acids and fats, which can cause malnutrition. Persons with this disease may also experience liver damage because the thick mucus can obstruct the liver. On average, people with CF in the United States currently live into their late 30s. Fortunately, as more advances have been made in treatment, this number has steadily increased.

Because of its medical significance, many scientists are interested in CF and are conducting studies aimed at gaining greater information regarding its underlying cause. The hope is that knowing more about the disease may lead to improved treatment options, and perhaps even a cure. As described next, discovery-based science and hypothesis testing have been critical to gaining a better understanding of this disease.

The CFTR Gene and Discovery-Based Science   In 1935, American physician Dorothy Andersen determined that cystic fibrosis is a genetic disorder. Persons with CF have inherited two faulty *CFTR* genes, one from each parent. (We now know this gene encodes a protein named the cystic fibrosis transmembrane regulator, abbreviated *CFTR*.) In the 1980s, researchers used discovery-based science to identify this gene. Their search for the *CFTR* gene did not require any preconceived hypothesis regarding the function of the gene. Rather, they used genetic strategies similar to those described in Chapter 21. Research groups headed by Lap-Chee Tsui, Francis Collins, and John Riordan identified the *CFTR* gene in 1989.

The discovery of the *CFTR* gene made it possible to devise diagnostic testing methods to determine if a person carries a faulty version of that gene. In addition, the characterization of the *CFTR* gene provided important clues about its function. Researchers observed striking similarities between the *CFTR* gene and other genes that were already known to encode proteins that function in the transport of substances across membranes. Based on this observation, as well as other kinds of data, the scientists hypothesized that the function of the normal *CFTR* gene is to encode a transport protein. In this way, the identification of the *CFTR* gene led them to conduct experiments aimed at testing a hypothesis about its function.

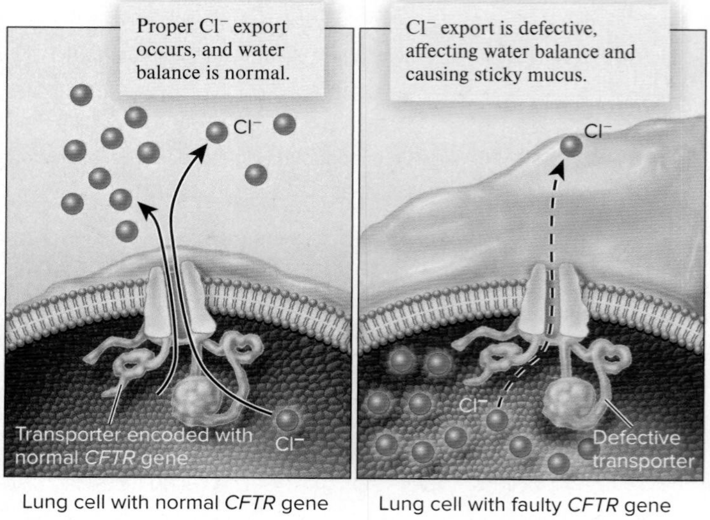

Figure 1.15   A hypothesis suggesting an explanation for the defective function of a gene in patients with cystic fibrosis. The normal *CFTR* gene, which does not carry a mutation, encodes a protein that transports chloride ions (Cl⁻) across the plasma membrane to the outside of the cell. In persons with CF, this protein is defective due to a mutation in the *CFTR* gene.

Concept Check: *Explain how discovery-based science helped researchers to hypothesize that the CFTR gene encodes a transport protein.*

The CFTR Gene and Hypothesis Testing   Researchers interested in the *CFTR* gene also considered studies showing that patients with CF have an abnormal regulation of salt balance across their plasma membranes. They hypothesized that the normal *CFTR* gene encodes a protein that functions in the transport of chloride ions (Cl⁻) across the membranes of cells (**Figure 1.15**). This hypothesis led to experimentation that tested normal cells and cells from CF patients for their ability to transport Cl⁻. The CF cells were found to be defective in chloride transport. In 1990, scientists successfully transferred the normal *CFTR* gene into cells from CF patients in the laboratory. The introduction of the normal gene corrected the cells' defect in chloride transport. Overall, the results showed that the *CFTR* gene encodes a protein that transports Cl⁻ across the plasma membrane. A mutation in this gene causes it to encode a defective protein, leading to a salt imbalance that affects water levels outside the cell, which explains the thick and sticky mucus in CF patients. In this example, hypothesis testing provided a way to evaluate a hypothesis about how a disease is caused by a genetic change.

Biology Is a Social Discipline

Finally, it is worthwhile to point out that biology is a social as well as a scientific discipline. Several laboratories often collaborate on scientific projects. After performing observations and experiments, biologists communicate their results in different ways. Most importantly, papers are submitted to scientific journals. Following submission, a paper usually undergoes a **peer-review process** in which other scientists, who are experts in the area, evaluate the paper and make comments regarding its quality. As a result of peer review, a paper is either accepted for publication or rejected, or the authors of the paper

Figure 1.16 **One of the social aspects of science.**
©Dita Alangkara/AP Images

 Core Skill: Communication and Collaboration At scientific meetings, researchers from various disciplines gather together to discuss new data and discoveries. Research that is conducted by professors, students, lab technicians, and industrial participants is sometimes hotly debated.

may be given suggestions for how to revise the work or conduct additional experiments to make it acceptable for publication.

Another social aspect of research is that biologists often attend meetings where they report their most recent work to the scientific community (**Figure 1.16**). They comment on each other's ideas and results, eventually putting together the information that builds into scientific theories over many years. As you develop your skills at scrutinizing experiments, it is helpful to discuss your ideas with other people, including fellow students and faculty members. Importantly, you do not need to "know all the answers" before you enter into a scientific discussion. Instead, a more realistic way to view science is as an ongoing and never-ending series of questions.

1.6 Core Skills of Biology

Learning Outcomes:

1. **CoreSKILL** » Describe the core skills of biology as identified by "Vision and Change."
2. **CoreSKILL** » Explain the process of science.
3. **CoreSKILL** » Describe what a model is in biology, and explain why models are useful.
4. **CoreSKILL** » List the types of problem-solving skills you will develop by completing BioTIPS.

In addition to the five core concepts of biology (see Section 1.2), the participants in "Vision and Change" also identified certain skills that students should develop so they can become successful in careers in biology. Educators need to focus on these skills, which are also referred to as core competencies:

- The ability to apply the process of science
- The ability to use quantitative reasoning

- The ability to use models and simulation
- The ability to tap into the interdisciplinary nature of science
- The ability to communicate and collaborate with professionals in other disciplines
- The ability to understand the relationship between science and society

In this section, we will consider the features of this textbook that will help you to develop these skills. These features are summarized below:

- Each chapter has a Feature Investigation that allows you to apply the process of science. Likewise, the BioTIPS features are aimed at helping you refine and apply your problem-solving skills.
- Quantitative reasoning is also a key component of the Feature Investigations. It is involved in answering many of the questions at the end of Feature Investigations, as well as many end-of-chapter questions and BioTIPS questions.
- A new feature of the fifth edition, introduced later in this section, is the Modeling Challenges. After learning about a particular topic in biology, you will be asked to either interpret a given model or propose your own model based on a scenario or data.
- The interdisciplinary nature of science is highlighted in features titled "Connections" that follow some figure legends.
- Another new feature of the fifth edition is the addition of a core skill called "Science and Society" following some of the figure legends.

The "Vision and Change" icon, ◉, that highlights core concepts throughout the text, also highlights material that promotes the core skills.

Core Skill: Process of Science

Feature Investigation | Observation and Experimentation Form the Core of Biology

Biology is largely about the process of discovery. Therefore, a recurring theme of this textbook is how scientists design experiments, analyze data, and draw conclusions. Although each chapter contains many examples of data collection and experiments, a consistent element is a Feature Investigation—which presents an actual study by current or past researchers. Some of these involve discovery-based science, in which biologists collect and interpret data in an attempt to make discoveries that are not hypothesis driven. Most Feature Investigations, however, involve hypothesis testing in which a hypothesis is stated and the experiment and resulting data are presented. Figure 1.14, illustrating the experiment with maple trees, shows the general form of Feature Investigations.

The Feature Investigations allow you to appreciate the connection between science and scientific theories. As you read a Feature Investigation, you may find yourself thinking about different approaches and alternative hypotheses. Different people can view the same data and arrive at very different conclusions. As you progress through the experiments in this textbook, we hope you will try to develop your own skills at formulating hypotheses, designing experiments, and interpreting data.

Experimental Questions

1. Discuss the difference between discovery-based science and hypothesis testing.
2. What are the steps in the scientific method, also called hypothesis testing?
3. **CoreSKILL »** In an experiment, explain how a control group and an experimental group differ from each other.

Model-Based Learning Will Enhance Your Understanding of Biological Concepts and Improve Your Critical-Thinking Skills

What is a model? A **scientific model**, or simply a model, is a conceptual, mathematical, or physical depiction of a real-world phenomenon. A model is a simplification and abstraction of a researcher's perception of reality. In biology, models are testable ideas that are usually derived from observations and experiments. Because of the vast amount of complexity and variation found in nature, all but the simplest models are imperfect depictions of living things, their working parts, and their interactions with the environment. The majority of figures in this textbook are models, based on the ideas of biologists and drawn by professional illustrators.

Why are models useful? One reason is they promote communication. Models allow scientists to convey their ideas in a relatively simple way. For example, a model of the human heart depicts how the parts of the heart work together to pump blood (look ahead to Figure 48.6). Another useful aspect of a model is that it can be used as a working hypothesis that helps researchers visualize or explain biological phenomena. Such models form the basis for conducting further experiments. Models are evaluated by their consistency with experimental data, which enables researchers to accept, reject, or refine them. Likewise, models allow biologists to make meaningful predictions. Such predictions can be refuted or supported via experimentation. A model for gene regulation in Chapter 14 predicts that a repressor protein inhibits gene expression (look ahead to Figure 14.7). This prediction was verified by experimentation, as shown in Figure 14.9. Finally, models can lead to conceptual frameworks. For example, the concept of a species niche, which is described in Chapter 57, was derived from species competition models and has subsequently become one of the most important concepts in ecology.

Models take on many different forms. Let's consider some common categories of models that you will see.

- *Structural models.* A structural model shows the physical structures of components that make up living organisms. Biochemists and biologists have proposed many different models that depict biological structures at the cellular and molecular level. Figure 3.13 is a collection of 20 models of the structures of amino acids that are found in proteins.
- *Mechanistic models.* A mechanistic model (also called a physiological model) describes the workings of the individual parts of a complex system, and the manner in which they interact. As an example, plant biologists have proposed two models, called symplastic and apoplastic transport, which describe two possible pathways by which minerals are taken into the root of a plant (look ahead to Figure 39.7).
- *Mathematical models.* A mathematical model is a description of a process or a system using mathematical concepts, symbols, and diagrams. Many mathematical models are presented as one or more equations. For example, ecologists use equations to describe two different modes of population growth, termed exponential and logistic growth. Such equations allow biologists to make predictions about population growth, which can be illustrated graphically (look ahead to Figure 56.10).
- *Temporal models.* A temporal model depicts a biological process as it occurs over a short or long period of time. In cell biology, some processes occur very quickly. For example, the absorption of light energy during photosynthesis occurs in less than a second (look ahead to Figure 8.11). In contrast, the evolution of new groups of species may occur on a timescale of millions of years (look ahead to Figure 26.4).
- *Hierarchical models.* In a hierarchical model, organisms, parts of organisms, or observations fall into nested levels. For example, the field of taxonomy organizes species into progressively smaller groups, such as kingdom, family, and genus (plural, genera). One or more genera are found within a family, and many different families are found within a kingdom (see Figure 1.11).

Some models incorporate two or more of these categories. Take a look at the model for DNA replication in Figure 11.17, which is a combination of a structural model, a mechanistic model, and a temporal model.

Model-based learning is an educational approach in which students evaluate or generate models as a way to enhance their understanding of scientific concepts and improve their critical-thinking skills. In this textbook, you will be engaged in this strategy via figures that present a modeling challenge. Each of these figures shows a model that pertains to a particular topic in biology. After you study this model, your modeling skills will be challenged in one of two different ways. In some cases, you will be given a second model and asked to explain it or describe what types of predictions can be made based on it (**Figure 1.17**). In other cases, you will be given a scenario and asked to generate your own model that is consistent with the scenario (**Figure 1.18**). Even though explaining and

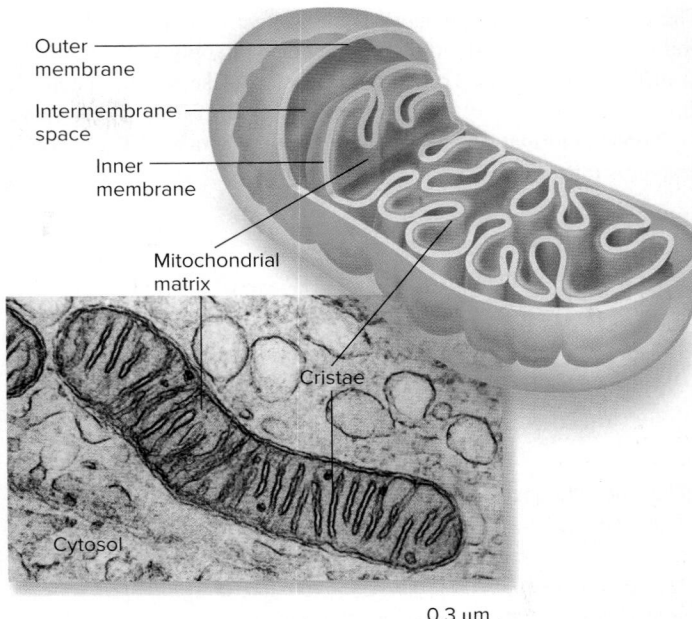

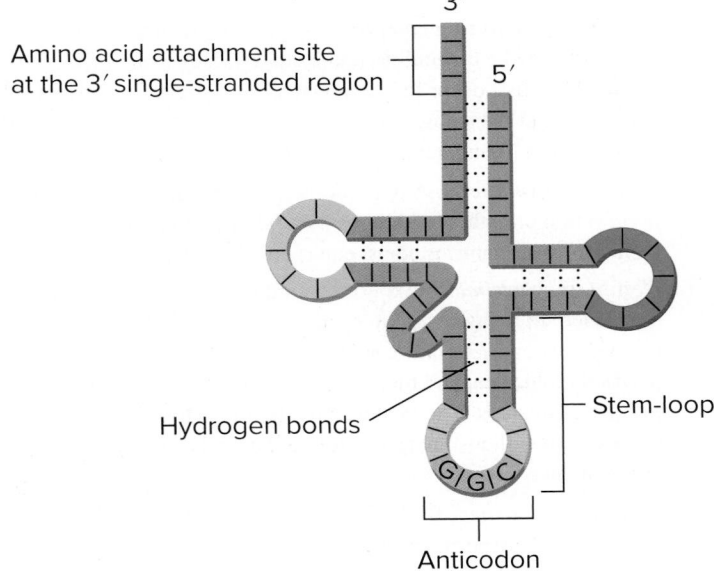

Figure 1.17 A modeling challenge to explain a revised model. This figure shows a model for the structure of a tRNA molecule, which is described in Chapter 12. The stem regions are regions where the RNA is double stranded as a result of complementary base pairing, in which A hydrogen-bonds to U, and G hydrogen-bonds with C. The modeling challenge below involves an alteration in this model.

Core Skill: Modeling In this modeling challenge, you are asked to explain how the model below differs from the one in Figure 1.17.

Modeling Challenge: In a tRNA molecule, four of the bases were changed. One A was changed to a G, and three C's were changed to U's. A model of the secondary structure of this altered tRNA is shown to the right. Explain where the altered bases are located and how the alteration affects the structure of the tRNA.

Figure 1.18 A modeling challenge to make a prediction. This figure shows the structure of a mitochondrion. It emphasizes the membrane organization of the mitochondrion, which has outer and inner membranes. The invaginations (infoldings) of the inner membrane, which are called cristae, occur because of the large surface area of that membrane. The modeling challenge below involves proposing an altered model. ©Don W. Fawcett/Science Source

Core Skill: Modeling This modeling challenge asks you to propose a model for the structure of a mitochondrion in the presence of a drug that decreases the surface area of the inner membrane.

Modeling Challenge: Let's suppose a cell is exposed to a drug that decreases the surface area of the inner mitochondrial membrane, but has no effect on the outer mitochondrial membrane. Draw a model of the structure of the mitochondrion in the presence of this drug.

generating models can be a challenge, the educational benefits are worth it. Give the modeling challenges a try.

BioTIPS Will Help You Improve Your Problem-Solving Skills

As you progress through this textbook, your learning will involve two general goals:

- You will gather foundational knowledge. In other words, you will be able to describe basic ideas and discoveries in biology. For example, you will be able to explain how photosynthesis works.

- You will develop skills that will allow you to apply that foundational knowledge in different ways. For example, you will learn how to use statistics to determine if a hypothesis is consistent with experimental data.

The combination of foundational knowledge and skills will enable you not only to understand biology but also to apply your knowledge in different situations. To help you develop these skills, Chapters 2 through 60 contain solved problems called **BioTIPS**, which stands for **T**opic, **I**nformation, and **P**roblem-Solving **S**trategy. These solved problems follow a consistent pattern.

THE QUESTION *All of the BioTIPS begin with a question. As an example, let's consider the following question:*

The following base sequence is found within a messenger RNA molecule:

AUG GGC CUU AGC

This segment carries the information to make a region of a polypeptide with the amino acid sequence methionine-glycine-leucine-serine. What would be the consequences if a mutation in the gene that encodes this mRNA changed the second cytosine (C) in the base sequence to an adenine (A)?

T OPIC **What topic in biology does this question address?** The topic is gene expression. More specifically, the question is about the relationship between a base sequence and the genetic code.

I NFORMATION **What information do you know based on the question and your understanding of the topic?** In the question, you are given the base sequence of a short segment of an mRNA and told that one of the bases has been changed. From your understanding of the topic, you may remember that a polypeptide sequence is determined by reading the mRNA (transcribed from a gene) in groups of three bases called codons.

P ROBLEM-SOLVING **S** TRATEGY **Compare and contrast. Predict the outcome.** One strategy to begin to solve this problem is to compare the mRNA sequence before and after the mutation:

Original: AUG GGC CUU AGC
Mutant: AUG GGC AUU AGC

↑

ANSWER *The mutation has altered the sequence of bases in the mRNA, changing the third codon from CUU to AUU (see the arrow). Because codons specify amino acids, this may change the third amino acid in the polypeptide to something else. Note: If you look ahead to Table 12.1, you will see that CUU specifies leucine, whereas AUU specifies isoleucine. Therefore, you can predict that the mutation will change the third amino acid from leucine to isoleucine.*

Though many different problem-solving strategies exist, **BioTIPS** will focus on 11 strategies that will help you solve problems. You will see these strategies over and over again as you progress through this textbook:

1. ***Make a drawing***. Biology problems are often difficult to solve in your head. Making a drawing may make a big difference in your ability to see the solution.

2. ***Compare and contrast***. Making a direct comparison between two biological structures or processes may help you understand how they are similar and how they are different.

3. ***Relate structure and function***. A recurring theme in biology is that structure determines function. This relationship holds true at many levels of biology, including the molecular, microscopic, and macroscopic levels. For some questions, you will need to understand how certain structural features are related to their biological functions.

4. ***Sort out the steps in a complicated process***. At first, some questions may be difficult to understand because they involve mechanisms that occur in a series of several steps. Sometimes, if you sort out the steps, you will be able to identify the key step that you need to understand to solve the problem.

5. ***Propose a hypothesis***. A hypothesis is an attempt to explain an observation or data. Hypotheses may be made in many forms including statements, models, equations, and diagrams.

6. ***Design an experiment***. Experimental design lies at the heart of science. In many cases, an experiment begins with some type of starting material(s), such as strains of organisms or purified molecules, and then the starting materials are subjected to a series of steps. The Feature Investigations throughout the textbook will also help you refine the skill of designing experiments.

7. ***Predict the outcome***. Biologists may want to predict the outcome of an experiment.

8. ***Interpret data***. Experimentation involves the analysis of data. Such an analysis often involves the use of statistics to determine if the experimental and control data show significant differences. The interpretation of data allows scientists to propose models that describe what the data may mean.

9. ***Use statistics***. A variety of different statistical methods are used to analyze data and make conclusions about what they mean.

10. ***Make a calculation***. Biology is a quantitative science. Researchers have devised mathematical relationships that help them understand and predict biological phenomena. Becoming familiar with these mathematical relationships will help you to better understand biological concepts and to make predictions.

11. ***Search the literature***. The goal here is to be able to read and explain a scientific article, and extract useful information.

For most problems in this textbook, one or more of these strategies may help you arrive at the correct solution. **BioTIPS** will provide you with practice in applying these problem-solving strategies.

Summary of Key Concepts

- Biology is the study of life. Discoveries in biology help us understand how life exists, and they also have many practical applications, such as the development of drugs to treat human diseases (Figures 1.1, 1.2, Table 1.1.).

1.1 Levels of Biology

- Living organisms can be viewed at different levels of biological organization: atoms, molecules and macromolecules, cells, tissues, organs, organisms, populations, communities, ecosystems, and the biosphere (Figure 1.3).

1.2 Core Concepts of Biology

- "Vision and Change" has identified five core concepts in biology (Figure 1.4). These are evolution; structure and function; information flow, exchange, and storage; pathways and transformations of energy and matter; and systems.

1.3 Biological Evolution

- Changes in species often occur as a result of modification of pre-existing structures (Figure 1.5).

- During vertical evolution, mutations in a lineage alter the characteristics of species from one generation to the next. Individuals with greater reproductive success are more likely to contribute to future generations, a process known as natural selection. Over the long run, this process alters species and may produce new species (Figure 1.6).

- Horizontal gene transfer is the transfer of genetic material from one organism to another organism that is not its offspring. Along with vertical descent with mutation, it is an important process in biological evolution, producing a web of life (Figures 1.7, 1.8).

- An analysis of genomes and proteomes helps us to understand how information at the molecular level relates to the characteristics of individuals and how they survive in their native environments (Figure 1.9).

1.4 Classification of Living Things

- Taxonomy is the grouping of species according to their evolutionary relatedness to other species. Going from broad to narrow groups, each species is placed into a domain, supergroup, kingdom, phylum, class, order, family, and genus (Figures 1.10, 1.11).

- The classification of species changes as biologists gather new information (Figure 1.12).

1.5 Biology as a Scientific Discipline

- Biological science is the observation, identification, experimental investigation, and theoretical explanation of natural phenomena.

- Biologists study life at different levels, ranging from ecosystems to the molecular components in cells (Figure 1.13).

- A hypothesis is a proposal to explain a natural phenomenon. A useful hypothesis makes a testable prediction. A biological theory is a broad explanation that is substantiated by a large body of evidence.

- Discovery-based science is an approach in which researchers conduct experiments and analyze data without a preconceived hypothesis.

- The scientific method, also called hypothesis testing, is a series of steps to formulate and test the validity of a hypothesis. The experimentation often involves a comparison between control and experimental groups (Figure 1.14).

- The study of cystic fibrosis provides an example in which both discovery-based science and hypothesis testing led to key insights regarding the nature of the disease (Figure 1.15).

- Biology is a social discipline in which scientists often work in teams. To be published, a scientific paper is usually subjected to a peer-review process in which other scientists evaluate the paper and make suggestions regarding its quality. Advances in science often occur when scientists gather and discuss their data (Figure 1.16).

1.6 Core Skills of Biology

- "Vision and Change" recognized the need to focus on the development of certain skills in students: the ability to apply the process of science; the ability to use quantitative reasoning; the ability to use models and simulation; the ability to tap into the interdisciplinary nature of science; the ability to communicate and collaborate with professionals in other disciplines; and the ability to understand the relationship between science and society.

- Each chapter in this textbook has a "Feature Investigation," an actual study by current or past researchers that highlights the experimental approach and helps you appreciate how science has led to key discoveries in biology.

- Biologists use models to convey their ideas, evaluate experiments, and make predictions that apply to their research studies. Modeling challenges will help you to understand and propose models (Figure 1.17, Figure 1.18).

- BioTIPS are intended to develop your problem-solving skills.

Assess & Discuss

Test Yourself

1. Which of the following is *not* a core concept of biology, as advocated by "Vision and Change"?
   a. Evolution
   b. Information flow, exchange, and storage
   c. Structure and function
   d. Taxonomy
   e. Pathways and transformation of energy and matter

2. Populations of organisms change over the course of many generations. Many of these changes are the result of greater reproductive success. This phenomenon is
   a. evolution.   d. genetics.
   b. homeostasis.   e. metabolism.
   c. development.

3. A biologist is studying the living organisms in a valley in western Colorado. She is studying
   a. an ecosystem.   d. a viable land mass.
   b. a community.   e. a population.
   c. the biosphere.

4. Which of the following is an example of horizontal gene transfer?
   a. the transmission of an eye color gene from father to daughter
   b. the transmission of a mutant gene causing cystic fibrosis from father to daughter

c. the transmission of a gene conferring pathogenicity (the ability to cause disease) from one bacterial species to another

d. the transmission of a gene conferring antibiotic resistance from a mother cell to its two daughter cells

e. all of the above.

5. The scientific name for humans is *Homo sapiens*. The name *Homo* is the _____ to which humans are classified.
   a. kingdom
   b. phylum
   c. order
   d. genus
   e. species

6. The complete genetic makeup of an organism is called its
   a. genus.
   b. genome.
   c. proteome.
   d. genotype.
   e. phenotype.

7. After observing certain desert plants in their native environment, a researcher proposes that they drop their leaves to conserve water. This is an example of
   a. a theory.
   b. a law.
   c. a prediction.
   d. a hypothesis.
   e. an experiment.

8. In science, a theory should
   a. be viewed as knowledge.
   b. be supported by a substantial body of evidence.
   c. provide the ability to make many correct predictions.
   d. do all of the above.
   e. b and c only.

9. Conducting research without a preconceived hypothesis is called
   a. discovery-based science.
   b. the scientific method.
   c. hypothesis testing.

d. a control experiment.

e. none of the above.

10. What is the purpose of using a control group in a scientific experiment?
    a. A control group allows the researcher to practice the experiment first before actually conducting it.
    b. A researcher can compare the results in the experimental group and control group to determine if a single variable is causing a particular outcome in the experimental group.
    c. A control group provides the framework for the entire experiment so the researcher can recall the procedures that should be conducted.
    d. A control group allows the researcher to conduct other experimental changes without disturbing the original experiment.
    e. all of the above.

Conceptual Questions

1. Of the five core concepts of biology described in Figure 1.4, which apply to individuals and which apply to populations?

2. Explain how it is possible for evolution to result in unity among different species yet also produce amazing diversity.

3. **Core Concept:** In your own words, describe the five core concepts of biology that are detailed at the beginning of this chapter in Figure 1.4.

Collaborative Questions

1. Discuss whether or not you think that theories in biology are true. Outside of biology, how do you decide if something is true?

2. In certain animals, such as alligators, sex is determined by temperature. When alligator eggs are exposed to low temperatures, most alligator embryos develop into females. Discuss how this phenomenon is related to genomes and proteomes.

UNIT I
CHEMISTRY

Living organisms are composed of chemicals, which are altered via chemical reactions. These reactions occur between atoms and molecules and may require, or in some cases release, energy. Chemical reactions and interactions between molecules play a role in virtually all aspects of a cell's activities. In order to understand how living organisms function, grow, develop, behave, and interact with their environments, therefore, we first need to understand some basic principles of atomic and molecular structure and the forces that allow atoms and molecules to interact with each other. We begin this unit with an overview of **inorganic chemistry**—that is, the nature of atoms and molecules, with the exception of those that contain rings or chains of carbon. Such carbon-containing molecules form the basis of **organic chemistry** and are covered in Chapter 3.

 The following Core Concepts and Core Skills will be emphasized in this unit:

- *Energy and matter: We will see how the chemical energy stored in the bonds of molecules, such as sugars and fats, can be released and used by living organisms to perform numerous functions that support life, including growth, digestion, and locomotion.*

- *Structure and function: As described in Chapter 3, the three-dimensional structure of molecules is critical in enabling them to carry out their function.*

- *Information: Nucleic acids, the basis of inherited genetic material, are first introduced in Chapter 3.*

- *Systems: You will learn in this unit how simple molecules are joined to create a more complex molecule with new biological properties. The newly created molecule has properties that are different from those of its component atoms.*

- *Science and society: In Chapter 2, we will see how an understanding of chemistry has transformed the ability of physicians to diagnose disease in humans. One example of an application of chemistry to medicine is the PET scan.*

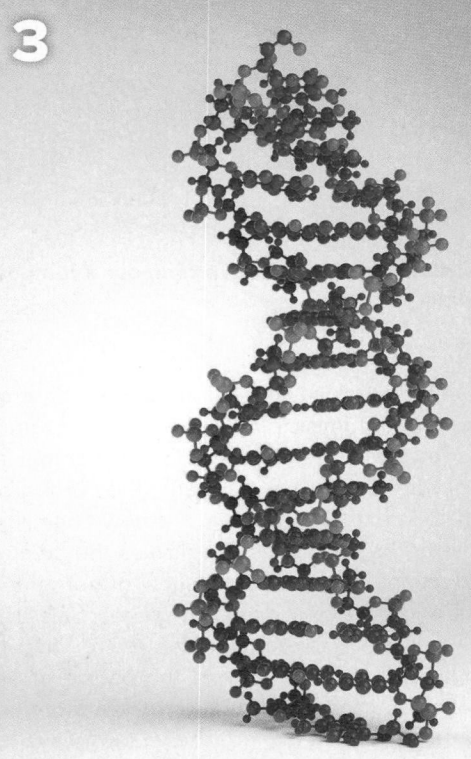

The Chemical Basis of Life I: Atoms, Molecules, and Water

2

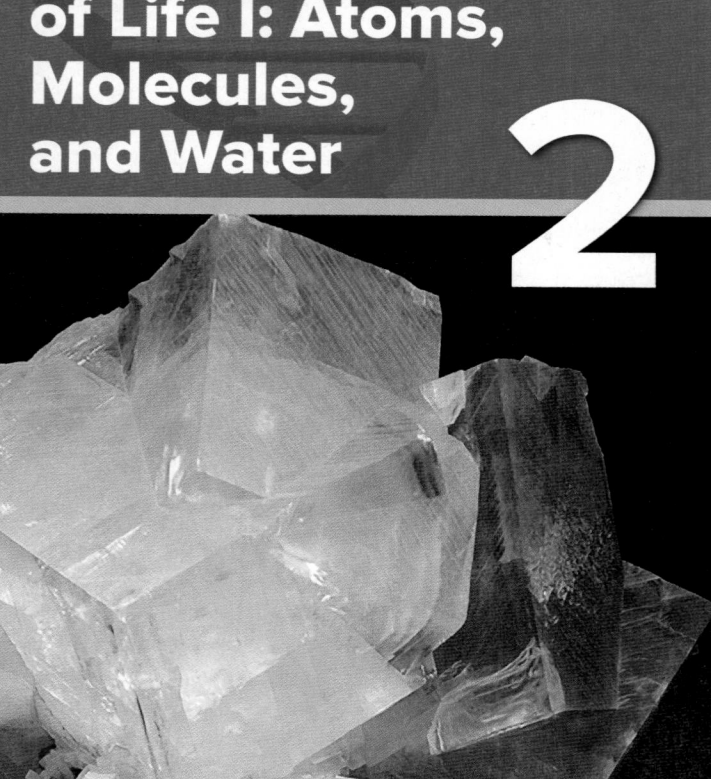

Crystals of sodium chloride (NaCl), a compound composed of two elements. ©Dr. Parvinder Sethi

Biology—the study of life—is founded on the principles of chemistry and physics. All living organisms are a collection of atoms and molecules bound together and interacting with each other through the forces of nature. Throughout this textbook, we will see how chemistry can be applied to living organisms as we discuss the components of cells, the functions of proteins, the flow of nutrients in plants and animals, and the evolution of new genes. This chapter lays the groundwork for understanding these and other concepts. We will begin with an overview of the nature of atoms and molecules, focusing on the structure of the atom and how it was discovered. We next explore the various ways that atoms combine with other atoms to create molecules, looking at the different types of chemical bonds between atoms, how these bonds form, and how they determine the structures of molecules. We end with an examination of the water molecule and the properties that make it a crucial component of living organisms and their environment.

2.1 Atoms

Learning Outcomes:

1. Describe the general structure of atoms.
2. **CoreSKILL »** Interpret the results of an experiment indicating that most of an atom is empty space.
3. Define orbital and electron shell.
4. Relate atomic structure to the periodic table of the elements.
5. **CoreSKILL »** Quantify atomic mass using units of daltons and moles.
6. Explain how a single element may exist in two or more forms, called isotopes, and how certain isotopes have importance in human medicine.
7. List the elements that make up most of the mass of all living organisms.

All life-forms are composed of **matter**, which is defined as anything that contains mass and occupies space. In living organisms, matter may exist in any of three states: solid, liquid, or gas. All matter is composed of **atoms**, which are the smallest functional units of matter that form all chemical substances and ultimately all organisms; they cannot be further broken down into other substances by ordinary chemical or physical means. Atoms, in turn, are composed of different types of smaller, subatomic particles. Chemists study the properties of atoms and **molecules**, which are two or more atoms bonded together. A major interest of the physicist, by contrast, is to uncover the properties of subatomic particles. Chemistry and physics merge in attempts to understand the mechanisms by which atoms and molecules interact. When atoms and molecules are studied in the context of a living organism, the science of biochemistry emerges. In this section, we will explore the physical properties of atoms so we can understand how atoms combine to form molecules of biological importance.

Atoms Are Composed of Subatomic Particles

The chemicals within living organisms are composed of many different types of atoms. The simplest atom, hydrogen, is approximately

0.1 nanometer (nm) in diameter, roughly one-millionth the diameter of a human hair. Each specific type of atom—nitrogen, hydrogen, oxygen, and so on—is called an **element** (or chemical element), which is defined as a pure substance made up of only one kind of atom.

Three subatomic particles—**protons** (p⁺), **neutrons** (n⁰), and **electrons** (e⁻)—are found within atoms (**Figure 2.1**). The protons and neutrons are confined to a very small volume at the center of an atom, the **atomic nucleus**, whereas the electrons are found in regions at various distances from the nucleus. In most atoms, the numbers of protons and electrons are identical, but the number of neutrons may vary. Each of the subatomic particles has a different electric charge. Protons have one unit of positive charge, electrons have one unit of negative charge, and neutrons are electrically neutral. Like charges repel each other, and opposite charges attract each other. The positive charges in the nucleus attract the negatively charged electrons.

Because the protons are located in the atomic nucleus, the nucleus has a net positive charge equal to the number of protons it contains. The entire atom has no net electric charge, however, because the number of negatively charged electrons around the nucleus is equal to the number of positively charged protons in the nucleus.

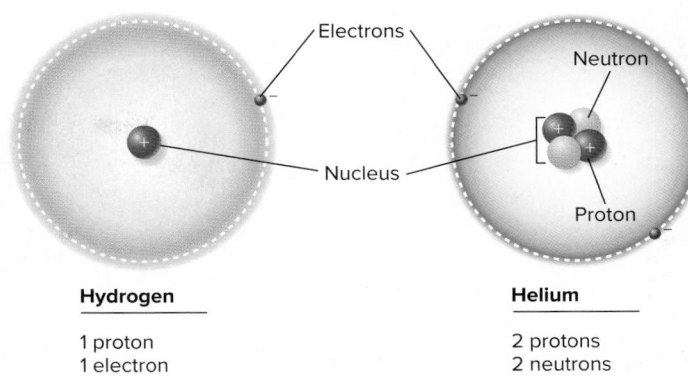

Hydrogen

1 proton
1 electron

Helium

2 protons
2 neutrons
2 electrons

Figure 2.1 Diagrams of two simple atoms. These are models of the two simplest atoms, hydrogen and helium. The nucleus consists of protons and neutrons, whereas electrons are found outside the nucleus. Note: In all figures of atoms, the sizes and distances are not to scale.

This basic concept of the structure of the atom was not established until a landmark experiment conducted by Ernest Rutherford during the years 1909–1911, as described next.

 Core Skill: Process of Science

Feature Investigation | Rutherford Determined the Modern Model of the Atom

Nobel laureate Ernest Rutherford was born in 1871 in New Zealand, but he did his greatest work at McGill University in Montreal, Canada, and later at the University of Manchester in England. At that time, scientists knew that atoms contained charged particles but had no idea how those particles were distributed. Neutrons had not yet been discovered, and many scientists, including Rutherford, hypothesized that the positive charge and the mass of an atom were evenly dispersed throughout the atom.

In a now-classic experiment, Rutherford aimed a fine beam of positively charged α (alpha) particles at an extremely thin sheet of gold foil only 400 atoms thick (**Figure 2.2**). α particles consist of two protons and two neutrons and are thus identical to the nuclei of helium atoms; you can think of them as helium atoms without their electrons (see Figure 2.1). Surrounding the gold foil were zinc sulfide screens that registered any α particles passing through or bouncing off the foil, much like film in a camera detects light. Rutherford hypothesized that if the positive charges of the gold atoms were uniformly distributed, many of the positively charged α particles would be slightly deflected, because one of the most important features of electric charge is that like charges repel each other. Due to their much smaller mass, he did not expect electrons in the gold atoms to have any effect on the ability of an α particle to move through the metal foil.

Figure 2.2 Rutherford's gold foil experiment, demonstrating that most of the volume of an atom is empty space.

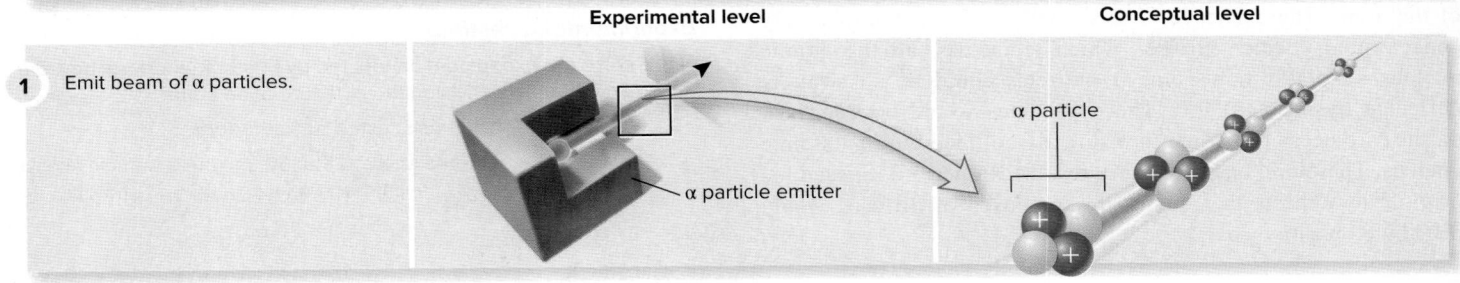

HYPOTHESIS Atoms in gold foil are composed of diffuse, evenly distributed positive charges that should usually cause α particles to be slightly deflected as they pass through.

KEY MATERIALS Thin sheet of gold foil, α particle emitter, zinc sulfide detection screen.

Experimental level

Conceptual level

1   Emit beam of α particles.

α particle emitter

α particle

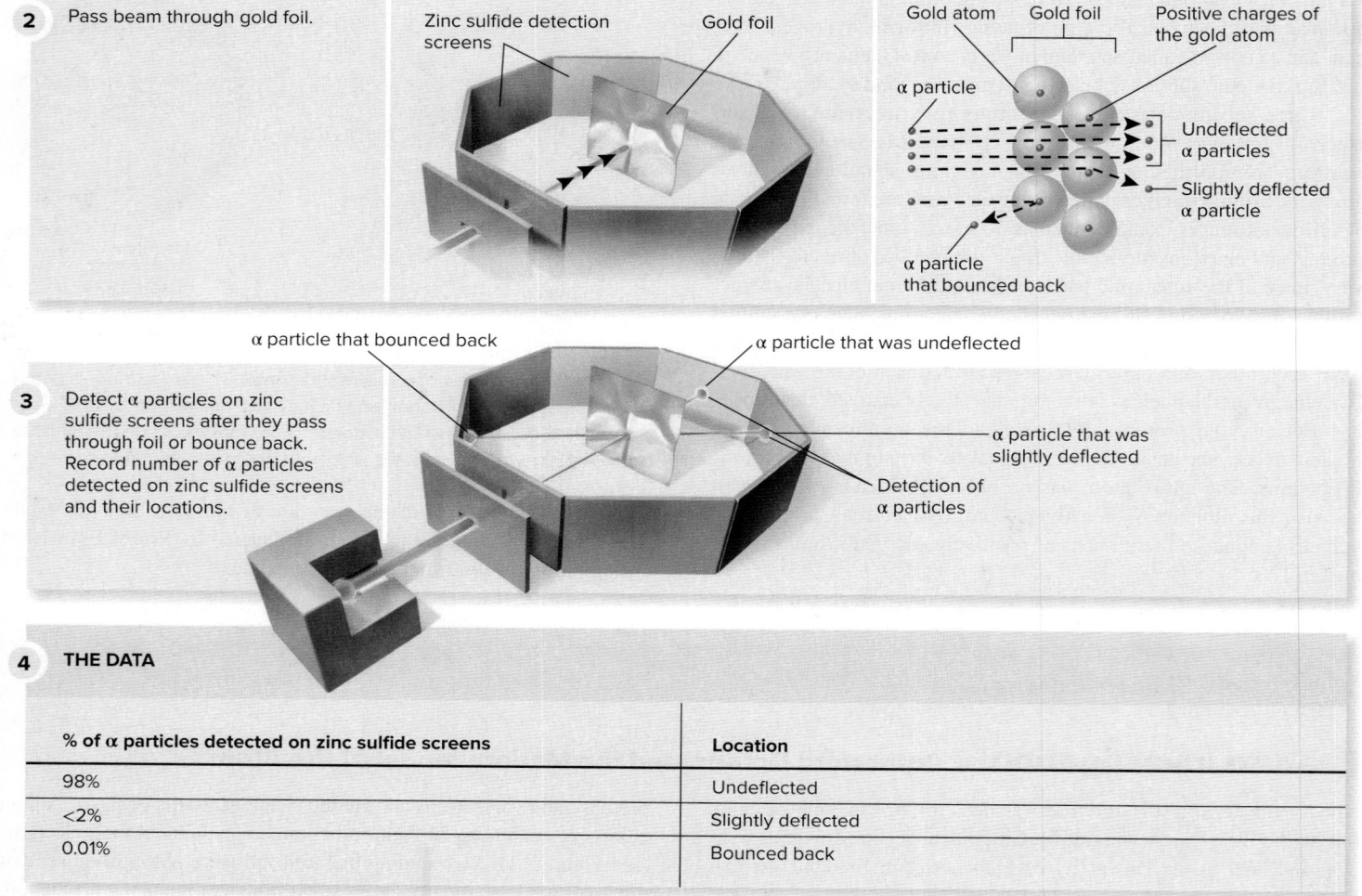

2 Pass beam through gold foil.

Zinc sulfide detection screens

Gold foil

Gold atom | Gold foil | Positive charges of the gold atom

α particle

Undeflected α particles

Slightly deflected α particle

α particle that bounced back

3 Detect α particles on zinc sulfide screens after they pass through foil or bounce back. Record number of α particles detected on zinc sulfide screens and their locations.

α particle that bounced back

α particle that was undeflected

α particle that was slightly deflected

Detection of α particles

4 THE DATA

% of α particles detected on zinc sulfide screens	Location
98%	Undeflected
<2%	Slightly deflected
0.01%	Bounced back

5 **CONCLUSION** The hypothesis is rejected. Most of the volume of an atom is empty space, with the positive charges concentrated in a small volume.

6 **SOURCE** Rutherford, E. 1911. The scattering of α and β particles by matter and the structure of the atom. *Philosophical Magazine* 21: 669–688.

Surprisingly, Rutherford discovered that more than 98% of the α particles passed right through the foil as though it was not there, and only a small percentage was slightly deflected; a few even bounced back at a sharp angle! To explain the 98% that passed right through, Rutherford concluded that most of the volume of an atom is empty space. To explain the few α particles that bounced back at a sharp angle, he postulated that most of the atom's positive charge was localized in a highly compact area at the center of the atom. The existence of this small, dense region of highly concentrated positive charge—which today we call the atomic nucleus—explains how some α particles could be so strongly deflected by the gold foil. The α particles would bounce back on the rare occasions when they directly collided with an atomic nucleus. Therefore, based on these results, Rutherford rejected his original hypothesis that atoms are composed of diffuse, evenly distributed positive charges.

From this experiment, without being able to actually visualize an atom, Rutherford proposed a model of an atom, with its small, positively charged nucleus surrounded at relatively great distances by negatively charged electrons. Today we know that more than 99.99% of an atom's volume is outside the nucleus. The nucleus accounts for only about 1/10,000 of an atom's diameter—most of an atom is empty space!

Experimental Questions

1. Before the experiment conducted by Ernest Rutherford, how did many scientists envision the structure of an atom?

2. What was the hypothesis tested by Rutherford?

3. **CoreSKILL »** The data showed that 98% of the α particles passed right through the gold foil. What is an interpretation of these results?

Electrons Occupy Orbitals Around an Atom's Nucleus

At one time, scientists visualized an atom as a mini–solar system, with the nucleus being the Sun and the electrons traveling in clearly defined orbits around it. Diagrams of the two simplest atoms—hydrogen and helium—which have the smallest numbers of protons, were shown in Figure 2.1. This model of the atom is now known to be an oversimplification, because as described shortly, electrons do not actually orbit the nucleus in defined paths like planets around the Sun. However, this depiction of an atom remains a convenient way to diagram atoms in two dimensions.

For complex reasons associated with the physics of subatomic particles, it is impossible to precisely predict the exact location of a given electron. We can only describe the region of space surrounding the atomic nucleus in which there is a high probability of finding that electron. Such a region is called an **orbital**. A better model of an atom, therefore, is a central nucleus surrounded by cloudlike orbitals. Some orbitals are spherical, called *s* orbitals, whereas others assume a shape that is often described as similar to a propeller or dumbbell and are called *p* orbitals (**Figure 2.3**). An orbital can contain a maximum of two electrons. Consequently, any atom with more than two electrons must contain more than one orbital.

Orbitals are found within **electron shells**, or energy levels. **Energy** can be defined as the capacity to do work or cause a change. Electrons have kinetic energy, that is, the energy of moving matter. The electron shells are numbered, with shell number 1 being closest to the nucleus. Different electron shells may contain one or more orbitals, each orbital holding up to two electrons. The innermost electron shell of all atoms has room for only two electrons, which spin in opposite directions within a spherical *s* orbital (1*s*). The second electron shell is composed of one spherical *s* orbital (2*s*) and

three dumbbell-shaped *p* orbitals (2*p*). Therefore, the second shell can hold up to four pairs of electrons, or eight electrons altogether (see Figure 2.3).

Electrons vary in the amount of energy they have. The shell closest to the nucleus fills up with the lowest energy electrons first, and then each subsequent shell fills with higher and higher energy electrons, one shell at a time. Within a given shell, the energy of electrons can also vary among different orbitals. In the second shell, for example, the *s* orbital has lower energy, whereas the three *p* orbitals have slightly higher and roughly equal energies. In that case, two electrons fill the *s* orbital first. Any additional electrons fill the *p* orbitals one electron at a time.

Although electrons are found in orbitals of varying shapes, as shown in Figure 2.3, scientists often use more simplified models when depicting the electron shells of atoms. **Figure 2.4a** presents an example of such a depiction of an atom of the element nitrogen. An atom of this element has seven protons and seven electrons. Two electrons fill the first shell, and five electrons are found in the outer shell. Two of these

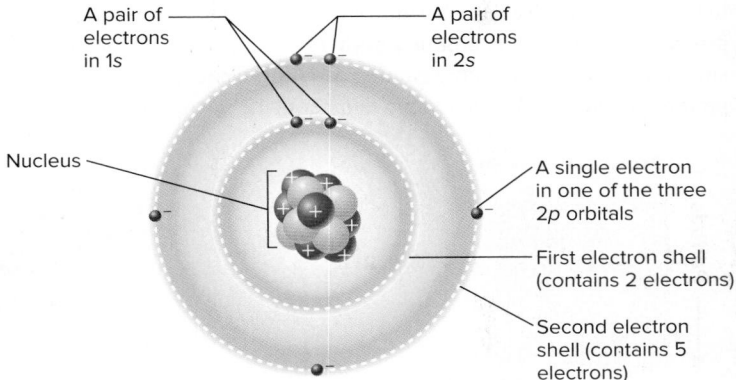

(a) Simplified depiction of a nitrogen atom

Orbital name	1s	2s	2p
	Nucleus		
Number of electrons per electron shell	2	2 per orbital; 8 total	
Orbital shape	Spherical	First orbital: spherical	Second to fourth orbital: dumbbell-shaped

Figure 2.3 **Diagrams of individual electron orbitals.** Electrons are found outside the nucleus in orbitals that may resemble spherical or dumbbell-shaped clouds. The orbital cloud represents a region in which the probability is high of locating a particular electron. For this illustration, only two shells are shown; the heaviest elements contain a total of seven shells.

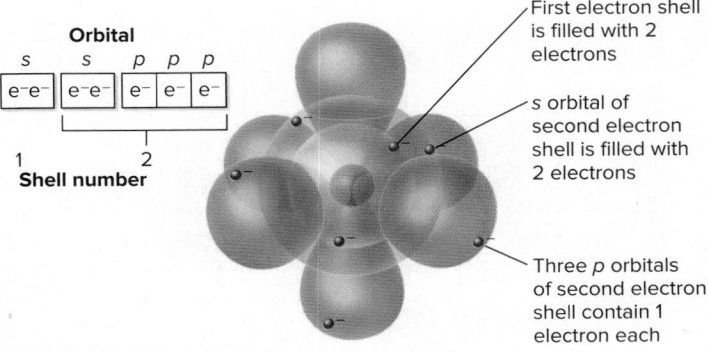

(b) Nitrogen atom showing electrons in orbitals

Figure 2.4 **Diagrams showing the multiple electron shells and orbitals of a nitrogen atom.** The nitrogen atom is shown **(a)** in a simplified depiction and **(b)** with all of its orbitals and shells. An atom's shells fill up one by one. In shells containing more than one orbital, the orbital with lowest energy fills first. Subsequent orbitals gain one electron at a time, shown schematically in boxes, where e⁻ represents an electron. Atoms of heavier elements contain additional shells and orbitals.

Concept Check: *Explain the difference between an electron shell and an orbital.*

fill the 2s orbital and are shown as a pair of electrons in the second shell. The other three electrons in the second shell are found singly in each of the three p orbitals. The diagram in Figure 2.4a makes it easy to see whether electrons are paired within the same orbital and whether the outer shell is full. **Figure 2.4b** is a more accurate model of a nitrogen atom, showing how the electrons occupy orbitals with different shapes.

Most atoms have outer shells that are not completely filled with electrons. Nitrogen, as we just saw, has a first shell filled with two electrons and a second shell with five electrons (see Figure 2.4a). Because the second shell can actually hold eight electrons, the outer shell of a nitrogen atom is not full. As discussed later in this chapter, atoms that have unfilled electron shells tend to share, release, or obtain electrons to fill their outer shell. Those electrons in the outermost shell are called the **valence electrons**. As you will learn shortly, such electrons allow atoms to form chemical bonds with each other, a process in which two or more atoms become joined together to create a new substance.

Each Element Has a Unique Number of Protons

Each chemical element has a specific and unique number of protons in its nucleus that distinguishes it from other elements. The number of protons in an atom is its **atomic number**. For example, hydrogen, the simplest atom, has an atomic number of 1, corresponding to its single proton. Magnesium has an atomic number of 12, corresponding to its

12 protons. With the exception of ions, which are described later, the number of protons and electrons in a given atom are identical. Therefore, the atomic number is also equal to the number of electrons in the atom, resulting in a net electric charge of zero.

Figure 2.5 shows the first three rows of the periodic table of the elements, which arranges the known elements according to their atomic numbers and electron shells (see Appendix A for the complete periodic table). A one- or two-letter symbol is used as an abbreviation for each element. The rows (known as periods) indicate the number of electron shells. For example, hydrogen (H) has one shell, lithium (Li) has two shells, and sodium (Na) has three shells. The columns (called groups) indicate the numbers of electrons in the outer shell. As you move along the columns from left to right, the outer shell of lithium (Li) has one electron, beryllium (Be) has two, boron (B) has three, and so forth. This organization of the periodic table tends to arrange elements based on similar chemical properties. The similarities of elements within a group occur because they have the same number of valence electrons, and therefore, they have similar chemical bonding properties.

Atoms Have a Small but Measurable Mass

Atoms are extremely small and thus have very little mass. A single hydrogen atom, for example, has a mass of about 1.67×10^{-24} g (grams). Protons and neutrons are nearly equal in mass, and each has

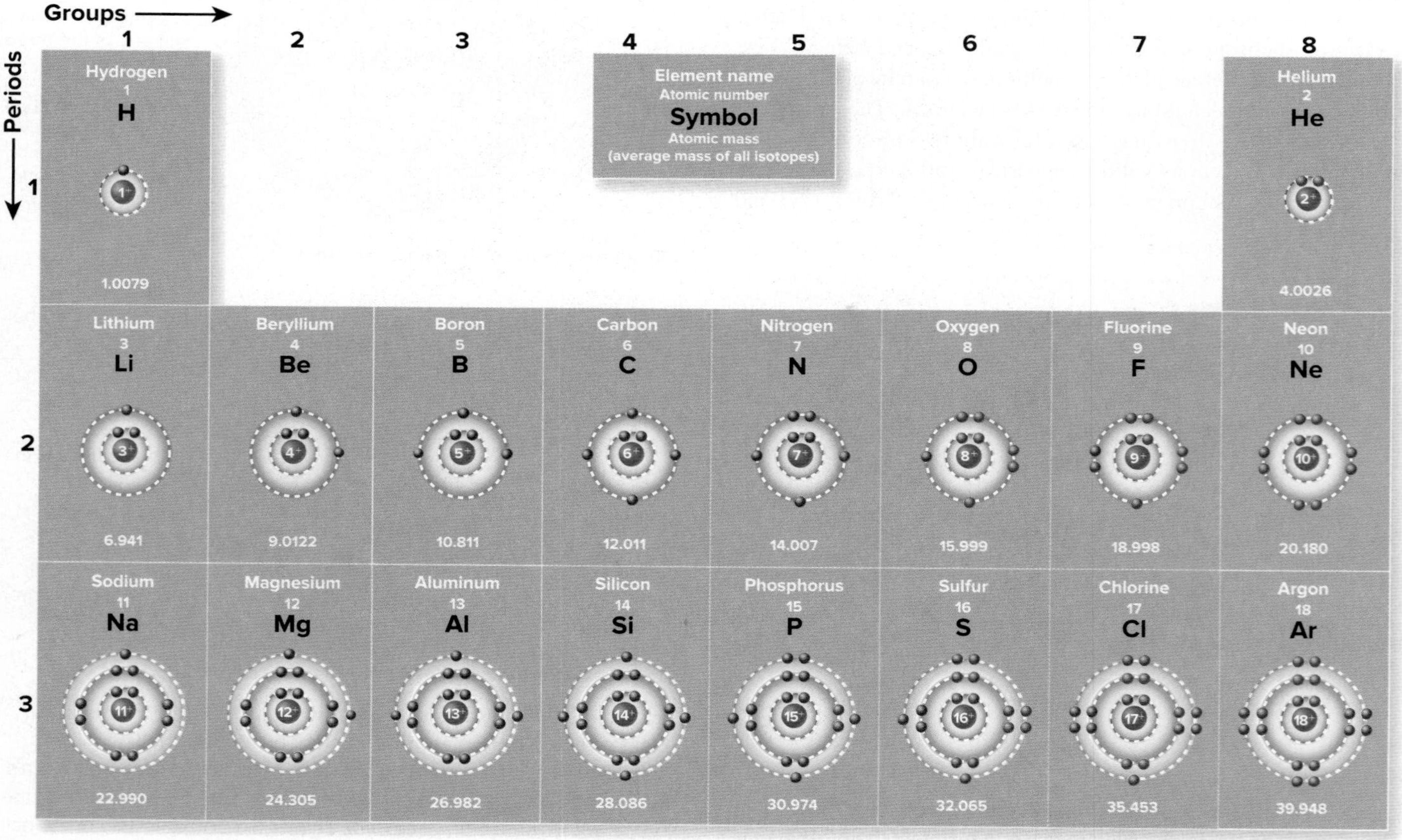

Figure 2.5 **The first three rows of the periodic table of the elements.** The elements are shown in models that depict the electron shells in different colors and show the total number of electrons in each shell. The occupancy of orbitals is that of the elements in their pure state. The red sphere represents the nucleus of the atom, and the numerical value with the $^+$ symbol represents the number of protons and, therefore, the positive charge of the nucleus. Elements are arranged in groups (columns) and periods (rows). For the complete periodic table, see Appendix A.

Table 2.1	Characteristics of Major Subatomic Particles		
Particle	Location	Charge	Mass relative to electron
Proton	Nucleus	+1	1,836
Neutron	Nucleus	0	1,839
Electron	Around the nucleus	−1	1

more than 1,800 times the mass of an electron (Table 2.1). Because of their tiny size relative to protons and neutrons, the mass of the electrons in an atom is ignored in calculations of atomic mass.

The **atomic mass** indicates an atom's mass relative to the masses of other atoms. By convention, the most common type of carbon atom, which has six protons and six neutrons, is assigned an atomic mass of exactly 12. On this scale, a hydrogen atom has an atomic mass of 1, indicating that it has 1/12 the mass of a carbon atom. A magnesium atom, with an atomic mass of 24, has twice the mass of a carbon atom.

The term mass is sometimes confused with weight, but these two terms refer to different features of matter. Weight is derived from the gravitational pull on a given mass. For example, a man who weighs 154 pounds on Earth would weigh only 25 pounds if he were standing on the Moon, and he would weigh 21 trillion pounds if he could stand on a neutron star. However, his mass is the same in all locations because he has the same amount of matter.

Atomic mass is measured in units called daltons, after the English chemist John Dalton, who postulated that matter is composed of tiny indivisible units he called atoms and laid the groundwork for atomic theory. One **dalton (Da)**, also known as an atomic mass unit (amu), equals 1/12 the mass of a carbon atom, or about the mass of a proton or a hydrogen atom. Therefore, the most common type of carbon atom has an atomic mass of 12 Da.

Because atoms such as hydrogen have a small mass, but atoms such as carbon have a larger mass, 1 g of hydrogen contains more atoms than 1 g of carbon. A **mole** (mol) of any substance contains the same number of particles as there are atoms in exactly 12 g of carbon. Twelve grams of carbon equals 1 mol of carbon, and 1 g of hydrogen equals 1 mol of hydrogen. As first described by Italian physicist Amedeo Avogadro, 1 mole of any element contains the same number of atoms—6.022×10^{23}. For example, 12 g of carbon contains 6.022×10^{23} atoms, and 1 g of hydrogen, whose atoms have 1/12 the mass of a carbon atom, also contains 6.022×10^{23} atoms. This number is known as Avogadro's number. To visualize the enormity of this number, imagine that people could pass through a turnstile at a rate of 1 million people per second. Even at that incredible rate, it would require almost 20 billion years for 6.022×10^{23} people to go through that turnstile!

Isotopes Vary in Their Number of Neutrons

Many elements can exist in multiple forms, called **isotopes**, that differ in the number of neutrons they contain. For example, the most abundant form of the carbon atom, ^{12}C, contains six protons and six neutrons, and thus has an atomic number of 6 and an atomic mass of 12 Da. The superscript placed to the left of ^{12}C is the sum of the protons and neutrons. The rare carbon isotope ^{14}C, however, contains six protons and eight neutrons. Although ^{14}C has an atomic number of 6, it has an atomic mass of 14 Da. Nearly 99% of the carbon in living organisms is ^{12}C. Consequently, the average atomic mass of carbon is slightly greater than 12 Da because of the existence of a small amount of heavier isotopes. This explains why the atomic masses given in the periodic table do not add up exactly to the predicted masses based on the atomic number and the number of neutrons of a given atom (for example, see carbon in Figure 2.5).

Isotopes of an atom have similar chemical properties but may have very different physical properties. For example, many isotopes found in nature are inherently unstable; the length of time they persist is measured in half-lives—a half-life is the time it takes for 50% of an isotope to decay. Such unstable isotopes are called **radioisotopes**. They emit radiation, which converts them to a stable form. At the very low amounts found in nature, radioisotopes usually pose no serious threat to life, but exposure of living organisms to high amounts of radioactivity can result in the disruption of cellular function, cancer, and even death.

Modern medical treatment and diagnosis make use of the special properties of radioactive compounds in many ways. For example, beams of high-energy radiation can be directed onto cancerous parts of the body to kill cancer cells. In another example, one or more atoms in the metabolically important sugar molecule glucose can be chemically replaced with a radioactive isotope of fluorine (^{18}F) to create a molecule called fluorodeoxyglucose (FDG). ^{18}F has a half-life of about 110 minutes. When a solution containing such modified radioactive glucose is injected into a person's bloodstream, the organs of the body take up the molecules from the blood just as they would ordinary glucose. Special imaging techniques, such as the positron-emission tomography (PET) scan shown in Figure 2.6, can detect the amount of the radioactive FDG in the body's organs. In this way, it is possible to visualize whether organs such as the lungs or brain are functioning normally, or at an increased or decreased rate. For example, cancer cells tend to take up much more glucose than normal cells do. Therefore, PET scans can reveal the presence of cancer—a disease characterized by uncontrolled cell growth. The scan of the individual shown in Figure 2.6, for example, identified numerous regions of high activity, suggestive of cancer.

The Mass of All Living Organisms Is Largely Composed of Four Elements

Just four elements—oxygen, carbon, hydrogen, and nitrogen—account for the vast majority of atoms in living organisms (Table 2.2). These elements typically make up about 95% of the mass of living organisms. Much of the oxygen and hydrogen occur in the form of water, which accounts for approximately 60% of the mass of most animals and up to 95% or more in some plants. Carbon is a major building block of all living matter, and nitrogen is a vital element in all proteins. Note in Table 2.2 that although hydrogen accounts for about 63% of the atoms in the body, it makes up only a small percentage of the mass of the human body. That is because the atomic mass of hydrogen is so much smaller than that of heavier elements such as oxygen.

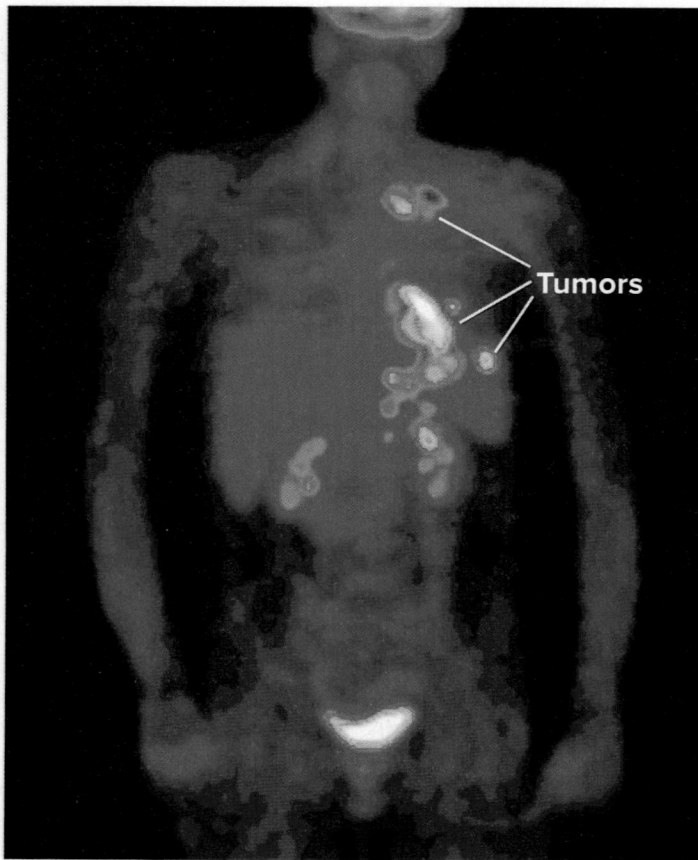

Figure 2.6 Diagnostic image of the human body using radioisotopes. An imaging technique called positron-emission tomography (PET) highlights regions of the body that are actively using glucose, the body's major energy source. Radioactivity in this image shows up as a color. The bright patches are regions of extremely intense activity, some of which were later determined to be cancer in this patient. Note: In this PET scan, the brain, kidneys, and bladder are not cancerous. The brain naturally uses a high amount of glucose. The kidneys filter the blood, and the bladder accumulates urine, which contains some glucose. ©Steven Needell/Science Source

 Core Skill: Science and Society Applying an understanding of chemistry to biology has transformed the ability of physicians to diagnose diseases in humans. In the United States alone, between 1 and 2 million PET scans such as this one are performed each year, helping to localize the sites and extent of diseased structures, greatly facilitating subsequent drug or surgical treatments.

Other important elements in living organisms include the mineral elements. Calcium and phosphorus, for example, are important constituents of the skeletons and shells of animals. Minerals such as potassium and sodium are key regulators of water movement and of electric currents that occur across the surfaces of many cells.

In addition, all living organisms require **trace elements**. These elements are present in extremely small quantities but are essential for normal growth and function. For example, iron plays an important role in how vertebrates transport oxygen in their blood, and copper serves a similar role in some invertebrates.

Table 2.2	Chemical Elements Essential for Life in Many Organisms*		
Most abundant in living organisms (approximately 95% of total mass)			
Element	Symbol	% Human body mass	% All atoms in human body
Oxygen	O	65	25.5
Carbon	C	18	9.5
Hydrogen	H	9	63.0
Nitrogen	N	3	1.4
Mineral elements (less than 1% of total mass)			
Calcium	Ca	Potassium	K
Chlorine	Cl	Sodium	Na
Magnesium	Mg	Sulfur	S
Phosphorus	P		
Trace elements (less than 0.01% of total mass)			
Boron	B	Manganese	Mn
Chromium	Cr	Molybdenum	Mo
Cobalt	Co	Selenium	Se
Copper	Cu	Silicon	Si
Fluorine	F	Tin	Sn
Iodine	I	Vanadium	V
Iron	Fe	Zinc	Zn

*Although these are the most common elements in living organisms, many other trace and mineral elements have reported functions. For example, aluminum is believed to be a cofactor for certain chemical reactions in animals, but it is generally toxic to plants.

2.2 Chemical Bonds and Molecules

Learning Outcomes:

1. Compare and contrast the types of atomic interactions that lead to the formation of molecules.
2. Explain the concept of electronegativity, and describe how it contributes to the formation of polar and nonpolar covalent bonds.
3. Describe how a molecule's shape is important to its ability to interact with other molecules.
4. Relate the concepts of a chemical reaction and chemical equilibrium.

The linkage of atoms with other atoms serves as the basis for life and also gives life its great diversity. Two or more atoms bonded together make up a molecule. For example, two oxygen atoms can combine to form one oxygen molecule, represented as O_2. This representation is called a **molecular formula**. It consists of the chemical symbols for all of the atoms that are present (here, O for oxygen) and a subscript that tells you how many of those atoms are present in the molecule (in this case, two). The term **compound** refers to a molecule composed of two or more different elements. Examples include water (H_2O), with two hydrogen atoms and one oxygen atom, and the sugar glucose ($C_6H_{12}O_6$), which has 6 carbon atoms, 12 hydrogen atoms, and 6 oxygen atoms.

One of the most important features of compounds is their emergent properties. This means that the properties of a compound differ greatly from those of its elements. Let's consider sodium as an example. Pure sodium (Na) is a soft, silvery white metal that can be cut with a knife. When sodium forms a compound with chlorine (Cl), table salt (NaCl) results. NaCl is a white, relatively hard crystal (as seen in the chapter opening photo) that dissolves in water. Thus, the properties of a compound can be dramatically different from the properties of the elements that combined to form it.

The atoms in molecules are held together by chemical bonds. In this section, we will examine the different types of chemical bonds, how those bonds form, and how they determine the structures of molecules.

Covalent Bonds Are Formed When Atoms Share Electrons to Fill Their Outer Shells

A **covalent bond** is a chemical bond in which two atoms share a pair of electrons. Covalent bonds can occur between atoms whose outer shells are not full. A fundamental principle of chemistry is the following:

Atoms tend to be most stable when their outer shells are filled with electrons.

Figure 2.7 shows this principle as it applies to the formation of hydrogen fluoride (HF), a molecule with many important industrial and medical applications, such as petroleum refining and pharmaceutical production. The outer shell of a hydrogen atom is full when it contains two electrons, though a hydrogen atom has only one electron. The outer shell of a fluorine atom is full when it contains eight electrons, though a fluorine atom has only seven electrons in its outer shell. In the HF molecule, the two atoms share a pair of electrons, which spend time in the outer shells of both atoms. This allows both of the outer shells to be full. Covalent bonds are strong chemical bonds, because the shared electrons behave as if they belong to each atom.

Chemists sometimes depict molecules with a **structural formula** in which each covalent bond is represented by a line indicating a pair of shared electrons. For example, HF is depicted as

H—F

A molecule of water (H_2O) can be represented as

H—O—H

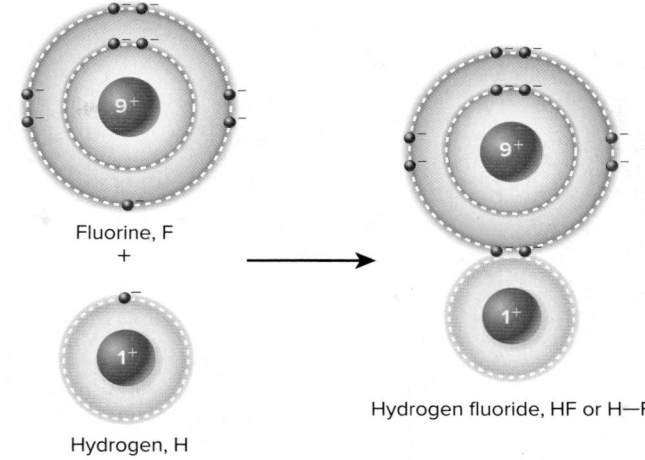

Fluorine, F
+
Hydrogen, H

Hydrogen fluoride, HF or H—F

Figure 2.7   The formation of a covalent bond. In a covalent bond, electrons from the outer shells of two atoms are shared with each other in order to complete both outer shells. This simplified illustration shows hydrogen forming a covalent bond with fluorine.

The structural formula of water indicates that the oxygen atom forms a covalent bond with both hydrogen atoms.

Each atom forms a characteristic number of covalent bonds, which depends on the number of electrons required to fill the outer shell. The atoms of some elements important for life, notably carbon, form more than one covalent bond and become linked simultaneously to two or more other atoms. Figure 2.8 shows the number of covalent bonds formed by several atoms commonly found in the molecules of living cells—hydrogen, oxygen, nitrogen, and carbon.

For many types of atoms, their outermost shell is full when it contains eight electrons, an octet. The **octet rule** states that many atoms are most stable when they have eight electrons in their outermost electron shell. This rule applies to most atoms found in living organisms, including oxygen, nitrogen, carbon, phosphorus, and sulfur. These atoms form a characteristic number of covalent bonds to make an octet in their outermost shell (see **Figure 2.8**). However, the octet rule does not always apply. For example, hydrogen has an outermost shell that can contain only two electrons, not eight.

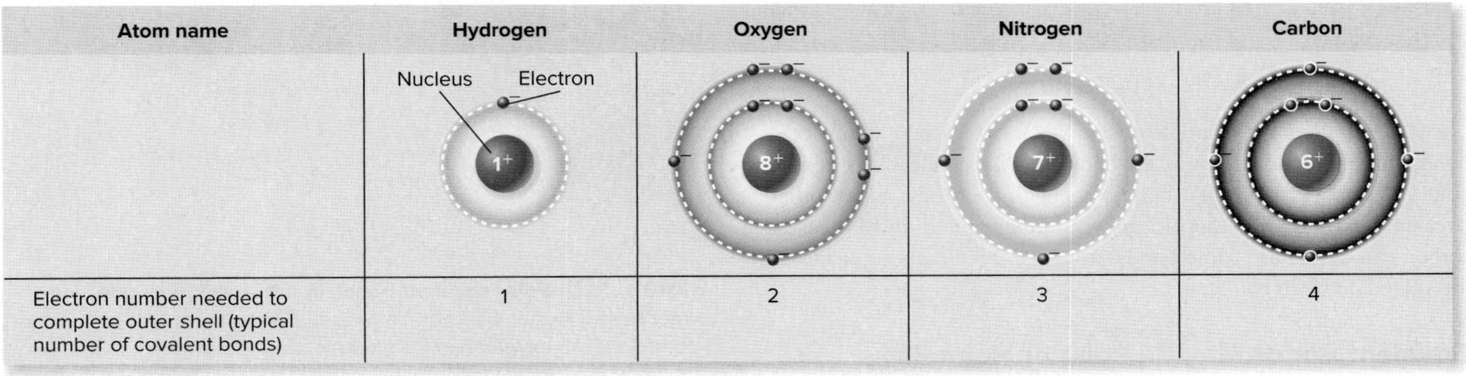

Atom name	Hydrogen	Oxygen	Nitrogen	Carbon
	Nucleus Electron			
Electron number needed to complete outer shell (typical number of covalent bonds)	1	2	3	4

Figure 2.8   The number of covalent bonds formed by common elements found in living organisms. These elements form different numbers of covalent bonds due to the electron configurations in their outer shells.

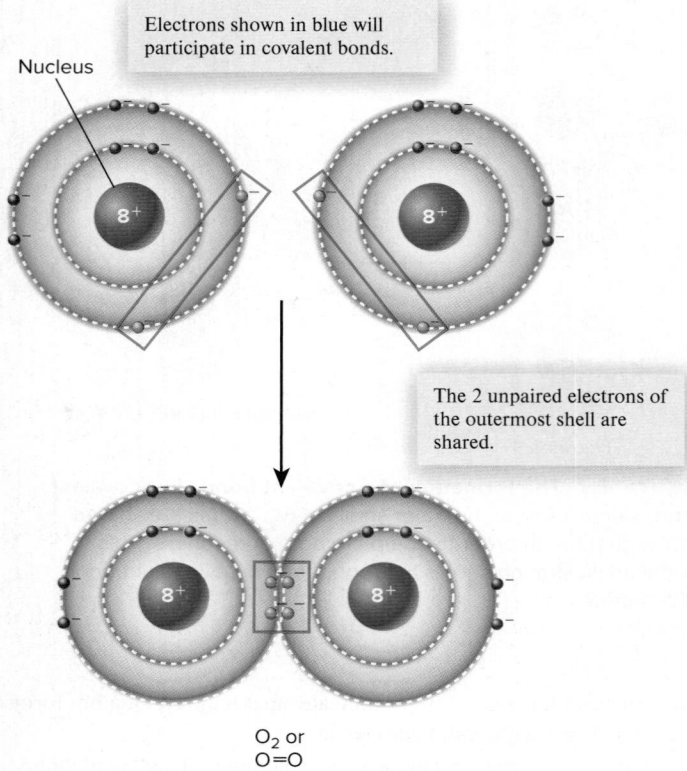

Electrons shown in blue will participate in covalent bonds.

Nucleus

The 2 unpaired electrons of the outermost shell are shared.

O_2 or
$O{=}O$

Figure 2.9 **A double bond between two oxygen atoms.**

 Core Skill: Modeling The goal of this modeling challenge is to apply your understanding of molecular structure and propose a model for carbon dioxide.

Modeling Challenge: Carbon dioxide (CO_2) is a colorless and odorless gas that plays a key role in photosynthesis, as discussed in Chapter 8. In a CO_2 molecule, each oxygen forms two covalent bonds with the carbon atom. Draw a model for CO_2, using the same format as shown for the model of O_2 in this figure.

In some molecules, a **double bond** occurs when atoms share two pairs of electrons (four electrons) rather than one pair. As shown in **Figure 2.9**, this is the case for an oxygen molecule (O_2), which can be represented as

$$O{=}O$$

Another common example occurs when two carbon atoms form bonds in compounds. They may share one pair of electrons (single bond) or two pairs (double bond), depending on how many other covalent bonds each carbon forms with other atoms. In rare cases, carbon can even form triple bonds, in which three pairs of electrons are shared between two atoms.

Covalent Bonds May Be Polar or Nonpolar

Some atoms attract shared electrons more strongly than do other atoms. The **electronegativity** of an atom is a measure of its ability to attract

electrons in a bond with another atom. When two atoms with different electronegativities form a covalent bond, the shared electrons are more likely to be closer to the nucleus of the atom of higher electronegativity than to the nucleus of the atom of lower electronegativity. Such bonds are called **polar covalent bonds**, because the distribution of the shared electrons around the nuclei creates a polarity, or difference in electric charge, across the molecule. Water is a classic example of a molecule containing polar covalent bonds. Because oxygen is much more electronegative than hydrogen, the shared electrons tend to be pulled closer to the oxygen nucleus than to either of the hydrogens. This unequal sharing of electrons gives the molecule a region of partial negative charge (indicated by the Greek letter δ and a minus sign, δ^-) and two regions of partial positive charge (δ^+) (**Figure 2.10**).

Atoms with high electronegativity, such as oxygen and nitrogen, have a relatively strong attraction for electrons. These atoms form polar covalent bonds with hydrogen atoms, which have low electronegativity. Examples of polar covalent bonds include O—H and N—H. In contrast, bonds between atoms with similar electronegativities, for example, between two carbon atoms (C—C) or between carbon and hydrogen atoms (C—H), are called **nonpolar covalent bonds**. Polar molecules usually have one or more polar covalent bonds, whereas nonpolar molecules tend to have bonds that are mostly nonpolar covalent. A single molecule may have different regions with nonpolar bonds and polar bonds. As we will explore later, the physical characteristics of polar and nonpolar molecules, especially their solubility in water, are quite different.

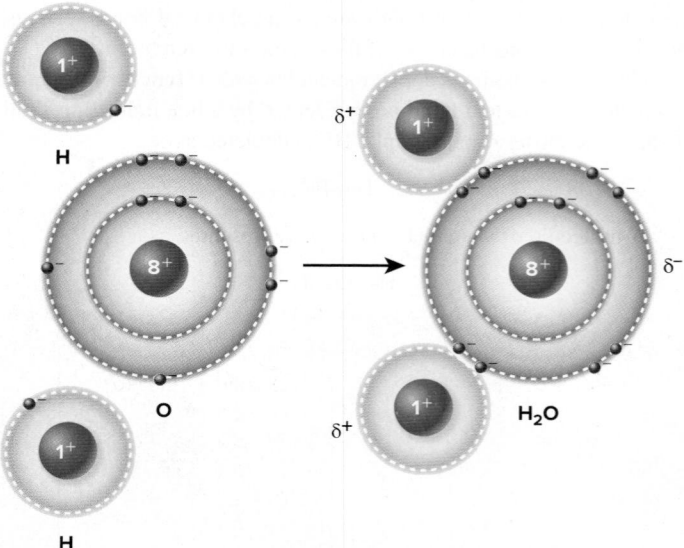

In water, the shared electrons tend to be closer to the oxygen atom. This gives oxygen a partial negative charge (δ^-) and each hydrogen a partial positive charge (δ^+).

H

O

H

δ^+

δ^-

δ^+

H_2O

Figure 2.10 **Polar covalent bonds in the water molecule.** In a water molecule, two hydrogen atoms share electrons with an oxygen atom. Because oxygen has a higher electronegativity, the shared electrons tend to be closer to the oxygen nucleus. This gives oxygen a partial negative charge, designated δ^-, and each hydrogen a partial positive charge, designated δ^+.

Hydrogen Bonds and van der Waals Dispersion Forces Promote Interactions Between and Within Molecules

An important effect of certain polar covalent bonds is the ability of one molecule to loosely associate with another molecule through a weak interaction called a **hydrogen bond**. A hydrogen bond forms when a hydrogen atom in one polar molecule becomes electrically attracted to an electronegative atom, such as an oxygen or nitrogen atom, in another polar molecule. Hydrogen bonds, like those between water molecules, are represented in diagrams by dashed or dotted lines to distinguish them from covalent bonds (**Figure 2.11a**). A single hydrogen bond is very weak. The strength of a hydrogen bond is only a small percentage of the strength of the polar covalent bonds linking the hydrogen and oxygen within a water molecule.

Hydrogen bonds can also occur within a single large molecule. Large molecules may have many hydrogen bonds within their structure. Collectively, many hydrogen bonds may provide a strong force that helps maintain the three-dimensional structure of a molecule. This is particularly true in deoxyribonucleic acid (DNA)—the molecule that makes up the genetic material of living organisms. DNA exists as two long, twisting strands of many millions of atoms. The two strands are held together along their length, in part, by hydrogen bonds between different portions of the molecule (**Figure 2.11b**). Due to the large number of hydrogen bonds, it takes considerable energy to separate the strands of DNA.

In contrast to the cumulative strength of many hydrogen bonds, the weakness of the individual bonds is also important. When an interaction between two molecules involves relatively few hydrogen bonds, such an interaction tends to be weak and readily disrupted. The reversible nature of hydrogen bonds allows molecules to interact and then to become separated again. For example, small molecules may bind to proteins called enzymes via hydrogen bonds. **Enzymes** are molecules that catalyze many biologically important chemical reactions. The small molecules are later released, after the enzymes have changed their structure.

In addition to hydrogen bonds, another type of weak molecular attraction is due to **van der Waals dispersion forces**. These van der Waals dispersion forces arise because electrons are located within orbitals in a random way, as described previously. At any moment, the electrons in the outer shells of the atoms in a nonpolar molecule may be evenly distributed or unevenly distributed. In the latter case, a fleeting electrical attraction to other nearby molecules may arise. As with hydrogen bonds, the collective strength of these temporary attractive forces between molecules can be quite strong.

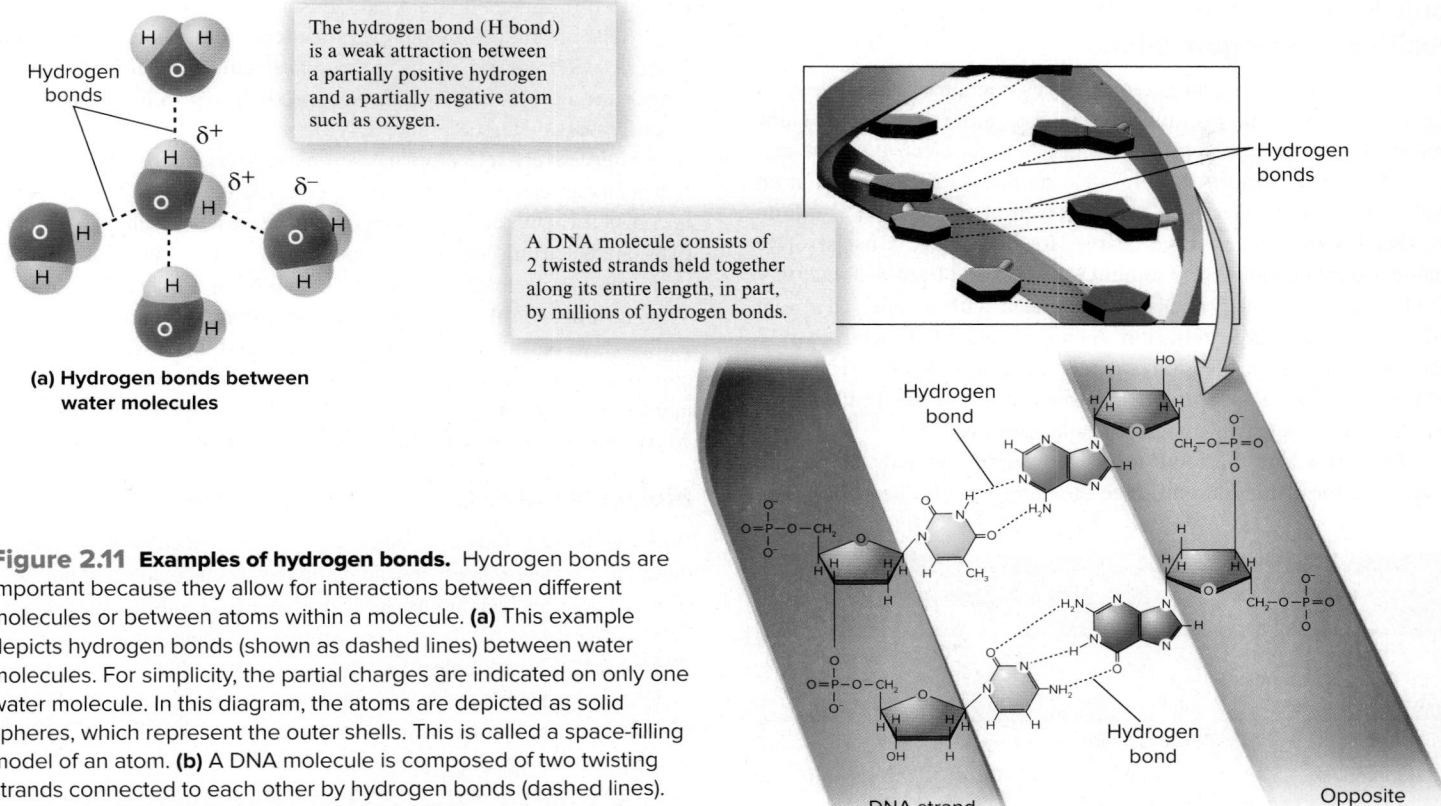

Figure 2.11 Examples of hydrogen bonds. Hydrogen bonds are important because they allow for interactions between different molecules or between atoms within a molecule. **(a)** This example depicts hydrogen bonds (shown as dashed lines) between water molecules. For simplicity, the partial charges are indicated on only one water molecule. In this diagram, the atoms are depicted as solid spheres, which represent the outer shells. This is called a space-filling model of an atom. **(b)** A DNA molecule is composed of two twisting strands connected to each other by hydrogen bonds (dashed lines). Although each individual bond is weak, the sum of all the hydrogen bonds in a large molecule like DNA imparts considerable stability to the molecule.

Concept Check: *In Chapter 11, you will learn that the two DNA strands must first separate into two single strands for DNA to be replicated. Do you think the process of strand separation requires energy, or do you think the strands can separate spontaneously?*

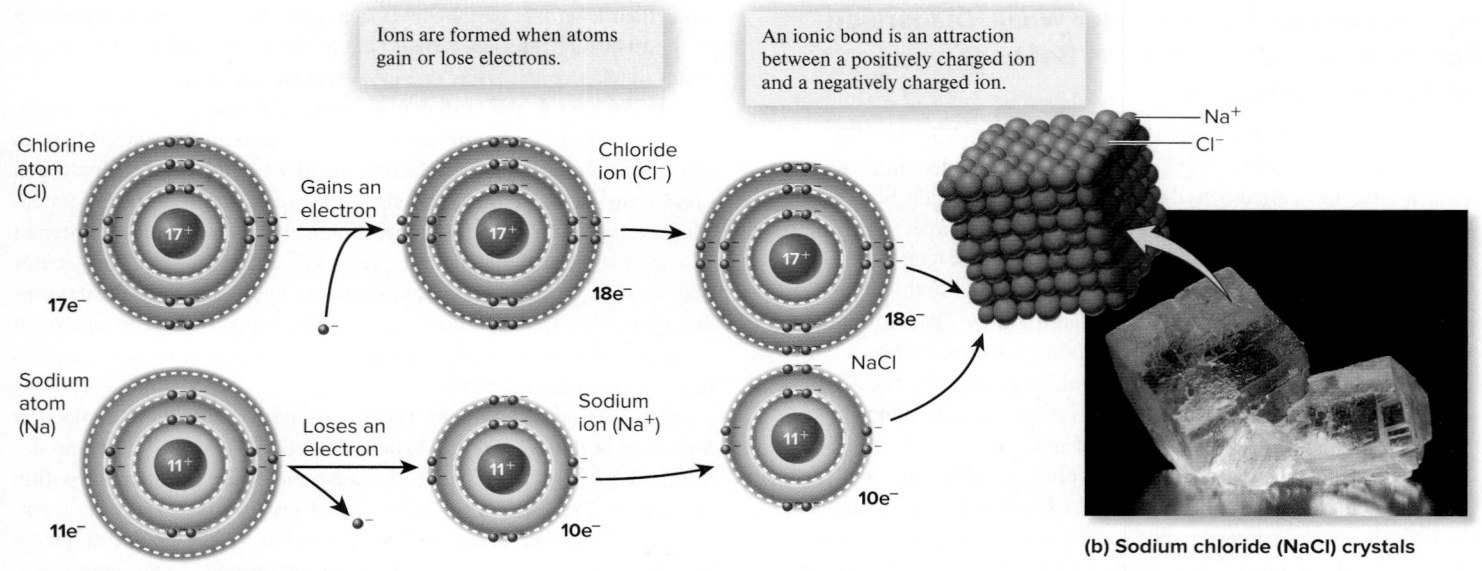

Ions are formed when atoms gain or lose electrons.

An ionic bond is an attraction between a positively charged ion and a negatively charged ion.

Chlorine atom (Cl)

17e⁻

Gains an electron

Chloride ion (Cl⁻)

18e⁻

Na⁺
Cl⁻

Sodium atom (Na)

11e⁻

Loses an electron

Sodium ion (Na⁺)

10e⁻

NaCl

(b) Sodium chloride (NaCl) crystals

(a) Formation of ions and an ionic bond

Figure 2.12 Ionic bonding in table salt (NaCl). (a) When a sodium atom loses an electron, a sodium ion is formed, and when a chlorine atom gains an election, a chloride ion is formed. The resulting ions are attracted to each other via an ionic bond. **(b)** In a salt crystal, a lattice is formed in which the positively charged sodium ions (Na^+) are attracted to negatively charged chloride ions (Cl^-). Note: Electrons do not exist free in solution; when an electron is removed from one atom, it must be transferred to some other atom. b: ©Charles D. Winters/Science Source

Ionic Bonds Involve an Attraction Between Positive and Negative Ions

Atoms are electrically neutral because they contain equal numbers of negative electrons and positive protons. If an atom or molecule gains or loses one or more electrons, it acquires a net electric charge and becomes an **ion** (**Figure 2.12a**). For example, when a sodium atom (Na), which has 11 electrons, loses 1 electron, it becomes a sodium ion (Na^+) with a net positive charge. Ions that have a net positive charge are called **cations**. A sodium ion still has 11 protons, but only 10 electrons. Ions such as Na^+ are depicted with a superscript that indicates the net charge of the ion. A chlorine atom (Cl), which has 17 electrons, can gain an electron and become a chloride ion (Cl^-) with a net negative charge—it still has 17 protons but now has 18 electrons. Ions with a net negative charge are called **anions**.

Table 2.3 lists the ionic forms of several elements. Hydrogen atoms and most mineral and trace elements readily form ions. The

ions listed in this table are relatively stable because their outer electron shells are full. For example, a sodium atom has one electron in its third (outermost) shell. If it loses this electron to become Na^+, it no longer has a third shell, and the second shell, which is full, becomes its outermost shell (see Figure 2.12a).

Alternatively, a Cl atom has seven electrons in its outermost shell. If it gains an electron to become a chloride ion (Cl^-), its outer shell becomes full with eight electrons. Some atoms can gain or lose more than one electron. For instance, a calcium atom, which has 20 electrons, loses 2 electrons to become a calcium ion, symbolized as Ca^{2+}.

An **ionic bond** occurs when a cation binds to an anion. Figure 2.12a shows an ionic bond between Na^+ and Cl^- to form NaCl, or common table salt. NaCl often exists as crystals in which the cations and anions form a regular array. Figure 2.12b shows a NaCl crystal, in which the sodium and chloride ions are held together by ionic bonds.

Molecules May Change Their Shapes

When atoms are linked together, they form molecules with various three-dimensional shapes, depending on the arrangements and numbers of bonds between their atoms. As an example, let's consider the arrangements of covalent bonds in a few simple molecules, including water (**Figure 2.13**). These molecules form new orbitals that cause the atoms to lie at defined angles relative to each other, giving the groups of atoms very specific shapes, as shown in the three examples of Figure 2.13.

Molecules containing covalent bonds are not rigid, inflexible structures. Think of a single covalent bond as an axle around which the joined atoms can rotate. Within certain limits, the shape of a molecule can change without breaking its covalent bonds. As illustrated in **Figure 2.14a**, a molecule of six carbon atoms bonded together can assume a number of shapes as a result of rotations around various covalent bonds. The three-dimensional, flexible shape of molecules

Table 2.3	Ionic Forms of Some Common Elements in Living Organisms			
Atom	Chemical symbol	Ion	Ion symbol	Electrons gained or lost
Calcium	Ca	Calcium ion	Ca^{2+}	2 lost
Chlorine	Cl	Chloride ion	Cl^-	1 gained
Hydrogen	H	Hydrogen ion	H^+	1 lost
Magnesium	Mg	Magnesium ion	Mg^{2+}	2 lost
Potassium	K	Potassium ion	K^+	1 lost
Sodium	Na	Sodium ion	Na^+	1 lost

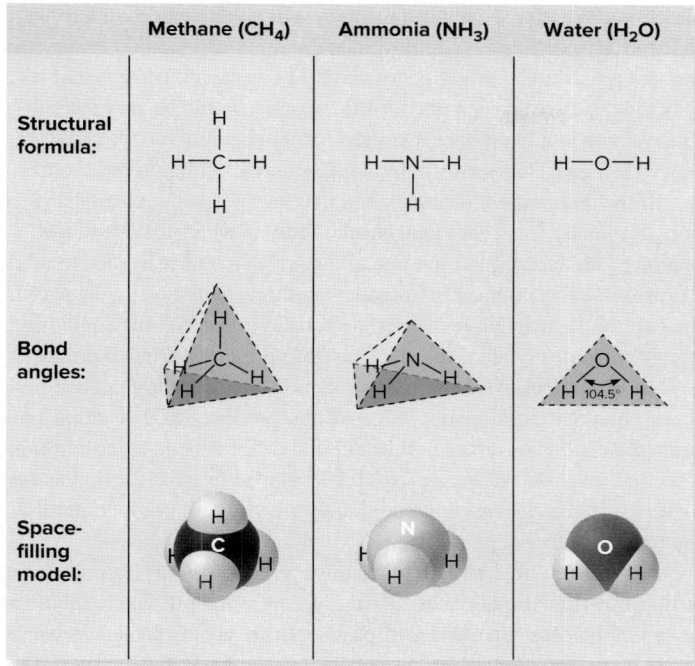

	Methane (CH₄)	Ammonia (NH₃)	Water (H₂O)
Structural formula:			
Bond angles:			
Space-filling model:			

Figure 2.13 Shapes of molecules. Molecules may assume different shapes, depending on the types of bonds between their atoms. The angles between the bonds are well defined. For example, in liquid water at room temperature, the angle formed by the covalent bonds between the two hydrogen atoms and the oxygen atom is approximately 104.5°. This bond angle can vary slightly, depending on the temperature and degree of hydrogen bonding between adjacent water molecules.

contributes to their biological properties. As shown in Figure 2.14b, the binding of one molecule to another may affect the shape of one of the molecules. A person can smell food, for instance, because odor molecules interact with special proteins called receptors in their nose (see Figure 44.24). When an odor molecule encounters a receptor, the two molecules recognize each other by their unique shapes, somewhat like a key fitting into a lock. As molecules in the food interact with the receptor, the shape of the receptor changes.

Free Radicals Are a Special Class of Highly Reactive Molecules

Recall that an atom or an ion is most stable when each of its orbitals is occupied by a full complement of electrons. A molecule containing an atom with a single, unpaired electron in its outer shell is known as a **free radical**. Free radicals can react with other molecules to "steal" an electron from one of their atoms, thereby filling the orbital in the free radical. In the process, a new free radical may be created from the donor molecule, setting off a chain reaction.

Free radicals can be formed in several ways, including exposure of cells to radiation and toxins. They are depicted with a dot (representing the unpaired electron) next to the atomic symbol. Examples of biologically important free radicals are superoxide anion, $O_2^{\cdot-}$; hydroxyl radical, $\cdot OH$; and nitric oxide, $NO\cdot$. Note that free radicals can be either charged or neutral.

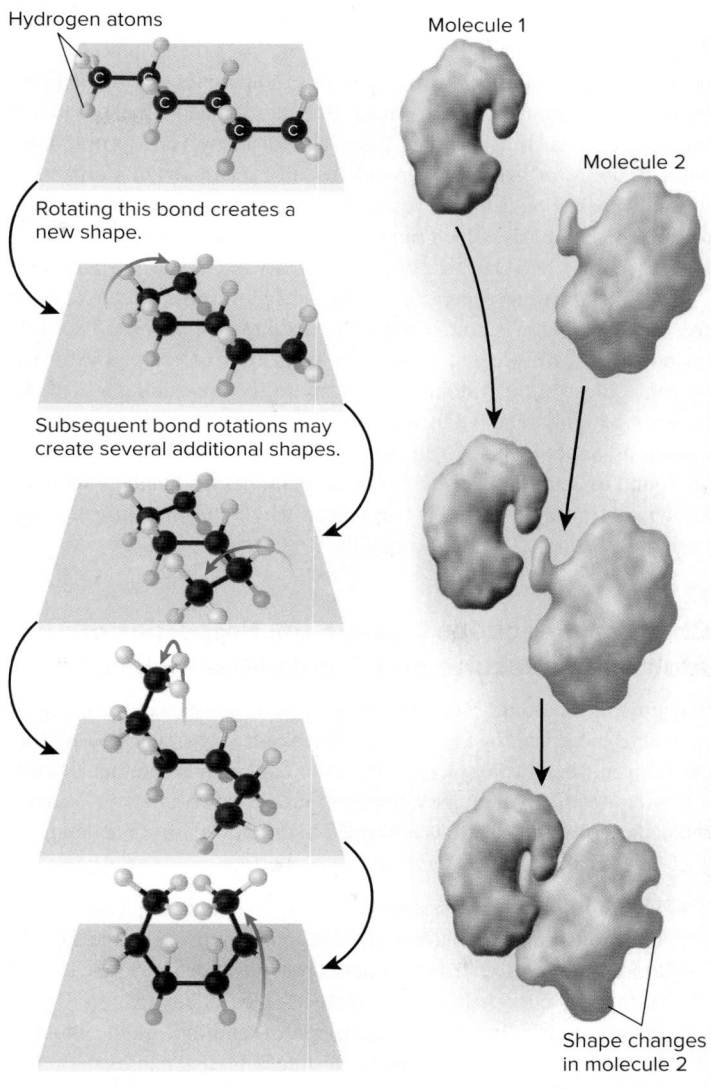

(a) Bond rotation in a small molecule

(b) Noncovalent interactions that may alter the shape of molecules

Figure 2.14 Shape changes in molecules. A single molecule may assume different three-dimensional shapes without breaking any of the covalent bonds between its atoms, as shown in **(a)** for a six-carbon molecule. Hydrogen atoms above the blue plane are shown in white; those below the blue plane are blue. **(b)** Two molecules are shown schematically as having complementary shapes that permit them to interact. During the interaction, the flexible nature of the molecules causes molecule 2 to twist sufficiently to assume a new shape. This change in shape is often an important mechanism by which one molecule influences the activity of another.

 Core Concept: Structure and Function The three-dimensional structure of the two molecules in Figure 2.14b is critical in ensuring that they are capable of specifically interacting with each other and not with other molecules. The function of the molecules is defined by their ability to bind to each other, which in turn depends on their unique structures.

Free radicals can do considerable harm to living cells—for example, by causing a cell to rupture or by damaging the genetic material. Surprisingly, the lethal effect of free radicals is sometimes put to good use. Some cells in animals' bodies create free radicals and use them to kill invading cells such as bacteria. Likewise, for many years people used weak solutions of hydrogen peroxide to kill bacteria, as in a dirty skin wound. When applied to the wound, hydrogen peroxide can break down to create free radicals, which can then attack bacteria (this practice is no longer recommended because of the possibility of damage to skin cells).

Aside from the exceptional case of fighting off bacteria, most free radicals that arise in an organism need to be inactivated so they do not kill healthy cells. Protection from free radicals is afforded by molecules that can donate electrons to the free radicals without becoming highly reactive themselves. Such protective compounds are known as antioxidants. Examples include vitamins C and E, which are found in fruits and vegetables, and the numerous plant compounds known as flavonoids. This is one reason why a diet rich in fruits and vegetables is beneficial to our health.

Chemical Reactions Change the Properties of Atoms or Molecules and Create New Molecules

A **chemical reaction** occurs when one or more substances are changed into other substances by the making or breaking of chemical bonds. This can happen when two or more elements or compounds combine to form a new compound, when one compound breaks down into two or more molecules, or when electrons are added to or removed from an atom. Chemical reactions share similar properties.

- First, they all require a source of energy so that atoms and molecules can encounter each other. The energy required for atoms and molecules to interact is provided partly by heat or thermal energy. In the complete absence of any heat (a temperature called absolute zero), atoms and molecules would be totally stationary and unable to interact. Heat causes them to vibrate and move, a phenomenon known as Brownian motion.

- Second, chemical reactions that occur in living organisms often require more than just Brownian motion to proceed at a reasonable rate. Such reactions need to be catalyzed. As discussed in Chapter 6, a **catalyst** is an agent that speeds up the rate of a chemical reaction. Enzymes are proteins that are found in all cells and catalyze most chemical reactions.

- Third, chemical reactions tend to proceed in a particular direction but eventually reach a state of equilibrium.

To understand what we mean by "direction" and "equilibrium," let's consider a chemical reaction between methane (a component of natural gas) and oxygen. When a single molecule of methane reacts with two molecules of oxygen, one molecule of carbon dioxide and two molecules of water are produced:

$$CH_4 + 2\,O_2 \rightleftharpoons CO_2 + 2\,H_2O$$
$$\text{(methane) (oxygen)} \quad \text{(carbon dioxide) (water)}$$

As it is written here, methane and oxygen are the starting materials, or **reactants**, and carbon dioxide and water are the **products**. The bidirectional arrows indicate that this reaction can proceed in both

directions. Whether a chemical reaction is likely to proceed in a forward (left to right) or reverse (right to left) direction depends on changes in free energy, which you will learn about in Chapter 6. If we began with only methane and oxygen, the forward reaction would be very favorable. The reaction would produce a large amount of carbon dioxide and water, as well as heat. This is why natural gas is used as a fuel to heat homes.

If the products are not converted to other molecules, chemical reactions eventually reach **chemical equilibrium**, in which the rate of the formation of products equals the rate of the formation of reactants. In other words, the concentrations of products and reactants do not change. In the case of the reaction involving methane and oxygen, this equilibrium occurs when nearly all of the reactants have been converted to products.

In biological systems, many reactions do not have a chance to reach chemical equilibrium, because the products of a reaction may immediately be converted within a cell to different substances through a second reaction. When a product is removed from a reaction as fast as it is formed, the reactants continue to form new products until all the reactants are used up.

A final feature common to chemical reactions in living organisms is that most reactions occur in watery environments. Such chemical reactions involve reactants and products that are dissolved in water. Next, we will examine the properties of this amazing liquid and its importance to biology.

2.3 Properties of Water

Learning Outcomes:

1. Describe how hydrogen bonding determines many properties of water.
2. List the properties of water that make it a good solvent, and distinguish between hydrophilic and hydrophobic substances.
3. **CoreSKILL »** Calculate the molarity of a solution, and explain its meaning.
4. Discuss the properties of water that are critical for the survival of living organisms.

It would be difficult to imagine life without **water**, which is the liquid form of H_2O. People can survive for a month or more without food but usually die in less than a week without water. The bodies of all organisms are composed largely of water; most of the cells in an organism's body are filled with water and surrounded by it. Up to 95% of the weight of certain plants comes from water. In humans, typically 60–70% of body weight is due to water. The brain is roughly 70% water, blood is about 80% water, and the lungs are nearly 90% water. Even our bones are about 20% water! In addition, water is an important liquid in the surrounding environments of living organisms. For example, many species are aquatic organisms that live in watery environments.

Thus far in this chapter, we have considered the features of atoms and molecules and the nature of bonds and chemical reactions between atoms and molecules. In this section, we will turn our attention to issues related to the liquid properties of living organisms and the environment in which they live. Most of the chemical reactions that occur in nature involve molecules that are dissolved in water, including those reactions that happen inside the cells of living organisms and in the spaces that surround the cells (**Figure 2.15**).

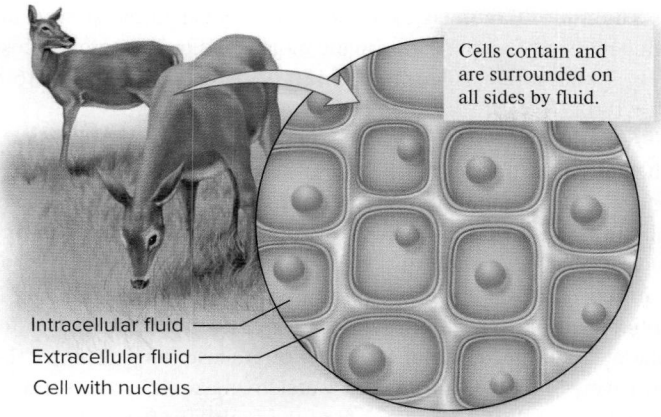

Figure 2.15 Fluids inside and outside of cells. Water is found in the intracellular fluid and in the extracellular fluid. Chemical reactions are always ongoing in both fluids.

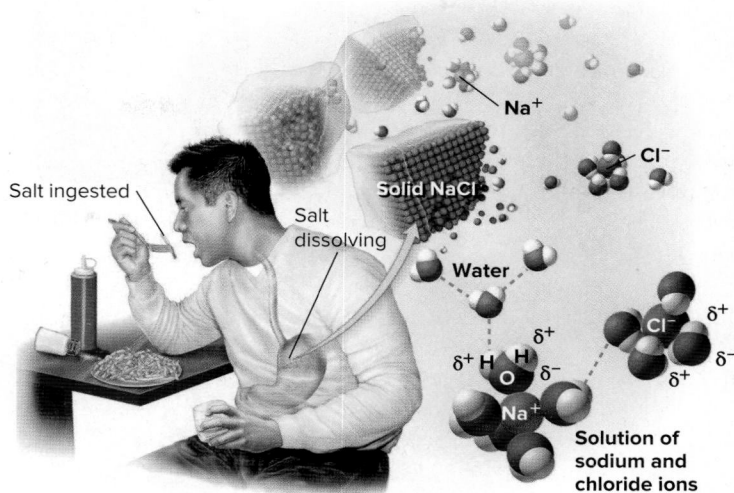

Figure 2.16 Table salt (NaCl crystals) dissolving in water. The ability of water to dissolve sodium chloride crystals depends on the electrical attraction between the polar water molecules and the charged sodium (Na^+) and chloride ions (Cl^-). Water molecules surround each ion as it becomes dissolved. For simplicity, the partial charges are indicated for only two water molecules.

In this section, we will examine the properties of chemicals that influence whether they dissolve in water and consider how biologists measure the amounts of dissolved substances. In addition, we will examine some of the other special properties of water that make it a vital component of living organisms and their environments.

Ions and Polar Molecules Readily Dissolve in Water

Substances dissolved in a liquid are known as **solutes**, and the liquid in which they are dissolved is the **solvent**. In all living organisms, the solvent for nearly all chemical reactions is water, which is the most abundant solvent in nature. Solutes dissolve in a solvent to form a **solution**. Solutions made with water are called **aqueous solutions**.

To understand why a substance dissolves in water, we need to consider the chemical bonds in the solute molecule and those in water. As discussed earlier, the covalent bonds linking the two hydrogen atoms to the oxygen atom in a water molecule are polar. Therefore, the oxygen in water has a slight negative charge, and each hydrogen has a slight positive charge. To dissolve in water, a substance must be electrically attracted to water molecules. For example, table salt (NaCl) is a solid crystalline substance because of the strong ionic bonds between positive sodium ions (Na^+) and negative chloride ions (Cl^-). When a crystal of sodium chloride is placed in water, the partially negatively charged oxygens of water molecules are attracted to Na^+, and the partially positively charged hydrogens are attracted to Cl^- (**Figure 2.16**). Clusters of water molecules surround the ions, allowing Na^+ and Cl^- to separate from each other and enter the water—that is, to dissolve.

Generally, molecules that contain ionic and/or polar covalent bonds dissolve in water. Such molecules are said to be **hydrophilic**, which literally means "water-loving." In contrast, molecules composed predominantly of carbon and hydrogen are relatively insoluble in water, because carbon-carbon and carbon-hydrogen bonds are nonpolar. These molecules do not have partial positive and negative charges and, therefore, are not attracted to water molecules. Such molecules are **hydrophobic**, or "water-fearing." Oils are a familiar example of hydrophobic molecules. Try mixing vegetable oil with water and observe the result. The two liquids separate into an oil layer and a water layer, with very little oil dissolving in the water.

Some Molecules Have Both Hydrophilic and Hydrophobic Regions

Molecules that have both hydrophilic regions at one or more sites and hydrophobic regions at other sites are called **amphipathic** (or amphiphilic, from the Greek for "both loves"). When mixed with water, long amphipathic molecules may aggregate into spheres called **micelles**, with their polar (hydrophilic) regions at the surface of each micelle, where they are attracted to the surrounding water molecules. The nonpolar (hydrophobic) ends are oriented toward the interior of the micelle (**Figure 2.17**). Such an arrangement minimizes the interaction between water molecules and the nonpolar ends of the amphipathic molecules, which face inward. Nonpolar molecules can dissolve in the central nonpolar regions of these clusters and thus exist in an aqueous environment in far higher amounts than would otherwise be possible based on their low solubility in water. Familiar examples of amphipathic molecules are those in detergents, which can form micelles that help to dissolve the oils and nonpolar molecules found in dirt. The detergent molecules found in soap have polar and nonpolar ends. Oils on your skin dissolve in the nonpolar regions of the detergent micelles, and the polar ends help the detergent rinse off in water, taking the oil with it.

In addition to micelles, amphipathic molecules may form structures consisting of double layers of molecules called bilayers. Such bilayers have two hydrophilic surfaces facing outside, in contact with water, and a hydrophobic interior facing away from water. As you will learn in Chapter 5, bilayers play a key role in cell membrane structure (look ahead to Figure 5.1).

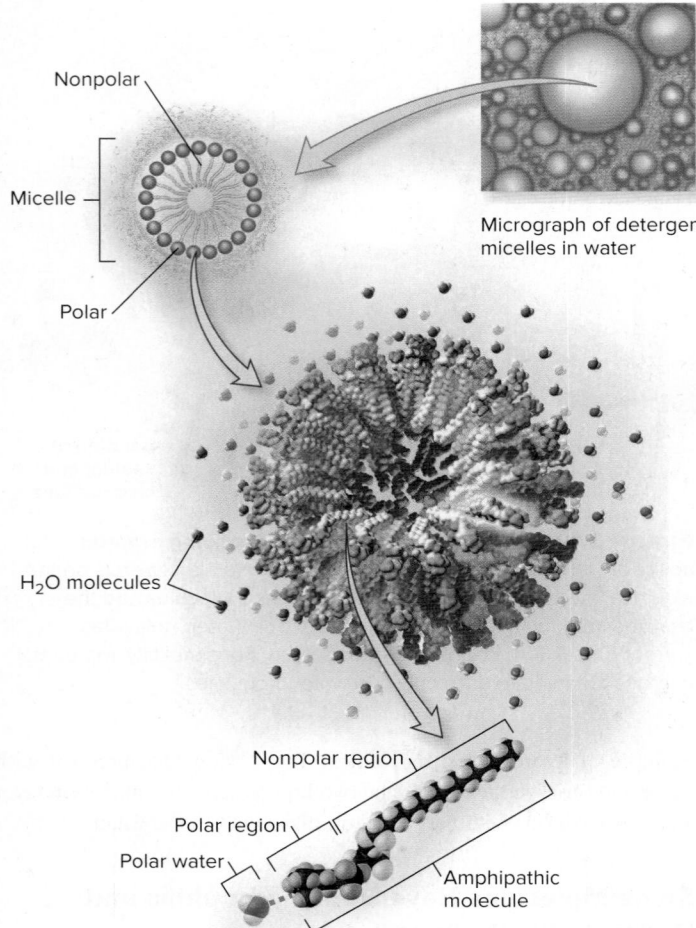

Nonpolar

Micelle

Polar

Micrograph of detergent micelles in water

H₂O molecules

Nonpolar region

Polar region

Polar water

Amphipathic molecule

Figure 2.17 The formation of a micelle by amphipathic molecules. In water, amphipathic molecules tend to arrange themselves so their nonpolar regions are directed away from water molecules and their polar regions are directed toward the water and can form hydrogen bonds with it. (top right): ©Jeremy Burgess/Science Source

Concept Check: *When oil dissolves in a soapy solution, where is the oil found?*

The Amount of a Dissolved Solute per Unit Volume of Liquid Is Its Concentration

Solute **concentration** is defined as the amount of a solute dissolved in a unit volume of solution. For example, if 1 gram (g) of NaCl was dissolved in enough water to make 1 liter (L) of solution, we would say that its solute concentration is 1 g/L.

A comparison of the concentrations of two different substances on the basis of the number of grams per liter of solution does not directly indicate how many molecules of each substance are present. For example, let's compare 10 g each of glucose ($C_6H_{12}O_6$) and sodium chloride (NaCl). Because the individual molecules of glucose have more mass than those of NaCl, 10 g of glucose contains fewer molecules than 10 g of NaCl. Therefore, another way to describe solute concentration is according to the moles of dissolved solute per volume of solution. To make this calculation, we must know three things: the amount of dissolved solute, the molecular mass of the dissolved solute, and the volume of the solution.

The **molecular mass** of a molecule is equal to the sum of the atomic masses of all the atoms in the molecule. For example, glucose ($C_6H_{12}O_6$) has a molecular mass of 180 ([6 × 12] + [12 × 1] + [6 × 16] = 180).

As mentioned earlier, 1 mole (abbreviated mol) of a substance is the amount of the substance in grams equal to its atomic or molecular mass. The **molarity** of a solution is defined as the number of moles of a solute dissolved in 1 L of solution. A solution containing 180 g of glucose (1 mol) dissolved in enough water to make 1 L is a 1 **molar** solution of glucose (1 mol/L). By convention, a 1 mol/L solution is usually written as 1 M, where the capital M stands for molar and is defined as mol/L. If 90 g of glucose (half its molecular mass) were dissolved in enough water to make 1 L, the solution would have a solute concentration of 0.5 mol/L, or 0.5 M.

The concentrations of solutes dissolved in the fluids of living organisms are usually much less than 1 M. Many have concentrations in the range of millimoles per liter (1 mM = 0.001 M = 10^{-3} M), and others are present in even smaller concentrations—micromoles per liter (1 μM = 0.000001 M = 10^{-6} M), nanomoles per liter (1 nM = 0.000000001 M = 10^{-9} M), picomoles per liter (1 pM = 0.000000000001 M = 10^{-12} M), or even less.

Core Skill: Quantitative Reasoning

BIO:TIPS **THE QUESTION** *Insulin is a hormone that regulates the uptake of glucose into muscle and fat cells. It is composed of 51 amino acids and has a molecular mass of approximately 5,808 g/mol. In healthy individuals, insulin levels in the bloodstream rise sharply after eating a meal, which increases the ability of muscle and fat cells to take up glucose. Two individuals, Alfonzo and Gordan, had their blood insulin levels tested before and after a meal.*

	Before meal (ng/L)	After meal (ng/L)
Alfonzo	475	2,850
Gordan	399	789

Calculate the molarity of insulin in each individual's bloodstream before and after the meal, expressed in units of picomoles/L (pM). (Note: 1 mole = 10^{12} picomoles.) Which person do you think may be diabetic because he does not release enough insulin into his bloodstream?

TOPIC *What topic in biology does this question address?* The topic is insulin levels in the bloodstream. More specifically, the question is about calculating the concentration of insulin (in pM) before and after a meal. You are also asked to consider if either individual may be diabetic.

INFORMATION *What information do you know based on the question and your understanding of the topic?* From the question, you have learned that insulin increases the ability of muscle and fat cells to take up glucose and that diabetic individuals have a diminished ability to produce insulin. You are given the blood insulin levels of two individuals before and after a meal. From your understanding of the topic, you may remember that molarity refers to the number of moles of a substance dissolved in a liter of solution.

PROBLEM-SOLVING **S**TRATEGY *Make a calculation. Compare and contrast.* To begin to solve this problem, you first need to calculate the molarities. After this is done, you can compare the insulin concentrations between Alfonzo and Gordan.

Let's go through the calculation for Alfonzo's insulin level before a meal. We begin with his blood insulin level, which is 475 ng/L.

To convert this value to g/L, remember that $1 g = 10^9$ ng.

$$475 \text{ ng/L} \times \frac{1 \text{ g}}{10^9 \text{ ng}} = 475 \times 10^{-9} \text{ g/L}$$

We then divide this value by the molecular mass of insulin, which is 5,808 g/mol.

$$\frac{475 \times 10^{-9} \text{ g/L}}{5,808 \text{ g/mol}} = 0.082 \times 10^{-9} \text{ mol/L}$$

The question asks you to express your value in pM, where 1 mole = 10^{12} picomoles:

$$0.082 \times 10^{-9} \text{ mol/L} \times \frac{10^{12} \text{ pmol}}{\text{mol}} = 82 \text{ pmol/L, or } 82 \text{ pM}$$

ANSWER

	Before meal (pM)	After meal (pM)
Alfonzo	82	492
Gordan	69	136

Alfonzo's blood insulin level after the meal is six times higher than before the meal, whereas Gordan's is only about twice as high. Gordan may be diabetic, but this would need to be substantiated by more extensive testing of his insulin and glucose levels.

H_2O Exists in Three States

H_2O is an abundant compound on Earth that exists in all three states of matter—solid (ice), liquid (water), and gas (water vapor). At the temperatures found over most regions of the planet, H_2O is found primarily as a liquid in which the weak hydrogen bonds between molecules are continuously being formed, broken, and formed again. If the temperature rises, the rate at which hydrogen bonds break increases, and molecules of water escape into the gaseous state, becoming water vapor. If the temperature falls, hydrogen bonds are broken less frequently, so larger and larger clusters of water molecules are formed, until at 0°C water freezes into a crystalline matrix—ice. The H_2O molecules in ice tend to lie in a more orderly and open arrangement, that is, with greater intermolecular distances, which makes ice less dense than water. This is why ice floats on water (**Figure 2.18**). Compared with water, ice is also less likely to participate in most types of chemical reactions.

Changes in state, such as changes between the solid, liquid, and gaseous states of H_2O, involve an input or a release of energy. For example, when energy is supplied to make water boil, it changes from the liquid to the gaseous state—a process called vaporization. The heat required to vaporize 1 mole of any substance at its boiling point is called the substance's **heat of vaporization**. For water, this value

Ice: Hydrogen bonds are more stable.

Liquid water: Hydrogen bonds continually break and reform.

Figure 2.18 Structure of liquid water and ice. In the liquid form of H_2O, the hydrogen bonds between molecules continually form, break, and re-form, resulting in a changing arrangement of molecules from instant to instant. At temperatures at or below its freezing point, H_2O forms a crystalline matrix called ice. In this solid form, hydrogen bonds are more stable. Ice has a hexagonal crystal structure. The greater space between H_2O molecules in this crystal structure causes ice to have a lower density than liquid water. For this reason, ice floats on water.

is very high, because of the high number of hydrogen bonds between the molecules. It takes more than five times as much heat to vaporize water than it does to raise the temperature of water from 0°C to 100°C. In contrast, energy is released when water freezes to form ice. A substance's **heat of fusion** is the amount of heat that must be withdrawn or released from a substance to cause it to change from the liquid to the solid state. For water, this value is also high.

Another important feature for living organisms is that water has a very high **specific heat**, defined as the amount of heat required to raise the temperature of 1 gram of a substance by 1°C (or conversely, the amount of heat that must be lost to lower the temperature by 1°C). The high specific heat means that it takes considerable heat to raise the temperature of water. A related concept is **heat capacity**, which refers to the amount of heat required to raise the temperature of an entire object or amount of substance. A large beaker of distilled water has a greater heat capacity than a small beaker of distilled water, but the water in both beakers has the same specific heat. These properties of water contribute to the relatively stable temperatures of large bodies of water compared with inland temperatures. Large bodies of water tend to have a moderating effect on the temperature of nearby land masses. These three features—the high heats of vaporization and fusion and the high specific heat of water—mean that water is extremely stable as a liquid. Not surprisingly, therefore, living organisms have evolved to function best within a range of temperatures consistent with the liquid phase of water.

The temperature at which a solution freezes or vaporizes is influenced by the amounts of dissolved solutes. These are examples of a solution's **colligative properties**, defined as those properties that depend strictly on the total number of dissolved solute particles, not on the specific type of solute. Pure water freezes at 0°C and vaporizes at 100°C. Addition of solutes to water lowers its freezing point below 0°C and raises its boiling point to above 100°C. Adding a small amount of the compound ethylene glycol—antifreeze—to the water in a car's radiator, for instance, lowers the freezing point of the water and consequently prevents it from freezing in cold weather. Similarly, the presence of large amounts of solutes partly explains why the oceans do not freeze when the temperature falls below 0°C.

Water Performs Many Important Roles in Living Organisms

As noted previously, water is the primary solvent in the fluids of all living organisms, from unicellular bacteria to the largest sequoia tree. Water permits atoms and molecules to interact in ways that would be impossible in their undissolved states. In Unit II, we will consider many ions and molecules that are solutes in living cells.

However, it is important to recognize that in addition to acting as a solvent, water serves many other remarkable functions that are critical for the survival of living organisms. For example, water molecules participate in many chemical reactions of this general type:

$$R_1{-}R_2 + H{-}O{-}H \rightarrow R_1{-}OH + H{-}R_2$$

R is a general symbol used in this case to represent a group of atoms. In this reaction, R_1 and R_2 are distinct groups of atoms. On the left side of the reaction, $R_1{-}R_2$ is a compound in which these groups of atoms are connected by a covalent bond. To be converted to products, a covalent bond is broken in each reactant, $R_1{-}R_2$ and H—O—H, and OH and H (from water) form covalent bonds with R_1 and R_2, respectively. Reactions of this type are known as **hydrolysis reactions** (from the Greek *hydro*, meaning water, and *lysis*, meaning to break apart), because water is used to break apart another molecule (**Figure 2.19a**). As discussed in Chapter 3 and later chapters, many large molecules are broken down into smaller, biologically important units by hydrolysis reactions.

Another property of water is that it is incompressible—its volume does not significantly decrease when subjected to high pressure. This has biological importance for many organisms that use water to provide force or support. For example, water supports the bodies of worms and some other invertebrates in a structure called a hydrostatic skeleton, and it provides turgidity (stiffness) and support for plants (**Figure 2.19b**).

Water is also the means by which unneeded and potentially toxic waste compounds are eliminated from an animal's body (**Figure 2.19c**). In mammals, for example, the kidneys filter out

—H_2O

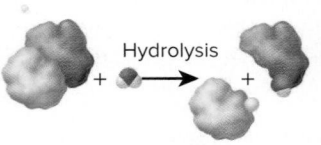
Hydrolysis

(a) Water participates in chemical reactions.

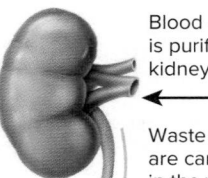
Blood enters and is purified by kidney cells.

Waste products are carried away in the watery urine.

(c) Water is used to eliminate soluble wastes.

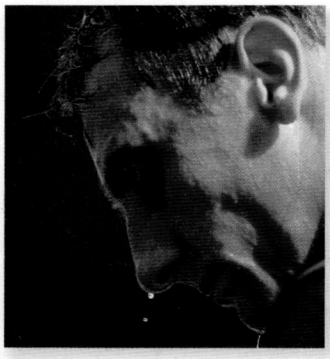
(b) Water provides support. The plant on the right is wilting due to lack of water.

(e) The cohesive force of water molecules aids in the movement of fluid through vessels in plants.

(g) The surface tension of water explains why this water strider doesn't sink.

(d) Evaporation helps some animals dissipate body heat.

(f) Water in saliva serves as a lubricant during—or as shown here, in anticipation of—feeding.

Figure 2.19 Some of the amazing functions of water. In addition to acting as a solvent, water serves many crucial functions in nature. b: ©Aaron Haupt/Science Source; d: ©Chris McGrath/Getty Images; e: ©Dana Tezarr/Getty Images; f: ©Gallo Images-Anthony Bannister/DigitalVision/Getty Images; g: ©Matti Suopajarvi/mattisj/Getty Images

Core Concept: Structure and Function The structure of water allows it perform a variety of functions as illustrated in this figure.

soluble waste products derived from the breakdown of proteins and other compounds. The filtered products remain in solution in a watery fluid, which eventually becomes urine and is excreted.

Recall from our earlier discussion of the three states of H_2O that it takes considerable energy in the form of heat to convert water from a liquid to a gas. Although you may be familiar with the phenomenon of boiling water being converted to water vapor, water can also vaporize into the gaseous state even at ordinary temperatures. This process is known as **evaporation**. The simplest way to understand this is to imagine that in any volume of water at any temperature, some vibrating water molecules have higher energy than others. Those with the highest energy break their hydrogen bonds and escape into the gaseous state. During this process, energy in the form of heat is released into the environment. Evaporation is an important mechanism by which many animals cool themselves on hot days (**Figure 2.19d**).

The hydrogen-bonding properties of water affect its ability to form droplets and to adhere to surfaces. The phenomenon of water molecules attracting each other is called **cohesion**. Water exhibits strong cohesion due to hydrogen bonding. Cohesion aids in the movement of water through the vessels of plants (**Figure 2.19e**). A property similar to cohesion is **adhesion**, which refers to the ability of water to be attracted to, and thus adhere to, a surface that is not electrically neutral. Water tends to cling to surfaces to which it can hydrogen bond. For example, the adhesive properties of water allow it to coat the surfaces of the digestive tract of animals and act as a lubricant for the passage of food (**Figure 2.19f**).

Surface tension is a measure of the attraction between molecules at the surface of a liquid. In the case of water, the attractive force between hydrogen-bonded water molecules at the interface between water and air is what causes water to form droplets. The surface water molecules attract each other into a configuration (roughly that of a sphere) that reduces the number of water molecules in contact with air. You can see this by slightly overfilling a glass with water; the water forms a rounded bulge above the rim. Likewise, surface tension allows certain insects, such as water striders, to walk on the surface of a pond without sinking (**Figure 2.19g**).

2.4 pH and Buffers

Learning Outcomes:

1. **CoreSKILL »** Calculate the concentrations of hydrogen and hydroxide ions at a given pH.
2. Give examples of how buffers maintain a stable environment in an animal's body fluids.

As we have seen, water is an essential solvent that is needed by all living organisms. In this section, we will examine the factors that determine the relative concentrations of H^+ and OH^- ions in water, and see how those concentrations are calculated. We will also consider how buffers are used by living organisms to minimize fluctuations in the H^+ and OH^- concentrations.

Hydrogen Ion Concentrations Are Changed by Acids and Bases

Pure water has the ability to ionize to a very small extent into **hydroxide ions (OH–)** and hydrogen ions (H^+). In pure water, the concentrations of H^+ and OH^- are both 10^{-7} mol/L, or 10^{-7} M. An inherent property of water is that the product of the concentrations of H^+ and OH^- is always 10^{-14} M at 25°C. Therefore, in pure water, $[H^+][OH^-] = [10^{-7}$ M$][10^{-7}$ M$] = 10^{-14}$ M. (The brackets around the symbols for the hydrogen and hydroxide ions indicate that we are considering their concentrations.)

When certain substances are dissolved in water, they may release or absorb H^+ or OH^-, thereby altering the relative concentrations of these ions. Substances that release hydrogen ions in solution are called **acids**. Two examples are hydrochloric acid and carbonic acid:

$$HCl \rightarrow H^+ + Cl^-$$

(hydrochloric acid)   (chloride ion)

$$H_2CO_3 \rightleftharpoons H^+ + HCO_3^-$$

(carbonic acid)   (bicarbonate ion)

Hydrochloric acid is called a **strong acid** because it completely dissociates into H^+ and Cl^- when added to water (which is why the arrow is not bidirectional in that reaction). By comparison, carbonic acid is a **weak acid** because some of it remains in the H_2CO_3 state when dissolved in water (note the bidirectional arrow, $\rightleftharpoons$).

Compared with an acid, a **base** has the opposite effect when dissolved in water—it decreases the H^+ concentration. This can occur in different ways. Some bases, such as sodium hydroxide (NaOH), release OH^- when dissolved in water:

$$NaOH \rightarrow Na^+ + OH^-$$

(sodium hydroxide)   (sodium ion)

Recall that the product of $[H^+]$ and $[OH^-]$ is always 10^{-14} M. When a base such as NaOH raises the OH^- concentration, some of the hydrogen ions bind to these hydroxide ions to form water. Therefore, increasing the OH^- concentration lowers the H^+ concentration.

Let's consider another example. Ammonia reacts with water to produce ammonium ion:

$$NH_3 + H_2O \rightleftharpoons NH_4^+ + OH^-$$

(ammonia)   (ammonium ion)

In this case, NH_3 increases the OH^- concentration by removing H^+ from H_2O. Both sodium hydroxide and ammonia have the same effect—they lower the concentration of H^+. NaOH achieves this by directly increasing the OH^- concentration, whereas NH_3 reacts with water to produce OH^-.

The pH Is a Measure of the H⁺ Concentration of a Solution

The addition of an acid or base to water can greatly change the H^+ and OH^- concentrations over a very broad range. Therefore, scientists use a log scale to describe the concentrations of these ions. The H^+ concentration is expressed as the solution's **pH**, which is defined as the negative logarithm to the base 10 of the H^+ concentration. A logarithmic scale is used because the concentrations of hydrogen ions can vary over a very wide range.

$$pH = -\log_{10}[H^+]$$

To understand what this equation means, let's consider a few examples. A solution with an H^+ concentration of 10^{-7} M has a pH of 7. A concentration of 10^{-7} M is the same as 0.1 μM. A solution in which $[H^+] = 10^{-6}$ M has a pH of 6. A concentration of 10^{-6} M is the same as 1.0 μM. A solution at pH 6 is said to be **acidic**, because it contains more H^+ ions than OH^- ions. Note that as the acidity increases, the pH decreases. A solution in which the pH is 7 is said to be neutral because $[H^+]$ and $[OH^-]$ are equal. A solution with a pH above 7 is considered to be **alkaline**. **Figure 2.20** considers the pH values of some familiar fluids. Keep in mind that each change of 1 pH unit represents a 10-fold difference in H^+ concentration.

Why is pH of importance to living organisms? The answer lies in the observation that H^+ and OH^- can readily bind to many kinds of ions and molecules. For this reason, the pH of a solution can affect:

- the shapes and functions of molecules,
- the rates of many chemical reactions,
- the ability of two molecules to bind to each other, and
- the ability of ions or molecules to dissolve in water.

Due to the various effects of pH, many biological processes function best within very narrow ranges of pH, and even small shifts can have a negative effect. In living cells, the pH ranges from about 6.5 to 7.8 and is carefully regulated to avoid major shifts. The blood of the human body has a normal range of about pH 7.35–7.45 and is therefore slightly alkaline. Certain diseases, such as kidney disease, can decrease or increase blood pH by a few tenths of a unit. When this happens, the enzymes in the body that are required for normal metabolism can no longer function optimally, leading to additional symptoms. As described next, living organisms have buffers to help prevent such changes in pH.

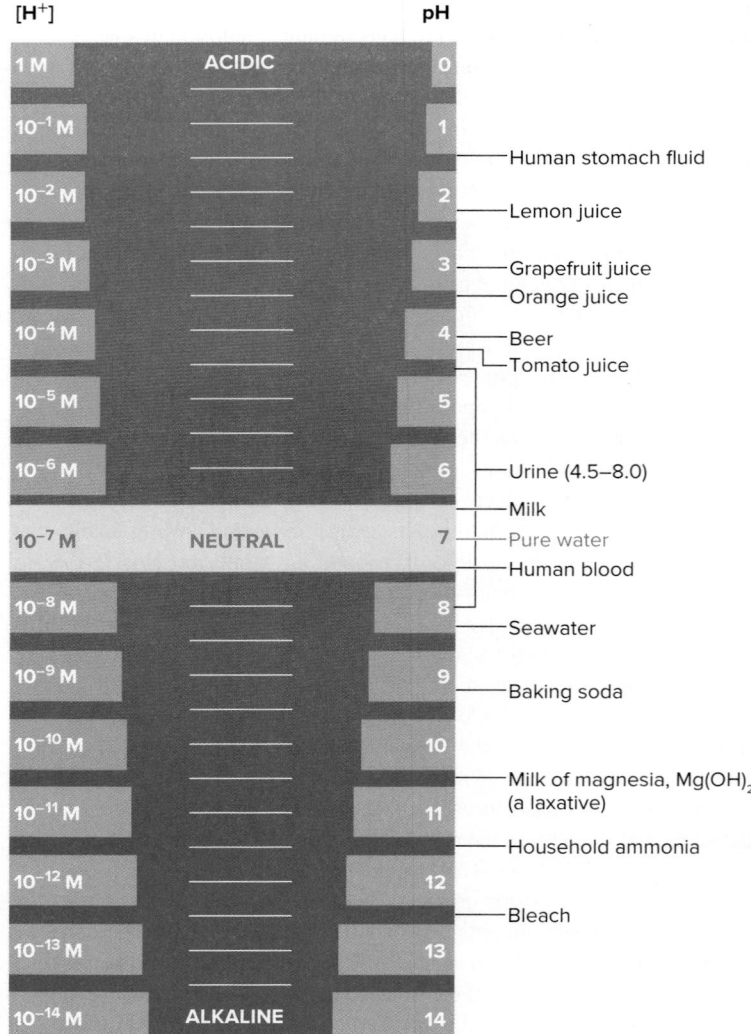

Figure 2.20   **The pH scale and the relative acidities of common substances.**

 Core Skill: Connections   Look ahead to Figure 54.14. The plant life shown growing in part (b) of that figure is sparse because the soil is very acidic. If the pH of the soil were 5.0, what would the H^+ concentration be?

Buffers Minimize Fluctuations in pH

What factors might alter the pH of an organism's fluids? In plants, external factors such as acid rain and other forms of pollution can reduce the pH of water entering the roots. In animals, exercise generates lactic acid, and certain disease states can raise or lower the pH of blood.

Organisms have several ways to cope with changes in pH. In mammals, for example, the kidneys secrete acidic or alkaline compounds into the bloodstream when the blood pH becomes imbalanced. Another mechanism by which pH balance is regulated in diverse organisms involves the actions of acid-base buffers. A **buffer** is usually a pair of substances, an acid and its related base, that minimizes pH fluctuations in the fluids of living organisms. For example, carbonic acid (H_2CO_3) and bicarbonate ions (HCO_3^-) function to keep the pH of an animal's body fluids within a narrow range:

$$CO_2 + H_2O \rightleftharpoons H_2CO_3 \rightleftharpoons H^+ + HCO_3^-$$
$$\text{(carbonic acid)}\quad\text{(bicarbonate ion)}$$

This buffer can affect pH in both directions. For example, if the pH of an animal's body fluids increases (that is, the H^+ concentration decreases), the reaction proceeds from left to right. Carbon dioxide combines with water to make carbonic acid, and then the carbonic acid dissociates into H^+ and HCO_3^-. This increases the H^+ concentration and thereby decreases the pH. Alternatively, when the pH of an animal's blood decreases (that is, the H^+ concentration increases), the reaction runs in reverse. Bicarbonate combines with H^+ to make H_2CO_3, which then dissociates to CO_2 and H_2O. This process removes H^+ from the blood, restoring it to its normal pH, and the CO_2 is exhaled from the lungs. Many buffers exist in nature. Buffers found in living organisms function most efficiently at the normal range of pH values found in that organism.

Summary of Key Concepts

2.1 Atoms

- Atoms are the smallest functional units of matter that form all chemical elements and cannot be further broken down into other substances by ordinary chemical or physical means. Atoms are composed of protons (p^+, positive charge), electrons (e^-, negative charge), and (except for hydrogen) neutrons (n^0, electrically neutral). Electrons are found in orbitals around the atomic nucleus (Figures 2.1, 2.2, 2.3, 2.4).

- Each element contains a unique number of protons—its atomic number. The periodic table organizes all known elements by atomic number and electron shells (Figure 2.5).

- Each atom has a small but measurable mass, measured in daltons (Da). The atomic mass scale indicates an atom's mass relative to the mass of other atoms (Table 2.1).

- Many atoms exist as isotopes, which differ in the number of neutrons they contain. Some isotopes are unstable radioisotopes and emit radiation (Figure 2.6).

- Four elements—oxygen, carbon, hydrogen, and nitrogen—account for the vast majority of atoms in living organisms. In addition, living organisms require mineral and trace elements that are essential for growth and function (Table 2.2).

2.2 Chemical Bonds and Molecules

- A molecule is two or more atoms bonded together. The properties of a molecule are different from the properties of the atoms that combined to form it. A compound is a molecule composed of two or more different elements.

- Atoms tend to form bonds that fill their outer shell with electrons. Covalent bonds, in which atoms share electrons, are strong chemical bonds. Atoms form two covalent bonds—a double bond—when they share two pairs of electrons (Figures 2.7, 2.8, 2.9).

- The electronegativity of an atom is a measure of its ability to attract electrons in a bond with another atom. When two atoms with different electronegativities combine, they form a polar covalent bond because the distribution of electrons around the atoms creates a difference in electric charge across the molecule. Polar molecules, such as water, typically have one or more polar covalent bonds, whereas nonpolar molecules tend to have mostly nonpolar covalent bonds (Figure 2.10).

- A hydrogen bond is a weak interaction between a hydrogen atom and an electronegative atom such as oxygen or nitrogen. The van der Waals dispersion forces are weak electrical attractions that arise between molecules due to variations in the locations of electrons in atoms (Figure 2.11).

- If an atom or molecule gains or loses one or more electrons, it acquires a net electric charge and becomes an ion. The strong attraction between two oppositely charged ions forms an ionic bond (Table 2.3, Figure 2.12).

- The three-dimensional, flexible shapes of molecules allow them to interact and contribute to their biological properties (Figures 2.13, 2.14).

- A free radical is an unstable molecule that can cause cellular damage by taking electrons away from other molecules.

- A chemical reaction occurs when one or more substances are changed into different substances. All chemical reactions eventually reach an equilibrium, unless the products of the reaction are continually removed.

2.3 Properties of Water

- Water is the solvent for most chemical reactions in all living organisms, both inside and outside of cells. Atoms and molecules dissolved in water interact in ways that would be impossible in their undissolved states (Figure 2.15).

- A solute dissolves in a solvent to form a solution. Solute concentration refers to the amount of a solute dissolved in a unit volume of solution. The molarity of a solution is defined as the number of moles of a solute dissolved in 1 L of solution (Figure 2.16).

- Molecules with ionic and polar covalent bonds are hydrophilic, whereas nonpolar molecules, composed predominantly of carbon and hydrogen, are hydrophobic. Amphipathic molecules, such as detergents, have both hydrophilic and hydrophobic regions (Figure 2.17).

- H_2O exists as ice, liquid water, and water vapor (gas) (Figure 2.18).

- The colligative properties of water depend on the number of dissolved solute particles and allow it to function as an antifreeze in certain organisms.

- Water's high heat of vaporization and high heat of fusion make it very stable in its liquid form.

- Water molecules participate in many chemical reactions in living organisms. Hydrolysis reactions break down large molecules into smaller units. In living organisms, water provides support, is used to eliminate wastes, dissipates body heat, aids in the movement of liquid through vessels, and serves as a lubricant; also, its surface tension allows certain insects to walk on water (Figure 2.19).

2.4 pH and Buffers

- The pH of a solution is the negative logarithm to the base 10 of the H^+ concentration. The pH of pure water is 7 (neutral). Alkaline solutions have a pH higher than 7, and acidic solutions have a pH lower than 7 (Figure 2.20).

- A buffer is usually a pair of substances, an acid and its related base, that minimizes pH fluctuations in the fluids of living organisms. Buffers in living cells or body fluids can raise or lower pH to keep its value within a narrow range.

Assess & Discuss

Test Yourself

1. _____ make(s) up the nucleus of an atom.
   a. Protons and electrons
   b. Protons and neutrons
   c. DNA and RNA
   d. Neutrons and electrons
   e. DNA only

2. Living organisms are composed mainly of which atoms?
   a. calcium, hydrogen, nitrogen, and oxygen
   b. carbon, hydrogen, nitrogen, and oxygen
   c. hydrogen, nitrogen, oxygen, and helium
   d. carbon, helium, nitrogen, and oxygen
   e. carbon, calcium, hydrogen, and oxygen

3. The ability of an atom to attract electrons in a bond with another atom is termed its
   a. hydrophobicity.
   b. electronegativity.

c. solubility.
d. valence.
e. both a and b.

4. Hydrogen bonds differ from covalent bonds in that
    a. covalent bonds can form between any type of atom, and hydrogen bonds form only between H and O.
    b. covalent bonds involve sharing of electrons, and hydrogen bonds involve the complete transfer of electrons.
    c. covalent bonds result from equal sharing of electrons, but hydrogen bonds involve unequal sharing of electrons.
    d. covalent bonds involve sharing of electrons between atoms, but hydrogen bonds are the result of weak attractions between a hydrogen atom of a polar molecule and an electronegative atom of another polar molecule.
    e. covalent bonds are weak bonds that break easily, but hydrogen bonds are strong links between atoms that are not easily broken.

5. A free radical
    a. is a positively charged ion.
    b. is an atom with one unpaired electron in its outer shell.
    c. is a stable atom that is not bonded to another atom.
    d. can cause considerable cellular damage.
    e. both b and d.

6. Chemical reactions in living organisms
    a. require energy to begin.
    b. usually require a catalyst to speed them up.
    c. are usually reversible.
    d. occur in liquid environments, such as water.
    e. are all of the above.

7. Solutes that easily dissolve in water are said to be
    a. hydrophobic.
    b. hydrophilic.
    c. polar molecules.
    d. all of the above.
    e. b and c only.

8. The molecular mass of glucose is about 180 g/mol. If 45 g of glucose is dissolved in water to make a final volume of 0.5 L, what is the molarity of the solution?
    a. 0.125 M
    b. 0.25 M
    c. 0.5 M
    d. 1.0 M
    e. 2.0 M

9. The sum of the atomic masses of all the atoms of a molecule is its
    a. atomic weight.
    b. molarity.
    c. molecular mass.
    d. concentration.
    e. polarity.

10. Reactions in which water is used to break apart other molecules are known as _____ reactions.
    a. hydrophilic
    b. hydrophobic
    c. dehydration
    d. anabolic
    e. hydrolysis

Conceptual Questions

1. Compare and contrast the different types of bonds commonly found in biological molecules.

2. What is the significance of molecular shape, and what may change the shapes of molecules?

3. **Core Concept: Systems** A core concept of biology is that systems are interconnected and interacting. As mentioned in Figure 1.4e, emergent properties arise from complex interactions within systems. How is this core concept of biology related to chemical reactions that make molecules from other starting materials? What examples can you cite from this chapter of emergent properties of molecules, in which atoms with one type of property combine to form molecules with completely different properties?

Collaborative Questions

1. Discuss the properties of the three subatomic particles of atoms.

2. Discuss several properties of water that make it possible for life to exist.

The Chemical Basis of Life II: Organic Molecules

3

A model showing the structure of DNA—a type of organic macromolecule that stores genetic information. ©Zoonar GmbH/ Alamy Stock Photo

In Chapter 2, we learned that all life is composed of atoms, which, in turn, combine to form molecules. Molecules may be simple in atomic composition, such as water (H_2O) or hydrogen gas (H_2), or may bind with other molecules to form larger ones. Of the countless possible molecules that can be produced from the known elements in nature, certain types contain carbon and are found in all forms of life. These carbon-containing molecules are collectively referred to as **organic molecules**, so named because they were first discovered in living organisms. Organic molecules include lipids and large, complex compounds called **macromolecules**, which can be carbohydrates, proteins, or nucleic acids. In this chapter, we will survey the structures of these molecules and examine their main functions. We begin with the element whose chemical properties are fundamental to the formation of biologically important molecules: carbon. This element provides the atomic scaffold on which life is built.

3.1 The Carbon Atom

Learning Outcomes:

1. Explain the properties of carbon that make it the chemical basis of all life.
2. Describe the variety and chemical characteristics of common functional groups of organic compounds.
3. Compare and contrast different types of isomers.

The science of carbon-containing molecules is known as **organic chemistry**. A long time ago, the study of organic molecules was considered a fruitless endeavor because of a concept called vitalism, which persisted into the 19th century. Vitalism held that organic molecules were created by, and therefore imparted with, a vital life force that was contained within a plant or an animal's body. Supporters of vitalism argued that chemists could not synthesize an organic compound, because such molecules could arise only through the intervention of mysterious qualities associated with life.

Vitalism was disproved by Friedrich Wöhler, a German physician and chemist interested in the properties of inorganic and organic compounds. He spent some time studying urea (($NH_2)_2CO$), a natural organic molecule formed from the breakdown of proteins in an animal's body. In mammals, urea accumulates in the urine formed by the kidneys, and then is excreted from the body. During the course of his studies, Wöhler purified urea from the urine of mammals. He noted the color, size, shape, and other characteristics of the urea crystals.

In 1828, while exploring the reactive properties of ammonia and cyanic acid, Wöhler attempted to synthesize an inorganic molecule, ammonium cyanate (NH_4OCN), which is not found in living organisms. Instead, to his surprise, Wöhler discovered that ammonia and cyanic acid reacted to produce a third compound, which, when heated, formed familiar-looking crystals. After careful analysis, he concluded that these crystals were urea. No mysterious life force was required to make this organic molecule. Other scientists, such as Hermann Kolbe, would soon demonstrate that organic compounds such as acetic acid (CH_3COOH) could also be synthesized directly from simpler molecules. These studies refuted the concept of vitalism, and so began the field of organic chemistry.

Central to Wöhler's and Kolbe's reactions is the carbon atom. Urea and acetic acid, like all organic compounds, contain carbon atoms bonded to other atoms. In this section, we will consider the chemical features of carbon that make it such an important element in living organisms.

Carbon Forms Four Covalent Bonds with Other Atoms

A key property of the carbon atom is its ability to form four covalent bonds with other atoms, including other carbon atoms. This occurs because carbon has four electrons in its outer (second) shell, and it requires eight electrons, or four additional electrons, to fill this shell (**Figure 3.1**). In living organisms, carbon atoms most commonly form covalent bonds with other carbon atoms and with hydrogen, oxygen, nitrogen, and sulfur atoms. Bonds between two carbon atoms, between carbon and oxygen, or between carbon and nitrogen can be single or double, or in the case of C≡C and C≡N bonds, triple. The variation in bonding of carbon with carbon and other atoms allows a vast number of organic compounds to be formed from only a few chemical elements. Carbon and other atoms may be bonded together in configurations that are linear, ringlike, or highly branched. Such molecular shapes can produce molecules with a variety of functions.

Carbon and hydrogen have similar electronegativities (see Chapter 2). Therefore, carbon-carbon and carbon-hydrogen bonds are nonpolar. As a consequence, molecules with a high proportion of hydrogen-carbon bonds, called **hydrocarbons**, are hydrophobic and poorly soluble in water. In contrast, when carbon forms polar

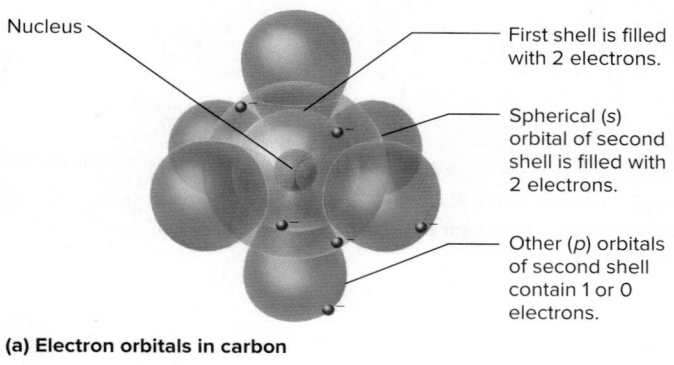

Nucleus

First shell is filled with 2 electrons.

Spherical (s) orbital of second shell is filled with 2 electrons.

Other (p) orbitals of second shell contain 1 or 0 electrons.

(a) Electron orbitals in carbon

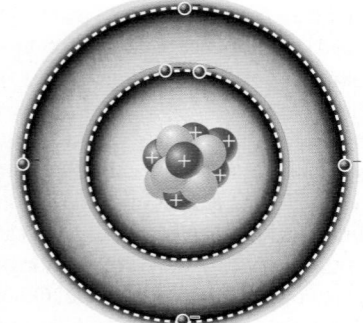

(b) Simplified depiction of carbon's electron shells

Figure 3.1   Models for the electron orbitals and shells of carbon. A carbon atom has four electrons in its outer (second) electron shell. When a carbon atom forms four covalent bonds with other atoms, its outer shell is full with eight electrons, which is a stable condition.

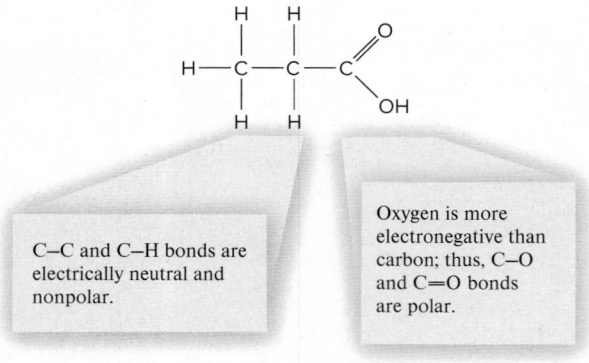

C–C and C–H bonds are electrically neutral and nonpolar.

Oxygen is more electronegative than carbon; thus, C–O and C=O bonds are polar.

Propionic acid

Figure 3.2   Nonpolar and polar bonds in an organic molecule. Carbon can form both nonpolar and polar bonds, and both single and double bonds, as shown here in the molecule propionic acid, a common food preservative.

covalent bonds with more electronegative atoms, such as oxygen or nitrogen, the resulting molecule is much more soluble in water because of its electrical attraction to polar water molecules. The ability of carbon to form both polar and nonpolar bonds (**Figure 3.2**) contributes to its ability to serve as the backbone for an astonishing variety of biologically important molecules.

Another feature of carbon that is important to living organisms is that carbon bonds are stable within the large range of temperatures associated with life. This property arises in part because the carbon atom is small relative to most other atoms. Therefore, the distance between carbon atoms forming a carbon-carbon bond is quite short. Shorter bonds tend to be stronger and more stable than longer bonds, which form between two large atoms. For this reason, carbon bonds are compatible with what we observe about life-forms today; namely, living organisms can inhabit environments with a range of temperatures, from the Earth's frigid icy poles to the superheated water of deep-sea vents.

Carbon Atoms Bond to Several Biologically Important Functional Groups

Aside from the simplest hydrocarbons, most organic molecules and macromolecules contain **functional groups**—groups of atoms with characteristic chemical structures and properties. Each type of functional group exhibits similar chemical properties in all molecules in which it occurs. For example, the amino group ($-NH_2$) acts like a base. In the pH range found in living organisms, an amino group readily binds H^+ to become NH_3^+, thereby removing H^+ from an aqueous solution and raising the pH. As discussed later in this chapter, amino groups are found in proteins and also in other types of organic molecules. **Table 3.1** describes examples of functional groups found in many different types of organic molecules. We will discuss each of these groups at numerous points throughout this textbook.

Carbon-Containing Molecules May Exist in Multiple Forms Called Isomers

Wöhler was surprised to discover that urea (($NH_2)_2CO$) and ammonium cyanate (NH_4OCN) contained the exact same ratio of carbon, nitrogen, hydrogen, and oxygen atoms, yet they were different molecules with distinct chemical and biological properties. Two (or more)

Table 3.1   Some Biologically Important Functional Groups That Bond to Carbon

Functional group* (with shorthand notation)	Formula†	Examples of where the group is found	Properties
Amino (–NH$_2$)	R–N(H)(H)	Amino acids (proteins)	Weakly basic (can accept H$^+$); polar; forms part of peptide bonds
Carbonyl (–CO)‡ Ketone	O‖ R–C–R′	Steroids, waxes, and proteins	Polar; highly chemically reactive; forms hydrogen bonds
Aldehyde (–CHO)	O‖ R–C–H	Linear forms of sugars and some odor molecules	
Carboxyl (–COOH)	O R–C(–OH)	Amino acids, fatty acids	Acidic (gives up H$^+$ in water); forms part of peptide bonds
Hydroxyl (–OH)	R–OH	Steroids, alcohol, carbohydrates, some amino acids	Polar; forms hydrogen bonds with water
Methyl (–CH$_3$)	H| R–C–H | H	May be attached to DNA, proteins, and carbohydrates	Nonpolar
Phosphate (–PO$_4{}^{2-}$)	O‖ R–O–P–O$^-$ | O$^-$	Nucleic acids, ATP, phospholipids	Polar; weakly acidic and negatively charged at typical pH of living organisms
Sulfate (–SO$_4{}^-$)	O‖ R–O–S–O$^-$ ‖ O	May be attached to carbohydrates, proteins, and lipids	Polar; negatively charged at typical pH of living organisms
Sulfhydryl (–SH)	R–SH	Proteins that contain the amino acid cysteine	Polar; forms disulfide bridges in many proteins

*This list contains many of the functional groups that are important in biology. However, many more functional groups have been identified by biochemists.
†R and R′ represent the remainder of the molecule.
‡A carbonyl group is C=O. In a ketone, the carbon of this group forms covalent bonds with two other carbon atoms. In an aldehyde, the carbon is bonded to a hydrogen atom.

molecules with the same chemical formula but different structures and characteristics are called **isomers**.

Figure 3.3 depicts three ways in which isomers may occur. **Structural isomers** contain the same atoms but in different bonding relationships. Urea and ammonium cyanate fall into this category. A simpler example of structural isomers (isopropyl alcohol and propyl alcohol) is illustrated in Figure 3.3a.

Stereoisomers have identical bonding relationships, but the spatial positioning of their atoms differs. Two types of stereoisomers are *cis-trans* isomers and enantiomers. In *cis-trans* **isomers**, like those shown in Figure 3.3b, the two hydrogen atoms linked to the two carbons of a C=C double bond may be on the same side of the carbons, in which case the C=C bond is called a *cis* double bond. If the hydrogens are on opposite sides, it is a *trans* double bond. *Cis-trans* isomers may have very different chemical properties from each other, most notably their stability and sensitivity to heat and light. For instance, the light-sensitive region of your eye contains a molecule called retinal, which exists in either a *cis* or *trans* form. In darkness, the *cis*-retinal form predominates.

The energy of sunlight, however, causes retinal to isomerize to the *trans* form. The *trans*-retinal activates the light-capturing cells in the eye.

A second type of stereoisomer, called an **enantiomer**, exists as one of a pair of molecules that are mirror images. Four different atoms can bind to a single carbon atom in two possible ways, designated as a left-handed and a right-handed structure. The resulting structures are not identical, but instead are mirror images of each other (Figure 3.3b). A convenient way to visualize the contrasting structures of enantiomers is to consider a pair of gloves. No matter which way you turn or hold a left-hand glove, it cannot fit properly on your right hand. Any given pair of enantiomers shares identical chemical properties, such as solubility and melting point. However, due to the different orientation of their atoms in space, their ability to noncovalently bond to other molecules can be strikingly different. For example, **enzymes** are molecules that catalyze (speed up) the rates of many biologically important chemical reactions. An enzyme that recognizes one enantiomer usually does not recognize the other.

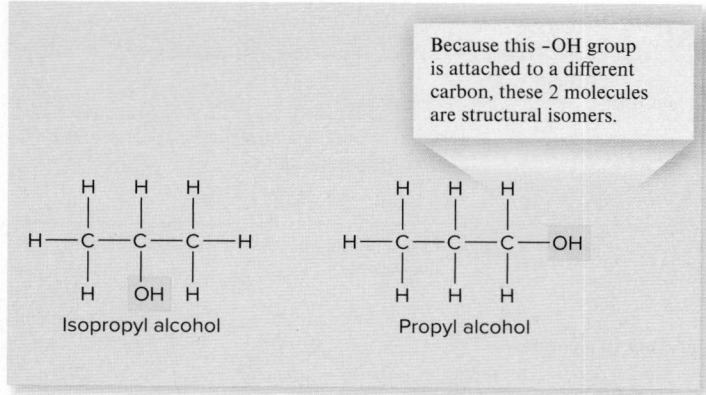

Because this –OH group is attached to a different carbon, these 2 molecules are structural isomers.

Isopropyl alcohol   Propyl alcohol

(a) Structural isomers

These 2 hydrogens are *cis* to each other.

These 2 hydrogens are *trans* to each other.

cis-Butene   *trans*-Butene

Cis-trans isomers

Molecule   Mirror image

Enantiomers

(b) Two types of stereoisomers

Figure 3.3 Types of isomers. Isomers are molecules with the same chemical formula but different structures. The differences in structure result in different biological properties. Isomers can be grouped into **(a)** structural isomers and **(b)** stereoisomers.

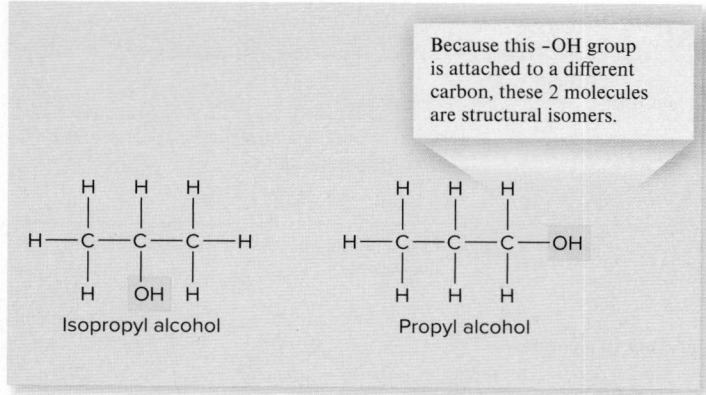

3.2 Formation of Organic Molecules and Macromolecules

Learning Outcome:

1. Explain how small molecules are assembled into larger ones by dehydration reactions and how hydrolysis reactions reverse this process.

As we have seen, organic molecules have various shapes due to the bonding properties of carbon. During the past two centuries,

---

biochemists have studied many organic molecules found in living organisms and determined their structures at the molecular level. Many of these are relatively small molecules. However, some organic molecules are extremely large macromolecules composed of thousands or even millions of atoms. Such large molecules are formed by linking together many smaller molecules called **monomers** (meaning one part) and are known as **polymers** (meaning many parts). When a polymer is being formed, two smaller molecules combine by a **condensation reaction**, which produces a larger organic molecule plus a water molecule. This specific type of condensation reaction is also called a **dehydration reaction**, because a molecule of water is removed when a monomer is added to a growing polymer.

The mechanism of a dehydration reaction is illustrated in **Figure 3.4a**. The length of a polymer is extended with each dehydration reaction. Some polymers reach great lengths by this mechanism. For example, during the synthesis of DNA, which is described in Chapter 11, dehydration reactions produce linear strands of DNA that contain millions of monomers called nucleotides.

Although DNA is a stable polymer, other polymers, such as large carbohydrates, are often broken down. As discussed later in this chapter, a large carbohydrate in plants, which is called starch, plays a role in storing energy. When a plant cell needs that stored energy, the starch is broken down into its constituent monomers. The process by which a polymer is broken down into monomers is called a **hydrolysis reaction**, because a molecule of water is added back each time a monomer is released (**Figure 3.4b**).

3.3 Overview of the Four Major Classes of Organic Molecules Found in Living Cells

Learning Outcome:

1. Compare and contrast the structures and functions of carbohydrates, lipids, proteins, and nucleic acids.

By analyzing the cells of many different species, researchers have determined that all forms of life have organic molecules and macromolecules that fall into four broad categories, based on their chemical and biological properties: carbohydrates, lipids, proteins, and nucleic acids. **Table 3.2** outlines the general structures and functions of these molecules and provides some examples. In the next sections, we will examine them in greater detail.

3.4 Carbohydrates

Learning Outcomes:

1. Distinguish among different forms of carbohydrate molecules, including monosaccharides, disaccharides, and polysaccharides.

2. Relate the functions of plant and animal polysaccharides to their structure.

Carbohydrates are organic molecules composed of carbon, hydrogen, and oxygen atoms in or close to the proportions represented by the general formula $C_n(H_2O)_n$, where *n* is a whole number. This

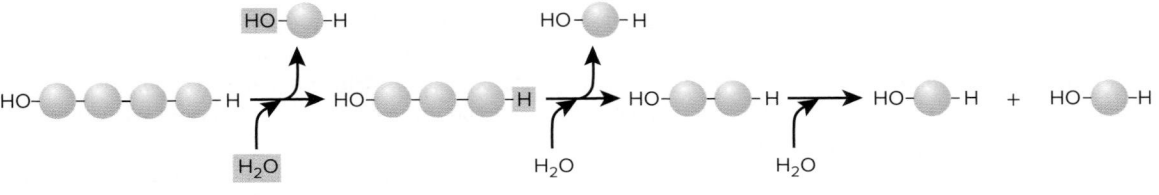

(a) Polymer formation by dehydration reactions

A polymer begins as two monomers combine in a dehydration reaction.

Elongation of the polymer continues with additional dehydration reactions.

The final polymer may consist of many monomers.

Polymers are broken down one monomer at a time by hydrolysis reactions.

(b) Breakdown of a polymer by hydrolysis reactions

Figure 3.4 Formation and breakdown of polymers. (a) Monomers combine to form polymers in living organisms by dehydration reactions, in which a molecule of water is removed each time a new monomer is added to the growing polymer. **(b)** Polymers can be broken down into their constituent monomers by hydrolysis reactions, in which a molecule of water is added each time a monomer is released.

formula gives carbohydrates their name—carbon-containing compounds that are hydrated, that is, contain water. Most of the carbon atoms in a carbohydrate are linked to a hydrogen atom and a hydroxyl functional group. However, other functional groups, such as amino and carboxyl groups, are also found in certain carbohydrates. As discussed next, sugars are relatively small carbohydrates, whereas polysaccharides are large macromolecules.

Sugars Are Small Carbohydrates That Usually Taste Sweet

Sugars are small carbohydrates that usually taste sweet. The simplest sugars are monomers known as **monosaccharides** (from the Greek, meaning single sugars). The most common types of monosaccharides contain either five carbons (pentoses) or six carbons

Table 3.2	A Comparison of the Four Types of Organic Molecules Found in Living Organisms		
Type	**Structure**	**Key functions**	**Examples**
Carbohydrates	The general formula is $C_n(H_2O)_n$, where n is a whole number.	Simple carbohydrates are broken down to make ATP, which is used as a source of energy. Larger carbohydrates store energy or may play a structural role, as in plant cell walls. Some carbohydrates function as molecular tags allowing recognition of specific cells and molecules.	Simple sugars, such as glucose; larger polymers, such as starch and cellulose
Lipids	Lipids are nonpolar molecules that are primarily composed of carbon and hydrogen, with some oxygen.	Lipids are a key part of cell membranes and also function as hormones and in energy storage; in animals, they act as insulators and shock absorbers.	Phospholipids, estrogen, testosterone, triglycerides
Proteins	A polypeptide is a structural unit composed of a linear sequence of amino acids. A protein is a functional unit composed of one or more polypeptides.	Proteins play a key role in cell structure and carry out a diverse array of cellular functions; for example, there are proteins involved with gene expression and regulation, motor proteins, defense proteins, cell-signaling proteins, metabolic enzymes, structural proteins, and transporters.	See Table 3.3
Nucleic acids	A nucleic acid is a linear sequence of nucleotides; DNA is double-stranded.	DNA stores genetic information in units called genes. RNA is made from DNA and provides access to that information.	DNA and RNA

(hexoses). Important pentoses are ribose ($C_5H_{10}O_5$) and the closely related deoxyribose ($C_5H_{10}O_4$), which are part of RNA and DNA molecules, respectively, and are described later in this chapter. The most common hexose is glucose ($C_6H_{12}O_6$). Like other monosaccharides, glucose is very water-soluble and circulates in the blood or fluids of animals, where it can be transported across cell membranes. Once inside a cell, enzymes can break down glucose into smaller molecules, releasing energy that was stored in glucose's chemical bonds. This energy is then stored in the bonds of another molecule, called adenosine triphosphate, or ATP (see Chapter 7), which, in turn, powers a variety of cellular processes. In this way, sugar is often used as a source of energy by living organisms.

Figure 3.5a depicts the bonds between atoms in a monosaccharide in both linear and ring forms, with the carbon atoms numbered by convention. The ring is made from the linear structure when the oxygen atom attached to carbon 5 forms a covalent bond with carbon 1. The hydrogen atoms and the hydroxyl groups may lie above or below the plane of the ring structure. The ring structure is the predominant type of structure found in living organisms.

Figure 3.5b compares different isomers of glucose. Glucose can exist as D- and L-glucose, which are mirror images of each other, or enantiomers. D-Glucose is the isomer of glucose that is commonly found in living cells. It is recognized by enzymes that can synthesize polymers of D-glucose, such as starch. By comparison, L-glucose is rarely found in living cells, and it binds poorly to enzymes that recognize D-glucose. Other types of isomers are formed by changing the relative positions of the hydrogens and hydroxyl groups along the sugar ring. For example, glucose exists in two interconvertible forms, with the hydroxyl group attached to the number 1 carbon atom lying either above (the β form of glucose, Figure 3.5b) or below (the α form, Figure 3.5a) the plane of the ring. As another example, if the hydroxyl group on carbon atom number 4 of glucose is above the plane of the ring instead of below it, the sugar is called galactose (Figure 3.5b).

Monosaccharides can be linked together by dehydration reactions to form larger carbohydrates. **Disaccharides** (meaning two sugars) are carbohydrates composed of two monosaccharides. A familiar disaccharide is sucrose, or table sugar, which is composed of the monomers glucose and fructose (**Figure 3.6**). Sucrose is the major transport form of sugar in plants. The linking together of most monosaccharides involves the removal of a hydroxyl group from one monosaccharide and a hydrogen atom from the other, giving rise to a molecule of water and covalently bonding the two sugars together through an oxygen atom. The bond formed between two sugar molecules by such a dehydration reaction is called a **glycosidic bond**. Other disaccharides frequently found in nature are maltose, formed in animals during the digestion of large carbohydrates in the intestinal tract, and lactose, present in the milk of mammals. Maltose is α-D-glucose linked to α-D-glucose, and lactose is β-D-galactose linked to β-D-glucose.

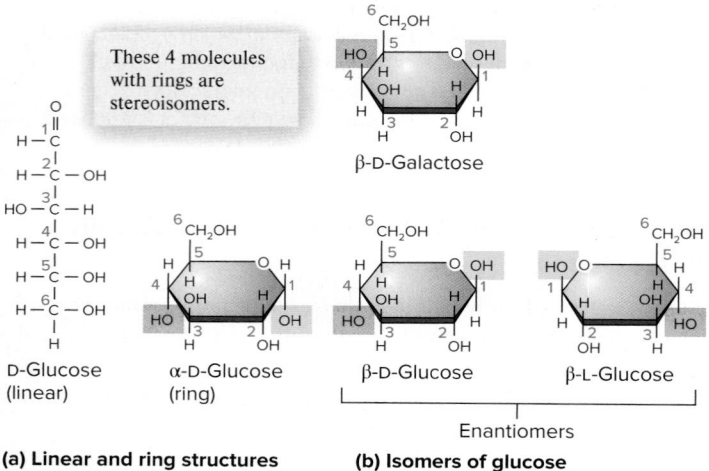

(a) Linear and ring structures of D-glucose

(b) Isomers of glucose

Enantiomers

Figure 3.5 Monosaccharide structure. (a) A comparison of the linear and ring structures of glucose. In solution, such as in the fluids of organisms, nearly all glucose is in the ring form. **(b)** Isomers of glucose. The locations of the hydroxyl groups on carbon 1 and carbon 4 are emphasized with green and orange boxes, respectively. Glucose exists as stereoisomers designated α- and β-glucose, which differ in the position of the —OH group attached to carbon atom number 1. Glucose and galactose differ in the position of the —OH group attached to carbon atom number 4. Enantiomers of glucose, called D-glucose and L-glucose, are mirror images of each other. D-Glucose is the form found in living cells.

 Core Concept: Energy and Matter Living organisms use energy. The chemical energy stored in the bonds of glucose molecules can be harnessed by living organisms. This energy is used to perform numerous functions that support life, including the synthesis of new molecules, growth, digestion, locomotion, and many others.

Concept Check: *Why do enantiomers such as D- and L-glucose differ in their ability to bind to enzymes?*

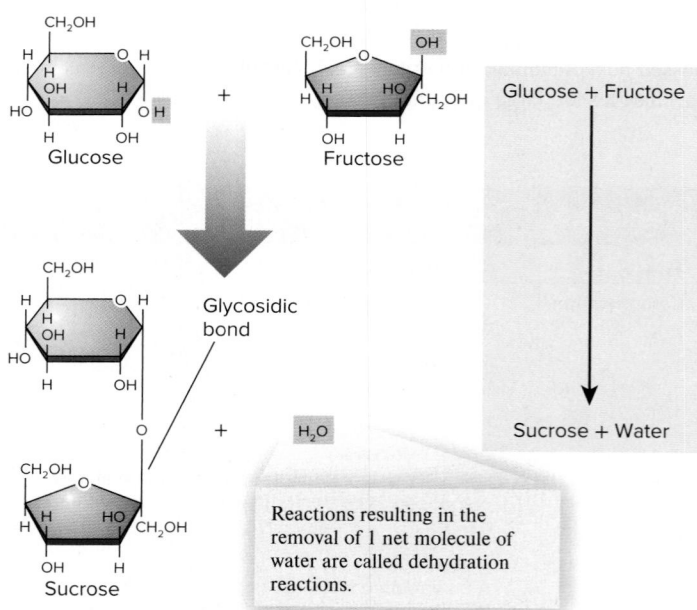

Glucose + Fructose

Glycosidic bond

Sucrose + Water

Reactions resulting in the removal of 1 net molecule of water are called dehydration reactions.

Figure 3.6 Formation of a disaccharide. Two monosaccharides can bond to each other to form a disaccharide, such as sucrose, maltose, or lactose, by a dehydration reaction.

Concept Check: *What type of reaction is the reverse of the one shown here, in which a disaccharide is broken down into two monosaccharides?*

Polysaccharides Are Carbohydrate Polymers That Include Starch, Glycogen, and Cellulose

When many monosaccharides are linked together to form long polymers, the products are **polysaccharides** (meaning many sugars). **Starch**, found in plant cells, and **glycogen**, found in animal cells, are examples of polysaccharides (**Figure 3.7**). Both of these polysaccharides are composed of thousands of α-D-glucose molecules linked together in long, branched chains, differing only in the extent of branching along the chain. The bonds that connect the monomers are very specific. In starch and glycogen, the bonds form between carbons 1 and 4 and between carbons 1 and 6. The high degree of branching in glycogen contributes to its solubility in animal tissues,

such as muscle tissue, because the extensive branching creates a more open structure in which many hydrophilic hydroxyl (—OH) side groups have access to water and can hydrogen-bond with it. Starch is less branched and less soluble, which contributes to the properties of plant structures (think of a potato or a kernel of corn).

Some polysaccharides, such as starch and glycogen, store energy in cells. Like disaccharides, these polysaccharides can be hydrolyzed to yield monosaccharides, which are broken down to produce ATP, a common energy source for cells. Starch and glycogen, the polymers of α-glucose, provide an efficient means of storing energy for those times when a plant or animal cannot obtain sufficient energy from its environment or diet for its metabolic requirements.

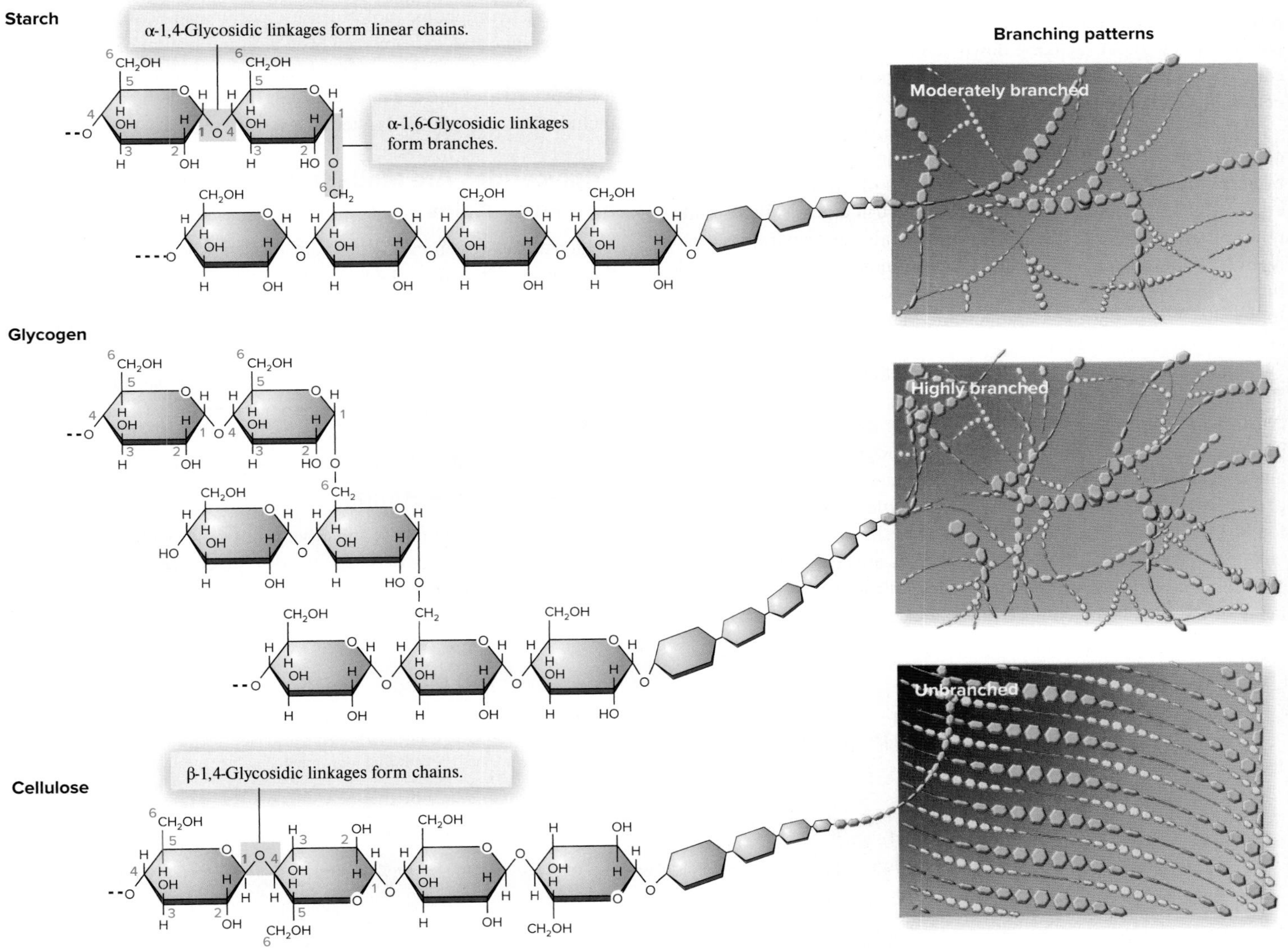

Figure 3.7 **Polysaccharides that are polymers of glucose.** These polysaccharides differ in their arrangement, extent of branching, and type of glucose isomer. In cellulose, the bonding arrangements cause every other glucose to be upside-down with respect to its neighbors.

 Core Skill: Connections Look ahead to Figures 10.5 and 10.6 for the role of cellulose in plant structure and to Figures 36.10 and 36.11 for its role in plant growth. Considering the amount of plant life on Earth, what might you conclude about the abundance of cellulose on the planet?

Other polysaccharides play a structural role, rather than storing energy. For example, cellulose is a major constituent of plant cell walls. **Cellulose** is a polymer of β-D-glucose, with a linear arrangement of carbon-carbon bonds and no branching (see Figure 3.7). Each glucose monomer in cellulose is in an opposite orientation from its adjacent monomers (flipped over), forming long chains of several thousand glucose monomers.

Linear chains of cellulose can form hydrogen bonds with each other and thereby arrange themselves in a parallel pattern (see the lower right panel in Figure 3.7). These sheets provide great strength to plant cell walls. The bond orientations in β-D-glucose prevent cellulose from being hydrolyzed in most types of organisms. The enzymes that break the bonds between monomers of α-D-glucose in starch do not recognize the shape of the polymer made by the bonds between β-D-glucose monomers in cellulose. Therefore, plant cells can break down starch without breaking down cellulose. In this way, cellulose can be used for other functions, notably in the formation of the rigid cell walls characteristic of plants.

Unlike most animals and plants, some organisms do have an enzyme capable of breaking down cellulose. For example, certain bacteria present in the gastrointestinal tracts of grass and wood eaters, such as cows and termites, respectively, can digest cellulose into usable monosaccharides because they contain an enzyme that can hydrolyze the bonds between β-D-glucose monomers. Humans lack this enzyme. Therefore, we eliminate in the feces most of the cellulose ingested in our diet. Undigestible plant matter we consume is commonly referred to as fiber.

Other polysaccharides also play structural roles. **Chitin**, a tough, structural polysaccharide, forms the external skeleton of insects and crustaceans (shrimp and lobsters) as well as the cell walls of fungi. The sugar monomers within chitin have nitrogen-containing groups attached to them. **Glycosaminoglycans** are large polysaccharides that play a structural role in animals. For example, they are abundantly found in cartilage, the tough, fibrous material found in joints and other animal structures. Glycosaminoglycans are also abundant in the extracellular matrix that provides a structural framework surrounding many of the cells in an animal's body (look ahead to Figure 10.4).

3.5 Lipids

Learning Outcomes:
1. List the classes of lipid molecules important in living organisms.
2. Diagram the structure of a triglyceride, and explain how it is affected by the presence of saturated and unsaturated fatty acids.
3. Explain why some fats are solid at room temperature and others are liquid.
4. Discuss how fats function as energy-storage molecules.
5. Explain why phospholipids form a bilayer when dissolved in water.
6. Describe the chemical nature of steroids, and give an example of their biological importance.

Lipids are hydrophobic molecules composed mainly of hydrogen and carbon atoms, and some oxygen. The defining feature of lipids is that they are nonpolar and therefore insoluble in water. Lipids account for about 40% of the organic matter in the average human body and include fats, phospholipids, steroids, and waxes.

Triglycerides Are Made from Glycerol and Fatty Acids

Triglycerides (often called fats) are formed when glycerol bonds to three fatty acids (**Figure 3.8**). Glycerol is a three-carbon molecule with one hydroxyl group (—OH) bonded to each carbon. A fatty acid is a chain of carbon and hydrogen atoms with a carboxyl group (—COOH) at one end. Each of the hydroxyl groups in glycerol is linked to the carboxyl group of a fatty acid by the removal of a molecule of water by a dehydration reaction. The resulting bond is an ester bond.

Fatty Acids May Differ in Length and Contain Double Bonds

The fatty acids found in fats and other lipids differ with regard to their lengths and the presence of double bonds (**Figure 3.9**). Most fatty acids in nature have an even number of carbon atoms, with 16- and 18-carbon fatty acids being the most common in the cells of plants and animals.

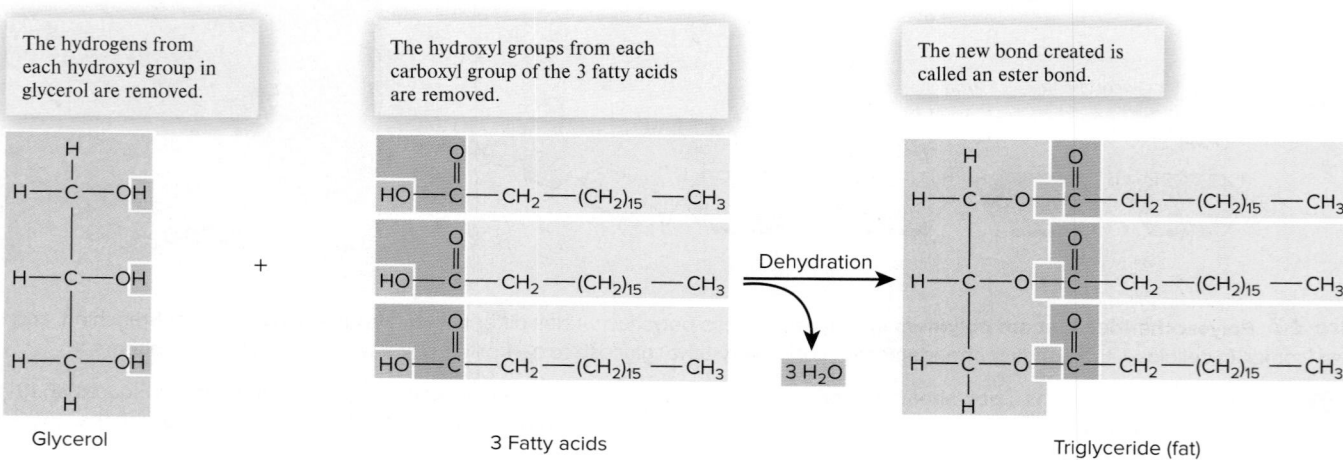

Figure 3.8 The formation of a triglyceride. The formation of a triglyceride occurs via three dehydration reactions in which fatty acids are bonded to glycerol. Note in this figure and in Figure 3.9 a common shorthand notation used for depicting fatty acid chains, in which a portion of the CH_2 groups forming the chain are represented as $(CH_2)_n$, where n is 2 or greater.

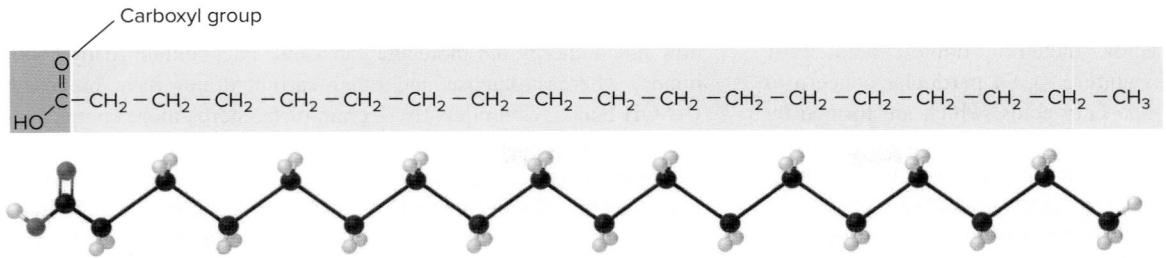

Carboxyl group

Saturated fatty acid
(Stearic acid)

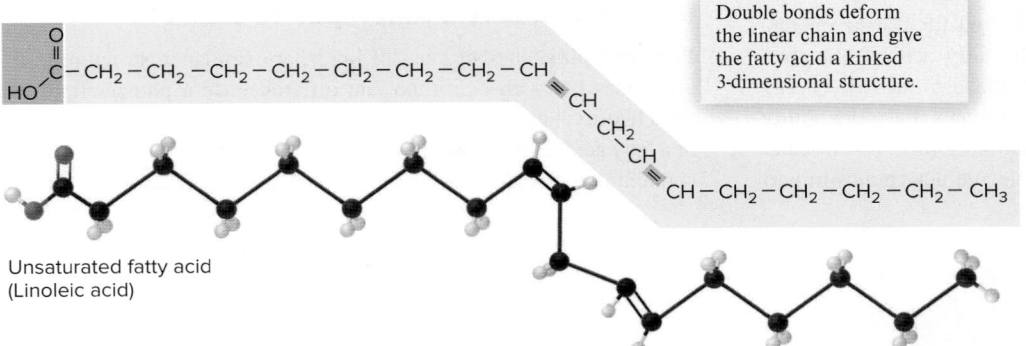

Double bonds deform
the linear chain and give
the fatty acid a kinked
3-dimensional structure.

Unsaturated fatty acid
(Linoleic acid)

Figure 3.9 Examples of fatty acids. Fatty acids are hydrocarbon chains that have a carboxyl functional group at one end and contain either no double bonds between carbons (saturated) or one or more double bonds (unsaturated). Stearic acid, for example, is an abundant saturated fatty acid in animals, whereas linoleic acid is an unsaturated fatty acid found in plants. Note that the presence of two C=C double bonds introduces two kinks into the chain structure of linoleic acid. As a consequence, unsaturated fatty acids are not able to pack together as tightly as saturated fatty acids.

Fatty acids also differ with regard to the presence of double bonds. When all of the carbons in a fatty acid are linked by single covalent bonds, the fatty acid is said to be a **saturated fatty acid**, because all of the carbons are saturated with covalently bonded hydrogens. Alternatively, some fatty acids contain one or more C=C double bonds. These fatty acids are known as **unsaturated fatty acids**. The C=C double bond introduces a kink into the linear shape of a fatty acid. A fatty acid with one C=C bond is a monounsaturated fatty acid, whereas a fatty acid with two or more C=C bonds is a polyunsaturated fatty acid.

In organisms such as mammals, certain fatty acids are necessary for good health but cannot be synthesized by the body. Such fatty acids are called essential fatty acids, because they must be obtained in the diet; one example is linoleic acid (see Figure 3.9).

Fats (triglycerides) that contain high amounts of saturated fatty acids pack together tightly, resulting in numerous intermolecular interactions that stabilize the fat. Saturated fats have a high melting point and tend to be solid at room temperature. Animal fats generally contain a high proportion of saturated fatty acids. For example, beef fat contains high amounts of stearic acid, a saturated fatty acid with a melting point of 70°C (see Figure 3.9). When you cook a hamburger on the stove, the stearic acid and other saturated animal fats melt, and liquid grease appears in the frying pan (**Figure 3.10**). When allowed to cool to room temperature, however, the liquid grease in the pan returns to its solid form.

Because of kinks in their chains, unsaturated fatty acids do not pack together as tightly as saturated fatty acids. Fats high in unsaturated fatty acids usually have low melting points and are liquid at room temperature. Such fats are called oils. Fats derived from plants generally contain unsaturated fatty acids. For example, olive oil contains high amounts of oleic acid, a monounsaturated fatty acid with a melting point of 16°C. Fatty acids with additional double bonds have even lower melting points. Linoleic acid (see Figure 3.9) has two double bonds and melts at −5°C. Safflower and sunflower oils contain high amounts of linoleic acid.

High temperature converts solid, saturated fats to liquid.

After cooling, saturated fats return to their solid form.

Unsaturated fats have low melting points and are liquid at room temperature.

Figure 3.10 Fats at different temperatures. Saturated fats found in animals tend to have higher melting points than do the unsaturated fats found in plants. a (left, right): ©Tom Pantages; b: ©Felicia Martinez Photography/PhotoEdit

(a) Animal fats at high and low temperatures

(b) Vegetable fats at low temperature

Concept Check: *Certain types of fats used in baking are called shortenings. Shortenings are often made from vegetable oils by a process called hydrogenation, in which the addition of hydrogens causes double bonds to become single bonds. How do you think hydrogenation affects the melting point of the resulting fat?*

Most unsaturated fatty acids, including linoleic acid, exist in nature in the *cis* form (see Figure 3.3). Of particular concern to human health, however, are *trans* fatty acids, which are formed by an artificial process in which the natural *cis* form is altered to a *trans* configuration. This alteration gives the fats that contain such fatty acids a more compact, linear structure and, therefore, a higher melting point. Although this process has been used for many years to produce fats with a longer shelf life and with better characteristics for baking, research has revealed that *trans* fats are linked to human diseases. Notable among these is coronary artery disease, caused by a narrowing of the blood vessels that supply the heart.

Like starch and glycogen, fats are important for storing energy. The hydrolysis of triglycerides releases the fatty acids from glycerol, and these products can then be metabolized to provide energy to make ATP. Certain organisms, such as mammals, have the ability to store large amounts of energy by accumulating fats. The number of C—H bonds in a fat or carbohydrate molecule determines in part how much energy the molecule can yield. Fats contain many C—H bonds, whereas glucose and other carbohydrates have numerous C—OH bonds. Consequently, 1 gram of fat stores more energy than does 1 gram of starch or glycogen. For this reason, fat is an efficient means of energy storage for mobile organisms for which excess body mass may be a disadvantage. In animals, fats can also play a structural role by forming cushions that support organs. In addition, fats provide insulation under the skin that helps protect many terrestrial animals during cold weather and marine mammals in cold water.

Phospholipids Are Amphipathic Lipids

Phospholipids, another class of lipids, are similar in structure to triglycerides but with one important difference. In a phospholipid, the third hydroxyl group of glycerol is linked to a phosphate group instead of a fatty acid. In most phospholipids, a small polar or charged nitrogen-containing molecule is attached to this phosphate (**Figure 3.11a**). The

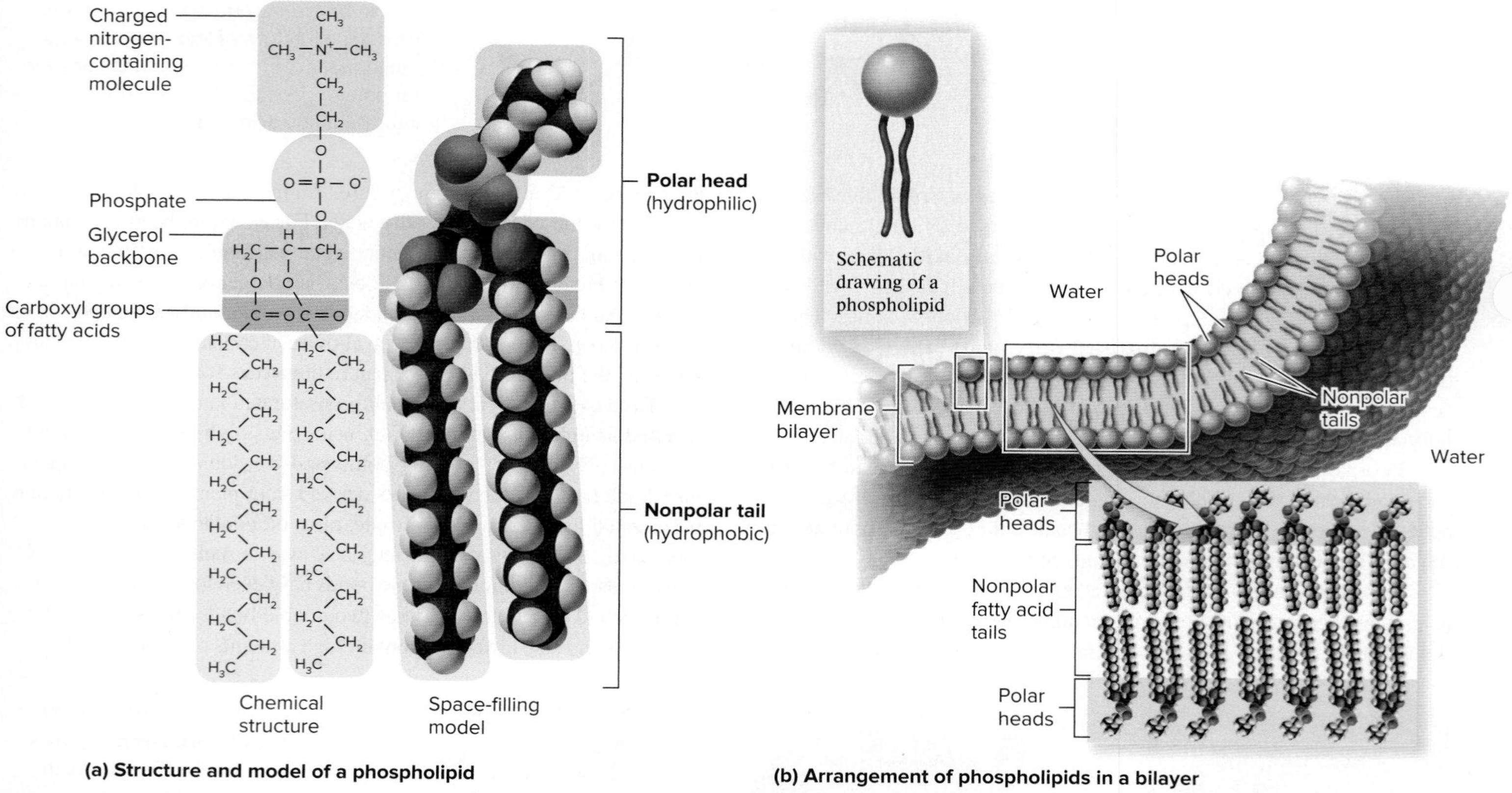

(a) Structure and model of a phospholipid

(b) Arrangement of phospholipids in a bilayer

Figure 3.11 **Structure of phospholipids.** **(a)** Chemical structure and space-filling model of phosphatidylcholine, a common phospholipid found in living organisms. Phospholipids contain both polar and nonpolar regions, making them amphipathic. The fatty-acid tails are nonpolar. The rest of the molecule is polar. **(b)** Arrangement of phospholipids in a biological membrane, such as the plasma membrane that encloses cells. The polar regions of the phospholipids face the watery environment, whereas the nonpolar regions associate with each other in the interior of the membrane, forming a bilayer.

 Core Skill: Modeling The goal of this modeling challenge is to propose a model for a lipid droplet based on a description of its components.

Modeling Challenge: Within human cells, lipids are stored in structures called lipid droplets. The surface of such a droplet has a monolayer of phospholipids and the interior is composed of neutral lipids, such as triglycerides. Some proteins are also attached to the polar head groups of the phospholipids. Draw a model showing the structure of a lipid droplet. In your model, draw phospholipids schematically as shown in part (b) of Figure 3.11, depict neutral lipids with blue dots, and depict proteins as green blobs.

glycerol backbone, phosphate group, and a charged molecule (in this case, choline) constitute a polar (hydrophilic) head at one end of the phospholipid, whereas the fatty acid chains form nonpolar (hydrophobic) tails at the opposite end. Recall from Chapter 2 that molecules with polar and nonpolar regions are called amphipathic molecules.

In water, phospholipids become organized into bilayers, with their polar heads interacting with the water molecules and their nonpolar tails facing the interior, where they are shielded from water. As you will learn in Chapter 5, this bilayer arrangement of phospholipids is critical for determining the structure of cellular membranes, as shown in **Figure 3.11b**.

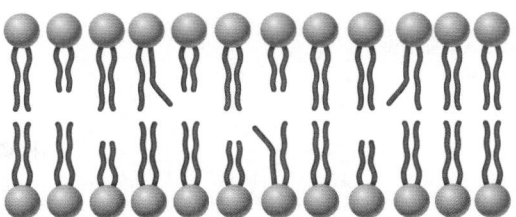

A mixture of long and short nonpolar tails, with double bonds in some of the long tails

ANSWER *When you compare the structures in the two drawings, you see that the lipids are more tightly packed in the membrane that is composed primarily of lipids with long nonpolar tails. As you can see, there is less open space in this membrane. It would be less fluid than the membrane containing a mixture of long and short nonpolar tails with double bonds in some of the long tails.*

BIO:**TIPS**   **THE QUESTION** *Biological membranes contain a phospholipid bilayer. As discussed in Chapter 5, membranes are somewhat fluid. For example, lipids move laterally within a membrane. When the lipid molecules are packed tightly together, the membrane tends to be less fluid than when they are more loosely packed.*

Let's suppose that one membrane is composed primarily of lipids with long nonpolar tails that do not have any double bonds. A second membrane has some lipids with long nonpolar tails and others with short nonpolar tails. Also, some of the longer tails in this second membrane contain double bonds. Which of these two membranes would you expect to be less fluid?

TOPIC *What topic in biology does this question address?* The topic is how lipid structure may affect the fluidity of a membrane.

INFORMATION *What information do you know based on the question and your understanding of the topic?* From the question, you have learned that membranes with tightly packed lipids are less fluid than membranes in which the lipids are loosely packed. From your understanding of the topic, you may recall that the hydrophobic lipid tails associate with each other in the nonpolar region of the membrane (see Figure 3.11b). You may also remember that phospholipids vary with regard to the lengths of their nonpolar tails and that a double bond introduces a kink into a tail.

PROBLEM-SOLVING **S**TRATEGY *Make a drawing. Compare and contrast.* One strategy to solve this problem is to make a drawing that shows the structures of the two membranes described in the question. Then compare the two structures, and decide which membrane is more tightly packed.

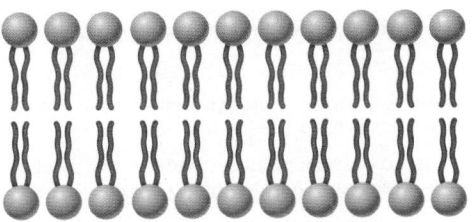

All long nonpolar tails

Steroids Contain Ring Structures

Steroids have a distinctly different chemical structure from the other types of lipid molecules discussed thus far. Four fused rings of carbon atoms form the general structure of all steroids. One or more polar hydroxyl groups are attached to the fused ring structure, but they are not numerous enough to make a steroid highly water-soluble. For example, steroids with a hydroxyl group are known as sterols—one of the most well known being cholesterol (**Figure 3.12**, top). Cholesterol is found in the blood and cellular membranes of animals.

In steroids, minor differences in chemical structure result in profoundly different biological properties. For example, all steroid hormones are derived from cholesterol and share similarities in structure, but with some important differences. Estrogen is a steroid hormone found in high amounts in female vertebrates. Estrogen differs from testosterone, a steroid hormone found largely in males, by having one less methyl group, a hydroxyl group instead of a ketone group (see Table 3.1), and additional double bonds in one of its rings (compare the structures in Figure 3.12). However, these small differences are sufficient to make these two molecules largely responsible for whether an animal exhibits male or female characteristics, including feather color in birds.

Waxes Are Complex Lipids That Prevent Water Loss from Organisms

Many plants and animals produce lipids called waxes that are secreted onto their surface, such as the leaves of plants and the cuticles of insects. Although any wax may contain hundreds of different compounds, all waxes contain one or more hydrocarbons and long structures that resemble a fatty acid attached by its carboxyl group to another long hydrocarbon chain. Waxes are very nonpolar and therefore exclude water, providing a barrier to water loss. They also are used as structural elements, such as the beeswax that forms the honeycomb produced by honeybees.

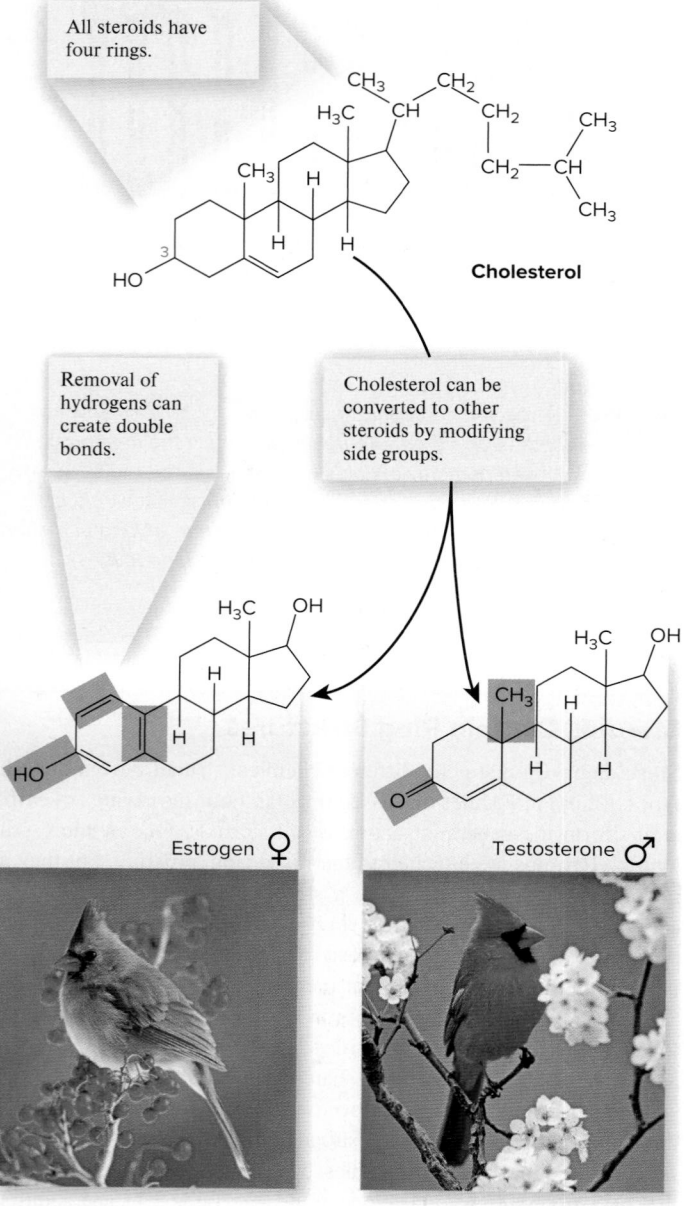

All steroids have four rings.

Cholesterol

Removal of hydrogens can create double bonds.

Cholesterol can be converted to other steroids by modifying side groups.

Estrogen ♀

Testosterone ♂

Female cardinal

Male cardinal

Figure 3.12 **Structures of cholesterol and steroid hormones derived from cholesterol.** The structure of a steroid has four rings. Steroids include cholesterol and molecules derived from cholesterol, such as steroid hormones. These include the reproductive hormones estrogen and testosterone. (left, right): ©Adam Jones/Science Source

 Core Concept: Structure and Function The minor structural differences between estrogen and testosterone dramatically affect their biological functions. The differences between female and male cardinals are one example from the animal world of sex-dependent differences in form and function that are due to these two hormones.

3.6   Proteins

Learning Outcomes:

1. Give examples of the general functions that are carried out by different proteins.
2. Describe how amino acids are joined to form a polypeptide, and distinguish between a polypeptide and a protein.
3. Explain the four levels of protein structure.
4. Outline the factors that determine protein shape and function.
5. Define domain, as it relates to protein structure.

Proteins play critical roles in nearly all life processes (**Table 3.3**). The word protein comes from the Greek *proteios* (meaning of the first rank), which aptly describes their importance. Proteins account for about 50% of the organic material in a typical animal's body. In this section, we will survey the structure and function of proteins.

Amino Acids Are the Building Blocks of Proteins

Proteins are composed of carbon, hydrogen, oxygen, nitrogen, and small amounts of other elements, notably sulfur. The monomers of proteins are **amino acids**, compounds with a structure in which a carbon atom, called the α-carbon, is linked to an amino group (—NH_2) and a carboxyl group (—COOH). The α-carbon also is linked to a hydrogen atom and a side chain, designated with the letter R. Proteins are polymers of amino acids.

When an amino acid is dissolved in water at neutral pH, the amino group accepts a hydrogen ion and is positively charged, whereas the

Table 3.3	Major Categories and Functions of Proteins	
Category	**Functions**	**Examples**
Proteins involved in gene expression and regulation	Make mRNA from a DNA template; synthesize polypeptides from mRNA; regulate genes	RNA polymerase catalyzes the synthesis of RNA using DNA as a template.
Motor proteins	Initiate movement	Myosin provides the contractile force of muscles.
Defense proteins	Protect organisms against disease	Antibodies help destroy bacteria or viruses.
Metabolic enzymes	Increase rates of chemical reactions	Hexokinase is an enzyme involved in sugar metabolism.
Cell-signaling proteins	Enable cells to communicate with each other and with the environment	Taste receptors in the tongue allow animals to taste molecules in food.
Structural proteins	Support and strengthen structures	Actin provides shape to the cytoplasm of plant and animal cells. Collagen gives strength to tendons.
Transporters	Promote movement of solutes across membranes	Glucose transporters move glucose from outside cells to inside cells, where it can be used for energy.

carboxyl group loses a hydrogen ion and is negatively charged. The name amino acid was given to such molecules because they have an amino group and also a carboxyl group that acts as an acid.

All amino acids except glycine exist in more than one isomeric form, called the D and L forms, which are enantiomers. Only L-amino acids are found in proteins. D-amino acids are not found in most cells. An exception is in the cell walls of certain bacteria, where D-amino acids may play a protective role against molecules secreted by the host organism in which the bacteria live.

The 20 amino acids in proteins are distinguished by their side chains (**Figure 3.13**). The amino acids are categorized by whether

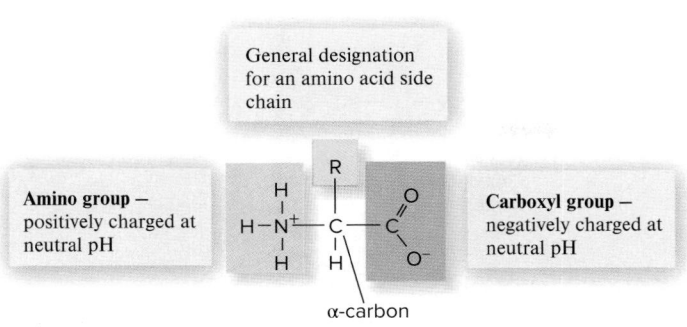

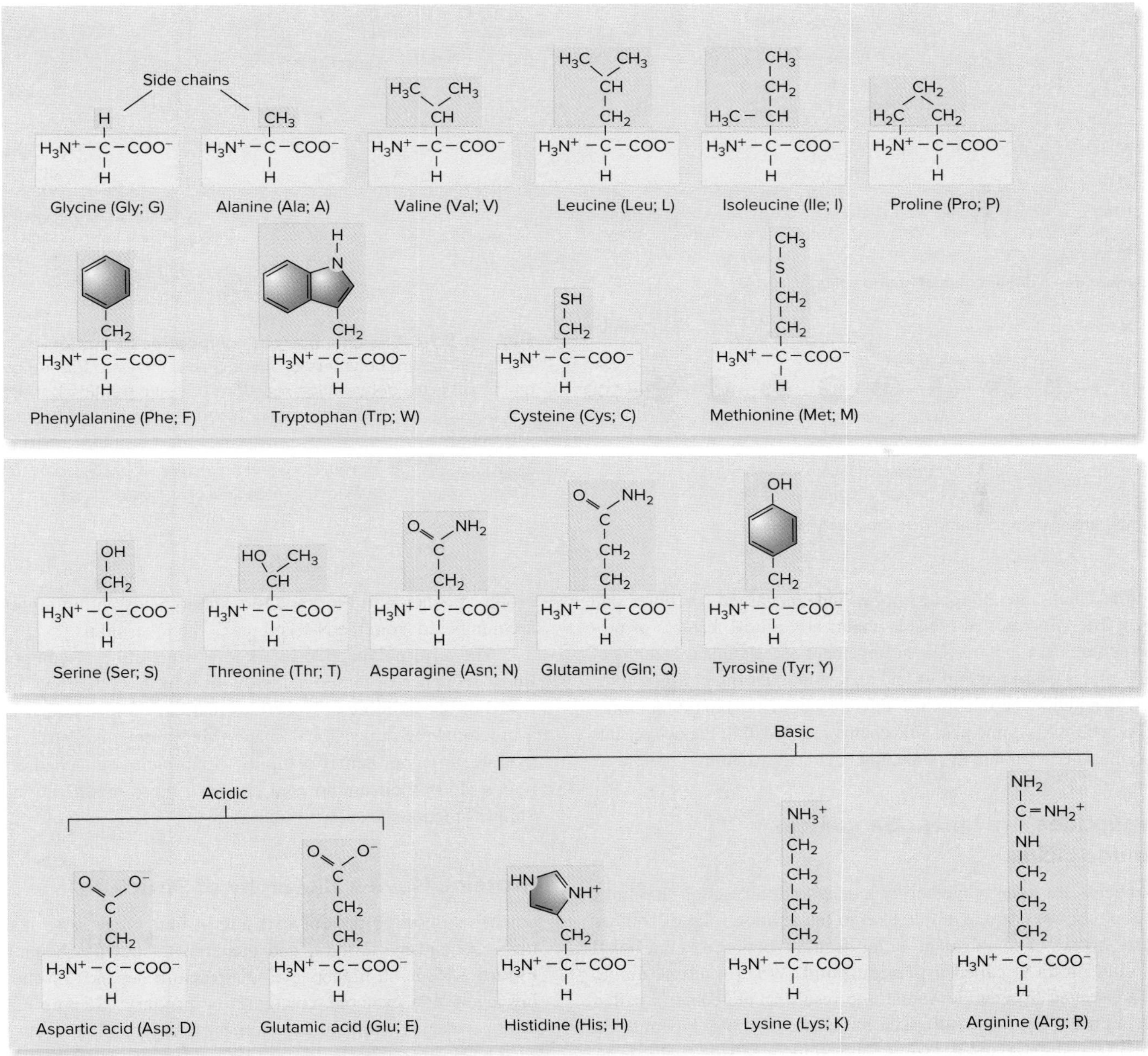

Figure 3.13 **The 20 amino acids found in living organisms.** Amino acids have different chemical properties (for example, nonpolar versus polar) due to their different side chains, which are highlighted in blue. These properties contribute to the differences in the three-dimensional shapes and chemical properties of proteins, which, in turn, influence proteins' biological functions. Note: Tyrosine has both polar and nonpolar characteristics and is listed in just one category for simplicity. The common three-letter and one-letter abbreviations for each amino acid are shown in parentheses.

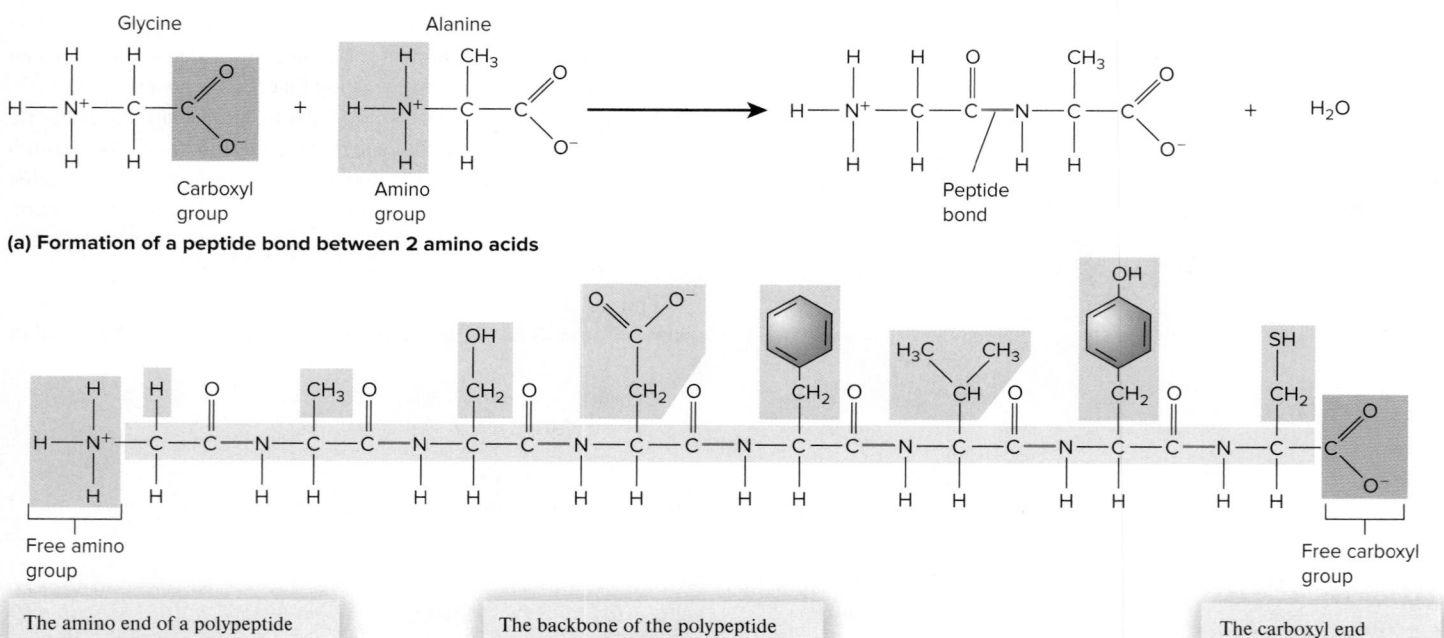

(a) Formation of a peptide bond between 2 amino acids

Free amino group

Free carboxyl group

| The amino end of a polypeptide is called the N-terminus. | The backbone of the polypeptide is highlighted in yellow. | The carboxyl end of a polypeptide is called the C-terminus. |

(b) Polypeptide—a linear chain of amino acids

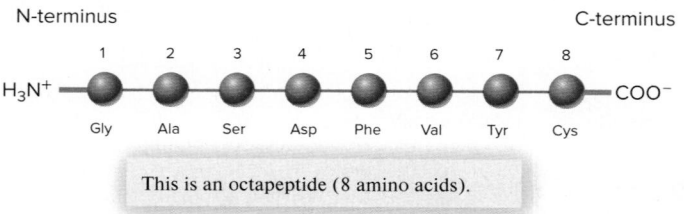

This is an octapeptide (8 amino acids).

(c) Numbering system of amino acids in a polypeptide

Figure 3.14 **The chemistry of polypeptide formation.**
Polypeptides are polymers of amino acids. They are formed by linking amino acids via dehydration reactions to make peptide bonds. Every polypeptide has an amino end, or N-terminus, and a carboxyl end, or C-terminus.

Concept Check: *How many water molecules would be produced during the formation of a polypeptide that is 72 amino acids long?*

their side chains are nonpolar, polar and uncharged, or polar and charged. The structures of the side chains are critical features of protein structure and function. The arrangement and chemical features of the side chains cause proteins to fold and adopt their three-dimensional shapes. In addition, certain amino acids may be critical in protein function. For example, amino acid side chains found within the active sites of enzymes are important in catalyzing chemical reactions.

Polypeptides Are Linear Sequences of Amino Acids

Amino acids are joined together by a dehydration reaction that links the carboxyl group of one amino acid to the amino group of another (**Figure 3.14a**). The covalent bond formed between a carboxyl and amino group is called a **peptide bond**. When multiple amino acids are joined by peptide bonds, the resulting molecule is called a **polypeptide** (**Figure 3.14b**). The backbone of the polypeptide in Figure 3.14 is highlighted in yellow. The amino acid side chains project from the backbone. When two or more amino acids are linked together, one end of the resulting molecule has a free amino group. This is the amino end, or **N-terminus**. The other end of the polypeptide, called the carboxyl end, or **C-terminus**, has a free carboxyl

group. As shown in **Figure 3.14c**, amino acids within a polypeptide are numbered from the N-terminus to the C-terminus.

The term polypeptide refers to a structural unit composed of a linear sequence of amino acids. A **protein** is a functional unit composed of one or more polypeptides that have folded and twisted into a precise three-dimensional shape. Many proteins also have carbohydrates (glycoproteins) or lipids (lipoproteins) attached at various points along their amino acid chain(s); these modifications impart unique functions to such proteins.

Proteins Have a Hierarchy of Structure

Scientists describe protein structure at four progressive levels: primary, secondary, tertiary, and quaternary, shown schematically in **Figure 3.15**. Each higher level of structure depends on the preceding levels. For example, changing the primary structure may affect the secondary, tertiary, and quaternary structures. Let's now consider each level separately.

Primary Structure   The **primary structure** (see Figure 3.15) of a protein is the amino acid sequence of its polypeptide(s). The primary structures of proteins are determined by genes. As we will explore in

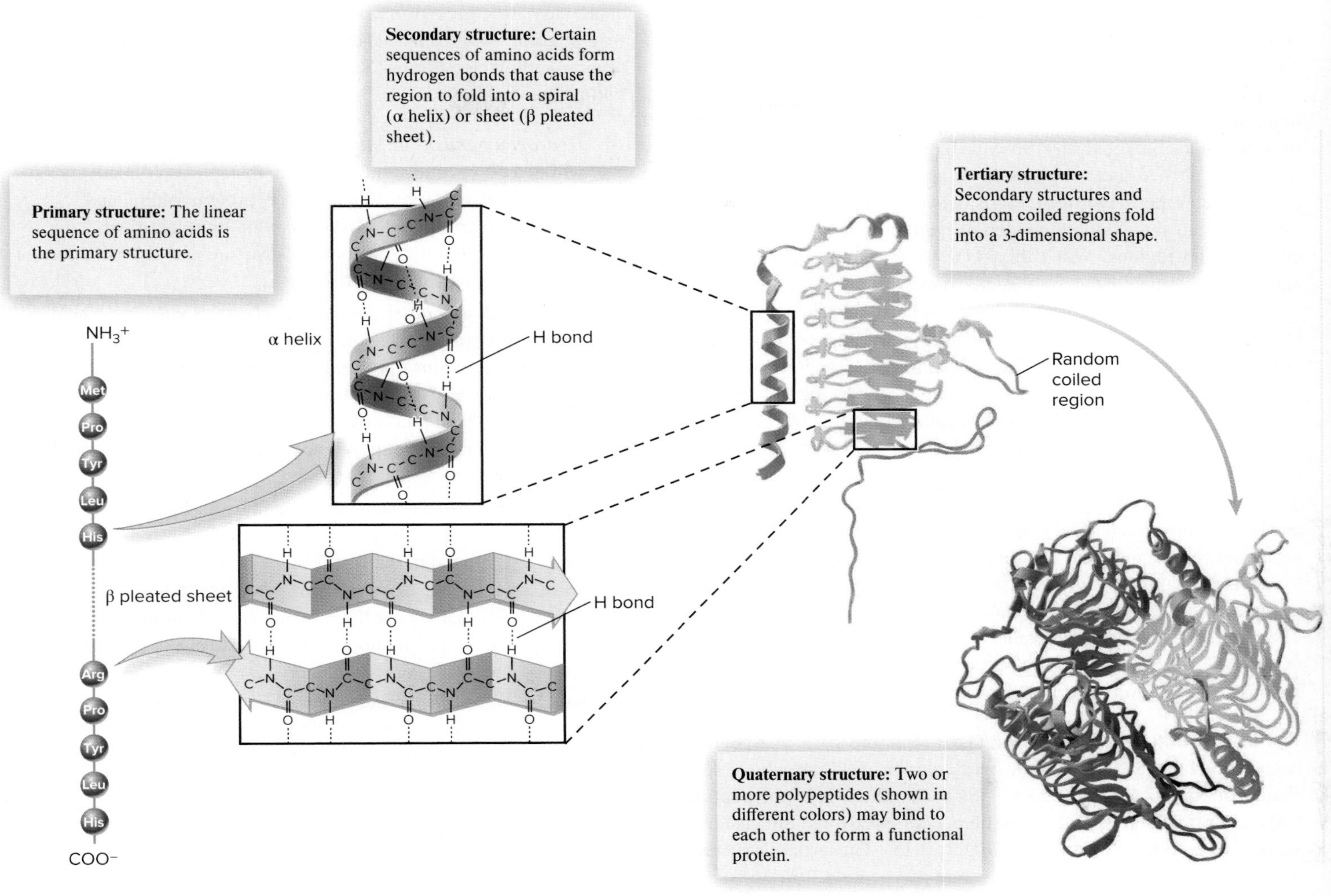

Secondary structure: Certain sequences of amino acids form hydrogen bonds that cause the region to fold into a spiral (α helix) or sheet (β pleated sheet).

Primary structure: The linear sequence of amino acids is the primary structure.

Tertiary structure: Secondary structures and random coiled regions fold into a 3-dimensional shape.

NH_3^+

Met
Pro
Tyr
Leu
His

α helix

H bond

β pleated sheet

H bond

Arg
Pro
Tyr
Leu
His

COO^-

Random coiled region

Quaternary structure: Two or more polypeptides (shown in different colors) may bind to each other to form a functional protein.

Figure 3.15 The hierarchy of protein structure. The R groups are omitted for simplicity.

Chapter 12, genes carry the information for the production of polypeptides with specific amino acid sequences.

Figure 3.16 shows the primary structure of ribonuclease, which functions as an enzyme to degrade ribonucleic acid (RNA) molecules after they are no longer required by a cell. As described later and in Unit III, RNA carries the information for protein synthesis. Ribonuclease is composed of a relatively short polypeptide consisting of 124 amino acids. An average polypeptide is about 300 to 500 amino acids in length, but some polypeptides in proteins are a few thousand amino acids long.

Secondary Structure   The amino acid sequence of a polypeptide, together with the laws of chemistry and physics, cause a protein to fold into a more compact structure. Amino acids can rotate around bonds within a polypeptide. Consequently, proteins are flexible and can fold into a number of shapes, just as a string of beads can be twisted into many configurations. Folding can be irregular, or certain regions can have a repeating folding pattern called **secondary structure**. The two basic types of a protein's secondary structure are the α helix and the β pleated sheet.

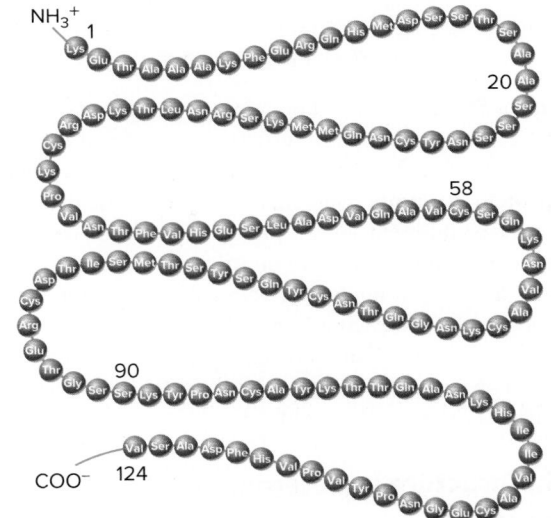

Figure 3.16 The primary structure of ribonuclease. The example shown here is ribonuclease from cattle, which contains 124 amino acids.

In an α helix, the polypeptide backbone forms a repeating helical structure that is stabilized by hydrogen bonds along the length of the backbone. As shown in Figure 3.15, the hydrogen linked to a nitrogen atom forms a hydrogen bond with an oxygen atom that is double-bonded to a carbon atom. These hydrogen bonds occur at regular intervals along the polypeptide backbone and cause the backbone to twist into a helix.

In a β pleated sheet, regions of the polypeptide backbone lie parallel to each other. Hydrogen bonds between a hydrogen linked to a nitrogen atom and a double-bonded oxygen form between these adjacent, parallel regions. When this occurs, the polypeptide backbone adopts a repeating zigzag, or pleated, shape.

The α helices and β pleated sheets are key determinants of a protein's characteristics. For example, α helices in certain proteins are composed primarily of nonpolar amino acids. Proteins containing stretches of nonpolar amino acids tend to anchor themselves into a lipid-rich environment, such as a cell's plasma membrane. In this way, a protein whose function is required in a specific location such as a plasma membrane can be retained there. Secondary structure also contributes to the great strength of certain proteins, including the keratins found in hair and hooves; the proteins that make up the silk webs of spiders; and collagen, the chief component of cartilage in vertebrate animals.

Some regions along a polypeptide chain do not assume an α helix or β pleated sheet conformation and do not have a secondary structure. These regions are sometimes called random coiled regions. However, this term is somewhat misleading because the shapes of random coiled regions are usually very specific and important for the protein's function.

Tertiary Structure   As the secondary structure of a polypeptide becomes established due to the particular primary structure, side chains of amino acids interact with each other. The polypeptide folds and refolds upon itself to assume a complex three-dimensional shape—its **tertiary structure** (see Figure 3.15). The tertiary structure is the three-dimensional shape of a single polypeptide. Tertiary structure includes all secondary structures plus any interactions involving amino acid side chains. For some proteins, such as ribonuclease, the tertiary structure is the final structure of a functional protein. However, as described next, other proteins are composed of two or more polypeptides and adopt a quaternary structure.

Quaternary Structure   Most proteins are composed of two or more polypeptides that each adopt a tertiary structure and then assemble with each other (see Figure 3.15). The individual polypeptides are called **protein subunits**. Subunits may be identical polypeptides or they may be different. When proteins consist of more than one polypeptide, they are said to have **quaternary structure**. A common example is the oxygen-binding protein called hemoglobin, found in the red blood cells of vertebrate animals. Four protein subunits combine to form one hemoglobin protein. Each subunit can bind a single molecule of oxygen; therefore, each hemoglobin protein can carry four molecules of oxygen in the blood.

Protein Structure Is Determined by Several Factors

The amino acid sequences of polypeptides distinguish the structure of one protein from another. As polypeptides are synthesized in a cell, they fold into secondary and tertiary structures, which assemble into quaternary structures for most proteins. Several factors determine the way proteins adopt their secondary, tertiary, and quaternary structures. As shown in **Figure 3.17**, five factors are critical for protein folding and stability:

1. *Hydrogen bonds.* The large number of weak hydrogen bonds within a polypeptide and between polypeptides collectively produce a strong force that promotes protein folding and stability. As mentioned, hydrogen bonding is a critical determinant of protein secondary structure and also is important in tertiary and quaternary structure.

2. *Ionic bonds and other polar interactions.* Some amino acid side chains are positively or negatively charged. Positively charged side chains may bind to negatively charged side chains via ionic bonds. Similarly, uncharged polar side chains in a protein may bind to ionic amino acids. Ionic bonds and polar interactions are particularly important in tertiary and quaternary structure.

3. *Hydrophobic effect.* Some amino acid side chains are nonpolar (hydrophobic). As a protein folds, the nonpolar amino acids are likely to be found in the center of the protein, minimizing their contact with water. Some proteins have stretches of nonpolar amino acids that anchor the proteins in the hydrophobic portion of membranes. The hydrophobic effect plays a major role in tertiary and quaternary structures.

4. *van der Waals dispersion forces.* Atoms within molecules have temporary weak attractions for each other if they are an optimal distance apart. These weak attractions are termed van der Waals dispersion forces (see Chapter 2). If two atoms are too close together, their electron clouds will repel each other. If they are far apart, the van der Waals dispersion forces will diminish. The van der Waals dispersion forces are important in determining tertiary structures.

5. *Disulfide bridges.* The side chain of the amino acid cysteine contains a sulfhydryl group (—SH), which can react with a sulfhydryl group in another cysteine side chain (see Figure 3.13). The result is a **disulfide bridge**, or disulfide bond, which links the two amino acid side chains together (—S—S—). Disulfide bridges are covalent bonds that can occur within a polypeptide or between different polypeptides. Though other forces are usually more important in protein folding, the covalent nature of disulfide bridges can help to stabilize the structure of a protein.

The first four factors just described are also important in the ability of different proteins to interact with each other. As discussed throughout Unit II and other parts of this textbook, many cellular processes involve steps in which two or more different proteins interact with each other. For such an interaction to occur, one protein must recognize and bind to the surface of the other. Such binding is usually very specific. The surface of one protein precisely fits into the surface of another (**Figure 3.18**). Such **protein-protein interactions** are critically important in allowing cellular processes to occur in a series of defined steps. In addition, protein-protein interactions are important in building complicated cellular structures that provide shape and organization to cells.

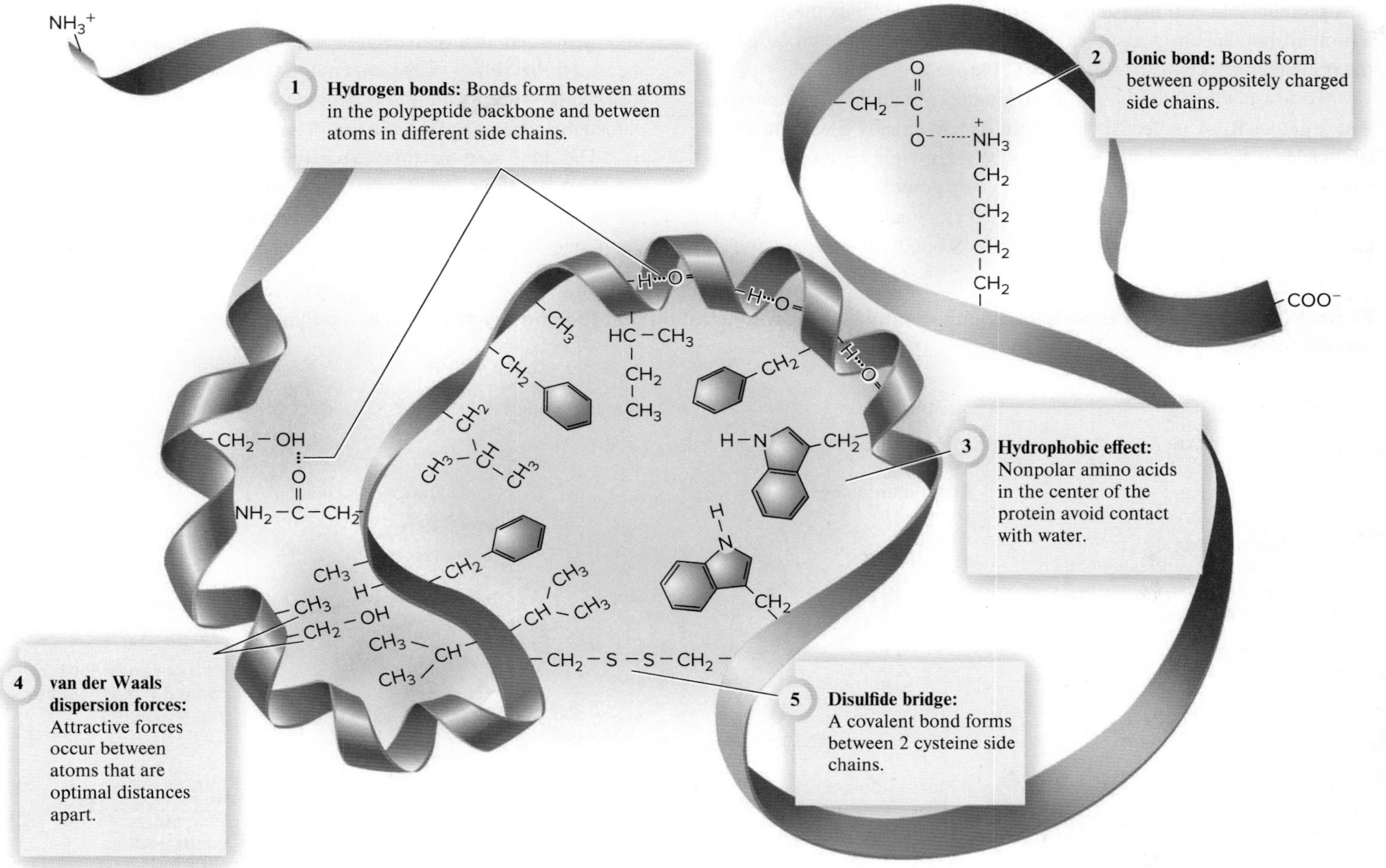

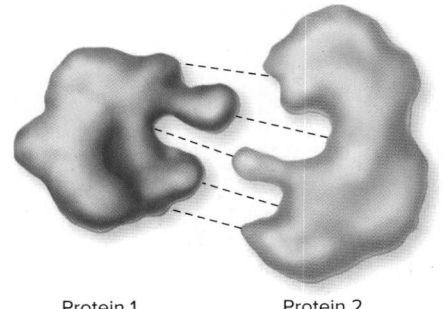

Figure 3.17 Factors that influence protein folding and stability.

 Core Concept: Structure and Function This core concept of biology is apparent even at the molecular level. As seen in this figure, several distinct types of chemical interactions produce a protein with a complex shape. The three-dimensional shapes of different proteins determine their functions and their ability to interact with other cellular components.

Figure 3.18 Protein-protein interaction. Two different proteins may interact with each other through hydrogen bonding, ionic bonding, the hydrophobic effect, and van der Waals dispersion forces.

Concept Check: *If the primary structure of protein 1 in this figure was experimentally altered by the substitution of several incorrect amino acids, would protein 1 still be able to interact with protein 2?*

Protein 1   Protein 2

 Core Skill: Process of Science

Feature Investigation | **Anfinsen Showed That the Primary Structure of Ribonuclease Determines Its Three-Dimensional Structure**

Prior to the 1960s, the mechanisms by which proteins assume their three-dimensional structures were not understood. Scientists hypothesized that the correct folding required cellular factors or that ribosomes, the sites where polypeptides are synthesized, somehow shaped proteins during their synthesis. American researcher Christian Anfinsen, however, postulated that the amino acid sequence is the primary factor that determines how proteins fold into their proper conformations. He hypothesized that a protein spontaneously assumes its most stable conformation based on the principles of chemistry and physics (**Figure 3.19**).

To test this hypothesis, Anfinsen studied ribonuclease, an enzyme that degrades RNA molecules. Biochemists had already determined that ribonuclease has four disulfide bridges between eight cysteines. Anfinsen began with purified ribonuclease. The key point is that other cellular components were not present. He exposed ribonuclease to a chemical called β-mercaptoethanol, which breaks S—S bonds, and to urea, which disrupts hydrogen and ionic bonds. This treatment caused ribonuclease to be denatured, that is, to become unfolded. Following this treatment, he measured the ability of the enzyme to degrade RNA. The enzyme had lost nearly all of its ability to degrade RNA. Therefore, Anfinsen concluded that when ribonuclease was denatured, it was no longer functional.

The key step in this experiment came when Anfinsen then removed the urea and β-mercaptoethanol. Because these molecules are much smaller than ribonuclease, removing them was accomplished via a size-exclusion chromatography column. As shown in step 3, a

Figure 3.19 **Anfinsen's experiments with ribonuclease, demonstrating that the primary structure of a polypeptide plays a key role in protein folding.**

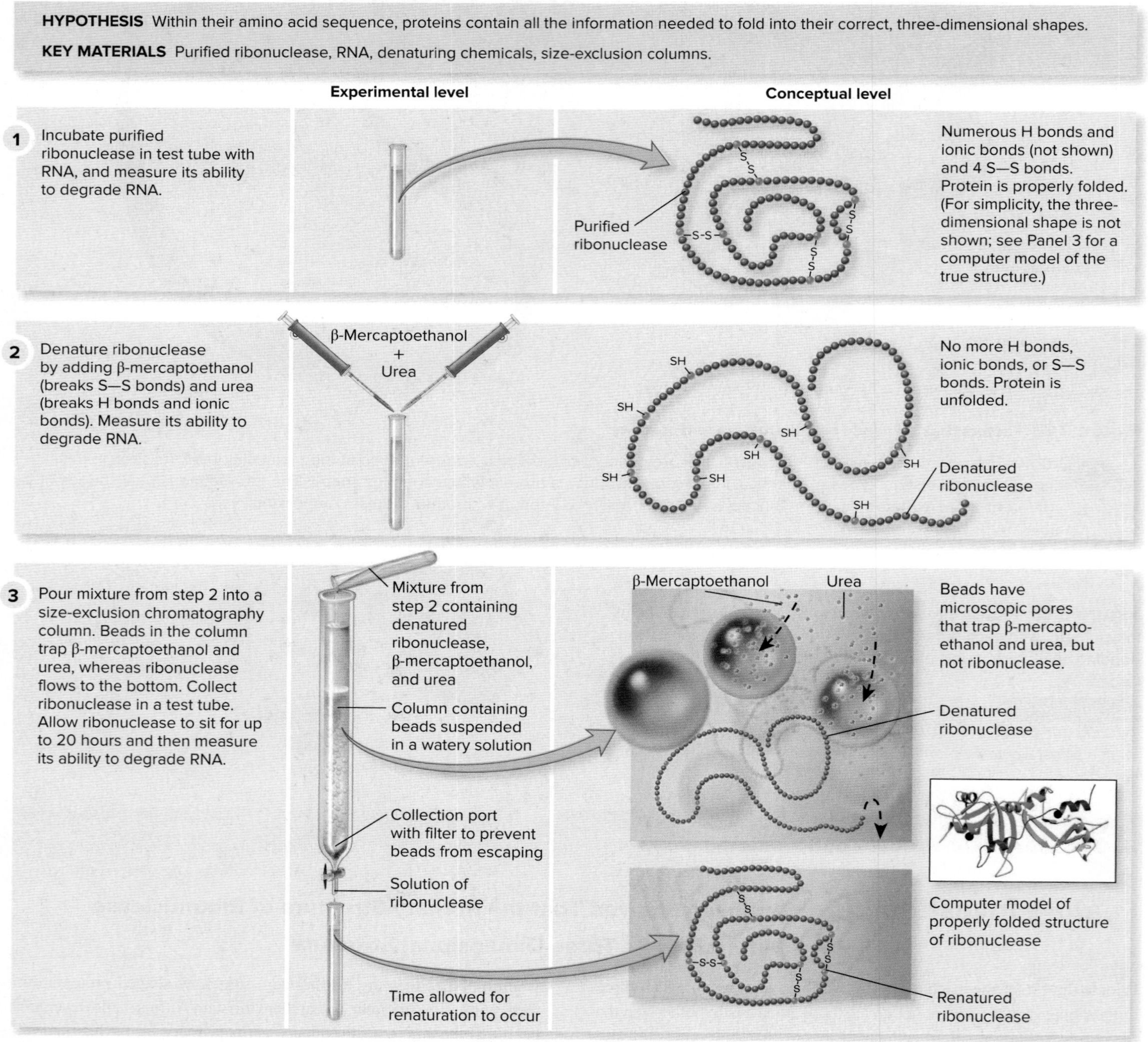

HYPOTHESIS Within their amino acid sequence, proteins contain all the information needed to fold into their correct, three-dimensional shapes.

KEY MATERIALS Purified ribonuclease, RNA, denaturing chemicals, size-exclusion columns.

Experimental level   Conceptual level

1 Incubate purified ribonuclease in test tube with RNA, and measure its ability to degrade RNA.

Purified ribonuclease

Numerous H bonds and ionic bonds (not shown) and 4 S—S bonds. Protein is properly folded. (For simplicity, the three-dimensional shape is not shown; see Panel 3 for a computer model of the true structure.)

2 Denature ribonuclease by adding β-mercaptoethanol (breaks S—S bonds) and urea (breaks H bonds and ionic bonds). Measure its ability to degrade RNA.

β-Mercaptoethanol + Urea

SH

Denatured ribonuclease

No more H bonds, ionic bonds, or S—S bonds. Protein is unfolded.

3 Pour mixture from step 2 into a size-exclusion chromatography column. Beads in the column trap β-mercaptoethanol and urea, whereas ribonuclease flows to the bottom. Collect ribonuclease in a test tube. Allow ribonuclease to sit for up to 20 hours and then measure its ability to degrade RNA.

Mixture from step 2 containing denatured ribonuclease, β-mercaptoethanol, and urea

Column containing beads suspended in a watery solution

Collection port with filter to prevent beads from escaping

Solution of ribonuclease

Time allowed for renaturation to occur

β-Mercaptoethanol   Urea

Beads have microscopic pores that trap β-mercaptoethanol and urea, but not ribonuclease.

Denatured ribonuclease

Renatured ribonuclease

Computer model of properly folded structure of ribonuclease

4 **THE DATA**

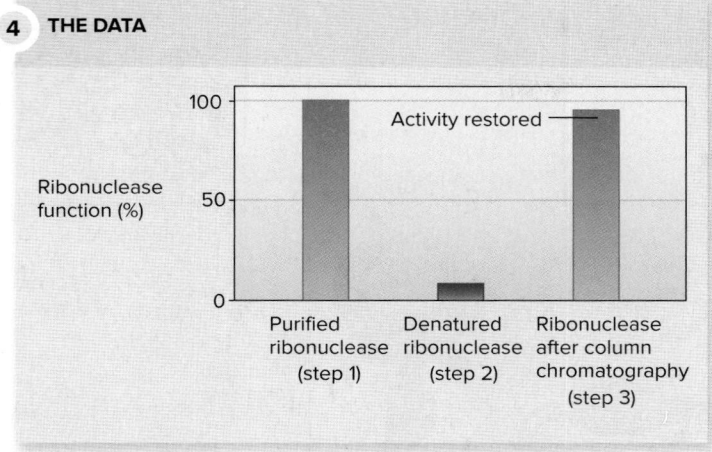

5 **CONCLUSION** Certain proteins, like ribonuclease, can spontaneously fold into their final, functional shapes without assistance from other cellular structures or factors. (However, as described in the text, this is not true of many other proteins.)

6 **SOURCE** Haber, E., and Anfinsen, C.B. 1961. Regeneration of enzyme activity by air oxidation of reduced subtilisin-modified ribonuclease. *Journal of Biological Chemistry* 236: 422–424.

solution containing ribonuclease, β-mercaptoethanol, and urea was poured on top of a column of small beads and allowed to flow down the column to an open collection port at the bottom. The beads in the column had microscopic pores that trapped small molecules like urea and β-mercaptoethanol but allowed large proteins such as ribonuclease to pass down the length of the column and out the collection port.

Using this chromatography column, Anfinsen separated ribonuclease from β-mercaptoethanol and urea. He allowed the ribonuclease to sit for up to 20 hours and then retested its ability to degrade RNA. The result revolutionized our understanding of proteins. The activity of the ribonuclease was almost completely restored! Therefore, even in the complete absence of any cellular factors or ribosomes, this unfolded protein can refold into its correct, functional structure.

Researchers have since learned that ribonuclease's ability to refold into its functional structure does not occur with all proteins.

Some proteins require assistance from enzymes and other proteins to achieve their proper folding. Even so, Anfinsen's experiments provided compelling evidence that the primary structure of a polypeptide is a key determinant of a protein's tertiary structure, an observation that earned him the Nobel Prize in Chemistry in 1972.

Experimental Questions

1. What hypothesis was Anfinsen testing?
2. Why did Anfinsen use urea and β-mercaptoethanol in his experiments?
3. **CoreSKILL »** Explain the result that was crucial to the discovery that the tertiary structure of ribonuclease may depend entirely on the primary structure.

 **Core Concept: Evolution**

Proteins Contain Functional Domains

By comparing the structures of many different proteins, researchers have determined many of them have a modular design. This means that portions within these proteins, called **domains**, have distinct structures and functions. These domains have been duplicated during evolution, so the same kind of domain is found in many different proteins. A domain that is found in different proteins has the same three-dimensional tertiary structure in all of them and performs a characteristic function.

As an example, **Figure 3.20** shows two members of a family of related proteins, known as nuclear receptors, which function in the nucleus of animal cells by regulating how certain genes are turned on. These types of proteins are involved in animal development, reproduction, metabolism, and homeostasis. Nuclear receptors contain four or more domains within their structure:

- One domain found in nuclear receptors is a ligand-binding domain. These receptors are activated by a ligand, which is a molecule that binds to the receptor. For the two examples in

Figure 3.20, the ligands are the steroid hormones estrogen and testosterone (a type of androgen), and the nuclear receptors are called the estrogen receptor and the androgen receptor, respectively. Though the ligand-binding domains in these two nuclear receptors have similar structures, slight structural differences allow one to bind estrogen and the other to bind testosterone (see the insets in Figure 3.20).

- A second domain, called the DNA-binding domain, binds to DNA once the receptor is activated by its ligand. The DNA-binding domains of these two receptors are sufficiently similar to enable both of them to bind to DNA, but dissimilar enough that they bind to different genes. Therefore, estrogen and testosterone have different effects, because they regulate different sets of genes.

- Another domain, called a nuclear localization domain, facilitates the movement of the protein into the cell nucleus, where the DNA is located.

- Once the protein binds to DNA, a fourth domain, called the activation domain, activates the transcription of the target gene.

Overall, a nuclear receptor is a single protein with multiple domains, each with a unique function.

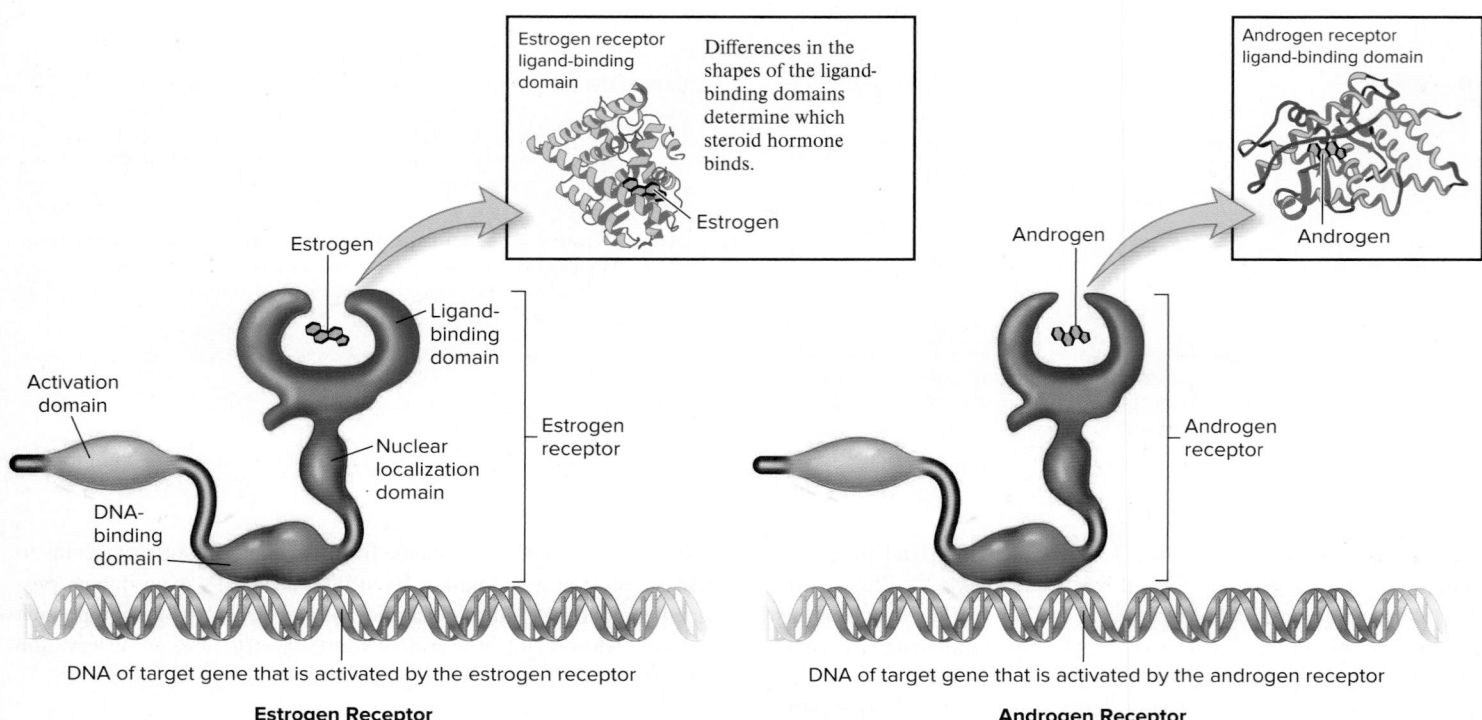

Figure 3.20 **The domains in two related proteins called nuclear receptors.** These schematic drawings do not depict the actual three-dimensional structures of the estrogen and androgen receptors but rather emphasize that both receptors are composed of a series of different domains. The insets show the actual structures of the ligand-binding domains for both receptors. Note: The estrogen and androgen receptors are each composed of two identical polypeptides. For simplicity, only one polypeptide is shown here.

3.7 | Nucleic Acids

Learning Outcomes:

1. Describe the three components of a nucleotide.
2. Distinguish between the structures of DNA and RNA.
3. Explain how bases form hydrogen bonds with other bases in DNA and RNA.

Nucleic acids account for only about 2% of the weight of animals like humans, yet these molecules are extremely important because they are responsible for the storage, expression, and transmission of genetic information. The expression of genetic information in the form of specific proteins determines whether an organism is a human, a frog, an onion, or a bacterium. In this section, we will survey the general features of DNA and RNA, which are discussed in greater detail in Chapter 11.

Nucleotides Are the Building Blocks of DNA and RNA

The two classes of nucleic acids are **deoxyribonucleic acid (DNA)** and **ribonucleic acid (RNA)**. DNA molecules store genetic information coded in the sequence of their building blocks. RNA molecules are involved in decoding this information into instructions for linking a specific sequence of amino acids to form a polypeptide. The monomers in DNA must be arranged in a precise way so that the correct code can be read.

Like other macromolecules, DNA and RNA are polymers consisting of linear sequences of repeating monomers. Each monomer, known as a **nucleotide**, has three components: (1) a phosphate group, (2) a pentose (five-carbon) sugar (either ribose or deoxyribose), and (3) a single or a double ring of carbon and nitrogen atoms known as a base (**Figure 3.21**). A nucleotide of DNA is called a deoxyribonucleotide; one of RNA is a ribonucleotide. The nucleotides in DNA contain the five-carbon sugar **deoxyribose**. Four different nucleotides are present in DNA, corresponding to the four different bases that can be linked to deoxyribose. The **purine** bases, **adenine (A)** and **guanine (G)**, have a fused double ring of carbon and nitrogen atoms, and the **pyrimidine** bases, **cytosine (C)** and **thymine (T)**, have a single-ring structure (look ahead to Figure 3.22).

DNA Is Composed of Two Strands of Nucleotides

Nucleotides are covalently linked together to form strands of DNA. The phosphates and sugar molecules form the backbone of a DNA strand, with the bases projecting from the backbone. The carbon atoms of the sugar are numbered 1′ through 5′ (**Figure 3.22**). The phosphate groups link the 3′ carbon of one nucleotide to the 5′ carbon of the next. A DNA molecule consists of two strands of nucleotides coiled around each other to form a double helix (**Figure 3.23**). The two strands are held together by hydrogen bonds between a purine base in one strand and a pyrimidine base in the opposite strand. The ring structure of each base lies in a flat plane perpendicular to the sugar-phosphate backbone, somewhat like steps on a spiral staircase.

Only certain bases can pair with each other, due to the locations of the hydrogen-bonding groups in the four bases (see Figure 3.23). In

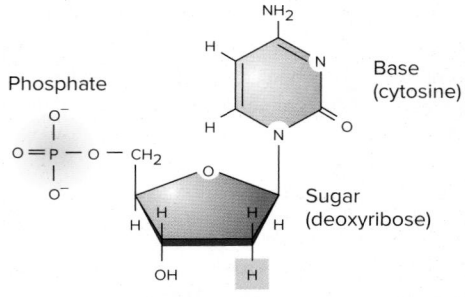

Figure 3.21
Examples of two nucleotides found in RNA or DNA.
A nucleotide has a phosphate group, a five-carbon sugar, and a base.

a DNA molecule, A on one strand is always paired with T on the opposite strand, and G is always paired with C. Two hydrogen bonds form between adenine and thymine (A-T pairing), whereas three hydrogen bonds are formed between guanine and cytosine (G-C pairing).

If we know the amount of one type of base in a DNA molecule, we can predict the relative amounts of each of the other three bases. For example, if a DNA molecule is composed of 20% A, it must also have 20% T. That leaves 60% of the bases that must be G and C combined. Because the amounts of G and C must be equal, this particular DNA molecule must contain 30% each of G and C. This specificity provides the mechanism for duplicating and transferring genetic information (see Chapter 11).

RNA Strands Have a Similar Structure to DNA Strands

RNA structure differs in only a few respects from DNA structure. Like DNA, RNA consists of nucleotides covalently linked together. RNA usually consists of a single strand of nucleotides. In RNA, the sugar in each nucleotide is **ribose** instead of deoxyribose. Also, the pyrimidine base thymine found in DNA is replaced in RNA with the pyrimidine base **uracil (U)** (see Figure 3.21). The other three bases—adenine, guanine, and cytosine—are found in both DNA and RNA.

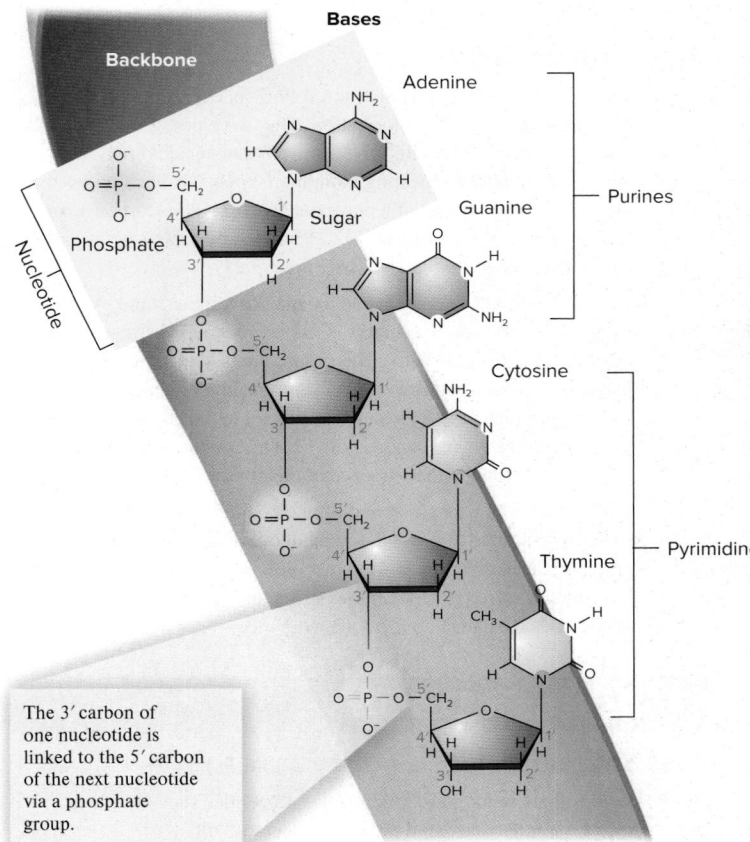

The 3′ carbon of one nucleotide is linked to the 5′ carbon of the next nucleotide via a phosphate group.

Figure 3.22 Structure of a DNA strand. Nucleotides are linked to each other to form a strand of DNA. The four bases found in DNA are shown. A strand of RNA is similar except the sugar is ribose, and uracil is substituted for thymine.

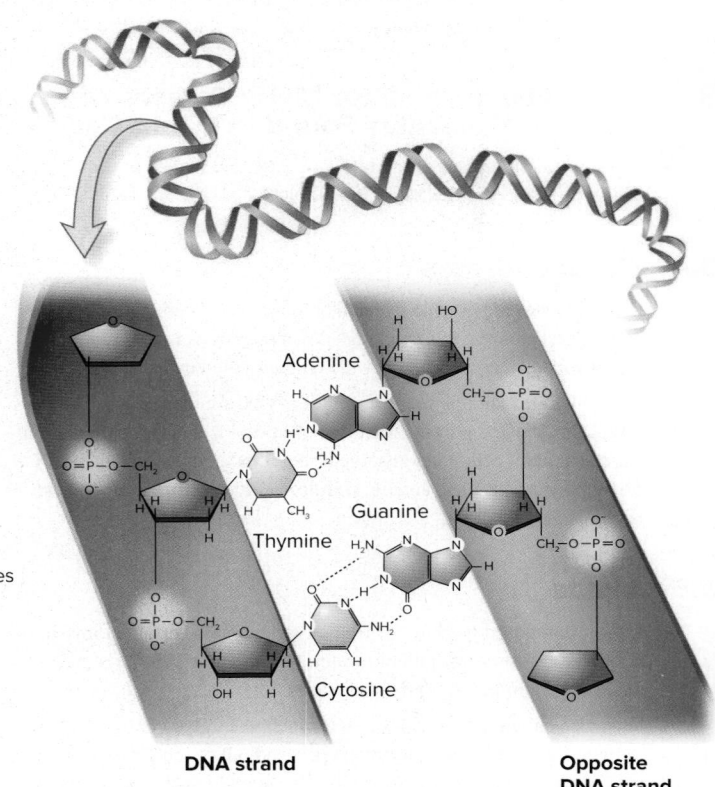

Figure 3.23 The double-stranded structure of DNA. DNA consists of two strands coiled around each other to form a double helix. The bases form hydrogen bonds (dashed lines) in which A pairs with T, and G pairs with C.

Concept Check: *If the sequence of bases in one strand of a DNA double helix is known, can the base sequence of the opposite strand be predicted?*

Summary of Key Concepts

3.1 The Carbon Atom

- Organic chemistry is the science of carbon-containing molecules, which are found in living organisms.

- A key property of the carbon atom is its ability to form four covalent bonds (polar or nonpolar) with other atoms. The combination of different elements and different types of bonds allows a vast number of organic compounds to be formed from relatively few chemical elements (Figures 3.1, 3.2).

- Carbon bonds are stable at the different temperatures associated with life.

- Organic compounds may contain functional groups with specific structures and chemical properties (Table 3.1).

- Carbon-containing molecules can exist as isomers, which have the same chemical formula but different structures and characteristics (Figure 3.3).

3.2 Formation of Organic Molecules and Macromolecules

- Organic molecules exist as monomers or polymers. Polymers are large macromolecules formed by dehydration reactions, in which individual monomers are attached to a growing polymer. Monomers are released from polymers by hydrolysis reactions (Figure 3.4).

3.3 Overview of the Four Major Classes of Organic Molecules Found in Living Cells

- The four major classes of organic molecules are carbohydrates, lipids, proteins, and nucleic acids (Table 3.2).

3.4 Carbohydrates

- Carbohydrates are organic molecules composed of carbon, hydrogen, and oxygen atoms. Cells can break down glucose, an important carbohydrate, releasing energy, which is then stored in the bonds of ATP.

- Carbohydrates include monosaccharides (the simplest sugars), disaccharides, and polysaccharides. The polysaccharides called starch (in plant cells) and glycogen (in animal cells) store energy. Some polysaccharides, notably cellulose, serve a structural function (Figures 3.5, 3.6, 3.7).

3.5 Lipids

- Lipids, composed predominantly of hydrogen and carbon atoms, are nonpolar and very insoluble in water. Major classes of lipids include fats, phospholipids, steroids, and waxes.

- Fats, also called triglycerides, are formed when glycerol bonds to three fatty acids. In a saturated fatty acid, all of the carbons are linked by single covalent bonds. Unsaturated fatty acids contain one or more C=C double bonds (Figures 3.8, 3.9, 3.10).

- Phospholipids are similar in structure to triglycerides, except that one glycerol is linked to a phosphate group instead of a fatty acid. Phospholipids contain both hydrophilic and hydrophobic regions, making them amphipathic (Figure 3.11).

- Steroids are constructed of four fused rings of carbon atoms. Small differences in steroid structure can lead to profoundly different biological properties, such as the differences between estrogen and testosterone (Figure 3.12).

- Waxes, another class of lipids, are nonpolar and repel water. They are often found as protective coatings on the leaves of plants and the outer surfaces of animals' bodies.

3.6 Proteins

- Proteins are composed of carbon, hydrogen, oxygen, nitrogen, and small amounts of other elements, notably sulfur. Proteins are macromolecules that play critical roles in almost all life processes. The proteins of all living organisms are composed of the same set of 20 amino acids, which contain 20 different side chains (Figure 3.13, Table 3.3).

- Amino acids are joined together by a dehydration reaction that links the carboxyl group of one amino acid to the amino group of another, forming a peptide bond. A polypeptide is a structural unit composed of a linear sequence of amino acids. A protein is a functional unit composed of one or more polypeptides that have folded and twisted into precise three-dimensional shapes (Figure 3.14).

- The four levels of protein structure are primary (the amino acid sequence), secondary (α helices or β pleated sheets), tertiary (folding to assume a three-dimensional shape), and quaternary (having two or more polypeptides as subunits). The three-dimensional structure of a protein determines its function (Figures 3.15, 3.16, 3.17, 3.18, 3.19).

- Proteins contain regions called domains that have particular functions (Figure 3.20).

3.7 Nucleic Acids

- Nucleic acids are responsible for the storage, expression, and transmission of genetic information. The two types of nucleic acids are deoxyribonucleic acid (DNA) and ribonucleic acid (RNA). DNA and RNA consist of repeating monomers known as nucleotides. Each nucleotide is composed of a phosphate group, a five-carbon sugar (either deoxyribose or ribose), and a single or double ring of carbon and nitrogen atoms called a base (Figure 3.21).

- Nucleotides are covalently linked together to form a strand. A DNA molecule consists of two strands of nucleotides coiled around each other to form a double helix. The strands are held together by hydrogen bonds between a purine base (adenine or guanine) in one strand and a pyrimidine base (cytosine or thymine) in the other (A always hydrogen-bonds with T, and G with C). DNA molecules store genetic information coded in the sequence of their bases (Figures 3.22, 3.23).

- RNA consists of a single strand of nucleotides. The sugar in each nucleotide is ribose rather than deoxyribose, and the base uracil replaces thymine. RNA molecules are involved in decoding information stored in DNA into instructions for linking amino acids in a specific sequence to form a polypeptide.

Assess & Discuss

Test Yourself

1. Molecules that are found in living cells and contain the element _____ are considered organic molecules.
   a. hydrogen
   b. carbon
   c. oxygen
   d. nitrogen
   e. calcium

2. The versatility of carbon that allows it to serve as the backbone for a variety of different molecules is due to
   a. the ability of carbon atoms to form four covalent bonds.
   b. the fact that carbon usually forms ionic bonds with many different atoms.
   c. the abundance of carbon in the environment.
   d. the ability of carbon to form covalent bonds with many different types of atoms.
   e. both a and d.

3. Which of the following type(s) of bonds are nonpolar?
   a. C—C
   b. C—O
   c. C—H
   d. both a and b
   e. both a and c

4. Which of the following molecules are isomers of each other?

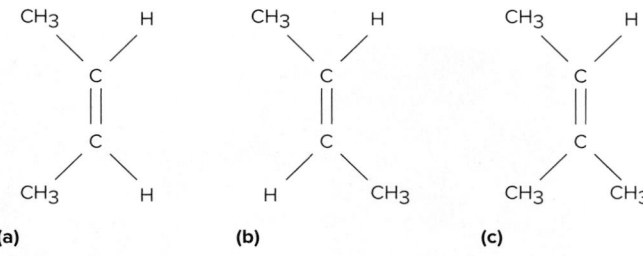

(a)   (b)   (c)

   a. a and b
   b. a and c
   c. b and c
   d. a, b, and c
   e. None of them are isomers of each other.

5. A polysaccharide that is commonly found in animal cells and stores energy is
   a. glucose.
   b. sucrose.
   c. glycogen.
   d. starch.
   e. cellulose.

6. In contrast to other fatty acids, essential fatty acids
   a. are always saturated fats.
   b. cannot be synthesized by a living organism and are necessary for survival.
   c. can act as building blocks for large, more complex macromolecules.
   d. are the simplest form of lipids found in plant cells.
   e. are structural components of plasma membranes.

7. The structures of three molecules are shown below. Which of them is (are) amphipathic?

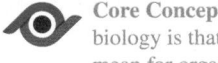

(a)

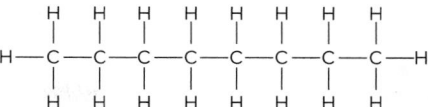

(b)

(c)

   a. a only
   b. b only
   c. c only
   d. b and c
   e. a and c

8. The monomers of proteins are _____, and these are linked by polar covalent bonds commonly referred to as _____.
   a. nucleotides, peptide bonds
   b. amino acids, ester bonds
   c. hydroxyl groups, ester bonds
   d. amino acids, peptide bonds
   e. monosaccharides, glycosidic linkages

9. A _____ is a portion of protein with a particular structure and function.
   a. peptide bond
   b. domain
   c. phospholipid
   d. wax
   e. monosaccharide

10. A DNA molecule contains 30% G. What percentage of its bases are A?
    a. 30%
    b. 20%
    c. 15%
    d. 10%
    e. none of the above

Conceptual Questions

1. Explain the similarities and differences between molecules that are isomers.

2. What is the difference between a saturated and an unsaturated fatty acid? How do the structural differences contribute to differences in their properties?

3. **Core Concept: Structure and Function** A core concept of biology is that *structure determines function*. What does this mean for organic molecules such as carbohydrates, lipids, and proteins?

Collaborative Questions

1. Discuss the differences between the various types of carbohydrates.

2. Discuss some of the roles that proteins play in living organisms.

UNIT II
CELL

Cell biology is the study of life at the cellular level. Although cells are the simplest units of life, biologists have come to realize that they are wonderfully complex and interesting, providing information about all living things. In this unit, Chapter 4 begins with a description of the evolutionary origin of cells and then provides an overview of cell structure and function. In Chapter 5, we will examine the structure and synthesis of cell membranes and the transport of substances in and out of the cell.

Chapters 6, 7, and 8 are largely devoted to metabolism, the sum of the chemical reactions in a cell or organism. Chapter 6 explores the topic of energy and considers how enzymes facilitate chemical reactions in a cell. Chapter 7 examines the pathways for carbohydrate breakdown and their production of an energy intermediate called ATP. In Chapter 8, we will explore the process of photosynthesis, in which the energy of sunlight drives the synthesis of carbohydrates.

Finally, Chapters 9 and 10 consider the ways that cells interact with their environment and with each other. In Chapter 9, we will examine how cells respond to signals, either those that come directly from their environment or those that are made by other cells. In Chapter 10, we will explore how cells interact with each other to produce a multicellular organism.

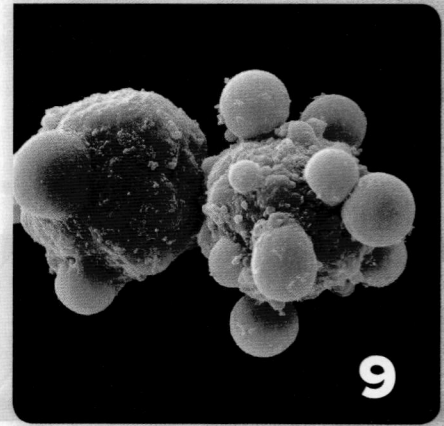

 The following Core Concepts **and** Core Skills **will be emphasized in this unit:**

- *Evolution: At the beginning of this unit, we will consider the evolutionary origin of cells, and also the origin of organelles, such as mitochondria and chloroplasts.*
- *Systems: As you will learn, a cell is a system with many interacting parts.*
- *Energy and Matter: Chapters 6, 7, and 8 examine how cells utilize and store energy contained within organic molecules such as glucose.*
- *Information: This unit provides many examples in which a cell's genome (its genetic makeup) results in a proteome (the proteins it makes) that largely determines cell structure and function.*
- *Structure and Function: Throughout this unit, we will see many examples in which the structure of proteins determines their cellular functions.*
- *Process of Science: Every chapter in this unit has a Feature Investigation that describes a pivotal experiment that provided insights into the workings of cells.*
- *Modeling: Every chapter has a Modeling Challenging that refines this important skill.*

(4): ©Steve Gschmeissner/Science Source; (5): ©Ramón Andrade, 3Dciencia/Science Source; (6): ©McGraw-Hill Education/Aaron Roeth, photographer; (7): ©Michael Dwyer/AP Images; (8): ©Travelpix Ltd/Getty Images; (9): ©David McCarthy/SPL/Science Source; (10): ©Altrendo Panoramic/Getty Images

Evolutionary Origin of Cells and Their General Features

4

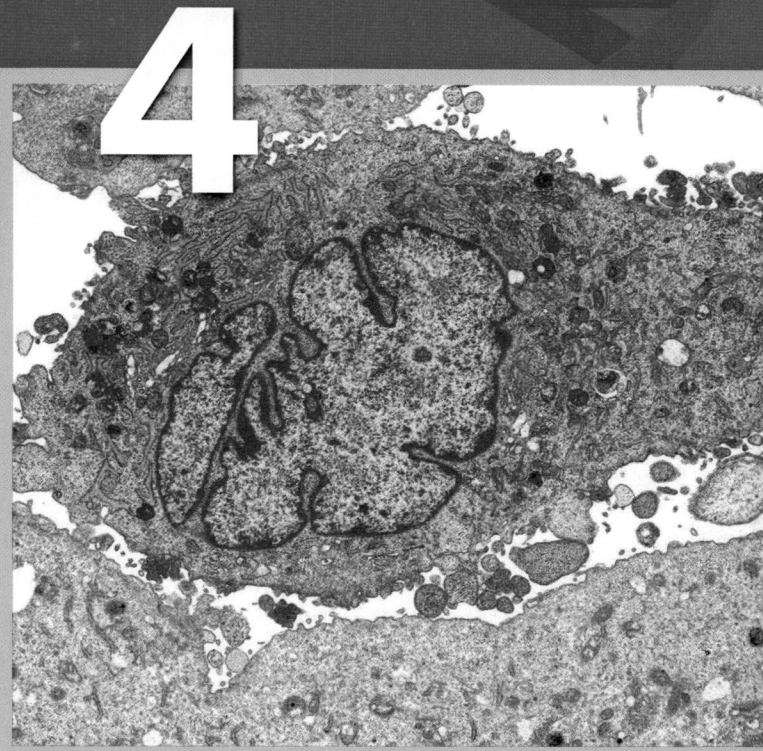

A cell from the lung of a person with lung cancer. The cell in this micrograph was viewed by a technique called transmission electron microscopy, which is described in this chapter. The micrograph was artificially colored using a computer to enhance the visualization of certain cell structures. ©Steve Gschmeissner/Science Source

Emily had a persistent cough ever since she started smoking cigarettes in college. However, at age 35, it seemed to be getting worse, and she was alarmed by the occasional pain in her chest. When she began to lose weight and became easily fatigued, Emily decided to see a doctor. The diagnosis was lung cancer. Despite aggressive treatment with chemotherapy and radiation therapy, she succumbed to lung cancer 14 months after the initial diagnosis. Emily was 36.

Topics such as cancer are within the field of **cell biology**—the study of individual cells and their interactions with each other. Researchers in this field want to understand the basic features of cells and apply their knowledge in the treatment of diseases such as cystic fibrosis, sickle cell disease, and lung cancer.

The idea that organisms are composed of cells originated in the mid-1800s. German botanist Matthias Schleiden studied plant material under the microscope and was struck by the presence of many similar-looking compartments, each of which contained a dark area. Today we call those compartments cells and the dark area the nucleus. In 1838, Schleiden speculated that cells are living entities and that plants are aggregates of cells arranged according to definite laws.

Schleiden was a good friend of the German physiologist Theodor Schwann. Over dinner one evening, their conversation turned to the nuclei of plant cells, and Schwann remembered having seen similar structures in animal tissue. Schwann conducted additional studies that showed that animal tissue contains large numbers of nuclei, which are located in cell-like compartments and occur at regular intervals. In 1839, Schwann extended Schleiden's hypothesis to animals. About two decades later, German biologist Rudolf Virchow proposed that *omnis cellula e cellula*, or "every cell originates from another cell." This idea arose from his research, which showed that diseased cells divide to produce more diseased cells.

The **cell theory**, which is credited to both Schleiden and Schwann with contributions from Virchow, has three parts.

1. All living organisms are composed of one or more cells.
2. Cells are the smallest units of life.
3. New cells come only from pre-existing cells by cell division.

Most cells are so small they cannot be seen with the unaided eye. However, as cell biologists have begun to unravel

cell structure and function at the molecular level, the cell has emerged as a unit of incredible complexity and adaptability. In this chapter, we will begin our exploration of cells with a description of hypotheses of how living cells arose on Earth. We will then consider the general features of cell structure and function. Later chapters in this unit will explore certain aspects of cell biology in greater detail.

4.1 Origin of Living Cells on Earth

Learning Outcomes:

1. Outline the four overlapping stages that are hypothesized to have led to the origin of living cells.
2. List various hypotheses about how complex organic molecules formed.
3. Explain the concept of an RNA world, and describe how it could have evolved into a DNA/RNA/protein world.

Living cells are complex collections of molecules and macromolecules. DNA stores genetic information, RNA acts as an intermediary in the process of protein synthesis and plays other important roles, and proteins form the foundation for the structure and activities of living cells. Life as we know it requires this interplay between DNA, RNA, and proteins for its existence and perpetuation. On modern Earth, every living cell is made from a pre-existing cell.

But how did life get started? Because DNA, RNA, and proteins are the central players in the enterprise of life, scientists who are interested in the origin of life have focused much of their attention on the formation of these macromolecules and their building blocks, namely, nucleotides and amino acids. To understand the origin of cells, we can view the process as occurring in four overlapping stages:

Stage 1: Nucleotides and amino acids were produced prior to the existence of cells.

Stage 2: Nucleotides became polymerized to form RNA and/or DNA, and amino acids became polymerized to form proteins.

Stage 3: Polymers became enclosed in membranes.

Stage 4: Polymers enclosed in membranes acquired properties that are associated with living cells.

Researchers have followed a variety of experimental approaches to determine how life may have begun, including the synthesis of organic molecules in the laboratory without the presence of living cells or cellular material. This work has led researchers to propose a variety of hypotheses regarding the origin of cells. In this section, we will examine the origin of life at each of these stages and consider a few scientific viewpoints that wrestle with the question "How did life on Earth begin?"

Stage 1: Organic Molecules Formed Prior to the Existence of Cells

Let's begin our inquiry into the first stage of the origin of life by considering how nucleotides and amino acids may have been made prior to the existence of living cells. In the 1920s, the Russian biochemist Alexander Oparin and the Scottish biologist J. B. S. Haldane independently proposed that organic molecules, such as nucleotides and amino acids, arose spontaneously under the conditions that occurred on early Earth. According to this hypothesis, the spontaneous appearance of organic molecules produced what they called a "primordial soup," which eventually gave rise to living cells.

The conditions on early Earth, which were much different from today, may have been more conducive to the spontaneous formation of organic molecules. Current hypotheses suggest that organic molecules, and eventually macromolecules, formed spontaneously. The formation of such molecules is termed prebiotic (before life) or abiotic (without life) synthesis. These organic molecules slowly accumulated because there was little free oxygen gas, so they were not spontaneously oxidized, and there were as yet no living organisms, so they were also not metabolized. The slow accumulation of these molecules in the early oceans over a long period of time formed what is now called the **prebiotic soup**. The formation of this medium was a key event that preceded the origin of life.

Though most scientists agree that life originated from the assemblage of nonliving matter on early Earth, the mechanism of how and where these molecules originated is widely debated. Many intriguing hypotheses have been proposed, which are not mutually exclusive. A few of the more widely debated ideas are the reducing atmosphere hypothesis, the extraterrestrial hypothesis, and the deep-sea vent hypothesis.

Reducing Atmosphere Hypothesis Based largely on geological data, many scientists in the 1950s proposed that the atmosphere on early Earth was rich in water vapor (H_2O), hydrogen gas (H_2), methane (CH_4), and ammonia (NH_3). These components, along with a lack of atmospheric oxygen (O_2), produced a reducing atmosphere because methane and ammonia readily give up electrons to other molecules, thereby reducing them. Such oxidation-reduction reactions, or redox reactions, are required for the formation of complex organic molecules from simple inorganic molecules.

In 1953, American chemist Stanley Miller, a student in the laboratory of physical chemist Harold Urey, was the first scientist to use experimentation to test whether the prebiotic synthesis of organic molecules is possible. His experimental apparatus was intended to simulate the conditions on early Earth that were postulated in the 1950s (**Figure 4.1**). Water vapor from a flask of boiling water rose into another chamber containing hydrogen gas (H_2), methane (CH_4), and ammonia

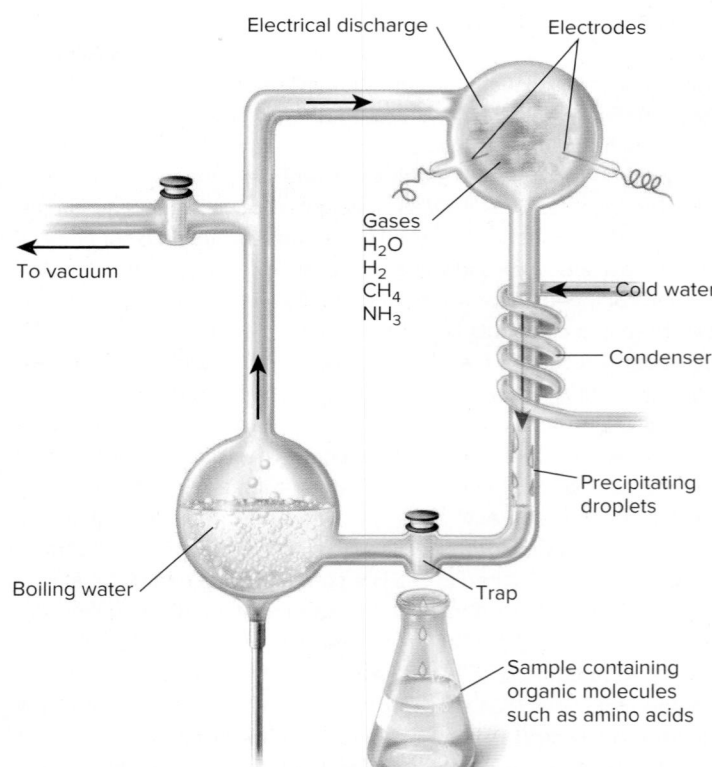

Figure 4.1 **Testing the reducing atmosphere hypothesis for the origin of life—the Miller and Urey experiment.**

 Core Skill: Process of Science By conducting experiments, researchers were able to demonstrate the feasibility of the synthesis of organic molecules prior to the emergence of living cells.

(NH_3). Miller inserted two electrodes that sent electrical discharges into the chamber to simulate lightning bolts. A condenser jacket cooled some of the gases from the chamber, causing droplets to form that fell into a trap. He then took samples from this trap for chemical analysis. In his first experiments, he observed the formation of hydrogen cyanide (HCN) and formaldehyde (CH_2O). Such molecules are precursors of more complex organic molecules. These precursors also combined to make larger molecules such as the amino acid glycine. At the end of 1 week of operation, 10–15% of the carbon had been incorporated into organic compounds. Later experiments by Miller and others demonstrated the formation of sugars, a few types of amino acids, lipids, and bases found in nucleic acids (for example, adenine).

In a study published in 2011, researchers analyzed samples that Miller had preserved from a 1958 experiment in which he used a mixture of CH_4, NH_3, hydrogen sulfide (H_2S), and carbon dioxide (CO_2). For unknown reasons, Miller had not analyzed what products were made in this experiment. When these preserved samples were analyzed using modern technology, they were found to contain 23 different amino acids and 4 amines (another type of organic molecule), more organic compounds than seen in Miller's classic experiments.

Why were these studies important? The work of Miller and Urey was the first attempt to apply scientific experimentation to our quest to understand the origin of life. Their pioneering strategy showed that the prebiotic synthesis of organic molecules is possible, although it could not prove that such synthesis did in fact occur. In spite of the importance of these studies, critics of the so-called reducing atmosphere hypothesis have argued that Miller and Urey were wrong about the composition of early Earth's environment. More recently, many scientists have suggested that the atmosphere on early Earth was not reducing, but instead was a neutral gaseous mixture consisting mostly of carbon monoxide (CO), carbon dioxide (CO_2), nitrogen (N_2), and H_2O. These newer ideas are derived from studies of volcanic gas, which has much more CO_2 and N_2 than CH_4 and NH_3, and from the observation that ultraviolet (UV) radiation destroys CH_4 and NH_3, so these molecules would have been short-lived on early Earth, which had high levels of UV radiation. Nevertheless, since the experiments of Miller and Urey, many newer investigations have shown that organic molecules can be made under a variety of conditions. For example, organic molecules can be made prebiotically from a neutral gaseous mixture composed primarily of CO, CO_2, N_2, and H_2O.

Extraterrestrial Hypothesis   Many scientists have argued that sufficient organic molecules may have been present in the materials from asteroids and comets that reached the surface of early Earth in the form of meteorites. A significant proportion of meteorites belong to a class known as carbonaceous chondrites. Such meteorites may contain a substantial amount of organic carbon, including amino acids and nucleic acid bases. Based on this observation, some scientists have postulated that such meteorites could have transported a significant amount of organic molecules to early Earth.

Opponents of this hypothesis argue that most of this material would have been destroyed by the intense heating that accompanies the passage of large bodies through the atmosphere and their subsequent collision with the surface of the Earth. Though some organic molecules are known to reach the Earth via such meteorites, the degree to which heat would have destroyed those organic molecules remains a matter of controversy.

Deep-Sea Vent Hypothesis   In 1988, German lawyer and organic chemist Günter Wächtershäuser proposed that key organic molecules may have originated in deep-sea vents, which are cracks in the Earth's surface where superheated water rich in metal ions and hydrogen sulfide (H_2S) mixes abruptly with cold seawater. These vents release hot gaseous substances from the interior of the Earth at temperatures in excess of 300°C (572°F). Supporters of this hypothesis propose that biologically important molecules may have been formed in the temperature gradient between the extremely hot vent water and the cold water that surrounds the vent (**Figure 4.2a**).

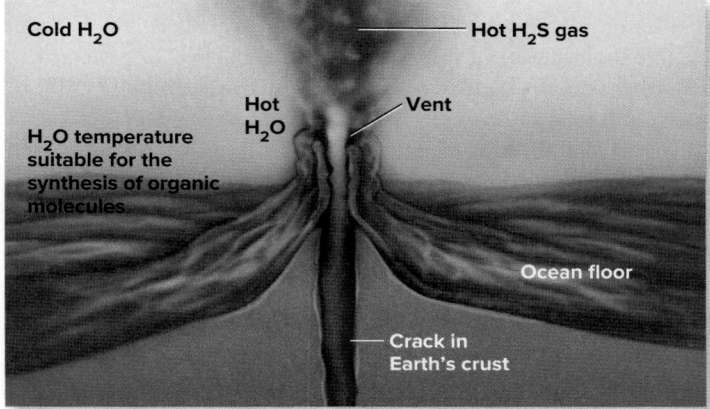

(a) Deep-sea vent hypothesis

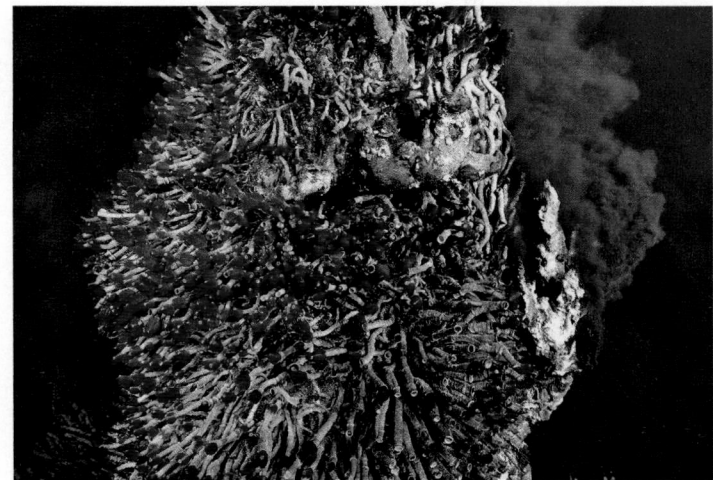

(b) A deep-sea vent community

Figure 4.2   The deep-sea vent hypothesis for the origin of life.
(a) Deep-sea vents are cracks in the Earth's surface that release hot gases such as hydrogen sulfide (H_2S). This heats the water near the vent and results in a gradient between the very hot water adjacent to the vent and the cold water farther from the vent. The synthesis of organic molecules can occur in this gradient. **(b)** Photograph of a biological community near a deep-sea vent, which includes giant tube worms and crabs. b: ©CSSF/Neptune Canada

Concept Check: *What properties of deep-sea vents made them suitable for the prebiotic synthesis of molecules?*

Experimentally, the temperatures within this gradient are known to be suitable for the synthesis of molecules that form components of biological molecules. For example, the reaction between iron and H_2S yields pyrites and H_2 and has been shown to provide the energy necessary for the reduction of N_2 to NH_3. Nitrogen is an essential component of both nucleic acids and amino acids—the molecular building blocks of life. But N_2, which is found abundantly on Earth, is chemically inert, so it is unlikely to have given rise to life. The conversion of N_2 to NH_3 at deep-sea vents may have led to the production of amino acids and nucleic acids.

Interestingly, complex biological communities are found in the vicinity of modern deep-sea vents. Various types of fish, worms, clams, crabs, shrimp, and bacteria are found in significant abundance in those areas (**Figure 4.2b**). Unlike most other forms of life on our planet, these organisms receive their energy from chemicals in the vent and not from the Sun. In 2007, American scientist Timothy Kusky and colleagues discovered 1.4-billion-year-old fossils of deep-sea microbes near ancient deep-sea vents. This study provided more evidence that life may have originated on the bottom of the ocean. However, debate continues as to the primary way organic molecules were made prior to the existence of life on Earth.

Stage 2: Organic Polymers May Have Formed on the Surface of Clay

The preceding three hypotheses provide reasonable mechanisms whereby small organic molecules could have accumulated on early Earth. Scientists hypothesize that the second stage in the origin of life was a period in which simple organic molecules polymerized to form more complex organic polymers such as DNA, RNA, or proteins. Most ideas regarding the origin of life assume that polymers with at least 30–60 monomers are needed to store enough information to make a viable genetic system. Because hydrolysis competes with polymerization, many scientists have speculated that the synthesis of polymers did not occur in a watery prebiotic soup, but instead took place on a solid surface or in evaporating tidal pools.

In 1951, Irish X-ray crystallographer John Bernal first suggested that the prebiotic synthesis of polymers took place on clay. In his book *The Physical Basis of Life*, he wrote that "clays, muds and inorganic crystals are powerful means to concentrate and polymerize organic molecules." Many clay minerals are known to bind organic molecules such as nucleotides and amino acids. Experimentally, many research groups have demonstrated the formation of nucleic acid polymers and polypeptides on the surface of clay, given the presence of monomer building blocks. During the prebiotic synthesis of RNA, the purine bases of the nucleotides could have interacted with the silicate surfaces of the clay. Cations, such as Mg^{2+}, bound the nucleotides to the negative surfaces of the clay, thereby positioning the nucleotides in a way that promoted bond formation between the phosphate of one nucleotide and the ribose sugar of an adjacent nucleotide. In this way, polymers such as RNA may have been formed.

Though the formation of polymers on clay remains a reasonable hypothesis, studies by American chemist Luke Leman and his colleagues English chemist Leslie Orgel and Iranian-American chemist M. Reza Ghadiri indicate that polymers can also form in aqueous solutions, contrary to the prevalent view. Their work in 2004 showed that carbonyl sulfide, a simple gas present in volcanic gases and deep-sea vent emissions, can bring about the formation of peptides from amino acids under mild conditions in water. These results indicate that the synthesis of polymers could have taken place in the prebiotic soup.

Stage 3: Cell-like Structures May Have Originated When Polymers Were Enclosed by a Boundary

The third stage in the origin of living cells is hypothesized to be the formation of a boundary that separated the polymers such as RNA from the environment. The term **protobiont** is used to describe an aggregate of prebiotically produced molecules and macromolecules that acquired a boundary, such as a lipid bilayer, that allowed it to maintain an internal chemical environment distinct from that of its surroundings. What characteristics make protobionts possible precursors of living cells? Scientists envision the existence of four key features:

1. A boundary, such as a membrane, separated the internal contents of the protobiont from the external environment.
2. Polymers inside the protobiont contained information.
3. Polymers inside the protobiont had catalytic functions.
4. The protobionts eventually developed the capability of self-replication.

Protobionts were not capable of precise self-reproduction like living cells, but could divide to increase in number. Such protobionts are thought to have exhibited basic metabolic pathways in which the structures of organic molecules were changed. In particular, the polymers inside protobionts must have gained the catalytic ability to link organic building blocks to produce new polymers. This would have been a critical step in the process that eventually provided protobionts with the ability to self-replicate. According to this scenario, metabolic pathways became more complex, and the ability of protobionts to self-replicate became more refined over time. Eventually, these structures exhibited the characteristics that we attribute to living cells. As described next, researchers have hypothesized that protobionts may have existed as coacervates or liposomes.

Coacervates   In 1924, Alexander Oparin hypothesized that living cells evolved from **coacervates**, droplets that form spontaneously from the association of charged polymers such as proteins, carbohydrates, or nucleic acids surrounded by water. Their name derives from the Latin *coacervare*, meaning to assemble together or cluster. Coacervates measure 1–100 μm (micrometers) across, are surrounded by a tight skin of water molecules, and possess osmotic properties (**Figure 4.3a**). The skin of water allows the selective absorption of simple molecules from the surrounding medium.

Enzymes trapped within coacervates can perform primitive metabolic functions. For example, researchers have made coacervates containing the enzyme glycogen phosphorylase. When

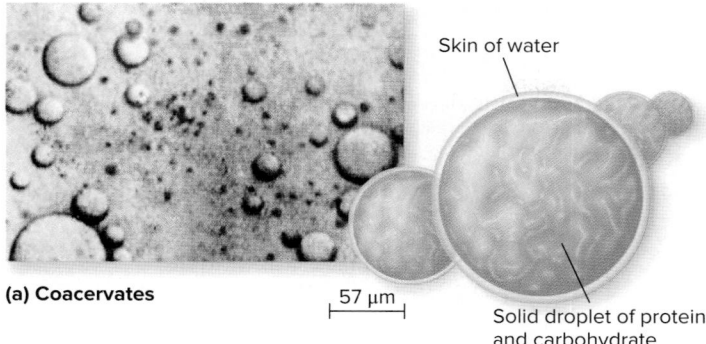

(a) Coacervates

57 μm

Skin of water

Solid droplet of protein and carbohydrate

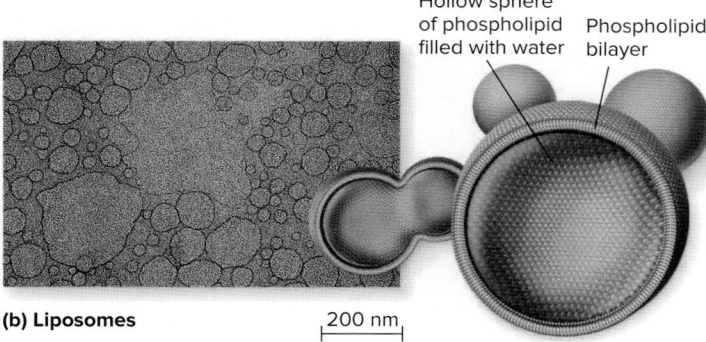

Hollow sphere of phospholipid filled with water

Phospholipid bilayer

(b) Liposomes

200 nm

Figure 4.3 Possible structures of protobionts. Primitive cell-like structures such as coacervates or liposomes could have given rise to living cells. **(a)** A micrograph and illustration of coacervates, which are droplets of charged polymers surrounded by a skin of water molecules. **(b)** An electron micrograph and illustration of liposomes. Each liposome is made of a phospholipid bilayer surrounding an aqueous compartment. a: Source: A. I. Oparin. From *The Origin of Life,* New York: Dover, 1952; b: ©Mary Kraft

Concept Check: *Which protobiont seems most similar to today's cells? Explain.*

 Core Skill: Connections Look back at Figure 3.11. What is the physical/chemical reason why phospholipids tend to form a bilayer?

glucose-1-phosphate was made available to these coacervates, it was taken up into them, and starch was produced. The starch merged with the wall of the coacervates, and they increased in size and eventually divided into two. When the enzyme amylase was included, the starch was broken down to maltose, which was released from the coacervates.

Liposomes As a second possibility, protobionts may have resembled **liposomes**—vesicles surrounded by a phospholipid bilayer (**Figure 4.3b**). When certain types of lipids are dissolved in water, they spontaneously form liposomes. As discussed in Chapter 5, phospholipid bilayers are selectively permeable (look ahead to Figure 5.10), and some liposomes can even store energy in the form of an electrical gradient. Such liposomes can discharge this energy in a neuron-like fashion, showing rudimentary signs of excitability, which is characteristic of living cells.

In 2003, Danish chemist Martin Hanczyc, American chemist Shelly Fujikawa, and Canadian-American biologist Jack Szostak showed that clay can catalyze the formation of liposomes that grow and divide, a primitive form of self-replication. Furthermore, if RNA was on the surface of the clay, the researchers discovered that liposomes that enclosed RNA were formed. These experiments are compelling because they showed that the formation of membrane vesicles containing RNA molecules is a plausible explanation for the emergence of cell-like structures based on simple physical and chemical properties.

Stage 4: Cellular Characteristics May Have Evolved via Chemical Selection, Beginning with an RNA World

The majority of scientists favor RNA as the first macromolecule that was found in protobionts. Unlike other polymers, RNA exhibits three key functions:

1. RNA has the ability to store information in its nucleotide base sequence.
2. Due to base pairing, its nucleotide sequence has the capacity for self-replication.
3. RNA can perform a variety of catalytic functions. The results of many experiments have shown that some RNA molecules can function as **ribozymes**—RNA molecules that catalyze chemical reactions.

By comparison, DNA and proteins are not as versatile as RNA. DNA has very limited catalytic activity, and proteins are not known to undergo self-replication. RNA can perform functions that are characteristic of proteins and, at the same time, can serve as genetic material with replicative and informational functions.

How did the RNA molecules that were first made prebiotically evolve into more complex molecules that developed cell-like characteristics? Researchers propose that a process called chemical selection was responsible. **Chemical selection** occurs when a chemical within a mixture has special properties or advantages that cause it to increase in number relative to other chemicals in the mixture. (As we will discuss in Chapter 23, natural selection is a similar process except that it promotes change in a population of living organisms over time due to survival and reproductive advantages.) Chemical selection results in **chemical evolution**—a population of molecules changes over time to become a new population with a different chemical composition.

Scientists speculate that initially the special properties that enabled certain RNA molecules to undergo chemical selection were their ability to self-replicate and to perform other catalytic functions. As a way to understand the concept of chemical selection, let's consider a hypothetical scenario showing two steps of this process. Step 1 of **Figure 4.4** shows a group of protobionts that contain RNA molecules that were made prebiotically. RNA molecules inside these protobionts could be used as templates for the prebiotic synthesis of complementary RNA molecules. Such a process of self-replication, however, would be very slow because it would not be catalyzed by enzymes in the protobiont. In a first step of chemical selection, the sequence of one of the RNA molecules has undergone

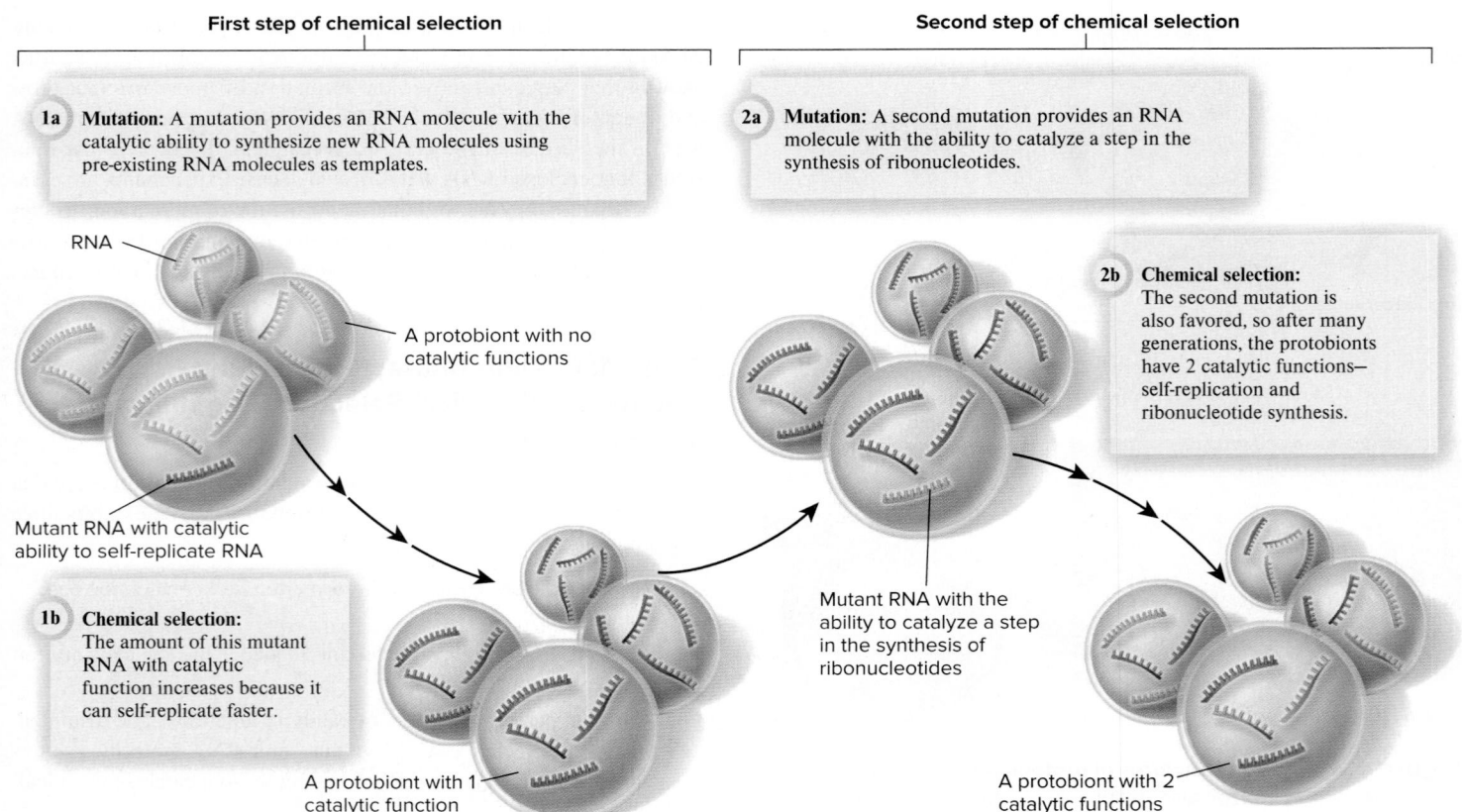

First step of chemical selection

1a **Mutation:** A mutation provides an RNA molecule with the catalytic ability to synthesize new RNA molecules using pre-existing RNA molecules as templates.

RNA

A protobiont with no catalytic functions

Mutant RNA with catalytic ability to self-replicate RNA

1b **Chemical selection:** The amount of this mutant RNA with catalytic function increases because it can self-replicate faster.

A protobiont with 1 catalytic function

Second step of chemical selection

2a **Mutation:** A second mutation provides an RNA molecule with the ability to catalyze a step in the synthesis of ribonucleotides.

2b **Chemical selection:** The second mutation is also favored, so after many generations, the protobionts have 2 catalytic functions—self-replication and ribonucleotide synthesis.

Mutant RNA with the ability to catalyze a step in the synthesis of ribonucleotides

A protobiont with 2 catalytic functions

Figure 4.4   A hypothetical scenario illustrating the process of chemical selection. This figure shows a two-step scenario. In the first step, RNAs that can self-replicate are selected, and in the second step, RNAs with the ability to catalyze a step in ribonucleotide synthesis are selected.

Concept Check: *What is meant by the term chemical selection?*

a mutation that gives it the catalytic ability to attach nucleotides together, using other RNA molecules as a template. This protobiont would have an advantage over others because it would be capable of faster self-replication of its RNA molecules. Over time, due to this enhanced rate of replication, protobionts carrying such RNA molecules would increase in number compared with the others. Eventually, the group of protobionts shown in the figure contains only this type of catalytic RNA.

In the second step of chemical selection (Figure 4.4, right side), a second mutation in an RNA molecule could produce the catalytic function that would help to promote the synthesis of ribonucleotides, the building blocks of RNA. For example, a hypothetical ribozyme may catalyze the attachment of a base to a ribose, thereby catalyzing one of the steps necessary for making a ribonucleotide. This protobiont would not rely solely on the prebiotic synthesis of ribonucleotides, which is a very slow process. Therefore, the protobiont having the ability to both self-replicate and synthesize ribonucleotides would have an advantage over a protobiont that could only self-replicate. Over time, the faster rate of self-replication and ribonucleotide synthesis would cause an increase in the numbers of protobionts with both functions.

The **RNA world** is a hypothetical period on early Earth when both the information needed for life and the catalytic activity of living cells were contained solely in RNA molecules. In this scenario, protobionts containing RNA exhibited the properties of life due to RNA genomes that were copied and maintained through the catalytic function of RNA molecules. Over time, scientists envision that mutations occurred in these RNA molecules, occasionally introducing new functional possibilities. Chemical selection would have eventually produced an increase in complexity in these protobionts, with RNA molecules accruing abilities such as the ability to link amino acids together into proteins and other catalytic functions.

But is an RNA world a plausible scenario? Remarkably, scientists have been able to perform experiments in the laboratory that can select for RNA molecules with a particular function. American biologists David Bartel and Jack Szostak conducted the first study of this type in 1993, in which they selected for RNA molecules with the catalytic ability to link nucleotides together. After 10 rounds of chemical selection, they obtained a collection of RNA molecules that had catalytic activity that was 3 million times higher than their original random collection of molecules!

Like the work of Miller and Urey, the study by Bartel and Szostak showed the feasibility of another phase of the prebiotic process that led to life. In this case, chemical selection resulted in chemical evolution. The results showed that chemical selection can change the functional characteristics of a group of RNA molecules over time by increasing the proportion of those molecules with enhanced function.

The RNA World Was Superseded by the Modern DNA/RNA/Protein World

Assuming that an RNA world was the origin of life, researchers have asked, "Why and how did the RNA world evolve into the DNA/RNA/protein world we see today?" The RNA world may have been superseded by a DNA/RNA world or an RNA/protein world before the emergence of the modern DNA/RNA/protein world. Let's now consider the advantages of a DNA/RNA/protein world as opposed to the simpler RNA world and explore how this modern biological world might have come into being.

Information Storage   RNA can store information in its base sequence. If so, why did DNA take over that function in modern cells? During the RNA world, RNA had to perform two roles: the storage of information and the catalysis of chemical reactions. Scientists have speculated that the incorporation of DNA into cells would have relieved RNA of its storage role, thereby allowing RNA to perform a variety of other functions. For example, if DNA stored the information for the synthesis of RNA molecules, such RNA molecules could bind cofactors, have modified bases, or bind peptides that might enhance their catalytic function. Cells with both DNA and RNA would have had an advantage over those with just RNA, and so they would have been selected. Another advantage of DNA is its stability. Compared with RNA, DNA strands are less likely to spontaneously break.

A second issue is how DNA came into being. Scientists have proposed that an ancestral RNA molecule had the ability to make DNA using RNA as a template. This function, known as reverse transcription, is described in Chapter 19 in the discussion of retroviruses. Interestingly, modern eukaryotic cells can use RNA as a template to make DNA. For example, an RNA sequence in the enzyme telomerase is used as a template to copy the ends of chromosomes, thus preventing progressive shortening of the chromosomes (look ahead to Figure 11.21).

Metabolism and Other Cellular Functions   Now let's consider the origin of proteins. The emergence of proteins as catalysts may have been a great benefit to early cells. Due to the different chemical properties of the 20 amino acids, proteins have vastly greater catalytic ability than do RNA molecules, again providing a major advantage to cells that had both RNA and proteins. In modern cells, proteins have taken over most, but not all, catalytic functions. In addition, proteins can perform other important tasks. For example, cytoskeletal proteins carry out structural roles, and certain membrane proteins are responsible for the uptake of substances into living cells.

How would proteins have come into being in an RNA world? Chemical selection experiments have shown that RNA molecules can catalyze the formation of peptide bonds and even attach amino acids to primitive tRNA molecules. Similarly, modern protein synthesis still includes a central role for RNA in the synthesis of polypeptides. First, mRNA provides the information for a polypeptide sequence. Second, tRNA molecules act as adaptors for the formation of polypeptides. And finally, ribosomes containing rRNA provide a site for polypeptide synthesis. Furthermore, rRNA within ribosomes acts as a ribozyme to catalyze peptide bond formation. Taken together, the analysis of translation in modern cells is consistent with an evolutionary history in which RNA molecules were instrumental in the emergence and formation of proteins.

4.2 Microscopy

Learning Outcomes:

1. **CoreSKILL »** Explain the three key parameters in microscopy: resolution, contrast, and magnification.
2. **CoreSKILL »** Compare and contrast the different types of light and electron microscopes and their uses.

Before we examine the general features of modern cells, we will first consider the **microscope**, which is a magnification tool that enables researchers to visualize the structure and inner workings of cells. A **micrograph** is an image taken with the aid of a microscope. The first compound microscope—a microscope with more than one lens—was first constructed in 1595 by Zacharias Jansen of Holland. In 1665, an English biologist, Robert Hooke, studied cork under a primitive compound microscope he had made. He actually observed cell walls because cork cells are dead and have lost their internal components. Hooke coined the word cell, derived from the Latin word *cellula*, meaning small compartment, to describe the structures he observed.

Three important parameters in microscopy are resolution, contrast, and magnification.

- **Resolution**, a measure of the clarity of an image, is the ability to observe two adjacent objects as distinct from one another. For example, a microscope with good resolution enables a researcher to distinguish as separate objects two adjacent chromosomes, which would appear as a single, blurry object under a microscope with poor resolution.

- **Contrast** refers to relative differences in the lightness, darkness, or color between adjacent regions in a sample. The ability to visualize a particular cell structure may depend on how different it looks from adjacent structures. Staining the cellular structure of interest with a dye can make viewing much easier. The application of stains, which selectively label individual components of the cell, greatly improves contrast. However, staining should not be confused with colorization. Many of the micrographs shown in this textbook are colorized, or artificially colored, to emphasize certain cellular structures, such as different parts of a cell (see the chapter opener, for example). In colorization, particular colors are added to micrographs with the aid of a computer.

- **Magnification** is the ratio between the size of an image produced by a microscope and the object's actual size. For example, if the image size is 100 times larger than the object's actual size, the magnification is designated 100×. Depending on the quality of the lens and the illumination source, every microscope has an optimal range of magnification before objects appear too blurry to be readily observed.

Microscopes are categorized into two groups based on the source of illumination. A **light microscope** utilizes light for illumination, whereas an **electron microscope** uses a beam of electrons for illumination. Very good light microscopes resolve structures that are as close as 0.2 μm (micron, or micrometer) from each other.

Resolution is improved when the illumination source has a shorter wavelength. A major advance in microscopy occurred in 1931 when Max Knoll and Ernst Ruska invented the first electron microscope. Because the wavelength of an electron beam is much shorter than visible light, the resolution of an electron microscope is far better than that of any light microscope. The resolution limit of an electron microscope is typically around 2 nm (nanometers), which is about 100 times better than a light microscope. **Figure 4.5** shows the ranges of resolving powers of the electron microscope, light microscope, and unaided eye and compares them with the sizes of various chemical and biological structures.

Over the past several decades, technological advances have made light microscopy a powerful research tool. Improvements in lens technology, microscope organization, sample preparation, sample illumination, and computerized image processing have enabled researchers to invent different types of light microscopes, each with its own advantages and disadvantages (**Figure 4.6**).

Similarly, improvements in electron microscopy occurred during the 1930s and 1940s, and by the 1950s, the electron microscope was playing a major role in advancing our understanding of cell structure. Two general types of electron microscopy have been developed: transmission electron microscopy and scanning electron microscopy. In **transmission electron microscopy (TEM)**, a beam of electrons is transmitted through a biological sample. To provide contrast, the sample is stained with a heavy metal, which binds to certain cellular structures such as membranes. The sample is then adhered to a copper grid and placed in a transmission electron microscope. When the beam of electrons strikes the sample, some of them hit the heavy metal and are scattered, while those that pass through without being scattered are focused to form an image on a photographic plate or screen (**Figure 4.7a**). The metal-stained regions of the sample that scatter electrons appear as darker areas, because of reduced electron penetration of those regions. TEM provides a cross-sectional view of a cell and its organelles and gives the best resolution compared with other forms of microscopy. However, such microscopes are expensive and cannot be used to view living cells.

Scanning electron microscopy (SEM) is used to view the surface of a biological sample. The sample is coated with a thin layer of heavy metal, such as gold or palladium, and then is exposed to an electron beam that scans its surface. Secondary electrons are emitted from the sample, which are detected and create an image of its three-dimensional surface (**Figure 4.7b**).

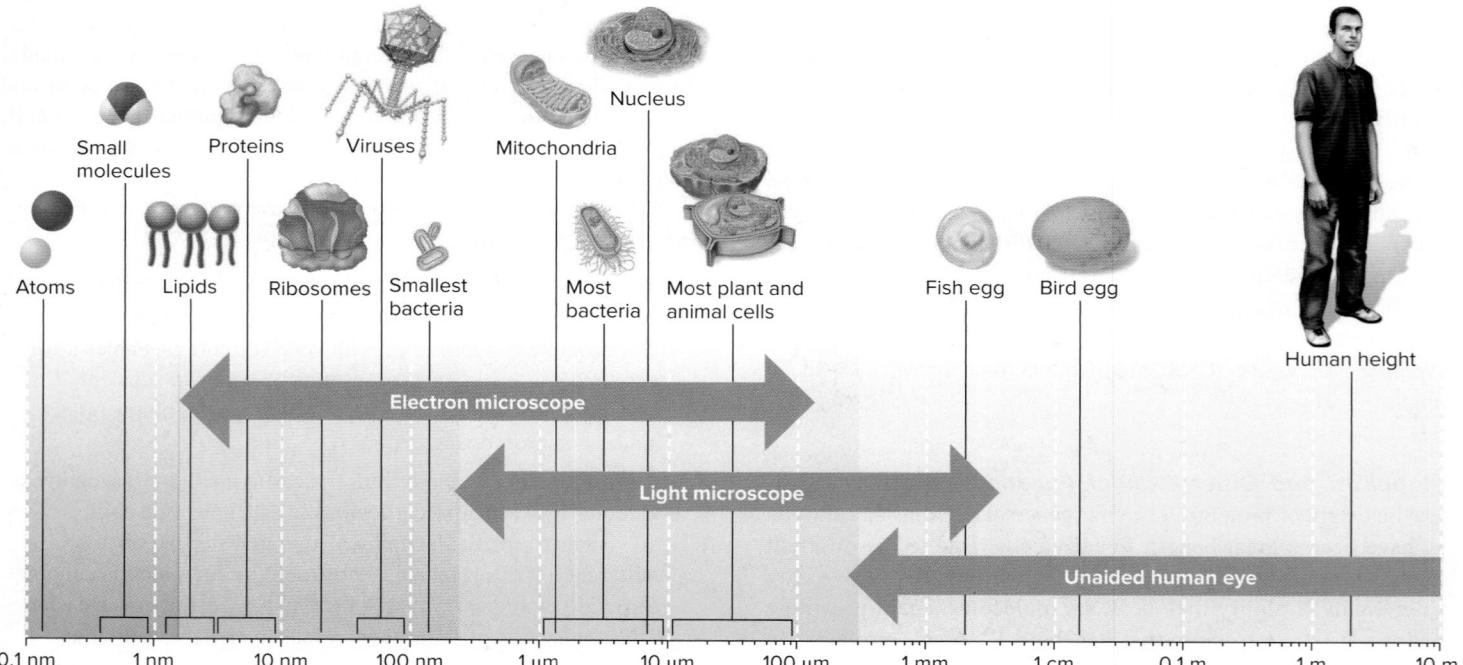

Figure 4.5 A comparison of the sizes of various chemical and biological structures with the resolving powers of the unaided eye, light microscope, and electron microscope. The scale at the bottom is logarithmic to accommodate the wide range of sizes in this drawing.

Concept Check: *Which type of microscope would you use to observe a virus?*

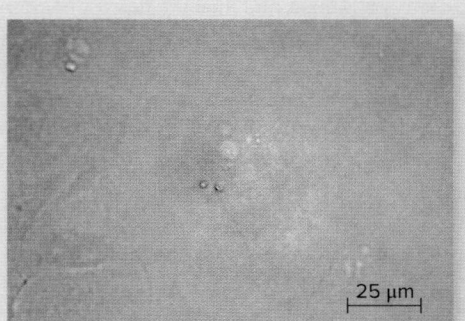 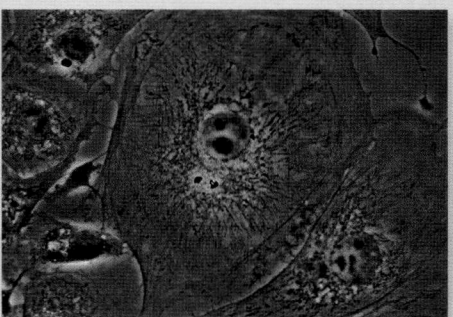 

Standard light microscopy (bright field, unstained sample).
Light is passed directly through a sample, and the light is focused using glass lenses. Simple, inexpensive, and easy to use but offers little contrast with unstained samples.

Phase contrast microscopy.
As an alternative to staining, this microscope controls the path of light and amplifies differences in the phase of light transmitted or reflected by a sample. The dense structures appear darker than the background, thereby improving the contrast in different parts of the specimen. Can be used to view living, unstained cells.

Differential interference contrast (Nomarski) microscopy.
Similar to a phase contrast microscope in that it uses optical modifications to improve contrast in unstained specimens. Can be used to visualize the internal structures of cells and is commonly used to view whole cells or large cell structures such as nuclei.

(a) Three different methods of light microscopy on the same unstained sample

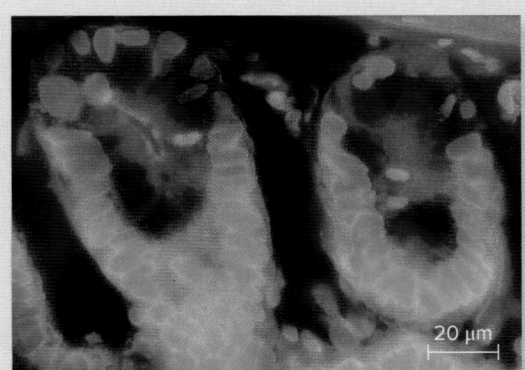 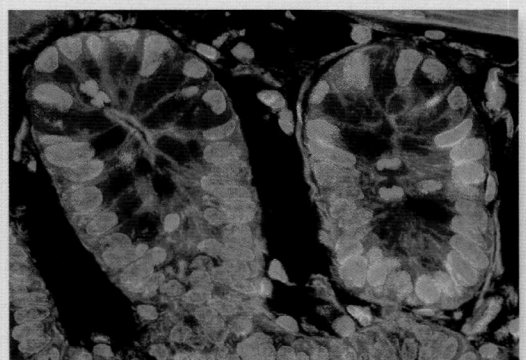

Standard (wide-field) fluorescence microscopy.
Fluorescent molecules specifically label a particular type of cellular protein or organelle. A fluorescent molecule absorbs light at a particular wavelength and emits light at a longer wavelength. This microscope has filters that illuminate the sample with the wavelength of light that a fluorescent molecule absorbs, and then only the light that is emitted by the fluorescent molecules is allowed to reach the observer. To detect their cellular location, researchers often label specific cellular proteins using fluorescent antibodies that bind specifically to a particular protein.

Confocal fluorescence microscopy.
Uses lasers that illuminate various points in the sample. These points are processed by a computer to give a very sharp focal plane. In this example, this microscope technique is used in conjunction with fluorescence microscopy to view fluorescent molecules within a cell.

(b) Two different methods of fluorescence microscopy on the same sample

Figure 4.6 **Examples of light microscopy.** **(a)** These micrographs compare the use of three types of light microscopy to view the same unstained sample of endothelial cells that line the interior surface of arteries in the lungs. **(b)** These two micrographs compare standard (wide-field) fluorescence microscopy with confocal fluorescence microscopy. The sample is a section through a mouse intestine, showing two villi, projections from the small intestine that are described in Chapter 46. In this sample, the nuclei are stained green, and the actin filaments (discussed later in this chapter) are stained red. a-b: Courtesy of Molecular Expressions

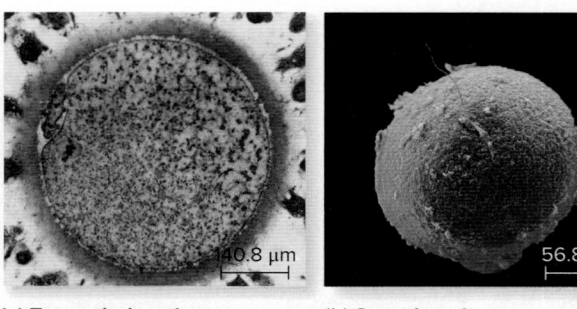

(a) Transmission electron micrograph (TEM)

(b) Scanning electron micrograph (SEM)

Figure 4.7 **A comparison of transmission and scanning electron microscopy.** **(a)** Section through a developing human egg cell, observed by TEM, shortly before it was released from an ovary. **(b)** An egg cell, with an attached sperm, was coated with heavy metal and observed via SEM. This SEM is colorized. a: ©Don W. Fawcett/Science Source; b: ©Eye of Science/Science Source

Concept Check: *What is the primary advantage of SEM?*

4.3 Overview of Cell Structure and Function

Learning Outcomes:

1. Compare and contrast the general features of prokaryotic and eukaryotic cells.
2. Explain how the proteome underlies the structure and function of a cell.
3. **CoreSKILL »** Analyze how cell size and shape affect the surface area/volume ratio.

Cell structure and function are primarily determined by four factors: (1) matter, (2) energy, (3) organization, and (4) information. In Chapters 2 and 3, we considered the first factor. The matter found in living organisms is composed of atoms, molecules, and macromolecules. Each type of cell synthesizes a unique set of molecules and macromolecules that contribute to cell structure and function. We will discuss the second factor, energy, throughout this unit, particularly in Chapters 6 through 8. Energy is needed to produce molecules and macromolecules and to carry out many cellular functions.

The third phenomenon that underlies a cell's structure and function is organization. A cell is not a haphazard bag of components. The molecules and macromolecules that constitute a cell are found at specific sites. For example, if we compare muscle cells from two different humans, or two muscle cells within the same individual, we would see striking similarities in their overall structures. All living cells have the ability to build and maintain their internal organization. Proteins often bind to each other in much the same way that toy building blocks snap together. These types of **protein-protein interactions** create intricate cell structures and also facilitate processes in which proteins interact in a consistent series of steps.

The fourth critical factor underlying cell structure and function is information. This information consists of instructions found in the blueprint of life, namely, the genetic material (DNA), which is

discussed in Unit III. Every organism and species has a distinctive **genome**, the entire complement of its genetic material. Likewise, each living cell has a copy of the genome. This genetic information is passed from cell to cell and from parent to offspring to yield new generations of cells and new generations of offspring. The **genes** within each species' genome contain the information to produce cellular proteins, which are largely responsible for determining cell structure and function. In this section, we will explore the general features of cells and examine how the genome contributes to those features.

Prokaryotic Cells Have a Simple Structure

Based on cell structure, all forms of life can be placed into two categories called prokaryotes and eukaryotes. We will first consider **prokaryotic cells**, which have a relatively simple structure. The term comes from the Greek *pro* and *karyon*, meaning before a kernel—a reference to the kernel-like appearance of what would later be named the cell nucleus. Prokaryotic cells lack a membrane-enclosed nucleus.

From an evolutionary perspective, the two categories of organisms that are composed of prokaryotic cells are **bacteria** and **archaea**. Both types are microorganisms that are usually small, with cell sizes that typically range between 1 micrometer (μm) and 10 μm in diameter. Bacteria are abundant throughout the world, being found in soil, water, and even our digestive tracts. Most bacterial species are not harmful to humans, and they play vital roles in ecology. However, some species are pathogenic—they cause disease. Examples of pathogenic bacteria include *Vibrio cholerae*, the source of cholera, and *Bacillus anthracis*, which causes anthrax. Archaea are also widely found throughout the world, though they are less common than bacteria and often occupy extreme environments such as hot springs and deep-sea vents.

Figure 4.8 shows a typical bacterial cell. The **plasma membrane**, which is a double layer of phospholipids and embedded proteins, forms an important barrier between the interior of the cell and its external environment. The cytoplasm is the region of the cell contained within the plasma membrane. Certain features in the bacterial cytoplasm are visible via microscopy. These include the **nucleoid** (not to be confused with the eukaryotic nucleus), where the genetic material is located. The nucleoid is not a membrane-bound compartment. **Ribosomes**, which are involved in polypeptide synthesis, are also found in the cytoplasm.

Some bacterial structures are located outside the plasma membrane. Nearly all species of bacteria and archaea have a relatively rigid **cell wall** that supports and protects the plasma membrane and cytoplasm. The cell-wall composition varies widely among prokaryotic cells but commonly contains peptides and carbohydrates. It is relatively porous, allowing most nutrients in the environment to reach the plasma membrane. Many bacteria also secrete a **glycocalyx**, an outer viscous covering surrounding the bacterium. The glycocalyx traps water and helps protect the bacterium from drying out. Certain strains of bacteria that invade animals' bodies produce a very thick, gelatinous glycocalyx called a **capsule** that may help them avoid being destroyed by an animal's immune (defense) system or may aid in the attachment to cell surfaces. Finally, many prokaryotic cells

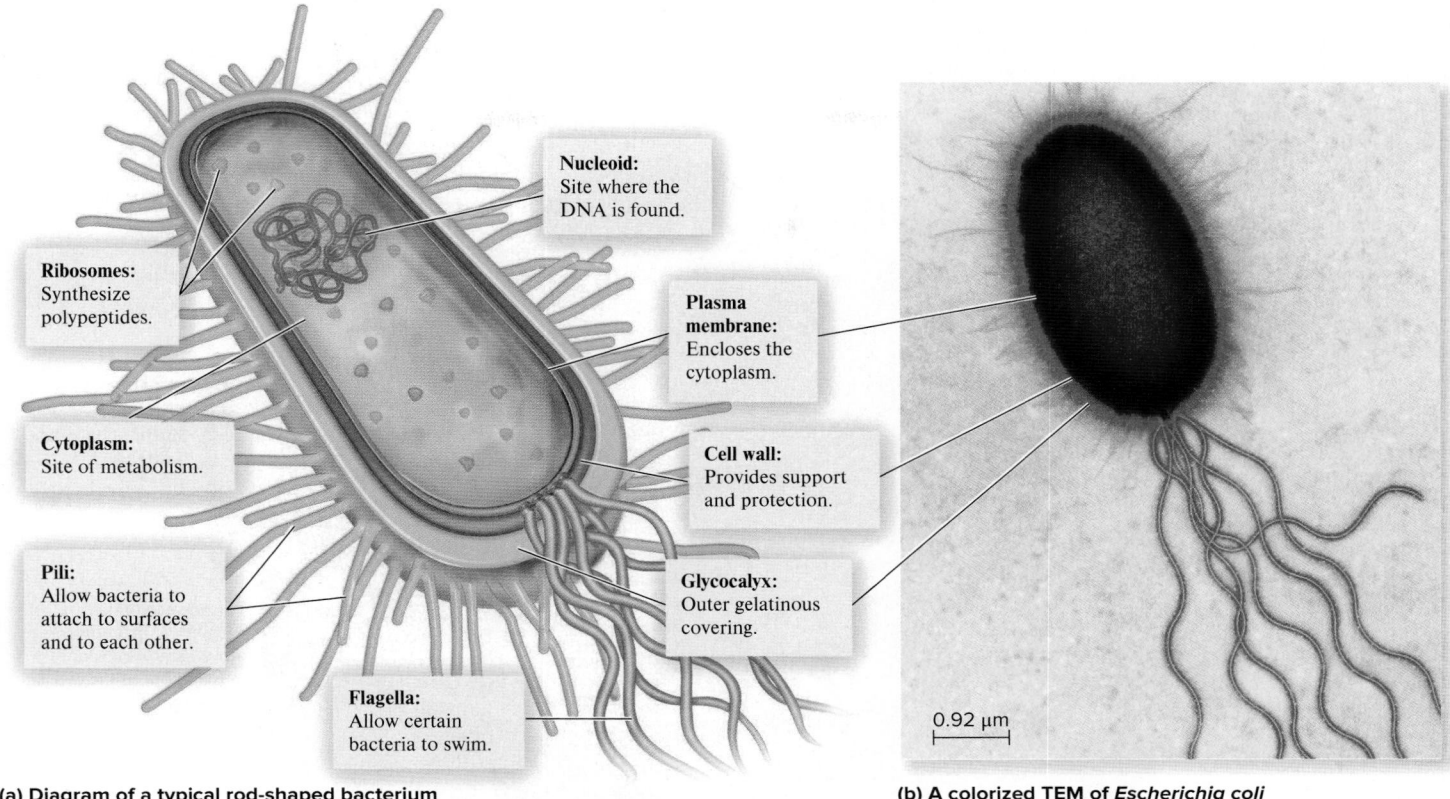

(a) Diagram of a typical rod-shaped bacterium

Nucleoid:
Site where the
DNA is found.

Ribosomes:
Synthesize
polypeptides.

Cytoplasm:
Site of metabolism.

Pili:
Allow bacteria to
attach to surfaces
and to each other.

**Plasma
membrane:**
Encloses the
cytoplasm.

Cell wall:
Provides support
and protection.

Glycocalyx:
Outer gelatinous
covering.

Flagella:
Allow certain
bacteria to swim.

0.92 µm

(b) A colorized TEM of *Escherichia coli*

Figure 4.8 **Structure of a typical bacterial cell. Prokaryotic cells, which include bacteria and archaea, lack internal compartmentalization.**
b: ©Dennis Kunkel Microscopy, Inc./Phototake

have appendages such as pili and flagella. **Pili** allow cells to attach to surfaces and to each other. **Flagella** provide prokaryotic cells with the ability to move, also called motility.

Eukaryotic Cells Are Compartmentalized by Internal Membranes to Create Organelles

Aside from bacteria and archaea, all other species are **eukaryotes** (from the Greek, meaning true nucleus), which include protists, fungi, plants, and animals. Paramecia and algae are types of protists; yeasts and molds are types of fungi. **Figure 4.9** illustrates the general structure of a typical animal cell. Eukaryotic cells possess a true nucleus, where most of the DNA is housed. A nucleus is a type of **organelle**—a membrane-bound compartment with its own unique structure and function. In contrast to prokaryotic cells, eukaryotic cells exhibit extensive **compartmentalization**, which means they have many membrane-bound organelles that separate the cell into different regions. Cellular compartmentalization allows a cell to carry out specialized chemical reactions in different places.

Some general features of cell organization, such as a nucleus, are found in nearly all eukaryotic cells. However, the shape, size, and organization of cells vary considerably among different species and even among different cell types of the same species. For example, micrographs of a human skin cell and a human neuron (a nervous system cell) show that, although these cells contain the same types of organelles, their overall morphologies are quite different (**Figure 4.10**).

Plant cells possess a collection of organelles similar to those found in animal cells (**Figure 4.11**). Additional structures found in plant cells but not animal cells include chloroplasts, a central vacuole, and a cell wall.

Droplet Organelles Are a Category of Organelles Whose Boundary Is Due to Phase Separation

Most of the organelles that are shown in Figures 4.9 and 4.11 are surrounded by a single or double membrane. Recently, however, researchers have discovered that cells can also become compartmentalized by a second mechanism called **liquid-liquid phase separation** in which aggregated solutes, such as proteins and RNA molecules, separate from the bulk solvent and form a droplet. The droplet has a spherical shape with a measurable surface tension and viscosity. Molecules can diffuse within the droplet and occasionally leave it and pass into the surrounding liquid phase. Cell biologists are beginning to recognize these droplets as organelles, hence the name, **droplet organelle**. An example is the nucleolus, the site for rRNA processing and the assembly of ribosomal subunits.

The internal environment of droplet organelles is thought to serve two purposes. First, molecules are brought close together and can assemble into complexes. For example, ribosomal subunits assemble within the nucleolus. Second, the environment within the droplet is chemically different from the surrounding medium, which may affect events such as RNA folding.

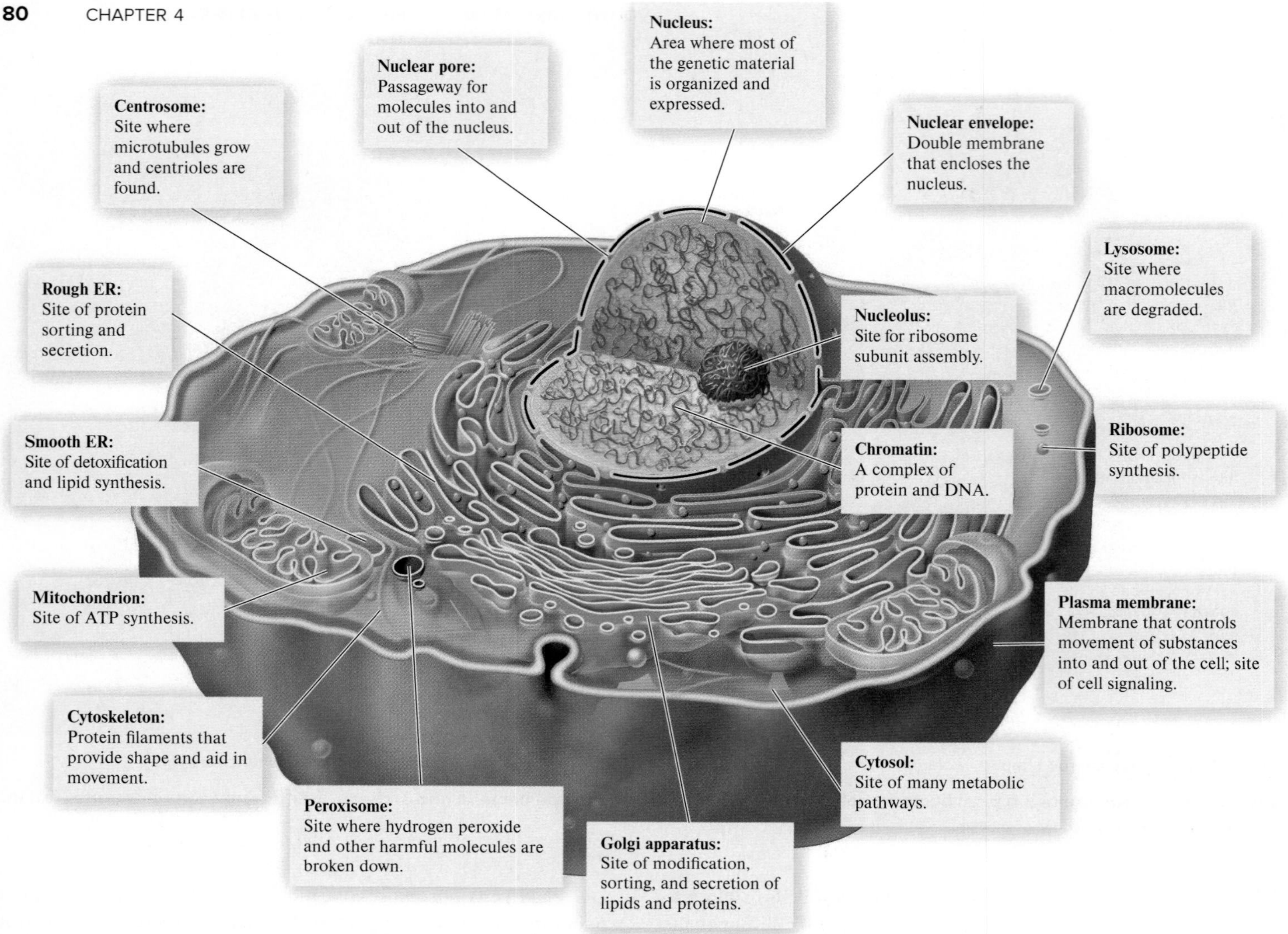

Centrosome:
Site where microtubules grow and centrioles are found.

Nuclear pore:
Passageway for molecules into and out of the nucleus.

Nucleus:
Area where most of the genetic material is organized and expressed.

Nuclear envelope:
Double membrane that encloses the nucleus.

Rough ER:
Site of protein sorting and secretion.

Lysosome:
Site where macromolecules are degraded.

Nucleolus:
Site for ribosome subunit assembly.

Smooth ER:
Site of detoxification and lipid synthesis.

Ribosome:
Site of polypeptide synthesis.

Chromatin:
A complex of protein and DNA.

Mitochondrion:
Site of ATP synthesis.

Plasma membrane:
Membrane that controls movement of substances into and out of the cell; site of cell signaling.

Cytoskeleton:
Protein filaments that provide shape and aid in movement.

Cytosol:
Site of many metabolic pathways.

Peroxisome:
Site where hydrogen peroxide and other harmful molecules are broken down.

Golgi apparatus:
Site of modification, sorting, and secretion of lipids and proteins.

Figure 4.9 General structure of an animal cell.

👁 **Core Concept: Systems** A cell, such as the animal cell illustrated here, is the smallest unit of life. As this diagram shows, it is composed of many interacting parts.

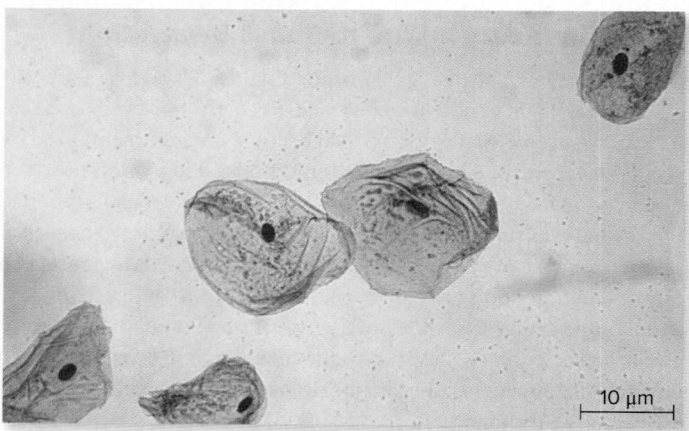

10 μm

(a) Human skin cell

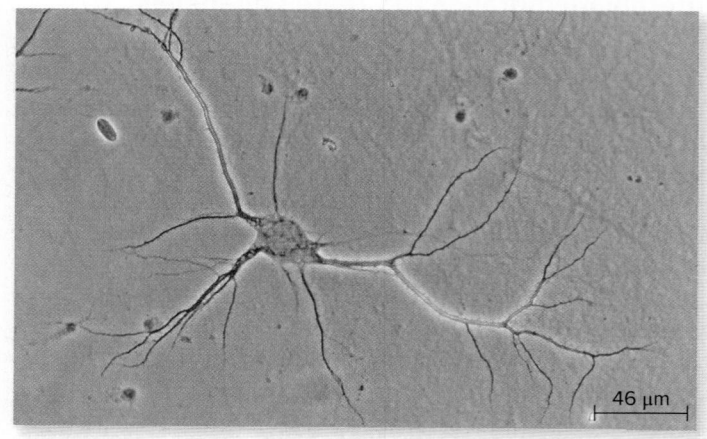

46 μm

(b) Human neuron

Figure 4.10 Variation in morphology of eukaryotic cells. Light micrographs of **(a)** a human skin cell and **(b)** a human neuron (a cell of the nervous system). Although these cells have the same genome and the same types of organelles, their general morphologies are quite different.

a: ©Ed Reschke/Getty Images; b: ©Eye of Science/Science Source

 Core Skill: Connections Look ahead to Figure 14.21. How does alternative splicing affect protein structure and function?

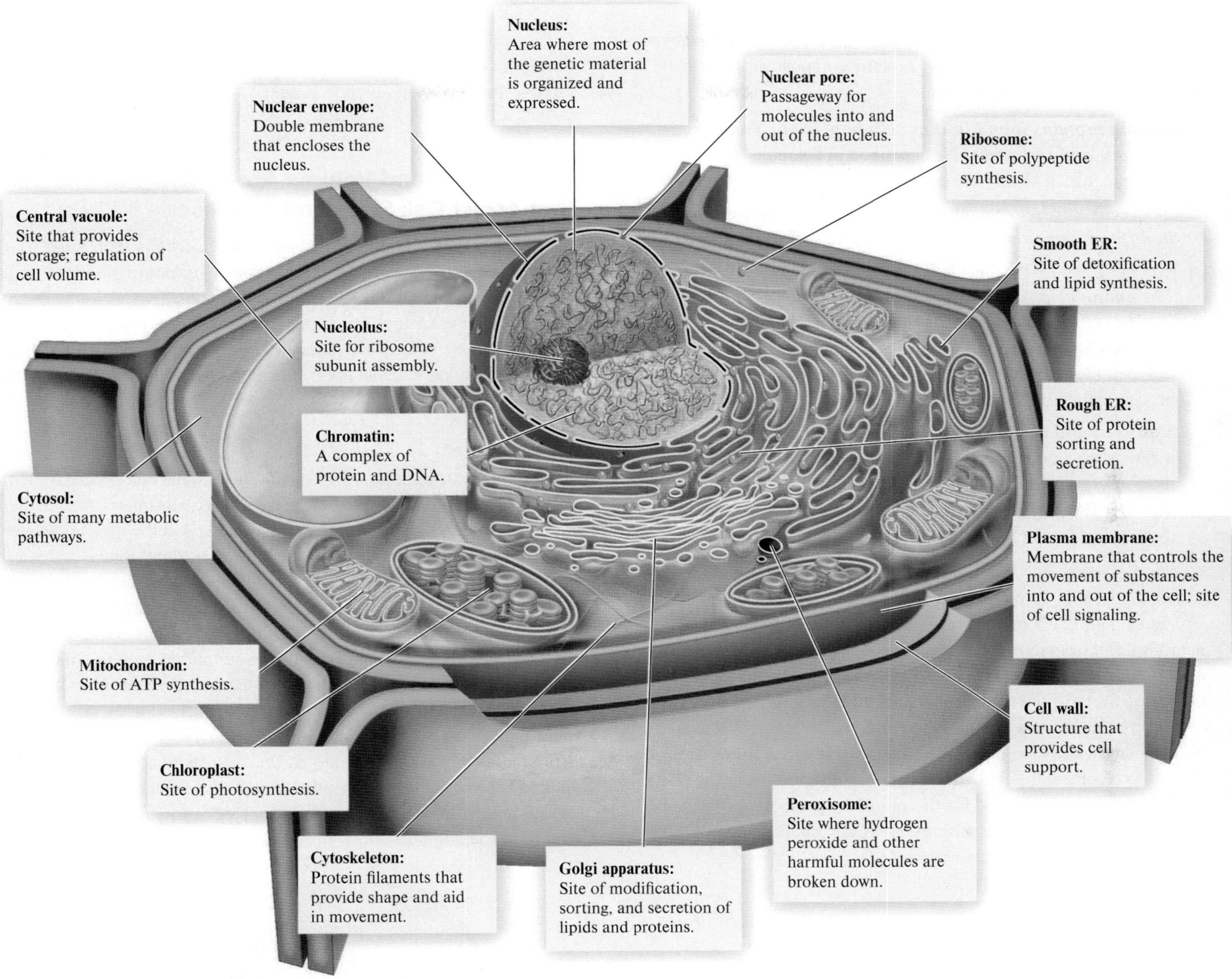

Nucleus:
Area where most of the genetic material is organized and expressed.

Nuclear pore:
Passageway for molecules into and out of the nucleus.

Ribosome:
Site of polypeptide synthesis.

Nuclear envelope:
Double membrane that encloses the nucleus.

Smooth ER:
Site of detoxification and lipid synthesis.

Central vacuole:
Site that provides storage; regulation of cell volume.

Nucleolus:
Site for ribosome subunit assembly.

Rough ER:
Site of protein sorting and secretion.

Chromatin:
A complex of protein and DNA.

Cytosol:
Site of many metabolic pathways.

Plasma membrane:
Membrane that controls the movement of substances into and out of the cell; site of cell signaling.

Mitochondrion:
Site of ATP synthesis.

Cell wall:
Structure that provides cell support.

Chloroplast:
Site of photosynthesis.

Peroxisome:
Site where hydrogen peroxide and other harmful molecules are broken down.

Cytoskeleton:
Protein filaments that provide shape and aid in movement.

Golgi apparatus:
Site of modification, sorting, and secretion of lipids and proteins.

Figure 4.11 General structure of a plant cell. Plant cells lack lysosomes and centrioles. Unlike animal cells, plant cells have an outer cell wall; a large central vacuole that functions in storage and the regulation of cell volume; and chloroplasts, which carry out photosynthesis.

 *What are the functions of the cell structures and organelles that are found in animal cells but not plant cells or found in plant cells but not animal cells?*

Core Concepts: Information, Structure and Function

The Characteristics of a Cell Are Largely Determined by the Proteins It Makes

Many organisms, such as animals and plants, are multicellular, meaning that a single organism is composed of many cells. However, the cells of most multicellular organisms are not all identical. For example, your body contains skin cells, neurons, muscle cells, and many other types. An intriguing question, therefore, is how does a single organism produce different types of cells?

To answer this question, we need to consider the distinction between a cell's genome and its proteome. Recall that the genome consists of all of an organism's genetic material, namely its DNA, which contains many different genes. Most genes encode the production of polypeptides, which assemble into functional proteins. The **proteome** is defined as the complete set of proteins that a cell is currently making or an organism can make. The set of proteins that is made by a given cell type is largely responsible for determining the structure and function of that cell.

The set of proteins made in one cell type is not the same as that made in a different cell type. As an example, let's consider human skin cells and neurons—two cell types that have dramatically different organization and structure (look back at Figure 4.10). In any particular individual, the genes in a skin cell are identical to those in a neuron. However, the cells' protein compositions are quite different for the following reasons:

1. ***Certain proteins found in skin cells may not be produced in neurons, and vice versa.*** As described in Chapter 14, genes can be regulated so they are turned on only in certain cell types.

2. ***Skin cells and neurons may produce the same protein but in different amounts.*** This is also due to gene regulation and to the rates at which a protein is synthesized and degraded.

3. ***The amino acid sequences of particular proteins can vary in skin cells and neurons.*** As discussed in Chapter 14, the mRNA from a single gene can produce two or more polypeptides with different amino acid sequences via a process called alternative splicing.

4. ***Skin cells and neurons may alter their proteins in different ways.*** After a protein is made, its structure may be changed in a variety of ways. These include the covalent attachment of molecules, such as phosphate and carbohydrates, and the cleavage of a protein to a smaller size.

For these reasons, skin cells and neurons produce different sets of proteins, that is, different proteomes, and therefore have different structures and functions. Likewise, the proteomes of skin cells and neurons differ from those of other cell types such as muscle and liver cells. Ultimately, the proteomes of cells are largely responsible for producing the traits of organisms, such as the color of a person's eyes.

During the last few decades, researchers have also discovered an association between proteome changes and disease. For example, the proteomes of healthy lung cells are different from the proteomes of lung cancer cells. Furthermore, the proteomes of cancer cells change as the disease progresses. A key challenge for biologists is to understand the synthesis and function of proteomes in different cell types and discover how proteome changes may lead to disease conditions such as cancer.

Surface Area and Volume Are Critical Parameters That Affect Cell Sizes and Shapes

As we have seen, a common feature of most cells is their small size. For example, most bacterial cells are about 1–10 μm in diameter, and a typical eukaryotic cell is 10–100 μm in diameter. Though some exceptions are known, such as an ostrich egg, small size is a nearly universal characteristic of cells. In general, large organisms attain their large sizes by having more cells, not by having larger cells. For example, the various types of cells found in an elephant and a mouse are roughly the same sizes. However, an elephant has many more cells than a mouse.

Why are cells usually small? One key factor is the interface between a cell and its extracellular environment, that is, the cell's plasma membrane. For cells to survive, they must import substances across their plasma membranes and export waste products. A cell with a large internal volume will require a greater amount of nutrient uptake and waste export. However, the rate of transport of substances across the plasma membrane is limited by its surface area. Therefore, a critical issue for sustaining a cell is the surface area/volume ratio. This concept is illustrated in **Figure 4.12**, which considers a simplified case in which cells are spherical. As cells get larger, the surface area of their plasma membrane increases with the square of the radius ($A = 4\pi r^2$), whereas the volume increases with the cube of the radius ($V = 4/3\pi r^3$). Therefore, as the radius of the cell gets larger, the surface area/volume ratio gets smaller. Biologists hypothesize that most cells are small because a high surface area/volume ratio is required for cells to sustain an adequate level of nutrient uptake and waste export.

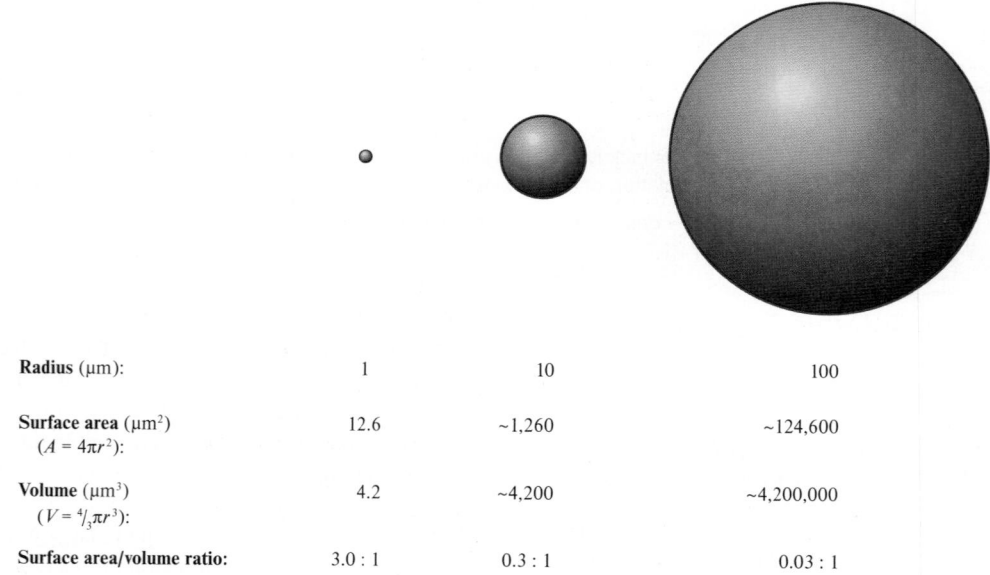

Radius (μm):	1	10	100
Surface area (μm²) ($A = 4\pi r^2$):	12.6	~1,260	~124,600
Volume (μm³) ($V = 4/3\pi r^3$):	4.2	~4,200	~4,200,000
Surface area/volume ratio:	3.0 : 1	0.3 : 1	0.03 : 1

Figure 4.12 **Relationship between cell size and the surface area/volume ratio.** As cells get larger, the surface area/volume ratio gets smaller. Note: The three spheres shown here are not drawn precisely to scale.

 Core Skill: Connections Look ahead to Figure 41.8a. How does the surface area/volume ratio relate to the shapes of structures involved with gas exchange?

Core Skill: Quantitative Reasoning

BIO **TIPS**   **THE QUESTION** *One way for cells to partially overcome the limitation imposed by the surface area/volume ratio is to be elongated and have an irregularly shaped surface. For example, look back at Figure 4.10. The skin cell is roughly spherical, whereas the neuron is very elongated and has an irregularly shaped surface. If a skin cell and a neuron cell had the same internal volume, the neuron would have a much higher surface area/volume ratio.*

Let's suppose that one cell is spherical with a radius of 21 μm. Another cell is cylindrical, with a smaller radius of 3 μm but a much greater length of 1,372 μm. Which of these cells has the greater volume? Which has the greater surface area/volume ratio? Note: For a cylinder, the volume and surface area are calculated as follows:

$$\text{Volume} = \pi r^2 h$$

$$\text{Surface area} = 2\pi r^2 + 2\pi r h$$

In these equations, h (height) corresponds to cell length.

TOPIC *What topic in biology does this question address?* The topic is cell volume and the surface area/volume ratio. More specifically, the question asks you to compare these parameters for two cells with different shapes.

INFORMATION *What information do you know based on the question and your understanding of the topic?* In the question, you are given the dimensions of two different cells and equations to calculate the volume and surface area of a cylindrical cell. From your understanding of the topic, you may remember the equations for finding the volume and surface area of a spherical cell (look back at Figure 4.12).

PROBLEM-SOLVING **S**TRATEGY *Make a drawing. Make a calculation.* To solve this problem, you need to use the equations for calculating cell volume and surface area. It may be helpful to begin with a drawing that depicts the variables in these equations, as shown below:

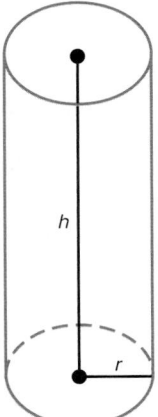 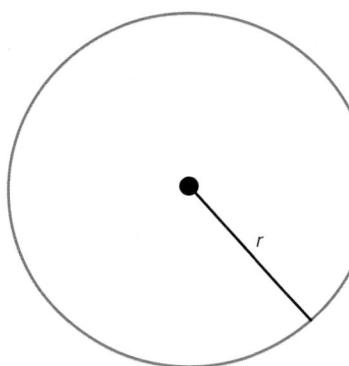

Let's begin by calculating the volume for both cell types. For the cylinder, we have

$$\text{Volume} = \pi r^2 h$$

$$\text{Volume} = 3.14(3 \ \mu m)^2(1372 \ \mu m) = 38{,}773 \ \mu m^3$$

For the sphere, we have

$$\text{Volume} = {}^4/_3 \pi r^3$$

$$\text{Volume} = {}^4/_3(3.14)(21 \mu m)^3 = 38{,}773 \ \mu m^3$$

Now let's calculate the surface area for both cell types. For the cylinder,

$$\text{Surface area} = 2\pi r^2 + 2\pi r h$$

$$\text{Surface area} = 2(3.14)(3 \ \mu m)^2 + 2(3.14)(3 \ \mu m)(1372 \ \mu m)$$

$$= 25{,}905 \ \mu m^2$$

For the sphere,

$$\text{Surface area} = 4\pi r^2$$

$$\text{Surface area} = 4(3.14)(21 \ \mu m)^2 = 5{,}539 \ \mu m^2$$

ANSWER *Though they have very different shapes, the two cell types have the same volume. The surface area/volume ratio for the cylindrical cell is 25,905/38,773 = 0.67. By comparison, the surface area/volume ratio for the spherical cell is 5,539/38,773 = 0.14. If we divide 0.67 by 0.14, we find that the cylindrical cell's surface area/volume ratio is about 4.8 times greater than that of the spherical cell.*

4.4 The Cytosol

Learning Outcomes:

1. Identify the location of the cytosol in a eukaryotic cell, and list its general functions.
2. Describe the three types of protein filaments that make up the cytoskeleton.
3. Explain how motor proteins interact with microtubules or actin filaments to promote cellular movements.

In Section 4.3, we focused on the general features of prokaryotic and eukaryotic cells. In the rest of this chapter, we will survey the various compartments of eukaryotic cells with an emphasis on structure and function. **Figure 4.13** highlights various regions in an animal cell and a plant cell. We will start with the **cytosol** (shown in yellow), the region of a eukaryotic cell that is outside the organelles but inside the plasma membrane. The other regions of the cell, which we will examine later in this chapter, include the interior of the nucleus (blue), the endomembrane system (purple and pink), and the semiautonomous organelles (orange and green). As in prokaryotic cells, the term cytoplasm refers to the region enclosed by the plasma membrane, which includes the cytosol and the organelles.

Synthesis and Breakdown of Molecules Occur in the Cytosol

Metabolism is defined as the sum of the chemical reactions by which cells produce the materials and utilize the energy necessary to sustain life. Although many steps of metabolism also occur in cell organelles, the cytosol is a central coordinating region for many metabolic activities of eukaryotic cells. Metabolism often involves a series of steps called a metabolic pathway. Each step in a metabolic pathway is catalyzed by a specific **enzyme**—a protein that accelerates the rate of a chemical

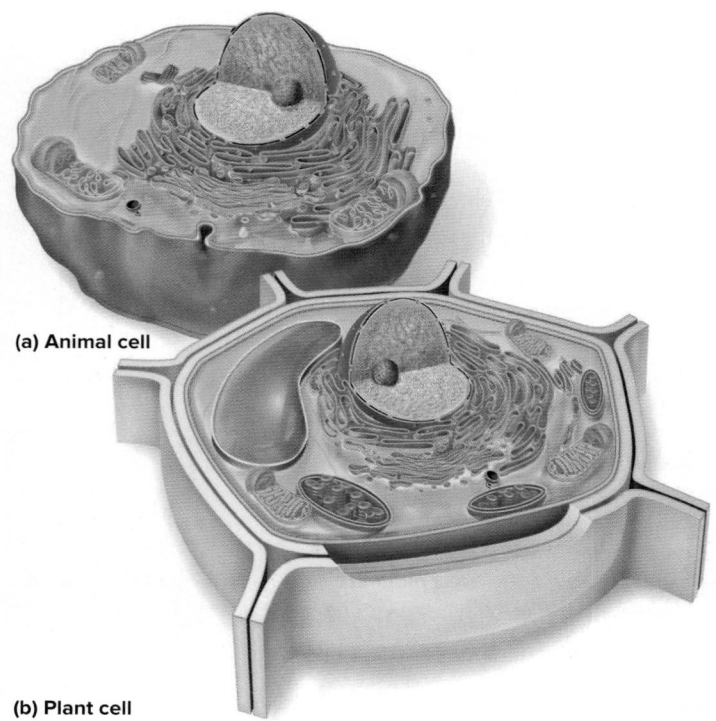

(a) Animal cell

(b) Plant cell

Figure 4.13 Compartments within (a) animal and (b) plant cells. The cytosol, which is outside the organelles but inside the plasma membrane, is shown in yellow. The membranes of the endomembrane system are shown in purple, and the fluid-filled interiors are pink. The peroxisome is dark purple. The interior of the nucleus is blue. Semiautonomous organelles are shown in orange (mitochondria) and green (chloroplasts).

reaction. In Chapters 6 and 7, we will examine enzymes and consider a few metabolic pathways that occur in the cytosol and cell organelles.

Some metabolic pathways involve the breakdown of a molecule into smaller components, a process termed **catabolism**. Such pathways are needed by the cell to utilize energy and also to generate molecules that provide the building blocks to construct macromolecules. Conversely, other pathways are involved in **anabolism**, the synthesis of molecules and macromolecules. For example, polysaccharides are made by linking sugar molecules. To make proteins, amino acids are covalently connected to form a polypeptide, using the information within an mRNA (see Chapter 12). Translation of that information occurs on ribosomes, which are found in various locations in the cell. Some ribosomes may float freely in the cytosol, others are attached to the outer membrane of the nuclear envelope and endoplasmic reticulum membrane, and still others are found within the mitochondria or chloroplasts.

The Cytoskeleton Provides Cell Shape, Organization, and Movement

The **cytoskeleton** is a network of three different types of protein filaments: **microtubules**, **intermediate filaments**, and **actin filaments** (Table 4.1). Each type is constructed from many protein monomers. The cytoskeleton is a striking example of protein-protein interactions. The cytoskeleton is found primarily in the cytosol and also in the nucleus along the inner nuclear membrane. Let's first consider the structure of

cytoskeletal filaments and their roles in the construction and organization of cells. Later, we will examine how they are involved in cell movement.

Microtubules   Microtubules are long, hollow, cylindrical structures about 25 nm in diameter composed of protein subunits called α- and β-tubulin. The assembly of tubulin to form a microtubule results in a structure with a plus end and a minus end (see Table 4.1). Microtubules grow only at the plus end, but can shorten at either the plus or minus end. A single microtubule can oscillate between growing and shortening phases, a phenomenon termed **dynamic instability**. This phenomenon is important in many cellular activities, including the sorting of chromosomes during cell division.

The sites where microtubules form within a cell vary among different types of organisms. Nondividing animal cells contain a single structure near their nucleus called the **centrosome**, also called a microtubule-organizing center (see Table 4.1). Within the centrosome are the **centrioles**, a conspicuous pair of structures arranged perpendicularly to each other. In animal cells, microtubule growth typically starts at the centrosome in such a way that the minus end is anchored there. In contrast, most plant cells and many protists lack centrosomes and centrioles. Microtubules are created at many sites that are scattered throughout a plant cell. In plants, the nuclear membrane appears to function as a microtubule-organizing center.

Microtubules are important for cell shape and organization. Organelles such as the Golgi apparatus are attached to microtubules. In addition, microtubules are involved in the organization and movement of chromosomes during mitosis and in the orientation of cells during cell division, events we will examine in Chapter 16.

Intermediate Filaments   Intermediate filaments are another class of cytoskeletal filaments found in the cells of many but not all animal species. Their name is derived from the observation that they are intermediate in diameter between actin filaments and microtubules. Intermediate filament proteins bind to each other in a staggered array to form a twisted, ropelike structure with a diameter of approximately 10 nm (see Table 4.1). They function as tension-bearing fibers that help maintain cell shape and rigidity. The lengths of intermediate filaments tend to be relatively permanent. By comparison, microtubules and actin filaments readily lengthen and shorten in cells.

Several types of proteins assemble into intermediate filaments. Keratins form intermediate filaments in skin, intestinal, and kidney cells, where they are important for cell shape and mechanical strength. They are also a major constituent of hair and nails. In addition, intermediate filaments are found inside the cell nucleus. As discussed later in this chapter, nuclear lamins form a network of intermediate filaments that line the inner nuclear membrane and provide anchor points for the nuclear pores.

Actin Filaments   Actin filaments are also known as **microfilaments**, because they are the thinnest cytoskeletal filaments. They are long, thin fibers approximately 7 nm in diameter (see Table 4.1). Like microtubules, actin filaments have plus and minus ends, and they are very dynamic structures in which each strand grows at the plus end by the addition of actin monomers. This assembly process produces a fiber composed of two strands of actin monomers that spiral around each other.

Despite their thinness, actin filaments play a key role in cell shape and strength. Although actin filaments are dispersed throughout the cytosol,

Table 4.1	Types of Cytoskeletal Filaments Found in Eukaryotic Cells		
Characteristic	**Microtubules**	**Intermediate filaments**	**Actin filaments**
Diameter	25 nm	10 nm	7 nm
Structure	Hollow tubule	Twisted filament	Spiral filament

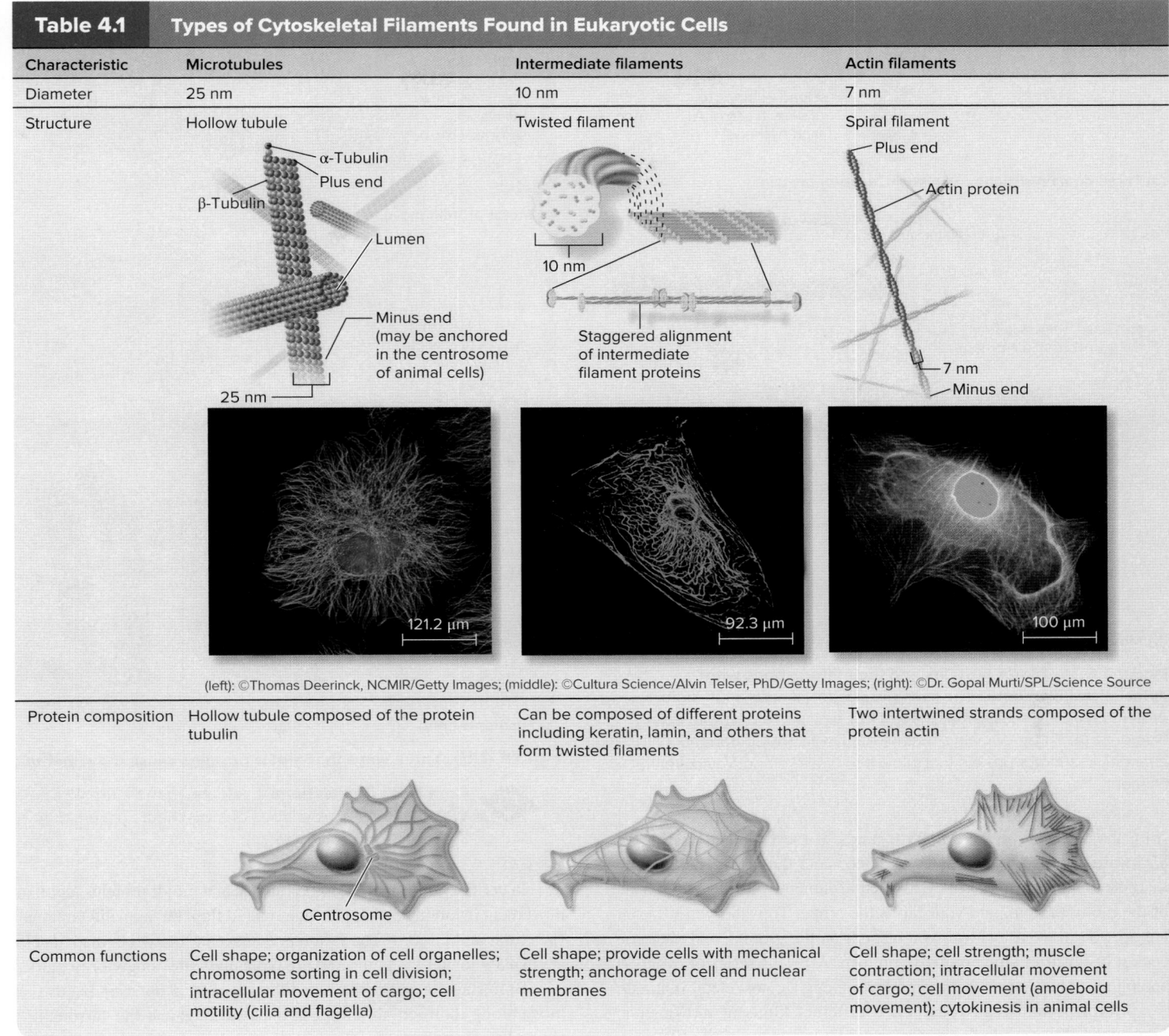

(left): ©Thomas Deerinck, NCMIR/Getty Images; (middle): ©Cultura Science/Alvin Telser, PhD/Getty Images; (right): ©Dr. Gopal Murti/SPL/Science Source

Protein composition	Hollow tubule composed of the protein tubulin	Can be composed of different proteins including keratin, lamin, and others that form twisted filaments	Two intertwined strands composed of the protein actin
Common functions	Cell shape; organization of cell organelles; chromosome sorting in cell division; intracellular movement of cargo; cell motility (cilia and flagella)	Cell shape; provide cells with mechanical strength; anchorage of cell and nuclear membranes	Cell shape; cell strength; muscle contraction; intracellular movement of cargo; cell movement (amoeboid movement); cytokinesis in animal cells

they tend to be highly concentrated near the plasma membrane. In many types of cells, actin filaments support the plasma membrane and provide shape and strength to the cell. The sides of actin filaments are often anchored to other proteins near the plasma membrane, which explains why actin filaments are typically found there. The plus ends grow toward the plasma membrane and play a key role in cell shape and movement.

Motor Proteins Interact with Cytoskeletal Filaments to Promote Movements

Motor proteins are a category of proteins that use ATP as a source of energy to promote various types of movements. As shown in

Figure 4.14a, a motor protein consists of three domains: head, hinge, and tail. Together, the hinge and tail make up a structure called the lever arm. The head is the site where ATP binds and is hydrolyzed to adenosine diphosphate (ADP) and inorganic phosphate (P_i). ATP binding and hydrolysis cause a bend in the hinge, which results in movement. The tail region is attached to other proteins or to other kinds of cellular molecules.

To implement movement, the head region of a motor protein interacts with a cytoskeletal filament, such as an actin filament (Figure 4.14b). When ATP binds and is hydrolyzed, the motor protein interacts with the filament in a series of steps. The head of the motor protein is initially attached to a filament. To move forward, the head detaches

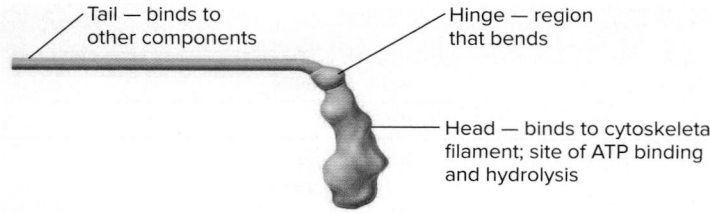

(a) Three-domain structure of myosin, a motor protein

Tail — binds to other components
Hinge — region that bends
Head — binds to cytoskeletal filament; site of ATP binding and hydrolysis

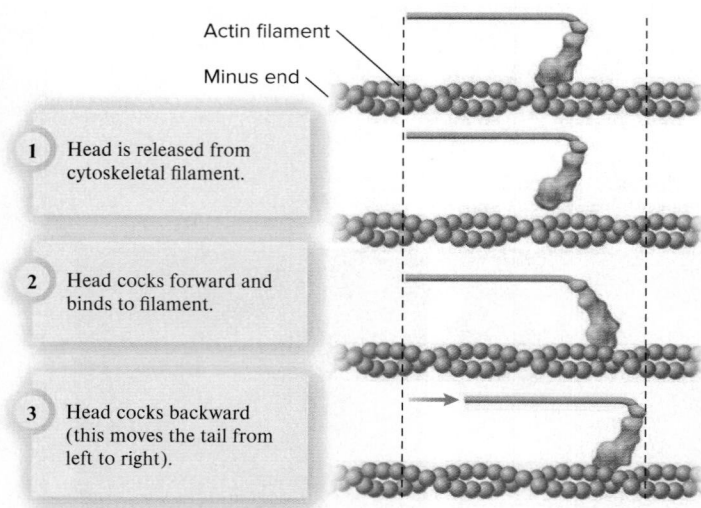

Actin filament
Minus end

1 Head is released from cytoskeletal filament.

2 Head cocks forward and binds to filament.

3 Head cocks backward (this moves the tail from left to right).

(b) Movement of a motor protein along a cytoskeletal filament

Figure 4.14 Motor proteins and their interactions with cytoskeletal filaments. The example illustrated here is the motor protein myosin (discussed in Chapter 45), which interacts with actin filaments. **(a)** Three-domain structure of myosin. **(b)** Conformational changes in a motor protein that allow it to "walk" along a cytoskeletal filament.

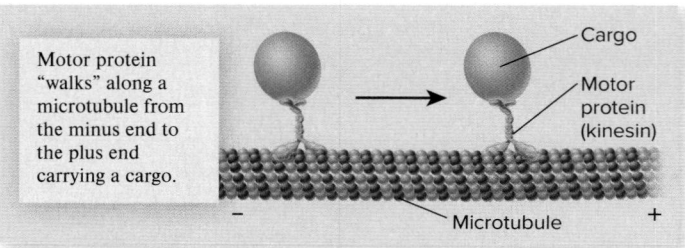

Motor protein "walks" along a microtubule from the minus end to the plus end carrying a cargo.

Cargo
Motor protein (kinesin)
Microtubule

(a) Motor protein moves

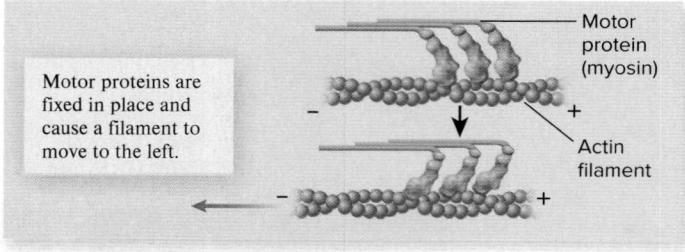

Motor proteins are fixed in place and cause a filament to move to the left.

Motor protein (myosin)
Actin filament

(b) Filament moves

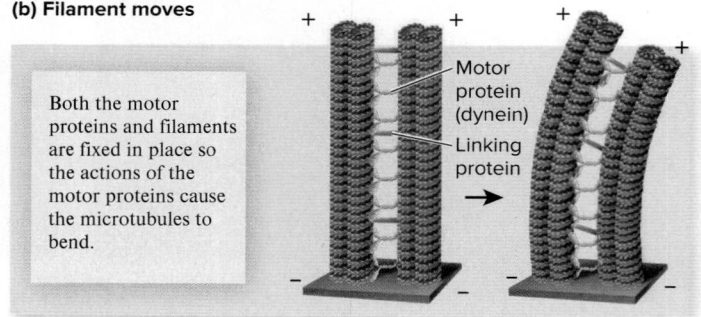

Both the motor proteins and filaments are fixed in place so the actions of the motor proteins cause the microtubules to bend.

Motor protein (dynein)
Linking protein

(c) Filaments bend

Figure 4.15 Three ways that motor proteins cause movements.

 Core Skill: Connections Look ahead to Figure 45.6. Which of these three types of movements occurs during muscle contraction?

from the filament, cocks forward, binds to the filament, and cocks backward. To picture how this works, consider the act of walking and imagine that the ground is a cytoskeletal filament, your leg is the head of the motor protein, and your hip is the hinge. To walk, you lift your leg up, you move it forward, you place it on the ground, and then you cock it backward (which propels you forward). This series of events is analogous to how a motor protein moves along a cytoskeletal filament.

Motor proteins can cause three different kinds of movements: movement of cargo via the motor protein, movement of the filament, or bending of the filament.

- In the example shown in **Figure 4.15a**, the tail region of a motor protein called kinesin is attached to a cargo, and the motor protein moves the cargo from one location to another.

- Alternatively, a motor protein called myosin can remain in place and cause the filament to move (**Figure 4.15b**). This occurs during muscle contraction, which is described in Chapter 45.

- A third possibility is that both the motor protein and filament are restricted in their movement due to the presence of linking proteins. In this case, when motor proteins called dynein attempt to walk toward the minus end, they exert a force that causes the microtubules to bend (**Figure 4.15c**).

In certain kinds of cells, microtubules and motor proteins facilitate movement involving cell appendages called **flagella** and **cilia** (singular, flagellum and cilium). The difference between the two is that flagella are usually longer than cilia and are typically found singly or in pairs.

Both flagella and cilia cause movement by generating bends that move along their length and push backward against the surrounding fluid. The flagellum of a sperm cell generates bends alternatively in each direction, which begin at the head and move (propagate) toward the tip of the flagellum (**Figure 4.16a**). Alternatively, a pair of flagella may move in a synchronized manner to pull a microorganism through the water (think of a human swimmer doing the breaststroke). Certain unicellular algae swim in this manner (**Figure 4.16b**). By comparison, cilia are typically shorter than flagella and tend to cover all or part of the surface of a cell. Protists such as paramecia may have hundreds of adjacent cilia that beat in a coordinated fashion to propel the organism through the water (**Figure 4.16c**).

Despite their differences in length, flagella and cilia have the same internal structure called the **axoneme**. The axoneme contains microtubules, the motor protein dynein, and linking proteins (**Figure 4.17**). In the cilia and flagella of most eukaryotic

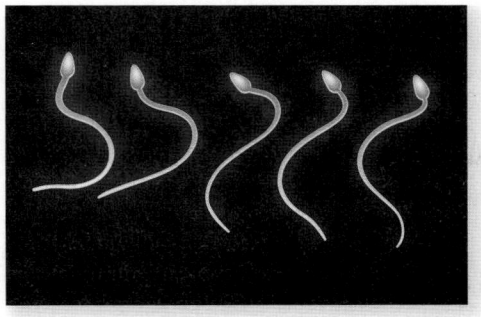
(a) Drawing of a sperm moving its flagellum

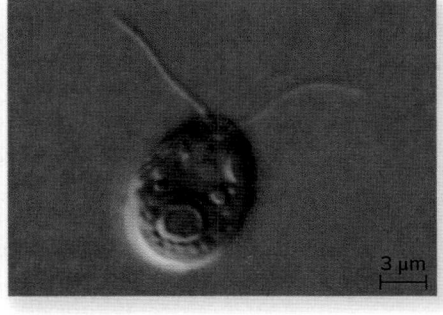
3 µm
(b) *Chlamydomonas* with 2 flagella

70 µm
(c) *Paramecium* with many cilia

Figure 4.16 **Cellular movements due to the actions of flagella and cilia.** **(a)** Spermatozoa (singular, spermatozoon) are sperm cells that are motile. They swim by producing repeated bends of a single, long flagellum, which move along its length. **(b)** The swimming of *Chlamydomonas reinhardtii*, a unicellular green algae, also involves a bending motion beginning at the base of flagella, but the motion is precisely coordinated between two flagella. This results in swimming behavior that resembles a human doing the breaststroke. **(c)** Ciliated protozoa such as this paramecium swim by coordinated beating of many shorter cilia. b: Courtesy of Dr. Barbara Surek, Culture Collection of Algae at the University of Cologne (CCAC); c: ©SPL/Science Source

Concept Check: *Describe the type of movements that occur between the motor proteins and microtubules when flagella or cilia bend.*

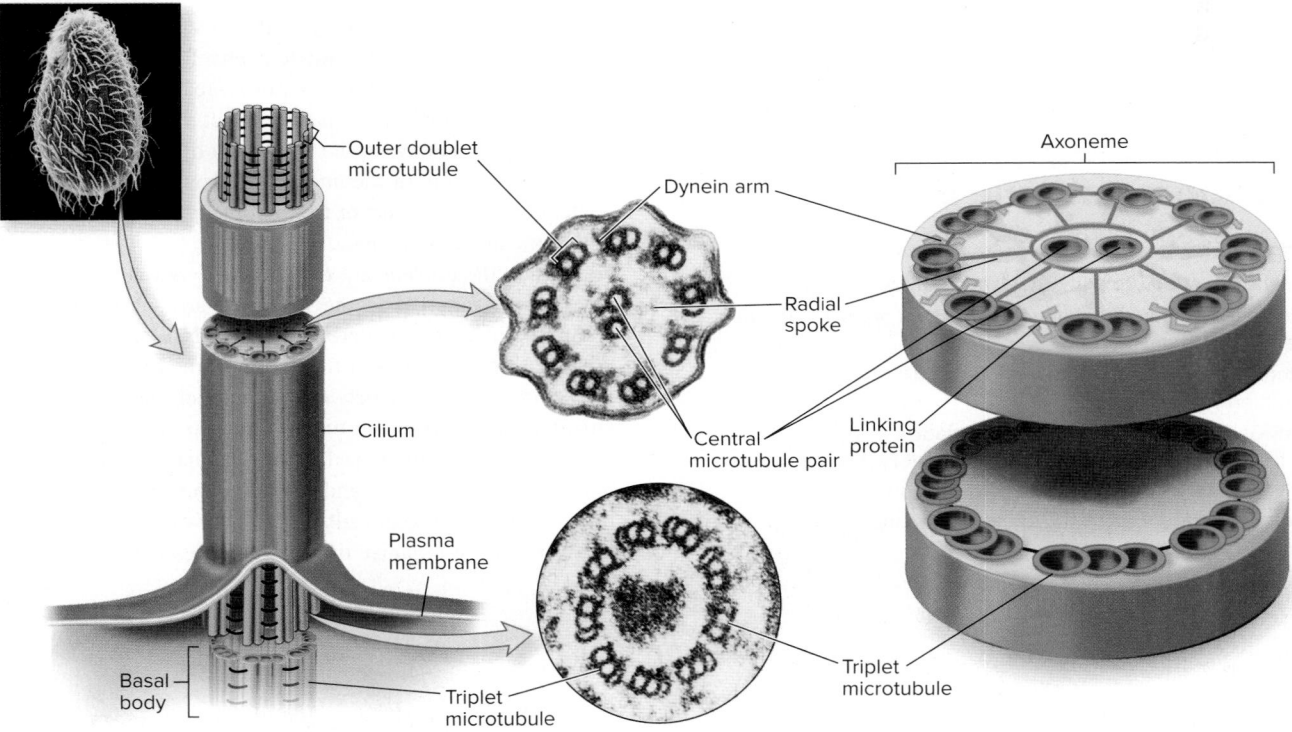

Figure 4.17 **Structure of a eukaryotic cilium or flagellum.** The structure of a cilium of a protist, *Tetrahymena thermophila* (see inset), consists of a 9 + 2 arrangement of nine outer doublet microtubules and two central microtubules. This structure is anchored to the basal body, which has nine triplet microtubules, in which three microtubules are fused together. Note: The structure of the basal body is very similar to that of centrioles in animal cells. (top left): ©Aaron J. Bell/Science Source; (top middle, bottom middle): ©Dr. William Dentler/University of Kansas

 Core Skill: Modeling The goal of this modeling challenge is to make a model of the circular structure formed by SAS-6 proteins based on information regarding which sites (A, B, and C) bind to other SAS-6 proteins or to doublet microtubules.

Modeling Challenge: A key protein that is a component of the radial spokes in an axoneme determines the nine-fold symmetry of the doublet microtubules. This protein is called SAS-6. A schematic drawing of its structure is shown to the right, with three sites labeled A, B, and C. Several SAS-6 proteins bind to each other to form a circular structure. During this process, the A site in one SAS-6 protein binds to the B site in another one. The C site binds to a doublet microtubule. Draw a model of the circular structure formed by SAS-6 proteins and indicate how many proteins make up this structure.

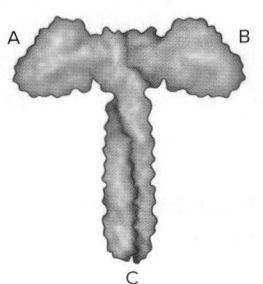
A   B

C

organisms, the microtubules form an arrangement called a 9 + 2 array. The outer nine are doublet microtubules, which are composed of a partial microtubule attached to a complete microtubule. Each of the two central microtubules is a single microtubule. Radial spokes project from the outer doublet microtubules toward the central pair. The microtubules in flagella and cilia emanate from **basal bodies**, which are anchored to the cytoplasmic side of the plasma membrane. At the basal body, the microtubules form a triplet structure. Much like the centrosome of animal cells, the basal bodies provide a site for microtubules to grow.

The movement of both flagella and cilia involves the propagation of a bend, which begins at the base of the structure and proceeds toward the tip (look back at Figure 4.16a). The bending occurs because dynein is activated to walk toward the minus end of the microtubules. However, the microtubules and dynein are not free to move relative to each other because of linking proteins. Therefore, instead of freely walking along the microtubules, the dyneins exert a force that bends the microtubules (look back at Figure 4.15c). The dyneins at the base of the flagellum or cilium are activated first, followed by dyneins that are progressively closer to the tip, and the resulting movement propels the organism.

4.5 The Nucleus and Endomembrane System

Learning Outcomes:

1. Describe the structure and organization of the cell nucleus.
2. Outline the structures and general functions of the components of the endomembrane system.
3. Distinguish between the rough endoplasmic reticulum and the smooth endoplasmic reticulum.
4. **CoreSKILL »** Analyze the results of Palade's study, and explain how they indicate the existence of a secretory pathway in eukaryotic cells.
5. List three important functions of the plasma membrane.

In Chapter 2, we learned that the nucleus of an atom contains protons and neutrons. In cell biology, the term **nucleus** has a different meaning. It is an organelle found in eukaryotic cells that contains most of the cell's genetic material. A small amount of genetic material is also found outside the nucleus, in mitochondria and chloroplasts.

The membranes that enclose the nucleus are part of a larger network of membranes called the **endomembrane system**. This system includes not only the nuclear envelope, which encloses the nucleus, but also the endoplasmic reticulum, Golgi apparatus, lysosomes, vacuoles, and peroxisomes. The prefix endo- (from the Greek, meaning inside) originally referred only to these organelles and internal membranes. However, we now know that the plasma membrane is also part of this integrated membrane system (**Figure 4.18**). In this section, we will examine the nucleus and survey the structures and functions of the organelles and membranes of the endomembrane system.

The Eukaryotic Nucleus Contains Chromosomes

The nucleus is the compartment that is enclosed by a double-membrane structure termed the **nuclear envelope** and houses the genetic material (**Figure 4.19**). **Nuclear pores** are formed where the inner and outer nuclear membranes make contact with each other. The pores provide a passageway for the movement of molecules and macromolecules into and out of the nucleus. Although cell biologists view the nuclear envelope as part of the endomembrane system, the materials within the nucleus are not.

Inside the nucleus are the chromosomes and a filamentous network of proteins called the nuclear matrix. Each **chromosome** is composed of genetic material, namely DNA, and many types of proteins that help to compact the chromosome to fit inside the nucleus. The complex formed between DNA and such proteins is termed **chromatin**. The **nuclear matrix** consists of two parts: the nuclear lamina, which is composed of intermediate filaments that line the inner nuclear membrane, and an internal nuclear matrix, which is connected to the lamina and fills the interior of the nucleus. The nuclear matrix serves to organize the chromosomes within the nucleus. Each

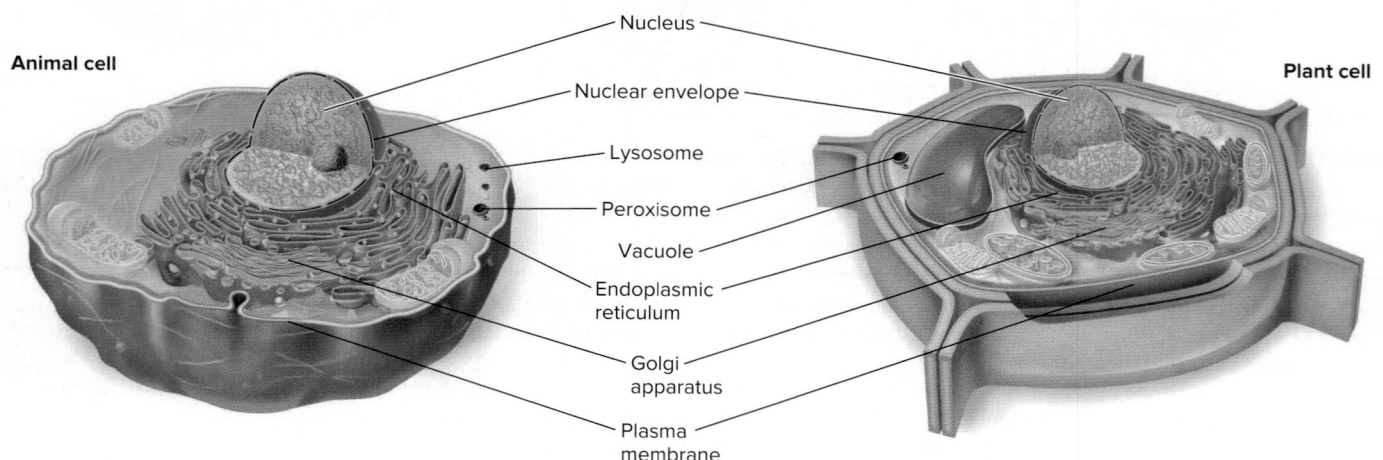

Figure 4.18 The nucleus and endomembrane system. This figure highlights the internal compartment of the nucleus (blue), the membranes of the endomembrane system (purple), and the fluid-filled interiors of the endomembrane system (pink). The nuclear envelope is part of the endomembrane system, but the interior of the nucleus is not.

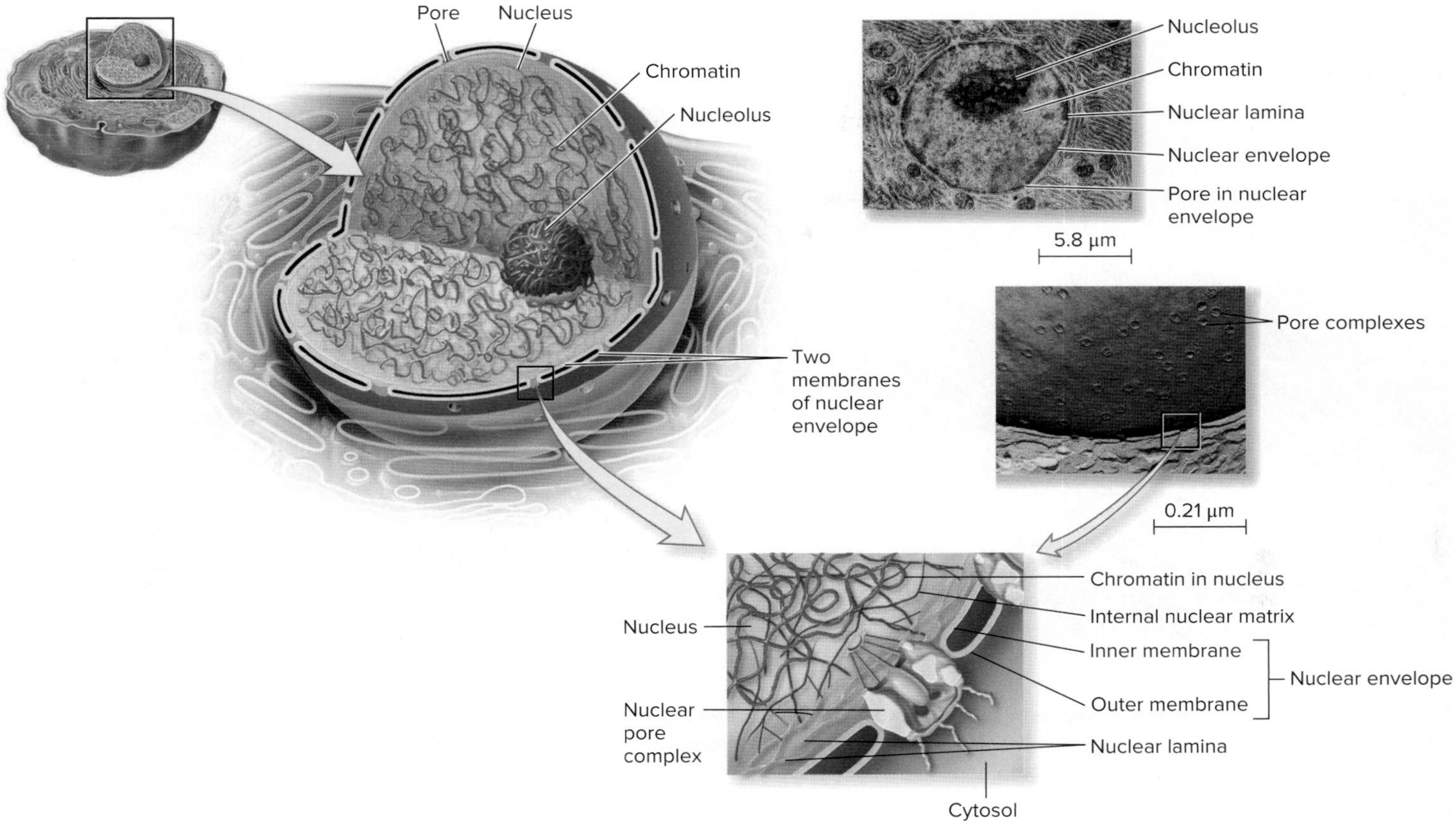

Pore   Nucleus

Chromatin

Nucleolus

Nucleolus

Chromatin

Nuclear lamina

Nuclear envelope

Pore in nuclear envelope

5.8 µm

Two membranes of nuclear envelope

Pore complexes

0.21 µm

Chromatin in nucleus

Internal nuclear matrix

Inner membrane

Nuclear envelope

Nucleus

Outer membrane

Nuclear pore complex

Nuclear lamina

Cytosol

Figure 4.19 The nucleus and nuclear envelope. The nuclear envelope is composed of an inner membrane and an outer membrane that come into contact at the nuclear pores. The inner nuclear membrane is lined with lamin proteins to form the nuclear lamina. The interior of the nucleus contains chromatin, which is attached to the nuclear matrix, and a nucleolus, where ribosome subunits are assembled. (top right, middle right): ©Don W. Fawcett/Science Source

`Concept Check:` *What is the function of the nuclear matrix?*

chromosome is located in a distinct **chromosome territory**, which is visible when cells are exposed to dyes that label specific types of chromosomes (**Figure 4.20**).

The primary function of the nucleus is the protection, organization, replication, and expression of the genetic material. These topics are discussed in Unit III. Another important function is the assembly of ribosome subunits—cellular structures involved in producing polypeptides during the process of translation (look ahead to Table 12.3). The assembly of ribosome subunits occurs in the **nucleolus** (plural, nucleoli), a droplet organelle in the nucleus of nondividing cells. A ribosome is composed of two subunits: one small and one large. Each subunit contains one or more RNA molecules and several types of proteins. Most of the RNA molecules that are components of ribosomes are made in the vicinity of the nucleolus. By comparison, the ribosomal proteins are produced in the cytosol and then imported into the nucleus through the nuclear pores. The ribosomal proteins and RNA molecules then enter the nucleolus and are assembled into ribosomal subunits. Finally, the subunits exit the nucleolus and then move through the nuclear pores into the cytosol, where they carry out polypeptide synthesis.

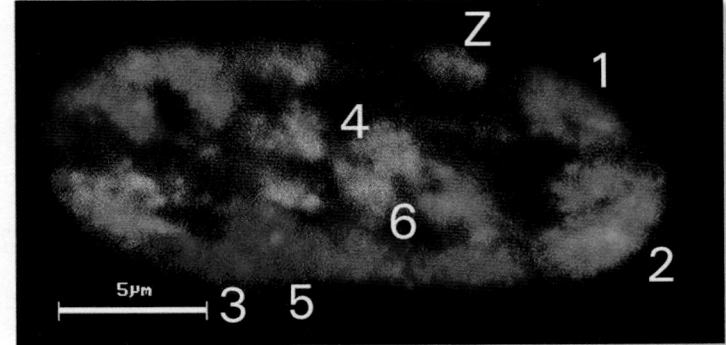

Figure 4.20 Chromosome territories in the cell nucleus. Chromosomes from a chicken were labeled with chromosome-specific probes. Seven types of chicken chromosomes are stained with a different dye. Each chromosome occupies its own distinct, nonoverlapping territory within the cell nucleus. Courtesy of Felix A. Habermann

 Core Skill: Connections Look ahead to Figure 16.8. What happens to chromosome territories during cell division?

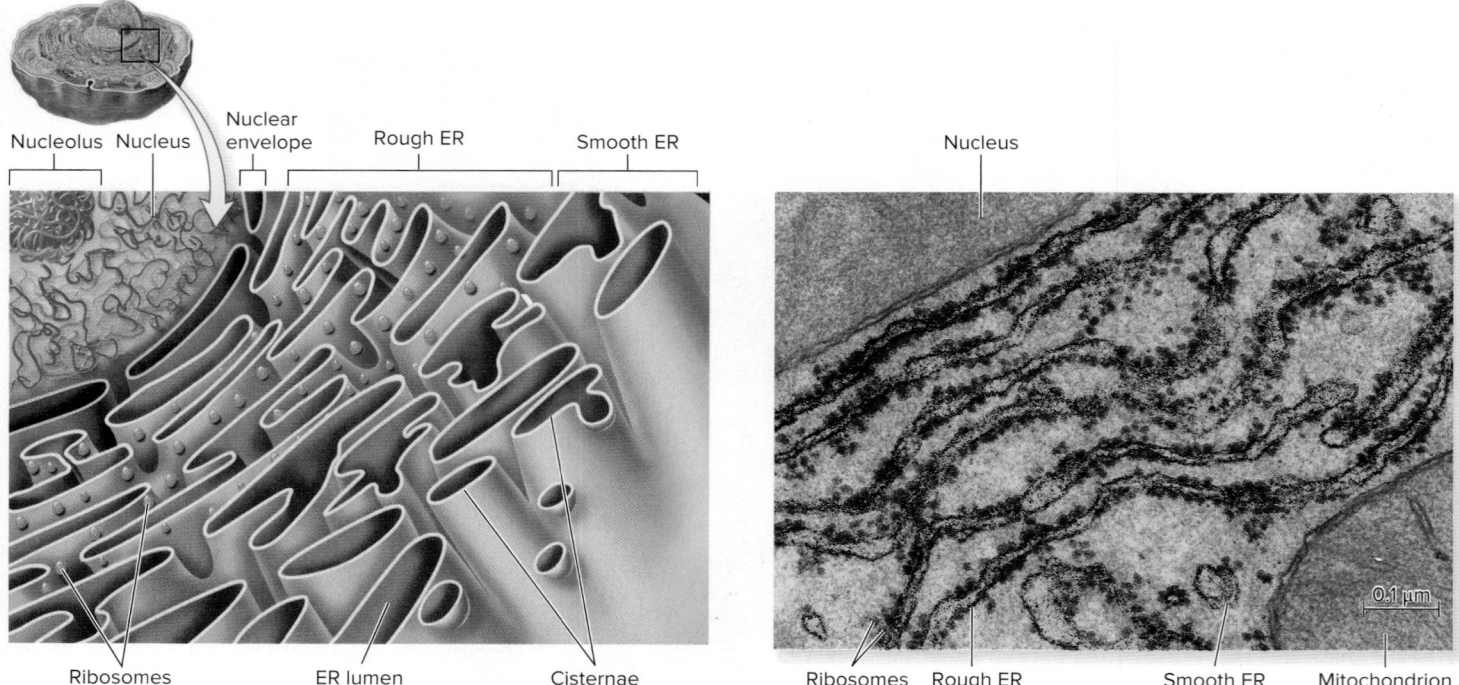

Figure 4.21 **Structure of the endoplasmic reticulum.** (Left side) The endoplasmic reticulum (ER) is composed of a network of flattened tubules called cisternae that enclose a continuous ER lumen. The rough ER is studded with ribosomes, whereas the smooth ER lacks ribosomes. The rough ER is continuous with the outer nuclear membrane. (Right side) A colorized TEM of the ER. The lumen of the ER is colored yellow and the ribosomes are red. (right): ©Dennis Kunkel Microscopy, Inc./Phototake

The Endoplasmic Reticulum Initiates the Sorting of Some Proteins and Carries Out Metabolic Functions

The **endoplasmic reticulum (ER)** is a network of membranes that form flattened, fluid-filled tubules, or **cisternae** (**Figure 4.21**). The terms endoplasmic (Greek, for in the cytoplasm) and reticulum (Latin, for little net) refer to the location and shape of this organelle when viewed under a microscope. The term **lumen** refers to the internal space of an organelle. The ER membrane encloses a single compartment called the **ER lumen**. There are two distinct, but continuous, types of ER: rough ER and smooth ER.

Rough ER   The outer surface of the **rough endoplasmic reticulum (rough ER)** is studded with ribosomes, giving it a bumpy appearance. Rough ER plays a key role in the sorting of proteins that are destined for the ER, Golgi apparatus, lysosomes, vacuoles, plasma membrane, or extracellular environment. Proteins are packaged into **membrane vesicles**—small spheres enclosed by a membrane—and moved from one location in the endomembrane system to another. This sorting process is described in Section 4.7. In conjunction with protein sorting, a second function of the rough ER is the insertion of certain newly made proteins into the ER membrane. A third important function of the rough ER is the attachment of carbohydrates to proteins and lipids. This process is called **glycosylation**. The topics of membrane protein insertion and protein glycosylation will be discussed in Chapter 5.

Smooth ER   The **smooth endoplasmic reticulum (smooth ER)**, which lacks ribosomes, functions in diverse metabolic processes. The extensive network of smooth ER membranes provides a large surface area for enzymes that play important metabolic roles. In liver cells, enzymes in the smooth ER detoxify many potentially harmful organic molecules, including barbiturate drugs and ethanol. These enzymes convert hydrophobic toxic molecules into more hydrophilic molecules, which are easily excreted from the body. Chronic alcohol consumption, as in alcoholics, leads to a greater amount of smooth ER in liver cells, which increases the rate of alcohol breakdown. This explains why people who consume alcohol regularly must ingest more alcohol to experience its effects.

The smooth ER of liver cells also plays a role in carbohydrate metabolism. The liver cells of animals store energy in the form of glycogen, which is a polymer of glucose. Glycogen granules sit very close to the smooth ER membrane. When chemical energy is needed, enzymes are activated that break down the glycogen to glucose-6-phosphate. Then, an enzyme in the smooth ER called glucose-6-phosphatase removes the phosphate group, and glucose is exported from the liver cell into the bloodstream.

Another important function of the smooth ER in all eukaryotes is the accumulation of calcium ions (Ca^{2+}). The smooth ER contains calcium pumps that transport Ca^{2+} into the ER lumen. The regulated release of Ca^{2+} into the cytosol is involved in many vital cellular processes, including muscle contraction in animals.

Finally, enzymes in the smooth ER are critical in the synthesis and modification of lipids. For example, the smooth ER is the primary site for the synthesis of phospholipids, which are the main lipid component of eukaryotic cell membranes. This topic is discussed in Chapter 5. In addition, enzymes in the smooth ER are necessary for certain modifications of the lipid cholesterol to produce steroid hormones such as estrogen and testosterone.

The Golgi Apparatus Directs the Processing, Sorting, and Secretion of Cellular Molecules

The **Golgi apparatus** (also called the Golgi body, Golgi complex, or simply Golgi) was discovered by the Italian microscopist Camillo Golgi in 1898. It consists of a stack of flattened membranes, with each flattened membrane enclosing a single compartment. The Golgi compartments are named according to their orientation in the cell. The *cis* Golgi is near the ER membrane, the *trans* Golgi is closest to the plasma membrane, and the medial Golgi is found in the middle.

Two models have been proposed to explain how materials move through the Golgi apparatus:

- *Vesicular transport model.* Materials are transported between the Golgi cisternae via membrane vesicles that bud from one compartment in the Golgi (for example, the *cis* Golgi) and fuse with another compartment (for example, the medial Golgi).

- *Cisternal maturation model.* Vesicles from the ER fuse to form a cisterna at the *cis* face; the cisterna that was previously at the *cis* face becomes a medial cisterna. This addition of a cisterna moves the other medial cisternae toward the *trans* face.

A cisterna at the *trans* face is lost as a result of the export of vesicles from its surface.

Further research is needed to determine the validity of these models.

The Golgi apparatus performs three overlapping functions: (1) processing, (2) protein sorting, and (3) secretion. We will discuss protein sorting in Section 4.7. Enzymes in the Golgi apparatus process, or modify, certain proteins and lipids. As mentioned earlier, carbohydrates can be attached to proteins and lipids in the endoplasmic reticulum. Glycosylation continues in the Golgi. For this to occur, a protein or lipid is transported via vesicles from the ER to the *cis* Golgi. Most glycosylation occurs in the medial Golgi.

A second type of processing event is **proteolysis**, whereby enzymes called **proteases** make cuts in polypeptides. For example, the hormone insulin is first made as a large precursor molecule termed proinsulin. In the Golgi apparatus, proinsulin is packaged with proteases into vesicles. The proteases cut out a portion of the proinsulin to create a smaller insulin polypeptide that is a functional hormone. This happens just prior to secretion, which is described next.

The Golgi apparatus packages different types of materials (cargo) into **secretory vesicles** that fuse with the plasma membrane, thereby releasing their contents outside the cell. Proteins destined for secretion are synthesized into the ER, travel to the Golgi, and then are transported by vesicles to the plasma membrane. The vesicles then fuse with the plasma membrane, and the proteins are secreted to the outside of the cell. The entire route is called the **secretory pathway** (Figure 4.22). In addition to secretory vesicles, the Golgi also produces vesicles that travel to other parts of the cell, such as the lysosomes.

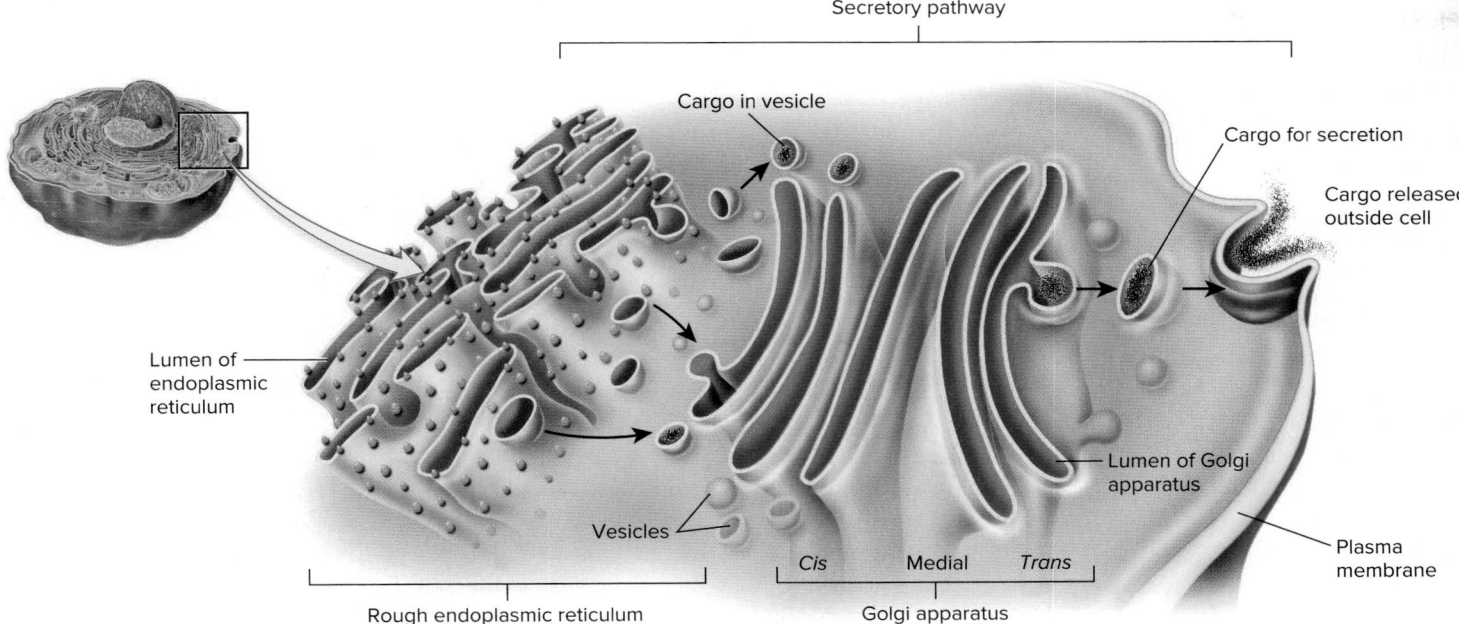

Figure 4.22 The Golgi apparatus and secretory pathway. The Golgi is composed of stacks of membranes that enclose distinct compartments. Transport to and from the Golgi compartments occurs via membrane vesicles. Vesicles bud from the ER and go to the Golgi, and vesicles from the Golgi fuse with the plasma membrane to release cargo to the outside. The pathway from the ER to the Golgi to the plasma membrane is termed the secretory pathway.

Concept Check: *If we consider the Golgi apparatus as three compartments (cis, medial, and trans), in what order does a protein travel through them before being secreted?*

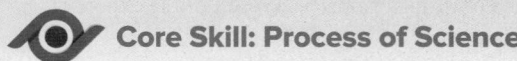

Core Skill: Process of Science

Feature Investigation | Palade Discovered That Proteins Destined for Secretion Move Sequentially Through Organelles of the Endomembrane System

As we have seen, a key function of the endomembrane system is protein secretion. The identification of the secretory pathway came from studies of George Palade and his colleagues in the 1960s. He hypothesized that proteins follow an intracellular pathway to be secreted. Palade's team conducted pulse-chase experiments, in which the researchers administered a pulse of radioactive amino acids to cells so they made radioactive proteins. A few minutes later, the cells were given a large amount of nonradioactive amino acids. This step is called a "chase" because it chases away the ability of the cells to make any more radioactive proteins. In this way, radioactive proteins were produced only briefly. Because they were labeled with radioactivity, the fate of these proteins could be monitored over time. The goal of a pulse-chase experiment is to determine where the radioactive proteins are produced and the pathway they take as they travel through a cell.

Palade chose to study the cells of the pancreas. This organ secretes enzymes and protein hormones that play a role in digestion and metabolism. Therefore, these cells were chosen because their primary activity is protein secretion. To study the pathway for protein secretion, Palade and colleagues injected a radioactive version of the amino acid leucine into the bloodstream of male guinea pigs. The radiolabeled leucine traveled in the bloodstream and was quickly taken up by cells of the body, including those in the pancreas. Three minutes later, the researchers injected nonradiolabeled leucine (**Figure 4.23**). At various times after the second injection, samples of pancreatic cells were removed from the animals. The cells were then prepared for transmission electron microscopy (TEM). The sample was stained with osmium tetroxide, a heavy metal compound that became bound to membranes and showed the locations of the cell organelles. In addition, the sample was coated with a radiation-sensitive emulsion containing silver. When radiation was emitted from the radiolabeled proteins, it interacted with the emulsion in a way that caused the precipitation of silver, which became tightly bound to the sample. In this way, the precipitated silver marked the location of the radiolabeled proteins. Unprecipitated silver in the emulsion was later washed away. Because silver atoms are electron-dense (allowing few electrons to pass), they produce dark spots in a TEM. Therefore, dark spots revealed the locations of radiolabeled proteins.

The schematic drawings shown as the data indicate the path of the proteins as they moved through the secretory pathway. Very dark objects, namely radiolabeled proteins, were first observed in the

Figure 4.23 Palade's use of the pulse-chase method to study protein secretion.

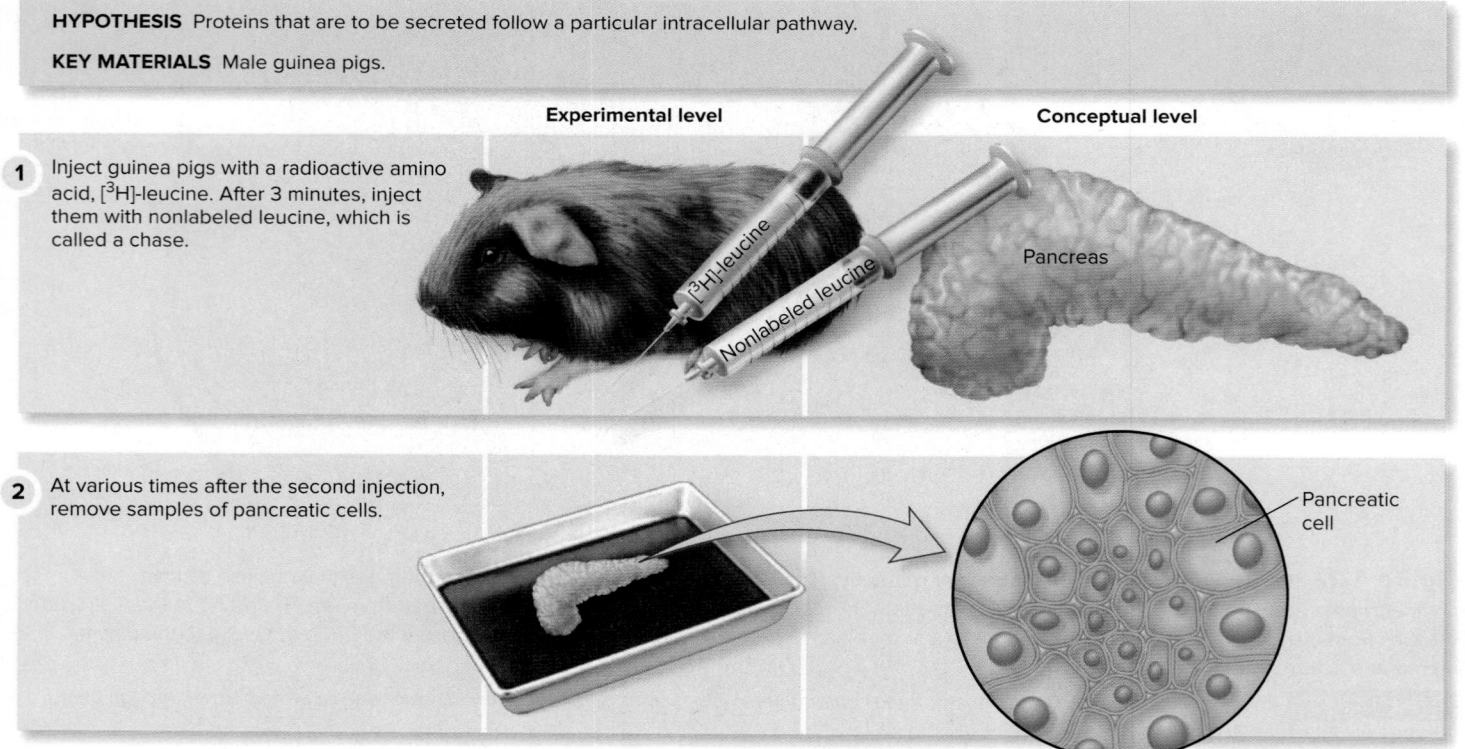

HYPOTHESIS Proteins that are to be secreted follow a particular intracellular pathway.

KEY MATERIALS Male guinea pigs.

Experimental level   Conceptual level

1 Inject guinea pigs with a radioactive amino acid, [³H]-leucine. After 3 minutes, inject them with nonlabeled leucine, which is called a chase.

[³H]-leucine

Nonlabeled leucine

Pancreas

2 At various times after the second injection, remove samples of pancreatic cells.

Pancreatic cell

3 Stain the sample with osmium tetroxide, which is a heavy metal that binds to membranes.

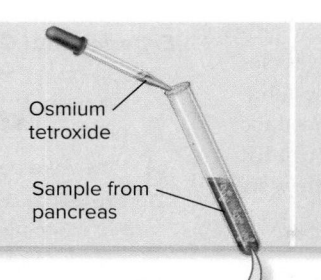

Osmium tetroxide

Sample from pancreas

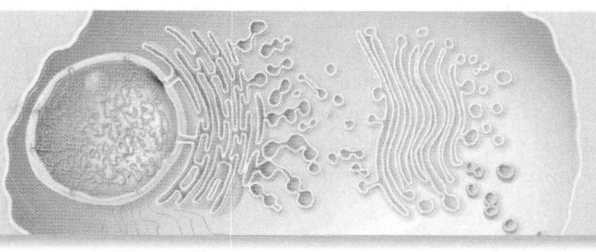

4 Cut thin sections of the samples, and place a thin layer of radiation-sensitive emulsion over the sample. Allow time for radioactive emission from radiolabeled proteins to precipitate silver atoms in the emulsion. Wash away unprecipitated silver atoms.

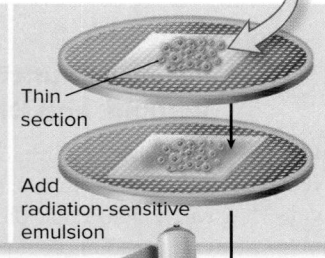

Thin section

Add radiation-sensitive emulsion

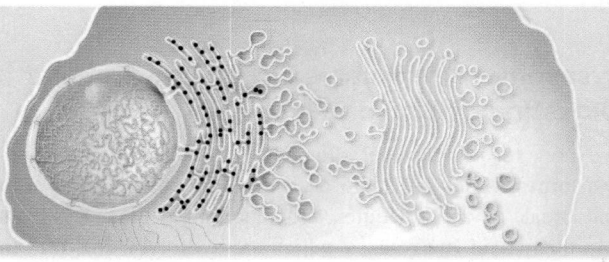

5 Observe the sample under a transmission electron microscope.

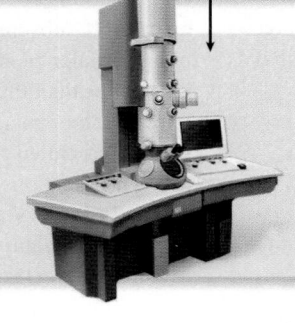

6 **THE DATA**

Schematic drawings of transmission electron micrographs

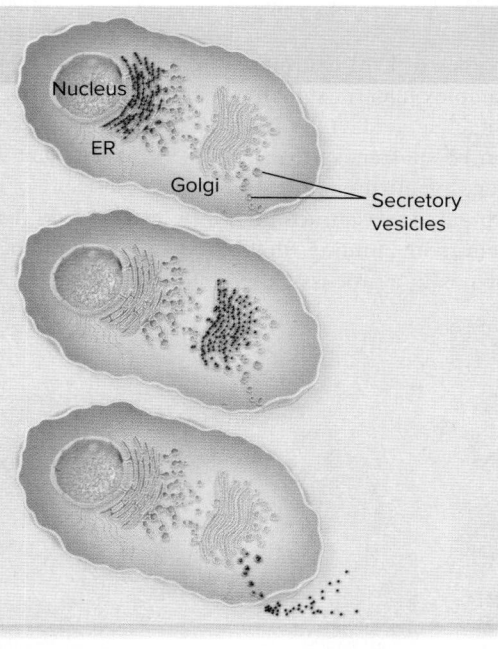

Nucleus

ER

Golgi

Secretory vesicles

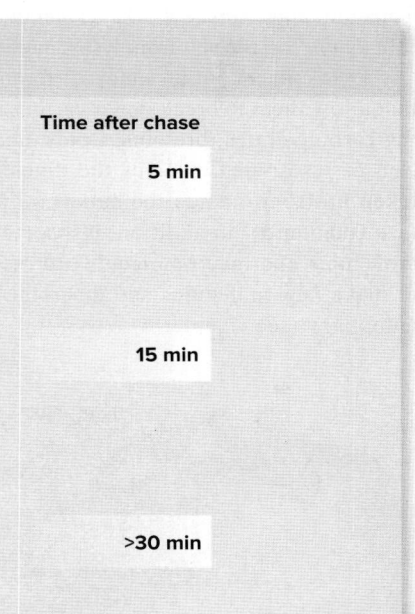

Time after chase

5 min

15 min

>30 min

7 **CONCLUSION** To be secreted, proteins move from the ER to the Golgi to secretory vesicles and then to the plasma membrane, where they are released to the outside of the cell.

8 **SOURCE** Caro, L.G., and Palade, G.E. 1964. Protein synthesis, storage, and discharge in the pancreatic exocrine cell. An autoradiographic study. *Journal of Cell Biology* 20: 473–495.

rough ER. Observations made at later times indicated that these proteins moved from the ER to the Golgi, and then to secretory vesicles near the plasma membrane. In this way, Palade followed the intracellular pathway of protein movement. His experiments provided the first evidence that secreted proteins are synthesized into the rough ER and move through a series of cellular compartments before they are secreted.

Experimental Questions

1. **CoreSKILL »** Explain the procedure of a pulse-chase experiment. What is the pulse, and what is the chase? What was the purpose of this approach?

2. Why were pancreatic cells used for this investigation?

3. **CoreSKILL »** Analyze the results of the experiment of Figure 4.23. What did the researchers conclude?

Lysosomes Are Involved in the Intracellular Digestion of Macromolecules

We now turn to another organelle of the endomembrane system, **lysosomes**, which are small organelles that are found in animal cells and break down molecules and macromolecules. Lysosomes contain many **acid hydrolases**, which are hydrolytic enzymes that use a molecule of water to break a covalent bond. As described in Chapter 3 (refer back to Figure 3.4b), this type of chemical reaction is called hydrolysis:

$$\text{Acid hydrolase}$$
$$R_1-R_2 + H_2O \xrightarrow{\hspace{2cm}} R_1-OH + R_2-H$$

The acid hydrolases in a lysosome function optimally at an acidic pH. The fluid-filled interior of a lysosome has a pH of approximately 4.8. If a lysosomal membrane breaks, releasing acid hydrolases into the cytosol, the enzymes are not very active because the cytosolic pH is neutral (approximately pH 7.2) and buffered. This prevents significant damage to the cell from lysosome breakage.

Lysosomes contain many different types of acid hydrolases that allow them to break down various complex materials, including carbohydrates, proteins, lipids, and nucleic acids. One function of lysosomes involves the digestion of substances that are taken up from outside the cell via a process called endocytosis (see Chapter 5). In addition, lysosomes break down intracellular molecules and macromolecules to recycle their building blocks to make new molecules and macromolecules in a process called autophagy (see Chapter 6).

Vacuoles Function in Storage, Regulation of Cell Volume, and Degradation

Vacuoles are prominent organelles in plant cells, fungal cells, and certain protists. The term vacuole (Latin, for empty space) came from early microscopic observations of these compartments. We now know that vacuoles are not empty but instead contain fluid and sometimes even solid substances. Most vacuoles are made from the fusion of many smaller membrane vesicles. Vacuoles in animal cells tend to be smaller than those in plants and are more commonly used to temporarily store materials or transport substances. Such vacuoles are sometimes called storage vesicles.

The functions of vacuoles are extremely varied, and they differ among cell types and even with environmental conditions. The best way to appreciate vacuole function is to consider a few examples. Mature plant cells usually have a large **central vacuole** that occupies 80% or more of the cell volume (**Figure 4.24a**). The central vacuole serves two important purposes. First, it stores a large amount of water, enzymes, and inorganic ions such as calcium. It also stores other materials including proteins and pigments. Second, it performs a space-filling function. The central vacuole exerts a pressure on the cell wall, called turgor pressure. If a plant becomes dehydrated and this pressure is lost, a plant will wilt. Turgor pressure is important in maintaining the structure of plant cells and the plant itself, and it helps to drive the expansion of the cell wall, which is necessary for growth.

Certain species of protists use vacuoles to maintain cell volume. Freshwater organisms such as the alga *Chlamydomonas reinhardtii* have small, water-filled **contractile vacuoles** that expand as water

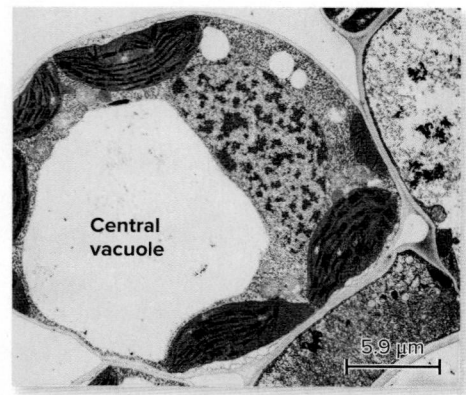

(a) Central vacuole in a plant cell

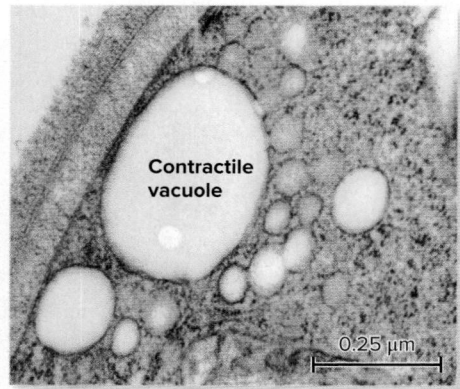

(b) Contractile vacuoles in an algal cell

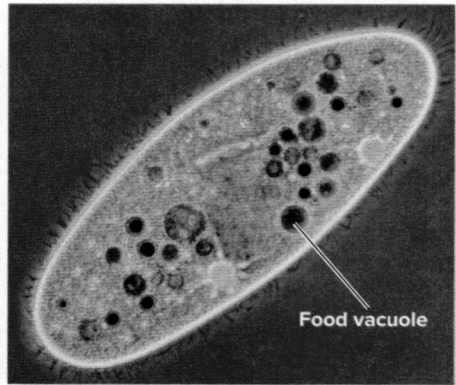

(c) Food vacuoles in a paramecium

Figure 4.24   Examples of vacuoles. These are TEMs. Part (c) is colorized. a: ©Biophoto Associates/Science Source; b: Courtesy of Dr. Peter Luykx, Biology, University of Miami; c: ©Dr. David Patterson/Science Source

enters the cell (Figure 4.24b). Once they reach a certain size, the vacuoles fuse with the plasma membrane, expelling their contents to the exterior of the cell (look ahead to Figure 5.14). This mechanism is necessary to remove excess water that continually enters the cell by diffusion across the plasma membrane.

Another function of vacuoles is degradation. Some protists engulf their food into large food vacuoles in the process of phagocytosis (Figure 4.24c). Food vacuoles contain hydrolytic enzymes that break down macromolecules within food. Macrophages, a type of cell found in animals' immune systems, engulf bacterial cells into phagocytic vacuoles, which then fuse with lysosomes, where the bacteria are destroyed.

Peroxisomes Catalyze Detoxifying Reactions

Peroxisomes, discovered by Christian de Duve in 1965, are small organelles found in all eukaryotic cells. Peroxisomes consist of a single membrane that encloses a fluid-filled lumen. A typical eukaryotic cell contains several hundred of them.

Peroxisomes catalyze a variety of chemical reactions, including some reactions that break down organic molecules and others that are biosynthetic. In mammals, large numbers of peroxisomes are found in liver cells, where toxic molecules accumulate and are broken down. A common by-product of the breakdown of toxins is hydrogen peroxide, H_2O_2:

$$RH_2 + O_2 \longrightarrow R + H_2O_2$$
$$\text{(toxin)}$$

Hydrogen peroxide has the potential to damage cellular components. In the presence of metals such as iron (Fe^{2+}), which are found naturally in living cells, H_2O_2 is broken down to form a hydroxide ion (OH^-) and a molecule called a hydroxide free radical ($\cdot OH$):

$$Fe^{2+} + H_2O_2 \rightarrow Fe^{3+} + OH^- + \cdot OH \text{ (hydroxide free radical)}$$

The $\cdot OH$ is highly reactive and can damage proteins, lipids, and DNA. Therefore, it is beneficial for cells to break down H_2O_2 in an alternative manner that does not form $\cdot OH$. Peroxisomes contain an enzyme called **catalase** that breaks down hydrogen peroxide to make water and oxygen gas (hence the name peroxisome):

$$2 H_2O_2 \xrightarrow{\text{Catalase}} 2 H_2O + O_2$$

Aside from detoxification, peroxisomes can play a role in the metabolism of fats and amino acids. For example, plant seeds contain specialized organelles called **glyoxysomes**, which are similar to peroxisomes. Seeds often store fats instead of carbohydrates. Because fats have higher energy per unit mass, seeds that store fats are smaller and less heavy than seeds that store carbohydrates would be. Glyoxysomes contain enzymes that are needed to convert fats to sugars. These enzymes become active when a seed germinates and the seedling begins to grow.

A general model for peroxisome formation is shown in **Figure 4.25**, though the details may differ among animal, plant, and fungal cells. To initiate peroxisome formation, vesicles bud from the ER membrane and form a premature peroxisome. Following the import of additional proteins, the premature peroxisome becomes a mature peroxisome. Once the mature peroxisome has formed, it may then divide to further increase the number of peroxisomes in the cell.

The Plasma Membrane Is the Interface Between a Cell and Its Environment

The cytoplasm of eukaryotic cells is surrounded by a plasma membrane, which is part of the endomembrane system and provides a boundary between a cell and the extracellular environment. Proteins

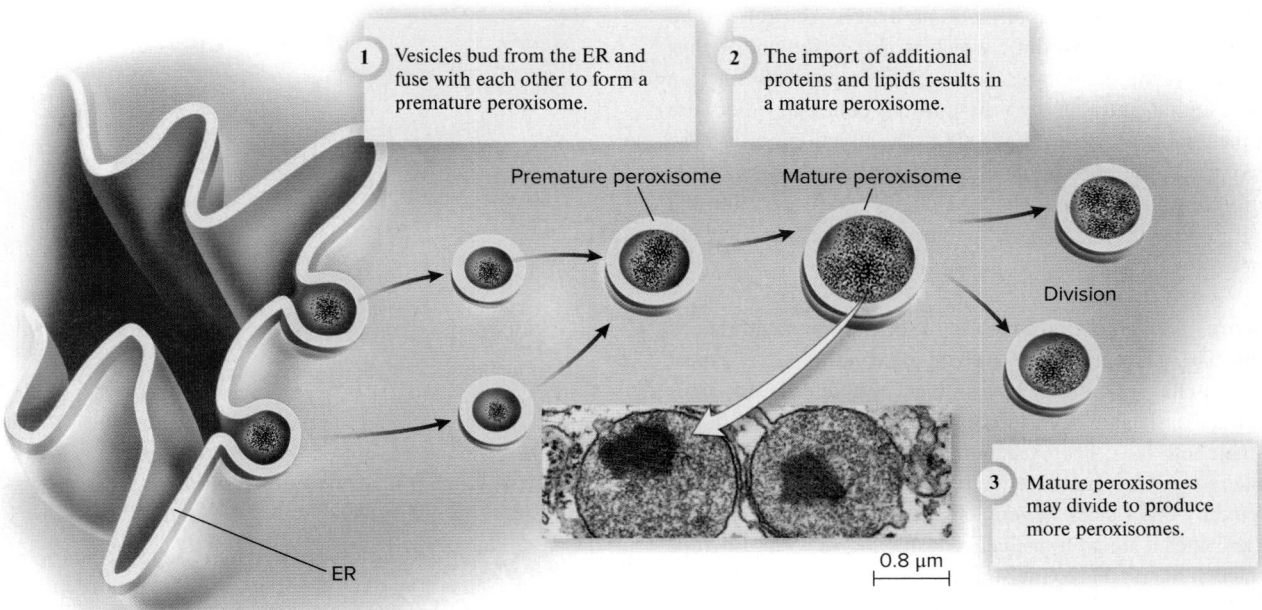

Figure 4.25 **Formation of peroxisomes.** The inset is a TEM of mature peroxisomes. (inset): ©Don W. Fawcett/Science Source

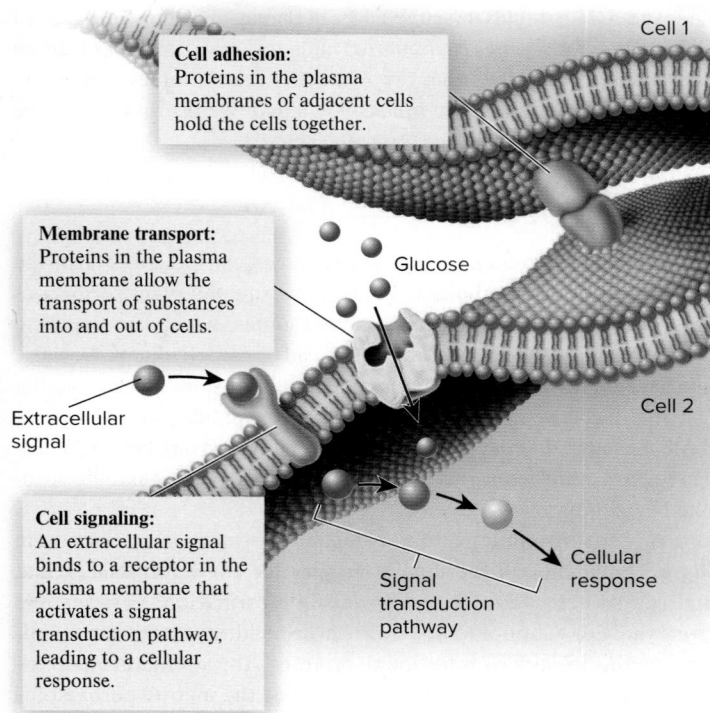

Figure 4.26 Major functions of the plasma membrane. Three important roles are membrane transport, cell signaling, and cell adhesion.

Concept Check: *Which of these three functions do you think is the most important for cellular metabolism?*

in the plasma membrane perform many important functions that affect the activities inside the cell (**Figure 4.26**).

Membrane Transport   First, many plasma membrane proteins are involved in **membrane transport** , which is the movement of ions or molecules across the membrane. Some of these proteins function to transport essential nutrients or ions into the cell, and others are involved in the export of substances. Due to the functioning of these protein transporters, the plasma membrane is selectively permeable; it allows only certain substances in and out. We will examine the structure and function of the plasma membrane, as well as a variety of transporters, in Chapter 5.

Cell Signaling   A second vital function of the plasma membrane is **cell signaling**. To survive and adapt to changing conditions, cells must be able to sense changes in their environment. In addition, the cells of a multicellular organism need to communicate with each other to coordinate their activities. The plasma membrane of all cells contains receptors that recognize signals—either environmental agents or molecules secreted by other cells. When a signaling molecule binds to a receptor, it activates a signal transduction pathway—a series of steps that cause the cell to respond to the signal. For example, when you eat a meal, the hormone insulin is secreted into your bloodstream. This hormone binds to receptors in the plasma membranes of your cells, which results in a cellular response that allows your cells to increase

their uptake of certain molecules found in food, such as glucose. We will explore the details of cell signaling in Chapter 9.

Cell Adhesion   A third important role of the plasma membrane in animal cells is **cell adhesion**. Protein-protein interactions among proteins in the plasma membranes of adjacent cells promote cell-to-cell adhesion. This phenomenon is critical for animal cells to properly interact to form a multicellular organism and for cells to recognize each other. The structures and functions of proteins involved in cell adhesion will be examined in Chapter 10.

4.6 Semiautonomous Organelles

Learning Outcomes:
1. Outline the structures and general functions of mitochondria and chloroplasts.
2. **CoreSKILL »** Evaluate the evidence for the endosymbiosis theory.

We now turn to those organelles in eukaryotic cells that are considered semiautonomous: mitochondria and chloroplasts. These organelles grow and divide, but they are not completely autonomous because they depend on other parts of the cell for their internal components (**Figure 4.27**). For example, most of the proteins found in mitochondria are imported from the cytosol. In this section, we will survey the structures and functions of the semiautonomous organelles in eukaryotic cells and consider

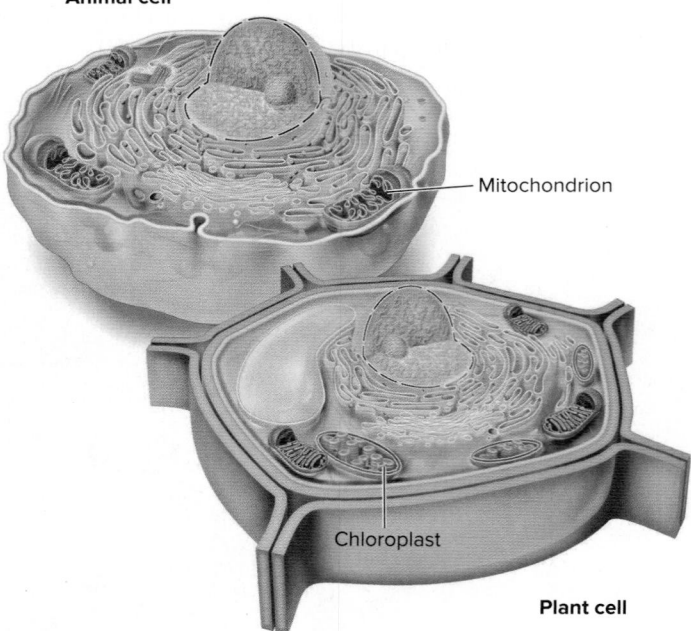

Figure 4.27 Semiautonomous organelles. Mitochondria and chloroplasts are the semiautonomous organelles.

 Core Concept: Energy and Matter Chloroplasts capture light energy and synthesize organic molecules. Mitochondria break down organic molecules and make ATP that is used as an energy source to drive many different cellular processes.

their evolutionary origins. In Chapters 7 and 8, we will explore the functions of mitochondria and chloroplasts in greater depth.

Mitochondria Supply Cells with Most of Their ATP

Mitochondrion (plural, mitochondria) literally means thread granule, which is what mitochondria look like under a light microscope—either threadlike or granular-shaped. They are similar in size to bacteria. A typical cell may contain a few hundred to a few thousand mitochondria. Cells with particularly heavy energy demands, such as muscle cells, have more mitochondria than other cells. Research has shown that regular exercise increases the number and size of mitochondria in human muscle cells to meet the expanded demand for energy.

A mitochondrion has an outer membrane and an inner membrane separated by a region called the intermembrane space (**Figure 4.28**). The inner membrane is highly invaginated (folded) to form projections called **cristae**. The cristae greatly increase the surface area of the inner membrane, which is the site where ATP is made. The compartment enclosed by the inner membrane is the **mitochondrial matrix**.

The primary role of mitochondria is to make ATP. Even though mitochondria produce most of a cell's ATP, mitochondria do not create energy. Rather, their primary function is to convert chemical energy that is stored within the covalent bonds of organic molecules into a form that can be readily used by cells. Covalent bonds in sugars, fats, and amino acids store a large amount of energy. The breakdown of these molecules into simpler molecules releases energy that is used

to make ATP. Many proteins in living cells use ATP as a source of energy to carry out their functions, such as muscle contraction, the uptake of nutrients, cell division, and many other cellular processes.

Mitochondria perform other functions as well. They are involved in the synthesis, modification, and breakdown of several types of cellular molecules. For example, the synthesis of certain hormones requires enzymes that are found in mitochondria. Another interesting role of mitochondria is to generate heat in specialized fat cells known as brown fat cells. Groups of brown fat cells serve as heating pads that help to revive hibernating animals and protect sensitive areas of young animals from the cold.

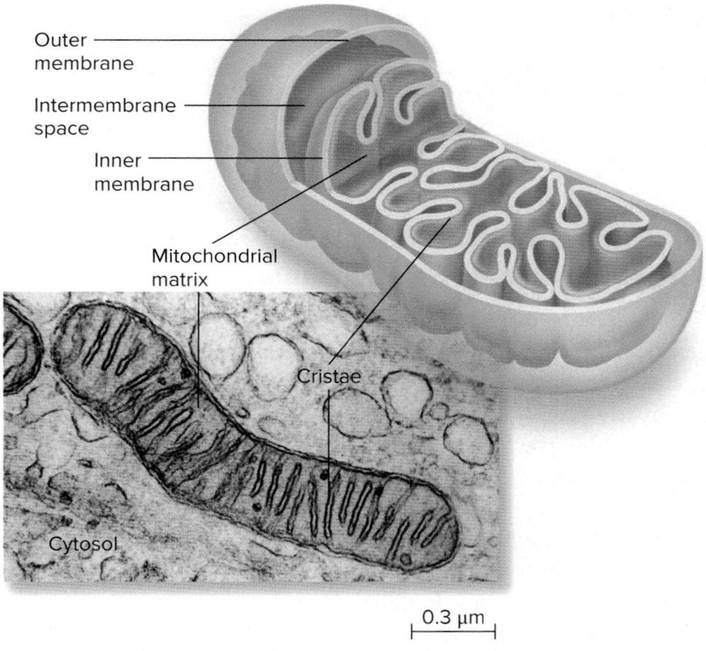

Chloroplasts Carry Out Photosynthesis

Chloroplasts are semiautonomous organelles that capture light energy and use some of that energy to synthesize organic molecules such as glucose. This process, called **photosynthesis**, is described in Chapter 8. Chloroplasts are found in nearly all species of plants and algae. **Figure 4.29** shows the structure of a typical chloroplast. Like a mitochondrion, a chloroplast contains an outer and inner membrane. An intermembrane space lies between these two membranes. A third membrane, the **thylakoid membrane**, forms many flattened, fluid-filled tubules that enclose a single, convoluted compartment called the thylakoid lumen. These tubules stack on top of each other to form a structure called a **granum** (plural, grana). The **stroma** is the compartment of the chloroplast that is enclosed by the inner membrane but outside the thylakoid membrane.

Chloroplasts are a specialized version of plant organelles that are more generally known as **plastids**. All plastids are derived from unspecialized **proplastids**. The various types of plastids are

Outer membrane
Intermembrane space
Inner membrane
Mitochondrial matrix
Cristae
Cytosol

0.3 µm

Figure 4.28 **Structure of a mitochondrion.** This figure emphasizes the membrane organization of a mitochondrion, which has an outer and inner membrane. The invaginations of the inner membrane are called cristae. The mitochondrial matrix lies inside the inner membrane. The micrograph is a colorized TEM. ©Don W. Fawcett/Science Source

Concept Check: *What is the advantage of the mitochondrion's highly invaginated inner membrane?*

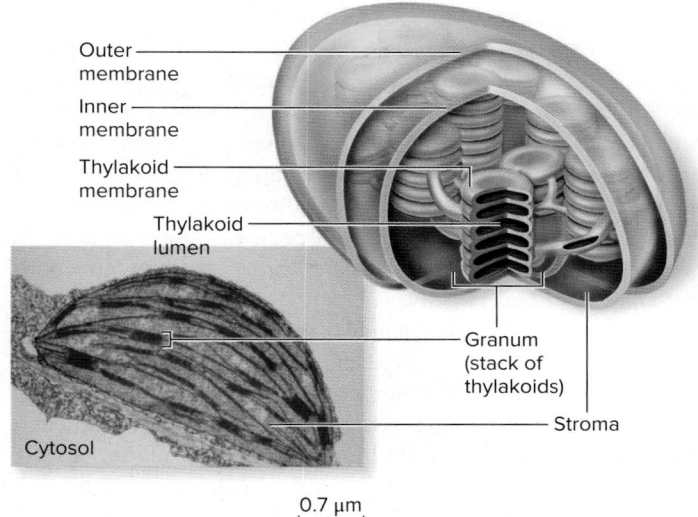

Outer membrane
Inner membrane
Thylakoid membrane
Thylakoid lumen
Granum (stack of thylakoids)
Stroma
Cytosol

0.7 µm

Figure 4.29 **Structure of a chloroplast.** Like a mitochondrion, a chloroplast is enclosed in a double membrane. In addition, it has an internal thylakoid membrane that forms flattened tubular compartments. These compartments stack on each other to form grana. The stroma is located inside the inner membrane but outside the thylakoid membrane. This micrograph is a colorized TEM. ©Dr. Jeremy Burgess/Science Source

distinguished by their synthetic abilities and the types of pigments they contain. Chloroplasts, which carry out photosynthesis, contain the green pigment chlorophyll. The abundant number of chloroplasts in the leaves of plants gives them their green color. Chromoplasts, a second type of plastid, function in synthesizing and storing the yellow, orange, and red pigments known as carotenoids. Chromoplasts give many fruits and flowers their colors. In autumn, the chromoplasts also give many leaves their yellow, orange, and red colors. A third type of plastid, leucoplasts, typically lacks pigment molecules. An amyloplast is a leucoplast that synthesizes and stores starch. Amyloplasts are common in underground plant structures such as roots and tubers.

Mitochondria and Chloroplasts Contain Their Own Genetic Material and Divide by Binary Fission

To fully appreciate the structure and organization of mitochondria and chloroplasts, we also need to briefly examine their genetic properties. In 1951, Yasutane Chiba exposed plant cells to Feulgen stain, a DNA-specific dye, and discovered that the chloroplasts became stained. Based on this observation, he was the first to suggest that chloroplasts contain their own DNA. Researchers in the 1970s and 1980s isolated DNA from both chloroplasts and mitochondria. These studies revealed that the DNA of these organelles resembled smaller versions of bacterial chromosomes.

The chromosomes found in mitochondria and chloroplasts are referred to as the **mitochondrial genome** and **chloroplast genome**, respectively, whereas the chromosomes found in the nucleus of a eukaryotic cell constitute the **nuclear genome**. Like bacterial genomes, the genomes of most mitochondria and chloroplasts are composed of a single circular chromosome. Compared with the nuclear genome, they are very small. For example, the amount of DNA in the human nuclear genome (about 3 billion base pairs) is about 200,000 times greater than the amount in the mitochondrial genome. In terms of genes, the human genome has approximately 22,000 different protein-encoding genes, whereas the human mitochondrial genome has only about a dozen protein-encoding genes. Chloroplast genomes tend to be larger than mitochondrial genomes, and they have a correspondingly greater number of genes. Depending on the particular species of plant or algae, a chloroplast genome is about 10 times larger than the mitochondrial genome of human cells.

Just as the genomes of mitochondria and chloroplasts resemble bacterial genomes, the production of new mitochondria and chloroplasts bears a striking resemblance to the division of bacterial cells. Like their bacterial counterparts, mitochondria and chloroplasts increase in number via **binary fission**, or splitting in two. **Figure 4.30** illustrates the process for a mitochondrion. The mitochondrial chromosome, which is found in a region called the nucleoid, is duplicated, and the organelle divides into two separate organelles. Mitochondrial and chloroplast divisions are needed to maintain a full complement of these organelles when cell growth occurs following cell division. In addition, environmental conditions may influence the sizes and numbers of these organelles. For example, when plants are exposed to more sunlight, the number of chloroplasts in leaf cells increases.

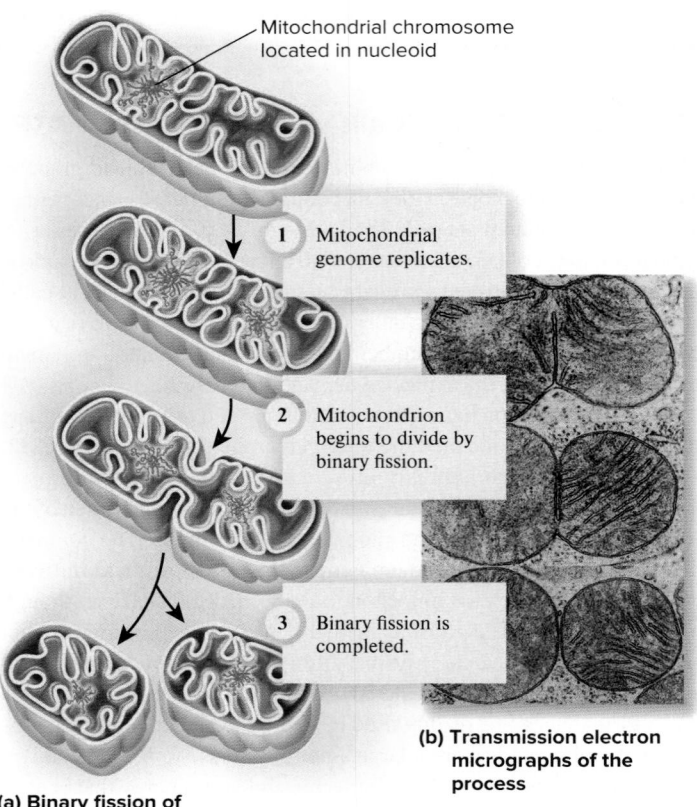

Mitochondrial chromosome located in nucleoid

1 Mitochondrial genome replicates.

2 Mitochondrion begins to divide by binary fission.

3 Binary fission is completed.

(a) Binary fission of mitochondria

(b) Transmission electron micrographs of the process

Figure 4.30 **Division of mitochondria by binary fission.** b: ©Don W. Fawcett/Science Source

 Core Skill: Connections Look ahead to Figure 19.13. How is the process of binary fission similar to bacterial cell division, and how is it different?

Mitochondria and Chloroplasts Are Derived from Ancient Symbiotic Relationships

The observation that mitochondria and chloroplasts contain their own genetic material may seem puzzling. Perhaps you might think that it would be simpler for a eukaryotic cell to have all of its genetic material in one place—the nucleus. The distinct genomes of mitochondria and chloroplasts can be traced to their evolutionary origin, which involved an ancient symbiotic association.

A symbiotic relationship occurs when two different species live in direct contact with each other. **Endosymbiosis** describes a symbiotic relationship in which the smaller species—the symbiont—lives inside the larger species. In 1883, Andreas Schimper proposed that chloroplasts evolved from an endosymbiotic relationship between cyanobacteria (a bacterium capable of photosynthesis) and eukaryotic cells. In 1922, Ivan Wallin also hypothesized an endosymbiotic origin for mitochondria.

In spite of these interesting proposals, the question of whether endosymbiosis gave rise to mitochondria and chloroplasts was largely ignored until the discovery that these organelles contain their own genetic material. In 1970, the idea of endosymbiosis as the origin of mitochondria and chloroplasts was revived by Lynn Margulis in her

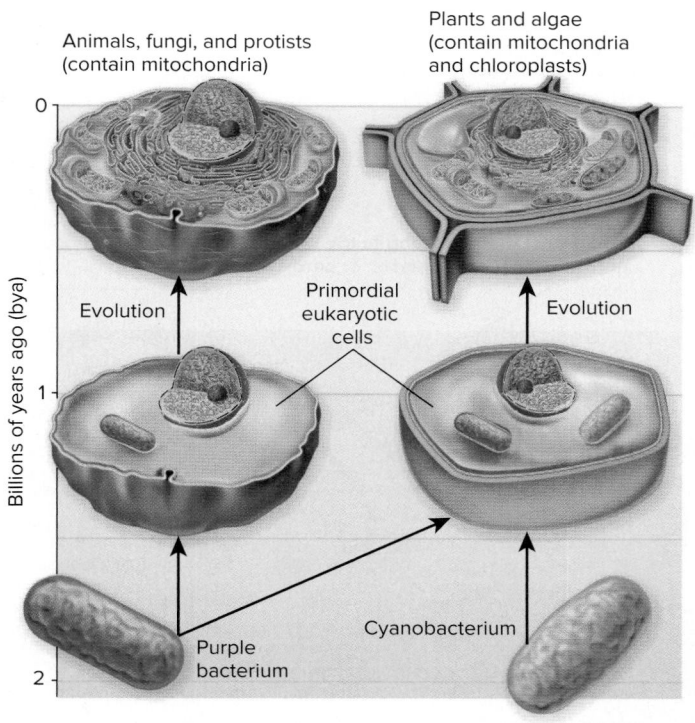

Animals, fungi, and protists
(contain mitochondria)

Plants and algae
(contain mitochondria
and chloroplasts)

Evolution

Primordial
eukaryotic
cells

Evolution

Purple
bacterium

Cyanobacterium

**(a) Mitochondria originated
from endosymbiotic
purple bacteria.**

**(b) Chloroplasts originated
from endosymbiotic
cyanobacteria.**

Figure 4.31 A simplified view of the endosymbiosis theory.

Core Concept: Evolution (a) According to the endosymbiosis theory, modern mitochondria were derived
from purple bacteria, also called α-proteobacteria.
Over the course of evolution, their characteristics
evolved into those found in mitochondria today. **(b)** A
similar phenomenon occurred for chloroplasts, which
were derived from cyanobacteria (blue-green bacteria), which are capable of photosynthesis.

book *Origin of Eukaryotic Cells.* During the 1970s and 1980s, the
advent of molecular genetic techniques allowed researchers to analyze genes from mitochondria, chloroplasts, bacteria, and eukaryotic
nuclear genomes. Researchers discovered that genes in mitochondria
and chloroplasts are very similar to bacterial genes. Likewise, mitochondria and chloroplasts are strikingly similar in size and shape to
certain bacterial species. These observations provided strong support
for the **endosymbiosis theory**, which proposes that mitochondria and
chloroplasts originated from bacteria that took up residence within
primordial eukaryotic cells (**Figure 4.31**). Over the next 2 billion
years, the characteristics of these intracellular bacterial cells gradually changed to those of mitochondria or chloroplasts. The origin of
eukaryotic cells is discussed in more detail in Chapter 26.

Symbiosis occurs because the relationship is beneficial to one
or both species. According to the endosymbiosis theory, such a relationship provided eukaryotic cells with useful cellular characteristics.
Chloroplasts, which were derived from cyanobacteria, have the ability to carry out photosynthesis. This benefits plant cells by giving
them the ability to use the energy from sunlight. By comparison,

mitochondria are thought to have been derived from a different type
of bacteria known as purple bacteria, or α-proteobacteria. In this case,
the endosymbiotic relationship enabled eukaryotic cells to synthesize
greater amounts of ATP. How the relationship would have been beneficial to a cyanobacterium or purple bacterium is less clear, though
the cytosol of a eukaryotic cell may have provided a stable environment with an adequate supply of nutrients.

During the evolution of eukaryotic species, many genes that were
originally found in the genomes of the primordial purple bacteria and
cyanobacteria have been transferred from the organelles to the nucleus.
This has occurred many times throughout evolution, so modern mitochondria and chloroplasts have lost most of the genes that still exist in
present-day purple bacteria and cyanobacteria. Some researchers speculate that the movement of genes into the nucleus makes it easier for the
cell to control the structure, function, and division of mitochondria and
chloroplasts. In modern cells, hundreds of different proteins that make
up these organelles are encoded by genes that have been transferred to
the nucleus. These proteins are made in the cytosol and then taken up
into mitochondria or chloroplasts. We will discuss this topic next.

4.7 Protein Sorting to Organelles

Learning Outcomes:

1. List the categories of proteins that are sorted cotranslationally and
   post-translationally.
2. Describe the steps that occur during the cotranslational sorting of
   proteins to the endoplasmic reticulum.
3. Outline the steps of post-translational sorting of proteins to
   mitochondria.

As we have seen, eukaryotic cells contain a variety of membrane-
bound organelles. Each protein that a cell makes usually functions
within one cellular compartment or is secreted from the cell. How
does each protein reach its appropriate destination? For example, how
does a mitochondrial protein get sent to the mitochondrion rather
than to a different organelle such as a lysosome? In eukaryotes, most
proteins contain short stretches of amino acid sequences that direct
them to their correct cellular location. These sequences are called
sorting signals, or **traffic signals**. Each sorting signal is recognized
by specific cellular components that facilitate the proper movement
of the protein carrying that signal to its correct location.

The synthesis of most eukaryotic proteins begins on ribosomes
in the cytosol, using messenger RNA (mRNA) that contains the information for polypeptide synthesis (**Figure 4.32**). The cytosol provides
amino acids, which are used as building blocks to make the proteins
during translation. Cytosolic proteins lack any sorting signal, so they
remain there. By comparison, the synthesis of proteins destined for
the ER, Golgi, lysosomes, vacuoles, or secretory vesicles begins in
the cytosol and then halts temporarily until the ribosome has become
bound to the ER membrane. After this occurs, translation resumes and
the polypeptide is synthesized into the ER. Proteins that are destined
for the ER, Golgi, lysosomes, vacuoles, plasma membrane, or secretion are first directed to the ER. This is called **cotranslational sorting**
because the first step in the sorting process begins while translation
is occurring. In contrast, the uptake of most proteins into the nucleus,

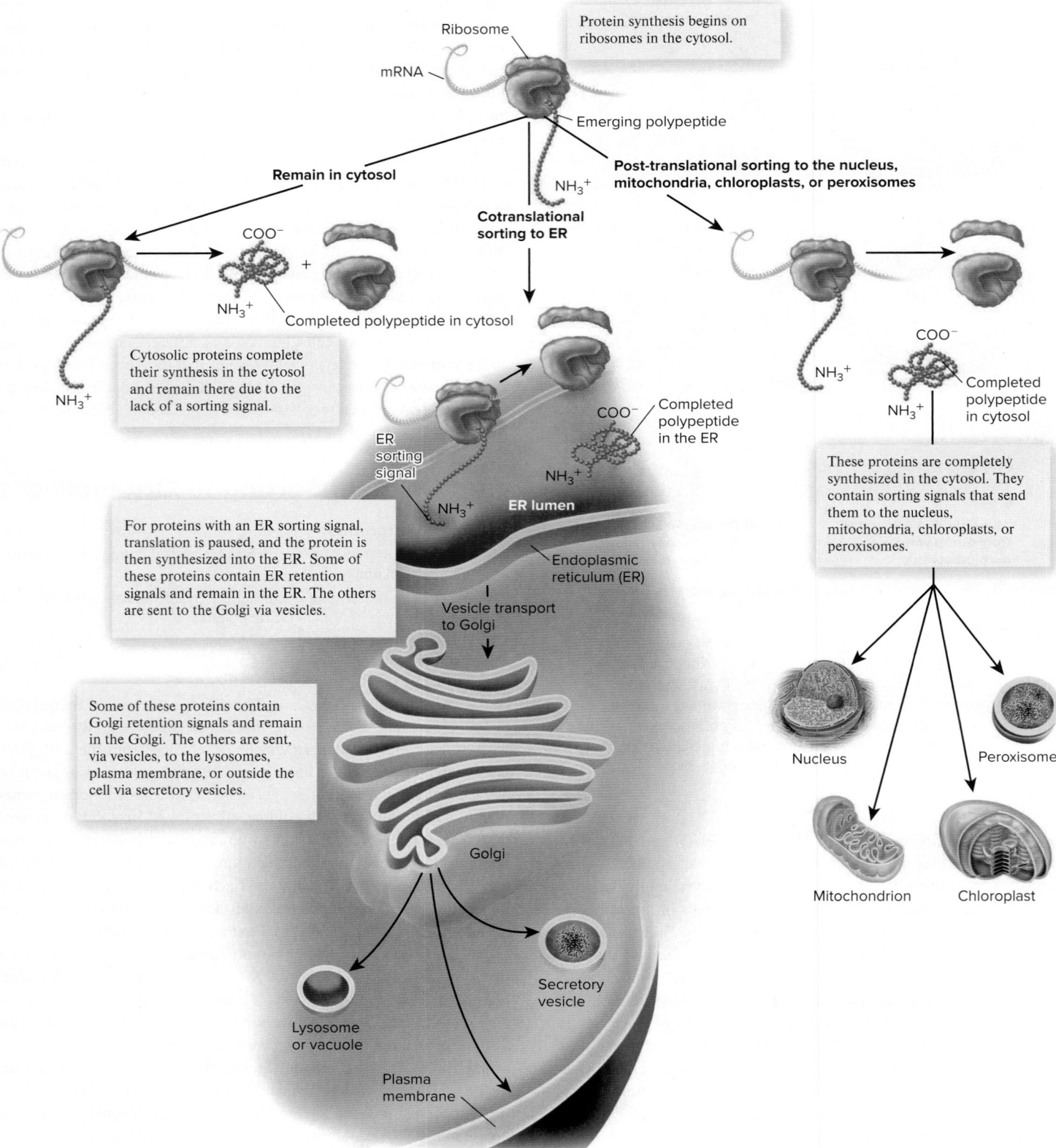

Figure 4.32 Three pathways for protein sorting in a eukaryotic cell. Proteins either remain in the cytosol, are sorted to the ER (cotranslational sorting), or are sorted after they are completely synthesized (post-translational sorting).

mitochondria, chloroplasts, and peroxisomes occurs after the protein is completely made (that is, completely translated) in the cytosol. This is called **post-translational sorting** because it does not happen until translation is finished. In this section, we will consider how cells carry out cotranslational and post-translational sorting.

The Cotranslational Sorting of Some Proteins Occurs at the Endoplasmic Reticulum Membrane

The concept of sorting signals in proteins was first proposed by Günter Blobel in the 1970s. Blobel and colleagues discovered a sorting signal in proteins that sends them to the ER membrane, which is the first step in cotranslational sorting (**Figure 4.33**, also see Figure 4.32). To be directed to the rough ER membrane, a polypeptide must contain a sorting signal called an **ER signal sequence**, which is a sequence of about 6–12 amino acids that are predominantly hydrophobic and usually located near the N-terminus. As the ribosome is making the polypeptide in the cytosol, the ER signal sequence emerges from the ribosome and is recognized by a protein-RNA complex called **signal recognition particle (SRP)**. SRP has two functions. First, it recognizes the ER signal sequence and pauses translation. Second, SRP binds to an SRP receptor in the ER membrane, which docks the ribosome over a channel. At this stage, SRP is released and translation resumes. The growing polypeptide is threaded through the channel to cross the ER membrane. If the protein is not a membrane protein, it will be released into the lumen of the ER. In most cases, the ER signal sequence is removed by an enzyme, signal peptidase. In 1999, Blobel won the Nobel Prize in Physiology or Medicine for his discovery of sorting signals in proteins. The process shown in Figure 4.33 illustrates another important role of protein-protein interactions—a series of interactions causes the steps of a process to occur in a specific order.

Some proteins are meant to function in the ER. Such proteins contain ER retention signals in addition to the ER signal sequence. Alternatively, other proteins that are destined for the Golgi, lysosomes, vacuoles, plasma membrane, or secretion leave the ER and are transported to their correct location. This transport process occurs via vesicles that are formed from one compartment and then move through the cytosol and fuse with another compartment. Vesicles from the ER may go to the Golgi, and then vesicles from the Golgi may go to the lysosomes, vacuoles, or plasma membrane. Sorting signals within proteins' amino acid sequences are responsible for directing them to the correct location.

Proteins Are Sorted Post-translationally to the Nucleus, Peroxisomes, Mitochondria, and Chloroplasts

The organization and function of the nucleus, peroxisomes, mitochondria, and chloroplasts depend on the uptake of proteins from the cytosol. Most of these proteins are synthesized in the cytosol and then taken up into their respective organelles. For example, most proteins involved in ATP synthesis are made in the cytosol and taken up into mitochondria after they have been completely synthesized. For this to occur, a protein must have the appropriate sorting signal as part of its amino acid sequence.

As one example of post-translational sorting, let's consider how a protein is directed to the mitochondrial matrix. Such a protein has a short amino acid sequence at the N-terminus called a matrix-targeting sequence. As shown in **Figure 4.34**, the process of protein import into the matrix involves a series of intricate protein-protein interactions. A protein destined for the mitochondrial matrix is first made in the cytosol, where proteins called **chaperones** keep it in an unfolded state. A

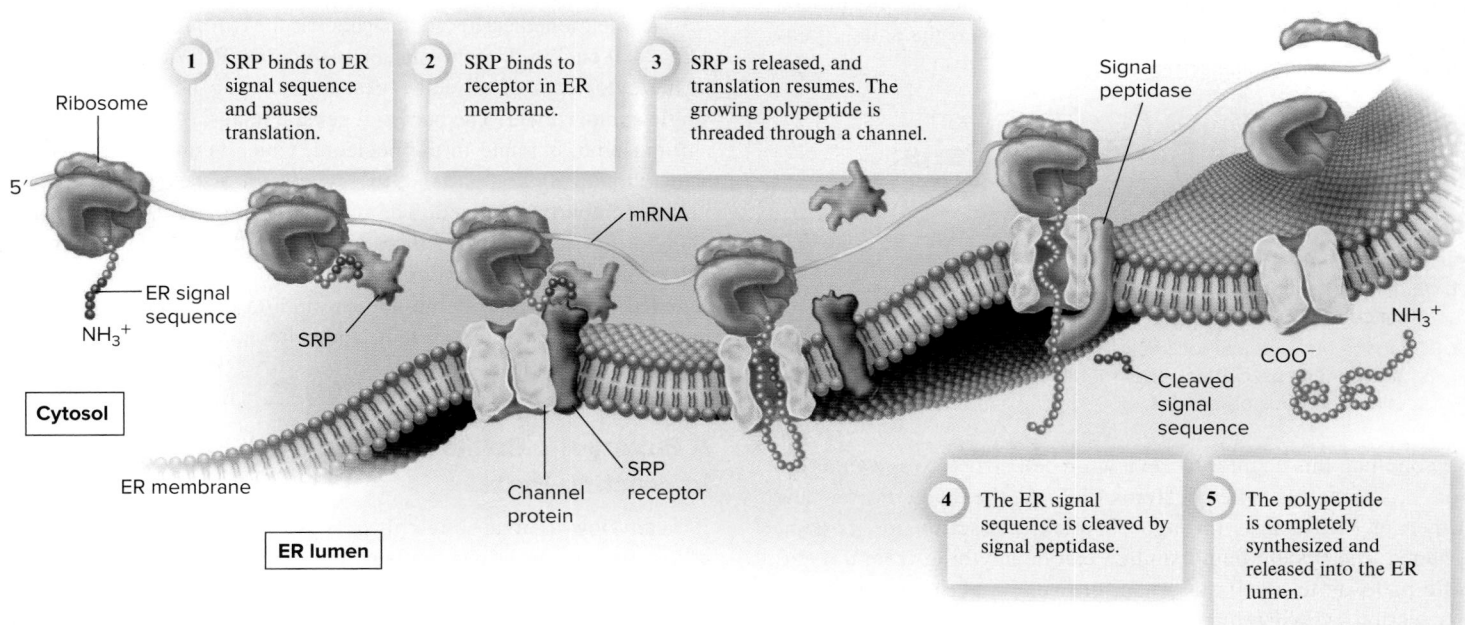

1 SRP binds to ER signal sequence and pauses translation.

2 SRP binds to receptor in ER membrane.

3 SRP is released, and translation resumes. The growing polypeptide is threaded through a channel.

Signal peptidase

Ribosome

5′

mRNA

ER signal sequence

NH₃⁺

SRP

Cytosol

ER membrane

Channel protein

SRP receptor

ER lumen

NH₃⁺

COO⁻

Cleaved signal sequence

4 The ER signal sequence is cleaved by signal peptidase.

5 The polypeptide is completely synthesized and released into the ER lumen.

Figure 4.33 **First step in cotranslational sorting: sending proteins to the ER.**

Concept Check: *What prevents a protein destined for the ER from being completely synthesized in the cytosol?*

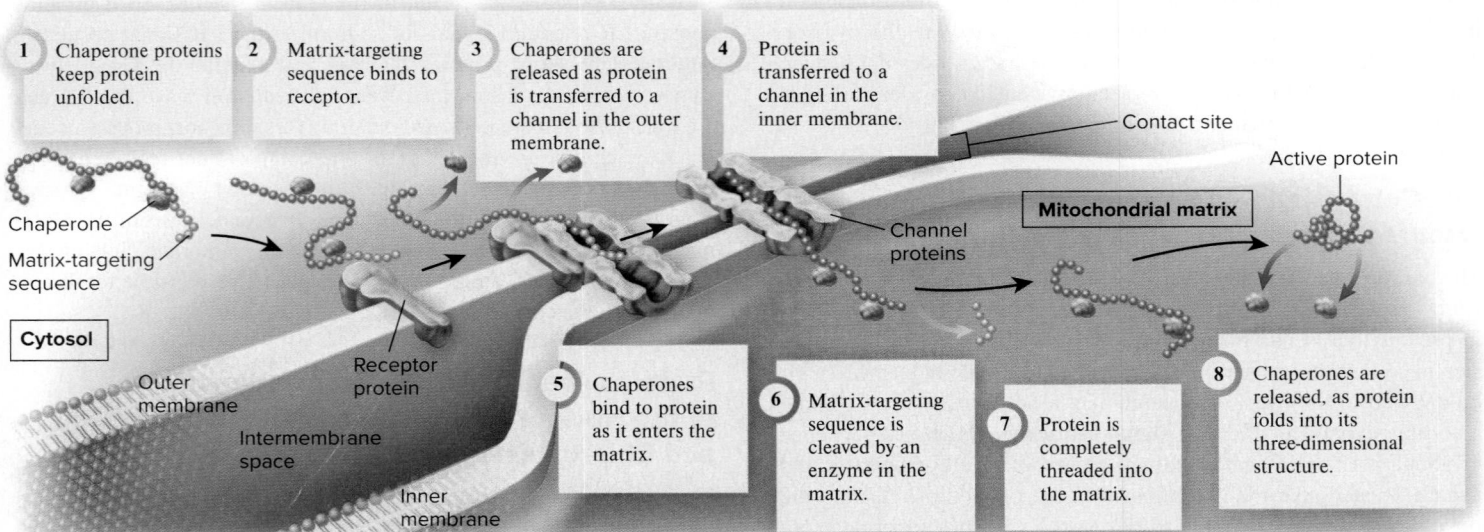

Figure 4.34 **Post-translational sorting of a protein to the mitochondrial matrix.**

Concept Check: *What do you think would happen if chaperone proteins did not bind to a protein before it was imported into the mitochondrial matrix?*

receptor protein in the outer mitochondrial membrane recognizes the matrix-targeting sequence. The protein is released from the chaperone as it is transferred to a channel in the outer mitochondrial membrane. Because it is in an unfolded state, the mitochondrial protein can be threaded through this channel, and then through another channel in the inner mitochondrial membrane. These channels lie close to each other at contact sites between the outer and inner membranes. As the protein emerges in the matrix, other chaperone proteins already in the matrix continue to keep it unfolded. Eventually, the matrix-targeting sequence is cleaved, and the entire protein is threaded into the matrix. At this stage, the chaperone proteins are released as the protein folds into its three-dimensional active structure.

4.8 Systems Biology of Cells: A Summary

Learning Outcomes:

1. Outline the differences in complexity among bacteria, animal, and plant cells.
2. Describe how a eukaryotic cell can be viewed as four interacting systems: nucleus, cytosol, endomembrane system, and semiautonomous organelles.

We conclude this chapter by reviewing cell structure and function from a perspective called **systems biology**, the study of how new properties of life arise through complex interactions of its components. The system being studied can be anything from a metabolic pathway to a cell, an organ, or even an entire organism. In this section, we view the cell as a system. First, we will compare prokaryotic and eukaryotic cells as systems, and then examine the four interconnected parts that make up the system that is the eukaryotic cell.

Bacterial Cells Are Relatively Simple Systems Compared to Eukaryotic Cells

Bacterial cells are relatively small and lack the extensive internal compartmentalization characteristic of eukaryotic cells (**Table 4.2**). On the outside, bacterial cells are surrounded by a cell wall, and many species have flagella. Animal cells lack a cell wall, and only certain cell types have flagella or cilia. Like bacteria, plant cells also have cell walls but the chemical composition of these walls is different from that of bacterial cells. Plant cells rarely have flagella.

As mentioned earlier in this chapter, the cytoplasm is the region of the cell enclosed by the plasma membrane. Ribosomes are found in the cytoplasm of all cell types. In bacteria, the cytoplasm is a single compartment. The bacterial genetic material, usually a single chromosome, is found in the nucleoid, which is not surrounded by a membrane. By comparison, the cytoplasm of eukaryotic cells is highly compartmentalized. The cytosol is the area that surrounds many different types of membrane-bound organelles. For example, eukaryotic chromosomes are found in the nucleus, which is surrounded by a double membrane. In addition, all eukaryotic cells have an endomembrane system, and mitochondria and plant cells also have chloroplasts.

A Eukaryotic Cell Is a System with Four Interacting Parts

We can view a eukaryotic cell as a system with four interacting parts: the interior of the nucleus, the cytosol, the endomembrane system, and the semiautonomous organelles. These four regions have their own structure and organization, while also playing a role in the structure and organization of the entire cell. The structures and functions of these four interacting parts are described in **Figure 4.35**.

Table 4.2	A Comparison of Cell Complexity Among Bacterial, Animal, and Plant Cells		
Structures	Bacteria	Animal cells	Plant cells
Extracellular structures			
Cell wall*	Present	Absent	Present
Flagella/cilia	Flagella sometimes present	Cilia or flagella present on certain cell types	Rarely present†
Plasma membrane	Present	Present	Present
Interior structures			
Cytoplasm	Usually a single compartment inside the plasma membrane	Composed of membrane-bound organelles that are surrounded by the cytosol	Composed of membrane-bound organelles that are surrounded by the cytosol
Ribosomes	Present	Present	Present
Chromosomes	Typically one circular chromosome per nucleoid; a nucleoid is not a membrane-bound compartment.	Multiple linear chromosomes in the nucleus, which is surrounded by a double membrane. Mitochondria also have chromosomes.	Multiple linear chromosomes in the nucleus, which is surrounded by a double membrane. Mitochondria and chloroplasts also have chromosomes.
Endomembrane system	Absent	Present	Present
Mitochondria	Absent	Present	Present
Chloroplasts	Absent	Absent	Present

*Note that the biochemical composition of bacterial cell walls is very different from plant cell walls.
†Some plant species produce sperm cells with flagella, but flowering plants produce sperm within pollen grains that lack flagella.

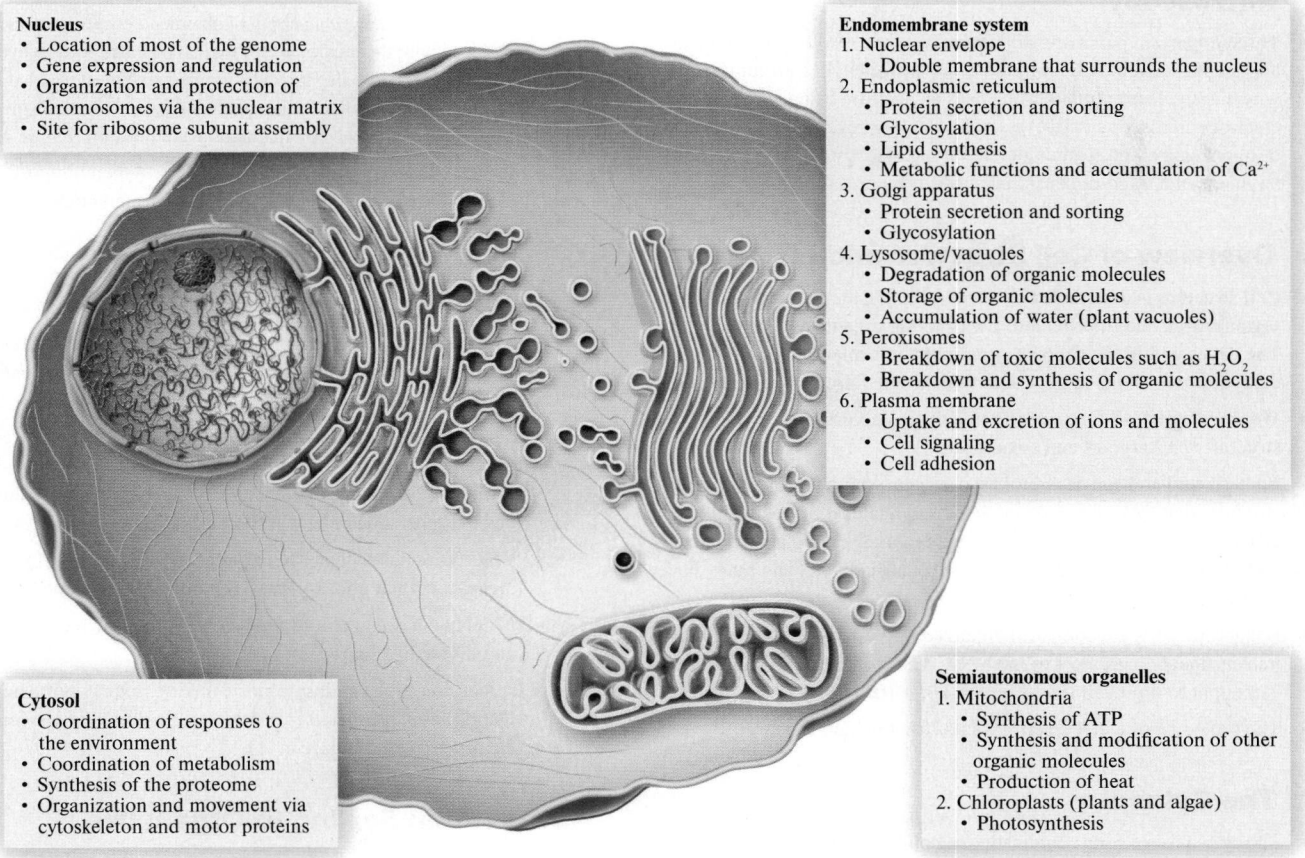

Figure 4.35 The four interacting parts of eukaryotic cells: nucleus, cytosol, endomembrane system, and semiautonomous organelles. An animal cell is illustrated here.

 Core Concept: Systems A eukaryotic cells is a system with four interacting parts.

Summary of Key Concepts

4.1 Origin of Living Cells on Earth

- Life on Earth is hypothesized to have arisen in four overlapping stages. The first stage involved the synthesis of organic molecules to form a prebiotic soup. Possible scenarios as to how this occurred are the reducing atmosphere, extraterrestrial, and deep-sea vent hypotheses (Figures 4.1, 4.2).
- The second stage was the formation of polymers from simple organic molecules. This may have occurred on the surface of clay.
- The third stage involved the emergence of protobionts, which were aggregates of polymers with a boundary that separated them from the external environment (Figure 4.3).
- In the fourth stage, polymers enclosed in membranes acquired properties of cells, such as self-replication and catalytic functions (Figure 4.4).
- During the hypothetical period called the RNA world, the first living cells used RNA for both information storage and catalytic functions.
- Bartel and Szostak demonstrated experimentally that chemical selection for RNA molecules that can catalyze covalent bond formation is possible.
- The RNA world was eventually superseded by the modern DNA/RNA/protein world.

4.2 Microscopy

- Three important parameters in microscopy are resolution, contrast, and magnification. A light microscope utilizes light for illumination, whereas an electron microscope uses an electron beam. Transmission electron microscopy (TEM) provides the best resolution of any form of microscopy, and scanning electron microscopy (SEM) produces an image of a three-dimensional surface (Figures 4.5, 4.6, 4.7).

4.3 Overview of Cell Structure and Function

- Cell structure is determined by four factors: matter, energy, organization, and information. Every living organism has a genome. The genes within the genome contain the information to produce the cellular proteins that largely determine a cell's structure and function.
- We can classify all forms of life into two categories based on cell structure: prokaryotes and eukaryotes.
- Bacteria and archaea have prokaryotic cells with a relatively simple structure that lacks a membrane-enclosed nucleus. Structures in prokaryotic cells include the plasma membrane, cytoplasm, nucleoid, and ribosomes. Prokaryotic cells also have a cell wall and many have a glycocalyx (Figure 4.8).
- Eukaryotic cells are compartmentalized into organelles and contain a nucleus that houses most of the DNA. The surface area/volume ratio is thought to limit cell size (Figures 4.9, 4.10, 4.11, 4.12).
- The proteome of a cell determines its structure and function.

4.4 The Cytosol

- The cytosol is a central coordinating region for many metabolic activities of eukaryotic cells, including polypeptide synthesis (Figure 4.13).
- The cytoskeleton is a network of three different types of protein filaments: microtubules, intermediate filaments, and actin filaments. Microtubules are important for cell shape, organization, and movement. Intermediate filaments help maintain cell shape, rigidity, and strength. Actin filaments support the plasma membrane and play a key role in cell strength, shape, and movement (Table 4.1, Figures 4.14, 4.15, 4.16, 4.17).

4.5 The Nucleus and Endomembrane System

- The primary function of the nucleus is the organization and expression of the genetic material. A second important function is the assembly of ribosomal subunits in the nucleolus (Figures 4.18, 4.19, 4.20).
- The endomembrane system includes the nuclear envelope, endoplasmic reticulum (ER), Golgi apparatus, lysosomes, vacuoles, peroxisomes, and plasma membrane. The rough endoplasmic reticulum (rough ER) plays a key role in the initial sorting of proteins. The smooth endoplasmic reticulum (smooth ER) functions in metabolic processes such as detoxification, carbohydrate metabolism, accumulation of calcium ions, and synthesis and modification of lipids. The Golgi apparatus performs three overlapping functions: processing, protein sorting, and secretion. Lysosomes degrade macromolecules and help digest substances taken up from outside the cell (endocytosis) and inside the cell (autophagy) (Figures 4.21, 4.22).
- Palade's pulse-chase experiments demonstrated that secreted proteins move sequentially through the ER and Golgi apparatus (Figure 4.23).
- Types of vacuoles include central vacuoles, contractile vacuoles, and food or phagocytic vacuoles (Figure 4.24).
- Peroxisomes catalyze a variety of chemical reactions, including those involved with the breakdown of toxic molecules such as hydrogen peroxide, and they also typically contain enzymes involved in the metabolism of fats and amino acids. Peroxisomes are formed by budding from the ER, followed by maturation and division (Figure 4.25).
- Proteins in the plasma membrane perform many important roles that affect activities inside the cell, including membrane transport, cell signaling, and cell adhesion (Figure 4.26).

4.6 Semiautonomous Organelles

- Mitochondria and chloroplasts are considered semiautonomous organelles because they grow and divide, but still depend on other parts of the cell for their internal components (Figure 4.27).
- Mitochondria produce most of a cell's ATP, which is utilized by many proteins to carry out their functions. Other mitochondrial functions include the synthesis, modification, and breakdown of cellular molecules and the generation of heat in specialized fat cells (Figure 4.28).
- Chloroplasts, which are found in nearly all species of plants and algae, carry out photosynthesis (Figure 4.29).
- Mitochondria and chloroplasts contain their own genetic material and divide by binary fission (Figure 4.30).
- According to the endosymbiosis theory, mitochondria and chloroplasts originated from bacteria that took up residence in early eukaryotic cells (Figure 4.31).

4.7 Protein Sorting to Organelles

- Proteins synthesized in eukaryotic cells are sorted to their correct cellular destination (Figure 4.32).
- The cotranslational sorting of proteins to the ER, Golgi, lysosomes, vacuoles, plasma membrane, and secretory vesicles begins in the

cytosol, while translation is occurring, and involves sorting signals and vesicle transport (Figure 4.33).

- Most proteins destined for the nucleus, mitochondria, chloroplasts, and peroxisomes are synthesized in the cytosol and taken up after synthesis is complete; this is called post-translational sorting (Figure 4.34).

4.8   Systems Biology of Cells: A Summary

- Systems biology is the study of how new properties of life arise by complex interactions of its components. In systems biology, the cell is viewed in terms of its structural and functional connections, rather than its individual molecular components.

- Prokaryotic and eukaryotic cells differ in their levels of organization. In eukaryotic cells, four parts—nucleus, cytosol, endomembrane system, and semiautonomous organelles—work together to produce dynamic organization (Table 4.2, Figure 4.35).

Assess & Discuss

Test Yourself

1. The cell theory states that
   a. all living things are composed of cells.
   b. cells are the smallest units of living organisms.
   c. new cells come from pre-existing cells by cell division.
   d. all of the above.
   e. only a and b are true.

2. For a microscope, resolution refers to
   a. the ratio between the size of the image produced by the microscope and the actual size of the object.
   b. the degree to which a particular structure looks different from other structures around it.
   c. how well a structure takes up certain dyes.
   d. the ability to observe two adjacent objects as being distinct from each other.
   e. the degree to which the image is magnified.

3. A spherical cell has a radius of 34 μm. What is its surface area/volume ratio?
   a. 0.088
   b. 0.12
   c. 11.3
   d. 55.7
   e. 127

4. If a motor protein was held in place and a cytoskeletal filament was free to move, what type of motion would occur when the motor protein was active?
   a. The motor protein would "walk" along the filament.
   b. The filament would move.
   c. The filament would bend.
   d. all of the above
   e. Only b and c would happen.

5. Each of the following is part of the endomembrane system except
   a. the nuclear envelope.
   b. the endoplasmic reticulum.
   c. the Golgi apparatus.
   d. lysosomes.
   e. mitochondria.

6. Vesicle transport occurs between the ER and the Golgi in both directions. Let's suppose a researcher exposed some cells to a drug that inhibited vesicle transport from the Golgi to the ER but did not affect vesicle transport from the ER to the Golgi. If you observed the cells microscopically after the drug was added, what would you expect to see happen over the course of 1 hour?
   a. The ER would get smaller, and the Golgi would get larger.
   b. The ER would get larger, and the Golgi would get smaller.
   c. The ER and Golgi would stay the same size.
   d. Both the ER and Golgi would get larger.
   e. Both the ER and Golgi would get smaller.

7. Functions of the smooth endoplasmic reticulum include
   a. detoxification of harmful organic molecules.
   b. metabolism of carbohydrates.
   c. protein sorting.
   d. all of the above.
   e. a and b only.

8. The central vacuole in many plant cells is important for
   a. storage.
   b. photosynthesis.
   c. structural support.
   d. all of the above.
   e. a and c only.

9. Let's suppose an abnormal protein contains three sorting signals: an ER signal sequence, an ER retention sequence, and a mitochondrial matrix-targeting sequence. The ER retention sequence is supposed to keep a protein within the ER. Where would you expect this abnormal protein to go? Note: Think carefully about the timing of events in protein sorting and which events occur cotranslationally and which occur post-translationally.
   a. It would go to the ER.
   b. It would go the mitochondria.
   c. It would go to both the ER and mitochondria equally.
   d. It would remain in the cytosol.
   e. It would be secreted.

10. Which of the following observations would *not* be considered evidence for the endosymbiosis theory?
    a. Mitochondria and chloroplasts have genomes that resemble smaller versions of bacterial genomes.
    b. Mitochondria, chloroplasts, and bacteria all divide by binary fission.
    c. Mitochondria, chloroplasts, and bacteria all have ribosomes.
    d. Mitochondria, chloroplasts, and bacteria all have similar sizes and shapes.
    e. All of the above are considered evidence for the theory.

Conceptual Questions

1. What are the four stages that led to the origin of living cells?

2. Explain how motor proteins and cytoskeletal filaments interact to promote three different types of movements: movement of a cargo, movement of a filament, and bending of a filament.

3.   **Core Concept: Structure and Function** A core concept of biology is that *structure determines function*. Explain how the invaginations of the inner mitochondrial membrane are related to mitochondrial function.

Collaborative Questions

1. Discuss the roles of the genome and proteome in determining cell structure and function.

2. Discuss and draw the structural relationship between the nucleus, the rough endoplasmic reticulum, and the Golgi apparatus.

Membrane Structure, Synthesis, and Transport

This is a model of a membrane in which a protein (shown in yellow) is embedded in a bilayer of lipids. The protein functions as a channel that allows ions to cross the membrane.
©Ramón Andrade, 3Dciencia/Science Source

When he was 28, Andrew began to develop a combination of symptoms that included fatigue, joint pain, abdominal pain, and a loss of sex drive. His doctor conducted some tests and discovered that Andrew had abnormally high levels of iron in his body. Iron is a mineral found in many foods. Andrew was diagnosed with a genetic disease called hemochromatosis, which caused him to absorb more iron than he needed. This was due to an overactive protein involved in the transport of iron across the membranes of intestinal cells and into the bloodstream. Unfortunately, when the human body takes up too much iron, it is stored in body tissues, especially the liver, heart, pancreas, and joints. The extra iron can damage a person's organs.

In Andrew's case, the disease was caught relatively early, and treatment—which includes a modification in diet along with medication that inhibits the absorption of iron—prevented more severe symptoms. Without treatment, however, hemochromatosis can cause organ failure. Later signs and symptoms include skin discoloration, arthritis, liver disease, diabetes mellitus, and heart failure.

The disease hemochromatosis illustrates the importance of membranes in regulating the traffic of ions and molecules into and out of cells.

All cells have a **plasma membrane** that encloses the cytoplasm, and eukaryotic cells have internal membranes that surround organelles (see Chapter 4). Both types are also called **biological membranes**. The plasma membrane separates the internal contents of a cell from its external environment. With such a role, you might imagine that the plasma membrane would be thick and rigid. Remarkably, the opposite is true. All biological membranes, including the plasma membrane, are thin (typically 5–10 nm) and somewhat fluid. It would take 5,000–10,000 of these membranes stacked on top of each other to equal the thickness of a piece of paper! Despite their thinness, however, membranes are impressively dynamic structures that effectively maintain the separation between a cell and its surroundings and also provide interfaces where many vital cellular activities occur (Table 5.1).

In this chapter, we will begin by considering the components that provide the structure and fluid properties of membranes and then explore how they are synthesized. Finally, we will examine one of a membrane's primary functions—membrane transport. Biological membranes regulate the traffic of substances into and out of the cell and its organelles. As you will learn, this occurs via transport proteins and via exocytosis and endocytosis.

Table 5.1	Important Functions of Biological Membranes
Function	
Selective uptake and export of ions and molecules	
Cell compartmentalization	
Protein sorting	
Anchoring of the cytoskeleton	
Production of energy intermediates such as ATP and NADPH	
Cell signaling	
Cell and nuclear division	
Adhesion of cells to each other and to the extracellular matrix	

5.1   Membrane Structure

Learning Outcomes:

1. Describe the fluid-mosaic model of membrane structure.
2. Identify the three different types of membrane proteins.

The two primary components of membranes are phospholipids, which form the basic matrix of a membrane, and proteins, which are embedded in the membrane or loosely attached to its surface. A third component is carbohydrates, which may be attached to membrane lipids and proteins. In this section, we will examine the organization of these components to form a biological membrane and their importance in the overall function of membranes.

Biological Membranes Are a Mosaic of Lipids, Proteins, and Carbohydrates

Figure 5.1 shows the biochemical organization of a membrane, which is similar in composition among all living organisms. The framework of the membrane is the **phospholipid bilayer**, which consists of two layers of phospholipids. Recall from Chapter 3 that phospholipids are **amphipathic** molecules. They have hydrophobic (water-fearing) or nonpolar tails, and also a hydrophilic (water-loving) or polar head. The nonpolar tails of the lipids are found in the interior of the membrane, and the polar heads are on the surface. Biological membranes also contain proteins, and most membranes have carbohydrates attached to lipids and proteins. Overall, the membrane is considered a mosaic of lipid, protein, and carbohydrate molecules.

The membrane structure illustrated in Figure 5.1 is referred to as the **fluid-mosaic model**, originally proposed by S. Jonathan Singer and Garth Nicolson in 1972. As discussed later, the membrane exhibits properties that resemble a fluid because lipids and proteins can move relative to each other within the membrane.

Half of a phospholipid bilayer is termed a **leaflet**. Each leaflet faces a different region. For example, the plasma membrane contains a cytosolic leaflet and an extracellular leaflet (see Figure 5.1). With regard to lipid composition, the two leaflets of membranes are asymmetrical. Certain types of lipids may be more abundant in one leaflet compared to the other. A striking asymmetry occurs with glycolipids—lipids with a carbohydrate attached. These are found primarily in the extracellular leaflet of the plasma membrane. The carbohydrate portion of a glycolipid protrudes into the extracellular medium.

Proteins Associate with Membranes in Three Different Ways

Although the phospholipid bilayer forms the basic foundation of cellular membranes, the protein component carries out many key functions. Some of these functions were considered in Chapter 4. For example, we saw how membrane proteins in the smooth ER membrane function as enzymes that break down glycogen. Later in this chapter, we will explore how membrane proteins are involved in transporting ions and molecules across membranes. In other chapters, we will examine how membrane proteins are responsible for other functions, including ATP synthesis (Chapter 7), photosynthesis (Chapter 8), cell signaling (Chapter 9), and cell-to-cell adhesion (Chapter 10).

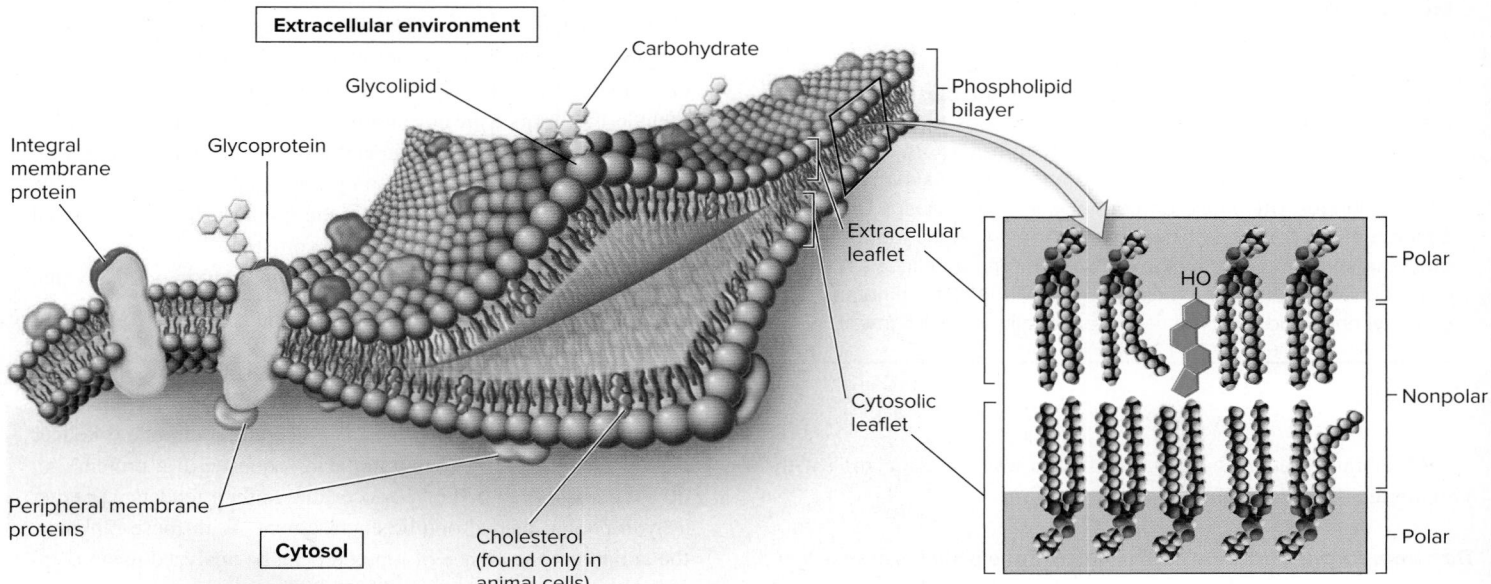

Figure 5.1   Fluid-mosaic model of membrane structure. The membrane shown here is a plasma membrane of a eukaryotic cell, which separates the extracellular environment from the cytosol. The basic framework of a membrane is a phospholipid bilayer, which may also contain other lipids such as cholesterol. Integral membrane proteins have regions that span the membrane. Peripheral membrane proteins are noncovalently attached to integral membrane proteins or to lipids. Proteins and lipids that have covalently bound carbohydrates are called glycoproteins and glycolipids, respectively. The inset shows nine phospholipids and one cholesterol molecule in a bilayer, and it emphasizes the polar and nonpolar regions of the two leaflets. Note: A portion of the bilayer is artificially pealed apart so you can more easily see the two leaflets.

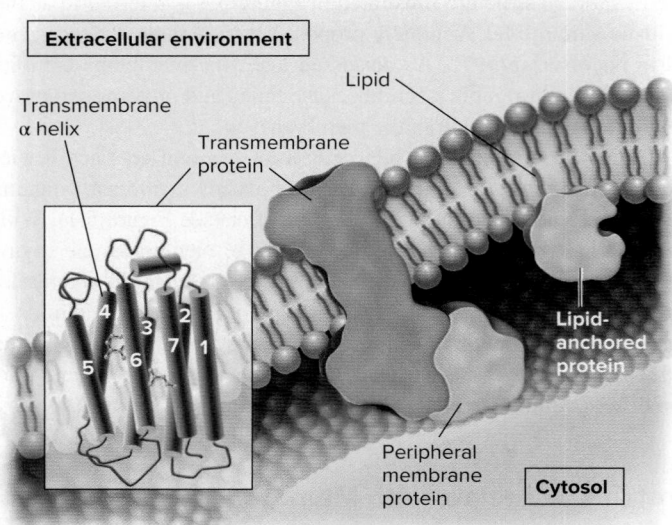

Figure 5.2 **Types of membrane proteins.** Integral membrane proteins are of two types: transmembrane proteins and lipid-anchored proteins. Peripheral membrane proteins are noncovalently bound to the hydrophilic regions of integral membrane proteins or to the polar head groups of lipids. Inset: The protein bacteriorhodopsin contains seven transmembrane segments, depicted as cylinders, each having an α-helical structure. Bacteriorhodopsin is found in halophilic (salt-loving) archaea.

 Core Skill: Modeling The goal of this modeling challenge is to propose a model for a transmembrane protein.

Modeling Challenge: As shown in Figure 5.2, some α helices, which are called transmembrane α helices, may be inserted into the hydrophobic region of a membrane and span the entire membrane. Let's suppose a protein in the plasma membrane has 5 transmembrane α helices. The loops that connect these 5 transmembrane segments are relatively short, except for the one that connects transmembrane segments 4 and 5, which is longer. The amino end projects into the cytosol. Draw a model of this transmembrane protein in the plasma membrane. In your model, draw the transmembrane α helices as cylinders and label them 1 through 5. Also label the amino and carboxyl ends and the cytosol and extracellular environment.

Membrane proteins have three different ways of associating with a membrane (**Figure 5.2**).

Transmembrane Proteins **Transmembrane proteins** have one or more regions that are physically inserted into the hydrophobic interior of the phospholipid bilayer. These regions, the transmembrane segments, are stretches of nonpolar amino acids that span or traverse the membrane from one leaflet to the other. In most transmembrane proteins, each transmembrane segment is folded into an α helix. Such a segment is stable in a membrane because the nonpolar amino acids interact favorably with the nonpolar lipid tails.

Lipid-Anchored Proteins A **lipid-anchored protein** associates with a membrane because it has a lipid molecule that is covalently attached to an amino acid side chain within the protein. The lipid tails are inserted into the hydrophobic portion of the membrane and thereby keep the protein firmly attached to the membrane. Both lipid-anchored proteins and transmembrane proteins are considered to be **integral membrane proteins** because they cannot be released from the membrane unless the membrane is dissolved with an organic solvent or detergent. In other words, they cannot be removed without disrupting the integrity of the membrane.

Peripheral Membrane Proteins **Peripheral membrane proteins** associate with membranes in a third way. They do not interact with the hydrophobic interior of the phospholipid bilayer. Instead, they are noncovalently bound to regions of integral membrane proteins that project out from the membrane (see Figure 5.2), or they are bound to the polar head groups of phospholipids. Peripheral membrane proteins are typically attached to the membrane by hydrogen and/or ionic bonds.

 **Core Concept: Information**

Approximately 20–30% of All Genes Encode Transmembrane Proteins

Membrane proteins participate in some of the most important cellular processes, including transport, energy transduction, cell signaling, secretion, cell recognition, metabolism, and cell-to-cell contact. Research studies have revealed that cells devote a sizable fraction of their energy and metabolic machinery to the synthesis of membrane proteins. These proteins are particularly important in human medicine—approximately 70% of all medications exert their effects by binding to membrane proteins. Examples include the drugs aspirin, ibuprofen, and acetaminophen, which are widely used to relieve pain and inflammatory conditions such as arthritis. These drugs bind to cyclooxygenase, a protein in the ER membrane that is necessary for the synthesis of chemicals that play a role in pain sensation and inflammation.

Because membrane proteins are so important biologically and medically, researchers have analyzed the genomes of many species and asked the question "What percentage of genes encode transmembrane proteins?" To answer this question, they have developed tools to predict the likelihood that a gene encodes a transmembrane protein. For example, the occurrence of transmembrane α helices can be predicted from the amino acid sequence of a protein. All 20 amino acids can be ranked according to their tendency to enter a hydrophobic or hydrophilic environment. With these rankings, the amino acid sequence of a protein can be analyzed using computer software to determine the average hydrophobicity of short amino acid sequences within the protein. A stretch of 18–20 amino acids in an α helix is long enough to span the membrane. If such a stretch contains a high percentage of hydrophobic amino acids, it is predicted to be a transmembrane α helix. However, such computer predictions must eventually be verified by experimentation.

Table 5.2	Estimated Percentage of Genes That Encode Transmembrane Proteins*
Organism	Percentage of protein-encoding genes that encode transmembrane proteins
Archaea	
Archaeoglobus fulgidus	24.2
Methanococcus jannaschii	20.4
Pyrococcus horikoshii	29.9
Bacteria	
Escherichia coli	29.9
Bacillus subtilis	29.2
Haemophilus influenzae	25.3
Eukaryotes	
Homo sapiens	29.7
Drosophila melanogaster	24.9
Arabidopsis thaliana	30.5
Saccharomyces cerevisiae	28.2

* Source: Stevens, A. J., and Arkin, T. I. 2000. Do More Complex Organisms Have a Greater Proportion of Membrane Proteins in Their Genomes? *Proteins* 39: 417–420.

Using computer analysis, many research groups have attempted to calculate the percentage of genes that encode transmembrane proteins in various species. Table 5.2 shows the results of one such study. The estimated percentage of transmembrane proteins is substantial: 20–30% of all genes may encode transmembrane proteins. This trend is found throughout all domains of life, including archaea, bacteria, and eukaryotes. For example, about 30% of human genes encode transmembrane proteins. With a genome size of about 22,000 different protein-encoding genes, the total number of human genes that encode transmembrane proteins is estimated to be 6,600. The functions of many of the proteins have yet to be determined. Identifying their functions will help researchers gain a better understanding of human biology. Likewise, medical researchers and pharmaceutical companies are interested in the identification of new transmembrane proteins that could be targets for effective new medications.

5.2 Fluidity of Membranes

Learning Outcomes:
1. Describe the fluidity of membranes.
2. **CoreSKILL** » Predict how changes in lipid composition affect membrane fluidity.
3. **CoreSKILL** » Analyze the results of experiments that showed the lateral diffusion of membrane proteins.

Let's now turn our attention to the dynamic properties of membranes. Although a membrane provides a critical interface between a cell or an organelle and its environment, it is not a solid, rigid structure. Rather, biological membranes exhibit properties of **fluidity**, which means that individual molecules remain in close association yet have

the ability to readily move within the membrane. In this section, we will examine the fluid properties of biological membranes.

Membranes Are Semifluid

Though membranes are often described as fluid, it is more appropriate to say they are **semifluid**, because the movement of membrane components occurs only in two dimensions. In a fluid substance, molecules can move in three dimensions. By comparison, most phospholipids can rotate freely around their long axes and move laterally within the membrane leaflet (**Figure 5.3a**). This type of motion is considered two-dimensional, which means it occurs within the plane of the membrane. Because rotational and lateral movements keep the lipid tails within the hydrophobic interior, such movements are energetically favorable. At 37°C, a typical lipid molecule exchanges places with its neighbors about 10^7 times per second, and it can move several micrometers per second. At this rate, a lipid can traverse the length of a bacterial cell (approximately 1 μm) in only 1 second and the length of a typical animal cell in 10 to 20 seconds.

In contrast to rotational and lateral movements, the flip-flop of lipids from one leaflet to the opposite leaflet does not occur spontaneously. Flip-flop is energetically unfavorable because the polar head of a phospholipid would have to travel through the hydrophobic interior of the membrane. How are lipids moved from one leaflet to the other? The transport of lipids between leaflets is due to the action of the enzyme flippase, which requires energy input in the form of ATP (**Figure 5.3b**).

Although most lipids diffuse rotationally and laterally within the plane of the lipid bilayer, researchers have discovered that certain types of lipids in animal cells tend to strongly associate with each other to form structures called lipid rafts. As the word raft suggests, a **lipid raft** is a group of lipids that float together as a unit within a larger sea of lipids. Lipid rafts have a lipid composition that differs from the surrounding membrane. For example, they usually have a high amount of cholesterol. In addition, lipid rafts may contain unique sets of lipid-anchored proteins and transmembrane proteins. The functional importance of lipid rafts is the subject of a large amount of current research. Lipid rafts may play an important role in endocytosis (discussed later in this chapter) and cell signaling.

Lipid Composition Affects Membrane Fluidity

The biochemical properties of phospholipids affect the fluidity of the phospholipid bilayer.

Length of Phospholipid Tails One key factor that affects membrane fluidity is the length of the lipid tails, which range from 14 to 24 carbon atoms, with 16 to 18 carbons being the most common. Shorter tails are less likely to interact with each other, which makes the membrane more fluid.

Double Bonds in Phospholipid Tails A second important factor is the presence of double bonds in the lipid tails. When a double bond is present, the lipid is said to be **unsaturated** with respect to the number of hydrogens that are bound to the carbon atoms (refer back to Figure 3.9). A double bond creates a kink in a lipid tail (see inset to Figure 5.1), making it more difficult for neighboring tails to interact and making the bilayer more fluid. As described in Chapter 3, unsaturated lipids tend to be more liquid than saturated lipids, which often form solids at room temperature (refer back to Figure 3.10).

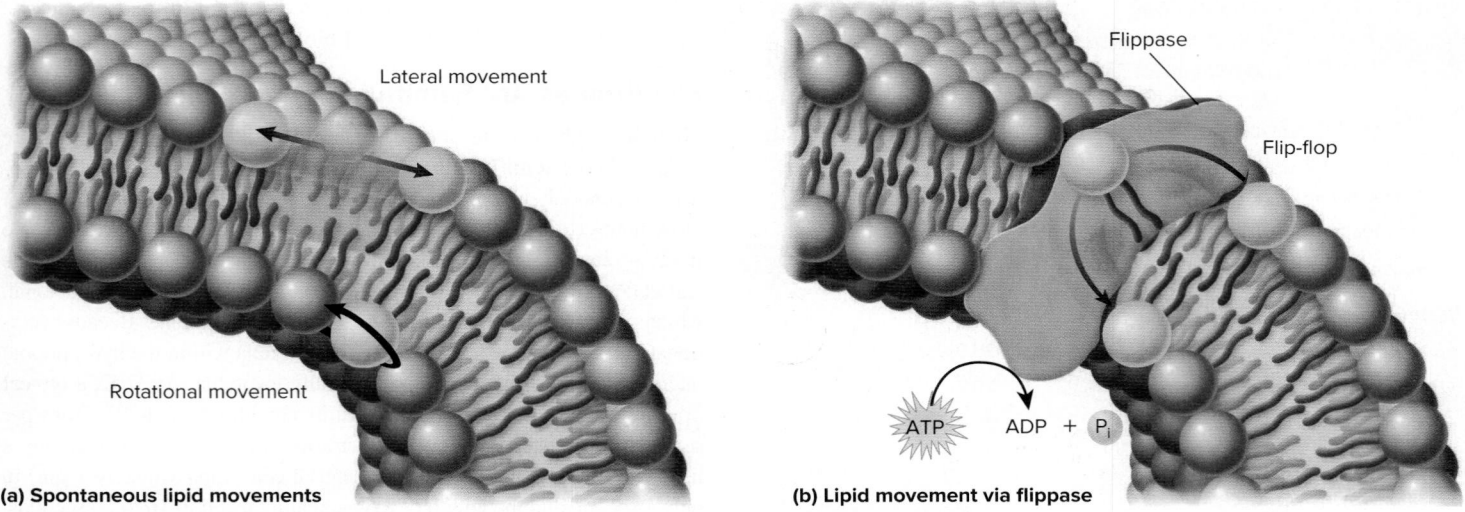

(a) Spontaneous lipid movements

(b) Lipid movement via flippase

Figure 5.3 Semifluidity of the lipid bilayer. (a) Spontaneous movements in the bilayer. Lipids can rotate (that is, move 360°) and move laterally (for example, from left to right in the plane of the bilayer). **(b)** Flip-flop does not happen spontaneously, because the polar head group would have to pass through the hydrophobic region of the bilayer. Instead, the enzyme flippase uses ATP to flip phospholipids from one leaflet to the other.

Cholesterol   A third factor affecting fluidity is the presence of cholesterol, a short and rigid molecule produced by animal cells (see inset to Figure 5.1). Plant cell membranes contain phytosterols that resemble cholesterol in their chemical structure. Cholesterol tends to stabilize membranes; its effects depend on temperature. At higher temperatures, such as those observed in mammals that maintain a constant body temperature, cholesterol makes the membrane less fluid. At lower temperatures, such as icy water, cholesterol has the opposite effect. It makes the membrane more fluid and prevents it from freezing.

An optimal level of bilayer fluidity is essential for normal cell function, growth, and division. If a membrane is too fluid, which may occur at higher temperatures, it can become leaky. However, if a membrane becomes too solid, which may occur at lower temperatures, the functioning of membrane proteins will be inhibited. How can organisms cope with changes in temperature? The cells of many species adapt to changes in temperature by altering the lipid composition of their membranes. For example, when the water temperature drops, the cells of certain fish will incorporate more cholesterol into their membranes, making the membrane more fluid. If a plant cell is exposed to high temperatures for many hours or days, it will alter the lipid composition of its cell membrane to have longer lipid tails and fewer double bonds, which will make the membrane less fluid.

Many Transmembrane Proteins Can Rotate and Move Laterally, but Some Are Restricted in Their Movement

Like lipids, many transmembrane proteins may rotate and move laterally throughout the plane of a membrane. Because transmembrane proteins are larger than lipids, they move within the membrane at a much slower rate. Flip-flop of transmembrane proteins does not occur, because the proteins also contain hydrophilic regions that project out from the phospholipid bilayer, and it would be energetically unfavorable for the hydrophilic regions of membrane proteins to pass through the hydrophobic portion of the phospholipid bilayer.

In 1970, Larry Frye and Michael Edidin conducted an experiment that verified the lateral movement of transmembrane proteins (**Figure 5.4**). Mouse and human cells were mixed together and

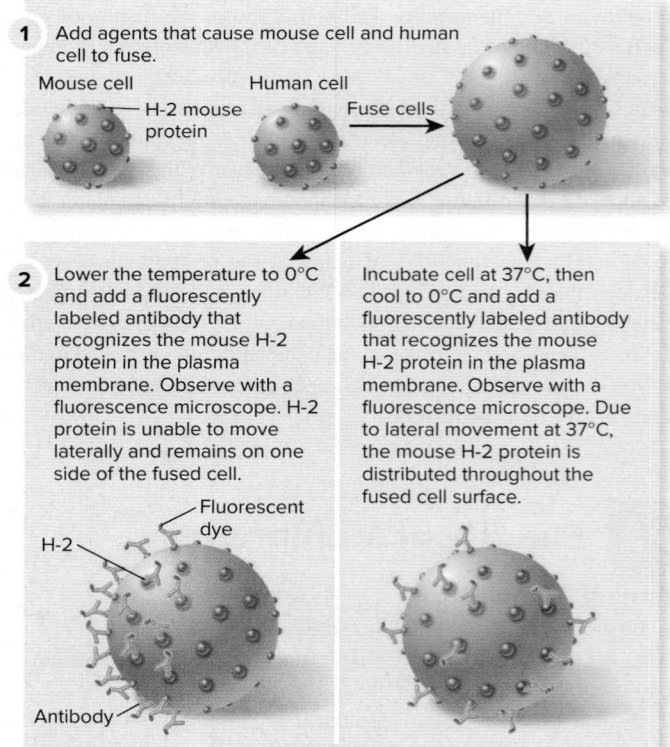

1. Add agents that cause mouse cell and human cell to fuse.
   Mouse cell   Human cell
   H-2 mouse protein   Fuse cells

2. Lower the temperature to 0°C and add a fluorescently labeled antibody that recognizes the mouse H-2 protein in the plasma membrane. Observe with a fluorescence microscope. H-2 protein is unable to move laterally and remains on one side of the fused cell.

   Incubate cell at 37°C, then cool to 0°C and add a fluorescently labeled antibody that recognizes the mouse H-2 protein in the plasma membrane. Observe with a fluorescence microscope. Due to lateral movement at 37°C, the mouse H-2 protein is distributed throughout the fused cell surface.

   Fluorescent dye
   H-2
   Antibody

Figure 5.4 A method to measure the lateral movement of membrane proteins.

 Core Skill: Process of Science This experiment verified that membrane proteins can diffuse laterally within the plane of the lipid bilayer.

exposed to agents that caused them to fuse with each other to produce mouse-human cell hybrids. Some cells were cooled to 0°C, while others were incubated at 37°C before being cooled. Both sets of cells were then exposed to fluorescently labeled antibodies that became specifically bound to a mouse transmembrane protein called H-2. The fluorescent label was observed with a fluorescence microscope. If the cells were maintained at 0°C, a temperature that greatly inhibits lateral movement, the fluorescence was seen on only one side of the fused cell. However, if the cells were incubated for several hours at 37°C and then cooled to 0°C, the fluorescence was distributed throughout the plasma membrane of the fused cell. This occurred because the higher temperature allowed the lateral movement of the H-2 protein throughout the fused cell.

Unlike the example shown in Figure 5.4, not all transmembrane proteins are capable of rotational and lateral movement. Depending on the cell type, 10–70% of membrane proteins may be restricted in their movement. Transmembrane proteins may be bound to components of the cytoskeleton, which restricts the proteins from moving (**Figure 5.5**), or they may be attached to molecules that are outside the cell, such as the interconnected network of proteins that forms the extracellular matrix of animal cells (see Chapter 10).

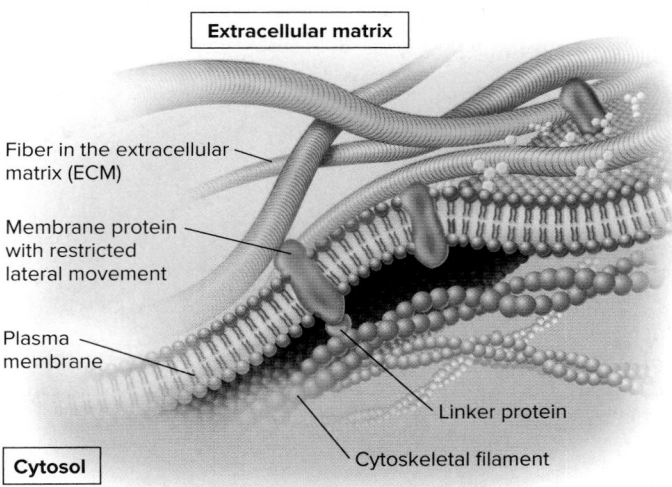

Figure 5.5 Attachment of transmembrane proteins to the cytoskeleton and extracellular matrix of an animal cell. Some transmembrane proteins have regions that extend into the cytosol and are anchored to large cytoskeletal filaments via linker proteins. Being bound to these large filaments restricts the movement of these proteins. Similarly, some transmembrane proteins are bound to large, immobile fibers in the extracellular matrix, which restricts their movement.

 Core Skill: Connections Look ahead to Figure 10.8. Discuss how transmembrane proteins are important in the binding of cells to each other and the binding of cells to the extracellular matrix.

5.3 Synthesis of Membrane Components in Eukaryotic Cells

Learning Outcomes:
1. Outline the synthesis of lipids at the ER membrane.
2. Explain how transmembrane proteins are inserted into the ER membrane.
3. Describe the process of glycosylation, and explain its functional consequences.

As we have seen, membranes are composed of lipids, proteins, and carbohydrates. Most of the membrane components of eukaryotic cells are made at the endoplasmic reticulum (ER). In this section, we will begin by considering how phospholipids are synthesized at the ER membrane. We will then examine the process by which transmembrane proteins are inserted into the ER membrane and explore how carbohydrates are attached to some proteins.

Lipid Synthesis Occurs at the ER Membrane

In eukaryotic cells, the cytosol and endomembrane system work together to synthesize most lipids. This process occurs at the cytosolic leaflet of the smooth ER membrane. **Figure 5.6** shows a simplified pathway for the synthesis of phospholipids. The building blocks of a phospholipid are two fatty acids, each with a long tail, one glycerol molecule, one phosphate, and a polar head group. These building blocks are made via enzymes in the cytosol, or they are taken into cells from food. To begin the process of phospholipid synthesis, the fatty acids are activated by attachment to an organic molecule called coenzyme A (CoA). This activation promotes the bonding of the two fatty acids to a glycerol-phosphate molecule, and the resulting molecule is inserted into the cytosolic leaflet of the ER membrane. The phosphate is removed from glycerol, and then a polar molecule already linked to phosphate is attached to glycerol. In the example shown in Figure 5.6, the polar head group contains choline, but many other types of head groups are possible. Phospholipids are initially inserted into the cytosolic leaflet. Flippases in the ER membrane transfer about half of the newly made phospholipids to the other leaflet so similar amounts of lipids are found in both leaflets.

The lipids made in the ER membrane are transferred to other membranes in the cell by a variety of mechanisms. Phospholipids in the ER can diffuse laterally to the nuclear envelope. In addition, lipids are transported via vesicles to the Golgi, lysosomes, vacuoles, or plasma membrane. A third mode of lipid transfer involves **lipid exchange proteins**, which extract a lipid from one membrane, diffuse through the cell, and insert the lipid into another membrane. Such transfer can occur between any two membranes, even between the endomembrane system and semiautonomous organelles. For example, lipid exchange proteins transfer lipids between the ER and mitochondria. In addition, chloroplasts and mitochondria synthesize certain types of lipids that are transferred from these organelles to other cellular membranes via lipid exchange proteins.

In figure labels: Extracellular matrix, Fiber in the extracellular matrix (ECM), Membrane protein with restricted lateral movement, Plasma membrane, Linker protein, Cytoskeletal filament, Cytosol

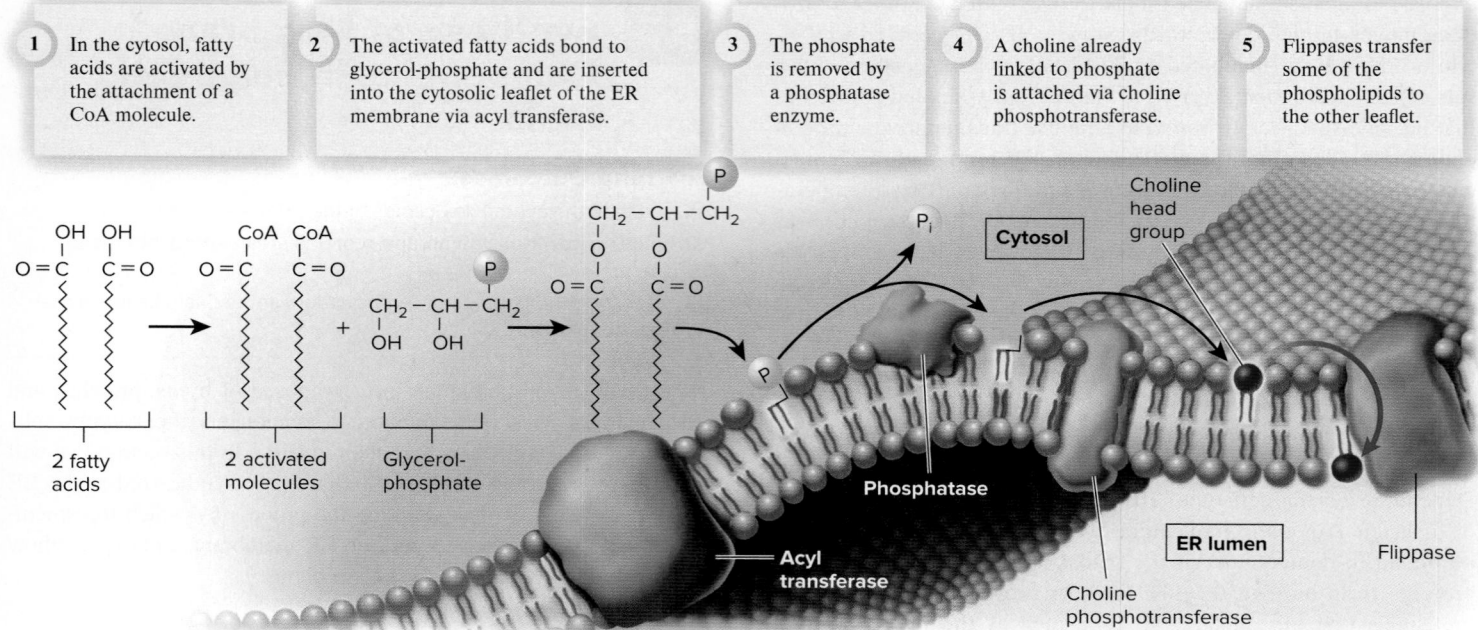

1 In the cytosol, fatty acids are activated by the attachment of a CoA molecule.

2 The activated fatty acids bond to glycerol-phosphate and are inserted into the cytosolic leaflet of the ER membrane via acyl transferase.

3 The phosphate is removed by a phosphatase enzyme.

4 A choline already linked to phosphate is attached via choline phosphotransferase.

5 Flippases transfer some of the phospholipids to the other leaflet.

Figure 5.6 **A simplified pathway for the synthesis of membrane phospholipids at the ER membrane.** Note: Phosphate is abbreviated P when it is attached to an organic molecule and P_i when it is unattached. The subscript i refers to the inorganic form of phosphate.

Concept Check: *How are phospholipids transferred to the leaflet of the ER membrane that faces the ER lumen?*

Most Transmembrane Proteins Are First Inserted into the ER Membrane

In Chapter 4, we considered how eukaryotic proteins contain sorting signals that direct them to their proper destination (look back at Figure 4.32). With the exception of proteins destined for semiautonomous organelles, most transmembrane proteins contain an ER signal sequence that directs them to the ER membrane. If a polypeptide also contains a stretch of 20 amino acids that are mostly hydrophobic and form an α helix, this region will become a transmembrane segment. In the example shown in **Figure 5.7**, the polypeptide contains one such sequence. After the ER signal sequence is removed by signal peptidase (refer back to Figure 4.33), a membrane protein with a single transmembrane segment is the result. Other polypeptides may contain more than one transmembrane segment. Each time a polypeptide sequence contains a region of 20 amino acids that are mostly hydrophobic and form an α helix, an additional transmembrane segment is synthesized into the membrane. From the ER, membrane proteins can be transferred via vesicles to other regions of the cell, such as the Golgi, lysosomes, vacuoles, or plasma membrane.

The Attachment of Carbohydrates to Proteins Occurs in the ER and Golgi Apparatus

Glycosylation refers to the process of covalently attaching a carbohydrate to a lipid or protein. When a carbohydrate is attached to a lipid, a **glycolipid** is created, whereas attachment of a carbohydrate to a protein produces a **glycoprotein**.

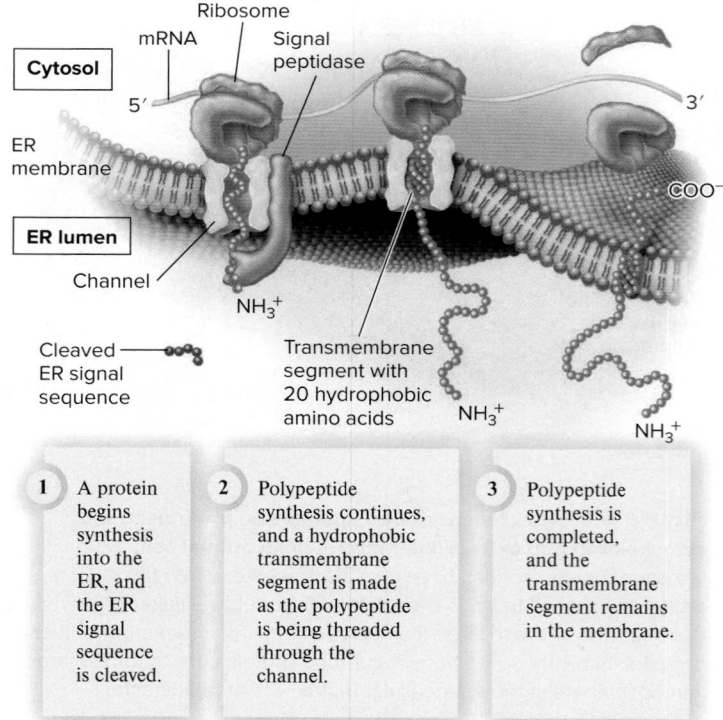

1 A protein begins synthesis into the ER, and the ER signal sequence is cleaved.

2 Polypeptide synthesis continues, and a hydrophobic transmembrane segment is made as the polypeptide is being threaded through the channel.

3 Polypeptide synthesis is completed, and the transmembrane segment remains in the membrane.

Figure 5.7 **Insertion of membrane proteins into the ER membrane.**

Concept Check: *What structural feature of a polypeptide causes a region of it to form a transmembrane segment?*

What is the function of glycosylation? Though the roles of carbohydrates in cell structure and function are not entirely understood, some functional consequences of glycosylation have emerged. Glycolipids and glycoproteins often play a role in cell surface recognition. When glycolipids and glycoproteins are found in the plasma membrane, the carbohydrate portion is located in the extracellular region. During embryonic development in animals, significant cell movement occurs. Layers of cells slide over each other to create body structures such as the spinal cord and internal organs. The proper migration of individual cells and cell layers relies on the recognition of cell types via the carbohydrates on their cell surfaces.

Carbohydrates often have a protective effect. The carbohydrate-rich zone on the surface of certain animal cells shields the cell from mechanical and physical damage. Similarly, the carbohydrate portion of glycosylated proteins protects them from the harsh conditions of the extracellular environment and degradation by extracellular proteases, which are enzymes that digest proteins.

Two forms of protein glycosylation occur in eukaryotes: N-linked and O-linked. N-linked glycosylation, which also occurs in archaea, involves the attachment of a carbohydrate to the amino acid asparagine in a polypeptide. It is called N-linked because the carbohydrate is attached to a nitrogen atom of the asparagine side chain. For this to occur, a group of 14 sugar molecules, called a carbohydrate tree, is first built onto a lipid found in the ER membrane (**Figure 5.8**). An enzyme in the ER, oligosaccharide transferase, transfers the carbohydrate tree from the lipid

to an asparagine in the polypeptide. N-linked glycosylation commonly occurs on membrane proteins that are transported to the cell surface.

The second form of glycosylation, O-linked glycosylation, occurs only in the Golgi apparatus. This form involves the addition of a string of sugars to the oxygen atom of a serine or threonine side chain in a polypeptide. In animals, O-linked glycosylation is important for the production of proteoglycans, which are highly glycosylated proteins that are secreted from cells and help to organize the extracellular matrix that surrounds cells. Proteoglycans are also a component of mucus, a slimy material that coats many cell surfaces and is secreted into fluids such as saliva. High concentrations of carbohydrates give mucus its slimy texture.

5.4 Overview of Membrane Transport

Learning Outcomes:

1. Compare and contrast simple diffusion, facilitated diffusion, passive transport, and active transport.

2. Describe the process of osmosis, and explain how it affects cell structure.

3. **CoreSKILL** » Predict the direction of water movement in response to solute gradients.

We now turn to one of the key functions of membranes, **membrane transport**—the movement of ions and molecules across biological membranes. All cells contain a plasma membrane that exhibits **selective permeability**, allowing the passage of some ions and molecules but not others. Essential molecules such as glucose and amino acids enter the cell, metabolic intermediates remain in the cell, and waste products exit. The selective permeability of the plasma membrane allows the cell to maintain a favorable internal environment.

Substances can move directly across a membrane in three general ways (**Figure 5.9**).

- **Simple diffusion** occurs when a substance moves across a membrane from an area of high concentration to one of lower concentration by passing directly through the phospholipid bilayer. This diffusion is an example of **passive transport**—the movement of a substance across a membrane from an area of high concentration to one of lower concentration, which does not require an input of energy.

- A second mechanism of passive transport is **facilitated diffusion**, in which a transport protein provides a passageway for a substance to cross a membrane from an area of higher concentration to one of lower concentration.

- A third mode of membrane transport, called **active transport**, moves a substance from an area of low concentration to one of high concentration with the aid of a transport protein. Active transport requires an input of energy from a source such as ATP.

In this section, we will begin with a discussion of how the phospholipid bilayer presents a barrier to the simple diffusion of ions and polar molecules across membranes. We will then consider the concept of gradients across membranes and how such gradients affect the movement of water.

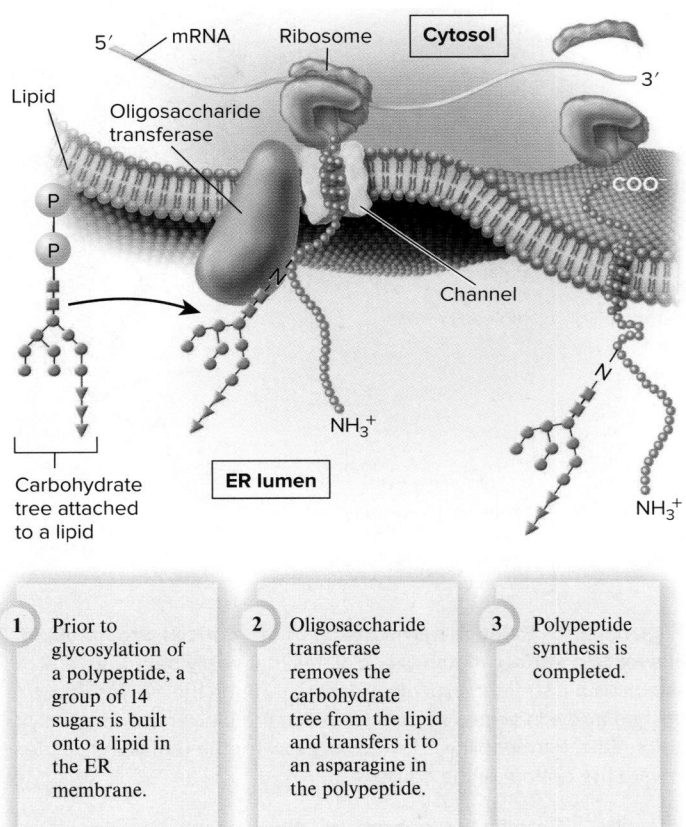

| 1 | Prior to glycosylation of a polypeptide, a group of 14 sugars is built onto a lipid in the ER membrane. | 2 | Oligosaccharide transferase removes the carbohydrate tree from the lipid and transfers it to an asparagine in the polypeptide. | 3 | Polypeptide synthesis is completed. |

Figure 5.8 **N-linked glycosylation in the ER.**

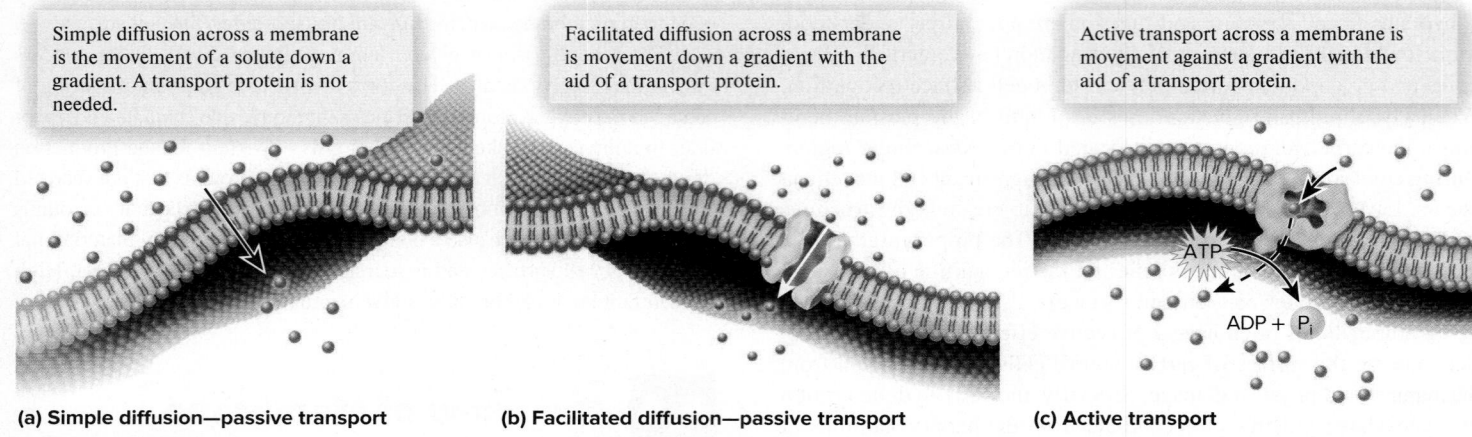

(a) Simple diffusion—passive transport

Simple diffusion across a membrane is the movement of a solute down a gradient. A transport protein is not needed.

(b) Facilitated diffusion—passive transport

Facilitated diffusion across a membrane is movement down a gradient with the aid of a transport protein.

(c) Active transport

Active transport across a membrane is movement against a gradient with the aid of a transport protein.

ATP

ADP + P_i

Figure 5.9 Three general types of membrane transport.

The Phospholipid Bilayer Is a Barrier to the Simple Diffusion of Hydrophilic Solutes

Because of their hydrophobic interiors, phospholipid bilayers are a barrier to the simple diffusion of ions and polar (hydrophilic) molecules. Such ions and molecules are called **solutes**; they are dissolved in water, which is a **solvent**. Four factors affect the ability of solutes to pass through a phospholipid bilayer.

- *Size.* Small solutes cross bilayers faster than larger ones.
- *Polarity.* Nonpolar solutes cross bilayers faster than polar ones.
- *Charge.* Noncharged solutes cross bilayers faster than charged ones.
- *Concentration.* The rate of movement of a solute across a membrane will be higher when its concentration is higher.

Figure 5.10 compares the relative permeabilities of an artificial phospholipid bilayer to various solutes. This artificial bilayer does not contain any proteins or carbohydrates. Gases and a few small, uncharged molecules can readily cross the bilayer by simple diffusion. However, the permeability of the bilayer to ions and larger polar molecules, such as sugars, is relatively low, and the permeability to macromolecules, such as proteins and polysaccharides, is even lower.

Cells Maintain Gradients Across Their Membranes

A hallmark of living cells is their ability to maintain a relatively constant internal environment that is distinctively different from their external environment. Solute gradients are formed across the plasma membrane and across internal membranes. When we speak of a **transmembrane gradient**, or **concentration gradient**, we mean that the concentration of a solute is higher on one side of a membrane than on the other. Transmembrane gradients of solutes are a universal feature of all living cells. For example, immediately after you eat a meal containing carbohydrates, a higher concentration of glucose is found outside your cells than inside; this is an example of a chemical gradient (**Figure 5.11a**).

Gradients involving ions have two components—electrical and chemical. An **electrochemical gradient** is a dual gradient with both electrical and chemical components (**Figure 5.11b**). It occurs with solutes that have a net positive or negative charge. For example, let's

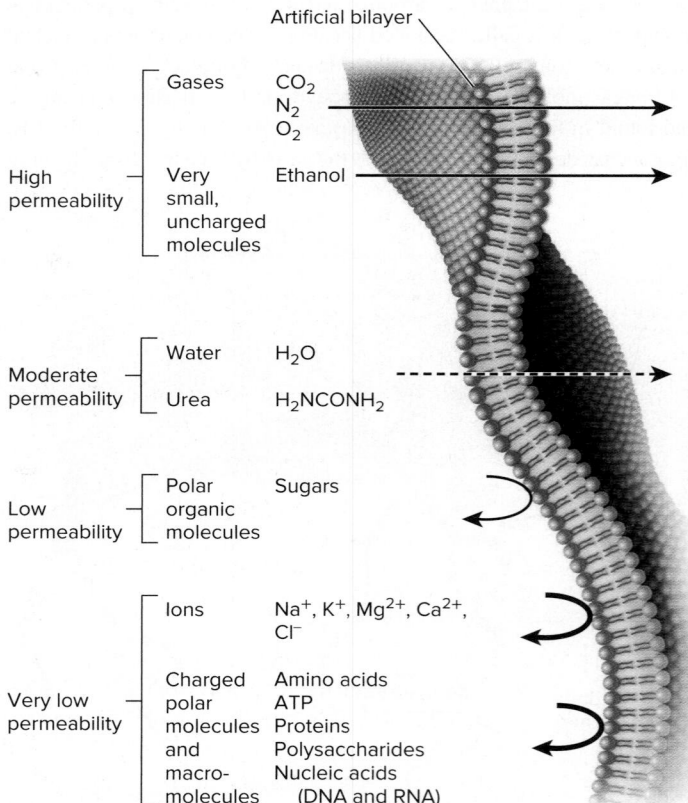

Artificial bilayer

High permeability	Gases	CO_2 N_2 O_2
	Very small, uncharged molecules	Ethanol
Moderate permeability	Water	H_2O
	Urea	H_2NCONH_2
Low permeability	Polar organic molecules	Sugars
Very low permeability	Ions	Na^+, K^+, Mg^{2+}, Ca^{2+}, Cl^-
	Charged polar molecules and macro-molecules	Amino acids ATP Proteins Polysaccharides Nucleic acids (DNA and RNA)

Figure 5.10 Relative permeability of an artificial phospholipid bilayer to a variety of solutes. Solutes that easily penetrate are shown with a straight arrow that passes through the bilayer. The dashed arrow indicates solutes for which the bilayer is moderately permeable. Permeability is low to very low for the remaining solutes, toward the bottom of the figure.

 Core Skill: Connections Which amino acid, described in Chapter 3 (see Figure 3.13), would you expect to be more likely to cross an artificial phospholipid bilayer, leucine or lysine?

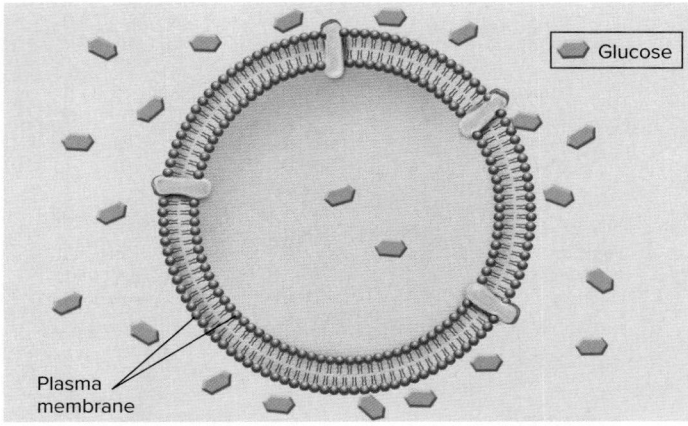

(a) Chemical gradient for glucose—a higher glucose concentration outside the cell

Glucose

Plasma membrane

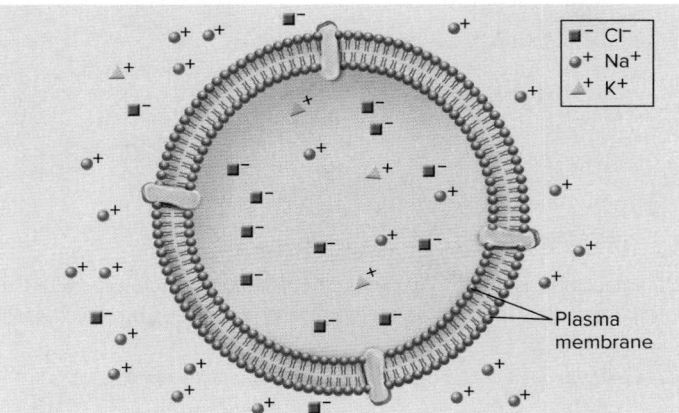

Cl⁻
Na⁺
K⁺

Plasma membrane

(b) Electrochemical gradient for Na⁺—more positive charges outside the cell and a higher Na⁺ concentration outside the cell

Figure 5.11 Gradients across cell membranes.

 Core Skill: Connections Look ahead to Figure 42.9. What types of ion gradients are important for the conduction of action potentials across the plasma membrane of a neuron?

consider a gradient involving Na⁺. An electrical gradient can exist in which the amount of net positive charge outside a cell is greater than inside. In Figure 5.11b, an electrical gradient is due to differences in the amounts of different types of ions—sodium, potassium, and chloride (Na⁺, K⁺, and Cl⁻)—on the two sides of the plasma membrane. At the same time, a chemical gradient—a difference in Na⁺ concentration across the membrane—also exists in which the concentration of Na⁺ outside is greater than inside. The Na⁺ electrochemical gradient is composed of both an electrical gradient due to charge differences across the membrane and a chemical gradient for Na⁺.

One way to view the transport of solutes across membranes is to consider how the transport process affects the pre-existing transmembrane gradients. Passive transport tends to dissipate a pre-existing gradient. Such a process is energetically favorable and does not require an input of energy. As noted earlier, passive transport can occur in two ways, via simple diffusion or facilitated diffusion (see Figure 5.9a,b).

By comparison, active transport produces a chemical or electrochemical gradient. The formation of a gradient requires an input of energy.

Osmosis Is the Movement of Water Across a Membrane to Balance Solute Concentrations

Let's now turn our attention to how gradients affect the movement of water across membranes. When the concentrations of solutes on both sides of the plasma membrane are equal, the two concentrations are said to be **isotonic** (**Figure 5.12a**). However, we have also seen that transmembrane gradients commonly exist across membranes. When the concentration of solutes outside the cell is higher, the outside is said to be **hypertonic** relative to the inside of the cell (**Figure 5.12b**). Alternatively, the outside of the cell could be **hypotonic**—have a lower concentration of solutes than the inside (**Figure 5.12c**).

If solutes cannot readily move across the membrane, water will do so and tend to balance the solute concentrations. In this process, called **osmosis**, water moves across a membrane from the hypotonic compartment (with a lower solute concentration) into the hypertonic compartment (with a higher solute concentration). Animal cells, which are not surrounded by a rigid cell wall, must maintain a balance between the extracellular and intracellular solute concentrations; the two solutions need to be isotonic. Animal cells contain a variety of transport proteins that sense changes in cell volume and allow the necessary movements of solutes across the membrane to prevent

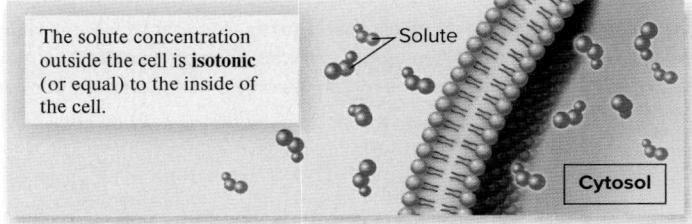

The solute concentration outside the cell is **isotonic** (or equal) to the inside of the cell.

Solute

Cytosol

(a) Outside isotonic

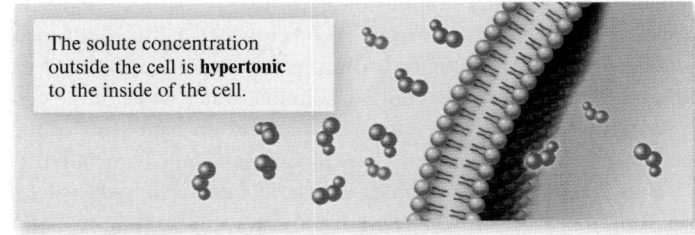

The solute concentration outside the cell is **hypertonic** to the inside of the cell.

(b) Outside hypertonic

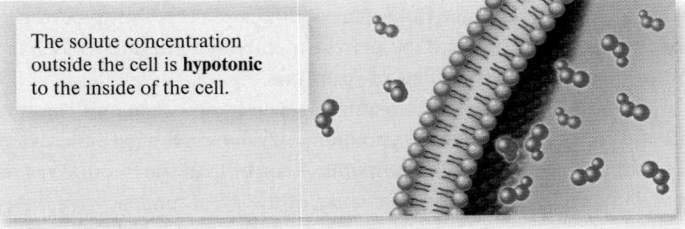

The solute concentration outside the cell is **hypotonic** to the inside of the cell.

(c) Outside hypotonic

Figure 5.12 Relative solute concentrations outside and inside cells.

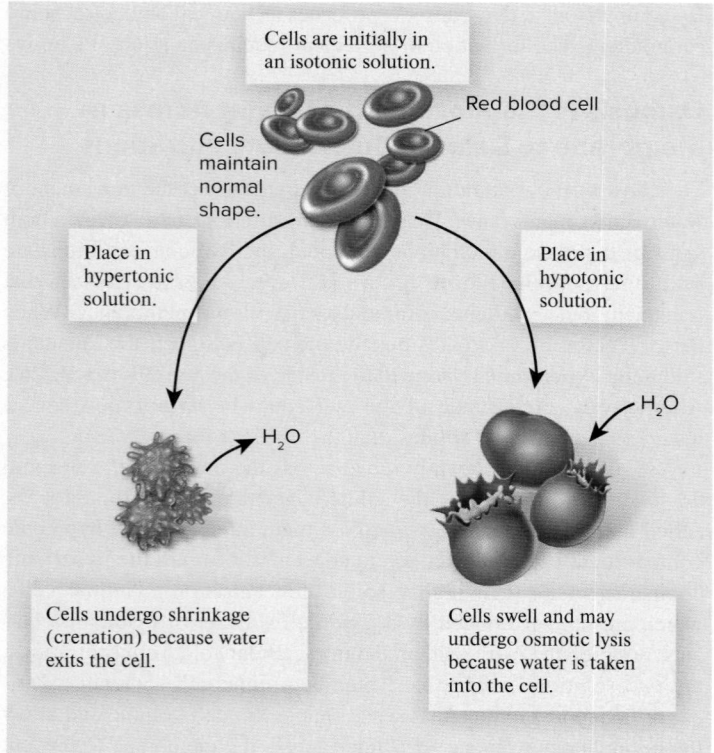

(a) Osmosis in animal cells

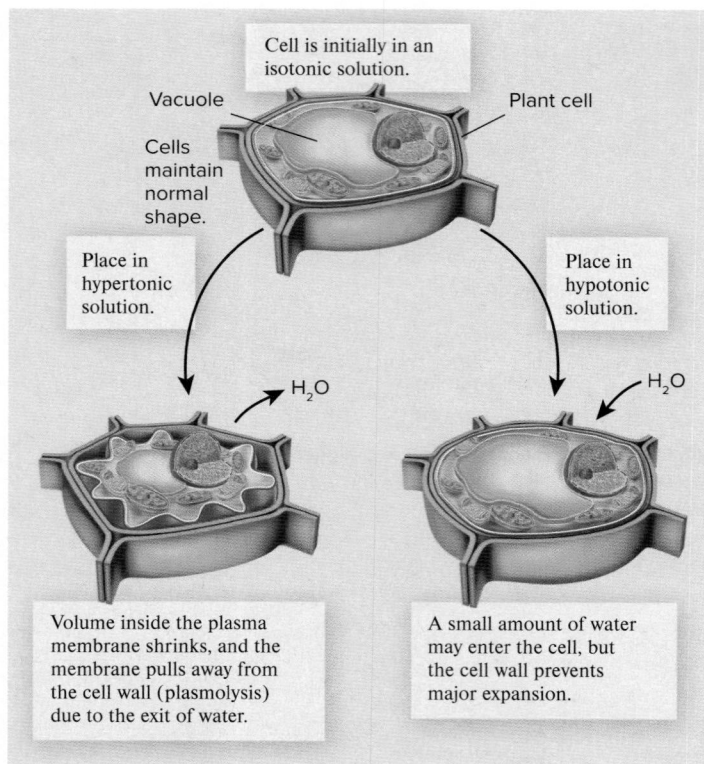

(b) Osmosis in plant cells

Figure 5.13 **The effects of osmosis.** **(a)** In cells that lack a cell wall, such as animal cells, osmosis may promote cell shrinkage (crenation) or swelling. **(b)** In cells that have a rigid cell wall, such as plant cells, a hypertonic medium causes the plasma membrane to pull away from the cell wall, whereas a hypotonic medium causes only a minor amount of expansion.

Concept Check: *Let's suppose the inside of a cell has a solute concentration of 0.3 M and the outside has a concentration of 0.2 M. If the membrane is impermeable to solutes, in which direction will water move?*

osmotic changes and maintain normal cell shape. However, if an animal cell is placed in a hypotonic solution, water will enter the cell to equalize solute concentrations on both sides of the membrane. In extreme cases, a cell may take up so much water that it ruptures, a phenomenon called osmotic lysis (**Figure 5.13a**). Alternatively, if an animal cell is placed in a hypertonic solution, water will exit the cell via osmosis and equalize solute concentrations on both sides of the membrane, causing the cell to shrink in a process called crenation.

How does osmosis affect cells with a rigid cell wall, such as bacteria, fungi, algae, and plant cells? If the extracellular fluid is hypotonic, a plant cell will take up a small amount of water, but the cell wall prevents osmotic lysis from occurring (**Figure 5.13b**). Alternatively, if the extracellular fluid surrounding a plant cell is hypertonic, water will exit the cell and the plasma membrane will pull away from the cell wall, a process called **plasmolysis**.

Some freshwater microorganisms, such as amoebae and paramecia, are found in extremely hypotonic environments where the external solute concentration is always much lower than the internal solute concentration in the cytosol. Because of the great tendency for water to move into these cells by osmosis, such organisms contain one or more contractile vacuoles to prevent osmotic lysis. A contractile vacuole takes up water from the cytosol and periodically discharges it by fusing with the plasma membrane (**Figure 5.14**).

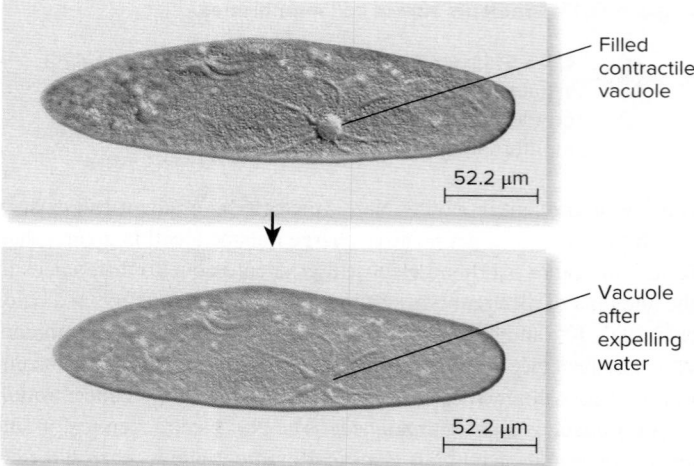

Figure 5.14 **The contractile vacuole in *Paramecium caudatum*.** In the upper photo, a contractile vacuole is filled with water from radiating canals that collect fluid from the cytosol. The lower photo shows the cell after the contractile vacuole has fused with the plasma membrane (which would be above the plane of this page) and released the water from the cell. (photos): ©Michael Abbey/Science Source

5.5 Transport Proteins

Learning Outcomes:

1. Outline the functional differences between channels and transporters.
2. Compare and contrast uniporters, symporters, and antiporters.
3. **CoreSKILL »** Analyze the results of Agre, and explain how they indicated the presence of a water channel.
4. Explain the difference between primary active transport and secondary active transport.
5. Describe the structure and function of pumps.

Because the phospholipid bilayer is a physical barrier to the movement of most polar molecules and ions across membranes, cells can separate their internal contents from the external environment. However, this barrier also poses a potential problem because cells must take up nutrients from the environment and export waste products. How do cells resolve this dilemma? Over the course of millions of years, species have evolved a multitude of **transport proteins**—transmembrane proteins that provide passageways for the movement of ions and hydrophilic molecules across the phospholipid bilayer. Transport proteins play a central role in the selective permeability of biological membranes. In this section, we will examine the two categories of transport proteins—channels and transporters—and see how they move solutes across the membrane.

Channels Provide Open Passageways for Solute Movement

A **channel** is a transmembrane protein that forms an open passageway for the facilitated diffusion of ions or molecules across the membrane (**Figure 5.15**). Solutes move directly through a channel to get to the

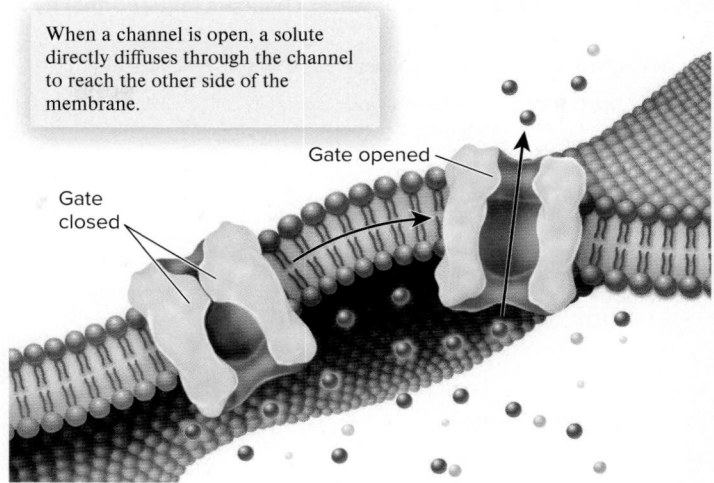

When a channel is open, a solute directly diffuses through the channel to reach the other side of the membrane.

Gate opened

Gate closed

Figure 5.15 Mechanism of solute transport via a channel.

Concept Check: *What is the purpose of gating?*

other side. When a channel is open, the transmembrane movement of solutes can be extremely rapid, up to 100 million ions or molecules per second!

Most channels are **gated**, which means they open to allow the diffusion of solutes and close to prohibit diffusion. The phenomenon of gating allows cells to regulate the movement of solutes. For example, gating may involve the direct binding of a molecule to the channel protein itself. These gated channels are controlled by the noncovalent binding of small molecules—called ligands—such as hormones or neurotransmitters. The ligands are often important in the transmission of signals between neurons and muscle cells or between two neurons.

 **Core Skill: Process of Science**

Feature Investigation | **Agre Discovered That Osmosis Occurs More Quickly in Cells with a Channel That Allows the Facilitated Diffusion of Water**

As discussed earlier in this chapter, osmosis is the movement of water to balance solute concentrations. Water can cross biological membranes slowly by simple diffusion through the phospholipid bilayer. However, in the 1980s, researchers discovered that certain cell types allow water to move across the plasma membrane at a much faster rate than would occur with simple diffusion alone. For example, water moves very quickly across the membrane of red blood cells, which causes them to shrink and swell in response to changes in extracellular solute concentrations. Likewise, bladder and kidney cells, which play a key role in regulating water balance in the bodies of vertebrates, allow the rapid movement of water across their membranes. Based on these observations, researchers speculated that certain cell types might have channels in their plasma membranes that enable the rapid movement of water.

One approach to characterizing a new protein is to first identify a protein based on its relative abundance in a particular cell type and then attempt to determine the protein's function. This rationale was applied to the discovery of proteins that allow the rapid movement of water across membranes. Peter Agre and his colleagues first identified a protein that was abundant in red blood cells and kidney cells but not found in high amounts in many other cell types. Though they initially did not know the function of the protein, its physical structure was similar to other proteins that were already known to function as channels. They named this protein CHIP28, which stands for channel-forming integral membrane protein with a molecular mass of 28,000 daltons. During the course of their studies, they also identified and isolated the gene that encodes CHIP28.

In 1992, Agre and his colleagues conducted experiments to determine if CHIP28 functions in the transport of water across membranes (**Figure 5.16**). Because they already had isolated the gene that encodes CHIP28, they could make many copies of

Figure 5.16 The discovery of water channels (aquaporins) by Agre. (4): Courtesy Dr. Peter Agre

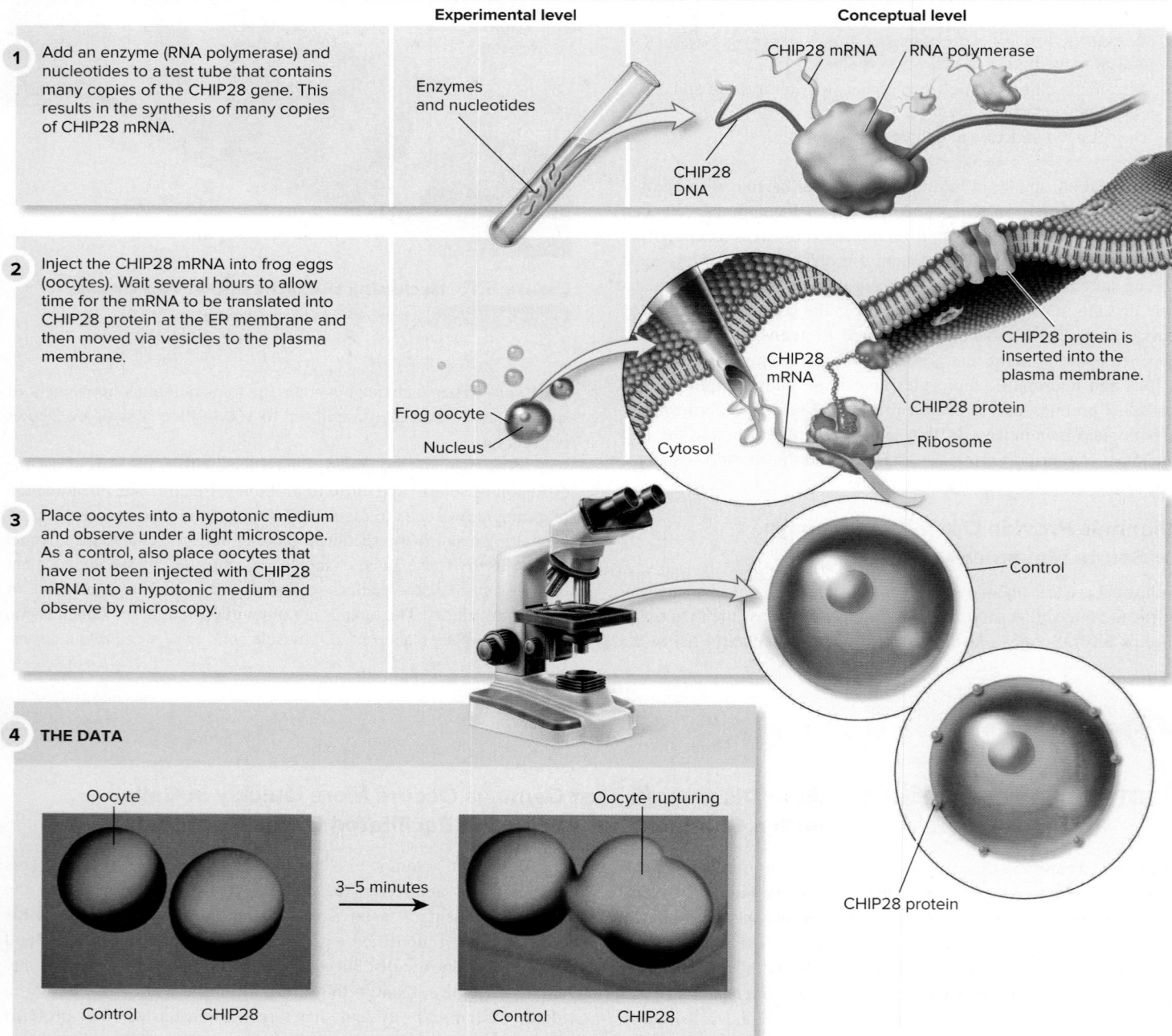

HYPOTHESIS CHIP28 may function as a water channel.

KEY MATERIALS Prior to this work, a protein called CHIP28 was identified that is abundant in red blood cells and kidney cells. The gene that encodes this protein was cloned, which means that many copies of the gene were made in a test tube.

Experimental level

Conceptual level

1 Add an enzyme (RNA polymerase) and nucleotides to a test tube that contains many copies of the CHIP28 gene. This results in the synthesis of many copies of CHIP28 mRNA.

Enzymes and nucleotides

CHIP28 mRNA   RNA polymerase

CHIP28 DNA

2 Inject the CHIP28 mRNA into frog eggs (oocytes). Wait several hours to allow time for the mRNA to be translated into CHIP28 protein at the ER membrane and then moved via vesicles to the plasma membrane.

CHIP28 mRNA

CHIP28 protein is inserted into the plasma membrane.

CHIP28 protein

Ribosome

Frog oocyte

Nucleus

Cytosol

3 Place oocytes into a hypotonic medium and observe under a light microscope. As a control, also place oocytes that have not been injected with CHIP28 mRNA into a hypotonic medium and observe by microscopy.

Control

4 **THE DATA**

Oocyte

Oocyte rupturing

3–5 minutes

Control   CHIP28

Control   CHIP28

CHIP28 protein

5 **CONCLUSION** The CHIP28 protein, now called aquaporin, allows the rapid movement of water across the membrane.

6 **SOURCE** Preston, G. M., Carroll, T. P., Guggino, W. B., and Agre, P. "Appearance of water channels in Xenopus oocytes expressing red cell CHIP28 protein." *Science.* 1992.

this gene in a test tube (in vitro) using gene cloning techniques (see Chapter 21). Starting with many copies of the gene in vitro, they added an enzyme to transcribe the gene into mRNA that encodes the CHIP28 protein. This mRNA was then injected into frog oocytes, chosen because these oocytes are large, easy to inject, and lack pre-existing proteins in their plasma membranes that allow the rapid movement of water. Following injection, the mRNA was translated into CHIP28 proteins that were inserted into the plasma membrane of the oocytes. After sufficient time had been allowed for this to occur, the oocytes were placed in a hypotonic medium. As a control, oocytes that had not been injected with CHIP28 mRNA were also exposed to a hypotonic medium.

As you can see in the data, a striking difference was observed between oocytes that expressed CHIP28 versus the control oocytes. Within minutes, oocytes that contained the CHIP28 protein were seen to swell due to the rapid uptake of water. Three to five minutes after being placed in a hypotonic medium, they actually ruptured! By comparison, the control oocytes did not swell as rapidly, and

they did not rupture even after 1 hour. Taken together, these results are consistent with the hypothesis that CHIP28 functions as a channel that allows the facilitated diffusion of water across the membrane. Many subsequent studies confirmed this observation. Later, CHIP28 was renamed **aquaporin** to indicate its newly identified function of allowing water to diffuse through a channel in the membrane. In 2003, Agre was awarded the Nobel Prize in Chemistry for this work.

Experimental Questions

1. What observations about particular cell types in the human body led to the experimental strategy of Figure 5.16?

2. What were the characteristics of CHIP28 that made Agre and associates speculate that it may transport water? In your own words, briefly explain how they tested the hypothesis that CHIP28 has this function.

3. **CoreSKILL »** Explain how the results of the experiment of Figure 5.16 support the proposed hypothesis.

Transporters Bind Their Solutes and Undergo Conformational Changes

Let's now turn our attention to a second category of transport proteins known as **transporters.**[*] These transmembrane proteins bind one or more solutes in a hydrophilic pocket and undergo a conformational change that switches the exposure of the pocket from one side of the membrane to the other side (**Figure 5.17**). For example, in 1995, American biologist Robert Brooker and colleagues proposed that a transporter called lactose permease, which is found in the bacterium *E. coli*, has a hydrophilic pocket that binds lactose. They further proposed that the two halves of the transporter protein come together at an interface that moves in such a way that the lactose-binding site alternates between an outwardly accessible pocket and an inwardly accessible pocket, as shown in Figure 5.17. This idea was later confirmed by studies that determined the structure of the lactose permease and related transporters.

Transporters provide the principal pathway for the cellular uptake of organic molecules, such as sugars, amino acids, and nucleotides. In animals, they also allow cells to take up certain hormones and neurotransmitters. In addition, many transporters play a key role in export. Waste products of cellular metabolism must be released from cells before they reach toxic levels. For example, a transporter removes lactic acid, a by-product of muscle cells during exercise. Other transporters, which are involved with ion transport, play an important role in regulating internal pH and controlling cell volume. Transporters tend to be much slower than channels. Their rate of transport is typically 100 to 1,000 ions or molecules per second.

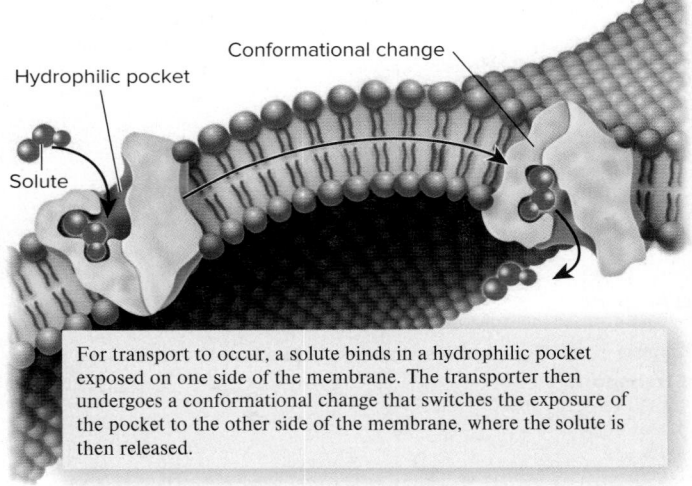

Conformational change

Hydrophilic pocket

Solute

For transport to occur, a solute binds in a hydrophilic pocket exposed on one side of the membrane. The transporter then undergoes a conformational change that switches the exposure of the pocket to the other side of the membrane, where the solute is then released.

Figure 5.17 Mechanism of transport by a transporter, also called a carrier.

 Core Concept: Structure and Function Two structural features—a hydrophilic pocket and the ability to switch back and forth between two conformations—allow transporters to move ions and molecules across the membrane.

Transporters are named according to the number of solutes they bind and the direction in which they transport those solutes (**Figure 5.18**). **Uniporters** bind a single ion or molecule and transport it across the membrane. **Symporters** bind two or more ions or molecules and transport them in the same direction. **Antiporters** bind two or more ions or molecules and transport them in opposite directions.

---

[*] Transporters are also called carriers. However, this term is misleading because transporters do not physically carry the solutes across the membrane.

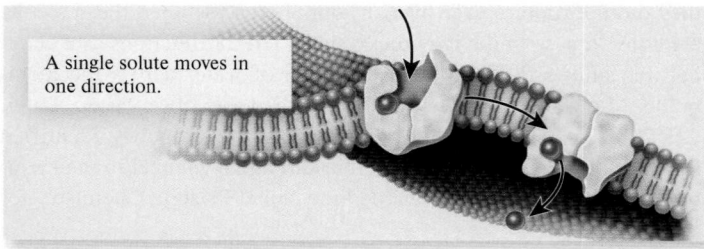

A single solute moves in one direction.

(a) Uniporter

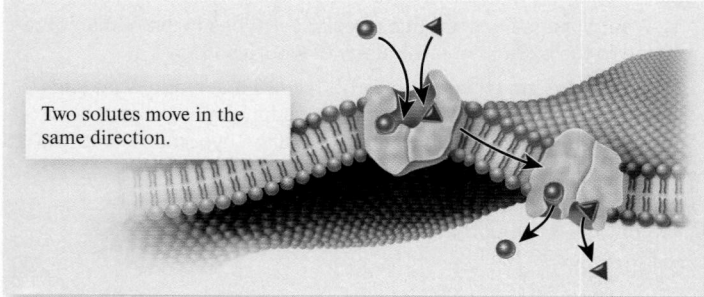

Two solutes move in the same direction.

(b) Symporter

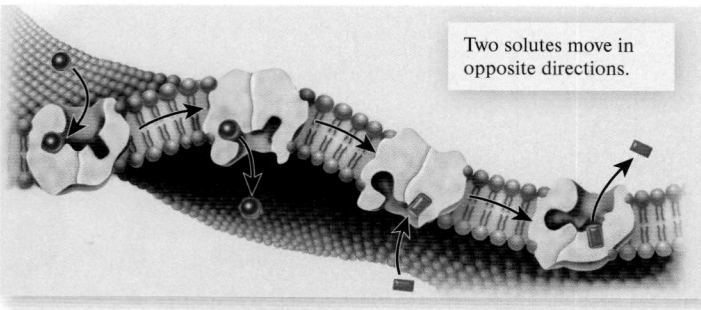

Two solutes move in opposite directions.

(c) Antiporter

Figure 5.18 **Types of transporters based on the direction of transport.**

BIO**TIPS**

THE QUESTION *Channels and transporters allow the passage of solutes across membranes. However, at the molecular level, they work in fundamentally different ways. Explain how each type can transport solutes across a membrane.*

Ⓣ**OPIC** *What topic in biology does this question address?* The topic is membrane transport. More specifically, the question asks you to compare the mechanisms of transport used by channels and transporters.

Ⓘ**NFORMATION** *What information do you know based on the question and your understanding of the topic?* From the question, you know that channels and transporters allow solutes to move across membranes. From your understanding of the topic, you may remember that channels and transporters are transmembrane proteins with different structures.

Ⓟ**ROBLEM-SOLVING** Ⓢ**TRATEGY** *Make a drawing. Relate structure and function.* One strategy to solve this problem is to make a drawing that compares the structures of channels and transporters and shows their abilities to transport solutes across membranes.

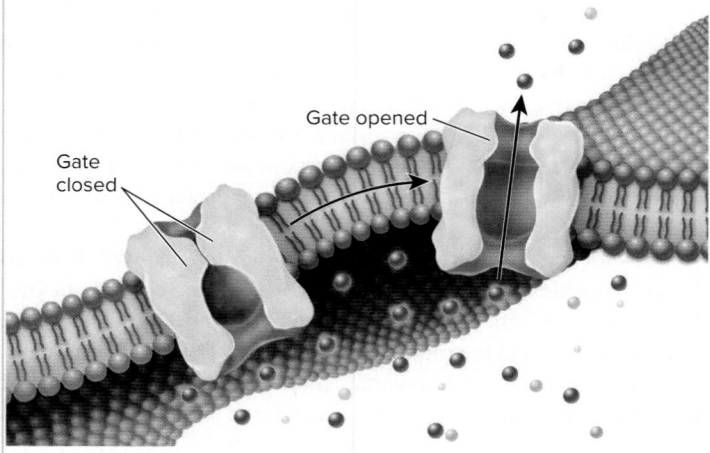

Gate opened

Gate closed

Channel

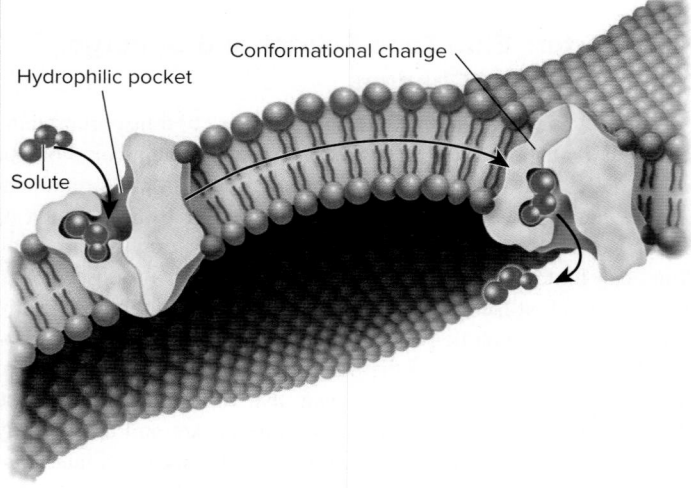

Conformational change

Hydrophilic pocket

Solute

Transporter

ANSWER *When its gate is open, a channel provides a direct passageway for the movement of a solute across a membrane. A transporter does not provide a direct passageway for such movement. Instead, a solute must first enter a hydrophilic pocket on one side of the membrane. The transporter then undergoes a conformational change that exposes the pocket on the other side of the membrane, where the solute is released.*

Active Transport Is the Movement of Solutes Against a Gradient

As described earlier, active transport is the movement of a solute across a membrane against its concentration gradient—that is, from a region of lower concentration to one of higher concentration. Active

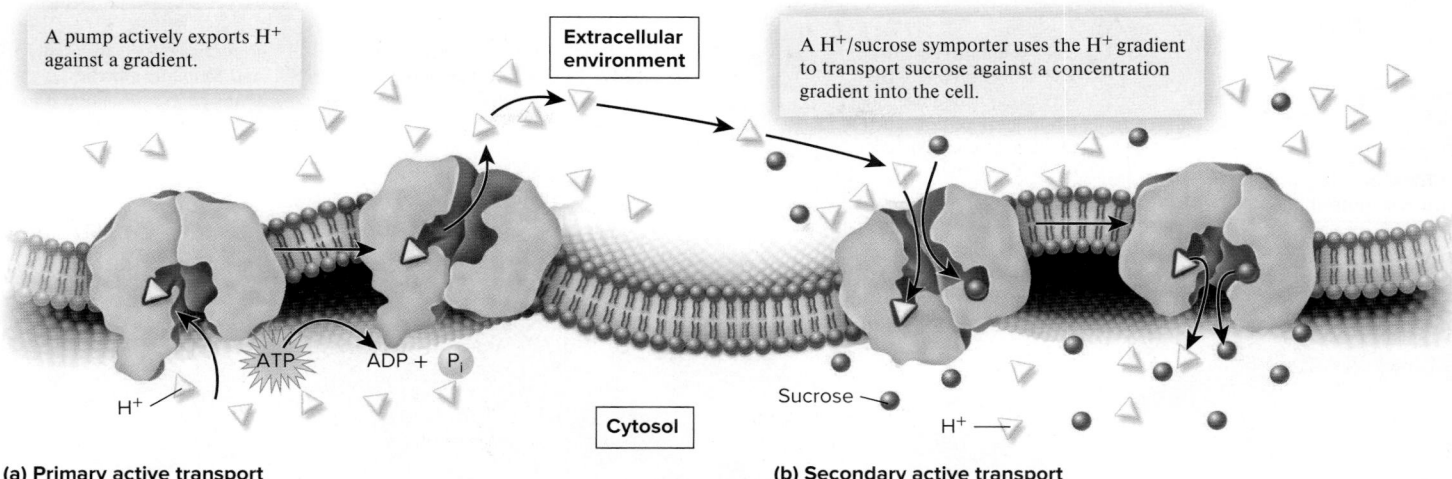

A pump actively exports H^+ against a gradient.

Extracellular environment

A H^+/sucrose symporter uses the H^+ gradient to transport sucrose against a concentration gradient into the cell.

ATP $ADP + P_i$

H^+

Cytosol

Sucrose

H^+

(a) Primary active transport

(b) Secondary active transport

Figure 5.19   Types of active transport. (a) During primary active transport, a pump directly uses energy, in this case from ATP, to transport a solute against a concentration gradient. The pump shown here uses ATP to establish an H^+ electrochemical gradient. **(b)** Secondary active transport via a symporter involves the use of this gradient to drive the active transport of a solute, such as sucrose.

transport is energetically unfavorable and requires an input of energy. **Primary active transport** involves the functioning of a **pump**— a type of transporter that directly uses energy to transport a solute against a concentration gradient. **Figure 5.19a** shows a pump that uses ATP to transport H^+ against a gradient. Such a pump can establish an H^+ electrochemical gradient across a membrane.

Secondary active transport is a process in which a pre-existing gradient drives the active transport of another solute. For example, an H^+/sucrose symporter uses an H^+ electrochemical gradient, established by a pump, to move sucrose against its concentration gradient (**Figure 5.19b**). In this case, only sucrose is actively transported. Hydrogen ions move down their electrochemical gradient. H^+/solute symporters are more common in bacteria, fungi, algae, and plant cells, because H^+ pumps are found in their plasma membranes. In animal cells, a pump that exports Na^+ maintains a Na^+ gradient across the plasma membrane. Na^+/solute symporters are prevalent in animal cells.

Symporters enable cells to actively import nutrients against a gradient. These proteins use the energy stored in the electrochemical gradient of H^+ or Na^+ to power the uphill movement of organic solutes such as sugars, amino acids, and other necessary molecules. Therefore, with symporters in their plasma membrane, cells can scavenge nutrients from the extracellular environment and accumulate them to high levels within the cytoplasm.

ATP-Driven Ion Pumps Generate Ion Electrochemical Gradients

The phenomenon of active transport was discovered in the 1940s based on the study of the transport of sodium ions (Na^+) and potassium ions (K^+). In animal cells, the concentration of Na^+ is lower inside the cell than outside, whereas the concentration of K^+ is higher inside the cell than outside. After analyzing the movement of these ions across the plasma membranes of muscle cells, neurons, and red blood cells, researchers determined that the export of Na^+ is coupled to the import of K^+. In the late 1950s, Danish biochemist Jens Skou

proposed that a single transporter is responsible for this phenomenon. He was the first to describe an ATP-driven ion pump, which was later named Na^+/K^+-ATPase. This pump actively transports Na^+ and K^+ against their gradients by using the energy from ATP hydrolysis. The plasma membrane of a typical animal cell contains thousands of Na^+/K^+-ATPase pumps that maintain large concentration gradients in which the concentration of Na^+ is higher outside the cell and the concentration of K^+ is higher inside the cell.

Let's take a closer look at the Na^+/K^+-ATPase that Skou discovered. Every time one ATP is hydrolyzed, the Na^+/K^+-ATPase functions as an antiporter that pumps three Na^+ into the extracellular environment and two K^+ into the cytosol (**Figure 5.20a**). Because one cycle of pumping results in the net export of one positive charge, the Na^+/K^+-ATPase also produces an electrical gradient across the membrane. For this reason, it is called an **electrogenic pump**, because it generates an electrical gradient.

By studying the interactions of Na^+, K^+, and ATP with the Na^+/K^+-ATPase pump, researchers have pieced together a molecular road map of the steps that direct the pumping of ions across the membrane (**Figure 5.20b**). The Na^+/K^+-ATPase alternates between two conformations, designated E1 and E2. In E1, the ion-binding sites are accessible from the cytosol—Na^+ binds tightly to this conformation, whereas K^+ has a low affinity. In E2, the ion-binding sites are accessible from the extracellular environment—Na^+ has a low affinity, and K^+ binds tightly.

To examine the pumping mechanism of Na^+/K^+-ATPase, let's begin with the E1 conformation. Three Na^+ bind to the Na^+/K^+-ATPase from the cytosol (Figure 5.20b). When this occurs, ATP is hydrolyzed to ADP and phosphate. Temporarily, the phosphate is covalently bound to the pump, an event called phosphorylation. The pump then switches to the E2 conformation. The three Na^+ are released into the extracellular environment, because they have a lower affinity for the E2 conformation. In this conformation, two K^+ bind from the outside. The binding of two K^+ causes the release of phosphate, which, in turn, causes a switch to E1. Because the E1 conformation has a low affinity

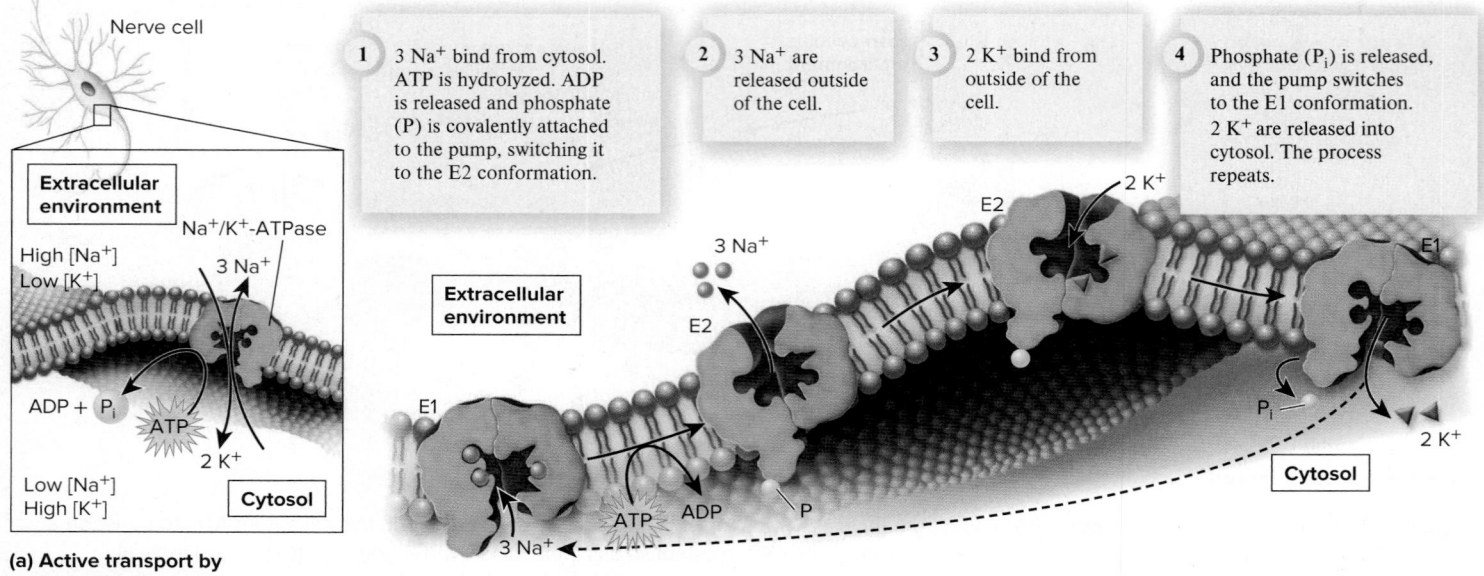

1 3 Na$^+$ bind from cytosol. ATP is hydrolyzed. ADP is released and phosphate (P) is covalently attached to the pump, switching it to the E2 conformation.

2 3 Na$^+$ are released outside of the cell.

3 2 K$^+$ bind from outside of the cell.

4 Phosphate (P$_i$) is released, and the pump switches to the E1 conformation. 2 K$^+$ are released into cytosol. The process repeats.

(a) Active transport by the Na$^+$/ K$^+$-ATPase

(b) Mechanism of pumping

Figure 5.20 Structure and function of the Na$^+$/K$^+$-ATPase. **(a)** Active transport by Na$^+$/K$^+$-ATPase. Each time this protein hydrolyzes one ATP molecule, it pumps out three Na$^+$ and pumps in two K$^+$. **(b)** Pumping mechanism. This figure illustrates the protein conformational changes between E1 and E2. As this occurs, ATP is hydrolyzed to ADP and phosphate. During the process, phosphate is covalently attached to the protein but is released after two K$^+$ bind.

 Core Concept: Energy and Matter The Na$^+$/K$^+$-ATPase uses energy to establish Na$^+$ and K$^+$ gradients across the plasma membrane of animal cells.

for K$^+$, the two K$^+$ are released into the cytosol. The Na$^+$/K$^+$-ATPase is now ready for another round of pumping.

Na$^+$/K$^+$-ATPase is a critical ion pump in animal cells because it maintains Na$^+$ and K$^+$ gradients across the plasma membrane. Many other types of ion pumps are also found in the plasma membrane and in the membranes of organelles. Ion pumps play the primary role in the formation and maintenance of ion electrochemical gradients that drive many important cellular processes (**Table 5.3**). ATP is commonly the source of energy that drives ion pumps, and cells typically use a substantial portion of their ATP to keep these pumps working. For example, neurons use up to 70% of their ATP to operate ion pumps!

5.6 Exocytosis and Endocytosis

Learning Outcome:

1. Describe the steps in exocytosis and endocytosis.

We have seen that most small substances are transported via transmembrane proteins such as channels and transporters, which provide passageways for the movement of ions and molecules directly across the membrane. Eukaryotic cells have two other mechanisms, exocytosis and endocytosis, for transporting larger molecules such as proteins and polysaccharides, and even very large particles. Both mechanisms involve the packaging of the transported substance, sometimes called the cargo, into a membrane vesicle or vacuole. **Table 5.4** describes some examples.

Exocytosis

During **exocytosis**, material inside the cell is packaged into vesicles and then excreted into the extracellular environment (**Figure 5.21**). These vesicles are usually derived from the Golgi apparatus. As a vesicle forms, a specific cargo is loaded into the interior. The budding process involves the formation of a protein coat around the emerging vesicle. The assembly of the proteins to make the coat on the surface of the Golgi membrane causes the bud to form. Eventually, the bud separates from the membrane to form a vesicle. After the vesicle is

Table 5.3	Important Functions of Ion Electrochemical Gradients
Function	**Description**
Transport of ions and molecules	Symporters and antiporters use H$^+$ and Na$^+$ gradients to take up nutrients and export waste products (see Figure 5.19).
Production of energy intermediates	In the mitochondrion and chloroplast, H$^+$ gradients are used to synthesize ATP.
Osmotic regulation	Animal cells control their internal volume by regulating ion gradients between the cytosol and extracellular fluid.
Neuronal signaling	Na$^+$ and K$^+$ gradients are involved in conducting action potentials, the signals transmitted by neurons.
Muscle contraction	Ca^{2+} gradients regulate the ability of muscle fibers to contract.
Bacterial swimming	H$^+$ gradients drive the rotation of bacterial flagella.

Table 5.4	Examples of Exocytosis and Endocytosis
Exocytosis	**Description**
Hormones	Certain hormones, such as insulin, are composed of polypeptides. To exert its effect, insulin is secreted via exocytosis into the bloodstream from beta cells of the pancreas.
Digestive enzymes	Digestive enzymes that function in the lumen of the small intestine are secreted via exocytosis from exocrine cells of the pancreas.
Endocytosis	**Description**
Uptake of vital nutrients	Many important nutrients are highly insoluble in the blood. Therefore, they are bound to proteins in the blood and then taken into cells via endocytosis. Examples include the uptake of lipids (bound to low-density lipoprotein) and iron (bound to transferrin protein).
Root nodules	Nitrogen-fixing root nodules found in certain species of plants, such as legumes, are formed by the endocytosis of bacteria. After being taken up, the bacterial cells are contained within a membrane-enclosed compartment in the nitrogen-fixing tissue of root nodules.
Immune system	Cells of the immune system, known as macrophages, engulf and destroy bacteria via phagocytosis.

released, the coat is shed. Finally, the vesicle fuses with the plasma membrane and releases the cargo into the extracellular environment.

Endocytosis

During **endocytosis**, the plasma membrane invaginates, or folds inward, to form a vesicle that brings substances into the cell. Three types of endocytosis are receptor-mediated endocytosis, pinocytosis, and phagocytosis.

Receptor-Mediated Endocytosis In **receptor-mediated endocytosis**, a receptor in the plasma membrane is specific for a given cargo

(**Figure 5.22**). Cargo molecules binding to their specific receptors stimulate many receptors to aggregate, and then coat proteins bind to the membrane. The protein coat causes the membrane to invaginate and form a vesicle. Once it is released into the cell, the vesicle sheds its coat. In most cases, the vesicle fuses with an internal organelle, such as a lysosome, and the receptor releases its cargo. Then, the cargo may be directly released into the cytosol, or it may be digested into simpler building blocks before release.

Pinocytosis Other specialized types of endocytosis occur in certain cells. **Pinocytosis** (from the Greek, meaning cell-drinking) involves the formation of membrane vesicles from the plasma membrane as a

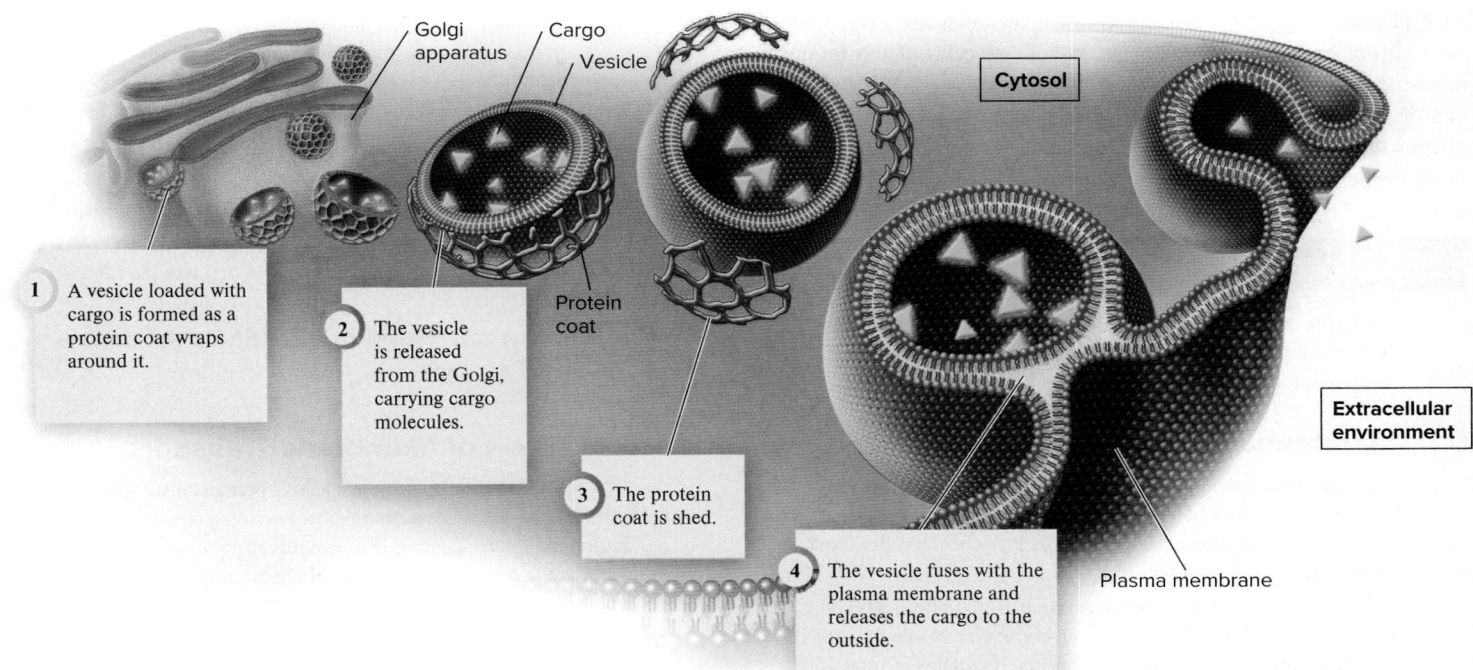

1 A vesicle loaded with cargo is formed as a protein coat wraps around it.

2 The vesicle is released from the Golgi, carrying cargo molecules.

3 The protein coat is shed.

4 The vesicle fuses with the plasma membrane and releases the cargo to the outside.

Figure 5.21 **Exocytosis.**

Concept Check: *What is the function of the protein coat?*

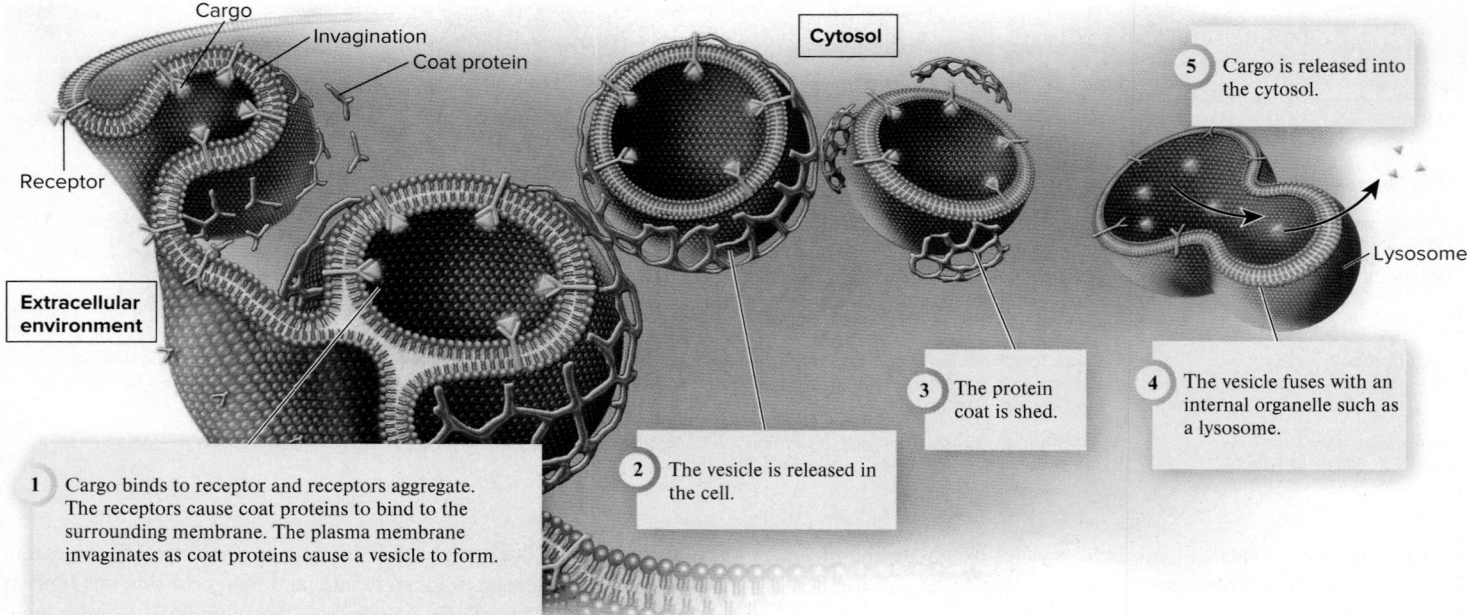

Figure 5.22 **Receptor-mediated endocytosis.**

way for cells to internalize the extracellular fluid. This allows cells to sample the extracellular solutes. Pinocytosis is particularly important in cells that are actively involved in nutrient absorption, such as cells that line the intestine in animals.

Phagocytosis Phagocytosis (from the Greek, meaning cell-eating) involves the formation of an enormous membrane vesicle called a phagosome, or phagocytic vacuole, which engulfs a large particle such as a bacterium. Only certain kinds of cells can carry out phagocytosis. For example, macrophages, which are cells of the immune system in mammals, kill bacteria via phagocytosis. Macrophages engulf bacterial cells into phagosomes. Once inside the cell, the phagosome fuses with a lysosome, and the digestive enzymes within the lysosome destroy the bacterium.

Summary of Key Concepts

- A plasma membrane separates a cell from its surroundings. The plasma membrane and the membranes of organelles provide interfaces for carrying out vital cellular activities (Table 5.1).

5.1 Membrane Structure

- The accepted model of membranes is the fluid-mosaic model, and the basic framework of a membrane is the phospholipid bilayer. Biological membranes also contain proteins, and some membranes have attached carbohydrates (Figure 5.1).

- The three main types of membrane proteins are transmembrane proteins, lipid-anchored proteins, and peripheral membrane proteins. Transmembrane proteins and lipid-anchored proteins are classified as integral membrane proteins. Researchers are working to identify new membrane proteins and their functions because these proteins are important biologically and medically (Figure 5.2, Table 5.2).

5.2 Fluidity of Membranes

- Membrane fluidity is essential for normal cell function, growth, and division. Lipids and many proteins can move rotationally and laterally, but the flip-flop of lipids from one leaflet to the opposite does not occur spontaneously. Some membrane proteins are restricted in their movements (Figures 5.3, 5.4, 5.5).

- The chemical properties of phospholipids—such as tail length and the presence of double bonds—and the amount of cholesterol present affect the fluidity of membranes.

5.3 Synthesis of Membrane Components in Eukaryotic Cells

- In eukaryotic cells, most membrane phospholipids are synthesized at the cytosolic leaflet of the smooth ER membrane. Flippases move some phospholipids to the other leaflet (Figure 5.6).

- Most transmembrane proteins are first inserted into the ER membrane (Figure 5.7).

- Glycosylation of proteins occurs in the ER and Golgi apparatus (Figure 5.8).

5.4 Overview of Membrane Transport

- Biological membranes exhibit selective permeability. Simple diffusion occurs when a solute moves across a membrane from a region of high concentration to a region of lower concentration without the aid of a transport protein, whereas facilitated diffusion involves a transport protein. Passive transport of a solute across a membrane can occur via simple diffusion or facilitated diffusion. Active transport is the movement of a substance against a gradient (Figure 5.9).

- The phospholipid bilayer is relatively impermeable to many hydrophilic substances (Figure 5.10).

- Living cells maintain an internal environment that is separated from their external environment. Transmembrane gradients are established across the plasma membrane and across internal membranes (Figure 5.11).

- In the process of osmosis, water moves through a membrane from an area of lower concentration of solute (hypotonic) into an area of higher concentration of solute (hypertonic). Solutions with identical concentrations are isotonic. Some microorganisms have contractile vacuoles to eliminate excess water (Figures 5.12, 5.13, 5.14).

5.5   Transport Proteins

- Two classes of transport proteins are channels and transporters.

- Channels provide open passageways for the facilitated diffusion of solutes across the membrane. One example is aquaporin, which allows the movement of water. Most channels are gated, which allows cells to regulate the movement of solutes (Figures 5.15, 5.16).

- Transporters, which tend to function at a slower rate than channels, bind their solutes in a hydrophilic pocket and undergo a conformational change that switches the exposure of the pocket to the other side of the membrane. They can be uniporters, symporters, or antiporters (Figures 5.17, 5.18).

- Primary active transport involves pumps that directly use energy to generate a solute gradient. Secondary active transport uses a pre-existing gradient (Figure 5.19).

- Na^+/K^+-ATPase is an electrogenic pump that uses energy from ATP to transport ions across the membrane. Ion electrochemical gradients perform several important cellular functions (Figure 5.20, Table 5.3).

5.6   Exocytosis and Endocytosis

- In eukaryotes, exocytosis and endocytosis are used to transport large molecules and particles. Exocytosis is a process in which material inside the cell is packaged into vesicles and excreted into the extracellular environment. During endocytosis, the plasma membrane folds inward to form a vesicle that brings substances into the cell. Receptor-mediated endocytosis, pinocytosis, and phagocytosis are types of endocytosis (Figures 5.21, 5.22, Table 5.4).

Assess & Discuss

Test Yourself

1. Which of the following statements best describes the chemical composition of biological membranes?
   a. Biological membranes are bilayers of proteins with associated lipids and carbohydrates.
   b. Biological membranes are composed of two layers—one layer of phospholipids and one layer of proteins.
   c. Biological membranes are bilayers of phospholipids with associated proteins and carbohydrates.
   d. Biological membranes are composed of equal numbers of phospholipids, proteins, and carbohydrates.
   e. Biological membranes are composed of lipids with proteins attached to the outer surface.

2. Which of the following events can never be energetically favorable in a biological membrane and therefore will not occur spontaneously?
   a. the rotation of phospholipids
   b. the lateral movement of phospholipids
   c. the flip-flop of phospholipids to the opposite leaflet
   d. the rotation of membrane proteins
   e. the lateral movement of membrane proteins

3. Let's suppose an insect, which doesn't maintain a constant body temperature, was exposed to a shift in temperature from 60°F to 80°F. Which of the following types of membrane changes would be the most beneficial in helping the insect cope with the temperature shift?
   a. increase the number of double bonds in the lipid tails of phospholipids
   b. increase the length of the lipid tails of phospholipids
   c. decrease the amount of cholesterol in the membrane
   d. decrease the amount of carbohydrate attached to membrane proteins
   e. decrease the amount of carbohydrate attached to phospholipids

4. Carbohydrates of the plasma membrane
   a. are bonded to a protein or lipid.
   b. are located on the outer surface of the plasma membrane.
   c. can function as cell markers for recognition by other cells.
   d. All of the above are true of the carbohydrates.
   e. Only a and c are true.

5. A transmembrane protein in the plasma membrane is glycosylated at two sites in the polypeptide sequence. Where in this protein would you expect these two sites to be?
   a. in transmembrane segments
   b. in hydrophilic regions that project into the extracellular environment
   c. in hydrophilic regions that project into the cytosol
   d. could be anywhere
   e. b and c only

6. The tendency for Na^+ to move into the cell can be due to
   a. the higher numbers of Na^+ outside the cell, resulting in a chemical concentration gradient.
   b. the net negative charge inside the cell attracting the positively charged Na^+.
   c. the attractive force of K^+ inside the cell pulling Na^+ into the cell.
   d. all of the above.
   e. a and b only.

7. Let's suppose the solute concentration inside the cells of a plant is 0.3 M and the concentration outside is 0.2 M. If we assume that the solute does not readily cross the membrane, which of the following statements best describes what will happen?
   a. The plant cells will lose water, and the plasma membrane will push against the cell wall.
   b. The plant cells will lose water, and the plasma membrane will pull away from the cell wall (plasmolysis).
   c. The plant cells will take up a lot of water and undergo osmotic lysis.
   d. The plant cells will take up a little water, and the plasma membrane will push against the cell wall.
   e. both a and b.

8. What features of a biological membrane are major contributors to its selective permeability?
   a. phospholipid bilayer
   b. transport proteins
   c. glycolipids on the outer surface of the membrane
   d. peripheral membrane proteins
   e. both a and b

9. What is the name given to the process in which solutes are moved across a membrane against their concentration gradient?
   a. simple diffusion
   b. facilitated diffusion
   c. osmosis
   d. passive diffusion
   e. active transport

10. Large particles or large volumes of fluid can be brought into the cell by
    a. facilitated diffusion.
    b. active transport.
    c. endocytosis.
    d. exocytosis.
    e. all of the above.

Conceptual Questions

1. With your textbook closed, draw and describe the fluid-mosaic model of membrane structure.

2. Describe two different ways that integral membrane proteins associate with a membrane. How do peripheral membrane proteins associate with a membrane?

3. **Core Concept: Energy and Matter** Discuss how the lipid bilayer, channels, and transporters influence the ability of cells to control the amounts of solutes they contain.

Collaborative Questions

1. Proteins in the plasma membrane are often the target of medicines. Discuss why you think this is the case. How would you determine experimentally that a specific membrane protein was the target of a drug?

2. With regard to bringing solutes into the cell across the plasma membrane, discuss the advantages and disadvantages of simple diffusion, facilitated diffusion, active transport, and endocytosis.

An Introduction to Energy, Enzymes, and Metabolism

6

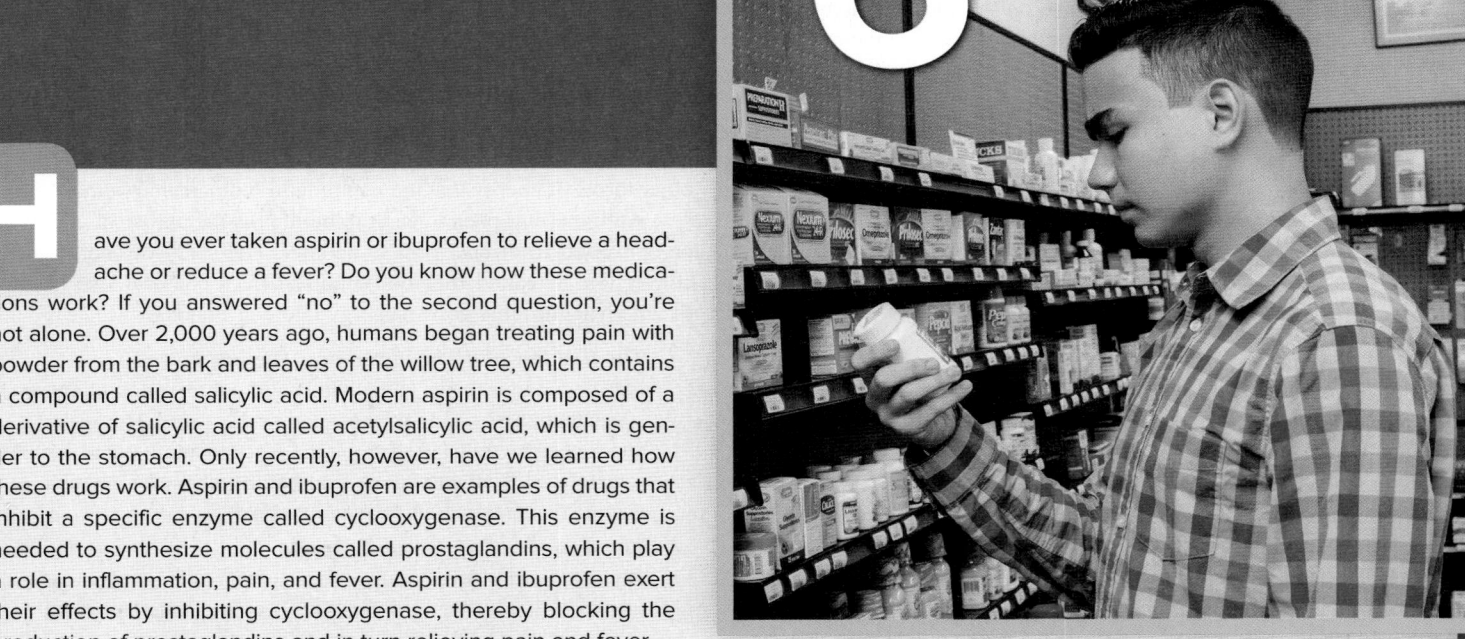

Have you ever taken aspirin or ibuprofen to relieve a headache or reduce a fever? Do you know how these medications work? If you answered "no" to the second question, you're not alone. Over 2,000 years ago, humans began treating pain with powder from the bark and leaves of the willow tree, which contains a compound called salicylic acid. Modern aspirin is composed of a derivative of salicylic acid called acetylsalicylic acid, which is gentler to the stomach. Only recently, however, have we learned how these drugs work. Aspirin and ibuprofen are examples of drugs that inhibit a specific enzyme called cyclooxygenase. This enzyme is needed to synthesize molecules called prostaglandins, which play a role in inflammation, pain, and fever. Aspirin and ibuprofen exert their effects by inhibiting cyclooxygenase, thereby blocking the production of prostaglandins and in turn relieving pain and fever.

Enzymes are proteins that act as critical catalysts to speed up thousands of different reactions in cells. As discussed in Chapter 2, a **chemical reaction** is a process in which one or more substances are changed into other substances. Such reactions may involve molecules attaching to each other to form larger molecules, molecules breaking apart to form two or more smaller molecules, rearrangements of atoms within molecules, or the transfer of electrons from one atom to another. Every living cell continuously performs thousands of such chemical reactions to sustain life. **Metabolism** is the sum total of all chemical reactions that occur within an organism. Metabolism also refers to a specific set of chemical reactions occurring at the cellular level. For example, biologists may speak of sugar metabolism or fat metabolism. Most types of metabolism involve the breakdown or synthesis of organic molecules. Cells maintain their structure by using organic molecules. Such molecules provide the building blocks for constructing cells, and the chemical bonds within organic molecules store energy that is used to drive cellular processes.

In this chapter, we begin with a general discussion of energy and chemical reactions. We will examine what factors control the direction of a chemical reaction and what determines its rate, paying particular attention to the role of enzymes. We then consider metabolism at the cellular level, examining how chemical reactions are often coordinated with each other in metabolic pathways. We

Common drugs that act as enzyme inhibitors. Drugs such as aspirin and ibuprofen exert their effects by inhibiting an enzyme that speeds up a cellular chemical reaction. ©McGraw-Hill Education/ Aaron Roeth, photographer

will also explore the variety of ways in which metabolic pathways are regulated and how organic molecules are recycled.

6.1 Energy and Chemical Reactions

Learning Outcomes:

1. Define energy, and distinguish between potential and kinetic energy.
2. State the first and second laws of thermodynamics, and discuss how they relate to living things.
3. Explain how the change in free energy determines the direction of a chemical reaction and how chemical reactions eventually reach a state of equilibrium.
4. Distinguish between exergonic and endergonic reactions in terms of the energy of the reactants and products and the free energy change.
5. Describe how cells use the energy released by the hydrolysis of ATP to drive endergonic reactions.

Two general factors govern the fate of a given chemical reaction in a living cell—its direction and rate. To illustrate this point, let's consider this generalized chemical reaction:

$$aA + bB \rightleftharpoons cC + dD$$

where A and B are the reactants, C and D are the products, and *a*, *b*, *c*, and *d* are the number of moles of reactants and products. This reaction is reversible, which means that A + B could be converted to C + D, or C + D could be converted to A + B. The direction of the reaction, whether C + D are made (the forward direction) or A + B are made (the reverse direction), depends on energy and on the concentrations of A, B, C, and D. In this section, we will begin by examining the interplay of energy and reactants' concentrations as they govern the direction of a chemical reaction. You will learn that cells use energy intermediate molecules, such as ATP, to drive chemical reactions in a desired direction.

Energy Exists in Different Forms

To understand why a chemical reaction occurs, we first need to consider **energy**, which is the ability to promote change or do work. Physicists often consider energy in two general forms: kinetic energy and potential energy (**Figure 6.1**). **Kinetic energy** is energy associated with movement, such as the movement of a baseball bat from one location to another. By comparison, **potential energy** is the energy that a substance or object possesses due to its structure or location. An electron in an atom has potential energy based on its position relative to other electrons and the positively charged nucleus. As you may recall from Chapter 2, electrons occupy orbitals of different shapes and sizes, which are found within electron shells, or energy levels (refer back to Figure 2.4). An electron in an outer shell has a higher amount of potential energy than one in an inner shell. If an electron drops to a lower shell, some of its potential energy is converted to kinetic energy.

The energy that is stored in atoms and in the bonds between atoms is called **chemical potential energy** (or simply, chemical energy). This energy can be released during chemical reactions. Organic molecules, such as glucose, store a great deal of potential energy. As discussed in Chapter 7, the breakdown of glucose releases energy that is harnessed to make molecules such as ATP that are energy

(a) Kinetic energy

(b) Potential energy

Figure 6.1 Examples of energy. (a) Kinetic energy, such as that of a swinging bat, is energy associated with motion. **(b)** Potential energy is stored energy, as in a bow that is ready to shoot an arrow. a: ©moodboard/Corbis; b: ©amanaimages/Corbis

intermediates. **Table 6.1** summarizes chemical potential energy and other forms of energy that are common in biological systems.

An important phenomenon in biology is the ability of energy to be converted from one form to another. The study of energy interconversions is called **thermodynamics**. Let's consider two laws of thermodynamics that govern energy interconversions:

1. *The first law of thermodynamics.* The first law of thermodynamics, also called the law of conservation of energy, states that energy cannot be created or destroyed. However, energy can be transferred from one place to another and can be transformed from one type to another (as when, for example, chemical energy is transformed into heat).

2. *The second law of thermodynamics.* The second law states that any energy transfer or transformation from one form to another increases the degree of disorder of a system, called **entropy** (**Figure 6.2**). Entropy is a measure of the randomness of molecules in a system. When a physical system becomes more disordered, the entropy increases. As the energy becomes more evenly distributed, that energy is less able to promote change or do work. When energy is converted from one form to another, some energy may become unusable by living organisms. For example, a chemical reaction may release unusable heat.

Table 6.1	Types of Energy That Are Important in Biology	
Energy type	**Description**	**Biological example**
Light	Light is a form of electromagnetic radiation that is visible to the eye. The energy of light is packaged in photons.	During photosynthesis, light energy is captured by pigments in chloroplasts (described in Chapter 8). Ultimately, this energy is used to produce organic molecules.
Heat	Heat is the transfer of kinetic energy from one object to another or from an energy source to an object. In biology, heat is often viewed as kinetic energy that can be transferred due to a difference in temperature between two objects or locations.	Many organisms, including humans, maintain their bodies at a constant temperature. This is achieved, in part, by chemical reactions that generate heat.
Mechanical	Mechanical energy is the energy possessed by an object due to its motion or its position relative to other objects.	In animals, mechanical energy is associated with movement due to muscle contraction, such as walking.
Chemical potential	Chemical potential energy is potential energy stored in the electrons of molecules. When bonds are broken and rearranged, energy may be released.	The covalent bonds in organic molecules, such as glucose and ATP, store large amounts of energy. When bonds are broken in larger molecules to form smaller molecules, the energy that is released can be used to drive cellular processes.
Electrical/ion gradient	The movement of charge or the separation of charges can provide energy. Also, a difference in ion concentration across a membrane constitutes an electrochemical gradient, which is a source of potential energy.	During a stage of cellular respiration called oxidative phosphorylation (described in Chapter 7), an H^+ gradient provides the energy to drive ATP synthesis.

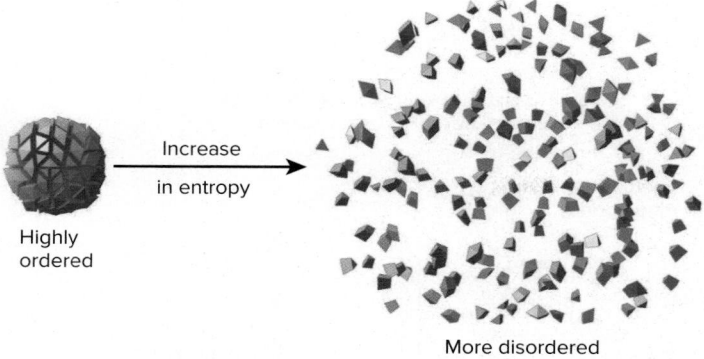

Figure 6.2 Entropy, a measure of the disorder of a system. An increase in entropy means an increase in disorder.

> **Concept Check:** *Which do you think has more entropy, a NaCl crystal at the bottom of a beaker of water or the solution that would be formed after the Na⁺ and Cl⁻ ions forming the crystal have dissolved in the water?*

Next, we will see how the two laws of thermodynamics place limits on the ways that living cells use energy for their own needs.

The Change in Free Energy Determines the Direction of a Chemical Reaction

Energy is required for many cellular processes, including chemical reactions, cellular movements such as those occurring in muscle contraction, and the maintenance of cell organization. To understand how organisms use energy, we need to distinguish between the energy that can be used to promote change or do work (usable energy) and the energy that cannot (unusable energy).

$$\text{Total energy} = \text{Usable energy} + \text{Unusable energy}$$

Why is some energy unusable? The main culprit is entropy. As stated by the second law of thermodynamics, energy transfers or transformations involve an increase in entropy, a degree of disorder that cannot be harnessed in a useful way. The total energy of a system is termed **enthalpy** *(H)*, and the usable energy—the amount of energy that is available and can be used to promote change or do work—is called the **free energy** *(G)*. The use of the letter *G* is in recognition of American physicist J. Willard Gibbs, who proposed the concept of free energy in 1878. The unusable energy is the system's entropy *(S)*. Gibbs proposed that these three components of a system's energy are related to each other in the following way:

$$H = G + TS$$

where *T* is the absolute temperature in kelvins (K). Because our focus is on free energy, we can rearrange this equation as

$$G = H - TS$$

A critical issue in biology is whether a process does or does not occur spontaneously. For example, will glucose be broken down into carbon dioxide and water? Another way of framing this question is to ask: "Is the breakdown of glucose a spontaneous, or favorable, reaction?" A spontaneous reaction or process is one that occurs without being driven by an input of energy. However, a spontaneous reaction does not necessarily proceed quickly. In some cases, the rate of a spontaneous reaction can be quite slow. For example, the breakdown of sugar is a spontaneous reaction, but the rate at which sugar in a sugar bowl breaks down into CO_2 and H_2O is very slow.

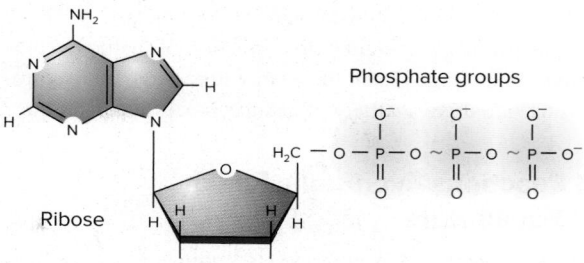

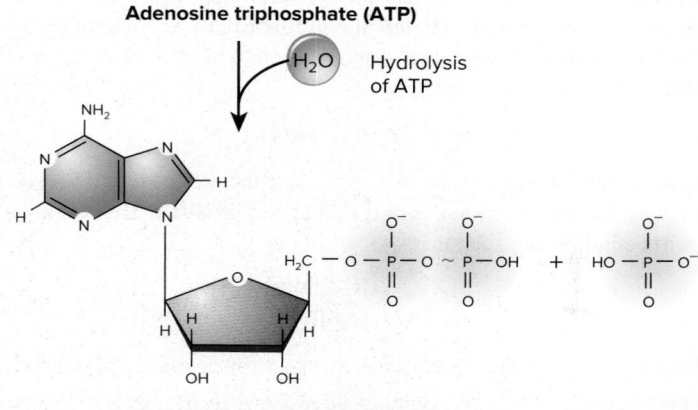

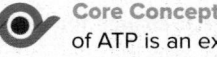

Figure 6.3 The hydrolysis of ATP to ADP and Pᵢ. As shown in this figure, ATP has a net charge of −4, while ADP and Pᵢ are shown with net charges of −2 each. When these compounds are shown in chemical reactions with other molecules, the net charges are also indicated. Otherwise, these compounds are simply designated ATP, ADP, and Pᵢ. At neutral pH, ADP^{2-} dissociates to ADP^{3-} and H^+.

> 👁 **Core Concept: Energy and Matter** The hydrolysis of ATP is an exergonic reaction that is used to drive many cellular processes, such as chemical reactions.

The key way to evaluate if a chemical reaction is spontaneous is to determine the free-energy change that occurs as a result of the reaction:

$$\Delta G = \Delta H - T \Delta S$$

where the symbol Δ (the Greek letter delta) indicates a change, such as before and after a chemical reaction. If a chemical reaction has a negative free-energy change ($\Delta G < 0$), the products have less free energy than the reactants, and, therefore, free energy is released during product formation. Such a reaction is said to be **exergonic**. Exergonic reactions are spontaneous. Alternatively, if a reaction has a positive free-energy change ($\Delta G > 0$), requiring the addition of free energy, it is termed **endergonic**. An endergonic reaction is not a spontaneous reaction.

If ΔG for a chemical reaction is negative, the reaction favors the conversion of reactants to products, whereas a reaction with a positive ΔG favors the formation of reactants. Chemists have determined free-energy changes for a variety of chemical reactions, which allows them to predict their direction. As an example, let's consider **adenosine triphosphate (ATP)**, which is a molecule that is a common energy source for all cells. ATP is broken down to adenosine diphosphate (ADP) and inorganic phosphate (HPO_4^{2-}, abbreviated Pᵢ). Because water is used to remove a phosphate group, chemists refer to this reaction as the hydrolysis of ATP (**Figure 6.3**). For the conversion of 1 mole of ATP to 1 mole of ADP and P$_i$, ΔG equals −7.3 kcal/mol. Because this is a negative value, the formation of the products is strongly favored. As discussed later, the energy liberated by the hydrolysis of ATP is used to drive a variety of cellular processes.

Chemical Reactions Eventually Reach a State of Equilibrium

Even when a chemical reaction is associated with a negative free-energy change, not all of the reactants are converted to products. The reaction reaches a state of **chemical equilibrium** in which the rate of formation of products equals the rate of formation of reactants. Let's consider the generalized reaction

$$a\text{A} + b\text{B} \rightleftharpoons c\text{C} + d\text{D}$$

where A and B are the reactants, C and D are the products, and a, b, c, and d are the number of moles of reactants and products. The reaction reaches equilibrium, such that

$$K_{eq} = \frac{[\text{C}]^c[\text{D}]^d}{[\text{A}]^a[\text{B}]^b}$$

where K_{eq} is the equilibrium constant. Each type of chemical reaction has a specific value for K_{eq}. When K_{eq} is greater than 1, the reaction favors the formation of products; when it is less than 1, the reaction favors the formation of reactants.

Cells Use ATP to Drive Endergonic Reactions

Many biological processes require the addition of free energy; that is, they are endergonic and do not occur spontaneously. How do cells overcome this problem? One strategy is to couple exergonic reactions with endergonic reactions. If an exergonic reaction is coupled with an endergonic reaction, the endergonic reaction will proceed spontaneously if the net free-energy change for both processes combined is negative. For example, consider the following reactions:

Glucose + Phosphate^{2-} → Glucose-6-phosphate^{2-} + H$_2$O
$$\Delta G = +3.3 \text{ kcal/mol}$$

ATP^{4-} + H$_2$O → ADP^{2-} + P$_i^{2-}$
$$\Delta G = -7.3 \text{ kcal/mol}$$

Coupled reaction:

Glucose + ATP^{4-} → Glucose-6-phosphate^{2-} + ADP^{2-}
$$\Delta G = -4.0 \text{ kcal/mol}$$

The first reaction, in which phosphate is covalently attached to glucose, is endergonic, and by itself is not spontaneous. The second reaction, the hydrolysis of ATP, is exergonic. If the two reactions are coupled, however, the combined net free-energy change for both is negative ($\Delta G = -4.0$ kcal/mol), and the coupled reaction is exergonic. In the coupled reaction, a phosphate is directly transferred from ATP to glucose, in a process called **phosphorylation**. This coupled reaction proceeds spontaneously because the net free-energy change is negative. Exergonic reactions, such as the breakdown of ATP, are commonly coupled to chemical reactions and other cellular processes that would otherwise be endergonic.

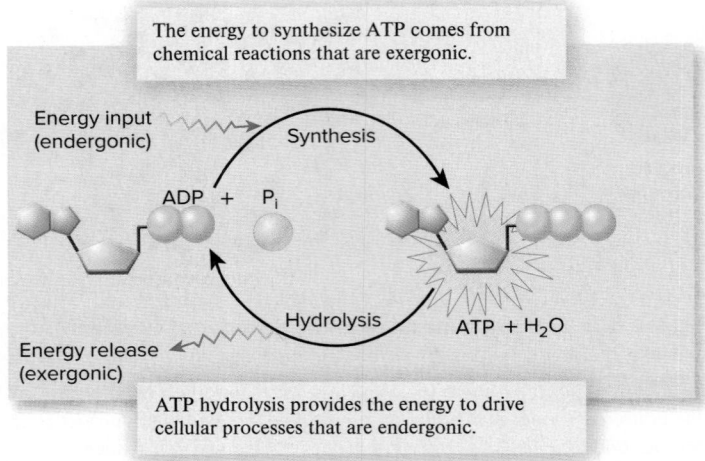

The energy to synthesize ATP comes from chemical reactions that are exergonic.

Energy input (endergonic)

Synthesis

ADP + P$_i$

Hydrolysis

ATP + H$_2$O

Energy release (exergonic)

ATP hydrolysis provides the energy to drive cellular processes that are endergonic.

Figure 6.4 **The ATP cycle.** Living cells continuously recycle ATP. The energy released from the breakdown of food molecules into smaller molecules is used to synthesize ATP from ADP and P$_i$. The hydrolysis of ATP to ADP and P$_i$ is used to drive many different endergonic reactions and processes that occur in cells.

Concept Check: *If a large amount of ADP was broken down in a cell, how would this affect the ATP cycle?*

In humans, a typical cell uses millions of ATP molecules per second to drive endergonic processes. At the same time, the breakdown of food molecules to form smaller molecules (an exergonic reaction) releases energy that allows cells to make more ATP from the phosphorylation of ADP (an endergonic reaction). The recycling of ATP from ADP and phosphate occurs at a remarkable pace. An average person hydrolyzes about 100 pounds of ATP per day, yet at any given time we do not have 100 pounds of ATP in our bodies. For this to happen, each molecule of ATP undergoes about 10,000 cycles of hydrolysis and regeneration during an ordinary day (**Figure 6.4**).

Core Concepts: Information, Energy and Matter

Genomes Encode Many Proteins That Use ATP as a Source of Energy

Over the past several decades, researchers have studied the functions of many proteins and **discovered** numerous examples in which a protein uses the hydrolysis of ATP to drive a chemical reaction or other type of cellular process (**Table 6.2**). By studying the structures of proteins that use ATP in this way, biochemists have discovered that particular amino acid sequences within proteins function as ATP-binding sites. This information has allowed researchers to predict whether a newly discovered protein uses ATP or not. When an entire genome sequence of a species has been determined, the genes that encode proteins can be analyzed to find out if the encoded proteins have ATP-binding sites in their amino acid sequences. Using this approach, researchers have been able to analyze **proteomes**—all of the proteins that a given cell

Table 6.2	Examples of Proteins That Use ATP for Energy
Type	**Description**
Metabolic enzymes	Many enzymes use ATP to catalyze endergonic reactions. For example, hexokinase uses ATP to attach phosphate to glucose, producing glucose-6-phosphate.
Transporters	Ion pumps, such as Na^+/K^+-ATPase, use ATP to pump ions against a gradient (see Chapter 5).
Motor proteins	Motor proteins, such as myosin, use ATP to facilitate cellular movement, as in muscle contraction (see Chapter 45).
Chaperones	Chaperones are proteins that use ATP to aid in the folding and unfolding of cellular proteins (see Chapter 4).
DNA-modifying enzymes	Many proteins, such as helicases and topoisomerases, use ATP to modify the conformation of DNA (see Chapter 11).
Aminoacyl-tRNA synthetases	These synthetases are enzymes that use ATP to attach amino acids to tRNAs (transfer RNAs; see Chapter 12).
Protein kinases	Protein kinases are regulatory proteins that use ATP to attach a phosphate to a protein, thereby phosphorylating the protein and affecting its function (see Chapter 9).

or organism makes—and estimate the percentage of proteins that are able to bind ATP. This approach has been applied to the proteomes of bacteria, archaea, and eukaryotes.

On average, over 20% of all proteins bind ATP. However, this number is likely an underestimate because all of the types of ATP-binding sites in proteins may not have been identified. In humans, whose genome has an estimated size of 22,000 different protein-encoding genes, a minimum of 4,400 of those genes encode proteins that use ATP. From these numbers, we can see the enormous importance of ATP as a source of energy for living cells.

6.2 Enzymes and Ribozymes

Learning Outcomes:

1. Explain how enzymes increase the rates of chemical reactions by lowering the activation energy.
2. Describe how enzymes bind their substrates with high specificity and undergo induced fit.
3. **CoreSKILL »** Analyze the velocity of chemical reactions, and evaluate the effects of competitive and noncompetitive inhibitors.
4. Explain how additional factors, such as nonprotein molecules or ions, temperature, and pH, influence enzyme activity.
5. Identify the unique feature of ribozymes.

For most chemical reactions in cells to proceed at a rapid pace, a catalyst is needed. A **catalyst** is an agent that speeds up the rate of a chemical reaction without being permanently changed or consumed by it. In living cells, the most common catalysts are **enzymes**, which are proteins. The term was coined in 1876 by a German physiologist,

Wilhelm Kühne, who discovered trypsin, an enzyme in pancreatic juice that is needed for the digestion of food proteins. In this section, we will explore how enzymes increase the rates of chemical reactions. Interestingly, some biological catalysts are RNA molecules called ribozymes. We will examine a few examples in which RNA molecules carry out catalytic functions.

Enzymes Increase the Rates of Chemical Reactions

If a chemical reaction has a negative free-energy change, the reaction will be spontaneous; it will tend to proceed in the direction of reactants to products. Although thermodynamics governs the direction of an energy transformation, it does not determine the rate of a chemical reaction. For example, the breakdown of the molecules in gasoline to smaller molecules is an exergonic reaction. Even so, we could place gasoline and oxygen in a container and nothing much would happen (provided the container wasn't near a flame). If we came back several days later, we would expect to see the gasoline still sitting there. Perhaps if we came back in a few million years, the gasoline would have been broken down. On a timescale of months or a few years, however, the chemical reaction would proceed very slowly.

In living cells, the rates of enzyme-catalyzed reactions typically occur millions of times faster than the corresponding uncatalyzed reactions. A dramatic example involves the enzyme catalase, which catalyzes the breakdown of hydrogen peroxide (H_2O_2) into water and oxygen. Catalase speeds up this reaction so that it occurs 10^{15}-fold faster than the uncatalyzed reaction!

Why are catalysts necessary to speed up a chemical reaction? Chemical reactions between molecules involve bond breaking and bond forming. When a covalent bond is broken or formed, this process initially involves the straining or stretching of one or more bonds in the starting molecule(s) and/or the positioning of two molecules so that they interact with each other properly. Enzymes help to facilitate these kinds of events.

As an example, let's consider the reaction in which ATP is used to phosphorylate glucose:

$$\text{Glucose} + \text{ATP}^{4-} \rightarrow \text{Glucose-6-phosphate}^{2-} + \text{ADP}^{2-}$$

For a reaction to occur between glucose and ATP, the molecules must collide in the correct orientation and possess enough energy so the chemical bonds can be changed. As glucose and ATP get close together, the electrons in the outer shells of their atoms repel each other. To overcome this repulsion, an initial input of energy, called the **activation energy**, is required (**Figure 6.5**). Activation energy (E_A) allows the molecules to get close enough to cause a rearrangement of bonds. With the input of activation energy, glucose and ATP can achieve a **transition state** in which the original bonds have stretched to their limit. Once the reactants have reached the transition state, the chemical reaction can readily proceed to the formation of products, which in this case are glucose-6-phosphate and ADP.

The activation energy required to achieve the transition state is a barrier to the formation of products. This barrier is the reason why the rate of many chemical reactions is very slow. Enzymes lower the activation energy to a point where a small amount of available heat can push the reactants to the transition state.

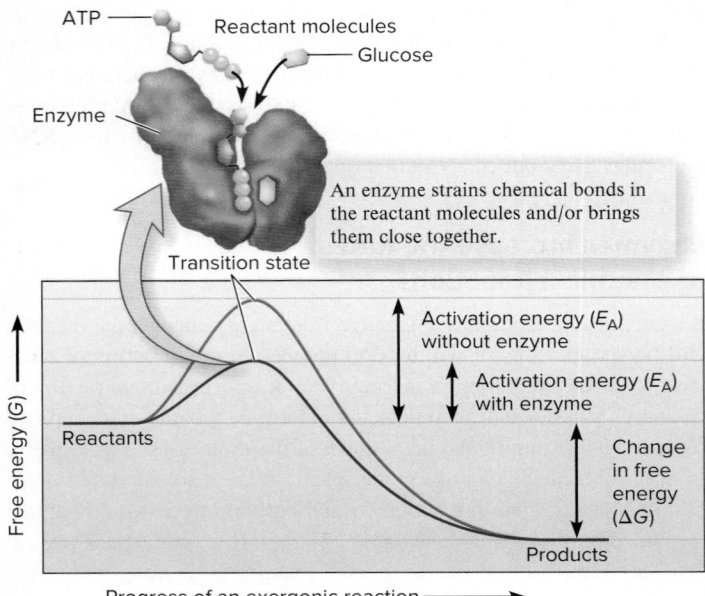

Figure 6.5 Activation energy of a chemical reaction. This figure depicts an exergonic reaction. The activation energy (E_A) is needed for molecules to achieve a transition state. One way that enzymes lower the activation energy is by straining chemical bonds in the reactants so less energy is required to attain the transition state. A second way is by binding two reactants so they are close to each other and in a favorable orientation.

Concept Check: *How does lowering the activation energy affect the rate of a chemical reaction? How does it affect the direction?*

How do enzymes lower the activation energy barrier of chemical reactions? Let's consider two common ways that enzymes exert their effects.

- Enzymes are proteins that bind relatively small reactants. When reactant molecules are bound to an enzyme, their bonds can be strained, thereby making it easier for them to achieve the transition state (see Figure 6.5).

- In addition, when a chemical reaction involves two or more reactants, the enzyme provides a site where the reactants are positioned very close to each other in an orientation that facilitates the formation of new covalent bonds. This favorable orientation also lowers the necessary activation energy for a chemical reaction.

Enzymes Recognize Their Substrates with High Specificity and Undergo Conformational Changes

Thus far, we have considered how enzymes lower the activation energy of a chemical reaction, and thereby increase its rate. Let's consider some other features of enzymes that enable them to serve as effective catalysts in chemical reactions. The **active site** is the location in an enzyme where the chemical reaction takes place. The **substrates** for an enzyme are the reactant molecules that bind to an enzyme at the active site and participate in the chemical reaction. For example, hexokinase is an enzyme whose substrates are glucose and ATP (**Figure 6.6**). The binding between enzyme and substrate produces an **enzyme-substrate complex**.

A key feature of nearly all enzymes is their ability to bind their substrates with a high degree of specificity. For example, hexokinase recognizes glucose but does not recognize other similar sugars, such as fructose and galactose, very well. In 1894, a German chemist Emil Fischer proposed that the recognition of a substrate by an enzyme resembles the interaction between a lock and key: Only the correctly shaped key (the substrate) will fit into the keyhole (active site) of the lock (the enzyme). Further research

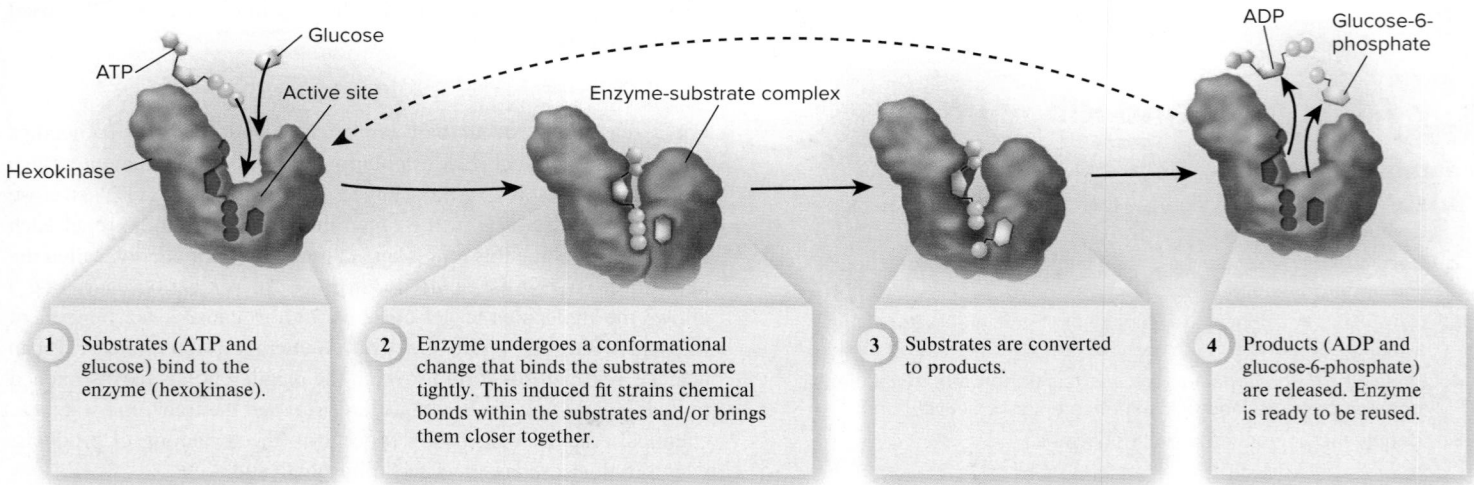

| 1 | Substrates (ATP and glucose) bind to the enzyme (hexokinase). | 2 | Enzyme undergoes a conformational change that binds the substrates more tightly. This induced fit strains chemical bonds within the substrates and/or brings them closer together. | 3 | Substrates are converted to products. | 4 | Products (ADP and glucose-6-phosphate) are released. Enzyme is ready to be reused. |

Figure 6.6 The steps of an enzyme-catalyzed reaction. The example shown here involves the enzyme hexokinase, which binds glucose and ATP. The products are glucose-6-phosphate and ADP, which are released from the enzyme.

 Core Concept: Structure and Function A key function of enzymes is their ability to bind their substrates with high specificity. This specificity is due to the structure of the enzyme's active site.

revealed that the interaction between an enzyme and its substrates also involves movements or conformational changes in the enzyme itself. As shown in step 2 in Figure 6.6, these conformational changes cause the substrates to bind more tightly to the enzyme, a phenomenon called **induced fit**, which was proposed by American biochemist Daniel Koshland in 1958. Only after induced fit takes place does the enzyme catalyze the conversion of reactants to products. Induced fit is a key phenomenon that lowers the activation energy.

Enzyme Function Is Influenced by the Substrate Concentration and by Inhibitors

The degree of attraction between an enzyme and its substrate(s) is called the **affinity** of the enzyme for its substrate(s). Some enzymes have very high affinity for their substrates, which means they readily recognize them. Such enzymes bind their substrates even when the substrate concentration is relatively low. Other enzymes have lower affinity for their substrates; the enzyme-substrate complex is likely to form only when the substrate concentration is higher.

Let's consider how biologists analyze the relationship between substrate concentration and enzyme function. In the experiment of **Figure 6.7a**, tubes labeled A, B, C, and D each contained 1 µg of enzyme, but they varied in the amount of substrate that was added. This enzyme recognizes a single substrate and converts it to a product. The samples were incubated for 60 seconds, and then the amount of product in each tube was measured. The velocity, or rate, of the chemical reaction is expressed as the amount of product produced per second. As we see in Figure 6.7a, the velocity increases as the substrate concentration increases, but eventually reaches a plateau. Why does the plateau occur? At high substrate concentrations, nearly all of the active sites of the enzyme are occupied with substrate, so further increasing the substrate concentration has a negligible effect. At this point, the enzyme is saturated with substrate, and the velocity of the chemical reaction is near its maximal rate, called its V_{max}.

Figure 6.7a also helps us understand the relationship between substrate concentration and velocity. The K_M is the substrate concentration at which the velocity is half its maximal value. The K_M is also called the Michaelis constant in honor of German biochemist Leonor Michaelis, who carried out pioneering work with Canadian biochemist Maud Menten on the study of enzymes. The K_M is a measure of the substrate concentration required for a chemical reaction to occur. An enzyme with a high K_M requires a higher substrate concentration to achieve a particular reaction velocity compared to an enzyme with a lower K_M.

For an enzyme-catalyzed reaction, we can view the formation of product as occurring in two steps: (1) binding or release of substrate and (2) formation of product:

$$E + S \rightleftharpoons ES \rightarrow E + P$$

where E is the enzyme, S is the substrate, ES is the enzyme-substrate complex, and P is the product.

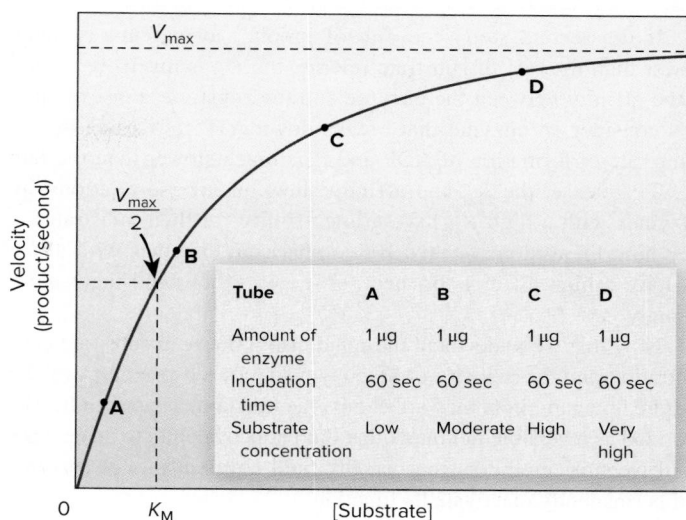

(a) **Reaction velocity in the absence of inhibitors**

Tube	A	B	C	D
Amount of enzyme	1 µg	1 µg	1 µg	1 µg
Incubation time	60 sec	60 sec	60 sec	60 sec
Substrate concentration	Low	Moderate	High	Very high

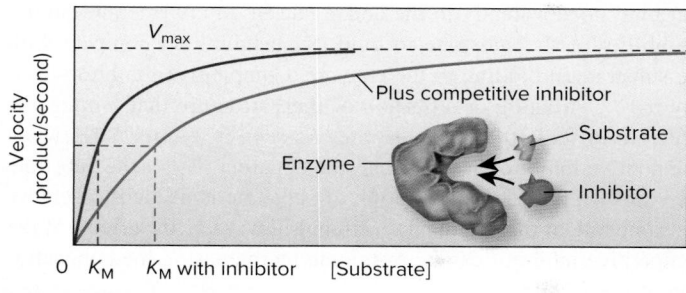

(b) **Competitive inhibition**

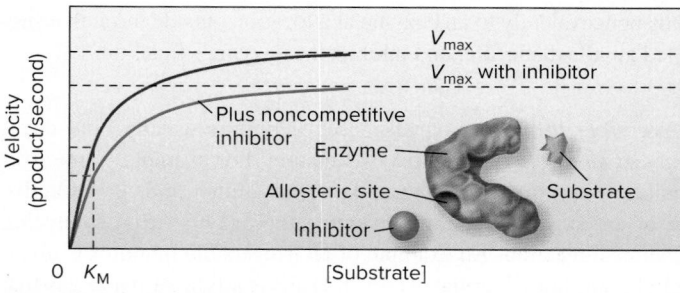

(c) **Noncompetitive inhibition**

Figure 6.7 The relationship between velocity and substrate concentration in an enzyme-catalyzed reaction, and the effects of inhibitors. (a) In the absence of an inhibitor, the maximal velocity (V_{max}) of an enzyme-catalyzed reaction is achieved when the substrate concentration is high enough to be saturating. The K_M value for an enzyme is the substrate concentration at which the velocity of the reaction is half the maximal velocity. **(b)** A competitive inhibitor binds to the active site of an enzyme and raises the K_M. **(c)** A noncompetitive inhibitor binds to an allosteric site outside the active site and lowers the V_{max}.

Concept Check: *Enzyme A has a K_M of 0.1 mM, whereas enzyme B has a K_M of 1.0 mM. The reactions the two enzymes catalyze both have the same V_{max}. If the substrate concentration was 0.5 mM, which reaction—the one catalyzed by enzyme A or the one catalyzed by enzyme B—would have the higher velocity?*

If the second step—the rate of product formation—is much slower than the rate of substrate release, the K_M is inversely related to the affinity between the enzyme and the substrate. For example, let's consider an enzyme that breaks down ATP into ADP and P_i. If the rate of formation of ADP and P_i is much slower than the rate of ATP release, the K_M and affinity show an inverse relationship. Enzymes with a high K_M have a low affinity for their substrates—they bind them more weakly. By comparison, enzymes with a low K_M have a high affinity for their substrates—they bind them more strongly.

Now that we understand the relationship between substrate concentration and the velocity of an enzyme-catalyzed reaction, we can explore how inhibitors may affect enzyme function. These can be categorized as reversible inhibitors that bind noncovalently to an enzyme or irreversible inhibitors that usually bind covalently to an enzyme and permanently inactivate its function.

Reversible Inhibitors Cells often use reversible inhibitors to modulate enzyme function. **Competitive inhibitors** are molecules that bind noncovalently to the active site of an enzyme and inhibit the ability of the substrate to bind. Such inhibitors compete with the substrate in binding to the enzyme. Competitive inhibitors usually have a structure or a portion of their structure that mimics the structure of the enzyme's substrate. As seen in **Figure 6.7b**, when competitive inhibitors are present, the apparent K_M for the substrate increases—a higher concentration of substrate is needed to achieve the same rate of the chemical reaction. In this case, the effects of the competitive inhibitor can be overcome by increasing the concentration of the substrate.

By comparison, **Figure 6.7c** illustrates the effects of a **noncompetitive inhibitor**. This type of inhibitor lowers the V_{max} for the reaction without affecting the K_M. A noncompetitive inhibitor binds noncovalently to an enzyme at a location outside the active site, called an **allosteric site**, and inhibits the enzyme's function.

Irreversible Inhibitors Irreversible inhibitors usually bind covalently to an enzyme to inhibit its function. For example, some irreversible inhibitors bind covalently to an amino acid at the active site of an enzyme, thereby preventing the enzyme from catalyzing a chemical reaction. An example of an irreversible inhibitor is diisopropyl phosphorofluoridate (DIFP). DIFP is a type of nerve gas that was developed as a chemical weapon. This molecule covalently reacts with the enzyme acetylcholinesterase, which is important for the proper functioning of neurons.

Irreversible inhibition is not a common way for cells to control enzyme function. Why do cells usually control enzymes via reversible inhibitors? The answer is that a reversible inhibitor allows an enzyme to be used again, when the inhibitor concentration becomes lower. Being able to reuse an enzyme is energy-efficient. In contrast, irreversible inhibitors permanently inactivate an enzyme, thereby preventing its further use.

Additional Factors Influence Enzyme Function

Enzymes, which are proteins, sometimes require nonprotein molecules or ions to carry out their functions.

- **Prosthetic groups** are small molecules that are permanently attached to the surface of an enzyme and aid in enzyme function.
- **Cofactors** are usually inorganic ions, such as Fe^{3+} or Zn^{2+}, that temporarily bind to the surface of an enzyme and promote a chemical reaction.
- Some enzymes use **coenzymes**, organic molecules that temporarily bind to an enzyme and participate in the chemical reaction that the enzyme catalyzes, but are left unchanged when the reaction is completed.

The ability of enzymes to increase the rate of a chemical reaction is also affected by their environment. In particular, the temperature, pH, and ionic conditions play an important role in the proper functioning of enzymes. Most enzymes function maximally in a narrow range of temperature and pH. For example, many human enzymes work best at 37°C (98.6°F), which is normal body temperature. If the temperature is several degrees above or below this optimal temperature due to infection or environmental causes, the function of many enzymes is greatly inhibited (**Figure 6.8**). Very high temperatures may denature a protein, causing it to unfold and lose its three-dimensional shape, thereby inhibiting its function.

Enzyme function is also sensitive to pH. Certain enzymes in the stomach function best at the acidic pH found in this organ. For example, pepsin is a protease—an enzyme that digests proteins into peptides—that is released into the stomach. The optimal pH for pepsin function is around pH 2.0, which is extremely acidic. By comparison, many cytosolic enzymes function optimally at a more neutral pH, such as pH 7.2, which is the pH normally found in the cytosol of human cells. If the pH was significantly above or below this value, function would be decreased for cytosolic enzymes.

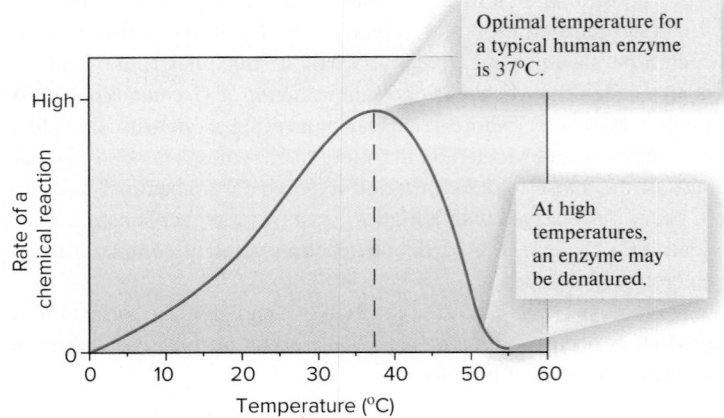

Figure 6.8 Effects of temperature on a typical human enzyme. Most enzymes function optimally within a narrow range of temperature. Many human enzymes function best at 37°C, which is normal body temperature.

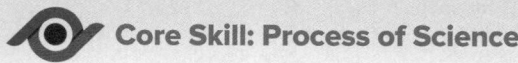

Core Skill: Process of Science

Feature Investigation | The Discovery of Ribozymes by Sidney Altman Revealed That RNA Molecules May Also Function as Catalysts

Until the 1980s, scientists thought that all biological catalysts are proteins. An avenue of study that dramatically changed this view came from the analysis of ribonuclease P (RNase P), a catalyst involved in the processing of tRNA molecules—a type of molecule required for protein synthesis. tRNA molecules are synthesized as longer precursor molecules called ptRNAs, which have 5′ and 3′ ends. (The 5′ and 3′ directionality of RNA molecules is described in Chapter 12.) RNase P breaks a covalent bond at a specific site in a ptRNA, which releases a fragment at the 5′ end and makes the precursor molecule shorter (**Figure 6.9**).

Sidney Altman and his colleagues became interested in the processing of tRNA molecules and turned their attention to RNase P in *E. coli*. During the course of their studies, they purified this enzyme and, to their surprise, discovered it has two subunits—one is an RNA molecule that contains 377 nucleotides, and the other is a small protein with a mass of 14 kDa. In the 1980s, the finding that a catalyst had an RNA subunit was very unexpected. Even so, a second property of RNase P would prove even more exciting.

Altman and colleagues were able to purify RNase P and study its properties in vitro. Cecilia Guerrier-Takada in Altman's laboratory determined that magnesium ion (Mg^{2+}) has a stimulatory effect on RNase P function. In the experiment described in **Figure 6.10**, the effects of Mg^{2+} were studied in greater detail. The researchers analyzed the effects of low (10 mM $MgCl_2$) and high (100 mM $MgCl_2$) magnesium concentrations on the processing of a ptRNA. At low or high magnesium concentrations,

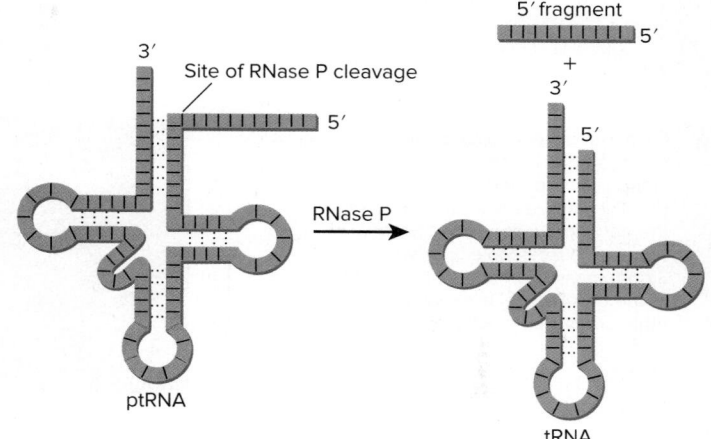

Figure 6.9 The function of RNase P. A specific bond in a precursor tRNA (ptRNA) is cleaved by RNase P, which releases a small fragment at the 5′ end. This results in the formation of a mature tRNA.

Core Skill: Connections Look ahead to Figure 12.20. How do you think translation would be affected if RNase P did not function properly?

Figure 6.10 The discovery that the RNA subunit of RNase P is a catalyst.

HYPOTHESIS The catalytic function of RNase P is carried out by its RNA subunit or by its protein subunit.

KEY MATERIALS Purified precursor tRNA (ptRNA) and purified RNA and protein subunits of RNase P from *E. coli*.

Experimental level	Conceptual level

1 Into each of five tubes, add ptRNA.

2 In tubes 1–3, add a low concentration of $MgCl_2$; in tubes 4 and 5, add a high $MgCl_2$ concentration.

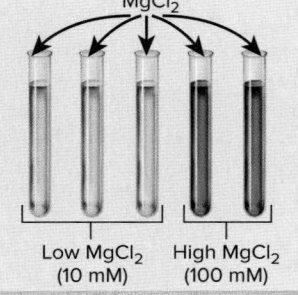

Low $MgCl_2$ (10 mM)   High $MgCl_2$ (100 mM)

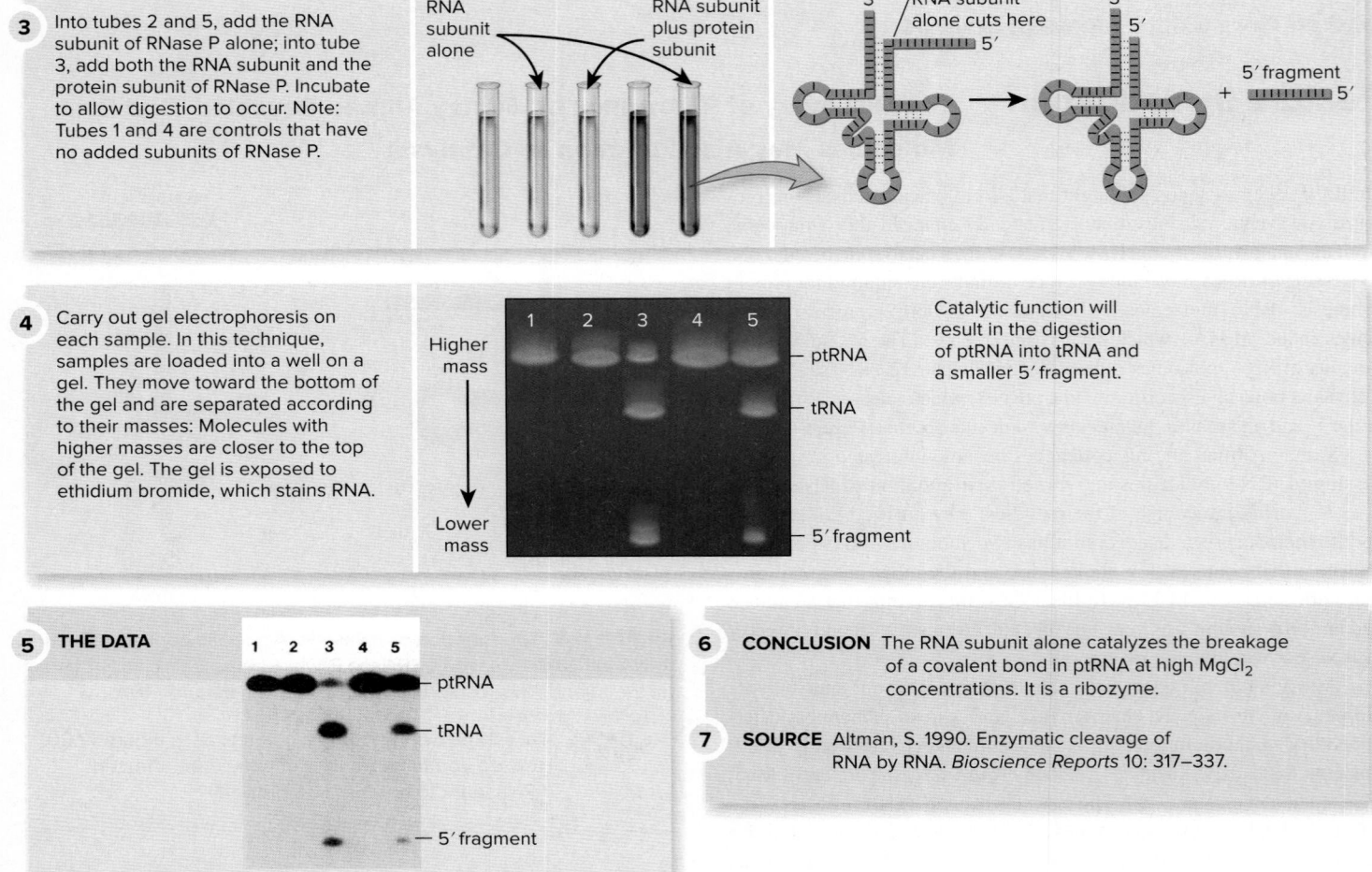

3 Into tubes 2 and 5, add the RNA subunit of RNase P alone; into tube 3, add both the RNA subunit and the protein subunit of RNase P. Incubate to allow digestion to occur. Note: Tubes 1 and 4 are controls that have no added subunits of RNase P.

4 Carry out gel electrophoresis on each sample. In this technique, samples are loaded into a well on a gel. They move toward the bottom of the gel and are separated according to their masses: Molecules with higher masses are closer to the top of the gel. The gel is exposed to ethidium bromide, which stains RNA.

Catalytic function will result in the digestion of ptRNA into tRNA and a smaller 5′ fragment.

5 THE DATA

6 CONCLUSION The RNA subunit alone catalyzes the breakage of a covalent bond in ptRNA at high $MgCl_2$ concentrations. It is a ribozyme.

7 SOURCE Altman, S. 1990. Enzymatic cleavage of RNA by RNA. *Bioscience Reports* 10: 317–337.

(4–5): Altman, S. 1990. Enzymatic Cleavage of RNA by RNA. *Bioscience Reports*, 10:317–337, Fig. 7. ©The Nobel Foundation

ptRNAs were incubated without RNase P (as a control), with the RNA subunit alone, or with intact RNase P (RNA subunit and protein subunit). Following incubation, the researchers performed gel electrophoresis on the samples to determine if the ptRNAs had been cleaved into two pieces—the tRNA and a 5′ fragment. (Gel electrophoresis separates molecules on the basis of their masses.)

Let's now look at the data. As a control, ptRNAs were incubated with low (lane 1) or high (lane 4) concentrations of $MgCl_2$ in the absence of RNase P. As expected, no processing to lower molecular mass tRNAs was observed. When the RNA subunit alone was incubated with ptRNA molecules in the presence of low $MgCl_2$ (lane 2), no processing occurred, but it did occur if the protein subunit was also included (lane 3).

The surprising result is shown in lane 5, in which the ptRNA was incubated with the RNA subunit alone in the presence of a high concentration of $MgCl_2$. The RNA subunit by itself was sufficient to cleave the ptRNA to a smaller tRNA and a 5′ fragment! Presumably, the high $MgCl_2$ concentration helps to keep the RNA subunit in a conformation that is catalytically active. Alternatively, the protein subunit plays a similar role in a living cell.

Subsequent work confirmed these observations and showed that the RNA subunit of RNase P is a true catalyst—it accelerates the rate of a chemical reaction and is not permanently altered by it. Around the same time, Thomas Cech and colleagues determined that a different RNA molecule found in the protist *Tetrahymena thermophila* also has

catalytic activity. The term **ribozyme** is now used to describe an RNA molecule that catalyzes a chemical reaction. In 1989, Altman and Cech received the Nobel Prize in Chemistry for their discovery of ribozymes.

Since the pioneering work of Altman and Cech, researchers have discovered that ribozymes play key catalytic roles in cells (**Table 6.3**).

Table 6.3	Types of Ribozymes
General function	**Biological examples**
Processing of RNA molecules	1. RNase P: As described earlier, RNase P cleaves precursor tRNA molecules (ptRNAs) to form mature tRNAs.
	2. Spliceosomal RNA: As described in Chapter 12, eukaryotic pre-mRNAs often have regions called introns. These introns are later removed by a spliceosome that is composed of RNA and protein subunits. The RNA within the spliceosome is believed to function as a ribozyme that removes the introns from pre-mRNA.
	3. Certain introns found in mitochondrial, chloroplast, and bacterial RNAs are removed by a self-splicing mechanism.
Synthesis of polypeptides	A ribosome has an RNA component that catalyzes the formation of covalent bonds between adjacent amino acids during polypeptide synthesis.

They are primarily involved in the processing of RNA molecules from precursor to mature forms. In addition, a ribozyme in ribosomes catalyzes the formation of covalent bonds between adjacent amino acids during polypeptide synthesis.

Experimental Questions

1. Briefly explain why it was necessary to purify the individual subunits of RNase P to show that it is a ribozyme.

2. **CoreSKILL** » Explain why the researchers conducted experiments in which they measured the formation of mature tRNAs without adding the protein subunit or without adding the RNA subunit.

3. **CoreSKILL** » Analyze the results of Altman and colleagues, and explain how they indicated that RNase P is a ribozyme. How does the concentration of Mg^{2+} affect the function of the RNA subunit in RNase P?

6.3 Overview of Metabolism

Learning Outcomes:

1. Explain the concept of a metabolic pathway, and distinguish between catabolic and anabolic reactions.
2. Describe how catabolic reactions are used to generate building blocks to make larger molecules and to produce energy intermediates.
3. Define redox reaction.
4. Compare and contrast three ways that metabolic pathways are regulated.

In the previous sections, we examined the underlying factors that govern individual chemical reactions and explored the properties of enzymes and ribozymes. In living cells, chemical reactions are coordinated with each other and often occur in a series of steps called a **metabolic pathway**, with each step catalyzed by a specific enzyme (**Figure 6.11**). These pathways are categorized according to whether the reactions lead to the breakdown or synthesis of substances. **Catabolic reactions** result in the breakdown of larger molecules into smaller ones. Such reactions are often exergonic. By comparison, **anabolic reactions** involve the synthesis of larger molecules from smaller precursor molecules. These reactions usually are endergonic and, in living cells, must be coupled to an exergonic reaction. In this section, we will survey the general features of catabolic and anabolic reactions and explore the ways in which metabolic pathways are controlled.

Catabolic Reactions Recycle Organic Building Blocks and Produce Energy Intermediates Such as ATP

Catabolic reactions result in the breakdown of larger molecules into smaller ones. Such catabolic reactions have two uses.

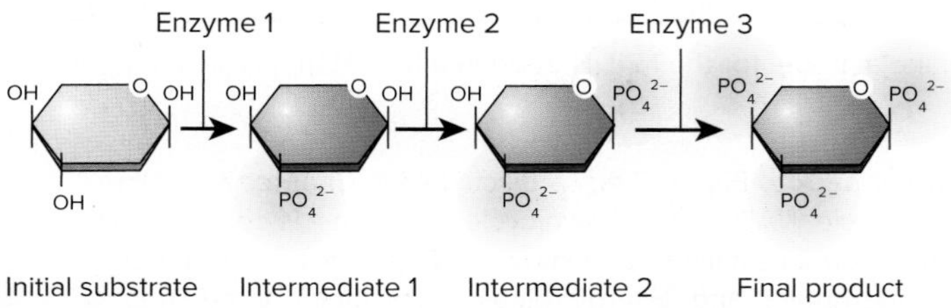

Recycling of Organic Building Blocks One reason to break down macromolecules is to recycle their organic molecules, which are used as building blocks to construct new molecules and macromolecules. For example, polypeptides, which make up proteins, are composed of a linear sequence of amino acids. When a protein is improperly folded or is no longer needed by a cell, the peptide bonds between the amino acids in the protein are broken by enzymes called proteases. This generates amino acids that can be used in the construction of new proteins.

$$Protein \xrightarrow{\text{Proteases}} \rightarrow \rightarrow \rightarrow \rightarrow \rightarrow \rightarrow \rightarrow \rightarrow \text{Many individual amino acids}$$

We will consider the mechanisms of recycling in Section 6.4.

Breakdown of Organic Molecules to Obtain Energy A second reason to break down macromolecules into smaller organic molecules is to obtain energy that is used to drive endergonic processes in the cell. Covalent bonds store a large amount of energy. However, when cells break covalent bonds in organic molecules such as glucose, they do not directly use the energy released in this process. Instead, the released energy is stored in **energy intermediates**, molecules such as ATP, which are directly used to drive endergonic reactions in cells.

As an example, let's consider the breakdown of glucose into two molecules of pyruvate. As discussed in Chapter 7, the breakdown of glucose to pyruvate involves a catabolic pathway called glycolysis. Some of the energy released during the breakage of covalent bonds in glucose is harnessed to synthesize ATP. Glycolysis involves a series of steps in which covalent bonds are broken and rearranged. This process produces molecules that readily donate a phosphate group to ADP, thereby producing ATP. For example, phosphoenolpyruvate has a phosphate group attached to pyruvate. Due to the arrangement of bonds in phosphoenolpyruvate, this phosphate bond is unstable and easily broken. Therefore, the phosphate can be readily transferred from phosphoenolpyruvate to ADP:

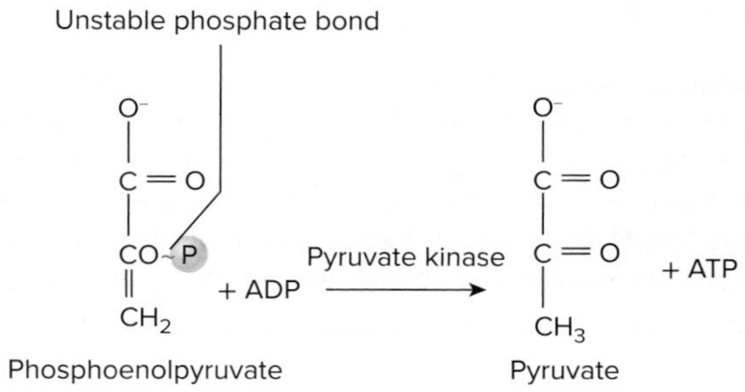

Figure 6.11 A metabolic pathway. In this metabolic pathway, a series of different enzymes catalyze the attachment of phosphate groups at various positions on a sugar molecule, beginning with a starting substrate and ending with a final product.

This is an exergonic reaction ($\Delta G = -7.5$ kcal/mol) and therefore favors the formation of products. In this step of glycolysis, the breakdown of an organic molecule, namely phosphoenolpyruvate, results in the formation of pyruvate and the synthesis of an energy intermediate, a molecule of ATP, which can then be used by a cell to drive an endergonic reaction. This way of synthesizing ATP, termed **substrate-level phosphorylation**, occurs when an enzyme directly transfers a phosphate from an organic molecule to ADP, thereby making ATP.

Another way to make ATP is via **chemiosmosis**. In this process, energy stored in an ion electrochemical gradient is used to make ATP from ADP and P_i. We will consider this other mechanism in Chapter 7.

Redox Reactions Involve the Transfer of Electrons

During the breakdown of small organic molecules, **oxidation**—the removal of one or more electrons from an atom or molecule—may occur. This process is called oxidation because oxygen is frequently involved in chemical reactions that remove electrons from other atoms or molecules. By comparison, **reduction** is the addition of one or more electrons to an atom or molecule. Reduction is so named because the addition of a negatively charged electron reduces the net charge of an atom or molecule.

Electrons do not exist freely in solution. When an atom or molecule is oxidized, the electron that is removed must be transferred to another atom or molecule, which becomes reduced. This type of reaction is termed a **redox reaction**, which is short for a reduction-oxidation reaction. An electron may be transferred from molecule A to molecule B as shown in the following generalized equation:

$$Ae^- \quad + \quad B \quad \rightarrow \quad A \quad + \quad Be^-$$
$$\text{(oxidized)} \quad \text{(reduced)}$$

As shown on the right side of this reaction, A has been oxidized (that is, had an electron removed), and B has been reduced (that is, had an electron added). In general, a substance that has been oxidized has less energy, whereas a substance that has been reduced has more energy.

During the oxidation of organic molecules such as glucose, the electrons that are removed may be used to produce energy intermediates such as NADH (**Figure 6.12**). In this process, an organic molecule

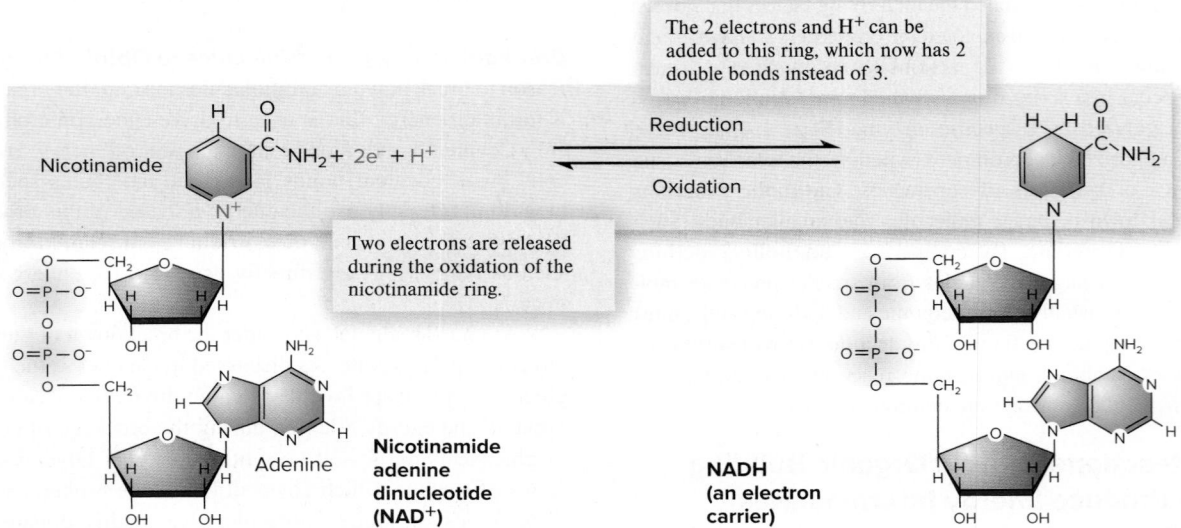

Figure 6.12   The reduction of NAD⁺ to produce NADH. NAD⁺ is composed of two nucleotides, one with an adenine base and one with a nicotinamide base. The oxidation of organic molecules releases electrons that bind to NAD⁺ (and along with a hydrogen ion) result in the formation of NADH. The two electrons and H⁺ are incorporated into the nicotinamide ring. Note: The actual net charges of NAD⁺ and NADH are −1 and −2, respectively. They are designated NAD⁺ and NADH to emphasize the net charge of the nicotinamide ring, which is involved in reduction-oxidation reactions.

Core Skill: Modeling   The goal of this modeling challenge is to make a model for the NADH cycle in a format that is similar to Figure 6.4.

Modeling Challenge: Earlier in this chapter, we considered the ATP cycle (refer back to Figure 6.4). As discussed in Chapter 7, NADH is used by mitochondria to make ATP. Therefore, it plays a key role in the ATP cycle. NADH has its own cycle, in which it is converted to NAD⁺ and then back to NADH again. Draw a model for the NADH cycle using a format similar to that shown in Figure 6.4. Your model should incorporate the red squiggly arrows that are labeled "Energy input (endergonic)" and "Energy release (exergonic)." In addition to using NADH, NAD⁺, H⁺, and 2e⁻ in your model (instead of ATP, etc.), you will need to change the sentences in the top and bottom text boxes of Figure 6.4 and to change the words "Synthesis" and "Hydrolysis."

is oxidized, and **NAD⁺** (**nicotinamide adenine dinucleotide**) is reduced to NADH. Cells use NADH in two common ways. First, as we will see in Chapter 7, the oxidation of NADH is a highly exergonic reaction that can be used to make ATP. Second, NADH can donate electrons to other organic molecules and thereby energize them. Such energized molecules can more readily form covalent bonds. Therefore, as described next, NADH is often needed in reactions that involve the synthesis of larger molecules through the formation of covalent bonds between smaller molecules.

Anabolic Reactions Require an Input of Energy to Make Larger Molecules

Anabolic reactions are also called **biosynthetic reactions**, because they are necessary to make larger molecules and macromolecules. We will examine the synthesis of macromolecules in several chapters of this textbook. For example, RNA and protein biosynthesis are described in Chapter 12. Cells also need to synthesize small organic molecules, such as amino acids and fats, if they are not readily available from food sources. Such molecules are made by the formation of covalent linkages between precursor molecules. For example, glutamate (an amino acid) is made by covalently linking α-ketoglutarate (a product of sugar metabolism) and ammonium (NH_4^+).

α-Ketoglutarate   Glutamate

An energy intermediate, a molecule of NADH, is needed to drive this reaction forward.

Metabolic Pathways Are Regulated in Three General Ways

The regulation of metabolic pathways is important for a variety of reasons. Catabolic pathways are regulated so organic molecules are broken down only when they are no longer needed or when the cell requires energy. During anabolic reactions, regulation ensures that a cell synthesizes molecules only when they are needed. The regulation of catabolic and anabolic pathways occurs at the genetic, cellular, and biochemical levels.

Gene Regulation Enzymes are protein molecules that are encoded by genes. One way that cells control metabolic pathways is via gene regulation. For example, if a bacterial cell is not exposed to a particular sugar in its environment, it will turn off the genes that encode the enzymes that are needed to break down

that sugar. Then, if the sugar becomes available, the genes are switched back on. Chapter 14 examines the steps of gene regulation in detail.

Cellular Regulation Metabolism is also coordinated at the cellular level. Cells integrate signals from their environment and adjust their metabolic pathways to adapt to those signals. As discussed in Chapter 9, cell-signaling pathways often lead to the activation of protein kinases—enzymes that covalently attach a phosphate group to a target protein. For example, when people are frightened, they secrete a hormone called epinephrine into their bloodstream. This hormone binds to the surface of muscle cells and stimulates an intracellular pathway that leads to the phosphorylation of specific enzymes involved in carbohydrate metabolism. These activated enzymes promote the breakdown of carbohydrates, an event that supplies the frightened individual with more energy. Epinephrine is sometimes called the fight-or-flight hormone because the added energy prepares an individual to either stay and fight or run away quickly. After a person no longer feels frightened, hormone levels drop, and other enzymes called phosphatases remove the phosphate groups from enzymes, thereby restoring the original level of carbohydrate metabolism.

Biochemical Regulation A third and very prominent way that metabolic pathways are controlled is at the biochemical level. In this case, the noncovalent binding of a molecule to an enzyme directly regulates the enzyme's function. As discussed earlier, one form of biochemical regulation involves the binding of molecules called competitive or noncompetitive inhibitors (see Figure 6.7). An example of noncompetitive inhibition is a type of regulation called **feedback inhibition**, in which the product of a metabolic pathway inhibits an enzyme that acts early in the pathway, thus preventing the overaccumulation of the product (**Figure 6.13**).

Many metabolic pathways use feedback inhibition as a form of biochemical regulation. In such cases, the inhibited enzyme has two binding sites. One site is the active site, where the reactants are converted to products. In addition, enzymes controlled by feedback inhibition also have an allosteric site, where a molecule can bind noncovalently and affect the enzyme's function. The binding of a molecule to an allosteric site causes a conformational change in the enzyme that inhibits its catalytic function. Allosteric sites are often found in the enzymes that catalyze the early steps in a metabolic pathway. Such allosteric sites typically bind molecules that are the products of the metabolic pathway. When the products bind to these sites, they inhibit the function of these enzymes, thereby preventing the formation of too much product. As described earlier, in Figure 6.7c, this phenomenon is also called noncompetitive inhibition.

Regulation of the Rate-Limiting Step Cellular regulation and biochemical regulation are important ways to control chemical reactions in a cell. For a metabolic pathway composed of several enzyme-catalyzed reactions, which enzyme should be controlled? In many cases, a metabolic pathway has a **rate-limiting step**, which is the slowest step in the pathway. If the rate-limiting step is inhibited or enhanced, such changes will have the greatest influence on the

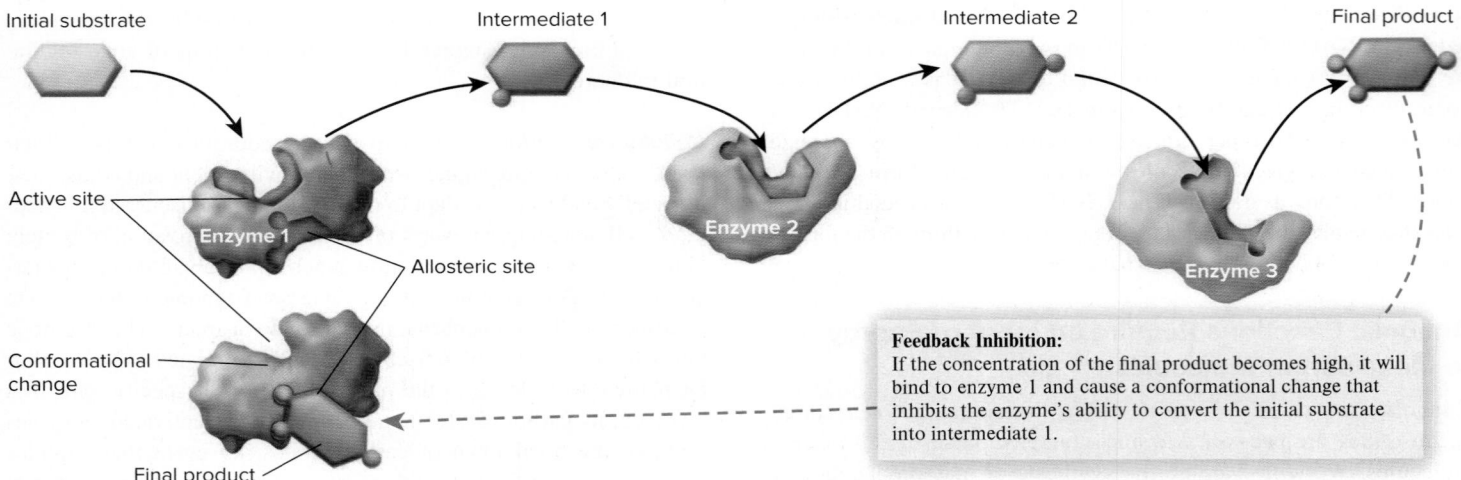

Initial substrate   Intermediate 1   Intermediate 2   Final product

Active site

Enzyme 1

Allosteric site

Enzyme 2

Enzyme 3

Conformational change

Feedback Inhibition:
If the concentration of the final product becomes high, it will bind to enzyme 1 and cause a conformational change that inhibits the enzyme's ability to convert the initial substrate into intermediate 1.

Final product

Figure 6.13 Feedback inhibition. In this process, the final product of a metabolic pathway inhibits an enzyme that functions early in the pathway, thereby preventing the overaccumulation of the product.

 Core Skill: Connections Look ahead to Figure 7.3, which describes a metabolic pathway called glycolysis. Feedback inhibition occurs during this process in that high levels of ATP inhibit phosphofructokinase, an enzyme that catalyzes the conversion of fructose-6-phosphate and ATP to fructose-1,6-bisphosphate and ADP. How is this beneficial to the cell?

formation of the product of the metabolic pathway. Rather than affecting all of the enzymes in a metabolic pathway, cellular or biochemical regulation is often directed at the enzyme that catalyzes the rate-limiting step. This is an efficient and rapid way to control the amount of product of a pathway.

 **THE QUESTION** *The enzyme called 3-phosphoglycerate dehydrogenase catalyzes the following chemical reaction:*

3-phospho-D-glycerate + NAD⁺ ⇌
3-phosphonooxypyruvate + NADH + H⁺

This reaction is the rate-limiting step in a metabolic pathway that synthesizes serine, which is an amino acid. Serine inhibits 3-phosphoglycerate dehydrogenase by binding to an allosteric site on the enzyme, thereby preventing the overaccumulation of serine in a cell. This is an example of feedback inhibition. Researchers have identified a mutant version of 3-phosphoglycerate dehydrogenase that does not exhibit feedback inhibition. Cells that make the mutant enzyme tend to overaccumulate serine. Make a drawing that depicts how the mutant enzyme is different from the normal one. Your drawing should include binding sites for 3-phospho-D-glycerate, NAD⁺, and serine.

T OPIC *What topic in biology does this question address?* The topic is enzymes and feedback inhibition. More specifically, the question is about a mutant version of 3-phosphoglycerate dehydrogenase that does not exhibit feedback inhibition.

I NFORMATION *What information do you know based on the question and your understanding of the topic?* From the question, you know that 3-phosphoglycerate dehydrogenase catalyzes the rate-limiting step in a metabolic pathway that

produces serine. Serine causes feedback inhibition of the normal version of the enzyme but does not inhibit a mutant version. From your understanding of the topic, you may recall that feedback inhibition occurs via an allosteric site.

P ROBLEM-SOLVING **S** TRATEGY *Compare and contrast. Make a drawing.* To solve this problem, you could begin by comparing the properties of the normal and mutant enzyme. The mutant enzyme does not exhibit feedback inhibition. However, because cells harboring the mutant version of the enzyme overaccumulate serine, you know that the catalytic properties of the enzyme must be functioning normally. In other words, the active site is functional. When making the drawing, you need to remember that the enzyme has two sites: an active site and an allosteric site.

ANSWER *The mutation, designated by an X in the enzyme on the right, is an alteration in the structure of the allosteric site that prevents serine from binding there.*

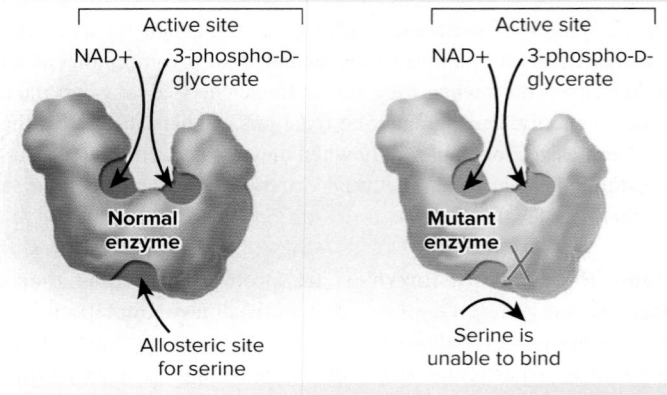

Active site

NAD+   3-phospho-D-glycerate

Normal enzyme

Allosteric site for serine

Active site

NAD+   3-phospho-D-glycerate

Mutant enzyme

X

Serine is unable to bind

6.4 Recycling of Organic Molecules

Learning Outcomes:

1. Explain the relationship between the recycling of organic molecules and cellular efficiency.
2. Outline how the building blocks of proteins are recycled.
3. Describe how the components of cellular organelles are recycled via autophagy.

As mentioned earlier in this chapter, an important feature of metabolism is the recycling of organic molecules, such as amino acids, which are the building blocks of proteins. Except for DNA, which is stably maintained and inherited from cell to cell, other large molecules such as RNA, proteins, lipids, and polysaccharides typically exist for a relatively short period of time. Biologists often speak of the **half-life** of molecules, which is the time it takes for 50% of a specific type of molecule in a cell to be broken down and recycled. For example, mRNA molecules in bacterial cells have an average half-life of about 5 minutes, whereas mRNAs in eukaryotic cells tend to exist for longer periods of time, on the order of 30 minutes to 24 hours or even several days.

Why is recycling important? To compete effectively in their native environments, all living organisms must efficiently use and recycle the organic molecules that are needed as building blocks to construct larger molecules and macromolecules. Otherwise, they would waste a great deal of energy making such building blocks from smaller molecules. For example, organisms conserve an enormous amount of energy by reusing the amino acids that are needed to construct proteins. In this section, we will explore how amino acids are recycled and consider a mechanism for recycling all of the materials found in an organelle.

Proteins in Eukaryotes and Archaea Are Broken Down in the Proteasome

Cells continually degrade proteins that are faulty or no longer needed. To be degraded, proteins are recognized by **proteases**—enzymes that cleave the bonds between adjacent amino acids. The primary pathway for protein degradation in archaea and eukaryotic cells occurs via a protein complex called a **proteasome**. The core of the proteasome consists of four stacked rings, each composed of seven protein subunits (**Figure 6.14a**). The proteasomes of eukaryotic cells also contain caps at each end that control the entry of proteins into the proteasome.

Figure 6.14b describes the steps of protein degradation via eukaryotic proteasomes. A string of small proteins called **ubiquitins** is covalently attached to the target protein. This event directs the target protein to a proteasome cap, which has binding sites for ubiquitins. The cap also has enzymes that unfold the protein and inject it into the internal cavity of the proteasome core. The ubiquitins are removed during entry and released to the cytosol for reuse. Inside the proteasome, proteases degrade the target protein into small peptides and amino acids. The process is completed when the peptides and

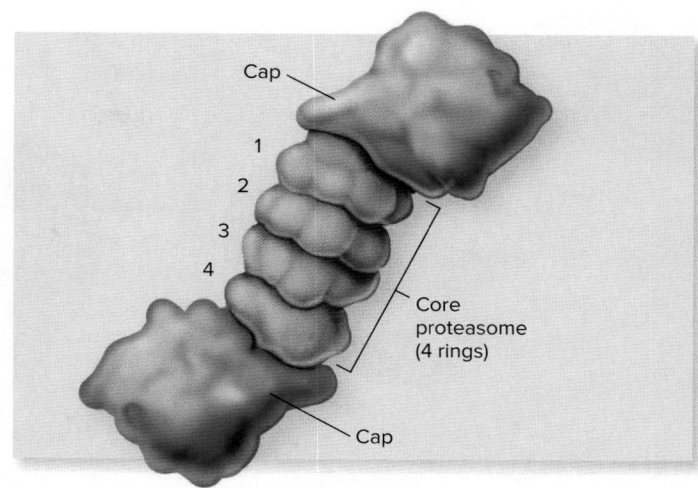

(a) Structure of the eukaryotic proteasome

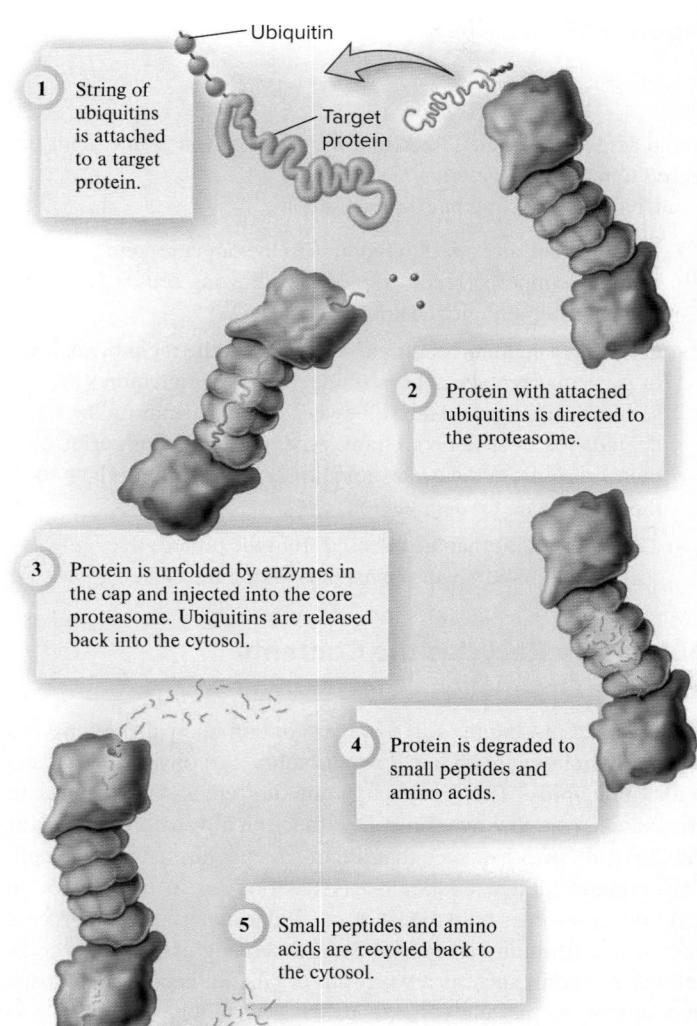

1. String of ubiquitins is attached to a target protein.

2. Protein with attached ubiquitins is directed to the proteasome.

3. Protein is unfolded by enzymes in the cap and injected into the core proteasome. Ubiquitins are released back into the cytosol.

4. Protein is degraded to small peptides and amino acids.

5. Small peptides and amino acids are recycled back to the cytosol.

(b) Steps of protein degradation in eukaryotic cells

Figure 6.14   Protein degradation via the proteasome.

Concept Check   *What are advantages of protein degradation?*

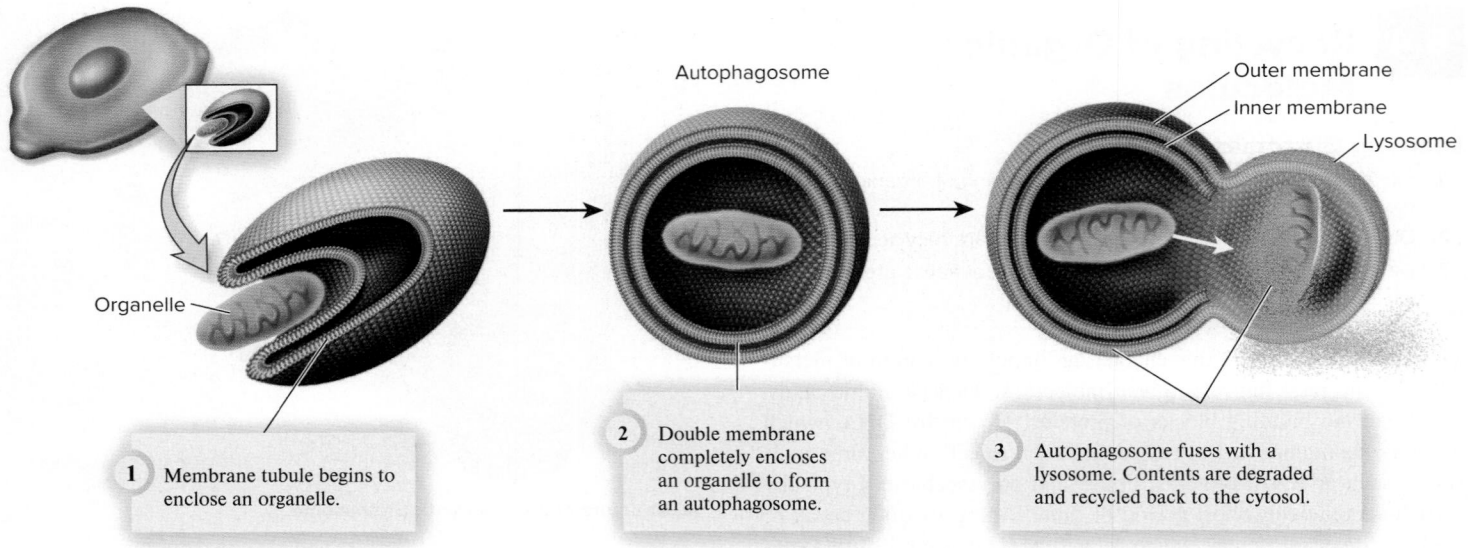

Autophagosome

Outer membrane

Inner membrane

Lysosome

Organelle

1 Membrane tubule begins to enclose an organelle.

2 Double membrane completely encloses an organelle to form an autophagosome.

3 Autophagosome fuses with a lysosome. Contents are degraded and recycled back to the cytosol.

Figure 6.15   Autophagy.

amino acids are recycled back into the cytosol. The amino acids are reused to make new proteins.

Ubiquitin targeting has three functions.

- The enzymes that attach ubiquitins to the target protein recognize improperly folded proteins, allowing cells to identify and degrade nonfunctional proteins.

- Changes in cellular conditions may warrant the rapid breakdown of particular proteins. For example, cell division requires a series of stages called the cell cycle, which depends on the degradation of specific proteins. After these proteins perform their functions in the cycle, ubiquitin targeting directs them to the proteasome for degradation.

- The amino acids that are released from the proteosome are recycled to make new proteins, thus saving the cell energy.

Autophagy Recycles the Contents of Entire Organelles

As described in Chapter 4, lysosomes contain many different types of acid hydrolases that break down proteins, carbohydrates, nucleic acids, and lipids. This enzymatic function enables lysosomes to break down complex materials. One function of lysosomes involves the digestion of substances that are taken up from outside the cell. This process, called endocytosis, is described in Chapter 5. In addition, lysosomes help digest intracellular materials. In a process known as **autophagy** (from the Greek, meaning eating one's self), cellular material, such as a worn-out organelle, becomes enclosed in a double membrane (**Figure 6.15**). This double membrane is formed from a tubule that elongates and eventually wraps around the organelle to form an **autophagosome**. The autophagosome then fuses with one or more lysosomes, and the material inside the autophagosome is digested. The small molecules released from this digestion are recycled back into the cytosol.

Summary of Key Concepts

6.1   Energy and Chemical Reactions

- The fate of a chemical reaction is determined by its direction and rate.

- Energy, the ability to promote change or do work, exists in many forms. According to the first law of thermodynamics, energy cannot be created or destroyed, but it can be converted from one form to another. The second law of thermodynamics states that energy interconversions involve an increase in entropy (Figures 6.1, 6.2, Table 6.1).

- Free energy is the amount of available energy that can be used to promote change or do work. Spontaneous or exergonic reactions, which release free energy, have a negative free-energy change, whereas endergonic reactions have a positive free-energy change (Figure 6.3).

- Chemical reactions proceed until they reach a state of chemical equilibrium, where the rate of formation of products equals the rate of formation of reactants.

- Exergonic reactions, such as the hydrolysis of ATP, are commonly coupled to cellular processes that would otherwise be endergonic. Cells continuously synthesize ATP from ADP and P_i and then hydrolyze it to drive endergonic reactions (Figure 6.4).

- Estimates from genome analysis indicate that over 20% of all proteins bind ATP (Table 6.2).

6.2   Enzymes and Ribozymes

- Enzymes are proteins that speed up the rate of a chemical reaction by lowering the activation energy (E_A) needed to achieve a transition state (Figure 6.5).

- Enzymes recognize reactant molecules, also called substrates, with high specificity. Conformational changes in an enzyme cause its substrate to bind more tightly to it, a phenomenon called induced fit (Figure 6.6).

- Each enzyme-catalyzed reaction has a maximal velocity (V_{max}). The K_M value for an enzyme is the substrate concentration at which the velocity of the reaction is half of the maximal value. Competitive inhibitors raise the K_M for the substrate, whereas noncompetitive inhibitors lower the V_{max} (Figure 6.7).

- Enzyme function may be affected by a variety of other factors, including prosthetic groups, cofactors, coenzymes, temperature, and pH (Figure 6.8).

- Altman and colleagues discovered that the RNA subunit within RNase P is a ribozyme, an RNA molecule that catalyzes a chemical reaction. Other ribozymes play key roles in the cell (Figures 6.9, 6.10, Table 6.3).

6.3 Overview of Metabolism

- Metabolism is the sum of the chemical reactions in a living organism. Metabolic pathways consist of coordinated chemical reactions that occur in steps and are catalyzed by specific enzymes (Figure 6.11).

- Catabolic reactions involve the breakdown of larger molecules into smaller ones. These reactions recycle organic molecules that are used as building blocks to make new molecules. The organic molecules are also broken down to make energy intermediates such as ATP.

- Some chemical reactions are redox reactions, in which electrons are transferred from one molecule to another. These reactions can be used to make energy intermediates such as NADH (Figure 6.12).

- Anabolic reactions require an input of energy to synthesize larger molecules and macromolecules.

- Metabolic pathways are controlled by gene regulation, cellular regulation, and biochemical regulation. An example of biochemical regulation is feedback inhibition. The enzyme that catalyzes the rate-limiting step in a pathway is often the target of cellular or biochemical regulation (Figure 6.13).

6.4 Recycling of Organic Molecules

- Recycling of organic molecules saves a great deal of energy for living organisms.

- Proteins in the cells of eukaryotes and archaea are degraded by proteasomes (Figure 6.14).

- Lysosomes digest intracellular material through the process of autophagy (Figure 6.15).

Assess & Discuss

Test Yourself

1. Reactions that release free energy are
   a. exergonic.
   b. spontaneous.
   c. endergonic.
   d. endothermic.
   e. both a and b.

2. Enzymes speed up reactions by
   a. providing chemical energy to fuel a reaction.
   b. lowering the activation energy necessary to initiate a reaction.

   c. causing an endergonic reaction to become an exergonic reaction.
   d. substituting for one of the reactants necessary for a reaction.
   e. none of the above.

3. For the idealized reaction aA + bB $\rightleftharpoons$ cC + dD, suppose that the equilibrium constant, K_{eq}, is 0.01. If the starting concentrations for A, B, C, and D are 1 M each, what would you predict based on the value of K_{eq}?
   a. The forward reaction is favored.
   b. The reverse reaction is favored.
   c. The forward reaction is fast.
   d. The reverse reaction is fast.
   e. both b and d.

4. Researchers analyzed a cell extract—a mixture of molecules isolated from a certain type of cell—and studied a chemical reaction in which a carbohydrate was broken down into smaller molecules. When they added a protease to the cell extract, they discovered that the protease greatly inhibited the rate of the reaction. Based on this observation, you could conclude that the reaction is
   a. exergonic.
   b. endergonic.
   c. catalyzed by an enzyme.
   d. catalyzed by a ribozyme.
   e. Both b and c are true of this reaction.

5. In biological systems, ATP functions by
   a. providing the energy to drive endergonic reactions.
   b. acting as an enzyme and lowering the activation energy of certain reactions.
   c. adjusting the pH of intracellular solutions to maintain optimal conditions for enzyme activity.
   d. regulating the speed at which endergonic reactions proceed.
   e. interacting with enzymes as a cofactor to stimulate chemical reactions.

6. In a chemical reaction, NADH is converted to NAD^+ + H^+. We say that NADH has been
   a. reduced.
   b. phosphorylated.
   c. oxidized.
   d. decarboxylated.
   e. methylated.

7. Scientists identify proteins that use ATP as an energy source by
   a. determining whether a protein functions in anabolic or catabolic reactions.
   b. determining if a protein has a known ATP-binding site.
   c. predicting the free energy necessary for a protein to function.
   d. determining if a protein has an ATP synthase subunit.
   e. all of the above.

8. For a particular chemical reaction, an inhibitor raises the K_M but does not affect the V_{max}. This inhibitor
   a. is a competitive inhibitor.
   b. is a noncompetitive inhibitor.
   c. binds to the active site of the enzyme.
   d. binds to an allosteric site of the enzyme.
   e. is a competitive inhibitor and binds to the active site of the enzyme.

9. Which of the following is (are) key benefits of catabolic reactions?
   a. recycling of organic building blocks
   b. breakdown of organic molecules to obtain energy
   c. synthesis of important polymers, such as polypeptides
   d. all of the above
   e. a and b only

10. Autophagy provides a way for cells to
    a. degrade entire organelles and recycle their components.
    b. control the level of ATP.
    c. engulf bacterial cells.
    d. export unwanted organelles out of the cell.
    e. inhibit the first enzyme in a metabolic pathway.

Conceptual Questions

1. With regard to rate and direction, discuss the differences between endergonic and exergonic reactions.

2. Describe the mechanism and purpose of feedback inhibition in a metabolic pathway.

3.  **Core Concept: Energy and Matter** A core concept of biology is that *living organisms use energy*. Explain why the recycling of amino acids and nucleotides is energy-efficient.

Collaborative Questions

1. Living cells are highly ordered units, yet the entropy of the universe is increasing. Discuss how life can maintain its order in spite of the second law of thermodynamics. Are we defying this law?

2. What is the advantage of using ATP as a common energy source; that is, how is using just ATP better than using a bunch of different food molecules? For example, instead of just having Na^+/K^+-ATPase in a cell, why not have many different ion pumps, each driven by a different food molecule, like Na^+/K^+-glucosase (a pump that uses glucose), Na^+/K^+-sucrase (a pump that uses sucrose), Na^+/K^+-fatty acidase (a pump that uses fatty acids), and so on?

Cellular Respiration and Fermentation

7

Physical endurance. Conditioned athletes, like these marathon runners, metabolize organic molecules such as glucose very efficiently. ©Michael Dwyer/AP Images

Carmen became inspired while watching the 2008 Summer Olympics and set a personal goal to run a marathon—a distance of 42.2 kilometers, or 26.2 miles. Although she was active in volleyball and downhill skiing in high school, she had never attempted distance running. At first, running an entire mile was pure torture. She was out of breath, overheated, and unhappy, to say the least. However, she became committed to endurance training and within a few weeks discovered that running a mile was a "piece of cake." Two years later, Carmen participated in her first marathon and finished with a time of 4 hours and 11 minutes—not bad for someone who had previously struggled to run a single mile!

How had Carmen's training allowed her to achieve this goal? Perhaps the biggest factor is that the training altered the metabolism in her leg muscles. For example, the network of small blood vessels supplying oxygen to her leg muscles became more extensive, providing more efficient delivery of oxygen and removal of wastes. Second, her muscle cells developed more mitochondria. Recall from Chapter 4 that the primary role of mitochondria is to make ATP, which cells use as a source of energy. With these changes, Carmen's leg muscles were better able to break down organic molecules in her food and utilize them to make ATP.

The cells in Carmen's leg muscles had become more efficient at **cellular respiration**, which comprises the metabolic reactions that a cell uses to get energy from food molecules and release waste products. When we eat food, we use much of that food for energy. People often speak of "burning calories." Although metabolism does generate some heat, the chemical reactions that take place in the cells of living organisms are uniquely different from those that occur, say, in a fire. When wood is burned, the reaction produces enormous amounts of heat in a short period of time—the reaction lacks control. In contrast, the metabolism that occurs in living cells is extremely controlled. The food molecules from which we harvest energy give up that energy in a very restrained manner rather than all at once, as in a fire. An underlying theme of metabolism is the remarkable control that cells possess when they coordinate chemical reactions. A key emphasis of this chapter is how cells use the energy stored within the chemical bonds of organic molecules.

We will begin by surveying a group of chemical reactions that accomplish the breakdown of the main carbohydrate cells use as an energy source, namely, the sugar glucose. As you will learn, cells carry out an intricate series of reactions so that glucose can be "burned" in a very controlled fashion when oxygen is available. We will then examine how cells use organic molecules in the absence of oxygen via processes known as anaerobic respiration and fermentation.

7.1   Overview of Cellular Respiration

Learning Outcome:

1. List and briefly describe the four metabolic pathways that are needed to break down glucose to CO_2 and H_2O.

Cellular respiration is a process by which living cells obtain energy from organic molecules and release waste products. A primary aim of cellular respiration is to make adenosine triphosphate, or ATP.

When oxygen (O_2) is used, this process is termed **aerobic respiration**. During aerobic respiration, O_2 is consumed, and carbon dioxide (CO_2) is released via the oxidation of organic molecules. When we breathe, we inhale the oxygen needed for aerobic respiration and exhale CO_2, a by-product of the process. For this reason, the term respiration has a second meaning, which is the act of breathing.

$$C_6H_{12}O_6 \; + \; 6\,O_2 \;\; \rightarrow \;\; 6\,CO_2 \; + \; 6\,H_2O$$
(Glucose)

$$\Delta G \; = \; -685\,\text{kcal/mol}$$

We will focus on the breakdown of glucose in a eukaryotic cell in the presence of oxygen. Certain covalent bonds within glucose store a large amount of chemical potential energy. When glucose is broken down via oxidation, ultimately to CO_2 and water,

a tremendous amount of free energy is released (-685 kcal/mol). Some of the energy is lost as heat, but much of it is used to make three energy intermediates: ATP, NADH, and $FADH_2$. This process involves four metabolic pathways: (1) glycolysis, (2) the breakdown of pyruvate, (3) the citric acid cycle, and (4) oxidative phosphorylation (**Figure 7.1**):

1. *Glycolysis.* In glycolysis, glucose (a compound with six carbon atoms) is broken down to two pyruvate molecules (with three carbons each), producing a net energy yield of two ATP molecules and two NADH molecules. The two ATP molecules are synthesized via **substrate-level phosphorylation**, which occurs when an enzyme directly transfers a phosphate from an organic molecule to ADP. In eukaryotes, glycolysis occurs in the cytosol.

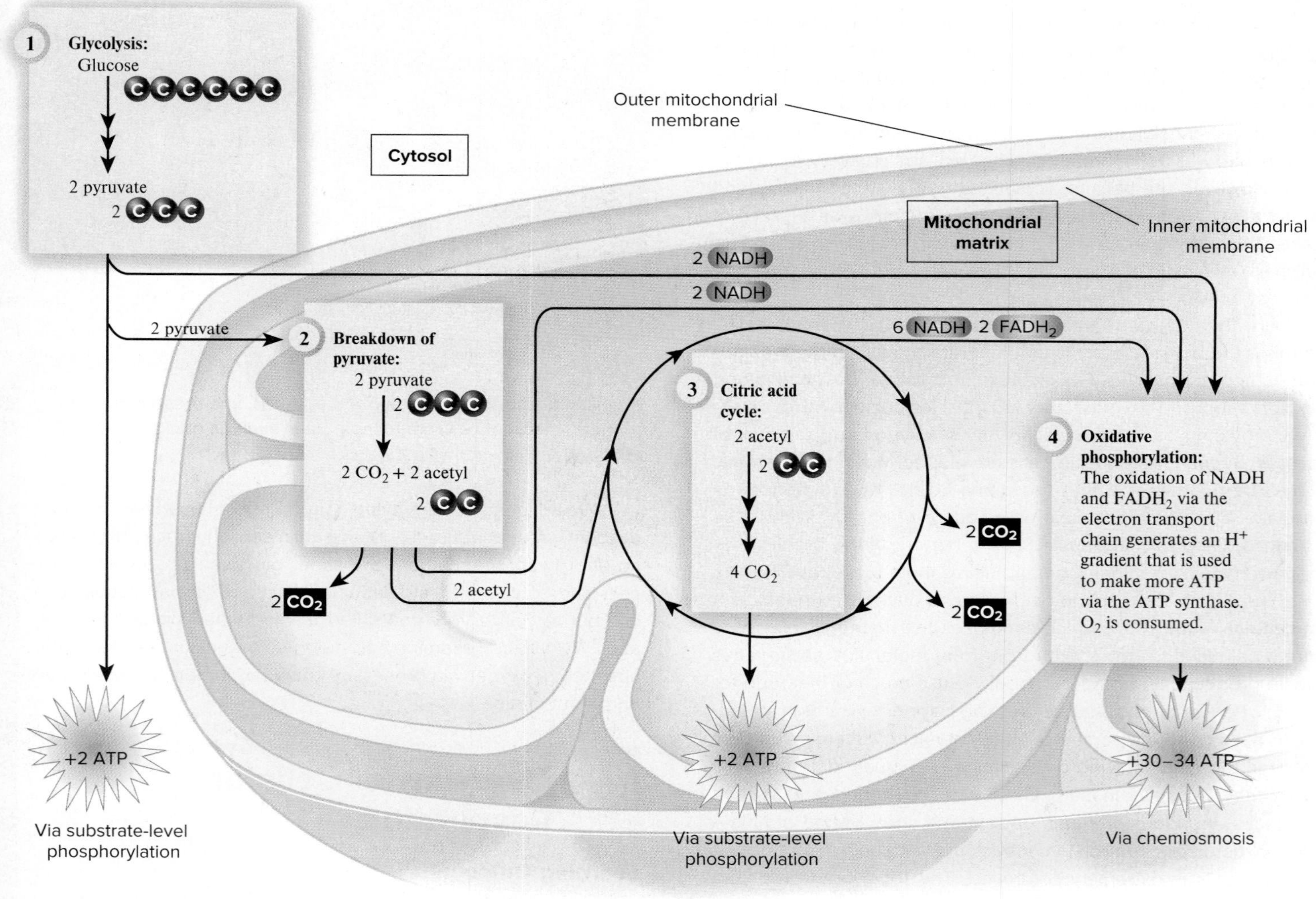

Figure 7.1 An overview of cellular respiration. The 30–34 ATP molecules produced via chemiosmosis represent the maximum number possible. As described later in this chapter, mitochondria may use NADH, $FADH_2$, and the H^+ electrochemical gradient for purposes other than ATP synthesis.

 Core Concept: Energy and Matter Molecules such as glucose store a large amount of energy. The breakdown of glucose is used to make energy intermediates, such as ATP molecules, which drive many types of cellular processes.

2. ***Breakdown of pyruvate.*** The two pyruvate molecules enter the mitochondrial matrix, where each one is broken down to an acetyl group (with two carbons each) and one CO_2 molecule. For each pyruvate broken down via oxidation, one NADH molecule is made by the reduction of NAD^+.

3. ***Citric acid cycle.*** Each acetyl group is incorporated into an organic molecule, which is later oxidized to liberate two CO_2 molecules. One ATP, three NADH, and one $FADH_2$ are made in this process. Because there are two acetyl groups (one from each pyruvate), the total yield is four CO_2, two ATP via substrate-level phosphorylation, six NADH, and two $FADH_2$. This process occurs in the mitochondrial matrix.

4. ***Oxidative phosphorylation.*** The NADH and $FADH_2$ made in the three previous stages contain high-energy electrons that can be readily transferred in a redox reaction to other molecules. Once removed from NADH or $FADH_2$, these high-energy electrons release some energy, and through an electron transport chain, that energy is harnessed to produce an H^+ electrochemical gradient. In **chemiosmosis**, energy stored in the H^+ electrochemical gradient is used to synthesize ATP from ADP and P_i. The overall process of electron transport and ATP synthesis is called oxidative phosphorylation because NADH or $FADH_2$ has been oxidized and ADP has become phosphorylated to make ATP. Approximately 30–34 ATP molecules can be made via oxidative phosphorylation.

In eukaryotes, oxidation phosphorylation occurs along the **cristae**, which are projections formed by the invagination of the inner mitochondrial membrane. The cristae greatly increase the surface area of the inner membrane and thereby increase the amount of ATP that can be made. In bacteria and archaea, oxidative phosphorylation occurs along the plasma membrane.

7.2 Glycolysis

Learning Outcomes:

Thus far, we have examined the general features of the four metabolic pathways that are involved in the breakdown of glucose. We will now turn our attention to a more detailed understanding of these pathways for glucose metabolism, beginning with glycolysis.

Glycolysis Is a Metabolic Pathway That Breaks Down Glucose to Pyruvate

Glycolysis (from the Greek *glykos*, meaning sweet, and *lysis*, meaning splitting) involves the breakdown of glucose, a simple sugar, into two molecules of a compound called pyruvate. This process can occur in the presence of oxygen, that is, under aerobic conditions, and it can also occur in the absence of oxygen. During the 1930s, the efforts of several German biochemists, including Gustav Embden, Otto Meyerhof, and Jacob Parnas, established that glycolysis involves 10 steps, each one catalyzed by a different enzyme. The elucidation of these steps was a major achievement in the field of **biochemistry**—the study of the chemistry of living organisms. Researchers have since discovered that glycolysis is the common pathway for glucose breakdown in bacteria, archaea, and eukaryotes. Remarkably, the steps of glycolysis are virtually identical in nearly all living species, suggesting that glycolysis arose very early in the evolution of life on our planet.

The 10 steps of glycolysis can be grouped into three phases (**Figure 7.2**).

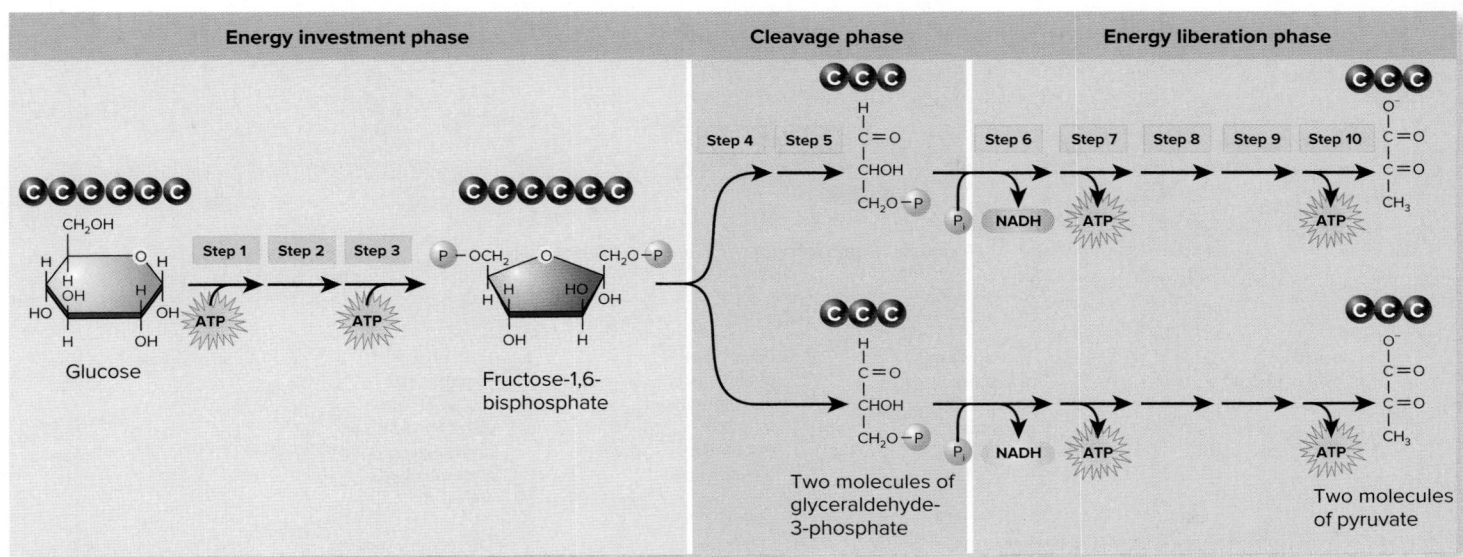

Figure 7.2 Overview of glycolysis.

 Core Skill: Connections Look ahead to Table 45.1. With regard to oxygen needs, what advantage do glycolytic muscle fibers provide?

- The first phase (steps 1–3) involves an energy investment. Two ATP molecules are hydrolyzed, and the phosphates from those ATP molecules are attached to glucose, which is converted to fructose-1,6-bisphosphate. The energy investment phase raises the free energy of glucose, thereby allowing later reactions to be exergonic.

- The cleavage phase (steps 4–5) breaks this six-carbon molecule into two molecules of glyceraldehyde-3-phosphate.

- The energy liberation phase (steps 6–10) produces four ATP, two NADH, and two molecules of pyruvate. Because two molecules of ATP are used in the energy investment phase, the net yield is two molecules of ATP.

Figure 7.3 describes the details of the 10 reactions of glycolysis. The net reaction of glycolysis is as follows:

$$C_6H_{12}O_6 \; + \; 2\,NAD^+ \; + \; 2\,ADP^{2-} \; + \; 2\,P_i^{2-} \; \rightarrow$$
Glucose

$$2\,CH_3(C{=}O)COO^- \; + \; 2\,H^+ \; + \; 2\,NADH \; + \; 2\,ATP^{4-} \; + \; 2\,H_2O$$
Pyruvate

Regulation of Glycolysis   How do cells control glycolysis? The rate of glycolysis is regulated by the availability of substrates, such as glucose, and by feedback inhibition. A key control point involves the enzyme phosphofructokinase, which catalyzes the third step in glycolysis, the step believed to be the slowest, or rate-limiting, step. When a cell has a sufficient amount of ATP, feedback inhibition occurs. At high concentrations, ATP binds to an allosteric site in phosphofructokinase, causing a conformational change that renders the enzyme functionally inactive. This prevents the further breakdown of glucose and thereby inhibits the overproduction of ATP.

BIO**TIPS**   **THE QUESTION** *During the process of glycolysis, glucose is broken down into two pyruvate molecules. As shown in Figure 7.3, this metabolic pathway consists of 10 consecutive chemical reactions. Describe the three major phases of glycolysis.*

TOPIC *What topic in biology does this question address?* The topic is glycolysis. More specifically, the question asks you to describe the three major phases of this process.

INFORMATION *What information do you know based on the question and your understanding of the topic?* In the question, you are reminded that glycolysis consists of 10 consecutive chemical reactions. From your understanding of the topic, you may remember that different types of chemical reactions are occurring.

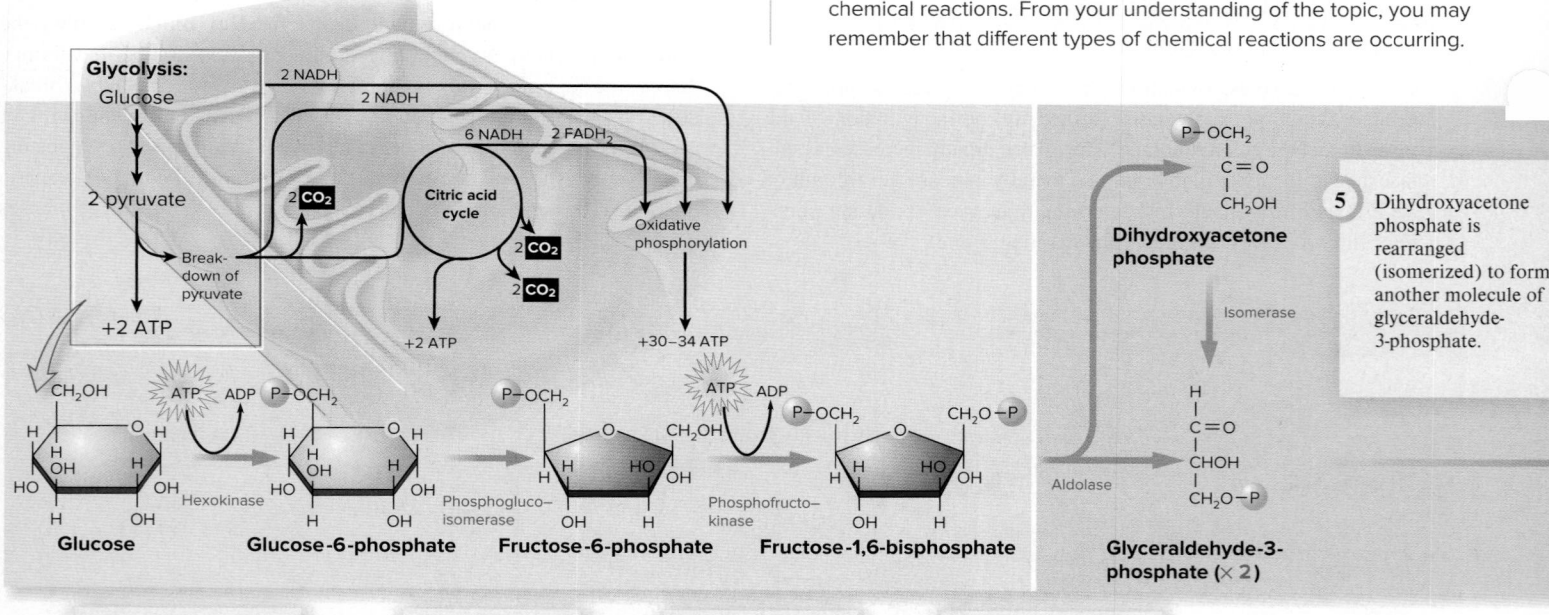

1. Glucose is phosphorylated by ATP. Glucose-6-phosphate is more easily trapped in the cell than glucose.

2. The structure of glucose-6-phosphate is rearranged to fructose-6-phosphate.

3. Fructose-6-phosphate is phosphorylated to make fructose-1,6-bisphosphate.

4. Fructose-1,6-bisphosphate is cleaved into dihydroxyacetone phosphate and glyceraldehyde-3-phosphate.

5. Dihydroxyacetone phosphate is rearranged (isomerized) to form another molecule of glyceraldehyde-3-phosphate.

Figure 7.3 A detailed look at the steps of glycolysis. The pathway begins with a six-carbon molecule (glucose) that is broken down into two molecules that contain three carbons each. The notation **x2** in the figure indicates that two of these three-carbon molecules are produced from each glucose molecule.

Concept Check: *Which organic molecules donate a phosphate group to ADP during substrate-level phosphorylation?*

(P)ROBLEM-SOLVING (S)TRATEGY *Sort out the steps in a complicated process.* To solve this problem, it may be helpful to examine the process in a step-by-step manner to identify the key events.

ANSWER *First phase: During steps 1–3 of glycolysis, ATP is used to phosphorylate two different sites in the glucose molecule. This stage is called the energy investment phase because ATP is used to fuel the process. The energy investment phase prepares the glucose molecule for the next two phases.*

Second phase: During steps 4 and 5, glucose is cleaved into two three-carbon molecules, and then one of those is isomerized to glyceraldehyde-3-phosphate. This phase is called the cleavage phase because a six-carbon molecule is split (cleaved) into two three-carbon molecules.

Third phase: During steps 6–10, ATP and NADH are made, molecules that are energy intermediates. ATP is made by substrate-level phosphorylation, in which a phosphate is removed from 1,3-bisphosphoglycerate or phosphoenolpyruvate and directly transferred to ADP. NADH is made when glyceraldehyde-3-phosphate is oxidized. This last phase is called the energy liberation phase because energy that was stored in organic molecules was released (liberated) and used to make energy intermediates (ATP and NADH).

Core Concept: Information

The Overexpression of Certain Genes Causes Cancer Cells to Exhibit High Levels of Glycolysis

In 1931, the German physiologist Otto Warburg discovered that certain cancer cells preferentially use glycolysis for ATP production, in contrast to healthy cells, which mainly generate ATP from oxidative phosphorylation. This phenomenon, termed the Warburg effect, is very common among different types of tumors. The Warburg effect is the basis for the detection of cancer via a procedure called positron-emission tomography (PET, see Figure 2.6). In this technique, patients are injected with a radioactive glucose analogue called [^{18}F]-fluorodeoxyglucose (FDG). FDG is taken up by cells that use high amounts of glucose, such as cancer cells. The scanner detects regions of the body that accumulate high amounts of FDG, which are visualized as bright spots on the PET scan.

Figure 7.4 shows a PET scan of a patient with lung cancer. The bright regions that the arrows point at are tumors that show abnormally high levels of glycolysis. The tumors show up so well because the genome found in cancer cells exhibits an increased expression of genes that encode enzymes involved with glycolysis. Research has shown that the enzymes of glycolysis are overexpressed in approximately 80% of all types of cancer, including

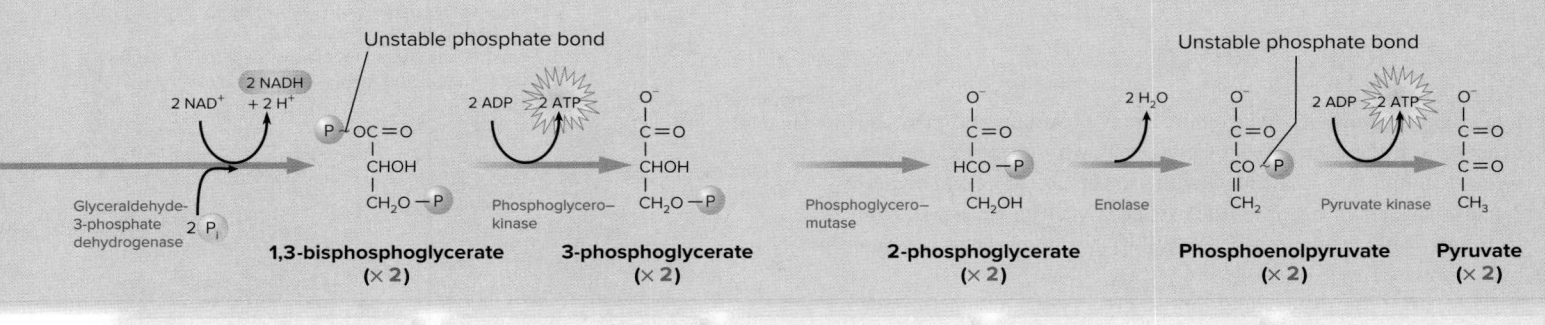

6 Glyceraldehyde-3-phosphate is oxidized to 1,3-bisphosphoglycerate. NADH is produced. In 1,3-bisphosphoglycerate, the phosphate group in the upper left is destabilized, meaning that the bond will break in a highly exergonic reaction.

7 A phosphate is removed from 1,3-bisphosphoglycerate to form 3-phosphoglycerate. The removed phosphate is transferred to ADP to make ATP via substrate-level phosphorylation.

8 The phosphate group in 3-phosphoglycerate is moved to a new location, creating 2-phosphoglycerate.

9 A water molecule is removed from 2-phosphoglycerate to form phosphoenolpyruvate. In phosphoenolpyruvate, the phosphate group is destabilized, meaning that the bond will break in a highly exergonic reaction.

10 A phosphate is removed from phosphoenolpyruvate to form pyruvate. The removed phosphate is transferred to ADP to make ATP via substrate-level phosphorylation.

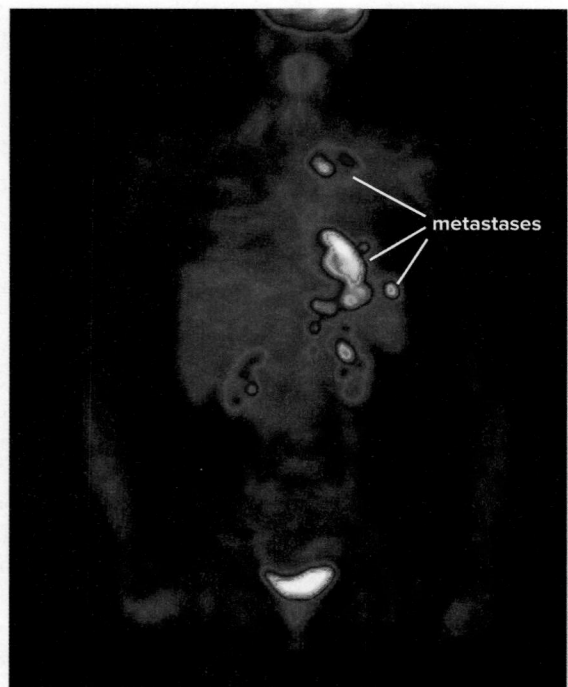

metastases

Figure 7.4 A PET scan of a patient with lung cancer. The bright regions in the lungs are tumors (indicated by the arrows). The brain, which is not cancerous in this patient, appears bright because it performs high levels of glucose metabolism. Also, the kidneys and bladder appear bright because they filter and accumulate FDG. (Note: FDG is taken up by cells and converted to FDG-phosphate by hexokinase, the first enzyme in glycolysis. However, because FDG lacks an —OH group, it is not metabolized further. Therefore, FDG-phosphate accumulates in cells that carry out glycolysis.) ©Steven Needell/Science Source

 Core Skill: Connections Look back at **Figure 2.6**. Why is FDG radiolabeled?

lung, skin, colon, liver, pancreatic, breast, ovarian, and prostate cancers. The three enzymes of glycolysis whose overexpression is most commonly associated with cancer are glyceraldehyde-3-phosphate dehydrogenase, enolase, and pyruvate kinase (shown in Figure 7.3). In many cancers, all 10 glycolytic enzymes are overexpressed!

How does the overexpression of glycolytic enzymes affect tumor growth? While the genetic changes associated with tumor growth are complex, researchers have speculated that an increase in glycolysis favors the growth as a result of changes in oxygen levels. As a tumor grows, the internal regions of the tumor tend to become hypoxic, or deficient in oxygen. The hypoxic state inside a tumor may contribute to the overexpression of glycolytic genes and lead to a higher level of glycolytic enzymes within the cancer cells. This favors glycolysis as a means of making ATP, because glycolysis does not require oxygen. Making ATP via glycolysis is an advantage to cancer cells, because such cells would have trouble making ATP via

oxidative phosphorylation, which requires oxygen. Based on these findings, some current research is aimed at discovering drugs that inhibit glycolysis in cancer cells as a way to prevent their growth.

7.3 Breakdown of Pyruvate

Learning Outcome:

1. Describe how pyruvate is broken down and acetyl CoA is made.

In eukaryotes, glycolysis produces pyruvate in the cytosol, which is then transported into the mitochondria. Once in the mitochondrial matrix, pyruvate molecules are broken down (oxidized) by an enzyme complex called pyruvate dehydrogenase (**Figure 7.5**). A molecule of CO_2 is removed from pyruvate, and the remaining acetyl group is attached to an organic molecule called coenzyme A (CoA) to produce acetyl CoA. (In chemical equations, CoA is depicted as CoA—SH to emphasize how the —SH group participates in the chemical reaction.) During this process, two high-energy electrons are removed from pyruvate and transferred to NAD^+, together with H^+, to produce a molecule of NADH. For each pyruvate, the net reaction is as follows:

$$^-O-\overset{\overset{\displaystyle O}{\|}}{C}-\overset{\overset{\displaystyle O}{\|}}{C}-CH_3 + CoA-SH + NAD^+ \rightarrow$$

Pyruvate   CoA

$$CoA-S-\overset{\overset{\displaystyle O}{\|}}{C}-CH_3 + CO_2 + NADH$$

Acetyl CoA

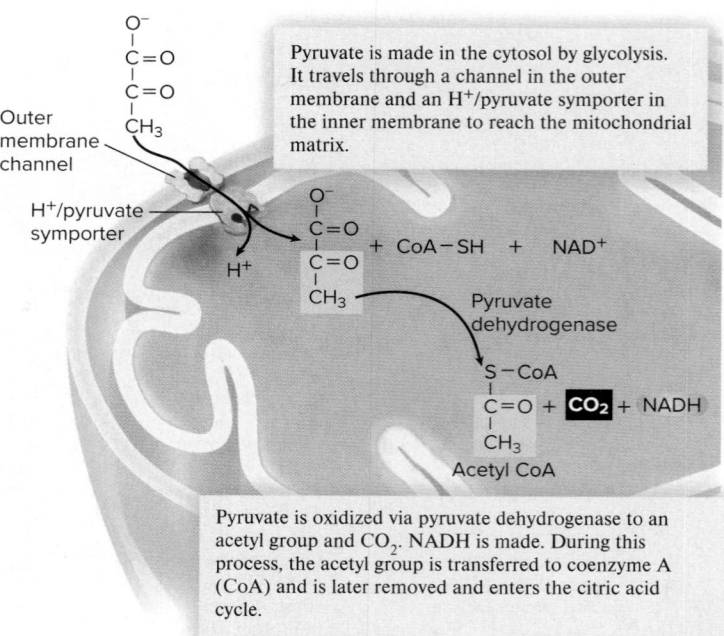

Pyruvate is made in the cytosol by glycolysis. It travels through a channel in the outer membrane and an H^+/pyruvate symporter in the inner membrane to reach the mitochondrial matrix.

Outer membrane channel

H^+/pyruvate symporter

Pyruvate dehydrogenase

Acetyl CoA

Pyruvate is oxidized via pyruvate dehydrogenase to an acetyl group and CO_2. NADH is made. During this process, the acetyl group is transferred to coenzyme A (CoA) and is later removed and enters the citric acid cycle.

Figure 7.5 Breakdown of pyruvate and the attachment of an acetyl group to CoA.

The acetyl group is attached to CoA via a covalent bond to a sulfur atom. The hydrolysis of this bond releases a large amount of free energy, making it possible for the acetyl group to be transferred to other organic molecules. As described next, the acetyl group is removed from CoA and enters the citric acid cycle.

7.4 Citric Acid Cycle

Learning Outcomes:

1. Explain the concept of a metabolic cycle.
2. Describe how an acetyl group enters the citric acid cycle, and list the net products of the cycle.

The third stage of glucose metabolism introduces a new concept, that of a **metabolic cycle**. During a metabolic cycle, particular molecules enter the cycle while others leave. The process is cyclical because it involves a series of organic molecules that are regenerated with each turn of the cycle. The idea of a metabolic cycle was first proposed in the early 1930s by German biochemist Hans Krebs. While studying carbohydrate metabolism in England, he analyzed cell extracts from pigeon muscle and determined that citric acid and other organic molecules participated in a cycle that resulted in the breakdown of carbohydrates to carbon dioxide. This cycle is called the **citric acid cycle**, or the Krebs cycle, in honor of Krebs, who was awarded the Nobel Prize in Physiology or Medicine in 1953.

An overview of the citric acid cycle is shown in **Figure 7.6**. In the first step of the cycle, the acetyl group (with two carbons) is removed from acetyl CoA and attached to oxaloacetate (with four carbons) to form citrate (with six carbons), also called citric acid. Then, in a series of several steps, two CO_2 molecules are released. As this occurs, three molecules of NADH, one molecule of $FADH_2$, and one molecule of guanosine triphosphate (GTP) are made. The GTP, which is made via substrate-level phosphorylation, is used to make ATP. After a total of eight steps, oxaloacetate is regenerated, so the cycle can begin again, provided acetyl CoA is available. **Figure 7.7** shows a more detailed view of the citric acid cycle. For each acetyl group attached to CoA, the net reaction of the citric acid cycle is as follows:

$$\text{Acetyl-CoA} + 2\,H_2O + 3\,NAD^+ + FAD + GDP^{2-} + Pi^{2-} \rightarrow$$

$$\text{CoA---SH} + 2\,CO_2 + 3\,NADH + FADH_2 + GTP^{4-} + 3\,H^+$$

Regulation of the Citric Acid Cycle   How is the citric acid cycle controlled? The rate of the cycle is largely regulated by the availability of substrates, such as acetyl-CoA and NAD^+, and by feedback

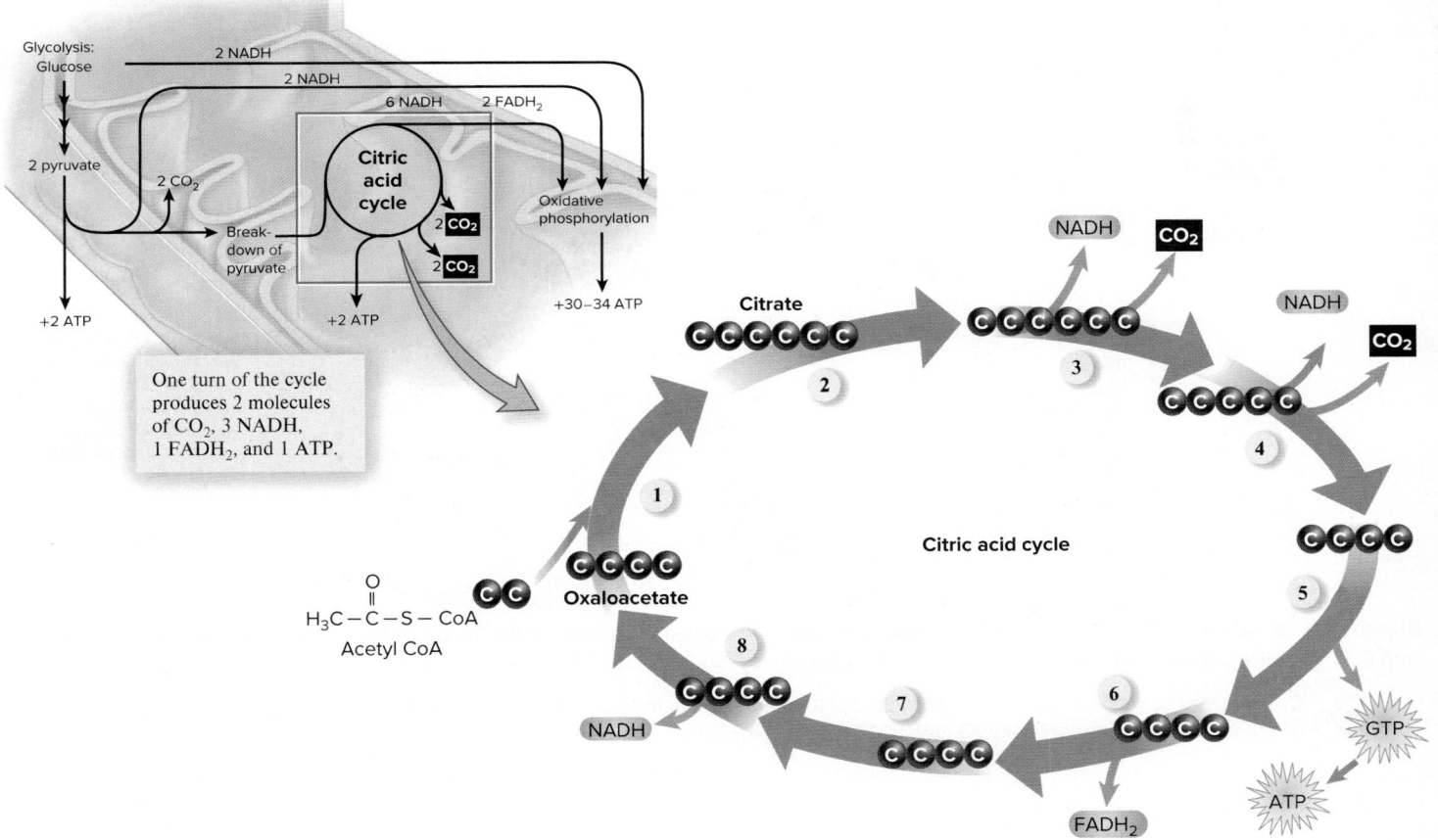

Figure 7.6 Overview of the citric acid cycle.

Concept Check: *What are the main products of the citric acid cycle?*

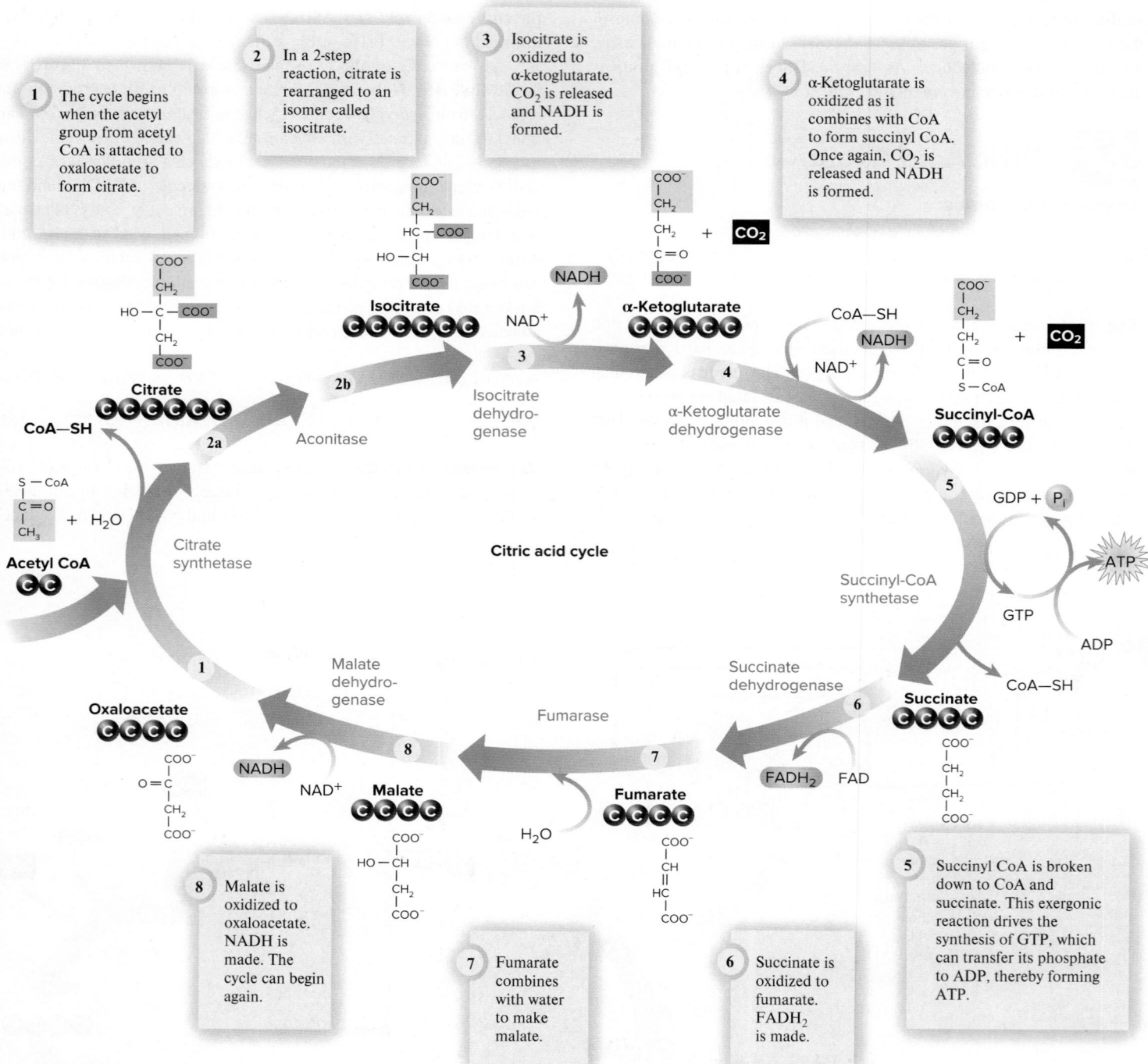

Figure 7.7 A detailed look at the steps of the citric acid cycle. The blue boxes indicate the location of the acetyl group, which is oxidized at step 6. (It is oxidized again in step 8.) The green boxes indicate the locations where CO_2 molecules are removed.

Core Concept: Systems A metabolic cycle, such as the citric acid cycle, can be viewed as a small system. This system oxidizes organic molecules and produces 3 NADH, 1 FADH$_2$, 1 ATP, and 2 CO_2.

inhibition. The three steps in the cycle that are highly exergonic are those catalyzed by citrate synthase, isocitrate dehydrogenase, and α-ketoglutarate dehydrogenase (see Figure 7.7). Each of these steps is rate-limiting under certain circumstances, and the way that each enzyme is regulated varies among different species. Let's consider an example. In mammals, NADH and ATP act as feedback inhibitors of isocitrate dehydrogenase, whereas NAD^+ and ADP act as activators. In this way, the citric acid cycle is inhibited when NADH and ATP levels are high, but it is stimulated when NAD^+ and ADP levels are high.

7.5   Overview of Oxidative Phosphorylation

Learning Outcomes:

1. Describe how the electron transport chain produces an H^+ electrochemical gradient.
2. Explain how ATP synthase utilizes the H^+ electrochemical gradient to synthesize ATP.

During the first three stages of glucose metabolism, the oxidation of glucose yields 6 molecules of CO_2, 4 molecules of ATP, 10 molecules of NADH, and 2 molecules of $FADH_2$. Let's now consider how high-energy electrons are removed from NADH and $FADH_2$ to produce more ATP. This process is called **oxidative phosphorylation**. As mentioned earlier, the term refers to the observation that electrons are removed from NADH and $FADH_2$, that is, these molecules are oxidized, and ATP is made by the phosphorylation of ADP. In this section, we will examine how the oxidative process involves the electron transport chain, whereas the phosphorylation of ADP occurs via ATP synthase.

The Electron Transport Chain Establishes an Electrochemical Gradient

The **electron transport chain (ETC)** consists of a group of protein complexes and small organic molecules embedded in the inner mitochondrial membrane. These components are referred to as an electron transport chain because electrons are passed from one component to the next in a series of redox reactions (**Figure 7.8**). Most members of the ETC are protein complexes (designated I–IV in the figure) that have prosthetic groups, which are small molecules permanently attached to the surface of proteins that aid in their function. For example, cytochrome oxidase contains two prosthetic groups, each with an iron atom. The iron in each prosthetic group can readily accept and release an electron. One member of the ETC, ubiquinone (Q), is not a protein. Rather, ubiquinone is a small organic molecule that can accept and release an electron.

The red line in Figure 7.8 shows the path of electron flow. The electrons, which are originally found in NADH or $FADH_2$, are transferred to components of the ETC. The electron path is

a series of redox reactions in which electrons are transferred to components with increasingly higher electronegativity. At the end of the chain is oxygen, which is the most electronegative component and the final electron acceptor. The ETC is also called the **respiratory chain** because the oxygen we breathe is used in this process.

NADH and $FADH_2$ donate their electrons at different points in the ETC. Two high-energy electrons from NADH are first transferred one at a time to NADH dehydrogenase (complex I). They are then transferred to ubiquinone (Q), cytochrome b-c_1 (complex III), cytochrome c, and cytochrome oxidase (complex IV). The final electron acceptor is O_2. By comparison, $FADH_2$ transfers electrons to succinate reductase (complex II), then to ubiquinone, and the rest of the chain.

As shown in Figure 7.8, some of the energy that is released during the movement of electrons is used to pump H^+ across the inner mitochondrial membrane into the intermembrane space. This active transport establishes a large **H^+ electrochemical gradient**, in which the concentration of H^+ is higher outside of the mitochondrial matrix than inside and an excess of positive charge exists outside the matrix.

Chemicals that inhibit the flow of electrons along the ETC have lethal effects. For example, one component of the ETC, cytochrome oxidase (complex IV), is inhibited by cyanide. The deadly effects of cyanide ingestion occur because the ETC is shut down, preventing cells from making enough ATP for survival.

ATP Synthase Makes ATP via Chemiosmosis

The second event of oxidative phosphorylation is the synthesis of ATP by an enzyme called **ATP synthase**. The H^+ electrochemical gradient across the inner mitochondrial membrane is a source of potential energy. How is this energy used? The passive flow of H^+ back into the matrix is an exergonic process. The lipid bilayer is relatively impermeable to H^+. However, H^+ can pass through the membrane-embedded portion of ATP synthase. This enzyme harnesses some of the free energy that is released as the H^+ ions flow through its membrane-embedded region to synthesize ATP from ADP and P_i (see bottom of Figure 7.8). This is an example of an energy conversion: Energy in the form of an H^+ gradient is converted to chemical potential energy in ATP. The synthesis of ATP that occurs as a result of pushing H^+ across a membrane is called chemiosmosis (from the Greek *osmos*, meaning to push). The theory behind it was proposed by Peter Mitchell, a British biochemist who was awarded the Nobel Prize in Chemistry in 1978.

Regulation of Oxidative Phosphorylation   How is oxidative phosphorylation controlled? This process is regulated by a variety of factors, including the availability of ETC substrates, such as NADH and O_2, and by the ATP/ADP ratio. When ATP levels are high, ATP binds to a subunit of cytochrome oxidase (complex IV), thereby inhibiting the ETC and oxidative phosphorylation. By comparison, when ADP levels are high, oxidative phosphorylation is

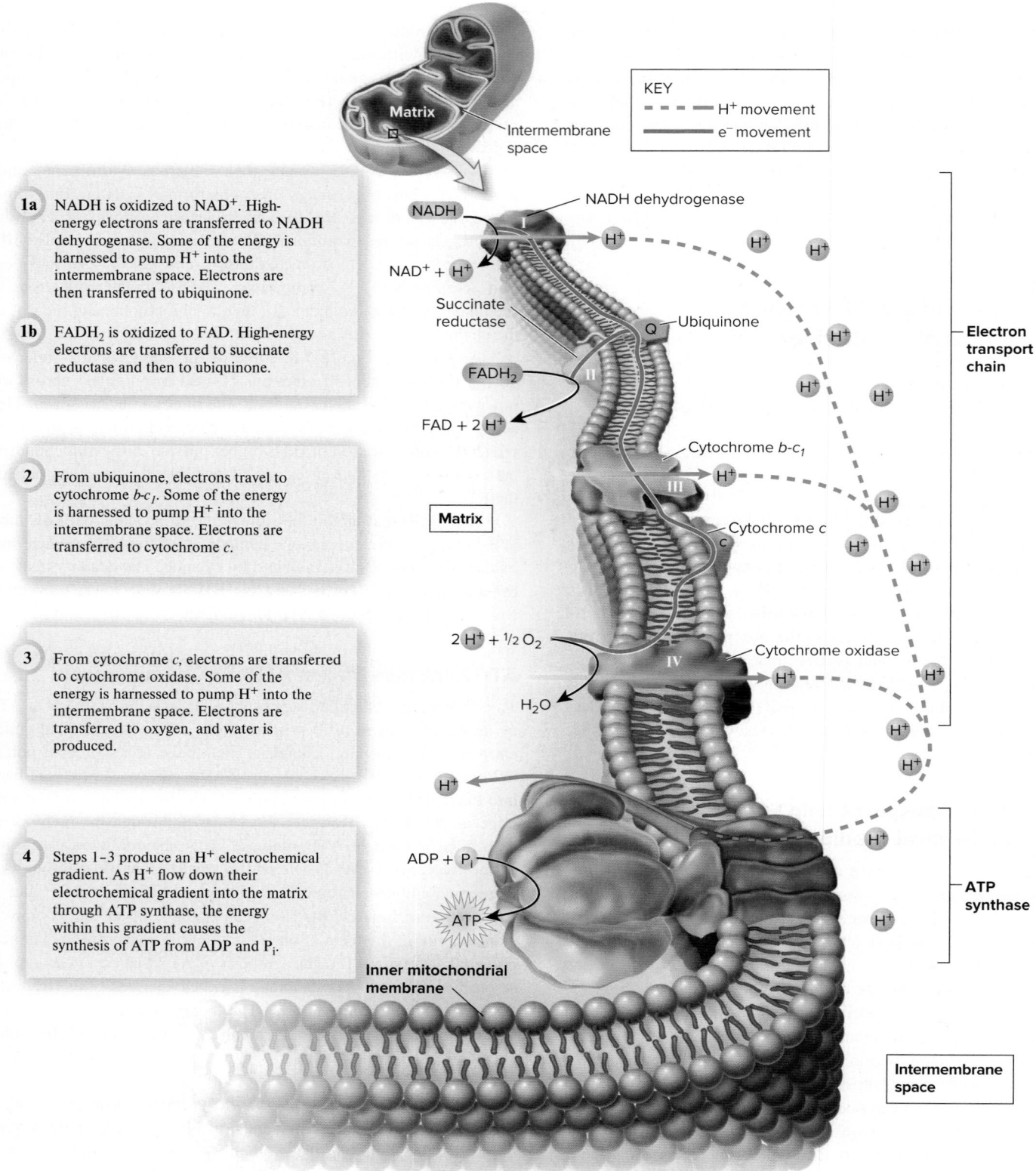

1a NADH is oxidized to NAD$^+$. High-energy electrons are transferred to NADH dehydrogenase. Some of the energy is harnessed to pump H$^+$ into the intermembrane space. Electrons are then transferred to ubiquinone.

1b FADH$_2$ is oxidized to FAD. High-energy electrons are transferred to succinate reductase and then to ubiquinone.

2 From ubiquinone, electrons travel to cytochrome b-c_1. Some of the energy is harnessed to pump H$^+$ into the intermembrane space. Electrons are transferred to cytochrome c.

3 From cytochrome c, electrons are transferred to cytochrome oxidase. Some of the energy is harnessed to pump H$^+$ into the intermembrane space. Electrons are transferred to oxygen, and water is produced.

4 Steps 1–3 produce an H$^+$ electrochemical gradient. As H$^+$ flow down their electrochemical gradient into the matrix through ATP synthase, the energy within this gradient causes the synthesis of ATP from ADP and P$_i$.

Figure 7.8 Oxidative phosphorylation. This process consists of two distinct events: the electron transport chain (ETC) and ATP synthesis. The ETC oxidizes, or removes electrons from, NADH or FADH$_2$ and pumps H$^+$ across the inner mitochondrial membrane. In chemiosmosis, ATP synthase uses the energy in this H$^+$ electrochemical gradient to phosphorylate ADP, thereby synthesizing ATP. In this figure, an oxygen atom is represented as $^1/_2$ O$_2$ to emphasize that the ETC reduces oxygen when it is in its molecular (O$_2$) form.

Concept Check: *Explain the meaning of the name cytochrome oxidase.*

stimulated for two reasons: (1) ADP stimulates cytochrome oxidase, and (2) ADP is a substrate that is used (with P_i) to make ATP.

NADH Oxidation Makes a Large Proportion of a Cell's ATP

For each molecule of NADH that is oxidized and each molecule of ATP that is made, the two chemical reactions of oxidative phosphorylation can be represented as follows:

$$NADH + H^+ + \tfrac{1}{2} O_2 \rightarrow NAD^+ + H_2O$$

$$ADP^{2-} + P_i^{2-} \rightarrow ATP^{4-} + H_2O$$

When we add up the maximal amount of ATP that can be made by oxidative phosphorylation, most researchers agree it is in the range of 30–34 ATP molecules for each glucose molecule that is broken down to CO_2 and H_2O. However, that maximal amount of ATP is rarely achieved, for two reasons.

- First, although 10 NADH and 2 $FADH_2$ are available to make the H^+ electrochemical gradient across the inner mitochondrial membrane, a cell uses some of these molecules for anabolic pathways. For example, NADH is used in the synthesis of organic molecules such as glycerol (a component of phospholipids).

- Second, the mitochondrion may use some of the energy in the H^+ electrochemical gradient for other purposes. For example, the gradient is used for the uptake of pyruvate into the matrix via an H^+/pyruvate symporter (see Figure 7.5).

Therefore, the actual amount of ATP synthesized is usually a little less than the maximum of 30 to 34 molecules. Even so, when we compare the amount of ATP that is made by glycolysis (2), the citric acid cycle (2), and oxidative phosphorylation (30–34), we see that oxidative phosphorylation provides a cell with a much greater capacity to make ATP.

Free-Energy Changes Drive Oxidative Phosphorylation and Other Stages of Glucose Breakdown

Thus far, we have considered (1) glycolysis, (2) the breakdown of pyruvate, (3) the citric acid cycle, and (4) oxidative phosphorylation. All four of these stages are ultimately driven by the oxidation of glucose, which is a highly exergonic process that releases free energy. However, the energy is not released in one big blast, as in an explosion, but rather in small step-wise increments. Releasing the energy in small increments allows cells to couple the breakdown of glucose with useful chemical processes. For example, as we saw earlier in this chapter, the breakdown of glucose to pyruvate is coupled to the synthesis of ATP. **Figure 7.9** shows how free energy is released as electrons move along the electron transport chain. At particular points along the ETC, some of the energy is used to pump H^+ across the inner mitochondrial membrane and establish an H^+ electrochemical gradient. This gradient is then used to power ATP synthesis.

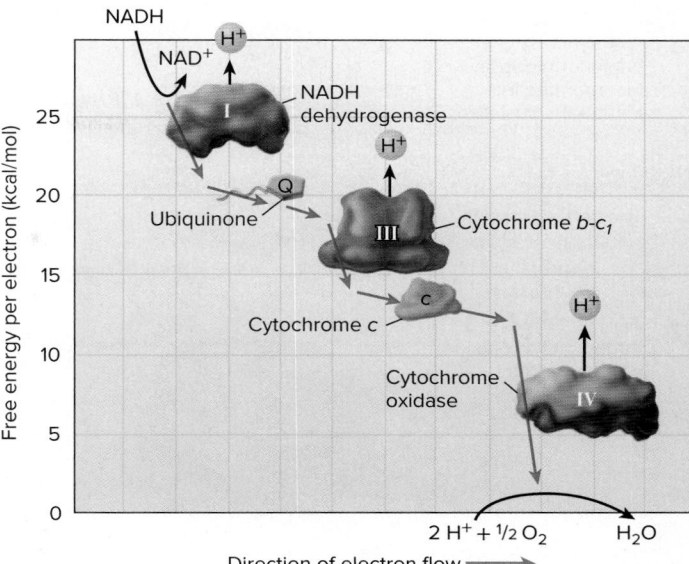

Figure 7.9 The relationship between free energy and electron movement along the electron transport chain. As electrons are transferred from one site to another along the electron transport chain, they release energy. Some of this energy is harnessed to pump H^+ across the inner mitochondrial membrane. The total energy released by a single electron is approximately −25 kcal/mol.

7.6 A Closer Look at ATP Synthase

Learning Outcomes:

1. **CoreSKILL »** Analyze the results of an experiment that verified that ATP synthase uses an H^+ electrochemical gradient to make ATP.
2. Describe the structure of ATP synthase.
3. Explain how a series of three conformational changes enables ATP synthase to make ATP.
4. **CoreSKILL »** Analyze the results of an experiment that showed that ATP synthase is a rotary machine.

The structure and function of ATP synthase are particularly intriguing and have received much attention over the past few decades. In this section, we will consider experiments that were aimed at elucidating this enzyme's function and explore, in greater depth, how it is able to synthesize ATP.

Experiments with Purified Proteins in Membrane Vesicles Verified Chemiosmosis

To show experimentally that ATP synthase makes ATP using an H^+ electrochemical gradient, researchers needed to purify the enzyme and study its function in vitro. In 1974, Efraim Racker and Walther Stoeckenius purified ATP synthase and another protein called bacteriorhodopsin, which is found in certain species of archaea. Previous research had shown that bacteriorhodopsin is a light-driven H^+ pump. Racker and Stoeckenius took both purified proteins and experimentally inserted them into membrane vesicles, a process called reconstitution (**Figure 7.10**). ATP synthase was oriented so its ATP-synthesizing region was on the outside of the

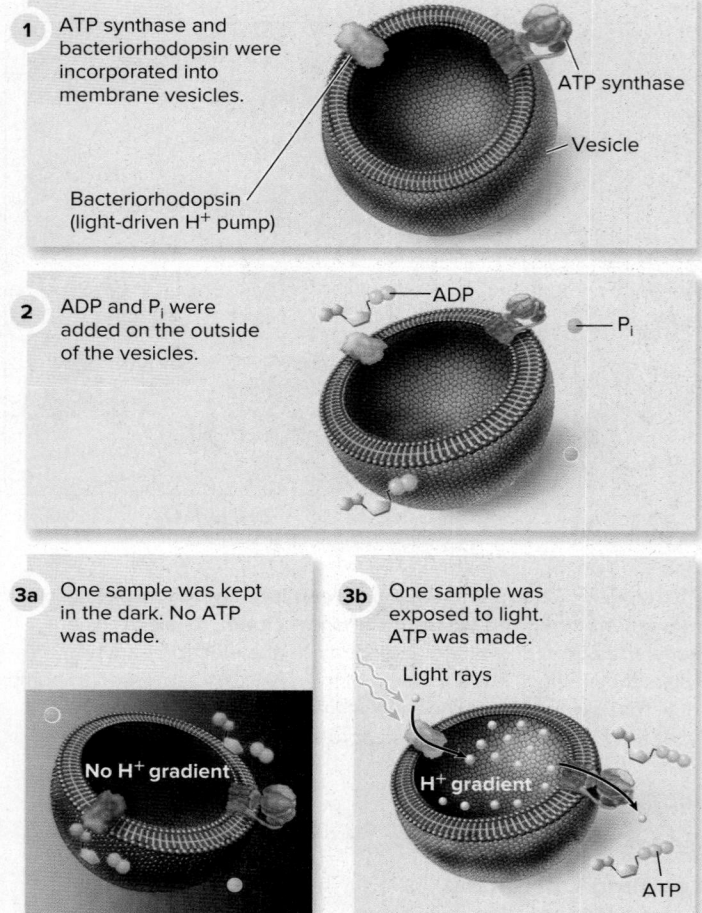

1 ATP synthase and bacteriorhodopsin were incorporated into membrane vesicles.

ATP synthase

Vesicle

Bacteriorhodopsin (light-driven H⁺ pump)

2 ADP and Pᵢ were added on the outside of the vesicles.

ADP

Pᵢ

3a One sample was kept in the dark. No ATP was made.

No H⁺ gradient

3b One sample was exposed to light. ATP was made.

Light rays

H⁺ gradient

ATP

Figure 7.10 The Racker and Stoeckenius experiment. In this experiment, bacteriorhodopsin pumped H⁺ into vesicles, and the resulting H⁺ electrochemical gradient was sufficient to drive ATP synthesis via ATP synthase.

Concept Check: *Is the functioning of the electron transport chain always needed to make ATP via ATP synthase?*

vesicles. Bacteriorhodopsin was oriented so it would pump H⁺ into the vesicles. The researchers added ADP and Pᵢ on the outside of the vesicles. In the dark, no ATP was made. However, when they shone light on the vesicles, a substantial amount of ATP was synthesized. Because bacteriorhodopsin was already known to be a light-driven H⁺ pump, these results convinced the researchers that ATP synthase uses an H⁺ electrochemical gradient as an energy source to make ATP.

ATP Synthase Is a Rotary Machine That Makes ATP as It Spins

ATP synthase is a rotary machine (**Figure 7.11**). It spins! The region embedded in the membrane is composed of three types of subunits called *a*, *b*, and *c*. Approximately 10–14 *c* subunits form a ring in the membrane. One *a* subunit is bound to this ring, and

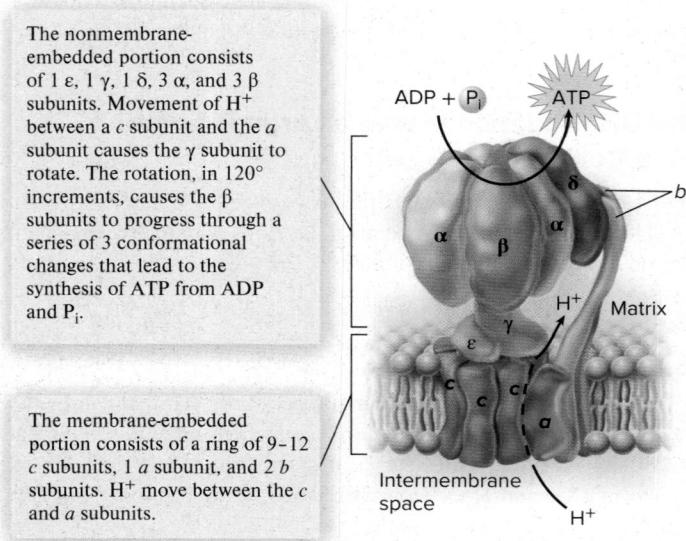

The nonmembrane-embedded portion consists of 1 ε, 1 γ, 1 δ, 3 α, and 3 β subunits. Movement of H⁺ between a *c* subunit and the *a* subunit causes the γ subunit to rotate. The rotation, in 120° increments, causes the β subunits to progress through a series of 3 conformational changes that lead to the synthesis of ATP from ADP and Pᵢ.

ADP + Pᵢ

ATP

δ

b

α

β

α

H⁺

Matrix

γ

ε

c c c

a

The membrane-embedded portion consists of a ring of 9–12 *c* subunits, 1 *a* subunit, and 2 *b* subunits. H⁺ move between the *c* and *a* subunits.

Intermembrane space

H⁺

Figure 7.11 The subunit structure and function of ATP synthase.

two *b* subunits are attached to the *a* subunit and protrude from the membrane. The nonmembrane-embedded subunits are designated with Greek letters. One ε and one γ subunit bind to the ring of *c* subunits. The γ subunit forms a long stalk that pokes into the center of another ring of three α and three β subunits. Each β subunit contains a catalytic site where ATP is made. Finally, the δ subunit forms a connection between the ring of α and β subunits and the two *b* subunits.

When hydrogen ions pass through a narrow channel at the contact site between a *c* subunit and the *a* subunit, a conformational change causes the γ subunit to turn clockwise (when viewed from the intermembrane space). Each time the γ subunit turns 120°, it changes its contacts with the three β subunits, which, in turn, causes the β subunits to change their conformations. How do these conformational changes promote ATP synthesis? The answer is that the conformational changes occur in a way that favors ATP synthesis and release. As shown in **Figure 7.12**, the conformational changes in the β subunits happen in the following order:

- Conformation 1: ADP and Pᵢ bind with good affinity.
- Conformation 2: ADP and Pᵢ bind very tightly, which strains chemical bonds so that ATP is made.
- Conformation 3: ATP binds very weakly and is released.

Each time the γ subunit turns 120°, it causes a β subunit to change to the next conformation. After conformation 3, a 120° turn by the γ subunit returns a β subunit back to conformation 1, and the cycle of ATP synthesis can begin again. Because ATP synthase has three β subunits, each subunit is in a different conformation at any given time.

American biochemist Paul Boyer proposed the concept of a rotary machine in the late 1970s. In his model, the three β subunits alternate between three conformations, as described previously. Boyer's

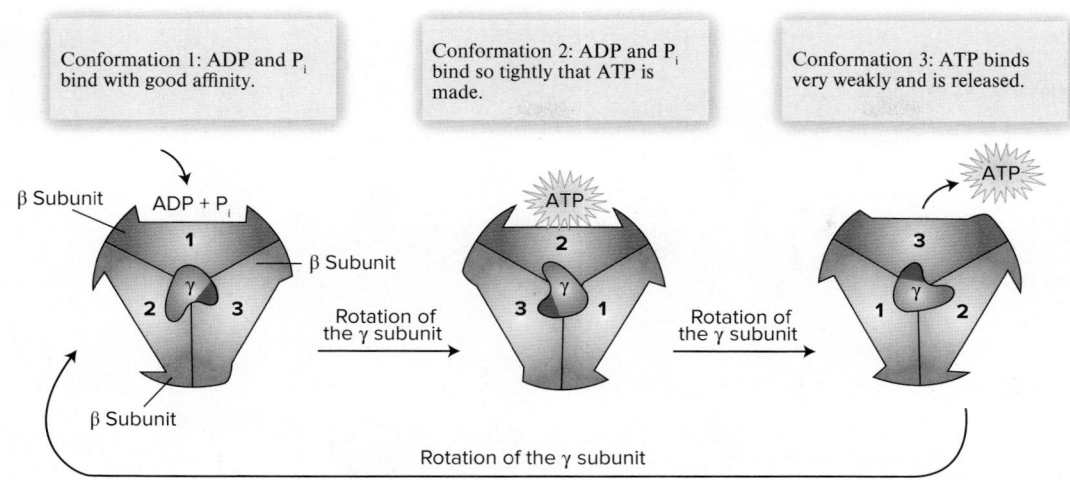

Conformation 1: ADP and P_i bind with good affinity.

Conformation 2: ADP and P_i bind so tightly that ATP is made.

Conformation 3: ATP binds very weakly and is released.

Figure 7.12 Conformational changes that result in ATP synthesis. For simplicity, the α subunits are not shown. This drawing emphasizes the conformational changes in the β subunit shown at the top. The other two β subunits also make ATP. All three β subunits alternate between three conformational states due to their interactions with the γ subunit.

original idea was met with great skepticism, because the concept that part of an enzyme could spin was very novel, to say the least. In 1994, British biochemist John Walker and his colleagues determined the three-dimensional structure of the nonmembrane-embedded portion of the ATP synthase. The structure revealed that each of the three β subunits had a different conformation—one with ADP bound, one with ATP bound, and one without any nucleotide bound. This result supported Boyer's model. In 1997, Boyer and Walker shared the Nobel Prize in Chemistry for their work on ATP synthase. As described next in the Feature Investigation, other researchers subsequently visualized the rotation of the γ subunit.

Core Skill: Modeling The goal of this modeling challenge is to predict how a mutation in the β subunit of ATP synthase would affect ATP synthesis.

Modeling Challenge: Let's suppose a researcher has identified a mutation in the β subunit that only affects conformation 3. A model that depicts the shape of the mutant β subunit is shown to the right. Look very carefully at the shape of the mutant subunit in conformation 3 and compare it to the normal β subunit in that conformation, as shown in Figure 7.12. Predict how this mutant subunit would affect ATP synthesis.

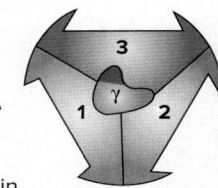

Mutant β subunit

Core Skill: Process of Science

Feature Investigation | Yoshida and Kinosita Demonstrated That the γ Subunit of ATP Synthase Spins

In 1997, Japanese biochemist Masasuke Yoshida, biophysicist Kazuhiko Kinosita, and colleagues set out to experimentally visualize the rotary nature of ATP synthase (Figure 7.13). The membrane-embedded region of ATP synthase can be separated from the rest of the protein by treating mitochondrial membranes with a high concentration of salt, releasing the portion of the protein containing one γ, three α, and three β subunits. The researchers adhered the $\gamma\alpha_3\beta_3$ complex to a glass slide so that the γ subunit was protruding upward. Because the γ subunit is too small to be seen with a light microscope, the rotation of this subunit cannot be visualized directly. To overcome this problem, the researchers attached a long, fluorescently labeled actin filament to the γ subunit via linker proteins. The fluorescently labeled actin filament is very long compared to the γ subunit and can be readily seen with a fluorescence microscope.

Because the membrane-embedded portion of the protein was missing, you may be wondering how the researchers could get the γ subunit to rotate. The answer is that they added ATP. Although the normal function of ATP synthase is to make ATP, it can also hydrolyze ATP. In other words, ATP synthase can run backward. As shown in the data

in **Figure 7.13**, when the researchers added ATP, they observed that the fluorescently labeled actin filament rotated in a counterclockwise direction, which is opposite to the direction that the γ subunit rotates when ATP is synthesized. Actin filaments were observed to rotate for more than 100 revolutions in the presence of ATP. These results convinced the scientific community that ATP synthase is a rotary machine.

Experimental Questions

1. **CoreSKILL »** The components of ATP synthase are too small to be visualized by light microscopy. For the experiment of Figure 7.13, how did the researchers observe the movement of ATP synthase?

2. **CoreSKILL »** In the experiment of Figure 7.13, what observation indicated to the researchers that ATP synthase is a rotary machine? What was the control of this experiment? What did it indicate?

3. **CoreSKILL »** Were the rotations seen by the researchers in the data of Figure 7.13 in the same direction as they are expected to occur in mitochondria during ATP synthesis? Why or why not?

Figure 7.13 **Yoshida and Kinosita provide evidence that ATP synthase is a rotary machine.** (5): From Noji, H., Yoshida, M. 2001. The Rotary Machine in the Cell, ATP Synthase. *Journal of Biological Chemistry 276: 1665–1668.* ©2001 The American Society for Biochemistry and Molecular Biology

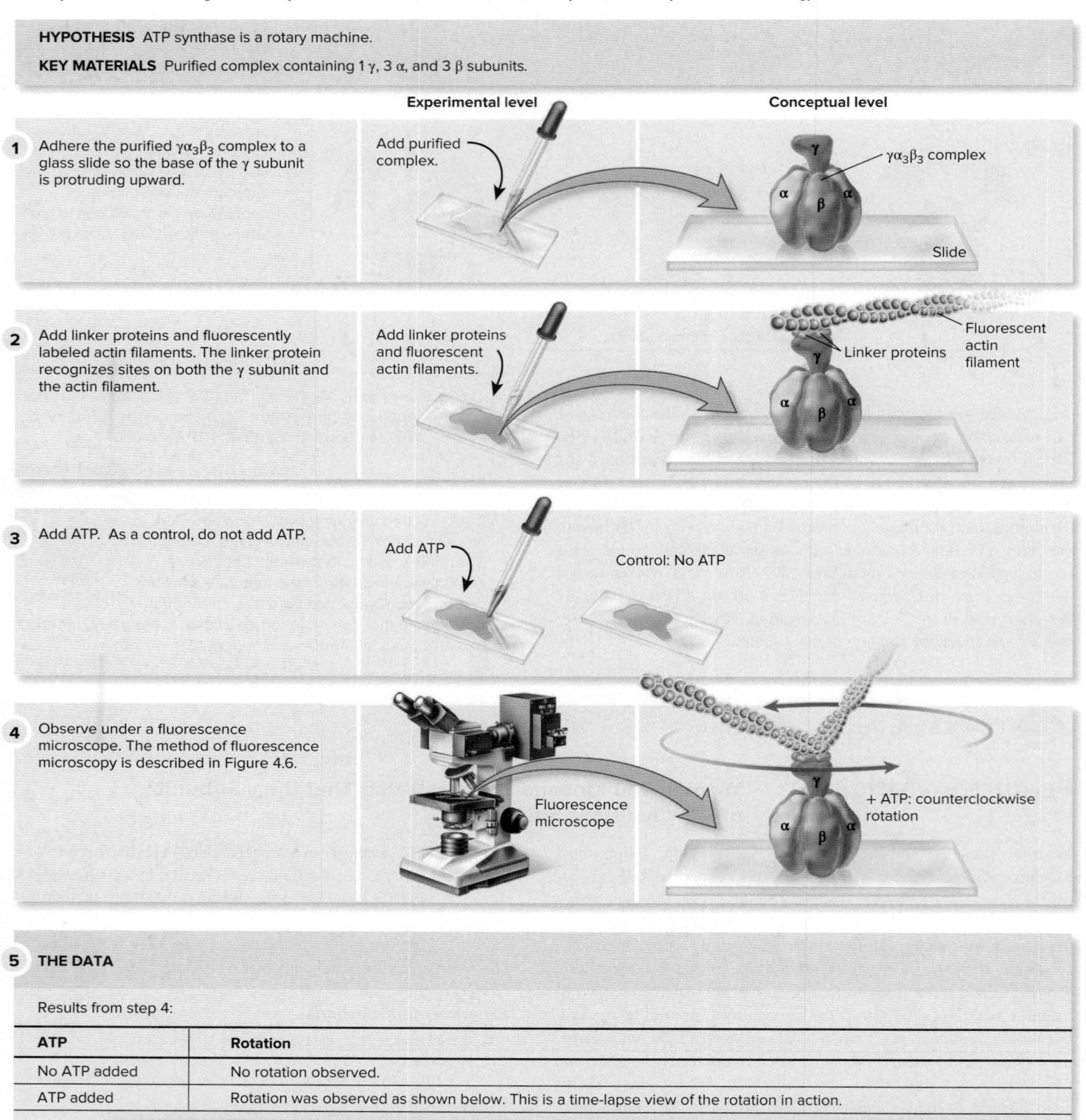

HYPOTHESIS ATP synthase is a rotary machine.

KEY MATERIALS Purified complex containing 1 γ, 3 α, and 3 β subunits.

Experimental level   **Conceptual level**

1. Adhere the purified $\gamma\alpha_3\beta_3$ complex to a glass slide so the base of the γ subunit is protruding upward.

   Add purified complex.

   γ
   $\gamma\alpha_3\beta_3$ complex
   α β α
   Slide

2. Add linker proteins and fluorescently labeled actin filaments. The linker protein recognizes sites on both the γ subunit and the actin filament.

   Add linker proteins and fluorescent actin filaments.

   Fluorescent actin filament
   γ
   Linker proteins
   α β α

3. Add ATP. As a control, do not add ATP.

   Add ATP

   Control: No ATP

4. Observe under a fluorescence microscope. The method of fluorescence microscopy is described in Figure 4.6.

   Fluorescence microscope

   γ
   + ATP: counterclockwise rotation
   α β α

5. **THE DATA**

   Results from step 4:

ATP	Rotation
No ATP added	No rotation observed.
ATP added	Rotation was observed as shown below. This is a time-lapse view of the rotation in action.

   Row 1

   Row 2

6 **CONCLUSION** The γ subunit rotates counterclockwise when ATP is hydrolyzed. It would be expected to rotate clockwise when ATP is synthesized.

7 **SOURCE** Noji, H., Yoshida, M. 2001. The rotary machine in the cell, ATP synthase. *Journal of Biological Chemistry* 276: 1665–1668.

7.7 Connections Among Carbohydrate, Protein, and Fat Metabolism

Learning Outcome:

1. Explain how carbohydrate, protein, and fat metabolism are interconnected.

When you eat a meal, it usually contains not only carbohydrates (including glucose), but also proteins and fats. These molecules are broken down by some of the same enzymes involved with glucose metabolism. The use of the same pathways for the breakdown of sugars, amino acids, and fats makes cellular metabolism more efficient because the same enzymes are used for the breakdown of different starting molecules.

As shown in **Figure 7.14**, proteins and fats can enter glycolysis or the citric acid cycle at different points.

- Proteins are first acted on by enzymes, either in digestive juices or within cells, that cleave the bonds connecting individual amino acids. Because the 20 amino acids differ in their side chains, amino acids and their breakdown products can enter at different points in the pathway. Breakdown products of some amino acids can enter at later steps of glycolysis, or an acetyl group can be removed from certain amino acids and become attached to CoA and then enter the citric acid cycle (see Figure 7.14). Other amino acids are modified and enter the citric acid cycle.

- Fats are typically broken down to glycerol and fatty acids. Glycerol can be modified to glyceraldehyde-3-phosphate and enter glycolysis. Lipid tails can have two carbon acetyl units removed, which bind to CoA and enter the citric acid cycle.

7.8 Anaerobic Respiration and Fermentation

Learning Outcomes:

1. Describe how certain microorganisms make ATP using a final electron acceptor in the electron transport chain that is not oxygen.
2. Explain how muscle and yeast cells use fermentation to synthesize ATP under anaerobic conditions.

Thus far, we have surveyed catabolic pathways that result in the complete breakdown of glucose in the presence of oxygen. Cells also commonly metabolize organic molecules in the absence of oxygen. The term **anaerobic** is used to describe an environment that lacks oxygen. Many bacteria and archaea and some fungi exist in anaerobic

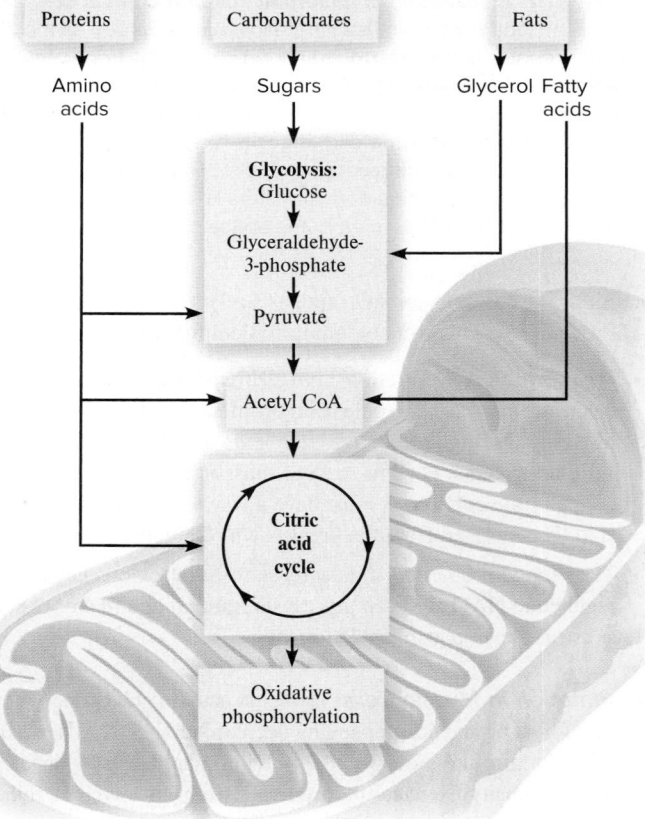

Figure 7.14 Integration of carbohydrate, protein, and fat metabolism. Breakdown products of proteins and fats are used as fuel for cellular respiration, entering the same pathways used to break down carbohydrates. ©Ernie Friedlander/Cole Group/Getty Images

Concept Check: *What advantage does integrating protein, carbohydrate, and fat metabolism have for cells?*

environments but still have to oxidize organic molecules to obtain sufficient amounts of energy. Examples include microbes living in your intestinal tract and those living deep in the soil. Similarly, when a person exercises strenuously, the rate of oxygen consumption by muscle cells may greatly exceed the rate of oxygen delivery—particularly at the start of the strenuous exercise. Under these conditions, muscle cells become anaerobic and must obtain sufficient energy in the absence of oxygen to maintain their level of activity.

Two different strategies may be used by cells to metabolize organic molecules in the absence of oxygen. One mechanism is to use a substance other than O_2 as the final electron acceptor of the electron transport chain, a process called **anaerobic respiration**. A second approach is to produce ATP via substrate-level phosphorylation only, without any net oxidation of organic molecules, a process called **fermentation**. In this section, we will consider examples of both strategies.

Some Microorganisms Carry Out Anaerobic Respiration

At the end of the ETC, as shown earlier in Figure 7.8, cytochrome oxidase recognizes O_2 and catalyzes its reduction to H_2O. The final electron acceptor of the chain is O_2. Many species of bacteria that live under anaerobic conditions have evolved enzymes that function similarly to cytochrome oxidase but recognize molecules other than O_2 and use them as the final electron acceptor.

For example, under anaerobic conditions *Escherichia coli*, a bacterial species found in your intestinal tract, produces an enzyme called nitrate reductase. This enzyme uses nitrate (NO_3^-) as the final electron acceptor of the electron transport chain. **Figure 7.15** shows a simplified ETC in *E. coli* in which nitrate is the final electron acceptor. In *E. coli* and other bacterial species, the ETC is in the plasma membrane that surrounds the cytoplasm. Electrons travel from NADH to NADH dehydrogenase to ubiquinone to cytochrome *b* and then to nitrate reductase. At the end of the chain, NO_3^- is converted to nitrite (NO_2^-). This process generates an H^+ electrochemical gradient in three ways. First, NADH dehydrogenase pumps H^+ out of the cytoplasm. Second, ubiquinone picks up H^+ in the cytoplasm and carries it to the other side of the membrane. Third, the reduction of nitrate to nitrite consumes H^+ in the cytoplasm. The generation of an H^+ electrochemical gradient via these three processes allows *E. coli* cells to make ATP via chemiosmosis under anaerobic conditions.

Fermentation Is the Breakdown of Organic Molecules Without Net Oxidation

Many organisms, including animals and yeast, use only O_2 as the final electron acceptor of their ETCs. When confronted with anaerobic conditions, these organisms must have a different way of producing sufficient ATP. One strategy is to make ATP via glycolysis, which can occur under either anaerobic or aerobic conditions. Under anaerobic conditions, cells do not use the citric acid cycle or the ETC, but make ATP only via glycolysis.

A key issue is that glycolysis requires NAD^+ and generates NADH. Under aerobic conditions, NADH is oxidized to NAD^+ to make more ATP. However, this cannot occur under anaerobic

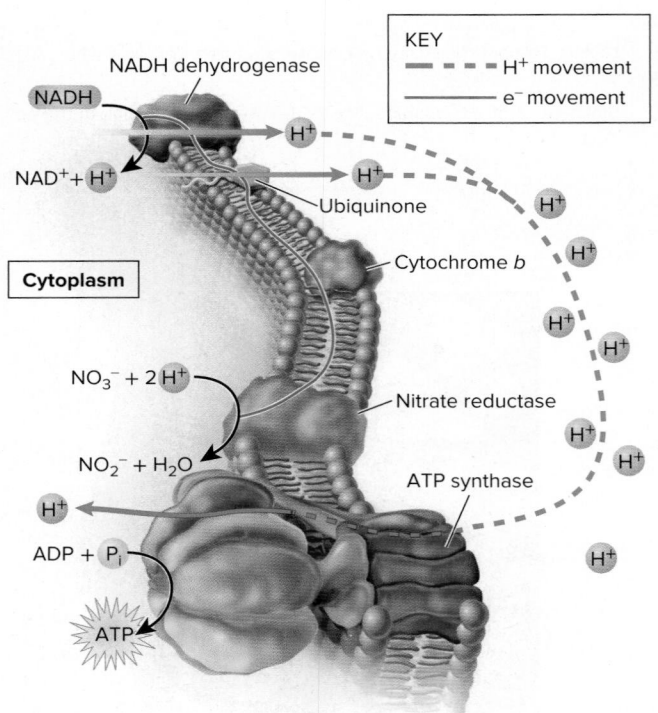

Figure 7.15 **An example of anaerobic respiration in *E. coli*.** When oxygen is absent, *E. coli* can use nitrate instead of oxygen as the final electron acceptor of the electron transport chain. This generates an H^+ electrochemical gradient that is used to make ATP via chemiosmosis. Note: As shown in this figure, ubiquinone picks up H^+ on one side of the membrane and deposits it on the other side. A similar event happens during aerobic respiration in mitochondria (see Figure 7.8), except that ubiquinone transfers H^+ to cytochrome b-c_1, which pumps it into the intermembrane space.

conditions in yeast and animals, and, as a result, NADH builds up and NAD^+ decreases. This is a potential problem for two reasons:

- First, at high concentrations, NADH haphazardly donates its electrons to other molecules and promotes the formation of free radicals, highly reactive chemicals that damage DNA and cellular proteins. For this reason, yeast and animal cells exposed to anaerobic conditions must have a way to remove the excess NADH generated from the breakdown of glucose.

- The second problem is the decrease in NAD^+. Cells need to regenerate NAD^+ to keep glycolysis running and make ATP via substrate-level phosphorylation.

Fermentation in Muscle Cells How do muscle cells cope with the buildup of NADH and accompanying decrease in NAD^+? When a muscle cell is working strenuously and its environment becomes anaerobic, as in high-intensity exercise, the pyruvate from glycolysis is reduced to make lactate. (The uncharged, or protonated, form is called lactic acid.) The electrons to reduce pyruvate are derived from NADH, which is oxidized to NAD^+ (**Figure 7.16a**). Therefore, this process decreases NADH and reduces its potentially harmful effects. It also increases the level of NAD^+, thereby allowing glycolysis to continue. The lactate is secreted from muscle cells. Once sufficient oxygen is restored, the

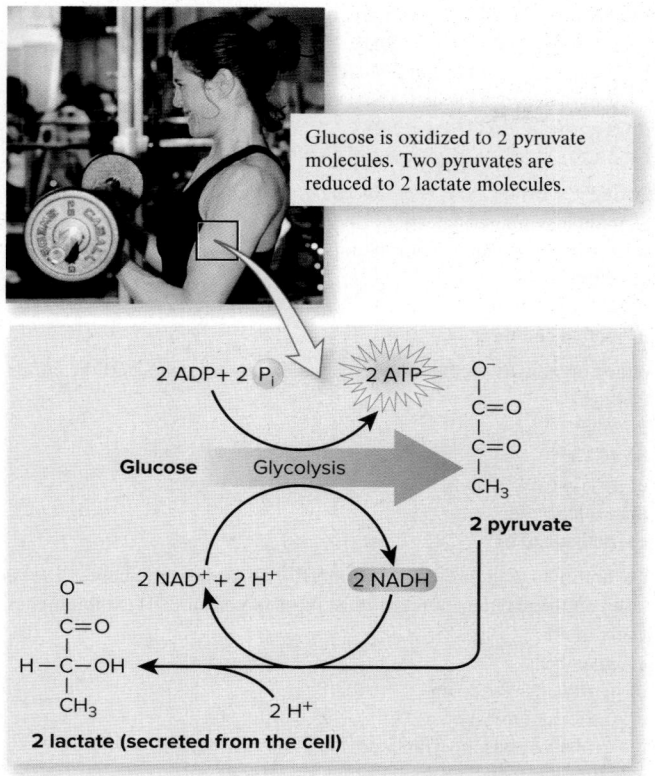

Glucose is oxidized to 2 pyruvate molecules. Two pyruvates are reduced to 2 lactate molecules.

(a) Production of lactic acid

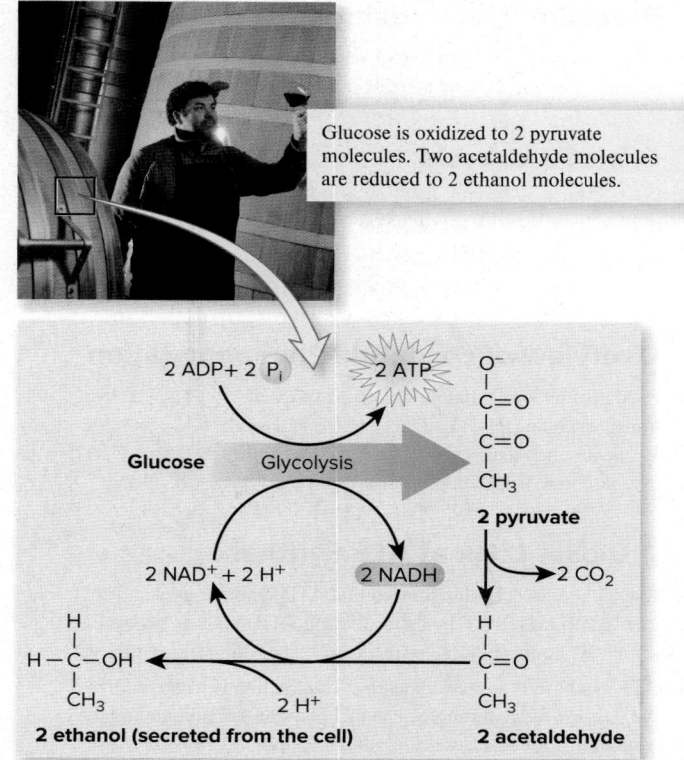

Glucose is oxidized to 2 pyruvate molecules. Two acetaldehyde molecules are reduced to 2 ethanol molecules.

(b) Production of ethanol

Figure 7.16 Examples of fermentation. In these examples, NADH is produced by the oxidation of an organic molecule, and then the NADH is converted back to NAD⁺ when it donates electrons to a different organic molecule such as pyruvate **(a)** or acetaldehyde **(b)**. a: ©Homer W Sykes/Alamy Stock Photo; b: ©FreeProd/Alamy Stock Photo

 Core Skill: Science and Society Fermentation by microorganisms is used in wine making, beer brewing, and bread making.

lactate produced during strenuous exercise can be taken up by cells, converted back to pyruvate, and used for energy, or this lactate may be used by the liver and other tissues to make glucose.

Fermentation in Yeast Cells Yeast cells cope with anaerobic conditions differently. During wine making, a yeast cell metabolizes sugar under anaerobic conditions. The pyruvate is broken down to CO_2 and a two-carbon molecule called acetaldehyde. The acetaldehyde is then reduced by NADH to make ethanol, while NADH is oxidized to NAD⁺ (**Figure 7.16b**). Similar to lactate production in muscle cells, this process decreases NADH and increases NAD⁺, thereby preventing the harmful effects of NADH and allowing glycolysis to continue.

The term fermentation is used to describe the breakdown of organic molecules to harness energy without any net oxidation (that is, without any removal of electrons). The pathways for breaking down glucose to lactate or ethanol are examples of fermentation. Although electrons are removed from an organic molecule such as glucose to make pyruvate and NADH, the electrons are donated back to an organic molecule in the production of lactate or ethanol. Therefore, there is no net removal of electrons from an organic molecule. Compared with oxidative phosphorylation, fermentation produces far less ATP, for two reasons. First, glucose is not oxidized completely to CO_2 and H_2O. Second, the NADH

made during glycolysis cannot be used to make more ATP. Overall, the complete breakdown of glucose in the presence of oxygen yields 34–38 ATP molecules. By comparison, the anaerobic breakdown of glucose to lactate or ethanol yields only 2 ATP molecules.

Summary of Key Concepts

7.1 Overview of Cellular Respiration

- Cells obtain energy via cellular respiration, which involves the breakdown of organic molecules and the export of waste products.
- The breakdown of glucose occurs in four stages: glycolysis, pyruvate breakdown, citric acid cycle, and oxidative phosphorylation (Figure 7.1).

7.2 Glycolysis

- During glycolysis, which occurs in the cytosol, glucose is split into two molecules of pyruvate, with a net yield of two ATP and two NADH. The ATP is made by substrate-level phosphorylation (Figures 7.2, 7.3).
- Cancer cells exhibit high levels of glycolysis, which enables the detection of tumors via a procedure called positron-emission tomography (PET) (Figure 7.4).

7.3 Breakdown of Pyruvate

- Pyruvate is broken down to CO_2 and an acetyl group that becomes attached to CoA. NADH is made during this process (Figure 7.5).

7.4 Citric Acid Cycle

- During the citric acid cycle, an acetyl group is removed from acetyl CoA and attached to oxaloacetate to make citrate. In a series of steps, two CO_2 molecules, three NADH, one $FADH_2$, and one ATP are made, after which the cycle begins again (Figures 7.6, 7.7).

7.5 Overview of Oxidative Phosphorylation

- Oxidative phosphorylation involves two events: (1) The electron transport chain (ETC) oxidizes NADH or $FADH_2$ and generates an H^+ electrochemical gradient, and (2) this gradient is used by ATP synthase to make ATP via chemiosmosis (Figures 7.8, 7.9).

7.6 A Closer Look at ATP Synthase

- Racker and Stoeckenius showed that ATP synthase uses an H^+ gradient to make ATP by reconstituting ATP synthase with a light-driven H^+ pump (Figure 7.10).

- ATP synthase is a rotary machine. The rotation is triggered by the passage of H^+ through a channel between a c subunit and the a subunit, which causes the γ subunit to spin, resulting in three conformational changes in the β subunits that promote ATP synthesis (Figures 7.11, 7.12).

- Yoshida and Kinosita demonstrated rotation of the γ subunit of ATP synthase by attaching a fluorescently labeled actin filament and observing its movement during the hydrolysis of ATP (Figure 7.13).

7.7 Connections Among Carbohydrate, Protein, and Fat Metabolism

- Proteins and fats can enter into glycolysis or the citric acid cycle at different points (Figure 7.14).

7.8 Anaerobic Respiration and Fermentation

- Anaerobic respiration occurs in the absence of oxygen. Certain microorganisms carry out anaerobic respiration by using as the final electron acceptor of the ETC a substance other than oxygen, such as nitrate (Figure 7.15).

- During fermentation, organic molecules are broken down without any net oxidation (that is, without any net removal of electrons). Examples include lactic acid production in muscle cells and ethanol production in yeast cells (Figure 7.16).

Assess & Discuss

Test Yourself

1. Which of the following pathways occurs in the cytosol?
   a. glycolysis
   b. breakdown of pyruvate to an acetyl group
   c. citric acid cycle
   d. oxidative phosphorylation
   e. all of the above

2. The net products of glycolysis are
   a. 6 CO_2, 4 ATP, and 2 NADH.
   b. 2 pyruvate, 2 ATP, and 2 NADH.
   c. 2 pyruvate, 4 ATP, and 2 NADH.
   d. 2 pyruvate, 2 GTP, and 2 CO_2.
   e. 2 CO_2, 2 ATP, and glucose.

3. During glycolysis, ATP is produced by
   a. oxidative phosphorylation.
   b. substrate-level phosphorylation.
   c. redox reactions.
   d. all of the above.
   e. both a and b.

4. Which organic molecule supplies a two-carbon group to start the citric acid cycle?
   a. ATP
   b. NADH
   c. acetyl CoA
   d. oxaloacetate
   e. both a and b

5. The ability to diagnose tumors using [^{18}F]-fluorodeoxyglucose (FDG) is based on the phenomenon that most types of cancer cells exhibit higher levels of
   a. glycolysis.
   b. pyruvate breakdown.
   c. citric acid metabolism.
   d. oxidative phosphorylation.
   e. all of the above.

6. In the experiment of Racker and Stoeckenius, bacteriorhodopsin was oriented in such a way that it pumped H^+ into a vesicle. Each vesicle actually contained many molecules of bacteriorhodopsin. How would the results of the experiment have been affected if 50% of the bacteriorhodopsin molecules pumped H^+ into the vesicle and 50% pumped H^+ out of the vesicles?
   a. The same amount of ATP would be made in the presence of light, and no ATP would be made in the dark.
   b. More ATP would be made in the presence of light, and no ATP would be made in the dark.
   c. No ATP would be made in the presence of light, and no ATP would be made in the dark.
   d. No ATP would be made in the presence of light, but some ATP would be made in the dark.
   e. Some ATP would be made in the presence of light, and some ATP would be made in the dark.

7. Certain drugs, which are called ionophores, cause the mitochondrial membrane to be highly permeable to H^+. How would such drugs affect oxidative phosphorylation?
   a. Movement of electrons down the ETC would be inhibited.
   b. ATP synthesis would be inhibited.
   c. ATP synthesis would be unaffected.
   d. ATP synthesis would be stimulated.
   e. Both a and b would occur.

8. The source of energy that *directly* drives the synthesis of ATP during oxidative phosphorylation is the
   a. oxidation of NADH.
   b. oxidation of glucose.
   c. oxidation of pyruvate.
   d. H^+ electrochemical gradient.
   e. reduction of O_2.

9. Compared with oxidative phosphorylation in mitochondria, anaerobic respiration in bacteria differs in that
    a. more ATP is made.
    b. ATP is made only via substrate-level phosphorylation.
    c. O_2 is converted to H_2O_2 rather than H_2O.
    d. something other than O_2 acts as a final electron acceptor of the ETC.
    e. both b and d occur.

10. When conditions in a muscle become anaerobic during strenuous exercise, why is it necessary to convert pyruvate to lactate?
    a. to decrease NAD^+ and increase NADH
    b. to decrease NADH and increase NAD^+
    c. to increase NADH and increase NAD^+
    d. to decrease NADH and decrease NAD^+
    e. to keep oxidative phosphorylation running

Conceptual Questions

1. The electron transport chain is so named because electrons are transported from one component to another. Describe the purpose of the ETC.

2. What causes the rotation of the γ subunit of ATP synthase? How does this rotation promote ATP synthesis?

3. **Core Concept: Energy and Matter** How is glucose breakdown regulated to avoid the overproduction of ATP and NADH? What would be some potentially harmful consequences if glucose metabolism was not regulated properly?

Collaborative Questions

1. Discuss the advantages and disadvantages of aerobic respiration, anaerobic respiration, and fermentation.

2. Read more about PET scans in other sources. Which types of cancers are most easily detected by this procedure, and which types are not readily detected? Is the ability to detect cancer via a PET scan related to the level of oxygen within a tumor?

Photosynthesis

8

A tropical rain forest in the Amazon. Plant life in tropical rain forests carries out a large amount of the world's photosynthesis and supplies the atmosphere with a sizable fraction of its oxygen.
©Travelpix Ltd/Getty Images

photosynthesis for their nourishment, either directly or indirectly. Photosynthesis is also responsible for producing the oxygen that makes up a large portion of the Earth's atmosphere. Therefore, all aerobic organisms rely on photosynthesis for cellular respiration.

We begin this chapter with an overview of photosynthesis as it occurs in plants and algae. We will then explore the two stages of photosynthesis in more detail. In the first stage, called the **light reactions**, light energy is absorbed by chlorophyll and converted to chemical energy in the form of two energy intermediates: ATP and NADPH. During the second stage, known as the **Calvin cycle**, ATP and NADPH are used to drive the synthesis of carbohydrates. We will conclude with a consideration of the variations in photosynthesis that occur in plants existing in hot and dry conditions.

8.1 Overview of Photosynthesis

Learning Outcomes:

1. Write the general equations that represent the process of photosynthesis.
2. Explain how photosynthesis powers the biosphere.
3. Describe the general structure of chloroplasts.
4. Compare and contrast the two phases of photosynthesis: the light reactions and the Calvin cycle.

In the mid-1600s, a Flemish physician, Jan Baptista Van Helmont, conducted an experiment in which he transplanted the shoot of a young willow tree into a bucket of soil and allowed it to grow for 5 years. After this time, the willow tree had added 164 pounds to its original weight, but the soil had lost only 2 ounces. Van Helmont correctly concluded that the willow tree did not get most of its nutrients from the soil. He also hypothesized that the mass of the tree came from the water he had added over the 5 years. This hypothesis was partially correct, but we now know that CO_2 from the air is also a major contributor to the growth and mass of plants.

In the 1770s, Jan Ingenhousz, a Dutch physician, immersed green plants under water and discovered that they released bubbles of oxygen. Ingenhousz determined that sunlight was necessary for oxygen production. During this same period, Jean Senebier, a Swiss botanist,

Take a deep breath. Nearly all of the oxygen in every breath you take is made by Earth's abundant plants, algae, and cyanobacteria. More than 20% of the world's oxygen is produced in the Amazon rain forest in South America alone (see the chapter opening photo). Biologists are alarmed about the rate at which such forests are being destroyed by human activities such as logging, mining, and oil extraction. Rain forests once covered 14% of the Earth's land surface, but they now occupy less than 6%. At their current rate of destruction, rain forests may be nearly eliminated in less than 40 years. Such a development may lower the level of oxygen in the atmosphere and thereby have a harmful effect on living organisms on a global scale.

In rain forests and across all of the Earth, the most visible color on land is green. The green color of plants is due to a pigment called chlorophyll. This pigment provides the starting point for the process of **photosynthesis**, in which the energy from light is captured and used to synthesize glucose and other organic molecules. Nearly all living organisms ultimately rely on

found that CO_2 is required for plant growth. With this accumulating information, Julius von Mayer, a German physicist, proposed in 1845 that plants convert light energy from the Sun into chemical energy.

For the next several decades, plant biologists studied photosynthesis in plants, algae, and species of bacteria that are capable of photosynthesis. They discovered that some photosynthetic bacteria use hydrogen sulfide (H_2S) instead of water (H_2O) for photosynthesis, and these organisms release sulfur instead of oxygen. In the 1930s, based on this information, Dutch-American microbiologist Cornelis van Niel proposed a general equation for photosynthesis that applies to plants, algae, and photosynthetic bacteria:

$$CO_2 + 2\,H_2A + \text{Light energy} \rightarrow CH_2O + A_2 + H_2O$$

where A is oxygen (O) or sulfur (S) and CH_2O is the general formula for a carbohydrate. This is a redox reaction in which CO_2 is reduced and H_2A is oxidized.

In plants and algae, A is oxygen and A_2 is a molecule of oxygen that is designated O_2. Therefore, this equation becomes

$$CO_2 + 2\,H_2O + \text{Light energy} \rightarrow CH_2O + O_2 + H_2O$$

When the carbohydrate produced is glucose ($C_6H_{12}O_6$), we multiply each side of the equation by 6 to obtain:

$$6\,CO_2 + 12\,H_2O + \text{Light energy} \rightarrow C_6H_{12}O_6 + 6\,O_2 + 6\,H_2O$$
$$\Delta G = +685 \text{ kcal/mol}$$

In this redox reaction, CO_2 is reduced during the formation of glucose, and H_2O is oxidized during the formation of O_2. Notice that the free-energy change required for the production of 1 mole of glucose from carbon dioxide and water is a whopping +685 kcal/mol! As we learned in Chapter 6, an endergonic reaction is driven forward by being coupled with an exergonic process that releases free energy. In this case, the energy from sunlight ultimately drives the synthesis of glucose.

In this section, we will survey the general features of photosynthesis as it occurs in plants and algae. The sections that follow will examine the various steps in this process.

Photosynthesis Powers the Biosphere

The term **biosphere** describes the regions on the surface of the Earth and in the atmosphere where living organisms exist. Organisms can be categorized as heterotrophs and autotrophs. **Heterotrophs** must consume food—organic molecules from their environment—to sustain life. Most species of bacteria and protists, as well as all species of fungi and animals, are heterotrophs. By comparison, **autotrophs** sustain themselves by producing organic molecules from inorganic sources such as CO_2 and H_2O. **Photoautotrophs** are autotrophs that use light as a source of energy to make organic molecules. These include plants, algae, and some bacterial species such as cyanobacteria.

Life in the biosphere is largely driven by the photosynthetic power of plants, algae, and cyanobacteria. The existence of most species relies on a key energy cycle that involves the interplay between organic molecules (such as glucose) and inorganic molecules, namely, O_2, CO_2, and H_2O (**Figure 8.1**). Photoautotrophs make a large proportion of the Earth's organic molecules via photosynthesis, using light

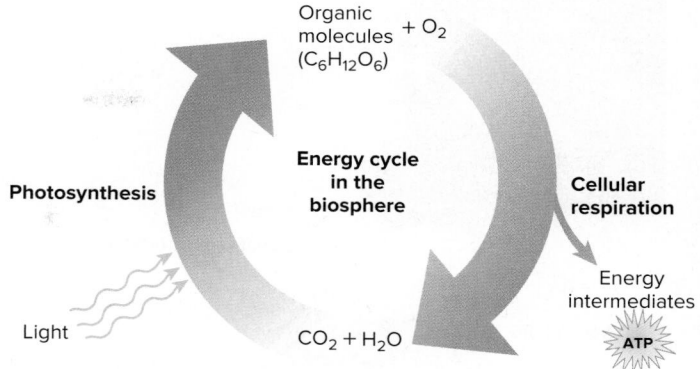

Figure 8.1 **An important energy cycle between photosynthesis and cellular respiration.** Photosynthesis is a process in which light, CO_2, and H_2O are used to produce O_2 and organic molecules. The organic molecules are broken down to CO_2 and H_2O via cellular respiration to supply energy in the form of ATP; O_2 is reduced to H_2O.

 Core Skill: Modeling The goal of this modeling challenge is to increase the complexity of the model shown in Figure 8.1 by adding organisms that carry out photosynthesis and those that carry out cellular respiration.

Modeling Challenge: The figure shows a simplified model for an energy cycle in the biosphere. Increase the complexity of the model in the following ways: On the left side, add drawings of three different broad categories of organisms that carry out photosynthesis. On the right, add drawings of three or more categories that carry out cellular respiration.

energy, CO_2, and H_2O. During this process, they also produce O_2. To supply their energy needs, both photoautotrophs and heterotrophs metabolize organic molecules via cellular respiration. As described in Chapter 7, cellular respiration generates CO_2 and H_2O and is used to make ATP. The CO_2 is released into the atmosphere and can be reused by photoautotrophs to make more organic molecules such as glucose. In this way, an energy cycle between photosynthesis and cellular respiration sustains life on our planet.

In Plants and Algae, Photosynthesis Occurs in the Chloroplasts

Chloroplasts are organelles found in plant and algal cells that carry out photosynthesis. These organelles contain large quantities of **chlorophyll**, which is a pigment that gives plants their green color. All green parts of a plant contain chloroplasts and can perform photosynthesis, although the majority of photosynthesis in most species of plants occurs in the leaves (**Figure 8.2**). The tissue in the internal part of the leaf, called the **mesophyll**, contains cells with chloroplasts. For photosynthesis to occur, the mesophyll cells must receive light, and also obtain water and carbon dioxide. The water is taken up by the roots of the plant and is transported to the leaves by small veins. Carbon dioxide gas enters the leaf, and oxygen exits, via pores called stomata (singular, stoma or stomate; from the Greek, meaning mouth).

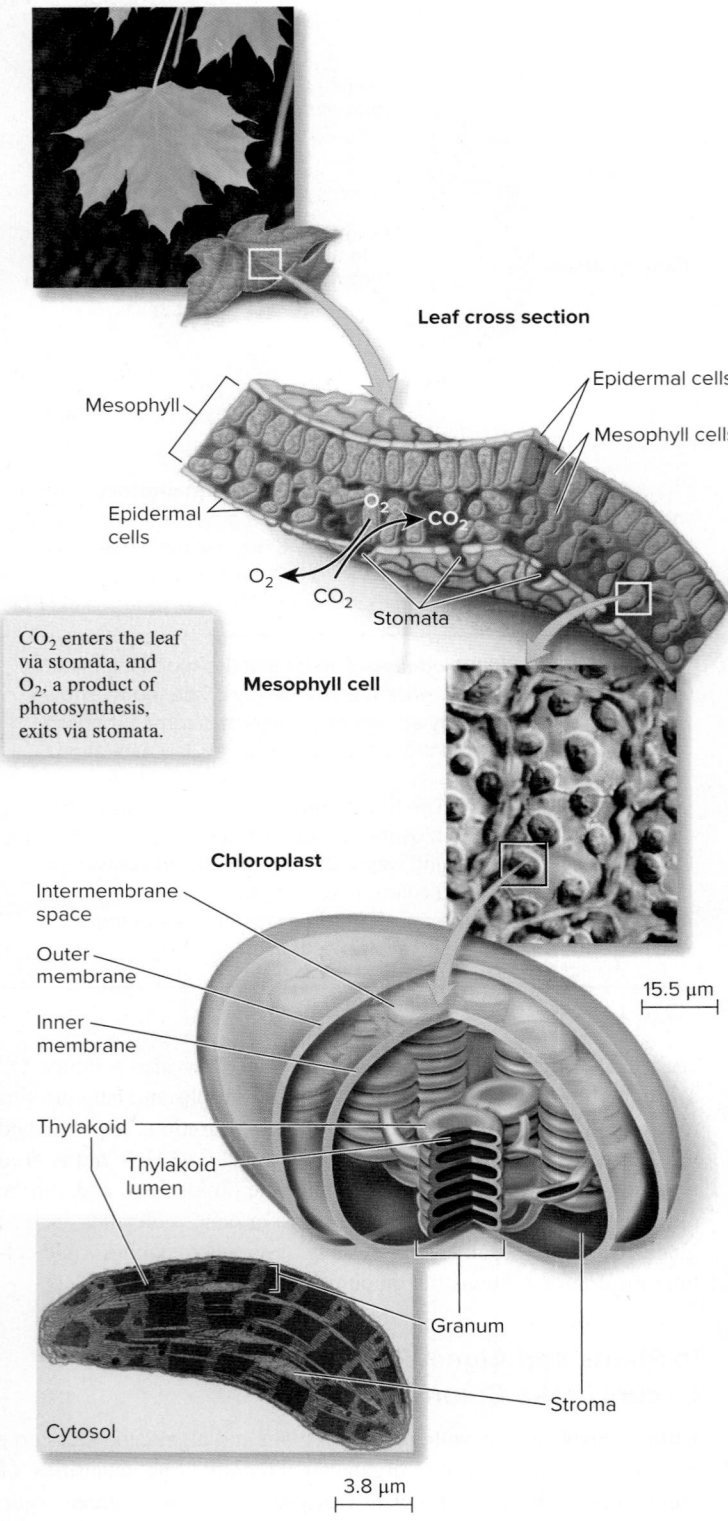

Like a mitochondrion, a chloroplast contains an outer and an inner membrane, with an intermembrane space lying between the two. A third membrane, called the **thylakoid membrane**, contains pigment molecules, including chlorophyll. The thylakoid membrane forms many flattened, fluid-filled tubules called **thylakoids**, each of which encloses a single compartment known as the **thylakoid lumen**. Thylakoids stack on top of each other to form a structure called a **granum** (plural, grana). The **stroma** is the fluid-filled region of the chloroplast between the thylakoid membrane and the inner membrane (see Figure 8.2).

Photosynthesis Occurs in Two Stages: Light Reactions and the Calvin Cycle

How does photosynthesis take place? As mentioned, the process of photosynthesis occurs in two stages called the light reactions and the Calvin cycle. The term photosynthesis is derived from the association between these two stages: Photo refers to the light reactions that capture the energy from sunlight needed for the synthesis of carbohydrates that occurs in the Calvin cycle. The light reactions take place at the thylakoid membrane, and the Calvin cycle occurs in the stroma (**Figure 8.3**).

The light reactions involve an amazing series of energy conversions, starting with light energy and ending with chemical energy that is stored in the form of covalent bonds. The light reactions produce three chemical products: ATP, NADPH, and O_2. ATP and NADPH are energy intermediates that provide the needed

CO₂ enters the leaf via stomata, and O₂, a product of photosynthesis, exits via stomata.

Leaf cross section

Mesophyll

Epidermal cells

Epidermal cells

Mesophyll cells

O_2

CO_2

O_2

CO_2

Stomata

Mesophyll cell

Chloroplast

Intermembrane space

Outer membrane

Inner membrane

15.5 μm

Thylakoid

Thylakoid lumen

Granum

Stroma

Cytosol

3.8 μm

Figure 8.2 Leaf organization. Leaves are composed of layers of cells. The epidermal cells are on the outer surface, both top and bottom, with mesophyll cells sandwiched in the middle. The mesophyll cells contain chloroplasts and are the primary sites of photosynthesis in most plants. (1): ©McGraw-Hill Education/Mark Dierker, photographer; (2): ©Biophoto Associates/SPL/Science Source; (3): ©Omikron/Science Source

Core Skill: Connections Look ahead to Figure 39.17. How many guard cells make up a stoma (plural, stomata)?

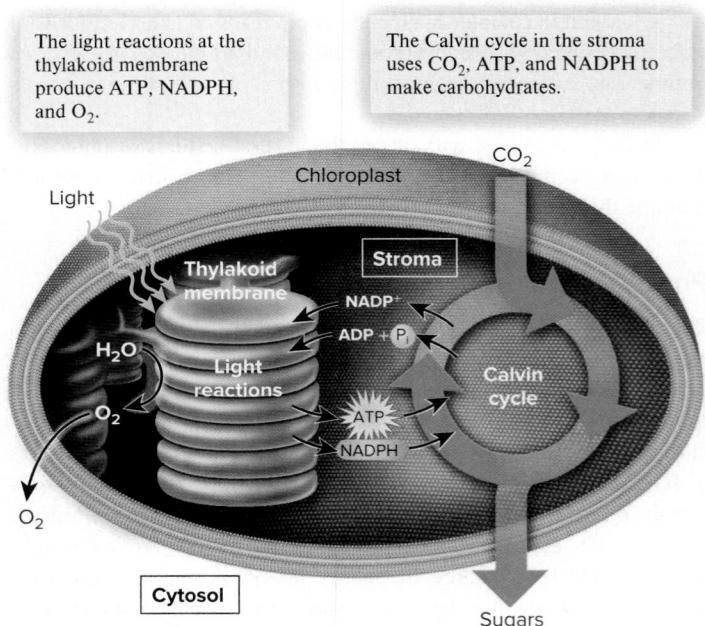

The light reactions at the thylakoid membrane produce ATP, NADPH, and O_2.

The Calvin cycle in the stroma uses CO_2, ATP, and NADPH to make carbohydrates.

Chloroplast

CO_2

Light

Thylakoid membrane

Stroma

$NADP^+$

$ADP + P_i$

H_2O

Light reactions

Calvin cycle

O_2

ATP

NADPH

O_2

Cytosol

Sugars

Figure 8.3 An overview of the two stages of photosynthesis: light reactions and Calvin cycle. The light reactions, through which ATP, NADPH, and O_2 are made, occur at the thylakoid membrane. The Calvin cycle, in which enzymes use ATP and NADPH to incorporate CO_2 into carbohydrates, occurs in the stroma.

Concept Check: *Can the Calvin cycle occur in the dark?*

energy and electrons to drive the Calvin cycle. Like NADH, **NADPH (nicotinamide adenine dinucleotide phosphate)** is an electron carrier that can accept two electrons. Its structure differs from NADH by the presence of an additional phosphate group. The structure of NADH is described in Chapter 6 (see Figure 6.12).

8.2 Reactions That Harness Light Energy

Learning Outcomes:

1. Describe the general properties of light.
2. Explain how pigments absorb light energy, and list the types of pigments found in plants and green algae.
3. Outline the steps by which photosystems II and I capture light energy and produce O_2, ATP, and NADPH.
4. Describe the process of cyclic photophosphorylation, which produces only ATP.

According to the first law of thermodynamics, discussed in Chapter 6, energy cannot be created or destroyed, but it can be transferred from one place to another and transformed from one form to another. During photosynthesis, energy in the form of light is transferred from the Sun, some 92 million miles away, to a pigment molecule in a photosynthetic organism such as a plant. What follows is an interesting series of energy transformations in which light energy is transformed into electrochemical energy and then into energy stored within chemical bonds.

In this section, we will explore this series of transformations, collectively called the light reactions of photosynthesis. We begin by examining the properties of light and then consider the features of chloroplasts that allow them to capture light energy. The remainder of this section focuses on how the light reactions of photosynthesis generate three important products: ATP, NADPH, and O_2.

Light Energy Is a Form of Electromagnetic Radiation

Light is essential to support life on Earth. Light is a type of electromagnetic radiation, so named because it consists of energy in the form of electric and magnetic fields. Electromagnetic radiation travels as waves caused by the oscillation of the electric and magnetic fields. The **wavelength** is the distance between the peaks in a wave pattern. The **electromagnetic spectrum** encompasses all possible wavelengths of electromagnetic radiation, from relatively short wavelengths (gamma rays) to much longer wavelengths (radio waves) (**Figure 8.4**). Visible light is the range of wavelengths detected by the human eye, commonly between 380 and 740 nm. As discussed later, visible light provides the energy to drive photosynthesis.

Physicists have also discovered that light has properties that are characteristic of particles. Albert Einstein formulated the photon theory of light, in which he proposed that light is composed of discrete particles called **photons**—massless particles traveling in a wavelike pattern and moving at the speed of light (about 300 million m/sec). Each photon contains a specific amount of energy. An important

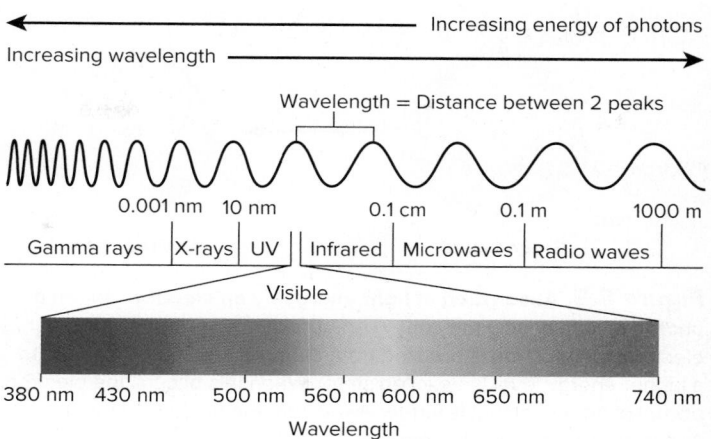

Figure 8.4 The electromagnetic spectrum. The bottom portion of this figure emphasizes visible light—the wavelengths of electromagnetic radiation visible to the human eye. Light in the visible portion of the electromagnetic spectrum drives photosynthesis.

Concept Check: *Which has higher energy, gamma rays or radio waves?*

difference between the various types of electromagnetic radiation, shown in Figure 8.4, is the amount of energy of the photons. Shorter wavelength radiation carries more energy per unit of time than longer wavelength radiation. For example, the photons of gamma rays carry more energy than those of radio waves.

The Sun radiates the entire spectrum of electromagnetic radiation, but the atmosphere prevents much of this radiation from reaching the Earth's surface. For example, the ozone layer forms a thin shield in the upper atmosphere, protecting life on Earth from much of the Sun's ultraviolet (UV) radiation. Even so, a substantial amount of electromagnetic radiation does reach the Earth's surface. The effect of light on living organisms is critically dependent on the energy of the photons that reach them. The photons in gamma rays, X-rays, and UV radiation have very high energy. When molecules in cells absorb such energy, the effects can be devastating. Such radiation can cause mutations in DNA and even lead to cancer. By comparison, the energy of photons in visible light is much less intense. Molecules can absorb this energy in a way that does not cause damage. Next, we will consider how molecules in living cells absorb the energy within visible light.

Pigments Absorb Light Energy

When light strikes an object, one of three things happens. First, light may simply pass through the object. Second, the object may change the path of light toward a different direction. A third possibility is that the object may absorb the light. The term **pigment** is used to describe a molecule that can absorb light energy. When light strikes a pigment, some of the wavelengths of light energy are absorbed, while others are reflected. For example, leaves look green to us because they reflect light energy with wavelengths in the green region of the visible spectrum. Various pigments in the leaves absorb the energy of other wavelengths. At the extremes of color reflection are white and black. A white object reflects nearly all of

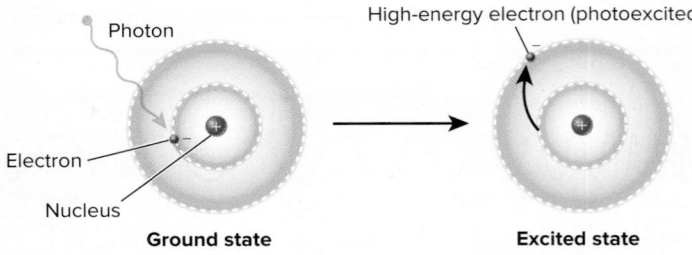

Figure 8.5   Absorption of light energy by an electron. When a photon of light having the correct amount of energy strikes an electron, the electron is boosted from the ground (unexcited) state to a higher energy level (an excited state). When this occurs, the electron occupies an orbital that is farther away from the nucleus of the atom. At this farther distance, the electron is held less firmly and is considered unstable.

Concept Check: *Describe the three events that can enable a photoexcited electron to become more stable.*

the visible light energy falling on it, whereas a black object absorbs nearly all of the light energy. This is why it is coolest to wear white clothes on a sunny, hot day.

What do we mean when we say that light energy is absorbed? Light energy in the visible spectrum can be absorbed by an atom when it boosts an electron to a higher energy level (**Figure 8.5**). The location in which an electron is found is called its orbital. Electrons in different orbitals possess different amounts of energy. For an electron to absorb light energy and be boosted to an orbital with a higher energy, it must overcome the difference in energy between the orbital it is in and the orbital to which it is going. For this to happen, an electron must absorb a photon that contains precisely that amount of energy. Different pigment molecules contain a variety of electrons that can be shifted to different energy levels. The wavelength of light that a pigment absorbs depends on the amount of energy needed to boost an electron to a higher orbital.

After an electron absorbs energy, it is said to be in an excited state. Usually, this is an unstable condition. To become stable again, one of four things can happen.

- To become stable, an excited electron may drop back down to a lower energy level and release heat. For example, on a sunny day, the sidewalk heats up because it absorbs light energy that is released as heat.

- Alternatively, an electron can become stable by releasing energy in the form of light. Certain organisms, such as jellyfish, possess molecules that make them glow. This glowing is due to the release of light when electrons drop down to lower energy levels, a phenomenon called fluorescence.

- An excited electron can transfer its extra energy to an electron in a nearby molecule, a process called **resonance energy transfer**.

- Rather than releasing energy or transferring it to another molecule, an excited electron can be removed from the molecule in which it is unstable and transferred to another molecule where it is stable. When this occurs, the energy in the electron is said to be captured, because the electron does not readily drop down to a lower energy level and release heat or light.

Plants Contain Different Types of Photosynthetic Pigments

In plants, different pigment molecules absorb the light energy used to drive photosynthesis. Two types of chlorophyll pigments, termed **chlorophyll *a*** and **chlorophyll *b***, are found in green plants and green algae. Their structure was determined in the 1930s by German chemist Hans Fischer (**Figure 8.6a**). In the chloroplast, both chlorophylls *a* and *b* are bound to integral membrane proteins in the thylakoid membrane.

The chlorophylls contain a porphyrin ring and a phytol tail. A magnesium ion (Mg^{2+}) is bound to the porphyrin ring. An electron in the porphyrin ring is able to hop from one atom in the ring to another. Because this electron isn't restricted to a single atom, it is called a delocalized electron. The delocalized electron can absorb light energy. The phytol tail in chlorophyll is a long hydrocarbon chain that is hydrophobic. Its function is to anchor the pigment to the surface of hydrophobic proteins within the thylakoid membrane of chloroplasts.

Carotenoids are another type of pigment found in chloroplasts (**Figure 8.6b**). These pigments impart a color that ranges from yellow to orange to red. Carotenoids are often the major pigments in flowers and fruits. In leaves, the more abundant chlorophylls usually mask the colors of carotenoids. In temperate climates where the leaves change colors, the quantity of chlorophyll in the leaf declines during autumn. The carotenoids become readily visible and produce the yellows, oranges, and reds of autumn foliage.

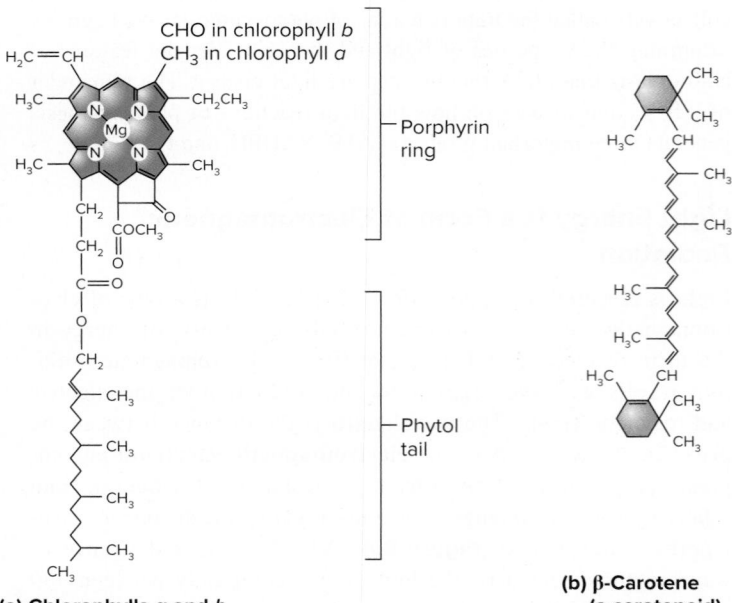

(a) Chlorophylls *a* and *b*

(b) β-Carotene (a carotenoid)

Figure 8.6   Structures of pigment molecules. **(a)** The structure of chlorophylls *a* and *b*. As indicated, chlorophylls *a* and *b* differ only at a single site, at which chlorophyll *a* has a —CH_3 group and chlorophyll *b* has a —CHO group. **(b)** The structure of β-carotene, an example of a carotenoid. The green- and orange-shaded areas of the structures in parts (a) and (b) are regions where a delocalized electron can hop from one atom to another.

An **absorption spectrum** is a graph that plots a pigment's light absorption as a function of the light's wavelength. Each of the photosynthetic pigments shown in **Figure 8.7a** absorbs light in different regions of the visible spectrum. The absorption spectra of chlorophylls *a* and *b* are slightly different, though both chlorophylls absorb light most strongly in the red and violet parts of the visible spectrum and absorb green light poorly. Green light is reflected, which is why leaves appear green during the growing season. Carotenoids absorb light in the blue and blue-green regions of the visible spectrum, reflecting yellow and red.

Why do plants have different pigments? Having different pigments allows plants to absorb light at many different wavelengths. In this way, plants are more efficient at capturing the energy in sunlight. This phenomenon is highlighted in an **action spectrum**, which plots the rate of photosynthesis as a function of wavelength (**Figure 8.7b**). The highest rates of photosynthesis in green plants correlate with the wavelengths that are strongly absorbed by the chlorophylls and carotenoids. Photosynthesis is poor in the green region of the spectrum, because these pigments do not readily absorb this wavelength of light.

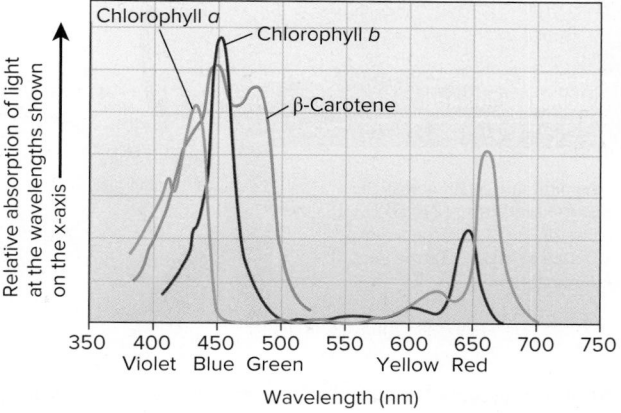

(a) Absorption spectra

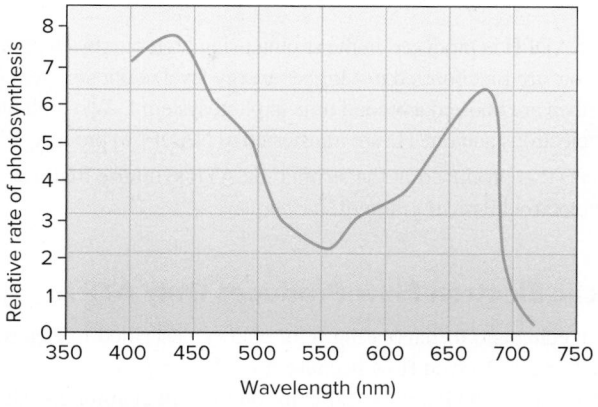

(b) Action spectrum

Figure 8.7 Properties of pigment function: absorption and action spectra. (a) These absorption spectra show the absorption of light by chlorophyll *a*, chlorophyll *b*, and β-carotene. **(b)** An action spectrum of photosynthesis depicting the relative rate of photosynthesis in green plants at different wavelengths of light.

Concept Check: *What is the advantage of having different pigment molecules?*

Photosystems II and I Work Together to Produce ATP and NADPH via Linear Electron Flow

A key feature of photosynthesis is the ability of pigments to absorb light energy and transfer it to other molecules that can hold the energy in a stable fashion and ultimately produce energy-intermediate molecules that can do cellular work. Let's now consider how chloroplasts capture light energy. The thylakoid membranes of the chloroplast contain two distinct complexes of proteins and pigment molecules called **photosystem I (PSI)** and **photosystem II (PSII)** (**Figure 8.8**). Photosystem I was discovered before photosystem II, but photosystem II is the initial step in photosynthesis. Working together, these two systems enable chloroplasts to capture light energy and synthesize ATP, NADPH, and O_2.

Events within Photosystem II   As described in step 1a of Figure 8.8, light excites electrons in pigment molecules, such as chlorophylls, which are located in a region of PSII called a light-harvesting complex. Rather than releasing their energy in the form of heat, the excited electrons begin to follow a path shown by the red arrow. Initially, the excited electrons move sequentially from a pigment molecule called P680 in PSII to other electron carriers called pheophytin (Pp), Q_A, and Q_B. PSII also oxidizes water, which generates O_2 and adds H^+ into the thylakoid lumen (see step 1b of Figure 8.8). The electrons released from oxidized water molecules replenish the electrons that are removed from P680.

Electron Transport Chain   Via Q_B, the electrons exit PSII and enter an electron transport chain (ETC)—a series of electron carriers—located in the thylakoid membrane (see Figure 8.8, step 1a). This ETC functions similarly to the one found in mitochondria. From Q_B, an electron goes to a cytochrome complex; then to plastocyanin (Pc), a small protein; and then to photosystem I. Along its journey from photosystem II to photosystem I, the electron releases some of its energy at particular steps and is transferred to the next component that has a higher electronegativity. The energy released is harnessed to pump H^+ into the thylakoid lumen.

Photosystem I and NADPH Synthesis   A key role of photosystem I is to make NADPH (see Figure 8.8, steps 2 and 3). When light strikes the light-harvesting complex of photosystem I, this energy is also transferred to a reaction center, where a high-energy electron is removed from a pigment molecule, designated P700, and transferred to a primary electron acceptor. A protein called ferredoxin (Fd) can accept two high-energy electrons, one at a time, from the primary electron acceptor. Fd then transfers the two electrons to the enzyme NADP$^+$ reductase. This enzyme transfers the two electrons to NADP$^+$, which also accepts an H^+ to produce NADPH. The formation of NADPH results in fewer H^+ in the stroma. The combined action of photosystem II and photosystem I is termed **linear electron flow** because the electrons move linearly from PSII to PSI and ultimately reduce NADP$^+$ to NADPH.

A key difference between PSII and PSI lies in the source of the electrons received by their respective pigment molecules. An oxidized pigment in PSII called P680 receives an electron from water. By comparison, an oxidized pigment in PSI called P700 receives an electron from the protein Pc. Therefore, PSI does not need to split water to reduce this pigment and does not generate oxygen.

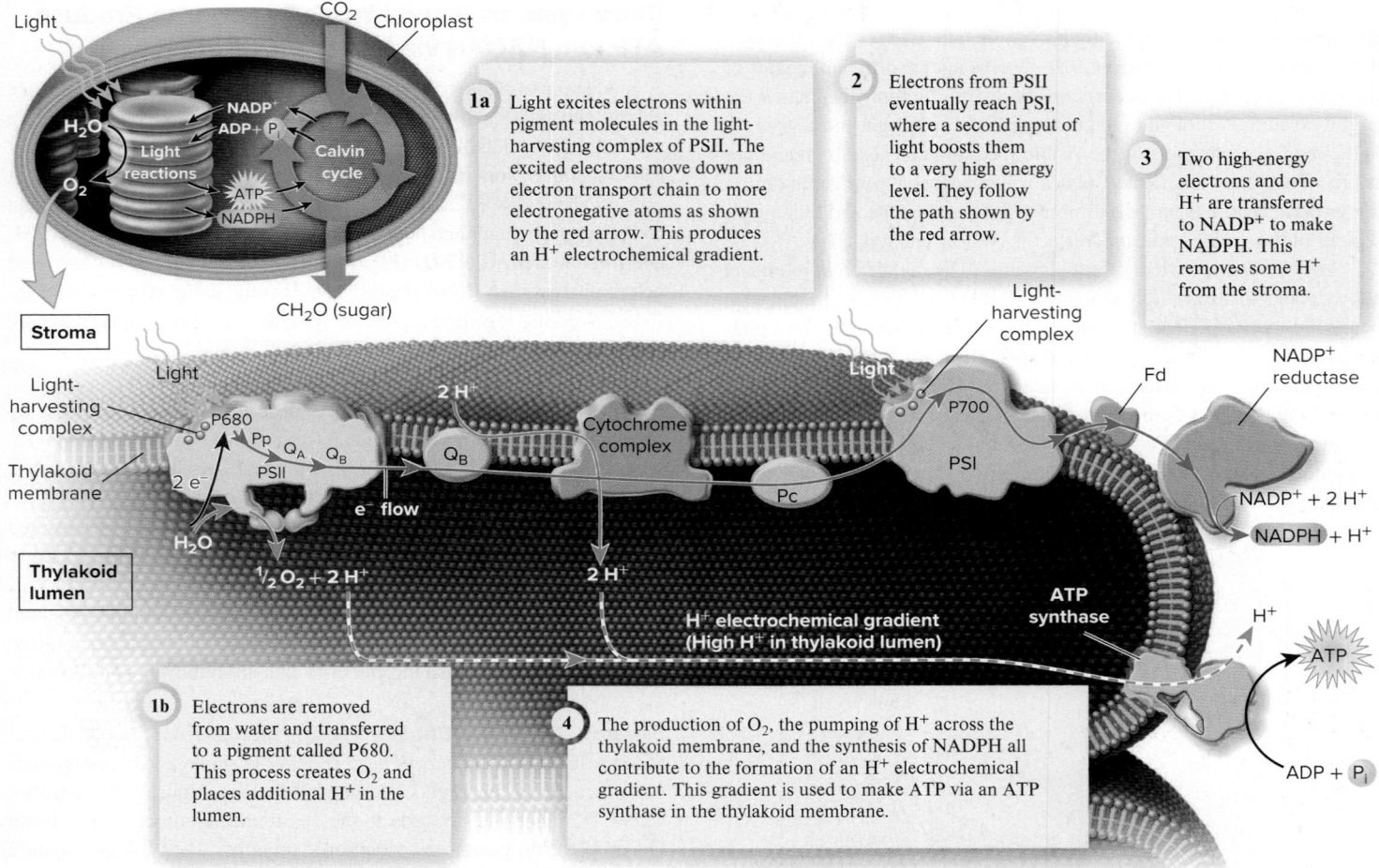

Figure 8.8 **The synthesis of ATP, NADPH, and O$_2$ by the concerted actions of photosystems II and I.** The movement of electrons from photosystem II to photosystem I to NADPH is called linear electron flow.

Concept Check: *Are ATP, NADPH, and O$_2$ produced in the stroma or in the thylakoid lumen?*

ATP Synthesis   The synthesis of ATP in chloroplasts is achieved by a chemiosmotic mechanism called **photophosphorylation**, which is similar to the oxidative phosphorylation used to make ATP in mitochondria. In chloroplasts, ATP synthesis is driven by the flow of H$^+$ from the thylakoid lumen into the stroma via ATP synthase (Figure 8.8, step 4). The light reactions produce an H$^+$ electrochemical gradient in which more H$^+$ is in the thylakoid lumen and less in the stroma. The gradient is generated in three ways:

1. The splitting of water places H$^+$ in the thylakoid lumen.
2. The movement of high-energy electrons along the ETC from photosystem II to photosystem I pumps H$^+$ into the thylakoid lumen.
3. The formation of NADPH consumes H$^+$ in the stroma.

Products of Photosynthesis   In summary, the steps of the light reactions of photosynthesis produce three chemical products: O$_2$, NADPH, and ATP:

1. O$_2$ is produced in the thylakoid lumen by the oxidation of water by photosystem II. Two electrons are removed from water, producing 2 H$^+$ and $^1/_2$ O$_2$. The two electrons are transferred to P680 molecules.

2. NADPH is produced in the stroma using high-energy electrons that are first boosted to a higher energy level in photosystem II and then are boosted a second time in photosystem I. Two high-energy electrons and one H$^+$ are transferred to NADP$^+$ to produce NADPH.

3. ATP is produced in the stroma via ATP synthase that uses an H$^+$ electrochemical gradient.

Cyclic Electron Flow Produces Only ATP

The mechanism of harvesting light energy described in Figure 8.8 is called linear electron flow because it is a linear process. This electron flow produces ATP and NADPH in roughly equal amounts. However, as we will see later, the Calvin cycle uses more ATP than NADPH. How can plant cells avoid making too much NADPH and not enough ATP? In 1959, Daniel Arnon discovered a pattern of electron flow that is cyclic and generates only ATP (**Figure 8.9**). Arnon termed the process **cyclic photophosphorylation** because (1) the path of electrons is cyclic, (2) light energizes the electrons, and (3) ATP is made via the phosphorylation of ADP. Due to the path of electrons, the mechanism is also called **cyclic electron flow**.

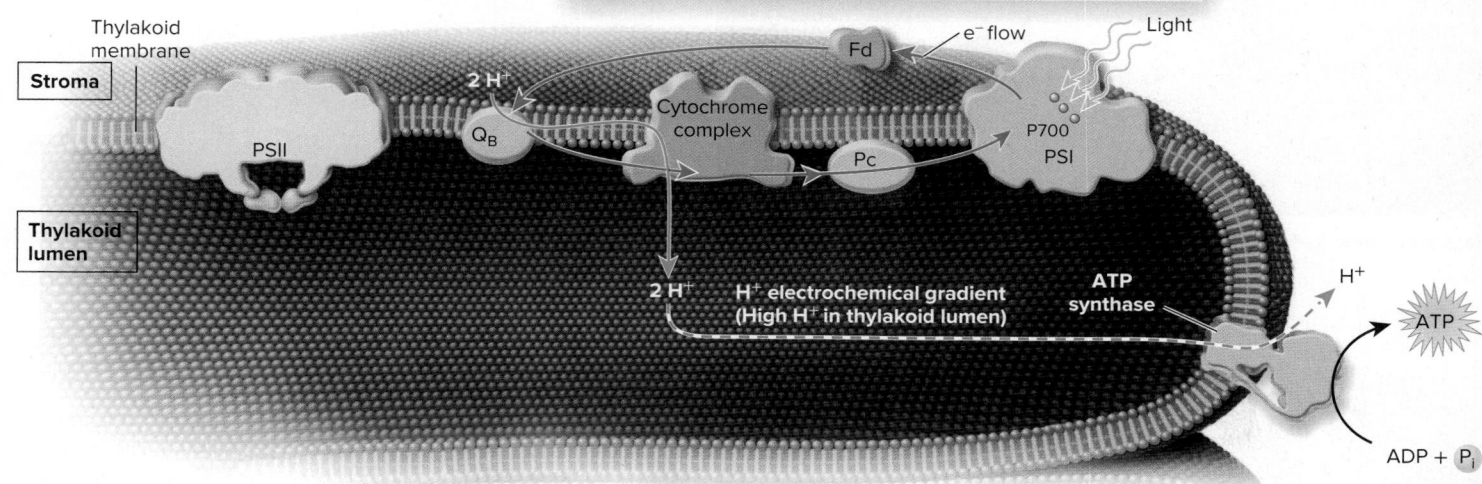

When light strikes photosystem I, electrons are excited and sent to ferredoxin (Fd). From Fd, the electrons are then transferred to Q_B, to the cytochrome complex, to plastocyanin (Pc), and back to photosystem I. This produces an H^+ electrochemical gradient, which is used to make ATP via ATP synthase.

Figure 8.9 Cyclic photophosphorylation. In this process, electrons follow a cyclic path that is powered by photosystem I (PSI). This contributes to the formation of an H^+ electrochemical gradient, which is then used by ATP synthase to make ATP.

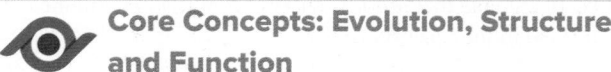 *Why does cyclic photophosphorylation provide an advantage to a plant over using only linear electron flow?*

When light strikes photosystem I, high-energy electrons are sent to the primary electron acceptor and then to ferredoxin (Fd). The key difference in cyclic photophosphorylation is that the high-energy electrons are transferred from Fd to Q_B. From Q_B, the electrons then go to the cytochrome complex, then to plastocyanin (P_c), and back to photosystem I. As the electrons travel along this cyclic route, they release energy, and some of this energy is used to transport H^+ into the thylakoid lumen. The resulting H^+ gradient drives the synthesis of ATP via ATP synthase.

Cyclic photophosphorylation is favored when the level of $NADP^+$ is low and NADPH is high. Under these conditions, there is sufficient NADPH to run the Calvin cycle, which is described later. Alternatively, when $NADP^+$ is high and NADPH is low, linear electron flow is favored, so more NADPH can be made. Cyclic photophosphorylation is also favored when ATP levels are low.

Core Concepts: Evolution, Structure and Function

The Cytochrome Complexes of Mitochondria and Chloroplasts Contain Evolutionarily Related Proteins

A recurring theme in cell biology is that evolution has resulted in groups of genes that encode proteins that play similar but specialized roles in cells—an example of descent with modification. When two or more genes are similar because they are derived from the same ancestral gene, they are called **homologous genes**. As discussed in Chapter 22, homologous genes encode proteins that have similar amino acid sequences and often perform similar functions.

A comparison of the electron transport chains of mitochondria and chloroplasts reveals homologous genes. In particular, let's consider the cytochrome complex found in the thylakoid membrane of plants and algae, called cytochrome b_6-f (**Figure 8.10a**), and the complex cytochrome b-c_1, which is found in the ETC of mitochondria (**Figure 8.10b**; also refer back to Figure 7.8). Both of these cytochrome complexes are composed of several proteins. One of the proteins is called cytochrome b_6 in cytochrome b_6-f and cytochrome b in cytochrome b-c_1.

By analyzing the sequences of the genes that encode these proteins, researchers discovered that cytochrome b_6 and cytochrome b are homologous proteins. These proteins carry out similar functions: Both of them accept electrons from a quinone (Q_B, or ubiquinone), and both donate an electron to another protein within their respective complexes (cytochrome f or cytochrome c_1). Likewise, both proteins function as H^+ pumps that capture some of the energy that is released from electrons to transport H^+ across the membrane. In this way, evolution has produced a family of cytochrome b proteins that play similar but specialized roles.

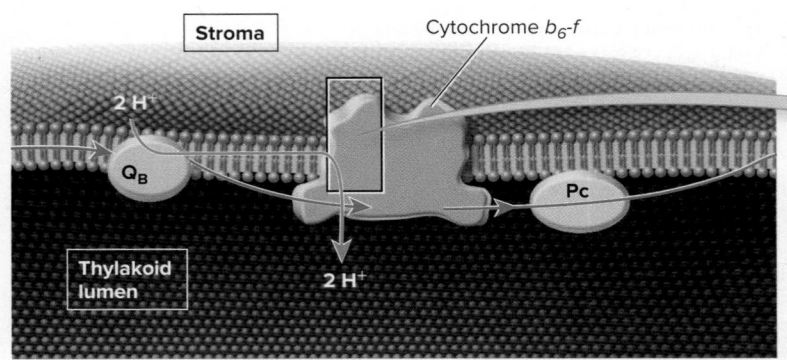

(a) Cytochrome b_6-f in the chloroplast

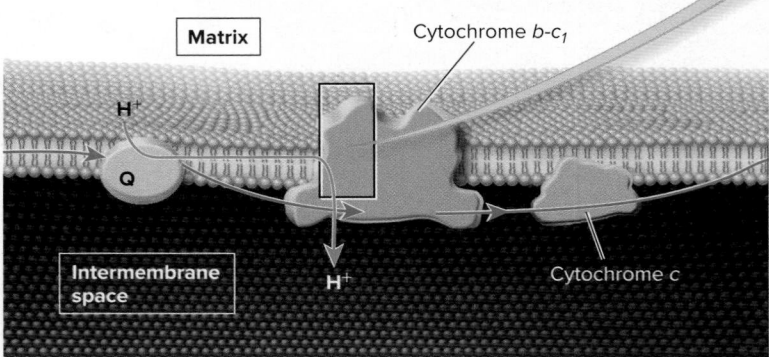

(b) Cytochrome b-c_1 in the mitochondrion

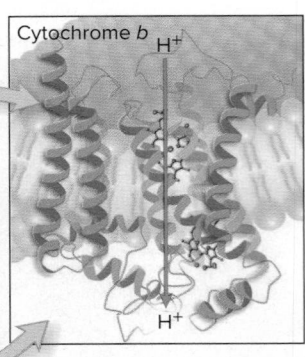

Figure 8.10 Homologous proteins in the electron transport chains of chloroplasts and mitochondria. (a) Cytochrome b_6-f is a complex of proteins involved in electron and H^+ transport in chloroplasts, and **(b)** cytochrome b-c_1 is a complex of proteins involved in electron and H^+ transport in mitochondria. These complexes contain homologous proteins designated cytochrome b_6 in chloroplasts and cytochrome b in mitochondria. The inset shows the three-dimensional structure of cytochrome b, which was determined by X-ray crystallography. It is an integral membrane protein with several transmembrane helices and two heme groups, which are prosthetic groups involved in electron transfer. The structure of cytochrome b_6 has also been determined and found to be very similar.

Concept Check: *Explain why the three-dimensional structures of cytochrome b and cytochrome b_6 are very similar.*

8.3 Molecular Features of Photosystems

Learning Outcomes:

1. Explain how PSII absorbs and captures light energy and how it produces O_2.
2. Diagram the variation in the energy of an electron as it moves from PSII to PSI to NADP+.

The previous section provided an overview of how chloroplasts absorb light energy and produce ATP, NADPH, and O_2. As you have learned, two photosystems—PSI and PSII—play critical roles in two aspects of photosynthesis. First, both PSI and PSII absorb light energy and capture that energy in the form of excited electrons. Second, PSII oxidizes water, thereby producing O_2. In this section, we will take a closer look at how these events occur at the molecular level.

Photosystem II Captures Light Energy and Produces O_2

PSI and PSII have two main components: a light-harvesting complex and a reaction center. **Figure 8.11** shows how these components function in PSII.

Absorption of Energy by the Light-Harvesting Complex and Its Transfer to P680 via Resonance Energy Transfer In 1932, American biologist Robert Emerson and an undergraduate student,

William Arnold, originally discovered the **light-harvesting complex** in the thylakoid membrane. It is composed of several dozen pigment molecules that are anchored to transmembrane proteins. The role of the complex is to directly absorb photons of light. When a pigment molecule absorbs a photon, an electron is boosted to a higher energy level. As shown in Figure 8.11, the energy (not the electron itself) is transferred to adjacent pigment molecules by a process called resonance energy transfer. The energy may be transferred among multiple pigment molecules until it is eventually transferred to a special pigment molecule designated P680, which is located within the reaction center of PSII. The P680 pigment is so named because it can directly absorb light at a wavelength of 680 nm. However, P680 is more commonly excited by resonance energy transfer from a chlorophyll pigment in the light-harvesting complex. In either case, when an electron in P680 is excited, the molecule is designated P680*. The light-harvesting complex is also called the antenna complex because it acts like an antenna that absorbs energy from light and funnels that energy to P680 in the reaction center.

Rapid Transfer of a High-Energy Electron from P680* to the Primary Electron Acceptor A high-energy (photoexcited) electron in a pigment molecule is very unstable. It may abruptly release its energy by giving off heat or light. Unlike the pigments in the light-harvesting complex that undergo resonance energy transfer, P680* can actually release its high-energy electron and become P680+.

$$P680^* \rightarrow P680^+ + e^-$$

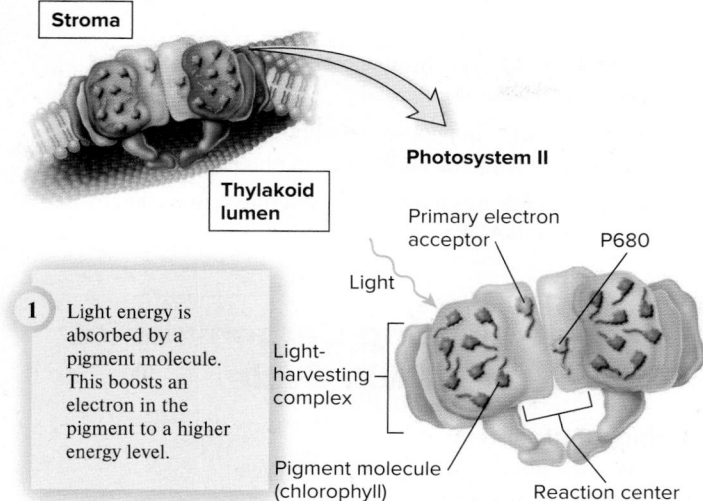

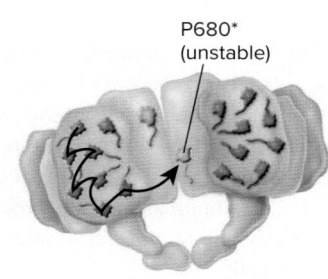

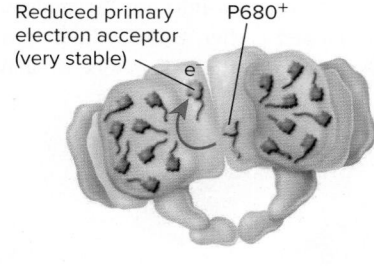

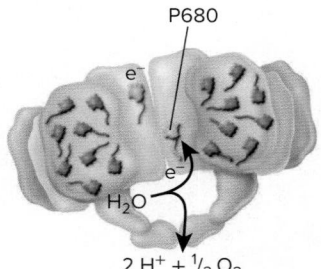

1 Light energy is absorbed by a pigment molecule. This boosts an electron in the pigment to a higher energy level.

2 Energy is transferred among pigment molecules via resonance energy transfer until it reaches P680, converting it to P680*.

3 The high-energy electron on P680* is transferred to the primary electron acceptor (pheophytin), where it is very stable. P680* becomes P680+.

4 A low-energy electron from water is transferred to P680+ to convert it to P680. O_2 is produced.

Figure 8.11 A closer look at how photosystem II harvests light energy and oxidizes water. Note: Two electrons are released during the oxidation of water, but they are transferred one at a time to P680+.

 Core Concept: Energy and Matter The pigments in PSII absorb light energy that is captured in a stable form when an excited electron is transferred to the primary electron acceptor (pheophytin).

The role of the reaction center is to quickly remove the high-energy electron from P680* and transfer it to another molecule, where the electron is stable. This molecule is called the **primary electron acceptor** (see Figure 8.11). The transfer of the electron from P680* to the primary electron acceptor is remarkably fast. It occurs in less than a few picoseconds! (One picosecond equals one-trillionth of a second, or 10^{-12} sec.) Because this occurs so quickly, the excited electron does not have much time to release its energy in the form of heat or light.

When the primary electron acceptor (pheophytin) has received this high-energy electron, the light energy has been captured and can be used to perform cellular work. As discussed earlier, the work it performs is to synthesize the energy intermediates ATP and NADPH (look back at Figure 8.8).

Transfer of a Low-Energy Electron from Water to P680+ Let's now consider what happens to P680+, which has given up its high-energy electron. After P680+ is formed, the electron that has been removed must be replaced so that P680 can function again. Therefore, another role of the reaction center is to replace the electron that is removed when P680* becomes P680+. This missing electron of P680+ is replaced with a low-energy electron from water (see Figure 8.11).

$$H_2O \rightarrow 2H^+ + \tfrac{1}{2}O_2 + 2e^-$$
$$2\,P680^+ + 2e^- \rightarrow 2\,P680$$
$$(\text{from water})$$

The oxidation of water results in the formation of oxygen gas (O_2), which is used by many organisms for cellular respiration. Photosystem II is the only known protein complex that can oxidize water, resulting in the release of O_2 into the atmosphere.

BIO TIPS **THE QUESTION** *Describe the roles of the light-harvesting complex, P680, and the primary electron acceptor during the absorption of light energy by photosystem II (PSII). At which step is the light energy captured?*

TOPIC *What topic in biology does this question address?* The topic is the absorption of light by PSII. More specifically, the question asks you to describe the various roles played by the light-harvesting complex, P680, and the primary electron acceptor.

INFORMATION *What information do you know based on the question and your understanding of the topic?* In the question, you are reminded that PSII has a light-harvesting complex, P680, and a primary electron acceptor. From your understanding of the topic, you may remember that light absorption begins at the light-harvesting complex, which funnels energy to P680. The energy transforms P680 to P680*, which then transfers a high-energy electron to the primary electron acceptor.

PROBLEM-SOLVING STRATEGY *Sort out the steps in a complicated process. Compare and contrast.* To begin to solve this problem, it may be helpful to review the steps of the light-absorption process shown in Figure 8.11. As you do so, compare and contrast the roles of the light-harvesting complex, P680, and the primary electron acceptor.

ANSWER *Light-harvesting complex: The role of the light-harvesting complex is to absorb light. Because it is composed of many pigment molecules (chlorophylls and β-carotene), the light-harvesting complex is the most likely place for visible light to be absorbed. When a pigment molecule absorbs light, an electron is boosted to a higher energy level, and that energy is transferred via resonance energy transfer to P680.*

P680: The role of P680 is to provide a link between the light-harvesting complex and the primary electron acceptor. Although P680 can directly absorb light, P680 is far more likely to gain energy from the light-harvesting complex, which converts it to P680*. The high-energy electron of P680* is then transferred to the primary electron acceptor.

Primary electron acceptor: The role of the primary electron acceptor is to capture the light energy. The high-energy electron of P680* is unstable. However, when it is transferred to the primary electron acceptor, the electron becomes stable, meaning that it will not drop down to a lower energy level.

Electrons Vary in Energy as They Move from Photosystem II to Photosystem I to NADP⁺

In 1960, Robin Hill and Fay Bendall proposed that the light reactions of photosynthesis involve two photoactivation events. According to their model, known as the **Z scheme**, an electron proceeds through a series of energy changes during photosynthesis (**Figure 8.12**). The Z refers to the zigzag shape of this energy curve. Based on our modern understanding of photosynthesis, we now know that these events involve increases and decreases in the energy of an electron as it moves linearly from photosystem II through photosystem I to NADP⁺.

- An electron on a nonexcited pigment molecule in photosystem II has the lowest energy.

- In photosystem II, light boosts such an electron to a much higher energy level.

- As the electron travels from photosystem II to photosystem I, some of the energy is released.

- The input of light in photosystem I boosts the electron to an even higher energy than it attained in photosystem II.

- The electron releases a little energy before it is eventually transferred to NADP⁺.

8.4 Synthesizing Carbohydrates via the Calvin Cycle

Learning Outcomes:

1. Outline the three phases of the Calvin cycle.
2. **CoreSKILL »** Analyze the results of Calvin and Benson, and explain how they identified the components of the Calvin cycle.

In the previous sections, we learned how the light reactions of photosynthesis produce ATP, NADPH, and O_2. We will now turn our attention to the second phase of photosynthesis, the Calvin cycle, in which ATP and NADPH are used to make carbohydrates. The Calvin cycle consists of a series of steps that occur in a metabolic cycle. In plants and algae, it occurs in the stroma of chloroplasts. In photosynthetic bacteria, the Calvin cycle occurs in the cytoplasm of the cell.

The Calvin cycle takes CO_2 from the atmosphere and incorporates the carbon into organic molecules, namely, carbohydrates. As mentioned earlier, carbohydrates are critical for two reasons. First, they provide the precursors to make the organic molecules and

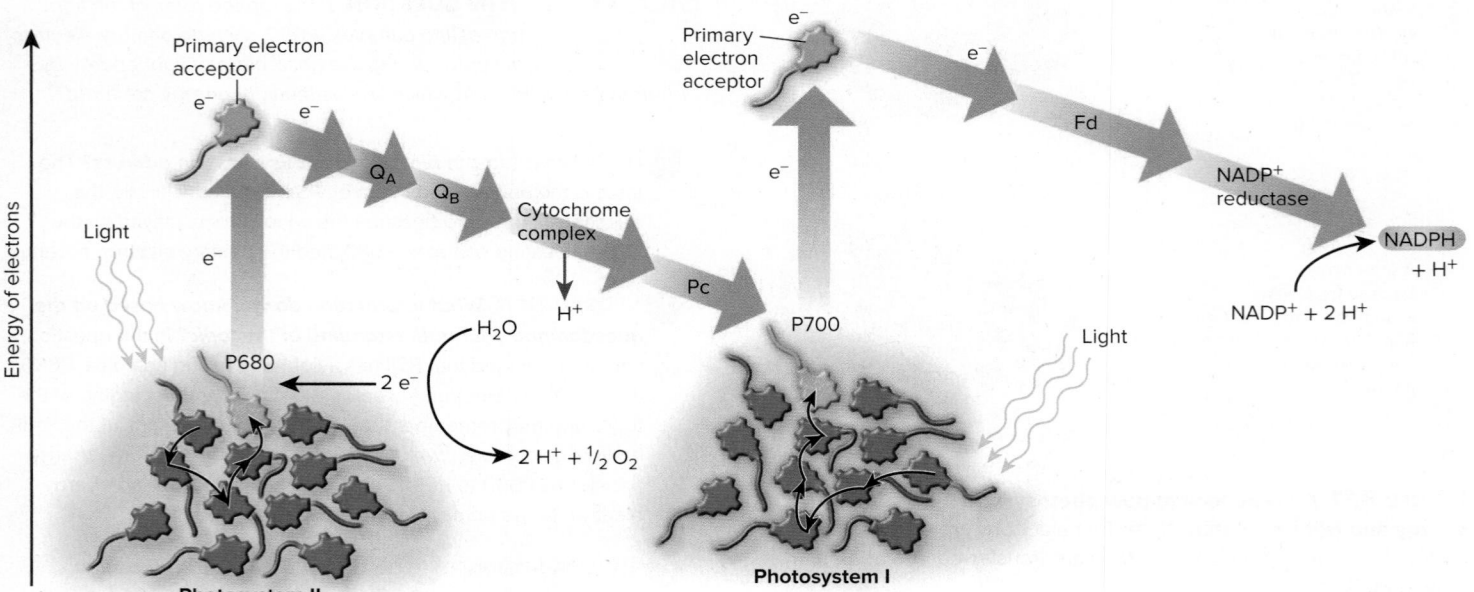

Figure 8.12   The Z scheme, showing the energy of an electron moving from photosystem II to NADP⁺. The oxidation of water releases two electrons that travel one at a time from photosystem II to NADP⁺. As seen here, the input of light boosts the energy of the electron twice. At the end of the pathway, two electrons are used to make NADPH.

Concept Check: *During its journey from photosystem II to NADP⁺, at what point does an electron have the highest amount of energy?*

macromolecules of nearly all living cells. The second key reason is the storage of energy. The Calvin cycle produces carbohydrates, which store energy. These carbohydrates are accumulated inside plant cells. When a plant is in the dark and not carrying out photosynthesis, the stored carbohydrates are used as a source of energy. Similarly, when an animal consumes a plant, it uses the carbohydrates as an energy source.

In this section, we will examine the three phases of the Calvin cycle. We will also explore the experimental approach of Melvin Calvin and his colleagues that enabled them to elucidate the steps of this cycle.

The Calvin Cycle Incorporates CO$_2$ into a Carbohydrate

The Calvin cycle, also called the Calvin-Benson cycle, was determined by chemists Melvin Calvin and Andrew Adam Benson and their colleagues in the 1940s and 1950s. This cycle requires a massive input of energy. For every 6 carbon dioxide molecules that are

incorporated into a carbohydrate such as glucose (C$_6$H$_{12}$O$_6$), 18 ATP molecules are hydrolyzed and 12 NADPH molecules are oxidized:

$$6 \text{ CO}_2 + 12 \text{ H}_2\text{O} \rightarrow \text{C}_6\text{H}_{12}\text{O}_6 + 6 \text{ O}_2 + 6 \text{ H}_2\text{O}$$
$$18 \text{ ATP} + 18 \text{ H}_2\text{O} \rightarrow 18 \text{ ADP} + 18 \text{ P}_i$$
$$12 \text{ NADPH} \rightarrow 12 \text{ NADP}^+ + 12 \text{ H}^+ + 24 \text{ e}^-$$

Although biologists commonly describe glucose as a product of photosynthesis, glucose is not directly made by the Calvin cycle. Instead, molecules of glyceraldehyde-3-phosphate, which are products of the Calvin cycle, are used as starting materials for the synthesis of glucose and other molecules, including sucrose. After glucose molecules are made, they may be linked together to form a polymer of glucose called starch, which is stored in the chloroplast for later use. Alternatively, the disaccharide sucrose may be made and transported out of the leaf to other parts of the plant.

The Calvin cycle can be divided into three phases: carbon fixation, reduction and carbohydrate production, and regeneration of ribulose bisphosphate (RuBP) (**Figure 8.13**).

Figure 8.13 The Calvin cycle. This cycle has three phases: (1) carbon fixation, (2) reduction and carbohydrate production, and (3) regeneration of RuBP.

Concept Check: *Why is NADPH needed during this cycle?*

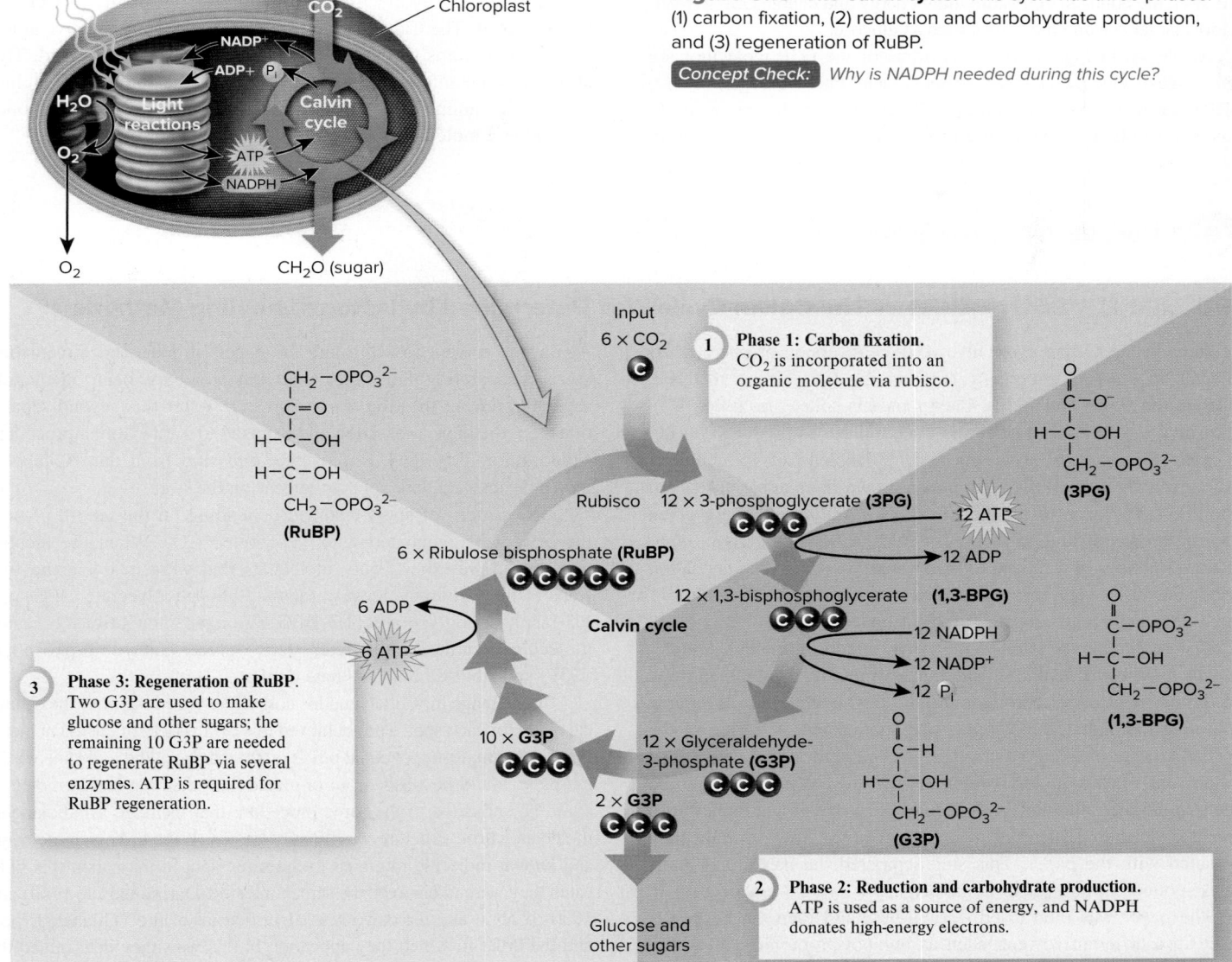

Carbon Fixation (Phase 1)   During **carbon fixation**, CO_2 is incorporated into RuBP, a five-carbon sugar. The term fixation means that the carbon has been removed from the atmosphere and incorporated into an organic molecule that is not a gas. More specifically, the product of this reaction in phase 1 is a six-carbon intermediate that immediately splits in half to form two molecules of 3-phosphoglycerate (3PG). The enzyme that catalyzes this step is named RuBP carboxylase/oxygenase, or **rubisco**. It is the most abundant protein in chloroplasts and perhaps the most abundant protein on Earth! This observation underscores the massive amount of carbon fixation that happens in the biosphere.

Reduction and Carbohydrate Production (Phase 2)   In the second phase of the Calvin cycle, ATP is used to convert 3PG to 1,3-bisphosphoglycerate (1,3-BPG). Next, electrons from NADPH reduce 1,3-BPG to glyceraldehyde-3-phosphate (G3P). G3P is a carbohydrate with three carbon atoms. The key difference between 3PG and G3P is that 3PG has a C—O bond, whereas the analogous carbon in G3P has a C—H bond (see Figure 8.13). The C—H bond results when the G3P molecule is reduced by the addition of two electrons from NADPH. Compared with 3PG, the bonds in G3P store more energy and enable G3P to readily form larger organic molecules such as glucose.

As shown in Figure 8.13, only some of the G3P molecules are used to make glucose or other carbohydrates. Phase 1 begins with 6 RuBP molecules and 6 CO_2 molecules. Twelve G3P molecules are made at the end of phase 2, and only 2 of these G3P molecules are used in carbohydrate production. As described next, the other 10 G3P molecules are needed to keep the Calvin cycle turning by regenerating RuBP.

Regeneration of RuBP (Phase 3)   In the last phase of the Calvin cycle, a series of enzymatic steps converts the 10 G3P molecules into 6 RuBP molecules, using 6 molecules of ATP. After the RuBP molecules are regenerated, they serve as acceptors for CO_2, thereby allowing the cycle to continue.

As we have just seen, the Calvin cycle begins by using carbon from an inorganic source, that is, CO_2, and ends with organic molecules that will be used by the plant to make other molecules. You may be wondering why CO_2 molecules cannot be directly linked to form these larger molecules. The answer lies in the number of electrons that are around the carbon atoms. In CO_2, the carbon atom is considered electron poor. Oxygen is a very electronegative atom that monopolizes the electrons it shares with other atoms. In a covalent bond between carbon and oxygen, the shared electrons are closer to the oxygen atom.

By comparison, in an organic molecule, the carbon atom is electron-rich. During the Calvin cycle, ATP provides energy and NADPH donates high-energy electrons, so the carbon originally in CO_2 has been reduced. The Calvin cycle combines less electronegative atoms with carbon atoms so that C—H and C—C bonds are formed. This allows the eventual synthesis of larger organic molecules, including glucose, amino acids, and so on. In addition, the covalent bonds within these molecules store large amounts of energy.

 **Core Skill: Process of Science**

Feature Investigation | The Calvin Cycle Was Determined by Isotope-Labeling Methods

The steps in the Calvin cycle involve the conversion of one type of molecule to another, eventually regenerating the starting material, RuBP. In the 1940s and 1950s, Calvin and his colleagues used ^{14}C, a radioisotope of carbon, to label and trace molecules produced during the cycle (**Figure 8.14**). They injected ^{14}C-labeled CO_2 into cultures of the green alga *Chlorella pyrenoidosa* grown in an apparatus called a "lollipop" (because of its shape). The *Chlorella* cells were given different lengths of time to incorporate the ^{14}C-labeled carbon, ranging from fractions of a second to many minutes. After this incubation period, the cells were abruptly placed into a solution of alcohol to inhibit enzymatic reactions and thereby stop the cycle.

The researchers separated the newly made radiolabeled molecules by a variety of methods. The most commonly used method was two-dimensional paper chromatography. In this approach, a sample containing radiolabeled molecules was spotted onto a corner of the paper at a location called the origin. The edge of the paper was placed in a solvent, such as phenol-water. As the solvent rose through the paper, so did the radiolabeled molecules. The rate at which they rose depended on their structures, which determined how strongly they interacted with the paper. This step separated the mixture of molecules spotted onto the paper at the origin.

The paper was then dried, turned 90°, and then the edge was placed in a different solvent, such as butanol-propionic acid-water.

Again, the solvent rose through the paper (in a second dimension), thereby separating molecules that may not have been adequately separated during the first separation step. After this second separation step, the paper was dried and exposed to X-ray film, a procedure called autoradiography. Radioactive emission from the ^{14}C-labeled molecules caused dark spots to appear on the film.

The pattern of spots changed depending on the length of time the cells were incubated with ^{14}C-labeled CO_2. When the incubation period was short, only molecules that were made in the first steps of the Calvin cycle were seen—3-phosphoglycerate (3PG) and 1,3-bisphosphoglycerate (1,3-BPG). Longer incubations revealed molecules synthesized in later steps—glyceraldehyde-3-phosphate (G3P) and ribulose bisphosphate (RuBP).

A challenge for Calvin and his colleagues was to identify the chemical nature of each spot. They achieved this by a variety of chemical methods. For example, a spot could be cut out of the paper, the molecule within the paper could be washed out or eluted, and then the eluted molecule could be subjected to the same procedure that included a radiolabeled molecule whose structure was already known. If the unknown molecule and known molecule migrated to the same spot in the paper, this indicated they were likely to be the same molecule. During the late 1940s and 1950s, Calvin and his coworkers identified all of the ^{14}C-labeled spots and the order in which they appeared. In this way, they determined the

Figure 8.14 The determination of the Calvin cycle using ^{14}C-labeled CO_2 and paper chromatography. (6): Calvin, M. 1961. The path of carbon in photosynthesis, *Nobel Lecture* pp. 618–644, Fig. 4. ©The Nobel Foundation

GOAL The incorporation of CO_2 into carbohydrate involves a biosynthetic pathway. The aim of this experiment was to identify the steps.

KEY MATERIALS The green alga *Chlorella pyrenoidosa* and ^{14}C-labeled CO_2.

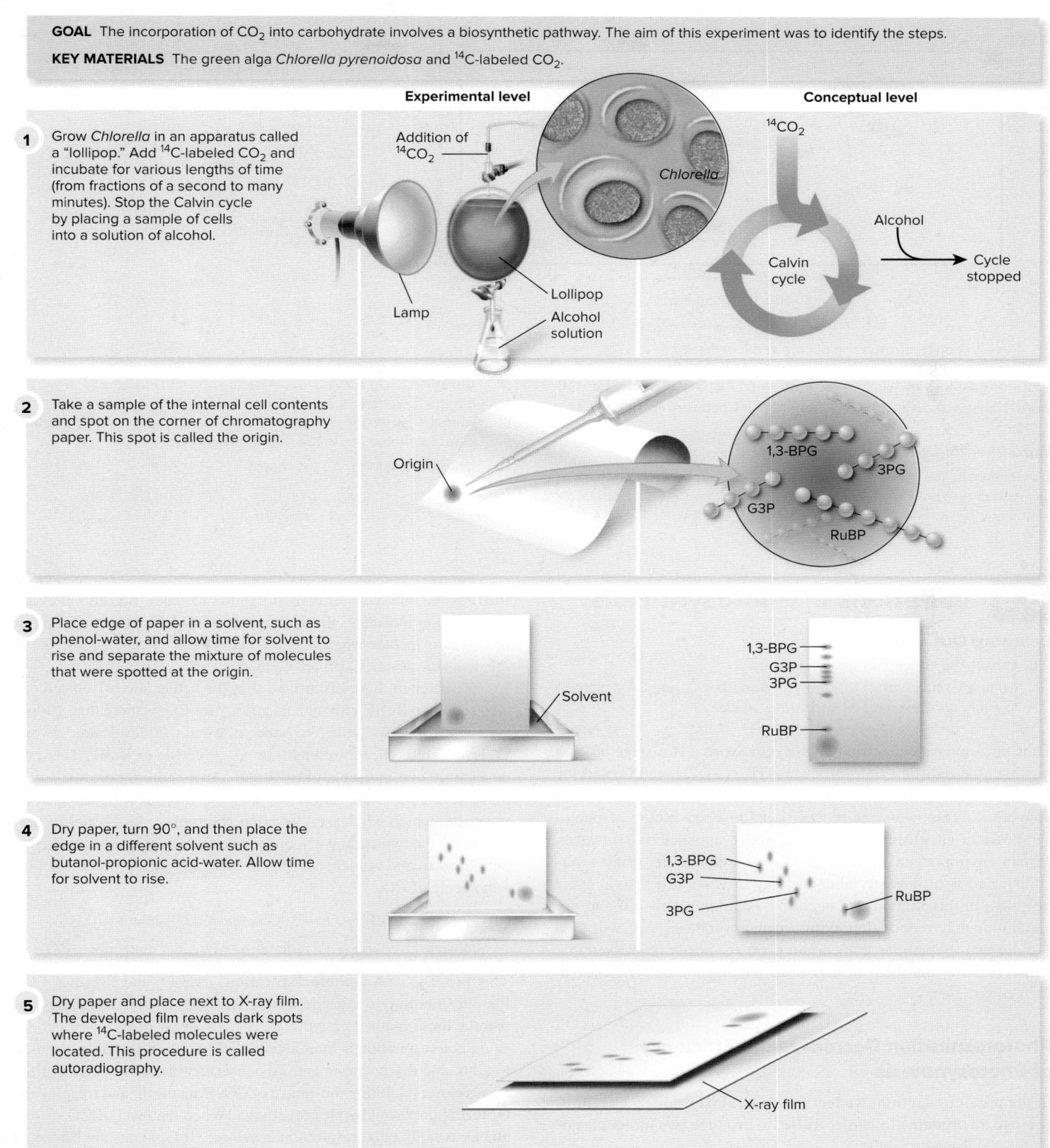

Experimental level   **Conceptual level**

1. Grow *Chlorella* in an apparatus called a "lollipop." Add ^{14}C-labeled CO_2 and incubate for various lengths of time (from fractions of a second to many minutes). Stop the Calvin cycle by placing a sample of cells into a solution of alcohol.

2. Take a sample of the internal cell contents and spot on the corner of chromatography paper. This spot is called the origin.

3. Place edge of paper in a solvent, such as phenol-water, and allow time for solvent to rise and separate the mixture of molecules that were spotted at the origin.

4. Dry paper, turn 90°, and then place the edge in a different solvent such as butanol-propionic acid-water. Allow time for solvent to rise.

5. Dry paper and place next to X-ray film. The developed film reveals dark spots where ^{14}C-labeled molecules were located. This procedure is called autoradiography.

6 THE DATA*

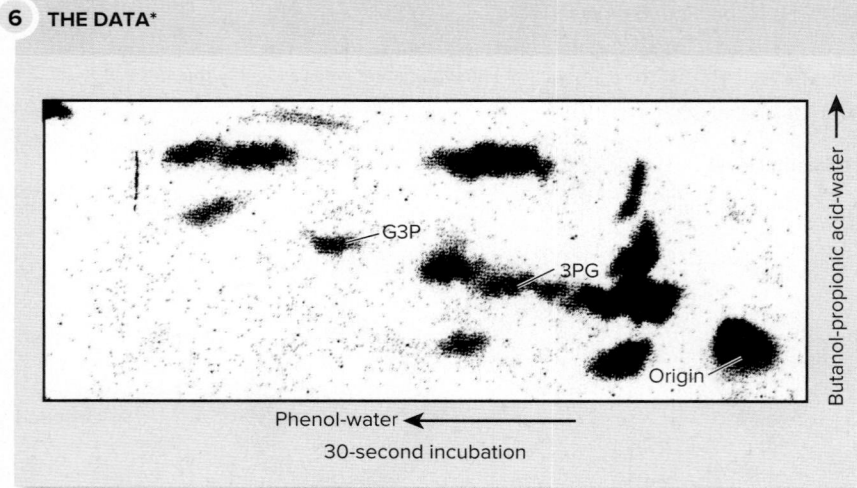

7 CONCLUSION The identification of the molecules in each spot elucidated the steps of the Calvin cycle.

8 SOURCE Calvin, M. 1961. The path of carbon in photosynthesis, *Nobel Lecture*, 618–644.

*An autoradiograph from one of Calvin's experiments.

series of reactions of what we now know as the Calvin cycle. For this work, Calvin was awarded the Nobel Prize in Chemistry in 1961.

Experimental Questions

1. What was the purpose of the study conducted by Calvin and his colleagues?

2. **CoreSKILL »** In Calvin's experiment shown in Figure 8.14, why did the researchers use ^{14}C-labeled CO_2? Why did they examine samples taken after several different time periods? How were the different molecules in the samples identified?

3. **CoreSKILL »** Interpret the results of Calvin's study.

8.5 Variations in Photosynthesis

Learning Outcomes:

1. Explain the concept of photorespiration.
2. Compare and contrast the strategies used by C_4 and CAM plants to avoid photorespiration and conserve water.

Thus far, we have considered photosynthesis as a two-stage process in which the light reactions produce ATP, NADPH, and O_2 and the Calvin cycle uses the ATP and NADPH for the synthesis of carbohydrates. This two-stage process is a universal feature of photosynthesis in all green plants, algae, and cyanobacteria. However, certain environmental conditions such as temperature, water availability, and light intensity alter the way in which the Calvin cycle operates. In this section, we begin by examining how hot and dry conditions may reduce the output of photosynthesis. We will then explore two adaptations that certain plant species have evolved that conserve water and help to maximize photosynthetic efficiency in such environments.

Photorespiration Decreases the Efficiency of Photosynthesis

In the previous section, we learned that rubisco adds a CO_2 molecule to an organic molecule, RuBP, to produce two molecules of 3-phosphoglycerate (3PG):

$$RuBP + CO_2 \rightarrow 2\ 3PG$$

For most species of plants, the incorporation of CO_2 into 3PG via RuBP is the only way for carbon fixation to occur. Because 3PG is a three-carbon molecule, these plants are called **C_3 plants**. Examples of C_3 plants include wheat and oak trees (**Figure 8.15**). About 90% of the plant species on Earth are C_3 plants.

Researchers have discovered that the active site of rubisco can also add O_2 to RuBP, although its affinity for CO_2 is more than 10-fold better than its affinity for O_2. Even so, when CO_2 levels are low and O_2 levels are high, rubisco adds an O_2 molecule to RuBP. This produces only one molecule of 3PG and a two-carbon molecule called phosphoglycolate. The phosphoglycolate is then dephosphorylated to glycolate, which is released from the chloroplast. In a series of several steps, the two-carbon glycolate molecule is eventually oxidized in peroxisomes and mitochondria to produce an organic molecule plus a molecule of CO_2:

$$RuBP + O_2 \rightarrow 3PG + Phosphoglycolate$$

$$Phosphoglycolate \rightarrow Glycolate \rightarrow\rightarrow Organic\ molecule + CO_2$$

This process, called **photorespiration**, uses O_2 and liberates CO_2. Photorespiration is considered wasteful because it releases CO_2, thereby limiting plant growth.

Photorespiration is more likely to occur when plants are exposed to a hot and dry environment. To conserve water, the stomata of the leaves close, inhibiting the uptake of CO_2 from the air and trapping the O_2 that is produced by photosynthesis. When the level of CO_2 is low and O_2 is high, photorespiration is favored. If C_3 plants are subjected to hot and dry environmental conditions, as much as 25–50% of their photosynthetic work is reversed by the process of photorespiration.

(a) Wheat plants

(b) Oak leaves

Figure 8.15 **Examples of C$_3$ plants.** The structures of **(a)** wheat and **(b)** oak leaves are similar to that shown in Figure 8.2. a: ©David Noton Photography/Alamy Stock Photo; b: ©McGraw-Hill Education/Vicki Copeland, photographer

Why do plants carry out photorespiration? The answer is not entirely clear. One possibility is that photorespiration may have a protective advantage. On hot and dry days when the stomata are closed, CO_2 levels within the leaves fall, and O_2 levels rise. Under these conditions, highly toxic oxygen-containing molecules such as free radicals may be produced that could damage the plant. Therefore, plant biologists have hypothesized that the role of photorespiration may be to protect the plant against the harmful effects of such toxic molecules by consuming O_2 and releasing CO_2.

C$_4$ Plants Have Evolved a Mechanism to Minimize Photorespiration

Certain species of plants have developed a way to minimize photorespiration. In the early 1960s, Hugo Kortschak discovered that the first product of carbon fixation in sugarcane is not 3GP but instead is a molecule with four carbon atoms. Species such as sugarcane are called **C$_4$ plants** because of this four-carbon molecule. Later, Marshall Hatch and Roger Slack confirmed this result and identified the molecule as oxaloacetate. For this reason, the pathway is sometimes called the Hatch-Slack pathway.

Some C$_4$ plants have a unique leaf anatomy that allows them to avoid photorespiration (**Figure 8.16**). An interior layer in the leaves of many C$_4$ plants has a two-cell organization composed of mesophyll cells and bundle-sheath cells. CO_2 from the atmosphere enters the mesophyll cells via stomata. Once inside, the enzyme PEP carboxylase attaches CO_2 to phosphoenolpyruvate (PEP), a three-carbon molecule, to produce oxaloacetate, a four-carbon molecule. PEP carboxylase does not recognize O_2. Therefore, unlike rubisco, PEP carboxylase does not promote photorespiration when CO_2 is low and O_2 is high. Instead, PEP carboxylase continues to fix CO_2.

As shown in Figure 8.16, oxaloacetate is converted to the four-carbon molecule malate, which is transported into the bundle-sheath cell. Malate is then broken down into pyruvate and CO_2. The pyruvate returns to the mesophyll cell, where it is converted to PEP via ATP, and the cycle in the mesophyll cell can begin again. The CO_2 enters the Calvin cycle in the chloroplasts of the bundle-sheath cells. Because the mesophyll cell supplies the bundle-sheath cell with a steady supply of CO_2, the concentration of CO_2 remains high in the bundle-sheath cell. Also, the mesophyll cells shield the bundle-sheath cells from high levels of O_2. This strategy minimizes photorespiration, which requires low CO_2 and high O_2 levels to proceed.

Which is better—being a C$_3$ or a C$_4$ plant? The answer is that it depends on the environment. In warm and dry climates, C$_4$ plants have an advantage. During the day, they can keep their stomata partially closed to conserve water. Furthermore, they minimize photorespiration. Examples of C$_4$ plants are sugarcane, crabgrass, and corn. In cooler climates, C$_3$ plants have the edge because they use less energy to fix CO_2. The process of carbon fixation that occurs in C$_4$ plants uses ATP to regenerate PEP from pyruvate (see Figure 8.16), and C$_3$ plants do not have to expend that ATP.

CAM Plants Are C$_4$ Plants That Take Up CO$_2$ at Night

We have just learned that certain C$_4$ plants prevent photorespiration by providing CO_2 to the bundle-sheath cells, where the Calvin cycle occurs. This mechanism spatially separates the processes of carbon fixation and the Calvin cycle. Another strategy followed by other C$_4$ plants, called **CAM plants**, separates these processes in time. CAM stands for crassulacean acid metabolism, because the process was first studied in members of the plant family Crassulaceae. Most CAM plants are water-storing succulents such as cacti, bromeliads (including pineapple), and sedums. To avoid water loss, CAM plants keep their stomata closed during the day and open them at night, when it is cooler and the relative humidity is higher.

How, then, do CAM plants carry out photosynthesis? **Figure 8.17** compares CAM plants with the other type of C$_4$ plants we considered in Figure 8.16. Photosynthesis in CAM plants occurs entirely within mesophyll cells, but the synthesis of a C$_4$ molecule and the Calvin cycle occur at different times. During the night when temperatures are cooler, the stomata of CAM plants open, thereby allowing the entry of CO_2 into mesophyll cells. CO_2 is joined with PEP to form the four-carbon molecule oxaloacetate. This is then converted to malate, which accumulates during the night in the central vacuoles of the cells. In the morning, the stomata close to conserve moisture. The accumulated malate in the mesophyll cells leaves the vacuole and is broken down to release CO_2, which then drives the Calvin cycle during the daytime.

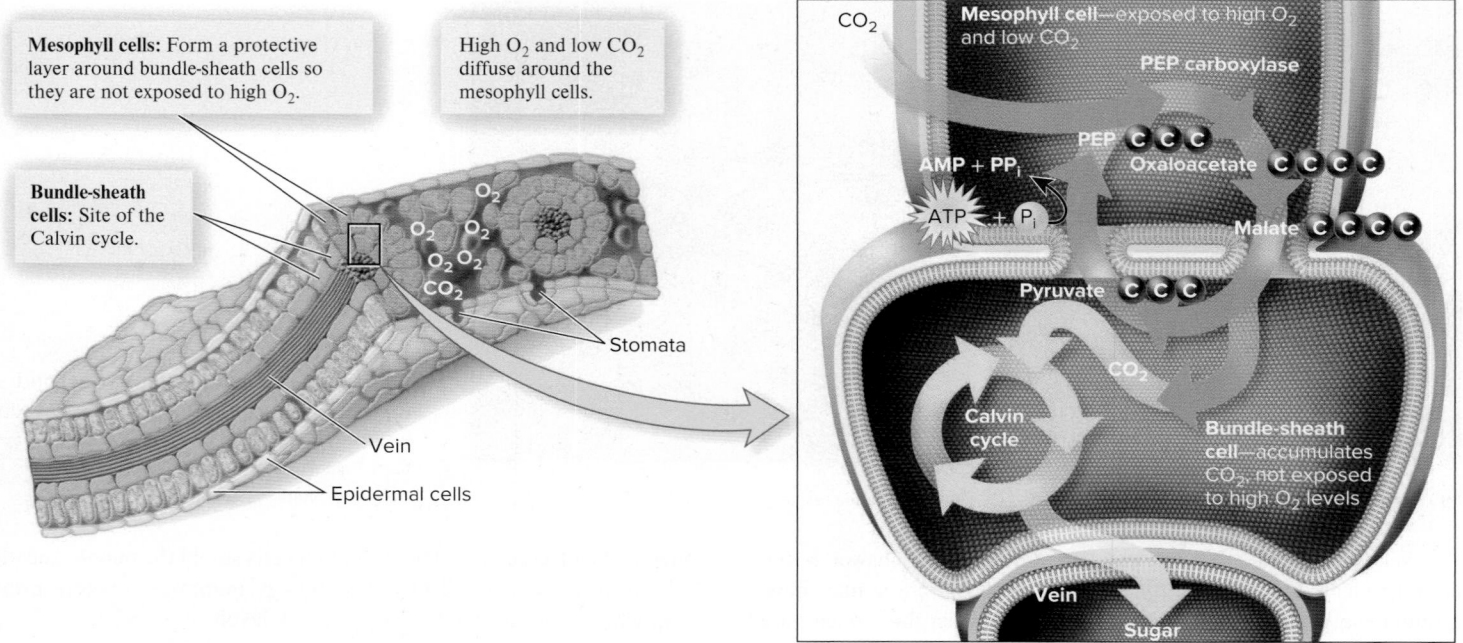

Figure 8.16 **Leaf structure and its relationship to the C₄ cycle.** C₄ plants have mesophyll cells, which initially take up CO₂, and bundle-sheath cells, where much of the carbohydrate synthesis occurs. Compare this leaf structure with the structure of C₃ leaves shown in Figure 8.2.

Concept Check: *How does the cellular arrangement in C₄ plants minimize photorespiration?*

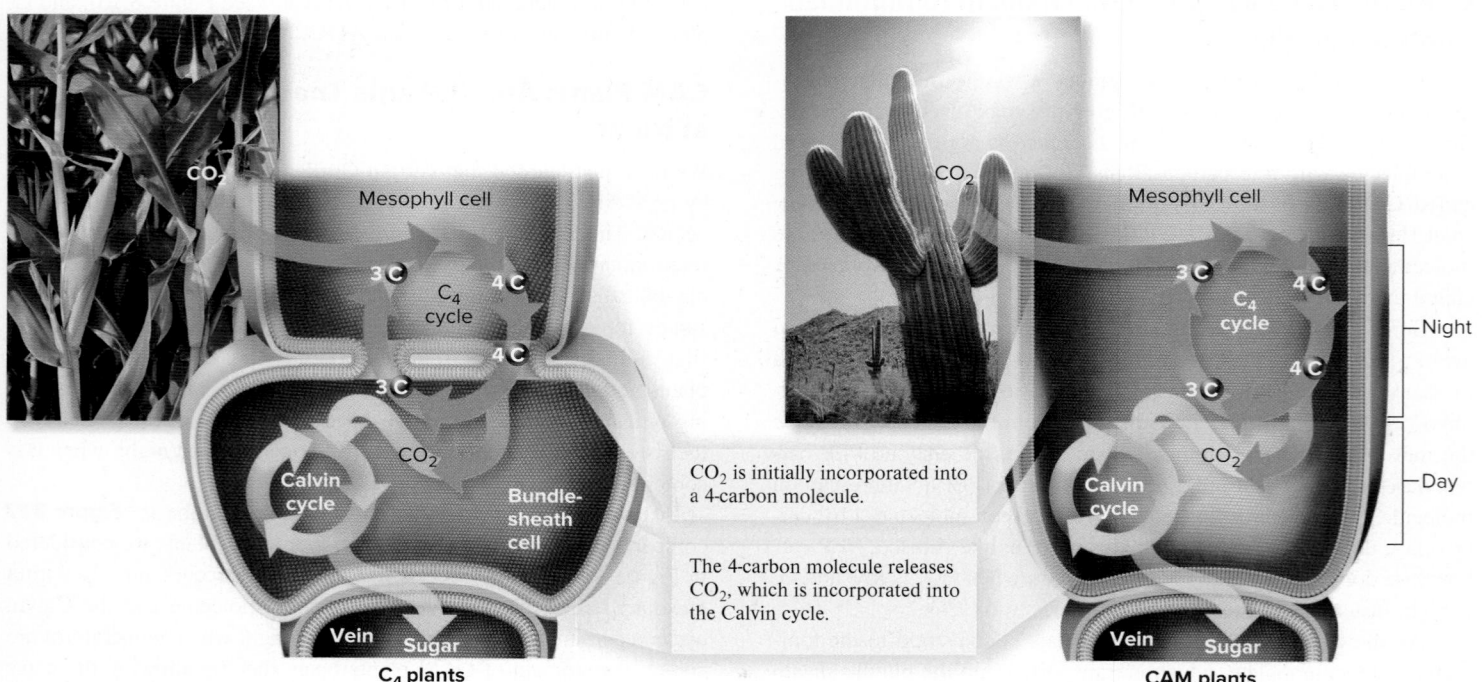

Figure 8.17 **A comparison of C₄ and CAM plants.** The name C₄ designates those plants in which the first organic product of carbon fixation is a four-carbon molecule. Using this definition, CAM plants are a type of C₄ plant. CAM plants, however, do not separate the functions of making a four-carbon molecule and the Calvin cycle into different types of cells. Instead, they make a four-carbon molecule at night and break down that molecule during the day so the CO₂ can be used in the Calvin cycle. (left): ©Wesley Hitt/Getty Images; (right): ©John Foxx/Getty Images

Concept Check: *What are the advantages for C₃, C₄, and CAM plants?*

Summary of Key Concepts

8.1 Overview of Photosynthesis

- Photosynthesis is the process by which plants, algae, and photosynthetic bacteria capture light energy that is used to synthesize carbohydrates.

- During photosynthesis, carbon dioxide, water, and energy are used to make carbohydrates and oxygen.

- Heterotrophs must obtain organic molecules in their food, whereas autotrophs make organic molecules from inorganic sources. Photoautotrophs use the energy from light to make organic molecules.

- An energy cycle occurs in the biosphere in which photosynthesis uses light, CO_2, and H_2O to make organic molecules, and the organic molecules are broken back down to CO_2 and H_2O via cellular respiration to supply energy in the form of ATP (Figure 8.1).

- In plants and algae, photosynthesis occurs within chloroplasts, organelles with an outer membrane, inner membrane, and thylakoid membrane. The stroma is the fluid-filled region between the thylakoid membrane and inner membrane. In plants, the leaves are the major site of photosynthesis (Figure 8.2).

- The light reactions of photosynthesis capture light energy to make ATP, NADPH, and O_2. These reactions occur at the thylakoid membrane. Carbohydrate synthesis via the Calvin cycle uses ATP and NADPH from the light reactions and happens in the stroma (Figure 8.3).

8.2 Reactions That Harness Light Energy

- Light is a form of electromagnetic radiation that travels in waves and is composed of photons with discrete amounts of energy (Figure 8.4).

- Electrons can absorb light energy and be boosted to a higher energy level—an excited state (Figure 8.5).

- Photosynthetic pigments include chlorophylls a and b and carotenoids. These pigments absorb light energy in the visible spectrum to drive photosynthesis (Figures 8.6, 8.7).

- During linear electron flow, electrons from photosystem II (PSII) follow a pathway along an electron transport chain (ETC) in the thylakoid membrane. This pathway generates an H^+ gradient that is used to make ATP. In addition, light energy striking photosystem I (PSI) boosts electrons to a very high energy level that allows the synthesis of NADPH (Figure 8.8).

- During cyclic photophosphorylation, electrons are activated in PSI and flow through the ETC back to PSI. This cyclic electron flow produces an H^+ gradient that is used to make ATP (Figure 8.9).

- Cytochrome b_6 in chloroplasts and cytochrome b in mitochondria are homologous proteins involved in electron transport and H^+ pumping (Figure 8.10).

8.3 Molecular Features of Photosystems

- In the light-harvesting complex of PSII, pigment molecules absorb light energy that is transferred to the reaction center via resonance energy transfer. A high-energy electron from P680* is transferred to a primary electron acceptor. An electron from water then replaces the electron lost by P680* (Figure 8.11).

- The Z scheme proposes that an electron absorbs light energy twice, at both PSII and PSI, losing some of that energy as it flows along the ETC in the thylakoid membrane (Figure 8.12).

8.4 Synthesizing Carbohydrates via the Calvin Cycle

- The Calvin cycle is composed of three phases: carbon fixation, reduction and carbohydrate production, and regeneration of ribulose bisphosphate (RuBP). In this cycle, ATP is used as a source of energy, and NADPH is used as a source of high-energy electrons to incorporate CO_2 into a carbohydrate (Figure 8.13).

- Calvin and Benson determined the steps in the Calvin cycle by isotope-labeling methods in which the products of the Calvin cycle were separated by paper chromatography (Figure 8.14).

8.5 Variations in Photosynthesis

- C_3 plants incorporate CO_2 into RuBP to make 3PG, a three-carbon molecule (Figure 8.15).

- Photorespiration occurs when the level of O_2 is high and CO_2 is low, which happens under hot and dry conditions. During this process, some O_2 is used and CO_2 is liberated. Photorespiration is inefficient because it reverses the incorporation of CO_2 into an organic molecule.

- Some C_4 plants avoid photorespiration by first incorporating CO_2, via PEP carboxylase, into a four-carbon molecule, which is pumped from mesophyll cells into bundle-sheath cells. This maintains a high concentration of CO_2 in the bundle-sheath cells, where the Calvin cycle occurs. The high CO_2 concentration minimizes photorespiration (Figure 8.16).

- CAM plants, a type of C_4 plant, prevent photorespiration by fixing CO_2 into a four-carbon molecule at night and then running the Calvin cycle during the day with their stomata closed to reduce water loss (Figure 8.17).

Assess & Discuss

Test Yourself

1. The water necessary for photosynthesis
   a. is split into H_2 and O_2.
   b. is directly involved in the synthesis of carbohydrates.
   c. provides the electrons to replace those lost in photosystem II.
   d. provides the H^+ needed to synthesize G3P.
   e. does none of the above.

2. In PSII, P680 differs from the pigment molecules of the light-harvesting complex in that it
   a. is a carotenoid.
   b. absorbs light energy and transfers that energy to other molecules via resonance energy transfer.
   c. transfers an excited electron to the primary electron acceptor.
   d. transfer an excited electron to O_2.
   e. acts like ATP synthase to produce ATP.

3. The cyclic electron flow that occurs via photosystem I produces
   a. NADPH.
   b. oxygen.
   c. ATP.
   d. all of the above.
   e. a and c only.

4. During linear electron flow, the high-energy electron from P680*
   a. eventually moves to NADP+.
   b. becomes incorporated in water molecules.
   c. is pumped into the thylakoid space to drive ATP production.
   d. provides the energy necessary to split water molecules.
   e. falls back to the low-energy state in photosystem II.

5. During the first phase of the Calvin cycle, carbon dioxide is incorporated into ribulose bisphosphate (RuBP) by
   a. oxaloacetate.
   b. rubisco.
   c. RuBP.
   d. quinone.
   e. G3P.

6. The NADPH produced during the light reactions is necessary for
   a. the carbon fixation phase, which incorporates carbon dioxide into an organic molecule during the Calvin cycle.
   b. the reduction phase, which produces carbohydrates in the Calvin cycle.
   c. the regeneration of RuBP of the Calvin cycle.
   d. all of the above.
   e. a and b only.

7. The majority of the G3P produced during the reduction and carbohydrate production phase is used in making
   a. glucose.
   b. ATP.
   c. RuBP to continue the cycle.
   d. rubisco.
   e. all of the above.

8. Photorespiration
   a. is the process in which plants use sunlight to make ATP.
   b. is an inefficient way that plants can produce organic molecules by using O_2 and releasing CO_2.
   c. is a process that plants use to convert light energy to NADPH.
   d. occurs in the thylakoid lumen.
   e. is the normal process of carbohydrate production in cool, moist environments.

9. Photorespiration is avoided by C_4 plants because
   a. these plants separate the formation of a four-carbon molecule from the rest of the Calvin cycle in different cells.
   b. these plants carry out only anaerobic respiration.
   c. the enzyme PEP carboxylase functions to maintain high CO_2 concentrations in the bundle-sheath cells.
   d. all of the above.
   e. a and c only.

10. Plants commonly found in hot and dry environments that carry out carbon fixation at night are
    a. oak trees.
    b. C_3 plants.
    c. CAM plants.
    d. all of the above.
    e. a and b only.

Conceptual Questions

1. What are the two stages of photosynthesis? What are the key products of each stage?

2. What is the function of NADPH in the Calvin cycle?

3.  **Core Concept: Energy and Matter** At the level of the biosphere, what is the role of photosynthesis in the utilization of energy by living organisms?

Collaborative Questions

1. Discuss the advantages and disadvantages of being a heterotroph or a photoautotroph.

2. Biotechnologists are trying to genetically modify C_3 plants to convert them to C_4 or CAM plants. Why would this be useful? What genes might you introduce into C_3 plants to convert them to C_4 or CAM plants?

Cell Communication

9

O ver 2 billion cells will die in your body during the next hour. In an adult human body, approximately 50–70 billion cells die each day due to programmed cell death—the process in which a cell breaks apart into small fragments (see the chapter opening photo). In a year, your body produces and purposely destroys a mass of cells that is equal to its total weight! Though this may seem like a scary process, it's actually keeping you healthy. Programmed cell death, also called apoptosis, ensures that your body maintains a proper number of cells. It also eliminates cells that are worn out or potentially harmful, such as cancer cells. Programmed cell death can occur via signals that intentionally cause particular cells to die, or it can result from a failure of proper cell communication. It may also happen when environmental agents cause damage to a cell. Programmed cell death is one example of a response that involves **cell communication**—the process by which cells can detect, interpret, and respond to signals in their environment. A **signal** is an agent that can influence the properties of cells.

In this chapter, we will examine how cells detect environmental signals and also how they produce signals that enable them to communicate with other cells. Communication at the cellular level involves not only receiving and sending signals but also their interpretation. For this to occur, a signal must be recognized by a cellular protein called a **receptor**. When a signal and a receptor interact, the receptor changes shape, or conformation, thereby changing the way the receptor interacts with cellular factors. These interactions eventually lead to some type of response in the cell. We begin the chapter with the general features of cell communication, and then discuss the main ways in which cells receive, process, and respond to signals sent by other cells. As you will learn, cell communication involves an amazing diversity of signaling molecules and cellular proteins that are devoted to this process. We conclude by looking at the role of cell communication in apoptosis, in which a cell becomes programmed to die.

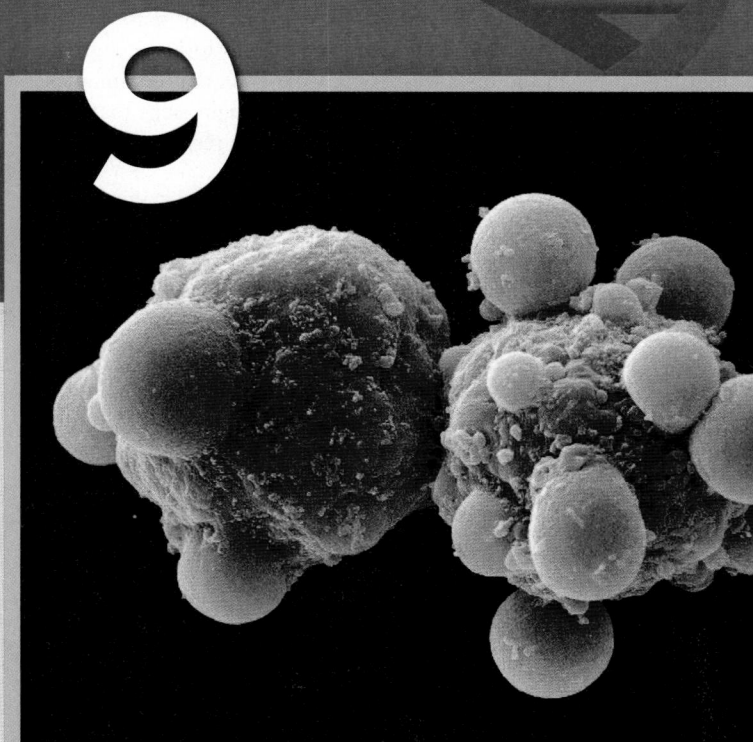

Programmed cell death. The two cells shown here are breaking apart because signaling molecules initiated a pathway that programmed their death. ©David McCarthy/SPL/Science Source

9.1 General Features of Cell Communication

Learning Outcomes:

1. Explain the two general reasons for cell signaling: responding to environmental changes and cell-to-cell communication.
2. Compare and contrast the five ways that cells communicate with each other based on the distance between them.
3. Outline the three-stage process of cell signaling.

All living cells, including those of bacteria, archaea, protists, fungi, plants, and animals, must engage in cell communication to survive. Cell communication, also known as cell signaling, involves both incoming and outgoing signals. For example, on a sunny day, cells can sense their exposure to ultraviolet (UV) light—a physical signal—and respond accordingly. In humans, UV light acts as an incoming signal to promote the synthesis of melanin, a protective pigment that helps to prevent the harmful effects of UV radiation. In addition, cells produce outgoing signals that influence the behavior of neighboring cells. Plant cells, for example, produce hormones that influence the pattern of cell elongation so the plant grows toward light. Cells of all living organisms both respond to incoming signals and produce outgoing signals. Cell communication is a two-way street.

In this section, we begin by considering why cells need to respond to signals. We will then examine various forms of signaling that are based on the distance between the cells that communicate with each other. Finally, we will examine the main steps that occur when a cell is exposed to a signal and produces a response to it.

Cells Detect and Respond to Signals from Their Environment and from Other Cells

Before getting into the details of cell communication, let's take a general look at why cell communication is necessary.

Responding to Changes in the Environment   The first reason for cell communication is that cells need to respond to a changing environment. Changes in the environment are a persistent feature of life, and living cells are continually faced with alterations in temperature and availability of nutrients, water, and light. A cell may even be exposed to a toxic chemical in its environment. Being able to respond to change at the cellular level is called a **cellular response**.

As an example, let's consider the response of a yeast cell to glucose in its environment (**Figure 9.1**). Some of the glucose acts as a signaling molecule that binds to a receptor and causes a cellular response. In this case, the cell responds by increasing the number of glucose transporters needed to take glucose into the cell and also by increasing the number of metabolic enzymes required to utilize glucose once it is inside. The cellular response allows the cell to use glucose efficiently.

Cell-to-Cell Communication   A second reason for cell communication is the need for cells to share information with each other—a

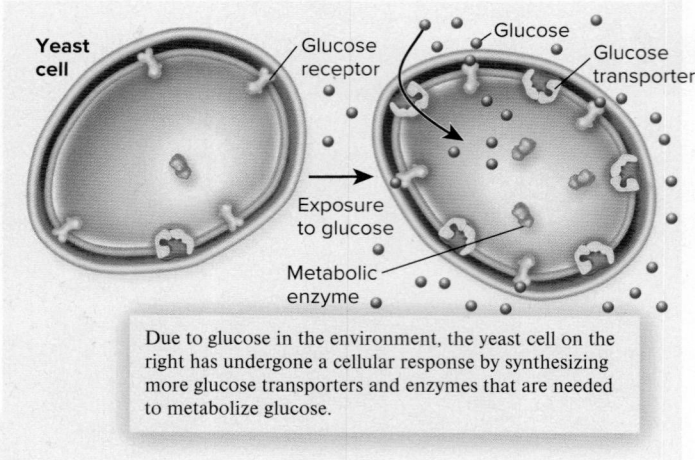

Due to glucose in the environment, the yeast cell on the right has undergone a cellular response by synthesizing more glucose transporters and enzymes that are needed to metabolize glucose.

Figure 9.1 Response of a yeast cell to glucose. When glucose is absent from the extracellular environment, the cell is not well prepared to take up and metabolize this sugar. However, when glucose is present, some of that glucose binds to receptors in the membrane, which leads to changes in the amounts and properties of intracellular and membrane proteins so the cell can readily use glucose.

Concept Check: *What is the signaling molecule in this example?*

type of cell communication called **cell-to-cell communication**. In one of the earliest experiments demonstrating cell-to-cell communication, Charles Darwin and his son Francis Darwin studied phototropism, the phenomenon in which plants grow toward light (**Figure 9.2**). The Darwins observed that the actual bending occurs in a zone below the growing shoot tip. They concluded that a signal must be transmitted from the growing tip to lower parts of the shoot. Later research revealed that the signal is a molecule called auxin, which is transmitted from cell to cell. A higher amount of auxin accumulates on the nonilluminated side of the shoot and promotes cell elongation on that side of the shoot only, thereby causing the shoot to bend toward the light source.

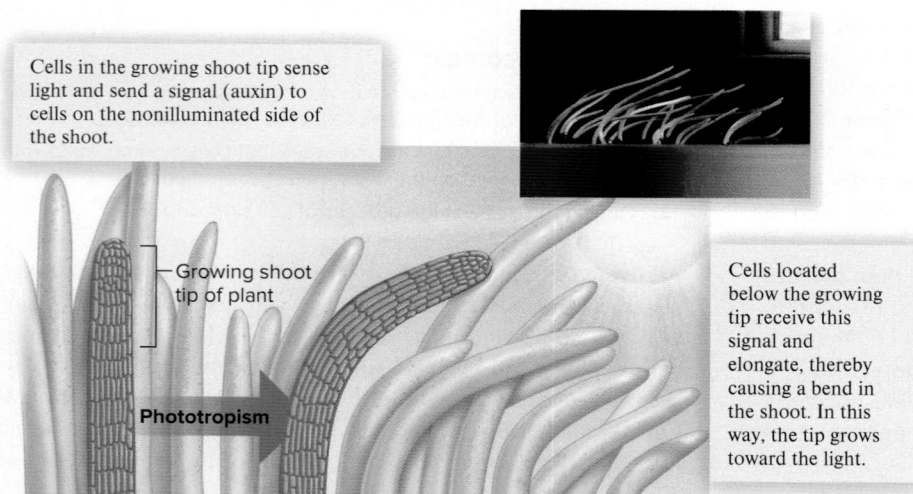

Cells in the growing shoot tip sense light and send a signal (auxin) to cells on the nonilluminated side of the shoot.

Growing shoot tip of plant

Phototropism

Cells located below the growing tip receive this signal and elongate, thereby causing a bend in the shoot. In this way, the tip grows toward the light.

Figure 9.2 Phototropism in plants. This process involves cell-to-cell communication that leads to a shoot bending toward light just beneath its actively growing tip. (inset): ©Cordelia Molloy/SPL/Science Source

 Core Skill: Connections Look ahead to Figure 37.5. How does light affect the distribution of auxin produced by a plant's growing shoot tip?

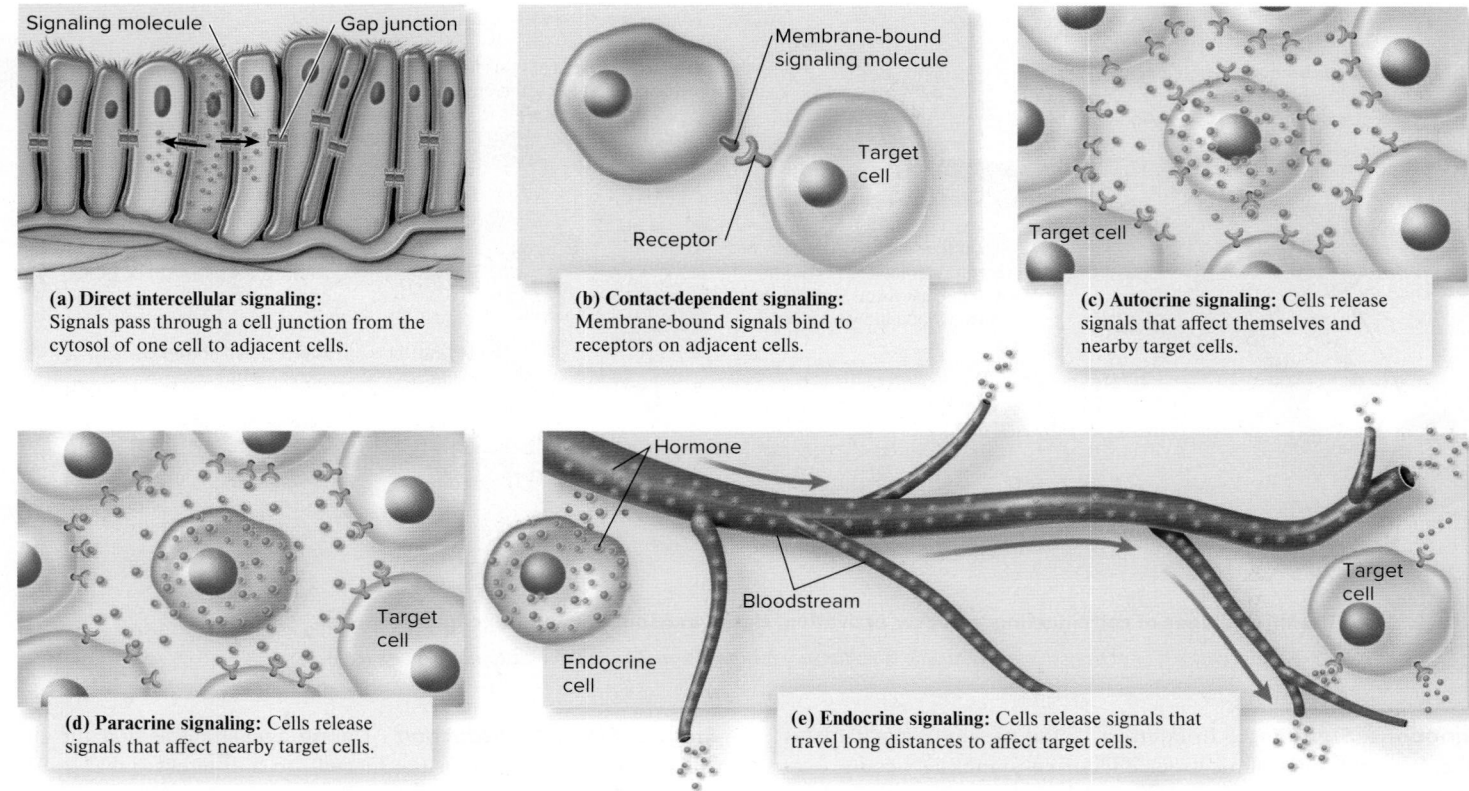

Figure 9.3 **Types of cell-to-cell communication based on the distance between cells.**

Concept Check: *Which type of signal, paracrine or endocrine, is likely to exist for a longer period of time? Explain why this longer existence is necessary.*

Cell-to-Cell Communication Can Occur Between Adjacent Cells and Between Cells That Are Long Distances Apart

Organisms have a variety of different mechanisms to achieve cell-to-cell communication. The mode of communication depends, in part, on the distance between the cells that need to communicate with each other. Let's first examine the various ways in which signals are transferred between cells. Later in this chapter, we will learn how such signals elicit a cellular response.

One way to categorize cell signaling is by the manner in which the signal is transmitted from one cell to another. Signals are relayed between cells in five common ways, all of which involve a cell that produces a signal and a target cell that receives the signal (**Figure 9.3**).

Direct Intercellular Signaling   In a multicellular organism, cells adjacent to each other may have contacts, called cell junctions, that enable them to pass ions, signaling molecules, and other materials between the cytosol of one cell and the cytosol of the other (Figure 9.3a). For example, cardiac muscle cells, which cause your heart to beat, have intercellular connections called gap junctions that allow the passage of ions needed for the coordinated contraction of these cells. We will examine how gap junctions work in Chapter 10.

Contact-Dependent Signaling   Not all signaling molecules diffuse from one cell to another. Some molecules are bound to the surface of

a cell and provide a signal to other cells that make contact with the surface of that cell (Figure 9.3b). In the case of contact-dependent signaling, one cell has a membrane-bound signaling molecule that is recognized by a receptor on the surface of another cell. This type of cell-to-cell communication occurs, for example, when portions of neurons (nerve cells) grow and make contact with other neurons. This is important for the formation of the proper connections between neurons.

Autocrine Signaling   In autocrine signaling, a cell secretes signaling molecules that bind to receptors on its own cell surface and on the surfaces of neighboring cells of the same cell type, stimulating a response (Figure 9.3c). What is the purpose of autocrine signaling? It is often important for groups of cells to sense cell density. When cell density is high, the concentration of autocrine signals is also high. In some cases, such signals inhibit further cell growth, thereby limiting cell density.

Paracrine Signaling   In paracrine signaling, a specific cell secretes a signaling molecule that does not affect that cell but instead influences the behavior of target cells in close proximity (Figure 9.3d). Paracrine signaling is typically of short duration. Usually, the signal is broken down too quickly to be carried to other parts of the body and affect distant cells. A specialized form of paracrine signaling occurs in the nervous systems of animals. Neurotransmitters—molecules made in neurons that transmit a signal to an adjacent cell—are released at the end of a neuron and traverse a narrow space called the synapse (see Chapter 42). The neurotransmitter then binds to a receptor in a target cell.

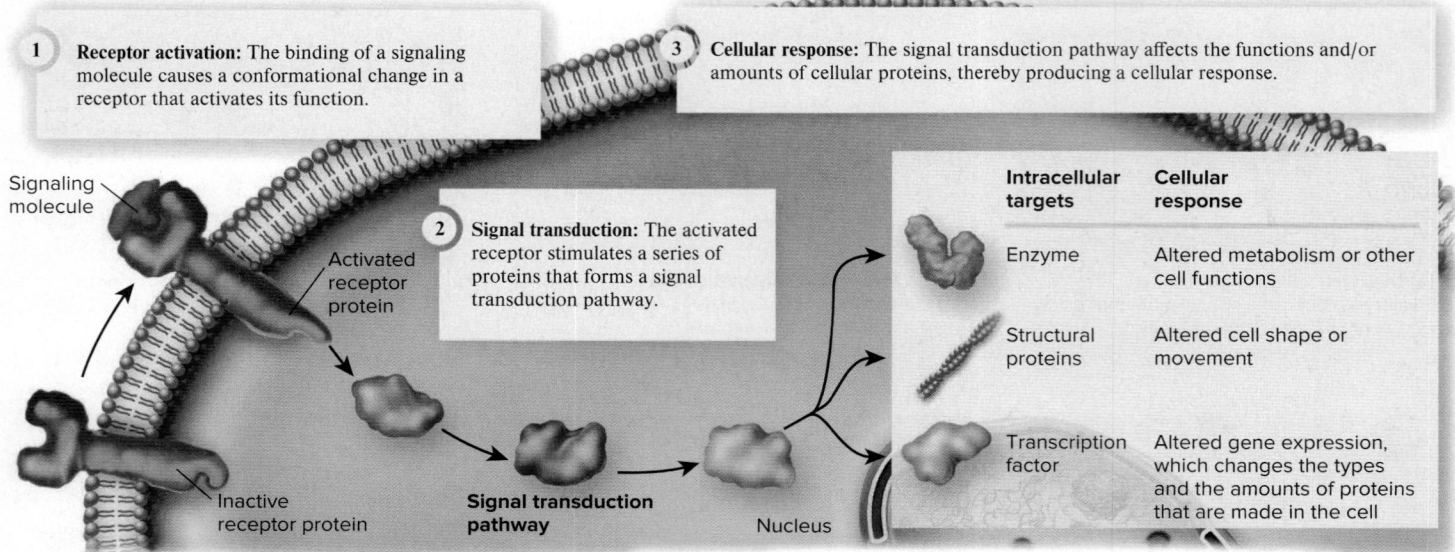

Figure 9.4 **The three stages of cell signaling: receptor activation, signal transduction, and a cellular response.**

Concept Check: *Explain why a signal transduction pathway is necessary for most signaling molecules to have an effect.*

Endocrine Signaling In contrast to the previous mechanisms of cell-to-cell communication, endocrine signaling occurs over relatively long distances (Figure 9.3e). In both animals and plants, molecules involved in long-distance signaling are called **hormones**. They usually last longer than signaling molecules involved in autocrine and paracrine signaling. In mammals, endocrine signaling involves the secretion of hormones into the bloodstream, which may affect virtually all cells of the body, including those that are far from the cells that secrete the signaling molecules. In flowering plants, hormones move through the plant vascular system and also move through adjacent cells. Some hormones are even gases that diffuse into the air. Ethylene, a gas given off by plants, plays a variety of roles, such as accelerating the ripening of fruit.

Cells Usually Respond to Signals via a Three-Stage Process

Up to this point, we have seen how signals influence the behavior of cells in close proximity or at long distances, interacting with receptors to elicit a cellular response. What events occur when a cell receives a signal? In most cases, the binding of a signaling molecule to a receptor causes the receptor to activate a signal transduction pathway, which then leads to a cellular response. **Figure 9.4** diagrams the three common stages of cell signaling: receptor activation, signal transduction, and a cellular response.

Stage 1: Receptor Activation In the initial stage, a signaling molecule binds to a receptor of the target cell, causing a conformational change in the receptor that activates its function. In most cases, the activated receptor initiates a response by causing changes in a series of proteins that collectively forms a signal transduction pathway, as described next.

Stage 2: Signal Transduction During signal transduction, the initial signal is converted—or transduced—to a different signal inside the cell. This process is carried out by a group of proteins that form a **signal transduction pathway**. These proteins undergo a series of changes that may result in the production of an intracellular signaling molecule. However, some receptors are intracellular and do not activate a signal transduction pathway. As discussed later, certain types of intracellular receptors directly cause a cellular response.

Stage 3: Cellular Response Cells respond to signals in several different ways. Figure 9.4 shows three common categories of proteins that are controlled by cell signaling: enzymes, structural proteins, and transcription factors.

1. Many signaling molecules exert their effects by altering the activity of one or more enzymes. For example, certain hormones provide a signal that the body needs energy. These hormones activate enzymes that are required for the breakdown of molecules such as carbohydrates.

2. Cells also respond to signals by altering the functions of structural proteins in the cell. For example, when animal cells move during embryonic development or when an amoeba moves toward food, signals play a role in the rearrangement of actin filaments, which are components of the cytoskeleton. The coordination of signaling and changes in the cytoskeleton enables a cell to move in the correct direction.

3. Signaling molecules may also affect the function of transcription factors—proteins that regulate the transcription of genes. Some transcription factors activate gene expression. For example, when cells are exposed to sex hormones, transcription factors activate genes that change the properties of cells, which can lead to changes in the sexual characteristics of entire organisms. As discussed in Section 51.3, estrogens and androgens are

responsible for the development of secondary sex characteristics in humans, including breast development in females and beard growth in males.

9.2 Cellular Receptors and Their Activation

Learning Outcomes:

1. **CoreSKILL »** Calculate the affinity, measured as a dissociation constant, that a receptor has for its signaling molecule, or ligand.
2. Explain how a signaling molecule activates a receptor.
3. Identify three general types of cell surface receptors.
4. Describe intracellular receptors, using estrogen receptors as an example.

In this section, we will take a closer look at receptors and their interactions with signaling molecules. We will compare receptors based on whether they are located on the cell surface or inside the cell. In this chapter, our focus will be on receptors that respond to chemical signaling molecules. Other receptors discussed in Units VI and VII respond to mechanical motion (mechanoreceptors), temperature changes (thermoreceptors), and light (photoreceptors).

Signaling Molecules Bind to Receptors

The ability of cells to respond to a signal usually requires precise recognition between a signal and its receptor. In many cases, the signal is a molecule, such as a steroid or a protein, that binds to the receptor. A signaling molecule binds to a receptor in much the same way that a substrate binds to the active site of an enzyme, as described in Chapter 6. The signaling molecule, which is called a **ligand**, binds noncovalently to the receptor with a high degree of specificity. The binding occurs when the ligand and receptor happen to collide in the correct orientation with enough energy to form a **ligand·receptor complex**.

$$[\text{Ligand}] + [\text{Receptor}] \underset{k_{\text{off}}}{\overset{k_{\text{on}}}{\rightleftharpoons}} [\text{Ligand·Receptor complex}]$$

Square brackets, [ ], indicate concentration. The value k_{on} is the rate at which binding occurs. After a complex forms between the ligand and its receptor, the noncovalent interaction between ligand and receptor remains stable for a finite period of time. The term k_{off} is the rate at which the ligand·receptor complex falls apart or dissociates.

In general, the binding and dissociation of a ligand and its receptor occur relatively rapidly, and therefore an equilibrium is reached when the rate of formation of new ligand·receptor complexes equals the rate at which existing ligand·receptor complexes dissociate:

$$k_{\text{on}} [\text{Ligand}][\text{Receptor}] = k_{\text{off}} [\text{Ligand·Receptor complex}]$$

Rearranging the equation gives

$$\frac{[\text{Ligand}][\text{Receptor}]}{[\text{Ligand·Receptor complex}]} = \frac{k_{\text{off}}}{k_{\text{on}}} = K_{\text{d}}$$

K_{d} is called the **dissociation constant** between a ligand and its receptor. The K_{d} value is inversely related to the affinity between the ligand and receptor. A low K_{d} value indicates that a receptor has a high affinity for its ligand.

Let's look carefully at the left side of this equation and consider what it means. At a ligand concentration at which half of the receptors are bound to a ligand, the concentration of the ligand·receptor complex equals the concentration of receptor that doesn't have ligand bound. At this ligand concentration, [Receptor] and [Ligand·Receptor complex] cancel out of the equation because they are equal. Therefore, at a ligand concentration at which half of the receptors have bound ligand:

$$K_{\text{d}} = [\text{Ligand}]$$

When the ligand concentration is above the K_{d} value, most of the receptors are likely to have ligand bound to them. In contrast, if the ligand concentration is substantially below the K_{d} value, most receptors will not be bound by their ligand. The K_{d} values for many different ligands and their receptors have been experimentally determined. How is this information useful? It allows researchers to predict when a signaling molecule is likely to cause a cellular response. If the concentration of a signaling molecule is far below the K_{d} value, a cellular response is not likely because relatively few receptors will form a complex with a signaling molecule.

Receptors Undergo Conformational Changes

Unlike enzymes, which convert their substrates into products, receptors do not usually alter the structure of their ligands. Instead, the ligands alter the structure of their receptors, causing a conformational change (**Figure 9.5**). In this case, the binding of the ligand to its receptor changes the receptor in a way that activates its ability to initiate a cellular response.

Because the binding of a ligand to its receptor is a reversible process, the ligand and receptor will dissociate. Once the ligand is released, the receptor is no longer activated.

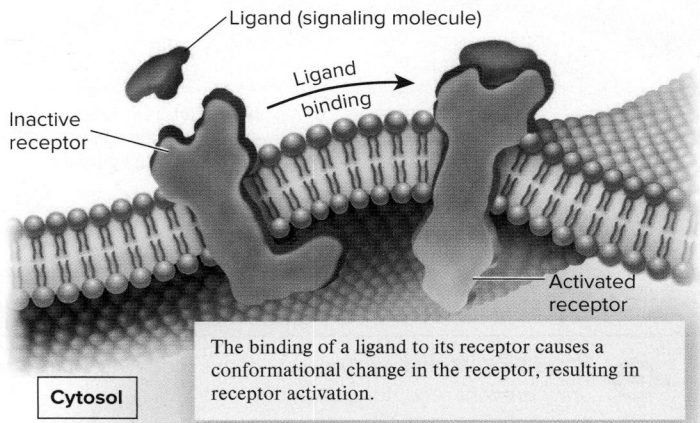

The binding of a ligand to its receptor causes a conformational change in the receptor, resulting in receptor activation.

Figure 9.5 Receptor activation.

 Core Skill: Connections Look back at Figure 6.6. How is the binding of a ligand to its receptor similar to the binding of a substrate to an enzyme? How are these processes different?

Cells Contain a Variety of Cell Surface Receptors That Respond to Extracellular Signals

Most signaling molecules are either small hydrophilic molecules or large molecules that do not readily pass through the plasma membrane of cells. Such extracellular signaling molecules bind to **cell surface receptors**—receptors found in the plasma membrane. A typical cell usually contains dozens or even hundreds of different cell surface receptors that enable the cell to respond to different kinds of extracellular signaling molecules. By analyzing the functions of cell surface receptors from many different organisms, researchers have determined that most fall into one of three categories: enzyme-linked receptors, G-protein-coupled receptors, and ligand-gated ion channels, which are described next.

Enzyme-Linked Receptors   Receptors known as **enzyme-linked receptors** are found in all living species. Many human hormones bind to this type of receptor. For example, when insulin binds to an enzyme-linked receptor in muscle cells, it enhances the ability of those cells to use glucose. Enzyme-linked receptors typically have two important domains: an extracellular domain, which binds to a signaling molecule, and an intracellular domain, which has a catalytic function (**Figure 9.6a**). When a signaling molecule binds to the extracellular domain, a conformational change is transmitted through the membrane-embedded portion of the protein and affects the conformation of the intracellular catalytic domain. In most cases, this conformational change causes the intracellular catalytic domain to become functionally active.

Most types of enzyme-linked receptors function as **protein kinases**, enzymes that transfer a phosphate group from ATP to specific amino acids in a protein (**Figure 9.6b**). For example, tyrosine kinases attach phosphate to the amino acid tyrosine, whereas serine/threonine kinases attach phosphate to the amino acids serine and threonine. In the example shown in Figure 9.6b, the catalytic domain of the receptor remains inactive when no signaling molecule is present. However, when a signal binds to the extracellular domain, the catalytic domain is activated. Under these conditions, the receptor may phosphorylate itself, or it may phosphorylate intracellular proteins. The attachment of a negatively charged phosphate changes the structure of a protein and thereby alters its function. Later in this chapter, we will explore how this event leads to a cellular response, such as the activation of enzymes that affect cell function.

G-Protein-Coupled Receptors   Receptors called **G-protein-coupled receptors (GPCRs)** are found in the cells of all eukaryotic species and are particularly common in animals. GPCRs typically contain seven transmembrane segments that wind back and forth through the plasma membrane. The receptors interact with intracellular proteins called **G proteins**, which are so named because of their ability to bind guanosine triphosphate (GTP) and guanosine diphosphate (GDP). GTP is similar in structure to ATP except it has guanine as a base instead of adenine. In the 1970s, the existence of G proteins was first proposed by Martin Rodbell and colleagues, who found that GTP is needed for certain hormone receptors to cause an intracellular response. Later,

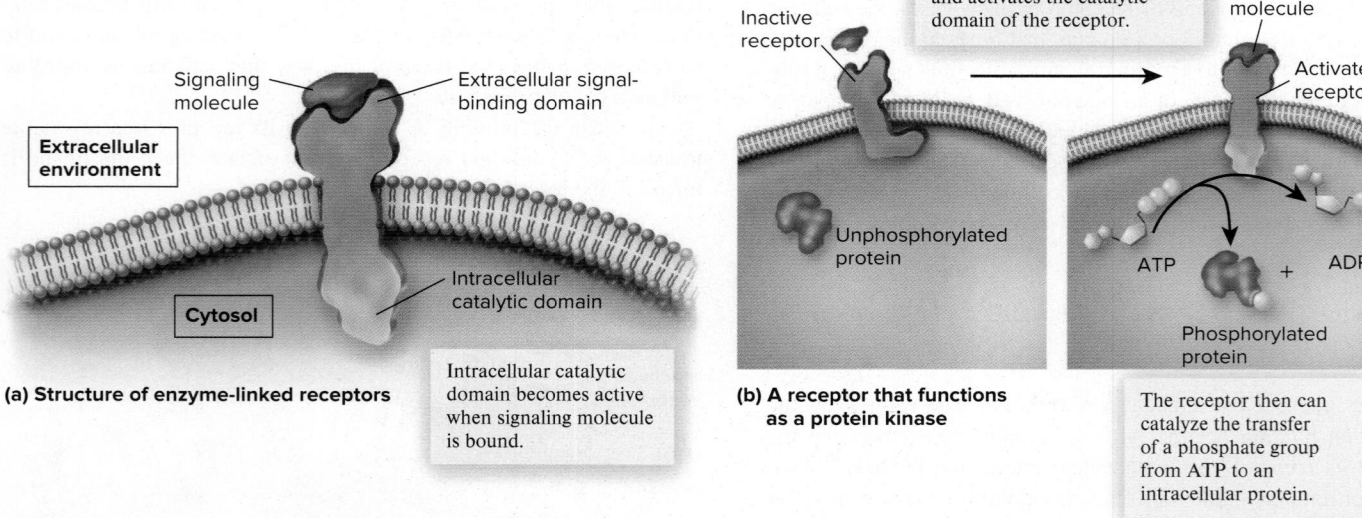

(a) **Structure of enzyme-linked receptors**

Intracellular catalytic domain becomes active when signaling molecule is bound.

(b) **A receptor that functions as a protein kinase**

The receptor then can catalyze the transfer of a phosphate group from ATP to an intracellular protein.

Figure 9.6   **Enzyme-linked receptors.**

Core Skill: Modeling   The goal of this modeling challenge is to predict the possible locations where an amino acid substitution may prevent receptor activation.

Modeling Challenge: Figure 9.6 is a general model that shows how the binding of a ligand to an enzyme-linked receptor results in receptor activation. Let's suppose that researchers have identified a mutant version of this type of receptor in which the ligand can still bind to the receptor correctly, but the receptor is not activated. In other words, the binding of the ligand does not cause the receptor to phosphorylate intracellular proteins. The mutation changes just one amino acid in the receptor protein by substituting a glycine (found in the normal protein) to a glutamic acid. On the model shown in part (a) of the figure, put two X's in places where you think the glutamic acid might be found in the mutant receptor, and place a Y where you think it would not be found. Briefly explain your chosen locations.

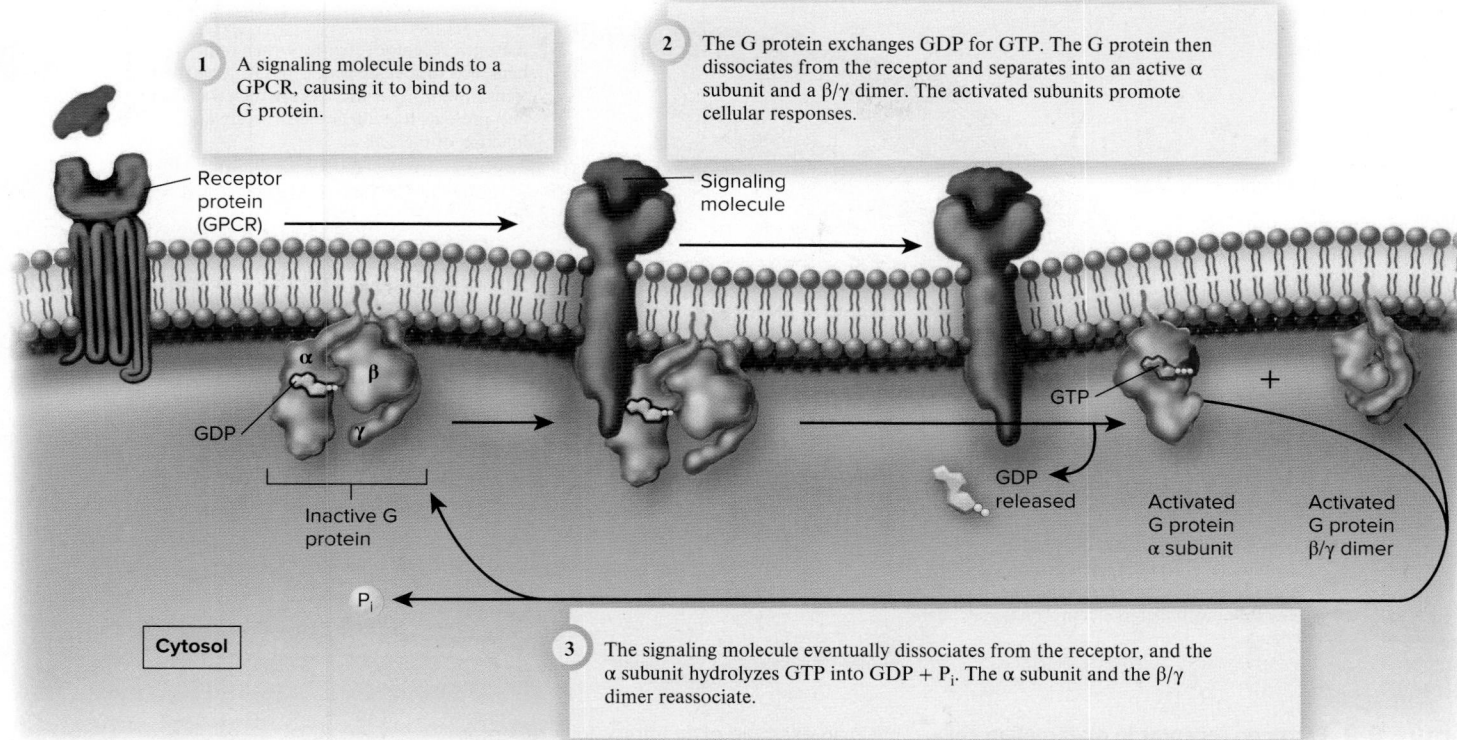

1 A signaling molecule binds to a GPCR, causing it to bind to a G protein.

2 The G protein exchanges GDP for GTP. The G protein then dissociates from the receptor and separates into an active α subunit and a β/γ dimer. The activated subunits promote cellular responses.

Receptor protein (GPCR)

Signaling molecule

α

β

γ

GDP

GTP

GDP released

Activated G protein α subunit

Activated G protein β/γ dimer

Inactive G protein

P$_i$

Cytosol

3 The signaling molecule eventually dissociates from the receptor, and the α subunit hydrolyzes GTP into GDP + P$_i$. The α subunit and the β/γ dimer reassociate.

Figure 9.7 **The activation of G-protein-coupled receptors (GPCRs) and G proteins.** Note: All three receptors shown in this figure are the same receptor, but the one on the left is drawn with greater detail to emphasize that it has seven transmembrane segments.

Concept Check: *What has to happen before the α and β/γ subunits of the G protein can reassociate with each other?*

Alfred Gilman and coworkers used genetic and biochemical techniques to identify and purify a G protein. In 1994, Rodbell and Gilman won the Nobel Prize in Physiology or Medicine for their pioneering work.

Figure 9.7 shows how a GPCR and a G protein interact. At the cell surface, a signaling molecule binds to a GPCR, causing a conformational change that activates the receptor, enabling it to bind to a G protein. The G protein, which is a lipid-anchored protein, releases GDP and binds GTP instead. The binding of GTP changes the conformation of the G protein, causing it to dissociate into an α subunit and a β/γ dimer. Later in this chapter, we will examine how the α subunit interacts with other proteins in a signal transduction pathway to elicit a cellular response. The β/γ dimer also plays a role in signal transduction. For example, it can regulate the function of ion channels in the plasma membrane.

When a signaling molecule and a GPCR dissociate, the GPCR is no longer activated, and the cellular response is reversed. For the G protein to return to the inactive state, the α subunit first hydrolyzes its bound GTP to GDP and P$_i$. After this occurs, the α and β/γ subunits reassociate with each other to form an inactive G protein.

Ligand-Gated Ion Channels   As described in Chapter 5, ion channels are proteins that allow the diffusion of ions across cell membranes. **Ligand-gated ion channels** are a third type of cell surface receptor found in the plasma membranes of animal, plant, and fungal cells. When signaling molecules (ligands) bind to this type of receptor, the ion channel opens and allows the flow of ions through the membrane, changing the concentration of the ions in the cell (**Figure 9.8**).

In animals, ligand-gated ion channels are important in the transmission of signals between neurons and muscle cells and between two

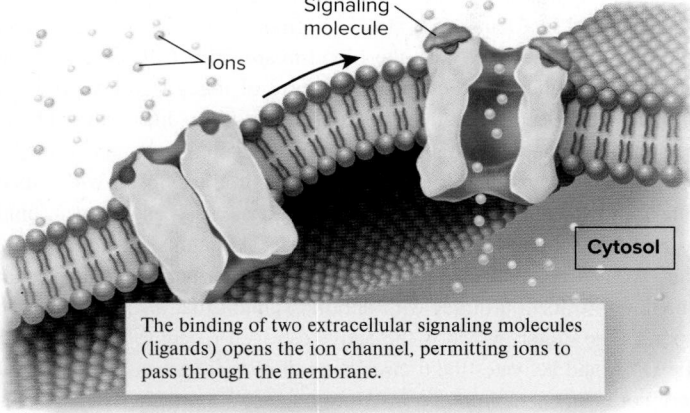

Signaling molecule

Ions

Cytosol

The binding of two extracellular signaling molecules (ligands) opens the ion channel, permitting ions to pass through the membrane.

Figure 9.8 **The function of a ligand-gated ion channel.**

neurons. In addition, ligand-gated ion channels in the plasma membrane allow the influx of Ca^{2+} into the cytosol. Changes in the cytosolic concentration of Ca^{2+} often play a role in signal transduction.

Cells Also Have Intracellular Receptors Activated by Signaling Molecules That Pass Through the Plasma Membrane

Although most receptors for signaling molecules are located in the plasma membrane, some are found inside the cell. In these cases, an extracellular signaling molecule must diffuse through the plasma membrane to gain access to its receptor.

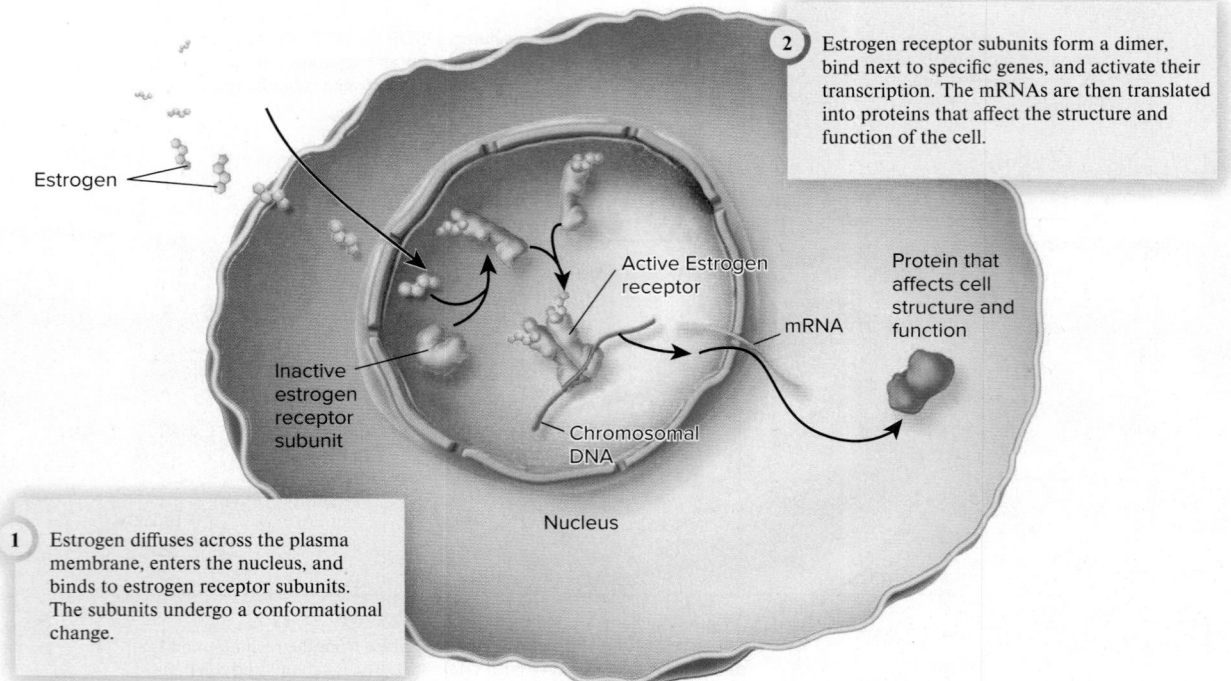

1 Estrogen diffuses across the plasma membrane, enters the nucleus, and binds to estrogen receptor subunits. The subunits undergo a conformational change.

2 Estrogen receptor subunits form a dimer, bind next to specific genes, and activate their transcription. The mRNAs are then translated into proteins that affect the structure and function of the cell.

Figure 9.9 **Estrogen receptor in mammalian cells.** This is an example of an intracellular receptor.

 Core Concept: Structure and Function The structure of the estrogen receptor, which is a dimer, has two important sites: the estrogen-binding site and the DNA-binding site. When estrogen binds to its receptor, a conformational change occurs that allows the DNA-binding site to function. The estrogen receptor then binds to the DNA and activates the transcription of specific genes.

In vertebrates, receptors for steroid hormones are intracellular. As discussed in Chapter 51, steroid hormones, such as estrogens and androgens, are secreted into the bloodstream from cells of endocrine glands. The behavior of estrogen is typical of many steroid hormones (**Figure 9.9**). Because estrogen is hydrophobic, it can diffuse through the plasma membrane of a target cell and bind to receptor subunits inside the cell. Some steroids bind to receptor subunits in the cytosol, which then travel into the nucleus. Other steroid hormones, such as estrogen, bind to receptor subunits already in the nucleus. After this binding occurs, the estrogen receptor subunit undergoes a conformational change that enables it to form a dimer with another subunit that also has estrogen bound. The dimer, which is the active estrogen receptor, then binds to the DNA and activates the transcription of specific genes. The estrogen receptor is an example of a transcription factor—a protein that regulates the transcription of genes. The expression of specific genes changes cell structure and function in a way that results in a cellular response.

9.3 Signal Transduction and the Cellular Response

Learning Outcomes:

1. For signaling molecules that bind to receptor tyrosine kinases or G-protein-coupled receptors, describe the signal transduction pathways and how those pathways lead to a cellular response.
2. Relate the function of second messengers to signal transduction pathways.

3. List examples of second messengers, and explain how they exert their effects.

We now turn our attention to the intracellular events that enable a cell to respond to a signaling molecule that binds to a cell surface receptor: signal transduction and a cellular response. In most cases, the binding of a signaling molecule to its receptor stimulates a signal transduction pathway. We will begin by examining a pathway that is controlled by an enzyme-linked receptor, and then consider G-protein-coupled receptors.

Receptor Tyrosine Kinases Activate Signal Transduction Pathways Involving a Protein Kinase Cascade That Alters Gene Transcription

Receptor tyrosine kinases are a category of enzyme-linked receptors that are found in all animals and also in choanoflagellates, which are the protists that are most closely related to animals (see Chapter 28). However, they are not found in bacteria, archaea, or other eukaryotic species. (Bacteria do have receptor histidine kinases, and all eukaryotes have receptor serine/threonine kinases.) The human genome contains about 60 different genes that encode receptor tyrosine kinases that recognize various types of signaling molecules such as hormones.

Figure 9.10 shows a simplified signal transduction pathway for epidermal growth factor (EGF). A **growth factor** is a signaling molecule that promotes cell division. Multicellular organisms, such as plants and animals, produce a variety of different growth factors to coordinate cell division throughout the body. In vertebrate animals,

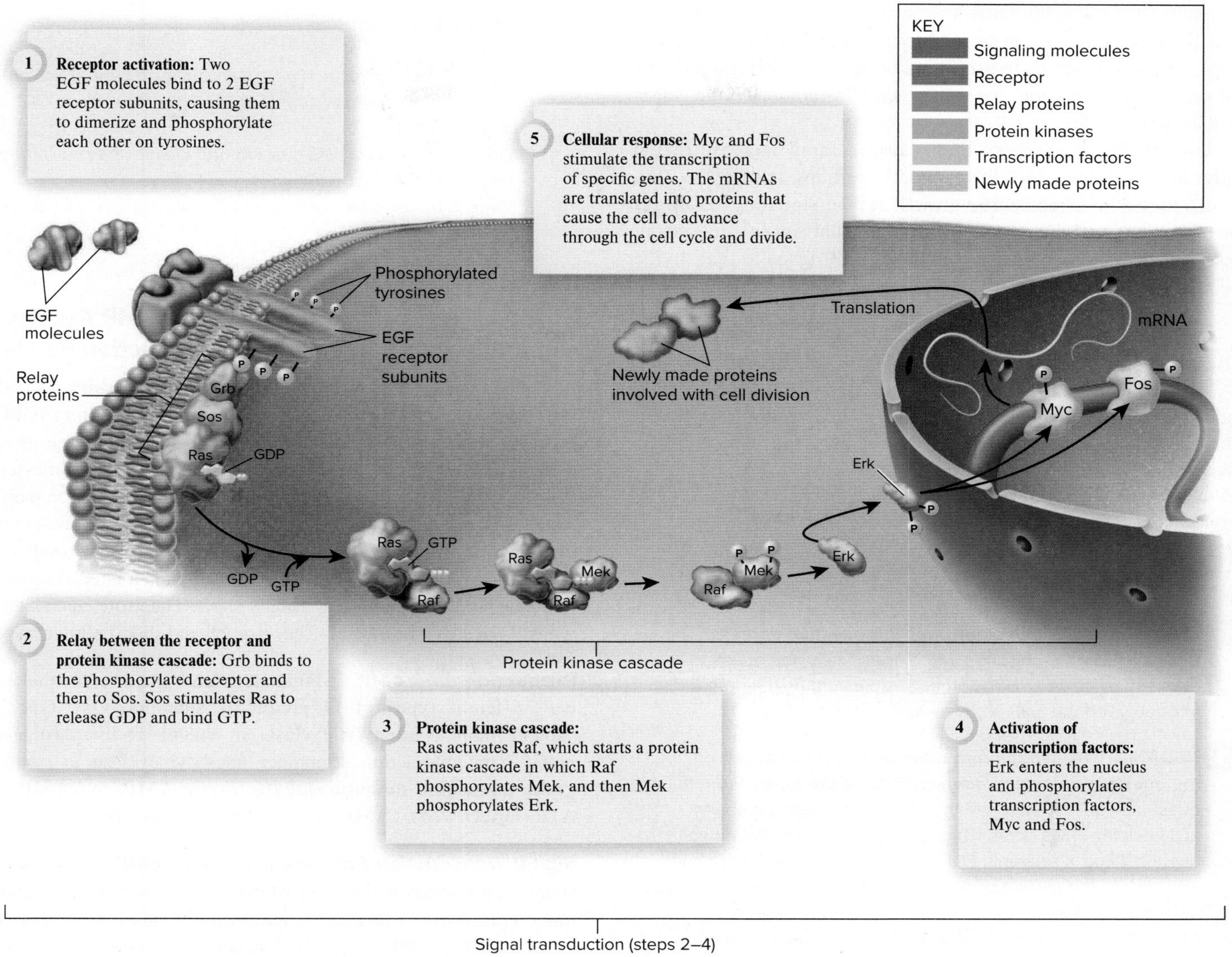

KEY
- Signaling molecules
- Receptor
- Relay proteins
- Protein kinases
- Transcription factors
- Newly made proteins

1 **Receptor activation:** Two EGF molecules bind to 2 EGF receptor subunits, causing them to dimerize and phosphorylate each other on tyrosines.

5 **Cellular response:** Myc and Fos stimulate the transcription of specific genes. The mRNAs are translated into proteins that cause the cell to advance through the cell cycle and divide.

EGF molecules

Relay proteins

Phosphorylated tyrosines

EGF receptor subunits

Grb

Sos

Ras

GDP

Translation

mRNA

Newly made proteins involved with cell division

Myc

Fos

Erk

Ras GTP

Raf

Ras Mek Raf

Mek Raf Erk

Erk

GDP GTP

2 **Relay between the receptor and protein kinase cascade:** Grb binds to the phosphorylated receptor and then to Sos. Sos stimulates Ras to release GDP and bind GTP.

Protein kinase cascade

3 **Protein kinase cascade:** Ras activates Raf, which starts a protein kinase cascade in which Raf phosphorylates Mek, and then Mek phosphorylates Erk.

4 **Activation of transcription factors:** Erk enters the nucleus and phosphorylates transcription factors, Myc and Fos.

Signal transduction (steps 2–4)

Figure 9.10 **The epidermal growth factor (EGF) pathway that promotes cell division.**

 Core Skill: Connections Look ahead to Figures 15.11 and, in particular, 15.12. Certain mutations alter the structure of the Ras protein so it does not hydrolyze GTP. Such mutations cause cancer. Explain why.

EGF is secreted from endocrine cells, travels through the bloodstream, and binds to a receptor tyrosine kinase, which is located on target cells and called the EGF receptor. EGF is responsible for stimulating epidermal cells, such as skin cells, to divide. Following receptor activation, the three general parts of the signal transduction pathway are (1) relay proteins activate a protein kinase cascade; (2) the protein kinase cascade phosphorylates intracellular proteins such as transcription factors; and (3) the phosphorylated transcription factors stimulate gene transcription. Next, we will consider the details of this pathway.

EGF Receptor Activation For receptor activation to occur, two EGF receptor subunits each bind to a molecule of EGF. The binding of EGF causes the subunits to dimerize and phosphorylate each other on tyrosines within the receptors, which is why they are named receptor tyrosine kinases. Once the EGF receptor is activated, the signal transduction pathway starts.

Relay Proteins The phosphorylated form of the EGF receptor is first recognized by a relay protein of the signal transduction pathway called Grb. This interaction changes the conformation of Grb, causing it to bind another relay protein in the signal transduction pathway termed Sos, causing it to undergo a conformational change. This activation of Sos causes a third relay protein called Ras to release GDP and bind GTP. The GTP form of Ras is the active form.

Protein Kinase Cascade The function of the relay proteins is to activate a **protein kinase cascade**. This cascade involves the sequential activation of three protein kinases. Activated Ras binds to Raf, the first protein kinase in the cascade. Raf then phosphorylates Mek, which becomes active and, in turn, phosphorylates Erk.

Activation of Transcription Factors and the Cellular Response
The phosphorylated form of Erk enters the nucleus and

phosphorylates transcription factors such as Myc and Fos. What is the cellular response? Once these transcription factors are phosphorylated, they stimulate the transcription of genes that encode proteins that promote cell division. After these proteins are made, the cell is stimulated to divide.

Growth factors such as EGF cause a rapid increase in the expression of many genes in mammals, perhaps as many as 100. As discussed in Chapter 15, growth factor signaling pathways are often involved in cancer. Mutations that cause proteins in these pathways to become hyperactive result in cells that divide uncontrollably!

BIO TIPS

THE QUESTION *One of the genes that is activated by the EGF signaling pathway is a gene called HSF1, which encodes a protein that is thought to be important for regulating cell division. Let's suppose that researchers have identified a drug that prevents EGF from activating the HSF1 gene. In the laboratory, this drug seems to prevent the growth of certain types of cancer cells. Propose a hypothesis for how this drug exerts its effect. In other words, which protein in the cell might drug X be binding to, and how does drug X affect that protein's function?*

TOPIC *What topic in biology does this question address?* The topic is cell communication. More specifically, the question asks you to propose a hypothesis explaining how a drug might interfere with the EGF pathway and prevent cancer.

INFORMATION *What information do you know based on the question and your understanding of the topic?* From the question, you have learned that the EGF signaling pathway activates the *HSF1* gene, which plays a role in regulating cell division. Drug X prevents EGF from turning on the *HSF1* gene and inhibits the growth of certain kinds of cancer cells. From your understanding of the topic, you may remember that the EGF pathway involves a series of steps, beginning with the binding of EGF to its receptor.

PROBLEM-SOLVING **S** STRATEGY *Sort out the steps in a complicated process. Propose a hypothesis.* One strategy to begin to solve this problem is to analyze the steps in the EGF pathway (see Figure 9.10) and identify the proteins involved. Any of these proteins could potentially be the target of drug X. Propose a hypothesis for how drug X could bind to one of these proteins and alter its function in a way that would prevent the expression of the *HSF1* gene and thus prevent cancer cells from dividing.

ANSWER *For drug X to exert its effect, it must be inhibiting one of the steps of the EGF pathway. Here are some possible hypotheses for how drug X works:*

1. *Drug X binds to the EGF receptor and inhibits the ability of EGF to bind to the receptor.*
2. *Drug X binds to the EGF receptor and inhibits its ability to phosphorylate itself.*
3. *Drug X binds to Grb and inhibits its ability to bind to the EGF receptor or to Sos.*
4. *Drug X binds to Sos and inhibits its ability to bind to Grb or to Ras.*
5. *Drug X binds to Ras and inhibits its ability to bind to Sos or Raf.*
6. *Drug X binds to Ras and inhibits its ability to release GDP or to bind GTP.*
7. *Drug X binds to Raf, Mek, or Erk and inhibits the phosphorylation of its target protein.*
8. *Drug X binds to Myc or Fos and inhibits the ability to activate a gene.*

Second Messengers Such as Cyclic AMP Are Key Components of Many Signal Transduction Pathways

Let's now turn to examples of signal transduction pathways and cellular responses that involve G-protein-coupled receptors (GPCRs). Extracellular signaling molecules that bind to cell surface receptors are sometimes referred to as first messengers. After first messengers bind to receptors such as GPCRs, many signal transduction pathways lead to the production of **second messengers**—small molecules or ions that relay signals inside the cell. The signals that result in second messenger production often act quickly, in a matter of seconds or minutes, but their duration is usually short. Therefore, such signaling typically occurs when a cell needs a quick and short cellular response.

Production of cAMP Mammalian and plant cells make several different types of G protein α subunits. One type of α subunit binds to **adenylyl cyclase**, an enzyme in the plasma membrane. This interaction stimulates adenylyl cyclase to synthesize **cyclic adenosine monophosphate (cyclic AMP,** or **cAMP)** from ATP (**Figure 9.11**). cAMP is an example of a second messenger.

Signal Transduction Pathway Involving cAMP Let's explore a signal transduction pathway in which the GPCR recognizes the hormone epinephrine (also called adrenaline). This hormone is sometimes called the fight-or-flight hormone. Epinephrine is produced when an individual is confronted with a stressful situation and helps the individual deal with a perceived threat or danger.

First, epinephrine binds to its receptor and activates a G protein (**Figure 9.12**). The α subunit then activates adenylyl cyclase, which catalyzes the production of cAMP from ATP. One effect of cAMP is to activate protein kinase A (PKA), which is composed of four subunits: two catalytic subunits that phosphorylate specific cellular proteins, and two regulatory subunits that inhibit the catalytic subunits when they are bound to each other. cAMP binds to the regulatory subunits of PKA. The binding of cAMP separates the regulatory and catalytic subunits, which allows each catalytic subunit to be active.

Cellular Response via PKA How does PKA activation lead to a cellular response? The catalytic subunit of PKA phosphorylates specific cellular proteins such as enzymes, structural proteins, and transcription factors. The phosphorylation of enzymes and structural proteins influences the structure and function of the cell. Likewise, the phosphorylation of transcription factors leads to the synthesis of new proteins that affect cell structure and function.

As a specific example of a cellular response, **Figure 9.13** shows how a skeletal muscle cell responds to elevated levels of epinephrine.

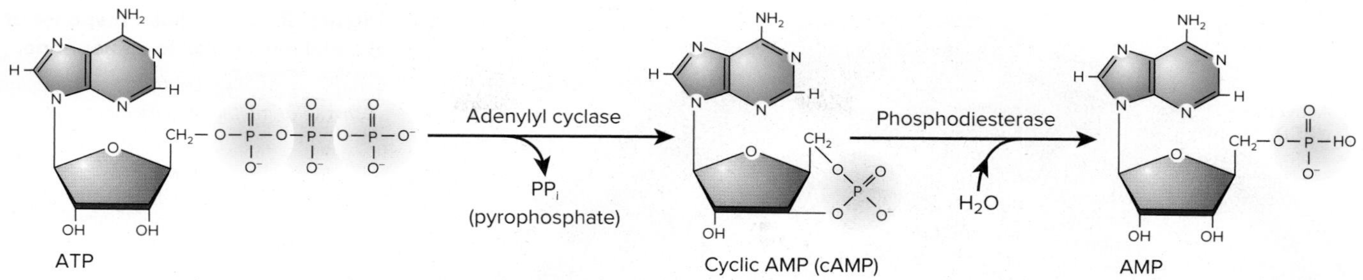

Figure 9.11 **The synthesis and breakdown of cyclic AMP.** Cyclic AMP (cAMP) is a second messenger formed from ATP by adenylyl cyclase, an enzyme in the plasma membrane. cAMP is inactivated by the action of an enzyme called phosphodiesterase, which converts cAMP to AMP.

When PKA becomes active, it phosphorylates two enzymes— phosphorylase kinase and glycogen synthase. Both of these enzymes are involved with the metabolism of glycogen, which is a polymer of glucose used to store energy.

- When phosphorylase kinase is phosphorylated, it becomes activated. The function of phosphorylase kinase is to phosphorylate another enzyme in the cell called glycogen phosphorylase, which then becomes activated. This enzyme causes glycogen breakdown by phosphorylating glucose units at the ends of a glycogen polymer, which releases individual glucose-phosphate molecules from glycogen:

$$\text{Glycogen}_n + \text{P}_i \xrightarrow{\text{Glycogen phosphorylase}} \text{Glycogen}_{n-1} + \text{Glucose-phosphate}$$

where n is the number of glucose units in the glycogen polymer.

- When PKA phosphorylates glycogen synthase, the function of this enzyme is inhibited rather than activated (see Figure 9.13). The function of glycogen synthase is to make glycogen. Therefore, the effect of cAMP is to prevent glycogen synthesis.

Taken together, the effects of epinephrine in skeletal muscle cells are to stimulate glycogen breakdown and inhibit glycogen synthesis. This provides these cells with more glucose molecules, which they can use for the energy needed for muscle contraction. In this way, the individual is better prepared to fight or flee.

Reversal of the Cellular Response   As mentioned, signaling that involves second messengers is typically of short duration. When the signaling molecule is no longer produced and its concentration falls, a larger percentage of the receptors are not bound by their ligands. When a ligand dissociates from a GPCR, the GPCR becomes deactivated. Intracellularly, the α subunit hydrolyzes its GTP to GDP, and the α subunit and β/γ dimer reassociate to form an inactive G protein

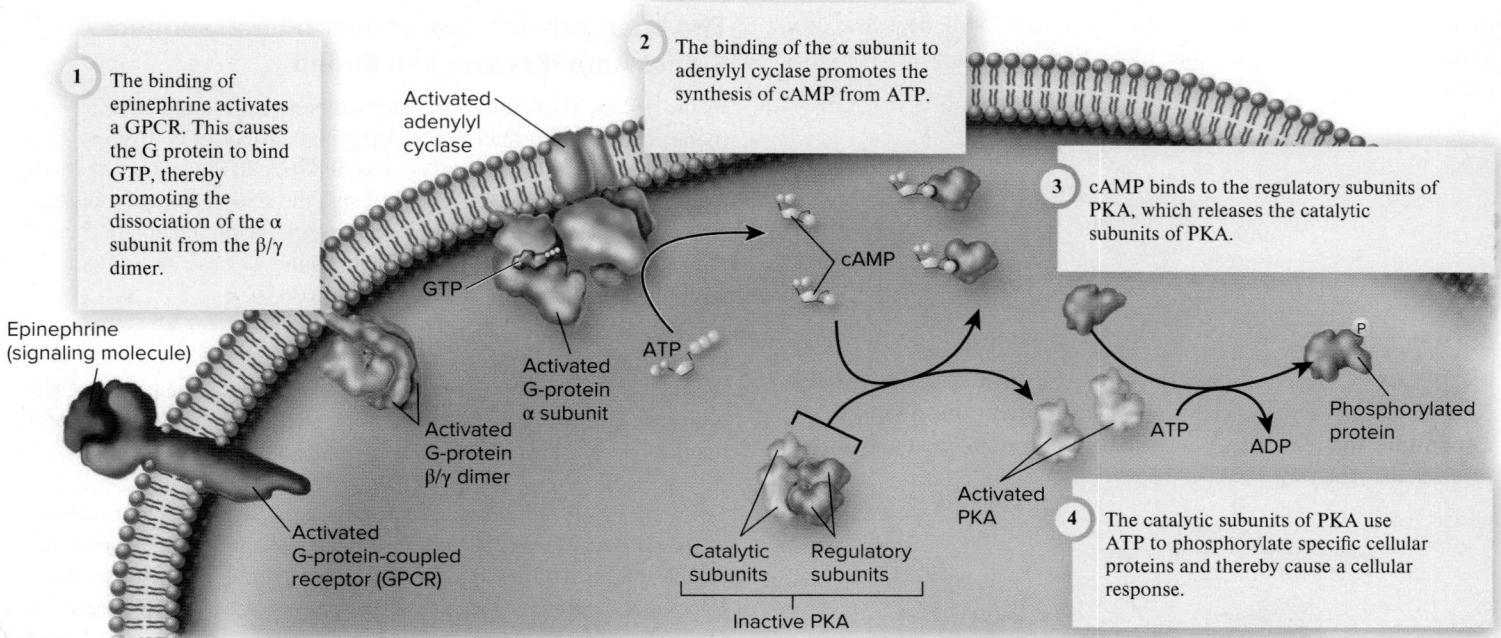

Figure 9.12 **A signal transduction pathway involving cAMP.** The pathway leading to the formation of cAMP and subsequent activation of protein kinase A (PKA), which is mediated by a G-protein-coupled receptor (GPCR).

Concept Check: *In this figure, where does the signal transduction pathway begin and end, and what is the cellular response?*

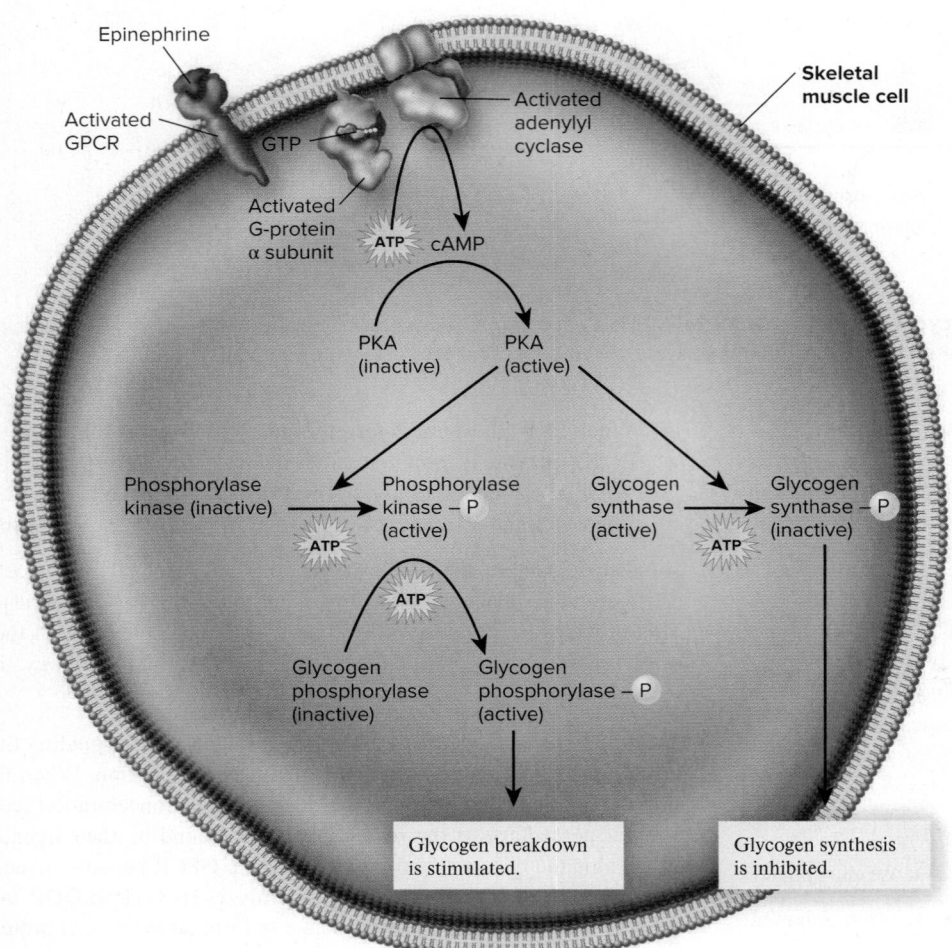

Figure 9.13 A cellular response of a skeletal muscle cell to epinephrine.

Concept Check: *Does phosphorylation activate or inhibit enzyme function?*

(refer back to step 3, Figure 9.7). The amount of cAMP decreases due to the action of an enzyme called **phosphodiesterase**, which converts cAMP to AMP:

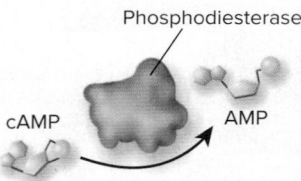

As the cAMP level falls, the regulatory subunits of PKA release cAMP, and the regulatory and catalytic subunits reassociate, thereby inhibiting PKA. Finally, enzymes called **protein phosphatases** are responsible for removing phosphate groups from proteins, which reverses the effects of PKA:

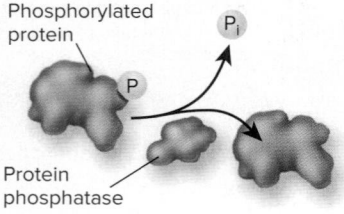

The Main Advantages of Second Messengers Are Signal Amplification and Speed

In the 1950s, Earl Sutherland determined that many different hormones cause the formation of cAMP in a variety of cell types. This observation, for which he won the Nobel Prize in Physiology or Medicine in 1971, stimulated great interest in the study of signal transduction pathways. Since Sutherland's discovery, the production of second messengers such as cAMP has been found to have two important advantages: signal amplification and speed.

Signal Amplification   Amplification of the signal involves the synthesis of many cAMP molecules, which, in turn, activate many PKA proteins (**Figure 9.14**). Likewise, each PKA protein phosphorylates many target proteins in the cell to promote a cellular response.

Speed   A second advantage of second messengers such as cAMP is speed. Because second messengers are relatively small and water-soluble, they can diffuse rapidly through the cytosol. For example, Brian Bacskai and colleagues studied the response of neurons to a signaling molecule called serotonin, which is a neurotransmitter that binds to a GPCR. In humans, low serotonin is believed to play a role in depression, anxiety, and other behavioral disorders. To monitor cAMP levels, neurons grown in a laboratory were injected with a fluorescent protein that

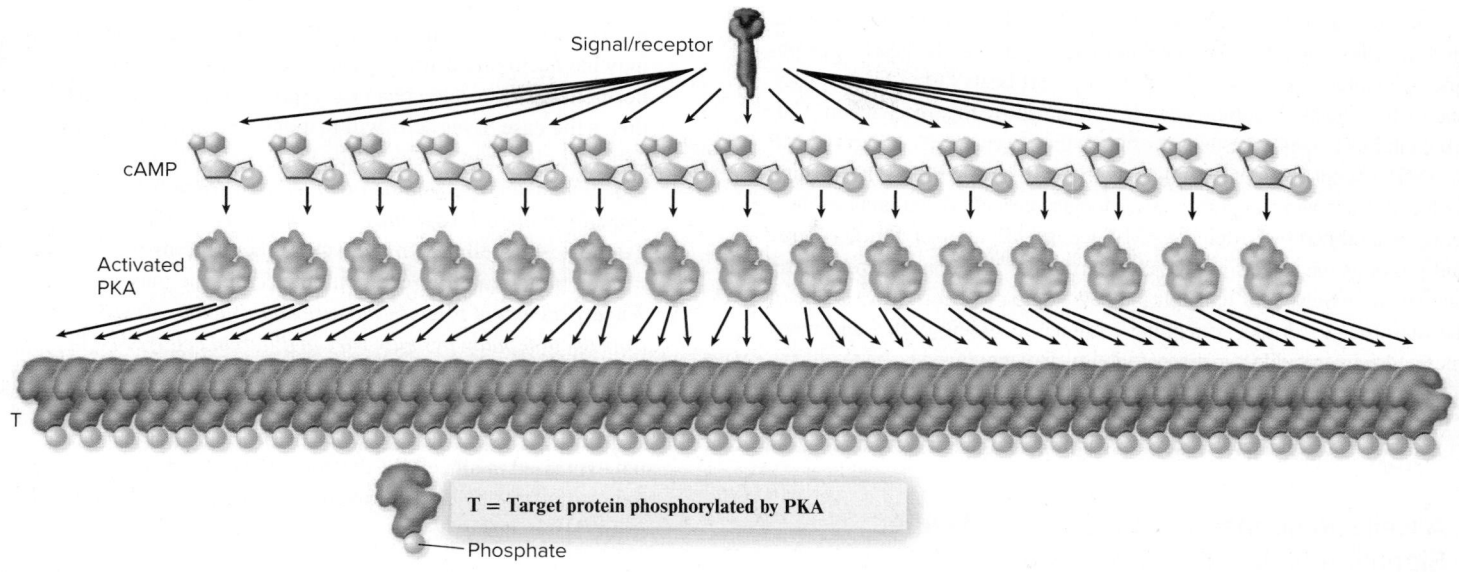

Signal/receptor

cAMP

Activated
PKA

T

T = Target protein phosphorylated by PKA

Phosphate

Figure 9.14 **Signal amplification.** An advantage of a signal transduction pathway is the amplification of a signal. In this case, a single signaling molecule leads to the phosphorylation of many, perhaps hundreds or thousands of, target proteins (designated T).

Concept Check: *In the case of signaling pathways involving hormones, why is signal amplification an advantage?*

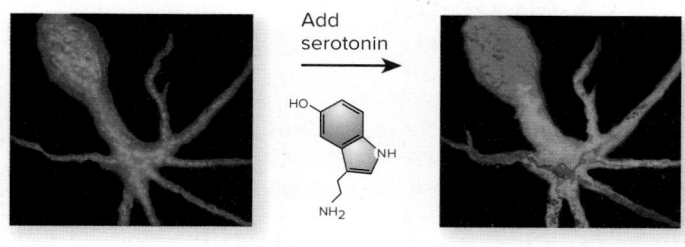

Add
serotonin

+ 20 seconds

Figure 9.15 **The rapid speed of cAMP production.** The schematic drawing on the left shows a neuron prior to its exposure to serotonin, a signaling molecule; the drawing on the right shows the same cell 20 seconds after exposure. Blue indicates a low level of cAMP, yellow is an intermediate level, and purple is a high level.

changes its fluorescence when cAMP is made. As shown schematically in the drawing on the right in **Figure 9.15**, such cells made a substantial amount of cAMP within 20 seconds after the addition of serotonin.

9.4 Hormonal Signaling in Multicellular Organisms

Learning Outcomes:

1. Explain how the cellular response to a particular hormone can vary among different cell types.
2. Describe how a cell's response to a hormone depends on the genes it expresses.

Thus far, we have considered how signaling molecules bind to particular types of receptors, thereby activating a signal transduction pathway that leads to a cellular response. In this section, we will consider how hormones in multicellular organisms exert a variety

of responses. As you will learn, the type of cellular response that is caused by a given hormone depends on the type of cell. Each cell type responds to a particular hormone in its own unique way. The variation in a cellular response is determined by the types of proteins, such as receptors and signal transduction proteins, that each cell type makes, which is determined by the genes expressed in that type of cell.

The Cellular Response to a Given Hormone Varies Among Different Cell Types

As we have seen, signaling molecules usually exert their effects on cells via signal transduction pathways that control the functions and/or synthesis of specific proteins. In multicellular organisms, one of the amazing effects of hormones is their ability to coordinate cellular activities. One example is epinephrine, which is secreted from endocrine cells. As mentioned earlier, epinephrine is also called the fight-or-flight hormone because it quickly prepares the body for strenuous physical activity in response to a perceived danger. Epinephrine is also secreted into the bloodstream when a person is exercising.

Epinephrine has different effects throughout the body (**Table 9.1**). We have already discussed how it promotes the breakdown of glycogen in

Table 9.1	Effects of Epinephrine in Humans
Organ/Tissue	**Effect**
Eye	Dilates pupils
Salivary glands	Inhibits the production of saliva
Skeletal muscle	Stimulates cells to break down glycogen and release glucose
Skin	Constricts blood vessels; stimulates sweating
Lungs	Relaxes airways so more oxygen is taken in
Heart	Increases the rate of beating

skeletal muscle cells (refer back to Figure 9.13). In the lungs, it relaxes the airways, allowing a person to take in more oxygen. In the heart, epinephrine stimulates heart muscle cells so the heart beats faster. Interestingly, one of the effects of caffeine can be explained by this mechanism. Caffeine inhibits phosphodiesterase, which is the enzyme that converts cAMP to AMP. Phosphodiesterase functions to remove cAMP once a signaling molecule, such as epinephrine, is no longer present. When phosphodiesterase is inhibited by caffeine, cAMP persists for a longer period of time and prolongs the effects of signaling molecules like epinephrine. Therefore, even low levels of epinephrine have a greater effect. This is one of the reasons why drinks containing caffeine, including coffee and many energy drinks, provide a feeling of vitality and energy.

 Core Concept: Information

A Cell's Response to Hormones and Other Signaling Molecules Depends on the Genes It Expresses

As Table 9.1 shows, the hormone epinephrine produces diverse responses throughout the body. How do we explain the observation that various cell types respond so differently to the same hormone? As a multicellular organism develops from a fertilized egg, the cells of the body become differentiated into particular types, such as heart and lung cells. The mechanisms that underlie this differentiation process are described in Chapter 20. Although different cell types, such as heart and lung cells, contain the same set of genes—the same genome—those genes are not expressed in the same pattern in all cells. Certain genes that are turned off in heart cells are turned on in lung cells, whereas some genes that are turned on in heart cells are turned off in lung cells. This phenomenon, which is called **differential gene regulation**, causes each cell type to have its own distinct proteome. The set of proteins made in any given cell type is critical to a cell's ability to respond to signaling molecules. The following are examples of how differential gene regulation affects the cellular response:

1. *A cell may or may not express a receptor for a particular signaling molecule.* For example, not all cells of the human body express a receptor for epinephrine. Cells without such a receptor are not affected when epinephrine is released into the bloodstream.

2. *Different cell types have different cell surface receptors that recognize the same signaling molecule.* In humans, for example, a signaling molecule called acetylcholine has two different types of receptors. One acetylcholine receptor is a ligand-gated ion channel that is expressed in skeletal muscle cells. Another acetylcholine receptor is a G-protein-coupled receptor (GPCR) that is expressed in heart muscle cells. Because of this, acetylcholine activates different signal transduction pathways in skeletal and heart muscle cells. Therefore, these cells respond differently to acetylcholine.

3. *Two (or more) receptors may work the same way in different cell types but have different affinities for the same signaling molecule.* For example, two different GPCRs may recognize

the same hormone, but the receptor expressed in liver cells may have a higher affinity (that is, a lower K_d) for the hormone than does the receptor expressed in muscle cells. If this is the case, liver cells will respond to a lower hormone concentration than muscle cells do.

4. *The expression of proteins involved in intracellular signal transduction pathways may vary in different cell types.* For example, one cell type may express the proteins that are needed to activate PKA, but another cell type may not.

5. *The expression of proteins that are controlled by signal transduction pathways may vary in different cell types.* For example, the presence of epinephrine in skeletal muscle cells leads to the activation of glycogen phosphorylase, an enzyme involved in glycogen breakdown. However, this enzyme is not expressed in all cells of the body. Glycogen breakdown is only stimulated by epinephrine if glycogen phosphorylase is expressed in that cell.

9.5 Apoptosis: Programmed Cell Death

Learning Outcomes:
1. Define and describe apoptosis.
2. **CoreSKILL »** Analyze the results of experiments indicating that certain hormones control apoptosis.
3. Outline the extrinsic pathway of apoptosis.

We will end our discussion of cell communication by considering one of the most dramatic responses that eukaryotic cells exhibit—**apoptosis**, or programmed cell death. During this process, a cell orchestrates its own destruction! The cell first shrinks and becomes rounder due to the internal destruction of its nucleus and cytoskeleton (**Figure 9.16**). The plasma membrane then forms irregular extensions that eventually become blebs—small cell fragments that break away from the cell as it destroys itself (also look back at the chapter opening photo).

Cell biologists have discovered that apoptosis plays many important roles.

- During embryonic development in animals, it is needed to sculpt the tissues and organs. For example, the fingers on a human hand are initially webbed, but become separated during embryonic development when the cells between the fingers undergo apoptosis (see Figure 20.4).

- Apoptosis is also necessary in adult organisms to maintain the proper numbers of cells in tissues and organs.

- Programmed cell death also eliminates cells that have become worn out or infected by viruses, or have the potential to cause cancer.

During the past few decades, clinical research has revealed that many human diseases are associated with irregularities in apoptosis. **Table 9.2** describes a few examples. In this section, we will examine the pioneering work that led to the discovery of apoptosis and explore its molecular mechanism.

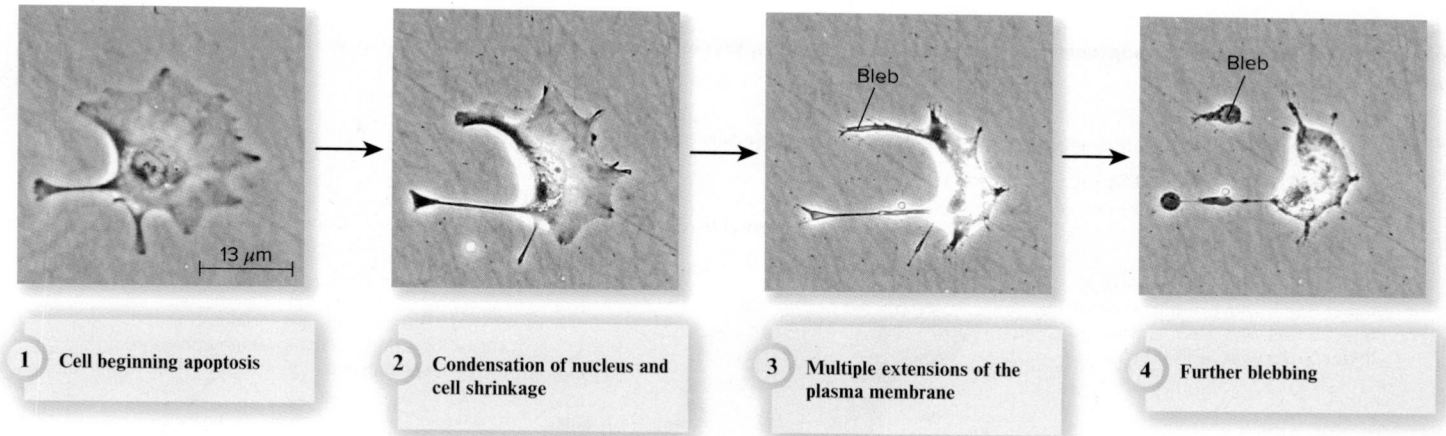

1 **Cell beginning apoptosis**

2 **Condensation of nucleus and cell shrinkage**

3 **Multiple extensions of the plasma membrane**

4 **Further blebbing**

Figure 9.16 Stages of apoptosis. (1–4): ©Prof. Guy Whitley/Reproductive and Cardiovascular Disease Research Group at St. George's University of London

Table 9.2	Relationship Between Certain Diseases and Abnormal Levels of Apoptosis
Disease	**Description/Examples**
Diminished levels of apoptosis	
Cancer	Cancer cells proliferate in an uncontrolled manner. In some forms of cancer, a decrease in the normal rate of apoptosis contributes to the faster proliferation rate. Examples include particular types of prostate and ovarian cancers.
Elevated levels of apoptosis	
Viral diseases	Certain viral diseases are associated with elevated levels of apoptosis. For example, infection by human immunodeficiency virus (HIV) results in an increased rate of apoptosis of helper T cells.
Neurodegenerative diseases	Some neurodegenerative diseases occur because specific neurons undergo an unusually high rate of apoptosis. An example is Parkinson's disease, which arises from a loss of dopaminergic neurons.

 **Core Skill: Process of Science**

Feature Investigation | Kerr, Wyllie, and Currie Found That Hormones May Control Apoptosis

How was apoptosis discovered? One line of evidence involved the microscopic examination of tissues in mammals. In the 1960s, British pathologist John Kerr microscopically examined liver tissue that was deprived of oxygen. He observed that, within hours of oxygen deprivation, some cells underwent a process that involved cell shrinkage. Around this time, similar results had been noted by other researchers, such as Scottish pathologists Andrew Wyllie and Alastair Currie, who had studied cell death in the adrenal glands. In 1973, Kerr, Wyllie, and Currie joined forces to study this process further.

Prior to that collaboration, other researchers had already established that certain hormones affect the growth of the adrenal glands, which sit atop the kidneys. Adrenocorticotropic hormone (ACTH) was known to increase the number of cells in the adrenal cortex, which is the outer layer of the adrenal glands. By contrast, the drug prednisolone was shown to suppress the synthesis of ACTH and cause a decrease in the number of cells in the cortex. In the experiment described in **Figure 9.17**, Kerr, Wyllie, and Currie wanted to understand how ACTH and prednisolone exert their effects. They subjected rats to four types of treatments. The control rats were injected with saline (salt water). Other rats were injected with prednisolone alone, prednisolone plus ACTH, or ACTH alone. After 2 days, samples of adrenal cortex were obtained from the rats and observed by light microscopy. Even in control samples,

the researchers occasionally observed cell death via apoptosis (see the micrograph in step 4). However, in prednisolone-treated rats, the cells in the adrenal cortex were found to undergo a dramatically higher rate of apoptosis. Multiple cells undergoing apoptosis were found in 9 out of every 10 samples observed under the light microscope. Such a high level of apoptosis was not observed in control samples or in samples obtained from rats treated with both prednisolone and ACTH or with ACTH alone. Therefore, ACTH appears to prevent apoptosis.

The results of Kerr, Wyllie, and Currie are important for two reasons. First, their results indicated that tissues decrease their cell number via a mechanism that involves cell shrinkage and eventually blebbing. Second, they showed that cell death followed a program that, in this case, was induced by the presence of prednisolone (which decreases ACTH). They coined the term apoptosis to describe this process.

As you may know, prednisone is an anti-inflammatory and immunosuppressive drug that is used to treat a wide variety of disorders, including asthma and rheumatoid arthritis. When taken into the body, it is converted to prednisolone by the liver. In recent years, prednisone has been used in conjunction with other therapies to treat certain forms of cancer, such as leukemia, which is cancer of white blood cells. Prednisone is thought to exert its effect by promoting apoptosis in the cancer cells.

Figure 9.17 Discovery of apoptosis in the adrenal cortex by Kerr, Wyllie, and Currie. (4): ©Dr. Thomas Caceci, Virginia-Maryland Regional College of Veterinary Medicine

---

HYPOTHESIS Hormones may affect cell number in the adrenal gland by controlling the rate of apoptosis.

KEY MATERIALS Laboratory rats, prednisolone, and ACTH.

	Experimental level	**Conceptual level**
1 Inject 5 rats with saline (control). Inject 5 rats with prednisolone alone. Inject 5 rats with prednisolone + ACTH. Inject 5 rats with ACTH alone.	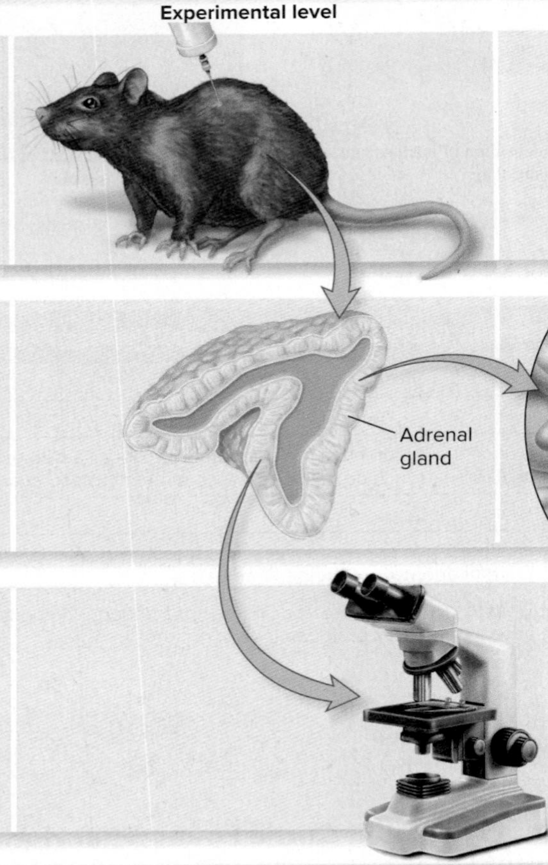	Previous studies indicated that prednisolone alone may promote apoptosis by lowering ACTH levels.
2 After 2 days, obtain samples of adrenal tissue from all 20 rats.	Adrenal gland	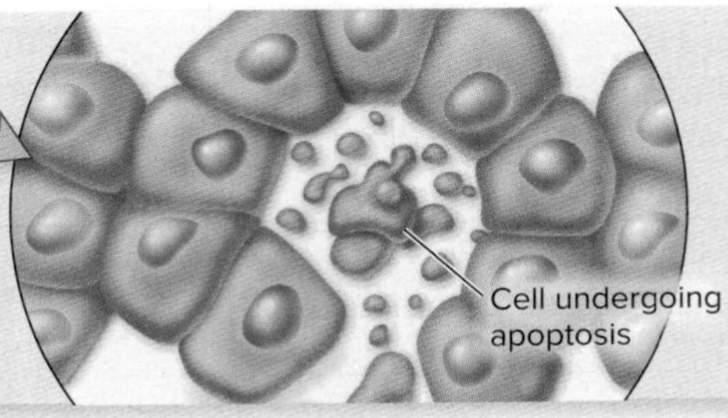 Cell undergoing apoptosis
3 Observe the samples via light microscopy, described in Chapter 4.		

4 THE DATA

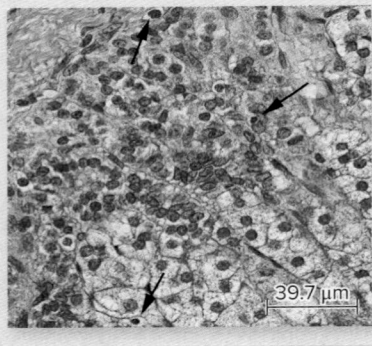

Micrograph of adrenal tissue showing occasional cells undergoing apoptosis (see arrows)

39.7 μm

Treatment	Number of animals	Glands with enhanced apoptosis*/Total number of animals
Saline	5	0/10
Prednisolone	5	9/10
Prednisolone + ACTH	5	0/10
ACTH	5	0/10

*Samples from two adrenal glands were removed from each animal. Enhanced apoptosis means that cells undergoing apoptosis were observed in every sample under the light microscope.

---

5 CONCLUSION Prednisolone alone, which lowers ACTH levels, causes some cells to undergo apoptosis. During this process, the cells shrink and form blebs as they kill themselves. Apoptosis is controlled by hormones.

6 SOURCE Wyllie, A. H., Kerr, J. F. R., Macaskill, I. A. M., and Currie, A. R. 1973. Adrenocortical cell deletion: the role of ACTH. *Journal of Pathology* 111: 85–94.

Experimental Questions

1. **CoreSKILL »** In the experiment of Figure 9.17, explain the effects on apoptosis in the control rats (injected with saline) versus those injected with prednisolone alone, predinisolone + ACTH, or ACTH alone.

2. Prednisolone inhibits the production of ACTH in rats. Do you think it inhibited the ability of rats to make their own ACTH when they were injected with both prednisolone and ACTH? Explain.

3. **CoreSKILL »** Of the four groups of rats—control, prednisolone alone, prednisolone + ACTH, and ACTH alone—which would you expect to have the lowest level of apoptosis? Explain.

Signal Transduction Pathways Lead to Apoptosis

Apoptosis involves the activation of cell-signaling pathways. One pathway, called the **extrinsic pathway**, begins with the activation of **death receptors** on the cell surface. When death receptors bind to extracellular signaling molecules, a pathway is stimulated that leads to apoptosis. **Figure 9.18** shows a simplified pathway for this process. In this example, the signaling molecule is a protein composed of three identical subunits—a trimeric protein. Such trimeric signaling molecules are typically produced by cells of the immune system that recognize abnormal cells and target them for destruction. For example, when a cell is infected with a virus, cells of the immune system may

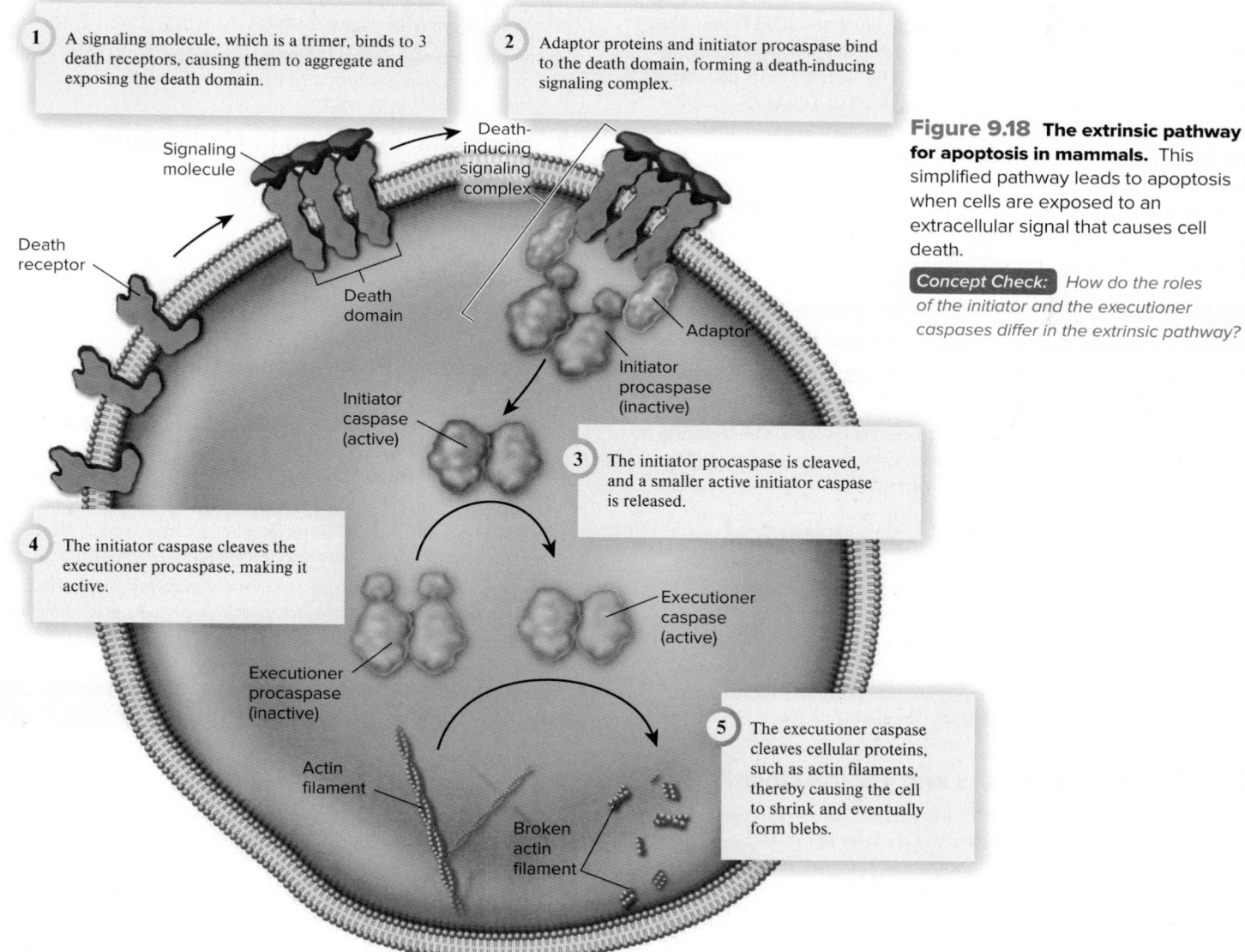

1   A signaling molecule, which is a trimer, binds to 3 death receptors, causing them to aggregate and exposing the death domain.

2   Adaptor proteins and initiator procaspase bind to the death domain, forming a death-inducing signaling complex.

Figure 9.18 The extrinsic pathway for apoptosis in mammals. This simplified pathway leads to apoptosis when cells are exposed to an extracellular signal that causes cell death.

Concept Check: *How do the roles of the initiator and the executioner caspases differ in the extrinsic pathway?*

Signaling molecule

Death-inducing signaling complex

Death receptor

Death domain

Adaptor

Initiator procaspase (inactive)

Initiator caspase (active)

3   The initiator procaspase is cleaved, and a smaller active initiator caspase is released.

4   The initiator caspase cleaves the executioner procaspase, making it active.

Executioner caspase (active)

Executioner procaspase (inactive)

Actin filament

5   The executioner caspase cleaves cellular proteins, such as actin filaments, thereby causing the cell to shrink and eventually form blebs.

Broken actin filament

target the infected cell for apoptosis. The signaling molecule binds to three death receptors, which causes them to aggregate into a trimer. This results in a conformational change that exposes a domain on the death receptors called the death domain. Once the death domain is exposed, it binds to adaptors, which then bind to an initiator procaspase. The complex between the death receptors, adaptors, and initiator procaspase is called the death-inducing signaling complex (DISC).

Once the initiator procaspase, which is inactive, is part of the death-inducing signaling complex, it is converted by proteolytic cleavage to an initiator caspase, which is active. An active **caspase** functions as a protease—an enzyme that digests other proteins. After it is activated, the initiator caspase is then released from the DISC. This caspase is called an initiator caspase because it initiates the activation of many other caspases in the cell. These other caspases are called executioner, or effector, caspases because they are directly responsible for digesting intracellular proteins and causing the cell to die. The executioner caspases digest a variety of intracellular proteins, including the proteins that constitute the cytoskeleton and nuclear lamina as well as proteins involved with DNA replication and repair. In this way, the executioner caspases cause the cellular changes shown in Figure 9.16. The caspases also activate an enzyme called DNase that chops the DNA in the cell into small fragments. This event may be particularly important for eliminating virally infected cells because it also destroys viral genomes that are composed of DNA.

Alternatively, another pathway of apoptosis, called the **intrinsic pathway** or **mitochondrial pathway**, is stimulated by DNA damage that could cause cancer. Mitochondria release cytochrome c (a small mitochondrial protein) into the cytosol, where it forms a complex with other proteins called an **apoptosome**. The apoptosome then initiates the activation of caspases.

Summary of Key Concepts

9.1 General Features of Cell Communication

- A signal is an agent that can influence the properties of cells. A signal binds to a receptor to elicit a cellular response. Cell signaling enables cells to sense and respond to environmental changes and to communicate with each other (Figures 9.1, 9.2).
- Cell-to-cell communication varies in terms of the mechanism of signal transmission and the distance that a signal travels. Signals are relayed between cells in five common ways: direct intercellular, contact-dependent, autocrine, paracrine, and endocrine signaling (Figure 9.3).
- Cell signaling is usually a three-stage process involving receptor activation, signal transduction, and a cellular response. A signal transduction pathway is a group of proteins that convert an initial signal to a different signal inside the cell (Figure 9.4).

9.2 Cellular Receptors and Their Activation

- A signaling molecule, also called a ligand, binds to a receptor with an affinity that is measured as the value of a dissociation constant, K_d. The binding of a ligand to a receptor is usually very specific and alters the conformation of the receptor (Figure 9.5).
- Enzyme-linked receptors have some type of catalytic function. Many of them are protein kinases that phosphorylate proteins (Figure 9.6).

- G-protein-coupled receptors (GPCRs) interact with G proteins to initiate a cellular response (Figure 9.7).
- Ligand-gated ion channels are receptors that allow the flow of ions across the plasma membrane (Figure 9.8).
- Although most receptors involved in cell signaling are found on the cell surface, some receptors, such as the estrogen receptor, are intracellular receptors (Figure 9.9).

9.3 Signal Transduction and the Cellular Response

- Signaling pathways influence whether or not a cell divides. An example is the pathway that is stimulated by epidermal growth factor, which binds to a receptor tyrosine kinase (Figure 9.10).
- Second messengers, such as cAMP, play a key role in signal transduction pathways, such as those that occur via GPCRs. These pathways are reversible once the signal is degraded (Figures 9.11, 9.12).
- An example of a pathway that uses cAMP is found in skeletal muscle cells responding to elevated levels of epinephrine, the fight-or-flight hormone. Epinephrine enhances the function of enzymes that increase glycogen breakdown and inhibits enzymes that cause glycogen synthesis (Figure 9.13).
- Second messengers amplify the signal and increase the speed of signaling pathways (Figures 9.14, 9.15).

9.4 Hormonal Signaling in Multicellular Organisms

- Hormones such as epinephrine exert different effects throughout the body (Table 9.1).
- The way in which any particular cell type responds to a signaling molecule depends on the set of proteins it makes. The amounts of these proteins are controlled by differential gene regulation.

9.5 Apoptosis: Programmed Cell Death

- Apoptosis is the process of programmed cell death in which the nucleus and cytoskeleton break down and eventually the cell breaks apart into blebs. Irregularities in apoptosis are associated with some diseases (Figure 9.16, Table 9.2).
- Microscopy studies of Kerr, Wyllie, and Currie, in which they studied the effects of ACTH on the adrenal cortex, were instrumental in the identification of apoptosis (Figure 9.17).
- Apoptosis occurs via extrinsic or intrinsic pathways. The extrinsic pathway is stimulated when an extracellular signaling molecule binds to death receptors (Figure 9.18).

Assess & Discuss

Test Yourself

1. An agent that allows a cell to respond to changes in its environment is termed
   a. a cell surface receptor.
   b. an intracellular receptor.
   c. a structural protein.
   d. a signal.
   e. apoptosis.

2. When a cell secretes a signaling molecule that binds to receptors on neighboring cells as well as the cell itself, this is called _____ signaling.
   a. direct intercellular
   b. contact-dependent
   c. autocrine
   d. paracrine
   e. endocrine

3. Which of the following does *not* describe a typical cellular response to signaling molecules?
   a. activation of enzymes within the cell
   b. change in the function of structural proteins, which determine cell shape
   c. alteration of levels of certain proteins in the cell by changing the level of gene expression
   d. change in a gene sequence that encodes a particular protein
   e. all of the above are examples of cellular responses.

4. A receptor has a K_d for its ligand of 50 nM. This receptor
   a. has a higher affinity for its ligand than does a receptor with a K_d of 100 nM.
   b. has a higher affinity for its ligand than does a receptor with a K_d of 10 nM.
   c. is mostly bound by its ligand when the ligand concentration is 100 nM.
   d. must be an intracellular receptor.
   e. both a and c are true of this ligand.

5. _____ binds to receptors inside cells.
   a. Estrogen
   b. Epinephrine
   c. Epidermal growth factor
   d. all of the above bind to such receptors.
   e. none of the above binds to such receptors.

6. The relay protein Ras is part of the EGF pathway that promotes cell division (see Figure 9.10). The active form of Ras has GTP bound to it, whereas the inactive form has GDP. GTP is hydrolyzed to GDP and P_i to switch Ras from the active to the inactive form. Researchers have discovered that certain forms of cancer involve mutations in the gene that encodes the Ras protein. Which of the following types of mutations would you expect to promote cell division and thereby lead to cancer?
   a. a mutation that prevents the synthesis of Ras
   b. a mutation that causes Ras to bind GDP more tightly
   c. a mutation that prevents the GTP bound to Ras from being hydrolyzed
   d. a mutation that prevents Ras from binding to Raf
   e. both b and c

7. The benefit of second messengers in signal transduction pathways is
   a. an increase in the speed of a cellular response.
   b. duplication of the ligands in the system.
   c. amplification of the signal.
   d. all of the above.
   e. a and c only.

8. All cells of a multicellular organism may not respond in the same way to a particular ligand (signaling molecule) that binds to a cell surface receptor. The difference in response may be due to
   a. the type of receptor for the ligand that the cell expresses.
   b. the affinity of the ligand for the receptor in a given cell type.
   c. the type of signal transduction pathways that the cell expresses.
   d. the type of target proteins that the cell expresses.
   e. all of the above.

9. Apoptosis is the process of
   a. cell migration.
   b. cell signaling.
   c. signal transduction.
   d. signal amplification.
   e. programmed cell death.

10. Which statement best describes the extrinsic pathway for apoptosis?
    a. Caspases recognize an environmental signal and expose their death domain.
    b. Death receptors recognize an environmental signal, which then leads to the activation of caspases.
    c. Initiator caspases digest the nuclear lamina and cytoskeleton.
    d. Executioner caspases are part of the death-inducing signaling complex (DISC).
    e. All of the above are true of the extrinsic pathway.

Conceptual Questions

1. What are the two general reasons that cell communication is essential?

2. What are the three stages of cell signaling? What stage does *not* occur when the estrogen receptor is activated?

3. **Core Concept: Systems** Discuss how cell signaling helps organisms to interact with their environment.

Collaborative Questions

1. Discuss and compare several different types of cell-to-cell communication. What are some advantages and disadvantages of each type?

2. How does differential gene regulation enable various cell types to respond differently to the same signaling molecule? Why is this useful to multicellular organisms?

Multicellularity

10

The General Sherman in Sequoia National Park, a striking example of the size that multicellular organisms can reach. This tree is thought to be the largest organism (by mass) in the world. ©Altrendo Panoramic/Getty Images

What is the largest living organism on Earth? The size of an organism can be defined by its volume, mass, height, length, or the area it occupies. A giant fungus (*Armillaria ostoyae*), growing in the soil in Malheur National Forest in Oregon, spans 8.9 km², or 2,200 acres, which makes it the largest known organism by area. Most of this organism lies below ground, so it is not visible from the surface. In the Mediterranean Sea, marine biologists discovered a giant aquatic plant (*Posidonia oceanica*) whose length is 8 km, or 4.3 miles, making it the world's longest known organism. With regard to mass, the largest organism is probably a tree named the General Sherman, which is 83.8 m tall (275 feet), nearly the length of a football field (see the chapter opening photo). This giant sequoia tree (*Sequoiadendron giganteum*) is estimated to weigh nearly 2 million kg (over 2,000 tons)—equivalent to a herd of 400 elephants!

An organism composed of more than one cell is said to be **multicellular**. The preceding examples illustrate the amazing sizes that certain multicellular organisms have attained.

As we will discuss in Chapter 26, multicellular organisms came into being approximately 1 billion years ago. Some species of protists are multicellular, as are most species of fungi. In this chapter, we will focus on plants and animals, which are always multicellular species.

The main benefit of multicellularity arises from the division of labor between different types of cells in an organism. For example, the intestinal cells of animals and the root cells of plants have become specialized for nutrient uptake. Other types of cells in a multicellular organism perform different roles, such as reproduction. In animals, most of the cells of the body—somatic cells—are devoted to the growth, development, and survival of the organism, whereas specialized cells—gametes—function in sexual reproduction.

Multicellular species usually have much larger genomes than unicellular species. The increase in genome size is associated with an increase in proteome size—multicellular organisms produce a larger array of proteins than do unicellular species. The additional proteins play a role in three general phenomena.

- First, in a multicellular organism, cell communication is vital for the proper organization and functioning of cells. Many more proteins involved in cell communication are made in multicellular species.
- Second, both the arrangement of cells within the organism and the attachment of cells to each other require a greater variety of proteins in multicellular species than in unicellular species.
- Finally, additional proteins play a role in cell specialization because proteins that are needed for the structure and function of one cell type may not be needed in a different cell type, and vice versa. Likewise, additional proteins are needed to regulate the expression of genes so that all proteins are expressed in the proper cell types.

In this chapter, we will consider the cellular characteristics that are specific to multicellular organisms. We begin by exploring the material that is produced by animal and plant cells to form an extracellular matrix or cell wall, respectively. This material plays many important roles in the structure, organization, and functioning of cells within multicellular organisms. We will then turn our attention to cell junctions, specialized structures that enable cells to make physical contact with one another. Cells within multicellular organisms form junctions that help the cells function in a cohesive and well-organized way. Finally, we will examine the organization and function of tissues, groups of cells that have a similar structure and function. In this chapter, we will survey the general features of tissues from a cellular perspective. Units VI and VII will explore the characteristics of particular plant and animal tissues in greater detail.

10.1 Extracellular Matrix and Cell Walls

Learning Outcomes:

1. Explain the functional roles of the extracellular matrix in animals.
2. Outline the major structural components of the ECM of animals.
3. Describe the structure and function of plant cell walls.

Organisms are not composed solely of cells. A large portion of an animal or plant consists of a network of material that is secreted from cells and forms a complex meshwork outside of cells. In animals, this is called the **extracellular matrix (ECM)**, whereas plant cells are surrounded by a **cell wall**. The ECM and cell walls are a major component of certain parts of animals and plants, respectively. For example, bones and cartilage in animals are composed largely of ECM, and the woody portions of plants are composed mostly of cell walls. Although the cells within wood eventually die, the cell walls they have produced provide a rigid structure that supports the plant for years or even centuries.

In this section, we begin by examining the structure and functions of the ECM in animals, focusing on the major ECM components: proteins and polysaccharides. We will then explore the cell wall that surrounds plant cells.

The Extracellular Matrix in Animals Supports and Organizes Cells and Plays a Role in Cell Signaling

Unlike the cells of bacteria, archaea, fungi, and plants, the cells of animals are not surrounded by a rigid cell wall that provides structure and support. However, animal cells secrete materials that form an ECM that provides support and helps to organize cells. Certain animal cells are completely embedded within an extensive ECM, whereas other cells may adhere to the ECM on only one side. **Figure 10.1** illustrates the general features of the ECM and its relationship to cells. The major macromolecules of the ECM are proteins and polysaccharides. The most abundant proteins are those that form large fibers. The polysaccharides attract water and give the ECM a gel-like character.

As we will see, the ECM found in animals performs many important functions, including strength, structural support, organization, and cell signaling.

- *Strength*. The ECM is the "tough stuff" of animals' bodies. The strength of the ECM in the skin of mammals prevents tearing.

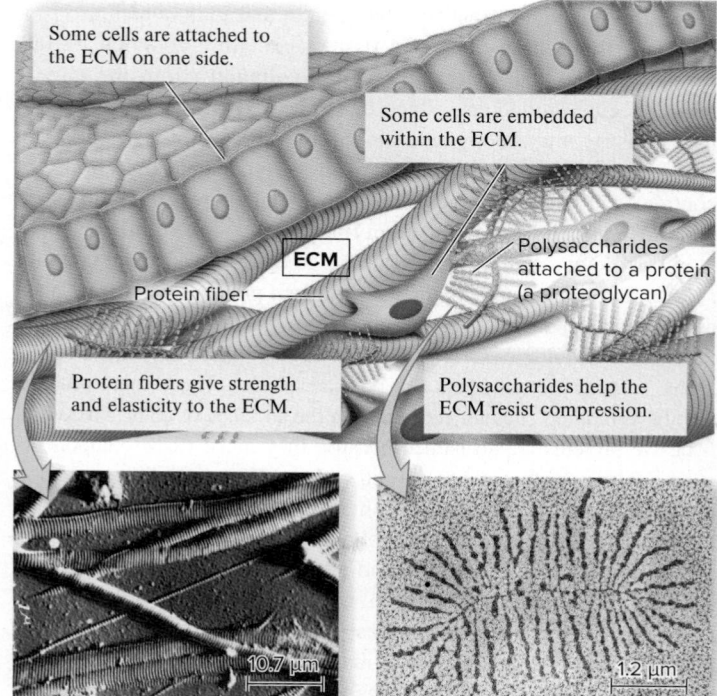

Figure 10.1 The extracellular matrix (ECM) of animal cells. The micrograph (SEM) at the bottom left shows collagen fibers, a type of protein fiber found in the ECM. The micrograph (TEM) at the bottom right shows a proteoglycan, which consists of polysaccharides attached to a protein. (left): ©Biophoto Associates/Science Source; (right): Courtesy of Dr. Joseph Buckwalter/University of Iowa

Concept Check: *What are the four functions of the ECM in animals?*

The ECM found in cartilage resists compression and provides protection to the joints. Similarly, the ECM protects the soft parts of the body, such as the internal organs.

- *Structural support*. The bones of many animals are composed primarily of ECM. Skeletons not only provide structural support but also facilitate movement via the functioning of attached muscles.

- *Organization*. The attachment of cells to the ECM plays a key role in the proper arrangement of cells throughout the body. In addition, the ECM binds many body parts together, such as tendons to bones.

- *Cell signaling*. A less obvious role of the ECM is cell signaling. One way that cells in multicellular organisms sense their environment is via changes in the ECM.

Let's now consider the synthesis and structure of ECM components found in animals.

Adhesive and Structural Proteins Are Major Components of the ECM of Animals

In the 1850s, German biologist Rudolf Virchow suggested that all extracellular materials are made and secreted by cells. Around the same time, biologists realized that gelatin and glue, which are produced by the boiling of animal tissues, contain a common fibrous substance. This substance was named **collagen** (from the Greek, meaning glue-producing). Since that time, experimental techniques in chemistry, microscopy, and biophysics have enabled scientists to probe the structure of the ECM. We now understand that the ECM contains a mixture of several different components, including proteins such as collagen, which form fibers.

The proteins found in the ECM are grouped into adhesive proteins, such as fibronectin and laminin, and structural proteins, such as collagen and elastin (**Table 10.1**). How do adhesive proteins work? Fibronectin and laminin have multiple binding sites that bind to other components in the ECM, such as protein fibers and polysaccharides. These same proteins also have binding sites for receptors on the surfaces of cells. Therefore, adhesive proteins are so named because they make ECM components adhere to one another and to the cell surface. They provide organization to the ECM and facilitate the attachment of cells to the ECM.

Structural proteins, such as collagen and elastin, form large fibers that give the ECM its strength and elasticity. A key function of collagen is to impart tensile strength, which is a measure of how much stretching force a material can bear without tearing apart. Collagen provides high tensile strength to many parts of an animal's body. It is the main protein found in bones, cartilage, tendons, skin, and the lining of blood vessels and internal organs. In the bodies of mammals, more than 25% of the total protein mass consists of collagen, much more than any other protein. Approximately 75% of the protein in mammalian skin is composed of collagen. Leather is largely a pickled and tanned form of collagen.

As described in Chapter 4 (see Figure 4.32), proteins, such as collagen, that are secreted from eukaryotic cells are first directed from the cytosol to the endoplasmic reticulum (ER), then to the Golgi apparatus, and subsequently are secreted from the cell via vesicles that fuse with the plasma membrane. **Figure 10.2** depicts the synthesis and assembly of collagen. Individual procollagen polypeptides (called α chains) are synthesized into the lumen of the ER. Three procollagen polypeptides then associate with each other to form a procollagen triple helix. The amino acid sequences at both ends of the polypeptides, termed extension sequences, promote the formation of procollagen and prevent the formation of a larger fiber. After procollagen is secreted from the cell, extracellular enzymes remove the extension sequences. Once this occurs, the protein, now called collagen, can form larger structures. Collagen proteins assemble in a staggered way to form relatively thin collagen fibrils, which then align and produce large collagen fibers. The many layers of these proteins give collagen fibers their great tensile strength.

Table 10.1	Proteins in the ECM of Animals	
General type	**Example**	**Function**
Adhesive	Fibronectin	Connects cells to the ECM and helps to organize components in the ECM.
	Laminin	Connects cells to the ECM and helps to organize components in the ECM.
Structural	Collagen	Forms large fibers and interconnected fibrous networks in the ECM. Provides tensile strength.
	Elastin	Forms elastic fibers in the ECM that can stretch and recoil.

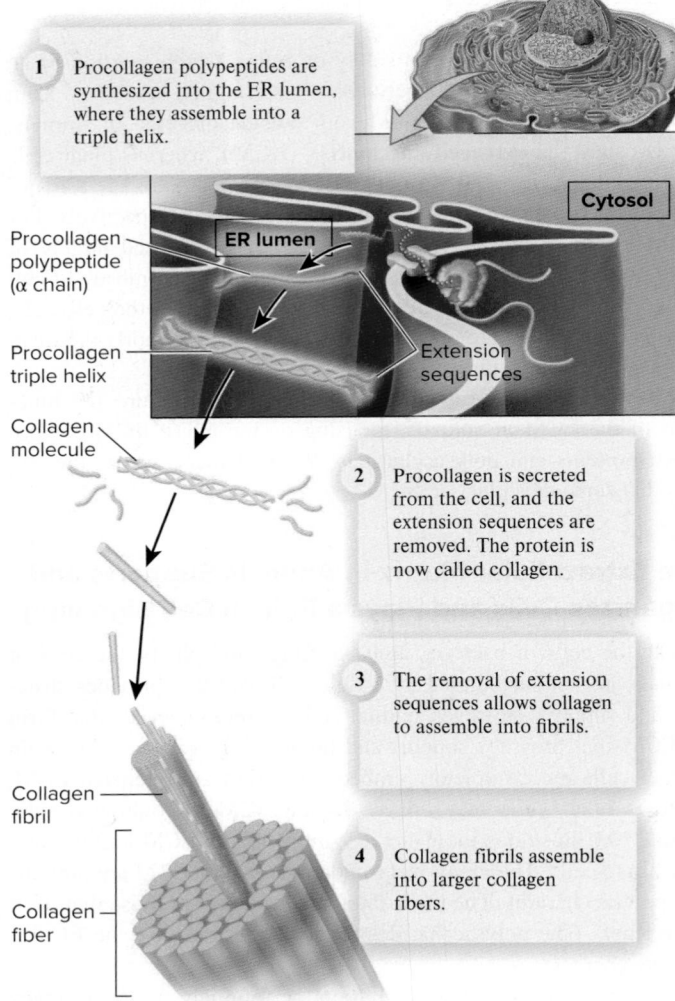

1. Procollagen polypeptides are synthesized into the ER lumen, where they assemble into a triple helix.

Cytosol

Procollagen polypeptide (α chain)

ER lumen

Procollagen triple helix

Extension sequences

Collagen molecule

2. Procollagen is secreted from the cell, and the extension sequences are removed. The protein is now called collagen.

3. The removal of extension sequences allows collagen to assemble into fibrils.

Collagen fibril

Collagen fiber

4. Collagen fibrils assemble into larger collagen fibers.

Figure 10.2 Formation of collagen fibers. Collagen is one type of structural protein found in the ECM of animal cells.

Concept Check: *What prevents large collagen fibers from forming intracellularly?*

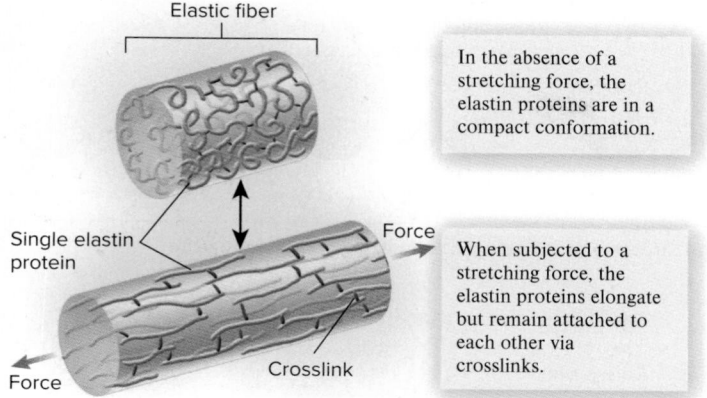

Elastic fiber

Single elastin protein

Force

Crosslink

Force

In the absence of a stretching force, the elastin proteins are in a compact conformation.

When subjected to a stretching force, the elastin proteins elongate but remain attached to each other via crosslinks.

Figure 10.3 Structure and function of elastic fibers. Elastic fibers are made of elastin, one type of structural protein found in the ECM surrounding animal cells.

Concept Check: *Suppose you started with an unstretched elastic fiber and treated it with a chemical that breaks the crosslinks between adjacent elastin proteins. What would happen when the fiber was stretched?*

In addition to tensile strength, elasticity is needed in regions of the body such as the lungs and blood vessels, which regularly expand and return to their original shape. In these places, the ECM contains elastic fibers composed primarily of the protein **elastin** (**Figure 10.3**). Elastin proteins form many covalent crosslinks to make a fiber with remarkable elastic properties. In the absence of a stretching force, each protein tends to adopt a compact conformation. When subjected to a stretching force, however, the compact proteins become more linear, with the covalent crosslinks holding the fiber together. When the stretching force stops, the proteins naturally return to their compact conformation. In this way, an elastic fiber behaves much like a rubber band, stretching under tension and snapping back when the tension is released.

BIO **TIPS**

THE QUESTION *Two structural proteins found in the ECM of animals are collagen and elastin. How are the structures of these proteins related to their functions?*

TOPIC *What topic in biology does this question address?* The topic is structural proteins in the ECM. More specifically, the question asks you to relate the structures and functions of collagen and elastin.

INFORMATION *What information do you know based on the question and your understanding of the topic?* In the question, you are reminded that collagen and elastin are structural proteins found in the ECM of animals. From your understanding of the topic, you may remember that collagen is composed of long, relatively thick fibers, and its role is to provide tensile strength. Elastin is a more compact protein that forms crosslinked elastic fibers, which provide elasticity.

PROBLEM-SOLVING **S**TRATEGY *Relate structure and function.* Take a closer look at the structures of these proteins, and consider how the structures determine the proteins' functions.

ANSWER *Collagen: A collagen fiber is composed of many smaller fibrils. Three procollagen polypeptides associate with each other to form a protein with a triple helix structure. These collagen proteins then assemble in a staggered way to form relatively thin collagen fibrils. The fibrils, in turn, align with each other and produce larger collagen fibers. The many layers of fibrils give collagen fibers their tensile strength.*

Elastin: Elastin has a very different structure from collagen. It is a fairly compact protein that forms elastic fibers with many covalent crosslinks between the proteins. In the absence of a stretching force, the elastin proteins remain in the compact conformation. However, when subjected to a stretching force, they become more linear. The covalent crosslinks keep the proteins within the elastic fiber from coming apart. When the stretching force ends, the proteins naturally return to their compact conformation.

 **Core Concepts: Evolution, Structure and Function**

Collagens Are a Family of Proteins That Give the ECM of Animals a Variety of Properties

Researchers have determined that animals make many different types of collagen fibers. These are designated as type I, type II, and so on. At least 27 different types of collagens have been identified in humans. To make different types of collagens, the human genome, as well as the genomes of other animals, has many different genes that encode procollagen polypeptides. Some inherited human diseases are caused by mutations in genes that encode collagen proteins. For example, Ehlers-Danlos syndrome is caused by mutations in one of several different collagen genes. Characteristic symptoms are very stretchable skin and hyperflexible joints.

Why are different collagens made? Each of the many different types of collagen polypeptides has a similar yet distinctive amino acid sequence that affects the structure of not only individual collagen proteins but also the resulting collagen fibers. For example, the amino acid sequence may cause the α chains within each collagen protein to bind to each other very tightly, thereby creating rigid proteins that form a relatively stiff fiber. Such collagen fibers are found in bone and cartilage.

The amino acid sequence of the α chains also influences the interactions between the collagen proteins within a fiber. For example, the amino acid sequences of certain α chains promote a looser interaction that produces a more bendable or thinner fiber. More flexible collagen fibers support the lining of your lungs and intestines. In addition, domains within the collagen polypeptide affect the spatial arrangement of collagen proteins. The collagen shown in Figure 10.2 forms fibers in which collagen proteins align themselves in parallel arrays. However, not all collagen proteins form long fibers. For example, type IV collagen proteins interact with each other in a meshwork pattern. This meshwork acts as a filter around capillaries.

Gene regulation controls which types of collagens are made throughout the body and in what amounts they are made. Of the

Table 10.2	Examples of Collagen Types in Humans	
Type	Sites of synthesis*	Structure and function
I	Tendons, ligaments, bones, and skin	Forms a relatively rigid and thick fiber. Very abundant, provides most of the tensile strength to the ECM.
II	Cartilage, discs between vertebrae	Forms a fairly rigid and thick fiber but is more flexible than type I. Permits smooth movements of joints.
III	Arteries, skin, internal organs, and around muscles	Forms thin fibers, often arranged in a meshwork pattern. Allows for greater elasticity in tissues.
IV	Skin, intestine, and kidneys; also found around capillaries	Does not form long fibers. Instead, the proteins are arranged in a meshwork pattern that provides organization and support to cell layers. Functions as a filter around capillaries.

*The sites of synthesis indicate where a large amount of the collagen type is made.

27 types of collagens identified in humans, **Table 10.2** considers types I to IV, each of which varies as to where it is primarily synthesized and its structure and function. In skin cells, for example, the genes that encode the polypeptides that make up collagen types I, III, and IV are turned on, but the synthesis of type II collagen is minimal.

The regulation of collagen synthesis has received a great deal of attention due to the phenomenon of wrinkling. As we age, the amount of collagen that is synthesized in our skin significantly decreases. The underlying network of collagen fibers, which provides scaffolding for the surface of our skin, loosens and unravels. This is one factor that causes the skin of older people to sink, sag, and form wrinkles. Various therapeutic and cosmetic agents have been developed to prevent or reverse the appearance of wrinkles, most with limited benefits. For example, many face and skin creams contain collagen as an ingredient. Another approach is collagen injections, in which small amounts of collagen (from cows) are injected into areas where the body's collagen has weakened, filling the depressions to the level of the surrounding skin. Because collagen is naturally broken down in the skin, the injections are not permanent and last only about 3 to 6 months.

Animal Cells Also Secrete Polysaccharides into the ECM

Polysaccharides are the second major component of the ECM of animals. As discussed in Chapter 3, polysaccharides are polymers of many simple sugars. Among vertebrates, the most abundant types of polysaccharides in the ECM are **glycosaminoglycans (GAGs)**. These macromolecules are long, unbranched polysaccharides containing a repeating disaccharide unit (**Figure 10.4a**). GAGs are highly negatively charged molecules that tend to attract positively charged ions and water. The majority of GAGs in the ECM are linked to core proteins, forming **proteoglycans** (**Figure 10.4b**).

Providing resistance to compression is the primary function of GAGs and proteoglycans. Once secreted from cells, these

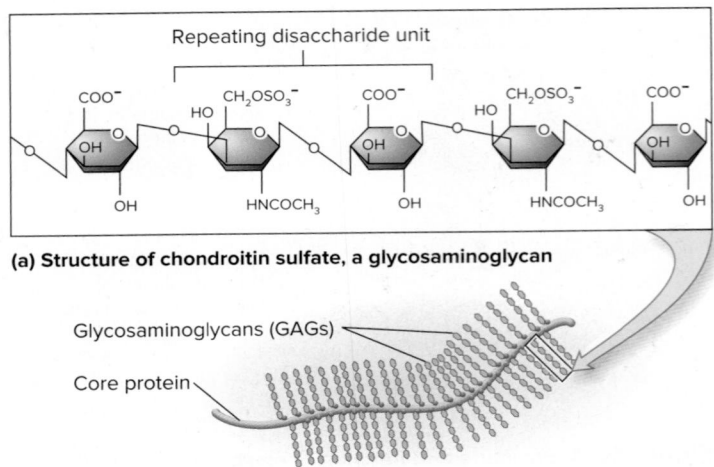

(a) Structure of chondroitin sulfate, a glycosaminoglycan

(b) General structure of a proteoglycan

Figure 10.4 **Structures of glycosaminoglycans and proteoglycans.** These macromolecules are found in the ECM, which is located outside of animal cells. **(a)** Glycosaminoglycans (GAGs) are composed of repeating disaccharide units. They range in length from several dozen to 25,000 disaccharide units. The GAG shown here is chondroitin sulfate, which is a component of cartilage. **(b)** Proteoglycans are composed of a long, linear core protein with many GAGs attached. Note that each GAG is typically 80 disaccharide units long but only a short chain of sugars is shown in this illustration.

Concept Check: *What structural feature of GAGs gives the ECM a gel-like character?*

macromolecules form a gel-like component in the ECM. How is this gel-like property important? Due to its high water content, the ECM is difficult to compress and thereby serves to protect cells. GAGs and proteoglycans are found abundantly in regions of the body that are subjected to harsh mechanical forces, such as the joints of the human body. Two examples of GAGs are chondroitin sulfate, which is a major component of cartilage, and hyaluronic acid, which is found in the skin, eyes, and joint fluid. Purified hyaluronic acid is also used to treat wrinkles and give skin fullness.

Among many invertebrates, an important ECM component is **chitin**, a nitrogen-containing polysaccharide. Chitin forms the hard protective outer covering (called an exoskeleton) of insects, such as crickets and grasshoppers, and crustaceans, such as lobsters and shrimp. As these animals grow, they periodically shed this rigid outer layer and secrete a new, larger one—a process called molting (look ahead to Figure 33.13).

The Cell Wall of Plants Provides Strength and Resistance to Compression

Let's now turn our attention to the cell walls of plants. Plant cells are surrounded by a cell wall, a protective layer that forms outside of the plasma membrane. Like animal cells, the cells of plants are surrounded by material that provides tensile strength and resistance to compression. The cell walls of plants, however, are usually thicker, stronger, and more rigid than the ECM found in animals. Plant cell walls provide rigidity for mechanical support and also play a role in the maintenance of cell shape and the direction of cell growth.

As described in Chapter 5, the cell wall also prevents expansion when water enters the cell, thereby preventing osmotic lysis.

The main macromolecule of the plant cell wall is **cellulose**, a polysaccharide made of repeating molecules of glucose attached end to end. These glucose polymers associate with each other via hydrogen bonding to form microfibrils that provide great tensile strength (**Figure 10.5**).

Cellulose was discovered in 1838 by French chemist Anselme Payen, who was the first scientist to attempt to separate wood into its component parts. After treating different types of wood with nitric acid, Payen obtained a fibrous substance that was also found in cotton and other plants. His chemical analysis revealed that the fibers were made of the carbohydrate glucose. Payen called this substance cellulose (from the Latin, meaning consisting of cells). Cellulose is probably the single most abundant organic molecule on Earth. Wood consists mostly of cellulose, and cotton and paper are almost pure cellulose.

Plant Cell Walls Consist of Primary and Secondary Walls

The cell walls of plants are composed of a primary cell wall and a secondary cell wall (**Figure 10.6**). These walls are named based on the timing of their synthesis—the primary cell wall is made before the secondary cell wall.

Primary Cell Wall During cell division, the **primary cell wall** develops between two newly formed daughter cells. It is usually very flexible and allows the new cells to increase in size. The main constituent of the primary cell wall is cellulose.

In addition to cellulose, other components found in the primary cell wall include hemicellulose, glycans, and pectins (see Figure 10.6).

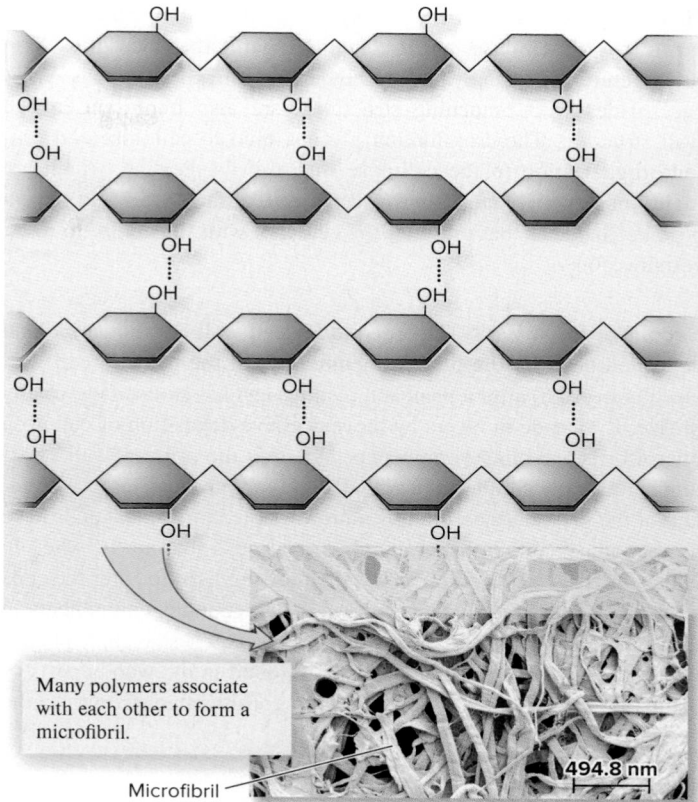

Many polymers associate with each other to form a microfibril.

Microfibril

494.8 nm

Figure 10.5 Structure of cellulose, the main macromolecule of the plant cell wall. Cellulose is made of repeating glucose units linked end to end that hydrogen-bond to each other to form microfibrils (SEM). ©SciMAT/Science Source

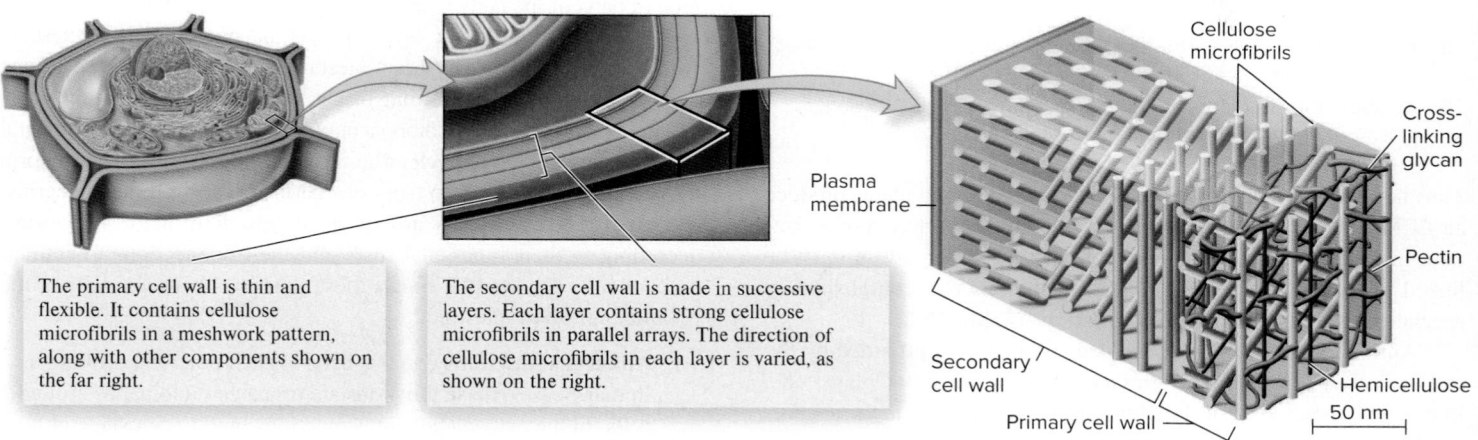

The primary cell wall is thin and flexible. It contains cellulose microfibrils in a meshwork pattern, along with other components shown on the far right.

The secondary cell wall is made in successive layers. Each layer contains strong cellulose microfibrils in parallel arrays. The direction of cellulose microfibrils in each layer is varied, as shown on the right.

Plasma membrane

Cellulose microfibrils

Cross-linking glycan

Pectin

Secondary cell wall

Hemicellulose

Primary cell wall

50 nm

Figure 10.6 Structure of the cell wall of plant cells. The primary cell wall is relatively thin and flexible. It contains cellulose (tan), hemicellulose (red), crosslinking glycans (blue), and pectin (green). The secondary cell wall, which is produced only by certain plant cells, is made after the primary cell wall and is synthesized in successive layers.

 Core Skill: Modeling The goal of this modeling challenge is to draw layers of a plant's secondary cell wall in colors that reflect the timing of their synthesis.

Modeling Challenge: After making its primary cell wall, a particular type of plant cell makes its secondary cell wall in three successive layers. Draw a model that is similar to the model shown in the middle of Figure 10.6, but don't show any components in the cytoplasm. The colors of your model should be as follows: primary cell wall, blue; first-made layer of the secondary cell wall, yellow; second-made layer of the secondary cell wall, green; and third-made layer of the secondary cell wall, black.

Hemicellulose is another linear polysaccharide, with a structure similar to that of cellulose, but it contains sugars other than glucose in its structure and usually forms thinner microfibrils. Glycans, polysaccharides with branching structures, are also important in cell wall structure. The crosslinking glycans bind to cellulose and provide organization to the cellulose microfibrils. Pectins, which are highly negatively charged polysaccharides, attract water and have a gel-like character that provides the cell wall with the ability to resist compression.

Secondary Cell Wall The **secondary cell wall** is synthesized and deposited between the plasma membrane and the primary cell wall (see Figure 10.6) after a plant cell matures and has stopped increasing in size. It is made in layers by the successive deposition of cellulose microfibrils and other components. Whereas the primary wall structure is relatively similar in nearly all cell types and species, the structure of the secondary cell wall is more variable. Some plant cells have no secondary cell wall. For example, leaf cells that are involved in photosynthesis lack a secondary wall, allowing light to enter the cells more readily. The secondary cell wall often contains components in addition to those found in the primary cell wall. These include phenolic compounds called lignins, which are found in the woody parts of plants. Lignins are very hard and impart considerable strength to the secondary wall structure.

10.2 Cell Junctions

Learning Outcomes:

1. Compare and contrast the structures and functions of anchoring junctions, tight junctions, and gap junctions found between animal cells.
2. **CoreSKILL** » Analyze the results of experiments that determined the size of gap junction channels.
3. Describe the structures and functions of the middle lamella and plasmodesmata that connect adjacent plant cells.

Thus far, we have learned that the cells of animals and plants produce an ECM or a cell wall that provides strength, support, and organization. In a multicellular organism, cells within the organism must be linked to each other. In animals and plants, this is accomplished by specialized structures called **cell junctions** (**Table 10.3**).

Animal cells, which lack the structural support provided by the cell wall, have a more varied group of cell junctions than plant cells. In animals, three types of junctions are found between cells: anchoring junctions play a role in anchoring cells to each other or to the ECM; tight junctions seal cells together to prevent small molecules from leaking across a layer of cells; and gap junctions allow the passage of materials between adjacent cells.

In plants, cellular organization is somewhat different because plant cells are surrounded by a rigid cell wall. Plant cells are connected to each other by a component called the middle lamella, which cements their cell walls together. They also have junctions termed plasmodesmata that allow the passage of materials between adjacent cells. In this section, we will examine these various types of junctions found between the cells of animals and plants.

Table 10.3	Common Types of Cell Junctions
Type	**Description**
Animals	
Anchoring junctions	Cell junctions that hold adjacent cells together or attach cells to the ECM. Anchoring junctions are mechanically strong.
Tight junctions	Junctions between adjacent cells in a layer that prevent the leakage of material between cells.
Gap junctions	A cluster of channels that permit the direct exchange of ions and small molecules between the cytosols of adjacent cells.
Plants	
Middle lamella	A polysaccharide layer that cements together the cell walls of adjacent cells.
Plasmodesmata	Passageways between the cell walls of adjacent cells that can be opened or closed. When open, they permit the direct diffusion of ions and molecules between the cytosols of the adjacent cells.

Anchoring Junctions Link Animal Cells to Each Other and to the ECM

Electron microscopy allows researchers to explore the types of junctions that occur between adjacent cells and between cells and the ECM. In the 1960s, Marilyn Farquhar, George Palade, and colleagues conducted several studies showing that various types of cell junctions connect cells to each other. Collectively called **anchoring junctions**, these junctions attach cells to each other and to the ECM. Anchoring junctions are common in parts of the body where the cells are tightly connected and form linings. An example is the layer of cells that line the small intestine. Anchoring junctions keep these intestinal cells tightly adhered to one another, thereby forming a strong barrier between the lumen of the intestine and the blood. A key component of anchoring junctions are integral membrane proteins called **cell adhesion molecules (CAMs)**, which form the actual connections. Two types of CAMs are cadherins and integrins.

Anchoring junctions are grouped into four main categories, according to their functional roles and their connections to cellular components. **Figure 10.7** shows these junctions between cells of the mammalian small intestine.

1. **Adherens junctions** connect cells to each other via cadherins. In many cases, these junctions are organized into bands around cells. In the cytosol, adherens junctions bind to cytoskeletal filaments called actin filaments.
2. **Desmosomes** also connect cells to each other via cadherins. They are spotlike points of intercellular contact that rivet cells together. Desmosomes are connected to cytoskeletal filaments called intermediate filaments.
3. **Hemidesmosomes** connect cells to the extracellular matrix via integrins. Like desmosomes, they interact with intermediate filaments.
4. **Focal adhesions** also connect cells to the ECM via integrins. In the cytosol, focal adhesions bind to actin filaments.

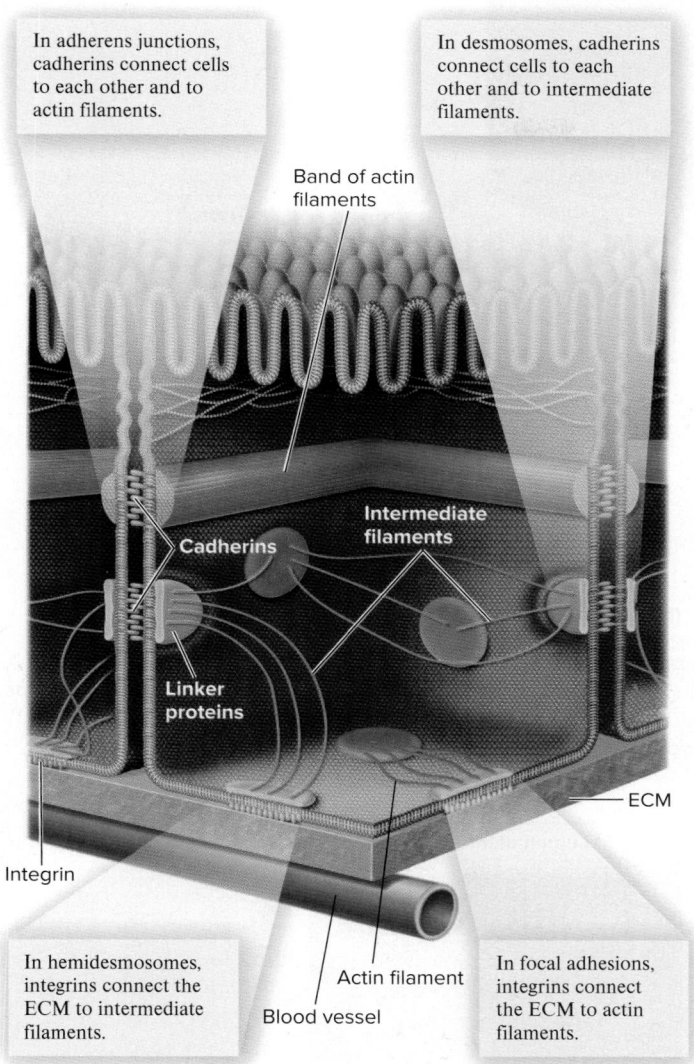

In adherens junctions, cadherins connect cells to each other and to actin filaments.

In desmosomes, cadherins connect cells to each other and to intermediate filaments.

Band of actin filaments

Cadherins

Intermediate filaments

Linker proteins

Integrin

ECM

In hemidesmosomes, integrins connect the ECM to intermediate filaments.

Actin filament

Blood vessel

In focal adhesions, integrins connect the ECM to actin filaments.

Figure 10.7 **Types of anchoring junctions.** This figure shows the four types of anchoring junctions in three adjacent intestinal cells. The tops of these cells face the lumen of the intestine, whereas the bottoms are adjacent to the ECM and a blood vessel.

Concept Check: *Which anchoring junctions are cell-to-cell junctions and which are cell-to-ECM junctions?*

Cell Adhesion Molecules (CAMs) Form Links Between Cells and to the ECM

Let's now consider the molecular components of anchoring junctions.

Cadherins   As shown in Figure 10.7, **cadherins** are CAMs that create cell-to-cell junctions. The extracellular domains of two cadherin proteins, each in adjacent cells, bind to each other to promote cell-to-cell adhesion (**Figure 10.8a**). This binding requires the presence of calcium ions (Ca^{2+}), which change the conformation of the cadherin protein such that cadherins in adjacent cells bind to each other. (This calcium dependence gives cadherin its name—Ca^{2+}-dependent adhering molecule.) On the interior of

the cell, linker proteins connect cadherins to actin or intermediate filaments of the cytoskeleton. This promotes a more stable interaction between two cells because their strong cytoskeletons are connected to each other.

The genomes of vertebrates and invertebrates contain multiple cadherin genes, which encode slightly different cadherin proteins. The expression of cadherins in particular cell types allows cells to recognize each other. Dimer formation follows a homophilic, or like-to-like, binding mechanism. To understand the concept of homophilic binding, let's consider an example. One type of cadherin is called E-cadherin, and another is N-cadherin. E-cadherin in one cell binds to E-cadherin in an adjacent cell to form a homodimer. However, E-cadherin in one cell does not bind to N-cadherin in an adjacent cell to form a heterodimer. Similarly, N-cadherin binds to N-cadherin but not to E-cadherin in an adjacent cell. Why is such homophilic binding important? By expressing only certain types of cadherins, each cell binds only to other cells that express the same cadherin types. This phenomenon plays a key role in the proper arrangement of cells throughout the body, particularly during embryonic development.

Integrins   Another type of CAM is a group of proteins called **integrins**, which form connections between cells and the ECM. Integrins do not require Ca^{2+} to function. Each integrin protein is composed of two nonidentical subunits. In the example shown in **Figure 10.8b**, an integrin is bound to fibronectin, an adhesive protein in the ECM that binds to other ECM components such as collagen fibers. Like cadherins, integrins also bind to actin or intermediate filaments in the cytosol of the cell, via linker proteins, to promote a strong association between the cytoskeleton and the ECM. Thus, integrins have an extracellular domain for the binding of ECM components and an intracellular domain for the binding of cytosolic proteins.

When CAMs were first discovered, researchers imagined that cadherins and integrins played only a mechanical role. In other words, their functions were described as holding cells together or to the ECM. More recently, however, experiments have shown that cadherins and integrins are important in cell communication. The formation or breaking of cell-to-cell and cell-to-ECM anchoring junctions affects signal transduction pathways within the cell. Similarly, intracellular signal transduction pathways affect cadherins and integrins in ways that alter intercellular junctions and the binding of cells to ECM components.

Abnormalities in CAMs such as integrins are associated with the ability of cancer cells to metastasize, that is, to move to other parts of the body. CAMs are critical for keeping cells in their correct locations. When these adhesion molecules become defective due to cancer-causing mutations, cells lose their proper connections with the ECM and adjacent cells and may move to other parts of the body.

Tight Junctions Prevent the Leakage of Materials Across Animal Cell Layers

In animals, **tight junctions** are a second type of junction, one that forms a tight seal between adjacent cells, thereby preventing material from leaking between the cells. As an example, let's consider the

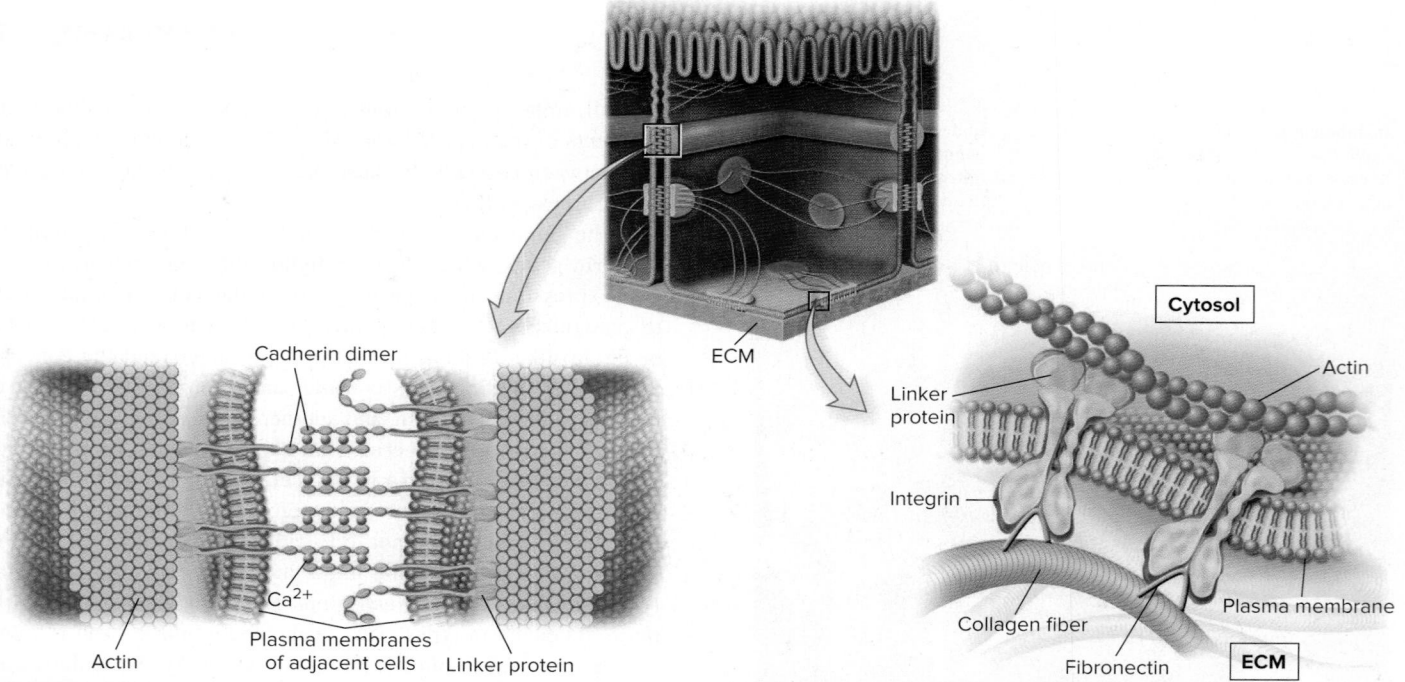

(a) Cadherins—link cells to each other

(b) Integrins—link cells to the extracellular matrix

Figure 10.8 Types of cell adhesion molecules (CAMs). Cadherins and integrins are CAMs that form connections in anchoring junctions. **(a)** A cadherin in one cell binds to a cadherin of an identical type in an adjacent cell. This binding requires Ca^{2+}. In the cytosol, cadherins bind to actin or intermediate filaments of the cytoskeleton via linker proteins. **(b)** Integrins link cells to the ECM and form intracellular connections to actin or intermediate filaments. Each integrin protein is a heterodimer, composed of two nonidentical subunits.

intestine. The cells that line the intestine form a sheet that is one cell thick. One side of each cell faces the intestinal lumen, and the other faces the ECM and a blood vessel (**Figure 10.9**). Tight junctions between these cells prevent the leakage of materials from the lumen of the intestine into the blood, and vice versa.

Tight junctions are made by integral membrane proteins, called occludin and claudin, that form interlaced strands in the plasma membrane (see inset in Figure 10.9). These strands of proteins, located in adjacent cells, bind to each other, thereby forming a tight seal between cells. Tight junctions are not mechanically strong like anchoring junctions, because they do not have strong connections with the cytoskeleton. Therefore, adjacent cells that have tight junctions also have anchoring junctions to hold them in place.

Tight junctions perform several important roles. Let's consider a few examples.

- Tight junctions between intestinal cells prevent leakage of materials between the lumen of the intestine and the blood.

- Tight junctions help maintain the polarity of intestinal cells by preventing the lateral diffusion of integral membrane proteins between the apical side (which faces the lumen of the intestine) and the basolateral side (which faces a blood vessel). For example, proteins involved with receptor-mediated endocytosis are restricted to the apical side, and proteins involved with exocytosis are located at the basolateral side. Thus, intestinal cells are able to take up nutrients from the intestinal lumen and export them into the bloodstream, a phenomenon called **transepithelial transport**.

- Tight junctions prevent microbes from entering the body. In mammals, the skin on the exterior of the body and the lining of

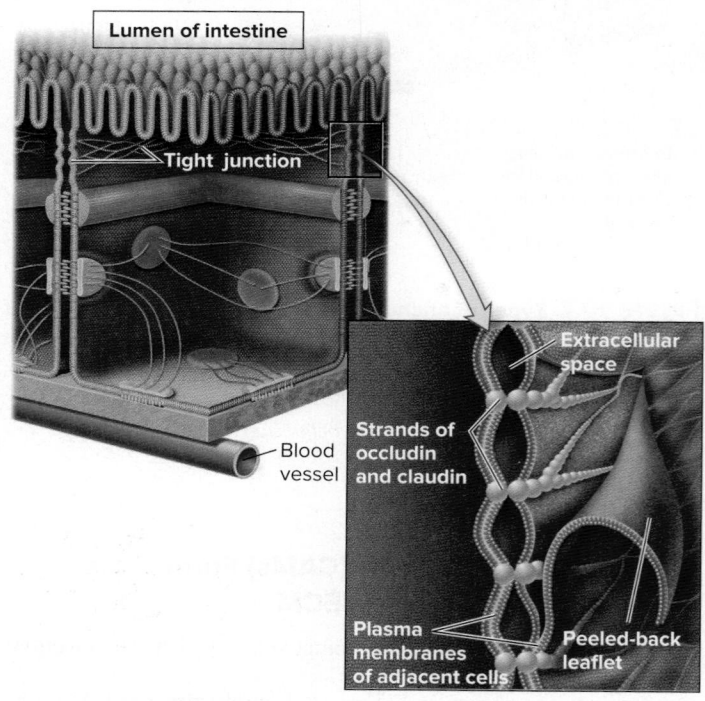

Figure 10.9 Tight junctions between adjacent intestinal cells. In this example, tight junctions form a seal between cells of the intestinal lining. The inset shows the interconnected network of occludin and claudin that forms the tight junction.

 Core Skill: Connections Look ahead to Figure 46.8. What problems might arise if tight junctions did not connect the cells that line your small intestine?

the digestive tract are formed from interconnected cells that have tight junctions. Some pathogenic microorganisms, such as those that cause certain forms of diarrhea, are able to cause infection by disrupting tight junctions.

The amazing ability of tight junctions to prevent the leakage of material across cell layers has been demonstrated by dye-injection studies. In 1972, Daniel Friend and Norton Gilula injected lanthanum into the bloodstream of a rat. Lanthanum is an electron-dense element that can be visualized using electron microscopy. A few minutes later, a sample of a cell layer in the digestive tract was removed and observed under an electron microscope. As seen in the micrograph in **Figure 10.10**, lanthanum diffused into the region between the cells that faces the blood, but it could not move past the tight junction to the side of the cell layer facing the lumen of the digestive tract.

Gap Junctions Between Animal Cells Provide Passageways for Intercellular Transport

A third type of junction found between animal cells is called a **gap junction**, because a small gap occurs between the plasma membranes of cells connected by these junctions (**Figure 10.11**). Gap junctions are abundant in tissues and organs where the cells need to communicate with each other. For example, cardiac muscle cells, which cause your heart to beat, are interconnected by many gap junctions. Because gap junctions allow the passage of ions, electrical changes in one cardiac muscle cell are easily transmitted to an adjacent cell that is connected via gap junctions. These connections are needed for the coordinated contraction of cardiac muscle cells.

In vertebrates, gap junctions are composed of an integral membrane protein called connexin. Invertebrates have a structurally similar protein called innexin. Six connexin proteins in one vertebrate cell form a channel called a **connexon**. A connexon in one cell aligns with a connexon in an adjacent cell to form an intercellular channel (see the middle drawing in Figure 10.11). The term gap junction refers to

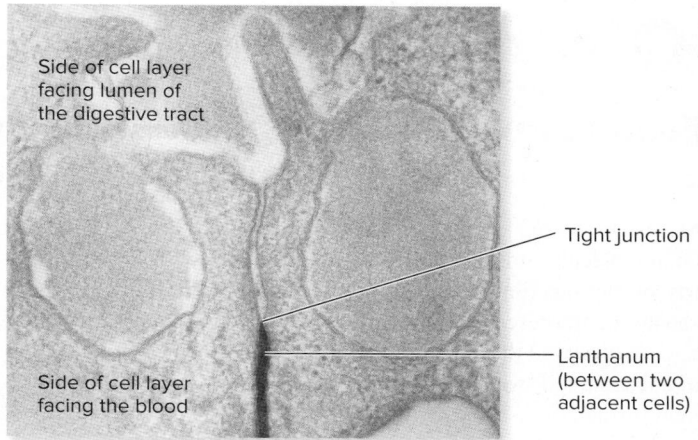

Figure 10.10 **An experiment demonstrating the function of a tight junction.** When lanthanum was injected into the bloodstream of a rat, it diffused between the cells in the region up to a tight junction but could not diffuse past the junction to the other side of the cell layer. ©Dr. Daniel Friend

Concept Check: *What results would you expect if a rat was fed lanthanum and then a sample of a cell layer in the digestive tract was observed under an electron microscope?*

a cluster of many connexons that are close to each other in the plasma membrane and form many intercellular channels.

Gap junction channels allow the passage of ions and small molecules, including amino acids, sugars, and signaling molecules such as Ca^{2+} and cAMP, between cells. In this way, gap junctions allow adjacent cells to share metabolites and directly signal each other. However, gap junction channels are too small to allow the passage of RNA, proteins, or polysaccharides. Therefore, cells that communicate via gap junctions still maintain their own distinctive sets of macromolecules.

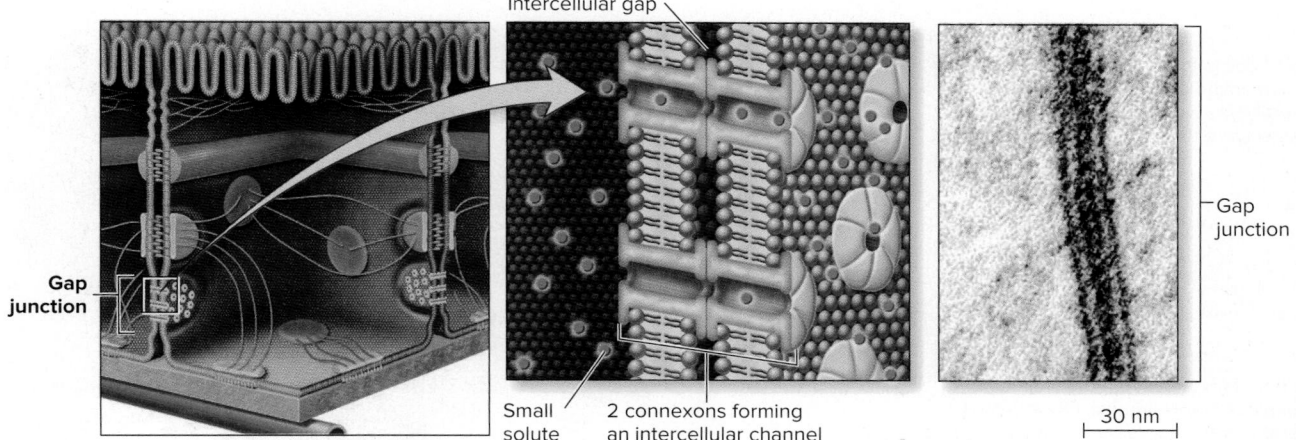

Figure 10.11 **Gap junctions between adjacent cells.** Gap junctions form intercellular channels that allow the passage of small solutes with masses less than 1,000 Da. One connexon consists of six proteins called connexins. Two connexons align to form an intercellular channel. The micrograph shows a gap junction, which is composed of many connexons, between intestinal cells. (right): Courtesy Dr. Dan Goodenough/Harvard Medical School

Core Skill: Process of Science

Feature Investigation | Loewenstein and Colleagues Followed the Transfer of Fluorescent Dyes to Determine the Size of Gap-Junction Channels

As just mentioned, gap junctions allow the passage of ions and small molecules, those with a mass up to about 1,000 Da. This property of gap junctions was determined in experiments involving the transfer of fluorescent dyes. In 1964, Werner Loewenstein and colleagues observed that a fluorescent dye could move from one cell to an adjacent cell, which prompted them to investigate this phenomenon further.

In the experiment shown in **Figure 10.12**, Loewenstein and colleagues grew rat liver cells in the laboratory, where they formed a single layer. The adjacent cells formed gap junctions. Single cells were injected with various dyes composed of fluorescently labeled amino acids or peptide molecules with different masses, and then the cell layers were observed via fluorescence microscopy. As the data in Figure 10.12 show, dyes with a molecular mass up to 901 Da passed from cell to cell. Dyes with a larger mass, however, did not move

intercellularly. Loewenstein and other researchers subsequently investigated dye transfer in other cell types and species. Though some variation is found among different cell types and species, the researchers generally observed that molecules with a mass greater than 1,000 Da do not pass through gap junctions.

Experimental Questions

1. What was the purpose of the study conducted by Loewenstein and colleagues?

2. **CoreSKILL »** Explain the experimental procedure used by Loewenstein and colleagues to determine the sizes of molecules that can pass through gap-junction channels.

3. **CoreSKILL »** What do the results of the experiment in Figure 10.12 indicate about the size of gap-junction channels?

Figure 10.12 Use of fluorescent molecules by Loewenstein and colleagues to determine the size of gap-junction channels.

HYPOTHESIS Gap-junction channels allow the passage of ions and molecules, but there is a limit to how large the molecules can be.

KEY MATERIALS Rat liver cells grown in the laboratory, a collection of fluorescent dyes.

	Experimental level	Conceptual level
1	Grow rat liver cells in a laboratory on solid growth medium until they become a single layer. At this point, adjacent cells have formed gap junctions.	

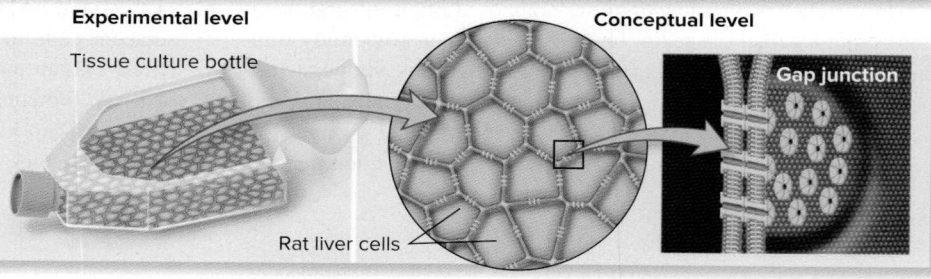

2. Inject 1 cell in the layer with fluorescently labeled amino acids or peptides. Note: Several dyes with different molecular masses were tested.

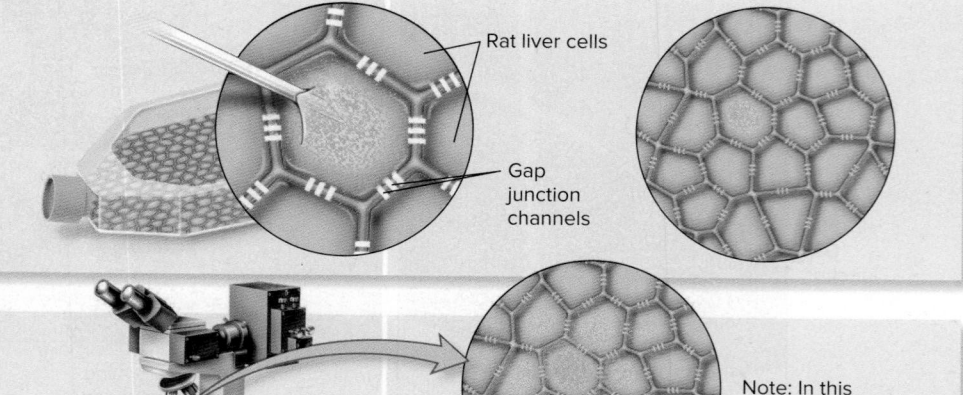

3. Incubate for various lengths of time (for example, 40–45 minutes). Observe cell layer under the fluorescence microscope to determine if the dye has moved to adjacent cells.

Note: In this case, the dye was transferred to adjacent cells.

4 THE DATA

Mass of dye (in daltons)	Transfer to adjacent cells*	Mass of dye	Transfer to adjacent cells*
376	++++	851**	–
464	++++	901	+++
536	+++	946	–
559	++++	1004	–
665	+	1158	–
688	++++	1678	–
817	+++	1830	–

*The number of pluses indicates the relative speed of transfer. Four pluses denotes fast transfer, whereas one plus is slow transfer. A minus indicates that transfer between cells did not occur. **In some cases, molecules with less mass did not pass between cells compared with molecules with a higher mass. This may be due to differences in their structures (for example, charges) that influence whether or not they can easily penetrate the channel.

5 CONCLUSION Gap junctions allow the intercellular movement of molecules that have a mass of approximately 900 Da or less.

6 SOURCE Flagg-Newton, J., Simpson, II, and Loewenstein, W. R. 1973. Permeability of the cell-to-cell membrane channels in mammalian cell junctions. *Science* 205: 404–407.

The Middle Lamella Cements Adjacent Plant Cell Walls Together

In animals, cell-to-cell contact via anchoring junctions, tight junctions, and gap junctions involves interactions between membrane proteins in adjacent cells. In plants, cell junctions are biochemically different. Rather than using membrane proteins to form cell-to-cell connections, plant cells make an additional component called the **middle lamella** (plural, lamellae), which is found between most adjacent plant cells (**Figure 10.13**). When plant cells are dividing, the middle lamella is the first layer formed. The primary cell wall is then made. The middle lamella is rich in pectins, negatively charged polysaccharides that are also found in the primary cell wall (see Figure 10.6). Pectins attract water and thus produce a hydrated gel. Ca^{2+} and Mg^{2+} interact with the negative charges in the pectins and cement the cell walls of adjacent cells together.

The process of fruit ripening illustrates the importance of pectins in holding plant cells together. An unripened fruit, such as a green tomato, is very firm because the rigid cell walls of adjacent cells are firmly attached to each other. During ripening, the cells secrete a group of enzymes called pectinases, which digest pectins in the middle lamella as well as those in the primary cell wall. As this process continues, the attachments between cells are broken, and the cell walls become less rigid. For this reason, a red ripe tomato is much less firm than an unripe tomato.

Plasmodesmata Are Channels Connecting the Cytoplasm of Adjacent Plant Cells

In 1879, Eduard Tangl, a Russian botanist, observed intercellular connections in the seeds of the strychnine tree and hypothesized that the cytoplasm of adjacent cells is connected by ducts in the cell walls.

He was the first to propose that direct cell-to-cell communication integrates the functioning of plant cells. The ducts or intercellular channels that Tangl observed are now known as **plasmodesmata** (singular, plasmodesma).

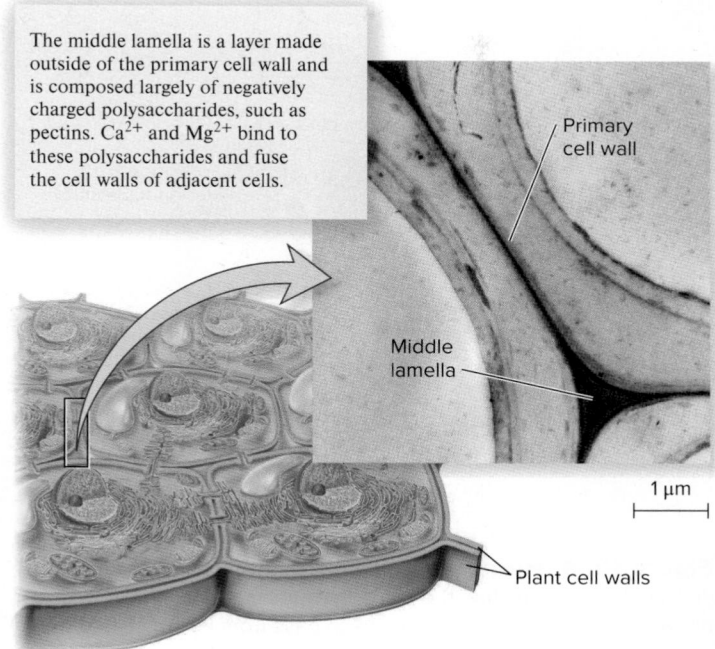

The middle lamella is a layer made outside of the primary cell wall and is composed largely of negatively charged polysaccharides, such as pectins. Ca^{2+} and Mg^{2+} bind to these polysaccharides and fuse the cell walls of adjacent cells.

Primary cell wall

Middle lamella

1 µm

Plant cell walls

Figure 10.13 **Plant cell-to-cell connections consist of middle lamellae.** ©Purbasha Sarkar

Concept Check: *How are middle lamellae similar to the anchoring junctions and desmosomes found between animal cells? How are they different?*

Plasmodesmata are functionally similar to gap junctions in animal cells because they are open pores that allow the passage of ions and molecules between the cytosols of adjacent plant cells. However, the structure of the plasmodesmata is quite different from that of gap junctions. As shown in **Figure 10.14**, the plasma membrane of one cell is continuous with the plasma membrane of the adjacent cell, which forms a pore that permits the diffusion of molecules from the cytosol of one cell to the cytosol of the other. In addition to a cytosolic connection, plasmodesmata also have a central tubule, called a desmotubule, connecting the smooth ER membranes of adjacent cells.

Plant cells can alter the diameter of the channel formed by plasmodesmata. The channel can occur in the closed, open, and dilated states. In the open state, plasmodesmata allow the passage of ions and small molecules, such as sugars and cAMP. In this state, plasmodesmata

play a similar role to gap junctions between animal cells. Plasmodesmata tend to close when a large pressure difference occurs between adjacent cells. Why does this happen? One reason is related to cell damage. When a plant is wounded, damaged cells lose their turgor pressure. (Turgor pressure is described in Chapter 39, look ahead to Figure 39.4.) The closure of plasmodesmata between adjacent cells helps to prevent the loss of water and nutrients from the wound site.

Unlike gap junctions between animal cells, plasmodesmata can dilate to also allow the passage of macromolecules and even viruses between adjacent plant cells. Though the mechanism of dilation is not well understood, the wider opening of plasmodesmata is important for the passage of proteins and mRNA during plant development. It also provides a key mechanism whereby viruses can move from cell to cell.

10.3 Tissues

Learning Outcomes:

1. List the six basic cell processes that produce tissues and organs.
2. Outline the structures and functions of the four types of animal tissues: epithelial, connective, nervous, and muscle tissues.
3. Summarize the structures and functions of the three types of plant tissues: dermal, ground, and vascular tissues.

A **tissue** is a part of an animal or plant consisting of a group of cells having a similar structure and function. In this section, we will view tissues from the perspective of cell biology. Animals and plants contain many different types of cells. Humans, for example, have over 200 different cell types, each with a specific structure and function. Even so, these cells can be grouped into a few general categories. For example, muscle cells found in your heart (cardiac muscle cells), in your biceps (skeletal muscle cells), and around your arteries (smooth muscle cells) look somewhat different under the microscope and have unique roles in the body. Yet due to structural and functional similarities, all three types are categorized as muscle tissue. In this section, we begin by surveying the basic processes that cells undergo to make tissues. Then, we will examine the main categories of animal and plant tissues.

Six Different Cellular Processes Produce Tissues and Organs

A multicellular organism, such as a plant or animal, contains many cells. For example, an adult human has somewhere between 10 and 100 trillion cells in her or his body. Cells are organized into tissues, and tissues are organized into organs. An **organ** is a collection of two or more tissues that performs a specific function or set of functions. The heart is an organ found in the bodies of complex animals, and a leaf is an organ found in plants. We will examine the structures and functions of organs in Units VI and VII.

How are tissues and organs formed? To form tissues and organs, cells undergo six different processes that influence their morphology, arrangement, and number: division, growth, differentiation, migration, apoptosis, and formation of connections.

1. ***Division.*** As discussed in Chapter 16, eukaryotic cells advance through a cell cycle that leads to cell division.

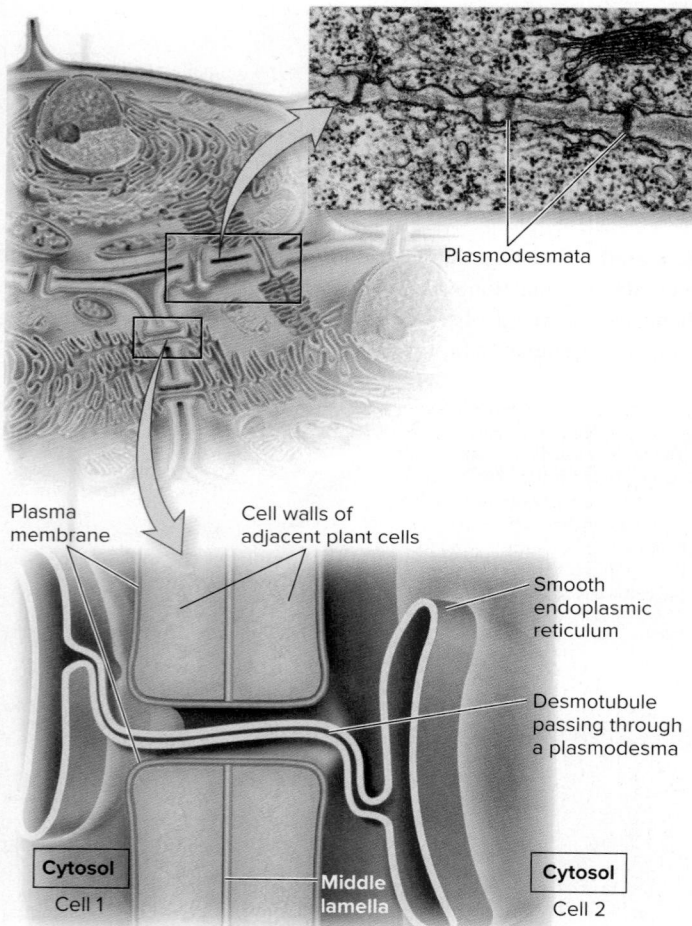

Figure 10.14 **Structure of a plasmodesma.** Plasmodesmata are cell junctions connecting the cytosols of adjacent plant cells, allowing water, ions, and molecules to pass from cell to cell. At these pores, the plasma membrane of one cell is continuous with the plasma membrane of an adjacent cell. In addition, the smooth ER from one cell is connected to that of the adjacent cell via a desmotubule. ©Biophoto Associates/Science Source

 Core Skill: Connections Look ahead to Figure 39.8. How do plasmodesmata play a role in the movement of nutrients through a plant root?

2. *Growth.* Following cell division, cells take up nutrients and usually expand in volume. Cell division and growth are the primary mechanisms for increasing the size of tissues, organs, and organisms.

3. *Differentiation.* Due to gene regulation, cells differentiate into specialized types of cells. Cell differentiation is described in Chapter 20.

4. *Migration.* During embryonic development in animals, cells migrate to their appropriate positions within the body. Also, adults have cells that can move into regions that have become damaged. Cell migration does not occur during plant development.

5. *Apoptosis.* Programmed cell death, also known as apoptosis (discussed in Chapter 9), is necessary to produce certain morphological features of the body. For example, during development in mammals, the formation of individual fingers and toes requires the removal, by apoptosis, of the skin cells between them.

6. *Formation of connections.* In the first section of this chapter, we learned that cells produce an extracellular matrix or cell wall that provides strength and support. In animals, the ECM serves to organize cells within tissues and organs. In plants, the connections and structures of cell walls are largely responsible for the shapes of plant tissues. Different types of cell junctions in both animal and plant cells enable cells to maintain physical contact and communicate with one another.

Animals Are Composed of Epithelial, Connective, Nervous, and Muscle Tissues

The body of an animal contains four general types of tissue—epithelial, connective, nervous, and muscle—that serve very different purposes (**Figure 10.15**).

Epithelial Tissue   **Epithelial tissue** is composed of cells that are joined together via tight junctions and form continuous sheets. (Epithelial cells are shown in Figure 10.9.) Epithelial tissue covers or forms the lining of all internal and external body surfaces. For example, epithelial tissue lines organs such as the lungs and digestive tract. In addition, epithelial tissue forms the outer layer of the skin, a protective surface that shields the body from the outside environment.

Connective Tissue   Most **connective tissue** provides support to the body and/or helps to connect different tissues to each other. Connective tissue is rich in ECM. Examples of connective tissue include cartilage, tendons, bone, fat tissue, and the inner layers of the skin. Blood is also considered a form of connective tissue because it provides liquid connections to various regions of the body.

Figure 10.16 shows a micrograph of cartilage, a connective tissue found in joints such as your knees. The cells that synthesize cartilage, known as chondrocytes, actually represent a small proportion of the total volume of cartilage. As shown in Figure 10.16, the chondrocytes are found in small cavities within the cartilage called lacunae (singular, lacuna). In some types of cartilage, the chondrocytes represent only 1–2% of the total volume of the tissue! Chondrocytes are the only cells found in cartilage. They are solely responsible for the synthesis of protein fibers, such as collagen, as well as the glycosaminoglycans and proteoglycans that are found in cartilage.

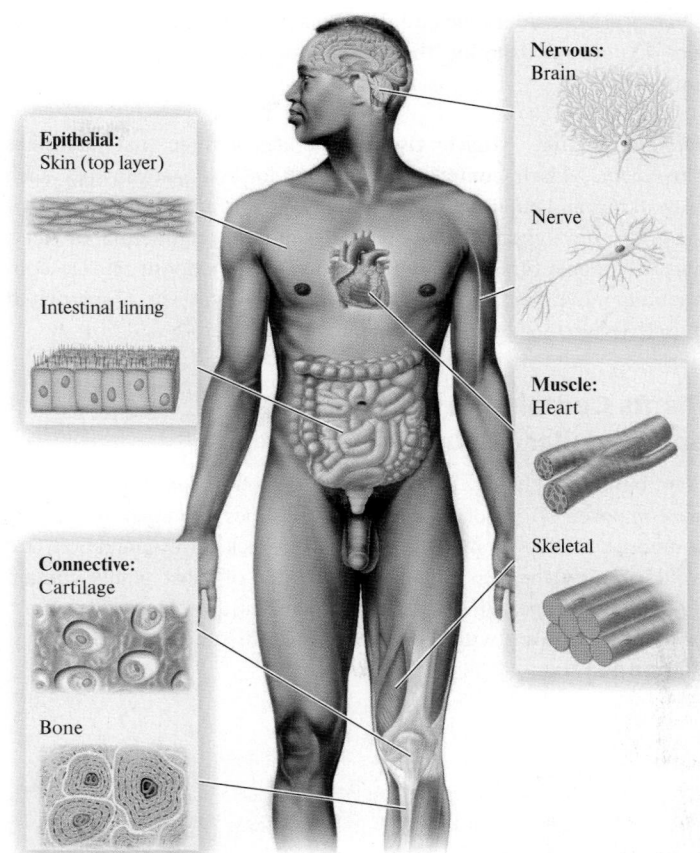

Figure 10.15 **Examples of the four general types of tissues—epithelial, connective, nervous, and muscle—found in animals.**

Concept Check: *Which of the four general types of tissues has the most extensive ECM?*

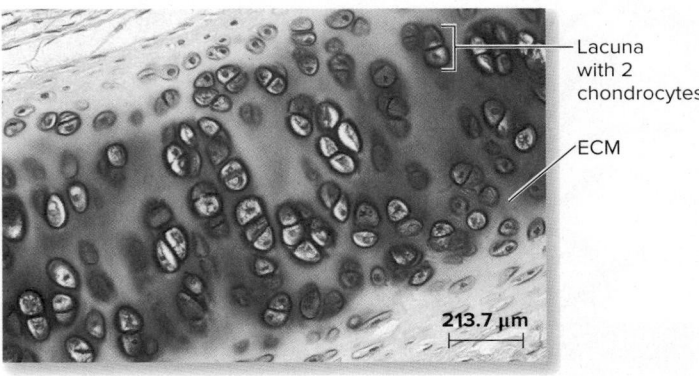

Figure 10.16 **An example of connective tissue in animals that is rich in extracellular matrix.** This micrograph of cartilage shows chondrocytes in the ECM. The chondrocytes, which are responsible for making the components of cartilage, are found in cavities called lacunae. ©Victor P. Eroschenko

Nervous Tissue   **Nervous tissue** receives, generates, and conducts electrical signals throughout the body. In vertebrates, these electrical signals are integrated by nervous tissue in the brain and transmitted down the spinal cord to the rest of the body.

Chapter 42 considers the cellular basis of nerve signals, and Chapters 43 and 44 examine the organization of nervous systems in animals.

Muscle Tissue   **Muscle tissue** generates a force that facilitates movement. Muscle contraction is needed for body movements, such as walking and running, and also plays a role in the movement of materials throughout the body. For example, contraction of heart muscle propels blood through your body, and smooth muscle contractions move food through the digestive system. The properties of muscle tissue in animals are examined in Chapter 45.

Plants Contain Dermal, Ground, and Vascular Tissues

Plant biologists classify tissues as simple or complex. Simple tissues are composed of one or possibly two cell types. Complex tissues are composed of two or more cell types but lack an organization that would qualify them as organs. The bodies of most plants contain three general types of simple or complex tissues—dermal, ground, and vascular—each with a different structure suited to its functions (**Figure 10.17**).

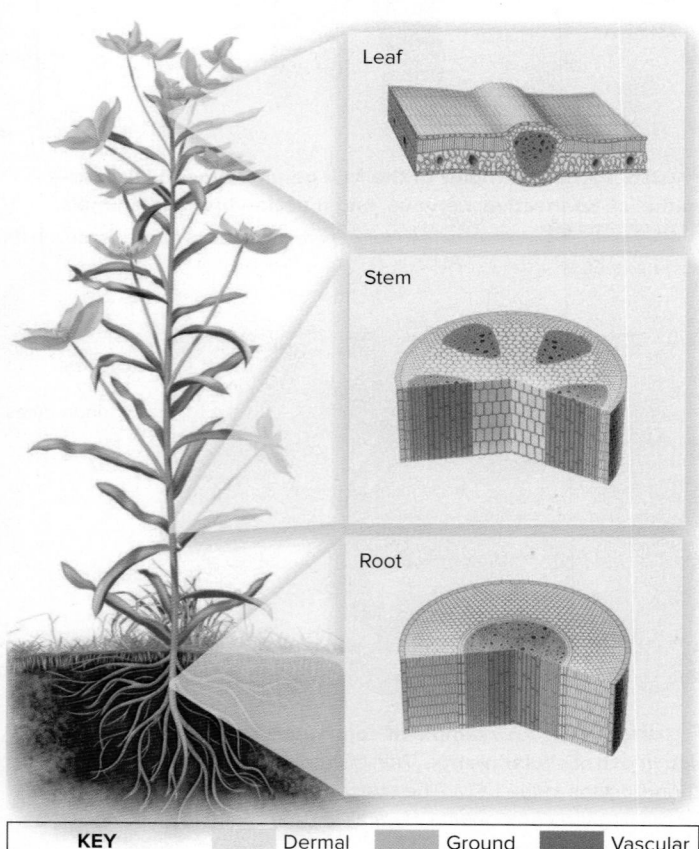

KEY	Dermal	Ground	Vascular

Figure 10.17 **Locations of the three general types of tissues— dermal, ground, and vascular—found in plants.**

Concept Check: *Which of these three types of plant tissues is found on the surfaces of leaves, stems, and roots?*

Dermal Tissue   **Dermal tissue** is a complex tissue that forms a covering on various parts of the plant. The term **epidermis** refers to the newly made dermal tissue on the surfaces of leaves, stems, and roots. Plant epidermal cells have a thick primary cell wall and are tightly interlocked by their middle lamellae. As a consequence, these cells are held closely together, much like epithelial cell layers in animals.

The epidermal cells of leaves usually secrete a waxy cuticle to prevent water loss. In addition, leaf epidermis often has hairs, or trichomes, which are specialized types of epidermal cells. Trichomes have diverse functions, including the secretion of oils and leaf protection. In leaves, epidermal cells called guard cells form pores known as stomata, which permit gas exchange. The function of the root epidermis is the absorption of water and nutrients. The root epidermis does not have a waxy cuticle because such a cuticle would inhibit water and nutrient absorption.

Ground Tissue   Most of a plant's body is made of **ground tissue**, which has a variety of functions, including photosynthesis, storage of carbohydrates, and support. Ground tissue is subdivided into three types of simple tissues: parenchyma, collenchyma, and sclerenchyma. Let's look briefly at each of these types of ground tissue (also see Figure 36.7).

1. Parenchyma is very active metabolically. The mesophyll, the central part of the leaf that carries out the bulk of photosynthesis, is composed of parenchyma. Parenchyma also functions in the storage of carbohydrates. The cells of parenchyma usually lack a secondary cell wall.

2. Collenchyma provides structural support to the plant body, particularly to growing regions such as the periphery of the stems and leaves. Cells in collenchyma tend to have thick, secondary cell walls but do not contain much lignin. Therefore, they provide support but are also able to stretch.

3. Sclerenchyma also provides structural support to the plant body, particularly to those parts that are no longer growing, such as the dense, woody parts of stems. The secondary cell walls of sclerenchyma cells tend to have large amounts of lignin, which provides rigid support. In many cases, sclerenchyma cells are dead at maturity, but their cell walls continue to provide structural support during the life of the plant.

Vascular Tissue   Some types of modern plants, such as mosses, are nonvascular plants that lack conducting vessels. These plants tend to be small and live in damp, shady places. Most plants living today, however, are vascular plants. In these species, which include ferns and seed plants, the **vascular tissue** is a complex tissue composed of cells that are interconnected and form conducting vessels for water and nutrients. As described in greater detail in Chapter 39, the two types of vascular tissue are called xylem and phloem. The xylem transports water and mineral ions from the root to the rest of the plant, and the phloem distributes the products of photosynthesis and a variety of other nutrients throughout the plant.

Summary of Key Concepts

10.1 Extracellular Matrix and Cell Walls

- The extracellular matrix (ECM) is a network of material that forms a complex meshwork outside of animal cells; the cell wall is a similar component of plant cells.

- Proteins and polysaccharides are the major constituents of the ECM in animals. These materials are involved in strength, structural support, organization, and cell signaling (Figure 10.1).

- Adhesive proteins, such as fibronectin and laminin, help adhere cells to the ECM. Structural proteins include collagen, which forms fibers and fibrous networks that provide tensile strength, and elastin, which forms elastic fibers that stretch and recoil (Table 10.1, Figures 10.2, 10.3).

- Animals make many different types of collagen fibers, and gene regulation controls the locations in the body where they are made (Table 10.2).

- Glycosaminoglycans (GAGs) are polysaccharides of repeating disaccharide units that give a gel-like character to the ECM of animals. Proteoglycans consist of a long, linear core protein with many GAGs attached (Figure 10.4).

- Plant cells are surrounded by a cell wall composed largely of cellulose. The primary cell wall is made first and tends to be thin and flexible. The secondary cell wall is made after the primary cell wall and is often thick and rigid (Figures 10.5, 10.6).

10.2 Cell Junctions

- The three common types of cell junctions found in animals are anchoring, tight, and gap junctions (Table 10.3).

- Key components of anchoring junctions are cell adhesion molecules (CAMs), which bind cells to each other or to the ECM. The four types of anchoring junctions are adherens junctions, desmosomes, hemidesmosomes, and focal adhesions (Figure 10.7).

- Cadherins and integrins are two types of CAMs. Cadherins link cells to each other, whereas integrins link cells to the ECM. In the cytosol, CAMs bind to actin or intermediate filaments (Figure 10.8).

- Tight junctions between cells, composed of occludin and claudin, prevent the leakage of materials across a layer of cells (Figures 10.9, 10.10).

- Gap junctions consist of many channels called connexons, which permit the direct passage of ions and small molecules between adjacent cells (Figure 10.11).

- Loewenstein and colleagues showed that gap junctions permit the passage of substances with a molecular mass of less than about 1,000 Da (Figure 10.12).

- The cell walls of adjacent plant cells are cemented together via middle lamellae, which are rich in pectins—negatively charged polysaccharides (Figure 10.13).

- The plasma membranes and endoplasmic reticula of adjacent plant cells are connected via plasmodesmata that allow the passage of water, ions, and molecules between the cytosols of adjacent cells (Figure 10.14).

10.3 Tissues

- Cells are organized into tissues, and tissues are organized into organs. A tissue is a group of cells that have a similar structure and function, and an organ is composed of two or more tissues that carry out a particular function or set of functions.

- Six processes—cell division, cell growth, differentiation, migration, apoptosis, and formation of cell-to-cell connections—produce tissues and organs.

- The four general kinds of tissues found in animals are epithelial, connective, nervous, and muscle tissues (Figures 10.15, 10.16).

- The three general kinds of tissues found in plants are dermal, ground, and vascular tissues (Figure 10.17).

Assess & Discuss

Test Yourself

1. The function of the extracellular matrix (ECM) in animals is
   a. to provide strength.
   b. to provide structural support.
   c. to organize cells and other body parts.
   d. cell signaling.
   e. all of the above.

2. The protein found in the ECM of animals that provides strength and resistance to tearing when stretched is
   a. elastin.
   b. cellulose.
   c. collagen.
   d. laminin.
   e. fibronectin.

3. The polysaccharide that forms the hard outer covering of many invertebrates is
   a. collagen.
   b. chitin.
   c. chondroitin sulfate.
   d. pectin.
   e. cellulose.

4. The extension sequence found in procollagen polypeptides
   a. causes procollagen to be synthesized into the ER lumen.
   b. causes procollagen to form a triple helix.
   c. prevents procollagen from forming large collagen fibers.
   d. causes procollagen to be secreted from the cell.
   e. both b and c.

5. The dilated state of plasmodesmata allows the passage of
   a. water.
   b. ions.
   c. small molecules.
   d. macromolecules and viruses.
   e. all of the above.

6. The gap junctions of animal cells differ from the plasmodesmata of plant cells in that
   a. gap junctions serve as communicating junctions and plasmodesmata serve as anchoring junctions.
   b. gap junctions prevent extracellular material from moving between adjacent cells but plasmodesmata do not.
   c. gap junctions allow for direct exchange of cellular material between cells but plasmodesmata cannot allow the same type of exchange.
   d. gap junctions are formed by specialized proteins that form channels through the membranes of adjacent cells and plasmodesmata are formed by connecting the plasma membranes of adjacent cells.
   e. all of the above are correct.

7. Which of the following is (are) involved in the process of tissue and organ formation in multicellular organisms?
   a. cell division
   b. cell growth
   c. cell differentiation
   d. cell connections
   e. all of the above

8. The tissue type common to animals that functions in the conduction of electrical signals is
   a. epithelial.
   b. dermal.
   c. muscle.
   d. nervous.
   e. ground.

9. A type of tissue that is rich in ECM or has cells with a thick cell wall is
   a. dermal tissue in plants.
   b. ground tissue in plants.
   c. nervous tissue in animals.
   d. connective tissue in animals.
   e. both b and d.

10. Which of the following is *not* a correct statement comparing plant tissues and animal tissues?
    a. Nervous tissue of animals plays the same role as vascular tissue in plants.
    b. The dermal tissue of plants is similar to epithelial tissue of animals in that both provide a covering for the organism.
    c. The epithelial tissue of animals and the dermal tissue of plants have special characteristics that limit the movement of material between cell layers.

d. The ground tissue of plants and the connective tissue of animals provide structural support for the organism.

e. The ground tissue of plants and the connective tissue of animals have large amounts of extracellular material (that is, thick cell walls in plants and lots of ECM in animals).

Conceptual Questions

1. What are key differences between the primary cell wall and the secondary cell wall of plant cells?

2. What are similarities and differences in the structures and functions of cadherins and integrins, proteins found in animal cells?

3. **Core Concept: Systems** We can view the body of a multicellular organism, such as a plant or animal, as a system of interconnected cells. Discuss how cell junctions play a key role in forming this system.

Collaborative Questions

1. Discuss the similarities and differences between the ECM of animals and the cell walls of plants.

2. Cell junctions in animals are important in preventing cancer cells from metastasizing—moving to other parts of the body. Certain drugs bind to CAMs and influence their structure and function. Some of these drugs may help to prevent the spread of cancer cells. What would you hypothesize to be the mechanism by which such drugs work? What might be some harmful side effects?

UNIT III
GENETICS

Genetics is the branch of biology that deals with **inheritance**—the transmission of characteristics from parent to offspring. We begin this unit by examining the structure of the genetic material, namely DNA, at the molecular and cellular levels. We will explore the structure and replication of DNA and see how it is packaged into chromosomes (Chapter 11). We will then consider how segments of DNA are organized into units called genes, and how those genes are expressed at the molecular level to produce mRNA, proteins, and noncoding RNAs (Chapters 12 and 13). In Chapter 14, we will consider how the expression of genes is regulated. We will also examine how mutations alter the properties of genes and even lead to diseases such as cancer (Chapter 15).

In Chapter 16, we turn our attention to the mechanisms by which genes are transmitted from parent to offspring, beginning with a discussion of how chromosomes are sorted and transmitted during cell division. Chapters 17 and 18 explore the relationships between the transmission of genes and the outcome of an offspring's traits. We will look at genetic patterns called Mendelian inheritance and more complex patterns that could not have been predicted from Mendel's work.

The remaining chapters of this unit explore additional topics that are of interest to biologists. In Chapter 19, we will examine some of the unique genetic properties of bacteria and viruses. Chapter 20 considers the central role genes play in the development of animals and plants from a fertilized egg to an adult. We end this unit by exploring genetic technologies that are used by researchers, clinicians, and biotechnologists to unlock the mysteries of genes and provide tools and applications that benefit humans (Chapter 21).

 **The following Core Concepts and Core Skills will be emphasized in this unit:**

- *Information: Throughout this unit, we will see how the genetic material carries the information to sustain life.*
- *Structure and Function: In Chapters 11 through 15, we will examine how the structures of DNA, RNA, genes, and chromosomes underlie their functions.*
- *Quantitative Reasoning: In Chapters 17 and 18, we will consider methods used to predict the outcome of genetic crosses.*
- *Science and Society: In Chapter 21, we will examine genetic technologies that have many applications in our society.*
- *Process of Science: Every chapter in this unit has a Feature Investigation that describes a pivotal experiment that provided insights into our understanding of genetics.*

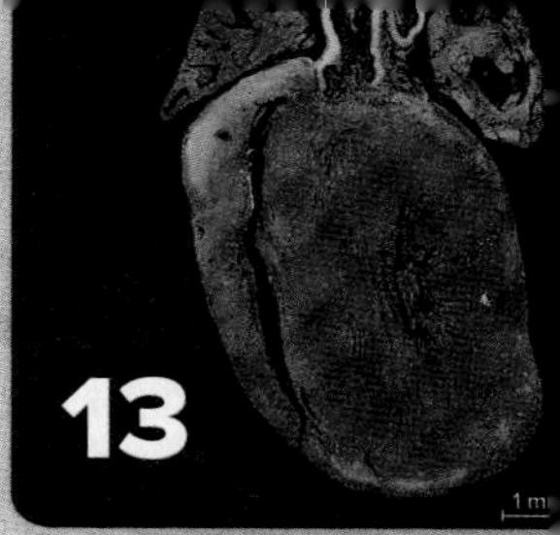

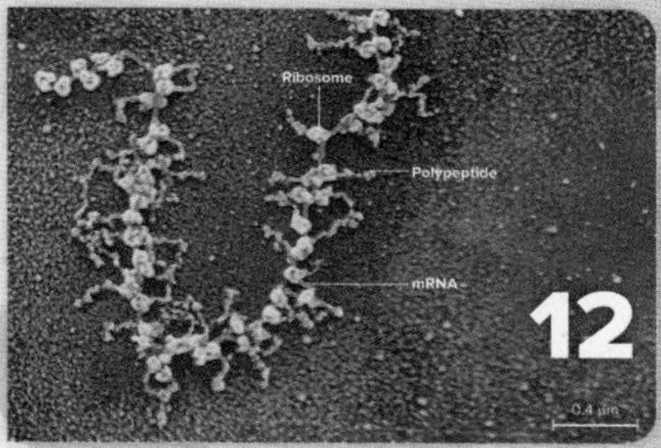

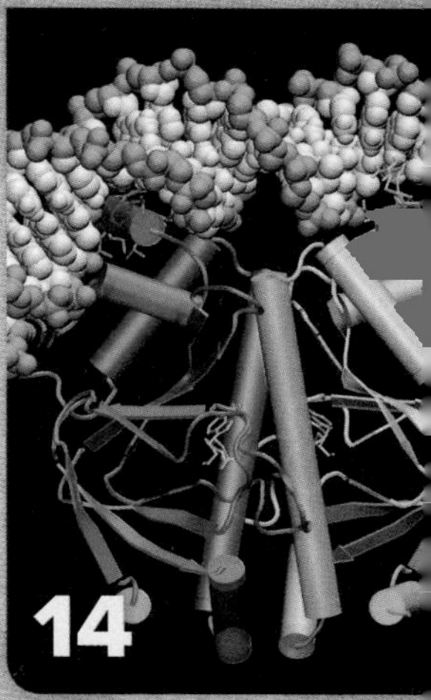

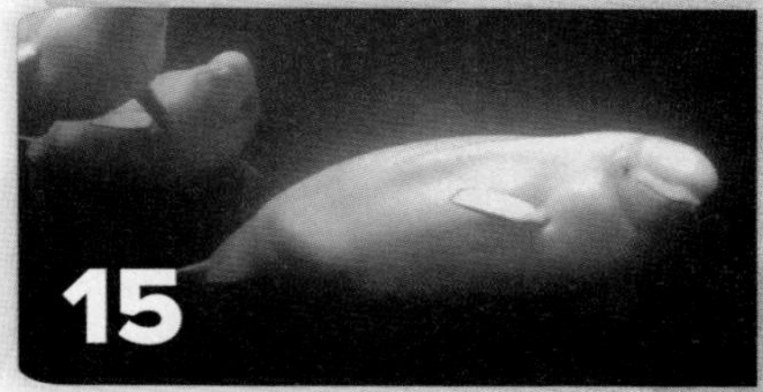

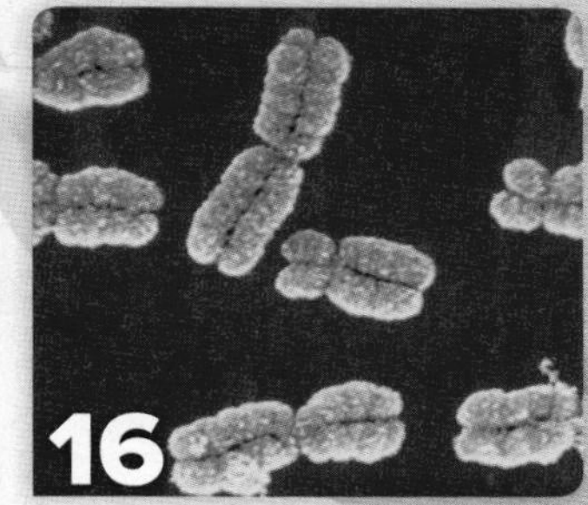

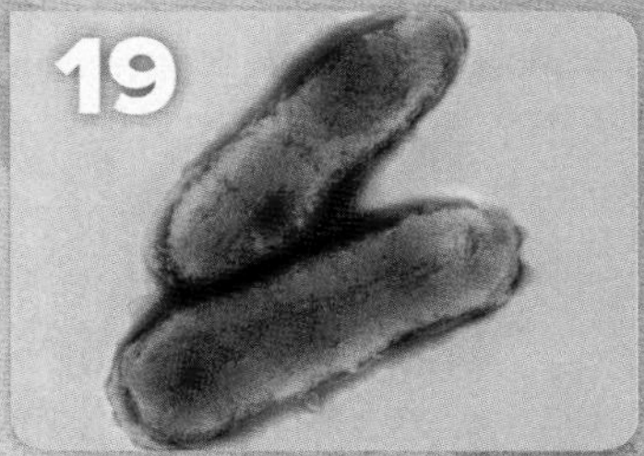

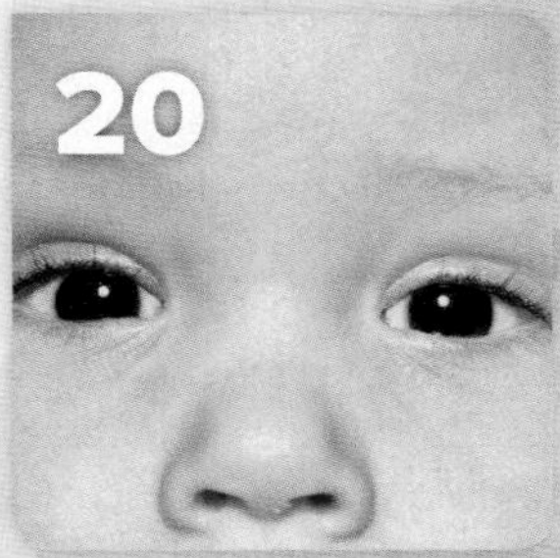

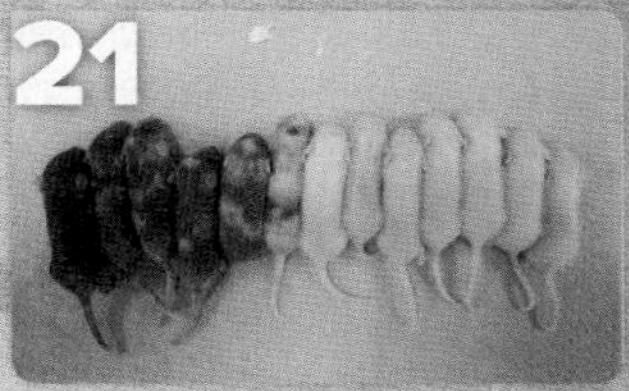

Nucleic Acid Structure, DNA Replication, and Chromosome Structure

11

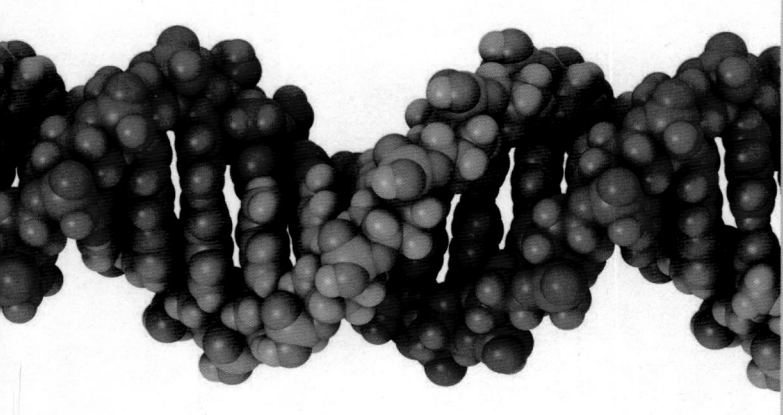

A molecular model for the structure of a DNA double helix.
©Pieter Van De Vijverl/Science Photo Library/Corbis

characteristics of unicellular and multicellular organisms. The past several decades have seen exciting advances in techniques and approaches for investigating and even altering the genetic material. These advances have greatly expanded our understanding of molecular genetics, and the techniques are widely used in related disciplines, including biochemistry, cell biology, and microbiology. Likewise, genetic techniques have many important applications in biotechnology and are used in the field of criminal justice, especially in forensics, to provide evidence of guilt or innocence.

To a large extent, our understanding of genetics comes from our knowledge of the molecular structure of DNA. In this chapter, we begin by considering some classic experiments that provided evidence that DNA is the genetic material. We will then survey the molecular features of DNA, which will allow us to appreciate how DNA can store information and be accurately copied. We will also consider the components of ribonucleic acid (RNA), which show striking similarities to those of DNA. Lastly, we will examine the molecular composition of chromosomes, where the DNA is found.

On October 17, 2001, Mario K. was set free after serving 16 years in prison. He had been convicted of a sexual assault and murder that occurred in 1985. The charges were dropped because investigators discovered that another person, Edwin M., had actually committed the crime. How was Edwin M. identified as the real murderer? In 2001, he committed another crime, and his DNA was entered into a computer database. Edwin's DNA matched the DNA that had been collected from the victim in 1985, and other evidence was then gathered indicating that Edwin M. was the true murderer. Like Mario K., over 200 other inmates have been exonerated when DNA tests have shown that a different person was responsible for the crime.

Deoxyribonucleic acid, or **DNA**, is the genetic material that provides the blueprint to produce an individual's traits. Each person's DNA is distinct and unique. Even identical twins show minor differences in their DNA sequences. We begin our survey of genetics by examining DNA at the molecular level. Once we understand how DNA works at this level, it becomes easier to see how DNA functions to control the properties of cells and ultimately the

11.1 Biochemical Identification of the Genetic Material

Learning Outcomes:

1. List the four key criteria that the genetic material must fulfill.
2. **CoreSKILL »** Analyze the results of experiments that identified DNA as the genetic material.

DNA carries the genetic instructions for the traits of living organisms. In the case of multicellular organisms such as plants and animals, the information stored in the genetic material enables a fertilized egg to develop into an embryo and eventually into an adult organism. In addition, the genetic material allows organisms to survive in their native environments. For example, an individual's DNA provides the blueprint to produce enzymes that are needed to metabolize nutrients in food. To fulfill its role, the genetic material must meet the following key criteria:

1. *Information.* The genetic material must contain the information necessary to construct an entire organism.

2. *Replication.* The genetic material must be accurately copied, a process known as **replication**.

3. *Transmission.* After it is replicated, the genetic material can be passed from parent to offspring. It also must be passed from cell to cell during the process of cell division.

4. *Variation.* Differences in the genetic material must account for the known variation within each species and among different species.

How was the genetic material discovered? The quest to identify the genetic material began in the late 19th century, when a few scientists postulated that living organisms possess a blueprint that has a biochemical basis. In 1883, German biologist August Weismann and his Swiss colleague Karl Nägeli championed the idea that a chemical substance exists within living cells that is responsible for the transmission of traits from parents to offspring. During the next 30 years, experimentation along these lines centered on the behavior of **chromosomes**, the cellular structures that we now know contain the genetic material. The term chromosome is from the Greek words *chromo* and *soma*, meaning colored body, which refers to the observation of early microscopists that chromosomes are easily stained by colored dyes. By studying the transmission patterns of chromosomes from cell to cell and from parent to offspring, researchers were convinced that chromosomes carry the determinants that control the outcome of traits.

Ironically, the study of chromosomes initially misled researchers regarding the biochemical identity of the genetic material. Chromosomes contain two classes of macromolecules: proteins and DNA. Scientists of that era viewed proteins as being more biochemically complex because they are made from 20 different amino acids. Furthermore, biochemists already knew that proteins perform an amazingly wide range of functions, and complexity seemed an important prerequisite for the blueprint of an organism. By comparison, DNA seemed less complex, because it contains only four types of repeating units, called nucleotides, which will be described later in this chapter. In addition, the functional role of DNA in the nucleus had not been extensively investigated prior to the 1920s. Therefore, from the 1920s to the 1940s, most scientists were expecting research studies to reveal that proteins are the genetic material. Contrary to this expectation, however, several different experiments revealed that DNA carries out this critical role. In this section, we will examine one early line of study that involved research in microbiology.

Griffith's Bacterial Transformation Experiments Indicated the Existence of a Genetic Material

In the late 1920s, an English microbiologist, Frederick Griffith, studied a type of bacterium known then as pneumococci and now classified as *Streptococcus pneumoniae*. Some strains of *S. pneumoniae* secrete a polysaccharide capsule, but other strains do not. When streaked on petri plates containing solid growth media, capsule-secreting strains have a smooth colony morphology. Those strains unable to secrete a capsule have a colony morphology that looks rough. In mammals, smooth strains of *S. pneumoniae* may cause pneumonia and other symptoms. In mice, such infections are usually fatal.

As shown in **Figure 11.1**, Griffith injected live and/or heat-killed bacteria into mice and then observed whether or not the bacteria caused them to die. He investigated the effects of two strains of *S. pneumoniae*: type S for smooth and type R for rough.

1. When injected into a live mouse, the type S strain killed the mouse (Figure 11.1, step 1). The capsule made by type S strains prevents the mouse's immune system from killing the bacterial cells. Following the death of the mouse, many type S bacteria were found in the mouse's blood.

2. When type R bacteria were injected into a mouse, the mouse survived, and after several days, living bacteria were not found in the live mouse's blood (Figure 11.1, step 2).

3. Griffith also heat-killed the type S bacteria and then injected them into a mouse. As expected, the mouse survived (Figure 11.1, step 3).

4. A surprising result occurred when Griffith mixed live type R bacteria with heat-killed type S bacteria and then injected them into a mouse—the mouse died (Figure 11.1, step 4). The blood from the dead mouse contained living type S bacteria! How did Griffith explain these results? He postulated that a substance from dead type S bacteria transformed the type R bacteria into

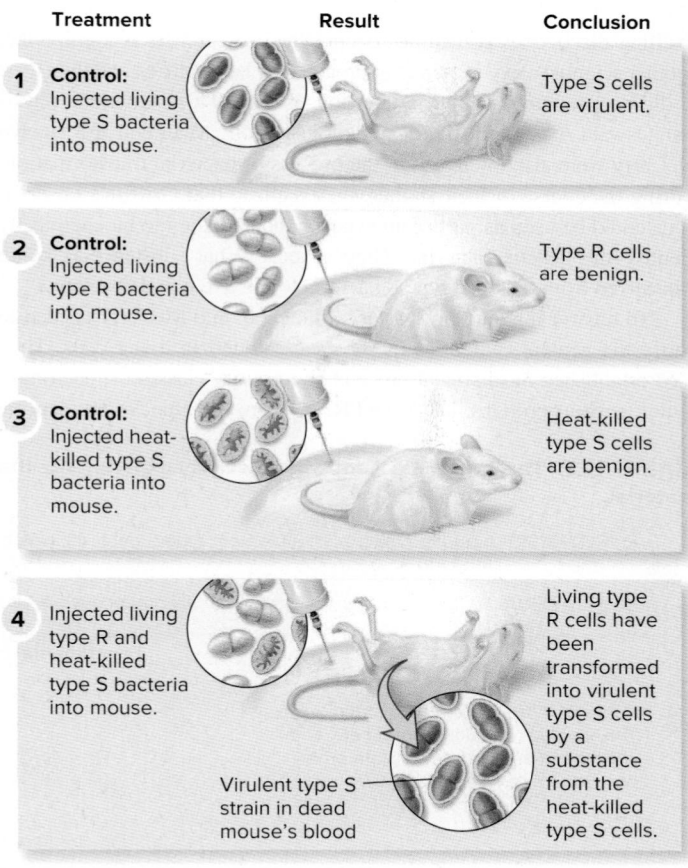

Figure 11.1 Griffith's experiments showing that genetic material can be transferred from one bacterium to another. Note: To determine if a mouse's blood contained live bacteria, a sample of blood was also applied to solid growth media. (This part of the procedure is not shown.) For steps 1 and 4, smooth bacterial colonies were observed. For step 2, no bacterial colonies were observed because the type R cells were killed by the immune system of the mouse.

 Core Skill: Connections Look ahead to Figure 19.17. How does bacterial transformation play a role in the transfer of genes, such as antibiotic resistance genes, from one bacterial species to another?

type S bacteria. Griffith called this process **transformation**, and he termed the unidentified material responsible for this phenomenon the "transformation principle."

Let's consider what these observations mean with regard to the four criteria of the genetic material: information, replication, transmission, and variation. According to Griffith's results, the transformed bacteria had acquired the information (criterion 1) to make a capsule from the heat-killed cells. For the transformed bacteria to proliferate and thereby kill the mouse, the substance conferring the ability to make a capsule must be replicated (criterion 2) and then transmitted

(criterion 3) from mother to daughter cells during cell division. Finally, Griffith already knew that variation (criterion 4) existed in the ability of his strains to produce a capsule (S strain) or not produce a capsule (R strain). Taken together, these observations are consistent with the idea that the formation of a capsule is governed by genetic material. In the experiment of Figure 11.1, step 4 indicated that some genetic material from the heat-killed type S bacteria had been transferred to the living type R bacteria and provided those bacteria with a new trait. At the time of his studies, however, Griffith could not determine the biochemical composition of the transforming substance.

 Core Skill: Process of Science

Feature Investigation | Avery, MacLeod, and McCarty Used Purification Methods to Reveal That DNA Is the Genetic Material

Exciting discoveries sometimes occur when researchers recognize that another scientist's experimental approach may be modified and then used to dig deeper into a scientific question. In the 1940s, American physician Oswald Avery and American biologists Colin MacLeod and Maclyn McCarty were also interested in the process of bacterial transformation. During the course of their studies, they realized that Griffith's observations could be used as part of an experimental strategy to biochemically identify the genetic material. They asked, "What substance is being transferred from the dead type S bacteria to the live type R bacteria?"

To answer this question, Avery, MacLeod, and McCarty needed to purify the general categories of substances found in living cells. They used established biochemical procedures to purify classes of macromolecules, such as proteins, DNA, and RNA, from the type S streptococcal

strain. Initially, they discovered that only the purified DNA could convert type R bacteria into type S. To further verify that DNA is the genetic material, they performed the investigation outlined in **Figure 11.2**. They purified DNA from the type S bacteria and mixed it with type R bacteria. After allowing time for DNA uptake into the type R bacteria, they added an antibody that aggregated any nontransformed type R bacteria, which were then removed by centrifugation. The remaining bacteria were placed on solid growth media within petri plates and incubated overnight to allow the division and growth of cells to form visible bacterial colonies.

As a control, no DNA extract was added, and no type S bacterial colonies were observed on the petri plates (see plate A in step 6). When the researchers mixed their S strain DNA extract with type R bacteria, some of the bacteria were converted to type S bacteria (see

Figure 11.2 The Avery, MacLeod, and McCarty experiments that identified DNA as Griffith's transformation principle—the genetic material.

HYPOTHESIS A purified macromolecule from type S bacteria, which functions as the genetic material, will be able to convert type R bacteria into type S.

KEY MATERIALS Type R and type S strains of *Streptococcus pneumoniae*.

	Experimental level	Conceptual level
1 Purify DNA from the type S strain. This involves breaking open cells and separating the DNA away from other components by centrifugation.	± DNase ± RNase ± Protease + Type R cells	DNA fragments in a purified DNA extract
2 Mix the DNA extract with type R bacteria. Also, carry out the same steps but add the enzyme DNase, RNase, or protease to the DNA extract, which digests DNA, RNA, or proteins, respectively. As a control, don't add any DNA extract to some type R cells.	A B C D E	A Control B + DNA C + DNA + DNase D + DNA + RNase E + DNA + Protease

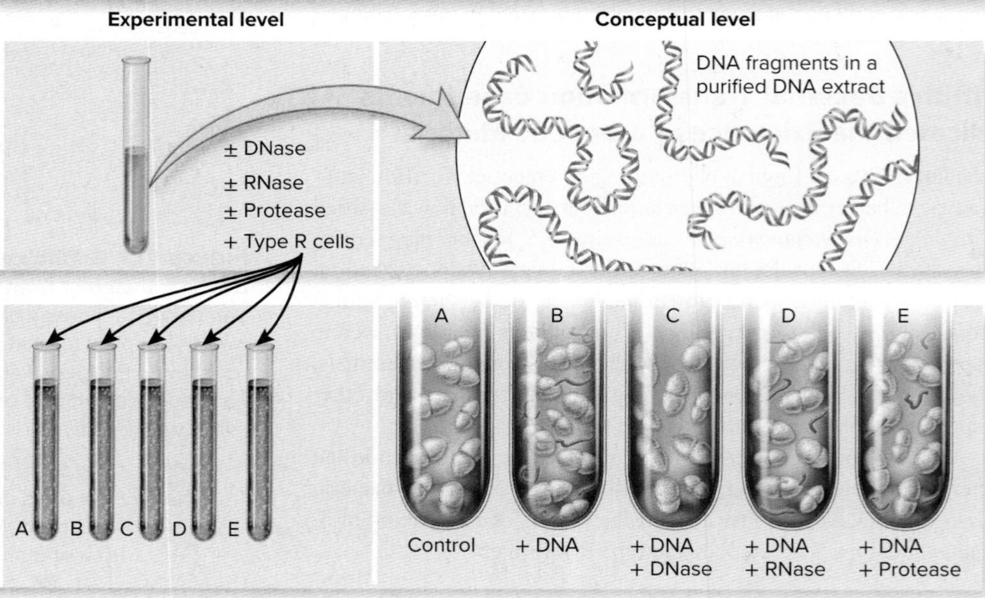

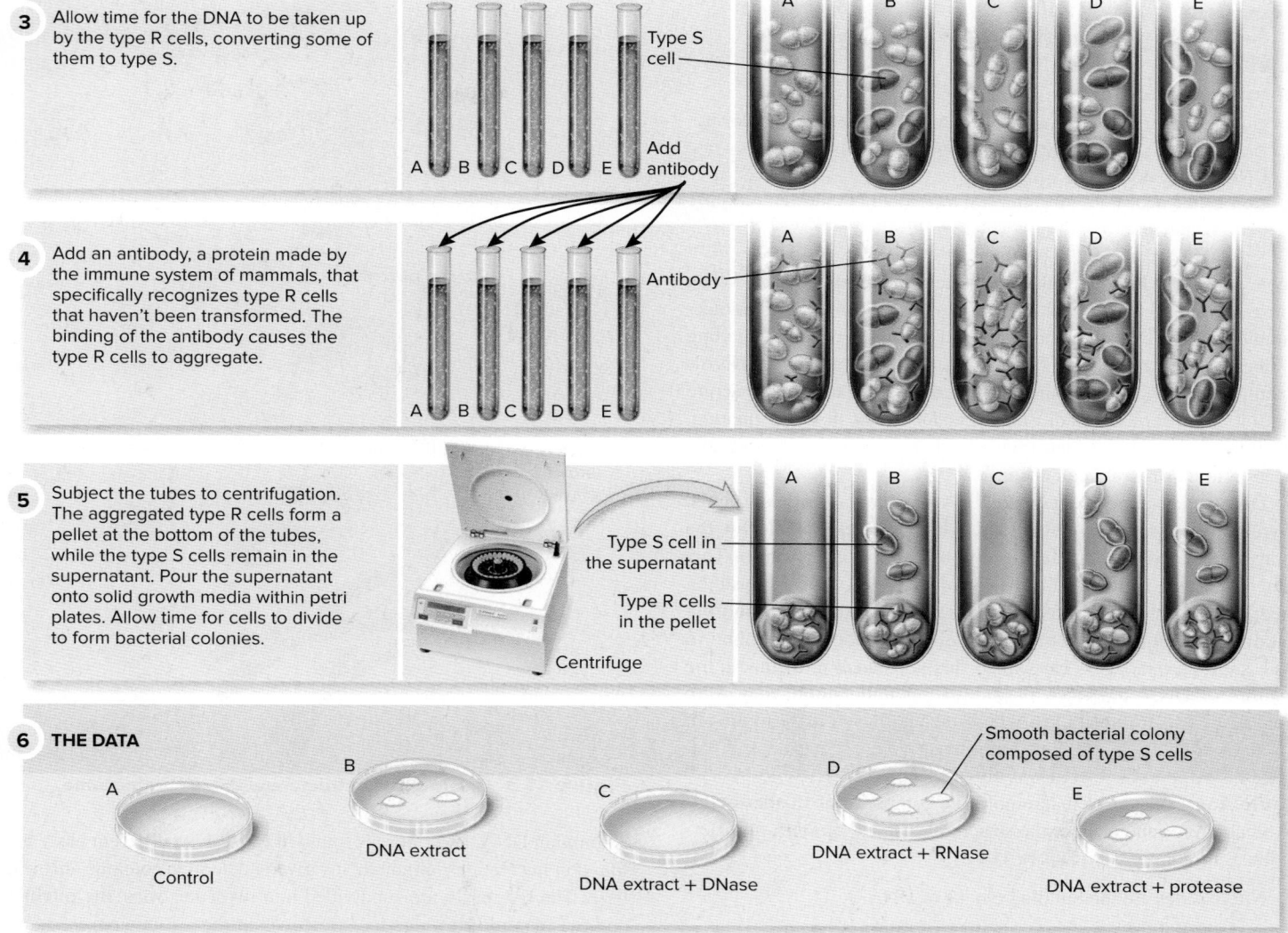

3 Allow time for the DNA to be taken up by the type R cells, converting some of them to type S.

Type S cell

Add antibody

4 Add an antibody, a protein made by the immune system of mammals, that specifically recognizes type R cells that haven't been transformed. The binding of the antibody causes the type R cells to aggregate.

Antibody

5 Subject the tubes to centrifugation. The aggregated type R cells form a pellet at the bottom of the tubes, while the type S cells remain in the supernatant. Pour the supernatant onto solid growth media within petri plates. Allow time for cells to divide to form bacterial colonies.

Type S cell in the supernatant

Type R cells in the pellet

Centrifuge

6 **THE DATA**

Smooth bacterial colony composed of type S cells

A — Control

B — DNA extract

C — DNA extract + DNase

D — DNA extract + RNase

E — DNA extract + protease

7 **CONCLUSION** DNA is responsible for transforming type R cells into type S cells.

8 **SOURCE** Avery, O.T., MacLeod, C.M., and McCarty, M. 1944. Studies on the Chemical Nature of the Substance Inducing Transformation of Pneumococcal Types. *Journal of Experimental Medicine* 79: 137–158.

plate B in step 6 of Figure 11.2). This result was consistent with the idea that DNA is the genetic material.

Even so, a careful biochemist could argue that the DNA extract might not have been 100% pure. For this reason, the researchers realized that a small amount of contaminating material in the DNA extract could actually be the genetic material. The most likely contaminating substances in this case would be RNA or protein.

To address this possibility, Avery, MacLeod, and McCarty treated the DNA extract with an enzyme that digests either DNA (called **DNase**), RNA (**RNase**), or protein (**protease**) (see step 2). When the DNA extracts were treated with RNase or protease, the type R bacteria were still converted into type S bacteria, indicating that contaminating RNA or protein in the extract was not acting as the genetic material (see step 6, plates D and E). Moreover, when

the extract was treated with DNase, it lost the ability to convert type R bacteria into type S bacteria (see plate C). Taken together, these results were consistent with the idea that DNA is the genetic material.

Experimental Questions

1. **CoreSKILL** » Avery, MacLeod, and McCarty worked with two strains of *Streptococcus pneumoniae* to determine the biochemical identity of the genetic material. Explain the characteristics of the *S. pneumoniae* strains that made them particularly well suited for the researchers' experiment.

2. What is a DNA extract?

3. **CoreSKILL** » In the experiment of Avery, MacLeod, and McCarty, what was the purpose of using protease, RNase, and DNase if only the DNA extract caused transformation?

11.2 Nucleic Acid Structure

Learning Outcomes:

1. Outline the structural features of DNA at five levels of complexity.
2. Describe the structures of nucleotides, a DNA strand, and the DNA double helix.
3. **CoreSKILL »** Discuss and interpret the work of Franklin; Chargaff; and Watson and Crick.

A core concept in biology is that structure determines function. When biologists want to understand the function of a material at the molecular and cellular level, they focus some of their efforts on determining its biochemical structure. In this regard, an understanding of DNA's structure has proven to be particularly exciting because the structure makes it easier for us to understand how DNA can store information, how it is replicated and then transmitted from cell to cell, and how variation in its structure can occur.

DNA and its molecular cousin, RNA, are known as **nucleic acids**, polymers consisting of nucleotides, which are responsible for the storage, expression, and transmission of genetic information. This term is derived from the discovery of DNA by Swiss physician Friedrich Miescher in 1869. He identified a novel phosphorus-containing substance from the nuclei of white blood cells found in waste surgical bandages. He named this substance nuclein. As the structure of DNA and RNA became better understood, they were found to be acidic molecules, which means they release hydrogen ions (H^+) in solution and have a net negative charge at neutral pH. Thus, the name nucleic acid was coined.

DNA is a very large macromolecule composed of smaller building blocks. We can consider the structural features of DNA at different levels of complexity (**Figure 11.3**):

1. **Nucleotides** are the building blocks of DNA.
2. A **strand** of DNA is formed by the covalent linkage of nucleotides in a linear manner.
3. Two strands of DNA hydrogen-bond with each other to form a **double helix**. In a DNA double helix, two DNA strands are twisted together to form a structure that resembles a spiral staircase.
4. In living cells, DNA is associated with an array of different proteins to form chromosomes. The association of proteins with DNA organizes the long double helix into a compact structure.
5. A **genome** is the complete complement of an organism's genetic material. For example, the genome of most bacteria is a single circular chromosome, whereas eukaryotic cells have DNA in their nucleus, mitochondria, and chloroplasts.

The first three levels of complexity will be the focus of this section. Level 4 will be discussed in Section 11.5, and level 5 is examined in Chapter 21.

Nucleotides Contain a Phosphate, a Sugar, and a Base

A nucleotide has three components: a phosphate group, a pentose (five-carbon) sugar, and a nitrogen-containing base (**Figure 11.4**). The nucleotides in DNA and RNA contain different sugars. Deoxyribose

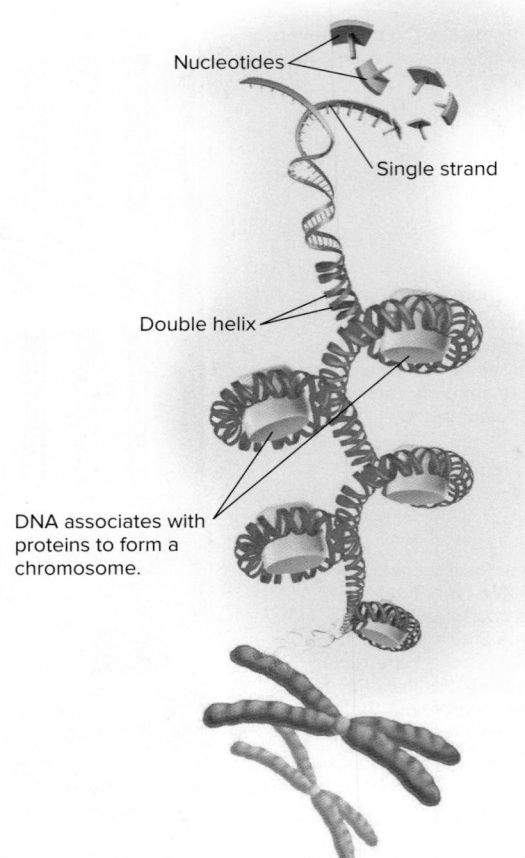

Nucleotides

Single strand

Double helix

DNA associates with proteins to form a chromosome.

Figure 11.3 **Levels of DNA structure within a chromosome.**

is found in DNA, and ribose is found in RNA. Five different bases are found in nucleotides, although any given nucleotide contains only one base. The five bases are subdivided into two categories, the **purines** and the **pyrimidines**, due to differences in their structures (see Figure 11.4). The purine bases, **adenine (A)** and **guanine (G)**, have a double-ring structure, whereas the pyrimidine bases, **thymine (T)**, **cytosine (C)**, and **uracil (U)**, have a single-ring structure. Adenine, guanine, and cytosine are found in both DNA and RNA. Thymine is found only in DNA, whereas uracil is found only in RNA.

A conventional numbering system describes the locations of carbon and nitrogen atoms in the sugars and bases (**Figure 11.5**). The prime symbol (′) is used to distinguish the numbering of carbons in the sugar. The atoms in the ring structures of the bases are not given the prime designation. The sugar carbons are designated 1′ (read as "one prime"), 2′, 3′, 4′, and 5′, with the carbon atoms numbered in a clockwise direction starting with the carbon atom to the right of the ring oxygen atom. The fifth carbon is outside the ring. A base is attached to the 1′ carbon atom, and a phosphate group is attached at the 5′ position. Compared with ribose (see Figure 11.4), deoxyribose lacks a single oxygen atom at the 2′ position; the prefix deoxy- (meaning without oxygen) refers to this missing atom.

A Strand Is a Linear Linkage of Nucleotides with Directionality

The next level of nucleic acid structure is the formation of a strand of DNA or RNA in which nucleotides are covalently attached to each other

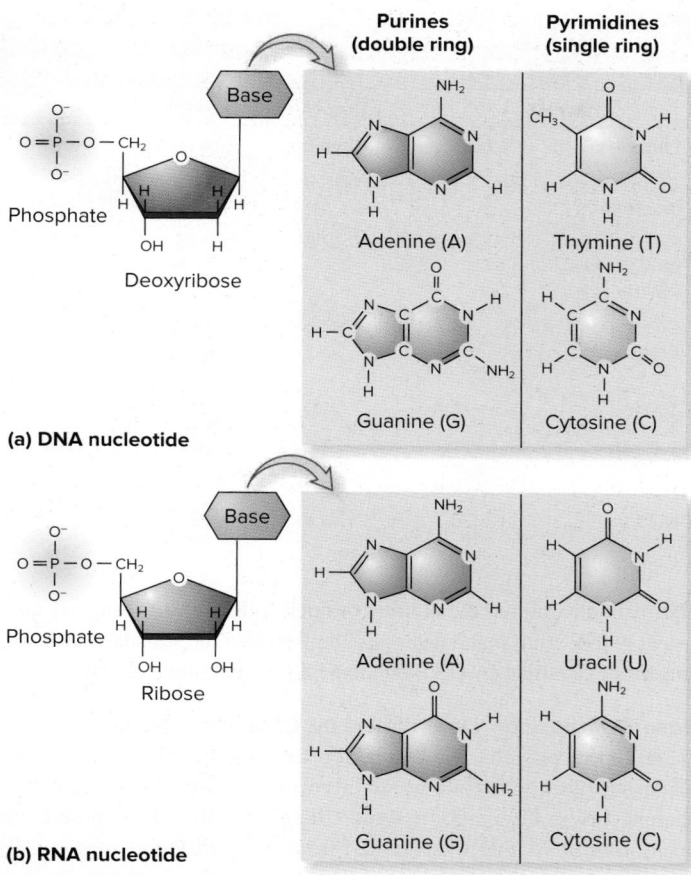

(a) DNA nucleotide

(b) RNA nucleotide

Figure 11.4 Nucleotides and their components. For simplicity, the carbon atoms in the ring structures are shown only for guanine and cytosine in part (a).

Concept Check: Which pyrimidine(s) is (are) found in both DNA and RNA?

Figure 11.5 Conventional numbering in a DNA nucleotide. The carbons in the sugar are given a prime designation, whereas those in the base are not.

Concept Check: What is the numbering designation of the carbon atom to which the phosphate is attached?

in a linear fashion. **Figure 11.6** depicts a short strand of DNA with four nucleotides. The linkage is a phosphoester bond (a covalent bond between phosphorus and oxygen) involving a sugar molecule in one nucleotide and a phosphate group in the next nucleotide. Another way of viewing this linkage is to notice that a phosphate group connects two sugar molecules. From this perspective, the linkage in DNA and RNA strands is called a **phosphodiester linkage**, which has two phosphoester bonds.

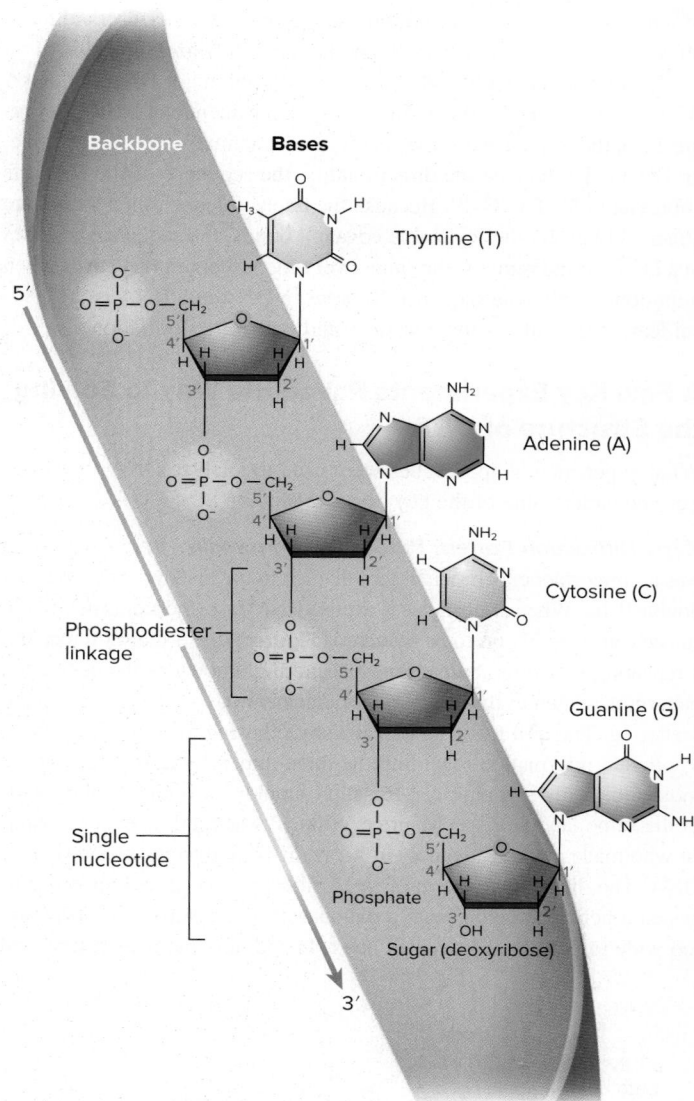

Figure 11.6 The structure of a DNA strand. Nucleotides are covalently bonded to each other in a linear manner. Notice the directionality of the strand and that it carries a particular sequence of bases. An RNA strand has a very similar structure, except the sugar is ribose rather than deoxyribose, and uracil is substituted for thymine.

👁 **Core Concept: Information** The covalent linkage of a sequence of bases allows DNA to store information.

The phosphates and sugar molecules form the **backbone** of a DNA or RNA strand, and the bases project from the backbone. The backbone is negatively charged due to the negative charges of the phosphate groups.

An important structural feature of a DNA strand is the orientation of the nucleotides. Each phosphate in a phosphodiester linkage is covalently bonded to the 5′ carbon in one nucleotide and to the 3′ carbon in the other. In a strand, all sugar molecules are oriented in the same direction. For example, in the strand shown in Figure 11.6, all of the 5′ carbons in every sugar molecule are above the 3′ carbons. A strand has a **directionality** based on the orientation of the sugar molecules within that strand. In Figure 11.6, the direction of the strand is said to be 5′ to

3′ when going from top to bottom. The 5′ end of a DNA strand has a phosphate group, whereas the 3′ end has an —OH group.

From the perspective of function, a key feature of DNA and RNA structure is that a strand contains a specific sequence of bases. In Figure 11.6, the sequence of bases is thymine–adenine–cytosine–guanine, or TACG. To indicate the directionality, the sequence of the strand is abbreviated 5′–TACG–3′. Because the nucleotides within a strand are attached to each other by stable covalent bonds, the sequence of bases in a DNA strand remains the same over time, except in rare cases when mutations occur. The sequence of bases in DNA and RNA is the critical feature that allows them to store and transmit information.

A Few Key Experiments Paved the Way to Solving the Structure of DNA

What experimental approaches were used to analyze DNA structure? Let's consider some of the key experiments.

X-ray Diffraction Pattern Produced by Franklin   X-ray diffraction was an important experimental tool that led to the discovery of the DNA double helix. When a substance is exposed to X-rays, the atoms in the substance cause the X-rays to be scattered (**Figure 11.7**). If the substance has a repeating structure, the pattern of scattering, known as the diffraction pattern, is related to the structural arrangement of the atoms causing the scattering. The diffraction pattern is analyzed using mathematical theory to provide information regarding the three-dimensional structure of the molecule. British biophysicist Rosalind Franklin, working in the 1950s in the same laboratory as Maurice Wilkins, was a gifted experimentalist who made marked advances in X-ray diffraction techniques involving DNA. The diffraction pattern of DNA fibers produced by Franklin suggested a helical structure with a diameter that is relatively uniform and too wide to be a single-stranded helix. In addition, the pattern provided

Table 11.1	Base Composition of DNA from a Variety of Organisms as Determined by Chargaff			
	Percentages of bases (%)			
Organism	Adenine	Thymine	Guanine	Cytosine
Escherichia coli (bacterium)	26.0	23.9	24.9	25.2
Streptococcus pneumoniae (bacterium)	29.8	31.6	20.5	18.0
Saccharomyces cerevisiae (yeast)	31.7	32.6	18.3	17.4
Turtle	28.7	27.9	22.0	21.3
Salmon	29.7	29.1	20.8	20.4
Chicken	28.0	28.4	22.0	21.6
Human	30.3	30.3	19.5	19.9

information regarding the number of nucleotides per turn and was consistent with a 2-nm (nanometer) spacing between the strands, which corresponds to a purine (A or G) bonding with a pyrimidine (T or C).

Base Composition Determined by Chargaff   Another piece of evidence that proved to be critical for the determination of the double helix structure came from the studies of Austrian-born American biochemist Erwin Chargaff. In 1950, Chargaff analyzed the base composition of DNA that was isolated from many different species. His experiments consistently showed that the amount of adenine in each sample was similar to the amount of thymine, and the amount of cytosine was similar to the amount of guanine (**Table 11.1**).

Model Building by Pauling   In the early 1950s, more information was known about the structure of proteins than that of nucleic acids. American biochemist Linus Pauling correctly proposed that some regions of proteins fold into a structure known as an α helix. To determine the structure of the α helix, Pauling built large models by linking together simple ball-and-stick units. In this way, he could see if atoms fit together properly in a complicated three-dimensional structure. This approach is still widely used today, except that now researchers construct three-dimensional models using computers. Use of the ball-and-stick approach was instrumental in solving the structure of the DNA double helix.

Watson and Crick Deduced the Double Helix Structure of DNA

Thus far, we have considered the experimental studies that led to the determination of the DNA double helix. American biologist James Watson and English biologist Francis Crick, working together at Cambridge University, assumed that nucleotides are linked together in a linear fashion and that the chemical linkage between two nucleotides is always the same. In collaboration with Wilkins, they then set out to build ball-and-stick models that incorporated all of the known experimental observations.

Modeling of chemical structures involves trial and error. Watson and Crick initially considered several incorrect models. One model was a double helix in which the bases were on the outside of the helix. In another model, each base formed hydrogen bonds with the identical base in the

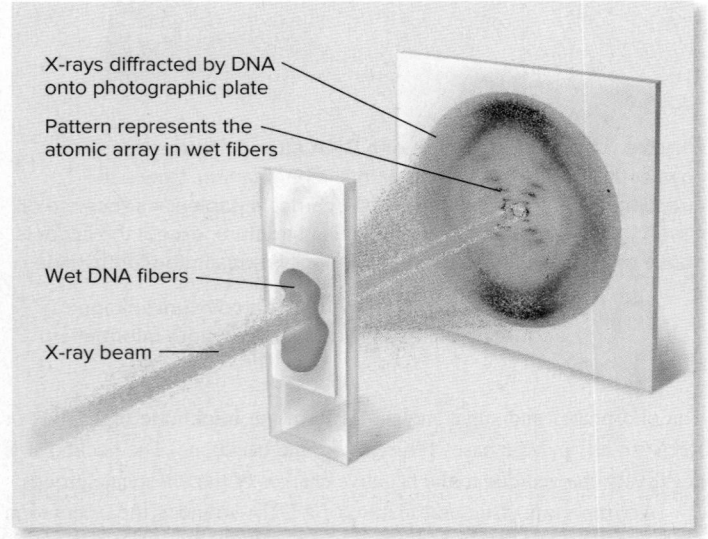

X-rays diffracted by DNA onto photographic plate

Pattern represents the atomic array in wet fibers

Wet DNA fibers

X-ray beam

Figure 11.7 Franklin's X-ray diffraction of DNA fibers. The exposure of DNA wet fibers to X-rays causes the X-rays to be scattered and the pattern of scattering is related to the position of the atoms in the DNA fibers.

 Core Skill: Process of Science This method was instrumental in solving the structure of the DNA double helix.

opposite strand (A to A, T to T, G to G, and C to C). However, model-building revealed that purine-purine pairs were too wide and pyrimidine-pyrimidine pairs were too narrow to fit the uniform diameter of DNA revealed from Franklin's work. Eventually, they realized that the hydrogen bonding of adenine to thymine was structurally similar to that of guanine to cytosine. In both cases, a purine base (A or G) bonds with a pyrimidine base (T or C). With an interaction between A and T and between G and C, the ball-and-stick models showed that the two strands would form a double helix structure in which all atoms would fit together properly.

Watson and Crick proposed the structure of DNA, which was published in the journal *Nature* in 1953. In 1962, Watson, Crick, and Wilkins were awarded the Nobel Prize in Physiology or Medicine.

Unfortunately, Rosalind Franklin had died before this time, and the Nobel Prize is awarded only to living recipients.

DNA Has a Repeating, Antiparallel Helical Structure Formed by the Complementary Base Pairing of Nucleotides

The structure that Watson and Crick proposed is a double-stranded, helical structure with the sugar-phosphate backbone on the outside and the bases on the inside (**Figure 11.8a**). This structure is stabilized by hydrogen bonding between the bases in opposite strands to form **base pairs**. A distinguishing feature of base pairing is its specificity. An adenine (A) base in one strand forms two hydrogen bonds with a

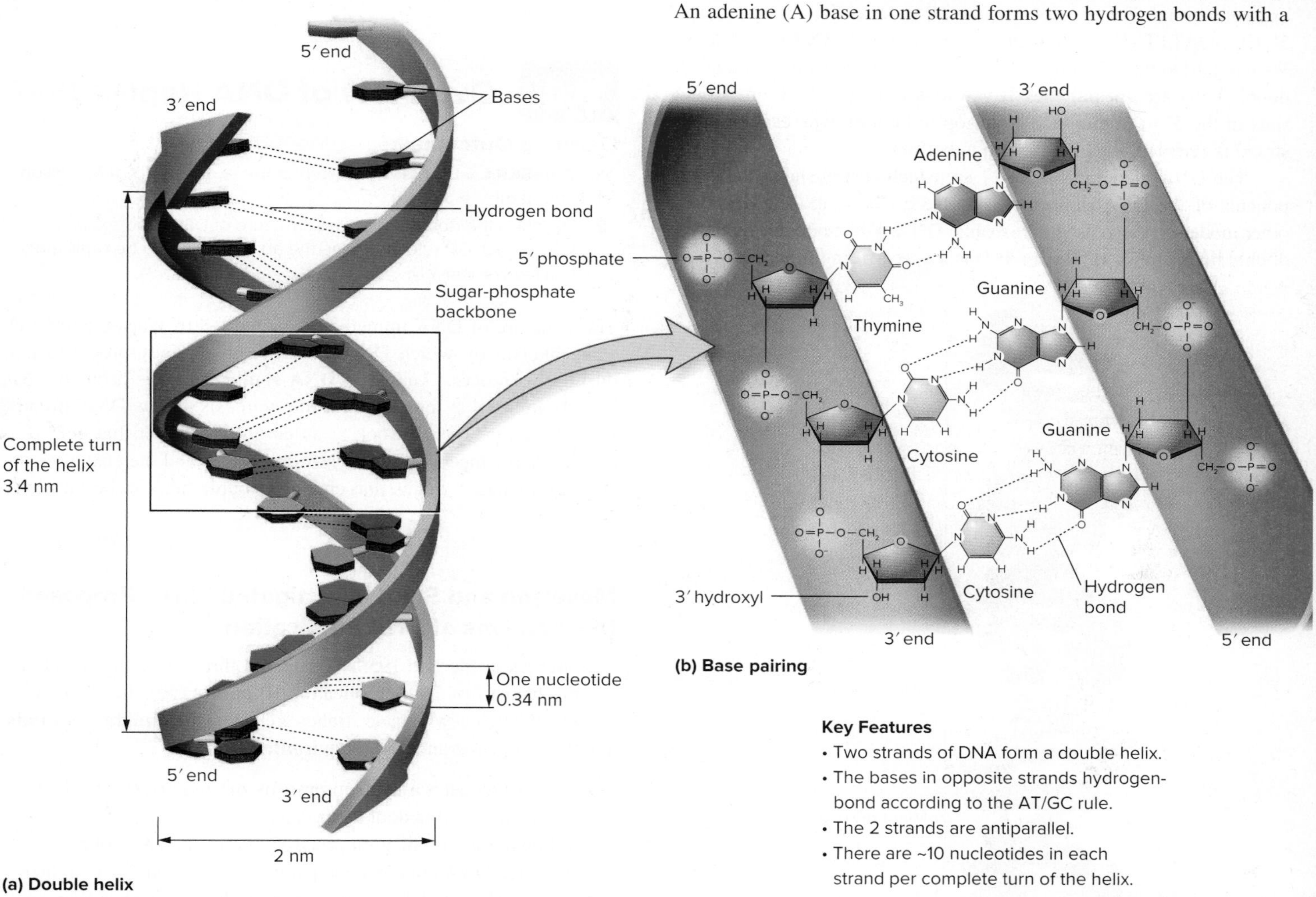

Key Features
- Two strands of DNA form a double helix.
- The bases in opposite strands hydrogen-bond according to the AT/GC rule.
- The 2 strands are antiparallel.
- There are ~10 nucleotides in each strand per complete turn of the helix.

Figure 11.8 Structure of the DNA double helix. As seen in part **(a)**, DNA is a helix composed of two antiparallel strands. Part **(b)** shows the AT/GC base pairing that holds the strands together via hydrogen bonds.

Core Skill: Modeling The goal of this modeling challenge is to predict the hydrogen-bonding relationship between O⁶-MeG and cytosine.

Modeling Challenge: As discussed in Chapter 15, certain chemicals, such as nitrogen mustard and ethyl methanesulfonate, can modify the structures of DNA bases. For example, a methyl group (–CH₃) can be attached to the oxygen atom on guanine, thereby creating 6-O-methylguanine (O⁶-MeG), as shown to the right. When O⁶-MeG is included in a DNA strand, it can form only two hydrogen bonds with cytosine instead of three. Draw a model for the base pairing between O⁶-MeG and cytosine.

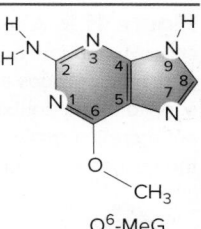

thymine (T) base in the opposite strand, or a guanine (G) base forms three hydrogen bonds with a cytosine (C) base (**Figure 11.8b**). This **AT/GC rule** is consistent with Chargaff's observation that DNA contains approximately equal amounts of A and T, and equal amounts of G and C. According to the AT/GC rule, purines (A and G) always bond with pyrimidines (T and C) (recall that purines have a double-ring structure, whereas pyrimidines have single rings). This keeps the width of the double helix relatively constant. One complete turn of the double helix is 3.4 nm in length and comprises about 10 base pairs.

Due to the AT/GC rule, the base sequences of two DNA strands are **complementary** to each other. That is, you can predict the sequence in one DNA strand if you know the sequence in the opposite strand. For example, if one DNA strand has the sequence 5′–GCGGATTT–3′, the opposite strand must be 3′–CGCCTAAA–5′. With regard to their 5′ and 3′ directionality, the two strands of a DNA double helix are **antiparallel**. If you look at Figure 11.8, one strand runs in the 5′ to 3′ direction from top to bottom, whereas the other strand is oriented 3′ to 5′ from top to bottom.

The DNA model in Figure 11.8a, which clearly shows the components of the DNA molecule, is called a ribbon model. However, other models are also used to visualize DNA. The model for the DNA double helix shown in **Figure 11.9** is a space-filling model in which the atoms are depicted as spheres. Why is this model useful? This type of structural model emphasizes the surface of DNA. As you can see in this model, the sugar-phosphate backbone is on the outermost surface of the double helix; the backbone has the most direct contact with water in the surroundings. The atoms of the bases are more internally located within the double-stranded structure. The indentations where the atoms of the bases make contact with the surrounding water are termed grooves. Two grooves, called the **major groove** and the **minor groove**, spiral around the double helix. As discussed in later chapters, the major groove provides a location where a protein can bind to a particular sequence of bases and affect the expression of a gene (for example, look ahead to Figure 14.10).

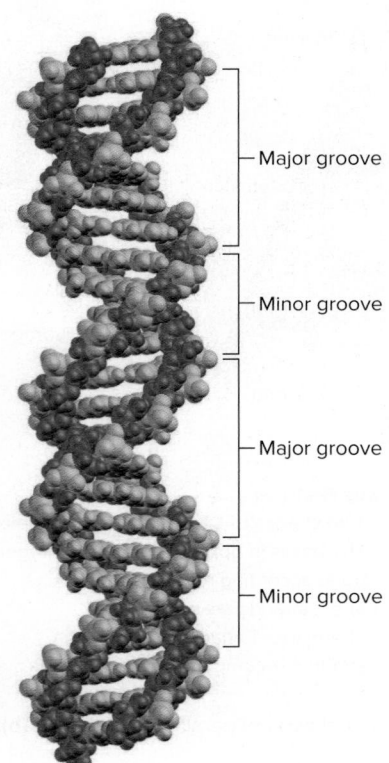

Figure 11.9 A space-filling model of the DNA double helix. In the sugar-phosphate backbone, sugar molecules are shown in blue, and phosphate groups are yellow. The backbone is on the outermost surface of the double helix. The atoms of the bases, shown in green, are more internally located within the double-stranded structure. Notice the major and minor grooves that are formed by this arrangement.

 Core Concept: Structure and Function The major groove provides a binding site for proteins that control the expression of genes.

11.3 Overview of DNA Replication

Learning Outcomes:

1. **CoreSKILL »** Discuss and interpret the experiments of Meselson and Stahl.
2. Describe the double-stranded structure of DNA, and explain how the AT/GC rule underlies the ability of DNA to be replicated semiconservatively.

The structure of DNA immediately suggested to Watson and Crick a mechanism by which DNA can be copied. They proposed that during this process, known as **DNA replication**, the original DNA strands are used as templates for the synthesis of new DNA strands. In this section, we will look at an early experiment that helped to determine the mechanism of DNA replication and then examine the structural characteristics that enable a double helix to be faithfully copied.

Meselson and Stahl Investigated Three Proposed Mechanisms of DNA Replication

Researchers in the late 1950s considered three different models for the mechanism of DNA replication (**Figure 11.10**). In all of these models, the two newly made strands are called the **daughter strands**, and the original strands are the **parental strands**.

- The first model is a **semiconservative mechanism** (Figure 11.10a). In this model, the double-stranded DNA is half conserved following the replication process; that is, the new double-stranded DNA contains one parental strand and one daughter strand. This model is consistent with the proposal of Watson and Crick.

- According to a second model, called a **conservative mechanism**, both parental strands of DNA remain together following DNA replication (Figure 11.10b). The original arrangement of parental strands is completely conserved, and the two newly made daughter strands are also together following replication.

- A third possibility, called a **dispersive mechanism**, proposed that segments of parental DNA and newly made daughter DNA are interspersed in both strands following the replication process (Figure 11.10c).

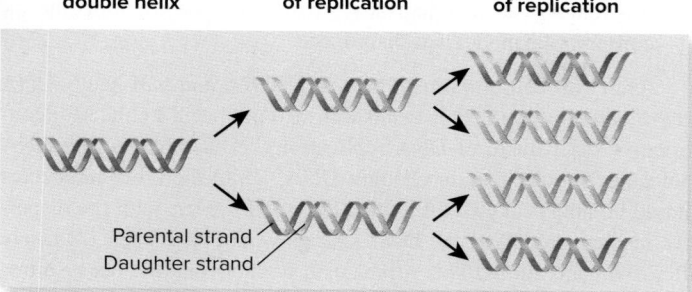

(a) Semiconservative mechanism. DNA replication produces DNA molecules with 1 parental strand and 1 newly made daughter strand.

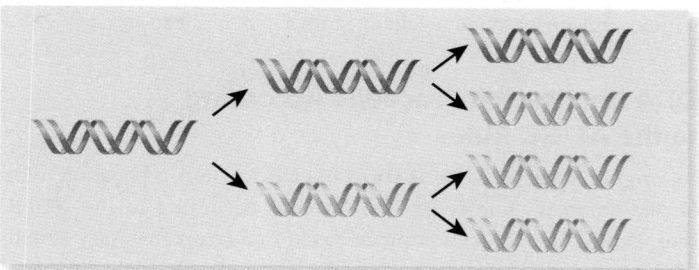

(b) Conservative mechanism. DNA replication produces 1 double helix with both parental strands and the other with 2 new daughter strands.

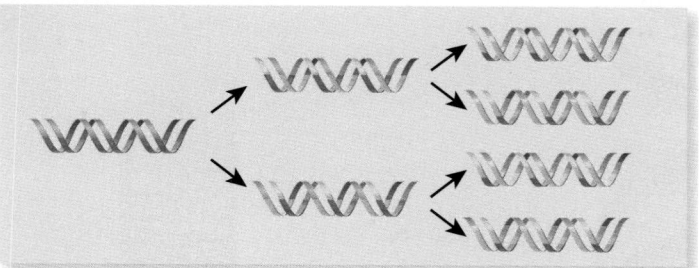

(c) Dispersive mechanism. DNA replication produces DNA strands in which segments of new DNA are interspersed with the parental DNA.

Figure 11.10 **Three proposed mechanisms for DNA replication.** The strands of the original (parental) double helix are shown in red. Two rounds of replication are illustrated with the daughter strands, which are shown in blue.

In 1958, American biologists Matthew Meselson and Franklin Stahl devised an experimental approach to distinguish among these three mechanisms. An important feature of their research was the use of isotope labeling. Nitrogen, which is found in DNA, occurs in a common light (^{14}N) form and a rare heavy (^{15}N) form. Meselson and Stahl studied DNA replication in the bacterium *Escherichia coli*.

1. They grew *E. coli* cells for many generations in a medium that contained only the ^{15}N form of nitrogen (**Figure 11.11**). This produced a population of bacterial cells in which all of the DNA was ^{15}N-labeled.

2. Then they switched the bacteria to a medium that contained only ^{14}N as the nitrogen source. The cells were allowed to divide,

1 Grow bacteria in ^{15}N media.

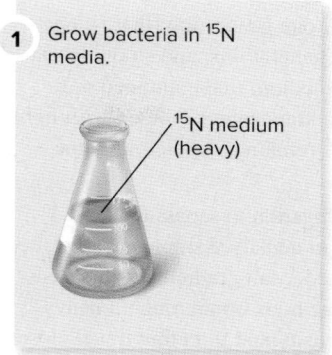

^{15}N medium (heavy)

2 Transfer to ^{14}N media and continue growth for <1.0, 1.0, 2.0, or 3.0 generations.

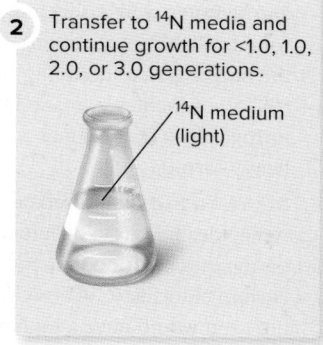

^{14}N medium (light)

3 Isolate DNA after each generation. Transfer DNA to CsCl gradient, and centrifuge.

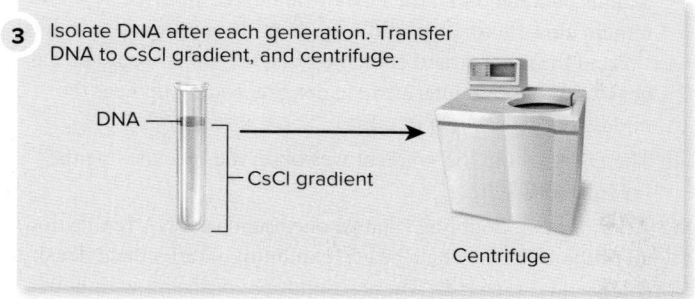

DNA — CsCl gradient — Centrifuge

4 Observe DNA under UV light.

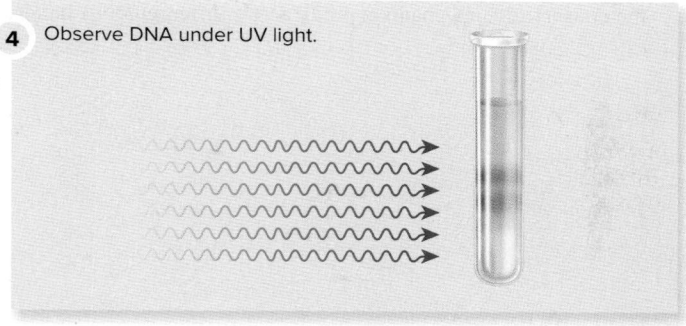

5 **THE DATA**

Approximate generations after transfer to ^{14}N medium.

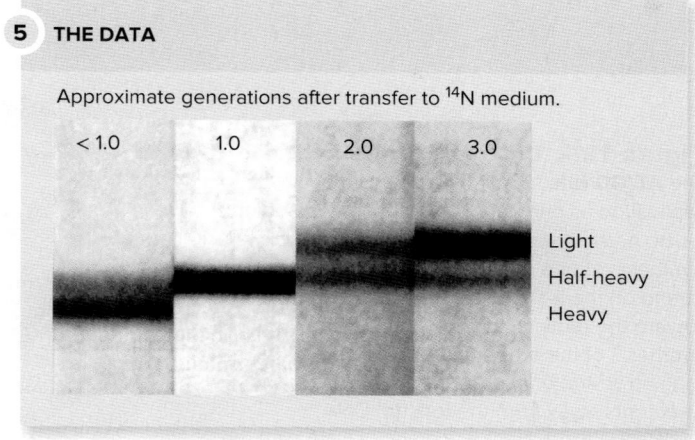

| < 1.0 | 1.0 | 2.0 | 3.0 |

Light
Half-heavy
Heavy

Figure 11.11 **The Meselson and Stahl experiment showing that DNA replication is semiconservative.** (5): ©Meselson, M., and Stahl, F. 1958. The replication of DNA in *Escherichia coli. PNAS* 44(7): 671–682, Fig. 4a

Concept Check: *If this experiment was conducted for four rounds of DNA replication (that is, four generations), what would be the expected fractions of light DNA and half-heavy DNA according to the semiconservative model?*

and samples were collected after one generation (that is, one round of DNA replication), two generations, and so on. Because the bacteria were doubling in a medium that contained only ¹⁴N, all of the newly made DNA strands were labeled with light nitrogen, but the original strands remained labeled with the heavy form.

3. Meselson and Stahl used centrifugation to separate DNA molecules based on differences in density. Samples were placed on top of a solution that contained a salt gradient, in this case, cesium chloride (CsCl). A double helix containing all heavy nitrogen would have a higher density and therefore travel closer to the bottom of the gradient. By comparison, if both DNA strands contained ¹⁴N, the DNA would have a low density and remain closer to the top of the gradient. If one strand contained ¹⁴N and the other strand contained ¹⁵N, the DNA would be half-heavy and have an intermediate density, ending up near the middle of the gradient.

4. The DNA within the gradient was observed by exposing the gradient to UV light.

5. After one cell doubling (that is, one round of DNA replication), all of the DNA was half-heavy, exhibiting intermediate density (Figure 11.11, step 5). These results are consistent with both the semiconservative and dispersive mechanisms. In contrast, the conservative mechanism predicts two different DNA bands:

one of high density and one of low density. Because the DNA was found in a single half-heavy band after one doubling, the conservative model was disproved.

After two cell doublings, both light DNA and half-heavy DNA bands were observed. This result was also predicted by the semiconservative mechanism of DNA replication, because half of the DNA molecules should contain all light DNA, while the other molecules should be half-heavy (see Figure 11.10a). However, with the dispersive mechanism, all of the DNA strands would have been 1/4 heavy after two generations. This mechanism predicts that the heavy nitrogen would be evenly dispersed among four double helices, each strand containing 1/4 heavy nitrogen and 3/4 light nitrogen (see Figure 11.10c). This prediction did not agree with the data. Taken together, the results of the Meselson and Stahl experiment are consistent only with a semiconservative mechanism for DNA replication.

DNA Replication Proceeds According to the AT/GC Rule

As originally proposed by Watson and Crick, DNA replication relies on the complementarity of DNA strands according to the AT/GC rule. During the replication process, the two complementary strands of DNA separate and serve as **template strands**, also called parental strands, for the synthesis of daughter strands of DNA (**Figure 11.12a**).

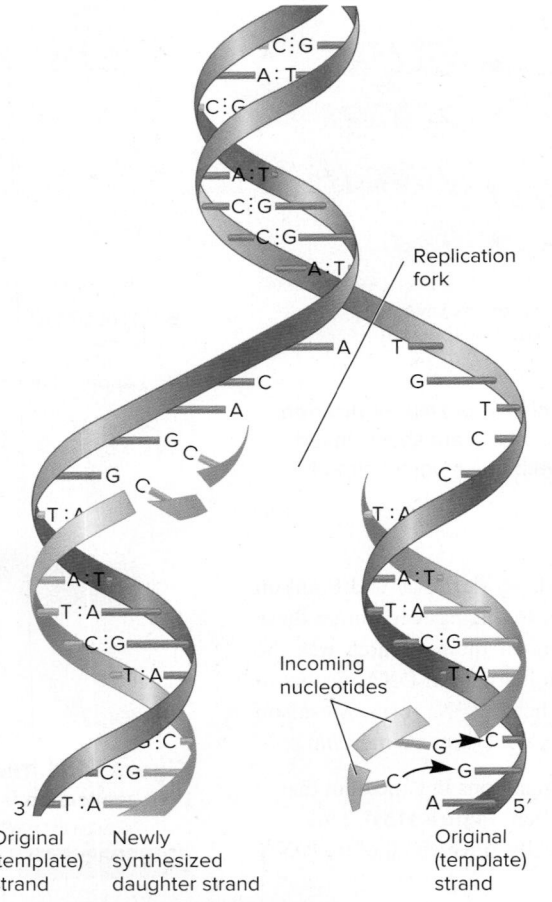
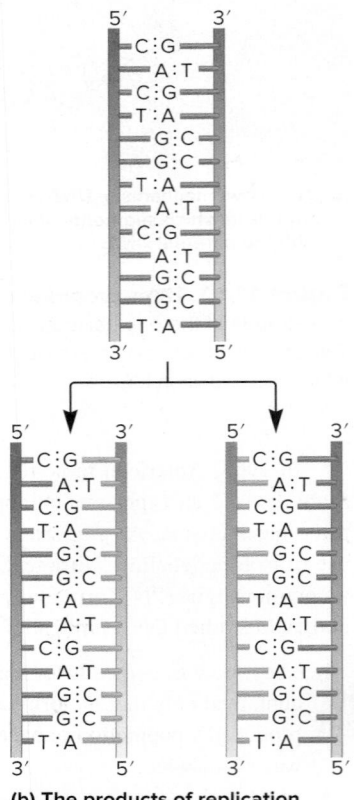

Figure 11.12 DNA replication according to the AT/GC rule. (a) The mechanism of DNA replication as originally proposed by Watson and Crick. As we will see in Section 11.4, the synthesis of one newly made strand (the leading strand on the left side) occurs in the direction toward the replication fork, whereas the synthesis of the other newly made strand (the lagging strand on the right side) occurs in small segments away from the fork. **(b)** DNA replication produces two copies of DNA with the same sequence as the original DNA molecule.

 Core Concept: Structure and Function A double-stranded structure whose base sequence obeys the AT/GC rule underlies the function of DNA replication.

Replication fork

Incoming nucleotides

Original (template) strand

Newly synthesized daughter strand

Original (template) strand

(a) The mechanism of DNA replication

(b) The products of replication

After the double helix has separated, individual nucleotides have access to the template strands in a region called the replication fork. First, individual nucleotides hydrogen-bond to the template strands according to the AT/GC rule: An adenine (A) base in one strand bonds with a thymine (T) base in the opposite strand, or a guanine (G) base bonds with a cytosine (C). Next, a covalent bond is formed between the phosphate of one nucleotide and the sugar of the previous nucleotide. The end result is that two double helices are made that have the same base sequence as the original DNA molecule (**Figure 11.12b**). This is a critical feature of DNA replication, because it enables the replicated DNA molecules to retain the same information (that is, the same base sequence) as the original molecule. In this way, DNA has the remarkable ability to direct its own duplication.

11.4 Molecular Mechanism of DNA Replication

Learning Outcomes:

1. Describe how the synthesis of new DNA strands begins at an origin of replication.

2. List the functions of helicase, topoisomerase, single-strand binding protein, primase, and DNA polymerase at the replication fork.

3. Outline the key differences in the synthesis of the leading and lagging strands.

4. List three reasons why DNA replication is very accurate.

5. Explain how DNA replication occurs at telomeres in eukaryotic chromosomes.

Thus far, we have examined the general mechanism of DNA replication, known as semiconservative replication, and considered how DNA synthesis obeys the AT/GC rule. In this section, we will explore the details of DNA replication as it occurs inside living cells. As you will learn, several different proteins are needed to initiate DNA replication and allow it to proceed quickly and accurately.

DNA Replication Begins at an Origin of Replication

Where does DNA replication begin? An **origin of replication** is a site within a chromosome that serves as a starting point for DNA replication. At the origin, the two DNA strands unwind (**Figure 11.13a**). DNA replication proceeds outward from two **replication forks**, a process termed **bidirectional replication**. The number of origins of replication varies among different organisms. In bacteria, which typically have a small circular chromosome, a single origin of replication is found. Bidirectional replication starts at the origin of replication and proceeds until the new strands meet on the opposite side of the chromosome (**Figure 11.13b**). Eukaryotes have larger chromosomes that are linear. They have multiple origins of replication so the DNA can be replicated in a reasonable length of time. The newly made

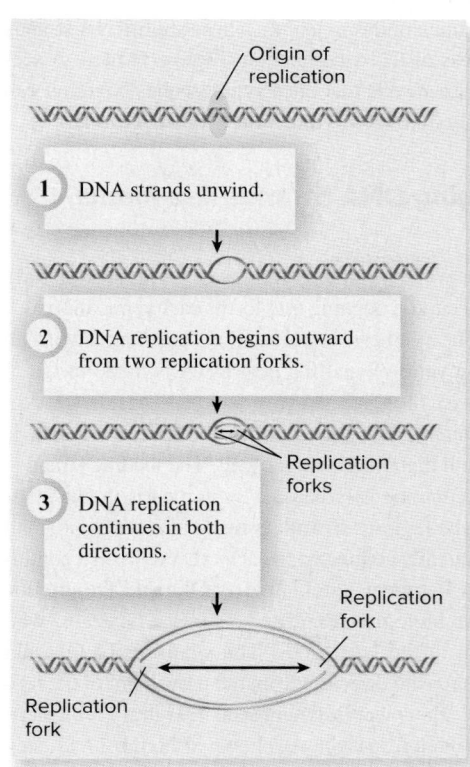

(a) Bidirectional replication

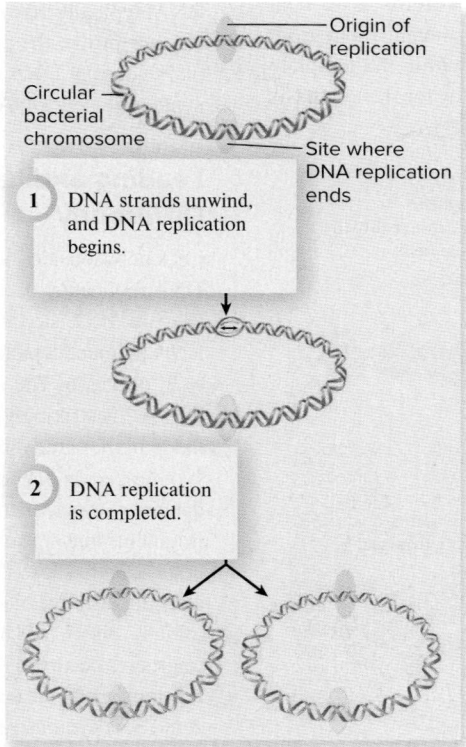

(b) Single origin of replication in bacteria

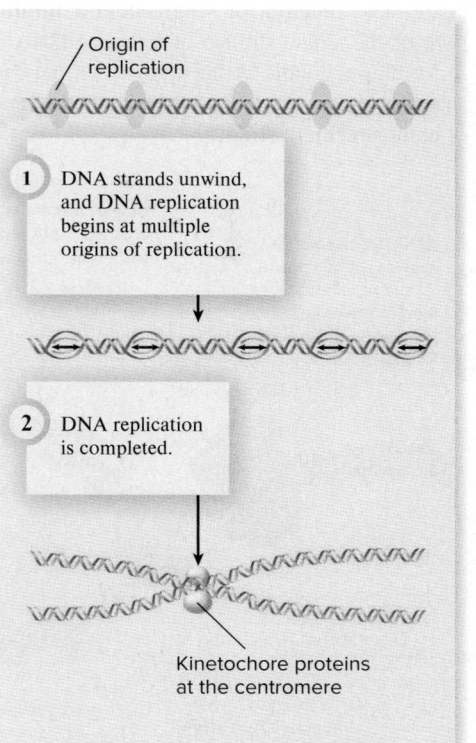

(c) Multiple origins of replication in eukaryotes

Figure 11.13 The bidirectional replication of DNA. (a) DNA replication proceeds in both directions from an origin of replication. **(b)** Bacterial chromosomes have a single origin of replication, whereas **(c)** eukaryotes have multiple origins. Following DNA replication in eukaryotes, the two copies remain attached to each other at the centromere via kinetochore proteins.

strands from each origin eventually make contact with each other to complete the replication process (**Figure 11.13c**).

DNA Replication Requires the Action of Several Different Proteins

Thus far, we have considered how DNA replication occurs outward from an origin of replication in a region called a DNA replication fork. In all living species, a set of several different proteins is involved in this process. An understanding of the functions of these proteins is critical to explaining the replication process at the molecular level.

Helicase, Topoisomerase, and Single-Strand Binding Proteins: Formation and Movement of the Replication Fork   To act as a template for DNA replication, the strands of a double helix must separate, and the resulting fork must move. As mentioned, an origin of replication serves as a site where this separation initially occurs. The strand separation at each fork then moves outward from the origin via the action of an enzyme called **DNA helicase**. At each fork, DNA helicase binds to one of the DNA strands and travels in the 5′ to 3′ direction toward the fork (**Figure 11.14**). It uses energy from ATP to break hydrogen bonds between base pairs. This separates the DNA strands and keeps the fork moving forward. The action of DNA helicase can cause knots (called supercoils) to form just ahead of the replication fork. These knots are removed by another enzyme called **DNA topoisomerase**.

After the two template DNA strands have separated, they must remain that way until the complementary daughter strands have been made. The function of **single-strand binding proteins** is to coat both of the single strands of template DNA and prevent them from re-forming a double helix. In this way, the bases within the template strands are kept exposed so they can act as templates for the synthesis of complementary strands.

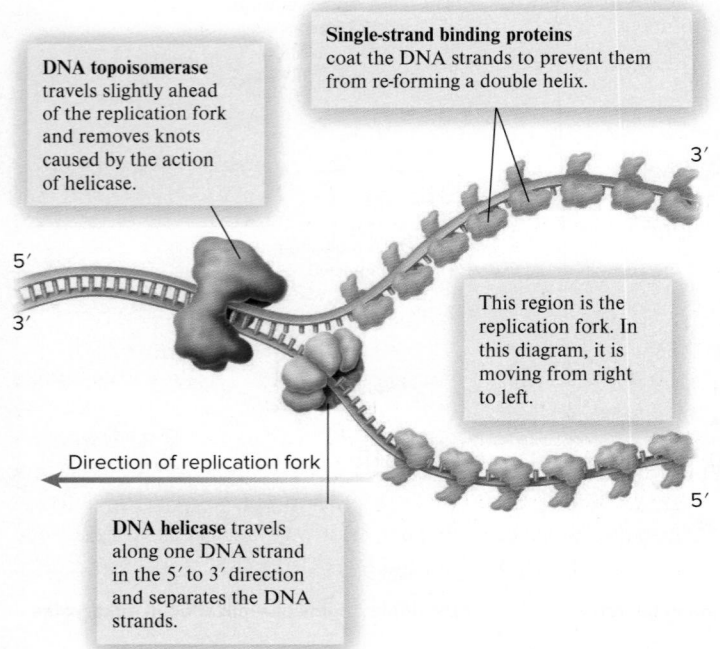

DNA topoisomerase travels slightly ahead of the replication fork and removes knots caused by the action of helicase.

Single-strand binding proteins coat the DNA strands to prevent them from re-forming a double helix.

This region is the replication fork. In this diagram, it is moving from right to left.

Direction of replication fork

DNA helicase travels along one DNA strand in the 5′ to 3′ direction and separates the DNA strands.

Figure 11.14 **Proteins that facilitate the formation and movement of a replication fork.**

DNA Polymerase and Primase: Synthesis of DNA Strands   The enzyme **DNA polymerase** is responsible for covalently linking nucleotides together to form DNA strands. American biochemist Arthur Kornberg discovered this enzyme in the 1950s. The structure of DNA polymerase resembles a human hand with the DNA threaded through it (**Figure 11.15a**). As DNA polymerase slides along the DNA, individual nucleotides with three phosphate groups, called **deoxynucleoside triphosphates**, hydrogen-bond to the exposed bases in the template strand according to the AT/GC rule. At the catalytic site, DNA polymerase breaks a bond between the first and second phosphate and then attaches the resulting nucleotide with one phosphate group (a deoxynucleoside monophosphate) to the 3′ end of a growing strand via a phosphoester bond. The breakage of the covalent bond releases pyrophosphate; this is an exergonic reaction that provides the energy to covalently connect adjacent nucleotides (**Figure 11.15b**). The pyrophosphate is broken down to two phosphates.

The rate of DNA synthesis is truly remarkable. In bacteria, DNA polymerase synthesizes DNA at a rate of 500 nucleotides per second, whereas eukaryotic species make DNA at a rate of about 50 nucleotides per second.

DNA polymerase has two additional enzymatic features that affect how DNA strands are made. First, if a DNA or RNA strand is already attached to a template strand, DNA polymerase can elongate such a pre-existing strand by making DNA. However, DNA polymerase is unable to begin DNA synthesis on a bare template strand. A different enzyme called **DNA primase** is required if the template strand is bare. DNA primase makes a complementary primer that is actually a short segment of RNA, typically 10 to 12 nucleotides in length. These short RNA strands start, or prime, the process of DNA replication (**Figure 11.16a**). A second feature of DNA polymerase is that once synthesis has begun, it can synthesize new DNA only in a 5′ to 3′ direction (**Figure 11.16b**).

Leading and Lagging DNA Strands Are Made Differently

Let's now consider how new DNA strands are made at a replication fork. DNA replication occurs near the opening that forms each replication fork (**Figure 11.17**, step 1). The synthesis of a strand always begins with an RNA primer (depicted in yellow), and the new DNA is made in the 5′ to 3′ direction. The manner in which the two daughter strands are synthesized is strikingly different. One strand, called the **leading strand**, is made in the same direction that the fork is moving. The leading strand is synthesized as one long continuous molecule. By comparison, the other daughter strand, termed the **lagging strand**, is made as a series of small fragments that are subsequently connected to each other to form a continuous strand. These DNA fragments are known as **Okazaki fragments**, after Japanese molecular biologists Reiji and Tsuneko Okazaki, who initially discovered them in the late 1960s. The synthesis of Okazaki fragments occurs in the opposite direction from the movement of the replication fork. For example, the lower fragment seen in Figure 11.17, steps 2 and 3, is synthesized from left to right. As shown in Figure 11.17, step 4, the RNA primer is eventually removed, and adjacent Okazaki fragments are connected to each other to form a continuous strand of DNA.

Figure 11.18 shows how the leading and lagging strands are made during bidirectional DNA replication from a single origin of replication. The fork moving to the left uses the top template strand to make

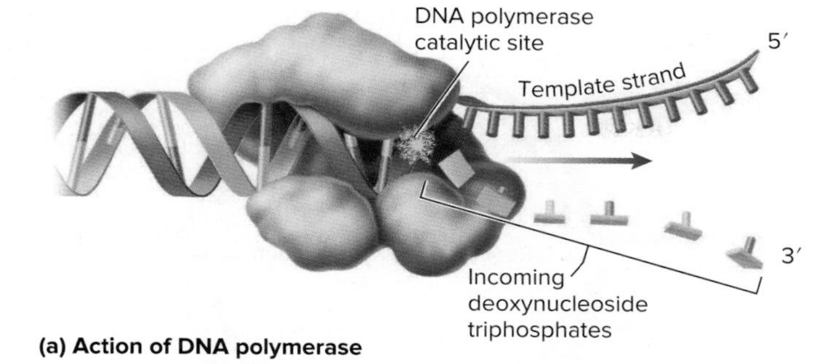

(a) Action of DNA polymerase

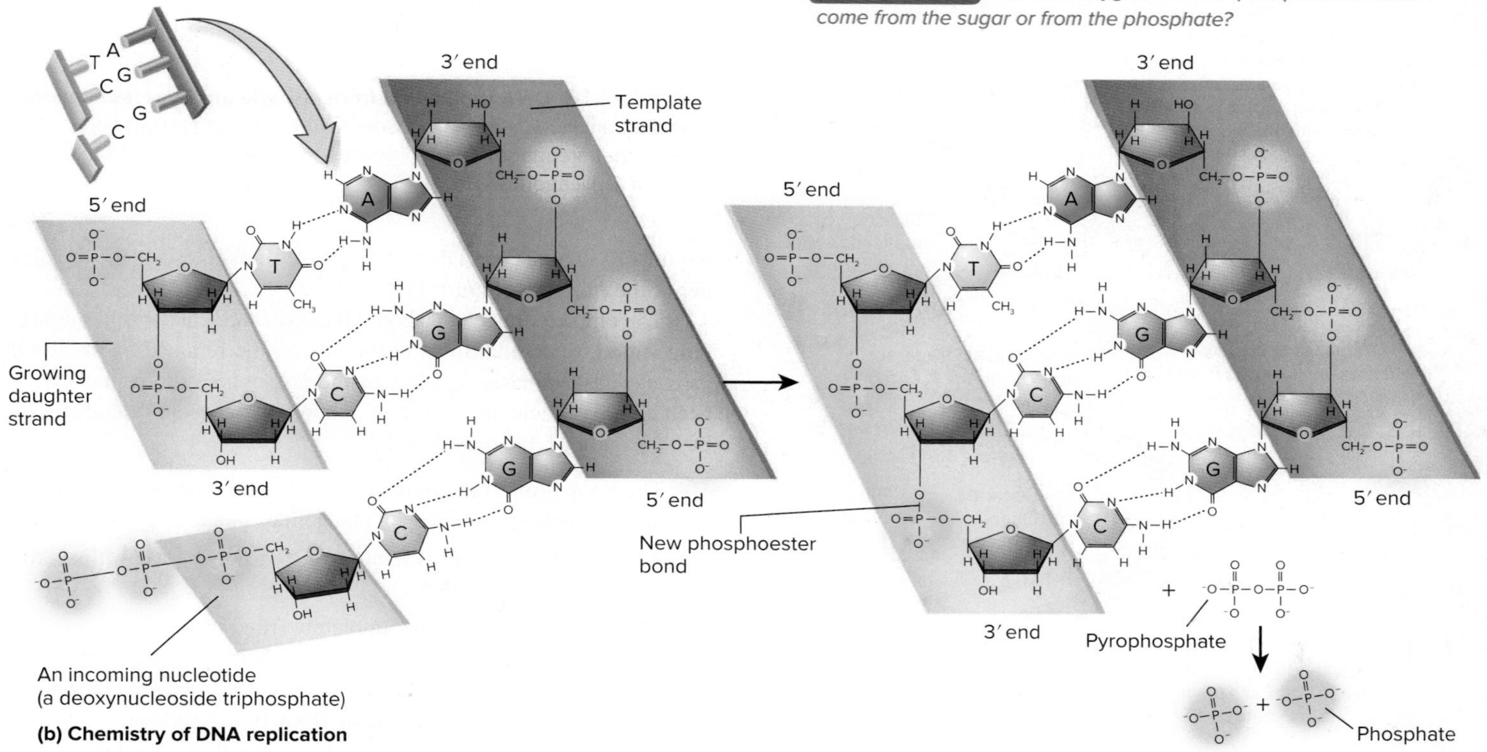

DNA polymerase catalytic site

Template strand

5'

Incoming deoxynucleoside triphosphates

3'

Figure 11.15 Enzymatic synthesis of DNA. (a) Incoming deoxynucleoside triphosphates first hydrogen-bond to the template strand according to the AT/GC rule. DNA polymerase recognizes these deoxynucleoside triphosphates and attaches a deoxynucleoside monophosphate to the 3' end of a growing strand. **(b)** DNA polymerase breaks the bond between the first and second phosphate in a deoxynucleoside triphosphate, causing the release of pyrophosphate. This provides the energy to form a covalent bond between the resulting deoxynucleoside monophosphate and the previous nucleotide in the growing strand. The pyrophosphate is broken down to two phosphates.

Concept Check: Does the oxygen in a new phosphoester bond come from the sugar or from the phosphate?

(b) Chemistry of DNA replication

Growing daughter strand

Template strand

3' end

5' end

3' end

An incoming nucleotide (a deoxynucleoside triphosphate)

New phosphoester bond

Pyrophosphate

Phosphate

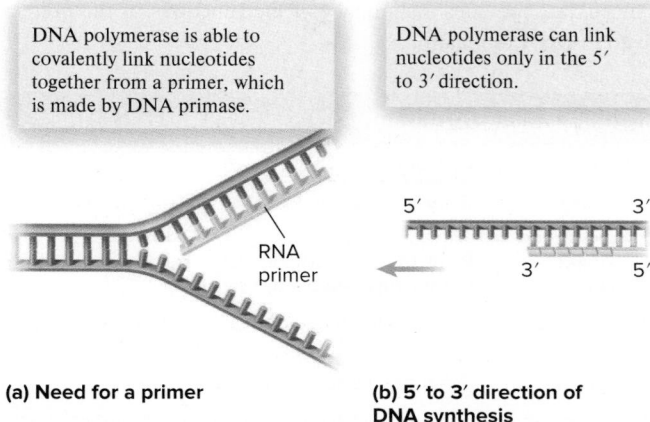

(a) Need for a primer

DNA polymerase is able to covalently link nucleotides together from a primer, which is made by DNA primase.

DNA polymerase can link nucleotides only in the 5' to 3' direction.

RNA primer

5'   3'
3'   5'

(b) 5' to 3' direction of DNA synthesis

Figure 11.16 Enzymatic features of DNA polymerase. (a) DNA polymerase needs a primer to begin DNA synthesis, and **(b)** it can synthesize DNA only in the 5' to 3' direction.

the leading strand and the bottom template strand to make the lagging strand. In contrast, the fork moving to the right uses the top strand to make the lagging strand and bottom strand to make the leading strand.

The synthesis of DNA shown in Figures 11.17 and 11.18 emphasizes the synthesis of new DNA strands. **Figure 11.19** also includes the proteins involved in the synthesis of the leading and lagging strands in *E. coli*. In this bacterium, two different DNA polymerases, called DNA polymerase I and III, are primarily responsible for DNA replication. In the leading strand, DNA primase makes one RNA primer at the origin, and then DNA polymerase III attaches nucleotides in a 5' to 3' direction as it slides toward the opening of the replication fork. DNA polymerase III has a subunit called the clamp protein that allows the enzyme to slide along the template strand without falling off, a characteristic called **processivity**.

In the lagging strand, DNA is also synthesized in a 5' to 3' direction, but this synthesis occurs in the direction away from the replication fork. In the lagging strand, short segments of DNA are made discontinuously as a series of Okazaki fragments, each of which

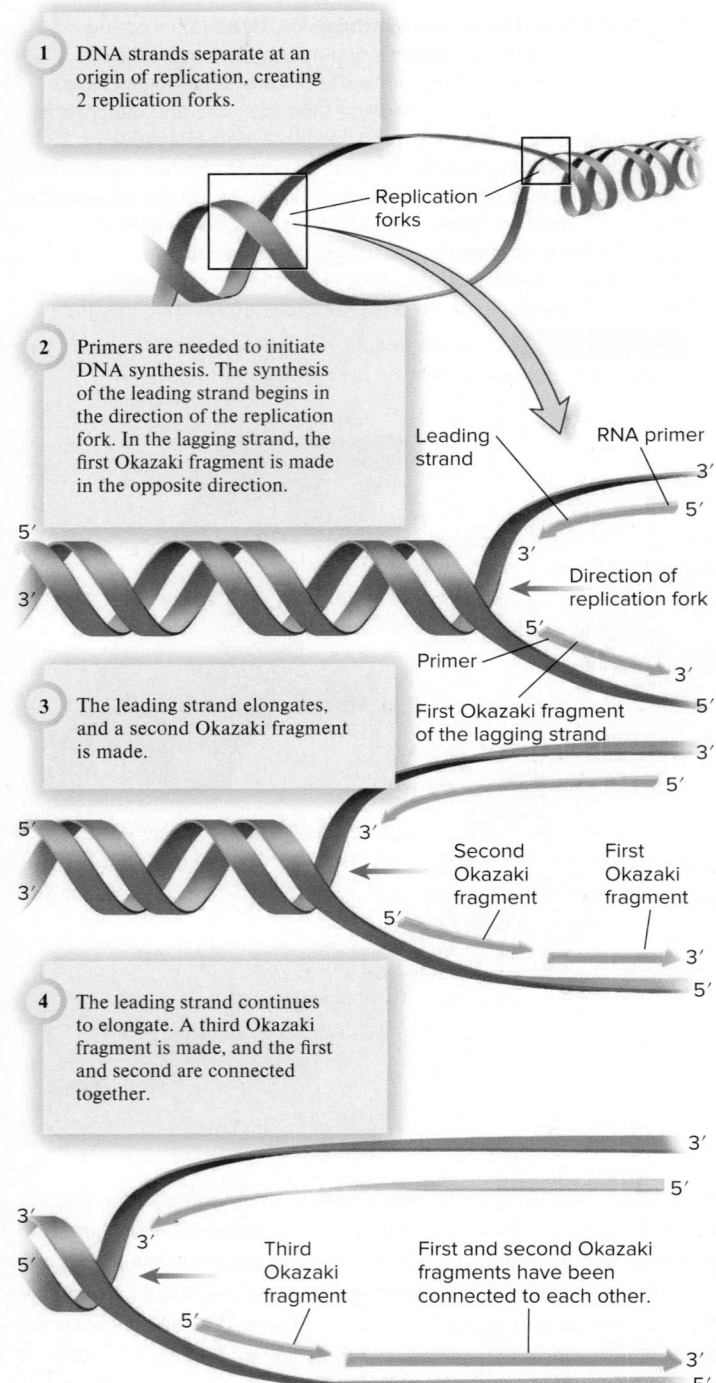

1 DNA strands separate at an origin of replication, creating 2 replication forks.

Replication forks

2 Primers are needed to initiate DNA synthesis. The synthesis of the leading strand begins in the direction of the replication fork. In the lagging strand, the first Okazaki fragment is made in the opposite direction.

Leading strand

RNA primer

3′

5′

5′

3′

3′

Direction of replication fork

5′

Primer

3′

First Okazaki fragment of the lagging strand

5′

3 The leading strand elongates, and a second Okazaki fragment is made.

3′

5′

5′

3′

3′

Second Okazaki fragment

First Okazaki fragment

5′

3′

5′

4 The leading strand continues to elongate. A third Okazaki fragment is made, and the first and second are connected together.

3′

5′

3′

5′

3′

3′

Third Okazaki fragment

First and second Okazaki fragments have been connected to each other.

5′

3′

5′

Figure 11.17 Synthesis of new DNA strands. The separation of DNA at the origin of replication produces two replication forks that move in opposite directions. New DNA strands are made near the opening of each fork. The leading strand is made continuously in the same direction the fork is moving. The lagging strand is made as small pieces in the opposite direction. These small pieces are then connected to each other to form a continuous lagging strand.

Concept Check: Which strand, the leading or lagging strand, is made discontinuously in the direction opposite to the movement of the replication fork?

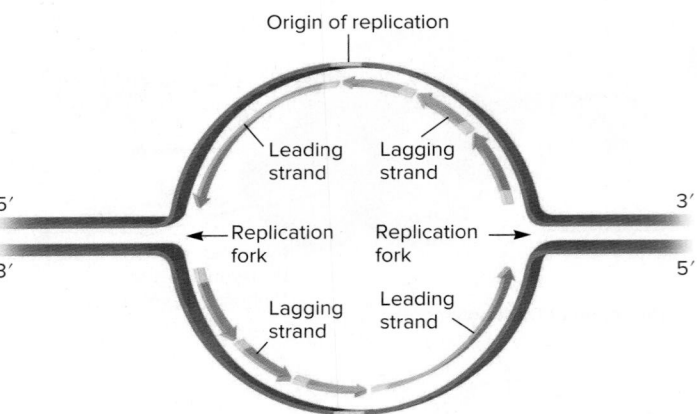

Origin of replication

Leading strand

Lagging strand

5′

3′

Replication fork

Replication fork

3′

5′

Lagging strand

Leading strand

Figure 11.18 DNA replication from a single origin of replication. This diagram illustrates the locations of the leading and lagging strands that are made during bidirectional DNA replication from one origin of replication.

requires its own primer. DNA polymerase III synthesizes the remainder of the fragment (Figure 11.19, step 2).

To complete the synthesis of Okazaki fragments within the lagging strand, three additional events occur: the removal of the RNA primers, the synthesis of DNA in the area where the primers have been removed, and the covalent joining of adjacent fragments of DNA (Figure 11.19, steps 3 and 4).

- The RNA primers are removed by DNA polymerase I, which digests the linkages between nucleotides in a 5′ to 3′ direction.
- After the RNA primer is removed, DNA polymerase I fills in the vacant region with DNA.
- After the DNA has been completely filled in, a covalent bond is missing between the last nucleotide added by DNA polymerase I and the first nucleotide in the adjacent Okazaki fragment. An enzyme known as **DNA ligase** catalyzes the formation of a covalent bond between these two DNA fragments to complete the replication process in the lagging strand (Figure 11.19, step 4).

Table 11.2 provides a summary of the functions of the proteins involved in DNA replication.

Table 11.2	Proteins Involved in DNA Replication
Common name	**Function**
DNA helicase	Separates double-stranded DNA into single strands
Single-strand binding protein	Binds to single-stranded DNA and prevents it from re-forming a double helix
Topoisomerase	Removes tightened coils ahead of the replication fork
DNA primase	Synthesizes short RNA primers
DNA polymerase	Synthesizes DNA in the leading and lagging strands, removes RNA primers, and fills in gaps
DNA ligase	Covalently attaches adjacent Okazaki fragments in the lagging strand

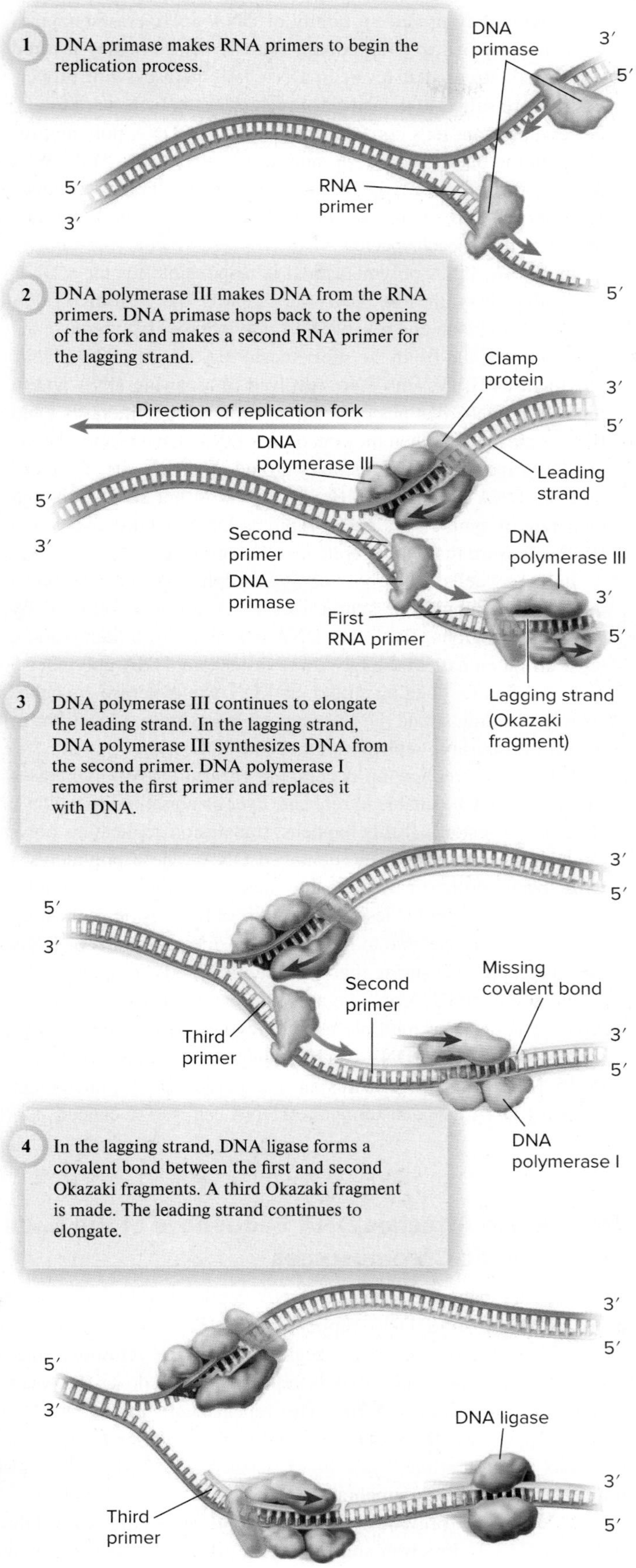

1 DNA primase makes RNA primers to begin the replication process.

DNA primase

3′
5′

5′
3′

RNA primer

5′

2 DNA polymerase III makes DNA from the RNA primers. DNA primase hops back to the opening of the fork and makes a second RNA primer for the lagging strand.

Clamp protein

3′
5′

Direction of replication fork

DNA polymerase III

Leading strand

5′
3′

Second primer

DNA polymerase III

DNA primase

First RNA primer

3′
5′

Lagging strand (Okazaki fragment)

3 DNA polymerase III continues to elongate the leading strand. In the lagging strand, DNA polymerase III synthesizes DNA from the second primer. DNA polymerase I removes the first primer and replaces it with DNA.

3′
5′

5′
3′

Second primer

Missing covalent bond

Third primer

3′
5′

DNA polymerase I

4 In the lagging strand, DNA ligase forms a covalent bond between the first and second Okazaki fragments. A third Okazaki fragment is made. The leading strand continues to elongate.

3′
5′

5′
3′

DNA ligase

Third primer

3′
5′

Figure 11.19 **Proteins involved with the synthesis of the leading and lagging strands in *E. coli*.**

Concept Check: *Briefly describe the movement of primase in the lagging strand in this figure. In which direction does it move when it is making a primer, from left to right or right to left? Describe how it must move after it is done making a primer and has to start making the next primer at a new location. Does it have to hop from left to right or from right to left?*

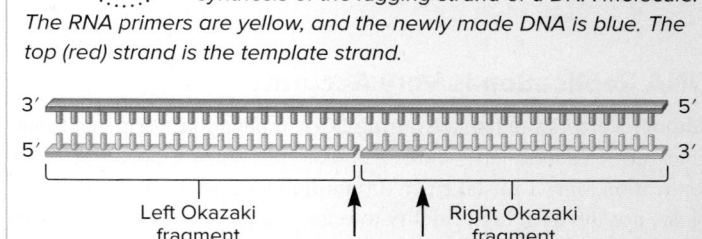

BIO TIPS   **THE QUESTION** *The drawing below shows the synthesis of the lagging strand of a DNA molecule. The RNA primers are yellow, and the newly made DNA is blue. The top (red) strand is the template strand.*

3′ ———————————————————————— 5′
5′ ———————————————————————— 3′

Left Okazaki fragment   Right Okazaki fragment

After DNA polymerase I removes the right RNA primer and fills in the gap with DNA, where will DNA ligase act? See the arrows on either side of the right RNA primer. Is the ligase needed at the left arrow, the right arrow, or both?

TOPIC *What topic in biology does this question address?* The topic is DNA replication. More specifically, the question asks you to determine where DNA ligase needs to act during replication of the lagging strand.

INFORMATION *What information do you know based on the question and your understanding of the topic?* In the question, you are given the arrangement of two adjacent Okazaki fragments, with arrows pointing to two possible places where DNA ligase may be needed. From your understanding of the topic, you may remember that in *E. coli*, DNA polymerase I removes the RNA primer and fills in the region with DNA; then DNA ligase connects the adjacent Okazaki fragments.

PROBLEM-SOLVING **S**TRATEGY *Sort out the steps in a complicated process. Make a drawing.* To solve this problem, it may be helpful to list the steps of the process. Also, you should consider how DNA polymerase I and DNA ligase function.

1. First, DNA polymerase I removes the right RNA primer.

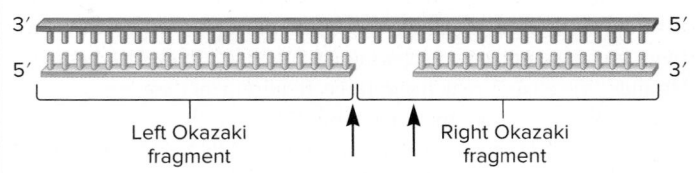

3′ ———————————————————————— 5′
5′ ———————————————————————— 3′

Left Okazaki fragment   Right Okazaki fragment

2. Starting at the 3′ end of the left Okazaki fragment, DNA polymerase I then extends the DNA until it fills in the region where the RNA primer was removed. DNA ligase is not needed at the left arrow.

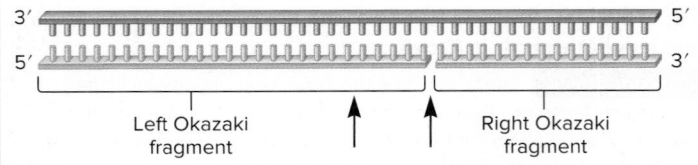

Left Okazaki fragment   Right Okazaki fragment

3. As shown above, when DNA polymerase I reaches the (blue) DNA of the right Okazaki fragment, a gap exists between the 3′ end of the left Okazaki fragment and the 5′ end of the DNA of the right Okazaki fragment.

ANSWER *DNA ligase is needed at the right arrow only.*

DNA Replication Is Very Accurate

Although errors can happen during DNA replication, permanent mistakes are extraordinarily rare. For example, during bacterial DNA replication, only 1 mistake per 100 million nucleotides is made. Biologists use the term high fidelity to refer to a process that occurs with relatively few mistakes. How can we explain such a remarkably high fidelity for DNA replication?

- First, hydrogen bonding between A and T or between G and C is more stable than hydrogen bonding between mismatched pairs of bases.

- Second, the active site of DNA polymerase is unlikely to catalyze bond formation between adjacent nucleotides if a mismatched base pair is formed.

- Third, DNA polymerase can identify a mismatched nucleotide and remove it from the daughter strand. This event, called **proofreading**, occurs when DNA polymerase detects a mismatch and then reverses its direction and digests the linkages between nucleotides at the end of a newly made strand in the 3′ to 5′ direction. Once it passes the mismatched base and removes it, DNA polymerase then changes direction again and continues to synthesize DNA in the 5′ to 3′ direction.

Core Concepts: Evolution, Structure and Function

DNA Polymerases Are a Family of Enzymes with Specialized Functions

Three important properties of DNA replication are speed, fidelity, and completeness. DNA replication must proceed quickly and with great accuracy, and gaps should not be left in the newly made strands. To ensure that these three requirements are met, living species produce more than one type of DNA polymerase, each of which may differ in the rate and accuracy of DNA replication and/ or the ability to prevent the formation of DNA gaps.

The genomes of living species have multiple DNA polymerase genes, which were produced by random gene duplication events. During evolution, mutations have altered each gene so that

collectively they produce a family of DNA polymerase enzymes with more specialized functions. Natural selection has favored certain mutations that result in DNA polymerases with properties that are suited to the species in which the enzymes are found. For comparison, let's consider the families of DNA polymerases found in the bacterium *E. coli* and in humans (**Table 11.3**). Why does *E. coli* produce 5 DNA polymerases and humans produce 12 or more? The answer lies in specialization and the functional requirements of each species.

In *E. coli*, DNA polymerase III is responsible for most DNA replication. It synthesizes DNA very rapidly and with high fidelity. By comparison, the role of DNA polymerase I is to remove the RNA primers and fill in the short vacant regions with DNA. DNA polymerases II, IV, and V are involved in repairing DNA and in replicating DNA that has been damaged. DNA polymerases I and III become stalled when they encounter DNA damage and may be unable to make a complementary strand at such a site. By comparison, DNA polymerases II, IV, and V do not stall. Although their rate of synthesis is not as rapid as DNA polymerases I and III, they ensure that DNA replication is complete.

In human cells, DNA polymerase α (alpha) has its own "built-in" primase subunit. It synthesizes RNA primers followed by short DNA regions. Two other DNA polymerases, δ (delta) and ε (epsilon), then extend the DNA at a faster rate. DNA polymerase δ synthesizes the lagging strand, and DNA polymerase ε synthesizes the leading strand. DNA polymerase γ (gamma) functions in the mitochondria to replicate mitochondrial DNA.

When DNA replication occurs, the general DNA polymerases (α, δ, or γ) may be unable to replicate over an abnormality in DNA structure (a lesion). If this happens, translesion-replicating polymerases are attracted to the damaged DNA. These polymerases have special properties that enable them to synthesize a complementary strand over the lesion. Each type of translesion-replicating polymerase may be able to replicate over different kinds of DNA damage, thereby ensuring that DNA replication is complete.

Other human DNA polymerases play an important role in DNA repair. The need for multiple repair enzymes arises because there are various ways that DNA can be damaged, as described in Chapter 15. Multicellular organisms must be particularly vigilant about repairing DNA, because unrepaired DNA can lead to cancer.

Telomerase Attaches DNA Sequences at the Ends of Eukaryotic Chromosomes

We will end our discussion of DNA replication by considering a specialized form of DNA replication that happens at the ends of eukaryotic chromosomes. This region, called the **telomere**, has a short nucleotide sequence that is repeated a few dozen to several hundred times (**Figure 11.20**). The repeat sequence shown here, 5′–GGGTTA–3′, is the sequence found in human telomeres. A telomere has a region at the 3′ end that is termed a 3′ overhang, because it does not have a complementary strand.

As discussed previously, DNA polymerase synthesizes DNA only in a 5′ to 3′ direction and requires a primer. For these reasons,

Table 11.3 — DNA Polymerases in *E. coli* and Humans

Polymerase types*	Functions
E. coli	
III	Replicates most of the DNA during cell division
I	Removes RNA primers and fills in the gaps
II, IV, and V	Repairs damaged DNA and replicates over DNA abnormalities
Humans	
α (alpha)	Makes RNA primers and synthesizes short DNA strands
δ (delta), ε (epsilon)	Displaces DNA polymerase α and then replicates DNA at a rapid rate
γ (gamma)	Replicates the mitochondrial DNA
η (eta), κ (kappa), ι (iota), ζ (zeta)	Replicates over DNA abnormalities
α, β (beta), δ, ε, σ (sigma), λ (lambda), μ (mu), φ (phi), θ (theta)	Repairs DNA or has other functions

*Certain DNA polymerases have more than one function.

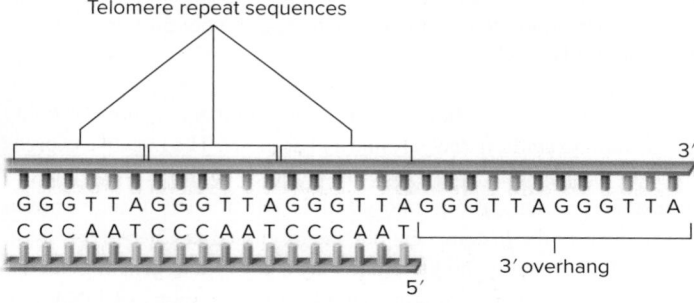

Figure 11.20 **Telomere sequences at the end of a human chromosome.** The telomere sequence shown here is found in humans and other mammals. The length of the telomere and the 3′ overhang varies among different species and cell types.

DNA polymerase cannot copy the tip of a DNA strand with a 3′ end. Therefore, if this replication problem was not overcome, a linear chromosome would become progressively shorter with each round of DNA replication. In 1984, American molecular biologist Carol Greider and Australian-born American molecular biologist Elizabeth Blackburn discovered an enzyme called **telomerase** that prevents chromosome shortening by attaching many copies of a DNA repeat sequence to the ends of chromosomes (**Figure 11.21**). Telomerase contains both protein and RNA. The RNA part of telomerase has a sequence that is complementary to the DNA repeat sequence. This allows telomerase to bind to the 3′ overhang region of the telomere. Following binding, the RNA sequence beyond the binding site functions as a template, allowing telomerase to synthesize a 6-nucleotide sequence at the end of the DNA strand. The enzyme then moves to the new end of this DNA strand and attaches another 6 nucleotides to the end. This occurs many times, thereby greatly lengthening the 3′ end of the DNA in the telomere. This lengthening

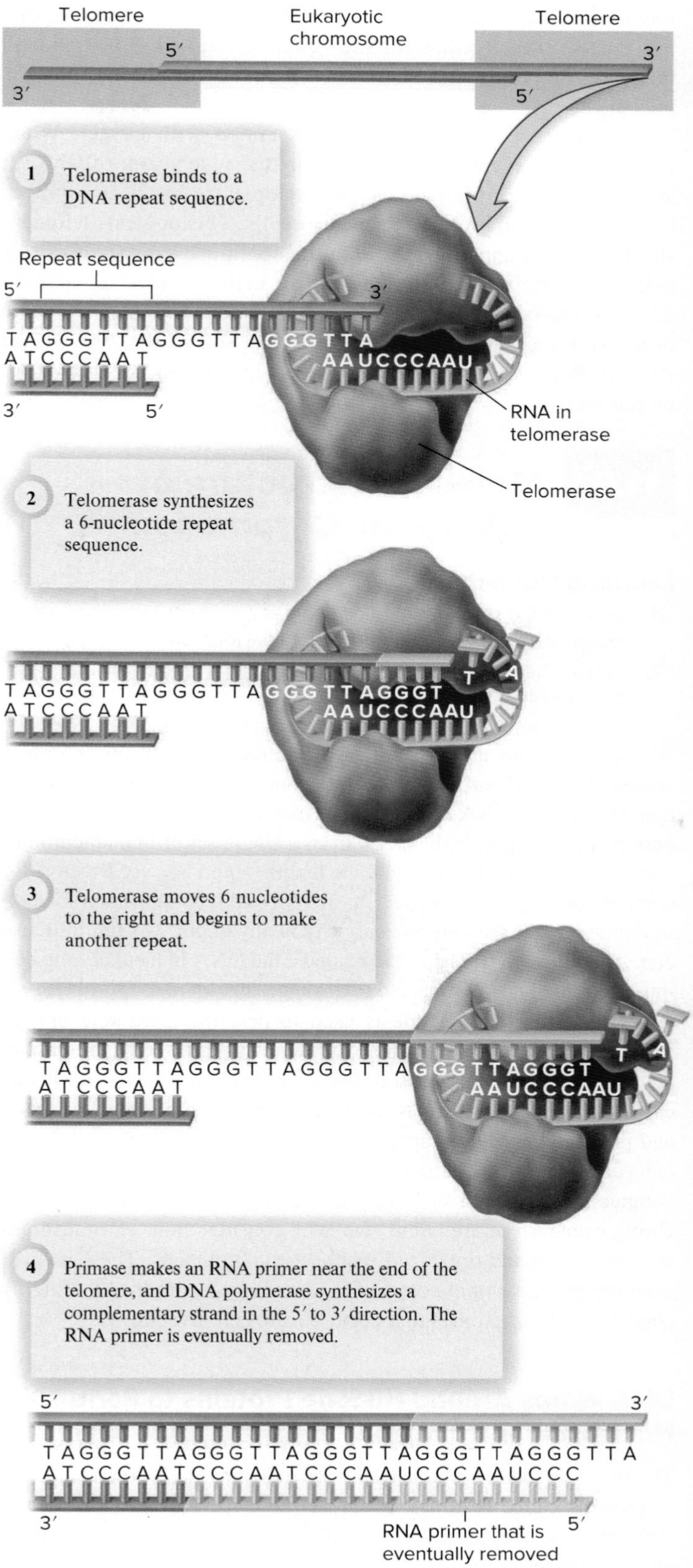

1. Telomerase binds to a DNA repeat sequence.

2. Telomerase synthesizes a 6-nucleotide repeat sequence.

3. Telomerase moves 6 nucleotides to the right and begins to make another repeat.

4. Primase makes an RNA primer near the end of the telomere, and DNA polymerase synthesizes a complementary strand in the 5′ to 3′ direction. The RNA primer is eventually removed.

Figure 11.21 **Mechanism of DNA replication by telomerase.**

Concept Check: What does telomerase use as a template to make the DNA repeat sequence?

provides an upstream site for an RNA primer to be made. DNA polymerase then synthesizes the complementary DNA strand. In this way, the progressive shortening of eukaryotic chromosomes is prevented.

Telomerase function is also associated with cancer. When cells become cancerous, they continue to divide uncontrollably. In 90% of all types of human cancers, telomerase has been found to be present at high levels in the cancer cells. This prevents telomere shortening and may play a role in the continued growth of cancer cells. The mechanism whereby cancer cells are able to increase the function of telomerase is not well understood and is a topic of active research. Greider and Blackburn shared the 2009 Nobel Prize in Physiology or Medicine with Jack Szostak for their work on telomeres.

11.5 Molecular Structure of Eukaryotic Chromosomes

Learning Outcomes:

1. Describe the structure of nucleosomes and the 30-nm fiber, and explain how the 30-nm fiber forms radial loop domains.
2. Outline the various levels of compaction that lead to a metaphase chromosome.

We now turn our attention to the structure of eukaryotic chromosomes. A typical eukaryotic chromosome contains a single, linear, double-stranded DNA molecule that may be hundreds of millions of base pairs in length. If the DNA from a single set of human chromosomes was stretched end to end, the length would be over 1 meter! By comparison, most eukaryotic cells are only 10–100 μm (micrometers) in diameter, and the cell nucleus is typically about 2–4 μm in diameter. Therefore, to fit inside the nucleus, the DNA in a eukaryotic cell must be folded and compacted to a staggering degree.

The term **chromosome** is used to describe a discrete unit of genetic material. For example, a human somatic cell contains 46 chromosomes. By comparison, the term chromatin has a biochemical meaning. **Chromatin** is used to describe the complex of DNA and proteins that makes up eukaryotic chromosomes. Chromosomes are very dynamic structures that alternate between tight and loose compaction states. In this section, we will focus on two issues of chromosome structure. First, we will consider how chromosomes are compacted and organized within the cell nucleus. Then, we will examine the additional compaction necessary to produce the highly condensed chromosomes that occur during cell division.

DNA Wraps Around Histone Proteins to Form Nucleosomes

The first way DNA is compacted is by wrapping itself around a group of proteins called **histones**. As shown in **Figure 11.22**, a repeating structural unit of eukaryotic chromatin is the **nucleosome**, which is 11 nm in diameter at its widest point. Each nucleosome is composed of 146 or 147 bp (base pairs) of DNA wrapped around an octamer of histone proteins. An octamer contains two molecules each of four types of histone proteins: H2A, H2B, H3, and H4. Histone proteins are very

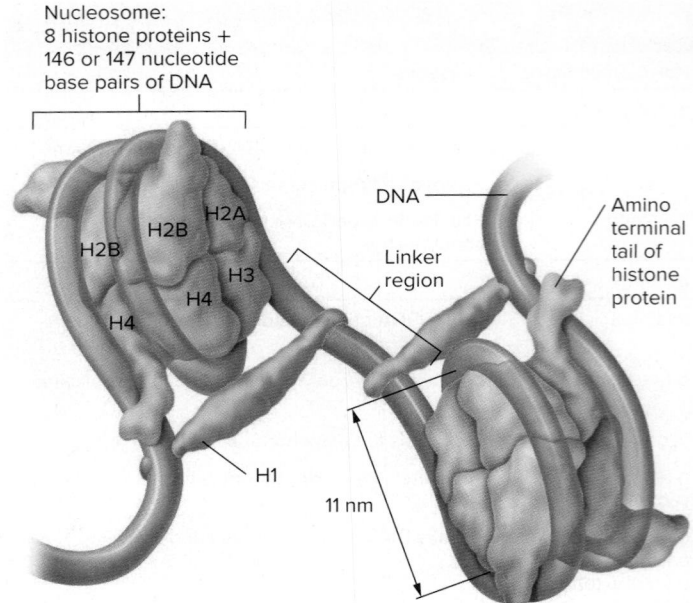

Figure 11.22 Structure of a nucleosome. A nucleosome is composed of double-stranded DNA wrapped around an octamer of histone proteins. A linker region connects two adjacent nucleosomes. Histone H1 is bound to the linker region, as are other proteins not shown in this figure.

basic proteins because they contain a large number of the positively charged amino acids, namely, lysine and arginine. The negative charges found in the phosphates of DNA are attracted to the positive charges on histone proteins. The amino terminal tail of each histone protein protrudes from the histone octamer. As discussed in Chapter 14, these tails can be covalently modified and play a key role in gene regulation.

The nucleosomes are connected by linker regions of DNA that vary in length from 20 to 100 bp, depending on the species and cell type. A particular histone named H1 is bound to the linker region, as are other types of proteins. The overall structure of connected nucleosomes resembles beads on a string. This structure shortens the length of the DNA molecule about sevenfold.

Nucleosomes Form a 30-nm Fiber

Nucleosome units are organized into a more compact structure that is 30 nm in diameter, known as the **30-nm fiber** (**Figure 11.23a**). Histone H1 and other proteins are important in the formation of the 30-nm fiber, which shortens the nucleosome structure another sevenfold. The structure of the 30-nm fiber has proven difficult to determine because the conformation of the DNA may be substantially altered when extracted from living cells. A model for the 30-nm fiber was proposed by Rachel Horowitz-Scherer and Christopher Woodcock in the 1990s (**Figure 11.23b**). According to their model, linker regions in the 30-nm structure are variably bent and twisted, with little direct contact between nucleosomes. The 30-nm fiber forms an asymmetric, three-dimensional zigzag of nucleosomes. At this level of compaction, the overall picture of chromatin that emerges is an irregular, fluctuating structure with stable nucleosome units connected by bendable linker regions.

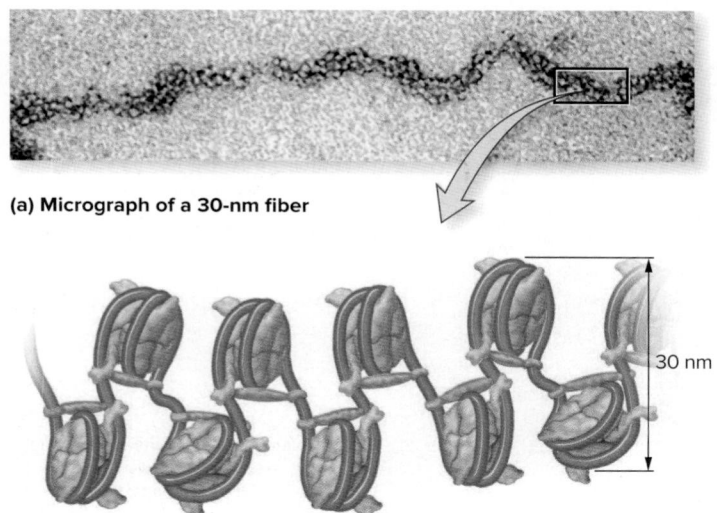

(a) Micrograph of a 30-nm fiber

30 nm

(b) Three-dimensional zigzag model

Figure 11.23 **The 30-nm fiber.** **(a)** A photomicrograph of the 30-nm fiber. **(b)** In this three-dimensional zigzag model, the linker DNA forms a bendable structure with little contact between adjacent nucleosomes. a: ©Dr. Barbara A. Hamkalo

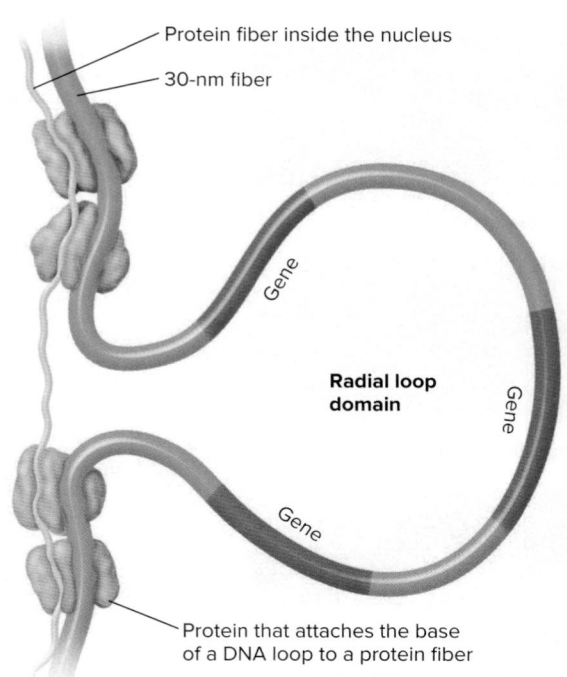

Protein fiber inside the nucleus

30-nm fiber

Gene

Gene

Gene

Radial loop domain

Protein that attaches the base of a DNA loop to a protein fiber

Figure 11.24 **Attachment of the 30-nm fiber to a protein fiber to form a radial loop domain.**

Concept Check: *What holds the bases of the radial loop domains in place?*

Chromatin Loops Are Anchored to the Nuclear Matrix

Thus far, we have examined two mechanisms that compact eukaryotic DNA: the formation of nucleosomes and their arrangement into a 30-nm fiber. Taken together, these two events shorten the folded DNA about 49-fold. A third level of compaction involves interactions between the 30-nm fibers and a filamentous network of proteins in the nucleus called the **nuclear matrix**. This matrix consists of the **nuclear lamina**, which is composed of protein fibers that line the inner nuclear membrane (refer back to Figure 4.19), and an internal nuclear matrix that is connected to the lamina and fills the interior of the nucleus. The internal nuclear matrix is an intricate network of irregular protein fibers plus many other proteins that bind to these fibers. The nuclear matrix aids in compaction by binding to the 30-nm fiber to form **radial loop domains**. These loops, often containing 25,000–200,000 bp, are anchored to the nuclear matrix (**Figure 11.24**).

How are chromosomes organized within the cell nucleus? In nondividing cells, each chromosome occupies its own discrete region in the cell nucleus that usually does not overlap with the territory of adjacent chromosomes (refer back to Figure 4.20). In other words, different chromosomes are not substantially intertwined with each other even when they are in a noncompacted condition.

The compaction level of chromosomes in the cell nucleus is not completely uniform. This variability can be seen with a light microscope and was first observed by German cytologist Emil Heitz in 1928. He coined the term **heterochromatin** to describe the highly compacted regions of chromosomes. The less condensed regions are known as **euchromatin**, which is the form of chromatin in which the 30-nm fiber forms radial loop domains. In heterochromatin, these radial loop domains are compacted even further. In nondividing cells, most chromosomal regions are euchromatic, and these are the regions where genes are usually located. By comparison, the centromeric and telomeric regions are often heterochromatic and may not contain genes.

During Cell Division, Chromosomes Undergo Maximum Compaction

When cells prepare to divide, the chromosomes become even more compacted or condensed. Each chromosome becomes entirely compacted into heterochromatin. This aids in their proper alignment during metaphase, which is a stage of eukaryotic cell division described in Chapter 16. **Figure 11.25** illustrates the levels of compaction that contribute to the formation of a metaphase chromosome. DNA in the nucleus is always compacted by forming nucleosomes and condensing into a 30-nm fiber (Figure 11.25a, b, c). In euchromatin, the 30-nm fibers are arranged in radial loop domains that are relatively loose, meaning that a fair amount of space is between the 30-nm fibers (Figure 11.25d). The average width of such loops is about 300 nm.

By comparison, heterochromatin involves a much tighter packing of the loops, so little space is left between the 30-nm fibers (Figure 11.25e). When cells prepare to divide, all of the euchromatin becomes highly compacted. The compaction of euchromatin greatly shortens the chromosomes. For a metaphase chromosome that contains two copies of the DNA (Figure 11.25f), the width averages about 1,400 nm, but the length of a metaphase chromosome is much shorter than the same chromosome in the nucleus of a nondividing cell.

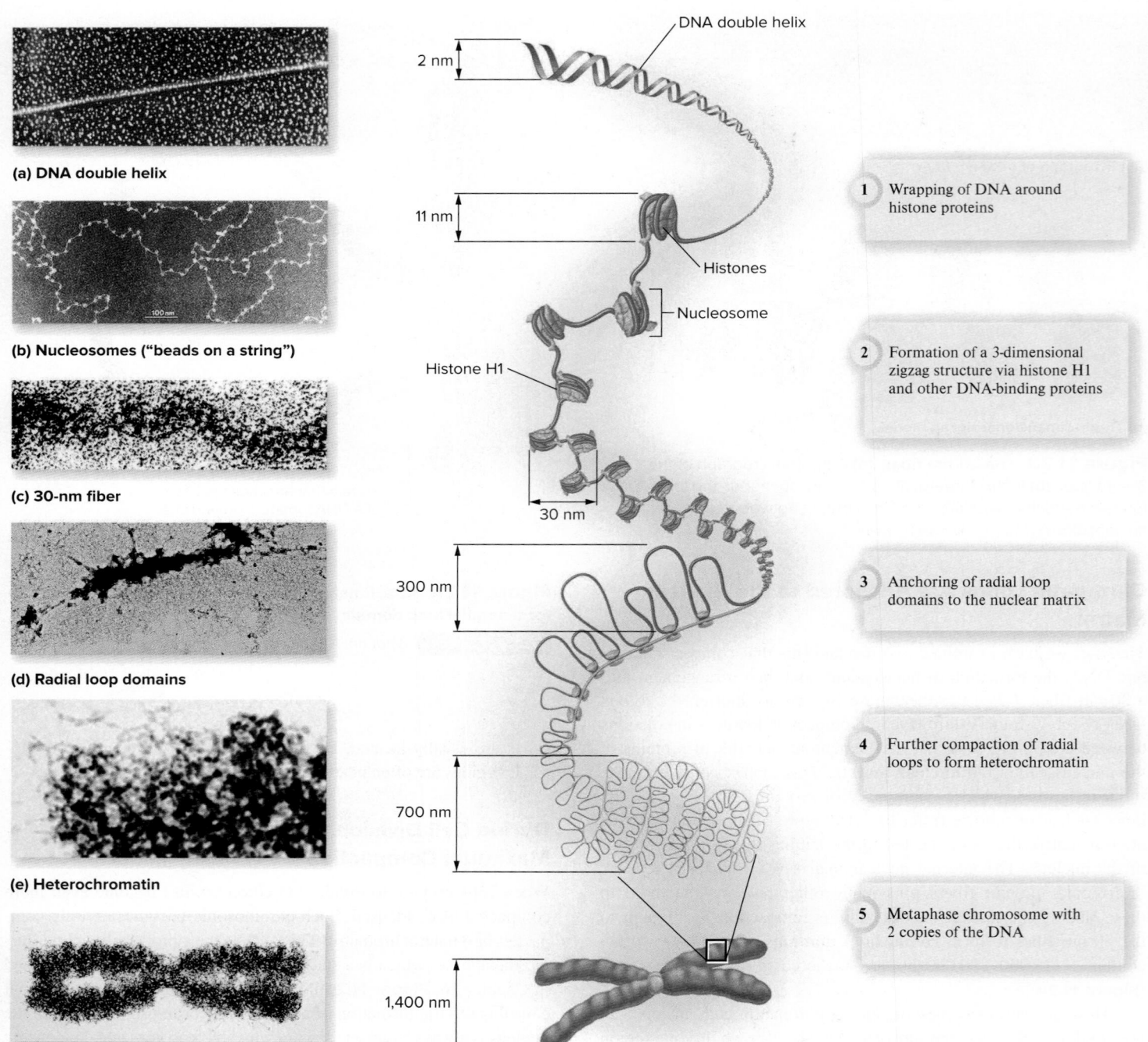

(a) DNA double helix

(b) Nucleosomes ("beads on a string")

(c) 30-nm fiber

(d) Radial loop domains

(e) Heterochromatin

(f) Metaphase chromosome

DNA double helix

2 nm

11 nm — Histones

Nucleosome

Histone H1

30 nm

300 nm

700 nm

1,400 nm

1. Wrapping of DNA around histone proteins

2. Formation of a 3-dimensional zigzag structure via histone H1 and other DNA-binding proteins

3. Anchoring of radial loop domains to the nuclear matrix

4. Further compaction of radial loops to form heterochromatin

5. Metaphase chromosome with 2 copies of the DNA

Figure 11.25 **The steps in eukaryotic chromosomal compaction leading to the metaphase chromosome.** a: ©Science Source; b: ©Dr. Barbara A. Hamkalo; c: Courtesy Dr. Jerome B. Rattner, Cell Biology and Anatomy, University of Calgary; d: ©Dr. James Paulson, Ph.D.; e-f: ©Peter Engelhardt/Department of Virology, Haartman Institute

Core Skill: Connections Look ahead to Figure 16.8. Why do you think it is necessary for the chromosomes to become highly compacted in preparation for cell division?

Summary of Key Concepts

11.1 Biochemical Identification of the Genetic Material

- The genetic material contains the information that produces the traits of organisms. It is accurately replicated and transmitted from cell to cell and parent to offspring. The genetic material has differences that explain the variation among different organisms.

- Griffith's work with type S and type R bacteria indicated the existence of a genetic material, which he called the transformation principle (Figure 11.1).

- Avery, MacLeod, and McCarty used biochemical methods to show that DNA is the genetic material (Figure 11.2).

11.2 Nucleic Acid Structure

- DNA is composed of nucleotides, which are covalently linked to form DNA strands. Two DNA strands are held together by hydrogen bonds between the bases to form a double helix. DNA associates with various proteins to form a chromosome (Figure 11.3).

- Nucleotides are composed of a phosphate, a sugar, and a nitrogen-containing base. The sugar can be deoxyribose (DNA) or ribose (RNA). The purine bases are adenine and guanine, and the pyrimidine bases are thymine (DNA only), cytosine, and uracil (RNA only). The atoms in a nucleotide are numbered in a conventional way (Figures 11.4, 11.5).

- In a strand of DNA (or RNA), the sugars are connected by covalent bonds in a 5′ to 3′ direction (Figure 11.6).

- The X-ray diffraction data of Franklin, the biochemical data of Chargaff, and the ball-and-stick modeling of Pauling helped reveal the structure of DNA (Figure 11.7, Table 11.1).

- Watson and Crick determined that DNA is a double helix in which the DNA strands are complementary, with base sequences that are antiparallel and obey the AT/GC rule (Figures 11.8, 11.9).

11.3 Overview of DNA Replication

- Meselson and Stahl used isotope labeling methods to show that DNA is replicated by a semiconservative mechanism in which the products are two DNA molecules, each with one parental strand and one daughter strand (Figures 11.10, 11.11).

- During DNA replication, the parental double-stranded DNA separates and each strand serves as a template for the synthesis of daughter strands. The bases within nucleotides hydrogen-bond to each other according to the AT/GC rule: An adenine (A) base in one strand bonds with a thymine (T) base in the opposite strand, or a guanine (G) base bonds with a cytosine (C) base. The result of DNA replication is two double helices with the same base sequence as the original DNA (Figure 11.12).

11.4 Molecular Mechanism of DNA Replication

- DNA synthesis occurs bidirectionally from an origin of replication. The synthesis of new DNA strands happens near each replication fork (Figure 11.13).

- DNA helicase separates DNA strands, single-strand binding proteins keep them separated, and DNA topoisomerase alleviates supercoiling ahead of the fork (Figure 11.14).

- Deoxynucleoside triphosphates bind to the template strands according to the AT/GC rule. DNA polymerase recognizes these deoxynucleoside triphosphates and attaches a deoxynucleoside monophosphate to the 3′ end of a growing strand (Figure 11.15).

- DNA polymerase requires a primer and synthesizes new DNA strands only in the 5′ to 3′ direction (Figure 11.16).

- The leading strand is made continuously, in the same direction that the fork is moving. The lagging strand is made in the opposite direction as short Okazaki fragments that are synthesized and connected together (Figure 11.17).

- The two replication forks from a single origin of replication use opposite DNA strands to synthesize the leading and lagging strands (Figure 11.18).

- DNA primase makes one RNA primer in the leading strand and multiple RNA primers in the lagging strand. In *E. coli*, DNA polymerase III extends these primers with DNA, and DNA polymerase I removes the primers when they are no longer needed and fills in with DNA. DNA ligase connects adjacent Okazaki fragments in the lagging strand (Figure 11.19, Table 11.2).

- DNA replication is very accurate because (1) hydrogen bonding that follows the AT/CG rule is more stable; (2) DNA polymerase is unlikely to catalyze bond formation if a mismatched base pair is formed; and (3) DNA polymerase carries out proofreading.

- Living organisms have several different types of DNA polymerases with specialized functions (Table 11.3).

- The ends of linear, eukaryotic chromosomes have telomeres composed of repeat sequences. Telomerase binds to the telomere repeat sequence and synthesizes a 6-nucleotide repeat. This happens many times in a row to lengthen one DNA strand of the telomere. DNA primase, DNA polymerase, and DNA ligase are needed to synthesize the complementary DNA strand (Figures 11.20, 11.21).

11.5 Molecular Structure of Eukaryotic Chromosomes

- Chromosomes are structures in living cells that carry the genetic material. Chromatin is the name given to the complex of DNA and proteins that makes up eukaryotic chromosomes.

- In eukaryotic chromosomes, the DNA is wrapped around histone proteins to form nucleosomes. Nucleosomes are further compacted into 30-nm fibers. The linker regions are variably twisted and bent into a zigzag pattern (Figures 11.22, 11.23).

- A third level of compaction of eukaryotic chromosomes involves the formation of radial loop domains in which the 30-nm fibers are anchored to a network of proteins called the nuclear matrix. This level of compaction is called euchromatin. In heterochromatin, the loops are even more closely packed together (Figure 11.24).

- During cell division, chromosomes become entirely heterochromatic (Figure 11.25).

Assess & Discuss

Test Yourself

1. Why did researchers initially believe that the genetic material was composed of proteins?
   a. Proteins are more biochemically complex than DNA.
   b. Proteins are found only in the nucleus, but DNA is found in many areas of the cell.
   c. Proteins are much larger molecules and can store more information than DNA.
   d. all of the above
   e. both a and c

2. Which component is always different when comparing a nucleotide in a DNA strand to one in an RNA strand?
   a. phosphate group
   b. pentose sugar
   c. nitrogenous base
   d. both b and c
   e. a, b, and c

3. Which of the following equations is accurate concerning DNA base composition?
   a. %A + %T = %G + %C
   b. %A = %G
   c. %A = %G = %T = %C
   d. %A + %G = %T + %C

4. If the sequence of a segment of DNA in one strand is 5′–CGCAACTAC–3′, what is the sequence of the corresponding segment in the opposite strand?
   a. 5′–GCGTTGATG–3′
   b. 3′–ATACCAGCA–5′
   c. 5′–ATACCAGCA–3′
   d. 3′–GCGTTGATG–5′

5. Which of the following statements about the process of DNA replication is correct?
   a. New DNA molecules are composed of two completely new strands.
   b. New DNA molecules are composed of one strand from the old molecule and one new strand.
   c. New DNA molecules are composed of strands that are a mixture of sections from the old molecule and sections that are new.
   d. None of the above statements is correct.

6. Meselson and Stahl were able to demonstrate semiconservative replication in *E. coli* by
   a. using radioactive isotopes of phosphorus to label the original strand and visually determining the relationship of original and new DNA strands.
   b. using different enzymes to eliminate old strands from DNA.
   c. using isotopes of nitrogen to label the DNA and determining the relationship of original and new DNA strands by density differences of the new DNA molecules.
   d. labeling viral DNA before it was incorporated into a bacterial cell and visually determining the location of the DNA after centrifugation.

7. During replication of a DNA molecule, the daughter strands are not produced in exactly the same manner. One strand, the leading strand, is made toward the replication fork, while the lagging strand is made in fragments in the opposite direction. This difference in the synthesis of the two strands is the result of which of the following?
   a. DNA polymerase is not fast enough to make two leading strands of DNA.
   b. The two template strands are antiparallel, and DNA polymerase makes DNA only in the 5′ to 3′ direction.
   c. The lagging strand is the result of DNA breakage due to UV light.
   d. The cell does not contain enough nucleotides to make two complete strands.

8. In living cells, chromosomes consist of
   a. DNA and RNA.
   b. DNA only.
   c. RNA and proteins.
   d. DNA and proteins.
   e. RNA only.

9. A nucleosome is
   a. a dark-staining body composed of RNA and proteins found in the nucleus.
   b. a protein that helps organize the structure of chromosomes.
   c. another word for a chromosome.
   d. a structure composed of DNA wrapped around eight histones.
   e. the short arm of a chromosome.

10. The conversion of euchromatin into heterochromatin involves
    a. the formation of more nucleosomes.
    b. the formation of less nucleosomes.
    c. a greater compaction of loop domains.
    d. a lesser compaction of loop domains.
    e. both a and c.

Conceptual Questions

1. What are the four key criteria that the genetic material must fulfill? What was Griffith's contribution to the study of DNA, and why was it so important?

2. A double-stranded DNA molecule contains 560 nucleotides. How many complete turns occur in this double helix?

3. **Core Concept: Structure and Function** Discuss how the structure of DNA underlies different aspects of its function.

Collaborative Questions

1. **CoreSKILL »** A trait that some bacterial strains exhibit is resistance to being killed by antibiotics. For example, certain strains of bacteria are resistant to the drug tetracycline, whereas other strains are sensitive to this antibiotic. Describe an experiment you would carry out to demonstrate that tetracycline resistance is an inherited trait carried in the DNA of the resistant strain.

2. **CoreSKILL »** How might you provide evidence that DNA is the genetic material in mice?

Gene Expression at the Molecular Level I: Production of mRNA and Proteins

12

An electron micrograph of many ribosomes that are translating an mRNA into polypeptides. This colorized electron micrograph shows ribosomes attached to a bacterial mRNA and synthesizing polypeptides. Ribosomes are blue, mRNA is red, and emerging polypeptides are green. The complex of one mRNA and many ribosomes is called a polysome. ©Elena Kiseleva/Science Source

Mina, age 21, works part-time in an ice-cream shop and particularly enjoys the double-dark chocolate and chocolate fudge brownie flavors on her breaks. She exercises little and spends most of her time studying or watching television. Mina is effortlessly thin. She never worries about what or how much she eats. By comparison, her close friend, Rezzy, has struggled with her weight as long as she can remember. Compared with Mina, she feels like she must constantly deprive herself of food just to maintain her current weight—a weight she would describe as 30 pounds too much.

How do we explain the differences between Mina and Rezzy? Two fundamental factors are involved. Our weight is strongly influenced by the environment, especially our diet, as well as by social and behavioral factors. The amount and types of food we eat are correlated with weight gain. However, there is little doubt that our weight is also influenced by variation in our genes. *Obesity, the condition of having too much body fat, runs in families. The degree of obesity is often similar between genetically identical twins who have been raised apart. Why has genetic variation resulted in some genes that cause certain people to gain weight? A popular hypothesis is that some people have inherited "thrifty genes" as hand-me-downs from their ancestors, who periodically faced famines and food scarcity. Such thrifty genes would be advantageous in allowing people to store body fat more easily and to use food resources more efficiently when times are lean. The negative side is that when food is abundant, unwanted weight gain, and associated diseases such as diabetes and heart disease, can constitute a serious health problem.

Why is knowing about our genes important? Let's consider this question with regard to obesity. Researchers have identified several key genes that influence a person's predisposition to becoming obese. Dozens more are likely to play a minor role. By identifying those genes and studying the proteins specified by them, researchers gain a better understanding of how genetic variation causes certain people to gain weight more easily than others. In addition, this knowledge has led to the development of drugs that are used to combat obesity.

*People are generally considered obese when their body mass index, a measurement obtained by dividing a person's weight by the square of the person's height, is over 30 kg/m².

We can broadly define a gene as a unit of heredity. Geneticists view gene function at different biological levels. In Chapter 17, we will examine how genes affect the traits, or characteristics, of individuals. For example, we will consider how the transmission of genes from parents to offspring affects the color of the offspring's eyes and the likelihood that the offspring will be color blind. In this chapter, we will begin to explore how genes work at the molecular level. You will learn how DNA sequences are organized to form genes and how those genes are used as a template to make RNA copies, ultimately leading to the synthesis of a functional protein. The term **gene expression** can refer to gene function either at the level of traits or at the molecular level. In reality, the two phenomena are intricately woven together. The expression of genes at the molecular level affects the structure and function of cells, which, in turn, determine the traits that an organism expresses.

We begin this chapter by considering how researchers came to realize that most genes store the information to make proteins. We then explore the steps of gene expression as they occur at the molecular level. These steps include the use of a gene as a template to make an RNA molecule, the modifications of the RNA into a functional molecule (in eukaryotes), and the use of RNA to direct the formation of a protein. This chapter focuses on the expression of genes that encode polypeptides, which are called **protein-encoding genes**. The next chapter focuses on some of the interesting functions of genes that produce **non-coding RNAs (ncRNAs)**, which are RNAs that do not encode polypeptides.

12.1 Overview of Gene Expression

Learning Outcomes:

1. **CoreSKILL »** Analyze the results of the experiments of Garrod and of Beadle and Tatum.
2. Outline the general steps of gene expression at the molecular level, which together constitute the central dogma.
3. Explain how proteins are largely responsible for determining an organism's characteristics.

Even before DNA was identified as the genetic material, scientists had asked, "How does the functioning of genes produce the traits of living organisms?" At the molecular level, a similar question can be asked: "How do genes affect the composition and/or function of molecules found within living cells?" An approach that was successful in answering these questions involved the study of **mutations**, which are changes in the genetic material that can be inherited. Mutations may affect the genetic blueprint by altering gene function. For this reason, research that focused on the effects of mutations proved instrumental in determining the molecular function of genes.

In this section, we will consider two early experiments in which researchers studied the effects of mutations in humans and in a bread mold. Both studies led to the conclusion that the role of some genes is to carry the information to produce enzymes, which are a type of protein. Then we will examine the general features of gene expression at the molecular level.

The Study of Inborn Errors of Metabolism Suggested That Some Genes Carry the Information to Make Enzymes

In 1908, Archibald Garrod, a British physician, proposed a relationship between genes and the production of enzymes. Prior to his work, biochemists had studied many metabolic pathways that consist of a series of conversions of one molecule to another, each step catalyzed by an enzyme. **Figure 12.1** illustrates part of the metabolic pathway for the breakdown of phenylalanine, an amino acid commonly found in human diets. The enzyme phenylalanine hydroxylase catalyzes the conversion of phenylalanine to tyrosine, another amino acid. A different enzyme, tyrosine aminotransferase, converts tyrosine into the next molecule in the pathway, called p-hydroxyphenylpyruvic acid. In each case, a specific enzyme catalyzes a single chemical reaction.

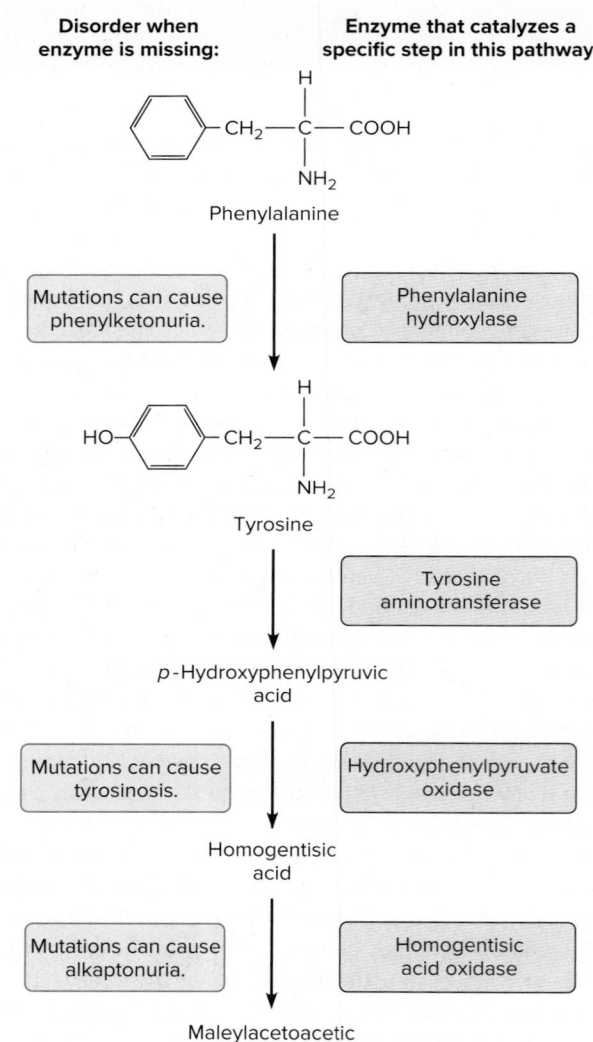

Figure 12.1 The metabolic pathway that breaks down phenylalanine and its relationship to certain genetic diseases. Each step in the pathway is catalyzed by a different enzyme, shown in the boxes on the right. If one of the enzymes is not functioning, the product of the previous step builds up, causing the disorders named in the boxes on the left.

Concept Check: *What disease would result if a person inherited two defective copies of the gene that encodes phenylalanine hydroxylase?*

Much of Garrod's early work centered on the inherited disease alkaptonuria, in which the patient's body accumulates abnormal levels of homogentisic acid (also called alkapton). This compound, which is bluish black, results in discoloration of the skin and cartilage and causes the urine to appear black. Garrod hypothesized that the accumulation of homogentisic acid in these patients is due to a defect in an enzyme, namely, homogentisic acid oxidase (see Figure 12.1). Furthermore, he already knew that alkaptonuria is an inherited condition that follows a recessive pattern of inheritance. As discussed in Chapter 17, if a disease is recessive, an individual with the disease has inherited the mutant (defective) gene that causes it from both parents.

How did Garrod explain these observations? In 1908, he proposed a relationship between the inheritance of a mutant gene and a defect in metabolism. In the case of alkaptonuria, if an individual inherited the mutant gene from both parents, she or he would not produce any normal enzyme and would be unable to metabolize homogentisic acid. Garrod described alkaptonuria as an **inborn error of metabolism**. An inborn error refers to a mutation in a gene that is inherited from one or both parents. At the turn of the last century, this was a particularly insightful idea because the structure and function of the genetic material were completely unknown.

Beadle and Tatum Proposed the One-Gene/One-Enzyme Hypothesis

In early 1940s, American geneticists George Beadle and Edward Tatum became aware of Garrod's work and were interested in the relationship between genes and enzymes. They focused their studies on *Neurospora crassa*, a common bread mold. *Neurospora* is easily grown in the laboratory and has only a few nutritional requirements: a carbon source (namely, sugar), inorganic salts, and one vitamin known as biotin. *Neurospora* has many different enzymes that synthesize the molecules, such as amino acids and vitamins, which are essential for growth.

Like Garrod, Beadle and Tatum hypothesized that genes carry the information to make specific enzymes. They reasoned that a mutation, that is, a change in a gene, might cause a defect in an enzyme required for the synthesis of an essential molecule, such as an amino acid. A mutant *Neurospora* strain (one that carries such a mutation) would be unable to grow unless the amino acid was supplemented in the growth medium. Strains without a mutation are called wild-type strains. One line of study involved the amino acid arginine. At the time of Beadle and Tatum's work in the early 1940s, the pathway leading to arginine synthesis was known to involve certain precursor molecules, including ornithine and citrulline. A simplified pathway for arginine synthesis is shown in **Figure 12.2a**. Each step is catalyzed by a different enzyme.

Beadle and Tatum exposed *Neurospora* cells to X-rays, which caused mutations to occur, and studied the resulting cells. By plating the cells on growth media with or without arginine, they were able to identify several different mutant strains that required arginine for growth. They hypothesized that each mutant strain might be blocked at only a single step in the consecutive series of reactions that lead to arginine synthesis. To test this hypothesis, the mutant strains were examined for their ability to grow in the presence of ornithine, citrulline, or arginine (**Figure 12.2b**). The wild-type strain could grow on minimal growth media that did not contain ornithine, citrulline, or arginine. Based on their growth properties, the mutant strains that had been originally identified as requiring arginine for growth could be placed into three groups, designated 1, 2, and 3:

- Group 1 mutants were missing enzyme 1, needed for the conversion of a precursor molecule into ornithine. They could grow only if ornithine, citrulline, or arginine was added to the growth medium.

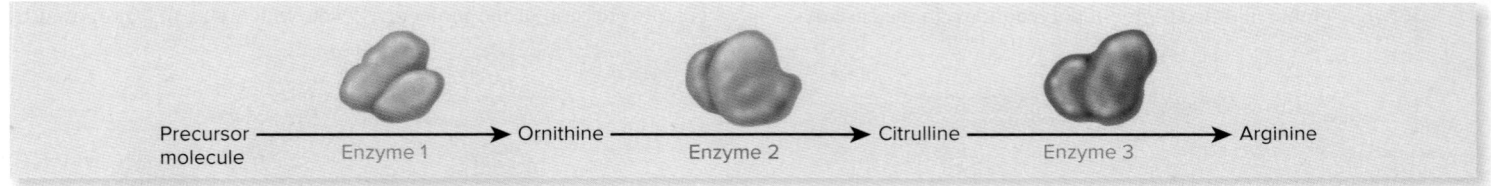

Precursor molecule → (Enzyme 1) → Ornithine → (Enzyme 2) → Citrulline → (Enzyme 3) → Arginine

(a) Simplified pathway for arginine synthesis

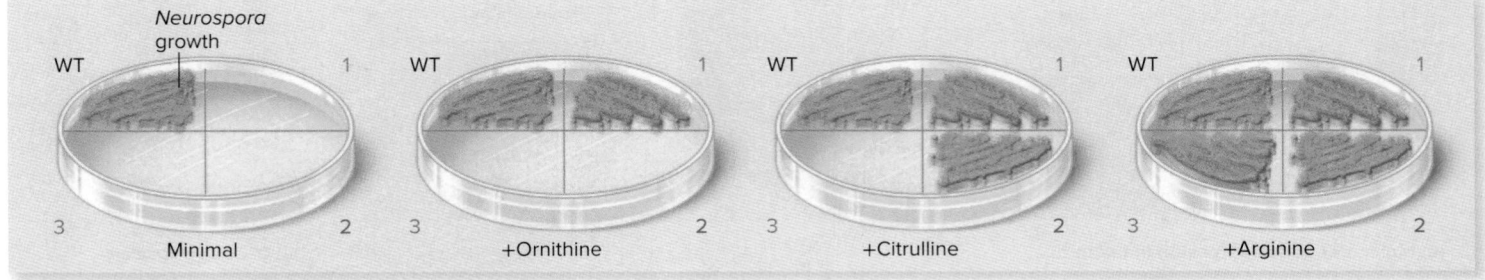

(b) Growth of strains on minimal and supplemented growth media

Figure 12.2 **An experiment that supported Beadle and Tatum's one-gene/one-enzyme hypothesis.** **(a)** This simplified metabolic pathway shows three enzymes that are required for arginine synthesis. **(b)** Growth of wild-type (WT) and mutant *Neurospora* strains (groups 1, 2, and 3) on minimal growth medium or in the presence of ornithine, citrulline, or arginine.

Concept Check: *What enzyme function was missing in group 2 mutants in this experiment?*

- Group 2 mutants were missing the second enzyme in this pathway that is needed for the conversion of ornithine into citrulline. The group 2 mutants would not grow if only ornithine was added, but could grow if citrulline or arginine was added.

- Group 3 mutants were missing the enzyme needed for the conversion of citrulline into arginine. These mutants could grow only if arginine was added.

How were these results interpreted? The researchers were able to order the functions of the genes involved in arginine synthesis in the following way:

$$\text{Precursor} \xrightarrow{\text{Group 1}} \text{Ornithine} \xrightarrow{\text{Group 2}} \text{Citrulline} \xrightarrow{\text{Group 3}} \text{Arginine}$$

From these results and earlier studies, Beadle and Tatum concluded that a single gene controlled the synthesis of a single enzyme. This was referred to as the **one-gene/one-enzyme hypothesis**. Beadle and Tatum received the 1958 Nobel Prize in Physiology or Medicine for their work on the role of genes in metabolism.

In later decades, their hypothesis was modified in four ways.

1. The information to make all proteins is contained within genes, and many proteins do not function as enzymes.

2. Some proteins are composed of two or more different polypeptides. The term **polypeptide** refers to a linear sequence of amino acids; it denotes structure. Most genes carry the information to make a particular polypeptide. By comparison, the term **protein** denotes function. Some proteins are composed of one polypeptide. In such cases, a single gene does contain the information to make a single protein. In other cases, however, a functional protein is composed of two or more different polypeptides. An example is hemoglobin—the protein that carries oxygen in red blood cells—which is composed of two α-globin and two β-globin polypeptides. In the case of hemoglobin, the expression of two genes (that is, the α-globin and β-globin genes) is needed to produce a functional protein.

3. As described in Chapter 14, some mRNAs (messenger RNAs) are spliced in alternative ways so they produce two or more polypeptides. This allows a single gene to encode more than one polypeptide.

4. A fourth modification to the one-gene/one-enzyme hypothesis is that some genes produce non-coding RNAs that do not specify the amino acid sequence of a polypeptide. This topic is discussed in Chapter 13.

Because of these additional complexities, the one-gene/one-enzyme hypothesis was modified and expanded as the functions of genes became better understood.

Molecular Gene Expression Involves the Processes of Transcription and Translation

Let's now examine the general steps of gene expression at the molecular level. The first step, known as **transcription**, produces an RNA copy of a gene, also called an RNA transcript (**Figure 12.3**). The term transcription literally means the act of making a copy. Most genes, which are termed protein-encoding genes, produce an RNA molecule that contains the information to specify a polypeptide with a particular amino acid sequence. This type of RNA is called **messenger RNA** (abbreviated **mRNA**), because its function is to carry information from the DNA to cellular components called ribosomes. As discussed later, ribosomes play a key role in the synthesis of polypeptides. The process of synthesizing a specific polypeptide on a ribosome is called **translation**. The term translation is used because a base sequence in an mRNA is "translated" into an amino acid sequence of a polypeptide.

Together, the transcription of DNA into mRNA and the translation of mRNA into a polypeptide constitute the **central dogma** of gene expression at the molecular level, which was first proposed by

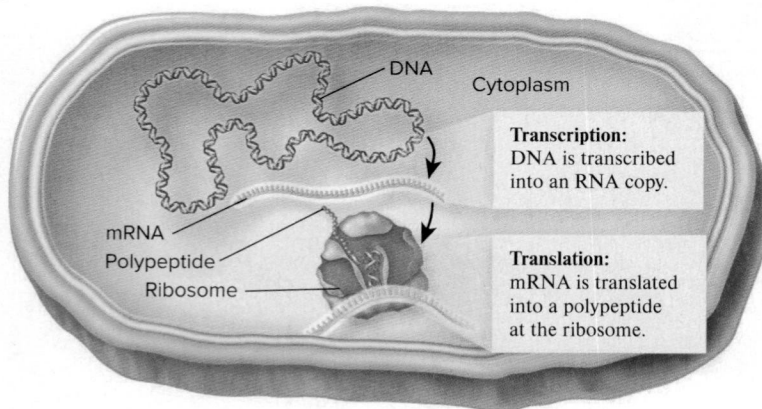

(a) Molecular gene expression in bacteria

Figure 12.3 **The central dogma of gene expression at the molecular level.** **(a)** In bacteria, transcription and translation occur in the cytoplasm. **(b)** In eukaryotes, transcription and RNA modification occur in the nucleus, whereas translation takes place in the cytosol.

Concept Check: *What is the direction of flow of genetic information?*

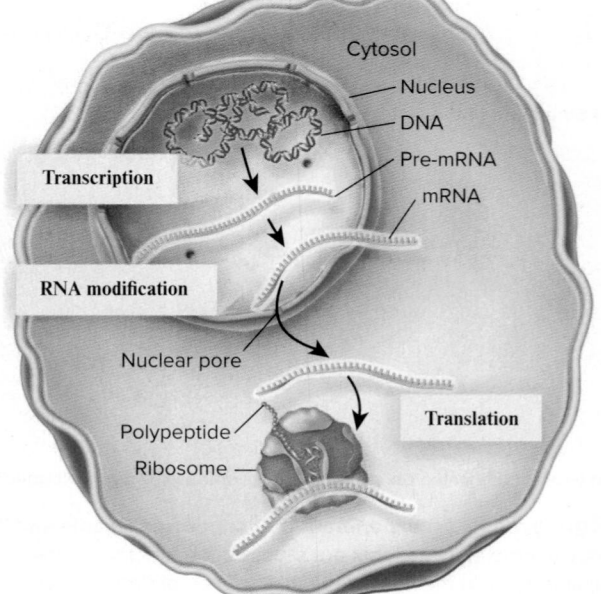

(b) Molecular gene expression in eukaryotes

Francis Crick in 1958 (see Figure 12.3). The central dogma applies equally to bacteria, archaea, and eukaryotes. However, in eukaryotes, an additional step occurs between transcription and translation. During **RNA modification**, which is described later in this chapter, the RNA transcript, termed **pre-mRNA**, is modified in ways that make it a functionally active mRNA (Figure 12.3b).

Another difference between bacteria and eukaryotes is the cellular location of transcription and translation. In bacteria, both events occur in the same location, namely, the cytoplasm. In eukaryotes, transcription occurs in the nucleus. The mRNA then exits the nucleus through a nuclear pore, and translation occurs in the cytosol.

Though the direction of information flow, that is, from DNA to RNA to protein, is the most common pathway, exceptions do occur. For example, certain viruses use RNA as a template to synthesize DNA. Such viruses are described in Chapter 19.

The Protein Products of Genes Largely Determine an Organism's Characteristics

The genes that constitute the genetic material provide a blueprint for the characteristics of every organism. They contain the information necessary to produce an organism and allow it to interact appropriately with its environment. Each protein-encoding gene stores the information for the production of a polypeptide, which then becomes a unit within a functional protein. The activities of proteins largely determine the structure and function of cells. Furthermore, the characteristics of an organism are rooted in the activities of cellular proteins.

A key purpose of the genetic material is to encode the production of proteins in the correct cell, at the proper time, and in suitable amounts. This is an intricate task, because living cells make thousands of different kinds of proteins. Genetic analyses have shown that a typical bacterium can make a few thousand different proteins, and estimates for eukaryotes range from several thousand in simpler eukaryotes to tens of thousands in more complex eukaryotes like humans.

12.2   Transcription

Learning Outcomes:

1. Give a molecular definition of the term gene.
2. Outline the three stages of transcription and the role of RNA polymerase in this process.
3. Explain how genes within the same chromosome vary in their direction of transcription.
4. Compare and contrast transcription in bacteria and eukaryotes.

DNA is an information storage unit. For genes to be expressed, the information in them must be accessed at the molecular level. Rather than accessing the information directly, however, a working copy of the DNA, composed of RNA, is made. This occurs by the process of transcription, in which a DNA sequence is copied into an RNA sequence. Importantly, transcription does not permanently alter the structure of DNA. Therefore, the same DNA can continue to store information even after an RNA copy has been made. In this section, we will examine the steps necessary for genes to act as transcriptional units. We will also consider some differences in these steps between bacteria and eukaryotes.

At the Molecular Level, a Gene Is Transcribed and Produces a Functional Product

What is a gene? At the molecular level, a **gene** is defined in the following way:

At the molecular level, a gene is defined as an organized unit of base sequences that enables a segment of DNA to be transcribed into RNA and ultimately results in the formation of a functional product.

When a protein-encoding gene is transcribed, an mRNA is made that specifies the amino acid sequence of a polypeptide. After it is made, the polypeptide becomes a functional product; one or more polypeptides form a functional protein. The mRNA is an intermediary in polypeptide synthesis. Among all species, most genes are protein-encoding genes. However, for some genes, the functional product is the RNA itself. The RNA from such a gene, which is called a non-coding RNA, is never translated. Two important examples of non-coding RNAs are transfer RNA and ribosomal RNA. **Transfer RNA (tRNA)** translates the language of mRNA into that of amino acids. **Ribosomal RNA (rRNA)** forms part of ribosomes, which provide the site where translation occurs. We'll learn more about these two types of RNA later in this chapter.

A gene is composed of specific base sequences organized in a way that allows the DNA to be transcribed into RNA. **Figure 12.4** shows the general organization of sequences in a protein-encoding gene. The **promoter** is a sequence of DNA that controls when and where transcription will begin. By comparison, the **terminator** specifies the end of transcription. Therefore, transcription occurs between these two boundaries. As shown in Figure 12.4, the DNA is transcribed into mRNA

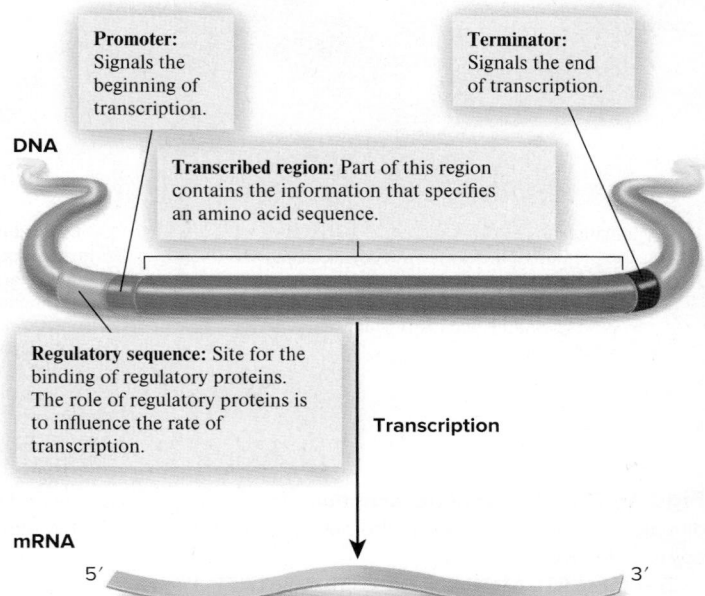

Figure 12.4   A protein-encoding gene as a transcriptional unit.

 Core Concept: Information Transcription is the first step in accessing the information that is stored in DNA.

from the end of the promoter through the coding sequence to the terminator. Within this transcribed region is the information that will specify the amino acid sequence of a polypeptide when the mRNA is translated.

Other DNA sequences are involved in the regulation of transcription. These **regulatory sequences** function as sites for the binding of regulatory proteins, which are discussed in Chapter 14. When a regulatory protein binds to a regulatory sequence, the rate of transcription is affected. Some regulatory proteins enhance the rate of transcription, whereas others inhibit it.

During Transcription, RNA Polymerase Uses a DNA Template to Make RNA

Transcription occurs in three stages, called initiation, elongation, and termination, during which various proteins interact with DNA sequences (**Figure 12.5**).

Initiation The stage called **initiation** is a recognition step. In bacteria such as *E. coli*, a protein called **sigma factor** binds to

RNA polymerase, the enzyme that synthesizes strands of RNA. Sigma factor recognizes the base sequence of a promoter and binds there. An example of a promoter sequence is described in the legend to Figure 12.5. The role of sigma factor is to cause RNA polymerase to bind to the promoter. The initiation stage is completed when the DNA strands are separated near the promoter to form an **open complex** that is approximately 10–15 bp long.

Elongation During **elongation**, RNA polymerase synthesizes the RNA transcript. For this to occur, sigma factor is released and RNA polymerase slides along the DNA in a way that maintains an open complex as it goes. The DNA strand that is used as a template for RNA synthesis is called the **template strand**. For protein-encoding genes, the opposite DNA strand is called the **coding strand**. The coding strand has the same sequence of bases as the resulting mRNA, except that the RNA has uracil instead of the thymine found in the DNA. The coding strand is so named because, like mRNA, it carries the information that codes for a polypeptide.

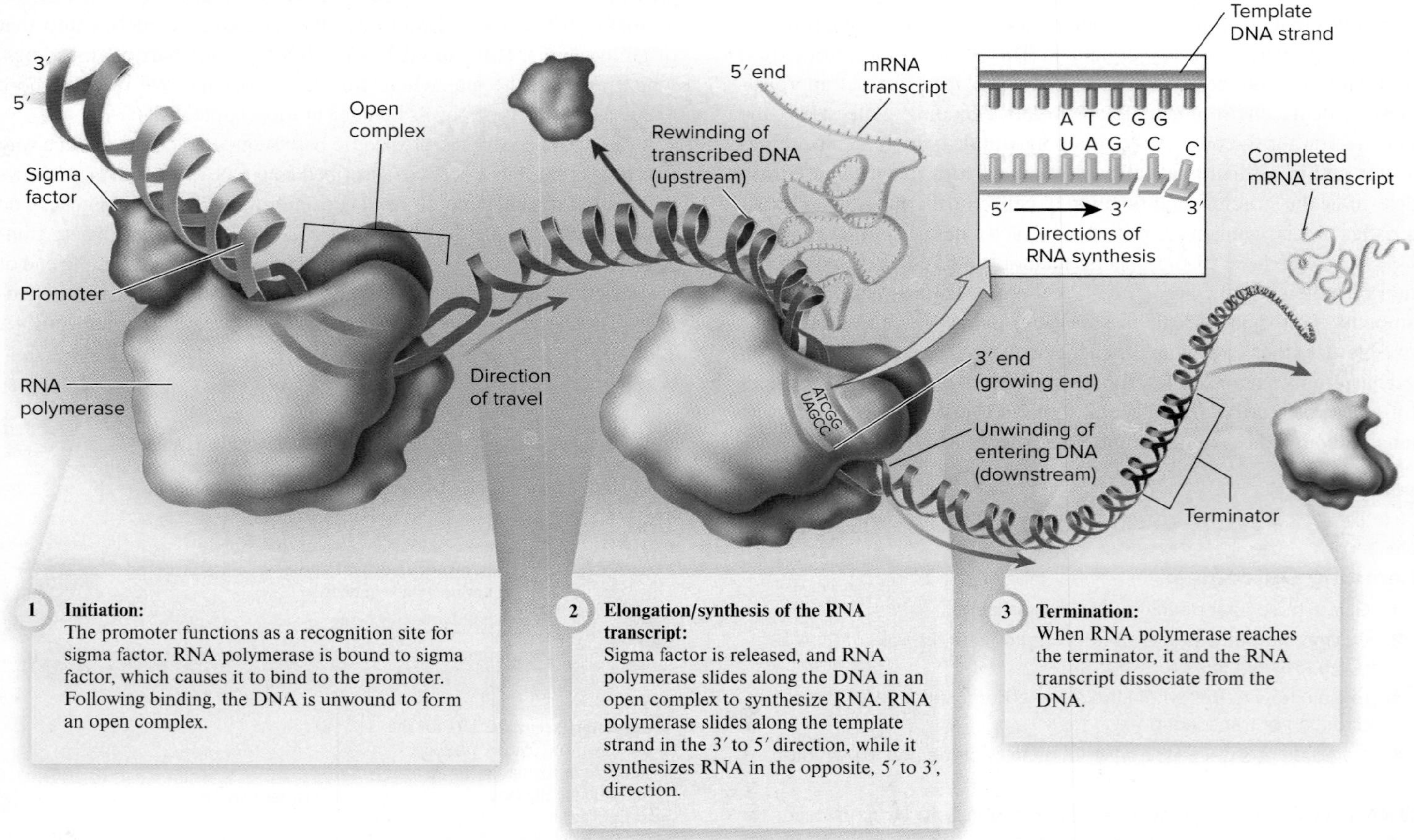

1 Initiation:
The promoter functions as a recognition site for sigma factor. RNA polymerase is bound to sigma factor, which causes it to bind to the promoter. Following binding, the DNA is unwound to form an open complex.

2 Elongation/synthesis of the RNA transcript:
Sigma factor is released, and RNA polymerase slides along the DNA in an open complex to synthesize RNA. RNA polymerase slides along the template strand in the 3′ to 5′ direction, while it synthesizes RNA in the opposite, 5′ to 3′, direction.

3 Termination:
When RNA polymerase reaches the terminator, it and the RNA transcript dissociate from the DNA.

Figure 12.5 Stages of transcription. Transcription can be divided into initiation, elongation, and termination. The inset emphasizes the direction of RNA synthesis and the base pairing between the DNA template strand and RNA. An example of a promoter sequence in the DNA of *E. coli* is as follows:

5′-TTGACATGATAGAAGCACTCTACTATATT-3′
3′-AACTGTACTATCTTCGTGAGATGATATAA-5′

This region is 29 bp long, and it immediately precedes the site where transcription begins. The bases that are specifically recognized by sigma factor are shown in red. The sequences of promoters for different genes are fairly diverse, particularly in eukaryotic species.

 Core Skill: Connections Look back at the role of DNA polymerase shown in Figure 11.15. What are similarities and differences between the function of DNA polymerase and that of RNA polymerase?

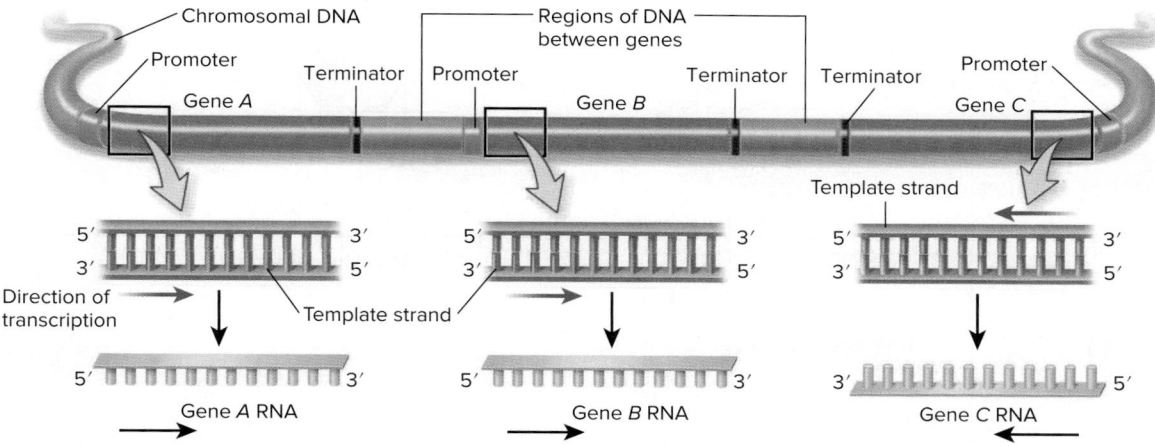

Figure 12.6 **The transcription of three different genes found in the same chromosome.** RNA polymerase synthesizes each RNA transcript in a 5′ to 3′ direction, sliding along a DNA template strand in a 3′ to 5′ direction. However, the strand used as the template can vary from gene to gene. For example, for transcribing genes *A* and *B*, the bottom strand is used as the template strand, while the top strand is used for transcribing gene *C*.

During the elongation stage of transcription, nucleotides bind to the template strand and are covalently connected in the 5′ to 3′ direction (see inset of step 2, Figure 12.5). The complementarity rule used in this process is similar to the AT/GC rule of DNA replication, except that uracil (U) in RNA substitutes for thymine (T) in DNA. For example, a DNA template with the sequence 3′–TACAATGTAGCC–5′ will be transcribed into an RNA sequence reading 5′–AUGUUACAUCGG–3′. In bacteria, the rate of RNA synthesis is about 40 nucleotides per second! Behind the open complex, the DNA rewinds back into a double helix.

Termination Eventually, RNA polymerase reaches a terminator, which causes it and the newly made RNA transcript to dissociate from the DNA. This event constitutes the **termination** of transcription.

When multiple genes within a chromosome are transcribed, the DNA strand that is used as the template strand varies among the genes. **Figure 12.6** shows three genes adjacent to each other within a chromosome. Genes *A* and *B* are transcribed from left to right, using the bottom DNA strand as the template strand. By comparison, gene *C* is transcribed from right to left, using the top DNA strand as a template strand. In all three cases, however, the synthesis of the RNA transcript begins at a promoter and always occurs in a 5′ to 3′ direction. The template strand is read in the 3′ to 5′ direction.

Transcription in Eukaryotes Involves More Proteins

The basic features of transcription are similar among all organisms. The genes of all species have promoters, and the transcription process occurs in the stages of initiation, elongation, and termination. However, the transcription of eukaryotic genes tends to involve a greater complexity of protein components than does the transcription of bacterial genes. For example, three forms of RNA polymerase, designated I, II, and III, are found in eukaryotes. RNA polymerase II is responsible for transcribing the mRNA from eukaryotic protein-encoding genes, whereas RNA polymerases I and III transcribe genes that specify non-coding RNAs, such as tRNAs and rRNAs. By comparison, bacteria have a single type of RNA polymerase that

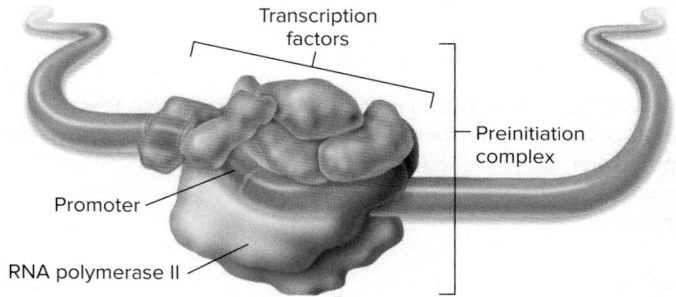

Figure 12.7 **The preinitiation complex.** Transcription factors and RNA polymerase II assemble into the preinitiation complex at the promoter in eukaryotic protein-encoding genes.

transcribes all genes, though many bacterial species have more than one type of sigma factor that can recognize different promoters.

The initiation stage of transcription in eukaryotes is also more complex. Recall that in bacteria such as *E. coli*, sigma factor recognizes the promoter of a gene. By comparison, RNA polymerase II of eukaryotes always requires five transcription factors to initiate transcription. **Transcription factors** are proteins that influence the ability of RNA polymerase to transcribe genes. The binding of RNA polymerase II to the promoter is an assembly process in which RNA polymerase II and the five transcription factors form a **preinitiation complex** (**Figure 12.7**). The complex then unwinds the DNA to initiate transcription.

12.3 RNA Modification in Eukaryotes

Learning Outcomes:

1. Describe the addition of the 5′ cap and 3′ poly A tail to eukaryotic mRNA.

2. Explain the process of splicing that produces mature eukaryotic mRNA.

As noted previously, eukaryotic mRNA transcripts undergo modifications to produce functional mRNAs. Transcription initially produces

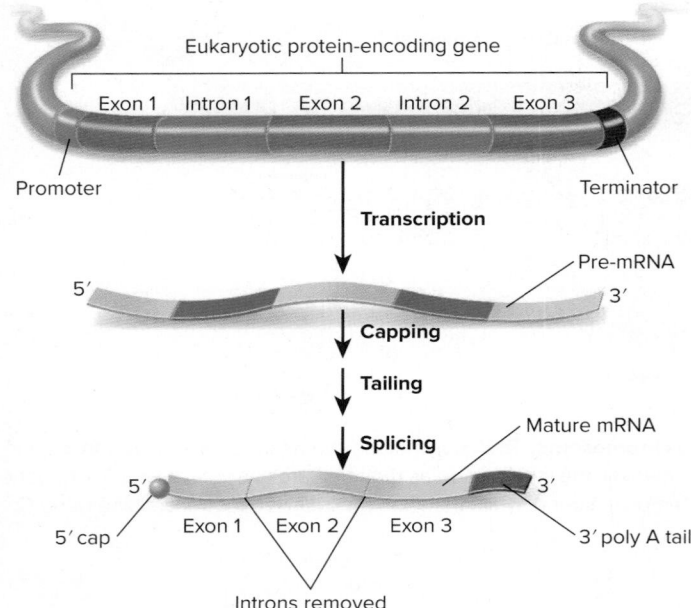

Figure 12.8 **Modifications to eukaryotic pre-mRNA that produce a mature mRNA molecule.** Note: Most RNA molecules are spliced after the pre-mRNA is completely synthesized. However, for some, splicing may begin before transcription of the pre-mRNA is completed.

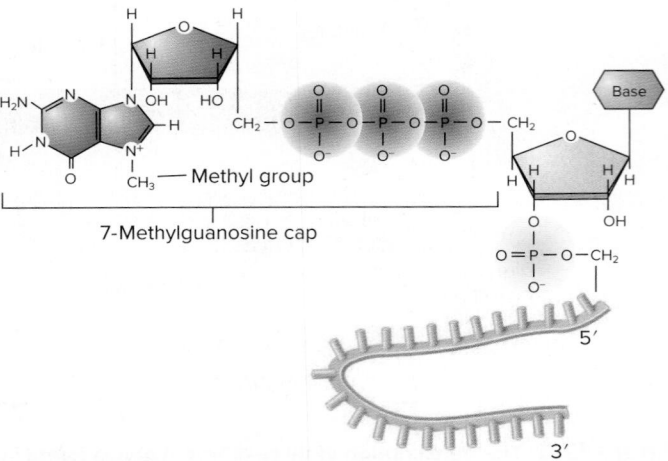

(a) Cap structure at the 5′ end of eukaryotic mRNA

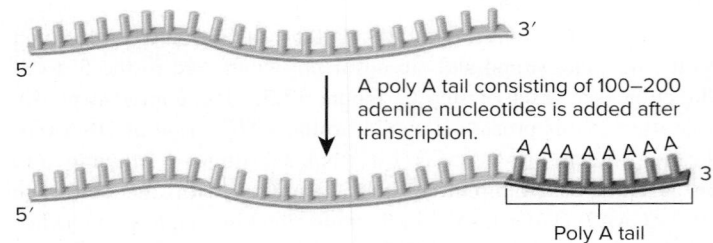

(b) A poly A tail at the 3′ end of eukaryotic mRNA

Figure 12.9 **Modifications that alter the ends of mRNA in eukaryotic cells. (a)** A 7-methylguanosine cap is attached to the 5′ end of a pre-mRNA. This is a guanine base modified by the attachment of a methyl group. The linkage between the cap and the mRNA is a 5′ to 5′ linkage. **(b)** A poly A tail is added to the 3′ end of a pre-mRNA.

Concept Check: *Do the ends of protein-encoding genes have a poly T region that acts as a template for the synthesis of a poly A tail in mRNA? Explain.*

a longer RNA, called a **pre-mRNA**, which undergoes certain modifications before it exits the nucleus. The final product is called a **mature mRNA**, or simply an mRNA. As shown in **Figure 12.8**, three different modifications are common. Two of them, called capping and tailing, are modifications to the ends of the pre-mRNA. As described later, these add a 5′ cap and a polyA tail. A third modification, called splicing, involves the removal of internal segments called introns. The segments that are retained in a mature mRNA are exons. After all of the RNA modifications have been completed, the mRNA leaves the nucleus and enters the cytosol, where translation occurs. In this section, we will examine the molecular mechanisms that account for these RNA modifications and consider why they are functionally important.

The Ends of Eukaryotic Pre-mRNAs Are Modified by the Addition of a 5′ Cap and a 3′ Poly A Tail

Mature mRNAs of eukaryotes have a modified form of guanine covalently attached at the 5′ end, an event known as **capping** (**Figure 12.9a**). Capping occurs while a pre-mRNA is being made by RNA polymerase, usually when the transcript is only 20 to 25 nucleotides in length. What are the functions of the cap?

- The 7-methylguanosine structure, called a **5′ cap**, is recognized by cap-binding proteins, which are needed for the proper exit of mRNAs from the nucleus.
- After an mRNA is in the cytosol, the cap structure helps to prevent its degradation.

- The cap structure is recognized by cap-binding proteins that enable the mRNA to bind to a ribosome for translation.

At the 3′ end, most mature eukaryotic mRNAs have a string of adenine nucleotides, typically 100 to 200 nucleotides in length, referred to as a **poly A tail** (**Figure 12.9b**). The poly A tail is not encoded in the gene sequence. Instead, the tail is added enzymatically after a pre-mRNA has been completely transcribed.

- A long poly A tail aids in the export of mRNA from the nucleus.
- It also stabilizes a eukaryotic mRNA so it can exist for a longer period of time in the cytosol.

Interestingly, new research has shown that some bacterial mRNAs also have poly A tails attached to them. However, the poly A tail has an opposite effect in bacteria, where it causes the mRNA to be rapidly degraded.

Splicing Involves the Removal of Introns and the Linkage of Exons

In the late 1970s, when the experimental tools became available to study eukaryotic genes at the molecular level, the scientific community was astonished by the discovery that the coding sequences within many eukaryotic protein-encoding genes are separated by DNA sequences that are transcribed but not translated into protein. These intervening sequences that are not translated are called **introns**, whereas sequences contained in the mature mRNA are termed **exons**. Exons are considered to be <u>expressed</u> regi<u>ons</u>, because they contain the coding sequence for a polypeptide. In contrast, introns are <u>intervening</u> regi<u>ons</u> that are not expressed, because they are removed from the pre-mRNA. To become a mature mRNA, the pre-mRNA transcribed from eukaryotic genes that contain introns must undergo a third RNA modification known as **RNA splicing**, or simply **splicing** (see Figure 12.8). During this process, introns are removed and the remaining exons are connected to each other.

Introns are found in many but not all eukaryotic genes. Splicing is less frequent among unicellular eukaryotic species, such as yeast, but is a widespread phenomenon among more complex eukaryotes. In animals and flowering plants, most protein-encoding genes have one or more introns. For example, an average human gene has about nine introns. The sizes of introns vary from a few dozen nucleotides to over 100,000! A few bacterial genes have been found to have introns, but they are rare among bacterial and archaeal species.

Introns are precisely removed from eukaryotic pre-mRNA by a large complex called a **spliceosome** that is composed of several different snRNPs (pronounced "snurps"); each snRNP contains <u>s</u>mall <u>n</u>uclear <u>RNA</u> and a set of <u>p</u>roteins. An intron in pre-mRNA is defined by a particular sequence within the intron termed the branch site and by two intron-exon boundaries, called the 5′ splice site and the 3′ splice site (**Figure 12.10**). Particular snRNPs bind to specific sequences at these three locations. This binding causes the intron to loop outward, which brings the two exons close together. The 5′ splice site is then cut, and the 5′ end of the intron becomes covalently attached to the branch site. In the final step, the 3′ splice site is cut, and the two exons are covalently attached to each other. The intron is released and eventually degraded.

In some cases, the function of the spliceosome is regulated so the splicing of a given mRNA can occur in two or more ways. This phenomenon, called **alternative splicing**, allows a single gene to encode two or more polypeptides with differences in their amino acid sequences. As described in Chapter 14, alternative splicing allows complex eukaryotic species to use the same gene to make different proteins at different stages of development or in different cell types. This increases the size of the proteome while minimizing the size of the genome.

Although primarily found in mRNAs, introns occasionally occur in rRNA and tRNA molecules of certain species. These introns, however, are not removed by the action of a spliceosome. Instead, such rRNAs and tRNAs are **self-splicing**, which means the RNA itself can catalyze the removal of its own intron(s). Portions of the RNA act like an enzyme to cleave the covalent bonds at the intron-exon boundaries and connect the exons together. An RNA molecule that catalyzes a chemical reaction is termed a **ribozyme**.

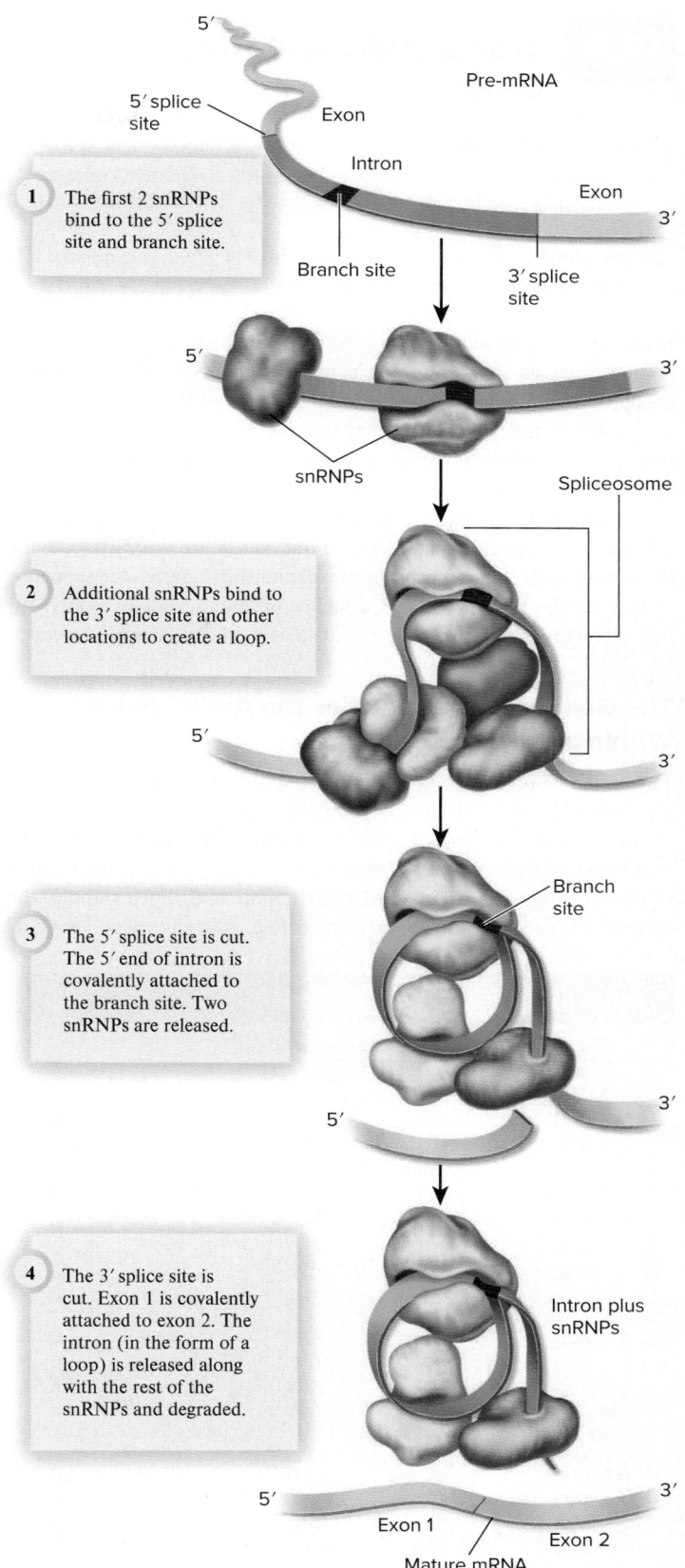

Figure 12.10 **The splicing of a eukaryotic pre-mRNA by a spliceosome.**

12.4 Translation and the Genetic Code

Learning Outcomes:

1. Explain how the genetic code specifies the relationship between the sequence of codons in mRNA and the amino acid sequence of a polypeptide.
2. **CoreSKILL »** Analyze the experiments of Nirenberg and Leder that led to the deciphering of the genetic code.

In the two previous sections, we considered the first stages of the central dogma—how an RNA transcript is made from DNA and how eukaryotes process that transcript. Recall that this type of RNA is called messenger RNA (mRNA), because its function is to transmit information from DNA to cellular components called ribosomes, where polypeptide synthesis occurs. In this section, we will consider the next stage, translation, which is the synthesis of polypeptides using information from the mRNA. To understand the process of translation, we will first examine the **genetic code**, which specifies the relationship between the sequence of bases in the mRNA and the sequence of amino acids in a polypeptide. We will also explore experiments that helped to "crack" the code.

The Genetic Code Specifies the Amino Acids Within a Polypeptide

The ability of mRNA to be translated into an amino acid sequence of a polypeptide relies on the genetic code. The code is read in groups of three nucleotide bases known as **codons**. The genetic code consists of 64 different codons (**Table 12.1**). The sequence of three bases in most codons specifies a particular amino acid. For example, the codon CCC specifies the amino acid proline, whereas the codon GGC

encodes the amino acid glycine. From the analysis of many different species, including bacteria, archaea, protists, fungi, plants, and animals, researchers have found that the genetic code is nearly universal. Only a few rare exceptions to the genetic code have been discovered.

Why are there 64 codons, as shown in Table 12.1? Because amino acids are found in 20 different types, at least 20 different codons are needed so each amino acid can be specified by a codon. With four types of bases in mRNA (U, C, A, and G), a genetic code containing two bases in a codon would not be sufficient, because only 4^2, or 16, different codons would be possible. A three-base system can specify 4^3, or 64, different codons, which is far more than the number of amino acids. The genetic code is said to be **degenerate** because more than one codon can specify the same amino acid (see Table 12.1). For example, the codons GGU, GGC, GGA, and GGG all code for the amino acid glycine. In most instances, the third base in the codon is the degenerate, or variable, base.

During Translation, mRNA Is Used to Make a Polypeptide with a Specific Amino Acid Sequence

Let's look at the organization of a bacterial mRNA to see how translation occurs (**Figure 12.11**). A ribosomal-binding site is located near the 5′ end of the mRNA. The **start codon**, which is AUG, is the site where translation begins. AUG specifies the amino acid methionine. The start codon is only a few nucleotides from the ribosomal-binding site. Beyond

Table 12.1	The Genetic Code*					
			Second position			
		U	C	A	G	
First Position	U	UUU } Phe UUC UUA } Leu UUG	UCU } Ser UCC UCA UCG	UAU } Tyr UAC UAA Stop UAG Stop	UGU } Cys UGC UGA Stop UGG Trp	U C A G
	C	CUU } Leu CUC CUA CUG	CCU } Pro CCC CCA CCG	CAU } His CAC CAA } Gln CAG	CGU } Arg CGC CGA CGG	U C A G
	A	AUU } Ile AUC AUA AUG Met/start	ACU } Thr ACC ACA ACG	AAU } Asn AAC AAA } Lys AAG	AGU } Ser AGC AGA } Arg AGG	U C A G
	G	GUU } Val GUC GUA GUG	GCU } Ala GCC GCA GCG	GAU } Asp GAC GAA } Glu GAG	GGU } Gly GGC GGA GGG	U C A G

Third Position (right column)

*The sequences of bases are in the 5' to 3' direction (from left to right) in the mRNA. Exceptions to the genetic code are sporadically found among various species. For example, AUA encodes methionine in yeast and mammalian mitochondria. The three-letter abbreviations for the amino acids are given in Chapter 3 (see Figure 3.13).

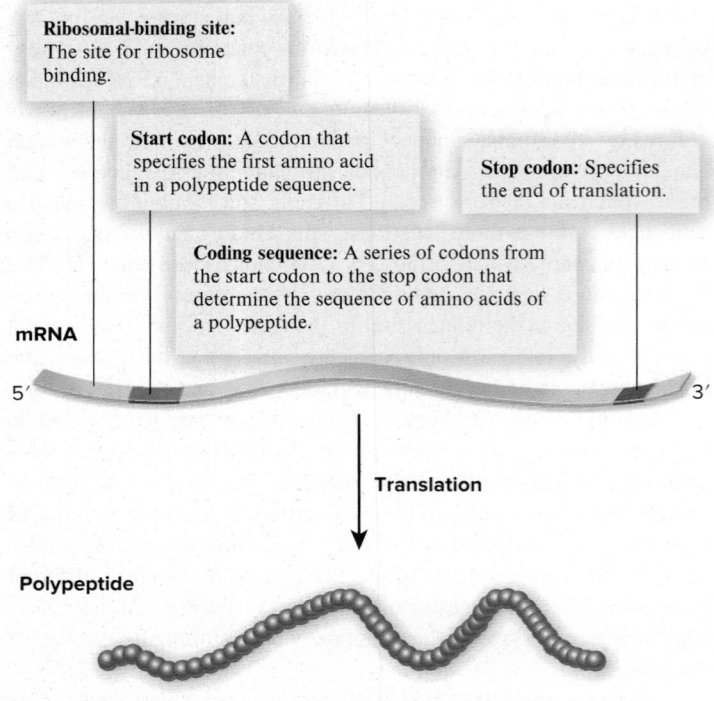

Figure 12.11 The organization of a bacterial mRNA as a translational unit. The string of blue balls represents a sequence of amino acids in a polypeptide. During and following translation, a sequence of amino acids folds into a more compact structure as described in Chapter 3 (see Figure 3.15).

Concept Check: If a mutation eliminated the start codon from a protein-encoding gene, how would the mutation affect transcription, and how would it affect translation?

this, a large portion of an mRNA functions as a **coding sequence**—a region that specifies the linear amino acid sequence of a polypeptide. A typical polypeptide is a few hundred amino acids in length. The coding sequence consists of a series of codons. Finally, one of three **stop codons** signals the end of translation. These codons, also known as **termination codons**, are UAA, UAG, and UGA.

The start codon also defines the **reading frame** of an mRNA, which refers to the order in which codons are read during translation. Beginning at the start codon, each adjacent codon is read as a group of three bases, also called a **triplet**, in the 5′ to 3′ direction. For example, look at the following two mRNA sequences and their corresponding amino acid sequences.

Ribosomal-binding site	Start codon					

mRNA 5′–<u>AUAAGGAGG</u>UUACG(<u>AUG</u>)(CAG)(CAG)(GGC)(UUU)(ACC)–3′

Polypeptide   Met - Gln - Gln - Gly - Phe - Thr

Ribosomal-binding site	Start codon					

mRNA 5′–<u>AUAAGGAGG</u>UUACG(<u>AUG</u>)(UCA)(GCA)(GGG)(CUU)(UAC)C–3′

Polypeptide   Met - Ser - Ala - Gly - Leu - Tyr

The first sequence shows how the mRNA codons would be correctly translated into amino acids. In the second sequence, an additional U has been added to the sequence after the start codon. This shifts the reading frame, thereby changing the codons as they occur in the 5′ to 3′ direction. The polypeptide produced from this series of codons has a very different sequence of amino acids. From this comparison, we can also see that the reading frame is not overlapping, which means that each base functions within a single codon.

DNA Stores Information, Whereas mRNA and tRNA Access That Information to Make Polypeptides

The relationships among the DNA sequence of a gene, the mRNA transcribed from the gene, and the polypeptide sequence are shown schematically in **Figure 12.12**. Recall that the template strand is used to make mRNA. The resulting mRNA strand corresponds to the coding strand of DNA, except that U in the mRNA substitutes for T in the DNA. The 5′ end of the mRNA contains an untranslated region (5′ UTR) as does the 3′ end (3′ UTR). The middle portion contains a series of codons that specify the amino acid sequence of a polypeptide.

To translate a nucleotide sequence of mRNA into an amino acid sequence, recognition occurs between mRNA and transfer RNA (tRNA) molecules. Transfer RNA, which is described in

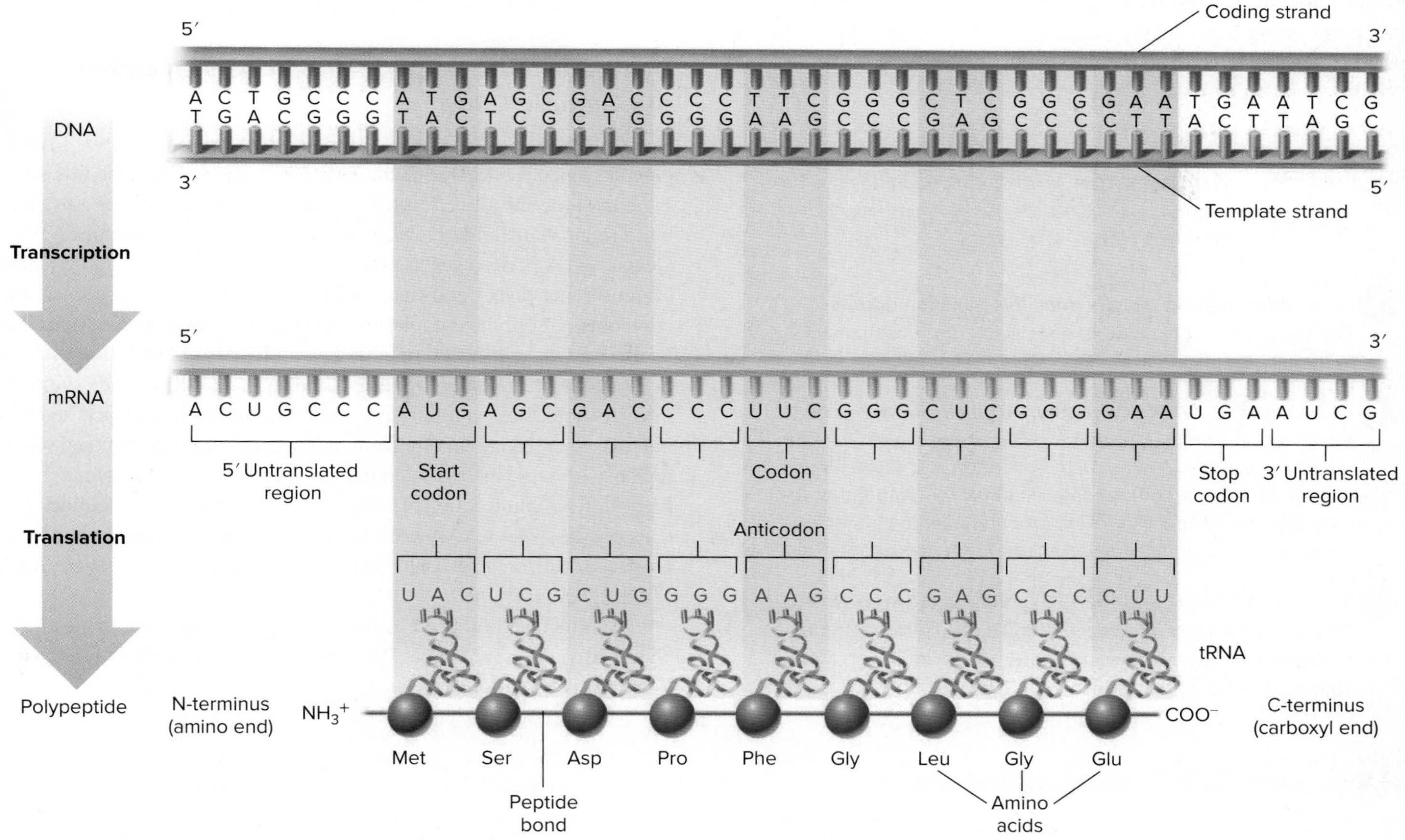

Figure 12.12 **Relationships among the coding sequence of a gene, the codon sequence of an mRNA, the anticodons of tRNA, and the amino acid sequence of a polypeptide.** Note: The tRNAs are detached from the polypeptide as it being synthesized. Also, this gene does not contain any introns.

 Core Concept: Information Figure 12.12 illustrates how DNA stores the information to make a polypeptide with a particular amino acid sequence. Messenger RNA is a temporary copy of that information that is directly used to make a polypeptide.

Section 12.5, functions as the "translator" or intermediary between an mRNA codon and an amino acid. The **anticodon** is a three-base sequence in a tRNA molecule that is complementary to a codon in mRNA. Due to this complementarity, the anticodon in a tRNA and a codon in an mRNA bind to each other. Furthermore, the anticodon in a tRNA corresponds to the amino acid that it carries. For example, if the anticodon in a tRNA is 3′–AAG–5′, it is complementary to a 5′–UUC–3′ codon. According to the genetic code, a UUC codon specifies phenylalanine (Phe). Therefore, a tRNA with a 3′–AAG–5′ anticodon must carry phenylalanine. As another example, a tRNA with a 3′–GGG–5′ anticodon is complementary to a 5′–CCC–3′ codon, which specifies proline. This tRNA must carry proline (Pro).

As seen at the bottom of Figure 12.12, the direction of polypeptide synthesis parallels the 5′ to 3′ orientation of mRNA. The first amino acid is said to be at the amino end, or **N-terminus**, of the polypeptide. The term N-terminus refers to the presence of a nitrogen atom (N) at this end, whereas amino end indicates the presence of an amino group (NH_2). **Peptide bonds** connect the amino acids together. These covalent bonds form between the carboxyl group (COOH) of the previous amino acid and the amino group of the next amino acid. The last amino acid in a completed polypeptide does not have another amino acid attached to its carboxyl group. This last amino acid is said to be located at the carboxyl end, or **C-terminus**. A carboxyl group is always found at this end of the polypeptide. Note that at neutral pH, the amino group is positively charged (NH_3^+), whereas the carboxyl group is negatively charged (COO^-).

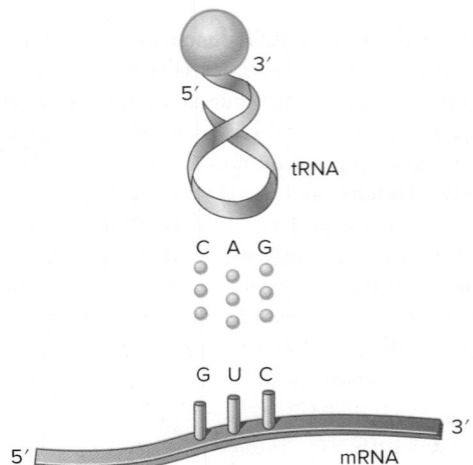

The basis of anticodon/codon recognition is that the anticodon and codon are complementary and antiparallel. The function of the codon is to specify a particular amino acid according to the genetic code.

ANSWER *The anticodon is 3′–CAG–5′, so it is complementary to a codon with the sequence 5′–GUC–3′. According to the genetic code, this codon specifies the amino acid valine. Therefore, this tRNA must carry a valine.*

Synthetic RNA Helped Researchers Decipher the Genetic Code

Now let's look at some early experiments that allowed scientists to decipher the genetic code. During the early 1960s, the genetic code was determined by the collective efforts of several researchers, including American biochemist Marshall Nirenberg, Spanish-American biochemist Severo Ochoa, and American geneticist Philip Leder. Prior to their studies, other scientists had discovered that bacterial cells can be broken open and components from the cytoplasm can synthesize polypeptides if mRNA is also present. This mixture is termed an **in vitro translation system**, or a **cell-free translation system**. Nirenberg and Ochoa made synthetic mRNA molecules using an enzyme that covalently connects nucleotides together. Using this synthetic mRNA, they then determined which amino acids were incorporated into polypeptides. For example, if a synthetic mRNA molecule had only adenine-containing nucleotides (for example, 5′–AAAAAAAAAAAAAAAAAAA–3′), a polypeptide was produced that contained only lysine. This result indicated that the AAA codon specifies lysine.

Another method used to decipher the genetic code involved the chemical synthesis of short RNA molecules, as described next in the Feature Investigation.

 BIO **TIPS**

THE QUESTION *A tRNA anticodon has the sequence 3′–CAG–5′. What amino acid does this tRNA carry?*

T OPIC *What topic in biology does this question address?* The topic is translation. More specifically, the question asks you to identify the amino acid that a tRNA carries.

I NFORMATION *What information do you know based on the question and your understanding of the topic?* From the question, you know that a tRNA anticodon is 3′–CAG–5′. From your understanding of the topic, you may remember that the anticodon and codon are complementary and antiparallel. The codon specifies an amino acid according to the genetic code.

P ROBLEM-SOLVING **S** TRATEGY *Make a drawing. Relate structure and function.* One strategy to begin to solve this problem is to make a drawing showing how the given tRNA anticodon binds to a codon in an mRNA.

 **Core Skill: Process of Science**

Feature Investigation | Nirenberg and Leder Found That RNA Triplets Can Promote the Binding of tRNA to Ribosomes

In 1964, Nirenberg and Leder discovered that RNA molecules containing three nucleotides (that is, a triplet) can cause a tRNA molecule to bind to a ribosome. In other words, an RNA triplet acts like a codon

within an mRNA molecule. To establish the relationship between triplet sequences and specific amino acids, Nirenberg and Leder made triplets with specific base sequences (**Figure 12.13**). For example, in one experiment they studied 5′–CCC–3′ triplets. This particular triplet was added to 20 different tubes. To each tube, they next added an in vitro translation system, which contained ribosomes and tRNAs that already had amino acids attached to them. However, each translation system had only one type of radiolabeled amino acid. One translation system had only proline that was radiolabeled, a second translation system had only serine that was radiolabeled, and so on.

As shown in step 2 of Figure 12.13, the triplets became bound to the ribosomes just like mRNAs bind to ribosomes. The tRNA with an anticodon that was complementary to the added triplet then bound to the triplet, which was already bound to the ribosome. For example, when the triplet was 5′–CCC–3′, a tRNA with a 3′–GGG–5′ anticodon bound to the triplet/ribosome complex. This tRNA carries proline.

To determine which tRNA had bound, the contents from each tube were poured through a filter that trapped the large ribosomes but did not trap tRNAs that were not bound to ribosomes (see step 3). If the tRNA carrying the radiolabeled amino acid was bound to the triplet/ribosome complex, radioactivity would be trapped on the

filter. Using a scintillation counter, the researchers determined the amount of radioactivity on each filter. Because only one amino acid was radiolabeled in each in vitro translation system, they could determine which triplet corresponded to which amino acid. In the example shown here, CCC corresponds to proline. Therefore, the in vitro translation system containing radiolabeled proline showed a large amount of radioactivity on the filter. As seen in the data, by studying triplets with different sequences, Nirenberg and Leder identified many codons of the genetic code.

Experimental Questions

1. Briefly explain how a triplet mimics the role of an mRNA molecule. How was this observation useful in the study done by Nirenberg and Leder?

3. **CoreSKILL »** What was the benefit of using radiolabeled amino acids in the Nirenberg and Leder experiment?

3. **CoreSKILL »** Predict the results that Nirenberg and Leder would have found for the following triplets: AUG, UAA, UAG, and UGA.

Figure 12.13 Nirenberg and Leder's use of triplet binding method to decipher the genetic code.

HYPOTHESIS An RNA triplet can bind to a ribosome and promote the binding of the tRNA that carries the amino acid that the RNA triplet specifies.

KEY MATERIALS The researchers made 20 in vitro translation systems, which included ribosomes, tRNAs, and 20 amino acids. The 20 translation systems differed with regard to which amino acid was radiolabeled. For example, in 1 translation system, radiolabeled glycine was added, and the other 19 amino acids were unlabeled. In another system, radiolabeled proline was added, and the other 19 amino acids were unlabeled. The in vitro translation systems also contained the enzymes that attach amino acids to tRNAs.

	Experimental level	**Conceptual level**
1 Mix together RNA triplets of a specific sequence and 20 in vitro translation systems. In the example shown here, the triplet is 5′–CCC–3′. Each translation system contained a different radiolabeled amino acid. (Note: Only 3 tubes are shown here.)	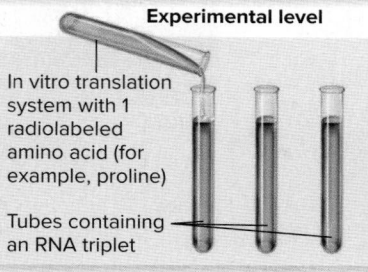 In vitro translation system with 1 radiolabeled amino acid (for example, proline) — Tubes containing an RNA triplet	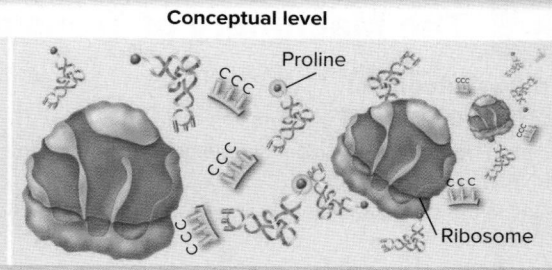 Proline — Ribosome
2 Allow time for the RNA triplet to bind to the ribosome and for the appropriate tRNA to bind to the RNA triplet.		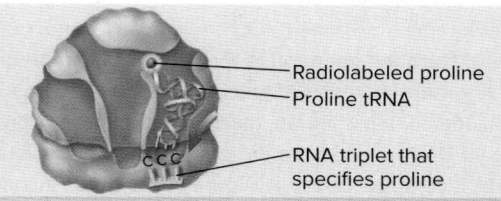 Radiolabeled proline — Proline tRNA — RNA triplet that specifies proline
3 Pour each mixture through a filter that allows the passage of unbound tRNA but does not allow the passage of ribosomes.	 Ribosomes trapped on filter — Filter	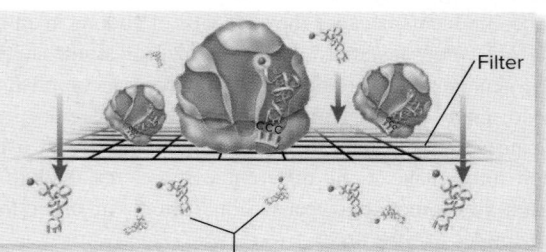 Filter — tRNAs not bound to a ribosome

4 Count radioactivity on the filter.

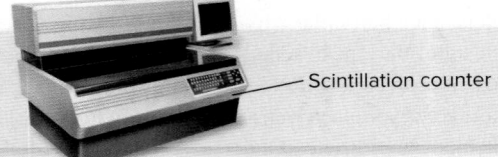

Scintillation counter

5 **THE DATA**

Triplet	Radiolabeled amino acid trapped on the filter	Triplet	Radiolabeled amino acid trapped on the filter
5′ – AAA – 3′	Lysine	5′ – GAC – 3′	Aspartic acid
5′ – ACA – 3′	Threonine	5′ – GCC – 3′	Alanine
5′ – ACC – 3′	Threonine	5′ – GGU – 3′	Glycine
5′ – AGA – 3′	Arginine	5′ – GGC – 3′	Glycine
5′ – AUA – 3′	Isoleucine	5′ – GUU – 3′	Valine
5′ – AUU – 3′	Isoleucine	5′ – UAU – 3′	Tyrosine
5′ – CCC – 3′	Proline	5′ – UGU – 3′	Cysteine
5′ – CGC – 3′	Arginine	5′ – UUG – 3′	Leucine
5′ – GAA – 3′	Glutamic acid		

6 **CONCLUSION** This method enabled the researchers to identify many of the codons of the genetic code.

7 **SOURCE** Leder, P., and Nirenberg, M. W. 1964. RNA Codewords and Protein Synthesis, III. On the nucleotide sequence of a cysteine and a leucine RNA codeword. *Proceedings of the National Academy of Sciences* 52: 1521–1529.

12.5   The Machinery of Translation

Learning Outcomes:

1. Describe the structure and function of tRNA.
2. Explain how aminoacyl-tRNA synthetases attach amino acids to tRNAs.
3. Outline the structural features of bacterial and eukaryotic ribosomes.
4. **CoreSKILL »** Analyze how ribosomal RNA (rRNA) is used to evaluate evolutionary relationships among different species.

Let's now turn our attention to the components in living cells that are needed to translate mRNAs into polypeptides. Earlier in this chapter, we considered transcription, the first step in gene expression. To transcribe an RNA molecule, a pre-existing DNA template strand is used to make a complementary RNA strand. A single enzyme, RNA polymerase, catalyzes this reaction. By comparison, translation requires more components because the sequence of codons in an mRNA molecule must be translated into a sequence of amino acids according to the genetic code. A single protein cannot accomplish such a task. Instead, many different proteins and RNA molecules interact in an intricate series of steps to achieve the synthesis of a polypeptide. A cell must make many different components, including mRNAs, tRNAs, ribosomes, and translation factors, in order to synthesize polypeptides (**Table 12.2**).

Table 12.2	Components of the Translation Machinery
Component	**Function**
mRNA	Contains the information for the amino acid sequence of a polypeptide according to the genetic code.
tRNA	A molecule with two functional sites: one site, termed the anticodon, binds to a codon in mRNA, and a second site is where an appropriate amino acid is attached.
Ribosome	Composed of many proteins and rRNA molecules, the ribosome provides a location where mRNA and tRNA molecules can properly interact with each other. The ribosome catalyzes the formation of covalent bonds between adjacent amino acids to make a polypeptide.
Translation factors	Proteins needed for the three stages of translation. Initiation factors are required for the assembly of mRNA, the first tRNA, and ribosomal subunits. Elongation factors are needed to synthesize the polypeptide. Release factors are needed to recognize the stop codon and disassemble the translation machinery. Several translation factors use GTP as an energy source to carry out their functions.

Though the estimates vary from cell to cell and from species to species, most cells use a substantial amount of their energy to translate mRNA into polypeptides. In *E. coli*, for example, approximately 90%

of the cellular energy is used for this process. This value underscores the complexity and importance of translation in living organisms. In this section, we will focus on the components of the translation machinery. The last section of the chapter will describe the stages of translation as they occur in living cells.

Transfer RNAs Share Common Structural Features

To understand how tRNAs function as carriers of the correct amino acids during translation, researchers have examined their structural characteristics. The tRNAs of bacteria, archaea, and eukaryotes share common features. As originally proposed in 1965 by American biochemist Robert Holley, the two-dimensional structure of a tRNA resembles a cloverleaf. The structure has three stem-loops and a fourth stem with a 3′ single-stranded region (**Figure 12.14a**). The stem in a stem-loop is a region where the RNA is double-stranded due to complementary base pairing via hydrogen bonding, whereas the loop is a region without base pairing. The anticodon is located in the loop of the middle stem-loop region. The 3′ single-stranded region is the amino acid attachment site. The three-dimensional structure of tRNA molecules involves additional folding of the secondary structure (**Figure 12.14b**).

The cells of every organism make many different tRNA molecules, each encoded by a different gene. A tRNA is named according to the amino acid it carries. For example, tRNA^Ser carries a serine. Because the genetic code contains six different serine codons, as shown in Table 12.1, a cell produces more than one type of tRNA^Ser.

Aminoacyl-tRNA Synthetases Charge tRNAs by Attaching an Appropriate Amino Acid

To perform its role during translation, a tRNA must have the appropriate amino acid attached to its 3′ end. The enzymes that catalyze the attachment of amino acids to tRNA molecules are known as **aminoacyl-tRNA synthetases**. Cells make 20 distinct types of aminoacyl-tRNA synthetase enzymes, with each type recognizing just one of the 20 different amino acids. Each aminoacyl-tRNA synthetase is named for the specific amino acid it attaches to tRNA. For example, alanyl-tRNA synthetase recognizes alanine and attaches this amino acid to all tRNAs with alanine anticodons.

Aminoacyl-tRNA synthetases catalyze chemical reactions involving an amino acid, a tRNA molecule, and ATP (**Figure 12.15**).

1. First, a specific amino acid and ATP bind to the enzyme.
2. Next, the amino acid is activated by the covalent attachment of adenosine monophosphate (AMP), and pyrophosphate is released.
3. In a third step, the activated amino acid is covalently attached to the 3′ end of a tRNA molecule, and AMP is released.
4. Finally, the tRNA with its attached amino acid, called a **charged tRNA**, or an **aminoacyl tRNA**, is released from the enzyme.

The ability of each aminoacyl-tRNA synthetase to recognize an appropriate tRNA has been called the second genetic code. A precise recognition process is necessary to maintain the fidelity of genetic information. If the wrong amino acid was attached to a tRNA, the amino acid sequence of the translated polypeptide would be incorrect. However, aminoacyl-tRNA synthetases are amazingly accurate enzymes. The wrong amino acid is attached to a tRNA less than

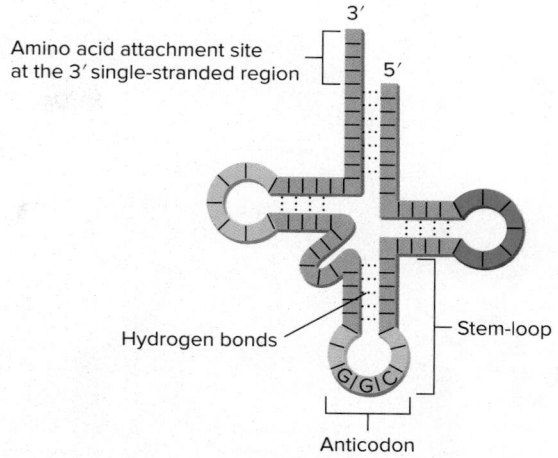

(a) Two-dimensional structure of tRNA

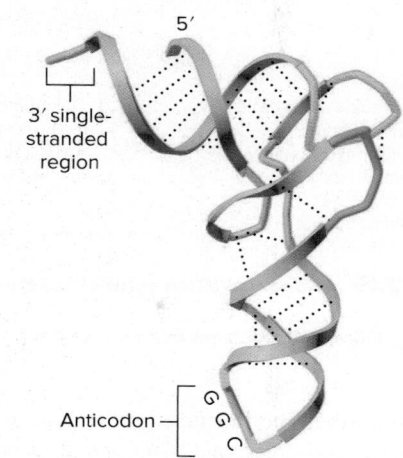

(b) Three-dimensional structure of tRNA

Figure 12.14 Structure of tRNA. (a) The two-dimensional or secondary structure of tRNA resembles a cloverleaf, with the anticodon in the loop of the middle stem-loop structure. The 3′ single-stranded region is where an amino acid can attach. **(b)** The actual three-dimensional structure folds in on itself.

 Core Concept: Structure and Function The structure of tRNA has two functional sites: a 3′ single-stranded region where an amino acid is attached and an anticodon that binds to a codon on mRNA.

once in 100,000 times! The anticodon region of the tRNA is usually important for recognition by the correct aminoacyl-tRNA synthetase. In addition, the base sequences in other regions may facilitate binding to an aminoacyl-tRNA synthetase.

Ribosomes Are Composed of rRNA and Proteins

Let's now turn our attention to the **ribosome**, the site where translation takes place. The ribosome is often described as a molecular machine. Bacterial cells have one type of ribosome, which translates all mRNAs in the cytoplasm. Because eukaryotic cells are compartmentalized into cellular organelles, biochemically distinct ribosomes are found in different cellular compartments. The most abundant type

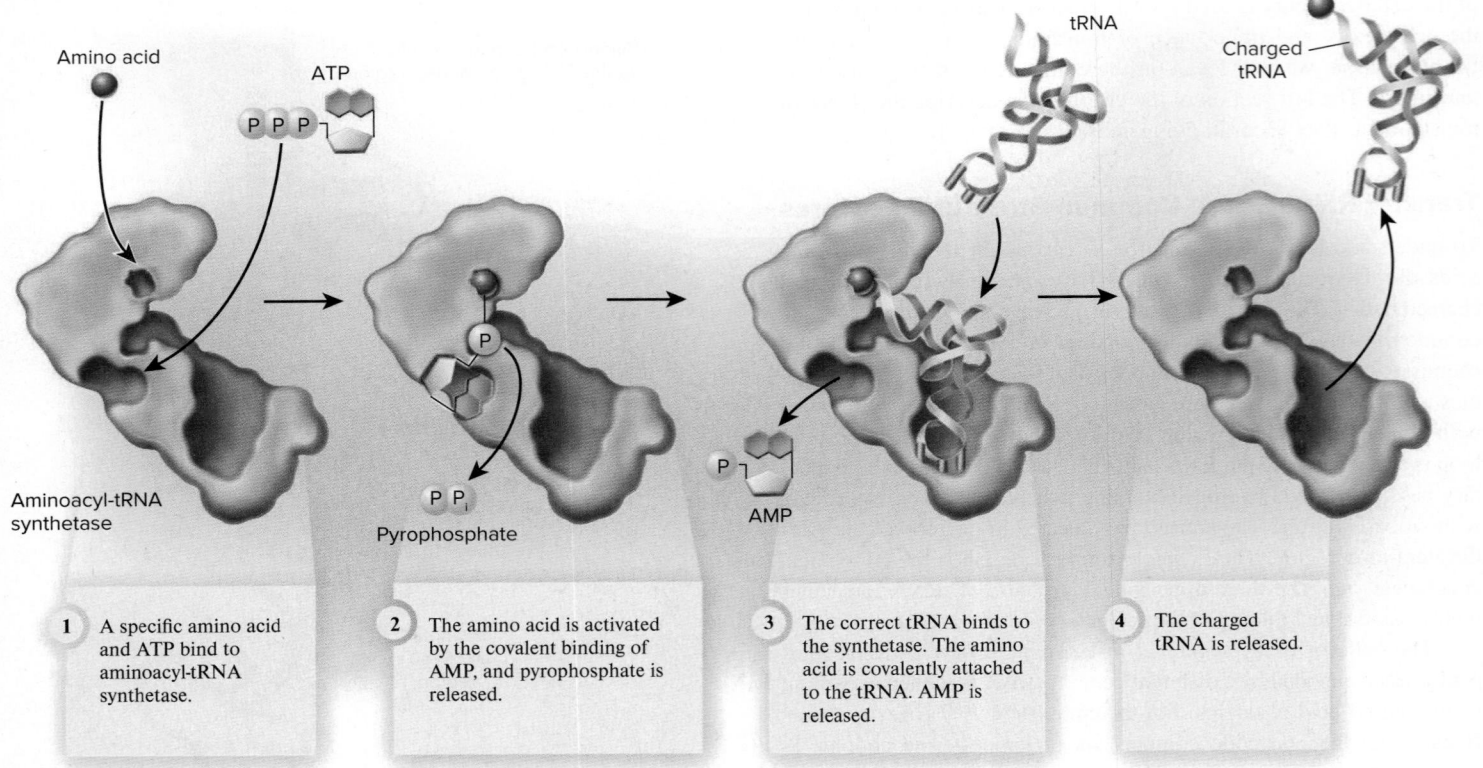

Figure 12.15 **Aminoacyl-tRNA synthetase charging a tRNA.**

Core Skill: Connections Look back at Figure 6.3, which describes the hydrolysis of ATP. Why is ATP needed to charge a tRNA?

of eukaryotic ribosome functions in the cytosol. In addition, mitochondria have ribosomes, and plant and algal cells have ribosomes in their chloroplasts. Unless otherwise noted, the term eukaryotic ribosome refers to ribosomes in the cytosol, not to those found in organelles.

A ribosome is a large complex composed of structures called the large and small subunits. The term subunit is perhaps misleading, because each ribosomal subunit is itself assembled from many different proteins and one or more RNA molecules. In the bacterium *E. coli*, the small ribosomal subunit is called 30S, and the large subunit is 50S (**Table 12.3**). The designations 30S and 50S refer to the rate at which these subunits sediment when subjected to a centrifugal force. This rate is described as a sedimentation coefficient in Svedberg units (S) in honor of Swedish chemist Theodor Svedberg, who invented the ultracentrifuge. The 30S subunit is formed from the assembly of 21 different ribosomal proteins and one 16S rRNA molecule. The 50S subunit contains 34 different proteins and two different rRNA molecules, called 5S and 23S. Together, the 30S and 50S subunits form a 70S ribosome. (Svedberg units don't add up linearly, because the sedimentation coefficient is a function of both size and shape.) In bacteria, ribosomal proteins and rRNA molecules are synthesized in the cytoplasm, and the ribosomal subunits are assembled there as well.

Eukaryotic ribosomes consist of subunits that are slightly larger than their bacterial counterparts (Table 12.3). In eukaryotes, 40S and 60S subunits combine to form an 80S ribosome. The 40S subunit is composed of 33 proteins and an 18S rRNA, and the 60S subunit has

Table 12.3	Composition of Bacterial and Eukaryotic Ribosomes		
	Small subunit	Large subunit	Assembled ribosome
Bacterial			
Sedimentation coefficient	30S	50S	70S
Number of proteins	21	34	55
rRNA	16S rRNA	5S rRNA, 23S rRNA	16S rRNA, 5S rRNA, 23S rRNA
Eukaryotic			
Sedimentation coefficient	40S	60S	80S
Number of proteins	33	49	82
rRNA	18S rRNA	5S rRNA, 5.8S rRNA, 28S rRNA	18S rRNA, 5S rRNA, 5.8S rRNA, 28S rRNA

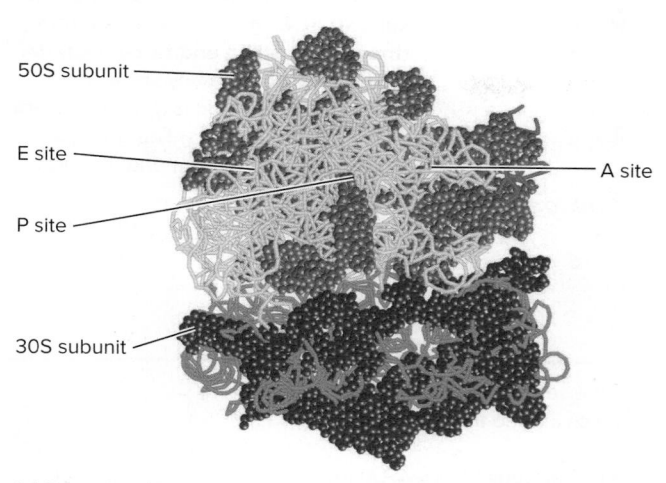

(a) Bacterial ribosome model based on X-ray diffraction studies

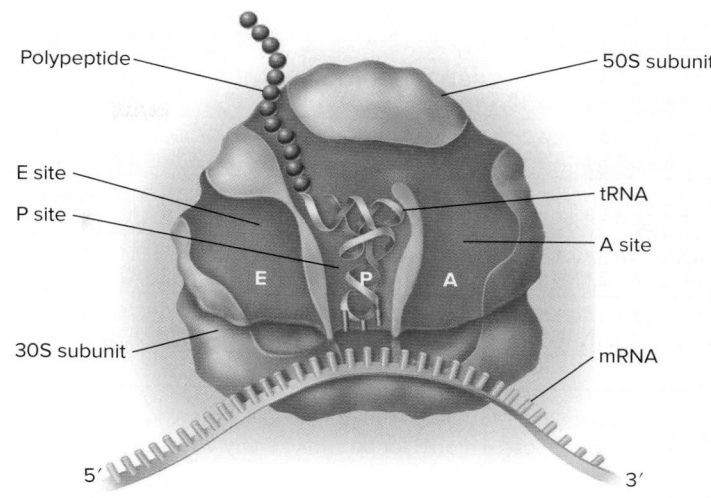

(b) Schematic model for ribosome structure

Figure 12.16 **Ribosome structure.** **(a)** A model for the structure of a bacterial ribosome based on X-ray diffraction studies, showing the large and small subunits and the major binding sites. The rRNA is shown in gray (large subunit) and turquoise (small subunit), whereas the ribosomal proteins are magenta (large subunit) and dark blue (small subunit). **(b)** A schematic model emphasizing functional sites in the ribosome, and showing bound mRNA and tRNA with an attached polypeptide.

 Core Concept: Structure and Function The structure of a ribosome has three discrete sites, called the E, P, and A sites, which carry out different functions in polypeptide synthesis, described in Section 12.6.

49 proteins and 5S, 5.8S, and 28S rRNAs. The synthesis of eukaryotic rRNA occurs in the nucleolus, a droplet organelle in the nucleus that is specialized for that purpose. The ribosomal proteins are made in the cytosol and imported into the nucleus. The rRNAs and ribosomal proteins are then assembled within the nucleolus to make the 40S and 60S subunits. The 40S and 60S subunits are exported into the cytosol, where they associate to form an 80S ribosome during translation.

Components of Ribosomal Subunits Form Functional Sites for Translation

To understand the structure and function of the ribosome at the molecular level, researchers have determined the locations and functional roles of individual ribosomal proteins and rRNAs. In recent years, a few research groups have succeeded in purifying ribosomes and causing them to crystallize in a test tube. When researchers use X-ray diffraction to study the crystallized ribosomes, they gain detailed information about ribosome structure. **Figure 12.16a** shows a model of a bacterial ribosome.

During bacterial translation, the mRNA lies on the surface of the 30S subunit, within a space between the 30S and 50S subunits (**Figure 12.16b**). As a polypeptide is synthesized, it exits through a hole within the 50S subunit. Ribosomes contain discrete sites where tRNAs bind and the polypeptide is synthesized. In 1964, James Watson proposed a two-site model for tRNA binding to the ribosome. These sites are known as the **peptidyl site (P site)** and **aminoacyl site (A site)**. In 1981, German geneticists Knud Nierhaus and Hans-Jörg Rheinberger expanded this to a three-site model (Figure 12.16b). The third site is known as the exit site (E site). In Section 12.6, we will examine the roles of these sites in the synthesis of a polypeptide.

 **Core Concept: Evolution**

Comparisons of Small Subunit rRNAs Among Different Species Provide a Basis for Establishing Evolutionary Relationships

Translation is a fundamental process that is vital for the existence of all living species. Research indicates that the components needed for translation arose very early in the evolution of life on our planet in ancestors that gave rise to all known living species. For this reason, all organisms have translational components that are evolutionarily related to each other. For example, the rRNA found in the small subunit of ribosomes is similar in all forms of life, though it is slightly larger in eukaryotic species (18S) than in bacterial species (16S). The gene for the small subunit rRNA (SSU rRNA) is found in the genomes of all organisms.

How is this observation useful? One way that geneticists explore evolutionary relationships is to compare the sequences of evolutionarily related genes. At the molecular level, gene evolution involves changes in DNA sequences. After two different species have diverged from each other during evolution, the genes of each species can accumulate changes, or mutations, that alter the sequences of those genes. After many generations, evolutionarily related species contain genes that are similar but not identical to each other, because each species accumulates different mutations. In general, if a very long time has elapsed since two species diverged evolutionarily, their genes tend to be quite different. In contrast, if two species diverged relatively recently on an evolutionary time scale, their genes tend to be more similar.

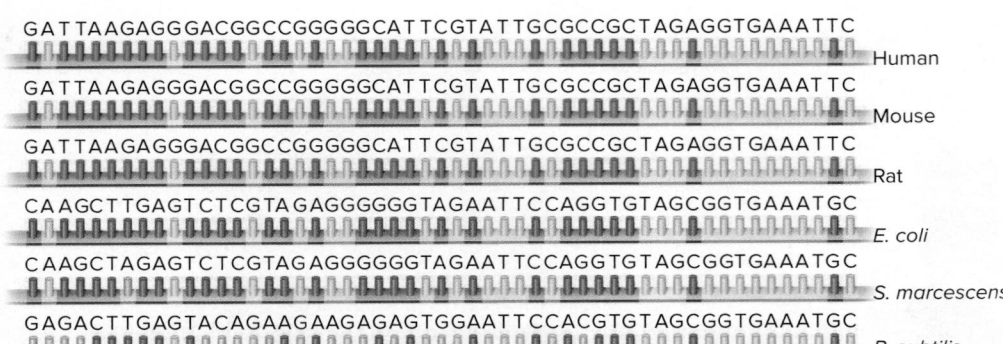

GATTAAGAGGGACGGCCGGGGGGCATTCGTATTGCGCCGCTAGAGGTGAAATTC Human

GATTAAGAGGGACGGCCGGGGGGCATTCGTATTGCGCCGCTAGAGGTGAAATTC Mouse

GATTAAGAGGGACGGCCGGGGGGCATTCGTATTGCGCCGCTAGAGGTGAAATTC Rat

CAAGCTTGAGTCTCGTAGAGGGGGGTAGAATTCCAGGTGTAGCGGTGAAATGC E. coli

CAAGCTAGAGTCTCGTAGAGGGGGGTAGAATTCCAGGTGTAGCGGTGAAATGC S. marcescens

GAGACTTGAGTACAGAAGAAGAGAGTGGAATTCCACGTGTAGCGGTGAAATGC B. subtilis

Figure 12.17 Comparison of small subunit rRNA gene sequences from three mammalian and three bacterial species. Note the many similarities (yellow) and differences (green and red) among the sequences. The gray color indicates differences among the three bacterial species.

 Core Skill: Modeling The goal of this modeling challenge is to analyze the sequences in Figure 12.17 and propose a model for an evolutionary tree that describes the relationships among these six species.

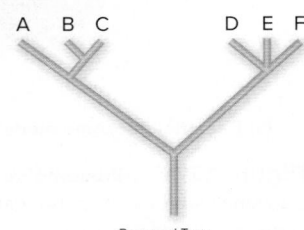
Proposed Tree

Modeling Challenge: As discussed in Chapter 25, phylogenetic trees are models that depict the evolutionary relationships among different species. Those species that are more closely related are closer together on a tree. The model to the right shows a tree with the tips of the branches labeled A through E. Relying only on the sequences shown in Figure 12.17, replace the 6 letters on this tree with the names of the six species. Note: More than one model is possible.

Figure 12.17 compares a portion of the sequence of the SSU rRNA gene from three mammalian and three bacterial species. The colors highlight different types of comparisons. The bases shaded in yellow are identical in five or six species. Sequences of bases that are identical or very similar in different species are said to be **evolutionarily conserved**. Presumably, these sequences were found in the primordial gene that gave rise to modern species. Perhaps because these sequences may have some critical function, they have not changed over evolutionary time. Those sequences shaded in green are identical in all three mammals, but differ from the sequences in one or more bacterial species. Actually, if you scan the mammalian species, you may notice that all three have identical sequences in this region. The sequences shaded in red are identical or very similar in the bacterial species, but differ from the mammalian SSU rRNA genes. The sequences from *Escherichia coli* and *Serratia marcescens* are more similar to each other than the sequence from *Bacillus subtilis* is to either of them. This observation suggests that *E. coli* and *S. marcescens* are more closely related evolutionarily than either of them is to *B. subtilis*.

12.6 The Stages of Translation

Learning Outcomes:

1. Describe the three stages of translation.
2. Summarize the similarities and differences between translation in bacteria and in eukaryotes.
3. Explain how some antibiotics inhibit the growth of bacteria by interfering with translation.

Like transcription, the process of translation occurs in three stages called initiation, elongation, and termination. **Figure 12.18** provides an overview of the process. During initiation, an mRNA, the first tRNA, and the ribosomal subunits assemble into a complex. Next, in the elongation stage, the ribosome moves in the 5′ to 3′ direction from the start codon in the mRNA toward the stop codon, synthesizing a polypeptide according to the sequence of codons in the mRNA. Finally, the process is terminated when the ribosome reaches a stop codon and the complex disassembles, releasing the completed polypeptide. In this section, we will examine the steps in this process as they occur in living cells.

Translation Is Initiated with the Assembly of mRNA, tRNA, and the Ribosomal Subunits

During **initiation**, a complex is formed between an mRNA molecule, the first tRNA, and the ribosomal subunits. In all species, the assembly of this complex requires the help of proteins called **initiation factors** that facilitate the interactions between these components (see Table 12.2). The assembly also requires an input of energy. Guanosine triphosphate (GTP) is hydrolyzed by certain initiation factors to provide the necessary energy.

When they are not involved in translation, the small and large ribosomal subunits exist separately.

1. To begin assembly of the complex in bacteria, mRNA binds to the small ribosomal subunit (**Figure 12.19**). The binding of mRNA to this subunit is facilitated by a short ribosomal-binding site near the 5′ end of the mRNA. The ribosomal binding site is a sequence of bases that is complementary to a portion of the 16S rRNA within the small ribosomal subunit. The mRNA becomes bound to the ribosome because the ribosomal-binding site and rRNA hydrogen-bond to each other by base-pairing. The start codon is usually just a few nucleotides downstream (that is, toward the 3′ end) from the ribosomal-binding site.

2. A specific tRNA, which functions as the initiator tRNA, recognizes the start codon in mRNA (AUG) and binds to it. In eukaryotes, this tRNA carries a methionine, whereas in bacteria it carries a methionine that has been modified by the attachment of a formyl group.

Figure 12.18 **An overview of the stages of translation.**

Core Concept: Energy and Matter The process of translation uses a sizable amount of a cell's energy and results in the synthesis of a cell's proteins.

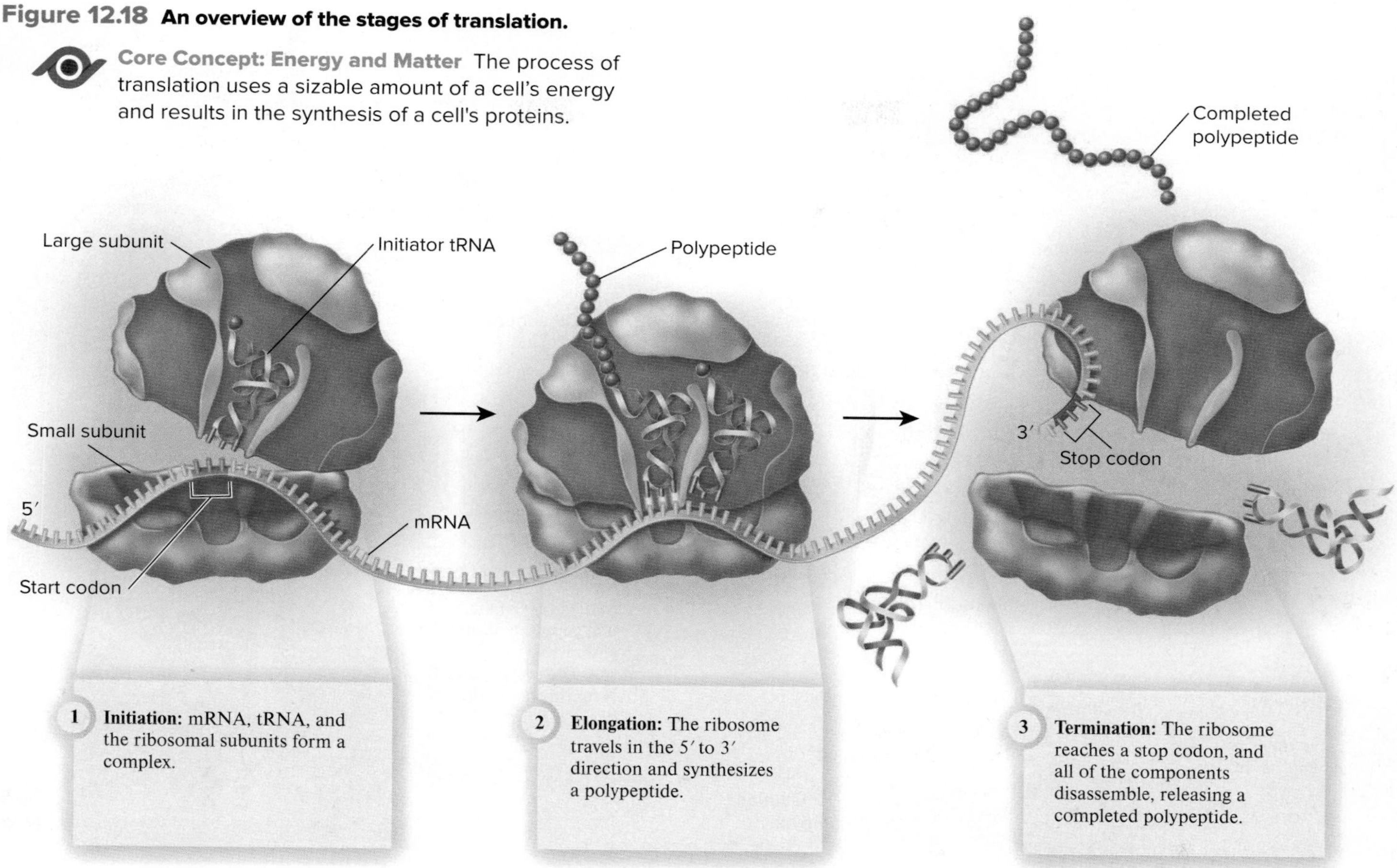

1. **Initiation:** mRNA, tRNA, and the ribosomal subunits form a complex.

2. **Elongation:** The ribosome travels in the 5′ to 3′ direction and synthesizes a polypeptide.

3. **Termination:** The ribosome reaches a stop codon, and all of the components disassemble, releasing a completed polypeptide.

3. To complete the initiation stage, the large ribosomal subunit associates with the small subunit. At the end of this stage, the initiator tRNA is located in the P site of the ribosome.

In eukaryotic species, the initiation phase of translation differs in two ways from the process in bacteria.

- First, instead of an RNA sequence that functions as a ribosomal-binding site, eukaryotic mRNAs have a 7-methylguanosine cap (5′ cap) at their 5′ end. This 5′ cap is recognized by cap-binding proteins that promote the binding of the mRNA to the small ribosomal subunit.

- Also, in bacteria, the start codon is very close to a ribosomal-binding site, but the location of start codons in eukaryotes is more variable.

In 1978, American biochemist Marilyn Kozak proposed that the small ribosomal subunit identifies a start codon by beginning at the 5′ end and then scanning along the mRNA in the 3′ direction in search of an AUG sequence. In many, but not all, cases, the first AUG codon is used as a start codon. By analyzing the sequences of many eukaryotic mRNAs, Kozak and her colleagues discovered that the sequence around an AUG codon is important for it to be recognized as a start codon. The sequence for optimal start codon recognition is shown here:

Upstream of start codon	Start codon	Downstream coding region

. . . G C C (A or G) C C **A U G** G . . . .

Aside from the AUG codon itself, a guanine just past the start codon and the sequence of six bases directly upstream from the start codon are important for start codon selection. If the first AUG codon is within a site that deviates markedly from this optimal sequence, the small subunit may skip this codon and instead use another AUG codon farther downstream. Once the small subunit selects a start codon, an initiator tRNA binds to the start codon, and then the large ribosomal subunit associates with the small subunit to complete the assembly process.

Polypeptide Synthesis Occurs During the Elongation Stage

As its name suggests, the stage of translation called **elongation** involves the covalent bonding of amino acids to each other, one at a time, to produce a polypeptide. Even though this process involves several different components, translation occurs at a remarkable rate. Under normal cellular conditions, the translation machinery can elongate a polypeptide at a rate of 15 to 18 amino acids per second in bacteria and 6 amino acids per second in eukaryotes!

tRNA Entry To elongate a polypeptide by one amino acid, a tRNA brings a new amino acid to the ribosome, where it is attached to the end of a growing polypeptide. In step 1 of **Figure 12.20**, translation has already proceeded to a point where a short polypeptide is attached to the tRNA located in the P site of the ribosome. This is called peptidyl tRNA. In the first step of elongation, a charged tRNA

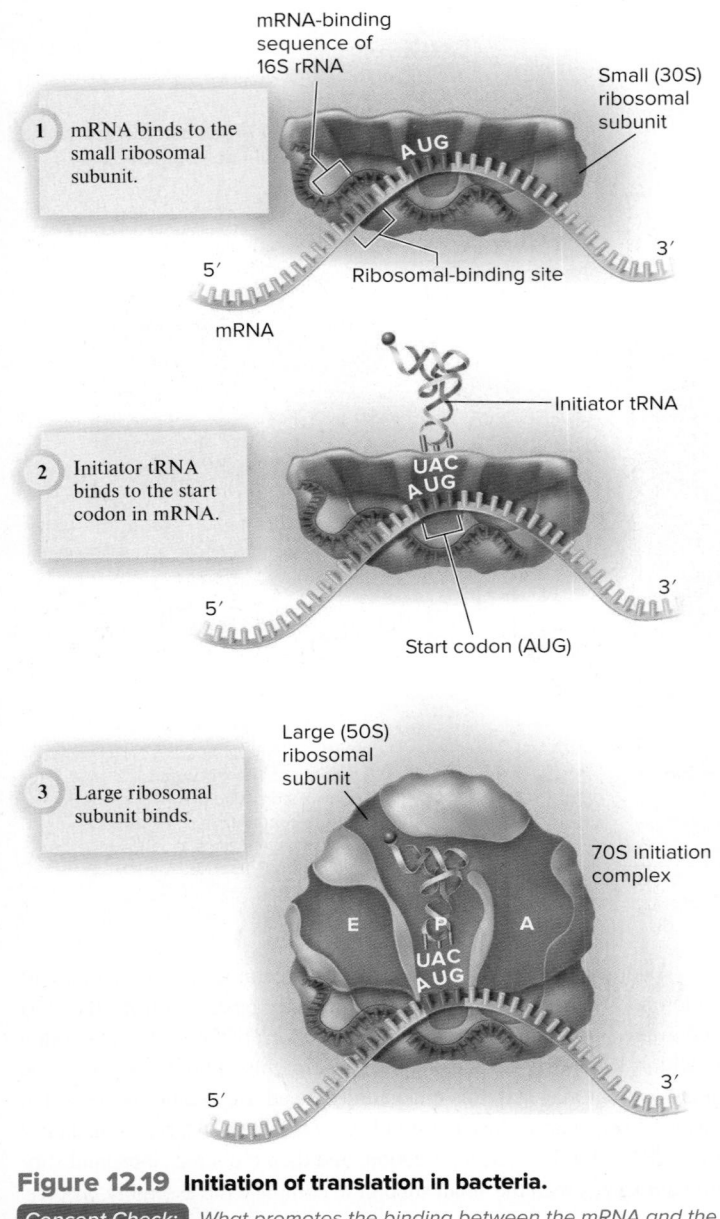

Figure 12.19 **Initiation of translation in bacteria.**

`Concept Check:` *What promotes the binding between the mRNA and the small ribosomal subunit?*

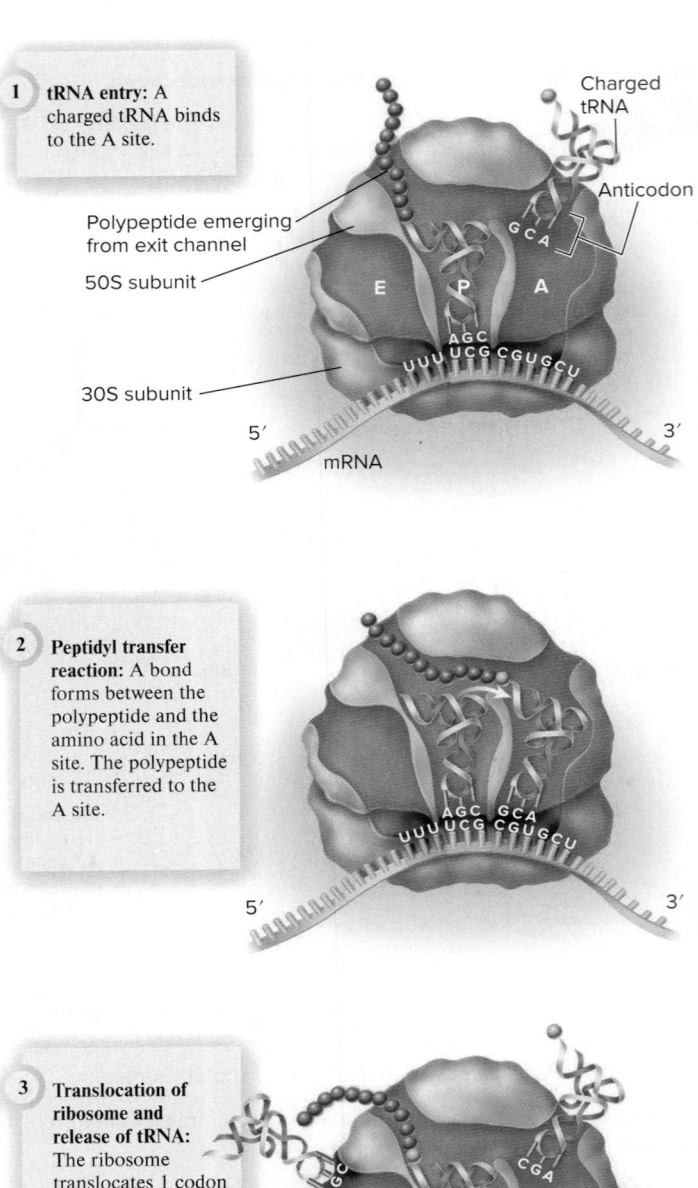

Figure 12.20 **Elongation stage of translation in bacteria.** In this drawing, the amino acids that were already part of the polypeptide are shown in blue. The amino acids attached to incoming tRNAs are shown in yellow.

carrying a single amino acid binds to the A site. This binding occurs because the anticodon in the tRNA is complementary to the codon in the mRNA. The hydrolysis of GTP by proteins that function as **elongation factors** provides the energy for the binding of the tRNA to the A site (see Table 12.2). At this step in elongation, a peptidyl tRNA is in the P site and a charged tRNA (an aminoacyl tRNA) is in the A site. This is how the P and A sites came to be named.

Peptidyl Transfer Reaction In the second step, a peptide bond is formed between the amino acid at the A site and the growing polypeptide, thereby lengthening the polypeptide by one amino acid. As this occurs, the polypeptide is removed from the tRNA in the P site and transferred to the amino acid at the A site, an event termed a **peptidyl transfer reaction**. This reaction is catalyzed by a region of the 50S subunit known as the peptidyltransferase center, which is composed of several proteins and rRNA. In 2000, American biochemist Thomas Steitz,

American biophysicist Peter Moore, and their colleagues proposed that the rRNA is responsible for catalyzing the peptide bond formation between adjacent amino acids. It is now accepted that the ribosome is a ribozyme.

Translocation of the Ribosome and Release of tRNA After the peptidyl transfer reaction is complete, the third step involves the movement or translocation of the ribosome toward the 3′ end of the mRNA by exactly one codon. This shifts the tRNAs in the P and A

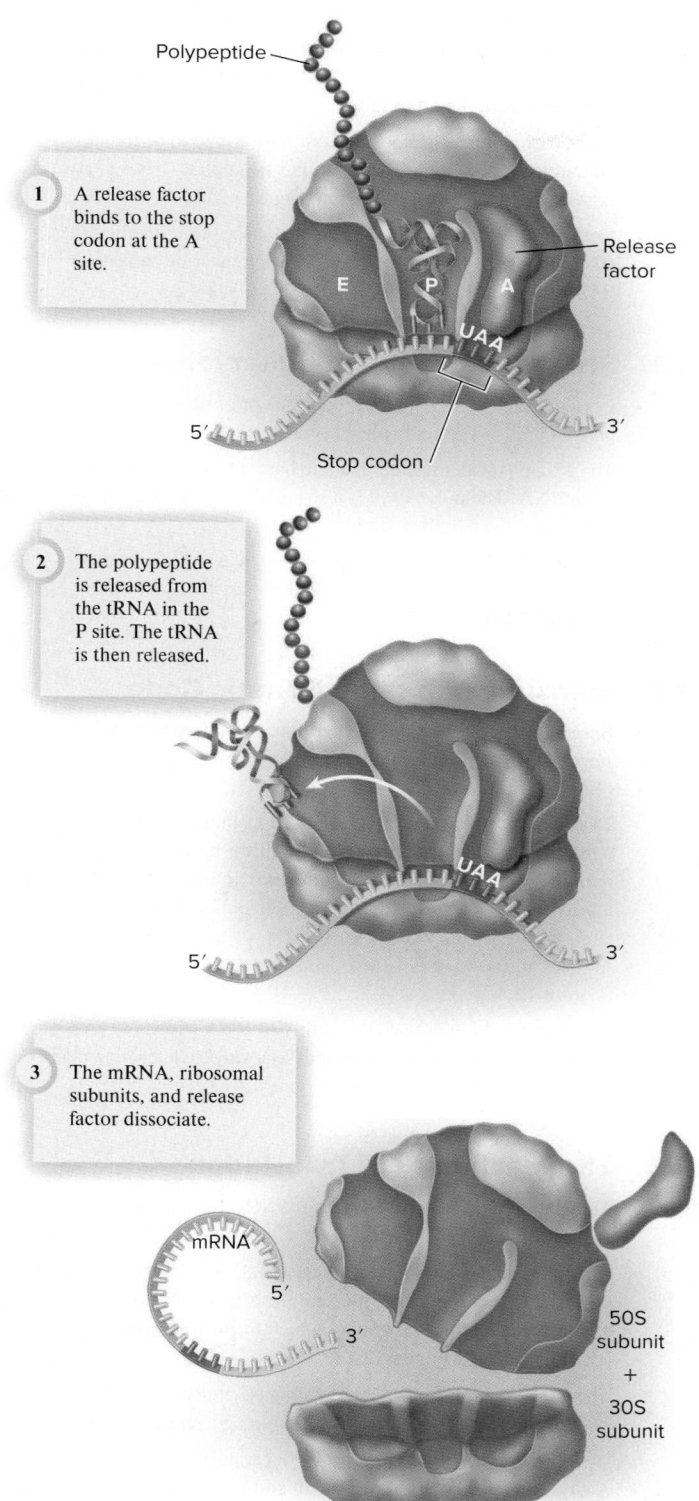

Polypeptide

1 A release factor binds to the stop codon at the A site.

Release factor

E   P   A

UAA

Stop codon

5′   3′

2 The polypeptide is released from the tRNA in the P site. The tRNA is then released.

UAA

5′   3′

3 The mRNA, ribosomal subunits, and release factor dissociate.

mRNA

5′

3′

50S subunit
+
30S subunit

Figure 12.21   **Termination of translation in bacteria.**

sites to the E and P sites, respectively. The uncharged tRNA exits the E site. Notice that the next codon in the mRNA (GCU in Figure 12.20) is now exposed at the unoccupied A site. At this point, a charged tRNA can enter the A site, and the same series of steps will add the next amino acid to the polypeptide.

Figure 12.20 shows a single ribosome in the act of translating an mRNA. In living cells, it is common for multiple ribosomes to be gliding along the same mRNA and synthesizing polypeptides. The complex of a single mRNA and multiple ribosomes is called a **polysome** (see the chapter opening micrograph).

Termination Occurs When a Stop Codon Is Reached in the mRNA

Elongation continues until a stop codon moves into the A site of a ribosome. The three stop codons, UAA, UAG, and UGA, are recognized by a protein known as a **release factor**. The three-dimensional structure of a release factor protein mimics the structure of tRNAs, which allows it to fit into the A site.

Figure 12.21 illustrates the **termination** of translation.

1. In step 1 of this figure, a release factor binds to the stop codon at the A site. The completed polypeptide is attached to a tRNA in the P site.

2. In step 2, the bond between the polypeptide and the tRNA is hydrolyzed, causing the polypeptide and tRNA to be released from the ribosome.

3. In step 3, the mRNA, ribosomal subunits, and release factor dissociate.

The termination stage of translation is similar in bacteria and eukaryotes except that bacteria have two different termination factors that recognize stop codons (RF1 and RF2), whereas eukaryotes have only one (eRF). **Table 12.4** compares some of the key differences between bacterial and eukaryotic translation.

Antibiotics That Inhibit Bacterial Translation Are Used to Treat Bacterial Infections

Many diseases that affect humans and domesticated animals are caused by pathogenic bacteria. An **antibiotic** is any substance produced by a

Table 12.4	Comparison of Bacterial and Eukaryotic Translation	
	Bacterial	**Eukaryotic**
Cellular location	Cytoplasm	Cytosol*
Ribosome composition	70S ribosomes:	80S ribosomes:
	30S subunit: 21 proteins + 1 rRNA	40S subunit: 33 proteins + 1 rRNA
	50S subunit: 34 proteins + 2 rRNAs	60S subunit: 49 proteins + 3 rRNAs
Initiator tRNA	tRNA$^{\text{Formyl-methionine}}$	tRNA^{Methionine}
Initial binding of mRNA	Requires a ribosomal-binding site	Requires a 7-methylguanosine cap
Selection of a start codon	Just downstream from the ribosomal-binding site	According to Kozak's sequences
Termination factors	Two factors: RF1 and RF2	One factor: eRF

*The components for eukaryotic translation described in this table refer to those that are used in the cytosol. Different types of ribosomes are used for translation inside mitochondria and chloroplasts.

Table 12.5	Mechanisms of Inhibition of Bacterial Translation by Selected Antibiotics
Antibiotic	**Description**
Chloramphenicol	Blocks elongation by acting as a competitive inhibitor of the peptidyltransferase complex.
Erythromycin	Binds to the 23S rRNA and blocks elongation by interfering with the translocation step.
Puromycin	Binds to the A site and causes premature release of the polypeptide. This early termination of translation results in polypeptides that are shorter than normal and usually nonfunctional.
Tetracycline	Blocks elongation by inhibiting the binding of aminoacyl tRNAs to the ribosome.
Streptomycin	Interferes with normal pairing between aminoacyl tRNAs and codons. This causes misreading of the code and thereby produces abnormal proteins.

microorganism that inhibits the growth of other microorganisms, such as pathogenic bacteria. Most antibiotics are small organic molecules, with masses of less than 2,000 Da. In some cases, antibiotics exert their effect because they inhibit or interfere with bacterial translation. Because the components of translation differ somewhat between bacteria and eukaryotes, some antibiotics inhibit bacterial translation without affecting eukaryotic translation. Therefore, they can be used to treat bacterial infections in humans, pets, and livestock. **Table 12.5** describes a few of these antibiotics.

Summary of Key Concepts

12.1 Overview of Gene Expression

- Based on his studies of inborn errors of metabolism, Garrod hypothesized that certain genetic diseases are caused by a defect in a gene encoding an enzyme (Figure 12.1).

- Based on their study of the nutritional requirements of a bread mold, Beadle and Tatum proposed the one-gene/one-enzyme hypothesis, in which a single gene controls the synthesis of a single enzyme (Figure 12.2).

- A polypeptide is a unit of structure. A protein, composed of one or more polypeptides, is a unit of function.

- At the molecular level, the central dogma states that most genes are transcribed into mRNA, and then the mRNA is translated into a polypeptide. Eukaryotes modify their RNA transcripts to make them functional (Figure 12.3).

- The molecular expression of genes is an underlying factor that determines an organism's characteristics.

12.2 Transcription

- A site in a gene called a promoter specifies where transcription begins. A terminator specifies where transcription will end (Figure 12.4).

- In bacteria, the initiation of transcription begins when sigma factor binds to RNA polymerase and to a promoter. During elongation, synthesis of an RNA transcript occurs via base pairing

of nucleotides to the template strand of DNA as RNA polymerase slides along the DNA. RNA polymerase and the RNA transcript dissociate from the DNA at the terminator (Figure 12.5).

- The genes along a chromosome are transcribed in different directions using either DNA strand as a template. RNA is always synthesized in a 5′ to 3′ direction (Figure 12.6).

- In eukaryotes, the initiation stage of transcription involves the assembly of RNA polymerase with five transcription factors (Figure 12.7).

12.3 RNA Modification in Eukaryotes

- In eukaryotes, transcription produces a pre-mRNA that is capped, given a poly A tail, and spliced (Figure 12.8).

- The 5′ cap is a methylated guanine base attached at the 5′ end of the mRNA. The poly A tail is a string of adenine nucleotides that is added to the 3′ end (Figure 12.9).

- During RNA splicing, intervening sequences called introns are removed from eukaryotic pre-mRNA by a spliceosome (Figure 12.10).

12.4 Translation and the Genetic Code

- Based on the genetic code, each of the 64 codons specifies a start codon (methionine), other amino acids, or a stop codon (Table 12.1, Figure 12.11).

- The template strand of DNA is used to make mRNA that contains a series of codons. Recognition between mRNA and many tRNA molecules determines the amino acid sequence of a polypeptide. A polypeptide has a directionality in which the first amino acid is at the N-terminus, or amino end, whereas the last amino acid is at the C-terminus, or carboxyl end (Figure 12.12).

- Nirenberg and Leder used the ability of RNA triplets to promote the binding of tRNAs to ribosomes as a way to determine many of the codons of the genetic code (Figure 12.13).

12.5 The Machinery of Translation

- Translation requires mRNA, charged tRNAs, ribosomes, and many translation factors (Table 12.2).

- tRNA molecules have a two-dimensional structure resembling a cloverleaf. Two important sites are the amino acid attachment site at the 3′ end and the anticodon, which forms base pairs with a codon in mRNA (Figure 12.14).

- The enzyme aminoacyl-tRNA synthetase attaches the correct amino acid to a tRNA molecule, producing a charged tRNA (Figure 12.15).

- A ribosome is composed of a small and large subunit, each consisting of rRNA molecules and many proteins. Bacterial and eukaryotic ribosomes differ in their molecular composition (Table 12.3).

- Ribosomes have three sites, termed the A, P, and E sites, which are locations for the binding and release of tRNA molecules (Figure 12.16).

- The gene that encodes the small subunit rRNA (SSU rRNA) has been used to determine evolutionary relationships among different species (Figure 12.17).

12.6 The Stages of Translation

- Translation occurs in three stages called initiation, elongation, and termination (Figure 12.18).

- During the initiation stage of translation, an mRNA assembles with the ribosomal subunits and an initiator tRNA molecule, which carries methionine, the first amino acid (Figure 12.19).

- During elongation, amino acids are added one at a time to a growing polypeptide (Figure 12.20).

- Termination of translation occurs when the binding of a release factor to a stop codon causes the release of the completed polypeptide from the tRNA and the disassembly of the mRNA, ribosomal subunits, and the release factor (Figure 12.21).

- Though translation in bacteria and eukaryotes is strikingly similar, some key differences have been observed (Table 12.4).

- Some antibiotics inhibit bacterial growth by interfering with translation (Table 12.5).

Assess & Discuss

Test Yourself

1. Which of the following best represents the central dogma of gene expression?
   a. During transcription, DNA codes for polypeptides.
   b. During transcription, DNA codes for mRNA, which codes for polypeptides during translation.
   c. During translation, DNA codes for mRNA, which codes for polypeptides during transcription.
   d. none of the above

2. A mutation prevents a gene from being transcribed into an mRNA. The mutation most likely disrupts
   a. the promoter.
   b. the terminator.
   c. the start codon.
   d. the stop codon.
   e. both a and c.

3. The functional product of a protein-encoding gene is
   a. tRNA.
   b. mRNA.
   c. rRNA.
   d. a polypeptide.
   e. a, b, and c.

4. Which of the following is *not* a property of the genetic code?
   a. It specifies the amino acids within a polypeptide.
   b. It is composed of codons, which are a specific sequences of three bases.
   c. It has a start codon, which specifies the starting point for polypeptide synthesis.
   d. It has stop codons, which specify the end of polypeptide synthesis.
   e. It determines the rate of transcription.

5. If a eukaryotic mRNA failed to have a cap attached to its 5′ end, what would the negative consequence(s) be?
   a. The mRNA would not properly exit the nucleus.
   b. The mRNA would not properly bind to a ribosome.
   c. The mRNA would not receive a poly A tail.
   d. The mRNA would not use the correct start codon.
   e. both a and b

6. The small subunit of a ribosome is composed of
   a. a protein.
   b. an rRNA molecule.
   c. many proteins.
   d. many rRNA molecules.
   e. many proteins and one rRNA molecule.

7. The part of a tRNA that is complementary to a codon in an mRNA is the
   a. acceptor stem.
   b. codon.
   c. peptidyl site.
   d. anticodon.
   e. adaptor loop.

8. During the initiation of translation, the first codon, _____, enters the _____ and associates with the initiator tRNA.
   a. UAG, A site
   b. AUG, A site
   c. UAG, P site
   d. AUG, P site
   e. AUG, E site

9. The movement of the polypeptide from the tRNA in the P site to the tRNA in the A site is referred to as
   a. peptide bonding.
   b. aminoacyl binding.
   c. translation.
   d. the peptidyl transfer reaction.
   e. initiation.

10. During which stage of translation does the synthesis of a polypeptide occur?
    a. initiation
    b. elongation
    c. termination
    d. splicing

Conceptual Questions

1. Briefly explain how studying the pathway that leads to arginine synthesis allowed Beadle and Tatum to conclude that one gene sometimes encodes one enzyme.

2. What is the function of an aminoacyl-tRNA synthetase?

3. **Core Concept: Information** The genetic material provides a blueprint for producing the characteristics of living organisms. Explain how the information within the blueprint is accessed at the molecular level.

Collaborative Questions

1. Why do you think some complexes, such as spliceosomes and ribosomes, have both protein and RNA components?

2. Discuss and make a list of the similarities and differences in the events that occur during the initiation, elongation, and termination stages of transcription and translation.

Gene Expression at the Molecular Level II: Non-coding RNAs

13

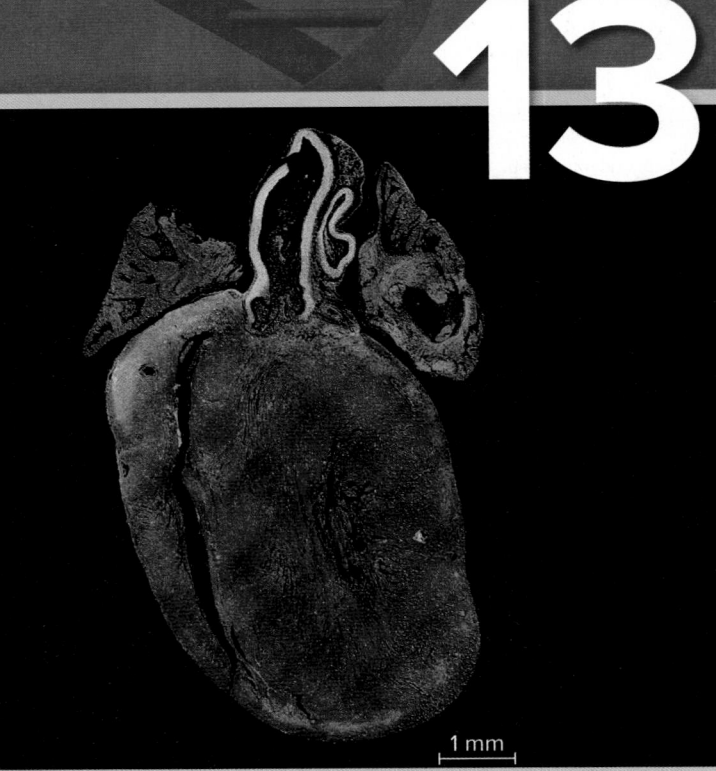

1 mm

Non-coding RNAs and heart repair. The muscles of the mammalian heart have poor regenerating abilities. Researchers have identified several non-coding RNAs that stimulate cardiac muscle regeneration. This heart is from a mouse that was treated with such a non-coding RNA, and it showed a significant increase in proliferating cells. This discovery may lead to new therapies to help heart attack victims regenerate new cardiac muscle. ©Mauro Giacca, Ana Eulalio, Miguel Mano

People with a rare genetic disorder called cartilage-hair hypoplasia (CHH) have short stature, underdeveloped hair, and short limbs with malformations in the cartilage. In addition, they have a higher predisposition to develop lymphomas and other cancers, and they may lack a normal immune response. Though CHH was first identified by American geneticist Victor McKusick in 1965, the underlying genetic cause remained a mystery for 36 years. In 2001, the function of a single mutant gene was linked to this disease. The gene specifies an RNA molecule that does not encode a protein. Rather, the RNA made from this gene is the RNA component of RNase MRP, which is an RNA-protein complex involved in the modification of some ribosomal and mitochondrial RNAs. This was the first case in which geneticists determined that a human genetic disease was due to a mutation in a nuclear gene that is not a protein-encoding

gene. By comparison, the first human genetic disease involving a protein-encoding gene was discovered nearly a century earlier! In 1909, Archibald Garrod proposed that patients with a disease called alkaptonuria, which is characterized by bluish-black discoloration of the cartilage and skin, is due to a mutation in a gene that encodes the protein homogentisic acid oxidase.

Why such a big time gap in our understanding of protein-encoding genes versus other types of genes? It's all about tools. The experimental tools to study the structure and function of proteins and to identify protein-encoding genes have been around for a long time. In contrast, the tools to study RNA structure and function and to identify genes that do not specify proteins are much more recent and are under rapid development. We are witnessing a revolution in molecular biology that is uncovering an unprecedented number of functions for RNA molecules.

In Chapter 12, we focused our attention on gene expression at the molecular level. The emphasis was on protein-encoding genes, which are transcribed into mRNA. During translation, the information within mRNAs is used to make polypeptides, which then assemble into functional proteins. The human genome has about 22,000 protein-encoding genes. In contrast, other genes are transcribed into **non-coding RNAs (ncRNAs),** which are RNA molecules that do not encode polypeptides. As this chapter will reveal, ncRNAs perform a very diverse set of functions. In humans, the number of genes that specify ncRNAs is still difficult to measure and a matter of controversy. Estimates range from several thousand to tens of thousands.

In the past, educators have tended to emphasize proteins and DNA in the teaching of biology at the molecular level. For example, in the cell unit (Chapters 4 through 10), we saw many examples of how proteins affect cell structure and function, and the genetics unit (Chapters 11 through 21) largely focuses on the structure and function of DNA. Although DNA, RNA, and proteins are key molecular players in living cells, a historical bias has existed against RNA. With a few exceptions, the educational exploration of RNA has been limited to its role in making proteins (see Chapter 12).

The purpose of this chapter is to lessen the bias against RNA. New molecular tools have enabled researchers to discover that ncRNAs perform a spectacular array of cellular functions in bacteria, archaea, protists, fungi, plants, and animals. ncRNAs play important roles in a variety of processes, including DNA replication, chromatin modification, transcription, translation, and genome defense. In most cell types, ncRNAs are more abundant than mRNAs. For example, in a typical human cell, only about 20% of transcription involves the production of mRNAs, whereas 80% is associated with making ncRNAs! This observation underscores the importance of RNA in the enterprise of life, and indicates why it deserves greater recognition and deeper study. Furthermore, abnormalities in ncRNAs are associated with a wide range of human diseases, including CHH, cancer, neurological disorders, and cardiovascular diseases. Many ncRNAs are also critical to the growth of plants, including the crop plants that are so essential to human survival.

In this chapter, we will begin with an overview of the general properties of ncRNAs, and then examine specific examples of the functions they perform. We will end the chapter by considering the role of ncRNAs in different human diseases and in plant health.

13.1 | Overview of Non-coding RNAs

Learning Outcomes:

1. Describe the ability of ncRNAs to bind to other molecules and macromolecules.
2. Outline the general functions of ncRNAs.
3. Define ribozyme.
4. List several examples of ncRNAs, and describe their functions.

The study of ncRNAs is a rapidly expanding field, and researchers speculate that many ncRNAs have yet to be discovered. Also, due to the relative youth of this field, not all researchers agree on the names of certain ncRNAs or their primary functions. Even so, some broad themes are beginning to emerge. In this section, we will survey the general features of ncRNAs, and in later sections, we will discuss specific examples in greater detail.

ncRNAs Can Bind to Different Types of Molecules

The ability of ncRNAs to carry out an amazing array of functions is largely related to their ability to bind to different types of molecules. **Figure 13.1a** shows four common types of molecules that are recognized by ncRNAs. Some ncRNAs bind to DNA or another RNA through complementary base pairing. This allows ncRNAs to affect processes such as DNA replication, transcription, and translation. In addition, ncRNAs can bind to proteins or small molecules.

As described in Chapter 12, RNA molecules, such as tRNAs, can form stem-loop structures (refer back to Figure 12.14). Similar structures in other ncRNAs may bind to pockets on the surface of proteins, or multiple stem-loops may form a binding site for a small molecule. In some cases, a single ncRNA may contain multiple binding sites. This allows an ncRNA to facilitate the formation of a large structure composed of multiple molecules, such as an ncRNA and three different proteins, as shown in **Figure 13.1b**.

ncRNAs Can Perform a Diverse Set of Functions

In recent decades, researchers have uncovered many examples in which ncRNAs play a critical role in different biological processes. Let's first consider how ncRNAs work in a general way. The common functions of ncRNAs are the following.

Scaffold   Some ncRNAs contain binding sites for multiple components, such as a group of different proteins. Much like the beams in a building, an ncRNA can act as a scaffold for the formation of a complex, as in Figure 13.1b.

Guide   Some ncRNAs guide a molecule to a specific location in a cell. For example, an ncRNA may bind to a protein and guide it to a target site in the DNA that is part of a particular gene (**Figure 13.2**). This function also relies on the ncRNA having multiple binding sites: one for the protein and another for the target site in the DNA.

Alteration of Protein Function or Stability   When it binds to a protein, an ncRNA can alter that protein's structure, which in turn can have a variety of effects. The binding of an ncRNA may affect

- the ability of the protein to act as a catalyst;
- the ability of the protein to bind to other molecules, such as proteins, DNA, or RNA;
- the stability of the protein.

Ribozyme   Another interesting feature of some ncRNAs is that they function as **ribozymes**, which are RNA molecules with catalytic function. For example, in Chapter 12, we saw how peptidyltransferase, which is a component of the large ribosomal subunit, catalyzes peptide bond formation during translation (refer back to Figure 12.20). An rRNA within peptidyltransferase plays the key role in this catalysis. In other words, a part of the ribosome is a ribozyme.

Blocker   An ncRNA may physically prevent or block a cellular process from happening. For example, in bacteria, an antisense RNA is a type of ncRNA that is complementary to an mRNA. When an antisense RNA binds to an mRNA, it blocks the ability of a ribosome to bind to the mRNA, thereby inhibiting translation.

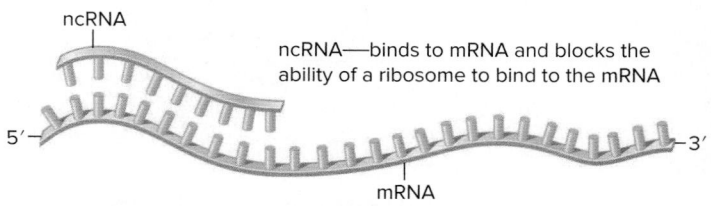

Decoy   Some ncRNAs recognize other ncRNAs and sequester them, thereby preventing them from working. For example, a decoy ncRNA may bind to a different ncRNA called a microRNA (miRNA), which is described later in this chapter (**Figure 13.3**). The function of

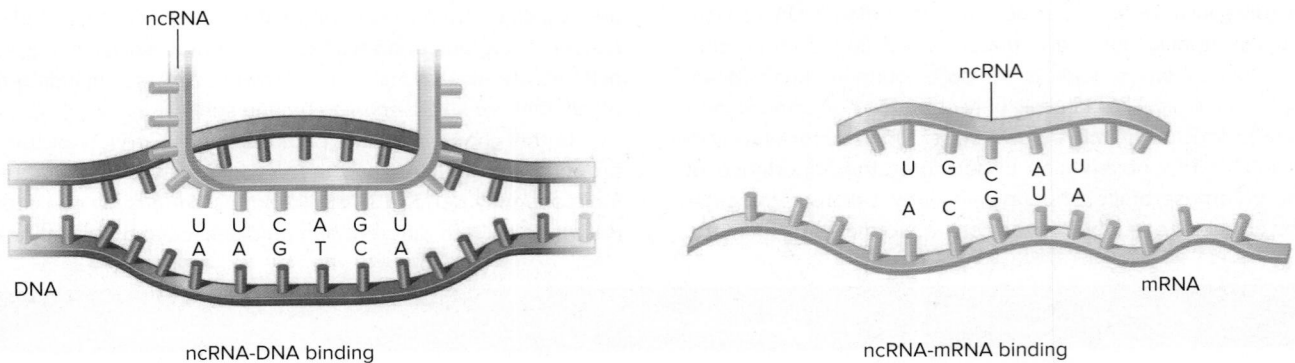

ncRNA-DNA binding

ncRNA-mRNA binding

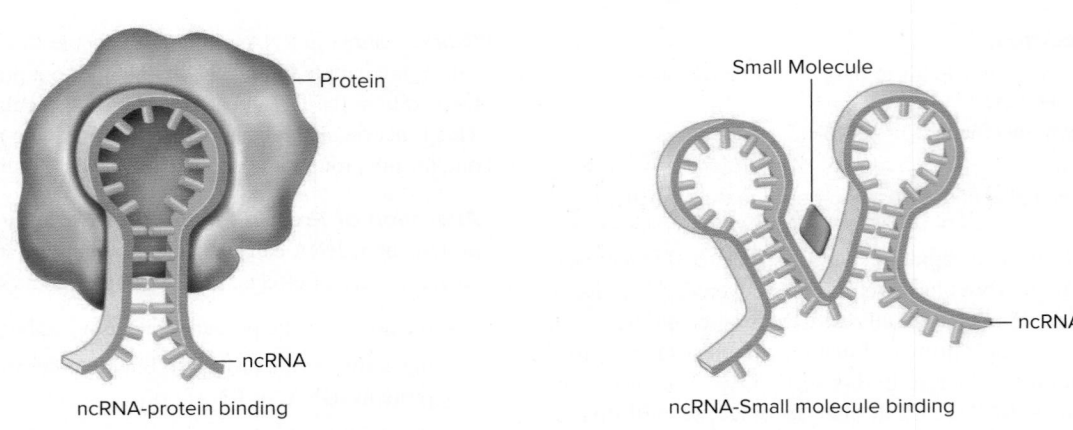

ncRNA-protein binding

ncRNA-Small molecule binding

(a) Common binding interactions between ncRNAs and other molecules

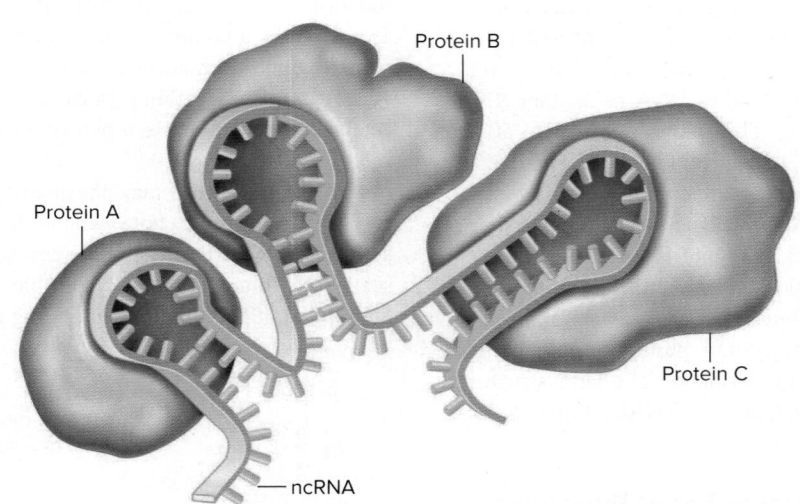

(b) Multiple binding sites in a single ncRNA

Figure 13.1 **Ability of ncRNAs to bind to other molecules.** **(a)** ncRNA molecules can bind to DNA, mRNA, proteins, and small molecules. **(b)** Some ncRNAs have multiple binding sites for different molecules, such as proteins.

Concept Check: *Which of these binding interactions might be inhibited by the formation of a stem-loop within the ncRNA?*

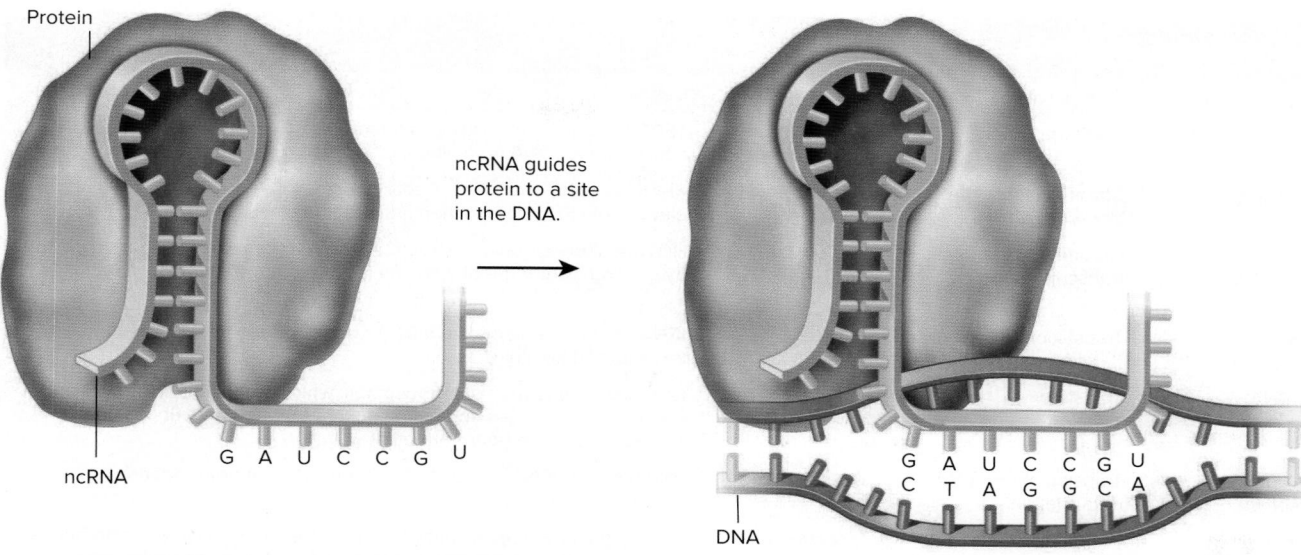

Figure 13.2 **Ability of an ncRNA to function as a guide.**

 Core Concept: Structure and Function This guide RNA has two key structural features: One part binds to a protein and another part binds to a specific sequence of DNA. These two structural features allow the ncRNA to carry out its function of guiding the protein to the DNA.

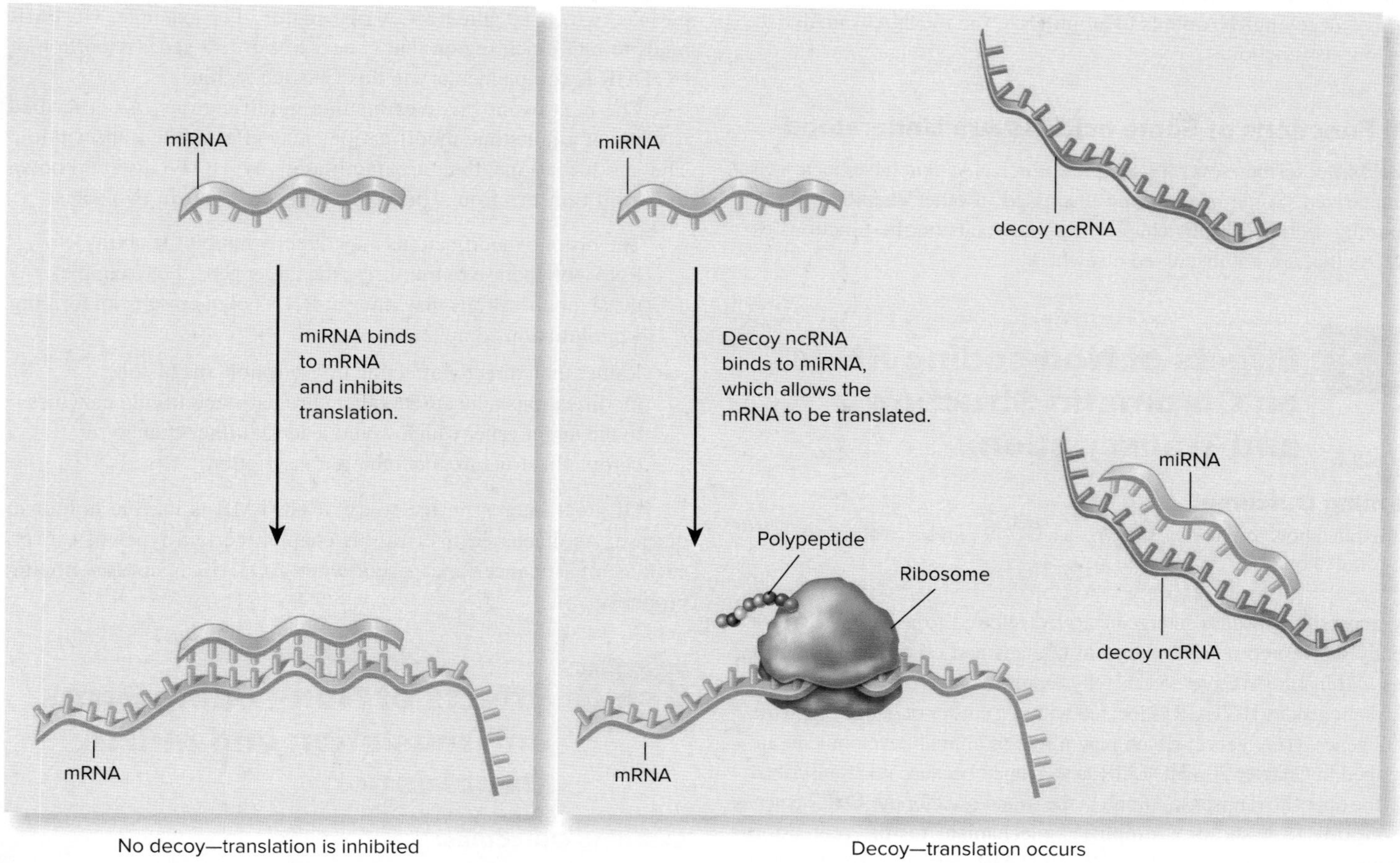

No decoy—translation is inhibited

Decoy—translation occurs

Figure 13.3 **Ability of an ncRNA to function as a decoy.**

Table 13.1	Examples of ncRNAs		
Type of ncRNA	Plays a role in	Discussed in	Description
Telomerase RNA component (TERC)	DNA replication	Chapter 11	TERC facilitates the binding of telomerase to the telomere and acts as a template for DNA replication.
X inactive specific transcript (Xist RNA)	Chromatin structure, transcription	Chapter 18	Xist RNA coats one of the X chromosomes in female mammals and plays a role in its compaction and resulting inactivation.
Hox transcript antisenseintergenic RNA (HOTAIR)	Chromatin structure, transcription	This chapter	HOTAIR alters chromatin structure and thereby represses transcription by guiding histone-modifying complexes to target genes.
Transfer RNA (tRNA)	Translation	Chapter 12	tRNA molecules recognize mRNA codons during translation and carry the appropriate amino acid.
Ribosomal RNA (rRNA)	Translation	Chapter 12	rRNAs are components of ribosomes, which are the site of polypeptide synthesis. Ribosomes contain an ncRNA that acts as a ribozyme by catalyzing peptide bond formation.
microRNA (miRNA), small-interfering RNA (siRNA)	Translation and RNA degradation	This chapter	miRNAs and siRNAs regulate the expression and degradation of mRNAs.
RNA component of signal recognition particle (SRP RNA)	Protein sorting and secretion	This chapter	In bacteria, SRP directs some polypeptides to the plasma membrane. In eukaryotes, it directs polypeptides to the endoplasmic reticulum.
CRISPR RNA (crRNA)	Genome defense	This chapter	crRNA, found in bacteria and archaea, guides an endonuclease to foreign DNA, such as the DNA of a bacteriophage.

an miRNA is to inhibit the translation of a particular mRNA. However, if a decoy ncRNA binds to an miRNA, the miRNA is unable to carry out its function.

The Functions of Some ncRNAs Are Understood

Table 13.1 describes several examples of ncRNAs that have been well characterized. Some of these are discussed in other chapters. In the remaining sections of this chapter, we will focus on the functions of ncRNAs that are not discussed elsewhere.

13.2 Effects of Non-coding RNAs on Chromatin Structure and Transcription

Learning Outcome:

1. Explain how the ncRNA known as HOTAIR plays a role in gene repression.

Hox transcript antisense intergenic RNA, referred to as HOTAIR, is a recently discovered ncRNA found in humans and other mammals that alters chromatin structure and thereby represses gene transcription. The gene that encodes HOTAIR is located within a cluster of genes called the *HoxC* genes. (*Hox* genes, which play a role in animal development, are described in Chapter 20.) HOTAIR is so named because it is transcribed from the opposite (antisense) strand to the strand used for the *HoxC* genes.

Figure 13.4 shows a simplified mechanism for the repression of gene transcription by HOTAIR. HOTAIR acts as a scaffold for the binding of two protein complexes that covalently modify histone proteins. One of these complexes binds to the 5′ end of HOTAIR, and the other binds to the 3′ end. HOTAIR then guides these complexes to

a target gene by binding to a region near the gene that contains many purines, which is called a GA-rich region. For example, HOTAIR binds to a GA-rich region that is next to a *HoxD* gene. A portion of HOTAIR is complementary to this GA-rich region.

The next event involves histone modifications. As described in Chapter 14, histone modifications may affect gene transcription. The modifications that are facilitated by HOTAIR are known to inhibit transcription. This inhibition can occur in two ways:

- The histone modifications may directly inhibit the ability of RNA polymerase to transcribe the target gene. For example, these modifications may prevent RNA polymerase from forming a preinitiation complex.
- Rather than directly affecting transcription, the histone modifications may attract other chromatin-modifying enzymes to the target gene, which would lead to further changes in chromatin structure that inhibit transcription.

Of great interest in the study of HOTAIR is its role in human disease. As discussed later in this chapter, certain types of cancer, such as breast cancer, may occur when HOTAIR is not functioning properly.

13.3 Effects of Non-coding RNAs on Translation and mRNA Degradation

Learning Outcomes:

1. **CoreSKILL »** Analyze experimental evidence that double-stranded RNA is more potent in silencing mRNA than antisense RNA is.
2. Outline the steps of RNA interference.

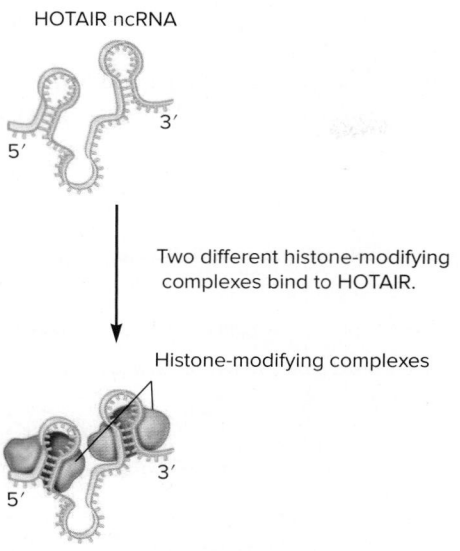

HOTAIR ncRNA

Two different histone-modifying complexes bind to HOTAIR.

Histone-modifying complexes

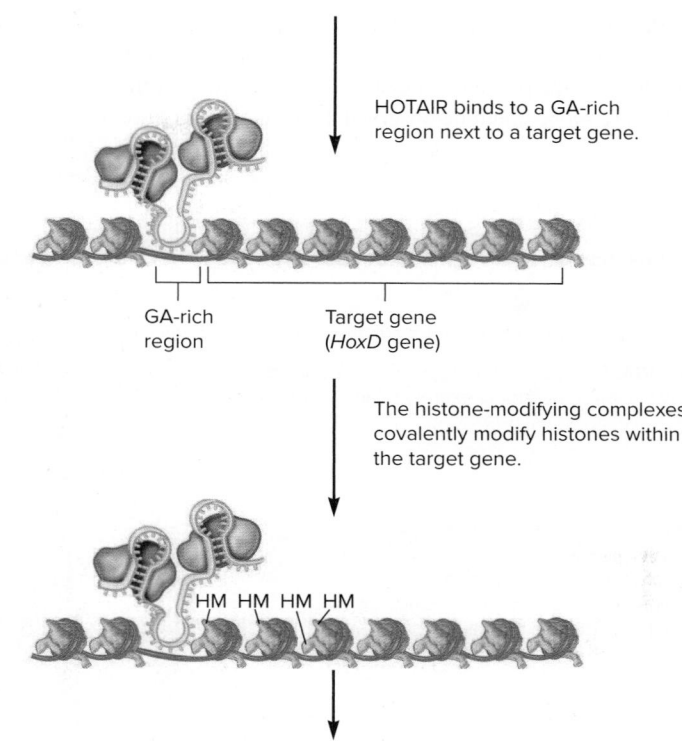

HOTAIR binds to a GA-rich region next to a target gene.

GA-rich region

Target gene (*HoxD* gene)

The histone-modifying complexes covalently modify histones within the target gene.

HM HM HM HM

Figure 13.4 **Simplified mechanism for inhibition of gene transcription by HOTAIR.** This is just one proposed role of HOTAIR. This ncRNA is known to interact with other proteins as well. Note: The abbreviation HM stands for histone modification.

Concept Check: *Explain why HOTAIR binds to the target gene. Why doesn't it bind next to every gene?*

These histone modifications may directly inhibit transcription, or they may lead to further changes in chromatin structure that inhibit transcription.

In the previous section, we considered how an ncRNA can affect the process of transcription. In recent years, researchers have discovered that ncRNAs often exert their effects on RNA molecules that are already made. In this section, we will consider how ncRNAs can affect the ability of mRNAs to be translated or degraded, as well as the ability of rRNAs to be covalently modified.

Feature Investigation | Fire and Mello Showed That Double-Stranded RNA Is More Potent Than Antisense RNA in Silencing mRNA

Specific mRNAs can be targeted for translational inhibition or degradation by a mechanism involving double-stranded RNA. This mechanism was discovered during research involving plants and the nematode worm *Caenorhabditis elegans*. The study described here involved an examination of gene expression in *C. elegans*.

American biologists Andrew Fire, Craig Mello, and colleagues used *C. elegans* as their experimental organism, because it is relatively easy to inject with RNA and the expression of many of its genes had been established. In 1998, Fire and Mello investigated the effects of injected RNA on the expression of specific mRNAs. In the investigation described in **Figure 13.5**, we will focus on one of their experiments involving an mRNA encoded by a gene called *mex-3*. This mRNA had already been shown to be made in high amounts in early embryos of *C. elegans*.

Prior to this work, the *mex-3* gene had been identified and inserted into a plasmid. The process of inserting genes into plasmids is described in Chapter 21 (look ahead to Figure 21.2). Let's first look at the upper plasmid shown in the "Conceptual level" column for step 1. When RNA polymerase, nucleotides, and this plasmid were mixed together in a test tube, *mex-3* mRNA was made, which is called the sense strand. In living cells, the sense strand is used to make the mex-3 protein. Fire and Mello also switched the location of the promoter so that it was at the other end of the gene and signaled transcription of the opposite strand, which is called the antisense strand (see the second plasmid in the "Conceptual level" column). The sense and antisense strands are complementary to each other.

Next, they injected these RNAs into the gonads of *C. elegans*. Into some worms, they injected antisense RNA alone. Alternatively, they mixed sense and antisense RNA, which formed double-stranded RNA, and injected this double-stranded RNA into the gonads of other worms. They also used uninjected worms as controls. After injection, the RNA was taken up by eggs, which later developed into embryos.

To determine the amount of *mex-3* mRNA present, Fire and Mello incubated the embryos with a probe that was complementary to *mex-3* mRNA. Because the probe was labeled, any *mex-3* mRNA that became bound to the probe could be observed under the microscope.

After this incubation step, any probe that was not bound to mRNA was washed away.

As seen in the schematic data of Figure 13.5, the control embryos were very darkly labeled as denoted by their green color. These

Figure 13.5 Injection of antisense and double-stranded RNA into *C. elegans* to compare their effects on mRNA silencing.

GOAL The goal was to further understand how the experimental injection of RNA was responsible for the silencing of particular mRNAs.

KEY MATERIALS The researchers used *C. elegans* as their model organism. They also had the cloned *mex-3* gene, which had been previously shown to be highly expressed in *C. elegans* embryos.

Experimental level	Conceptual level

1 Make sense and antisense *mex-3* RNA in vitro using cloned genes for *mex-3* with promoters on either side of the gene. RNA polymerase and nucleotides are added to synthesize the RNAs.

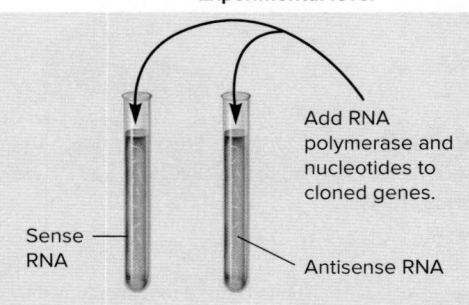

Add RNA polymerase and nucleotides to cloned genes.

Sense RNA

Antisense RNA

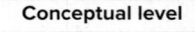
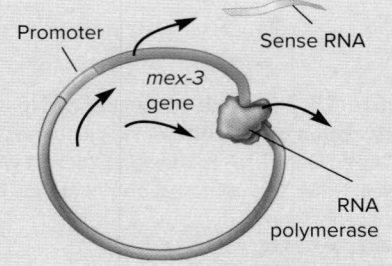

Promoter

Sense RNA

mex-3 gene

RNA polymerase

2 Inject either *mex-3* antisense RNA or a mixture of *mex-3* sense and antisense RNA into the gonads of *C. elegans*. This RNA is taken up by the eggs and early embryos. As a control, do not inject any RNA.

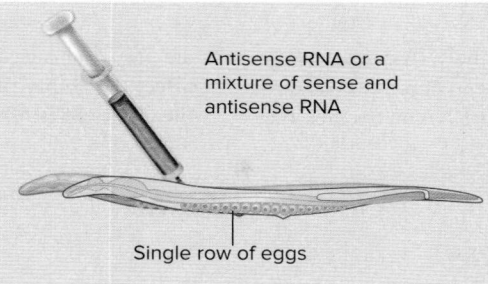

Antisense RNA or a mixture of sense and antisense RNA

Single row of eggs

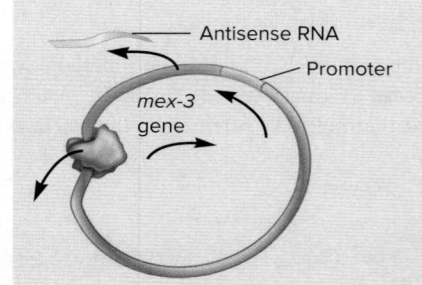

Antisense RNA

Promoter

mex-3 gene

3 Incubate and then subject early embryos to in situ hybridization. In this method, a labeled probe is added that is complementary to *mex-3* mRNA. If cells express *mex-3*, the mRNA in the cells will bind to the probe and become labeled. After incubation with a labeled probe, the cells are washed to remove unbound probe.

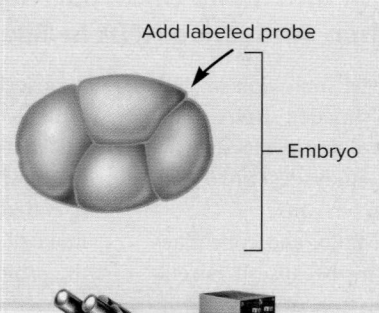

Add labeled probe

Embryo

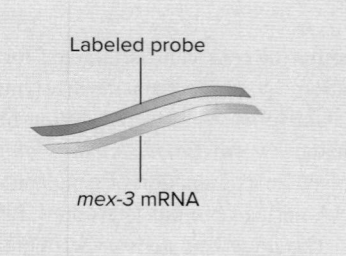

Labeled probe

mex-3 mRNA

4 Observe embryos under the microscope.

5 THE DATA

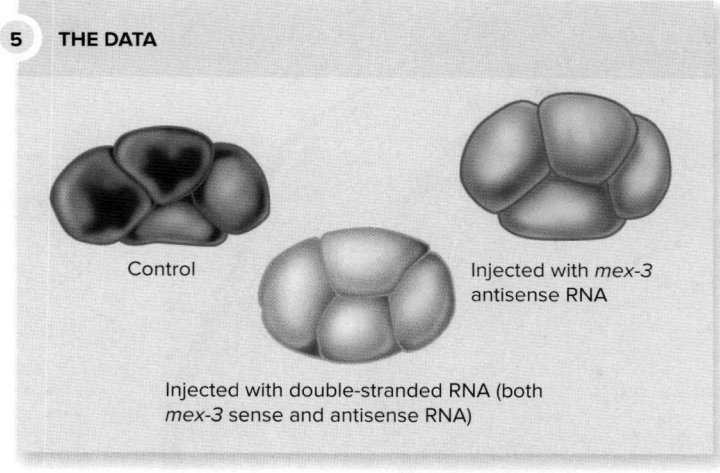

Control

Injected with *mex-3* antisense RNA

Injected with double-stranded RNA (both *mex-3* sense and antisense RNA)

6 CONCLUSION   Double-stranded RNA is more potent at inhibiting *mex-3* mRNA than antisense RNA alone.

7 SOURCE   Fire, A., Xu, S., Montgomery, M.K., et al. 1998. Potent and Specific Genetic Interference by Double-Stranded RNA in *Caenorhabditis elegans. Nature* 391: 806–811.

results indicated that the control embryos contained a high amount of *mex-3* mRNA, which was known from previous research. In the embryos that had received antisense RNA, *mex-3* mRNA levels were decreased, but detectable, as shown by faint labeling. Remarkably, in embryos that had received double-stranded RNA, no *mex-3* mRNA was detected! These results indicated that double-stranded RNA is more potent at silencing mRNA than is antisense RNA. In this case, the double-stranded RNA caused the *mex-3* mRNA to be degraded. Fire and Mello used the term **RNA interference (RNAi)** to describe the phenomenon in which double-stranded RNA causes the silencing of mRNA. This surprising observation led researchers to investigate the underlying molecular mechanism that accounts for this phenomenon, as described next.

Experimental Questions

1. In this experiment, does the *mex-3* mRNA correspond to the sense strand or antisense strand?

2. CoreSKILL » Explain how the sense and antisense *mex-3* RNAs were made.

3. CoreSKILL » According to the data, which material was the most effective at causing the degradation of *mex-3* mRNA?

RNA Interference Is Mediated by MicroRNAs or Small-Interfering RNAs via the RNA-Induced Silencing Complex

RNA interference is found in most eukaryotic species, including animals and plants. It can arise from two sources: microRNAs and small-interfering RNAs. **MicroRNAs (miRNAs)** are ncRNAs that are transcribed from endogenous eukaryotic genes—genes that are normally found in the genome. They play key roles in regulating gene expression, particularly during embryonic development in animals and plants. Most commonly, a single type of miRNA inhibits the translation of several different mRNAs. An miRNA and an mRNA bind to each other because they have base sequences that are partially complementary. In humans, over 2,000 genes encode miRNAs. Researchers estimate that 60% of human protein-encoding genes are regulated by miRNAs.

By comparison, **small-interfering RNAs (siRNAs)** are ncRNAs that usually originate from sources that are exogenous, which means they are not normally made by cells. The siRNAs can come from viruses that infect a cell, or they might be synthesized by researchers to study gene function experimentally, as in Figure 13.5. In most cases, siRNAs are a perfect match to a single type of mRNA. The functioning of siRNAs is thought to play a key role in preventing certain types of viral infections. In addition, siRNAs have become important experimental tools in molecular biology.

How do miRNAs and siRNAs cause the silencing of specific mRNAs? **Figure 13.6** shows how an miRNA or an siRNA leads to RNA interference. The miRNA is first synthesized as a pri-miRNA (for primary-miRNA) in the nucleus. Due to complementary base pairing, the pri-miRNA folds into a hairpin structure (also called a stem-loop) with long, single-stranded 5′ and 3′ ends. The pri-miRNA is cleaved at both ends to form a pre-miRNA (for precursor-miRNA, not to be confused with pri-miRNA). The pre-miRNA is then exported from the nucleus.

As shown in Figure 13.6, siRNAs do not go through the processing events that occur in the nucleus. Instead, pre-siRNAs may be derived from viral RNAs, or they may be made by researchers and taken up by cells. For example, in the work of Fire and Mello described in Figure 13.5, the double-stranded *mex-3* RNA is an example of a pre-siRNA. The pre-siRNA is formed from two complementary RNA molecules that base-pair with each other.

In the cytosol, both pre-miRNAs and pre-siRNAs are cut by an endonuclease called dicer (see Figure 13.6). This releases a double-stranded RNA molecule that is typically 20–25 bp long. This double-stranded RNA associates with proteins to form a complex called the **RNA-induced silencing complex (RISC).** One of the RNA strands is degraded. The remaining single-stranded miRNA or siRNA is complementary to specific mRNAs that will be silenced. The miRNA or siRNA acts as a guide that causes RISC to recognize and bind to such mRNA molecules.

After RISC binds to an mRNA, one of two things may happen:

- RISC may inhibit translation without degrading the mRNA. This is more common for miRNAs, which often are only partially complementary to their target mRNAs.

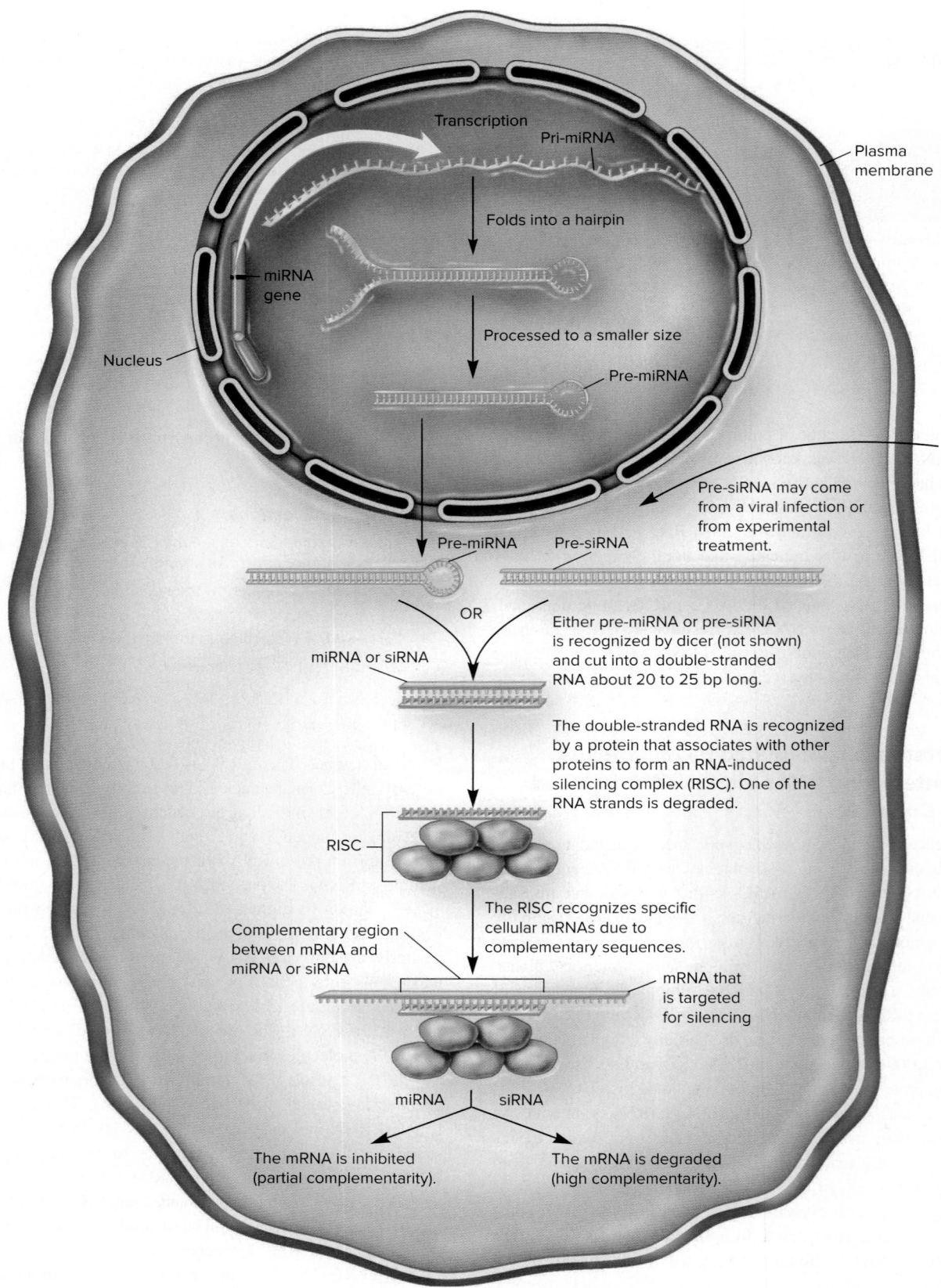

Transcription

Pri-miRNA

Plasma membrane

Folds into a hairpin

miRNA gene

Processed to a smaller size

Nucleus

Pre-miRNA

Pre-siRNA may come from a viral infection or from experimental treatment.

Pre-miRNA   Pre-siRNA

OR

Either pre-miRNA or pre-siRNA is recognized by dicer (not shown) and cut into a double-stranded RNA about 20 to 25 bp long.

miRNA or siRNA

The double-stranded RNA is recognized by a protein that associates with other proteins to form an RNA-induced silencing complex (RISC). One of the RNA strands is degraded.

RISC

The RISC recognizes specific cellular mRNAs due to complementary sequences.

Complementary region between mRNA and miRNA or siRNA

mRNA that is targeted for silencing

miRNA   siRNA

The mRNA is inhibited (partial complementarity).

The mRNA is degraded (high complementarity).

Figure 13.6 **Mechanism of RNA interference.**

Concept Check: *Explain why RISC binds to a specific mRNA. What type of bonding occurs?*

- RISC may direct the degradation of the mRNA. One of the proteins in RISC can cleave the mRNA. This usually occurs for siRNAs that typically are a perfect match (or highly complementary) to their target mRNA.

These two effects are termed RNA interference because the miRNA or siRNA interferes with the proper expression of an mRNA. In 2006, Fire and Mello received the Nobel Prize in Physiology or Medicine for their discovery of this mechanism.

RNA interference is believed to have at least two benefits:

- This mechanism represents an important form of regulation. When genes encoding pri-miRNAs are turned on, the production of miRNAs silences the expression of specific mRNAs.

- RNA interference provides a defense against viruses. This mechanism is widely used by plants to prevent viral infections.

13.4 Non-coding RNAs and Protein Sorting

Learning Outcome:

1. Describe the function of SRP, and explain the roles of SRP RNA with regard to its function.

To carry out their functions, proteins need to be directed to particular locations (refer back to Figure 4.32). For example, some proteins function extracellularly and need to be secreted from the cell. For such proteins to be secreted, they are first sorted to the plasma membrane in bacteria and archaea, or to the endoplasmic reticulum (ER) membrane in eukaryotic cells (refer back to Figure 4.33). This process is facilitated by a protein-RNA complex called **signal recognition particle (SRP).** In bacteria, SRP is composed of one ncRNA and one protein. In eukaryotes, SRP is composed of one ncRNA and six different proteins.

Figure 13.7 takes a closer look at how SRP works in eukaryotes. To be directed to the ER membrane, a polypeptide must contain a sorting signal called an **ER signal sequence**, which is a sequence of about 6–12 amino acids that are predominantly hydrophobic and usually located near the N-terminus. As the ribosome is making the polypeptide in the cytosol, the ER signal sequence emerges from the ribosome and is recognized by a protein in SRP. The binding of SRP to the polypeptide pauses translation.

SRP then binds to an SRP receptor in the ER membrane, which docks the ribosome over a channel. For this binding to occur, proteins within SRP and the SRP receptor must also be bound by GTP. Next, these GTP-binding proteins hydrolyze their GTP, which causes the release of SRP from the SRP receptor and the polypeptide. Once SRP is released, translation resumes and the growing polypeptide is threaded through a channel to cross the ER membrane. In the case of a secreted protein, the newly made polypeptide then travels through the Golgi apparatus and then to the plasma membrane, where it is released outside of the cell.

Researchers have identified at least two key roles for SRP RNA:

1. SRP RNA provides a scaffold for the binding of SRP proteins.
2. After SRP binds to the SRP receptor in the ER membrane, the SRP RNA stimulates proteins within both SRP and the SRP

receptor to hydrolyze their GTP. In other words, SRP RNA alters the structures of these proteins to enhance their GTPase activities. This stimulation is essential for the release of SRP.

13.5 Non-coding RNAs and Genome Defense

Learning Outcome:

1. Explain how the CRISPR-Cas system defends bacteria against bacteriophages.

Much like the immune system found in vertebrates, a system called the **CRISPR-Cas system** provides some species of bacteria and archaea with a means of defense against foreign invaders. CRISPR-Cas systems are an effective defense against bacteriophages, which are viruses that infect bacteria (discussed in Chapter 19), and transposons, which are small segments of DNA that can be inserted into the chromosomes of all species (discussed in Chapter 21). ncRNAs play a key role in CRISPR-Cas systems. About half of all bacterial species and most archaeal species have such a system. Three general types are known, designated type I, II, and III. In this section, we will focus on the type II CRISPR-Cas system and its role in providing bacteria with defense against bacteriophages.

The CRISPR-Cas System Provides Bacteria with Defense Against Bacteriophages

In 1993, Spanish microbiologist Francisco Mojica and colleagues were the first to recognize that different species of bacteria and archaea have a site in their chromosome, now called the CRISPR locus, that contains a series of repeated sequences. In 2005, by analyzing the DNA sequences of the CRISPR locus in a variety of bacterial species, Mojica, Spanish geneticist Giles Vergnaud, and Russian microbiologist Alexander Bolotin independently proposed that this locus provides protection against bacteriophage infection. This hypothesis was based on the observation that the CRISPR locus contains segments that are derived from bacteriophage DNA. The hypothesis was confirmed in 2007 by French microbiologist Philippe Horvath and colleagues, who showed experimentally that the CRISPR-Cas locus provides defense against bacteriophage infection.

Figure 13.8a shows a common organization of the CRISPR-Cas system (also called the CRISPR locus), which has five genes: *tracr, Cas9, Cas1, Cas2,* and *Crispr.* A key feature of the *Crispr* gene is a group of clustered, regularly interspaced, short, palindromic repeats—hence the name CRISPR. The repeats within the *Crispr* gene are interspersed by short, unique sequences, which are called spacers. The CRISPR-Cas type II system also includes a gene that encodes an ncRNA called tracrRNA and a few protein-encoding CRISPR-associated genes (*Cas* genes), which are usually adjacent to the *Crispr* gene. These genes are needed to mediate the defense against bacteriophages.

The CRISPR-Cas system is considered an adaptive defense system because a bacterial cell must first be exposed to an agent, such as a bacteriophage, to elicit a response from the system. As shown in **Figure 13.8b–d**, the defense mechanism occurs in three phases.

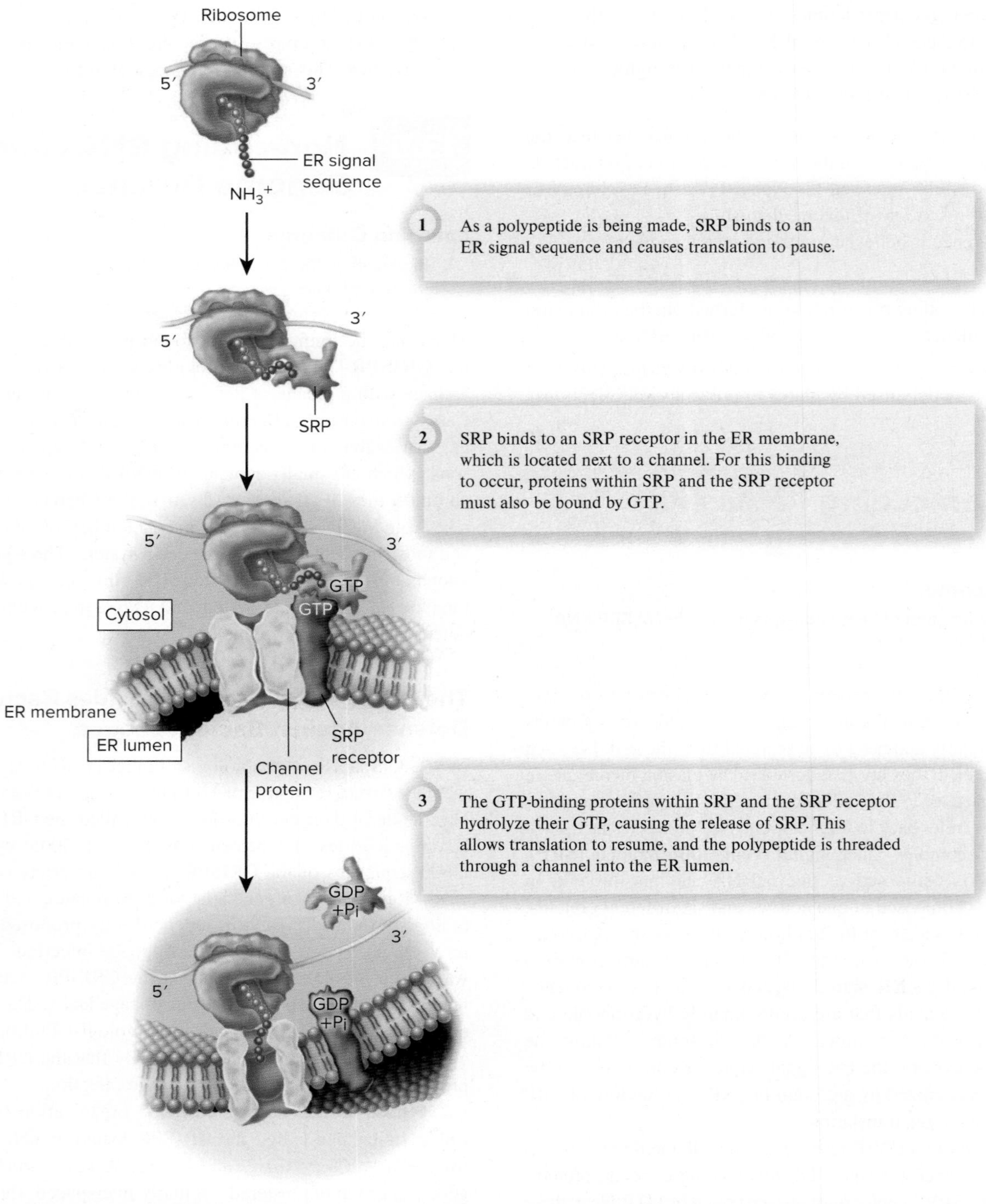

Ribosome

5′   3′

ER signal
sequence

NH_3^+

1 As a polypeptide is being made, SRP binds to an ER signal sequence and causes translation to pause.

5′   3′

SRP

2 SRP binds to an SRP receptor in the ER membrane, which is located next to a channel. For this binding to occur, proteins within SRP and the SRP receptor must also be bound by GTP.

5′   3′

GTP
GTP

Cytosol

ER membrane

ER lumen

SRP
receptor

Channel
protein

3 The GTP-binding proteins within SRP and the SRP receptor hydrolyze their GTP, causing the release of SRP. This allows translation to resume, and the polypeptide is threaded through a channel into the ER lumen.

GDP
+Pi

3′

5′

GDP
+Pi

Figure 13.7 **Directing of polypeptides to the endoplasmic reticulum membrane via SRP.** In eukaryotes, several categories of proteins are first directed to the ER via SRP. These include proteins that are secreted from the cells as well as proteins that are destined to stay in the ER, Golgi, lysosomes, or vacuoles.

 Core Skill: Connections Refer back to Figure 4.32. Which types of proteins need SRP to reach their proper location, and which do not?

Adaptation The process of adaptation (also called spacer acquisition) occurs after a bacterial cell has been exposed to a bacteriophage. The proteins encoded by the *Cas1* and *Cas2* genes form a complex that recognizes the bacteriophage DNA as being foreign and cleaves it into small pieces. As shown in Figure 13.8b, a piece of bacteriophage DNA, usually between 20 and 50 bp in length, is inserted into the *Crispr* gene. The mechanism of insertion is not entirely understood. The newly inserted piece of bacteriophage DNA is called a spacer because it acts as a space between adjacent repeats. The different spacers found in

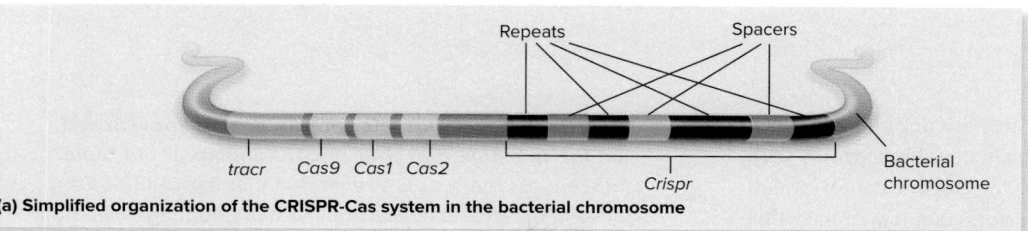

(a) Simplified organization of the CRISPR-Cas system in the bacterial chromosome

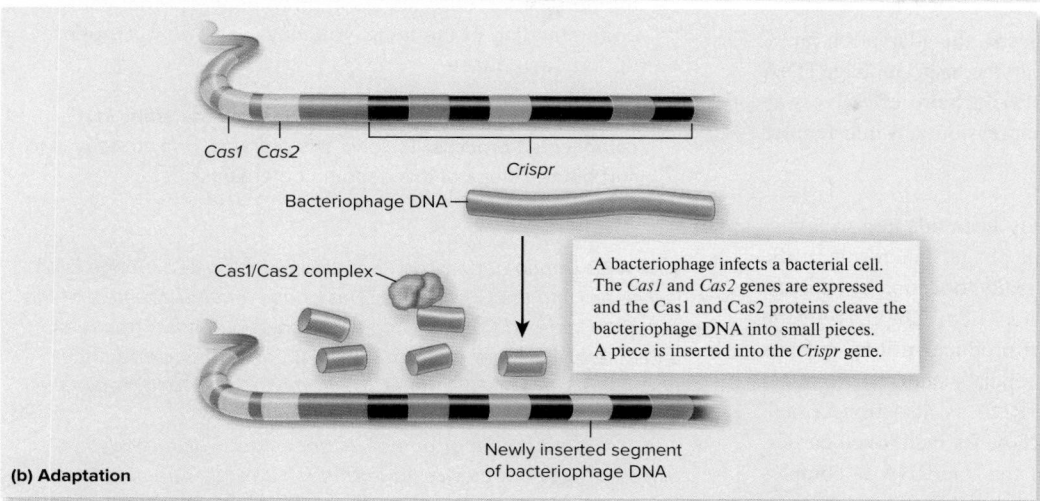

A bacteriophage infects a bacterial cell. The *Cas1* and *Cas2* genes are expressed and the Cas1 and Cas2 proteins cleave the bacteriophage DNA into small pieces. A piece is inserted into the *Crispr* gene.

(b) Adaptation

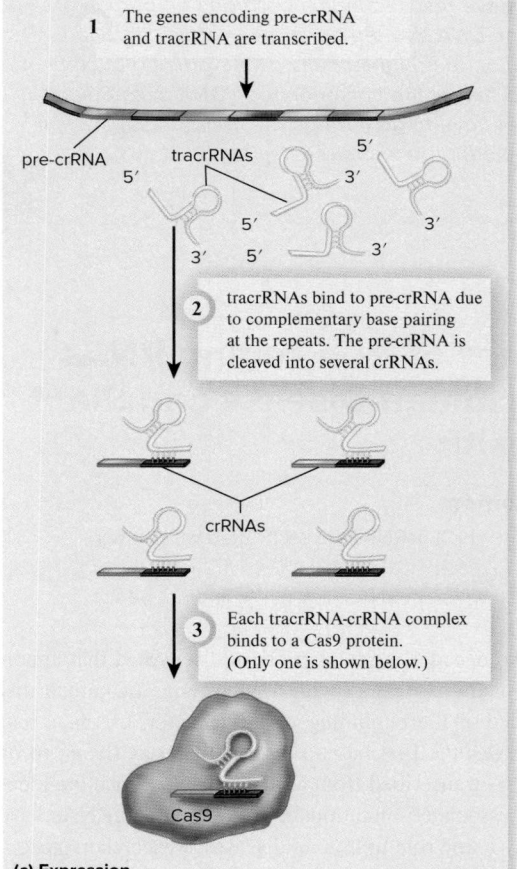

1 The genes encoding pre-crRNA and tracrRNA are transcribed.

2 tracrRNAs bind to pre-crRNA due to complementary base pairing at the repeats. The pre-crRNA is cleaved into several crRNAs.

3 Each tracrRNA-crRNA complex binds to a Cas9 protein. (Only one is shown below.)

(c) Expression

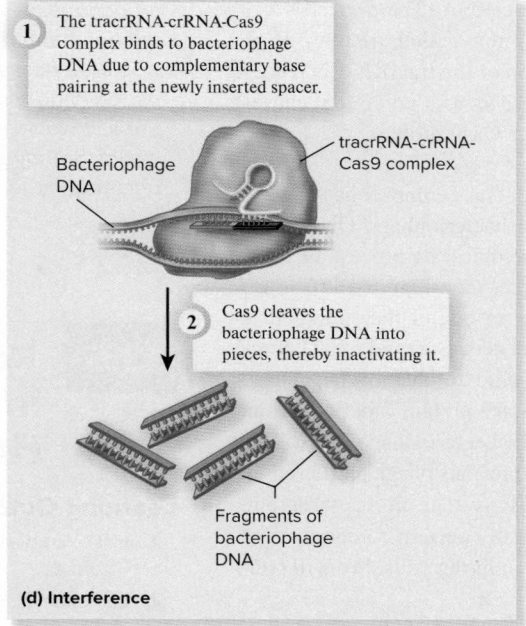

1 The tracrRNA-crRNA-Cas9 complex binds to bacteriophage DNA due to complementary base pairing at the newly inserted spacer.

2 Cas9 cleaves the bacteriophage DNA into pieces, thereby inactivating it.

(d) Interference

Figure 13.8 **The CRISPR-Cas system of genome defense in bacteria.** The system shown here is a type II system, which is found in the chromosome of certain bacterial species but not in archaea. **(a)** Organization of the CRISPR-Cas system in a bacterial chromosome. This drawing shows a typical organization, but different species have variations. **(b–d)** A simplified mechanism of the CRISPR-Cas system. The defense occurs in three phases, called adaptation, expression, and interference.

 Core Skill: Modeling The goal of this modeling challenge is to increase the complexity of the model shown in Figure 13.8d by including sequences in the crRNA and bacteriophage DNA that bind to each other.

Modeling Challenge: For simplicity, the structure of the crRNAs in Figure 13.8 is shown shorter than it really is. Let's suppose that the part of a crRNA that recognizes the bacteriophage DNA is 20 nucleotides long with the following base sequence: 3'-GAUCCCAUACGGCU-AAUCAA-5'. (Note: This is only part of the sequence of the crRNA; it does not include the part that binds to tracrRNA.) Suppose this crRNA is within a tracrRNA-crRNA-Cas9 complex, and draw a model that shows the binding of the complex to a bacteriophage. The general features of the model should be similar to those in Figure 13.8d, except you should include the sequences of the crRNA and the bacteriophage DNA that bind to each other. Label the 5' and 3' ends of the tracrRNA, crRNA and bacteriophage DNA.

the *Crispr* gene of modern bacterial species are derived from past bacteriophage infections. Each spacer provides a bacterium with defense against a particular bacteriophage. Once a bacterial cell has become adapted to a particular bacteriophage, it will pass this trait on to its daughter cells.

By cleaving the bacteriophage into pieces, the adaptation phase can protect a bacterial cell, because it cuts up the bacteriophage DNA and thereby inactivates the phage. However, a more effective way of destroying phages is provided by the expression and interference phases of this system.

Expression   If a bacterial cell has already been adapted to a bacteriophage, a subsequent infection by that phage will result in the expression phase, in which the system gets ready for action by expressing the *Crispr, tracr,* and *Cas9* genes (Figure 13.8c). The *Crispr* gene is transcribed from a single promoter and produces a long ncRNA called pre-crRNA, which contains several repeat sequences separated by spacers. The gene encoding the tracrRNA is also transcribed, which produces many molecules of tracrRNA. As mentioned earlier, tracrRNA is also an ncRNA. A region of the tracrRNA is complementary to the repeat sequences of the pre-crRNA. Several molecules of tracrRNA base-pair with the pre-crRNA. The pre-crRNA is then cleaved into many small molecules, now called crRNAs. Each crRNA is attached to a tracrRNA. A region of the tracrRNA is recognized by the Cas9 protein. The tracrRNA acts as a guide that causes the tracrRNA-crRNA complex to bind to a Cas9 protein.

Interference   After the tracrRNA-crRNA-Cas9 complex has formed, the bacterial cell is ready to destroy the bacteriophage DNA. This phase is called interference because it resembles the process of RNA interference described earlier in this chapter (see Figure 13.6). Each spacer within a crRNA is complementary to one of the strands of a bacteriophage DNA. Therefore, the crRNA acts as a guide that causes the tracrRNA-crRNA-Cas9 complex to bind to that bacteriophage DNA (Figure 13.8d). After binding, the Cas9 protein functions as an endonuclease that breaks both strands in the bacteriophage DNA. This cleavage inactivates the phage and thereby prevents phage proliferation.

Since discovering the CRISPR-Cas system in bacteria and archaea, researchers have been able to modify certain components of this system and use them to mutate genes in living cells. We will consider this technology in Chapter 21.

BIO **TIPS**   **THE QUESTION** *With regard to the CRISPR-Cas system that defends bacteria against bacteriophages, what happens during the adaptation, expression, and interference phases? When a bacterium is exposed to a particular bacteriophage, is the adaptation phase always necessary?*

T OPIC *What topic in biology does this question address?* The topic is the CRISPR-Cas system that provides bacteria with defense against bacteriophages. More specifically, the question asks you to sort out what happens during each phase of the genome defense process and decide whether or not the first phase is always needed.

I NFORMATION *What information do you know based on the question and your understanding of the topic?* In the question, you are reminded that the CRISPR-Cas system defends bacteria against bacteriophages, and that the defense process occurs in three phases. From your understanding of the topic, you may recall what happens during each phase.

P ROBLEM-SOLVING **S** TRATEGY *Sort out the steps in a complicated process.* To solve this problem, one strategy is to sort out the steps of this genome defense process.

ANSWER *During adaptation, a portion of the bacteriophage DNA is inserted into the Crispr gene. This phase requires the help of the proteins Cas1 and Cas2. During the expression phase, tracrRNA, crRNA, and Cas9 are produced. Finally, during the interference phase, tracrRNA, crRNA, and Cas9 come together and cleave the bacteriophage DNA, thereby inactivating it.*

If the bacterium or one of its ancestors was already exposed to the bacteriophage that is currently infecting it, the adaptation phase is not necessary. Prior exposure to the bacteriophage may have resulted in the insertion of a portion of the bacteriophage DNA into the Crispr gene. This alteration would be passed on to daughter cells. Therefore, if a bacterium already had a portion of the bacteriophage DNA in its Crispr gene, it would not have to go through the adaptation phase; it would already be adapted to defend itself against that bacteriophage.

13.6 Roles of Non-coding RNAs in Human Disease and Plant Health

Learning Outcomes:
1. List examples in which ncRNAs are associated with human diseases.
2. List examples in which ncRNAs play a role in plant health.

During the past two decades, researchers have discovered that abnormalities in ncRNAs are associated with a wide range of human diseases. As mentioned at the beginning of this chapter, cartilage-hair hypoplasia (CHH) was the first human disease that was shown to be caused by an ncRNA transcribed from a nuclear gene. Since the identification of CHH-associated mutations in 2001, many ncRNAs have been shown to play a key role in human diseases. Researchers speculate that we are still seeing only the "tip of the iceberg" with regard to identifying the roles of ncRNAs in human pathology. Likewise, the impact of ncRNAs on plant health is only beginning to be appreciated but has exciting potential in the field of agriculture. In this section, we will focus on the roles of ncRNAs in the development of cancer, neurological disorders, and cardiovascular diseases, as well as their effects on plant health.

Table 13.2	Examples of ncRNAs Associated with Human Diseases
Type of ncRNA	**Disease(s)***
A group of miRNAs called the miR-200 family	Several types of cancer, including bladder cancer, melanoma, stomach cancer, and colorectal cancer
HOTAIR	Several types of cancer, including breast cancer, lung cancer, and colorectal cancer
Many miRNAs	Alzheimer disease
Many miRNAs	Multiple sclerosis
An miRNA called miR-1	Heart arrhythmias
Several different miRNAs, including miR10a, miR145, and miR143	Formation of arterial plaques

*The diseases listed in this table show an association with abnormal levels of ncRNAs. In many cases, it is not yet clear if the disease symptoms are caused, in part, by the abnormal levels of ncRNAs or if the abnormal levels are a consequence of the disease symptoms.

ncRNAs Play a Role in Many Forms of Cancer and Other Human Diseases

As we have seen throughout this chapter, ncRNAs play important roles in chromatin modification, gene transcription, mRNA translation, and protein function. When certain ncRNAs are expressed abnormally, that is, at too high or too low a level, disease conditions are known to occur. Such abnormal expression levels can be caused by mutations in specific genes or by epigenetic changes, described in Chapter 18, that alter the expression of genes that encode ncRNAs. Several examples of human diseases associated with the abnormal expression of ncRNAs are listed in **Table 13.2**.

ncRNAs and Cancer   The topic of cancer is described in Chapter 15 (look ahead to Section 15.4). The roles of ncRNAs in cancer have been most thoroughly studied with respect to miRNAs. In nearly all forms of human cancer, levels of expression of particular miRNAs differ between normal and cancer cells. In some cases, the genes that encode the miRNAs behave as tumor-suppressor genes, because a lower level of expression of particular miRNAs allows tumor growth. In other cases, the genes that encode certain miRNAs act as oncogenes; their overexpression promotes cancer.

A well-studied example of the role of miRNAs in cancer involves a group of several different miRNAs called the miR-200 family. The miR-200 family plays an essential role in tumor suppression by inhibiting metastasis—the process by which cancer cells can spread through the bloodstream to other parts of the body. Low levels of expression of miR-200 members have been associated with many types of cancer, including bladder cancer, melanoma, stomach cancer, and colorectal cancer.

Though they have been less well studied, other ncRNAs are also associated with particular types of human cancers. HOTAIR, which was discussed in Section 13.2, is an ncRNA that is highly expressed in a variety of cancers, including breast cancer, lung cancer, and colorectal cancer. When overexpressed, the gene that encodes HOTAIR behaves as an oncogene. High levels of HOTAIR expression in primary breast tumors are a significant predictor of metastasis and death. HOTAIR is known to interact with a variety of cellular components, but the mechanism by which it promotes cancer is not well understood.

ncRNAs and Neurological Disorders   Many miRNAs are essential for the proper development and functioning of the nervous system. Approximately 70% of all miRNAs are expressed in the brain, and many of them are specific to neurons. miRNAs are involved in neuron growth and the overall development of the nervous system. Abnormal levels of expression of miRNAs have been associated with nearly all neurological disorders in which these ncRNAs have been investigated! Table 13.2 describes some examples in which the expression of miRNAs has been altered and associated with neurological disorders. For example, in Alzheimer disease, abnormally expressed miRNAs are thought to be involved in down-regulating the expression of the enzyme β-secretase, which leads to the overproduction of certain β-amyloid peptides—a key feature of the disease. miRNAs are also known to control the inflammatory process that leads to the development of multiple sclerosis.

ncRNAs and Cardiovascular Diseases   Abnormalities in miRNA levels have been linked to several cardiovascular diseases. A particular miRNA, called miR-1, is associated with the development of arrhythmias—irregularities in the rate or rhythm of the heartbeat. This miRNA regulates the expression of genes that encode ion channel proteins, which are important for proper signaling between cardiac muscle cells. Other miRNAs appear to play a role in vascular disease. The formation of arterial plaques is associated with abnormal expression levels of several miRNAs, including miR10a, miR145, and miR143.

ncRNAs Are Essential to Plant Health

In parallel to the growing knowledge of the role of ncRNAs in human diseases, plant biologists are discovering that abnormalities in ncRNAs play many essential roles that contribute to the health of plants. This realization is likely to have great impact in the field

Table 13.3	Importance of ncRNAs in Plant Health
Type of ncRNA*	**Normal role in plant structure and function**
Several miRNAs, including miR156, miR157, and miR159	Control the time of year when flowering occurs
An ncRNA called COOLAIR	Promotes vernalization, the process in which certain plants will only flower after being exposed to cold winter temperatures
Two miRNAs called miR167 and miR397	Play a role in seed development
An miRNA called miR402	Affects the rate of seed germination and seedling growth under stress conditions
An miRNA called miR824	Plays a role in the development of stomata
An ncRNA called IPS1	Affects the ability of plants to cope with phosphate starvation

*Most of the examples listed are miRNAs, which are short ncRNAs. COOLAIR and IPS1 are longer ncRNAs.

of agriculture as we develop methods to change the expression of ncRNAs in order to modify the characteristics of agriculturally important plants. **Table 13.3** describes several ncRNAs that are known to play key roles in plant health.

Summary of Key Concepts

13.1 Overview of Non-coding RNAs

- Non-coding RNAs (ncRNAs) are RNA molecules that do not encode polypeptides.
- ncRNAs bind to different types of molecules, including DNA, other RNAs, proteins, and small molecules (Figure 13.1).
- An ncRNA can provide a scaffold, act as a guide, alter protein function or stability, function as a ribozyme, function as a blocker, and/or act as a decoy (Figures 13.2, 13.3).
- ncRNAs play a role in DNA replication, chromatin structure, transcription, translation, RNA degradation, RNA modification, protein sorting and secretion, and genome defense (Table 13.1).

13.2 Effects of Non-coding RNAs on Chromatin Structure and Transcription

- HOTAIR is an ncRNA found in humans and other mammals that regulates transcription by forming a scaffold that binds to two protein complexes and guides them to particular genes. The protein complexes covalently modify histones, and these modifications inhibit transcription of the target genes (Figure 13.4).

13.3 Effects of Non-coding RNAs on Translation and mRNA Degradation

- Fire and Mello showed that double-stranded RNA is more potent at silencing mRNA than is antisense RNA (Figure 13.5).
- RNA interference is a mechanism of mRNA silencing in which miRNA or siRNA becomes part of an RNA-induced silencing complex (RISC) that inhibits the translation of a specific mRNA or causes its degradation, respectively (Figure 13.6).

13.4 Non-coding RNAs and Protein Sorting

- Signal recognition particle (SRP), which is composed of one or more proteins and an ncRNA, plays a role in directing proteins to the plasma membrane of prokaryotic cells and to the ER membrane of eukaryotic cells (Figure 13.7).

13.5 Non-coding RNAs and Genome Defense

- The CRISPR-Cas system in bacteria and archaea provides defense against bacteriophages and transposons. The defense occurs in three phases: adaptation, expression, and interference (Figure 13.8).

13.6 Role of Non-coding RNAs in Human Disease and Plant Health

- Abnormalities in the expression of ncRNAs have been associated with many human diseases, including cancer, neurological disorders, and cardiovascular diseases (Table 13.2).
- The proper level of expression of ncRNAs is also important for plant health (Table 13.3).

Assess & Discuss

Test Yourself

1. Which of the following types of molecules could bind to an ncRNA through base pairing?
   a. DNA
   b. RNA
   c. protein
   d. small molecule
   e. both a and b

2. Which of the following is *not* a general function of an ncRNA?
   a. encoding a polypeptide
   b. acting as a ribozyme
   c. acting as a guide
   d. acting as a scaffold
   e. acting as a decoy

3. ncRNAs play an important role in
   a. DNA replication.
   b. chromatin structure and transcription.
   c. translation and RNA degradation.

d. genome defense.

e. all of the above.

4. HOTAIR causes certain genes to be repressed by facilitating

a. the binding of a repressor protein.

b. the release of an activator protein.

c. the covalent modification of histones.

d. the removal of nucleosomes.

e. both a and c.

5. One of the roles of the RNA component of signal recognition particle (SRP) is to stimulate certain proteins to hydrolyze GTP. If this function of SRP RNA did not work properly, what would you expect to happen?

a. SRP would not bind to the ER signal sequence of a polypeptide.

b. SRP would not cause translation to pause.

c. SRP would not bind to an SRP receptor in the ER membrane.

d. SRP would not be released from the ER membrane.

e. both a and b

6. During RNA interference, what binds to an mRNA to inhibit translation?

a. a pri-miRNA

b. a pre-miRNA or pre-siRNA

c. a double-stranded miRNA or double-stranded siRNA

d. a single-stranded miRNA or single-stranded siRNA

e. dicer

7. With regard to miRNAs and siRNAs, which of the following statements is (are) correct?

a. miRNAs are transcribed from endogenous genes.

b. miRNAs are usually a perfect match to an mRNA.

c. siRNAs are transcribed from endogenous genes.

d. siRNAs cause mRNA degradation.

e. both a and d

8. Cas1 and Cas2 proteins play a role during which of the following phases of genome defense?

a. adaptation

b. expression

c. interference

d. both adaptation and expression

e. both expression and interference

9. Which of the following components bind to tracrRNA?

a. crRNA and Cas1 protein

b. crRNA and Cas2 protein

c. crRNA and Cas9 protein

d. crRNA only

e. Cas1 and Cas2 proteins

10. Abnormalities in the expression of ncRNAs are associated with

a. many forms of cancer.

b. neurological disorders.

c. cardiovascular diseases.

d. all of the above.

e. only a and b.

Conceptual Questions

1. An ncRNA may have one or more of the following functions: scaffold, guide, alterer of protein function or stability, ribozyme, blocker, and decoy. Which of those functions are exhibited by the following examples: HOTAIR, SRP RNA, miRNA, and crRNA? Note: A single ncRNA may have more than one function.

2. What is RNA interference (RNAi)? Explain how the double-stranded RNA is processed during RNAi and how it leads to the silencing of a complementary mRNA.

3. **Core Concept: Structure and Function** Explain how the structure of HOTAIR allows it to carry out its function.

Collaborative Questions

1. Review the concept of an RNA world described in Section 4.1. Discuss which ncRNAs described in Table 13.1 may have arisen during the RNA world, and which probably arose after the modern DNA/RNA/protein world came into being.

2. Go to the PubMed website and search for "non-coding RNA and disease." Scan through the journal articles you retrieve, and make a list of the roles that ncRNAs may play in human diseases.

Gene Expression at the Molecular Level III: Gene Regulation

14

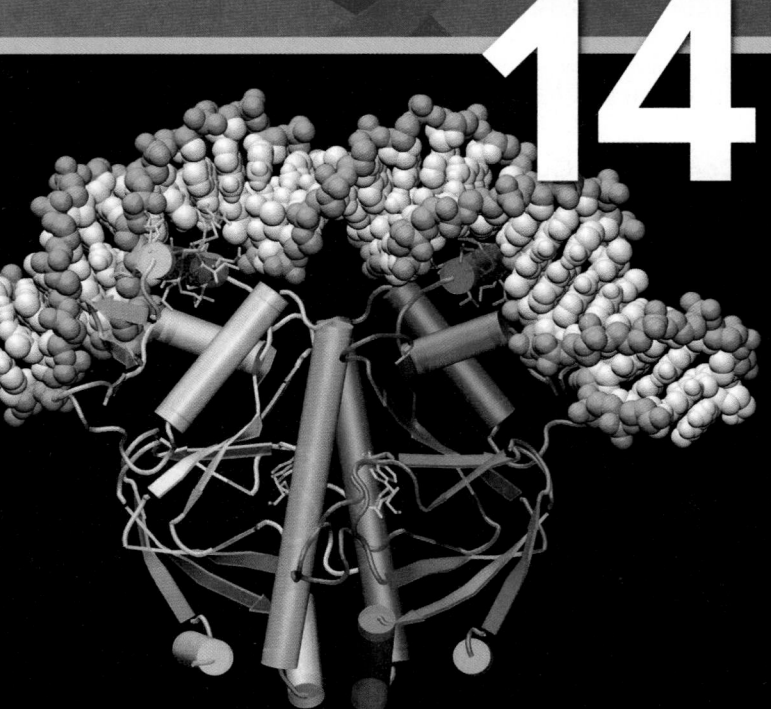

A model for a protein that binds to DNA and regulates genes. The catabolite activator protein (CAP), shown in dark and light blue, is binding to the DNA double helix, shown in orange and white. CAP, shown again in Figure 14.10, activates gene transcription. ©Daniel Gage, University of Connecticut

Emilio took a weight-lifting class in college and was surprised by the results. Within a few weeks, he was able to lift substantially more weight. He was inspired by his progress and continued lifting weights after the semester-long course ended. A year later, he was not only much stronger, but he could see physical changes in his body. Certain muscles, such as the biceps and triceps in his upper arms, were noticeably larger. How can we explain the increase in mass of Emilio's muscles? Unknowingly, when he was lifting weights, Emilio was affecting the regulation of his genes. Certain genes in his muscle cells were being "turned on" during his workouts, which then led to the synthesis of proteins that increased the mass of Emilio's muscles.

At the molecular level, **gene expression** is the process by which the information within a gene is made into a functional product, such as an RNA molecule or a protein. Most genes in all species are regulated so that the proteins they specify are produced at appropriate times and in specific amounts. The term **gene regulation** refers to the ability of cells to control the expression of their genes. By comparison, some genes have relatively constant levels of expression in all conditions over time. These are called **constitutive genes**. In most cases, constitutive genes encode proteins that are constantly required for the survival of an organism, such as certain metabolic enzymes.

The importance of gene regulation is underscored by the number of genes devoted to this process in an organism. For example, in *Arabidopsis thaliana*, a plant that is studied by many plant geneticists, over 5% of the genome is involved with regulating gene transcription. This species has more than 1,500 different genes that encode proteins that regulate the transcription of other genes.

In this chapter, we will begin with an overview that emphasizes the benefits of gene regulation and the general mechanisms that achieve such regulation in bacteria and in eukaryotes. The following sections will describe how bacteria regulate gene expression in the face of environmental change and the more complex nature of gene regulation in eukaryotes.

14.1 Overview of Gene Regulation

Learning Outcomes:

1. Discuss the various ways that organisms benefit from gene regulation.
2. Identify where gene regulation can occur during the process of gene expression in bacteria and eukaryotes.

How do living organisms benefit from gene regulation? One benefit is that gene regulation conserves energy. Proteins that are encoded by genes are produced only when needed. In multicellular organisms, gene regulation also ensures that genes are expressed in the appropriate cell types and at the correct stage of development. In this section, we will examine a few examples that illustrate the important consequences of gene regulation. We will also survey the major points in the gene expression process at which genes are regulated in bacterial and eukaryotic cells.

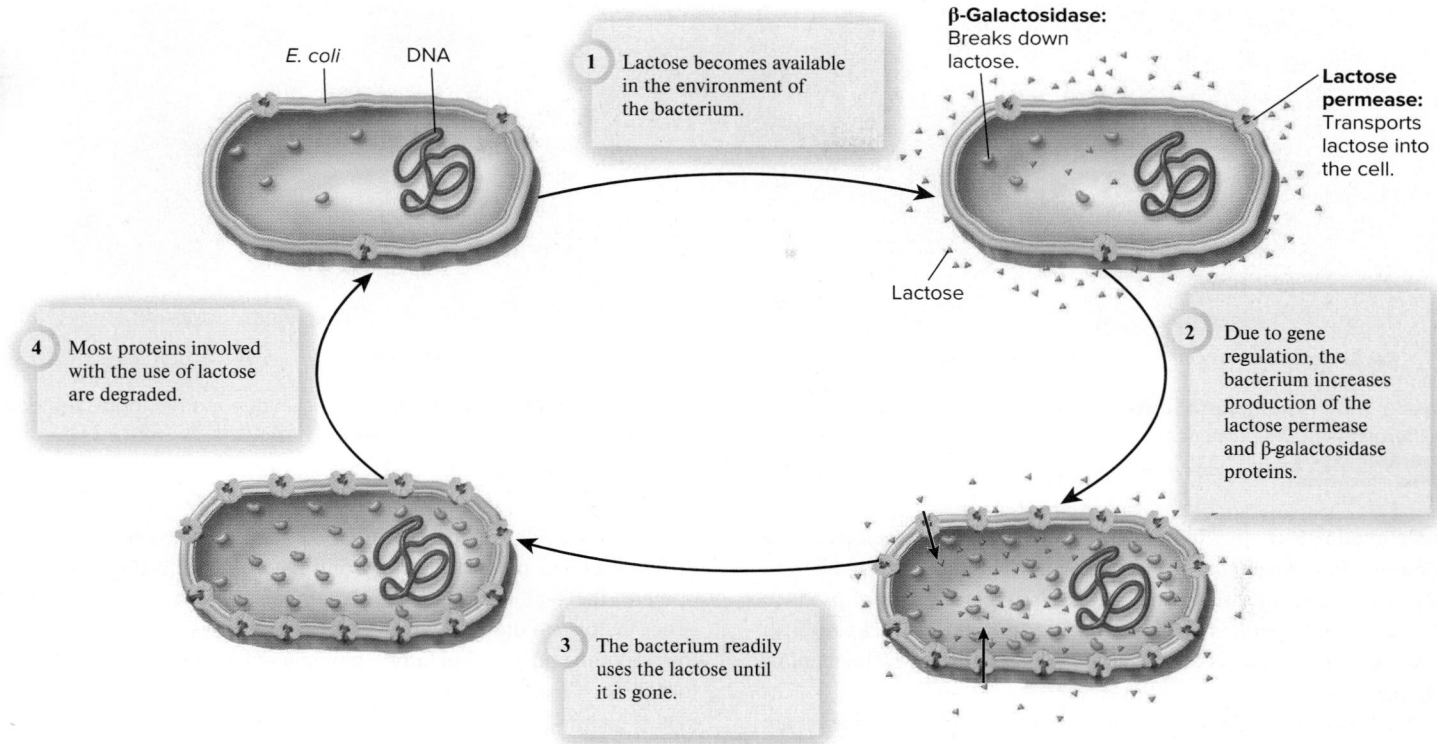

Figure 14.1 **Gene regulation of lactose utilization in *E. coli*.**

 Core Concept: Energy and Matter Gene regulation provides a way for organisms to avoid wasting energy. Their cells make proteins only when the proteins are needed.

Bacteria Regulate Genes in Response to Changes in Their Environment

The bacterium *Escherichia coli* can use many types of sugars as food sources, thereby increasing its chances of survival. With regard to gene regulation, we will focus on how it uses lactose, which is a sugar found in milk. The genome of *E. coli* carries genes that code for proteins that enable the bacterium to take up lactose from the environment and metabolize it.

Figure 14.1 illustrates the effects of lactose on the regulation of those genes. In order to utilize lactose, an *E. coli* cell requires a transporter, called lactose permease, that facilitates the uptake of lactose into the cell, and an enzyme, called β-galactosidase, that catalyzes the breakdown of lactose. When lactose is not present in the environment, an *E. coli* cell makes very little of these proteins. However, when lactose becomes available, the bacterium produces many more of these proteins, enabling it to readily use lactose from its environment. Eventually, all of the lactose in the environment will be used up. At this point, the genes encoding these proteins will be shut off, and most of the proteins will be degraded. Overall, gene regulation conserves energy because it ensures that the proteins needed for lactose utilization are made only when lactose is present in the environment.

Eukaryotic Gene Regulation Produces Different Cell Types in a Single Organism

One of the most amazing examples of gene regulation is the phenomenon of **cell differentiation**, the process by which cells become specialized into particular types. In humans, for example, cells may differentiate into muscle cells, neurons, skin cells, or other types. **Figure 14.2** shows micrographs of three types of cells found in humans. As the images show, their morphologies are strikingly different. Likewise, their functions within the body are also quite different. Muscle cells are important in body movements, neurons function in cell signaling, and skin cells form a protective outer surface to the body.

Gene regulation is responsible for producing different types of cells within a multicellular organism. The three cell types shown in Figure 14.2 contain the same **genome**, meaning they carry the same set of genes. However, their **proteomes**—the sets of proteins they make—are quite different. Certain proteins are found in particular cell types but not in others. Alternatively, a protein may be present in all three cell types, but the relative amounts of the protein may be different. The amount of a given protein depends on many factors, including how strongly the corresponding gene is turned on and how much protein is synthesized from mRNA. Gene regulation plays a major role in determining the proteome of each cell type.

Eukaryotic Gene Regulation Enables Multicellular Organisms to Proceed Through Developmental Stages

In multicellular organisms that progress through developmental stages, certain genes are expressed at particular stages of development but not others. Let's consider an example of such gene regulation in mammals. Early stages of development occur in the uterus of

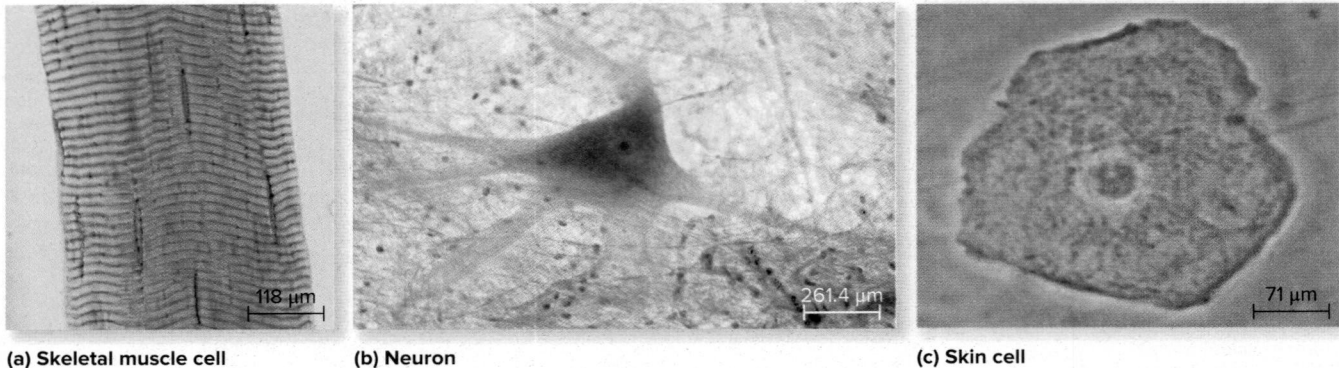

(a) **Skeletal muscle cell**   (b) **Neuron**   (c) **Skin cell**

Figure 14.2 Examples of different cell types in humans. These cells have the same genetic composition. Their unique morphologies are due to differences in the proteins they make. a: ©Ed Reschke/Getty Images; b: ©McGraw-Hill Education/Al Telser, photographer; c: Source: M. Rein/CDC

Concept Check: *How does gene regulation underlie the different morphologies of the various types of cells?*

female mammals. Following fertilization, an embryo develops inside the uterus. In humans, the embryonic stage lasts from fertilization to 8 weeks. During this stage, major developmental changes produce the various body parts. The fetal stage occurs from 8 weeks to birth (41 weeks). This stage is characterized by a continued refinement of body parts and a large increase in size.

The oxygen demands of a rapidly growing embryo and fetus are quite different from the needs of the mother. Gene regulation plays a vital role in ensuring that an embryo and fetus get the proper amount of oxygen. Hemoglobin is a protein that delivers oxygen to the cells of a mammal's body. A hemoglobin protein is composed of four globin polypeptides, two encoded by one globin gene and two encoded by another globin gene (**Figure 14.3**). The genomes of mammals carry

several genes (designated with Greek letters) that encode slightly different globin polypeptides. During the embryonic stage of development, the ε-globin and ζ-globin (epsilon-globin and zeta-globin) genes are turned on. At the fetal stage, these genes are turned off, and the α-globin and γ-globin (alpha-globin and gamma-globin) genes are turned on. Finally, at birth, the γ-globin gene is turned off, and the beta β-globin (beta-globin) gene is turned on.

How do the embryo and fetus acquire oxygen from their mother's bloodstream? The hemoglobin produced during the embryonic and fetal stages has a higher binding affinity for oxygen than does the hemoglobin produced after birth. Therefore, the embryo and fetus can remove oxygen from the mother's bloodstream and use that oxygen for their own needs. This occurs across the placenta, where the mother's bloodstream is adjacent to the bloodstream of the embryo or fetus. In this way, gene regulation enables mammals to develop inside the mother's body, even though the embryo and fetus are not breathing on their own. Gene regulation ensures that the correct hemoglobin protein is produced at the right time in development. We'll discuss how gene expression controls the process of development in greater detail in Chapter 20.

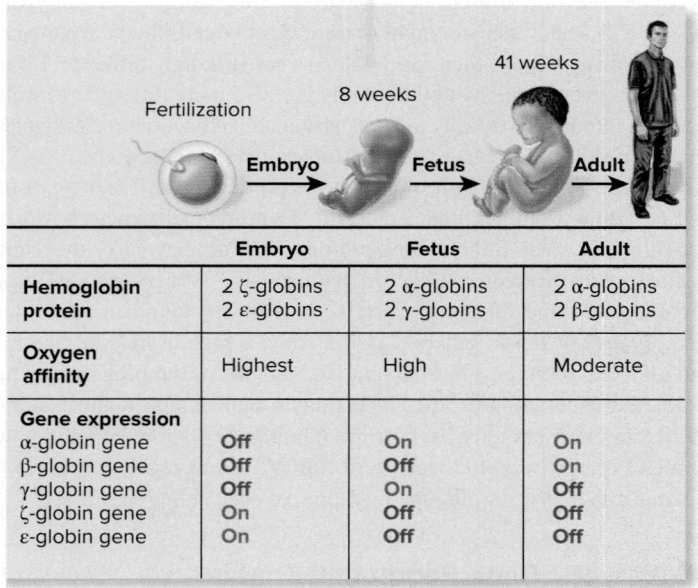

	Embryo	Fetus	Adult
Hemoglobin protein	2 ζ-globins 2 ε-globins	2 α-globins 2 γ-globins	2 α-globins 2 β-globins
Oxygen affinity	Highest	High	Moderate
Gene expression α-globin gene β-globin gene γ-globin gene ζ-globin gene ε-globin gene	 Off Off Off On On	 On Off On Off Off	 On On Off Off Off

Figure 14.3 Regulation of human globin genes at different stages of development.

 Core Concept: Information Gene regulation is an important process that allows organisms to properly access the information within their genomes and proceed through developmental stages.

Gene Regulation Occurs at Different Points in the Process from DNA to Protein

Thus far, we have learned that gene regulation has a dramatic influence on the ability of organisms to respond to environmental changes, produce different types of cells, and progress through developmental stages. For protein-encoding genes, the regulation of gene expression can occur at any of the steps in the process that produces a functional protein.

In bacteria, gene regulation most commonly occurs at the level of transcription, which means that bacteria regulate how much mRNA is made from genes (**Figure 14.4a**). When geneticists say a gene is "turned off," they mean that very little or no mRNA is made from that gene, whereas a gene that is "turned on" is transcribed into mRNA. Because transcription is the first step in gene expression, transcriptional regulation is a particularly efficient way to regulate genes because cells avoid wasting energy when the product of the gene is not needed. A second way for bacteria to regulate gene expression is to control the ability of an mRNA to be translated into a protein. This form of gene regulation is less common in bacteria. Last, gene

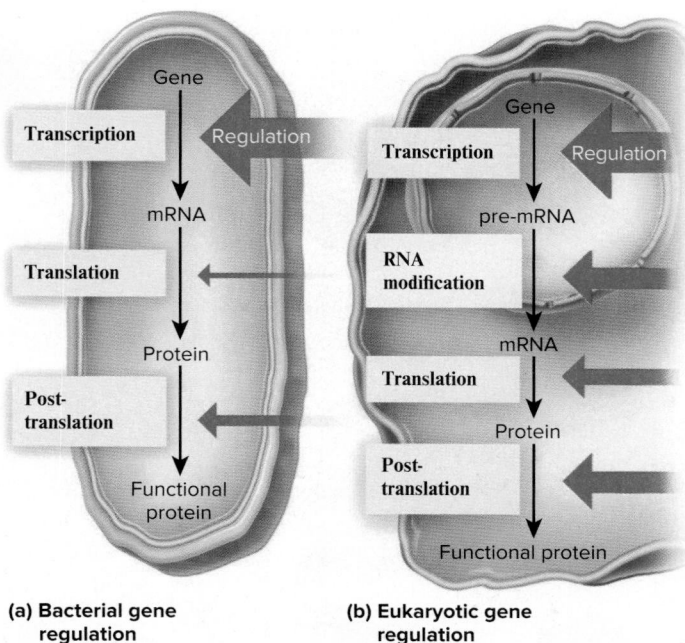

(a) Bacterial gene regulation

(b) Eukaryotic gene regulation

Figure 14.4   Overview of gene regulation in (a) bacteria and (b) eukaryotes. The relative widths of the red arrows indicate the prominence with which gene regulation is used to control the production of functional proteins.

expression can be regulated at the post-translational level in which a protein's function is controlled after it is synthesized via translation.

In eukaryotes, gene regulation occurs at many levels, including transcription, RNA modification, translation, and after translation of a protein is completed (**Figure 14.4b**). As it is for their bacterial counterparts, transcriptional regulation is a prominent form of gene regulation for eukaryotes. As discussed later in this chapter, eukaryotic genes are transcriptionally regulated in several different ways, some of which do not occur in bacteria. Regulation of RNA modification and of the rate of translation of mRNAs is also common.

Like bacterial proteins, eukaryotic proteins can be regulated in a variety of ways, including cellular regulation and biochemical regulation (such as feedback inhibition). These various types of regulation are best understood within the context of cell biology, so they were primarily discussed in Unit II (look back at Chapter 6, especially Figure 6.13).

14.2   Regulation of Transcription in Bacteria

Learning Outcomes:

1. Explain how regulatory transcription factors and small effector molecules are involved in the regulation of transcription.
2. Describe the organization of the *lac* operon and how it is under negative and positive control.
3. **CoreSKILL »** Analyze the results of the experiments of Jacob, Monod, and Pardee.
4. Describe how the *trp* operon is under negative control.

As we have seen, when a bacterium is exposed to a particular nutrient in its environment, such as a sugar, the genes are expressed that encode proteins needed for the uptake and metabolism of that sugar. In addition, bacteria have genes that encode enzymes that synthesize molecules such as particular amino acids. For these genes, the control of expression often occurs at the level of transcription. In this section, we will examine the underlying molecular mechanisms that bring about transcriptional regulation in bacteria.

Transcriptional Regulation Involves Regulatory Transcription Factors and Small Effector Molecules

In most cases, regulation of transcription involves the actions of **regulatory transcription factors**—proteins that bind to **regulatory sequences**, usually in the DNA in the vicinity of a promoter, and affect the rate of transcription of one or more nearby genes. These transcription factors either decrease or increase the rate of transcription of a gene. **Repressors** are regulatory transcription factors that bind to the DNA and decrease the rate of transcription. This is a form of regulation called **negative control**. **Activators** bind to the DNA and increase the rate of transcription, a form of regulation termed **positive control** (**Figure 14.5a**).

In conjunction with regulatory transcription factors, molecules called **small effector molecules** often play a critical role in transcriptional regulation. A small effector molecule exerts its effects by binding to a regulatory transcription factor and causing a conformational change in the protein. In many cases, the effect of the conformational change determines whether or not the protein can bind to the DNA. **Figure 14.5b** illustrates an example involving a repressor. When the small effector molecule is not present in the cytoplasm, the repressor binds to the DNA and inhibits transcription. However, when the small effector molecule is present in the cytoplasm, it will bind to the repressor and cause a conformational change that inhibits the ability of the protein to bind to the DNA. Transcription can occur because the repressor is not able to bind to the DNA. Repressors and activators that respond to small effector molecules have two functional regions called domains. One domain is a site where the protein binds to the DNA, whereas the other is the binding site for the small effector molecule.

The *lac* Operon Contains Genes That Encode Proteins Involved in Lactose Metabolism

In bacteria, a set of two or more genes may be under the transcriptional control of a single promoter. This arrangement is known as an **operon**. The group of genes are transcribed as a single unit, resulting in the production of a **polycistronic mRNA**, an mRNA that encodes more than one protein. What advantage does this arrangement provide? An operon allows a bacterium to coordinately regulate a group of genes that encode proteins whose functions are used in a common pathway.

The genome of *E. coli* carries an operon, called the **lac operon**, that contains the genes for the proteins that allow the bacterium to

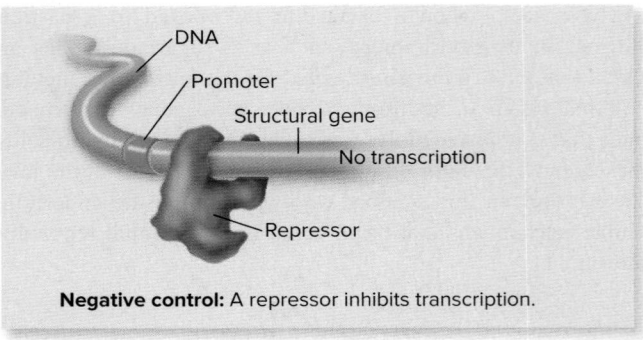
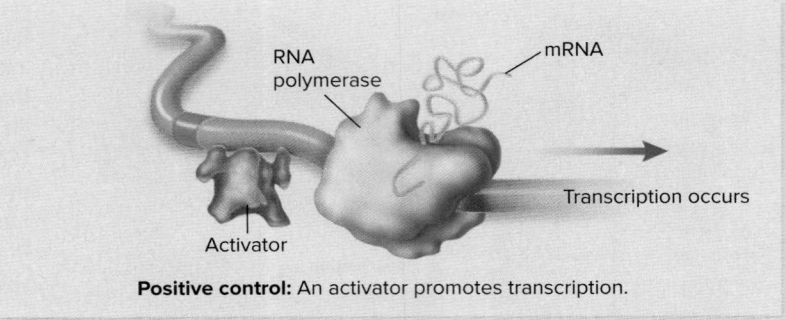

Negative control: A repressor inhibits transcription.

Positive control: An activator promotes transcription.

(a) Actions of regulatory transcription factors

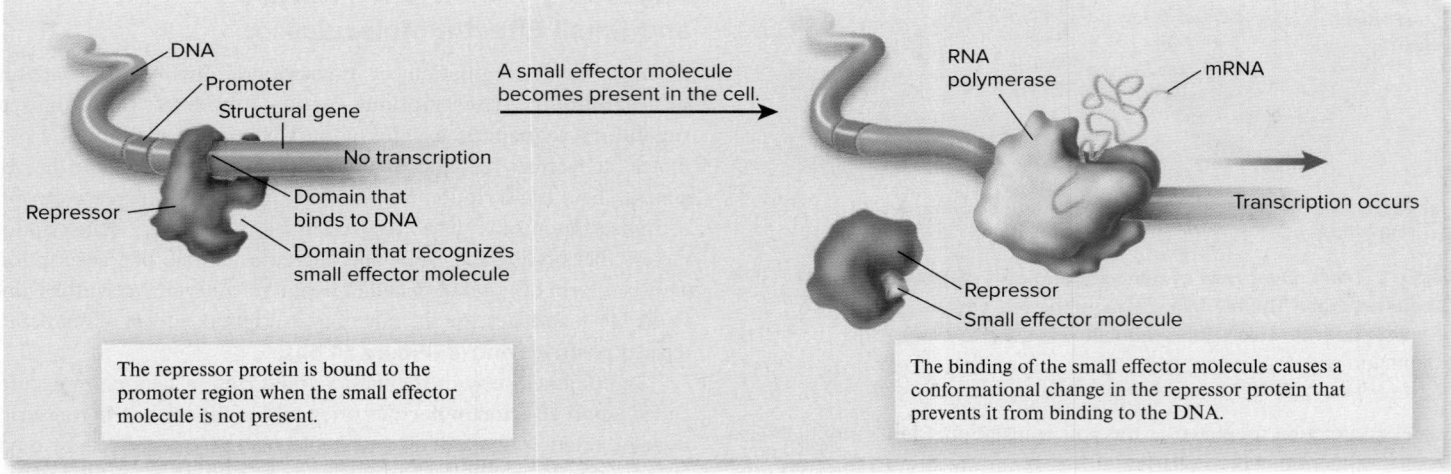

The repressor protein is bound to the promoter region when the small effector molecule is not present.

The binding of the small effector molecule causes a conformational change in the repressor protein that prevents it from binding to the DNA.

(b) Action of a small effector molecule on a repressor

Figure 14.5   Actions of regulatory transcription factors and small effector molecules. (a) Regulatory transcription factors are proteins that exert negative or positive control. **(b)** One way that a small effector molecule may exert its effects is by preventing a repressor protein from binding to the DNA.

metabolize lactose (refer back to Figure 14.1). **Figure 14.6a** shows the organization of this operon as it is found in the *E. coli* chromosome, as well as the polycistronic mRNA that is transcribed from it. The *lac* operon contains a promoter, *lacP*, that is involved in the transcription of three protein-encoding genes: *lacZ*, *lacY*, and *lacA*.

- The *lacZ* gene encodes β-galactosidase, which is an enzyme that breaks down lactose (**Figure 14.6b**). As a side reaction, β-galactosidase also converts a small percentage of lactose into allolactose, a structurally similar sugar, or lactose analogue. As described later, allolactose is important in the regulation of the *lac* operon.

- The *lacY* gene encodes lactose permease, which is a membrane protein required for the transport of lactose into the cytoplasm of the bacterium.

- The *lacA* gene encodes galactoside transacetylase, which covalently modifies lactose and lactose analogues by attaching an acetyl group (—COCH_3). The attachment of acetyl groups to nonmetabolizable lactose analogues prevents their toxic buildup in the cytoplasm.

Near the *lac* promoter are two regulatory sequences designated the operator and the CAP site (see Figure 14.6a). The **operator** (*lacO*) is a regulatory sequence in the DNA. The sequence of bases at the operator provides a binding site for a repressor protein. The **CAP site** is a regulatory sequence recognized by an activator protein.

Adjacent to the *lac* operon is the *lacI* gene, which encodes the **lac repressor**. This repressor protein is important for the regulation of the *lac* operon. The *lacI* gene, which is constitutively expressed at a fairly low level, has its own promoter called the *i* promoter. The *lacI* gene is not considered a part of the *lac* operon. Let's now take a look at how the *lac* operon is regulated by the lac repressor.

The *lac* Operon Is Under Negative Control by a Repressor Protein

In the late 1950s, the first researchers to investigate gene regulation were French biologists François Jacob and Jacques Monod at the Pasteur Institute in Paris, France. Their focus on gene regulation stemmed from an interest in the phenomenon known as enzyme adaptation, which had been identified early in the 20th century. Enzyme adaptation occurs when a particular enzyme appears within a living cell only after the cell has been exposed to the substrate for that enzyme. Jacob and Monod studied lactose metabolism in *E. coli* to investigate this phenomenon. When they exposed bacteria to lactose, the levels of lactose-utilizing enzymes in the cells increased by

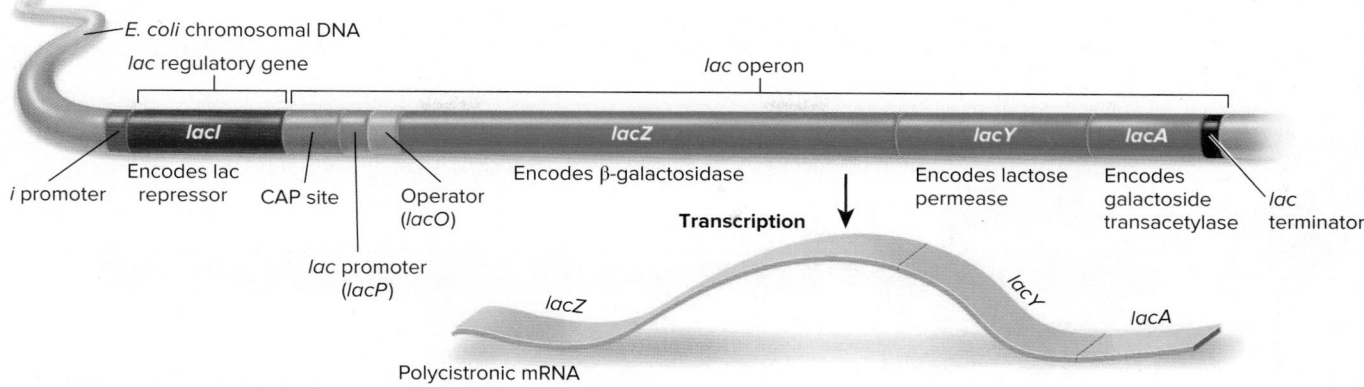

(a) Organization of DNA sequences in the *lac* region of the *E. coli* chromosome

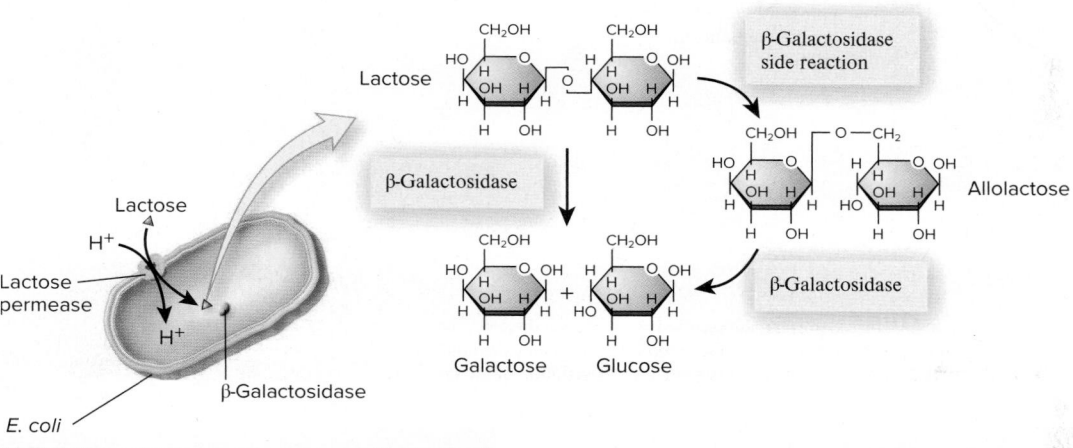

(b) Functions of lactose permease and β-galactosidase

Figure 14.6 **The *lac* operon.** **(a)** This diagram depicts a region of the *E. coli* chromosome that contains the *lacI* gene and the adjacent *lac* operon, as well as the polycistronic mRNA transcribed from the operon. The mRNA is translated into three proteins: β-galactosidase, lactose permease, and galactoside transacetylase. **(b)** Lactose permease cotransports H⁺ with lactose. Bacteria maintain an H⁺ gradient across their cytoplasmic membrane that drives the active transport of lactose into the cytoplasm. β-Galactosidase cleaves lactose into galactose and glucose. As a side reaction, it can also convert lactose into allolactose.

Concept Check: *Which genes are under the control of the lac promoter?*

1,000- to 10,000-fold. After lactose was removed, the synthesis of the enzymes abruptly stopped.

The first mechanism of regulation that Jacob and Monod discovered involved the lac repressor, which binds to the sequence of bases found at the *lac* operator site. Once bound, the lac repressor prevents RNA polymerase from transcribing the *lacZ*, *lacY*, and *lacA* genes (**Figure 14.7a**). RNA polymerase can bind to the promoter when the lac repressor is bound to the operator site, but cannot move past the operator to transcribe the *lacZ*, *lacY*, and *lacA* genes.

Whether or not the lac repressor binds to the operator site depends on allolactose, the previously mentioned side product of the β-galactosidase enzyme (see Figure 14.6b). How does allolactose control the lac repressor? Allolactose is an example of a small effector molecule. The lac repressor protein contains four identical subunits, each of which recognizes a single allolactose molecule. When four allolactose molecules bind to the lac repressor, a conformational change occurs that prevents the repressor from binding to the operator. Under these conditions, RNA polymerase is free to transcribe the operon (**Figure 14.7b**).

The regulation of the *lac* operon enables *E. coli* to conserve energy because lactose-utilizing proteins are made only when lactose is present in the environment. Allolactose is an **inducer**, a small effector molecule that increases the rate of transcription, and the *lac* operon is said to be an **inducible operon**. When the bacterium is not exposed to lactose, no allolactose is available to bind to the lac repressor. Therefore, the lac repressor binds to the operator site and inhibits transcription. In reality, the repressor does not completely inhibit transcription, so very small amounts of β-galactosidase, lactose permease, and galactoside transacetylase are made. However, the levels are far too low for the bacterium to readily use lactose. When the bacterium is exposed to lactose, a small amount can be transported into the cytoplasm via lactose permease, and β-galactosidase converts some of it to allolactose (see Figure 14.6b). The cytoplasmic level of allolactose gradually rises until allolactose binds to the lac repressor, which induces the *lac* operon and promotes a high rate of transcription of the *lacZ*, *lacY*, and *lacA* genes. Translation of the encoded polypeptides produces the proteins needed for lactose uptake and metabolism, as described previously in Figure 14.1.

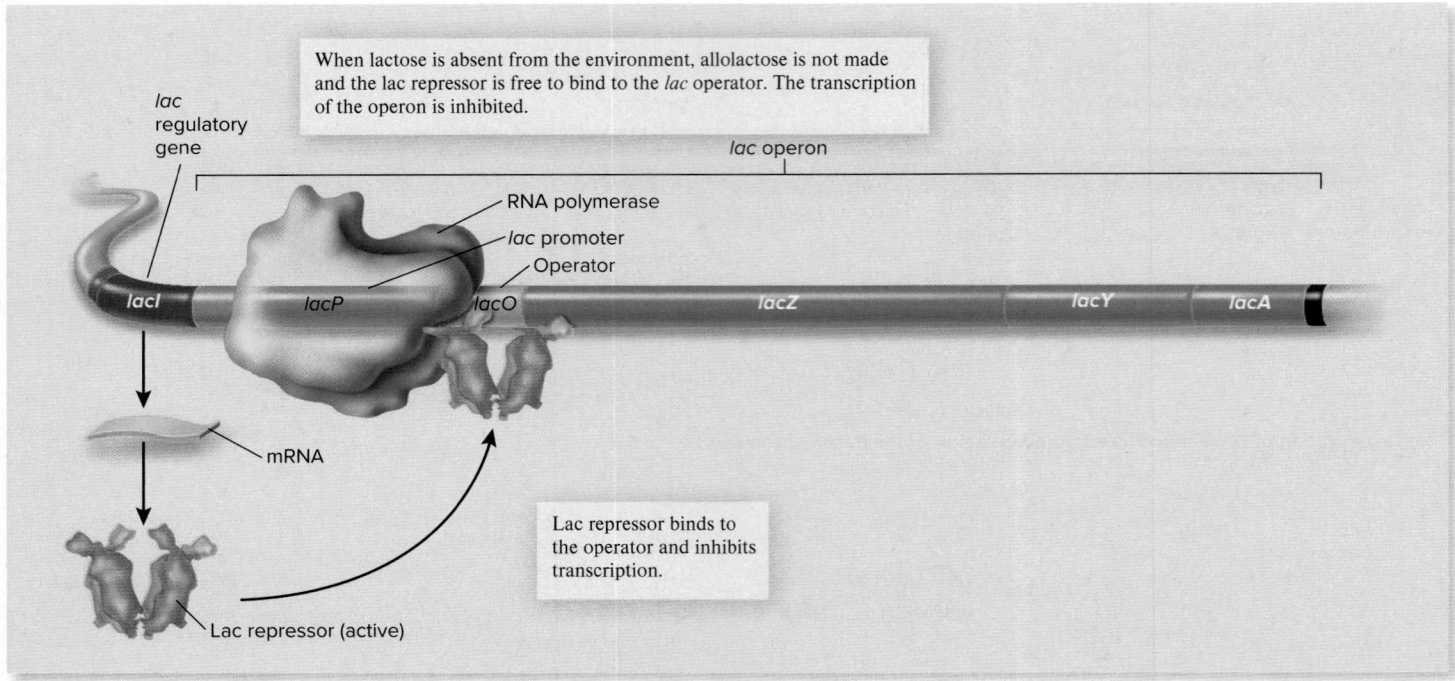

When lactose is absent from the environment, allolactose is not made and the lac repressor is free to bind to the *lac* operator. The transcription of the operon is inhibited.

lac operon

lac regulatory gene

RNA polymerase

lac promoter

Operator

lacI   *lacP*   *lacO*   *lacZ*   *lacY*   *lacA*

mRNA

Lac repressor binds to the operator and inhibits transcription.

Lac repressor (active)

(a) Lactose absent from the environment

When lactose is present, allolactose is made inside the cell. The binding of allolactose to the lac repressor prevents it from binding to the *lac* operator site. This permits the transcription of the *lac* operon.

RNA polymerase

lacI   *lacP*   *lacO*   *lacZ*   *lacY*   *lacA*

Transcription

Polycistronic mRNA

mRNA

Translation

β-Galactosidase

Lactose permease

Galactoside transacetylase

Allolactose

Conformational change

The binding of allolactose to the lac repressor causes a conformational change that prevents the lac repressor from binding to the operator site.

Lac repressor (inactive)

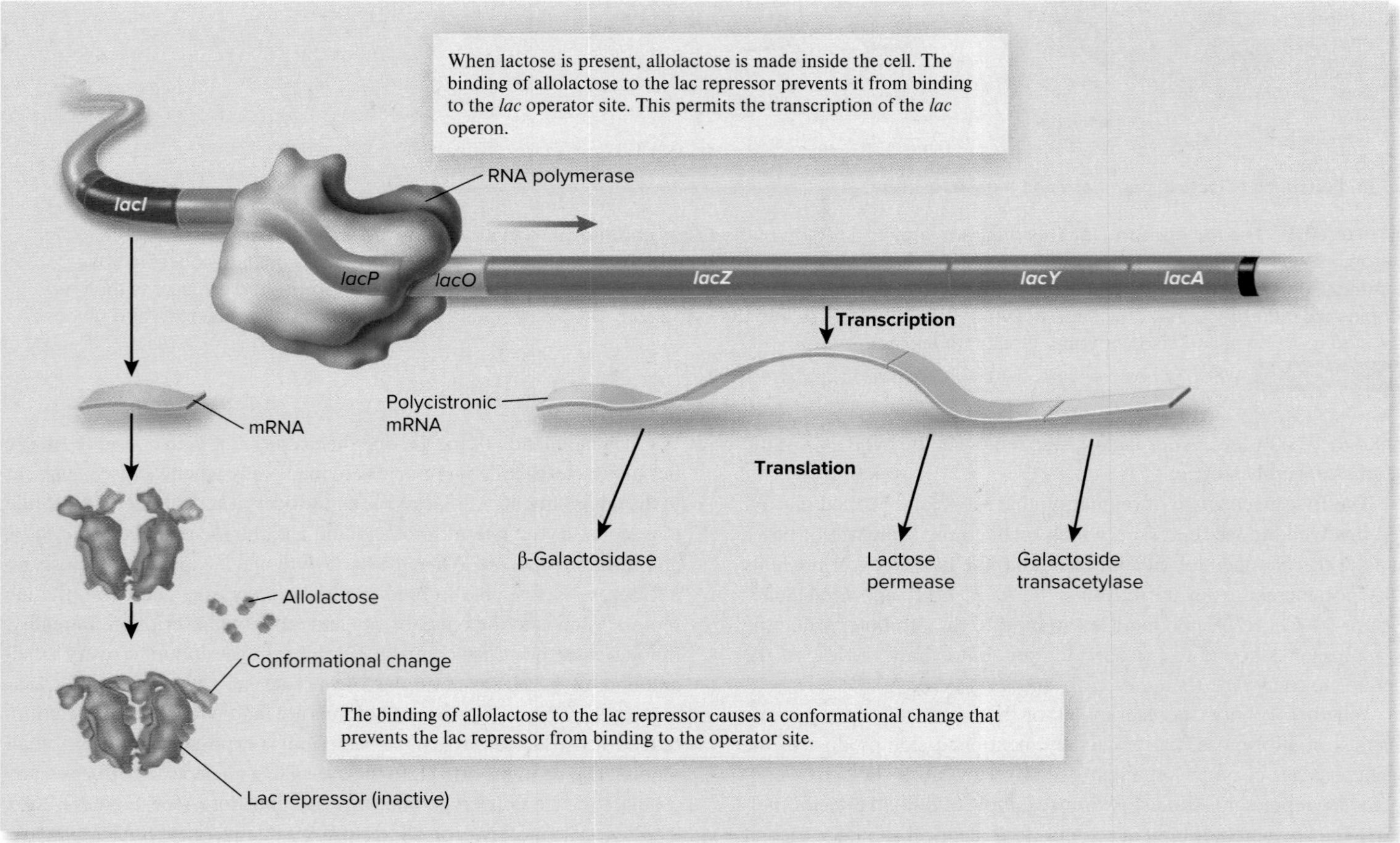

(b) Lactose present

Figure 14.7 **Negative control of an inducible set of genes: function of the lac repressor in regulating the *lac* operon.**

Concept Check: *With regard to regulatory proteins and small effector molecules, explain the meaning of negative control and inducible.*

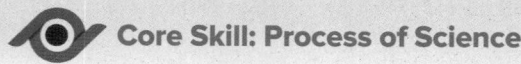

Core Skill: Process of Science

Feature Investigation | Jacob, Monod, and Pardee Studied a Constitutive Mutant to Determine the Function of the Lac Repressor

Thus far, we have learned that the lac repressor binds to the *lac* operator site to exert its effects. Let's now take a look at experiments that helped researchers determine the function of the lac repressor. Our understanding of *lac* operon regulation came from studies involving *E. coli* strains that showed abnormalities in the process. In the 1950s, French biologist François Jacob, French biochemist Jacques Monod, and their colleague, American biochemist Arthur Pardee, had identified a few rare mutant bacteria that expressed the genes of the *lac* operon constitutively, meaning that the *lacZ*, *lacY*, and *lacA* genes were expressed even in the absence of lactose in the environment. The researchers discovered that some mutations that caused this abnormality had occurred in the *lacI* region of the DNA. Such strains were termed *lacI⁻* (*lacI* minus) to indicate that the *lacI* region was not functioning properly. Normal, or wild-type, *lacI* strains of *E. coli* are called *lacI⁺* (*lacI* plus).

The researchers initially hypothesized that the *lacI* gene encodes an enzyme that degrades an internal inducer of the *lac* operon. The *lacI⁻* mutation was thought to inhibit this enzyme, thereby allowing the internal inducer to be synthesized continuously. In this way, the *lacI⁻* mutation made it unnecessary for cells to be exposed to lactose for induction. However, over the course of this study and other studies, the researchers eventually arrived at the hypothesis that the *lacI* gene encodes a repressor protein, which proved to be correct (**Figure 14.8**). A mutation in the *lacI* gene that eliminates the synthesis of a functional lac repressor prevents the lac repressor protein from inhibiting transcription. At the time of Jacob, Monod, and Pardee's work, however, the function of the lac repressor was not yet known.

To understand the nature of the *lacI⁻* mutation, Jacob, Monod, and Pardee applied a genetic approach. Although the transfer of DNA from one bacterial cell to another is described in Chapter 19, let's briefly examine this process in order to understand this experiment. Bacteria sometimes exchange circular segments of DNA known as F factors. Some F factors also carry genes that were originally found within the bacterial chromosome. These types of F factors are called F′ factors (F prime factors). A bacterial cell that contains an F′ factor is called a **merozygote**. The study of merozygotes was instrumental in allowing Jacob, Monod, and Pardee to elucidate the function of the *lacI* gene.

As shown in **Figure 14.9**, these researchers studied the *lac* operon in a bacterial strain carrying a *lacI⁻* mutation that caused constitutive expression of the *lac* operon. In addition, a F′ factor was transferred to the mutant strain, thereby producing a merozygote that also carried a normal *lac* operon and a normal *lacI⁺* gene on this F′ factor. The merozygote contained both *lacI⁺* and *lacI⁻* genes. The constitutive mutant and corresponding merozygote were grown separately in liquid media and then divided into two tubes each. In half of the tubes, the cells were incubated with lactose to determine if lactose was needed to induce the expression of the operon. In the other tubes, lactose was omitted. To monitor the expression of the *lac* operon, the cells were broken open and then tested for the amount of β-galactosidase they released by measuring the ability of any β-galactosidase present to convert a colorless compound into a yellow product.

The data table in Figure 14.9 summarizes the effects of this constitutive mutation and its analysis in a merozygote. As Jacob, Monod, and Pardee already knew, the *lacI⁻* mutant strain expressed the *lac* operon constitutively, in both the presence and the absence of lactose. However, when a normal *lac* operon and *lacI⁺* gene on an F′ factor were introduced into a cell harboring the mutant *lacI⁻* gene on the chromosome, the normal *lacI⁺* gene could regulate both operons. In the absence of lactose, both operons were shut off. How did Jacob, Monod, and Pardee explain these results? They concluded that a single *lacI⁺* gene on the F′ factor produces enough repressor protein to bind to both operator sites. Furthermore, this protein is diffusible—can spread through the cytoplasm—and binds to *lac* operons that are on the F′ factor and on the bacterial chromosome. Taken together, the data indicated that the normal *lacI* gene encodes a diffusible protein that represses the *lac* operon.

The interactions between regulatory proteins and DNA sequences illustrated in this experiment led to the definition of three genetic terms. A ***cis*-acting element** is a DNA segment that must be adjacent to the gene(s) that it regulates. The *lac* operator site is an example of a *cis*-acting element. A ***trans*-effect** is a form of gene regulation that can occur even though two DNA segments are not physically adjacent. The action of the lac repressor on the *lac* operon is a *trans*-effect. A ***cis*-effect** is mediated by a *cis*-acting element that binds regulatory proteins, whereas a *trans*-effect is mediated by genes that encode diffusible regulatory proteins.

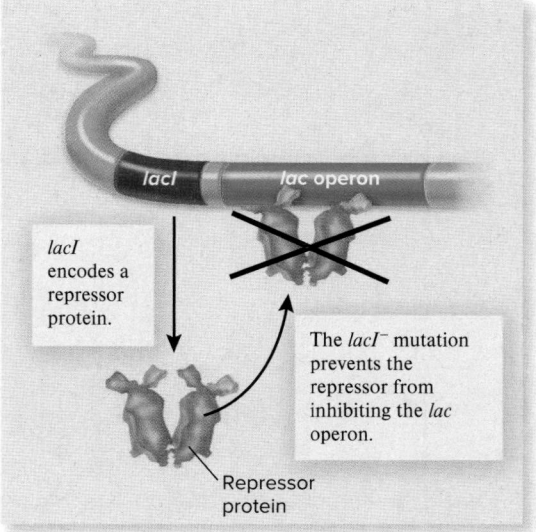

lacI encodes a repressor protein.

The *lacI⁻* mutation prevents the repressor from inhibiting the *lac* operon.

Repressor protein

Figure 14.8 A hypothesis for the function of the *lacI* gene.

Figure 14.9 The experiment performed by Jacob, Monod, and Pardee to study a constitutive *lacI⁻* mutant.

HYPOTHESIS The *lacI⁻* mutation inhibits the lac repressor and thereby allows the constitutive expression of the *lac* operon. Note: This correct hypothesis actually arose from the results of this study and other studies.

KEY MATERIALS A constitutive *lacI⁻* mutant strain was already characterized. An F′ factor carrying a normal *lacI⁺* gene and *lac* operon was introduced into this strain to produce a merozygote strain. Note: POZ⁺Y⁺A⁺ refers to a normal *lac* operon.

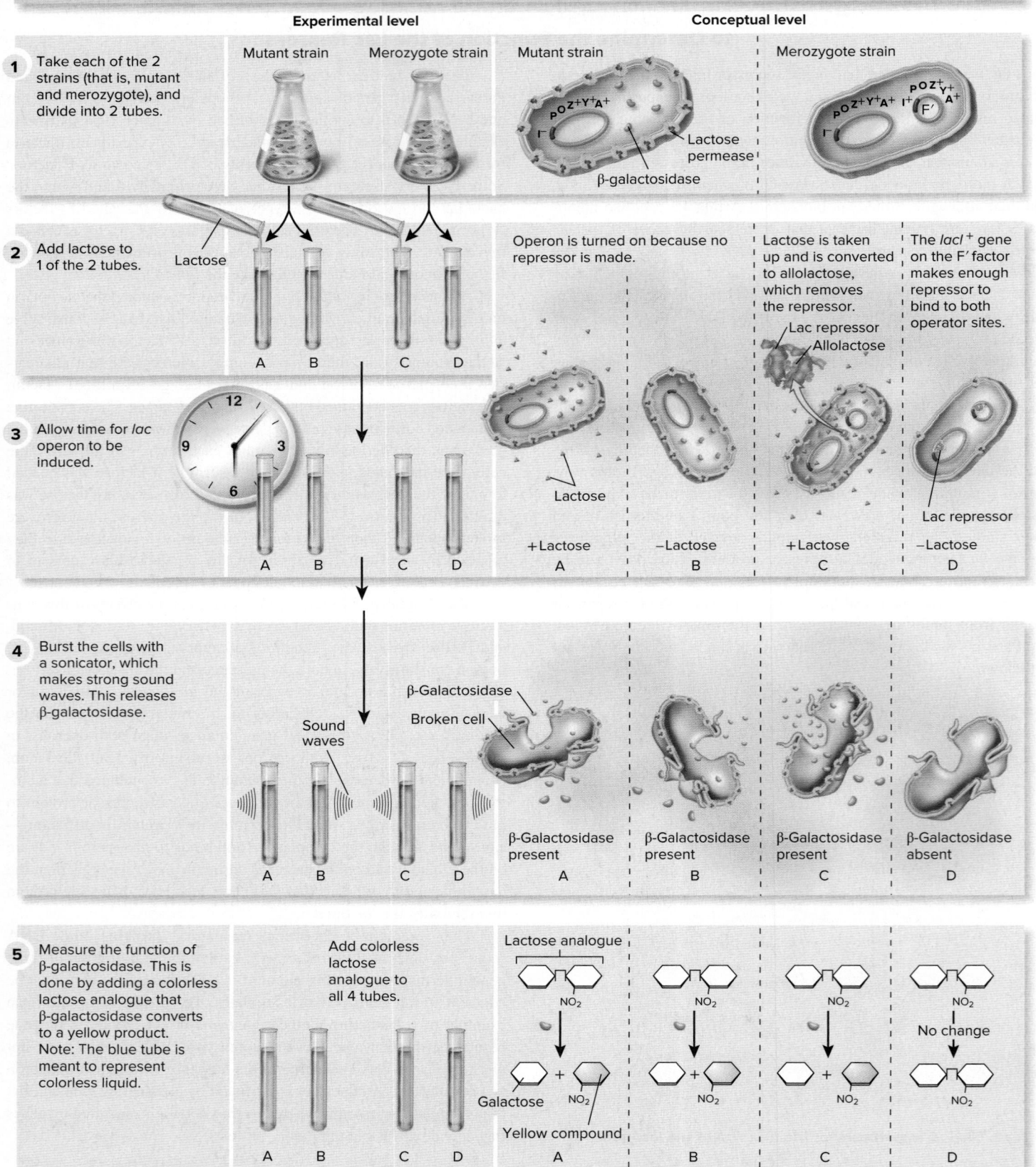

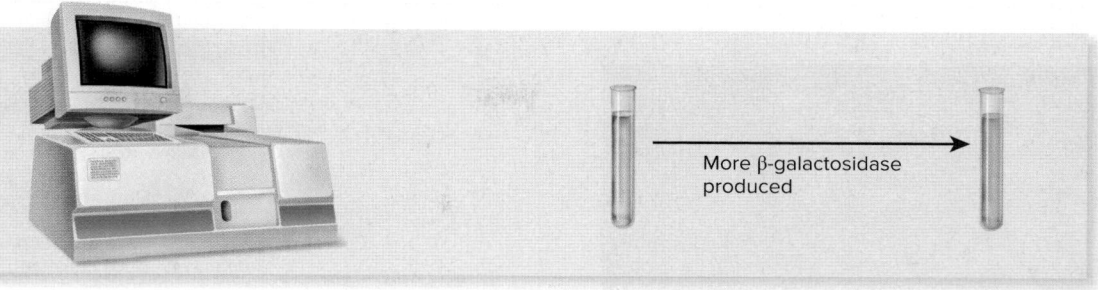

6 The amount of yellow color is measured with a spectrophotometer; the deeper the yellow color, the more β-galactosidase was produced.

More β-galactosidase produced

7 THE DATA

Results from step 6:

	Expression of the *lac* operon	
	With lactose	**Without lactose**
Mutant strain	100%	100%
Merozygote strain	220%	<1%

8 CONCLUSION The *lacI* gene encodes a diffusible repressor protein.

9 SOURCE Jacob, F., and Monod, J. 1961. Genetic regulatory mechanisms in the synthesis of proteins. *Journal of Molecular Biology* 3: 318–356.

Experimental Questions

1. What were the key observations made by Jacob, Monod, and Pardee that led to the development of their hypothesis regarding the *lacI* gene and the regulation of the *lac* operon?

2. **CoreSKILL »** What was the eventual hypothesis proposed by the researchers to explain the function of the *lacI* gene and the regulation of the *lac* operon?

3. **CoreSKILL »** How did Jacob, Monod, and Pardee test the hypothesis? What were the results of the experiment? How do these results support the idea that the *lacI* gene produces a repressor protein?

The *lac* Operon Is Also Under Positive Control by an Activator Protein

In addition to being under negative control by a repressor protein, the *lac* operon is also positively regulated by an activator called the **catabolite activator protein (CAP)**. CAP is controlled by a small effector molecule, **cyclic AMP (cAMP)**, which is produced from ATP via an enzyme known as adenylyl cyclase. Gene regulation involving CAP and cAMP is an example of positive control (**Figure 14.10**). When cAMP binds to CAP, the cAMP-CAP complex binds to the CAP site near the *lac* promoter. This causes a bend in the DNA that enhances the ability of RNA polymerase to bind to the promoter. In this way, the rate of transcription is increased.

The key functional role of CAP is to allow *E. coli* to choose between different sugars as an energy source. In a process known as **catabolite repression**, the presence of a preferred energy source inhibits the use of other energy sources. In this case, transcription of the *lac* operon is inhibited by the presence of glucose, which is a catabolite (it is broken down—catabolized—inside the cell). This gene regulation allows *E. coli* to preferentially use glucose instead of other sugars, such as lactose. How does this occur? Glucose inhibits the production of cAMP, thereby preventing the binding of CAP to the DNA. In this way, glucose blocks the activation of the *lac* operon by inhibiting transcription. Though it may

seem puzzling, the term catabolite repression was coined before the action of the cAMP-CAP complex was understood at the molecular level. Historically, the primary observation of researchers was that glucose (a catabolite) inhibited (repressed) lactose metabolism. Further experimentation revealed that CAP is actually an activator protein.

Figure 14.11 considers the four possible environmental conditions that an *E. coli* bacterium might experience with regard to these two sugars.

- When both lactose and glucose levels are high (Figure 14.11a), CAP does not bind to the CAP site, which inhibits transcription. However, a low level of transcription does occur. Under these conditions, the bacterium primarily uses glucose rather than lactose. Why is this a benefit to the bacterium? The bacterium conserves energy by using one type of sugar at a time.

- If the lactose level is high and the glucose level is low (Figure 14.11b), the transcription rate of the *lac* operon is very high because CAP is bound to the CAP site and the lac repressor is not bound to the operator site. Under these conditions, the bacterium metabolizes lactose.

- When the lactose level is low, the lac repressor prevents transcription of the *lac* operon, whether the glucose level is high or low (Figure 14.11c,d).

CAP site

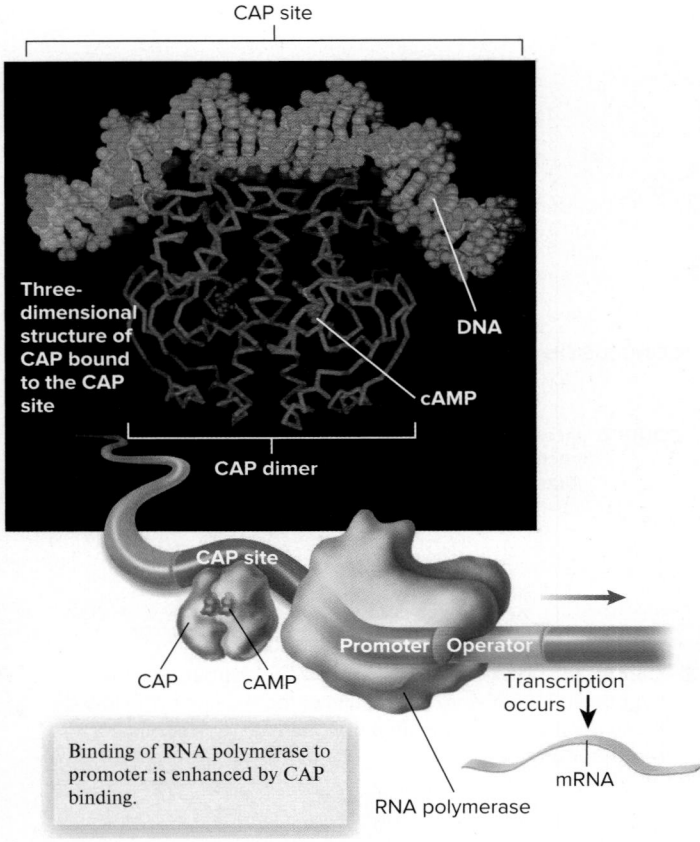

Three-dimensional structure of CAP bound to the CAP site

DNA

cAMP

CAP dimer

CAP site

Promoter   Operator

CAP   cAMP

Transcription occurs ↓

mRNA

RNA polymerase

Binding of RNA polymerase to promoter is enhanced by CAP binding.

Figure 14.10 **Positive control of the *lac* operon by the catabolite activator protein (CAP).** When cAMP is bound to CAP, CAP binds to the DNA and causes it to bend. This bend facilitates the binding of RNA polymerase. ©Thomas Steitz, Howard Hughes Medical Institution, Yale University

 Core Skill: Connections Look back at Figure 9.12. What is the function of cAMP in eukaryotic cells?

BIO TIPS   **THE QUESTION** *Let's suppose you have isolated a mutant strain of E. coli in which the lac operon is constitutively expressed. In other words, the operon is turned on in the presence or the absence of lactose. One possibility is that the mutation is blocking transcription of the lacI gene, thereby preventing the synthesis of lac repressor. A second possibility is that the mutation altered the sequence of the lac operator site in a way that prevents the lac repressor protein from binding there. How could you distinguish between these two possibilities?*

TOPIC **What topic in biology does this question address?**
The topic is gene regulation. More specifically, the question asks how you could determine the way a mutation is affecting the expression of the *lac* operon.

INFORMATION **What information do you know based on the question and your understanding of the topic?** From the question, you know that the mutation is either inhibiting the expression of *lacI* or has altered *lacO* in a way that prevents the binding of lac repressor. From your understanding of the topic, you may

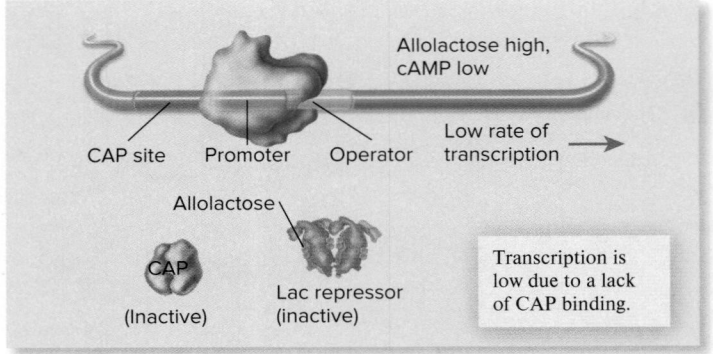

Allolactose high, cAMP low

CAP site   Promoter   Operator

Low rate of transcription →

Allolactose

CAP (Inactive)

Lac repressor (inactive)

Transcription is low due to a lack of CAP binding.

(a) Lactose high, glucose high

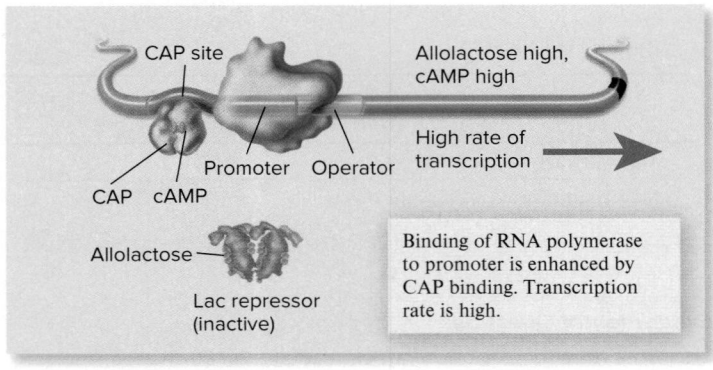

CAP site

Allolactose high, cAMP high

Promoter   Operator

High rate of transcription →

CAP   cAMP

Allolactose

Lac repressor (inactive)

Binding of RNA polymerase to promoter is enhanced by CAP binding. Transcription rate is high.

(b) Lactose high, glucose low

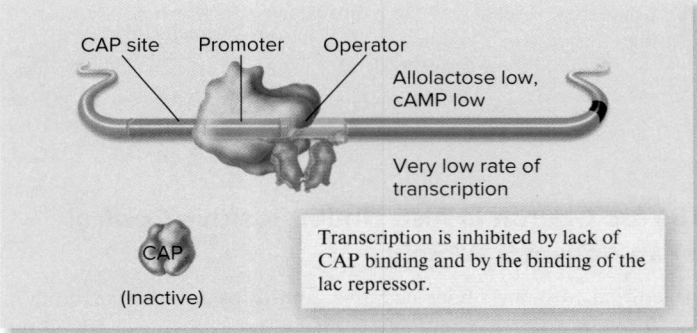

CAP site   Promoter   Operator

Allolactose low, cAMP low

Very low rate of transcription

CAP (Inactive)

Transcription is inhibited by lack of CAP binding and by the binding of the lac repressor.

(c) Lactose low, glucose high

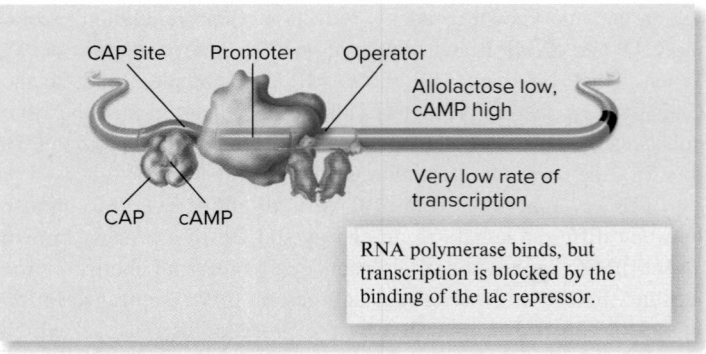

CAP site   Promoter   Operator

Allolactose low, cAMP high

Very low rate of transcription

CAP   cAMP

RNA polymerase binds, but transcription is blocked by the binding of the lac repressor.

(d) Lactose low, glucose low

Figure 14.11 **Effects of lactose and glucose on the expression of the *lac* operon.**

Concept Check: *What are the advantages of having both an activator and a repressor protein?*

remember that the lac repressor exhibits a *trans*-effect because it is a diffusible protein, whereas *lacO* is a *cis*-acting element.

(P)ROBLEM-SOLVING (S)TRATEGY *Design an experiment.* **Predict the outcome.** One strategy to solve this problem is to design an experiment that can distinguish between a mutation that results in a *cis*-effect versus one that produces a *trans*-effect. The use of a merozygote is one way to accomplish that goal.

ANSWER

Key materials: The constitutive strain of E. coli and a merozygote that carries a normal lac operon and a normal lacI gene on an F ' factor (see Figure 14.9).

Procedure:

1. Place each strain into separate tubes with or without lactose.
2. Allow induction to occur.
3. Burst the cells with a sonicator.
4. Add the lactose analogue, and measure yellow color production.

Expected results: If the mutation is in lacI, the repressor encoded on the F ' factor will inhibit the expression of the lac operon on the chromosome and the one on the F ' factor. There will be very little yellow color in the absence of lactose in the tube with the merozygote. (This was the result obtained in Figure 14.9.) Alternatively, if the mutation is in lacO, the lac operon on the chromosome will still be turned on even in the absence of lactose. The merozygote will produce a strong yellow color in the absence of lactose.

The *trp* Operon Is Under Negative Control by a Repressor Protein

So far in this section, we have examined the regulation of the *lac* operon. Let's now consider an example of an operon that encodes enzymes involved in biosynthesis rather than breakdown. Our example is the ***trp* operon** of *E. coli*, which encodes enzymes that are required to make the amino acid tryptophan, a building block of proteins. More specifically, the *trpE, trpD, trpC, trpB,* and *trpA* genes encode enzymes that are involved in a pathway that leads to tryptophan synthesis.

The *trp* operon is regulated by a repressor protein that is encoded by the *trpR* gene. The binding of the repressor to the *trp* operator site inhibits transcription. The ability of the trp repressor to bind to the *trp* operator is controlled by tryptophan, which is the product of the metabolic pathway controlled by the enzymes that are encoded by the operon.

- When the tryptophan level within the cell is very low, the trp repressor cannot bind to the operator site. Under these conditions, RNA polymerase readily transcribes the operon (**Figure 14.12a**). In this way, the cell expresses the genes that encode enzymes that result in the synthesis of tryptophan, which is in short supply.

- When the tryptophan level within the cell is high, tryptophan turns off the *trp* operon. Tryptophan acts as a small effector molecule, or **corepressor**, by binding to the trp repressor protein. This causes a conformational change in the repressor that allows it to bind to the *trp* operator site, inhibiting

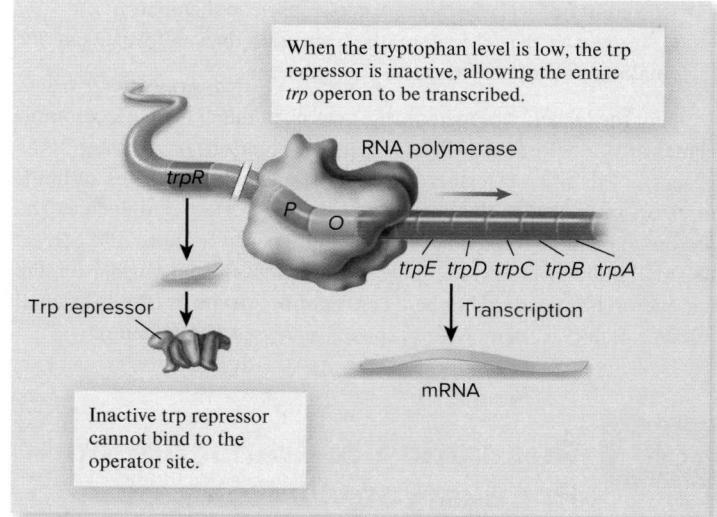

When the tryptophan level is low, the trp repressor is inactive, allowing the entire *trp* operon to be transcribed.

Inactive trp repressor cannot bind to the operator site.

(a) Low tryptophan

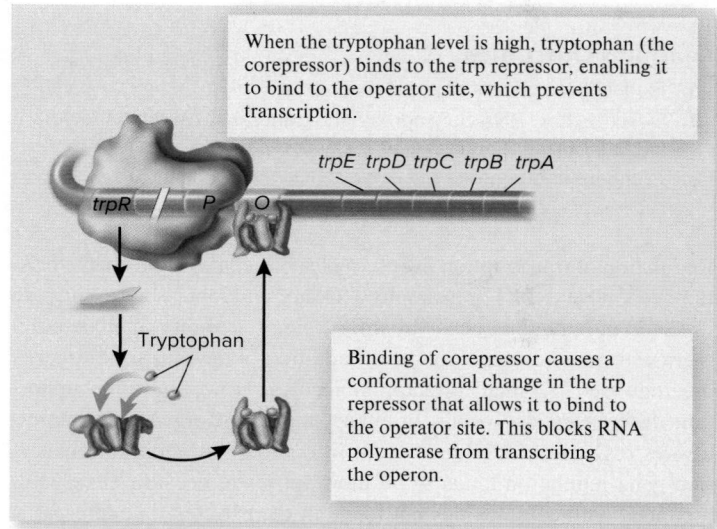

When the tryptophan level is high, tryptophan (the corepressor) binds to the trp repressor, enabling it to bind to the operator site, which prevents transcription.

Binding of corepressor causes a conformational change in the trp repressor that allows it to bind to the operator site. This blocks RNA polymerase from transcribing the operon.

(b) High tryptophan

Figure 14.12 **Negative control of a repressible set of genes: function of the trp repressor and corepressor (tryptophan) in regulating the *trp* operon.**

 Core Skill: Modeling The goal of this modeling challenge is to propose a model for the structure of a mutant trp repressor that cannot bind to tryptophan and to predict the mutant's effect on the expression of the *trp* operon.

Modeling Challenge: Let's suppose that researchers identified a mutant form of the trp repressor that cannot bind to tryptophan. Draw a model for the structure of the repressor in the presence of tryptophan and in its absence. Based on your model, would you predict that the *trp* operon would be repressed in the presence of tryptophan?

the ability of RNA polymerase to transcribe the operon (**Figure 14.12b**). Therefore, the bacterium does not waste energy making tryptophan when it is abundant.

For the *lac* and *trp* operons, the actions of their small effector molecules are quite different. The lac repressor binds to its operator in the absence of its small effector molecule, whereas the trp repressor binds to its operator only in the presence of its small effector molecule. The *lac* operon is categorized as an inducible operon because allolactose, its small effector molecule, induces transcription. By comparison, the *trp* operon is considered to be a **repressible operon** because its small effector molecule, namely tryptophan, represses transcription.

14.3 Regulation of Transcription in Eukaryotes I: Roles of Transcription Factors and Mediator

Learning Outcomes:

1. Explain the concept of combinatorial control.
2. Describe how RNA polymerase and general transcription factors initiate transcription at the core promoter.
3. Compare and contrast the roles of activators, coactivators, repressors, TFIID, and mediator in gene regulation.

Regulation of transcription in eukaryotes has some of the characteristics seen in bacteria. For example, activator and repressor proteins are involved in regulating genes by influencing the ability of RNA polymerase to initiate transcription. In addition, many eukaryotic genes are regulated by small effector molecules. However, some important differences also occur. In eukaryotic species, genes are almost always organized individually, not in operons. In addition, eukaryotic gene regulation tends to be more intricate, because eukaryotes are faced with complexities not found in their bacterial counterparts. For example, eukaryotes have more complicated cell structures that contain many more proteins and a variety of cell organelles. Many eukaryotes, such as animals and plants, are multicellular and contain different cell types. As discussed earlier in this chapter, animal cells may differentiate into neurons, muscle cells, and skin cells, and so on. Furthermore, animals and plants progress through developmental stages that require changes in gene expression.

By studying transcriptional regulation, researchers have discovered that most eukaryotic genes, particularly those found in multicellular species, are regulated by many factors. This phenomenon is called **combinatorial control** because the combination of many factors determines the expression of any given gene. At the level of transcription, the following factors contribute to combinatorial control:

1. One or more activators may stimulate the ability of RNA polymerase to initiate transcription.
2. One or more repressors may inhibit the ability of RNA polymerase to initiate transcription.
3. The function of activators and repressors may be modulated in several ways, which include the binding of small effector

molecules, protein-protein interactions, and covalent modifications.

4. Activators are necessary to alter chromatin structure in the region where a gene is located, thereby making it easier for the gene to be recognized and transcribed by RNA polymerase.
5. DNA methylation usually inhibits transcription, either by preventing the binding of an activator or by recruiting proteins that inhibit transcription.

All five of these factors may contribute to the regulation of a single gene, or possibly only three or four will play a role. In most cases, transcriptional regulation is aimed at controlling the initiation of transcription at the promoter. In this section and the following section, we will survey these basic types of gene regulation in eukaryotic species.

Eukaryotic Protein-Encoding Genes Have a Core Promoter and Regulatory Elements

To understand gene regulation in eukaryotes, we first need to consider the DNA sequences that are needed to initiate transcription. For eukaryotic protein-encoding genes, three features are common among most promoters: **regulatory elements**, a **TATA box**, and a **transcriptional start site** (**Figure 14.13**).

The TATA box and transcriptional start site form the **core promoter**. The transcriptional start site is the place in the DNA where transcription actually begins. The TATA box, which is a 5′–TATAAA–3′ sequence, is usually about 25 bp upstream from a transcriptional start site. The TATA box determines the precise starting point for transcription. If it is missing from the core promoter, transcription may start at a variety of different locations. The core promoter, acting alone, results in a low level of transcription that is termed **basal transcription**.

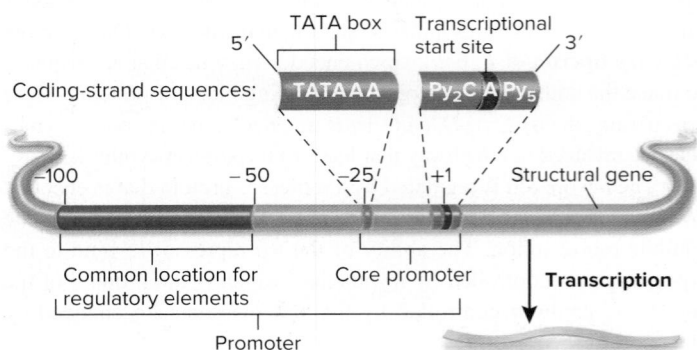

Figure 14.13 A common organization of sequences for the promoter of a eukaryotic protein-encoding gene. The core promoter has a TATA box and a transcriptional start site. The TATA box sequence is 5′–TATAAA–3′. However, not all protein-encoding genes in eukaryotes have a TATA box. The A highlighted in dark blue is the transcriptional start site. This A marks the site of the first adenine in the RNA transcript. The sequence that flanks the A of the transcriptional start site is two pyrimidines, then a cytosine (C), then five pyrimidines. Py stands for a pyrimidine—cytosine or thymine. Regulatory elements, such as enhancers and silencers, are usually found upstream from the core promoter.

Regulatory elements (or regulatory sequences) are DNA segments that regulate eukaryotic genes. As described later, regulatory elements are recognized by regulatory transcription factors that control the ability of RNA polymerase to initiate transcription at the core promoter. Some regulatory elements, known as **enhancers**, play a role in the ability of RNA polymerase to begin transcription, thereby enhancing the rate of transcription. When enhancers are not functioning, most eukaryotic genes have very low levels of transcription. Other regulatory elements, known as **silencers**, prevent transcription of a given gene when its expression is not needed. When these sequences function, the rate of transcription is decreased.

A common location for regulatory elements is the region that is 50–100 bp upstream from the transcriptional start site (see Figure 14.13). However, the locations of regulatory elements vary greatly among different eukaryotic genes. Regulatory elements can be quite distant from the promoter, even 100,000 bp away, yet exert strong effects on the ability of RNA polymerase to initiate transcription at the core promoter! Regulatory elements were first discovered by Japanese molecular biologist Susumu Tonegawa and coworkers in the 1980s. While studying genes that play a role in immunity, they identified a region that was far away from the core promoter but was needed for high levels of transcription to take place.

RNA Polymerase II, General Transcription Factors, and Mediator Are Needed to Transcribe Eukaryotic Protein-Encoding Genes

As discussed in Chapter 12, three forms of RNA polymerases, designated I, II, and III, are found in eukaryotes. RNA polymerase II transcribes protein-encoding genes. By studying transcription in a variety of eukaryotic species, researchers have identified three types of proteins that play a role in initiating transcription at the core promoter of protein-encoding genes. These are RNA polymerase II, five different proteins called **general transcription factors (GTFs)**, and a large protein complex called mediator.

RNA polymerase II and GTFs must come together at the TATA box of the core promoter so transcription can be initiated. A series of interactions that occurs between these proteins enables RNA polymerase II to bind to the DNA. The completed assembly of RNA polymerase II and GTFs at the TATA box is known as the **preinitiation complex** (**Figure 14.14**).

Another component needed for transcription in eukaryotes is the protein complex called mediator. **Mediator** is composed of many proteins that bind to each other to form an elliptically shaped complex that partially wraps around RNA polymerase II and the GTFs. Mediator derives its name from the observation that it mediates interactions between the preinitiation complex and regulatory transcription factors such as activators or repressors that bind to enhancers or silencers. The function of mediator is to control the rate at which RNA polymerase begins to transcribe RNA at the transcriptional start site.

Activators and Repressors May Influence the Function of GTFs or Mediator

In eukaryotes, regulatory transcription factors called activators and repressors bind to enhancers or silencers, respectively, and regulate

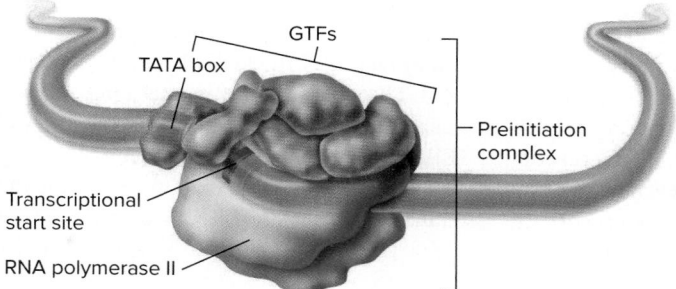

Figure 14.14 The preinitiation complex. General transcription factors (GTFs) and RNA polymerase II assemble into the preinitiation complex at the core promoter of eukaryotic protein-encoding genes.

the rate of transcription of genes. Activators and repressors commonly regulate the function of RNA polymerase II by binding to GTFs or mediator.

Affecting the Function of GTFs   As shown in **Figure 14.15**, some activators bind to an enhancer and then influence the function of GTFs. For example, an activator may improve the ability of a GTF called transcription factor II D (TFIID) to initiate transcription. The

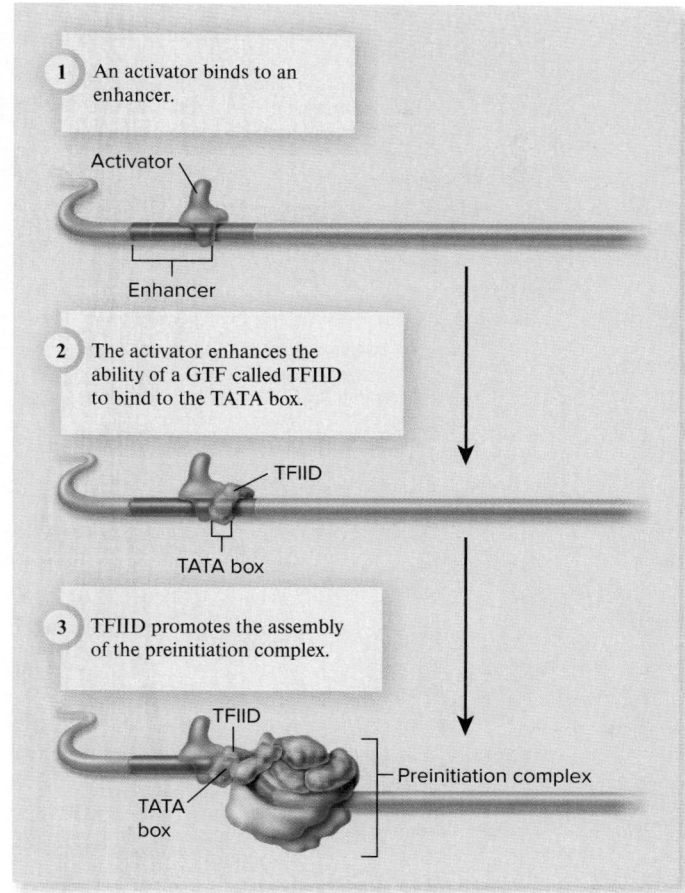

1 An activator binds to an enhancer.

2 The activator enhances the ability of a GTF called TFIID to bind to the TATA box.

3 TFIID promotes the assembly of the preinitiation complex.

Figure 14.15 Effect of an activator via TFIID, a general transcription factor.

function of TFIID is to recognize the TATA box and begin the assembly process. An activator may recruit TFIID to the TATA box, thereby promoting the assembly of GTFs and RNA polymerase II into the pre-initiation complex. In contrast, repressors may bind to a silencer and inhibit the function of TFIID. Certain repressors exert their effects by preventing the binding of TFIID to the TATA box or by inhibiting the ability of TFIID to assemble other GTFs and RNA polymerase II at the core promoter.

Affecting the Function of Mediator In addition to affecting GTFs, a second way that regulatory transcription factors control RNA polymerase II is via mediator (**Figure 14.16**). In this example, an activator also interacts with a **coactivator**—a protein that increases the rate of transcription but does not directly bind to the DNA itself. The activator-coactivator complex stimulates the function of mediator, thereby causing RNA polymerase II to proceed to the elongation phase of transcription more quickly. Alternatively, repressors have the opposite effect to those seen in Figure 14.16. When a repressor inhibits mediator, RNA polymerase II cannot progress to the elongation stage.

A third way that regulatory transcription factors influence transcription is by recruiting proteins that affect chromatin structure in the promoter region, as described in the next section.

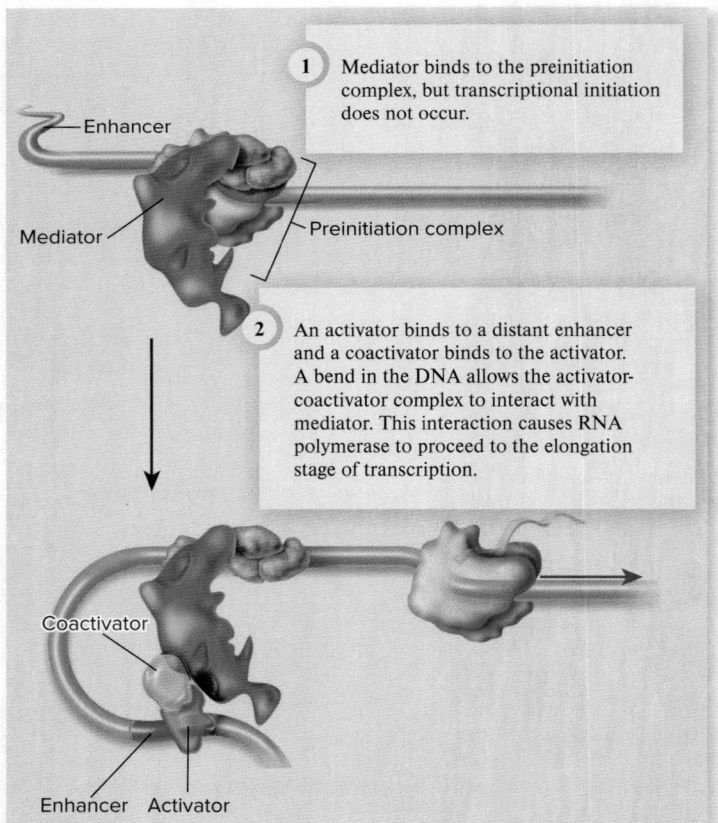

Figure 14.16 **Effect of an activator via mediator.**

Concept Check: *When an activator interacts with mediator, how does this affect the function of RNA polymerase?*

14.4 Regulation of Transcription in Eukaryotes II: Changes in Chromatin Structure and DNA Methylation

Learning Outcomes:

1. Describe the flanking of eukaryotic genes by nucleosome-free regions, and explain how nucleosomes are altered during gene transcription.
2. Explain how DNA methylation affects transcription.

In eukaryotes, DNA is associated with proteins to form a structure called **chromatin**—the complex of DNA and proteins that makes up eukaryotic chromosomes (refer back to Figures 11.22 through 11.25). How does the structure of chromatin affect gene transcription? Recall from Chapter 11 that nucleosomes are composed of DNA wrapped around an octamer of histone proteins. Depending on the locations and arrangements of nucleosomes, a region of chromatin containing a gene may be in a **closed conformation**, and transcription may be difficult or impossible. Transcription requires changes in chromatin structure that allow transcription factors to gain access to and bind to the DNA in the promoter region. Such chromatin, said to be in an **open conformation**, is accessible to GTFs and RNA polymerase II, so transcription can take place. In this section, we will examine how chromatin is converted from a closed to an open conformation. We will also explore how **DNA methylation**—the attachment of methyl groups to cytosine bases—affects chromatin conformation and gene expression.

Transcription Is Controlled by Changes in Chromatin Structure

In recent years, geneticists have been trying to identify the steps that promote the interconversion between the closed and open conformations of chromatin. One way to change chromatin structure is through **ATP-dependent chromatin-remodeling complexes**, which are complexes of proteins that alter chromatin structure. Such complexes use energy from ATP hydrolysis to drive a change in the locations and/or compositions of nucleosomes, thereby making the DNA more or less amenable to transcription. Therefore, chromatin remodeling is important for both the activation and repression of transcription.

How do ATP-dependent chromatin-remodeling complexes change chromatin structure? Three effects are possible.

- One effect is that these complexes may bind to chromatin and change the locations of nucleosomes (**Figure 14.17a**). This may involve a shift of the relative positions of a few nucleosomes or a change in the relative spacing of nucleosomes over a long stretch of DNA.

- A second effect is that remodeling complexes may evict histone octamers from the DNA, thereby creating gaps where nucleosomes are not found (**Figure 14.17b**).

- A third possibility is that chromatin-remodeling complexes may change the composition of nucleosomes by removing

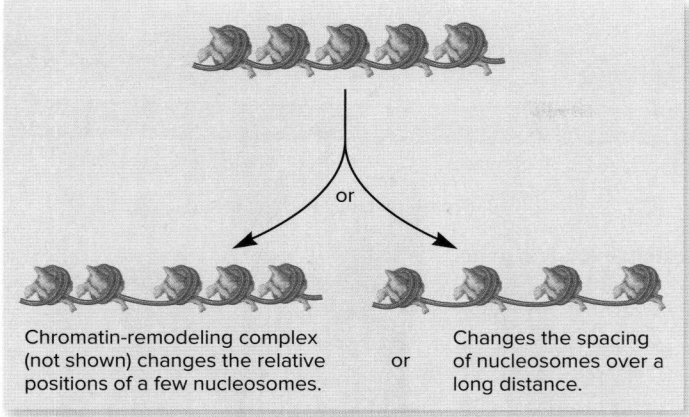

Chromatin-remodeling complex (not shown) changes the relative positions of a few nucleosomes.

or

Changes the spacing of nucleosomes over a long distance.

(a) Change in nucleosome position

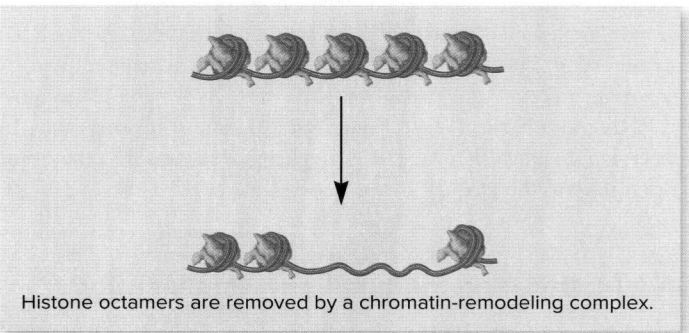

Histone octamers are removed by a chromatin-remodeling complex.

(b) Histone eviction

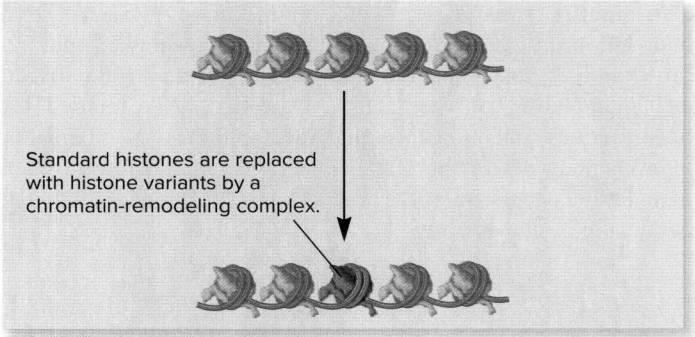

Standard histones are replaced with histone variants by a chromatin-remodeling complex.

(c) Replacement with histone variants

Figure 14.17 **ATP-dependent chromatin remodeling.** Chromatin-remodeling complexes may **(a)** change the locations of nucleosomes, **(b)** remove histones from the DNA, or **(c)** replace standard histones with histone variants. The chromatin-remodeling complex, which is a complex of proteins, is not shown in this figure.

standard histone proteins from an octamer and replacing them with histone variants (**Figure 14.17c**). A **histone variant** is a histone protein that has a slightly different amino acid sequence than that of the standard histone proteins described in Chapter 11. Some histone variants promote gene transcription, whereas others inhibit it.

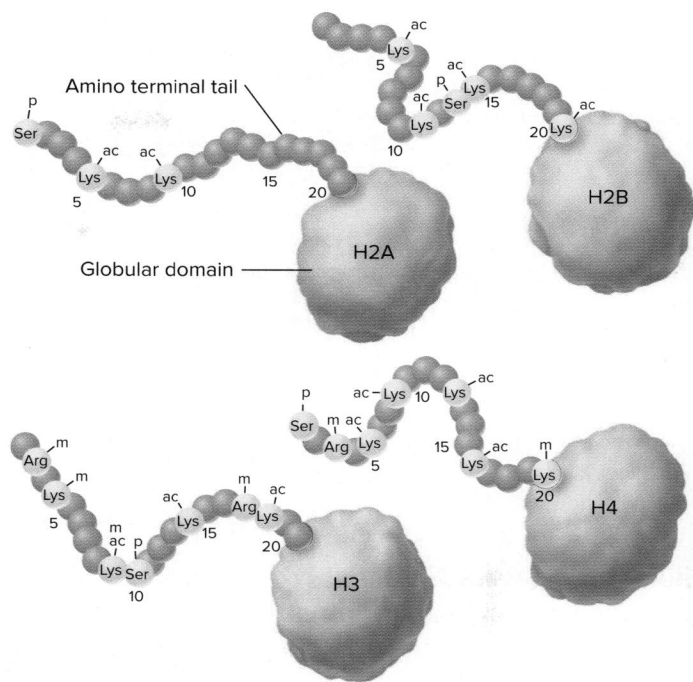

Figure 14.18 **Examples of covalent modifications of the amino terminal tails of histone proteins.** The amino acids are numbered from the N-terminus, or amino end. The modifications shown here are labeled m for methylation, p for phosphorylation, and ac for acetylation. Many more modifications can be made to the amino terminal tails. These modifications are reversible.

Concept Check: *What are the two opposing effects that histone modifications may have on transcription?*

Histone Modifications Affect Gene Transcription

In recent years, researchers have learned that the amino terminal tails of histone proteins are subject to several types of covalent modifications. For example, an enzyme called **histone acetyltransferase** attaches acetyl groups (—COCH$_3$) to the amino terminal tails of histone proteins. When acetylated, histone proteins do not bind as tightly to the DNA, which aids in transcription. Over 50 different enzymes that selectively modify amino terminal tails have been found in mammals. **Figure 14.18** shows how the amino terminal tails of histone proteins H2A, H2B, H3, and H4 can be modified by the attachment of acetyl, methyl, and phosphate groups.

What are the effects of covalent modifications of histones? First, modifications may directly influence interactions between DNA and histone proteins, and between adjacent nucleosomes. As mentioned, the acetylation of histones loosens their binding to DNA and aids in transcription. Second, histone modifications provide binding sites that are recognized by other proteins. According to the **histone code hypothesis**, proposed by American biologists Brian Strahl and David Allis in 2000, the pattern of histone modification is recognized by proteins much like a language or code. One pattern of histone modification may attract proteins that inhibit transcription. Alternatively, a different combination of histone modifications may attract proteins, such as ATP-dependent chromatin-remodeling

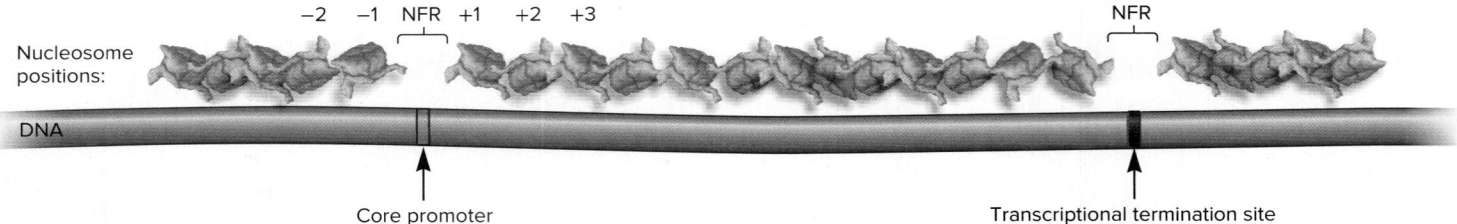

Figure 14.19 **Nucleosome arrangements in the vicinity of a eukaryotic protein-encoding gene.**

 Core Skill: Connections Look back at Figure 11.22. What is the composition of a nucleosome?

complexes, that promote gene transcription. In this way, the histone code plays a key role in accessing the information within the genomes of eukaryotic species.

Eukaryotic Genes Are Flanked by Nucleosome-Free Regions

Studies over the last 10 years or so have revealed that many eukaryotic genes show a common pattern of nucleosome organization (**Figure 14.19**). For active genes or those genes that can be activated, the core promoter is found at a **nucleosome-free region (NFR)**, which is a site in the chromatin that is missing nucleosomes. The NFR is typically 150 bp in length. Although the NFR may be required for transcription, it is not, by itself, sufficient for gene activation. At any given time in the life of a eukaryotic cell, many genes that contain an NFR are not being actively transcribed. The NFR is flanked by two nucleosomes that are termed the –1 and +1 nucleosomes. These nucleosomes often contain histone variants that promote transcription. The end of many eukaryotic genes is followed by another NFR. This arrangement at the end of genes may be important for transcriptional termination.

Transcriptional Activation Involves Changes in Nucleosome Locations and Changes in Histones

A key role of certain activators is to recruit ATP-dependent chromatin-remodeling complexes and histone-modifying enzymes to the promoter region of eukaryotic genes. Though the order of recruitment may differ among specific activators, the recruiting appears to be critical for transcriptional initiation and elongation. In the scenario shown in **Figure 14.20**, an activator binds to an enhancer in the NFR. The activator then recruits chromatin-remodeling complexes and histone-modifying enzymes to this region. A chromatin-remodeling complex may shift nucleosomes or temporarily evict nucleosomes from the promoter region. Nucleosomes containing certain histone variants are thought to be more easily removed from the DNA than those containing the standard histones. Histone-modifying enzymes, such as histone acetyltransferase, covalently modify histone proteins and may affect nucleosome contact with the DNA. The actions of chromatin-remodeling complexes and histone-modifying enzymes facilitate the binding of general transcription factors and RNA polymerase II to the core promoter, thereby allowing the formation of a preinitiation complex (see Figure 14.20, step 2).

Further changes in chromatin structure are necessary for elongation to occur. RNA polymerase II cannot transcribe DNA that is tightly wrapped in nucleosomes. For transcription to occur, histones are evicted, partially displaced, or destabilized so RNA polymerase II can pass. Evicted histones are then reassembled by chaperone proteins and placed back on the DNA behind the moving RNA polymerase II (see Figure 14.20). These histones may be deacetylated—have their acetyl groups removed—so that they bind more tightly to the DNA.

DNA Methylation Inhibits Gene Transcription

Let's now turn our attention to a mechanism that usually silences gene expression. DNA structure can be modified by the covalent attachment of methyl groups ($-CH_3$) by an enzyme called **DNA methyltransferase**. This modification, termed DNA methylation, is common in some eukaryotic species but not all. For example, yeast and *Drosophila* have little or no detectable methylation of their DNA, whereas DNA methylation in vertebrates and plants is relatively abundant. In mammals, approximately 5% of the DNA is methylated. Eukaryotic DNA methylation occurs on the cytosine base. The sequence that is methylated is shown here:

$$
\begin{array}{c}
CH_3 \\
| \\
5'-CG-3' \\
3'-GC-5' \\
| \\
CH_3
\end{array}
$$

DNA methylation usually inhibits the transcription of eukaryotic genes, particularly when it occurs in the vicinity of the promoter. In vertebrates and flowering plants, many genes contain sequences called **CpG islands** near their promoters. CpG refers to the bases cytosine (C) and guanine (G) in DNA whose nucleotides are connected by a phosphodiester linkage. A CpG island is a cluster of CpG sites. Unmethylated CpG islands are usually correlated with active genes, whereas repressed genes contain methylated CpG islands. In this way, DNA methylation may play an important role in the silencing of particular genes.

How does DNA methylation inhibit transcription? This can occur in two general ways. First, methylation of CpG islands may prevent an activator from binding to an enhancer element, thus inhibiting

Many genes are flanked by nucleosome-free regions (NFR) and well-positioned nucleosomes.

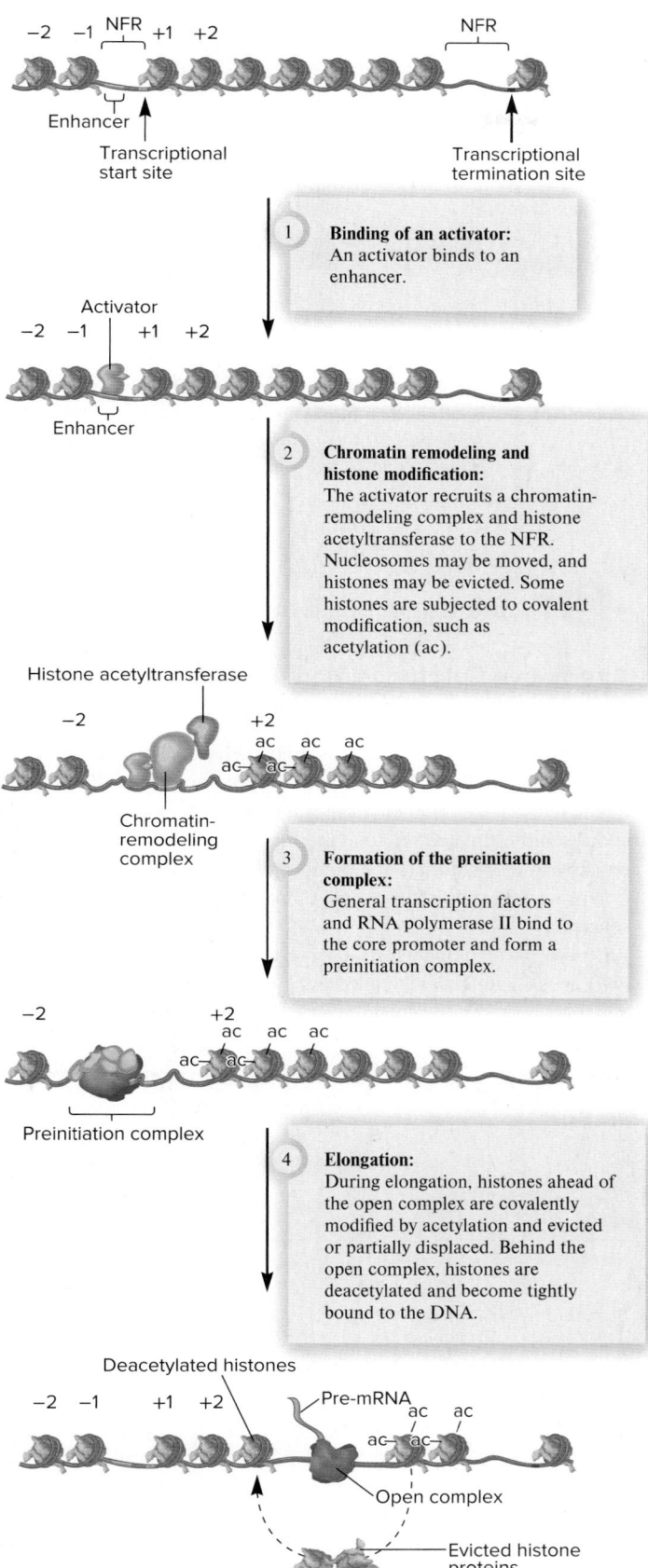

1 **Binding of an activator:** An activator binds to an enhancer.

2 **Chromatin remodeling and histone modification:** The activator recruits a chromatin-remodeling complex and histone acetyltransferase to the NFR. Nucleosomes may be moved, and histones may be evicted. Some histones are subjected to covalent modification, such as acetylation (ac).

3 **Formation of the preinitiation complex:** General transcription factors and RNA polymerase II bind to the core promoter and form a preinitiation complex.

4 **Elongation:** During elongation, histones ahead of the open complex are covalently modified by acetylation and evicted or partially displaced. Behind the open complex, histones are deacetylated and become tightly bound to the DNA.

Figure 14.20 **A simplified model for the transcriptional activation of a eukaryotic protein-encoding gene.**

the initiation of transcription. A second way that methylation inhibits transcription is by altering chromatin structure. Proteins known as **methyl-CpG-binding proteins** bind methylated sequences. Once bound to the DNA, the methyl-CpG-binding protein recruits to the site other proteins that inhibit transcription.

14.5 Regulation of RNA Modification and Translation in Eukaryotes

Learning Outcomes:
1. Outline the process of alternative splicing, and explain how it increases protein diversity.
2. Explain how RNA-binding proteins regulate the translation of specific mRNAs, using the regulation of iron absorption in mammals as an example.

In the preceding sections of this chapter, we focused on gene regulation at the level of transcription in bacteria and eukaryotes. Eukaryotic gene expression is also commonly regulated at the levels of RNA modification and translation. These added levels of regulation provide important benefits to eukaryotic species. First, by regulating RNA modification, eukaryotes can produce more than one mRNA transcript from a single gene. This allows a gene to encode two or more polypeptides, thereby increasing the complexity of eukaryotic proteomes. A second issue is timing. Regulation of transcription in eukaryotes takes a fair amount of time before its effects are observed at the cellular level. During transcription (1) the chromatin must be converted to an open conformation, (2) the gene must be transcribed, (3) the RNA must be modified and exported from the nucleus, and (4) the protein must be made via translation. All four steps take time, on the order of several minutes. One way to achieve faster regulation is to control steps that occur after an RNA transcript is made. In eukaryotes, regulation of translation provides a faster way to regulate the levels of gene products, namely, proteins.

During the past few decades, many critical advances have been made in our knowledge of the regulation of RNA modification and translation. Even so, molecular geneticists are still finding new forms of regulation, making this an exciting area of modern research. In Chapter 13, we considered RNA interference (RNAi), which is a mechanism for regulating translation that involves the use of noncoding RNAs. In this section, we will examine two other mechanisms of RNA regulation: (1) alternative splicing and (2) translational regulation via RNA-binding proteins.

Alternative Splicing of Pre-mRNAs Increases Protein Diversity

In eukaryotes, a pre-mRNA transcript is modified before it becomes a mature mRNA (refer back to Figure 12.8). When a pre-mRNA has multiple introns and exons, splicing may occur in more than one way, resulting in the production of two or more different polypeptides. Such **alternative splicing** is a form of gene regulation that allows an organism to use the same gene to make different proteins at different

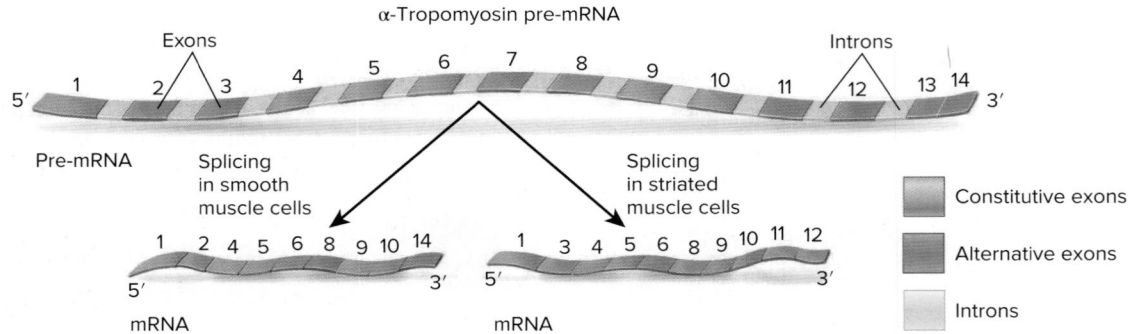

Figure 14.21 **Alternative splicing of the rat α-tropomyosin pre-mRNA.** The top part of this figure depicts the structure of the rat α-tropomyosin pre-mRNA. Exons are red or green, and introns are yellow. The lower part of the figure shows the final mRNA products in smooth and striated muscle cells after alternative splicing. Note: Exon 8 is found in the final mRNA of smooth and striated muscle cells, but not in the mRNA of some other cell types.

`Concept Check:`   *What is the biological advantage of alternative splicing?*

stages of development, in different cell types, and/or in response to a change in the environmental conditions. Alternative splicing is an important form of gene regulation in complex eukaryotes such as animals and plants. An advantage of alternative splicing is that two or more different polypeptides can be derived from a single gene, thereby increasing the size of the proteome while minimizing the size of the genome.

Let's consider an example of alternative splicing for a pre-mRNA that encodes a protein known as α-tropomyosin, which functions in the regulation of cell contraction in animals. It is located along the thin filaments found in smooth muscle cells, such as those in the uterus and small intestine, and in striated muscle cells that are found in cardiac and skeletal muscle. α-Tropomyosin is also synthesized in many types of nonmuscle cells but in lower amounts. Within a multicellular organism, different types of cells must regulate their contractibility in subtly different ways. One way this may be accomplished is by the production of different forms of α-tropomyosin.

Figure 14.21 shows the intron-exon structure of the rat α-tropomyosin pre-mRNA and two alternative ways that the pre-mRNA can be spliced. The pre-mRNA contains 14 exons, 6 of which are constitutive exons (shown in red), which are always found in the mature mRNA from all cell types. Presumably, constitutive exons encode polypeptide segments of the α-tropomyosin protein that are necessary for its general structure and function. By comparison, alternative exons (shown in green) are not always found in the mRNA after splicing has occurred. The polypeptide sequences encoded by alternative exons may subtly change the function of α-tropomyosin to meet the needs of the cell type in which it is found. For example, Figure 14.21 shows the predominant splicing products found in smooth muscle cells and striated muscle cells. Exon 2 encodes a segment of the α-tropomyosin protein that alters its function to make it suitable for smooth muscle cells. By comparison, the α-tropomyosin mRNA found in striated muscle cells does not include exon 2. Instead, this mRNA contains exon 3, leading to the production of an α-tropomyosin more suitable for that cell type.

 **Core Concepts: Evolution, Information**

Alternative Splicing Is More Prevalent in Complex Eukaryotic Species

In the past few decades, many technical advances have improved our ability to analyze the genomes and proteomes of many different species. Researchers have sequenced the DNA from many species and estimated the total number of genes. In addition, scientists can also estimate the number of polypeptides if information is available about the degree of alternative splicing in a given species.

Table 14.1 compares six species: a bacterium (*Escherichia coli*), a eukaryotic single-celled organism (yeast—*Saccharomyces cerevisiae*), a small nematode worm (*Caenorhabditis elegans*),

Table 14.1	Genome Size and Biological Complexity			
Species	Level of complexity	Genome size (million bp)	Approximate number of protein-encoding genes	Percentage of genes alternatively spliced
Escherichia coli	A unicellular bacterium	4.2	4,300	0
Saccharomyces cerevisiae	A unicellular eukaryote	12	6,300	<1
Caenorhabditis elegans	A tiny worm (about 1,000 cells)	97	20,500	2
Drosophila melanogaster	An insect	137	15,600	7
Arabidopsis thaliana	A flowering plant	142	27,000	11
Homo sapiens	A complex mammal	3,000	22,000	70

a fruit fly (*Drosophila melanogaster*), a flowering plant (*Arabidopsis thaliana*), and a human (*Homo sapiens*). One general trend is that less complex organisms tend to have fewer genes. For example, unicellular organisms have only a few thousand genes, whereas multicellular species have tens of thousands. However, the trend is by no means a linear one. If we compare *C. elegans* and *D. melanogaster*, the fruit fly actually has fewer genes, even though it is more complex morphologically.

A second trend you can see in Table 14.1 concerns alternative splicing. This phenomenon does not occur in bacteria and is rare in *S. cerevisiae*. The frequency of alternative splicing increases from worms to flies to humans. For example, the level of alternative splicing is 10-fold higher in humans than in *Drosophila*. This trend can partially explain the increase in complexity among these species. Even though humans have only about 22,000 different protein-encoding genes, their cells make well over 100,000 different polypeptides because most genes are alternatively spliced in multiple ways. This increases the level of information contained within the human genome.

The Prevention of Iron Toxicity in Mammals Involves the Regulation of Translation

In Chapter 13, we considered how microRNAs (miRNAs) and small-interfering RNAs (siRNAs) can silence mRNAs via RNA interference (RNAi). Another way to regulate mRNAs involves RNA-binding proteins that directly affect the initiation of translation. The regulation of iron absorption in mammals provides a well-studied example. Although iron is a vital cofactor for many cellular enzymes, it is toxic at high levels. To prevent toxicity, mammalian cells synthesize a protein called ferritin, which forms a hollow, spherical complex that stores excess iron.

The mRNA that encodes ferritin is controlled by an RNA-binding protein known as the **iron regulatory protein (IRP)**. When the iron level in the cytosol is low and more ferritin is not needed, IRP binds to a regulatory element within the ferritin mRNA known as the **iron regulatory element (IRE)**. The IRE is located between the 5′ cap, where the ribosome binds, and the start codon where translation begins. Due to base pairing, it forms a stem-loop structure. The binding of IRP to the IRE inhibits translation of the ferritin mRNA (**Figure 14.22a**). However, when iron is abundant in the cytosol, the iron binds directly to IRP, which changes its conformation and prevents it from binding to the IRE. Under these conditions, the ferritin mRNA is translated to make more ferritin protein (**Figure 14.22b**).

Why is translational regulation of ferritin mRNA an advantage over transcriptional regulation of the ferritin gene? This mechanism of translational control allows cells to rapidly respond to changes in their environment. When cells are confronted with high levels of iron, they can quickly make more ferritin protein to prevent the toxic buildup of iron. This mechanism is faster than transcriptional regulation, which would require the activation of the ferritin gene and the transcription of ferritin mRNA prior to the synthesis of more ferritin protein.

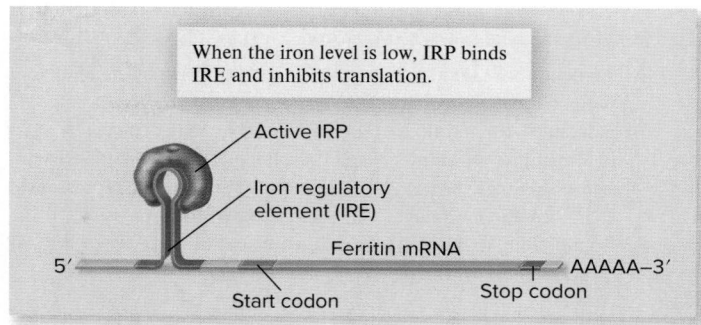

(a) Low iron level

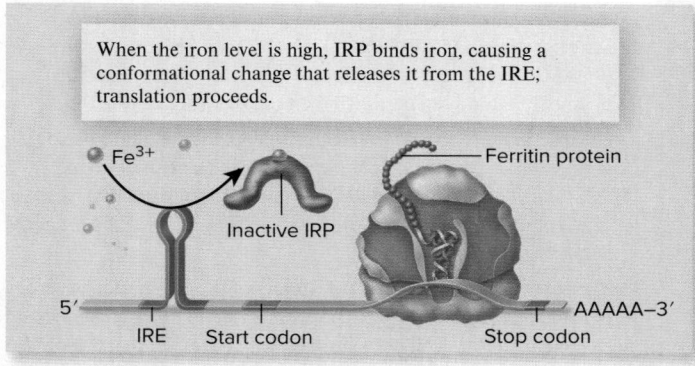

(b) High iron level

Figure 14.22 **Translational regulation of ferritin mRNA by the iron regulatory protein (IRP).**

Concept Check: *Poisoning may occur if a young child finds a bottle of vitamins, such as those that taste like candy, and eats a large number of them. One of the toxic effects involves the ingestion of too much iron. How does the IRP protect people from the toxic effects of too much iron?*

Summary of Key Concepts

14.1 Overview of Gene Regulation

- Most genes are regulated so that the level of gene expression can vary under different conditions. By comparison, constitutive genes are expressed at constant levels.

- Gene regulation ensures that gene products are made only when they are needed. An example is the synthesis of the gene products needed for lactose utilization in bacteria (Figure 14.1).

- In eukaryotes, gene regulation leads to the production of different cell types, such as neurons, muscle cells, and skin cells, within an organism (Figure 14.2).

- In eukaryotes, gene regulation also enables gene products to be produced at different developmental stages (Figure 14.3).

- All organisms regulate gene expression at a variety of levels, including transcription, translation, and post-translation. Eukaryotes also regulate RNA modification (Figure 14.4).

14.2 Regulation of Transcription in Bacteria

- Repressors and activators are regulatory transcription factors that bind to the DNA and affect the transcription of genes. Small effector molecules control the ability of regulatory transcription factors to bind to DNA (Figure 14.5).

- An operon is a set of two or more genes controlled by a single promoter and an operator. The *lac* operon is an example of an inducible operon. The lac repressor exerts negative control by binding to the operator site and preventing RNA polymerase from transcribing the operon. When allolactose binds to the repressor, a conformational change occurs that prevents the repressor from binding to the operator site so transcription can proceed (Figures 14.6, 14.7).

- By constructing a merozygote, Jacob, Monod, and Pardee determined that the *lacI* gene encodes a diffusible protein that represses the *lac* operon (Figures 14.8, 14.9).

- Positive control of the *lac* operon occurs when the catabolite activator protein (CAP) binds to the CAP site in the presence of cAMP. This causes a bend in the DNA, which promotes the binding of RNA polymerase to the promoter (Figure 14.10).

- Glucose inhibits cAMP production, which, in turn, inhibits the expression of the *lac* operon, because CAP cannot bind to the CAP site. This form of regulation provides bacteria with a more efficient utilization of their resources because they use one sugar at a time (Figure 14.11).

- The *trp* operon is an example of a repressible operon. The presence of tryptophan causes the trp repressor to bind to the *trp* operator and stop transcription. This prevents the excessive buildup of tryptophan in the cell, which would be a waste of energy (Figure 14.12).

14.3 Regulation of Transcription in Eukaryotes I: Roles of Transcription Factors and Mediator

- Eukaryotic genes exhibit combinatorial control, meaning that many factors control the expression of a single gene.

- Eukaryotic promoters consist of a core promoter (containing a TATA box and transcriptional start site) and regulatory elements, such as enhancers or silencers, that regulate the rate of transcription (Figure 14.13).

- General transcription factors (GTFs) are needed for RNA polymerase II to bind to the core promoter, forming a preinitiation complex (Figure 14.14).

- Activators and repressors regulate RNA polymerase II by affecting the function of TFIID (a GTF) or mediator, a protein complex that wraps around RNA polymerase II and the GTFs (Figures 14.15, 14.16).

14.4 Regulation of Transcription in Eukaryotes II: Changes in Chromatin Structure and DNA Methylation

- ATP-dependent chromatin-remodeling complexes change the positions and compositions of nucleosomes (Figure 14.17).

- The pattern of covalent modification of the amino terminal tails of histone proteins, also called the histone code, can inhibit or promote transcription (Figure 14.18).

- Eukaryotic genes are usually flanked by nucleosome-free regions (Figure 14.19).

- For eukaryotic protein-encoding genes, a preinitiation complex forms at a nucleosome-free region. During elongation,

nucleosomes are displaced ahead of RNA polymerase and re-form after RNA polymerase has passed (Figure 14.20).

- DNA methylation, which occurs at CpG islands near promoters, usually inhibits transcription by (1) preventing the binding of activator proteins or (2) promoting the binding of proteins that inhibit transcription.

14.5 Regulation of RNA Modification and Translation in Eukaryotes

- In alternative splicing, a single type of pre-mRNA can be spliced in more than one way, producing polypeptides with somewhat different sequences. This is a common way for complex eukaryotes to increase the size of their proteomes (Figure 14.21, Table 14.1).

- RNA-binding proteins can regulate the translation of specific mRNAs. An example is the regulation of iron absorption, in which the iron regulatory protein (IRP) regulates the translation of ferritin mRNA (Figure 14.22).

Assess & Discuss

Test Yourself

1. Genes that are expressed at all times at relatively constant levels are known as _____ genes.
   a. inducible
   b. repressible
   c. positive
   d. constitutive
   e. negative

2. Which of the following is *not* a level at which gene regulation occurs in bacteria?
   a. transcription
   b. RNA modification
   c. translation
   d. post-translation
   e. All of the above are levels at which bacteria are able to regulate gene expression.

3. Transcription factors that bind to DNA and stimulate transcription are
   a. repressors.
   b. small effector molecules.
   c. activators.
   d. promoters.
   e. operators.

4. In bacteria, the unit of DNA that contains multiple genes under the control of a single promoter is called _____. The mRNA produced from this unit is referred to as _____ mRNA.
   a. an operator, a polycistronic
   b. a template, a protein-encoding
   c. an operon, a polycistronic
   d. an operon, a monocistronic
   e. a template, a monocistronic

5. For the *lac* operon, what would be the expected effects of a mutation in the operator site that prevented the binding of the repressor protein?
   a. The operon would always be turned on.
   b. The operon would always be turned off.
   c. The operon would always be turned on, except when glucose is present.
   d. The operon would be turned on only in the presence of lactose.

e. The operon would be turned on only in the presence of lactose and the absence of glucose.

6. The presence of _____ in a bacterium's environment prevents CAP from binding to the DNA, resulting in _____ in transcription of the *lac* operon.
   a. lactose, an increase
   b. glucose, an increase
   c. cAMP, a decrease
   d. glucose, a decrease
   e. lactose, a decrease

7. The *trp* operon is considered _____ operon because the protein-encoding genes necessary for tryptophan synthesis are not expressed when the level of tryptophan in the cell is high.
   a. an inducible
   b. a positive
   c. a repressible
   d. a negative
   e. both c and d

8. Regulatory elements that function to increase transcription levels in eukaryotes are called
   a. promoters.
   b. silencers.
   c. enhancers.
   d. transcriptional start sites.
   e. activators.

9. The iron regulatory protein (IRP) binds to the iron regulatoty element (IRE) when iron levels are _____ and _____ translation of ferritin mRNA.
   a. high, stimulates
   b. high, inhibits
   c. low, stimulates
   d. low, inhibits
   e. both a and d

10. _____ refers to the process that allows a single type of pre-mRNA to give rise to multiple types of mRNAs due to different patterns of intron and exon removal.
   a. Spliceosomes
   b. Variable expression
   c. Alternative splicing
   d. Polycistronic mRNA
   e. Induced silencing

Conceptual Questions

1. What is the difference between inducible and repressible operons? Give an example of each.

2. Transcriptional regulation often involves a regulatory protein that binds to a segment of DNA and a small effector molecule that binds to the regulatory protein. Does each of the following terms apply to a regulatory protein, a segment of DNA, or a small effector molecule?
   a. repressor
   b. inducer
   c. operator
   d. corepressor
   e. activator

3.  **Core Concept: Information** Explain the importance of gene regulation as a mechanism for properly accessing the information within genes.

Collaborative Questions

1. Discuss the advantages and disadvantages of genetic regulation at the different levels shown in Figure 14.4.

2. Discuss the advantages and disadvantages of combinatorial control of eukaryotic genes.

Mutation, DNA Repair, and Cancer

15

During the past two decades, over 25% of the beluga whales in Canada's St. Lawrence Seaway have died of cancer. Biologists speculate that these deaths are caused by cancer-causing pollutants, such as polycyclic aromatic hydrocarbons (PAHs).

©Yvette Cardozo/Workbook Stock/Getty Images

A t a summer camp, the children enjoy ice cream, horseback riding, hay rides, swimming, and learning about the habits of owls. Not such an unusual camp, you might be thinking. However, what makes Camp Sundown unique is that the outdoor fun begins at dusk and runs all night. The children at this camp have inherited a disorder called xeroderma pigmentosum (XP), which makes them highly sensitive to sunlight. Their skin will blister or freckle on minimum exposure to sunlight. Of greater concern, however, is skin cancer. Persons with XP may have a 1,000-fold greater risk of developing skin cancer, though such a risk is greatly decreased if exposure to sunlight is minimized.

What explains the symptoms of XP? Individuals with this condition are highly susceptible to **mutation,** which is defined as a heritable change in the genetic material. When a mutation occurs, the order of nucleotide bases in a DNA molecule, its base sequence, is changed permanently, an alteration that can be passed from mother to daughter cells during cell division. Mutations that lead to cancer cause particular genes to be expressed in an abnormal way.

For example, a mutation could affect the transcription of a gene, or it could alter the functional properties of the polypeptide that is specified by a gene. In addition to mutations, changes in chromatin structure can also affect gene expression and contribute to cancer.

Should we be afraid of mutations? Yes and no. On the positive side, mutations are essential to the long-term continuity of life. Mutations provide the foundation for evolutionary change. They supply the variation that enables species to evolve and become better adapted to their environments. On the negative side, however, new mutations are more likely to be harmful than beneficial to the individual. The genes within modern species are the products of billions of years of evolution and have evolved to work properly. Random mutations are more likely to disrupt genes rather than enhance their function. As we will see in this chapter, mutations can cause cancer. In addition, many inherited disorders, such as XP and cystic fibrosis, are caused by gene mutations. For these and many other reasons, understanding the molecular nature of mutations is a compelling area of research.

All species have evolved several ways to repair damaged DNA. Such DNA repair systems reverse DNA damage before a permanent mutation can occur. DNA repair systems are vital to the survival of all organisms. If these systems did not exist, mutations would be so prevalent that few species, if any, would survive. In this chapter, we will examine how these DNA repair systems operate. But first, let's explore the consequences and causes of mutations.

15.1 Consequences of Mutations

Learning Outcomes:

1. List several ways that mutations can alter the amino acid sequence of a polypeptide.
2. Outline how mutations in protein-encoding genes may affect the amino acid sequence of a polypeptide.
3. Explain how mutations that occur outside of the coding sequence can affect the expression of a gene.
4. Compare and contrast the effects of mutations in somatic cells versus germ-line cells.

How do mutations affect traits? To answer this question at the molecular level, we must understand how changes in the DNA sequence of a gene ultimately affect gene function. Most of our understanding of mutations has come from the study of experimental organisms, such as bacteria and *Drosophila*. Researchers can expose these organisms to agents that cause mutations and then study the consequences of the mutations that arise. In addition, because these organisms have a short generation time, researchers can investigate the effects of mutations when they are passed from cell to cell and from parent to offspring.

The structure and amount of genetic material can be altered in a variety of ways. For example, the structure and number of chromosomes can change. We will examine these types of genetic changes in Chapter 16. In this section, we will focus our attention on gene mutations, which are relatively small changes in the sequence of bases in a particular gene. We will also consider how the timing of new mutations during an organism's development has important consequences.

Gene Mutations Alter the DNA Sequence of a Gene

Mutations cause two basic types of changes to a gene: (1) the base sequence within a gene can be changed; and (2) one or more base pairs can be added to or removed from a gene. A **point mutation** affects only a single base pair within the DNA. For example, the DNA sequence shown here has been altered by a **base substitution** in which a T (in the top strand) has been replaced by a G and the corresponding A in the bottom strand is replaced with a C:

5′–CCCGCTAGATA–3′   5′–CCCGCGAGATA–3′
3′–GGGCGATCTAT–5′ → 3′–GGGCGCTCTAT–5′

A point mutation could also involve the addition or deletion of a single base pair to a DNA sequence. For example, in the following sequence, a single base pair (A-T) has been added to the DNA:

5′–GGCGCTAGATC—3′   5′–GGCAGCTAGATC–3′
3′–CCGCGATCTAG—5′ → 3′–CCGTCGATCTAG–5′

Though point mutations may seem like small changes to a DNA sequence, they can have important consequences when genes are expressed, as we will see next.

Gene Mutations May Affect the Amino Acid Sequence of a Polypeptide

If a mutation occurs within the coding region of a protein-encoding gene, the mutation may alter that sequence in a variety of ways. Table 15.1 considers the potential effects of point mutations.

Silent Mutations **Silent mutations** do not alter the amino acid sequence of the polypeptide, even though the nucleotide sequence has changed. As discussed in Chapter 12, the genetic code is degenerate; that is, more than one codon can specify the same amino acid. Silent mutations occur in the third base of many codons without changing the type of amino acid that is encoded.

Missense Mutations A **missense mutation** is a base substitution that changes a single amino acid in a polypeptide sequence.

Table 15.1 Consequences of Point Mutations Within the Coding Sequence of a Protein-Encoding Gene

Mutation in the DNA	Effect on polypeptide	Example*
None	None	ATGGCCGGCCCGAAAGAGACC Met–Ala–Gly–Pro–Lys–Glu–Thr
Base substitution	Silent—causes no change	ATGGCCGGCCCCAAAGAGACC Met–Ala–Gly–Pro–Lys–Glu–Thr
Base substitution	Missense—changes one amino acid in the polypeptide	ATGCCCGGCCCGAAAGAGACC Met–Pro–Gly–Pro–Lys–Glu–Thr
Base substitution	Nonsense—changes a normal codon to a stop codon	ATGGCCGGCCCGTAAGAGACC Met–Ala–Gly–Pro–STOP
Addition of a single base	Frameshift—produces a different amino acid sequence	ATGGCCGGCACCGAAAGAGACC Met–Ala–Gly–Thr–Glu–Arg–Asp

*DNA sequence in the coding strand. This sequence is the same as the mRNA sequence except that RNA contains uracil (U) instead of thymine (T).

A missense mutation may not alter protein function because it changes only a single amino acid within a polypeptide that is typically hundreds of amino acids in length. A missense mutation that substitutes an amino acid with a chemistry similar to the original amino acid is less likely to alter protein function. For example, a missense mutation that substitutes a glutamic acid for an aspartic acid may not alter protein function because both amino acids are negatively charged and have similar side chain structures.

Alternatively, some missense mutations have a dramatic effect on protein function. A striking example occurs in the human disease known as **sickle cell disease**. This disease involves a missense mutation in the β-globin gene, which encodes one of the polypeptide subunits that make up hemoglobin, the oxygen-carrying protein in red blood cells. In the most common form of this disease, a missense mutation alters the polypeptide sequence such that the sixth amino acid is changed from a glutamic acid to a valine (**Figure 15.1**). Because glutamic acid is hydrophilic but valine is hydrophobic, this single amino acid substitution alters the structure and function of the hemoglobin protein. The mutant hemoglobin subunits tend to stick to one another when the oxygen concentration is low. The aggregated proteins form fiber-like structures within red blood cells, which causes the cells to lose their normal disc-shaped morphology and become sickle-shaped. It is amazing that a single amino acid substitution could have such a profound effect on the structure of cells.

Nonsense Mutations A **nonsense mutation** involves a change from a normal codon to a stop, or termination, codon. This causes translation to be terminated earlier than expected, producing a truncated polypeptide (see Table 15.1). Compared with a normal polypeptide, a shorter polypeptide is much less likely to function properly.

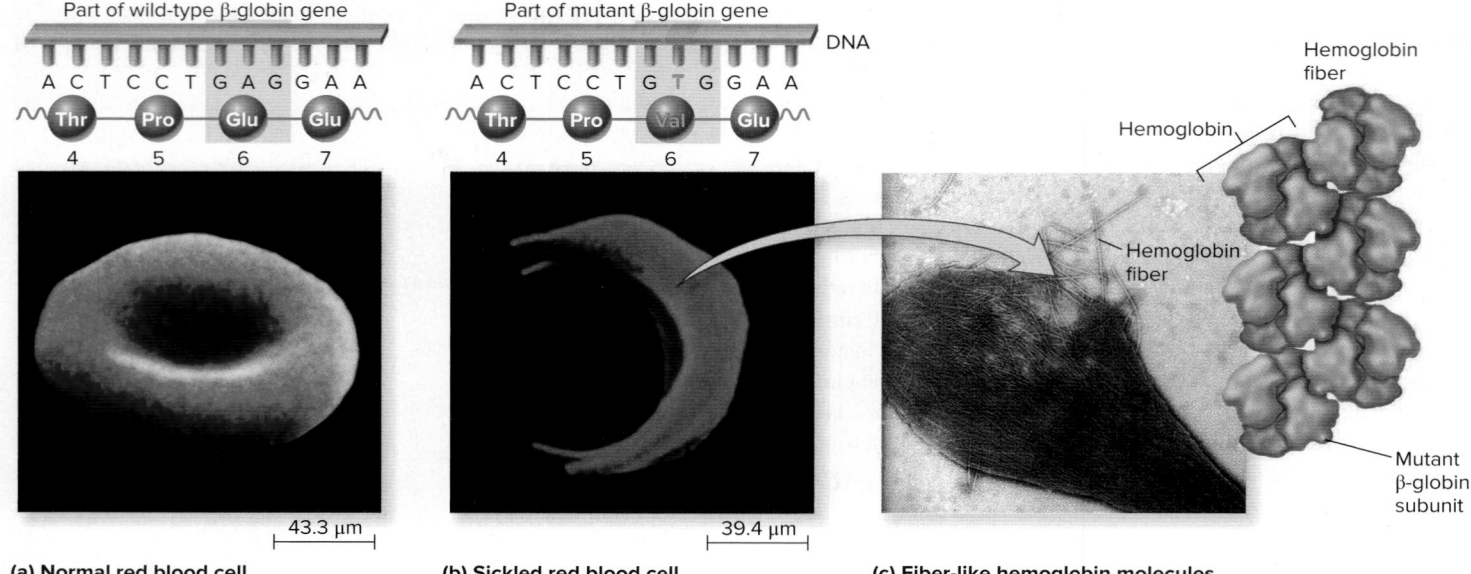

(a) Normal red blood cell

(b) Sickled red blood cell

(c) Fiber-like hemoglobin molecules

Figure 15.1 **A missense mutation that causes red blood cells to sickle in sickle cell disease.** Scanning electron micrographs of **(a)** a normal red blood cell and **(b)** a sickled red blood cell. As shown above the micrographs, a missense mutation in the β-globin gene (which codes for a subunit of hemoglobin) changes the sixth amino acid in the β-globin polypeptide from glutamic acid (Glu) to valine (Val). **(c)** This micrograph shows how this alteration to the structure of β-globin causes the formation of abnormal fiber-like structures. In normal red blood cells, hemoglobin proteins do not form fibers. a: ©Mary Martin/Science Source; b: ©Science Source; c: Courtesy of Thomas Wellems and Robert Josephs. Electron Microscopy and Image Processing Laboratory, University of Chicago

Concept Check: *Based on the fiber-like structures seen in part (c) of this figure, what aspect of hemoglobin structure does a glutamic acid at the sixth position in normal β-globin prevent? Speculate as to how the charge of this amino acid may play a role.*

Frameshift Mutations Finally, a **frameshift mutation** involves the addition or deletion of a number of nucleotides that is not a multiple of three. For example, a frameshift mutation could involve the addition or deletion of one, two, four, or five nucleotides. Because the codons are read in multiples of three, these types of insertions or deletions shift the reading frame so a completely different amino acid sequence occurs downstream from the mutation (see Table 15.1). Such a large change in polypeptide structure is likely to inhibit protein function.

Changes in protein function may affect the ability of an organism to survive and to reproduce. Except for silent mutations, new mutations are more likely to produce polypeptides that have reduced rather than enhanced function. However, mutations can occasionally produce a polypeptide that has an enhanced function. Such mutations may change in frequency in a population over the course of many generations due to natural selection. This topic is discussed in Chapter 23.

Gene Mutations That Occur Outside of Coding Sequences Can Influence Gene Expression

Thus far, we have focused our attention on mutations in the coding regions of protein-encoding genes. In Chapters 12 and 14, we explored the role of DNA sequences in gene expression. A mutation can occur within a noncoding DNA sequence and affect gene expression (**Table 15.2**). For example, a mutation may alter the sequence within the promoter of a gene, thereby affecting the rate of transcription. A mutation that improves the ability of RNA polymerase to bind

to the promoter may enhance transcription, whereas other mutations may inhibit transcription.

Mutations in regulatory elements or operator sites can alter the regulation of gene transcription. For example, in Chapter 14, we considered the roles of regulatory elements such as the *lac* operator site in *E. coli*, which is recognized by the lac repressor protein (refer back to Figure 14.7). Mutations in the *lac* operator site can disrupt the proper regulation of the *lac* operon. An operator mutation may change the DNA sequence so the lac repressor protein does not bind to it. This mutation would cause the operon to be constitutively expressed.

Table 15.2	Effects of Mutations Outside of the Coding Sequence of a Gene
Sequence	**Effect of mutation**
Promoter	May increase or decrease the rate of transcription
Transcriptional regulatory element/operator site	May alter the regulation of transcription
Splice sites	May alter the ability of pre-mRNA to be properly spliced
Translational regulatory element	May alter the ability of mRNA to be translationally regulated
Intergenic region	Not as likely to have an effect on gene expression

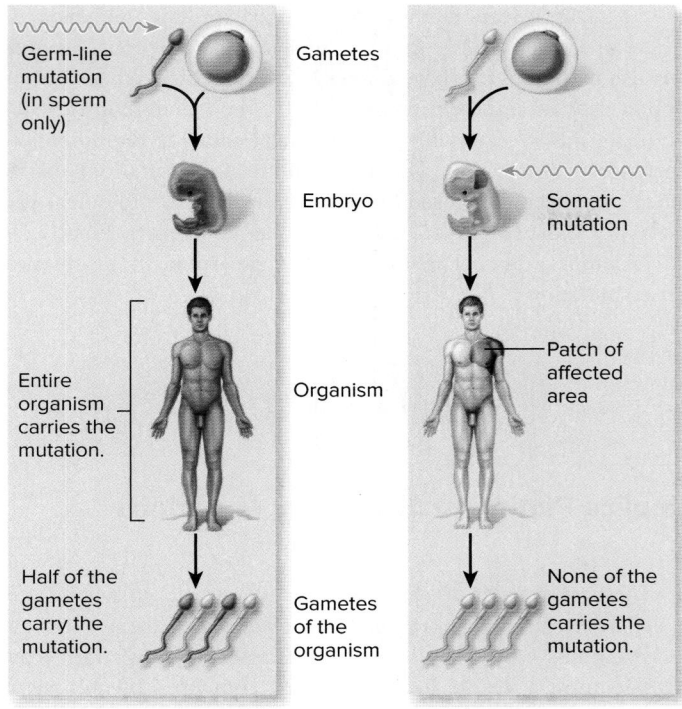

(a) Germ-line mutation

(b) Somatic cell mutation

Figure 15.2 **The effects of germ-line versus somatic cell mutations.** The red color indicates which cells carry the mutation. **(a)** In this example, a mutation occurs in a gamete. This germ-line mutation will be passed to every cell of the body. Because humans have two copies of most genes, a germ-line mutation in one of those two copies is transmitted to only half of the gametes. **(b)** Somatic mutations affect a limited area of the body and are not transmitted to offspring.

 Core Concept: Information As a multicellular organism grows and develops, a germ-line mutation is transmitted to all cells of the body, whereas a somatic mutation is found only in a particular region.

Mutations Can Occur in Germ-Line or Somatic Cells

Let's now consider how the timing of a mutation may have important consequences for its potential effects. Multicellular organisms typically begin their lives as a single fertilized egg cell that divides many times to produce all the cells of an adult organism. A mutation can occur in any cell of the body, either very early in life, such as in a gamete (egg or sperm) or a fertilized egg, or later in life, such as in the embryonic or adult stages. The number and location of cells with a mutation are critical both to the severity of the genetic effect and to the ability of the mutation to be passed on to offspring.

Geneticists classify the cells of animals into two types: germ-line cells and somatic cells. The term **germ line** refers to cells that give rise to gametes, such as egg and sperm cells. A germ-line mutation can occur directly in an egg or sperm cell, or it can occur in a precursor cell that produces the gamete. If a mutant human

gamete participates in fertilization, all the cells of the resulting offspring will contain the mutation, as indicated by the red color in **Figure 15.2a**. Likewise, when such an individual produces gametes, the mutation may be transmitted to future generations of offspring. Because humans carry two copies of most genes, a new mutation in a single gene has a 50% chance of being transmitted from parent to offspring.

The **somatic cells** constitute all cells of the body except for the germ line. Examples include skin cells and muscle cells. Mutations can also occur within somatic cells at early or late stages of development. What are the consequences of a mutation that happens during the embryonic stage? As shown in **Figure 15.2b**, a mutation occurred within a single embryonic cell. This single somatic cell was the precursor for many cells of the adult. Therefore, in the adult, a patch of tissue contains cells that carry the mutation. The size of any patch depends on the timing of a new mutation. In general, the earlier a mutation occurs during development, the larger the patch. An individual with somatic regions that are genetically different from each other is called a **mosaic**.

Figure 15.3 illustrates a child who had a somatic mutation during an early stage of development. In this case, the child has a streak of white hair while the rest of his hair is black. Presumably, a single mutation happened in an embryonic cell that ultimately gave rise to the patch that produced the white hair.

Although a change in hair color is not a harmful consequence, mutations during early stages of life can be quite harmful, especially if they disrupt essential developmental processes. Even though it is sensible to avoid environmental agents that cause mutations at any stage of life, the possibility of somatic mutations is a compelling reason to avoid such agents during the early stages of life such as embryonic and fetal development, infancy, and early childhood.

Figure 15.3 **Example of a somatic mutation.** This child has a streak of white hair. This is due to a somatic mutation in a single cell during embryonic development. This cell continued to divide to produce a streak of white hair. ©Otero/GTphoto

Concept Check: *Can this child with a streak of white hair transmit this trait to his future offspring?*

15.2 Causes of Mutations

Learning Outcomes:

1. **CoreSKILL** » Analyze the replica plating experiments of the Lederbergs.
2. Describe the difference between spontaneous and induced mutations.
3. **CoreSKILL** » Analyze the results of an Ames test for determining if a substance is a mutagen.

As we have seen, mutations affect the expression of genes in a variety of ways, and their timing can have important consequences. Because mutations can have dramatic effects on individuals' traits, a great deal of research has focused on their underlying causes. We begin this section with an experiment showing that mutations are random events. We will then explore how mutations can be either spontaneous (caused by mistakes in natural biological processes) or induced (caused by environmental agents). Finally, we will examine a testing method used to determine if a substance causes mutations.

 Core Skill: Process of Science

Feature Investigation | The Lederbergs Used Replica Plating to Show That Mutations Are Random Events

Prior to understanding the causes of mutations at the molecular level, scientists considered the following question: Are mutations that affect the traits of an individual caused by pre-existing circumstances, or are they random events that may happen in any gene of any individual? In the 19th century, French naturalist Jean-Baptiste Lamarck proposed that physiological events (such as use or disuse) determine whether traits are passed along to offspring. For example, his hypothesis suggested that an individual who practiced and became adept at a physical activity, such as the long jump, would pass that quality on to his or her offspring. Alternatively, geneticists in the early 20th century suggested that genetic variation occurs as a matter of chance. According to this view, those individuals whose genes happen to contain beneficial mutations are more likely to survive and pass those genes to their offspring.

These opposing views were tested in bacterial studies in the 1940s and 1950s. One such study, by American microbiologists Joshua and Esther Lederberg, focused on the occurrence of mutations

in bacteria (**Figure 15.4**). First, the Lederbergs placed a few dozen *E. coli* bacteria onto growth media and incubated them overnight. Following this growth period, each bacterial cell had divided many times to form a visible bacterial colony composed of millions of cells (see step 2). This is called the master plate. Next, in a technique known as **replica plating,** a sterile piece of velvet cloth was lightly touched to the master plate to pick up bacterial cells from each colony on the master plate. The Lederbergs then transferred this replica to two secondary plates containing an agent that selected for the growth of bacterial cells with a particular mutation.

In the example shown in Figure 15.4, the secondary plates contained T1 bacteriophages, which are viruses that infect bacteria and cause them to lyse. On these plates, only those rare cells that had acquired a mutation conferring resistance to T1, termed *ton^r*, could grow. All other cells were lysed by the proliferation of bacteriophages in the bacteria. Therefore, only a few colonies were observed on the secondary plates. Strikingly, these colonies occupied the same

Figure 15.4 **The experiment performed by the Lederbergs showing that mutations are random events.**

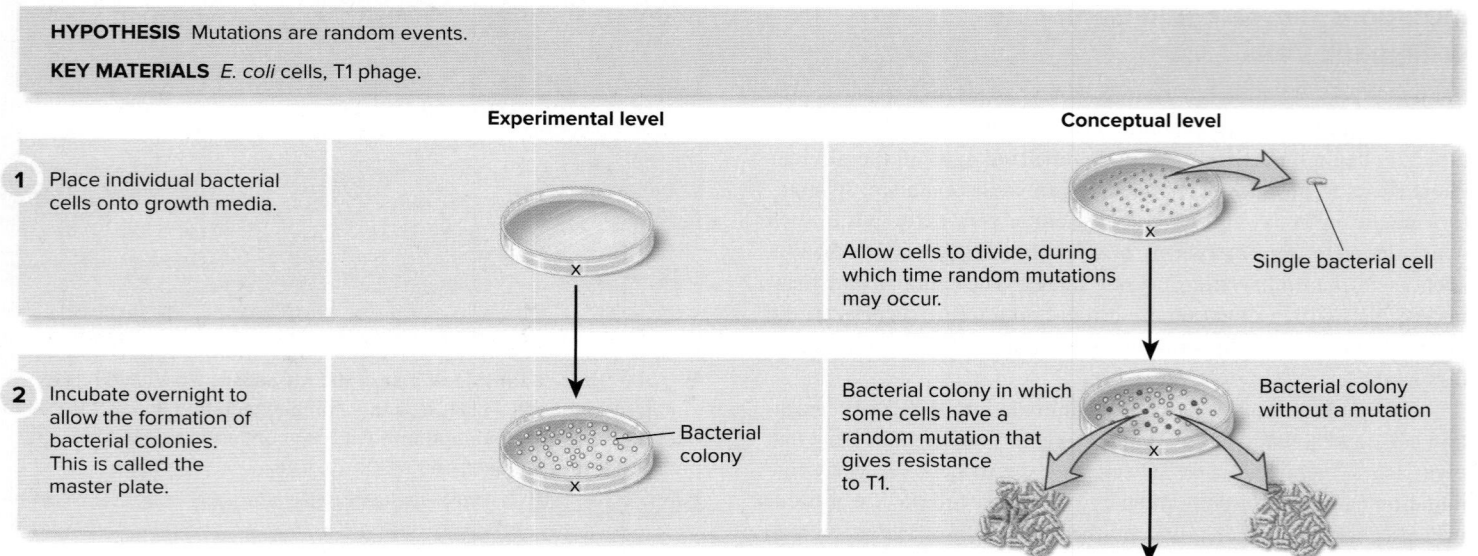

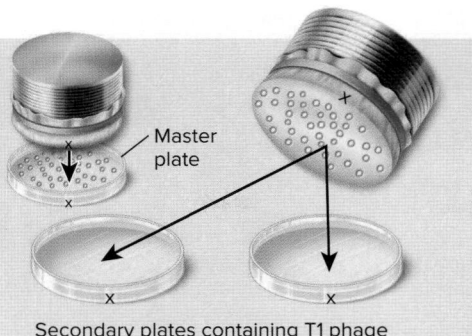

3 Press a velvet cloth (wrapped over a cylinder) onto the master plate, and then lift gently to obtain a replica of each bacterial colony. Press the replica onto 2 secondary plates that contain T1 bacteriophage. Incubate overnight to allow bacterial growth.

Master plate

Secondary plates containing T1 phage

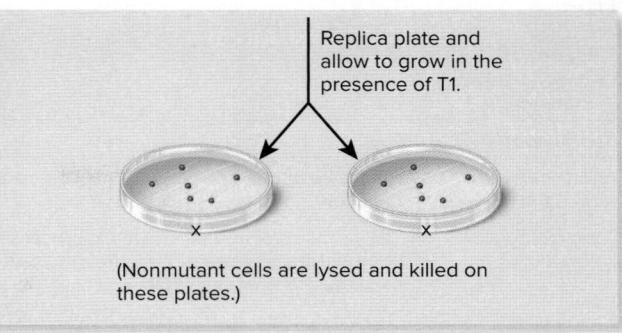

Replica plate and allow to grow in the presence of T1.

(Nonmutant cells are lysed and killed on these plates.)

4   THE DATA

Colonies on each plate are in the same locations.

5   CONCLUSION Mutations are random events. In this case, the mutations occurred on the master plate prior to exposure to T1 bacteriophage.

6   SOURCE Lederberg, J., and Lederberg, E. M. 1952. Replica Plating and Indirect Selection of Bacterial Mutants. *Journal of Bacteriology* 63: 399–406.

locations on each plate. How did the Lederbergs interpret these results? The data indicated that the *ton*^r mutations occurred randomly while the bacterial cells were forming colonies on the nonselective master plate. The presence of T1 bacteriophages in the secondary plates did not cause the mutations to develop. Rather, the T1 bacteriophages simply selected for the growth of *ton*^r mutants that were already in the population. These results supported the idea that mutations are random events.

Experimental Questions

1. Explain the opposing views of mutation prior to the Lederbergs' study.
2. **CoreSKILL »** What hypothesis was being tested by the Lederbergs?
3. **CoreSKILL »** How did the results of the Lederbergs support or falsify the hypothesis?

Mutations May Be Spontaneous or Induced

Biologists categorize the causes of mutation as spontaneous or induced (**Table 15.3**). **Spontaneous mutations** result from abnormalities in biological processes. Spontaneous mutations reflect the observation that biology isn't perfect. Enzymes, for example, can function abnormally. In Chapter 11, we learned that DNA polymerase can make mistakes during DNA replication by putting the wrong base in a newly synthesized daughter strand. Though such errors are rare, due to the proofreading function of DNA polymerase, they do occur. In addition, normal metabolic processes within the cell may produce toxic chemicals such as free radicals that can react directly with the DNA and alter its structure. Finally, the structures of nucleotides are not absolutely stable. On occasion, the structure of a base may spontaneously change, and such a change may cause a mutation if it occurs immediately prior to DNA replication.

The rates of spontaneous mutations vary from species to species and from gene to gene. Larger genes are usually more likely to incur a mutation than are smaller ones. A common rate of spontaneous mutation among various species is approximately 1 mutation for every 1 million genes per cell division, which equals 1 in 10^6, or simply 10^{-6}.

This is the expected rate of spontaneous mutation, which creates the variation that is the raw material of evolution.

Induced mutations are caused by environmental agents that enter the cell and alter the structure of DNA. They cause the mutation rate to be higher than the spontaneous mutation rate. Agents that cause mutation are called **mutagens**. Mutagenic agents can be categorized as **chemical** or **physical mutagens** (**Table 15.4**). We will consider their effects next.

Mutagens Alter DNA Structure in Different Ways

Researchers have discovered that an enormous array of agents act as mutagens. We often hear in the news media that we should avoid these agents in our foods and living environments. We even use products such as sunscreens that help us avoid the mutagenic effects of ultraviolet (UV) light from the Sun. The public is often concerned about mutagens for two important reasons. First, mutagenic agents are usually involved in the development of human cancers. Second, because new mutations may be deleterious, people want to avoid mutagens to prevent mutations that may have harmful effects in their future offspring.

Table 15.3 — Some Common Causes of Gene Mutations

Common causes of mutations	Description
Spontaneous	
Errors in DNA replication	A mistake by DNA polymerase may cause a point mutation.
Toxic metabolic products	The products of normal metabolic processes may be reactive chemicals such as free radicals that can alter the structure of DNA.
Changes in nucleotide structure	On rare occasions, the linkage between a purine and deoxyribose can spontaneously break. Changes in base structure (isomerization) may cause mispairing during DNA replication.
Transposons	As discussed in Chapter 21, transposons are small segments of DNA that can insert at various sites in the genome. If they insert into a gene, they may inactivate the gene.
Induced	
Chemical agents	Chemical substances, such as benzo(a)pyrene, a chemical found in cigarette smoke, may cause changes in the structure of DNA.
Physical agents	Physical agents such as UV (ultraviolet) light and X-rays can damage DNA.

Table 15.4 — Examples of Mutagens

Mutagen	Effect(s) on DNA structure
Chemical	
Nitrous acid	Deaminates bases
5-Bromouracil	Acts as a base analogue
2-Aminopurine	Acts as a base analogue
Nitrogen mustard	Alkylates bases
Ethyl methanesulfonate (EMS)	Alkylates bases
Benzo(a)pyrene	Inserts between bases in the DNA double helix and causes additions or deletions
Physical	
X-rays	Causes base deletions, single nicks in DNA strands, crosslinking, and chromosomal breaks
UV light	Promotes pyrimidine dimer formation, which involves covalent bonds between adjacent pyrimidines (C and T)

Chemical Mutagens How do mutagens affect DNA structure? Some chemical mutagens act by covalently modifying the structure of nucleotides. For example, nitrous acid (HNO_2) deaminates bases by replacing amino groups with keto groups (replacing —NH_2 with =O). This can change cytosine to uracil. When this altered DNA replicates, the modified base does not pair with the appropriate base in the newly made strand. In this case, uracil pairs with adenine (**Figure 15.5**).

Similarly, 5-bromouracil and 2-aminopurine, which are called base analogues, have structures that are similar to particular bases in DNA

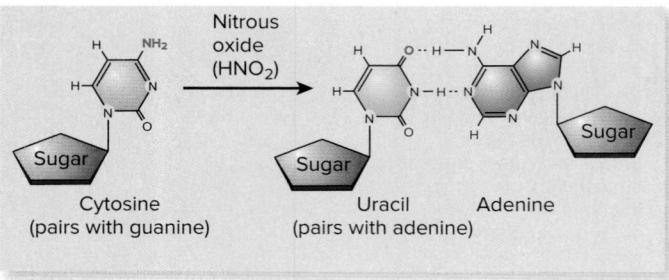

Template strand   **After replication**

Figure 15.5 Deamination and mispairing of modified bases by a chemical mutagen. Nitrous acid changes cytosine to uracil by replacing NH_2 with an oxygen. During DNA replication, uracil pairs with adenine, thereby creating a mutation in the newly replicated strand.

and can substitute for them. When incorporated into DNA, they also cause errors in DNA replication. Other chemical mutagens disrupt the appropriate pairing between nucleotides by alkylating bases within the DNA. During alkylation, methyl or ethyl groups are covalently attached to the bases. Examples of alkylating agents include nitrogen mustards (used as a chemical weapon during World War I) and ethyl methanesulfonate (EMS), which is used as a mutagen in laboratory experiments.

Some chemical mutagens exert their effects by interfering with DNA replication. For example, benzo(a)pyrene, which is found in automobile exhaust, cigarette smoke, and charbroiled food, is metabolized to a compound (benzopyrene diol epoxide) that inserts between the bases of the double helix, thereby distorting the helical structure. When DNA containing such a mutagen is replicated, single-nucleotide additions and deletions may be incorporated into the newly made strands.

Physical Mutagens DNA molecules are also sensitive to physical agents such as radiation. In particular, radiation of short wavelength and high energy, known as ionizing radiation, is known to alter DNA structure. Ionizing radiation includes X-rays and gamma rays. This type of radiation can penetrate deeply into biological materials, where it creates free radicals. These molecules can alter the structure of DNA in a variety of ways. Exposure to high doses of ionizing radiation can cause base deletions, breaks in one DNA strand, or even a break in both DNA strands.

Nonionizing radiation, such as UV light, contains less energy, and so it penetrates only the surface of biological materials, such as the skin. Nevertheless, UV light is known to cause mutations. For example, UV light can cause the formation of a **thymine dimer**, which is a site where two adjacent thymine bases become covalently crosslinked to each other (**Figure 15.6**).

Thymine dimers are typically repaired before or during DNA replication. However, if such repair fails to occur, a thymine dimer may cause a mutation when that DNA strand is replicated. When DNA polymerase attempts to replicate over a thymine dimer, proper base pairing does not occur between the template strand and the incoming nucleotides. This mispairing can cause gaps in the newly made strand or the incorporation of incorrect bases. Plants, in particular, must have effective ways to prevent UV damage because they are exposed to sunlight throughout the day.

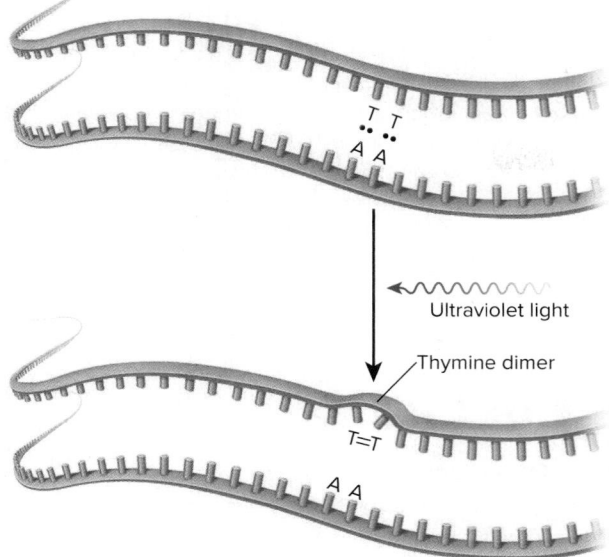

Figure 15.6 **Formation and structure of a thymine dimer.**

Concept Check: *Why is a thymine dimer harmful?*

Testing Methods Determine If an Agent Is a Mutagen

Because mutagens are harmful, researchers have developed testing methods to evaluate the ability of a substance to cause mutation. One commonly used test is the **Ames test**, which was developed by American biochemist Bruce Ames in the 1970s. This test uses a strain of a bacterium, *Salmonella typhimurium*, that cannot synthesize the amino acid histidine. This strain contains a point mutation within a gene that encodes an enzyme required for histidine biosynthesis. The mutation renders the enzyme inactive. The bacteria cannot grow unless histidine has been added to the growth medium. However, a second mutation may correct the first mutation, thereby restoring the ability to synthesize histidine. The Ames test monitors the rate at which this second mutation occurs and thereby indicates whether an agent increases the mutation rate above the spontaneous rate.

Figure 15.7 outlines the steps in the Ames test. The suspected mutagen is mixed with a rat liver extract and the strain of *S. typhimurium* that cannot synthesize histidine. Because some potential mutagens may require activation by cellular enzymes, the rat liver extract provides a mixture of enzymes that may cause such activation. This step improves the ability to identify agents that cause mutations in mammals. As a control, bacteria that have not been exposed to the mutagen are also tested. After an incubation period in which mutations may occur, a large number of bacteria are plated on a growth medium that does not contain histidine. The *S. typhimurium* strain is not expected to grow on these plates. However, if a mutation has occurred that allows a cell to synthesize histidine, the bacterium harboring this second mutation will proliferate during an overnight incubation period to form a visible bacterial colony.

To estimate the mutation rate, the colonies that grow in the absence of histidine are counted and compared with the total number of bacterial cells that were originally placed on the plate for both the suspected-mutagen sample and the control. The control condition is a measure of the spontaneous mutation rate, whereas

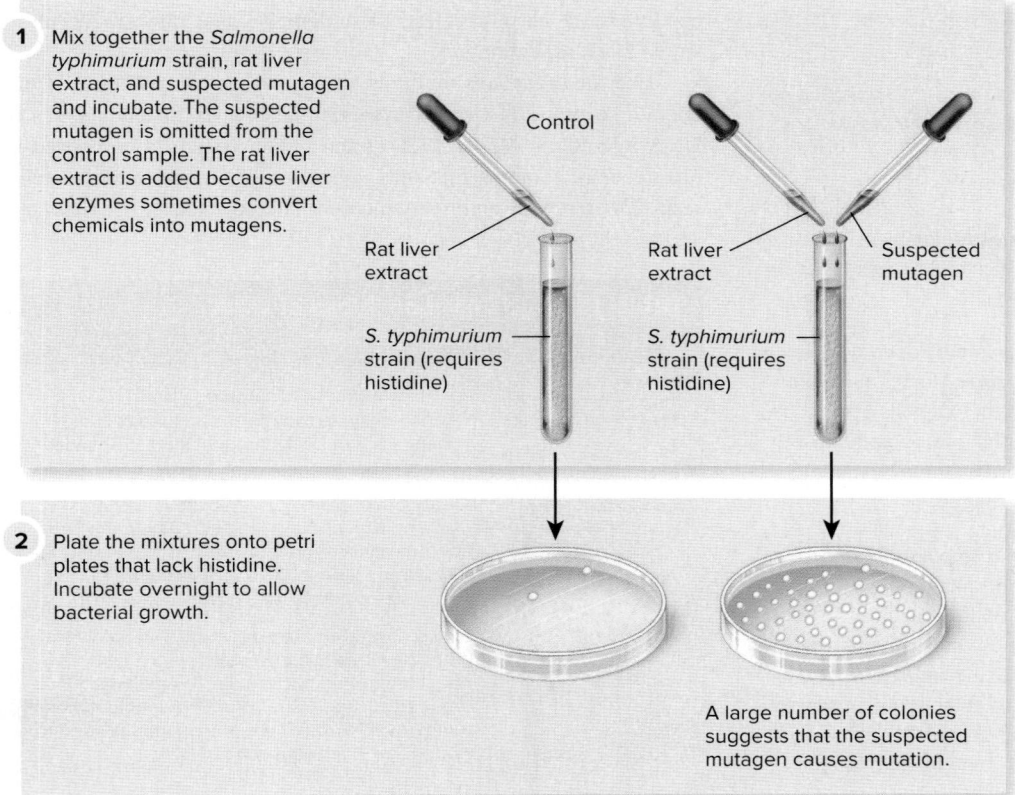

1 Mix together the *Salmonella typhimurium* strain, rat liver extract, and suspected mutagen and incubate. The suspected mutagen is omitted from the control sample. The rat liver extract is added because liver enzymes sometimes convert chemicals into mutagens.

Control

Rat liver extract

S. typhimurium strain (requires histidine)

Rat liver extract

Suspected mutagen

S. typhimurium strain (requires histidine)

2 Plate the mixtures onto petri plates that lack histidine. Incubate overnight to allow bacterial growth.

A large number of colonies suggests that the suspected mutagen causes mutation.

Figure 15.7 **The Ames test for mutagenicity.** In this example, 2 million bacterial cells were placed on plates lacking histidine. Two colonies arose from the control sample, whereas 44 arose from the sample exposed to a suspected mutagen.

Core Skill: Science and Society Biologists have developed many methods, including the Ames test, for determining if a substance is a mutagen. The results of these tests have prevented the use of many different chemicals in the production of food and also resulted in warning labels on products such as cigarettes.

the other sample measures the rate of mutation in the presence of the suspected mutagen. As an example, let's suppose that 2 million bacteria were plated from both the control and the suspected-mutagen tubes. In the control experiment, 2 bacterial colonies were observed. The spontaneous mutation rate is calculated by dividing 2 (the number of mutants) by 2 million (the number of original cells). This equals 1 in 1 million, or 1×10^{-6}. By comparison, 44 colonies arose from the suspected-mutagen sample (see Figure 15.7). In this case, the mutation rate would be 44 divided by 2 million, which equals 2.2×10^{-5}. The mutation rate in the presence of the mutagen is over 20 times higher than the spontaneous mutation rate.

How do we judge if an agent is a mutagen? Researchers compare the mutation rate in the presence and absence of the suspected mutagen. The experimental procedure shown in Figure 15.7 is conducted several times. If statistics reveal that the mutation rate in the suspected-mutagen sample is significantly higher than in the control sample, they may tentatively conclude that the agent is a mutagen. Interestingly, many studies have used the Ames test to compare the urine from cigarette smokers with that from nonsmokers. This research has shown that urine from smokers contains much higher levels of mutagens.

BIO TIPS

THE QUESTION *Let's suppose a researcher studied the effects of a suspected mutagen, mutagen X, using the protocol described in Figure 15.7. The following data were obtained after placing 2 million cells on each plate:*

	Number of colonies	
Trial	Control (no mutagen)	With mutagen X
1	3	62
2	2	77
3	5	46
4	2	55

Calculate the average mutation rate in the presence and absence of mutagen X. Conduct a t-test to determine if suspected mutagen X is significantly affecting the mutation rate.

T OPIC *What topic in biology does this question address?* The topic is identifying a mutagen. More specifically, the question is about analyzing results from the Ames test.

I NFORMATION *What information do you know based on the question and your understanding of the topic?* In the question, you are given data regarding the outcome of four trials using the Ames test. From your understanding of the topic, you may remember that a higher number of colonies on the experimental plate may indicate that a substance is a mutagen.

P ROBLEM-SOLVING **S** TRATEGY *Make a calculation. Use statistics.* To begin to solve this problem, you first need to calculate the average mutation rates. To do this, take the average of the four trials and then divide the average number of mutant colonies by the total number of cells applied to each plate (in this case, 2 million). You also need to conduct a t-test to determine if the control and experimental data are significantly different. A description of a t-test can be found in various statistics textbooks.

ANSWER *In the control trials, the average mutation rate is 1.5 in 1 million, or 1.5×10^{-6}. In the presence of the suspected mutagen, the average rate is 30 in 1 million, or 30×10^{-6}. From a t-test of these data, P < 0.01, so you can reject the null hypothesis that the control and experimental data are not different from each other. Therefore, you can accept the hypothesis that the suspected mutagen is causing a higher mutation rate. Note: This hypothesis is not proven; you are simply able to accept it based on this statistical outcome.*

15.3 DNA Repair

Learning Outcomes:
1. List the general features of DNA repair systems.
2. Describe the steps of nucleotide excision repair.
3. Explain the connection between a defect in DNA repair and the inherited human disease xeroderma pigmentosum.

In the previous sections, we considered the consequences and causes of mutations. As we have seen, mutations are random events that often have negative consequences. To minimize mutations, all living organisms have the ability to repair changes that occur in the structure of DNA. For example, in Chapter 11, we considered how DNA polymerase has a proofreading function that helps to prevent mutations from arising during DNA replication. In this section, we will examine DNA repair systems that can detect abnormalities in DNA structure and repair them. The importance of these systems becomes evident when they are missing. For example, as discussed at the beginning of this chapter, persons with xeroderma pigmentosum are highly susceptible to the harmful effects of sunlight because they are missing a single DNA repair system.

How do organisms minimize the occurrence of mutations? Cells contain several DNA repair systems that can fix different types of DNA alterations (**Table 15.5**). Each repair system is composed of one or more proteins that play specific roles in the repair mechanism. DNA repair requires two coordinated events. In the first step,

Table 15.5	Common Types of DNA Repair Systems*
System	**Description**
Direct repair	A repair enzyme recognizes an incorrect structure in the DNA and directly restores the correct structure.
Base excision and nucleotide excision repair	An abnormal base or nucleotide is recognized, and a portion of the strand containing the abnormality is removed. The complementary DNA strand is then used as a template to synthesize a normal DNA strand.
Methyl-directed mismatch repair	Similar to excision repair except that the DNA defect is a base pair mismatch in the DNA, not an abnormal nucleotide. The mismatch is recognized, and a strand of DNA in this region is removed. The complementary strand is used to synthesize a normal strand of DNA.

*Other types of repair systems exist; these are common examples.

one or more proteins in the repair system detect an irregularity in DNA structure. In the second step, the abnormality is repaired. In some cases, the change in DNA structure can be directly repaired. For example, DNA may be modified by the attachment of an alkyl group, such as —CH₂CH₃, to a base. In **direct repair**, an enzyme removes this alkyl group, thereby restoring the structure of the original base. More commonly, however, the altered DNA is removed, and a new segment of DNA is synthesized. In this section, we will examine nucleotide excision repair as an example of how such systems operate. This system, which is found in all species, is an important mechanism of DNA repair.

Nucleotide Excision Repair Removes Segments of Damaged DNA

In **nucleotide excision repair (NER)**, a region encompassing several nucleotides in the damaged strand is removed from the DNA, and the intact undamaged strand is used as a template for the resynthesis of a normal complementary strand. NER can fix many different types of DNA damage, including UV-induced damage, chemically modified bases, missing bases, and various types of crosslinks (such as thymine dimers). The system is found in all species, although its molecular mechanism is best understood in bacteria.

In *E. coli*, the NER system is composed of four key proteins: UvrA, UvrB, UvrC, and UvrD. They are named Uvr because they are involved in ultraviolet light repair of thymine dimers, although these proteins are also important in repairing chemically damaged DNA. In addition, DNA polymerase and DNA ligase are required to complete the repair process.

How does the NER system work?

1. Two UvrA proteins and one UvrB protein form a complex that tracks along the DNA (**Figure 15.8**). Damaged DNA will have a distorted double helix, which is sensed by the UvrA-UvrB complex.

2. When the complex identifies a damaged site, the two UvrA proteins are released, and UvrC binds to UvrB at the site.

3. The UvrC protein makes incisions in one DNA strand on both sides of the damaged site.

4. After this incision process, UvrC is released. UvrD binds to UvrB. UvrD then begins to separate the DNA strands, and UvrB is released. The action of UvrD unravels the DNA, which removes a short DNA strand that contains the damaged region. UvrD is released.

5. After the damaged DNA strand is removed, a gap is left in the double helix. DNA polymerase fills in the gap using the undamaged strand as a template. Finally, DNA ligase makes the final covalent connection between the newly made DNA and the original DNA strand.

Human Genetic Diseases Occur When a Component of the NER System Is Missing

Thus far, we have considered the NER system in *E. coli*. In humans, NER systems were discovered by the analysis of genetic diseases that affect DNA repair. These include xeroderma pigmentosum (XP),

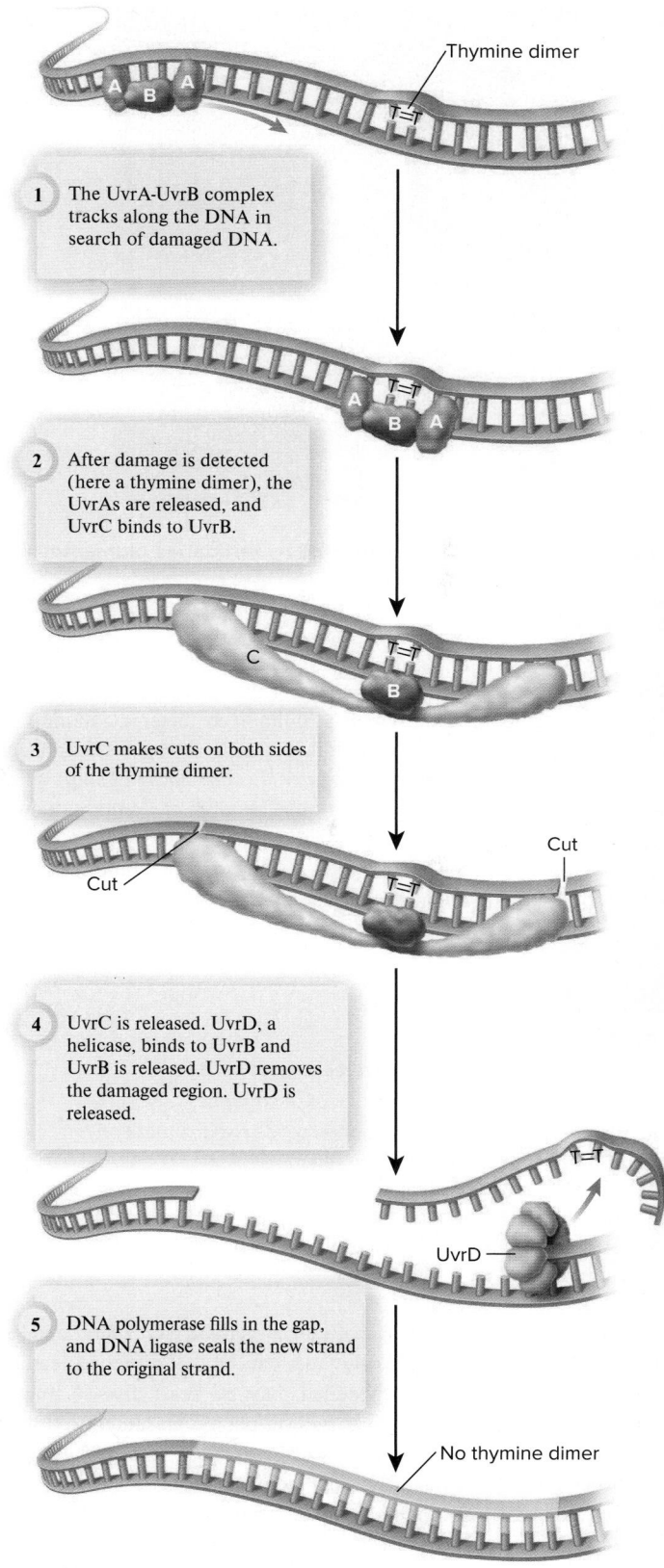

Thymine dimer

1 The UvrA-UvrB complex tracks along the DNA in search of damaged DNA.

2 After damage is detected (here a thymine dimer), the UvrAs are released, and UvrC binds to UvrB.

3 UvrC makes cuts on both sides of the thymine dimer.

Cut

Cut

4 UvrC is released. UvrD, a helicase, binds to UvrB and UvrB is released. UvrD removes the damaged region. UvrD is released.

UvrD

5 DNA polymerase fills in the gap, and DNA ligase seals the new strand to the original strand.

No thymine dimer

Figure 15.8 **Nucleotide excision repair in *E. coli*.**

Concept Check: *Which components of the NER system are responsible for removing the damaged DNA?*

Figure 15.9 **An individual affected by xeroderma pigmentosum.**
©Barcroft Media/Getty Images

`Concept Check:` *Why is this person so sensitive to sunlight?*

which was discussed at the beginning of this chapter, and Cockayne syndrome (CS). Photosensitivity is a common characteristic in individuals with these syndromes because of an inability to repair UV-induced lesions. Therefore, people with either of these syndromes must avoid prolonged exposure to sunlight, as do the children at Camp Sundown. **Figure 15.9** shows a photograph of a child with XP who had some exposure to sunlight. Such individuals may have pigmentation changes, precancerous lesions, and a predisposition to developing skin cancer.

15.4 Cancer

Learning Outcomes:

1. Outline the steps in the development of cancer.
2. Describe the general functions of oncogenes.
3. List the four common types of genetic changes that convert proto-oncogenes into oncogenes.
4. Identify the two general functions of the proteins encoded by tumor-suppressor genes.
5. Describe three common ways that tumor-suppressor genes are silenced.

Cancer is a disease of multicellular organisms characterized by uncontrolled cell division. Worldwide, cancer is the second leading cause of death in humans, exceeded only by heart disease. In the United States, approximately 1.5 million people are diagnosed with cancer each year; over 0.5 million will die from the disease. Overall, about one in four Americans will die from cancer.

For about 10% of cancers, a higher predisposition to develop the disease is an inherited trait. Most cancers, though, perhaps 90%, do not involve genetic changes that are passed from parent to offspring. Rather, cancer is usually an acquired condition that typically occurs later in life. At least 80% of all human cancers are related to exposure to **carcinogens**, agents that increase the likelihood of developing

cancer. Most carcinogens, such as UV light and certain chemicals in cigarette smoke, are mutagens that promote genetic changes in somatic cells. These genetic changes can alter gene expression in a way that ultimately affects cell division, leading to cancer. In this section, we will explore such genetic abnormalities.

How does cancer occur? In most cases, the development of cancer is a multistep process (**Figure 15.10**). Cancers originate from a single cell. This single cell and its lineage of daughter cells undergo a series of mutations and other genetic changes that cause the cells to grow abnormally. At an early stage, the cells form a **tumor**, which is an abnormal overgrowth of cells. For most types of cancer, growth begins as a precancerous mass, or a **benign tumor**. Such tumors do not invade adjacent tissues and do not spread throughout the body. This may be followed by additional genetic changes that cause some cells in the tumor to lose their normal growth regulation and it becomes a **malignant tumor**. At this stage, the individual has cancer. Cancerous tumors invade adjacent healthy tissues, and cancer cells may spread through the bloodstream or surrounding body fluids, a process called **metastasis**. If left untreated, malignant cells will cause the death of the organism.

Over the past few decades, researchers have identified many genes that promote cancer when they are mutant. By comparing the function of each mutant gene with the corresponding nonmutant gene found in healthy cells, these cancer-promoting genes have been placed into two categories.

- In some cases, a mutation causes a gene to be overactive—have an abnormally high level of expression. This overactivity contributes to the uncontrolled cell growth that is observed in cancer cells. This type of mutant gene is called an **oncogene**.
- Alternatively, when a **tumor-suppressor gene** is normal (that is, not mutant), it encodes a protein that helps to prevent cancer. However, when a mutation eliminates its function, cancer may occur.

Thus, the two categories of cancer-causing genes are based on the effects of mutations. Oncogenes are the result of mutations that cause overactivity, whereas cancer-causing mutations in tumor-suppressor genes are due to a loss of activity. In this section, we will begin with a discussion of oncogenes and then consider tumor-suppressor genes.

Oncogenes May Result from Mutations That Cause the Overactivity of Proteins Involved with Cell Division

Over the past four decades, researchers have identified many oncogenes. A large number of oncogenes encode proteins that function in signal transduction pathways involved in cell growth. Cell division is regulated, in part, by growth factors. A growth factor binds to a receptor, which results in receptor activation (**Figure 15.11**). This stimulates an intracellular signal transduction pathway that activates transcription factors. In this way, the transcription of specific genes is activated in response to a growth factor. After they are made, the gene products promote cell division.

Eukaryotic species produce many different growth factors that play a role in cell division. Likewise, cells have several different types of signal transduction pathways, which are composed of proteins that respond to growth factors and promote cell division. Mutations in the

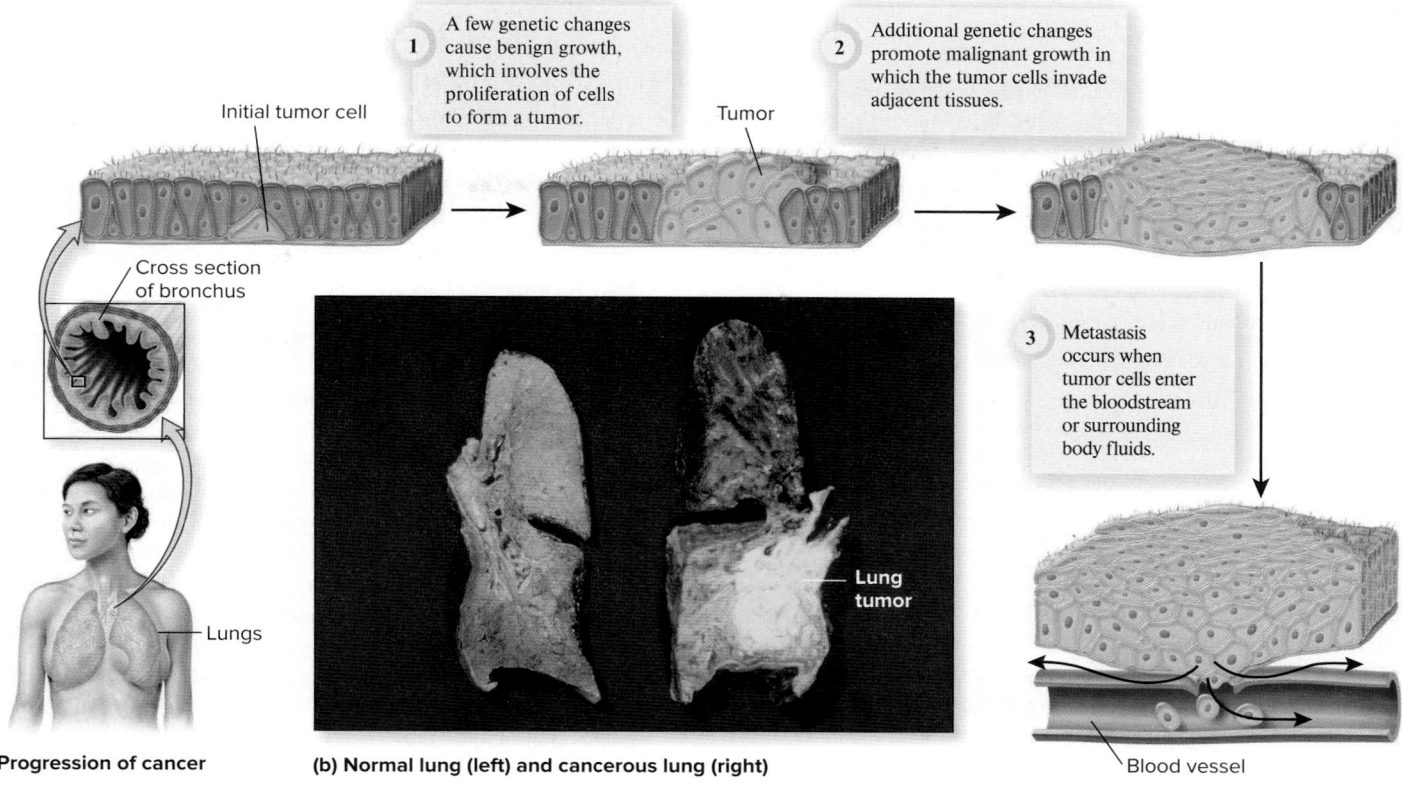

1 A few genetic changes cause benign growth, which involves the proliferation of cells to form a tumor.

2 Additional genetic changes promote malignant growth in which the tumor cells invade adjacent tissues.

3 Metastasis occurs when tumor cells enter the bloodstream or surrounding body fluids.

Initial tumor cell

Tumor

Cross section of bronchus

Lungs

Lung tumor

Blood vessel

(a) Progression of cancer

(b) Normal lung (left) and cancerous lung (right)

Figure 15.10 **Cancer: its typical progression and effects.** **(a)** In a healthy individual, a few mutations convert a normal cell into a tumor cell. This cell divides to produce a benign tumor. Additional mutations and other changes in the tumor cells may occur, leading to a malignant tumor. At a later stage in malignancy, the tumor cells invade surrounding tissues, and some malignant cells may metastasize by traveling through the bloodstream to other parts of the body. **(b)** On the left of the photo is a human lung that was obtained from a healthy nonsmoker. The lung shown on the right has been ravaged by lung cancer. This lung was taken from a person who was a heavy smoker. b: ©St. Bartholomew's Hospital/Science Source

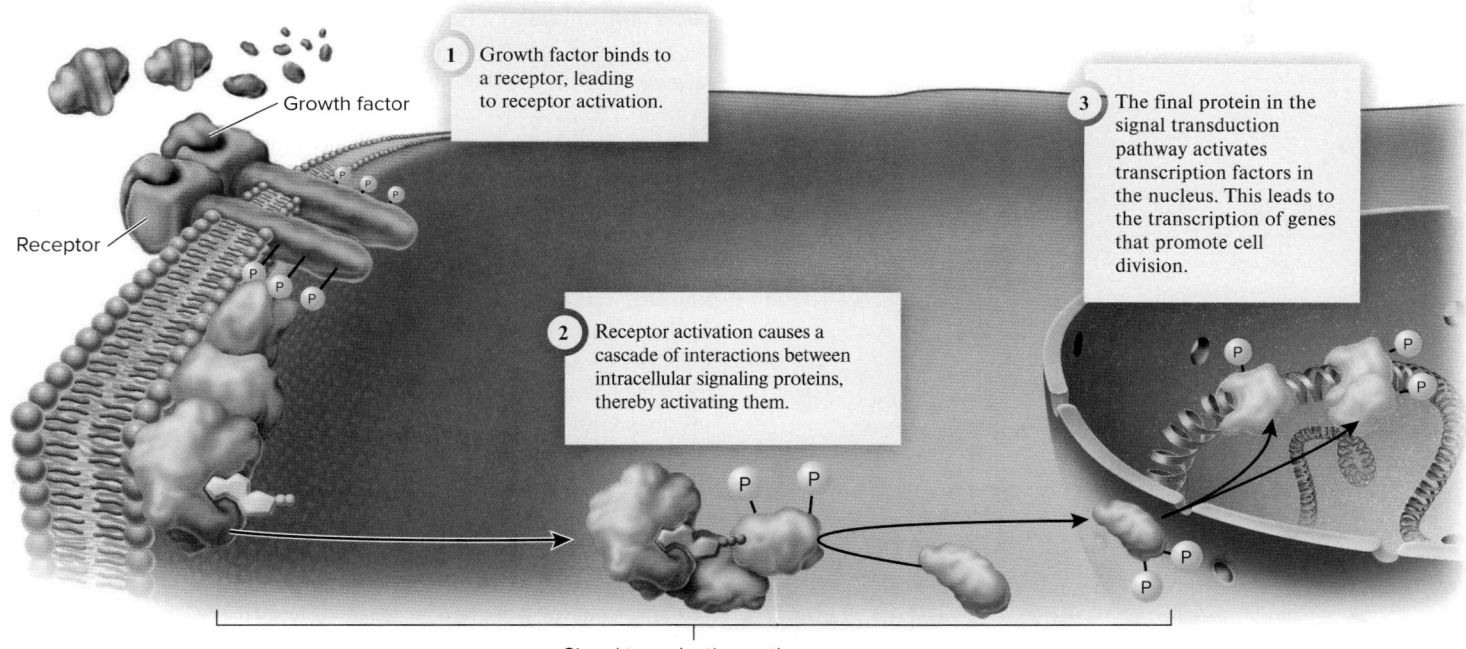

1 Growth factor binds to a receptor, leading to receptor activation.

Growth factor

Receptor

2 Receptor activation causes a cascade of interactions between intracellular signaling proteins, thereby activating them.

3 The final protein in the signal transduction pathway activates transcription factors in the nucleus. This leads to the transcription of genes that promote cell division.

Signal transduction pathway

Figure 15.11 **General features of a signal transduction pathway involving a growth factor that promotes cell division.** A detailed description of this pathway is found in Chapter 9 (look back at Figure 9.10).

Concept Check: *How does the presence of a growth factor ultimately affect the function of a cell?*

 Core Skill: Connections Look back at Figure 9.10. Could drugs that inhibit protein kinases be used to combat cancer? Explain.

Table 15.6	Examples of Genes That Encode Signal Transduction Proteins and Can Become Oncogenes
Gene*	**Cellular function of encoded protein**
erbB	Growth factor receptor for EGF (epidermal growth factor)
ras	Intracellular signaling protein
raf	Intracellular signaling protein
src	Intracellular signaling protein
fos	Transcription factor
jun	Transcription factor

*The genes described in this table are found in humans as well as other vertebrate species. Most of the genes have been given three-letter names that are abbreviations for the type of cancer the oncogene causes or the type of virus in which the gene was first identified.

genes that encode these signal transduction proteins can change them into oncogenes (**Table 15.6**).

How does an oncogene promote cancer? In some cases, an oncogene may keep a signal transduction pathway for cell division in a permanent "on" state. One way oncogenes keep cell division turned on is by producing a functionally overactive protein. As a specific example, let's consider how a mutation alters an intracellular signaling protein called Ras (refer back to Figure 9.10). The Ras protein is a GTPase that hydrolyzes GTP to GDP + P_i (**Figure 15.12**). When a signal transduction pathway is activated, the Ras protein releases GDP and binds GTP. When GTP is bound, the activated Ras protein promotes cell division. The Ras protein returns to its inactive state by hydrolyzing its bound GTP, and cell division is inhibited. Mutations that convert the normal *ras* gene into an oncogenic *ras* either decrease the ability of Ras protein to hydrolyze GTP or increase the rate of exchange

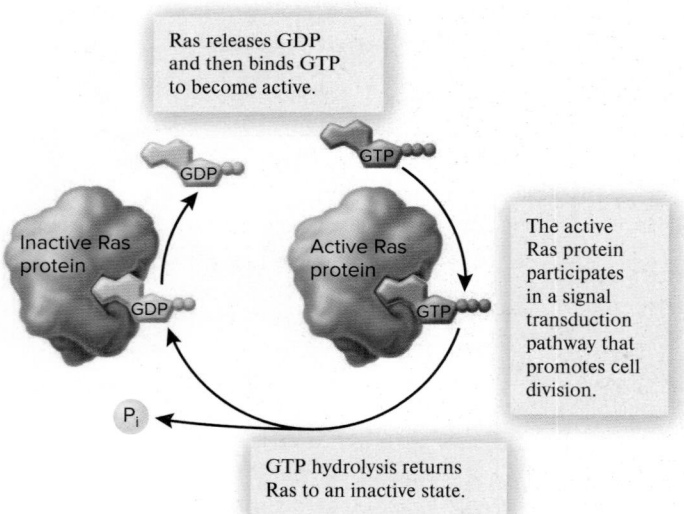

Ras releases GDP and then binds GTP to become active.

Inactive Ras protein

Active Ras protein

The active Ras protein participates in a signal transduction pathway that promotes cell division.

GTP hydrolysis returns Ras to an inactive state.

Figure 15.12 **The function of Ras, a protein that is part of signal transduction pathways.** When GTP is bound, the activated Ras protein promotes cell division. When GTP is hydrolyzed to GDP and P_i, Ras is inactivated, and cell division is inhibited.

of bound GDP for GTP. Both of these functional changes result in a greater amount of the active GTP-bound form of the Ras protein. In this way, these mutations keep the signal transduction pathway turned on when it should not be, resulting in uncontrolled cell division.

Mutations in Proto-Oncogenes Convert Them to Oncogenes

Thus far, we have examined the functions of proteins that cause cancer when they become overactive, resulting in uncontrolled cell division. Let's now consider the common types of genetic changes that create such oncogenes. A **proto-oncogene** is a normal gene that, if mutated, can become an oncogene. An oncogene is a gene that has been altered in a way that causes it to be overexpressed or expressed in the wrong cell type. Several types of genetic changes may convert a proto-oncogene into an oncogene. **Figure 15.13** describes four common types: missense mutations, gene amplifications, chromosomal translocations, and retroviral insertions.

Missense Mutation A missense mutation (Figure 15.13a), which changes a single amino acid in a protein, alters the function of the encoded protein in a way that promotes cancer. This type of mutation is responsible for the conversion of the *ras* gene into an oncogene. An example is a mutation in the *ras* gene that changes a specific glycine to a valine in the Ras protein. This mutation decreases the ability of the Ras protein to hydrolyze GTP, which promotes cell division (see Figure 15.12). Experimentally, chemical mutagens have been shown to cause this missense mutation, thereby leading to cancer.

Gene Amplification Another genetic event that occurs in some cancer cells is an increase in the number of copies of a proto-oncogene (Figure 15.13b). An abnormal increase in the number of genes results in too much of the encoded protein. Many human cancers are associated with the amplification of particular proto-oncogenes. In 1982, American molecular biologist Mark Groudine discovered that the *myc* gene, which encodes a transcription factor, was amplified in a human leukemia.

Chromosomal Translocation A third type of genetic alteration that can lead to cancer is a chromosomal translocation (Figure 15.13c). This occurs when one segment of a chromosome becomes attached to a different chromosome. In 1960, American pathologist Peter Nowell discovered that a form of leukemia called chronic myelogenous leukemia (CML)—a type of cancer involving white blood cells—was correlated with the presence of a shortened version of a human chromosome. This shortened chromosome is the result of a chromosome translocation in which two different chromosomes, chromosomes 9 and 22, exchange pieces. This activates a proto-oncogene, *abl*, in an unusual way (**Figure 15.14**). In healthy individuals, the *bcr* gene and the *abl* gene are located on different chromosomes. In CML, these chromosomes break and rejoin in a way that causes the promoter and the first part of *bcr* to fuse with part of *abl*. This fused gene acts as an oncogene and encodes a fusion protein whose functional overactivity leads to leukemia.

Retroviral Insertion Certain types of viruses convert proto-oncogenes into oncogenes during the viral replication cycle (see

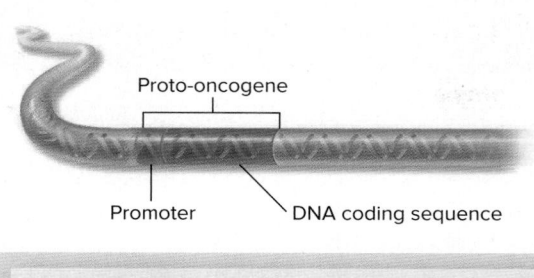

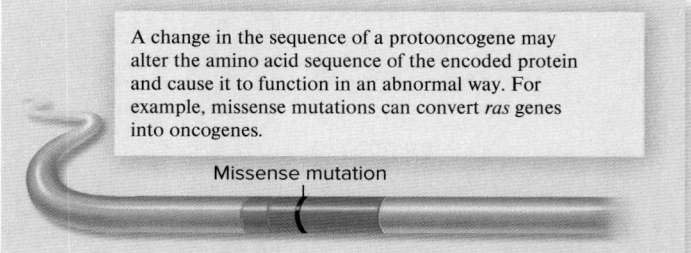

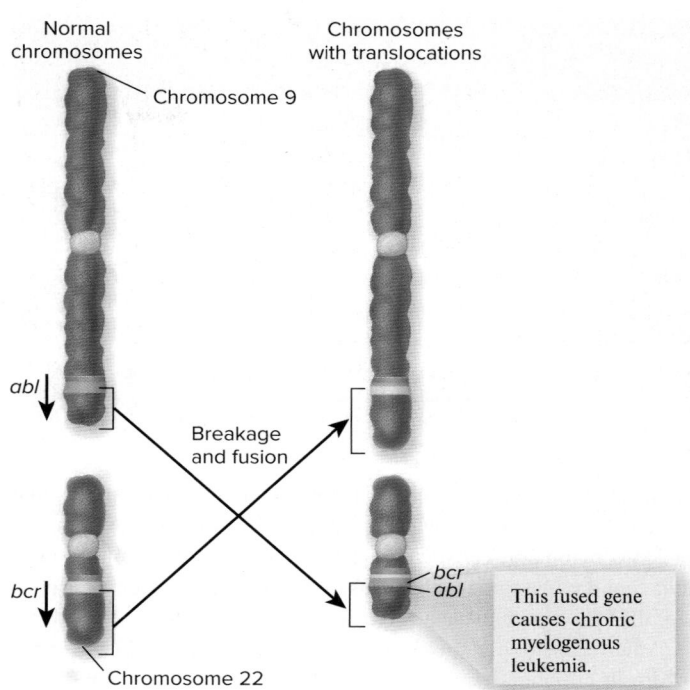

Figure 15.14 The formation of a fused gene found in people with certain forms of leukemia. The fusion of the *bcr* and *abl* genes creates a fused gene that encodes a fusion protein, leading to leukemia. The blue regions are the promoters for the *bcr* and *abl* genes.

Concept Check: *The bcr gene is normally expressed in white blood cells. Explain how this observation is related to the type of cancer that the translocation between chromosomes 9 and 22 causes.*

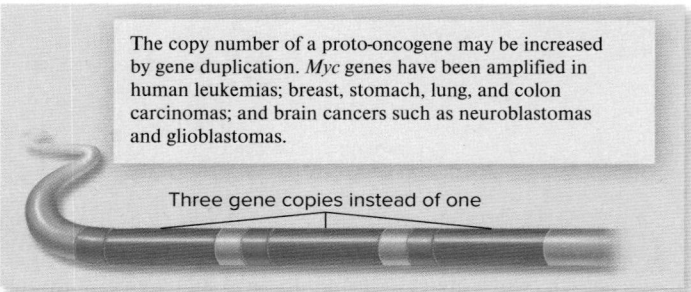

Figure 15.13d). Retroviruses insert their DNA into the chromosomal DNA of the host cell. The viral genome contains promoter and regulatory elements that cause a high level of expression of viral genes. On occasion, the viral DNA may insert into a host chromosome in such a way that a viral promoter and regulatory elements are next to a proto-oncogene. This may result in the overexpression of the proto-oncogene, thereby promoting cancer. This is one way for a virus to cause cancer. Alternatively, a virus may cause cancer because it carries an oncogene in its viral genome. This phenomenon is described next.

Some Types of Cancer Are Caused by Viruses

The majority of cancers are caused by mutagens or other changes that alter the structure and expression of genes that are found in somatic cells. A few viruses, however, are known to cause cancer in plants and animals, including humans (**Table 15.7**).

In 1911, the first cancer-causing virus to be discovered was isolated from chicken sarcomas by American pathologist Peyton Rous. A **sarcoma** is a tumor of connective tissue such as bone or cartilage. The virus was named the Rous sarcoma virus (RSV). In the 1970s, research involving RSV led to the identification of a viral gene that acts as an oncogene. Researchers investigated RSV by using it to infect chicken cells grown in the laboratory. This infection causes the chicken cells to grow like cancer cells, continuously and in an

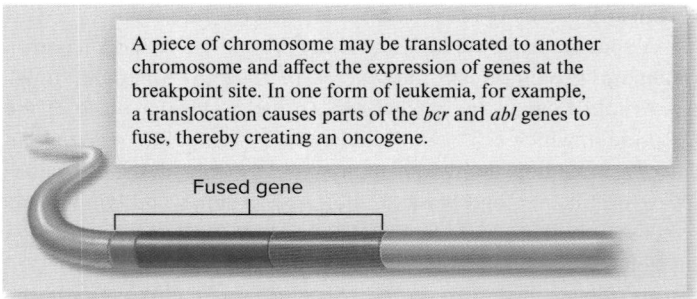

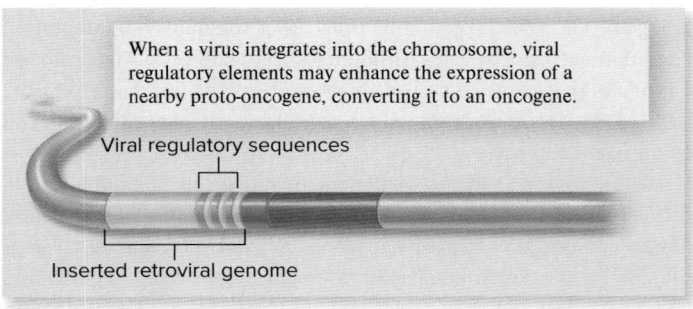

Figure 15.13 Common genetic changes that convert proto-oncogenes to oncogenes.

Table 15.7	Examples of Viruses That Cause Cancer
Virus	**Description**
Rous sarcoma virus	Causes sarcomas in chickens
Simian sarcoma virus	Causes sarcomas in monkeys
Abelson leukemia virus	Causes leukemia in mice
Hardy-Zuckerman 4 feline sarcoma virus	Causes sarcomas in cats
Hepatitis B	Causes liver cancer in several species, including humans

Table 15.8	Functions of Selected Tumor-Suppressor Genes
Gene	
Maintenance of genome integrity	
p53	p53 is a transcription factor that acts as a sensor of DNA damage. It can promote DNA repair, prevent the progression through the cell cycle, and promote apoptosis.
BRCA-1 *BRCA-2*	BRCA-1 and BRCA-2 proteins are both involved in the cellular defense against DNA damage. They play a role in sensing DNA damage and facilitate DNA repair. These genes are mutant in persons with certain inherited forms of breast cancer.
XPD	This represents one of several different genes whose products function in DNA repair. These genes are defective in patients with xeroderma pigmentosum.
Negative regulation of cell division	
Rb	The Rb protein is a negative regulator that represses the transcription of genes required for DNA replication and cell division.
NF1	The NF1 protein stimulates Ras to hydrolyze its GTP to GDP. Loss of NF1 function causes the Ras protein to be overactive, which promotes cell division.
p16	The p16 protein is a negative regulator of cyclin-dependent kinases (cdks).

uncontrolled manner. Researchers identified mutant RSV strains that infected and proliferated within chicken cells without transforming them into malignant cells. These RSV strains were missing a gene that is found in the form of the virus that does cause cancer. This gene was called the *src* gene because it causes sarcoma.

Americans, biologist Harold Varmus and microbiologist Michael Bishop, in collaboration with molecular biologist Peter Vogt, later discovered that normal (nonviral-infected) chicken cells also contain a copy of the *src* gene in their chromosomes. This gene is a proto-oncogene. When it is incorporated into a viral genome, it is overexpressed because it is transcribed from a very active viral promoter. This overexpression ultimately produces too much of the Src protein in infected cells and promotes uncontrolled cell division.

Tumor-Suppressor Genes Prevent Mutation or Cell Proliferation

Thus far, we have examined one category of genes that promote cancer, namely oncogenes. We now turn our attention to the second category, those called tumor-suppressor genes. The functioning of a normal (nonmutant) tumor-suppressor gene prevents cancerous growth. The proteins encoded by tumor-suppressor genes usually have one of two functions: maintenance of genome integrity or negative regulation of cell division (Table 15.8).

Maintenance of Genome Integrity Some tumor-suppressor genes encode proteins that maintain the integrity of the genome by monitoring and/or repairing genome alterations. The proteins encoded by these genes are vital for the prevention of abnormalities such as gene mutations, DNA breaks, and improperly segregated chromosomes. Therefore, when these proteins are functioning properly, they minimize the chance that a cancer-causing mutation will occur. In some cases, the proteins encoded by tumor-suppressor genes prevent a cell from progressing through the cell cycle if an abnormality is detected. These are termed **checkpoint proteins** because their role is to check the integrity of the genome and prevent a cell from progressing past a certain point in the cell cycle. Checkpoint proteins are not always required to regulate normal, healthy cell division, but they can stop cell division if an abnormality is detected.

How do checkpoint proteins stop the cell cycle? One way is by controlling proteins called cyclins and cyclin-dependent

kinases (cdks), which are responsible for advancing a cell through the four phases of the cell cycle (see Chapter 16). The formation of activated cyclin/cdk complexes can be stopped by checkpoint proteins.

A specific example of a tumor-suppressor gene that encodes a checkpoint protein is *p53*, discovered in 1979 by American biologist Arnold Levine. Its name refers to the molecular mass of the p53 protein, which is 53 kDa (kilodaltons). About 50% of all human cancers, including malignant tumors of the lung, breast, esophagus, liver, bladder, and brain, as well as leukemias and lymphomas (cancer of the lymphatic system), are associated with mutations in this gene.

As shown in Figure 15.15, p53 is a protein that controls the ability of cells to advance from the G_1 stage of the cell cycle to the S phase. The expression of the *p53* gene is induced when DNA is damaged. The p53 protein functions as a regulatory transcription factor that activates several different genes, leading to the synthesis of proteins that stop the cell cycle and other proteins that repair the DNA. If the DNA is eventually repaired, a cell may later proceed through the cell cycle.

Alternatively, if the DNA damage is too severe, the p53 protein will also activate other genes that promote programmed cell death. This process, called **apoptosis**, involves cell shrinkage and DNA degradation. As described in Chapter 9, enzymes known as caspases are activated during apoptosis (refer back to Figure 9.18). They function as proteases that are sometimes called the "executioners" of the cell. Caspases digest selected cellular proteins such as microfilaments, which are components of the cytoskeleton. The destruction of the

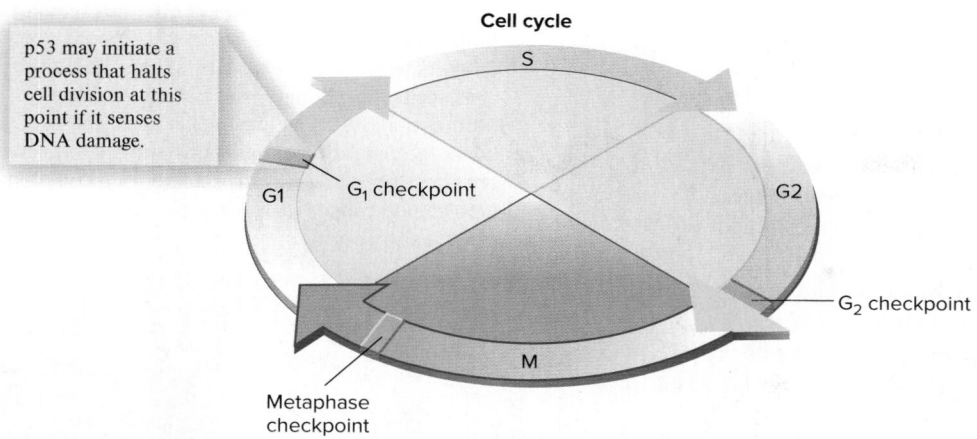

Cell cycle

p53 may initiate a process that halts cell division at this point if it senses DNA damage.

G1

G_1 checkpoint

S

G2

G_2 checkpoint

M

Metaphase checkpoint

Figure 15.15 **The cell cycle and checkpoints.** As discussed in Chapter 16, eukaryotic cells advance through a cell cycle composed of G_1, S, G_2, and M phases (look ahead to Figure 16.2). The yellow bars indicate common checkpoints where the cell cycle is stopped if genetic abnormalities are detected. The p53 protein stops a cell at the G_1 checkpoint if it senses DNA damage.

Concept Check: *Why is it an advantage for an organism to have checkpoints where the cell cycle can be stopped?*

microfilaments causes the cell to break into small vesicles that are eventually phagocytized by cells of the immune system. It is beneficial for a multicellular organism to kill an occasional cell with cancer-causing potential.

Negative Regulation of Cell Division

A second category of tumor-suppressor genes encodes proteins that are negative regulators or inhibitors of cell division. These proteins must function properly to halt cell division. If their function is lost, cell division is abnormally accelerated.

An example of such a tumor-suppressor gene is the *Rb* gene. It was the first tumor-suppressor gene to be identified in humans, from studies of patients with a disease called retinoblastoma, a cancerous tumor that occurs in the retina of the eye. The Rb protein negatively controls a regulatory transcription factor called E2F that activates genes required for cell cycle progression from G_1 to S phase. The binding of the Rb protein to E2F inhibits its activity and prevents cell division (**Figure 15.16**). When a normal cell is supposed to divide, cyclins bind to cyclin-dependent kinases (cdks). This binding activates the kinases, which catalyze the transfer of a phosphate to the Rb protein. The phosphorylated form of the Rb protein is released from E2F, thereby allowing E2F to activate genes needed to advance through the cell cycle. When both copies of Rb are defective due to mutations, the E2F protein is always active. This explains why uncontrolled cell division occurs in retinoblastoma.

Gene Mutations, Chromosome Loss, and Changes in Chromatin Structure Can Inhibit the Expression of Tumor-Suppressor Genes

Cancer biologists want to understand how tumor-suppressor genes are inactivated, because this knowledge may ultimately help them to prevent or combat cancer. How are tumor-suppressor genes silenced? The function of tumor-suppressor genes is lost in three common ways.

Inactivation of Tumor-Suppressor Genes via Mutation

First, a mutation can occur within a tumor-suppressor gene to inactivate its function. For example, a mutation could abolish the function

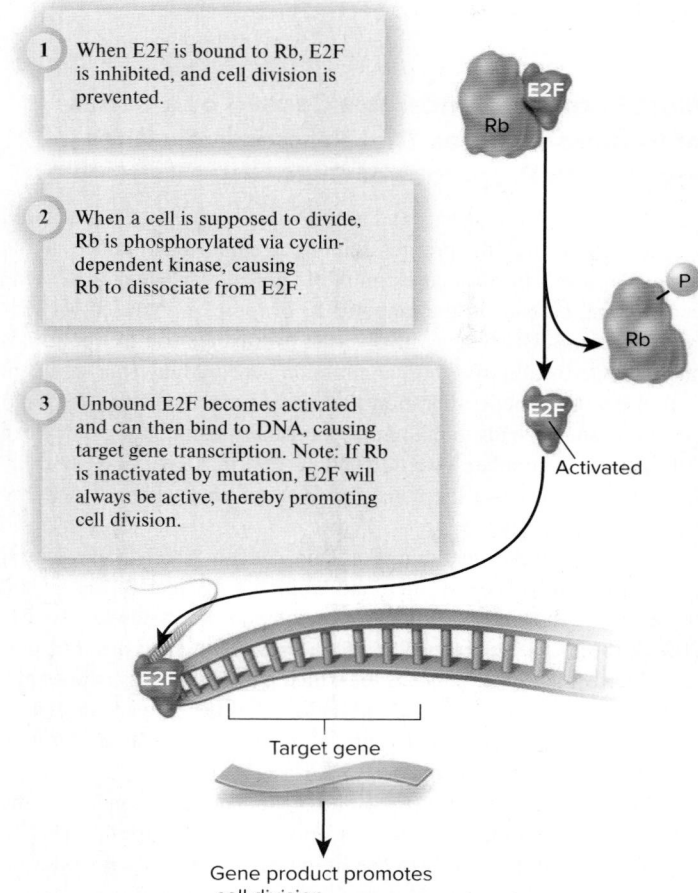

1 When E2F is bound to Rb, E2F is inhibited, and cell division is prevented.

E2F
Rb

2 When a cell is supposed to divide, Rb is phosphorylated via cyclin-dependent kinase, causing Rb to dissociate from E2F.

P
Rb

3 Unbound E2F becomes activated and can then bind to DNA, causing target gene transcription. Note: If Rb is inactivated by mutation, E2F will always be active, thereby promoting cell division.

E2F
Activated

E2F

Target gene

Gene product promotes cell division.

Figure 15.16 **Function of the Rb protein.** The Rb protein inhibits the function of E2F, which turns on genes that cause a cell to divide. When cells are supposed to divide, Rb is phosphorylated by cyclin-dependent kinase, which allows E2F to function.

Concept Check: *Would cancer occur if both copies of the Rb gene and both copies of the E2F gene were rendered inactive due to mutations?*

of the promoter for a tumor-suppressor gene or introduce an early stop codon in its coding sequence. Either of these would prevent the expression of a functional protein.

Chromosome Loss   Chromosome loss is a second way that the function of a tumor-suppressor gene is lost. Chromosome loss may contribute to the progression of cancer if the missing chromosome carries one or more tumor-suppressor genes.

Epigenetic Changes   Researchers have discovered a third way that tumor-suppressor genes may be inactivated. Epigenetic changes involve changes in chromatin structure that alter gene expression without altering the base sequence of DNA (see Chapter 18). For example, tumor-suppressor genes found in cancer cells are sometimes abnormally methylated. As discussed in Chapter 14, transcription is inhibited when CpG islands near a promoter are methylated. Such DNA methylation near the promoters of tumor-suppressor genes has been found in many types of tumors, suggesting that this form of gene inactivation plays an important role in the formation and/or progression of malignancy.

Most Forms of Cancer Are Caused by a Series of Genetic Changes That Progressively Alter the Growth Properties of Cells

The discovery of oncogenes and tumor-suppressor genes has allowed researchers to study the progression of certain forms of cancer at the molecular level. In most cases, multiple genetic changes to the same cell lineage, perhaps in the range of 10 or more, are needed for cancer to occur. Such changes involve the overexpression of oncogenes and the inactivation of tumor-suppression genes. Many cancers begin with a benign genetic alteration that, over time and with additional genetic changes, leads to malignancy. Furthermore, a malignancy can continue to accumulate genetic changes that make it even more difficult to treat because the cells divide faster or invade surrounding tissues more readily.

As an example, lets consider lung cancer, which is diagnosed in approximately 170,000 men and women each year in the United States. More than 1.2 million cases are diagnosed worldwide. Nearly 90% of these cases are caused by tobacco smoking and are thus preventable. Unlike other cancers for which early diagnosis is possible, lung cancer is usually detected only after it has become advanced and is difficult if not impossible to cure. The 5-year survival rate for lung cancer patients is approximately 15%.

What is the cellular basis for lung cancer? Most cancers of the lung are **carcinomas**—cancers of epithelial cells (Figure 15.17). (Epithelial cells, which form the lining of all internal and external body surfaces, are described in Chapter 10.) The top images in **Figure 15.17** show the normal epithelium found in a healthy lung. The rest of the figure shows the progression of a carcinoma that is due to mutations in basal cells, a type of epithelial cell. Keep in mind that cancer occurs due to the accumulation of mutations in a cell lineage, beginning with an initial mutant cell that then divides multiple times to produce a population of many daughter cells (see Figure 15.10). As mutations accumulate in a lineage of basal cells, the number of these cells increases dramatically. This

Figure 15.17   Progression of changes leading to lung cancer. Lung tissue is largely composed of different types of connective tissue and epithelial cells, including columnar and basal cells. A progression of cellular changes in basal cells, caused by the accumulation of mutations and epigenetic changes, leads to basal cell carcinoma, a common type of lung cancer. (photos): ©Dr. Oscar Auerbach, reproduced with permission

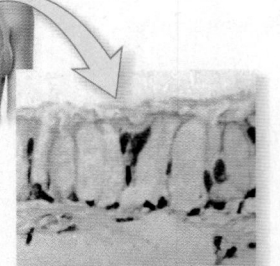
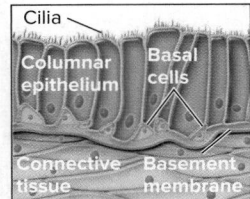

Normal lung epithelium

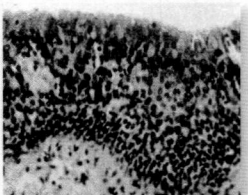
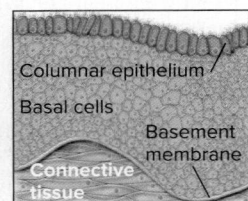

Hyperplasia

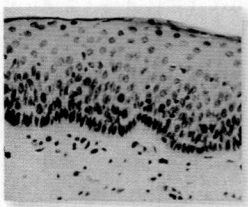
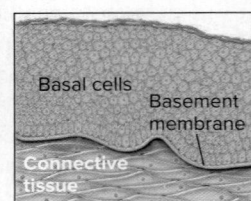

Loss of ciliated cells

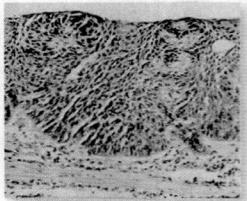
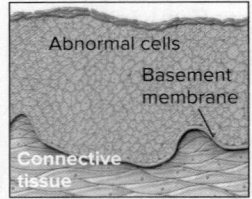

Dysplasia (initially precancerous, then cancerous)

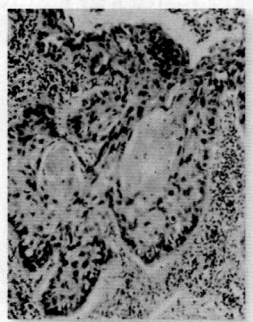
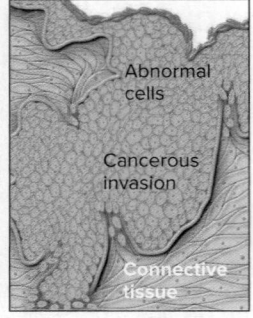

Invasive cancerous cells that can metastasize

causes a thickening of the epithelium, a condition called hyperplasia. The proliferation of the basal cells causes the loss of the ciliated, columnar epithelial cells that normally line the airways and help remove mucus and its trapped particles from the lungs. As additional mutations accumulate in this cell lineage, the basal cells develop more abnormal morphologies, a condition known as dysplasia. In the early stages of dysplasia, the abnormal basal cells are precancerous. If the source of chronic irritation (usually cigarette smoke) is eliminated, the abnormal cells are likely to disappear. Alternatively, if smoking continues, these abnormal cells may accumulate additional genetic changes and lose the ability to stop dividing. Such cells have become cancerous—the person has basal cell carcinoma.

The basement membrane is a sheetlike layer of extracellular matrix that provides a barrier between the lung cells and the bloodstream. If the cancer cells have not yet penetrated the basement membrane, they will not have metastasized, that is, spread into the blood and to other parts of the body. If the entire tumor is removed at this stage, the patient should be cured. The lower images in Figure 15.17 show a tumor that has broken through the basement membrane. The metastasis of these cells to other parts of the body will likely kill the patient, usually within a year of diagnosis.

The cellular changes that lead to lung cancer are correlated with genetic changes. These include the occurrence of mutations that create oncogenes and inhibit tumor-suppressor genes. The order of mutations is not absolute. It takes time for multiple changes to accumulate, so cancer is usually a disease of older people. Reducing your exposure to mutagens such as cigarette smoke throughout your lifetime helps minimize the risk of mutations to your genes that could promote cancer.

 **Core Concept: Evolution**

Mutations in Approximately 300 Human Genes May Promote Cancer

Researchers have identified a large number of genes that are mutated in cancer cells. Though not all of these mutant genes have been directly shown to affect the growth rate of cells, such mutations are likely to be found in tumors because they provide some type of growth advantage for the cell population from which the cancer developed. For example, certain mutations may affect the functions of proteins that enable cells to metastasize to neighboring locations. These mutations may not affect growth rate, but they provide a growth advantage in that cancer cells are not limited to growing in a particular location. They can migrate to new locations.

How many genes can contribute to cancer when they become mutant? Researchers have estimated that about 300 different genes may play a role in the development of human cancer. With an approximate human genome size of 22,000 genes, this observation indicates that over 1% of our genes have the potential to promote cancer if their expression is altered by a mutation or an epigenetic change.

Summary of Key Concepts

15.1 Consequences of Mutations

- A mutation is a heritable change in the genetic material; gene mutations are relatively small changes in the base sequence of a gene.
- Point mutations affect a single base pair and can alter the coding sequence of genes in several ways. These mutations include silent, missense, nonsense, and frameshift mutations (Table 15.1).
- Sickle cell disease is caused by a missense mutation that results in a single amino acid substitution in β-globin (Figure 15.1).
- Gene mutations also alter gene function by changing DNA sequences that are not within the coding region (Table 15.2).
- Germ-line mutations affect gametes, whereas mutations in somatic cells affect only a part of the body and cannot be passed to offspring (Figures 15.2, 15.3).

15.2 Causes of Mutations

- The Lederbergs used replica plating to show that mutations are random events (Figure 15.4).
- Spontaneous mutations are the result of abnormalities in biological processes. Induced mutations are caused by agents in the environment that alter DNA structure (Table 15.3).
- Mutagens are chemical or physical agents that lead to mutations in DNA (Table 15.4, Figures 15.5, 15.6).
- The Ames test is a method of testing whether an agent is a mutagen (Figure 15.7).

15.3 DNA Repair

- DNA repair systems consist of proteins that sense DNA damage and repair it before a mutation occurs (Table 15.5).
- In nucleotide excision repair (NER), proteins recognize various types of DNA damage, such as thymine dimers. A region in the damaged strand is excised, and a new strand is synthesized, using the intact strand as a template (Figure 15.8).
- Certain inherited diseases in humans, such as xeroderma pigmentosum (XP), are due to defects in the NER system (Figure 15.9).

15.4 Cancer

- Cancer is due to the accumulation of mutations and epigenetic changes in a lineage of cells that leads to uncontrolled cell growth (Figure 15.10).
- Mutations in proto-oncogenes that result in overactivity produce cancer-causing genes called oncogenes.
- Oncogenes often encode proteins involved in signal transduction pathways that promote cell division (Figures 15.11, 15.12, Table 15.6).
- Four common types of genetic changes, namely, missense mutations, gene amplifications, chromosomal translocations, and retroviral insertions, can change proto-oncogenes into oncogenes (Figures 15.13, 15.14).
- Some types of cancer are caused by viruses (Table 15.7).

- The normal function of tumor-suppressor genes is to prevent cancer. Mutations of these genes may affect this function and thus promote cancer. Tumor-suppressor genes often encode proteins that maintain the integrity of the genome or function as negative regulators of cell division (Table 15.8).

- Checkpoint proteins such as p53 monitor the integrity of the genome and prevent the cell from progressing through the cell cycle if abnormalities are detected (Figure 15.15).

- The Rb protein is an inhibitor of the cell cycle, because it negatively controls E2F, a transcription factor that promotes cell division (Figure 15.16).

- Tumor-suppressor genes can be inactivated by gene mutations, chromosome loss, and epigenetic changes such as DNA methylation.

- Most forms of cancer, such as lung cancer, involve multiple genetic changes that lead to malignancy (Figure 15.17).

- Over 300 human genes, or over 1% of the total, are known to be associated with cancer when they become mutant.

Assess & Discuss

Test Yourself

1. A mutation removes a single base pair within the coding sequence of a gene and inactivates the protein encoded by the gene. Such a mutation is
   a. a silent mutation.
   b. a missense mutation.
   c. a nonsense mutation.
   d. a frameshift mutation.
   e. both b and c.

2. Some point mutations lead to an mRNA that produces a shorter polypeptide. This type of mutation is known as a _____ mutation.
   a. neutral
   b. silent
   c. missense
   d. nonsense
   e. chromosomal

3. In which location is a mutation least likely to affect gene function?
   a. promoter
   b. coding region
   c. splice junction
   d. intergenic region
   e. regulatory site

4. Mutagens can cause mutations by
   a. chemically altering DNA nucleotides.
   b. disrupting DNA replication.
   c. altering the genetic code of an organism.
   d. doing all of the above.
   e. doing a and b only.

5. The mutagenic effect of UV light is
   a. the alteration of cytosine bases to adenine bases.
   b. the formation of adenine dimers that interfere with genetic expression.
   c. the breaking of the sugar-phosphate backbone of the DNA molecule.
   d. the formation of thymine dimers that disrupt DNA replication.
   e. the deletion of thymine bases along the DNA molecule.

6. The Ames test
   a. provides a way to determine if any type of cell has experienced a mutation.
   b. provides a way to determine if an agent is a mutagen.
   c. allows researchers to experimentally disrupt gene activity by causing a mutation in a specific gene.
   d. provides a way to repair mutations in bacterial cells.
   e. does all of the above.

7. Xeroderma pigmentosum
   a. is a genetic disorder that results in uncontrolled cell growth.
   b. is a genetic disorder in which the NER system is not fully functional.
   c. is a genetic disorder that results in the loss of pigment in certain patches of skin.
   d. results from the lack of DNA polymerase proofreading.
   e. both b and d are true of this disorder.

8. If a mutation eliminated the function of UvrC, which aspect of the nucleotide excision repair system would not work?
   a. sensing a damaged DNA site
   b. endonuclease cleavage of the damaged strand
   c. removal of the damaged strand
   d. synthesis of a new strand, using the undamaged strand as a template
   e. none of the above

9. Cancer cells are said to be metastatic when they
   a. begin to divide uncontrollably.
   b. invade healthy tissue.
   c. migrate to other parts of the body.
   d. cause mutations in other healthy cells.
   e. do all of the above.

10. Oncogenes can be produced by
    a. missense mutations.
    b. gene amplification.
    c. chromosomal translocation.
    d. retroviral insertion.
    e. all of the above.

Conceptual Questions

1. Is a random mutation more likely to be beneficial or harmful? Explain your answer.

2. Distinguish between spontaneous and induced mutations. Which are more harmful? Which are avoidable?

3. **Core Concept: Information** Explain how mutations may cause alterations to the genetic material that are detrimental for reproduction and sustaining life.

Collaborative Questions

1. Discuss the pros and cons of mutation.

2. A large amount of research is aimed at studying mutation. However, there is not an infinite supply of research funding. Where would you put your money for mutation research?
   a. testing of potential mutagens
   b. investigating molecular effects of mutagens
   c. investigating DNA repair mechanisms
   d. some other area

The Eukaryotic Cell Cycle, Mitosis, and Meiosis

16

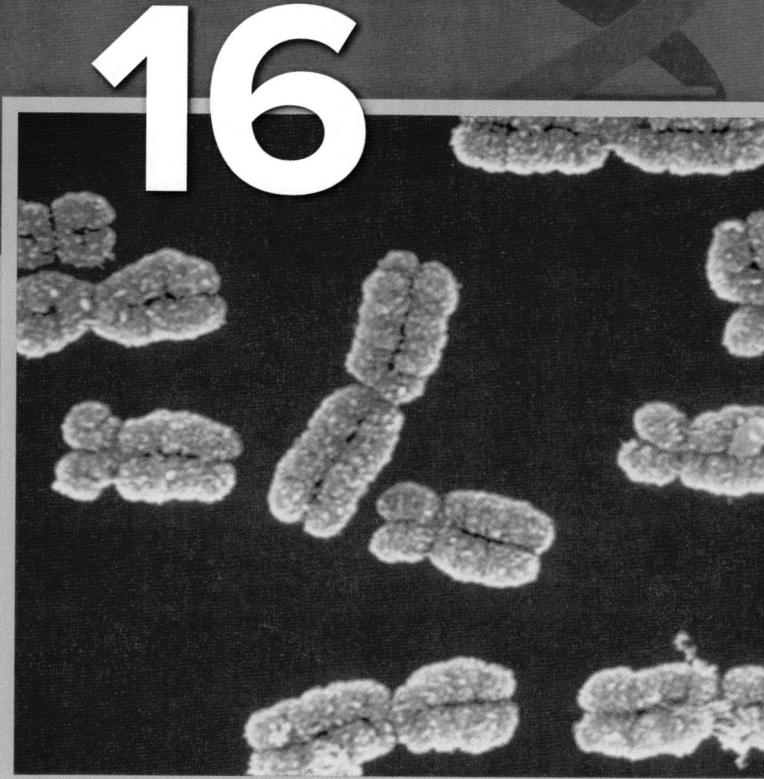

O ver 10,000,000,000,000! Researchers estimate that the adult human body contains somewhere between 10 trillion and 50 trillion cells. It is an almost incomprehensible number. Even more amazing is the accuracy of the process that produces these cells. After a human sperm and egg unite, the fertilized egg goes through a long series of cell divisions to produce an adult with over 10 trillion cells. Let's suppose you randomly removed a cell from your arm and compared it with a cell from your foot. If you examined the chromosomes in both cells under the microscope, they would look identical. The DNA sequences along those chromosomes would also be the same, barring rare mutations. Similar comparisons could be made among the trillions of cells in your body. When you consider how many cell divisions are needed to produce an adult human, the precision of cell division is truly remarkable.

What accounts for this high level of accuracy? As we will examine in this chapter, **cell division**, the reproduction of cells, is a highly regulated process that distributes and monitors the integrity of the genetic material. The eukaryotic cell cycle is a series of phases needed for cell division. The cells of eukaryotic species follow one of two different sorting processes so that new daughter cells receive the correct number and types of chromosomes. The first sorting process we will explore, called mitosis, ensures that two daughter cells receive the same amount of genetic material as the mother cell that produced them. The second sorting process we will consider, called meiosis, is needed for sexual reproduction. In meiosis, cells that have two sets of chromosomes produce daughter cells with a single set of chromosomes. Lastly, we will look at variation in the structure and number of chromosomes. As you will see, certain mechanisms that alter chromosome structure and number have important consequences for the organisms that carry them.

A scanning electron micrograph of human chromosomes. These highly compacted chromosomes were found in a dividing cell.
©Biophoto Associates/Science Source

16.1 The Eukaryotic Cell Cycle

Learning Outcomes:

1. **CoreSKILL »** Describe the features of chromosomes, and explain how sets of chromosomes are examined microscopically.
2. Outline the phases of the eukaryotic cell cycle.
3. Explain how cyclins and cdks work together to advance a cell through the eukaryotic cell cycle.

Life is a continuum in which new living cells are formed by the division of pre-existing cells. The Latin axiom *Omnis cellula e cellula*, meaning "Every cell originates from another cell," was first proposed in 1858 by Rudolf Virchow, a German biologist. From an evolutionary perspective, cell division has a very ancient origin. All living organisms, from unicellular bacteria to multicellular plants and animals, have been produced by a series of repeated rounds of cell growth and division extending back to the beginnings of life nearly 4 billion years ago.

A **cell cycle** is a series of events that leads to cell division. In all species, it is a highly regulated process, to ensure that cell division occurs at the appropriate time. As discussed in Chapter 19, bacterial cells produce more cells via binary fission. The cell cycle in eukaryotes is more complex, in part, because eukaryotic cells have sets of chromosomes that need to be sorted properly. In this section, we will examine the phases of the eukaryotic cell cycle and see how the cell cycle is controlled by proteins that carefully monitor the division process to ensure its accuracy. But first, we need to consider some general features of chromosomes in eukaryotic species.

Chromosomes Are Inherited in Sets and Occur in Homologous Pairs

To understand the chromosomal composition of cells and the behavior of chromosomes during cell division, scientists use microscopes to observe cells and chromosomes. **Cytogenetics** is the field of genetics that involves the microscopic examination of chromosomes. When a cell prepares to divide, the chromosomes become more tightly compacted, a process that decreases their apparent length and increases their diameter. A consequence of this compaction is that distinctive shapes and numbers of chromosomes become visible under a light microscope.

Microscopic Examination of Chromosomes **Figure 16.1** shows the general procedure for preparing and viewing chromosomes from a eukaryotic cell. In this example, the cells were obtained from a sample of human blood. Specifically, the chromosomes within leukocytes

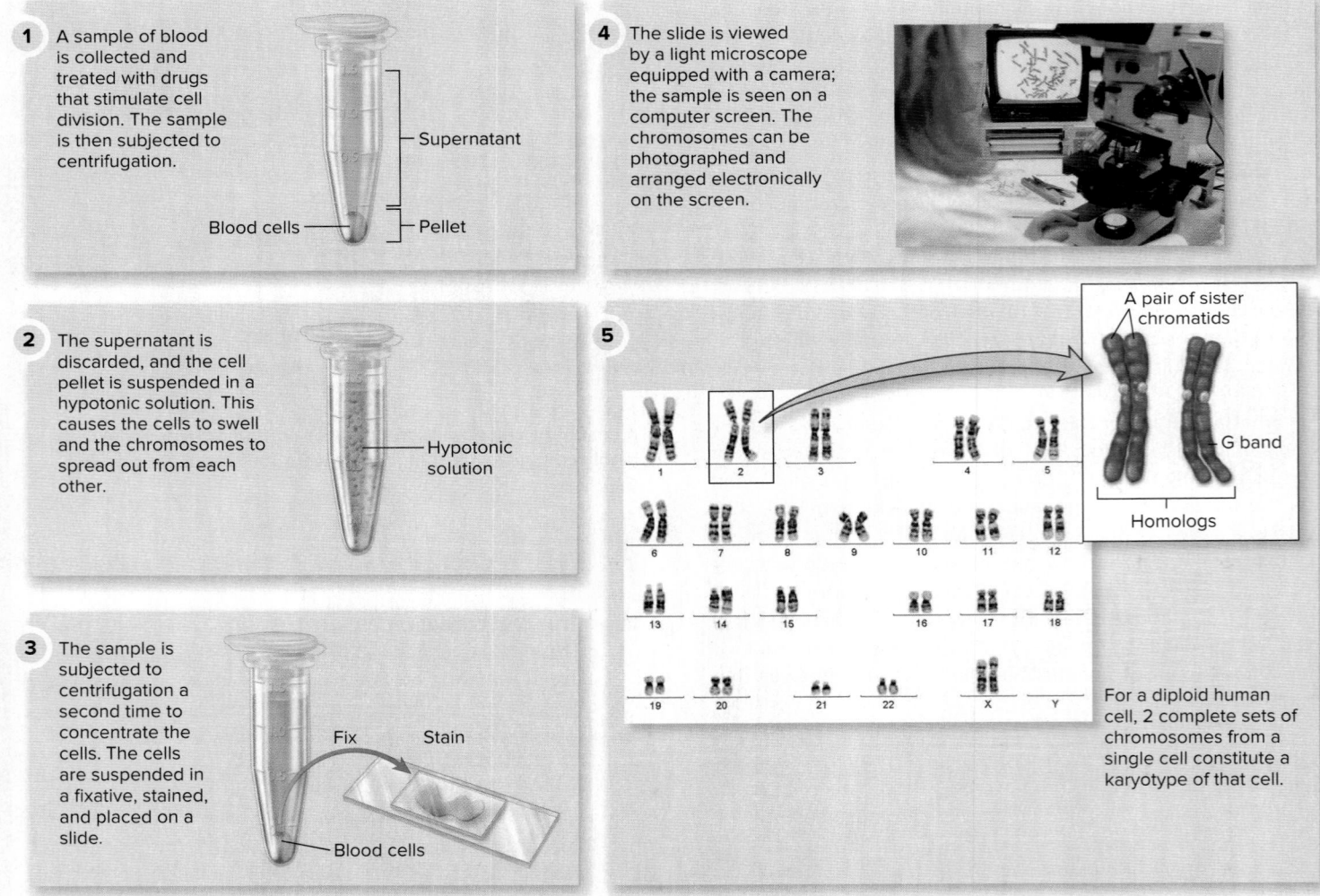

Figure 16.1   The procedure for making a karyotype. In this example, the chromosomes were treated with Giemsa stain, and the resulting bands are called G bands. (4): ©Burger/Science Source; (5): Courtesy of the Genomic Centre for Cancer Research and Diagnosis, CancerCare Manitoba, University of Manitoba, Winnipeg, Manitoba, Canada

Concept Check: *Researchers usually treat cells with drugs that stimulate them to divide before beginning the procedure for making a karyotype. Why is this treatment useful?*

(white blood cells) were examined. A sample of the blood cells was treated with drugs that stimulated them to divide. The actively dividing cells were centrifuged to concentrate them into a pellet, which was then mixed with a hypotonic solution that caused the cells to swell. The expansion of the cells caused the chromosomes to spread out from each other, making it easier to see each individual chromosome.

Next, the cells were concentrated by a second centrifugation and treated with a fixative, which chemically fixed them in place so the chromosomes could no longer move around. The cells were then exposed to a chemical dye, such as Giemsa stain, that binds to the chromosomes and stains them. This gives chromosomes a distinctive banding pattern that greatly enhances their contrast and ability to be uniquely identified; in this case, the bands are called G bands.

The cells were then placed on a slide and viewed with a light microscope. In a cytogenetics laboratory, microscopes are equipped with an electronic camera to photograph the chromosomes. On a computer screen, the images of the chromosomes are organized in a standard way, usually from largest to smallest. This type of photographic representation of chromosomes, such as the photo in step 5 of Figure 16.1, is called a **karyotype**. A karyotype reveals the number, size, and form of chromosomes found within an actively dividing cell. It should also be noted that the chromosomes viewed in actively dividing cells have already replicated. The two copies are still joined to each other and referred to as a pair of **sister chromatids** (see inset to Figure 16.1).

Sets of Chromosomes What type of information is learned from a karyotype? By studying the karyotypes of many species, scientists have discovered that eukaryotic chromosomes occur in sets. Each set is composed of several different types of chromosomes. For example, one set of human chromosomes contains 23 different types of chromosomes (see Figure 16.1). By convention, the chromosomes are numbered according to size, with the largest chromosomes having the smallest numbers. For example, human chromosomes 1, 2, and 3 are relatively large, whereas 21 and 22 are the two smallest. This numbering system does not apply to the **sex chromosomes**, which determine the sex of the individual. Sex chromosomes in humans are designated with the letters X and Y; females are XX and males are XY. The chromosomes that are not sex chromosomes are called **autosomes**. Humans have 22 different types of autosomes.

A second feature of many eukaryotic species is that most cells contain two sets of chromosomes. The karyotype shown in Figure 16.1 contains two sets of chromosomes, with 23 different chromosomes in each set. Therefore, this human cell contains a total of 46 chromosomes. Each cell has two sets because the individual inherited one set from the father and one set from the mother. When the cells of an organism carry two sets of chromosomes, that organism is said to be **diploid**. Geneticists use the letter n to represent a set of chromosomes. Diploid organisms are referred to as $2n$, because they have two sets of chromosomes. For example, humans are $2n$, where $n = 23$. Most human cells are diploid. An exception is the **gametes**, the sperm and egg cells. Gametes are **haploid**, or $1n$, which means they contain one set of chromosomes.

Homologous Pairs of Chromosomes When an organism is diploid, the members of a pair of chromosomes are called **homologs** (see inset to Figure 16.1). The term **homology** refers to any similarity that is due to common ancestry. Pairs of homologous chromosomes are evolutionarily derived from the same chromosome. However, homologous chromosomes are not usually identical because over many generations they have accumulated some genetic changes that make them distinct.

How similar are homologous chromosomes to each other? Each of the two chromosomes in a homologous pair is nearly identical in size and contains a very similar composition of genetic material. A particular gene found on one copy of a chromosome is usually found on the homolog. However, because one homolog is received from each parent, the two homologs may vary in the way that a gene affects an organism's traits. As an example, let's consider a gene in humans called *OCA2*, which plays a major role in determining eye color. The *OCA2* gene is found on chromosome 15. One copy of chromosome 15 might carry the form of this eye color gene that confers brown eyes, whereas the gene on the homolog could confer blue eyes. The topic of how genes affect an organism's traits will be considered in Chapter 17.

The DNA sequences on homologous chromosomes are very similar. In most cases, the sequence of bases on one homolog differs by less than 1% from the sequence on the other homolog. For example, the DNA sequence of chromosome 1 that you inherited from your mother is likely to be more than 99% identical to the DNA sequence of chromosome 1 that you inherited from your father. Nevertheless, keep in mind that the sequences are not identical. The slight differences in DNA sequence provide important variation in gene function. Again, if we use the eye color gene *OCA2* as an example, a minor difference in DNA sequence distinguishes two forms of the gene, brown versus blue.

The striking similarity between homologous chromosomes does not apply to the sex chromosomes (for example, X and Y). These chromosomes differ in size and genetic composition. Certain genes found on the X chromosome are not found on the Y chromosome, and vice versa. The X and Y chromosomes are not considered homologous chromosomes, although they do have short regions of homology.

The Cell Cycle Is a Series of Phases That Lead to Cell Division

Eukaryotic cells that are destined to divide advance through the cell cycle, a series of changes that involves growth, replication, and division, and ultimately produces new cells. **Figure 16.2** provides an overview of the cell cycle. In this diagram, the mother cell has three pairs of chromosomes, for a total of six individual chromosomes. Such a cell is diploid ($2n$) and contains three chromosomes per set ($n = 3$). The paternal set is shown in blue, and the homologous maternal set is shown in red.

The phases of the cell cycle are G_1 (first gap), S (synthesis of DNA, the genetic material), G_2 (second gap), and **M phase** (mitosis and cytokinesis). The G_1 and G_2 phases were originally described as gap phases to indicate the periods between DNA synthesis and mitosis. In actively dividing cells, the G_1, S, and G_2 phases are collectively known as **interphase**. During interphase, the cell grows and copies its chromosomes in preparation for cell division. Alternatively, a cell may exit the cell cycle and remain for long periods of time in a phase called G_0 (G zero). The G_0 phase is an alternative to proceeding through G_1. A cell in the G_0 phase has postponed division or, in the case of terminally differentiated cells (such as muscle cells in an adult animal), will never divide again. G_0 is a nondividing phase.

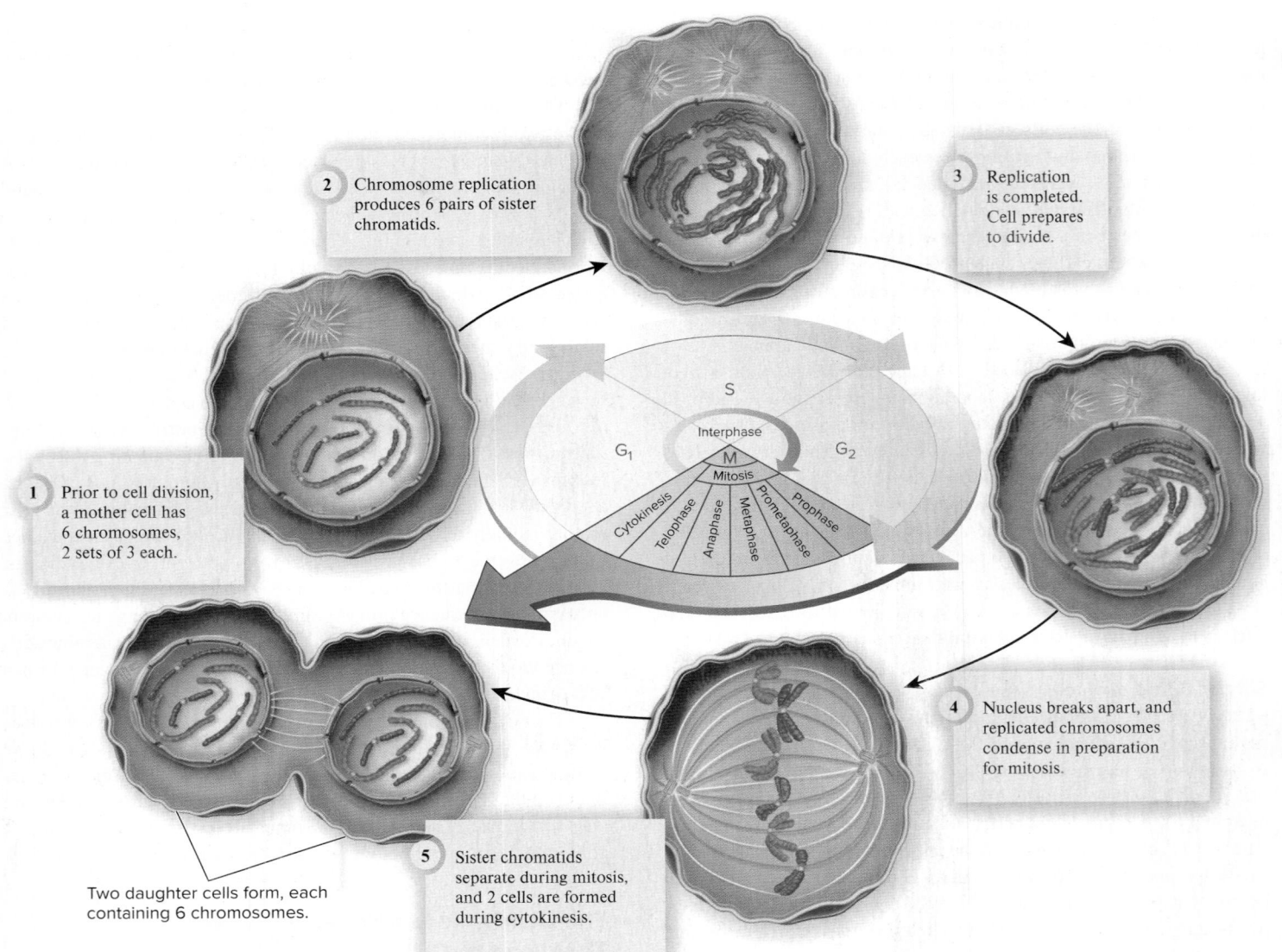

① Prior to cell division, a mother cell has 6 chromosomes, 2 sets of 3 each.

② Chromosome replication produces 6 pairs of sister chromatids.

③ Replication is completed. Cell prepares to divide.

④ Nucleus breaks apart, and replicated chromosomes condense in preparation for mitosis.

⑤ Sister chromatids separate during mitosis, and 2 cells are formed during cytokinesis.

Two daughter cells form, each containing 6 chromosomes.

Figure 16.2 The eukaryotic cell cycle. Dividing cells advance through a series of phases denoted G₁, S, G₂, and M. This diagram shows the advancement of a cell through the cell cycle to produce two daughter cells. The original diploid cell had three pairs of chromosomes, for a total of six individual chromosomes. During S phase, these replicate to yield 12 chromatids. After mitosis is complete, the two daughter cells each contain six individual chromosomes. The width of the phases shown in this figure is not meant to reflect their actual length. G₁ is typically the longest phase of the cell cycle, whereas M phase is relatively short.

Concept Check: *Which phases make up interphase?*

G₁ Phase   The G₁ phase is a period in a cell's life when it may become committed to divide. Depending on the environmental conditions and the presence of signaling molecules, a cell in the G₁ phase may accumulate molecular changes that cause it to advance through the rest of the cell cycle. Cell growth typically occurs during the G₁ phase.

S Phase   During the S phase, each chromosome is replicated to form a pair of sister chromatids (see Figure 16.1). When S phase is completed, a cell has twice as many chromatids as the number of chromosomes in the G₁ phase. For example, a human cell in G₁ phase has 46 distinct chromosomes, whereas the same cell in G₂ phase will have 46 pairs of sister chromatids, for a total of 92 chromatids.

G₂ Phase   During the G₂ phase, a cell synthesizes the proteins necessary for chromosome sorting and cell division. Some cell growth may occur.

M Phase   The first part of M phase is **mitosis**. The purpose of mitosis is to divide one cell nucleus into two nuclei, distributing the duplicated chromosomes so that each daughter cell receives the same complement of chromosomes. As noted previously, a human cell in G₂ phase has 92 chromatids, which are found in 46 pairs. During mitosis, these pairs of chromatids are separated and sorted so that each daughter cell receives 46 chromosomes. In most cases, mitosis is followed by **cytokinesis**, which is the division of the cytoplasm to produce two distinct daughter cells.

The length of the cell cycle varies considerably among different cell types, ranging from several minutes in quickly growing embryos to several months in slow-growing adult cells. For fast-dividing mammalian cells in adults, such as skin cells, the length of the cycle is often in the range of 10 to 24 hours. The various phases within the cell cycle also vary in length. G_1 is often the longest and also the most variable phase, and M is the shortest. For a cell that divides in 24 hours, the following lengths of time for each phase are typical:

- G_1 phase: 11 hours
- S phase: 8 hours
- G_2 phase: 4 hours
- M phase: 1 hour

What factors determine whether or not a cell will divide? First, cell division is controlled by external factors, such as environmental conditions and signaling molecules. The effects of growth factors on cell division are discussed in Chapter 9 (refer back to Figure 9.10). Second, internal factors affect cell division. These include cell cycle control molecules and checkpoints, as we will discuss next.

The Cell Cycle Is Controlled by Checkpoint Proteins

The advancement through the cell cycle is a process that is highly regulated to ensure that the genome remains intact and that the conditions are appropriate for a cell to divide. As discussed in Chapter 15, this regulation is necessary to minimize the occurrence of mutations, which could have harmful effects and potentially lead to cancer. Proteins called **cyclins** and **cyclin-dependent kinases (cdks)** are responsible for advancing a cell through the phases of the cell cycle. Cyclins

are so named because their amount varies throughout the cell cycle. To be active, the cyclin-dependent kinases controlling the cell cycle must bind to (are dependent on) cyclins. The numbers of different types of cyclins and cdks vary from species to species.

Figure 16.3 provides a simplified description of how cyclins and cdks work together to advance a cell through G_1 and mitosis. During G_1, the amount of a particular cyclin termed G_1 cyclin increases in response to sufficient nutrients and growth factors. The G_1 cyclin binds to a cdk to form an activated G_1 cyclin/cdk complex. Once activated, cdk functions as a protein kinase that phosphorylates other proteins needed to advance the cell to the next phase in the cell cycle. For example, certain proteins involved with DNA synthesis are phosphorylated and activated, thereby allowing the cell to replicate its DNA in S phase. After the cell passes into the S phase, G_1 cyclin is degraded. Similar events advance the cell through other phases of the cell cycle. A different cyclin, called mitotic cyclin, accumulates late in G_2. It binds to a cdk to form an activated mitotic cyclin/cdk complex. This complex phosphorylates proteins that are needed to advance the cell into M phase.

Three critical regulatory points called **checkpoints** are found in the cell cycle of eukaryotic cells (see Figure 16.3). At these checkpoints, a variety of proteins, referred to as checkpoint proteins, act as sensors to determine if a cell is in the proper condition to divide. At the G_1 checkpoint, also called the **restriction point**, the checkpoint proteins determine if conditions are favorable for cell division. In addition, G_1 checkpoint proteins sense if the DNA has incurred damage. What happens if DNA damage is detected? The checkpoint proteins prevent the formation of active cyclin/cdk complexes, thereby stopping the advancement of the cell cycle.

A second checkpoint exists in G_2. At this checkpoint, proteins also check the DNA for damage and ensure that all of the DNA has been replicated. In addition, the G_2 checkpoint proteins monitor the

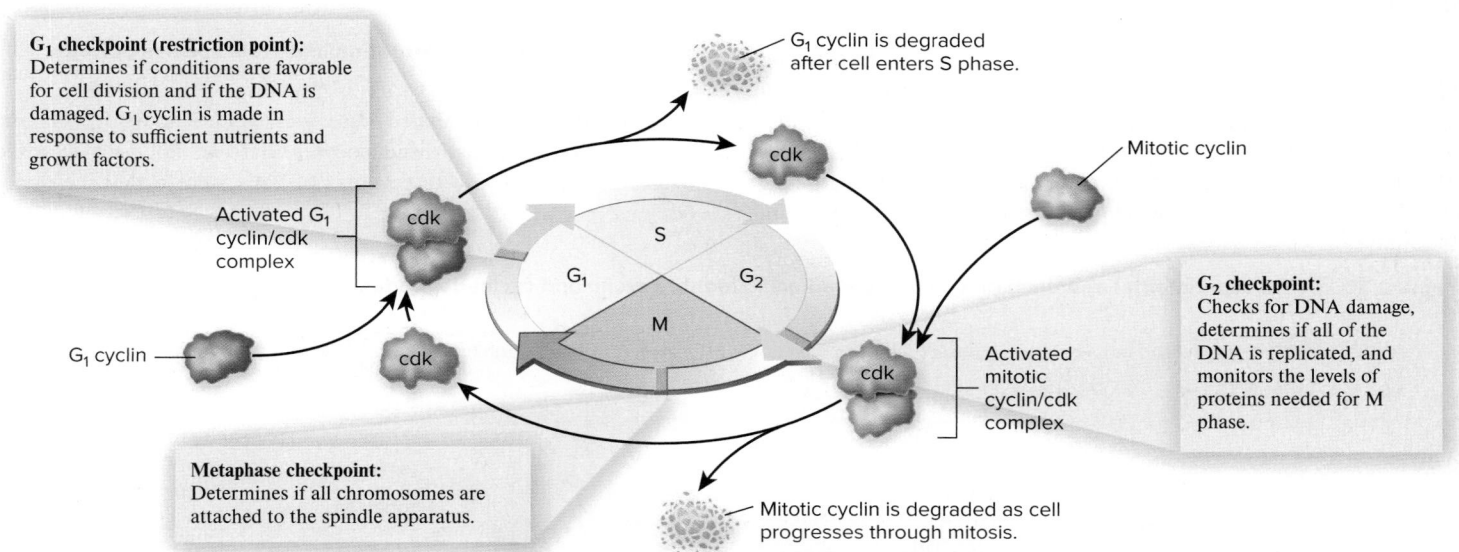

G₁ checkpoint (restriction point): Determines if conditions are favorable for cell division and if the DNA is damaged. G_1 cyclin is made in response to sufficient nutrients and growth factors.

Activated G_1 cyclin/cdk complex

G_1 cyclin

Metaphase checkpoint: Determines if all chromosomes are attached to the spindle apparatus.

G_1 cyclin is degraded after cell enters S phase.

Mitotic cyclin

G₂ checkpoint: Checks for DNA damage, determines if all of the DNA is replicated, and monitors the levels of proteins needed for M phase.

Activated mitotic cyclin/cdk complex

Mitotic cyclin is degraded as cell progresses through mitosis.

Figure 16.3 Checkpoints in the cell cycle. This is a general diagram of the eukaryotic cell cycle. Advancement through the cell cycle requires the formation of activated cyclin/cdk complexes. Cells make different types of cyclin proteins, which are typically degraded after the cell has advanced to the next phase. The formation of activated cyclin/cdk complexes is regulated by checkpoint proteins.

 Core Skill: Connections Look back at Figure 15.15. How do checkpoint proteins prevent cancer?

levels of the proteins that are needed to advance through M phase. A third checkpoint, called the metaphase checkpoint, has proteins that monitor the integrity of the spindle apparatus. As we will see later, the spindle apparatus is involved in chromosome sorting. Metaphase is a step in mitosis during which all of the chromosomes should be attached to the spindle apparatus. If a chromosome is not correctly attached, the metaphase checkpoint proteins will stop the cell cycle. This checkpoint prevents cells from incorrectly sorting their chromosomes during division.

Checkpoint proteins delay the cell cycle until problems are fixed or prevent cell division when problems cannot be fixed. A primary aim of checkpoint proteins is to prevent the division of a cell that has incurred DNA damage or harbors abnormalities in chromosome number. As discussed in Chapter 15, when the functions of checkpoint genes are lost due to mutation, the likelihood increases that undesirable genetic changes will occur that can cause additional mutations and cancerous growth.

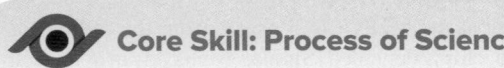

Core Skill: Process of Science

Feature Investigation | Masui and Markert's Study of Oocyte Maturation Led to the Identification of Cyclins and Cyclin-Dependent Kinases

During the 1960s and 1970s, researchers were intensely searching for the factors that promote cell division. In 1971, Japanese zoologist Yoshio Masui and American biologist Clement Markert developed a way to test whether a substance causes a cell to advance from one phase of the cell cycle to the next. They chose to study frog oocytes—cells that mature into egg cells. At the time of their work, researchers had already determined that frog oocytes naturally become dormant in the G_2 phase of the cell cycle for up to 8 months (**Figure 16.4**). During mating season, female frogs produce a hormone called progesterone. After progesterone enters an oocyte and binds to intracellular receptors, the oocyte advances from G_2 to the beginning of M phase, where the chromosomes condense and become visible under the microscope. This phenomenon is called maturation. When a sperm fertilizes the egg, M phase is completed, and the zygote continues to undergo cellular divisions.

Because progesterone is a signaling molecule, Masui and Markert speculated that this hormone affects the functions and/or amounts of proteins that trigger the oocyte to advance through the cell cycle. To test this hypothesis, they developed the procedure described in **Figure 16.5**, using the oocytes of the leopard frog (*Rana pipiens*). They began by exposing oocytes to progesterone in

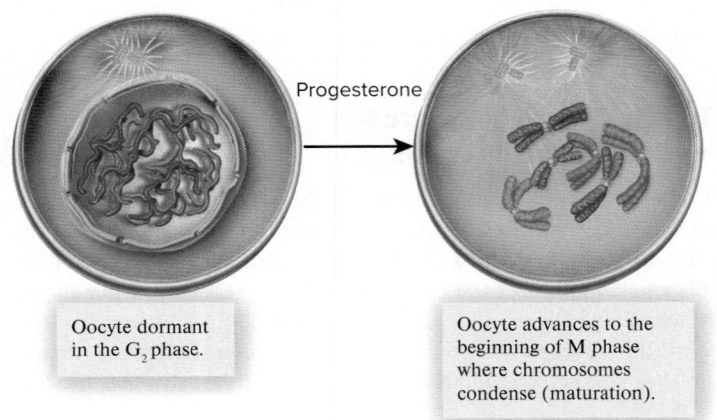

Progesterone

Oocyte dormant in the G_2 phase.

Oocyte advances to the beginning of M phase where chromosomes condense (maturation).

Figure 16.4 Oocyte maturation in certain species of frogs.

vitro, and then they incubated these oocytes for 2 hours or 12 hours. As a control, they also used oocytes that had not been exposed to progesterone. These three types of cells were called the donor oocytes.

Figure 16.5 The experimental approach of Masui and Markert to identify cyclin and cyclin-dependent kinase (cdk).

HYPOTHESIS Progesterone induces the synthesis of factor(s) that advance(s) frog oocytes through the cell cycle from G_2 to M phase.

KEY MATERIALS Oocytes from *Rana pipiens*.

Experimental level | Conceptual level

1 Expose oocytes to progesterone, then incubate for 2 or 12 hours. As a control, also use oocytes that have not been exposed to progesterone. All 3 types are donor oocytes.

Progesterone | Progesterone | No progesterone (control)

02:00 | 12:00

Donor oocytes

Progesterone

Donor oocyte

Progesterone enters cell and activates intracellular receptor.

Factors are made that advance oocyte to M phase. One such factor is called maturation-promoting factor (MPF).

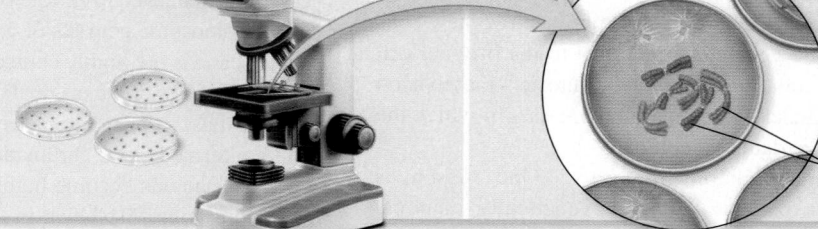

2 Using a micropipette, transfer some cytosol from the 3 types of donor oocytes to recipient oocytes that have not been exposed to progesterone.

Donor cytosol

Micropipette tip

Donor oocytes

Recipient oocyte

Recipient oocyte

Cytosol

MPF

Recipient oocyte received MPF from donor oocyte if donor oocyte was incubated for 12 hours with progesterone.

3 Incubate for several hours, and observe the recipient oocytes under the microscope to determine if the recipient oocytes advance to M phase. Advancement to M phase can be determined by the condensation of the chromosomes.

Recipient oocyte that had received cytosol containing MPF from donor oocyte

Condensed chromosomes

4 **THE DATA**

Donor oocytes	Recipient oocytes proceeded to M phase?
Control, no progesterone exposure	No
Progesterone exposure, incubation for 2 hours	No
Progesterone exposure, incubation for 12 hours	Yes

5 **CONCLUSION** Exposure of oocytes to progesterone for 12 hours results in the synthesis of factor(s) that advance(s) frog oocytes through the cell cycle from G_2 to M phase.

6 **SOURCE** Masui, Y., and Markert, C. L. 1971. Cytoplasmic Control of Nuclear Behavior During Meiotic Maturation of Frog Oocytes. *Journal of Experimental Zoology* 177: 129–145.

Next, Masui and Markert used a micropipette to transfer a small amount of cytosol from the three types of donor oocytes to recipient oocytes that had not been exposed to progesterone. As seen in the data, the recipient oocytes that had been injected with cytosol from the control donor oocytes or from oocytes that had been incubated with progesterone for only 2 hours did not advance to M phase. However, cytosol from donor oocytes that had been incubated with progesterone for 12 hours caused the recipient oocytes to advance to M phase. Masui and Markert concluded that a cytosolic factor, which required more than 2 hours to be synthesized after progesterone treatment, had been transferred to the recipient oocytes and induced maturation. The factor that caused the oocytes to advance (or mature) from G_2 to M phase was originally called the maturation-promoting factor (MPF).

After MPF was discovered in frogs, it was found in all eukaryotic species that researchers studied. MPF is important in the division of all types of cells, not just oocytes. It took another 17 years before Manfred Lohka, Marianne Hayes, and James Maller were able to purify the components that make up MPF. This was a difficult undertaking because these components are found in very small amounts in the cytosol and are easily degraded during purification procedures. We now know that MPF is a complex made of a mitotic cyclin and a cyclin-dependent kinase (cdk), as shown in Figure 16.3.

Experimental Questions

1. At the time of Masui and Markert's study, summarized in Figure 16.5, what was known about the effects of progesterone on oocytes?

2. **CoreSKILL »** What hypothesis did Masui and Markert propose to explain the function of progesterone? Describe the procedure used to test the hypothesis.

3. **CoreSKILL »** How did the researchers explain the difference between the results with 2-hour-exposed donor oocytes versus 12-hour-exposed donor oocytes?

16.2 Mitotic Cell Division

Learning Outcomes:

1. Describe how the replication of eukaryotic chromosomes produces sister chromatids.
2. Explain the structure and function of the mitotic spindle.
3. Outline the key events that occur during the phases of mitosis.

We now turn our attention to a mechanism of cell division and its relationship to chromosome replication and sorting. During the process of **mitotic cell division**, a cell divides to produce two new cells (the daughter cells) that are genetically identical to the original cell (the mother cell). Mitotic cell division involves mitosis—the division of one nucleus into two nuclei—and then cytokinesis—in which the mother cell divides into two daughter cells.

Why is mitotic cell division important? One reason is **asexual reproduction**, a process in which genetically identical offspring are produced from a single parent. Certain unicellular eukaryotic organisms, such as baker's yeast (*Saccharomyces cerevisiae*) and the amoeba, increase their numbers in this manner. A second important reason for mitotic cell division is the production and maintenance of multicellularity. Organisms such as plants, animals, and most fungi are derived from a single cell that subsequently undergoes repeated cell divisions to become a multicellular organism.

In this section, we will explore the process of mitotic cell division, which requires the replication, organization, and sorting of chromosomes. We will also examine how a single cell is separated into two daughter cells by cytokinesis.

In Preparation for Cell Division, Eukaryotic Chromosomes Are Replicated and Compacted to Produce Pairs Called Sister Chromatids

We now turn our attention to how chromosomes are replicated and sorted during cell division. In Chapter 11, we examined the molecular process of DNA replication. **Figure 16.6** describes the process at the chromosomal level. Prior to DNA replication, the DNA of each eukaryotic chromosome consists of a linear double helix that is found in the nucleus and is not highly compacted. When the DNA is replicated, two identical copies of the original double helix are produced. As discussed earlier, these copies, along with associated proteins, lie side-by-side and are termed sister chromatids. When a cell prepares to divide, the sister chromatids become highly compacted and readily visible under the microscope. As shown in Figure 16.6b, the two sister chromatids are tightly associated at a region called the **centromere**. A protein called cohesin holds the sister chromatids together. In addition, the centromere serves as an attachment site for a group of proteins that form the **kinetochore**, a structure necessary for sorting the chromosomes.

The Mitotic Spindle Organizes and Sorts Chromosomes During Cell Division

What structure is responsible for organizing and sorting the chromosomes during cell division? The answer is the **mitotic spindle**

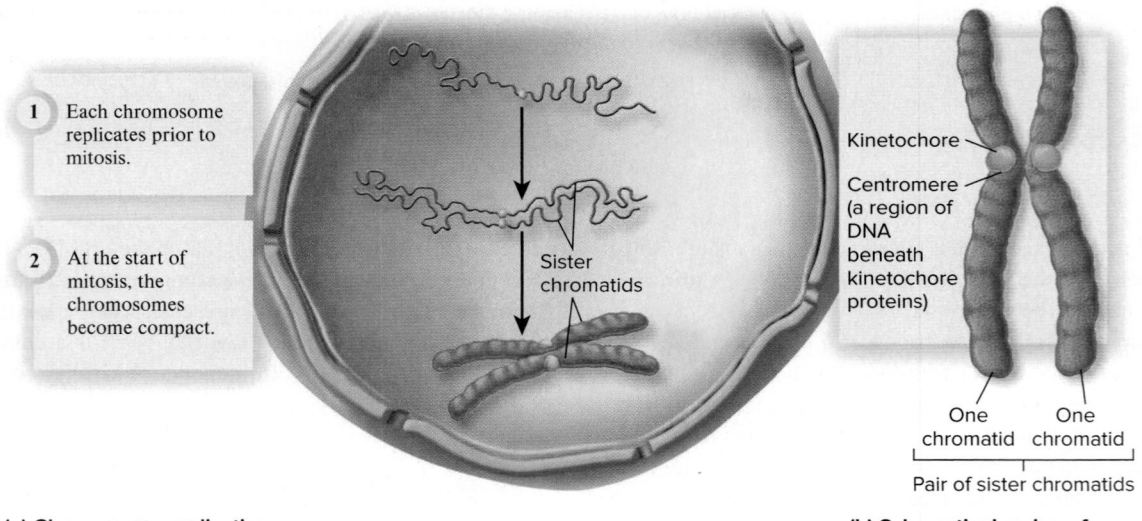

1 Each chromosome replicates prior to mitosis.

2 At the start of mitosis, the chromosomes become compact.

Sister chromatids

Kinetochore

Centromere (a region of DNA beneath kinetochore proteins)

One chromatid · One chromatid

Pair of sister chromatids

(a) Chromosome replication and compaction

(b) Schematic drawing of a metaphase chromosome

Figure 16.6 Replication and compaction of chromosomes into pairs of sister chromatids. **(a)** Chromosomal replication produces a pair of sister chromatids. While the chromosomes are elongated, they are replicated to produce two copies that are connected and lie parallel to each other. This is a pair of sister chromatids. Later, when the cell is preparing to divide, the sister chromatids condense into more compact structures that are easily seen with a light microscope. **(b)** A schematic drawing of a metaphase chromosome. This structure has two chromatids that lie side-by-side. The two chromatids are held together by cohesin proteins (not shown in this drawing). The kinetochore is a group of proteins that are attached to the centromere and play a key role during chromosome sorting.

 Core Concept: Information The process of mitosis ensures that each daughter cell receives a complete copy of the genetic material.

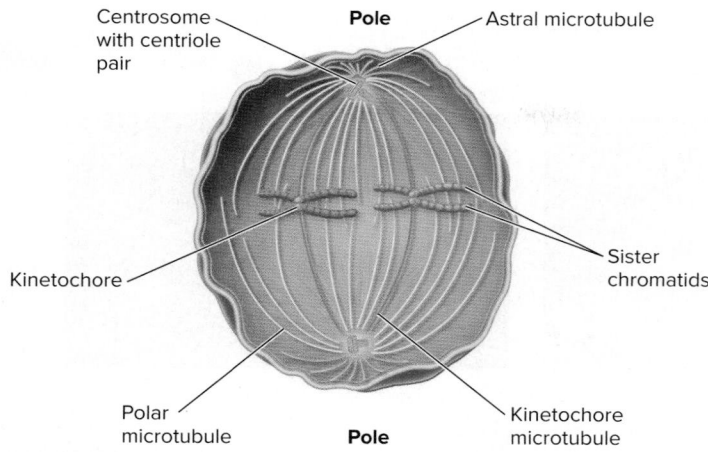

Figure 16.7 **The structure of the mitotic spindle.** The mitotic spindle in animal cells is formed by the centrosomes, which produce three types of microtubules. The astral microtubules emanate away from the region between the poles. The polar microtubules project into the region between the two poles. The kinetochore microtubules are attached to the kinetochores of sister chromatids. Note: For simplicity, this diagram shows only one pair of homologous chromosomes. Eukaryotic species typically have multiple chromosomes per set.

(**Figure 16.7**). It is composed of microtubules—protein fibers that are components of the cytoskeleton (refer back to Table 4.1). In animal cells, microtubule growth and organization start at two **centrosomes**, structures that are also referred to as microtubule-organizing centers (MTOCs). A single centrosome duplicates during interphase. When the cell enters mitosis, each centrosome defines a **pole** of the spindle apparatus, one within each of the future daughter cells. The centrosome in animal cells has a pair of **centrioles**. Each one is composed of nine sets of triplet microtubules. However, centrioles are not found in many other eukaryotic species, such as plants, and are not required for spindle formation.

Each centrosome organizes the construction of the microtubules by rapidly polymerizing tubulin proteins. The three types of spindle microtubules are termed astral, polar, and kinetochore microtubules (see Figure 16.7).

The Transmission of Chromosomes Requires a Sorting Process Known as Mitosis

Mitosis is the sorting process for dividing one cell nucleus into two nuclei (**Figure 16.8**). The duplicated chromosomes are distributed so that each daughter cell receives the same complement of chromosomes. Mitosis was first observed microscopically in the 1870s by a German biologist, Walther Flemming, who coined the term (from the Greek *mitos*, meaning thread). He studied the large, transparent skin cells of salamander larvae as they were dividing and noticed that chromosomes are constructed of "threads" that are doubled in appearance along their length. These double threads divided and moved apart, one going to each of the two daughter nuclei. By this

mechanism, Flemming pointed out, the two daughter cells receive an identical group of threads, the same as the number of threads in the mother cell.

Figure 16.8 depicts the process of mitosis in an animal cell, though the process is quite similar in a plant cell. Mitosis occurs as a continuum of phases known as prophase, prometaphase, metaphase, anaphase, and telophase. In the simplified diagrams shown along the bottom of Figure 16.8, the original cell contains six chromosomes. One set of chromosomes is depicted in red, whereas the homologous set is blue. The different colors are intended to distinguish maternal and paternal chromosomes.

Interphase   Prior to mitosis, the cells are in interphase, which consists of the G_1, S, and G_2 phases of the cell cycle. The chromosomes have replicated in S phase and are decondensed and found in the nucleus (Figure 16.8a). The nucleolus, which is the site where the components of ribosomes assemble into ribosomal subunits, is visible during interphase.

Prophase   At the start of mitosis, in **prophase**, the chromosomes have already replicated to produce 12 chromatids, joined as six pairs of sister chromatids that have condensed into highly compacted structures readily visible by light microscopy (Figure 16.8b). As prophase proceeds, the nuclear envelope begins to dissociate into small vesicles. The nucleolus is no longer visible.

Prometaphase   During **prometaphase**, the nuclear envelope completely fragments into small vesicles, and the mitotic spindle is fully formed (Figure 16.8c). As prometaphase advances, the centrosomes move apart and demarcate the two poles. Once the nuclear envelope has dissociated, the spindle fibers can interact with the sister chromatids. How do the sister chromatids become attached to the spindle apparatus? Initially, microtubules are rapidly formed and can be seen under a microscope growing out from the two poles. As it grows, if a microtubule happens to make contact with a kinetochore, it is said to be captured and remains firmly attached to the kinetochore. Alternatively, if a microtubule does not collide with a kinetochore, the microtubule eventually depolymerizes and retracts to the centrosome. This random process is how sister chromatids become attached to kinetochore microtubules. As the end of prometaphase nears, the two kinetochores on each pair of sister chromatids are attached to kinetochore microtubules from opposite poles. As these events are occurring, the sister chromatids are seen under the microscope to undergo jerky movements as they are tugged, back and forth, between the two poles by the kinetochore microtubules.

Metaphase   Eventually, the pairs of sister chromatids are aligned in a single row along the **metaphase plate**, a plane halfway between the poles of the spindle. When this alignment is complete, the cell is in **metaphase** of mitosis (Figure 16.8d). The chromatids can then be equally distributed into two daughter cells.

Anaphase   During **anaphase**, the connections between the pairs of sister chromatids are broken (Figure 16.8e). Each chromatid, now an

(a) Interphase   **(b) Prophase**   **(c) Prometaphase**

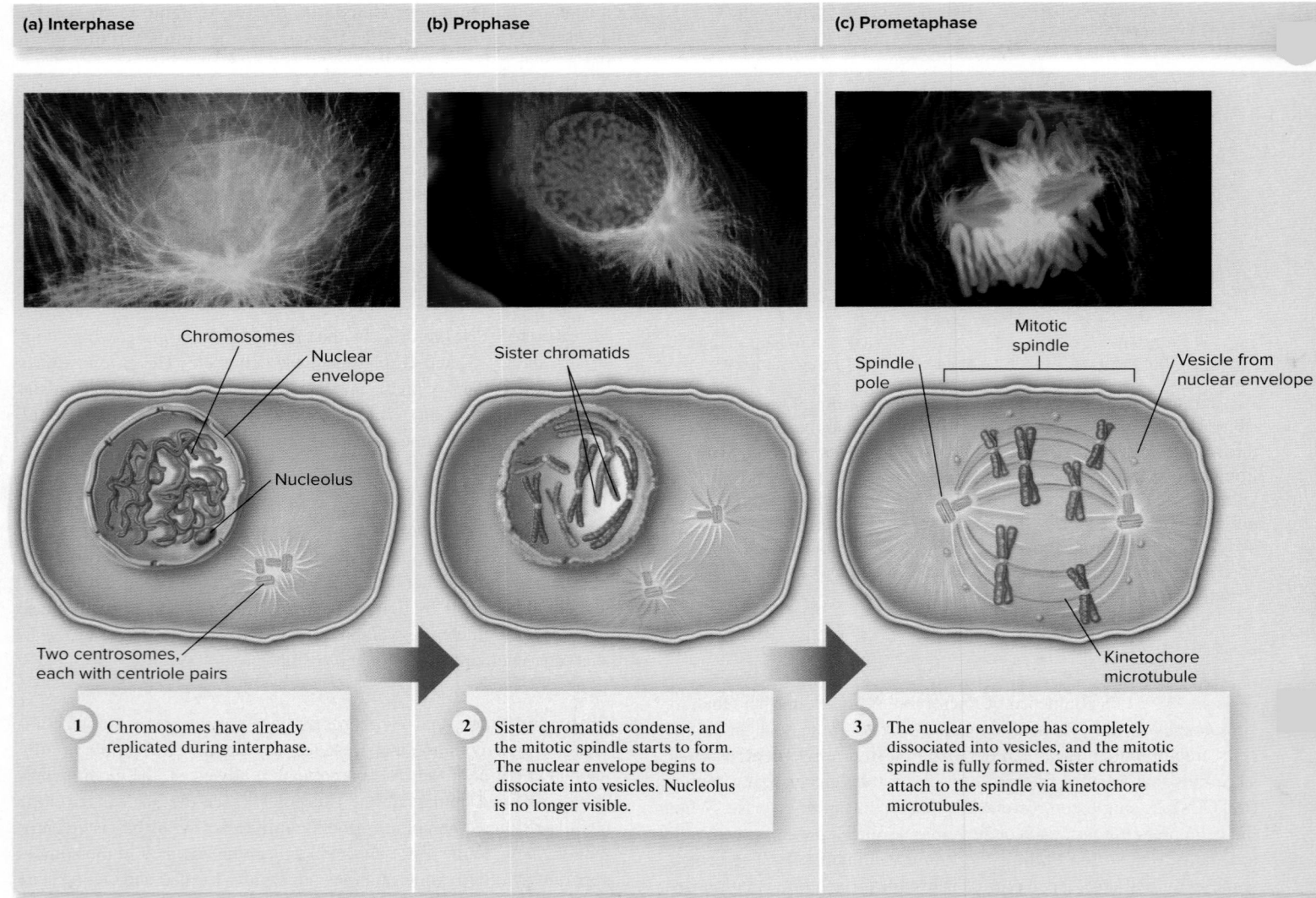

Figure 16.8 **The process of mitosis in an animal cell.** The top panels are fluorescence micrographs of a newt cell advancing through mitosis. The drawings below emphasize the sorting of the chromosomes, in which the diploid mother cell had six chromosomes (three in each set). At the start of mitosis, these have already replicated into 12 chromatids. The final result is two daughter cells, each containing six chromosomes.

a–f: ©Photographs by Dr. Conly L. Rieder, East Greenbush, New York, 12061

Concept Check: *What are the functions of the three types of microtubules?*

individual chromosome, is linked to only one of the two poles by one or more kinetochore microtubules. As anaphase proceeds, the kinetochore microtubules shorten, pulling the chromosomes toward the pole to which they are attached. In addition, the two poles move farther away from each other. This occurs because the overlapping polar microtubules lengthen and push against each other, thereby pushing the poles farther apart.

Telophase During **telophase**, the chromosomes have reached their respective poles and decondense. The nuclear envelope now re-forms to produce two separate nuclei. In Figure 16.8f, two nuclei that contain six chromosomes each are being produced.

Cytokinesis In most cases, mitosis is quickly followed by cytokinesis, in which the two nuclei are segregated into separate daughter cells. Whereas the phases of mitosis are similar between plant and animal cells, the process of cytokinesis is quite different.

- In animal cells, cytokinesis involves the formation of a **cleavage furrow**, which constricts like a drawstring to separate the cells (**Figure 16.9a**).

- In plants, vesicles from the Golgi apparatus move along microtubules to the center of the cell and coalesce to form a **cell plate** (**Figure 16.9b**), which then forms a cell wall between the two daughter cells.

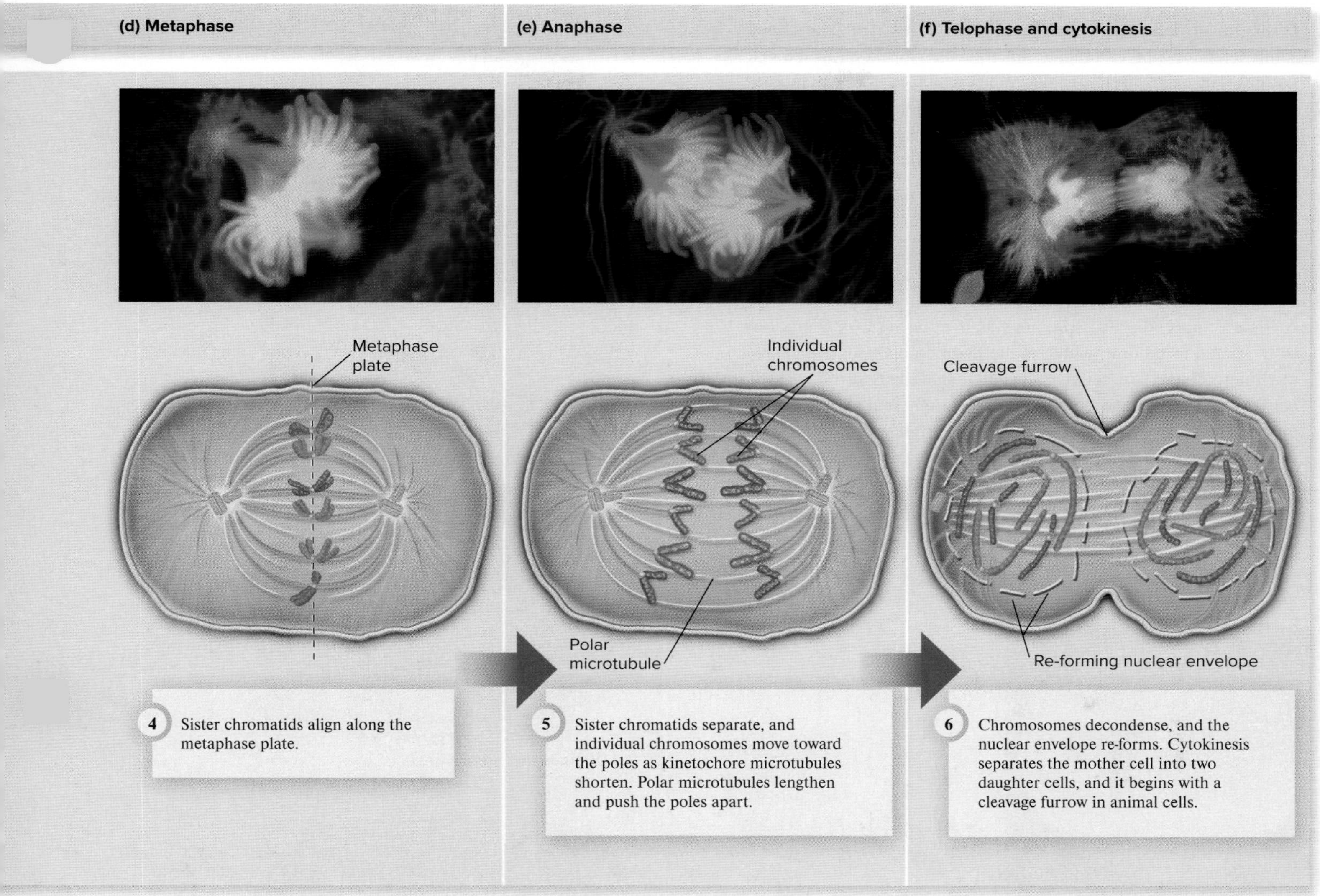

(d) Metaphase	(e) Anaphase	(f) Telophase and cytokinesis

Metaphase plate

Individual chromosomes

Cleavage furrow

Polar microtubule

Re-forming nuclear envelope

4 Sister chromatids align along the metaphase plate.

5 Sister chromatids separate, and individual chromosomes move toward the poles as kinetochore microtubules shorten. Polar microtubules lengthen and push the poles apart.

6 Chromosomes decondense, and the nuclear envelope re-forms. Cytokinesis separates the mother cell into two daughter cells, and it begins with a cleavage furrow in animal cells.

What are the results of mitosis and cytokinesis? These processes ultimately produce two daughter cells with the same number of chromosomes as the mother cell. Barring rare mutations, the two daughter cells are genetically identical to each other and to the mother cell from which they were derived. The critical consequence of this sorting process is ensuring genetic consistency from one cell to the next. The development of multicellularity relies on the repeated process of mitosis and cytokinesis.

 Core Concept: Evolution

Mitosis in Eukaryotes Evolved from the Binary Fission That Occurs in Prokaryotic Cells

The process of mitosis allows eukaryotic cells to properly sort their chromosomes during cell division. By comparing cell division among prokaryotic cells, simple eukaryotes, and more com-

plex eukaryotes, biologists have pieced together a progression of how mitosis may have evolved.

Binary Fission in Bacterial Cells As described in Chapter 19 (look ahead to Figure 19.13), bacterial cells divide by a relatively simple process known as binary fission (**Figure 16.10a**). After chromosome replication, each copy of the bacterial chromosome becomes anchored to the plasma membrane. Proteins called FtsZ form a ring at the site where the mother cell will divide into two daughter cells.

Dinoflagellates In protists known as dinoflagellates, nuclear division is much simpler than in animal and plant cells (**Figure 16.10b**). After chromosome replication, the chromosomes become attached to the nuclear envelope. The nuclear envelope does not break apart. Microtubules, which are described in Chapter 4 (see Table 4.1), are formed in the cytosol and pass through tunnels in the nuclear envelope. The nucleus then divides by a process that resembles binary fission.

Diatoms and Some Yeasts In diatoms (a type of protist) and some yeasts (a type of fungus), microtubules form within the cell nucleus (**Figure 16.10c**). Kinetochore microtubules attach to chromosomes and facilitate their sorting, and other microtubules promote the separation of the nucleus into two separate nuclei. As in dinoflagellates, the nuclear envelope does not break apart during this process.

Complex Eukaryotes As we have seen, mitosis in complex eukaryotes, such as animals and plants, involves the breaking apart of the nuclear envelope and the formation of the spindle apparatus (**Figure 16.10d**). After the chromosomes are sorted, the nuclear envelope then re-forms.

Interestingly, the FtsZ protein found in bacteria is evolutionarily related to tubulin, which is the main component of eukaryotic microtubules. Researchers speculate that the first role of FtsZ was to form a ring and promote cell division (Figure 16.10a). In eukaryotic cells, the homologous protein, tubulin, forms linear microtubules and has acquired additional roles in cell division. These include the division of the cell nucleus and the sorting of chromosomes. The relationship of tubulin to FtsZ is an example of descent with modification.

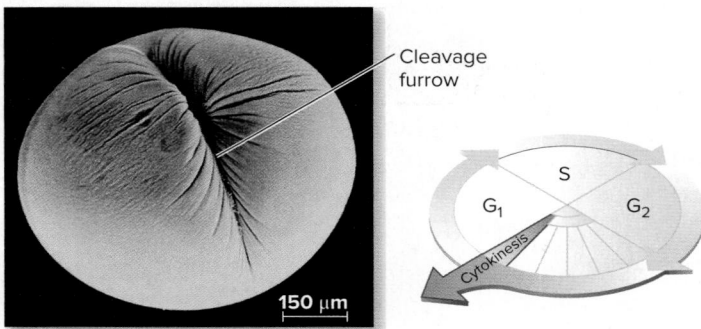

(a) Cleavage of an animal cell

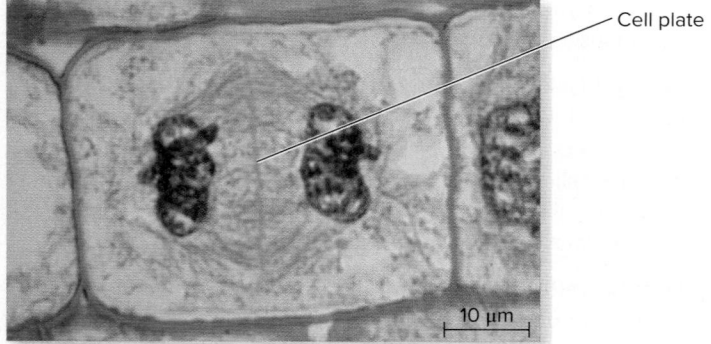

(b) Formation of a cell plate in a plant cell

Figure 16.9 Micrographs showing cytokinesis in animal and plant cells. a: ©Don W. Fawcett/Science Source; b: ©Carolina Biological Supply Company/Phototake

Concept Check: *What are the similarities and differences between animal and plant cells with regard to cytokinesis?*

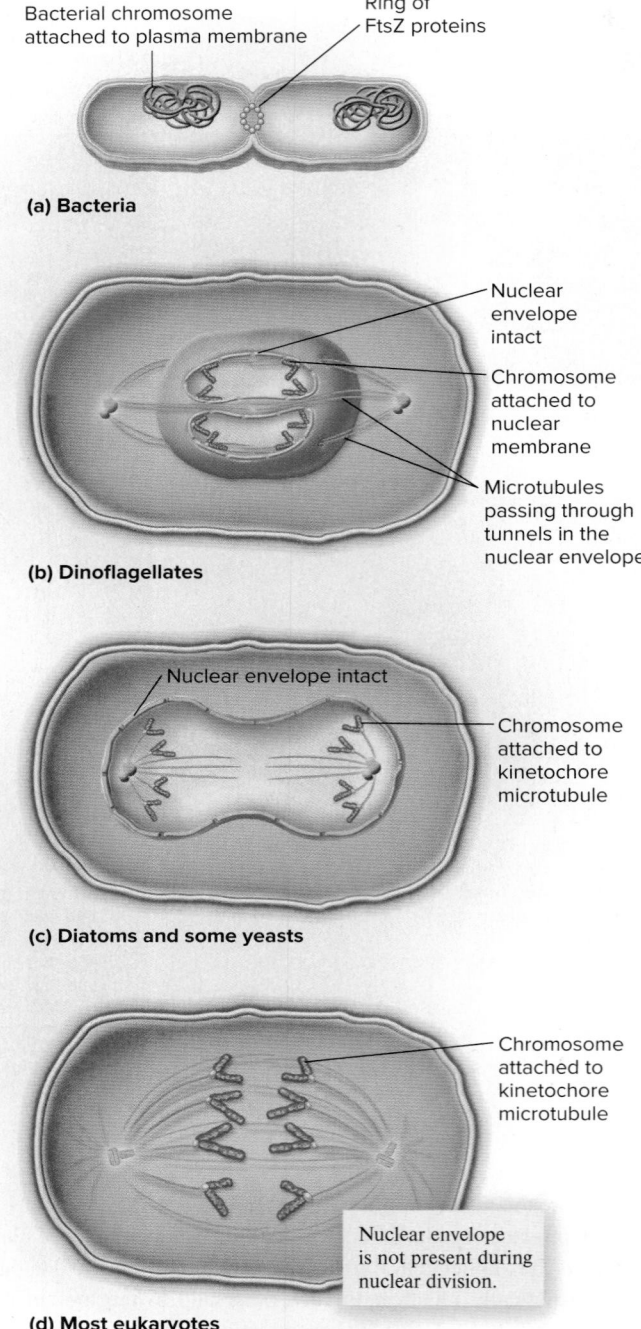

(a) Bacteria

(b) Dinoflagellates

(c) Diatoms and some yeasts

Nuclear envelope is not present during nuclear division.

(d) Most eukaryotes

Figure 16.10 A comparison of cell division among bacteria, simple eukaryotes, and more complex eukaryotes.

16.3 Meiosis

Learning Outcomes:

1. Describe the processes of synapsis and crossing over.
2. Outline the key events that occur during the phases of meiosis.
3. Compare and contrast mitosis and meiosis, focusing on key steps that account for the different outcomes of these two processes.

As discussed earlier, a diploid cell contains two homologous sets of chromosomes, whereas a haploid cell contains a single set. For example, a diploid human cell contains 46 chromosomes, but a human gamete—sperm or egg cell—is a haploid cell that contains only 23 chromosomes. **Meiosis** is the process by which haploid cells are produced from a cell that was originally diploid. The term meiosis, which means to make smaller, refers to the fewer chromosomes found in cells that have undergone this process. For haploid cells to be produced, the chromosomes must be correctly sorted and distributed in a way that reduces the chromosome number to half its original diploid value. In the case of human gametes, for example, each gamete must receive one chromosome from each of the 23 pairs. For this to happen, two rounds of divisions are necessary, termed meiosis I and meiosis II (**Figure 16.11**). When

a cell begins meiosis, it contains chromosomes that are found in homologous pairs. When meiosis is completed, a single diploid cell with homologous pairs of chromosomes has produced four haploid cells.

In this section, we will examine the cellular events of meiosis that reduce the chromosome number from diploid to haploid. In the following section, we will consider how this process plays a role in the sexual reproduction of animals, plants, fungi, and protists.

Bivalent Formation and Crossing Over Occur at the Beginning of Meiosis

Like mitosis, meiosis begins after a cell has progressed through the G_1, S, and G_2 phases of the cell cycle. However, two key events occur at the beginning of meiosis that do not occur in mitosis. First, homologous pairs of sister chromatids associate with each other, lying side by side to form a **bivalent**, also called a tetrad (**Figure 16.12**). The process of forming a bivalent is termed **synapsis**. In most eukaryotic species, a protein structure called the synaptonemal complex connects homologous chromosomes during a portion of meiosis. However, the synaptonemal complex is not required for the pairing of homologous chromosomes because some species of fungi completely lack such a complex, yet their chromosomes associate with each other correctly.

The second event that occurs at the beginning of meiosis, but not usually during mitosis, is **crossing over**, which involves a physical exchange between chromosome segments of the bivalent (Figure 16.12). As discussed in Chapter 18, crossing over increases the genetic variation of sexually reproducing species. After crossing over occurs, the arms of the chromosomes tend to separate but remain adhered at a crossover site. This connection is called a chiasma (plural, chiasmata), because the connected chromosomal arms resemble the Greek letter chi, χ. The number of crossovers is carefully controlled by cells and depends on the size of the chromosome and the species. The range of crossovers for eukaryotic chromosomes is typically one or two to a couple dozen. During the formation of sperm in humans, for example, an average chromosome undergoes slightly more than two crossovers, whereas chromosomes in certain plant species may undergo 20 or more.

Meiosis I Separates Homologous Chromosomes

Now that you have an understanding of bivalent formation and crossing over, we are ready to consider the phases of meiosis (**Figure 16.13**). These simplified diagrams depict a diploid cell (*2n*) that contains a total of six chromosomes (as in the diagram of mitosis in Figure 16.8). Prior to meiosis, the chromosomes are replicated in S phase to produce pairs of sister chromatids. This single replication event is then followed by sequential divisions called meiosis I and II. Like mitosis, each of these processes is a continuous series of stages called prophase, prometaphase, metaphase, anaphase, and telophase. The sorting that occurs during **meiosis I** separates homologous chromosomes from each other (Figure 16.13a–e).

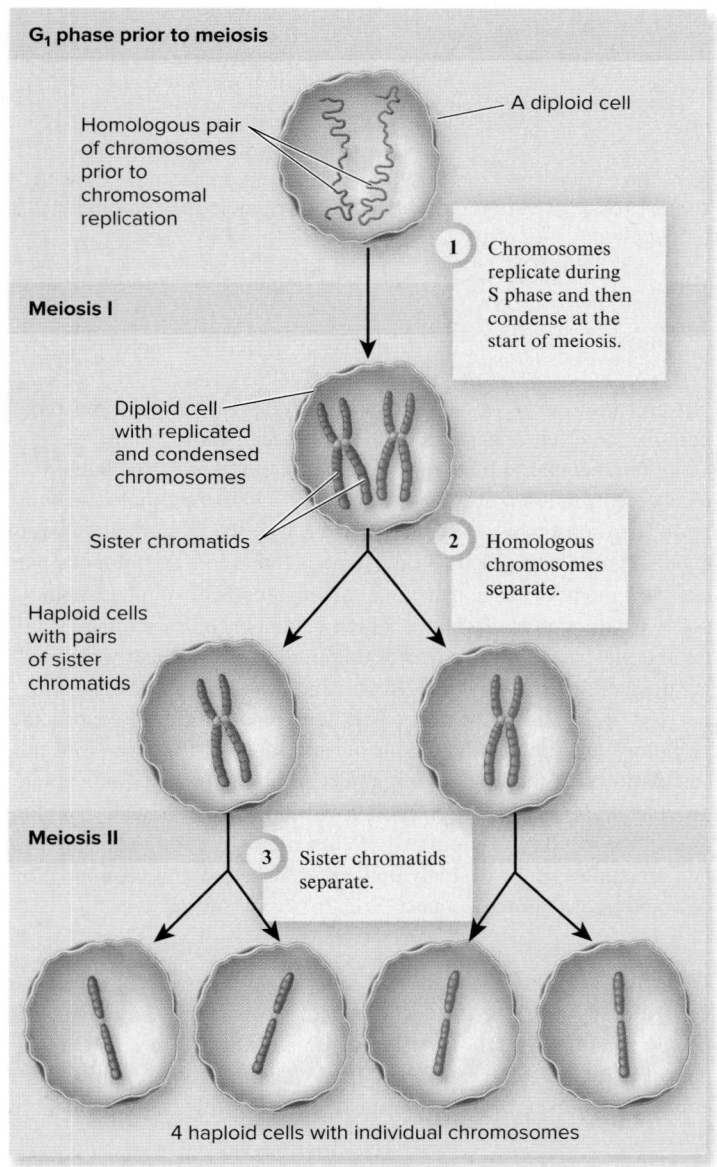

G₁ phase prior to meiosis

A diploid cell

Homologous pair of chromosomes prior to chromosomal replication

1 Chromosomes replicate during S phase and then condense at the start of meiosis.

Meiosis I

Diploid cell with replicated and condensed chromosomes

Sister chromatids

2 Homologous chromosomes separate.

Haploid cells with pairs of sister chromatids

Meiosis II

3 Sister chromatids separate.

4 haploid cells with individual chromosomes

Figure 16.11 How the process of meiosis reduces chromosome number. This simplified diagram emphasizes the reduction in chromosome number as a diploid cell divides by meiosis to produce four haploid cells.

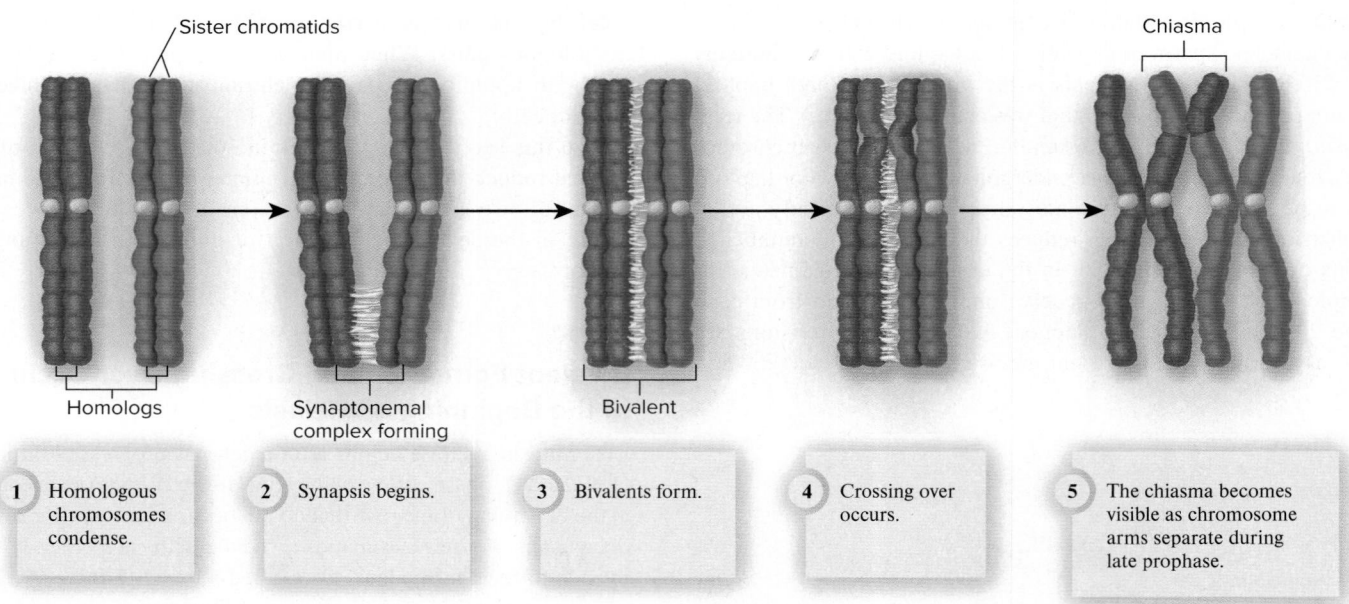

Figure 16.12 Formation of a bivalent and crossing over during meiosis I. At the beginning of meiosis, homologous chromosomes pair with each other to form a bivalent, usually with a synaptonemal complex between them. Crossing over then occurs between homologous chromatids within the bivalent. During this process, homologs exchange segments of chromosomes.

Prophase I During prophase I, the replicated chromosomes condense, the homologous chromosomes form bivalents, and crossing over occurs. The nuclear envelope then starts to fragment into small vesicles.

Prometaphase I In prometaphase I, the nuclear envelope is completely broken apart into vesicles, and the spindle apparatus is entirely formed. The sister chromatids become attached to kinetochore microtubules. However, a key difference exists between mitosis and meiosis I. In mitosis, each pair of sister chromatids is attached to both poles (see Figure 16.8c). In meiosis I, each pair of sister chromatids is attached to just one pole via kinetochore microtubules (Figure 16.13b).

Metaphase I At metaphase I, the bivalents are organized along the metaphase plate. Notice how this pattern of alignment is strikingly different from that observed during mitosis (see Figure 16.8d). In particular, the sister chromatids are aligned in a double row rather than a single row (as in mitosis). Furthermore, the arrangement of sister chromatids within this double row is random with regard to the (red and blue) homologs. (Remember that these different colors indicate maternal and paternal chromosomes.) In Figure 16.13c, one of the red homologs is to the left of the metaphase plate, and the other two are to the right, whereas two of the blue homologs are to the left of the metaphase plate and the other one is to the right. In other cells, homologs could be arranged differently along the metaphase plate (for example, three blues to the left and none to the right, or none to the left and three to the right).

Because eukaryotic species typically have many chromosomes per set, maternal and paternal homologs can be randomly aligned along the metaphase plate in a variety of ways. The possible number of different, random alignments equals 2^n, where n equals the number of chromosomes per set. The reason why the random alignments equals 2^n is because each chromosome is found in a homologous pair and each member of the pair can align on either side of the metaphase plate. It is a matter of chance which daughter cell of meiosis I will get the maternal chromosome of a homologous pair, and which will get the paternal chromosome. In humans, who have 23 chromosomes per set, 2^n equals 2^{23}, or over 8 million possibilities. Because the homologs are genetically similar but not identical, we see from this calculation that the random alignment of homologous chromosomes provides a mechanism to promote a vast amount of genetic diversity among the resulting haploid cells. When meiosis is complete, any two human gametes are extremely unlikely to have the same combination of homologous chromosomes.

Anaphase I The segregation of homologs occurs during anaphase I (Figure 16.13d). The connections between bivalents break, but not the connections that hold sister chromatids together. Each joined pair of chromatids migrates to one pole, and the homologous pair of chromatids moves to the opposite pole, both pulled by kinetochore microtubules.

Telophase I At telophase I, the sister chromatids have reached their respective poles and then decondense. The nuclear envelope now reforms to produce two separate nuclei.

If we consider the end result of meiosis I, we see that two nuclei are produced, each with three pairs of sister chromatids; this is called a reduction division. The original diploid cell had its chromosomes in homologous pairs, whereas the two cells produced as a result of meiosis I and cytokinesis are considered haploid—they do not have pairs of homologous chromosomes.

Meiosis II Separates Sister Chromatids

Meiosis I is followed by cytokinesis and then **meiosis II** (see Figure 16.13f–j). DNA replication does not occur between meiosis I and meiosis II. The sorting events of meiosis II are similar to those of mitosis, but the starting point is different. For a diploid cell with six chromosomes, mitosis begins with 12 chromatids that are joined as six pairs of sister chromatids (see Figure 16.8). By comparison, the two cells that begin meiosis II each have six chromatids that are joined as three pairs of sister chromatids. Otherwise, the steps that occur during prophase, prometaphase, metaphase, anaphase, and telophase of meiosis II are analogous to a mitotic division. Sister chromatids are separated during anaphase II.

Mitosis and Meiosis Differ in a Few Key Steps

How are the outcomes of mitosis and meiosis different? Mitosis produces two diploid daughter cells that are genetically identical. In our example shown in Figure 16.8, the starting cell had six chromosomes (three homologous pairs of chromosomes), and both daughter cells received copies of the same six chromosomes. By comparison, meiosis reduces the number of sets of chromosomes. In the example shown in Figure 16.13, the starting cell also had six chromosomes, whereas the resulting four daughter cells have only three chromosomes. However, the daughter cells do not contain a random mix of three chromosomes. Each haploid daughter cell contains one complete set of chromosomes, whereas the original diploid mother cell had two complete sets.

How do we explain the different outcomes of mitosis and meiosis? **Table 16.1** emphasizes the differences between certain key steps in mitosis and meiosis that account for the different outcomes of these two processes. DNA replication occurs prior to mitosis and meiosis I, but not between meiosis I and II. During prophase of meiosis I, the homologs synapse to form bivalents. This explains why crossing over occurs commonly during meiosis, but rarely during mitosis. During prometaphase of mitosis and meiosis II, pairs of sister chromatids are attached to both poles. In contrast, during meiosis I, each pair of sister chromatids (within a bivalent) is attached to a single pole. Bivalents align along the metaphase plate during metaphase of meiosis I, whereas sister chromatids align along the metaphase plate during metaphase of mitosis and meiosis II. At anaphase of meiosis I, the homologous chromosomes separate, but the sister chromatids remain together. In contrast, sister chromatid separation occurs during anaphase of mitosis and meiosis II. Taken together, the steps of mitosis produce two diploid cells that are genetically identical, whereas the steps of meiosis involve two sequential cell divisions that produce four haploid cells that may not be genetically identical.

 BIO**TIPS**

THE QUESTION *A diploid cell has 12 chromosomes, or 6 pairs. In the following diagram, in what phase of mitosis, meiosis I or meiosis II, is this cell?*

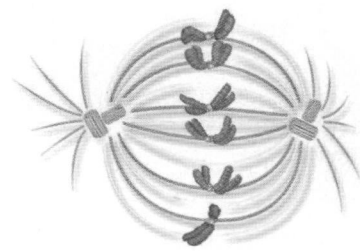

TOPIC *What topic in biology does this question address?* The topic is cell division. More specifically, the question is asking you to be able to look at a drawing and discern which phase of cell division a particular cell is in.

INFORMATION *What information do you know based on the question and your understanding of the topic?* In the question, you are given a diagram of a cell at a particular phase of the cell cycle. This cell is derived from a mother cell with 6 pairs of chromosomes. From your understanding of the topic, you may remember the various phases of mitosis, meiosis I, and meiosis II, which are described in Figures 16.8 and 16.13. If so, you may initially realize that the cell is in metaphase.

PROBLEM-SOLVING **S**TRATEGY *Sort out the steps in a complicated process.* To solve this problem, you may need to describe the steps, starting with a mother cell that has 6 pairs of chromosomes. Keep in mind that a mother cell with 6 pairs of chromosomes has 12 chromosomes during G_1, which then replicate to form 12 pairs of sister chromatids during S phase. Therefore, at the beginning of M phase, this mother cell will have 12 pairs of sister chromatids. During mitosis, the 12 pairs of sister chromatids will align at metaphase. During meiosis I, 6 bivalents will align along the metaphase plate in the mother cell. During meiosis II, 6 pairs of sister chromatids will align along the metaphase plate in the two cells.

ANSWER *The cell is in metaphase of meiosis II. You can tell because the chromosomes are lined up in a single row along the metaphase plate, and the cell has only 6 pairs of sister chromatids. If it were mitosis, the cell would have 12 pairs of sister chromatids. If it were in meiosis I, bivalents would be aligned along the metaphase plate.*

Meiosis I

(a) Prophase I	(b) Prometaphase I	(c) Metaphase I

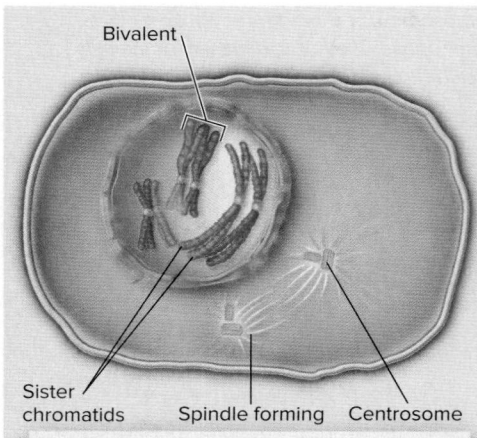

Bivalent

Sister chromatids   Spindle forming   Centrosome

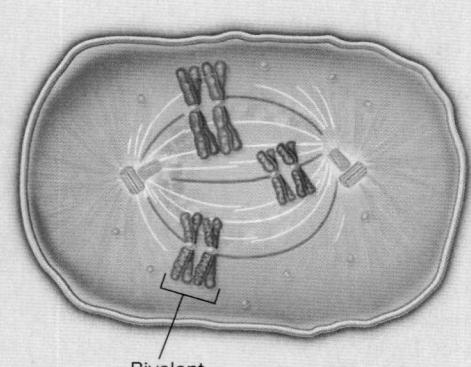

Bivalent

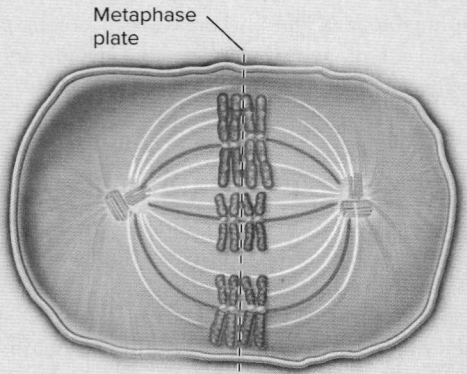

Metaphase plate

1 Homologous chromosomes synapse to form bivalents, and crossing over occurs. Chromosomes condense, and the nuclear envelope begins to dissociate into vesicles.

2 The nuclear envelope completely dissociates into vesicles, and bivalents become attached to kinetochore microtubules.

3 Bivalents randomly align along the metaphase plate. Each pair of sister chromatids is attached to one pole.

Meiosis II

(f) Prophase II	(g) Prometaphase II	(h) Metaphase II

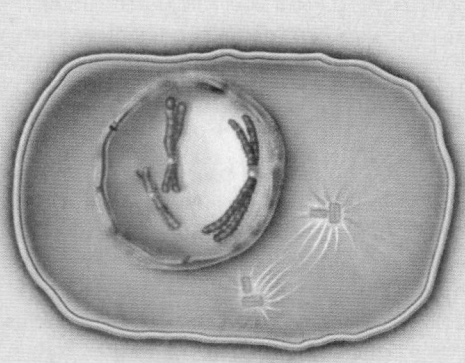

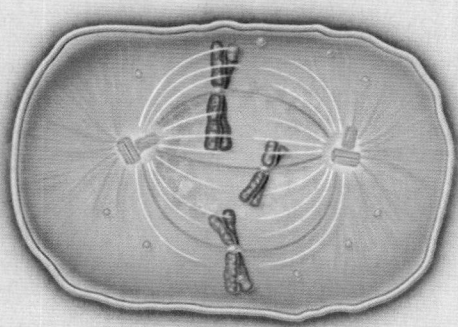

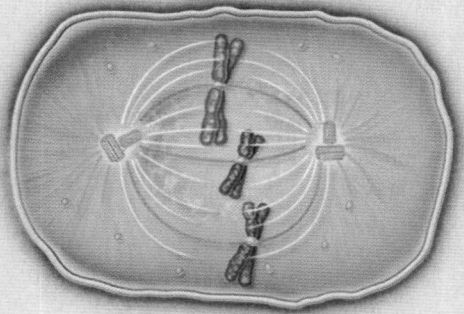

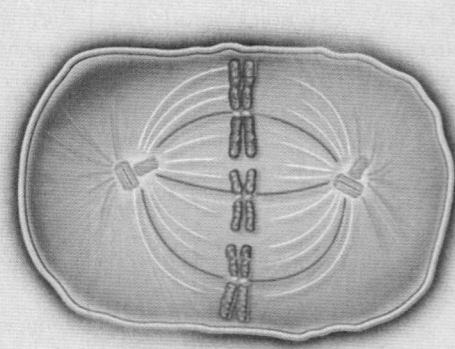

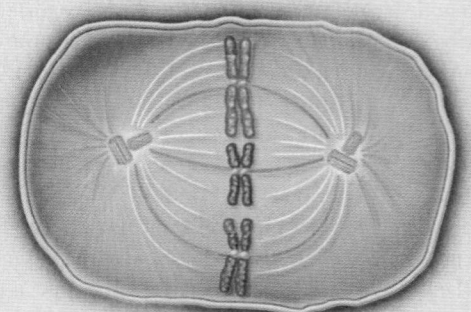

6 Sister chromatids condense, and the spindle starts to form. The nuclear envelope begins to dissociate into vesicles.

7 The nuclear envelope completely dissociates into vesicles. Sister chromatids attach to the spindle via kinetochore microtubules.

8 Sister chromatids align along the metaphase plate. Each pair of sister chromatids is attached to both poles.

(d) Anaphase I

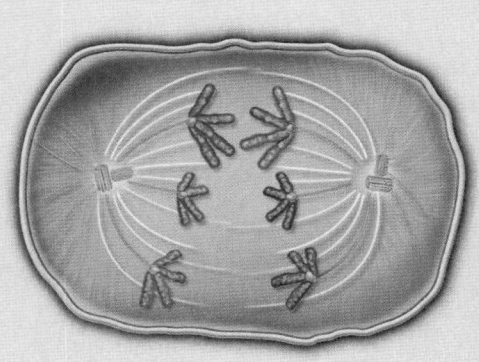

4 Homologous chromosomes separate and pairs of sister chromatids move toward opposite poles.

(e) Telophase I and cytokinesis

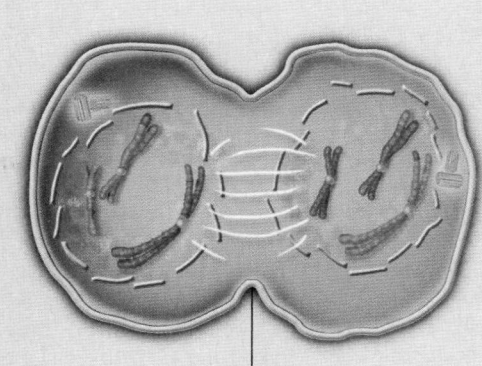

Cleavage furrow

5 The chromosomes decondense, and the nuclear envelope re-forms. The 2 daughter cells are separated by a cleavage furrow.

(i) Anaphase II

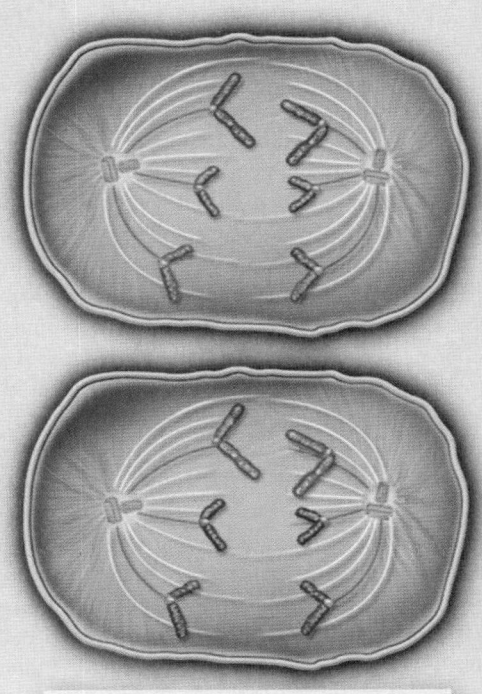

9 Sister chromatids separate, and individual chromosomes move toward the poles as kinetochore microtubules shorten. Polar microtubules lengthen and push the poles apart.

(j) Telophase II and cytokinesis

Four haploid cells

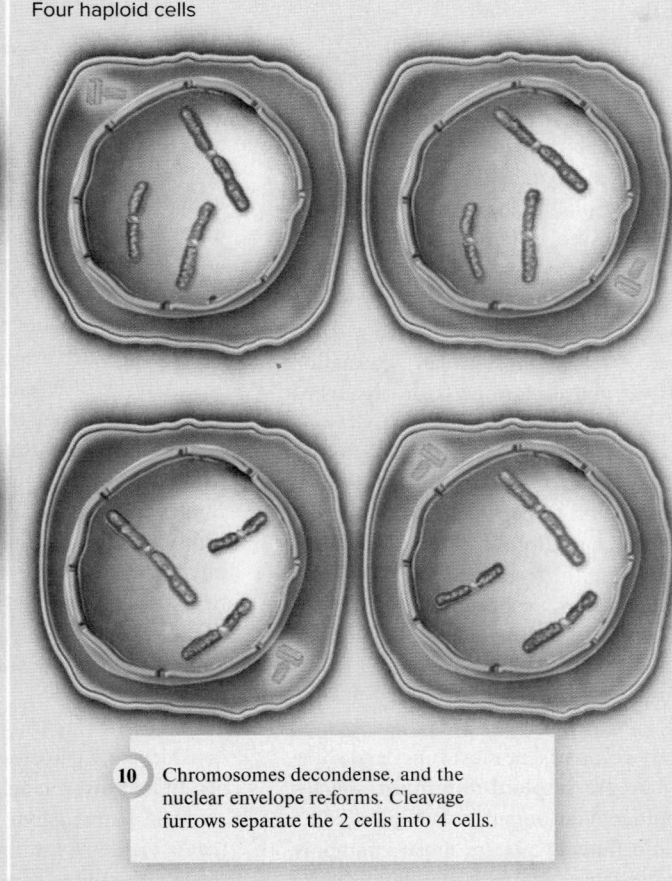

10 Chromosomes decondense, and the nuclear envelope re-forms. Cleavage furrows separate the 2 cells into 4 cells.

Figure 16.13 **The phases of meiosis in an animal cell.**

 Core Skill: Modeling
The goal of this modeling challenge is to predict the outcome of meiosis if one pair of chromosomes does not separate properly during meiosis ll.

Modeling Challenge: In Figure 16.13, the starting cell in meiosis I has 3 homologous pairs of chromosomes that differ in length: short, medium, and long. Let's suppose that during meiosis I, the segregation of the long chromosomes into the two daughter cells occurs abnormally, and both of the long chromosomes go into the same daughter cell. Draw a model showing the chromosomal composition of the four daughter cells at the end of meiosis II. For each pair of homologs, draw one red and the other blue, as in the figure. You do not need to include crossovers in your model.

Table 16.1	A Comparison of Mitosis, Meiosis I, and Meiosis II		
Event	**Mitosis**	**Meiosis I**	**Meiosis II**
DNA replication:	Occurs prior to mitosis	Occurs prior to meiosis I	Does not occur between meiosis I and II
Synapsis during prophase:	No	Yes, bivalents are formed.	No
Crossing over during prophase:	Rarely	Commonly	Rarely
Attachment to poles at prometaphase:	A pair of sister chromatids is attached to kinetochore microtubules from both poles.	A pair of sister chromatids is attached to kinetochore microtubules from just one pole.	A pair of sister chromatids is attached to kinetochore microtubules from both poles.
Alignment along the metaphase plate:	Sister chromatids align.	Bivalents align.	Sister chromatids align.
Type of separation at anaphase:	Sister chromatids separate. A single chromatid, now called a chromosome, moves to each pole.	Homologous chromosomes separate. A pair of sister chromatids moves to each pole.	Sister chromatids separate. A single chromatid, now called a chromosome, moves to each pole.
End result when the mother cell is diploid:	Two daughter cells that are diploid	—	Four daughter cells that are haploid

16.4 Sexual Reproduction

Learning Outcome:

1. Distinguish between the life cycles of diploid-dominant species, haploid-dominant species, and species that exhibit an alternation of generations.

Sexual reproduction is a process in which two haploid gametes unite in a fertilization event to form a diploid cell called a zygote. For multicellular species such as animals and plants, the zygote then grows and divides by mitotic cell divisions into a multicellular organism with many diploid cells.

For any given species, the sequence of events that produces another generation of organisms is known as a **life cycle**. For sexually reproducing organisms, this usually involves an alternation between haploid cells or organisms and diploid cells or organisms (**Figure 16.14**).

Diploid-Dominant Species Most species of animals are diploid, and their haploid gametes are considered to be a specialized type of cell. For this reason, animals are viewed as **diploid-dominant species** (Figure 16.14a). Certain diploid cells in the testes or ovaries undergo meiosis to produce haploid sperm or eggs, respectively. During fertilization, sperm and egg unite to form a diploid zygote, which then undergoes repeated mitotic cell divisions to produce a diploid multicellular organism.

Haploid-Dominant Species By comparison, most fungi and some protists are just the opposite; they are **haploid-dominant species** (Figure 16.14b). In fungi, the multicellular organism is haploid ($1n$); only the zygote is diploid. Haploid fungal cells are most commonly produced by mitosis. During sexual reproduction, haploid cells unite to form a diploid zygote, which then immediately proceeds through meiosis to produce four haploid cells called spores. Each spore goes through mitotic cellular divisions to produce a haploid multicellular organism.

Alternation of Generations Plants and some algae have life cycles that are intermediate between diploid and haploid dominance. Such species exhibit an **alternation of generations** (Figure 16.14c). The species alternate between diploid multicellular organisms called **sporophytes**, and haploid multicellular organisms called **gametophytes**. Meiosis in certain cells within the sporophyte produces haploid spores, which divide by mitosis to produce the gametophyte. Particular cells within the gametophyte differentiate into haploid gametes. Fertilization occurs between two gametes, producing a diploid zygote that then undergoes repeated mitotic cell divisions to produce a sporophyte.

Among different plant species, the relative sizes of the haploid and diploid organisms vary greatly. In mosses, the haploid gametophyte is a visible multicellular organism, whereas the diploid sporophyte is smaller and remains attached to the haploid organism. In other plants, such as ferns (Figure 16.14c), both the diploid sporophyte and haploid gametophyte grow independently. The sporophyte is considerably larger and is the organism we commonly think of as a fern. In seed-bearing plants, such as roses and oak trees, the diploid sporophyte is the large multicellular plant, whereas the gametophyte is composed of only a few cells and is formed within the sporophyte.

When comparing animals, plants, and fungi, it's interesting to consider how gametes are made. Animals produce gametes by meiosis. In contrast, plants and fungi produce reproductive cells by mitosis. The gametophyte of plants is a haploid multicellular organism that is created by mitotic cellular divisions of a haploid spore. Within the multicellular gametophyte, certain cells become specialized as gametes.

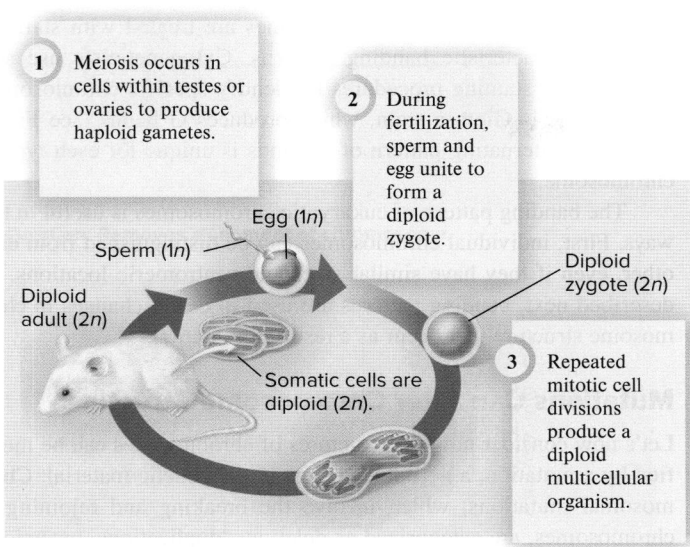

(a) Animal life cycle—diploid dominant

1. Meiosis occurs in cells within testes or ovaries to produce haploid gametes.
2. During fertilization, sperm and egg unite to form a diploid zygote.
3. Repeated mitotic cell divisions produce a diploid multicellular organism.

Sperm (1n)
Egg (1n)
Diploid adult (2n)
Diploid zygote (2n)
Somatic cells are diploid (2n).

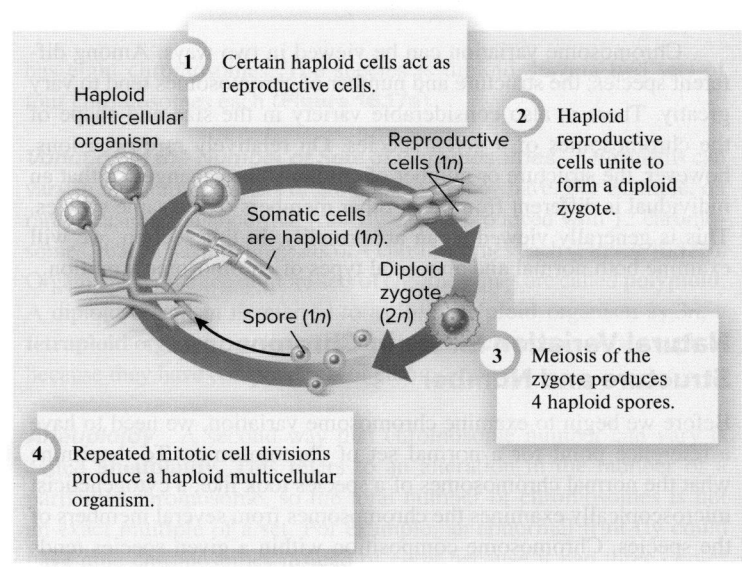

(b) Fungal life cycle—haploid dominant

1. Certain haploid cells act as reproductive cells.
2. Haploid reproductive cells unite to form a diploid zygote.
3. Meiosis of the zygote produces 4 haploid spores.
4. Repeated mitotic cell divisions produce a haploid multicellular organism.

Haploid multicellular organism
Reproductive cells (1n)
Somatic cells are haploid (1n).
Diploid zygote (2n)
Spore (1n)

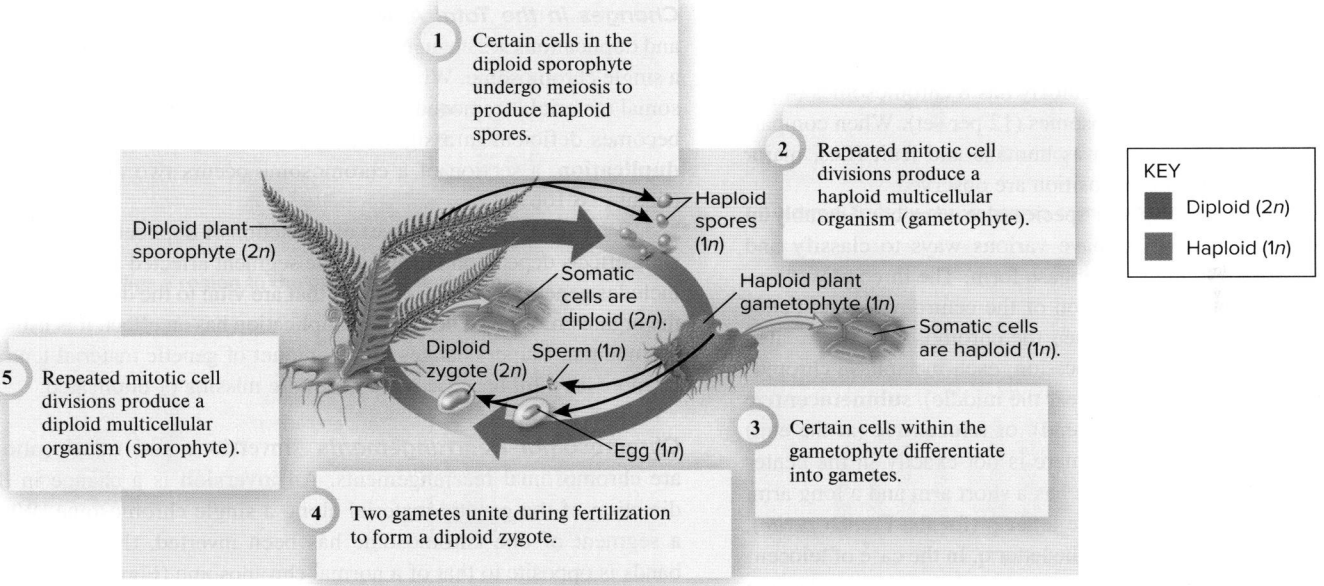

(c) Plant life cycle—alternation of generations

1. Certain cells in the diploid sporophyte undergo meiosis to produce haploid spores.
2. Repeated mitotic cell divisions produce a haploid multicellular organism (gametophyte).
3. Certain cells within the gametophyte differentiate into gametes.
4. Two gametes unite during fertilization to form a diploid zygote.
5. Repeated mitotic cell divisions produce a diploid multicellular organism (sporophyte).

Diploid plant sporophyte (2n)
Haploid spores (1n)
Somatic cells are diploid (2n).
Haploid plant gametophyte (1n)
Somatic cells are haploid (1n).
Diploid zygote (2n)
Sperm (1n)
Egg (1n)

KEY
■ Diploid (2n)
■ Haploid (1n)

Figure 16.14 **A comparison of three types of life cycles for sexually reproducing organisms.**

Concept Check: *What is the main purpose of meiosis in animals? What is the main purpose of mitosis in animals?*

16.5   Variation in Chromosome Structure and Number

Learning Outcomes:

1. Describe how chromosomes can vary in size, centromere location, and number.
2. Identify the four ways that the structure of a chromosome can be changed via mutation.
3. Compare and contrast changes in the number of sets of chromosomes and changes in the number of individual chromosomes.
4. Give examples of how changes in chromosome number affect the characteristics of animals and plants.

In the previous sections of this chapter, we examined two important features of chromosomes: They occur in sets, and two sorting processes determine the number of sets of chromosomes following cell division. In this section, we will examine how the structures and numbers of chromosomes may vary between different species and within the same species.

Why is the study of chromosomal variation important? First, geneticists have discovered that variations in chromosome structure and number can have major effects on the characteristics of an organism. We now know that several human genetic diseases are caused by such changes. In addition, changes in chromosome structure and number have been an important factor in the evolution of new species, which is a topic we will consider in Chapter 24.

of chromosome 2 instead of the normal two copies (**Figure 16.17c**). Instead of being perfectly diploid, a trisomic animal is $2n + 1$. Such an animal is said to have trisomy 2. By comparison, a fruit fly could be lacking a single chromosome, such as chromosome 3, and have a total of seven chromosomes ($2n - 1$). This animal is said to be monosomic and is described as having monosomy 3.

Variations in chromosome number are fairly widespread and have a significant effect on the characteristics of plants and animals. For these reasons, researchers want to understand the mechanisms that cause these variations. In some cases, a change in chromosome number is the result of the abnormal sorting of chromosomes during cell division. The term **nondisjunction** refers to an event in which the chromosomes do not separate properly during cell division. Nondisjunction can occur during meiosis I or meiosis II and produces haploid cells that have too many or too few chromosomes. **Figure 16.18** illustrates the consequences of nondisjunction during meiosis I. In this case, one pair of homologs moved into the cell on the left instead of separating from each other. This results in the production of aneuploid cells, with either too many or too few chromosomes. If such a cell becomes a gamete that fuses with another gamete during fertilization, the zygote and the resulting organism will have an abnormal number of chromosomes in all of its cells.

Changes in Chromosome Number Have Important Consequences

How do changes in chromosome number affect the characteristics of animals and plants? Let's consider a few examples.

Changes in Chromosome Number in Animals   In many cases, animals do not tolerate deviations from diploidy well. For example, polyploidy in mammals is generally a lethal condition. However, a few cases of naturally occurring variations from diploidy do occur in animals. Male bees, which are produced from unfertilized eggs, contain a single set of chromosomes and are therefore haploid organisms. By comparison, fertilized eggs become female bees, which are diploid. A few examples of vertebrate polyploid animals have been discovered. Interestingly, on rare occasions, animals that are morphologically very similar to each other can be found as a diploid species as well as a separate polyploid species. This situation occurs among certain amphibians and reptiles. **Figure 16.19** shows photographs of a diploid and a tetraploid frog. As you can see, they look very similar.

One important reason that geneticists are so interested in aneuploidy is its relationship to certain inherited disorders in humans. Even though most people are born with 46 chromosomes, alterations in chromosome number occur at a surprising frequency during gamete formation. About 5% to 10% of all fertilized human eggs result in an embryo with an abnormality in chromosome number. In most cases, these abnormal embryos do not develop properly and result in a spontaneous abortion very early in pregnancy. Approximately 50% of all spontaneous abortions are due to alterations in chromosome number.

In some cases, an abnormality in chromosome number produces an offspring that can survive. Several human disorders are the result of abnormalities in chromosome number. The most common are trisomies of chromosomes 21, 18, or 13 and abnormalities in the number of the sex chromosomes (**Table 16.2**). These syndromes are most likely

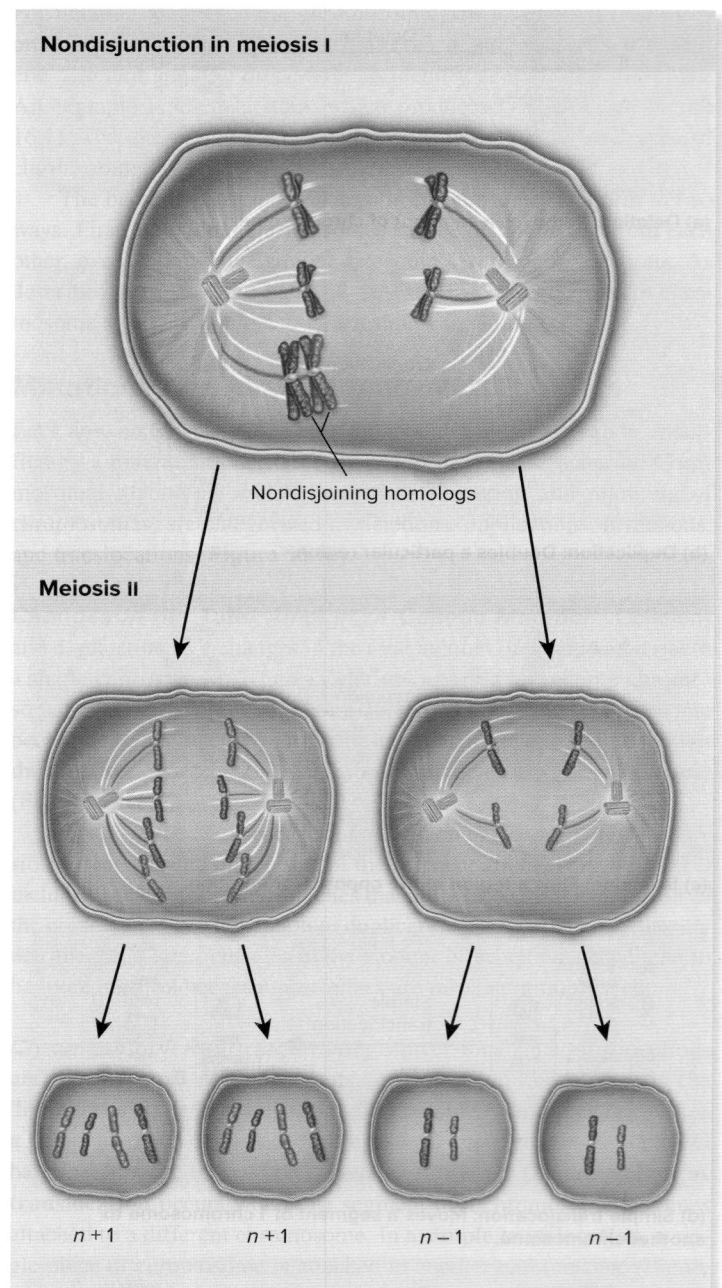

Figure 16.18 Nondisjunction during meiosis I. For simplicity, this cell shows only three pairs of homologous chromosomes. One of the three pairs does not disjoin (separate) properly, and both homologs have moved into the cell on the left. The resulting haploid cells shown at the bottom are all aneuploid, resulting in gametes with four chromosomes and two chromosomes, instead of three.

due to nondisjunction. For example, Turner syndrome (XO) may occur when a gamete that is lacking a sex chromosome due to nondisjunction has fused with a gamete carrying an X chromosome. By comparison, triple X syndrome (XXX) occurs when a gamete carrying two X chromosomes fuses with a gamete carrying a single X chromosome.

Most of the known trisomies involve chromosomes that are relatively small, so they carry fewer genes. Trisomies of the other human

(a) *Hyla chrysoscelis* (diploid)

(b) *Hyla versicolor* (tetraploid)

Figure 16.19 **Differences in chromosome number in two closely related frog species.** The frog in **(a)** is diploid, whereas the frog in **(b)** is tetraploid. These frogs are in the act of performing their mating calls, which is why the skin under their mouths is distended, forming a large bubble. a–b: ©A. B. Sheldon

Table 16.2	Aneuploid Conditions in Humans		
Condition	Frequency (per number of live births)	Syndrome	Characteristics
Autosomal			
Trisomy 21	1/800	Down	Mental impairment, abnormal pattern of palm creases, slanted eyes, flattened face, short stature
Trisomy 18	1/6,000	Edward	Mental and physical impairment, facial abnormalities, extreme muscle tone, early death
Trisomy 13	1/15,000	Patau	Mental and physical impairment, wide variety of defects in organs, large triangular nose, early death
Sex chromosomal			
XXY	1/1,000 (males)	Klinefelter	Sexual immaturity (no sperm), breast swelling (males)
XYY	1/1,000 (males)	Jacobs	Tall
XXX	1/1,500 (females)	Triple X	Tall and thin, menstrual irregularity
XO	1/5,000 (females)	Turner	Short stature, webbed neck, sexually undeveloped

chromosomes and most monosomies are presumed to be lethal and have been found in spontaneously aborted embryos and fetuses.

Human abnormalities in chromosome number are influenced by the age of the parents. Older parents are more likely to produce children with abnormalities in chromosome number, possibly because meiotic nondisjunction is more likely to occur in older cells. **Down syndrome**, which was first described by the English physician John Langdon Down in 1866, provides an example. This disorder is caused by the inheritance of three copies of chromosome 21 (see Table 16.2). The incidence of Down syndrome rises with the age of either parent. In males, however, the rise occurs relatively late in life, usually past the age when most men have children. By comparison, the likelihood of having a child with Down syndrome rises dramatically during the later reproductive ages of women.

Changes in Chromosome Number in Plants In contrast to animals, plants commonly exhibit polyploidy, which is important in agriculture. In many instances, polyploid strains of plants display characteristics that are helpful to humans. They are often larger in size and more robust. These traits are clearly advantageous in the production of food. For example, the species of wheat that we use to make bread, *Triticum aestivum*, is a hexaploid (with six sets of chromosomes) that arose from the union of diploid genomes from three closely related species (**Figure 16.20**). During the course of its domestication, a

Figure 16.20 **Example of a polyploid plant** Cultivated wheat, *Triticum aestivum*, is a hexaploid. It was derived from three different diploid species of grasses that originally were found in the Middle East and were cultivated by ancient farmers in that region. Modern varieties of wheat have been produced from this hexaploid species. ©irin-k/age fotostock

wild species became a tetraploid, and then a second diploid species interbred with the tetraploid to produce a hexaploid. Plant polyploids tend to exhibit a greater adaptability, which allows them to withstand harsher environmental conditions. Polyploid ornamental plants commonly produce larger flowers than their diploid counterparts.

Although polyploidy is often beneficial in plants, aneuploidy usually has detrimental consequences for the characteristics of an organism of any eukaryotic species. Why is aneuploidy usually detrimental? To answer this question, we need to consider the relationship between gene expression and chromosome number. For many, but not all genes, the level of gene expression is correlated with the number of genes per cell. For example, if a gene is carried on a chromosome that is present in a cell as three copies instead of two, approximately 150% of the normal amount of gene product is usually made. Alternatively, if only one copy of that gene is present due to a missing chromosome, only 50% of the gene product is typically made. For some genes, producing too much or too little of the gene product may not have adverse effects. However, for other genes, over- or underexpression may interfere with the proper functioning of cells.

Summary of Key Concepts

16.1 The Eukaryotic Cell Cycle

- Cytogeneticists examine cells microscopically to determine their chromosome composition. A micrograph that shows the alignment of chromosomes from a given cell is called a karyotype. Eukaryotic chromosomes are inherited in sets. A diploid cell has two sets of chromosomes. The members of each pair are called homologs (Figure 16.1).

- The eukaryotic cell cycle consists of four phases called G_1 (first gap), S (synthesis of DNA), G_2 (second gap), and M (mitosis and cytokinesis). The G_1, S, and G_2 phases are collectively known as interphase (Figure 16.2).

- An interaction between cyclin and cyclin-dependent kinase (cdk) is necessary for cells to advance through the cell cycle. Checkpoint proteins sense the environmental conditions and the integrity of the genome and control whether or not the cell advances through the cell cycle (Figure 16.3).

- Masui and Markert studied the maturation of frog oocytes to identify a substance necessary for the oocytes to progress through the cell cycle. This substance was initially called maturation-promoting factor (MPF) and was later identified as a complex of mitotic cyclin and cyclin-dependent kinase (Figures 16.4, 16.5).

16.2 Mitotic Cell Division

- In the process of mitotic cell division, a cell divides to produce two new cells (the daughter cells) that are genetically identical to the original cell.

- During S phase, eukaryotic chromosomes are replicated to produce a pair of identical sister chromatids that remain attached to each other (Figure 16.6).

- The mitotic spindle is a network of microtubules that plays a central role in chromosome sorting during cell division (Figure 16.7).

- Mitosis occurs in five phases called prophase, prometaphase, metaphase, anaphase, and telophase. During prophase, the

chromosomes condense, and the nuclear envelope begins to dissociate. The spindle apparatus is completely formed by the end of prometaphase. At metaphase, the chromosomes are aligned in a single row along the metaphase plate of the spindle. During anaphase, the sister chromatids separate from each other and move to opposite poles; the poles themselves also move farther apart. During telophase, the chromosomes decondense, and the nuclear envelope re-forms (Figure 16.8).

- Cytokinesis, which occurs after mitosis, is the division of the cytoplasm to produce two distinct daughter cells. In animal cells, cytokinesis involves the formation of a cleavage furrow. In plant cells, two separate cells are produced by the formation of a cell plate (Figure 16.9).

- The analysis of cell division in prokaryotic cells and in simple and complex eukaryotes has revealed an evolutionary progression in which the protein FtsZ plays a role in bacterial cell division and microtubules gain new functions in eukaryotes, such as sorting chromosomes and promoting nuclear division (Figure 16.10).

16.3 Meiosis

- The process of meiosis begins with a diploid cell and produces four haploid cells with one set of chromosomes each (Figure 16.11).

- During prophase of meiosis, homologous pairs of sister chromosomes synapse, and crossing over occurs. After crossing over, chiasmata—the sites where crossing over occurs—become visible (Figure 16.12).

- Meiosis consists of two divisions—meiosis I and II—each composed of prophase, prometaphase, metaphase, anaphase, and telophase. During meiosis I, the homologs are separated into two different cells, and during meiosis II, the sister chromatids are separated into four different cells (Figure 16.13, Table 16.1).

16.4 Sexual Reproduction

- Animals are diploid-dominant species, whereas most fungi and some protists are haploid-dominant species. Plants alternate between diploid and haploid forms (Figure 16.14).

16.5 Variation in Chromosome Structure and Number

- Chromosomes are classified as metacentric, submetacentric, acrocentric, and telocentric, based on their centromere location. Each type of chromosome can be uniquely identified by its banding pattern after staining (Figure 16.15).

- Deletions, duplications, inversions, and translocations are different ways in which mutations alter chromosome structure (Figure 16.16).

- A euploid organism has chromosomes that occur in complete sets. A polyploid organism has three or more sets of chromosomes. An organism that has one too many (trisomy) or one too few (monosomy) chromosomes is termed aneuploid. Aneuploidy can be caused by nondisjunction, an event in which the chromosomes do not separate properly during cell division (Figures 16.17, 16.18).

- Aneuploidy in humans is responsible for several types of inherited disorders, including Down syndrome (Table 16.2).

- Polyploid animals are relatively rare, but polyploid plants are common and tend to be larger and more robust than their diploid counterparts (Figures 16.19, 16.20).

Assess & Discuss

Test Yourself

1. In which phase of the cell cycle are chromosomes replicated?
   a. G_1 phase
   b. S phase
   c. M phase
   d. G_2 phase
   e. none of the above

2. If two chromosomes are homologous, they
   a. look similar under the microscope.
   b. have very similar DNA sequences.
   c. carry the same types of genes.
   d. may carry different versions of the same gene.
   e. are all of the above.

3. Checkpoints during the cell cycle are important because they
   a. allow the organellar activity to catch up to cellular demands.
   b. ensure the integrity of the cell's DNA.
   c. allow the cell to generate sufficient ATP for cellular division.
   d. are the only time DNA replication can occur.
   e. do all of the above.

4. Which of the following is a reason for mitotic cell division?
   a. asexual reproduction
   b. gamete formation in animals
   c. multicellularity
   d. all of the above
   e. both a and c

5. A replicated chromosome is composed of
   a. two homologous chromosomes held together at the centromere.
   b. four sister chromatids held together at the centromere.
   c. two sister chromatids held together at the centromere.
   d. four homologous chromosomes held together at the centromere.
   e. one chromosome with a centromere.

6. Which of the following is *not* an event of anaphase of mitosis?
   a. The nuclear envelope breaks apart.
   b. Sister chromatids separate.
   c. Kinetochore microtubules shorten, pulling the chromosomes to the poles.
   d. Polar microtubules push against each other, moving the poles farther apart.
   e. All of the above occur during anaphase.

7. A student is looking at cells under the microscope. The cells are from an organism that has a diploid chromosome number of 14. In one particular case, the cell has seven replicated chromosomes (sister chromatids) aligned at the metaphase plate of the cell. Which of the following statements accurately describes this particular cell?
   a. The cell is in metaphase of mitosis.
   b. The cell is in metaphase of meiosis I.
   c. The cell is in metaphase of meiosis II.
   d. All of the above are correct.
   e. Both b and c are correct.

8. Which of the following statements accurately describes a difference between mitosis and meiosis?
   a. Mitosis may produce diploid cells, whereas meiosis produces haploid cells.
   b. Homologous chromosomes synapse during meiosis but do not synapse during mitosis.
   c. Crossing over commonly occurs during meiosis, but it does not commonly occur during mitosis.
   d. All of the above are correct.
   e. Both a and c are correct.

9. During crossing over in meiosis I,
   a. homologous chromosomes are not altered.
   b. homologous chromosomes exchange genetic material.
   c. chromosomal damage occurs.
   d. genetic information is lost.
   e. cytokinesis occurs.

10. Aneuploidy may be the result of
    a. duplication of a region of a chromosome.
    b. inversion of a region of a chromosome.
    c. nondisjunction during meiosis.
    d. interspecies breeding.
    e. all of the above.

Conceptual Questions

1. Distinguish between homologous chromosomes and sister chromatids.

2. The *OCA2* gene, which influences eye color in humans, is found on chromosome 15. How many copies of this gene are found in the karyotype in the inset in Figure 16.1? Is it one, two, or four?

3. **Core Concept: Information** Explain why mitosis is a key process for passing genetic information to new cells.

Collaborative Questions

1. Why is it necessary for chromosomes to condense during mitosis and meiosis? What do you think might happen if chromosomes did not condense?

2. A diploid eukaryotic cell has 10 chromosomes (5 per set). As a group, take turns having one student draw the cell as it would look during a phase of mitosis, meiosis I, or meiosis II; then have the other students guess which phase it is.

Mendelian Patterns of Inheritance

17

An African girl with albinism. This condition results in very light skin and hair color. ©Radu Sigheti/Reuters

Ntombi knew she looked different as long as she can remember. Born in Nigeria in 1997, she has accepted her appearance, though she still finds the occasional stare from strangers to be disturbing. Ntombi has albinism, a condition characterized by a total or partial lack of pigmentation of the skin, hair, and eyes. As a result, she has very fair skin, blond hair, and blue eyes.* In contrast, her parents and three brothers have dark skin, black hair, and brown eyes, as do most of her relatives and most of the people in the city where she lives. Ntombi is very close to her aunt, who also has albinism.

Cases like Ntombi's have intrigued people for many centuries. How do we explain the traits that are found in people, plants, and other organisms? Can we predict what types of offspring two parents will produce? To answer such questions, researchers have studied the characteristics among related individuals and tried to make some sense of the data. Their goal is to understand

*In contrast to popular belief, most people with albinism have blue eyes, not pink eyes. This is particularly the case among Africans with albinism.

inheritance—the acquisition of traits by their transmission from parent to offspring.

The first systematic attempt to understand inheritance was carried out by German plant breeder Joseph Kolreuter between 1761 and 1766. In crosses between two strains of tobacco plants, Kolreuter found that the offspring were usually intermediate in appearance between the two parents. He concluded that parents make equal genetic contributions to their offspring and that their genetic material blends together as it is passed to the next generation. This interpretation was consistent with the concept known as blending inheritance, which was incorrect but widely accepted at that time. In the late 1700s, Jean-Baptiste Lamarck, a French naturalist, hypothesized that physiological events (such as use or disuse) could modify traits and such modified traits would be inherited by offspring. For example, an individual who became adept at archery would pass that skill to his or her offspring. Overall, the prevailing view prior to the 1800s was that hereditary traits were rather malleable and could change and blend over the course of one or two generations.

In contrast, microscopic observations of chromosome transmission during mitosis and meiosis in the second half of the 19th century provided compelling evidence for **particulate inheritance**—the idea that the determinants of hereditary traits are transmitted in discrete units, or particles, from one generation to the next. Remarkably, this idea was first put forward in the 1860s by a researcher who knew nothing about chromosomes. Gregor Mendel used statistical analysis of carefully designed plant breeding experiments to arrive at the concept of a gene, which is broadly defined as a unit of heredity. Forty years later, through the convergence of Mendel's work and that of cell biologists, this concept became the foundation of the modern science of genetics.

In this chapter, we will consider inheritance patterns known as Mendelian inheritance. Although these patterns can vary, they all obey Mendel's laws of inheritance, which we will examine in Section 17.1. As summarized in **Table 17.1**, our emphasis will be on two aspects of inheritance. First, we will explore how the various types of inheritance patterns produce different outcomes in a genetic cross. Second, we will examine the underlying molecular mechanisms that explain these different outcomes. In Chapter 18, we will explore some inheritance patterns that violate Mendel's laws.

Table 17.1	Different Types of Mendelian Inheritance Patterns and Their Molecular Basis
Type	**Description**
Simple Mendelian inheritance	**Inheritance pattern:** Pattern of traits is determined by a pair of alleles that display a dominant/recessive relationship and are located on an autosome. The presence of the dominant allele masks the presence of the recessive allele.
	Molecular basis: In many cases, the recessive allele is nonfunctional. Though a heterozygote may produce 50% of the functional protein compared with a dominant homozygote, this is sufficient to produce the dominant trait.
X-linked inheritance	**Inheritance pattern:** Pattern of traits is determined by genes that display a dominant/recessive relationship and are located on the X chromosome. In mammals and fruit flies, males are hemizygous for X-linked genes. In these species, X-linked recessive traits occur more frequently in males than in females.
	Molecular basis: In a female with one recessive X-linked allele (a heterozygote), the protein encoded by the dominant allele is sufficient to produce the dominant trait. A male with a recessive X-linked allele does not have a dominant allele and does not make any of the functional protein.
Incomplete dominance	**Inheritance pattern:** Pattern that occurs when the heterozygote has a phenotype intermediate to the phenotypes of the homozygotes, as when a cross between red-flowered and white-flowered plants produces pink-flowered offspring.
	Molecular basis: Fifty percent of the protein encoded by the functional (wild-type) allele results in an intermediate phenotype.
Codominance	**Inheritance pattern:** Pattern that occurs when the heterozygote expresses both alleles simultaneously. For example, a human carrying the A and B alleles for the ABO antigens of red blood cells produces both the A and the B antigens (has an AB blood type).
	Molecular basis: The codominant alleles encode proteins that function somewhat differently from each other. In a heterozygote, the function of each protein affects the phenotype uniquely.
Epistasis	**Inheritance pattern:** A type of gene interaction in which the alleles of one gene mask the effects of an allele of another gene.
	Molecular basis: Two different genes are needed to produce a given phenotype. Loss of function of one of the genes alters the phenotype.
Continuous variation	**Inheritance pattern:** A pattern in which the offspring display a continuous range of phenotypes.
	Molecular basis: This pattern is produced by the additive interactions of several genes, along with environmental influences.

17.1 Mendel's Laws of Inheritance

Learning Outcomes:

1. List the advantages of using the garden pea to study inheritance.
2. Describe the difference between dominant and recessive traits.
3. Distinguish between genotype and phenotype.
4. **CoreSKILL** » Predict the outcome of genetic crosses using a Punnett square.
5. State Mendel's law of segregation and law of independent assortment.

Gregor Johann Mendel (**Figure 17.1**) grew up on a small farm in northern Moravia, then a part of the Austrian Empire and now in the Czech Republic. At the age of 21, he entered the Augustinian monastery of St. Thomas in Brno and was ordained a priest in 1847. Mendel then worked for a short time as a substitute teacher, but to continue teaching he needed a license. Surprisingly, he failed the licensing exam due to poor answers in physics and natural history, so he enrolled at the University of Vienna to expand his knowledge in these two areas. Mendel's training in physics and mathematics taught him to perceive the world as an orderly place, governed by natural laws that could be stated as simple mathematical relationships.

In 1856, Mendel began his historic studies on pea plants. For 8 years, he analyzed thousands of pea plants that he grew on a small plot in his monastery garden. In 1866, he published the results of his work in

Figure 17.1 Gregor Johann Mendel. ©SPL/Science Source

a paper entitled "Experiments on Plant Hybrids." This paper was largely ignored by scientists at that time, partly because of its title. Also, Mendel was clearly ahead of his time. During this period, biology had not yet become a quantitative, experimental science. In addition, the behavior of chromosomes during mitosis and meiosis, which provides a framework for understanding inheritance patterns, had yet to be studied. Prior to his death in 1884, Mendel reflected, "My scientific work has brought me a great deal of satisfaction and I am convinced it will be appreciated before long by the whole world." Sixteen years later, in 1900, Mendel's work was independently rediscovered by three biologists with an interest in plant genetics: Hugo de Vries of Holland, Carl Correns of Germany, and Erich von Tschermak of Austria. Within a few years, the influence of Mendel's landmark studies was felt around the world.

In this section, we will examine Mendel's experiments and see how they led to the formulation of basic genetic principles known as Mendel's laws. We will discover that these principles apply not only to the pea plants Mendel studied, but also to a wide variety of sexually reproducing organisms, including humans.

Mendel Chose the Garden Pea to Study Inheritance

When two individuals of the same species with different characteristics are bred or crossed to each other, the process is called **hybridization**, and the offspring are referred to as hybrids. For example, a hybridization experiment could involve breeding a purple-flowered plant to a white-flowered plant. Mendel was particularly intrigued by the consistency with which offspring of such crosses showed characteristics of one or the other parent in successive generations. His intellectual foundation in physics and the natural sciences led him to consider that this regularity might be rooted in natural laws that could be expressed mathematically. To uncover these laws, he carried out quantitative experiments in which he carefully analyzed the numbers of offspring carrying specific traits.

Mendel chose the garden pea, *Pisum sativum*, to investigate the natural laws that govern inheritance. Why did he choose this species? Several properties of the garden pea were particularly advantageous for studying inheritance. First, it was available in many varieties that differed in characteristics, such as the appearance of seeds, pods, flowers, and stems. Such general features of an organism are called **characters**. **Figure 17.2** illustrates the seven characters that Mendel eventually chose to follow in his breeding experiments. Each of these characters was found in two discrete variants. For example, one character he followed was height, which had the variants known as tall and dwarf. Another was seed color, which had the variants yellow and green. A **trait** is an identifiable characteristic of an organism. The term trait usually refers to a variant for a character.[*] For example, seed color is a character, and green and yellow seed colors are traits.

A second advantageous property of garden peas is they are normally self-fertilizing. In **self-fertilization**, a female gamete is fertilized by a male gamete from the same plant. Like many flowering plants, peas have male and female sex organs in the same flower (**Figure 17.3**). Male gametes (sperm cells) are produced within pollen grains, which are formed in structures called stamens. Female gametes (egg cells) are produced in structures called ovules, which form within an organ called an ovary. For fertilization to occur, a pollen grain must land on the receptacle called a stigma, enabling a sperm to migrate to an ovule and fuse with an egg cell. In peas, the stamens and the ovaries are enclosed by a modified petal, an arrangement that greatly favors self-fertilization. Self-fertilization makes it easy to produce plants that breed true for a given trait, meaning the trait does not vary from generation to generation. For example, if a pea plant with yellow seeds breeds true for seed color, all of the plants that grow from these seeds will also produce yellow seeds. A strain that continues

---

[*]Geneticists may also use the term trait to refer to a character.

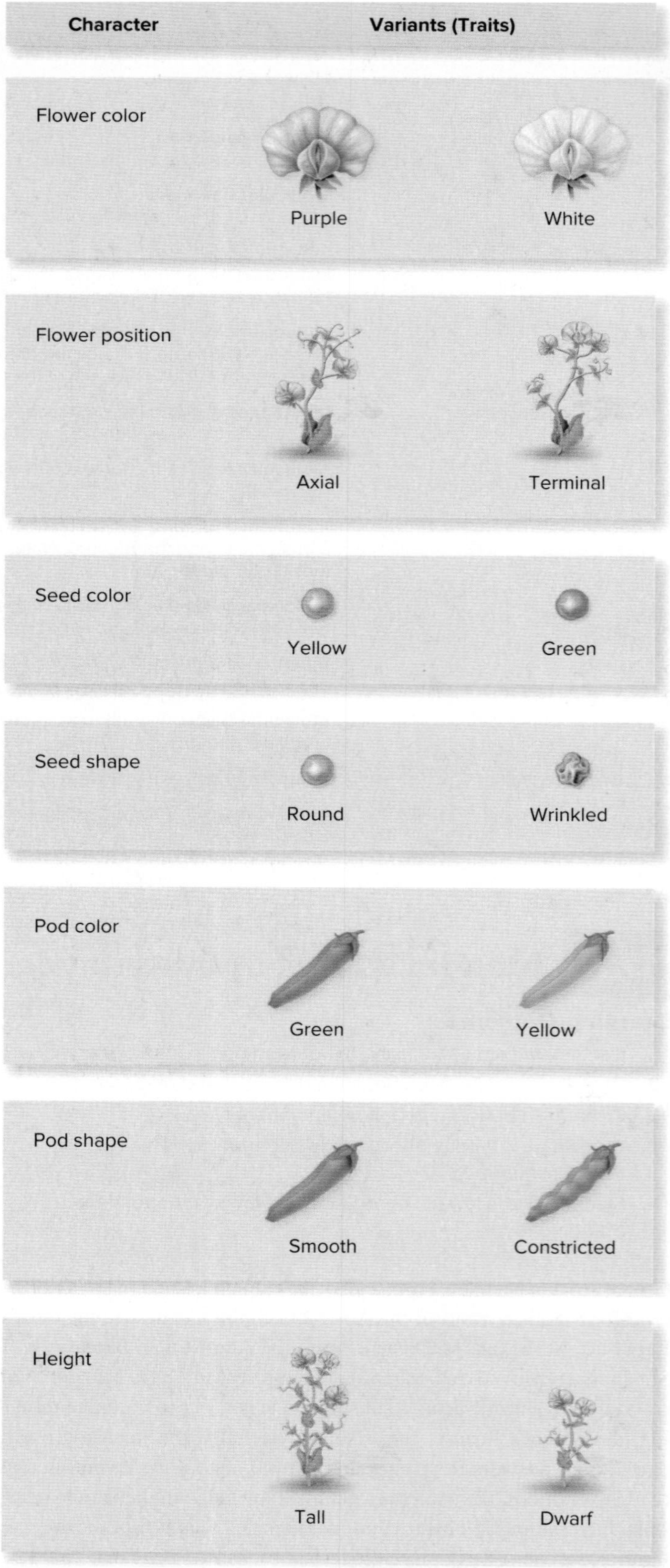

Character	Variants (Traits)	
Flower color	Purple	White
Flower position	Axial	Terminal
Seed color	Yellow	Green
Seed shape	Round	Wrinkled
Pod color	Green	Yellow
Pod shape	Smooth	Constricted
Height	Tall	Dwarf

Figure 17.2 **The seven characters that Mendel studied.**

 Core Concept: Information The traits that Mendel studied in pea plants are governed by the genetic material of this species.

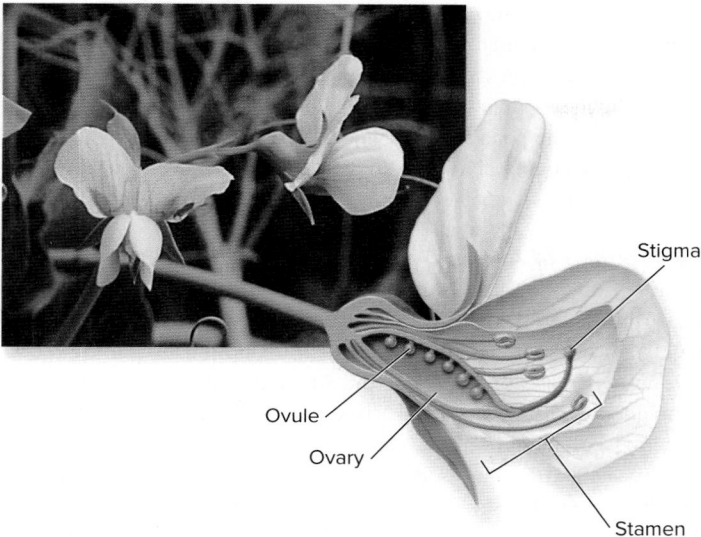

Figure 17.3 **Flower structure in pea plants.** The pea flower produces both male and female gametes. Sperm form in the pollen produced within the stamens; egg cells form in ovules within the ovary. A modified petal encloses the stamens and stigma, encouraging self-fertilization. ©Nigel Cattlin/Science Source

to exhibit the same trait after several generations of self-fertilization is called a **true-breeding line**. Prior to conducting the studies described in this chapter, Mendel had already established that the seven characters he chose to study were true-breeding in the strains of pea plants he had obtained.

A third reason for using garden peas in hybridization experiments is the ease of making crosses: The flowers are fairly large and easy to manipulate. In some cases, Mendel wanted his pea plants to self-fertilize, but in others, he wanted to cross plants that differed with respect to some character, a process called hybridization, or **cross-fertilization**. In garden peas, cross-fertilization requires placing pollen from one plant onto the stigma of a flower on a different plant (**Figure 17.4**). Mendel would pry open an immature flower

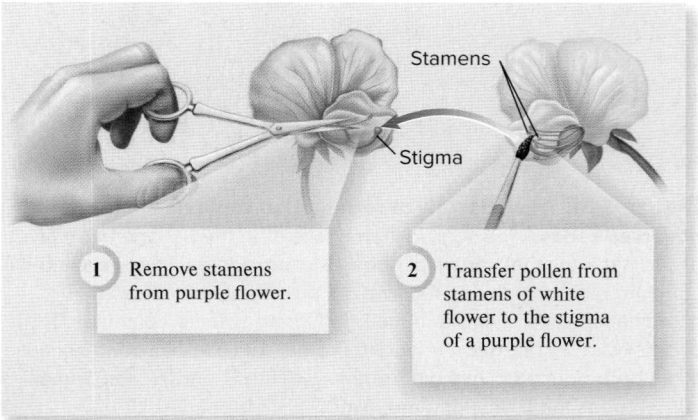

Figure 17.4 **A procedure for cross-fertilizing pea plants.**

Concept Check: *Why are the stamens removed from the purple flower in this cross-fertilization procedure?*

and remove the stamens before they produced pollen, so the flower could not self-fertilize. He then used a paintbrush to transfer pollen from another plant to the stigma of the flower that had its stamens removed. In this way, Mendel was able to cross-fertilize any two of his true-breeding pea plants and obtain any type of hybrid he wanted.

By Following the Inheritance Pattern of Single Traits, Mendel's Work Revealed the Law of Segregation

Mendel began his investigations by studying the inheritance patterns of pea plants that differed in a single character. A cross in which an experimenter follows the variants of only one character is called a **single-factor cross**. As an example, we will consider a single-factor cross in which Mendel followed the tall and dwarf variants for height (**Figure 17.5**). The left side of Figure 17.5a shows his experimental approach. The true-breeding parents are termed the **P generation** (parental generation), and their offspring constitute the F_1 **generation** (first filial generation, from the Latin *filius*, meaning son). When the true-breeding parents differ in a single character, their F_1 offspring are called single-trait hybrids, or **monohybrids**. When Mendel crossed true-breeding tall and dwarf plants, he observed that all plants of the F_1 generation were tall.

Next, Mendel followed the transmission of this character for a second generation. To do so, he allowed the F_1 monohybrids to self-fertilize, producing a generation called the F_2 **generation** (second filial generation). The dwarf trait reappeared in the F_2 offspring: Three-fourths of the plants were tall and one-fourth were dwarf. Mendel obtained similar results for each of the seven characters he studied, as shown in the data of Figure 17.5b. A quantitative analysis of his data allowed Mendel to postulate three important ideas about the properties of traits and their transmission from parents to offspring:

1. Traits may exist in two forms, dominant and recessive.
2. An individual carries two genes for a given character, and genes have variant forms (now called **alleles**).
3. The two alleles of a gene separate during the process that gives rise to haploid cells and gametes, so each sperm and egg receives only one allele.

Dominant and Recessive Traits Perhaps the most surprising outcome of Mendel's work was that the data argued strongly against the prevailing notion of blending inheritance. In each of the seven cases, the F_1 generation displayed a trait distinctly like one of the two parents rather than an intermediate trait. Using genetic terms that Mendel originated, we describe the alternative traits as dominant and recessive. The term **dominant** describes the displayed trait, whereas the term **recessive** describes a trait that is masked by the presence of a dominant trait. Tall stems and purple flowers are examples of dominant traits; dwarf stems and white flowers are examples of recessive traits. In this case, we say that tall is dominant over dwarf, and purple is dominant over white.

Genes and Alleles Mendel's results were consistent with particulate inheritance, in which the determinants of traits are inherited as unchanging, discrete units. In all seven cases, the recessive trait reappeared in the F_2 generation: Most F_2 plants displayed the dominant trait, whereas a smaller proportion showed the recessive trait. This

Experimental approach

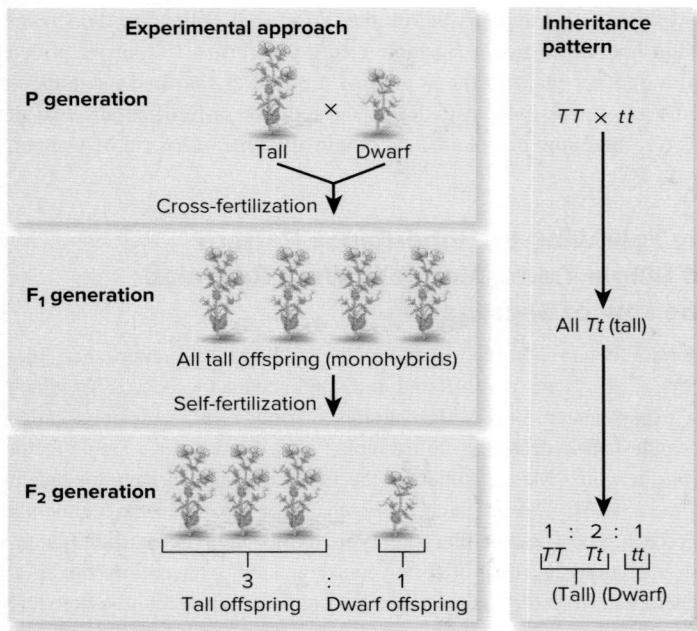

P generation

Tall × Dwarf

Cross-fertilization

F₁ generation

All tall offspring (monohybrids)

Self-fertilization

F₂ generation

3 : 1
Tall offspring Dwarf offspring

Inheritance pattern

$TT \times tt$

All Tt (tall)

1 : 2 : 1
TT Tt tt
(Tall) (Dwarf)

(a) Mendel's protocol for making single-factor crosses

THE DATA

P cross	F₁ generation	F₂ generation	Ratio
Purple × white flowers	All purple	705 purple, 224 white	3.15:1
Axial × terminal flowers	All axial	651 axial, 207 terminal	3.14:1
Yellow × green seeds	All yellow	6,022 yellow, 2,001 green	3.01:1
Round × wrinkled seeds	All round	5,474 round, 1,850 wrinkled	2.96:1
Green × yellow pods	All green	428 green, 152 yellow	2.82:1
Smooth × constricted pods	All smooth	882 smooth, 299 constricted	2.95:1
Tall × dwarf stem	All tall	787 tall, 277 dwarf	2.84:1
Total	**All dominant**	**14,949 dominant, 5,010 recessive**	**2.98:1**

(b) Mendel's observed data for all 7 traits

Figure 17.5 **Mendel's analyses of single-factor crosses.**

Concept Check: *Why do offspring of the F₁ generation exhibit only one variant of each character?*

observation led Mendel to conclude that the genetic determinants of traits are "unit factors" that are passed intact from generation to generation. These unit factors are what we now call **genes** (from the Greek *genos*, meaning birth), a term coined by the Danish botanist Wilhelm Johannsen in 1909. Mendel postulated that every individual carries two genes for a given character and that the gene for each character in his pea plants exists in two variant forms, which we now call alleles.

For example, the gene controlling height in Mendel's pea plants occurs in two variants, called the tall allele and the dwarf allele. The right side of Figure 17.5a shows Mendel's conclusions, using genetic symbols (italic letters) that were adopted later. The letters *T* and *t* represent the alleles of the gene for plant height. By convention, the uppercase letter represents the dominant allele (in this case, tall), and the same letter in lowercase represents the recessive allele (dwarf).

Segregation of Alleles When Mendel compared the numbers of F₂ offspring exhibiting dominant and recessive traits, he noticed a recurring pattern. Although some experimental variation occurred, he always observed a 3:1 ratio between the dominant and the recessive trait (Figure 17.5b). How did Mendel interpret this ratio? He concluded that each F₁ plant carried two versions (alleles) of a gene affecting height (or another character) and that the two alleles carried by such an F₁ plant separate, or segregate, from each other during the process that gives rise to gametes. Therefore, each sperm or egg carried only one allele. The diagram in **Figure 17.6** shows that

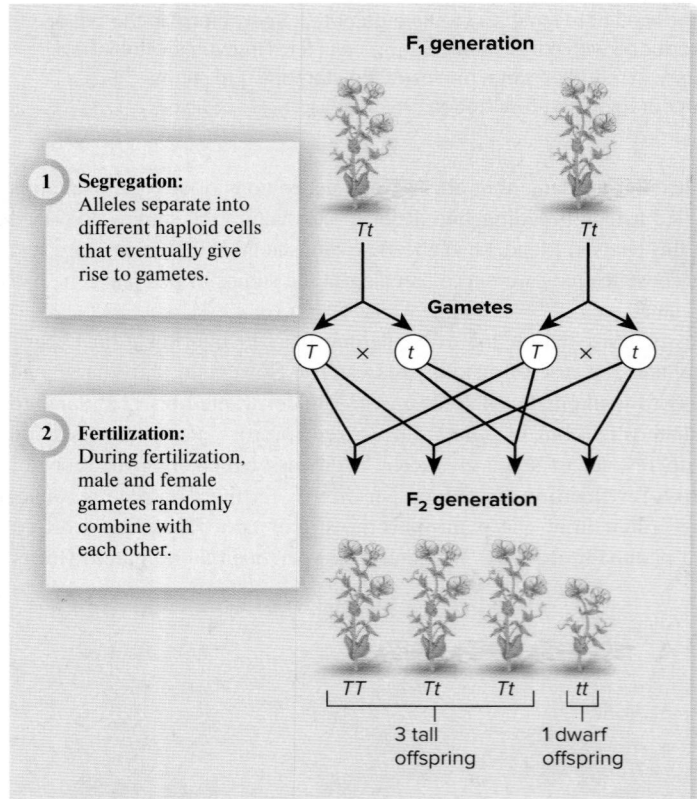

F₁ generation

Tt Tt

1 Segregation: Alleles separate into different haploid cells that eventually give rise to gametes.

Gametes

$T \times t$ $T \times t$

2 Fertilization: During fertilization, male and female gametes randomly combine with each other.

F₂ generation

TT Tt Tt tt

3 tall offspring   1 dwarf offspring

Figure 17.6 **How the law of segregation explains Mendel's observed ratios.** The segregation of alleles in the F₁ generation gives rise to gametes that carry just one of the two alleles. These gametes combine randomly during fertilization, producing the allele combinations *TT*, *Tt*, and *tt* in the F₂ offspring. The combination *Tt* occurs twice as often as either of the other two combinations because it can be produced in two different ways. The *TT* and *Tt* offspring are tall, whereas the *tt* offspring are dwarf.

Concept Check: *What is the ratio of the T allele to the t allele in the F₂ generation? Does this ratio differ from the 3:1 phenotype ratio? If so, explain why.*

the segregation of the F_1 alleles should result in equal numbers of gametes carrying the dominant allele (T) and the recessive allele (t). If these gametes combine with one another randomly at fertilization, as shown in the figure, this would account for the 3:1 ratio of the F_2 generation. Note that a Tt individual can be produced by two different combinations of alleles—the T allele can come from the male gamete and the t allele from the female gamete, or vice versa. This accounts for the observation that Tt offspring are produced twice as often as either TT or tt. The results of the study of traits in pea plants gave rise to **Mendel's law of segregation**, which can be stated as follows:

The two alleles of a gene separate (segregate) from each other during the process that gives rise to gametes, so every gamete receives only one allele.

Genotype Describes an Organism's Genetic Makeup, Whereas Phenotype Describes Its Characteristics

To continue our discussion of Mendel's results, we need to introduce a few more genetic terms. The term **genotype** refers to the genetic composition of an individual. In the example shown in Figure 17.5a, TT and tt are the genotypes of the P generation, and Tt is the genotype of the F_1 generation. In the P generation, both parents are true-breeding plants, which means that each has identical copies of the allele of the gene for height. An individual with two identical alleles of a gene is said to be **homozygous** with respect to that gene. In the specific cross we are considering, the tall plant (TT) is homozygous for T, and the dwarf plant (tt) is homozygous for t. In contrast, a **heterozygous** individual carries two different alleles of a gene. Plants of the F_1 generation are heterozygous, with the genotype Tt, because every individual carries one copy of the tall allele (T) and one copy of the dwarf allele (t). The F_2 generation includes both homozygous individuals (homozygotes) and heterozygous individuals (heterozygotes).

The term **phenotype** refers to the characteristics of an organism that are the result of the expression of its genes. In the example in Figure 17.5a, one of the parent plants is phenotypically tall, and the other is phenotypically dwarf. Although the F_1 offspring are heterozygous (Tt), they are phenotypically tall because each of them has a copy of the dominant tall allele. In contrast, the F_2 plants display both phenotypes in a ratio of 3:1.

A Punnett Square Is Used to Predict the Outcome of Crosses

A common way to predict the outcome of simple genetic crosses is to make a **Punnett square**, a method originally proposed by the British geneticist Reginald Punnett. To construct a Punnett square, you must know the genotypes of the parents. What follows is a step-by-step description of the Punnett-square approach, using a cross of heterozygous tall plants.

Step 1. *Write down the genotypes of both parents.* In this example, a heterozygous tall plant is crossed to another heterozygous tall plant. The plant providing the pollen is considered the male parent and the plant providing the eggs, the female parent. (In self-pollination, a single individual produces both types of gametes.)

Male parent: Tt
Female parent: Tt

Step 2. *Write down the possible gametes that each parent can make.* Remember the law of segregation tells us that a gamete contains only one copy of each allele.

Male gametes: T or t
Female gametes: T or t

Step 3. *Create an empty Punnett square.* The number of columns equals the number of male gametes, and the number of rows equals the number of female gametes. Our example has two rows and two columns. Place the male gametes across the top of the Punnett square and the female gametes along the side.

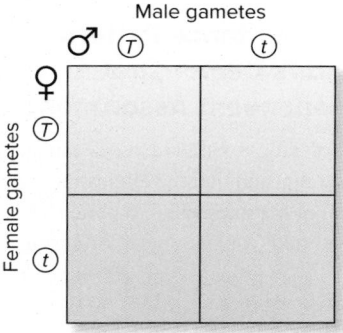

Step 4. *Fill in the possible genotypes of the offspring by combining the alleles of the gametes in the empty boxes.*

Step 5. *Determine the relative proportions of genotypes and phenotypes of the offspring.* The genotypes are obtained directly from the Punnett square. In this example, the genotype ratio is 1 TT : 2 Tt : 1 tt. To determine the phenotypes, you must know which allele is dominant. For plant height, T (tall) is dominant to t (dwarf). The genotypes TT and Tt are tall, whereas the genotype tt is dwarf. Therefore, our Punnett square shows us that the phenotype ratio is expected to be 3 tall : 1 dwarf.

A Testcross Is Used to Determine an Individual's Genotype

When a character has two variants, one of which is dominant over the other, we know that an individual with a recessive phenotype is homozygous for the recessive allele. A dwarf pea plant, for example, must have the genotype *tt*. But an individual with a dominant phenotype may be either homozygous or heterozygous—a tall pea plant may have the genotype *TT* or *Tt*. How can we distinguish between these two possibilities? Mendel devised a method called a **testcross** to address this question. In a testcross, the researcher crosses the individual of interest to a homozygous recessive individual and observes the phenotypes of the offspring.

Figure 17.7 shows how this procedure can be used to determine the genotype of a tall pea plant. If the testcross produces some dwarf offspring, as shown in the Punnett square on the right side, these offspring must have two copies of the recessive allele, one inherited from each parent. Therefore, the tall parent must be a heterozygote, with the genotype *Tt*. Alternatively, if all of the offspring are tall, as shown in the Punnett square on the left, the tall parent is likely to be a homozygote, with the genotype *TT*.

Analyzing the Inheritance Pattern of Two Characters Demonstrated the Law of Independent Assortment

Mendel's analysis of single-factor crosses suggested that traits are inherited as discrete units and that the alleles for a given gene segregate during the formation of haploid cells. To obtain additional insights into how genes are transmitted from parents to offspring, Mendel conducted crosses in which he simultaneously followed the inheritance of two different characters. A cross of this type is called a **two-factor cross**. We will examine a two-factor cross in which Mendel simultaneously followed the inheritance of seed color and seed shape (**Figure 17.8**). He began by crossing strains of pea plants that bred true for both characters. The plants of one strain had yellow, round seeds, and plants of the other strain had green, wrinkled seeds. He then allowed the F_1 offspring to self-fertilize and observed the phenotypes of the F_2 generation.

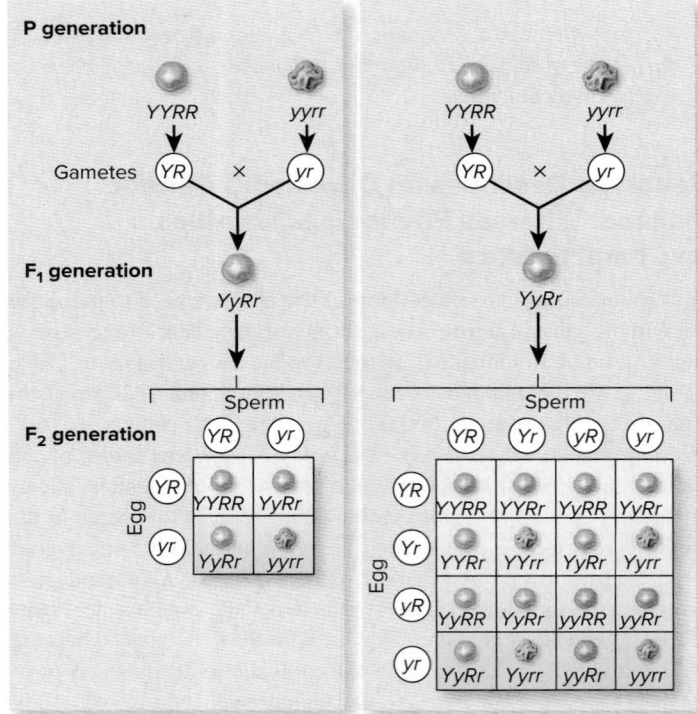

(a) **Hypothesis: linked assortment**

(b) **Hypothesis: independent assortment**

P cross	F_1 generation	F_2 generation
Yellow, round seeds × Green, wrinkled seeds	Yellow, round seeds	315 yellow, round seeds 101 yellow, wrinkled seeds 108 green, round seeds 32 green, wrinkled seeds

(c) **The data observed by Mendel**

Figure 17.8 Two hypotheses for the assortment of two different genes. In a cross between two true-breeding pea plants, one with yellow, round seeds and one with green, wrinkled seeds, all of the F_1 offspring have yellow, round seeds. When the F_1 offspring self-fertilize, the two hypotheses predict different ratios of phenotypes in the F_2 generation. (a) Linked assortment, in which parental alleles stay associated with each other, or (b) independent assortment, in which each allele assorts independently. (c) Mendel's data supported the independent assortment hypothesis.

Concept Check: What ratio of phenotypes would have occurred in the F_2 generation if the linked assortment hypothesis had been correct?

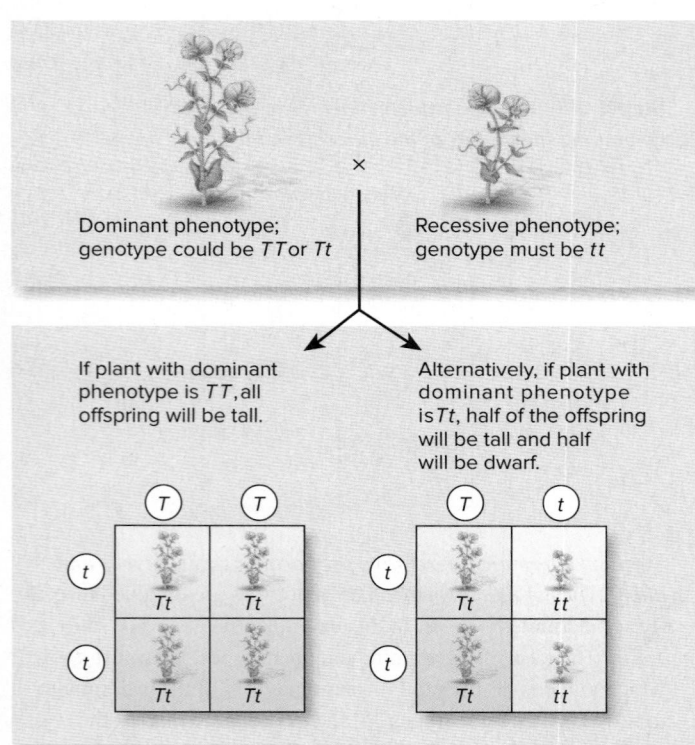

Figure 17.7 A testcross. The purpose of this experiment is to determine if an organism with the dominant phenotype, in this case a tall pea plant, is a homozygote (*TT*) or a heterozygote (*Tt*).

Concept Check: Let's suppose you had a pea plant with purple flowers and unknown genotype and conducted a testcross to determine its genotype. You obtained 41 offspring plants: 20 with white flowers and 21 with purple flowers. What was the genotype of the original purple-flowered plant?

What are the possible patterns of inheritance for two characters? One possibility is that the two genes are linked in some way, so variants that occur together in the parents are always inherited as a unit. In our example, the allele for yellow seeds (*Y*) would always be inherited with the allele for round seeds (*R*), and the alleles for green seeds (*y*) would always be inherited with the allele for wrinkled seeds (*r*), as shown in Figure 17.8a. A second possibility is that the two genes are independent of one another, so their alleles are randomly distributed into gametes (Figure 17.8b). By following the transmission pattern of two characters simultaneously, Mendel could determine whether the genes that determine seed shape and seed color assort (are distributed) together as a unit or independently of each other.

What experimental results could Mendel predict for each of these two models? The two homozygous plants of the P generation can produce only two kinds of gametes, *YR* and *yr*, so in either case the F$_1$ offspring would be heterozygous for both genes; that is, they would have the genotype *YyRr*. Because Mendel knew from his earlier experiments that yellow was dominant over green and round over wrinkled, he could predict that all the F$_1$ plants would have yellow, round seeds. In contrast, as shown in Figure 17.8, the ratios he obtained in the F$_2$ generation would depend on whether the alleles of both genes assort together or independently.

If the two genes are linked, as in Figure 17.8a, the F$_1$ plants could produce gametes that are only *YR* or *yr*. These gametes would combine to produce offspring with the genotypes *YYRR* (yellow, round), *YyRr* (yellow, round), and *yyrr* (green, wrinkled). The ratio of phenotypes would be 3 yellow, round to 1 green, wrinkled. Every F$_2$ plant would be phenotypically like one P-generation plant or the other. None would display a new combination of the parental traits. However, if the alleles assorted independently, the F$_2$ generation would have a wider range of genotypes and phenotypes, as shown by the Punnett square in Figure 17.8b. In this case, each F$_1$ parent produces four kinds of gametes—*YR*, *Yr*, *yR*, and *yr*—instead of two, so the square is constructed with four rows on each side and shows 16 possible genotypes. The F$_2$ generation includes plants with yellow, round seeds; yellow, wrinkled seeds; green, round seeds; and green, wrinkled seeds, in a ratio of 9:3:3:1.

The actual results of this two-factor cross are shown in Figure 17.8c. Crossing the true-breeding parents produced **dihybrid** offspring—offspring that are hybrids with respect to both traits. These F$_1$ dihybrids all had yellow, round seeds, confirming that yellow and round are dominant traits. This result was consistent with either hypothesis. However, the data for the F$_2$ generation were consistent only with the independent assortment hypothesis. The F$_2$ offspring showed four different phenotypes in a ratio that was reasonably close to 9:3:3:1.

In his original studies, Mendel reported that he had obtained similar results for every pair of characters he analyzed. This work gave rise to **Mendel's law of independent assortment**, which can be stated as follows:

The alleles of different genes assort independently of each other during the process that gives rise to gametes.

Independent assortment means that a specific allele for one gene may be found in a gamete regardless of which allele for a different gene is found in the same gamete. In our example, the yellow and green alleles assort independently of the round and wrinkled alleles.

The union of gametes from F$_1$ plants carrying these alleles produces the F$_2$ genotype and phenotype ratios shown in Figure 17.8b.

As we will see in Chapter 18, not all two-factor crosses exhibit independent assortment. In some cases, the alleles of two genes that are physically located near each other on the same chromosome do not assort independently.

17.2 The Chromosome Theory of Inheritance

Learning Outcomes:

1. Outline the principles of the chromosome theory of inheritance.
2. Relate the behavior of chromosomes during meiosis to Mendel's laws of inheritance.

Mendel's studies with pea plants eventually led to the concept of a gene, which is the foundation for our understanding of inheritance. However, at the time of Mendel's work, the physical nature and location of genes were a complete mystery. The idea that inheritance has a physical basis was not even addressed until 1883, when German biologist August Weismann and Swiss botanist Karl Nägeli championed the idea that a substance in living cells is responsible for the transmission of hereditary traits. This idea challenged other researchers to identify the genetic material. Several scientists, including German biologists Eduard Strasburger and Walther Flemming, observed dividing cells under the microscope and suggested that the chromosomes are the carriers of the genetic material. As we now know, the genetic material is the DNA within chromosomes.

In the early 1900s, the idea that chromosomes carry the genetic material gained increasing support as researchers continued to study the processes of mitosis, meiosis, and fertilization. It became increasingly clear that the characteristics of organisms are rooted in the continuity of cells during the life of an organism and from one generation to the next. Several scientists noted striking parallels between the segregation and assortment of traits noted by Mendel and the behavior of chromosomes during meiosis. Among these scientists were German biologist Theodor Boveri and American biologist Walter Sutton, who independently proposed the chromosome theory of inheritance. According to this theory, the inheritance patterns of traits can be explained by the transmission of chromosomes during meiosis and fertilization.

A modern version of the **chromosome theory of inheritance** consists of a few fundamental principles:

1. Chromosomes contain DNA, which is the genetic material. Genes are found within the chromosomes.
2. Chromosomes are replicated and passed from parent to offspring. They are also passed from cell to cell during the development of a multicellular organism.
3. The nucleus of a diploid cell contains two sets of chromosomes, which are found in homologous pairs. The maternal and paternal sets of homologous chromosomes are functionally equivalent; each set carries a full complement of genes.
4. At meiosis, one member of each chromosome pair segregates into one daughter nucleus, and its homolog segregates into the other daughter nucleus. During the formation of haploid

cells, the members of different chromosome pairs segregate independently of each other.

5. Gametes are haploid cells that combine to form a diploid cell during fertilization, with each gamete transmitting one set of chromosomes to the offspring.

In this section, we will relate the chromosome theory of inheritance to Mendel's laws of inheritance.

Mendel's Law of Segregation Is Explained by the Segregation of Homologous Chromosomes During Meiosis

Now that you have an understanding of the basic tenets of the chromosome theory of inheritance, let's relate these ideas to Mendel's laws of inheritance. To do so, it will be helpful to introduce another genetic term. The physical location of a gene on a chromosome is called the gene's **locus** (plural, loci). As shown in **Figure 17.9**, each member of a homologous chromosome pair carries an allele of the same gene at the same locus. The individual in this example is heterozygous (*Tt*), so each homolog has a different allele.

How can we relate the chromosome theory of inheritance to Mendel's law of segregation? **Figure 17.10** follows a pair of homologous chromosomes through the events of meiosis. This example involves a pea plant, heterozygous for height, *Tt*. The top of Figure 17.10 shows the two homologous chromosomes prior to DNA replication. When a cell prepares to divide, the homologs replicate to produce pairs of sister chromatids. Each chromatid carries a copy of the allele found on the original homolog, either *T* or *t*. During meiosis I, the homologs, each consisting of two sister chromatids, pair up and then segregate into two daughter cells. One of these cells has two copies of the *T* allele, and the other has two copies of the *t* allele. The sister chromatids separate during meiosis II, which produces four haploid cells. The end result of meiosis is that each haploid cell has a copy of just one of the two original homologs. Two of the cells have a chromosome carrying the *T* allele, and the other two have a chromosome carrying the *t* allele at the same locus.

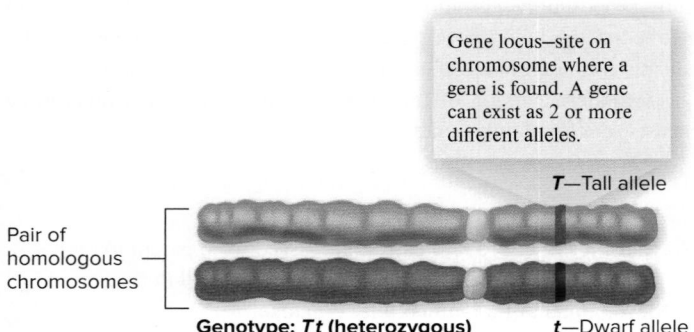

Gene locus—site on chromosome where a gene is found. A gene can exist as 2 or more different alleles.

T—Tall allele

Pair of homologous chromosomes

Genotype: *Tt* (heterozygous)   *t*—Dwarf allele

Figure 17.9 A gene locus. The locus (location) of a gene is the same for each member of a homologous pair, whether the individual is homozygous or heterozygous for that gene. This individual is heterozygous (*Tt*) for a gene for plant height.

 Core Skill: Connections Look back at Section 16.4. Explain the relationship between sexual reproduction and homologous chromosomes.

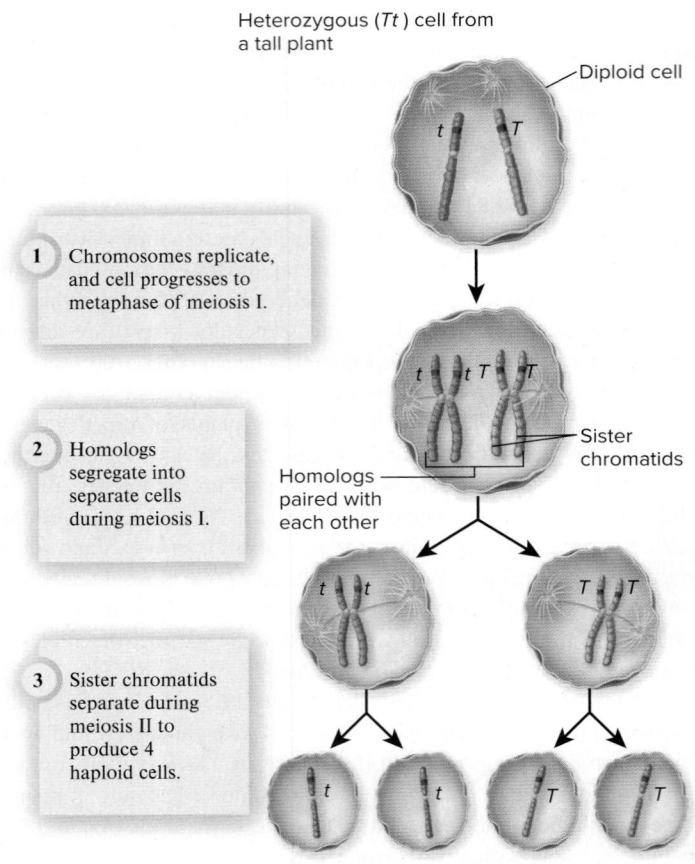

Heterozygous (*Tt*) cell from a tall plant

Diploid cell

1 Chromosomes replicate, and cell progresses to metaphase of meiosis I.

2 Homologs segregate into separate cells during meiosis I.

Sister chromatids

Homologs paired with each other

3 Sister chromatids separate during meiosis II to produce 4 haploid cells.

Four haploid cells

Figure 17.10 The chromosomal basis of allele segregation. This example shows a pair of homologous chromosomes in a cell of a pea plant. The blue chromosome was inherited from the male parent, and the red chromosome was inherited from the female parent. This individual is heterozygous (*Tt*) for a height gene. The two homologs segregate from each other during meiosis, leading to segregation of the tall allele (*T*) and the dwarf allele (*t*) into different haploid cells. Note: For simplicity, this diagram shows a single pair of homologous chromosomes, though eukaryotic cells typically have several different pairs of homologous chromosomes.

 Core Skill: Connections When we say that alleles segregate, what does the word segregate mean? How is this related to meiosis, shown in Figure 16.13?

If the haploid cells shown at the bottom of Figure 17.10 give rise to gametes that combine randomly during fertilization, they produce diploid offspring with the genotype and phenotype ratios shown earlier in Figure 17.6.

Mendel's Law of Independent Assortment Is Explained by the Independent Alignment of Different Chromosomes During Meiosis

How can we relate the chromosome theory of inheritance to Mendel's law of independent assortment? **Figure 17.11** shows the alignment and segregation of two pairs of chromosomes in a pea plant. One pair carries the gene for seed color: The yellow allele (*Y*) is on one chromosome, and the green allele (*y*) is on its homolog. The other

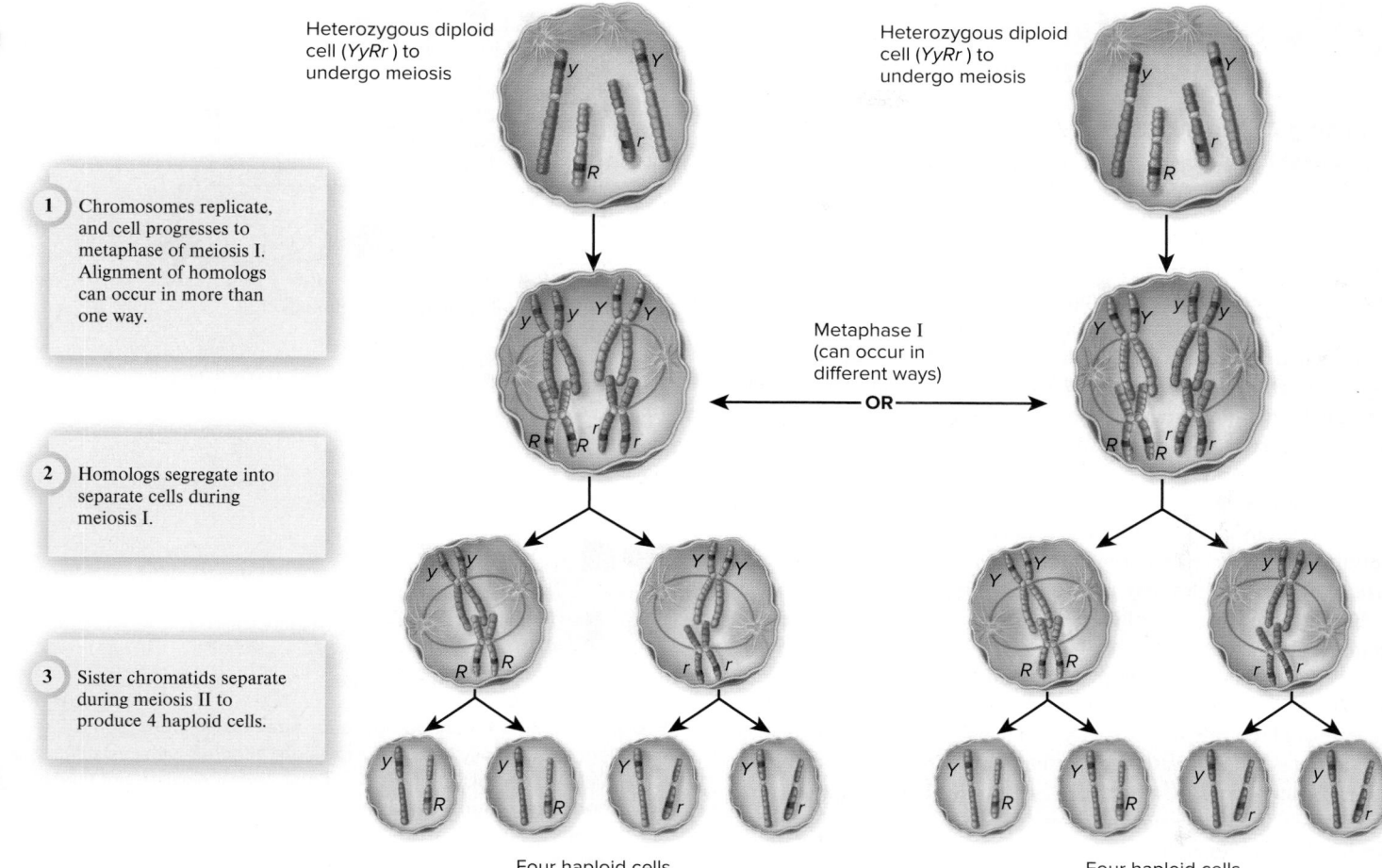

Heterozygous diploid cell (*YyRr*) to undergo meiosis

Heterozygous diploid cell (*YyRr*) to undergo meiosis

1 Chromosomes replicate, and cell progresses to metaphase of meiosis I. Alignment of homologs can occur in more than one way.

Metaphase I (can occur in different ways)

— **OR** —

2 Homologs segregate into separate cells during meiosis I.

3 Sister chromatids separate during meiosis II to produce 4 haploid cells.

Four haploid cells

Four haploid cells

Figure 17.11 The chromosomal basis of independent assortment. The alleles for seed color (*Y* or *y*) and seed shape (*R* or *r*) in peas are on different chromosomes. During metaphase of meiosis I, different arrangements of the two chromosome pairs lead to different combinations of the alleles in the resulting haploid cells. On the left, the chromosome carrying the recessive y allele has segregated with the chromosome carrying the dominant *R* allele. On the right, the two chromosomes carrying the dominant alleles (*Y* and *R*) have segregated together. Note: For simplicity, this diagram shows only two pairs of homologous chromosomes, though eukaryotic cells typically have several different pairs of homologous chromosomes.

Concept Check: *Let's suppose that a cell is heterozygous for three different genes (Aa, Bb, and Cc) and that each gene is on a different chromosome. How many different ways can the three pairs of homologous chromosomes align themselves during metaphase I, and how many different types of gametes can be produced?*

pair of chromosomes carries the gene for seed shape: One member of the pair has the round allele (*R*), whereas its homolog carries the wrinkled allele (*r*). Therefore, this individual is heterozygous for both genes, with the genotype *YyRr*.

When meiosis begins, the DNA in each chromosome has already replicated, producing two sister chromatids. At metaphase I of meiosis, the two pairs of chromosomes randomly align themselves along the metaphase plate. This alignment can occur in two equally probable ways, shown on the two sides of the figure. On the left, the chromosome carrying the *y* allele is aligned on the same side of the metaphase plate as the chromosome carrying the *R* allele; *Y* is aligned with *r*. On the right, the opposite has occurred: *Y* is aligned with *R*, and *y* is with *r*. In each case, the chromosomes that aligned on the same side of the metaphase plate segregate into the same daughter cell. In this way, the random alignment of chromosome pairs during meiosis I

leads to the independent assortment of alleles found on different chromosomes. For two genes found on different chromosomes, each with two variant alleles, meiosis produces four allele combinations in equal numbers (*yR*, *Yr*, *YR*, and *yr*), as seen at the bottom of the figure.

If a *YyRr* (dihybrid) plant undergoes self-fertilization, any two gametes can combine randomly during fertilization. Because four kinds of gametes are made, 4^2, or 16, possible allele combinations are possible in the offspring. These genotypes, in turn, produce four phenotypes in a 9:3:3:1 ratio, as seen earlier in Figure 17.8. This ratio is the expected outcome when a heterozygote for two genes on different chromosomes undergoes self-fertilization.

But what if two different genes are located on the same chromosome? In this case, the transmission pattern may not conform to the law of independent assortment. We will discuss this phenomenon, known as linkage, in Chapter 18.

17.3   Pedigree Analysis of Human Traits

Learning Outcomes:

1. **CoreSKILL »** Apply pedigree analysis to deduce inheritance patterns in humans.
2. Distinguish between recessively inherited disorders and dominantly inherited disorders.

As we have seen, Mendel conducted experiments by making selective crosses of pea plants and analyzing large numbers of offspring. Later geneticists also relied on crosses of experimental organisms, especially fruit flies (*Drosophila melanogaster*). However, geneticists studying human traits cannot use this approach, for ethical and practical reasons. Instead, human geneticists must rely on information from family trees, or pedigrees. In this approach, called **pedigree analysis**, an inherited trait is analyzed over the course of a few generations in one family. The results of this method may be less definitive than the results of breeding experiments because the small size of human families may lead to large sampling errors. Nevertheless, a pedigree analysis often provides important clues concerning human inheritance.

Pedigree analysis has been used to understand the inheritance of human genetic diseases that follow simple Mendelian patterns. Many genes that play a role in disease exist in two forms: the common allele and a rare allele that has arisen by mutation. The disease symptoms are associated with the mutant allele. Pedigree analysis allows us to determine whether the mutant allele is dominant or recessive and to predict the likelihood of an individual being affected.

Let's consider a recessive condition to illustrate pedigree analysis. The pedigree in **Figure 17.12** concerns a human genetic disease known as cystic fibrosis (CF), which involves a mutation in a gene that encodes the cystic fibrosis transmembrane regulator (the *CFTR* gene, also see Figure 1.15). Approximately 3% of Americans of European descent are heterozygous carriers of the recessive (disease-causing) *CFTR* allele. Individuals who are homozygous for this allele exhibit the disease symptoms, which include abnormalities of the lungs, pancreas, intestine, and sweat glands. A human pedigree, like the one in Figure 17.12, shows the oldest generation (designated by the Roman numeral I) at the top, with later generations (II and III) below it. A male (represented by a square) and a female (represented by a circle) who produce offspring are connected by a horizontal line; a vertical line connects parents with their offspring. Siblings (brothers and sisters) are placed on downward projections from a single horizontal line, from left to right in the order of their birth. For example, individuals I-1 and I-2 are the parents of individuals II-2, II-3, and II-4, who are all siblings. Individuals affected by the disease, such as individual II-3, are depicted by filled symbols.

Why does this pedigree indicate a recessive pattern of inheritance for CF? The answer is that two unaffected individuals can produce an affected offspring. Such individuals are presumed to be heterozygotes (designated by a half-filled symbol). However, the same unaffected parents can also produce unaffected offspring (depicted by an unfilled symbol), because an individual must inherit two copies of the mutant allele to exhibit the disease. A recessive

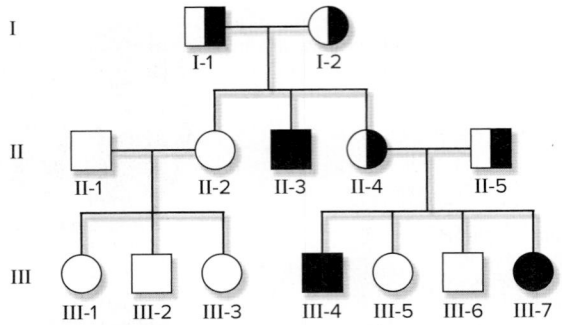

(a) Human pedigree showing cystic fibrosis

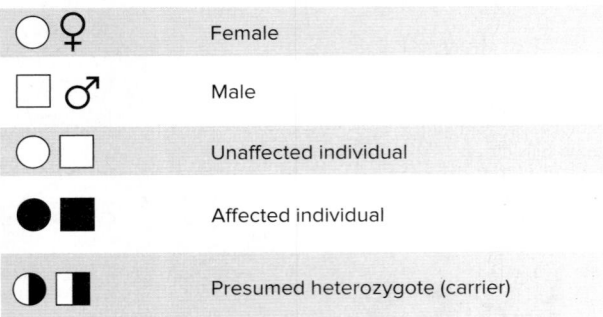

(b) Symbols used in a human pedigree

Figure 17.12   A family pedigree for a recessive trait. Some members of the family in this pedigree are affected with cystic fibrosis. Individuals I-1, I-2, II-4, and II-5 do not have cystic fibrosis, but they are presumed to be heterozygotes (carriers) because they have produced affected offspring.

Concept Check: *Let's suppose a genetic disease is caused by a mutant allele. If two affected parents produce an unaffected offspring, can the mutant allele be recessive?*

mode of inheritance is also indicated by the observation that all of the offspring of two affected individuals are affected themselves. However, for genetic diseases that limit survival or fertility, there are rarely if ever cases where two affected individuals produce offspring.

Although many of the alleles causing human genetic diseases are recessive, some are known to be dominant. Let's consider Huntington disease, a condition that causes the degeneration of brain cells involved in emotions, intellect, and movement. The symptoms of Huntington disease, which usually begin to appear when people are 30 to 50 years old, include uncontrollable jerking movements of the limbs, trunk, and face; progressive loss of mental abilities; and the development of psychiatric problems. If you examine the pedigree shown in **Figure 17.13**, you will see that every affected individual has one affected parent. This pattern is characteristic of most dominant disorders. However, affected parents do not always produce affected offspring. For example, II-6 is a heterozygote that has passed the nondisease-causing allele to his offspring, thereby producing unaffected offspring (III-3 and III-4).

Most human genes are found on the paired chromosomes known as **autosomes**, which are the same in both sexes. Mendelian inheritance patterns involving these autosomal genes are described as autosomal inheritance patterns. Huntington disease is an example of a

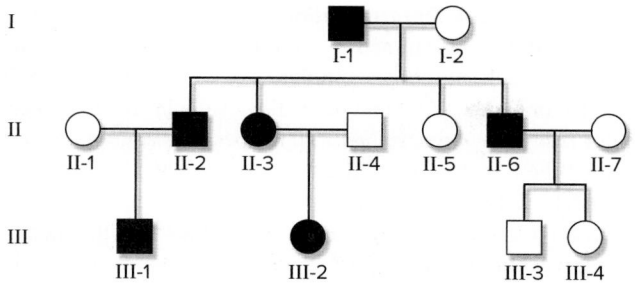

Figure 17.13 A family pedigree for a dominant trait. Huntington disease is caused by a dominant allele.

Concept Check: *What observation in a pedigree suggests a dominant pattern of inheritance?*

trait with an autosomal dominant inheritance pattern, whereas cystic fibrosis displays an autosomal recessive pattern. However, some human genes are located on sex chromosomes, which are different in males and females. These genes have their own characteristic inheritance patterns, which we will consider next.

17.4 Sex Chromosomes and X-Linked Inheritance Patterns

Learning Outcomes:

1. Describe different systems of sex determination in animals and plants.
2. **CoreSKILL »** Predict the outcome of crosses when genes are located on sex chromosomes.
3. Explain why X-linked recessive traits are more likely to occur in males.

Earlier in this chapter, we discussed Mendel's experiments that established the basis for understanding how traits are transmitted from parents to offspring. We also examined the chromosome theory of inheritance, which provided a framework for explaining Mendel's observations. Mendelian patterns of gene transmission are observed for most genes located on autosomes in a wide variety of eukaryotic species.

We will now turn our attention to genes located on **sex chromosomes**. This term refers to a distinctive pair of chromosomes that are different in males and females and that determine the sex of the individuals. Sex chromosomes are found in many but not all species with two sexes. The study of sex chromosomes proved pivotal in confirming the chromosome theory of inheritance. The distinctive transmission patterns of genes on sex chromosomes helped early geneticists show that particular genes are located on particular chromosomes. Later, other researchers became interested in these genes because some of them were found to cause inherited disorders in humans.

In this section, we will consider a few mechanisms by which sex chromosomes in various species determine an individual's sex. We

will then explore the inheritance patterns of genes on sex chromosomes and see that recessive alleles are expressed more frequently in males than in females. Last, we will examine some of the early research involving sex chromosomes that provided convincing evidence for the chromosome theory of inheritance.

In Many Species, Sex Differences Are Due to the Presence of Sex Chromosomes

Some early evidence supporting the chromosome theory of inheritance involved a consideration of sex determination. In 1901, American biologist C. E. McClung suggested that the inheritance of particular chromosomes is responsible for determining sex in fruit flies. Following McClung's initial observations, several mechanisms of sex determination were found in different species of animals. Some examples are described in **Figure 17.14**. All of these mechanisms involve chromosomal differences between the sexes, and most involve a difference in a single pair of sex chromosomes.

X-Y System In the X-Y system of sex determination, which operates in mammals, the somatic cells of males have one X and one Y chromosome, whereas female somatic cells contain two X chromosomes (Figure 17.14a). For example, the 46 chromosomes carried by human cells consist of 22 pairs of autosomes and one pair of sex chromosomes (either XY or XX). Which chromosome, the X or Y, determines sex? In mammals, the presence of the Y chromosome causes maleness. This is known from the analysis of rare individuals who carry chromosomal abnormalities. For example, mistakes that occasionally occur during meiosis may produce an individual who carries two X chromosomes and one Y chromosome. Such an individual develops into a male. A gene called the *SRY* gene located on the Y chromosome of mammals plays a key role in the developmental pathway that leads to maleness.

X-O System The X-O system operates in many insects (Figure 17.14b). Unlike the X-Y system in mammals, the presence of the Y chromosome in the X-O system does not determine maleness. Females in this system have a pair of sex chromosomes and are designated XX. In some insect species that follow the X-O system, the male has only one sex chromosome, the X. In other X-O insect species, such as *Drosophila melanogaster*, the male has both an X chromosome and a Y chromosome. In all cases, an insect's sex is determined by the ratio between its X chromosomes and its sets of autosomes. If a fly has one X chromosome and is diploid for the autosomes ($2n$), this ratio is 1/2, or 0.5. This fly will become a male whether or not it receives a Y chromosome. On the other hand, if a diploid fly receives two X chromosomes, the ratio is 2/2, or 1.0, and the fly becomes a female.

Z-W System Thus far, we have considered examples where females have two similar copies of a sex chromosome, the X. However, in other animal species, such as birds and some fish, the male carries two similar chromosomes (Figure 17.14c). This is called the Z-W system to distinguish it from the X-Y system found in mammals. The male is ZZ, and the female is ZW.

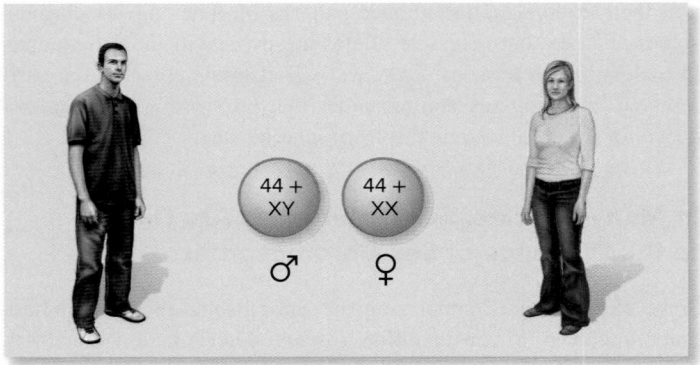

(a) The X-Y system in mammals

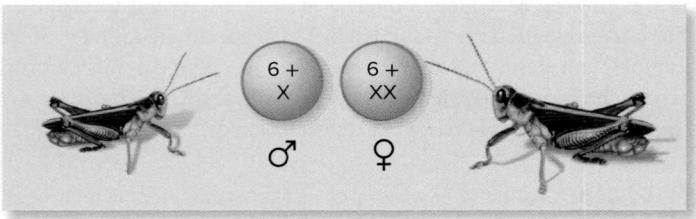

(b) The X-O system in certain insects

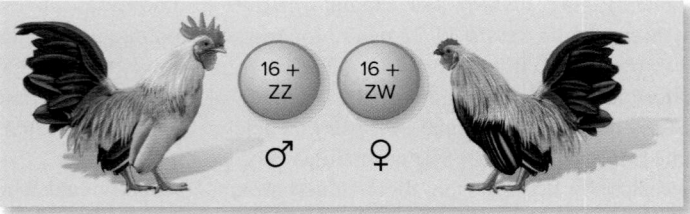

(c) The Z-W system in birds

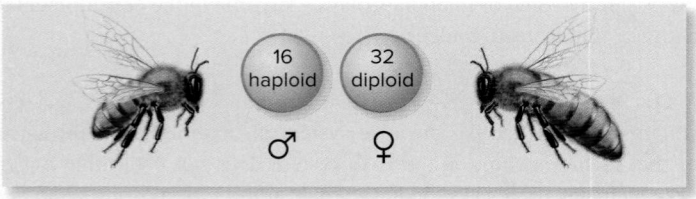

(d) The haplodiploid system in bees

Figure 17.14 Different mechanisms of sex determination in animals. The numbers shown in the circles indicate the numbers of autosomes.

Concept Check: *If a person is born with only one X chromosome and no Y chromosome, would you expect that person to be a male or a female? Explain your answer.*

Haplodiploid System   Not all chromosomal mechanisms of sex determination involve a special pair of sex chromosomes. An interesting mechanism known as the haplodiploid system is found in bees (Figure 17.14d). The male bee, or drone, is produced from an unfertilized haploid egg. Therefore, male bees are haploid individuals. Females, both worker bees and queen bees, are produced from fertilized eggs and are diploid.

Environmental Sex Determination   Although sex in many species of animals is determined by chromosomes, other mechanisms are known. In certain reptiles and fish, sex is controlled by environmental factors such as temperature. For example, in the American alligator (*Alligator mississippiensis*), temperature controls sex development. When eggs of this alligator are incubated at 33°C, nearly all of them produce male individuals. When the eggs are incubated at a temperature significantly below 33°C, they produce nearly all females, whereas increasing percentages of females are produced above 34°C.

Sex Determination in Plants   Most species of flowering plants, including pea plants, have a single type of diploid plant, or sporophyte, that makes both male and female gametophytes. However, the sporophytes of some species have two sexually distinct types of individuals, one with flowers that produce male gametophytes, and the other with flowers that produce female gametophytes. Examples include hollies, willows, poplars, and date palms. Sex chromosomes, designated X and Y, are responsible for sex determination in many such species. The male plant is XY, whereas the female plant is XX. However, in some plant species with separate sexes, microscopic examination of the chromosomes does not reveal distinct types of sex chromosomes.

In Humans, Recessive X-Linked Traits Are More Likely to Occur in Males

In humans, the X chromosome is rather large and carries over 1,000 genes, whereas the Y chromosome is quite small and has less than 100 genes. Therefore, many genes are found on the X chromosome but not on the Y; these are known as **X-linked genes**. By comparison, fewer genes are known to be Y-linked, meaning they are found on the Y chromosome but not on the X. **Sex-linked genes** are found on one sex chromosome but not on the other. Because fewer genes are found on the Y chromosome, the term usually refers to X-linked genes. In mammals, a male cannot be described as being homozygous or heterozygous for an X-linked gene, because these terms apply to genes that are present in two copies. Instead, the term **hemizygous** is used to describe an individual with only one copy of a particular gene. A male mammal is said to be hemizygous for an X-linked gene.

Many recessive X-linked alleles cause diseases in humans, and these diseases occur more frequently in males than in females. An example is the X-linked recessive disorder called classical hemophilia (hemophilia A). In individuals with hemophilia, blood does not clot properly, and a minor cut may bleed for a long time. Common accidental injuries that are minor in most people pose a threat of severe internal or external bleeding for hemophiliacs. Hemophilia A is caused by a recessive X-linked allele that encodes a defective form of a clotting protein. If a mother is a heterozygous carrier of hemophilia A, each of her children has a 50% chance of inheriting the recessive allele. The following Punnett square shows a cross between an unaffected father and a heterozygous mother. X^H designates an X chromosome carrying the dominant functional allele, and X^{h-A} is the X chromosome that carries the recessive nonfunctional allele for hemophilia A.

Although each child has a 50% chance of inheriting the hemophilia allele from the mother, only 1/2 of the sons will exhibit the disorder. Because a son inherits only one X chromosome, a son who inherits the recessive (disease-causing) allele from his mother will have hemophilia. However, a daughter inherits an X chromosome from both her mother and her father. In this example, a daughter who inherits the recessive allele from her mother also inherits a dominant allele from her father. This daughter will not have hemophilia, but if she passes the recessive allele to a son, he will have hemophilia.

👁 **Core Skill: Process of Science**

Feature Investigation | Morgan's Experiments Showed a Correlation Between a Genetic Trait and the Inheritance of a Sex Chromosome in *Drosophila*

The distinctive inheritance pattern of X-linked alleles provides a way of demonstrating that a specific gene is on an X chromosome. An X-linked gene was the first gene to be located on a specific chromosome. In 1910, American geneticist Thomas Hunt Morgan began work on a project in which he reared large populations of fruit flies, *Drosophila melanogaster*, in the dark to determine if their eyes would atrophy from disuse and disappear in future generations. Even after many consecutive generations, the flies showed no noticeable changes. After 2 years of looking at many flies, Morgan happened to discover a male fly with white eyes rather than red,

which is the common (wild-type) color. The white-eye trait must have arisen from a new mutation that converted a red-eye allele into a white-eye allele.

To study the inheritance of the white-eye trait, Morgan followed an approach similar to Mendel's in which he made crosses and quantitatively analyzed their outcome. In the experiment described in **Figure 17.15**, Morgan crossed his white-eyed male to a red-eyed female. All of the F₁ offspring had red eyes, indicating that red is dominant to white. The F₁ offspring were then mated to each other to obtain an F₂ generation. As seen in the data table, this cross

Figure 17.15 Morgan's crosses of red-eyed and white-eyed *Drosophila*.

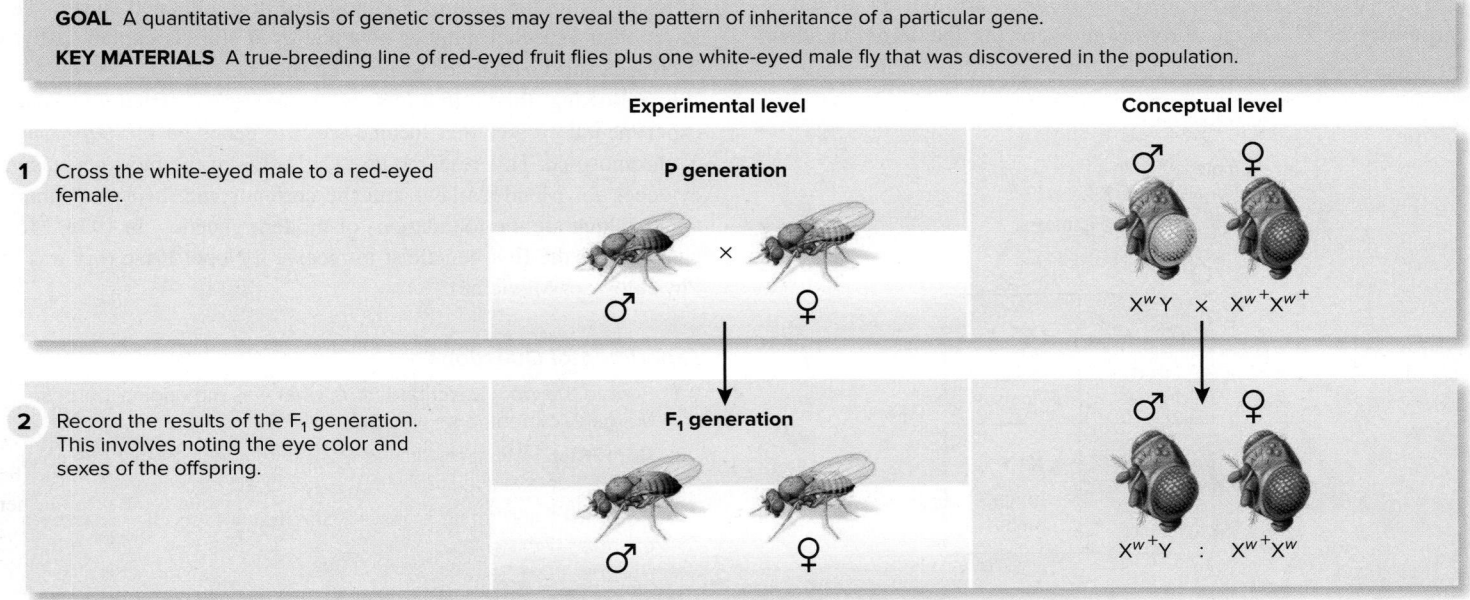

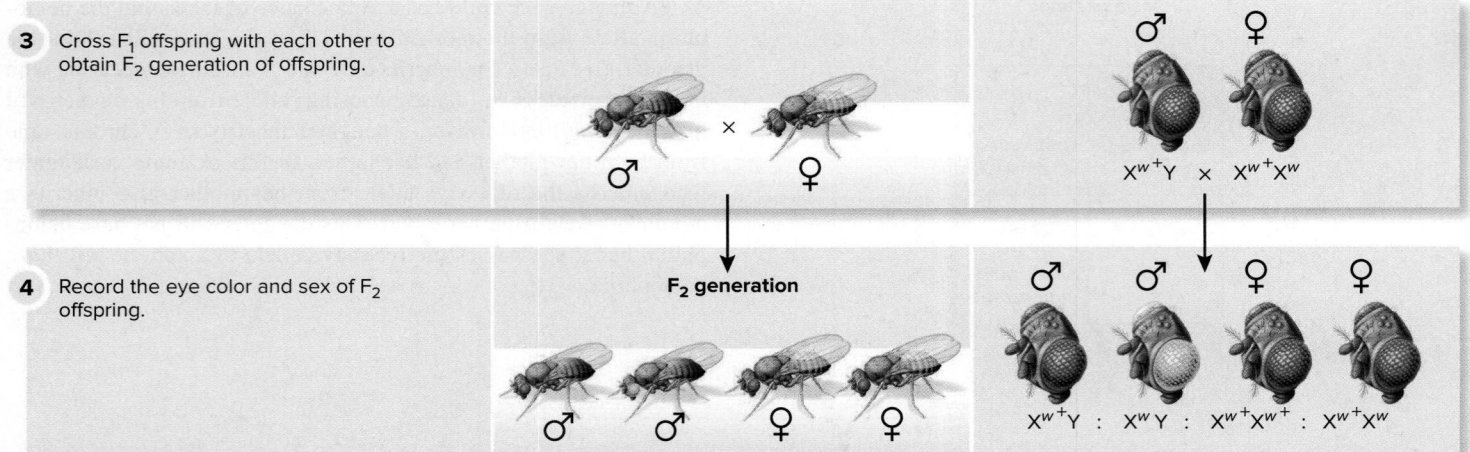

3 Cross F₁ offspring with each other to obtain F₂ generation of offspring.

4 Record the eye color and sex of F₂ offspring.

F₂ generation

$X^{w^+}Y \times X^{w^+}X^w$

$X^{w^+}Y : X^wY : X^{w^+}X^{w^+} : X^{w^+}X^w$

5 **THE DATA**

Cross	Results	
Original white-eyed male to a red-eyed female	F₁ generation	All red-eyed flies
F₁ males to F₁ females	F₂ generation	1,011 red-eyed males 782 white-eyed males 2,459 red-eyed females 0 white-eyed females

6 **CONCLUSION** The data are consistent with an inheritance pattern in which an eye-color gene is located on the X chromosome.

7 **SOURCE** Morgan, T. H. 1910. Sex limited inheritance in *Drosophila*. *Science* 32: 120–122.

produced 1,011 red-eyed males, 782 white-eyed males, and 2,459 red-eyed females. Surprisingly, no white-eyed females were observed in the F₂ generation.

How did Morgan interpret these results? The results suggested a connection between the alleles for eye color and the sex of the offspring. As shown in the conceptual column of Figure 17.15 and in the following Punnett square, his data were consistent with the idea that the eye-color alleles in *Drosophila* are located on the X chromosome. X^{w^+} is the chromosome carrying the common allele

for red eyes, and X^w is the chromosome with the mutant allele for white eyes.

The Punnett square predicts that the F₂ generation will not have any white-eyed females. This prediction was confirmed by Morgan's experimental data. However, it should also be pointed out that the experimental ratio of red eyes to white eyes in the F₂ generation is (2,459 + 1,011) : 782, which equals 4.4 : 1. This ratio deviates significantly from the ratio of 3:1 predicted in the Punnett square. The lower than expected number of white-eyed flies is explained by a decreased survival rate for white-eyed flies.

Following this initial discovery, Morgan carried out many experimental crosses that located specific genes on the *Drosophila* X chromosome. This research provided some of the most persuasive evidence for Mendel's laws and the chromosome theory of inheritance, which are the foundations of modern genetics. In 1933, Morgan became the first geneticist to receive a Nobel Prize (his was in Physiology or Medicine).

Experimental Questions

1. Prior to the work described here, what was the original purpose of Morgan's experiments with *Drosophila*?

2. **CoreSKILL »** What results led Morgan to conclude that eye color in fruit flies is associated with the sex of the individual?

3. **CoreSKILL »** What crosses between fruit flies could yield female offspring with white eyes?

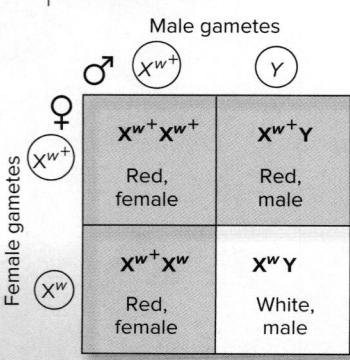

F₁ male is $X^{w^+}Y$
F₁ female is $X^{w^+}X^w$

Male gametes

♂ X^{w^+} | Y

♀ Female gametes

X^{w^+} | $X^{w^+}X^{w^+}$ Red, female | $X^{w^+}Y$ Red, male

X^w | $X^{w^+}X^w$ Red, female | X^wY White, male

17.5 ## Variations in Inheritance Patterns and Their Molecular Basis

Learning Outcomes:

1. Relate dominant and recessive traits to protein function.
2. Define pleiotropy, and explain why it occurs.
3. **CoreSKILL »** Predict the outcomes of crosses that exhibit incomplete dominance and codominance.
4. Discuss how the environment plays a critical role in determining the expression of traits.

The term **Mendelian inheritance** describes the inheritance patterns of genes that segregate and assort independently. In the first section of this chapter, we considered the inheritance pattern of traits affected by a single gene that is found in two variants, one of which is dominant over the other. This pattern is called **simple Mendelian inheritance**, because the phenotype ratios in the offspring clearly demonstrate Mendel's laws. We will begin this section by discussing the molecular basis of dominant and recessive traits and see how the molecular expression of a gene can have widespread effects on an organism's phenotype. In addition, we will examine the inheritance patterns of genes that segregate and assort independently but do not display a simple dominant/recessive relationship. The transmission of these genes from parents to offspring does not usually produce the ratios of phenotypes we would expect on the basis of Mendel's observations. This does not mean that Mendel was wrong. Rather, the inheritance patterns of many traits are different from the simple patterns he chose to study. In this section, we will explore these variations in Mendelian inheritance.

Protein Function Explains the Phenomenon of Dominance

As described at the beginning of this chapter, Mendel studied seven characters that were found in two variants each (see Figure 17.2). The dominant variants are caused by the common alleles for these traits in pea plants. For any given gene, geneticists refer to a prevalent allele in a population as a **wild-type allele**. In most cases, a wild-type allele encodes a protein that is made in the proper amount and functions properly. By comparison, alleles that have been altered by mutation are called **mutant alleles**; these tend to be rare in natural populations. In the case of Mendel's seven characters in pea plants, the recessive alleles are due to rare mutations.

How do we explain why one allele is dominant and another allele is recessive? By studying genes and their gene products at the molecular level, researchers have discovered that a recessive allele is often defective in its ability to express a functional protein. In other words, mutations that produce recessive alleles are likely to decrease or eliminate the synthesis or functional activity of a protein. These are called loss-of-function alleles. To understand why many loss-of-function alleles are recessive, we need to take a quantitative look at protein function.

In a simple dominant/recessive relationship, the recessive allele does not affect the phenotype of the heterozygote. In this type of relationship, a single copy of the dominant (wild-type) allele is sufficient to mask the effects of the recessive allele. How do we explain the dominant phenotype of the heterozygote? **Figure 17.16** considers the example of flower color in a pea plant. The gene encodes an enzyme (protein P) that is needed to convert a colorless molecule into a purple pigment. The *P* allele is dominant because one *P* allele encodes enough of the functional protein—50% of the amount found in a *PP* homozygote—to provide a purple phenotype. Therefore, the *PP* homozygote and the *Pp* heterozygote both make enough of the purple pigment to yield purple flowers. The *pp* homozygote cannot make any of the functional protein required for pigment synthesis, so its flowers are white.

This explanation—that 50% of the functional protein is enough—is true for many dominant alleles. In such cases, the homozygote with two dominant alleles is making much more of the protein than necessary, so if the amount is reduced to 50%, as it is in the heterozygote, the individual still has plenty of this protein to accomplish whatever cellular function it performs. In other cases, however, an allele may be dominant because the heterozygote actually produces more than 50% of the functional protein. This increased production is due to the phenomenon of gene regulation. The dominant allele is up-regulated in the heterozygote to compensate for the lack of function of the recessive allele.

Genotype	*PP*	*Pp*	*pp*
Amount of functional protein P produced	100%	50%	0%
Phenotype	**Purple**	**Purple**	**White**

Only 50% of the functional protein is needed to produce the purple phenotype

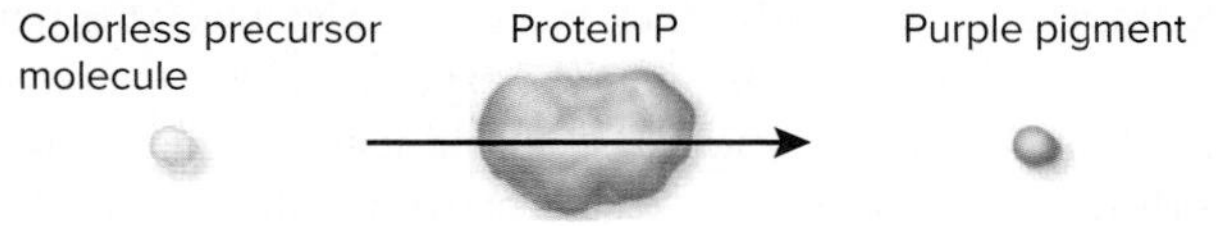

Colorless precursor molecule   Protein P   Purple pigment

Figure 17.16 How genes give rise to traits during simple Mendelian inheritance. In the heterozygote, the amount of protein encoded by a single dominant allele is sufficient to produce the dominant phenotype. In this example, the gene encodes an enzyme that is needed to produce a purple pigment. A plant with one or two copies of the dominant allele makes enough pigment to produce purple flowers. In a *pp* homozygote, the complete lack of functional protein (enzyme) results in white flowers.

Core Skill: Quantitative Reasoning In a simple dominant/recessive relationship, even though the heterozygote may produce less of a functional protein compared to the homozygote that has two copies of the dominant allele, the amount made by the heterozygote is sufficient to yield the dominant phenotype.

The Expression of a Single Gene Often Has Multiple Effects on Phenotype

By studying mutations in humans and model organisms, researchers have discovered that genes usually exhibit **pleiotropy**, which means that a mutation in a single gene can have multiple effects on an individual's phenotype. Pleiotropy occurs for several reasons, including the following:

1. The expression of a single gene can affect cell function in more than one way. For example, a defect in a microtubule protein may affect cell division and cell movement.

2. A gene may be expressed in different cell types in a multicellular organism.

3. A gene may be expressed at different stages of development.

In this genetics unit, we tend to discuss genes as they affect a single trait. This educational approach allows us to appreciate how genes function and how they are transmitted from parents to offspring. However, in all or nearly all cases, the expression of a gene is pleiotropic with regard to the characteristics of an organism. The expression of any given gene influences the expression of many other genes in the genome, and vice versa. Pleiotropy is revealed when researchers study the effects of gene mutations.

As an example of a pleiotropic effect, let's consider cystic fibrosis (CF), which we discussed earlier as an example of a recessive human disorder (see Figure 17.12). In the late 1980s, the gene for CF was identified. The gene encodes a protein called the cystic fibrosis transmembrane regulator (CFTR), which regulates ion balance by allowing the transport of chloride ions (Cl^-) across cell membranes. The mutation that causes CF diminishes the function of this Cl^- transporter, affecting several parts of the body in different ways. Because the movement of Cl^- affects water transport across membranes, the most severe symptom of CF is the production of thick mucus in the lungs, which occurs because of a water imbalance. Similarly, thick mucus can also block the tubes that carry digestive enzymes from the pancreas to the small intestine. Without these enzymes, certain nutrients are not properly absorbed into the body. As a result, persons with CF may show poor weight gain. Another effect is seen in the sweat glands. The Cl^- transporter has the function of recycling salt out of the glands and back into the skin before it can be lost to the outside world. Persons with CF have excessively salty sweat due to their inability to recycle salt back into their skin cells. A common test for CF is the measurement of salt on the skin. Taken together, we can see that a defect in CFTR has multiple effects throughout the body.

Incomplete Dominance Results in an Intermediate Phenotype

We will now turn our attention to examples in which the alleles for a given gene do not show a simple dominant/recessive relationship. In some cases, a heterozygote that carries two different alleles exhibits a phenotype that is intermediate between those of the

corresponding homozygous individuals. This phenomenon is known as **incomplete dominance**.

In 1905, Carl Correns discovered this pattern of inheritance for alleles affecting flower color in the four-o'clock plant (*Mirabilis jalapa*). **Figure 17.17** shows a cross between two four-o'clock plants: a red-flowered homozygote and a white-flowered homozygote. The allele for red flower color is designated C^R, and the white allele is C^W. These alleles are designated with superscripts rather than upper- and lowercase letters because neither allele is dominant. The offspring of this cross have pink flowers—they are $C^R C^W$ heterozygotes with an intermediate phenotype. If these F_1 offspring are allowed to self-fertilize, the F_2 generation has 1/4 red-flowered plants, 1/2 pink-flowered plants, and 1/4 white-flowered plants. This is a 1:2:1 phenotype ratio rather than the 3:1 ratio observed for simple Mendelian inheritance. What is the molecular explanation for this ratio? In this

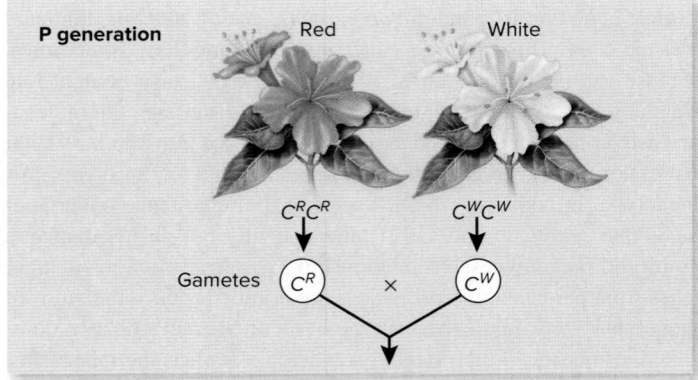

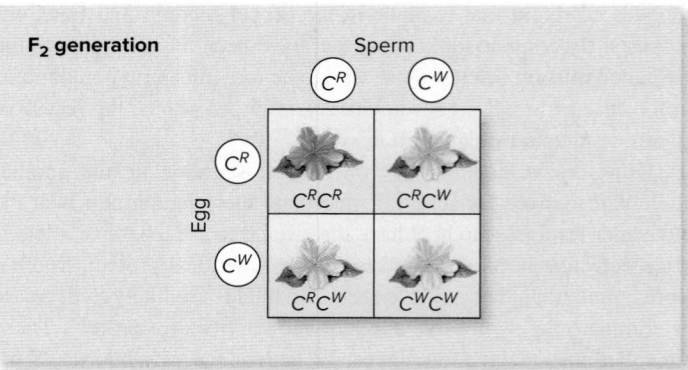

Figure 17.17 Incomplete dominance in the four-o'clock plant. When red-flowered and white-flowered homozygotes ($C^R C^R$ and $C^W C^W$) are crossed, the resulting heterozygote ($C^R C^W$) has an intermediate phenotype of pink flowers.

case, the red allele encodes a functional protein needed to produce a red pigment, whereas the white allele is a mutant allele that is non-functional. In the $C^R C^W$ heterozygote, 50% of the protein encoded by the C^R allele is not sufficient to produce the red-flower phenotype, but it does provide enough pigment to give pink flowers.

ABO Blood Types Provide an Example of Multiple Alleles and Codominance

Although diploid individuals have only two copies of most genes, the majority of genes have three or more variants in natural populations. We describe such genes as occurring in **multiple alleles**. Particular phenotypes depend on which two alleles each individual inherits. ABO blood types in humans are an example of phenotypes produced by multiple alleles.

As shown in **Table 17.2**, human red blood cells have structures on their plasma membrane known as surface antigens, which are constructed from several sugar molecules that are connected to form a carbohydrate tree. The carbohydrate tree is attached to a lipid or membrane protein to form a glycolipid or a glycoprotein, respectively. As noted in Chapter 5, glycolipids and glycoproteins often play a role in cell surface recognition.

Antigens are substances (in this case, carbohydrates) that may be recognized as foreign material when introduced into the body of an animal. Let's consider two types of surface antigens, known as A and B, which may be found on red blood cells. The synthesis of these antigens is determined by enzymes that are encoded by a gene that exists in three alleles, designated I^A, I^B, and i, respectively. The i allele is recessive to both I^A and I^B. A person who is ii homozygous does not produce surface antigen A or B and has blood type O. The red blood cells of an $I^A I^A$ homozygous or $I^A i$ heterozygous

individual have surface antigen A (blood type A). Similarly, a homozygous $I^B I^B$ or heterozygous $I^B i$ individual produces surface antigen B (blood type B). A person who is $I^A I^B$ heterozygous makes both antigens, A and B, on every red blood cell (blood type AB). The phenomenon in which a single individual expresses two alleles is called **codominance**.

What is the molecular explanation for codominance? Biochemists have analyzed the carbohydrate tree produced in people of differing blood types. The differences are shown schematically in Table 17.2. In type O, the carbohydrate tree is smaller than in type A or type B because a sugar has not been attached to a specific site on the tree. People with blood type O have a loss-of-function mutation in the gene that encodes the enzyme that attaches a sugar at this site. This enzyme, called a glycosyl transferase, is inactive in type O individuals. In contrast, the type A and type B antigens have sugars attached to this site, but each of them has a different sugar. This difference occurs because the enzymes encoded by the I^A allele and the I^B allele have slightly different active sites. As a result, the enzyme encoded by the I^A allele attaches a sugar called N-acetylgalactosamine to the carbohydrate tree, whereas the enzyme encoded by the I^B allele attaches galactose. N-Acetylgalactosamine is represented by an orange hexagon in Table 17.2, and galactose by a green triangle.

The Environment Plays a Vital Role in the Making of a Phenotype

In this chapter, we have been mainly concerned with the effects of genes on phenotypes. In addition, phenotypes are shaped by an organism's environment. An organism cannot exist without its genes or without an environment in which to live. Both are indispensable for life. An organism's genotype provides the plan to create a phenotype,

Table 17.2	The ABO Blood Group			
		Antigen A	Antigen B	Antigen A Antigen B
		N-Acetyl-galactosamine	Galactose	
Blood type:	O	A	B	AB
Genotype:	ii	$I^A I^A$ or $I^A i$	$I^B I^B$ or $I^B i$	$I^A I^B$
Surface antigen:	Neither A nor B	A	B	A and B
Antibodies:	Against A and B	Against B	Against A	None

Core Skill: Modeling The goal of this modeling challenge is to create a pair of models that depict the key difference between the forms of glycosyl transferase encoded by the I^A and I^B alleles.

Modeling Challenge: Glycosyl transferase is an enzyme that recognizes the structure of a carbohydrate tree on the surface of a cell and attaches an additional sugar to that tree. Based on the schematic drawings of carbohydrate trees in Table 17.2, draw a pair of models that highlight the key difference between the glycosyl transferase encoded by the I^A allele and that encoded by the I^B allele. Before drawing your models, refer back to Figure 6.6, which shows a model for a different enzyme, called hexokinase, and use that style for your models for glycosyl transferase.

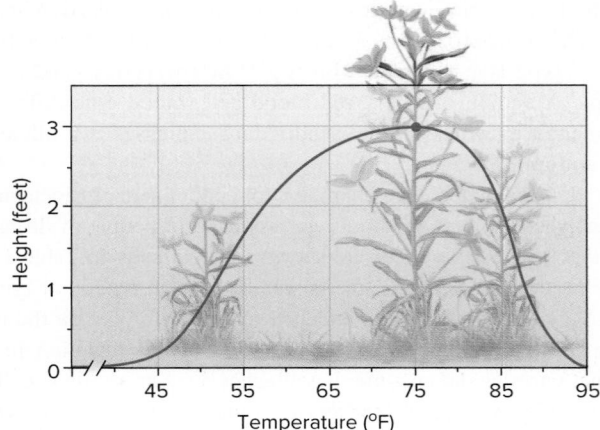

Figure 17.18 **The norm of reaction.** The norm of reaction is the range of phenotypes that a population of organisms with a particular genotype exhibit under different environmental conditions. In this example, genetically identical plants were grown at different temperatures in a greenhouse and then measured for height.

Concept Check: *Could you study the norm of reaction in a wild population of squirrels?*

and the environment provides nutrients and energy so that plan can be executed.

The **norm of reaction** is the phenotype range that individuals with a particular genotype exhibit under differing environmental conditions. To evaluate the norm of reaction, researchers study members of true-breeding strains that have the same genotypes and subject them to different environmental conditions. For example, **Figure 17.18** shows the norm of reaction for genetically identical plants raised at different temperatures. As shown in the figure, these plants attain a maximal height when raised at 75°F. At 50°F and 85°F, the plants are substantially shorter. Growth cannot occur below 40°F or above 95°F.

17.6 Gene Interaction

Learning Outcomes:

1. Describe how the alleles of one gene can mask or be epistatic to the alleles of a different gene.
2. Explain why polygenic traits usually show a continuum of phenotype variation.

The study of single genes was pivotal in establishing the science of genetics. This focus allowed Mendel to formulate the basic laws of inheritance for traits with a simple dominant/recessive inheritance pattern. Likewise, this approach helped later researchers understand inheritance patterns involving incomplete dominance and codominance, as well as traits that are influenced by an individual's sex. However, all or nearly all traits are influenced by many genes. For example, in both plants and animals, height is affected by genes that encode proteins involved in the production of growth hormones, cell division, the uptake of nutrients, metabolism, and many other functions. Variation in any of the genes involved in these processes is likely to influence an individual's height.

If height is controlled by many genes, how was Mendel able to study the effects of a single gene that produced tall or dwarf pea plants? The answer lies in the genotypes of his strains. Although many genes affect the height of pea plants, Mendel chose true-breeding strains that differed with regard to only one of those genes. As a hypothetical example, let's suppose that pea plants have 10 genes affecting height, which we will call K, L, M, N, O, P, Q, R, S, and T. The genotypes of two hypothetical strains of pea plants may be:

Tall strain: *KK LL MM NN OO PP QQ RR SS TT*
Dwarf strain: *KK LL MM NN OO PP QQ RR SS tt*

In this example, the tall and dwarf strains differ at only a single gene. One strain is *TT* and the other is *tt*, and this accounts for the difference in their height. If we make crosses of tall and dwarf plants, the genotypes of the F_2 offspring will differ with regard to only one gene; the other nine genes will be identical in all of them. This approach allows a researcher to study the effects of a single gene even though many genes may affect a single character.

In this section, we will examine situations in which a single character is controlled by two or more different genes, each of which has two or more alleles. This phenomenon is called **gene interaction**. As you will see, allelic variation of two or more genes may affect the outcome of traits in different ways. First, we will look at a gene interaction in which an allele of one gene prevents the phenotypic expression of an allele of a different gene. Then we will discuss an interaction in which multiple genes have additive effects on a single character. These additive effects, together with environmental influences, account for the continuous phenotypic variation that we see in most traits.

In an Epistatic Gene Interaction, the Alleles of One Gene Mask the Phenotypic Effects of a Different Gene

In some gene interactions, the alleles of one gene mask the expression of the alleles of another gene. This phenomenon is called **epistasis** (from the Greek *ephistanai*, meaning stopping). An example is the unexpected gene interaction discovered by English geneticists William Bateson and Reginald Punnett in the early 1900s, when they were studying crosses involving the sweet pea, *Lathyrus odoratus*. A cross between a true-breeding purple-flowered plant and a true-breeding white-flowered plant produced an F_1 generation with all purple-flowered plants and an F_2 generation with a 3:1 ratio of purple- to white-flowered plants. Mendel's laws predicted this result. The surprise came when the researchers crossed two different true-breeding varieties of white-flowered sweet peas (**Figure 17.19**). All of the F_1 generation plants had purple flowers! When these plants were allowed to self-fertilize, the F_2 generation had purple-flowered and white-flowered plants in a 9:7 ratio. From these results, Bateson and Punnett deduced that two different genes were involved. To have purple flowers, a plant must have one or two dominant alleles for each of these genes. The relationships among the alleles are as follows:

C (one allele for purple) is dominant to *c* (white)
P (an allele of a different gene for purple) is dominant to *p* (white)
cc masks *P*, or *pp* masks *C*, resulting in white flowers in either case

A plant that is homozygous for either *c* or *p* has white flowers even if it has a dominant purple-producing allele for the other gene.

How do we explain these results at the molecular and cellular level? Epistatic interactions often arise because two or more different proteins are involved in a single cellular function. For example, two or more proteins may be part of a metabolic pathway leading to the formation of a single product. This is the case for the formation of a purple pigment in the sweet pea strains we have been discussing:

$$\text{Colorless precursor} \xrightarrow{\text{Enzyme C}} \text{Colorless intermediate} \xrightarrow{\text{Enzyme P}} \textbf{Purple pigment}$$

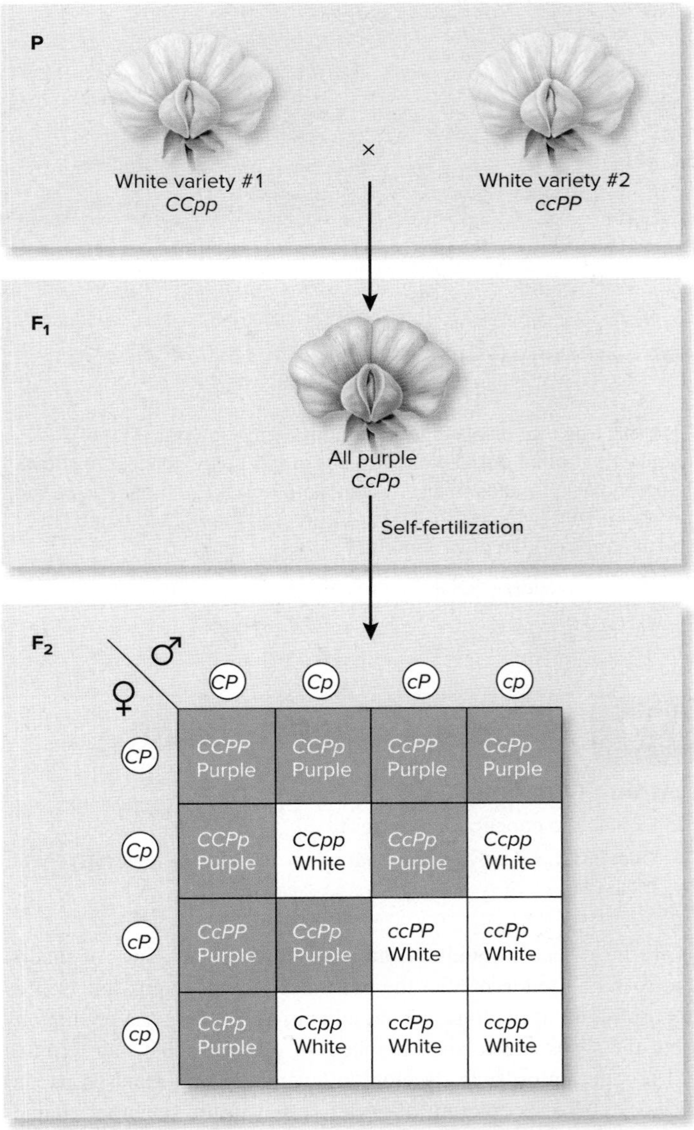

Figure 17.19 Epistasis in the sweet pea. The color of the sweet pea flower is controlled by two genes, each with a dominant and a recessive allele. Each of the dominant alleles (*C* and *P*) encodes an enzyme required for the synthesis of purple pigment. A plant that is homozygous recessive for either gene (*cc* or *pp*) cannot synthesize the pigment and has white flowers.

Concept Check: *In a Ccpp individual, which functional enzyme is missing? Is it the enzyme encoded by the C or P gene?*

In this example, a colorless precursor molecule must be acted on by two different enzymes to produce the purple pigment. Gene *C* encodes a functional protein called enzyme C, which converts the colorless precursor into a colorless intermediate. The recessive *c* allele results in a lack of production of enzyme C in the *cc* homozygote. Gene *P* encodes the functional enzyme P, which converts the colorless intermediate into the purple pigment. Like the *c* allele, the *p* allele results in an inability to produce a functional enzyme. A plant homozygous for either of the recessive alleles does not make any functional enzyme C or enzyme P. When either of these enzymes is missing, the plant cannot make the purple pigment and has white flowers. Note that the results observed in Figure 17.19 do not conflict with Mendel's laws of segregation or independent assortment. Mendel investigated the effects of only a single gene on a given character. The 9:7 ratio is due to a gene interaction in which two genes affect a single character.

Polygenic Inheritance and Environmental Influences Produce Continuous Phenotypic Variation

Until now, we have discussed the inheritance of characters with clearly defined phenotypic variants, such as red or white eyes in fruit flies and round or wrinkled seeds in garden peas. These are known as **discrete traits**, because the phenotypes do not overlap. For most traits, however, the phenotypes cannot be sorted into discrete categories. Traits that show continuous variation over a range of phenotypes are called **quantitative traits**. In humans, quantitative traits include height, weight, skin color, metabolic rate, and heart size. In the case of domestic animals and plant crops, many of the traits that people consider desirable are quantitative in nature, such as the number of eggs a chicken lays, the amount of milk a cow produces, and the number of apples on an apple tree. Consequently, much of our modern understanding of quantitative traits comes from agricultural research.

Quantitative traits are usually **polygenic**, which means that multiple genes contribute to the outcome of the trait. For many polygenic traits, genes contribute to the phenotype in an additive way. Also, environmental factors often have a major effect on quantitative traits. For example, an animal's diet affects its weight, and the amounts of rain and sunlight that fall on an apple tree affect how many apples it produces.

Because quantitative traits are polygenic and greatly influenced by environmental conditions, the phenotypes among different individuals may vary substantially in any given population. As an example, let's consider grain pigmentation in wheat. In certain strains of wheat, this character is influenced by three genes that interact in an additive way. Let's call them genes *A*, *B*, and *C*. Each gene may exist as a red allele, designated A^R, B^R, or C^R, or a white allele, designated A^W, B^W, or C^W, respectively. The red alleles encode enzymes that cause the synthesis of grain pigment, whereas the white alleles are the result of loss-of-function mutations. The color of wheat grains varies along a continuum, ranging from white to dark red.

Figure 17.20 considers a hypothetical case in which wheat plants that were heterozygous for all three genes produced a large population of offspring. The bar graph shows the genotypes of the offspring, grouped according to the total number of red and white alleles. As shown by the shading in the figure, red pigmentation increases as the number of red alleles increases. Offspring that have all white alleles

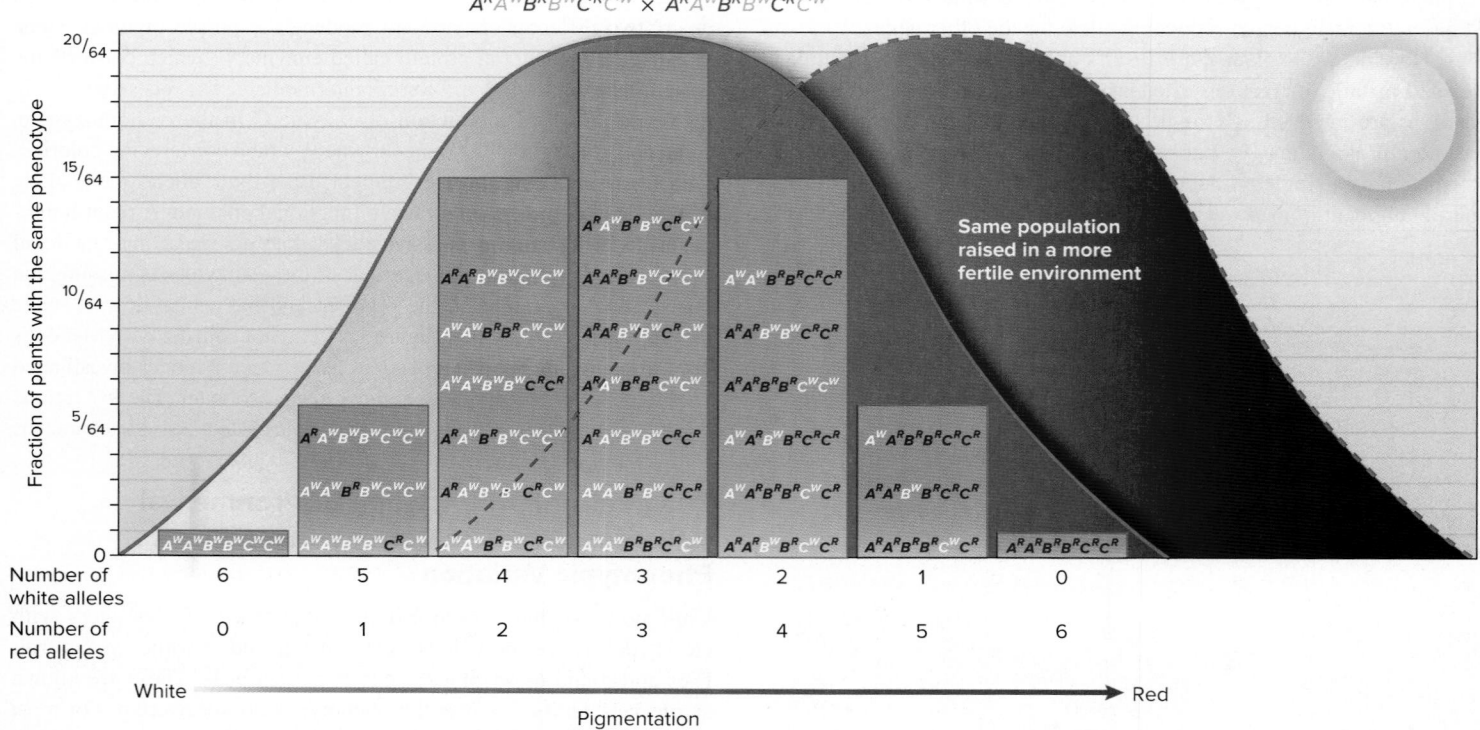

$A^RA^WB^RB^WC^RC^W \times A^RA^WB^RB^WC^RC^W$

Figure 17.20 Continuous variation in a polygenic trait. Grain color is a polygenic trait that displays a continuum of phenotypes. The bell curve on the left (solid line) shows the range of grain pigmentation in a hypothetical wheat-plant population. The bar graph below this curve shows the additive effects of three genes that affect pigment production in this population; the frequencies of all six alleles are equal. Each bar shows the fraction of plants with a particular number of dark alleles (A^R, B^R, and C^R) and light alleles (A^W, B^W, and C^W). The bell curve on the right (dashed line) represents the expected range of phenotypes if the same population were raised in a more fertile environment.

 Core Concept: Information The genetic blueprint usually involves the expression of several different genes that affect the same trait. In many cases, this results in continuous variation.

or have all red alleles—that is, those that are homozygous for all three genes—are fewer in number than those with some combination of light and dark alleles. As indicated by the bell-shaped curve above the bar graph, the phenotypes of the offspring fall along a continuum. This continuous phenotypic variation, which is typical of quantitative traits, is produced by genotypic differences together with environmental effects.

A second bell-shaped curve (dashed) depicts the expected phenotypic range if the same population of offspring had been raised in a more fertile environment (i.e., richer soil and more sunlight), which increases pigment production. This curve illustrates how the environment can also have a significant influence on the range of phenotypes.

In our discussion of genetics, we tend to focus on discrete traits because this makes it easier to relate a specific genotype with a phenotype. Identifying such a clear relationship is usually not possible for continuous traits. For example, as depicted in the middle bar of Figure 17.20, seven different genotypes can produce plants with a medium amount of pigmentation. It is important to emphasize that the majority of traits in all organisms are continuous, not discrete. Most traits are influenced by multiple genes, and the environment has an important influence on the phenotypic outcome.

17.7 Genetics and Probability

Learning Outcomes:

1. Explain the concept of probability.
2. **CoreSKILL »** Apply the product rule to problems involving genetic crosses.

As we have seen throughout this chapter, Mendel's laws of inheritance can be used to predict the outcomes of genetic crosses. How is this useful? In agriculture, plant and animal breeders use predictions about the types and relative numbers of offspring that their crosses will produce in order to develop commercially important crops and livestock. Also, people are often interested in the potential characteristics of their future children. This has particular importance to individuals who may carry alleles that cause inherited diseases. Of course, no one can see into the future and definitively predict what will happen. Nevertheless, genetic counselors can help couples predict the likelihood of having an affected child. This probability is one factor that may influence a couple's decision about whether to have children.

Earlier in this chapter, we considered how a Punnett square can be used to predict the outcome of simple genetic crosses. In addition to Punnett squares, we can apply the tools of mathematics and probability to solve more complex genetic problems. In this section, we will examine a couple of ways to calculate the outcomes of genetic crosses using these tools.

Genetic Predictions Are Based on the Rules of Probability

The chance that an event will have a particular outcome is called the **probability** of that outcome. The probability of a given outcome depends on the number of possible outcomes. For example, if you draw a card at random from a 52-card deck, the probability that you will get the jack of diamonds is 1 in 52, because 52 outcomes are possible. In contrast, only two outcomes are possible when you flip a coin, so the probability is one in two (1/2, or 0.5, or 50%) that the heads side will be showing when the coin lands. The general formula for the probability (P) that an event will have a specific outcome is

$$P = \frac{\text{Number of times an event occurs}}{\text{Total number of possible outcomes}}$$

For a single coin toss, the chance of getting heads is

$$P_{\text{heads}} = \frac{1 \text{ heads}}{(1 \text{ heads} + 1 \text{ tails})} = \frac{1}{2}$$

Earlier in this chapter, we used Punnett squares to predict the fractions of offspring with a given genotype or phenotype. In a cross between two pea plants that were heterozygous for the height gene (Tt), our Punnett square predicted that one-fourth of the offspring would be dwarf. We can make the same prediction by using a probability calculation.

$$P_{\text{dwarf}} = \frac{1 \; tt}{(1 \; TT + 2 \; Tt + 1 \; tt)} = \frac{1}{4} = 0.25, \text{ or } 25\%$$

A probability calculation allows us to predict the likelihood that a future event will have a specific outcome. However, the accuracy of this prediction depends to a great extent on the number of events we observe—in other words, on the size of our sample. For example, if we toss a coin six times, the calculation we just presented for P_{heads} suggests we should get heads three times and tails three times. However, each coin toss is an independent event, meaning that every time we toss the coin there is an equal chance that it will come up heads or tails, regardless of the outcome of the previous toss. With only six tosses, we would not be too surprised if we got four heads and two tails instead of the expected three heads and three tails. The deviation between the observed and expected outcomes due to random chance is called the **random sampling error**. With a small sample, the random sampling error may cause the observed data to be quite different from the expected outcome. By comparison, if we flipped a coin 1,000 times, the percentage of heads would be fairly close to the predicted 50%. With a larger sample, we expect the sampling error to be smaller.

The Product Rule Is Used to Predict the Outcome of Independent Events

Punnett squares allow us to predict the likelihood that a genetic cross will produce an offspring with a particular genotype or phenotype. To predict the likelihood of producing multiple offspring with particular genotypes or phenotypes, we can use the **product rule**, which states:

The probability that two or more independent events will occur is equal to the product of their individual probabilities.

As we have already discussed, events are independent if the outcome of one event does not affect the outcome of another. In our coin-toss example, each toss is an independent event—if one toss comes up heads, another toss still has an equal chance of coming up either heads or tails. If we toss a coin twice, what is the probability that we will get heads both times? The product rule says that it is equal to the probability of getting heads on the first toss (1/2) times the probability of getting heads on the second toss (1/2), or one in four (1/2 × 1/2 = 1/4).

To see how the product rule can be applied to a genetics problem, let's consider a rare recessive human trait known as congenital analgesia. (Congenital refers to a condition present at birth; analgesia means insensitivity to pain.) People with this trait can distinguish between sensations such as sharp and dull, or hot and cold, but they do not perceive extremes of sensation as painful. The first known case of congenital analgesia, described in 1932, was a man who made his living entertaining the public as a "human pincushion." For a couple, each heterozygous for the recessive allele causing congenital analgesia, we can ask, "What is the probability that their first three offspring will have the disorder?" To answer this question, we must first determine the probability of a single offspring having the disorder. By using a Punnett square, we would find that the probability of an individual offspring being homozygous recessive is 1/4. Thus, each of this couple's children has a one in four chance of having congenital analgesia.

We can now use the product rule to calculate the probability of this couple having three affected offspring in a row. The phenotypes of the first, second, and third offspring are independent events; that is, the phenotype of the first offspring does not affect the phenotype of the second or third offspring. The product rule tells us that the probability of all three children having the disorder is

$$\frac{1}{4} \times \frac{1}{4} \times \frac{1}{4} = \frac{1}{64} = 0.016, \text{ or } 1.6\%$$

The probability of the first three offspring having the disorder is 0.016, or 1.6%. In other words, we can say that this couple's chance of having three children in a row with congenital analgesia is very small—only 1.6 out of 100.

The product rule can also be used to predict the outcome of a cross involving two or more genes. Let's suppose a pea plant with the genotype $TtYy$ was crossed with a plant with the genotype $Ttyy$. We could ask, "What is the probability that an offspring will have the genotype $ttYy$?" If the two genes independently assort, the probability of inheriting alleles for one gene is independent of the probability for other gene. Therefore, we can separately calculate the probability of the desired outcome for each gene. By constructing two small Punnett squares, we can determine the probability of genotypes for each gene individually, as shown in the following Punnett squares.

Cross: *TtYy* × *Ttyy*

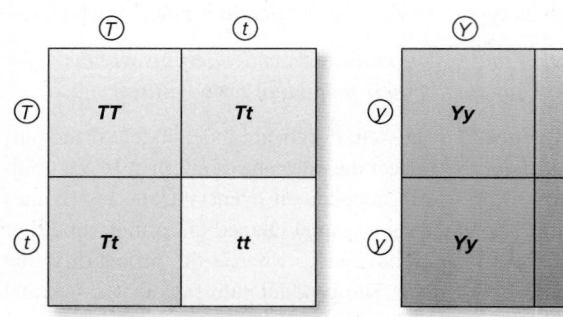

The probability that an offspring will be *tt* is 1/4, or 0.25.

The probability that an offspring will be *Yy* is 1/2, or 0.5.

We can now use the product rule to determine the probability that an offspring will be *ttYy*:

$$P = (0.25)(0.5) = 0.125, \text{ or } 12.5\%$$

Core Skill: Quantitative Reasoning

BIO TIPS **THE QUESTION** *As described earlier in this chapter, the human disease known as cystic fibrosis (CF) is inherited via a recessive allele. Two individuals, who do not have disease symptoms, have a first child who has CF. What is the probability that their next two children will not have the disease?*

TOPIC *What topic in biology does this question address?*
The topic is Mendelian inheritance. More specifically, the question is about a single-factor cross involving cystic fibrosis.

INFORMATION *What information do you know based on the question and your understanding of the topic?*
From the question, you know that both parents are unaffected, but they produced an affected offspring, who must be homozgyous for the recessive allele. Therefore, both parents must be heterozygotes. If *C* is the dominant allele and *c* is the recessive, disease-causing allele, the genotype of each parent must be *Cc*. From your understanding of the topic, you may remember that alleles segregate during the process that yields gametes and parents pass one allele to their offspring, when gametes combine at fertilization.

PROBLEM-SOLVING **S**TRATEGY *Predict the outcome. Make a calculation.* One strategy to predict the outcome is to use a Punnett square, as shown next.

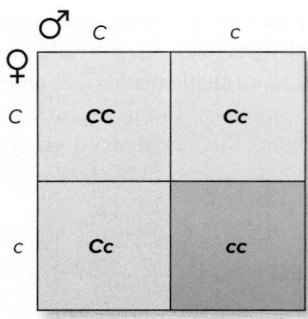

C = dominant allele
c = recessive, disease-causing allele

To calculate the probability, you need to consider two things. First, you need to know the probability of having an unaffected offspring. This probability can be deduced from the Punnett square. Once this is known, you can use the product rule to calculate the likelihood of having two unaffected offspring in a row, because these are independent outcomes.

ANSWER *The genotype ratio for the offspring is 1 CC : 2 Cc : 1 cc. The ratio of the phenotypes is 3 unaffected with CF : 1 affected with CF.*

The probability of these parents having a single unaffected offspring is

$$P_{\text{unaffected}} = \frac{3}{(3 + 1)} = \frac{3}{4}$$

To obtain the probability that they will have two unaffected offspring in a row, you need to apply the product rule.

$$\frac{3}{4} \times \frac{3}{4} = \frac{9}{16} = 0.56, \text{ or } 56\%$$

The chance that their next two children will not have CF is 56%.

Summary of Key Concepts

- Mendelian inheritance patterns obey Mendel's laws (Table 17.1).

17.1 Mendel's Laws of Inheritance

- Mendel studied seven characters of garden peas that existed in two variants each (Figures 17.1, 17.2).
- Mendel allowed his pea plants to self-fertilize, or he carried out cross-fertilization, also known as hybridization (Figures 17.3, 17.4).
- Mendel determined that certain traits exist in two forms, dominant and recessive. An individual carries two genes for a given character, and genes have variant forms, which are called alleles.
- By following the inheritance pattern of a single character (using a single-factor cross) for two generations, Mendel proposed the law of segregation, which states that two alleles segregate during the process that gives rise to gametes, so every gamete receives only one allele (Figures 17.5, 17.6).
- The genotype is the genetic makeup of an organism. Phenotype is a description of the traits that an organism displays.
- A Punnett square is constructed to predict the outcome of crosses.

- A testcross is conducted to determine if an individual displaying a dominant trait is a homozygote or a heterozygote (Figure 17.7).
- By conducting a two-factor cross, Mendel determined the law of independent assortment, which states that the alleles of different genes assort independently of each other during the process that gives rise to gametes. In a two-factor cross, this yields a 9:3:3:1 ratio in the F_2 generation (Figure 17.8).

17.2   The Chromosome Theory of Inheritance

- The chromosome theory of inheritance explains how the behavior of chromosomes during meiosis accounts for Mendel's laws of inheritance. Each gene is located at a particular site, or locus, on a chromosome (Figures 17.9, 17.10, 17.11).

17.3   Pedigree Analysis of Human Traits

- The inheritance patterns in humans are determined from pedigree analysis (Figures 17.12, 17.13).

17.4   Sex Chromosomes and X-Linked Inheritance Patterns

- Most species of animals and some species of plants have separate male and female sexes. In many species, sex is determined by differences in sex chromosomes (Figure 17.14).
- X-linked genes are found on the X chromosome but not the Y chromosome. Recessive X-linked alleles in humans can cause disorders such as hemophilia, which are more likely to occur in males.
- Morgan's experiments showed that an eye-color gene in *Drosophila* is located on the X chromosome (Figure 17.15).

17.5   Variations in Inheritance Patterns and Their Molecular Basis

- Several inheritance patterns have been discovered that obey Mendel's laws but yield differing ratios of offspring compared with Mendel's crosses.
- Recessive inheritance is often due to a loss-of-function mutation. In many simple dominant/recessive relationships, the heterozygote has a dominant phenotype because 50% of the functional protein is sufficient to produce that phenotype (Figure 17.16).
- The effects of a mutant gene are often pleiotropic, meaning the gene affects several different aspects of bodily structure and function.
- Incomplete dominance occurs when a heterozygote has a phenotype that is intermediate between either homozygote. This occurs because 50% of the functional protein is not enough to produce the same phenotype as a homozygote (Figure 17.17).
- ABO blood types are produced by the expression of a gene that exists in multiple alleles in humans. The I^A and I^B alleles show codominance, a phenomenon in which both alleles are expressed in a heterozygous individual (Table 17.2).
- Genes and the environment interact to determine an individual's phenotype. The norm of reaction is the phenotype range that individuals with the same genotype exhibit under different environmental conditions (Figure 17.18).

17.6   Gene Interaction

- Epistasis is a gene interaction that occurs when the alleles of one gene mask the effects of the alleles of a different gene (Figure 17.19).
- Quantitative traits such as height and weight are polygenic, which means that they are determined by multiple genes. Often, the alleles of such genes contribute in an additive way to the phenotype and are greatly affected by the environment. This interaction produces continuous variation in the trait, resulting in a phenotype range that can be graphed as a bell-shaped curve (Figure 17.20).

17.7   Genetics and Probability

- Probability is the likelihood that an event will occur in the future. Random sampling error is the deviation between observed and expected values.
- The product rule states that the probability of two or more independent events occurring is equal to the product of their individual probabilities.

Assess & Discuss

Test Yourself

1. Based on Mendel's experiments, what is the expected phenotype ratio in the F_2 generation from a single-factor cross?
   a. 1:2:1
   b. 2:1
   c. 3:1
   d. 9:3:3:1
   e. 4:1

2. During which phase of nuclear division does the phenomenon described in Mendel's law of segregation occur?
   a. mitosis
   b. meiosis I
   c. meiosis II
   d. all of the above
   e. b and c only

3. An individual that has two different alleles of a particular gene is said to be
   a. dihybrid.   d. heterozygous.
   b. recessive.   e. hemizygous.
   c. homozygous.

4. Which of Mendel's laws cannot be observed in a single-factor cross?
   a. segregation
   b. dominance/recessiveness
   c. independent assortment
   d. codominance
   e. All of the above can be observed in a single-factor cross.

5. During a_____ , an individual with the dominant phenotype and an unknown genotype is crossed with a_____ individual to determine the unknown genotype.
   a. single-factor cross, homozygous recessive
   b. two-factor cross, heterozygous
   c. testcross, homozygous dominant
   d. single-factor cross, homozygous dominant
   e. testcross, homozygous recessive

the normal-size and dwarf offspring have the same genotype *(Igf2 Igf2⁻)* but different phenotypes! In mice, the *Igf2* gene is imprinted in such a way that only the paternal allele is expressed, which means it is transcribed into mRNA. The maternal allele is not transcribed. The newborn mice shown on the left side of the photograph of Figure 18.1 are normal size, because they express a functional paternal allele. By contrast, the mice on the right side are dwarf because they express a paternal allele that is defective and results in a nonfunctional hormone.

Transcription of an Imprinted Gene Depends on Methylation

Why is the maternal gene encoding Igf2 not transcribed into mRNA? To answer this question, we need to consider the regulation of gene transcription in eukaryotes. As discussed in Chapter 14, DNA methylation, which is the attachment of methyl (—CH₃) groups to bases of DNA, can alter gene transcription. Researchers have discovered that DNA methylation is the marking process that occurs during the imprinting of certain genes, including the *Igf2* gene. For most genes, DNA methylation silences gene expression by inhibiting the initiation of transcription or by causing the chromatin in a region to become more compact. By contrast, for a few imprinted genes, DNA methylation may enhance gene expression by attracting activator proteins to the promoter or by preventing the binding of repressor proteins.

Figure 18.2 shows the imprinting process in which a maternal gene is methylated. The left side of the figure follows the marking process during the life of a female individual; the right side follows the same process in a male. Both individuals received a methylated gene from their mother and a nonmethylated copy of the same gene from their father. Via cell division, the zygote develops into a multicellular organism. Each time a somatic cell divides, enzymes in the cell maintain the methylation of the maternal gene, but the paternal gene remains unmethylated. If methylation inhibits transcription of this gene, only the paternal copy will be expressed in the somatic cells of both the male and female offspring.

The methylation state of an imprinted gene may be altered when individuals make gametes. First, the methylation is erased (Figure 18.2, step 2). Next, the gene may be methylated again, but that depends on whether the individual is female or male. In females making eggs, both copies of the gene are methylated; in males making sperm, neither copy is methylated. When we consider the effects of methylation over the course of two or more generations, we can see how this phenomenon results in an epigenetic transmission pattern. The male in Figure 18.2 has inherited a methylated gene from his mother that is transcriptionally silenced in his somatic cells. Although he does not express this gene during his lifetime, he can pass on an active, nonmethylated copy of this exact same gene to his offspring.

Genomic imprinting is a recently discovered phenomenon that has been shown to occur for a many genes in mammals. For some genes, such as *Igf 2*, the maternal allele is silenced, but for other genes, the paternal allele is silenced. Although several hypotheses have been advanced, biologists are still trying to identify possible advantages that this curious marking process may confer.

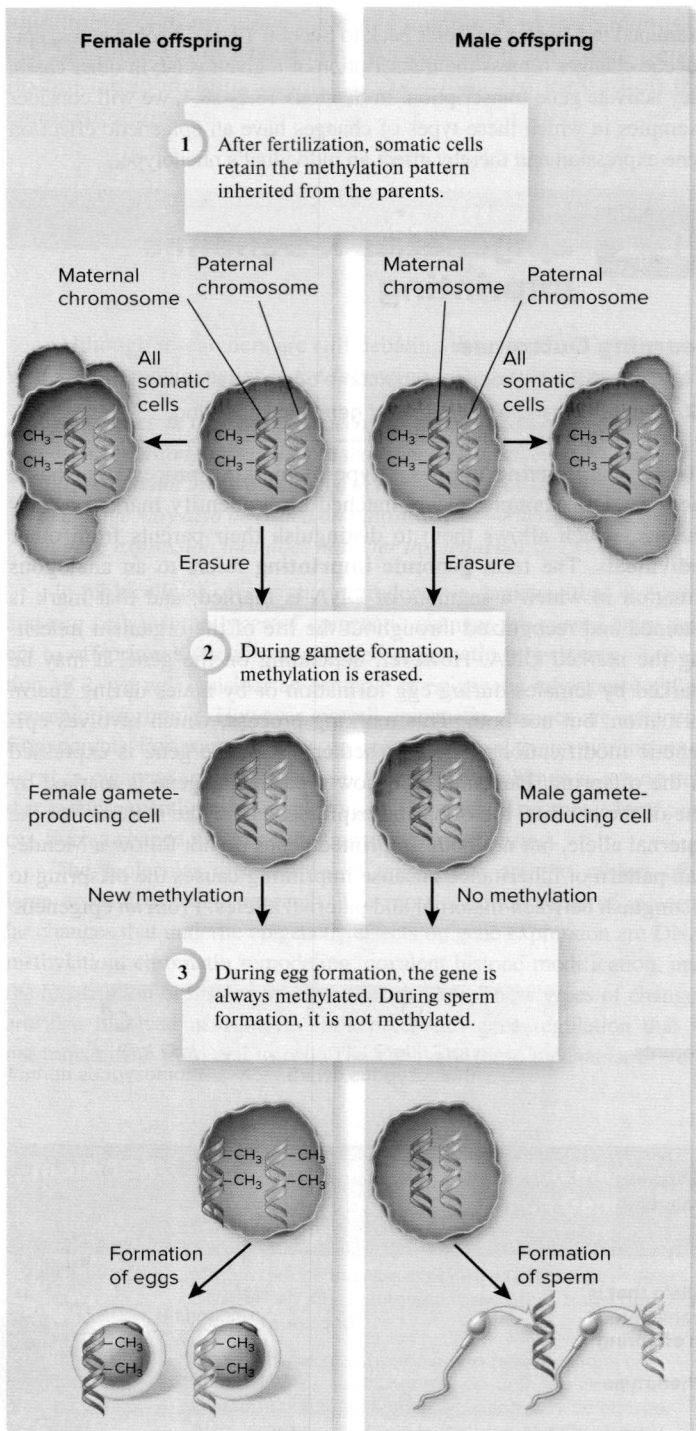

Figure 18.2 Genomic imprinting via DNA methylation. The cells of the female and male offspring at the top of this figure have a methylated gene inherited from the mother and a nonmethylated version of the same gene inherited from the father. This pattern of methylation is maintained in the somatic cells of both female and male offspring. The methylation is erased during gamete formation, but in females, the gene is methylated again at a later stage in the formation of eggs. Therefore, females always transmit a methylated, transcriptionally silent copy of this gene, whereas males transmit a nonmethylated, transcriptionally active copy.

Epigenetics II: X-Chromosome Inactivation

Learning Outcomes:

1. Explain how X-chromosome inactivation may affect the phenotype of female mammals.

2. Describe the process of X-chromosome inactivation at the cellular level.

As we have seen, genomic imprinting involves epigenetic changes that occur during gamete formation and are passed from parent to off-spring. Other types of epigenetic changes begin later, such as during embryonic development, and then persist into adulthood. For example, as mentioned in Section 18.1, epigenetic changes may silence actin and myosin genes in some embryonic cells, and these changes are passed from cell to cell so that the same genes are silenced in nonmuscle cells of the adult.

In this section, we will consider an example of epigenetic silencing that begins during embryonic development in female mammals. As discussed in Chapter 17, female mammals carry two X chromosomes in their cells, whereas males carry one X and one Y. During embryonic development in female mammals, one of the X chromosomes undergoes an epigenetic change called **X-chromosome inactivation (XCI)**. This process causes that X chromosome to become highly compacted, which silences the genes that it carries. In this section, we will examine how XCI may affect a female mammal's phenotype and how the process occurs at the cellular and molecular levels.

In Female Mammals, One X Chromosome Is Inactivated in Each Somatic Cell

In 1961, British geneticist Mary Lyon proposed the epigenetic phenomenon of XCI. Its discovery was based on two lines of evidence. The first came from microscopic studies of mammalian cells. In 1949, Canadian physicians Murray Barr and Ewart Bertram identified a highly condensed structure in the cells of female cats that was not found in the cells of male cats. This structure was named a **Barr body** after one of its discoverers (**Figure 18.3**). In 1960, Asian-American geneticist Susumu Ohno correctly proposed that a Barr body is a highly condensed X chromosome. Lyon's second line of evidence was the inheritance pattern of variegated coat colors in certain female mammals. A classic case is the calico cat, which has randomly distributed patches of black and orange fur (look ahead to the bottom of **Figure 18.4**).

How do we explain this patchwork phenotype? According to Lyon's hypothesis, the calico pattern is due to the permanent inactivation of one X chromosome in each cell that forms a patch of the cat's skin, as shown in Figure 18.4. The gene involved is an X-linked gene that occurs as an orange allele, X^O, and a black allele, X^B. A female cat heterozygous for this gene will be calico. (The cat's white underside is due to a dominant allele of a different autosomal gene.) At an early stage of embryonic development, one of the two X chromosomes is randomly inactivated in each of the cat's somatic cells, including those that will give rise to the hair-producing skin cells. As the embryo grows and matures, the pattern of XCI is maintained during

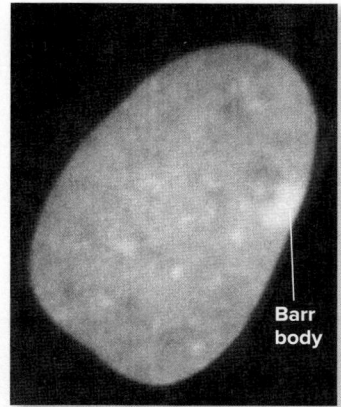
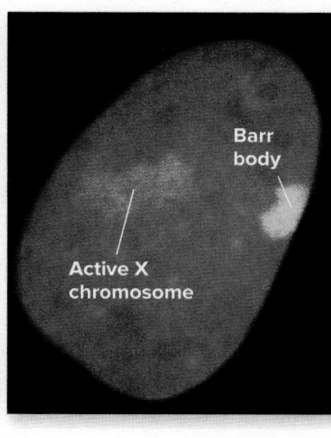

(a)   **(b)**

Figure 18.3 X-chromosome inactivation in female mammals.
(a) A Barr body is seen on the periphery of a human nucleus (during interphase) after the nucleus has been stained with a DNA-specific dye. Because it is compact, the Barr body is the most brightly stained feature. **(b)** The same nucleus was labeled using a yellow fluorescent probe that recognizes the X chromosome. The Barr body is more compact than the active X chromosome, which is to the left of the Barr body. a–b: Courtesy of I. Solovei, University of Munich (LMU)

Concept Check: *How is the Barr body different from the other X chromosome in this cell?*

subsequent cell divisions. Skin cells derived from a single embryonic cell in which the X^B-carrying chromosome has been inactivated produce a patch of orange fur, because they express only the X^O allele that is carried on the active chromosome. Alternatively, a group of skin cells in which the chromosome carrying X^O has been inactivated express only the X^B allele, producing a patch of black fur. If female mammals are heterozygous for X-linked genes, approximately half of their somatic cells express one allele, whereas the rest of their somatic cells express the other allele. The result is an animal with randomly distributed patches of black and orange fur. These heterozygotes are called **mosaics** because they have somatic regions that are composed of two types of cells.

For many X-linked traits in humans, females who are heterozygous for recessive X-linked alleles usually show the dominant trait because the expression of the dominant allele in 50% of their cells is sufficient to produce the dominant phenotype. For example, let's consider the recessive X-linked form of hemophilia that was discussed in Chapter 17 (hemophilia A). This type of hemophilia is caused by a defect in a gene that encodes a blood-clotting protein, called factor VIII, which is made by cells in the liver and secreted into the bloodstream. In a heterozygous female, approximately half of her liver cells make and secrete this clotting factor, which is sufficient to prevent hemophilia. Therefore, she exhibits the dominant trait of proper blood clotting.

On rare occasions, a female who is heterozygous may show mild or even severe disease symptoms. How is this possible? X-chromosome inactivation in humans occurs when an embryo is 10 days old. At this stage, the liver contains only about a dozen cells. In most females who are heterozygous for the dominant and recessive (hemophilia-causing) alleles, roughly half of their liver cells express the dominant

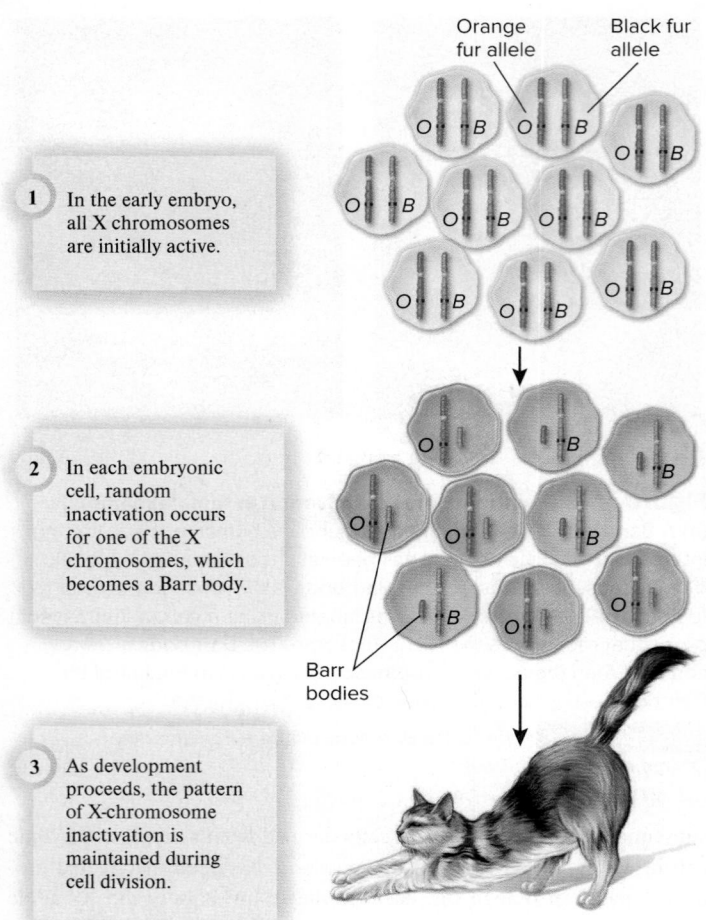

1 In the early embryo, all X chromosomes are initially active.

Orange fur allele Black fur allele

2 In each embryonic cell, random inactivation occurs for one of the X chromosomes, which becomes a Barr body.

Barr bodies

3 As development proceeds, the pattern of X-chromosome inactivation is maintained during cell division.

Figure 18.4 X-chromosome inactivation (XCI) in a calico cat. The calico pattern is due to random XCI in a female that is heterozygous for an X-linked gene with black (X^B) and orange (X^O) alleles. The cells at the top of this figure represent a small mass of cells making up the very early embryo. In these cells, both X chromosomes are active. At an early stage of embryonic development, one X chromosome is randomly inactivated in each cell. The initial inactivation pattern is an epigenetic change that is maintained in the descendants of each cell as the embryo matures into an adult. The pattern of orange and black fur in the adult cat reflects the pattern of XCI in the embryo.

 Core Skill: Modeling The goal of this modeling challenge is to create a model that shows the pattern of X-chromosome inactivation (XCI) in a clump of cells after XCI has occurred.

Modeling Challenge: Step 2 of Figure 18.4 shows a model of early embryonic cells after XCI has occurred. Let's suppose you could remove the (orange) embryonic cell on the top left and the (gray) embryonic cell on the top right from this embryo. You then place each of these cells on solid growth media and allow them to grow and divide to form a small clump of cells. Draw a model that depicts the pattern of XCI in these two clumps of cells after 2 cell divisions.

allele. However, on rare occasions, all or most of the dozen embryonic liver cells may inactivate the X chromosome carrying the dominant functional allele. Following growth and development, such a female will have a very low level of factor VIII and as a result will show symptoms of hemophilia.

Why does X-chromosome inactivation occur? Researchers have proposed that XCI achieves **dosage compensation**, an equalization of the expression of X-linked genes in male and female mammals. The inactivation of one X chromosome in the female reduces the number of expressed copies (doses) of X-linked genes from two to one, the same as expressed in males. As a result, the expression of X-linked genes in females and males is roughly equal.

The X Chromosome Has an X Inactivation Center That Controls Compaction into a Barr Body

After Lyon's hypothesis was confirmed, researchers became interested in the cellular and molecular control of X-chromosome inactivation. The cells of humans and other mammals have the ability to count their X chromosomes and allow only one of them to remain active. Additional X chromosomes are converted to Barr bodies. In females, two X chromosomes are counted and one is inactivated. In males, one X chromosome is counted and none inactivated.

On rare occasions, people are born with abnormalities in the number of their sex chromosomes. In the disorders known as Turner syndrome, triple X syndrome, and Klinefelter syndrome, the cells inactivate the number of X chromosomes necessary to leave a single active chromosome (**Table 18.2**). For example, in triple X syndrome, in which an extra X chromosome is found in each cell, two X chromosomes are converted to Barr bodies. In spite of X-chromosome inactivation, people with these three syndromes do exhibit some phenotypic abnormalities. The symptoms associated with these disorders may be due to effects that occur prior to XCI or may arise because not all of the genes on the Barr body are completely silenced.

Although the mechanism of inactivation is not entirely understood at the molecular level, a short region on the X chromosome called the **X inactivation center (Xic)** is known to play a critical role. Finnish-born American geneticist Eeva Therman and German-born American geneticist Klaus Patau determined that XCI is

Table 18.2	Relationship Between X-Chromosome Inactivation and the Number of X Chromosomes		
Phenotype	Chromosome composition	Number of Barr bodies	Number of active X chromosomes
Female	XX	1	1
Male	XY	0	1
Turner syndrome (female)	XO	0	1
Triple X syndrome (female)	XXX	2	1
Klinefelter syndrome (male)	XXY	1	1

accomplished by counting the number of Xics and inactivating all X chromosomes except for one. In cells with two X chromosomes, if one of them is missing its Xic due to a chromosome mutation, neither X chromosome will be inactivated, because only one Xic is counted. Having two active X chromosomes is a lethal condition for a human female embryo.

The expression of a specific gene within the Xic is required for compaction of the X chromosome into a Barr body. This gene, discovered in 1991, is named *Xist* (for X inactive specific transcript). The *Xist* gene product is a long RNA molecule that does not encode a protein. Instead, the role of *Xist* RNA is to coat one of the two X chromosomes during the process of X-chromosome inactivation. After coating, proteins associate with the *Xist* RNA and promote compaction of the chromosome into a Barr body. The *Xist* gene on the Barr body continues to be expressed after other genes on this chromosome have been silenced. The expression of the *Xist* gene also maintains a chromosome as a Barr body during cell division. Whenever a somatic cell divides in a female mammal, the Barr body is replicated to produce two Barr bodies.

18.4 Epigenetics III: Effects of Environmental Agents

Learning Outcomes:

1. Explain how chemicals in the diet may affect an individual's phenotype.
2. List examples of chemicals that cause epigenetic changes that may contribute to cancer.

One of the most active fields in genetics is the study of how certain environmental agents cause epigenetic changes and thereby affect gene expression. Two areas that have received a great deal of attention are the effects of diet and the potential effects of toxic agents, such as carcinogens—cancer-causing agents. In this section, we will consider examples in which environmental agents promote epigenetic changes that affect an individual's phenotype or cause a disease such as cancer.

Chemicals in an Individual's Diet May Cause Epigenetic Changes That Affect Phenotype

At the beginning of this chapter, we considered how chemicals in royal jelly are responsible for producing queen bees (see the chapter opening photo). Another striking example of how chemicals in the diet can promote epigenetic changes is illustrated by studies of the *Agouti* gene (designated *A*) found in mice. This gene encodes the Agouti signaling peptide that controls the deposition of yellow pigment in developing hairs. In mice that are homozygous for a functional allele, *AA*, the expression of this gene promotes the synthesis of pheomelanin, a yellow pigment. During the growth of a hair, melanocytes (pigment-producing cells) within a hair follicle initially make eumelanin, which is black. The transient expression of the *Agouti* gene causes the melanocytes to make pheomelanin. The melanocytes then revert to making black pigment. The result is a band of yellow pigment sandwiched between layers of black

pigment, which gives a brown color. The yellow pigment is not synthesized near the tip of the hair, so the hair of *AA* mice is brown with black tips.

Researchers have identified several mutations that affect the expression of the *Agouti* gene. For example, mice that are homozygous for a loss-of-function allele, *aa,* have black fur because pheomelanin is not made. Alternatively, a gain-of-function mutation that causes the *Agouti* gene to be overexpressed results in a mouse with yellow fur. One such mutation is designated A^{vy}. (*A* refers to Agouti, *v* refers to viable, and *y* refers to yellow. The letter *v* is used because other mutations in the *Agouti* gene are not viable.) By characterizing the A^{vy} allele at the molecular level, researchers determined that it is due to the insertion of a new promoter next to the normal promoter of the *Agouti* gene. This new promoter is very active, which causes the overexpression of the *Agouti* gene.

An intriguing observation of mice carrying the A^{vy} allele is that they exhibit a wide phenotypic variation, ranging from yellow to mottled to pseudo-agouti (**Figure 18.5a**). Why should mice with the same genotype show such a wide range of phenotypic variation? Although the answer is not entirely understood, researchers have speculated that the new promoter in mice carrying the A^{vy} allele is very sensitive to epigenetic changes. In particular, this promoter may be more likely to be modified by DNA methylation, which would inhibit its function. Furthermore, a variety of environmental factors may cause this epigenetic change to occur. The sensitivity of this promoter to epigenetic modifications, together with variation in environmental factors, may explain the phenotypic variation seen in these mice.

A key factor that may affect epigenetic changes is diet. With regard to the A^{vy} allele, the exposure of pregnant female mice to different diets affects the phenotypes of the resulting offspring. In 2003, American geneticists Robert Waterland and Randy Jirtle conducted a study in which they investigated the effects of certain dietary supplements. Their goal was to determine if nutrients that are known to inhibit DNA methylation would alter the expression of the *Agouti* gene and thereby affect coat color. A variety of dietary factors can inhibit the enzyme DNA methyltransferase, which methylates DNA. These include folic acid, vitamin B_{12}, betaine, and choline chloride.

Waterland and Jirtle began with female mice carrying the A^{vy} allele and divided them into a control group (which was fed a standard diet) and an experimental group (which was fed a diet supplemented with folic acid, vitamin B_{12}, betaine, and choline chloride). Both groups were fed their respective diets before and during pregnancy and up to the stage of weaning. Offspring that inherited the A^{vy} allele were then analyzed with regard to their coat color and levels of DNA methylation.

As expected, a range of coat colors was observed among the offspring (**Figure 18.5b**). However, the offspring of females that had been fed a supplemented diet tended to have darker coats. For example, over 25% of the offspring with heavily mottled coats had mothers that were fed a supplemented diet (blue bars), whereas less than 10% had mothers that were given a standard diet (red bars).

The coat colors of the offspring were correlated with the degree of methylation that occurred at the new promoter—offspring

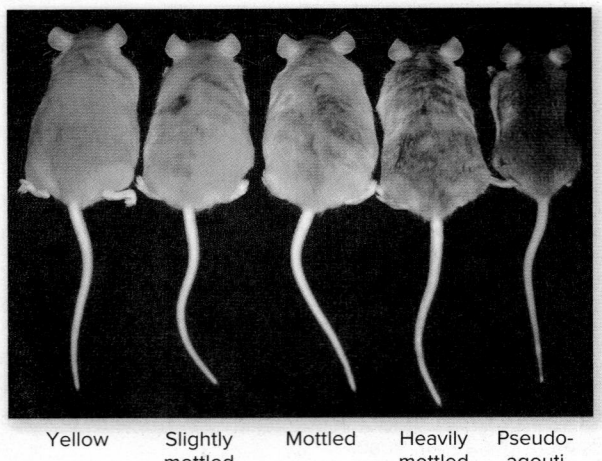

(a) Range in coat-color phenotypes in $A^{vy}a$ mice due to epigenetic changes

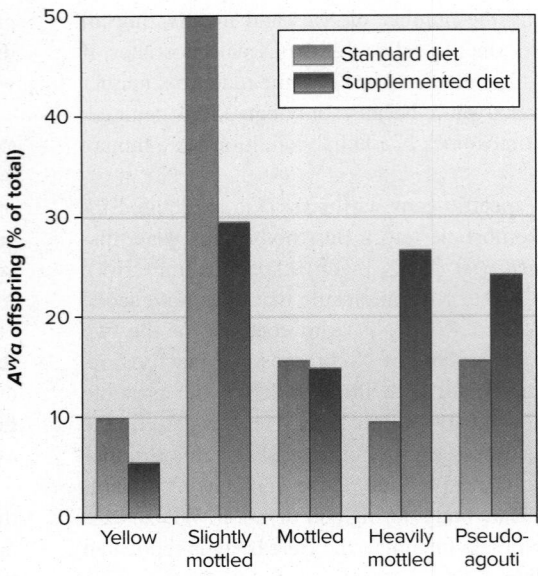

(b) Effect of diet on coat color

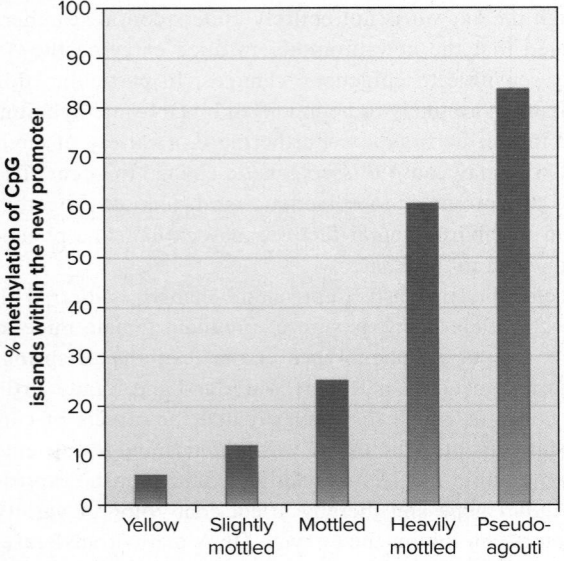

(c) Level of DNA methylation of CpG islands within the new promoter among mice with different coat colors

Figure 18.5 **Dietary effects on coat color in mice.** **(a)** Mice carrying the A^{vy} allele exhibit a range of phenotypes. The mice shown here are heterozygotes, $A^{vy}a$; they carry the A^{vy} allele and a loss-of-function allele, a. **(b)** Effects of diet supplementation on coat color. Red bars represent offspring from females given a standard diet, and blue bars represent offspring from females given a supplemented diet. **(c)** DNA methylation patterns among mice with different coat colors. a–c: Source: Waterland, R. A., and Jirtle, R. L. 2003. Transposable Elements: Targets for Early Nutritional Effects on Epigenetic Gene Regulation, *Molecular and Celular Biology* 23: 5293–5300

with darker coat color had greater levels of DNA methylation (**Figure 18.5c**). How do we explain these results? In the mice that are more yellow, the new promoter has undergone less DNA methylation. Therefore, the promoter remains active, leading to

the transcription of the *Agouti* gene and the overproduction of yellow pigment. By contrast, the new promoter in the darker mice has undergone more methylation. Such methylation inhibits the overexpression of the *Agouti* gene and thereby prevents the overproduction of yellow pigment, resulting in darker fur.

Environmental Agents May Cause Epigenetic Changes That Are Associated with Human Diseases, Such as Cancer

One of the most active fields in genetics involves the study of epigenetic changes that contribute to human diseases. We have probably seen only "the tip of the iceberg" with respect to our understanding of this topic. Many medical studies have identified correlations between epigenetic changes and particular diseases. For example, some research studies have compared one variable, such as the level of DNA methylation of a specific gene, to a second variable, such as the severity of a disease. If a high level of DNA methylation is associated with an increase in disease severity, this is a positive correlation. Researchers analyze the data to decide if such a correlation is statistically significant. When a statistically significant correlation is obtained, how do we interpret its meaning? Such a result suggests a true **association**—changes in the two variables follow a pattern. For example, in a positive correlation, when one variable increases, the other variable also increases.

However, an association does not necessarily imply a cause-and-effect relationship. When considering the role of epigenetic changes and human disease, an association can arise in three common ways:

- The epigenetic changes directly contribute to the disease symptoms. There is a cause-and-effect relationship.
- Conversely, the disease symptoms may arise first, and then they cause subsequent epigenetic changes to happen. This is also a cause-and-effect relationship, but in the opposite direction.

- The association is indirect because a third factor is involved. For example, a toxic agent in the environment may cause a disease and also cause particular types of epigenetic changes even though those epigenetic changes do not contribute to the disease.

Correlations identify associations between two variables. We should use caution, however, because the correlation by itself cannot prove that the association is due to cause and effect. Even so, research studies that identify associations are very useful because they provide the rationale to carry out further research to determine if a cause-and-effect relationship exists.

Researchers have identified many examples in which epigenetic changes are associated with a particular disease. These include Alzheimer disease, cardiovascular diseases, diabetes, multiple sclerosis, and asthma. For these diseases, further research is needed to determine if these epigenetic changes are directly contributing to the disease symptoms. The role of epigenetics in disease has been most extensively studied with regard to cancer. **Table 18.3** describes several examples in which an environmental factor is associated with a particular type of cancer.

In some of the examples listed in Table 18.3, scientific evidence indicates that the association is causative. For example, certain agents in tobacco smoke have been shown to cause epigenetic changes that underlie lung cancer. As described in Chapter 15, cancer-causing genes are placed into two categories: oncogenes, which are overexpressed in cancer, and tumor-suppressor genes, which are inhibited. In cases where research has shown that an environmental agent results in an epigenetic effect that contributes to cancer, it is more common for that agent to inhibit tumor-suppressor genes. However, in some cases, it may activate oncogenes. Alternatively, some of the agents listed in

Table 18.3 show an association with particular cancers, but researchers are still trying to determine if the epigenetic changes caused by these agents actually promote the changes that result in cancer.

18.5 Extranuclear Inheritance: Organelle Genomes

Learning Outcomes:

1. Describe the general features of mitochondrial and chloroplast genomes.
2. **CoreSKILL »** Predict the outcome of crosses that exhibit maternal inheritance.
3. List human diseases associated with mutations in mitochondrial genes.

In this section, we will explore inheritance patterns that violate the law of segregation. As described in Chapter 17, the segregation of genes is explained by the pairing and segregation of homologous chromosomes during meiosis. However, some genes are not found on the chromosomes in the cell nucleus, and these genes do not segregate in the same way. The transmission of genes located outside the cell nucleus is called **extranuclear inheritance**. Two important types of extranuclear inheritance patterns involve genes found in chloroplasts and mitochondria. Extranuclear inheritance is also called cytoplasmic inheritance because these organelles are in the cytoplasm of the cell. In this section, we will examine the transmission patterns observed for genes found in the chloroplast and mitochondrial genomes and consider how mutations in these genes may affect an individual's traits.

 Core Concepts: Evolution, Information

Chloroplast and Mitochondrial Genomes Are Relatively Small, but Contain Genes That Encode Important Proteins

As discussed in Chapter 4, mitochondria and chloroplasts are found in eukaryotic cells because of an ancient endosymbiotic relationship. They contain their own genetic material, called the mitochondrial genome and chloroplast genome, respectively (**Figure 18.6**). Mitochondrial and chloroplast genomes are composed of a single, circular DNA molecule. The mitochondrial genome of many mammalian species has been analyzed and usually contains a total of 37 genes. Twenty-four genes encode tRNAs and rRNAs, which are needed for translation inside the mitochondrion, and 13 genes encode proteins that are involved in oxidative phosphorylation. As discussed in Chapter 7, the primary function of the mitochondrion is the synthesis of ATP via oxidative phosphorylation. Among different species of flowering plants, chloroplast genomes typically contain between 100 and 200 genes. Many of these genes encode proteins that are vital to the process of photosynthesis, which is discussed in Chapter 8.

Table 18.3	Environmental Agents That Are Associated with Cancer and Are Known to Cause Epigenetic Changes	
Environmental agent	**Occurrence**	**Associations with particular cancers**
Polycyclic aromatic hydrocarbons	Tobacco smoke, automobile exhaust, charbroiled food	Lung, breast, stomach, and skin cancer
Benzene	Tobacco smoke, automobile exhaust	Leukemia, lymphoma, multiple myeloma
Endocrine disruptors (such as diethylstilbestrol)	Insecticides, fungicides, herbicides, some types of plastic	Breast, prostate, and thyroid cancer
Cadmium	Tobacco products, production of batteries	Lung and breast cancer
Nickel	Occupational exposure in mining, welding, and electroplating and in the manufacturing of jewelry, stainless steel, and batteries	Lung and nasal cancer
Arsenic	Lead alloy, feed additive in agriculture, insecticides	Skin, bladder, kidney, and liver cancer

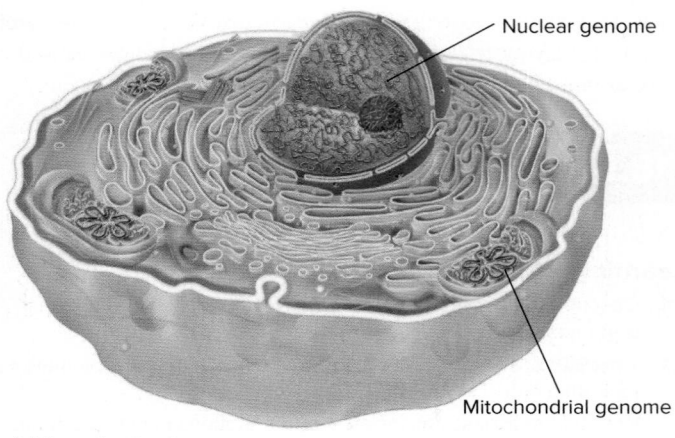

(a) An animal cell

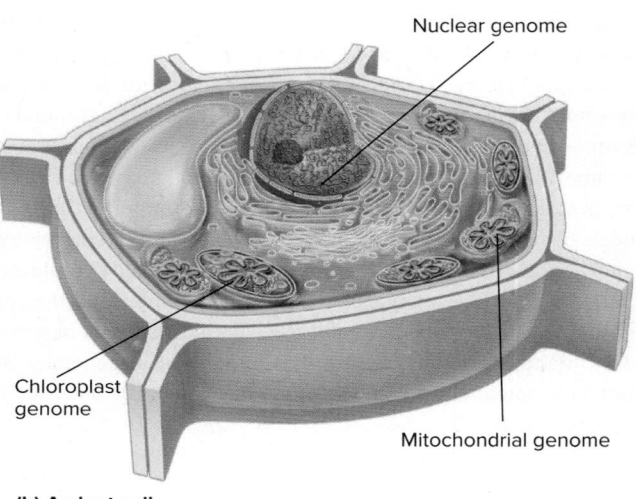

(b) A plant cell

Figure 18.6 **The locations of genetic material in animal and plant cells.** The chromosomes in the cell nucleus are collectively known as the nuclear genome. Mitochondria and chloroplasts have small circular chromosomes called the mitochondrial and chloroplast genomes, respectively.

 Core Skill: Connections Look back at Figure 4.31. What is the evolutionary origin of mitochondria and chloroplasts in eukaryotic cells?

Chloroplast Genomes Are Often Maternally Inherited

One of the first experiments showing an extranuclear inheritance pattern was carried out by German botanist Carl Correns in 1909. Correns discovered that leaf pigmentation in the four-o'clock plant (*Mirabilis jalapa*) follows a pattern of inheritance that does not obey Mendel's law of segregation. Four-o'clock leaves may be green, white, or variegated. Correns observed that the pigmentation of the offspring depended solely on the pigmentation of the female parent, a phenomenon called **maternal inheritance** (**Figure 18.7**). In cross 1, if the female parent providing the eggs had white leaves and the male parent providing the pollen had green leaves, all of the offspring had white leaves like the

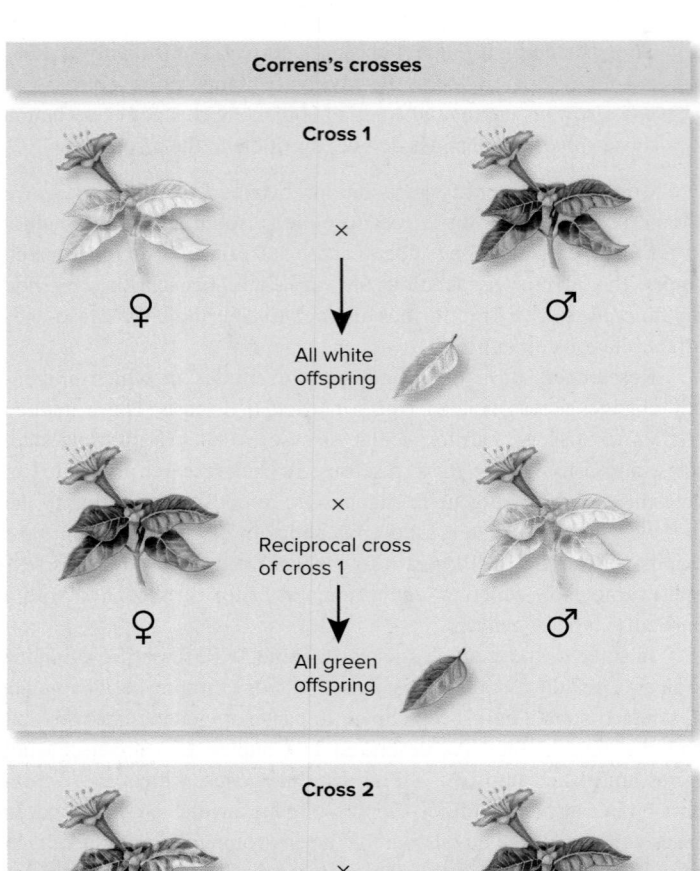

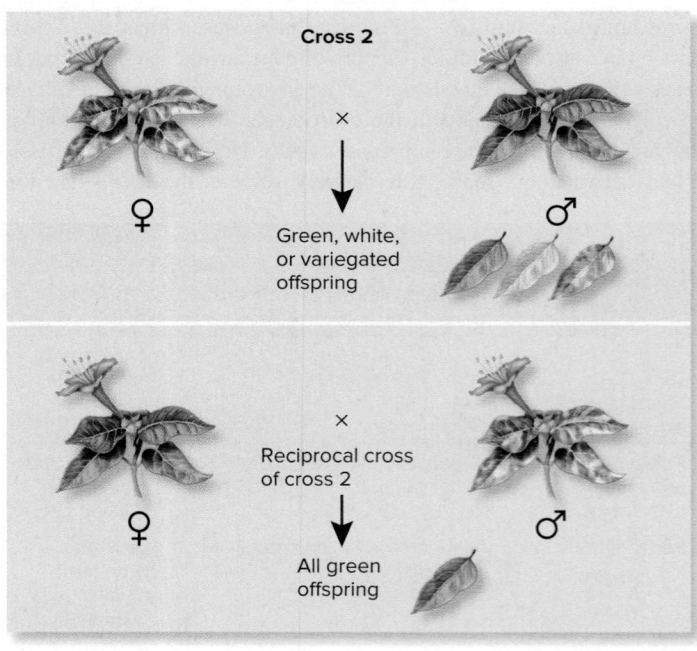

Figure 18.7 **Maternal inheritance in the four-o'clock plant.** In four-o'clocks, the egg contains all of the proplastids, which develop into chloroplasts, that are inherited by the offspring. The phenotype of the offspring is determined by the maternal parent. The green phenotype is due to the presence of normal chloroplasts. The white phenotype is due to chloroplasts with a mutant allele that greatly reduces green pigment production. The variegated phenotype is due to a mixture of normal and mutant chloroplasts.

Concept Check: *In this example, where is the gene located that causes the green color of four-o'clock leaves? How is this gene transmitted from parent to offspring?*

female parent. Correns also conducted a **reciprocal cross**—a cross in which the sexes and phenotypes are reversed compared to another cross. In the reciprocal cross of cross 1, the female parent had green leaves and the male parent had white leaves. Again, the offspring exhibited a phenotype like the female parent. Similarly, if the female was green, so were all of the offspring. In cross 2, the offspring of a variegated female parent could be green, white, or variegated.

What accounts for maternal inheritance? At the time, Correns did not understand that chloroplasts contain genetic material. Subsequent research identified DNA present in chloroplasts as responsible for the unusual inheritance pattern observed. We now know that the pigmentation of four-o'clock leaves can be explained by the occurrence of genetically different types of chloroplasts in the leaf cells. As discussed in Chapter 8, chloroplasts are the site of photosynthesis, and their green color is due to the presence of the pigment called chlorophyll. Certain genes required for chlorophyll synthesis are found within the chloroplast DNA. For four-o'clock plants, the green phenotype is due to the presence of chloroplasts that have functional genes and synthesize the usual quantity of chlorophyll. The white phenotype is caused by a mutation in a gene within the chloroplast DNA that prevents the synthesis of most of the chlorophyll. (Enough chlorophyll is made for the plant to survive.) The variegated phenotype occurs in leaves that have a mixture of the two types of chloroplasts.

Leaf pigmentation follows a maternal inheritance pattern because the chloroplasts in four-o'clocks are transmitted only through the cytoplasm of the egg (**Figure 18.8**). In most species of plants, the egg cell provides most of the zygote's cytoplasm, whereas the much smaller male gamete often provides little more than a nucleus. Therefore, chloroplasts are most often inherited via the egg. Recall from Chapter 4 that chloroplasts are derived from proplastids. In four-o'clocks, the egg cell contains several proplastids that are inherited by the offspring. The sperm cell does not contribute any proplastids. For this reason, the phenotype of a four-o'clock plant reflects the types of proplastids it inherits from the maternal parent.

- If the maternal parent transmits only normal proplastids, all offspring will have green leaves (**Figure 18.8a**).

- Alternatively, if the maternal parent transmits only mutant proplastids, all offspring will have white leaves (**Figure 18.8b**).

- Because an egg cell contains several proplastids, an offspring from a variegated maternal parent may inherit only normal proplastids, only mutant proplastids, or a mixture of normal and mutant proplastids. Consequently, the offspring of a variegated maternal parent can be green, white, or variegated individuals (**Figure 18.8c**).

How do we explain the variegated phenotype at the cellular level? This phenotype is due to events that occur after fertilization. As a zygote containing both types of proplastids grows via cellular division to produce a multicellular plant, some cells may receive mostly protoplastids that develop into normal chloroplasts. Further division of these cells gives rise to a patch of green tissue. Alternatively, as a matter of chance, other cells may receive all or mostly mutant protoplastids that develop into chloroplasts that are defective in chlorophyll synthesis. The result is a patch of white tissue.

In seed-bearing plants, maternal inheritance of chloroplasts is the most common transmission pattern. However, certain species

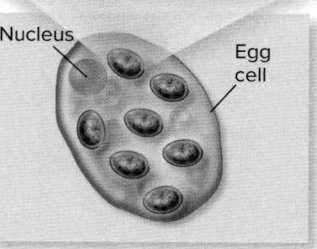

Normal proplastid will produce chloroplasts with a normal amount of green pigment.

Mutant proplastid will produce chloroplasts with very little pigment.

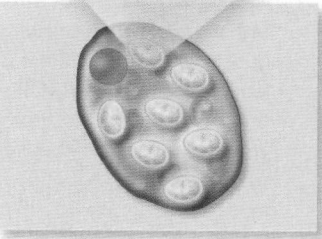

Nucleus

Egg cell

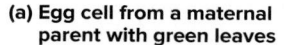

(a) Egg cell from a maternal parent with green leaves

(b) Egg cell from a maternal parent with white leaves

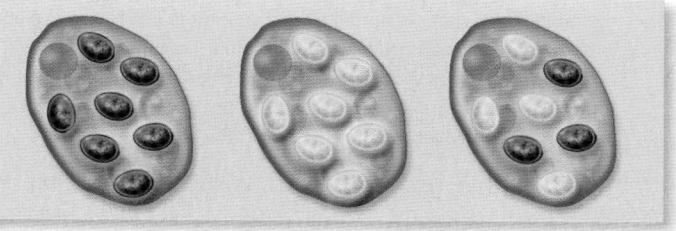

(c) Possible egg cells from a maternal parent with variegated leaves

Figure 18.8 **Plastid compositions of egg cells from green, white, and variegated four-o'clock plants.** In this drawing of four-o'clock egg cells, normal proplastids are represented as green and mutant proplastids as white. (Note: This drawing is schematic. Proplastids do not differentiate into chloroplasts in egg cells, and they are not actually green.) **(a)** A green plant produces eggs carrying normal proplastids. **(b)** A white plant produces eggs carrying mutant proplastids. **(c)** A variegated plant produces eggs that may contain either or both types of proplastids.

exhibit a pattern called **biparental inheritance**, in which both the pollen and the egg contribute chloroplasts to the offspring. Others exhibit **paternal inheritance**, in which only the pollen contributes these organelles. For example, most types of pine trees show paternal inheritance of chloroplasts.

THE QUESTION *One strain of periwinkle plants has green leaves, and another strain has variegated leaves. You do not know if the difference in the phenotypes is due to a mutation in a nuclear gene or in an organellar gene (one found in the chloroplasts or mitochondria). Using reciprocal crosses of the two strains, the following results were obtained:*

Variegated plant pollinated by green plant	Green plant pollinated by variegated plant
↓	↓
Offspring with green, white, or variegated leaves	All offspring with green leaves

Explain this pattern of inheritance.

T OPIC *What topic in biology does this question address?* The topic is inheritance. More specifically, the question is about distinguishing nuclear and extranuclear (organellar) inheritance patterns.

I NFORMATION *What information do you know based on the question and your understanding of the topic?* From the question, you know there are green-leaved and variegated-leaved strains of periwinkles. You are also given the results of reciprocal crosses. From your understanding of the topic, you may remember that some genes are found in the nucleus, whereas others are found in organelles, chloroplasts or mitochondria.

P ROBLEM-SOLVING S TRATEGY *Predict the outcome. Compare and contrast.* Crosses of these two strains will yield different results depending on the mode of inheritance. For example, if the gene is a nuclear gene and the green-leaved allele is dominant, you can predict that all of the F_1 offspring will be green-leaved. On the other hand, if the gene is in the chloroplasts and follows maternal inheritance, the phenotype of the offspring will depend on which plant contributed the egg.

ANSWER *The results of the reciprocal crosses are consistent with maternal inheritance, because the phenotypes of the offspring correlate with inheriting the gene from the plant contributing the egg cells. Since this gene affects the synthesis of chlorophyll, it is likely to be found in the chloroplasts.*

Mitochondrial Genomes Are Maternally Inherited in Humans and Most Other Species

Mitochondria are found in nearly all eukaryotic species. As with the transmission of chloroplasts in plants, maternal inheritance is the most common pattern of mitochondrial transmission in eukaryotes, although some species do exhibit biparental or paternal inheritance.

In humans, mitochondria are maternally inherited. Researchers have discovered that mutations in human mitochondrial genes cause a variety of rare diseases (**Table 18.4**). These are usually chronic degenerative disorders that affect organs, such as the brain, eyes, heart, muscle, kidneys, and endocrine glands, whose cells require high levels of ATP. For example, Leber's hereditary optic neuropathy (LHON) affects the optic nerve and leads to the progressive loss of vision in one or both eyes. LHON is caused by point mutations in several different mitochondrial genes.

Table 18.4	Examples of Human Mitochondrial Disease
Disease	Causes and symptoms
Leber's hereditary optic neuropathy (LHON)	A mutation in one of several mitochondrial genes that encode electron transport proteins. The main symptom is loss of vision.
Neurogenic muscle weakness	A mutation in a mitochondrial gene that encodes a subunit of mitochondrial ATP synthase, which is required for ATP synthesis. Symptoms involve abnormalities in the nervous system that affect the muscles and eyes.
Maternal myopathy and cardiomyopathy	A mutation in a mitochondrial gene that encodes a tRNA for leucine. The primary symptoms involve muscle abnormalities, most notably in the heart.
Myoclonic epilepsy and ragged-red muscle fibers	A mutation in a mitochondrial gene that encodes a tRNA for lysine. Symptoms include epilepsy, dementia, blindness, deafness, and heart and kidney malfunctions.

18.6 Genes on the Same Chromosome: Linkage and Recombination

Learning Outcomes:
1. Describe how linkage violates the law of independent assortment.
2. Explain how experimental crosses can demonstrate linkage.
3. **CoreSKILL »** Calculate the distance between genes that are linked on the same chromosome.

In Chapter 17, we saw that the independent assortment of alleles is due to the random alignment of homologous chromosomes during meiosis (refer back to Figure 17.11). But what happens when the alleles of different genes are on the same chromosome and do not independently assort? A typical chromosome contains many hundreds or even a few thousand different genes. When two genes are close together on the same chromosome, they tend to be transmitted as a unit, a phenomenon known as **linkage**. A group of genes that usually stay together during meiosis is called a **linkage group**, and the genes in the group are said to be linked. In a two-factor cross, linked genes that are close together on the same chromosome do not follow the law of independent assortment.

In this section, we will begin by examining the first experimental cross that demonstrated linkage. This pattern was subsequently explained by Thomas Hunt Morgan, who proposed that different genes located close to each other on the same chromosome tend to be inherited together. We will also see how crossing over between such genes provided the first method of mapping genes along chromosomes.

 **Core Skill: Process of Science**

Feature Investigation | **Bateson and Punnett's Cross of Sweet Peas Showed That Genes Do Not Always Assort Independently**

The first study showing linkage between two different genes was a cross of sweet peas carried out by William Bateson and Reginald Punnett in 1911. A surprising result occurred when they conducted

a two-factor cross involving flower color and pollen shape (**Figure 18.9**). One of the parent plants had purple flowers (*PP*) and long pollen (*LL*); the other had red flowers (*pp*) and round pollen (*ll*).

Figure 18.9   A cross of sweet peas showing that independent assortment does not always occur.

HYPOTHESIS The alleles of different genes assort independently of each other.

KEY MATERIALS True-breeding sweet pea strains that differ with regard to flower color and pollen shape.

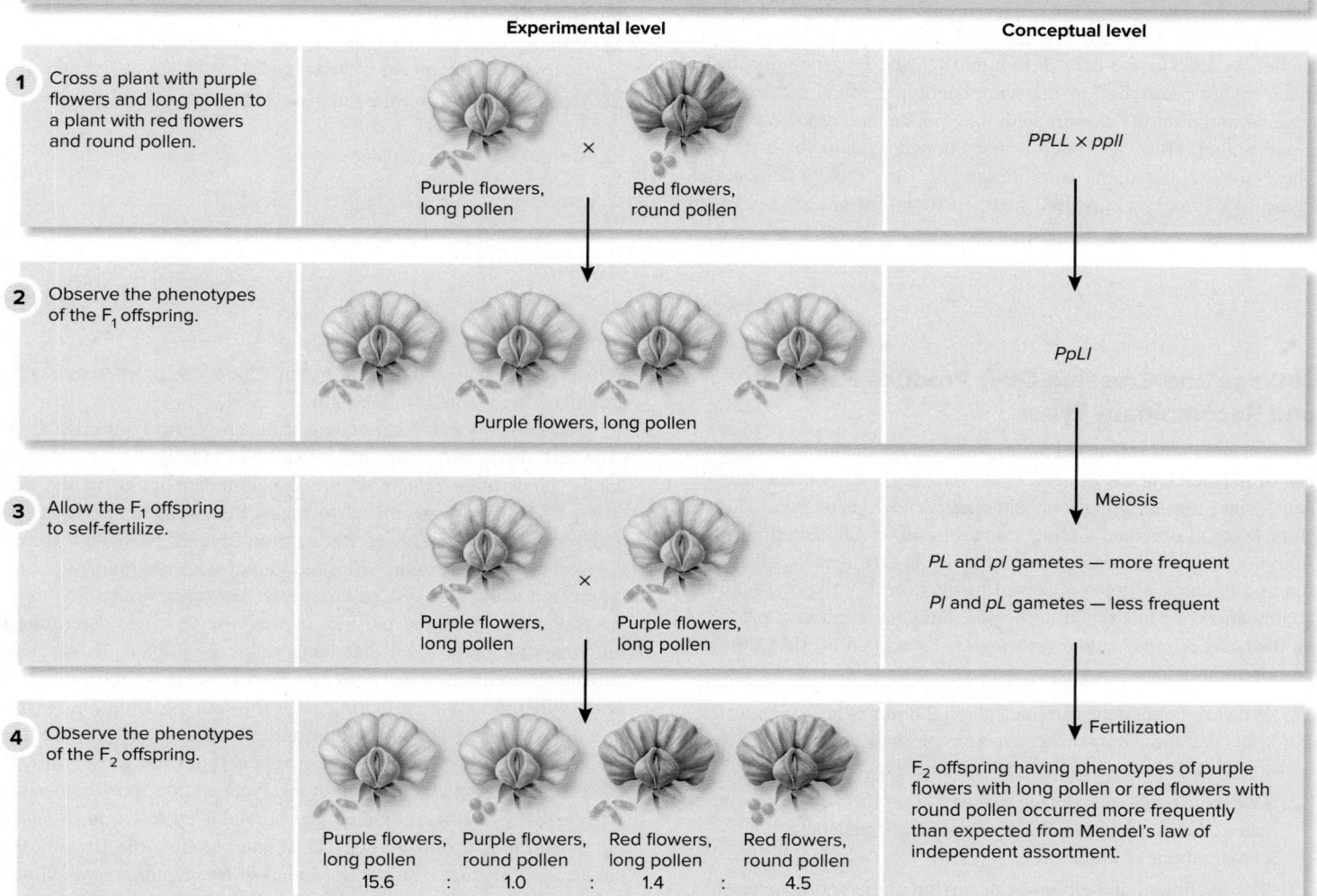

	Experimental level	Conceptual level
1 Cross a plant with purple flowers and long pollen to a plant with red flowers and round pollen.	Purple flowers, long pollen × Red flowers, round pollen	$PPLL \times ppll$
2 Observe the phenotypes of the F_1 offspring.	Purple flowers, long pollen	$PpLl$
3 Allow the F_1 offspring to self-fertilize.	Purple flowers, long pollen × Purple flowers, long pollen	Meiosis PL and pl gametes — more frequent Pl and pL gametes — less frequent
4 Observe the phenotypes of the F_2 offspring.	Purple flowers, long pollen : Purple flowers, round pollen : Red flowers, long pollen : Red flowers, round pollen 15.6 : 1.0 : 1.4 : 4.5	Fertilization F_2 offspring having phenotypes of purple flowers with long pollen or red flowers with round pollen occurred more frequently than expected from Mendel's law of independent assortment.

5   THE DATA

Phenotypes of F_2 offspring	Observed number	Observed ratio	Expected number	Expected ratio
Purple flowers, long pollen	296	15.6	240	9
Purple flowers, round pollen	19	1.0	80	3
Red flowers, long pollen	27	1.4	80	3
Red flowers, round pollen	85	4.5	27	1

6   CONCLUSION The data are not consistent with the law of independent assortment.

7   SOURCE Bateson, W., and Punnett, R. C. 1911. On the inter-relations of genetic factors. *Proceedings of the Royal Society of London, Series B* 84: 3–8.

As Bateson and Punnett expected, the F_1 plants all had purple flowers and long pollen (*PpLl*). The unexpected result came in the F_2 generation.

Although the F_2 offspring displayed the four phenotypes predicted by Mendel's laws, the observed numbers of offspring did not conform to the predicted 9:3:3:1 ratio (refer back to Figure 17.8). Rather, as seen in the data in Figure 18.9, the F_2 generation had a much higher proportion of the two phenotypes found in the parental generation: purple flowers with long pollen, and red flowers with round pollen. How did Bateson and Punnett explain these results? They suggested that the transmission of flower color and pollen shape was somehow coupled, so these traits did not always assort independently. Although the law of independent assortment applies to many other genes, in this example, the hypothesis of independent assortment was rejected.

Experimental Questions

1. What hypothesis were Bateson and Punnett testing when conducting the crosses of sweet peas?

2. **CoreSKILL »** What were the expected results of Bateson and Punnett's cross of F_1 plants?

3. **CoreSKILL »** How did the observed results differ from the expected results?

Linkage and Crossing Over Produce Parental and Recombinant Types

Bateson and Punnett realized their results did not conform to Mendel's law of independent assortment. However, they did not know why the genes were not assorting independently. A few years later, Thomas Hunt Morgan obtained similar ratios in crosses of fruit flies while studying the transmission pattern of genes in *Drosophila*. Like Bateson and Punnett, Morgan observed many more F_2 offspring with the combination of traits found in the parental generation than predicted on the basis of independent assortment. To explain his data, Morgan proposed three ideas:

1. When different genes are located on the same chromosome, the traits determined by those genes are more likely to be inherited together. This violates the law of independent assortment.

2. Due to crossing over during meiosis, homologous chromosomes can exchange pieces of chromosomes and create new combinations of alleles.

3. The likelihood of a crossover occurring in the region between two genes depends on the distance between the two genes. Crossovers between homologous chromosomes are much more likely to occur between two genes farther apart along a chromosome compared to two genes that are closer together.

To illustrate the first two ideas, **Figure 18.10** considers a series of crosses involving two genes linked on the same chromosome in *Drosophila*. The two genes are located on an autosome, not on a sex chromosome. The P generation cross is between flies that are homozygous for alleles that affect body color and wing shape. The female is homozygous for the dominant wild-type alleles that produce gray body color (b^+b^+) and straight wings (c^+c^+); the male is homozygous for recessive mutant alleles that produce black body color (*bb*) and curved wings (*cc*). The symbols for the genes are based on the names of the mutant phenotypes; the dominant wild-type allele is indicated by a superscript plus sign ($^+$). The chromosomes next to the flies in Figure 18.10 show the arrangement of these alleles. If the two genes are on the same chromosome, we know the arrangement of alleles in the P generation flies because these flies are homozygous for both genes ($b^+b^+c^+c^+$ for one parent and *bbcc* for the other parent). In the P generation female, on the left, b^+ and c^+ are linked, whereas *b* and *c* are linked in the male, on the right.

Let's now look at the outcome of the crosses in Figure 18.10. As expected, the F_1 offspring (b^+bc^+c) all had gray bodies and straight wings, confirming that these are the dominant traits. In the next cross, F_1 females were mated to males that were homozygous for both recessive alleles (*bbcc*). Recall from Chapter 17 that a **testcross** is conducted to determine if an individual with a dominant phenotype is a homozygote or a heterozygote. However, in the crosses we are discussing here, the purpose of the testcross is to determine if the genes for body color and wing shape are linked. If the genes are on different chromosomes and assort independently, this testcross will produce F_2 offspring with the four possible phenotypes in a 1:1:1:1 ratio. The observed numbers clearly conflict with this prediction. The two most abundant phenotypes are those with the combinations of characteristics in the P generation: gray bodies and straight wings or black bodies and curved wings. These offspring are termed **nonrecombinants**. The smaller number of offspring that have a combination of traits not found in the parental generation— gray bodies and curved wings or black bodies and straight wings— are called **recombinants**.

How do we explain the occurrence of recombinants when genes are linked on the same chromosome? As shown beside the flies of the F_2 generation in Figure 18.10, each recombinant individual has a chromosome that is the product of a crossover. The crossover occurred during the process of egg formation in the F_1 female fly. As shown below, four different egg cells are possible:

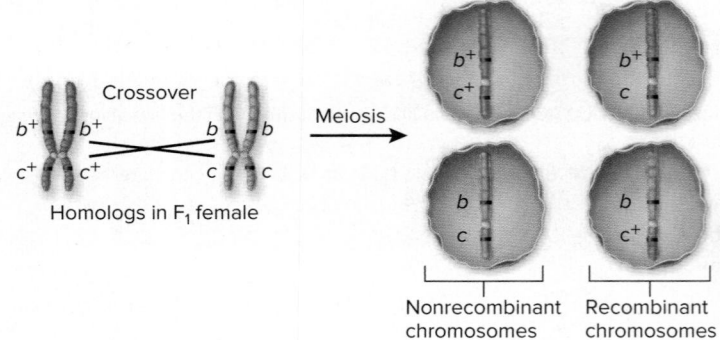

Crossover

b^+ b^+ b b
c^+ c^+ c c

Homologs in F_1 female

Meiosis →

b^+ b^+
c^+ c

b b
c c^+

Nonrecombinant   Recombinant
chromosomes   chromosomes

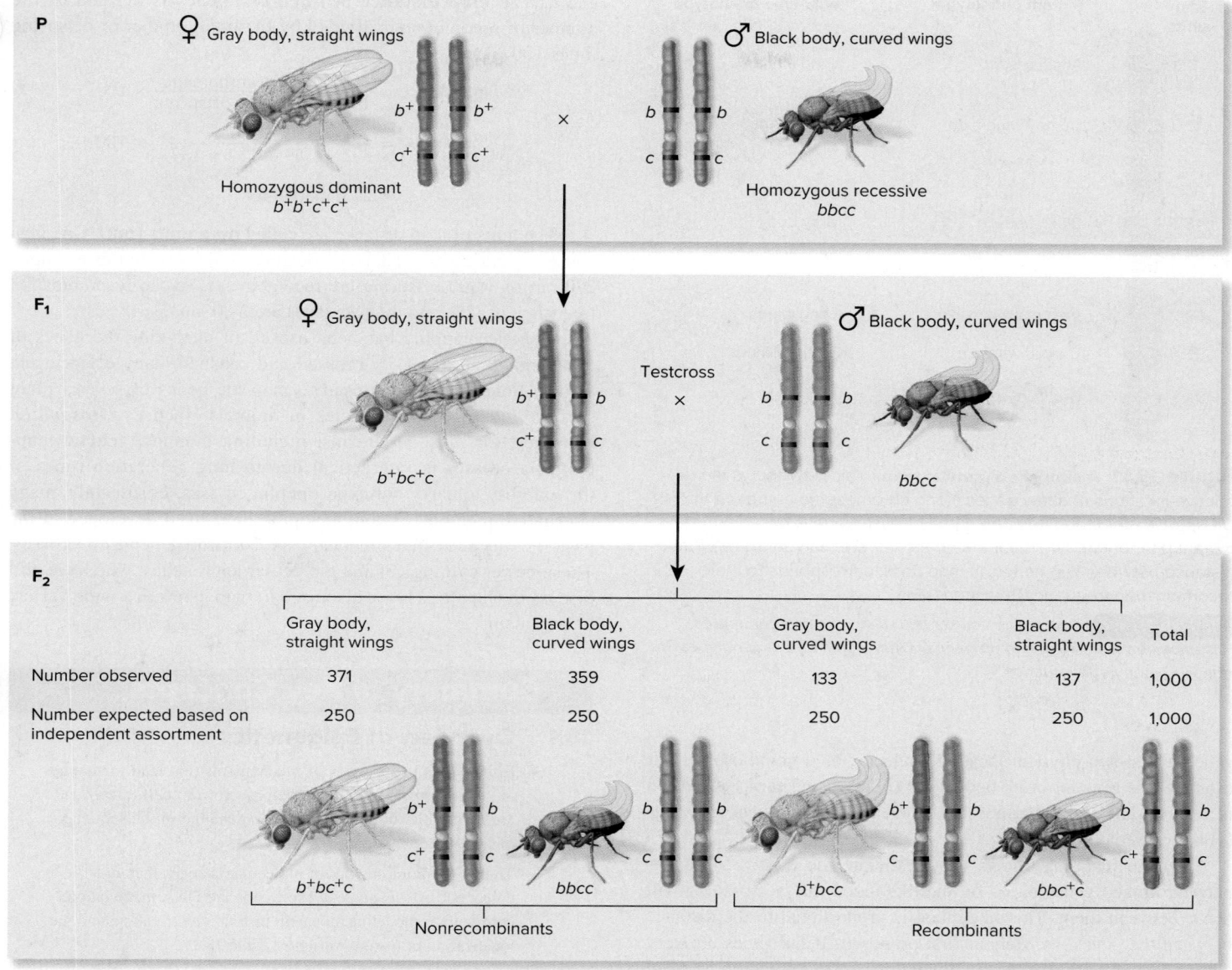

Figure 18.10 **Linkage and recombination of alleles.** An experimenter crossed $b^+b^+c^+c^+$ and $bbcc$ flies to produce F_1 heterozygotes. F_1 females were then testcrossed to $bbcc$ males. F_2 nonrecombinants have phenotypes that are the same as the parental (P) generation, whereas recombinants have a new combination of traits that is different from the P generation. The large number of nonrecombinant phenotypes in the F_2 generation suggests that the two genes are linked on the same chromosome. F_2 recombinant phenotypes occur because the alleles can be rearranged by crossing over. Note: The b^+ and c^+ alleles are dominant, and the b and c alleles are recessive.

Concept Check: *In which fly or flies did crossing over occur to produce the recombinant offspring of the F_2 generation?*

Due to crossing over, two of the four egg cells produced by meiosis have recombinant chromosomes. What happens when eggs containing such chromosomes are fertilized in the testcross? Each of the male fly's sperm cells carries a chromosome with the two recessive alleles. If the egg contains the recombinant chromosome carrying the b^+ and c alleles, the testcross will produce an F_2 offspring with a gray body and curved wings. If the egg contains the recombinant chromosome carrying the b and c^+ alleles, F_2 offspring will have a black body and straight wings. Therefore, crossing over in the F_1 female can explain the occurrence of both types of F_2 recombinant offspring.

Morgan's third idea regarding linkage was that the frequency of crossing over between linked genes depends on the distance between them. This suggested a method for determining the relative positions of genes on a chromosome, as we will discuss next.

Recombination Frequencies Provide a Method for Mapping Genes Along Chromosomes

The study of the arrangement of genes in a species' genome is called **genetic mapping**. As depicted in **Figure 18.11**, the linear order of genes along a chromosome is shown in a chart known as a **genetic map**. Each

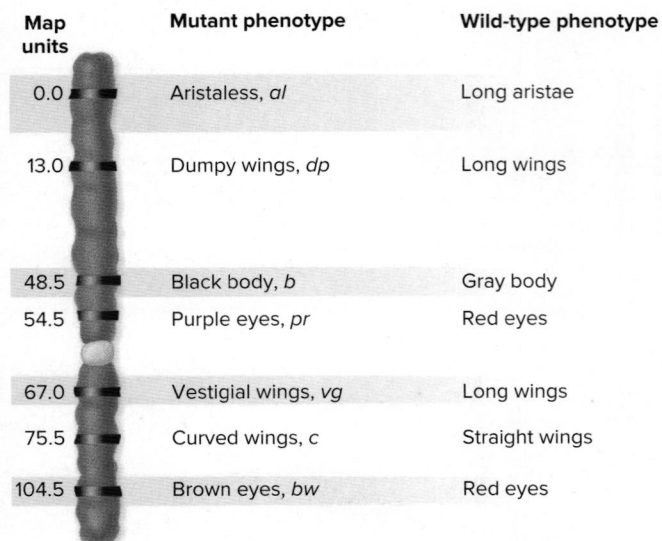

Map units	Mutant phenotype	Wild-type phenotype
0.0	Aristaless, *al*	Long aristae
13.0	Dumpy wings, *dp*	Long wings
48.5	Black body, *b*	Gray body
54.5	Purple eyes, *pr*	Red eyes
67.0	Vestigial wings, *vg*	Long wings
75.5	Curved wings, *c*	Straight wings
104.5	Brown eyes, *bw*	Red eyes

Figure 18.11 A simplified genetic map. This map shows the relative locations of a few genes along chromosome number 2 in *Drosophila melanogaster*. The name of each gene is based on the mutant phenotype. The numbers on the left are map units (mu). The distance between two genes, in map units, corresponds to their recombination frequency in testcrosses.

Concept Check: *How would you set up a testcross to determine the distance between the al and dp genes? What would be the genotypes of the P, F$_1$, and F$_2$ generations?*

gene has its own physical location, or locus, on a chromosome. For example, the gene for black body color (*b*) discussed earlier is located near the middle of the chromosome, whereas the gene for curved wings (*c*) is closer to one end.

Genetic mapping allows us to estimate the relative distances between linked genes based on the likelihood that a crossover will occur between them. This likelihood is proportional to the distance between the genes, as Morgan first proposed. If the genes are very close together, a crossover is unlikely to occur in the region between them. However, if the genes are very far apart, a crossover is more likely to occur in the region between the genes and thereby recombine the alleles. Therefore, in a testcross involving two genes on the same chromosome, the percentage of recombinant offspring is correlated with the distance between the genes. If a two-factor testcross produces many recombinants, the experimenter concludes that the two genes are far apart. If very few recombinants are observed, the two genes must be close together.

To find the distance between two genes, the experimenter must determine the frequency of crossing over between them, called their **recombination frequency**. This is accomplished by conducting a testcross. As an example, let's refer back to the *Drosophila* testcross described in Figure 18.10. As we discussed, the genes for body color and wing shape are on the same chromosome. The recombinants are the result of crossing over during egg formation in the F$_1$ female. We can use the data from the testcross shown in Figure 18.10 to estimate the distance between these two

genes. The **map distance** between two genes is defined as the number of recombinants divided by the total number of offspring times 100.

$$\text{Map distance} = \frac{\text{Number of recombinants}}{\text{Total number of offspring}} \times 100$$

$$= \frac{133 + 137}{371 + 359 + 133 + 137} \times 100$$

$$= 27.0 \text{ map units}$$

The units of map distance are called **map units (mu)**. One map unit is equivalent to a 1% recombination frequency. In this example, 270 out of 1,000 offspring are recombinants, so the recombination frequency is 27%, and the two genes are 27.0 mu apart.

Genetic mapping has been useful for analyzing the genes of organisms that are easily crossed and produce many offspring in a short time. It has been used to map the genes of several plant species and of certain species of animals, such as *Drosophila*. However, for most organisms, including humans, genetic mapping via crosses is impractical due to long generation times or the inability to carry out experimental crosses. Fortunately, many alternative methods of gene mapping have been developed in the past few decades that are faster and do not depend on crosses. These newer cytological and molecular approaches, which we will discuss in Chapter 21, are also used to map genes in a wide variety of organisms.

Summary of Key Concepts

18.1 Overview of Epigenetics

- Epigenetics is the study of mechanisms that lead to changes in gene expression that can be passed from cell to cell and are reversible, but do not involve a change in the sequence of DNA.

- The most common types of molecular changes that underlie epigenetic effects on gene expression are DNA methylation, chromatin remodeling, covalent histone modification, and the localization of histone variants (Table 18.1).

18.2 Epigenetics I: Genomic Imprinting

- As a result of genomic imprinting, offspring express either a maternal or paternal allele, depending on how a particular gene is marked, or imprinted (Figure 18.1).

- During gamete formation, DNA methylation of an allele from one parent is a mechanism to achieve imprinting (Figure 18.2).

18.3 Epigenetics II: X-Chromosome Inactivation

- If a female is heterozygous for an X-linked gene, this can lead to a mosaic phenotype, with some of the somatic cells expressing one allele and some expressing the other (Figures 18.3, 18.4).

- XCI in female mammals occurs when one X chromosome in every somatic cell is randomly inactivated. The counting of X inactivation centers (Xics) causes somatic cells to have only one active X chromosome (Table 18.2)

18.4 Epigenetics III: Effects of Environmental Agents

- Dietary factors during early stages of development cause epigenetic changes that affect phenotype (Figure 18.5).

- Environmental agents have been shown to cause epigenetic changes that are associated with human diseases such as cancer (Table 18.3).

18.5 Extranuclear Inheritance: Organelle Genomes

- Mitochondria and chloroplasts carry a small number of genes. The inheritance of such genes is called extranuclear inheritance (Figure 18.6).

- Chloroplasts in the four-o'clock plant are transmitted via the egg, a pattern called maternal inheritance (Figures 18.7, 18.8).

- Several human diseases are known to be caused by mutations in mitochondrial genes, which follow a maternal inheritance pattern (Table 18.4).

18.6 Genes on the Same Chromosome: Linkage and Recombination

- When two different genes are on the same chromosome, they are said to be linked. Linked genes tend to be inherited as a unit, unless crossing over separates them (Figures 18.9, 18.10).

- Genetic mapping allows us to determine the order of genes along a chromosome and the relative distances between them, based on the frequency of crossing over observed in testcrosses (Figure 18.11).

Assess & Discuss

Test Yourself

1. Which of the following is an example of an epigenetic change that alters gene expression?
   a. chromatin remodeling
   b. covalent histone modification
   c. localization of histone variants
   d. DNA methylation
   e. all of the above

2. In mice, the allele of the *Igf2* gene that is inherited from the mother is never expressed in her offspring. This happens because the *Igf2* gene from the mother
   a. always undergoes a mutation that inactivates its function.
   b. is deleted during oogenesis.
   c. is deleted during embryonic development.
   d. is not transcribed in the somatic cells of her offspring.
   e. is affected by all of the above.

3. A female mouse that is *Igf2 Igf2⁻* is crossed to a male that is also *Igf2 Igf2⁻*. The expected outcome for the phenotypes of the offspring from this cross is
   a. all normal size.
   b. all dwarf.
   c. 1 normal size : 1 dwarf.
   d. 3 normal size : 1 dwarf.
   e. 1 normal size : 3 dwarf.

4. The marking process for genomic imprinting initially occurs during
   a. gametogenesis.
   b. fertilization.
   c. embryonic development.
   d. adulthood.
   e. both b and c.

5. According to Lyon's hypothesis, the patchwork pattern on a calico cat can be explained by which of the following?
   a. One of the X chromosomes is converted to a Barr body in somatic cells of female mammals.
   b. One of the X chromosomes is converted to a Barr body in all cells of female mammals.
   c. Both of the X chromosomes are converted to Barr bodies in somatic cells of female mammals.
   d. Both of the X chromosomes are converted to Barr bodies in all cells of female mammals.
   e. One of the X chromosomes is lost in the somatic cells of female mammals.

6. A female mouse that is homozygous for the A^{vy} allele is mated to a male that is homozygous for a loss-of-function *(a)* allele. How would you expect the diet of this female during pregnancy to affect her offspring?
   a. Dietary agents that promote a greater level of DNA methylation would produce offspring with more yellow fur.
   b. Dietary agents that promote a lower level of DNA methylation would produce offspring with more yellow fur.
   c. Dietary agents that promote a greater level of DNA methylation would produce offspring with darker fur.
   d. Dietary agents that promote a lower level of DNA methylation would produce offspring with darker fur.
   e. Both b and c are correct.

7. Environmental agents may cause epigenetic changes that alter the expression of specific genes. Which of the following epigenetic changes would be expected to promote cancer?
   a. a change that resulted in the overexpression of a tumor-suppressor gene
   b. a change that resulted in the inhibition of a tumor-suppressor gene
   c. a change that resulted in the overexpression of an oncogene
   d. a change that resulted in the inhibition of an oncogene
   e. Both b and c are correct.

8. In many organisms, organelles, such as the mitochondria, are transmitted only by the egg. This phenomenon is known as
   a. biparental inheritance.
   b. paternal inheritance.
   c. X-linked inheritance.
   d. maternal inheritance.
   e. both c and d.

9. Based on the ideas proposed by Morgan, which of the following statements concerning linkage is *false?*
   a. Traits determined by genes located close together on the same chromosome are likely to be inherited together.
   b. Crossing over between homologous chromosomes can create new allele combinations.
   c. A crossover is more likely to occur in a region between two genes that are close together than in a region between two genes that are farther apart.
   d. The probability of crossing over depends on the distance between the genes.
   e. Genes that tend to be transmitted together are physically located on the same chromosome.

10. Extranuclear inheritance occurs because
     a.   certain genes are found on the X chromosome.
     b.   chromosomes in the nucleus may be transferred to the
          cytoplasm.
     c.   some cellular organelles contain DNA.
     d.   the nuclear membrane breaks apart during cell division.
     e.   both a and c.

Conceptual Questions

1.   Define epigenetics. Are all epigenetic changes passed from parent to
     offspring? Explain.

2.   What is a Barr body? How is its structure different from that of other
     chromosomes in the cell? How does the structure of a Barr body affect
     the level of X-linked gene expression?

3.      **Core Concept: Information** A core concept of biology is
     that the genetic material provides a blueprint for reproduction.
     Explain how epigenetics affects that blueprint.

Collaborative Questions

1.   Go to the PubMed website and search the words epigenetic and cancer.
     Scan through the journal articles you retrieve, and make a list of
     environmental agents that may cause epigenetic changes that contribute
     to cancer.

2.   Mendel studied seven traits in garden pea plants, and this species
     happens to have seven different chromosomes. It has been pointed out
     that Mendel was very lucky not to have conducted crosses involving
     two traits governed by genes that are closely linked on the same
     chromosome, because the results would have confounded his theory of
     independent assortment. It has even been suggested that Mendel may
     not have published data involving traits that were linked! An article by
     Stig Blixt 1975. (Why Didn't Gregor Mendel Find Linkage? *Nature* 256:
     206, 1975) considers this issue. Look up this article, and discuss why
     Mendel did not find linkage.

Genetics of Viruses and Bacteria

19

A colorized micrograph of *Haemophilus influenzae*, type b. This bacterium is a common cause of meningitis—a serious infection of the fluid in the spinal cord and the fluid that surrounds the brain. ©CAMR/A. Barry Dowsett/Science Source

While studying for his calculus test, Jason was having trouble concentrating due to a severe headache and fever. He thought he must be coming down with a cold. Though he had taken some aspirin, it didn't seem to be working. As he was eating some potato chips, one dropped in his lap. When he tried to look down to see where the chip had fallen, he realized that his neck was extremely stiff; he could barely move his head to look downward. Also, the brightness of his desk light seemed freakishly painful to his eyes. Over the course of that evening, Jason became confused and lethargic, and his roommate urged him to see a doctor. Fortunately, Jason took his advice and went to the college clinic. The diagnosis was bacterial meningitis—an inflammation of the protective membranes that cover the brain and spinal cord, collectively called the meninges. Although a relatively rare disease, bacterial meningitis is up to six times more common among people living in close quarters, such as college dormitories. Because Jason sought help early enough, his disease was successfully treated with antibiotics. Had he not gotten help, the disease could have progressed to the point of causing severe brain damage and even death.

Jason's story highlights a primary reason why biologists are so interested in viruses and bacteria. Many of them are **pathogens**—agents that cause disease symptoms in their hosts. Infectious diseases caused by viruses and bacteria are a leading cause of human suffering and death, accounting for one-quarter to one-third of deaths worldwide. The spread of infectious diseases results from human behavior, and in recent times, it has been accelerated by changes in land-use patterns, increased trade and travel, and the inappropriate use of antibiotic drugs. Although the incidence of fatal infectious diseases in the U.S. is low compared to the worldwide average, an alarming increase in more deadly strains of viruses and bacteria has occurred over the past few decades. Since 1980, the number of deaths in the U.S. due to infectious diseases has approximately doubled.

In this chapter, we turn our attention to the genetic analyses of viruses and bacteria. We will begin by examining viruses and other nonliving particles that infect living cells. All organisms are thought to be susceptible to infection by one or more types of viruses, which use the host's cellular machinery to replicate. Once a cell is infected, the genetic material of a virus orchestrates a series of events that ultimately leads to the production of new virus particles. We will consider the biological complexity of viruses and explore viral reproductive cycles. We will also examine some of the simplest and smallest infectious agents, called viroids and prions.

In the remaining sections of this chapter, we will examine the bacterial genome and the methods used in its investigation. Like their eukaryotic counterparts, bacteria have genetic differences that affect their cellular traits, and techniques of modern microbiology make many of these differences, such as sensitivity to antibiotics and differences in nutritional requirements, easy to study. Although bacteria reproduce asexually by cell division, their genetic variety is enhanced by the phenomenon called gene transfer, in which genes are passed from one bacterial cell to another. Like sexual reproduction in eukaryotes, gene transfer enhances the genetic diversity observed among bacterial species. In this chapter, we will explore three interesting ways that bacteria transfer genetic material.

19.1 General Properties of Viruses

Learning Outcome:

1. Compare and contrast types of viruses with regard to their host range, structure, and genomes.

Viruses are nonliving particles with nucleic acid genomes. Why are viruses considered nonliving? The answer is that they do not exhibit key properties associated with living organisms. Viruses are not composed of cells, and by themselves, they do not use energy or carry out metabolism, maintain homeostasis, or even reproduce. A virus or its genetic material must be taken up by a living cell to replicate.

The first virus to be discovered was tobacco mosaic virus (TMV). This virus infects many species of plants and causes mosaic-like patterns in which normal-colored patches are interspersed with light green or yellowish patches on the leaves (**Figure 19.1**). TMV damages leaves, flowers, and fruit but almost never kills the plant. In 1883, German chemist Adolf Mayer determined that this disease could be spread by spraying the sap from one plant onto another. By subjecting this sap to filtration, Russian scientist Dmitri Ivanovski demonstrated that the disease-causing agent was not a bacterium. Sap that had been passed through filters with pores small enough to prevent the passage of bacterial cells was still able to spread the disease. At first, some researchers suggested the agent was a chemical toxin. However, Dutch botanist Martinus Beijerinck ruled out this possibility by showing that sap continued to transmit the disease after many plant generations. A toxin would have been diluted after many generations, but Beijerinck's results indicated the disease agent was multiplying in the plant. Around the same time, animal viruses were discovered in connection with a disease of cattle called foot-and-mouth disease. In 1900, the first human virus, the virus that causes yellow fever, was identified.

Figure 19.1 A plant infected with tobacco mosaic virus. ©Norm Thomas/Science Source

Since these early studies, microbiologists, geneticists, and molecular biologists have taken a great interest in the structure, genetic composition, and replication of viruses. In this section, we will discuss their general properties.

Viruses Are Remarkably Varied, Despite Their Simple Structure

A **virus** is a small infectious particle that consists of nucleic acid enclosed in a protein coat. Researchers have identified and studied over 4,000 different types of viruses. Although all viruses share some similarities, such as small size and the reliance on a living cell for replication, they vary greatly in their characteristics, including their host range, structure, and genome composition. Some of the major differences are described next, and characteristics of selected viruses are shown in **Table 19.1**.

Table 19.1	Hosts and Characteristics of Selected Viruses				
Virus or group of viruses	**Host**	**Effect on host**	**Nucleic acid***	**Genome size (kb)†**	**Number of genes†**
Phage λ	*E. coli*	Can exist harmlessly in the host cell or cause lysis	dsDNA	48.5	36
Phage T4	*E. coli*	Causes lysis	dsDNA	169	288
Tobacco mosaic virus (TMV)	Many plants	Causes mottling and necrosis of leaves and other plant parts	ssRNA	6.4	6
Baculoviruses	Insects	Most baculoviruses are species specific; they usually kill the insect	dsDNA	133.9	154
Influenza virus	Mammals	Causes classical "flu," with fever, cough, sore throat, and headache	ssRNA	13.5	11
Epstein-Barr virus	Humans	Causes mononucleosis, with fever, sore throat, and fatigue	dsDNA	172	80
Adenovirus	Humans	Causes respiratory symptoms and diarrhea	dsDNA	34	35
Herpes simplex type II	Humans	Causes blistering sores around the genital region	dsDNA	158.4	77
HIV (type I)	Humans	Causes AIDS, an immunodeficiency syndrome eventually leading to death	ssRNA	9.7	9

*The abbreviations ss and ds refer to single-stranded and double-stranded, respectively.
†Several of the viruses listed in this table are found in different strains that vary with regard to genome size and number of genes. The numbers reported in this table are typical values. The abbreviation kb means kilobase, which equals 1,000 bases.

Differences in Host Range   A cell that is infected by a virus is called a **host cell**, and a species that can be infected by a specific virus is called a host species for that virus. Viruses differ greatly in their **host range**—the number of species and cell types they can infect. Table 19.1 lists a few examples of viruses with widely different ranges of host species. Tobacco mosaic virus, which we discussed earlier, has a broad host range. TMV is known to infect over 150 different species of plants. By comparison, other viruses have a narrow host range, with some infecting only a single species. Furthermore, a virus may infect only a specific cell type in a host species. **Figure 19.2** shows some viruses that infect particular human cells and cause disease.

Structural Differences   Viruses cannot be resolved by even the best light microscope. Although the existence of viruses was postulated in the 1890s, viruses were not observed until the 1930s when the electron microscope was invented. Viruses range in size from 20 to 400 nm in diameter (1 nm [nanometer] = 10^{-9} meter).

For comparison, a typical bacterium is 1,000 nm in diameter, and the diameter of most eukaryotic cells is 10 to 1,000 times that of a bacterium. Adenoviruses, which cause infections of the respiratory and gastrointestinal tracts, have an average diameter of 75 nm. Over 50 million adenoviruses could fit into an average-sized human cell.

What are the common structural features of all viruses? As shown in **Figure 19.3**, all viruses have a protein coat called a **capsid**, which encloses a genome consisting of one or more molecules of nucleic acid (DNA or RNA). Capsids are composed of one or several different protein subunits called capsomers. Capsids have a variety of shapes, including helical and polyhedral. Figure 19.3a shows the structure of TMV, which has a helical capsid made of identical capsomers. Figure 19.3b shows an adenovirus, which has a polyhedral capsid. Protein fibers with a terminal knob are located at the corners of the polyhedral capsid. Many viruses that infect animal cells, such as the influenza virus shown in Figure 19.3c, have a **viral envelope** enclosing the capsid. The envelope consists of a lipid bilayer that is derived from the plasma membrane of the host cell and is embedded with virally encoded spike glycoproteins.

In addition to encasing and protecting the genetic material, the capsid and envelope enable viruses to infect their hosts. Many viruses have protein fibers with a knob (Figure 19.3b) or spike glycoproteins (Figure 19.3c) that help them bind to the surface of a host cell. Viruses that infect bacteria, called **bacteriophages**, or simply **phages**, may have more complex protein coats, with accessory structures used for anchoring the virus to a host cell and injecting the viral nucleic acid (Figure 19.3d). As discussed later, the tail fibers of such bacteriophages are needed to attach the virus to the bacterial cell wall.

Genome Differences   The genetic material in a virus is called a **viral genome**. The composition of viral genomes varies markedly among different types of viruses, as suggested by the examples in Table 19.1. The nucleic acid of some viruses is DNA, whereas in others it is RNA. These are referred to as DNA viruses and RNA viruses, respectively. It is striking that some viruses use RNA for their genome, whereas all living organisms use DNA. In some viruses, the nucleic acid is single stranded, whereas in others, it is double stranded. The genome can be linear or circular, depending on the type of virus. Some kinds of viruses have more than one copy of the genome.

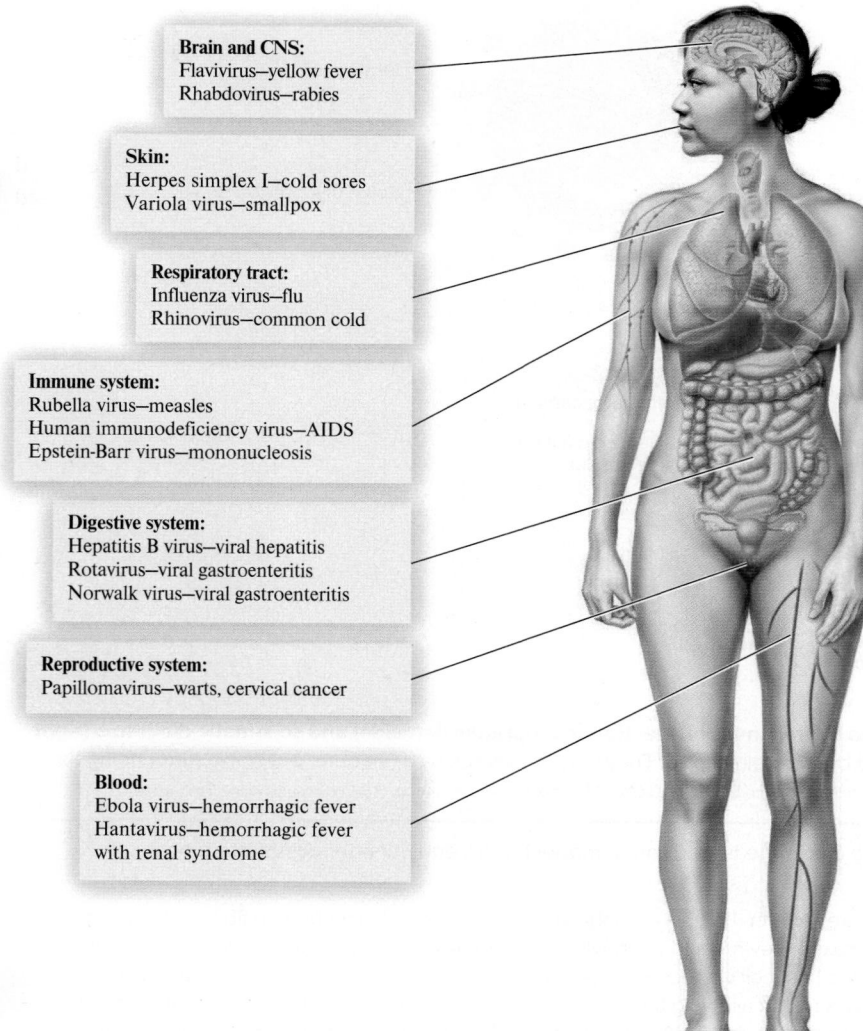

Brain and CNS:
Flavivirus—yellow fever
Rhabdovirus—rabies

Skin:
Herpes simplex I—cold sores
Variola virus—smallpox

Respiratory tract:
Influenza virus—flu
Rhinovirus—common cold

Immune system:
Rubella virus—measles
Human immunodeficiency virus—AIDS
Epstein-Barr virus—mononucleosis

Digestive system:
Hepatitis B virus—viral hepatitis
Rotavirus—viral gastroenteritis
Norwalk virus—viral gastroenteritis

Reproductive system:
Papillomavirus—warts, cervical cancer

Blood:
Ebola virus—hemorrhagic fever
Hantavirus—hemorrhagic fever with renal syndrome

Figure 19.2 Some viruses that cause human diseases. Most viruses that cause disease in humans infect cells of specific tissues, as illustrated by the examples in this figure.

 Core Concept: Science and Society
By studying viruses, biologists have developed vaccines and drugs to help prevent their spread.

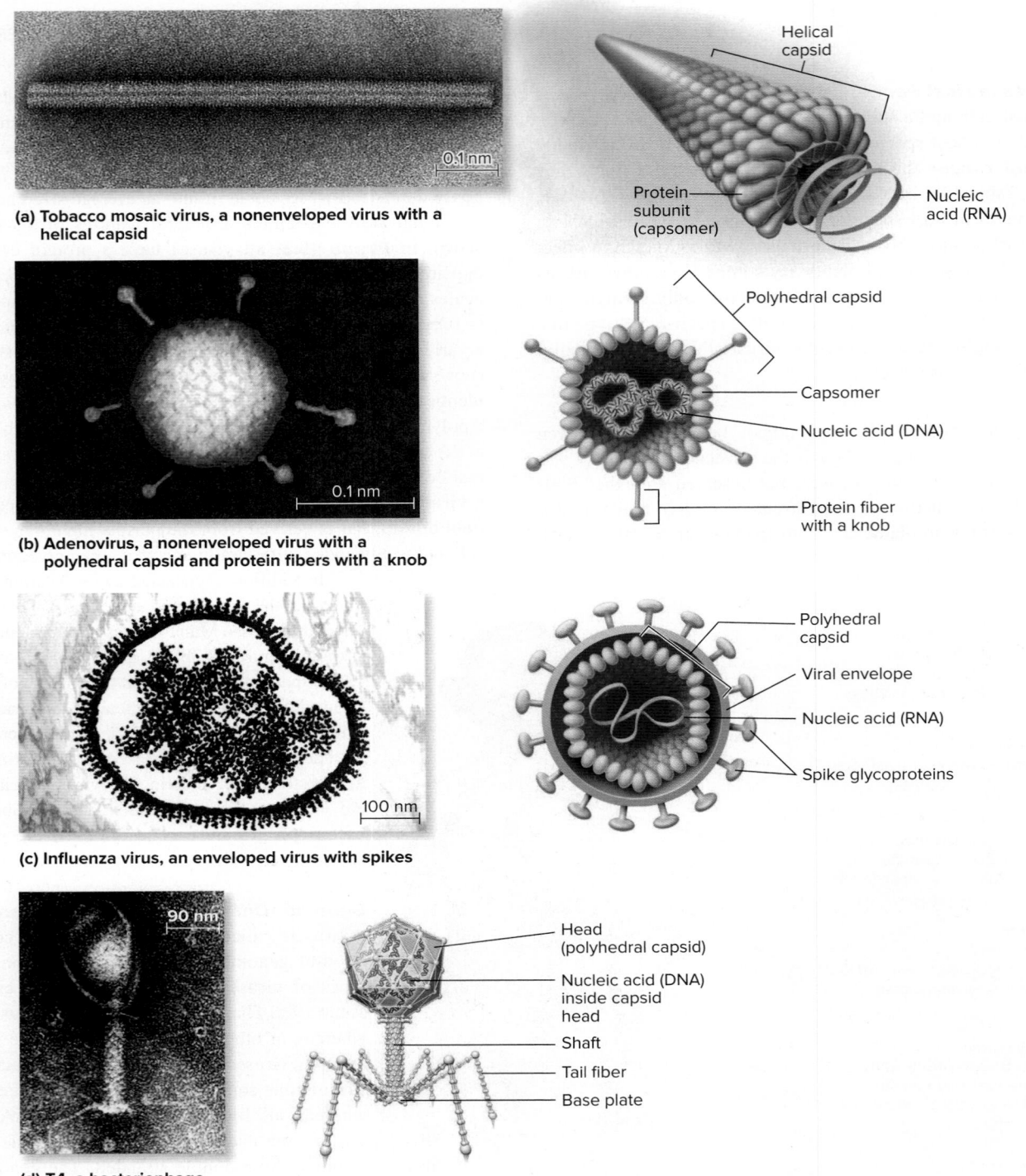

(a) Tobacco mosaic virus, a nonenveloped virus with a helical capsid

Helical capsid

Protein subunit (capsomer)

Nucleic acid (RNA)

(b) Adenovirus, a nonenveloped virus with a polyhedral capsid and protein fibers with a knob

Polyhedral capsid

Capsomer

Nucleic acid (DNA)

Protein fiber with a knob

(c) Influenza virus, an enveloped virus with spikes

Polyhedral capsid

Viral envelope

Nucleic acid (RNA)

Spike glycoproteins

(d) T4, a bacteriophage

Head (polyhedral capsid)

Nucleic acid (DNA) inside capsid head

Shaft

Tail fiber

Base plate

Figure 19.3 **Variations in the structure of viruses, as shown by transmission electron micrographs (left side) and schematic diagrams (right side).** All viruses contain nucleic acid (DNA or RNA) surrounded by a protein capsid. They may or may not have an outer envelope surrounding the capsid. a: ©Science Source; b: ©Dr. Linda M. Stannard, University of Cape Town/SPL/Science Source; c: ©Chris Bjornberg/Science Source; d: ©Omikron/Science Source

Core Skill: Modeling The goal of this modeling challenge is to create a model for the entry of adenovirus into a host cell.

Modeling Challenge The capsid of an adenovirus plays a key role in the uptake of the virus into a host cell. The protein fiber with a knob binds to a receptor on the surface of the host cell called the coxsackievirus and adenovirus receptor (CAR), because it can recognize either coxsackievirus or adenovirus. Adenovirus is then taken into the host cell via receptor-mediated endocytosis (see Figure 5.22). After an intracellular vesicle carrying the virus forms, capsid proteins also play a role in allowing the virus to enter the cytosol by breaking through the vesicle membrane. During this process, the capsid breaks apart, releasing the viral DNA that subsequently enters the nucleus and provides the information to make thousands of new viruses. Draw a model that is similar to the one shown in Figure 5.22 that depicts the binding of adenovirus to a host cell and its subsequent uptake into the cell. Your model should also include the entry of viral DNA into the cell nucleus.

Viral genomes also vary considerably in size, ranging from a few thousand to more than a hundred thousand nucleotides in length (see Table 19.1). For example, the genome of TMV is only 6,400 base pairs in length and contains only six genes. Other viruses, particularly those with a complex structure, such as phage T4, contain many more genes. These extra genes encode many different proteins that are involved in the formation of the elaborate structure shown in Figure 19.3d.

19.2 Viral Reproductive Cycles

Learning Outcomes:

1. List the steps in a viral reproductive cycle, and distinguish between the lysogenic and lytic cycles.
2. Describe how emerging viruses such as HIV arise and spread through a population.
3. Explain how an understanding of viral structure and reproduction can aid in the development of drugs to combat viruses.
4. Outline three hypotheses regarding the origin of viruses.

When a virus infects a host cell, the expression of viral genes leads to a series of steps, called a **viral reproductive cycle**, which results in the production of new viruses. The details of the steps differ among various types of viruses, and a given type of virus may follow alternative cycles. Even so, by studying hundreds of different viruses, researchers have determined that the viral reproductive cycle consists of five or six common steps. In this section, we will examine viral reproductive cycles in detail, paying particular attention to human immunodeficiency virus (HIV), which causes acquired immunodeficiency syndrome (AIDS) in humans.

Viral Reproductive Cycles Consist of a Few Common Steps

To illustrate the general features of viral reproductive cycles, **Figure 19.4** considers these steps for two types of viruses. Figure 19.4a shows the cycle of phage λ (lambda), a bacteriophage with double-stranded DNA as its genome, and Figure 19.4b depicts the cycle of HIV, an enveloped animal virus containing single-stranded RNA. The descriptions that follow compare the reproductive cycles of these two very different viruses.

Step 1: Attachment In the first step of a viral reproductive cycle, the virus attaches to the surface of a host cell. This attachment is usually specific for one or just a few types of cells because proteins in the virus recognize and bind to specific molecules on the cell surface. In the case of phage λ, the tail fibers bind to proteins in the outer bacterial cell membrane of *E. coli* cells. In the case of HIV, spike glycoproteins in the viral envelope bind to protein receptors in the plasma membrane of human white blood cells called helper T cells.

Step 2: Entry After attachment, the viral genome enters the host cell. Attachment of phage λ stimulates a conformational change in its coat proteins, so the shaft contracts, and the phage injects its DNA into the bacterial cytoplasm. In contrast, the envelope of HIV fuses with the plasma membrane of the host cell, so both the capsid and its contents are released into the cytosol. Some of the HIV capsid proteins are then removed by host cell enzymes, a process called uncoating. This releases two copies of the viral RNA and molecules of two enzymes called reverse transcriptase and integrase into the cytosol. As discussed shortly, these enzymes are needed for step 3.

Once a viral genome has entered the cell, one or a few viral genes are expressed immediately due to the action of host cell enzymes and ribosomes. Expression of these early genes leads quickly to either step 3 or step 4 of the reproductive cycle, depending on the specific virus. The genome of some viruses, including both phage λ and HIV, can integrate into a chromosome of the host cell. For such viruses, the cycle may proceed from step 2 to step 3 as described next, delaying the production of new viruses. Alternatively, the cycle for phage λ may proceed directly from step 2 to step 4 and quickly lead to the production of new viruses.

Step 3: Integration Viruses capable of integration carry a gene that encodes an enzyme called **integrase**, which cuts the host's chromosomal DNA and inserts the viral genome into the chromosome. In the case of phage λ, the double-stranded DNA that entered the cell can be directly integrated into the double-stranded DNA of the chromosome. Once integrated, the phage DNA in a bacterium is called a **prophage**. When a bacterial cell divides, the prophage DNA is copied and transmitted to daughter cells along with the bacterial chromosomal DNA. When a prophage has been integrated into a bacterial chromosome, this type of viral reproductive cycle is called the **lysogenic cycle**. As discussed later, new phages are not made during the lysogenic cycle, and the host cell is not destroyed. On occasion, a prophage can be excised from the bacterial chromosome and proceed to step 4.

How can an RNA virus integrate its genome into the host cell's DNA? For this to occur, the viral genome must be copied into DNA. HIV accomplishes this by means of a viral enzyme called **reverse transcriptase**, which is carried within the capsid and released into the host cell along with the viral RNA. Reverse transcriptase uses the viral RNA strand to make a complementary copy of DNA. The complementary DNA is then used as a template to make double-stranded viral DNA. This process is called reverse transcription because it is the reverse of the usual transcription process, in which a DNA strand is used to make a complementary strand of RNA. The viral double-stranded DNA enters the host cell nucleus and is inserted into a host chromosome via integrase. Like reverse transcriptase, integrase is carried within the HIV capsid and released into the host cell during uncoating. Once integrated, the viral DNA in a eukaryotic cell is called a **provirus**. Viruses that follow this mechanism are called **retroviruses**.

Step 4: Synthesis of Viral Components The production of new viruses by a host cell involves the replication of the viral genome and the synthesis of viral proteins that make up the protein coat. A prophage must be excised as described in step 3 before the synthesis of new viral components can occur. An enzyme called excisionase is required for this process. Following excision, host cell enzymes make many copies of the phage DNA and transcribe the genes within these copies into mRNA. Host cell ribosomes translate this viral mRNA

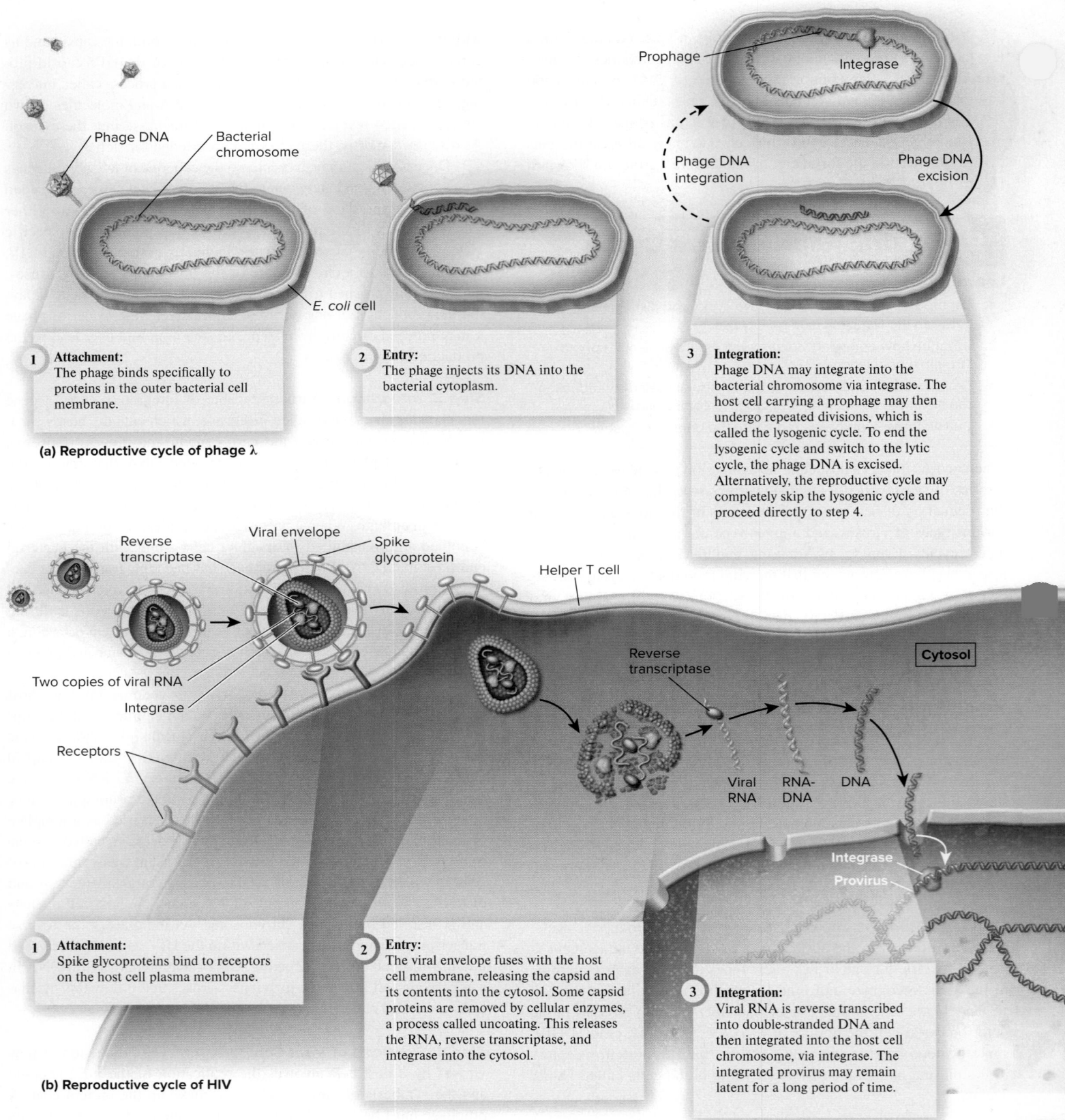

1 Attachment:
The phage binds specifically to proteins in the outer bacterial cell membrane.

2 Entry:
The phage injects its DNA into the bacterial cytoplasm.

3 Integration:
Phage DNA may integrate into the bacterial chromosome via integrase. The host cell carrying a prophage may then undergo repeated divisions, which is called the lysogenic cycle. To end the lysogenic cycle and switch to the lytic cycle, the phage DNA is excised. Alternatively, the reproductive cycle may completely skip the lysogenic cycle and proceed directly to step 4.

(a) Reproductive cycle of phage λ

1 Attachment:
Spike glycoproteins bind to receptors on the host cell plasma membrane.

2 Entry:
The viral envelope fuses with the host cell membrane, releasing the capsid and its contents into the cytosol. Some capsid proteins are removed by cellular enzymes, a process called uncoating. This releases the RNA, reverse transcriptase, and integrase into the cytosol.

3 Integration:
Viral RNA is reverse transcribed into double-stranded DNA and then integrated into the host cell chromosome, via integrase. The integrated provirus may remain latent for a long period of time.

(b) Reproductive cycle of HIV

Figure 19.4 Comparison of the steps of two viral reproductive cycles. (a) The reproductive cycle of phage λ, a bacteriophage with a double-stranded DNA genome. (b) The reproductive cycle of HIV, an enveloped animal virus with a single-stranded RNA genome.

Core Skill: Connections Look back at Figure 5.21. How does the release of HIV resemble exocytosis?

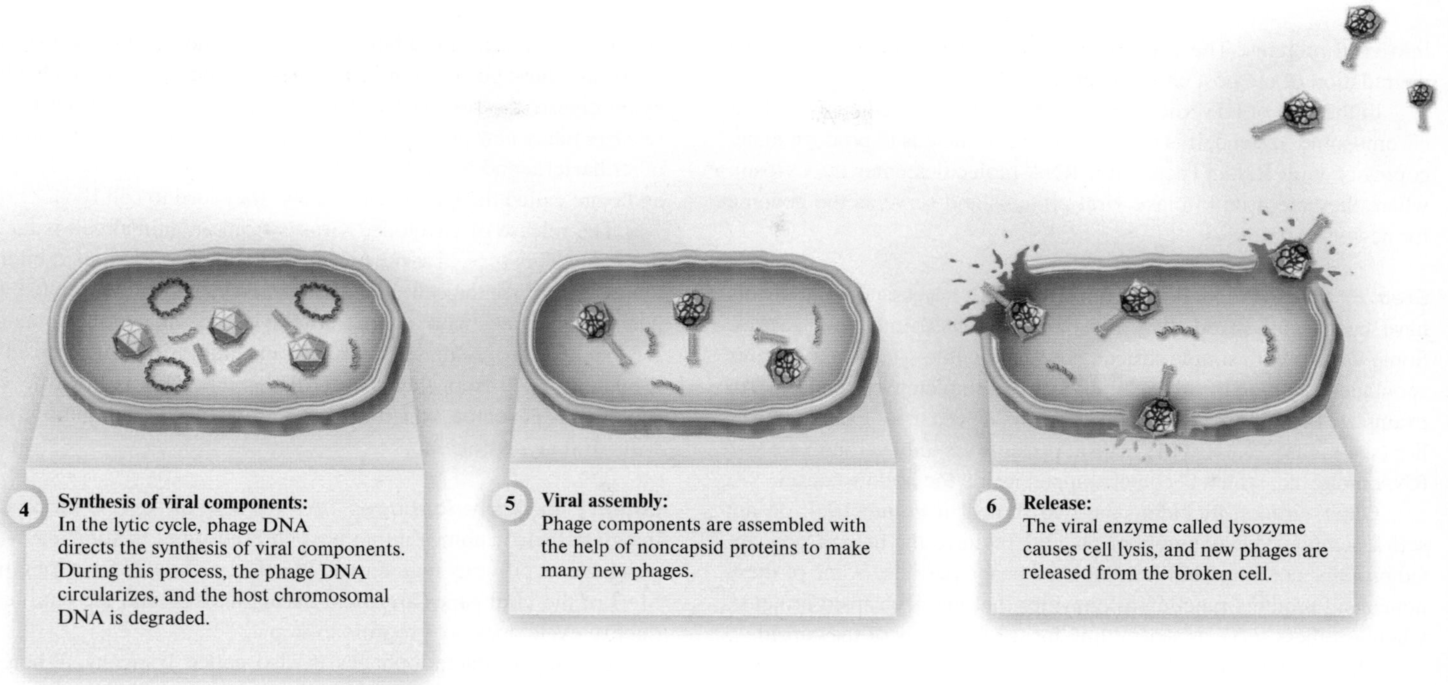

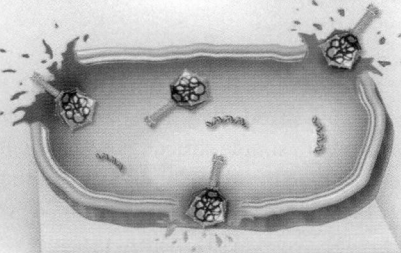

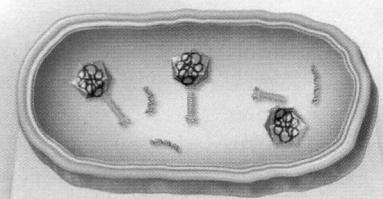

4   **Synthesis of viral components:**
In the lytic cycle, phage DNA
directs the synthesis of viral components.
During this process, the phage DNA
circularizes, and the host chromosomal
DNA is degraded.

5   **Viral assembly:**
Phage components are assembled with
the help of noncapsid proteins to make
many new phages.

6   **Release:**
The viral enzyme called lysozyme
causes cell lysis, and new phages are
released from the broken cell.

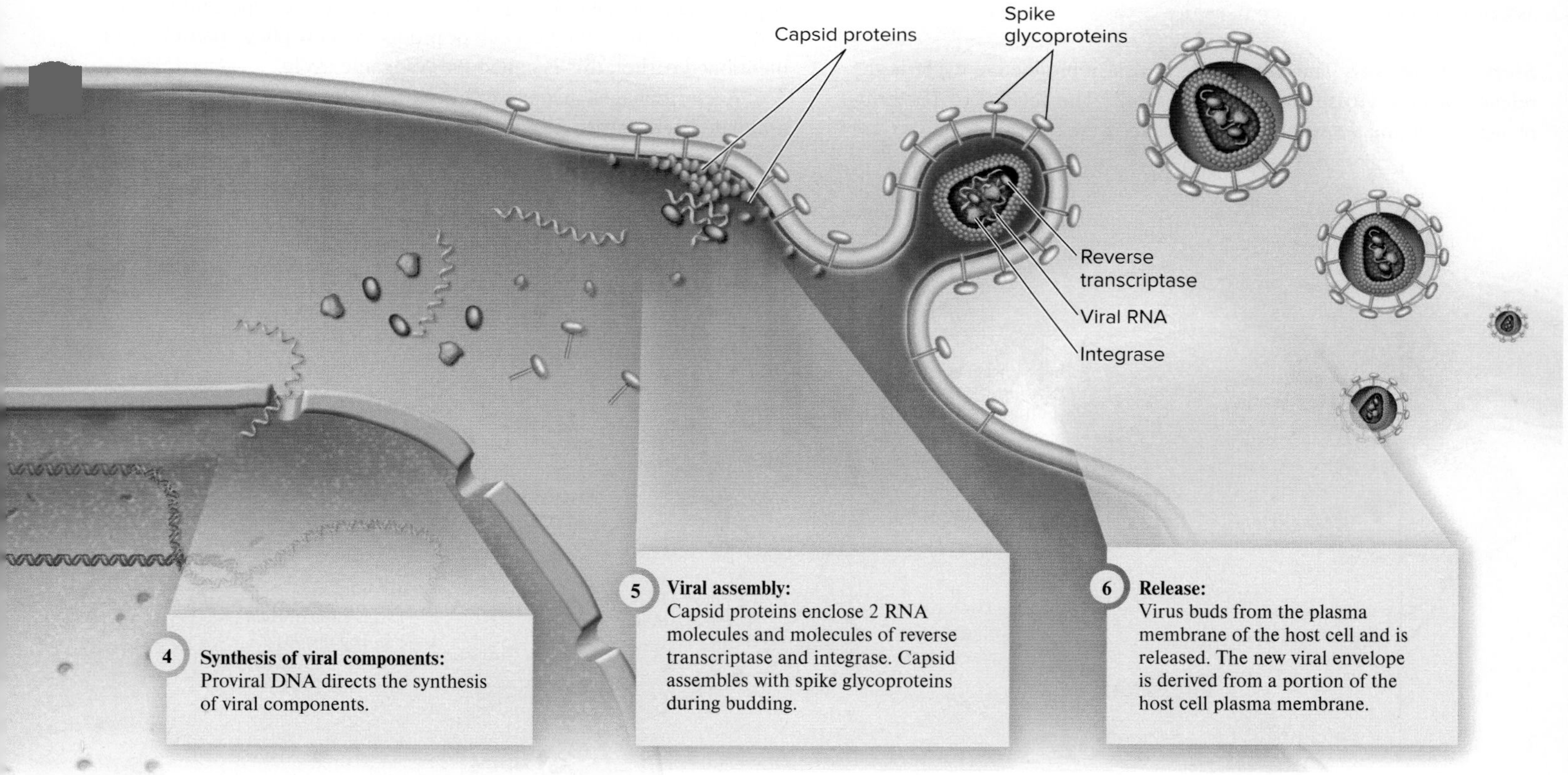

Capsid proteins

Spike
glycoproteins

Reverse
transcriptase

Viral RNA

Integrase

4   **Synthesis of viral components:**
Proviral DNA directs the synthesis
of viral components.

5   **Viral assembly:**
Capsid proteins enclose 2 RNA
molecules and molecules of reverse
transcriptase and integrase. Capsid
assembles with spike glycoproteins
during budding.

6   **Release:**
Virus buds from the plasma
membrane of the host cell and is
released. The new viral envelope
is derived from a portion of the
host cell plasma membrane.

into viral proteins. The expression of phage genes also leads to the degradation of the host chromosomal DNA.

In the case of HIV, the provirus DNA is not excised from the host chromosome. Instead, it is transcribed in the nucleus to produce many copies of viral RNA. These viral RNA molecules enter the cytosol, where they are used to make viral proteins and serve as the genome for new viral particles.

Step 5: Viral Assembly   After all of the necessary components have been synthesized, they must be assembled into new viruses. Some viruses with simple structures self-assemble—viral components spontaneously bind to each other to form a complete virus particle. An example of a self-assembling virus is TMV, which we examined earlier (see Figure 19.3a). TMV capsid proteins assemble around a TMV RNA molecule, which becomes trapped inside the hollow capsid.

Other viruses, including the two shown in Figure 19.4, do not self-assemble. The assembly of phage λ requires the help of noncapsid proteins not found in the completed phage particle. Some of these noncapsid proteins function as enzymes that modify capsid proteins, whereas others serve as scaffolding for the assembly of the capsid.

The assembly of HIV occurs in two stages. First, capsid proteins assemble around two molecules of viral RNA and molecules of reverse transcriptase and integrase. Next, the newly formed capsid acquires its outer envelope in a budding process. This second phase of assembly occurs during step 6, as the virus is released from the cell.

Step 6: Release   The last step of a viral reproductive cycle is the release of new viruses from the host cell. The release of bacteriophages is a dramatic event. Because bacteria are surrounded by a rigid cell wall, the phages must burst, or lyse, their host cell to escape. After the phages have been assembled, a phage-encoded enzyme called lysozyme digests the bacterial cell wall, causing the cell to burst. Lysis releases many new phages into the environment, where they can infect other bacteria and begin the cycle again. Collectively, steps 1, 2, 4, 5, and 6 are called the **lytic cycle** because they lead to cell lysis.

The release of enveloped viruses from an animal cell is far less dramatic. This type of virus escapes by a mechanism called budding that does not lyse the cell. In the case of HIV, a newly assembled virus particle associates with a portion of the plasma membrane containing HIV spike glycoproteins. The membrane enfolds the viral capsid and eventually buds from the surface of the cell. This is how the virus acquires its envelope, which is a piece of host cell membrane studded with viral glycoproteins.

Latency in Bacteriophages   As we saw in step 3, viruses can integrate their genomes into a host chromosome. In some cases, the prophage or provirus may remain inactive, or **latent**, for a long time. Most of the viral genes are silent during latency, and the viral reproductive cycle does not progress to step 4.

Latency in bacteriophages is also called lysogeny. When this occurs, both the prophage and its host cell are said to be lysogenic. When a lysogenic bacterium prepares to divide, it copies the prophage DNA along with its own DNA, so each daughter cell inherits a copy of the prophage. A prophage can be replicated repeatedly in this way without killing the host cell or producing new phage particles. As mentioned earlier, this is called the lysogenic cycle.

Bacteriophages that can follow either a lysogenic or a lytic cycle are called **temperate phages** (**Figure 19.5**). Phage λ is an example

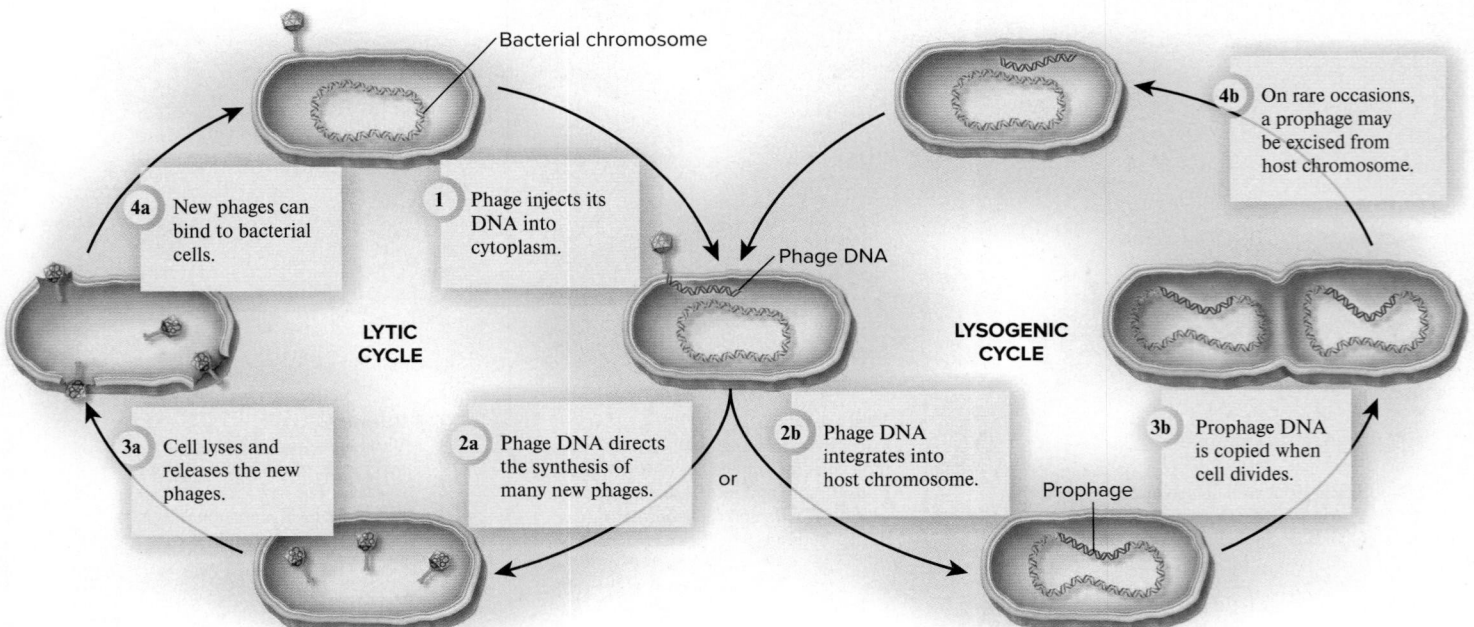

Figure 19.5 Lytic and lysogenic cycles of bacteriophages. Some phages, such as phage λ, may follow either a lytic or a lysogenic reproductive cycle. During the lytic cycle, new phages are made, and the bacterial cell lyses. During the lysogenic cycle, the integrated phage DNA, or prophage, is replicated along with the DNA of the host cell. Environmental conditions influence how long the phage remains in the lysogenic cycle.

Concept Check: *From the perspective of the bacteriophage, what are the primary advantages of the lytic and lysogenic cycles?*

of a temperate phage. Upon infection, it can either enter the lysogenic cycle or proceed directly to the lytic cycle. Other phages, called **virulent phages**, have only lytic cycles. The genome of a virulent phage is not capable of integrating into a host chromosome. Phage T4 is a virulent phage that infects *E. coli* (see Figure 19.3d). Unlike phage λ, which may coexist harmlessly with *E. coli*, T4 always lyses the host cell.

For temperate phages such as phage λ, environmental conditions influence whether or not viral DNA is integrated into a host chromosome and how long the virus remains in the lysogenic cycle. If nutrients are readily available, phage λ usually proceeds directly to the lytic cycle after its DNA enters the cell. Alternatively, if nutrients are in short supply, the lysogenic cycle is favored because sufficient material may not be available to make new viruses. If more nutrients become available later, the prophage may become activated. At this point, the viral reproductive cycle switches to the lytic cycle, and new viruses are made and released.

Latency in Human Viruses   Latency among human viruses can occur in two different ways. For HIV, latency occurs because the virus has integrated into the host genome and may remain dormant for a long time. In addition, the genome of some other viruses can exist as an **episome**—a genetic element that replicates independently of the chromosomal DNA but also can occasionally integrate into chromosomal DNA. Examples of viral genomes that exist as episomes include different types of herpesviruses that cause cold sores (usually herpes simplex type I), genital herpes (usually herpes simplex type II), and chickenpox (varicella-zoster). A person infected with a given type of herpesvirus may have periodic outbreaks of disease symptoms when the virus switches from the latent, episomal form to the active form that produces new virus particles.

As an example, let's consider the herpesvirus called varicella-zoster. The initial infection by this virus causes chickenpox, after which the virus may remain latent for many years as an episome. The disease called shingles occurs when varicella-zoster switches from the latent state and starts making new virus particles. Shingles begins as a painful rash that eventually erupts into blisters. The blisters follow the path of the neurons that carry the latent varicella-zoster virus. The blisters often form a ring around the back of the patient's body. The name shingles is derived from a Latin word meaning girdle, referring to the observation that the blisters girdle a part of the body.

Emerging Viruses, Such as HIV and Zika Virus, May Spread Rapidly Through a Population

A key reason researchers have been interested in viral reproductive cycles is the ability of many viruses to cause diseases in humans and other hosts. **Emerging viruses** are ones that have arisen recently or have recently shown a greater probability of causing infection. Because the base sequences of many viruses are already known, researchers have determined that emerging viruses typically result from mutations in pre-existing viruses. Emerging viruses can lead to significant loss of human life and often cause public alarm. New strains of influenza virus arise fairly regularly due to mutations. An example is the strain H1N1, also called swine flu. In the U.S., despite

attempts to minimize deaths by vaccination, over 30,000 people die annually from influenza.

Another example of an emerging virus is Zika virus, an enveloped virus with a genome composed of single-stranded RNA. Its name comes from the Zika Forest of Uganda, where the virus was first isolated in 1947. Zika virus is primarily spread by mosquitoes of the genus *Aedes*. The most common symptoms of a Zika infection are fever, rash, joint pain, and conjunctivitis. In most people, the illness is usually mild, but in rare cases, a Zika infection in an adult can cause a more serious illness called Guillain-Barré syndrome. In addition, Zika virus infection during pregnancy can result in serious brain abnormalities, including the condition microcephaly, in which the infant's head is smaller than normal. The Zika virus has spread globally from Africa into Asia, South America, and North America. Though estimates for infection rates vary, some epidemiologists predict that millions of people will become infected with the virus in the coming years.

During the past few decades, the most devastating example of an emerging virus is **human immunodeficiency virus (HIV)**, the causative agent of acquired immune deficiency syndrome (AIDS). HIV is primarily spread by sexual contact between infected and uninfected individuals, but it can also be spread by the transfusion of HIV-infected blood, by the sharing of needles among drug users, and from infected mother to unborn child. Since AIDS was first recognized in 1981, the total number of AIDS deaths has been nearly 40 million, making it one of the most deadly diseases in human history. More than 0.6 million of these deaths have occurred in the U.S. In 2016, over 30 million people were living with HIV; approximately 3 million of them were infected that year. In that same year, nearly 2 million died from AIDS. Worldwide, nearly 1 in every 100 adults between ages 15 and 49 is infected. In the U.S., about 50,000 new HIV infections occur each year, 70% of those infections in men and 30% in women.

The devastating effects of AIDS result from viral destruction of helper T cells, a type of white blood cell that plays an essential role in the immune system of mammals. **Figure 19.6** shows HIV virus particles invading a helper T cell. As described in Chapter 52, helper T cells interact with other cells of the immune system to facilitate the production of antibodies and other molecules that target and kill

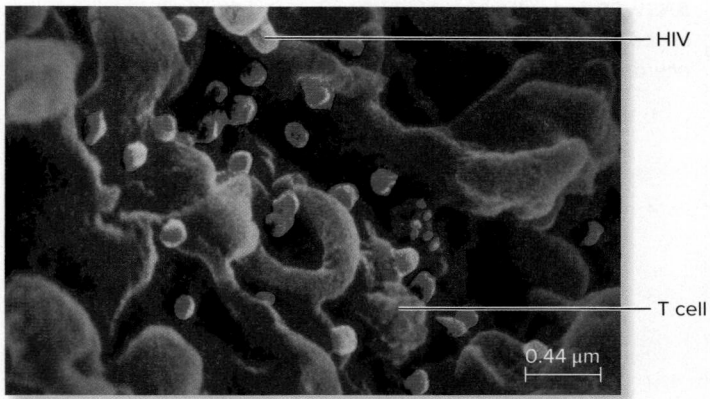

Figure 19.6 Micrograph of HIV invading a human helper T cell. This is a colorized scanning electron micrograph. The surface of the T cell is purple, and HIV particles are red. Source: Cynthia Goldsmith/CDC

foreign invaders of the body. When large numbers of helper T cells are destroyed by HIV, the function of the immune system is seriously compromised, and the individual becomes susceptible to infectious diseases called opportunistic infections that would not normally occur in a healthy person. For example, *Pneumocystis jiroveci*, a fungus that causes a type of pneumonia, is easily destroyed by a healthy immune system. However, in people with AIDS, *Pneumocystis jiroveci* pneumonia can be fatal.

An insidious feature of HIV replication, which is summarized in Figure 19.4b, is that reverse transcriptase, the enzyme that copies the RNA genome into DNA, lacks a proofreading function. In Chapter 11, we learned that DNA polymerase can identify and remove mismatched nucleotides in newly synthesized DNA. Because reverse transcriptase lacks this function, it makes more errors and thereby tends to create mutant strains of HIV. This undermines the ability of the body to combat HIV because mutant strains may be resistant to the body's defenses.

 **BIO TIPS**

THE QUESTION *Propose an experiment to explain how an emerging virus could arise.*

T OPIC *What topic in biology does this question address?* The topic is emerging viruses. More specifically, the question asks you to propose an experiment whose results could explain how they come into existence.

I NFORMATION *What information do you know based on the question and your understanding of the topic?* From your understanding of the topic, you may remember that emerging viruses typically arise via mutations in pre-existing viruses.

P ROBLEM-SOLVING S TRATEGY *Design an experiment. Compare and contrast.* In designing an experiment that may explain how an emerging virus could arise, you want to keep in mind that new forms of viruses typically result from the genetic alteration of pre-existing viruses. Another important point to keep in mind is that the base sequences of many viruses have already been determined.

ANSWER *The rationale behind the design of this experiment is based on the premise that emerging viruses arise from genetic alterations in pre-existing viruses. Here is a possible procedure:*

1. *Determine the base sequence of the emerging virus that you are interested in. (Note: The topic of DNA sequencing is described in Chapter 21.)*
2. *Compare its base sequence with those of other viruses. The expectation is that the emerging virus will be closely related to some other virus that is already known.*
3. *Analyze the differences in DNA sequences between the emerging virus and its closest relative. You may identify differences in particular genes in the emerging virus that may have altered the infectivity of the virus. For example, a mutation may have altered a viral protein in a way that allows the virus to bind more easily to host cells and enter them.*

Drugs Have Been Developed to Combat the Proliferation of HIV

A compelling reason to understand the reproductive cycle of HIV and other disease-causing viruses is that such knowledge may be used to develop drugs that stop viral proliferation. For example, in the U.S., the highest rate of AIDS-related deaths was approximately 17 per year per 100,000 people in 1994 and 1995. The current rate is about 4 to 5 deaths per year per 100,000 people, owing in part to the use of new antiviral drugs. These drugs inhibit viral proliferation, though they cannot eliminate the virus from the body.

One approach to the design of antiviral treatments is to develop drugs that specifically bind to proteins encoded by the viral genome. For example, azidothymidine (AZT) mimics the structure of a normal nucleotide and binds to the enzyme reverse transcriptase. In this way, AZT inhibits reverse transcription, thereby inhibiting viral replication. Another way to combat HIV involves the use of antiviral drugs that inhibit proteases, enzymes that are needed during the assembly of the HIV capsid. Certain HIV proteases cut capsid proteins, which makes them smaller and able to assemble into a capsid structure. If the proteases do not function, the capsid will not assemble, and new HIV particles will not be made. Several drugs known as protease inhibitors have been developed that bind to HIV proteases and inhibit their function.

A major challenge in AIDS research is to discover drugs that inhibit viral proteins without also binding to host cell proteins and inhibiting normal cellular functions. A second challenge is to develop drugs to which mutant strains will not become resistant. As mentioned, HIV readily accumulates mutations during viral replication. A current strategy is to treat HIV patients with a "cocktail" of three or four HIV drugs, making it less likely that any mutant strain will overcome all of the inhibitory effects.

 **Core Concept: Evolution**

Several Hypotheses Have Been Proposed to Explain the Origin of Viruses

Because viruses are such small particles, no fossil record is available to provide evidence about their evolution. Researchers must rely on analyses of modern viruses to develop hypotheses about their origin. Viral genomes follow the same rules of gene expression as the genomes of their host cells. Viral genes have promoter sequences similar to those of their host cells, and the translation of viral proteins relies on the genetic code. Viruses depend entirely on host cells for their proliferation. No known virus makes its own ribosomes or generates the energy it requires to make new viruses. Therefore, many biologists have argued that cells must have evolved before viruses.

How did viruses come into existence? A few hypotheses have been proposed.

Progressive Evolution from Genetic Elements Within Cells A common hypothesis for the origin of viruses is that they evolved from macromolecules inside living cells. The precursors of the first viruses may have been RNA molecules or they may have been plasmids—small, circular DNA molecules that exist independently of chromosomal DNA. (Plasmids are described later in this chapter.) Biologists have hypothesized that such RNA or DNA molecules may have become more complex by acquiring genes that code for proteins that facilitate their own replication.

Regressive Evolution from Cells Though many biologists favor the idea that viruses originated from primitive plasmids or other chromosomal elements, some have suggested they are an example of regressive evolution—the reduction of a trait or traits over time. This hypothesis proposes that viruses are degenerate cells that have retained the minimal genetic information essential for reproduction. For example, some viruses may have originated as small cells that infected larger cells. Over time, genes not required for their independent existence were lost.

Parallel Evolution with Cells A new and interesting hypothesis is that viruses did not evolve from living cells but instead evolved in parallel with cellular organisms. As discussed in Chapter 4, the precursors of cellular DNA genomes may have been RNA molecules that could replicate independently of cells. An early stage of evolution, termed the RNA world, could have involved the parallel evolution of both viruses and cellular organisms.

19.3 Viroids and Prions

Learning Outcomes:

1. Distinguish between a viroid and a virus.
2. Describe the structure of prions, and explain how they cause disease.

Some nonliving infectious agents are simpler than viruses. Viroids are composed solely of RNA, and prions are composed solely of protein. In this section, we begin by examining viroids, infectious agents that cause diseases in plants. Next, we will discuss infectious proteins known as prions, which cause devastating neurological diseases in humans and other mammals.

Viroids Are RNA Molecules That Infect Plant Cells

In 1971, Swiss-born American plant pathologist Theodor Diener discovered that the agent of potato spindle tuber disease is a small RNA molecule devoid of any protein. He coined the term **viroid** for this newly discovered infectious particle. Viroids are composed solely of a single-stranded circular RNA molecule that is a few hundred nucleotides in length.

Viroids infect plant cells, where they depend entirely on host enzymes for their replication. Some viroids are replicated in the host cell nucleus, whereas others replicate in a chloroplast. In contrast to viral genomes, the RNA genomes of viroids do not code for any proteins. How do viroids affect plant cells? The RNA of some viroids has ribozyme activity, and researchers have hypothesized that this activity may damage plants by interfering with the function of host cell molecules. However, the mechanism by which viroids induce disease is not well understood.

Since Diener's initial discovery, many more viroids have been characterized as the agents of diseases that affect many economically important plants, including potato, tomato, cucumber, orange, coconut, grape, avocado, peach, apple, pear, and plum. Some viroids have devastating effects, as illustrated by the case of the coconut cadang-cadang viroid, which has killed more than 20 million coconut trees in Southeast Asia and New Guinea (**Figure 19.7**). Other viroids produce less severe damage, causing necrosis on leaves, shortening of stems, bark cracking, and delays in foliation, flowering, and fruit ripening. A few viroids induce mild symptoms or no symptoms at all.

Prions Are Infectious Proteins That Cause Neurodegenerative Diseases

Before we end our discussion of nonliving, infectious particles, let's consider an unusual infectious agent that causes a group of rare, fatal brain diseases affecting humans and other mammals. Until the 1980s, biologists thought that any infectious agent, whether living or

Figure 19.7 Effects of a viroid. This palm tree (left foreground) in Papua, New Guinea, has been infected with the coconut cadang-cadang viroid and shows symptoms of stunting and yellowing.

©Photograph by J. W. Randles, at Albay Research Center, Philippines

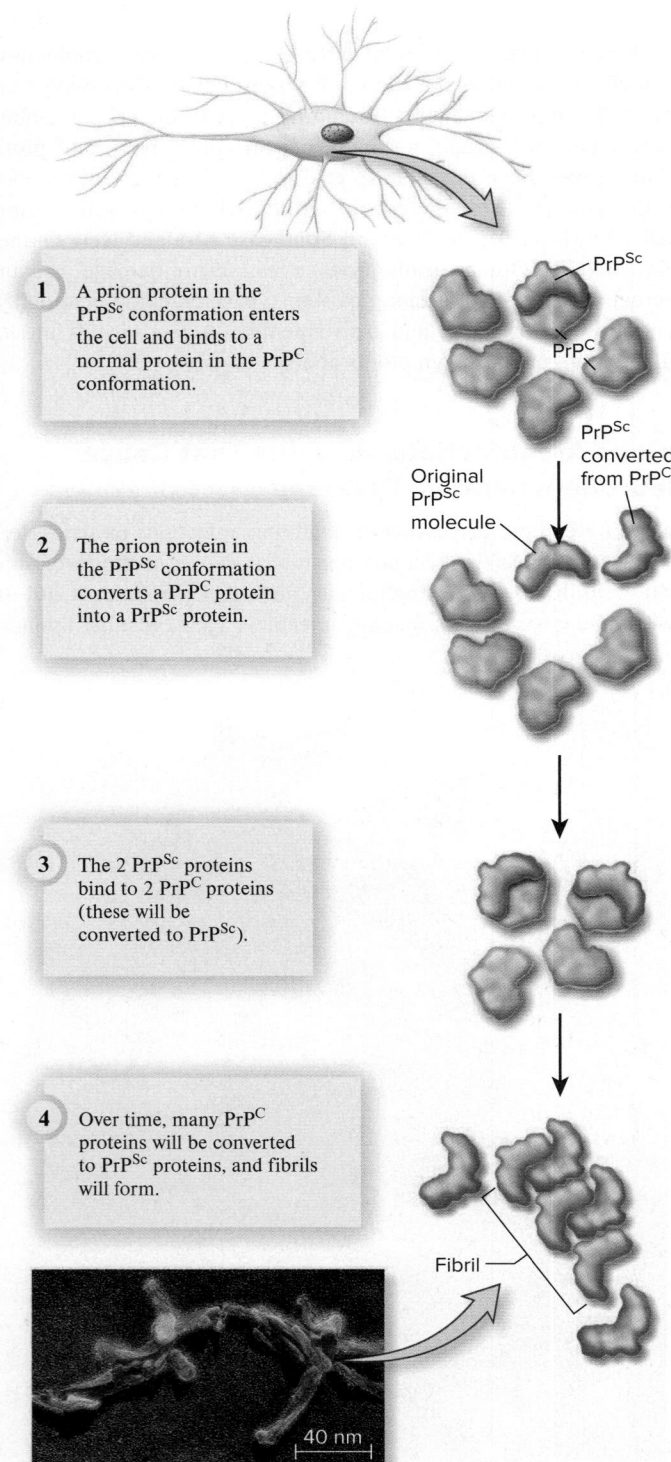

1. A prion protein in the PrP^{Sc} conformation enters the cell and binds to a normal protein in the PrP^{C} conformation.

2. The prion protein in the PrP^{Sc} conformation converts a PrP^{C} protein into a PrP^{Sc} protein.

3. The 2 PrP^{Sc} proteins bind to 2 PrP^{C} proteins (these will be converted to PrP^{Sc}).

4. Over time, many PrP^{C} proteins will be converted to PrP^{Sc} proteins, and fibrils will form.

PrP^{Sc}

PrP^{C}

PrP^{Sc} converted from PrP^{C}

Original PrP^{Sc} molecule

Fibril

40 nm

Figure 19.8 A proposed molecular mechanism of prion diseases. A healthy neuron contains only the PrP^{C} conformation of the protein. The abnormal PrP^{Sc} conformation catalyzes the conversion of PrP^{C} proteins into PrP^{Sc} proteins, thereby causing the symptoms of the prion disease. ©Eye of Science/Science Source

 Core Concept: Structure and Function The prion and normal protein conformations have different structures. The abnormal conformation of the prion has the functional ability to convert normal proteins to the abnormal conformation.

nonliving, must have genetic material. It seemed logical that genetic material is needed to store the information to produce new infectious particles.

In the 1960s, British researchers Tikvah Alper and John Stanley Griffith discovered that preparations from animals with certain neurodegenerative diseases remained infectious even after exposure to radiation that would destroy any DNA or RNA. They suggested that the infectious agent was a protein. In the early 1970s, American neurologist Stanley Prusiner, moved by the death of a patient from such a neurodegenerative disease, began to search for the causative agent. In 1982, Prusiner isolated a disease-causing particle composed entirely of protein, which he called a **prion**. The term was based on his characterization of the particle as a proteinaceous infectious agent. In 1997, Prusiner was awarded the Nobel Prize in Physiology or Medicine for his work on prions.

Prion diseases arise from the ability of the prion to induce abnormal folding in normal protein molecules (**Figure 19.8**). The prion exists in a disease-causing conformation designated PrP^{Sc}. The superscript Sc refers to scrapie, an example of a prion disease. A normal conformation of this same protein, which does not cause disease, is termed PrP^{C}. The superscript C stands for cellular. The normal protein is encoded by an individual's genome, and it is expressed at low levels in certain types of neurons.

How does someone contract a prion disease? A healthy person may become "infected" with the abnormal protein by eating meat of an animal with the disease. Unlike most other proteins in the diet, the prion escapes digestion in the stomach and small intestine and is absorbed into the bloodstream. After being taken up by neurons, the prion gradually converts the cell's normal proteins to the abnormal conformation. As a prion disease progresses, the PrP^{Sc} proteins are deposited as dense aggregates that form tough fibrils in the cells of the brain and peripheral nervous tissues, causing the disease symptoms. Some of the abnormal proteins are also secreted from infected cells, where they travel through the bloodstream. In this way, a prion disease spreads through the body like many viral diseases.

Prions cause several types of fatal neurodegenerative diseases affecting humans, livestock, and wildlife (**Table 19.2**). Prion diseases are termed transmissible spongiform encephalopathies (TSEs). The postmortem examination of the brains of affected individuals

Table 19.2	Examples of Neurodegenerative Diseases Caused by Infectious Prions
Disease	**Description**
Scrapie	A disease of sheep and pigs characterized by intense itching, causing the animals to scrape themselves against trees or other objects, followed by neurodegeneration.
Mad cow disease	Begins with changes in posture and temperament, followed by loss of coordination and neurodegeneration.
Chronic wasting disease	A disease of deer (genus *Odocoileus*) and Rocky Mountain elk (*Cervus elaphus*). A consistent symptom is weight loss over time. The disease is progressive and fatal.

reveals a substantial destruction of brain tissue. The brain has a spongy appearance. Most prion diseases progress fairly slowly. Over the course of a few years, symptoms proceed from a loss of motor control to dementia, paralysis, wasting, and eventually death. These symptoms are correlated with an increase in the level of prions in the neurons of infected individuals. No current treatment can halt the progression of any of the TSEs. For this reason, great public alarm occurs when an outbreak of a TSE is reported. For example, in 2003, a report of a single cow in the U.S. with a TSE commonly known as mad cow disease prompted several countries to restrict the import of American beef.

19.4   Genetic Properties of Bacteria

Learning Outcomes:

1. Outline the key features of a bacterial chromosome.
2. Explain the two processes that compact the bacterial chromosome.
3. Outline the structure and functions of plasmids.
4. Diagram the process of cell division in bacteria.

Many bacteria exist as unicellular organisms. However, some of them may remain associated with each other after cell division, forming pairs, chains, or clumps. Bacteria are widespread on Earth, and numerous species are known to cause various types of infectious diseases, such as bacterial meningitis, discussed at the beginning of this chapter (see the chapter opening photo). We begin this section by exploring the structure and replication of the bacterial genome and the organization of DNA sequences along a bacterial chromosome. We then examine how the chromosome is compacted to fit inside a bacterium and how it is transmitted during asexual reproduction.

Bacteria Typically Have Circular Chromosomes That Carry a Few Thousand Genes

The genes of bacteria are within structures known as bacterial chromosomes.

- Although a bacterial cell usually has a single type of chromosome, it may have more than one copy of that chromosome. The number of copies depends on the bacterial species and on growth conditions, but a bacterium typically has one to four identical chromosomes.

- Each bacterial chromosome is tightly packed within a distinct **nucleoid** of the cell (**Figure 19.9**). Unlike the eukaryotic nucleus, the bacterial nucleoid is not a separate cellular compartment bounded by a membrane. The DNA in a nucleoid is in direct contact with the cytoplasm of the cell.

- Bacterial chromosomes contain molecules of double-stranded DNA along with many different proteins. They are usually circular and are typically a few million base pairs (bp) long. For example, the chromosome of *Escherichia coli* has approximately 4.6 million bp, and the *Haemophilus influenzae* chromosome has roughly 1.8 million bp.

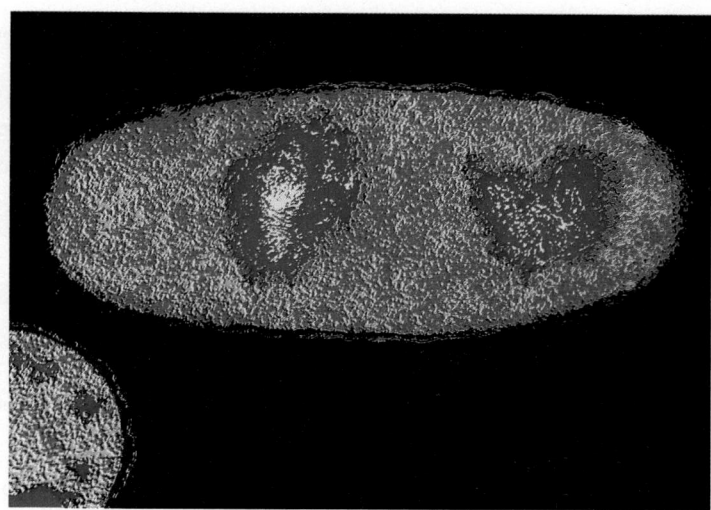

Figure 19.9   Nucleoids within the bacterium *Bacillus subtilis*. In this light micrograph, the nucleoids are fluorescently labeled and seen as purple, oval-shaped areas within the bacterial cytoplasm. Two or more nucleoids are usually found within each cell. ©M. Wurtz/Biozentrum, University of Basel/Science Source

 Core Skill: Connections Look back at Figures 4.8 and 4.9. How is a nucleoid different from a nucleus found in a eukaryotic cell?

- A typical bacterial chromosome contains a few thousand genes that are found throughout the chromosome. Gene sequences, primarily those that encode proteins, account for the largest part of bacterial DNA.

- Other nucleotide sequences in the chromosome play a role in DNA replication, gene expression, and chromosome structure. One of these sequences is the origin of replication, which is a few hundred base pairs long. Bacterial chromosomes have a single origin of replication that functions as an initiation site for the assembly of several proteins that are required for DNA replication (refer back to Figure 11.13b).

The Formation of Chromosomal Loops and DNA Supercoiling Make the Bacterial Chromosome Compact

Bacterial cells are much smaller than most eukaryotic cells. *E. coli* cells, for example, are approximately 1 μm wide and 2 μm long. To fit within a bacterial cell, the DNA of a typical bacterial chromosome must be compacted about 1,000-fold. How does this occur? The compaction of a bacterial chromosome, shown in **Figure 19.10**, occurs by two processes: the formation of loops and DNA supercoiling.

Unlike eukaryotic DNA, bacterial DNA is not wound around histone proteins to form nucleosomes. However, the binding of proteins to bacterial DNA is important in the formation of **loop domains**—chromosomal segments that are folded into loops. As seen in Figure 19.10, DNA-binding proteins anchor the bases of the loops in place. The number of loops varies according to the size of a bacterial chromosome and the species. The *E. coli* chromosome has 400 to 500 loop domains, each with about 10,000 bp. This looping

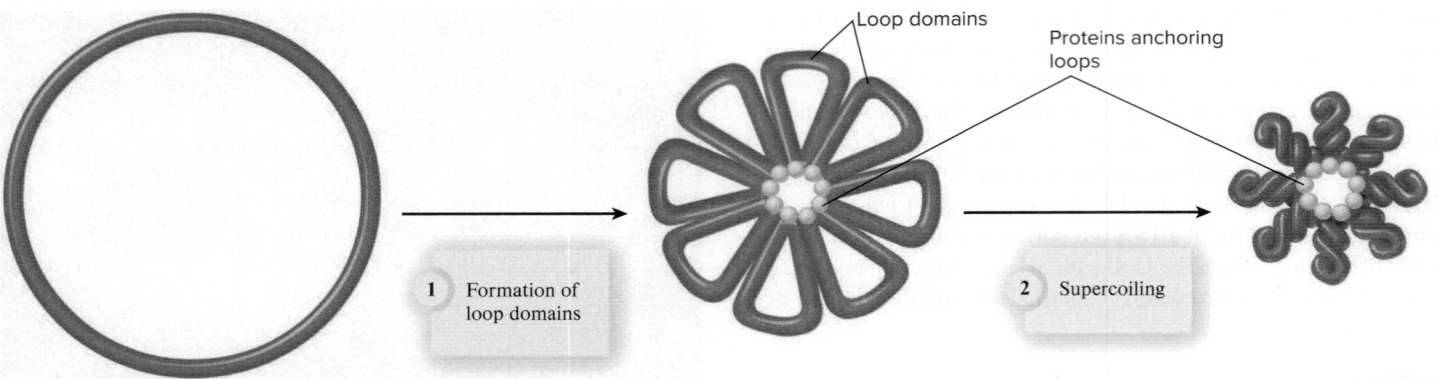

Loop domains

Proteins anchoring loops

1 Formation of loop domains

2 Supercoiling

Circular chromosomal DNA

Looped chromosomal DNA with associated proteins

Supercoiled and looped DNA

Figure 19.10 **The compaction of a bacterial chromosome.** To compact the large, circular chromosome, segments are organized into smaller loop domains by binding to proteins at the bases of the loops. These loops are made more compact by DNA supercoiling. Note: This is a simplified drawing; bacterial chromosomes typically have between 400 and 500 loop domains

Concept Check: *Describe how the loop domains are held in place.*

compacts the circular chromosome about 10-fold. A similar process of loop-domain formation occurs in eukaryotic chromatin compaction, which is described in Chapter 11 (Figure 11.24).

DNA supercoiling is a second important compaction process for the bacterial chromosome. Because DNA is a long, thin molecule, twisting can dramatically change its conformation. This compaction process is similar to what happens to a rubber band if you twist it in one direction. Because the two strands of DNA already coil around each other, the formation of additional coils due to twisting is referred to as supercoiling. Bacterial enzymes called topoisomerases twist the DNA and control the degree of DNA supercoiling.

Plasmids Are Small, Circular Pieces of Extrachromosomal DNA

In addition to chromosomal DNA, bacterial cells commonly contain **plasmids**, small, circular pieces of DNA that exist separately from the bacterial chromosome (**Figure 19.11**). Plasmids occur naturally in many strains of bacteria and in a few types of eukaryotic cells, such as yeast. The smallest plasmids consist of just a few thousand base pairs and carry only a gene or two. The largest are in the range of 100,000 to 500,000 bp and carry several dozen or even hundreds of genes. A plasmid has its own origin of replication that allows it to be replicated independently of the bacterial chromosome. The DNA sequence of the origin of replication influences how many copies of the plasmid are found within a cell. Some origins are said to be very strong because they result in many copies of the plasmid, perhaps as many as 100 per cell. Other origins of replication have sequences that are much weaker, so the number of copies is relatively low, such as one or two per cell.

Why do bacteria have plasmids? Certain genes within a plasmid usually provide some type of growth advantage to the cell or may aid in survival under certain conditions. By studying plasmids in many different species, researchers have discovered that most plasmids fall into a few different categories:

1. Resistance plasmids, also known as R factors, contain genes that confer resistance against antibiotics and other types of toxins.

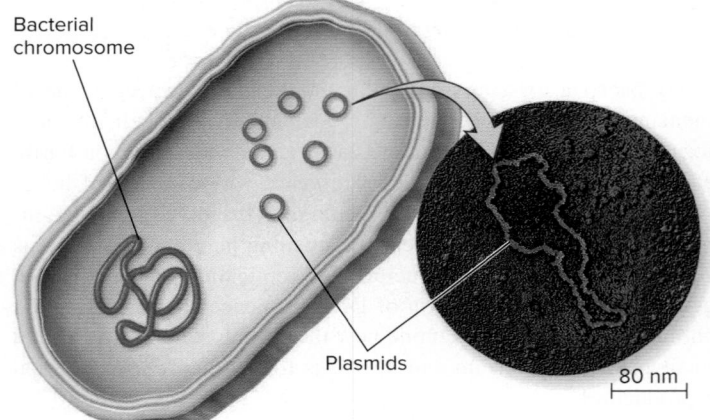

Bacterial chromosome

Plasmids

80 nm

Figure 19.11 **Plasmids in a bacterial cell.** Plasmids are small, circular DNA molecules that exist independently of the bacterial chromosome. (right) ©Stanley Cohen/Science Source

Concept Check: *Describe the similarities and differences between a bacterial chromosome and a plasmid.*

2. Degradative plasmids carry genes that enable the bacterium to digest and utilize an unusual substance. For example, a degradative plasmid may carry genes that allow a bacterium to digest an organic solvent such as toluene.

3. Virulence plasmids carry genes that turn a bacterium into a pathogenic strain.

4. Fertility plasmids, also known as F factors, allow bacteria to transfer genes to each other, as described later in this chapter.

On occasion, a plasmid may integrate into the bacterial chromosome. Such plasmids, which can integrate or remain independent of the chromosome, are also termed episomes.

Most Bacteria Reproduce by Binary Fission

Thus far, we have considered the genetic material of bacteria and the compaction of the bacterial chromosome to fit inside the cell. Let's now turn our attention to the process of cell division. The capacity of bacteria to divide is really quite astounding. The cells of some species, such as *E. coli*, can divide every 20–30 minutes. When placed on a solid growth medium in a petri dish, an *E. coli* cell and its daughter cells undergo repeated cellular divisions and form a clone of genetically identical cells called a **bacterial colony** (**Figure 19.12**). Starting with a single cell that is invisible to the unaided eye, a visible bacterial colony containing 10–100 million cells forms in less than a day!

Cell division of most bacterial species occurs by a process called **binary fission**, during which a cell divides into two daughter cells. **Figure 19.13** shows this process for a cell with a single chromosome.

Before it divides, the cell replicates its DNA. This produces two identical copies of the chromosome. Next, the cell's plasma membrane is drawn inward and deposits new cell-wall material, separating the two daughter cells. Each daughter cell receives one of the copies of the original chromosome. Therefore, except when a mutation occurs, each daughter cell contains an identical copy of the mother cell's genetic material.

Binary fission in most bacterial species requires proteins named FtsA and FtsZ, which are evolutionarily related to eukaryotic actin and tubulin proteins, respectively. With the aid of FtsA, the FtsZ proteins assemble into a ring at the site where a septum will be formed

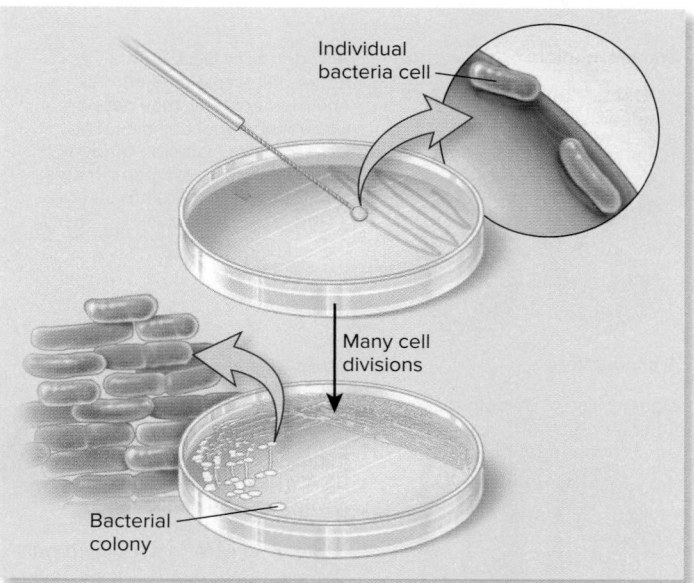

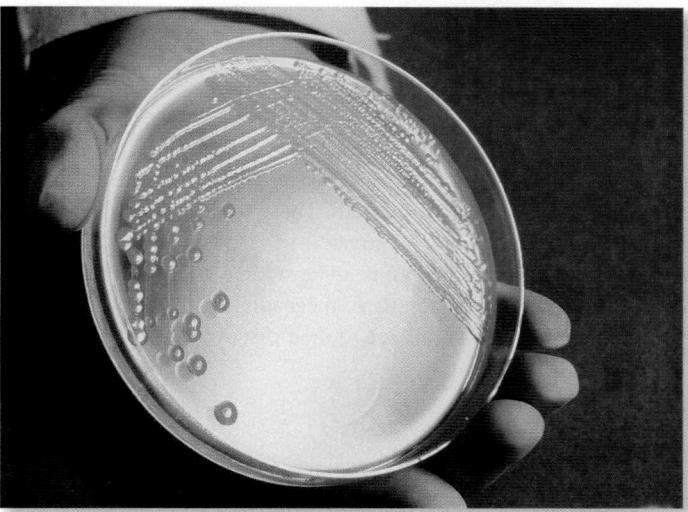

Figure 19.12 Growth of a bacterial colony. Through successive cell divisions, a single bacterial cell of *E. coli* forms a genetically identical group of cells called a bacterial colony.
©Dr. Jeremy Burgess/SPL/Science Source

Concept Check: *Suppose a bacterial strain divides every 30 minutes. If a single cell is placed on a plate, how many cells will be in the colony after 16 hours?*

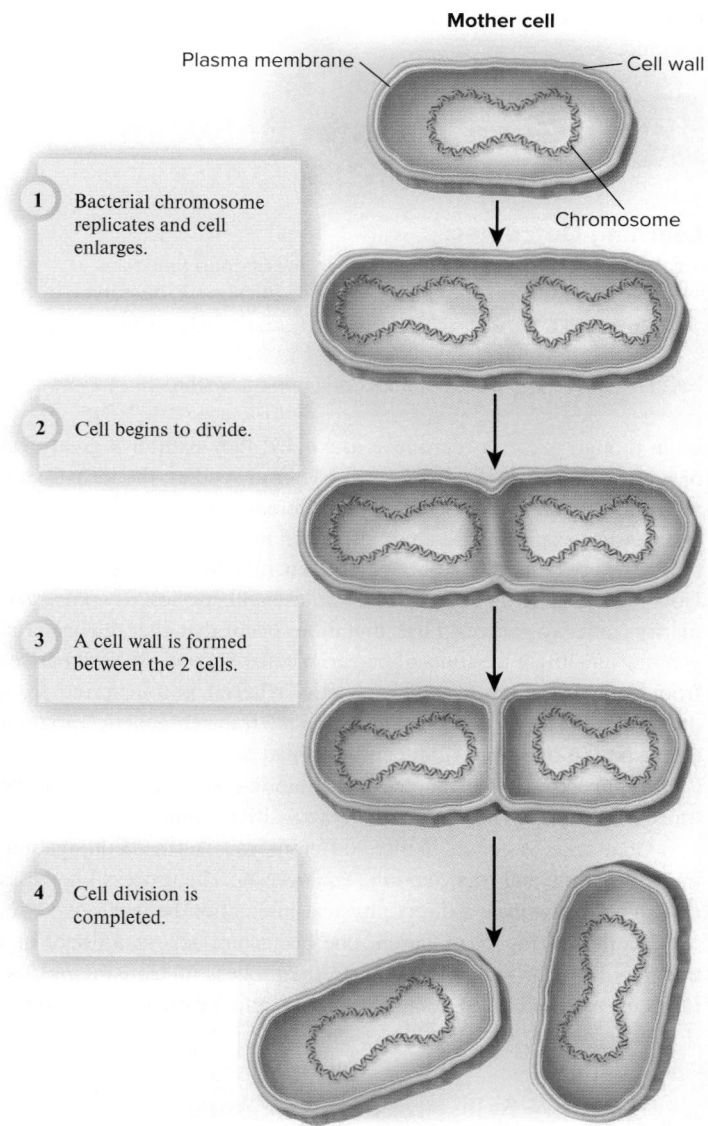

Mother cell

Plasma membrane   Cell wall

① Bacterial chromosome replicates and cell enlarges.

Chromosome

② Cell begins to divide.

③ A cell wall is formed between the 2 cells.

④ Cell division is completed.

Two daughter cells

Figure 19.13 Bacterial cell division. Bacteria reproduce by binary fission. Before a bacterium divides, the bacterial chromosome is replicated to produce two identical copies. These two copies segregate from each other, with one copy going to each daughter cell.

  Core Concept: Information After cell division, each daughter cell has a copy of the genetic material that was in the mother cell.

that separates the daughter cells. While the mechanism by which Fts proteins promote septum formation is not well understood, their role is thought to involve the binding of other proteins that are needed in the process. For example, FtsZ proteins attract enzymes that are involved with synthesizing peptidoglycan. Researchers have proposed that FtsZ proteins may guide the insertion of new cell wall by building smaller and smaller rings of peptidoglycan to eventually divide the cell into two daughter cells. Some archaea also use Fts proteins during cell division, but others utilize different mechanisms.

Plasmids replicate independently of the bacterial chromosome. During binary fission, the plasmids are distributed to the daughter cells so that each one usually receives one or more copies of each plasmid.

19.5 Gene Transfer Between Bacteria

Learning Outcomes:

1. Compare and contrast the three forms of gene transfer—conjugation, transformation, and transduction—in bacteria.
2. **CoreSKILL »** Analyze the results of Lederberg and Tatum, and explain how they led to the discovery of conjugation.
3. Describe the process of horizontal gene transfer.

Even though bacteria reproduce asexually, they exhibit a great deal of genetic diversity. Within a given bacterial species, the term **strain** refers to a lineage that has genetic differences compared to another lineage. For example, one strain of *E. coli* may be resistant to an antibiotic, whereas another strain may be sensitive to the same antibiotic. How does genetic diversity arise in an asexual species? It comes primarily from two sources. First, mutations occur that alter the bacterial genome and affect the traits of bacterial cells. Second, diversity arises from **gene transfer**, in which genetic material is transferred from one bacterial cell to another. Through gene transfer, genetic variation that arises in one bacterium can be spread to other strains and even to other species. For example, an antibiotic-resistance gene may be transferred from a resistant strain to a sensitive strain.

Gene transfer occurs in three different ways, termed conjugation, transformation, and transduction (**Table 19.3**). The process known as **conjugation** involves a direct physical interaction between two bacterial cells. During conjugation, one bacterium acts as a donor and transfers DNA to a recipient cell. In the process of **transformation**, DNA is released into the environment and taken up by another

Table 19.3	Mechanisms of Gene Transfer Between Bacterial Cells
Mechanism	**Description**
Conjugation: 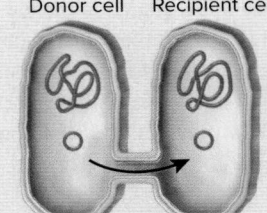 Donor cell Recipient cell	Requires direct contact between a donor cell and a recipient cell. The donor cell transfers a strand of DNA to the recipient. In the example shown here, DNA from a plasmid is transferred to the recipient cell. The end result is that both donor and recipient cells have a plasmid.
Transformation: 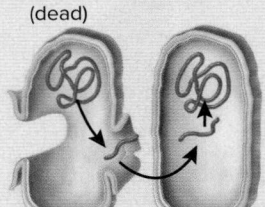 Donor cell (dead) Recipient cell	A fragment of DNA from a donor cell is released into the environment. This may happen when a bacterial cell dies. This DNA fragment is taken up by a recipient cell, which incorporates the DNA into its chromosome.
Transduction: 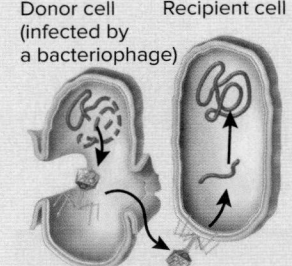 Donor cell (infected by a bacteriophage) Recipient cell	When a bacteriophage infects a donor cell, it causes the bacterial chromosome of the donor cell to break up into fragments. A fragment of bacterial chromosomal DNA is incorporated into a newly made bacteriophage. The bacteriophage then transfers this fragment of DNA to a recipient cell.

bacterial cell. **Transduction** occurs when a bacteriophage infects a bacterial cell and then a newly made bacteriophage transfers some of that cell's DNA to another bacterium. These three types of gene transfer have been extensively investigated in research laboratories, and their molecular pathways continue to be studied with great interest. In this section, we will examine these mechanisms in greater detail and consider the experiments that led to their discovery.

 Core Skill: Process of Science

Feature Investigation | Lederberg and Tatum's Work with *E. coli* Demonstrated Gene Transfer Between Bacteria and Led to the Discovery of Conjugation

In 1946 and 1947, Joshua Lederberg and Edward Tatum carried out the first experiments that showed gene transfer from one bacterial cell to another (**Figure 19.14**). The researchers studied strains of *E. coli* that had different nutritional requirements for growth. They designated

one strain *met⁻bio⁻thr⁺pro⁺* because its growth required the amino acid methionine (met) and the vitamin biotin (bio) in the growth medium. This strain did not require the amino acids threonine (thr) or proline (pro) for growth. Another strain, designated *met⁺bio⁺thr⁻pro⁻*, had just

Figure 19.14   **Experiment of Lederberg and Tatum demonstrating gene transfer between *E. coli* cells.**

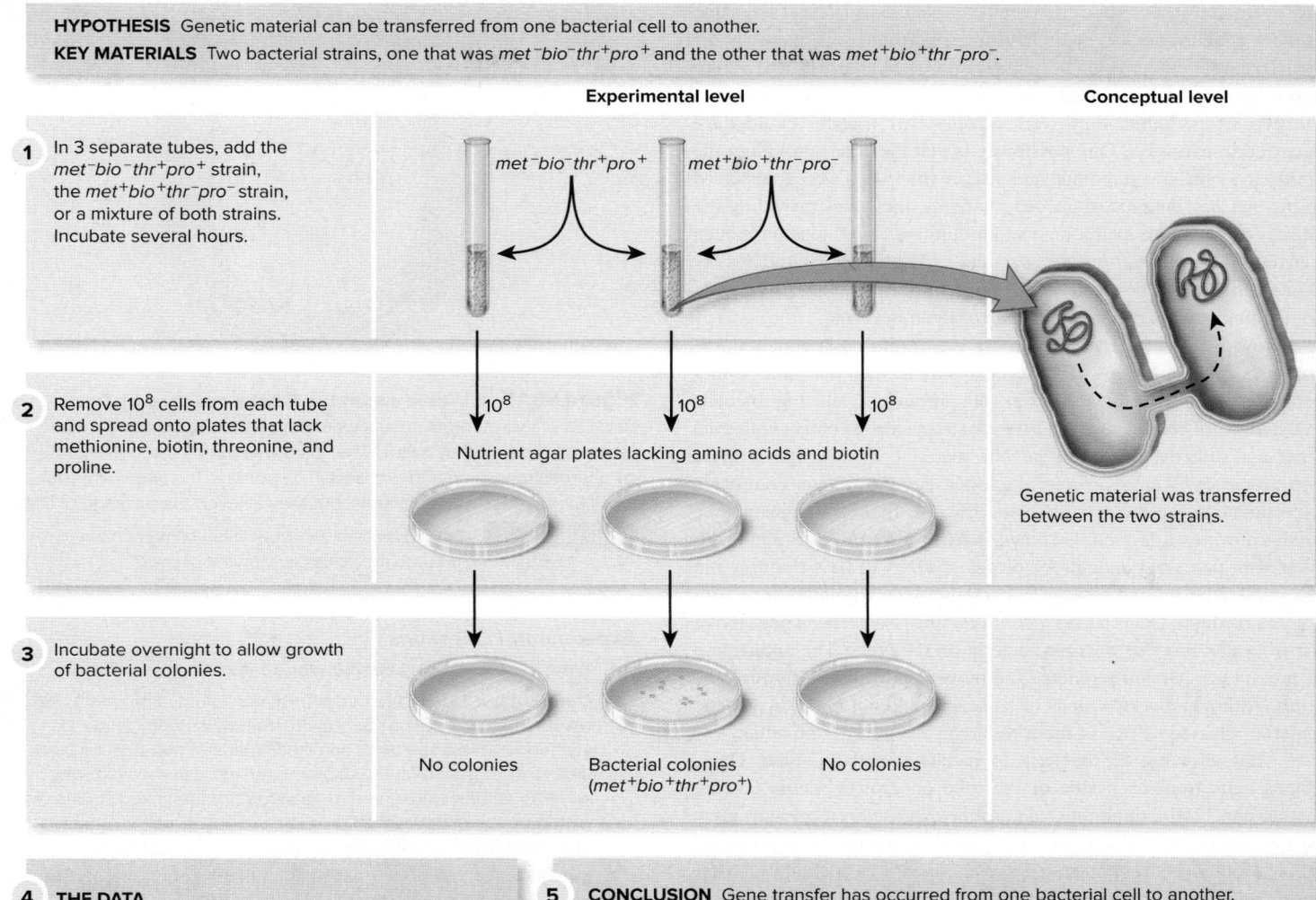

HYPOTHESIS   Genetic material can be transferred from one bacterial cell to another.

KEY MATERIALS   Two bacterial strains, one that was *met⁻bio⁻thr⁺pro⁺* and the other that was *met⁺bio⁺thr⁻pro⁻*.

Experimental level   Conceptual level

1   In 3 separate tubes, add the *met⁻bio⁻thr⁺pro⁺* strain, the *met⁺bio⁺thr⁻pro⁻* strain, or a mixture of both strains. Incubate several hours.

met⁻bio⁻thr⁺pro⁺   *met⁺bio⁺thr⁻pro⁻*

2   Remove 10⁸ cells from each tube and spread onto plates that lack methionine, biotin, threonine, and proline.

10⁸   10⁸   10⁸

Nutrient agar plates lacking amino acids and biotin

Genetic material was transferred between the two strains.

3   Incubate overnight to allow growth of bacterial colonies.

No colonies   Bacterial colonies (*met⁺bio⁺thr⁺pro⁺*)   No colonies

4   **THE DATA**

Strain	Number of colonies after overnight growth
met⁻bio⁻thr⁺pro⁺	0
met⁺bio⁺thr⁻pro⁻	0
Both strains together	~10

5   **CONCLUSION**   Gene transfer has occurred from one bacterial cell to another.

6   **SOURCES**   Lederberg, J., and Tatum, E. L. 1946. Novel genotypes in mixed cultures of biochemical mutants of bacteria, *Cold Spring Harbor Symposia on Quantitative Biology* 11: 113–114.

Tatum, E. L., and Lederberg, J. 1947. Genetic recombination in the bacterium *Escherichia coli. Journal of Bacteriology* 53: 673–684.

the opposite requirements. It needed threonine and proline, but not methionine or biotin. These differences in nutritional requirements correspond to allelic differences between the two strains. The *met⁻bio⁻ thr⁺pro⁺* strain had defective genes encoding enzymes necessary for methionine and biotin synthesis, whereas the *met⁺bio⁺thr⁻pro⁻* strain had defective genes encoding the enzymes required to make threonine and proline.

Figure 19.14 compares the results of mixing the two *E. coli* strains with the results when they were not mixed. The tube on the left contained only *met⁻bio⁻thr⁺pro⁺* cells, and the tube on the right had only *met⁺bio⁺thr⁻pro⁻* cells. The middle tube contained a mixture

of the two kinds of cells. In each case, the researchers applied about 100 million (10⁸) cells to plates containing a growth medium lacking amino acids and the vitamin biotin. When the unmixed strains were applied to these plates, no colonies were observed to grow. This result was expected because the plates did not contain the methionine and biotin that the *met⁻bio⁻thr⁺pro⁺* cells needed for growth or the threonine and proline that the *met⁺bio⁺thr⁻pro⁻* cells required. The striking result occurred when the researchers plated 10⁸ cells from the tube containing the mixture of the two strains. In this case, approximately 10 cells multiplied and formed visible bacterial colonies on the plates. Because these cells multiplied without supplemental amino acids or vitamins, their genotype must have been *met⁺bio⁺thr⁺pro⁺*. Mutations cannot account for the occurrence of this new genotype because colonies were not observed on the other two plates, which had the same number of cells and also could have incurred mutations.

To explain the results of their experiment, Lederberg and Tatum hypothesized that some genetic material had been transferred between the two strains when they were mixed. This transfer could have occurred in two ways. One possibility is that the genes providing the ability to synthesize threonine and proline (*thr⁺pro⁺*) were transferred to the *met⁺bio⁺thr⁻pro⁻* strain. Alternatively, the genes providing the ability to synthesize methionine and biotin (*met⁺bio⁺*) may have been transferred to the *met⁻bio⁻thr⁺pro⁺* cells. The experimental results cannot distinguish between these two possibilities, but they provide compelling evidence that at least one of them occurred.

How did the bacteria in Lederberg and Tatum's experiment transfer genes between strains? Two mechanisms seemed plausible. Either genetic material was released from cells of one and taken up by cells of the other, or cells of the two different strains made contact with each other and directly transferred genetic material. To distinguish these two scenarios, American microbiologist Bernard Davis conducted experiments using the same two strains of *E. coli*. The apparatus he used, known as a U-tube, is shown in **Figure 19.15**. The tube had a filter with pores big enough for pieces of DNA to pass through, but too small to permit the passage of bacteria. After filling the tube with a liquid medium, Davis added *met⁻bio⁻thr⁺pro⁺* bacteria on one side of the filter and *met⁺bio⁺thr⁻pro⁻* bacteria on the other. The application of pressure or suction promoted the movement of liquid through the pores. Although the two kinds of bacteria could not mix, any genetic material released by one of them would be available to the other.

After allowing the bacteria to incubate in the U-tube, Davis placed cells from each side of the tube on growth media lacking methionine, biotin, threonine, and proline. No bacterial colonies grew on the media. How did Davis interpret these results? He proposed that without physical contact, the two *E. coli* strains could not transfer genetic material from one cell to the other. The conceptual level of Figure 19.14, step 1, shows the physical connection that explains Lederberg and Tatum's results. Conjugation is the process of gene transfer that requires direct cell-to-cell contact. It has been subsequently observed in other species of bacteria. Many, but not all, species of bacteria can conjugate.

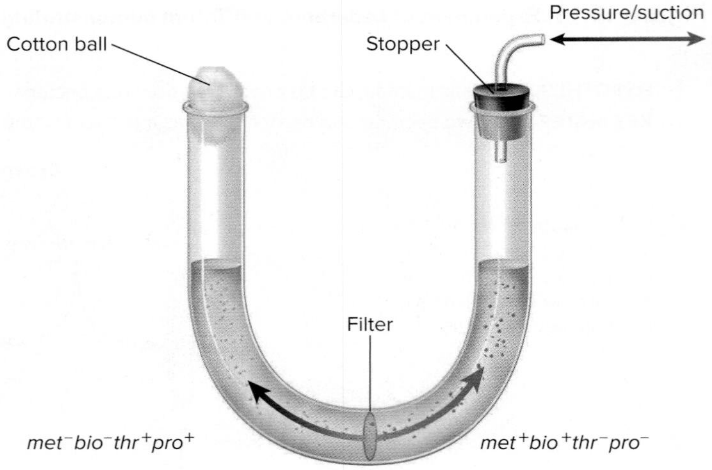

Figure 19.15 A U-tube apparatus like the one used by Davis. Bacteria of two different strains were suspended in the liquid in the tube and separated by a filter. The liquid was forced through the filter by alternating suction and pressure. The pores in the filter were too small for the passage of bacteria, but they allowed the passage of DNA.

Concept Check: Would Davis's results have been different if the pore size was larger and allowed the passage of bacterial cells?

Experimental Questions

1. What hypothesis did Lederberg and Tatum test?

2. **CoreSKILL »** During the Lederberg and Tatum experiment, the researchers compared the growth of mutant strains under two scenarios: mixed strains or unmixed strains. When the unmixed strains were plated on the experimental growth medium, why were no colonies observed to grow? When the mixed strains were plated on the experimental growth medium, 10 colonies were observed. What was the significance of these colonies?

3. **CoreSKILL »** The gene transfer seen in the Lederberg and Tatum experiment could have occurred in one of two ways: by bacteria taking up DNA released into the environment or by contact between two bacterial cells that allowed for direct transfer. Davis conducted an experiment to determine the correct process. Explain how his results indicated the correct gene transfer process.

During Conjugation, DNA Is Transferred from a Donor Cell to a Recipient Cell

In the early 1950s, American microbiologists Joshua and Esther Lederberg, Irish physician William Hayes, and Italian geneticist Luca Cavalli-Sforza independently discovered that only certain bacterial strains can donate genetic material during conjugation. For example, about 5% of *E. coli* strains found in nature act as donor strains. Further research showed that a strain that is incapable of acting as a donor can acquire this ability after being mixed with a donor strain. Hayes correctly proposed that donor strains contain a type of plasmid called a fertility factor, or **F factor**, that can be transferred to recipient strains. Also, other donor *E. coli* strains were later identified that

transfer portions of the bacterial chromosome at high frequencies. After a segment of the chromosome is transferred, it then inserts, or recombines, into the chromosome of the recipient cell. Such donor strains were named *Hfr* (for **H**igh **f**requency of **r**ecombination). In our discussion, we will focus on donor strains that carry F factors.

The micrograph in **Figure 19.16a** shows two conjugating *E. coli* cells. The cell on the left is designated *F⁺*, meaning that it has an F factor. This donor cell is transferring genetic material to the recipient cell on the right, which lacks an F factor and is designated *F⁻*. F factors carry several genes that are required for conjugation and also may carry genes that confer a growth advantage for the bacterium.

Figure 19.16b describes the events that occur during conjugation in *E. coli*. **Sex pili** (singular, pilus) are made by *F⁺* cells that bind

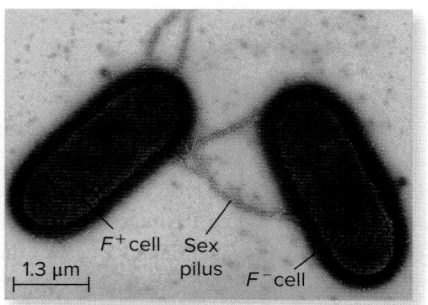

F⁺ cell   Sex pilus   F⁻ cell
1.3 μm

(a) Micrograph of conjugating cells

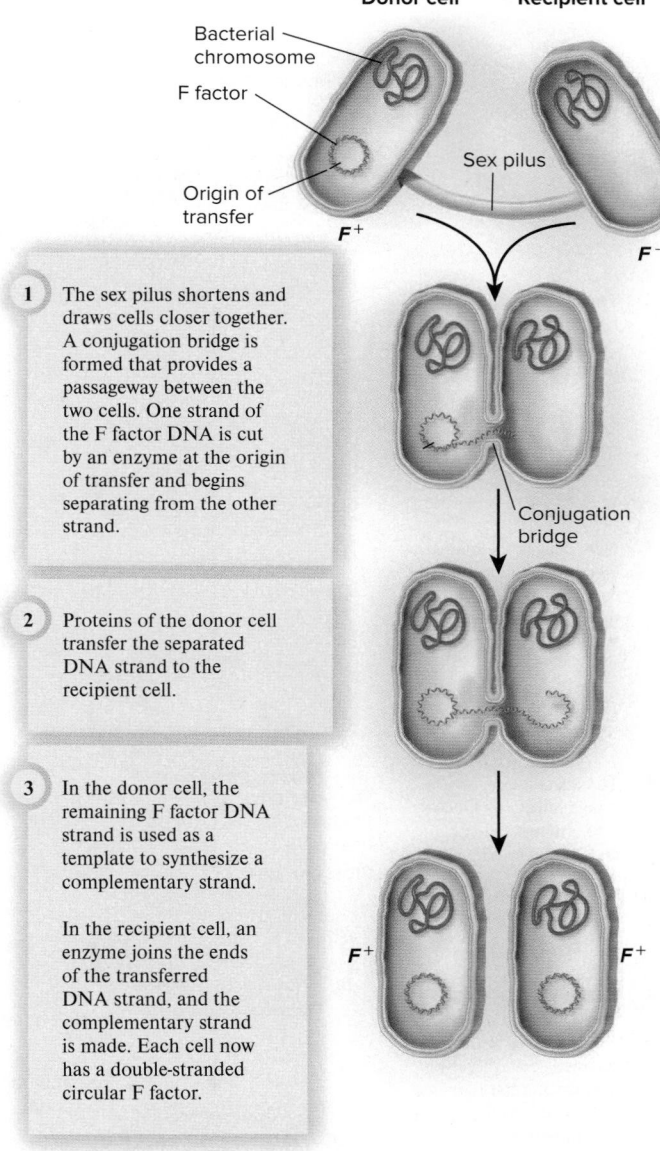

Donor cell   Recipient cell

Bacterial chromosome

F factor

Sex pilus

Origin of transfer

F⁺   F⁻

1   The sex pilus shortens and draws cells closer together. A conjugation bridge is formed that provides a passageway between the two cells. One strand of the F factor DNA is cut by an enzyme at the origin of transfer and begins separating from the other strand.

2   Proteins of the donor cell transfer the separated DNA strand to the recipient cell.

Conjugation bridge

3   In the donor cell, the remaining F factor DNA strand is used as a template to synthesize a complementary strand.

In the recipient cell, an enzyme joins the ends of the transferred DNA strand, and the complementary strand is made. Each cell now has a double-stranded circular F factor.

F⁺   F⁺

(b) Transfer of an F factor

Figure 19.16   Bacterial conjugation. (a) A micrograph of two *E. coli* cells that are conjugating. The cell on the left, designated *F⁺*, is the donor; the cell on the right, designated *F⁻*, is the recipient. The two cells make contact via sex pili made by the *F⁺* cell. **(b)** The transfer of an F factor during conjugation. At the end of conjugation, both the donor cell and the recipient cell are *F⁺*. a: ©Dr. L. Caro/SPL/Science Source

Concept Check: *If a donor cell has only one F factor, explain how the donor and recipient cell both contain one F factor following the transfer of an F factor during conjugation.*

specifically to *F⁻* cells. They are so named because conjugation has been called bacterial mating. However, this term is a bit misleading because the process does not involve equal genetic contributions from two gametes and it does not produce offspring. Donor strains have genes responsible for the formation of sex pili. In *F⁺* strains, the genes are located on the F factor. In *E. coli* and some other species, *F⁺* cells make very long pili that attempt to make contact with nearby *F⁻* cells. Once contact is made, the pili shorten, drawing the donor and recipient cells closer together.

After the pili have shortened, contact between donor and recipient cell stimulates the donor cell to begin the transfer process. First, a conjugation bridge is formed that provides a direct passageway for DNA transfer. One strand of F factor DNA is cut at the origin of transfer and then travels through the conjugation bridge into the recipient cell. The other strand remains in the donor cell, and the complementary strand is synthesized, thereby restoring the F factor DNA to its original double-stranded condition. In the recipient cell, the two ends of the newly acquired F factor DNA strand are joined to form a circular molecule, and its complementary strand is synthesized to produce a double-stranded F factor. If conjugation is successful, the end result is that the recipient cell has acquired an F factor, converting it from an *F⁻* to an *F⁺* cell. The genetic composition of the donor strain has not been changed.

In Transformation, Bacteria Take Up DNA from the Environment

In contrast to conjugation, the process of gene transfer known as bacterial transformation does not require direct contact between bacterial cells. Frederick Griffith first discovered this process in 1928 while working with strains of *Streptococcus pneumoniae*. We discussed early experiments involving transformation in Chapter 11 (refer back to Figures 11.1 and 11.2).

How does a bacterial cell become transformed? First, it imports a strand of DNA from the environment. This DNA strand, which is typically derived from a dead bacterial cell, may then insert or recombine into the bacterial chromosome. The live bacterium then carries genes from the dead bacterium—the live bacterium has been transformed.

Not all bacterial strains have the ability to take up DNA. Those that do have this ability are described as naturally **competent**, and they have genes that encode proteins called competence factors. Competence factors facilitate the binding of DNA fragments to the bacterial cell surface, the uptake of DNA into the cytoplasm, and the incorporation of the imported DNA into the bacterial chromosome. Temperature, ionic conditions, and the availability of nutrients affect whether or not a bacterium will be competent to take up genetic material.

In recent years, biologists have unraveled some of the steps that occur when competent bacterial cells are transformed by taking up genetic material from the environment. In the example shown in **Figure 19.17**, the DNA released from a dead bacterium carries a gene, *tetᴿ*, that confers resistance to the antibiotic tetracycline. First, a large fragment of the DNA binds to a cell surface receptor on the outside of a bacterial cell that is sensitive to tetracycline. Enzymes secreted by the bacterium cut this large fragment into fragments small enough to enter the cell. In our example, one of the two strands of a fragment of DNA containing the *tetᴿ* gene is degraded. The other strand enters the bacterial cytoplasm via a DNA uptake system that transports the DNA across the

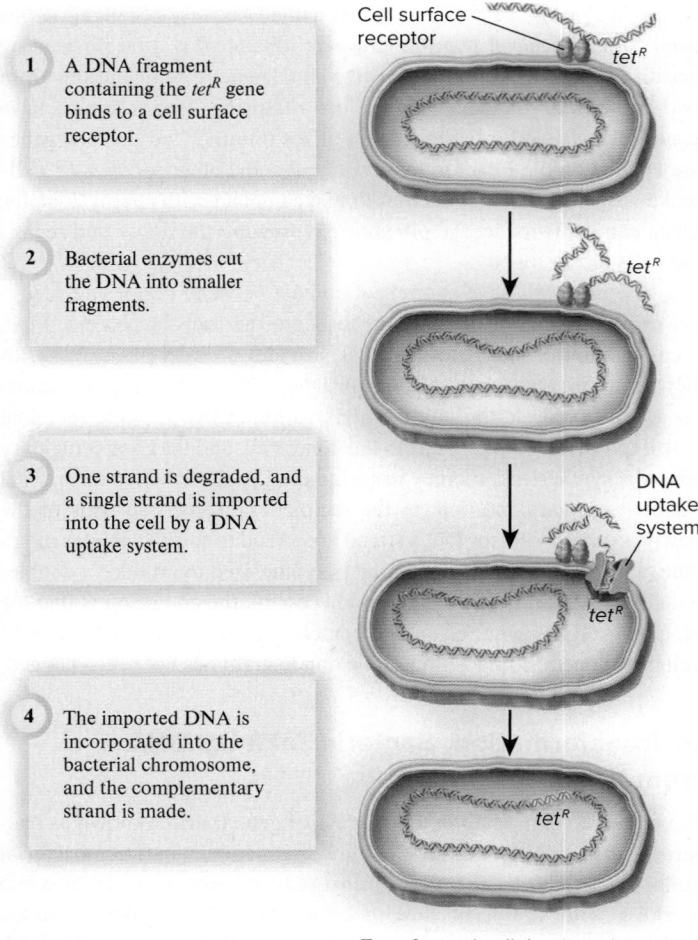

1   A DNA fragment containing the *tet*^R gene binds to a cell surface receptor.

Cell surface receptor

tet^R

2   Bacterial enzymes cut the DNA into smaller fragments.

tet^R

3   One strand is degraded, and a single strand is imported into the cell by a DNA uptake system.

DNA uptake system

tet^R

4   The imported DNA is incorporated into the bacterial chromosome, and the complementary strand is made.

tet^R

Transformed cell that is resistant to the antibiotic tetracycline

Figure 19.17   Bacterial transformation. This process has transformed a bacterium that was sensitive to the antibiotic tetracycline into one that is resistant to this antibiotic.

 Core Skill: Connections Look back at Figures 11.1 and 11.2. How did the phenomenon of transformation allow researchers to demonstrate that DNA is the genetic material?

plasma membrane. Finally, the imported DNA strand is incorporated into the bacterial chromosome, and the complementary strand is synthesized. Following transformation, the recipient cell has been transformed from a tetracycline-sensitive cell to a tetracycline-resistant cell.

In Transduction, Bacteriophages Transfer Genetic Material from One Bacterium to Another

A third mechanism of gene transfer is transduction, in which bacteriophages transfer bacterial genes from one bacterium to another. As discussed earlier in this chapter, a bacteriophage (or simply phage) is a virus that uses the cellular machinery of a bacterium for its own replication. The new viral particles made in this way usually contain only viral genes. On rare occasions, however, a phage may pick up a piece of DNA from the bacterial chromosome. When a phage carrying a

segment of bacterial DNA infects another bacterium, it transfers this segment into the chromosome of its new bacterial host.

Transduction is actually an error in a phage lytic cycle, as shown in **Figure 19.18**. In this example, a phage called P1 infects an *E. coli* cell that has a gene (*his*⁺) for histidine synthesis. Phage P1 causes the host cell chromosome to be degraded into small pieces. New phage DNA and proteins are synthesized. When new phages are assembled, coat proteins may accidentally enclose a piece of host DNA that carries the *his*⁺ gene, creating a phage that carries the gene. In the

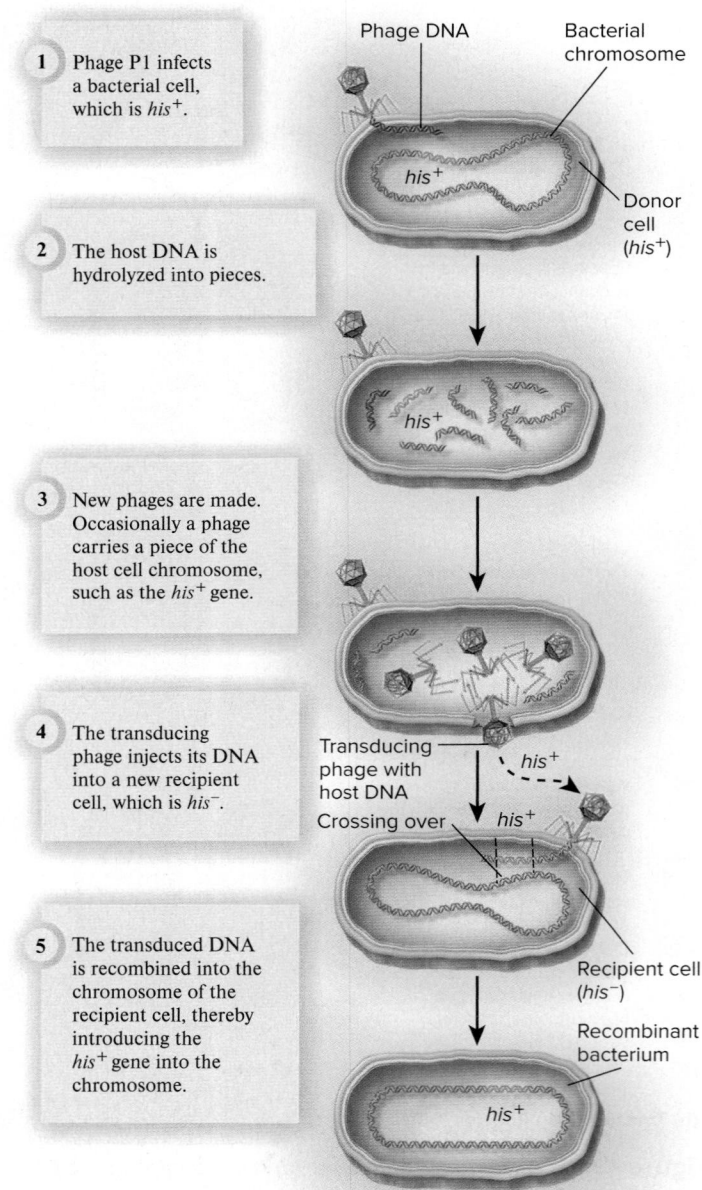

1   Phage P1 infects a bacterial cell, which is *his*⁺.

Phage DNA

Bacterial chromosome

his⁺

Donor cell (*his*⁺)

2   The host DNA is hydrolyzed into pieces.

his⁺

3   New phages are made. Occasionally a phage carries a piece of the host cell chromosome, such as the *his*⁺ gene.

4   The transducing phage injects its DNA into a new recipient cell, which is *his*⁻.

Transducing phage with host DNA

Crossing over

his⁺

his⁺

5   The transduced DNA is recombined into the chromosome of the recipient cell, thereby introducing the *his*⁺ gene into the chromosome.

Recipient cell (*his*⁻)

Recombinant bacterium

his⁺

The recombinant bacterium has a genotype (*his*⁺) that is different from the original recipient bacterial cell (*his*⁻).

Figure 19.18   Bacterial transduction by phage P1.

Concept Check: *Is transduction a normal part of the phage life cycle? Explain.*

example shown in Figure 19.18, this transducing phage is released and binds to an *E. coli* cell that lacks the *his⁺* gene. It inserts the bacterial DNA fragment into the recipient cell, which then integrates this fragment into its own chromosome. In this case, gene transfer by transduction converts a *his⁻* strain of *E. coli* to a *his⁺* strain.

 Core Concept: Evolution

Horizontal Gene Transfer Can Occur Within a Species or Between Different Species

The term **horizontal gene transfer** refers to a process in which an organism incorporates genetic material from another organism without being the offspring of that organism. Conjugation, transformation, and transduction are examples of horizontal gene transfer. In contrast, vertical gene transfer occurs when genes are passed from one generation to the next—from parents to offspring and from mother cells to daughter cells.

Conjugation, transformation, and transduction occasionally occur between cells of different bacterial species. In recent years, analyses of bacterial genomes have shown that a sizable percentage of bacterial genes are derived from horizontal gene transfer. For example, roughly 17% of the genes of *E. coli* and of *Salmonella typhimurium* have been acquired from other species by horizontal gene transfer during the past 100 million years. Many of these acquired genes affect traits that give cells a selective advantage, including genes that confer antibiotic resistance, the ability to degrade toxic compounds, and the ability to withstand extreme environments. Some horizontally transferred genes confer pathogenicity, turning a harmless bacterial strain into one that can cause disease. Geneticists have suggested that horizontal gene transfer has played a major role in the evolution of different bacterial species. In many cases, the acquisition of new genes allows a bacterium to survive in a new type of environment and can eventually lead to the formation of a new species.

A second reason why horizontal gene transfer is important is its medical relevance. Let's consider the topic of antibiotic resistance. Antibiotics are widely prescribed to treat bacterial infections in humans. They are also used in agriculture to control bacterial diseases. Unfortunately, the widespread use of antibiotics has greatly increased the prevalence of antibiotic-resistant strains of bacteria, strains that have a selective advantage over those that are susceptible to antibiotics. Resistant strains carry genes that counteract the action of antibiotics in various ways. A resistance gene may encode a protein that breaks down the antibiotic, pumps it out of the cell, or prevents it from inhibiting cellular processes.

The term **acquired antibiotic resistance** refers to the common phenomenon in which a previously susceptible strain becomes resistant to a specific antibiotic. This change may result from genetic alterations in the genome of the susceptible strain, but it is often due to the horizontal transfer of resistance genes from a resistant strain. As often mentioned in the news media, antibiotic resistance has increased dramatically worldwide over the past few decades, with resistant strains reported in almost all pathogenic strains of bacteria. As an example, some *Staphylococ-*

cus aureus strains have developed resistance to methicillin and all penicillins. Evidence suggests that these so-called methicillin-resistant strains of *Staphlococcus aureus* (MRSA) acquired the methicillin-resistance gene by horizontal gene transfer, possibly from a strain of *Enterococcus faecalis*. MRSA strains cause skin infections that are more difficult to treat than ordinary "staph" infections caused by nonresistant strains of *S. aureus*.

Summary of Key Concepts

19.1 General Properties of Viruses

- Viruses are nonliving particles that do not exhibit all of the properties associated with living organisms. A virus or its genetic material must be taken up by a living cell to replicate. Tobacco mosaic virus (TMV) was the first virus to be discovered (Figure 19.1).

- Viruses vary with regard to their host range, structure, and genome composition (Table 19.1, Figures 19.2, 19.3).

19.2 Viral Reproductive Cycles

- The viral reproductive cycle consists of a series of steps: attachment, entry, integration, synthesis of components, assembly, and release (Figure 19.4).

- Some bacteriophages can follow two different reproductive cycles: the lytic cycle and the lysogenic cycle (Figure 19.5).

- Emerging viruses, such as human immunodeficiency virus (HIV) and Zika virus, can cause significant loss of human life. HIV, the causative agent of the disease AIDS, is a retrovirus whose reproductive cycle involves the integration of the viral genome into a chromosome in the host cell (Figure 19.6).

- Drugs to combat viral proliferation are often developed to specifically inhibit viral proteins.

19.3 Viroids and Prions

- Viroids are RNA molecules that infect plant cells (Figure 19.7).

- Prions are infectious proteins that induce abnormal folding in normal proteins. They cause several fatal neurodegenerative diseases in humans (Figure 19.8, Table 19.2).

19.4 Genetic Properties of Bacteria

- Bacteria typically have a single type of circular chromosome found in the nucleoid of the cell. The chromosome contains many genes and one origin of replication (Figure 19.9).

- The bacterial chromosome is made more compact by the formation of loop domains and by DNA supercoiling (Figure 19.10).

- Plasmids are small, circular DNA molecules that exist independently of the bacterial chromosome (Figure 19.11).

- When placed on solid growth media, a single bacterial cell will divide many times to produce a colony composed of many cells (Figure 19.12).

- Bacterial cells reproduce by asexual reproduction in a process called binary fission, during which a cell divides to form two daughter cells (Figure 19.13).

- Positional information may stimulate a cell to divide.
- Positional information in animals may cause the migration of a cell or group of cells in a particular direction from one region of the embryo to another. (Cell migration does not occur during development in plants.)
- Positional information may cause a cell to differentiate into a specific cell type such as a neuron.
- Positional information may promote **apoptosis**, or programmed cell death, which is described in Chapter 9. Apoptosis plays a key role in sculpting the bodies of animals. In vascular plants, certain cells undergo programmed cell death to form tracheids, specialized cells that function in water transport.

As an example of how the coordination of these four processes is required for pattern formation, **Figure 20.4** shows the embryonic development of a human limb, which has an arm and hand.

- Cell division with accompanying cell growth increases the size of the limb.

- Cell migration is also important for limb development. For example, embryonic cells that eventually form muscles in the arm and hand must migrate from outside the limb to reach their correct location within the limb.
- As development proceeds, cell differentiation produces the various tissues that will eventually be found in the fully developed limb. Some cells become neurons, others muscle cells, and still others become epidermal cells, forming the outer layer of skin.
- Finally, apoptosis is important in the formation of fingers. If apoptosis did not occur, a human hand would have webbed fingers.

Morphogens and Cell-to-Cell Contacts Convey Positional Information

How does positional information lead to the development of a body plan? Though the details of pattern formation vary widely among different species, two main mechanisms are commonly used to

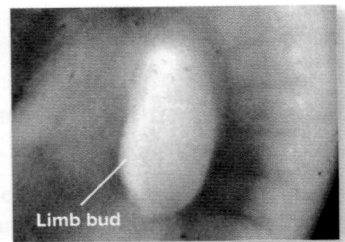 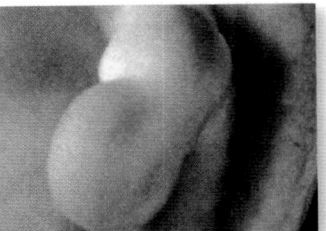 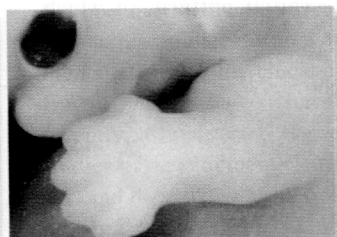 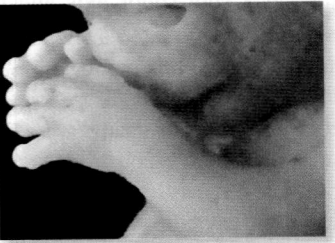

Limb bud

(a) Limb development in a human embryo

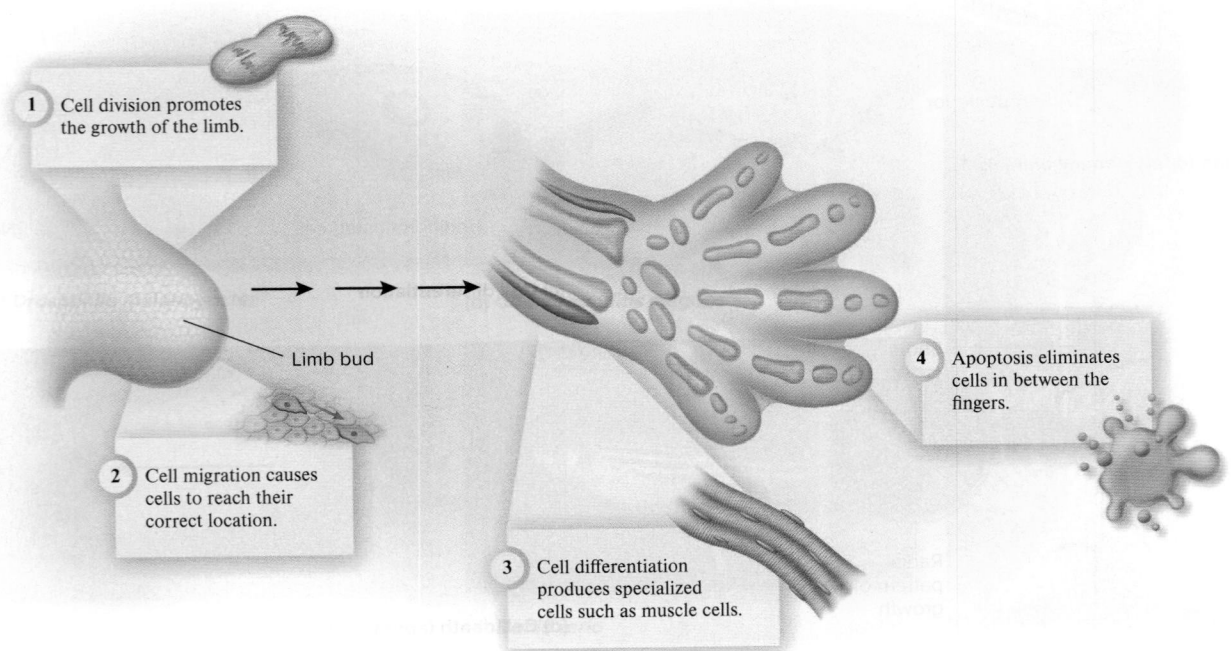

1. Cell division promotes the growth of the limb.

Limb bud

2. Cell migration causes cells to reach their correct location.

3. Cell differentiation produces specialized cells such as muscle cells.

4. Apoptosis eliminates cells in between the fingers.

(b) Four cellular processes that promote limb formation

Figure 20.4 Limb development in humans. (a) Photographs of limb development in human embryos. The limb begins as a protrusion called a limb bud that eventually forms an arm and hand. **(b)** The development of a human hand from an embryonic limb bud. a: Courtesy of the National Museum of Health and Medicine, Washington, D.C.

Concept Check: *How would human finger formation be affected if apoptosis did not occur?*

communicate positional information. One of these mechanisms involves molecules called morphogens. **Morphogens** impart positional information and promote developmental changes at the cellular level. Many morphogens are proteins, but they can also be small signaling molecules. A morphogen influences the fate of a cell by promoting cell division, cell migration, cell differentiation, or apoptosis. A key feature of morphogens is that they act in a concentration-dependent manner. At a high concentration, a morphogen restricts a cell into a particular developmental pathway, whereas at a lower concentration, it does not. There is often a critical **threshold concentration** above which the morphogen exerts its effects.

Morphogens typically are distributed asymmetrically along a concentration gradient. Morphogen gradients may be established in the **oocyte**, a cell that matures into an egg cell (**Figure 20.5a**). In addition, a morphogen gradient can be established in the embryo by secretion and diffusion (**Figure 20.5b**). A certain cell or group of cells may synthesize and secrete a morphogen at a specific stage of development.

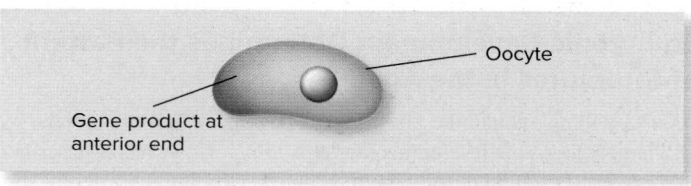

(a) Asymmetric distribution of morphogens in the oocyte

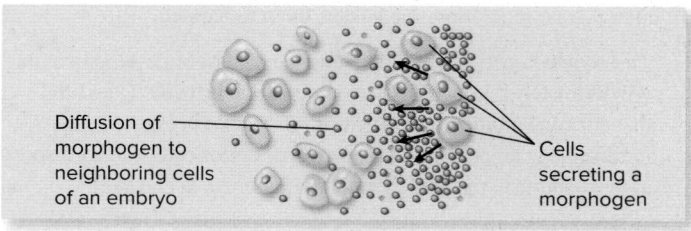

(b) Induction: asymmetric synthesis and extracellular distribution of a morphogen

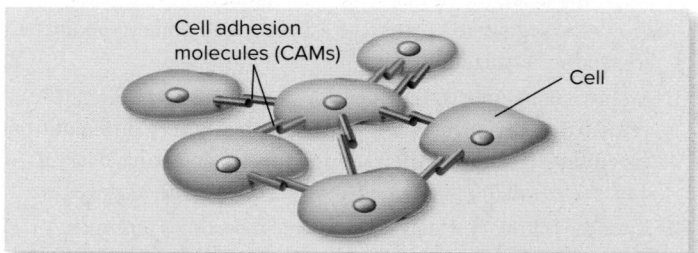

(c) Cell adhesion: Cell-to-cell contact conveys positional information.

Figure 20.5 Molecular mechanisms that convey positional information. Morphogen gradients may be established in the **(a)** oocyte or **(b)** embryo. **(c)** Positional information may also be conveyed by cell-to-cell contact. Different colors indicate different CAMs on the surfaces of the cells.

 Core Skill: Connections Look back at Chapter 9. Discuss the role of cell surface receptors in responding to positional information.

After secretion, the morphogen diffuses to neighboring cells, as in Figure 20.5b, or it may be transported to cells that are distant from the cells that secrete it. The morphogen may then influence the fate of cells exposed to it. The process by which a cell or group of cells governs the developmental fate of other cells is known as **induction**.

Another mechanism to convey positional information is **cell adhesion** (**Figure 20.5c**). Each animal cell makes its own collection of surface receptors that enable it to adhere to other cells and to the extracellular matrix (ECM). Such receptors, known as **cell adhesion molecules (CAMs)**, are described in Chapter 10 (refer back to Figure 10.8). The positioning of a cell within a multicellular organism is strongly influenced by the combination of contacts it makes with other cells and with the ECM.

The phenomenon of cell adhesion and its role in multicellular development was first recognized by American biologist Henry V. Wilson in 1907. He took multicellular sponges and passed them through a sieve, dissociating them into individual cells. Remarkably, the cells actively migrated until they adhered to one another to form a new sponge, complete with the chambers and canals that characterize a sponge's internal structure! When sponge cells from different species were mixed, they sorted themselves properly, adhering only to cells of the same species. Overall, these results indicate that cells possess specific CAMs, which are critical in cell-to-cell recognition. Cell adhesion plays an important role in governing the position that an animal cell will adopt during development.

Pattern Formation Occurs in Phases That Are Controlled by Transcription Factors

The formation of a body, in both animals and plants, occurs in a series of overlapping organizational phases. As an overview of this process, let's consider four general phases of pattern formation in an animal (**Figure 20.6**). This example involves human development, but research suggests that pattern formation in all complex animals follows a similar plan.

1. The first phase organizes the body along major axes. The anteroposterior axis is organized from head to tail, the dorsoventral axis is organized from back (dorsal) to front/abdomen (ventral), and the left-right axis is organized from side to side (refer back to Figure 20.2a).

2. During the second phase, the body becomes organized into smaller regions, a process called **segmentation**. In insects, these regions form well-defined segments. In mammals, some segmentation of the body is apparent during embryonic development, but defined boundaries are lost as the embryo proceeds to the fetal and adult stages.

3. In the third phase, the cells within the segments organize themselves in ways that will produce particular body parts.

4. Finally, during the fourth phase, the cells change their morphologies and become differentiated. This final phase of development produces an organism with many types of tissues, organs, and other body parts with specialized functions.

It should be noted that the four phases of development are overlapping. For example, cell differentiation begins to occur as the cells are adopting their correct locations.

Hierarchy of transcription factors

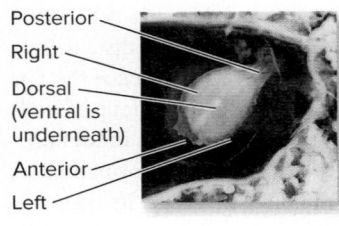

Posterior
Right
Dorsal
(ventral is
underneath)
Anterior
Left

1 **Phase 1:**
Transcription factors determine the formation of the body axes and control the expression of transcription factors of phase 2.

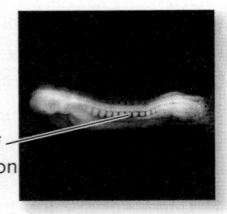

Evidence of segmentation

2 **Phase 2:**
Transcription factors cause the embryo to become subdivided into regions that have properties of individual segments. They also control transcription factors of phase 3.

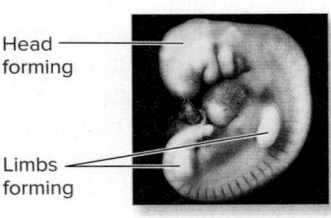

Head forming

Limbs forming

3 **Phase 3:**
Transcription factors cause each segment and groups of segments to develop specific characteristics. They also control transcription factors of phase 4.

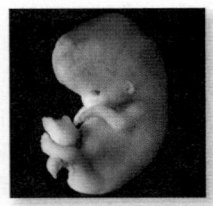

4 **Phase 4:**
Transcription factors cause cells to differentiate into specific cell types such as skin, nerve, and muscle cells.

Figure 20.6 Pattern formation in a human embryo. The ideas in this scenario are based largely on analogies between pattern formation in *Drosophila* and mammals. Many of the transcription factors that control the early phases of pattern formation in mammals have yet to be identified. (1, 3, 4): Courtesy of the National Museum of Health and Medicine, Washington, D.C.; (2): ©Congenital Anomaly Research Center of Kyoto University

 Core Concept: Information Pattern formation in animals occurs in four phases controlled by a hierarchy of transcription factors that cause some genes to be expressed and others to be repressed.

How does genetics underlie the phases of animal development? Geneticists have discovered a parallel between the expression of specific transcription factors, which are described in Chapters 12 and 14, and the four major phases of animal development. As noted in Figure 20.6, a hierarchy of transcription factors controls whether or not certain genes are expressed at a specific phase of development in a particular cell type, a phenomenon called **differential gene regulation**. Many morphogens, particularly those that act during early phases of development, function as transcription factors.

Development in Animals I: Pattern Formation

Learning Outcomes:

1. **CoreSKILL »** Explain how the analysis of mutants has been an important tool in our understanding of development in animals.
2. Distinguish the functions of maternal effect genes, segmentation genes, and homeotic genes in animal development.

In this section, we will begin by examining the general stages of *Drosophila* development and then focus our attention on its embryonic stage. During this stage, the overall body plan is determined. We will see how the differential expression of particular genes within the embryo controls pattern formation. Although the roles of genes in the organization of mammalian embryos are not as well understood as they are in *Drosophila*, the analysis of the genomes of mammals and many other species has revealed many interesting parallels in the developmental program of all animals.

Embryonic Development Determines the Pattern of Structures in the Adult

As a way to appreciate the phases of pattern formation in animals, we will largely focus on development in *Drosophila*. However, as described in Chapter 51, animal development is quite varied among different species. **Figure 20.7** illustrates a simplified sequence of events in *Drosophila* development. Let's examine these steps before we consider the differential gene regulation that causes them to happen.

1. The oocyte is critical to establishing the pattern of development that will ultimately produce an adult organism. It is an elongated cell that contains positional information. As shown in Figure 20.7a, the fertilized egg already has anterior and posterior ends that correspond to those found in the adult (compare Figure 20.7a and e).

2. A key process in the embryonic development of *Drosophila* is the formation of a segmented body pattern. The embryo is subdivided into visible segments grouped into three general areas: the head, the thorax, and the abdomen. Figure 20.7b shows the segmented pattern of a *Drosophila* embryo about 10 hours after fertilization.

3. A *Drosophila* embryo then develops into a **larva** (Figure 20.7c), a free-living organism that is morphologically very different from the embryo and adult. Many animal species do not have larval stages. *Drosophila* undergoes three successive larval stages.

4. After the third larval stage, the organism becomes a **pupa** (Figure 20.7d), a transitional stage between the larva and the adult.

5. Through a process known as **metamorphosis**, the pupa transforms into a mature adult that emerges from the pupal case (Figure 20.7e). Each segment in the adult has its own characteristic structures. For example, the wings are on a thoracic segment.

From beginning to end, this developmental process takes about 10 days.

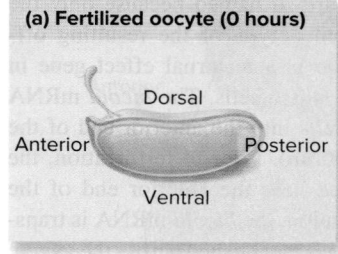

(a) Fertilized oocyte (0 hours)

Dorsal

Anterior — Posterior

Ventral

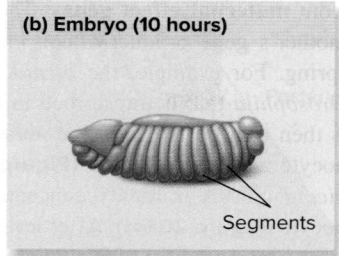

(b) Embryo (10 hours)

Segments

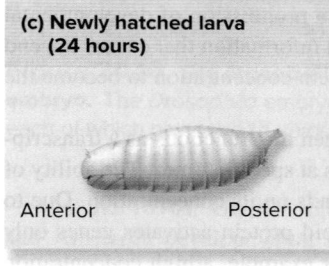

(c) Newly hatched larva (24 hours)

Anterior   Posterior

(d) Pupa (5 days)

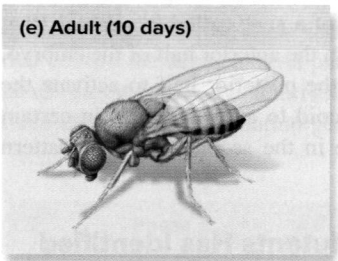

(e) Adult (10 days)

Figure 20.7 **Developmental stages of the fruit fly,** *Drosophila.*

Core Skill: Quantitative Reasoning

BIO **TIPS** **THE QUESTION** *One approach to studying development is to isolate mutants that cause abnormal development. This approach helps researchers identify the genes that regulate normal development. However, one problem with this approach is that mutations in genes that control the early stages of development are often lethal because they prevent the embryo from developing properly. To circumvent this problem, developmental biologists may try to isolate temperature-sensitive developmental mutations, or ts alleles. If an embryo carries a ts allele, it will develop correctly if incubated at the permissive temperature (for example, 25°C) but will fail to develop if incubated at the nonpermissive temperature (for example, 30°C). In most cases, ts alleles are mutations that slightly alter the amino acid sequence of a protein, causing a change in its structure that prevents it from working properly at the nonpermissive temperature. Such mutations are useful because they can provide insight regarding the stage of development at which the protein encoded by the gene is necessary. Researchers can take groups of embryos that carry the same ts allele and expose them to the permissive and nonpermissive temperatures at different stages of development. In the experiment described next, embryos carrying a ts allele were divided*

into five groups and exposed to the permissive or nonpermissive temperature at different times after fertilization. This experiment yielded the following results:

Time after fertilization (hours)	Group				
	1	2	3	4	5
0–1	30°C	25°C	25°C	25°C	25°C
1–2	25°C	30°C	25°C	25°C	25°C
2–3	25°C	25°C	30°C	25°C	25°C
3–4	25°C	25°C	25°C	30°C	25°C
4–5	25°C	25°C	25°C	25°C	30°C
Survival	Yes	Yes	Yes	No	Yes

Explain these results.

T OPIC **What topic in biology does this question address?** The topic is development. More specifically, the question asks you to analyze the effects of a temperature-sensitive mutation that affects development.

I NFORMATION **What information do you know based on the question and your understanding of the topic?** From the question, you have learned that developmental biologists can isolate ts alleles that are lethal only at nonpermissive temperatures. You are also given data about the survival of embryos in an experiment in which the temperature was shifted to a nonpermissive temperature at different times after fertilization.

P ROBLEM-SOLVING S TRATEGY **Interpret data. Compare and contrast.** To solve this problem, you need to interpret data that relate embryo survival to the timing of exposure to the nonpermissive temperature. You want to compare and contrast: When do the embryos survive, and when don't they survive?

ANSWER *The embryos do not survive if they are subjected to the nonpermissive temperature between 3 and 4 hours after fertilization, but they do survive if subjected to the nonpermissive temperature at other times during development. These results indicate that the protein encoded by the ts allele plays a crucial role in development at 3–4 hours after fertilization.*

Phase 1 Pattern Formation: Maternal Effect Genes Promote the Formation of the Body Axes

The first phase in *Drosophila* pattern formation is the establishment of the body axes, which occurs before the embryo becomes segmented. The morphogens necessary to establish these axes are distributed prior to fertilization. In most invertebrates and some vertebrates, certain morphogens, which are important in early developmental stages, are deposited asymmetrically within the egg as it develops (refer back to Figure 20.5a). Later, after the egg has been fertilized and development begins, these morphogens initiate developmental programs that govern the formation of the body axes of the embryo.

As an example of one morphogen that plays a role in axis formation, let's consider the product of a gene in *Drosophila* called *bicoid.* Its name is derived from the observation that a mutation

is the fertilized egg, which, via multiple cellular divisions, gives rise to an entire organism. A fertilized egg is said to be **totipotent** because it produces all of the cell types in the adult organism. The early embryonic structure called the blastocyst contains **embryonic stem cells (ES cells)**, which are located in the inner cell mass. The inner cell mass is a cluster of cells that give rise to the embryo. Embryonic stem cells are **pluripotent**, which means they can also differentiate into every or nearly every cell type of the body. However, a single embryonic stem cell by itself has lost the ability to produce an entire, intact individual. At an early fetal stage of development, the cells that later give rise to sperm or eggs cells, known as the **embryonic germ cells (EG cells)**, also are pluripotent.

During the embryonic and fetal stages of mammalian development, cells lose their ability to differentiate into a wide variety of cell types. Adults have both multipotent and unipotent stem cells. A **multipotent** stem cell can differentiate into several cell types, but far fewer than a pluripotent embryonic stem cell. For example, hematopoietic stem cells (HSCs) found in the bone marrow give rise to multiple blood cell types (**Figure 20.20**). Multipotent HSCs can follow a pathway in which cell division produces a myeloid cell, which then differentiates into various cells of the blood and immune systems. Alternatively, an HSC follows a path in which it becomes a lymphoid cell that develops into different blood cell types. A **unipotent** stem cell produces daughter cells that differentiate into only one cell type. For example, stem cells in the skin produce daughter cells that develop into skin cells.

Stem Cells in Medicine   Why are researchers interested in stem cells? Beyond shedding light on the process of development, stem cells have a potential use in the treatment of human diseases or injuries. This application has already become a reality in certain cases.

Table 20.1	Some Potential Uses of Stem Cells to Treat Diseases
Cell/tissue type	**Disease treatment**
Nerve	Implantation of cells into the brain to treat Parkinson disease; treatment of spinal cord injuries
Skin	Treatment of burns and skin disorders
Cardiac	Repair of heart damage associated with heart attacks
Cartilage	Repair of joints damaged by injury or arthritis
Bone	Repair or replacement of damaged bone
Liver	Repair or replacement of liver tissue damaged by injury or disease
Skeletal muscle	Repair or replacement of damaged muscle

For example, bone marrow transplants are used to treat patients with certain forms of cancer, such as leukemia. When bone marrow from a healthy person is injected into the body of a patient whose immune system has been wiped out via radiation, the stem cells within the transplanted marrow have the ability to proliferate and differentiate into various types of blood cells within the body of the patient.

Renewed interest in the use of stem cells in the potential treatment of many other diseases has been fostered by studies in 1998 in which researchers obtained ES cells from blastocysts and EG cells from aborted fetuses and successfully propagated them in the laboratory. Because ES and EG cells are pluripotent, they could potentially be used to treat a wide variety of diseases associated with cell and tissue damage (**Table 20.1**). Much progress has been made in testing

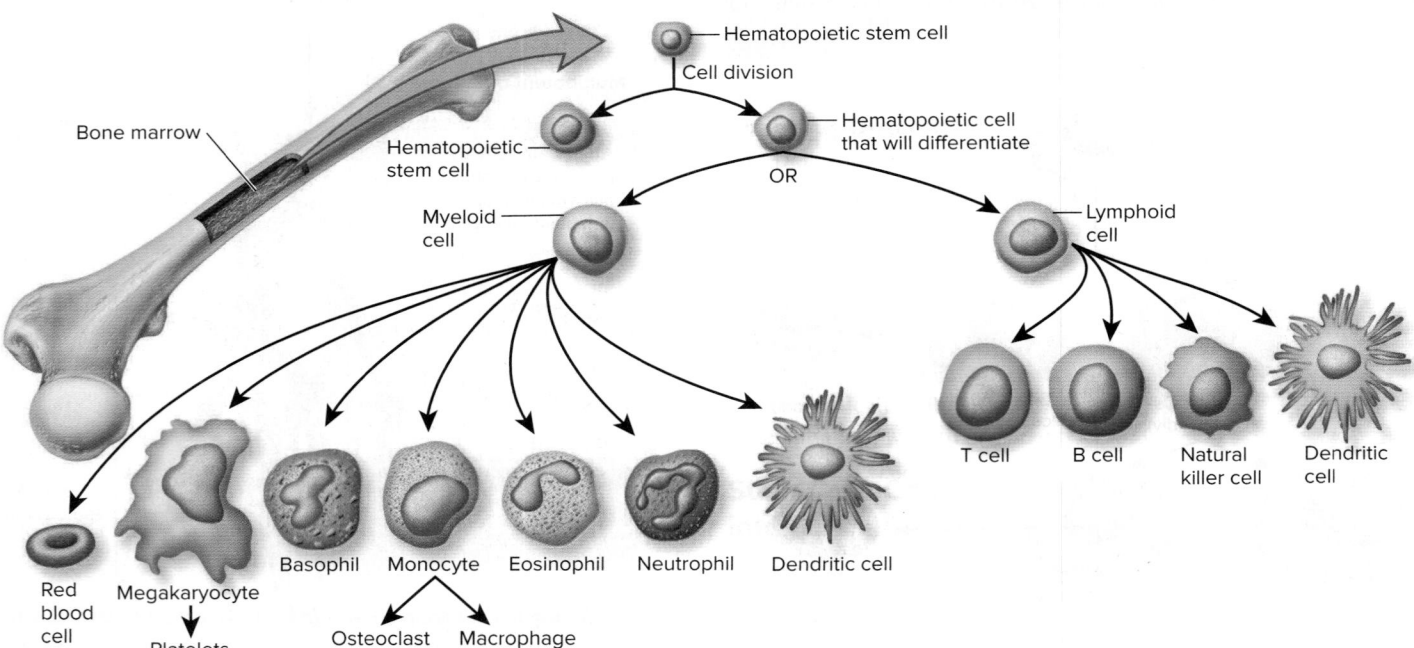

Figure 20.20   Fates of hematopoietic stem cells (HSCs). HSCs can follow two pathways: one in which cell division produces a myeloid cell and one that produces a lymphoid cell. Each develops into different blood cell types.

Concept Check: Are hematopoietic stem cells totipotent, pluripotent, multipotent, or unipotent?

the use of stem cells in animal models. However, more research is needed before the use of stem cells to treat such diseases in humans is realized.

From an ethical perspective, the primary issue that raises debate is the source of stem cells for research and potential treatments. Most ES cells have been derived from human embryos that were produced from in vitro fertilization, a method of assisted conception in which fertilization occurs outside of the mother's body and a limited number of the resulting embryos are transferred to the uterus. Most EG cells are obtained from aborted fetuses, either those that spontaneously aborted or those in which the decision to abort was not related to donating the fetal tissue to research. Some feel that it is morally wrong to use such tissue in research and/or the treatment of disease. Furthermore, some people fear this technology could lead to intentional abortions for the sole purpose of obtaining fetal tissues for transplantation. Others feel the embryos and fetuses that have been the sources of ES and EG cells were not going to become living

individuals, and therefore it is beneficial to study these cells and to use them in a positive way to treat human diseases and injury. It is not clear whether these two opposing viewpoints can reach a common ground.

If stem cells could be obtained from adult cells and induced to become pluripotent cells in the laboratory, an ethical dilemma may be avoided, because most people do not have moral objections to current procedures that use adult cells such as bone marrow transplantation. In 2006, work by Japanese physician Shinya Yamanaka and colleagues showed that adult mouse fibroblasts (a type of connective tissue cell) could become pluripotent by the introduction of four different genes that encode transcription factors. In 2007, Yamanaka's laboratory and two other research groups were able to show that such induced pluripotent stem cells can differentiate into all cell types when injected into mouse blastocysts and grown into baby mice. These results indicate that adult cells can be reprogrammed to become embryonic stem cells.

 Core Skill: Process of Science

Feature Investigation | Davis, Weintraub, and Lassar Identified Genes That Promote Muscle Cell Differentiation

A key question regarding stem cells is "What causes a stem cell to differentiate into a particular cell type?" Researchers have discovered that certain proteins function as master transcription factors that cause cells to differentiate into specific types of cells. The investigation described here was one of the first studies to reveal this phenomenon.

In 1987, Robert Davis, Harold Weintraub, and Andrew Lassar conducted a study to identify genes that promote skeletal muscle cell differentiation. The initial strategy for their experiments was to identify genes that are expressed only in differentiating skeletal muscle cells, not in nonmuscle cells. Though methods of gene cloning are described in Chapter 21, we will briefly consider these scientists' cloning methods in order to understand their approach. The researchers began with two different laboratory cell lines that could differentiate into muscle cells. From these two cell lines, they cloned and identified about 10,000 different genes that were transcribed into mRNA. Next, they compared the expressed genes in these two muscle cell lines with genes that were expressed in a nonmuscle cell line. Their comparison revealed 26 genes that were expressed only in the two muscle cell lines but not in the nonmuscle cell line. To narrow their search further, they compared these 26 genes with other nonmuscle cell lines they had available. Among the 26, only 3 of them, which the researchers termed *MyoA*, *MyoD*, and *MyoH*, were expressed exclusively in the two muscle cell lines.

In the experiment shown in **Figure 20.21**, the scientists' goal was to determine if any of these three genes could cause nonmuscle cells to differentiate into muscle cells. Using techniques described in Chapter 21, the coding sequence of each gene was placed next to an

active promoter that caused a high level of transcription, and then the genes were introduced into fibroblasts, which are a type of cell that normally differentiates into osteoblasts (bone cells), chondrocytes (cartilage cells), adipocytes (fat cells), and smooth muscle cells, but never differentiates into skeletal muscle cells in vivo. The cells were plated on growth media and allowed to grow for 3 to 5 days. When the cloned *MyoD* gene was introduced into fibroblast cells in a laboratory, the fibroblasts differentiated into skeletal muscle cells! These cells contained large amounts of myosin, which is a protein expressed in muscle cells. The other two cloned genes (*MyoA* and *MyoH*) did not cause muscle cell differentiation or promote myosin production.

Since this initial discovery, researchers have found that *MyoD* belongs to a small group of genes that initiate muscle cell development. These myogenic genes encode transcription factors. They are found in all vertebrates and have been identified in several invertebrates, such as *Drosophila* and *C. elegans*. In all cases, myogenic genes are activated during skeletal muscle cell development.

Experimental Questions

1. What was the goal of the research conducted by Davis, Weintraub, and Lassar?

2. **CoreSKILL** » How did Davis, Weintraub, and Lassar's research identify the candidate genes for muscle cell differentiation?

3. **CoreSKILL** » Once the researchers identified the candidate genes for muscle cell differentiation, how did they test the effect of each gene on cell differentiation? What were the results of the study?

Figure 20.21 Davis, Weintraub, and Lassar study showing that promotion of skeletal muscle cell differentiation in fibroblasts is caused by the expression of *MyoD*.

HYPOTHESIS Muscle differentiation is induced by particular genes.

KEY MATERIALS Three cloned genes had been identified that were expressed only in differentiating muscle cell lines. The researchers also had fibroblast cell lines, which do not normally differentiate into muscle cells.

Experimental level | Conceptual level

1. In 3 separate tubes, add each of the 3 cloned genes, designated *MyoA*, *MyoD*, and *MyoH*.

2. Add fibroblast cells to the tubes and incubate in the presence of calcium phosphate ($CaPO_4$), which promotes the uptake of DNA into the cells.

3. Plate the cells on solid growth media. Allow the cells to grow for 3 to 5 days. Cells will express the cloned gene.

4. Examine the cells under a microscope to determine if they have the morphology of muscle cells.

5. Determine if the cells are synthesizing myosin, which is a protein that is abundantly made in muscle cells. This is done by adding a labeled antibody that recognizes myosin and determining the amounts of antibody that bind.

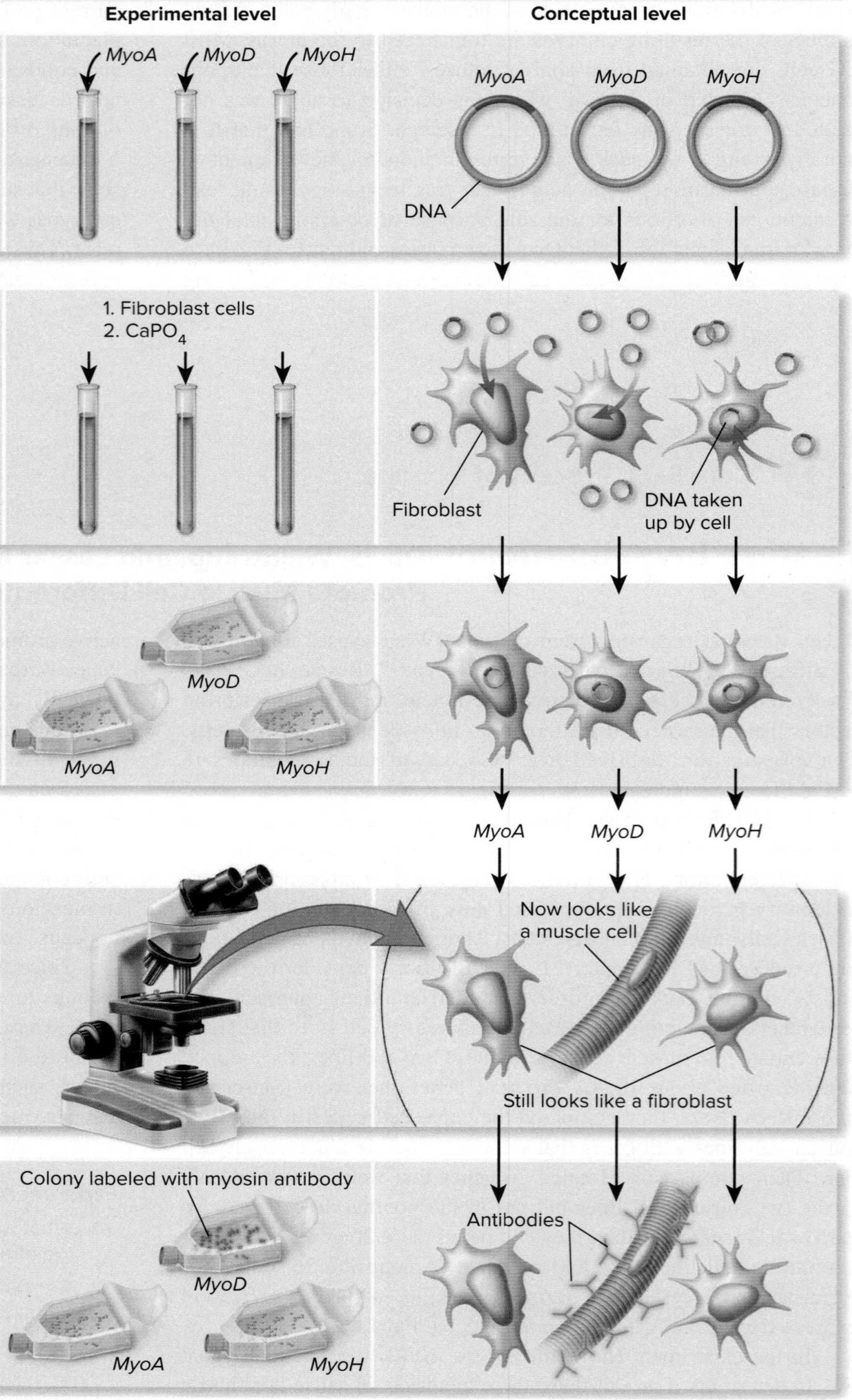

6 THE DATA

Results from step 4:

DNA added	Microscopic morphology of cells
MyoA	Fibroblasts
MyoD	Muscle cells
MyoH	Fibroblasts

Results from step 5:

DNA added	Colonies labeled with antibody that binds to myosin?
MyoA	No
MyoD	Yes
MyoH	No

7 CONCLUSION The *MyoD* gene encodes a protein that causes cells to differentiate into skeletal muscle cells.

8 SOURCE Davis, R. L., Weintraub, H., and Lassar, A. B. 1987. Expression of a single transfected cDNA converts fibroblasts to myoblasts. *Cell* 51: 987–1000.

20.4 Development in Plants

Learning Outcomes:
1. Outline the stages of pattern formation in plants.
2. **CoreSKILL »** Explain the ABC model for flower development.

Because all eukaryotic organisms share an evolutionary history, animals and plants have many common features, including the types of events that occur during development. However, the general morphology of plants is quite different from that of animals. Plant morphology exhibits two key features (see Figure 20.2b). The first is the root-shoot axis. Most plant growth occurs via cell division near the tips of the shoots and the bottoms of the roots. Second, this growth occurs in a well-defined radial pattern, which means that growth in the stems and roots occurs in concentric rings of tissues (**Figure 20.22**).

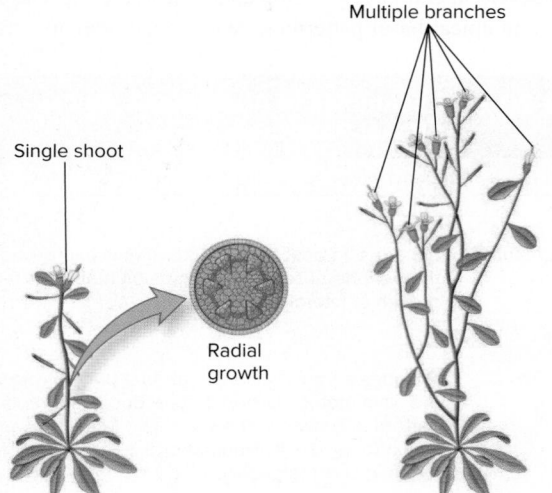

Figure 20.22 Pattern of shoot growth in plants. Early in development, as shown here in *Arabidopsis*, a single shoot promotes the formation of early leaves on the plant. Later, buds will form from this main shoot and grow into branches.

At the cellular level too, plant development shows some differences from animal development. For example, cell migration does not occur during plant development. In addition, the development of a plant does not rely on morphogens that are deposited in the oocyte, as in many animals. In plants, an entirely new individual can be regenerated from many types of somatic cells—cells that do not give rise to gametes. Such somatic cells of plants are totipotent.

In spite of these apparent differences, the underlying molecular mechanisms of pattern formation in plants share striking similarities with those in animals. Like animals, plants use the mechanism of differential gene regulation to coordinate the development of a body plan. Like their animal counterparts, plants have a developmental program that relies on transcription factors to determine when gene products are made and in what quantity. In this section, we will consider pattern formation in plants and examine how transcription factors play a key role in plant development.

Plant Development Occurs from Meristems That Are Formed in the Embryo

How does pattern formation occur in plants? **Figure 20.23** illustrates a common order of events in the embryonic development of flowering plants such as *Arabidopsis*. After fertilization, the first cellular division is asymmetrical and produces a smaller apical cell and a larger basal cell (Figure 20.23a). In 2009, Danish geneticist Martin Bayer and colleagues conducted experiments indicating that the sperm carries mRNA molecules that are critical for this asymmetric cell division. The apical cell gives rise to most of the embryo and later develops into the shoot of the plant. In *Arabidopsis*, the basal cell gives rise to the root, along with a structure called the suspensor, which channels nutrients from the parent plant to the young embryo (Figure 20.23b).

At the heart stage, which is composed of only about 100 cells, the basic organization of the plant has been established (Figure 20.23c). Plants have organized groups of actively dividing stem cells called **meristems**. As discussed earlier, stem cells retain the ability both to divide and to differentiate into multiple cell types. The meristem produces offshoots of proliferating and differentiating cells.

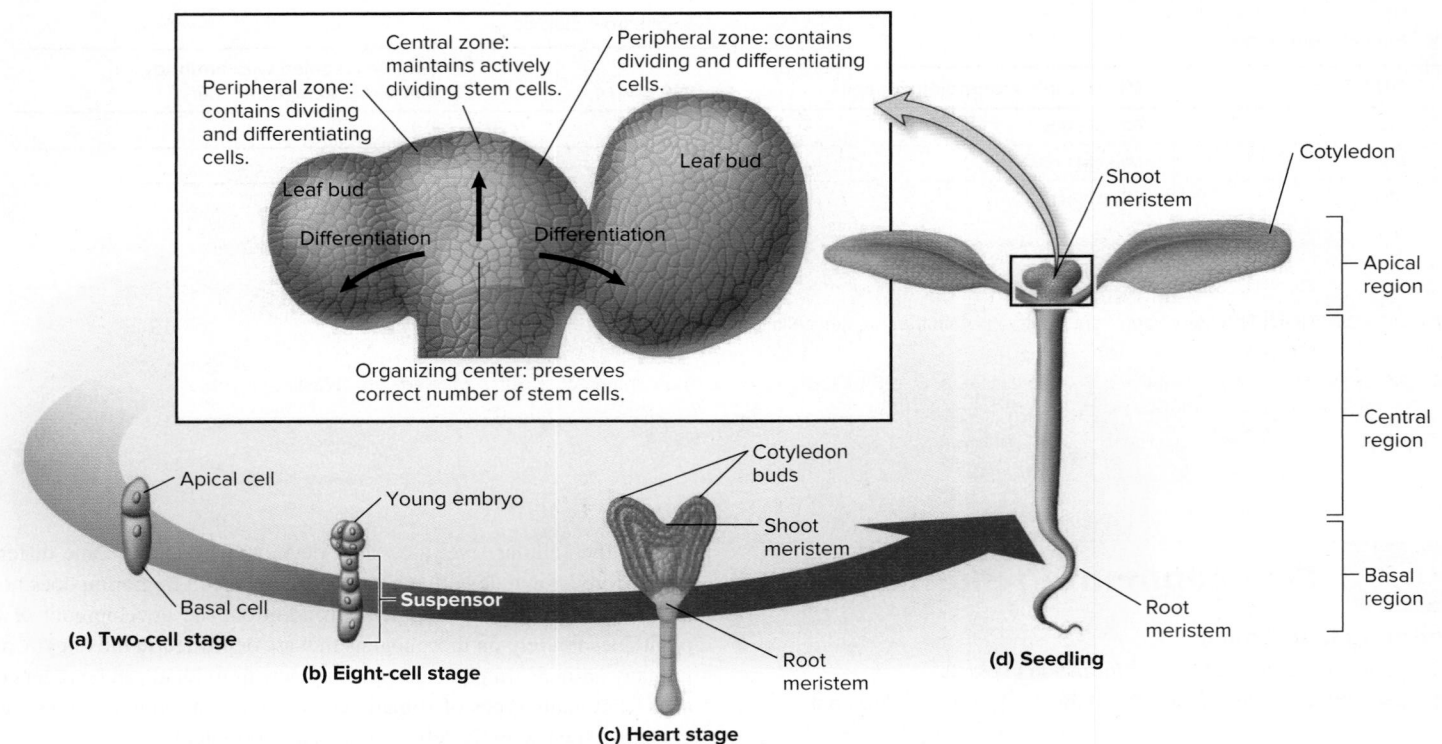

Figure 20.23 Developmental steps in the formation of a plant embryo. (a) The two-cell stage consists of the apical cell and basal cell. **(b)** The eight-cell stage consists of a young embryo and a suspensor. The suspensor channels nutrients to the young embryo from the parent plant. **(c)** At the heart stage, all of the plant tissues have begun to form. The shoot meristem is located between the future cotyledons, and the root meristem is on the opposite side. **(d)** A seedling showing apical, central, and basal regions. The inset shows the organization of the shoot meristem. Note: The steps shown in parts (a), (b), and (c) occur during seed formation, when the embryo is enclosed within a seed.

Concept Check: *Where are stem cells found in a growing plant?*

The **root apical meristem** gives rise only to the root, whereas the **shoot apical meristem** produces all aerial parts of the plant, which include the stem as well as lateral structures such as branches, leaves, and flowers.

The heart stage then progresses to the formation of a seedling that has two cotyledons, which are embryonic leaves that store nutrients for the developing embryo and seedling. In the seedling shown in Figure 20.23d, you can see three main regions. The **apical region** produces the leaves and flowers of the plant. The **central region** creates the stem. Finally, the **basal region** produces the roots. Each of these three regions develops differently, as indicated by their unique cell division patterns and distinct morphologies.

As seen in the inset to Figure 20.23d, the shoot meristem is organized into three areas: the organizing center, the central zone, and the peripheral zone. The **organizing center** ensures the proper organization of the meristem and preserves the correct number of actively dividing stem cells. The **central zone** is an area where undifferentiated stem cells are always maintained. The **peripheral zone** contains dividing cells that eventually differentiate into plant structures. For example, the peripheral zone may form a bud that will produce a leaf or flower.

By analyzing mutations that disrupt the developmental process, researchers have discovered that the apical, central, and basal regions of a growing plant express different sets of genes. A category of genes

called **apical-basal-patterning genes** are important in early stages of plant development. A few examples are described in **Table 20.2**. Mutations in apical-basal-patterning genes cause dramatic effects in

Table 20.2	Examples of *Arabidopsis* Apical-Basal-Patterning Genes
Region: *Gene*	**Description**
Apical:	
Aintegumenta	Encodes a transcription factor that is expressed in the peripheral zone. Its expression maintains the growth of lateral buds.
Central:	
Scarecrow	Encodes a transcription factor that plays a role in the asymmetric division that produces the radial pattern of growth in the stem. The Scarecrow protein also affects cell division patterns in roots and plays a role in sensing gravity.
Basal:	
Monopterous	Encodes a transcription factor. When the *Monopterous* gene is defective, the plant embryo cannot initiate the formation of root structures, although root structures can be formed postembryonically. This gene seems to be required for organizing root formation in the embryo.

one of these three regions. For example, the *Aintegumenta* gene is necessary for apical development. When it is defective, the growth of lateral buds is defective.

Plant Homeotic Genes Control Flower Development

Although William Bateson coined the term homeotic to describe mutations in animals in which one body part is replaced by another, the first known homeotic mutations were described in plants. Naturalists in ancient Greece and Rome, for example, recorded their observations of double flowers in which stamens were replaced by petals. In current research, geneticists are studying these types of mutations to better understand developmental pathways in plants. Many homeotic mutations affecting flower development have been identified in *Arabidopsis* and also in the snapdragon (*Antirrhinum majus*).

A normal *Arabidopsis* flower is composed of four concentric whorls of structures (**Figure 20.24a**). The first, outer whorl has four **sepals**, which protect the flower bud before it opens. The second whorl is composed of four **petals**, and the third whorl has six **stamens**, structures that make male gametophytes, pollen. Finally, the fourth, innermost whorl contains two carpels that are fused together. The **carpels** produce, enclose, and nurture the female gametophytes.

After analyzing the effects of many different homeotic mutations in *Arabidopsis*, British plant biologist Enrico Coen and his American colleague, plant geneticist, Elliot Meyerowitz, proposed the **ABC model** for flower development in 1991. In this model, three classes of genes, called *A*, *B*, and *C*, govern the formation of sepals, petals, stamens, and carpels. More recently, a fourth class, called the *E* genes, was found to be required for this process. All four types of genes encode transcription factors that control flower development in *Arabidopsis* (Figure 20.24a). In whorl 1, gene *A* product is made. This promotes sepal formation. In whorl 2, *A*, *B*, and *E* gene products are made, which promotes petal formation. In whorl 3, the expression of genes *B*, *C*, and *E* causes stamens to be made. Finally, in whorl 4, the products of *C* and *E* genes promote carpel formation.

What happens in certain homeotic mutants that undergo transformations of particular whorls? According to the original ABC model, genes *A* and *C* repress each other's expression, and gene *B* functions independently. In a mutant defective in gene *A* expression, gene *C* is also expressed in whorls 1 and 2. This produces a carpel-stamen-stamen-carpel arrangement in which the sepals have been transformed into carpels and the petals into stamens (**Figure 20.24b**). When gene *B* is defective, a flower cannot make petals or stamens. Therefore, a gene *B* defect yields a flower with a sepal-sepal-carpel-carpel arrangement. When gene *C* is defective, gene *A* is expressed in all four whorls. This results in a sepal-petal-petal-sepal pattern. If the expression of *E* genes is defective, the flower consists entirely of sepals.

Working together, the genes shown in Figure 20.24 promote a pattern of development that leads to sepal, petal, stamen, or carpel structures. But what happens if genes *A*, *B*, and *C* are all defective? This produces a flower composed entirely of leaves (**Figure 20.24c**). These results indicate that the leaf structure is the default pathway

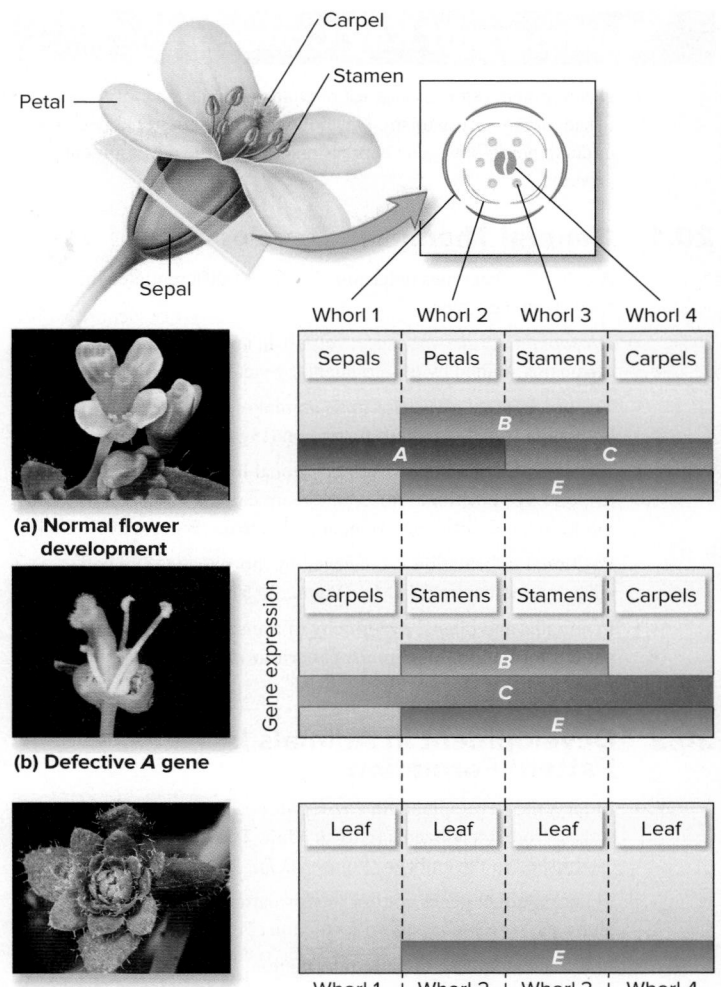

(a) Normal flower development

(b) Defective *A* gene

(c) Triple mutant

Figure 20.24 Normal and mutant homeotic gene action in *Arabidopsis*. (a) A normal flower is composed of four concentric whorls of structures: sepals, petals, stamens, and carpels. To the right is the ABC model of homeotic gene action that has been revised to include *E* genes. (b) A homeotic mutant defective in gene *A* in which the sepals have been transformed into carpels and the petals have been transformed into stamens. (c) A triple mutant defective in the *A*, *B*, and *C* genes, producing a flower with all leaves. a: ©Darwin Dale/Science Source; b–c: ©John Bowman

Concept Check: *What flower pattern would you expect if the B gene was expressed in whorls 2, 3, and 4?*

and that the *A*, *B*, and *C* genes cause development to deviate from a leaf structure in order to make something else. In this regard, the sepals, petals, stamens, and carpels of flowers can be viewed as modified leaves.

Like the *Drosophila* homeotic genes, plant homeotic genes are part of a hierarchy of gene regulation. Most plant homeotic genes belong to a family of genes called MADS-box genes, which encode transcription factor proteins that contain a DNA-binding domain called a MADS domain. The *Arabidopsis* homeotic genes do not contain a sequence similar to the homeobox found in animal homeotic genes.

Summary of Key Concepts

- Development refers to a series of changes in the state of a cell, tissue, organ, or organism. Developmental genetics is aimed at understanding how gene expression controls the development process.

20.1 General Themes in Development

- A cell's fate becomes determined before it differentiates into a specialized cell type.
- *Drosophila*, *C. elegans*, mice, zebrafish, and *Arabidopsis* are model organisms studied by developmental geneticists (Figure 20.1).
- The process that gives rise to an animal or plant with a particular body plan is called pattern formation (Figure 20.2).
- Pattern formation depends on positional information. Four responses to positional information are cell division, cell migration, cell differentiation, and apoptosis (Figures 20.3, 20.4).
- Positional information is conveyed by morphogens and cell adhesion molecules (CAMs) (Figure 20.5).
- In animals and plants, a hierarchy of transcription factors controls pattern formation. In animals, pattern formation occurs in four general phases (Figure 20.6).

20.2 Development in Animals I: Pattern Formation

- Embryonic development in *Drosophila* occurs in a sequence of stages, from a fertilized egg to an adult. The basic body plan is established in the embryo (Figure 20.7).
- Maternal effect genes control the formation of body axes, the first phase in *Drosophila* pattern formation (Figures 20.8, 20.9).
- In the second phase of pattern formation, the sequential expression of three categories of segmentation genes divides the embryo into segments. Mutations that alter *Drosophila* development have allowed scientists to understand the normal process (Figures 20.10, 20.11).
- During the third phase of pattern formation, each segment begins to develop its own unique characteristics. Homeotic genes control the development of a particular segment or group of segments (Figures 20.12, 20.13, 20.14, 20.15).
- Invertebrates and vertebrates have a homologous set of homeotic genes. These genes are called *Hox* genes (Figures 20.16, 20.17).

20.3 Development in Animals II: Cell Differentiation

- In the fourth phase of pattern formation, stem cells divide and differentiate into specialized cell types (Figure 20.18).
- Stem cells are categorized according to their developmental stage and their ability to differentiate. In mammals, a fertilized egg is totipotent; certain embryonic and fetal cells are pluripotent; and stem cells in the adult are multipotent or unipotent (Figures 20.19, 20.20).
- Stem cells have the potential to be used to treat a variety of human diseases (Table 20.1).
- The differentiation of cell types within certain tissues or organs is controlled by master transcription factors. An example is a transcription factor encoded by *MyoD*, a gene that initiates skeletal muscle cell development (Figure 20.21).

20.4 Development in Plants

- Plants grow along a root-shoot axis and in a well-defined radial pattern. Cell migration does not occur in plants (Figure 20.22).
- Plant stem cells within meristems promote the development of plant structures such as roots, stems, leaves, and flowers (Figure 20.23).
- The apical, central, and basal regions of the growing plant express different apical-basal-patterning genes (Table 20.2).
- According to the ABC model, four classes of homeotic genes in plants, *A*, *B*, *C*, and *E*, control flower development (Figure 20.24).

Assess & Discuss

Test Yourself

1. The process whereby a cell's morphology and function change is called
   a. determination.
   d. genetic engineering.
   b. cell fate.
   e. both a and c.
   c. differentiation.

2. Pattern formation in plants occurs along the _____ axis.
   a. dorsoventral
   d root-shoot
   b. anteroposterior
   e. all of the above are correct.
   c. left-right

3. Positional information is important in determining the fate of a cell in a multicellular organism. Animal cells may respond to positional information by
   a. dividing.
   d. undergoing apoptosis.
   b. migrating.
   e. doing any of the above.
   c. differentiating.

4. Morphogens are
   a. molecules that disrupt normal development.
   b. molecules that convey positional information and promote changes in development.
   c. mutagenic agents that cause apoptosis.
   d. receptors that allow cells to adhere to the extracellular matrix.
   e. both a and c.

5. What group of proteins play a key role in controlling the program of developmental changes?
   a. motor proteins
   d. restriction endonucleases
   b. transporters
   e. cyclins
   c. transcription factors

6. Arrange the following phases of pattern formation in animals in the correct sequence:
   1. Tissues, organs, and other body structures in each segment are formed.
   2. Axes of the entire animal are determined.
   3. Cells become differentiated.
   4. The entire animal is divided into segments.
   a. 2, 3, 4, 1   c. 2, 4, 3, 1   e. 2, 4, 1, 3
   b. 1, 2, 4, 3   d. 3, 2, 4, 1

7. Homeotic genes in *Drosophila*
   a. determine the structural and functional characteristics of different segments of the developing fly.
   b. encode motor proteins that transport morphogens throughout the embryo.
   c. are dispersed randomly throughout the genome.
   d. are expressed in similar levels in all parts of the developing embryo.
   e. Both a and c are correct.

8. Which of the following genes do *not* play a role in the process whereby segments are formed in the fruit fly embryo?
   a. *MyoD*
   b. gap genes
   c. pair-rule genes
   d. segment-polarity genes
   e. All of the above play a role in segmentation.

9. An embryonic stem cell that can give rise to any type of cell of an adult organism but cannot produce an entire, intact individual is called
   a. totipotent.
   b. pluripotent.
   c. multipotent.
   d. unipotent.
   e. antipotent.

10. During plant development, the leaves and the flowers of the plant are derived from
    a. the central region.
    b. the basal region.
    c. the suspensor.
    d. the apical region.
    e. both a and d.

Conceptual Questions

1. If you observed fruit flies with each of the following developmental abnormalities, would you guess that a mutation had occurred in a segmentation gene or a homeotic gene? Explain your guess.
   a. Three abdominal segments are missing.
   b. One abdominal segment has legs.

2. The *MyoD* gene in mammals plays a role in muscle cell differentiation. The *Hox* genes are homeotic genes that play a role in the differentiation of particular regions of the body. Compare and contrast the functions of these genes.

3. **Core Concept: Information** Discuss how maternal effect genes, segmentation genes, and homeotic genes control the process of development in animals.

Collaborative Questions

1. It seems that developmental genetics boils down to a complex network of gene regulation. Starting with maternal effect genes and ending with master transcription factors, draw or describe this network for the development of *Drosophila*. How many genes do you think are necessary to specify a complete developmental network for the fruit fly? How many genes do you think are needed for a network to specify one segment?

2. Is it possible for a phenotypically normal female fly to be homozygous for a loss-of-function allele in the *bicoid* gene? What would be the phenotype of the offspring that such a fly would produce if it was mated to a male that was homozygous for the normal *bicoid* allele?

Genetic Technologies and Genomics

21

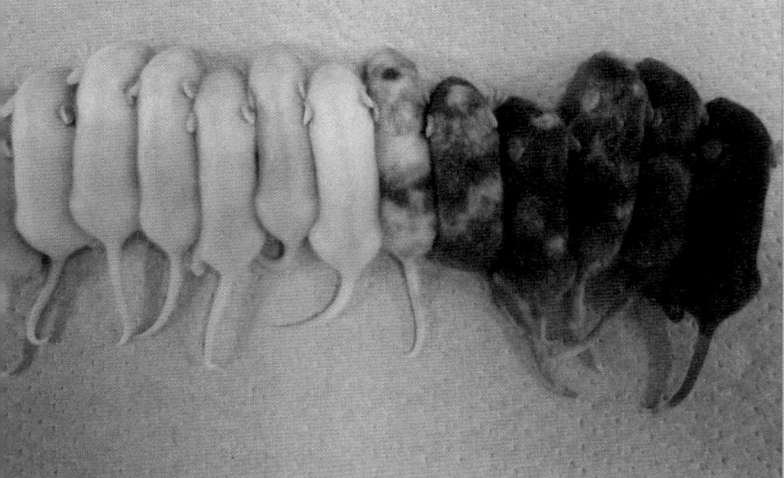

Japanese researchers used an exciting new genetic approach, called CRISPR-Cas technology, to silence a gene in mice that encodes tyrosinase, an enzyme needed for pigment production. In the seven albino newborn mice on the left, both copies of this gene have been silenced. In the ones with a mottled appearance, partial silencing was achieved. The gene was not silenced in the black newborn on the right. ©Fumihiro Sugiyama

J on was born with hemophilia A, which is a blood clotting disorder. As discussed in Chapter 17, hemophilia is inherited as an X-linked recessive trait. Jon's blood is unable to clot properly because he is missing a protein, called factor VIII, that is needed in a pathway required for normal blood clotting. Fortunately, Jon can take injections of purified factor VIII and thereby minimize the harmful effects of hemophilia. You might be surprised to learn that purified factor VIII is not obtained from human blood. Instead, it's made by cells grown in the laboratory. These cells have been genetically modified to synthesize factor VIII in large amounts. This process is just one example of how researchers have been able to apply **recombinant DNA technology**—the use of laboratory techniques to bring together fragments of DNA from multiple sources—to benefit humans.

In the early 1970s, the first successes in making recombinant DNA molecules were accomplished independently by two groups at Stanford University: David Jackson, Robert Symons, and Paul Berg; and Peter Lobban and A. Dale Kaiser. Both groups were able to isolate and purify pieces of DNA in a test tube and then covalently link two or more DNA fragments. Once inside a host cell, the recombinant molecules were replicated to produce many identical copies. The process of making multiple copies of a particular gene is known as **gene cloning**. In the first section of this chapter, we will explore recombinant DNA technology and gene cloning, techniques that have enabled geneticists to probe the relationships between gene sequences and phenotypic consequences.

In the second section, we will consider the topic of **genomics**—the molecular analysis of the entire genome of a species. In recent years, molecular techniques have progressed to the point where researchers can study the structure and function of many genes as large, integrated networks and can make changes to the genome in order to silence a particular gene (see the chapter opening photo) or alter its DNA sequence in a specific way.

In the remaining sections of this chapter, we will consider the genome characteristics of bacteria, archaea, and eukaryotes. In many species, such as multicellular plants and animals, the genome shows a high abundance of repetitive sequences—sequences that are repeated multiple times in the same genome. We will examine how such repetitive sequences increase in number.

21.1 Gene Cloning

Learning Outcomes:

1. Outline the steps of gene cloning using vectors.
2. Distinguish between a genomic library and a cDNA library.
3. Explain how gel electrophoresis is used to separate DNA fragments.
4. Describe the steps of gene cloning using polymerase chain reaction (PCR).

As already mentioned, the term gene cloning refers to the process of making many copies of a particular gene. Why is gene cloning useful? **Figure 21.1** provides an overview of the steps and goals of

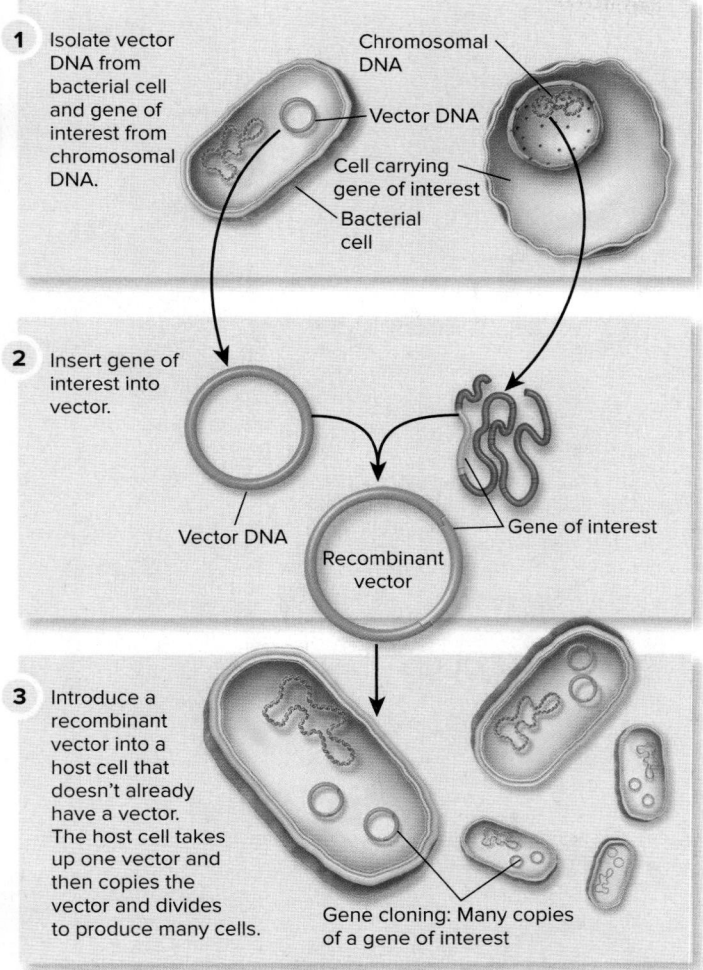

1 Isolate vector DNA from bacterial cell and gene of interest from chromosomal DNA.

Chromosomal DNA

Vector DNA

Cell carrying gene of interest

Bacterial cell

2 Insert gene of interest into vector.

Vector DNA

Gene of interest

Recombinant vector

3 Introduce a recombinant vector into a host cell that doesn't already have a vector. The host cell takes up one vector and then copies the vector and divides to produce many cells.

Gene cloning: Many copies of a gene of interest

Gene cloning is done to achieve one of two main goals:

Producing large amounts of DNA of a specific gene	Expressing the cloned gene to produce the encoded protein
Examples	*Examples*
• Cloned genes provide enough DNA for DNA sequencing. The sequence of a gene can help us understand how a gene works and identify mutations that cause diseases.	• Large amounts of the protein can be purified to study its structure and function.
• Cloned DNA can be used as a probe to identify the same gene or similar genes in other organisms.	• Cloned genes can be introduced into bacteria or livestock to make pharmaceutical products such as insulin.
	• Cloned genes can be introduced into plants and animals to alter their traits.
	• Cloned genes can be used to treat diseases—a clinical approach called gene therapy.

Figure 21.1 **Overview of gene cloning.** The process of gene cloning is used to produce large amounts of a gene or its protein product.

 Core Skill: Process of Science The technique of gene cloning allows researchers to study genes and gene products in greater detail.

gene cloning. The process is usually done with one of two goals in mind. One is that a researcher or clinician wants many copies of the gene, perhaps to study the DNA directly or to use the DNA as a tool. For example, geneticists may want to determine the sequence of a gene from a person with a disease to see if the gene carries a mutation. Alternatively, the goal may be to obtain a large amount of the gene product, such as a specific protein. For example, biochemists use gene cloning to obtain large amounts of proteins to study their structure and function. In recent years, gene cloning has provided the foundation for critical technical advances in a variety of disciplines, including molecular biology, genetics, cell biology, biochemistry, and medicine. In this section, we will examine the procedures that are used in gene cloning.

Step 1: Vector DNA and Chromosomal DNA Are the Starting Materials for Gene Cloning

One way to carry out gene cloning uses a type of DNA known as a **vector** (from the Latin, for "one who carries") (see Figure 21.1). Vector DNA acts as a carrier of the DNA segment that is to be cloned. In cloning experiments, a vector may carry a small segment of chromosomal DNA, perhaps only a single gene. By comparison, a chromosome carries up to a few thousand genes. When a vector is introduced into a living cell, it can replicate, and so the DNA that it carries is also replicated. This produces many identical copies of the inserted gene.

The vectors commonly used in gene cloning experiments were originally derived from two natural sources: plasmids or viruses.

- **Plasmids** are small, circular pieces of DNA that are found naturally in many strains of bacteria and exist independently of the bacterial chromosome. Commercially available plasmids have been genetically engineered for effective use in cloning experiments. They contain unique sites into which geneticists can easily insert pieces of chromosomal DNA.

- **Viral vectors** are derived from viruses, which can infect living cells and propagate themselves by taking control of the host cell's metabolic machinery. When a chromosomal gene is inserted into a viral vector, the gene is replicated whenever the viral DNA is replicated. Therefore, viruses can be used as vectors to carry other pieces of DNA.

The second material necessary for cloning a gene is the gene itself, which we will call the gene of interest. The source of the gene is the chromosomal DNA that carries the gene. The preparation of chromosomal DNA involves breaking open cells and extracting and purifying the DNA using biochemical separation techniques such as chromatography and centrifugation.

Step 2: Cutting Chromosomal and Vector DNA into Pieces and Linking Them Together Produces Recombinant Vectors

The second step in a gene cloning experiment is the insertion of the gene of interest into the vector (see Figure 21.1, step 2). How is this accomplished? DNA molecules are cut and pasted into vectors to produce recombinant vectors. To cut DNA, researchers use enzymes known as **restriction enzymes**. These enzymes, which were

Table 21.1	Examples of Restriction Enzymes Used in Gene Cloning	
Restriction enzyme*	Bacterial source	Sequence recognized†
EcoRI	Escherichia coli (strain RY13)	↓ 5′–GAATTC–3′ 3′–CTTAAG–5′ ↑
SacI	Streptomyces achromogenes	↓ 5′–GAGCTC–3′ 3′–CTCGAG–5′ ↑

*Restriction enzymes are named according to the species in which they are found. The first three letters are italicized because they indicate the genus and species names. Because a species may produce more than one restriction enzyme, the enzymes are designated I, II, III, and so on, to indicate the order in which they were discovered in a given species.

†The arrows show the locations in the two DNA strands where the restriction enzymes cleave the DNA backbone.

discovered by Swiss geneticist Werner Arber and American microbiologists Hamilton Smith and Daniel Nathans in the 1960s and 1970s, are made naturally by many different species of bacteria. Restriction enzymes protect bacterial cells from invasion by viruses by degrading the viral DNA into small fragments. Several hundred different restriction enzymes from various bacterial species have been identified and are commercially available to molecular biologists.

The restriction enzymes used in cloning experiments bind to a specific base sequence and then cleave the DNA backbone at two defined locations, one in each strand. Most restriction enzymes recognize sequences that are palindromic, which means a sequence is identical when read in the opposite directions on the two strands (**Table 21.1**). For example, the sequence recognized by the restriction enzyme *Eco*RI is 5′−GAATTC−3′ in the top strand shown in Table 21.1. Read in the opposite direction in the bottom (complementary) strand, this sequence is also 5′−GAATTC−3′. Certain restriction enzymes are useful in cloning because they digest DNA into fragments with single-stranded ends (termed "sticky" ends) that hydrogen-bond to other DNA fragments that are cut with the same enzyme and thus have complementary sequences.

Figure 21.2 shows the action of a restriction enzyme (*Eco*RI) and the insertion of a gene into a vector. This vector, which is a plasmid, carries the *amp^R* and *lacZ* genes, whose useful functions will be discussed later. *Eco*RI binds to specific sequences in both the vector and chromosomal DNA. It then cleaves the DNA backbones, producing DNA fragments with sticky ends (Figure 21.2, step 1). The sticky ends of a piece of chromosomal DNA and the vector DNA can hydrogen-bond with each other (Figure 21.2, step 2), a process called annealing. However, this interaction is not stable, because it involves only a few hydrogen bonds between complementary bases. To establish a permanent connection between two DNA fragments, the sugar-phosphate backbones of the DNA strands must be covalently linked, or ligated. This linkage is catalyzed by DNA ligase (Figure 21.2, step 3). Recall from Chapter 11 that DNA ligase is an enzyme that catalyzes the formation of a covalent bond between two adjacent DNA fragments.

In some cases, the two ends of the vector simply ligate back together, restoring it to its original circular structure; this forms

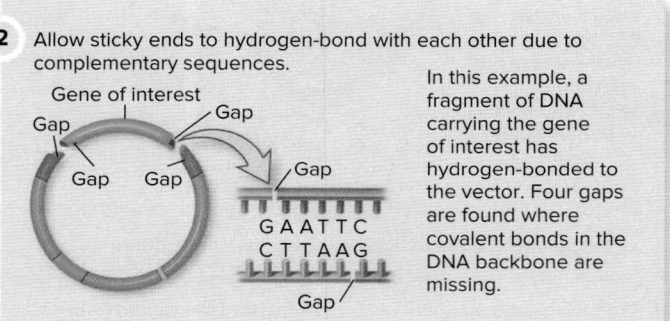

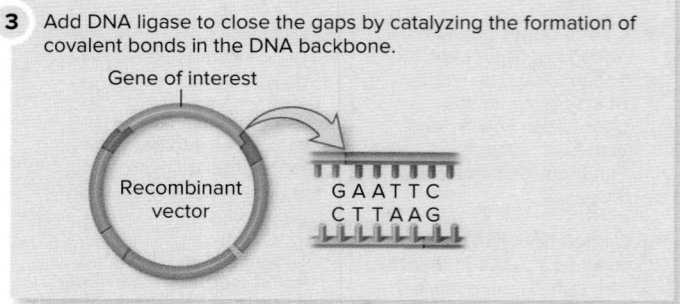

Figure 21.2 **Step 2 of gene cloning: the actions of a restriction enzyme and DNA ligase to produce a recombinant vector.**

 Core Skill: Connections Refer back to Figure 19.11. What are the general properties of plasmids?

a recircularized vector. In other cases, a fragment of chromosomal DNA may become ligated to both ends of the vector. When this happens, a segment of chromosomal DNA has been inserted into the vector. The result is a vector containing a piece of chromosomal DNA, which is called a **recombinant vector**. Such a vector is ready to be cloned. A recombinant vector may contain the gene of interest, or it may contain a different piece of chromosomal DNA.

Step 3: Putting Recombinant Vectors into Host Cells and Allowing Those Cells to Propagate Achieves Gene Cloning

The third step in gene cloning is the actual cloning of the gene of interest. In this step, the goal is for the recombinant vector carrying the desired gene to be taken up by bacterial cells that have been treated with agents that render them permeable to DNA molecules (**Figure 21.3**). The process, called transformation, is described in Chapter 19 (refer back to Figure 19.17). Bacterial cells with the ability to take up DNA are called **competent**. After the bacteria are combined with a mixture of recircularized vectors and recombinant vectors, some bacterial cells take up a single vector, although most cells fail to take up any vector. The bacteria are then inoculated onto petri plates containing a bacterial growth medium and ampicillin.

In the experiment shown in Figure 21.3, the bacterial cells were originally sensitive to ampicillin. The vector, which is a plasmid, carries an antibiotic-resistance gene, called the *amp^R* gene. What is the purpose of this gene in a cloning experiment? Such a gene is called a **selectable marker** because the presence of the antibiotic selects for the growth of cells expressing the *amp^R* gene. The *amp^R* gene encodes an enzyme known as β-lactamase that degrades the antibiotic ampicillin, which normally kills bacteria. Bacteria that have not taken up a plasmid are killed by the antibiotic. In contrast, any bacterium that has taken up a plasmid carrying the *amp^R* gene grows and divides many times to form a visible bacterial colony containing tens of millions of cells. Because each cell in a single colony is derived from the same original cell that took up a single plasmid, all cells within a colony contain the same type of plasmid DNA.

The experimenter also needs a way to distinguish bacterial colonies that contain cells with a recombinant vector from those containing cells with a recircularized vector. In a recombinant vector, a piece of chromosomal DNA has been inserted into a region of the vector that contains the *lacZ* gene, which encodes the enzyme β-galactosidase. The insertion of chromosomal DNA into the vector disrupts the *lacZ* gene, thereby preventing the synthesis of β-galactosidase. By comparison, a recircularized vector has a functional *lacZ* gene. The functionality of *lacZ* can be determined by adding to the growth medium a colorless compound, X-Gal, which is cleaved by β-galactosidase into a blue dye. Bacteria grown in the presence of X-Gal form blue colonies if they produce a functional β-galactosidase enzyme, and white colonies if they do not. In this experiment, therefore, bacterial colonies containing recircularized vectors form blue colonies, whereas colonies containing recombinant vectors carrying a segment of chromosomal DNA are white.

After a bacterial cell has taken up a recombinant vector, two subsequent events lead to the production of many copies of that vector. First, when the vector has a highly active origin of replication, the bacterial host cell produces many copies of the recombinant vector per cell. Second, the bacterial cells divide approximately every

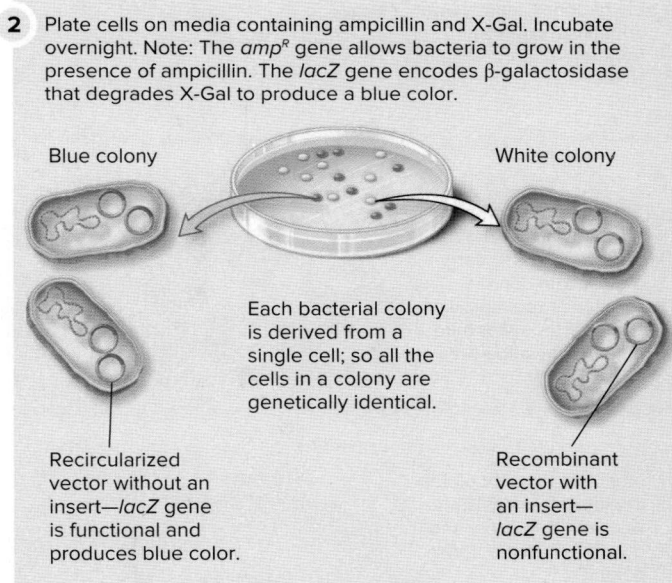

1 Mix plasmid DNA with many *E. coli* cells that have been treated with agents that make them permeable to DNA.

Gene of interest

Part of *lacZ*

Part of *lacZ*

amp^R

Origin of replication

In this example, the gene of interest was inserted into a plasmid. This disrupts the *lacZ* gene and renders it nonfunctional. It is also possible for any other chromosomal DNA fragment to be inserted into the plasmid, or the plasmid may recircularize without an insert.

This shows a bacterial cell that has taken up the plasmid carrying the gene of interest. Many bacterial cells fail to take up a plasmid.

2 Plate cells on media containing ampicillin and X-Gal. Incubate overnight. Note: The *amp^R* gene allows bacteria to grow in the presence of ampicillin. The *lacZ* gene encodes β-galactosidase that degrades X-Gal to produce a blue color.

Blue colony

White colony

Each bacterial colony is derived from a single cell; so all the cells in a colony are genetically identical.

Recircularized vector without an insert—*lacZ* gene is functional and produces blue color.

Recombinant vector with an insert—*lacZ* gene is nonfunctional.

Figure 21.3 **Step 3 of gene cloning: introduction of a recombinant vector into a host cell.** For cloning to occur, a recombinant vector is introduced into a host cell, which copies the vector and divides to produce many cells. This produces many copies of the gene of interest.

Concept Check: In this cloning experiment, what is the purpose of having the lacZ gene in the vector?

20 minutes. Following overnight growth, a population of many millions of bacteria is obtained from a single cell. For example, a bacterial colony may comprise 10 million cells, with each cell containing 50 copies of the recombinant vector. Therefore, this bacterial colony has 500 million copies of the cloned gene!

A DNA Library Is a Collection of Many Different DNA Fragments Cloned into Vectors

In a typical cloning experiment, such as the one described in Figures 21.2 and 21.3, the treatment of chromosomal DNA with restriction enzymes actually yields many different DNA fragments. Therefore, after the DNA fragments are ligated individually to vectors, a researcher has a collection of many recombinant vectors, with each vector containing a particular fragment of chromosomal DNA. A collection of recombinant vectors containing DNA fragments of a given organism is known as a **DNA library** (**Figure 21.4**). Researchers make DNA libraries using the methods shown in Figures 21.2 and 21.3 and then use those libraries to obtain clones that carry a gene of interest.

Two types of DNA libraries are commonly made. When the inserts are derived from chromosomal DNA, the library is called a

genomic library. Alternatively, researchers can isolate mRNA and use the enzyme reverse transcriptase, which is described in Chapter 19, to make DNA molecules using mRNA as a starting material. Such DNA is called **complementary DNA**, or **cDNA**. A **cDNA library** is a collection of recombinant vectors that have inserts derived from cDNA. From a research perspective, an important advantage of cDNA is that it lacks introns—intervening sequences that are not

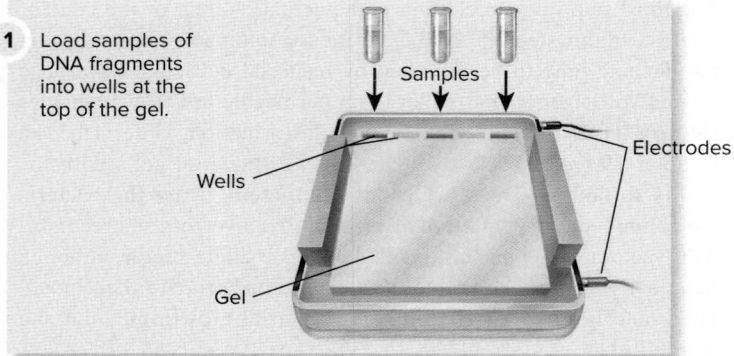

1 Load samples of DNA fragments into wells at the top of the gel.

Samples

Electrodes

Wells

Gel

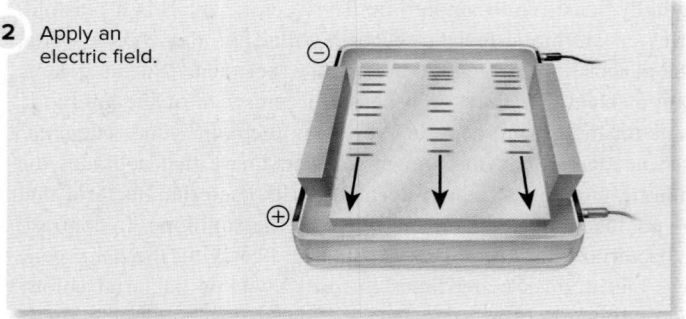

2 Apply an electric field.

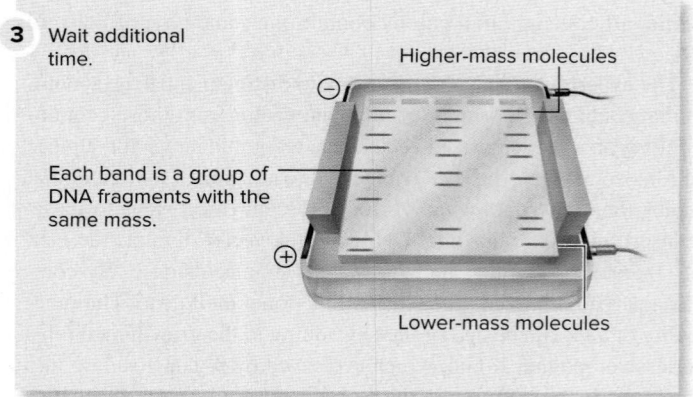

3 Wait additional time.

Higher-mass molecules

Each band is a group of DNA fragments with the same mass.

Lower-mass molecules

Figure 21.5 Separation of molecules by gel electrophoresis. In this example, samples containing many fragments of DNA are loaded into wells at the top of the gel and then subjected to an electric current that causes the fragments to move toward the positively charged electrode at the bottom of the gel. This separates the fragments according to their masses, with the smaller DNA fragments near the bottom of the gel.

Concept Check: One DNA fragment contains 600 bp and another has 1,300 bp. Following electrophoresis, which will be closer to the bottom of the gel?

1 As described in Figure 21.2, digest chromosomal DNA with a restriction enzyme and ligate the pieces into vectors.

Each recombinant vector contains a different fragment of chromosomal DNA.

Vector

2 Transform bacteria with recombinant vectors. The vectors also carry a gene that confers resistance to ampicillin. Only bacteria that take up a vector will grow.

3 Inoculate on petri plates containing ampicillin. Allow cells to grow and divide to form bacterial colonies.

Each bacterial colony contains millions of cells that were derived from a single transformed cell.

Figure 21.4 A DNA library. Each colony in a DNA library contains a vector with a different piece of chromosomal DNA.

translated into proteins. Because introns can be quite large, it is much simpler for researchers to insert cDNAs into vectors rather than chromosomal DNA segments if they want to focus their attention on the coding sequence of a gene. In addition, because bacteria do not splice out introns, using cDNAs provides an advantage if researchers want to express the gene of interest in bacteria.

Gel Electrophoresis Separates Macromolecules, Such as DNA Fragments

Gel electrophoresis is a technique for separating macromolecules, such as DNA and proteins, as they migrate through a gel. This method is often used to evaluate the results of a cloning experiment. For example, gel electrophoresis is used to determine the sizes of DNA fragments that have been inserted into recombinant vectors.

Gel electrophoresis can separate molecules based on their charge, size/length, and mass. In the example shown in **Figure 21.5**, gel electrophoresis is used to separate different fragments of chromosomal DNA based on their masses. The flat slab of semisolid gel has depressions at the top called wells, where samples are added. Electrodes are located at each end of the gel. An electric current is applied to the gel, which causes charged molecules, either proteins or nucleic acids, to migrate from the top of the gel toward the bottom—a process called electrophoresis. DNA is negatively charged and moves toward the positively charged electrode, which is at the bottom in this figure. As gel electrophoresis occurs, the DNA fragments are separated into distinct bands within the gel. Smaller DNA fragments move more quickly through the gel than larger ones in a given amount of time and therefore are located closer to the bottom of the gel than the larger ones. The fragments in each band can then be stained with a dye for identification.

Polymerase Chain Reaction (PCR) Is Also Used to Make Many Copies of DNA

As we have seen, one method of cloning involves an approach in which the gene of interest is inserted into a vector, introduced into a host cell, and then propagated. Another cloning technique, in which DNA is copied without the aid of vectors and host cells, is a process called **polymerase chain reaction (PCR)**, which was developed by American biochemist Kary Mullis in 1985 (**Figure 21.6**). The goal of PCR is to make many copies of DNA in a defined region, perhaps encompassing a gene or part of a gene. Several reagents are required for the synthesis of DNA. First, two different primers are needed that

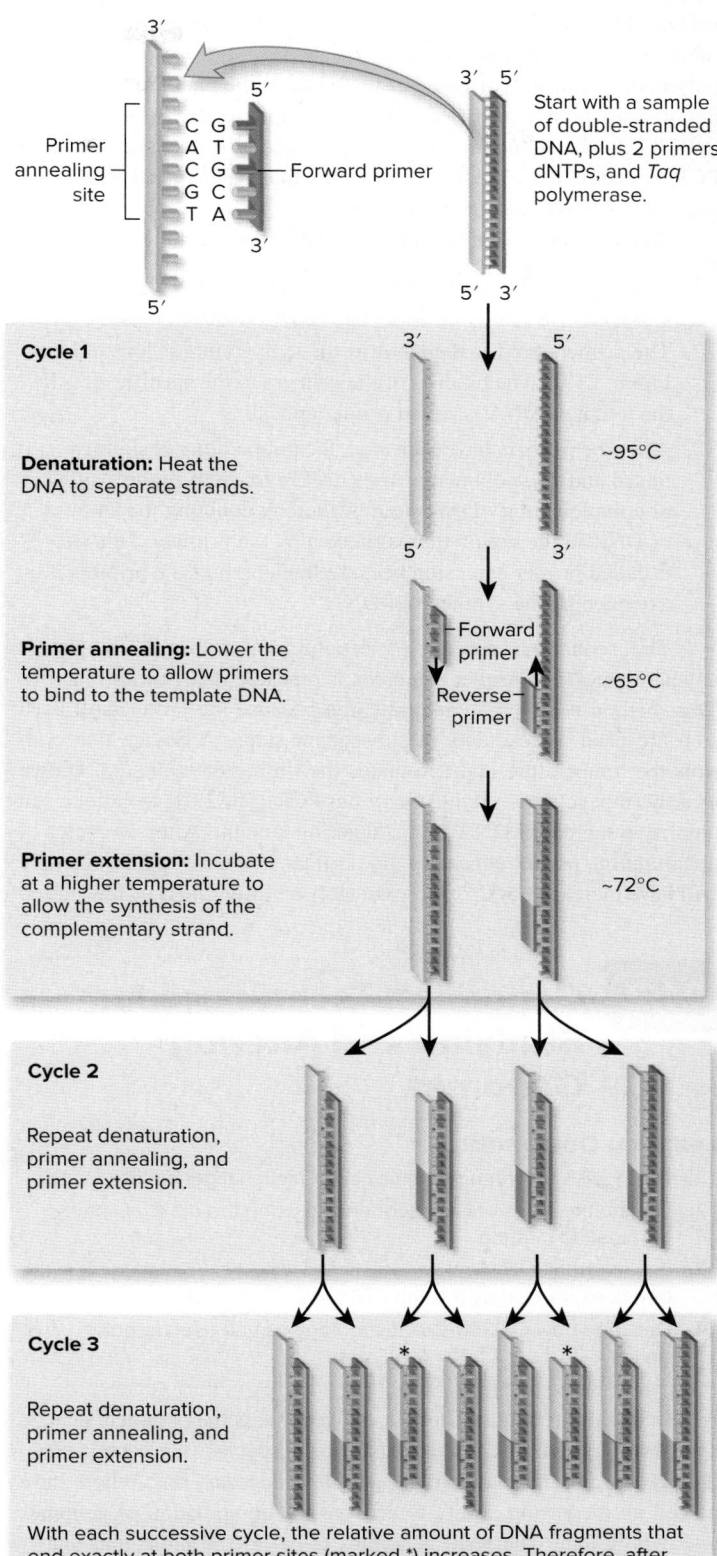

Figure 21.6 Polymerase chain reaction (PCR). During each PCR cycle, the steps of denaturation, primer annealing, and primer extension take place. The net result of PCR is the synthesis of many copies of DNA in the region that is flanked by the two primers. To conduct this type of PCR experiment, researchers must have prior knowledge about the base sequence of the template DNA so they can make primers with base sequences that are complementary to the ends of the template DNA. Note: The temperatures shown in this figure are approximate and may vary depending on the primer sequence and length.

Concept Check: *Why do the primers used in PCR bind specifically to the primer-annealing sites?*

are complementary to sequences at each end of the DNA region to be amplified. These primers are usually about 20 nucleotides long. One primer is called the forward primer, and the other is the reverse primer. PCR also requires all four deoxynucleoside triphosphates (dNTPs) and a heat-stable form of DNA polymerase called *Taq* polymerase. *Taq* polymerase is isolated from the bacterium *Thermus aquaticus*, which lives in hot springs and can tolerate temperatures up to 95°C. A heat-stable form of DNA polymerase is necessary because PCR is conducted at high temperatures that would inactivate DNA polymerase from most other bacteria.

To make copies of a DNA region, the following three steps occur:

1. A sample of chromosomal DNA, called the template DNA, is heated to separate (denature) the DNA into single-stranded molecules.

2. The primers bind to the DNA as the temperature is lowered (see Figure 21.6). The binding of the primers to the specific sites in the template DNA is called primer annealing.

3. After the primers have annealed, the temperature is slightly raised and *Taq* polymerase uses dNTPs to catalyze the synthesis of complementary DNA strands, thereby doubling the amount of DNA in the region that is flanked by the primers. This step is called primer extension because the length of the primers is extended by the synthesis of DNA.

The sequential process of denaturation followed by primer annealing and then primer extension is repeated many times in a row. This method is called a chain reaction because the products of each step are used as reactants in subsequent steps. A device that controls the temperature and automates the timing of each step, known as a thermocycler, is used to carry out PCR. The PCR technique can amplify a sample of DNA by a staggering amount. After 30 cycles of denaturation, primer annealing, and primer extension, a DNA sample will have increased by 2^{30}, approximately a billionfold, in a few hours!

21.2 Genomics: Techniques for Studying and Altering Genomes

Learning Outcomes:

1. Distinguish between genomics and functional genomics.
2. Outline the steps of DNA sequencing using the dideoxy chain-termination method.
3. Explain what a DNA microarray is and how it is used to identify the genes expressed by a sample of cells.
4. Describe how CRISPR-Cas technology can be used to edit genes.

As discussed throughout Unit III, the genome is the complete genetic composition of a cell, an organism, or a species. As genetic technology has progressed over the past few decades, researchers have gained an increasing ability to analyze the composition of genomes as a whole unit. The term genomics refers to the molecular analysis of the entire genome of a species. Segments of chromosomes are cloned and analyzed in progressively smaller pieces, the locations of which are known on the intact chromosomes. This is the mapping

phase of genomics. The mapping of a genome ultimately progresses to the determination of the complete DNA sequence, which provides the most detailed description available of an organism's genome at the molecular level. By comparison, **functional genomics** studies the expression of a genome. For example, functional genomics can be used to analyze which genes are turned on or off in normal versus cancer cells. In this section, we will consider a few of the methods that are used in genomics and functional genomics.

The Dideoxy Chain-Termination Method Is Used to Determine the Base Sequence of DNA

The term **DNA sequencing** refers to a procedure that is aimed at determining the base sequence of DNA. Scientists can learn a great deal about the function of a gene if its nucleotide sequence is known. For example, the investigation of genetic sequences has been vital in our understanding of the genetic basis of human diseases.

One type of DNA sequencing, developed in 1977 by English biochemist Frederick Sanger and colleagues, is known as the **dideoxy chain-termination method**, or more simply, **dideoxy sequencing**. Dideoxy sequencing is based on our knowledge of DNA replication. As described in Chapter 11, DNA polymerase connects adjacent deoxynucleoside triphosphates (dNTPs) by catalyzing a covalent linkage between the phosphate group at the 5' position on an incoming nucleotide and the —OH group at the 3' position on the growing strand. Chemists, however, can synthesize nucleotides, called dideoxynucleoside triphosphates (ddNTPs), that are missing the —OH group at the 3' position (**Figure 21.7**). What happens if a ddNTP is incorporated during DNA replication? If a ddNTP is added to a growing DNA strand, the strand can no longer grow because the 3' —OH group, the site of attachment for the next nucleotide, is missing. This ending of DNA synthesis is called chain termination.

Before describing the steps of this DNA sequencing procedure, let's first consider the DNA segment that is analyzed in such an experiment. The segment of DNA to be sequenced, the target DNA, is obtained in large amounts by using the gene cloning techniques that were described earlier in this chapter. In **Figure 21.8a**, the target DNA has been inserted into a vector next to a primer-annealing site, the place where a primer will bind. The target DNA is initially double stranded, but Figure 21.8a shows the DNA after it has been denatured into a single strand by heat treatment.

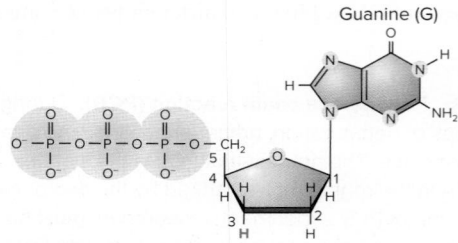

Figure 21.7 Structure of a dideoxynucleotide triphosphate. This figure shows the structure of dideoxyguanosine triphosphate (ddGTP). It has a hydrogen, shown in red, instead of a hydroxyl group at the 3' position. The prefix dideoxy- means that the sugar has two (di) missing (de) oxygens (oxy) compared with ribose, which has —OH groups at both the 2' and 3' positions.

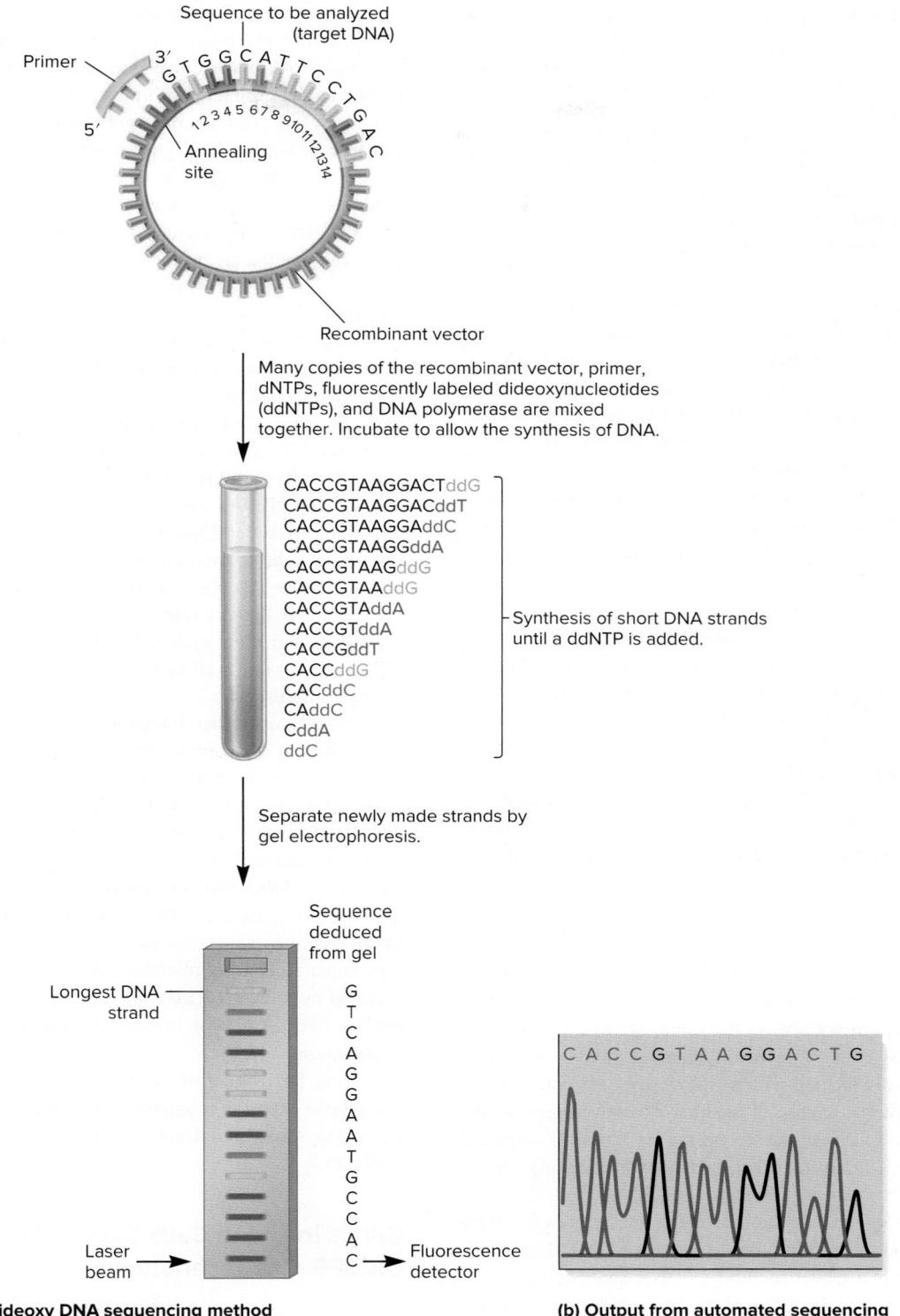

Figure 21.8   Dideoxy sequencing of DNA.   (a) The procedure of dideoxy sequencing uses fluorescently labeled ddNTPs. **(b)** This method uses a fluorescence detector that measures the four kinds of ddNTPs as they emerge from the gel.

Concept Check: *What happens when a ddNTP is incorporated into a growing DNA strand?*

Let's now examine the steps involved in DNA sequencing.

1. Many copies of single-stranded template DNA are placed into a tube and mixed with primers that bind to the primer-annealing site. DNA polymerase and all four types of dNTPs are also added. In addition, a low concentration of each of the four possible dideoxynucleoside triphosphates—ddGTP, ddATP, ddTTP, and ddCTP—is added. Each type of ddNTP is tagged with a different colored fluorescent molecule; typically, ddA is green, ddT is red, ddG is yellow, and ddC is blue.

2. The tube is then incubated to allow DNA polymerase to synthesize strands that are complementary to the target DNA sequence. However, addition of a ddNTP causes DNA synthesis to terminate early, preventing further elongation of the strand. For example, let's consider ddTTP. Synthesis of new DNA strands stops at the sixth or thirteenth position after the annealing site if a ddTTP, instead of a dTTP, is incorporated into the growing DNA strand (Figure 21.8a). This means the target DNA has a complementary A at the sixth and thirteenth positions. Eventually, a set of fluorescently tagged strands results, with the color of the ddNTP representing the last nucleotide added to the strand.

3. After the samples have been incubated for several minutes, the newly made DNA strands are separated according to their lengths by subjecting them to gel electrophoresis. This can be done using a slab gel, as shown in Figure 21.8a, or more commonly by running them through a gel-filled capillary tube. The shorter strands move to the bottom of the gel more quickly than the longer ones. Electrophoresis is continued until each band emerges from the bottom of the gel, where a laser excites the fluorescent dye. A fluorescence detector records the amount of fluorescence emission at four wavelengths, corresponding to the four dyes.

An example of a printout from a fluorescence detector is shown in **Figure 21.8b.** The peaks of fluorescence correspond to the DNA sequence that is complementary to the target DNA. The heights of the fluorescent peaks are not always the same, because ddNTPs get incorporated at some sites more readily than at others. Note that although ddG is usually labeled with a yellow dye, it is converted to black ink on the printout for ease of reading. Though improvements in automated sequencing continue to be made, a typical sequencing run can provide a DNA sequence that is approximately 700 to 900 bases long, and perhaps even longer.

Researchers are also developing alternative methods to the dideoxy chain-termination method in order to sequence DNA. For example, pyrosequencing is a newer method of DNA sequencing that is based on the detection of released pyrophosphate (PP_i) during DNA synthesis.

A Microarray Can Identify Which Genes Are Transcribed by a Cell

Let's now turn our attention to functional genomics. Researchers have developed a technology, called a **DNA microarray**, that is used to monitor the expression of thousands of genes simultaneously. A DNA microarray is a small silica, glass, or plastic slide that is dotted with many different sequences of single-stranded DNA, each corresponding to a short sequence within a known gene. Each spot contains multiple copies of a known DNA sequence. For example, one spot in a microarray may correspond to a sequence within the β-globin gene; another might correspond to a different gene, such as a gene that encodes a glucose transporter. A single slide contains tens of thousands of different spots in an area the size of a postage stamp. These microarrays are typically produced using a technology that "prints" spots of DNA sequences onto a slide, similar to the way that an inkjet printer deposits ink on paper.

What is the purpose of using a DNA microarray? In the experiment shown in **Figure 21.9,** the goal is to determine which genes are transcribed into mRNA from a particular sample of cells. In other words, which genes in the genome of these cells are expressed? To conduct this experiment, the mRNA was isolated from the cells and then used to make fluorescently labeled cDNAs. The labeled cDNAs were then incubated with a DNA microarray. The single-stranded DNA in the microarray corresponds to the coding strand—the strand that has a sequence that is similar to mRNA. Those cDNAs that are complementary to the DNAs in the microarray hybridize, thereby remaining bound to the microarray. The array is washed and then analyzed using a microscope equipped with a computer that scans all of the spots and generates an image of their relative fluorescence.

If the fluorescence intensity in a spot is high, a large amount of cDNA was in the sample that hybridized to the DNA at this location. For example, if the β-globin gene was expressed in the cells being tested, a large amount of cDNA for this gene would be made, and the fluorescence intensity for that spot would be high. Because the DNA sequence of each spot is already known, a fluorescent spot identifies a cDNA that is complementary to that DNA sequence. Furthermore, because the cDNA was generated from mRNA, this technique identifies genes that have been transcribed in a particular cell type under a given set of conditions. However, the amount of protein encoded by an mRNA may not always correlate with the amount of mRNA, due to variation in the rates of mRNA translation and protein degradation.

Thus far, the most common use of DNA microarrays is to study gene expression patterns. In addition, the technology of DNA microarrays has found several other important uses, described in **Table 21.2.**

Genes in Living Cells Can Be Altered Using CRISPR-Cas Technology

In Chapter 13, we considered how the CRISPR-Cas system provides bacteria with a defense against bacteriophages. Researchers realized that the components of this system can be used to alter genes, an approach called **gene editing.** This particular method is named **CRISPR-Cas technology.** Researchers have made a modification to the natural system to make it efficient for gene editing. They create a single RNA in which tracrRNA and crRNA are linked to each other (**Figure 21.10a**). This is called the single guide RNA (sgRNA). The spacer region of the sgRNA is designed

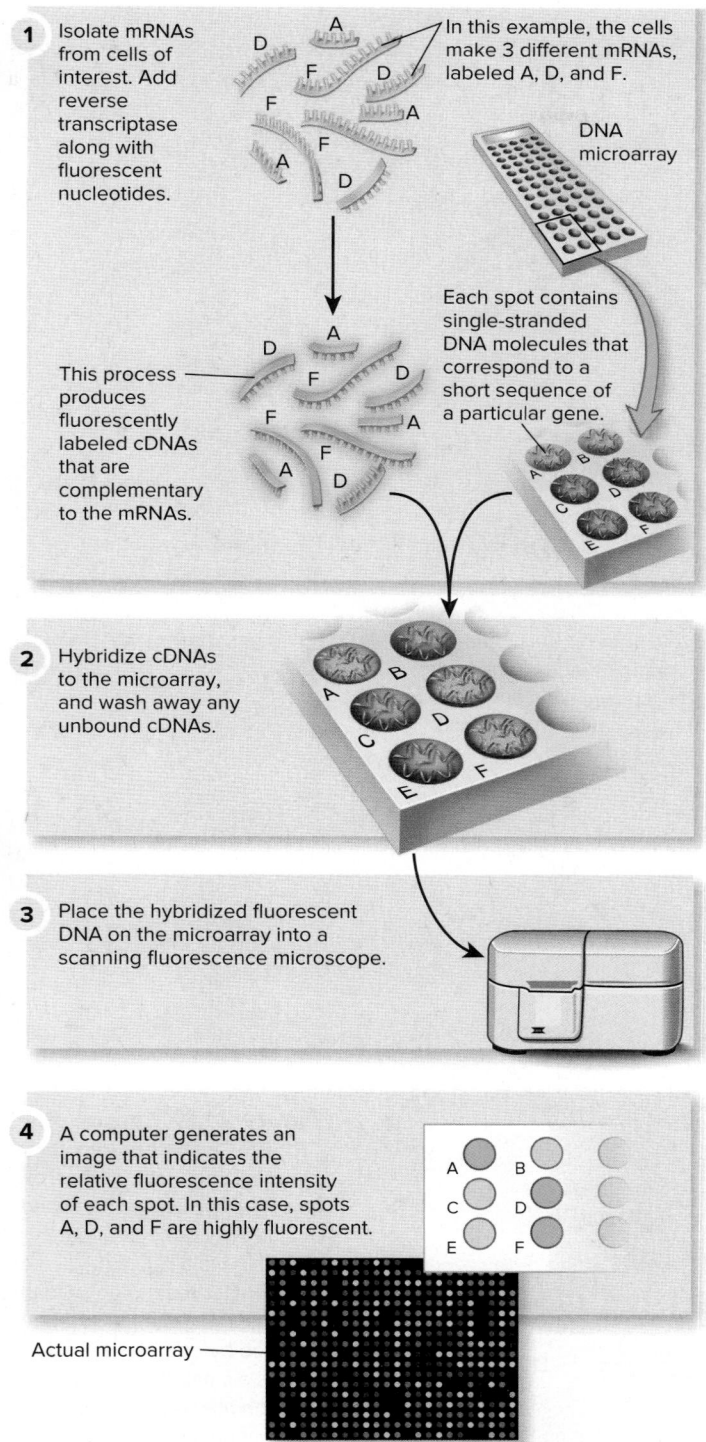

1 Isolate mRNAs from cells of interest. Add reverse transcriptase along with fluorescent nucleotides.

In this example, the cells make 3 different mRNAs, labeled A, D, and F.

DNA microarray

This process produces fluorescently labeled cDNAs that are complementary to the mRNAs.

Each spot contains single-stranded DNA molecules that correspond to a short sequence of a particular gene.

2 Hybridize cDNAs to the microarray, and wash away any unbound cDNAs.

3 Place the hybridized fluorescent DNA on the microarray into a scanning fluorescence microscope.

4 A computer generates an image that indicates the relative fluorescence intensity of each spot. In this case, spots A, D, and F are highly fluorescent.

Actual microarray

Figure 21.9 **Identifying transcribed genes within a DNA microarray.** In this simplified example, only three cDNAs specifically hybridize to spots on the microarray. Those genes were expressed in the cells from which the mRNA was isolated. In an actual experiment, the array typically contains hundreds or thousands of different cDNAs and tens of thousands of different spots.
(bottom) ©Alfred Pasieka/Science Source

Concept Check: *If a fluorescent spot appears on a microarray, what information does this provide regarding gene expression?*

Table 21.2	Applications of DNA Microarrays
Application	**Description**
Cell-specific gene expression	A comparison of microarray data using cDNAs derived from mRNAs of different cell types can identify genes that are expressed in a cell-specific manner.
Gene regulation	Because environmental conditions play an important role in gene regulation, a comparison of microarray data using cDNAs derived from mRNAs from cells exposed to two different environmental conditions may reveal genes that are induced under one set of conditions and repressed under another set.
Elucidation of metabolic pathways	Genes that encode proteins that participate in a common metabolic pathway are often expressed together and can be revealed from a microarray analysis.
Tumor profiling	Different types of cancer cells exhibit striking differences in their gene expression profiles, which can be revealed by a DNA microarray analysis. This approach is gaining use as a tool to classify tumors that are sometimes morphologically indistinguishable.
Genetic variation	A mutant allele may not hybridize to a spot on a microarray as well as a wild-type allele. Therefore, microarrays are gaining use as a tool for detecting genetic variation. This application has been used to identify disease-causing alleles in humans and to identify mutations that contribute to quantitative traits in plants and other species.
Microbial strain identification	Microarrays can distinguish between closely related bacterial species and subspecies.

to be complementary to one of the DNA strands of a target gene that a researcher wants to edit. The sgRNA binds to Cas9 and guides it to the target gene. Cas9 then makes a double-strand break in this gene.

Following this break, two different DNA repair events are possible. If the break is repaired by a process called end joining, the gene may incur a small deletion (see the left side of **Figure 21.10b**). This deletion may inactivate the gene, particularly if it causes a frameshift mutation in the coding sequence. Alternatively, a researcher can add a double-stranded segment of DNA, called the donor DNA, that is homologous to the region where the break occurs (see the right side of Figure 21.10b). This homologous DNA is made synthetically and is designed to carry a particular mutation, such as a point mutation, that the researcher wants to introduce. A different DNA repair system swaps in the donor DNA by a double crossover. In this way, researchers can introduce a specific mutation into a gene.

The experiment described in Figure 21.10b can be performed on different cell types and even on whole organisms. By studying how a gene mutation affects cell structure and function or by examining the phenotypic effects of a mutation in a whole organism (see the chapter opening photo), researchers often gain a better understanding of how genes function.

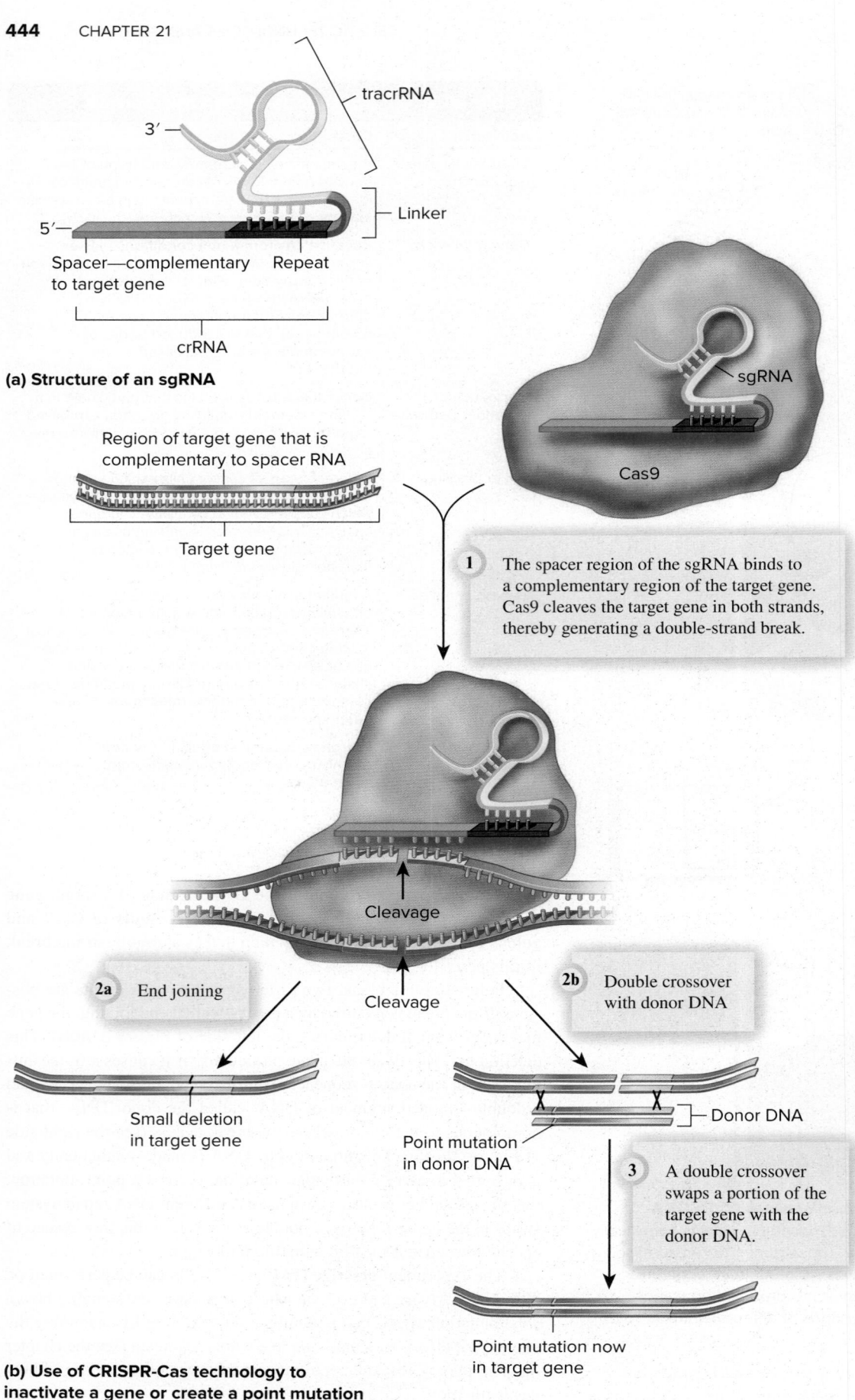

(a) Structure of an sgRNA

Region of target gene that is
complementary to spacer RNA

Target gene

Cas9

sgRNA

1 The spacer region of the sgRNA binds to
a complementary region of the target gene.
Cas9 cleaves the target gene in both strands,
thereby generating a double-strand break.

Cleavage

Cleavage

2a End joining

2b Double crossover
with donor DNA

Small deletion
in target gene

Point mutation
in donor DNA

Donor DNA

3 A double crossover
swaps a portion of the
target gene with the
donor DNA.

Point mutation now
in target gene

**(b) Use of CRISPR-Cas technology to
inactivate a gene or create a point mutation**

**Figure 21.10 The use of
CRISPR-Cas technology for
gene editing. (a)** Structure of
an sgRNA, which is composed
of a crRNA connected to a
tracrRNA via a linker. **(b)** Use of
CRISPR-Cas technology. On the
left side, the gene has been
repaired by end joining and
suffers a small deletion. This
deletion may result in gene
inactivation. On the right side, a
double crossover has occurred
that swaps in the donor DNA.
The target gene now carries a
point mutation.

Concept Check: How is the
sgRNA different from certain
components of the bacterial
defense system described
in Chapter 13 (refer back
to Figure 13.8)?

Core Skills: Process of Science, Quantitative Reasoning

BIO **TIPS**

THE QUESTION *Gene editing is often used to explore the structure and function of proteins. For example, changes can be made to the coding sequence of a gene to determine how the resulting alterations in the amino acid sequence affect the function of a protein. Let's suppose that you are interested in the functional importance of a particular asparagine (an amino acid) within a protein you are studying. By gene editing, you make mutant proteins in which this asparagine has been changed to other amino acids. You then test the encoded mutant proteins for functionality. The results are as follows:*

	Functionality (%)
Wild-type (nonmutant) protein	100
Mutant proteins in which the asparagine is changed to:	
Leucine	7
Phenylalanine	3
Glutamine	98
Proline	4

From these results, what would you conclude about the functional significance of this asparagine within the protein? Note: The structures of the amino acids are shown in Chapter 3 (refer back to Figure 3.13).

T OPIC **What topic in biology does this question address?** The topic is gene editing. More specifically, the question is about the effects of gene editing on protein structure and function.

I NFORMATION **What information do you know based on the question and your understanding of the topic?** From the question, you know that gene editing can be used to study protein structure and function. You are also given data on the results of a gene editing experiment, and reminded where to find the structures of the amino acids in this textbook. From your understanding of the topic, you may recall that if an amino acid is important for a protein's structure and function, then changing that amino acid is likely to inhibit the protein's function. Conservative substitutions, which involve changes to amino acids with similar side chains, are more likely than nonconservative ones to retain functionality.

P ROBLEM-SOLVING **S** TRATEGY **Interpret data. Compare and contrast.** One strategy to solve this problem is to look at the results of this experiment and compare and contrast the level of functionality that the mutant proteins have compared to the wild-type protein.

ANSWER *These results suggest that the asparagine is important for this protein's function. When this asparagine is replaced with glutamine, which has a very similar structure, the protein retains most of its functionality. However, if it is replaced with other types of amino acids, most of the functionality is lost.*

21.3 Bacterial and Archaeal Genomes

Learning Outcomes:
1. List the key characteristics of bacterial and archaeal genomes.
2. Describe the method of shotgun DNA sequencing.

The past decade has seen remarkable advances in our overall understanding of the entire genomes of many species. As genetic technology has progressed, researchers have gained an increasing ability to analyze the composition of a genome as a whole unit. The complete DNA sequence is now known for many species, providing the most detailed description available of an organism's genome at the molecular level. In this section, we will survey the sizes and compositions of genomes in selected species of bacteria and archaea.

Studying the Genomes of Bacteria and Archaea Has Important Applications

Why are researchers interested in the genomes of bacteria and archaea?

1. Bacteria cause many different diseases that affect humans as well as other animals and plants. Studying the genomes of bacteria reveals important clues about the process of infection, which may also help us find ways to combat bacterial infections.
2. The knowledge that is obtained by studying bacterial and archaeal genomes often applies to larger and more complex organisms.
3. A third reason is evolution. The origin of the first eukaryotic cell probably involved a union between an archaeal cell and a bacterial cell, as we will explore in Chapter 26. The study of bacterial and archaeal genomes helps us understand how all living species evolved.
4. Bacteria are often used as tools in research, as discussed in Section 21.1. A better understanding of their genomes can make them more effective tools.

The Genomes of Bacteria and Archaea Typically Consist of a Circular Chromosome with a Few Thousand Genes

Geneticists have made great progress in the study of bacterial and archaeal genomes. The genomes of thousands of bacterial and archaeal species have been sequenced and analyzed. The chromosomes of bacteria and archaea are usually a few million base pairs in length. Genomic researchers refer to 1 million base pairs as 1 megabase pair, abbreviated 1 Mb. Most bacteria and archaea contain a single type of chromosome, though multiple copies may be present in a single cell. However, some bacteria are known to have more than one type of chromosome. For example, *Vibrio cholerae*, the bacterium that causes the diarrheal disease cholera, has two different chromosomes in each cell, one has 2.9 Mb and the other 1.1 Mb.

Bacterial and archaeal chromosomes are usually circular. For example, the two chromosomes in *V. cholerae* are circular, as is the single type of chromosome found in *E. coli*. However, linear chromosomes are found in some species, such as *Borrelia burgdorferi*,

Table 21.3	Examples of Bacterial and Archaeal Genomes That Have Been Sequenced*		
Species	**Genome size (Mb)†**	**Number of genes‡**	**Description**
Methanobacterium thermoautotrophicum	1.7	1,921	An archaeal species that produces methane
Haemophilus influenzae	1.8	1,753	One of several different bacterial species that cause respiratory illness and meningitis
Sulfolobus solfataricus	3.0	3,032	An archaeal species that metabolizes sulfur-containing compounds
Lactobacillus plantarum	3.3	3,052	A type of lactic acid–producing bacterium used in the production of cheese and yogurt
Mycobacterium tuberculosis	4.4	4,294	The bacterium that causes the respiratory disease tuberculosis
Escherichia coli	4.6	4,377	A naturally occurring intestinal bacterium; certain strains cause human illness
Bacillus anthracis	5.2	5,439	The bacterium that causes the disease anthrax

*Bacterial and archaeal species often exist in different strains that may differ slightly in their genome size and number of genes. The data are from common strains of the indicated species. The species shown in this table have only one type of chromosome.
†Mb equals 1 million base pairs, or a megabase pair.
‡The number of genes is an estimate based on the analysis of genome sequences.

the bacterium that causes Lyme disease, the most common tick-borne disease in the United States. Certain bacterial species even contain both linear and circular chromosomes. *Agrobacterium tumefaciens*, which infects plants and causes crown gall tumors, has one linear chromosome (2.1 Mb) and one circular chromosome (3.0 Mb).

Table 21.3 compares the sequenced genomes from several bacterial and archaeal species. These genomes range in size from 1.7 to 5.2 Mb. The total number of genes is correlated with the total genome size. Roughly 1,000 genes are found for every megabase pair of DNA. Compared with eukaryotic genomes, bacterial and archaeal genomes are less complex. Their chromosomes lack centromeres and telomeres and have a single origin of replication. Also, chromosomes of bacteria and archaea have relatively little repetitive DNA, whereas repetitive sequences, which are discussed later in this chapter, are often abundant in eukaryotic genomes.

In addition to one or more chromosomes, bacteria may have plasmids, circular pieces of DNA that exist independently of the bacterial chromosome (refer back to Figure 19.11). Plasmids are typically small, ranging in length from a few thousand to tens of thousands of base pairs, though some can be quite large, with hundreds of thousands of base pairs. The various functions of plasmids were described in Chapter 19, and their use as vectors in gene cloning was discussed in Section 21.1.

 Core Skill: Process of Science

Feature Investigation | Venter, Smith, and Colleagues Sequenced the First Genome in 1995

The first genome to be entirely sequenced was that of the bacterium *Haemophilus influenzae*. This bacterium causes a variety of diseases in humans, including respiratory illnesses and bacterial meningitis. *H. influenzae* has a relatively small genome consisting of approximately 1.8 Mb of DNA in a single circular chromosome.

The most commonly used strategy for sequencing an entire genome is called **shotgun DNA sequencing**. In this approach, researchers use a DNA sequencing method, such as the dideoxy chain-termination method (see Figure 21.8), to randomly sequence many DNA fragments from the genome. As a matter of chance, some of the fragments are overlapping—the end of one fragment contains the same DNA region as the beginning of another fragment. Computers are used to align the overlapping regions and assemble the DNA fragments into a contiguous sequence identical to that found in the intact chromosome. This procedure is called shotgun DNA sequencing because the process generates many tiny pieces of DNA, reminding people of the tiny metal pellets of shot sprayed by a shotgun blast.

To obtain a complete sequence of a genome with the shotgun approach, how do researchers decide how many fragments to sequence? We can calculate the probability that a base will not be sequenced (P) using this equation:

$$P = e^{-m}$$

where e is the base of the natural logarithm ($e = 2.72$), and m is the number of sequenced bases divided by the total genome size. For example, in the case of *H. influenzae*, with a genome size of 1.8 Mb, if researchers sequenced 9.0 Mb, $m = 5$ (that is, 9.0 Mb divided by 1.8 Mb):

$$P = e^{-m} = e^{-5} = 0.0067, \text{ or } 0.67\%.$$

This means that if researchers randomly sequence 9.0 Mb, which is five times the length of a single genome, they are likely to miss only 0.67% of the genome. With a genome size of 1.8 Mb, they would miss about 12,000 bp out of approximately 1.8 million. Such missed sequences are typically on small DNA fragments that, as a matter of random chance, did not happen to be sequenced. Though it is beyond the scope of this textbook, these missed sequences can be identified and sequenced using more advanced types of cloning methods.

In their discovery-based investigation, American biologists Craig Venter and Hamilton Smith and their colleagues used a shotgun DNA sequencing approach (**Figure 21.11**). The researchers isolated

Figure 21.11 Determination of the complete genome sequence of *Haemophilus influenzae*.

GOAL The goal is to obtain the entire genome sequence of *Haemophilus influenzae*. This information will reveal its genome size and also which genes the organism has.

KEY MATERIALS A strain of *H. influenzae*.

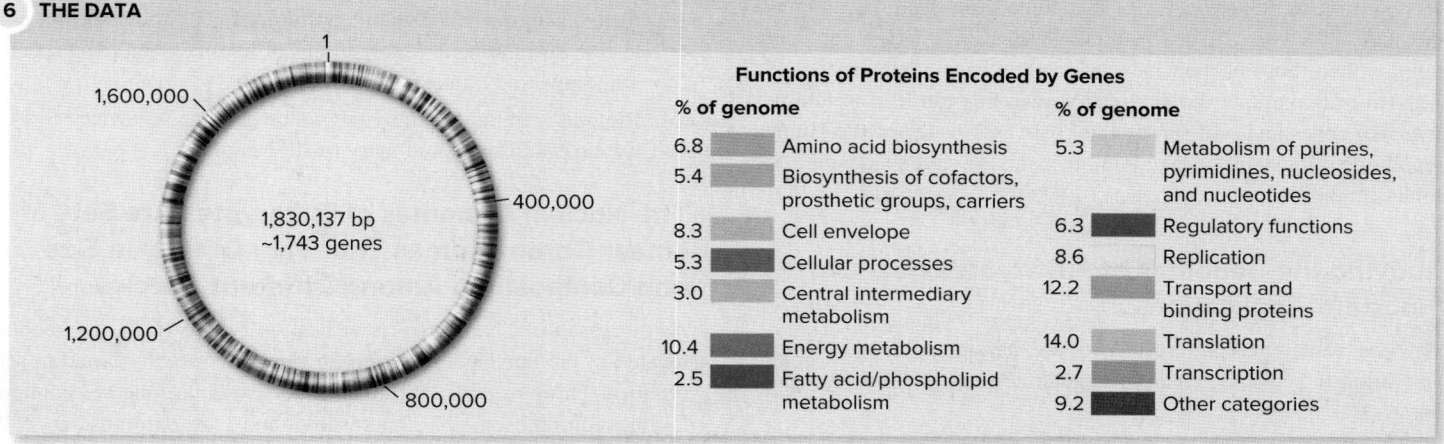

Experimental level   Conceptual level

1 Purify DNA from a strain of *H. influenzae*. This involves breaking the cells open by adding phenol and chloroform. Most protein and lipid components go into the phenol-chloroform phase. DNA remains in the aqueous (water) phase.

DNA in aqueous (water) phase
Proteins and lipids in phenol-chloroform phase
H. influenzae chromosomal DNA

2 Sonicate the DNA to break it into small fragments of about 2,000 bp in length.

Sound waves
DNA fragments in aqueous phase
Sound waves

3 Clone the DNA fragments into vectors. The procedures for cloning are described in Section 21.1. This produces a DNA library.

Refer back to Figures 21.2 and 21.3.

Vector DNA
A DNA library
Piece of *H. influenzae* DNA

4 Subject many clones to the procedure of dideoxy sequencing, described in Section 21.2. A total of 10.8 Mb was sequenced.

Refer back to Figure 21.8.

CCAGTCCCATGCCATGGCCCAGTCCC

Produces a large number of sequences with overlapping regions.

5 Use computer methods to identify various types of genes in the genome.

CCATGCCATGGCCCCCATCC

Explores the genome sequence and identifies and characterizes genes.

6 **THE DATA**

1,830,137 bp
~1,743 genes

1,600,000
1
400,000
800,000
1,200,000

Functions of Proteins Encoded by Genes

% of genome			% of genome		
6.8		Amino acid biosynthesis	5.3		Metabolism of purines, pyrimidines, nucleosides, and nucleotides
5.4		Biosynthesis of cofactors, prosthetic groups, carriers	6.3		Regulatory functions
8.3		Cell envelope	8.6		Replication
5.3		Cellular processes	12.2		Transport and binding proteins
3.0		Central intermediary metabolism	14.0		Translation
10.4		Energy metabolism	2.7		Transcription
2.5		Fatty acid/phospholipid metabolism	9.2		Other categories

chromosomal DNA from *H. influenzae* and used sound waves to break the DNA into small fragments of approximately 2,000 bp in length. These fragments were randomly inserted into vectors, allowing the DNA to be propagated in *E. coli*. Each *E. coli* clone carried a vector with a different piece of DNA from *H. influenzae*. The complete set of vectors, each containing a different fragment of DNA, is called a DNA library (refer back to Figure 21.4). The researchers then subjected many of these clones to the procedure of DNA sequencing. They sequenced a total of approximately 10.8 Mb of DNA.

The outcome of this genome-sequencing project was a very long DNA sequence. In 1995, Venter, Smith, and colleagues published the entire DNA sequence of *H. influenzae*. The researchers then analyzed the genome sequence using a computer to obtain information about the properties of the genome. Questions they asked included "How many genes does the genome contain, and what are the likely functions of those genes?" The data in Figure 21.11 summarize these researchers' results. The *H. influenzae* genome is composed of 1,830,137 bp of DNA. The computer analysis predicted 1,743 genes. Based on the similarities of the sequences in *H. influenzae* to sequences of genes identified in other species, the researchers also predicted the functions of proteins encoded by nearly two-thirds of the genes. The diagram shown in the data of Figure 21.11 places proteins in various categories based on their predicted function. These results gave the first comprehensive "genome picture" of a living organism!

Experimental Questions

1. What was the goal of the investigation conducted by Venter, Smith, and colleagues?

2. **CoreSKILL »** Let's suppose that researchers used the shotgun DNA sequencing approach and sequenced 20 Mb of DNA from a bacterium with a genome size of 4.1 Mb. What percentage of the genome would be left unsequenced?

3. **CoreSKILL »** What were the results of the study by Venter, Smith, and colleagues?

21.4 Eukaryotic Genomes

Learning Outcomes:

1. Describe the key features of eukaryotic genomes.
2. Explain how gene duplications occur and lead to the formation of gene families.
3. List the goals and results of the Human Genome Project.

In the previous section, we examined bacterial and archaeal genomes. We now turn to eukaryotes, which include protists, fungi, animals, and plants. As you will learn, their genomes are larger and more complex than those of their bacterial and archaeal counterparts. We will also examine how the duplication of genes can lead to families of related genes and will survey the goals and results of the Human Genome Project, which was aimed at mapping and sequencing the human genome.

Studying the Genomes of Eukaryotes Has Important Applications

Why are researchers interested in the genomes of eukaryotes? Motivation to sequence eukaryotic genomes comes from four main sources.

1. The availability of genome sequences makes it easier for researchers to identify and characterize the genes of model organisms. This was the impetus for genome projects involving baker's yeast (*Saccharomyces cerevisiae*), the fruit fly (*Drosophila melanogaster*), a nematode worm (*Caenorhabditis elegans*), the flowering plant called thale cress (*Arabidopsis thaliana*), and the mouse (*Mus musculus*).

2. Studying eukaryotic genomes enables researchers to gather more information for identifying and treating human diseases. Researchers hope that knowing the DNA sequence of the human genome will help to identify genes in which mutation plays a role in disease.

3. Sequencing the genomes of agriculturally important species can lead to development of new strains of livestock and plant species with improved traits.

4. Biologists are increasingly relying on genome sequences as a way to establish evolutionary relationships.

The Nuclear Genomes of Eukaryotes Are Sets of Linear Chromosomes That Vary Greatly in Size and Composition Among Different Species

As discussed in Chapter 16 (refer back to Figure 16.1), the genome located in the nucleus of eukaryotic species is usually found in sets of linear chromosomes. In humans, for example, one set contains 23 linear chromosomes—22 autosomes and 1 sex chromosome, X or Y. In addition, certain organelles in eukaryotic cells contain a small amount of DNA, including the mitochondrion, which plays a role in

Table 21.4   Examples of Eukaryotic Nuclear Genomes That Have Been Sequenced

Species	Nuclear Genome size (Mb)*	Number of protein-encoding genes	Description
Saccharomyces cerevisiae (baker's yeast)	12.1	~6,600	One of the simplest eukaryotic species, which has been extensively studied by researchers trying to understand eukaryotic molecular biology
Caenorhabditis elegans (a nematode worm)	100	~20,000	A model organism used to study animal development
Drosophila melanogaster (fruit fly)	180	~15,000	A model organism used to study many genetic phenomena, including development
Arabidopsis thaliana (thale cress)	120	~26,000	A model organism studied by plant biologists
Oryza sativa (rice)	440	~40,000	A cereal grain that has a relatively small genome and is very important worldwide as a food crop
Mus musculus (mouse)	2,500	~21,000	A model mammalian organism used to study genetics, cell biology, and development
Homo sapiens (humans)	3,200	~22,000	Our own genome, the sequencing of which will help in our understanding of inherited traits and aid in the identification and treatment of diseases

*The genome size refers to the number of megabase (Mb) pairs in one set of chromosomes. For species with sex chromosomes, it includes both sex chromosomes.

ATP synthesis, and the chloroplast (found in plants and algae), which carries out photosynthesis. The genetic material in these organelles is referred to as the mitochondrial or the chloroplast genome to distinguish it from the nuclear genome, which is located in the cell nucleus. In this chapter, we will focus on the nuclear genome of eukaryotes.

Sizes of Nuclear Genomes   In the past decade or so, the DNA sequence of entire nuclear genomes has been determined for hundreds of eukaryotic species, including several dozen mammalian genomes. Examples are shown in **Table 21.4**.

Relationship Between Genome Sizes and Repetitive Sequences   Eukaryotic genomes are generally larger than bacterial and archaeal genomes, in terms of both the number of genes and genome size. The genomes of simpler eukaryotes, such as yeast, carry several thousand different protein-encoding genes, whereas the genomes of more complex eukaryotes contain tens of thousands (see Table 21.4). Note that the number of genes is not the same as genome size. When we speak of genome size, we mean the total amount of DNA, often measured in megabase pairs (1 million bp). The relative sizes of nuclear genomes vary dramatically among different eukaryotic species (**Figure 21.12a**). In general, increases in the amount of DNA are correlated with increases in cell complexity and body complexity. For example, yeasts have smaller genomes than animals.

However, major variations in genome sizes are often observed among species that are similar in form and function. For example, the total amount of DNA found within different species of amphibians varies over 100-fold. As another example, let's consider two closely related species of the plant called the globe thistle, *Echinops bannaticus* and *Echinops nanus* (**Figure 21.12b, c**). These species have similar numbers of chromosomes, but *E. bannaticus* has nearly double the amount of DNA that *E. nanus* has. What is the

explanation for the larger genome of *E. bannaticus*? The genome of *E. bannaticus* is not likely to contain twice as many genes. Rather, its genome composition includes many repetitive sequences, which are

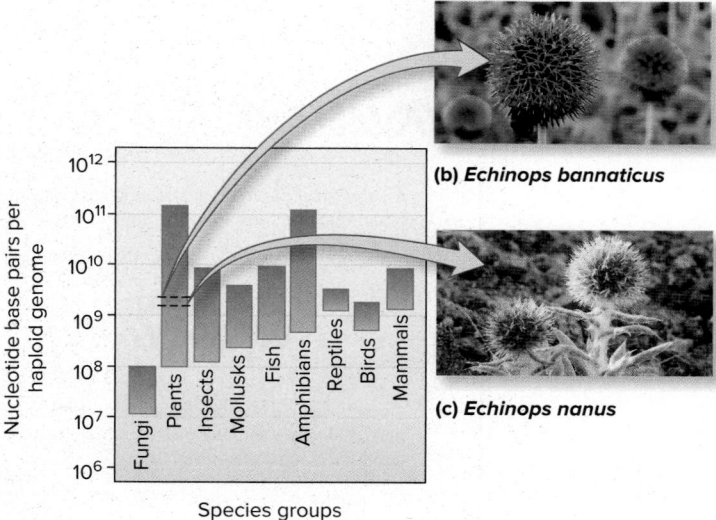

(b) *Echinops bannaticus*

(c) *Echinops nanus*

(a) Genome size

Figure 21.12   Genome sizes among selected groups of eukaryotes. (a) Genome sizes among various groups of eukaryotes are shown on a log scale. As an example for comparison, two closely related species of globe thistle are pictured. These species have similar characteristics, but *Echinops bannaticus* **(b)** has nearly double the amount of DNA that *E. nanus* **(c)** has, as a result of the accumulation of repetitive DNA sequences. b: ©The Picture Store/SPL/Science Source; c: ©Photo by Michael Beckmann, Institute of Geobotany and Botanical Garden, Halle, Germany

Concept Check: *What are two reasons that the groups of species shown in part (a) vary in their total amount of DNA?*

short DNA sequences that are present in many copies throughout the genome. Repetitive sequences are often abundant in eukaryotic species. We will examine the characteristics of such repetitive sequences in Section 21.5.

 Core Concept: Evolution

Gene Duplications Provide Additional Material for Genome Evolution, Sometimes Leading to the Formation of Gene Families

Let's now turn our attention to gene duplications, a way of increasing the number of genes in a genome. Gene duplications are important because they provide raw material for the addition of more genes into a species' genome. Such duplications produce **homologous genes**, two or more genes that are derived from the same ancestral gene (**Figure 21.13a**). Over the course of many generations, each version of the gene accumulates different mutations, resulting in genes with similar but not identical DNA sequences.

How do gene duplications occur? One mechanism that produces gene duplications is a misaligned crossover (**Figure 21.13b**). In this example, two homologous chromosomes have paired with each other during meiosis, but the homologs are misaligned. A crossover produces one chromosome with a gene duplication, one with a gene deletion, and two normal chromosomes. Each of these chromosomes is segregated into different haploid cells. If a haploid cell carrying the chromosome with the gene duplication participates in fertilization with another gamete, an offspring with a gene duplication is produced. In this way, gene duplications can form and be transmitted to future generations.

During evolution, gene duplications can occur several times. Two or more homologous genes within a single species are also called paralogous genes, or **paralogs**. Multiple gene duplications followed by the accumulation of mutations in each paralog result in a **gene family**—a group of paralogs that carry out related functions. A well-studied example is the globin gene family found in animals. The globin genes encode polypeptides that are subunits of proteins that function in oxygen binding. Hemoglobin, which is made in red blood cells, carries oxygen throughout the body. In humans, the globin gene family is composed of 14 paralogs that were originally derived from a single ancestral globin gene (**Figure 21.14**). According to an evolutionary analysis, the ancestral globin gene duplicated between 500 and 600 mya. Since that time, additional duplication events and chromosomal rearrangements have occurred to produce the current number of 14 genes on three different human chromosomes. Four of these are pseudogenes—genes that have been produced by gene duplication but have accumulated mutations that make them nonfunctional, so they are not transcribed into RNA.

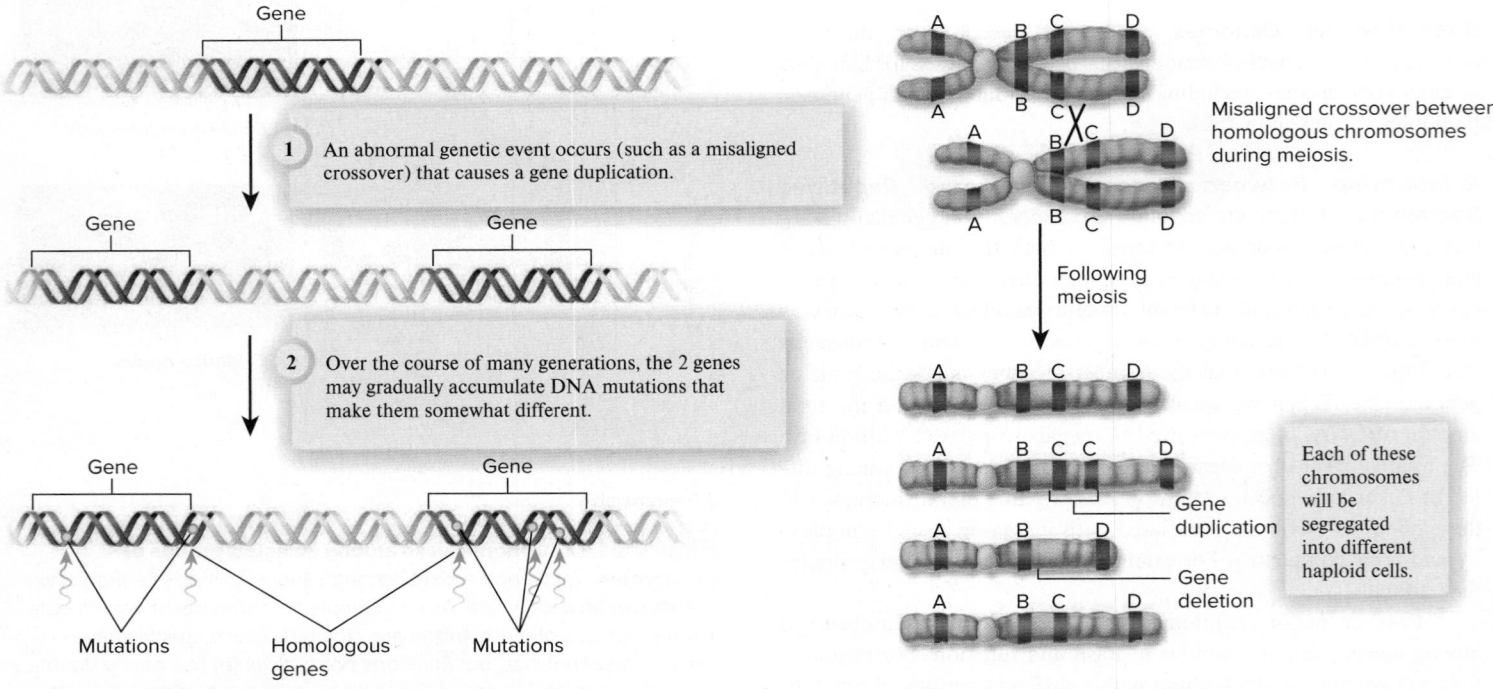

(a) Gene duplication and the formation of homologous genes

(b) Mechanism of gene duplication

Figure 21.13 Gene duplication and the evolution of homologous genes. (a) A gene duplication produces two copies of the same gene. Over time, these copies accumulate different random mutations, which results in homologous genes with similar but not identical DNA sequences. **(b)** A mechanism of gene duplication. If two homologous chromosomes misalign during meiosis, a crossover may produce a chromosome with a gene duplication.

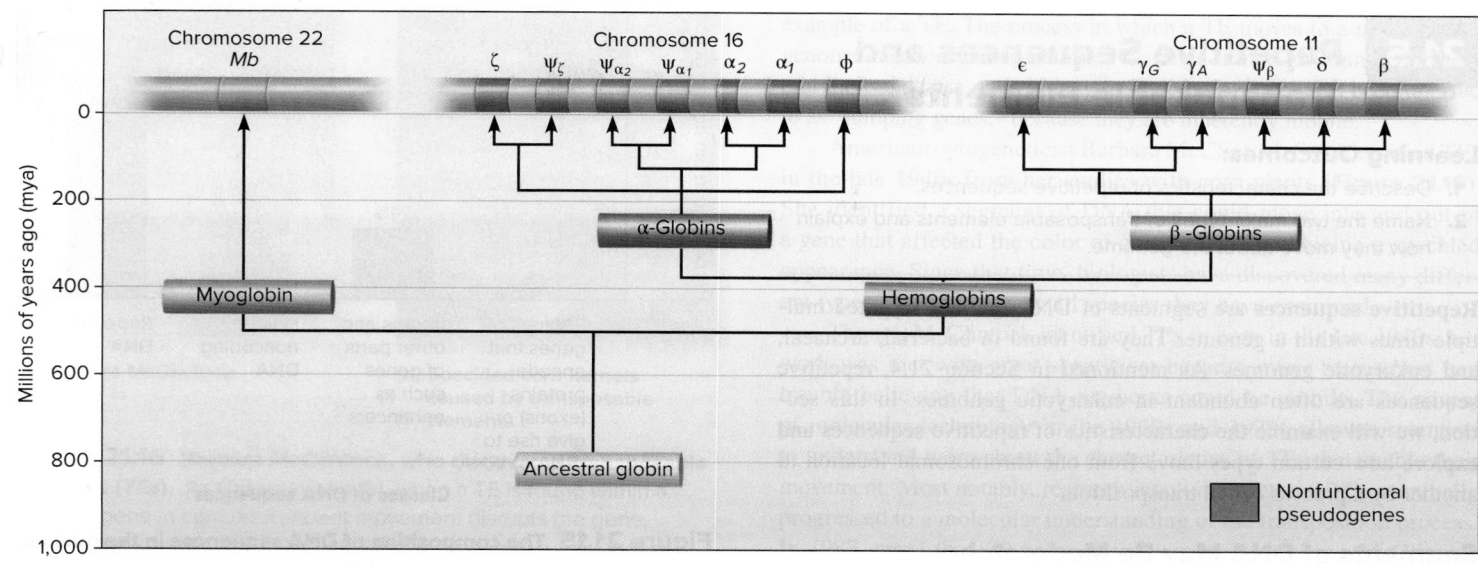

Figure 21.14 **The evolution of the globin gene family in humans.** The globin gene family evolved from a single ancestral globin gene.

 Core Skill: Connections Refer back to Figure 14.3. How do the proteins encoded by different members of the globin gene family vary in their affinity for oxygen?

The accumulation of different mutations in the various family members has produced globins that are specialized in their function. For example, myoglobin binds and stores oxygen in muscle cells, whereas the hemoglobins bind and transport oxygen via red blood cells. Also, different globin genes are expressed during different stages of development. The zeta (ζ)-globin and epsilon (ε)-globin genes are expressed very early in embryonic life. During the second trimester of gestation, the alpha (α)-globin and gamma (γ)-globin genes are turned on. Following birth, the γ-globin genes are turned off, and the β-globin gene is turned on. These differences in the expression of the globin genes reflect the differences in the oxygen transport needs of humans during the embryonic, fetal, and postpartum stages of life (refer back to Figure 14.3).

The Human Genome Project Has Stimulated Genomic Research

Before ending our discussion of genomes, let's consider the **Human Genome Project**, a research effort to identify and map all human genes. Scientists had been discussing how to undertake this project beginning in the mid-1980s. In 1988, the National Institutes of Health (NIH) in Bethesda, Maryland, established an Office of Human Genome Research, with James Watson as its first director. The Human Genome Project officially began on October 1, 1990, and was largely finished by the end of 2003. It was an international consortium that included research institutions in the U.S., U.K., France, Germany, Japan, and China. From its outset, the Human Genome Project had the following goals:

- *To obtain the DNA sequence of the entire human genome.* The first draft of a nearly completed DNA sequence was published in February 2001, and a second draft was published in 2003. The entire human genome is approximately 3.2 billion base pairs in length.

- *To identify all human genes.* This involved mapping the locations of genes throughout the entire genome.

- *To develop technology for the generation and management of human genome information.* Some of the efforts of the Human Genome Project have involved improvements in molecular genetic technology, such as gene cloning, DNA sequencing, and so forth. The Human Genome Project has also developed computer tools that allow scientists to easily access up-to-date information from the project and analytical tools to interpret genomic information.

- *To analyze the genomes of model organisms.* These include *E. coli, S. cerevisiae, D. melanogaster, C. elegans, A. thaliana,* and *M. musculus.*

- *To develop programs focused on understanding and addressing the ethical, legal, and social implications of the results obtained from the Human Genome Project.* The Human Genome Project raised many ethical issues regarding genetic information and genetic engineering. Who should have access to genetic information? Should employers, insurance companies, law enforcement agencies, and schools have access to our genetic makeup?

Some current and potential applications of the results from the Human Genome Project include the improved diagnosis and treatment of genetic diseases such as cystic fibrosis, Huntington disease, and Duchenne muscular dystrophy. The results may also enable researchers to identify the genetic basis of common disorders such as cancer, diabetes, and heart disease, which involve alterations in several genes.

5. Let's suppose you want to clone a gene that has never been analyzed before by DNA sequencing. Which of the following statements is the most accurate?
   a. Do PCR to clone the gene because it is much faster.
   b. Do PCR to clone the gene because it is very specific and gives a high yield.
   c. You can't do PCR because you can't make forward and reverse primers.
   d. Do cloning using a vector because it will give you a higher yield.
   e. Do cloning by insertion into a vector because it is easier than PCR.

6. In the CRISPR-Cas technology for editing genes, what is (are) the function(s) of sgRNA?
   a. to bind to the target gene
   b. to bind to Cas9
   c. to cause a double-strand break in the target gene
   d. all of the above
   e. both a and b

7. Which of the following is *not* an important reason for studying the genomes of bacteria and archaea?
   a. It may provide information that helps us understand how bacteria infect other organisms.
   b. It may provide a basic understanding of cellular processes that allows us to determine eukaryotic cellular function.
   c. It may provide the means of understanding evolutionary processes.
   d. It will reveal the approximate number of genes that an organism has in its genome.
   e. All of the above are important reasons.

8. The enzyme that helps short segments of DNA move from one chromosomal location to another is
   a. transposase.
   b. DNA polymerase.
   c. protease.
   d. restriction endonuclease.
   e. DNA ligase.

9. A gene family includes
   a. one specific gene found in several different species.
   b. all of the genes on the same chromosome.
   c. two or more homologous genes found within a single species.
   d. genes that code for structural proteins.
   e. both a and c.

10. Which of the following was *not* a goal of the Human Genome Project?
    a. identify all human genes
    b. sequence the entire human genome
    c. address the legal and ethical implications resulting from the project
    d. develop programs to manage the information gathered from the project
    e. be able to clone a human

Conceptual Questions

1. Draw the structure of a dideoxyribonucleotide triphosphate, and explain how it causes chain termination.

2. Briefly describe whether or not each of the following can be appropriately described as a genome.
   a. the *E. coli* chromosome
   b. human chromosome 11
   c. a complete set of 10 chromosomes in corn
   d. a copy of the single-stranded RNA packaged into the human immunodeficiency virus (HIV)

3. **Core Concept: Information** Explain the role of the genome at the molecular, cellular, and organism levels.

Collaborative Questions

1. Identify and discuss three important advances that have resulted from gene cloning.

2. Compare and contrast the characteristics of the genomes of bacteria, archaea, and eukaryotes.

UNIT IV
EVOLUTION

Evolution is a heritable change in one or more characteristics of a population from one generation to the next. This process not only alters the characteristics of populations, it also leads to the formation of new species.

We will begin this unit by considering the fundamental concepts of evolution, with an emphasis on natural selection (Chapter 22). We will examine observations of evolutionary change, which includes (1) the fossil record, (2) a comparison of the characteristics of modern species, and (3) an analysis of molecular data. Chapter 23 continues our discussion of evolution at the molecular level and focuses on how changes in allele and genotype frequencies from one generation to the next are driven by a variety of different factors. By comparison, Chapter 24 shifts the emphasis of evolution to the level of species. We will examine how species are identified and discuss the mechanisms by which new species arise via evolution. In Chapter 25, we will examine how biologists determine the evolutionary relationships among different species and produce diagrams called evolutionary trees to describe those relationships. Finally, in Chapter 26, we will examine a timeline for the evolution of species from 4 billion years ago to the present and consider the topic of human evolution.

 The following Core Concepts and Core Skills will be emphasized in this unit:

- *Evolution: This concept will be emphasized throughout the entire unit.*
- *Information: As discussed in Chapters 22 and 23, evolution involves changes in genes.*
- *Systems: Living organisms interact with their environment. As discussed in Chapters 22 through 24, natural selection is a process in which certain individuals have greater reproductive success. This success is often due to their ability to survive in a given environment.*
- *Structure and Function: Chapters 22 and 24 will also consider how structural features change during the evolution of new species. Such changes are related to changes in function.*
- *Process of Science: Every chapter has a Feature Investigation describing a pivotal experiment that provided insights into our understanding of evolution.*
- *Quantitative Reasoning: Chapter 23 focuses on changes in allele and genotype frequencies in populations.*
- *Modeling: Every chapter has a Modeling Challenging to help you refine this important skill.*

An Introduction to Evolution

22

Selective breeding. The horses in this race have been bred for a particular trait: speed. Such a practice, called selective breeding, can dramatically change the traits of organisms over several generations. ©Mark Dadswell/Getty Images

O rganic life beneath the shoreless waves
Was born and nurs'd in Ocean's pearly caves
First forms minute, unseen by spheric glass,
Move on the mud, or pierce the watery mass;
These, as successive generations bloom,
New powers acquire, and larger limbs assume;
Whence countless groups of vegetation spring,
And breathing realms of fin, and feet, and wing.

> By Erasmus Darwin, grandfather of Charles Darwin.
> Published posthumously in 1803.

The term **evolution** is used to describe a heritable change in one or more characteristics of a population from one generation to the next. Evolution can be viewed on different scales. **Microevolution** involves changes in a single gene or in allele frequencies in a population over time. **Macroevolution** refers to the formation of a new species or groups of related species.

For our discussion of evolution, let's begin with a working definition of a species. Biologists often define a **species** as a group of related organisms that share a distinctive form. Among species that reproduce sexually, such as plants and animals, members of the same species are capable of interbreeding in nature to produce viable and fertile offspring. The term **population** refers to all members of a species that live in the same area at the same time and have the opportunity to interbreed. As we will see in Chapter 24, some of the emphasis in the study of evolution is on understanding how populations change over the course of many generations to produce new species.

In the first section of this chapter, we will examine the development of evolutionary thought and some of the basic tenets of evolution, particularly those proposed by the British naturalist Charles Darwin in the mid-1800s. The theory of evolution has been refined over the past 170 years or so, but the fundamental principle of evolution remains unchanged and has provided a cornerstone for our understanding of biology. Ukrainian-born American geneticist Theodosius Dobzhansky, an influential evolutionary scientist of the 1900s, once said, "Nothing in biology makes sense except in the light of evolution." The extraordinarily diverse and often seemingly bizarre array of species on our planet can be explained within the context of evolution. As is the case with all scientific theories, evolution is called a theory because it is supported by a substantial body of evidence and because it explains a wide range of observations. The theory of evolution provides answers to many questions related to the diversity of life. In biology, theories such as this are viewed as scientific knowledge.

In the second section of this chapter, we will survey the extensive data that illustrate the processes by which evolution occurs. These data not only support the theory of evolution but also allow us to understand the interrelatedness of different species, whose similarities are often due to descent from a common ancestor. Much of the early evidence supporting evolution came from direct observations and comparisons of living and extinct species. More recently, advances in molecular genetics, particularly those related to DNA sequencing and genomics, have revolutionized the study of evolution. Scientists now have information that allows us to understand how evolution involves changes in the DNA sequences of a given species. These changes affect both a species' genes and the proteins they encode.

Molecular evolution refers to the process of evolution at the level of genes and proteins. Comparisons of gene or protein sequences in different organisms can reveal evolutionary relationships that cannot be seen in morphology. A major focus of this textbook is to provide an understanding of these changes. In the last section of this chapter, we consider some of the exciting new ways of exploring evolutionary change at the molecular level. In the following chapters of this unit, we will examine how such changes are acted upon by evolutionary factors in ways that alter the traits of a given species and may eventually lead to the formation of new species.

22.1 Overview of Evolution

Learning Outcomes:

1. Define evolution.
2. Describe the factors that led Darwin to the theory of evolution.
3. Explain the process of natural selection.

Undoubtedly, the question "Where did we come from?" has been asked and debated by people for thousands of years. Many of the early ideas regarding the existence of living organisms were strongly influenced by religion and philosophy. Some of these ideas suggested that all forms of life have remained the same since their creation. In the 1600s, however, scholars in Europe began a revolution that created the basis of empirical and scientific thought. **Empirical thought** relies on observation to form an idea or hypothesis rather than trying to understand life from a nonphysical or spiritual point of view. As described in this section, the shift toward empirical thought encouraged scholars to look for the basic rationale behind a given process or phenomenon. This perspective played a key role in the development of the theory of evolution.

The Work of Several Scientists Set the Stage for Darwin's Ideas

In the mid- to late-1600s, the first scientist to carry out a thorough study of the living world was an English naturalist named John Ray, who developed an early classification system for plants and animals based on anatomy and physiology. He established the modern concept of a species, noting that organisms of one species do not interbreed with members of another, and used it as the basic unit of his classification system. Ray's ideas on classification were later expanded by the Swedish naturalist Carolus Linnaeus. How did their work contribute to the development of evolutionary theory? Neither Ray nor Linnaeus proposed that evolutionary change promotes the formation of new species. However, their systematic classification of plants and animals helped scholars of this period perceive the similarities and differences among living organisms.

Late in the 1700s, a small number of European scientists began to quietly suggest that life-forms are not fixed and unchanging. A French zoologist, Georges Buffon, actually proposed that populations of living things change through time. However, Buffon was careful to hide his views in a 44-volume series of books on natural history. Around the same time, a French naturalist named Jean-Baptiste Lamarck suggested an intimate relationship between variation and evolution. By examining fossils, he realized that some species had remained the same over the millennia and others had changed. Lamarck hypothesized that species change over the course of many generations by adapting to new environments. He believed that living things evolved in a continuously upward direction, from dead matter, through simple to more complex forms, toward "human perfection." According to Lamarck, organisms altered their behavior in response to environmental change. He thought that behavioral changes could modify traits and hypothesized that these modified traits were inherited by offspring. He called this idea the inheritance of acquired characteristics. For example, according to Lamarck's hypothesis, giraffes developed their elongated necks and front legs by feeding on the leaves at the top of trees. The exercise of stretching up to the leaves altered the neck and legs, and Lamarck presumed that these acquired characteristics were transmitted to offspring. However, further research has rejected Lamarck's idea that most acquired traits can be inherited. (Note: An acquired trait can sometimes be transmitted from parent to offspring via epigenetic changes, which are described in Chapter 18.) Lamarck's work was important in promoting the idea of evolutionary change.

Interestingly, Erasmus Darwin, the grandfather of Charles Darwin, was a contemporary of Buffon and Lamarck and an early advocate of evolutionary change. He was a physician, a plant biologist, and also a poet (see the poem at the beginning of the chapter). He was aware that modern species were different from similar types of fossilized organisms, and he noted how plant and animal breeders used breeding practices to change the traits of domesticated species (see the chapter opening photo). He knew that offspring inherited features from their parents and went so far as to say that life on Earth could have descended from a common ancestor.

Darwin Suggested That Existing Species Are Derived from Pre-existing Species

Charles Darwin played a central role in developing the theory that existing species have evolved from pre-existing ones. Darwin's unique perspective and his ability to formulate evolutionary theory were shaped by several different fields of study, including ideas of his time about geology and population growth, as well as his own observations.

Hypotheses about Geology Two main hypotheses about geological processes predominated in the early 19th century. Catastrophism was first proposed by French zoologist and paleontologist Georges Cuvier to explain the age of the Earth. Cuvier suggested that the Earth is just 6,000 years old and that only catastrophic events have changed its geological structure. This idea fit well with certain religious teachings. Alternatively, uniformitarianism, proposed by Scottish geologist James Hutton and popularized by another Scottish geologist, Charles Lyell, suggested that changes in the Earth are directly caused by recurring events. For example, they suggested that geological processes such as erosion existed in the past and happened at the same gradual rate as they do now. For such slow geological processes to eventually lead to substantial changes in the Earth's characteristics, a great deal of time is required. Hutton and Lyell were the first to propose that the age of the Earth is well beyond 6,000 years. The ideas of Hutton and Lyell helped to shape Darwin's view of the world.

Population Growth   Darwin's thinking was also influenced by a paper published in 1798 called *An Essay on the Principle of Population* by Thomas Malthus, an English economist. Malthus asserted that the population size of humans can, at best, increase linearly due to increased land usage and improvements in agriculture, whereas our reproductive potential is exponential (for example, doubling with each generation). He argued that famine, war, and disease, especially among the poor, keep population growth within existing resources. The relevant message from Malthus's work was that not all members of any population will survive and reproduce.

Voyage of the Beagle   Darwin's ideas, however, were most influenced by his own experiences and observations. His work as a young man aboard the HMS *Beagle*, a survey ship, lasted from 1831 to 1836 and involved a careful examination of many different species (**Figure 22.1**). The main mission of the *Beagle* was to map the coastline of southern South America and take oceanographic measurements. As the ship's naturalist, Darwin's job was to record information about the weather, geological features, plants, animals, fossils, rocks, minerals, and indigenous people.

Though Darwin made many interesting observations on his journey, he was particularly struck by the distinctive traits of island species. For example, Darwin observed several species of finches found on the Galápagos Islands, a group of volcanic islands 600 miles from the coast of Ecuador. Though it is often assumed that Darwin's personal observations of these finches directly inspired his theory of evolution, this is not the case. Initially, Darwin thought the birds were various species of blackbirds, grosbeaks, and finches. Later, however, the bird specimens from the islands were given to the British ornithologist John Gould, who identified them as several new finch species. Gould's observations helped Darwin in the later formulation of his theory.

As seen in **Table 22.1**, the finches differed widely in the size and shape of their beaks and in their feeding habits. Darwin clearly saw the similarities among these species, yet he noted the differences that provided them with specialized feeding strategies. We now know that these finches all evolved from a single species similar to the dull-colored grassquit finch (*Tiaris obscura*), commonly found along the Pacific Coast of South America. Once they arrived on the Galápagos Islands, the finches' ability to obtain particular types of food in their new habitat depended, in part, on the relative sizes and shapes of their beaks, which, in turn, influenced their abilities to survive and reproduce.

With an understanding of geology and population growth, and his observations from his voyage on the *Beagle*, Darwin had formulated his theory of evolution by the mid-1840s. He had also catalogued and described all of the species he had collected on his *Beagle* voyage except for one type of barnacle. Some have speculated that Darwin may have felt that he should establish himself as an expert on one species before making generalizations about all of them. Therefore, he spent several additional years studying barnacles. During this time, the geologist Charles Lyell, who had greatly influenced Darwin's thinking, strongly encouraged Darwin to publish his theory of evolution. In 1856, Darwin began to write a long book to explain his

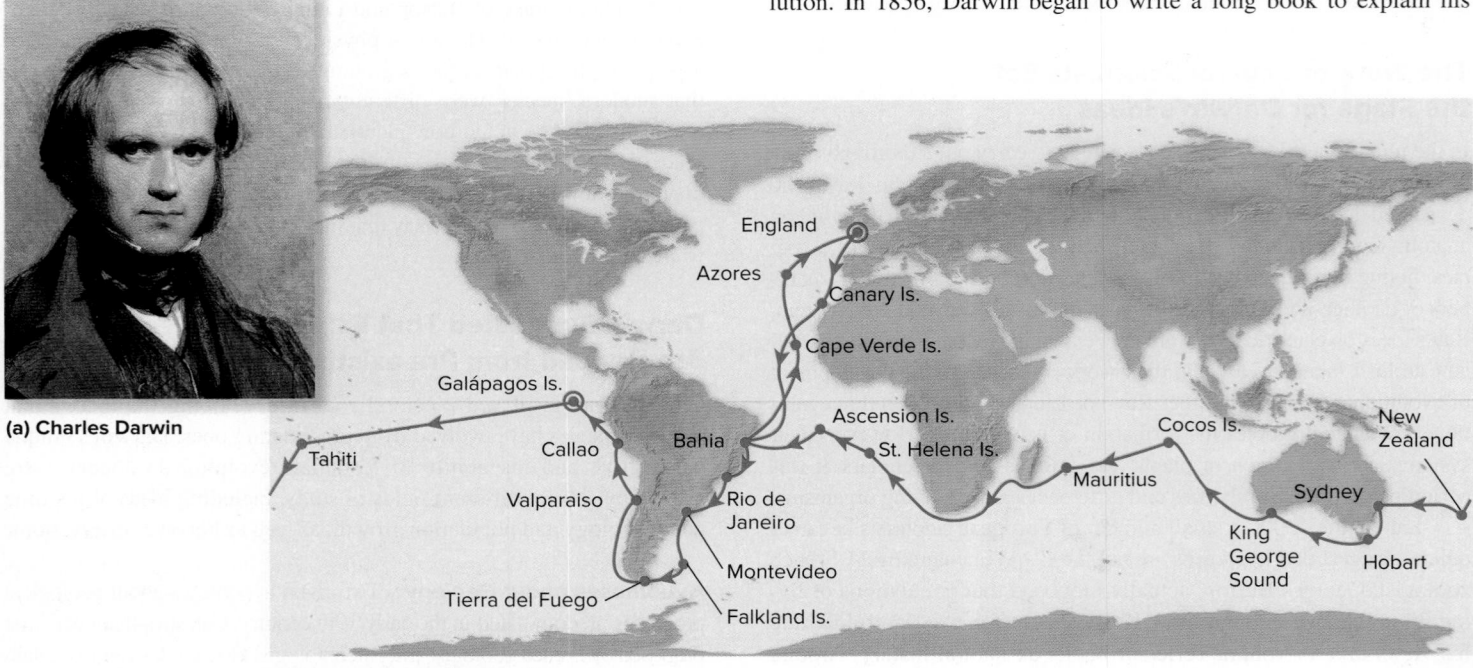

(a) Charles Darwin

(b) The voyage of the Beagle

Figure 22.1 Charles Darwin and the voyage of the Beagle, 1831–1836. **(a)** A portrait of Charles Darwin (1809–1882) at age 31. **(b)** Darwin's voyage on the *Beagle*, which took almost 5 years to circumnavigate the world. a: ©GraphicaArtis/Archive Photos/Getty Images

Table 22.1	A Comparison of Beak Type and Diet Among the Galápagos Finches That Darwin Studied		
Type of finch/diet	**Species**		**Type of beak**
Ground finches			
Ground finches have beaks shaped to crush various sizes of seeds; large beaks can crush large seeds, whereas smaller beaks are better for crushing small seeds.	Large ground finch (*Geospiza magnirostris*)		Crushing
	Medium ground finch (*G. fortis*)		
	Small ground finch (*G. fuliginosa*)		
	Sharp-billed ground finch (*G. difficilis*)		
Vegetarian finch			
Vegetarian finches have crushing beaks to pull buds from branches.	Vegetarian finch (*Platyspiza crassirostris*)		Crushing
Tree finches			
Tree finches have grasping beaks to pick insects from trees. Those with heavier beaks can also break apart wood in search of insects.	Large tree finch (*Camarhynchus psittacula*)		Grasping
	Medium tree finch (*Camarhynchus pauper*)		
	Small tree finch (*Camarhynchus parvulus*)		
Tree and warbler finches			
These finches have probing beaks to search for insects in crevices and then pick them up. The woodpecker finch can also use a cactus spine for probing.	Mangrove finch (*Cactospiza heliobates*)		Probing
	Woodpecker finch (*Camarhynchus pallidus*)		
	Warbler finch (*Certhidea olivacea*)		
Cactus finches			
Cactus finches have probing beaks to open cactus fruits and take out seeds.	Large cactus finch (*G. conirostris*)		Probing
	Cactus finch (*G. scandens*)		

ideas. In 1858, however, Alfred Wallace, a British naturalist working in the East Indies, sent Darwin an unpublished manuscript to read prior to its publication. In it, Wallace proposed the same ideas concerning evolution. In response to this, Darwin decided to use some of his own writings on this subject, and two papers, one by Darwin and one by Wallace, were published in the *Proceedings of the Linnaean Society of London*. These papers were not widely recognized. A year later, however, Darwin finished his book *On the Origin of Species* (1859), which described his ideas in greater detail and included observational support. Although some of his ideas were incomplete because the genetic basis of traits was not understood at that time, Darwin's work remains a foundation of our understanding of biology.

Natural Selection Changes Populations from Generation to Generation

Darwin hypothesized that existing life-forms on our planet result from the modification of pre-existing life-forms. He expressed this concept of evolution as "the theory of descent with modification through variation and natural selection." The term evolution refers to change. What factors bring about evolutionary change? According to Darwin's ideas, evolution occurs from generation to generation due to two interacting factors, genetic variation and natural selection:

1. Variation in traits may occur among individuals of a given species. The heritable traits are then passed from parents to offspring. The genetic basis for variation within a species was not understood at the time Darwin proposed his theory of evolution. We now know that such variation is due to different types of genetic changes such as random mutations in genes. Even though Darwin did not fully appreciate the genetic basis of variation, he and many other people before him observed that offspring resemble their parents more than they do unrelated individuals. Therefore, he assumed that some traits are passed from parent to offspring.

2. In each generation, many more offspring are usually produced than will survive and reproduce. Often, resources in the environment are limiting for an organism's survival. During the process of **natural selection**, individuals with heritable traits that make them better suited to their native environment tend to flourish and reproduce, whereas other individuals are less likely to survive and reproduce. As a result of natural selection, certain traits that favor reproductive success become more prevalent in a population over time.

As an example, we can consider a population of finches that migrates from the South American mainland to a distant island (**Figure 22.2**). Variation exists in the beak sizes among the migrating birds. Let's suppose the seeds produced on the distant island are larger than those produced on the mainland. Those birds with larger beaks would be better able to feed on these larger seeds and therefore would be more likely to survive and pass that trait to their offspring. What are the consequences of this selection process? In succeeding generations, the population tends to have a greater proportion of finches with larger beaks. Alternatively, if a trait happens to be detrimental to an individual's ability to survive and reproduce, natural selection is likely to eliminate this type of variation. For example, if a finch in the same environment had a small beak, this bird would be less likely to acquire enough food, which would decrease its ability

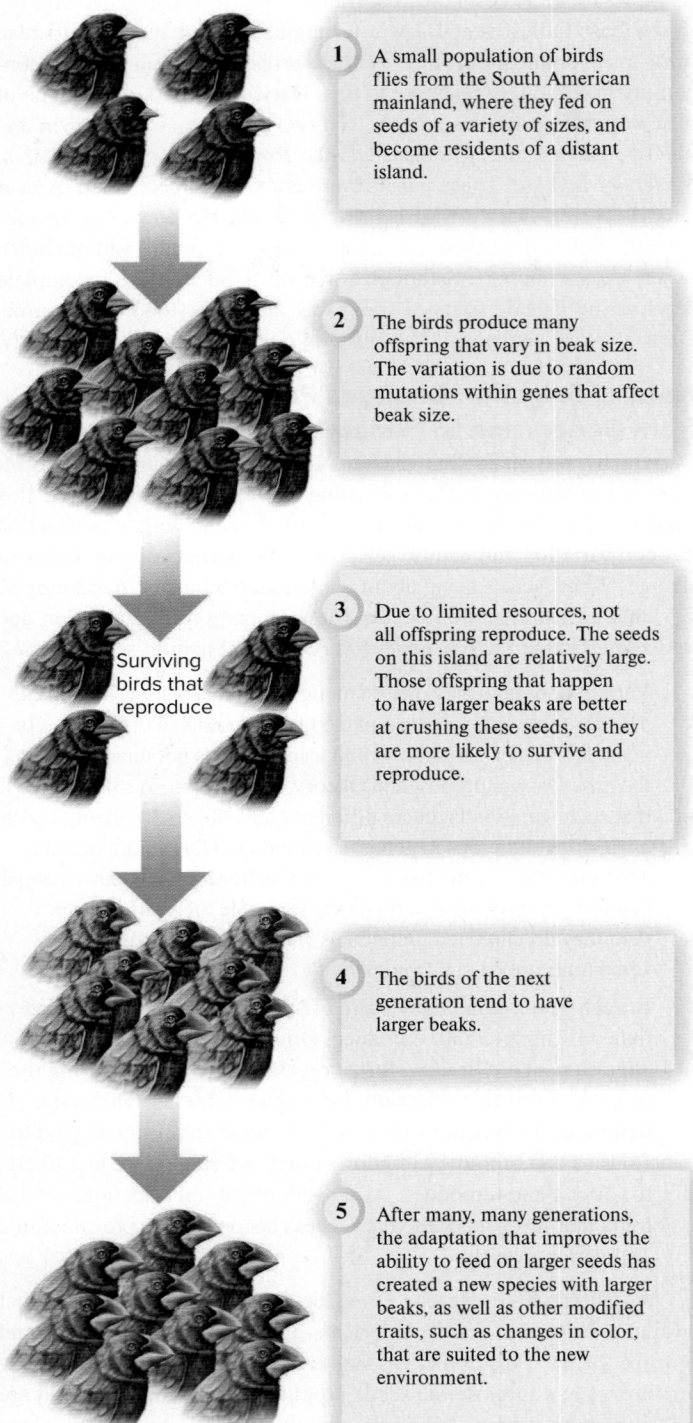

1. A small population of birds flies from the South American mainland, where they fed on seeds of a variety of sizes, and become residents of a distant island.

2. The birds produce many offspring that vary in beak size. The variation is due to random mutations within genes that affect beak size.

Surviving birds that reproduce

3. Due to limited resources, not all offspring reproduce. The seeds on this island are relatively large. Those offspring that happen to have larger beaks are better at crushing these seeds, so they are more likely to survive and reproduce.

4. The birds of the next generation tend to have larger beaks.

5. After many, many generations, the adaptation that improves the ability to feed on larger seeds has created a new species with larger beaks, as well as other modified traits, such as changes in color, that are suited to the new environment.

Figure 22.2 Evolutionary adaptation to a new environment via natural selection. The example shown here involves a species of finch adapting to a new environment on a distant island. According to Darwin's theory of evolution, the process of adaptation can lead to the formation of a new species with traits that are better suited to the new environment.

Concept Check: *The phrase "an organism evolves" is incorrect. Explain why.*

to survive and pass this trait to its offspring. Natural selection may ultimately result in a new species with a combination of multiple traits that are quite different from those of the original species, such as finches with larger beaks and changes in coloration. In other words, the newer species has evolved from a pre-existing one.

BIO TIPS **THE QUESTION** *Antibiotics are medicines used to treat various types of bacterial infections. Examples include streptomycin, tetracycline, and amoxicillin. These drugs inhibit bacterial growth by interfering with processes such as the synthesis of the cell wall, bacterial translation, or vital metabolic pathways. When a strain of bacteria that was originally sensitive to an antibiotic is no longer sensitive, such a strain is said to be antibiotic resistant. Resistant to antibiotics can arise in two common ways:*

- *A new mutation in a bacterium may render the antibiotic ineffective. For example, suppose an antibiotic blocks bacterial growth by binding to a protein that is needed for cell wall synthesis and inhibiting its function. A mutation could occur in the bacterial gene that encodes this protein, altering the protein's structure in a way that prevents the antibiotic from binding.*

- *A bacterium may acquire a gene that confers antibiotic resistance via horizontal gene transfer, which is discussed later in this chapter. For example, a bacterium may acquire a gene that encodes an enzyme that breaks down the antibiotic, thereby rendering it ineffective.*

The bacterium Staphylococcus aureus causes skin infections commonly called staph infections. One antibiotic that has been used to treat staph infections is methicillin. However, resistance to this antibiotic has become a widespread problem. The graph below shows the percentage of S. aureus strains that became resistant to methicillin over a 20-year period in the United States. As you may have heard, methicillin-resistant S. aureus strains are called MRSA (pronounced "mersa"). Explain these data. Is evolution occurring? If so, propose a hypothesis to explain why S. aureus populations are evolving with regard to antibiotic resistance.

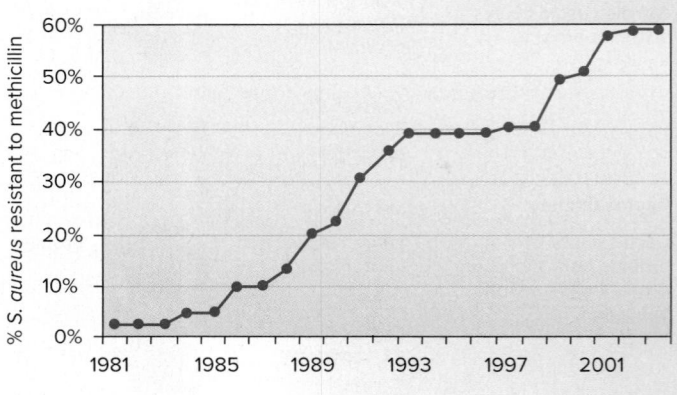

T OPIC *What topic in biology does this question address?* The topic is antibiotic resistance. More specifically, the question asks you to analyze data regarding resistance to methicillin exhibited by *S. aureus*.

I NFORMATION *What information do you know based on the question and your understanding of the topic?* From the question, you have learned what antibiotics are and how antibiotic resistance can arise. You are also given data regarding methicillin resistance in *S. aureus* over a 20-year period. From your understanding of the topic, you may remember that evolution involves heritable changes in a population that are passed from one generation to the next. Natural selection can facilitate evolution.

P ROBLEM-SOLVING S TRATEGY *Interpret data. Propose a hypothesis.* To solve this problem, you can start by observing the trend in the data over time. As you can see in the graph, the level of methicillin resistance dramatically increased over a 20-year

period. The trait that is measured by these data is the ability of *S. aureus* to survive when exposed to methicillin. The population in 2001 had a much higher percentage of bacteria that survived and reproduced when exposed to methicillin compared to the population in 1981.

ANSWER *Evolution is occurring. The U.S. population of S. aureus changed over a 20-year period such that more of these bacteria are resistant to methicillin compared to the original population. One hypothesis to explain these data is natural selection. In the original population in 1981, relatively few bacteria were resistant. However, a very small percentage of them may have been resistant due to a new mutation or horizontal gene transfer. The use of methicillin to treat staph infections may have selected for the survival of these MRSA strains. Therefore, over the course of many bacterial generations, MRSA strains became more common.*

👁 Core Skill: Process of Science

Feature Investigation | The Grants Observed Natural Selection in Galápagos Finches

Since 1973, British evolutionary biologists Peter Grant, Rosemary Grant, and their colleagues have studied natural selection in finches found on the Galápagos Islands. For over 40 years, the Grants have focused much of their work on one of the Galápagos Islands known as Daphne Major (**Figure 22.3a**). This small island (0.34 km²) has a moderate degree of isolation (it is 8 km from the nearest island), an undisturbed habitat, and a resident population of *Geospiza fortis*, the medium ground finch (**Figure 22.3b**).

To study natural selection, the Grants observed various traits in finches over the course of many years. One trait they observed is beak size. The medium ground finch has a relatively small crushing beak, allowing it to more easily feed on small, tender seeds (see Table 22.1). The Grants quantified beak size among the medium ground finches of Daphne Major by carefully measuring beak depth—a measurement of the beak from top to bottom (**Figure 22.4**). The small size of the island made it possible for them to measure a large percentage of birds and their offspring. During the course of their studies, they compared the beak depths of parents and offspring by examining many broods over several years and found that the depth of the beak was transmitted from parents to offspring, regardless of environmental conditions, indicating that differences in beak depths are due to genetic differences in the population. In other words, they found that beak depth was a heritable trait.

By measuring many birds every year, the Grants were able to assemble a detailed portrait of natural selection in action. In the study shown in Figure 22.4, they measured beak depth from 1976 to 1978. In the wet year of 1976, the plants of Daphne Major produced an abundance of the small, tender seeds that these finches could easily eat. However, a severe drought occurred in 1977. During this year, the plants on Daphne Major tended to produce few of the smaller seeds, which the finches

(a) Daphne Major   **(b) Medium ground finch**

Figure 22.3 The Grants' investigation of natural selection in finches. (a) Daphne Major, one of the Galápagos Islands. (b) One of the medium ground finches (*Geospiza fortis*) that populate this island.
a: ©Worldwide Picture Library/Alamy Stock Photo; b: ©Ralph Lee Hopkins/Getty Images

 Core Concept: Evolution This study was aimed at analyzing how beak size may change from one generation to the next.

rapidly consumed. Therefore, the finches resorted to eating larger, drier seeds, which are harder to crush. As a result, birds with larger beaks were more likely to survive and reproduce because they were better at breaking open the large seeds. As shown in the data, the average beak depth of birds in the population increased substantially, from 8.8 mm in predrought offspring to 9.8 mm in postdrought offspring.

How do we explain these results? According to evolutionary theory, birds with larger beaks were more likely to survive and pass this trait to their offspring. Overall, these results illustrate the

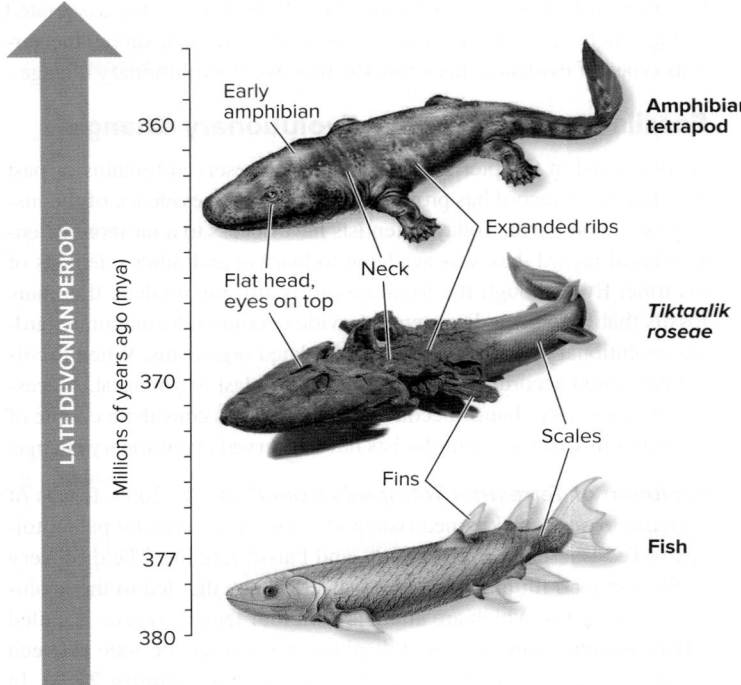

LATE DEVONIAN PERIOD

Millions of years ago (mya)

360 — Early amphibian

Amphibian tetrapod

Expanded ribs

Neck

Flat head, eyes on top

Tiktaalik roseae

370 —

Scales

Fins

Fish

377 —

380 —

Figure 22.5 A transitional form in the tetrapod lineage. This figure shows two early tetrapod ancestors, a Devonian fish and the transitional form *Tiktaalik roseae*, as well as one of their descendants, an early amphibian. An analysis of the fossils shows that *T. roseae*, also known as a fishapod, had both fish and amphibian characteristics, so it was likely able to survive brief periods out of the water.
(middle): ©Corbin17/Alamy Stock Photo

 Core Skill: Modeling The goal of this modeling challenge is to propose a model that describes a transitional form between dinosaurs and birds.

Modeling Challenge: Maniraptora includes a group of dinosaurs that is thought to have given rise to modern birds. As shown below, an example of a maniraptora is *Falcarius utahensis*. Propose a model that describes a transitional form between dinosaurs and birds. As in Figure 22.5, place the more recent species at the top and the earlier form at the bottom. In this case, copy and paste an image of a turkey at the top and *F. utahensis* at the bottom. In the middle, draw a model for a transitional form. Next to your model, list 4 key characteristics of the transitional form.

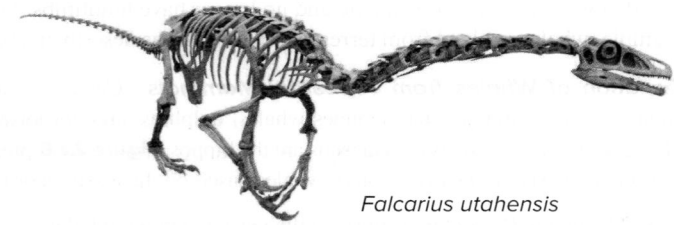

Falcarius utahensis

close together and high on the skull, which is characteristic of aquatic animals that peer out of the water. A particularly striking trait was a thick, bony wall around the middle ear, which is found in modern whales but not in other mammals.

- The genus *Ambulocetus* consisted of semi-aquatic whales of brackish (slightly salty) waters. They were roughly the size of a male sea lion and had short and powerful legs. The tail vertebrae were particularly large, suggesting that the tail was very muscular and possibly used for swimming. The eyes were more toward the sides but still high on the skull.

- The members of the genus *Remingtonocetus* were similar to those of *Ambulocetus* but with a longer snout and a fat pad in the jaw that aided in underwater hearing. They lived in saltwater habitats.

- In members of the genus *Rodhocetus*, the eyes were on the side of the head, and the nasal opening was beginning to shift away from the tip of the snout. The forelimbs had five fingers, and the hindlimbs had only four toes, suggesting the degeneration of the hindlimbs.

- The genus *Dorudon* was composed of whales that were completely aquatic animals. The nasal opening was shifted back toward the eyes to form a blowhole. The forelimbs became flippers, and the hindlimbs were very tiny. The tail was modified at the end to form a fluke.

- Odontoceti and Mysticeti are suborders of the order Cetacea, which includes many extinct species as well as all modern species of whales, dolphins, and porpoises. These animals show a complete loss of the hindlimbs in the adult. The nasal opening is the blowhole seen in modern whales. In odontocetes, echolocation is used for hunting. In mysticetes, baleen is used for filtering food.

Taken together, the changes observed in the fossil record of whales reveal a progression over the past 50 million years from a terrestrial tetrapod to aquatic animals that lack hindlimbs and have many adaptations that are beneficial in an aquatic environment.

Biogeography Indicates That Species in a Given Area Have Evolved from Pre-existing Species

Biogeography is the study of the geographic distribution of extinct and living species. Patterns of past evolution are often found in the natural geographic distribution of related species. From such studies, scientists have discovered that isolated continents and island groups have evolved their own distinct plant and animal communities.

Islands Islands, which are isolated from other landmasses, provide numerous examples in which geography has played a key role in the evolution of new species. Islands often have many species of plants and animals that are **endemic**, which means they are naturally found only in a particular location. Most endemic island species have closely related relatives on nearby islands or the mainland.

As an example, let's consider the island fox (*Urocyon littoralis*), which lives on the Channel Islands located off the coast near Santa Barbara in southern California (**Figure 22.7**). This type of fox is found nowhere else in the world. It weighs about 3–6 pounds and feeds largely on insects, mice, and fruits. The island fox evolved from the mainland gray fox (*Urocyon cinereoargenteus*), which is much larger, usually 7–11 pounds. During the last Ice Age, about 16,000–18,000 years ago, the Santa Barbara channel was frozen and narrow enough for ancestors of the mainland gray fox to cross over to the Channel Islands. When the Ice Age ended, the ice melted and sea levels rose, causing the foxes

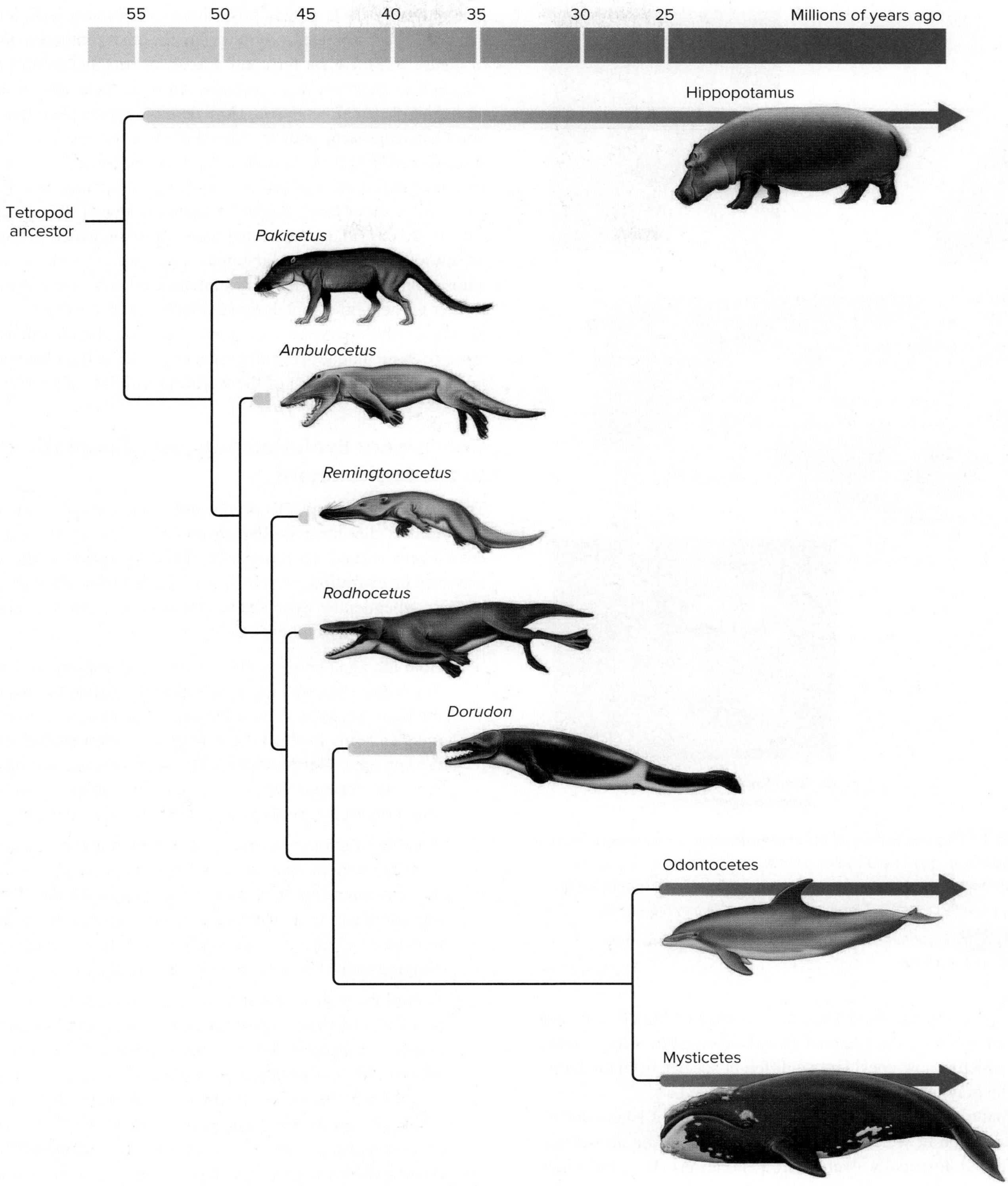

Figure 22.6 **Evolution of whales.** *Pakicetus*, *Ambulocetus*, *Remingtonocetus*, *Rodhocetus*, and *Dorudon* are extinct genera of whales. Odontocetes and Mysticetes are suborders of the order Cetacea, which includes all modern species of whales, dolphins, and porpoises. This simplified representation of whale evolution is a type of diagram called a phylogenetic tree, which is explained in Chapter 25. Note: The genera described in this phylogenetic tree are not depicted as direct ancestors to modern whales, but they all shared common ancestors.

Core Concept: Structure and Function This diagram shows the morphological (structural) changes that occurred in the evolution of whales that made them better suited to an aquatic environment.

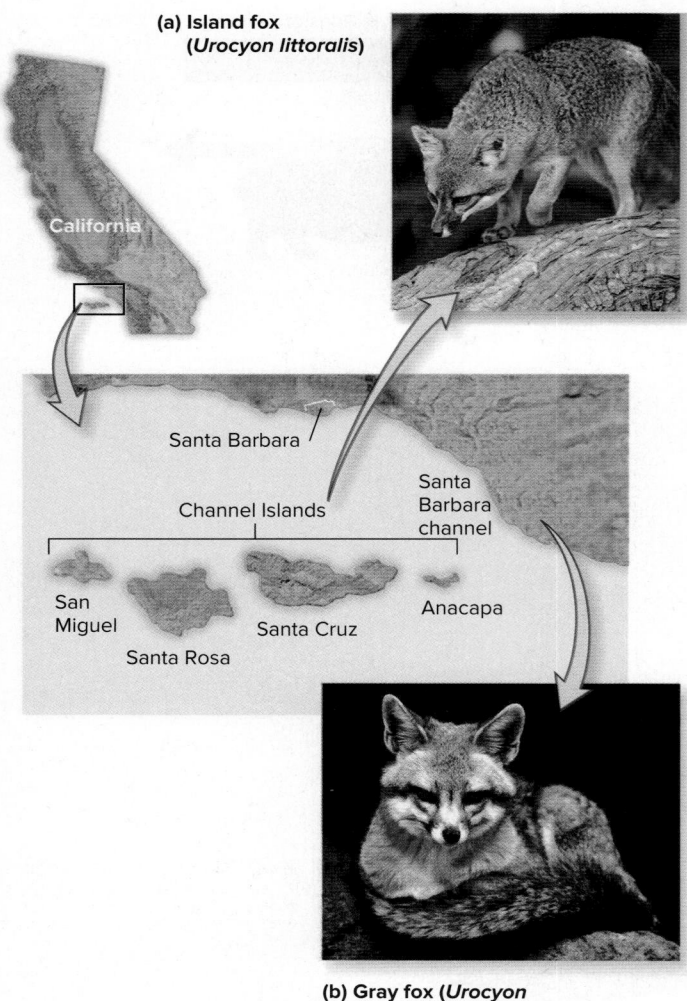

(a) Island fox (*Urocyon littoralis*)

California

Santa Barbara

Channel Islands

Santa Barbara channel

San Miguel

Santa Rosa

Santa Cruz

Anacapa

(b) Gray fox (*Urocyon cinereoargenteus*)

Figure 22.7 **The evolution of an endemic island species from a mainland species. (a)** The smaller island fox found on the Channel Islands evolved from **(b)** the gray fox found on the California mainland.
a: ©Kevin Schafer/Getty Images; b: ©Prisma Bildagentur AG/Alamy Stock Photo

Concept Check: *Explain how geography played a key role in the evolution of the island fox.*

to be cut off from the mainland. Over the last 16,000–18,000 years, the population of foxes on the Channel Islands evolved into the smaller island fox, which is now considered a different species from the larger gray fox. The gray fox is still found on the mainland.

The smaller size of the island fox is an example of island dwarfing, a phenomenon in which the size of large animals on an isolated island shrinks dramatically over many generations. It is the result of natural selection in which a smaller size provides a survival and reproductive advantage, probably because of the limited availability of food and other resources.

Isolated Continents The evolution of major animal groups is also correlated with known changes in the distribution of landmasses on the Earth. The first mammals arose approximately 200 mya, when the area that is now Australia was still connected to the other continents. However, the first placental mammals, which have a long internal gestation and

give birth to well-developed offspring, evolved much later, after continental drift had separated Australia from the other continents (look ahead to Figure 26.5). Except for a few species of bats and rodents that have migrated to Australia more recently, Australia lacks any of the larger, terrestrial placental mammals. How do biologists explain this observation? It is consistent with the idea that placental mammals first arose somewhere other than Australia, and that the barrier of a large ocean prevented most terrestrial placental mammals from migrating there.

On the other hand, Australia has more than 100 species of kangaroos, koalas, and other marsupials, most of which are not found on any other continent. Marsupials are a group of mammal species whose young are born in a very immature condition and then develop further in the mother's abdominal pouch, which covers the mammary glands. Evolutionary theory is consistent with the idea that the existence of these unique Australian species is due to their having evolved in isolation from the rest of the world for millions of years.

Convergent Evolution Suggests Adaptation to the Environment

The process of natural selection is also evident in the study of plants and animals that have similar characteristics, even though they are not closely related evolutionarily. This similarity is the result of **convergent evolution**, in which two species from different lineages have independently evolved similar characteristics because they occupy similar environments.

- Both the giant anteater (*Myrmecophaga tridactyla*), found in South America, and the echidna (*Tachyglossus aculeatus*), found in Australia, have a long snout and tongue. Both species independently evolved these adaptations that enable them to feed on ants (**Figure 22.8a**). The giant anteater is a placental mammal, whereas the echidna is an egg-laying mammal known as a monotreme, so they are not closely related evolutionarily.

- Another example of convergent evolution involves aerial rootlets found in vines such as English ivy (*Hedera helix*) and wintercreeper (*Euonymus fortunei*) (**Figure 22.8b**). Based on differences in their structures, these aerial rootlets appear to have developed independently as an effective means of clinging to the support on which a vine attaches itself.

- A third example of convergent evolution is revealed by the molecular analysis of fishes that live in very cold water. Antifreeze proteins enable certain species of fishes to survive the subfreezing temperatures of Arctic and Antarctic waters by inhibiting the formation of ice crystals in body fluids. Researchers have determined that these fishes are an interesting case of convergent evolution (**Figure 22.8c**). Among different species of fishes, one of five different genes has independently evolved to produce antifreeze proteins. For example, in the sea raven (*Hemitripterus americanus*), the antifreeze protein is rich in the amino acid cysteine, and the secondary structure of the protein is in a β pleated sheet conformation. In contrast, the antifreeze protein in the longhorn sculpin (*Trematomus nicolai*) is encoded by an entirely different gene. The antifreeze protein in this species is rich in the amino acid glutamine, and the secondary structure of the protein is largely composed of α helices.

(a) The long snouts and tongues of the giant anteater (left) and the echidna (right) allow them to feed on ants.

(b) The aerial rootlets of English ivy (left) and wintercreeper (right) enable them to climb up supports.

Figure 22.8 **Examples of convergent evolution.** The species in each of the pairs shown in this figure are not closely related evolutionarily but occupy similar environments, suggesting that natural selection results in similar adaptations to a particular environment. a (left): ©Peter Schoen/ Getty Images; a (right): ©Tom McHugh/Science Source; b (left): ©mm88/Getty Images; b (right): ©2003 Steve Baskauf/bioimages.vanderbilt.edu; c (left): ©Jonathan Bird/Getty Images; c (right): ©David Wrobel/SeaPics.com

`Concept Check:` *Can you think of another example in which two species that are not closely related have a similar adaptation?*

(c) The sea raven (left) and the longhorn sculpin (right) have antifreeze proteins that enable them to survive in frigid waters.

The similar characteristics in the examples shown in Figure 22.8— for example, the snouts of the anteater and the echidna—are called **analogous structures**, or convergent traits. They represent cases in which characteristics have arisen independently, two or more times, because different species have occupied similar types of environments on the Earth.

Selective Breeding Is a Human-Driven Form of Selection

The term **selective breeding** refers to programs and procedures designed to modify traits in domesticated species. This practice, also called **artificial selection**, is related to natural selection. In forming his theory of evolution, Charles Darwin was influenced by his observations of selective breeding by pigeon breeders. The primary difference between natural and artificial selection is how the parents are

chosen. Natural selection occurs because of genetic variation in reproductive success. Organisms that are able to survive and reproduce are more likely to pass their genes to future generations. Environmental factors often determine which individuals will be successful parents. In artificial selection, the breeder chooses as parents those individuals with traits that are desirable from a human perspective.

The underlying phenomenon that makes selective breeding possible is genetic variation. Within a population, variation may exist in a trait of interest. For selective breeding to be successful, the underlying cause of the phenotypic variation is typically due to differences in **alleles**, variant forms of a particular gene, that determine the trait. The breeder chooses parents with desirable phenotypic characteristics. For centuries, humans have employed selective breeding to obtain domesticated species with interesting or agriculturally useful characteristics.

23.1   Genes in Populations

Learning Outcomes:

1. Define a gene pool.
2. Distinguish between allele frequency and genotype frequency.
3. **CoreSKILL »** Use the Hardy-Weinberg equation to calculate allele and genotype frequencies in a given population.
4. List the conditions that must be met for a population to be in Hardy-Weinberg equilibrium.
5. Describe the factors that cause microevolution to occur.

Population genetics is an extension of our understanding of Darwin's theory of natural selection, Mendel's laws of inheritance, and newer studies in molecular genetics. All of the alleles for every gene in a given population make up the **gene pool**. Each member of the population receives its genes from its parents. Individuals that reproduce contribute to the gene pool of the next generation. Population geneticists study the genetic variation within the gene pool and how such variation changes from one generation to the next. The emphasis is often on understanding the variation in alleles among members of a population. In this section, we will examine some of the general features of populations and gene pools.

Populations Are Dynamic Units

Recall that a population is a group of individuals of the same species that occupy the same environment at the same time and can interbreed with one another. Certain species occupy a wide geographic range and are divided into discrete populations due to geographic isolation. For example, distinct populations of a given species may be located on different sides of a physical barrier, such as a mountain range.

Populations change from one generation to the next. How might populations become different? Populations may change in size and geographic location. As the size and location of a population change, the genetic composition generally changes as well. Some of the genetic changes involve adaptation, in which a population becomes better suited to its environment, making it more likely to survive and reproduce. For example, a population of mammals may move from a warmer to a colder geographic location. Over the course of many generations, natural selection may change the population such that animals whose fur is thicker and provides better insulation against the colder temperatures become more prevalent.

 **Core Concept: Evolution**

Genes Are Usually Polymorphic

The term **polymorphism** (from the Greek, meaning many forms) refers to the presence of two or more variations for a given character within a population. **Figure 23.1** illustrates a striking example of polymorphism in the elder-flowered orchid (*Dactylorhiza sambucina*). Throughout the range of this species in Europe, both yellow- and red-flowered individuals are prevalent.

Polymorphism of a character is usually due to the existence of two or more alleles of a gene that influences the character.

Figure 23.1 An example of polymorphism: the two color variations found in the orchid *Dactylorhiza sambucina*. ©Paul Harcourt Davies/SPL/Science Source

Geneticists also use the term polymorphism to describe the variation in the DNA sequence of genes. A gene that commonly exists as two or more alleles in a population is a **polymorphic gene**. To be considered polymorphic, a gene must exist in at least two alleles, and each allele must occur at a frequency that is greater than 1%. By comparison, a **monomorphic gene** exists predominantly as a single allele in a population. When 99% or more of the alleles of a given gene are identical in a population, the gene is considered to be monomorphic.

What types of molecular changes cause genes to be polymorphic? A polymorphism may involve various types of changes, such as a deletion of a significant region of the gene, a duplication of a region, or a change in a single nucleotide. This last type of variation is called a **single-nucleotide polymorphism (SNP)**. SNPs (or "snips") are the smallest type of genetic variation that can occur within a given gene and also the most common. For example, the sickle cell allele discussed at the beginning of the chapter involves a single-nucleotide change in the β-globin gene, which encodes a subunit of the oxygen-carrying protein called hemoglobin. The non-disease-causing allele and the sickle cell allele represent a SNP of the β-globin gene:

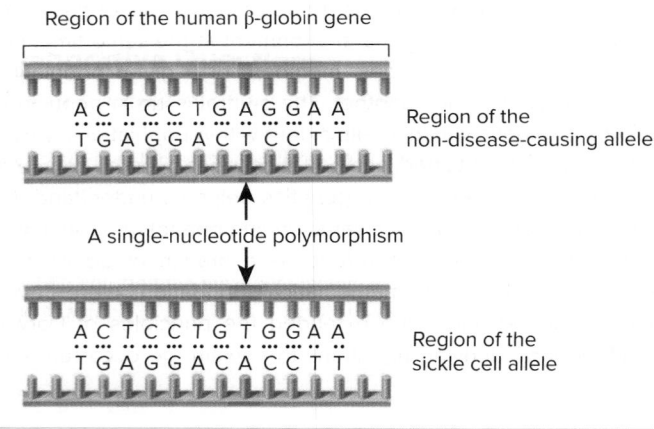

In this single-nucleotide polymorphism, the single nucleotide A (in the top strand) of the non-disease-causing allele changes to a T in the sickle cell allele.

SNPs represent 99% of all variation in human gene sequences that occurs among different people. In human populations, a gene that is 2,000–3,000 bp in length, on average, contains 10 different SNPs. Likewise, SNPs with a frequency of 1% or more are found very frequently among genes of nearly all species. Polymorphism is the norm for relatively large, healthy populations of nearly all species, as evidenced by the occurrence of SNPs within most genes.

Why do we care about SNPs? One reason is their importance in human health. By analyzing SNPs in human genes, researchers have determined that these small variations in DNA sequences can affect the function of the proteins encoded by the genes. These effects on the proteome, in turn, may influence how humans develop diseases, such as heart disease, diabetes, and sickle cell disease. Variations in SNPs in the human population are also associated with how people respond to viruses, drugs, and vaccines. The analysis of SNPs may be instrumental in the current and future development of **personalized medicine**—a medical practice in which information about a patient's genotype is used to tailor her or his medical care. For example, an analysis of a person's SNPs may be used to select between different types of medication or to customize the dosage. In addition, SNP analysis may reveal that a person has a high predisposition to develop a particular disease, such as heart disease. Such information may be used to initiate preventative measures to minimize the chances of developing the disease.

Population Genetics Is Concerned with Allele and Genotype Frequencies

One approach to analyzing genetic variation in populations is to consider the frequency of specific alleles and genotypes in a quantitative way. Two fundamental calculations are central to population genetics: **allele frequency** and **genotype frequency**. Allele and genotype frequencies are defined as follows:

$$\text{Allele frequency} = \frac{\text{Number of copies of a specific allele in a population}}{\text{Total number of all alleles for that gene in the population}}$$

$$\text{Genotype frequency} = \frac{\text{Number of individuals with a particular genotype in a population}}{\text{Total number of individuals in the population}}$$

Although allele and genotype frequencies are related, make sure you clearly distinguish between them. As an example, let's consider a population of 100 four-o'clock plants (*Mirabilis jalapa*) with the following genotypes:

49 red-flowered plants with the genotype $C^R C^R$

42 pink-flowered plants with the genotype $C^R C^W$

9 white-flowered plants with the genotype $C^W C^W$

When calculating an allele frequency for a diploid species, remember that homozygous individuals have two copies of a given allele, whereas heterozygotes have only one. For example, in tallying the C^W allele, each of the 42 heterozygotes has one copy of the C^W allele, and each white-flowered plant has two copies. Therefore, the allele frequency for C^W (the white color allele) equals

$$\text{Frequency of } C^W = \frac{(C^R C^W) + 2(C^W C^W)}{2(C^R C^R) + 2(C^R C^W) + 2(C^W C^W)}$$

$$\text{Frequency of } C^W = \frac{42 + (2)(9)}{(2)(49) + (2)(42) + (2)(9)}$$

$$= \frac{60}{200} = 0.3, \text{ or } 30\%$$

This result tells us that the allele frequency of C^W is 0.3. In other words, 30% of the alleles for this gene in the population are the white color (C^W) allele.

Let's now calculate the genotype frequency of $C^W C^W$ homozygotes (white-flowered plants).

$$\text{Frequency of } C^W C^W = \frac{9}{49 + 42 + 9}$$

$$= \frac{9}{100} = 0.09, \text{ or } 9\%$$

We see that 9% of the individuals in this population have the white-flower genotype.

The Hardy-Weinberg Equation Relates Allele and Genotype Frequencies in a Population

In 1908, Godfrey Harold Hardy, an English mathematician, and Wilhelm Weinberg, a German physician, independently derived a simple mathematical expression, now called the Hardy-Weinberg equation, that describes the relationship between allele and genotype frequencies when a population is not evolving. Let's examine the Hardy-Weinberg equation using the population of four-o'clock plants that we just considered. If the allele frequency of C^R is denoted by the symbol p and the allele frequency of C^W by q, then

$$p + q = 1$$

For example, if $p = 0.7$, then q must be 0.3. In other words, if the allele frequency of C^R equals 70%, the remaining 30% of alleles must be C^W, because together they equal 100%.

For a gene that exists in two alleles, the **Hardy-Weinberg equation** states that

$$p^2 + 2pq + q^2 = 1$$

If we apply this equation to our flower color gene, then

p^2 = the genotype frequency of $C^R C^R$ homozygotes

$2pq$ = the genotype frequency of $C^R C^W$ heterozygotes

q^2 = the genotype frequency of $C^W C^W$ homozygotes

If $p = 0.7$ and $q = 0.3$, then

$$\text{Frequency of } C^R C^R = p^2 = (0.7)^2 = 0.49$$

$$\text{Frequency of } C^R C^W = 2pq = 2\,(0.7)\,(0.3) = 0.42$$

$$\text{Frequency of } C^W C^W = q^2 = (0.3)^2 = 0.09$$

In other words, if the allele frequency of C^R is 70% and the allele frequency of C^W is 30%, the expected genotype frequency of $C^R C^R$ is 49%, of $C^R C^W$ is 42%, and of $C^W C^W$ is 9%.

Figure 23.2 uses a Punnett square to illustrate the relationship between allele frequencies and the way that gametes combine to produce genotypes. The validity of the Hardy-Weinberg equation rests on the assumption that two gametes combine randomly with each other to produce offspring. In a population, the frequency of a gamete carrying a particular allele is equal to the allele frequency in that population. For example, if the allele frequency of C^R equals 0.7, the frequency of a gamete carrying the C^R allele also equals 0.7. The probability of producing a $C^R C^R$ homozygote with red flowers is $0.7 \times 0.7 = 0.49$, or 49%. The probability of inheriting both C^W alleles, which produces white flowers, is $0.3 \times 0.3 = 0.09$, or 9%. Two different gamete combinations produce heterozygotes with pink flowers. An offspring could inherit the C^R allele from the pollen and C^W from the egg, or C^R from the egg and C^W from the pollen. Therefore, the frequency of heterozygotes is $pq + pq$, which equals $2pq$. In our example, this is $2(0.7)(0.3) = 0.42$, or 42%. Note that the frequencies for all three genotypes total 100%.

The Hardy-Weinberg equation predicts that allele and genotype frequencies will remain the same, generation after generation, provided that a population is in equilibrium. To be in equilibrium, the population must not be affected by evolutionary mechanisms that can change allele and genotype frequencies. For this to occur, the following conditions must be met:

- No new mutations occur to alter allele frequencies.
- No natural selection occurs; that is, no survival or reproductive advantage exists for any of the genotypes.
- The population is so large that allele frequencies do not change due to random chance.
- No migration occurs between different populations, altering the allele frequencies.
- Random mating occurs; that is, the members of the population mate with each other without regard to their genotypes.

Why is Hardy-Weinberg equilibrium a useful concept? An equilibrium is a null hypothesis, which suggests that evolutionary change is not occurring. In reality, however, populations rarely achieve an equilibrium, though in large natural populations with little migration and negligible natural selection, Hardy-Weinberg equilibrium may be nearly approximated for certain genes. Sometimes, when researchers experimentally examine allele and genotype frequencies for one or more genes in a given species, they discover that the frequencies are not in Hardy-Weinberg equilibrium. In such cases, they assume that one or more of the conditions are being violated—in other words, mechanisms of evolutionary change are affecting the population. Conservation biologists and wildlife managers may wish to determine why such disequilibrium has occurred because it may affect the future survival of the species.

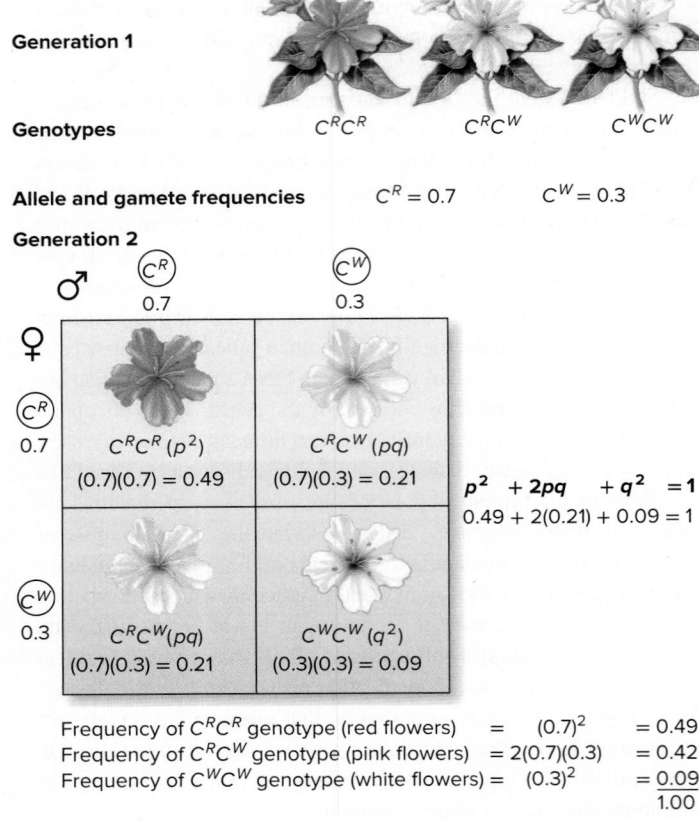

Generation 1

Genotypes $C^R C^R$ $C^R C^W$ $C^W C^W$

Allele and gamete frequencies $C^R = 0.7$ $C^W = 0.3$

Generation 2

	$\male$ $\boxed{C^R}$ 0.7	$\boxed{C^W}$ 0.3
$\female$ $\boxed{C^R}$ 0.7	$C^R C^R$ (p^2) (0.7)(0.7) = 0.49	$C^R C^W$ (pq) (0.7)(0.3) = 0.21
$\boxed{C^W}$ 0.3	$C^R C^W$ (pq) (0.7)(0.3) = 0.21	$C^W C^W$ (q^2) (0.3)(0.3) = 0.09

$$p^2 \; + \; 2pq \; + \; q^2 \; = 1$$
$$0.49 + 2(0.21) + 0.09 = 1$$

Frequency of $C^R C^R$ genotype (red flowers) $=$ $(0.7)^2$ $= 0.49$
Frequency of $C^R C^W$ genotype (pink flowers) $= 2(0.7)(0.3)$ $= 0.42$
Frequency of $C^W C^W$ genotype (white flowers) $=$ $(0.3)^2$ $= \underline{0.09}$
                                                                                  1.00

Figure 23.2 Calculating allele and genotype frequencies with the Hardy-Weinberg equation. A population of four-o'clock plants has allele and gamete frequencies of 0.7 for the C^R allele and 0.3 for the C^W allele. Knowing the allele frequencies allows us to calculate the genotype frequencies in the population.

 Core Skill: Modeling The goal of this modeling challenge is to make a mathematical model for a gene that exists in three alleles in a population that is in Hardy-Weinberg equilibrium.

Modeling Challenge: The Hardy-Weinberg equation is a mathematical model in which a gene exists as two alleles, designated p and q. The equation is derived from the concept that alleles combine randomly at fertilization when diploid offspring are produced. If p and q are the only two alleles, $(p + q)^2 = 1$, which is the same as $p^2 + 2pq + q^2 = 1$. Let's suppose that a gene exists in a population in three alleles, designated $A1$, $A2$, and $A3$. $A1$ is represented by p, $A2$ is represented by q, and $A3$ is represented by r. Propose an equation that describes the relationship between allele and genotype frequencies, assuming that the population is in Hardy-Weinberg equilibrium. If $p = 0.2$, $q = 0.7$, and $r = 0.1$, what would be the genotype frequencies of $A2A2$ homozygotes and $A2A3$ heterozygotes?

BIO TIPS

THE QUESTION *In human populations, the phenotype frequency of the inability to taste the bitter substance phenylthiocarbamide (PTC) is approximately 0.3. This inability is due to a recessive allele. Assuming that there are only two alleles in a population (namely, tasters, T, and nontasters, t) and that the population is in Hardy-Weinberg equilibrium, calculate the frequencies of these two alleles.*

TOPIC *What topic in biology does this question address?* The topic is predicting the allele frequencies in a population. More specifically, the question is about predicting the frequency of alleles that affect the tasting of PTC.

INFORMATION *What information do you know based on the question and your understanding of the topic?* From the question, you know the frequency of homozygotes who are nontasters. From your understanding of the topic, you may realize that you can use the Hardy-Weinberg equation to determine allele frequencies if you know the genotype frequencies.

PROBLEM-SOLVING **S**TRATEGY *Make a calculation.* One strategy to solve this problem is to use the components of the Hardy-Weinberg equation to determine the allele frequencies. If q represents the allele frequency of the recessive allele (t) that confers nontasting, then q^2 is the genotype frequency of homozygous nontasters:

$$q^2 = 0.3$$

We take the square root to determine q:

$$q = \sqrt{0.3}$$
$$q = 0.55$$

If p represents the frequency of the taster allele (T), then

$$p = 1 - q$$
$$p = 1 - 0.55 = 0.45$$

ANSWER *The frequency of the nontaster allele is 0.55, or 55%, and that of the taster allele is 0.45, or 45%.*

Microevolution Involves Changes in Allele Frequencies from One Generation to the Next

The term **microevolution** is used to describe changes in a population's gene pool, such as changes in allele frequencies, from generation to generation. What causes microevolution to happen? Such change is rooted in two related phenomena (**Table 23.1**). First, the introduction of new genetic variation into a population is one essential aspect of microevolution. New alleles of pre-existing genes arise by random mutation, and, as discussed in Chapters 21 and 22, new genes can be introduced into a population by gene duplication and horizontal gene transfer. Such mutations, albeit rare, provide a continuous source of new variation in populations. In 1926, Russian geneticist Sergei

Table 23.1	Factors That Govern Microevolution
*Sources of new genetic variation**	
New mutations within genes that produce new alleles	Random mutations within pre-existing genes introduce new alleles into populations, but at a very low rate. New mutations may be neutral, deleterious, or beneficial. Because mutations are rare, the change from one generation to the next is very small. For alleles to rise to a significant percentage in a population, evolutionary mechanisms, such as natural selection, genetic drift, and migration, must operate on them.
Gene duplication†	Abnormal crossover events and transposable elements may increase the number of copies of a gene. Over time, the additional copies accumulate random mutations and constitute a gene family.
Horizontal gene transfer‡	A gene from one species may be introduced into another species. The transferred gene may be acted on by evolutionary mechanisms.
Evolutionary mechanisms that alter the prevalence of a given allele or genotype	
Natural selection	The process by which individuals that possess certain traits are more likely to survive and reproduce than individuals without those traits. Over the course of many generations, beneficial traits that are heritable become more common and detrimental traits become less common.
Genetic drift	A change in genetic variation from generation to generation due to random chance. Allele frequencies may change as a matter of chance from one generation to the next. Genetic drift has a greater influence in a small population.
Migration	Migration can occur between two populations that have different allele frequencies. The introduction of migrants into a recipient population may change the allele frequencies of that population.
Nonrandom mating	The phenomenon in which individuals select mates based on their genotypes or phenotypes. This alters the relative proportion of homozygotes and heterozygotes that is predicted by the Hardy-Weinberg equation, but it does not change allele frequencies.

* These are examples that affect single genes. Other events, such as crossing over, independent assortment, and changes in chromosome structure and number, may alter the genetic variation among many genes.
† Described in Chapter 21. See Figures 21.13 and 21.14.
‡ Described in Chapter 22. See Figure 22.15.

Chetverikov was the first to suggest that random mutations are the raw material for evolution. However, due to their low rate of occurrence, mutations by themselves do not play a major role in changing allele frequencies in a population over time. They do not significantly disrupt a Hardy-Weinberg equilibrium.

The second phenomenon that is required for evolution to occur is one or more mechanisms that alter the prevalence of a given allele or genotype in a population. These mechanisms are natural selection, genetic drift, migration, and nonrandom mating (see Table 23.1). Over the course of many generations, these mechanisms may promote widespread genetic changes in a population. In the remainder of this chapter, we will examine how natural selection, genetic drift, migration, and nonrandom mating affect the type of genetic variation that occurs when a gene exists as two alleles in a population.

Figure 23.9 A study by Seehausen and van Alphen evaluating the effects of male coloration on female choice in African cichlids.

HYPOTHESIS Female African cichlids choose mates based on the males' coloration.

KEY MATERIALS Two species of cichlid, *Pundamilia pundamilia* and *P. nyererei*, were chosen. The males differ with regard to their coloration. A total of 8 males and 8 females (4 males and 4 females from each species) were tested.

	Experimental level	Conceptual level

1 Place 1 female and 2 males in an aquarium. Each male is within a separate glass enclosure. The enclosures contain 1 male from each species.

This is a method to evaluate sexual selection via female choice in 2 species of cichlid.

2 Observe potential courtship behavior for 1 hour. If a male exhibited lateral display (a courtship invitation) and then the female approached the enclosure that contained the male, this was scored as a positive encounter. This protocol was performed under normal light and under orange monochromatic light.

3 THE DATA

Female	Male	Light condition	Percentage of positive encounters*
P. pundamilia	*P. pundamilia*	Normal	16
P. pundamilia	*P. nyererei*	Normal	2
P. nyererei	*P. nyererei*	Normal	16
P. nyererei	*P. pundamilia*	Normal	5
P. pundamilia	*P. pundamilia*	Monochromatic	20
P. pundamilia	*P. nyererei*	Monochromatic	18
P. nyererei	*P. nyererei*	Monochromatic	13
P. nyererei	*P. pundamilia*	Monochromatic	18

*A positive encounter occurred when a male's lateral display was followed by the female approaching the male.

4 CONCLUSION Under normal light, where colors can be distinguished, *P. pundamilia* females prefer *P. pundamilia* males, and *P. nyererei* females prefer *P. nyererei* males.

5 SOURCE Seehausen, O., and van Alphen, J. J. M. 1998. The effect of male coloration on female mate choice in closely related Lake Victoria cichlids (Haplochromis nyererei complex). *Behavioral Ecology and Sociobiology* 42: 1–8.

male swims toward a female and exhibits a lateral display (that is, shows the side of his body to the female). If the female is interested, she will approach the male, and then the male will display a quivering motion. Such courtship behavior was examined under normal light and under orange monochromatic light.

As seen in the data, Seehausen and van Alphen found that the females' preference for males was dramatically different depending on the illumination conditions. Under normal light, *P. pundamilia* females preferred *P. pundamilia* males, and *P. nyererei* females preferred *P. nyererei* males. However, such mating preference was lost when colors were masked by artificial light. If the light conditions in their native habitats are similar to the normal light used in this experiment, female choice would be expected to separate cichlids into two populations, with *P. pundamilia* females mating with

P. pundamilia males and *P. nyererei* females mating with *P. nyererei* males. In this case, sexual selection appears to have followed a diversifying mechanism in which certain females prefer males with one color pattern, whereas other females prefer males with a different color pattern. A possible outcome of such sexual selection is that it can separate one large population into smaller populations that selectively breed with each other and eventually become distinct species. We will discuss the topic of species formation in more depth in Chapter 24.

23.4 Genetic Drift

Learning Outcomes:

1. Define genetic drift, and explain its effects on allele frequencies over time.

2. Compare and contrast the bottleneck and founder effects.

3. Explain how neutral mutations can spread through a population.

Thus far, we have focused on natural selection as a mechanism that can promote widespread genetic changes in a population. Let's now turn our attention to a second important way the gene pool of a population can change. In the 1930s, Sewall Wright played a large role in developing the concept of **genetic drift** (also called random genetic drift), which refers to changes in allele frequencies due to random chance. The term genetic drift is derived from the observation that allele frequencies may "drift" randomly from generation to generation as a matter of chance.

Changes in allele frequencies due to genetic drift happen regardless of the fitness of individuals that carry those alleles. For example, an individual with a high fitness value may, by chance, not encounter a member of the opposite sex. Likewise, random chance can influence which alleles happen to be carried in the gametes that fuse with each other in a successful fertilization. In this section, we will examine how genetic drift alters allele frequencies in populations.

Genetic Drift Has a Greater Effect in Small Populations

What are the effects of genetic drift? Over the long run, genetic drift favors either the elimination (frequency of 0%) or the fixation (frequency of 100%) of an allele in a population. However, the number of generations it takes for an allele to be lost or fixed greatly depends on the population size. **Figure 23.10** illustrates the potential consequences of genetic drift in one large ($N = 1{,}000$) and two small ($N = 10$) populations (N is the number of individuals that each population contains). This simulation involves the frequency of hypothetical B and b alleles of a gene for fur color in a population of mice—B is the black allele, and b is the white allele.

At the beginning of this hypothetical simulation, which ran for 50 generations, all three populations had identical allele frequencies: $B = 0.5$ and $b = 0.5$. In the small populations, the allele frequencies

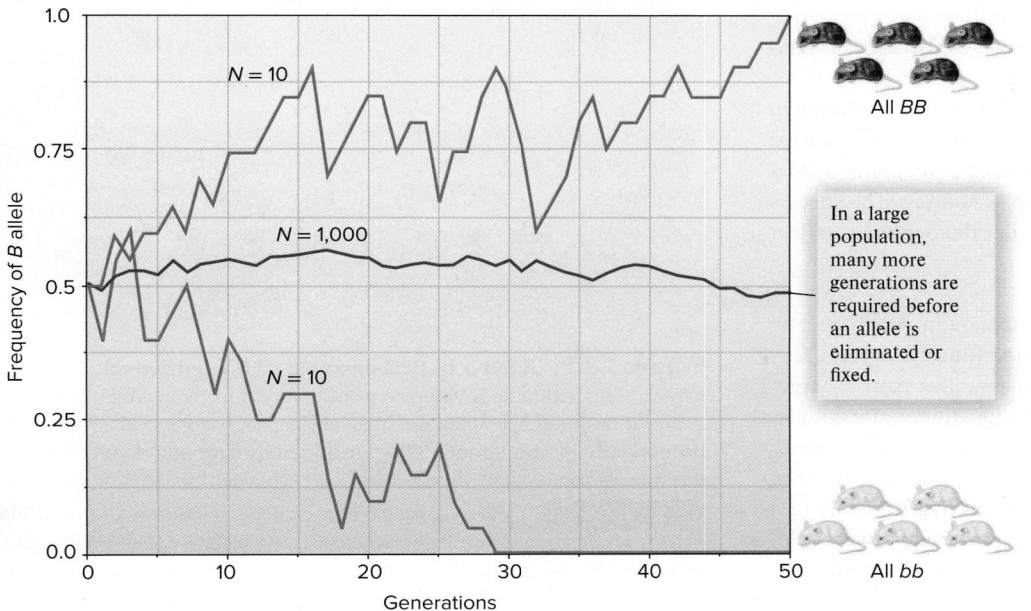

In a large population, many more generations are required before an allele is eliminated or fixed.

All *BB*

All *bb*

Figure 23.10 Genetic drift and population size. This graph shows three hypothetical simulations of genetic drift and their effects on small and large populations of black (B allele) and white (b allele) mice. In all cases, the starting allele frequencies are $B = 0.5$ and $b = 0.5$. The red lines illustrate two populations of mice in which $N = 10$; the blue line shows a population in which $N = 1{,}000$.

Core Skill: Quantitative Reasoning After many generations, random fluctuations in allele frequencies can lead to dramatic differences in the genetic compositions of different populations.

fluctuated substantially from generation to generation. Eventually, in one population, the *b* allele was eliminated; in another, it was fixed at 100%. These small populations then consisted of only black mice or white mice, respectively. At this point, the gene became monomorphic, and allele frequencies could no longer fluctuate due to genetic drift.

By comparison, the frequencies of *B* and *b* in the large population fluctuated much less. As discussed in Chapter 17, the relative effect of random chance, termed random sampling error, is much smaller when the sample size is large. Nevertheless, genetic drift can eventually lead to allele loss or fixation even in large populations, but this will take many more generations to occur than it does in small populations.

In nature, genetic drift may rapidly alter allele frequencies when the size of a population dramatically decreases. Two examples of this phenomenon are the bottleneck effect and the founder effect, which are described next.

Bottleneck Effect   A population can be dramatically reduced in size by events such as earthquakes, floods, drought, and human destruction of habitat. These occurrences may eliminate most members of the population without regard to their genetic composition. The population is said to have passed through a bottleneck. The change in allele frequencies of the resulting population due to genetic drift is called the **bottleneck effect**. Some alleles may be over-represented whereas others may even be eliminated. Such changes may happen for two reasons. First, the surviving population often has allele frequencies that differ from those of the original population that was much larger. Second, as we saw in Figure 23.10, genetic drift acts more quickly to reduce genetic variation when the population size is small. Eventually, a population that has gone through a bottleneck may regain its original size. However, the new population is likely to have less genetic variation than the original one.

A hypothetical example of the bottleneck effect is shown with a population of frogs in **Figure 23.11**. In this example, a starting population of frogs is found in three phenotypes: yellow, dark green, and striped. Due to a bottleneck caused by a drought, the dark green variety is lost from the population.

As a real-life example, the northern elephant seal (*Mirounga angustirostris*) has lost much of its genetic variation. This was caused by a bottleneck in which the population decreased to approximately 20 to 30 surviving members in the 1890s due to hunting. The species has rebounded in numbers to over 100,000, but the bottleneck effect reduced its genetic variation to very low levels.

Founder Effect   Another common phenomenon in which genetic drift may rapidly alter allele frequencies is the **founder effect**. This occurs when a small group of individuals separates from a larger population and establishes a colony in a new location. For example, a few individuals from a large population on a continent may move to an island and become the founders of an island population. The founder effect differs from a bottleneck effect in that it occurs in a new location, although both effects are related to a reduction in population size. The founder effect has two important consequences.

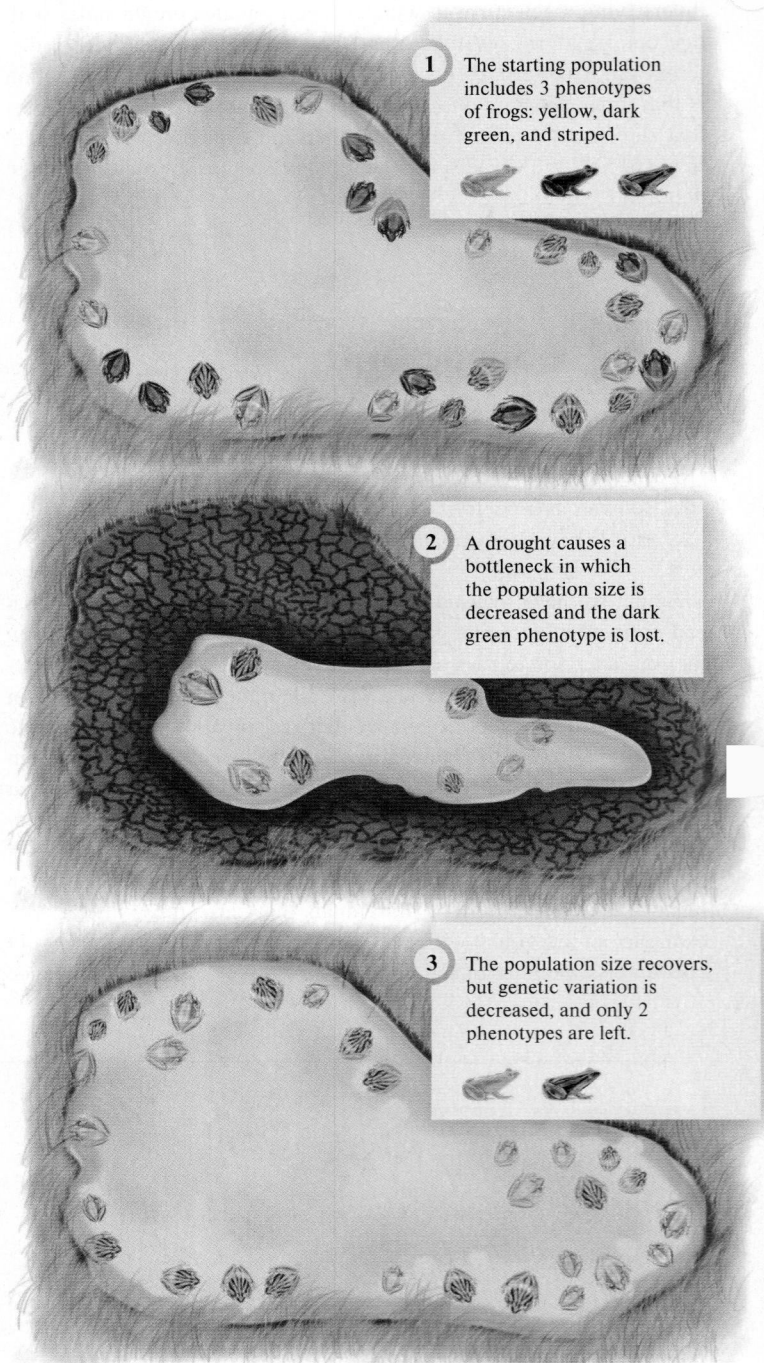

1. The starting population includes 3 phenotypes of frogs: yellow, dark green, and striped.

2. A drought causes a bottleneck in which the population size is decreased and the dark green phenotype is lost.

3. The population size recovers, but genetic variation is decreased, and only 2 phenotypes are left.

Figure 23.11 A hypothetical example of the bottleneck effect. This example involves a population of frogs in which a drought dramatically reduced population size, resulting in a bottleneck. The bottleneck effect reduced the genetic diversity in the population.

Concept Check: How does the bottleneck effect undermine the efforts of conservation biologists who are trying to save species nearing extinction?

- First, the founding population, which is relatively small, is expected to have less genetic variation than the larger original population from which it was derived.

- Second, as a matter of chance, the allele frequencies in the founding population may differ markedly from those of the original population.

Population geneticists have studied many examples in which isolated populations were founded via colonization by members of another population. For example, in the 1960s, American geneticist Victor McKusick studied allele frequencies in the Amish of Lancaster County, Pennsylvania. At that time, this group included about 8,000 people, descended from just three couples that immigrated to the U.S. in 1770. Among this population of 8,000, a genetic disease known as Ellis–van Creveld syndrome (a recessive form of dwarfism) was found at a frequency of 0.07, or 7%. By comparison, this disorder is extremely rare in other human populations, even the population from which the founding members had originated. Evidence suggests that the high frequency in the Lancaster County population can be traced to one couple, one of whom carried the mutated gene that causes the syndrome.

Genetic Drift Plays an Important Role in Promoting Genetic Change

In 1968, Japanese evolutionary biologist Motoo Kimura proposed that much of the DNA sequence variation seen in genes in natural populations is the result of genetic drift rather than natural selection. Genetic drift is a random process that does not preferentially select for any particular allele—it can alter the frequencies of both beneficial and deleterious alleles. Much of the time, genetic drift promotes **neutral variation**—changes in genes and proteins that do not have an effect on reproductive success.

According to Kimura, most variation in DNA sequences is due to the accumulation of neutral mutations that have attained high frequencies in a population via genetic drift. For example, a new mutation within a gene that changes a glycine codon from GGG to GGC would not affect the amino acid sequence of the encoded protein. Both genotypes may be equal in fitness. However, such new mutations can spread throughout a population due to genetic drift (**Figure 23.12**). This phenomenon has been called **non-Darwinian evolution** and also "survival of the luckiest." Kimura agreed with Darwin that natural selection is responsible for adaptive changes in a species during evolution. The long snout of an anteater is the result of natural selection. His main idea is that much of the variation in DNA sequences is explained by neutral variation rather than adaptive variation.

The sequencing of genomes from many species is consistent with Kimura's proposal. When researchers examine changes of the coding sequence within protein-encoding genes, nucleotide substitutions are found to be more prevalent in the third base of a codon than in the first or second base. Mutations in the third base are often neutral; that is, they do not change the amino acid sequence of the protein (refer back to Table 12.1). In contrast, random mutations at the first or second base are more likely to be harmful than beneficial and tend to be eliminated from a population.

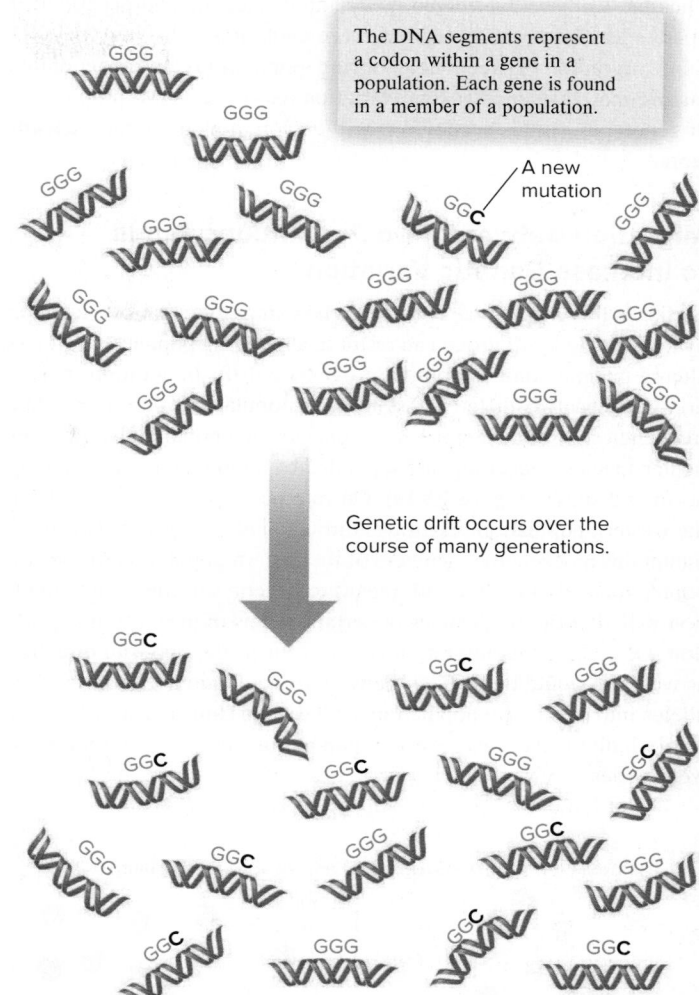

Figure 23.12 Non-Darwinian evolution in a population. In this example, a mutation within a gene changes a glycine codon from GGG to GGC, which does not affect the amino acid sequence of the encoded protein. Each gene shown represents a copy of the gene in a member of a population. Over the course of many generations, genetic drift may cause this altered allele to become prevalent in the population, perhaps even monomorphic.

 Core Skill: Connections Look back at the genetic code described in Table 12.1. Describe three different genetic changes that you would expect to be neutral.

23.5 Migration and Nonrandom Mating

Learning Outcomes:

1. Describe how gene flow affects genetic variation in neighboring populations.
2. Define inbreeding, and explain how it may have detrimental consequences.

Thus far, we have considered how natural selection and genetic drift operate as key mechanisms that cause evolution to happen. In addition, migration between neighboring populations and nonrandom mating may influence genetic variation and the relative proportions of genotypes. In this section, we will explore how these mechanisms work.

Migration Between Two Populations Tends to Increase Genetic Variation

Earlier in this chapter, we considered how migration to a new location by a relatively small group can result in a founding population with an altered genetic composition due to genetic drift. In addition, migration between two different established populations can alter allele frequencies. As an example, let's consider two populations of a particular species of deer that are separated by a mountain range running north and south (**Figure 23.13**). On rare occasions, a few deer from the western population may travel through a narrow pass between the mountains and become members of the eastern population. If the two populations are different with regard to genetic variation, this migration will alter the frequencies of certain alleles in the eastern population. Of course, this migration could occur in the opposite direction as well and would then affect the western population. This transfer of alleles into or out of a population, called **gene flow**, occurs whenever fertile individuals move between populations having different allele frequencies.

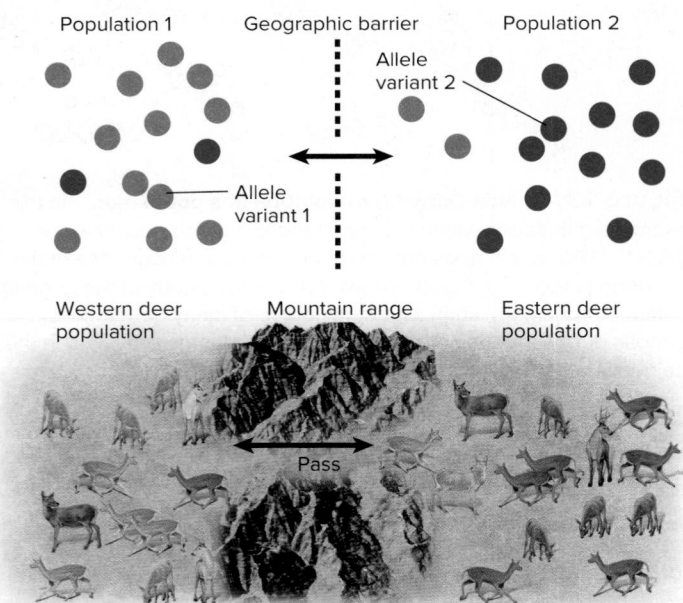

Figure 23.13 **Migration and gene flow.** In this example, two populations of a deer species are separated by a mountain range. On rare occasions, a few deer from one population travel through a narrow pass and become members of the other population. If the two populations differ in regard to genetic variation, this migration will alter the frequencies of alleles in the populations.

Concept Check: *How does migration affect the genetic compositions of populations?*

What are the consequences of migration? First, migration tends to reduce differences in allele frequencies between neighboring populations. Population geneticists can evaluate the extent of migration between two populations by analyzing the similarities and differences between their allele frequencies. Populations that frequently mix their gene pools via migration tend to have similar allele frequencies, whereas the allele frequencies of isolated populations are more disparate, due to the effects of natural selection and genetic drift. Second, migration tends to increase genetic diversity within populations. As discussed earlier in this chapter, new mutations are relatively rare events. Therefore, a new mutation may arise in only one population, and migration may then introduce this new allele into a neighboring population.

Nonrandom Mating Affects the Relative Proportion of Homozygotes and Heterozygotes in a Population

As mentioned earlier, one of the conditions required to establish Hardy-Weinberg equilibrium is random mating, which means that members of a population choose their mates irrespective of their genotypes or phenotypes. In many species, including human populations, this condition is violated. Such **nonrandom mating** takes different forms. Assortative mating occurs when individuals with similar phenotypes are more likely to mate. If the similar phenotypes are due to similar genotypes, assortative mating tends to increase the proportion of homozygotes and decrease the proportion of heterozygotes in the population. The opposite situation, where dissimilar phenotypes mate preferentially, causes heterozygosity to increase.

Another form of nonrandom mating involves the choice of mates based on their genetic history rather than their phenotypes. Individuals may choose a mate that is part of the same genetic lineage. The mating of two genetically related individuals, such as cousins, is called **inbreeding**. This sometimes occurs in human societies and is more likely to take place in nature when population size becomes very small.

In the absence of other evolutionary factors, nonrandom mating does not affect allele frequencies in a population. However, it will alter the balance of genotypes predicted by the Hardy-Weinberg equation. As an example, let's consider a human pedigree involving a mating between cousins (**Figure 23.14**). Individuals III-2 and III-3 are cousins and have produced the daughter labeled IV-1. She is said to be inbred, because her parents are genetically related. The parents of an inbred individual have one or more common ancestors. In the pedigree of Figure 23.14, I-2 is the grandfather of both III-2 and III-3.

Inbreeding increases the relative proportions of homozygotes and decreases the likelihood of heterozygotes in a population. Why does this happen? An inbred individual has a higher chance of being homozygous for any given gene because the same allele for that gene could be inherited twice from a common ancestor. For example, individual I-2 is a heterozygote, *Cc*. The *c* allele could pass from I-2 to II-2 to III-2 and finally to IV-1 (see red arrows in Figure 23.14). Likewise, the *c* allele could pass from I-2 to II-3 to III-3 and then to IV-1. Therefore, IV-1 has a chance of being homozygous because she inherited both copies of the *c* allele from a common ancestor to both of her parents. Inbreeding does not favor any particular allele—it does

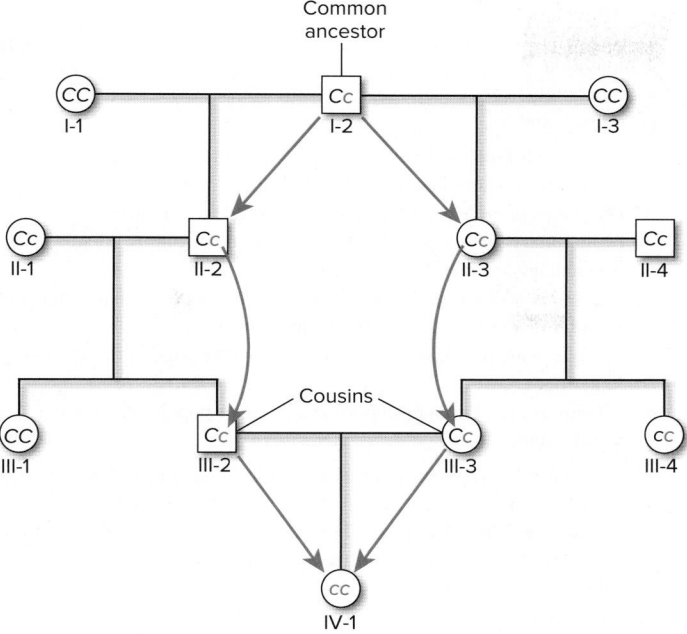

Figure 23.14 A human pedigree containing inbreeding. The parents of individual IV-1 are genetically related (cousins), and, therefore, individual IV-1 is inbred. Inbreeding increases the likelihood that an individual will be homozygous for any given gene. The red arrows show how IV-1 could become homozygous by inheriting the same allele (c) that the common ancestor (I-2) passed to both of her parents.

not favor *c* over *C*—but it does increase the likelihood that an individual will be homozygous for any given gene.

Although inbreeding by itself does not affect allele frequencies, it may have negative consequences with regard to recessive alleles. Rare recessive alleles that are harmful in the homozygous condition are found in all natural populations. Such alleles do not usually pose a problem because heterozygotes carrying a rare recessive allele are also rare, making it very unlikely that two such heterozygotes will mate with each other. However, related individuals share some of their genes, including recessive alleles. Therefore, if inbreeding occurs, homozygous offspring are more likely to be produced. For example, rare recessive diseases in humans are more frequent when inbreeding occurs.

In natural populations, inbreeding lowers the mean fitness of the population if homozygous offspring have lower fitness values. This can be a serious problem as natural populations become smaller due to human destruction of habitat. As a population shrinks, inbreeding becomes more likely because individuals have fewer potential mates from which to choose. The inbreeding, in turn, produces homozygotes that are less fit, thereby decreasing the reproductive success of the population. This phenomenon is called **inbreeding depression**. Conservation biologists sometimes try to circumvent this problem by introducing individuals from one population into another. For example, the endangered Florida panther (*Puma concolor coryi*) suffers from inbreeding-related defects, which include poor sperm quality and quantity and morphological abnormalities. To alleviate these effects, panthers from Texas have been introduced into the Florida population of panthers.

Summary of Key Concepts

23.1 Genes in Populations

- Population genetics is the study of genes and genotypes in a population. A population is a group of individuals of the same species that occupy the same environment at the same time and can interbreed if the species reproduces sexually. All of the alleles for every gene in a population constitute the population's gene pool.
- Polymorphism, which is very common in nearly all populations, refers to the presence of two or more variations of a character in a population. In contrast, a monomorphic gene exists as a single allele (comprising more than 99% of the alleles of the gene) in a population (Figure 23.1).
- Allele frequency is the number of copies of a specific allele divided by the total number of all alleles for that gene in a population. Genotype frequency is the number of individuals with a given genotype divided by the total number of individuals in a population.
- The Hardy-Weinberg equation ($p^2 + 2pq + q^2 = 1$) predicts that allele and genotype frequencies will remain in equilibrium if no new mutations arise, no natural selection occurs, the population size is very large, migration does not occur, and mating is random (Figure 23.2).
- Sources of new genetic variation include random gene mutations, gene duplications, and horizontal gene transfer. Natural selection, genetic drift, migration, and nonrandom mating may alter allele and genotype frequencies and cause a population to evolve (Table 23.1).

23.2 Natural Selection

- Natural selection is the process by which individuals with certain heritable traits that favor survival and reproduction tend to become more prevalent in a population. Fitness, the relative likelihood that a genotype will contribute to the gene pool of the next generation, is a measure of reproductive success.
- Directional selection is the process by which one extreme of a phenotypic distribution is favored (Figure 23.3).
- During stabilizing selection, individuals with an intermediate phenotype have greater reproductive success (Figure 23.4).
- Diversifying selection is the process by which two or more phenotypes are favored. An example is a population that occupies a heterogeneous environment (Figure 23.5).
- Balancing selection maintains balanced polymorphism in a population. Examples of the ways in which balancing selection occurs include heterozygote advantage and negative frequency-dependent selection (Figure 23.6).

23.3 Sexual Selection

- Sexual selection is a form of natural selection in which individuals with certain traits are more likely than others to engage in successful reproduction. In intrasexual selection, members of one sex compete for the opportunity to mate with individuals of the opposite sex. In intersexual selection, members of one sex choose their mates on the basis of certain desirable characteristics (Figure 23.7).
- Seehausen and van Alphen discovered that female cichlids' choice of mates is influenced by male coloration. This is an example of sexual selection (Figures 23.8, 23.9).

23.4 Genetic Drift

- Genetic drift involves changes in allele frequencies over time due to random chance. It occurs more rapidly in small populations and leads to either the elimination or the fixation of alleles (Figure 23.10).

- In the bottleneck effect, an environmental event dramatically reduces a population size, and the allele frequencies of the resulting population change due to genetic drift (Figure 23.11).

- The founder effect occurs when a small population moves to a new geographic location and genetic drift alters the genetic composition of that population.

- Kimura proposed that genetic drift promotes neutral variation, or the accumulation of changes in genes and proteins that do not affect reproductive success. Much of the genetic variation in DNA sequences in populations appears to be the result of genetic drift rather than natural selection (Figure 23.12).

23.5 Migration and Nonrandom Mating

- Gene flow occurs when individuals migrate between populations with different allele frequencies. It reduces differences in allele frequencies between populations and enhances genetic diversity (Figure 23.13).

- Inbreeding, a form of nonrandom mating in which genetically related individuals have offspring with each other, tends to increase the proportion of homozygotes relative to heterozygotes. When the resulting homozygotes have lower fitness, the phenomenon called inbreeding depression is the result (Figure 23.14).

Assess & Discuss

Test Yourself

1. Population geneticists are interested in the genetic variation in populations. The most common type of genetic change that causes polymorphism in a population is
   a. a deletion of a gene sequence.
   b. a duplication of a region of a gene.
   c. a rearrangement of a gene sequence.
   d. a single-nucleotide substitution.
   e. an inversion of a segment of a chromosome.

2. The Hardy-Weinberg equation characterizes the allele and genotype frequencies
   a. of a population that is experiencing selection for mating success.
   b. of a population that is extremely small.
   c. of a population that is very large and not evolving.
   d. of a community of species that is not evolving.
   e. of a community of species that is experiencing selection.

3. In the Hardy-Weinberg equation, what portion represents the frequency of individuals that do not exhibit a recessive disease but are carriers of a recessive allele?
   a. q
   b. p^2
   c. $2pq$
   d. q^2
   e. both b and d

4. By itself, which of the following is *not* likely to have a major influence on allele frequencies?

   a. natural selection
   b. genetic drift
   c. mutation
   d. inbreeding
   e. either c and d

5. Which of the following statements regarding mutations is correct?
   a. Mutations are not important in evolution.
   b. Mutations provide a source of genetic variation, but other evolutionary factors are more important in determining allele frequencies in a population.
   c. Mutations occur at such a high rate that they promote major changes in the gene pool from one generation to the next.
   d. Mutations are of greater importance in smaller populations than in larger ones.
   e. Mutations are of greater importance in larger populations than in smaller ones.

6. In a population of fish, body coloration varies from a light shade, almost white, to a very dark shade of green. If changes in the environment resulted in decreased predation of individuals with the lightest coloration, this would be an example of _____ selection.
   a. diversifying
   b. stabilizing
   c. directional
   d. sexual
   e. artificial

7. For the population of fish described in question 6, if the stream environment included some areas with a sandy, light-colored bottom and some with a lot of dark-colored vegetation, both the light- and dark-colored fish would have a selective advantage and increased survival in certain places. This scenario could explain the occurrence of
   a. genetic drift.
   b. diversifying selection.
   c. mutation.
   d. stabilizing selection.
   e. sexual selection.

8. The microevolutionary factor most sensitive to population size is
   a. mutation.
   b. migration.
   c. selection.
   d. genetic drift.
   e. all of the above.

9. Kimura's proposal regarding neutral variation differs from Darwinian evolution in that
   a. natural selection does not exist.
   b. most of the genetic variation in a population is due to mutations that do not affect reproductive success.
   c. neutral variation alters survival and reproductive success.
   d. neutral mutations are not affected by population size.
   e. it differs with respect to both b and c.

10. Populations that experience inbreeding may also experience
    a. a decrease in fitness due to an increased frequency of recessive genetic diseases.
    b. an increase in fitness due to increases in heterozygosity.
    c. very little genetic drift.
    d. no apparent change.
    e. increased mutation rates.

Conceptual Questions

1. The percentage of individuals exhibiting a recessive disease in a population is 0.04, or 4%. Based on the Hardy-Weinberg equation, what percentage of individuals in this population are expected to be heterozygous carriers?

2. Compare and contrast the four patterns of natural selection that result in adaptation to a given environment and also describe sexual selection.

3. **Core Concept: Evolution** Explain how genetic drift results in evolution.

Collaborative Questions

1. Antibiotics are commonly used to combat bacterial and fungal infections. During the past several decades, however, antibiotic-resistant strains of microorganisms have become alarmingly prevalent. This has undermined the ability of physicians to treat many types of infectious disease. Discuss how the following processes that alter allele frequencies may have contributed to the emergence of antibiotic-resistant strains:

    a. random mutation
    b. genetic drift
    c. natural selection

2. Discuss the similarities and differences among directional, disruptive, balancing, and stabilizing selection.

Dendrobates tinctorius, commonly called the dyeing poison frog. This species exists in many different-colored morphs, which are individuals of the same species that have noticeably dissimilar appearances. In contrast, **Figure 24.1b** shows two different species of frogs, the northern leopard frog (*Rana pipiens*) and the southern leopard frog (*Rana utricularia*), which look fairly similar.

Reproductive Isolation   Why would biologists describe two types of organisms, such as the northern leopard frog and southern leopard frog, as being different species if they are morphologically similar? One reason is that biologists have discovered that the two species of frogs are unable to breed with each other in nature. Therefore, a second way of identifying a species is by the ability of its members to interbreed. In the late 1920s, geneticist Theodosius Dobzhansky proposed that each species is reproductively isolated from other species. Such **reproductive isolation** prevents one species from successfully interbreeding with other species. In 1942, German evolutionary biologist Ernst Mayr expanded on the ideas of Dobzhansky to provide a definition of a species. According to Mayr, a key feature of sexually reproducing species is that, in nature, the members of one species have the potential to interbreed with one another to produce viable, fertile offspring but cannot successfully interbreed with members of other species. As discussed later in this section, reproductive isolation among species of plants and animals occurs by an amazing variety of different mechanisms.

Reproductive isolation has been used to distinguish many plant and animal species, especially those that look alike but do not interbreed. Even so, this criterion suffers from four main problems.

1. In nature, it may be difficult to determine if two populations are reproductively isolated, particularly if the populations have nonoverlapping geographic ranges.

2. Biologists have noted many cases in which two different species can interbreed in nature yet consistently maintain themselves as separate species. For example, different species of yucca plants, such as *Yucca pallida* and *Yucca constricta,* do interbreed in nature yet typically maintain populations with distinct characteristics. For this reason, they are viewed as distinct species.

3. Reproductive isolation does not apply to asexual species such as bacteria. Likewise, some species of plants and fungi reproduce only asexually.

4. Reproductive isolation cannot be applied to extinct species.

For these reasons, reproductive isolation has been primarily used to distinguish closely related species of modern animals and plants that reproduce sexually.

Molecular Features   Molecular features are now commonly used to determine if two different populations are different species. Evolutionary biologists often compare DNA sequences of genes, gene order along chromosomes, chromosome structure, and chromosome number in order to identify similarities and differences among different populations. For example, researchers may compare the DNA sequence of the *16S rRNA* gene between different bacterial populations as a way of determining if two populations represent different species. When the sequences are very similar, such populations would

probably be judged to be the same species. However, it may be difficult to draw the line when separating groups into different species. How much difference must be present for species to be considered separate? Is a 2% difference in their genome sequences sufficient to warrant placement into two different species, or do we need a 5% difference?

Ecological Factors   A variety of factors related to an organism's habitat may be used to distinguish one species from another. For example, certain species of warblers are distinguished by the habitat in which they forage for food. Some species search the ground for food, others forage in bushes or small trees, and some species primarily forage in tall trees. Such habitat differences are used to distinguish different species that look morphologically similar.

Many bacterial species have been categorized as distinct based on ecological factors. Bacterial cells of the same species are likely to use the same resources (such as sugars and vitamins) and grow under the same conditions (such as particular temperature and pH ranges). However, a drawback of this approach is that different groups of bacteria sometimes display very similar growth characteristics, and even the same species may show great variation in the growth conditions it will tolerate.

Evolutionary Relationships   In Chapter 25, we will examine the methods that are used to produce evolutionary trees that describe the relationships between ancestral species and modern species. In some cases, such relationships are based on an analysis of the fossil record. For example, the fossil record was used to construct a tree that shows the ancestors that led to modern horse species. Alternatively, another way of establishing evolutionary relationships is by the analysis of DNA sequences. Researchers obtain samples of cells from different individuals and compare the genes within those cells to see how similar or different they are.

BIO **TIPS**   **THE QUESTION** *A biologist has discovered two populations of snakes that live on opposite sides of a large canyon. The snakes look very similar, but those on the western side of the canyon have a red spot on the top of their heads, whereas those on the eastern side have an orange spot. How would decide if these two populations represent one species or two species?*

T **OPIC** *What topic in biology does this question address?* The topic is species identification. More specifically, the question is about deciding if two different populations of snakes are the same or different species.

I **NFORMATION** *What information do you know based on the question and your understanding of the topic?* In the question, you are given information about two populations of snakes that are found on opposite sides of a canyon. From your understanding of the topic, you may remember that biologists analyze five different characteristics to identify species: (1) morphological traits, (2) reproductive isolation (the ability to interbreed), (3) molecular features, (4) ecological factors, and (5) evolutionary relationships.

PROBLEM-SOLVING STRATEGY *Design an experiment.*
Interpret data. One strategy for solving this problem is to design
an experiment to examine one of the five characteristics that
biologists use to identify species.

ANSWER *Here are two possible experimental designs:*

1. *Reproductive isolation. Move a few snakes from the western
   side to the eastern side, and vice versa. Observe whether or
   not the introduced snakes interbreed with the ones already
   there. If they do readily interbreed, you can probably conclude that they are not separate species. Alternatively, if they
   don't interbreed, you may conclude that the two populations
   are reproductively isolated and are different species.*
2. *Molecular features. Obtain samples of cells from several
   western and eastern snakes, and analyze their genetic material. If the gene sequences are very similar and the chromosomal composition is very similar, you may conclude that the
   two populations are the same species. Alternatively, if the
   gene sequences show significant differences and the chromosomes differ with regard to structure and/or number, you
   may conclude that the two populations are different species.*

Species Concepts Emphasize Particular Features to Define and Distinguish Species

A **species concept** is a way of defining the concept of a species and/
or of providing an approach to distinguish one species from another.
Since 1942, over 20 different species concepts have been proposed by
a variety of evolutionary biologists.

Biological Species Concept   Ernst Mayr proposed one of the first
species concepts, called the **biological species concept**. According to
Mayr's concept, a species is a group of individuals whose members
have the potential to interbreed with one another in nature to produce
viable, fertile offspring but cannot successfully interbreed with members of other species. The biological species concept emphasizes reproductive isolation as the most important criterion for delimiting species.

Evolutionary Lineage Concept   Another example of a species concept is the **evolutionary lineage concept** proposed by American paleontologist George Gaylord Simpson in 1961. A **lineage** is a series of species
that forms a line of descent, with each new species the direct result of
speciation from an immediate ancestral species. According to Gaylord,
species should be defined based on their unique evolution of lineages.

Ecological Species Concept   A third example is the **ecological
species concept**, described by American evolutionary biologist Leigh
Van Valen in 1976. According to this viewpoint, each species occupies an ecological niche, which is the unique set of habitat resources
that a species requires, as well as its influence on the environment
and other species.

General Lineage Concept   Most evolutionary biologists would
agree that different methods are needed to distinguish the vast array of
species on Earth. Even so, some evolutionary biologists have questioned

whether it is valid to have many different species concepts. In 1998,
American zoologist Kevin de Queiroz suggested that there is only a
single general species concept, which concurs with Simpson's evolutionary lineage concept and includes all previous concepts. According
to de Queiroz's **general lineage concept**, each species is a population
of an independently evolving lineage. Each species has evolved from
a specific series of ancestors and, as a consequence, forms a group of
organisms with a particular set of characteristics. Multiple criteria are
used to determine if a population is part of an independent evolutionary lineage, and thus a species, which is distinct from others. Typically,
researchers use analyses of morphology, reproductive isolation, DNA
sequences, and ecology to determine if a population or group of populations is distinct from others. Because of its generality, the general
lineage concept has received significant support.

Reproductive Isolating Mechanisms Help to Maintain the Distinctiveness of Each Species

Thus far in this section, we have considered various ways of differentiating species. From the discussion, you may have realized that
the identification of a species is not always a simple matter. The phenomenon of reproductive isolation has played a major role in the way
biologists study plant and animal species, partly because it identifies a possible mechanism for the process of forming new species.
For this reason, much research has been done to try to understand
reproductive isolating mechanisms, the mechanisms that prevent
interbreeding between different species.

Why do reproductive isolating mechanisms occur? Populations
do not intentionally erect these reproductive barriers. Rather, reproductive isolation is a consequence of genetic changes that occur
usually because a species becomes adapted to its own particular
environment. The view of evolutionary biologists is that reproductive isolation typically evolves as a by-product of genetic divergence.
Over time, as a species evolves its own unique characteristics, some
of those traits are likely to prevent breeding with other species.

Reproductive isolating mechanisms fall into two categories:
prezygotic isolating mechanisms, which prevent the formation of a
zygote, and **postzygotic isolating mechanisms**, which block the development of a viable and fertile individual after fertilization has taken
place. **Figure 24.2** summarizes some of the more common ways that
reproductive isolating mechanisms prevent reproduction between different species. When members of two different species interbreed and
produce offspring, such an offspring is called an **interspecies hybrid**.

Prezygotic Isolating Mechanisms   We will consider five types of
prezygotic isolating mechanisms.

Habitat Isolation: One obvious way to prevent interbreeding is
for members of different species to never come in contact with each
other. This phenomenon, called habitat isolation, may involve a geographic barrier to interbreeding. For example, a large body of water
may separate two different plant species that live on nearby islands.

Temporal Isolation: In temporal isolation, species happen to reproduce at different times of the day or year. In the northeastern U.S.,
for example, the two most abundant field crickets, *Gryllus veletis* and
Gryllus pennsylvanicus (spring and fall field crickets, respectively),

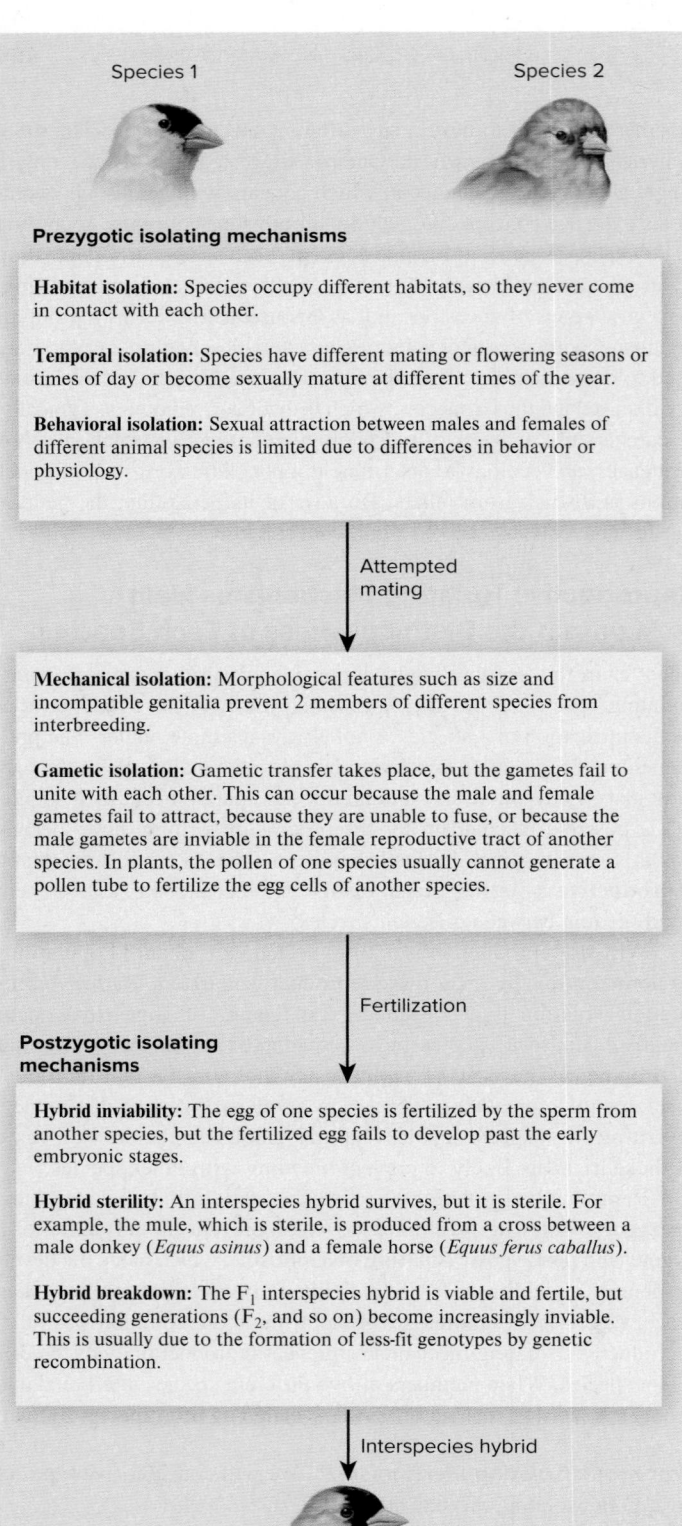

Prezygotic isolating mechanisms

Species 1   Species 2

Habitat isolation: Species occupy different habitats, so they never come in contact with each other.

Temporal isolation: Species have different mating or flowering seasons or times of day or become sexually mature at different times of the year.

Behavioral isolation: Sexual attraction between males and females of different animal species is limited due to differences in behavior or physiology.

↓ Attempted mating

Mechanical isolation: Morphological features such as size and incompatible genitalia prevent 2 members of different species from interbreeding.

Gametic isolation: Gametic transfer takes place, but the gametes fail to unite with each other. This can occur because the male and female gametes fail to attract, because they are unable to fuse, or because the male gametes are inviable in the female reproductive tract of another species. In plants, the pollen of one species usually cannot generate a pollen tube to fertilize the egg cells of another species.

↓ Fertilization

Postzygotic isolating mechanisms

Hybrid inviability: The egg of one species is fertilized by the sperm from another species, but the fertilized egg fails to develop past the early embryonic stages.

Hybrid sterility: An interspecies hybrid survives, but it is sterile. For example, the mule, which is sterile, is produced from a cross between a male donkey (*Equus asinus*) and a female horse (*Equus ferus caballus*).

Hybrid breakdown: The F_1 interspecies hybrid is viable and fertile, but succeeding generations (F_2, and so on) become increasingly inviable. This is usually due to the formation of less-fit genotypes by genetic recombination.

↓ Interspecies hybrid

Figure 24.2 Reproductive isolating mechanisms. These mechanisms prevent successful breeding between different species. They can occur prior to fertilization (prezygotic) or after fertilization (postzygotic).

 Core Skill: Connections Look back at Figure 23.9. Is female choice an example of a prezygotic or postzygotic isolating mechanism?

(a) Spring field cricket (*Gryllus veletis*)   **(b)** Fall field cricket (*Gryllus pennsylvanicus*)

Figure 24.3 Temporal isolation. Interbreeding between these two species of crickets does not usually occur because *Gryllus veletis* matures in the spring, whereas *Gryllus pennsylvanicus* matures in the fall. a: ©C. Allan Morgan/Getty Images; b: ©Bryan E. Reynolds

Concept Check: Is temporal isolation an example of a prezygotic or a postzygotic isolating mechanism?

do not differ in song or habitat and are morphologically very similar (**Figure 24.3**). How do the two species maintain reproductive isolation? *G. veletis* matures in the spring, whereas *G. pennsylvanicus* matures in the fall. This minimizes interbreeding between the two species.

Behavioral Isolation: In the case of animals, mating behavior and anatomy often play key roles in promoting reproductive isolation. An example of the third type of prezygotic isolation, behavioral isolation, separates the western meadowlark (*Sturnella neglecta*) and eastern meadowlark (*Sturnella magna*). Both species are nearly identical in shape, coloration, and habitat, and their ranges overlap in the central U.S. (**Figure 24.4**). For many years, they were thought to be the same species. When biologists discovered that the western meadowlark is a separate species, it was given the species name *S. neglecta* to reflect the long delay in its recognition. In the zone of overlap, very little interspecies mating takes place between western and eastern meadowlarks, largely due to differences in their songs. The song of the western meadowlark is a long series of flutelike gurgling notes that go down the scale. By comparison, the eastern meadowlark's song is a simple series of whistles, typically about four or five notes. These differences in songs enable meadowlarks to recognize potential mates as members of their own species.

Mechanical Isolation: A fourth type of prezygotic isolation, called mechanical isolation, occurs when morphological features such as size or incompatible genitalia prevent two species from interbreeding. For example, male dragonflies use a pair of special appendages to grasp females during copulation. When a male tries to mate with a female of a different species, his grasping appendages do not fit her body shape.

Gametic Isolation: A fifth type of prezygotic isolating mechanism occurs when two species attempt to interbreed, but the gametes fail to unite in a successful fertilization event. This phenomenon, called gametic isolation, is widespread among plant and animal species. In aquatic animals that release sperm and egg cells into the water, gametic isolation is important in preventing interspecies hybrids. For example, closely related species of sea urchins may release sperm and eggs into the water at the same time. Researchers have discovered that sea urchin sperm have a protein on their surface called bindin, which

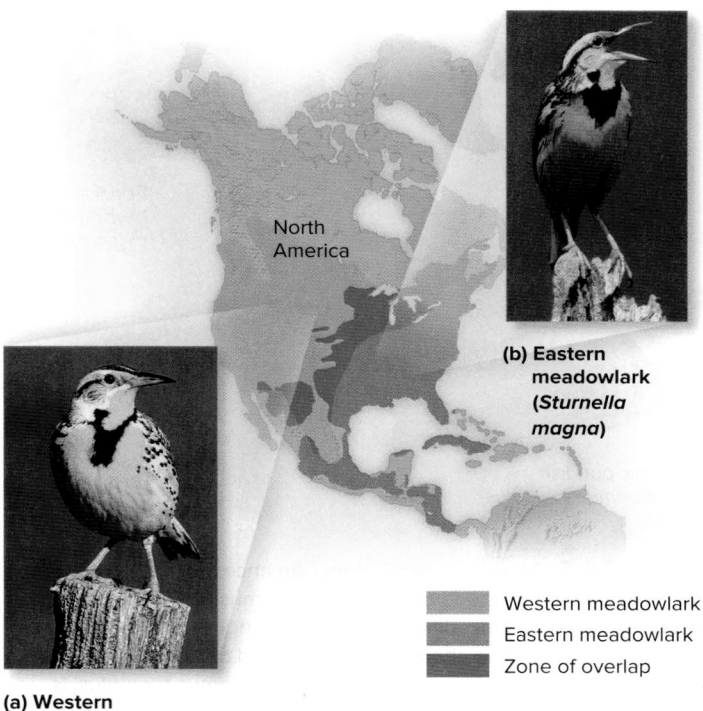

Western meadowlark
Eastern meadowlark
Zone of overlap

(a) Western meadowlark (*Sturnella neglecta*)

Figure 24.4 Behavioral isolation. (a) The western meadowlark (*Sturnella neglecta*) and **(b)** eastern meadowlark (*Sturnella magna*) are very similar in appearance. The red region in this map shows where the two species' ranges overlap. However, very little interspecies mating takes place due to differences in their songs. a: ©Rod Planck/ Science Source; b: ©Ron Austing/Science Source

 Core Concept: Evolution For these two species of meadowlarks, one evolutionary change that took place is that their mating songs became different.

mediates sperm-egg attachment and membrane fusion. The structure of bindin is significantly different among different sea urchin species, thereby ensuring that fertilization occurs only between sperm and egg cells of the same species.

In flowering plants, gametic isolation is commonly associated with pollination. As discussed in Chapter 40, plant fertilization is initiated when a pollen grain lands on the stigma of a flower and sprouts a pollen tube that ultimately reaches an egg cell (look ahead to Figure 40.4). When pollen is released from a plant, it could be transferred to the stigma of many different plant species. In most cases, when a pollen grain lands on the stigma of a different species, it either fails to generate a pollen tube or the tube does not grow properly and thus does not reach the egg cell.

Postzygotic Isolating Mechanisms Let's now turn to postzygotic mechanisms of reproductive isolation, of which there are three common types.

Hybrid Inviability: The mechanism of hybrid inviability occurs when an egg of one species is fertilized by a sperm from another species, but the fertilized egg cannot develop past the early embryonic stages.

Male donkey (*Equus asinus*) × **Female horse (*Equus ferus caballus*)**

Mule

Figure 24.5 Hybrid sterility. When a male donkey (*Equus asinus*) mates with a female horse (*Equus ferus caballus*), their offspring is a mule, which is usually sterile. (top left): ©Mark Boulton/Science Source; (top right): ©MyLoupe/UIG/Getty Images; (bottom): ©Stephen L. Saks/Science Source

Concept Check: *Is hybrid sterility an example of a prezygotic or a postzygotic isolating mechanism?*

Hybrid Sterility: A second postzygotic isolating mechanism is hybrid sterility, in which an interspecies hybrid may be viable but sterile. A classic example of hybrid sterility is the mule, which is produced by a mating between a male donkey (*Equus asinus*) and a female horse (*Equus ferus caballus*) (**Figure 24.5**). All male mules and most female mules are sterile. Why are mules usually sterile? Two reasons explain the sterility. Because the horse has 32 chromosomes per set and a donkey has 31, a mule inherits 63 chromosomes (32 + 31). Due to the uneven number, all of the chromosomes cannot pair evenly. Also, the chromosomes of the horse and donkey have structural differences, which either prevent them from pairing correctly or lead to chromosomal abnormalities if crossing over occurs during meiosis. For these reasons, mules usually produce inviable gametes. Note that the mule has no species name because it is not considered a species due to this sterility.

Hybrid Breakdown: Finally, interspecies hybrids may be viable and fertile, but the subsequent generation(s) may harbor genetic abnormalities that are detrimental. This third mechanism, called hybrid breakdown, can be caused by changes in chromosome structure. The chromosomes of closely related species may have structural differences from each other, such as inversions. In hybrids, a crossover may occur in the region that is inverted in one species but not the other. This will produce gametes with too little or too much genetic material. Such hybrids often have offspring with developmental abnormalities.

Postzygotic isolating mechanisms tend to be uncommon in nature compared with prezygotic mechanisms. Why are postzygotic mechanisms rare? One explanation is that they are more costly in terms

pass that connects two deer populations. For speciation to occur, the amount of gene flow within hybrid zones must become very limited. How does this happen? As the two populations accumulate different genetic changes, the ability of individuals from different populations to mate with each other in the hybrid zone may decrease. For example, natural selection in the western deer population may favor an increase in body size that is not favored in the eastern population. Over time, as this size difference between members of the

two populations becomes greater, breeding in the hybrid zone may decrease. Larger individuals may not interbreed easily with smaller ones due to mechanical isolation. In addition, larger individuals may prefer larger individuals as mates, and smaller individuals may also prefer each other. Once gene flow through the hybrid zone is greatly diminished, the two populations are reproductively isolated. Over the course of many generations, such populations may evolve into distinct species.

 **Core Skill: Process of Science**

Feature Investigation | Podos Found That an Adaptation for Feeding May Have Promoted Reproductive Isolation in Finches

In 2001, American evolutionary biologist Jeffrey Podos analyzed the songs of Darwin's finches on the Galápagos Islands to determine how environmental adaptation may contribute to reproductive isolation. As in honeycreepers, the differences in beak sizes and shapes among the various species of finches are adaptations to different feeding strategies. Podos hypothesized that changes in beak morphology could also affect the songs that the birds produce, thereby having the potential to affect mate choice. The components of the vocal tract of birds, including the trachea, larynx, and beak, work collectively to produce a bird's song. Birds actively modify the shape of their vocal tracts during singing, and beak movements are normally very rapid and precise.

Podos focused on two aspects of a bird's song. The first feature is the frequency range, which is a measure of the minimum and maximum frequencies in a bird's song, measured in kilohertz (kHz). The second feature is the trill rate. A trill is a series of notes or group of notes repeated in succession. **Figure 24.9** shows a graphical depiction of the songs of Darwin's finches. As you can see, the song patterns of these finches are quite different from each other

To study the relationship between beak size and song in a quantitative way, Podos first captured male finches on Santa Cruz, one of the Galápagos Islands, and measured their beak sizes (**Figure 24.10**).

The birds were banded and then released into the wild. The banding provided a way of identifying the birds whose beaks had already been measured. After release, the songs of the banded birds were recorded on a tape recorder, and their range of frequencies and trill rate were analyzed. Podos then compared the data for the Galápagos finches to a large body of data that had been collected on many other bird species. This comparison was used to evaluate whether beak size, in this case, beak depth—the measurement of the beak from top to bottom, at its base—constrained the frequency range and/or the trill rate of the finches.

The results of this comparison are shown in the data of Figure 24.10. As seen here, the relative constraint on vocal performance became higher as the beak depth became larger. This means that birds with larger beaks had a narrower frequency range and/or a slower trill rate. Podos proposed that as jaws and beaks became adapted for strength to crack open larger, harder seeds, they became less able to perform the rapid movements associated with certain types of songs. In contrast, the finches with smaller beaks adapted to probe for insects or eat smaller seeds had less constraint on their vocal performance. From the perspective of evolution, the changes observed in song patterns for the Galápagos finches could have played an important role in promoting reproductive isolation, because song pattern is an important factor in mate selection

Figure 24.9 Differences in the songs of Galápagos finches. These spectrograms depict the frequency of each bird's song over time, measured in kilohertz (kHz). The songs are produced in a series of trills that have a particular pattern and occur at regular intervals. Notice the differences in frequency and trill rate between different species of birds.

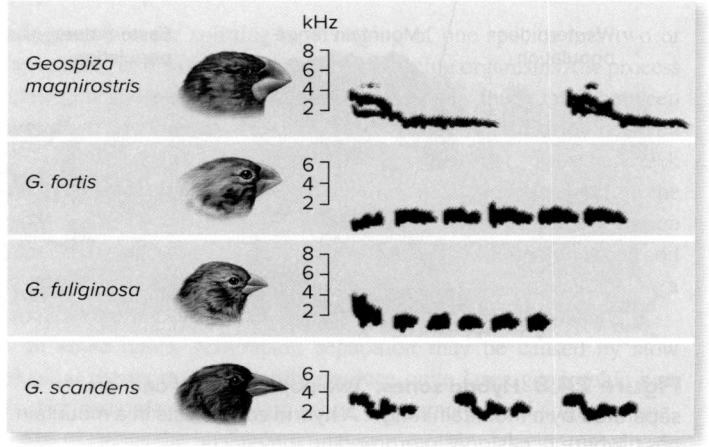

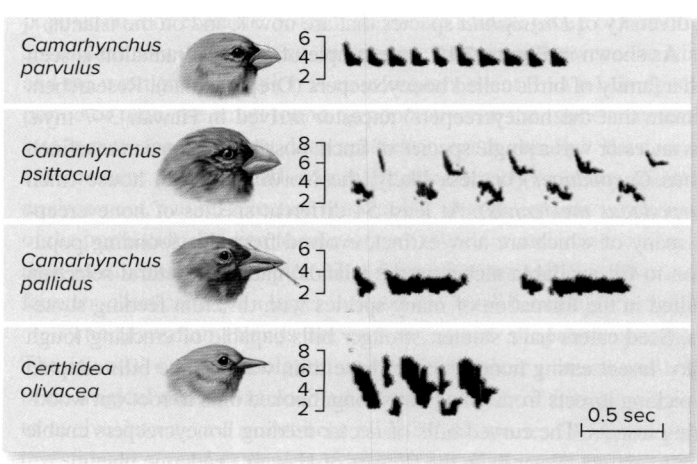

Figure 24.10 **Study by Podos investigating the effects of beak depth on song among different species of Galápagos finches.**

HYPOTHESIS Changes in beak morphology that are an adaptation for feeding may also affect the songs of Galápagos finches and thereby lead to reproductive isolation between species.

KEY MATERIALS This study was conducted on finch populations of the Galápagos Island of Santa Cruz.

Experimental level	Conceptual level

1 Capture male finches and measure their beak depth. Beak depth is measured at the base of the beak, from top to bottom.

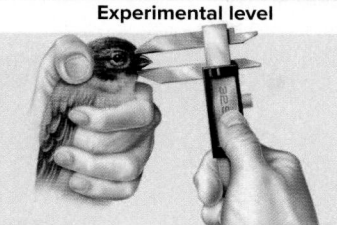

This is a measurement of phenotypic variation in beak size.

2 Band the birds and release them back into the wild.

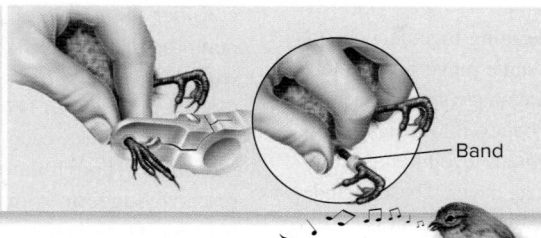

Band

Banding allows identification of birds with known beak depths.

3 Record the bird's songs on a tape recorder.

This is a measurement of phenotypic variation in song.

4 Analyze the songs with regard to frequency range and trill rate.

kHz

Time

The frequency range is the value between high and low frequencies. The trill rate is the number of repeats per unit time.

5   **THE DATA**

The data for the Galápagos finches were compared to a large body of data that had been collected on many other bird species. The relative constraint on vocal performance is higher if a bird has a narrower frequency range and/or a slower trill rate. These constraints were analyzed with regard to each bird's beak depth.

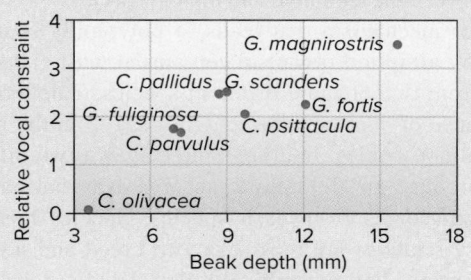

6   **CONCLUSION** Larger beak size, which is an adaptation to cracking open large, hard seeds, constrains vocal performance. This may affect mating song patterns and thereby promote reproductive isolation and, in turn, speciation.

7   **SOURCE** Podos, J. 2001. Correlated evolution of morphology and vocal signal structure in Darwin's finches. *Nature* 409: 185–188.

in birds. Therefore, a by-product of beak adaptation for feeding is that it also appears to have affected song pattern, possibly promoting reproductive isolation and eventually the formation of distinct species.

Experimental Questions

1. What did Podos hypothesize regarding the effects of beak size on a bird's song? How could changes in beak size and shape lead to reproductive isolation among the finches?

2. **CoreSKILL** » How did Podos test the hypothesis that beak morphology caused changes in the birds' songs?

3. **CoreSKILL** » Analyze the results of Podos's study, and explain whether they support his original hypothesis. What is meant by the phrase "by-product of adaptation," and how does it apply to this particular study?

Sympatric Speciation Occurs When Populations Are in Direct Contact

Sympatric speciation (from the Greek *sym*, meaning together) occurs when members of a species that are within the same range diverge into two or more different species even though there are no physical barriers to interbreeding. Although sympatric speciation is believed to be less common than allopatric speciation, particularly in animals, evolutionary biologists have discovered several ways in which it can occur. These include polyploidy, adaptation to local environments, and sexual selection.

Polyploidy   A type of genetic change that can cause immediate reproductive isolation is **polyploidy**, in which an organism has more than two sets of chromosomes. Plants tend to be more tolerant of changes in chromosome number than animals. For example, many crops and decorative species of plants are polyploid. How does polyploidy occur? One mechanism is complete nondisjunction of chromosomes, which increases the number of chromosome sets in a given species (autopolyploidy). Such changes can result in an abrupt sympatric speciation. For example, nondisjunction could produce a tetraploid plant with four sets of chromosomes from a species that was diploid with two sets. A cross between a tetraploid and a diploid produces a triploid offspring with three sets of chromosomes. Triploid offspring are usually sterile because an odd number of chromosomes cannot be evenly segregated during meiosis. This hybrid sterility causes reproductive isolation between the tetraploid and diploid species.

Another mechanism that leads to polyploidy is interspecies breeding. An **alloploid** organism contains at least one set of chromosomes from two or more different species. This term refers to the occurrence of chromosome sets (ploidy) from the genomes of different (allo-) species. Interbreeding between two different species may produce an allodiploid, an organism that has only one set of chromosomes from each species. Species that are close evolutionary relatives are most likely to breed and produce allodiploid offspring. For example, closely related species of grasses may interbreed to produce allodiploids. An organism containing two or more complete sets of chromosomes from two or more different species is called an allopolyploid. An allopolyploid can be the result of interspecies breeding between species that are already polyploid, or it can occur as a result of nondisjunction in an allodiploid organism. For example, complete nondisjunction in an allodiploid could produce an allotetraploid, which is an allopolyploid with two complete sets of chromosomes from two species for a total of four sets.

The formation of an allopolyploid can also abruptly lead to reproductive isolation, thereby promoting speciation. As an example, let's consider the origin of a natural species of plant called the common hemp nettle, *Galeopsis tetrahit*. This species is thought to be an allotetraploid derived from two diploid species, *Galeopsis pubescens* and *Galeopsis speciosa* (**Figure 24.11a**). These two diploid species have 16 chromosomes each ($2n = 16$), whereas *G. tetrahit* has 32 chromosomes. Though the origin of *G. tetrahit* is not completely certain, research suggests it may have originated from an interspecies cross between *G. pubescens* and *G. speciosa*, which initially produced an allodiploid with 16 chromosomes (one set from each species). The allodiploid then underwent complete nondisjunction to become an allotetraploid carrying four sets of chromosomes—two from each species.

How do these genetic changes cause reproductive isolation? The allotetraploid, *G. tetrahit*, is fertile, because all of its chromosomes occur in homologous pairs that can segregate evenly during meiosis. However, a cross between *G. tetrahit* and a diploid, *G. pubescens* or *G. speciosa*, produces an offspring that is monoploid for one chromosome set and diploid for the other set (**Figure 24.11b**). The chromosomes of the monoploid set cannot be evenly segregated during meiosis. These offspring are expected to be sterile, because they will produce gametes that have incomplete sets of chromosomes. This hybrid sterility causes the allotetraploid to be reproductively isolated from both diploid species. Therefore, this process could have led to the formation of a new species, *G. tetrahit*, by sympatric speciation.

Polyploidy is so frequent in plants that it is a major mechanism of their speciation. In ferns and flowering plants, about 40–70% of the species are polyploid. By comparison, polyploidy can occur in animals, but it is much less common. For example, less than 1% of reptiles and amphibians are polyploids derived from diploid ancestors. The reason why polyploidy is not usually tolerated in animals is not understood.

Adaptation to Local Environments   In some cases, populations that occupy different local environments, which are continuous with each other, may diverge into different species. An early example of this type of sympatric speciation was described by American biologists Jeffrey Feder, Guy Bush, and colleagues. They studied the North American apple maggot fly (*Rhagoletis pomenella*). This fly originally fed on native hawthorn trees. However, the introduction of apple trees approximately 200 years ago provided a new local environment for this species. The apple-feeding populations of this species develop more rapidly because apples mature more quickly than hawthorn fruit. The result is partial temporal isolation, which is an

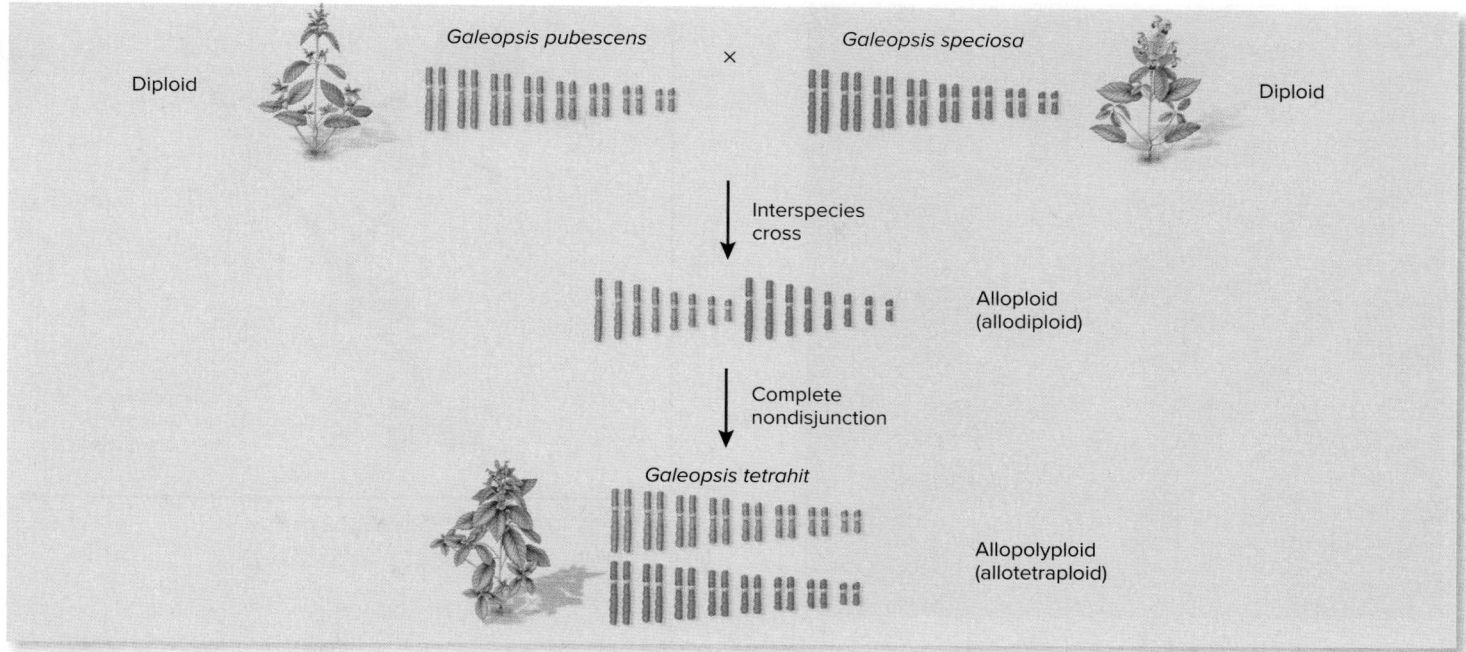

(a) Possible formation of G. tetrahit

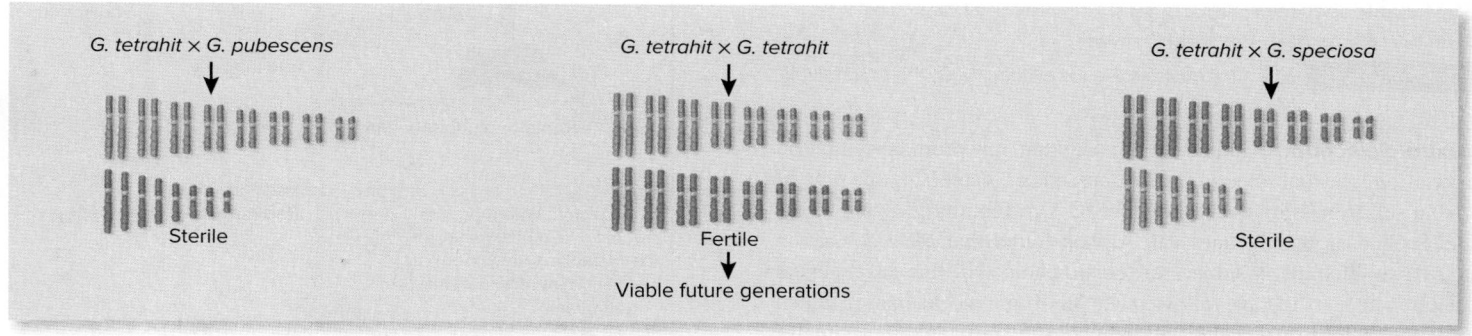

(b) Outcome of breeding among G. tetrahit, G. pubescens, and G. speciosa

Figure 24.11 **Polyploidy and sympatric speciation.** **(a)** *Galeopsis tetrahit* may have arisen from an interspecies cross between *Galeopsis pubescens* and *Galeopsis speciosa*, which was followed by a subsequent nondisjunction event. **(b)** Polyploidy may have caused reproductive isolation between these three natural species of hemp nettle. If *G. tetrahit* is crossed with either of the other two species, the resulting offspring will be monoploid for one chromosome set and diploid for the other set, making them sterile. Therefore, *G. tetrahit* is reproductively isolated from the diploid species, making it a new species.

Concept Check: *Suppose that G. tetrahit was crossed to G. pubescens to produce an interspecies hybrid, as shown at the left side of part (b). If this interspecies hybrid was crossed to G. tetrahit, how many chromosomes do you think an offspring would have? The answer you give should be a range, not a single number.*

example of a prezygotic isolating mechanism. Although the two populations—those that feed on apple trees and those that feed on hawthorn trees—are considered subspecies, evolutionary biologists speculate they may eventually become distinct species due to reproductive isolation and the accumulation of independent mutations.

American entomologist Sara Via and colleagues have studied the beginnings of sympatric speciation in pea aphids (*Acyrthosiphon pisum*), a small, plant-eating insect. Pea aphids in the same geographic area can be found on both alfalfa (*Medicago sativa*) and red clover (*Trifolium pratenae*) (**Figure 24.12**). Although pea aphids on these two host plants look identical, they show significant genetic differences and are highly ecologically specialized. Pea aphids that are found on alfalfa exhibit a lower fitness when transferred to red clover, whereas pea aphids found on red clover exhibit a lower fitness when transferred to alfalfa. The same traits involved in this host specialization cause these two groups of pea aphids to be substantially reproductively isolated. Taken together, the observations of the North American apple maggot fly, pea aphids, and other insect species suggest that diversifying selection (described in Chapter 23) occurs because some members within the same range evolve to feed on a different host. This may be an important mechanism of sympatric speciation among insects.

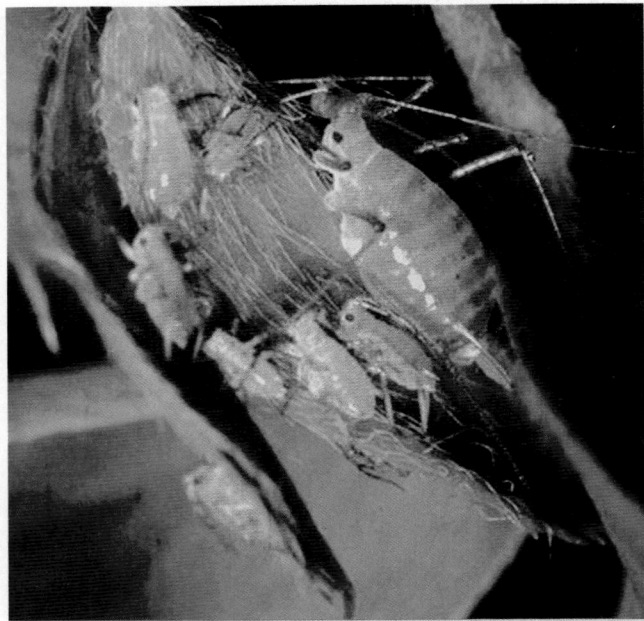

Figure 24.12 Pea aphids, a possible example of sympatric speciation in progress. Some pea aphids prefer alfalfa, whereas others prefer red clover. These two populations may be in the process of sympatric speciation. (left): ©Dr. Sara Via, Department of Biology and Department of Entomology, University of Maryland

Concept Check: *How may host preference eventually lead to speciation?*

Sexual Selection Another mechanism that may promote sympatric speciation is sexual selection. As discussed in Chapter 23, one type of sexual selection is mate choice (refer back to Figures 23.8 and 23.9). Ole Seehausen and Jacques van Alphen found that male coloration in African cichlids is subject to female choice. In this case, sexual selection appears to have followed a diversifying mechanism in which certain females prefer males with one color pattern and other females prefer males with a different color pattern. A possible outcome of such sexual selection is that it can separate one large sympatric population into smaller populations that eventually become distinct species because they selectively breed among themselves.

24.3 The Pace of Speciation

Learning Outcome:

1. Compare and contrast the concepts of gradualism and punctuated equilibrium.

Throughout the history of life on Earth, the rate of evolutionary change and speciation has not been constant. **Figure 24.13** illustrates two contrasting views concerning the rate of evolutionary change. These ideas are not mutually exclusive but represent two different ways to consider the tempo of evolution. The concept of **gradualism** suggests that each new species evolves continuously over long spans of time (Figure 24.13a). The principal idea is that large phenotypic differences that produce new species are due to the gradual accumulation of many small genetic changes.

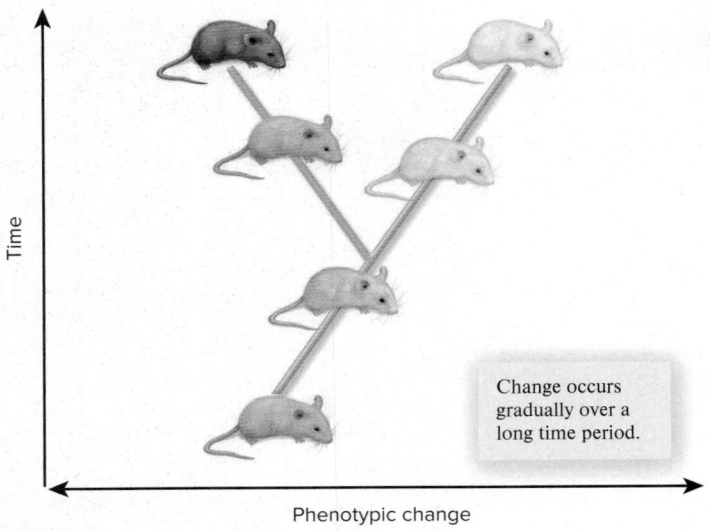

Change occurs gradually over a long time period.

(a) Gradualism

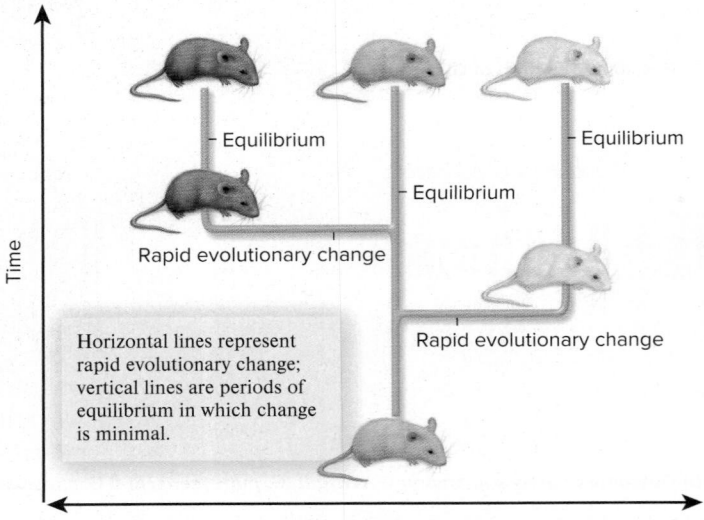

Equilibrium

Equilibrium

Equilibrium

Rapid evolutionary change

Rapid evolutionary change

Horizontal lines represent rapid evolutionary change; vertical lines are periods of equilibrium in which change is minimal.

(b) Punctuated equilibrium

Figure 24.13 A comparison of gradualism and punctuated equilibrium. **(a)** In gradualism, the phenotypic characteristics of a species gradually change due to the accumulation of small genetic changes. **(b)** In punctuated equilibrium, long periods of equilibrium in which species exist essentially unchanged are punctuated by relatively short periods of evolutionary change during which phenotypic characteristics may change rapidly.

 Core Concept: Evolution Gradualism and punctuated equilibrium are two different views regarding the pace of evolution.

By comparison, the concept of **punctuated equilibrium**, advocated in the 1970s by American paleontologist Niles Eldredge and American evolutionary biologist Stephen Jay Gould, suggests that the tempo of evolution is more sporadic (Figure 24.13b). According to this hypothesis, species exist relatively unchanged for many generations. During this equilibrium period, genetic changes are likely to accumulate, particularly neutral changes. However, genetic changes that significantly alter phenotype do not substantially change the overall composition of a population. These long periods of equilibria are punctuated by relatively short periods (that is, on a geological timescale) during which the frequencies of certain phenotypes in a population change substantially at a far more rapid rate.

A rapid rate of evolution could commonly occur via allopatric speciation, in which a small group migrates away from a larger population to a new environment in which different alleles provide better adaptation to the surroundings. By natural selection, the small population may rapidly evolve into a new species. In addition, events such as polyploidy may abruptly produce individuals with new phenotypic traits. On an evolutionary timescale, these types of events can be rather rapid, because a few genetic changes can have a major influence on phenotype.

In conjunction with genetic changes, species may also be subjected to sudden environmental shifts that quickly drive the gene pool in a particular direction via natural selection. For example, the climate may change or a new predator may infiltrate the geographic range of a species. Natural selection may lead to a rapid evolution of the gene pool by favoring those alleles that allow members of the population to survive the climatic change or to have phenotypic characteristics that allow them to avoid the predator.

Which viewpoint is correct, punctuated equilibrium or gradualism? Both have merit. The occurrence of punctuated equilibrium is often supported by the fossil record. New species seem to arise rather suddenly in a layer of rocks, persist relatively unchanged for a very long period of time, and then become extinct. In such cases, scientists hypothesize that the period during which a previous species evolved into a new species was so short that few, if any, of the transitional forms of the species were preserved as fossils. Even so, these rapid periods of change were probably followed by long periods that likely involved the additional accumulation of many small genetic changes, consistent with gradualism.

Finally, another issue associated with the speed of speciation is generation time. Species of large animals with long generation times tend to evolve much more slowly than do microbial species with short generations. Many new species of bacteria will come into existence during our lifetime, whereas new species of large animals tend to arise on a much longer timescale. This is an important consideration because bacteria have great environmental effects. They are decomposers of organic materials and pollutants in the environment, and they play a role in many diseases of plants and animals, including humans.

24.4   Evo-Devo: Evolutionary Developmental Biology

Learning Outcomes:

1. Describe how the spatial expression of genes, such as *BMP4* and *Gremlin*, affects pattern formation.
2. Explain the relationship between the number of *Hox* genes and the body pattern of an animal species.

3. Outline how differences in the growth rates of body parts can change the characteristics of species.
4. Describe how the study of the *Pax6* gene suggests that the eyes of different animal species evolved from a common ancestor.

As described earlier in this chapter, the origin of new species involves genetic changes that lead to adaptations to environmental niches and/or to reproductive isolating mechanisms that prevent closely related species from interbreeding. These genetic changes result in morphological and physiological differences that distinguish one species from another. In recent years, many evolutionary biologists have begun to investigate how genetic variation produces species and groups of species with novel shapes and forms. The underlying reasons for such changes are often rooted in the developmental pathways that control an organism's morphology.

Evolutionary developmental biology (referred to as **evo-devo**) is an exciting and relatively new field of biology that compares the development of different organisms in an attempt to understand ancestral relationships between organisms and the mechanisms that bring about evolutionary change. During the past few decades, developmental geneticists have gained a better understanding of biological development at the molecular level. Much of this work has involved the discovery of genes that control development in model organisms. As the genomes of more organisms have been analyzed, researchers have become interested in the similarities and differences that occur between closely related and distantly related species. The field of evolutionary developmental biology arose out of this interest.

How do new morphological forms come into being? For example, how does a nonwebbed foot evolve into a webbed foot? How does a new organ, such as an eye, come into existence? As we will explore, such novelty arises through genetic changes, also called genetic innovations. Certain types of genetic innovations have been so advantageous they have resulted in groups of new species. For example, the innovation of wings resulted in the evolution of many different species of birds. In this section, we will see that proteins that control developmental changes, such as cell-signaling proteins and transcription factors, often play a key role in promoting the morphological changes that occur during evolution.

The Spatial Expression of Genes That Affect Development Has a Dramatic Effect on Phenotype

In Chapter 20, we considered the role of genetics in the development of plants and animals. Genes that play a role in development influence cell division, cell migration, cell differentiation, and cell death. The interplay among these four processes produces an organism with a specific body pattern, a process called **pattern formation**. As you might imagine, genes that control development are very important to the phenotypes of individuals. They affect traits such as the shape of a bird's beak, the length of a giraffe's neck, and the size of a plant's flower. In recent years, the study of development has revealed that particular genes are key players in the evolution of many types of traits. Changes in such genes affect traits that can be acted on by natural selection. Furthermore, variation in the expression of these genes may be commonly involved in the acquisition of new traits that promote speciation.

As an example, let's compare pattern formation of a chicken's foot with that of a duck's foot. Two different patterns occur: a nonwebbed pattern in which the digits are not inconnected, and a webbed pattern in which the digits are connected by sheets of skin. Developmental biologists have discovered that the morphological differences between a nonwebbed and a webbed pattern are due to the differential expression of two different cell-signaling proteins called bone morphogenetic protein 4 (BMP4) and gremlin. The *BMP4* gene is expressed throughout the developing limb of both the chicken and duck; this is shown in **Figure 24.14a**, in which the BMP4 protein is stained purple. BMP4 causes cells to undergo apoptosis and die. The gremlin protein, which is stained brown in **Figure 24.14b**, inhibits the function of BMP4, thereby allowing cells to survive. In the developing chicken limb, the *Gremlin* gene is expressed throughout the limb, except in the regions between each digit. Therefore, in these regions, the cells die, and a chicken develops a nonwebbed foot (**Figure 24.14c**). By comparison, in the duck, *Gremlin* is expressed throughout the entire limb, including the interdigit regions, and the duck develops a webbed foot. Interestingly, researchers have been able to introduce gremlin protein into the interdigit regions of developing chicken limbs. This produces a chicken with webbed feet!

How are these observations related to evolution? During the evolution of birds, genetic variation arose such that some individuals expressed the *Gremlin* gene in the regions between each digit, but others did not. This variation determined whether or not a bird's feet were webbed. In terrestrial settings, having nonwebbed feet is an advantage because it enables the individual to hold onto perches, run along the ground, and snatch prey. Therefore, natural selection would favor nonwebbed feet in terrestrial environments. This process explains the occurrence of nonwebbed feet in chickens, hawks, crows, and many other terrestrial birds. In aquatic environments, however, webbed feet are an advantage because they act as paddles for swimming, so genetic variation that produced webbed feet in aquatic birds would have been acted on by natural selection. Over time, this gave rise to the webbed feet now found in a wide variety of aquatic birds, including ducks, geese, and penguins.

The *Hox* Genes Have Been Important in the Evolution of a Variety of Body Patterns

The study of developmental genes has revealed interesting trends among large groups of species. *Hox* genes, which are discussed in Chapter 20, are found in nearly all animals, indicating that they originated very early in animal evolution. *Hox* genes are homeotic genes, which specify the fate of a particular segment or region of the body. Developmental biologists have hypothesized that variation in the *Hox* genes has spawned the formation of many new body patterns. As shown in **Figure 24.15**, the number and arrangement of *Hox* genes vary considerably among different types of animals. Sponges, the simplest of animals, have at least one gene that is homologous to *Hox* genes. Insects typically have nine or more *Hox* genes. In most cases, multiple *Hox* genes occur in a cluster, lying

Chicken   Duck

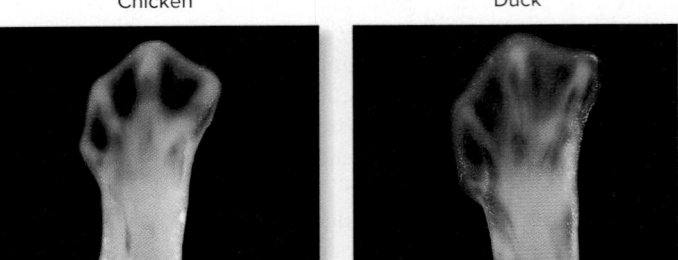

(a) BMP4 protein levels—similar expression in chicken and duck

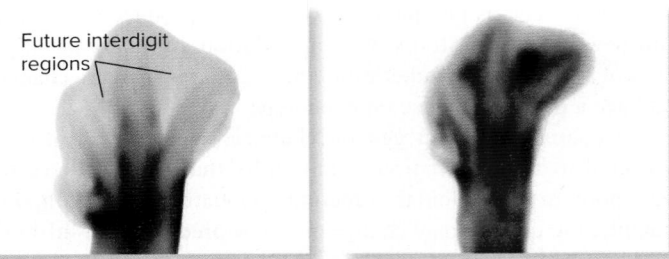

Future interdigit regions

(b) Gremlin protein levels—not expressed in interdigit regions in chicken

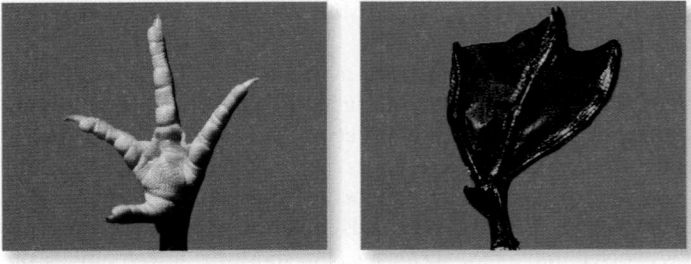

(c) Comparison of a chicken foot and a duck foot

Figure 24.14   The role of cell-signaling proteins in the pattern formation of birds' feet. This figure shows how changes in gene expression can affect webbing between the toes. **(a)** Expression of the *BMP4* gene in the developing limbs. BMP4 protein is stained purple here and is expressed throughout the limb. **(b)** Expression of the *Gremlin* gene in the developing limbs. Gremlin protein is stained brown here. Note that *Gremlin* is not expressed in the interdigit regions of the chicken but is expressed in these regions of the duck. Gremlin inhibits the ability of BMP4 to cause programmed cell death. **(c)** Because BMP4 is not inhibited in the interdigit regions in the chicken, the cells in this region die, and the foot is not webbed. By comparison, inhibition of BMP4 in the interdigit regions in the duck results in a webbed foot.

a (left and right): Zou, H. and NISWANDER, L. 1996. Requirement for BMP signaling in interdigital apoptosis and scale formation. *Science* 272: 738–741. PMID: 8614838; b (left and right): Courtesy Ed Laufer; c (left): Courtesy of Dr. J. M. Hurle 1999. Originally published in *Development* 126(23):5515–22; c (right): Courtesy of Dr. J. M. Hurle 1999. Originally published in *Development* 126(23):5515–23

Concept Check: *What would you expect to happen to the pattern of the feet of ducks if the Gremlin gene was underexpressed?*

close to each other along a chromosome. In mammals, *Hox* gene clusters have been duplicated twice during the course of evolution to form four clusters, all slightly different, containing a total of 39 genes.

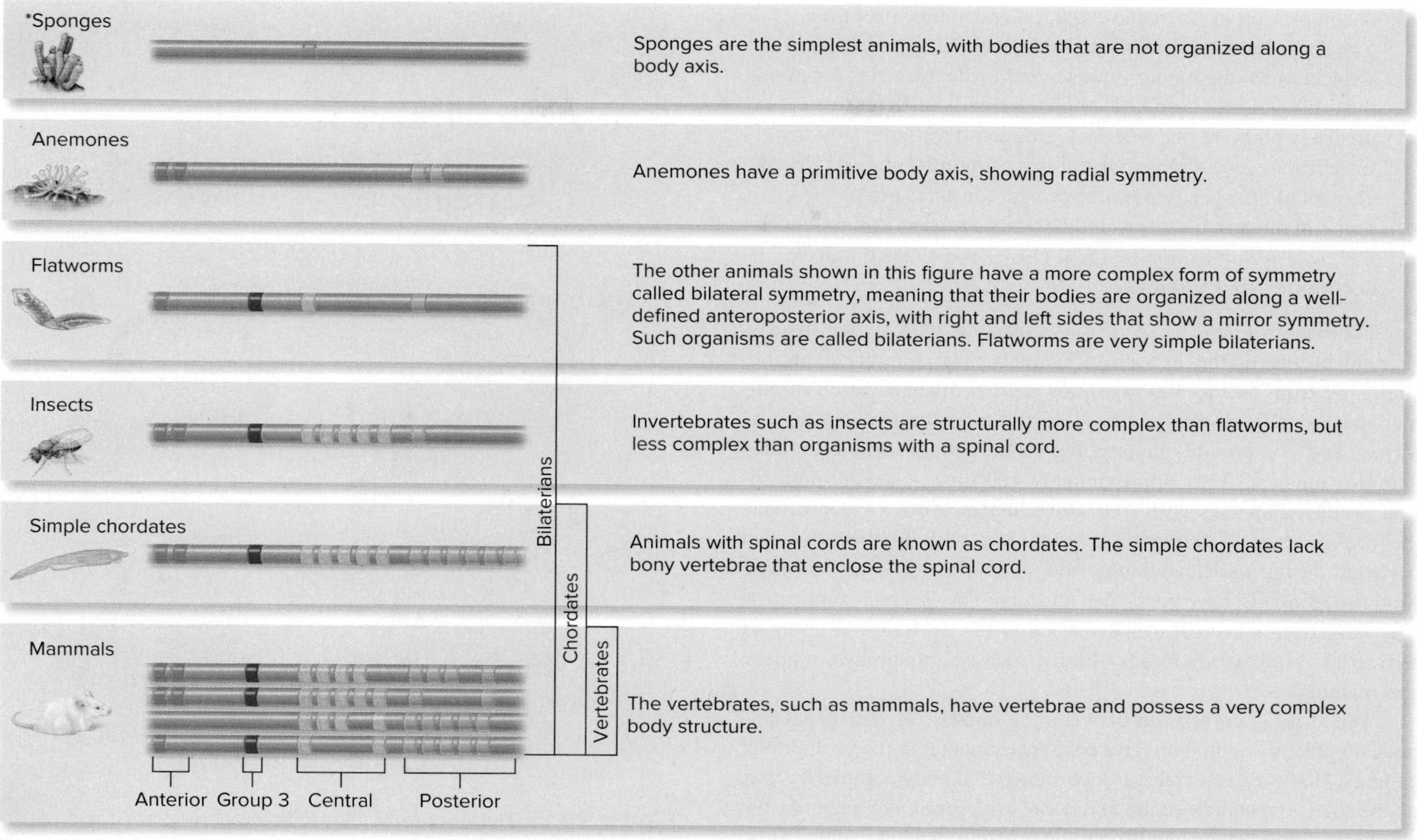

*Sponges
Sponges are the simplest animals, with bodies that are not organized along a body axis.

Anemones
Anemones have a primitive body axis, showing radial symmetry.

Flatworms
The other animals shown in this figure have a more complex form of symmetry called bilateral symmetry, meaning that their bodies are organized along a well-defined anteroposterior axis, with right and left sides that show a mirror symmetry. Such organisms are called bilaterians. Flatworms are very simple bilaterians.

Insects
Invertebrates such as insects are structurally more complex than flatworms, but less complex than organisms with a spinal cord.

Simple chordates
Animals with spinal cords are known as chordates. The simple chordates lack bony vertebrae that enclose the spinal cord.

Mammals
The vertebrates, such as mammals, have vertebrae and possess a very complex body structure.

Bilaterians

Chordates

Vertebrates

Anterior   Group 3   Central   Posterior

*Sponges are early diverging animals with no true tissues. They do not have true *Hox* genes, though they have an evolutionarily related gene called an *NK-like* gene.

Figure 24.15 *Hox* **gene number and body complexity in different types of animals.**   Researchers speculate that the duplication of *Hox* genes and *Hox* gene clusters played a key role in the evolution of more complex body patterns in animals. A correlation is observed between increasing numbers of *Hox* genes and increasing complexity of body patterns. The *Hox* genes are divided into four groups, called anterior, group 3, central, and posterior, based on their relative similarities. Each group is represented with a different color in this figure.

 Core Skill: Connections Look back at Figures 20.16 and 20.17. How is the expression of Hox genes related to segmentation and development along the anteroposterior axis?

Researchers propose that increases in the number of *Hox* genes have been instrumental in the evolution of many animal species whose body structures show greater complexity. To understand how, let's first consider *Hox* gene function. All *Hox* genes encode transcription factors that act as master control proteins for directing the formation of particular regions of the body. Each *Hox* gene controls a hierarchy of many regulatory genes that control the expression of genes encoding proteins that ultimately affect the morphology of the organism. The evolution of complex body patterns is associated with an increase not only in the number of regulatory genes—as evidenced by the increase in *Hox* gene complexity during evolution—but also in genes that encode proteins that directly affect an organism's form and function.

How would an increase in *Hox* genes enable more complex body patterns to evolve? Part of the answer lies in the spatial expression of the *Hox* genes. Different *Hox* genes are expressed in different regions of the body along the anteroposterior axis (refer back to **Figure 20.16**). Therefore, an increase in the number of *Hox* genes allows each of

these master control genes to become more specialized in the region that it controls. In fruit flies, one segment in the middle of the body can be controlled by a particular *Hox* gene and form wings and legs, whereas a segment in the head region can be controlled by a different *Hox* gene and develop antennae. Therefore, research suggests that one way for new, more complex body patterns to evolve is by increasing the number of *Hox* genes, thereby making it possible to form many specialized parts of the body that are organized along a body axis.

Three lines of evidence support the idea that increases in *Hox* gene number have been instrumental in the evolution and speciation of animals with more complex body patterns.

- As discussed in Chapter 20, *Hox* genes are known to control the fate of regions along the anteroposterior axis.

- As shown in Figure 24.15, a general trend is observed in which animals with a more complex body structure tend to have more *Hox* genes and *Hox* clusters in their genomes than do simpler animals.

- A comparison of *Hox* gene evolution and animal evolution reveals striking parallels. Researchers have analyzed *Hox* gene sequences among modern species and made estimates regarding the timing of past events. Though the date is difficult to precisely pinpoint, the first *Hox* gene arose well over 600 mya. In addition, gene duplications of this primordial gene produced clusters of *Hox* genes in other species. Clusters such as those found in modern insects were likely to be present approximately 600 mya. A duplication of a *Hox* cluster is estimated to have occurred around 520 mya.

Estimates of *Hox* gene origins correlate with major diversification events in the history of animals. The Cambrian period, stretching from 543 to 490 mya, saw a great diversification of animal species. This diversification occurred after the *Hox* cluster was formed and was possibly undergoing its first duplication to produce two *Hox* clusters. Also, approximately 420 mya, a second duplication produced species with four *Hox* clusters. This event preceded the proliferation of tetrapods—vertebrates with four limbs—that occurred during the Devonian period, approximately 417–354 mya. Modern tetrapods have four *Hox* clusters. This second duplication may have been a critical event that led to the evolution of complex terrestrial vertebrates with four limbs, such as amphibians, reptiles, and mammals.

The striking correlation between the number of *Hox* genes and body complexity is thought have been instrumental in the evolution of animals. However, research has also shown that body complexity may not be solely dependent on the number of *Hox* genes. For example, the number of *Hox* clusters in most tetrapods is four, whereas some fishes, which do not have more complex bodies than tetrapods, have seven or eight *Hox* clusters. In addition, researchers have discovered that specialized body structures can be formed by influencing the regulation of *Hox* genes and the other genes that are controlled by *Hox* genes. These findings indicate that changes in body complexity do not always have to be related to the total number of *Hox* genes or *Hox* clusters.

Variation in Growth Rates Can Have a Dramatic Effect on Phenotype

Another way that genetic variation can influence morphology is by controlling the relative growth rates of different parts of the body during development. The term **heterochrony** refers to differences among species in the rate or timing of developmental events. The speeding up or slowing down of growth appears to be a common occurrence in evolution and leads to different species with striking morphological differences. With regard to the pace of evolution, such changes may rapidly lead to the formation of new species.

As an example, **Figure 24.16** compares the progressive growth of human and chimpanzee skulls. At the fetal stage, the sizes and shapes of the skulls look fairly similar. However, after this stage, the relative growth rates of certain regions become markedly different, thereby affecting the shape and size of the adult skull. In the chimpanzee, the jaw region grows faster, giving the adult chimpanzee a much larger and longer jaw. In the human, the jaw grows more slowly, and the region of the skull that surrounds the brain—the cranium—grows faster. The result is that adult humans have a smaller jaw but a larger cranium than adult chimpanzees.

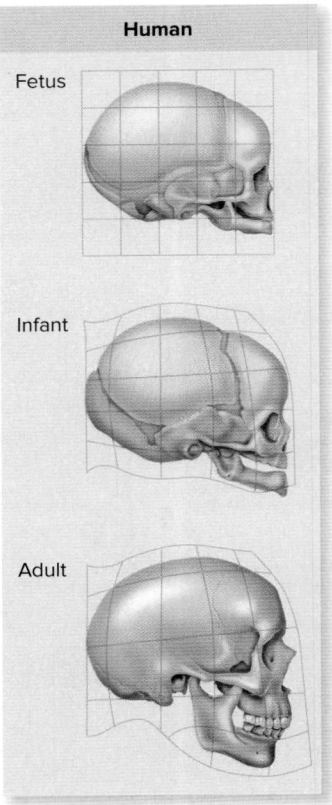
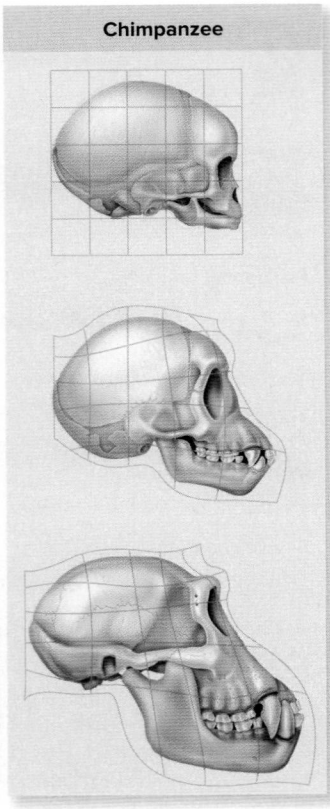

Figure 24.16 Heterochrony. Due to heterochrony, one region of the body may grow faster than another during development in different species. For example, the skulls of adult chimpanzees and humans have different shapes even though their fetal skull shapes are quite similar.

 Core Skill: Modeling The goal of this modeling challenge is to make a series of models that show the differences in limb lengths among orangutans, chimpanzees, and humans.

Modeling Challenge: Search the Internet and look at photos of orangutans, chimpanzees, and humans. Even though these species look similar, one noticeable difference is the relative lengths of their limbs. Although the limbs in an early fetus look similar in all three species, the limbs in the adults show significant differences in their relative lengths. Draw models, similar to those in **Figure 24.16**, that show an early fetus, infant, and adult for all three species. Include an explanation of how heterochrony affects limb development.

 **Core Concept: Evolution**

The Study of the *Pax6* Gene Indicates That Different Types of Eyes Evolved from One Simple Form

Thus far in this section, we have focused on the roles of particular genes as they influence the development of species with different body structures. Explaining how a complex organ comes into existence is another major challenge for evolutionary biologists. Although it is relatively easy to comprehend how a limb could undergo evolutionary modifications to become a wing, flipper, or arm, it is more difficult to understand how a body structure, such as a limb, comes into being in the first place. In his book *The Origin of Species*, Darwin addressed this question and admitted that the evolution and development of a complex organ such as the eye was difficult to understand.

As noted by Darwin, the eyes of vertebrate species are exceedingly complex, being able to adjust focus, let in different amounts of light, and detect a spectrum of colors. Darwin speculated that such complex eyes must have evolved from a simpler structure through the process of descent with modification. With amazing insight, he suggested that a very simple eye would be composed of two cell types, a photoreceptor cell and an adjacent pigment cell. The photoreceptor cell, which is a type of nerve cell, is able to absorb light and respond to it. The function of the pigment cell is to stop the light from reaching one side of the photoreceptor cell. This primitive, two-cell arrangement would allow an organism to sense both light and the direction from which the light comes.

A primitive eye would provide an additional way for an organism to sense its environment, possibly allowing it to avoid predators or locate food. Vision is nearly universal among animals, which indicates a strong selective advantage for eyesight. Over time, eyes could become more complex by enhancement of the ability to absorb different amounts and wavelengths of light and also by refinements in structures such as the addition of lenses that focus the incoming light.

Since the time of Darwin, many evolutionary biologists have wrestled with the question of eye evolution. From an anatomical point of view, researchers have discovered many different types of eyes. For example, the eyes of fruit flies, squid, and humans are quite different from each other. This observation led Austrian zoologist Luitfried von Salvini-Plawen and German evolutionary biologist Ernst Mayr to propose that eyes may have independently arisen multiple times during evolution. Based solely on morphology, such a hypothesis seemed reasonable and for many years was accepted by the scientific community.

The situation took a dramatic turn when geneticists began to study eye development. Researchers identified a master control gene, *Pax6*.[*] The protein encoded by the *Pax6* gene is a transcription factor that controls the expression of many other genes, including those involved in the development of the eye in both rodents and humans. In mice and rats, a mutation in the *Pax6* gene results in small eyes. A mutation in the human *Pax6* gene causes an eye disorder called aniridia, in which the iris and other structures of the eye do not develop properly. Similarly, *Drosophila* has a gene named *eyeless* that also causes a defect in eye development when mutant. *Eyeless* and *Pax6* are homologous genes; they are derived from the same ancestral gene.

In 1995, Swiss geneticist Walter Gehring and his colleagues were able to show experimentally that the expression of the

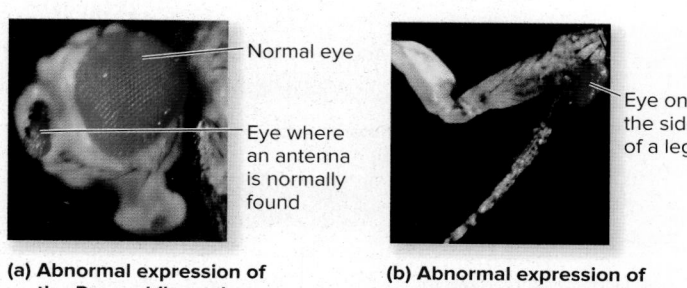

(a) Abnormal expression of the *Drosophila eyeless* gene in the antenna region

(b) Abnormal expression of the mouse *Pax6* gene in a fruit fly leg

Figure 24.17 **Formation of additional eyes in *Drosophila* due to the abnormal expression of a master control gene for eye morphogenesis. (a)** When the *Drosophila eyeless* gene is expressed in the antenna region, eyes are formed where antennae should be located. **(b)** When the mouse *Pax6* gene is expressed in the leg region of *Drosophila,* a small eye is formed there. a–b: ©Prof. Walter J. Gehring, University of Basel

Concept Check: *What do you think would happen if the Drosophila eyeless gene was expressed at the tip of a mouse's tail?*

eyeless gene in parts of *Drosophila* where it is normally inactive could promote the formation of additional eyes. For example, using genetic engineering techniques, they were able to express the *eyeless* gene in the region where antennae should form. As seen in **Figure 24.17a**, this resulted in the formation of an eye where antennae are normally found! Remarkably, the expression of the mouse *Pax6* gene in *Drosophila* can also cause the formation of eyes in unusual places. For example, **Figure 24.17b** shows the formation of an eye on the leg of *Drosophila*.

Note that when the mouse *Pax6* gene switches on eye formation in *Drosophila*, the eye produced is a *Drosophila* eye, not a mouse eye. Why does this occur? It happens because the *Pax6* gene activates genes from the *Drosophila* genome. In *Drosophila*, the *Pax6* homolog called *eyeless* switches on a cascade involving several hundred genes required for eye morphogenesis.

Since the discovery of the *Pax6* and *eyeless* genes, homologs of this gene have been discovered in many different species. In all cases where it has been tested, the homologous gene is involved with eye development. Gehring and colleagues have hypothesized that the eyes of many different species have evolved from a common ancestral form consisting of, as proposed by Darwin, one photoreceptor cell and one pigment cell (**Figure 24.18**). As mentioned, such a very simple eye can accomplish a rudimentary form of vision by detecting light and its direction. Eyes such as these are still found in modern species, such as the larvae of certain types of mollusks. Over time, simple eyes evolved into more complex types of eyes by modifications that resulted in the addition of more types of cells, such as lens cells and nerve cells. Alternatively, other researchers propose that *Pax6* may control only certain features of eye development and that different types of eyes may have evolved independently. Future research will be needed to resolve this controversy.

*[*]*Pax* is an abbreviation for paired box. The protein encoded by this gene contains a domain called a paired box.

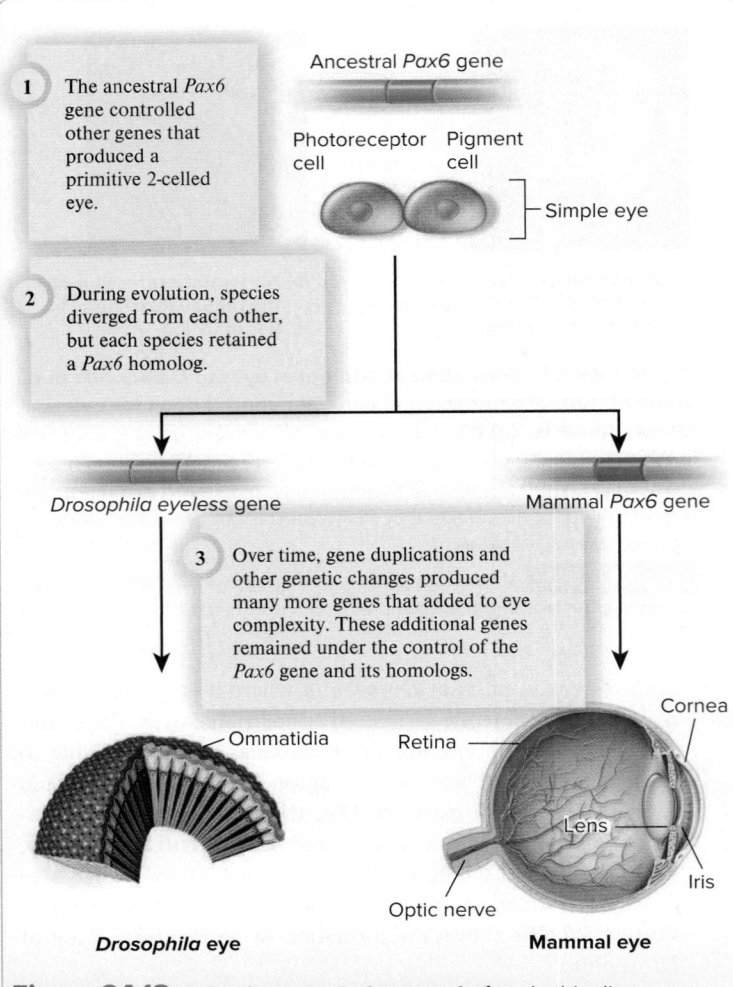

1. The ancestral *Pax6* gene controlled other genes that produced a primitive 2-celled eye.

Ancestral *Pax6* gene

Photoreceptor cell   Pigment cell

Simple eye

2. During evolution, species diverged from each other, but each species retained a *Pax6* homolog.

Drosophila eyeless gene

Mammal *Pax6* gene

3. Over time, gene duplications and other genetic changes produced many more genes that added to eye complexity. These additional genes remained under the control of the *Pax6* gene and its homologs.

Ommatidia

Retina

Cornea

Lens

Iris

Optic nerve

Drosophila eye

Mammal eye

Figure 24.18 Genetic control of eye evolution. In this diagram, genetic changes, under the control of the ancestral Pax6 gene, led to the evolution of different types of eyes.

Summary of Key Concepts

24.1 Identification of Species

- A species is a group of related organisms that shares a distinctive set of attributes in nature. Speciation is the process by which new species are formed. Macroevolution refers to evolutionary changes that produce new species and groups of species.

- Different characteristics, including morphological traits, reproductive isolation, molecular features, ecological factors, and evolutionary relationships, are used to identify species (Figure 24.1).

- Reproductive isolating mechanisms prevent two different species from breeding with each other (Figure 24.2).

- Prezygotic isolating mechanisms include habitat isolation, temporal isolation, behavioral isolation, mechanical isolation, and gametic isolation (Figures 24.3, 24.4).

- Postzygotic isolating mechanisms include hybrid inviability, hybrid sterility, and hybrid breakdown (Figure 24.5).

24.2 Mechanisms of Speciation

- Allopatric speciation occurs when a population becomes isolated from other populations and evolves into one or more new species. When speciation from a single ancestral species occurs multiple times, the process is called adaptive radiation. If two populations are incompletely separated, interbreeding may occur in hybrid zones (Figures 24.6, 24.7, 24.8).

- Podos hypothesized that changes in beak depth, associated with adaptation for feeding, promoted reproductive isolation by altering the song patterns of finches (Figures 24.9, 24.10).

- Sympatric speciation involves the formation of different species in populations that are not geographically isolated from one another. Polyploidy, adaptation to local environments, and sexual selection are mechanisms that promote sympatric speciation (Figures 24.11, 24.12).

24.3 The Pace of Speciation

- The pace of evolution may seem relatively constant or it may vary. Gradualism refers to steady evolution due to many small genetic changes, whereas punctuated equilibrium is a pattern of evolution in which new species arise more rapidly and then remain unchanged for long periods of time (Figure 24.13).

24.4 Evo-Devo: Evolutionary Developmental Biology

- Evolutionary developmental biology (evo-devo) compares the development of different species in order to understand ancestral relationships and the mechanisms that bring about evolutionary change. These changes often involve variation in the expression of cell-signaling proteins and transcription factors.

- The spatial expression of genes that affect development can affect phenotypes dramatically, as shown by the expression of the *BMP4* and *Gremlin* genes in birds, resulting in nonwebbed or webbed feet (Figure 24.14).

- An increase in the number of *Hox* genes played an important role in the evolution of more complex body patterns in animals (Figure 24.15).

- Heterochrony, which is a difference in the relative growth rates of body parts among different species, can have a major effect on phenotype (Figure 24.16).

- The *Pax6* gene and its homologs control eye development in many species of animals (Figures 24.17, 24.18).

Assess & Discuss

Test Yourself

1. Macroevolution refers to evolutionary changes that
   a   occur in multicellular organisms.
   b   produce new species and groups of species.
   c   occur over long periods of time.
   d   cause changes in allele frequencies.
   e   occur in large mammals.

2. The biological species concept classifies a species based on
   a   morphological characteristics.
   b   reproductive isolation.
   c   the niche the organism occupies in the environment.
   d   genetic relationships between an organism and its ancestors.
   e   both a and b.

3. Which of the following is considered an example of a postzygotic isolating mechanism?
   a incompatible genitalia
   b different mating seasons
   c incompatible gametes
   d mountain range separating two populations
   e failure of fertilized eggs to develop normally

4. Hybrid breakdown occurs when interspecies hybrids
   a do not develop past the early embryonic stages.
   b have a reduced life span.
   c are infertile.
   d are fertile but produce offspring with reduced viability and fertility.
   e produce offspring that express the traits of only one of the original species.

5. The evolution of one species into two or more species is called
   a gradualism.
   b punctuated equilibrium.
   c cladogenesis.
   d horizontal gene transfer.
   e microevolution.

6. The large number of honeycreeper species on the Hawaiian Islands is an example of
   a adaptive radiation.
   b genetic drift.
   c stabilizing selection.
   d horizontal gene transfer.
   e microevolution.

7. A major mechanism of speciation in plants but not in animals is
   a adaptation to new environments.
   b polyploidy.
   c hybrid breakdown.
   d genetic changes that alter the organism's niche.
   e both a and d.

8. The concept of punctuated equilibrium suggests that
   a the rate of evolution is constant, with short time periods of no evolutionary change.
   b evolution occurs gradually over time.
   c small genetic changes accumulate over time to allow for phenotypic change and speciation.
   d long periods of little evolutionary change are interrupted by short periods of major evolutionary change.
   e both b and c

9. Researchers suggest that an increase in the number of *Hox* genes
   a leads to reproductive isolation in all cases.
   b could explain the evolution of color vision.
   c allows for the evolution of more complex body patterns in animals.
   d results in the decrease in the number of body segments in insects.
   e does all of the above.

10. The observation that the mammalian *Pax6* gene and the *Drosophila eyeless* gene are homologous genes that promote the formation of different types of eyes suggests that
    a *Drosophila* eyes are more complex.
    b mammalian eyes are more complex.
    c eyes arose once during evolution.
    d eyes arose at least twice during evolution.
    e eye development is a simple process.

Conceptual Questions

1. What is the key difference between prezygotic and postzygotic isolating mechanisms? Give an example of each type. Which type is more costly in terms of energy expenditure?

2. What are the key differences between gradualism and punctuated equilibrium? How are genetic changes related to these two models?

3. **Core Concept: Evolution** Describe one example in which genes that control development played an important role in the evolution of different species.

Collaborative Questions

1. What is a species? Discuss how geographic isolation can lead to speciation, and explain how reproductive isolation plays a role.

2. Discuss the type of speciation (allopatric or sympatric) that is most likely to occur under each of the following conditions:
   a A pregnant female rat is transported by an ocean liner to a new continent.
   b A meadow containing several species of grasses is exposed to a pesticide that promotes nondisjunction.
   c In a very large lake containing several species of fishes, the water level gradually falls over the course of several years. Eventually, the large lake becomes subdivided into smaller lakes, some of which are connected by narrow streams.

Table 25.1	Distinguishing Cellular and Molecular Features of Domains Bacteria, Archaea, and Eukarya*		
Characteristic	Bacteria	Archaea	Eukarya
Chromosomes	Usually circular	Circular	Usually linear
Nucleosome structure	No	No	Yes
Chromosome segregation/cell division	Binary fission	Binary fission	Mitosis/meiosis
Introns in genes	Rarely	Rarely	Commonly
Ribosomes	70S	70S	80S
Initiator tRNA	Formylmethionine	Methionine	Methionine
Operons	Yes	Yes	No
Capping of mRNA	No	No	Yes
RNA polymerases	One	Several	Three
Promoters of structural genes	–35 and –10 sequences	TATA box	TATA box
Cell compartmentalization	No	No	Yes
Membrane lipids	Ester-linked	Ether-linked	Ester-linked

*The descriptions in this table represent the general features of most species in each domain. Some exceptions exist. For example, certain bacterial species have linear chromosomes, and operons occasionally are found in eukaryotes, such as the nematode worm *Caenorhabditis elegans*.

classes, then **orders**, **families**, **genera** (singular, genus), and **species**. As noted in Chapter 24, species may be divided into subspecies, often based on geographical distribution. Each of these taxa contains progressively fewer species that are more similar to each other than they are to the members of the taxa above them in the hierarchy. For example, the taxon Animalia, which is at the kingdom level, has a larger number of fairly diverse species than does the class Mammalia, which contains fewer species that are relatively similar to each other.

To further understand taxonomy, let's consider the classification of the gray wolf (*Canis lupus*) (**Figure 25.2**). The gray wolf is placed in the domain Eukarya, the supergroup Opisthokonta, and then within the kingdom Animalia. This kingdom contains all animals and has over 1 million species. Next, the gray wolf is classified in the phylum Chordata. The 50,000 species of animals in this phylum all have four common features at some stage of their development. These are a notochord (a cartilaginous rod that runs along the back of all chordates at some point in their life cycle), a tubular nerve or spinal cord located above the notochord, gill slits or arches, and a postanal tail. Examples of animals in the phylum Chordata include fishes, reptiles, and mammals.

The gray wolf is in the class Mammalia, which includes 5,513 species of mammals. Two distinguishing features of animals in this class are hair, which helps the body maintain a warm, constant body temperature, and mammary glands, which produce milk to nourish the young. There are 26 orders of mammals; the order that includes the gray wolf

Taxonomic group	Gray wolf found in	Number of current species
Domain	Eukarya	~4–10 million
Supergroup	Opisthokonta	>1 million
Kingdom	Animalia	>1 million
Phylum	Chordata	~50,000
Class	Mammalia	5,513
Order	Carnivora	282
Family	Canidae	34
Genus	*Canis*	7
Species	*lupus*	1

Figure 25.2 A taxonomic classification of the gray wolf (*Canis lupus*).

 Core Concept: Evolution A goal of taxonomy is to relate the diversity of species to their evolutionary relationships. Note: The numbers in this figure will change as new species are discovered and some species become extinct.

Concept Check: *Which group is broader, a phylum or a family?*

is called Carnivora and has 282 species that are meat-eating animals with prominent canine teeth. The gray wolf is placed in the family Canidae, which is a relatively small family of 34 species, including different species of wolves, jackals, foxes, wild dogs, and the coyote and domestic dog. All species in the family Canidae are doglike animals. The smallest grouping that contains the gray wolf is the genus *Canis*, which has four species of jackals, the coyote, and two types of wolves. The species *Canis lupus* encompasses several subspecies, including the domestic dog (*Canis lupus familiaris*).

Binomial Nomenclature Is Used to Name Species

As originally advocated by Linnaeus, **binomial nomenclature** is the standard format for naming species. The scientific name of every species has two names, its genus name and its unique specific epithet. For the gray wolf, the genus is *Canis* and the species epithet is *lupus*. The genus name is always capitalized, but the specific epithet is not. Both names are italicized. After the first mention, the genus name is abbreviated to a single letter. For example, we write that *Canis lupus* is the gray wolf, and in subsequent sentences, the species is referred to as *C. lupus*.

When naming a new species, genus names are always nouns or treated as nouns, whereas species epithets may be either nouns or adjectives. The names often have a Latin or Greek origin and refer to characteristics of the species or to features of its habitat. For example, the genus name of the newly discovered African forest elephant, *Loxodonta*, is from the Greek *loxo*, meaning slanting, and *odonta*, meaning tooth. The species epithet *cyclotis* refers to the observation that the ears of this species are rounder than those of *L. africana*.

The rules for naming animal species, such as *Canis lupus* and *Loxodonta africana*, were established by the International Commission on Zoological Nomenclature (ICZN). The ICZN provides and regulates a uniform system of nomenclature to ensure that every animal has a unique and universally accepted scientific name. Who is allowed to identify and name a new species? As long as ICZN rules are followed, new animal species can be named by anyone, not only scientists. The rules for naming plants are described in the International Code of Botanical Nomenclature (ICBN), and the naming of bacteria and archaea is overseen by the International Committee on Systematics of Prokaryotes (ICSP).

25.2 Phylogenetic Trees

Learning Outcomes:

1. Define phylogeny, and explain how it is depicted in phylogenetic trees.
2. Explain the process of cladogenesis, the primary way that new species arise.
3. Describe how homology is used to construct phylogenetic trees.

Systematics is the study of biological diversity and evolutionary relationships. By studying the similarities and differences among species, biologists can construct a **phylogeny**, which is the evolutionary history of a species or group of species. To propose a phylogeny, biologists use the tools of systematics. For example, the classification of the gray wolf in Figure 25.2 is based on systematics. Therefore, one use of systematics is to place species into taxa and to understand the evolutionary relationships among different taxa.

In this section, we will consider the features of diagrams or trees that describe the evolutionary relationships among various species, both extant and extinct. As you will learn, such trees are usually based on morphological or genetic data.

A Phylogenetic Tree Depicts Evolutionary Relationships Among Species

A **phylogenetic tree** is a diagram that describes the evolutionary relationships among various species, based on the information available to and gathered by systematists. Phylogenetic trees should be viewed as hypotheses that are proposed, tested, and later refined as additional data become available. Let's look at what information a phylogenetic tree contains and the form in which it is presented. **Figure 25.3** shows a hypothetical phylogenetic tree of the relationships among various flowering plant species, in which the species are labeled A through K. The vertical axis represents time, and the oldest species is at the bottom.

New species can be formed by **anagenesis**, in which a single species evolves into a different species. However, the primary way that new species arise is by **cladogenesis**, in which a species diverges into two or more species. The branch points in a phylogenetic tree, also called **nodes**, indicate times when cladogenesis has occurred. For example, approximately 12 mya, species A diverged into species A and species B. Figure 25.3 also shows anagenesis in which species C evolved into species G. The tips of branches represent species that became extinct in the past, such as species B and E, or living species, such as F, I, G, J, H, and K, which are at the top of the tree. Species A and D are also extinct but gave rise to species that are still in existence.

The branch points of a phylogenetic tree group species according to common ancestry. A **clade** consists of a common ancestral species and all of its descendant species. For example, the group highlighted in light green in Figure 25.3 is a clade derived from the common ancestral species labeled D. Likewise, the entire tree forms a clade, with species A as a common ancestor. Therefore, smaller and more recent clades are nested within larger clades that have older common ancestors.

Systematics Constructs Taxonomic Groups Based on Evolutionary Relationships

A key goal of modern systematics is to create taxonomic groups that reflect evolutionary relationships. Systematics attempts to organize species into clades, so that each group includes an ancestral species and all of its descendants. A **monophyletic group** is a taxon that is a clade. Ideally, every taxon, whether it is a domain, supergroup, kingdom, phylum, class, order, family, or genus, should be a monophyletic group.

What is the relationship between a phylogenetic tree and taxonomy? The relationship depends on how far back we go to identify a common ancestor. For broader taxa, such as a kingdom, the common ancestor existed a very long time ago, on the order of hundreds of millions or even billions of years ago. For smaller taxa, such as a family or genus, the common ancestor occurred much more recently, on the order of millions or tens of millions of years ago. This concept is shown in a schematic way in **Figure 25.4**. This small, hypothetical kingdom is a clade that contains 64 living species. (Actual kingdoms

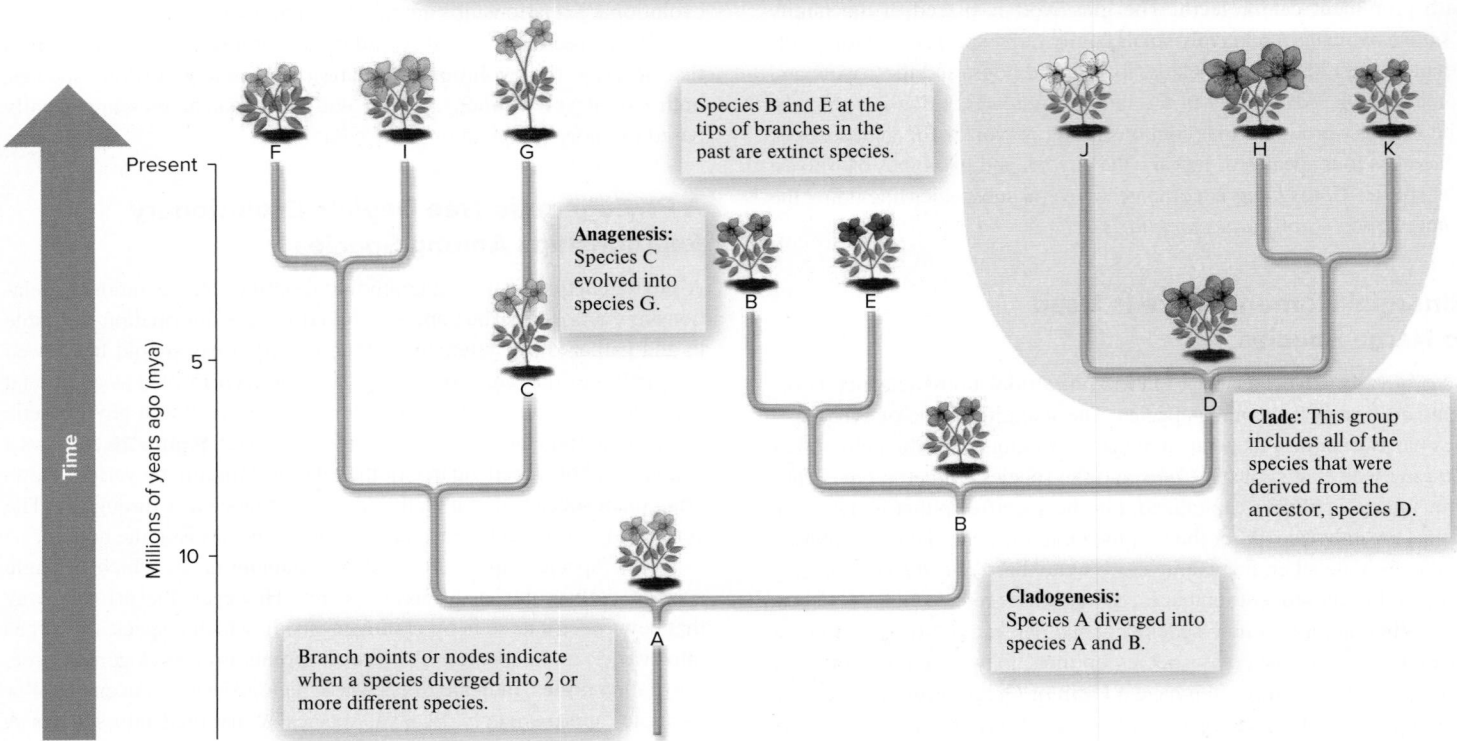

Species F, I, G, J, H, and K at the tips of branches in the present are extant species that still exist.

Species B and E at the tips of branches in the past are extinct species.

Anagenesis: Species C evolved into species G.

Clade: This group includes all of the species that were derived from the ancestor, species D.

Cladogenesis: Species A diverged into species A and B.

Branch points or nodes indicate when a species diverged into 2 or more different species.

Figure 25.3 **How to read a phylogenetic tree.** This hypothetical tree shows the proposed relationships between various flowering plant species. Species are placed into clades, groups of organisms containing an ancestral organism and all of its descendants. Note: Anagenesis is a possible way for a new species to arise, but as shown in this figure, cladogenesis is the primary mechanism.

Concept Check: *Can two different species have more than one common ancestor?*

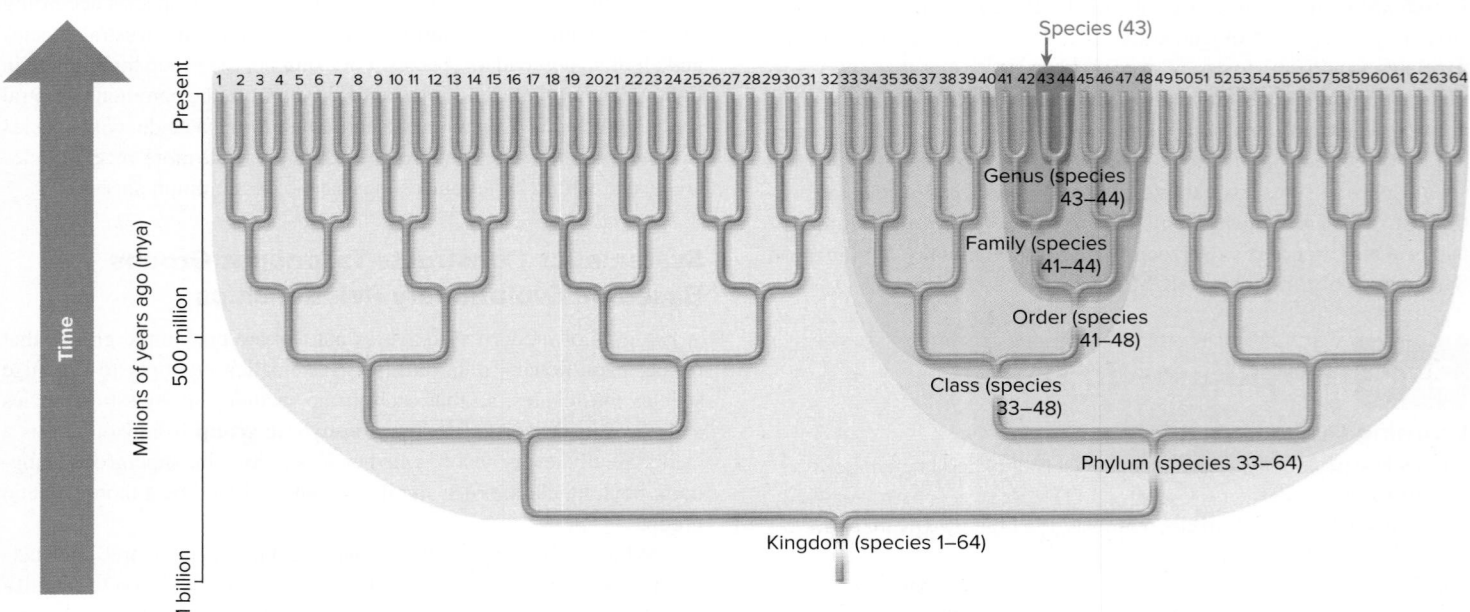

Species (43)

Genus (species 43–44)

Family (species 41–44)

Order (species 41–48)

Class (species 33–48)

Phylum (species 33–64)

Kingdom (species 1–64)

Figure 25.4 **Schematic relationship between a phylogenetic tree and taxonomy, when taxonomy is correctly based on evolutionary relationships.** The shaded areas highlight the kingdom, phylum, class, order, family, and genus for species number 43. All of the taxa are clades. Broader taxa, such as phyla and classes, are derived from more ancient common ancestors. Smaller taxa, such as families and genera, are derived from more recent common ancestors. These smaller taxa are subsets of the broader taxa.

Concept Check: *Which taxon would have a more recent common ancestor, a phylum or an order?*

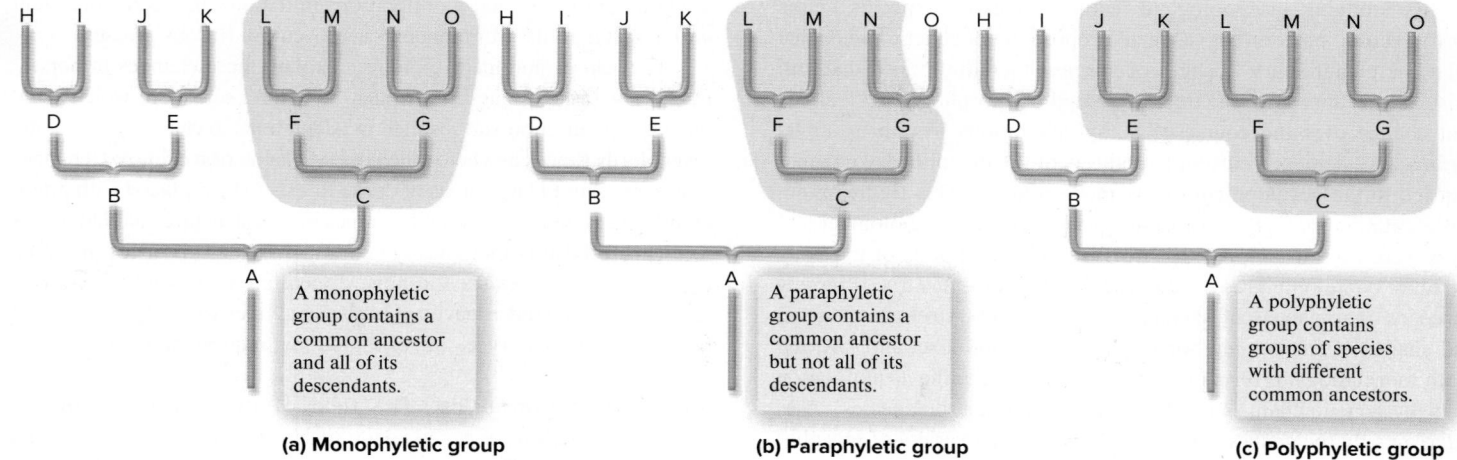

Figure 25.5 **A comparison of monophyletic, paraphyletic, and polyphyletic taxonomic groups.**

are obviously larger and exceedingly more complex.) The diagram emphasizes the taxa that contain the species designated number 43. The common ancestor that gave rise to this kingdom existed approximately 1 billion years ago. Over time, more recent species arose that subsequently became the common ancestors to the phylum, class, order, family, and genus that contain species number 43.

How does research in systematics affect taxonomy? As researchers gather new information, they sometimes discover that some of the current taxonomic groups are not monophyletic. **Figure 25.5** compares a monophyletic group with taxonomic groups that are not. A **paraphyletic group** contains a common ancestor and some, but not all, of its descendants (Figure 25.5b). In contrast, a **polyphyletic group** consists of members of several evolutionary lines and does not include the most recent common ancestor of the included lineages (Figure 25.5c).

As scientists learn more about evolutionary relationships, taxonomic groups are reorganized to recognize only monophyletic groups. For example, traditional classification schemes once separated birds and reptiles into separate classes (**Figure 25.6a**). In this scheme, the reptile class (officially named Reptilia) contained orders that included turtles, lizards and snakes, and crocodiles, with birds constituting a different class. Research indicated that the reptile taxon was paraphyletic, because birds were excluded from the group. This group can be made monophyletic by including birds as a class within the reptile clade and elevating the other groups to a class status (**Figure 25.6b**).

The Study of Systematics Is Usually Based on Morphological or Genetic Homology

As discussed in Chapter 22, the term **homology** refers to a similarity that occurs due to descent from a common ancestor. Such features are said to be homologous. For example, the arm of a human, the wing of a bat, and the flipper of a whale are homologous structures (refer back to Figure 22.12). Similarly, genes found in different species are homologous if they have been derived from the same ancestral gene (refer back to Figure 22.13).

In systematics, researchers identify homologous features that are shared by some species but not by others, which allows them to group

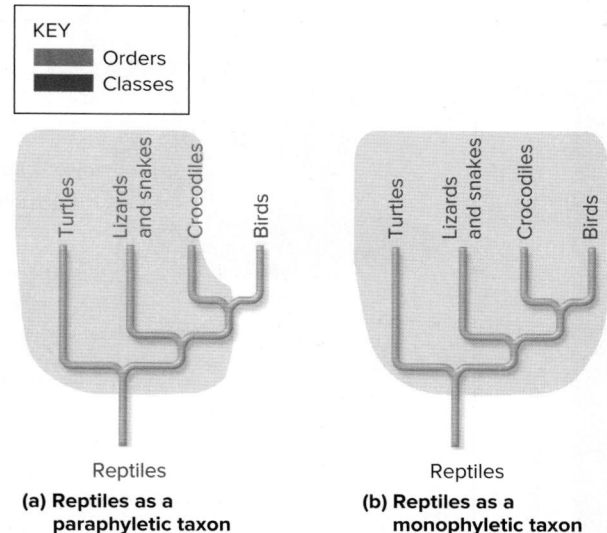

Figure 25.6 **An example of a taxon that is not monophyletic.** **(a)** The class of reptiles as a paraphyletic taxon. **(b)** The group can be made monophyletic if birds and the other orders are classified as classes within the reptile clade.

species based on shared similarities. Researchers usually study homology by examining morphological features or genetic data. In addition, the data they gather are viewed in light of geographic data. Many organisms do not migrate extremely long distances. Species that are closely related evolutionarily are relatively likely to inhabit neighboring or overlapping geographic regions, though many exceptions are known to occur.

Morphological Analysis The first studies in systematics focused on morphological features of extinct and living species. Morphological traits continue to be widely used in systematic studies, particularly in those studies pertaining to extinct species and those involving groups that have not been extensively studied at the molecular level. To establish evolutionary relationships based on morphological homology, many traits have to be analyzed to identify similarities and differences.

By studying morphological features of extinct species in the fossil record, paleontologists can propose phylogenetic trees that chart the evolutionary lineages of species, including those that still exist. In this approach, the trees are based on morphological features that change over the course of many generations. As an example, **Figure 25.7** depicts a current hypothesis of the evolutionary changes that led to the development of the modern horse. This figure shows representative species from various genera. Many morphological features were used to propose this tree. Because hard parts of the body are more commonly preserved in the fossil record, this tree is largely based on the analysis of skeletal changes in foot structure, lengths and shapes of various leg bones, skull shape and size, and jaw and tooth morphology. Over an evolutionary timescale, the accumulation of many genetic changes has had a dramatic effect on species' characteristics. In the genera depicted in this figure, a variety of morphological changes occurred, such as an increase in size, a reduction in

the number of toes, and modifications in the jaw and teeth consistent with a dietary shift from tender leaves to more fibrous grasses.

How do evolutionary biologists explain these changes in horses' traits? The changes can be attributed to natural selection, which acted on existing variation and resulted in adaptations to changes in climate. Over North America, where much of horse evolution occurred, changes in climate caused large areas of dense forests to be replaced with grasslands. The increase in size and changes in foot structure enabled horses to escape predators more easily and travel greater distances in search of food. The changes seen in horses' teeth are consistent with a shift from eating the tender leaves of bushes and trees to eating grasses and other more abrasive types of vegetation that require more chewing.

Molecular Systematics   The field of **molecular systematics** involves the analysis of genetic data, such as DNA sequences or amino acid sequences, to identify and study genetic homologies and propose

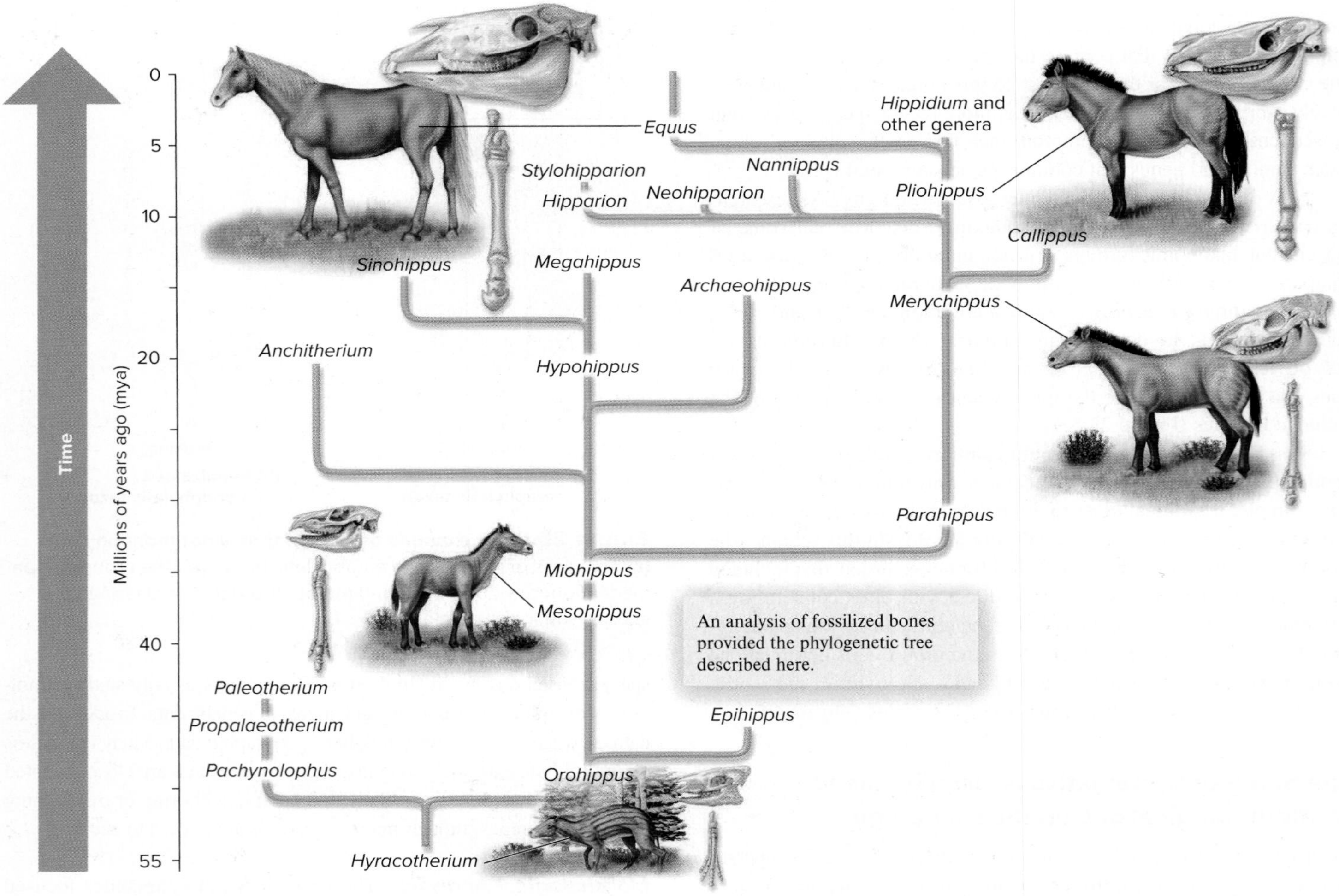

Figure 25.7   Evolution of horse populations. An analysis of morphological traits was used to produce this phylogenetic tree, which shows the evolutionary history that gave rise to the modern horse. As shown next to some of the genera, three important morphological changes were larger size, fewer toes, and a shift toward teeth suited for grazing.

 Core Concept: Structure and Function   The changes in structural features during horse evolution are related to changes in functional needs. During the course of their evolution, horse populations shifted from feeding on leaves in forested regions to feeding on grasses in more open spaces.

phylogenetic trees. In 1963, Austrian biologist Emile Zuckerkandl and American chemist Linus Pauling were the first to suggest that molecular data could be used to establish evolutionary relationships. How can a comparison of genetic sequences help to establish evolutionary relationships? As discussed later in this chapter, DNA sequences change over the course of many generations due to the accumulation of mutations. Therefore, when comparing homologous sequences in different species, DNA sequences from closely related species are more similar to each other than they are to sequences from distantly related species.

25.3 Cladistics

Learning Outcomes:

1. Distinguish between shared primitive characters and shared derived characters.

2. Outline the steps involved in using a cladistics approach to construct a phylogenetic tree, and explain how the principle of parsimony is used to choose among phylogenetic trees.

3. Describe how maximum likelihood is also used to discriminate among phylogenetic trees.

4. CoreSKILL » Explain how DNA can be analyzed to explore relationships among extant and extinct species.

Cladistics is the classification of species based on evolutionary relationships. A **cladistic approach** constructs phylogenetic trees by considering the possible pathways of evolutionary change that involve characteristics that are shared or not shared among various species. Such trees are known as **cladograms**. In this section, we will consider how biologists produce phylogenetic trees.

Species Differ with Regard to Primitive and Derived Characters

A cladistic approach compares homologous features, also called **characters**, which may exist in two or more **character states**. For example, among different species, a front limb, which is a character, may exist in different character states such as a wing, an arm, or a flipper. The various character states are either shared or not shared by different species.

To understand the cladistic approach, let's take a look at a simplified phylogeny (**Figure 25.8**). We can place the species that currently exist into two groups: D and E, and F and G. The most recent common ancestor to D and E is B, whereas species C is the most recent common ancestor to F and G. With these ideas in mind, let's focus on the front limbs (flippers versus legs) and eyes.

A character that is shared by two or more different taxa and inherited from ancestors older than their last common ancestor is called a **shared primitive character**, or **symplesiomorphy**. Such characters are viewed as being older—ones that occurred earlier in evolution. With regard to species D, E, F, and G, having two eyes is a shared primitive character. It originated prior to species B and C.

By comparison, a **shared derived character**, or **synapomorphy**, is a character that is shared by two or more species or taxa and originated in their most recent common ancestor. With regard to species D and E, having two front flippers is a shared derived character that originated in species B, their most recent common ancestor (see Figure 25.8). Compared with shared primitive characters, shared derived characters are more

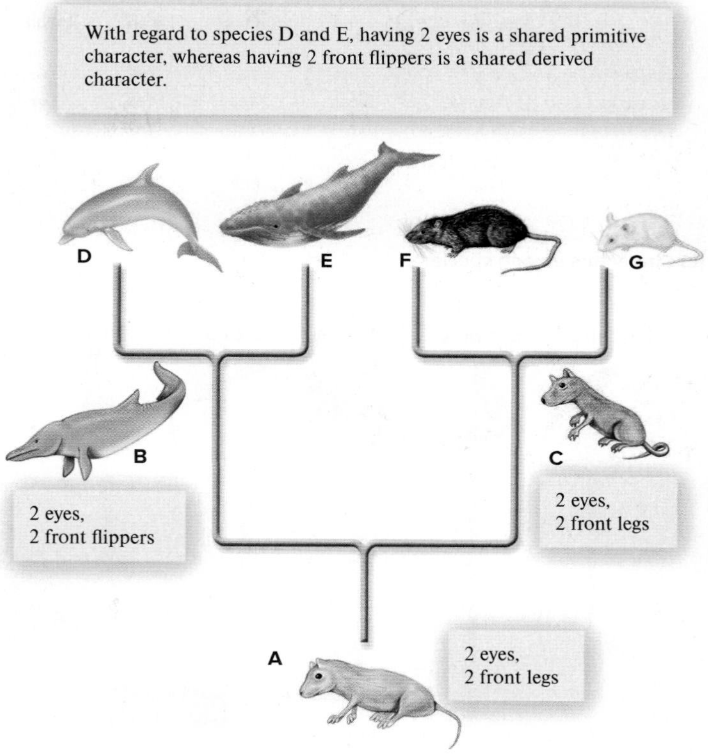

Figure 25.8 A comparison of shared primitive characters and shared derived characters.

recent traits on an evolutionary timescale. For example, among mammals, only some species, such as whales and dolphins, have flippers. In this case, flippers were derived from the two front limbs of an ancestral species. The word derived indicates that evolution involves the modification of traits in pre-existing species. In other words, populations of organisms with new traits are derived from changes in pre-existing populations. The basis of the cladistic approach is to analyze many shared derived characters among groups of species to deduce the pathway that gave rise to those species.

The terms primitive and derived do not indicate the complexity of a character. For example, the flippers of a dolphin do not appear more complex than the front limbs of ancestral species A (see Figure 25.8), which were limbs with individual toes. Derived characters can be similar in complexity, less complex, or more complex than primitive characters.

A Cladistic Approach Produces a Cladogram Based on Shared Derived Characters

To illustrate how shared derived characters are used to propose a phylogenetic tree, **Figure 25.9a** compares several characters among five species of animals. The proposed cladogram in **Figure 25.9b** is consistent with the distribution of shared derived characters among these species. A branch point is where two species differ in a character. The oldest common ancestor, which is now extinct, had a notochord and was an ancestor to all five species. Vertebrae are a shared derived character of the lamprey, salmon, lizard, and rabbit, but not the lancelet, which is an invertebrate. By comparison, a hinged jaw is a shared derived character of the salmon, lizard, and rabbit, but not of the lamprey or lancelet.

	Lancelet	Lamprey	Salmon	Lizard	Rabbit
Notochord	Yes	Yes	Yes	Yes	Yes
Vertebrae	No	Yes	Yes	Yes	Yes
Hinged jaw	No	No	Yes	Yes	Yes
Tetrapod	No	No	No	Yes	Yes
Mammary glands	No	No	No	No	Yes

(a) Characters among species

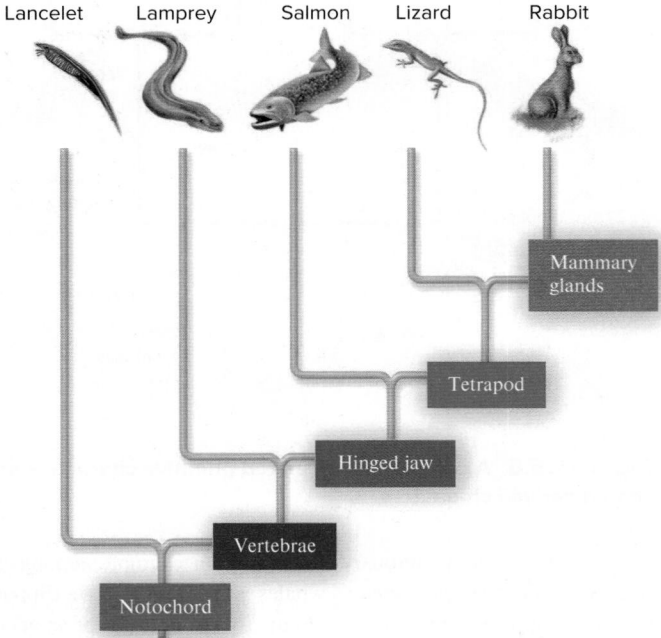

(b) Cladogram based on morphological traits

Figure 25.9 **Using shared primitive characters and shared derived characters to propose a phylogenetic tree. (a)** A comparison of characters among these species. **(b)** This phylogenetic tree illustrates both shared primitive and shared derived characters in a cladogram of five animal species.

Concept Check: *What shared derived character is common to the salmon, lizard, and rabbit, but not the lamprey?*

In a cladogram, an **ingroup** is the group whose evolutionary relationships we wish to understand. By comparison, an **outgroup** is a species or group of species that is assumed to have diverged before the species in the ingroup. An outgroup lacks one or more shared derived characters that are found in the ingroup. A designated outgroup can be closely related or more distantly related to the ingroup. In the tree shown in Figure 25.9, if the salmon, lizard, and rabbit are an ingroup, the lamprey is an outgroup. The lamprey has a notochord and vertebrae but lacks a character shared by the ingroup, namely, a hinged jaw. Thus, for the ingroup, the notochord and vertebrae are shared primitive characters, whereas the hinged jaw is a shared derived character not found in the outgroup.

Likewise, the concept of shared derived characters can apply to molecular data, such as a gene sequence. Let's consider an example

to illustrate this idea. Our example involves molecular data obtained from seven different hypothetical plant species called A–G. In these species, a homologous region of DNA was sequenced as shown here:

12345678910

A: GATAGTACCC
B: GATAGTTCCC
C: GATAGTTCCG
D: GGTATTACCC
E: GGTATAACCC
F: GGTAGTACCA
G: GGTAGTACCC

The cladogram of **Figure 25.10** is a hypothesis of how these DNA sequences arose. A mutation that changes the sequence of nucleotides is comparable to a modification of a character. For example, let's designate species D as an outgroup and species A, B, C, F, and G as the ingroup. In this case, a G (guanine) at the fifth position is a shared derived character. The genetic sequence carrying this G is derived from an older primitive sequence.

Now that you have an understanding of shared primitive and derived characters, let's consider the steps a researcher would follow to propose a cladogram using a cladistic approach.

1. ***Choose the species whose evolutionary relationships are of interest.*** In a simple cladogram, such as those described in this chapter, individual species are compared with each other. In more complex cladograms, species may be grouped into larger taxa (for example, families) and compared with each other. If such grouping is done, the results are not reliable if the groups are not clades.

2. ***Choose characters for comparing the species selected in step 1.*** As mentioned, a character is a general feature of an organism and may come in different versions called character states. For example, a front limb is a character in mammals, which exists in different character states including wing, arm, and flipper.

3. ***Determine the polarity of character states.*** In other words, determine if a character state came first and is primitive or came later and is a derived character. This information may be available by examining the fossil record, for example, but is usually done by comparing the ingroup with the outgroup. For a character with two character states, an assumption is made that a character state shared by the outgroup and ingroup is primitive. A character state shared only by members of the ingroup is derived.

4. ***Analyze cladograms based on the following principles:***

   - All species (or higher taxa) are placed on tips in a phylogenetic tree, not at branch points.

   - Each cladogram branch point should have a list of one or more shared derived characters that are common to all species above the branch point unless the character is later modified.

   - All shared derived characters appear together only once in a cladogram unless they arose independently during evolution more than once.

5. ***Among many possible options, choose the cladogram that provides the simplest explanation for the data.*** A common approach is to use a computer program that generates many

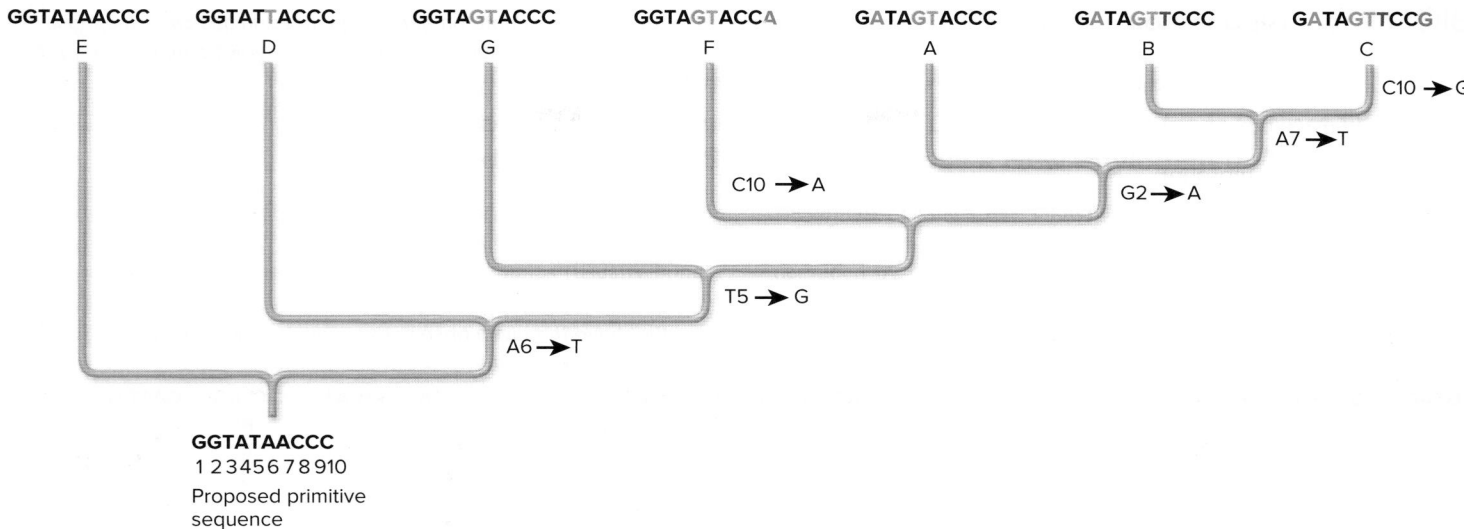

Figure 25.10 **The use of shared derived characters applied to molecular data.** This phylogenetic tree illustrates a cladogram involving homologous gene sequences found in seven hypothetical plant species. Mutations that alter a primitive DNA sequence are shared among certain species but not others. Note: A, T, G, and C refer to nucleotide bases, and the numbers refer to the position of the base in the nucleotide sequences. For example, A6 refers to an adenine at the sixth position.

Concept Check: *What nucleotide change is a shared derived character for species A, B, and C, but not for species G?*

possible cladograms. Analyzing the data and choosing among the possibilities are key aspects of this process. As described later, different theoretical approaches, such as the principle of parsimony, can be used to choose among possible phylogenies.

6. ***Provide a root to the phylogenetic tree by choosing a noncontroversial outgroup.*** In this textbook, most phylogenetic trees are rooted, which means that a single node at the bottom of the tree corresponds to a common ancestor for all of the species or groups of species in the tree. A method for rooting trees is the use of a noncontroversial outgroup. Such an outgroup typically shares morphological traits and/or DNA sequence similarities with the members of the ingroup, to allow a comparison between the ingroup and outgroup. Even so, the outgroup must be noncontroversial in that it has enough distinctive differences with the ingroup to be considered a clear outgroup. For example, if the ingroup was a group of mammalian species, an outgroup could be a reptile species.

The Principle of Parsimony Is Used to Choose from Among Possible Cladograms

One approach for choosing among possible cladograms is to assume that the best hypothesis is the one that requires the fewest number of evolutionary changes. This concept, called the **principle of parsimony**, states that the preferred hypothesis is the one that is the simplest for all the characters and their states. For example, if two species possess a tail, we would initially assume that a tail arose once during evolution and that both species have descended from a common ancestor with a tail. Such a hypothesis is simpler, and more likely to be correct, than assuming that tails arose

twice during evolution and that the tails in the two species are not due to descent from a common ancestor.

Maximum Likelihood Is Also Used to Discriminate Among Possible Phylogenetic Trees

In addition to the principle of parsimony, evolutionary biologists also apply other approaches to the evaluation of phylogenetic trees. These methods involve the use of an evolutionary model—a set of assumptions about how evolution is likely to happen. For example, mutations affecting the third base in a codon are often neutral because they don't affect the amino acid sequence of the encoded protein and therefore don't affect the fitness of an organism. As discussed in Chapter 23, such neutral mutations are more likely to become prevalent in a population than are mutations in the first or second base. Therefore, one possible assumption of an evolutionary model is that neutral mutations are more likely than nonneutral mutations.

According to an approach called **maximum likelihood**, researchers may ask, "What is the probability that an evolutionary model and a proposed phylogenetic tree would give rise to observed molecular data?" To answer this question, they must devise rules about how DNA sequences change over time. For example, one rule may be that neutral mutations are more likely to occur than nonneutral mutations. A second rule might be that the rate of change of DNA sequences is relatively constant from one generation to the next in a particular lineage. With a set of probability rules, researchers can analyze different possible trees and predict the relative probabilities for each of them. The phylogenetic tree that gives the highest probability of producing the observed data is preferred to any trees that give lower probabilities.

5 Align the DNA sequences to each other, using computer techniques.

Align sequences, using computer programs.

Align sequences to compare the degree of similarity.

6 **THE DATA**

```
Moa 1       GCTTAGCCCTAAATCCAGATACTTACCCTACACAAGTATCCGCCCGAGAACTACGAGCACAAACGCTTAAAACTCTAAGGACTTGGCGGTGCCCCAAACCCA
Kiwi 1      ···················T·G······GT··CT····C······································T······
Emu         ···············TT····C··T··CAG··C····T······································T······
Cassowary   ···············TT····CG·TA··CTG·······································T······
Ostrich     ·······T····AT······C··CT······································T······
Rhea 1      ···············T······C··CT······································T······

Moa 1       CCTAGAGGAGCCTGTTCTATAATCGATAATCCACGATACACCCGACCATCCCTCGCCCGT–GCAGCCTACATACCGCCGTCCCCAGCCCGCCT––AATGAAA
Kiwi 1      ···················C············A····A··T··T··AAC–A····T······G····T····AA····G
Emu         ···················C············A····A··T··T··AA–A····G····––····G
Cassowary   ···················C············AG···T··T··AA·TA···G····––·G··G
Ostrich     ················T···A····C··T··A––T····G····C––··G
Rhea 1      ···················C············T··T··A·–····G····TA·G····

Moa 1       G–AACAATAGCGAGCACAACAGCCCTCCCCCGCTAACAAGACAGGTCAAGGTATAGCATATGAGATGGAAGAAATGGGCTACATTTTCTAACATAGAACACC
Kiwi 1      ·–····C···A······TA·–··A····C····A···T··T
Emu         ·–········T··AC––TT····G······T·T·
Cassowary   ·–··········T····AC––T····G····T···
Ostrich     ·–········T···A––····GAG····T··A
Rhea 1      ·–····C···AG··T·T··TA––····G····TC···A

Moa 1       C––––––––––––––ACGAAAGAGAAGGTGAAACCCTCCTCAAAAGGCGGATTTAGCAGTAAAATAGAACAAGAATGCCTATTTTAAGCCCGGCCCTGGGGC
Kiwi 1      –··············A·GGT····T·–C··T·G····C··T···GA·T····–·T····A·
Emu         –············AG·T···T·AC·T··G····C··T···GA·T····A–·T··T·A···
Cassowary   –············A·G·T···T·A···T·G····C··T···GA·T····A–·····A·
Ostrich     –··············G·TA····T·A······T··T···GA·T····–·T··T·A···
Rhea 1      –··········G····GGCA·····–AC····CG····G··G·TC····A··C·C····–·······A·
```

7 **CONCLUSION** This discovery-based investigation led to a hypothesis regarding the evolutionary relationships among these bird species, which is described in Figure 25.12.

8 **SOURCE** Cooper, A., et al. 1992. Independent origins of New Zealand moas and kiwis. *Proceedings of the National Academy of Sciences* 89: 8741–8744.

investigated the evolutionary relationships among some extant and extinct species of flightless birds. In this example of discovery-based science, the researchers gathered data with the goal of proposing a hypothesis about the evolutionary relationships among several bird species. The kiwis and moas are two groups of flightless birds that existed in New Zealand during the Pleistocene. Species of kiwis still exist, but the moas are now extinct. Eleven known species of moas formerly existed. In this study, the researchers investigated the phylogenetic relationships among four extinct species of moas, which were available as museum samples; three species of New Zealand kiwis; and living species of other flightless birds, including the emu and the

cassowary (both found in Australia and/or New Guinea), the ostrich (found in Africa and formerly Asia), and two rheas (found in South America).

Samples from the various species were subjected to polymerase chain reaction (PCR) to amplify a region of the gene that encodes SSU rRNA (an RNA found in the small subunits of mitochondrial ribosomes of all organisms, as discussed in Chapter 12). This provided enough DNA for sequencing. The data in Figure 25.11 illustrate a comparison of the sequences of a continuous region of the SSU rRNA gene from these species. The first line shows the DNA sequence for one of the four extinct moa species. Below it are the sequences of several of the other species that were analyzed. When the other sequences are identical to the first sequence, a dot is placed in the corresponding position. When the sequences are different, the changed nucleotide base (A, T, G, or C) is placed there. In a few regions, the genes are different lengths. In these cases, a dash is placed to indicate missing nucleotides.

As you can see from the large number of dots, the gene sequences among these flightless birds are very similar, though some differences occur. If you look carefully at the data, you will notice that the sequence from the kiwi (a New Zealand species) is actually more similar to the sequence from the ostrich (an African species) than it is to that of the moa, which was once found in New Zealand. Likewise, the kiwi is more similar to the emu and cassowary (found in Australia and New Guinea) than to the moa. How were these results interpreted? The researchers concluded that the kiwis are more closely related to African and Australian flightless birds than they are to the moas. From these results, they concluded that New Zealand was colonized twice by ancestors of flightless birds. The researchers used a maximum likelihood analysis to propose a new phylogenetic tree that illustrates the revised relationships among these living and extinct species (**Figure 25.12**).

Experimental Questions

1. What is molecular paleontology? What was the purpose of the study conducted by Cooper and colleagues?

2. What birds were examined in the Cooper study, and what are their geographic distributions? Why were the different species selected for this study?

3. **CoreSKILL »** What results did Cooper and colleagues obtain by comparing these DNA sequences? How did the results of this study affect the proposed phylogeny of flightless birds?

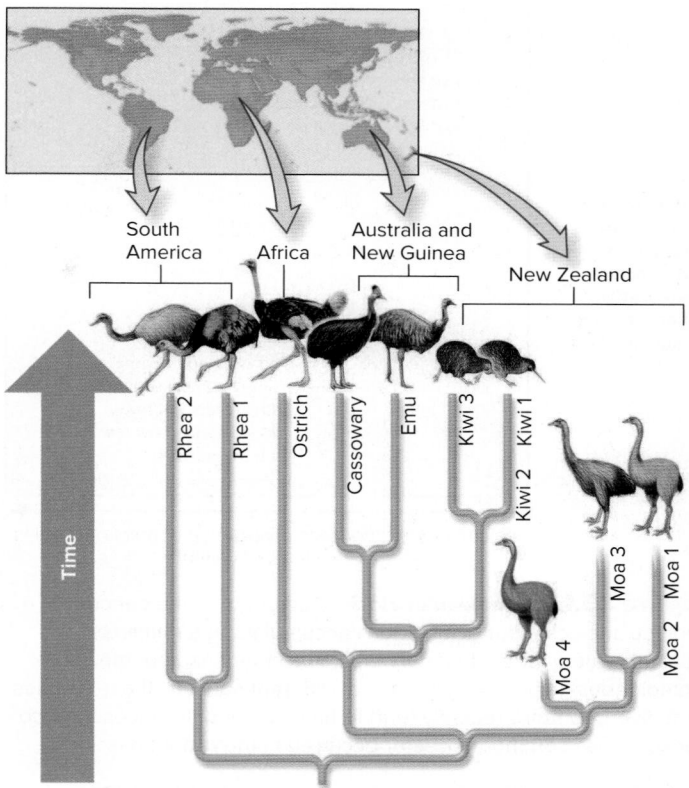

Figure 25.12 A revised phylogenetic tree of flightless birds. This tree is based on a comparison of DNA sequences from extinct and living flightless birds, as described in Figure 25.11.

Concept Check: *With regard to geography, why are the results of Cooper and his colleagues surprising?*

25.4 Molecular Clocks

Learning Outcomes:

1. Explain how molecular clocks are used in the dating of evolutionary events.

2. **CoreSKILL »** Compare and contrast the use of different genes to produce phylogenetic trees.

As we have seen, researchers employ different methods to choose a phylogeny that describes the evolutionary relationships among various species. Researchers are interested not only in the most likely pathway of evolution (the branches of the trees), but also the timing of evolutionary change (the lengths of the branches). How can researchers determine when different species diverged from each other in the past? As shown earlier in Figure 25.7, the fossil record can sometimes help researchers apply a timescale to a phylogeny.

Another way to infer the timing of past events is by analyzing genetic sequences. The **neutral theory of evolution** proposes that most genetic variation that exists in populations is due to the accumulation of neutral mutations—changes in genes and proteins that are not acted on by natural selection. The reasoning behind this concept is that

favorable mutations are likely to be very rare and detrimental mutations are likely to be eliminated from a population by natural selection. A large body of evidence supports the idea that much of the genetic variation observed in living species is due to the accumulation of neutral mutations. From an evolutionary point of view, if neutral mutations occur at a relatively constant rate, they can serve as a **molecular clock** to measure evolutionary time. In this section, we will consider the concept of a molecular clock and its application in phylogenetic trees.

The Timing of Evolutionary Change May Be Inferred from Molecular Clock Data

Figure 25.13 illustrates the concept of a molecular clock. The graph's vertical axis measures the number of base differences in a homologous gene between different pairs of species. The horizontal axis plots the amount of time that has elapsed since each pair of species shared a common ancestor.

As an example, let's suppose a researcher compared a gene sequence that was 500 bp long. Between species A and species B, this sequence might differ at 10 places and be identical at 490 places. By comparison, the 500-bp sequence might differ at 20 places between species A and species C and be the same at 480 places. Such a result is consistent with

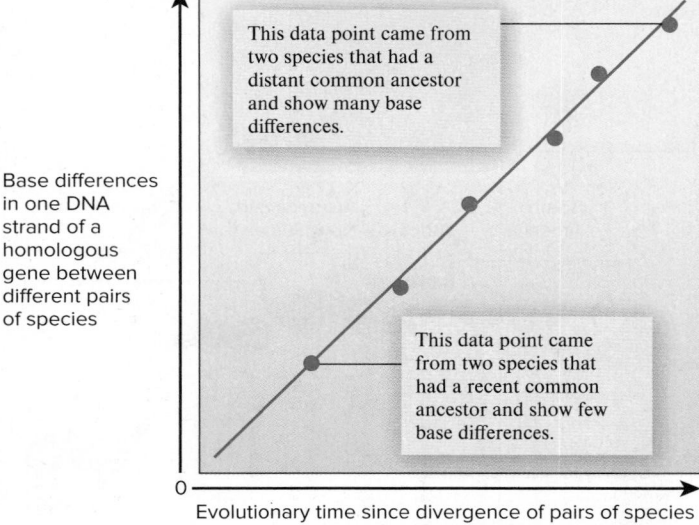

Base differences in one DNA strand of a homologous gene between different pairs of species

This data point came from two species that had a distant common ancestor and show many base differences.

This data point came from two species that had a recent common ancestor and show few base differences.

0

Evolutionary time since divergence of pairs of species (millions of years)

Figure 25.13 A molecular clock. According to the concept of a molecular clock, neutral mutations accumulate at a relatively constant rate over evolutionary time. In a comparison of the same homologous gene between pairs of different species, those species that diverged more recently tend to have fewer differences than do those whose common ancestor occurred in the distant past.

 Core Skill: Connections Look back at Table 12.1, which shows the genetic code. Propose three changes to a codon sequence that you think would be neutral mutations.

the idea that species A and species B shared a more recent common ancestor than do species A and species C. The explanation for this phenomenon is that the gene sequences of various species accumulate independent mutations after they have diverged from each other. A longer period of time since their divergence allows for a greater accumulation of mutations, which makes their sequences of bases more different.

Figure 25.13 suggests a linear relationship between the number of base changes and the time of divergence. For example, a linear relationship predicts that a pair of species with, say, 20 base differences in a given gene sequence would have a common ancestor that lived roughly twice as long ago as a pair showing 10 nucleotide differences. Although actual data sometimes show a relatively linear relationship over a defined time period, evolutionary biologists do not think that molecular clocks are perfectly linear over very long periods of time. Several factors can contribute to nonlinearity of molecular clocks. These include differences in the generation times of the species being analyzed and variation in the mutation rates of genes between different species.

To obtain reliable data, researchers must calibrate their molecular clocks. How much time does it take to accumulate a certain percentage of base changes? To perform such a calibration, researchers must have information regarding the date when two species diverged from a common ancestor. Such information could come from the fossil record, for instance. The genetic differences between those species are then divided by the amount of time since their last common ancestor to calculate a rate of evolutionary change.

As an example of clock calibration, let's consider primates. The fossil evidence suggests that humans and chimpanzees diverged from a common ancestor approximately 6 mya. The percentage of base differences between the mitochondrial DNA of humans and chimpanzees is 12%. From these data, the molecular clock for changes in the sequence of bases in mitochondrial DNA of primates is calibrated at roughly 2% base changes per million years. However, molecular dating based on the use of a single fossil as a calibration point can lead to significant inaccuracies in the molecular clock. When possible, researchers advocate using multiple fossils in the calibration process.

Different Genes Are Analyzed to Study Phylogeny and Evaluate the Timing of Evolutionary Change

For evolutionary comparisons, the DNA sequences of many genes have been obtained from a wide range of sources. Many different genes have been studied to propose phylogenetic trees and evaluate the timing of past events. For example, the SSU rRNA gene used by Cooper and colleagues in their research on flightless birds (see Figure 25.11) is commonly used in evolutionary studies. As noted in Chapter 12, the gene for SSU rRNA is found in the genomes of all living organisms. Therefore, its function must have been established at an early stage in the evolution of life on this planet, and its sequence has changed fairly slowly. Furthermore, SSU rRNA is a rather large molecule, so it contains a large amount of sequence information. This gene has been sequenced for thousands of different species (see Figure 12.17). Slowly changing genes such as the gene that encodes SSU rRNA are useful for evaluating distant evolutionary relationships, such as comparing higher taxa. For example, SSU rRNA data can be used to place eukaryotic species into their proper phyla or orders.

Other genes have changed more rapidly during evolution because of a greater tolerance of neutral mutations. For example, the mitochondrial genome and DNA sequences within introns can more easily incur neutral mutations (compared to the coding sequences of genes), and so their sequences change frequently during evolution. More rapidly changing DNA sequences have been used to study recent evolutionary relationships, particularly among eukaryotic species such as species of large animals that have long generation times and therefore tend to evolve more slowly. In these cases, slowly evolving genes may not be very useful for establishing evolutionary relationships because two closely related species may have identical or nearly identical DNA sequences for such genes.

Figure 25.14 shows a simplified phylogeny of closely related species of primates. A molecular clock was used to give a timescale to this phylogenetic tree. The tree was proposed by comparing DNA sequence changes in the gene for cytochrome oxidase subunit II, one of several subunits of cytochrome oxidase, a protein in the mitochondrial inner membrane that is involved in cellular respiration. This gene tends to change fairly rapidly on an evolutionary timescale. The vertical scale of Figure 25.14 represents time, and the branch points labeled with letters represent common ancestors. Let's take a look at three branch points (labeled A, D, and E) and relate them to the accumulation of neutral mutations.

Ancestor A: This ancestor diverged into two species that ultimately gave rise to siamangs and the other five species. Since this divergence,

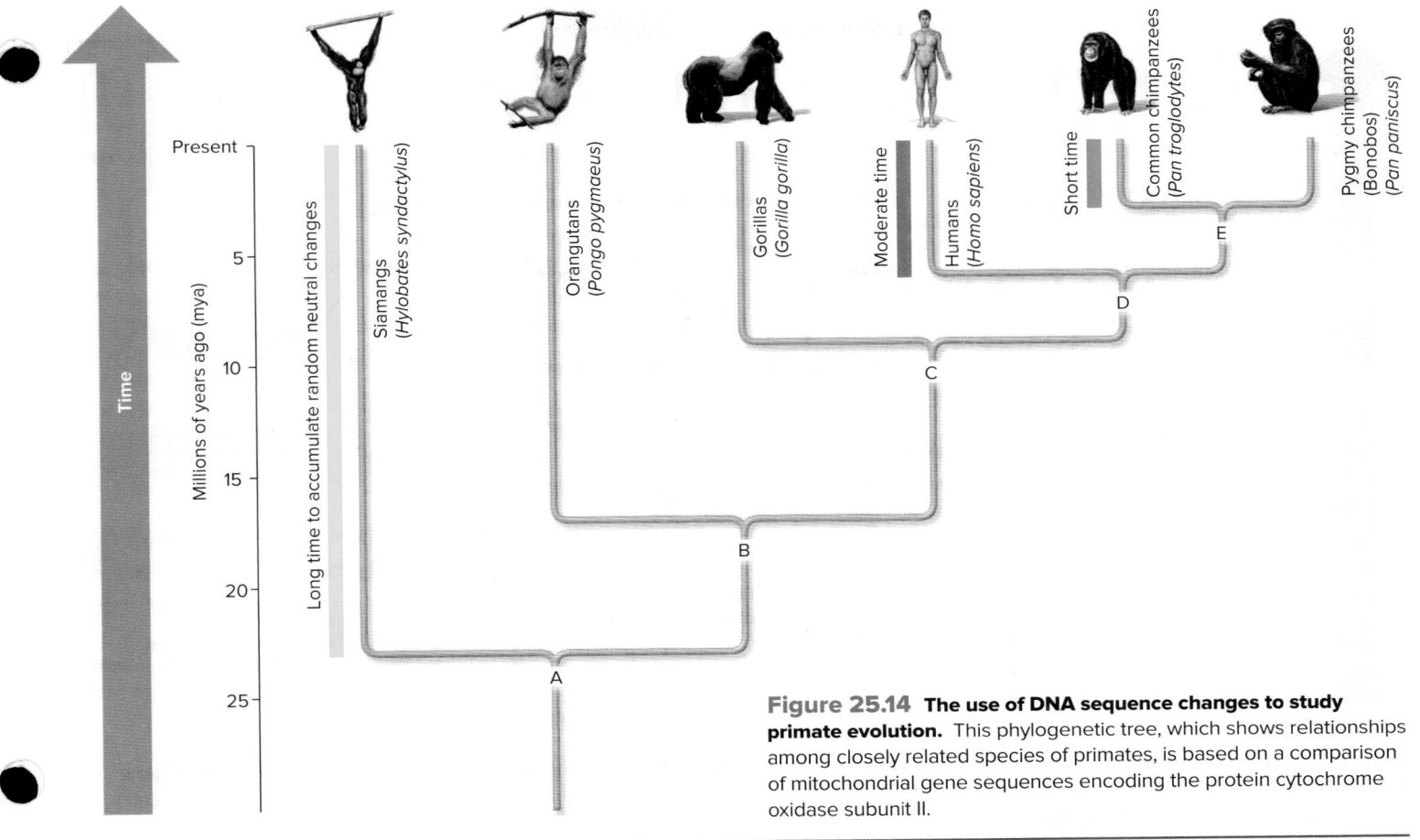

Figure 25.14 The use of DNA sequence changes to study primate evolution. This phylogenetic tree, which shows relationships among closely related species of primates, is based on a comparison of mitochondrial gene sequences encoding the protein cytochrome oxidase subunit II.

Core Skill: Modeling The goal of this modeling challenge is to propose a phylogenetic tree based on molecular data.

Modeling Challenge: Figure 22.13 compares a short amino acid sequence within the p53 protein among nine species. Propose an evolutionary tree that describes the evolutionary relationships of these species. You should also consider the data in the right column of Figure 22.13, which shows the percentages of amino acids in the whole p53 protein that are identical to the human sequence. The top of your tree should show the nine species with their names (as in Figure 25.14). Above the name of each species, put the number amino acid differences that occur within the short amino acid sequence for each species compared with that of humans.

there has been a long time (approximately 23 million years) for the siamang genome to accumulate a relatively high number of random neutral changes that would be different from the random changes that have occurred in the genomes of the other five species (see the yellow bar in Figure 25.14). Therefore, the gene in the siamangs is fairly different from the genes in the other five species.

Ancestor D: This ancestor diverged into two species that eventually gave rise to humans and chimpanzees. This divergence occurred a moderate time ago, approximately 6 mya, as illustrated by the red bar. The differences in gene sequences between humans and chimpanzees are relatively moderate.

Ancestor E: This ancestor diverged into two species of chimpanzees. Since the divergence of species E into two species, approximately 3 mya, the time for the molecular clock to "tick" (that is, accumulate random mutations) is relatively short, as depicted by the green bar in

Figure 25.14. Therefore, the two existing species of chimpanzees have fewer differences in their gene sequences compared to other primates.

25.5 Horizontal Gene Transfer

Learning Outcome:

1. Explain how horizontal gene transfer affects evolution and the relationships among different taxa.

Thus far, we have considered various ways to construct phylogenetic trees, which describe the relationships between ancestors and their descendents. The type of evolution depicted in the phylogenetic trees in previous sections, which involves changes in groups of species due to descent from a common ancestor, is sometimes called vertical evolution. Since the time of Darwin, vertical evolution has been the traditional way biologists have viewed the evolutionary process. However, over the past

4. Which of the following characteristics is (are) not shared by bacteria, archaea, and eukaryotes?
   a. DNA is the genetic material.
   b. Messenger RNA encodes the information to produce proteins.
   c. All cells are surrounded by a plasma membrane.
   d. The cytoplasm is compartmentalized into organelles.
   e. Both a and d are not shared by bacteria, archaea, and eukaryotes.

5. Which of the following occur at branch points, or nodes, in a phylogenetic tree?
   a. anagenesis   d. a and b
   b. cladogenesis   e. b and c
   c. horizontal gene transfer

6. The evolutionary history of a species is its
   a. systematics.   d. phylogeny.
   b. taxonomy.   e. embryology.
   c. evolution.

7. A taxon composed of all species derived from a common ancestor is referred to as
   a. a phylum.
   b. a monophyletic group or clade.
   c. a genus.
   d. an outgroup.
   e. all of the above.

8. A goal of modern taxonomy is to
   a. classify all organisms based on morphological similarities.
   b. classify all organisms into monophyletic groups.
   c. classify all organisms based solely on genetic similarities.
   d. determine the evolutionary relationships only between similar species.
   e. None of the above is a goal of modern taxonomy.

9. The concept that the preferred hypothesis is the one that is the simplest is
   a. phylogeny.   d. maximum likelihood.
   b. cladistics.   e. both b and d.
   c. the principle of parsimony.

10. Research indicates that horizontal gene transfer is less prevalent in eukaryotes because of
    a. the presence of organelles.
    b. multicellularity.
    c. sexual reproduction.
    d. all of the above.
    e. b and c only.

Conceptual Questions

1. Explain how the names of species conform to binomial nomenclature. Give an example of a species' name.

2. What is a molecular clock? How is it useful in the construction of phylogenetic trees?

3. **Core Concept: Evolution** What are some advantages and potential pitfalls of using changes in morphology to construct phylogenetic trees?

Collaborative Questions

1. Discuss how taxonomy is useful. Make a list of some practical applications that are derived from taxonomy.

2. Discuss how systematics is used to propose a phylogenetic tree and the rationale behind using the principle of parsimony to evaluate such a tree.

History of Life on Earth and Human Evolution

26

A fossil fish. This 50-million-year-old fossil of a unicorn fish (*Naso rectifrons*) is an example of the many different kinds of organisms that have existed during the history of life on Earth.
©George Bernard/SPL/Science Source

The amazing origin of the universe is difficult to comprehend. Astronomers think the universe began with a cosmic explosion called the Big Bang about 13.7 billion years ago (bya), after which the first clouds of the elements hydrogen and helium were formed. Over a long time period, gravitational forces collapsed these clouds to create stars that converted hydrogen and helium into heavier elements, including carbon, nitrogen, and oxygen, which are the atomic building blocks of life on Earth. These elements were returned to interstellar space by exploding stars called supernovas, which created clouds in which simple molecules such as water, carbon monoxide, and hydrocarbons formed. The clouds then collapsed to make a new generation of stars and solar systems.

Our solar system began about 4.6 bya after one or more local supernova explosions. According to one widely accepted scenario, hundreds of planetesimals (small celestial bodies like asteroids) occupied the region where Venus, Earth, and Mars are now found. The Earth, which is estimated to be 4.55 billion years old, grew from the aggregation of such planetesimals over a period of 100–200 million years. For the first half billion years or so after its formation, the Earth was too hot to allow liquid water to accumulate on its surface. By 4 bya, the Earth had cooled enough for the outer layers of the planet to solidify and for oceans to begin to form.

The period between 4.0 and 3.5 bya marked the emergence of life on our planet. The first forms of life that we know about produced well-preserved microscopic fossils, such as those found in western Australia. These fossils, estimated to be about 3.5 billion years old, resemble modern cyanobacteria, which are photosynthetic bacteria (**Figure 26.1**).

This chapter emphasizes when particular forms of life arose. We will begin by considering how researchers analyze and date fossils, which are the remains of past life-forms. We will then consider how fossils, such as the one shown in the chapter opening photo, have provided biologists with evidence of the history of life on Earth from its earliest beginnings to the present day. The last section focuses on one of the most interesting stories of evolution, which is the lineage that gave rise to modern humans.

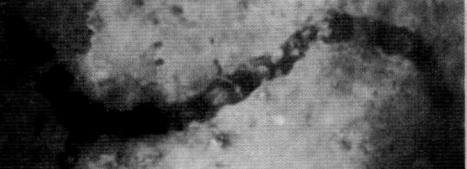

(a) Fossil prokaryote

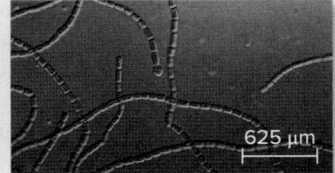

625 μm

(b) Modern cyanobacteria

Figure 26.1 Earliest fossils and living cyanobacteria. (a) A fossilized prokaryote about 3.5 billion years old that is thought to be an early cyanobacterium. (b) A modern cyanobacterium, which has a similar morphology. Cyanobacterial cells are connected to each other to form chains, as shown here. a: ©J. W. Schopf; b: ©Michael Abbey/Science Source

26.1 The Fossil Record

Learning Outcomes:

1. Describe how fossils are formed.
2. **CoreSKILL** » Explain how radiometric dating is used to estimate the age of a fossil.
3. List several factors that affect the completeness of the fossil record.

We will begin this chapter by considering a process that has given us a window into the history of life over the past 3.5 billion years. **Fossils** are the preserved remains of past life on Earth. They can take many forms, including bones, shells, and leaves, and the impression of cells or other evidence, such as footprints or burrows. Scientists who study fossils are called **paleontologists** (from the Greek *palaios*, meaning ancient). Because our understanding of the history of life is derived primarily from the fossil record, it is important to appreciate how fossils are formed and dated and to understand why the fossil record cannot be viewed as complete.

Fossils Are Formed Within Sedimentary Rock

How are fossils usually formed? Many of the rocks observed by paleontologists are sedimentary rocks that were formed from particles of older rocks broken apart by water or wind. These particles, in the form of gravel, sand, or mud, settle and bury living and dead organisms at the bottoms of rivers, lakes, and oceans. Over time, more particles pile up, and sediments at the bottom of the pile eventually become rock. Gravel particles form rock called conglomerate, sand becomes sandstone, and mud becomes shale. Most fossils are formed when organisms are buried quickly, and then during the process of sedimentary rock formation, their hard parts are gradually replaced over millions of years by minerals, producing a recognizable representation of the original organism (see, for example, the chapter opening photo).

The relative ages of fossils can sometimes be revealed by their locations in sedimentary rock formations. Because sedimentary rocks are formed by small particles settling in layers, the layers are piled one on top of the other. In a sequence of layered rock, the lower layers are usually older than the upper layers. Paleontologists often study changes in life-forms over time by studying the fossils in layers from bottom to top (**Figure 26.2**). The more ancient life-forms are found in the lower layers, and newer species are found in the upper layers. However, such an assumption can occasionally be misleading when geological processes such as folding have flipped the layers.

The Analysis of Radioisotopes Is Used to Date Fossils

A common way to estimate the age of a fossil is by analyzing the decay of radioisotopes within the accompanying rock, a process called **radiometric dating**. As discussed in Chapter 2, many elements occur in multiple forms, called isotopes, that differ in

Figure 26.2 **An example of layers of sedimentary rock that contain fossils.** ©Simon Fraser/SPL/Science Source

Concept Check: *Which rock layer in this photo is most likely to be the oldest?*

the number of neutrons their atoms contain. A radioisotope is an unstable isotope of an element that decays spontaneously, releasing radiation at a constant rate. The **half-life** is the length of time required for a radioisotope to decay to exactly one-half of its initial quantity. Each radioisotope has its own unique half-life (**Figure 26.3a**). Within a sample of rock, scientists can measure the amount of a given radioisotope as well as the amount of the decay product—the isotope that is produced when the original isotope decays. For dating geological materials, several types of isotope decay patterns are particularly useful: carbon to nitrogen, potassium to argon, rubidium to strontium, and uranium to lead (**Figure 26.3b**).

To determine the age of a rock using radiometric dating, paleontologists need to have a way to set the clock—extrapolate back to a starting point at which a rock did not have any amount of the decay product. Except for fossils less than 50,000 years old, in which carbon-14 (^{14}C) dating can be employed, fossil dating is not usually conducted on the fossil itself or on the sedimentary rock in which the fossil is found. Most commonly, igneous rock—rock formed through the cooling and solidification of lava—in the vicinity of the sedimentary rock is dated. Why is igneous rock chosen? One reason is that igneous rock derived from an ancient lava flow initially contains uranium-235 (^{235}U) but no lead-207 (^{207}Pb). The decay product of ^{235}U is ^{207}Pb. By comparing the relative proportions of ^{235}U and ^{207}Pb in a sample, the age of igneous rock can be accurately determined.

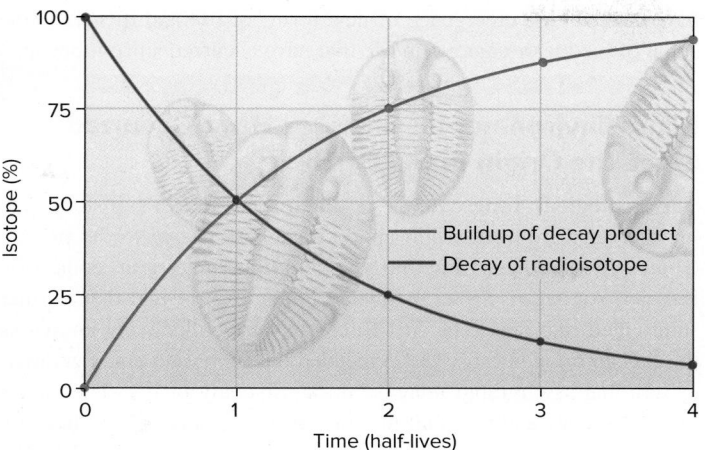

(a) Decay of a radioisotope

Radioisotope	Decay product	Half-life (years)	Useful dating range (years)
Carbon-14	Nitrogen-14	5,730	100–50,000
Potassium-40	Argon-40	1.3 billion	100,000–4.5 billion
Rubidium-87	Strontium-87	47 billion	10 million–4.5 billion
Uranium-235	Lead-207	710 million	10 million–4.5 billion
Uranium-238	Lead-206	4.5 billion	10 million–4.5 billion

(b) Radioisotopes that are useful for geological dating

Figure 26.3 **Radiometric dating of fossils.** **(a)** A rock can be dated by measuring the relative amounts of a radioisotope and its decay product within the rock. **(b)** These five radioisotopes are particularly useful for the dating of fossils.

`Concept Check:` *If you suspected a fossil to be 50 million years old, which pair of radioisotope and decay product would you choose to analyze?*

 **THE QUESTION** *The process of decay for a radioisotope is represented by the following equation:*

$$N = N_0 e^{-(0.693t/T_{1/2})}$$

where
N is the number of atoms of a radioisotope after a certain time,
N_0 is the number of atoms of the radioisotope that were originally present (prior to any decay),
e is the natural logarithm,
t is the time during which decay has occurred, and
T_{1/2} is the half-life of the radioisotope.

A paleontologist discovered a fossil of a previously unidentified reptile. A sample of nearby igneous rock contained 0.11 mg of uranium-235 (^{235}U) and 0.035 mg of lead-207 (^{207}Pb). Estimate the age of this fossil.

T **OPIC** *What topic in biology does this question address?* The topic is radiometric dating of fossils. More specifically, the question asks you to calculate an estimated age for a particular fossil.

I **NFORMATION** *What information do you know based on the question and your understanding of the topic?* In the question, you are given an equation that describes the decay process for a radioisotope. You are also given the relative amounts of uranium-235 and lead-207 in an igneous rock that was near the fossil of interest. From your understanding of the topic, you may recall that very old fossils are often dated by analyzing nearby igneous rock because such rock initially contains only uranium-235.

P **ROBLEM-SOLVING** **S** **TRATEGY** *Make a calculation.* You first need to calculate the number of atoms of ^{235}U and ^{207}Pb in the sample of igneous rock. The atomic masses of ^{235}U and ^{207}Pb are approximately 235 g/mol and 207 g/mol, respectively. For ^{235}U, the number of atoms in the sample, which is N, is

$$N = \frac{0.11}{235} \times 6.022 \times 10^{23} = 2.82 \times 10^{20}$$

For ^{207}Pb, the number of atoms in the sample is

$$\frac{0.035}{207} \times 6.022 \times 10^{23} = 1.02 \times 10^{20}$$

It is assumed that all of the ^{207}Pb is the decay product of ^{235}U. Therefore, the original number of atoms of ^{235}U, which is N_0, was

$$N_0 = (2.82 \times 10^{20}) + (1.02 \times 10^{20}) = 3.84 \times 10^{20}$$

The half-life ($T_{1/2}$) for ^{235}U is 710 million years (see Figure 26.3). You substitute these values for N, N_0, and $T_{1/2}$ into the given equation and solve for t.

ANSWER *The fossil is approximately 316 million years old.*

Several Factors Affect the Completeness of the Fossil Record

The fossil record should not be viewed as a complete and balanced representation of the species that existed in the past. Several factors affect the likelihood that extinct organisms have been preserved as fossils and will be identified by paleontologists (**Table 26.1**). First, certain organisms are more likely than others to become fossilized. Organisms with hard shells or bones tend to be over-represented in the fossil record. Factors such as anatomy, size, number, and the environment and time in which they lived also play important roles in determining the likelihood that organisms will be preserved in the fossil record. In addition, geological processes may favor the fossilization of certain types of organisms. Finally, unintentional biases arise that are related to the efforts of paleontologists. For example, scientific interests may favor searching for and analyzing certain species over others: Many paleontologists have been greatly interested in finding the remains of dinosaurs.

Table 26.1	Factors That Affect the Fossil Record
Factor	**Description**
Anatomy	Organisms with hard body parts, such as animals with a skeleton or thick shell, are more likely to be preserved than are organisms composed of soft tissues.
Size	The fossil remains of larger organisms are more likely to be found than those of smaller organisms.
Number	Species that existed in greater numbers or over a larger area are more likely to be preserved within the fossil record than those that existed in smaller numbers or in a smaller area.
Environment	Inland species are less likely to become fossilized than are those that lived in a marine environment or near the edge of water because sedimentary rock is more likely to be formed in or near water.
Time	Species that lived relatively recently or existed for a long time are more likely to be found as fossils than species that lived very long ago or for a relatively short time.
Geological processes	Due to the chemistry of fossilization, certain organisms are more likely to be preserved than are other organisms.
Paleontology	Certain types of fossils may be more interesting to paleontologists. In addition, a significant bias exists with regard to the locations where paleontologists search for fossils. For example, they tend to search in regions where other fossils have already been found.

Although the fossil record is incomplete, it has provided a wealth of information regarding the history of the types of life that existed on Earth. The rest of this chapter will survey the emergence of life-forms from 3.5 bya to the present.

26.2 History of Life on Earth

Learning Outcomes:

1. List the types of environmental changes that have affected the history of life on Earth.
2. Describe the cell structure and energy utilization of the first living organisms that arose during the Archaean eon.
3. Explain how the origin of eukaryotic cells involved a union between bacterial and archaeal cells.
4. Describe the key features of multicellular organisms, which arose during the Proterozoic eon.
5. Outline the major events and changes in species diversity during the Paleozoic, Mesozoic, and Cenozoic eras.

In Chapter 4, we considered hypotheses concerning how the first cells came into existence. The first known fossils of single-celled organisms were preserved approximately 3.5 bya. In this section, we will begin with a brief description of the geological changes on Earth that have affected the emergence of new forms of life and then examine some of the major changes in life that have occurred since it began.

Many Environmental Changes Have Occurred Since the Origin of the Earth

The **geological timescale** is a timeline of Earth's history and major events from its origin approximately 4.55 bya to the present (**Figure 26.4**). This timeline is subdivided into four eons—the Hadean, Archaean, Proterozoic, and Phanerozoic—and then further subdivided into eras. The first three eons are collectively known as the Precambrian because they preceded the Cambrian era, a geological era that saw a rapid increase in the diversity of life. The names of several eons and eras end in -zoic (meaning animal life), because these time intervals have been defined on the basis of animal life. We will examine these time periods later in this chapter.

The changes that occurred in living organisms over the past 4 billion years are the result of two interactive processes. First, as discussed in the previous chapters, genetic changes in organisms can affect their characteristics. Such changes influence organisms' abilities to survive and reproduce in their native environment. Second, the environment on Earth has undergone dramatic changes that have profoundly influenced the types of organisms that have existed during different periods of time. In some cases, an environmental change has allowed new types of organisms to flourish. Alternatively, environmental changes have resulted in **extinction**—the complete loss of a species or group of species. Major types of environmental changes are described next.

Temperature During the first 2.5 billion years of its existence, the surface of the Earth gradually cooled. However, during the last 2 billion years, the Earth has undergone major fluctuations in temperature, producing Ice Ages that alternate with warmer periods. Furthermore, the temperature on Earth is not uniform, which produces environments where the temperatures are quite different, such as tropical rain forests and the arctic tundra.

Atmosphere The chemical composition of the gases surrounding the Earth has changed substantially over the past 4 billion years. One notable change involves the amount of oxygen. Prior to 2.4 bya, relatively little oxygen gas was in the atmosphere, but at that time, levels of oxygen in the form of O_2 began to rise significantly. The emergence of organisms that are capable of photosynthesis added oxygen to the atmosphere. Our current atmosphere contains about 21% O_2.

Increased levels of oxygen are thought to have a played a key role in various aspects of the history of life, including the following:

- The origin of many animal body plans coincided with a rise in atmospheric O_2.
- The conquest of land by arthropods (about 410 mya) and a second conquest by arthropods and vertebrates (about 350 mya) occurred during periods in which O_2 levels were high or increasing.
- Increases in animal body sizes are associated with higher O_2 levels.

Higher levels of O_2 could have contributed to these events because higher O_2 levels may enhance the ability of animals to carry out

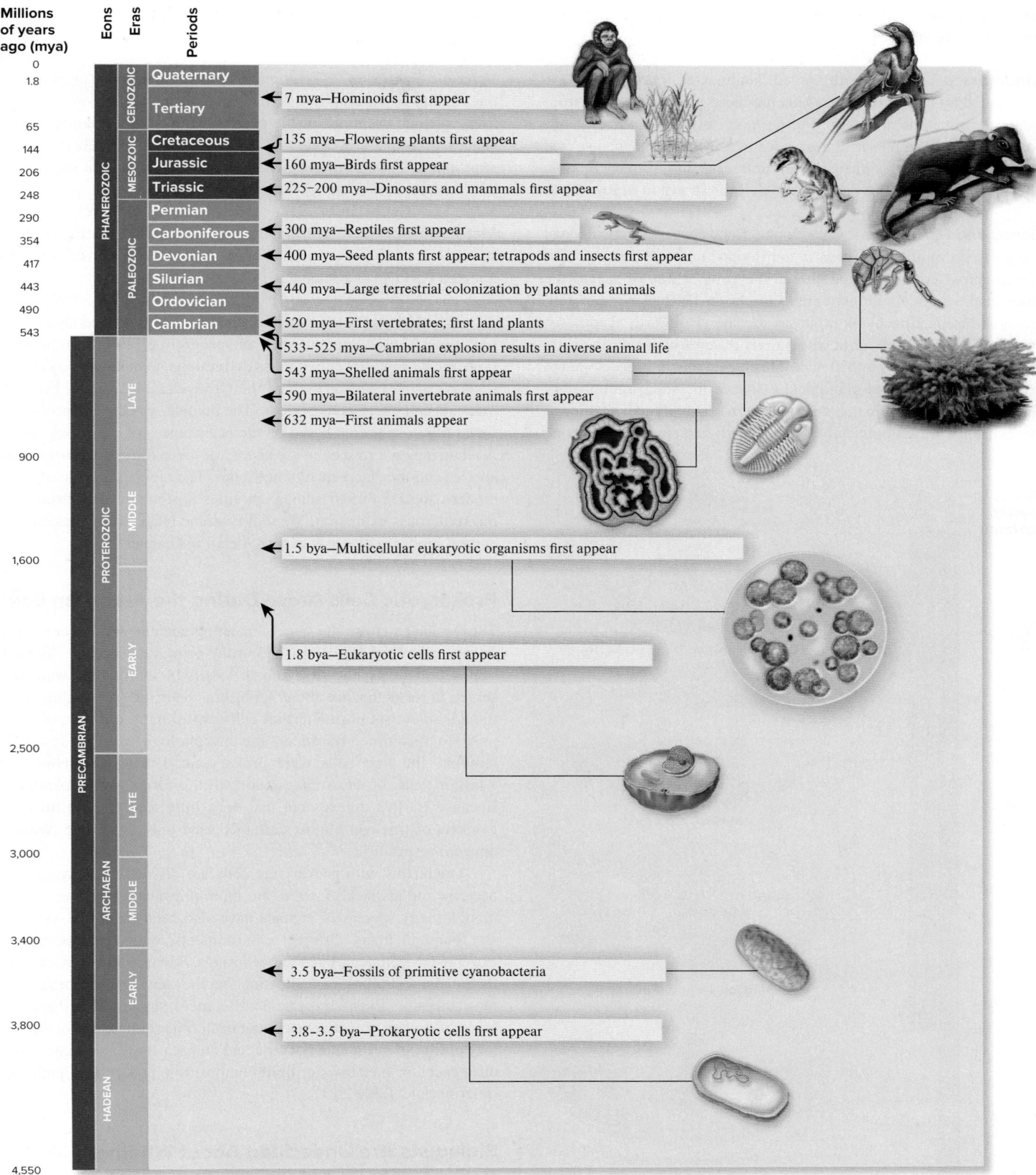

Figure 26.4 **The geological timescale and an overview of the history of life on Earth.**

aerobic respiration. These events are discussed later in this chapter and in more detail in Unit V.

Landmasses As the Earth cooled, landmasses formed that were surrounded by bodies of water. This produced two different environments: terrestrial and aquatic. Furthermore, over the course of billions of years, the major landmasses, known as the continents, shifted their positions, changed their shapes, and separated from each other. This phenomenon, called **continental drift**, is shown in **Figure 26.5**.

Floods and Glaciations Catastrophic floods have periodically had major effects on the organisms in the flooded regions. Glaciers have moved across continents and altered the composition of species on those landmasses. As an extreme example, in 1992, American geobiologist Joseph Kirschvink proposed the snowball Earth hypothesis, which suggests that the Earth was entirely covered by ice during parts of the period from 790 to 630 mya. This hypothesis was developed to explain various types of geological evidence including sedimentary deposits of glacial origin that are found at tropical latitudes. Although the existence of a completely frozen Earth remains controversial,

massive glaciations over our planet have had an important effect on the history of life.

Volcanic Eruptions The eruptions of volcanoes harm organisms in the vicinity of an eruption, sometimes causing extinctions. In addition, volcanic eruptions in the oceans lead to the formation of new islands. Massive eruptions may also spew so much debris into the atmosphere that they affect global temperatures and limit solar radiation, which restricts photosynthetic production.

Meteorite Impacts During its long history, the Earth has been struck by many meteorites. Large meteorites have significantly affected Earth's environment.

The effects of one or more of the changes described above have sometimes caused large numbers of species to go extinct at the same time. Such events are called **mass extinctions**. Five large mass extinctions occurred near the ends of the Ordovician, Devonian, Permian, Triassic, and Cretaceous periods. The boundaries between geological time periods are often based on the occurrences of mass extinctions. A recurring pattern seen in the history of life is the extinction of some species and the emergence of new ones. The rapid extinction of many modern species due to human activities is sometimes referred to as the sixth mass extinction. We will examine mass extinctions and the current biodiversity crisis in more detail in Chapter 60.

Prokaryotic Cells Arose During the Archaean Eon

The Archaean (from the Greek, meaning ancient) was an eon when diverse microbial life flourished in the primordial oceans. As mentioned previously, the first known fossils of living cells were preserved in rocks that are about 3.5 billion years old (see Figure 26.1), though scientists postulate that cells arose many millions of years prior to this time. Based on the morphology of their fossilized remains, the first cells were prokaryotic. During the more than 1 billion years of the Archaean eon, all life-forms were prokaryotic. Because Earth's atmosphere had very little free O_2, the microorganisms of this eon almost certainly used only anaerobic (without oxygen) respiration.

Organisms with prokaryotic cells are divided into two groups: bacteria and archaea. Bacteria are more prevalent on modern Earth, though many species of archaea have also been identified. Archaea are found in many different environments, with some occupying extreme environments such as hot springs. Bacteria and archaea share fundamental similarities, indicating that they are derived from a common ancestor. Even so, certain differences suggest that these two types of prokaryotes diverged from each other quite early in the history of life. In particular, bacteria and archaea show some interesting differences in metabolism, lipid composition, and genetic pathways (refer back to Table 25.1).

Biologists Are Undecided About Whether Heterotrophs or Autotrophs Came First

An important factor that greatly influenced the emergence of new species is the availability of energy. As we learned in Unit II, all

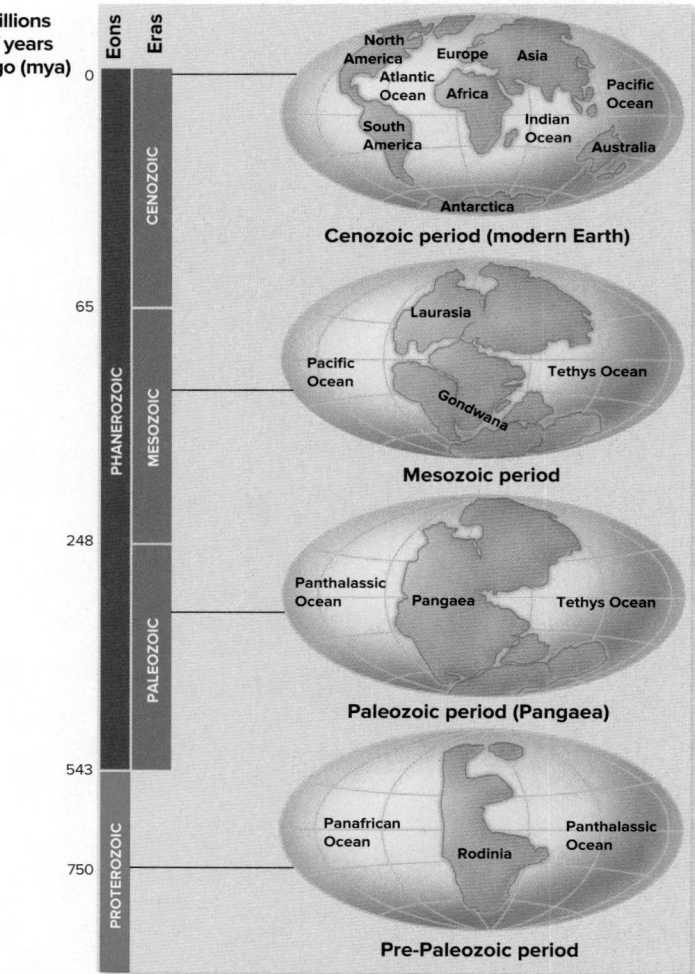

Figure 26.5 Continental drift. The relative locations of the continents on Earth have changed dramatically over time.

organisms require energy to survive and reproduce. Organisms follow two different strategies to obtain energy.

- Some are **heterotrophs**, which means their energy is derived from the chemical bonds within the organic molecules they consume. Because the most common sources of organic molecules today are other organisms, heterotrophs typically consume other organisms or materials from other organisms.

- Alternatively, many organisms are **autotrophs**, which directly harness energy from either inorganic molecules or light. Among modern species, plants are an important example of autotrophs. Plants directly absorb light energy and use it (via photosynthesis) to synthesize organic molecules such as glucose. On modern Earth, heterotrophs ultimately rely on autotrophs for the production of food.

Were the first forms of life heterotrophs or autotrophs? The answer is not resolved. Some biologists have speculated that autotrophs, such as those living near deep-sea vents, may have arisen first. These organisms would have used chemicals that were made near the vents as an energy source to make organic molecules. Alternatively, many scientists have hypothesized that the first living cells were heterotrophs. They reason that it would have been simpler for the first primitive cells to use the organic molecules in the prebiotic soup as a source of energy.

If heterotrophs came first, why were cyanobacteria preserved in the earliest fossils, rather than heterotrophs? One possible reason is related to their manner of growth. Certain cyanobacteria promote the formation of a layered structure called a **stromatolite (Figure 26.6)**. The aquatic environment where these cyanobacteria survive is rich in minerals such as calcium. The cyanobacteria grow in large mats that form layers. As they grow, they deplete the carbon dioxide (CO_2) in the surrounding water. This causes calcium carbonate in the water to gradually precipitate over the bacterial cells, calcifying the older cells in the lower layers and also trapping grains of sediment. Newer cells produce a layer on top. Over time, many layers of calcified cells and sediment are formed, thereby producing a stromatolite. This process still occurs today in places such as Shark Bay in western Australia, which is renowned for the stromatolites along its beaches (Figure 26.6b).

The emergence and proliferation of ancient cyanobacteria had two critical consequences. First, the autotrophic nature of these bacteria enabled them to produce organic molecules from CO_2. This ability prevented the depletion of organic foodstuffs that would have been exhausted if only heterotrophs existed. Second, cyanobacteria produce O_2 as a waste product of photosynthesis. During the Archaean and Proterozoic eons, the activity of cyanobacteria led to the gradual rise in atmospheric O_2 noted earlier. The increase in O_2 spelled doom for many anaerobic species, which became restricted to a few anoxic (without oxygen) environments, such as deep within the soil. However, O_2 enabled the emergence of new bacterial and archaeal species that used aerobic (with oxygen) respiration (see Chapter 7). In addition, aerobic respiration is likely to have played a key role in the emergence and eventual explosion of eukaryotic life-forms, which typically have high energy demands. These eukaryotic life-forms are described next.

 **Core Concept: Evolution**

The Origin of Eukaryotic Cells Involved a Union Between Bacterial and Archaeal Cells

Eukaryotic cells arose during the Proterozoic eon, which began 2.5 bya and ended 543 mya (see Figure 26.4). The manner in which the first eukaryotic cell originated is not entirely understood. In modern eukaryotic cells, genetic material is found in three distinct organelles. All eukaryotic cells contain DNA in the nucleus and mitochondria, and plant and algal cells also have DNA in their chloroplasts. To address the issue of the origin of

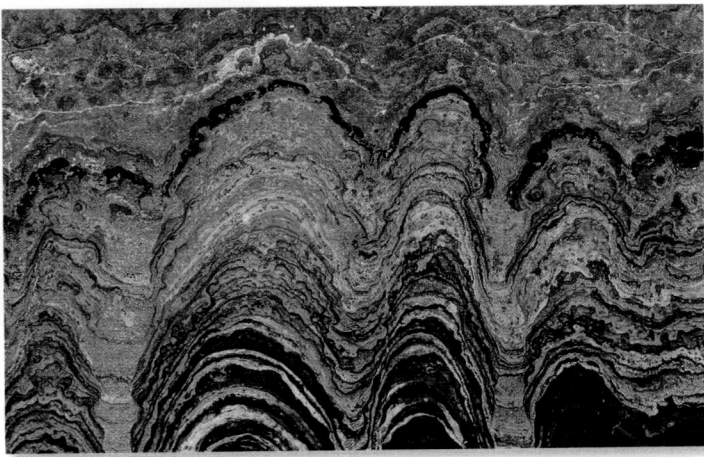

(a) Fossil stromatolite

(b) Modern stromatolites

Figure 26.6 Fossil and modern stromatolites: evidence of autotrophic cyanobacteria. Each stromatolite is a rocklike structure, typically 1 m in diameter. **(a)** Section of a fossilized stromatolite. The layers are mats of mineralized cyanobacteria, one layer on top of the other. The existence of fossil stromatolites provides evidence of early autotrophic organisms. **(b)** Modern stromatolites that have formed in western Australia.

Devonian. Early tetrapods included amphibians, which lived on land but required water in which to lay their eggs.

In the oceans, many types of invertebrates flourished, including brachiopods, echinoderms, and corals. This period is sometimes called the Age of Fishes, as many new types of fishes emerged. During a period of approximately 20 million years near the end of the Devonian period, a prolonged series of extinctions eliminated many marine species. The cause of this mass extinction is not well understood.

Carboniferous Period (354–290 mya) The term Carboniferous refers to the deposits of coal, a sedimentary rock primarily composed of carbon, that were formed during this period. The Carboniferous period had the ideal conditions for the subsequent formation of coal. It was a cooler period, and much of the land was covered by forest swamps. Coal was formed over many millions of years from compressed layers of rotting vegetation.

Plants and animals further diversified during the Carboniferous period. Very large plants and trees became prevalent. For example, tree ferns such as *Psaronius* grew to a height of 15 m or more (**Figure 26.12**). The first flying insects emerged. Giant dragonflies with a wingspan of over 2 ft inhabited the forest swamps. Terrestrial vertebrates also became more diverse. Amphibians were very prevalent. One innovation that seemed particularly beneficial was the amniotic egg. In reptiles, the amniotic egg was covered with a leathery or hard shell, which prevented the desiccation of the embryo inside. This innovation was critical for the emergence of reptiles during this period.

Permian Period (290–248 mya) At the beginning of the Permian, continental drift had brought much of the Earth's total land together into a supercontinent known as Pangaea (see Figure 26.5). The interior regions of Pangaea were dry, with great seasonal fluctuations.

The forests of fernlike plants were replaced with gymnosperms. Species resembling modern conifers first appeared in the fossil record. Amphibians were prevalent, but reptiles became the dominant vertebrate species.

At the end of the Permian period, the largest known mass extinction in the history of life on Earth occurred; 90–95% of marine species and a large proportion of terrestrial species were eliminated. The cause of the Permian extinction is the subject of much research and controversy. One possibility is that glaciation destroyed the habitats of terrestrial species and lowered ocean levels, which would have caused greater competition among marine species. Another hypothesis is that enormous volcanic eruptions in Siberia produced large ash clouds that abruptly changed the climate on Earth.

Phanerozoic Eon: The Mesozoic Era Saw the Rise and Fall of the Dinosaurs

The Permian extinction marks the division between the Paleozoic and Mesozoic eras. Mesozoic means middle animals. It was a time that saw great changes in animal and plant species. This era is sometimes called the Age of Dinosaurs, because those animals flourished during this time. The climate during the Mesozoic era was consistently hot, and terrestrial environments were relatively dry. Little if any ice was found at either pole. The Mesozoic is divided into three periods: the Triassic, Jurassic, and Cretaceous.

Triassic Period (248–206 mya) Reptiles were plentiful in this period, including new groups such as crocodiles and turtles. The first dinosaurs emerged during the middle of the Triassic. Dinosaurs were reptiles that shared certain anatomical features, including an erect posture. The first mammals also emerged, such as the small *Megazostrodon* (**Figure 26.13**). Gymnosperms were the dominant

Figure 26.12 A giant tree fern, *Psaronius*, from the Carboniferous period. This genus became extinct during the Permian. The illustration is a re-creation based on fossil evidence. The inset shows a fossilized section of the trunk, also known as petrified wood. ©Natural History Museum, London/SPL/Science Source

Figure 26.13 *Megazostrodon*, the first known mammal of the Triassic period. The illustration is a re-creation based on fossilized skeletons. The *Megazostrodon* was 10 to 12 cm long.

 Core Skill: Connections Look ahead to Table 35.1. What are the common characteristics of mammals?

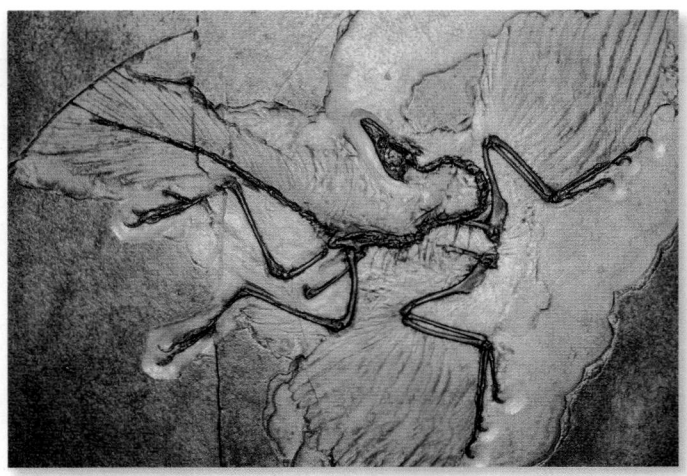

Figure 26.14 A fossil of an early birdlike animal, *Archaeopteryx*, which emerged in the Jurassic period. ©Jason Edwards/Getty Images

land plant. Volcanic eruptions near the end of the Triassic are thought to have caused global warming, resulting in mass extinctions that eliminated many marine and terrestrial species.

Jurassic Period (206–144 mya) Gymnosperms, such as conifers, continued to be the dominant vegetation in the Jurassic period. Mammals were not prevalent. Reptiles continued to be the dominant land vertebrate. Some dinosaurs attained enormous sizes, including the massive *Brachiosaurus*, which reached a length of 25 m (80 ft) and weighed up to 100 tons! Modern birds are descendants of a dinosaur lineage called theropod (meaning beast-footed) dinosaurs. *Tyrannosaurus rex* is one of the best known theropod dinosaurs. An early birdlike animal, *Archaeopteryx* (**Figure 26.14**), emerged in the Jurassic period. However, paleontologists are debating whether or not *Archaeopteryx* is a true ancestor of modern birds.

Cretaceous Period (144–65 mya) On land, dinosaurs continued to be the dominant animals in the Cretaceous period. The earliest flowering plants, called angiosperms, which form seeds within a protective chamber, emerged and began to diversify.

The end of the Cretaceous witnessed another mass extinction, which brought an end to many previously successful groups of organisms. Except for the lineage that gave rise to birds, dinosaurs abruptly died out, as did many other species. As with the Permian extinction, the cause or causes of this mass extinction are still debated. One plausible hypothesis suggests that a large meteorite hit the region that is now the Yucatan Peninsula of Mexico, lifting massive amounts of debris into the air and thereby blocking the sunlight from reaching the Earth's surface. Such a dense haze could have cooled the Earth's surface by 11–15°C (20–30°F). Evidence also points to strong volcanic eruptions as a contributing factor for this mass extinction.

Phanerozoic Eon: Mammals and Flowering Plants Diversified During the Cenozoic Era

The Cenozoic era spans the most recent 65 million years. It is divided into two periods: Tertiary and Quaternary. In many parts of the world,

tropical conditions were replaced by a colder, drier climate. During this time, mammals became the largest terrestrial animals, which is why the Cenozoic is sometimes called the Age of Mammals. However, the Cenozoic era also saw an amazing diversification of many types of organisms, including birds, fishes, insects, and flowering plants.

Tertiary Period (65–1.8 mya) On land, the mammals that survived from the Cretaceous began to diversify rapidly during the early part of the Tertiary period. Angiosperms became the dominant land plant, and insects became important for their pollination. Fishes also diversified, and sharks became abundant.

Toward the end of the Tertiary period, about 7 mya, hominoids came into existence. **Hominoids** include humans, chimpanzees, gorillas, orangutans, and gibbons, plus all of their recent ancestors. The subset of hominoids called hominins includes modern humans, extinct human species (for example, of the *Homo* genus), and our immediate ancestors. In 2002, a fossil of the earliest known hominin, *Sahelanthropus tchadensis*, was discovered in Central Africa. This fossil was dated at between 6 and 7 million years old. Another early hominin genus, called *Australopithecus*, first emerged in Africa about 4 mya. Australopithecines walked upright and had a protruding jaw, prominent eyebrow ridges, and a small braincase.

Quaternary Period (1.8 mya–present) Periodic Ice Ages have been prevalent during the last 1.8 million years, covering much of Europe and North America. This period has witnessed the widespread extinction of many species of mammals, particularly larger ones. Certain species of hominins became increasingly more like living humans. Fossils of *Homo habilis*, or handy man, so called because stone tools were found with the fossil remains, have been dated to close to the beginning of the Quaternary period. *Homo sapiens*—modern humans—first appeared about 200,000 years ago. The evolution of hominins is discussed in more detail in the next section.

26.3 Human Evolution

Learning Outcomes:

1. List the common characteristics of primates and describe their evolutionary relationships.
2. Explain how human species evolved from other primate species, and describe how they spread across the Earth.
3. Provide examples of how populations of *Homo sapiens* are still evolving.
4. Compare and contrast modern human variation at the phenotype and genotype levels.

Hardly a topic in biology has evoked more interest or public debate than human evolution. The question of "where did we come from" has been considered by people for thousands of years. In this section, we will tackle this question from an evolutionary perspective.

We begin with an overview of primate evolution, in which we explore how humans are evolutionarily related to their closest nonhuman relatives. We then take a closer look at the evolutionary events that gave rise to modern humans. As you will see, many extinct species of humans have existed, including the Denisovans, which were

Core Concept: Evolution

Comparing the Genomes of Humans and Chimpanzees

A male chimp called Clint, which lived at a primate research center in Atlanta provided the DNA used to sequence the chimp genome. In 2005, the Chimpanzee Sequencing and Analysis Consortium published an initial sequence of the chimpanzee genome. The draft sequence followed the 2003 publication of the human genome (see Chapter 21) and allowed scientists to make detailed comparisons between the two species. These comparisons revealed that the sequences of base pairs of the two genomes differ by only 1.23%, which is 10 times less than the difference between the mouse and rat genomes. Comparisons of human and chimpanzee proteomes also showed that 29% of all proteins are identical, with most others differing by one or two amino acid substitutions.

Many of the genetic differences between chimps and humans result from chromosome inversions and duplications. Over 1,500 inversions occur between the chimp and human genomes. Although many inversions are in the noncoding regions of the genome, the DNA in these regions may regulate the expression of the genes in the coding regions. Duplications and deletions are also common. For example, humans have lost a gene called *caspase-12,* which in other primates may protect against Alzheimer's disease.

Some interesting genetic differences were apparent between chimps and humans even before their entire genomes were sequenced. In 2002, Swedish molecular geneticist Svante Pääbo discovered differences between humans and chimps in a gene called *FOXP2,* which plays a role in speech development. Proteins encoded by this gene differ in just two amino acids of a 715-amino-acid sequence. Researchers propose that the mutations in this gene have been crucial for the development of human speech.

In 2006, a team led by American geneticist David Reich discovered that the human X chromosome diverged from the chimpanzee X chromosome about 1.2 million years more recently than the other chromosomes. This indicated to the researchers that the human and chimp lineages split apart, then began interbreeding before diverging again. If so, the interbreeding explains why many fossils appear to exhibit traits of both humans and chimps: Those primates may actually have been human-chimpanzee hybrids.

Bipedalism Is a Distinguishing Feature of Humans

About 7 mya in Africa, a lineage that led to modern humans diverged from other primate lineages. The evolution of humans should not be viewed as a neat, stepwise progression from one species to another. Rather, human evolution, like the evolution of all species, can be visualized more like a tree, with one or two **hominin** species—members of the Hominini tribe—likely coexisting at the same point in time, with some eventually going extinct and some giving rise to other species (**Figure 26.18**).

The key characteristic differentiating hominins from other apes is that hominins walk on two feet; that is, they are **bipedal**. At about the time when hominins diverged from other ape lineages, the Earth's climate had cooled, and the forests of Africa gave way to grassy savannas. Bipedal locomotion and an upright stance may have been advantageous in allowing hominins to peer over the tall grasses of the savanna to see predators or prey.

Bipedalism is correlated with important anatomical changes in hominins. First, the opening of the skull where the spinal cord enters shifted forward, causing the spine to be more directly underneath the head. Second, the hominin pelvis became broader to support the additional weight. And third, the lower limbs, used for walking, became relatively larger than those in other apes. These are the types of anatomical changes paleontologists look for in the fossil record to determine whether fossil remains are hominins.

The earliest known hominin, *Sahelanthropus tchadensis*, was discovered in Central Africa in 2002. Fossils of this species are dated at 7 million years old. The evolutionary relationship between *S. tchadensis* and later hominin species is unclear. Another early group of hominins included several species of the genus *Australopithecus,* which first emerged in Africa about 4 mya. As shown in Figure 26.18, *Australopithecus afarensis* is generally regarded as the direct ancestor of most hominin species, but it could be a close relative of an unknown species that was the direct ancestor. From there, the evolution of different human species is still debated. It is generally agreed that two genera evolved from *Australopithecus:* the more robust *Paranthropus* and the genus *Homo*. The early stages of the evolution of *Homo* species, and their differentiation from at least two possible *Australopithecus* species, have not yet been determined with great certainty. However, the later divergence of various *Homo* species is better understood.

Australopithecus and *Paranthropus* Are Early Human Genera

Let's consider some of the general features of the two early human genera, *Australopithecus* and *Paranthropus*. In 1924, the first fossil was found in South Africa for a member of the genus *Australopithecus* (from the Latin *austral,* meaning southern, and the Greek *pithecus*, meaning ape). Since then, hundreds of fossils of this group have been unearthed all over southern and eastern Africa, the areas where fossil deposits are best exposed to paleontologists. This group was widespread, with at least six species. In 1974, American paleontologist Donald Johanson discovered the skeleton of a female *A. afarensis* in the Afar region of Ethiopia and dubbed her Lucy. (The Beatles' song "Lucy in the Sky with Diamonds" was playing in the camp the night when Johanson was sorting the unearthed bones.) Over 40% of the skeleton had been preserved, enough to provide a good idea of the physical appearance of australopithecines. Compared with modern humans, they were relatively small, about 1–1.5 m in height and approximately 18 kg in weight (**Figure 26.19**). Females were much smaller than males, a characteristic known as sexual dimorphism. Examination of the bones revealed that *A. afarensis* walked on two legs. They had a facial structure and a brain size (about 500 cubic centimeters [cm^3]) similar to those of a chimp.

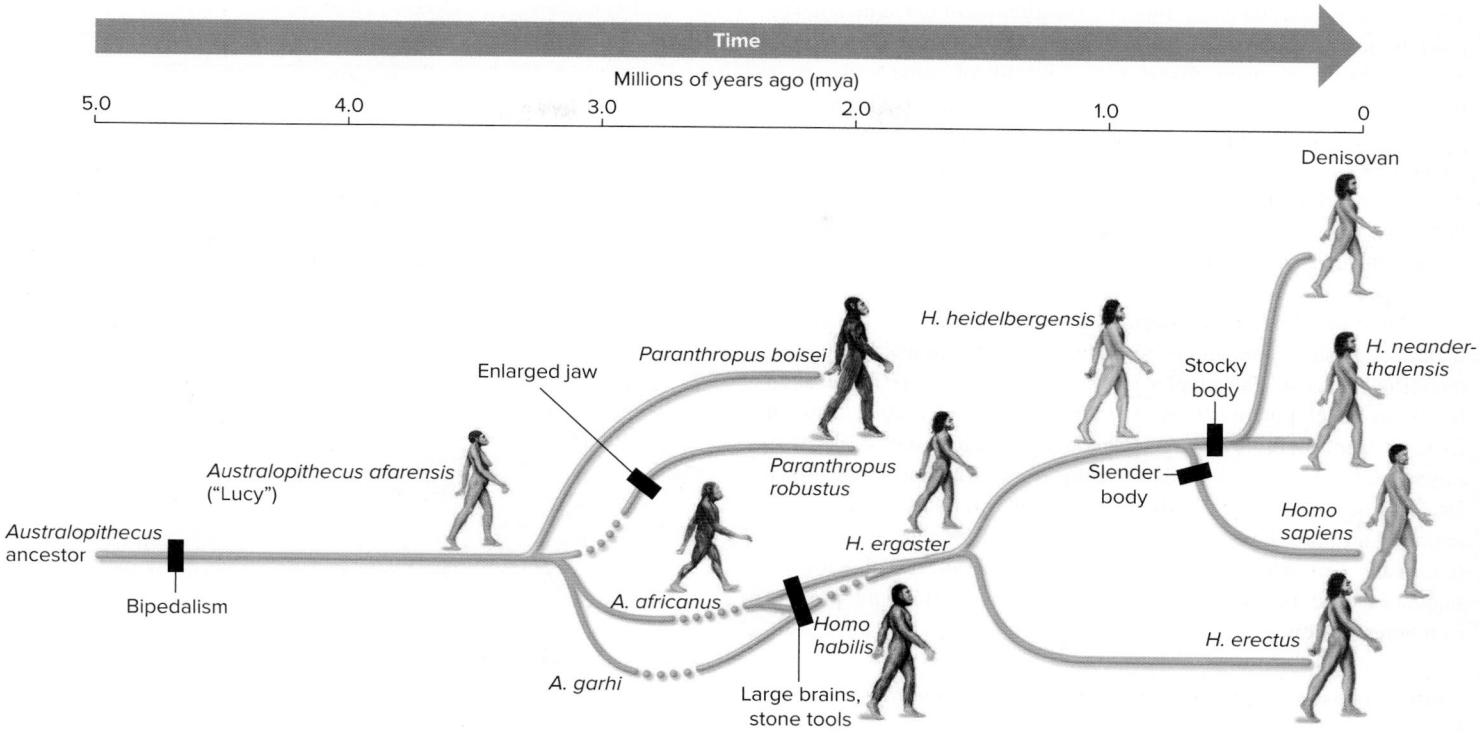

Figure 26.18 A possible scenario for human evolution. In this human family tree (based on the work of Donald Johanson and others), several hominin species lived during the same time period as others, but only one lineage gave rise to modern humans (*Homo sapiens*).

In the 1930s, the remains of bigger-boned hominins were found. Two of these larger species, now considered to be a separate genus, *Paranthropus,* weighed about 40 kg and lived during the same time period as australopithecines and early *Homo* species. *Paranthropus* were vegetarians with enormous jaws used for grinding tough roots and tubers. Both *Paranthropus* species died out rather suddenly about 1.5–2.0 mya.

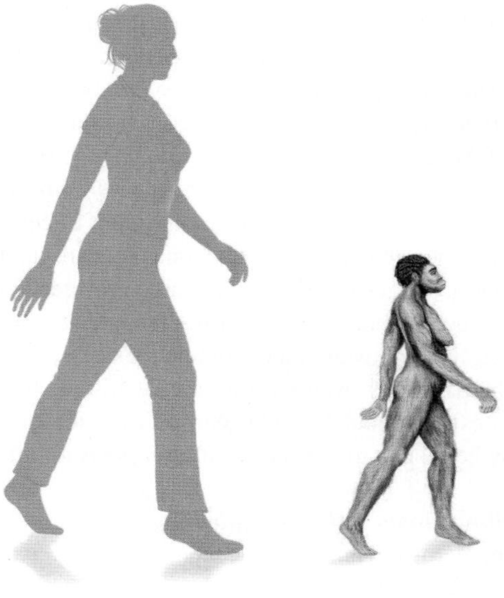

Although *Australopithecus africanus* was thought to have evolved slightly later than *A. afarensis,* its bones had been found much earlier than those of *A. afarensis.* In the 1920s, Australian anthropologist Raymond Dart described *A. africanus* from infant bones discovered in a cave in Taung, South Africa. The well-preserved skull was small but was well rounded, unlike the skulls of chimpanzees and gorillas. Also, the positioning of the head on the vertebral column indicated bipedalism. These observations suggested to Dart that he had found a transitional form between apes and humans. However, it would take another 20 years and the discovery of more fossils to convince the scientific world to support Dart's view. In 1996, remains of another species, *Australopithecus garhi,* were also found in the Afar region. The discoverers were surprised to find that the teeth had similarities with *Paranthropus boisei.* Garhi means surprise in the local Afar language. The proposal that both *A. garhi* and *A. africanus* are ancestors of modern humans has been the subject of much debate. They have been viewed as either dead-end cousins or the ancestors of the first members of the genus *Homo.*

The Genus *Homo* Includes Modern Humans and Their Most Recent Relatives

Seven different species in the *Homo* genus are shown in Figure 26.18. Let's consider how they are evolutionarily related to each other.

Homo habilis   In the 1960s, British paleontologist Louis Leakey found hominin fossils estimated to be about 2 million years old in Olduvai Gorge, Tanzania. Two particularly interesting observations

Figure 26.19 A modern woman compared to an australopithecine. Compared with modern humans, australopithecines, as illustrated by this reconstruction based on the famous fossil called Lucy, were much smaller and lighter.

about these fossils stand out. First, reconstruction of the skull showed a brain size of about 680 cm³, larger than that of *Australopithecus.* Second, the fossils were found with a wealth of stone tools. As a result, Leakey assigned the fossils to a new species, *Homo habilis,* from the Latin, meaning handy man. The discovery of several more *Homo* fossils followed, but there have been no extensive finds, as there were for australopithecines. This relative scarcity of fossils makes it difficult to determine which *Australopithecus* lineage gave rise to the *Homo* lineage (see Figure 26.17), and paleontologists remain divided on this point.

Homo habilis lived alongside *Paranthropus* in East Africa but had much smaller jaws and teeth, indicating that it probably ate large quantities of meat. The smaller jaw provided more space in the skull for brain development. *Homo habilis* probably scavenged most of its meat from the kills of large predators. A meatier diet is easier to digest and is rich in nutrients and calories. The human brain uses a lot of energy, 20% of the body's total energy production. The meat-eating habit thus helped propel the evolution of increasing brain size in humans. Cut marks on animal bones of the period reveal that early humans used stone tools to smash open bones and extract the protein-rich bone marrow.

Homo ergaster   Although the evidence is not entirely clear, *H. habilis* probably gave rise to one of the most important species of *Homo: Homo ergaster.* This hominin species arose in Africa about 2 million years ago; it had a human-looking face and skull, with downward-facing nostrils. *H. ergaster* was also a tool user, and the tools, such as hand axes, were larger and more sophisticated than those associated with *H. habilis. H. ergaster* evolved in a period of global cooling and drying that reduced tropical forests even more and promoted savanna conditions. Hairlessness and the regulation of body temperature through sweating may also have evolved at this time as adaptations to the sunny environment. A leaner body shape was evident. We know this from so-called Turkana boy, a fossil teenage boy found in Kenya in 1984. Though only 13 years old, scientists predict he would have been about 185 cm (6 ft 1 in.) when adult, much the same height as the Masai tribesman that inhabit the area today. A dark skin probably protected *H. ergaster* from the Sun's rays. The pelvis had narrowed, promoting efficiencies in walking upright, and the size of the brain and hence the skull increased, which may have produced more difficulty in childbirth. Mothers had to push increasingly large-brained infants through a narrowed pelvis. Researchers think that as a result, the human gestation period was shortened. Earlier birth leads to prolonged care of human infants compared with that in other apes. Prolonged child care required well-nourished mothers, who would have benefited from the support of their male partner and other members of a social group. Some anthropologists have suggested this was the beginning of the family.

H. ergaster is thought to have given rise to many species, including *Homo erectus, Homo heidelbergensis, Homo neanderthalensis,* and *Homo sapiens.* A possible timeline and geographic locations for these species are shown in **Figure 26.20**. *H. ergaster* probably was the first type of human to leave Africa, as similar bones have been found in the Eurasian country of Georgia. This species is believed to be a direct ancestor of modern humans, with *Homo heidelbergensis* viewed as an intermediary step. Living at the same time as

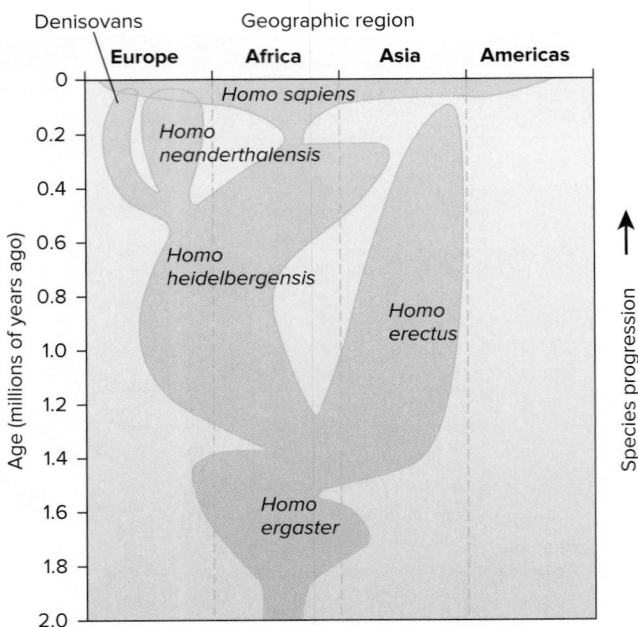

Figure 26.20   One view of the temporal and geographic evolution of hominid populations. Though not shown in this figure, the range of the Denisovans and *Homo neanderthalensis* also extended into Asia.

H. heidelbergensis was another descendent of *H. ergaster, H. erectus,* though some researchers consider *H. ergaster* and *H. erectus* as the same species. We will treat them as separate species here.

Homo erectus   *Homo erectus* was a large hominin, as large as a modern human but with heavier bones and a smaller brain capacity of between 750 and 1,225 cm³ (modern human brain size is about 1,350 cm³). Fossil evidence shows that *H. erectus* was a social species that used tools, hunted animals, and cooked over fires. The meat-eating habit may have sparked the migration of *H. erectus.* Carnivores tend to have larger ranges than similar-sized herbivores, because the food sources of carnivores (prey) are usually scarcer per unit area. *H. erectus* spread out of Africa soon after the species appeared, over a million years ago, and fossils have been found as far away as China and Indonesia. The first fossil was found by Dutch physician Eugene Dubois in 1891 on the Indonesian island of Java. Stone tools are rarely found in these Asian sites, suggesting *H. erectus* based their technology on other materials, such as bamboo, which was abundant at that time. Bamboo is strong yet lightweight and could have been used to make spears. These humans may even have used rafts to take to the seas. *H. erectus* went extinct about 100,000 years ago, for reasons that are unclear but may be related to the spread of *H. sapiens* into its range.

Homo heidelbergensis   *Homo heidelbergensis* was similar in body form to modern humans. Large caches of this species' bones were found in Spain, at the bottom of a 14-m (45-ft) shaft known as La Sima de Los Huesos (the pit of bones). Similar remains were also found at Boxgrove in England. Shinbones recovered from Boxgrove suggest that males had heights around 180 cm (6 ft) and weighed 88 kg (196 pounds). Skulls were large, with brain volumes from 1,100 to

1,400 cm³, similar to those of modern humans. Animal bones from these sites showed cut marks from stone blades beneath tooth marks from carnivores. This indicated that humans were killing large prey before scavengers arrived. Horses, giant deer, and rhinoceroses were common prey, and successfully hunting them would have required much skill and cooperation. *H. heidelbergensis* gave rise to three species, *Homo neanderthalensis,* the Denisovans, and *Homo sapiens.* However, some scientists view these as three subspecies. In the discussion that follows, we will consider them to be three different species.

Homo neanderthalensis

Homo neanderthalensis was named for the Neander Valley of Germany, where the first fossils of this species were found. In the Pleistocene epoch, glaciers were locked in a cycle of advance and retreat, and the European landscape was often covered with snow. Over the course of many generations, the more slender body form of *H. heidelbergensis* evolved into a shorter, stockier build that was better equipped to conserve heat; we now call this type of human Neanderthal. Neanderthals also possessed a more massive skull and larger brain size than modern humans, about 1,450 cm³, perhaps associated with their bulk. Males were about 168 cm (5 ft 6 in.) tall and would have been very strong by modern standards. They had a large face with a prominent bridge over the eyebrows, a large nose, and no chin (**Figure 26.21a**). They lived predominantly in Europe, with a range extending to the Middle East and Asia (**Figure 26.21b**). Their stocky and muscular physique was well suited to the rigors of cold climates and hunting prey. Paleontologists have found a high rate of head and neck injuries in Neanderthal bones, similar to that seen in present-day rodeo riders. This suggests that close encounters with large prey often resulted in blows that knocked the hunters off their feet. The hyoid bone, which holds the larynx (voice box) in place, was well developed, suggesting speech was used. The Neanderthals went extinct about 40,000 to 30,000 years ago.

Denisovans

In 2010, scientists sequenced DNA from a fossilized pinky finger of a young female found in Denisova Cave in Siberia, Russia, and found it to be genetically distinct from the DNA of *H. neanderthalensis* and *H. sapiens.* Because it is such a recent discovery, its species name is yet to be agreed upon. The common name given to this type of human is a Denisovan. Using carbon radioisotope dating, the fossil was estimated to be about 400,000 years old. Thus far, the remains of 4 Denisovans have been discovered.

(a) An adult male Neanderthal

Figure 26.21 Neanderthals. (a) Artist's rendition of a Neanderthal human. Neanderthals were shorter and stockier than modern humans, with larger elbow and ankle joints, shorter forearms, and a larger, broader rib cage. **(b)** The range of Neanderthals was confined to Europe and western Asia, with a northerly limit that corresponds to about 50° north, the southern limit of glaciation. Total population size may only have been 70,000 at its peak.

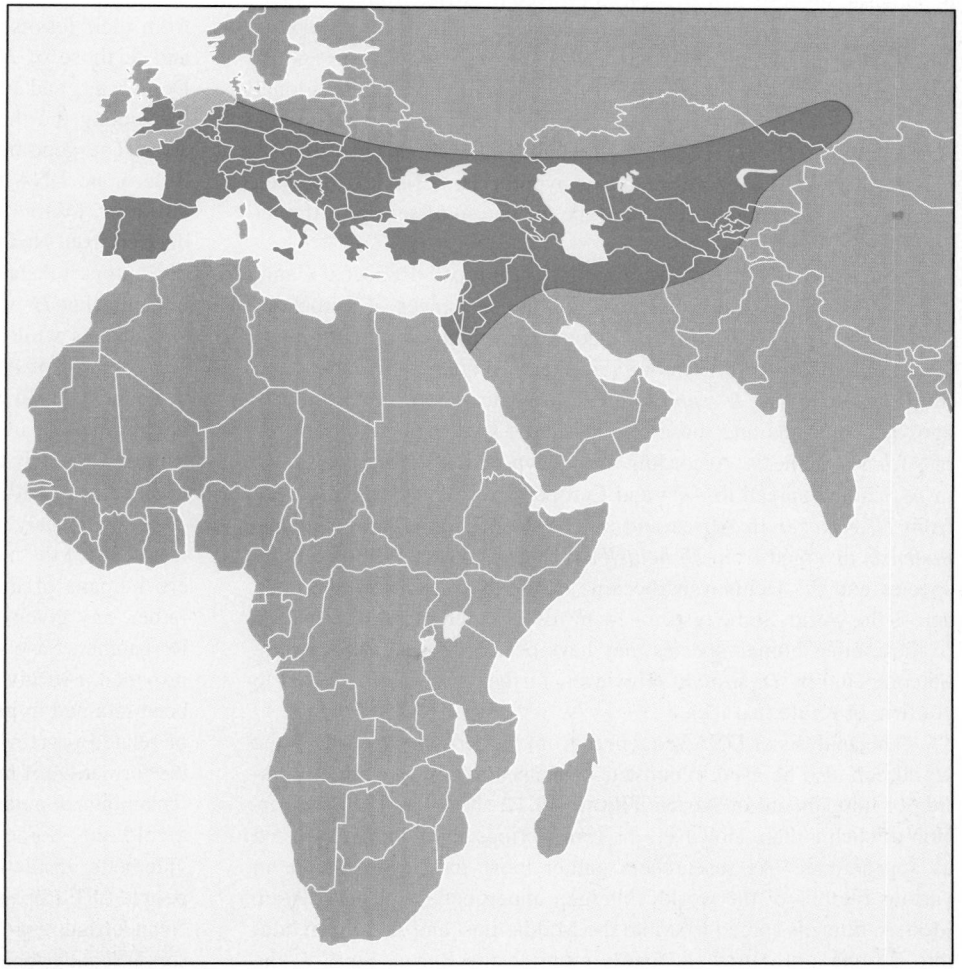

(b) Geographic range of Neanderthals

Scientists now hypothesize that Denisovans were a sister group to the Neanderthals, diverging from the Neanderthals about 400,000 years ago. It is difficult to reconstruct the physical traits of Denisovans, because only a finger bone, a toe bone, and a few molar teeth have been discovered thus far. Even so, the finger bone was unusually broad and robust, suggesting the Denisovans were similar in build to the Neanderthals. Like the Neanderthals, the Denisovans are thought to have gone extinct about 40,000 to 30,000 years ago.

Homo sapiens   *Homo sapiens* (from the Latin, meaning wise man) is our own species. *H. sapiens* is a slender, lighter-weight species with a slightly smaller brain capacity than that of the Neanderthals. Researchers hypothesize a variety of reasons why *H. sapiens* thrived while the Neanderthals disappeared; it may have been due to a more efficient body type with lower energy needs, increased longevity, and/or differences in social structure and cultural adaptations.

Evidence Suggests That *Homo sapiens* Arose in Africa and Then Migrated to Other Parts of the World

Two models have been proposed to explain where the species of modern humans, *Homo sapiens,* arose. The first model, the out-of-Africa hypothesis, suggests that *H. sapiens* evolved in Africa from *H. heidelbergensis.* Some members of *H. sapiens* later migrated to other parts of the world, and gradually replaced species such as *H. erectus* and *H. neanderthalensis.* An alternative hypothesis, called the multiregional hypothesis, which is not widely accepted, suggests that human groups have evolved from *H. ergaster* populations in a number of different parts of the world. According to this hypothesis, gene flow between neighboring populations prevented the formation of several different *H. sapiens* species.

In 1987, American evolutionary biologists Rebecca Cann, Allan Wilson, and colleagues analyzed the sequences of mitochondrial DNA (mtDNA) that was collected from many different people from around the world. By comparing these sequences to each other, they concluded that *H. sapiens* arose in Africa about 200,000 years ago. These results and those of subsequent studies support the out-of-Africa hypothesis. According to this hypothesis, *H. ergaster* arose in Africa and spread to Asia and Europe. Later, *H. erectus* diverged from *H. ergaster* in Africa and spread into Asia, and *H. neanderthalensis* diverged from *H. heidelbergensis* in Europe. Both of these species and the Denisovans became extinct as *H. sapiens* migrated across the world. Some researchers have suggested that the extinction of these other human species may have occurred because they were outcompeted by *H. sapiens.* However, further research is needed to confirm or refute that idea.

The analysis of DNA sequences from modern humans across the world can also be used to construct a map that describes the migration of humans out of Africa. **Figure 26.22** shows a simplified version of such a map. However, the time periods should be considered as approximate. As researchers gather more data from people in various regions of the world, this map undergoes frequent revision. Modern humans spread first into the Middle East and Asia, then later into Europe and Australia, finally crossing the Bering Strait to the Americas.

Much remains to be resolved in our understanding of human evolution, and new data provide paleontologists with information to revise their hypotheses. For example, in 2004, the remains of a small human were discovered on the Indonesian island of Flores and were given the name *Homo florensiensis,* nicknamed hobbits by the media. Many species—for example, deer and elephants—develop into small forms in insular situations, so hobbit-sized humans seemed plausible. Since then, many researchers have suggested these people were modern humans who were suffering from a genetic disorder. Even modern humans on Flores are pygmies. Pathological dwarfism would have made these people even smaller. Only tools associated with *H. sapiens* have been found at the area where the bones occur, suggesting these individuals were indeed dwarf forms of modern humans.

A 2014 study showed that the small brain size of one of the *H. floresiensis* fossils was in the range predicted for an individual with Down syndrome, and it was suggested that this is evidence that *H. floresiensis* is an invalid species.

Human Evolution Has Involved Interbreeding Among Closely Related Species

Because the remains of Neanderthals and Denisovans are less than 50,000 years old, researchers have been able to extract DNA from their fossils and compare their DNA sequences to each other and to those of *H. sapiens.* Detailed comparisons of Neanderthal, Denisovan, and modern human genomes have revealed interbreeding among the three species as *H. sapiens* spread into Europe and Asia. The genomes of modern humans of African descent contain little or no DNA that is derived from Neanderthals or Denisovans. However, 1% to 4% of the DNA from a person of European descent is derived from Neanderthals, and 4% to 6% of the DNA from a person of Southeast Asia descent is derived from Denisovans. These results indicate that *H. sapiens* ancestors interbred with Neanderthals and Denisovans while spreading across Europe and Asia. Interestingly, some people of African descent carry very small amounts of Neanderthal DNA. How is this possible? By analyzing the DNA sequences of certain African people, researchers speculate that some *H. sapiens* from Europe may have migrated back to Africa about 3,000 years ago and interbred with a few isolated African populations of *H. sapiens.*

When analyzing the human genome on a population level, at least 20% of the Neanderthal genome is found in the genome of modern humans of European descent. No one individual has all 20%; rather, any given person of European descent has about 1% to 4%. Researchers have speculated that certain Neanderthal genes may have provided a survival advantage, and that may explain why they have been retained in particular human populations. For example, a group of related proteins called keratins form filaments that play a role in the formation of human skin, hair, and nails. Such filaments may differ among populations that have evolved in a warm climate versus a cold one. Some alleles of keratin genes encode keratins that provide better insulation, a trait that is advantageous in cold climates. In people of European descent, genes that encode keratins are often of Neanderthal origin. This observation is consistent with the idea that some Neanderthal alleles may have helped European *H. sapiens* adapt to colder European environments.

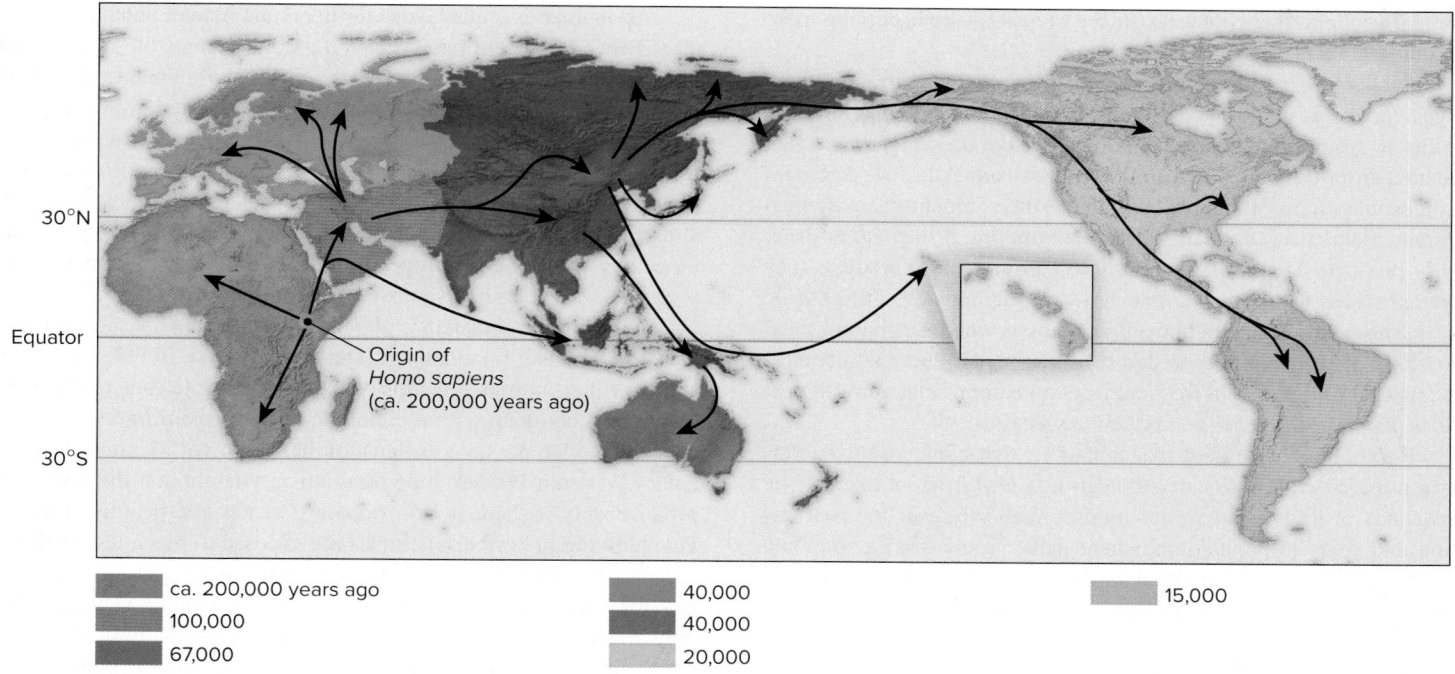

30°N

Equator

Origin of
Homo sapiens
(ca. 200,000 years ago)

30°S

ca. 200,000 years ago	40,000	15,000
100,000	40,000	
67,000	20,000	

Figure 26.22 **A simplified model for the origin and spread of *Homo sapiens* throughout the world.** This map, based on differences of mtDNA throughout current members of the world's population, suggests *Homo sapiens* originated in East Africa. About 100,000 years ago, the species spread into the Middle East and from there to Europe, Asia, Australia, and the Americas.

 Core Skill: Modeling The goal of this modeling challenge is to revise the model shown in Figure 26.22 to account for recent data indicating that some modern Africans have a small amount of Neanderthal DNA.

Modeling Challenge: As discussed in this section, between 1% and 4% of the DNA of modern humans of European descent is derived from that of Neanderthals. Though most modern humans of African descent do not carry Neanderthal DNA, recent evidence has shown that some of them carry a very small amount. Assuming that the presence of this Neanderthal DNA is not due to recent interbreeding between modern humans of European and African descent, revise the model shown in Figure 26.22 to account for the observation.

On the downside, scientists also speculate that Neanderthals carried an allele of a gene involved with fatty acid uptake that helped them store fat better than *H. sapiens*. Such a gene was an advantage for a Neanderthal lifestyle in which hunter-gatherers gorged on prey and then went for days without eating. However, in modern humans, fat storage can put them at risk for developing various diseases, such as type 2 diabetes mellitus. In certain human populations, particularly native Americans and those of Latin American descent, this Neanderthal allele is fairly common. Some people are heterozygous, carrying one allele that is derived from the Neanderthal genome and one from the *H. sapiens* genome. Such individuals are 20% more likely to develop type 2 diabetes compared to people who are homozygous for the *H. sapiens* allele. Furthermore, people who are homozygous for the Neanderthal allele are 40% more likely to develop diabetes.

Are Human Populations Still Evolving?

As discussed in Chapter 23, natural selection is the process by which individuals with greater reproductive success are more likely to pass

their genes to future generations. Natural selection results in evolution. (Other processes, such as genetic drift, can also promote evolutionary change.) One factor that often plays a role in natural selection is the environment. Various types of environmental factors such as temperature, predators, and food sources can affect reproductive success and thereby cause a population to evolve in a particular direction. For example, a prolonged decrease in temperature may favor the survival of mammals with thicker fur, a trait that will increase in frequency over the course of many generations.

Modern humans have great control over their environment. They live in dwellings where they can control the temperature, they can largely avoid predators, and they usually don't rely entirely on locally grown food for their survival. For such reasons, the impact of the natural environment on the evolution of human populations may have lessened compared to its impact on humans that lived long ago. Even so, human evolution via natural selection is still occurring. For example, we continue to evolve genetic resistance to infectious diseases. The bubonic plague of the 14th century killed about one-third of the Asian and European populations, yet many people survived and passed on alleles that confer greater resistance to this deadly disease.

Similarly, alleles that confer resistance to malaria are becoming more common in certain African populations.

A classic example of recent human evolution is the ability to digest lactose, a sugar found in milk. In most human populations, the ability to readily digest lactose is lost after the age when babies are weaned from their mother's milk. After weaning, lactose becomes indigestible to most people and they suffer bloating, abdominal cramps, flatulence, diarrhea, nausea, or vomiting if they eat or drink dairy products. However, the ability to consume dairy products may have provided a survival advantage as people began to domesticate cows, sheep, and goats. In human populations where such domestication took place, the ability to digest lactose, called lactose tolerance, is expected to increase in frequency due to natural selection if it provides people with greater reproductive success.

Recent studies suggest that mutations that confer lactose tolerance arose several thousand years ago in a few different places. The frequency of this mutation increased dramatically over the past few thousand years in populations where dairy products are commonly consumed. The genetic mutation for digesting lactose after weaning is now carried by most northern Europeans. Lactose intolerance is less common in this geographical region (**Figure 26.23**). For this population, the trait is linked to a single mutation that affects the expression of the lactase gene, which encodes an enzyme that is needed to digest lactose. The mutation prevents the gene from being turned off after weaning. Lactose tolerance has also been found in other populations, such as Africa and the Middle East, but these mutations occurred independently of the one that is usually found in lactose-tolerant people of European descent.

As another example, eye color in certain human populations has also changed in recent times. Over 10,000 years ago, all or nearly all humans had brown eyes. About 10,000 years ago, someone who lived near the Baltic Sea inherited a mutation that resulted in blue eyes in the homozygous state. In 2008, researchers discovered that this mutation decreases the expression of the *Oca2* gene, which encodes a protein that is needed for the production of melanin pigment in the iris and other parts of the body. The frequency of this allele increased, especially in northern Europe (**Figure 26.24**), and by about 3,000 years ago, blue eyes had spread across Europe.

Why did the frequency of blue eyes increase in such a rapid fashion in human populations? The dramatic rise in blue eye color suggests that natural selection was playing a role, but researchers have yet to come up with a definitive answer regarding its selective advantage. One possible explanation has to do with vitamin D deficiency. Vitamin D is an important human vitamin that the body can produce only if there is skin exposure to the UV rays in sunlight. People living in northern latitudes are exposed to much less sunlight compared to those living nearer the equator, putting them at greater risk for vitamin D deficiency. A decrease in melanin synthesis not only affects eye color (brown to blue) but also results in lighter skin, which more easily absorbs UV rays. Therefore, one hypothesis for the spread of blue eyes (and lighter skin) through the human population is that it may have enabled humans to avoid the harmful health effects of vitamin D deficiency, which includes weakness and bone abnormalities. In this scenario, natural selection acted on skin color, and the eye color phenotype increased due to its association with a lighter skin color.

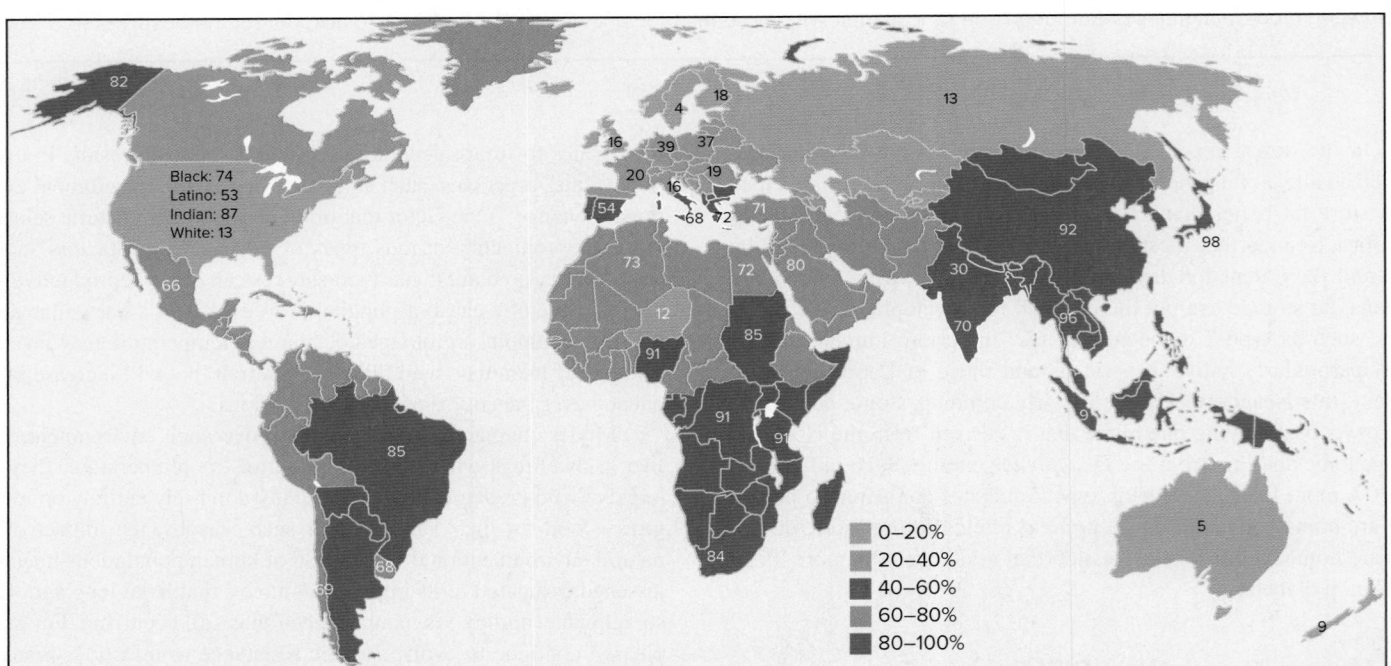

Figure 26.23 **The frequency of lactose intolerance in human populations.** This map emphasizes lactose intolerance, which is the inability to digest lactose after weaning. In contrast, most northern Europeans can digest the sugar lactose found in dairy products; they are lactose tolerant.

(a) Blue eye color

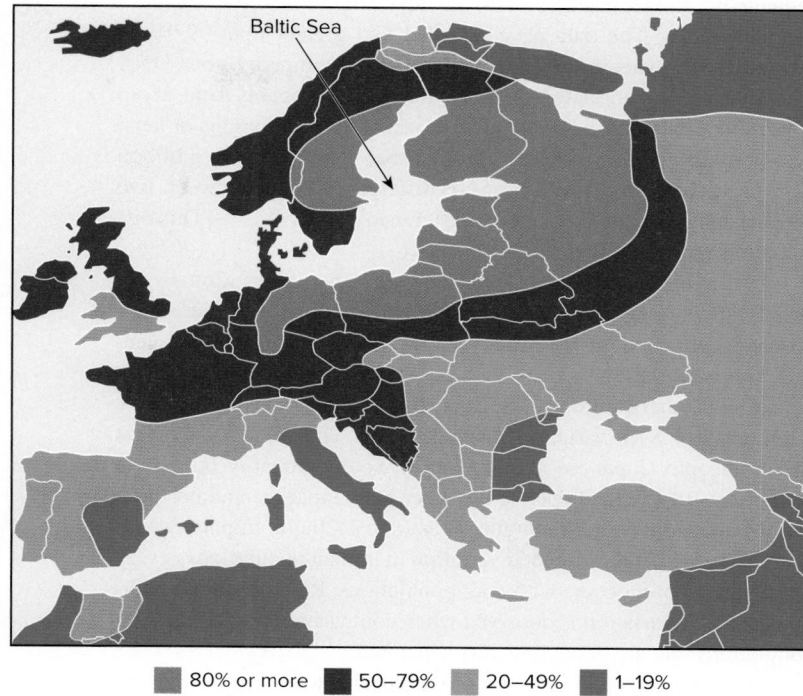

80% or more 50–79% 20–49% 1–19%

(b) Percentage of people with blue eye color in Europe and surrounding regions

Figure 26.24 **Blue eye color and its spread throughout Europe.** **(a)** In humans, blue eye color is due to a lack of melanin in the iris. This mutation probably appeared only about 10,000 years ago. **(b)** Many people in western and northern Europe have blue eyes due to the spread of this single mutation that originated in someone living near the Baltic Sea. Note: The indicated percentages include blue eye color and other light eye colors, such as green. a: ©harpazo_hope/Getty Images

Modern Humans Show Relatively Little Genetic Variation Yet Exhibit a Significant Amount of Phenotypic Variation

Looks can be deceiving. If you take a plane ride around the world and make stops in Japan, Nigeria, Norway, Brazil, and Australia, you might get the impression that the human species is genetically diverse (**Figure 26.25**). The physical differences among humans in many parts of the globe are striking. To assess the level of genetic variation, the **1000 Genomes Project** was launched in January 2008; it is an international research effort to establish the level of human genetic variation. By 2015, this project had sequenced the genomes of over 2,500 people from around the world and compared those sequences to each other. The results indicate that, genetically speaking, humans are very, very similar to each other. Our level of genetic variation is lower than most species of mammals whose genomes have been sequenced, and it is even lower than the variation within certain fruit fly species. This may seem surprising; if you compared two fruit flies of the same species to each other, they would probably look very similar!

Most human genetic variation is in the form of single nucleotide polymorphisms (SNPs), which are places where two humans' genomes differ at a single base pair (see Chapter 23). DNA

(a) Japan   **(b) Nigeria**   **(c) Norway**   **(d) Brazil**   **(e) Australia**

Figure 26.25 **Examples of human phenotypic variation in different parts of the world.** The women seen here are from **(a)** Japan, **(b)** Nigeria, **(c)** Norway, **(d)** Brazil, and **(e)** Australia. They are genetically very similar even though they look somewhat different. a: ©William Perugini/123RF; b: ©Filipe Frazao/Shutterstock; c: ©Andrea Magugliani/Alamy Stock Photo; d: ©Daniel Ernst/Alamy Stock Photo; e: ©David Freund/Getty Images

sequencing allows researchers to identify sites where two people's genomes differ. The data have revealed that greater than 99.9% of those differing sites are due to SNPs. If you compared your DNA with that of any unrelated person, you would probably find about 4.5 million SNP sites where your SNP was different from his or hers. This might sound like a lot, but consider that your genome is 3 billion base pairs long. If 4.5 million SNP differences occur between two people, this amounts to a genome difference of only 0.15%. This difference is much less than 1%!

Furthermore, this very low value of genetic variation is not greatly affected by the pairs of people who are analyzed. Let's suppose you compared the SNPs between two people of Japanese descent and compared the SNPs between a person of Japanese descent and a person of northern European descent. Both comparisons would show a low level of SNP variation, around 0.15%. The value for the first pair of people (Japanese and Japanese) would probably be a little lower (say, 0.14%), and that for the other pair (Japanese and northern European) might be a little higher (say, 0.16%), but both pairs would be remarkably similar. Genetic variation in human populations is very low and most of it occurs within all populations. Relatively little additional genetic variation is observed when comparing individuals from populations that are geographically separated.

Why is the genetic diversity of our species low? Various factors are involved. First, *Homo sapiens* has not been around that long. Even though 200,000 years might seem like a long time, humans have a long generation time, and evolution occurs over the course of generations. Second, until recently, human populations have been relatively small. About 10,000 years ago, the human population size is estimated to have been about 5 million. Small populations tend to be less genetically diverse than larger ones. Although the human population has grown enormously over the past few centuries, this expansion is very recent on an evolutionary timescale.

How do we explain the disparity between a low level of genetic variation and a seemingly higher level of phenotypic diversity? The answer is not entirely understood, but it may be related to the traits that influence our perception of diversity. Some of the traits that are most visually obvious, such as eye and skin color, may be dramatically influenced by natural selection even though they involve changes in a relatively small number of genes. For example, we have already considered how blue eye color and light skin color spread rapidly throughout Europe, and this phenotypic change involved a mutation in a single gene. This observation underscores how our visual perception of diversity may be biased by traits not rooted in major genetic differences.

Summary of Key Concepts

- Life began on Earth between 4.0 and 3.5 bya (Figure 26.1).

26.1 The Fossil Record

- Fossils, which are preserved remnants of past life-forms, are formed in sedimentary rock (Figure 26.2).
- Radiometric dating is one way of estimating the age of a fossil. Fossils provide an extensive record of the history of life on Earth, though the record is incomplete (Figure 26.3, Table 26.1).

26.2 History of Life on Earth

- The geological timescale, which is divided into four eons and many eras and periods, charts the major events that occurred during the history of life on Earth (Figure 26.4).
- Both the emergence of new species and mass extinctions are correlated with changes in temperature, amount of O_2 in the atmosphere, landmass locations, floods and glaciation, volcanic eruptions, and meteorite impacts (Figure 26.5).
- During the Archaean eon, bacteria and archaea arose. The proliferation of cyanobacteria led to a gradual rise in O_2 levels (Figure 26.6).
- Eukaryotic cells arose during the Proterozoic eon. This origin involved a union between bacterial and archaeal cells that is hypothesized to have been endosymbiotic. The origins of mitochondria and chloroplasts were also the result of endosymbiosis (Figure 26.7).
- Multicellular eukaryotes arose about 1.5 bya during the Proterozoic eon. Multicellularity now occurs via cell division and the adherence of the resulting cells to each other. A multicellular organism can have multiple cell types (Figure 26.8).
- The first animal showing bilateral symmetry emerged toward the end of the Proterozoic eon (Figure 26.9).
- The Phanerozoic eon is subdivided into the Paleozoic, Mesozoic, and Cenozoic eras. During the Paleozoic era, invertebrates greatly diversified, particularly during the Cambrian explosion, and the land became colonized by plants and animals. Terrestrial vertebrates, including tetrapods, became more diverse (Figures 26.10–26.12).
- Dinosaurs were prevalent during the Mesozoic era, particularly during the Jurassic period. Mammals and birds also emerged (Figures 26.13, 26.14).
- During the Cenozoic era, mammals diversified, and flowering plants became the dominant plant species. The first hominoids emerged approximately 7 mya. *Homo sapiens*, our species, first appeared about 200,000 years ago.

26.3 Human Evolution

- Many defining characteristics of primates relate to their tree-dwelling nature; these include grasping hands, large brain, nails instead of claws, and binocular vision (Figures 26.15–26.17).
- About 7 mya in Africa, a lineage that led to humans began to separate from other primate lineages. A key characteristic of hominins (extinct and modern humans) is bipedalism. Human evolution can be visualized like a tree, with a few hominin species coexisting at the same point in time, some eventually going extinct, and some giving rise to other species (Figures 26.18–26.21).
- Data from the sequencing of human mitochondrial DNA suggest that *H. sapiens* originated in East Africa. From there, *H. sapiens* spread to Asia and then to all other parts of the globe (Figure 26.22).
- Human evolution has involved interbreeding between closely related species, such as *H. sapiens* and the Neanderthals and the Denisovans.
- Evidence that human populations are still evolving includes traits such as lactose tolerance and blue eye color (Figures 26.23, 26.24).
- Modern humans show relatively little genetic variation yet exhibit a significant amount of phenotypic variation (Figure 26.25).

Assess & Discuss

Test Yourself

1. The movement of landmasses that has changed their positions, shapes, and association with other landmasses is called
   a. glaciation.
   b. Pangaea.
   c. continental drift.
   d. biogeography.
   e. geological scale.

2. Paleontologists estimate the dates of fossils using
   a. the layer of rock in which the fossils are found.
   b. analysis of radioisotopes found in nearby igneous rock.
   c. the complexity of the body plan of the organism.
   d. all of the above.
   e. a and b only.

3. The fossil record does not give us a complete picture of the history of life on Earth because
   a. not all past organisms have become fossilized.
   b. only organisms with hard skeletons can become fossilized.
   c. fossils of very small organisms have not been found.
   d. fossils of early organisms are located too deep in the crust of the Earth to be found.
   e. All of the above are true.

4. The endosymbiosis hypothesis explaining the evolution of eukaryotic cells is supported by
   a. DNA-sequencing analysis comparing bacterial genomes, mitochondrial genomes, and eukaryotic nuclear genomes.
   b. naturally occurring examples of endosymbiotic relationships between bacterial cells and eukaryotic cells.
   c. the presence of DNA in mitochondria and chloroplasts.
   d. all of the above.
   e. a and b only.

5. Which of the following evolutionary innovations was advantageous for survival in a terrestrial environment?
   a. the amniotic egg in animals
   b. the seed in plants
   c. the shell in marine invertebrates
   d. all of the above
   e. both a and b

6. Which of the following explanations of multicellularity in eukaryotes is seen in the development of complex, multicellular organisms today?
   a. endosymbiosis
   b. aggregation of cells to form a colony
   c. division of cells followed by cell adhesion of the resulting cells
   d. multiple cell types aggregating to form a complex organism
   e. None of the above phenomena are evident today.

7. The earliest fossils of vascular plants were formed during the _____ period.
   a. Ordovician
   b. Silurian
   c. Devonian
   d. Triassic
   e. Jurassic

8. The first mammal arose during the _____ period.
   a. Triassic
   b. Jurassic
   c. Cretaceous
   d. Tertiary
   e. Quaternary

9. The appearance of the first hominoids dates to the _____ period.
   a. Triassic
   b. Jurassic
   c. Cretaceous
   d. Tertiary
   e. Quaternary

10. Which of the following statements regarding modern humans, *H. sapiens*, is *false?*
    a. Some modern humans have a small amount of DNA that is derived from Neanderthals.
    b. Some modern humans have a small amount of DNA that is derived from Denisovans.
    c. *H. sapiens* probably arose in Africa.
    d. Modern humans are very genetically diverse compared to most other species.
    e. Modern humans are still evolving.

Conceptual Questions

1. How are the ages of fossils determined? In your answer, you should discuss which types of rocks are analyzed and explain the concepts of radiometric dating and half-life.

2. How was the phenomenon of endosymbiosis important in the evolution of the first eukaryotic cells?

3. **Core Concept: Evolution** Describe two examples in which changes in the global climate affected the evolution of species.

Collaborative Questions

1. Discuss the factors that have contributed to the dramatic changes in life-forms since the origin of life on Earth about 3.5 to 4 billion years ago.

2. Discuss how the human body has changed since the human lineage diverged from other primates about 7 million years ago.

Some archaea prefer habitats having both high temperatures and extremely low pH. For example, the archaeal genus *Sulfolobus* was discovered in samples taken from sulfur hot springs having a pH of 3 or lower. Archaea help biologists better understand the origin of life, the origin of eukaryotes, how life on Earth has evolved in extreme environments, and what kinds of extraterrestrial life might exist.

The domain Archaea includes several phyla, including Lokiarchaeota, Korarchaeota, Thaumarchaeota, Crenarchaeota, and Euryarchaeota (see Figure 27.1). Lokiarchaeota and close relatives named for Norse deities are collectively known as the Asgard superphylum and are particularly closely related to eukaryotes (Eukarya). Members of Korarchaeota are primarily known from hot springs. Thaumarchaeota species are widespread in terrestrial and aquatic environments, and include archaea that oxidize ammonia, making them important in global nitrogen cycling. Crenarchaeota includes organisms that live in extremely hot or cold habitats and also some that are widespread in aquatic and terrestrial habitats. Early-diverging Euryarchaeota includes some hyperthermophiles, diverse methane producers, and extreme halophiles—species able to grow in higher than usual salt concentrations.

Domain Bacteria Includes Cyanobacteria, Proteobacteria, and Many Other Phyla

Domain Bacteria is considerably more diverse than Archaea. Molecular studies suggest the existence of 50 or more bacterial phyla, though many are poorly characterized. Though some members of domain Bacteria live in extreme environments, most favor moderate conditions. Many bacteria form symbiotic associations with eukaryotes and are thus of concern in medicine and agriculture.

The characteristics of 10 prominent bacterial phyla are briefly summarized in **Table 27.1**. Bacterial phyla mentioned later in this chapter because of their medical, ecological, or evolutionary significance include Firmicutes, Bacteroidetes, Chlamydiae, Planctomycetes, Spirochaetes, Actinobacteria, Chloroflexi, and Deinococcus-Thermus. Because Cyanobacteria and Proteobacteria are particularly diverse and relevant to eukaryotic cell evolution, global ecology, and human affairs, we will consider them in greater detail next.

Cyanobacteria The phylum Cyanobacteria contains photosynthetic bacteria that are abundant in fresh waters, oceans, and wetlands and on the surfaces of arid soils. Cyanobacteria are named for the typical blue-green (cyan) coloration of their cells. Blue-green pigmentation results from the presence of photosynthetic pigments called phycobilins that help chlorophyll absorb light energy. Cyanobacteria are the only bacteria known to generate oxygen as a product of photosynthesis. Ancient cyanobacteria produced Earth's first oxygen-rich atmosphere, which allowed the eventual rise of eukaryotes. The chloroplasts of eukaryotic algae and plants were derived from cyanobacteria.

Cyanobacteria display the greatest diversity in body type found among bacterial phyla (**Figure 27.3**). Some occur as single cells called unicells (Figure 27.3a); others form colonies of cells held

Table 27.1	Representative Bacterial Phyla
Phyla	**Characteristics**
Firmicutes	Diverse Gram-positive bacteria, some of which produce endospores. The disease-causing *Clostridium difficile* is an example.
Bacteroidetes	Includes representatives with diverse metabolic processes; some are common in the human intestinal tract, and others are primarily aquatic.
Chlamydiae	Notably tiny, obligate intracellular parasites. Some cause eye disease in newborns or sexually transmitted diseases.
Planctomycetes	Reproduce by budding rather than binary fission; cell walls lack peptidoglycan; cytoplasm may contain nucleus-like bodies, and endocytosis may occur.
Spirochaetes	Motile bacteria having distinctive corkscrew shapes, with flagella held close to the body. They include the pathogens *Treponema pallidum*, the agent of syphilis, and *Borrelia burgdorferi*, which causes Lyme disease.
Actinobacteria	Gram-positive bacteria producing branched filaments; many form spores. *Mycobacterium tuberculosis*, the agent of tuberculosis in humans, is an example. Actinobacteria are notable antibiotic producers; over 500 different antibiotics are known from this group. Some fix nitrogen in association with plants.
Chloroflexi	Known as the green nonsulfur bacteria; conduct photosynthesis without releasing oxygen (anoxygenic photosynthesis).
Deinococcus-Thermus	Extremophiles. The genus *Deinococcus* is known for high resistance to ionizing radiation, and the genus *Thermus* inhabits hot springs. *Thermus aquaticus* has been used in commercial production of *Taq* polymerase, an enzyme used in polymerase chain reaction (PCR), an important procedure in molecular biology laboratories.
Cyanobacteria	Includes the oxygen-producing photosynthetic bacteria (some are also capable of anoxygenic photosynthesis). Photosynthetic pigments include chlorophyll *a* and phycobilins, which often give cells a blue-green pigmentation. Occur as unicells, colonies, unbranched filaments, and branched filaments. Many of the filamentous species produce specialized cells: dormant akinetes and heterocytes in which nitrogen fixation occurs. In waters having excess nutrients, cyanobacteria produce blooms and may release toxins harmful to the health of humans and wild and domesticated animals.
Proteobacteria	A very large group of Gram-negative bacteria, collectively having high metabolic diversity. Includes many species important in medicine, agriculture, and industry such as *Agrobacterium tumifaciens, Escherichia coli*, and *Haemophilus influenzae*. *Myxococcus xanthus* is a Gram-negative bacterium that is able to glide across surfaces, forming swarms of thousands of cells. This behavior aids feeding by concentrating digestive enzymes secreted by the bacteria. When food is scarce, the swarms form tiny tree-shaped structures from which tough spores disperse. By this means, cells move to new, food-rich places.

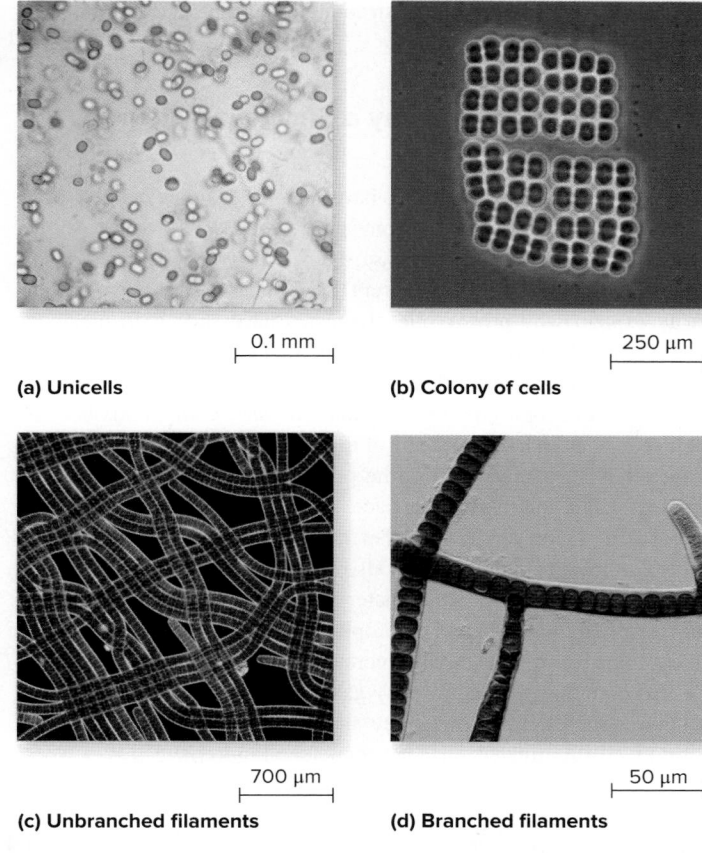

(a) Unicells

(b) Colony of cells

0.1 mm

250 µm

700 µm

50 µm

(c) Unbranched filaments

(d) Branched filaments

Figure 27.3 **Major body types found in the phylum Cyanobacteria.** **(a)** The genus *Chroococcus* occurs as unicells. **(b)** The genus *Merismopedia* forms a flat colony of cells held together by mucilage. **(c)** The genus *Oscillatoria* forms an unbranched filament. **(d)** The genus *Stigonema* forms a branched filament having a mucilage sheath; sunscreen compounds that protect the cells from damage by ultraviolet (UV) radiation cause the brown color of the sheath. a: ©Linda Graham; b: ©Michael Abbey/Science Source; c: ©Sinclair Stammers/SPL/Science Source; d: ©Lee W. Wilcox

together by a thick gluey substance called mucilage (Figure 27.3b), and many cyanobacteria form filaments in which cells are attached end-to-end (Figure 27.3c) or filaments that branch (Figure 27.3d). Some of the filamentous cyanobacteria display hallmarks of multicellularity: cellular attachment, specialized cells, intercellular chemical communication, and programmed cell death.

Proteobacteria Though Proteobacteria share molecular and cell-wall features, this phylum displays amazing diversity of form and metabolism. Genera of this phylum are classified into five major subgroups: alpha (α), beta (β), gamma (γ), delta (δ), and epsilon (ε). As we saw in Chapter 26 (refer back to Figure 26.7), the ancestry of mitochondria can be traced to the α-proteobacteria, which also include several genera noted for mutually beneficial relationships with animals and plants. For example, *Rhizobium* and related genera of α-proteobacteria form nutritionally beneficial associations with the roots of legume plants such as beans and peas and are thus agriculturally important. Another α-proteobacterium, *Agrobacterium*

Figure 27.4 ***Agrobacterium tumifaciens* infection.** This proteobacterium causes cancer-like tumors to grow on plants (see the arrows). ©Linda Graham

tumifaciens, causes destructive cancer-like tumors called galls to develop on susceptible plants, including grapes and ornamental crops (**Figure 27.4**). *A. tumifaciens* induces gall formation by injecting DNA into plant cells. This property has allowed researchers to use the bacterium in the production of transgenic plants, which are plants that carry genes from another species.

The genus *Nitrosomonas*, soil inhabitants important in the global nitrogen cycle, represents the β-proteobacteria. *Neisseria gonorrhoeae*, the agent of the sexually transmitted disease gonorrhea, is one of the γ-proteobacteria. *Vibrio cholerae*, another γ-proteobacterium, causes cholera epidemics when drinking water becomes contaminated with animal waste during floods and other natural disasters. The γ-proteobacteria *Salmonella enterica* and *Escherichia coli* strain O157:H7 also cause human disease, so food and water are widely tested for their presence. The δ-proteobacteria include the colony-forming myxobacteria and predatory bdellovibrios, which drill through the cell walls of other bacteria in order to consume them. *Helicobacter pylori*, which causes stomach ulcers, belongs to the ε-proteobacteria.

Horizontal Gene Transfer Influences the Diversity and Evolution of Archaea and Bacteria

As we have seen, Bacteria and Archaea are domains of life displaying an amazing level of diversity. One reason for this diversity is **horizontal gene transfer**, the process in which an organism receives genetic material from another organism without being the offspring of that organism. Horizontal gene transfer is common among archaea and bacteria, occurring most frequently between species that are closely related or that live in close proximity. Evolutionary change due to horizontal gene transfer contrasts with **vertical evolution**, in which gene transfer occurs from parent to progeny. During vertical evolution, genetic changes occur in a series of ancestors that form a lineage; species evolve from pre-existing species by the accumulation of mutations.

Horizontal gene transfer can result in large genetic changes that confer new metabolic capacities. For example, at least 17% of the genes present in the common human gut inhabitant *E. coli* were horizontally transferred from other bacteria. Studies of nearly 200 genomes have revealed that about 80% of prokaryotic genes have been involved in horizontal transfer at some point in their history. Genes also move among the bacterial, archaeal, and eukaryotic domains. For example, salt-tolerant (halophytic) archaea originated after an ancient horizontal transfer of more than a thousand genes from bacteria.

Horizontal gene transfer can occur between different bacterial species via transduction, transformation, and conjugation, as discussed in Chapter 19. In addition, horizontal gene transfer occurs by means of endosymbiosis, the process in which one species—the endosymbiont—lives in the body or cells of another species—the host. For example, certain γ-proteobacteria occupy the cells of β-proteobacterial hosts, which themselves live within insect cells. Such close proximity increases the odds that gene exchange will occur between distantly related species. During the process by which the mitochondria of eukaryotic cells originated from α-proteobacteria and plastids originated from cyanobacteria (see Chapter 26), so many bacterial genes were transferred to host nuclei that modern mitochondria and chloroplasts cannot reproduce outside the host cell.

27.2 Structure and Movement

Learning Outcomes:

1. Discuss the structural adaptations that have increased the complexity of prokaryotic cells.
2. Explain how mucilage influences the behavior of bacterial cells.
3. **CoreSKILL »** Make a drawing that shows the structural differences between Gram-positive and Gram-negative bacterial cells, and predict how these features might influence disease treatments.
4. List the different means by which prokaryotic cells can move.

Bulbnose unicorn fish (*Naso tonganus*) living in Australian coastal ocean waters contain cigar-shaped bacterial symbionts (*Epulopiscium*) whose cells are more than 600 µm long, larger than most eukaryotic cells (whose largest dimension is between 10 and 100 µm). Spherical cells of the bacterial species *Thiomargarita namibiensis*, which lives in African coastal regions, likewise reach record-setting sizes, some being 800 µm in diameter and large enough to be seen without a microscope. However, most bacteria (and archaea) are much smaller: a few micrometers in diameter. Small cell size limits the amount of materials that can be stored within each cell but allows much faster cell division. When nutrients are sufficient, many bacteria can divide many times within a single day. This explains how bacteria can spoil food rapidly and why bacterial infections can spread quickly within the human body. Despite their generally small size, bacteria display a high level of variation in cell structure and shape, surface and cell-wall features, and movement.

Prokaryotic Cells Display a Surprising Degree of Complexity

Although bacteria, like archaea, have a much simpler cellular organization than do eukaryotes, many prokaryotic cells display cellular structural adaptations that increase their complexity. Features of this complexity illustrate the core concept that structure determines function, partly explain why prokaryotic organisms have such high metabolic diversity, and help us understand how the first eukaryotes arose.

Cyanobacteria and other photosynthetic bacteria, for example, are able to use light energy to produce organic compounds because their cells contain large numbers of thylakoids, flattened tubular membranes that grow inward from the plasma membrane (**Figure 27.5**). The extensive membrane surface of the thylakoids bears large amounts of chlorophyll and other components that are needed for photosynthesis. Thylakoids are also abundant in plant chloroplasts, which descended from cyanobacterial ancestors. Thylakoids enable photosynthetic bacteria and chloroplasts to take maximum advantage of light energy in their environments. Aquatic photosynthetic bacteria also commonly contain many gas vesicles. These protein-walled structures increase cell buoyancy and thus help the organisms float within well-illuminated surface waters (see Figure 27.5).

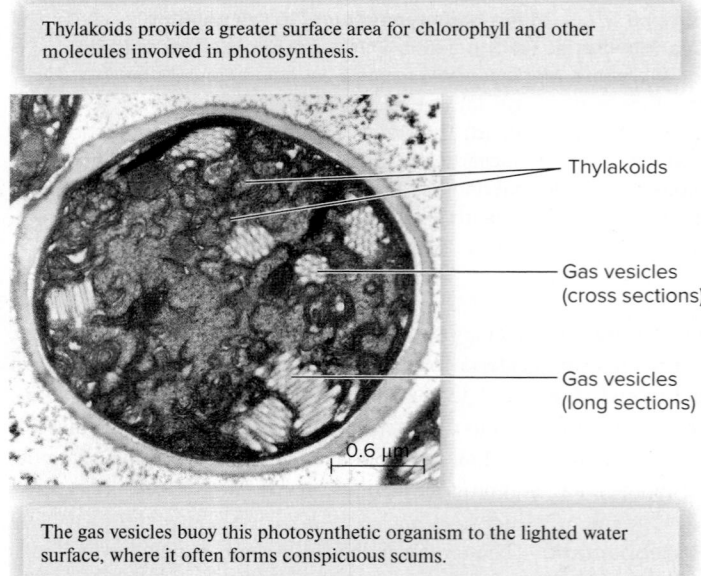

Thylakoids provide a greater surface area for chlorophyll and other molecules involved in photosynthesis.

Thylakoids

Gas vesicles (cross sections)

Gas vesicles (long sections)

0.6 µm

The gas vesicles buoy this photosynthetic organism to the lighted water surface, where it often forms conspicuous scums.

Figure 27.5 Photosynthetic thylakoid membranes and numerous gas vesicles in a cell of an aquatic cyanobacterium. ©Norma Lang

 Core Concept: Structure and Function Thylakoids, which contain chlorophyll and other components that are needed for photosynthesis, are the locations of the light-harvesting reactions. Gas vesicles allow photosynthetic cells to float in well-lit surface waters.

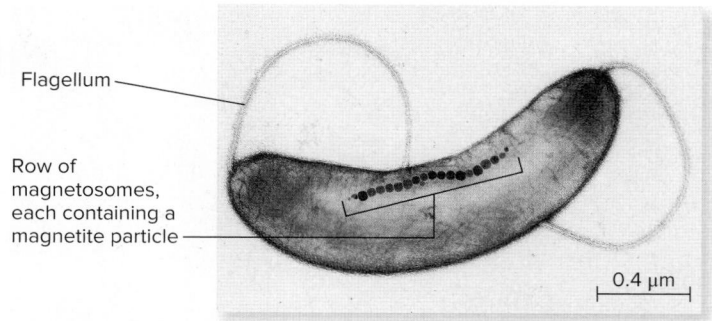

Flagellum

Row of magnetosomes, each containing a magnetite particle

0.4 μm

Figure 27.6 **Magnetosomes found in *Magnetospirillum magnetotacticum*.** An internal row of iron-rich magnetite crystals, each enclosed by a membrane derived from the plasma membrane, functions like a compass needle, allowing this bacterium to detect the Earth's magnetic field. This feature allows *M. magnetotacticum* to orient itself in space and thereby locate its preferred habitat, low-oxygen subsurface waters. These and other bacterial cells use flagella to move to more favorable locations. ©Dr. Richard P. Blakemore, University of New Hampshire

 Core Skill: Connections Look ahead to Section 44.4, which describes electromagnetic sensing by animals. What animals are like *M. magnetotacticum* in being able to sense and respond to magnetic fields?

In other bacteria, plasma membrane ingrowth has generated additional intriguing adaptations—magnetosomes and nucleus-like bodies—that are sometimes described as bacterial organelles. Magnetosomes are tiny crystals of an iron mineral known as magnetite, each surrounded by a membrane. These structures occur in the bacterium *Magnetospirillum* and related genera (**Figure 27.6**). In each of these bacteria, about 15 to 20 magnetosomes occur in a row, together acting as a compass needle that responds to the Earth's magnetic field. Magnetosomes help the bacteria to orient themselves in space and

thereby locate the submerged, low-oxygen habitats they prefer. Magnetosome development begins with invagination of the plasma membrane to form a row of spherical vesicles. If *Magnetospirillum* cells are grown in media having low iron levels, the vesicles remain empty. But if iron is available, a magnetite crystal forms within each vesicle. Fibrils of an actin-like protein keep the magnetosomes aligned in a row. (Recall from Chapter 4 that actin is a major cytoskeletal protein of eukaryotes.) Mutant bacteria lacking a functional form of this protein produce magnetosomes, but they do not remain aligned in a row. Instead, magnetosomes scatter around mutant cells, disrupting their ability to detect a magnetic field.

Plasma membrane invaginations produce nucleus-like bodies in *Gemmata obscuriglobus* and other members of the bacterial phylum Planctomycetes. In *G. obscuriglobus*, an envelope composed of a double membrane encloses all cellular DNA and some ribosomes. Although this bacterial envelope lacks the nuclear pores characteristic of the eukaryotic nuclear envelope, it likely plays a similar adaptive role in isolating DNA from other cellular influences. *G. obscuriglobus* and related bacterial species are also known to accomplish endocytosis by means of membrane coat proteins similar to those present in eukaryotic cells. The cellular diversity and surprising complexity of bacterial cell structure help us to understand not only how bacteria function in nature, but also how important features of eukaryotic cells first evolved.

Prokaryotic Cells Vary in Shape

Although prokaryotic cells occur in multiple forms, they have five common shapes (**Figure 27.7**): spheres (**cocci**), elongate rods (**bacilli**), comma-shaped cells (**vibrios**), and spiral-shaped cells that are either flexible (**spirochaetes**) or rigid (**spirilli**; see Figure 27.6). Cytoskeletal proteins similar to those present in eukaryotic cells control these cell shapes. For example, helical strands of an actin-like protein are responsible for the rod shape of bacilli; if this protein is not produced, bacilli become spherical in shape. Cellular shape

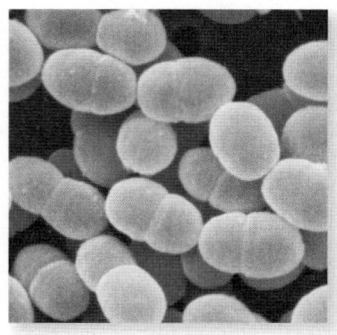

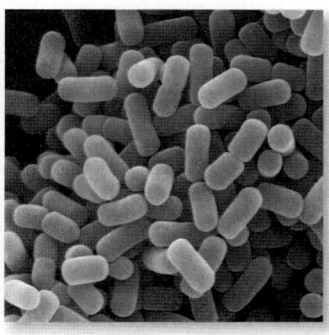

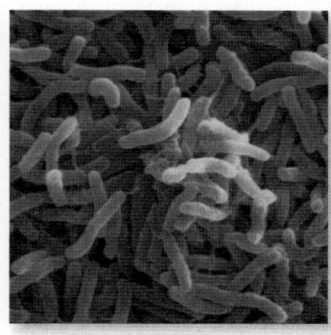

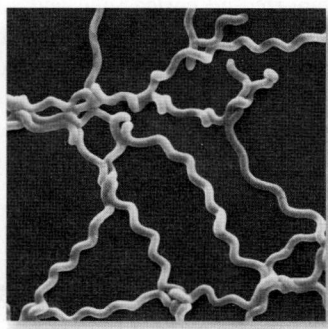

1 μm

11.4 μm

2.5 μm

7.5 μm

(a) Sphere-shaped cocci (*Lactococcus lactis*)

(b) Rod-shaped bacilli (*Lactobacillus plantarum*)

(c) Comma-shaped vibrios (*Vibrio cholerae*)

(d) Spiral-shaped spirochaetes (*Leptospira* sp.)

Figure 27.7 **Major types of prokaryotic cell shapes.** These images are scanning electron micrographs. a: ©SciMAT/Science Source; b, d: ©Dennis Kunkel Microscopy, Inc./Phototake; c: ©Media for Medical/UIG/Getty Images

 Core Concept: Systems In the case of unicellular bacteria and archaea, a single cell constitutes an entire organism.

is an important component of bacterial function in nature. Cocci tend to have a greater surface area/volume ratio, which facilitates exchange of materials with the environment, but bacilli can often store more nutrients.

Slimy Mucilage Often Coats Cellular Surfaces

Many bacteria exude a coat of slimy mucilage, sometimes called a glycocalyx, capsule, or extracellular polymeric substance (EPS). Mucilage, which varies in consistency and thickness, is composed of hydrated polysaccharides and proteins, as well as lipids and nucleic acids. A capsule helps some disease-causing bacteria evade the defense system of their host. You may recall that Frederick Griffith discovered the transfer of genetic material while experimenting with capsule-producing pathogenic strains and capsule-less nonpathogenic strains of the bacterium *Streptococcus pneumoniae* (refer back to Figure 11.1). The immune system cells of mice are able to destroy this bacterium only if it lacks a capsule.

Mucilage plays many additional roles: holding cells together closely enough for chemical communication and DNA exchange to occur, helping aquatic species to float in water, binding mineral nutrients, and repelling attack. Pigmented slime sheaths (see Figure 27.3d) coat some bacterial filaments, helping to prevent UV damage.

Biofilms are aggregations of microorganisms that secrete adhesive mucilage, thereby gluing themselves to surfaces. Formation of a biofilm helps microbes remain in favorable locations for growth; otherwise body or environmental fluids would wash them away. A mechanism known as **quorum sensing** fosters biofilm formation. During quorum sensing, individual microbes secrete small molecules having the potential to influence the behavior of nearby microbes. If enough individuals are present (a quorum), the concentration of signaling molecules builds to a level that causes collective behavior. In the case of biofilms, populations of microbes respond to chemical signals by moving to a common location and producing mucilage.

Biofilms are environmentally and medically important. From a human standpoint, biofilms have both beneficial and harmful consequences. In aquatic and terrestrial environments, biofilms help to stabilize and enrich sand and soil surfaces, and help form mineral deposits. Biofilms that form on the surfaces of animal tissues, however, can be harmful. Dental plaque is an example of a harmful biofilm (**Figure 27.8**); if allowed to remain, the bacterial community secretes acids that can damage tooth enamel. Biofilms may also develop in industrial pipelines, where the attached microbes can contribute to corrosion by secreting enzymes that chemically degrade metal surfaces.

Prokaryotic Cells Vary in Cell-Wall Structure

Whether coated with mucilage or not, most prokaryotic cells possess a rigid cell wall outside the plasma membrane. Cell walls maintain cell shape and help protect against attack by viruses or predatory bacteria. Cell walls also help microbes avoid lysing in hypotonic conditions, when the solute concentration is higher inside the cell than outside. The structure and composition of bacterial cell walls are medically important.

Although some archaea lack cell walls, most possess a wall composed of protein. In contrast, the polymer known as **peptidoglycan**,

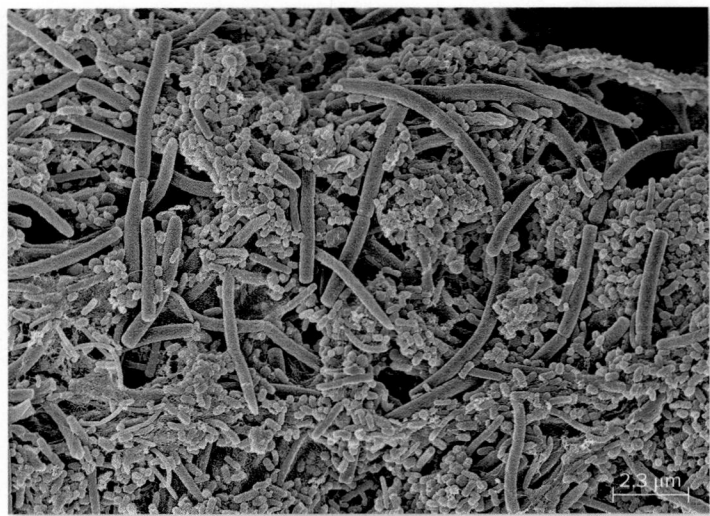

Figure 27.8 A biofilm composed of a community of microorganisms glued by mucilage to a surface. This SEM shows a view of the top surface of dental plaque, consisting of several types of bacteria—falsely colored purple, green, and blue—attached by mucilage to a tooth surface lying beneath. ©Science Photo Library/Alamy Stock Photo

 Core Skill: Modeling The goal of this modeling challenge is to make a model for the development of a biofilm of dental plaque. Such models are proving useful in finding new ways to reduce or prevent oral disease.

Modeling Challenge: Using the SEM of dental plaque shown in Figure 27.8, which illustrates the relative positions and abundances of three types of bacteria, draw a flow diagram showing several sequential stages that hypothetically model the process by which this biofilm might have developed. Your model should indicate which bacteria are most likely to have attached first (purple, green, or blue) and which most recently.

lacking in archaea, is an important component of most bacterial cell walls. Peptidoglycan is composed of carbohydrates that are cross-linked by peptides. Bacterial cell walls occur in two major forms that differ in thickness of the peptidoglycan layer, staining properties, and response to antibiotics. Bacteria having these chemically different walls are called Gram-positive or Gram-negative bacteria, after the staining process used to distinguish them (**Figure 27.9**). The stain is named for its inventor, Danish scientist Hans Christian Gram.

Gram-positive bacteria classified in the phyla Firmicutes and Actinobacteria have walls with a relatively thick peptidoglycan layer (**Figure 27.10a**). By contrast, the Gram-negative cell walls of Cyanobacteria, Proteobacteria, and other species have a thinner peptidoglycan layer and are enclosed by a thin, outer envelope whose outer leaflet is rich in **lipopolysaccharides**, which are lipids that have polysaccharides covalently attached to them (**Figure 27.10b**; see also Figure 27.2a). This outer envelope of Gram-negative bacteria contains a phospholipid bilayer that surrounds the outside of the cell wall, whereas the plasma membrane is found inside the cell wall.

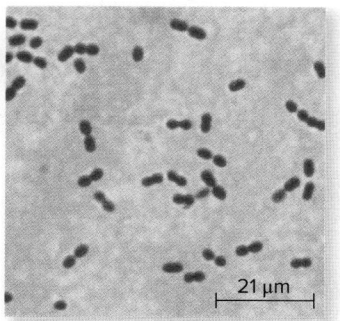 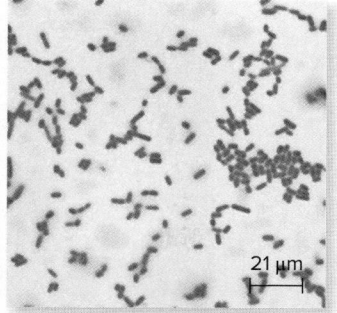

(a) Gram-positive bacteria **(b) Gram-negative bacteria**

Figure 27.9 **Gram-positive and Gram-negative bacteria.**
(a) *Streptococcus pneumoniae*, a member of the phylum Firmicutes, stains positive (purple) with the Gram stain. **(b)** *Escherichia coli*, a member of the Proteobacteria, stains negative (pink) when the Gram stain procedure is applied. a: ©CNRI/Science Source; b: ©Lee W. Wilcox

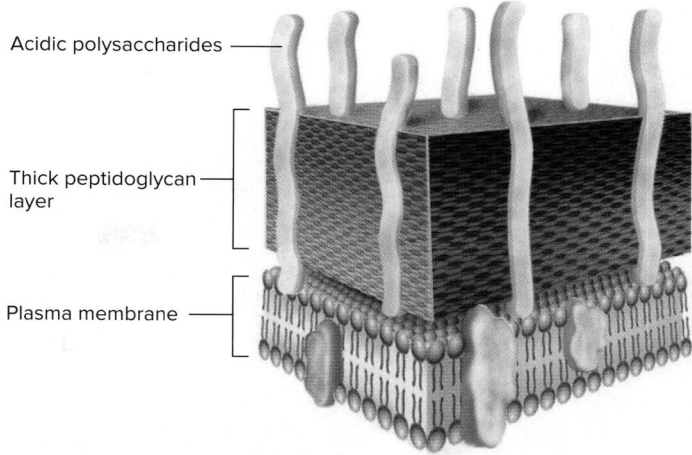

Acidic polysaccharides

Thick peptidoglycan layer

Plasma membrane

(a) Gram-positive: thick peptidoglycan layer, no outer envelope

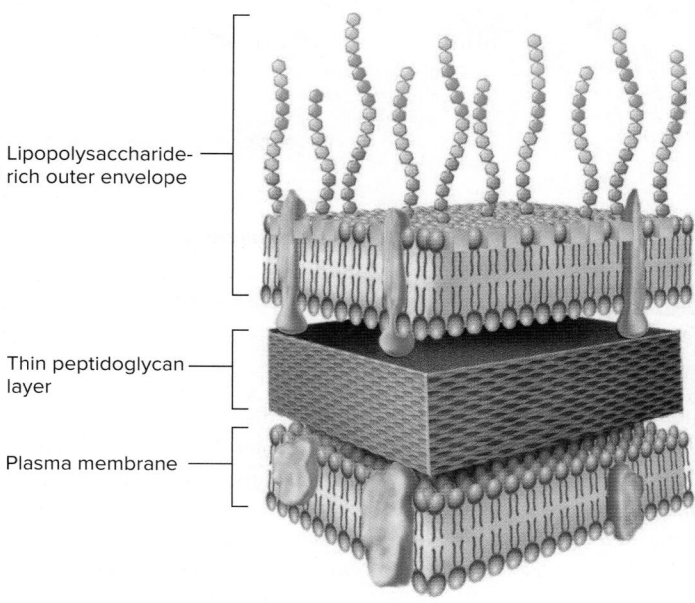

Lipopolysaccharide-rich outer envelope

Thin peptidoglycan layer

Plasma membrane

(b) Gram-negative: thinner peptidoglycan layer, with outer envelope

Figure 27.10 **Cell-wall structures of Gram-positive and Gram-negative bacteria.** **(a)** The structure of the cell wall of Gram-positive bacteria. **(b)** The structure of the cell wall and lipopolysaccharide-rich envelope typical of Gram-negative bacteria.

Peptidoglycan and lipopolysaccharides can affect disease symptoms, the composition of vaccines, and bacterial responses to antibiotics. For example, part of the peptidoglycan covering of the Gram-negative bacterial species *Bordetella pertussis* is responsible for the extensive tissue damage to the respiratory tract associated with whooping cough, and whooping cough vaccines are improved by including antibodies that reduce the ability of the lipopolysaccharide layer to attach to host cells.

The lipopolysaccharide-rich outer envelope of Gram-negative bacteria helps them to resist the entry of some antibiotics. However, this outer envelope also impedes the secretion of proteins from bacterial cells into the environment, a process that normally allows cells to communicate with each other, as in quorum sensing. Gram-negative bacteria have adapted to the presence of an outer envelope by evolving several types of protein systems that function in secretion. In Section 27.5, we will see how some of these secretion systems have been modified in ways that allow disease-causing bacteria to attack eukaryotic cells.

Distinguishing Gram-positive from Gram-negative bacteria is an important factor in choosing the best antibiotics for treating infectious diseases. For example, Gram-positive bacteria are typically more susceptible than Gram-negative bacteria to penicillin and related antibiotics because these antibiotics interfere with synthesis of peptidoglycan, which Gram-positive bacteria require in larger amounts. For this reason, penicillin and related antibiotics such as methicillin are widely used to treat infections caused by Gram-positive bacteria. However, it is of societal concern that some strains of bacteria have become resistant to some antibiotics, an example being methicillin-resistant *Staphylococcus aureus*, or MRSA.

Bacteria and Archaea Display Diverse Types of Movements

Many bacteria and archaea have structures at the cell surface or within the cell that enable them to change position in their environment, an ability known as **motility**. Diverse motility adaptations allow microbes to respond to chemical signals emitted from other cells during quorum sensing and mating, and to move to favorable conditions within gradients of light, gases, or nutrients. For example, we have already learned that gas vesicles help cyanobacteria float into well-illuminated waters close to the surface, where photosynthesis can occur (see Figure 27.5). In addition, prokaryotic cells may move by twitching, gliding, or swimming by means of flagella.

Bacterial **flagella** (singular, flagellum) differ from eukaryotic flagella in several ways. Although bacterial flagella are largely built of about 30 types of proteins, they lack a plasma membrane covering, an internal cytoskeleton of microtubules made of the protein

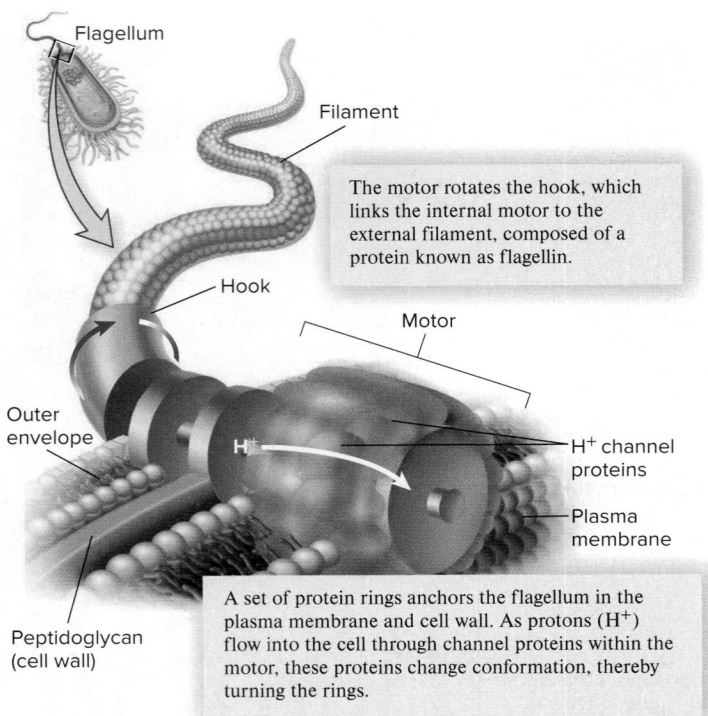

Figure 27.11 **Diagram of a bacterial flagellum, showing a filament, hook, and motor.**

Concept Check: *Does the filament move more like the arms of a human swimmer or the shaft of a boat propeller?*

tubulin, and the motor protein dynein—all features that characterize eukaryotic flagella (look back to Chapter 4). Unlike eukaryotic flagella, bacterial flagella do not repeatedly bend and straighten. Instead, bacterial flagella spin, propelled by molecular machines composed of a filament, hook, and motor that work together somewhat like a boat's outboard motor and propeller (**Figure 27.11**). Lying outside the cell, the long, stiff, curved filament acts as a propeller. The hook links the filament with the motor that contains a set of protein rings at the cell surface. Hydrogen ions (protons), which have been pumped out of the cytoplasm, usually via an electron transport chain, diffuse back into the cell through channel proteins within the motor. This proton flow powers the turning of the hook and filament at rates of hundreds of revolutions per second. Archaeal flagella also rotate but are much thinner than bacterial flagella, are composed of different proteins, and are powered differently (by the hydrolysis of ATP).

Prokaryotic species differ in the number and location of flagella, which may occur singly or in tufts at one pole or may emerge from around the cell (**Figure 27.12**). Differences in flagellar number and location cause microorganisms to exhibit different modes or rates of swimming. Some bacterial species are known to swim at rates of more than 150 μm per second! By contrast, spirochaetes tend to move slowly. Their flagella are located outside the peptidoglycan cell wall but within the confines of an outer membrane that holds them close to the cell. Rotation of these flagella causes spirochaetes to display characteristic bending, flexing, and twirling

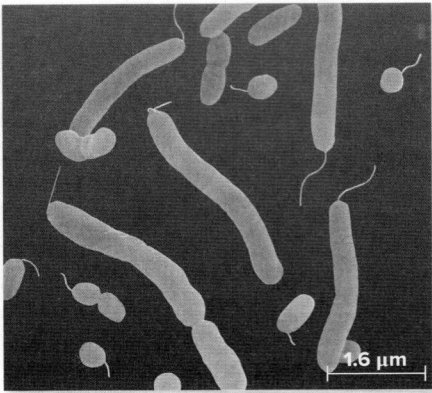

(a) Bacteria with a single short flagellum

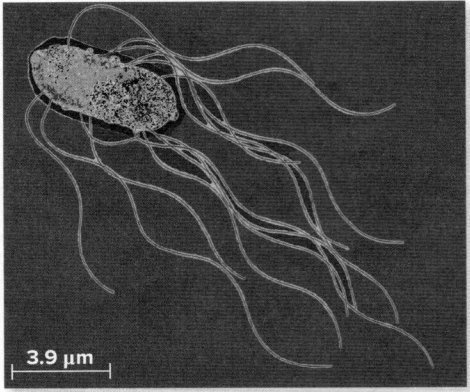

(b) Bacterium with multiple long flagella

Figure 27.12 **Differences in the number and location of flagella.** Depending on the species, microbial cells can produce one or more flagella at the poles or numerous flagella around the periphery. **(a)** *Vibrio parahaemoliticus*, a bacterium that causes seafood poisoning, has a single short flagellum. **(b)** *Salmonella enterica*, another bacterium that causes food poisoning, has many flagella distributed around the cell periphery. a: ©Dennis Kunkel Microscopy, Inc./ Phototake; b: ©Dr. Linda Stannard, UCT/SPL/Science Source

 Core Skill: Connections Look ahead to Figure 29.8b. Like the bacteria shown here, what heterotrophic eukaryote moves to its food source in the human gut by means of flagella?

motions. This allows spirochaetes to move within the thick bodily fluids of their hosts.

Some prokaryotic species twitch or glide across surfaces, using threadlike cell surface structures known as **pili** (singular, pilus) (**Figure 27.13a**). *Myxococcus xanthus* cells, for example, move by alternately extending and retracting pili from one pole or the other. This process allows directional movement toward food materials. If nutrients are low, cells of these bacteria glide together to form tiny treelike colonies, which are part of a reproductive process **Figure 27.13b**. These and other motility adaptations help bacteria and archaea survive in their environments.

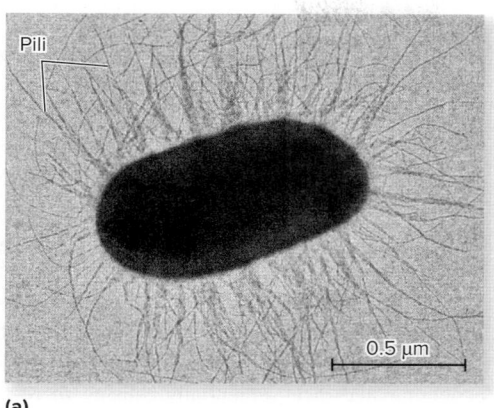

(a)   (b)

Figure 27.13 **Pili that extend from prokaryotic cell surfaces may allow motility and sometimes foster the formation of complex colonies.**
a: Courtesy Dr. Esther Bullitt; b: ©Yoav Levy/Medical Images.com

27.3 Reproduction

Learning Outcomes:

1. Explain how populations of prokaryotic organisms increase in number.
2. **CoreSKILL** » Describe how bacteria can be counted in medical and environmental samples.
3. Give examples of how some bacteria survive under stressful conditions.

Bacteria and archaea do not engage in the process of sexual reproduction used by eukaryotes, involving specialized gametes, gamete fusion, and meiosis. However, they can exchange some genes by conjugation, transformation, and transduction (described in Chapter 19). Bacteria and archaea usually reproduce asexually, generally by means of a type of cell division known as binary fission, but sometimes by forming small cells, known as buds, from one end. Both types of bacterial cell division increase the number of cells in populations. In addition, some bacteria produce tough cells that can withstand deleterious conditions for long periods in a dormant condition.

Prokaryotic Cells Generally Divide by Binary Fission

The cells of most bacteria and archaea divide by splitting in two, a process known as **binary fission** (**Figure 27.14a**; refer back to Figure 19.13). When sufficient nutrients are available, an entire population of identical cells can be produced from a single parental cell by repeated binary fission. This growth process allows microbes to become very numerous in water, food, or animal tissues, potentially causing harm.

Binary fission is the basis of a widely used method for detecting and counting bacteria in food, water samples, or patients' body fluids. Microbiologists who study the spread of disease need to quantify bacterial cells in samples taken from the environment. Medical technicians often need to count bacteria in body fluid samples to assess the likelihood of infection. However, because bacterial cells are small and often unpigmented, they are difficult to count directly. One way that microbiologists count bacteria is to place a measured volume of sample into laboratory dishes filled with a semisolid nutrient medium. Bacteria in the sample undergo repeated binary fission to form colonies of cells visible to the unaided eye (**Figure 27.14b**). Because each colony represents a single cell that was present in the original sample,

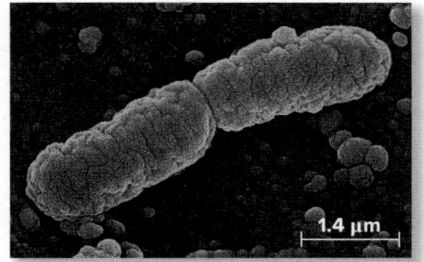
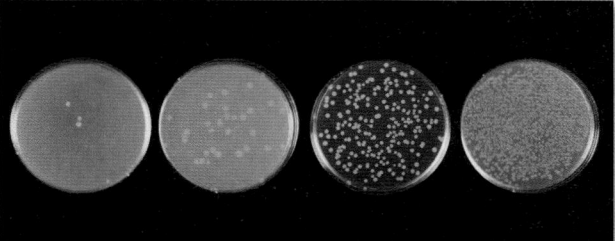
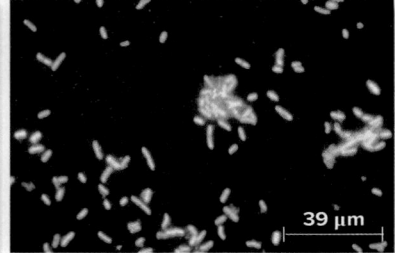

(a) Bacterium undergoing binary fission   **(b) Colonies developed from single cells**   **(c) Bacteria stained with fluorescent DNA-binding dye**

Figure 27.14 **Binary fission and counting microbes.** **(a)** Division of a bacterial cell as viewed by scanning electron microscopy. **(b)** When samples are spread onto the surfaces of laboratory dishes containing nutrients, single cells of bacteria or archaea may divide repeatedly to form visible colonies, which can be easily counted. The number of colonies is an estimate of the number of culturable cells in the original sample. **(c)** If a fluorescence microscope is available, cells can be counted directly by applying a fluorescent stain that binds to their DNA. Each cell glows brightly when illuminated with UV light. a: ©David Scharf/Science Source; b: ©Linda Graham; c: ©Lee W. Wilcox

the number of colonies in the dish reflects the number of living bacteria in the original sample.

Another way to detect and count prokaryotic cells is to treat samples with a stain that binds to bacterial DNA, causing cells to glow brightly when illuminated with UV light. The glowing cells can be viewed and counted by the use of a fluorescence microscope (**Figure 27.14c**). The fluorescence method must be used when the microbes of interest cannot be cultivated in the laboratory. For many bacteria and archaea, the conditions needed to foster population growth in the laboratory are not known.

Some Bacteria Survive Harsh Conditions as Akinetes or Endospores

Some bacteria produce thick-walled cells that are able to survive unfavorable conditions in a dormant state. These specialized cells develop when bacteria have experienced stressful conditions, such as low nutrients or unfavorable temperatures. Such dormant cells may be able to germinate into metabolically active cells when conditions improve again. For example, aquatic filamentous cyanobacteria often produce **akinetes**, thick-walled, food-filled cells, when winter approaches (**Figure 27.15a**). Akinetes are able to survive winter at the bottoms of lakes, and they produce new filaments in spring when they are carried by water currents to the brightly lit surface. Persistence of such akinetes explains how harmful cyanobacterial blooms can develop year after year in overly fertile lakes.

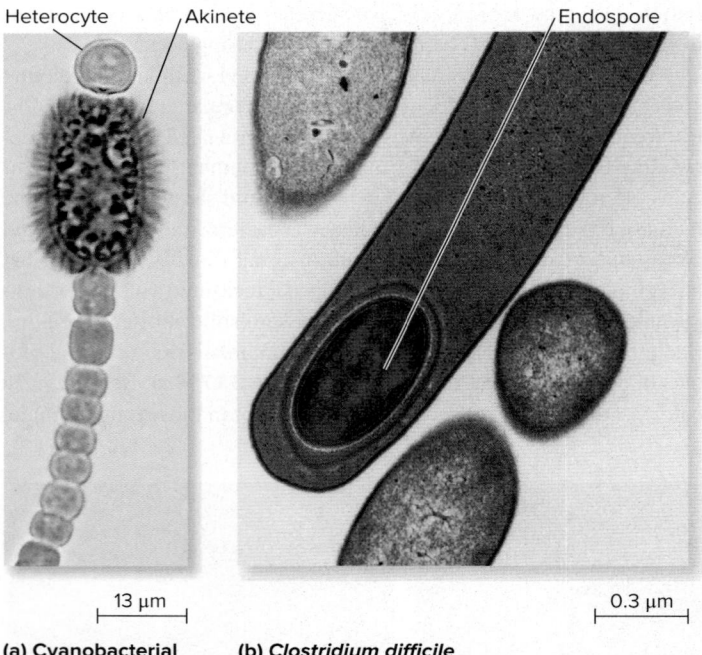

Heterocyte   Akinete   Endospore

13 μm   0.3 μm

(a) Cyanobacterial akinete   **(b)** *Clostridium difficile*

Figure 27.15 **Specialized cells capable of dormancy.**
(a) Akinetes are thick-walled, food-filled cells produced by some cyanobacteria. Akinetes are able to resist stressful conditions and generate new populations when conditions improve. As discussed later, the heterocyte is a specialized cell in which nitrogen fixation occurs. **(b)** An endospore with a resistant wall develops within the cytoplasm of the pathogen *Clostridium difficile*. a: ©Lee W. Wilcox; b: ©Dr. Kari Lounatmaa/Science Source

Concept Check: *How do endospores affect the ability of some bacteria to cause disease?*

Endospores (**Figure 27.15b**) are produced inside bacterial cells by the enclosure of DNA and other materials within a tough coat, and then are released when the enclosing cell dies and breaks down. Endospores can remain alive, though in a dormant state, for long periods, then reactivate when conditions are suitable.

The ability to produce endospores allows some Gram-positive bacteria in the phylum Firmicutes to cause serious diseases. For example, *Bacillus anthracis* causes the disease anthrax and is thus a potential agent in bioterrorism and germ warfare. Most cases of human anthrax result when endospores of *B. anthracis* enter breaks in the skin, causing skin infections that are relatively easily cured by antibiotic treatment. But sometimes the endospores are inhaled or consumed in undercooked, contaminated meat, potentially causing more serious illness or death. *Clostridium botulinum* can contaminate improperly canned food that has not been heated to temperatures high enough to destroy its tough endospores. When the endospores germinate and bacterial cells grow in the food, they produce a deadly toxin, as well as NH_3 and CO_2 gases, which cause can lids to bulge. If humans consume the food, the toxin causes botulism, a severe type of food poisoning that can lead to respiratory and muscular paralysis. The botulism toxin is marketed commercially as Botox, which is injected into the skin, where it paralyzes facial muscles, thereby reducing the appearance of wrinkles. The toxin has also been used as a migraine treatment. *Clostridium tetani* produces a nerve toxin that causes lockjaw, also known as tetanus, when bacterial cells or endospores from soil enter wounds. The ability of the genera *Bacillus* and *Clostridium* to produce resistant endospores helps explain their widespread presence in nature and their effect on humans.

27.4 Nutrition and Metabolism

Learning Outcomes:

1. List the major mechanisms of nutrition displayed by prokaryotic species.

2. **CoreSKILL** » Compare and contrast the effects of oxygen on the metabolism of different types of prokaryotic species; then predict the outcome when a gas gangrene patient is treated with oxygen.

3. Outline the process of biological nitrogen fixation, and explain why it is important and how oxygen interferes with this process.

All living cells require energy and a source of carbon to build their organic molecules. Bacteria and archaea use a wide variety of strategies to obtain energy and carbon for growth (**Table 27.2**). These microbes can be classified according to their energy source, carbon source, response to oxygen, and presence of specialized metabolic processes.

Mechanisms of Nutrition and Responses to Oxygen

Cyanobacteria and some other prokaryotic species are **autotrophs** (from the Greek, meaning self-feeders), organisms that are able to produce all or most of their own organic molecules from inorganic sources. Autotrophs fall into two categories: photoautotrophs and chemoautotrophs. **Photoautotrophs**, including cyanobacteria, use light as a source of energy for the synthesis of organic molecules from CO_2 and H_2O or H_2S. **Chemoautotrophs** use energy obtained by chemical modifications of inorganic compounds to synthesize organic compounds. Such chemical modifications include

Table 27.2	Major Types of Archaea and Bacteria Based on Energy and Carbon Source		
Type	Energy source	Carbon source	Example
Autotroph			
Photoautotroph	Light	CO_2	Cyanobacteria
Chemoautotroph	Inorganic compounds	CO_2	*Sulfolobus* (Archaea)
Heterotroph			
Photoheterotroph	Light	Organic compounds	Chloroflexi (Bacteria)
Chemoheterotroph	Organic compounds	Organic compounds	Many

nitrification (the conversion of ammonia to nitrate) and the oxidation of sulfur, iron, or hydrogen. For example, archaea of the genus *Sulfolobus* can oxidize certain sulfur-containing minerals.

Heterotrophs (from the Greek, meaning other feeders) are organisms that require at least one organic compound, and often more, from their environment. Some microorganisms, including bacteria in the phylum Chloroflexi, are **photoheterotrophs**, meaning that they are able to use light energy to generate ATP, but they must take in organic compounds from their environment as a source of carbon. **Chemoheterotrophs** must obtain organic molecules both for energy and as a carbon source.

Prokaryotic species differ in their need for and responses to oxygen. Like most eukaryotes (including humans), many prokaryotes are **obligate aerobes**, meaning that they require O_2 to survive. In contrast to obligate aerobes, obligate anaerobes, such as the Firmicutes genus *Clostridium*, are poisoned by O_2. People suffering from gas gangrene (caused by *Clostridium perfringens* and related species) are usually treated by placement in a chamber having a high oxygen content (called a hyperbaric chamber), which kills the organisms and deactivates the toxins. **Aerotolerant anaerobes** do not use O_2, but they are not poisoned by it either. These organisms obtain their energy by fermentation or anaerobic respiration, which are described in Chapter 7 (look back at Section 7.8). Anaerobic metabolic processes include denitrification (the conversion of nitrate into N_2 gas) and the reduction of manganese, iron, and sulfate, which are all important in the Earth's cycling of minerals.

Facultative anaerobes can use O_2 via aerobic respiration, obtain energy via anaerobic fermentation, or use inorganic chemical reactions to obtain energy—shifting between modes depending on environmental conditions. One fascinating example of a facultative anaerobe is the species *Thiomargarita namibiensis*, a large proteobacterium mentioned earlier in this chapter. This chemoheterotroph obtains its energy in two ways: by oxidizing sulfide with oxygen when oxygen is available or, when oxygen is low or unavailable, by oxidizing sulfide with nitrate. In either case, the cells convert sulfide to elemental sulfur, which is stored within the cells in large globules.

Some Prokaryotic Species Play Important Roles as Nitrogen Fixers

Many cyanobacteria and some other prokaryotic organisms carry out a specialized metabolic process called biological **nitrogen fixation**. The removal of nitrogen from the gaseous phase is called fixation, and microbes that perform this process are known as nitrogen fixers.

Nitrogen fixation is an important component of the cycling of nitrogen on a global basis. During nitrogen fixation, the enzyme nitrogenase converts inert atmospheric nitrogen gas (N_2) into ammonia (NH_3). Plants and algae can use ammonia (though not N_2) to produce proteins and other essential nitrogen-containing molecules. As a result, many plants have developed close relationships with nitrogen fixers, which provide ammonia fertilizer to their plant partners. In addition to the aquatic photosynthetic cyanobacteria mentioned in the chapter opening, many types of heterotrophic soil bacteria also fix nitrogen. Examples include protobacteria of the genus *Rhizobium*, which live within the roots of legume plants (see Chapter 38).

Nitrogenase is inhibited by O_2, so most nitrogen fixers conduct nitrogen fixation only in low-oxygen conditions. Many cyanobacteria generate low-oxygen conditions in specialized cells known as heterocytes, allowing nitrogen fixation to occur in these cells (see Figure 27.15a). Heterocytes display adaptations that reduce nitrogenase exposure to oxygen. These include thick walls that reduce inward O_2 diffusion, increased occurrence of cellular reactions that consume oxygen, and down-regulation of the oxygen-producing components of photosynthesis. The latter adaptation, involving reduction in chlorophyll synthesis, explains why heterocytes are paler in color than neighboring photosynthetic cells.

27.5 Ecological Roles and Biotechnology Applications

Learning Outcomes:

1. Discuss the roles of bacteria and archaea in the carbon cycle.
2. List examples of bacteria-eukaryote symbiosis and of pathogenic microbes.
3. List ways in which bacteria contribute to industrial and biotechnology applications.

Bacteria and archaea play many key ecological roles. In addition to their roles in nitrogen fixation and other aspects of the global nitrogen cycle, bacteria and archaea produce or break down organic carbon, important in the global carbon cycle. Bacteria function as beneficial symbionts in plants and animals and as disease agents. In this section, we will focus on these ecological roles and also provide examples of ways that humans use the metabolic capabilities of bacteria in industry and biotechnology.

Bacteria and Archaea Play Important Roles in Earth's Carbon Cycle

The Earth's carbon cycle is the sum of all the chemical changes that occur among compounds that contain carbon. (Look ahead to Chapter 59 for a detailed discussion of the carbon cycle.) One way that bacteria and archaea influence Earth's carbon cycle is by producing and consuming methane. Methane (CH_4)—the major component of natural gas—is a greenhouse gas more powerful than CO_2; CH_4 increases global warming over 20 times more per molecule than does CO_2. Therefore, atmospheric CH_4 has the potential to alter the Earth's climate, and in recent years the level of CH_4 has been increasing in Earth's atmosphere as the result of human activities. Several groups of anaerobic archaea known as **methanogens** convert CO_2, methyl groups, or acetate to CH_4 and release CH_4 from their cells into the atmosphere. Methanogens live in swampy wetlands, in deep-sea habitats, or in the digestive systems of animals, including cattle

and *Trypanosoma brucei*, the causative agent of sleeping sickness, are serious pathogens of humans and other animals (**Figure 28.8c**). Structural analyses of proteins specific to glycosomes have enabled the development of new ways to selectively kill *Trypanosoma* by interfering with these proteins.

Metamonads   Metamonads (formally Metamonada) are heterotrophic flagellates; some are parasitic species that attack the cells of animal hosts and absorb food molecules released from them. For example, *Trichomonas vaginalis* causes a sexually transmitted infection of the human genitourinary tract. In this location, *T. vaginalis* uses phagocytosis to consume bacteria and host epithelial and red blood cells, as well as carbohydrates and proteins released from damaged host cells. More than 170 million cases of infection by *T. vagnalis* are estimated to occur each year around the globe, and such an infection can predispose humans to other diseases. *T. vaginalis* has an undulating membrane and flagella that allow it to move over mucus-coated skin (**Figure 28.9a**).

Giardia intestinalis (previously known as *G. lamblia*), another parasitic protist, contains two active nuclei and produces eight flagella (**Figure 28.9b**). *G. intestinalis* causes giardiasis, an intestinal

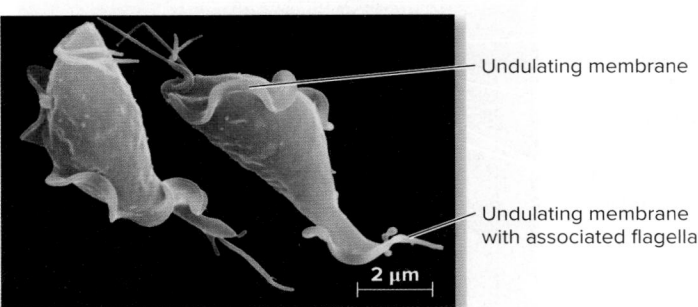

Undulating membrane

Undulating membrane with associated flagella

2 μm

(a) *Trichomonas vaginalis*

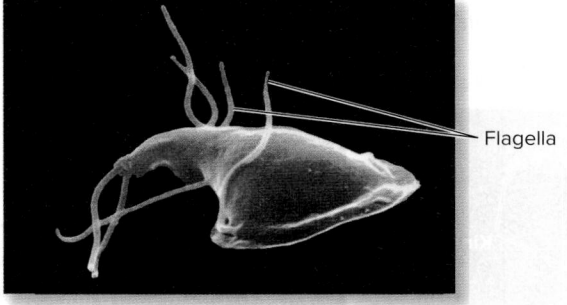

Flagella

(b) *Giardia intestinalis*

Figure 28.9 Parasitic members of the supergroup Excavata.
(a) *Trichomonas vaginalis*. **(b)** *Giardia intestinalis*. These specialized heterotrophic flagellates use flagella to disperse across the surfaces of moist host tissues; the flagellates then absorb nutrients from living cells. These images were made with a scanning electron microscope (SEM) that employs electrons rather than visible light, with the result that cellular structures do not appear in color. a: ©David M. Phillips/Science Source; b: Source: CDC/Dr. Stan Erlandsen, Dr. Dennis Feely

Concept Check: *How do these two parasitic protists differ in how they are transmitted from one human host to another?*

infection that can result from drinking untreated water or from unsanitary conditions in day-care centers. Nearly 300 million human infections occur every year, and the disease also harms young farm animals, dogs, cats, and wild animals. In the animal body, flagellate cells cause disease and also produce infectious stages known as cysts that are transmitted in feces and can survive several weeks outside a host. When an animal ingests as few as 10 of these cysts, within 15 minutes stomach acids induce the flagellate stage to develop and adhere to cells of the small intestine. *T. vaginalis* and *G. intestinalis* were once thought to lack mitochondria, but they are now known to possess simple structures that are highly modified mitochondria.

 **Core Concept: Evolution**

Genome Sequences Reveal the Different Evolutionary Pathways of *Trichomonas vaginalis* and *Giardia intestinalis*

In 2007, genome sequences were reported for *T. vaginalis* and *G. intestinalis*. A comparison of their genomes reveals similarities and differences in the evolution of their parasitic lifestyles. One common feature is that horizontal gene transfer from bacterial or archaeal donors has powerfully affected both genomes. About 100 *G. intestinalis* genes are likely to have been acquired via horizontal gene transfer. In *T. vaginalis*, more than 150 cases of likely horizontal gene transfer were identified, with most transferred genes encoding metabolic enzymes such as those involved in carbohydrate or protein metabolism. Another similarity between *T. vaginalis* and *G. intestinalis* revealed by comparative genomics is the apparent absence of the cytoskeletal protein myosin, which is present in most eukaryotic cells.

Despite these similarities, the genome sequences of *T. vaginalis* and *G. lamblia* reveal some dramatic differences. The *G. intestinalis* genome is quite compact, with only 11.7 megabase pairs (Mb), and the organism has relatively simple metabolic pathways and machinery for DNA replication, transcription, and RNA processing. In contrast, the *T. vaginalis* genome is a surprisingly large 160 Mb in size. *T. vaginalis* has a core set of about 60,000 protein-encoding genes, one of the greatest coding capacities known among eukaryotes. The additional genes provide an expanded capacity for biochemical degradation. Because most trichomonads inhabit animal intestines, the genomic data suggest that the large genome size of *T. vaginalis* is related to its ecological transition to a new habitat, the urogenital tract.

Land Plants and Related Algae Share Similar Genetic Features

The supergroup that includes land plants also encompasses several protist phyla (**Figure 28.10**). The land plants, also known as the kingdom Plantae (described more fully in Chapters 31 and 32), evolved from green algal ancestors. Together, plants and some closely related

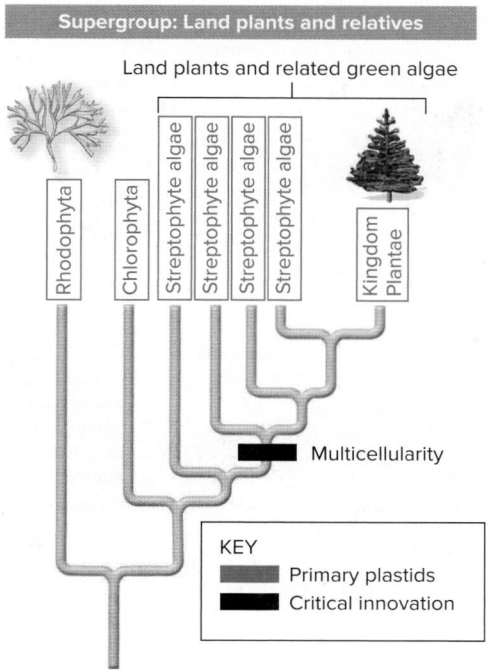

Supergroup: Land plants and relatives

Land plants and related green algae

Rhodophyta
Chlorophyta
Streptophyte algae
Streptophyte algae
Streptophyte algae
Streptophyte algae
Kingdom Plantae

Multicellularity

KEY
Primary plastids
Critical innovation

Figure 28.10 A phylogenetic tree of the supergroup that includes land plants and their close protist relatives. Note that plant multicellularity first arose in closely related streptophyte algae. Many chlorophyte and red algae are macroalgae in which multicellularity arose independently.

green algae form the clade Streptophyta, informally known as streptophytes, whereas most green algae are classified in the phylum Chlorophyta. The red algae, classified in the phylum Rhodophyta, are also regarded as close relatives of green algae and land plants.

Green Algae   Diverse structural types of green algae (see Figure 28.3) occur in fresh water, the ocean, and on land or ice surfaces. Most of the green algae are photosynthetic, and their cells contain the same types of plastids and photosynthetic pigments that are present in land plants. Some green algae are responsible for harmful algal growths, but others are useful as food for aquatic animals, as model organisms, and as sources of renewable oil supplies. Many green algae possess flagella or the ability to produce them during the development of reproductive cells. Green algae are increasingly important in medicine because they produce channel rhodopsins, light-activated ion channels. Green algae use these channel proteins to detect and respond to light, and researchers are studying the proteins in an attempt to understand and possibly treat blindness in animals.

Red Algae   Most species of the protists known as red algae are multicellular marine macroalgae (**Figure 28.11**). The red appearance of these algae is caused by the presence of distinctive photosynthetic pigments that are absent from green algae and land plants. Red algae characteristically lack flagella—a feature that has strongly influenced the evolution of this group, resulting in unusually complex life cycles (illustrated in Figure 28.26b). These life cycles are important to humans because red algae are cultivated in ocean waters for the production of billions of dollars worth of food or industrial and scientific materials yearly. For

(a) *Calliarthron*   **(b)** *Chondrus crispus*

Figure 28.11 Representative red algae (Rhodophyta). (a) The genus *Calliarthron* has cell walls that are impregnated with calcium carbonate. This stony, white material makes the red alga appear pink. **(b)** *Chondrus crispus* is an edible red seaweed. a: ©Lee W. Wilcox; b: ©Andrew J. Martinez/Science Source

example, the sushi wrappers called nori are composed of the sheetlike red algal genus *Porphyra*, which is grown in ocean farms. Carrageenan, agar, and agarose are complex polysaccharides that are extracted from red algae and are essential to the food industry and in biology laboratories for cultivating microorganisms and working with DNA.

Primary Plastids and Primary Endosymbiosis   The plastids of red algae resemble those of green algae and land plants (and differ from those of most other algae) in having an enclosing envelope composed of two membranes (**Figure 28.12**). Such plastids, known as **primary plastids**, are thought to have originated via a process known as **primary endosymbiosis** (**Figure 28.13**). During primary endosymbiosis, heterotrophic host cells captured cyanobacterial cells via phagocytosis but did not digest them. These endosymbiotic cyanobacteria provided host cells with photosynthetic capability and other useful biochemical pathways and eventually evolved into primary plastids (Figure 28.13a).

Endosymbiotic acquisitions of plastids and mitochondria resulted in massive horizontal gene transfer from the endosymbiont to the host nucleus. As a result of such gene transfer, many of the proteins needed by plastids and mitochondria are synthesized in the host cytosol and then targeted to these organelles. All cells of plants, green algae, and red algae contain one or more plastids, and most of these

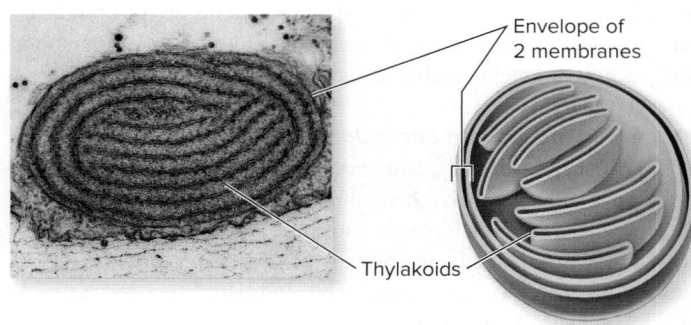

Envelope of 2 membranes

Thylakoids

Figure 28.12 A primary plastid, showing an envelope composed of two membranes. The plastid shown here is red, but primary plastids can also be green or blue-green in color. ©Joe Scott, Department of Biology, College of William and Mary, Williamsburg, VA 23187

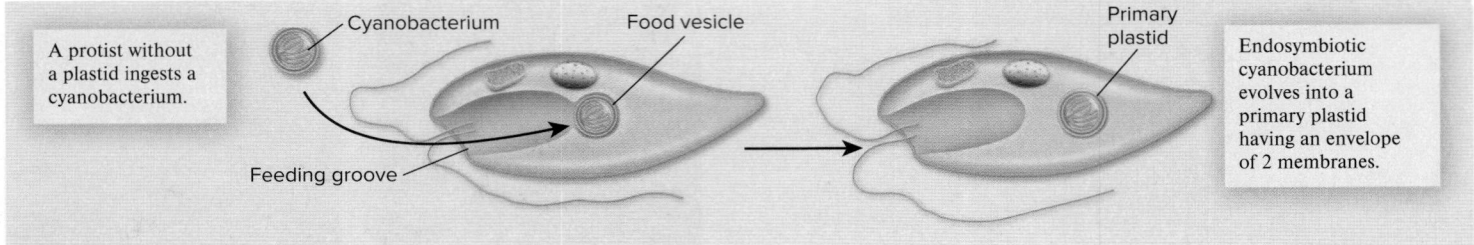

(a) Primary endosymbiosis

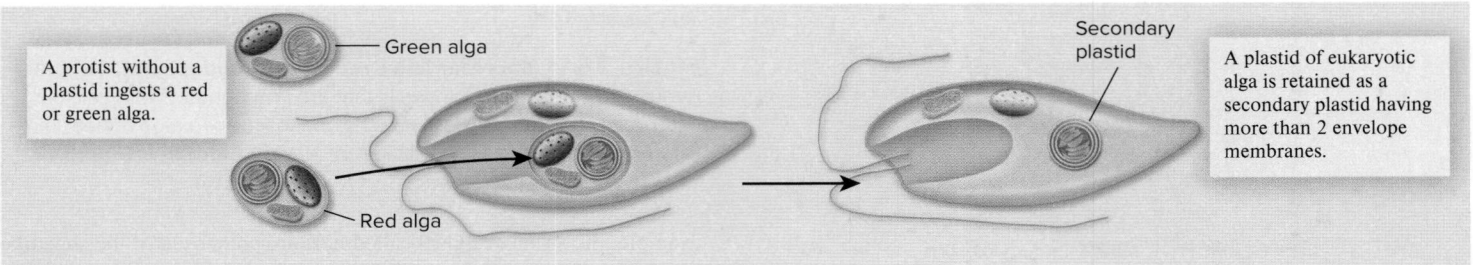

(b) Secondary endosymbiosis

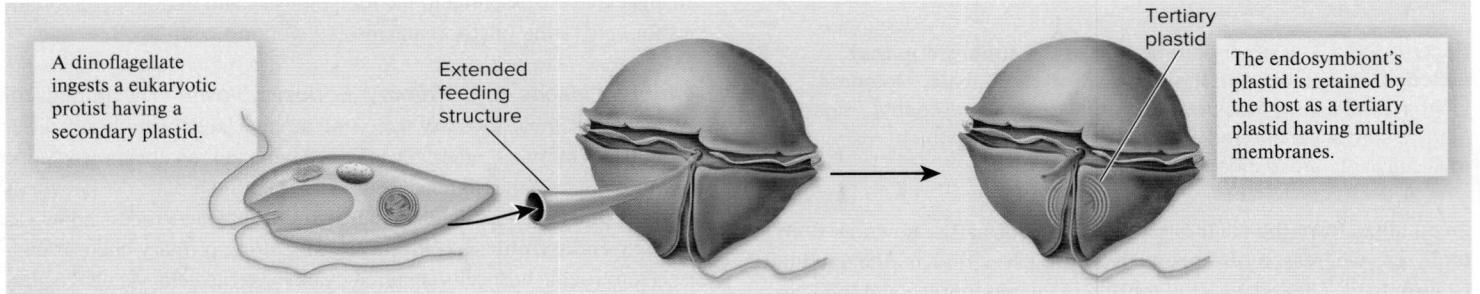

(c) Tertiary endosymbiosis

Figure 28.13 Primary, secondary, and tertiary endosymbiosis. (a) Primary endosymbiosis involves the acquisition of a cyanobacterial endosymbiont by a host cell without a plastid. During the evolution of a primary plastid, the bacterial cell wall is lost, and most endosymbiont genes are transferred to the host nucleus. **(b)** Secondary endosymbiosis involves the acquisition by a host cell of a eukaryotic endosymbiont that contains one or more primary plastids. During the evolution of a secondary plastid, most components of the endosymbiont cell are lost, but a plastid is often retained within an envelope of endoplasmic reticulum. **(c)** Tertiary endosymbiosis involves the acquisition by a host cell of a eukaryotic endosymbiont that possesses secondary plastids.

organisms are photosynthetic. However, some species (or some of the cells within the multicellular bodies of photosynthetic species) are heterotrophic because photosynthetic pigments are not produced in the plastids. In these cases, plastids play other essential metabolic roles, such as producing amino acids and fatty acids.

Secondary Plastids and Secondary Endosymbiosis In contrast to the primary plastids of plants and green and red algae, the plastids of most other photosynthetic protists are derived from a photosynthetic eukaryote. Such plastids are known as **secondary plastids** because they originated by the process of **secondary endosymbiosis** (see Figure 28.13b). Secondary endosymbiosis occurs when a eukaryotic host cell ingests and retains another type of eukaryotic cell that already has one or more primary plastids, such as a red or green alga. Such eukaryotic endosymbionts are often enclosed by the endoplasmic reticulum (ER), explaining why secondary plastids typically have envelopes of more than two membranes. Although most of the

endosymbiont's cellular components are digested over time, its plastids are retained, providing the host cell with photosynthetic capacity and other biochemical capabilities.

Cryptomonads (**Figure 28.14a**) and haptophytes are algal phyla that include single-celled flagellates whose plastids originated by secondary endosymbiosis involving the incorporation of plastids derived from a red alga. Occurring in marine and fresh waters, cryptomonads are excellent sources of the fatty-acid-rich food essential to aquatic animals. Haptophytes are primarily unicellular marine photosynthesizers; some have flagella and others do not. Some haptophytes are known as the coccolithophorids because they produce a covering of intricate white calcium carbonate discs known as coccoliths (**Figure 28.14b**). Coccolithophorids often form massive ocean growths that are visible from space and play important roles in Earth's climate by reflecting sunlight. In some places, coccoliths produced by huge populations of ancient coccolithophorids accumulated on the ocean floor, together with the calcium carbonate remains of other protists, for millions

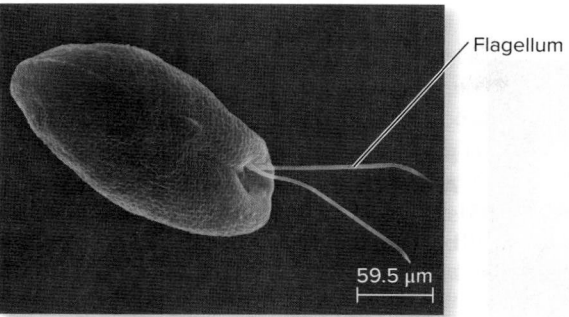

(a) A cryptomonad

Flagellum

59.5 µm

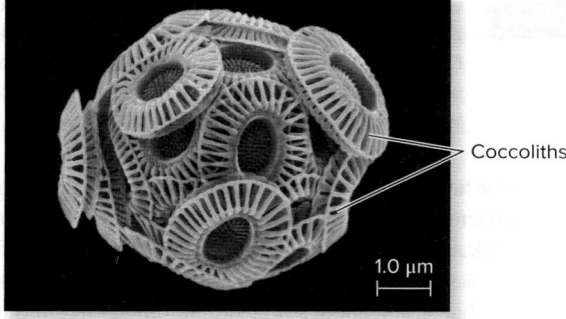

Coccoliths

1.0 µm

(b) A haptophyte coccolithophorid

(c) Fossil deposit containing coccolithophorids

Figure 28.14 Representative cryptomonads and haptophytes. **(a)** A cryptomonad flagellate. **(b)** A type of haptophyte known as a coccolithophorid, covered with disc-shaped coccoliths made of calcium carbonate. **(c)** Fossil carbonate remains of haptophyte algae and protozoan protists known as foraminifera that were deposited over millions of years formed the white cliffs of Dover in England. a: ©Dennis Kunkel Microscopy, Inc./Phototake; b: ©Steve Gschmeissner/Science Source; c: ©Stockbyte/Getty Images

of years. These deposits were later raised above sea level, forming massive limestone formations or chalk cliffs such as those visible at Dover, on the southern coast of England (**Figure 28.14c**).

Membrane Sacs Lie at the Cell Periphery of Alveolata

The three supergroups Alveolata, Stramenopila, and Rhizaria seem to be closely related, based on recent phylogenetic studies (**Figure 28.15**). These photosynthetic protists have plastids acquired by secondary endosymbiosis or, in some cases, by tertiary endosymbiosis.

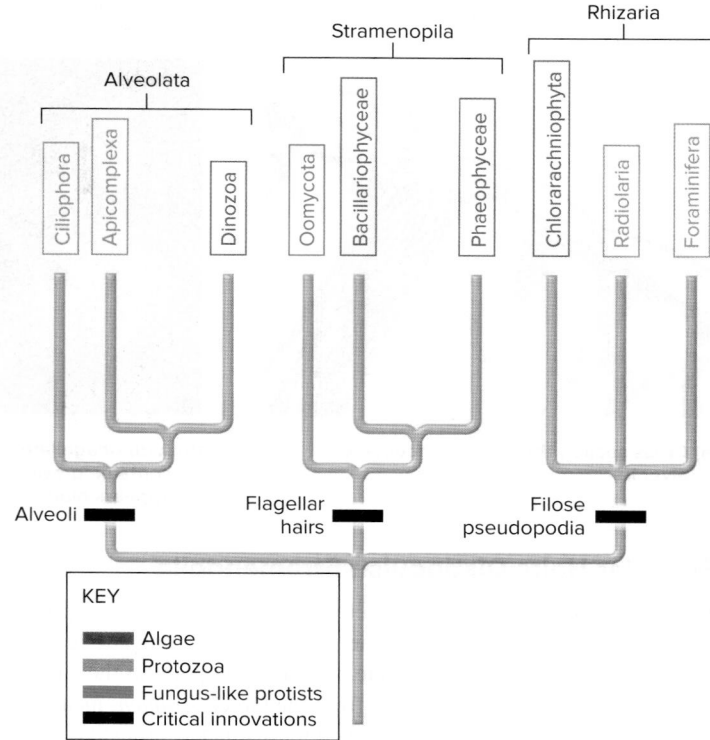

Alveolata

Stramenopila

Rhizaria

Ciliophora | Apicomplexa | Dinozoa | Oomycota | Bacillariophyceae | Phaeophyceae | Chlorarachniophyta | Radiolaria | Foraminifera

Alveoli

Flagellar hairs

Filose pseudopodia

KEY
- Algae
- Protozoa
- Fungus-like protists
- Critical innovations

Figure 28.15 A phylogenetic tree illustrating the close relationship among the supergroups Alveolata, Stramenopila, and Rhizaria. Some stramenopiles, such as giant kelps, are multicellular.

Turning first to Alveolata, we see that it includes three important phyla: (1) the Ciliophora, or ciliates; (2) the Apicomplexa, a medically important group of parasites; and (3) the Dinozoa, known as dinoflagellates. Apicomplexans include the malarial agent *Plasmodium* (see Section 28.4), the related protist *Cryptosporidium parvum*, whose effects were noted in the chapter opening, and other serious pathogens of humans and other animals. Dinoflagellates are recognized both for their mutualistic relationship with reef-building corals (look ahead to Figure 54.26b) and for the harmful blooms (red tides) that some species produce (see Section 28.3). The supergroup Alveolata is named for saclike membranous vesicles known as alveoli that are present at the cell periphery in all of these phyla (**Figure 28.16a**).

The alveoli of some dinoflagellates seem empty, so the cell surface appears smooth. By contrast, the alveoli of many dinoflagellates contain plates of cellulose, which form an armor-like enclosure (**Figure 28.16b**). These plates are often modified in ways that provide an adaptive advantage, such as protection from predators or increased ability to float.

About half of dinoflagellate species are heterotrophic, and half possess photosynthetic plastids of diverse types that originated by secondary or even tertiary endosymbiosis; therefore, these are known as secondary or tertiary plastids. **Tertiary plastids** were obtained by **tertiary endosymbiosis**—the acquisition by hosts of plastids from cells that possessed secondary plastids (see Figure 28.13c). Species having tertiary plastids have received genes by horizontal transfer from diverse genomes.

Core Skill: Process of Science

Feature Investigation | Cook and Colleagues Demonstrated That Cellulose Helps Green Algae Avoid Chemical Degradation

The periphytic, branched green alga *Cladophora* (see Figure 28.3d) is common along marine and freshwater shorelines around the world, where it provides essential habitat for dense populations of diverse microorganisms on its extensive surfaces. Amazingly tough cellulose cell walls allow this alga to harbor extensive microbial diversity without readily decomposing. Acting in this host role, *Cladophora* provides such an important ecological service that it has been called an

ecological engineer, which is a species that strongly affects its habitat. *Cladophora* is known to be resistant to microbial decay, leading to the buildup of organic carbon in aquatic environments, but the basis of this resistance was unknown until recently. In 2013, American cell biologist Martha Cook and associates performed an experiment to examine the effects of extreme chemical treatment on the cell structure of *Cladophora* (**Figure 28.23**).

Figure 28.23 Cook and colleagues showed that the green alga *Cladophora* produces tough cellulose walls that survive exposure to strong acids and high temperatures, suggesting the potential to leave fossil remains. (left): ©Martha Cook; (middle): ©Linda Graham; (right): ©Nicholas Butterfield

GOAL To determine the degree and chemical basis of the resistance to degradation of *Cladophora* and compare the results to ancient fossils of related algae.

KEY MATERIALS Samples of *Cladophora* collected from natural waters; concentrated acids

Experimental level

Conceptual level

1 Treat the algae with a standard mixture of acids, heated to boiling for 30 minutes, then centrifuge to sediment the algal remains and remove acid.

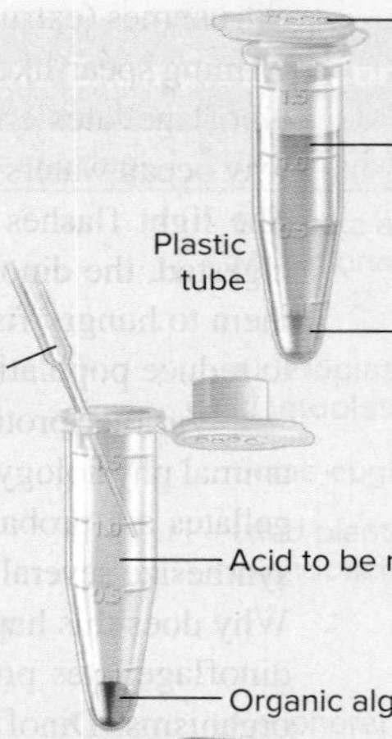

Holes in lid to release vapor

Acid mixture

Plastic tube

Green algae

Pipette tip

Acid to be removed

Organic algal remains

High-temperature acid treatment, known as acetolysis, would be expected to break down the cellulose microfibrils in land plants and other types of algae.

2 Examine algal remains by means of scanning electron microscopy to determine their structure.

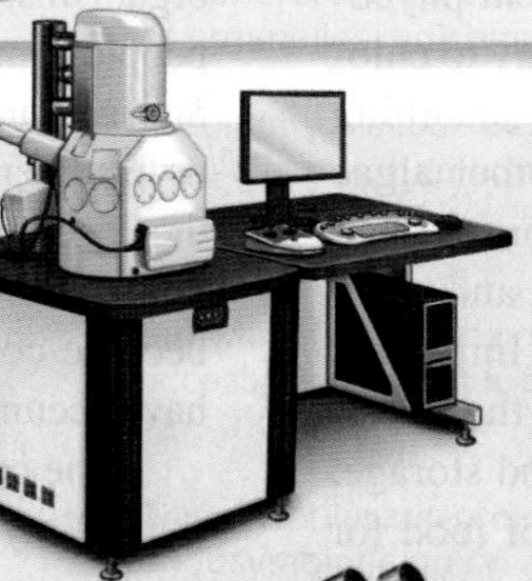

Structure of the algal remains suggests that the biochemical composition includes fibrils made of cellulose. Dimensions of microfibrils indicate the degree of chemical resistance: Microfibrils of greater width are known to have greater resistance to degradation.

3 Examine algal remains using a light microscope equipped with crossed polarizers. Compare microscopic appearance of the remains to that of 750-million-year-old fossils.

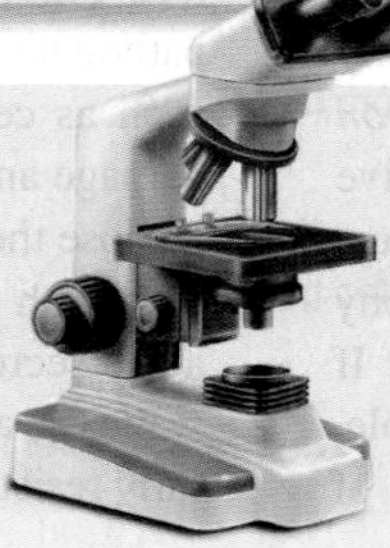

Crossed polarizers reveal birefringence, a sparkling white appearance typical of highly crystalline cellulose.

4 Compare the results of steps 3 and 4 to ancient fossils of related algae. | Compare modern *Cladophora* to ancient algal fossils. | *Cladophora* and the ancient algal fossils look similar. Biochemical materials that survive high-temperature acid treatment are also likely to have survived microbial degradation long enough to have formed organic fossils.

5 **THE DATA**

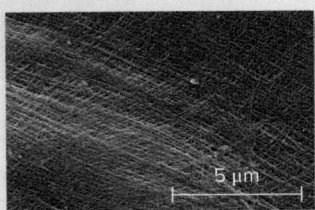

SEM of *Cladophora* after acetolysis. Microfibrils of cellulose are 100 nanometers in diameter, thicker than those in land plant cell walls, which are only 3.5 nm thick.

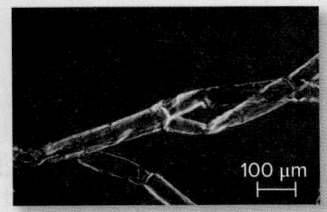

Light microscope view of acetolyzed *Cladophora* using crossed-polarizers. The sparkling white appearance is typical of highly crystalline cellulose.

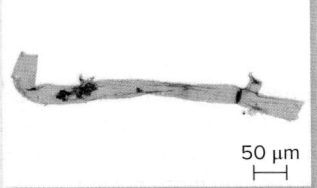

A 750-million-year-old fossil, *Pterocladus*, shows similar dimensions and distinctive branching pattern to modern *Cladophora*, even when the latter has been treated by acetolysis.

6 **CONCLUSION** Tough cell-wall cellulose resists chemical degradation, allowing *Cladophora*-like algae to form as fossils and explaining modern ecological persistence in aquatic ecosystems.

7 **SOURCE** Graham, L. E., Cook, M. E., et al. 2013. Resistance of filamentous chlorophycean, ulvophycean, and xanthophycean algae to acetolysis: Testing Proterozoic and Paleozoic microfossil attributions. *International Journal of Plant Sciences* 174: 947–957.

In the first step of the experiment, the investigators treated the algae with concentrated acids at a boiling temperature to mimic harsh chemical and microbial degradation processes. The second and third steps used two different microscopy methods to examine the algal remains and to determine their chemical makeup. In a final step, the investigators compared the algal remains to fossils of related algae from deposits about 750 million years old. As seen in the data, they found that the remains of modern *Cladophora* after acid treatment contained cellulose microfibrils that are thicker than those found in plants. The researchers inferred that the microbial resistance of modern *Cladophora* is derived from the relatively thick cellulose microfibrils present in its cell walls. In addition, the remains of *Cladophora* closely resembled the ancient fossils of related algae. These results are consistent with the idea that a cell wall that can withstand acetolysis may also have resisted microbial degradation long enough to allow the formation of fossils.

Experimental Questions

1. Why did the investigators collect the alga *Cladophora* from its natural habitat?

2. Why is boiling in concentrated acid a reasonable way to investigate the presence of biological materials that may resist decay long enough to form fossils?

BIO **TIPS** **THE QUESTION** *The experiment by Cook and colleagues revealed that the relatively thick cellulose microfibrils found in the cell walls of* Cladophora *resist chemical degradation. How much thicker are these algal cellulose microfibrils than the cellulose microfibrils in less-resistant plant cell walls?*

T **OPIC** *What topic in biology does this question address?* The topic is protist defensive structures. More specifically, the question is about the biochemical makeup of the cellulose-rich cell walls of a common green alga.

I **NFORMATION** *What information do you know based on the question and your understanding of the topic?* From Chapter 10, you may remember that plant cells are typically enclosed by a cell wall that is rich in cellulose, a biochemical material that provides strength and compression resistance. You learned that the strength of cellulose derives from extensive hydrogen bonding between adjacent chains. In this chapter, you learned that protist cells are enclosed by a variety of protective materials, including cellulose that differs in structure (for example, forms microfibrils that are thicker) and is consequently

10. What are the alternate hosts of the malarial parasite *Plasmodium falciparum*?
    a. humans and ticks
    b. ticks and mosquitoes
    c. humans and *Anopheles* mosquitoes
    d. humans and all types of mosquitoes
    e. sporophytes and gametophytes

Conceptual Questions

1. Explain why protists are classified into multiple supergroups, rather than as a single kingdom or phylum.

2. Why have molecular biologists sequenced the genomes of several parasitic protists?

3.  **Core Concept: Science and Society** Why are the cysts of protists important to epidemiologists, the biologists who study the spread of disease?

Collaborative Questions

1. Imagine you are studying an insect species and you discover that the insects are dying of a disease that results in the production of cysts of the type that protists often generate. Thinking that the cysts might have been produced by a parasitic protist that could be used as an insect control agent, how would you go about identifying the disease-causing organism?

2. Imagine you are part of a marine biology team seeking to catalogue the organisms inhabiting a threatened coral reef. The team has found two new types of macroalgae (seaweeds), each of which occurs during a particular time of the year when the water temperature is at a certain point. You suspect that the two macroalgae might be different generations of the same species that have differing optimal temperature conditions. How would you go about testing your hypothesis?

Fungi

29

You might think that the largest organism in the world is a whale or perhaps a giant redwood tree. Amazingly, giant fungi would also be good candidates. For example, an individual of the fungus species *Armillaria ostoyae* weighs hundreds of tons, is more than 2,000 years old, and spreads across 2,200 acres of Oregon forest soil! Scientists discovered the extent of this enormous fungus when they found identical DNA sequences in soil samples taken over this wide area. Other examples of such huge fungi have been found, and mycologists—scientists who study fungi—suspect that they may be fairly common, existing underfoot yet largely unseen.

Regardless of their size, fungi typically occur within soil or other materials, becoming conspicuous only when the reproductive portions such as mushrooms extend above the surface. Even though fungi can be inconspicuous, they play essential roles in the Earth's environment; are associated in diverse ways with other organisms, including humans; and have many applications in biotechnology. In this chapter, we will explore the distinctive features of fungal structure, growth, nutrition, reproduction, and diversity. In the process, we will see how fungi are connected to decomposition, forest growth, food production and food toxins, sick building syndrome, and other phenomena of great importance to humans.

The aboveground reproductive parts of the fungus *Armillaria ostoyae*. Because of the large extent of its underground components, a member of this species may be the largest organism in the world. ©Brian Lightfoot/naturepl.com

Figure 28.6). The kingdom Fungi, also known as the true fungi, diverged from Animalia more than a billion years ago, during the Middle Proterozoic Era. Several types of slime molds, disease-causing oomycetes, and other fungus-like protists—though often studied with fungi—are not classified as true fungi (see Chapter 28).

The true fungi form a monophyletic group of an estimated 1.5 million species. Even greater diversity of this group is suggested by molecular evidence indicating the existence of many species that have not yet been cultivated or named. The earliest fungi probably originated in aquatic habitats, where they diverged from opisthokont protists closely related to the modern genus *Nuclearia*—an amoeba that feeds by ingesting algal and bacterial cells. Feeding on particles such as cells is a process known as phagocytosis (see Figure 28.7).

The earliest-diverging phylum of modern fungi, known as Cryptomycota, are unicellular and mostly occur in soil and water. Later-diverging fungi regularly produce a cell wall containing **chitin**, a tough polysaccharide polymer that contains nitrogen. Such a cell wall enables most fungi to resist the high osmotic pressure

29.1 Evolution and Distinctive Features of Fungi

Learning Outcomes:

1. **CoreSKILL** » Use information about groups of fungi to draw a diagram showing their evolutionary relationships.

2. Outline the distinctive features of fungi, including how they obtain food.

3. Discuss how fungal feeding is related to fungal growth.

The eukaryotes known as fungi are so distinct from other organisms that they are placed in their own kingdom, the kingdom Fungi (**Figure 29.1**). Together with certain closely related protists, the kingdom Fungi and the kingdom Animalia form a eukaryotic supergroup known as Opisthokonta (refer back to

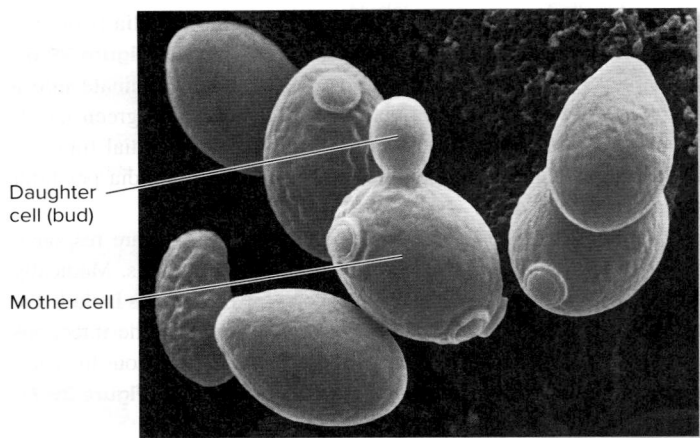

Daughter
cell (bud)

Mother cell

Figure 29.7 **The budding yeast *Saccharomyces cerevisiae.*** In budding, a small daughter cell is formed on the surface of a larger mother cell, eventually pinching off and forming a new cell. ©Medical-on-Line/Alamy Stock Photo

 Core Skill: Connections Look back at Table 14.1, which shows the genome characteristics of some model organisms. How does the genome of *S. cerevisiae* compare with genomes of other model organisms?

Fruiting Bodies Under appropriate environmental conditions, such as a seasonal change, a mated mycelium may produce a fleshy fruiting body, such as a mushroom. Fungal fruiting bodies typically emerge from the substrate and produce haploid spores (see Figure 29.2). Each spore acquires a tough chitin-rich wall that protects it from drying out and other stresses. Wind, rain, or animals disperse the mature spores, which grow into haploid mycelia. If a haploid mycelium encounters hyphae of an appropriate mating type, hyphal branches will fuse and start the sexual cycle over again.

Mycelium growth requires organic molecules, minerals, and water provided by the substrate, but in most cases, spores are more easily dispersed if released outside of the substrate. The structures of fruiting bodies vary in ways that reflect different adaptations that foster spore dispersal by wind, rain, or animals. For example, mature puffballs have delicate surfaces, and even a slight pressure on one causes the spores to puff out into wind currents (**Figure 29.8a**). Birds' nest fungi form characteristic egg-shaped spore clusters. Raindrops splash on these clusters and disperse the spores. The fruiting bodies of stinkhorn fungi smell and look like rotting meat (**Figure 29.8b**), which attracts carrion flies. The flies land on the fungi to investigate the potential meal and then fly away, in the process dispersing spores that stick to their bodies. The fruiting bodies of fungal truffles are unusual in being produced underground. Truffles have evolved a spore dispersal process that depends on animals that eat fungi. Mature truffles emit an odor that attracts wild pigs and dogs, which break up the fruiting structures while digging for them, thereby dispersing the spores (look ahead to Figure 29.19). Collectors use trained leashed pigs or dogs to locate valuable truffles from forests for the market.

Many fungal fruiting bodies such as truffles and morels are edible, and several species of edible fungi are cultivated for human consumption (**Figure 29.9**). However, many other fungi produce toxic substances that may deter animals from consuming them (**Figure 29.10**). For example, several fungi that attack stored grains,

Spores
in a
sticky
matrix

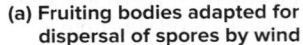

(a) Fruiting bodies adapted for dispersal of spores by wind

(b) Fruiting body adapted for dispersal of spores by insects

Figure 29.8 **Fruiting body adaptations that foster spore dispersal.** **(a)** When disturbed by wind gusts or animal movements, spores puff from fruiting bodies of the puffball fungus (*Lycoperdon perlatum*). **(b)** The fruiting bodies of stinkhorn fungi, such as this *Phallus impudicus*, smell and look like dung or rotting meat. This attracts carrion flies, which come into contact with the sticky fungal spores, thereby dispersing them. a: ©Bob Gibbons/ardea.com; b: ©RF Company/Alamy Stock Photo.

fruits, and spices produce **aflatoxins** that cause liver cancer and are a major health concern worldwide. When people consume the forest mushroom *Amanita virosa*, known as the "destroying angel," they ingest a powerful toxin that may cause liver failure so severe that death may ensue unless a liver transplant is performed. Each year, many people in North America are poisoned when they consume similarly toxic mushrooms gathered in the wild. There is no reliable way for amateurs to distinguish poisonous from nontoxic fungi; it is essential to receive instruction from an expert before foraging for mushrooms in the woods. Therefore, many authorities recommend that it is better to search for mushrooms in the grocery store than in the wild.

Several types of fungal fruiting structures produce hallucinogenic or psychoactive substances. As in the case of fungal toxins, fungal hallucinogens may have evolved as herbivore deterrents, but humans have

Figure 29.9 **Several types of edible fungi available in supermarkets.** ©Rob Casey/Alamy Stock Photo

Figure 29.10 Toxic fruiting body of *Amanita muscaria.* Common in conifer forests, *A. muscaria* is both toxic and hallucinogenic. Ancient people used this fungus to induce spiritual visions and to reduce fear during raids. This fungus produces a toxin, amanitin, which specifically inhibits RNA polymerase II in eukaryotes. ©MyLoupe/UIG CALC/ Universal Images Group/Getty Images

 Core Skill: Connections Look back at Figure 14.14, which illustrates the cellular role of RNA polymerase II in eukaryotes. What effect would the toxin amanitin have on human cells?

inadvertently experienced their effects. For example, *Claviceps purpurea*, which causes a disease of rye crops and other grasses known as ergot, produces a psychogenic compound related to LSD (lysergic acid diethylamide) (**Figure 29.11**). Some experts speculate that cases of hysteria, convulsions, infertility, and a burning sensation of the skin that occurred in Europe during the Middle Ages and that were attributed to witchcraft resulted from ergot-contaminated rye used in foods. Another example of a hallucinogenic fungus is the "magic mushroom" (*Psilocybe*), which is used in traditional rituals in some cultures. Like ergot, the magic mushroom produces a compound similar to LSD. Consuming hallucinogenic fungi is risky because the amount used to achieve psychoactive effects is dangerously close to a poisonous dose.

29.3 Diversity of Fungi

Learning Outcome:

1. Outline the distinguishing features of the fungal phyla Mucoromycota, Ascomycota, and Basidiomycota.

As noted earlier, the kingdom Fungi is a monophyletic group that arose from a protist ancestor, diversifying first in aquatic habitats, then later in terrestrial environments (see Figure 29.1). In this section, we will

Figure 29.11 Ergot of rye. The fungus *Claviceps purpurea* infects rye and other grasses, producing hard masses of mycelia known as ergots in place of some of the grains (fruits). ©imageBROKER/Superstock

 Core Skill: Science and Society Ergots such as the one illustrated produce alkaloids related to LSD and thus cause psychotic delusions in humans. LSD also harms pets that may accidentally consume it and farm animals that eat infected grains, causing lameness among other symptoms.

begin with a brief description of the early-diverging fungi and then focus on the largely terrestrial fungal lineages listed in **Table 29.1**: Mucoromycota, Ascomycota, and Basidiomycota. We will survey the habitats and characteristics of these groups of fungi and examine their distinctive ecological, structural, growth, and reproductive features.

Cryptomycota, Chytridiomycota, and Blastocladiomycota Occur in Moist Habitats

Single or few-celled Cryptomycota, Chytridiomycota, and Blastocladiomycota primarily live in moist locales, where they may reproduce using flagellate cells. Some classification schemes of

Table 29.1	Distinguishing Features of Later-Diverging Fungal Phyla			
Phylum	**Habitat**	**Ecological role**	**Reproduction**	**Examples cited in this chapter**
Mucoromycota	Terrestrial	Form mutually beneficial associations with plants	Distinctive multinucleate asexual spores or sexual zygospores	The genus *Glomus*, the genus *Rhizopus*
Ascomycota	Mostly terrestrial	Decomposers; pathogens; many form lichens; some are plant symbionts	Asexual conidia; nonflagellate sexual spores (ascospores) in sacs (asci) on fruiting bodies (ascocarps)	*Aleuria aurantia, Venturia inaequalis, Saccharomyces cerevisiae, Tuber melanosporum*
Basidiomycota	Terrestrial	Decomposers; many are plant symbionts; less commonly form lichens	Several types of asexual spores; nonflagellate sexual spores (basidiospores) on club-shaped basidia on fruiting bodies (basidiocarps)	*Coprinus disseminatus, Rhizoctonia solani, Armillaria mellea, Puccinia graminis, Ustilago maydis, Phanerochaete chrysosporium, Laccaria bicolor, Amanita muscaria, Phallus impudicus, Lycoperdon perlatum*

Figure 29.19 The black truffle *Tuber melanosporum,* an ascomycete fungus. ©Nacivet/Getty Images

(a) Corn smut   **(b) Shelf fungi**

Figure 29.21 Fruiting bodies of basidiomycetes. (a) Corn smut (*Ustilago maydis*) produces dikaryotic mycelial masses within the kernels (fruits) of infected corn plants. These mycelia produce many dark spores in which karyogamy and meiosis occur. Masses of these dark spores cause an infected kernel to enlarge and results in the smutty appearance. When the spores germinate, they produce basidiospores that can infect other corn plants. **(b)** Shelf fungi, such as this sulfur shelf fungus (*Laetiporus sulphureus*), are the fruiting bodies of basidiomycete fungi that have infected trees. a: ©Scott Camazine/Alamy Stock Photo; b: ©Mark Turner/Botanica/Getty Imagess

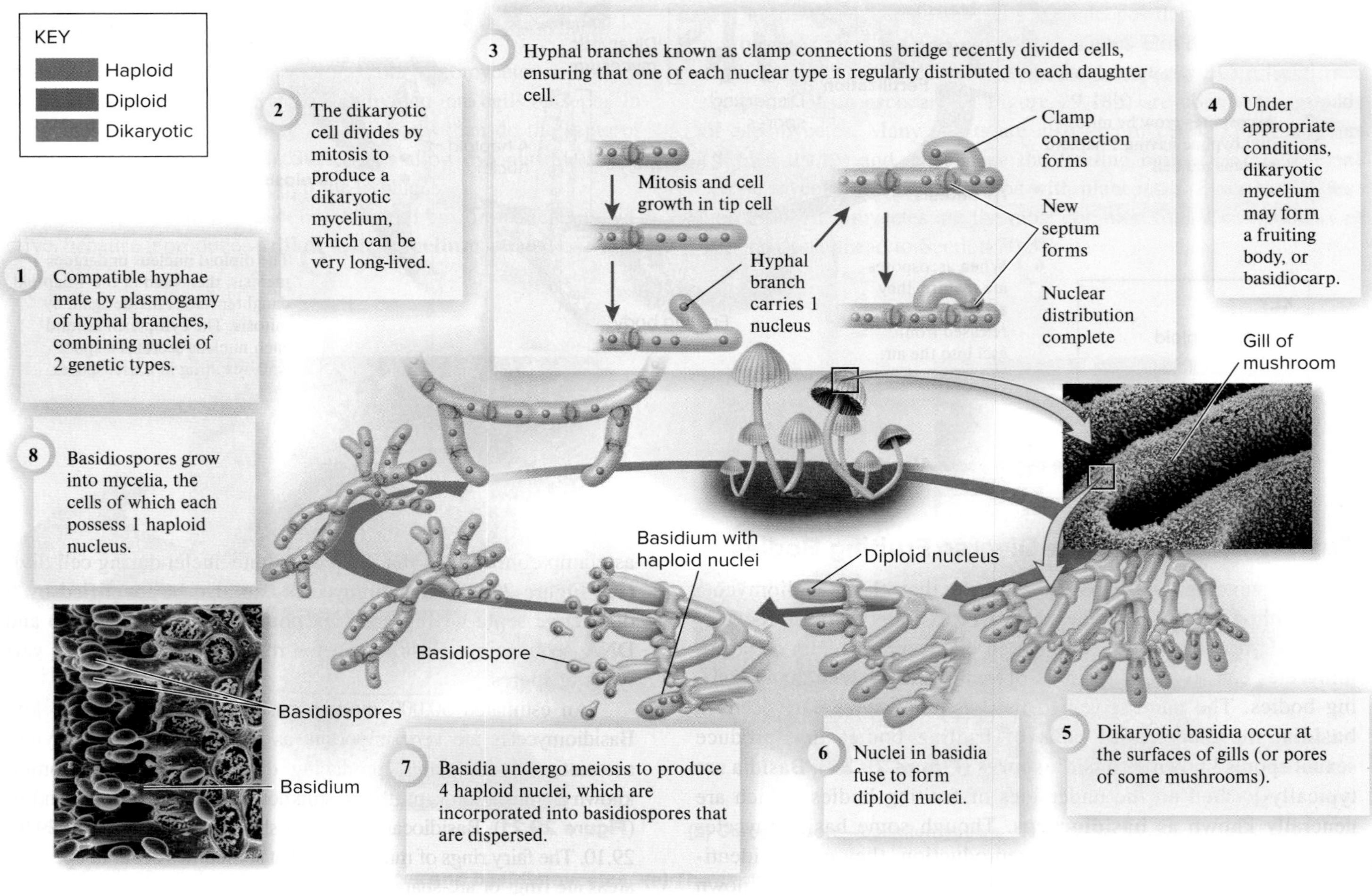

KEY
- Haploid
- Diploid
- Dikaryotic

3 Hyphal branches known as clamp connections bridge recently divided cells, ensuring that one of each nuclear type is regularly distributed to each daughter cell.

2 The dikaryotic cell divides by mitosis to produce a dikaryotic mycelium, which can be very long-lived.

Mitosis and cell growth in tip cell

Hyphal branch carries 1 nucleus

Clamp connection forms

New septum forms

Nuclear distribution complete

4 Under appropriate conditions, dikaryotic mycelium may form a fruiting body, or basidiocarp.

1 Compatible hyphae mate by plasmogamy of hyphal branches, combining nuclei of 2 genetic types.

8 Basidiospores grow into mycelia, the cells of which each possess 1 haploid nucleus.

Gill of mushroom

Basidium with haploid nuclei

Diploid nucleus

Basidiospore

Basidiospores

Basidium

7 Basidia undergo meiosis to produce 4 haploid nuclei, which are incorporated into basidiospores that are dispersed.

6 Nuclei in basidia fuse to form diploid nuclei.

5 Dikaryotic basidia occur at the surfaces of gills (or pores of some mushrooms).

Figure 29.20 The sexual life cycle of the basidiomycete fungus *Coprinus disseminatus.* (left): ©Biophoto Associates/Science Source; (right): ©Dr. Jeremy Burgess/Science Source

29.4   Fungal Ecology and Biotechnology

Learning Outcomes:

1. List several ecological roles of fungi.
2. Give examples of fungal diseases of plants and animals, including humans.
3. List several uses of fungi in biochemistry, biological studies, and industrial processes.

Fungi play diverse important ecological roles in addition to previously mentioned beneficial associations with plant roots (mycorrhizae), which are discussed in detail in the next chapter. These additional roles, which include decomposition, predation, disease agent, and protection, allow fungi to be useful in technological applications.

Many Fungi Play Ecological Roles as Decomposers and Some Fungi Are Predators

Decomposer fungi are essential components of the Earth's ecosystems. Together with bacteria, they decompose dead organisms and wastes, preventing the buildup of organic debris in ecosystems. For example, only certain bacteria and fungi can break down cellulose and lignin, the main components of wood. Decomposer fungi and bacteria are Earth's recycling engineers. They release CO_2 into the air and other minerals into the soil and water, making these essential nutrients available to plants and algae.

More than 200 species of predatory soil fungi use special adhesive or noose-like hyphae to trap tiny soil animals, such as nematodes, and absorb nutrients from their bodies (**Figure 29.22**). Such fungi help to control populations of nematodes, some of which attack plant roots. Other fungi obtain nutrients by attacking insects, and certain of these species have been used as biological control agents to kill black field crickets, red-legged earth mites, and other pests.

Pathogenic Fungi Cause Plant and Animal Diseases

One of the most important ways in which fungi affect humans is by causing diseases of crop plants and animals. Five thousand fungal species are known to be plant pathogens that cause serious crop diseases. Plant pathogenic fungi typically produce specialized balloon-shaped cells known as haustoria, whose increased cell membrane surface area aids in the absorption of organic food from plant cells (**Figure 29.23**). Pathogenic fungi use the absorbed organic compounds to grow, attack more plant cells, and produce reproductive spores capable of infecting more plants.

Wheat rust is an example of a common crop disease caused by fungi (**Figure 29.24**). Rusts are named for the reddish spores that emerge from the surfaces of infected plants. Many types of plants can be attacked by rust fungi, but rusts are of particular concern when new strains attack crops. To control the spread of fungal diseases, agricultural experts work to identify effective fungicidal chemicals and develop resistant crop varieties. Agricultural customs inspectors closely monitor the entry of plants, soil, foods, and other materials that might harbor pathogenic fungi.

Some fungi cause disease in animals. For example, the ascomycete *Geomyces destructans* is associated with white nose syndrome in bats, which has killed more than 1 million hibernating bats in the U.S. Athlete's foot and ringworm are common human skin diseases caused by several types of fungi that are known as dermatophytes because they colonize the human epidermis. The ascomycete *Pneumocystis jiroveci* and the basidiomycete *Cryptococcus neoformans* are fungal pathogens that infect individuals with weakened immune systems, such those with AIDS, sometimes causing death.

Dimorphic fungi (from the Greek, meaning two forms) live as spore-producing hyphae in the soil but transform into pathogenic yeasts when mammals inhale their wind-dispersed spores

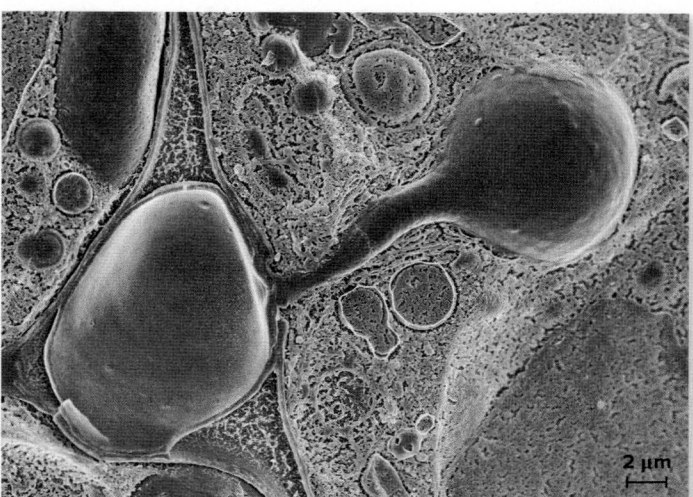

Figure 29.23 Fungal haustoria. Fungi that parasitize plants often produce specialized balloon-shaped cells called haustoria that absorb organic food from plant cells, as shown in this electron micrograph. ©Dr. Eric Kemen and Dr. Kurt W. Mendgen

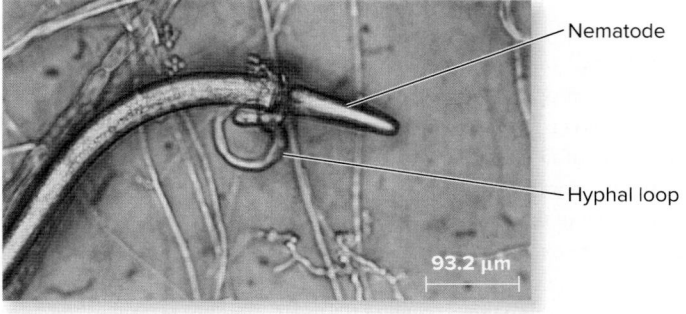

Nematode

Hyphal loop

93.2 μm

Figure 29.22 A predatory fungus. The fungus *Arthrobotrys anchonia* traps nematode worms in hyphal loops that suddenly swell in response to the animal's presence. Fungal hyphae then grow into the worm's body and digest it. ©Science Source

Figure 29.24 **Wheat rust.** The plant pathogenic fungus *Puccinia graminis* grows within the tissues of wheat plants, using plant nutrients to produce rusty streaks of red spores that erupt at the stem and leaf surfaces where they can be dispersed. Red spore production is but one stage of a complex life cycle involving several types of spores. Rusts infect many other crops in addition to wheat, causing immense economic damage. (left): ©Nigel Cattlin/Science Source; (right): ©Herve Conge/ISM/Phototake

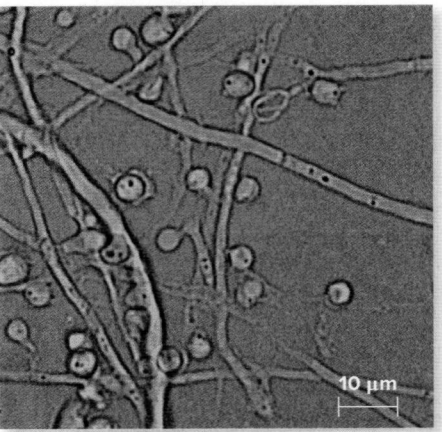

Soil-dwelling hyphal phase

Figure 29.25 **Dimorphic fungi.** The soil-dwelling hyphal stage reproduces by airborne spores. When a mammal inhales the spores, body heat causes the budding yeast phase to develop and attack host tissues. Courtesy Bruce Klein. Reprinted with permission

(**Figure 29.25**). Dimorphic fungi include the ascomycetes *Blastomyces dermatitidis*, which causes the disease blastomycosis; *Coccidioides immitis*, the cause of coccidiomycosis; and *Histoplasma capsulatum*, the agent responsible for histoplasmosis. These fungal diseases affect the lungs and may spread to other parts of the body, causing severe illness. The host's body temperature triggers the change from the hyphal form, which produces spores, to a yeast form. In an infected mammal, these pathogenic yeasts reproduce by forming buds that more effectively stick to lung cells, spread within lung tissue, and move to other organs.

Some Fungi Play Protective Roles

Although some fungi cause disease, some have recently been discovered to have protective roles. For example, fungi known as endophytes commonly live within plant tissues, providing protection against pathogens and physical stresses such as heat. Some endophytic associations also involve viruses.

 **Core Skill: Process of Science**

Feature Investigation | Márquez and Associates Discovered That a Three-Partner Symbiosis Allows Plants to Cope with Heat Stress

The endophytic fungus *Curvularia protuberata* commonly lives within aboveground tissues of the grass *Dichanthelium lanuginosum*. It can grow on very hot soils in areas of Yellowstone National Park. When the soil reaches 38°C, *D. lanuginosum* plants and *C. protuberata* fungi both die—unless they live together in a symbiosis. In the symbiotic association, the partners can survive temperatures near 65°C!

In 2007, a team of investigators led by Luis Márquez investigated the role of a virus in the symbiotic relationship between *D. lanuginosum* plants and *C. protuberata* fungi. Prior to the study described in **Figure 29.26**, these researchers discovered that *C. protuberata* may carry a virus, which they named *Curvularia* thermal tolerance virus (CthTV) to indicate its host and phenotype. In the laboratory, the investigators also noticed that some of their fungal cultures contained very little virus. They were able to use drying and freeze-thaw cycles to cure such cultures of the virus. This procedure allowed them to experimentally determine the relative abilities of virus-infected and virus-free *C. protuberata* fungus to tolerate high temperatures and to confer this property to plant partners.

As shown in step 1 of Figure 29.26, the researchers began with containers of *D. lanuginosum* plants. One set of containers had neither the fungus nor the virus, another set had the virus-infected fungus, and a third set had the virus-free fungus. The plants in the three sets of containers were exposed to heat stress for 2 weeks, and then categorized as dead, dying, or healthy. As seen in the data, the researchers found that plants having virus-infected fungal endophytes tolerated high temperatures much better than plants that lacked fungal endophytes or possessed only virus-free fungal endophytes. In other experiments, the researchers determined that virus-infected fungi (but not virus-free fungi) could also protect a distantly related crop plant (tomato) from

Figure 29.26 Márquez and associates discovered that a three-partner symbiosis allows plants to cope with heat stress.

GOAL To determine if a virus is essential to the protective role of endophytic fungi to host plants under heat stress.

KEY MATERIALS *Curvularia* thermal tolerance virus (CthTV), cultures of the endophytic fungus *Curvularia protuberata* infected with CthTV, *C. protuberata* cultures free of CthTV, and *Dichanthelium lanuginosum* plants.

	Experimental level	Conceptual level

1 Plant 25 replicate containers with *D. lanuginosum* lacking fungal symbionts (a) or having *C. protuberata* endophytes that either did (b) or did not (c) have virus.

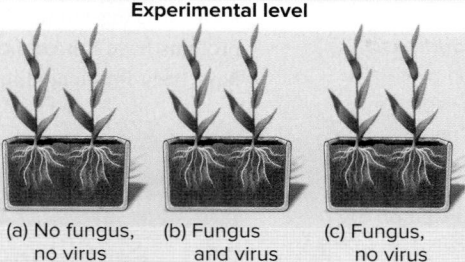

(a) No fungus, no virus   (b) Fungus and virus   (c) Fungus, no virus

Compare the effects of virus on the ability of the fungus to confer heat stress protection.

2 Expose plants to heat stress treatment (up to 65°C) for 2 weeks in a greenhouse.

Keep environmental conditions constant to reduce experimental error.

3 Count the number of plants that were green (alive), yellow (dying), or brown (dead).

(a)   (b)   (c)

Assess plant survival in the presence or absence of fungus and/or virus.

4 THE DATA

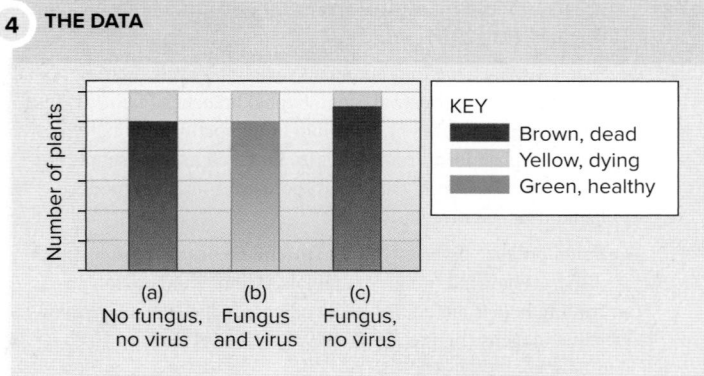

KEY
- Brown, dead
- Yellow, dying
- Green, healthy

(a) No fungus, no virus   (b) Fungus and virus   (c) Fungus, no virus

5 CONCLUSION A virus enhances the protective role of endophytic fungi in this grass species. The next step will be to try to determine just how the virus changes the fungus so that the fungus is able to protect the plant from heat stress.

6 SOURCE Marquez, L. M., et al. 2007. A virus in a fungus in a plant: three-way symbiosis required for thermal tolerance. *Science* 315: 513–515.

heat stress. These results add to accumulating evidence that multipartner symbioses are more common than previously realized and suggest that endophytic fungi may have useful agricultural applications.

Experimental Questions

1. Would you expect plants that grow on unusually hot soils to have endophytic fungi or not?

2. **CoreSKILL »** How did Márquez and associates demonstrate that a virus was important in the heat tolerance due to the symbiosis between *Dichanthelium lanuginosum* and *Curvularia protuberata*?

3. How might the results of the work by Márquez and associates be usefully applied in agriculture?

BIO TIPS   **THE QUESTION** *The data presented in step 4 of Figure 29.26 provide additional information about the relative effects of an endophytic fungus and a virus on heat tolerance in a species of plant. Compare the three bars in the graph and explain what these data mean.*

TOPIC *What topic in biology does this question address?* The topic is related to species diversity involved in protective interactions. More specifically, the question addresses the relative effects of fungal endophytes and viruses on plant heat tolerance.

INFORMATION *What information do you know based on the question and your understanding of the topic?* Step 4 in Figure 29.26 presents experimental data in the form of a bar graph that shows the relative numbers of plants in each of three groups that were dead, dying, and healthy at the end of the heat stress experiment. The three groups of plants differed as to whether an endophytic fungus and/or a virus was present in their containers. You have learned in this chapter what endophytic fungi are and how they can affect plants.

PROBLEM-SOLVING **S**TRATEGY *Compare and contrast. Interpret data.* Compare and contrast the bars in the graph, looking for differences in the responses of plants in each group.

ANSWER *First, compare the bars labeled (a) and (b). From this comparison, the presence of the virus-infected fungus is seen to confer heat resistance to the plant. However, from this comparison alone, you could infer that either the fungus or the virus or the combination of the two provided plants with protection from heat, but you could not discriminate among these possibilities. A comparison of the bars labeled (b) and (c) reveals that the fungus by itself does not confer thermal protection. Therefore, it is the virus-infected fungus that provides the plant with thermal protection.*

Interestingly, a careful comparison of the bars labeled (a) and (c) reveals that the proportion of dead plants to dying plants in the (c) group (fungus present but no virus) is higher than in the (a) group (no fungus or virus). These results suggest that the fungus by itself might actually make the plant more sensitive to heat.

Fungi Have Many Applications in Biotechnology

In addition to the potential use of fungal endophytes to protect agricultural plants suggested by the experiments conducted by Márquez and associates, fungi have diverse additional technology applications. Enzymes extracted from fungi are widely used to break down tough plant materials for renewable bioenergy applications. A variety of industrial processes employ fungi to convert inexpensive organic compounds into valuable materials such as the citric acid used in the soft-drink industry, glycerol, antibiotics such as penicillin, and cyclosporine, a drug widely used to prevent rejection of organ transplants. In the food industry, fungi are used to produce the distinctive flavors of blue cheese and other cheeses. Other fungi secrete enzymes that are used in the manufacture of protein-rich tempeh and other food products from soybeans.

The brewing and winemaking industries find yeasts essential, and the baking industry depends on the yeast *Saccharomyces cerevisiae* (see Figure 29.7) for bread production. *S. cerevisiae* is also widely used as a model organism for fundamental biological studies. Yeasts are useful in the laboratory because they have short life cycles, they are easy and safe for lab workers to maintain, and their genomes show striking similarities to those of humans. About 31% of yeast proteins have human homologs, and nearly 50% of human genes that have been implicated in heritable diseases have homologs in yeasts.

Summary of Key Concepts

29.1 Evolution and Distinctive Features of Fungi

- Fungi form a monophyletic group of heterotrophs that, together with the animal kingdom and certain protists, form the supergroup Opisthokonta (Figure 29.1).
- Fungal cells typically possess cell walls rich in the polysaccharide chitin. Fungal bodies, known as mycelia, are composed of microscopic branched filaments known as hyphae. Early-diverging fungi have aseptate hyphae that are not subdivided into cells. The hyphae of later-diverging fungi are subdivided into cells by cross walls known as septa (Figures 29.2, 29.3).
- Fungal hyphae feed and grow at their tips (Figure 29.4).
- Mycelial shape depends on the distribution of nutrients in the environment, which determines the direction in which cell division and hyphal growth will occur (Figure 29.5).

29.2 Overview of Asexual and Sexual Reproduction in Fungi

- Fungi spread rapidly by means of spores produced by asexual or sexual reproduction.
- Asexual reproduction does not involve mating or meiosis, and it occurs by means of asexual spores called conidia or by budding (Figures 29.6, 29.7).
- Fungi display a haploid-dominant sexual life cycle. During sexual reproduction of terrestrial fungi, hyphal branches (gametes) fuse with those of a different mycelium of compatible mating type. Mated hyphae form fruiting bodies in which haploid spores are produced by meiosis. Dispersed spores germinate to produce haploid fungal mycelia.
- Fungi produce diverse types of fruiting bodies that foster spore dispersal by wind, water, or animals. Although many fungal fruiting bodies are edible, many others produce defensive toxins or hallucinogens (Figures 29.8, 29.9, 29.10, 29.11).

29.3 Diversity of Fungi

- The fungi include several early-diverging lineages and the later-diverging phyla Mucoromycota, Ascomycota (ascomycetes), and Basidiomycota (basidiomycetes) (Table 29.1).
- Cryptomycota, Chytridiomycota, and Blastocladiomycota are among the simplest and earliest-diverging fungi. They commonly occur in aquatic habitats and moist soil, where they produce flagellate reproductive cells. Some are parasites of protists, animals, or plants (Figures 29.12, 29.13).

- Mucoromycota includes fungi that reproduce asexually or sexually by distinctive spores (Figures 29.14, 29.15, 29.16).
- Ascomycetes produce sexual ascospores in saclike asci located at the surfaces of fruiting bodies known as ascocarps. The septa of hyphae have simple pores (Figures 29.17, 29.18, 29.19).
- Basidiomycetes produce sexual basidiospores on club-shaped basidia located on the surfaces of fruiting bodies known as basidiocarps. Such fruiting bodies take a wide variety of forms, including mushrooms, puffballs, stinkhorns, shelf fungi, rusts, and smuts. The hyphae display complex septal pores and clamp connections. Mating commonly generates a long-lived dikaryotic mycelium that can produce many fruiting bodies (Figures 29.20, 29.21).

29.4 Fungal Ecology and Biotechnology

- Fungi play important roles in nature as decomposers, predators, and pathogens and in beneficial associations with other organisms. Pathogenic fungi cause plant and animal diseases (Figures 29.22, 29.23, 29.24, 29.25).
- Endophytic fungi live within the tissues of plants, providing protective services (Figure 29.26).
- Fungi are useful in the chemical, food-processing, waste-treatment, and renewable biofuel industries. The yeast *Saccharomyces cerevisiae* is a model organism and also important to the brewing and baking industries.

Assess & Discuss

Test Yourself

1. Fungal cells differ from animal cells in that fungal cells
   a. lack ribosomes, though these are present in animal cells.
   b. lack mitochondria, though these occur in animal cells.
   c. have chitin-rich cell walls, whereas animal cells lack cell walls.
   d. lack cell walls, whereas animal cells possess cell walls.
   e. None of the above is true.

2. Conidia are
   a. cells produced by some fungi as the result of sexual reproduction.
   b. fungal asexual reproductive cells produced by the process of mitosis.
   c. structures that occur in septal pores.
   d. the unspecialized gametes of fungi.
   e. none of the above.

3. What are mycelia?
   a. the bodies of fungi, composed of hyphae
   b. fungi that attack plant roots, causing disease
   c. fungal hyphae that are massed together into stringlike structures
   d. fungi that produce harmful toxins
   e. protists that are closely related to fungi

4. Where could you find diploid nuclei in an ascomycete or basidiomycete fungus?
   a. in spores
   b. in cells at the surfaces of fruiting bodies
   c. in conidia
   d. in zygospores
   e. in all of the above

5. Which fungi are examples of hallucinogen producers?
   a. *Claviceps* and *Psilocybe*
   b. *Epidermophyton* and *Candida*
   c. *Pneumocystis jiroveci* and *Histoplasma capsulatum*
   d. *Saccharomyces cerevisiae* and *Phanerochaete chrysosporium*
   e. *Cryphoenectria parasitica* and *Ventura inaequalis*

6. What role do fungal endophytes play in nature?
   a. They are decomposers.
   b. They are human pathogens that cause skin diseases.
   c. They are plant pathogens that cause serious crop diseases.
   d. They live within the tissues of plants, helping to protect them from herbivores, pathogens, and heat stress.
   e. All of the above are correct.

7. What determines whether a mycelium is flat or spherical?
   a. sunlight
   b. the nature of the substrate
   c. the amount of carbon dioxide in the air
   d. the amount of phosphorus available
   e. all of the above

8. Among fungi, nutrition is
   a. photosynthetic.
   b. mixotrophic.
   c. absorptive.
   d. all of the above.
   e. none of the above.

9. How can ascomycetes be distinguished from basidiomycetes?
   a. Ascomycete hyphae have simple pores in their septa, whereas basidiomycete hyphae display complex septal pores.
   b. Ascomycetes produce sexual spores in sacs, whereas basidiomycetes produce sexual spores on the surfaces of club-shaped structures.
   c. Ascomycetes lack clamp connections, whereas basidiomycetes display clamp connections.
   d. Ascomycetes fruiting bodies include cup structures and morels, whereas basidiomycete fruiting bodies take different forms that include shelf fungi on tree trunks.
   e. All of the above are correct.

10. Which of the following groups of organisms is most closely related to the kingdom Fungi?
    a. the animal kingdom
    b. the green algae
    c. the land plants
    d. the bacteria
    e. the archaea

Conceptual Questions

1. List three ways in which fungi are like animals and two ways in which fungi resemble plants.
2. Explain why some fungi produce toxic or hallucinogenic compounds.
3. **Core Concept: Systems** Describe three ways in which fungi affect their environments.

Collaborative Questions

1. Thinking about the natural habitats closest to you, where can you find fungi, and what roles do these fungi play?
2. Imagine that you are helping to restore the natural grassland vegetation in a region that has recently been used to grow crops. In what ways might you consider using fungi to aid in this restoration?

Microbiomes: Microbial Systems On and Around Us

30

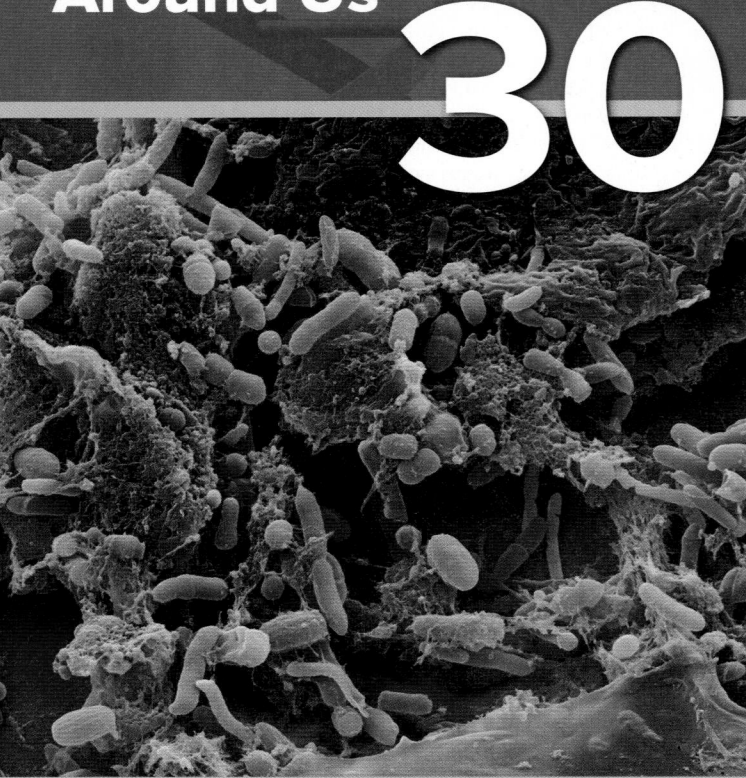

In this SEM image of a human fecal sample, the different colors indicate a diversity of bacteria present in the gut microbiome.
©Eye of Science/Science Source

Ideally, all of the world's children would have enough good food to start healthy lives. Unfortunately, malnutrition has left nearly 180 million children around the world stunted in their growth. Public health experts have tried to use dietary supplements to restore normal growth, a strategy that does not always work. New research on microbes living in the bodies of the stunted children has revealed why. These children retain an infantile set of gut microbes, in contrast to children whose more mature collection of gut microbes (illustrated by the chapter opening image) stimulates growth hormones. This understanding may help people to devise new ways to improve the health of millions of children.

Chapters 27–29 introduced the diverse groups of microorganisms—archaea, bacteria, protists, and fungi—that influence our health and environments in many ways. This chapter builds on that foundation by describing how these diverse microbes occur together in **microbiomes**, assemblages of microbes

that are associated with a particular environment, such as the human body. Microbiologists are learning that oceans, ice, fresh waters, soils, and the bodies of organisms other than humans have distinctive microbiomes that influence nature and human life.

Because microbes are generally small, microbiomes are often inconspicuous. New molecular approaches described in this chapter have enabled biologists to study microbiome compositions and functions. Using these new methods, medical scientists are identifying new ways in which people can improve their health. Agricultural scientists are discovering new strategies for engineering crop microbiomes to promote plant health. Exploring the microbiomes of other organisms and environments has revealed previously unrecognized global ecological effects. In this chapter, we will learn why the study of microbiomes has become an important and fast-growing area of modern biology.

30.1 Microbiomes: Diversity of Microbes and Functions

Learning Outcomes:

1. Define microbiome.
2. List some reasons why microbiomes are considered to be complex systems.
3. Discuss how biologists use ribosomal RNA gene sequences and whole metagenomic sequencing to catalog the diverse types of microbes in a microbiome.
4. Explain how biologists identify microbiome functions.

As noted in the chapter opener, a microbiome is a particular assemblage of microbes (including their genes) that is associated with a particular environment. Microorganisms commonly present in microbiomes include archaea, bacteria, viruses, protists, and fungi (see Chapters 27–29), and sometimes microscopic animals. Visualizing such microbes requires the use of microscopes, such as scanning or transmission electron microscopes.

Microbiomes can be associated with physical biomes such as water, ice, or soil, or with living hosts, such as animals, plants, fungi, and algae. Bacteria dominate the microbiomes of humans and other animals, though certain protists and fungi may also be present (**Figure 30.1**). Microbes are found in many different places in the human body. The microbiomes of plants commonly harbor many types of fungi, and algal microbiomes often include many species of bacteria and protists (**Figure 30.2**). For example, the surface of *Cladophora* is covered with a biofilm of diverse bacteria (Figure 30.2b). A biofilm is a group of microbes that use mucilage to stick to each other and to surfaces.

Microbiomes Are Complex Biological Systems

Microbiomes are complex systems, in part, because they contain many different microbial species that interact with each other in complicated ways. Microbiome studies often reveal new types of microbes that have not been studied in the lab and, so, have not even been formally named. These diverse life forms carry out many types of metabolism that influence their environments and other members of the same microbiome, but such ecological interactions are not fully understood. Microbes communicate with each other by means of chemical or electrical signals that biologists are just beginning to explore. Particular microbes seem to serve as network hubs, receiving information from the environment and transmitting information to the broader microbial community. In these ways, microbiomes resemble culturally diverse human groups whose social networks and responses to outside influences are complex. Identifying what species occur together, how microbes affect each other and their environments, and the effects of environmental change are major goals of microbiome research.

Determining the species compositions, functions, and responses of microbiomes are challenging because microbes are so small and difficult to distinguish. For example, different bacterial species often have similar body structure, such as single cells only

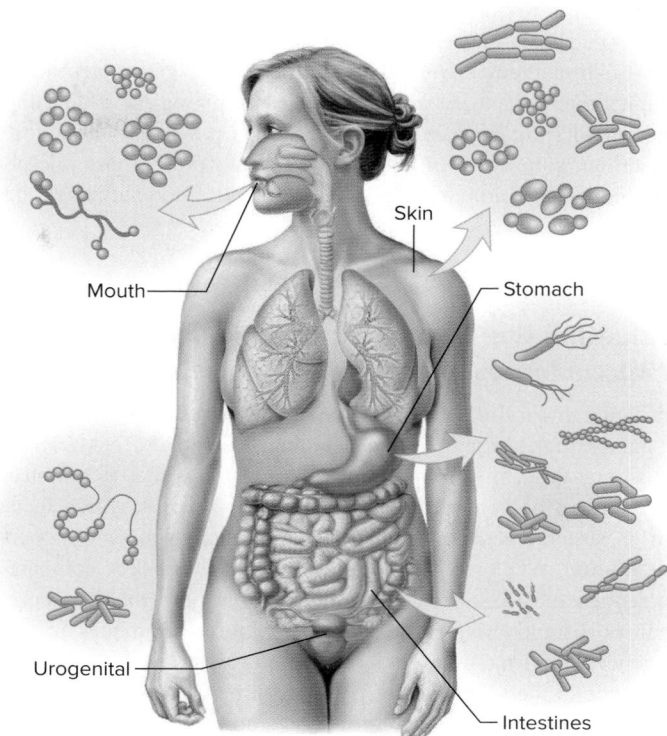

Figure 30.1 The human microbiome includes diverse bacteria, but also some protists and fungi.

a few micrometers in diameter (see Figure 30.2b). Likewise, the bodies of millions of fungal species are composed of thin hyphae that often look alike, even with the use of a microscope (see Chapter 29).

(a)

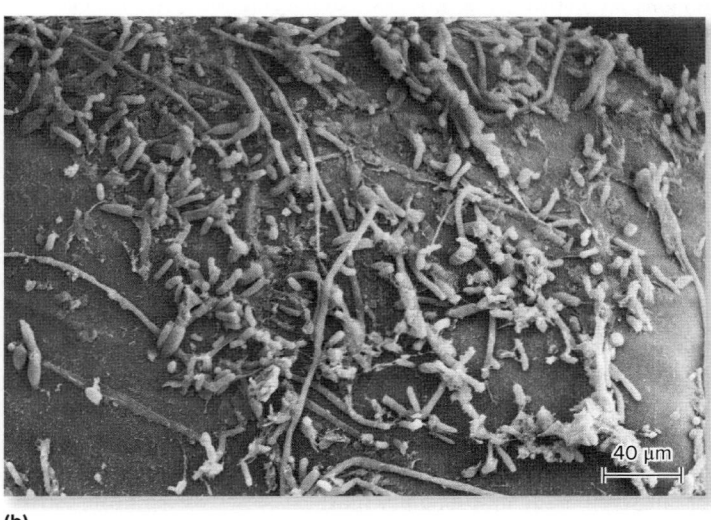

(b)

Figure 30.2 An algal microbiome that includes diverse bacterial and protist species. **(a)** The green alga *Cladophora* provides living space, organic food, and oxygen to hundreds of species of bacteria, protists, fungi, and microscopic animals, visible as clouds of white, golden, and brown particles on the algal surface. **(b)** This SEM reveals that the algal surface is covered with a biofilm of structurally diverse bacteria. These bacteria have important ecological functions. a: ©Lee W. Wilcox; b: ©Linda Graham

For these reasons, biologists commonly use genetic techniques to distinguish and identify microbial species within a given microbiome. Such methods involve the identification of genes present in a complex microbiome, which may also allow biologists to infer their functions if similar genes have been studied previously. In addition to cataloging the types of microbes and genes present in a microbiome, biologists examine proteins and metabolites to gain insight into function.

Evaluating the Taxonomic Complexity of Microbiomes by Amplicon Analysis

All of Earth's living things, including microbes, produce proteins by means of ribosomes, which contain ribosomal RNA (rRNA). Ribosomal RNA is so important to living things that rRNA structure tends to be conserved among different species, which means that its structure does not undergo major changes over the course of evolution. When rRNAs of closely related species are compared, the sequence of bases is usually very similar or highly conserved, whereas distantly related species show more differences in their sequences (refer back to Figure 12.17). For this reason, the level of difference in the sequences of rRNAs can be used to evaluate evolutionary relationships. In microbiome studies, sequences of genes that encode rRNAs are commonly used to identify and classify microbes, even if the microbiome includes thousands of microbial species. Other types of genes may also be amplified for evaluating microbiome complexity.

Biologists usually begin a microbiome study by obtaining a sample from a living organism or a physical environment and then extracting the DNA (**Figure 30.3**). As seen in step 3a, polymerase chain reaction (PCR) can be used to copy a particular region of an rDNA gene. This process yields many copies of that region from many different species that are in the sample. These copied rDNA regions are known as **amplicons**. Amplifying the DNA is generally required to generate sufficient DNA for sequencing (described in Chapter 21).

The amplicons are then subjected to DNA sequencing, which yields the base sequence of each gene that was amplified in the original sample. Biologists use computers to compare the DNA sequences of each amplicon to reference sequences in databases. These reference sequences come from microbes, the names and metabolic functions of which are already known. This relatively inexpensive way to examine the microbial diversity in a microbiome is called **amplicon analysis**.

In amplicon analysis, researchers often use PCR primers that amplify a region of genes that encode 16S, 23S, 18S, and/or 28S rRNA (refer back to Table 12.3). 16S rRNA and 23S rRNA occur in the small and large ribosomal subunits of bacteria and archaea; 18S rRNA and 28S rRNA occur in the corresponding ribosomal subunits of eukaryotes. As an example, **Figure 30.4** shows the evolutionary relationships for members of a particular microbiome that plays a role in mineral formation. This phylogenetic tree was constructed by comparing the genes encoding 16S rRNA. As you can see, the microbiome composition is complex, containing representatives of many bacterial phyla and one archaeal phylum.

Core Skill: Quantitative Reasoning

THE QUESTION *Which prokaryotic phylum dominates the microbiome shown in Figure 30.4? Note: In this figure, the sizes of circles indicate the relative abundances of sequences, which are related to organism abundances. For reference, Figure 27.1 and Table 27.1 list prokaryotic phyla that occur in Figure 30.4.*

TOPIC ***What topic in biology does this question address?*** The topic is microbiomes. More specifically, the question focuses on the composition of a particular microbiome and identification of the prokaryotic phylum that is the most prevalent.

INFORMATION ***What information do you know based on the question and your understanding of the topic?*** In the question, you are referred to Figure 30.4, which is a phylogenetic tree that provides information about the prokaryotic genera, families, orders, classes, and phyla present in one microbiome. You are also reminded that Figure 27.1 and Table 27.1 list prokaryotic phyla that occur in Figure 30.4.

PROBLEM-SOLVING **S**TRATEGY ***Make a calculation. Interpret data.*** The common bacterial phyla Bacteroidetes, Verrucomicrobia, Chloroflexi, Cyanobacteria, Firmicutes, Planctomycetes, Proteobacteria, and Spirochaetes and the archaeal phylum Euryarchaeota, listed in Figure 27.1 and Table 27.1, are represented in this microbiome. Count the number of representatives of each phylum, giving greater weight to larger circles. Use these calculations to make a pie chart that groups bacteria and archaea into different phyla.

ANSWER *Of the nearly 60 taxa listed along the right edge of the phylogentic tree, more than half are classified in the phylum Proteobacteria, and the two most abundant genera inferred from sequence abundances (Rhodoferax and Rheinheimera) belong to this phylum. Your pie chart should show the phylum Proteobacteria making up its largest sector, indicating that this prokaryotic phylum dominates this particular microbiome.*

Evaluating Taxonomic and Functional Complexity of Microbiomes by Whole Metagenomic Sequencing

An alternative method for characterizing microbiome diversity is to obtain base sequences of all the DNA present in a sample, a process known as **whole metagenomic sequencing (WMS)** (see Figure 30.3, step 3b). A **metagenome** is defined as the genomes of all the organisms present in a sample. WMS is carried out using an approach known as **shotgun DNA sequencing**, in which DNA fragments from a genome are randomly sequenced (refer back to Figure 21.11). This approach does not have to focus on the sequencing of one particular gene, such as the gene encoding 16S rRNA. Instead, many fragments of DNA are randomly sequenced, and then biologists use computers to identify places where the ends of DNA fragments have the same DNA

1　Obtain a sample to analyze.

Sample from living organism

Sample from physical environment

2　Extract the DNA from the sample. This yields a collection of many DNA fragments from many different microbial species.

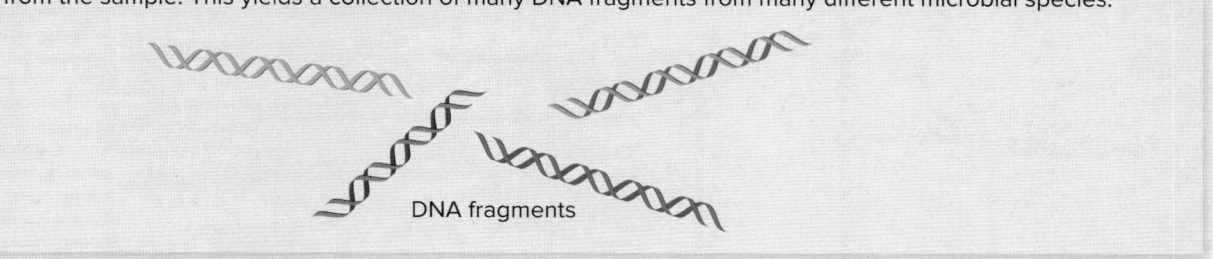

DNA fragments

3　**3a Amplicon Analysis:** Use primers that recognize a region of an rDNA gene and make many copies of that region using polymerase chain reaction (PCR). Subject the amplified segments of the *rDNA* gene to DNA sequencing.

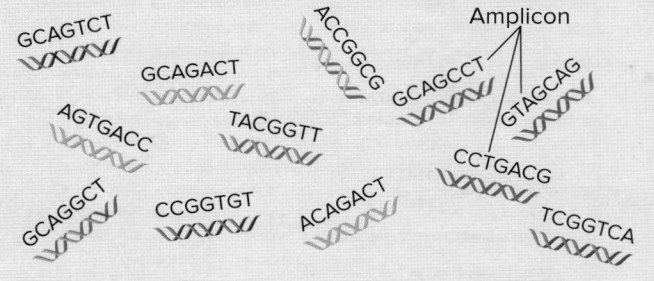

Sequences of rDNA genes that were in the sample.

3b Whole metagenome sequencing: Subject all of the DNA in the sample to shotgun DNA sequencing.

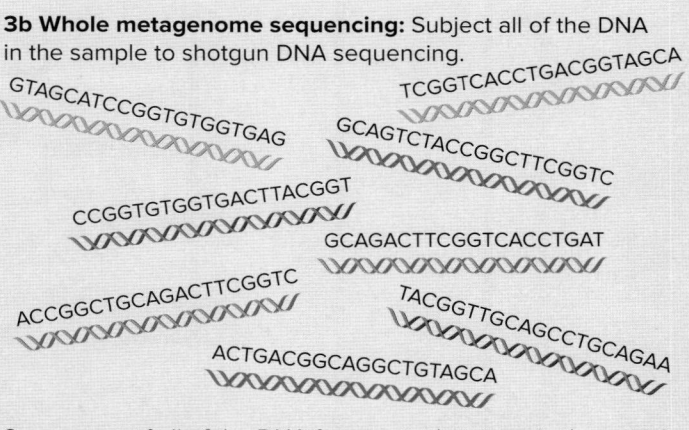

Sequences of all of the DNA fragments that were in the sample.

4　Compare the DNA sequences obtained in step 3 to DNA sequences in a database. The database sequences are already known to come from particular microbial species. This allows researchers to match the sequences obtained in step 3 to known sequences. For example, if a DNA sequence obtained in step 3a matches an rDNA sequence from the bacterium *E. coli*, this result indicates that *E. coli* was in the microbiome of that sample.

Figure 30.3 **Characterization of microbiome taxonomic complexity via amplicon analysis or whole metagenome sequencing.**
(right) ©Goodshoot/Alamy Stock Photo

Core Concept: Information The information contained in DNA sequences can be used to gain information about taxonomic and functional diversity in microbiomes.

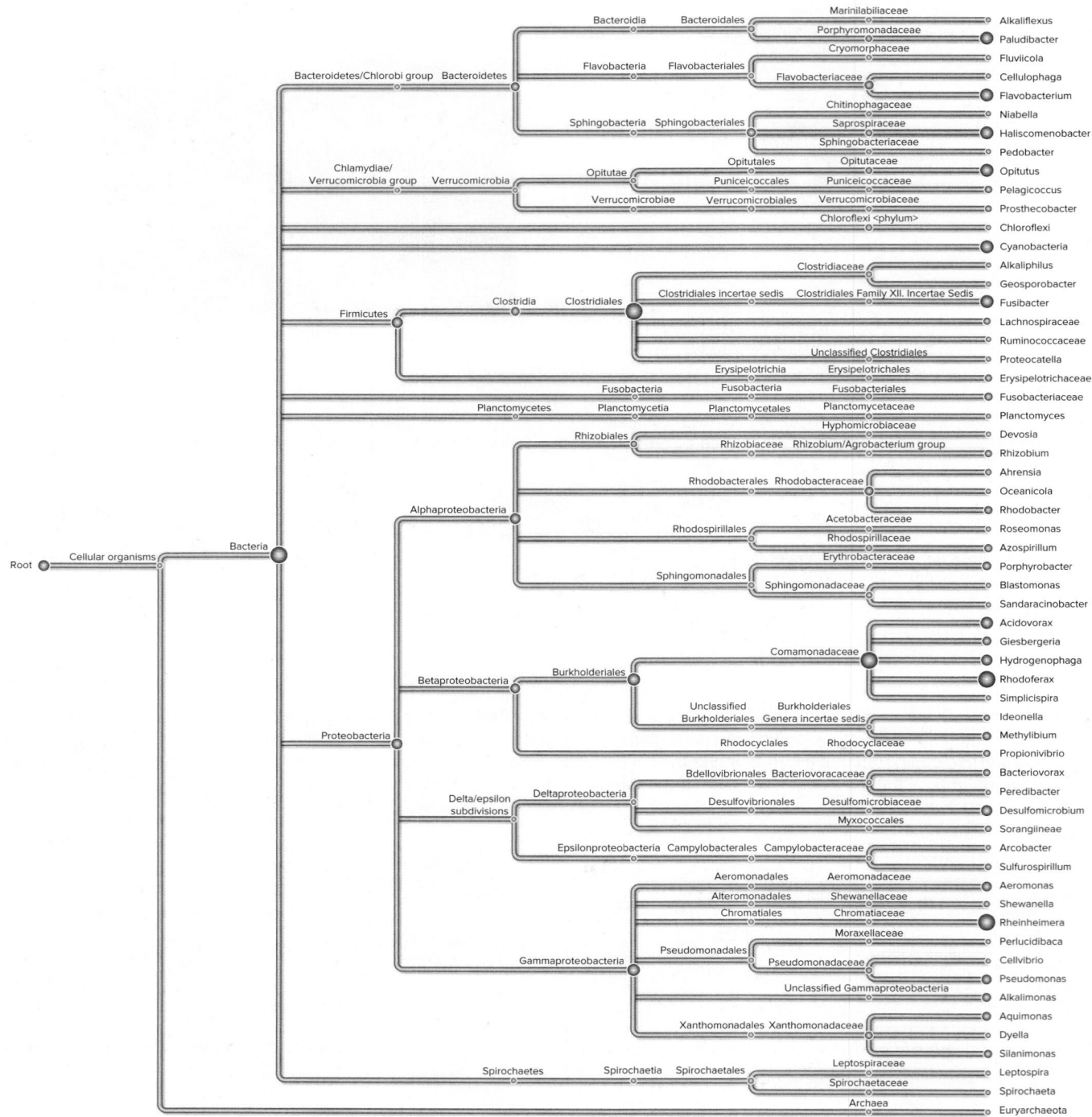

Figure 30.4 Example of the use of gene sequences encoding 16S rRNA to detect bacteria and archaea present in the microbiome of a photosynthetic organism and to produce a phylogenetic tree. This phylogenetic tree shows how genera are clustered into phyla and intermediate taxonomic groups. The sizes of circles indicate relative sequence abundances, which are approximately related to organism abundances. Graham, L. E., Knack, J. J., Piotrowski, M. J., Wilcox, L. W., Cook, M. E., Wellman, C. H., Taylor, W., Lewis, L. A., and Arancibia-Avila, P. 2014. Lacustrine *Nostoc* (Nostocales) and associated microbiome generate a new type of modern clotted microbialite. *Journal of Phycology* 50: 280–291. doi: 10.1111/jpy.12152. This work is licensed under a Creative Commons Attribution 3.0 License.

sequences (**Figure 30.5**). These overlapping regions allow researchers to align the DNA fragments into longer sequences known as contiguous sequences, or **contigs**. What is the advantage of constructing contigs? One advantage is that longer contigs provide greater amounts of information needed for more detailed classification.

If metagenomic sequences are relatively long, or if a microbiome contains relatively few microbes, it may be possible to use computer methods to assemble contigs into whole microbial genomes. A number of microbial species were discovered in this way and even today are known only from their genomic sequence. Some experts consider

Overlapping region

```
TTACGGTACCAGTTACAAATTCCAGACCTAGTACC
AATGCCATGGTCAATGTTTAAGGTCTGGATCATGG
                        GACCTAGTACCGGACTTATTCGATCCCCAATTTTGCAT
                        CTGGATCATGGCCTGAATAAGCTAGGGGTTAAAACGTA
```

Figure 30.5 **A comparison of two DNA fragments that contain an overlapping region.** A contig consists of a series of DNA fragments that contain overlapping regions.

that one goal of WMS should be to assemble entire genome sequences of microbes, a process known as **genome-centric metagenomics**.

If sufficient DNA has been analyzed, WMS and computer methods can be used to identify both prokaryotic and eukaryotic species in a microbiome at the same time. By contrast, amplicon analyses typically focus on the amplification of a particular gene from a selected group of species. For this reason, many experts consider that the term microbiome should be limited to microbial communities characterized by WMS. The term **microbiota** is commonly used to describe collections of microbial life cataloged by amplicon analysis.

Microbiome Functions Can Be Inferred by Identifying Protein-Encoding Genes

In the analysis of microbiomes by WMS, another goal is to find and classify protein-encoding genes, providing a deeper view of microbial function. To gain more information about microbiome function, biologists may look for particular protein-coding genes that indicate specialized microbial functions. For example, biologists have used metagenomic sequencing of DNA from natural microbiomes to find bacterial and archaeal genes that encode many previously undiscovered proteins involved in CRISPR-Cas systems. These proteins, which serve as microbial immune systems, have become important tools in modern genetics (see Chapter 21). Three additional examples of important microbiome functions that are inferred from protein-coding genes are described next.

Nitrogen Fixation   One important microbial function is nitrogen fixation, the process in which atmospheric nitrogen gas is reduced to form ammonia, which is useful as fertilizer. Only certain prokaryotic species have the natural ability to accomplish nitrogen fixation (see Chapter 27). Plants and other photosynthetic organisms commonly require ammonia or another source of fixed nitrogen to make amino acids, chlorophyll, and other essential molecules. Consequently, algal and plant microbiomes often include nitrogen-fixing prokaryotes. To obtain evidence for microbial species that are able to fix nitrogen, plant scientists may identify gene sequences known to encode enzymes essential for nitrogen fixation. One such gene is *nifH*, an indicator of nitrogen fixation. Such genes are known as **marker genes**, because they "mark" the occurrence of a particular function—in this case, nitrogen fixation.

Methane Oxidation   Additional marker genes encode subunits of the enzyme methane monooxygenase (MMO). This enzyme uses oxygen gas to oxidize the greenhouse gas methane, which plays an important role in global carbon cycles and climate warming. Lakes and wetlands are sources of methane, so it is not surprising that methane-oxidizing bacteria are commonly found in these places, often in association with oxygen-producing algae and plants. For example, peat mosses that dominate vast wetland areas, known as peatlands, play an important role in global carbon cycling by hosting methane-oxidizing bacteria. Peat moss leaves display both oxygen-producing green photosynthetic cells and larger non-green cells that have undergone programmed cell death and whose cell walls are perforated by large pores. Methane-oxidizing bacteria, many other types of bacteria, and diverse protists enter through the pores (**Figure 30.6**), and many of these microbes use mucilage to attach to inner cell wall surfaces (**Figure 30.7**). Peat moss microbiomes commonly contain MMO marker genes, indicating that a microbiome function is to oxidize methane.

Metabolites   Some microbes produce very specific compounds that are not produced by most species of microbes. These compounds are called metabolites, because they are the products of metabolic pathways. Examples include vitamins, toxins, and antibiotics. In many cases, previous research has identified the enzymes that are needed to produce a particular metabolite. When analysis by WMS identifies the genes that encode these enzymes, this result indicates that one function of the microbiome is to produce that metabolite. Microbiomes are potential sources of new antibiotic compounds and other metabolites of industrial importance.

The Analysis of mRNAs, Proteins, and Metabolites Provides Additional Information About Microbiome Function

Catalogs of microbial species and genes obtained by amplicon analysis or WMS don't reveal which genes were actually being transcribed and which transcripts were being translated at the time a sample was collected. Large data collections known as metatranscriptomes, metaproteomes, and meta-metabolomes can help provide the missing information.

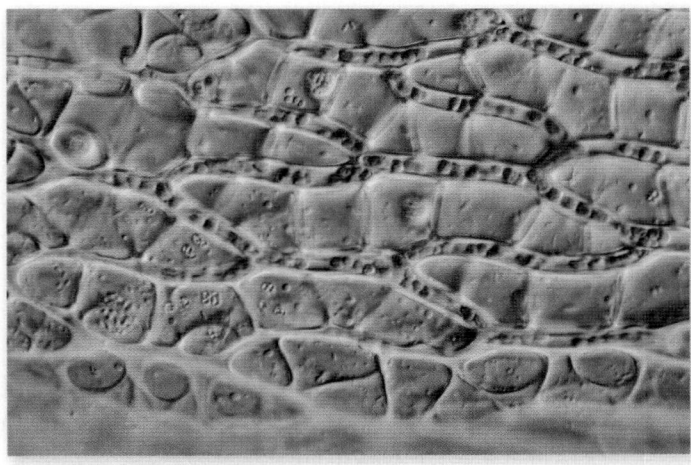

Figure 30.6 **Peat moss leaf harboring microbes within specialized cells having wall pores.** Peat moss leaves feature narrow living cells having green chloroplasts and larger, non-green, water-filled cells having cell wall pores. Diverse prokaryotic and eukaryotic microbes enter through the pores and live within the larger cells. ©Lee W. Wilcox

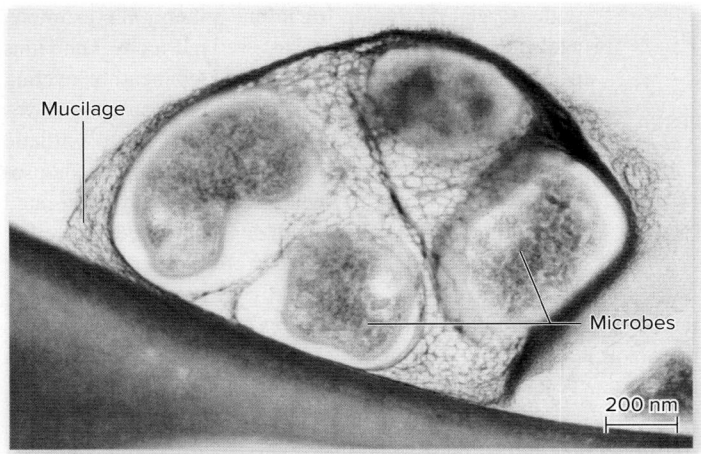

Figure 30.7 **TEM showing a biofilm of microbes attached by mucilage to the inner cell wall surfaces of peat moss leaf cells.**
©Linda Graham

Metatranscriptome To learn which mRNAs were present in a microbiome at the time of sampling, biologists analyze transcriptomes. A **transcriptome** is a collection of all the mRNA sequences produced by a single organism under defined conditions. A **metatranscriptome** is a collection of all the mRNA sequences present in an environmental sample, that is, all of the mRNAs produced by all of the organisms sampled from a particular place at a particular time.

Metaproteome Biologists sometimes use the number of mRNA sequences of a particular type to infer abundance or activity level of a translated protein. However, mRNA abundance is influenced by the extent to which microbes were actively growing when they were collected, the lifetime of a particular transcript, and how often that transcript is translated. A proteome analysis can provide more direct information about what proteins are present in a particular microbiome. A proteome analysis, accomplished by chromatographic and spectroscopy methods, reveals which proteins are present in a particular sample. A **metaproteome** is all the proteins produced by all the members of a microbiome.

Meta-metabolome Because proteins, even if present, might not be functionally active, researchers may analyze the products of metabolism. **Metabolomes** are collections of information about the types and abundances of molecules, such as sugars and fatty acids, produced by metabolism in a single organism. A **meta-metabolome** provides similar information for an entire microbiome.

30.2 Microbiomes of Physical Systems

Learning Outcomes:

1. List some types of microbiomes that are found within physical systems.
2. Explain how microbiome analyses can help monitor environments for microbial activities that affect human health.

Having discussed microbiomes as complex systems and examined the methods that biologists use to study microbiome composition and function, we have a foundation for surveying the diversity of Earth's microbiomes. We have seen that some microbiomes are found within **physical systems** such as oceans, ice, fresh waters, and soils, and others are associated with living organisms known as hosts. In this section, we focus on microbiomes within physical systems and the societal concerns related to them.

Microbiomes Are Abundant in the World's Oceans and in Its Ice

Although you might imagine that animals such as fish and whales dominate Earth's oceans, in fact, microbes are far more numerous. Oceans occupy 71% of Earth's surface and have a volume of 1.37 billion cubic kilometers. The concentration of microbes in ocean water is typically 10^4–10^6 microbial cells per mL. Therefore, the number of microbes in 1 liter of seawater reaches into the billions. That's a lot of microbes!

Collectively, ocean microbes represent an immense amount of genetic and functional diversity that influences the entire planet. For example, photosynthetic cyanobacteria and algae produce about half of the organic carbon and oxygen formed on Earth each year. Other ocean microbes play essential roles in degrading organic molecules and recycling dissolved minerals, a process essential to ocean productivity. The cyanobacterial genus *Synechococcus* and its phages, together with stramenopile, alveolate, and rhizarian protists (see Chapters 27–28), are key to the movement of organic molecules into deep-ocean waters. Retention of carbon in the deep oceans for long periods affects global climate and is the mechanism by which extensive oil and methane (fossil-fuel) deposits form in undersea locations. Biologists have recently used gene-sequencing techniques (described in Section 30.1) to catalog viruses, prokaryotic species, and small eukaryotes from 68 ocean locations worldwide. By also monitoring the physical features of these places, they have discovered that water temperature is a major factor influencing the compositions of ocean microbiomes, raising questions about the impact of global climate change.

Earth's icy environments—collectively known as the **cryosphere**—likewise contain a surprisingly large number of microbes, an estimated 10^{25}–10^{28} cells. The sampling of microbes from sea ice and glaciers is challenging, so adventurous biologists use ice-breaking ships, helicopters, planes, tractors, drilling rigs, and remotely operated vehicles to access polar oceans, sea ice sheets, snowfields, and glaciers (**Figure 30.8a**). Biologists are intrigued by the possibility that Earth's cold microbiomes might be similar to life on bodies such as Mars, Jupiter's moon Europa, and Saturn's moon Enceladus.

Microbiome studies of cold habitats have revealed surprisingly diverse types of microbiota that colorize otherwise white environments. Beneath floating sheets of sea ice live conspicuous growths of brown diatoms that dangle into the cold ocean. These photosynthetic algae supply organic molecules and oxygen to heterotrophic bacteria; ciliate, flagellate, and foraminiferan protists (see Chapter 28); and small animals. Algal cells on the surfaces of glaciers can be so abundant that they color the ice green, red,

(a) Researchers sampling the cryosphere. Darker areas of ice indicate growth of algae and other microbes.

(b) A glacier colored by algae in ice microbiomes

(c) Blood Falls in Antarctica colored red by iron released by bacteria in ice microbiomes

Figure 30.8 **Microbiomes within and on ice.** **(a)** Researchers obtaining samples growing on and within ice for microbiome analysis. **(b)** The color of the ice seen here is due to the presence of algae. **(c)** Blood Falls in Antarctica. The red color is from iron that is released by bacteria, which are part of a microbiome within the ice. a: Courtesy of Cody S. Sheik; b: ©Jason Edwards/National Geographic Creative; c: Source: Peter Rejcek, NSF

yellow, purple, or gray, in this way influencing the amount of light energy that glaciers reflect into space (**Figure 30.8b**). Blood Falls in Antarctica gets its dramatic red color from dissolved iron released from subsurface minerals by iron-metabolizing bacteria living in the cold darkness (**Figure 30.8c**).

Microbiomes Affect the Quality of Fresh Water and Soil

Freshwater and soil microbiomes are also important to many human concerns, including drinking water safety and agricultural production. Marker genes are commonly analyzed to detect infectious or toxic organisms in the water used for drinking and recreation. Experts are particularly concerned about the effects of global warming on freshwater and soil cyanobacteria, because these organisms grow more abundantly in warmer temperatures, particularly where humans have polluted environments with excess minerals.

Some abundant cyanobacteria produce persistent and potent toxins that harm people and wildlife. For example, the cyanobacterial genus *Microcystis* (**Figure 30.9**) produces more than 100 different chemical forms of the toxin **microcystin**, which binds to and inhibits eukaryotic phosphatases, cellular enzymes that remove

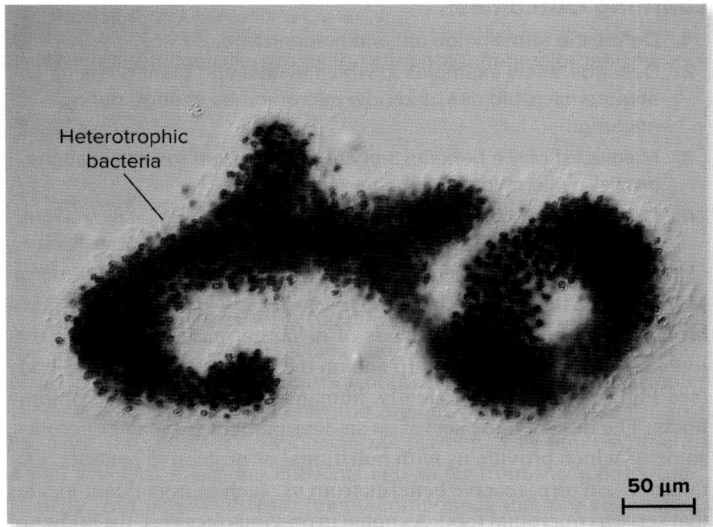

Heterotrophic bacteria

50 μm

Figure 30.9 **The colony-forming cyanobacterial genus** ***Microcystis.*** This cyanobacterial colony has cells that look dark because they contain many light-refracting gas vesicles that aid in flotation. In addition to being an important microbial component of a physical (freshwater) microbiome, *Microcystis* hosts other microbes, such as smaller colorless heterotrophic bacteria. *Microcystis* and associated bacteria produce toxins harmful to human health. ©Lee W. Wilcox

 Core Skill: Science and Society Microbiome characterization is important in evaluating the safety of water used by humans for drinking and recreation.

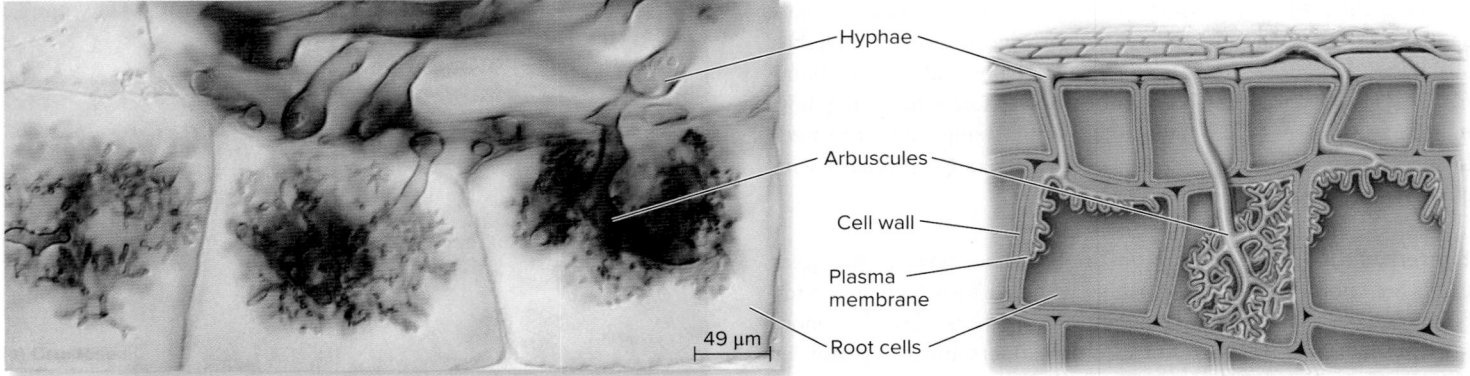

(a) Micrograph of arbuscular mycorrhizae

(b) Hyphae growing between cell walls and plasma membranes

Figure 30.14 Endomycorrhizae. (a) Light micrograph showing black-stained endomycorrhizal fungi within the roots of the forest herb *Asarum canadensis*. The fungal hyphae penetrate plant root cell walls, then branch into the space between root cell walls and plasma membranes. **(b)** Diagram showing the position of highly branched arbuscules. Hyphal branches or arbuscules are found on the surface of the plasma membrane, which becomes highly invaginated. The result is that both hyphae and plant membranes have very large surface areas.
a: ©Mark Brundrett

 Core Concept: Structure and Function The highly branched structure of intracellular portions of endomycorrhizal fungi is key to the ability of the fungus to take up sufficient organic nutrients and efficiently deliver minerals to the host plant.

and reliance on that fat during hibernation in winter. Amplicon analysis of rRNAs (see Figure 30.3) reveals that the microbiomes in bear guts differ in winter versus summer. Winter microbiomes are less diverse and include higher numbers of bacteria from the phylum Bacteroidetes, which are associated with the breakdown of lipids and proteins. Bacteria linked to diets rich in plant fiber are also lower in winter than in summer, when plants are part of a bear's diet.

The most intensively studied animal microbiome is that of humans, the subject of several large scientific projects involving many biologists. The Human Microbiome Project, for example, characterized the microbes of 18 body sites on 300 healthy U.S. adults,

finding that humans have distinctive microbiomes in the gut, vagina, urogenital tract, mouth, nose, skin, and teeth. This and other studies have shown that human bodies host 100 trillion microbes that make up 1–3% of our body weight! The microbiomes associated with humans affect our health in many ways.

- The microbiomes of teeth form biofilms, known as plaque, that are detrimental to dental health.

- Up to 240 bacterial genera can be associated with human skin alone, performing beneficial functions. Some species within skin microbiomes break down dead skin, and others help to prevent infections or transform skin oil into natural moisturizer.

(a) Ectomycorrhizal fruiting body

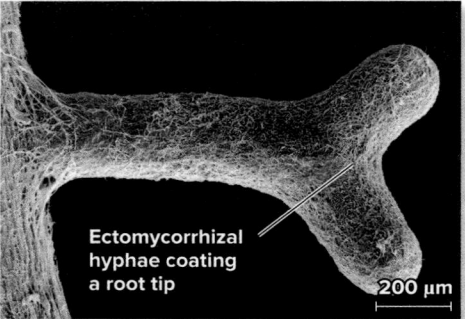

(b) SEM of ectomycorrhizal hyphae

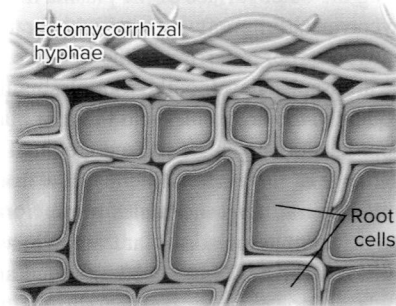

(c) Hyphae invading intercellular spaces

Figure 30.15 Ectomycorrhizae. (a) The fruiting structure of the common forest fungus *Laccaria bicolor*. This is an ectomycorrhizal fungus that is associated with tree roots. **(b)** SEM showing ectomycorrhizal fungal hyphae of *L. bicolor* covering the surfaces of young *Pinus resinosa* root tips. **(c)** Diagram showing that the hyphae of ectomycorrhizal fungi do not penetrate root cell walls but grow within intercellular spaces. By doing this, fungal hyphae are able to obtain organic food molecules produced by plant photosynthesis. a: ©Jacques Landry, Mycoquebec.org; b: Courtesy of Larry Peterson and Hugues Massicotte

Concept Check: *What benefits do plants obtain from the association with fungi?*

- Microbes of the digestive system, particularly the gut, are very important in early life. *Bifidobacterium longum* subspecies *infantis*, for example, is the most prevalent microbe in the gut of healthy infants. This bacterium has genes encoding proteins that bind, import, and metabolize milk polysaccharides into short fatty acids such as acetate. Some of these fatty acids serve as food for the infant's colon cells, aid the immune system, and reduce gut pH, which deters some disease microbes. The best foods for *B. longum* are polysaccharides that are abundant in human milk but rare or absent in that of other animals. Breastfeeding thereby fosters the growth of these beneficial microbes.

 **Core Skill: Process of Science**

Feature Investigation | Blanton, Gordon, and Associates Found That Gut Microbiomes Affect the Growth of Malnourished Children

In a study published in 2016, Laura Blanton, Jeffrey Gordon, and colleagues described the effects of differences in gut microbiomes on the growth of malnourished children. These researchers began their work by analyzing DNA sequences that encode 16S rDNA to determine how microbiome bacteria change during the first 32 months of life in malnourished children from the same locale (**Figure 30.16**). Some of these malnourished children appeared healthy based on their growth, but others were stunted in their growth and were underweight. The results revealed that the healthy children had microbiomes that changed over time, so that

Figure 30.16 **Impact of the gut microbiome on growth.**

HYPOTHESIS Microbiomes from children who were stunted in their growth due to malnourishment will impair the growth of mice.

KEY MATERIALS Fecal samples from healthy and stunted children, germ-free mice which are mice that have been raised in an aseptic environment and do not have any microbes in or on their bodies.

	Experimental level	Conceptual level
1 Obtain fecal samples from many healthy and stunted children of the same locale from birth to 32 months of age.	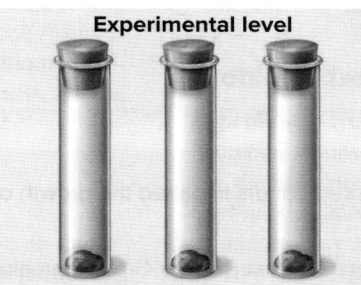	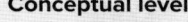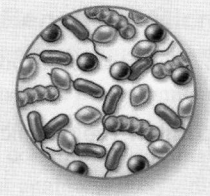
2 Perform an amplicon analysis on the fecal samples from birth to 32 months old.	See Figure 24.3.	This method reveals which prokaryote species are in the gut microbiome and how they change over the course of 32 months.
3 Using a tube, introduce fecal samples from healthy and stunted children into the gut of 5-week-old germ-free mice.	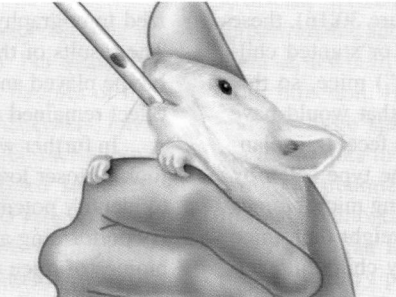	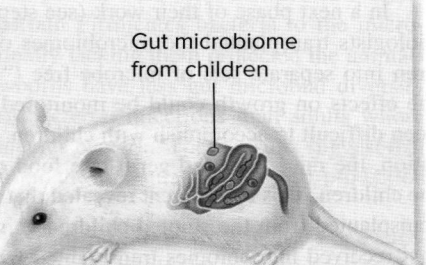Gut microbiome from children

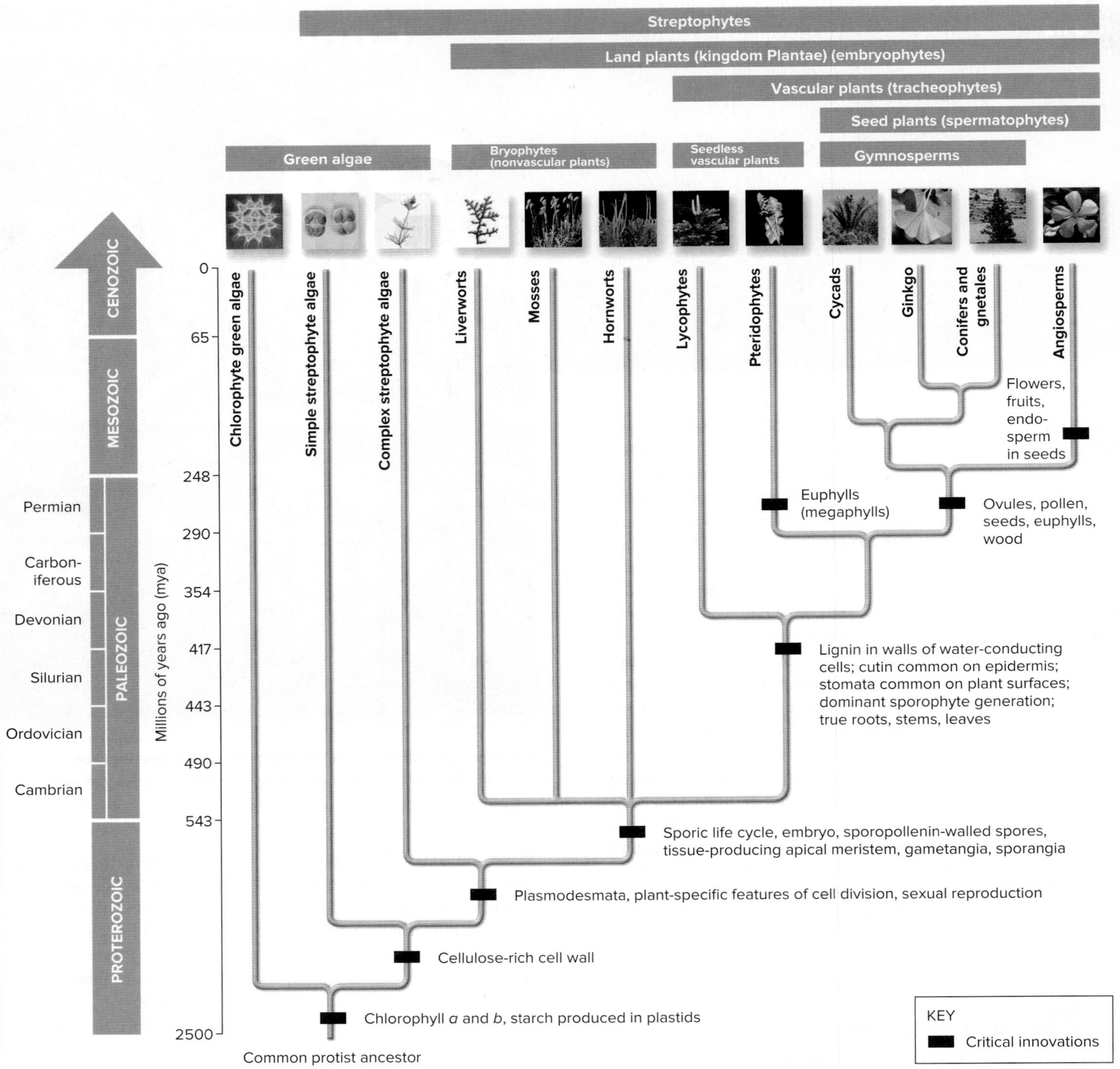

Figure 31.1 **Evolutionary relationships among green algae and modern plant phyla.** The blue bars in the arrow on the left side show maximal evolutionary divergence times indicated by molecular clock and some fossil evidence, suggesting when clades may first have arisen. This is a simplified diagram; fewer branches of streptophyte algae are shown here than actually exist. (inset 1): ©Roland Birke/Phototake; (inset 2): ©the CAUP image database, http://botany.natur.cuni.cz/algo/database; (inset 3–6): ©Lee W. Wilcox; (inset 7): ©Ed Reschke/Getty Images; (inset 8): ©Patrick Johns/Corbis/VCG/Getty Images; (inset 9): ©Philippe Psaila/Science Source; (inset 10): ©Fancy Photography/Veer/Getty Images; (inset 11): ©imageBROKER/Alamy Stock Photo; (inset 12): ©Gallo Images/Corbis/Getty Images

Core Concept: Evolution Land plants evolved from green algae and gradually acquired diverse structural, biochemical, and reproductive adaptations, allowing them to better survive in terrestrial habitats.

Modern Green Algae Are Closely Related to the Ancestors of Land Plants

Molecular, biochemical, and structural data indicate that the kingdom Plantae originated from a photosynthetic protist ancestor that, if present today, would be classified among the **streptophyte algae** (**Figure 31.2**). The streptophyte algae are related to other green algae, but have more features in common with land plants. The more complex, later-diverging streptophyte algae display several **critical innovations**—derived features shared with land plants that fostered plant success on land. Examples of these shared features are a distinctive type of cytokinesis,

(a) Complex streptophyte algae: *Chara zeylanica* **(left) and** *Coleochaete pulvinata* **(right)**

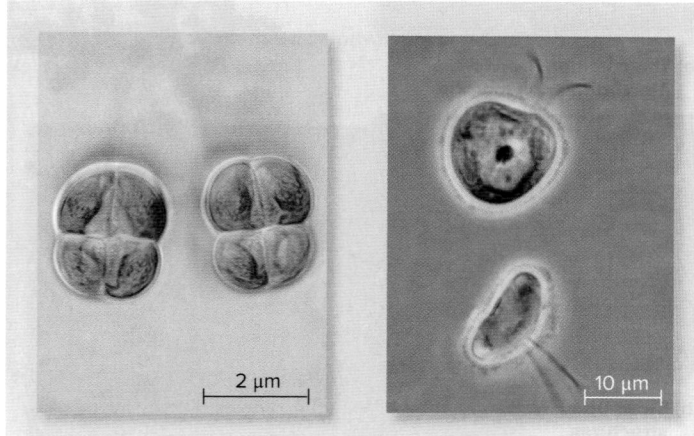

(b) Simple streptophyte algae: *Chlorokybus atmophyticus* **(left) and** *Mesostigma viridae* **(right)**

Figure 31.2 Streptophyte green algal relatives of the land plants. Streptophyte green algae occur **(a)** as more complex branched filaments or **(b)** as small colonies (left side) or single cells (right side). Streptophyte algae share cellular, biochemical, and molecular features with land plants. a (left, right): ©Lee W. Wilcox; b (left): ©the CAUP image database, http://botany.natur.cuni.cz/algo/database; b (right): ©Lee W. Wilcox

intercellular connections known as plasmodesmata (see Chapter 10), and sexual reproduction (see Figure 31.1). For this reason, complex streptophyte algae are good sources of information about the ancestors of land plants.

Distinctive Features of the Land Plants

Land plants can be distinguished from their close algae relatives by several features that represent early adaptations to the land habitat. For example, the bodies of all land plants are primarily composed of three-dimensional tissues, defined as close associations of cells of the same type. Tissues provide land plants with an increased ability to avoid water loss at their surfaces. Water loss is decreased in land plants because bodies composed of tissues have lower surface area/volume ratios than do branched filaments or simpler algal bodies. Land plant tissues arise from one or more actively dividing cells that occur at growing tips. Such localized regions of cell division are known as **apical meristems**. The tissue-producing apical meristems of land plants produce relatively thick, robust bodies able to withstand drought and mechanical stress and produce tissues and organs with specialized functions.

The land plants also have distinctive reproductive features.

- Land plants feature a life cycle involving alternation of generations. **Alternation of generations** means that two types of multicellular bodies alternate in time (refer back to Figure 16.14c). The diploid (2*n*) **sporophyte** generation produces spores by meiosis, and the haploid (*n*) **gametophyte** generation produces gametes by mitosis. By contrast, streptophyte algae feature a haploid-dominant life cycle (refer back to Figure 16.14b).

- During land plant sexual reproduction, a diploid zygote divides by mitosis to form a multicellular sporophyte embryo. A key feature is that the sporophyte embryo is nourished by maternal tissues. Although maternal cells of streptophyte algae may nourish zygotes, the algal zygotes do not develop into multicellular embryos.

- A mature land plant sporophyte undergoes meiosis to produce tough-walled non-flagellate reproductive cells known as **spores** that survive dispersal through dry air. Streptophyte algae differ in that spores produced by meiosis are adapted for dispersal in water; they possess flagella and lack protective walls.

We will take a closer look at the reproductive features of land plants in Sections 31.3–31.5, and also in Chapter 32.

How can we know about past events such as the origin and diversification of land plants? Some information comes from comparing molecular and other features of modern plants. For example, the genome sequence of the moss *Physcomitrella patens*, first reported in 2007, reveals the presence of genes that aid heat and drought tolerance, which are especially useful in the terrestrial habitat. Plant fossils, the preserved remains of plants that lived in earlier times, provide further information (**Figure 31.3**). The distinctive plant organic materials sporopollenin, cutin, and lignin (discussed later in this chapter) do not readily decay and thereby foster plant

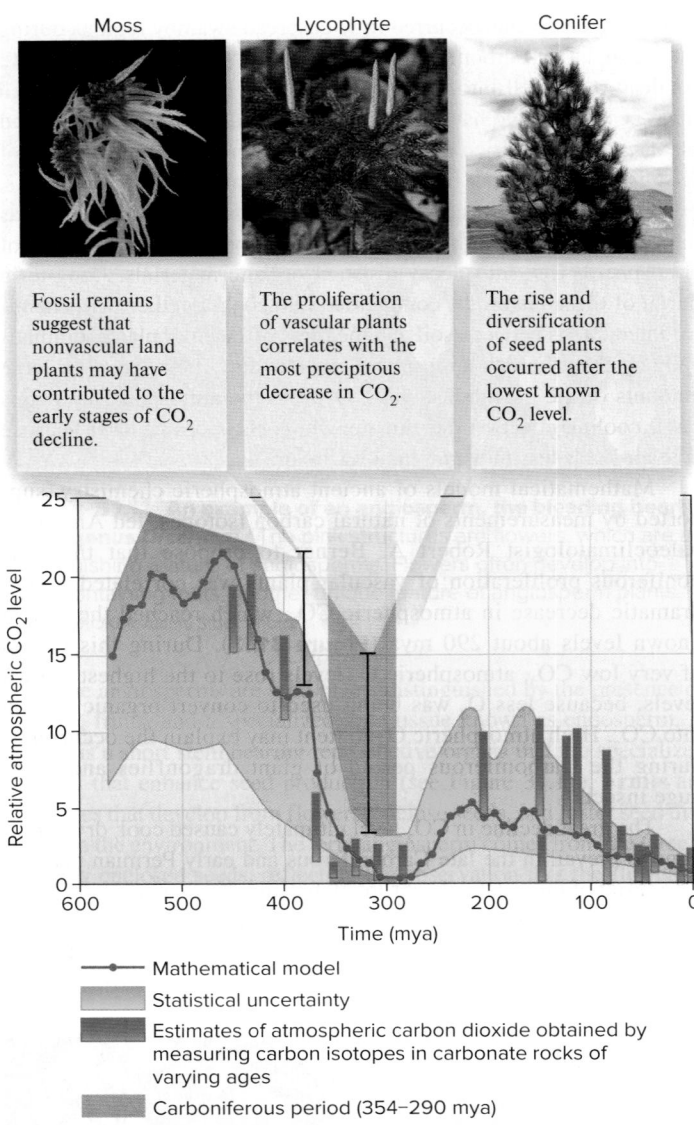

Moss | Lycophyte | Conifer

Fossil remains suggest that nonvascular land plants may have contributed to the early stages of CO_2 decline.

The proliferation of vascular plants correlates with the most precipitous decrease in CO_2.

The rise and diversification of seed plants occurred after the lowest known CO_2 level.

— Mathematical model
  Statistical uncertainty
  Estimates of atmospheric carbon dioxide obtained by measuring carbon isotopes in carbonate rocks of varying ages
  Carboniferous period (354–290 mya)

Figure 31.13 Changes in Earth's atmospheric carbon dioxide levels over geological time. Geological evidence indicates that carbon dioxide levels in Earth's atmosphere were once higher than they are now, but that the rise of land plants caused atmospheric CO_2 to reach the lowest known level about 300 mya. (left): ©Linda Graham; (middle): ©Darlyne A. Murawski/Getty Images; (right): ©David R. Frazier/The Image Works

Cooler, drier conditions favored extensive diversification of the first seed plants, the gymnosperms. Compared with seedless plants, seed plants were better at reproducing in cooler, drier habitats (as we will see in Section 31.5). As a result, seed plants came to dominate Earth's terrestrial communities, as they still do.

Plant Evolution Has Greatly Impacted the Survival and Evolution of Animals

Diverse phyla of gymnosperms dominated Earth's vegetation through the Mesozoic era (248–65 mya), which is sometimes called the Age of Dinosaurs. In addition, fossils provide evidence that early

mammals and flowering plants existed in the Mesozoic. Gymnosperms and early angiosperms were probably sources of food for early mammals as well as for herbivorous dinosaurs. For example, fossils of an aquatic angiosperm named *Cobbania corrugata* have been found with bones of the dinosaur *Ornithomimus* in Dinosaur Park, Alberta, Canada. This dinosaur may have fed on the plant when alive (**Figure 31.14**).

One fateful day about 65 mya, disaster struck from the sky, causing a dramatic change in the types of plants and animals that dominated terrestrial ecosystems. That day, at least one large meteorite crashed into the Earth near the present-day Yucatán Peninsula in Mexico. This collision is known as the Cretaceous-Paleogene event (also sometimes referred to as the K/T event). The impact, together with substantial volcanic activity that also occurred at this time, is thought to have produced huge amounts of ash, smoke, and haze that dimmed the Sun's light long enough to kill many of the world's plants. Many types of plants, including *Cobbania*, became extinct, though others survived and their descendants persist to the present time. With a severely reduced food supply, most dinosaurs were also doomed, the exceptions being their descendants, the birds. The demise of the dinosaurs left room for birds and mammals to adapt to many kinds of terrestrial habitats formerly inhabited by dinosaurs.

After the Cretaceous-Paleogene event, ferns dominated long enough to leave huge numbers of fossil spores, and then surviving groups of flowering plants began to diversify into the space opened up by the extinction of earlier plants. The rise of angiosperms fostered the diversification of beetles (see Chapter 34) and other insects that associate with modern plants.

Figure 31.14 Early angiosperms as sources of food for large herbivorous dinosaurs of the Mesozoic era. In this artist's habitat reconstruction from fossils, the extinct angiosperm *Cobbania corrugata* is shown growing in wetlands that were also inhabited by large dinosaurs such as *Ornithomimus*, whose head is illustrated here. ©Marjorie C. Leggitt

Evolution of Reproductive Features in Land Plants

Learning Outcomes:

1. Compare and contrast a haploid-dominant life cycle and alternation of generations.
2. List critical innovations in bryophytes that result in reproductive features different from those of streptophyte algae.
3. Discuss additional reproductive changes that occurred during the evolution of vascular plants.

In Section 31.1, we considered the diversity of land plants and some critical innovations associated with life in a terrestrial environment. In this section, we will take a closer look at the evolution of reproductive adaptations. We will compare and contrast such adaptions among green algae, bryophytes, and seedless vascular plants. In Chapter 32, we will examine some additional reproductive adaptions that have arisen in the seed plants—gymnosperms and angiosperms.

A Comparison of Algal and Bryophyte Reproduction Highlights an Early Plant Adaptation to Life on Land: Alternation of Generations

Because bryophytes diverged early in the evolutionary history of land plants (see Figure 31.1), they serve as models of the earliest terrestrial plants. A comparison of the life cycle of aquatic streptophyte algae with that of bryophytes reveals the adaptive value on land of bryophyte reproductive features.

Streptophyte algae display a haploid-dominant life cycle in which the only diploid cell is the zygote, whose meiotic division produces relatively few spores (**Figure 31.15a**). By contrast, land plant zygotes do not undergo meiosis. Instead, they undergo mitosis to form a multicellular sporophyte in which many cells can undergo meiosis and thereby produce a large number of spores (**Figure 31.15b**). Producing more spores not only aids dispersal but also increases the genetic diversity of progeny. This life cycle difference allows bryophytes and other land plants to increase the number of spores generated per sexual cycle, an important advantage in terrestrial habitats.

Like related algae (see Figure 31.15a) and modern seedless plants, early land plants likely produced flagellate sperm that needed liquid water to swim to eggs to accomplish fertilization (see Figure 31.15b). On dry land, the number of successful fertilizations and resulting zygotes can be limited by lack of sufficient water. By producing multicellular sporophytes to greatly increase the number of spores resulting from each fertilization, land plants have overcome this problem. Genomic comparisons indicate that transcription factors encoded by *KNOX* genes were key to the origin of plant sporophytes. These transcription factors suppress gametophyte development, thereby allowing multicellular sporophytes to develop from zygotes.

Bryophyte Reproduction Illustrates Other Terrestrial Adaptations

In addition to alternation of generations, other key features aided in terrestrial reproduction (**Figure 31.16**). As shown in step 3, the gametophytes of bryophytes and many other land plants produce

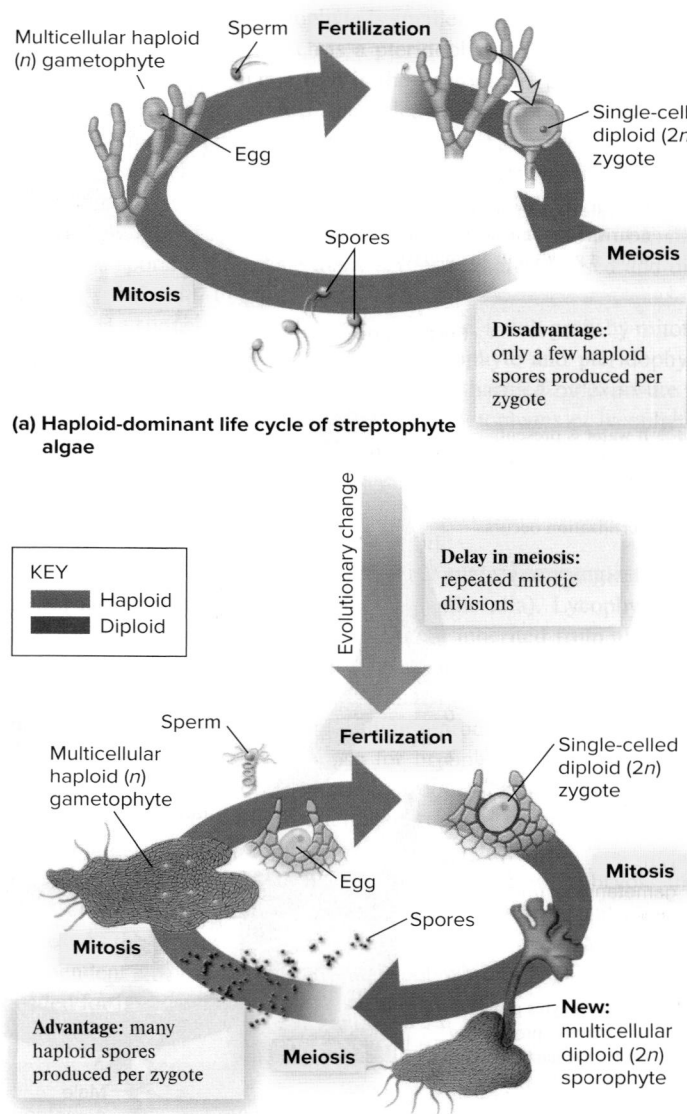

(a) Haploid-dominant life cycle of streptophyte algae

(b) Alternation of generation of early plants

Figure 31.15 Evolutionary transition from (a) the life cycle of primarily aquatic streptophyte algae to (b) the derived life cycle of primarily terrestrial bryophytes.

gametes in structures known as **gametangia** (from the Greek, meaning gamete containers). Certain cells of gametangia develop into gametes, and other cells form an outer protective jacket of tissue. This jacket protects the delicate gametes from drying out and from microbial attack while they develop. Flask-shaped gametangia that each enclose a single egg cell are known as **archegonia** (singular, archegonium). Spherical or elongate gametangia that each produce many sperm are known as **antheridia** (singular, antheridium). When bryophyte sperm are mature and moist conditions exist, antheridia open and release sperm into films of water. Under the influence of sex-attractant molecules secreted from archegonia, the sperm swim toward the eggs, twisting their way

31.5 The Origin and Evolutionary Importance of Leaves and Seeds

Learning Outcomes:

1. Describe how the leaves of ferns and seed plants likely evolved from branched-stem systems.
2. Discuss how seeds develop from fertilized ovules.
3. Name several advantages that seeds provide.

Like embryos, leaves and seeds are critical innovations that increased plant fitness and fostered diversification. Unlike the plant embryo, which likely originated just once at the birth of the plant kingdom, leaves and seeds may have independently evolved several times during plant evolutionary history. Comparative studies of diverse types of leaves and seeds in fossil and living plants suggest how these critical innovations originated.

The Large Leaves of Ferns Evolved from Branched-Stem Systems

Leaves are the solar panels of the plant world. Their flat structure provides a large surface area that effectively captures sunlight for photosynthesis. Among the vascular plants, lycophytes produce the simplest and most ancient type of leaves. Modern lycophytes have tiny leaves, known as **lycophylls** (also known as microphylls), which typically have only a single unbranched vein (**Figure 31.21a**). Some experts think that these small leaves may have evolved from sporangia.

By contrast to lycophytes, ferns and seed plants have leaves with extensively branched veins. Such leaves are known as **euphylls** (from the Greek, meaning true leaves) (**Figure 31.21b**). The branched veins of euphylls are able to supply relatively large areas of photosynthetic tissue with water and minerals. For this reason, euphylls are typically much larger than lycophylls, explaining why euphylls are also known as megaphylls. Euphylls provide considerable photosynthetic advantage to ferns and seed plants, because they provide more surface area for solar energy absorption than do small leaves. The evolution of relatively large leaves allowed plants to more effectively accomplish photosynthesis, enabling them to grow larger and produce more progeny.

The study of fern fossils indicates that euphylls likely arose from leafless, cylindrical, branched-stem systems by a series of steps (**Figure 31.21c**). First, one branch assumed the role of the main axis, while the other was reduced in size and became flattened in one plane, and then the spaces between the branches of this flattened system became filled with photosynthetic tissue. Such a process explains why euphylls have branched vascular systems; individual veins apparently originated from the separate branches of an ancestral branched stem. Plant evolutionary biologists suspect that euphylls arose several times by means of similar, parallel processes, and that leaves of ferns and seed plants are not homologous structures.

Seeds Develop from the Interaction of Ovules and Pollen

The seed plants dominate modern ecosystems, suggesting that seeds offer reproductive advantages. Seed plants are also the plants with the greatest importance to humans, as described in Chapter 32. For these reasons, plant biologists are interested in understanding why seeds are so advantageous and how they evolved. To consider these questions, we must first take a closer look at seed structure and development.

As mentioned earlier, plants produce spores by meiosis within sporangia, and seed plants are no exception. However, seed plants produce two distinct types of spores in two types of sporangia, a trait known as **heterospory**, meaning different spores. Microsporangia produce small **microspores** that give rise to male gametophytes, which develop into pollen grains. Megasporangia produce larger **megaspores** that give rise to female gametophytes, which develop and produce eggs while enclosed by protective megaspore walls. The enclosed female gametophytes are not photosynthetic, so they need help in feeding the embryos that develop from fertilized eggs. Female gametophytes get this help by remaining attached to the previous sporophyte generation, which provides gametophytes with the nutrients needed for embryo development.

Plants produce seeds by reproductive structures known as ovules and pollen, which are unique to seed plants. An **ovule** is a sporangium that typically contains only a single spore that develops into a very small egg-producing gametophyte; the entire structure is enclosed by leaflike structures known as **integuments** (**Figure 31.22a**). You can think of an ovule as being like a nesting doll with four increasingly smaller dolls inside. The smallest doll corresponds to an egg cell; intermediate-sized doll represents the gametophyte, spore wall, and megasporangium; and the largest doll represents the integuments. Fertilization converts such layered ovules into seeds. In seed plants, the sperm needed for fertilization are supplied by **pollen**, tiny male gametophytes enclosed by protective sporopollenin-containing microspore walls.

Embryos and seeds develop as the result of fertilization, which cannot occur until after **pollination**, the process by which pollen comes into contact with ovules. Pollination typically occurs by means of wind or animal transport (see Chapter 32). Fertilization occurs in seed plants when a male gametophyte extends a slender pollen tube that carries two sperm toward an egg. The pollen tube enters through an opening in the integument called the micropyle and releases the

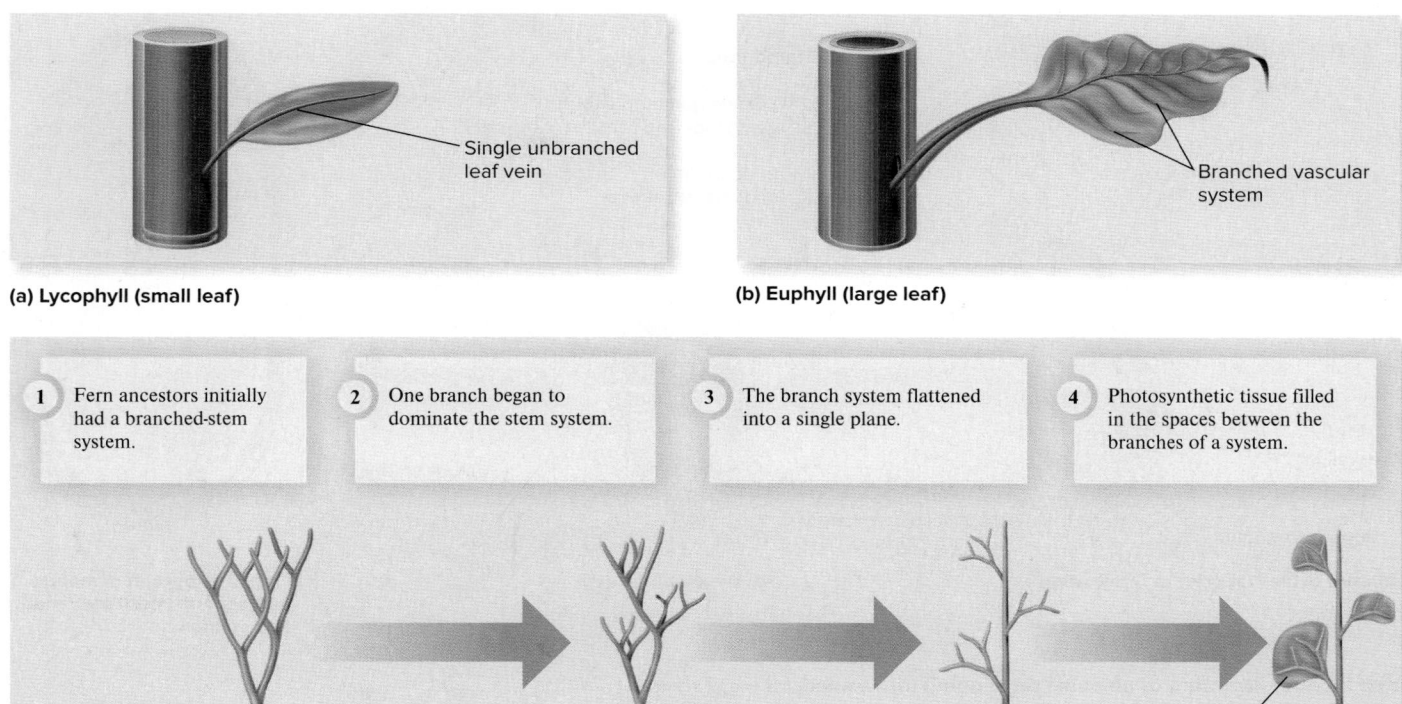

(a) Lycophyll (small leaf)

Single unbranched leaf vein

(b) Euphyll (large leaf)

Branched vascular system

1. Fern ancestors initially had a branched-stem system.

2. One branch began to dominate the stem system.

3. The branch system flattened into a single plane.

4. Photosynthetic tissue filled in the spaces between the branches of a system.

Euphyll

(c) Euphyll evolution process in pteridophytes

Figure 31.21 Lycophylls and euphylls. (a) Most lycophylls possess only a single unbranched leaf vein with limited conduction capacity, explaining why lycophylls are generally quite small. (b) Euphylls possess branched vascular systems with greater conduction capacity, explaining why many euphylls are relatively large. (c) Fossil evidence suggests how pteridophyte euphylls might have evolved from ancestors with branched-stem systems.

 Core Skill: Modeling The goal of this modeling challenge is to propose a visual model that compares the density of leaf veins between ferns and another plant group.

Modeling Challenge: Figure 31.21 provides a model of the process by which fern leaves having branched vascular systems (euphylls) are hypothesized to have evolved from ancestors with branching stems. Imagine that the leaves of some other plant group evolved similarly, but from stem systems that were twice as highly branched. In other words, when flattened, the stem system ancestral to this other plant group had twice as many branches per unit area. Assuming that the branch density of ancestors is directly related to vein density of leaves in descendant plants, draw a pair of models that compare the leaves of ferns and this other plant group, emphasizing the vein density in each type of leaf. How does the venation differ in the two leaf models?

---

sperm. The fertilized egg becomes an embryo, and the ovule's integument develops into a protective, often hard and tough **seed coat** (**Figure 31.22b** and **c**).

Gymnosperm seeds contain female gametophyte tissue that has accumulated large amounts of proteins, lipids, and carbohydrates prior to fertilization. These nutrients feed both embryo development and seed germination. Angiosperm seeds also contain this useful food supply, but most angiosperm ovules do not store food materials before fertilization. Instead, angiosperm seeds generally store food only after fertilization occurs, ensuring that the food is not wasted if an embryo does not form. How is this accomplished? The answer is a process known as **double fertilization**. This process produces

both a zygote and a food storage tissue known as endosperm, a feature unique to angiosperms. One of the two sperm delivered by each pollen tube fuses with the egg, producing a diploid zygote, as you might expect. The other sperm fuses with different gametophyte nuclei to form an unusual cell that has more than the diploid number of chromosomes; this cell continues to divide and generates the endosperm food tissue. Endosperm will be discussed in more detail in Chapter 40.

Seeds allow plant embryos access to food supplied by the previous sporophyte generation, an option not available to seedless plants. The layered structure of ovules explains why seeds are also layered, with a protective seed coat enclosing the embryo and

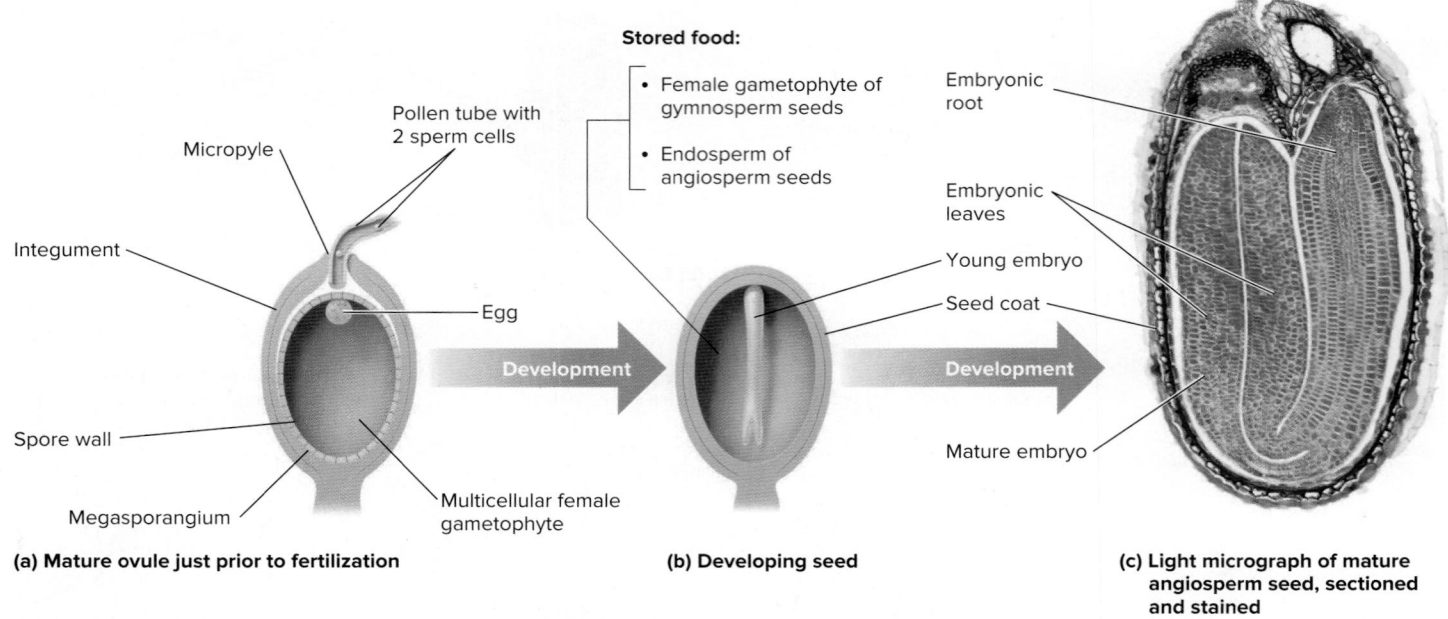

Figure 31.22 **Structure of an ovule developing into a seed.** c: ©Lee W. Wilcox

Concept Check: *Can you hypothesize why the mature angiosperm seed does not show obvious endosperm tissue?*

stored food. As described next, these seed features improve the chances of embryo and seedling survival, thereby increasing seed plant fitness.

Seeds Confer Important Reproductive Advantages

Seeds provide plants with numerous reproductive advantages.

- First, many seeds are able to remain dormant in the soil for long periods, until conditions become favorable for germination and seedling growth. Furthermore, seed coats are often adapted in ways that improve dispersal in diverse habitats. For example, many plants produce winged seeds that are effectively dispersed by wind. Other plants produce seeds with fleshy coverings that attract animals, which consume the seeds, digest the fleshy covering, and eliminate the bare seeds at some distance from the originating plants.

- Another advantage of seeds is that they can store considerable amounts of food, which supports embryo growth and helps plant seedlings grow large enough to compete for light, water, and minerals. This is especially important for seeds that must germinate in shady forests.

- Finally, the sperm of most seed plants can reach eggs without having to swim through water, because pollen tubes deliver sperm directly to ovules. Consequently, seed plant fertilization is not typically limited by lack of water, in contrast to fertilization of seedless plants. Consequently, seed plants are better able to reproduce in arid and seasonally dry habitats.

For these reasons, seeds are considered to be a key adaptation to reproduction in a land habitat.

Ovule and Seed Evolution Illustrates Descent with Modification

As we have seen, seed plants reproduce using both spores and seeds, but seed plants have not replaced spores with seeds. Seed plants still produce spores. Ovules and seeds have evolved from spore-producing structures by descent with modification. Recall that this evolutionary principle involves changes in pre-existing structures and processes. Fossils provide some clues about ovule and seed evolution, and other information can be obtained by comparing reproduction in living lycophytes and pteridophytes.

Most modern lycophytes and pteridophytes release one type of spore that develops into one type of gametophyte. Such plants are considered to be homosporous, and their gametophytes live independently and produce both male and female gametangia (see Figure 31.18). However, some lycophytes and pteridophytes produce and release two distinct kinds of spores: relatively small microspores and larger megaspores, which grow into male and female gametophytes, respectively. As mentioned previously, production of two kinds of spores is called heterospory. As shown in steps 2a and 2b of **Figure 31.23**, an early step in the evolution of seed plants may have been a switch from homospory to heterospory.

What are advantages of heterospory? One advantage is that it mandates cross-fertilization. The eggs and sperm that fuse are derived from different gametophytes, which are likely to be genetically different. Cross-fertilization increases the potential for genetic variation. As described in Chapter 23, such variation may enhance the survival and reproduction of individuals with favorable phenotypes and result in evolution from one

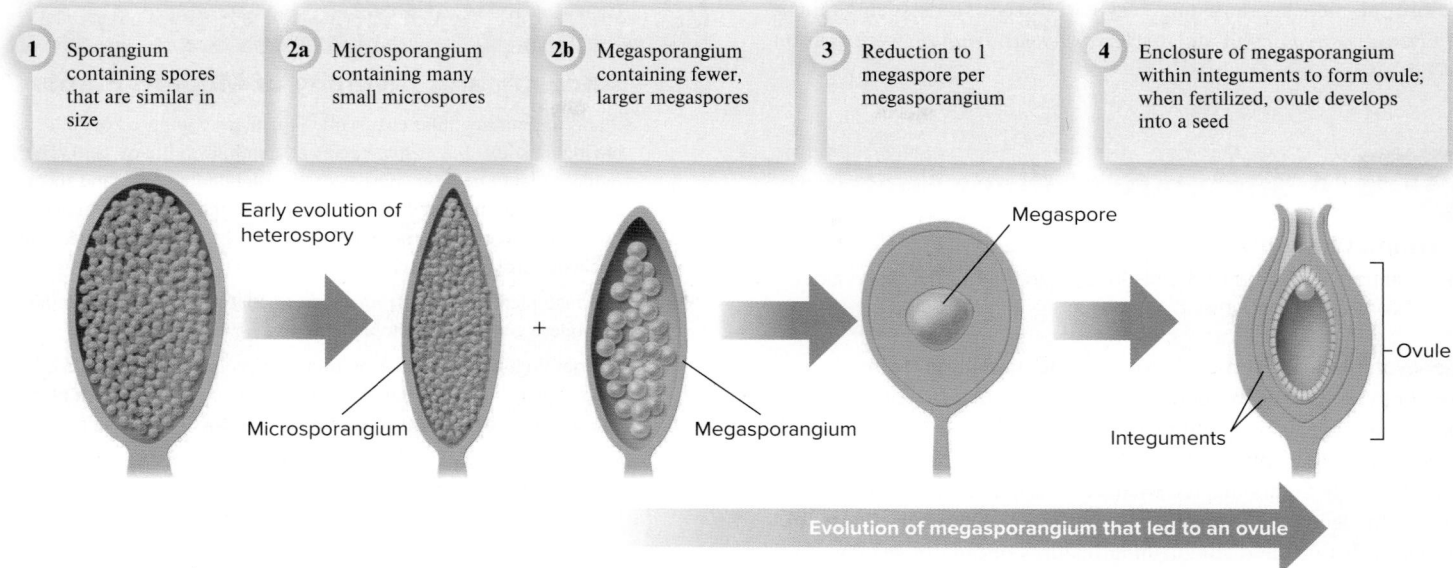

1 Sporangium containing spores that are similar in size

2a Microsporangium containing many small microspores

2b Megasporangium containing fewer, larger megaspores

3 Reduction to 1 megaspore per megasporangium

4 Enclosure of megasporangium within integuments to form ovule; when fertilized, ovule develops into a seed

Early evolution of heterospory

Microsporangium

Megasporangium

Megaspore

Integuments

Ovule

Evolution of megasporangium that led to an ovule

Figure 31.23 **Hypothetical stages in the evolution of seeds.** The parallel evolution of heterospory and endosporic gametophytes in some lycophytes and pteridophytes as well as in the seed plants suggests that these features were acquired early in the evolution of seeds. Later-occurring events in the evolution of seeds included reduction of the number of megaspores to one per megasporangium and enclosure of the megasporangium by protective integuments.

 Core Skill: Connections Look ahead to Figure 35.14, which illustrates the amniotic egg produced by many terrestrial animals. How is the plant seed like the amniotic egg?

generation to the next. A second advantage is that the gametophytes produced by heterosporous plants grow within the confines of microspore and megaspore walls and therefore are known as **endosporic gametophytes**. Endosporic gametophytes receive protection from environmental damage from the surrounding spore walls. Plant evolutionary biologists infer that heterospory and endosporic gametophytes were features of seed plant ancestors and constitute early steps toward seed evolution.

Whereas seedless plants produce multiple spores per sporangium, another key step in seed evolution may have been the production of only one megaspore per sporangium (see step 3 in Figure 31.23). Having a single megaspore allowed plants to channel more nutrients into each megaspore, thereby enabling megaspores to store more food. Following fertilization, this increased food confers an advantage by providing greater nutritive support to developing sporophytes.

A final step in seed evolution might have been the retention of megasporangia on parental sporophytes by the development of integuments (see step 4 in Figure 31.23). As mentioned earlier, this adaptation would allow food materials to flow from mature photosynthetic sporophytes to their dependent gametophytes and young embryos. Integuments also help ovules to receive pollen.

Fossils provide information about when and how the process of ovule and seed evolution first occurred. Fossil reproductive structures of an extinct Devonian plant named *Runcaria heinzelinii* may represent a precursor to an ovule or seed (see **Figure 31.24**). These fossil structures had a lacy integument that did not completely

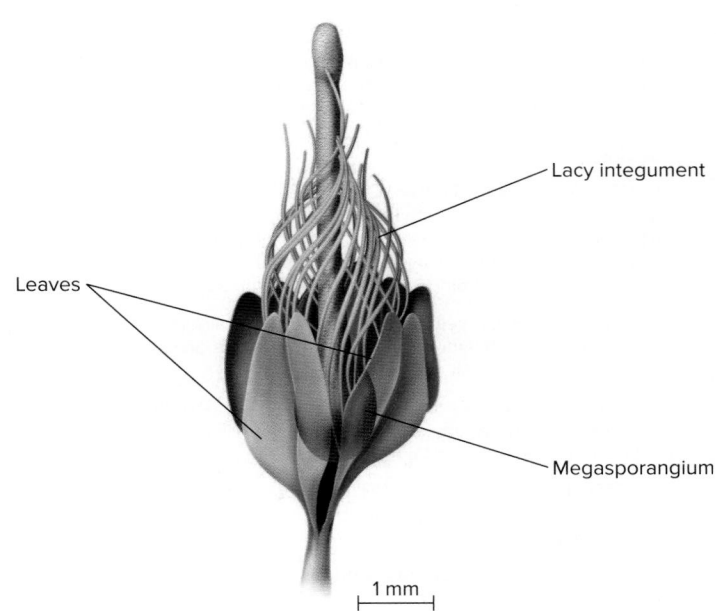

Lacy integument

Leaves

Megasporangium

1 mm

Figure 31.24 **Reconstruction of reproductive parts of the fossil *Runcaria heinzelinii*, a plant with a probable precursor to an ovule or seed.**

Concept Check: *Based on your knowledge of integument function in modern seed plants, can you hypothesize a function for the lacy integument of R. heinzelinii?*

enclose the megasporangium. Very early fossil seeds such as those of *Elkinsia polymorpha* and *Archaeosperma arnoldii* were present by 365 mya.

31.6   A Summary of Plant Features

Learning Outcome:

1. Compare and contrast the distinguishing features of green algae and modern plant phyla.

The evolutionary journey involving the transition from aquatic streptophyte algae to bryophytes, to seedless plants, and finally to seed plants reveals adaptations to a terrestrial environment, as well as ways in which plants themselves have shaped Earth's ecosystems. Throughout this chapter, we have considered many critical innovations that led to the development of modern plant phyla. **Table 31.1** provides a list of the distinguishing features of land plants and their algal relatives.

Table 31.1	**Distinguishing Features of Modern Streptophyte Algae and Land Plants**

STREPTOPHYTES

Streptophyte algae: Primarily aquatic habitat; haploid-dominant life cycle; sporangia absent; sporophytes absent

EMBRYOPHYTES: Primarily terrestrial habitat; life cycle consisting of alternation of two multicellular generations (diploid sporophyte and haploid gametophyte); multicellular embryos nutritionally dependent on maternal gametophyte for at least some time during development; spore-producing sporangia; gamete-producing gametangia; spores with sporopollenin-containing walls

Nonvascular plants (bryophytes) (**liverworts, mosses, hornworts**): Dominant gametophyte generation; supportive, lignin-containing vascular tissue absent; true roots, stems, and leaves absent; sporophytes unbranched and unable to grow independently of gametophytes

VASCULAR PLANTS (TRACHEOPHYTES) (lycophytes, pteridophytes, spermatophytes): Dominant sporophyte generation; lignified water-conducting tissue (xylem); specialized organic food-conducting tissue (phloem); sporophytes branched and eventually becoming independent of gametophytes

LYCOPHYTES: Leaves generally small with a single, unbranched vein (lycophylls); sporangia borne on sides of stems; seeds absent

PTERIDOPHYTES: Leaves relatively large with extensively branched vein system (euphylls or megaphylls); sporangia borne on leaves; seeds absent

SEED PLANTS (SPERMATOPHYTES): Seeds present; leaves are euphylls that evolved independently from those of pteridophytes

GYMNOSPERMS (**cycads, ginkgos, conifers**): Flowers and fruits absent; seed food stored before fertilization in female gametophyte; endosperm absent

ANGIOSPERMS (flowering plants): Flowers and fruit present; seed food stored after fertilization in endosperm tissue

Key: **Phyla**; LARGER MONOPHYLETIC CLADES (FORMAL SYNONYMS). All other classification terms are not clades.

Summary of Key Concepts

31.1   Ancestry and Diversity of Modern Plants

- Plants are multicellular eukaryotic organisms composed of cells having plastids; they display many adaptations to life on land. The modern plant kingdom consists of several hundred thousand species classified into nine phyla, informally called the liverworts, mosses, hornworts, lycophytes, pteridophytes, cycads, ginkgos, conifers, and angiosperms (Figure 31.1).

- The land plants evolved from ancestors that were probably similar to modern complex streptophyte algae (Figure 31.2).

- Paleobiologists and plant evolutionary biologists infer the history of land plants by analyzing the molecular features of modern plants and by comparing the structural features of fossil and modern plants (Figure 31.3).

- The nonvascular plants include the liverworts, mosses, and hornworts, phyla that are collectively known as the bryophytes (Figures 31.4, 31.5, 31.6).

- Lycophytes, pteridophytes, and other vascular plants generally possess stems, roots, and leaves having conductive vascular tissues composed of phloem and xylem, in addition to cuticle, and stomata. These features promote stable body water content (Figures 31.7, 31.8, 31.9).

- Cycads, ginkgos, conifers, and gnetophytes are collectively known as gymnosperms. Gymnosperms produce seeds, but not flowers and fruits. Angiosperms, the flowering plants, produce seeds, flowers, fruits, and seed endosperm (Figures 31.10, 31.11).

31.2   How Land Plants Have Changed the Earth

- Ancient seedless plants and later-emerging vascular plants transformed Earth's ecology by altering atmospheric chemistry and climate (Figures 31.12, 31.13, 31.14).

- The Cretaceous-Paleogene event, a probable meteorite collision with Earth that occurred 65 mya, helped cause the extinction of previously dominant dinosaurs and many types of gymnosperms, leaving space into which angiosperms, insects, birds, and mammals diversified.

31.3   Evolution of Reproductive Features in Land Plants

- Bryophytes illustrate early-evolved features of land plants, which include a life cycle featuring alternation of generations, involving embryos that develop within protective, nourishing gametophyte tissues (Figure 31.15).

- Bryophytes differ from other plants in having a dominant gametophyte generation and a dependent, nonbranching, short-lived sporophyte generation (Figure 31.16).

- The evolution of vascular plants involved a shift in the relative sizes of gametophytes and sporophytes, with the sporophyte becoming the dominant generation (Figure 31.17).

- The fern life cycle includes the dominant sporophyte characteristic of vascular plants (Figure 31.18).

31.4   Evolutionary Importance of the Plant Embryo

- The origin of the plant embryo was a critical innovation that fostered diversification of the land plants. Like placental mammal mothers, plant female gametophytes provide embryos with nutrients through specialized placental tissues (Figure 31.19).

- In a classic experiment, Browning and Gunning demonstrated that placental transfer tissues were responsible for an enhanced rate of nutrient flow from plant gametophytes to embryos (Figure 31.20).

31.5 The Origin and Evolutionary Importance of Leaves and Seeds

- Leaves are specialized photosynthetic organs that evolved more than once during plant evolutionary history. The lycophylls of lycophytes are relatively small leaves having a single unbranched vein. The larger leaves of ferns and seed plants, known as euphylls, have extensively branched vascular systems. Fossils indicate that fern euphylls evolved from branched-stem systems (Figure 31.21).

- Seeds develop from ovules, integument-enclosed sporangia that typically contain only a single spore that develops into an egg-producing gametophyte. Pollen produces thin cellular tubes that deliver sperm to eggs produced by female gametophytes. Following pollination and fertilization, ovules develop into seeds. Mature seeds contain stored food and an embryonic sporophyte that develops from the zygote (Figure 31.22).

- Seeds confer many reproductive advantages, including dormancy through unfavorable conditions, greater protection for embryos from mechanical and pathogen damage, seed coat modifications that enhance seed dispersal, and reduction of plant dependence on water for fertilization (Figures 31.23, 31.24).

31.6 A Summary of Plant Features

- The distinctive traits of modern streptophyte algae and the different phyla of land plants indicate the occurrence of descent with modification (Table 31.1).

Assess & Discuss

Test Yourself

1. The simplest and most ancient phylum of modern land plants is probably
   a. the pteridophytes.
   b. the cycads.
   c. the liverworts, mosses, or hornworts.
   d. the angiosperms.
   e. none of the above.

2. An important feature of land plants that originated during the diversification of streptophyte algae is
   a. the sporophyte.
   b. spores, which are dispersed in air and coated with sporopollenin.
   c. tracheids.
   d. plasmodesmata.
   e. fruits.

3. A seedless plant phylum that is included in the informal group known as bryophytes is
   a. liverworts.
   b. hornworts.
   c. mosses.
   d. All of the above phyla are included in the bryophytes.
   e. None of the above is included in the bryophytes.

4. Plants possess a life cycle that involves alternation of two multicellular generations: the gametophyte and
   a. the lycophyte.   d. the lignophyte.
   b. the bryophyte.   e. the sporophyte.
   c. the pteridophyte.

5. The seed plants are also known as
   a. bryophytes.
   b. spermatophytes.
   c. pteridophytes.
   d. lycophytes.
   e. none of the above.

6. A waxy cuticle is an adaptation that
   a. helps to prevent water loss from tracheophyte stem and leaf surfaces.
   b. helps to prevent water loss from streptophyte algae.
   c. helps to prevent water loss from spores.
   d. aids in water transport within the bodies of vascular plants.
   e. does all of the above.

7. Plant photosynthesis transformed a very large amount of atmospheric carbon dioxide into decay-resistant organic compounds, thereby contributing to a dramatic decrease in atmospheric carbon dioxide levels during the geological period known as the
   a. Cambrian.   d. Permian.
   b. Ordovician.   e. Pleistocene.
   c. Carboniferous.

8. Which of these plant phyla is likely to have the largest leaves?
   a. liverworts
   b. hornworts
   c. mosses
   d. lycophytes
   e. pteridophytes

9. Fern euphylls, also known as megaphylls, probably evolved from
   a. the leaves of mosses.
   b. lycophylls.
   c. branched-stem systems.
   d. modified roots.
   e. none of the above.

10. A seed develops from
    a. a spore.
    b. a fertilized ovule.
    c. a microsporangium covered by integuments.
    d. endosperm.
    e. none of the above.

Conceptual Questions

1. List several common traits that lead evolutionary biologists to infer that land plants evolved from ancestors related to modern streptophyte algae.

2. Why have bryophytes such as mosses been able to diversify into so many species even though they have relatively small, dependent sporophytes?

3. **Core Concept: Structure and Function** Explain how several structural features help vascular plants maintain stable internal water content.

Collaborative Questions

1. Discuss at least one difference in the environmental conditions experienced by early land plants and ancestral streptophyte algae.

2. Identify and describe as many plant adaptations to land as you can.

The Evolution and Diversity of Modern Gymnosperms and Angiosperms

32

The Madagascar periwinkle (*Catharanthus roseus*), one of the many seed plants on which humans depend. ©Gallo Images/Corbis/Getty Images

animals, and they also aid plant growth and reproduction. Though all plants produce secondary metabolites, these natural products are exceptionally diverse in gymnosperms and angiosperms.

In this chapter, we will explore the many important roles that the hundreds of thousands of modern seed plants play in the lives of humans and modern ecosystems. This chapter builds on the introduction to seeds and seed plants provided in Chapter 31. We begin by focusing on the diversity of modern lineages of gymnosperms and angiosperms. Coevolutionary interactions among angiosperms and animals are presented as major factors influencing the diversification of these groups. This chapter concludes by considering human influences on seed plant evolution and the importance of seed plants in modern agriculture.

32.1 Overview of Seed Plant Diversity

Learning Outcomes:

1. Describe the evolutionary relationships among seedless vascular plants and seed plants.
2. List the critical innovations that occurred during the evolution of seed plants.

The seed plants—gymnosperms and angiosperms—evolved from the seedless vascular plants, which were described in Chapter 31. Fossils indicate that gymnosperms originated from now extinct seedless plants known as progymnosperms, some of which were woody, representing the first trees. Gymnosperms then diversified into multiple lineages, some of which became extinct. However, a few gymnosperm phyla, including the conifers, have persisted to the modern day. Angiosperms arose from an unknown gymnosperm lineage, thereby inheriting the capacity to produce wood and other seed plant features. **Figure 32.1** shows our current understanding of the evolutionary relationships among seedless vascular plants and modern seed plants, which include three modern phyla of gymnosperms and the flowering plants (angiosperms). **Table 32.1** provides a summary of the critical innovations of all modern seed plants, conifers, and angiosperms.

The seed plants—gymnosperms and angiosperms—are particularly important in our everyday lives because they are the sources of many products, including wood, paper, beverages, food, cosmetics, and medicines. Leukemia, for example, is effectively treated with vincristine, a drug extracted from the beautiful flowering plant known as the Madagascar periwinkle (*Catharanthus roseus*), pictured in the chapter opening photo. Vinblastine—another extract from *C. roseus*—is used to treat lymphatic cancers. Taxol, a compound used in the treatment of breast and ovarian cancers, was first discovered in extracts of the bark of the Pacific yew tree, a gymnosperm called *Taxus brevifolia*. Vincristine, vinblastine, taxol, and many other plant-derived medicines are examples of plant secondary metabolites, which are distinct from the products of primary metabolism (carbohydrates, lipids, proteins, and nucleic acids). Secondary metabolites play essential roles in protecting plants from disease-causing organisms and plant-eating

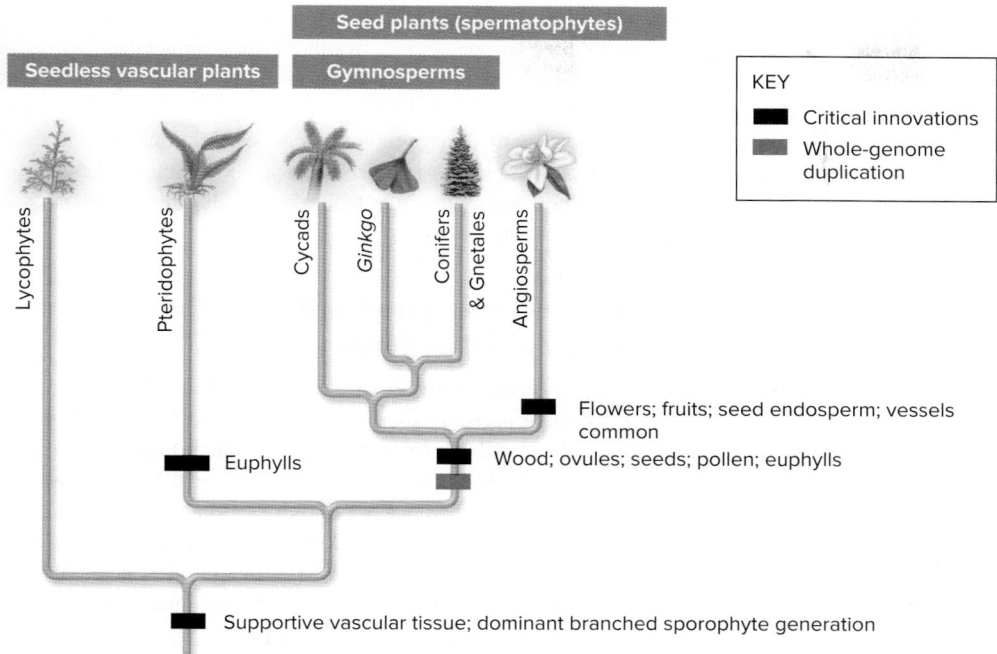

Figure 32.1 A phylogenetic tree for modern seedless vascular plants and seed plants.

Table 32.1	Critical Innovations of Some Seed Plant Groups	
Plant group	**Innovation**	**Advantages**
All seed plants	Vascular cambium that makes vascular tissue and also makes wood and inner bark in woody plants	Seed plants have the potential to grow tall and produce many branches and reproductive structures.
	Pollen, ovules, seeds	Pollen allows seed plants to disperse male gametophytes. Ovules provide protection and nutrition to female gametophytes and developing embryos. Seeds allow seed plants to reproduce in arid or shady habitats.
Conifers	Tracheid torus	Fosters water flow in arid or cold conditions
	Scales or needle-shaped leaves	Retard water loss from leaf surfaces
	Conical shape	Sheds snow, preventing damage
	Resin	Protects against pathogens and herbivores
Angiosperms	Flowers	Foster pollen dispersal, ovule protection, pollination, and seed production
	Fruits	Foster seed dispersal
	Endosperm	Efficiently provides food to embryo of developing seed
	Vessels	Relatively wide diameter fosters water flow
	Many secondary compounds	Provide flower colors and fragrances and protect against herbivores

32.2 The Evolution and Diversity of Modern Gymnosperms

Learning Outcomes:

1. Describe how gymnosperms diversified.
2. Identify three gymnosperm phyla, and describe their importance to humans.

Gymnosperms are defined as plants that produce seeds that are exposed rather than enclosed in fruits, as is the case for angiosperms. The word gymnosperm comes from the Greek *gymnos*, meaning naked (referring to the unclothed state of ancient athletes), and *sperma*, meaning seed. Most modern gymnosperms are woody plants that occur as shrubs or trees. Conifers, which are widely harvested for wood and produce other valuable materials, are familiar examples. In this section, we will examine the evolution and key features of the gymnosperms.

Modern Gymnosperms Arose from Woody Ancestors

Modern gymnosperms include the famous giant sequoias (*Sequoia-dendron giganteum*) native to the Sierra Nevada mountains of the western U.S. Giant sequoias are among Earth's largest organisms, weighing as much as 6,000 tons and reaching an amazing 100 m in height. The large size of sequoias and other trees is based on the presence of **wood**, a tissue composed of numerous pipelike arrays of empty, water-conducting cells whose walls are strengthened by an exceptionally tough polymer known as lignin. These properties enable woody tissues to transport water upward for great distances and also to provide the structural support needed for trees to grow tall and produce many branches and leaves.

In modern seed plants, a special tissue known as the **vascular cambium** produces both thick layers of wood and thinner layers of inner bark. The **inner bark** transports watery solutions of organic compounds. (The structure and function of the vascular cambium, wood, and inner bark are described in more detail in Chapters 36 and 39.) Vascular cambium, wood, and inner bark help gymnosperms and woody angiosperms to compete effectively for light and other resources needed for photosynthesis.

Wood first appeared in a group of ancient seedless plants known as the **progymnosperms** (from the Greek, meaning before gymnosperms). Woody progymnosperms, such as the fossil plant *Archaeopteris*, which lived 370 mya, were the first trees that had leafy twigs (**Figure 32.2**). The vascular tissue of progymnosperms differed from that of earlier vascular plants in being arranged in a ring around a central pith of nonvascular tissue. Seed plants inherited the capacity to make this new arrangement of vascular tissue, which is called a **eustele**. A eustele contains cells that can develop into a vascular cambium as seedlings grow into saplings. The vascular cambium generates wood, allowing saplings to grow into tall trees.

The greatest diversity of gymnosperms occurred during the Mesozoic era, when gymnosperms were the major vegetation present. This period was also known as the Age of Dinosaurs, and gymnosperms are thought to have been the major food for plant-eating dinosaurs during most of their history. Some groups of gymnosperms became extinct before or as a result of the Cretaceous-Paleogene event (K/T event) about 66 mya. Surviving gymnosperm phyla are the cycads (formally, Cycadophyta); *Ginkgo biloba*, the only surviving member of a once large phylum termed Ginkgophyta; and conifers plus Gnetales, which comprise about 800 species. These phyla display distinctive reproductive features and play important roles in ecology and human affairs.

Cycads Are Endangered in the Wild but Are Widely Used as Ornamentals

Cycads are regarded as the earliest diverging modern gymnosperm phylum, originating more than 300 mya. Nearly 300 cycad species occur today, primarily in tropical and subtropical regions. However, many species of cycads are rare, and their tropical forest homes are increasingly threatened by human activities. Many cycads are listed as endangered, and commercial trade in cycads is regulated by CITES (Convention on International Trade in Endangered Species of Wild Fauna and Flora), a voluntary international agreement between governments to protect such species.

The structure of cycads is so interesting and attractive that many species are cultivated for use in outdoor plantings or as houseplants. The nonwoody stems of some cycads emerge from the ground much like tree trunks, some reaching 15 m in height, whereas the stems of other cycads are not conspicuous because they are subterranean (**Figure 32.3**). Cycads display spreading, palmlike leaves (cycad comes from a Greek word meaning palm). Mature leaves of the African cycad *Encephalartos laurentianus* can reach an astounding 8.8 m in length!

Figure 32.2 An early forest in which the only trees were the progymnosperm *Archaeopteris*. This illustration was reconstructed from fossil data.

 Core Skill: Connections Look ahead to Figure 54.26a–e. In what way did ancient *Archaeopteris* forests differ from most forests of the present time?

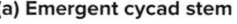
(a) Emergent cycad stem   **(b) Submergent cycad stem**

Figure 32.3 Cycads. Palmlike foliage and conspicuous seed-producing cones are features of most cycads. **(a)** The stems of some cycads emerge from the ground. **(b)** The stems of other cycads are submerged in the ground, so the leaves emerge at ground level. This image also shows a conspicuous orange conelike structure that bears seeds. a: ©Philippe Psaila/Science Source; b: ©Ed Reschke/Getty Images

Root surface

Cyanobacteria

(a) Coralloid roots

(b) Coralloid root cross section

Figure 32.4 Coralloid roots of cycads. (a) Many cycads produce aboveground branching roots that resemble branched corals. **(b)** This magnified cross section of a coralloid root shows a ring of symbiotic blue-green cyanobacteria, which provide the plant with a form of nitrogen that can be used to make essential cellular compounds.
©Lee W. Wilcox

Concept Check: *Why do the coralloid roots grow aboveground?*

In addition to underground roots, which provide anchorage and take up water and minerals, many cycads produce coralloid roots. Such roots extend aboveground and have branching shapes resembling corals (**Figure 32.4a**). Coralloid roots harbor light-dependent, photosynthetic cyanobacteria within their tissues. The cyanobacteria, which form a bright blue-green ring beneath the root surfaces (**Figure 32.4b**), convert atmospheric nitrogen (N_2) into ammonia (NH_3), providing their plant hosts with the nitrogen that is crucial to growth (see Chapter 38).

Cycad reproduction is distinctive in several ways. Individual cycad plants produce conspicuous conelike structures that bear either ovules and seeds or pollen (see Figure 32.3b). When mature, both types of reproductive structures emit odors that attract beetles. These insects carry pollen to ovules, where the pollen produces tubes that deliver sperm to eggs.

Ginkgo biloba Is the Last Survivor of a Once Diverse Group

The beautiful tree *Ginkgo biloba* (**Figure 32.5a**) is the single remaining species of a phylum that was much more diverse during the Age of Dinosaurs. *G. biloba* takes its species name from the two-lobed shape of its leaves, which have unusual forked veins (**Figure 32.5b**). Widely cultivated modern *Ginkgo* trees are descended from seeds produced by a tree found in a remote Japanese temple garden and brought to Europe by 17th-century explorers.

G. biloba trees are widely planted along city streets because they are ornamental and also tolerate cold, heat, and pollution better than many other trees. In addition, these trees are long-lived—individuals can live for more than a thousand years and grow to 30 m in height. Individual trees produce either ovules and seeds or pollen, based on a sex chromosome system much like that of humans. Ovule-producing trees have two X chromosomes; pollen-producing trees have one X and one Y chromosome. Wind disperses pollen to ovules, where pollen grains germinate to produce pollen tubes. These tubes grow through ovule tissues for several months, absorbing nutrients that are used for sperm development. Eventually the pollen tubes burst, delivering flagellate sperm to egg cells. After fertilization, zygotes develop into embryos, and the ovule integument develops into a fleshy, foul-smelling outer seed coat and a hard, inner seed coat (**Figure 32.5c**). For streetside or garden plantings, people usually select the pollen-producing trees to avoid the stinky seeds.

(a) *Ginkgo biloba* **tree**

b) *Ginkgo biloba* **leaf**

(c) *Ginkgo biloba* **seeds**

Figure 32.5 *Ginkgo biloba.* **(a)** A *Ginkgo biloba* tree; **(b)** fan-shaped leaves with forked veins; and **(c)** seeds with fleshy, foul-smelling seed coats (because of their fleshy, colorful appearance, mature *Ginkgo* seeds are often mistaken for fruits). a: ©Karlene V. Schwartz; b: ©Fancy Photography/ Veer/Getty Images; c: ©Topic Photo Agency IN/age fotostock

Conifers Are the Most Diverse Modern Gymnosperm Lineage

The conifers (**Figure 32.6**) are a lineage of trees named for their seed cones, of which pinecones are familiar examples. Modern conifer families include more than 50 genera. Conifers are particularly common in mountain and high-latitude forests and are important sources of wood and paper pulp.

Conifer Reproduction   Conifers produce simple pollen cones and more complex ovule-bearing cones (see step 1 of **Figure 32.7**). The ovule cones, also called seed cones, are composed of many short branch systems that bear ovules. Ovules contain female gametophytes, within which eggs develop (see step 3a of Figure 32.7). The pollen cones of conifers have many leaflike structures, each bearing a microsporangium in which meiosis occurs and pollen grains develop (see step 3b of Figure 32.7).

When conifer pollen is mature, it is released into the wind, which transports it to ovules. When released from pollen tubes, sperm fuse with eggs, generating zygotes that grow into the embryos within seeds (see steps 4–7 of Figure 32.7). Altogether, it takes nearly 2 years for pines (the genus *Pinus*) to complete the processes of male and female gamete development, fertilization, and seed development.

Conifer seeds may also display features that aid in dispersal. For example, the seeds of pines and some other conifers develop wings that aid in wind dispersal (**Figure 32.8a**). Other conifers, such as yew and juniper, produce seeds or cones with bright-colored, fleshy coatings that are attractive to birds, which help to disperse the seeds (**Figure 32.8b** and **c**).

Conifer Tracheids   The wood of conifers contains many specialized vascular cells known as tracheids that are adapted for efficient water and mineral conduction even in dry conditions. Like the tracheids of other vascular plants, those of conifers are devoid of cytoplasm and occur in long columns that function like plumbing pipelines (**Figure 32.9a**). Tracheid side and end walls possess many thin-walled, circular **pits** through which water moves both vertically and laterally from one tracheid to another. Conifer pits are unusual in having a porous outer region that lets water flow through and a nonporous, flexible central region called the **torus** (plural, tori) that functions like a valve (**Figure 32.9b**).

If conifer tracheids become dry, a common event in arid or cold habitats, they fill with air and are no longer able to conduct water. In this case, the torus presses against the pit opening, sealing it (**Figure 32.9c**). The torus valve thereby prevents air bubbles from spreading to the next tracheid. This conifer adaptation localizes air bubbles, preventing them from stopping water conduction in other tracheids. The presence of tori in their tracheids helps to explain why conifers have been so successful for hundreds of millions of years.

Conifer wood (and leaves) may also display conspicuous resin ducts, passageways for the flow of syrup-like resin that helps to prevent attack by pathogens and herbivores. Resin that exudes from tree surfaces may trap insects and other organisms, then harden in the air and fossilize, preserving the inclusions in amber.

Adaptations to Cold Climates   Many conifers occur in cold climates and thus display numerous adaptations to such environments. Their conical shapes and flexible branches help conifer trees shed snow, preventing heavy snow accumulations from breaking branches. People who use conifers in landscape plantings also value these traits.

Conifer leaf shape and structure are adapted to resist damage from drought that occurs in both summer and winter, when liquid water is scarce. Conifer leaves are often scalelike (**Figure 32.10a**) or needle-shaped (**Figure 32.10b**); these shapes reduce the area of leaf surface from which water can evaporate. In addition, a thick, waxy cuticle coats conifer leaf surfaces (**Figure 32.10c**), retarding water loss and attack by disease organisms.

Many conifers are evergreen; that is, their leaves live for more than 1 year before being shed and are not all shed during the same season. Retaining leaves through winter helps conifers start up

Figure 32.6 Representative conifers. (a) Many conifers, such as pines, are not deciduous, meaning that they do not lose all their leaves at the same time in the autumn. **(b)** Some conifers, such as the dawn redwood, are deciduous, meaning that they drop their leaves in the autumn.

a: ©Lee W. Wilcox; b: ©Bryan Pickering/Eye Ubiquitous/Corbis/Getty Images

(a) Pine (*Pinus ponderosa*)

(b) Dawn redwood (*Metasequoia glyptostroboides*)

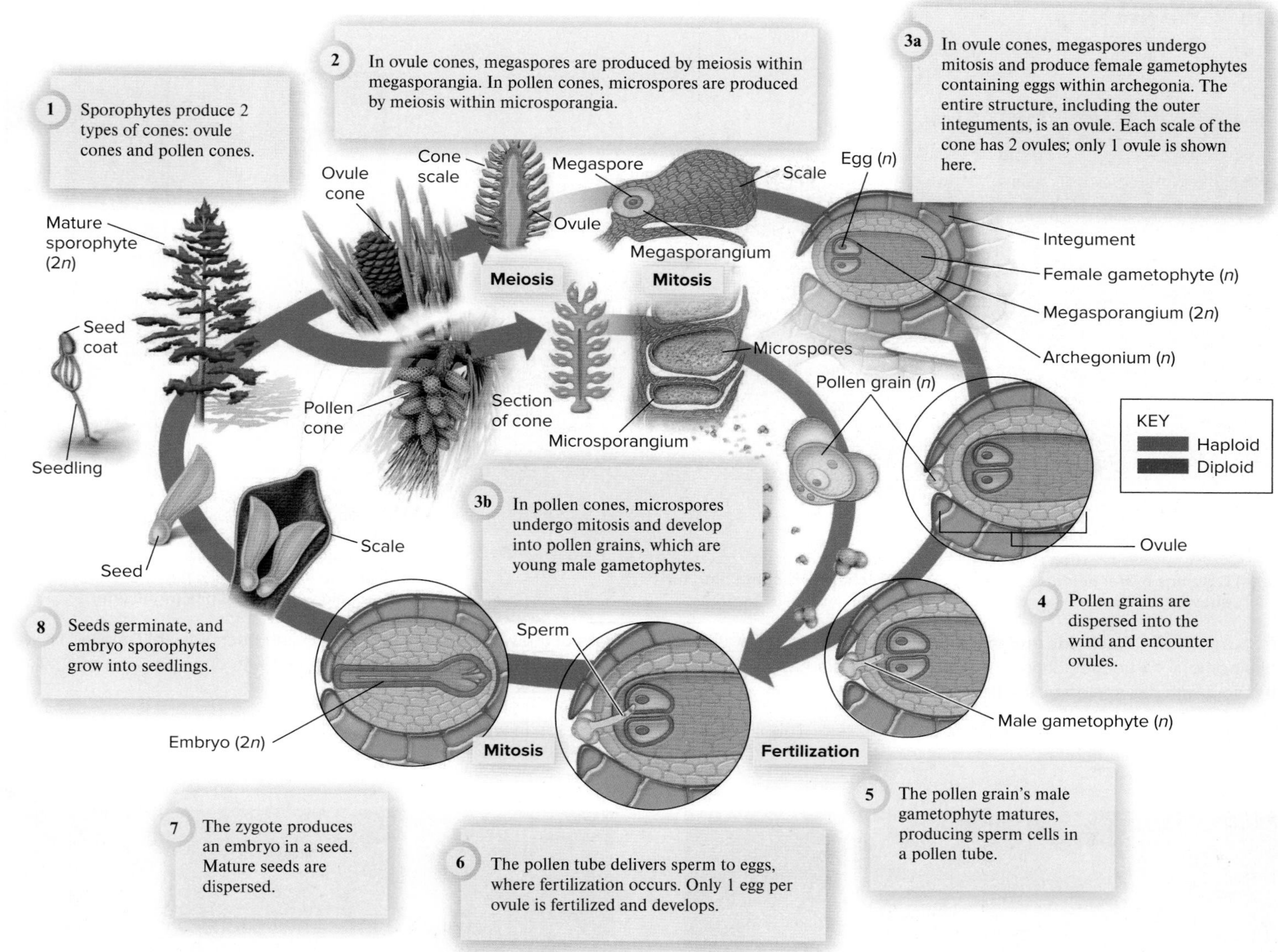

1 Sporophytes produce 2 types of cones: ovule cones and pollen cones.

2 In ovule cones, megaspores are produced by meiosis within megasporangia. In pollen cones, microspores are produced by meiosis within microsporangia.

3a In ovule cones, megaspores undergo mitosis and produce female gametophytes containing eggs within archegonia. The entire structure, including the outer integuments, is an ovule. Each scale of the cone has 2 ovules; only 1 ovule is shown here.

3b In pollen cones, microspores undergo mitosis and develop into pollen grains, which are young male gametophytes.

4 Pollen grains are dispersed into the wind and encounter ovules.

5 The pollen grain's male gametophyte matures, producing sperm cells in a pollen tube.

6 The pollen tube delivers sperm to eggs, where fertilization occurs. Only 1 egg per ovule is fertilized and develops.

7 The zygote produces an embryo in a seed. Mature seeds are dispersed.

8 Seeds germinate, and embryo sporophytes grow into seedlings.

Mature sporophyte (2n)
Seed coat
Seedling
Ovule cone
Cone scale
Megaspore
Ovule
Megasporangium
Scale
Egg (n)
Integument
Female gametophyte (n)
Megasporangium (2n)
Archegonium (n)
Pollen cone
Section of cone
Microspores
Microsporangium
Pollen grain (n)
Ovule
Scale
Seed
Sperm
Embryo (2n)
Male gametophyte (n)

Meiosis **Mitosis** **Mitosis** **Fertilization**

KEY
Haploid
Diploid

Figure 32.7 The life cycle of the genus *Pinus*.

Core Concept: Structure and Function This diagram illustrates the entire seed-to-seed growth and development cycle of conifers, illustrating structure-function relationships.

(a) Pine seed **(b) Yew seeds** **(c) Juniper cones with seeds**

Figure 32.8 **Conifer seeds. (a)** Winged, wind-dispersed seed of the genus *Pinus*. **(b)** Fleshy-coated, bird-dispersed seeds of yew (*Taxus baccata*). **(c)** Fleshy cones of juniper (*Juniperus scopularum*) contain one or more seeds and are dispersed by birds. Juniper seeds are used to flavor gin. a: ©Zach Holmes Photography; b: ©Carmen Hauser/Shutterstock; c: ©Ed Reschke/Getty Images

Core Skill: Connections Look ahead to Figure 32.21h. How are wind-dispersed pine seeds similar to wind-dispersed fruits of the angiosperm maple?

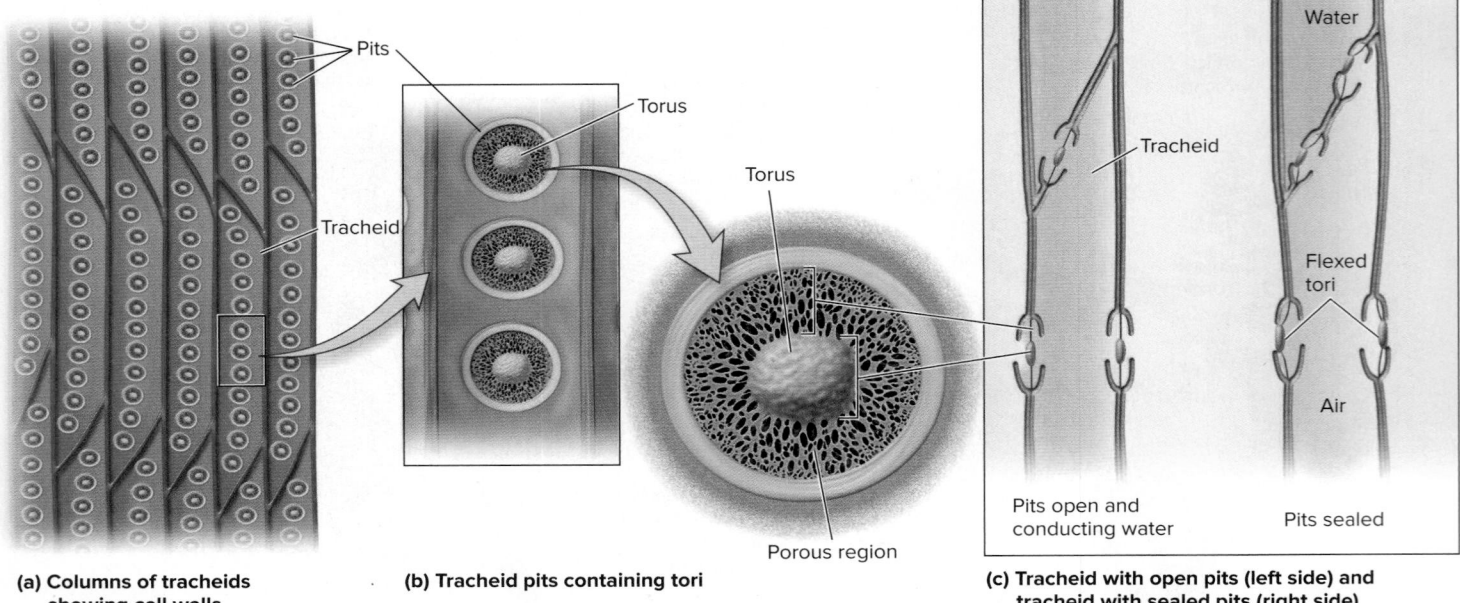

(a) Columns of tracheids showing cell walls

(b) Tracheid pits containing tori

(c) Tracheid with open pits (left side) and tracheid with sealed pits (right side)

Figure 32.9 Tracheids and tori in conifer wood. (a) The lignin-rich cell walls of the water-conducting cells called tracheids. **(b)** Detailed view of a portion of a tracheid that shows the thin-walled areas known as pits, each with a torus. **(c)** A water-filled tracheid with open pits and an air-filled tracheid with pits sealed by the flexed tori.

👁 **Core Concept: Structure and Function** This illustration shows how tori in water-conducting cells of conifers aid survival in arid or cold habitats.

(a) Scale-shaped leaves of Eastern red cedar

(b) Needle-shaped leaves of pine

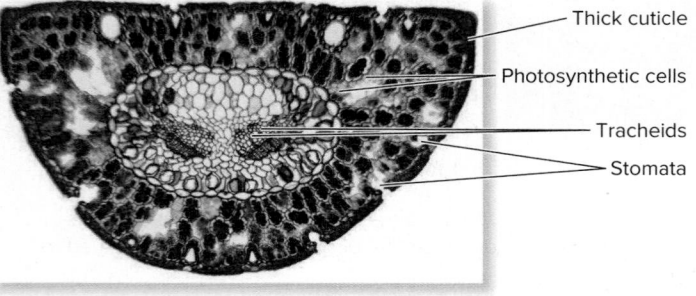

Thick cuticle

Photosynthetic cells

Tracheids

Stomata

(c) Stained cross section of pine needle, showing the thick cuticle

Figure 32.10 Conifer leaves. The leaves of conifers are typically shaped as small scales or long needles, with similar internal structure. a: ©Steven P. Lynch; b: ©Ken Wagner/Phototake; c: ©Lee W. Wilcox

Concept Check: *In what ways are conifer leaves adapted to resist water loss from their surfaces?*

Reproductive structures

Broad leaf

(a) Genus *Gnetum*

Reproductive structures

Leaves

(c) *Welwitschia mirabilis*

Photosynthetic stem

Tiny scale-like leaves

Reproductive structures

(b) *Ephedra californica*

Figure 32.11 Gnetales. (a) A tropical plant of the genus *Gnetum*, displaying broad leaves and reproductive structures. **(b)** *Ephedra californica* growing in deserts of North America, showing minuscule brown leaves on green, photosynthetic stems and reproductive structures. **(c)** *Welwitschia mirabilis* growing in the Namib Desert of southwestern Africa, showing long, wind-shredded leaves and reproductive structures. a: ©Robert & Linda Mitchell; b: ©2004 James M. Andre; c: ©Wildlife GmbH/Alamy Stock Photo

photosynthesis earlier than deciduous trees, which in spring must replace leaves lost during the previous autumn. Evergreen leaves thus provide an advantage in the short growth season of alpine or high-latitude environments. However, some conifers do lose all their leaves in the autumn. The bald cypress (*Taxodium distichum*) of southern U.S. floodplains, tamarack (*Larix laricina*) of northern bogs, and dawn redwood (*Metasequoia glyptostroboides*; see Figure 32.6b) are examples of deciduous conifers.

Gnetales The conifer clade also includes the Gnetales, an order of three genera, *Gnetum*, *Ephedra*, and *Welwitschia*, that feature distinctive adaptations. *Gnetum* is unusual among modern gymnosperms in having broad leaves similar to those of many tropical plants (**Figure 32.11a**). Such leaves maximize light capture in dim forest habitats. More than 30 species of the genus *Gnetum* occur as vines, shrubs, or trees in tropical Africa or Asia. *Ephedra*, native to arid regions of the southwestern U.S., has tiny brown scalelike leaves and green, photosynthetic stems (**Figure 32.11b**). These adaptations help the plant conserve water by preventing water loss that would otherwise occur from the surfaces of larger leaves. *Ephedra* produces secondary metabolites that aid in plant protection but also affect human physiology. Early settlers of the western U.S. used *Ephedra* to treat colds and other medical conditions. The modern decongestant drug pseudoephedrine is based on the chemical structure of ephedrine, a substance that was named for and originally obtained from *Ephedra*.

Welwitschia has only one living representative species. *Welwitschia mirabilis* is a strange-looking plant that grows in the coastal

Namib Desert of southwestern Africa, one of the driest places on Earth (**Figure 32.11c**). A long taproot anchors a stubby stem that barely emerges from the ground. Two very long leaves grow from the stem but are rapidly shredded by the wind into many strips. The plant is thought to obtain most of its water from coastal fog that accumulates on the leaves, explaining how it can grow and reproduce in such a dry place.

32.3 The Evolution and Diversity of Modern Angiosperms

Learning Outcomes:

1. List four flower organs and their functions, and explain how each flower part may have first evolved.
2. Describe how diversification of flowers and fruits enhances seed production and dispersal.
3. Name three major types of angiosperm secondary metabolites, and explain how these affect animals.

More than 124 mya, one extinct gymnosperm group, although it's unclear which one, gave rise to the angiosperms—the flowering plants. Charles Darwin famously referred to the origin of the flowering plants as "an abominable mystery," one that has not been fully solved even today. Recent geological studies indicate that the rise of angiosperms may be related to a global climate change that brought more humid conditions, arising from the breakup of the supercontinent Pangaea (see Chapter 26). Angiosperms have

Figure 32.12 **Angiosperm flowers and fruits.** Citrus plants display the critical innovations of flowering plants: the flowers and fruits shown here and seed endosperm (not shown). ©Bill Ross/Corbis/Getty Images

Concept Check: *What other trait occurs widely among angiosperms but rarely among other plants?*

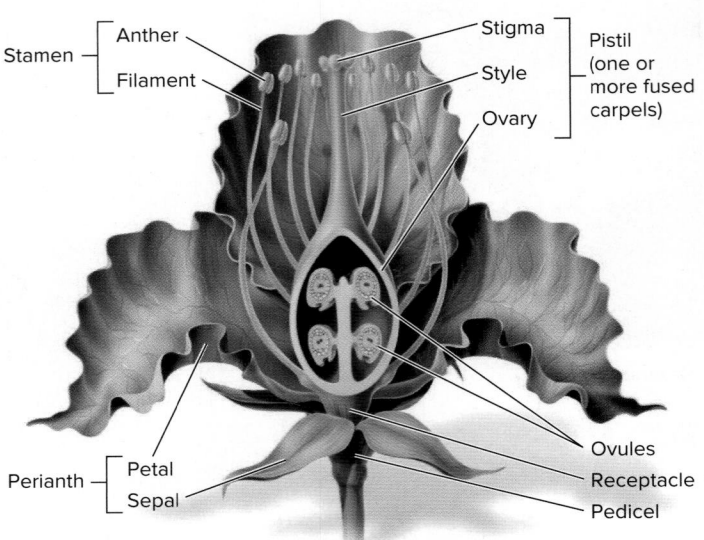

Figure 32.13 **Generalized flower structure.** Although flowers are diverse in size, shape, and color, many have the parts illustrated here.

retained many structural and reproductive features from ancestral seed plants, but have also evolved several distinctive traits.

Flowers and fruits are two of the defining features of angiosperms (**Figure 32.12**). These two features do not occur in other modern plants. The term **angiosperm** is from Greek words meaning enclosed seed, which reflects the presence of seeds within fruits. The seed nutritive material known as endosperm is another defining feature of the flowering plants (see Chapters 31 and 40). Flowers, fruits, and seed endosperm are critical innovations that aid reproduction. Flowers foster seed production, fruits favor seed dispersal, and endosperm food helps embryos within seeds grow into seedlings. In addition, most angiosperms possess distinctive water-conducting cells, known as **vessels**, which are wider than tracheids and therefore increase the efficiency of water flow through plants. Although similar conducting cells occur in some seedless plants and certain gymnosperms, the vessels of angiosperms are thought to have evolved independently.

Although humans obtain wood, medicines, and other valuable products from gymnosperms, we depend even more on the angiosperms. Our food, beverages, and spices—flavored by an amazing variety of secondary metabolites—primarily come from flowering plants. People surround themselves with ornamental flowering plants and decorative items displaying flowers or fruit. We also commonly use flowers and fruit in ceremonies. In this section, we will focus on how flowers, fruits, and secondary metabolites played key roles in angiosperm diversification. We will also examine how features of flowers, fruits, and secondary metabolites are used to classify and identify angiosperm species.

Flower Organs Evolved from Leaflike Structures

Flowers are complex reproductive structures that are specialized for the efficient production of pollen and seeds. The sexual reproduction process of angiosperms depends on flowers. As the flowering plants diversified, flowers of varied types evolved as reproductive adaptations to differing environmental conditions. To understand this process, we can start by considering the basic flower parts and their roles in reproduction.

Flower Parts and Their Reproductive Roles Flowers are produced at stem tips, and may contain four types of organs: sepals, petals, pollen-producing stamens, and ovule-producing carpels (**Figure 32.13**). These flower organs are supported by tissue known as a **receptacle**, located at the tip of a flower stalk—a **pedicel**. The functioning of several genes that control flower organ development explains why carpels are the most central flower organs, why stamens surround carpels, and why petals and sepals are the outermost flower organs (refer back to Figure 20.24).

Many flowers produce attractive **petals** that play a role in **pollination**, the transfer of pollen among flowers. **Sepals** of many flowers are green and form the outer layer of flower buds. By contrast, the sepals of other flowers look similar to petals, in which case both sepals and petals are known as **tepals**. Sepals and petals of a flower are collectively known as the **perianth**. Most flowers have one or more **stamens**, the structures that produce and disperse pollen. Most flowers also contain a single or multiple **carpels**, structures that produce ovules.

Some flowers lack perianths, stamens, or carpels. Flowers that possess all four types of flower organs are known as **complete flowers**, and flowers lacking one or more organ types are known as **incomplete flowers**. Flowers that contain both stamens and carpels are described as **perfect flowers**, and flowers lacking either stamens or carpels are **imperfect flowers**.

Flowers also differ in the numbers of organs they produce. Some flowers produce only a single carpel, others display several separate carpels, and many possess several carpels that are fused together into a compound structure. Both single and compound carpels are referred to as a **pistil** (from the Latin *pistillum*, meaning pestle) because of a resemblance to the device people use to grind materials to powder in a mortar (see Figure 32.13). Only one pistil is present in flowers that have only one carpel and in flowers with fused carpels. By contrast, flowers possessing several separate carpels display multiple pistils.

Pistil structure can be divided into three regions having distinct functions. The topmost portion of the pistil, known as the **stigma**, receives and recognizes pollen of the appropriate species or genotype. The elongate middle portion of the pistil is called the **style**. The lowermost portion of the pistil is the **ovary**, which encloses and protects ovules.

During the flowering plant life cycle, the stigma allows pollen of the appropriate genetic type to germinate, producing a long pollen tube that grows through the style (see steps 1–4 of **Figure 32.14**). The pollen tube thereby delivers two sperm cells to ovules. In the distinctive angiosperm process known as **double fertilization**, one sperm fuses with the egg to form a zygote, and the other sperm fuses with other haploid cells of the

female gametophyte (see step 5 of Figure 32.14). The latter is the first step in the development of a characteristic angiosperm nutritive tissue known as endosperm. Fed by the endosperm, the zygote develops into an embryo, and the ovule develops into a seed (see steps 6 and 7 of Figure 32.14). Ovaries (and sometimes additional flower parts) develop into fruits.

Early Flowers Fossils of whole plants with recognizable flowers and fruits have been identified from geological deposits that are about 124 million years old, though molecular data and fossil pollen grains suggest that angiosperms may have originated earlier. Flowers were a critical innovation that led to extensive angiosperm diversification. Comparative studies of the structures of modern and fossil flowers suggest how modern stamens and carpels might have arisen.

Structural comparisons and molecular data indicate that stamens are homologous to gymnosperm microsporophylls, leaflike structures

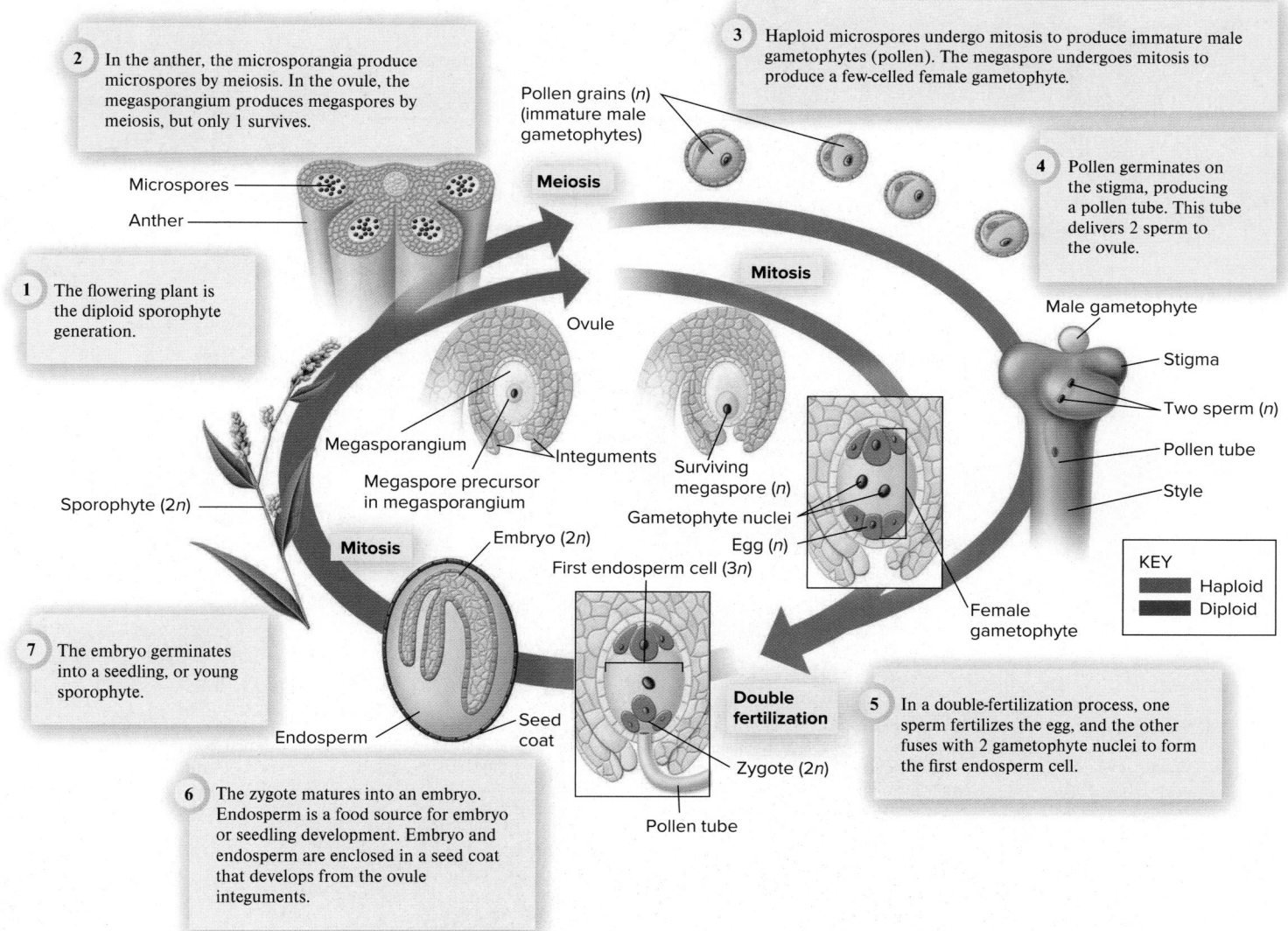

Figure 32.14 The life cycle of a flowering plant, illustrated by the genus *Polygonum*. Flowering plant life cycles differ in length and in the number of cells and nuclei occurring in the female gametophyte, with the seven cells and eight nuclei of *Polygonum* being common.

that produce microspores (young pollen). Early fossil flowers and some modern flowers have broad stamens that are leaf-shaped, with elongated, pollen-producing microsporangia on the stamen surface (**Figure 32.15a**). During angiosperm evolution, the stamens of most modern plants have narrowed to form **filaments**, or stalks, that elevate **anthers**, clusters of microsporangia that produce pollen and then open to release it (see steps 2 and 3 of Figure 32.15a). Filaments and anthers are adaptations that foster pollen dispersal.

Plant biologists likewise hypothesize that carpels are homologous to gymnosperm megasporophylls, leaflike structures that bear ovules on their surfaces. In early angiosperms, such leaves folded over ovules, protecting them (see step 1 of **Figure 32.15b**). In support of this hypothesis is the observation that the carpels of some early-diverging modern plants are leaflike structures that fold over ovules, with the carpel edges stuck together by secretions (see step 2 of Figure 32.15b). During evolution, this folding resulted in carpels that developed specialized regions and completely enclosed ovules (see steps 3 and 4 of Figure 32.15b). Most modern flowers produce carpels whose edges have fused together into a tube whose lower portion (ovary) encloses ovules. Plant biologists hypothesize that such evolutionary change increased ovule protection, which would improve plant fitness.

In contrast, flower sepals and petals have no recognizable homologs in modern gymnosperms. These perianth structures are unique

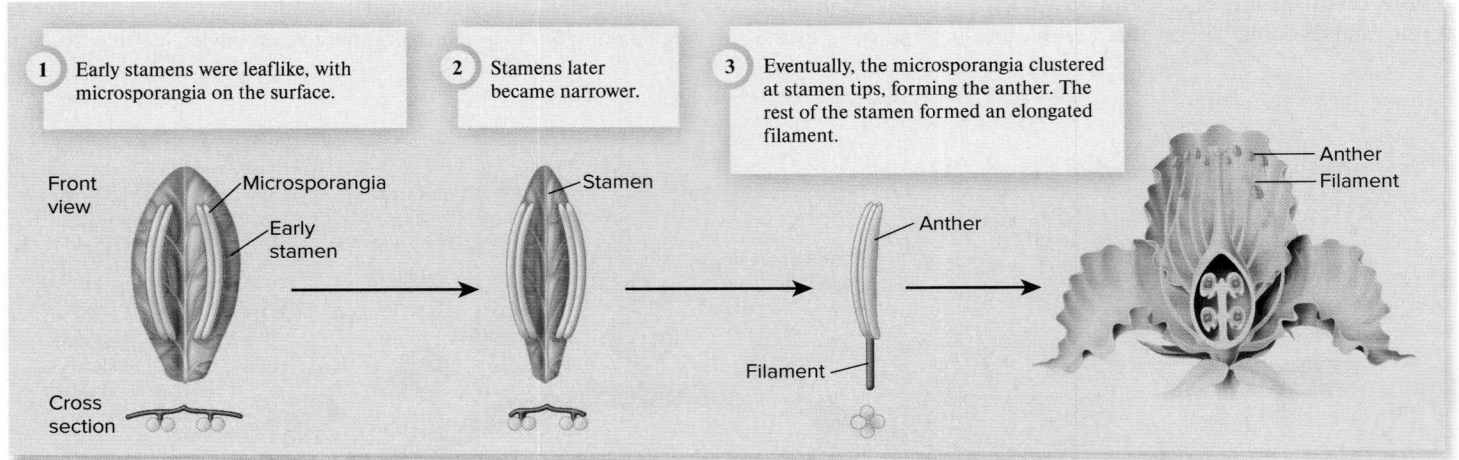

(a) Stamen evolution

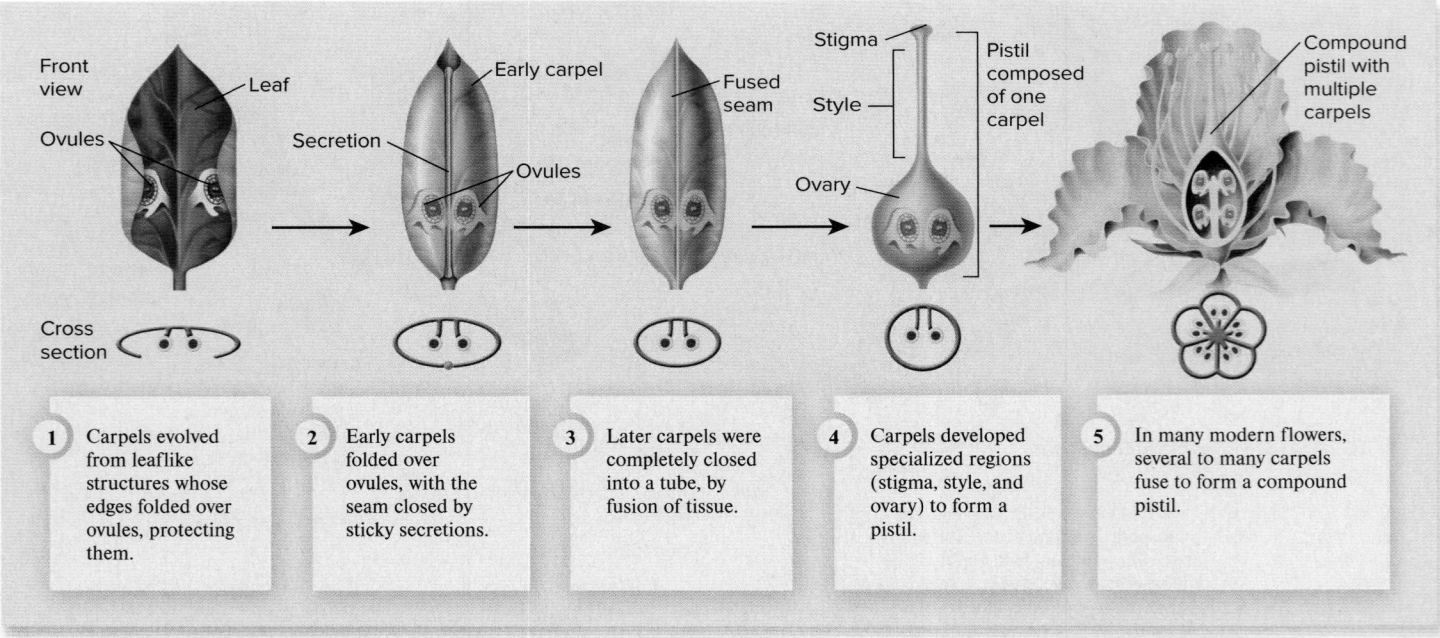

(b) Carpel evolution

Figure 32.15 Hypothetical evolutionary origin of stamens, carpels, and pistils. Plant biologists test these models by searching for new fossils or generating additional molecular data.

to angiosperms, so plant biologists have long wondered how sepals and petals arose. Recent analyses indicate that the gene expression patterns of the pollen cones of gymnosperms (see Figure 32.7) share features with flower stamens, as expected, but also with the flower perianth. These data suggest that perianth parts originated from stamen-like structures, by loss of sporangia. The first flowers arose when early stamens, carpels, and perianth parts became aggregated into a single structure.

Flowering Plants Diversified into Several Lineages, Including Monocots and Eudicots

Figure 32.16 presents our current understanding of the relationships among modern angiosperm groups. According to gene-sequencing studies, the earliest-diverging modern angiosperms are represented by a single species called *Amborella trichopoda*, a shrub that lives in cloud forests on the South Pacific island of New Caledonia. The flowers of *A. trichopoda* display hypothesized ancient features. For example, the fairly small flowers have stamens with broad filaments and several separate carpels (**Figure 32.17**). *A. trichopoda* also lacks vessels in the water-conducting tissues, but typical angiosperm vessels are present in later-diverging groups of

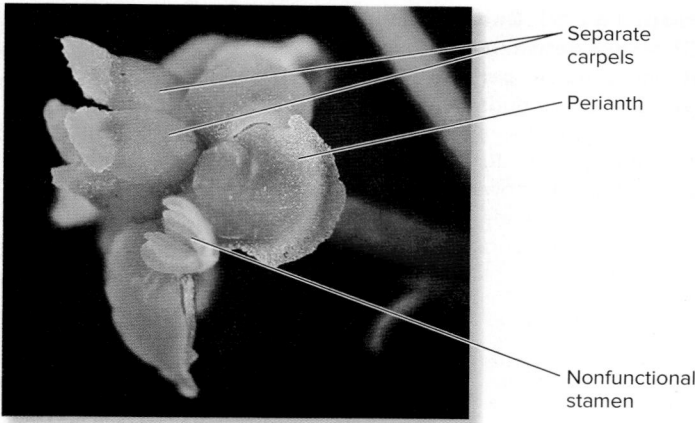

Figure 32.17 *Amborella trichopoda* **flower, similar to a hypothesized early flower.** This small flower is only about 3–4 mm in diameter. It displays several central, greenish carpels; nonfunctional stamens; and a pink perianth of tepals. This plant species also produces flowers that lack carpels but have many functional stamens. ©Sangtae Kim, Ph.D.

angiosperms, including water lilies, the star anise plant, and other close relatives (see Figure 32.16). Magnoliids, represented by the genus *Magnolia*, are the next-diverging group. Magnoliids are closely related to two very large and diverse angiosperm lineages: the **monocots** and the **eudicots**.

Monocots and eudicots are named for differences in the number of embryonic leaves called cotyledons. Monocot embryos possess one cotyledon, whereas eudicots possess two cotyledons. Monocots differ from eudicots in several additional ways (look ahead to Table 36.1). For example, monocots typically have flowers with parts numbering three or some multiple of three (**Figure 32.18a**). In contrast, eudicot flower parts often occur in fours, fives, or a multiple of four or five (**Figure 32.18b**).

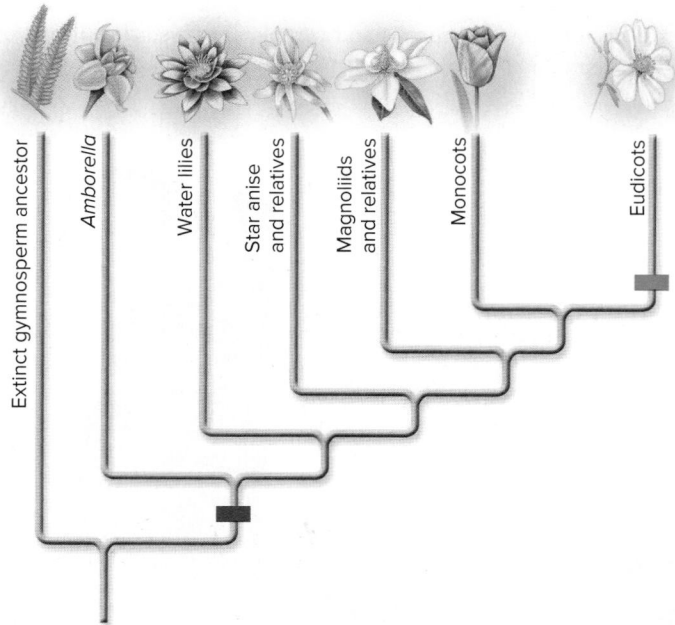

Figure 32.16 **A phylogenetic tree showing the major modern angiosperm lineages and examples of whole-genome duplication events.** In a whole-genome duplication event, the genome size doubles. Molecular data indicate that the size of plant genomes underwent major increases at different time points and in particular lineages (only some of which are indicated here). For example, a whole genome duplication occurred before the divergence of *Amborella* (blue bar), and the genome size tripled (a whole-genome triplication) during the evolution of eudicots (green bar). Plant evolutionary biologists speculate that these duplication and triplication events strongly influenced the diversification of modern angiosperms.

Core Concept: Evolution

Whole-Genome Duplications Influenced the Evolution of Flowering Plants

During evolution, whole-genome duplication has occurred in a wide variety of eukaryotes and has happened on multiple occasions during the evolutionary history of plants. For example, a whole-genome duplication event occurred early in the evolution of seed plants (see the red bar in Figure 32.1). Additional examples include duplication of the entire plant genome before the divergence of *Amborella* (see the blue bar in Figure 32.16) and during eudicot diversification (green bar in Figure 32.16). After such whole-genome duplications, a plant's genome operates as a diploid system. Although genome sizes vary, the number of genes estimated for plants whose genomes have been studied is about 25,000. Whole-genome duplication has the potential to affect species' evolutionary pathways because it offers the opportunity for many genes to diverge, forming gene families.

Figure 32.18 One characteristic difference between monocots and eudicots: flower part number. **(a)** Flowers and buds of a lily (genus *Lilium*), displaying six tepals. **(b)** A flower and buds of apple (genus *Malus*), showing five flower petals. Green sepals are visible around the pink buds. a: ©Dudakova Elena/Shutterstock; b: ©Ed Reschke/Getty Images

(a) A monocot with six tepals

(b) A eudicot with five petals

Flower Diversification Has Fostered Efficient Seed Production

During the diversification of flowering plants, flower evolution has involved several types of changes that foster the transfer of pollen from one plant to another. Effective pollination is essential to efficient seed production because it minimizes the amount of energy plants must expend to accomplish sexual reproduction. Fusion of flower organs, clustering of flowers into groups, and reduction in size of the perianth are some examples of changes leading to effective pollination.

Many flowers have fused petals that form floral tubes. Such tubes tend to accumulate sugar-rich nectar that provides a reward for **pollinators**, animals that transfer pollen among plants. The diameters of floral tubes vary among flowers and are evolutionarily tuned to the feeding structures of diverse animals, which range from the narrow tongues of butterflies to the wider bills of nectar-feeding birds (**Figure 32.19**). Nectar-feeding bats stick their heads into even larger tubular flowers to lap up nectar with their tongues. Orchids provide another example of ways in which flower parts have become fused; stamens and carpels are fused together into a single reproductive column that is surrounded by attractive tepals

(a) Zinnia flower and butterfly

(b) Hibiscus flower and hummingbird

(c) Saguaro cactus flower and bat

Figure 32.19 Flowers whose perianths form nectar-containing floral tubes of different widths that accommodate different pollinators. **(a)** This zinnia is composed of an outer rim of showy flowers and a central disc of narrow tubular flowers that produce nectar. Butterflies, but not other pollinators, are able to reach the nectar by means of their narrow tongues. **(b)** The hibiscus flower produces nectar in a floral tube whose diameter corresponds to the dimensions of a hummingbird bill. **(c)** The flower of a saguaro cactus (*Carnegiea gigantea*) forms a floral tube that is wide enough for nectar-feeding bats to get their heads inside. The cactus flower has been drawn here as if it were transparent, to illustrate bat pollination.

(**Figure 32.20a**). This arrangement of flower organs fosters orchid pollination by particular insects and is a distinctive feature of the orchid family.

Many plants produce **inflorescences**, groups of flowers tightly clustered together, which occur in several types. The sunflower family features a type of inflorescence in which many small flowers are clustered into a head (**Figure 32.20b**). The flowers at the center of a sunflower head function in reproduction and lack showy petals, but flowers at the rim have showy petals that attract pollinators. Flower heads allow pollinators to transfer pollen among a large number of flowers at the same time.

The grass family features flowers with few or no perianths, which explains why grass flowers are not showy (**Figure 32.20c**). This adaptation fosters pollination by wind, since petals would only get in the way of such pollen transfer.

(a) An orchid flower with fused pistil and stamens

Tepals

Fused pistil and stamens

Tepals

(b) A sunflower plant showing inflorescence

(c) Grass flowers lacking showy perianth

Figure 32.20 Evolutionary changes in flower structure. **(a)** An orchid of the genus *Cattleya* has fused stamens and pistil, and six tepals, one of which is specialized to form a lower lip. **(b)** An inflorescence (head) of sunflower (genus *Helianthus*). This inflorescence includes a rim of flowers with conspicuous petals that attract pollinators and an inner disc of flowers that lack attractive perianths. **(c)** Grass flowers of the grass genus *Triticum* lack a showy perianth. a: ©Neil Joy/Science Source; b: ©Pixtal/age fotostock; c: ©blickwinkel/Alamy Stock Photo

Concept Check: *What advantage does the nonshowy perianth of grass flowers provide?*

Diverse Types of Fruits Function in Seed Dispersal

Fruits are structures that develop from ovary walls and function in the dispersal of enclosed seeds. Seed dispersal helps to prevent seedlings from competing with their larger parents for scarce resources such as water and light. Dispersal of seeds also allows plants to colonize new habitats. Diverse fruit types illustrate the many ways in which plants have become adapted for effective seed dispersal. Like flower types, fruit types are useful in classifying and identifying angiosperms.

These are just a few examples of the diverse mechanisms that flowering plants use to disperse their seeds.

- Many mature angiosperm fruits, such as cherries, grapes, and lemons, are attractively colored, soft, juicy, and tasty (**Figure 32.21a–c**). Such fruits are adapted to attract animals that consume the fruits, digest the outer portion as food, and eliminate the seeds, thereby dispersing them. Hard seed coats prevent such seeds from being destroyed by the animal's digestive system.

- Strawberries are aggregate fruits, structures consisting of many fruits that all develop from a single flower having multiple pistils (Figure 32.21d). The ovaries of these pistils develop into tiny, single-seeded yellow fruits on a strawberry surface; the fleshy, red, sweet portion of a strawberry develops from a flower receptacle. Aggregate fruits allow a single animal consumer, such as a bird, to disperse many seeds at the same time.

- Pineapples (Figure 32.21e) are juicy multiple fruits that develop when many ovaries of an inflorescence fuse together. Such multiple fruits attract relatively large animals that have the ability to disperse seeds for long distances.

- The plant family informally known as **legumes** is named for its distinctive fruits, dry pods that open down both sides when seeds are mature, thereby releasing them (Figure 32.21f).

- Nuts and grains are additional examples of dry fruits. **Grains** are the characteristic single-seeded fruits of cereal grasses such as rice, corn (maize), barley, and wheat.

- Coconut fruits are adapted for dispersal in ocean currents and can float for months before being cast ashore (Figure 32.21g).

- Maple trees produce dry and thus lightweight fruits having wings, features that foster effective wind dispersal (Figure 32.21h).

- Other plants produce dry fruits with surface burrs that attach to animal fur.

(a) A fleshy fruit (cherry)

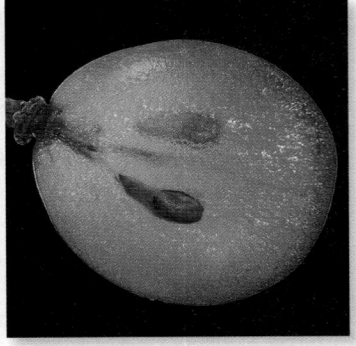

(b) A fleshy berry fruit (grape)

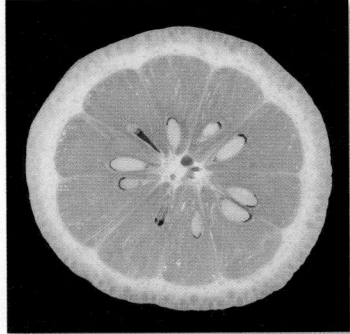

(c) A fleshy fruit (lemon)

(d) An aggregate fruit (strawberry)

(e) A multiple fruit (pineapple)

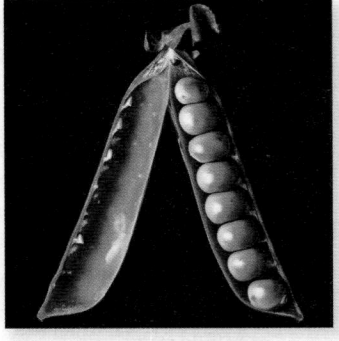

(f) Legumes with dry pods (peas)

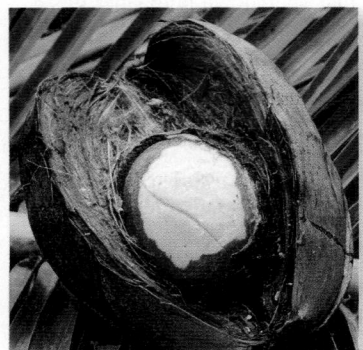

(g) Fruit with husk (coconut)

(h) A dry, winged fruit (maple)

Angiosperms Produce Diverse Secondary Metabolites That Play Important Roles in Plant Structure, Reproduction, and Protection

Secondary metabolism involves the synthesis of organic compounds that are not essential for cell structure and growth in organisms but aid their survival and reproduction. These molecules, called **secondary metabolites**, are produced by various prokaryotes, protists, fungi, some animals, and all plants, but are most diverse in the angiosperms. About 100,000 different types of secondary metabolites are known, most of which are produced by flowering plants. Because secondary metabolites play essential roles in plant structure, reproduction, and protection, diversification of these compounds has influenced flowering plant evolution. Three major classes of plant secondary metabolites occur: (1) terpenes and terpenoids; (2) phenolics, which include flavonoids and related compounds; and (3) alkaloids (**Figure 32.22**).

About 25,000 types of plant terpenes and terpenoids are constructed from different arrangements of the simple hydrocarbon gas isoprene. Taxol, whose use in the treatment of cancer was noted earlier, is a terpene, as are citronella and a variety of other compounds that repel insects. Rubber, turpentine, rosin, and amber are complex terpenoids that likewise serve important roles in plant biology as well as having useful human applications.

Phenolic compounds are responsible for some flower and fruit colors as well as the distinctive flavors of cinnamon, nutmeg, ginger, cloves, chilies, and vanilla. Phenolics absorb UV radiation, thereby preventing damage to a plant's DNA. They also help to defend plants against insects and disease microbes. Some phenolic compounds found in tea, red wine, grape juice, and blueberries are antioxidants that detoxify free radicals, thereby preventing cellular damage.

Alkaloids are nitrogen-containing secondary metabolites that often ave potent effects on the animal nervous system. Plants produce at least 12,000 types of alkaloids, and certain species produce many alkaloids. Caffeine, nicotine, morphine, ephedrine, cocaine, and codeine are examples of alkaloids that influence the physiology and behavior of humans and are thus of societal concern. Like flower and fruit structures, secondary metabolites are useful in distinguishing among Earth's hundreds of thousands of flowering plant species.

Figure 32.21 Representative fruit types. (a–c) The cherry, grape, and lemon are fleshy fruits adapted to attract animals that consume the fruits and excrete the seeds. **(d)** Strawberry is an aggregate fruit, consisting of many tiny, single-seeded fruits produced by a single flower. The fruits are embedded in the surface of a fleshy receptacle that is adapted to attract animal seed-dispersal agents. **(e)** Pineapple is a large multiple fruit formed by the aggregation of smaller fruits, each produced by one of the flowers in an inflorescence. **(f)** Peas produce legumes, fruits that open on two sides to release seeds. **(g)** Coconut fruits possess a fibrous husk that aids dispersal in water. **(h)** Maple trees produce dry fruits with wings adapted for wind dispersal. a–e: ©Lee W. Wilcox; f: ©Gloomerique/Getty Images; g: ©foodanddrinkphotos co/age fotostock; h: ©blickwinkel/Alamy Stock Photo

Terpene

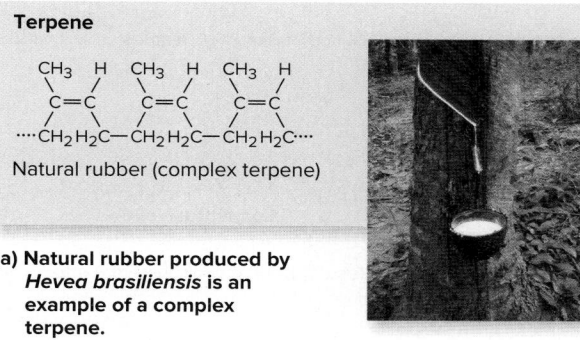

Natural rubber (complex terpene)

(a) Natural rubber produced by *Hevea brasiliensis* is an example of a complex terpene.

Phenolic

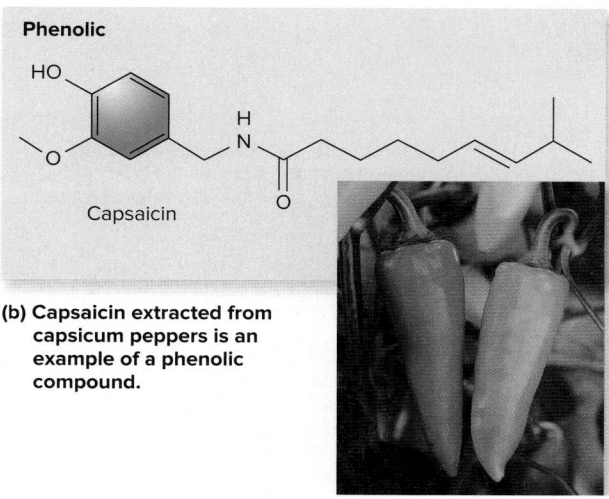

Capsaicin

(b) Capsaicin extracted from capsicum peppers is an example of a phenolic compound.

Alkaloid

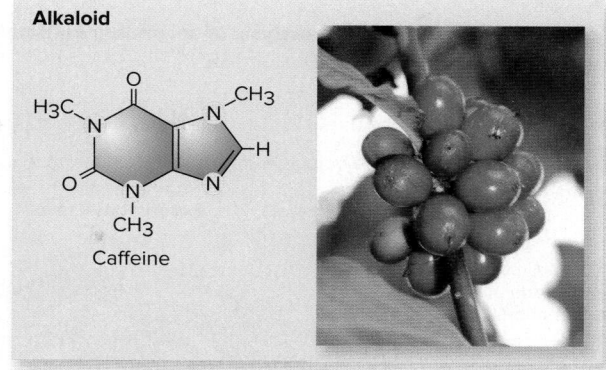

Caffeine

(c) Caffeine produced by *Coffea arabica* is an example of an alkaloid.

Figure 32.22 Major types of plant secondary metabolites. Note that the structures of these plant secondary metabolites differs from that of the primary compounds produced by all cells; primary compounds include sugars and amino acids, described in Chapter 3. The production by plants of terpenes, phenolics, and alkaloids helps to explain how plants survive and reproduce and why plants are useful to humans in so many ways. a: ©Suphatthra China/Shutterstock; b: ©Jonathan Buckley/ GAP Photo/Getty Images; c: ©Science Photo Library/Alamy Stock Photo

 **Core Skill: Process of Science**

Feature Investigation | Hillig and Mahlberg Analyzed Secondary Metabolites to Explore Species Diversification in the Genus *Cannabis*

The genus *Cannabis* has long been a source of hemp fiber used for ropes and fabric. People have also used *Cannabis* (also known as marijuana) in traditional medicine and as a hallucinogenic drug. *Cannabis* produces THC (tetrahydrocannabinol), a type of alkaloid called a cannabinoid. THC and other cannabinoids are produced in glandular hairs that cover most of the *Cannabis* plant's surface but are particularly rich in leaves located near the flowers. THC mimics compounds known as endocannabinoids, which are naturally produced and act in the animal brain and elsewhere in the body. THC affects humans by binding to receptor proteins in plasma membranes in the same way as natural endocannabinoids do. People sometimes use cannabis to ease pain and other medical conditions.

Because humans have subjected cultivated *Cannabis* plants to artificial selection for so long, plant biologists have been uncertain how cultivated *Cannabis* species are related to those in the wild. In the past, plants cultivated for drug production were often identified as *Cannabis indica*, whereas those grown for hemp were typically known as *Cannabis sativa*. However, these species are difficult to distinguish on the basis of structural features, and the relevance of these names to wild cannabis was unknown. At the same time, species identification has become important for biodiversity studies, agriculture, and law enforcement. For these reasons, plant biologists Karl Hillig and Paul Mahlberg hypothesized that ratios of THC to another cannabinoid known as CBD

(cannabidiol) might aid in defining *Cannabis* species and identifying plant samples at the species level, as shown in **Figure 32.23**.

To test their hypothesis, the investigators began by collecting *Cannabis* fruits (containing seeds) from nearly a hundred diverse locations around the world. As shown in step 1 of Figure 32.23, they used the seeds to grow new plants under uniform conditions in a greenhouse. The investigators next extracted cannabinoids, analyzed them by means of gas chromatography (a laboratory technique used to identify components of a mixture), and determined the ratios of THC to CBD. The results, published in 2004, suggested that the wild and cultivated *Cannabis* samples evaluated in this study could be classified into distinct species: *C. sativa*, displaying relatively low THC levels, and *C. indica*, having relatively high THC levels. More recent genetic studies suggest that the genus *Cannabis* is even more diverse than previously thought.

Experimental Questions

1. **CoreSKILL »** Designing an experiment requires a plan to achieve an adequate number of samples, in order to allow statistical analysis. Hillig and Mahlburg obtained nearly a hundred *Cannabis* fruit samples from around the world. Why were so many samples needed?

2. Why did Hillig and Mahlberg collect samples from the leaves growing nearest the flowers?

Figure 32.23 **Hillig and Mahlberg's analysis of secondary metabolites in the genus *Cannabis*.** (top inset): ©Phil Schermeister/National Geographic/
Getty Images; (middle inset): ©Matthew Kellett/Alamy Stock Photo

GOAL To determine if cannabinoids aid in distinguishing *Cannabis* species.

KEY MATERIALS *Cannabis* fruits obtained from nearly 100 different worldwide sources.

Experimental level		Conceptual level

1 Grow multiple *Cannabis* plants from seeds under standard conditions in a greenhouse.

Eliminates differential environmental effects on cannabinoid content.

2 Extract cannabinoids from leaves surrounding flowers.

Extracts were made from tissues richest in cannabinoids; this reduces the chance that cannabinoids present in lower levels would be missed.

3 Analyze cannabinoids by gas chromatography. Determine ratios of THC (tetrahydrocannabinol) to CBD (cannabidiol) in about 200 *Cannabis* plants.

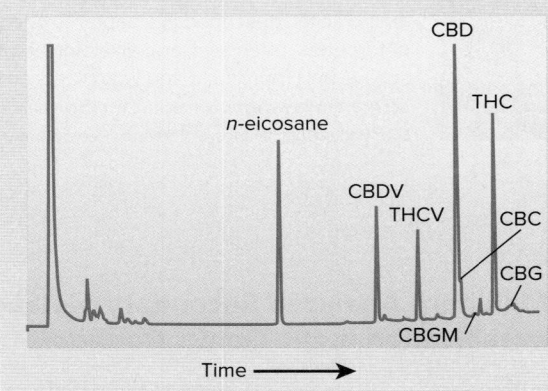

Previous data suggested that ratios of THC to CBD might be different in separate species.

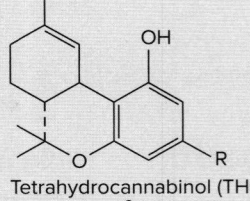

Cannabidiol (CBD)
($R = C_5H_{11}$)

Tetrahydrocannabinol (THC)
($R = C_5H_{11}\ \Delta^9$)

4 **THE DATA**

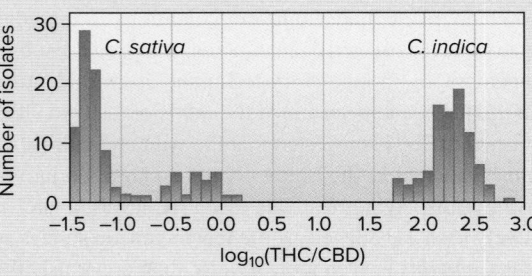

Cannabis plants isolated from diverse sources worldwide formed 2 groups—those having relatively high THC to CBD ratios and those having lower THC to CBD ratios.

Plants having low THC to CBD ratios, often used as hemp fiber sources, corresponded to the species *C. sativa*.

Plants having high THC to CBD ratios, often used as drug sources, corresponded to the species *C. indica*.

5 **CONCLUSION** Differing cannabinoid ratios support a concept of 2 *Cannabis* species.

6 **SOURCE** Hillig, K.W., and Mahlberg, P.G. 2004. A chemotaxonomic analysis of cannabinoid variation in Cannabis (Cannabaceae). *American Journal of Botany* 91: 966–975. ©2004 Botanical Society of America. All rights reserved. Used with permission.

BIO TIPS

THE QUESTION   *The study by Hillig and Mahlburg revealed that samples of Cannabis plants from diverse sources varied in their ratios of alkaloids known as cannabinoids. Why did the investigators grow plants from seeds in a greenhouse before conducting their analyses of cannabinoid content?*

TOPIC   *What topic in biology does this question address?* The topic is the use of secondary metabolites to differentiate species of plants. More specifically, the question addresses the relative effects of genes and environment on plants' production of secondary metabolites.

INFORMATION   *What information do you know based on the question and your understanding of the topic?* You know from earlier chapters of this textbook that the traits organisms express depend on both genes and environment and that genetically determined traits are used for classifying organisms. In this chapter, you have learned that plants, and flowering plants in particular, produce diverse types of secondary metabolites that play important roles in reproduction and protection. Consequently, you might expect that the ratios of cannabinoids in *Cannabis* plants reflect environmental conditions, genetic composition, or both.

PROBLEM-SOLVING **S**TRATEGY   *Design an experiment.* Consider how you might design an experiment to determine how cannabinoid ratios differ among individual plants grown from seeds collected from different sources. Because the seeds came from different sources, they may be from different species of *Cannabis*, defined by genetic characteristics. In your experiment, you would have to control for possible environmental effects, so that such effects would not mask any differences due to genetics.

ANSWER   *Growing experimental plants from seeds in a greenhouse under the same (standard) conditions is a way to minimize variation in cannabinoid ratios due to environmental effects. During their development, all of the experimental plants will experience the same conditions of light, moisture, soil minerals, day length, and other factors that affect plant growth and the production of secondary metabolites. Under standardized growth conditions, observed differences in cannabinoid ratios will reflect genetic variation that can be used to classify Cannabis plants into species, as Hillig and Mahlburg were able to do.*

32.4   The Role of Coevolution in Angiosperm Diversification

Learning Outcomes:

1. Explain the concept of coevolution.
2. List examples of coevolution between plants and animal pollinators.
3. List examples of coevolution between plants and animal seed dispersal agents.

The preceding section described how flowering plants are commonly associated with animals in ways that strongly influence plant evolution. Likewise, plants have influenced animal evolution in a diversity-generating process known as **coevolution**, which is the process by which two or more species of organisms influence each other's evolutionary pathway. During the diversification of flowering plants, coevolution with animals has been a major evolutionary factor. For example, the diversification of bees about 123 million years ago correlates with the diversification of the eudicots, which today make up three-quarters of all angiosperm species. Coevolution is reflected in the diverse forms of most flowers and many fruits and the many ways that plants accomplish effective pollen and seed dispersal. Human attraction to flowers and fruit also is an example of coevolution. This is because human sensory systems are similar to those of various animals that have coevolved with angiosperms.

Pollination Coevolution Influences the Diversification of Flowers and Animals

Animal pollinators transfer pollen from the anthers of one flower to the stigmas of other flowers of the same species. Pollinators thereby foster genetic variation and enhance the potential for evolutionary change among plants. Insects, birds, bats, and other pollinators learn the characteristics of particular flowers, visiting them preferentially. This animal behavior, known as constancy or fidelity, increases the odds that a flower stigma will receive pollen of the appropriate species. Animal pollinators increase the precision of pollen transfer, which reduces the amount of pollen that plants must produce to achieve pollination. By contrast, wind-pollinated plants must produce much larger amounts of pollen because windblown pollen reaches appropriate flowers by chance.

Flowers attract the most appropriate pollinators by means of attractive colors, odors, shapes, and sizes. Secondary metabolites influence the colors and odors of many flowers. Flavonoids, for example, color many blue, purple, or pink flowers. More than 700 types of chemical compounds contribute to floral odors.

Most flowers reward pollinators with food: sugar-rich nectar, lipid- and protein-rich pollen, or both. In this way, flowering plants provide an important biological service, providing food for many types of animals. However, some flowers "trick" pollinators into visiting or trap pollinators temporarily, thereby achieving pollination without actually rewarding the pollinator. Examples include flowers that look and smell like dead meat, thereby attracting flies, which are fooled but accomplish pollination anyway.

Although many flowers are pollinated by a variety of animals, others have flowers that have become specialized for particular pollinators, and vice versa. These specializations, which have resulted from coevolution, are known as **pollination syndromes** (Table 32.2). For example, odorless red flowers, such as those of hibiscus (see Figure 32.19b), are attractive to birds, which can see the color red but have a poor sense of smell. By contrast, bees are not typically attracted to red flowers because bee vision does not extend to the red end of the visible light spectrum. Rather, bees are attracted to blue, purple, yellow, and white flowers having sweet odors. If you are allergic to bee stings or just want to reduce the possibility of being stung, avoid dressing in bee-attracting flower colors and wearing flowery fragrances when in locales frequented by bees.

Table 32.2	Pollination Syndromes
Animal features	**Coevolved flower features**
Bees	
Color vision includes ultraviolet (UV), not red	Often blue, purple, yellow, white (not red) colors
Good sense of smell	Fragrant
Require nectar and pollen	Nectar and abundant pollen
Butterflies	
Good color vision	Blue, purple, deep pink, orange, red colors
Sense odors with feet	Light floral scent
Need landing place	Landing place
Feed with long, tubular tongue	Nectar in deep, narrow floral tubes
Moths	
Active at night	Open at night; white or bright colors
Good sense of smell	Heavy, musky odors
Feed with long, thin tongue	Nectar in deep, narrow floral tubes
Birds	
Color vision, includes red	Often colored red
Often require perch	Strong, damage-resistant structure
Poor sense of smell	No fragrance
Feed in daytime	Open in daytime
High nectar requirement	Copious nectar in floral tubes
Hover (hummingbirds)	Pendulous (dangling) flowers
Bats	
Color blind	Light, reflective colors
Good sense of smell	Strong odors
Active at night	Open at night
High food requirements	Copious nectar and pollen provided
Navigate by echolocation	Pendulous or borne on tree trunks

 Core Skill: Modeling The goal of this modeling challenge is to propose a model that shows a series of steps in the process by which a pollinator accomplishes pollination.

Modeling Challenge: Table 32.2 lists pollination syndromes, features of animal pollinators and flowers that have coevolved. Pick one of these pollination syndromes and propose a model that shows a series of steps in the pollination process. The model should begin with the pollinator close to, but not touching the flower, and should end with pollination, pollen attachment to the flower stigma. Your model should answer two key questions: Why does the pollinator visit the flower? How does the pollinator deliver pollen to the stigma?

Pollination syndromes are of practical importance in agriculture and in conservation biology. Fruit growers often import colonies of bees to pollinate flowers of fruit crops and thereby increase

Figure 32.24 *Brighamia insignis*, **a plant endangered by the loss of its pollinator.** The pollinator that coevolved with *B. insignis* has become extinct, with the result that the plant is unable to produce seeds unless artificially pollinated by humans. ©Garden World Images Ltd/Alamy Stock Photo

Concept Check: *What kind of animal likely pollinated B. insignis?*

crop yields. In recent years, widespread die-offs of bee colonies have become an environmental and agricultural concern. When bee pollinators are not available, growers cannot produce some fruit crops. Some plants have become so specialized to particular pollinators that if the pollinator becomes extinct, the plant becomes endangered. An example is the Hawaiian cliff-dwelling *Brighamia insignis* (**Figure 32.24**), whose presumed moth pollinator has become extinct. Humans that hand-pollinate *B. insignis* are all that stand between this plant and extinction.

Seed-Dispersal Coevolution Influences the Characteristics of Fruits and Animals

As in the case of pollination, coevolution between plants and their animal seed-dispersal agents has influenced characteristics of both fruits and the seed-dispersing animals. In addition, flowering plant fruits provide food for animals, an important biological service. For example, many of the plants of temperate forests produce fruits that are attractive to resident birds. Such juicy, sweet fruits have small seeds that readily pass through bird guts. Many plants signal fruit ripeness by undergoing color changes from unripe green fruits to red, orange, yellow, blue, or black (**Figure 32.25**). Because birds have good color vision, they are able to detect the presence of ripe fruits and consume them before the fruits drop from plants and rot.

Apples, strawberries, cherries, blueberries, and blackberries are examples of fruits whose seed dispersal adaptations have made them attractive food for humans. By contrast, the lipid-rich fruits of Virginia creeper (*Parthenocissus quinquefolia*) and some other autumn-fruiting plants energize migratory birds but are not tasty to

Figure 32.25 **Fruits attractive to animal seed-dispersal agents.** Color and odor signals alert coevolved animal species that fruits are ripe, thus favoring the dispersal of mature seeds. ©Beng & Lundberg/naturepl.com

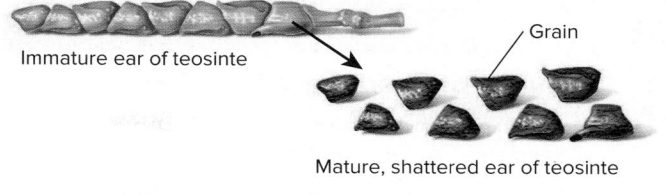
Immature ear of teosinte
Grain

Mature, shattered ear of teosinte

Nonshattering ear of *Z. mays,* subspecies mays.

Figure 32.26 **Ears and grains of modern corn and its ancestor, teosinte.** This illustration shows that domesticated corn ears are much larger than those of the ancestral grass teosinte. In addition, corn grains are softer and more edible than the grains of teosinte, which are enclosed in a hard casing.

 Core Skill: Science and Society The domestication of corn from a wild grass into one of the world's largest production crops is an amazing feat of artificial selection.

humans. The Virginia creeper's leaves often turn fall colors earlier than surrounding plants, thereby signaling the availability of nutritious, ripe fruit to high-flying birds. Such lipid-rich fruits must be consumed promptly because they rot easily, in which case seed dispersal cannot occur.

32.5 Human Influences on Angiosperm Diversification

Learning Outcome:

1. **CoreSKILL** » Describe how molecular information about modern crop plants is used to infer their evolutionary origin by domestication.

By means of the process known as **domestication**, which involves artificial selection for traits desirable to humans, ancient humans transformed wild plant species into new crop species. Cultivated bread wheat (*Triticum aestivum*) was probably among the earliest food crops, having originated more than 8,000 years ago, in what is now southeastern Turkey and northern Syria. Bread wheat originated by a series of steps that included hybridization and whole-genome duplication from wild ancestors (*Triticum boeoticum* and *Triticum dicoccoides*).

Among the earliest changes that occurred during wheat domestication was the loss of **shattering**, the process by which ears of wild grain crops break apart and disperse their grains. A mutation probably caused the ears of some wheat plants to remain intact, a trait that is disadvantageous in nature but beneficial to humans. Nonshattering ears would have been easier for humans to harvest than normal ears. Early farmers probably selected seed stock from plants having nonshattering ears and other favorable traits such as larger grains. These ancient artificial selection processes, together with modern breeding efforts, explain why cultivated wheat differs from its wild relatives in shattering and other properties. The accumulation of these trait differences is why cultivated and wild wheat plants are classified as different species.

About 9,000 years ago, people living in what is now Mexico domesticated one type of the native grass known as teosinte

(formally, *Zea mays* subspecies *parviglumis*). The domestication process produced a new species, *Zea mays* subspecies *mays*, commonly known as corn or maize. The evidence for this pivotal event includes ancient ears that were larger than wild ones and distinctive fossil pollen. Modern ears of corn are much larger than those of teosinte, with many more rows and larger and softer corn grains, and modern corn ears do not shatter, as do those of ancestral teosinte (**Figure 32.26**). These and other trait changes reflect artificial selection accomplished by humans. An analysis of the corn genome, reported in 2005 by Canadian biologist Stephen Wright, American evolutionary biologist Brandon Gaut, and coworkers, suggests that 1,200 corn genes have been affected by artificial selection.

Molecular analyses indicate that domesticated rice (*Oryza sativa*) originated from ancestral wild species of grasses (*Oryza nivara* and/or *Oryza rifipogon*). As in the cases of wheat and corn, domestication of rice involved loss of ear shattering. Researchers have identified a mutation in domesticated strains of rice that alters the amino acid sequence of a protein that regulates shattering. Ancient humans might have unconsciously selected for this mutation while gathering rice from wild populations, because the mutants would not so easily have shed grains during the harvesting process. Eventually, the nonshattering mutant became a widely planted crop throughout Asia, and today it is the food staple for millions of people.

Although humans generated these and other plant species, modern humans have also caused the extinction of plants as the result of habitat destruction and other threats to species. Protecting biodiversity will continue to challenge humans as populations and demands on the Earth's resources increase. Plant biologists are working to identify one or more molecular sequencing tools for use in barcoding plants, a process that is widely used to identify and catalog animals. The ability to bar code plants, which would enable researchers to quickly analyze the DNA of a species and identify it based on existing barcodes, is important to organizations like CITES and others that monitor international trade in endangered plant species.

Summary of Key Concepts

32.1 Overview of Seed Plant Diversity

- Modern seed plants include three phyla of gymnosperms and the angiosperms (Figure 32.1, Table 32.1).

32.2 The Evolution and Diversity of Modern Gymnosperms

- Gymnosperms are plants that produce exposed seeds rather than seeds enclosed in fruits. Gymnosperms originated from seedless woody plants known as progymnosperms (Figure 32.2).

- The modern gymnosperms include three phyla: cycads, *Ginkgo biloba*, and the conifers (which include the Gnetales). Nearly 300 species of cycads primarily live in tropical and subtropical regions. Features of cycads include palmlike leaves, nonwoody stems, coralloid roots with cyanobacterial endosymbionts, toxins, and large conelike seed-producing structures (Figures 32.3, 32.4).

- The tree *Ginkgo biloba* is the last surviving species of a phylum that was diverse during the Mesozoic, also known as the Age of Dinosaurs. Individual trees produce ovules and seeds or pollen, with a sex chromosome system much like that of humans (Figure 32.5).

- Conifers have been widespread and diverse members of plant communities for the past 300 million years and are important sources of wood and paper pulp for humans. Reproduction involves simple pollen cones and complex ovule-producing cones. Many conifers display adaptations that aid survival in cold climates. Three genera of Gnetales display distinctive adaptations (Figures 32.6, 32.7, 32.8, 32.9, 32.10, 32.11).

32.3 The Evolution and Diversity of Modern Angiosperms

- Angiosperms inherited seeds, the capacity to produce wood, and other features from gymnosperm ancestors, but display distinctive features not found in other land plants, including flowers and fruits (Figure 32.12).

- Flowers foster seed production and are adapted in various ways that aid pollination. The major flower organs are sepals and petals (or tepals), stamens, and carpels, which may occur singly or in fused groups. Both single carpels and compound carpels take a distinctive shape known as a pistil, which displays regions of specialized function. The stigma is a receptive surface for pollen, pollen tubes grow through the style, and ovules develop within the ovary. Pollination is the transfer of pollen from a stamen to a pistil, a process distinct from fertilization. Double fertilization, the production of both a zygote and a nutritive tissue known as endosperm, is a critical innovation of angiosperms. This process allows ovules to develop into seeds containing embryos and endosperm, and ovaries to develop into fruits. Stamens and carpels may have evolved from leaflike structures bearing sporangia (Figures 32.13, 32.14, 32.15).

- Whole-genome duplications have influenced plant evolution, particularly the diversification of the angiosperms. The two largest and most diverse lineages of flowering plants are the monocots and eudicots (Figures 32.16, 32.17, 32.18).

- Flower diversification involved evolutionary changes such as fusion of petals, clustering of flowers into inflorescences, and reduction in size of the perianth. These changes improve the effectiveness of pollination, which enhances seed production (Figures 32.19, 32.20).

- Fruits are structures that enclose seeds and aid in their dispersal. Fruits occur in many types that foster seed dispersal (Figure 32.21).

- Angiosperms produce three main groups of secondary metabolites: (1) terpenes and terpenoids; (2) phenolics, which include flavonoids and related compounds; and (3) alkaloids, which play essential roles in plant structure, reproduction, and defense, respectively (Figure 32.22).

- Hillig and Mahlberg demonstrated the use of particular secondary metabolites in distinguishing species of the societally important genus *Cannabis* (Figure 32.23).

32.4 The Role of Coevolution in Angiosperm Diversification

- Coevolutionary interactions between flowering plants and animals that serve as pollen- and seed-dispersal agents played a powerful role in the diversification of both angiosperms and animals (Table 32.2, Figures 32.24, 32.25).

- Human appreciation of flowers and fruits is based on sensory systems similar to those present in the animals with which angiosperms coevolved.

32.5 Human Influences on Angiosperm Diversification

- Humans have produced new crop species by domesticating wild plants. The process of domestication involved artificial selection for traits such as nonshattering ears of wheat, corn, and rice (Figure 32.26).

Assess & Discuss

Test Yourself

1. What feature(s) must be present for a plant to produce wood?
   a. a type of conducting system in which vascular bundles occur in a ring around pith
   b. a eustele
   c. a vascular cambium
   d. all of the above
   e. none of the above

2. Which sequence of critical innovations reflects the order of their appearance in time?
   a. embryos, vascular tissue, wood, seeds, flowers
   b. vascular tissue, embryos, wood, flowers, seeds
   c. vascular tissue, wood, seeds, embryos, flowers
   d. wood, seeds, embryos, flowers, vascular tissue
   e. seeds, vascular tissue, wood, embryos, flowers

3. How long have ancient and modern groups of gymnosperms been important members of plant communities?
   a. 10,000 years, since the dawn of agriculture
   b. 100,000 years
   c. 300,000 years
   d. 65 million years, since the Cretaceous-Paleogene (K/T) event
   e. 300 million years, since the Coal Age

4. What similar features do gymnosperms and angiosperms possess that differ from other modern vascular plants?
   a. Gymnosperms and angiosperms both produce flagellate sperm.
   b. Gymnosperms and angiosperms both produce flowers.
   c. Gymnosperms and angiosperms both have tracheids, but not vessels, in their vascular tissues.
   d. Gymnosperms and angiosperms both produce fruits.
   e. None of the above statements is true.

5. Which part of a flower receives pollen transported by the wind or a pollinating animal?
   a. perianth   d. pedicel
   b. stigma   e. ovary
   c. filament

6. The primary function of a fruit is to
   a. provide food for the developing seed.
   b. provide food for the developing seedling.
   c. foster pollen dispersal.
   d. foster seed dispersal.
   e. None of the above identifies the primary function of a fruit.

7. Flowers have diversified with regard to
   a. color.
   b. number of flower parts.
   c. fusion of organs.
   d. aggregation into inflorescences.
   e. all of the above.

8. Plants of the genus *Fuchsia* produce deep pink to red flowers that dangle from plants, produce nectar in floral tubes, and have no scent. Based on these features, which animal is most likely to be a coevolved pollinator of these plants?
   a. bee
   b. bat
   c. hummingbird
   d. butterfly
   e. moth

9. Which type of plant secondary metabolite is best known for the antioxidant properties of human foods such as blueberries, tea, and grape juice?
   a. alkaloids
   b. cannabinoids
   c. carotenoids
   d. phenolics
   e. terpenoids

10. What feature(s) of domesticated grain crops might differ from those of wild ancestors?
   a. the degree to which ears shatter, allowing for seed dispersal
   b. grain size
   c. number of grains per ear
   d. softness and edibility of grains
   e. all of the above

Conceptual Questions

1. Make a diagram that shows how plant biologists think flowers arose.

2. Explain why fruits such as apples, strawberries, and cherries are attractive, nutritious, and harmless foods for humans.

3. **Core Concept: Structure and Function** Compare the structures of an apple flower and a sunflower, explaining how they relate to differences in pollination and seed dispersal.

Collaborative Questions

1. Where in the world would you have to travel to find wild plants representing all of the gymnosperm phyla, including the three types of Gnetales?

2. How would you go about trying to solve what Darwin called "an abominable mystery," that is, the identity of the seed plant group that was ancestral to the flowering plants?

An Introduction to Animal Diversity

33

The variety of life forms on Earth is staggering. Naked mole rats, *Heterocephalus glaber,* are long-lived rodents that remain cancer free. ©John Visser/Photoshot

Naked mole rats (*Heterocephalus glaber*) are a species of rodent that live in arid areas of the Horn of Africa, including Ethiopia, Somalia, and Kenya. Their large protruding teeth are used for digging, and their lips are sealed behind the teeth to keep out soil. Naked mole rats have a unique reproductive process in which only one dominant female, the queen, reproduces. But these rats have an even more intriguing claim to fame. Whereas most species of mice and rats live only 4 years on average, naked mole rats can live for at least 30 years. And they are cancer free! Scientists discovered that the rats produce a polysaccharide called high-molecular-mass hyaluronan, or HMM-HA. Secretion of HMM-HA from mole rat cells causes contact inhibition, preventing the cells from overcrowding and forming tumors. This ability is lost in cancer cells. When researchers inhibited the synthesis of HMM-HA by naked mole rat cells, the cells lost their contact inhibition and tumors formed. From these results, biologists are interested in pursuing this line of research to prevent cancer and extend the life in humans. This is just one example

in which the study of animal diversity could lead to dramatic improvements in human health.

Animals constitute the most species-rich kingdom. About 1.3 million species have been found and described, and an estimated 2–5 million more species await discovery and classification. Beyond being members of this kingdom ourselves, humans depend on animals. Many different kinds of animals and their products are part of our diet. Humans also enjoy animal species as companions and depend on other species for tests of lifesaving drugs. We share parts of our genome with other organisms such as fruit flies, nematodes, and zebrafish—all of which are used as model organisms for understanding aspects of human molecular and developmental biology.

However, we are also in conflict with animals such as insects that threaten our food supply and transmit deadly diseases. Malaria is transmitted by mosquitoes; sleeping sickness, by tsetse flies; and rabies, by a number of animals, including dogs, raccoons, and bats. With such a huge number and diversity of existing animals and with animals featuring so prominently in our lives, understanding animal diversity is of great importance. Therefore, researchers have spent a great deal of effort in determining the unique characteristics of different taxonomic groups and identifying their evolutionary relationships.

Since the time of Carolus Linnaeus in the 1700s, scientists have classified animals based on their morphology, that is, on their physical structure. In the 1990s, animal classifications based on similarities in DNA and rRNA sequences became more common. Quite often, classifications based on morphology and those based on molecular data were similar, but some important differences arose. In this chapter, we will begin by defining the key characteristics of animals and then take a look at the major features of animal body plans that form the basis of classification. We will explore how new molecular data have enabled scientists to revise and refine the animal phylogenetic tree. As more molecular-based evidence becomes available, systematists will likely continue to redraw the tree of animal life. Therefore, as you read this chapter, keep in mind that the classification of animals is now, and will continue to be, a work in progress.

Characteristics of Animals

Learning Outcomes:

1. List the key characteristics of animals that distinguish them from other organisms.
2. Provide a brief overview of the history of animal life on Earth.

The Earth contains a dazzling diversity of animal species, living in environments from the deep sea to the desert and exhibiting an amazing array of characteristics. Most animals move and eat multicellular prey, and therefore, they are loosely differentiated from species in other kingdoms. However, a single definition of an animal is difficult because they are so diverse that biologists can find exceptions to nearly any given characteristic. Even so, a number of key features can help us broadly characterize the group we call animals (**Table 33.1**).

Animals Are Multicellular Heterotrophs

Animals have several characteristics relating to cell structure, mode of nutrition, movement, and reproduction that collectively distinguish them from other organisms. If we focus on these characteristics, **animals** can be defined as multicellular heterotrophs with cells that lack cell walls,

Table 33.1	Common Characteristics of Animals
Characteristic	**Example**
Multicellularity	Even relatively simple types of animals such as sponges are multicellular, in contrast to the mostly single-celled eukaryotic microorganisms called protists (see Chapter 28).
Heterotrophs	Animals obtain their food by eating other organisms or their products. This contrasts with plants and algae, most of which are autotrophs and essentially make their own food.
No cell walls	The cells of plants, fungi, bacteria, archaea, and most protists have a rigid cell wall, but animal cells lack a cell wall and are quite flexible.
Nervous tissue	The presence of a nervous system in most animals enables them to respond rapidly to environmental stimuli.
Movement	Most animals have a muscle system, which, combined with a nervous system, allows them to move in their environment.
Sexual reproduction	Most animals reproduce sexually, with small, mobile sperm uniting with a much larger egg to form a fertilized egg, or zygote.
Extracellular matrix	Proteins such as collagen bind animal cells together to give them added support and strength (see Figure 10.1).
Characteristic cell junctions	Animals have characteristic cell junctions, called anchoring, tight, and gap junctions (see Figures 10.7, 10.9, 10.11).
Special clusters of *Hox* genes	Most animals possess *Hox* genes, which function in patterning the body axis (see Figures 20.16, 24.15).
Similar rRNA	Animals all have very similar genes that encode for RNA of the small ribosomal subunit (SSU rRNA; see Figure 12.17).

the capacity to move at some point in their life cycle, and the ability to reproduce sexually, with sperm fusing directly with eggs.

Cell Structure   Like some protists, plants, and most fungi, animals are multicellular. However, animal cells lack cell walls and are flexible. This flexibility facilitates movement. Animal cells gain structural support from an extensive extracellular matrix (ECM) that forms strong fibers outside the cell (refer back to Figure 10.1). Additionally, a group of unique cell junctions—anchoring, tight, and gap junctions—play an important role in holding animal cells in place and allowing communication between cells (refer back to Table 10.3).

Mode of Nutrition   All animals are **heterotrophs**; that is, they cannot synthesize their own organic molecules using energy from inorganic substances. Instead, animals must ingest other organisms or their products to sustain life. Many different modes of feeding exist among animals, including suspension feeding (filtering food out of the surrounding water); bulk feeding (eating large food pieces, as done by carnivores and herbivores); and fluid feeding (sucking plant sap or animal body fluids) (**Figure 33.1**). Although fungi and animals both rely on absorptive nutrition—that is, they secrete enzymes that break down complex materials and absorb the resulting small organic molecules—fungi use external digestion to obtain their nutrients. Animals ingest their food into an internal gut and then break it down using enzymes.

Movement   Most animals have muscle cells and nerve cells organized into tissues. Muscle tissue is unique to animals, and most animals are capable of some type of locomotion, the ability to move from place to place, in order to acquire food or escape predators. This ability has led to the development of muscular-skeletal systems, systems of sensory structures, and a nervous system that coordinates movement and prey capture. Sessile species such as barnacles, which stay in one place, use bristled appendages to obtain nearby food. However, in many sessile species, although adults are immobile, the larvae can swim.

Reproduction   Nearly all members of the animal kingdom reproduce sexually, although certain insects, fish, and lizard species can reproduce asexually. During sexual reproduction, a small, mobile sperm generally unites with a much larger egg to form a fertilized egg, or zygote. Fertilization may occur internally, which is common in terrestrial species, or externally, which is more common in aquatic species. Similarly, embryos develop inside the mother or outside in the mother's environment.

Animal Life Began More Than a Half Billion Years Ago

The history of animal life spans over 630 million years, starting at the end of the Proterozoic eon, when multicellular animals emerged (refer back to Figure 26.4). The first animals were invertebrates, animals without a vertebral column, or backbone. A profusion of animal phyla appeared during the Cambrian explosion, 533–525 million years ago (mya), including sponges, jellyfish, corals, flatworms, mollusks, annelid worms, the first arthropods, and echinoderms, plus many phyla that no longer exist today (**Figure 33.2**).

(a)

(b)

(c)

Figure 33.1 **Modes of animal nutrition.** **(a)** Suspension feeders, such as these tube worms, filter food particles from the water column. **(b)** Grizzly bears and other bulk feeders tear off large pieces of their food and chew it or swallow it whole. **(c)** Fluid feeders, such as these aphids, suck fluid from their food source. a: ©waldhaeusl.com/age fotostock; b: ©Enrique R Aguirre Aves/Getty Images; c: ©Bartomeu Borrell/age fotostock

The causes of the sudden increase in animal life at that time are not fully understood, but three explanations have been proposed.

- Species proliferation may have been related to a warm favorable environment. At the same time, atmospheric and aquatic oxygen levels were increasing, permitting increased metabolic rates, and an ozone layer had developed, blocking out harmful UV radiation and allowing complex life to thrive in shallow water and eventually on land.

- The evolution of the *Hox* gene complex may have permitted much variation in morphology.

- As new types of predators evolved, prey developed adaptations that enabled them to avoid their predators, leading to counteradaptations by predators, and so on. This evolutionary "arms race" may have resulted in a proliferation of predator and prey types.

These hypotheses are not mutually exclusive and may well have operated at the same time.

Around 520 mya, the first vertebrates, fishes, appeared at roughly the same time as the first plants invaded land. The appearance of land plants introduced a viable food source for any organisms that could utilize them. However, the realm of land and air presented organisms with many challenges. For colonization of land to occur, certain species evolved adaptations that prevented them from drying out and enabled them to breathe, move, and reproduce in the new environment, in much the same way as the plant embryo, leaves, seeds, and other adaptations permitted plants to colonize terrestrial habitats (see Chapter 31). For animal species, such features included lungs and internal fertilization. The development of the amniotic egg, which features a tough, protective shell to prevent drying out, enabled animals to be terrestrial for their entire life cycle. The amniotic egg, which is described in Chapter 35, appeared during the Carboniferous period, about 300 mya, and was responsible for the success of the reptiles, which appeared during this period. Reptiles were to dominate the Earth for many millions of years during the rise and fall of the dinosaurs. Mammals appeared at the same time as dinosaurs, although they were not prevalent. The number and diversity of mammals exploded only after the dinosaurs abruptly died out at the end of the Cretaceous era, about 65 mya.

Figure 33.2 **The profusion of animal life in the Cambrian period, about 520 mya.** This artist's reconstruction of marine life shows many different phyla, some of which are now extinct.
©Publiphoto/Science Source

33.2 Animal Classification

Learning Outcomes:

1. Discuss why choanoflagellates are believed to be the closest living relatives of animals.
2. Describe each of the major morphological and developmental features of animal body plans that form the basis of the classification of animals.

All animals are classified in the domain Eukarya, the supergroup Opisthokonka, and the kingdom Animalia (informally called the animal kingdom) (refer back to Figure 25.1). Although extremely diverse, most biologists agree that the animal kingdom is monophyletic, meaning that all taxa have evolved from a single common ancestor. Today, scientists recognize about 35 animal phyla.

At first glance, many of the animal phyla seem so distantly related to one another (for example, chordates and jellyfish) that making sense of this diversity with a classification scheme seems very challenging. Fortunately, by carefully examining body features and, more recently, by analyzing molecular data such as DNA sequences, evolutionary biologists have been able to propose models that describe the evolutionary relationships among animals. The model shown in **Figure 33.3** describes those relationships for 13 common phyla. In this section, we will explore the major features of animal body plans that form the basis of this animal phylogeny.

Animals Evolved from a Choanoflagellate-like Ancestor

With the monophyletic nature of the animal kingdom in mind, scientists have attempted to identify the species from which animals most likely evolved. Molecular data indicate that the closest living relative of animals is the flagellated protist known as a choanoflagellate. These tiny, single-celled organisms have a single flagellum surrounded by a collar of cytoplasmic tentacles (refer back to Figure 28.21b).

Some species of choanoflagelles form colonies consisting of many individual organisms on a single stalk. Scientists hypothesize that the first simple animals may have arisen when some of these cells gradually acquired specialized functions—for example, movement or nutrition—while still maintaining coordination with other cells and cell types. As discussed later, evolutionary changes to this simple body plan resulted in critical innovations that led to the more complex body plans found in modern animals.

Animal Phyla Have Broad Differences Related to Body Plan, Germ Layers, and Features of Embryonic Development

Prior to the use of molecular data in phylogeny, biologists traditionally classified animal diversity in terms of three main morphological and developmental features of animal body plans:

1. Type of body symmetry
2. Number of germ layers
3. Specific features of embryonic development

We will discuss each of these major features of animal body plans next.

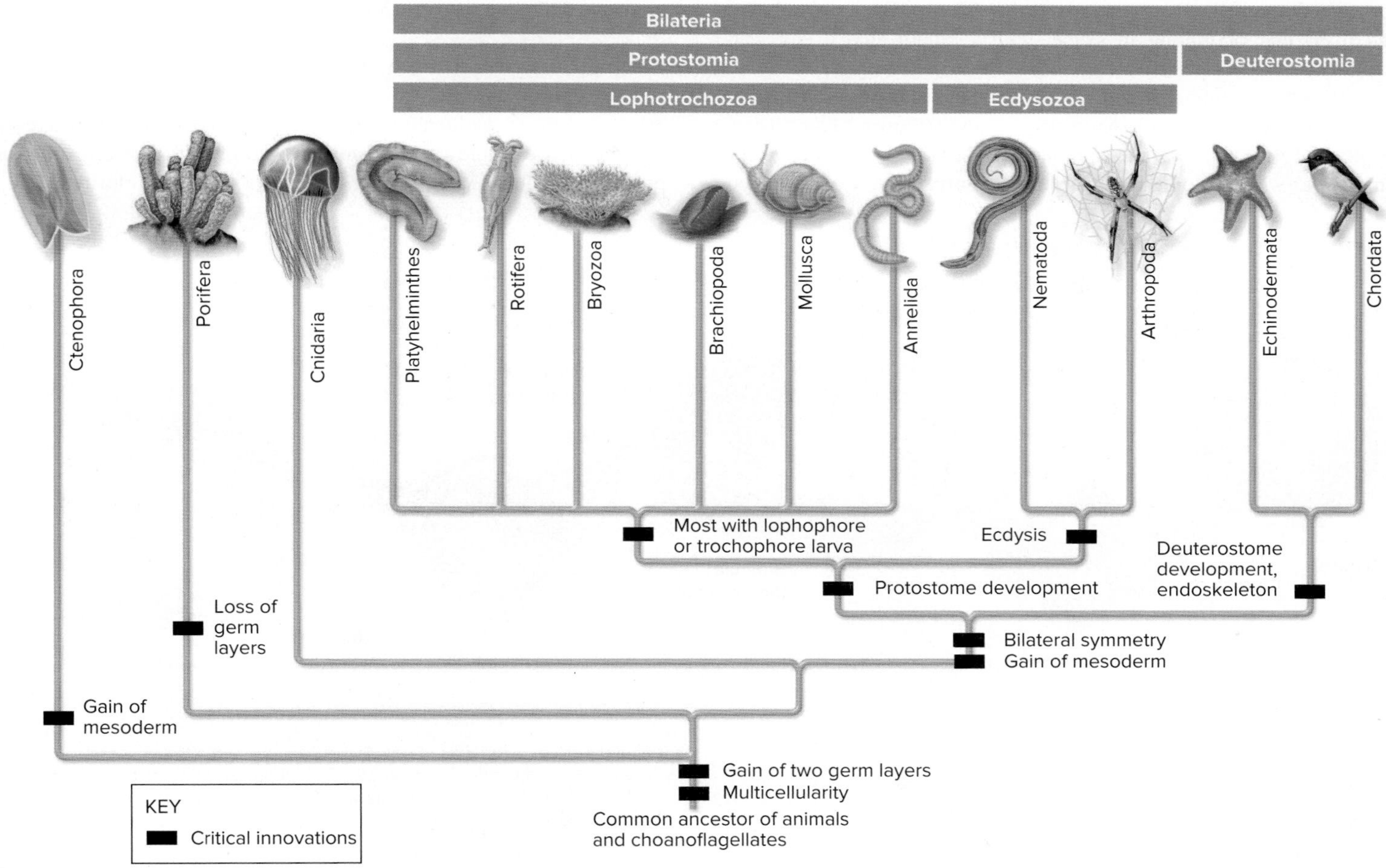

Figure 33.3 An animal phylogenetic tree based on body plans and molecular data. Biologists have identified about 35 different animal phyla. We will focus our discussions here and in the next two chapters on the 13 most abundant and recognizable phyla.

 Core Concept: Evolution As shown at the bottom of this tree, the first animals evolved from a choanoflagellate-like ancestor.

(a) Parazoa: no symmetry

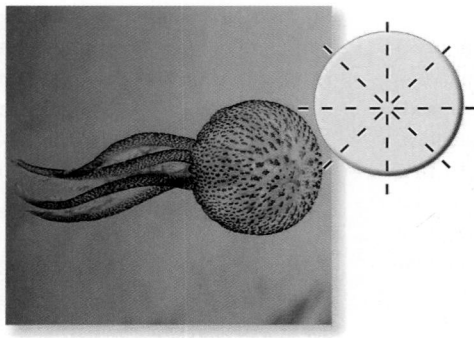

(b) Cnidaria: radial symmetry

(c) Bilateria: bilateral symmetry

Figure 33.4 **Early divisions in the animal phylogeny.** Animals can be categorized based on body symmetry **(a)** the absence of symmetry (Parazoa, the sponges); **(b)** radial symmetry (the cnidarians); or **(c)** bilateral symmetry (Bilateria, all other animals). a: ©E Teister/age fotostock; b: ©Gavin Parsons/Getty Images; c: ©Jens Kuhfs/Getty Images

Symmetry Animals may be categorized according to the type of symmetry their body displays. Symmetry refers to the existence of balanced proportions of the body on either side of a median plane. Some of the earliest-diverging animals, such as sponges, were asymmetric, meaning they had no plane of symmetry (**Figure 33.4a**). Radially symmetric animals can be divided equally by any longitudinal plane passing through the central axis (**Figure 33.4b**). Such animals are often circular or tubular in shape, with a mouth at one end, and include cnidarians (jellyfish).

Bilaterally symmetric animals, the **Bilateria**, can be divided along a vertical plane at the midline to create two halves (**Figure 33.4c**). Thus, a bilateral animal has a left side and a right side, which are mirror images, as well as a **dorsal** (upper) and a **ventral** (lower) side, which

are not identical, and an **anterior** (head) and a **posterior** (tail) end. Bilateral symmetry is strongly correlated with both the ability to move through the environment and **cephalization**—the localization of sensory structures at the anterior end of the body. Such abilities allow animals to encounter their environment initially with their head, which is best equipped to detect and consume prey and to detect and respond to predators and other dangers. Most animals are bilaterally symmetric.

Germ Layers Fertilization of an egg by a sperm creates a diploid zygote. During the earliest stage of embryonic development, the zygote becomes a multicellular embryo by a process called **cleavage**—a succession of rapid cell divisions with no significant growth that produces a hollow sphere of cells called a **blastula** (**Figure 33.5**).

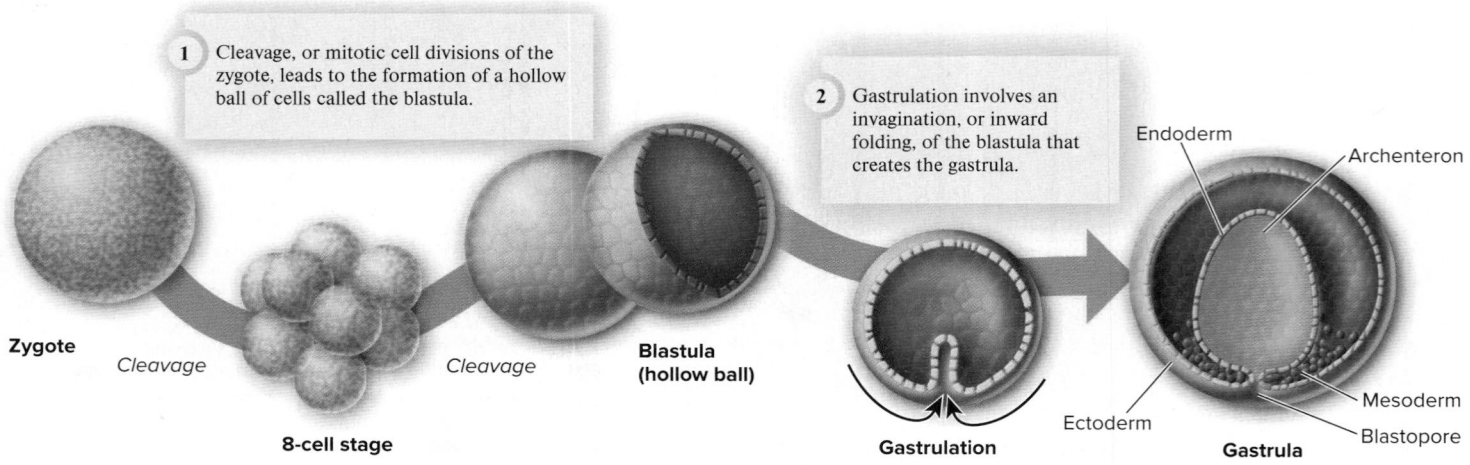

1. Cleavage, or mitotic cell divisions of the zygote, leads to the formation of a hollow ball of cells called the blastula.

2. Gastrulation involves an invagination, or inward folding, of the blastula that creates the gastrula.

Zygote

Cleavage

8-cell stage

Cleavage

Blastula (hollow ball)

Gastrulation

Endoderm

Archenteron

Ectoderm

Gastrula

Mesoderm

Blastopore

3. In the gastrula, the layer of cells lining the archenteron becomes the endoderm. The cells on the outside of the blastula form the ectoderm. In the Bilateria, a middle layer termed the mesoderm develops between the ectoderm and endoderm.

Figure 33.5 **Formation of germ layers.** Note: Radially symmetric animals (cnidarians) do not form mesoderm.

 Core Skill: Connections Look back to Figure 25.8. Is the existence of three germ layers in triploblastic animals a shared primitive character or a shared derived character?

In all animals except the sponges, the growing embryo then develops different layers of cells, called **germ layers**. During **gastrulation**, an area in the blastula folds inward, or invaginates, creating in the process a structure called a **gastrula**. The inner layer of cells becomes the **endoderm**, which lines the primitive digestive tract. The outer layer, or **ectoderm**, covers the surface of the embryo and differentiates into the epidermis and nervous system.

A key difference between Bilateria and most other animals is that the Bilateria develop a third layer of cells, termed the **mesoderm**, between the ectoderm and endoderm. Mesoderm forms the muscles and most other organs between the digestive tract and the ectoderm. Because the Bilateria have these three distinct germ layers, they are referred to as **triploblastic**, whereas the cnidarians, which have only ectoderm and endoderm, are termed **diploblastic**. Interestingly, the mesoderm of the earliest-diverging animals, the ctenophores, probably originated independently of the mesoderm found in bilaterians.

Specific Features of Embryonic Development in the Bilateria In the Bilateria, a key feature of embryonic development concerns the development of a mouth and anus (**Figure 33.6a**). In gastrulation, the endoderm forms an indentation, the **blastopore**, which is the opening of the archenteron to the outside. In **protostomes** (from the Greek *protos*, meaning first, and *stoma*, meaning mouth) (see Figure 33.3), the blastopore becomes the mouth. If an anus is formed in a protostome species, it develops from a secondary opening. In contrast, in **deuterostomes** (from the Greek *deuteros*, meaning second), the blastopore becomes the anus, and the mouth is formed from a secondary opening.

Protostomes and deuterostomes also differ at the cleavage stage of embryonic development. As mentioned, the earliest stage of embryonic development involves a process known as cleavage (see Figure 33.5). Protostome development is generally characterized by so-called **determinate cleavage**, in which the fate of each embryonic cell is determined very early (**Figure 33.6b**). If one of the cells

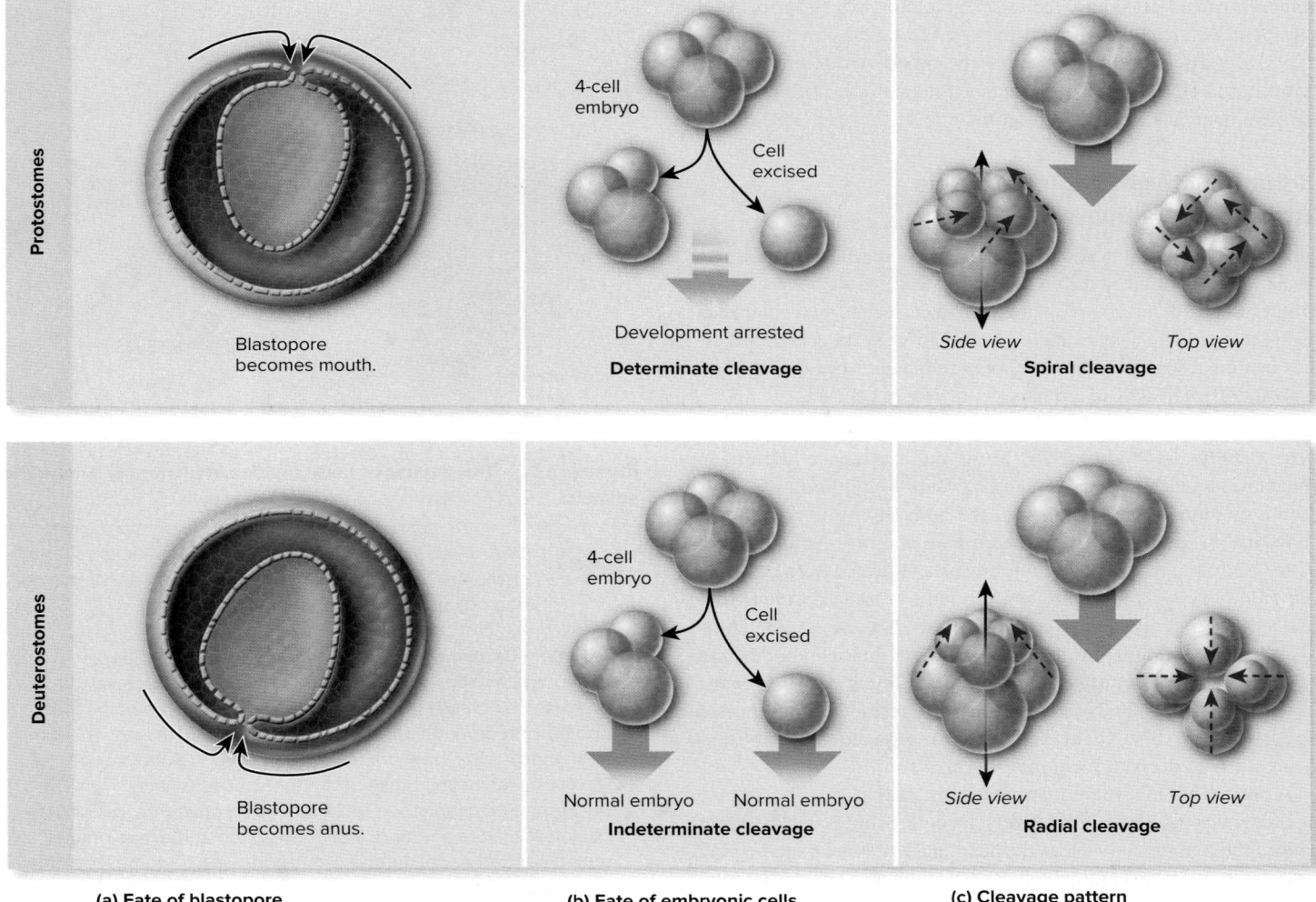

(a) Fate of blastopore   (b) Fate of embryonic cells   (c) Cleavage pattern

Figure 33.6 Differences in embryonic development between protostomes and deuterostomes. (a) In protostomes, the blastopore becomes the mouth. In deuterostomes, the blastopore becomes the anus. **(b)** Protostomes have determinate cleavage, whereas deuterostomes have indeterminate cleavage. **(c)** Many protostomes have spiral cleavage, whereas all deuterostomes have radial cleavage. The dashed arrows indicate the direction of cleavage.

is removed from a four-cell protostome embryo, neither the single cell nor the remaining three-cell mass can form viable embryos, and development is halted. In contrast, deuterostome development in most species is characterized by **indeterminate cleavage**, in which each cell produced by early cleavage retains the ability to develop into a complete embryo. For example, when one cell is excised from a four-cell sea urchin embryo, both the single cell and the remaining three can go on to form viable embryos. Other embryonic cells compensate for the missing cells. In human embryos, if individual embryonic cells separate from one another early in development, identical twins can result.

Another distinguishing feature of the early bilaterian embryo is the cleavage pattern (**Figure 33.6c**). In **spiral cleavage**, the planes of cell cleavage are oblique to the vertical axis of the embryo, resulting in an arrangement in which newly formed upper cells lie centered between the underlying cells. Many protostomes, including mollusks and annelid worms, exhibit spiral cleavage. The coiled shells of some mollusks result from spiral cleavage. Organisms with spiral cleavage are also known as spiralians. In **radial cleavage**, the cleavage planes are either parallel or perpendicular to the vertical axis of the embryo. This results in tiers of cells, one directly above the other. All deuterostomes exhibit radial cleavage, as do insects and nematodes, suggesting it may have been an ancestral condition.

Additional Morphological Criteria Distinguish the Bilateria

In older phylogenetic trees of animal life, classification was also based on morphological features, such as features of body cavities or the presence of body segmentation. More recent molecular data suggest that although these features are helpful in describing differences in animal structure, they are not as reliable in shedding light on the evolutionary history of animals as previously believed.

Body Cavity A body cavity is an internal space within an animal that houses internal organs. A fluid-filled body cavity is called a **coelom**. In many animals, the body cavity is completely lined with mesoderm and is called a true coelom. Animals with a true coelom are termed **coelomates** (**Figure 33.7a**). If the fluid-filled cavity is not completely lined by tissue derived from mesoderm, it is known as a pseudocoelom (**Figure 33.7b**). Animals with a pseudocoelom, including rotifers and nematodes, are termed **pseudocoelomates**. Some animals, such as flatworms, lack a fluid-filled body cavity and are termed **acoelomates** (**Figure 33.7c**). Instead of fluid, this region contains mesenchyme, a tissue derived from mesoderm.

A coelom has many important functions, perhaps the most important being that its fluid is relatively incompressible and therefore cushions internal organs such as the heart and intestinal tract, helping to prevent injury from external forces. A coelom also enables internal organs to move and grow independently of the outer body wall. Furthermore, in some soft-bodied invertebrates, such as earthworms, the coelom functions as a **hydrostatic skeleton**—a fluid-filled body cavity surrounded by muscles that gives support and shape to the body of organisms. Muscle contractions at one part of the body push this

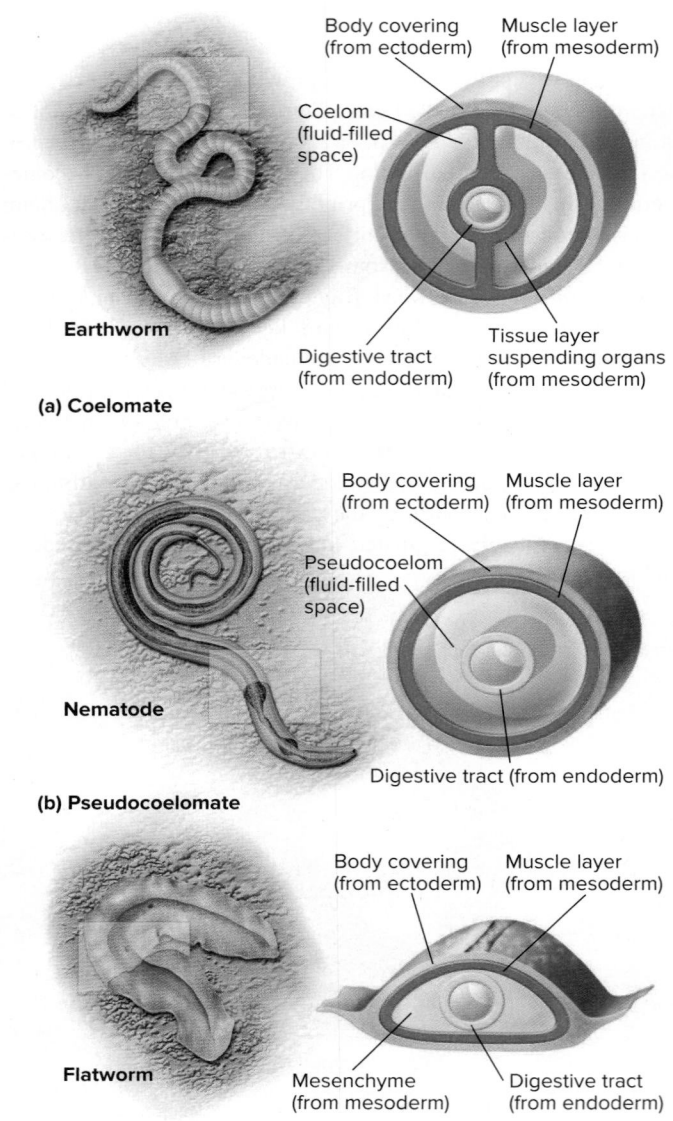

(a) Coelomate

(b) Pseudocoelomate

(c) Acoelomate

Figure 33.7 Three types of body cavities of bilaterally symmetric animals. Cross sections of each animal are shown on the right.

 Core Skill: Modeling The goal of this modeling challenge is to draw a phylogenetic tree based on morphological and developmental information.

Modeling Challenge: Older phylogenetic trees of animal life were based on developmental and morphological features, such as protostome versus deuterostome development, coelom type, and body segmentation. Let's consider eight of the phyla described earlier in Figure 33.3 with regard to these three features: Platyhelminthes—protostome, acoelomate, unsegmented; Nematoda and Rotifera—protostome, pseudocoelomate, unsegmented; Mollusca—protostome, coelomate, unsegmented; Annelida and Arthropoda—protostome, coelomate, segmented; Echinodermata—deuterstome, coelomate, unsegmented; and Chordata—deuterostome, coelomate, segmented. Based on these three features, draw a phylogenetic tree for the eight phyla. On your tree, place horizontal black bars to indicate the occurrence of these three critical innovations.

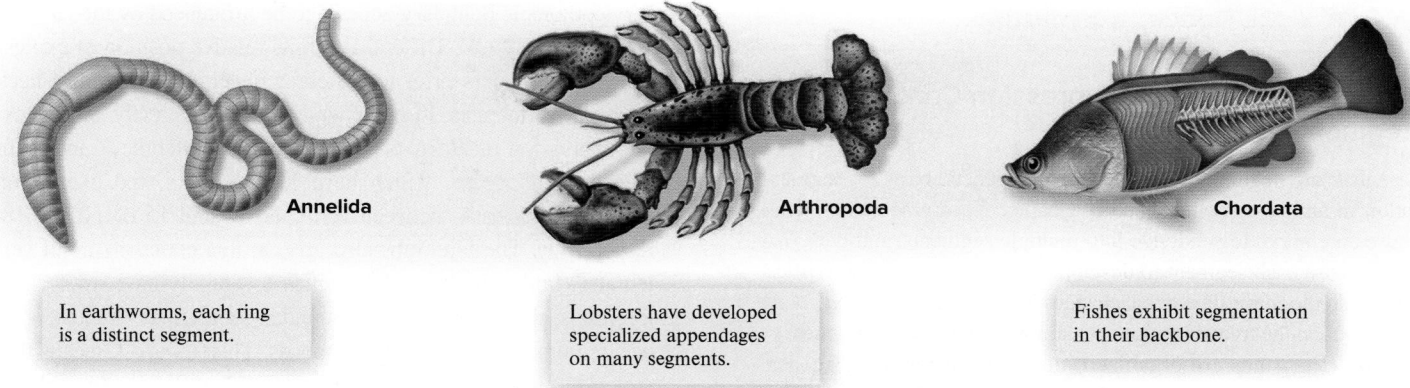

Annelida

In earthworms, each ring is a distinct segment.

Arthropoda

Lobsters have developed specialized appendages on many segments.

Chordata

Fishes exhibit segmentation in their backbone.

Figure 33.8 **Segmentation.** Annelids, arthropods, and chordates all exhibit segmentation.

fluid toward another part of the body. This type of movement can best be observed in an earthworm. Finally, in some organisms, the fluid in the body cavity also acts as a simple circulatory system.

The presence or absence of a coelom or pseudocoelom was previously used in the construction of animal phylogenies. However, scientists now believe this feature may not be useful in classification because animals that once possessed coeloms may have lost them over long periods of evolutionary time, as is true for the ancestors of flatworms. In addition, the coelom may have arisen twice in animal evolution, once in protostomes and once in deuterostomes.

Segmentation Another feature of the animal body plan is the presence or absence of segmentation. In segmentation, the body is divided into regions called segments. Even though segmentation is a common feature of the Bilateria, its presence is more obvious in some phyla compared to others. In annelids (segmented worms), most segments contain the same set of blood vessels, nerves, and muscles (**Figure 33.8**). Some segments may differ, such as those containing the brain or sex organs. Segmentation is also evident in arthropods (such as lobsters and insects), but less so in chordates (such as fish and mammals) (Figure 33.8). Most species of chordata are vertebrates, which possess a series of small bones called vertebrae that form the backbone. The repeating pattern of vertebrae indicates segmentation.

The advantage of segmentation is that it allows specialization of body regions. For example, as we will see in Chapter 34, arthropods exhibit a vast degree of specialization of their segments. Many insects have wings and only three pairs of legs, whereas centipedes have no wings and many legs. Crabs, lobsters, and shrimp have highly specialized thoracic appendages that aid in feeding.

BIO**TIPS**

THE QUESTION *Three phyla containing species with obvious segmentation are Annelida, Arthropoda, and Chordata. Are such segmented animals a monophyletic, polyphyletic, or paraphyletic group?*

TOPIC *What topic in biology does this question address?* The topic is evolutionary relationships based on segmentation.

INFORMATION *What information do you know based on the question and your understanding of the topic?* In the question, you are reminded that a taxonomic group can be monophyletic, polyphyletic, and paraphyletic. From your understanding of taxonomy and systematics, discussed in Chapter 25, you may remember that a monophyletic group contains a common ancestor and all of its descendants, a paraphyletic group contains a common ancestor but not all of its descendants, and a polyphyletic group contains groups of species with different common ancestors. You should also remember which phyla are segmented.

PROBLEM-SOLVING **S**TRATEGY *Make a drawing.* One strategy for solving this problem is to draw a simple version of Figure 33.3 with just the names of the phyla and the branches, and then place a star next to each phylum with segmented animals. Next, look at the comparison of monophyletic, polyphyletic, and paraphyletic taxonomic groups shown in Figure 25.5. Decide which pattern best matches your drawing.

ANSWER *Because segmented animals have different common ancestors, the group is polyphyletic.*

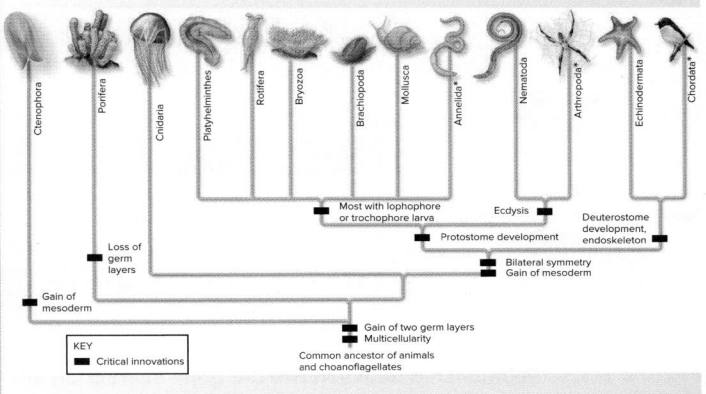

Core Concept: Evolution

Changes in *Hox* Gene Expression Control Body Segment Specialization

Scientists are beginning to understand the genetic basis for segmentation in animals. As described in Chapter 20, segmentation genes cause an embryo to subdivide into multiple segments, and then *Hox* genes cause each segment to develop its own unique characteristics. Recent studies have shown that changes in specialization among body segments can be traced to relatively simple changes in *Hox* genes.

The *Hox* genes are organized into four clusters of 13 genes, each designated with a number from 1 through 13. Some of these genes are expressed in anterior segments; others are expressed in posterior segments (refer back to Figure 20.17). In the 1990s, Greek molecular biologist Michalis Averof and coworkers showed how relatively simple shifts in the expression patterns of *Hox* genes along the anteroposterior axis can account for the large variation in arthropod appendage types. More recent work by Averof and colleagues (2010) has shown how specific changes in *Hox* expression are linked to changes in crustacean maxillipeds—appendages near the mouth that are used for feeding. Maxillipeds arise in the anterior thoracic segments and display a mixture of locomotory and feeding functions. By knocking out *Hox* genes or expressing *Hox* genes in an abnormal position, the researchers could change maxillipeds into leglike appendages or transform leglike appendages into maxillipeds.

Shifts in the patterns of expression of *Hox* genes in the embryo along the anteroposterior axis are similarly prominent in vertebrate evolution. In vertebrates, the transition from one type of vertebra to another, for example, from cervical (neck) to thoracic (chest) vertebrae, is controlled by particular *Hox* genes. The site of the cervicothoracic boundary appears to be influenced by the *HoxC-6* gene (**Figure 33.9**). Differences in its relative position of expression, which occurs prior to vertebrae development, control neck length in vertebrates. In mice, which have a relatively short neck, the expression of *HoxC-6* begins between vertebrae 7 and 8. In chickens and geese, which have longer necks, the expression begins farther back, between vertebrae 14 and 15 or 17 and 18, respectively. The forelimbs also arise at this boundary in all vertebrates. Interestingly, snakes, which essentially have no neck or forelimbs, do not exhibit this boundary, and *HoxC-6* expression occurs immediately behind their heads. This, in effect, means that snakes got longer by losing their neck and lengthening their chest.

American molecular biologist Sean Carroll has remarked that it is very satisfying to find that the evolution of body forms and novel structures in two of the most successful and diverse animal groups, arthropods and vertebrates, is shaped by the shifting of *Hox* genes. It also reminds us of one of the core concepts of biology—that evolution often involves descent with modification. Much of the diversity in animal phyla can be seen as modifications to a general body plan.

The Animal Kingdom Encompasses Many Diverse Phyla

Table 33.2 summarizes the basic characteristics of the major animal phyla. In Chapter 34, we will discuss the Ctenophora, Porifera, Cnidaria, Lophotrochozoa, and Ecdysozoa, and also the invertebrate members of Deuterostomia; these are all the animals without a backbone. In Chapter 35, we will turn our attention to the the phylum Chordata, which is the largest group of deuterostomes. These include fishes, amphibians, reptiles, and mammals, which possess a backbone.

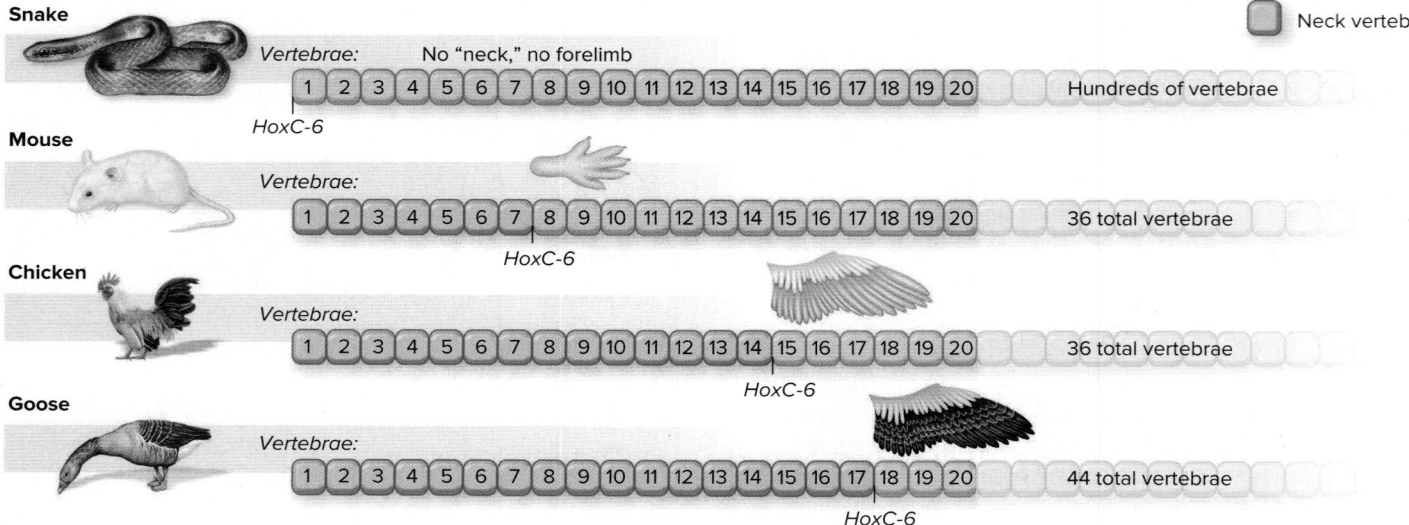

Figure 33.9 **Relationship between *HoxC-6* gene expression and neck length.** In vertebrates, the transition between neck and trunk vertebrae is controlled by the position of the *HoxC-6* gene. In snakes, the expression of this gene is shifted so far forward that a neck does not develop.

Table 33.2	**Summary of the Basic Characteristics of the Major Animal Phyla**											
Feature	**Ctenophora** (comb jellies)	**Porifera** (sponges)	**Cnidaria** (hydra, anemones, jellyfish)	**Platyhel-minthes** (flatworms)	**Rotifera** (rotifers)	**Bryozoa and Brachiopoda** (bryozoans and brachiopods)	**Mollusca** (snails, clams, squids)	**Annelida** (segmented worms)	**Nematoda** (round-worms)	**Arthropoda** (insects, arachnids, crustaceans)	**Echinoder-mata** (sea stars, sea urchins)	**Chordata** (vertebrates and others)
Estimated number of species	200	8,500	9,000	20,000	2,200	4,800	110,000	18,000	25,000	1,000,000+	7,400	69,730
Level of organization	Tissue; lack organs	Cellular; lack tissues and organs	Tissue; lack organs	Organs	Organs	Organs	Organs	Organs	Organs	Organs	Organs	Organs
Symmetry	Radial	Absent	Radial	Bilateral	Bilateral	Bilateral	Bilateral	Bilateral	Bilateral	Bilateral	Bilateral larvae, radial adults	Bilateral
Cephalization	Absent	Absent	Absent	Present	Present	Reduced	Present	Present	Present	Present	Absent	Present
Germ layers	Three	Absent	Two	Three	Three	Three	Three	Three	Three	Three	Three	Three
Body cavity, or Coelom	Absent	Absent	Absent	Absent	Pseudo-coelom	Coelom	Reduced Coelom	coelom	Pseudo-Coelom	Reduced coelom	Coelom	Coelom
Obvious segmentation in the adult	Absent	Absent	Absent	Absent	Absent	Absent	Absent	Present	Absent	Present	Absent	Present

33.3 The Use of Molecular Data in Constructing Phylogenetic Trees for Animals

Learning Outcomes:

1. Discuss how molecular data are used to construct and revise phylogenetic trees.
2. List the morphological features of the Ecdysozoa and the Lophotrochozoa.

In Chapter 25 (see Sections 25.2 and 25.3), we considered how molecular data can be used to construct phylogenetic trees. This approach involves the comparison of genetic data, such as DNA, RNA, and amino acid sequences from different species to estimate their evolutionary relationships based on the degree of similarities between the sequences. More closely related species exhibit fewer sequence differences than distantly related ones.

In Section 33.2, we explored the relationships between major features of animal body plans and animal phylogeny. Early phylogenetic trees for the animal kingdom were based largely on morphological features. In the past few decades, however, major revisions to such trees have occurred when biologists have compared molecular data, such as DNA sequences, with morphological data. The phylogenetic tree shown earlier, in Figure 33.3, is derived from morphological data and also from more recent molecular data.

In this section, we will consider how molecular data are used to refine our understanding of the evolutionary relationships among animals.

The Sequences of SSU rRNA Genes and *Hox* Genes Are Analyzed to Determine Broad Evolutionary Relationships Among Animals

As discussed in Chapter 25, the sequences of some genes change fairly slowly during evolution. Such slowly changing genes are particularly useful for evaluating broad evolutionary relationships, such as comparing phyla. Scientists have often focused on comparing base sequences in the gene that encodes RNA of the small ribosomal subunit (SSU rRNA) (see Chapter 12). SSU rRNA is universal in all organisms, and its base sequence has changed very slowly over long periods of time. We can appreciate this phenomenon by comparing a very small portion of the sequence of the SSU rRNA gene of a sponge, flatworm, seagull, and paramecium (**Figure 33.10**) in much the same way as we did in Chapter 12 (refer back to Figure 12.17). The three animal sequences are very similar to each other, and all of them differ from that of the paramecium (a protist).

The three animal species shown in Figure 33.10 are members of different phyla. If we compared three different species of sponges with three different species of flatworms, we would find that the sequences from the three species of sponges are more similar to each other than they are to those of the flatworms, and vice versa.

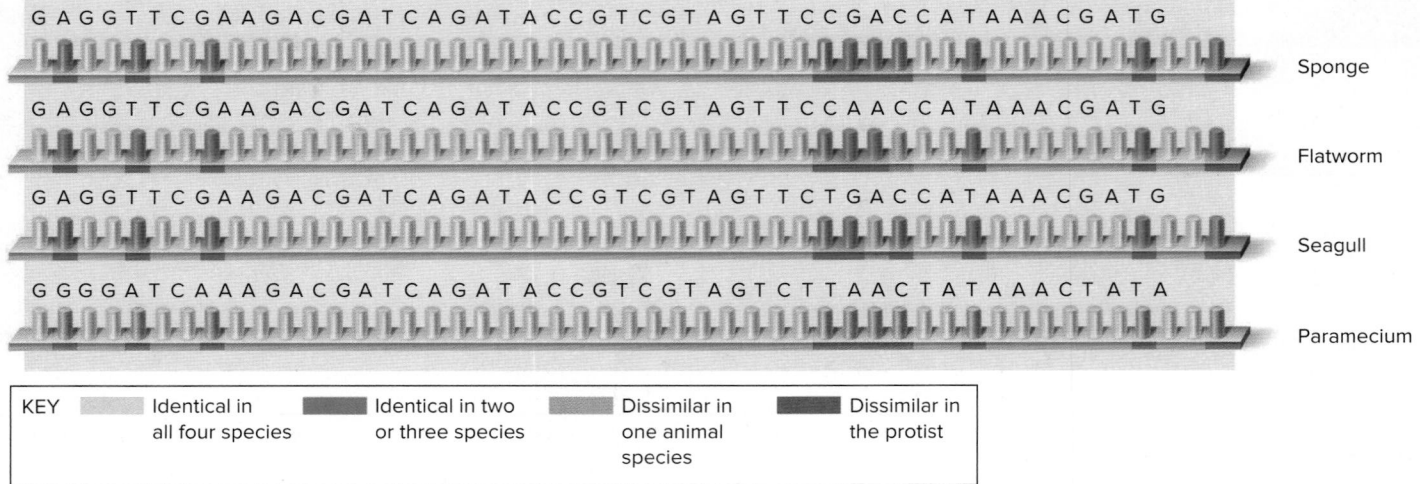

Figure 33.10 **Comparison of small subunit (SSU) rRNA gene sequences from three animals and a protist.** Note the similarities between the animals, even though they are very distantly related within the animal kingdom.

 Core Skill: Connections Look back at Figure 12.17. Which color represents sequences of bases that are the most evolutionarily conserved?

A second approach for understanding broad evolutionary relationships among animals is to analyze genes that have played a major role in animal diversification. Researchers have studied *Hox* genes, which are found in cnidarians and bilaterians, to study the evolution of body plans (refer back to Figure 24.15). They hypothesize that the duplication of *Hox* genes and gene clusters has led to the evolution of more complex animal body forms. Examination of the genes that regulate early developmental differences has provided insight into the evolution of animal development and the mechanisms by which animal body plans have diversified.

Studies using molecular data have resulted in major revisions to phylogenetic trees that were previously based on morphological data. As an example, **Figure 33.11** compares the phyla in Protostomia. Figure 33.11a is the current view, which was also shown as part of Figure 33.3. Figure 33.11b is a previous model that was based on morphological data. As described next, the revisions that created our current view of the phylogeny of Protostomia are derived from molecular studies.

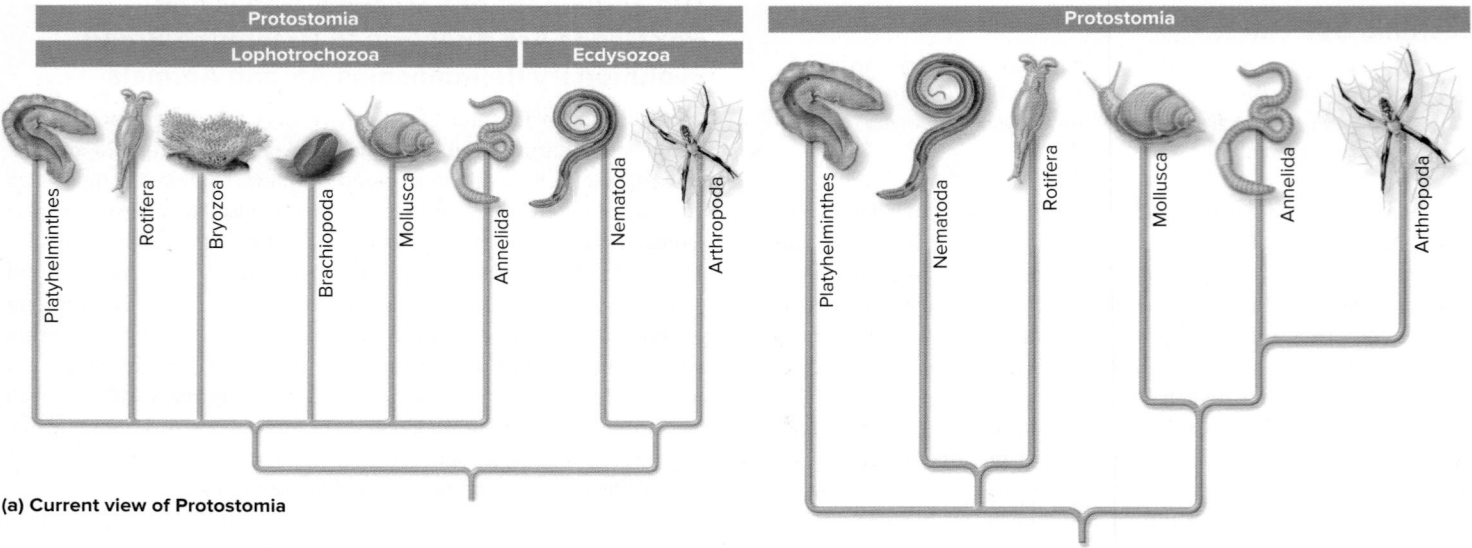

Figure 33.11 **A comparison of a current phylogenetic tree for Protostomia with an older tree based on morphological data.** The current tree shown in **(a)** is part of the tree shown earlier in Figure 33.3. The model shown in part **(b)** is no longer accepted.

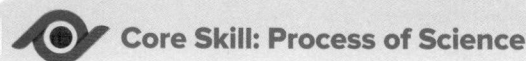 **Core Skill: Process of Science**

Feature Investigation | **Aguinaldo and Colleagues Analyzed SSU rRNA Sequences to Determine the Taxonomic Relationships of Arthropods to Other Phyla in Protostomia**

In 1997, American molecular biologists Anna Marie Aguinaldo, James Lake, and colleagues analyzed the relationships of arthropods to other phyla by sequencing the complete gene that encodes SSU rRNA from a variety of representative phyla (**Figure 33.12**). Total genomic DNA was isolated using standard techniques and amplified by polymerase chain reaction (PCR; refer back to Figure 21.6). PCR fragments were then subjected to DNA sequencing, a technique also described in Chapter 21, and the evolutionary relationships among 50 species were examined.

The resulting data indicated the existence of a monophyletic clade—the Ecdysozoa—containing the nematodes and arthropods (see step 3 in Figure 33.12 and Figure 33.11a). The hypothesis that nematodes are more closely related to arthropods than previously thought has important ramifications. First, it implies that

Figure 33.12 A revised animal phylogeny based on a comparison of SSU rRNA genes.

GOAL To determine the evolutionary relationships among many animal species, especially the relationship of arthropods to other species.

KEY MATERIALS Cellular samples from about 50 animals in different taxa.

	Experimental level	Conceptual level
1 Isolate DNA from animals and subject the DNA to polymerase chain reaction (PCR) to obtain enough material for DNA sequencing. PCR is described in Chapter 21.	For more detail, refer back to Figure 21.6. 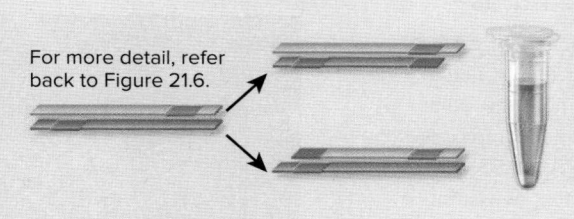	The goal of PCR is to amplify a region in the SSU rRNA gene.
2 Sequence the amplified DNA by dideoxy sequencing, also described in Chapter 21.	For more detail, refer back to Figure 21.8. 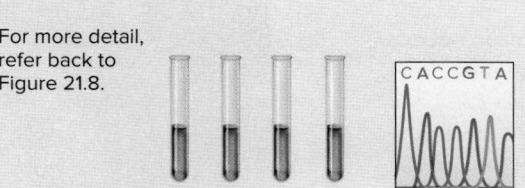	Dideoxy sequencing, in which DNA strands are separated according to their lengths by subjecting them to gel electrophoresis, is used to determine the base sequence of DNA.
3 Compare the DNA sequences and infer phylogenetic relationships using the cladistic approach described in Chapter 25.	Lophotrochozoa Ecdysozoa 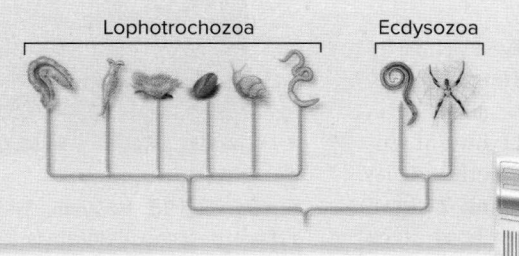	The approach compares traits that are either shared or not shared by different species and creates clades, consisting of a common ancestral species.

4 **THE DATA**

This process resulted in a large group of DNA sequences that were then analyzed with the use of computer programs.

5   **CONCLUSION** The arthropods are most closely related to the nematodes, and both phyla are placed in the clade Ecdysozoa. All other protostomes belong to a new clade called the Lophotrochozoa.

6   **SOURCE** Aguinaldo, A.M. et al. 1997. Evidence for a clade of nematodes, arthropods, and other moulting animals. *Nature* 387 (6632): 489–493.

two well-researched model organisms, *Caenorhabditis elegans* (a nematode) and the fruit fly *Drosophila melanogaster* (an arthropod), are more closely related than had been believed. Second, morphological classification had assumed that arthropods and annelids were closely related to each other based on the presence of segmentation. Molecular data does not support the previous hypothesis that annelids and arthropods form a clade of segmented animals (see Figure 33.11b).

Experimental Questions

1. What was the purpose of the study conducted by Aguinaldo and colleagues?
2. **CoreSKILL »** What was the major finding of this particular study?
3. What impact does the new view of nematode and arthropod phylogeny have on other areas of research?

The Ecdysozoa and Lophotrochozoa Have Some Distinctive Morphological Features

The study by Aguinaldo and colleagues provided evidence for a new clade of molting animals, the **Ecdysozoa**, consisting of the nematodes and arthropods. According to molecular evidence, the other major protostome clade is the **Lophotrochozoa**, which encompasses the mollusks, annelids, and several other phyla (see Figure 33.11a). When some morphologists reviewed their data given this new information, they found morphological support for these new groupings. Let's look at what morphological features make each of these groups unique.

The Ecdysozoa is so named because all of its members secrete a nonliving cuticle, an external skeleton (exoskeleton); think of the hard shell of a beetle or that of a crab. As these animals grow, the exoskeleton becomes too small, and the animal molts, or breaks out of its old exoskeleton, and secretes a newer, larger one (**Figure 33.13**). This molting process is called ecdysis; hence the name Ecdysozoa. Although this group was named for this morphological characteristic, it was first strongly supported as a separate clade by molecular evidence.

Similarly, the Lophotrochozoa clade was organized primarily through analyses of molecular data. Its name stems from two morphological features seen in many organisms of this clade: Lopho is derived from the **lophophore**, a horseshoe-shaped crown of tentacles used for feeding that is present on some phyla in this clade, such as the rotifers, bryozoans, and brachiopods (**Figure 33.14a**); trocho refers to the **trochophore larva**, a distinct larval stage characterized by a band of cilia around its middle that is used for swimming (**Figure 33.14b**). Trochophore larvae are found in several Lophotrochozoa phyla, such as annelid worms and mollusks, indicating their similar ancestry. However, other members of the clade, such as the platyhelminthes, have neither of these morphological features and are classified as lophotrochozoans based strictly on molecular data.

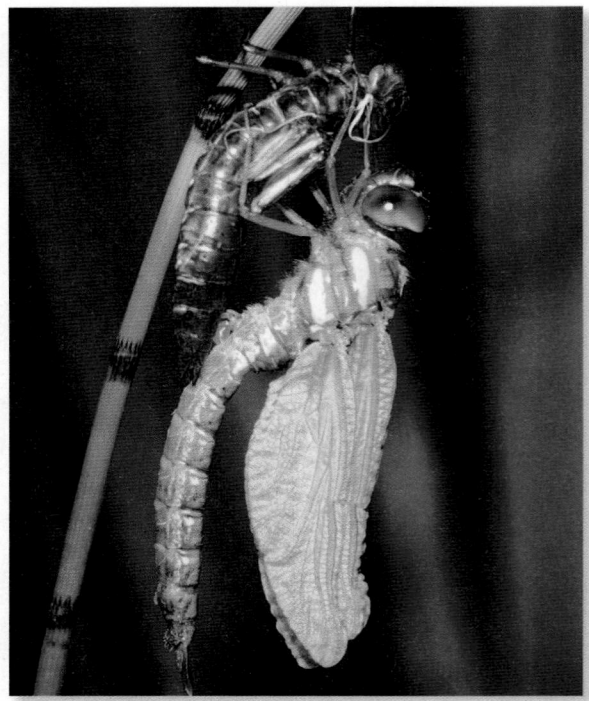

Figure 33.13 Ecdysis. The dragonfly, shown here emerging from a discarded exoskeleton, is a member of the Ecdysozoa—a clade of animals exhibiting ecdysis, the periodic shedding (molting) and re-formation of the exoskeleton. ©Dwight Kuhn

 Core Concept: Structure and Function For animals with exoskeletons, growth and development necessitate molting.

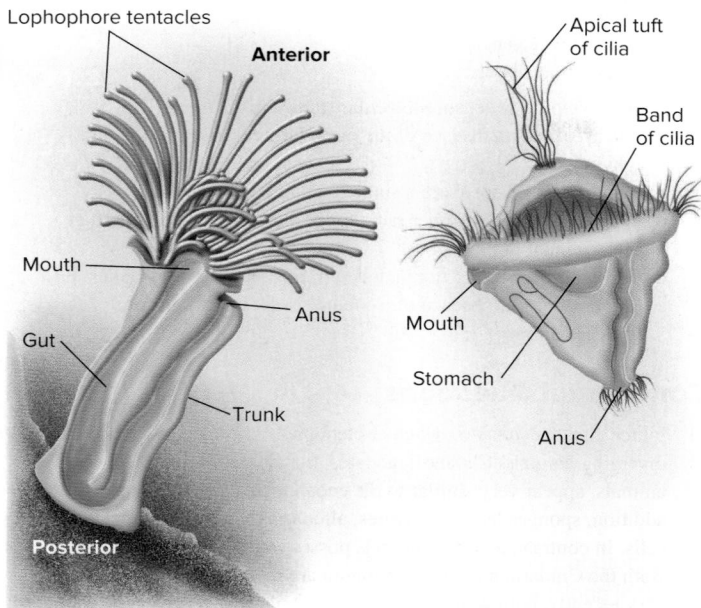

Lophophore tentacles

Anterior

Mouth

Anus

Gut

Trunk

Posterior

(a) Lophophore of a phoronid worm

Apical tuft of cilia

Band of cilia

Mouth

Stomach

Anus

(b) Trochophore larva

Figure 33.14 **Characteristics of the Lophotrochozoa. (a)** A lophophore, a crown of ciliated tentacles, generates a current to bring food particles into the mouth. **(b)** The trochophore larval form is found in several animal lineages.

Summary of Key Concepts

33.1 Characteristics of Animals

- Animals constitute a very species-rich kingdom, with a number of characteristics that distinguish them from other organisms, including multicellularity, an extracellular matrix, and unique cell junctions, in addition to heterotrophic feeding and internal digestion and the possession of nervous and muscle tissues (Table 33.1).

- Many different feeding modes are used by animals, including suspension feeding, bulk feeding and fluid feeding (Figure 33.1).

- The history of animal life on Earth spans over 630 million years. A profusion of animal phyla appeared in the Cambrian explosion (533–525 mya). Animals evolved adaptations to deal with the colonization of land, starting about 520 mya, and the number and diversity of mammals exploded after dinosaurs died out at the end of the Cretaceous period, 65 mya (Figure 33.2).

33.2 Animal Classification

- The animal kingdom is monophyletic, meaning that all taxa have evolved from a single common ancestor (Figure 33.3).

- Biologists hypothesize that animals evolved from a choanoflagellate-like ancestor.

- Animals can be categorized according to their type of symmetry, whether asymmetric (the sponges), radial (the cnidarians and ctenophores), or bilateral (Bilateria, all other animals) (Figure 33.4).

- The Cnidaria have two embryonic germ layers, the endoderm and the ectoderm, whereas the Bilateria and Ctenophora have a third

germ layer termed the mesoderm, which develops between the endoderm and the ectoderm (Figure 33.5).

- Animals are also classified according to patterns of embryonic development. In protostomes, the blastopore becomes the mouth; in deuterostomes, the blastopore becomes the anus. Most protostomes have spiral cleavage, and all deuterostomes have radial cleavage (Figure 33.6).

- Animals with a coelom, a body cavity that is completely lined with mesoderm, are termed coelomates. Animals that possess a coelom that is not completely lined by tissue derived from mesoderm are called pseudocoelomates. Those animals lacking a fluid-filled body cavity are termed acoelomates (Figure 33.7).

- Segmentation, the division of the body into identical subunits called segments, is an obvious feature of the animal body plan in certain phyla (Figure 33.8).

- Shifts in the pattern of expression of *Hox* genes are prominent in evolution. In vertebrates, the transition from one type of vertebra to another is controlled by certain *Hox* genes (Figure 33.9).

- Each animal phylum shows a distinctive set of general characteristics (Table 33.2).

33.3 The Use of Molecular Data in Constructing Phylogenetic Trees for Animals

- Phylogenetic trees are constructed and revised by comparing similarities in DNA, RNA, and amino acid sequences among different species (Figure 33.10).

- Molecular studies resulted in a revision to the animal phylogenetic tree; the protostomes were divided into two major clades: the Ecdysozoa and the Lophotrochozoa (Figures 33.11, 33.12).

- Members of the Ecdysozoa secrete and periodically shed a nonliving cuticle that is typically an exoskeleton, or external skeleton (Figure 33.13).

- The Lophotrochozoa are grouped primarily through analyses of molecular data, but some members are distinguished by two morphological features: the lophophore, a crown of tentacles used for feeding, and the trochophore larva, a distinct larval stage (Figure 33.14).

Assess & Discuss

Test Yourself

1. Which of the following is *not* a distinguishing characteristic of animals?
   a. the capacity to move at some point in the life cycle
   b. possession of cell walls
   c. multicellularity
   d. heterotrophy
   e. All of the above are characteristics of animals.

2. Which is the correct hierarchy of divisions in the animal kingdom, from most inclusive to least inclusive?
   a. Protostomia, Ecdysozoa, Bilateria
   b. Ecdysozoa, Protostomia, Bilateria
   c. Bilateria, Protostomia, Ecdysozoa
   d. Protostomia, Bilateria, Ecdysozoa
   e. none of the above

34.1 Ctenophores: The Earliest Animals

Learning Outcome:

1. Outline the unique features of ctenophores.

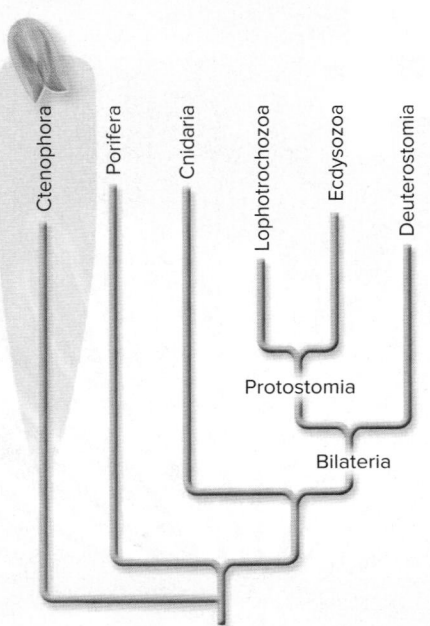

Ctenophores, also known as comb jellies, constitute the earliest-diverging animal lineage. Comb jellies are a small phylum of about 200 species, all of which are marine and look very much like jellyfish (**Figure 34.2**). They have on their surfaces eight rows of cilia that resemble combs. Based on morphological data, the ctenophores were once classified as close relatives to cnidarians, which include jellyfish and corals. However, recent molecular analyses have changed this view and placed them farther apart on the animal evolutionary tree.

The name Ctenophora (pronounced teen-o-for'-ah) comes from the Greek *ktenos,* meaning comb, and *phora,* meaning bearing. The coordinated beating of the cilia propels the ctenophores. Averaging

Figure 34.2 A ctenophore. Ctenophores are called comb jellies because the eight rows of cilia on their surfaces resemble combs.
©Matthew J. D'Avella/SeaPics.com

about 1–10 cm in length, comb jellies are probably the largest animals to use cilia for locomotion.

Most comb jellies possess two long tentacles that secrete a sticky substance onto which small prey adhere. The tentacles are then drawn over the mouth. Digestion occurs in a body cavity called a **gastrovascular cavity**, and waste and water are eliminated through two anal pores. Prey are generally small and may include tiny crustaceans called copepods and small fishes.

Comb jellies are often transported around the world in ships' ballast water. *Mnemiopsis leidyi*, a ctenophore species native to the Atlantic coast of North and South America, was accidentally introduced into the Black and Caspian Seas in the 1980s. With a plentiful food supply and a lack of predators, *M. leidyi* underwent a population explosion and ultimately devastated the local fishing industries.

All ctenophores are **hermaphrodites** (from the Greek, for the god Hermes and the goddess Aphrodite), possessing both ovaries and testes, and gametes are shed into the water to unite and eventually form a free-swimming larva that is very similar in form to the adult. Nearly all ctenophores exhibit **bioluminescence**, a phenomenon that results from chemical reactions that give off light. Ctenophores are particularly evident at night. Sometimes, they wash up on shore and make the sand or mud appear luminescent.

Like jellyfish, ctenophores have both muscle and nerve cells organized as a diffuse net centralized at an elementary brain. However, the ctenophore nervous system uses different neurotransmitters than those in bilaterians and jellyfish and has different types of synapses. The presence of muscle cells originating from mesoderm suggests that ctenophores share a three-germ-layer embryonic structure with bilaterians. Even so, recent analyses of the genome of the ctenophore *M. leidyi* suggests that ctenophores lack many of the genes involved in specifying bilaterian mesoderm. In addition, ctenophores lack true *Hox* genes and possess a ctenophore-specific cleavage program. Finally, many bilaterian neuron-specific genes are absent or not expressed in ctenophores. These findings argue against a linear march of evolutionary forms from more simple animals such as ctenophores and sponges to complex bilaterians. Instead, evolutionary studies suggest that ctenophores were the earliest animals to diverge from a choanoflagellate-like ancestor that was multicellular and had a simple nervous system. Later, the ctenophores evolved their own unique way of forming mesoderm, which is different from the bilaterians.

34.2 Porifera: The Sponges

Learning Outcomes:

1. Outline the body plan and unique characteristics of sponges.
2. Describe how sponges defend themselves against predators.

Members of the phylum Porifera (from the Latin, meaning pore bearers), are commonly referred to as sponges. Sponges lack true tissues—groups of cells that have a similar structure and function. However, sponges are multicellular and produce different types of specialized

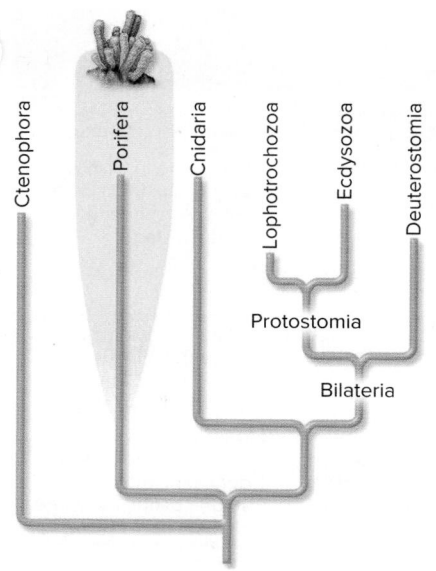

cells. Even though sponges carry most of the genes that are needed for a functioning nervous system, they have lost the ability to produce neurons during evolution. Biologists have identified approximately 8,000 species of sponges, the vast majority of which are marine. Sponges range in size from only a few millimeters across to more than 2 m in diameter. Smaller sponges may be radially symmetric, but most have no apparent symmetry. Some sponges have a low, encrusting growth form, whereas others grow tall and erect (**Figure 34.3a**). Although adult sponges are sessile—that is, anchored in place—the larvae are free-swimming.

Choanocytes Help Circulate Water

The body of a sponge looks similar to a vase pierced with small holes or pores (**Figure 34.3b**). Water is drawn through these pores into a central cavity, the **spongocoel**, and flows out through the large opening at the top, called the osculum. The water enters the pores by the beating action of the flagella of the **choanocytes**, or collar cells, that line the spongocoel (**Figure 34.3c**). In the process, the choanocytes trap and eat small particulate matter and tiny plankton.

A layer of flattened epithelial cells similar to those making up the outer layer of animals in other phyla protects the sponge body. In between the choanocytes and the epithelial cells lies a gelatinous, protein-rich matrix called the **mesohyl**. Within this matrix are mobile cells called **amoebocytes** that absorb food from choanocytes, digest it, and carry the nutrients to other cells. Thus, considerable cell-to-cell contact and communication exist in sponges. Sponges are unique among the major animal phyla in using intracellular digestion, the uptake of food particles by cells, as a mode of feeding.

Sponges Have Mechanical and Chemical Defenses Against Predators

Some amoebocytes can form tough skeletal fibers that support the sponge's body. In many sponges, this skeleton consists of sharp **spicules** formed of protein, calcium carbonate, or silica. For example, some deep-ocean species, called glass sponges, are distinguished by having needle-like silica spicules that form elaborate lattice-like skeletons. The presence of such tough spicules

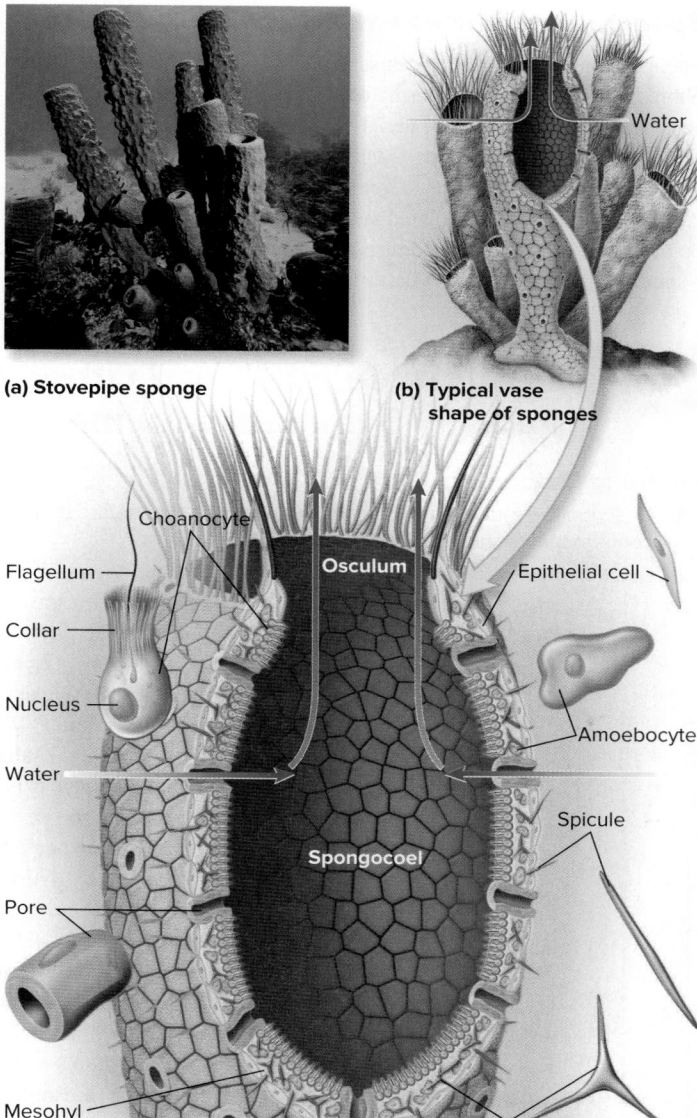

(a) Stovepipe sponge

(b) Typical vase shape of sponges

(c) Cross section of sponge morphology

Figure 34.3 **Sponge body plan.** **(a)** The stovepipe sponge (*Aplysina archeri*) is a common sponge found on Caribbean reefs. **(b)** Many sponges have a vaselike shape. **(c)** A cross section reveals that sponges are multicellular animals, having various cell types but no distinct tissues. a: ©Norbert Probst/age fotostock

Concept Check: *If sponges are soft and sessile, why aren't they eaten by other organisms?*

may explain why predation of sponges is rare. Other sponges have fibers of a tough protein called **spongin** that lend skeletal support. Spongin skeletons are still commercially harvested and sold as bath sponges. Many species produce toxic defensive chemicals, some of which are being tested as possible anticancer and anti-inflammatory agents in humans.

Sponges Reproduce Sexually and Asexually

Sponges reproduce through both sexual and asexual means. Like cteno-phores, most sponges are hermaphrodites, and thus can produce both sperm and eggs. Gametes are derived from amoebocytes or choanocytes. The eggs remain in the mesohyl, and the sperm are released into the water and carried by water currents to fertilize the eggs of neighboring sponges. Zygotes develop into flagellated swimming larvae that eventually settle on a suitable substrate to become sessile adults. In asexual reproduction, a small fragment or bud may detach and form a new sponge.

34.3 Cnidaria: Jellyfish and Other Radially Symmetric Animals

Learning Outcomes:

1. Describe the four main classes of cnidarians, and compare and contrast the polyp and medusa body forms.
2. Describe how cnidarians defend themselves and capture prey.

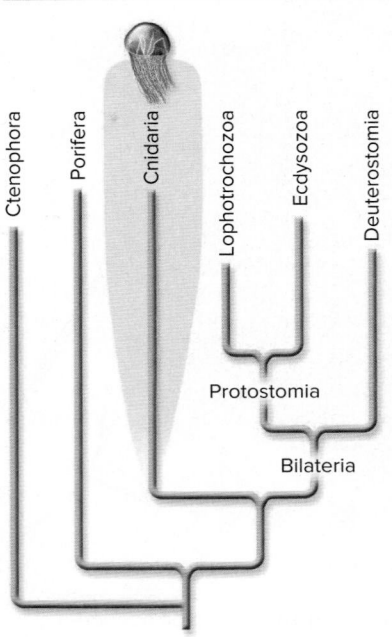

The members of the phylum Cnidaria (from the Greek *knide*, meaning nettle, and *aria*, meaning related to; pronounced nid-air'-e-ah) are mostly found in marine environments, although a few are freshwater species. Cnidaria includes hydra, jellyfish, box jellies, sea anemones, and corals. The cnidarians have only two embryonic germ layers: the ectoderm and the endo-derm. A gelatinous sub-stance called the **mesoglea** connects the two layers. In jellyfish, the mesoglea is enlarged and forms a trans-parent jelly, whereas in hydra and corals, the meso-glea is very thin. Most cnidarians have tentacles around the mouth that aid in prey detection and capture.

The phylum Cnidaria consists of four classes: Hydrozoa (includ-ing the Portuguese man-of-war), Scyphozoa (jellyfish), Anthozoa (sea anemones and corals), and Cubozoa (box jellies). The distinguishing characteristics of these classes are shown in **Table 34.1**.

Cnidarians Exist in Two Different Body Forms

Most cnidarians exist in one of two different body forms with an asso-ciated lifestyle: the sessile **polyp** or the motile **medusa** (**Figure 34.4**). For example, corals and sea anemones exhibit only the polyp form, and jellyfish exist predominantly in the medusa form.

The polyp form has a tubular body with an opening at the oral (top) end that is surrounded by tentacles and functions as both mouth and anus

Table 34.1	Main Classes and Characteristics of the Cnidaria	
	Class and examples (est. number of species)	Class characteristics
	Hydrozoa: Portuguese man-of-war, *Hydra*, some corals (2,700)	Mostly marine; polyp stage usually dominant and colonial, reduced medusa stage
	Scyphozoa: jellyfish (200)	All marine; medusa stage dominant and large (up to 2 m); reduced polyp stage
	Anthozoa: sea anemones, sea fans, most corals (6,000)	All marine; polyp stage dominant; medusa stage absent; many are colonial
	Cubozoa: box jellies, sea wasps (20)	All marine; medusa stage dominant; box-shaped

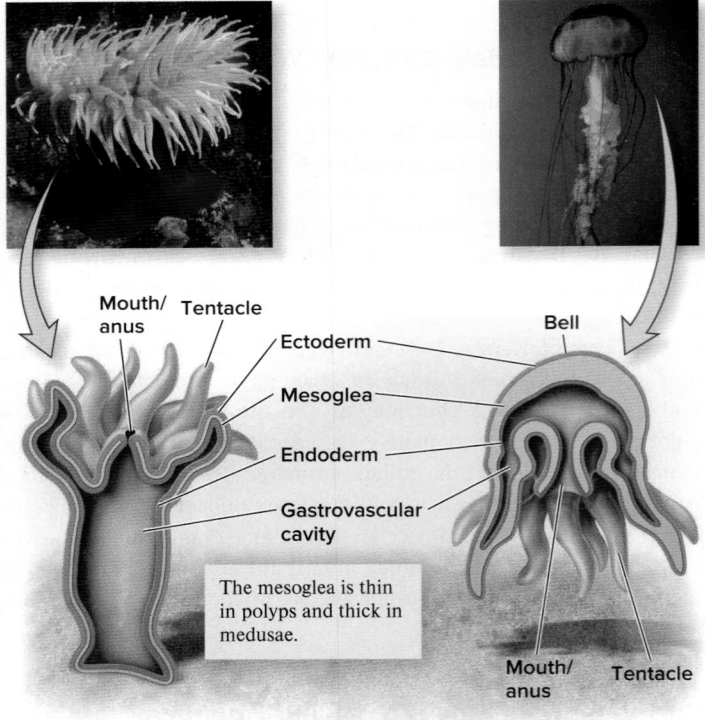

Figure 34.4 Polyp and medusa forms of cnidarians. Both **(a)** polyp and **(b)** medusa forms have two layers of cells, an outer layer of ectoderm and an inner layer of endoderm. In between is a layer of mesoglea, which is thin in polyps, such as corals, and thick in medusae, such as most jellyfish. a: Source: Linda Snook, NOAA/CBNMS; b: ©Kick Images/Getty Images

Concept Check: What are the body forms of the following types of cnidarians: jellyfish, sea anemone, and Portuguese man-of-war?

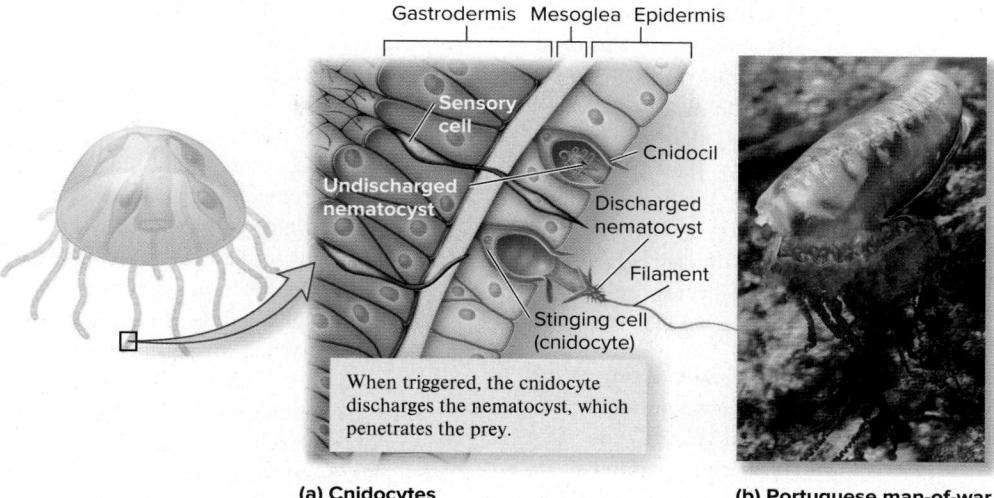

Gastrodermis Mesoglea Epidermis

Sensory cell

Undischarged nematocyst

Cnidocil

Discharged nematocyst

Filament

Stinging cell (cnidocyte)

When triggered, the cnidocyte discharges the nematocyst, which penetrates the prey.

(a) Cnidocytes

(b) Portuguese man-of-war

Figure 34.5 **Specialized stinging cells of cnidarians, called cnidocytes.** **(a)** Cnidocytes, which contain stinging capsules called nematocysts, are situated in the tentacles. **(b)** The Portuguese man-of-war (*Physalia physalis*) employs cnidocytes that can be lethal to humans. b: ©Nature/UIG/Getty Images

Concept Check: *Are cnidocytes recycled for reuse once they have been fired?*

(see Figure 34.4a). The aboral (bottom) end is attached to the substrate. Polyps exist colonially, as in corals, or alone, as in sea anemones. Corals take dissolved calcium and carbonate ions from seawater and precipitate them as limestone underneath their bodies. With some species, this leads to a buildup of limestone deposits. As each successive generation of polyps dies, the limestone remains in place, and new polyps grow on top. Thus, huge underwater limestone deposits called coral reefs are formed (look ahead to Figure 54.26b). The largest of these is Australia's Great Barrier Reef, which stretches over 2,300 km. Many other extensive coral reefs are known, including the reef system along the Florida Keys. All coral reefs occur in warm water, generally between 20°C and 30°C.

The free-swimming medusa form has an umbrella-shaped body with an opening that serves as both mouth and anus located on the concave underside and surrounded by tentacles (see Figure 34.4b). More mobile medusae possess simple sense organs near the bell margin, including organs of equilibrium called statocysts and photosensitive organs known as **ocelli**. When one side of the bell tips upward, the statocysts on that side are stimulated, and muscle contraction is initiated to right the medusa. The ocelli allow medusae to position themselves in particular light levels.

Cnidarians Have Specialized Stinging Cells

One of the unique and characteristic features of the cnidarians is the existence of stinging cells called **cnidocytes**, which function in defense or the capture of prey (**Figure 34.5a**). Cnidocytes contain **nematocysts**, powerful capsules with an inverted coiled and barbed thread. Each cnidocyte has a hairlike trigger called a **cnidocil** on its surface. When the cnidocil is touched or detects a chemical stimulus, the nematocyst is discharged, and its filament penetrates the prey and injects a small amount of toxin. Small prey are immobilized and passed into the mouth by the tentacles. After discharge, the cnidocyte is absorbed, and a new one grows to replace it. The nematocysts of most cnidarians are not harmful to humans, but those on the tentacles of the larger jellyfish and the Portuguese man-of-war (**Figure 34.5b**) can cause extreme pain or even death.

34.4 Lophotrochozoa: The Flatworms, Rotifers, Bryozoans, Brachiopods, Mollusks, and Annelids

Learning Outcomes:

1. Describe the unique features of platyhelminthes, rotifers, bryozoans, and brachiopods.
2. Outline the main features and list the major classes of the mollusks.
3. **CoreSKILL »** Analyze the results of Fiorito and Scotto's experiments, and explain how they show that octopuses can learn by watching each another.
4. List the advantages of segmentation in the annelids.

As we explored in Chapter 33 (refer back to Figure 33.3), molecular data suggest three clades of bilateral animals: the Lophotrochozoa and the Ecdysozoa (collectively known as the protostomes) and the Deuterostomia. In this section, we will explore the distinguishing characteristics of the Lophotrochozoa, a diverse group that includes taxa that possess either a lophophore (a crown of ciliated tentacles, seen in Bryozoa and Brachiopoda) or a distinct larval stage called a trochophore (Mollusca and Annelida). Also included in this clade are the Platyhelminthes (some of which have trochophore-like larvae) and the Rotifera (which have a lophophore-like feeding device), both of which share molecular similarities with the other members of the Lophotrochozoa.

The Phylum Platyhelminthes Consists of Flatworms with No Coelom

Platyhelminthes (from the Greek *platy*, meaning flat, and *helminth*, meaning worm), or flatworms, lack a specialized respiratory or

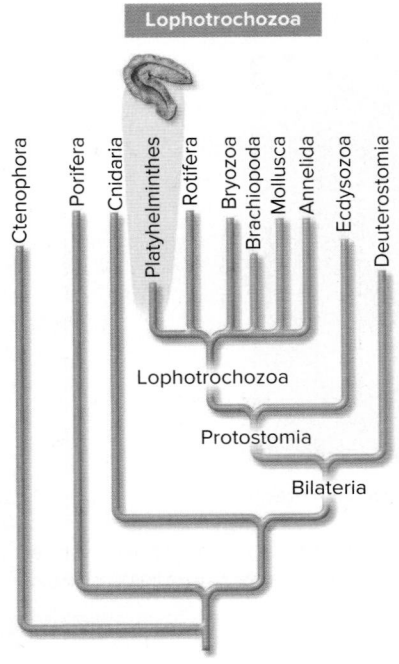

Lophotrochozoa

Ctenophora
Porifera
Cnidaria
Platyhelminthes
Rotifera
Bryozoa
Brachiopoda
Mollusca
Annelida
Ecdysozoa
Deuterostomia

Lophotrochozoa

Protostomia

Bilateria

circulatory system and must respire by diffusion. Thus, no cell can be too far from the surface, making a flattened shape necessary. Flatworms were among the first animals to develop an active predatory lifestyle. However, most species are internal or external parasites.

Flatworm Body Plan

The flatworms are hypothesized to be the first bilaterian animals to evolve three distinctive embryonic germ layers—ectoderm, endoderm, and mesoderm—with mesoderm replacing the simpler gelatinous mesoglea of cnidarians. For this reason, they are said to be triploblastic. The muscles in flatworms, which are derived from mesoderm, are well developed. The evolution of mesoderm was a critical innovation in animals, leading to the development of more sophisticated organs.

Flatworms lack a coelem—a fluid-filled body cavity in which the gut is suspended. Therefore, they are described as acoelomates. Instead, mesoderm fills the body spaces around the gastrovascular cavity (**Figure 34.6**). The digestive system of flatworms is incomplete, with only one opening, which serves as both a mouth and an anus, as in cnidarians. Most flatworms possess a muscular pharynx that may be extended through the mouth. The pharynx opens to a gastrovascular cavity, where food is digested. In large flatworms, the gastrovascular cavity is highly branched to distribute nutrients to all parts of the body.

Flatworms have a distinct excretory system consisting of **protonephridia**, two lateral canals with branches capped by **flame cells**. Protonephridia are dead-end tubules lacking internal openings. The flame cells, which are ciliated and waft water through the lateral canals to the outside (look ahead to Figure 49.2), primarily function in maintaining osmotic balance between the flatworm's body and the surrounding fluids. Simple though this system is, its development was key to permitting the movement of animals into freshwater habitats and even moist terrestrial areas.

Platyhelminthes are bilaterally symmetrical with a head bearing sensory appendages, the result of the process called **cephalization** (see Figure 34.6). At the anterior end of some free-living flatworms are light-sensitive eyespots, called ocelli, as well as chemoreceptive and sensory cells that are concentrated in organs called auricles. A pair of **cerebral ganglia**, clusters of nerve cell bodies, receives input from photoreceptors in eyespots and sensory cells. From the ganglia, a pair of lateral nerve cords running the length of the body allow rapid movement of information from anterior to posterior. In addition, transverse nerves form a nerve net on the ventral surface, similar to that of cnidarians. Thus, flatworms show the beginnings of the more centralized type of nervous system seen throughout much of the rest of the animal kingdom.

The Classes of Flatworms The four classes of flatworms are the Turbellaria, Monogenea, Cestoda (tapeworms), and Trematoda (flukes) (**Table 34.2**).

- Turbellarians are the only free-living class of flatworms and are widespread in lakes, ponds, and marine environments (**Figure 34.7a**).

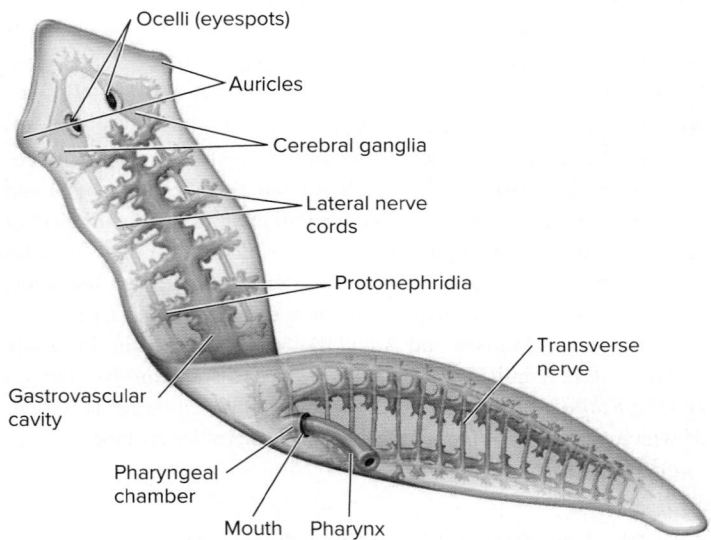

- Ocelli (eyespots)
- Auricles
- Cerebral ganglia
- Lateral nerve cords
- Protonephridia
- Transverse nerve
- Gastrovascular cavity
- Pharyngeal chamber
- Mouth
- Pharynx

Figure 34.6 Body plan of a flatworm. Flatworm morphology is represented by a planarian, a member of the class Turbellaria.

Concept Check: *How do flatworms breathe?*

Table 34.2	Main Classes and Characteristics of Platyhelminthes	
	Class and examples (est. number of species)	**Class characteristics**
	Turbellaria: planarian (3,000)	Mostly marine; free-living flatworms; predatory or scavengers
	Monogenea: fish flukes (1,000)	Marine and freshwater; usually external parasites of fish; simple life cycle (no intermediate host)
	Cestoda: tapeworms (5,000)	Internal parasites of vertebrates; complex life cycle, usually with one intermediate host; no digestive system; nutrients absorbed across epidermis
	Trematoda: flukes (11,000)	Internal parasites of vertebrates; complex life cycle with several intermediate hosts

(a)

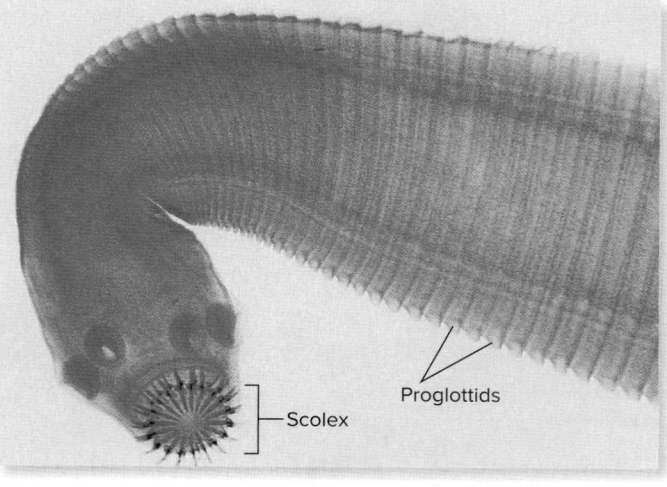

Proglottids

Scolex

(b)

Figure 34.7 Flatworms. (a) Many free-living marine turbellarians are brightly colored, such as this racing stripe flatworm, *Pseudoceros bifurcus*, from Bali, Indonesia. **(b)** A tapeworm, *Taenia pisiformis*, a member of the class Cestoda. Note the tiny hooks and suckers that make up the scolex. Each segment is a proglottid, which may be filled with eggs.

a: ©Wolfgang Poelzer/age fotostock; b: ©Biophoto Associates/Science Source

 Core Skill: Science and Society About 1% of U.S. cattle are infected by beef tapeworms. Consuming beef that is not sufficiently well cooked can lead to infection by these parasites. At least 1,000 hospitalizations a year in the U.S. are due to tapeworm infection, most as a result of eating uncooked pork.

- Monogeneans are relatively simple external parasites with just one host species (a fish).

- Cestodes and trematodes are internally parasitic in humans and other animals and therefore are of great medical and veterinary importance. They possess a variety of organs of attachment, such as hooks and suckers, that enable them to remain embedded within their hosts. For example, cestodes attach to their host by means of an organ at the head end called a scolex

(**Figure 34.7b**). They have no mouth or gastrovascular cavity and absorb nutrients across the body surface.

Reproduction in Flatworms In Platyhelminthes, reproduction is either sexual or asexual. Most species are hermaphroditic but do not fertilize their own eggs. Flatworms can also reproduce asexually by splitting into two parts, with each half regenerating the missing fragment.

Flatworm life cycles can be complex. Cestodes often require two different vertebrate host species, such as pigs or cattle, to begin their life cycle and another host, such as humans, to complete their development. Behind the scolex in cestodes is a long ribbon of identical segments called proglottids, which are segments of sex organs that produce thousands of eggs. The proglottids are continually shed in the host's feces. Human feces passed out onto the ground are eaten with grass by pigs and cattle. Many tapeworms are ingested by humans who consume undercooked, infected meat—hence it is important to cook meat thoroughly.

The life cycle of trematodes is typically more complex than that of cestodes, involving multiple hosts. The first host, called the intermediate host, is usually a mollusk, and the final host, or definitive host, is usually a vertebrate, but often a second or even a third intermediate host is involved. In the case of the Chinese liver fluke (*Clonorchis sinensis*), the adult parasite lives and reproduces in the definitive host, a human (see step 1, **Figure 34.8**). Structures, which are sometimes called eggs, contain encapsulated miracidia; these pass from the host via the feces, and then an intermediate host, such as a snail, eats the miracidia, which transform into sporocysts (see steps 2 and 3). The sporocysts asexually produce more sporocysts called rediae, which develop into a free-swimming life stage called cercariae (see steps 4 and 5). In the last stages of the life cycle, cercariae bore their way out of the snail and infect their second intermediate host, fishes, by entering via the gills. Here, the cercariae develop into juvenile flukes and lodge in fish muscle, which the definitive host will eat (see steps 6 and 7). From the small intestine of the definitive host, the juvenile flukes travel to the liver and grow into adult flukes, and the life cycle begins anew. The probability of each trematode stage reaching a suitable host is low, so trematodes produce large numbers of offspring to ensure that some survive.

Blood flukes, genus *Schistosoma*, are the most common parasitic trematodes infecting humans; they cause the disease known as schistosomiasis. Over 200 million people worldwide, primarily in tropical Asia, Africa, and South America, are infected with schistosomiasis. The inch-long adult flukes may live for years in human hosts, and the release of eggs may cause chronic inflammation and blockage in many organs. Untreated schistosomiasis can result in severe damage to the liver, intestines, and lungs and eventually lead to death. Sewage treatment and access to clean water greatly reduce infection rates.

Members of the Phylum Rotifera Have a Pseudocoelom and a Ciliated Crown

Members of the phylum Rotifera (from the Latin *rota*, meaning wheel, and *fera*, meaning to bear) get their name from their ciliated crown, or **corona**, which, when beating, looks similar to a rotating wheel

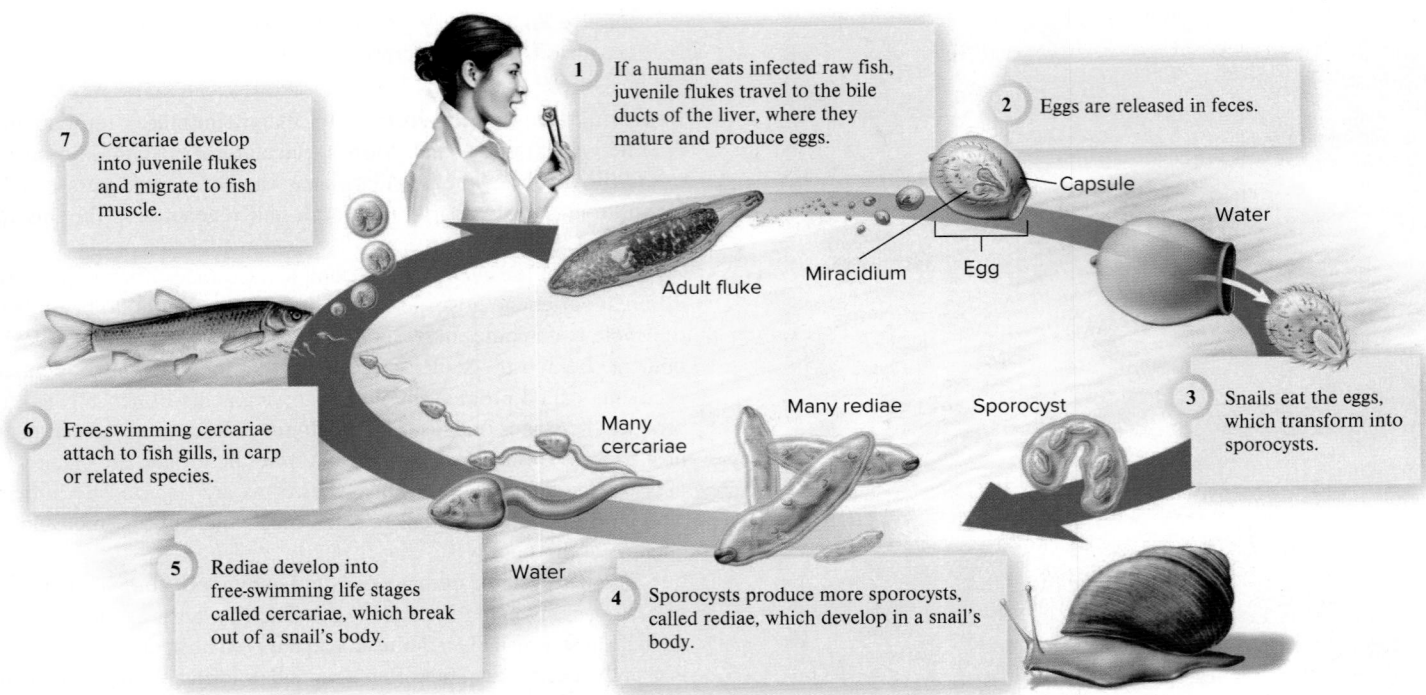

Figure 34.8 The complete life cycle of a trematode. This figure shows the life cycle of the Chinese liver fluke (*Clonorchis sinensis*).

1. If a human eats infected raw fish, juvenile flukes travel to the bile ducts of the liver, where they mature and produce eggs.

2. Eggs are released in feces.

3. Snails eat the eggs, which transform into sporocysts.

4. Sporocysts produce more sporocysts, called rediae, which develop in a snail's body.

5. Rediae develop into free-swimming life stages called cercariae, which break out of a snail's body.

6. Free-swimming cercariae attach to fish gills, in carp or related species.

7. Cercariae develop into juvenile flukes and migrate to fish muscle.

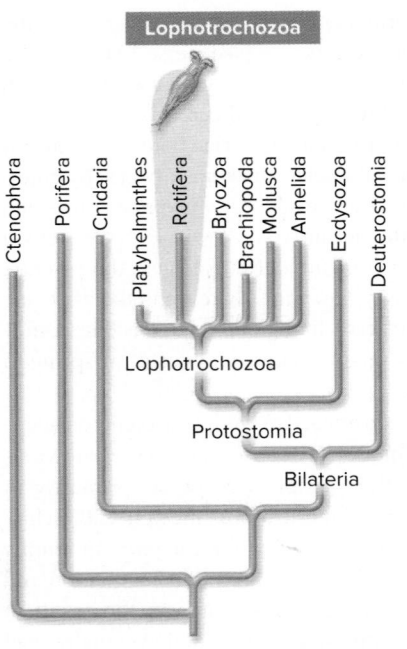

(**Figure 34.9**). Most rotifers are microscopic animals, usually less than 1 mm long, and some have beautiful colors. About 2,200 species of rotifers have been identified. They typically inhabit fresh water, with a few marine and terrestrial species. Most often they are bottom-dwelling organisms, living on a pond floor or along lakeside vegetation. The body of the rotifer bears a jointed foot with one to four toes. **Pedal glands** in the foot secrete a sticky substance that aids in attachment to a substrate.

The internal organs of rotifers lie within a pseudocoelom, a fluid-filled body cavity that is not completely lined with mesoderm. The pseudocoelom serves as a hydrostatic skeleton and as a medium for the internal transport of nutrients and wastes. Rotifers have an alimentary canal, a digestive tract with a separate mouth and anus. For this reason, rotifers can feed more frequently compared to simpler animals that have a single opening to their digestive system, such as cnidarians. The corona of rotifers creates water currents that propel the animal through the water and waft small planktonic organisms or decomposing organic material

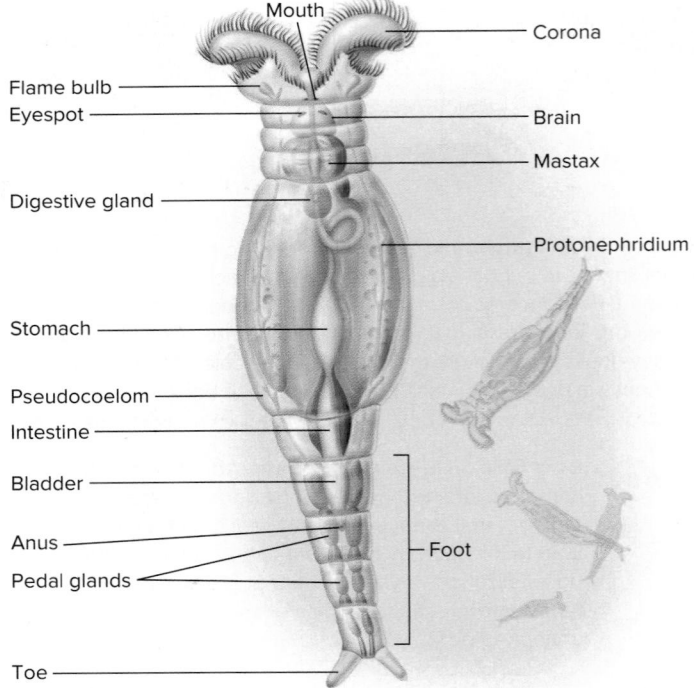

Figure 34.9 Body plan of a common rotifer, *Philodina* genus.

toward the mouth. The mouth opens into a circular, muscular pharynx called a **mastax**, which has jaws for grasping and chewing. The mastax, which in some species can protrude through the mouth to seize small prey, is a structure unique to rotifers. They also have a pair of protonephridia with flame bulbs that collect excretory and digestive waste and drain into a bladder, which passes waste to the anus. The nervous system consists of nerves that extend from the sensory organs, especially the eyespots and some bristles on the corona, to the brain.

Reproduction in rotifers is unique. In some species, unfertilized diploid eggs that have not undergone meiotic division develop into females through a process known as **parthenogenesis**. In other species, some unfertilized eggs develop into females, whereas others develop into males that live only long enough to produce and release sperm that fertilize the eggs. The resultant fertilized eggs form zygotes, which have a thick shell and can survive for long periods of harsh conditions, for example, if a water supply dries up, before developing into new females. Because the tiny zygotes are easily transported, rotifers show up in the smallest of aquatic environments, such as birdbaths or roof gutters.

Bryozoa and Brachiopoda Have a Lophophore for Feeding and Gas Exchange

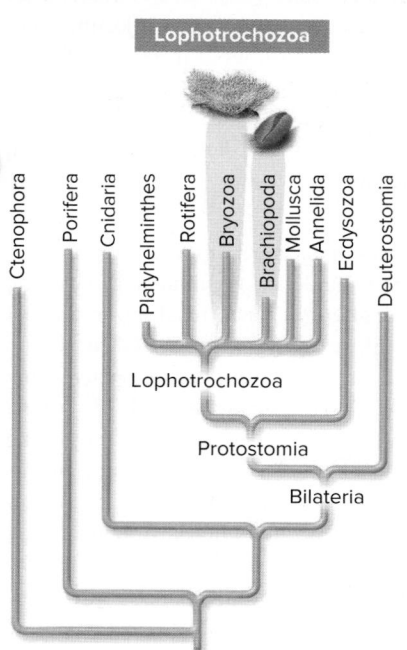

The Bryozoa and the Brachiopoda both possess a lophophore, a ciliary feeding device (refer back to Figure 33.14a), and a true coelom (refer back to Figure 33.7a). The lophophore is a circular fold of the body wall bearing tentacles that draw water toward the mouth. Because a thin extension of the coelom penetrates each tentacle, the tentacles also serve as a respiratory organ. Gases diffuse across the tentacles and into or out of the coelomic fluid and are carried throughout the body. Both phyla have a U-shaped alimentary canal, with the anus located near the mouth but outside of the lophophore.

Phylum Bryozoa   The bryozoans (from the Greek *bryon*, meaning moss, and *zoon*, meaning animal) are small colonial animals, most of which are less than 0.5 mm long, that can be found on rocks in shallow aquatic environments. They look very much like plants. Within a colony, each animal secretes and lives inside a nonliving exoskeleton called a zoecium that is composed of chitin or calcium carbonate (**Figure 34.10a**). For this reason, bryozoans have been important reef-builders. Also, many of them encrust boat hulls and have to be scraped off periodically. About 4,500 species of bryozoans currently exist. They date back to the Paleozoic era, and thousands of fossil forms have been discovered and identified.

(a) A bryozoan

(b) A brachiopod, the northern lamp shell

Figure 34.10 **Bryozoans and brachiopods.** (a) Bryozoans are colonial animals that reside in a nonliving case called a zoecium. (b) Brachiopods, such as this northern lamp shell (*Terebratulina septentrionalis*), have dorsal and ventral shells. a: ©G. Guenther/age fotostock; b: ©Gordon MacSkimming/age fotostock

Concept Check: *What are the two main functions of the lophophore?*

Phylum Brachiopoda   Brachiopods (from the Greek *brachio*, meaning arm, and *podos*, meaning foot) are marine organisms with two shell halves, much like clams (**Figure 34.10b**). In clams, however, the shell halves are considered to be left and right sides with the plane of symmetry lying parallel to the site at which the shells join. In contrast, brachiopods have a dorsal and ventral shell, with the plane of symmetry perpendicular to the site at which the shells join. The dorsal and ventral shells of brachiopods are of slightly different sizes and shapes. Brachiopods are bottom-dwelling species that attach to the substrate via a muscular pedicle. Although they are now a relatively small group, with about 300 living species, brachiopods flourished in the Paleozoic and Mesozoic eras—about 30,000 fossil species have been identified. Some of these fossil forms represent organisms that reached 30 cm in length, although their modern relatives are only 0.5–8.0 cm long.

Mollusca Is a Large Phylum Containing Snails, Slugs, Clams, Oysters, Octopuses, and Squids

Mollusks (from the Latin *mollis*, meaning soft) constitute a very large phylum, with over 100,000 living species, including organisms as diverse as snails, clams, octopuses, and chitons. They are an ancient group, as evidenced by the classification of about 35,000 fossil species. Mollusks have considerable economic, aesthetic, and ecological importance to humans. Many serve as sources of food, including scallops, oysters, clams, and squids. A significant industry involves the farming of oysters to produce cultured pearls, and rare and beautiful mollusk shells are extremely valuable to collectors. Snails and slugs can damage vegetables and ornamental plants, and boring mollusks can penetrate wooden ships and wharfs. Mollusks are intermediate hosts to many parasites, and several invasive species have become serious pests. For example, populations of the zebra mussel (*Dreissena polymorpha*) have been introduced into North America from Asia, probably via ballast water from transoceanic ships. Since their introduction, they have spread rapidly throughout the Great Lakes and an increasing number of inland waterways, adversely impacting native organisms and clogging water intake valves of municipal water-treatment plants around the lakes.

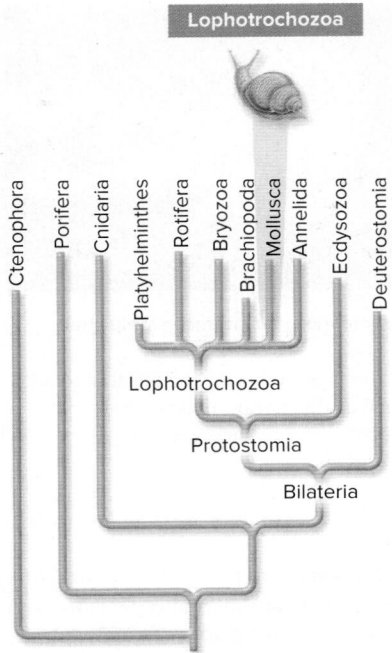

Lophotrochozoa

Ctenophora
Porifera
Cnidaria
Platyhelminthes
Rotifera
Bryozoa
Brachiopoda
Mollusca
Annelida
Ecdysozoa
Deuterostomia

Lophotrochozoa

Protostomia

Bilateria

Mollusk Body Plan   One common feature of mollusks is their soft body, which in many species is found under a protective external shell. Most mollusks are marine, although some have colonized fresh water. Many snails and slugs have moved onto land, but they survive only in humid areas and where the calcium necessary for shell formation is abundant in the soil. The ability to colonize freshwater and terrestrial habitats has led to a diversification of mollusk body plans. The amazing diversity of mollusks demonstrates how species diversity is related to environmental diversity.

Although great variation in morphology occurs between classes, mollusks have a basic body plan consisting of three parts (**Figure 34.11**).

- A muscular **foot** is usually used for movement, and a **visceral mass** containing the internal organs rests atop the foot.

- The **mantle**, a fold of skin draped over the visceral mass, secretes a shell in those species that form shells.

- The **mantle cavity** houses delicate **gills**, filamentous organs that are specialized for gas exchange. A continuous current of water, often induced by cilia present on the gills or by muscular pumping, flushes out the wastes from the mantle cavity and brings in new oxygen-rich water.

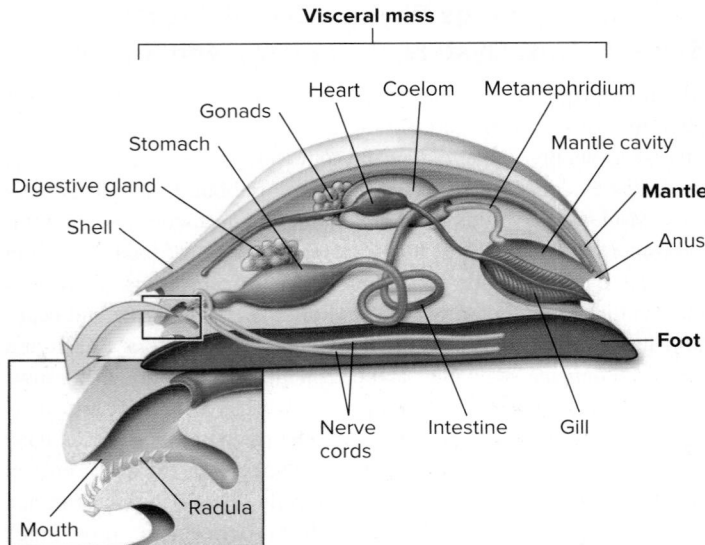

Figure 34.11 The mollusk body plan. The generalized body plan of a mollusk includes the characteristic foot, mantle, and visceral mass.

Concept Check: *Do molluscan hearts pump blood?*

Mollusks are coelomate organisms, but the coelom is confined to a small area around the heart. Most species of mollusks have an **open circulatory system** with a heart that pumps a body fluid called hemolymph through vessels and into sinuses. Sinuses are open, fluid-filled cavities between the internal organs. The organs and tissues are therefore continually bathed in hemolymph. The sinuses coalesce to form an open cavity known as the hemocoel (blood cavity). From these sinuses, the hemolymph drains into vessels that take it to the gills and then back to the heart.

Excretory organs called **metanephridia** remove nitrogenous and other wastes. Metanephridia have ciliated funnel-like openings inside the coelom that are connected to ducts that lead to the exterior mantle cavity. The pores from the metanephridia discharge wastes into this cavity. The anus also opens into the mantle cavity. The metanephridial ducts may also serve to discharge sperm or eggs from the gonads. The nervous system varies from simple ganglia and nerve chords in most species to much larger brains and sophisticated organs of touch, smell, taste, and vision in octopuses.

The mollusk's mouth may contain a **radula**, a unique, protrusible, tonguelike organ that has many teeth and is used to eat plants, scrape food particles off rocks, or, if the mollusk is predatory, bore into shells of other species and tear flesh. In the cone shells (genus *Conus*), the radula is reduced to a few poison-injecting teeth on the end of a long proboscis that is cast about in search of prey, such as a worm or even a fish. Some cone shell species produce a neuromuscular toxin that can kill humans. Other mollusks, particularly bivalves, have lost their radula and are filter feeders that strain water brought in by ciliary currents.

Mollusk Shells   Most mollusk shells are complex three-layered structures that are secreted by the mantle and continue to grow as the mollusk grows. Shell growth is often seasonal, resulting in distinct growth lines on the shell, much like tree rings (**Figure 34.12a**). Using shell growth patterns, biologists have discovered some bivalves that are over 100 years old. The innermost layer of the shells of oysters, mussels, abalone, and other mollusks is a smooth, iridescent lining called nacre, which is commonly known as mother-of-pearl and is often collected from abalone shells for jewelry. Actual pearl production in mollusks, primarily oysters, occurs when a foreign object, such as a grain of sand, becomes lodged between the shell and the mantle, and layers of nacre are laid down around it to reduce the irritation.

Reproduction in Mollusks   Most mollusks species have separate sexes, although some exist as hermaphrodites. Gametes are usually released into the water, where they mix and fertilization occurs. In some snails, however, fertilization is internal, with the male inserting sperm directly into the female. Internal fertilization was a critical innovation enabling some snails to colonize land. In many species, reproduction involves the production of a trochophore larva that develops into a **veliger**, a free-swimming larva that has a rudimentary foot, shell, and mantle (**Figure 34.13**).

The Major Molluscan Classes   Of the eight molluscan classes, the four most common are the Bivalvia (clams and mussels),

(a) A quahog clam, class Bivalvia

(c) A snail, class Gastropoda

(b) A chiton, class Polyplacophora

(d) A nudibranch, class Gastropoda

Figure 34.12 Mollusks. (a) A bivalve shell, class Bivalvia, with growth rings. This quahog clam (*Mercenaria mercenaria*) can live over 20 years. **(b)** A chiton (*Tonicella lineata*), a polyplacophoran with a shell made up of eight separate plates. **(c)** A gastropod, the tree snail, *Liguus fasciatus*, from the Florida Everglades showing its characteristic coiled shell. **(d)** A nudibranch (*Phyllidia ocellata*). The nudibranchs are a gastropod subclass whose members have lost their shell altogether. **(e)** The highly poisonous blue-ringed octopus (*Hapalochlaena lunulata*), a cephalopod. a: ©Andrew J. Martinez/Science Source; b: ©Kjell B. Sandved/Science Source; c: ©ImageBROKER/Alamy Stock Photo; d: ©Hal Beral/Corbis /Getty Images; e: ©Richard Merritt FRPS/Getty Images

(e) A blue-ringed octopus, class Cephalopoda

Polyplacophora (chitons), Gastropoda (snails and slugs), and Cephalopoda (octopuses, squids, and nautiluses) (**Table 34.3**).

- Bivalves are freshwater or marine mollusks whose bodies are enclosed within a hinged shell of two valves, or halves. Prominent members of this class include oysters, clams, mussels, and scallops (**Figure 34.12a**).
- Polyplacophora are marine mollusks with a shell composed of eight separate plates (**Figure 34.12b**). Chitons are common in the intertidal zone, an area above water at low tide and under water at high tide, and they creep along when covered by the tide. Feeding occurs by scraping algae off rock surfaces. When the tide recedes, the muscular foot holds the chiton tight to the rock surface, preventing desiccation.

- The class Gastropoda (from the Greek *gaster*, meaning stomach, and *podos*, meaning foot) is the largest group of mollusks and encompasses about 75,000 living species, including snails, periwinkles, and limpets (**Figure 34.12c**). Most gastropods have a one-piece shell, into which the animal can withdraw to escape predators, However, the class also includes species such as slugs and nudibranchs, whose shells have been greatly reduced or completely lost during their evolution (**Figure 34.12d**). Although gastropods usually occupy marine or freshwater habitats, some species, including snails and slugs, have also colonized land.

The 780 species of Cephalopoda (from the Greek *kephalo*, meaning head, and *podos*, meaning foot) are the most

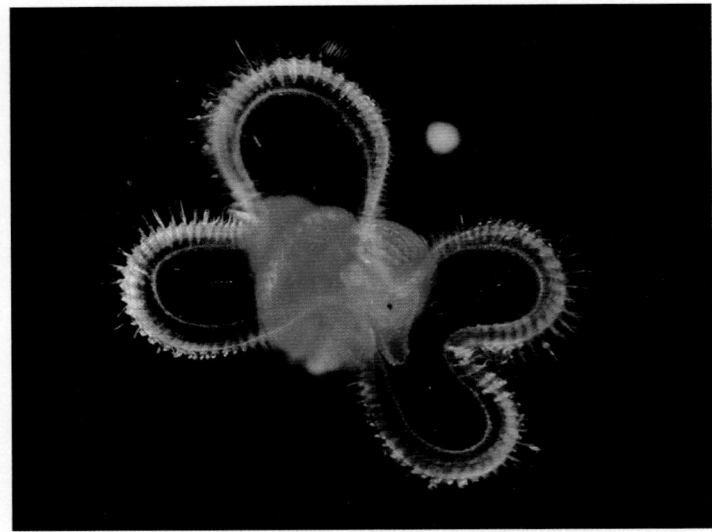

Figure 34.13 A snail veliger. Veligers are free-swimming larval forms of mollusks that look more like adults than the trocophore larvae from which they develop. ©Solvin Zankl/Alamy Stock Photo

Table 34.3	Major Classes and Characteristics of Mollusks	
	Class and examples (est. number of species)	Class characteristics
	Bivalvia: clams, mussels, oysters, scallops (30,000)	Marine or freshwater; shell with two halves or valves; primarily filter feeders with siphons
	Polyplacophora: chitons (860)	Marine; eight-plated shell
	Gastropoda: snails, slugs, nudibranchs (75,000)	Marine, freshwater, or terrestrial; most with coiled shell, but shell absent in slugs and nudibranchs; radula present
	Cephalopoda: octopuses, squids, nautiluses (780)	Marine; predatory, with tentacles around mouth, often with suckers; shell often absent or reduced; closed circulatory system; jet propulsion via siphon

morphologically complex of the mollusks and indeed among the most complex of all invertebrates. Most are fast-swimming marine predators that range from organisms just a few centimeters in size to the colossal squid (*Mesonychoteuthis hamiltoni*), which is known to reach over 13 m in length and 495 kg (1,091 lb) in weight. A cephalopod's mouth is surrounded by many long arms commonly armed with suckers. All cephalopods have a beaklike jaw that allows them to bite their prey, and some, such as the blue-ringed octopus (*Hapalochlaena lunulata*), deliver a deadly poison through their saliva (**Figure 34.12e**).

The foot of some cephalopods has become modified into a muscular siphon. Water drawn into the mantle cavity is quickly expelled through the siphon, propelling the organism forward or backward in a kind of jet propulsion. Such vigorous movement requires powerful muscles and a very efficient circulatory system to deliver oxygen and nutrients to the muscles. Cephalopods are the only mollusks with a **closed circulatory system**, in which

blood flows throughout an animal entirely within a series of vessels. One of the advantages of this type of system is that the heart can pump blood through the tissues rapidly, making oxygen more readily available. The blood of cephalopods contains the copper-rich protein hemocyanin for transporting oxygen. Less efficient than the iron-rich hemoglobin of vertebrates, hemocyanin gives the blood a blue color.

Cephalopods have a well-developed nervous system and brain that support their active lifestyle. Their sense organs, especially their eyes, are also very well developed. Many cephalopods (with the exception of nautiluses) have an ink sac that contains the pigment melanin; the sac can be emptied to provide a "smokescreen" to confuse predators. In many species, melanin is also distributed in special pigment cells in the skin, which allows for color changes. Octopuses often change color when disturbed, and they can change color rapidly to blend in with their background and escape detection.

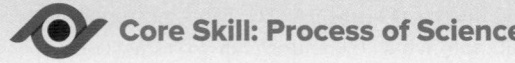

Core Skill: Process of Science

Feature Investigation | **Fiorito and Scotto's Experiments Showed That Invertebrates Can Exhibit Sophisticated Observational Learning Behavior**

The ability to learn by observing the behavior of others has commonly been observed in vertebrates, especially among species that live in social groups. For example, young rhesus macaques (*Macaca mulatta*) that observed their parents fearfully responding to model snakes also developed a fear of snakes and maintained this fear

for 3 months after observing their parent's behavior. In 1992, Italian researchers Graziano Fiorito and Pietro Scotto set out to test the hypothesis that octopuses (invertebrates) can learn by observing the behavior of other octopuses (**Figure 34.14**).

Figure 34.14 **Observational learning in octopuses.**

HYPOTHESIS Octopuses can learn by observing another's behavior.

STUDY LOCATION Laboratory setting with *Octopus vulgaris* collected from the Bay of Naples, Italy.

	Experimental level	Conceptual level

1 Train 2 groups of octopuses, one to attack white balls, one to attack red. These are called the demonstrator octopuses.

Reward choice of correct ball (with fish) and punish choice of incorrect ball (with electric shock). Training is complete when octopus makes no "mistakes" in 5 trials.

Conditions a demonstrator octopus to attack a particular color of ball.

2 In an adjacent tank, allow observer octopus to watch trained demonstrator octopus.

Observer   Demonstrator

Observer octopus may be learning the correct ball to attack by watching the demonstrator octopus.

3 Drop balls into the tank of the observer octopus. Test the observer octopus to see if it makes the same decisions as the demonstrator octopus.

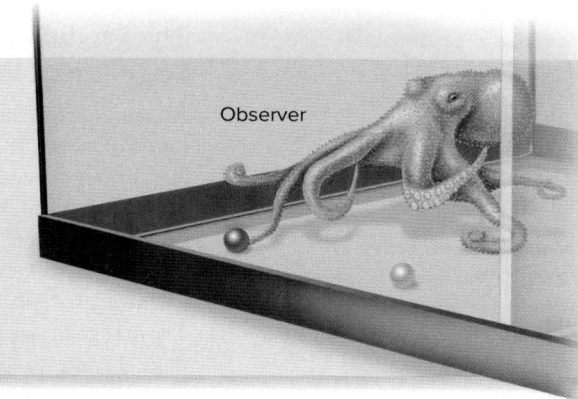

Observer

If the observer octopus is learning from the demonstrator octopus, the observer octopus should attack the ball of the same color as the demonstrator octopus was trained to attack.

4 **THE DATA**

Participant	Color of ball chosen in 5 trials*	
	Red	White
Observers (watched demonstrator attack red)	4.31	0.31
Observers (watched demonstrator attack white)	0.40	4.10
Untrained (did not watch demonstrations)	2.11	1.94

*Average of 5 trials; data do not always sum to 5, because some trials resulted in no balls being chosen.

5 **CONCLUSION** Invertebrate animals are capable of learning from watching other individuals behave, in much the same way as vertebrate species learn from watching others.

6 **SOURCE** Fiorito, G., and Scotto, P. 1992. Observational learning in Octopus vulgaris. *Science* 256: 545–547.

In their experiments, they used a system of reward (a small piece of fish placed behind a ball so that the octopus could not see it) and punishment (a small electric shock for choosing the wrong ball) to train octopuses to attack either a red or a white ball. This type of learning is called classical conditioning (see Chapter 55). Because octopuses are color blind, they must distinguish between the relative brightness of the balls. Octopuses were considered to be trained when they made no mistakes in five trials.

Observer octopuses in adjacent tanks were then allowed to watch the trained octopuses attacking the balls. In step 3, the observer octopuses were themselves tested, as were untrained octopuses that had never watched the demonstrators. As seen in the data, observers nearly always attacked the same color ball as they had observed the demonstrators attacking. In contrast, the untrained octopuses were equally likely to attack a red or white ball. These results indicate that one octopus can learn by watching the behavior of another octopus. This was a unexpected finding because many researchers thought that such complex learning would not be found in invertebrate species. It is also surprising because *Octopus vulgaris*, the species they studied, lives a solitary existence for most of its life.

Experimental Questions

1. What was the hypothesis tested by Fiorito and Scotto?
2. **CoreSKILL »** What were the results of the experiment? Did these results support the hypothesis?
3. **CoreSKILL »** Explain the significance of performing the experiment on both observer octopuses and untrained octopuses.

BIO·TIPS

THE QUESTION *To determine if the observer octopuses would retain their learning, Fiorito and Scotto conducted follow-up trials. Five days after their initial testing, the observer octopuses were retested for their ability to choose the correct ball. The observers that had watched a demonstrator that was trained to attack a red ball made the following choices of color: red, 3.88; white, 0.50. The observers that had watched a demonstrator trained to attack a white ball made the following choices: red, 0.50; white, 3.70. Were the observer octopuses retaining their learning after 5 days?*

TOPIC *What topic in biology does this question address?* The topic is learning; more specifically it is about learning retention in octopuses.

INFORMATION *What information do you know based on the question and your understanding of the topic?* In the data of Figure 34.14, you are given the initial frequency of color choices made by the observers. From the question, you know the frequency of color choices made 5 days later.

PROBLEM-SOLVING **S**TRATEGY *Make a calculation.* To solve this problem, you determine percentages of correct responses, initially (on day 1) and after 5 days, for both groups of observer octopuses.

For the octopuses that watched a demonstrator trained to attack a red ball, the percentages are as follows.

$$\text{Day 1: } \left(\frac{4.31}{4.31 + 0.31}\right) \times 100 = 93.3\%$$

$$\text{Day 5: } \left(\frac{3.88}{3.88 + 0.50}\right) \times 100 = 88.6\%$$

For the octopuses that watched a demonstrator trained to attack a white ball, the percentages are as follows.

$$\text{Day 1: } \left(\frac{4.10}{4.10 + 0.40}\right) \times 100 = 91.1\%$$

$$\text{Day 5: } \left(\frac{3.70}{3.70 + 0.50}\right) \times 100 = 88.1\%$$

ANSWER *The octopuses appeared to retain their learning fairly well, because only a slight drop (less than 5%) was observed after 5 days.*

The Phylum Annelida Consists of the Segmented Worms

Annelids are a large phylum with about 18,000 species of segmented worms. The members include free-ranging marine worms, tube worms, the familiar earthworm, and leeches. They range in size from less than 1 mm to enormous Australian earthworms that can reach a length of 3 m.

Annelid Body Plan The phylum name Annelida is derived from the Latin *annulus*, meaning little ring. Each ring is a distinct segment of the annelid's body; adjacent segments are separated by septa (**Figure 34.15**). Segmentation in the adult confers three advantages:

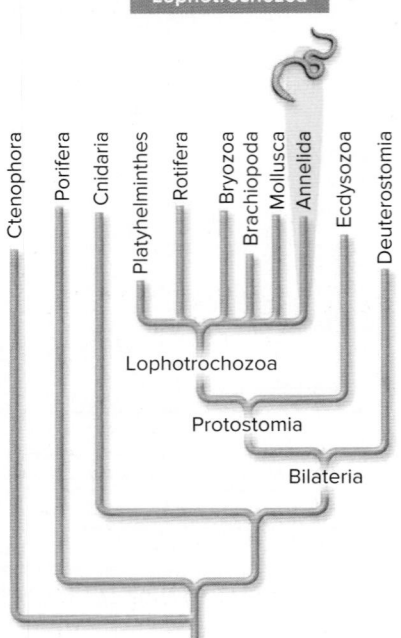

- Many components of the body are repeated in each segment, including blood vessels, nerves, and excretory and reproductive organs. If the components in one segment fail, those of another segment will still function.

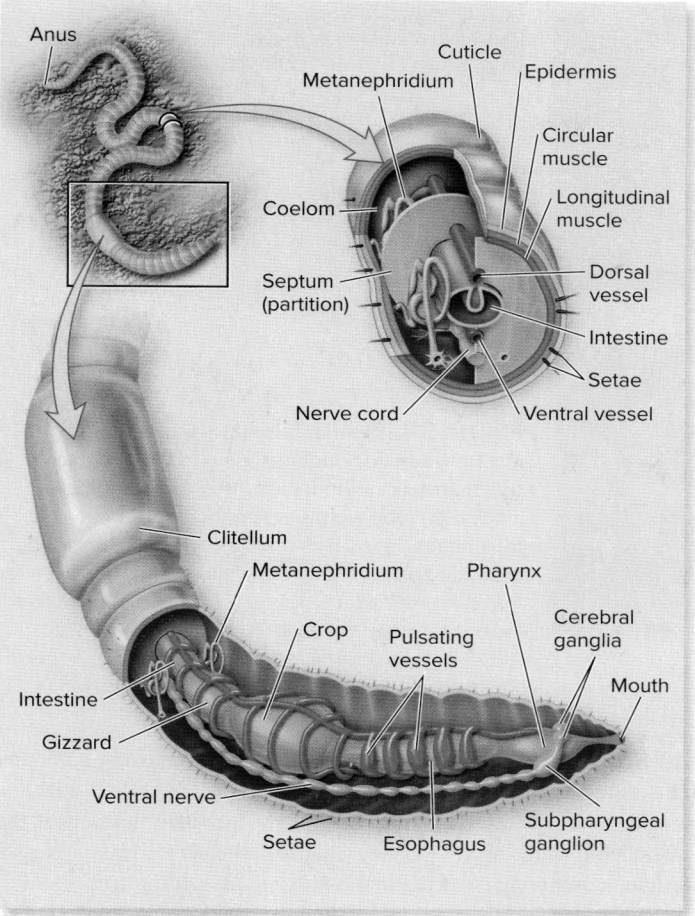

Figure 34.15 **The segmented body plan of an annelid, as illustrated by an earthworm.** The segmented nature of the worm is apparent internally as well as externally. Individual segments are separated by septa.

Concept Check: *What are some of the advantages of segmentation?*

- Annelids possess a fluid-filled coelom that acts as a hydrostatic skeleton. In unsegmented coelomate animals, muscle contractions can distort the entire body during movement. However, such distortion is minimized in segmented animals, which allows for more effective locomotion over solid surfaces.

- Segmentation permits specialization of some segments, especially at the annelid's anterior end. Animals with more complex body plans tend to produce a greater variety of specialized segments.

All annelids except the leeches have chitinous bristles, called **setae**, on each segment. In some annelids, these are situated on fleshy, footlike **parapodia** (from the Greek, meaning almost feet) that are pushed into the substrate to provide traction during movement. In others, the setae are held closer to the body. Many annelid species burrow into soil or into muddy marine sediments and extract nutrients from ingested soil or mud. Some annelids also feed on dead or living vegetation, whereas others are predatory or parasitic.

Annelids have a nervous system with a pair of cerebral ganglia that connect to a subpharyngeal ganglion (Figure 34.15). From there,

a large ventral nerve cord runs down the entire length of the body. The ventral nerve cord is unusual because it contains a few very large nerve cells called **giant axons** that facilitate high-speed neuronal conduction and rapid responses to stimuli.

Annelids have an internal transport system in which the circulatory system and the coelomic fluid both carry nutrients, wastes, and respiratory gases. The circulatory system is closed, with dorsal and ventral vessels connected by pairs of pulsating vessels. The blood of most annelid species contains the respiratory pigment hemoglobin. Respiration occurs directly through the permeable skin surface, which restricts annelids to moist environments. The digestive system is complete and unsegmented, with many specialized regions: mouth, pharynx, esophagus, crop, gizzard, intestine, and anus.

Reproduction in Annelids Sexual reproduction in annelids involves two individuals, often of separate sexes, but sometimes hermaphrodites, which exchange sperm via internal fertilization. In some species, asexual reproduction by fission occurs, in which the posterior part of the body breaks off and forms a new individual.

The Major Annelidan Groups In 2011, a study by German evolutionary biologist Torsten Struck and colleagues suggested that the phylum Annelida contains two major groups: the Errantia and the Sedentaria. Members of the Errantia have many long setae bristling out of their body and are supported on footlike parapodia (**Figure 34.16a**). Most of them are free-ranging predators with well-developed eyes and powerful jaws. Many are brightly colored. In turn, most species are important prey for fishes and crustaceans.

In the Sedentaria, setae are in close proximity to the body wall, which facilitates anchorage in tubes and burrows. The more sedentary lifestyle of the Sedentaria is associated with reductions in head appendages. Within this group, three types of lifestyles are apparent: those of tube worms, earthworms, and leeches.

Tube worms are marine sedentarians that exhibit beautiful tentacle crowns for filtering food items, such as plankton, from the water (**Figure 34.16b**). The bulk of the worm remains hidden in a tube deep in the mud or sand.

Earthworms play a unique and beneficial role in conditioning the soil, primarily due to the effects of their burrows and excretion. Earthworms ingest soil and leaf tissue to extract nutrients and in the process create burrows in the earth. As plant material and soil pass through the earthworm's digestive system, it is finely ground in the gizzard into smaller fragments. Once excreted, this material—called castings—enriches the soil (**Figure 34.16c**). Because a worm can eat its own weight in soil every day, worm castings on the soil surface can be extensive. The biologist Charles Darwin was interested in earthworm activity, and his last work, *The Formation of Vegetable Mould, through the Actions of Worms, with Observations on Their Habits*, was the first detailed study of earthworm ecology. In it, he wrote, "All the fertile areas of this planet have at least once passed through the bodies of earthworms."

Leeches are usually found in freshwater environments, but some are marine species and others are terrestrial species that inhabit warm, moist areas such as tropical forests. They have a fixed number of segments, usually 34, though in most species septa are not present. Most leeches are blood-sucking parasites of vertebrates. Unlike

(b)

(d)

(a)

(c)

Figure 34.16 Annelids. (a) This free-ranging marine worm from Indonesia is a member of the group Errantia. Members of the group Sedentaria include **(b)** tube worms, **(c)** earthworms, and **(d)** leeches. This leech species, *Hirudo medicinalis*, is sucking blood from a patient to reduce the swelling that can occur after surgery. a: ©WaterFrame/Alamy Stock Photo; b: ©J W Alker/age fotostock; c: ©Colin Varndell/Getty Images; d: ©St. Bartholomew's Hospital/Science Source

cestode and trematode flatworms, which are internally parasitic and host-specific, leeches are generally external parasites that feed on a broad range of hosts, including fishes, amphibians, and mammals. Leeches have powerful suckers at both ends of the body, and the anterior sucker is equipped with razor-sharp jaws that can bore or slice into the host's tissues. The salivary secretion (hirudin) acts as an anticoagulant to stop the prey's blood from clotting and an anesthetic to numb the pain. Leeches can suck up to several times their own weight in blood. They were once used in the medical field in the practice of bloodletting, the withdrawal of often considerable quantities of blood from a patient in the erroneous belief that this would prevent or cure illness and disease. Even today, leeches may be used after surgeries (Figure 34.16d). If the blood vessels are not fully reconnected and excess blood accumulates, a swelling called a hematoma may form. The accumulated blood blocks the delivery of new blood and stops the formation of new vessels. The leeches remove the accumulated blood, and new capillaries are more likely to form.

34.5 Ecdysozoa: The Nematodes and Arthropods

Learning Outcomes:

1. List the distinguishing characteristics of nematodes.
2. Describe the arthropod body plan and its major features.
3. Give examples of the arthropod subphyla Chelicerata, Myriapoda, Hexapoda, and Crustacea.
4. List the features that help to account for the diversity of insect species.
5. **CoreSKILL »** Explain how DNA barcoding can be useful in analyzing and controlling insect populations.

The Ecdysozoa is the sister group to the Lophotrochozoa. Although the separation is supported by molecular evidence, the Ecdysozoa is named for a process called **ecdysis**, or the periodic molting of the exoskeleton (refer back to Figure 33.13). All ecdysozoans possess a **cuticle**, a nonliving covering that both supports and protects the animal. Once formed, however, the cuticle typically cannot increase in size, which restricts the growth of the animal inside. The solution for growth is the formation of a new, softer cuticle under the old one. The old one then splits open and is sloughed off, allowing the new, soft cuticle to expand to a bigger size before it hardens.

The evolution of a cuticle was a critical innovation that led to other changes in ecdysoans. A thick cuticle, as in arthropods, impedes the diffusion of oxygen across the skin. Such species acquire oxygen by lungs, gills, or a set of branching, air-filled tubes called tracheae. The ability to shed the cuticle also opened up developmental options for the ecdysozoans. For example, many species undergo complete metamorphosis, changing from a wormlike larva into a winged adult. Animals with internal skeletons cannot do this because growth occurs only by adding more minerals to the existing skeleton. Another significant adaptation is the development of internal fertilization, which permitted species to live in dry environments. A variety of appendages specialized for locomotion evolved in many species, including legs for walking or swimming and wings for flying.

Because of these innovations, ecdysozoans are an incredibly successful group. Of the eight ecdysozoan phyla, we will consider the two most common: the nematodes and arthropods. The grouping of nematodes and arthropods is a relatively new concept supported by molecular data, and it implies that the process of molting arose only once in animal evolution. In support of this, certain hormones that stimulate molting have been discovered to exist only in both nematodes and arthropods.

The Phylum Nematoda Consists of Small Pseudocoelomate Worms Covered by a Tough Cuticle

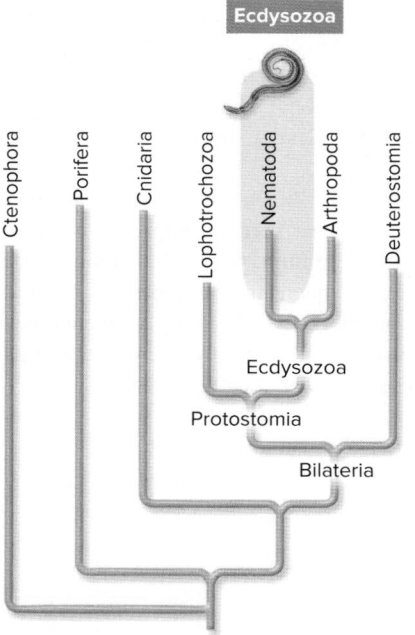

The nematodes (from the Greek *nematos*, meaning thread), also called roundworms, are small, thin worms that range in size from less than 1 mm to about 5 cm (**Figure 34.17**), although some parasitic species measuring 1 m or more have been found in the placenta of sperm whales. Nematodes are ubiquitous organisms that exist in nearly all habitats, from the poles to the tropics. They are found in the soil, in both freshwater and marine environments, and inside plants and animals as parasites. A shovelful of soil may contain a million nematodes. Over 25,000 species are known, but there are probably at least four times as many undiscovered species.

Key Features of Nematodes Nematodes have several distinguishing characteristics. A tough cuticle covers the body. The cuticle is secreted by the epidermis and is made primarily of **collagen**, a structural protein also present in vertebrates. The cuticle is shed periodically as the nematode grows. Beneath the epidermis are longitudinal muscles but no circular muscles, which means that muscle contraction results in thrashing of the body rather than smoother wormlike movement. The pseudocoelom functions as both a fluid-filled skeleton and a circulatory system. Diffusion of gases occurs through the cuticle. Nematodes have a complete digestive tract composed of a mouth, pharynx, intestine, and anus. The mouth often contains sharp, piercing organs called **stylets**, and the muscular pharynx functions to suck in food. Excretion of metabolic waste occurs via two simple tubules that have no cilia or flame cells.

Reproduction in Nematodes Nematode reproduction is usually sexual, with separate males and females, and fertilization takes place internally. Females are generally larger than males and can produce prodigious numbers of eggs, in some cases, over 100,000 per day. In some species, such as *Caenorhabditis elegans,* both hermaphrodites and males are produced. Hermaphrodites can undergo self fertilization, or they can achieve cross fertilization if they mate with a male. *C. elegans* has become a model organism for researchers to study the process of development (refer back to Figure 20.1b). Development is easily observed because the organism is transparent and composed of relatively few cells, and the generation time is short. An adult *C. elegans* has about 1000 somatic cells.

Parasitic Nematodes A large number of nematodes are parasitic in humans and other vertebrates.

- The large roundworm *Ascaris lumbricoides* is a parasite of the small intestine that can reach up to 30 cm in length. Over a billion people worldwide carry this parasite. Although infections are most prevalent in tropical or developing countries, the prevalence of *A. lumbricoides* is relatively high in rural areas of the southeastern U.S. Eggs pass out in feces and can remain viable in the soil for years, although they require ingestion before hatching into an infective stage.

- Hookworms (*Necator americanus*), so named because their anterior end curves dorsally like a hook, are also parasites of the human intestine. The eggs pass out in feces, and recently hatched hookworms can penetrate the skin of a host's foot to establish a new infection. In areas with modern plumbing, these infections are uncommon.

- Pinworms (*Enterobius vermicularis*), although a nuisance, have relatively benign effects on their hosts. The rate of infection in the U.S., however, is staggering: 30% of children and 16% of adults are believed to be hosts. Adult pinworms live in the large intestine and migrate to the anal region at night to lay their eggs, which causes intense itching. The resultant scratching can spread the eggs from the hand to the mouth.

- In the tropics, some 250 million people are infected with *Wuchereria bancrofti*, a fairly large (100 mm) worm that lives in the lymphatic system, blocking the flow of lymph, and, in extreme cases, causing elephantiasis, an extreme swelling of the legs and other body parts (**Figure 34.18**). Females release tiny, live young called microfilariae, which are transmitted to new hosts via mosquitoes.

The Phylum Arthropoda Contains Species with Jointed Appendages

The arthropods (from the Greek *arthron*, meaning joint, and *podos*, meaning foot) constitute perhaps the most diverse phylum on Earth, including familiar organisms such as spiders, insects, and crustaceans.

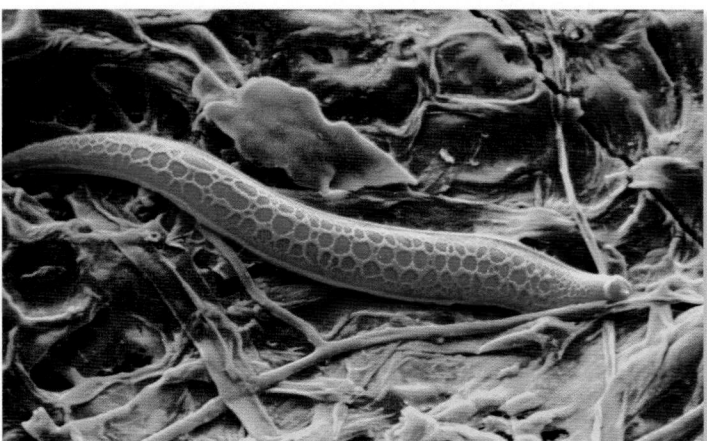

Figure 34.17 **Scanning electron micrograph of a nematode within a plant leaf.** ©Biophoto Associates/Science Source

Concept Check: *Both nematodes and annelids are wormlike in appearance. How are they different?*

[Cladogram labels: Ctenophora, Porifera, Cnidaria, Lophotrochozoa, Nematoda, Arthropoda, Deuterostomia, Ecdysozoa, Protostomia, Bilateria; box labeled Ecdysozoa]

Figure 34.18 Elephantiasis in a human leg. The disease is caused by the nematode parasite *Wuchereria bancrofti*, which lives in the lymphatic system and blocks the flow of lymph. ©Noah Seelam/Stringer/ Getty Images

crustaceans, the exoskeleton is reinforced with calcium carbonate to make it extra hard. The exoskeleton provides protection and also a point of attachment for muscles, all of which are internal. It is also relatively impermeable to water, a feature that may have enabled many arthropods to conserve water and colonize land, in much the same way as a tough seed coat allowed plants to colonize land (see Chapter 31). From this point of view, the development of a hard cuticle was a critical innovation. It also reminds us that the ability to adapt to diverse environmental conditions can itself lead to increased diversity of organisms.

Arthropods are segmented, and many of the segments bear jointed appendages. Jointed appendages permit complex movements and functions such as walking, swimming, sensing, breathing, food handling, and reproduction. These appendages are operated by muscles within each segment. In many orders, the body segments have become fused into functional units, or **tagmata**, such as the head, thorax, and abdomen of an insect (**Figure 34.19a**).

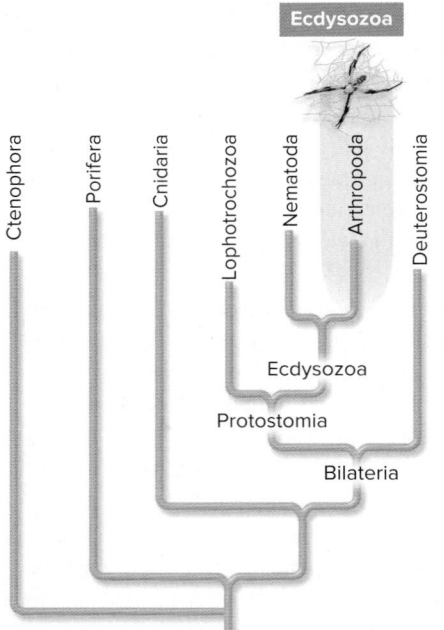

About three-quarters of all described living species present on Earth are arthropods, and scientists have estimated they are also numerically common, with an estimated 10^{18} (a billion billion) individual organisms. The huge success of the arthropods, in terms of their sheer numbers and diversity, is related to features that permit these animals to live in all the major areas on Earth, from the poles to the tropics and from marine and freshwater habitats to dry land. These features include an exoskeleton, segmentation, and jointed appendages.

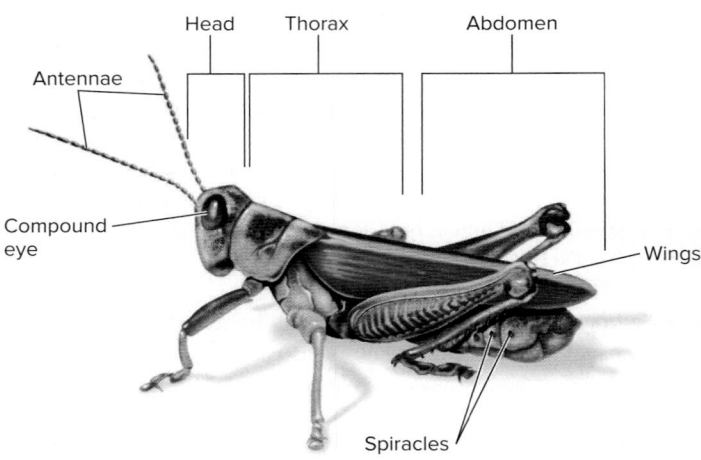

(a) External anatomy

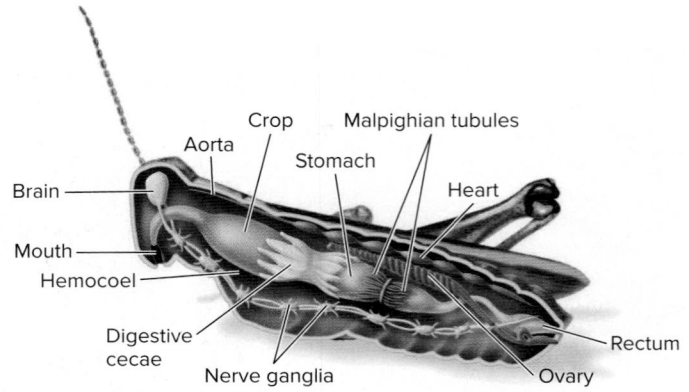

(b) Internal anatomy

Figure 34.19 Body plan of an arthropod, as represented by a grasshopper.

 Core Skill: Connections Look ahead to Figure 49.5. Why did the Malpighian tubule system play a key role in the colonization of land by insects and other arthropods?

Arthropod Body Plan The body of a typical arthropod is covered by a hard cuticle, an **exoskeleton** (external skeleton), made of layers of chitin and protein. The cuticle can be extremely tough in some parts, as in the shells of crabs, lobsters, and even beetles, yet be soft and flexible in other parts, between body segments and segments of appendages, to allow for movement. In the class of arthropods called

In arthropods, cephalization has resulted in a well-defined head, which includes a brain consisting of two or three cerebral ganglia connected to several smaller ventral nerve ganglia. Arthropods have multiple sensory organs, including organs of sight, touch, smell, hearing, and balance. They have compound eyes composed of many independent visual units called **ommatidia** (singular, ommatidium) (look ahead to Figure 44.13). Together, these lenses render a mosaic-like image of the environment. Some species, particularly some insects, possess additional simple eyes, or ocelli, that are probably only capable of distinguishing light from dark.

Like most mollusks, arthropods have an open circulatory system (look ahead to Figure 48.1a), in which hemolymph is pumped from a tubelike heart into the aorta or short arteries and then into the open sinuses that coalesce to form a cavity called the hemocoel. From the hemocoel, gases and nutrients from the hemolymph diffuse into tissues. The hemolymph flows back into the heart via pores, called ostia, that are equipped with valves.

Because the cuticle impedes the diffusion of gases through the body surface, arthropods require special organs that permit gas exchange. In aquatic arthropods, these consist of feathery gills that have an extensive surface area in contact with the surrounding water. Terrestrial species have a highly developed **tracheal system** (look ahead to Figure 48.18). On the body surface, pores called **spiracles** provide openings to a series of finely branched air tubes within the body called trachea. The tracheal system delivers oxygen directly to tissues and cells, and the circulatory system does not play a role in gas exchange.

The digestive system of arthropods is complex and often includes a mouth, crop, stomach, intestine, and rectum (**Figure 34.19b**). The stomach has glands called digestive cecae that secrete digestive enzymes. Excretion is accomplished by specialized metanephridia or, in insects and some other taxa, by **Malpighian tubules**, extensive tubes that extend from the digestive tract into body cavity, where they are surrounded by hemolymph (look ahead to Figure 49.5). Nitrogenous wastes are absorbed by the tubules and emptied into the gut, where the intestine and rectum reabsorb water and salts and the waste is excreted through the anus. This excretory system, allowing the retention of water, was another critical innovation that permitted the colonization of land by arthropods.

Major Subphyla of Arthropods

The history of arthropod classification is extensive and active. Although many classifications have been proposed, a 1995 study of the mitochondrial DNA of arthropod species by American geneticist Jeffrey Boore and colleagues suggests a phylogeny with five main subphyla: one now-extinct subphyla, Trilobita (trilobites); and four living subphyla, Chelicerata (spiders and scorpions), Myriapoda (millipedes and centipedes), Hexapoda (insects and relatives), and Crustacea (crabs and relatives) (**Table 34.4**).

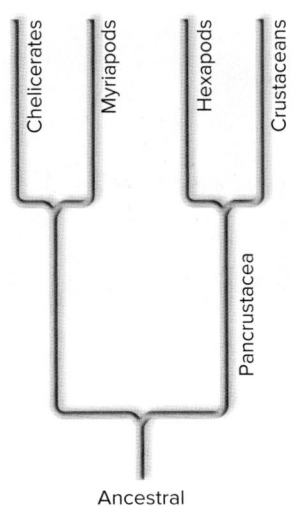
Chelicerates — Myriapods — Hexapods — Crustaceans — Pancrustacea — Ancestral arthropod

Table 34.4	Main Subphyla and Characteristics of Arthropods	
	Subphyla and examples (est. number of species)	Class characteristics
	Chelicerata: spiders, scorpions, mites, ticks, horseshoe crabs, and sea spiders (74,000)	Body usually with cephalothorax and abdomen only; six pairs of appendages, including four pairs of legs, one pair of fangs, and one pair of pedipalps; terrestrial; predatory or parasitic
	Myriapoda: millipedes and centipedes (13,000)	Body with head and highly segmented trunk. In millipedes, each segment with two pairs of walking legs; terrestrial; herbivorous. In centipedes, each segment with one pair of walking legs; terrestrial; predatory, poison jaws
	Hexapoda: insects such as beetles, butterflies, flies, fleas, grasshoppers, ants, bees, wasps, termites, and springtails (>1 million)	Body with head, thorax, and abdomen; mouthparts modified for biting, chewing, sucking, or lapping; usually with two pairs of wings and three pairs of legs; mostly terrestrial, some freshwater; herbivorous, parasitic, or predatory
	Crustacea: crabs, lobsters, shrimp (45,000)	Body of two to three parts; three or more pairs of legs; chewing mouthparts; usually marine

Boore's research showed that the Trilobita were among the earliest-diverging arthropods. The lineage then split into two groups. One, often referred to as the Pancrustacea, contains the insects and crustaceans. The other, with no overarching name, contains the myriapods and chelicerates. Molecular evidence suggests that insects are more closely related to crustaceans than they are to spiders or millipedes and centipedes. We will take a closer look at insects and crustaceans due to their relative sizes and importance to humans.

Subphylum Trilobita: Extinct Early Arthropods

The trilobites were among the earliest arthropods, flourishing in shallow seas of the Paleozoic era, some 500 mya, and dying out about 250 mya. Most trilobites were bottom feeders and were generally 3–10 cm in size, although some reached almost 1 m in length (**Figure 34.20**). They had three main tagmata: the head, thorax, and tail. Trilobites also had two dorsal grooves that divided the body longitudinally into three lobes—an axial lobe and two pleural lobes—a structural characteristic that gave the subphylum its name. Most of the body segments showed little specialization. In contrast, later-diverging arthropods developed specialized appendages on many segments, including appendages for grasping, walking, and swimming.

Head   Thorax   Tail

Pleural lobe

Axial lobe

Figure 34.20   A fossil trilobite. About 4,000 fossil species of these early arthropods, including *Modocia centralis*, shown here, which was about 20 cm long, have been described. ©Sinclair Stammers/Getty Images

Subphylum Chelicerata: The Spiders, Scorpions, Mites, and Ticks

The Chelicerata consists mainly of the class Arachnida, which contains predatory spiders and scorpions as well as the ticks and mites, some of which are blood-sucking parasites that feed on vertebrates. The two other living classes are the Merostomata, the horseshoe crabs (four species), and the Pycnogonida, the sea spiders (1,000 species), both of which are marine, reflecting the group's marine ancestry. All species have a body consisting of two tagmata: a fused head and thorax, called a cephalothorax, and an abdomen. They also possess six pairs of appendages: the chelicerae, or fangs; a pair of pedipalps, which have various sensory, predatory, or reproductive functions; and four pairs of walking legs.

Spider fangs are supplied with venom from poison glands. Most spider bites are harmless to humans, although they are very effective in immobilizing and/or killing their insect prey. Venom from some species, including the black widow (*Latrodectus mactans*; **Figure 34.21a**) and the brown recluse (*Loxosceles recluse*), are potentially, although rarely, fatal to humans. The toxin of the black widow is a neurotoxin, which interferes with the functioning of the nervous system, whereas that of the brown recluse is hemolytic,

meaning it destroys red blood cells around the bite. After the spider has subdued its prey, it pumps digestive fluid into the tissues via the fangs and sucks out the partially digested meal.

Spiders have abdominal silk glands, called spinnerets, and many spin webs to catch prey (**Figure 34.22a**). The silk is a protein that stiffens after extrusion from the body because the mechanical shearing causes a change in the organization of the protein's structure. Silk is stronger than steel of the same diameter and is more elastic than Kevlar, the material used in bulletproof vests. Each spider family constructs a characteristic size and style of web and can do it perfectly on its first attempt, indicating that web spinning is an innate (instinctual) behavior (see Chapter 55). Spiders also use silk to wrap up prey and to construct egg sacs. Interestingly, spiders that are fed drugged prey spin their webs differently than do undrugged spiders (**Figure 34.22b** and **c**).

Scorpions (order Scorpionida) are generally tropical or subtropical animals that feed primarily on insects, though they may eat spiders and other arthropods as well as smaller reptiles and mice. Their pedipalps are modified into large claws, and the abdomen tapers into a stinger, which is used to inject venom. Although the venom of most North American species is generally not fatal to humans, that of the *Centruroides* genus from deserts in the U.S. Southwest and Mexico can be deadly. Fatal species are also found in India, Africa, and other countries. Unlike spiders, which lay eggs, scorpions bear live young that the mother then carries around on her back until they have their first molt (**Figure 34.21b**).

In mites and ticks (order Acari), the two main body segments (cephalothorax and abdomen) are fused and appear as one large segment. Many mite species are free-living scavengers that feed on dead plant or animal material. Other mites are serious pests on crops, and some, like chiggers (*Trombicula alfreddugesi*), are parasites of humans that spread diseases such as typhus (**Figure 34.21c**). Chiggers are parasites only on their larval stage. Chiggers do not bore into the skin; their bite and salivary secretions cause skin irritation. *Demodex brevis* is a hair-follicle mite that is common in animals and humans. The mite is estimated to be present on over 90% of adult humans. Although the mite causes no irritation in most humans,

(a) Black widow spider

(b) Scorpion with young

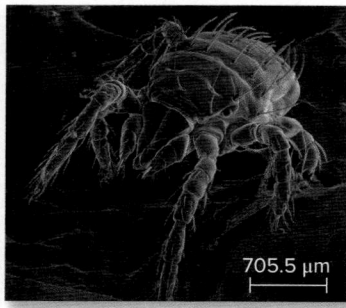

705.5 µm

(c) Chigger mite

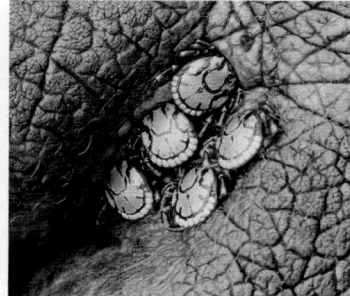

(d) Bont ticks

Figure 34.21   Common arachnids. (a) Female black widow spider (*Latrodectus mactans*). **(b)** The Central American black scorpion (*Centruroides gracilis*) is highly venomous and carries its young on its back. **(c)** SEM of a chigger mite (*Trombicula alfreddugesi*) that can cause irritation to human skin and spread disease. **(d)** These South African bont ticks (*Amblyomma hebraeum*) are feeding on a white rhinoceros. a: ©George Grall/Getty Images; b: ©Mark Smith/Science Source; c: ©David Scharf/Science Source; d: ©Roger De LaHarpe/Gallo Images/Corbis/Getty Images

Concept Check: *What is one of the main characteristics distinguishing arachnids from insects?*

(a) Normal web

(b) Web spun by spider fed with prey containing caffeine

(c) Web spun by spider fed with prey containing marijuana

Figure 34.22 Spider-web construction by normal and drugged spiders. a–c: ©NASA/SPL/Science Source

 Core Concept: Science and Society Some scientists have suggested using web-spinning spiders to test substances for the presence of drugs or even to indicate environmental contamination.

Demodex canis causes the skin disease known as mange in domestic animals, particularly dogs.

Ticks are larger than mites, and all are ectoparasitic, feeding on the body surface of vertebrates. Their life cycle includes attachment to a host, sucking blood until they are replete, and dropping off the host to molt (**Figure 34.21d**). Ticks can carry a variety of viral and bacterial diseases, including Lyme disease, a bacterial disease so named because it was first observed in the town of Lyme, Connecticut, in the 1970s.

Subphylum Myriapoda: The Millipedes and Centipedes Myriapods have one pair of antennae on the head and three pairs of appendages that are modified as mouthparts, including mandibles that act like jaws. The millipedes and centipedes, both wormlike arthropods with legs, are among the earliest terrestrial animal phyla known. Millipedes (class Diplopoda) have two pairs of legs per segment, as their class name denotes (from the Latin *diplo*, meaning two, and *podos*, meaning feet), not 1,000 legs, as their common name suggests (**Figure 34.23a**). They are slow-moving herbivores that eat decaying leaves and other plant material. When threatened, the millipede's response is to roll up into a protective coil. Many millipede species

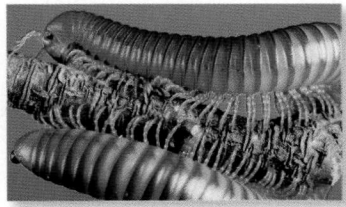
(a) Two millipedes

(b) A centipede

Figure 34.23 Millipedes and centipedes. (a) Millipedes have two pairs of legs per segment. **(b)** The venom of the giant centipede (Scolopendra heros) is known to produce significant swelling and pain in humans. a: ©David Aubrey/Corbis/Getty Images; b: ©Larry Miller/Science Source

also have glands on their underside that can eject a variety of toxic, repellent secretions. Some millipedes are brightly colored, warning potential predators that they can protect themselves.

Class Chilopoda (from the Latin *chilo*, meaning lip, and *podos*, meaning feet), or centipedes, are fast-moving carnivores that have one pair of walking legs per segment (**Figure 34.23b**). The head has many sensory appendages, including a pair of antennae and three pairs of appendages modified as mouthparts, including powerful claws connected to poison glands. The venom of some larger species, such as *Scolopendra heros*, is powerful enough to cause pain in humans. Most species do not have a waxy waterproofing layer on their cuticle and so are restricted to moist environments under leaf litter or in decaying logs, usually coming out at night to actively hunt their prey.

Subphylum Hexapoda: Insects and Relatives Hexapods are six-legged arthropods. Most are insects, but a few earlier-diverging noninsect hexapods have been identified, including soil-dwelling groups such as collembolans, and molecular studies have shown that these represent a separate but related lineage. Insects are in a class by themselves (Insecta), literally and figuratively. Biologists have classified more species of insects than all other species of animal life combined. Approximately 1 million species of insects have been described thus far, and according to a 2015 estimate by British Entomologist Nigel Stork, 4 million more species await description. At least 90,000 species of insects have been identified in the U.S. and Canada alone. DNA barcoding, which is discussed later in this chapter, can help resolve many taxonomic dilemmas between closely related species.

Insects are the subject of an entire field of scientific study, **entomology**. They are studied in large part because of their significance as pests of the world's agricultural crops and carriers of some of the world's most deadly diseases. Insects live in all terrestrial habitats, and virtually all species of plants are fed upon by at least one, usually tens, and sometimes, in the case of large trees, hundreds of insect species. Because approximately one-quarter of the world's crops are lost annually to insects, researchers are constantly trying to find ways to reduce pest densities. Insect pest reduction often involves chemical control (the use of pesticides) or biological control (the use of living organisms). Many species of insects are also important pests or parasites of humans and livestock, both by their own actions and as vectors of diseases such as malaria and sleeping sickness.

In contrast, insects also provide us with many types of essential biological services. We depend on insects such as honeybees, butterflies, and moths to pollinate our crops. Bees also produce honey, and silkworms are the source of silk fiber. Despite the revulsion they provoke in us, fly larvae (maggots) are important in the decomposition process of both dead plants and animals. In addition, we use insects in the biological control of other insects.

Key Features of Insects Of paramount importance to the success of insects was the evolution of wings, a feature possessed by no other arthropod and indeed no other living animal except birds and bats. Unlike vertebrate wings, however, insect wings are outgrowths of the body wall cuticle and are not true segmental appendages. This means that insects still have all their walking legs. Insects are thus like the mythological horse Pegasus, which sprouted wings out of its back while retaining all four legs. In contrast, birds and bats have one pair of appendages (arms) modified for flight, which leaves them considerably less agile on the ground.

Insects in different orders have also evolved a variety of mouthparts in which the constituent parts, the mandibles and maxillae, are modified for different functions (**Figure 34.24**). Many of these mouthparts are modified walking appendages and are bilaterally paired. As a result, the jaws of many insects, such as grasshoppers, move in a side-to-side motion, rather than up and down as human jaws do.

- Grasshoppers, beetles, dragonflies, and many others have mouthparts adapted for chewing.
- Mosquitoes and many plant pests have mouthparts adapted for piercing and sucking.
- Butterflies and moths have a coiled tongue (**proboscis**) that can be uncoiled, enabling them to drink nectar from flowers.
- Some flies have lapping, spongelike mouthparts that sop up liquid food.

Their varied mouthparts are adaptations that allow insects to specialize their feeding on virtually anything: plant matter, decaying organic matter, and other living animals. The biological diversity of insects is therefore related to environmental diversity, in this case, the variety of foods that insects eat. Parasitic insects attach themselves to other species, and some insect parasites (called hyperparasites) even feed on other parasites, as noted in a verse sometimes attributed to the 18th-century English poet and satirist Jonathan Swift:

> Big fleas have little fleas
>
> upon their backs to bite 'em;
>
> and little fleas have lesser fleas
>
> and so, ad infinitum.

Major Orders of Insects The diversity of insects is astounding: Hexapoda is composed of 35 orders, some of which have over 100,000 species. The most common orders are described in **Table 34.5**.

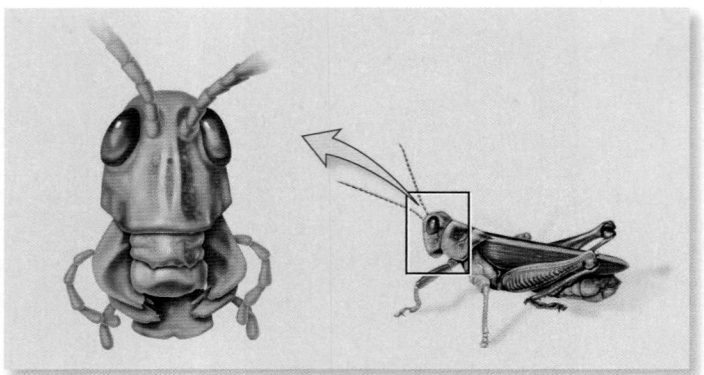

(a) Chewing (grasshopper)

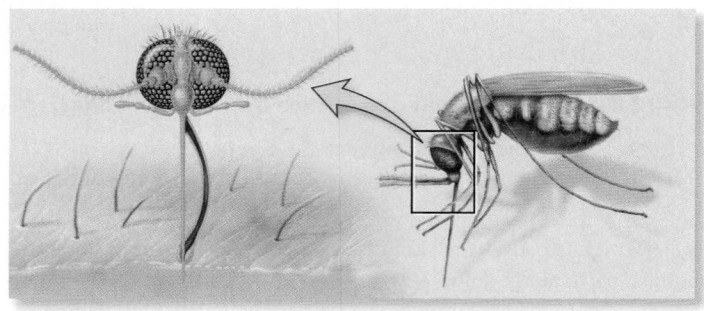

(b) Piercing and blood sucking (mosquito)

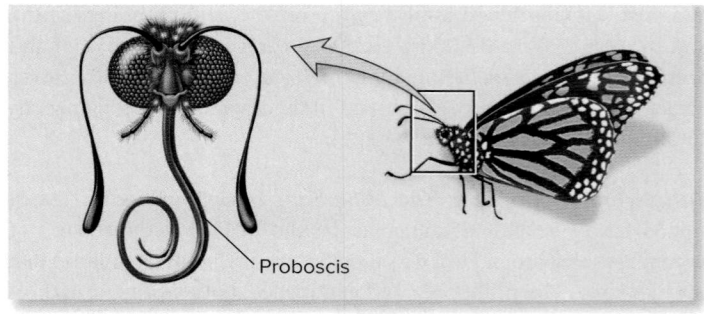

Proboscis

(c) Nectar sucking (butterfly)

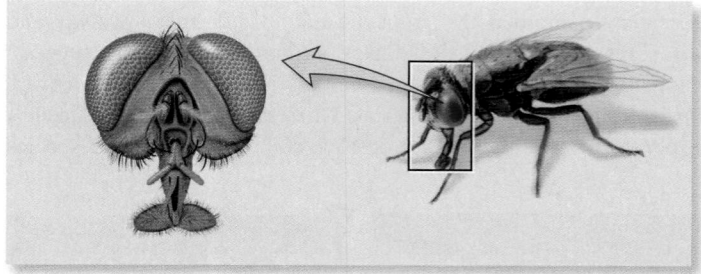

(d) Sponging liquid (housefly)

Figure 34.24 A variety of insect mouthparts. Insect mouthparts have become modified in ways that allow insects to feed by a variety of methods, including **(a)** chewing (Orthoptera, Coleoptera, and others), **(b)** piercing and blood sucking (Diptera), **(c)** nectar sucking (Lepidoptera), and **(d)** sponging up liquid (Diptera).

Concept Check: *Insects have a variety of mouthparts. Name two other key insect adaptations.*

Table 34.5   Major Orders and Characteristics of Insects

Order and examples (approx. number of described species)		Order characteristics
Coleoptera: beetles, weevils (400,000)		Two pairs of wings (front pair thick and leathery, acting as wing cases, back pair membranous); armored exoskeleton; biting and chewing mouthparts; complete metamorphosis; largest order of insects
Hymenoptera: ants, bees, wasps (130,000)		Two pairs of membranous wings; chewing or sucking mouthparts; many have posterior stinging organ on females; complete metamorphosis; many species social; important pollinators
Diptera: flies, mosquitoes (120,000)		One pair of wings with hind wings modified into halteres (balancing organs); sucking, piercing, or lapping mouthparts; complete metamorphosis; larvae are grublike maggots in various food sources; some adults are disease vectors
Lepidoptera: butterflies, moths (150,000)		Two pairs of colorful wings covered with tiny scales; long tubelike tongue for sucking; complete metamorphosis; larvae are plant-feeding caterpillars; adults are important pollinators
Hemiptera: true bugs; assassin bug, bedbug, chinch bug, cicada (82,000)		Two pairs of membranous wings; piercing or sucking mouthparts; incomplete metamorphosis; many are plant feeders; some are predatory or blood feeders; vectors of plant diseases
Orthoptera: crickets, grasshoppers (20,000)		Two pairs of wings (front pair leathery, back pair membranous); chewing mouthparts; mostly herbivorous; incomplete metamorphosis; powerful hind legs for jumping
Odonata: damselflies, dragonflies (5,500)		Two pairs of long, membranous wings; chewing mouthparts; large eyes; predatory on other insects; incomplete metamorphosis; nymphs aquatic; considered early-diverging insects
Siphonaptera: fleas (2,400)		Wingless, laterally flattened; piercing and sucking mouthparts; adults are bloodsuckers on birds and mammals; jumping legs; complete metamorphosis; vectors of plague
Phthiraptera: sucking lice (3,000)		Wingless ectoparasites; sucking mouthparts; flattened body; reduced eyes; legs with clawlike tarsi for clinging to skin; incomplete metamorphosis; very host-specific; vectors of typhus
Isoptera: termites (2,300)		Two pairs of membranous wings when present; some stages wingless; chewing mouthparts; social species; incomplete metamorphosis

 Core Skill: Modeling The goal of this modeling challenge is to develop a mathematical model that allows you to estimate the number of insect species on Earth.

Modeling Challenge: Some biologists have suggested that we don't know within an order of magnitude how many species exist on Earth. Because insects represent by far the largest taxa on Earth, the answer to this question is dependent on knowing the number of insect species. Of the insects, the best known are the showy butterflies, with 15,000–20,000 species known worldwide. In Britain, insect diversity is almost completely known, with 67 species of butterflies and a total of 24,043 insect species. Create a mathematical model that allows you to estimate the number of insect species on Earth. (Hint: Look ahead to Section 56.1 and read about the mark-recapture technique if you get stuck.) Can you think of some assumptions your model makes?

Although all insects have six legs, different orders have slightly different wing structures, and many of the orders are based on wing type (their names often include the root *pter-*, from the Greek *pteron*, meaning wing).

- In beetles (Coleoptera), only the back pair of wings is functional; the front wings have become protective shell-like coverings under which the back pair folds when not in use.

- Wasps and bees (Hymenoptera) have two pairs of wings that are hooked together and move as one wing.

- Flies (Diptera) possess only one pair of wings (the front pair); the back pair has been modified into a small pair of balancing organs, called halteres, that act like miniature gyroscopes.

- Butterflies (Lepidoptera) have wings that are covered in scales (from the Greek *lepido*, meaning scale); other insects generally have clear, membranous wings.

- In ant and termite colonies, the queen and the drones (males) retain their wings, whereas female individuals called workers have lost theirs. Other orders, such as fleas and lice, are completely wingless.

Reproduction and Development of Insects

All insects have separate sexes, and fertilization is internal. During development, the majority (approximately 85%) of insects undergo a change in body form known as **complete metamorphosis** (from the Greek *meta*, meaning change, and *morph*, meaning form) (**Figure 34.25a**). Animals that undergo complete metamorphosis advance through four stages: egg, larva, pupa, and adult. The dramatic body transformation from larva to adult occurs in the pupa stage. The larval stage is often spent in an entirely different habitat from that of the adult, and larval and adult forms use different food sources. Consequently, they do not compete directly for the same resources. The larval stage, such as a caterpillar, is focused on eating and growth, whereas the adult stage involves sexual reproduction. Most adult insects have wings, allowing them to disperse their fertilized eggs over a larger area.

A smaller percentage of insect species undergo **incomplete metamorphosis**, in which morphological changes are more gradual (**Figure 34.25b**). Incomplete metamorphosis has only three stages: egg, nymph, and adult. Young insects, called nymphs, look like miniature adults when they hatch from their eggs, but usually don't have wings. As they grow and feed, they shed their exoskeleton and replace it with a larger one several times, each time entering a new instar, or stage of growth. When the insects reach their adult size, they have also grown wings.

Some insects, such as bees, wasps, ants, and termites, have developed complex social behavior and live cooperatively in underground or aboveground nests. Such colonies exhibit a division of labor, in that some individuals forage for food and care for the brood (workers), others protect the nest (soldiers), and some only reproduce (the queen and drones) (**Figure 34.26**).

Subphylum Crustacea: Crabs, Lobsters, Barnacles, and Shrimp

The crustaceans are common inhabitants of marine environments, although some species live in fresh water and a few are terrestrial. Many species, including crabs, lobsters, crayfish, and shrimp, are

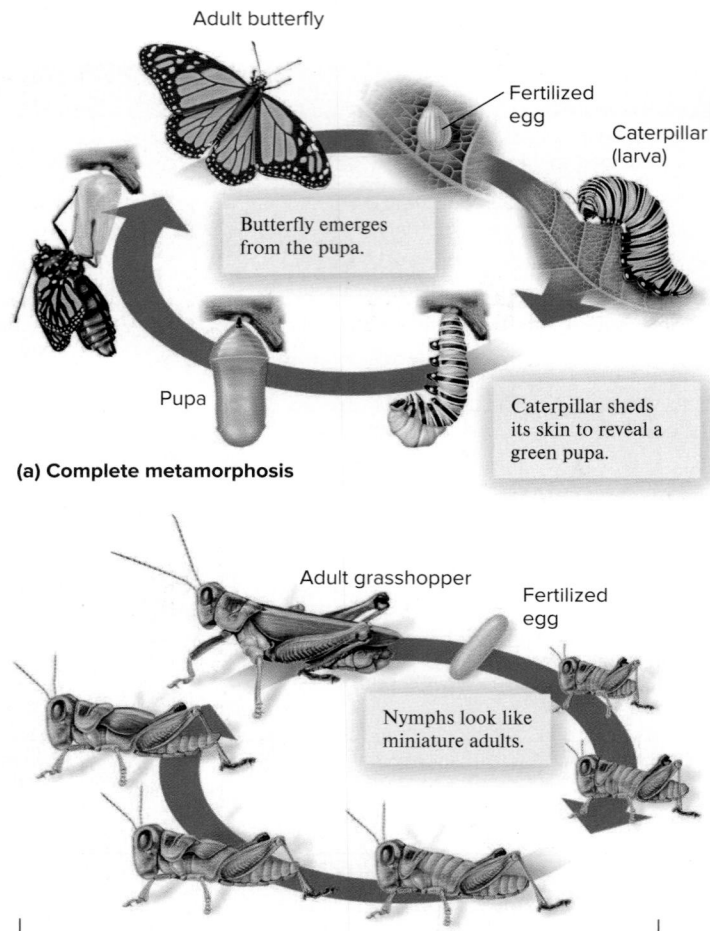

(a) Complete metamorphosis

(b) Incomplete metamorphosis

Figure 34.25 Metamorphosis. (a) Complete metamorphosis, as illustrated by the life cycle of a monarch butterfly. The adult butterfly has a completely different appearance than the larval caterpillar. **(b)** Incomplete metamorphosis, as illustrated by the life cycle of a grasshopper. The eggs hatch into nymphs, essentially miniature versions of the adult.

(a) Worker and soldier ants　　**(b) Queen ant**

Figure 34.26 The division of labor in insect societies. Individuals from the same insect colony may appear very different. Among these army ants (*Eciton burchelli*) from Paraguay, **(a)** workers forage for the colony, soldiers (with large mandibles) protect the colony from predators, and **(b)** the queen produces eggs. a: Source: Alex Wild/myrmecos .net; b: ©Oxford Scientific/Getty Images

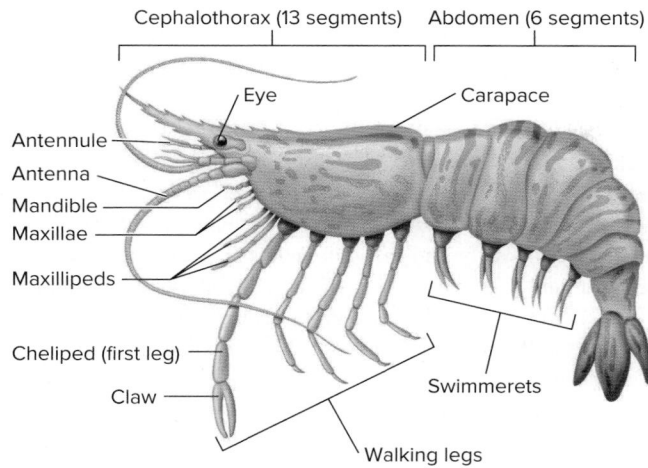

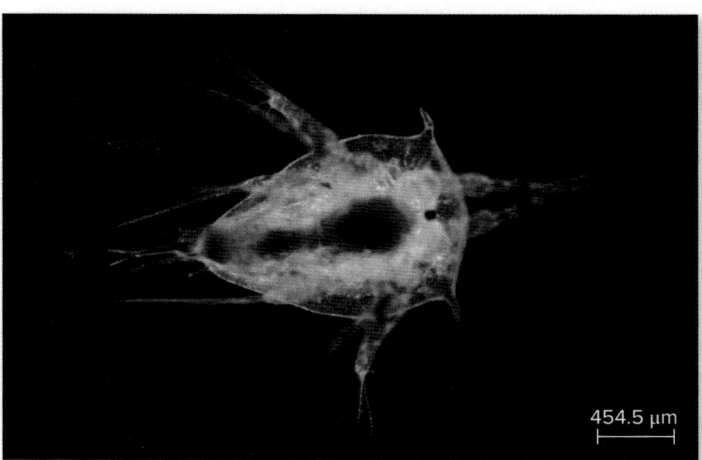

Figure 34.27 Body plan of a crustacean, as represented by a shrimp.

 Core Skill: Connections Look ahead to Figure 44.8. Where are a crustacean's organs of balance located?

Figure 34.28 Crustacean larva. The nauplius, a distinct larval stage exhibited by most crustaceans, molts several times before reaching maturity. Many of these larvae are less than 0.01 mm long.
©FLPA/D P Wilson/age fotostock

economically important food items for humans; smaller species are important food sources for other predators.

Crustacean Body Plan The crustaceans are unique among the arthropods in that they possess two pairs of antennae at the anterior end of the body—the antennule (first pair) and antenna (second pair) (**Figure 34.27**). In addition, they have three or more sensory and feeding appendages that are modified mouthparts: the mandibles, maxillae, and maxillipeds. These are followed by walking legs and, often, additional abdominal appendages, called swimmerets, and a powerful tail. In some orders, the first pair of walking legs, or chelipeds, is modified to form powerful claws. The head and thorax are often fused together, forming the cephalothorax. In many species, the cuticle covering the head extends over most of the cephalothorax, forming a hard protective covering called the **carapace**. For growth to occur, a crustacean must shed the entire exoskeleton.

Many crustaceans are predators, but others are scavengers, and some, such as barnacles, are filter feeders. Gas exchange typically

occurs via gills, and crustaceans, like other arthropods, have an open circulatory system. Crustaceans possess two excretory organs: antennal glands and maxillary glands, both modified metanephridia, which open at the bases of the antennae and the maxillae, respectively. Reproduction usually involves separate sexes, and fertilization is internal. Most species carry their eggs in brood pouches under the female's body. Eggs of most species produce larvae that must go through many different molts prior to assuming adult form. The first of these larval stages, called a **nauplius**, is very different in appearance from the adult crustacean (**Figure 34.28**).

Crustacean Diversity Crustacean clades are numerous, but most are small and obscure, although many orders contain important prey items for other marine organisms. For example, copepods are tiny and abundant planktonic crustaceans, which are a food source for filter-feeding organisms and small fish. The clade Cirripedia is composed of the barnacles, crustaceans whose carapace forms calcified plates that cover most of the body (**Figure 34.29a**). Their legs are modified into feathery filter-feeding structures.

(a) Goose barnacles—order Cirripedia

(b) Pill bug—order Isopoda

(c) Coral crab—order Decapoda

Figure 34.29 Common crustaceans. (a) Goose barnacles (*Lepas anatifera*). **(b)** Pill bug, or wood louse (*Armadillium vulgare*). **(c)** Coral crab (*Carpilius maculates*). a: ©NHPA/Photoshot; b: ©Miyuki Satake/iStock/Getty Images; c: ©Masa Ushioda/Waterframe/age fotostock

Malacostraca is the largest class of the crustaceans and is divided into many orders. For example, Euphausiacea are shrimplike krill that grow to about 3 cm and provide a large part of the diet of many whales, seals, penguins, fish, and squid. The order Isopoda contains many small species that are parasitic on marine fishes. Terrestrial isopods, better known as pill bugs, or wood lice, retain a strong connection to water and need to live in moist environments such as leaf litter or decaying logs (**Figure 34.29b**). When threatened, they curl up into a tight ball, making it difficult for predators to get a grip on them.

The most familiar Malacostracan order is Decapoda, which includes the crabs and lobsters, the largest crustacean species (**Figure 34.29c**). As their name suggests, these decapods have 10 walking legs (five pairs), although the first pair is invariably modified to support large claws. Most decapods are marine, but many are freshwater species, such as crayfish. In hot, moist tropical areas, some species, called land crabs, are terrestrial.

 Core Concept: Information

DNA Barcoding: A New Tool for Species Identification

The International Barcoding of Life (IBOL) project, begun in 2003 by Canadian biologist Paul Hebert, is a broad initiative that seeks to create a digital identification system for all life-forms. Hebert made the analogy that the large diversity of products in a grocery store can each be distinguished with a relatively small barcode. Though the diversity of the world's animal species is considerably larger, he reasoned that all species could be distinguished using their DNA. The complete genome would be too large to analyze rapidly, so Hebert suggested analyzing a small piece of DNA of all species. The DNA sequence he proposed for animals is the first 648 base pairs of a gene called *CO1*, for cytochrome oxidase, an enzyme in the electron transport chain of mitochondria (refer back to Figure 7.8). All animals have this gene in their mitochondrial DNA. A key observation is that although this part of the *CO1* gene varies widely between species, it hardly varies at all between individuals of the same species—only 2%.

From a practical perspective, DNA barcoding may be used to analyze and control insect populations For example, about 3,500 species of mosquitoes have been identified, but many of them are hard to tell apart, especially in the field. Some mosquitoes transmit deadly diseases such as malaria and yellow fever and are subject to stringent control measures in many countries. The Mosquito Barcoding Initiative aims to catalog each mosquito species by analyzing the *CO1* gene and thereby build up a DNA barcode database. Field researchers will be able to quickly analyze the DNA of some individuals in a given area and identify them based on existing barcodes. Appropriate control measures can then be instigated against a mosquito population if it contains members of a species that is known to be a disease carrier.

For blood-feeding insects, scientists can also bar code their blood meals, target their feeding preferences, and optimize control measures accordingly. For example, tsetse flies transmit tryptosomiasis, a parasitic disease that causes sleeping sickness in humans, and African animal trypanosomiasis, a disease that leads to serious economic losses of livestock. Tsetse flies are hard to track in nature because of their solitary habits and secretive nature, hiding in bushes and waiting for prey to pass by. Capturing tsetse flies and DNA barcoding their blood meals avoids the necessity of costly and difficult field behavioral studies. If cattle are found to be the source of most blood, spraying them with insecticides is an effective control strategy. If wildlife such as buffalo, giraffe, elephants, and warthogs are the source, then trapping devices may be used.

Hebert foresees the day when all species can be identified by their DNA barcodes. A huge advantage is that only a small sample of cells is necessary. The sample can come from an adult or immature individual, which is a great help since much insect taxonomy is based solely on adults. Many scientists anticipate the day when handheld field barcoding identification devices will be commonly used. At the moment, barcoding involves a laboratory analysis taking about an hour and costing $2.00 per sample.

34.6 Deuterostomia: The Echinoderms and Chordates

Learning Outcomes:

1. Identify the distinguishing characteristics of echinoderms.
2. Describe the four critical innovations in the body plan of chordates.
3. List the two invertebrate subphyla of Chordata, and explain their relationship to the vertebrates.

As discussed in Chapter 33, the deuterostomes are grouped together because they share similarities in patterns of development (refer back to Figure 33.6). Molecular evidence also supports a deuterostome clade. All animals in the phylum Chordata (from the Greek *chorde*, meaning string, referring to the spinal cord), which includes the vertebrates, are deuterostomes. Interestingly, so is one invertebrate group, the phylum Echinodermata, which includes the sea stars, sea urchins, and sea cucumbers. Although there are far fewer phyla and species of deuterostomes than

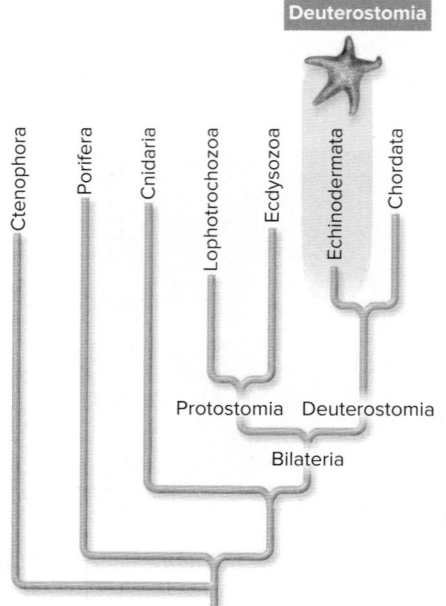

protostomes, the deuterostomes are generally much more familiar to us. After all, we humans are deuterostomes.

We will conclude our discussion of invertebrate biology by turning our attention to the invertebrate deuterostomes. In this section, we will explore the phylum Echinodermata and then introduce the phylum Chordata, looking in particular at its distinguishing characteristics and at its two invertebrate subphyla: the cephalochordates, commonly referred to as the lancelets, and the urochordates, also known as the tunicates. We will discuss the subphylum Vertebrata in Chapter 35.

The Phylum Echinodermata Includes Sea Stars and Sea Urchins—Species with a Water Vascular System

The phylum Echinodermata (from the Greek *echinos*, meaning spiny, and *derma*, meaning skin) consists of a unique grouping of deuterostomes. A striking feature of all echinoderms is their modified radial symmetry. The body of most species can be divided into five parts pointing out from the center. As a consequence, cephalization is absent in most classes. There is no brain and only a simple nervous system consisting of a central nerve ring from which arise radial branches to each limb. The radial symmetry of echinoderms is secondary, present only in adults. The free-swimming larvae have bilateral symmetry and metamorphose into the radially symmetrical adult form.

Echinoderm Body Plan   Most echinoderms have an **endoskeleton**, an internal hard skeleton composed of calcareous plates overlaid by a thin skin (**Figure 34.30**). The skeleton is covered with spines and jawlike pincers called pedicellariae, the primary purpose of which is to deter settling of animals such as barnacles. These structures can also have poison glands.

Echinoderms possess a true coelom, and a portion of the coelom has been adapted to serve as a unique **water vascular system**, a network of canals that branch into tiny **tube feet** that function in movement, gas exchange, feeding, and excretion (see inset to Figure 34.30). The water vascular system uses hydraulic power (water pressure generated by the contraction of muscles), which enables the tube feet to extend and contract, allowing echinoderms to move, but only very slowly.

Water enters the water vascular system through the **madreporite**, a sievelike plate on the animal's surface. From there it flows into the **ring canal** in the central disc, into five radial canals, and into the tube feet. At the base of each tube foot is a muscular sac called an **ampulla**, which stores water. Contractions of the ampullae force water into the tube feet, causing them to straighten and extend. When the foot contacts a solid surface, muscles in the foot contract, forcing water back into the ampulla. Sea stars also use their tube feet in feeding, by exerting a constant, strong pressure on bivalves, whose adductor muscles open and close the shell. The adductor muscles eventually tire, allowing the shell to open slightly. At this stage, the sea star everts its stomach and inserts it into the opening. It then digests its prey, using juices secreted from extensive digestive glands. Sea stars also feed on sea urchins, brittle stars, and sand dollars, prey that cannot easily escape them.

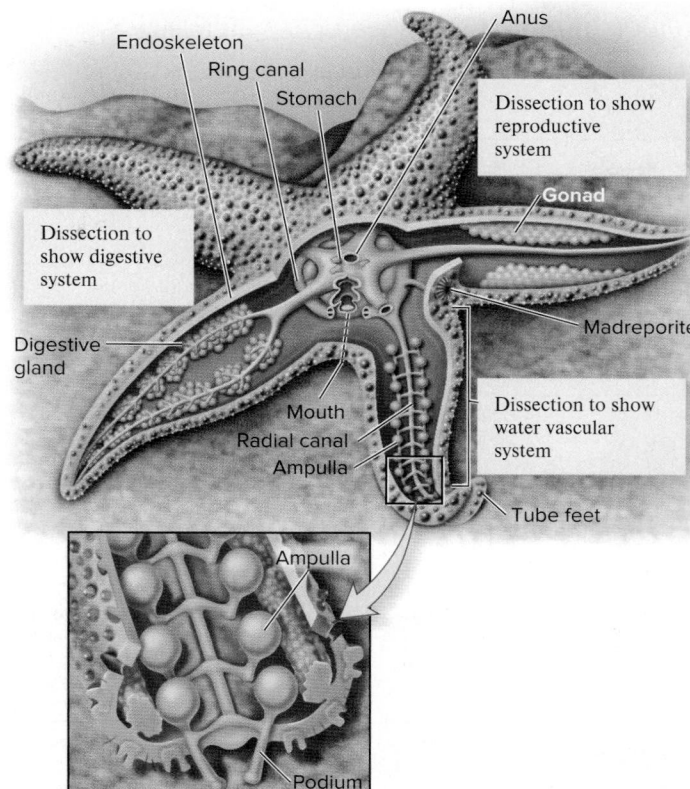

Figure 34.30   Body plan of an echinoderm, as represented by a sea star. The arms of this sea star have been dissected to different degrees to show the echinoderm's various organs. The inset shows a close-up view of the tube feet, part of the water vascular system characteristic of echinoderms.

Concept Check: *Echinoderms and chordates are both deuterostomes. What are three defining features of deuterostomes?*

Echinoderms cannot osmoregulate, so no species have entered freshwater environments. No excretory organs are present. For some species, both respiration and excretion of nitrogenous waste take place by diffusion across their tube feet. Coelomic fluid circulates around the body.

Most echinoderms exhibit **autotomy**, the ability to intentionally detach a body part, such as a limb, that will later regenerate. In some species, a broken limb can even regenerate into a whole animal. Some sea stars regularly reproduce by breaking in two. Most echinoderms reproduce sexually and have separate sexes. Fertilization is usually external, with gametes shed into the water. Fertilized eggs develop into free-swimming larvae, which become sedentary adults.

The Major Echinoderm Classes   Although over 20 classes of echinoderms have been described from the fossil record, only 5 main classes of echinoderms exist today: the Asteroidea (sea stars), Ophiuroidea (brittle stars), Echinoidea (sea urchins and sand dollars), Crinoidea (sea lilies and feather stars), and Holothuroidea (sea cucumbers). The key features of the echinoderms and their classes are listed in **Table 34.6**, and several members are shown in **Figure 34.31**.

Table 34.6	Main Classes and Characteristics of Echinoderms	
	Class and examples (est. number of species)	Class characteristics
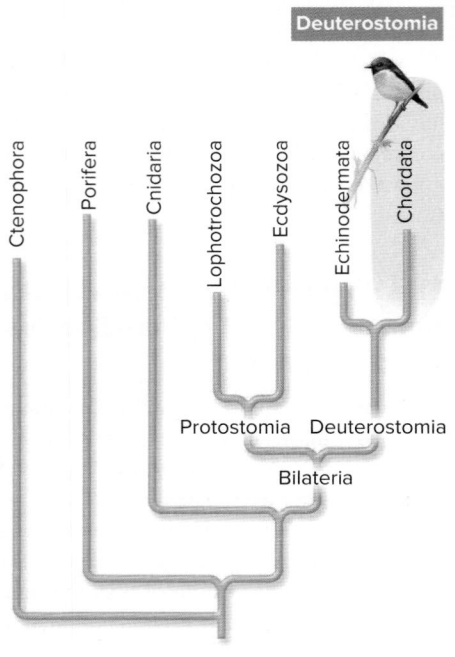	Asteroidea: sea stars (1,600)	Five arms; tube feet; predatory on bivalves and other echinoderms; eversible stomach
	Ophiuroidea: brittle stars (2,000)	Five long, slender arms; tube feet not used for locomotion; no pedicellariae; browse on sea bottom or filter feed
	Echinoidea: sea urchins, sand dollars (1,900)	Spherical (sea urchins) or disc-shaped (sand dollars); no arms; tube feet and moveable spines; pedicellariae present; many feed on seaweeds
	Crinoidea: sea lilies and feather stars (700)	Cup-shaped; often attached to substrate via stalk; arms feathery and used in filter feeding; very abundant in fossil record
	Holothuroidea: sea cucumbers (1,200)	Cucumber-shaped; no arms; spines absent; endoskeleton reduced; tube feet; browse on sea bottom

The Phylum Chordata Includes All Vertebrates and Some Invertebrates

The deuterostomes consist of two major phyla: the echinoderms and the chordates. As deuterostomes, both phyla share similar developmental traits. In addition, both have an endoskeleton, consisting in the echinoderms of calcareous plates and in chordates, for the most part, of bone. However, the echinoderm endoskeleton functions in much the same way as the arthropod exoskeleton, in that an important function is providing protection. The chordate endoskeleton serves a very different purpose. In early-diverging chordates, the endoskeleton is composed of a single flexible rod situated dorsally, deep inside the body. Muscles move this rod, and their contractions cause the back

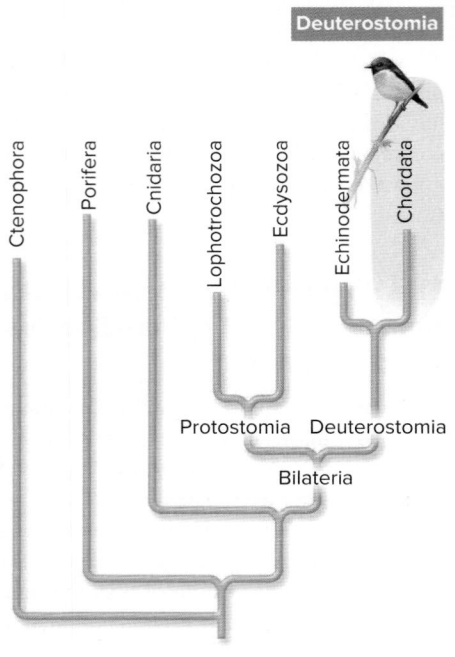

Deuterostomia

Ctenophora · Porifera · Cnidaria · Lophotrochozoa · Ecdysozoa · Echinodermata · Chordata

Protostomia   Deuterostomia

Bilateria

(a) Necklace Sea star, *Fromia monilis*, Baa Atoll, Maldives

(b) Brittle star, *Ophiarachna* spp., Gulf of Mexico

(c) Sea urchin, *Heterocentrotus trigonarius*, Hawaii

(d) Sea Lily, *Proisocrinus ruberrimus*, Indonesia

(e) Bronze-spot sea cucumber, *Holothuria argus*.

Figure 34.31 Echinoderms. (a) Sea star. **(b)** Brittle star. **(c)** Sea urchin. **(d)** Sea lily. **(e)** Sea cucumber. a: ©ullstein bild/Getty Images; b: Source: NOAA Okeanos Explorer Program, Gulf of Mexico 2012 Expedition; c: Source: David Burdick/NOAA; d: Source: NOAA Okeanos Explorer Program, INDEX-SATAL 2010; e: ©Poelzer Wolfgang/Alamy Stock Photo

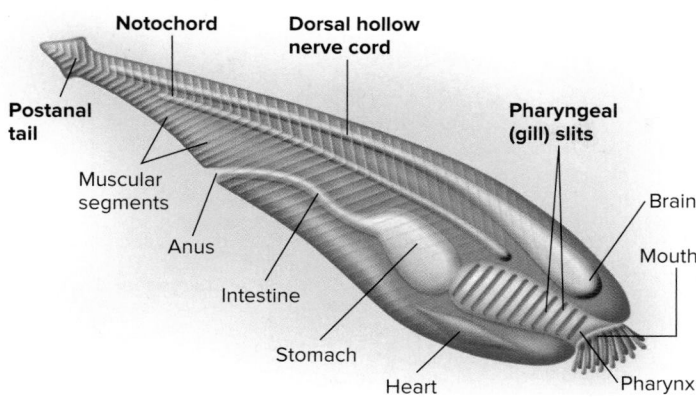

Figure 34.32 Chordate characteristics. The generalized chordate body plan has four main features: notochord, dorsal hollow nerve cord, pharyngeal slits, and postanal tail.

and tail end to move from side to side, permitting a swimming motion in water. The endoskeleton becomes more complex in different lineages that develop limbs, as we will see in Chapter 35, but it is always internal, with muscles attached.

Let's take a look at the four critical innovations in the body plan of chordates that distinguish them from all other animal life (**Figure 34.32**):

1. *Notochord.* Chordates are named for the **notochord**, a single flexible rod that lies between the digestive tract and the nerve cord. Composed of fibrous tissue encasing fluid-filled cells, the notochord is stiff yet flexible and provides skeletal support for all early-diverging chordates. In most chordates, such as vertebrates, a more complex jointed backbone usually replaces the notochord; its remnants exist only as the soft material within the discs between each vertebrae.

2. *Dorsal hollow nerve cord.* Many animals have a long nerve cord, but in nonchordate invertebrates, it is a solid tube that lies ventral to the alimentary canal. In contrast, the nerve cord in chordates is a hollow tube that develops dorsal to the alimentary canal. In vertebrates, the dorsal hollow nerve cord develops into the brain and spinal cord.

3. *Pharyngeal slits.* Chordates, like many animals, have a complete gut, from mouth to anus. However, in chordates, slits develop in the pharyngeal region, close to the mouth, that open to the outside. This permits water to enter through the mouth and exit via the slits, without having to go through the digestive tract. In early-diverging chordates, **pharyngeal slits** function as a filter-feeding device, whereas in later-diverging chordates, they develop into gills for gas exchange. In terrestrial chordates, the slits do not fully form, and they become modified for other purposes.

4. *Postanal tail.* Chordates possess a **postanal tail** of variable length that extends posterior to the anal opening. In aquatic chordates such as fishes, the tail is used in locomotion. In terrestrial chordates, the tail may be used for a variety of functions. In virtually all other nonchordate phyla, the anus is at the end of the body.

Although few chordates apart from fishes possess all of these characteristics in their adult life, they all exhibit them at some time during development. For example, in adult humans, the notochord becomes the spinal column, and the dorsal hollow nerve cord becomes the central nervous system. However, humans exhibit pharyngeal slits and a postanal tail only during early embryonic development. All the pharyngeal slits, except one, which forms the auditory (Eustachian) tubes in the ear, are eventually lost, and the postanal tail regresses to form the tailbone (the coccyx).

The phylum Chordata consists of the invertebrate chordates—the subphylum Cephalochordata (lancelets) and the subphylum Urochordata (tunicates)—along with the subphylum Vertebrata. Although the Vertebrata is by far the largest of these subphyla, biologists have focused on the Cephalochordata and Urochordata for clues as to how the chordate phylum may have evolved. Comparisons of gene sequences for the small subunit rRNA (SSU rRNA) show that these two subphyla are our closest invertebrate relatives (**Figure 34.33**).

Subphylum Cephalochordata: The Lancelets The cephalochordates (from the Greek *cephalo*, meaning head) look a lot more chordate-like than do tunicates. They are commonly referred to as lancelets, in reference to their bladelike shape and size, about 5–7 cm in length (**Figure 34.34a**). Lancelets are a small subphylum of 26 species, all marine filter feeders, with 4 species occurring in North American waters. Most of them belong to the genus *Branchiostoma*.

The lancelets live mostly buried in sand, with only the anterior end protruding into the water. Lancelets have the four distinguishing chordate characteristics: a clearly discernible notochord (extending well into the head), dorsal hollow nerve cord, pharyngeal slits, and postanal tail (**Figure 34.34b**). They are filter feeders, drawing

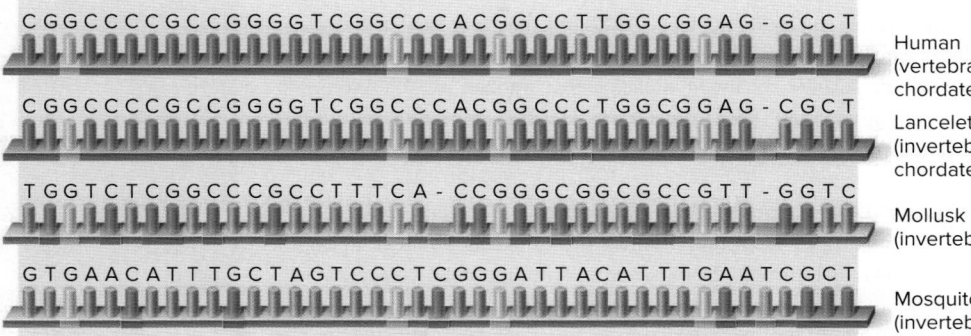

Figure 34.33 Comparison of SSU rRNA gene sequences of chordate and nonchordate species. Note the many similarities (yellow) and differences (green and red) among the sequences.

 Core Concept: Evolution The DNA sequence similarities between the invertebrate chordates (represented by the lancelet) and the vertebrates (represented by a human) suggest that the former are indeed our closest invertebrate relatives.

(a) Lancelet in the sand

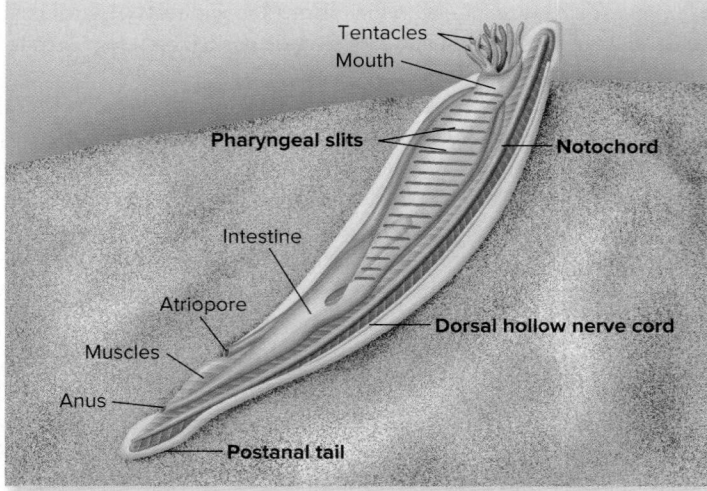

(b) Body plan of the lancelet

Figure 34.34   Lancelets. (a) A bladelike lancelet. **(b)** The body plan of the lancelet clearly displays the four characteristic chordate features. a: ©Natural Visions/Alamy Stock Photo

water through the mouth and into the pharynx, where it is filtered through the pharyngeal slits. A mucous net across the pharyngeal slits traps food particles, and ciliary action takes the food into the intestine, while water exits via the atriopore. Gas exchange generally takes place across the body surface. Although the lancelet is usually sessile, it can leave its sandy burrow and swim to a new spot, using a sequence of serially arranged muscles that appear like chevrons (<<<<) along its sides. These muscles reflect the segmented nature of the lancelet body and permit a fishlike swimming motion.

Subphylum Urochordata: The Tunicates   The urochordates (from the Greek *oura*, meaning tail) are a group of 3,000 marine species also known as tunicates. Looking at an adult tunicate, you might never guess that it is a relative of modern vertebrates. Of the four distinguishing chordate characteristics, it only has pharyngeal slits (**Figure 34.35a**). The larval tunicate, in contrast, looks like a tadpole and exhibits all four chordate hallmarks (**Figure 34.35b**). The larval tadpole swims for only a few days, usually without feeding. Larvae settle on and attach to a rock surface via rootlike extensions called stolons. Here the larvae metamorphose into adult tunicates and in the process lose most of their chordate characteristics.

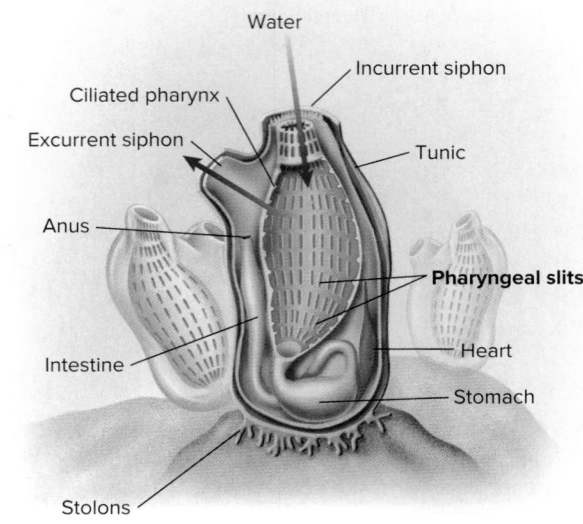

(a) Adult tunicate

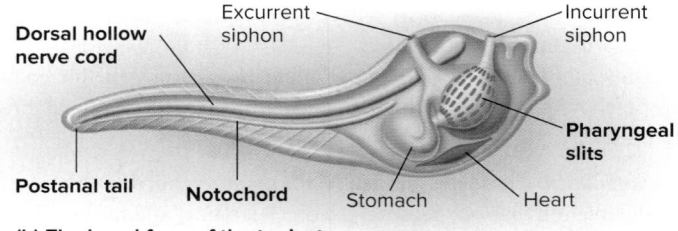

(b) The larval form of the tunicate

(c) Typical tunicate

Figure 34.35   Tunicates. (a) Body plan of the sessile, filter-feeding adult tunicate. **(b)** The larval form, which shows the four characteristic chordate features, has been proposed as a possible ancestor of modern vertebrates. **(c)** The blue tunicate, *Rhopalaea crassa*. c: ©Franco Banfi/Getty Images

In 1928, the English marine biologist Walter Garstang suggested modern vertebrates arose from a larval tunicate form that had somehow acquired the ability to reproduce. Analysis of molecular data in 2006 led French evolutionary biologist Frédéric Delsuc and colleagues to propose that tunicates are the closest living relatives of vertebrates. These researchers group the cephalochordates more closely with the echinoderms. This means the common ancestor of living deuterostomes was a free-living, bilaterally symmetrical animal with pharyngeal slits, a segmented body, and a dorsal hollow nerve cord. This ancestral line split into two groups, the echinoderm–cephalochordate group and the tunicate–vertebrate group. Echinoderms lost most of their ancestral features, but cephalochordates did not. According to this view, tunicates lost their segmentation and most became sedentary, whereas vertebrates did not.

Adult tunicates are marine animals, some colonial and others solitary, that superficially resemble sponges or cnidarians. Tunicates are filter feeders that draw in water through an **incurrent siphon**, using a ciliated pharynx, and filter it through extensive pharyngeal slits. The food is trapped on a mucous sheet and then passes via ciliary action to the stomach, intestine, and anus; waste products exit

through the excurrent siphon. The whole animal is enclosed in a nonliving **tunic** made of protein and a cellulose-like material called tunicin. Tunicates are also known as sea squirts for their ability to squirt out water from the excurrent siphon when disturbed. They have a rudimentary circulatory system with a heart and a simple nervous system of relatively few nerves connected to sensory tentacles around the incurrent siphon. The animals are mostly hermaphroditic.

34.7 A Comparison of Animal Phyla

Learning Outcome:

1. Compare and contrast the key characteristics of animal phyla.

Table 34.7 describes the common characteristics of the various animal phyla. In Sections 34.1–34.6, we explored all of the invertebrate phyla and two invertebrate subphyla of the chordates—Cephalochordata (lancelets) and Urochordata (tunicates). In Chapter 35, we will examine the vertebrates.

Table 34.7 — Summary of the Physical Characteristics of the Major Invertebrate Phyla

	Ctenophora (comb jellies)	Porifera (sponges)	Cnidaria (hydra, anemones, jellyfish)	Platyhelminthes (flatworms)	Rotifera (rotifers)	Bryozoa and Brachiopoda	Mollusca (snails, clams, squid)	Annelida (segmented worms)	Nematoda (roundworms)	Arthropoda (insects, arachnids, crustaceans)	Echinodermata (sea stars, sea urchins)	Chordata (vertebrates and others)
Digestive system	Complete gut	Absent	Gastrovascular cavity	Gastrovascular cavity	Complete gut (usually)	Complete gut	Complete gut	Complete gut	Complete gut	Complete gut	Usually complete gut	Complete gut
Circulatory system	Absent	Absent	Absent	Absent	Absent	Absent; open or closed	Open; closed in cephalopods	Closed	Absent	Open	Absent	Closed
Respiratory system	Absent	Absent	Absent	Absent	Absent	Absent	Gills	Absent	Absent	Trachae; gills or book lungs (a structure in spiders)	Tube feet; respiratory tree	Gills; lungs
Excretory system	Absent	Absent	Absent	Protonephridia with flame cells	Protonephridia	Metanephridia	Metanephridia	Metanephridia	Excretory tubules	Excretory glands resembling metanephridia	Absent	Kidneys
Nervous system	Nerve Net	Absent	Nerve net	Brain; cerebral ganglia; lateral nerve chords; nerve net	Brain; nerve cords	No brain; nerve ring	Ganglia; nerve cords	Brain; ventral nerve cord	Brain; nerve cords	Brain; ventral nerve cord	No brain; nerve ring and radial nerves	Well-developed brain; dorsal hollow nerve cord
Reproduction	Sexual (hemaphrodite)	Sexual; asexual (budding)	Sexual; asexual (budding)	Sexual (most hermaphroditic); asexual (body splits)	Mostly parthenogenetic; males appear only rarely	Sexual (some hermaphroditic); asexual (budding)	Sexual (some hermaphroditic)	Sexual (some hermaphroditic)	Sexual (some hermaphroditic)	Usually sexual (some hermaphroditic)	Sexual (some hermaphroditic); parthenogenetic; asexual by regeneration (rare)	Sexual; rarely parthenogenetic
Support	Mesoglea	Endoskeleton of spicules and collagen	Mesoglea	Parenchyma	Tissue	Exoskeleton	Hydrostatic skeleton and shell	Hydrostatic skeleton	Fluid skeleton	Exoskeleton	Endoskeleton of plates beneath outer skin	Endoskeleton of cartilage or bone

Summary of Key Concepts

34.1 Ctenophores: The Earliest Animals

- Invertebrates, or animals without a backbone, make up more than 95% of all animal species. Ctenophores are the earliest-diverging animals. They possess a unique nervous system and a mesoderm germ layer. They are predatory, possess a complete gut and use cilia to propel themselves (Figures 34.1, 34.2).

34.2 Porifera: The Sponges

- The phylum Porifera, or sponges, lack true tissues, but are multicellular animals possessing several types of cells. They are asymmetric marine filter feeders (Figure 34.3).

34.3 Cnidaria: Jellyfish and Other Radially Symmetric Animals

- The phylum Cnidaria includes hydra, jellyfish, box jellies, sea anemones, corals, and the Portuguese man-of-war (Table 34.1). Cnidarians have only two embryonic germ layers: the ectoderm and the endoderm, with a gelatinous substance (mesoglea) connecting the two layers.

- Cnidarians exist in one of two forms: polyp or medusa. A characteristic feature of cnidarians is their stinging cells, or cnidocytes, which function in defense and prey capture (Figures 34.4, 34.5).

34.4 Lophotrochozoa: The Flatworms, Rotifers, Bryozoans, Brachiopods, Mollusks, and Annelids

- Most Lophotrochozoa possess either a lophophore or a larval stage called a trochophore. Platyhelminthes, or flatworms, are hypothesized to be the first bilaterian animals to evolve three distinctive embryonic germ layers—ectoderm, endoderm, and mesoderm (Figure 34.6).

- The four classes of flatworms are the Turbellaria, Monogenea, Cestoda (tapeworms), and Trematoda (flukes). Flukes and tapeworms are internally parasitic, with complex life cycles (Figures 34.7, 34.8, Table 34.2).

- Rotifers are microscopic animals that have a complete digestive tract with separate mouth and anus; the mastax, a muscular pharynx, is a structure unique to the rotifers (Figure 34.9).

- The bryozoa and brachiopods both possess a lophophore, a ciliary feeding structure (Figure 34.10).

- The mollusks, which constitute a large phylum with over 100,000 diverse living species, have a basic body plan with three parts—a foot, a visceral mass, and a mantle—and an open circulatory system (Figures 34.11, 34.12, 34.13).

- The four most common mollusk classes are the polyplacophora (chitons), gastropoda (snails and slugs), bivalvia (clams and mussels), and cephalopoda (octopuses, squids, and nautiluses) (Table 34.3).

- Cephalopods are among the most complex of all invertebrates. They are the only mollusks with a closed circulatory system; they have a well-developed nervous system and brain and are believed to exhibit learning by observation (Figure 34.14).

- A striking feature of the annelids is segmentation, in which the body is divided into compartments; specialization of segments is only minimally present at the anterior end (Figure 34.15).

- Annelids are a large phylum containing two main groups: Errantia, which includes free-ranging marine worms, and Sedentaria, which includes tube worms, earthworms, and leeches (Figure 34.16).

34.5 Ecdysozoa: The Nematodes and Arthropods

- The ecdysozoans are named for their ability to shed their cuticle, a nonliving covering that provides support and protection. The two most common ecdysozoan phyla are the nematodes and the arthropods.

- Nematodes, which exist in nearly all habitats, have a cuticle made primarily of collagen, a structural protein. The small, free-living nematode *Caenorhabditis elegans* is a model organism. Many nematodes are parasitic in humans (Figures 34.17, 34.18).

- Arthropods are perhaps the most species-rich phylum on Earth. The arthropod body is covered by a cuticle (exoskeleton) made of layers of chitin and protein, and it is segmented, with segments fused into functional units called tagmata (Figure 34.19).

- The five main subphyla of arthropods are Trilobita (trilobites; now extinct), Chelicerata (spiders, scorpions, and relatives), Myriapoda (millipedes and centipedes), Hexapoda (insects and relatives), and Crustacea (crabs and relatives) (Table 34.4, Figures 34.20, 34.21, 34.22, 34.23).

- More insect species are known than all other animal species combined. The development of a variety of wing structures and mouthparts were keys to the success of insects (Figure 34.24, Table 34.5).

- Insects undergo a change in body form during development, either complete metamorphosis or incomplete metamorphosis, and have developed complex social behaviors (Figures 34.25, 34.26).

- Most crustacean orders contain small species and feature prominently in marine food chains. The most well-known order of crustaceans is the Decapoda, which includes the crabs, lobsters, and shrimp (Figures 34.27, 34.28, 34.29).

34.6 Deuterostomia: The Echinoderms and Chordates

- The Deuterostomia include the phyla Echinodermata and Chordata. A striking feature of the echinoderms is their radial symmetry, which is present only in adults; the free-swimming larvae are bilaterally symmetrical. Echinoderms possess a unique water vascular system (Figure 34.30).

- Five main classes of echinoderms exist today: the Asteroidea (sea stars), Ophiuroidea (brittle stars), Echinoidea (sea urchins and sand dollars), Crinoidea (sea lilies and feather stars), and Holothuroidea (sea cucumbers) (Table 34.6, Figure 34.31).

- The phylum Chordata is distinguished by four critical innovations: the notochord, dorsal hollow nerve chord, pharyngeal slits, and postanal tail (Figure 34.32).

- The subphylum Cephalochordata (lancelets) and subphylum Urochordata (tunicates) are invertebrate chordates. Genetic studies have shown that tunicates are the closest invertebrate relatives of the vertebrate chordates (subphylum Vertebrata) (Figures 34.33, 34.34, 34.35).

34.7   A Comparison of Animal Phyla

- Each of the major animal phyla is distinguished by a unique set of characteristics (Table 34.7).

Assess & Discuss

Test Yourself

1. Choanocytes are
   a. a group of protists that are believed to have given rise to animals.
   b. specialized cells of sponges that function to trap and eat small particles.
   c. cells that make up the gelatinous layer in sponges.
   d. cells of sponges that function to transfer nutrients to other cells.
   e. cells that form spicules in sponges.

2. Why aren't sponges eaten more often by predators?
   a. They are protected by silica spicules.
   b. They are protected by toxic defensive chemicals.
   c. They are often eaten; it's just that the leftover cells reaggregate into new, smaller sponges.
   d. Both a and b are correct.
   e. All three explanations, a, b, and c, are correct.

3. Which of the following organisms can produce female offspring through parthenogenesis?
   a. cnidarians   d. rotifers
   b. flukes   e. annelids
   c. choanocytes

4. What organisms survive without a mouth, digestive system, or anus?
   a. cnidarians   d. cestodes
   b. rotifers   e. nematodes
   c. echinoderms

5. Which phylum does not have at least some members with a closed circulatory system?
   a. Lophophorata
   b. Arthopoda
   c. Annelida
   d. Mollusca
   e. All of the above phyla have some members with a closed circulatory system.

6. A defining feature of the Ecdysozoa is a
   a. segmented body.
   b. closed circulatory system.
   c. cuticle.
   d. complete gut.
   e. lophophore.

7. In arthropods, the tracheal system is
   a. a unique set of structures that function in ingestion and digestion of food.
   b. a series of branching tubes extending into the body that allow for gas exchange.
   c. a series of tubules that allow waste products in the blood to be released into the digestive tract.
   d. the series of ommatidia that form the compound eye.
   e. none of the above.

8. Characteristics of the class Arachnida include
   a. two tagmata.
   b. six walking legs.
   c. an aquatic lifestyle.
   d. a lobed body.
   e. both b and d.

9. Incomplete metamorphosis
   a. is characterized by distinct larval and adult stages that do not compete for resources.
   b. is typically seen in arachnids.
   c. involves gradual changes in life stages in which the young resemble the adult stage.
   d. is characteristic of the majority of insects.
   e. always includes a pupal stage.

10. Which clade includes echinoderms?
    a. Protostomia
    b. Bilateria
    c. Ecdysozoa
    d. Lophotrochozoa
    e. Echinoderms are a member of all the above clades.

Conceptual Questions

1. Compare and contrast the five main feeding methods discussed in the chapter.

2. Why is external fertilization common in aquatic invertebrates but rare in terrestrial species?

3. **Core Concept: Structure and Function** Explain the difference between complete metamorphosis and incomplete metamorphosis.

Collaborative Questions

1. Revisit the animal phylogeny outlined in Figure 34.1 and discuss the critical innovations that led to the separation of each of the clades shown.

2. Discuss reasons why insects are the most species-rich taxon.

The Vertebrates

35

The star-nosed mole (*Condylura cristata*). This species is a vertebrate, a fascinating group of animals that includes human beings. ©Gary Meszaros/Science Source

The star-nosed mole, *Condylura cristata,* lives in tunnels in wet areas of eastern Canada and the northeastern United States. It is one of the most distinctive mammals anywhere on Earth. The mole lives for the most part in complete darkness and is virtually blind. It feels its way around and finds prey by means of 22 fleshy appendages on its nose, which contain more than 25,000 minute and highly sensitive sensory receptors called Eimer's organs. The mole has a voracious appetite and needs to eat frequently. In fact, the star-nosed mole has been identified as the world's fastest-eating mammal, averaging less than a quarter of a second to identify and consume a food item. Its astoundingly acute sensory abilities more than make up for its poor eyesight. The moles can swim underwater in search of food and smell their prey by exhaling air bubbles then inhaling them to detect scents.

The star-nosed mole is a **vertebrate** (from the Latin *vertebratus,* meaning joint of the spine), an animal with a backbone. Vertebrates range in size from tiny fishes weighing 0.1 g to huge whales with weights over 100,000 kg. They occupy nearly all of Earth's habitats, from the deepest depths of the oceans to mountaintops and the sky beyond. Throughout history, humans have depended on many vertebrate species for their welfare: by domesticating species such as horses, cattle, pigs, sheep, and chickens; using skin and fur for clothes; and keeping countless species, including cats and dogs, as pets. Many vertebrate species are the subjects of conservation efforts, as we will see in Chapter 60.

In Chapter 34, we discussed two chordate subphyla: the cephalochordates (lancelets) and urochordates (tunicates). The third subphylum of chordates, the Vertebrata, with about 66,000 species, is by far the largest and most dominant group of the phylum. The vertebrates include fishes, amphibians, reptiles, and mammals. In this chapter, we will explore the characteristics of vertebrates and the evolutionary development of the major vertebrate clades.

35.1 Vertebrates: Chordates with a Backbone

Learning Outcome:

1. List the main distinguishing characteristics of vertebrates.

Our current understanding of the relationships between the vertebrate groups is shown in **Figure 35.1**. Nested within the vertebrates are various clades based on morphological characteristics. For example, most vertebrates have jaws and are collectively known as gnathostomes. Many gnathostomes have four limbs for movement and are known as tetrapods.

The vertebrates retain all chordate characteristics outlined in Chapter 34, as well as possessing several additional traits, including the following:

1. *Vertebral column.* During development in vertebrates, the notochord is replaced by a bony or cartilaginous column of interlocking **vertebrae** that provides support and also protects the nerve cord, which lies within its tubelike structure.

2. *Cranium.* The anterior end of the nerve cord elaborates to form a well-developed brain that is encased in a protective bony or

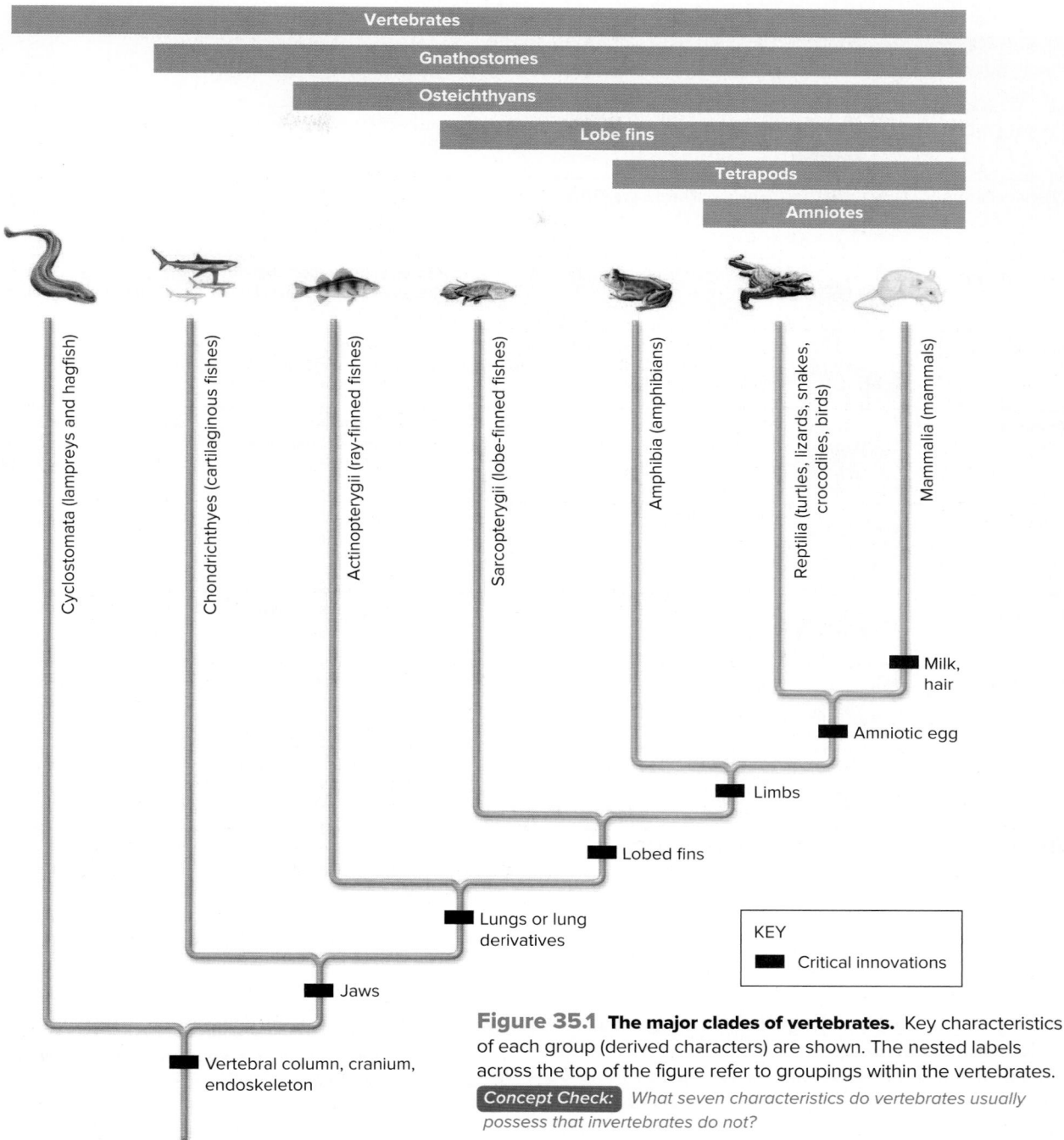

Figure 35.1 **The major clades of vertebrates.** Key characteristics of each group (derived characters) are shown. The nested labels across the top of the figure refer to groupings within the vertebrates.

Concept Check: *What seven characteristics do vertebrates usually possess that invertebrates do not?*

cartilaginous housing called the **cranium**. This continues the trend of cephalization—the development of the head end in animals.

3. ***Endoskeleton of cartilage or bone.*** The cranium and vertebral column are parts of the endoskeleton, the living skeleton of vertebrates that forms within the animal's body. Most vertebrates also have two pairs of appendages, such as fins, legs, or arms. The endoskeleton is composed of either bone or cartilage, materials that are very strong yet more flexible than the chitin found in insects and other arthropods.

Although these are the main distinguishing characteristics of vertebrates, there are others. For example, vertebrates have multiple clusters of *Hox* genes, compared with the single cluster of *Hox* genes in tunicates and lancelets. These additional gene clusters are believed to have permitted increasingly complex morphologies beyond those possessed by invertebrate chordates. Vertebrates also possess a great diversity of internal organs, including a liver, kidneys, endocrine glands, and a heart with at least two chambers. The liver is unique to vertebrates, and the vertebrate kidneys, endocrine system, and heart are more complex than are analogous structures in invertebrate taxa.

Although these features are exhibited in all vertebrate classes, some classes evolved critical innovations that helped them succeed in specific environments such as on land or in the air. For

Table 35.1 — The Main Clades and Characteristics of Living Vertebrates

Clade	Examples (approx. number of species)	Main characteristics
Cyclostomata	Lampreys and hagfish (100)	Jawless fishes, no appendages
Chondrichthyes	Sharks, skates, rays (970)	Fishes with cartilaginous skeleton; teeth not fused to jaw; no swim bladder; well-developed fins; internal fertilization; single blood circulation
Actinopterygii	Ray-finned fishes, most bony fish (31,830)	Fishes with ossified skeleton; single gill opening covered by operculum; fins supported by rays, fin muscles within body; swim bladder often present; mucous glands in skin
Sarcopterygii	Lobe-finned fishes, of which coelacanths (2) and lungfishes (6) are the only living members	Fishes with ossified skeleton; bony extensions, together with muscles, project into pectoral and pelvic fins
Amphibia	Frogs, toads, salamanders (7,600)	Adults able to live on land; fresh water needed for reproduction; development usually involving metamorphosis from tadpoles; adults with lungs and double blood circulation; moist skin; shell-less eggs
Testudines	Turtles (346)	Body encased in hard shell; no teeth; head and neck retractable into shell; eggs laid on land
Squamata	Lizards, snakes (9,900)	Lower jaw not attached to skull; skin covered in scales
Crocodilia	Crocodiles, alligators (25)	Four-chambered heart; large aquatic predators; parental care of young
Aves	Birds (10,425)	Feathers; hollow bones; air sacs; reduced internal organs; endothermic; four-chambered heart
Mammalia	Mammals (5,500)	Mammary glands; hair; specialized teeth; enlarged skull; external ears; endothermic; four-chambered heart; highly developed brains; diversity of body forms

example, birds developed feathers and wings, structures that enable most species to fly. Each of the vertebrate clades is distinctly different from one another, as outlined in **Table 35.1**. One of the earliest innovations was the development of jaws. All vertebrates except some early-diverging fishes possessed jaws. Today, the only jawless vertebrates are hagfish and lampreys, which are described in Section 35.2.

BIO **TIPS**

THE QUESTION *What derived characters (called critical innovations in Figure 35.1) are common to reptiles, amphibians, and lobe-finned fish, but not sharks?*

T OPIC *What topic in biology does this question address?* The topic is systematics. More specifically, the question concerns the use of a phylogenetic tree to determine derived characters that are shared among certain taxa.

I NFORMATION *What information do you know based on the question and your understanding of the topic?* From the question, you know you are comparing osteichthyans, tetrapods, and amniotes to chondrichthyans. From your understanding of systematics, which is described in Chapter 25, you may remember the definition of shared derived characters. You were given the derived characters (also called critical innovations) in Figure 35.1.

P ROBLEM-SOLVING S TRATEGY *Compare and contrast.* Look back at Figure 25.9. Construct a table with the derived characters listed on the left side and the four groups being compared across the top. Fill in the table with "Yes" or "No" as done in Figure 25.9a, according to whether a group does or does not possess a derived character.

ANSWER *Reptiles, amphibians, and lobe-finned fish all possess lungs or lung derivatives and lobe fins, but sharks do not.*

35.2 Cyclostomata: Jawless Fishes

Learning Outcome:

1. Describe the two classes of existing jawless vertebrates.

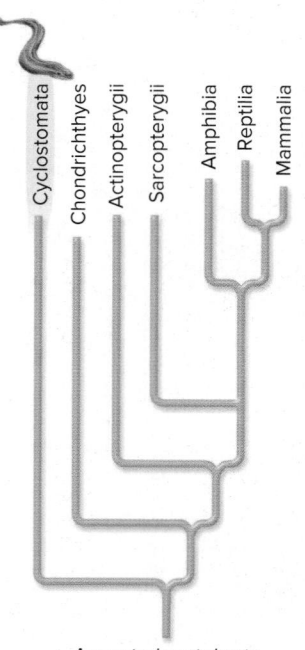

Ancestral vertebrate

Although many species of jawless fishes are known from the fossil record, most became extinct by the end of the Devonian period. Today, the only jawless vertebrates are hagfish and lampreys, together known as the Cyclostomata. Cyclostomes, or "circle mouths," are eel-like animals that do not possess jaws. Sequencing of RNA libraries in 2010, together with genomic surveys, yielded strong support that Cyclostomata is monophyletic. In addition, hagfish and lampreys share a very distinct type of immune system. In this section, we will examine the characteristics of hagfish and lampreys.

The Hagfish Are the Simplest Living Cyclostomes

The hagfish are entirely marine cyclostomes that lack eyes, jaws, fins and even vertebrae (**Figure 35.2**). The hagfish skeleton consists largely of a notochord and a cartilaginous skull that encloses the brain. The lack of a vertebral column leads to extensive flexibility. So how can hagfish be vertebrates without a vertebral column? The strong molecular support for a cyclostome clade suggests that hagfish anatomy has degenerated to a remarkable degree and only the cranium and diversity of organs provide evidence of vertebrate ancestry.

Hagfish live in the cold waters of northern oceans, close to the muddy bottom, feeding on marine worms and other invertebrates. Essentially blind, hagfish have a very keen sense of smell and are attracted to dead and dying fish. They attach themselves to such fish via toothed plates on the mouth. The powerful tongue then rasps off pieces of tissue. Though the hagfish cannot see approaching predators, they have special glands that produce copious amounts of slime. When provoked, the hagfish increases its slime production dramatically, enough to potentially distract predators or coat their gills and interfere with breathing. Hagfish can sneeze to free their nostrils of their own slime.

The Lampreys Are Eel-like Animals That Lack Jaws

Lampreys are similar to hagfish because they lack both a hinged jaw and true appendages. However, lampreys do possess a notochord surrounded by a cartilaginous rod that represents a rudimentary vertebral column.

Figure 35.2   The hagfish. ©Pat Morris/ardea.com

Lampreys are found in both marine and freshwater environments. Marine lampreys are parasitic as adults. They grasp other fish with their circular mouth (**Figure 35.3a**) and rasp a hole in the fish's side, sucking blood, tissue, and fluids until they are replete (**Figure 35.3b**).

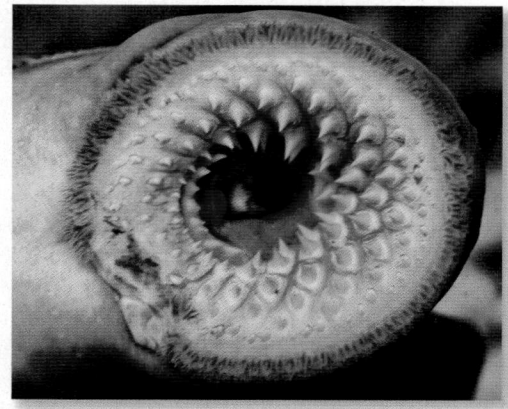

(a) Jawless mouth of a sea lamprey

(b) A sea lamprey feeding

Figure 35.3   The lamprey, a modern jawless fish. (a) The sea lamprey (*Petromyzon marinus*) has a circular, jawless mouth. **(b)** A sea lamprey feeding on a fish. a: ©R. Duran/Getty Images; b: ©Jacana/Science Source

Reproduction of all species, whether they live in marine or freshwater environments, is similar. Males and females spawn in freshwater streams, and the resultant larval lampreys bury into the sand or mud, much like lancelets (refer back to Figure 34.34a), emerging to feed on small invertebrates or detritus at night. This stage can last for 3–7 years, at the end of which the larvae metamorphose into adults. In most freshwater species, the adults do not feed at all but quickly mate and die. Young marine lampreys migrate from fresh water to the ocean, and later return to fresh water to spawn and then die.

35.3 Gnathostomes: Jawed Vertebrates

Learning Outcomes:

1. Describe how jaws evolved.
2. Discuss the distinguishing features of sharks.
3. List the three features that distinguish bony fishes from cartilaginous fishes.
4. Outline the differences between the ray-finned fish and the lobe-finned fish.

All vertebrate species that possess jaws are called **gnathostomes** (from the Greek, meaning jaw mouth) (see Figure 35.1). Gnathostomes are a diverse clade of vertebrates that include fishes, amphibians, reptiles, and mammals. The earliest-diverging gnathostomes were fishes. Jawed fishes, which appeared in the mid-Ordovician period (about 470 mya), radiated in both fresh and salt water.

Biologists have identified about 32,800 species of living fishes with jaws, more speices than in any other clade of vertebrates. Most jawed fishes are aquatic, gill-breathing species that usually possess fins and a scaly skin. The three clades of jawed fishes are the Chondrichthyes (cartilaginous fishes), Actinopterygii (ray-finned fishes), and Sarcopterygii (coelacanths and lungfishes) (see Table 35.1). In this section, we will examine the evolution of the vertebrate jaw and then consider these three classes of jawed fishes. The remaining sections of this chapter will explore the characteristics of the other jawed vertebrates.

A Hinged Jaw Was a Critical Innovation That Aided in Feeding

A hinged jaw was an important evolutionary development that led to a great diversification of vertebrates. It enabled an animal to grip its prey more firmly, thereby increasing its likelihood of capturing the prey and allowing it to attack larger prey. Accompanying the jawed mouth was the development of more sophisticated head and body structures, including two pairs of appendages called fins. Gnathostomes also possess at least two more *Hox* gene clusters than do the cyclostomes (bringing their total to four or more). Developmental biologists speculate that additional *Hox* gene clusters led to increased morphological complexity.

The hinged jaw developed from the gill arches, cartilaginous or bony rods that help to support gills. Similarities between cells that make up jaws and gill arches support this view. Primitive jawless fishes had nine gill arches surrounding the eight gill slits (**Figure 35.4a**). During the late Silurian period (about 417 mya),

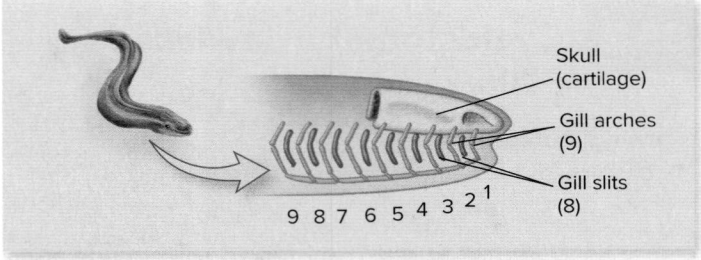

(a) Primitive jawless fishes

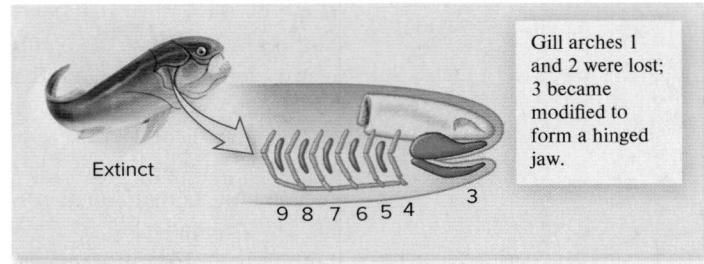

(b) Early jawed fishes (placoderms)

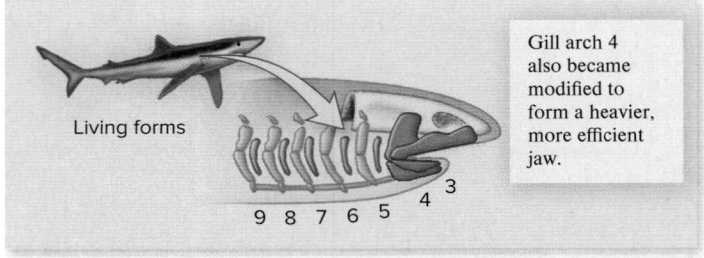

(c) Modern jawed fishes (cartilaginous and bony fishes)

Figure 35.4 The evolution of the vertebrate jaw. (a) Primitive fishes and extant jawless fishes such as lampreys have nine cartilaginous gill arches that support eight gill slits. **(b)** In early jawed fishes such as the placoderms, the first two pairs of gill arches were lost, and the third pair became modified to form a hinged jaw. This left six gill arches (4–9) to support the remaining five gill slits, which were still used in breathing. **(c)** In modern jawed fishes, the fourth gill arch also contributes to jaw support, allowing more powerful bites to be delivered.

 Core Concept: Structure and Function The development of a jaw increased the predatory capabilities of gnathostomes.

some of these gill arches became modified. The first and second gill arches were lost, and the third and fourth pairs evolved to form the jaws (**Figure 35.4b** and **c**). This is how evolution typically works; body features do not appear de novo, but instead, existing features become modified to serve other functions.

By the mid-Devonian period, several classes of jawed fishes were common. Two of them, the Acanthodii (spiny fishes) and Placodermi (armored fishes) died out during a mass extinction late in the Devonian. The reasons for this extinction are not well understood, but other types of jawed fishes present at the same time—the cartilaginous and bony fishes—did not go extinct and flourished in the aftermath of the mass extinction.

Chondrichthyans Are Fishes with Cartilaginous Skeletons

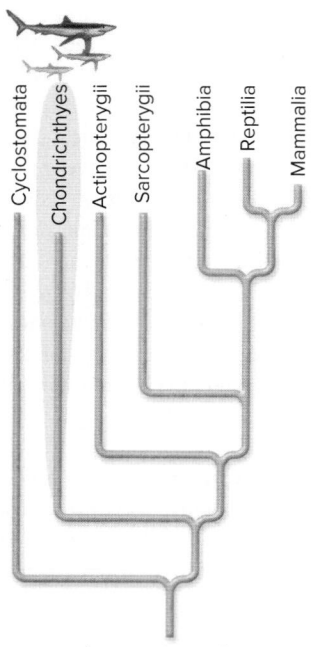

Members of the clade Chondrichthyes (the **chondrichthyans**)—sharks, skates, and rays—are also called cartilaginous fishes because their skeleton is composed of flexible cartilage rather than bone. The cartilaginous skeleton is not considered an ancestral character but rather a derived character. This means that the ancestors of the chondrichthyans had bony skeletons, but members of this class subsequently lost this feature. This hypothesis is reinforced by the observation that during development, the skeleton of most vertebrates is cartilaginous, and then it becomes bony (ossified) as a hard calcium-phosphate matrix replaces the softer cartilage. Genetic changes in the cartilaginous fishes are believed to prevent the ossification process.

Cyclostomata
Chondrichthyes
Actinopterygii
Sarcopterygii
Amphibia
Reptilia
Mammalia

Ancestral vertebrate

Key Features of Chondrichthyans All chondrichthyans are denser than water, which means that they will sink if they stopped swimming. Many sharks never stop swimming and maintain buoyancy via the use of their fins and a large oil-filled liver. Perhaps the most important fin for propulsion is the large and powerful caudal fin, or tail fin, which, when swept from side to side, thrusts the fish forward at great speed (**Figure 35.5a**). For example, great white sharks (*Carcharodon carcharias*) can swim at over 40 km per hour, and Mako sharks (*Isurus oxyrinchus*) have been clocked at nearly 50 km per hour. The paired pelvic fins (at the back) and pectoral fins (at the front) act like flaps on airplane wings, allowing the shark to dive deeper or rise to the surface. They also aid in steering. In addition, the dorsal fin (on the shark's back) acts as a stabilizer to prevent the shark from rolling in the water as the tail fin pushes it forward. During swimming, water continually enters the mouth and is forced over the gills, allowing sharks to extract oxygen and breathe.

Skates and rays are essentially flattened sharks that cruise along the ocean floor, using hugely expanded pectoral fins. In addition, their thin, whiplike tails are often equipped with a venomous barb used in defense (**Figure 35.5b**). Most of the 475 or so species of skates and rays feed on bottom-dwelling crustaceans and mollusks. At times, they may rest on the ocean floor. How do skates and rays breathe when they are not swimming? These species, and a few sharks such as the nurse shark, use a muscular pharynx and jaw muscles to pump water over the gills.

Sharks were among the earliest fishes to develop teeth. Shark teeth evolved from rough scales on the skin that contained dentin and enamel. Although shark's teeth are very sharp and hard, they are not set into the jaw, as are human teeth, so they break off easily. Teeth are

(a) Silvertip shark

Caudal fin
Dorsal fin
Pelvic fin
Pectoral fin

(b) Stingray

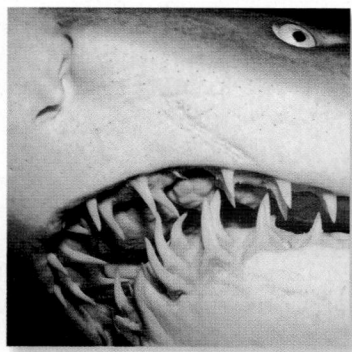

(c) Rows of shark teeth

(d) Shark egg pouch

Figure 35.5 Cartilaginous fishes. (a) The silvertip shark (*Carcharhinus albimarginatus*) is one of the ocean's most powerful predators. **(b)** Stingrays are essentially flattened sharks with very large pectoral fins. **(c)** Close-up of the mouth of a sand tiger shark (*Carcharias taurus*), showing rows of teeth. **(d)** This mermaid's purse (egg pouch) of a dogfish shark (*Scyliorhinus canicula*) is entwined in vegetation to keep it stationary. a: ©Valerie & Ron Taylor/ardea.com; b: ©Bill Curtsinger/National Geographic/Getty Images; c: ©Jeff Rotman/naturepl.com; d: ©Oxford Scientific/Getty Images

 Core Skill: Connections Are "fish" a monophyletic group?

continually replaced, row by row (**Figure 35.5c**). Sharks may have 20 rows of teeth, with the front pair in active use and the ones behind ready to grow in as replacements when needed.

In the chondrichthyans, and indeed in all species of fishes, the heart consists of two chambers, an atrium and a ventricle, that contract in sequence. All fishes employ what is known as single circulation, in which blood is pumped from the heart to capillaries in the gills to collect oxygen, and then it flows through arteries to the tissues of the body, before returning to the heart (look ahead to Figure 48.2a).

Chondrichthyan Senses Sharks have a powerful sense of smell, facilitated by sense organs in the nostrils (sharks and other fishes do not use nostrils for breathing). They can see well but cannot distinguish colors. Although sharks have no eardrum, they can detect pressure waves generated by moving objects. All jawed fishes have a row of microscopic organs in the skin, arranged in a line that runs laterally down each side of the body, that can sense movements in the surrounding water. This system of sense organs, known as the **lateral line**, senses pressure waves and sends nervous signals to the inner ear and then on to the brain. Sharks have an extra sense that helps them find and track prey. The ampullae of Lorenzini, vesicles and pores found around the shark's head, are sensory organs that detect electromagnetic fields produced by other organisms.

Reproduction in Chondrichthyans Fertilization is internal in chondrichthyans, with the male transferring sperm to the female via a pair of **claspers**, extensions of the pelvic fins. Some shark species are **oviparous**; that is, they lay eggs, often inside a protective pouch called a mermaid's purse (Figure 35.5d). In **ovoviviparous** species, the eggs are retained within the female's body, but there is no placenta to nourish the young. A few species are **viviparous**; the eggs develop within the uterus, receiving nourishment from the mother via a placenta. Both ovoviviparous and viviparous sharks give birth to live young.

Sharks never stop growing, so larger individuals are the oldest. Radiocarbon dating of the eye lenses of large Greenland sharks, *Somniosus microcephalus*, revealed the age at sexual maturity to be at least 156 years and showed an average life span of 272 years; the largest animal, at 502 cm long, was determined to be 392±120 years old, making this species the longest-lived vertebrate known.

The Earliest-Diverging Osteichthyans Are Fishes with Bony Skeletons

Unlike the cartilaginous fishes, all other gnathostomes have a bony skeleton and belong to the clade known as osteichthyes. This term means "bony fish" and was originally proposed for just that group. With the advent of modern phylogenetic systematics, the term **osteichthyans** was expanded to include all vertebrates with a bony skeleton, including tetrapods (refer back to Figure 35.1).

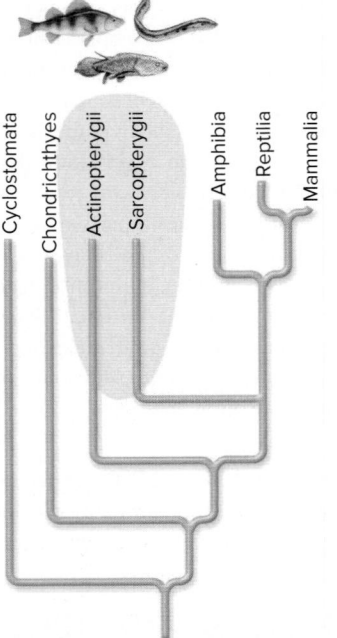

Ancestral vertebrate

Bony fishes are the most numerous of all types of fishes, with more individuals and more species (about 31,830) than any other group. Most biologists now recognize two living clades: the Actinopterygii (ray-finned fishes) and the Sarcopterygii (lobe-finned fishes).

Body Plan of Bony Fishes Fishes in both clades possess a bony skeleton and scale-covered skin. The skin of bony fishes, unlike the rough skin of sharks, is covered by a thin epidermal layer containing glands that produce mucus, an adaptation that reduces drag during swimming. Just as in the cartilaginous fishes, water is drawn over the gills for breathing, but in bony fishes, a protective flap called an **operculum** covers the gills (**Figure 35.6**). Muscle contractions around the gills and operculum draw water across the gills so that bony fishes do not need to swim continuously to breathe.

Some early bony fishes lived in shallow, oxygen-poor waters and developed lungs as an embryological offshoot of the pharynx. These fish could rise to the water surface and gulp air. As discussed later, modern lungfishes can breathe in this manner. However, in most bony

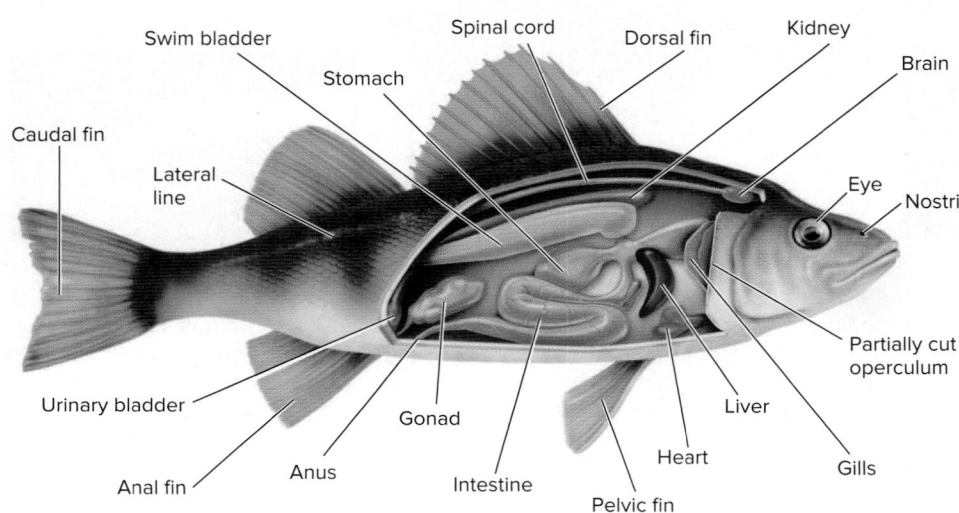

Figure 35.6 Generalized body plan of a bony fish. Bony fish possess a swim bladder and an operculum that covers the gills.

(a) Lionfish (*Pterois volitans*)

**(b) Whitemouth moray eel
(*Gymnothorax meleagris*)**

(c) Leafy sea dragon (*Phycodurus eques*)

Figure 35.7   The diversity of ray-finned fishes. Ray-finned fishes exhibit many different sizes and body shapes. a: Source: Julie Bedford/NOAA; b: ©Andrew Dawson/age fotostock; c: ©Luc Novovitch/Getty Images

 *Concept Check:* *What features distinguish ray-finned fishes from sharks?*

fishes, the lungs evolved into a **swim bladder**, a gas-filled, balloon-like structure that helps the fish remain buoyant in the water even when it is completely stationary. In early-diverging bony fishes, the gut and swim bladder are connected via a duct, and the fishes can fill their swim bladder by gulping air. In later-diverging species, the swim bladder is connected to the circulatory system, and gases are transported in and out of the blood, allowing the fishes to change the volume of the swim bladder and so to rise and sink. Therefore, unlike the sharks, many bony fishes can remain motionless and use a "sit-and-wait" ambush style. These three features—bony skeleton, operculum, and swim bladder—distinguish bony fishes from cartilaginous fishes.

Some fishes, known as bimodal breathers, can breathe through their gills and by gulping air, absorbing oxygen through their digestive tracts or accessory organs. For example, Siamese fighting fish (*Betta splendens*, known as betta), a popular freshwater aquarium fish, is a bimodal breather that is relatively easy to care for, since it can survive without an air pump in its aquarium.

Bony fishes have colonized nearly all aquatic habitats. Following the cooling of the newly formed Earth, water condensed into rain and over a vast period of time filled what are now the oceans. Later, as water evaporated from the oceans and sodium, potassium, and calcium were added via runoff from the land, the oceans became salty. Therefore, most fishes probably evolved in freshwater habitats and secondarily became adapted to marine environments. This, of course, required the development of physiological adaptations to the different osmotic problems seawater presents compared with fresh water (look ahead to Figure 41.17).

Reproduction in Bony Fishes   Reproductive strategies of bony fishes vary tremendously, but most species reproduce via external fertilization, with the female shedding her eggs and the male depositing sperm on top of them. Although adult bony fishes can maintain their buoyancy, their eggs tend to sink. This is why many species spawn in shallow, more oxygen- and food-rich waters and why coastal areas are important fish nurseries.

Actinopterygii, the Ray-Finned Fish   The most species-rich clade of bony fishes is the Actinopterygii, or **ray-finned fishes**, which includes all bony fishes except the coelacanths and lungfishes. In Actinopterygii, the fins are supported by thin, bony, flexible rays and are moved by muscles on the interior of the body. The clade has a diversity of forms, from lionfish and large predatory moray eels to delicate sea dragons (**Figure 35.7**). Whole fisheries are built around the harvest of species such as cod, anchovies, and salmon.

Sarcopterygii, the Lobe-Finned Fish   The Actinistia (coelacanths) and Dipnoi (lungfishes) are both considered Sarcopterygii, or **lobe-finned fishes**. The term Sarcopterygii used to refer solely to the lobe-finned fishes. More recently, evolutionary studies have shown that terrestrial vertebrates (tetrapods) evolved from such fishes. Therefore, the term Sarcopterygii has been expanded to include both lobe-finned fishes and tetrapods (see Figure 35.1). In the lobe-finned fishes, the fins are supported by skeletal extensions of the pectoral and pelvic areas that are moved by muscles within the fins.

The fossil record revealed that the Actinistia, or coelacanths, were a very successful group in the Devonian period, but all fishes of the class were believed to have died off at the end of the Mesozoic era (some 65 mya). You can therefore imagine the scientific excitement when in 1938, a modern coelacanth was discovered as part of the catch of a boat fishing near the Chalumna River in South Africa (**Figure 35.8a**). Intensive searches in the area revealed that coelacanths were living in deep waters off the southern African coast and especially off a group of islands near the coast of Madagascar called the Comoros Islands. Another species was found more recently in Indonesian waters.

Early-diverging lobe-finned fishes probably evolved in fresh water and had lungs, but the coelacanth lost lungs and returned to the sea. One distinctive feature of this group is a special joint in the skull that allows the jaws to open extremely wide and gives the coelacanth a powerful bite. As further evidence of the coelacanth's unusual body plan, its swim bladder is filled with oil rather than gas, although it serves a similar purpose—to increase buoyancy.

The Dipnoi, or **lungfishes**, like the coelacanths, are also not currently a very species-rich group, having just three genera and six species (**Figure 35.8b**). Lungfishes live in oxygen-poor freshwater swamps and ponds. They have both gills and lungs, the latter of which enable them to come to the surface and gulp air. Surprisingly, lungfish will drown if they are unable to breathe air. When ponds dry out, some species of lungfish can dig a burrow and survive in it until the next rain. Because they also have muscular lobe fins, lungfish are often able to successfully traverse quite long distances over shallow-bottomed lakes that may be drying out.

Figure 35.8 The Sarcopterygii (lobe-finned fish). (a) An actinisian, the coelacanth (*Latimeria chalumnae*). **(b)** A dipnoi, the Australian lungfish (*Neoceratodus forsteri*). a: ©Peter Scoones/SPL/Science Source; b: ©D. R. Schrichte/SeaPics.com

Concept Check: *How are lungfishes similar to coelacanths?*

The morphological features of coelacanths, lungfishes, and primitive terrestrial vertebrates, together with the similarity of their nuclear genes, suggest to many scientists that lobe-fin ancestors gave rise to three lineages: the coelacanths, the lungfishes, and the tetrapods. In the next section, we will examine the characteristics of tetrapods in more detail.

35.4 Tetrapods: Gnathostomes with Four Limbs

Learning Outcomes:

1. Describe adaptations that were beneficial for a terrestrial lifestyle.
2. List the amphibian orders, and describe the features that differentiate them.
3. **CoreSKILL** » Explain how relatively simple experiments with mice showed that mutations in just two genes can cause large changes in limb development.

During the Devonian period (from about 417 to 354 mya), a diversity of plants and animals colonized the land. The plants served as both a source of oxygen and a potential food source for animals that ventured out of the aquatic environment. Terrestrial arthropods and vertebrates appeared during the Devonian. The transition to life on land involved

a large number of adaptations. Paramount among these were adaptations preventing desiccation and making locomotion and reproduction on land possible. In this section, we begin by outlining the development of the **tetrapods**, vertebrate animals having four legs or leglike appendages. We will discuss the first terrestrial vertebrates and their immediate descendants, the amphibians. We will then explore the characteristic features and diversity of modern amphibians.

The Origin of Tetrapods Involved the Development of Four Limbs

The fossil record of the Devonian period demonstrates the evolution of sturdy lobe-finned fishes to fishes with four limbs. The abundance of light and nutrients in shallow waters encouraged a profusion of plant life and the invertebrates that fed on them. The development of lungs enabled lungfishes to colonize these productive yet often oxygen-poor waters. Here, the ability to move in shallow water clogged with plants and debris was more vital than the ability to swim swiftly through open water and may have favored the progressive development of sturdy limbs. As an animal's weight began to be borne more by the limbs, the vertebral column strengthened, and hip bones and shoulder bones were braced against the backbone for added strength.

Early Transitional Forms One of the transitional forms between fish and tetrapods was *Tiktaalik roseae*, nicknamed fishapod (refer back to Figure 22.5). Fishapods had broad skulls with eyes mounted on the top, lungs, and pectoral fins with five finger-like bones. *T. roseae* is an important species, for it represents a transitional form, displaying an intermediate state between an ancestral form and the form of its descendants. Eventually, species more like modern amphibians evolved, species that were still tied to water for reproduction but increasingly lived on land. In these species, the vertebral column, hip bones, and shoulder bones grew sturdier. Such changes were needed as the animal's weight was no longer supported by water but was borne entirely on the limbs.

Hox Genes and Limb Formation The modifications leading to the emergence of tetrapods are the result of changes in the expression of genes, especially *Hox* genes. In tetrapods, *Hox* genes 9–13 work together to specify limb formation from proximal to distal, meaning from close to the point of attachment to the body to the terminal end of the limb (**Figure 35.9**). For example, *Hox9* plays a role in the formation of the scapula, which is attached to the shoulder, whereas *Hox13* plays a role in the formation of metacarpals found in the claws or fingers. As described next in the Feature Investigation, our understanding of *Hox* gene function has come from genetic studies involving *Hox* mutations.

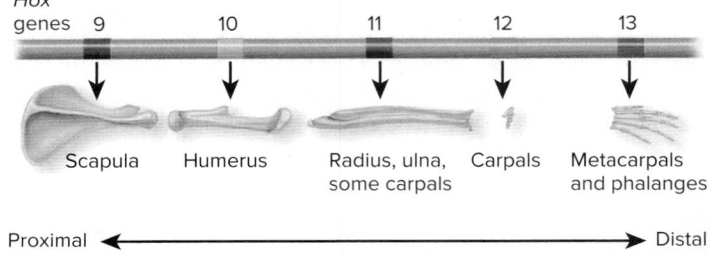

Figure 35.9 The roles of *Hox* genes 9–13 in specifying limb formation from proximal to distal. The axis of limb development in mice is shown, together with the associated genes.

Core Skill: Process of Science

Feature Investigation | Davis and Colleagues Provided a Genetic-Developmental Explanation for Limb Length in Tetrapods

The development of limbs in tetrapods was a vital step that allowed animals to colonize land. The diversity of vertebrate limb types is amazing, from fins in fish and marine mammals to different wing types in bats and birds to legs and arms in primates. Early in vertebrate evolution, an ancestral gene complex was duplicated twice to give rise to four groups of genes, called *HoxA*, *HoxB*, *HoxC*, and *HoxD*, which control limb development. Among the four groups, 13 different types of *Hox* genes can be found, but any given group does not contain all 13 types (refer back to Figure 20.16).

In 1995, Allen Davis, Mario Capecchi, and colleagues analyzed the effects of mutations in specific *Hox* genes that are responsible for determining limb formation in mice. The vertebrate forelimb is divided into three zones: humerus (upper arm); radius and ulna (forearm); and carpals, metacarpals, and phalanges (digits). The researchers had no specific hypothesis in mind; their goal was to understand the role of *Hox* genes in limb formation. As described in **Figure 35.10**, they began with strains of mice carrying loss-of-function mutations

Figure 35.10 Relatively simple changes in *Hox* genes control limb formation in tetrapods.

GOAL To determine the role of *Hox* genes in limb development in mice.

KEY MATERIALS Mice with individual mutations in *HoxA-11* and *HoxD-11* genes.

Experimental level	Conceptual level

1 Breed mice with individual mutations in *HoxA-11* and *HoxD-11* genes. (The *A* and *D* refer to wild-type alleles; *a* and *d* are mutant alleles.)

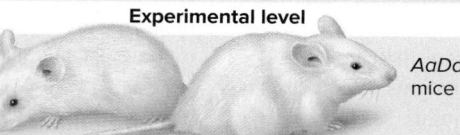

AaDd mice

The mice bred were heterozygous for both genes (*AaDd*).

Based on previous studies, researchers expect mutant mice to produce viable offspring, perhaps with altered limb morphologies.

2 Using molecular techniques described in Chapter 20, obtain DNA from the tail and determine the genotypes of offspring.

The resulting genotypes occur in Mendelian ratios, generating mice with different combinations of wild-type and mutant alleles.

	(AD)	(Ad)	(aD)	(ad)
(AD)	AADD	AADd	AaDD	AaDd
(Ad)	AADd	AAdd	AaDd	Aadd
(aD)	AaDD	AaDd	aaDD	aaDd
(ad)	AaDd	Aadd	aaDd	aadd

← Double mutant

9:3:3:1 phenotypic ratio expected a two-factor cross

3 Stain the skeletons and compare the limb characteristics of the wild-type mice (*AADD*) to those of strains carrying mutant alleles in one or both genes.

Mutant mice may have altered bone morphologies.

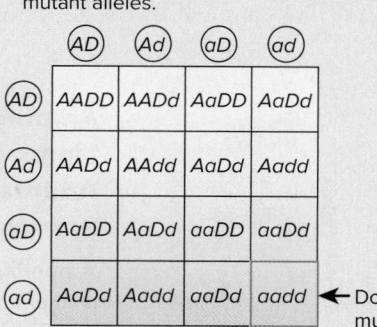

aadd

AADD

4   **THE DATA**

Genotype	Carpal bone fusions (% of mice showing the fusion)			
	Normal (none fused)	NL fused to T	T fused to P	NL fused to T and P
AADD	100	0	0	0
AaDD	100	0	0	0
aaDD	33	17	50	0
AADd	100	0	0	0
AAdd	0	17	17	67
AaDd	17	17	33	33

5   **CONCLUSION** Relatively simple mutations involving two genes can cause large changes in limb development.

6   **SOURCE** Davis, A.P. et al. 1995. Absence of radius and ulna in mice lacking Hoxa-11 and Hoxd-11. *Nature* 375: 791–795.

in *HoxA-11* or *HoxD-11* that, on their own, did not cause dramatic changes in limb formation. They bred the mice and obtained offspring carrying one, two, three, or four loss-of-function mutations. The mice were then analyzed with regard to the morphology of their limbs.

Taken together, the data indicate that the mutations affected the formation of limbs. For example, the wrist contains seven bones: three proximal carpals—called navicular lunate (NL), triangular (T), and pisiform (P)—and four distal carpals (d1–d4). In mice with the genotypes *aaDD* and *AAdd*, the proximal carpal bones are usually fused together. Individuals having one recessive allele (*AADd* and *AaDD*) do not show this defect, but individuals having two recessive alleles (*AaDd*) often do. Therefore, any two mutant alleles (either in both *HoxA-11* and *HoxD-11* or one in each locus) cause carpal fusions. Deformities became even more severe with three mutant alleles (*Aadd* or *aaDd*) or four mutant alleles (*aadd*) (data not shown in the figure). Thus, the researchers showed that relatively simple mutations can control relatively large changes in limb development.

Experimental Questions

1. What was the purpose of the study conducted by Davis and colleagues?

2. **CoreSKILL** ≫ Explain how the researchers were able to study the effects of individual genes.

3. **CoreSKILL** ≫ Summarize the results of the experiment, and explain how they relate to limb development in vertebrates.

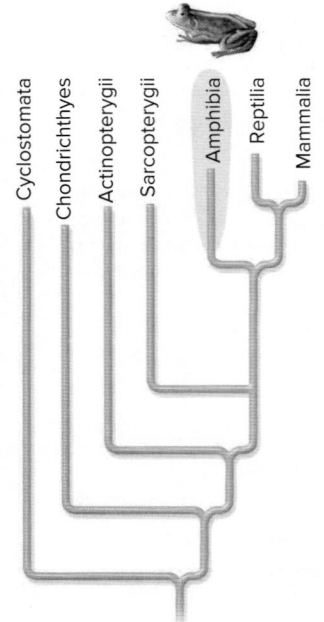

Amphibian Lungs and Limbs Are an Adaptation to a Semiterrestrial Lifestyle

Amphibians (from the Greek *amphibios*, meaning both ways of life) live in two worlds: They have successfully invaded the land, but most must return to the water to reproduce. By the middle of the Carboniferous period (about 320 mya), species similar to modern amphibians had become common in the terrestrial environment. Although most were small, *Cacops* was a large amphibian, as big as a pony (**Figure 35.11**). Its skin was heavy and tough, an adaptation that helped prevent water loss; its breathing was accomplished more

Figure 35.11 A primitive tetrapod. *Cacops* was a large, early amphibian of the Permian period.

Concept Check: *What were the advantages to animals of moving onto land?*

by lungs than by skin; and it possessed **pentadactyl limbs** (limbs ending in five digits).

With a bonanza of terrestrial arthropods to feast on, the amphibians became very numerous and species rich, and the mid-Permian period (some 260 mya) is sometimes known as the Age of Amphibians. However, most of the large amphibians became extinct at the end of the Permian period. This was the largest known mass extinction in Earth's history, with the extinction of 90–95% of marine species and a large proportion of terrestrial species. Most surviving amphibians were relatively small organisms resembling modern species.

Key Features of Amphibians   One of the first challenges terrestrial animals had to overcome was breathing air when on land. Like lungfishes, most amphibians open their mouths to let in air. Alternatively, air may enter through the nostrils. Amphibians then close and raise the floor of the mouth, creating a positive pressure that pumps air into the lungs. This method of breathing is called **buccal pumping**. In addition, the skin of amphibians is much thinner than that of fishes, and amphibians absorb oxygen from the air directly through their outer moist skin or through the skin lining of the inside of the mouth or pharynx. Because the skin of amphibians is usually thin, these animals face the problem of desiccation, or drying out. As a consequence, even amphibian adults are more abundant in damp habitats, such as swamps or rain forests, than in dry areas.

Amphibians have a three-chambered heart, with two atria and one ventricle. One atrium receives blood from the body, and the other receives blood from the lungs. Both atria pump blood into the single ventricle, which pumps some blood to the lungs and some to the rest of the body (look ahead to Figure 48.2b). This form of circulation allows the tissues to receive well-oxygenated blood at a higher pressure than is possible via single circulation, because some of the blood that returns to the heart is directly pumped to the tissues without being slowed down by passage through the lung capillaries. Oxygenated and deoxygenated bloods are kept somewhat separate, which enhances the delivery of nutrients and oxygen to the tissues.

Reproduction   In frogs and toads, fertilization is generally external, with males shedding sperm over the gelatinous egg masses laid by the females in water (**Figure 35.12a**). The fertilized eggs lack a shell and would quickly dry out if exposed to the air. The eggs soon hatch into tadpoles (**Figure 35.12b**), small fishlike animals that lack limbs and breathe through gills. As the tadpole nears the adult stage, the tail and gills are resorbed, and limbs and lungs appear (**Figure 35.12c**). Such a dramatic change in body form, from juvenile to adult, is known as **metamorphosis**. A few species of amphibians do not require water to reproduce. These species are ovoviviparous or viviparous—retaining the eggs in the reproductive tract and giving birth to live young.

Orders of Amphibians   Approximately 7,600 living amphibian species are known, and the vast majority of these, some 6,700 species, are frogs and toads of the order Anura (from the Greek, meaning tail-less ones) (**Figure 35.13a**). The other two orders are the Apoda (from the Greek, meaning legless ones), the wormlike caecilians; and the Urodela (from the Latin, meaning tailed ones), the salamanders. Global warming is currently threatening many anurans with extinction.

Adult anurans are carnivores, eating a variety of invertebrates by catching them on a long, sticky tongue. In contrast, the aquatic larvae (tadpoles) are primarily herbivores. Frogs generally have smooth, moist skin and long hind legs, making them excellent jumpers and swimmers. In addition to secreting mucus, which keeps their skin moist, some frogs can also secrete poisonous chemicals that deter would-be predators. Some amphibians advertise the poisonous nature of their skin with warning coloration (look ahead to Figure 57.9b). Others use camouflage as a way of avoiding detection by predators. Toads have a drier, bumpier skin and shorter legs than frogs. They are less impressive leapers than frogs, but they can better tolerate drier conditions.

Caecilians (order Apoda) comprise a small order of about 200 species of legless, nearly blind amphibians (**Figure 35.13b**). Most are tropical and burrow in forest soils, but a few live in ponds and streams. They are secondarily legless, which means they evolved from legged ancestors. Caecilians have tiny jaws equipped with teeth and eat worms and other soil invertebrates. In this order, fertilization is internal, and females usually bear live young. The young are nourished inside the mother's body by a thick, creamy secretion known as uterine milk. In most caecilian species, the young grow into adults about 30 cm long, though species up to 1.3 m in length are known.

The salamanders (order Urodela, about 700 species) possess a tail and have a more elongate body than that of anurans (**Figure 35.13c**). During locomotion, they seem to sway from side to side, perhaps reminiscent of how the earliest tetrapods may have walked. Like frogs,

(a) Gelatinous mass of amphibian eggs

(b) Tadpole

(c) Tadpole undergoing metamorphosis

Figure 35.12   Amphibian development in the wood frog (_Rana sylvatica_). (a) Amphibian eggs are laid in gelatinous masses in water. **(b)** The eggs develop into tadpoles, aquatic herbivores with a fishlike tail that breathe through gills. **(c)** During metamorphosis, the tadpole loses its gills and tail and develops limbs and lungs. a: ©Don Vail/Alamy Stock Photo; b–c: ©Dwight Kuhn

(a) Tree frog

(b) A caecilian   (c) Mud salamander

Figure 35.13 Amphibians. (a) Most amphibians are frogs and toads of the order Anura, including this red-eyed tree frog (*Agalychnis callidryas*). **(b)** The order Apoda includes wormlike caecilians such as this species from Ecuador, *Siphonops annulatus*. **(c)** The order Urodela includes species such as this mud salamander (*Pseudotriton montanus*). a: ©Gregory G. Dimijian/Science Source; b: ©Danita Delimont/Alamy Stock Photo; c: ©Gary Meszaros/Science Source

 **Concept Check:** *Do all amphibians produce tadpoles?*

salamanders often have colorful skin patterns that advertise their distastefulness to predators. Salamanders retain their moist skin by living in damp areas under leaves or logs or beneath lush vegetation. They generally range in size from 10 to 30 cm. Fertilization is usually internal, with females using their cloaca, a common opening for the digestive and urogenital tracts, to pick up sperm packets deposited by males. A very few salamander species do not undergo metamorphosis, and the newly hatched young resemble tiny adults. However, some species, such as Cope's giant salamander (*Dicamptodon copei*), retain the gills and tail fins characteristic of the larval stage into adulthood, and mature sexually in the larval stage, a phenomenon known as paedomorphosis.

35.5 Amniotes: Tetrapods with a Desiccation-Resistant Egg

Learning Outcomes:

1. Diagram the structure of the amniotic egg.
2. Identify the critical innovations of the amniotes.
3. Describe the distinguishing features of the major amniote classes.
4. List the features that allowed birds to fly.

Although amphibians live successfully in a terrestrial environment, they must lay their eggs in water or in a very moist place, so that the shell-less eggs do not dry out on exposure to air. Thus, a critical innovation in animal evolution was the development of a shelled egg that sheltered the embryo from desiccating conditions on land. A shelled

egg containing fluids was like a personal enclosed pond for each developing individual. Such an egg evolved in the common ancestor of turtles, lizards, snakes, crocodiles, birds, and mammals—a group of tetrapods collectively known as the **amniotes**. The amniotic egg permitted animals to lay their eggs in a dry place so that reproduction was no longer tied to water. It was truly a critical innovation, untethering animals from water in much the same way as the development of seeds liberated plants from water (see Chapter 31).

In time, the amniotes became very diverse in species and morphology. Mammals are considered amniotes, too, because even though most of them do not lay eggs, they retain other features of amniotic reproduction. In this section, we begin by discussing the structure of the amniotic egg and other adaptations that permitted animal species to become fully terrestrial. We will then discuss the biology of the reptiles, the first group of vertebrates to fully exploit land.

The Amniotic Egg and Other Innovations Permitted Life on Land

The **amniotic egg** (**Figure 35.14**) contains the developing embryo and the four separate extraembryonic membranes that it produces:

1. The innermost membrane is the **amnion**, which protects the developing embryo in a fluid-filled sac called the amniotic cavity.
2. The **yolk sac** encloses a stockpile of nutrients, in the form of yolk, for the developing embryo.
3. The **allantois** functions as a disposal sac for metabolic wastes.
4. The **chorion**, along with the allantois, provides gas exchange between the embryo and the surrounding air.

Surrounding the chorion is the albumin, or egg white, which also stores nutrients. The **shell** provides a tough, protective covering that is not very permeable to water and prevents the embryo from drying out. However, the shell remains permeable to oxygen and carbon dioxide, so the embryo can breathe. In birds, this shell is hard and calcareous, whereas in reptiles and early-diverging mammals such as the platypus and echidna, it is soft and leathery. In most mammals, however, the embryos embed into the wall of the uterus and receive their nutrients directly from the mother.

Along with the amniotic egg, other critical innovations that enabled animals' conquest of land include the following:

- *Desiccation-resistant skin.* Whereas the skin of amphibians is usually moist and aids in respiration, the skin of amniotes is thicker and water resistant and contains keratin, a tough protein. As a result, most gas exchange takes place through the lungs.

- *Thoracic breathing.* Amphibians use buccal pumping to breathe, contracting the mouth to force air into the lungs. In contrast, amniotes use **thoracic breathing**, in which coordinated contractions of muscles expand the rib cage, creating a negative pressure to suck air in and then forcing it out later. This results in a greater volume of air being displaced with each breath than with buccal pumping.

- *Water-conserving kidneys.* The ability to concentrate wastes prior to elimination and thus conserve water is an important role of the amniotes' kidneys.

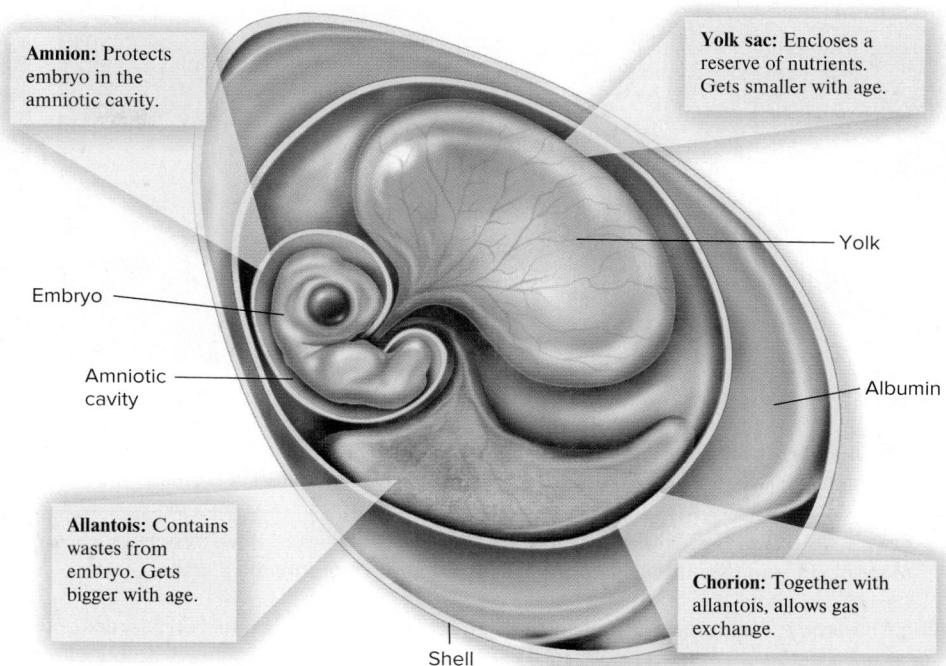

Amnion: Protects embryo in the amniotic cavity.

Yolk sac: Encloses a reserve of nutrients. Gets smaller with age.

Yolk

Embryo

Amniotic cavity

Albumin

Allantois: Contains wastes from embryo. Gets bigger with age.

Chorion: Together with allantois, allows gas exchange.

Shell

Figure 35.14 The amniotic egg.

Concept Check: *What are the other critical innovations of amniotes?*

- *Internal fertilization.* Because sperm cannot penetrate a shelled egg, fertilization occurs internally, within the female's body before the shell is secreted. In **internal fertilization,** the male of the species often uses a copulatory organ (penis) to transfer sperm into the female reproductive tract. However, birds usually transfer sperm from cloaca to cloaca.

Reptiles Include Turtles, Lizards, Snakes, Crocodilians, Dinosaurs, and Birds

Early amniote ancestors gave rise to all modern amniotes that exist today, from lizards and snakes to birds and mammals. The traditional view of amniotes identified three living classes: the reptiles (turtles, lizards, snakes, and crocodilians), birds, and mammals. As we will see later in the chapter, modern systematists have argued that enough similarities exist between birds and the classic reptiles that birds should be considered part of the reptilian lineage. This classification scheme, which is also based on molecular evidence, will be followed in this chapter. The fossil record reveals other reptilian clades, all of which are extinct, including two clades of dinosaurs (ornithischian and saurischian dinosaurs), flying reptiles (pterosaurs), and two clades of ancient aquatic reptiles (icthyosaurs and plesiosaurs).

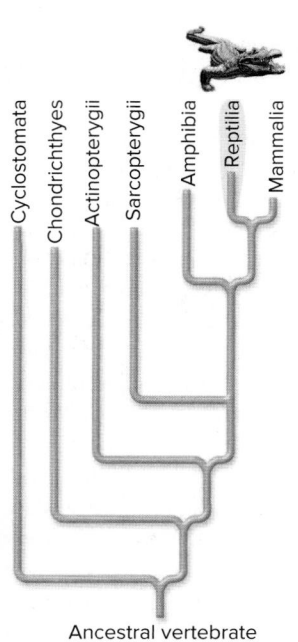

Cyclostomata

Chondrichthyes

Actinopterygii

Sarcopterygii

Amphibia

Reptilia

Mammalia

Ancestral vertebrate

Testudines: The Turtles   Turtles is an umbrella term for terrestrial species, also called tortoises, and aquatic species, sometimes known as terrapins. The turtle lineage is ancient and has remained virtually unchanged for 200 million years. The major distinguishing characteristic of the turtles is a hard protective shell into which the animal can withdraw its head and limbs. In most species, the vertebrae and ribs are fused to form this shell. All turtles lack teeth but have sharp beaks for biting.

Most turtles are aquatic and have webbed feet. The forelimbs of marine species have evolved to become large flippers. All turtles, even the aquatic species, lay their eggs on land, usually in soft sand. The gender of hatchlings is dependent on temperature, with high temperatures producing more females. Marine species often make long migrations to sandy beaches to lay their eggs (**Figure 35.15a**). Most land turtles are quite slow movers, possibly due to a low metabolic rate and a heavy shell. However, they are very long-lived species, often surviving for 120 years or more. Furthermore, turtles do not appear to show reproductive senescence or aging, reproducing continually throughout their lifetime. Most organs such as the liver, lungs, and kidneys of a centenarian turtle function as effectively as do organs in young individuals, prompting genetic researchers to examine the turtle genome for longevity genes. Many turtle species are in danger of extinction, due to egg hunting, harvesting for shells or meat, destruction of habitat and nesting sites, and death in fishing nets.

Squamata: Lizards and Snakes   The clade Squamata is a large clade with about 6,270 species of lizards and 3,630 species of snakes. Many species have an elongated body form. One of the defining characteristics of lizards and snakes is a **kinetic skull,** in which the joints between various parts of the skull are extremely mobile. The lower jaw does not join directly to the skull but rather is connected by a multijointed hinge, and the upper jaw is hinged and movable from the rest of the head. This allows the jaws to open relatively wider than other vertebrate jaws, with the

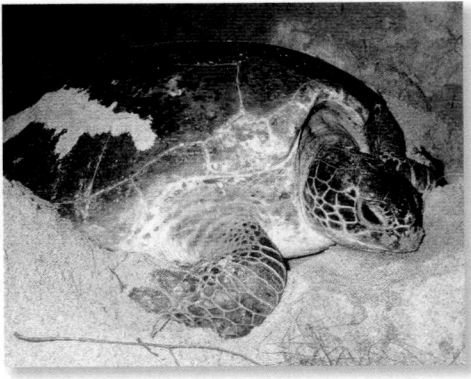

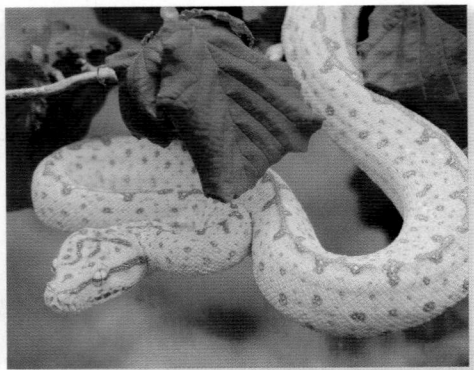

(a) Green turtle   **(b) Common collared lizard**   **(c) Juvenile tree python**

Figure 35.15 **A variety of reptiles.** **(a)** A green turtle (*Chelonia mydas*) laying eggs in the sand in Malaysia. **(b)** The common collared lizard (*Crotaphytus collarus*). **(c)** A juvenile tree python (*Morelia veridis*). a: ©Pat Morris/ardea.com; b: ©Royalty-Free/Corbis; c: ©Mark Kostich/Getty Images

 Core Skill: Modeling The goal of this modeling challenge is to draw a reptilian phylogenetic tree that distinguishes the four recognized taxa based on critical innovations that are morphological traits.

Modeling Challenge: Turtles, lizards and snakes, crocodiles, and birds are all considered reptilians, yet we recognize them as distinct taxa. Construct a model of a phylogenetic tree using six critical innovations: three- or four-chambered heart, scales, endothermy, a hard protective shell, a kinetic skull, and feathers. Be sure to show these critical innovations on your phylogenetic tree with black bars and labels. The four taxa have the following combinations of traits: Crocodilia (four-chambered heart, scales, not endothermic, no protective shell, no kinetic skull, no feathers); Squamata (three-chambered heart, scales, not endothermic, no protective shell, kinetic skull, no feathers); Testudines (three-chambered heart, scales, not endothermic, hard protective shell, no kinetic skull, no feathers); Aves (four-chambered heart, scales, endothermic, no protective shell, no kinetic skull, feathers).

result that lizards and especially snakes can swallow large prey (**Figure 35.16**). Nearly all species are carnivores. Snakes may be venomous, whereas lizards usually are not.

A main difference between lizards and snakes is that lizards generally have limbs, whereas snakes do not (**Figure 35.15b,c**).

Figure 35.16 **The kinetic skull.** In snakes and lizards, both the upper and lower jaw are movable, thereby permitting large prey to be swallowed. This horned bush viper (*Atheris ceratophora*) is swallowing a leaf-folding frog. ©Michele Menegon/ardea.com

Concept Check: *Snakes are limbless, so how can they be considered tetrapods?*

Leglessness is a derived character, meaning snake ancestors possessed legs but later lost them. In tetrapods, the expression of many different genes is needed for limb formation. In addition to *Hox* genes, the *SHH* gene is needed for limb formation and other developmental events. A genetic switch next to this gene is needed for *SHH* gene expression. In 2016, researchers found that pythons, which have tiny little leg bones inside their bodies, have three deletions in this genetic switch, and even more deletions are found in snake species with no leg bones at all. In the same year, a second research team used the CRISPR-Cas system (described in Chapter 21) to modify the expression of the *SHH* gene in mice. When they replaced the genetic switch of mice with the genetic switch from snakes, the resulting mice developed little nubs instead of legs. Taken together, these results indicate that the expression of the *SHH* gene plays an important role in limb formation.

Crocodilia: The Crocodiles and Alligators The Crocodilia is a small clade of large, carnivorous, aquatic animals that have remained essentially unchanged for nearly 200 million years (**Figure 35.17**). Indeed, these animals existed at the same time as the dinosaurs. Most of the 25 recognized species live in tropical or subtropical regions. There are only two extant species of alligators: one living in the southeastern U.S. and one found in China.

Crocodiles have a four-chambered heart, a feature they share with birds and mammals (look ahead to Figure 48.2b). In this regard, crocodiles are more closely related to birds than to any other living reptiles. Their teeth are set in sockets, a feature typical of the dinosaurs and the earliest birds. Similarly, crocodiles care for their young, another trait they have in common with birds. These and other features suggest that crocodiles and

(a) American alligator

(b) American crocodile

Figure 35.17 Crocodilians. The Crocodilia is an ancient clade that has existed unchanged for millions of years. **(a)** Alligators, such as this American alligator (*Alligator mississippiensis*), have a broad snout, and the lower jaw teeth close on the inside of the upper jaw (and thus are almost completely hidden when the mouth is closed). **(b)** Crocodiles, including this American crocodile (*Crocodylus acutus*), have a longer, thinner snout, and the lower jaw teeth close on the outside of the upper jaw (and thus are visible when the mouth is closed). a: ©Warren Jacobi/Corbis; b: ©SteveByland/ Getty Images

 Core Skill: Connections Look ahead to Figure 48.2b. In what ways are crocodilians similar to birds and mammals?

birds are more closely related than crocodiles and lizards. As with turtles, the sex of crocodiles' offspring is dependent on nest temperature.

Ornithischia and Saurischia: The Dinosaurs In 1841, English paleontologist Richard Owen coined the term **dinosaur** (from the Greek, meaning terrible lizard) to describe some of the wondrous fossil animals discovered in the 19th century. About 215 mya, dinosaurs were the dominant tetrapods on Earth and remained so for 150 million years, far longer than any other vertebrate. The two main clades were the ornithischians, or bird-hipped dinosaurs, which were herbivores such as *Stegosaurus*; and the saurischians, or lizard-hipped dinosaurs, which were fast, bipedal carnivores such as *Tyrannosaurus rex* (**Figure 35.18**). In contrast to the limbs of lizards, amphibians, and crocodiles, which splay out to the side, the legs of dinosaurs were positioned directly under the body, like pillars, a position that may have helped support their heavy bodies. Because less energy was devoted to lifting the body from the ground, some dinosaurs are believed to have been fast runners. Members of different but closely related clades—the pterosaurs (the first vertebrates to fly) and ichthyosaurs and plesiosaurs (marine reptiles)—were also common at the same time as the ornithishichians and saurischians.

Dinosaurs were the biggest animals ever to walk on the planet, with some weighing up to 50 tonnes (metric tons), or over 100,000 pounds. The variety of the thousands of dinosaur species found in fossil form around the world is staggering. However, perhaps not surprisingly for such long-extinct species, scientists are still hotly debating many details of their lives. For example, an issue still unresolved is whether some dinosaur species were **endothermic**, capable of generating body heat through their own metabolism, as birds and mammals are, or whether they were **ectothermic**, dependent on external heat as the main source of their body heat, as most reptiles are. Another issue is whether dinosaurs exhibited parental care of their young.

All nonavian dinosaurs, and many other animals, died out abruptly during a mass extinction at the end of the Cretaceous period (about 65 mya). Although widely attributed to climatic change brought about by the impact of a meteorite, scientists continue to debate the cause or causes of this mass extinction. We do not yet know why dinosaurs died out, while many other animals, including birds and small mammals, survived.

(a) Ornithischian (*Stegosaurus*)   (b) Saurischian (*Tyrannosaurus*)

Figure 35.18 Dinosaurs. (a) Herbivorous ornithischians included *Stegosaurus*, and **(b)** carnivorous saurischians included bipedal species such as *Tyrannosaurus rex.*

Aves: The Birds The defining characteristics of birds (Aves, plural of the Latin *avis*, meaning bird) are feathers and nearly all species can fly. As we will see, the ability to fly has shaped nearly every feature of the bird body. The other vertebrates that have evolved the ability to fly, the bats and the now-extinct pterosaurs, used skin stretched tight over elongated limbs to fly. Such a surface can be irreparably damaged, though some holes may heal remarkably quickly. In contrast, birds use feathers, epidermal outgrowths that can be replaced if damaged. Recent research shows that feathers evolved in dinosaurs before the appearance of birds.

Modern Birds Evolved from Small, Feather-Covered Dinosaurs

To trace the evolution of birds, paleontologists look at transitional forms, the earliest animals that had feathers. One of the first known fossils exhibiting the faint impression of feathers was *Archaeopteryx lithographica* (from the Greek, meaning ancient wings and stone picture), found in a limestone quarry in Germany in 1861. The fossil was dated at 150 million years old, which places it during the Jurassic period. Except for the presence of feathers, *Archaeopteryx* had features similar to those of dinosaurs (**Figure 35.19a**; see also Figure 26.14). First, the fossil included an impression of a long tail with many vertebrae, a dinosaur feature. Some modern birds have long tails, but they are made of feathers, with the actual tailbone being much reduced. Second, the wings had claws halfway down the leading edge, another dinosaur-like character. Among modern birds, only the hoatzin, a South American swamp-inhabiting bird, has claws on its wings, which enable the chicks to climb back into the nest if they fall out. A third dinosaur-like feature is *Archaeopteryx*'s toothed beak. Fourth, the fossil shows that *Archaeopteryx* lacked an enlarged breastbone, a feature that modern birds possess to anchor their large flight muscles, so it likely could not fly.

Structural similarities of the skull, feet, and hind leg bones have led scientists to conclude that *Archaeopteryx* is closely related to **theropods**, a group of bipedal saurischian dinosaurs. The wings and feathers of *Archaeopteryx* may have enabled it to glide from tree to tree, helped to keep it warm, or cut out the glare when folded over its head when hunting, in much the same way as some herons fold their wings over their heads when they are fishing. Later, the wings and feathers may have taken on functions of flight.

In China in the mid-1990s, paleontologists unearthed fossils of about the same age as *Archaeopteryx* that similarly suggest a close kinship between dinosaurs and modern birds. *Caudipteryx zoui* was a dinosaur-like animal with feathers on its wings and tail and a toothed beak (**Figure 35.19b**). *Confuciusornis sanctus* was a small, flightless but completely feathered dinosaur lacking the long, bony tail and toothed jaw found in other theropod dinosaurs. Its large tail feathers may have functioned in courtship displays (**Figure 35.19c**).

These three species—*Archaeopteryx, Caudipteryx,* and *Confuciusornis*—help trace a lineage from dinosaurs to birds. By the early Cretaceous period, and only a relatively short period after *Archaeopteryx* evolved, the fossil record shows the existence of a huge array of bird types resembling modern species. These were to share the skies with pterosaurs for 70 million years, before eventually having the airways to themselves.

Birds Have Feathers, a Lightweight Skeleton, Air Sacs, and Reduced Organs

Modern birds possess many characteristics, including scales on their feet and legs and shelled eggs, that reveal their reptilian ancestry. In addition, however, birds have four features that are unique among living animals and associated with flight.

1. **Feathers.** Feathers are modified scales that keep birds warm and enable flight (**Figure 35.20a**). Soft, downy feathers, which are close to the body, maintain heat, whereas stiffer contour feathers, supported on a modified forelimb, give the wing the airfoil shape it needs to generate lift. Each contour feather develops from a follicle, a tiny pit in the skin. If a feather is lost, a new one can be regrown. The contour feathers consist of many paired barbs, each of which supports barbules that contain hooks that interlock with barbules from neighboring barbs to give the feather its shape (**Figure 35.20b**).

(a) *Archaeopteryx lithographica*

Avian features:
1. Feathered wings and tail

Reptilian features:
1. Long, bony tail
2. Claws on wings
3. Toothed beak
4. No large breastbone

(b) *Caudipteryx zoui*

Avian features:
1. Feathered wings and tail

Reptilian features:
1. Short, bony tail
2. Claws on wings
3. Toothed beak
4. No large breastbone

(c) *Confuciusornis sanctus*

Avian features:
1. Completely feathered
2. No bony tail
3. No teeth in beak

Reptilian features:
1. Flightless
2. Claws on wings
3. No large breastbone

Figure 35.19 Transitional forms between dinosaurs and birds. (a) *Archaeopteryx lithographica* was a Jurassic animal with dinosaur-like features as well as wings and feathers. **(b)** *Caudipteryx zoui* was a dinosaur with feathers on its tail and wings. **(c)** *Confuciusornis sanctus* was a birdlike animal with a horny, toothless beak.

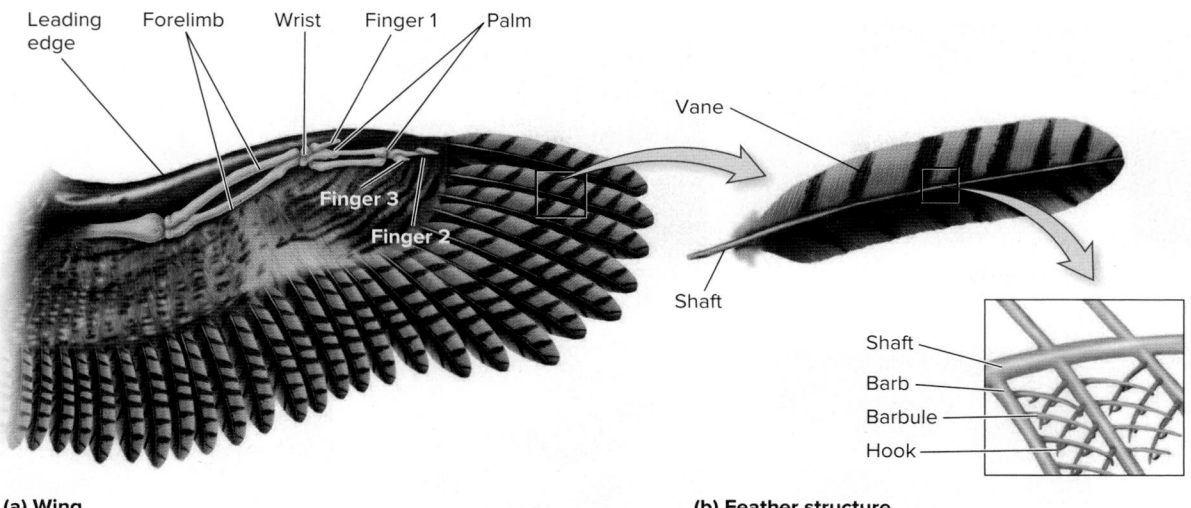

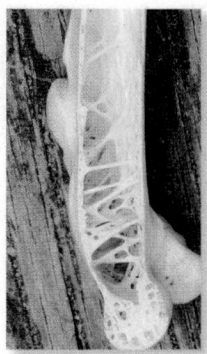

(a) Wing   (b) Feather structure   (c) Pelican bone
                                                                                          *(Pelicanus
                                                                                          occidentalis)*

Figure 35.20 Features of the bird wing and feather. **(a)** The wing is supported by an elongated and modified forelimb with three extended fingers. **(b)** Each feather has a hollow shaft that supports many barbs, which, in turn, support barbules that interlock with hooks to give the feather its form. **(c)** The bones of a pelican (*Pelicanus occidentalis*) are hollow but crisscrossed with a honeycomb structure that provides added strength.

c: ©Gilbert S. Grant/Science Source

Concept Check: *What adaptations in birds help reduce their body weight to enable flight?*

2. ***Air sacs.*** Flight requires a great deal of energy generated by an active metabolism that requires abundant oxygen. Birds have nine air sacs—large, hollow sacs that may extend into the bones—that expand and contract when a bird inhales and exhales, while the lungs remain stationary. Air is therefore being constantly moved across the lungs during inhalation and exhalation. Although making bird breathing very efficient, this process also makes birds especially susceptible to airborne toxins (hence, the utility of the canary in the coal mine; the bird's death signaled the presence of harmful carbon dioxide or methane gas that was otherwise unnoticed by miners).

3. ***Reduction of organs.*** Some organs are reduced in size or are lacking altogether in birds, which reduces the total mass of a bird's body. For example, birds have only one ovary and can carry relatively few eggs. As a result, they lay fewer eggs than most other reptile species. In fact, the gonads of both males and females are reduced, except during the breeding season, when they increase in size. Most birds also lack a urinary bladder. In addition, the lack of teeth reduces weight at the head end.

4. ***Lightweight bones.*** Most bird bones are thin and hollow and are crisscrossed internally by thin strips of bone, giving them a honeycomb structure (**Figure 35.20c**). An enlarged breastbone, or **sternum**, provides an anchor on which a bird's powerful flight muscles attach. These muscles may contribute up to 30% of the bird's body weight.

Other bird characteristics are related to flight. Rapid flight requires good vision, and bird vision is the best in the vertebrate world. Birds are endotherms. Their body temperatures are generally 40–42°C, considerably warmer than the human body's average of 37°C. This warm temperature ensures rapid metabolism and the quick production of adenosine triphosphate (ATP), which is needed to fuel flight and other activities. Like mammals, birds have a double circulation and a four-chambered heart. This type of circulatory system is more efficient at rapidly providing oxygen to the body, especially to the wings during flight.

Most birds are carnivores, eating insects or other invertebrates. However, some birds, such as parrots, eat just nutrient-rich fruits and seeds. The keratin of bird beaks is tough and malleable, and a wide assortment of beaks has evolved, with the form dependent on the function (**Figure 35.21**).

Bird reproduction involves parental care. Eggs need be kept warm for successful development, which entails brooding by an adult bird. Often, the males and females take turns brooding so that each parent can feed and maintain its strength. Picking successful partners is therefore an important task, and birds often engage in complex courtship rituals (look ahead to Figure 55.21).

Birds Are Placed into Many Different Orders

Birds are the most species-rich clade of terrestrial vertebrates, with 28 orders, 166 families, and about 10,425 species (**Table 35.2**). Despite this diversity, birds lack the variety of body shapes that exist in the mammals, some of which can swim, others fly, others walk on four legs, and yet others walk only on two legs. Most birds fly, and therefore, most have the same general body shape. The biggest departures from this body shape are the flightless birds, including the cassowaries, emus, and ostriches. These birds have smaller wing bones, and the keel on the breastbone is greatly reduced or absent. Penguins are also flightless birds whose upper limbs are modified as flippers used in swimming.

(a) Cracking beak

(b) Scooping beak

(c) Tearing beak

(d) Probing beak

(e) Nectar-feeding beak

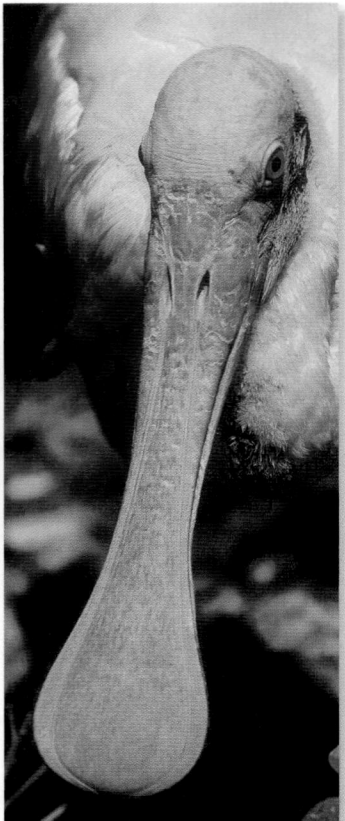

(f) Sieving beak

Figure 35.21 **A variety of bird beaks.** Birds have evolved a variety of beak shapes used in different types of food gathering. **(a)** Hyacinth macaw (*Anodorhynchus hyacinthinus*)—cracking. **(b)** White pelican (*Pelecanus onocrotalus*)—scooping. **(c)** Verreaux's eagle (*Aquila verreauxii*)—tearing. **(d)** American avocet (*Recurvirostra americana*)—probing. **(e)** Anna's hummingbird (*Calypte anna*)—nectar feeding. **(f)** Roseate spoonbill (*Platalea ajaja*)—sieving. a: ©B. G. Thomson/Science Source; b: ©Jean-Claude Canton/Bruce Coleman Inc./Photoshot; c: ©Morales/age fotostock; d: ©Max Allen/Shutterstock; e: Source: Robert McMorran/USFWS; f: ©Mervyn Rees/Alamy Stock Photo

 Core Concept: Structure and Function Each of these beak shapes permits a different method of feeding.

35.6 Mammals: Milk-Producing Amniotes

Learning Outcomes:

1. Identify four features that distinguish mammals from other vertebrate clades.
2. Describe the main orders of mammals.
3. Outline the phylogenetic relationships among the major clades of mammals.

About 225 mya, the first mammals appeared in the mid-Triassic period (refer back to Figure 26.13). They evolved from small mammal-like reptiles that went extinct about 170 mya. Until recently, the earliest mammals were believed to have been small, insect-eating species that lived in the shadows of dinosaurs. However, in 2005, the discovery of two fossils of a 130-million-year-old mammalian genus called *Repenomamus* challenged the notion that all early mammals were small insect eaters. One fossil was of an animal estimated to weigh about 13 kg (30 pounds), about the size of a small dog, which is larger than some dinosaurs living in the same region at the time. The other fossil had the remains of a baby dinosaur in its stomach area.

The extinction of the dinosaurs in the Cretaceous period, some 65 mya, paved the way for mammals to increase in numbers. Today, biologists have identified about 5,500 species of mammals with a diverse array of lifestyles, from fishlike dolphins to birdlike bats, and

from small insectivores such as shrews to large herbivores such as giraffes and elephants. The range of sizes and body forms of mammals is unmatched by any other vertebrate group, and mammals are prime illustrations of the concept that organismal diversity is related to environmental diversity. In this section, we will outline the features that distinguish mammals from other taxa and examine the diversity of mammals that exist on Earth.

Mammals Have Mammary Glands, Hair, Specialized Teeth, and an Enlarged Skull

Four characteristics distinguish mammals: the possession of mammary glands, hair, specialized teeth, and an enlarged skull.

- *Mammary glands.* Mammals, or the clade Mammalia (from the Latin *mamma*, meaning breast), are

Cyclostomata
Chondrichthyes
Actinopterygii
Sarcopterygii
Amphibia
Reptilia
Mammalia

Ancestral vertebrate

Table 35.2		The Main Orders of Birds, in Order of Species Richness	
Order		**Examples (approx. number of species)**	**Main characteristics**
Passeriformes		Robins, starlings, sparrows, warblers (5,900)	Perching birds with perching feet; songbirds
Apodiformes		Hummingbirds, swifts (430)	Fast fliers with rapidly beating wings; small bodies
Piciformes		Woodpeckers, toucans (403)	Large with specialized beaks; two toes pointing forward and two backward
Psittaciformes		Parrots, cockatoos (360)	Large, powerful beaks
Charadriiformes		Gulls, sandpipers (340)	Shorebirds
Columbiformes		Doves, pigeons (310)	Round bodies; short legs
Galliformes		Chickens, pheasants, quail (285)	Often large birds; weak flyers; ground nesters
Accipitriformes		Eagles, hawks, vultures (300)	Large diurnal carnivores; birds of prey; powerful talons; strong beaks
Coraciiformes		Hornbills, kingfishers (206)	Large beaks; cavity nesters
Strigiformes		Owls (205)	Nocturnal carnivores; powerful talons; strong beaks
Anseriformes		Ducks, swans, waterfowl (165)	Able to swim; webbed feet; broad bills
Pelecaniformes		Pelicans, frigate birds (65)	Large, water inhabiting
Sphenisciformes		Penguins (17)	Flightless; wings modified into flippers for swimming; marine; Southern Hemisphere

named after the female's distinctive mammary glands, which secrete milk. Milk is a fluid rich in fat, sugar, protein, and vital minerals, especially calcium. Newborn mammals suckle this fluid, which helps promote rapid growth.

- **Hair.** All mammals have hair, although some have more than others. Whales have hair in utero, but adults are hairless or retain only a few hairs on their snout. Compared with many mammals, humans are relatively hairless. In some animals, the hair is dense and is referred to as fur. In some aquatic species such as beavers, the fur is so dense it cannot be thoroughly wetted, so the hair underneath remains dry. Mammals are endothermic, and their fur is an efficient insulator. Hair can also take on functions other than insulation. Many mammals, including cats, dogs, walruses, and whales, have sensory hairs called vibrissae (**Figure 35.22a**). Hair can be of many colors, to allow the mammals to blend

into their background (**Figure 35.22b**). In some cases, as in porcupines and hedgehogs, the hairs become long, stiffened, and sharp (quills) and serve as a defense mechanism (**Figure 35.22c**).

- **Specialized teeth.** Mammals are the only vertebrates with highly differentiated teeth—incisors, canines, premolars, and molars—that are adapted for different types of diets (**Figure 35.23**). Although teeth are generally present in all mammalian species, some teeth are larger, smaller, lost, or reduced, depending on diet. Of particular importance to carnivores such as wolves are the piercing canine teeth, whereas herbivorous species such as deer depend on their chisel-like incisors to snip off vegetation and their many molars to grind plant material. Only mammals chew their food in this fashion. Rodent incisors grow continuously throughout life, and species such as beavers wear them down by gnawing tough plant material such as

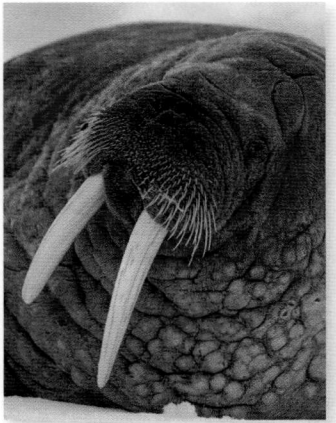
(a) Sensory hairs

(b) Camouflaged coat

(c) Defensive quills

Figure 35.22 Mammalian hair. (a) The sensory hairs (vibrissae) of the walrus (*Odobenus rosmarus*). **(b)** The camouflaged coat of a bobcat (*Lynx rufus*). **(c)** The defensive quills of the crested porcupine (*Hystrix africaeaustralis*). a: ©National Geographic Creative/Alamy Stock Photo; b: ©Charles Krebs/Corbis/Getty Images; c: ©Anthony Bannister/Science Source

wood. Mammals that have different types of teeth are called heterodonts; others, such as dolphins, whose teeth are of uniform size and shape, are called homodonts.

- **Enlarged skull.** The mammalian skull differs from other amniote skulls in several ways. First, the brain is enlarged and contained within a relatively large skull. Second, mammals have a single lower jawbone, unlike reptiles, whose lower jaw is composed of multiple bones. Third, mammals have three bones in the middle ear, as opposed to reptiles, which have only one. Fourth, most mammals, except some seals, have external ears.

In addition to those uniquely mammalian characteristics, some, but not all, mammals have the following additional features:

- **The ability to digest plants.** Apart from geese, tortoises and marine iguanas, certain species of mammals are the only large vertebrates alive today that can exist on a steady diet of grasses or tree leaves; indeed, most large mammals are herbivores. Though mammals cannot digest cellulose, the principal constituent of the cell wall of many plants, some species have a large four-chambered stomach containing cellulose-digesting bacteria. These bacteria can break down the cellulose and make the plant cell contents available to the animal. Other species have an extensive cecum or large intestine where digestion occurs.

- **Horns or antlers.** Mammals are the only living class of vertebrates to possess horns or antlers. Many mammals, especially antelope, cattle, and sheep, have horns, typically consisting of a bony core that is a permanent outgrowth of the skull surrounded by a hairlike keratin sheath, as shown in the large antelope called a kudu (**Figure 35.24a**). Hooves, also made of keratin, protect an animal's toes from the force of impact of its feet against the ground.

(a) Biting teeth

(b) Grinding teeth

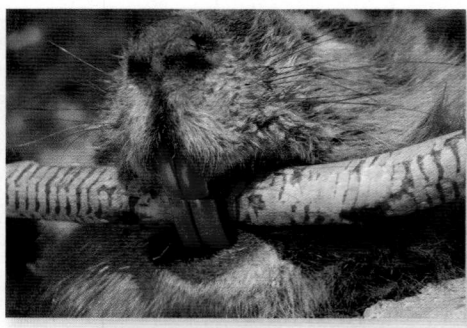
(c) Gnawing teeth

(d) Tusks

(e) Grasping teeth

Figure 35.23 Mammalian teeth. Mammals have different types of teeth, according to their diet. **(a)** The wolf has long canine teeth that bite its prey. **(b)** The deer has a long row of molars that grind plant material. **(c)** The beaver, a rodent, has long, continually growing incisors used to gnaw wood. **(d)** The elephant's incisors are modified into tusks. **(e)** Dolphins and other fish or plankton feeders have numerous small teeth used to grasp prey. a: ©Image Source/Corbis; b: ©Sam Camp/Getty Images; c: ©mauritius images GmbH/Alamy Stock Photo; d: ©Gallo Images ROOTS Collection/Getty Images; e: ©Jim Watt/Getty Images

Figure 35.24 Horns and antlers in mammals. Mammals have a variety of outgrowths that are used for defense or by males as weapons in contests over females. **(a)** The horns of this male kudu (*Tragelaphus strepsiceros*) are bony outgrowths of the skull covered in a keratin sheath. **(b)** The horns of the black rhinoceros (*Diceros bicornis*) are outgrowths of the epidermis, made of tightly matted hair. **(c)** The antlers of the caribou (*Rangifer tarandus*), also known as reindeer, are made entirely of bone and are grown and shed each year. a: ©Peter Chadwick/Getty Images; b: Source: Karl Stromayer/USFWS; c: ©Paul A. Souders/Corbis/Getty Images

(a) Skull outgrowths **(b) Epidermal outgrowths** **(c) Bony antlers**

Rhinoceros horns are outgrowths of the epidermis, consisting of very tightly matted hair (**Figure 35.24b**). In contrast, deer antlers are made entirely of bone (**Figure 35.24c**). Deer grow a new set of antlers each year and shed them after the mating season.

Mammals Are Morphologically Diverse and Occupy a Wide Range of Environments

Modern mammals are incredibly diverse in morphology and lifestyle (**Table 35.3**). They vary in size from tiny insect-eating bats,

Table 35.3	The Main Orders of Mammals, in Order of Species Richness		
Order		**Examples (approx. number of species)**	**Main characteristics**
Rodentia		Mice, rats, squirrels, beavers, porcupines (2,277)	Plant eating; gnawing habit, with two pairs of continually growing incisor teeth
Chiroptera		Bats (1,157)	Insect or fruit eating; small; have ability to fly; navigate by sonar; nocturnal
Eulipotyphla		Shrews, moles, hedgehogs (462)	Insect eaters; primitive placental mammals
Primates		Monkeys, apes, humans (437)	Opposable thumb; binocular vision; large brains
Carnivora		Cats, dogs, weasels, bears, seals, sea lions (295)	Flesh-eating mammals; canine teeth
Artiodactyla		Deer, antelopes, cattle, sheep, goats, camels, pigs (240)	Herbivorous hoofed mammals, usually with two toes, hippopotamus and others with four toes; many with horns or antlers
Diprotodontia		Kangaroos, koalas, opossums, wombats (147)	Pouched mammals mainly found in Australia
Lagomorpha		Rabbits, hares (92)	Powerful hind legs; rodent-like teeth
Cetacea		Whales, dolphins (84)	Marine fishes or plankton feeders; front limbs modified into flippers; no hind limbs; little hair except on snout
Perissodactyla		Horses, zebras, tapirs, rhinoceroses (18)	Hoofed herbivorous mammals with odd number of toes, one (horses) or three (rhinoceroses)
Monotremata		Duck-billed platypuses, echidna (5)	Egg-laying mammals found only in Australia and New Guinea
Proboscidea		Elephants (3)	Long trunk; large, upper incisors modified as tusks

weighing in at only 2 g, to leviathans such as the blue whale, the largest animal ever known, which tips the scales at 100 tonnes (over 200,000 pounds). Mammalian orders are divided into two distinct subclasses (**Figure 35.25**). The subclass Prototheria contains only the order Monotremata, or **monotremes**, which are found in Australia and New Guinea. There are only five species: the duck-billed platypus (**Figure 35.26a**) and four species of echidna, a spiny animal resembling a hedgehog. Monotremes are early-diverging mammals that lay eggs rather than bear live young, lack a placenta, and have mammary glands with poorly developed nipples. The mothers incubate the eggs, and after hatching, the young simply lap up the milk as it oozes onto the fur.

The subclass Theria contains all remaining live-bearing mammals. The Theria are divided into two clades, the Metatheria and the Eutheria. The clade Metatheria, or the **marsupials**, is a group of seven orders, with about 280 species, including the swamp wallaby pictured in **Figure 35.26b**. Once widespread, members of this order are now largely confined to Australia, although some marsupials exist in South America, and one species—the opossum—is found in North America. Fertilization is internal, and reproduction is viviparous in marsupials. Marsupials have a placenta that nourishes the embryo. Unlike other mammals, however, marsupials are extremely small when they are born (often only 1–2 cm) and make their way to a ventral pouch called a marsupium for further development.

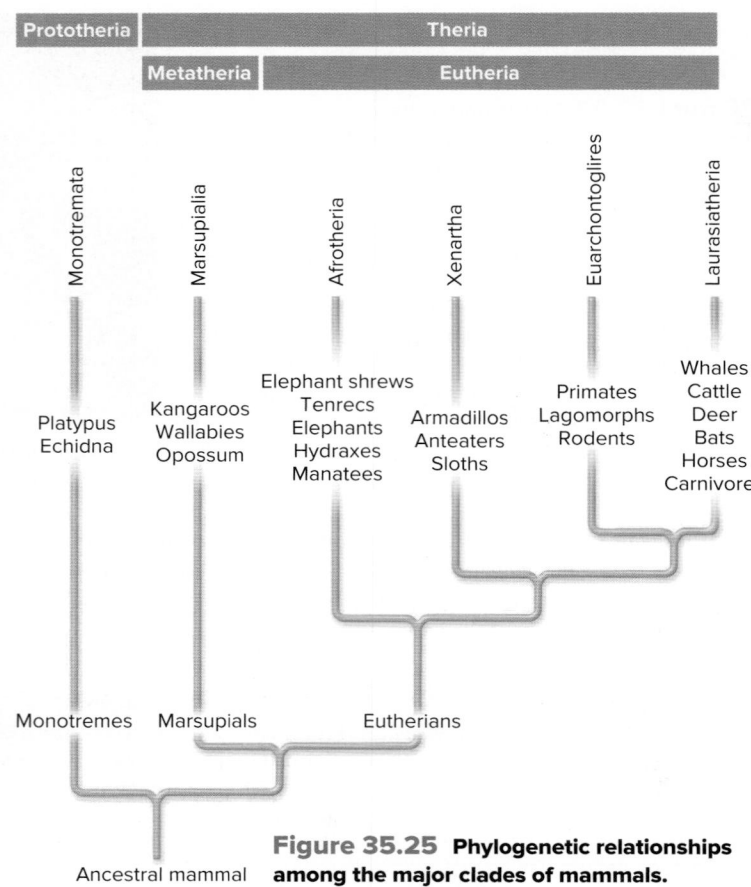

Figure 35.25 **Phylogenetic relationships among the major clades of mammals.**

(a) Prototherian (duck-billed platypus)

(b) Metatherian (swamp wallaby)

Figure 35.26 **Diversity among mammals.**
(a) Prototherians, such as this duck-billed platypus (*Ornithorhynchus anatinus*), lay eggs, lack a placenta, and possess mammary glands with poorly developed nipples. **(b)** Metatherians, or marsupials, such as this swamp wallaby (*Wallabia bicolor*), feed and carry their developing young, or "joeys," in a ventral pouch. **(c)** Gestation lasts longer in eutherians, and their young are more developed at birth, as illustrated by this young langur monkey (*Presbytis entellus*). a: ©Dave Watts/naturepl.com; b: ©Nigel Pavitt/Getty Images; c: ©Education Images/Contributor/Getty Images

 Core Skill: Connections Look ahead to Figure 51.10. The placenta serves as the provisional lungs, intestine, and kidneys of the developing fetus. How much mixing is there of maternal and fetal blood?

(c) Eutherian (gray langur)

All other mammalian orders are members of the clade Eutheria and are considered **eutherians**, or placental mammals, such as the langur monkeys shown in **Figure 35.26c**. Eutherians have a long-lived and complex placenta, compared with that of marsupials. In eutherians, fertilization is internal, and reproduction is viviparous, but the developmental period, or gestation, of the young is prolonged. Molecular studies suggest four clades of placental mammals diverged in the Cretaceous. The earliest diverging clade was the Afrotheria, which evolved in the African landmass starting about 110–100 mya. This clade includes the elephant shrews, tenrecs, golden moles, manatees and dugongs, hyraxes, aardvark, and elephants. Shortly thereafter, about 100–95 mya, the Xenartha evolved in South America, where the armadillos, anteaters, and sloths appeared. The other two clades, the Euarchontoglires, containing the primates (refer back to Section 26.3), lagomorphs, and rodents, and the Laurasiatheria, containing the whales, artiodactyla, bats, horses, and carnivores, both evolved in the northern continent of Laurasia and became separate about 95–85 mya. Later, following continental drift, Africa and Arabia collided with Laurasia, and the Isthmus of Panama joined North and South America. These new land bridges facilitated animal movement between once separated continents.

The diversity of mammals is often threatened by human activities such as habitat destruction. In addition, many species are hunted for food. Others, such as wild cats and whales, are hunted for their products (fur and oil, respectively), and still others, such as the oryx, have simply been shot for sport. We will revisit the conservation of such endangered species in Chapter 60.

Summary of Key Concepts

35.1 Vertebrates: Chordates with a Backbone

- Vertebrates have several characteristic features, including a vertebral column, a cranium, and an endoskeleton of cartilage or bone (Figure 35.1, Table 35.1).

35.2 Cyclostomata: Jawless Fishes

- Early-diverging vertebrates lacked jaws. Today, the only jawless vertebrates are the hagfish and lampreys (Figures 35.2, 35.3).

35.3 Gnathostomes: Jawed Vertebrates

- A critical innovation in vertebrate evolution was the hinged jaw, which first developed in fishes. Gnathostomes are vertebrate species that possess a hinged jaw (Figure 35.4).

- The chondrichthyans (sharks, skates, and rays) have a skeleton composed of flexible cartilage and powerful appendages called fins. They are active predators with acute senses and were among the earliest fishes to develop teeth (Figure 35.5).

- Bony fishes consist of the Actinopterygii (ray-finned fishes, the most species-rich clade), and the Sarcopterygii (lobe-finned fishes). In Actinopterygii, the fins are supported by thin, flexible rays and moved by muscles inside the body (Figures 35.6, 35.7).

- The Sarcopterygii comprise the lobe-finned fishes (Actinistia and Dipnoi) and the tetrapods. In the lobe-finned fishes, the fins are supported by extensions of the pectoral and pelvic areas and are moved by their own muscles (Figure 35.8).

35.4 Tetrapods: Gnathostomes with Four Limbs

- The fossil record reveals the evolution of lobe-finned fishes into fishes with four limbs. Recent research has shown that relatively simple mutations control large changes in limb development (Figures 35.9, 35.10, 35.11).

- Amphibians live on land but return to the water to reproduce. The larval stage undergoes metamorphosis, losing gills and tail and gaining lungs and limbs (Figure 35.12).

- The majority of amphibians belong to the order Anura (frogs and toads). Other orders are the Apoda (caecilians) and Urodela (salamanders) (Figure 35.13).

35.5 Amniotes: Tetrapods with a Desiccation-Resistant Egg

- The amniotic egg permitted animals to become fully terrestrial. Other critical innovations that enabled the conquest of land included desiccation-resistant skin, thoracic breathing, water-conserving kidneys, and internal fertilization (Figure 35.14).

- Living reptilian clades include the Testudines (turtles), Squamata (lizards and snakes), Crocodilia (crocodiles), and Aves (birds). The Ornithischia and Saurischia are two extinct clades of dinosaurs (Figures 35.15, 35.16, 35.17, 35.18).

- Three species—*Archaeopteryx*, *Caudipteryx*, and *Confuciusornis*—help trace a lineage from dinosaurs to birds (Figure 35.19).

- The four key characteristics of birds are feathers, air sacs, reduced size of organs, and a lightweight skeleton. Birds are the most species-rich clade of terrestrial vertebrates. Many of their unique features are related to flying. Their beak structures reflect varied methods for feeding (Figures 35.20, 35.21, Table 35.2).

35.6 Mammals: Milk-Producing Amniotes

- The distinguishing characteristics of mammals are mammary glands, hair, specialized teeth, and an enlarged skull. Mammalian tooth shape varies according to diet. Other distinguishing characteristics of some mammals are the ability to digest plants and horns or antlers (Figures 35.22, 35.23, 35.24).

- Two subclasses of mammals exist: the Prototheria (monotremes) and the Theria (the live-bearing mammals). The live-bearing mammals are, in turn, divided into the Metatheria (marsupials) and Eutheria (placental mammals). The Eutheria have been divided into four different clades (Table 35.3, Figures 35.25, 35.26).

Assess & Discuss

Test Yourself

1. Which of the following is *not* a defining characteristic of vertebrates?
   a. cranium
   b. hinged jaw
   c. vertebral column
   d. endoskeleton

2. Which of the following organisms are considered cyclostomes?
   a. tunicates
   b. hagfish
   c. lampreys
   d. both a and b
   e. both b and c

3. The presence of a bony skeleton, an operculum, and a swim bladder are all defining characteristics of
   a. Myxini.   d. bony fishes.
   b. lampreys.   e. amphibians.
   c. Chondrichthyes.

4. Which type of fish is a lobe-fin?
   a. moray eel   d. stingray
   b. sea dragon   e. lungfish
   c. lamprey

5. Organisms that lay eggs are said to be
   a. oviparous.   d. placental.
   b. ovoviparous.   e. none of the above.
   c. viviparous.

6. Which clade does not include frogs?
   a. vertebrates   d. amniotes
   b. gnathostomes   e. lobe fins
   c. tetrapods

7. In some amphibians, the adult retains certain larval characteristics, a phenomenon known as
   a. metamorphosis.   d. paedomorphosis.
   b. parthenogenesis.   e. hermaphrodism.
   c. cephalization.

8. The membrane of the amniotic egg that serves as a site for waste storage is the
   a. amnion.   d. chorion.
   b. yolk sac.   e. albumin.
   c. allantois.

9. Which characteristic qualifies lizards as gnathostomes?
   a. a cranium
   b. a skeleton of bone or cartilage
   c. a hinged jaw
   d. the possession of limbs
   e. amniotic eggs

10. Which of the following is *not* a distinguishing characteristic of birds?
    a. amniotic egg   d. lack of certain organs
    b. feathers   e. lightweight skeletons
    c. air sacs

Conceptual Questions

1. How is vertebrate movement similar to arthropod movement, and how is it different?

2. Why aren't all reptiles endothermic given that both birds and mammals are?

3. **Core Concept: Evolution** Are birds considered to be living dinosaurs?

Collaborative Questions

1. By what means can vertebrates move?

2. Why are amphibians considered good indicator species, which are species whose status provides information on the overall health of an ecosystem?

UNIT VI
FLOWERING PLANTS

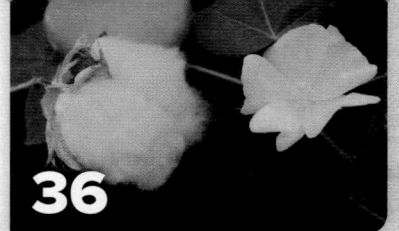

Flowering plants, also known as the angiosperms, are essential to the lives of humans and most other organisms on Earth. Flowering plants provide most of our food, either directly in the form of vegetables and grains and other fruits or indirectly as animal fodder. Cotton, linen, and other fibers that we use for clothing and wood that we use for construction and fuel, as well as powerful cancer drugs and many other medicines, come from flowering plants. This unit reveals molecular, biochemical, structural, evolutionary, and ecological features of the hundreds of thousands of flowering plants that support Earth's life.

The unit begins with Chapter 36, which provides an overview of flowering plant structure and function, focusing on the seed-to-seed life cycle. By comparing plant bodies with those of animals, we will discover how plants are constructed and how they grow. Building on this background, Chapter 37 explains the genetic and physiological bases of plant behavior—plant responses to external stimuli such as day length that are mediated by internally produced hormones. In this chapter, we will see that, like animals, plants have evolved sophisticated sensory systems that monitor environmental conditions and allow plants to respond in predictable ways. Chapter 38 explains the nutritional requirements of plants, a deep understanding of which is critical to human agriculture and our ability to feed our increasing populations. In Chapter 39, we see how plant water transport influences global climate and how plants import organic food into nonphotosynthetic

(36) ©Linda Graham;
(37) ©William D. Bowman;
(38) ©Dwight Kuhn;
(39) ©Barry Mason/Alamy
Stock Photo; (40) ©Michael
Roach/Alamy Stock Photo

organs and tissues. Chapter 40 focuses on the molecular and cellular bases of plant reproduction, the process that generates seeds and fruits. This chapter ties together key concepts presented throughout the unit: the seed-to-seed life cycle of plants and their distinctively structured bodies, plant development and growth in response to environmental and hormonal influences, and plant acquisition and transport of materials that support growth and reproduction.

 The following Core Concepts and Core Skills will be emphasized in this unit:

- *Energy and Matter: Though sunlight is the major source of energy for photosynthetic plants, hundreds of flowering plant species as well as diverse tissues occurring in all flowering plants are heterotrophic and thus require a supply of organic food as a source of energy.*
- *Systems: Some of the ways in which plants detect and respond to light and other environmental factors are similar to those operating in microbes or animals, but others are distinctive.*
- *Energy and Matter: As is the case for animals, it is essential for flowering plants to maintain body water content and energy balance within tolerance limits, or they will die.*
- *Information: Some of the cellular and molecular bases of plant growth and development are also found in microbes and animals, but plants display some unique growth and development modes.*
- *Structure and Function: Have you ever wondered why and how trees become so tall? The unique features of plant bodies as well as variations occurring among plants explain how flowering plants function in nature and in human agriculture.*
- *Process of Science: A modern understanding of flowering plant structure, function, and behavior—such as flower blooming—has been derived from experimental studies, some of which are described in Feature Investigations in this unit.*
- *Modeling: Every chapter has a Modeling Challenge to help you refine this important skill.*

An Introduction to Flowering Plant Form and Function

36

Cotton is an economically important crop harvested from the seeds of a flowering plant. ©Linda Graham

Anyone who seeks to improve human life by reducing the effects of disease, producing more food, or improving our environment needs to know something about plant form and function. That's because humans depend on flowering plants not only for nutritious food, fibers such as cotton and linen, wood and paper, medicines, and biofuels, but also for plentiful fresh air and clean water. Knowledge of basic plant form and function, including how plants develop from and produce seeds, is essential to human society.

The flowering plant *Gossypium*, shown in the chapter opening photo, provides an example. Flowering plants are distinguished by flowers that produce fruits containing seeds. As *Gossypium* seeds mature, their surfaces develop a thick blanket of 10,000–20,000 cellulose-rich hairs that may aid dispersal to environments favorable for seedling growth. Such seed hairs form the valuable commodity called cotton, which is harvested from mature *Gossypium* seeds as the fruit opens. Understanding seed hair form and function fosters agricultural production of this renewable organic material, which has many uses.

This chapter provides an introduction to the flowering plants, focusing on fundamental principles of body form and function—anatomy and physiology. These principles are basic to human efforts to use genetic methods to improve crops in ways that enhance human society, such as developing cotton plants that resist pest attack. The principles of plant form and function are equally important to evolutionary biologists who seek to understand how and why variations in plant body structure arise, and to ecologists who want to know how plants respond to environmental changes.

We will begin by considering the seed-to-seed life of a flowering plant, from seed germination to the production of a new generation. Next, an overview of how plants grow and develop reveals some fascinating similarities to animals, but also intriguing differences. Finally, centering our attention on the adult plant body reveals how adaptation to different environments has generated diverse species whose form and function vary dramatically. This background supports subsequent chapters in this unit that focus on flowering plant behavior, nutrition, transport, and reproduction.

36.1 From Seed to Seed—The Life of a Flowering Plant

Learning Outcomes:

1. List ways in which flowering plant reproduction and growth resemble or differ from those of animals.

2. Describe how the two major types of flowering plants—monocots and eudicots—differ in form.

3. **CoreSKILL »** Distinguish among annual, biennial, and perennial plants, and explain how their differences influence human uses of plants as food.

Several major events punctuate the lives of flowering plants, also known as the **angiosperms**. When seeds germinate, dormant embryos begin metabolic activity and start the process of seedling development. Seedlings grow and develop into mature plants capable of reproduction. Finally, flowers produce fruits that disperse the next generation of seeds. In this section, we will briefly survey the life cycle of flowering plants, focusing on the basic structural features of each life stage.

Seedlings Develop from Embryos in Seeds

Seeds are reproductive structures produced by flowering plants and other seed plants, usually as the result of sexual reproduction. Seeds contain embryos that develop into young plants—seedlings—when seeds germinate. As in animals, the embryo is an essential stage in the sexual cycle of plants. The plant sexual cycle explains how embryos typically arise (**Figure 36.1**; see also Figure 32.14).

Unlike animals, sexual reproduction in plants requires two multicellular stages: a gamete-producing **gametophyte** and a spore-producing **sporophyte**. In the life cycle of plants, these two life stages alternate with one another in a process called **alternation of generations**. Flowering plants produce relatively large sporophytes and microscopic gametophytes that grow and develop within flowers (see Figure 36.1). Diploid sporophytes produce haploid spores by the process of meiosis. These spores grow into gametophytes that produce plant gametes—eggs and sperm. Fusion of egg and sperm in the process of fertilization generates a diploid zygote, which undergoes repeated mitotic divisions to form the plant **embryo**.

The plant embryo is a very young sporophyte that lies dormant within a seed, accompanied by a supply of stored food and enclosed by a tough, protective seed coat (**Figure 36.2a**), much like the animal amniotic egg. Like an eggshell, the seed coat protects the delicate plant embryo during the dispersal of seeds from parent plants into the environment. Dispersed seeds may remain dormant in the soil—sometimes for long periods—and then germinate when temperature, moisture, and light conditions are favorable. Such conditions activate

embryo metabolism, in which stored food is respired for energy needed for cell division and growth.

As is the case for animals, **growth** of plants is an increase in weight or size, and **development** is a series of changes in the state of a cell, tissue, organ, or organism. Enlarging plant embryos break the seed coat and grow into seedlings (**Figure 36.2b**). If sufficient resources such as water and minerals are available, seedlings may develop into mature sporophyte plants (**Figure 36.2c**).

The angiosperm plant body is simpler in form than most animal bodies and is composed of only three types of organs: stems, leaves, and roots. **Stems** produce leaves and branches and bear the reproductive structures of mature plants. **Leaves** are flattened structures that emerge from stems and are often specialized in ways that enable photosynthesis. Stems and leaves together make up the plant **shoot** (see Figure 36.2b). Mature plants often possess multiple stems bearing many leaves, which together form the **shoot system**. **Roots** provide anchorage in the soil and also foster efficient uptake of water and minerals. The aggregate of a plant's roots make up the **root system** (see Figure 36.2c).

As in animals, the process of body and organ development in plants involves the differentiation of specialized cells having distinctive structures and functions. But unlike animals, plant seedlings and mature plants produce new tissues in specific areas called meristems. A **meristem** (from the Greek *merizein*, meaning to divide) is a region of undifferentiated cells that produces new tissue by cell division. A dormant meristem occurs at the shoot and root tips of seed embryos, and these meristems become active in seedlings (see Figure 36.2a and b). Active meristems also occur at stem and root tips of mature plants. Such meristems are known as shoot and root **apical meristems** because they occur at shoot and root tips, also known as apices.

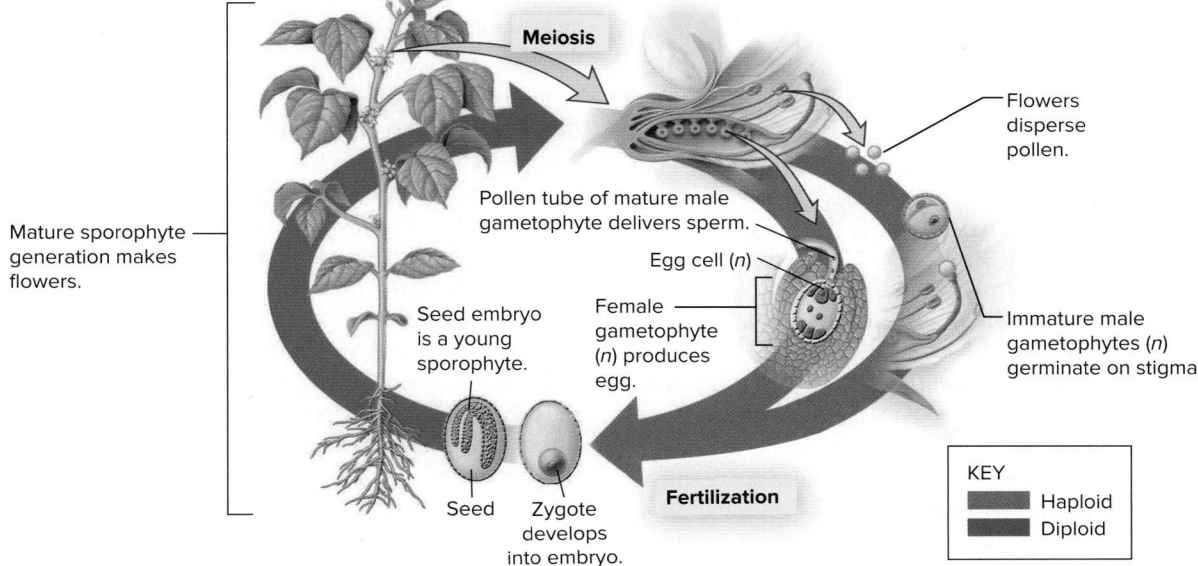

Figure 36.1 The plant sexual cycle. The sexual cycle of flowering plants involves alternation of sporophyte and gametophyte generations. In flowering plants, the spore-producing sporophyte is the dominant, conspicuous generation, whereas the tiny gametophytes are mostly hidden within flowers. Flowers produce haploid spores via meiosis. These spores undergo mitosis to grow into male or female gametophytes. Male gametophytes (pollen) contain sperm, and female gametophytes contain egg cells that are fertilized by sperm delivered by male gametophytes. Zygotes develop into embryonic plants that are dispersed in seeds.

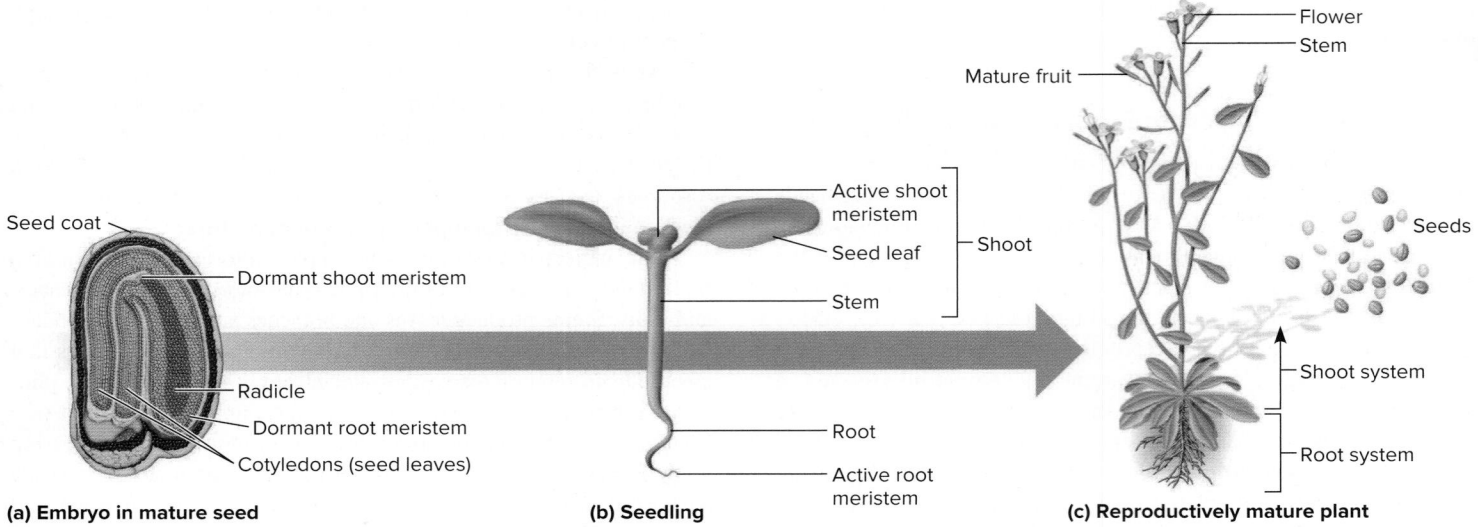

(a) Embryo in mature seed   (b) Seedling   (c) Reproductively mature plant

Figure 36.2 **The seed-to-seed life cycle of flowering plants, illustrated by *Arabidopsis thaliana*.** **(a)** Seed embryos possess embryonic leaves, known as cotyledons; a dormant shoot meristem; an embryonic root, known as a radicle; and a dormant root meristem. **(b)** When seeds germinate, the shoot and root meristems become active. Meristem activity allows the radicle to produce the seedling root and the young shoot of the seedling to grow and produce leaves. **(c)** Reproductively mature plants have branched shoot and root systems and bear flowers and fruits that disperse seeds.

 Core Skill: Process of Science The plant *Arabidopsis thaliana* is widely used as a model organism for understanding the genetics of plant form and development.

Mature Sporophytes Develop from Seedlings

As seedlings develop into mature sporophytes, the shoot typically becomes green and photosynthetic and thus able to produce organic food. Photosynthesis powers the transformation of seedlings into mature plants. The development of mature plants encompasses both **vegetative growth**, a process that increases the size of the shoot and root systems, and reproductive development. Vegetative growth and reproductive development involve **organ systems**, structures that are composed of multiple organs, tissues, and specialized cells. Branches, buds, flowers, seeds, and fruits are organ systems, analogous to organ systems such as the circulatory, skeletal, and reproductive systems in the animal body. The hierarchy of structure in a mature plant, ranging from specialized cells, tissues, organs, and organ systems to root and shoot systems, is shown in **Figure 36.3**.

Vegetative Growth and Development During their growth, plant shoots produce **buds**—miniature shoots, each having a dormant shoot apical meristem. Scaly modified leaves protect the bud contents. Under favorable conditions, the bud scales fall off, and the vegetative buds open. Newly opened buds display young leaves on a short shoot. The shoot apical meristem then becomes active, producing new stem tissue and leaves. In this way, buds generate leafy branches. A bud is an example of an organ system because it contains more than one organ.

Vegetative shoots often display **indeterminate growth**, meaning that apical meristems continuously produce new stem tissues and leaves as long as conditions remain favorable. This process explains how very large plants, such as trees, can develop from seedlings (**Figure 36.4a**). However, plant size is also under genetic control, so

some plants remain small even when they are mature. The tiny floating plants of *Lemna* species, commonly known as duckweeds, which sometimes cover the surfaces of ponds in summer, are examples of plants whose small size is genetically determined (**Figure 36.4b**). Indeterminate growth allows plants to adapt their vegetative body structure to environmental conditions. By contrast, animal bodies and flowers display **determinate growth**, which is growth of limited duration.

Reproductive Development Under favorable conditions, mature plants produce reproductive structures: flowers, seeds, and fruits. **Flowers** and floral buds are reproductive shoots that develop when shoot apical meristems produce flower parts instead of new stem tissues and leaves. Flower development occurs under the control of several genes whose roles are well understood (refer back to Figure 20.24). In contrast to shoots, which often show indeterminate growth, flowers are produced by determinate growth. A floral shoot no longer produces new stem growth or leaves. Therefore, vegetative growth and reproductive development are alternative processes. In order to flower, a plant must give up some of its potential to continue vegetative growth.

Flower tissues produce, enclose, and protect tiny male and female gametophytes during their growth and development (see Figure 36.1). Female gametophytes contain eggs within structures known as ovules, produced in the ovary of a flower pistil. Male gametophytes begin their development within pollen grains produced in the anthers of a flower stamen. Pollen is dispersed to the flower pistil, where the pollen grains may germinate, producing a tube that delivers sperm to eggs. Fertilization generates zygotes, which develop into

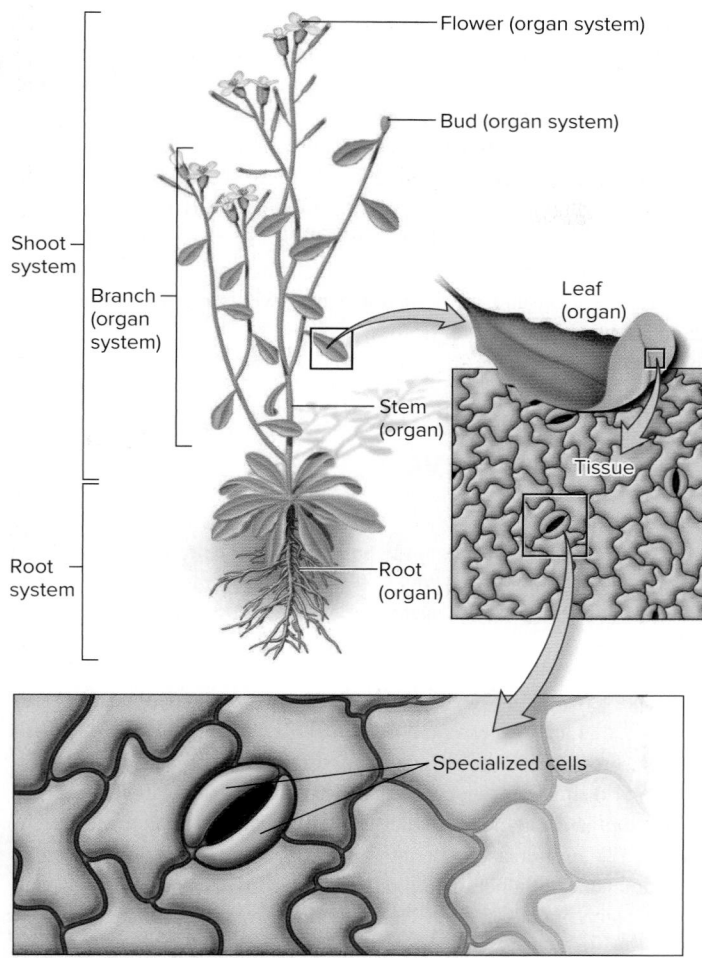

Figure 36.3 Levels of biological organization in a plant.
Flowering plant sporophyte bodies consist of a root system and a shoot system. Shoot systems produce organ systems such as buds, flowers, fruits, and seeds, which are composed of organs, tissues, and specialized cells. Root systems are likewise composed of organs, tissues, and specialized cells.

(a) *Brachychiton*, a tree native to Australia

(b) *Lemna* (common duckweed)

Figure 36.4 Plants display indeterminate growth, but vary in size. A large woody angiosperm **(a)** and tiny duckweed plants **(b)** display indeterminate growth, but genetic differences confer different plant dimensions. a: ©Linda Graham; b: ©Howard Rice/Getty Images

embryos, and also triggers the process by which ovules develop into seeds and flower parts develop into fruits. **Fruits** thus enclose seeds and function in seed dispersal. As noted earlier, flower buds, flowers, fruits, and seeds are organ systems because they consist of more than one organ. For example, flowers typically contain several leafy organs, including sepals and petals, as well as stamens and pistils, which evolved from leaves (refer back to Figure 32.15).

Flowering Plants Vary in the Structure of Organs and Organ Systems

With some exceptions, flowering plants are classified into two major groups, informally known as the **eudicots** and the **monocots** (refer back to Figure 32.18). These groups take their names from the number of seed leaves (cotyledons) that are present on seed embryos. For example, bean plants and relatives, which possess two (*di*) seed leaves, are examples of eudicots. Most woody trees, shrubs, and vines

are also eudicots. Corn, which has only one (*mono*) seed leaf, is an example of a monocot, as is tiny duckweed (see Figure 36.4b). Eudicots and monocots also vary in the structure of other organs and organ systems. For example, eudicot flowers typically have petals and other parts numbering four, five, or a multiple of those numbers, whereas monocot flower parts usually occur in threes or a multiple of three. Stems, roots, leaves, and pollen of eudicots and monocots also vary in distinctive ways, as shown in **Table 36.1**.

Flowering Plants Vary in Seed-to-Seed Lifetime

The lifetime of a flowering plant can vary from a few weeks to many years. Plants that die after producing seed during their first year of life are known as **annuals**. Corn and the common bean are examples of annual crops whose nutrient-rich seeds are harvested within a few months after planting and must be replanted at the beginning of each new growing season. Plants that do not reproduce during the first year of life but may reproduce within the following year are known as **biennials**. Such plants often store food in fleshy roots during the first year of growth, and this food fuels reproduction during the second

Table 36.1	Distinguishing Features of Eudicots and Monocots, Two Major Groups of Flowering Plants	
Feature	Eudicots	Monocots
Number of seed leaves (cotyledons)	Two	One
Number of flower parts	Usually four, five, or multiples of these	Usually three or a multiple of three
Stem vascular bundles	Arranged in a ring	Scattered
Root system	Branched taproot	Fibrous; adventitious
Leaf venation	Netted or branched	Often parallel
Pollen	Three pores or slits	One pore or slit

Core Skill: Modeling The goal of this modeling challenge is to sketch a diagram that shows the two major lineages of angiosperms, monocots and eudicots, and helps to explain why nearly three-quarters of flowering plant species are eudicots.

Modeling Challenge: Use Figure 32.16, reproduced at the right, to make a simplified sketch that shows only the two major lineages (monocots and eudicots). Use an arrow to indicate an event that may have led to the increased evolutionary diversification of eudicots.

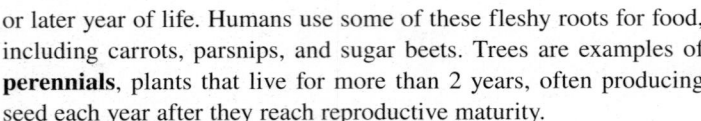

or later year of life. Humans use some of these fleshy roots for food, including carrots, parsnips, and sugar beets. Trees are examples of **perennials**, plants that live for more than 2 years, often producing seed each year after they reach reproductive maturity.

Many flowering plants use environmental signals to time flowering in ways that enhance seed production. Temperature and day length are examples of environmental factors that determine flowering time. Plant seed-to-seed lifetimes are also influenced by the longevity of their seeds. Seeds of some plants are able to germinate after more than a thousand years of dormancy, whereas other plant seeds are unable to remain alive for long periods.

36.2 How Plants Grow and Develop

Learning Outcomes:

1. **CoreSKILL »** Compare and contrast the body architecture and development of plants with those of animals.
2. Explain how the shoot system of a plant differs from the root system.

As plants grow from seedlings, their development depends on four processes that are also essential to animal growth and development: cell division, growth, cell specialization, and programmed cell death. Additional and distinctive aspects of plant growth and development include (1) development and maintenance of a plant-specific architecture throughout life, (2) an increase in length by the activity of apical meristems, (3) maintenance of a population of youthful stem cells in meristems, and (4) expansion of cells in controlled directions, by water uptake.

Plants Display a Distinctive Architecture

In plant biology, the term apical has two distinct meanings. As we have seen, apical refers to the tips (apices) of shoots and roots, as in shoot apical meristems or root apical meristems. A second meaning for apical is the part of a plant that typically projects upward, which is the top of the shoot. By contrast, the bottom of a root is termed the basal region. So the shoot apical meristem occurs at the apical pole, and the root apical meristem occurs at the basal pole. This property, known as **apical-basal polarity**, explains why plants produce shoots at their tops and roots at their lower regions.

Apical-basal polarity originates during embryo development. As seedlings and maturing plants grow in length by the activity of shoot and root meristems, apical-basal polarity is maintained (**Figure 36.5a**). Animals likewise have anterior and posterior ends, whose development is influenced by *Hox* genes (refer back to Chapter 20). In contrast, plant apical-basal polarity is under the control of genes such as *GNOM*; mutations in these genes result in plant embryos that are cone-shaped or spherical and thus lack normal apical-basal architecture (**Figure 36.5b**).

A second anatomical feature of plants is **radial symmetry**. Plant embryos normally display a cylindrical shape, also known as an axis, which is retained in the stems and roots of seedlings and mature plants. A thin slice or cross section of an embryo, stem, or root is typically circular in shape. Most plants produce new leaves or flower parts in circular whorls, or spirals, around shoot tips (**Figure 36.6**).

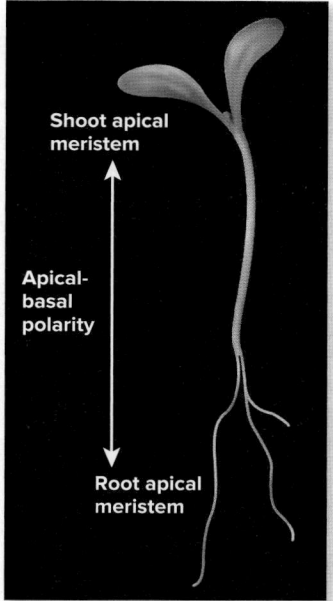
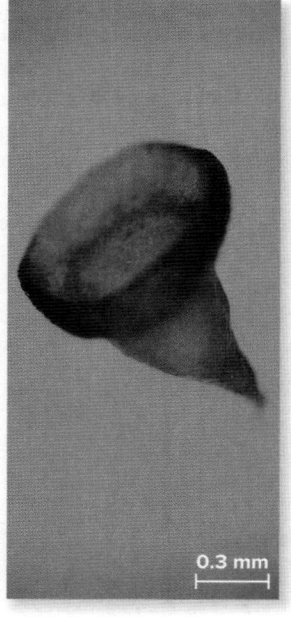

(a) Normal seedling   **(b) Abnormal**
                                  ***GNOM* mutants**

Figure 36.5 Plant apical-basal polarity. (a) Normal plants exhibit apical-basal polarity, as shown by this seedling. Growth occurs at two meristems, one at the shoot and one at the root. **(b)** *GNOM* mutants of *Arabidopsis thaliana* lack apical-basal polarity and thus produce abnormal embryos and seedlings. b: ©Prof. Dr. Gerd Jürgens/Universität Tübingen. Image Courtesy Hanno Wolters

 Core Skill: Connections Look back to Figure 20.17 to see the relationship between expression of *Hox* genes and body organization in the mouse, as a model animal. How is animal body polarity similar to that of plants?

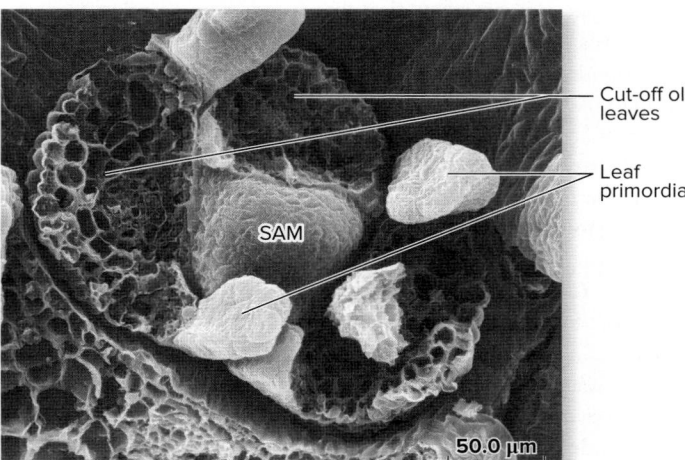

Figure 36.6 Plant radial symmetry. This top-down SEM view of a shoot apical meristem (SAM) reveals the radial symmetry of the shoot, indicated by its cylindrical shape. Leaf primordia are produced in circles or spirals around the shoot axis. ©Beth Krizek

Buds and branches likewise emerge from stems in radial patterns, as do lateral roots from a central root axis. Together, apical-basal polarity and radial symmetry explain why diverse plant species have a fundamentally similar architecture. Although radial symmetry also characterizes early-diverging animals, most animals exhibit bilateral symmetry (look back at Figure 33.4).

Primary Meristems Increase Plant Length and Produce Plant Organs

We previously discussed how plant embryos grow into seedlings by adding new cells from distinctive growth points, the **shoot apical meristem (SAM)** and the **root apical meristem (RAM)**. During plant development, the SAM and RAM of the embryo give rise to many apical meristems located in the buds of shoots and at the tips of roots.

A SAM produces tissues that increase plant length and generate new organs. Such meristems are known as the **primary meristems**, and in a process known as **primary growth**, they ultimately produce primary tissues and organs of diverse types (**Table 36.2**). Tissues differ in their cellular complexity. Simple primary tissues are those composed of only one or two cell types; complex primary tissues are

Table 36.2	Examples of Tissues and Specialized Cells Found in Flowering Plants*
Primary Growth	
Simple primary tissues (composed of one or two cell types)	**Plant cell types found in those tissues**
Parenchyma	Parenchyma cells
Collenchyma	Collenchyma cells
Sclerenchyma	Fibers and sclereids
Root endodermis	Endodermal cells
Root pericycle	Pericycle cells
Complex primary tissues (composed of at least two cell types)	**Plant cell types found in those tissues**
Leaf or stem epidermis	Flattened epidermal cells, trichomes, stomatal guard cells
Root epidermis	Flattened epidermal cells, root hairs
Leaf mesophyll	Spongy parenchyma cells, palisade parenchyma cells
Leaf, stem, or root xylem	Tracheids, vessel elements, fibers, parenchyma cells
Leaf, stem, or root phloem	Sieve-tube elements, companion cells, fibers, parenchyma cells
Secondary Growth	
Simple and complex secondary tissues	**Plant cell types found in those tissues**
Secondary xylem (wood)	Tracheids, vessel elements, fibers, parenchyma
Secondary phloem (inner bark)	Sieve-tube elements, companion cells, fibers, parenchyma
Outer bark	Cork cells

*This list does not include all of the tissues and cell types found in flowering plants. Some of these examples will be described later in this chapter.

made of more cell types. As described in Section 36.3, the primary meristems of woody plants also give rise to secondary or lateral meristems. In a process known as **secondary growth**, the secondary meristems increase the girth of woody plant stems and roots by producing secondary tissues (Table 36.2).

Plant biologists have discovered that plant cell specialization and tissue development do not depend on the lineage (the parentage) of a cell or tissue. Chemical influences such as hormones, proteins known as transcription factors, and microRNAs (miRNAs) that move through plants are much more important in determining the type of specialized tissue produced by unspecialized plant cells.

Primary Stem Structure and Development New primary stem tissues arise via cell divisions in shoot apical meristems. A layer of outermost tissue known as the **epidermis** develops at the stem surface. The epidermis produces a waxy surface coating known as the **cuticle**, which helps to reduce water loss from the plant surface and to protect plants from damage by ultraviolet (UV) light, animals, and disease-causing microorganisms.

Beneath the epidermis lies the stem **cortex**, which is largely composed of a type of tissue called **parenchyma** (**Figure 36.7a**). This tissue is composed of only one cell type, thin-walled cells known as **parenchyma cells**. These cells often store starch in plastids and

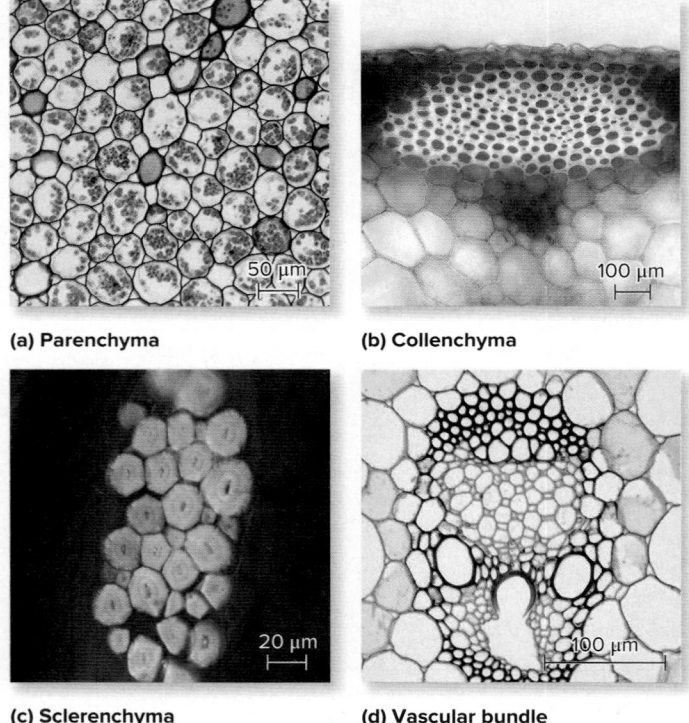

(a) Parenchyma 50 μm

(b) Collenchyma 100 μm

(c) Sclerenchyma 20 μm

(d) Vascular bundle 100 μm

Figure 36.7 **Examples of tissues produced by primary shoot meristems.** **(a)** Parenchyma, **(b)** collenchyma, **(c)** sclerenchyma, and **(d)** a vascular bundle composed of complex xylem and phloem tissues. The purple-stained particles in parenchyma cells are stored starch. The flexible walls of collenchyma cells appear white here, as do the more rigid and thicker walls of sclerenchyma cells. In the vascular bundle, darker-stained and thicker walls of xylem cells contrast with lighter-stained and thinner-walled cells of phloem. a–d: ©Lee W. Wilcox

therefore serve as an organic food reserve. Stem parenchyma also has the ability to undergo cell division (meristematic capacity), which aids wound healing when stems are damaged. The cell division capability of stem parenchyma also explains how people are able to grow new plants from stem cuttings. Stems also contain **collenchyma** (**Figure 36.7b**), tissue composed of flexible **collenchyma cells**, and rigid **sclerenchyma** (**Figure 36.7c**), tissue composed of two types of tough-walled sclerenchyma cells termed **fibers** and **sclereids**. These tough cells provide strength and protection to the plant stem.

New water- and food-conducting tissues develop at the core of a young shoot. These conducting tissues are known as **primary vascular tissues** because they develop from new cells produced by the SAM. Vascular bundles, also known as veins, contain two types of complex tissues—**xylem** and **phloem** (see Section 36.3 and Table 36.2). Newly formed stem xylem and phloem connect with older conducting tissues that extend throughout the stem system. Stem xylem and phloem link to vascular tissues of the root system, forming a continuous route for conduction of water, minerals, and organic compounds through the plant.

In contrast to the circulatory system of most animals, the plant conduction system is not closed, but instead is open to the environment. The open plant conduction system is key to the transport of materials within plants (described more completely in Chapter 39). Primary vascular tissues are typically arranged in elongate clusters known as **vascular bundles** that appear round or oval when cross-cut (**Figure 36.7d**). In the primary stems of beans and other eudicots, the vascular bundles are arranged in a ring, which is easily seen in thin slices made across a stem (see Table 36.1). By contrast, in the stems of corn and other monocots, the vascular bundles are scattered.

Leaf Structure and Development Young leaves are produced at the sides of a SAM as small bumps known as **leaf primordia** (see Figure 36.6). As young leaves develop, they acquire vascular tissue that connects to the stem xylem and phloem (**Figure 36.8a**) and leaves also become flattened. Leaf flattening expands the area of leaf surface available for light collection during photosynthesis. For some leaves, thinness is an adaptation that helps them to release excess heat. Leaves also become bilaterally symmetrical, meaning that they can be divided into two equal halves in only one direction, from the leaf tip to its base (**Figure 36.8b**).

Upper and lower leaf tissues develop differently in several ways that foster photosynthesis (**Figure 36.8c**). For example, the more shaded lower epidermis of a leaf usually displays larger numbers of pores, known as **stomata** (from the Greek word *stoma*, meaning mouth), than the sunnier upper surface (refer back to Figure 31.9b). When open, stomata allow CO_2 to enter and water vapor and O_2 to escape leaf tissues. Closure of stomata helps to prevent excess water loss from plant surfaces. Locating most stomata on the cooler, shadier leaf underside helps to reduce water loss by evaporation. Many plants produce surface leaf hairs, known as trichomes, that also help to reduce water loss.

Palisade parenchyma consists of closely packed, elongated cells of the inner leaf that are adapted to absorb sunlight efficiently (see Figure 36.8c). **Spongy parenchyma**, located closer to the lower leaf surface, contains rounder cells separated by abundant air spaces. These air spaces foster CO_2 absorption and O_2 release by leaves. Together, the palisade and spongy parenchyma are known as the leaf **mesophyll**.

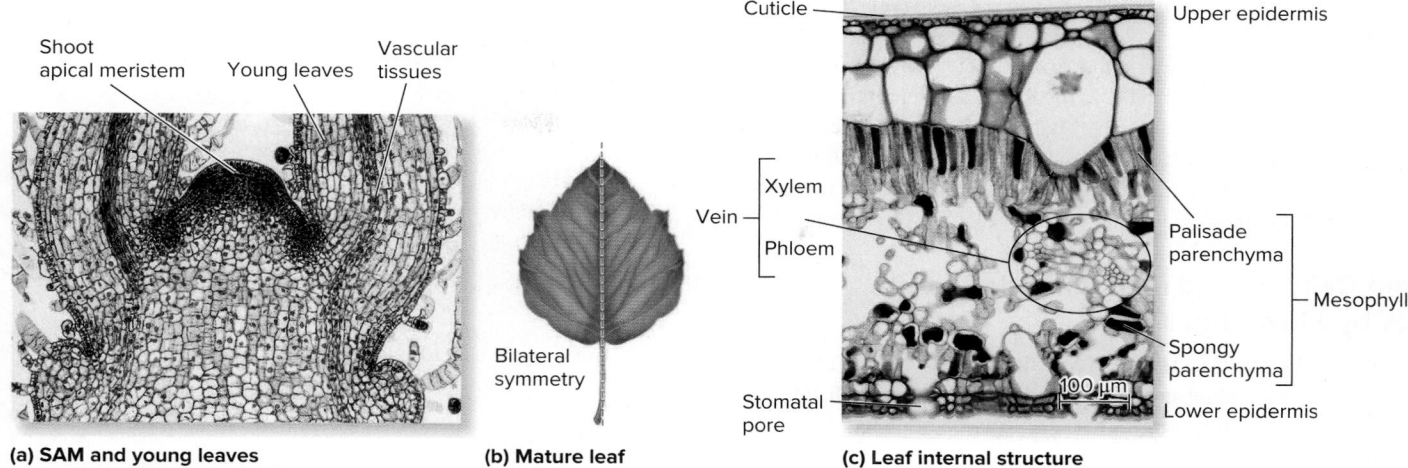

(a) SAM and young leaves   **(b) Mature leaf**   **(c) Leaf internal structure**

Figure 36.8 Leaf development and structure. (a) Young leaves develop at the sides of SAMs, as shown in this thinly sliced, stained shoot tip. The SAM is darkly stained because the cells at this location are small and densely packed. Note that the vascular tissues of young leaves, which also stain darkly, are connected to stem vascular tissues. **(b)** Mature leaves are typically thin and flat and show bilateral symmetry. **(c)** An internal view of a thinly sliced and stained leaf reveals tissue differentiation from the upper to the lower surface. A layer of palisade parenchyma lies just beneath the upper epidermis, which is capped with a waxy cuticle. Veins of conducting tissue (xylem and phloem) are embedded in the photosynthetic mesophyll. Spongy parenchyma lies above the lower epidermis, which displays stomata. These structural features of mature foliage leaves facilitate photosynthesis. a,c: ©Lee W. Wilcox

Concept Check: *What advantage do plant leaves obtain by having stomata located on the lower epidermis?*

Leaf veins composed of vascular tissue commonly occur at the junction of palisade and spongy parenchyma or within the spongy parenchyma (see Figure 36.8c). Palisade parenchyma and spongy parenchyma are typically green and active in photosynthesis, a process that requires water, carbon dioxide, and dissolved minerals. Parenchyma cells can only take up carbon dioxide that has first dissolved into water, a feature inherited from ancient aquatic algal ancestors. Therefore, to perform photosynthesis, leaf parenchyma cells must be bathed in water. The xylem tissues of veins conduct water and minerals throughout leaf tissues, fostering photosynthesis. Phloem tissues of leaf veins carry the sugar products of photosynthesis from leaf cells to stem vascular tissues. In this way, sugar produced in leaves can be exported to other parts of the plant.

The leaves of flowering plants have one or more larger main veins, with smaller veins branching from them. The density of veins in angiosperm leaves is about four times that of other vascular plants. This allows plants to conduct materials more efficiently, which helps to explain why flowering plants are the dominant type of vegetation in most habitats today.

Root System Structure and Development In beans and most other eudicots, a main root develops from the embryonic root and then produces branch roots, also known as lateral roots. Such a root system of eudicots is known as a **taproot system**, which has one main root with many branch roots (see Table 36.1). In contrast, the embryonic root of most monocots dies soon after seed germination, and it is replaced by a **fibrous root system** consisting of multiple roots that grow from the stem base (see Table 36.1). Fibrous roots are examples of **adventitious roots**, structures that are produced on the surfaces of stems (and sometimes leaves). They constitute the fibrous root system of most monocots and also can form on eudicots. Roots that develop at the bases of stem cuttings are also adventitious.

As noted earlier, the tips of roots and their branches each possess an apical meristem that adds new cells. Expansion of these new cells allows roots to grow into the soil. As they lengthen, roots produce branches but not from buds, as is the case for stems. Instead, branch roots develop from meristematic tissues located within the root (see Section 36.4). The root system both anchors the plant in the soil and plays an essential role in harvesting water and mineral nutrients. Root tissues are usually not green and photosynthetic, so must rely on organic compounds transported from the shoot. A plant's root system and shoot system depend on each other.

Plant Meristems Contain Youthful Stem Cells

Plant meristems include undifferentiated cells referred to as **stem cells**. In the late 19th century, the Russian-born American biologist Alexander Maximow coined the term Stammzelle, which is derived from the German words *stamm*, meaning stem, such as a plant stem, and *zelle*, meaning cell. Maximow used the term stem cell to describe animal cells that remain undifferentiated but are able to generate specialized tissues. Animal stem cells are often in the news because of their potential for use in the treatment of human diseases that cause cell or tissue damage. The term stem cell is also widely used for cells located within the plant meristem that likewise remain undifferentiated but can divide and produce cells that generate new tissues. In the context of plant development, the term does not mean any cell located in a plant stem, only the undifferentiated cells located within the meristems of the shoot and root.

When plant stem cells divide, they produce two cells: one that remains young and unspecialized and divides relatively rarely, plus another cell. This second cell may differentiate into various types of specialized cells, but it often continues to divide, thereby adding new cells to shoot and root tips. The indeterminate growth typical of plant shoots and roots is based on the localization of stem cells in the SAM and RAM.

In the SAM of plants, a transcription factor (a type of protein) called WUS maintains stem cells. In the RAM, a different transcription factor, WOX, maintains stem cells. Maintaining apical caches of stem cells that divide relatively rarely helps plants avoid accumulating mutations. Cells that divide frequently tend to acquire mutations because a polymerase that copies the lagging strand of DNA is error-prone.

Plant Cells Expand in a Controlled Way by Absorbing Water

As we have observed, meristem production of new cells is an important component of plant growth. In addition, plant growth involves cell expansion, which is a much less important component of animal growth. The diameters of newly formed stem and root cells are usually equal in all dimensions, but many soon begin to extend lengthwise, thereby helping shoots and roots to grow longer. Recall that plant cells typically possess a relatively large central vacuole (refer back to Figure 4.24a). Cell extension occurs when water enters the central vacuole by osmosis (**Figure 36.9**). As the central vacuole expands, the cell wall also expands and increases the cell's volume. By taking up water, plant cells can enlarge quickly, allowing rapid plant growth. Bamboo, for instance, can grow taller by 2 m within a week and can grow up to 30 m in less than 3 months! The importance of water uptake in cell expansion helps to explain why plant growth is so dependent on water supply.

Plant cell walls contain cellulose microfibrils that are held together by crosslinking polysaccharides. When plant cells and their vacuoles absorb water, pressure builds on cell walls. In response to this pressure and under acidic conditions, proteins unique to plants—known as expansins—are produced. **Expansins** unzip the crosslinking polysaccharides from cellulose microfibrils so that the cell wall can stretch (**Figure 36.10**). As a result, cells enlarge, often by elongating in a particular direction, which is important to plant form. Some plant cells are able to elongate up to 20 times their original length.

The direction in which a plant cell expands depends on the arrangement of cellulose microfibrils in its cell wall, which is in turn determined by the orientation of cytoplasmic microtubules. These

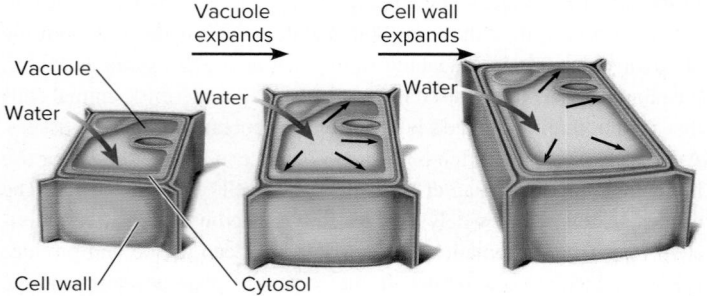

Figure 36.9 **Plant cells expand by taking up water into their vacuoles.**

 Core Skill: Connections Look back at Figure 4.24a to see an electron micrograph of a plant vacuole and at Figures 4.9 and 4.11, which compares generalized animal and plant cells. How do plant cells differ from animal cells in terms of vacuoles?

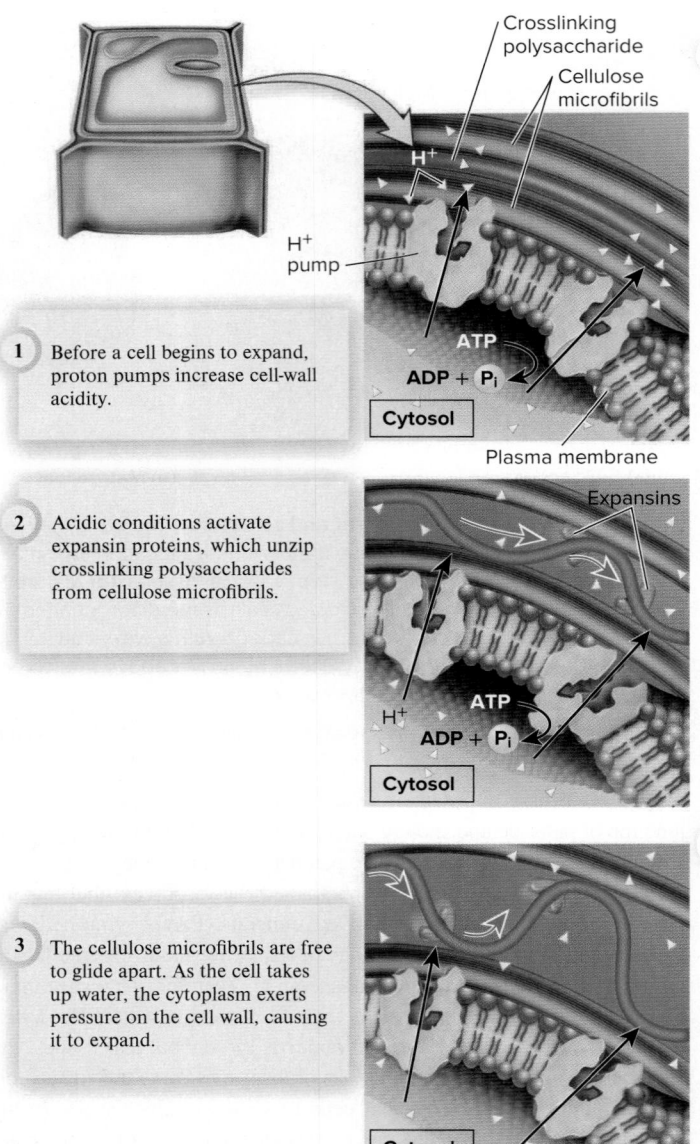

1. Before a cell begins to expand, proton pumps increase cell-wall acidity.

2. Acidic conditions activate expansin proteins, which unzip crosslinking polysaccharides from cellulose microfibrils.

3. The cellulose microfibrils are free to glide apart. As the cell takes up water, the cytoplasm exerts pressure on the cell wall, causing it to expand.

Figure 36.10 **A hypothetical model of the process of cell-wall expansion.**

microtubules are thought to influence the positions of cellulose-synthesizing protein complexes located in the plant plasma membrane. The protein complexes connect sugars to form cellulose polymers, spinning cellulose microfibrils onto the cell surface to form the cell wall. As a result, cell-wall cellulose microfibrils encircle cells in the same orientation as underlying cytoplasmic microtubules (**Figure 36.11**). Because cellulose microfibrils do not extend lengthwise, plant cell walls expand more easily in a direction perpendicular to the microfibrils.

Microtubules control not only the direction of cell expansion but also the plane of cell division, which is also critical to plant form. Mutation of the *FASS* gene in the model plant *A. thaliana* illustrates the importance of microtubule orientation to plant structure. In cells of the mutant plants, microtubules are randomly arranged, causing cells to divide and grow abnormally, and producing plants with stubby organs.

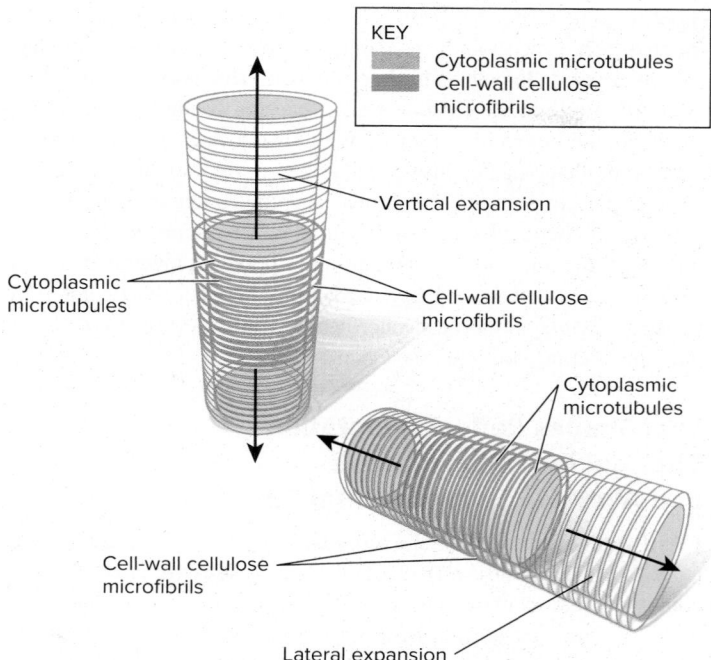

Figure 36.11 **Control of the direction of plant cell expansion by microfibrils and microtubules.** Plant cells enlarge in the direction perpendicular to encircling cell-wall cellulose microfibrils, which run parallel to the orientation of underlying cytoplasmic microtubules.

 Core Skill: Connections Look back to Table 4.1 to see an image of microtubules. Are the structures of plant and animal microtubules different?

 **36.3** **The Shoot System: Stem and Leaf Adaptations**

Learning Outcomes:

1. Explain why plant shoots are said to have a modular structure.
2. Explain why leaves having different shapes and vein patterns exist in nature.
3. Compare the structure and function of the conducting tissues xylem and phloem.
4. **CoreSKILL »** Create a drawing showing how bark and wood originate in woody plants.

As we have seen, the shoot system includes all of a plant's stems, branches, leaves, and buds. The shoot system also produces flowers and fruits when the plant has reached reproductive maturity. Thus, the shoot system is essential to plant growth, photosynthesis, and reproduction. Features of stems and leaves vary among plants in ways that explain their ecological functions and are useful in distinguishing plant species. In this section, we will examine the general features of shoot systems with an emphasis on stems and leaves.

Shoot Systems Have a Modular Structure

More than 200 years ago, the German author, politician, and scientist Johann Wolfgang von Goethe realized that plants are modular organisms, composed of repeating units. Shoots are notably modular (**Figure 36.12**).

Each shoot module consists of four parts: a stem node, an internode, a leaf, and an axillary meristem or bud. A **node** is the stem

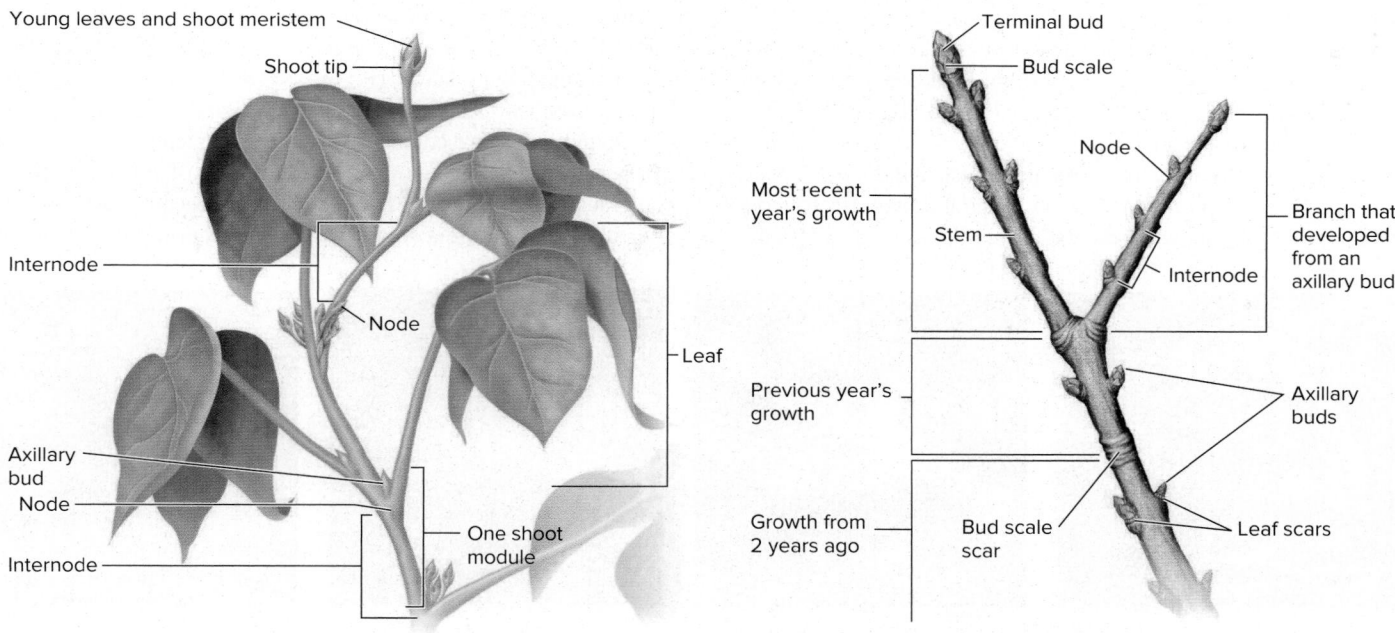

(a) Modular structure of herbaceous shoot

(b) Modular structure of woody shoot in winter

Figure 36.12 **The modular organization of plant shoots.** **(a)** The top end of an herbaceous stem showing the shoot modules. Each module consists of a node with its associated leaf and axillary meristem or bud and an internode. **(b)** The modular organization shown by a woody stem as it appears during winter. Axillary buds lie above the scars left by leaf fall. Regions between successive sets of bud scale scars mark each year's growth

Concept Check: *If a twig has five sets of bud scale scars, how old is the twig likely to be?*

region from which one or more leaves emerge. An **internode** is the region of stem between adjacent nodes. Differences in numbers and lengths of internodes help to explain why plants differ in height (look back to Figure 36.4).

Each time a young leaf is produced at a SAM, a new meristem develops in the upper angle formed where the leaf emerges from the stem. This angle is known as an axil (from the Greek *axilla*, meaning armpit), and the meristem formed there is called an **axillary meristem**. Such axillary meristems generate **axillary buds**, which can produce flowers or branches known as lateral shoots. Such new branches bear a SAM at their tips. SAMs located at the apices of both main and lateral shoots produce new leaves under the direction of chemical messengers known as hormones.

Hormones, Mechanical Forces, and miRNAs Influence Leaf Development

As we have noted, leaf primordia are surface bumps of tissue that develop at the sides of a SAM (see Figure 36.6). Production of leaf primordia is under the control of a plant hormone known as an **auxin**. In general, **hormones** are signaling molecules that exert their effects at a site distant from the place where they are produced. Plant hormones are important in coordinating both plant development and plant responses to environmental conditions and are described more completely in Chapter 37.

The outermost epidermal layer of cells at shoot tips produces an auxin, which moves from cell to cell by means of specific membrane transport proteins. The auxin accumulates in particular locations because cells of the shoot apex differ in their ability to import and export the hormone. When auxin accumulates in a particular apical region, it causes increased expression of the gene that encodes expansin. When expansin allows their cell walls to stretch (see Figure 36.10), cells expand by taking up water, thereby forming a tissue bulge—a leaf primordium. The development of leaf primordia depletes auxin from nearby tissue, with the result that the next leaf primordium will develop in a different place on the shoot apex, where the auxin level is higher. Such changes in auxin concentration on the surface of the shoot explain why leaf (and flower) primordia develop in spiral or whorled patterns around the shoot tip. The youngest leaf primordia occur closest to the shoot tip, and successively older leaf primordia occur on the sides of the stem below the shoot tip (see Figure 36.6). Leaf primordia produce a plant hormone known as **gibberellic acid**. This hormone stimulates both cell division and cell enlargement, causing young leaves to grow.

Computer modeling studies have shown that, as the largest major veins rapidly elongate during early leaf development, mechanical stresses play important roles in leaf shaping. Later in leaf development, local chemical signaling becomes more important. For example, leaf flattening and differentiation of upper and lower leaf surface structures are determined by interactions between particular transcription factors and a set of microRNAs (miRNAs) (for more information about microRNAs, see Chapter 13).

Leaf Shapes Reflect Adaptations That Aid in Photosynthesis and Alleviate Environmental Stress

Leaf flatness facilitates solar energy collection as described in Chapter 8. Leaf shapes also reflect adaptations to stressful environmental conditions. For example, thinness helps leaves to avoid overheating.

The flattened portion of a leaf is known as the leaf **blade**. In beans and most other eudicots, blades are attached to the stem by means of a stalk known as a **petiole**. An axillary bud occurs at the junction of stem and petiole (**Figure 36.13a**). In contrast, corn and other monocots have leaf blades that grow directly from the stem, encircling it to form a leaf sheath (**Figure 36.13b**).

Leaf shape can be simple or compound, each having particular advantages. Simple leaves have only one blade, though the edges may be smooth, toothed, or lobed (**Figure 36.13c**). Simple leaves are advantageous in shady environments because they provide maximal light absorption surface, but they can overheat in sunny environments. As an evolutionary response to heating stress, the blades of some leaves have become highly dissected into leaflets. Such leaves are known as compound leaves (**Figure 36.13d**). Leaflets can be distinguished from leaves because leaflets lack axillary buds at their bases. Compound leaves are common in hot environments because leaflets foster heat dissipation. During the development of at least some compound leaves, the transcription factor KNOX becomes active shortly after the leaf primordia form, causing these primordia to produce

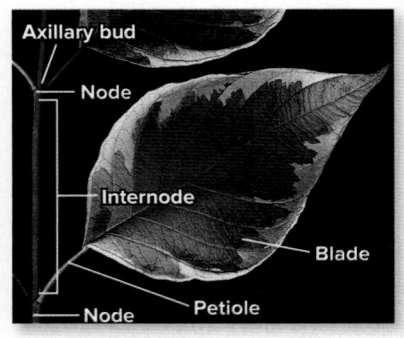

(a) Eudicot stem with simple leaf having pinnate venation

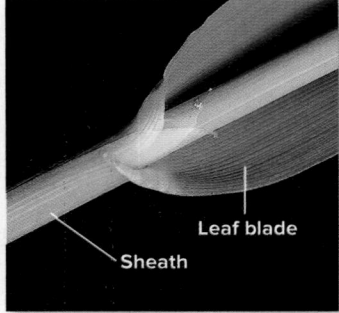

(b) Monocot stem and leaf

(c) A simple leaf with palmate venation

(d) A compound leaf

Figure 36.13 Examples of variation in leaf form. (a) A simple eudicot leaf, showing blade, petiole, and axillary bud. This leaf has a pinnate venation pattern. **(b)** The leaf of a monocot, showing parallel veins. The base of the leaf encircles the stem. **(c)** A simple leaf having palmate venation. **(d)** A compound leaf divided into leaflets. a–d: ©Lee W. Wilcox

multiple growth points that generate the leaflets. By contrast, during simple leaf development, KNOX is not active, because the presence of other proteins suppresses expression of the *KNOX* gene.

Leaf Vein Patterns Can Be Pinnate or Palmate

Leaf vein patterns are known as **venation**. Eudicot leaves occur in two major venation forms. In **pinnate** venation, one main vein extends from the base to the tip of the leaf and smaller veins branch off the main vein (Figure 36.13a). Alternatively, several main veins may radiate from the base of the leaf like the fingers of your hand, a pattern known as **palmate** venation (Figure 36.13c). In eudicot leaves, small veins connect in a netted pattern, but most monocot leaves have a distinctive parallel venation (Figure 36.13b and Table 36.1).

 Core Skill: Process of Science

Feature Investigation | Sack and Colleagues Showed That Palmate Venation Confers Tolerance of Leaf Vein Breakage

In 2008, Lawren Sack and colleagues studied the adaptive value of leaf venation patterns by comparing water conduction after injury in pinnately and palmately veined leaves (**Figure 36.14**). Leaves with palmate venation have several main veins, whereas leaves with pinnate venation have just one main vein. The investigators hypothesized that the multiple main veins of palmate leaves could confer greater tolerance of vein breakage of the type that would occur during mechanical injury or insect damage; if one main vein were damaged, water flow could continue through the other main veins.

Figure 36.14 Sack and colleagues investigated the function of palmate venation.

HYPOTHESIS Palmate venation provides vascular redundancy, which allows leaves to tolerate vein breakage.

KEY MATERIALS Seven species of trees or shrubs at Harvard Forest, Petersham, MA.

	Experimental level	Conceptual level
1 Identify 7 species, 4 with pinnately veined leaves and 3 with palmately veined leaves. For each species, the researchers analyzed 10 leaves on 3 different plants.	Single primary vein connecting directly to petiole — Pinnately veined leaves — Petiole — *Quercus rubra* *Betula alleghaniensis* *Viburnum cassinoides* *Kalmia latifolia* — More than one primary vein connecting directly to petiole — Palmately veined leaves — *Viburnum acerifolium* *Acer saccharum* *Acer rubrum*	Locate pinnate and palmate leaves for comparison.
2 With the leaf still attached to the plant, use a scalpel to cut across 1 primary vein in 5 experimental leaves but not 5 control leaves.		This procedure initially cuts off water supply via 1 primary vein.

3 Cover the cuts with medical tape on both top and bottom of leaves. Tape same area of uncut control leaves.

Tape

The tape prevents infection. Controls: Tape is applied to controls for experimental consistency.

4 Fold cardboard over base of cut leaves, forming a splint. Splint the same area of uncut control leaves.

Splint

The cardboard prevents leaf collapse. Controls: Cardboard is applied to controls for experimental consistency.

5 Measure water conduction 2–9 weeks after treatment, in 2 regions (A, B) of each pinnate leaf and in 3 regions (A, B, C) of each palmate leaf.

Pinnate leaf   Palmate leaf

After 2–9 weeks, the cuts had healed. Measurement of water conduction will determine the effect of the vein cut.

6 THE DATA

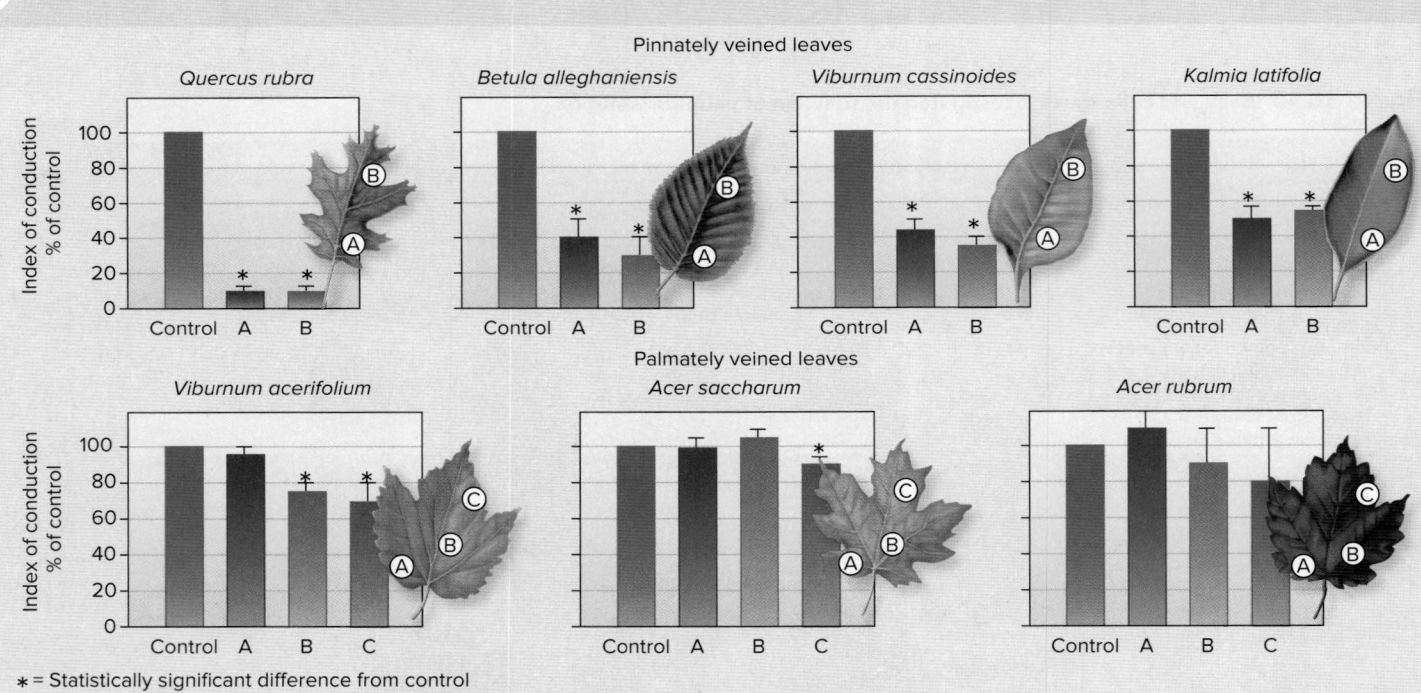

Pinnately veined leaves

Quercus rubra   *Betula alleghaniensis*   *Viburnum cassinoides*   *Kalmia latifolia*

Index of conduction % of control

Control A B

Palmately veined leaves

Viburnum acerifolium   *Acer saccharum*   *Acer rubrum*

Index of conduction % of control

Control A B C

✳ = Statistically significant difference from control

7 **CONCLUSION** Palmately veined leaves did not suffer as much conduction loss from a primary vein cut as did pinnately veined leaves.

8 **SOURCE** Sack, L., et al. 2008. Leaf palmate venation and vascular redundancy confer tolerance of hydraulic disruption. *Proceedings of the National Academy of Sciences of the U.S.* 105:1567–1572. Copyright ©2008 National Academy of Sciences, U.S.A. Used with permission.

To test the hypothesis, the investigators experimentally cut a main vein in the leaves of several plants belonging to seven different plant species: four having pinnately veined leaves and three having palmately veined leaves. They conducted the experiments in vivo, that is, in living trees. After the wounds had healed, the investigators measured the water flow within the leaves at two or three places on each leaf (see steps 3–5 of (Figure 36.14). The rate of water flow, called the index of conduction, is expressed as the percentage of water flow of the control leaves, which are uncut leaves. As seen in the data, they found that across all species examined, palmately veined leaves tolerated the disruption in water flow better than pinnately veined leaves.

What are the advantages and disadvantages of these two venation patterns? Although palmate venation provides redundancy in case a main vein becomes damaged, it is more costly in terms of materials needed to construct the additional main veins. Leaves with pinnate venation are less costly to produce and work well when the potential for vein damage is low.

Experimental Questions

1. Why did Sack and colleagues conduct their studies of palmate venation on plants growing in a forest rather than in a greenhouse?

2. **CoreSKILL »** Why did Sack and colleagues splint leaves having cut veins as well as controls?

3. **CoreSKILL »** Why did Sack and colleagues measure leaf water conduction at two or more places on each leaf?

THE QUESTION *Which species of tree or shrub tested by Sack and colleagues showed the greatest tolerance to damaged primary veins? In other words, in which leaves was water flow least inhibited by leaf damage?*

TOPIC   ***What topic in biology does this question address?***
The topic is variation in leaf venation, which many people first encounter as young children making leaf collections for school projects. More specifically, the question is about the relationship between leaf venation and the effects of damage on water flow.

INFORMATION   ***What information do you know based on the question and your understanding of the topic?***
In the question, you are reminded that Sack and colleagues did experiments to study the relationship between leaf venation pattern and the effects of vein damage on water flow. You also have the data in Figure 36.14, which compares the effects of leaf damage among seven different species.

PROBLEM-SOLVING **S**TRATEGY   ***Interpret data.*** The data in step 6 of Figure 36.14 are presented in the form of histogram bars, showing differences in water conduction among the species studied when leaf veins were cut. Look for the species that displays the least difference between control leaves and experimentally cut leaves. Pay particular attention to the indicator of statistical significance (the asterisk). In displays of numerical data, asterisks are commonly used to indicate significant differences in outcomes between experimentally manipulated organisms and unmanipulated controls.

ANSWER *Bars indicating results for leaves of pinnately veined species that were experimentally cut are all noticeably shorter than bars for control leaves, and all are marked with an asterisk,* *indicating statistical significance. Among the palmately veined species, the histogram bars for experimentally cut leaves of Viburnum acerifolium are taller than those for pinnately veined species, but shorter than those for the other palmately veined species studied. For the Acer species, the heights of the histogram bars for the Acer saccharum leaves that were experimentally cut are approximately the same as the height of the control bar, except for the bar for leaves cut at point C, which shows a significant difference from the control. By contrast, the heights of the histogram bars for all manipulations of the palmately veined Acer rubrum are similar, and no bars display an asterisk indicating a significant difference from the control. These results indicate that, of the species examined, Acer rubrum showed the greatest tolerance to the experimental leaf cuts.*

Leaf Surface Features Prevent Desiccation, Provide Protection, and Aid in Photosynthesis

Leaf surfaces also show adaptive features. As we have previously discussed, a layer of epidermal tissue occurs at upper and lower leaf surfaces (see Figure 36.8c). These epidermal cells secrete a cuticle composed of protective wax and polyester compounds. The cuticle helps plants to avoid drying in the same way that enclosure in waxed paper keeps food moist. Plants that grow in very arid climates often have thick cuticles, whereas plants native to moist habitats typically have thinner cuticles.

As previously mentioned, some leaf epidermal cells may differentiate into protective spiky or hairlike projections known as **trichomes** (**Figure 36.15**). Broken trichomes of the stinging nettle, for example, release a caustic substance that irritates animals' skin, causing them to avoid consuming these plants. Production of leaf trichomes is under the control of transcription factors; similar proteins control the formation of hairs on seeds, as in cotton plants (see the chapter opening photo).

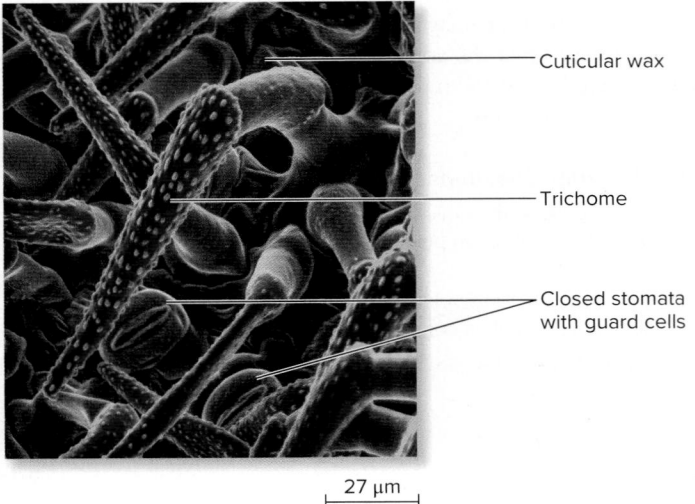

Cuticular wax

Trichome

Closed stomata
with guard cells

|— 27 μm —|

Figure 36.15 Leaf surface features. The features shown in this artificially colored SEM are cuticular wax, trichomes, and stomatal pores with guard cells. ©Eye of Science/Science Source

Leaf epidermal cells include pairs of specialized guard cells located on either side of stomata (see Figure 36.15). These **guard cells** allow stomata to be open during moist conditions, which allows a leaf to take up CO_2 and release O_2 during photosynthesis. Alternatively, the stomata will close when conditions are dry, thereby preventing plants from losing too much water. The genetic basis of guard-cell development is becoming increasingly well understood, as described next.

👁 Core Concept: Information

Genetic Control of Stomatal Guard-Cell Development

The flowering plant *Arabidopsis thaliana* is a model organism that is widely used to explore the genetic basis for plant structure and development. Several features of *A. thaliana* make it suitable for such studies. It is small in size, it has a fast seed-to-seed life cycle, it produces a relatively large number of seeds, and the

genome has been sequenced. Mutants of this plant have been used to identify the genes controlling many aspects of plant structure and development, including the development of specialized stomatal guard cells.

Guard-cell development begins when an unspecialized surface cell divides unequally (Figure 36.16). Unequal cell division is controlled by the protein RBR, which is related to the animal tumor suppressor Rb (Retinoblastoma). Plant cells having mutations in the gene that encodes RBR fail to differentiate normally. The larger of the two leaf cells arising from unequal division becomes a flat, puzzle piece–shaped epidermal cell, and the smaller is called a meristemoid because it functions as a stem cell. Meristemoids undergo one or more unequal cell divisions, producing more puzzle piece–shaped epidermal cells, before finally dividing equally to produce a pair of guard cells. Genetic studies of *A. thaliana* have revealed that the meristemoid secretes a protein that inhibits division by adjacent cells but does not affect cells farther away. This process distributes stomata evenly and prevents too many of them from forming, which could increase the loss of water from plant surfaces.

In 2007, two teams, led by Lynn Pillitteri and Cora MacAlister, respectively, independently reported experiments with *A. thaliana* showing how three closely related genes control guard-cell development at three consecutive steps. A gene called *SPEECHLESS* starts the process by establishing the first unequal cell divisions of meristemoids. A protein encoded by the *MUTE* gene then causes meristemoids to stop dividing unequally and produces the cell that will eventually divide to produce guard cells (guard cells precursor) (see **Figure 36.16**). Disabling mutations of these two genes cause the plant epidermis to completely lack stomatal pores (and so lack epidermal "mouths" and be speechless, or mute). Finally, the gene *FAMA* directs the production of guard cells and their specialization. The proteins encoded by these plant genes are members of a type known as basic helix-loop-helix (bHLH) proteins. Similar bHLH proteins control the development of muscle and nerve cells in animals, such as the protein encoded by *MyoD* (refer back to Figure 20.21).

Modified Leaves Perform Diverse Functions

Though most leaves function primarily as photosynthetic organs, some plants produce leaves that are modified in ways that allow them to play other roles. For example, threadlike tendrils that help some plants attach to a supporting structure are modified leaves or leaflets (**Figure 36.17a**). The tough scales that protect buds on plants such as the sycamore from winter damage are modified

Leaf
primordium

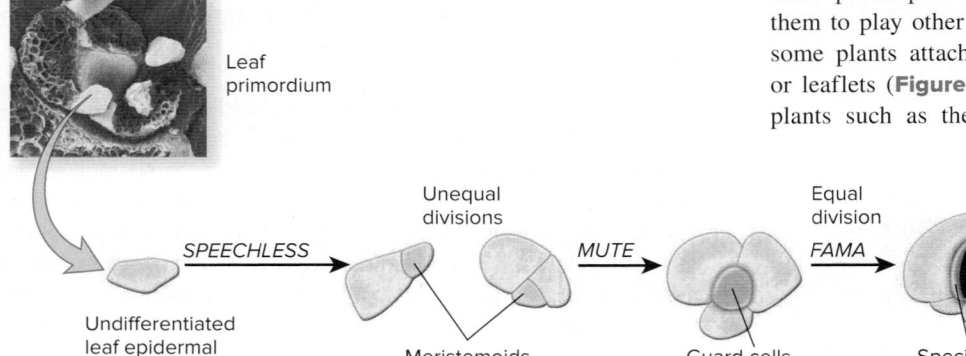

Undifferentiated
leaf epidermal
cell

Unequal
divisions

Meristemoids

Equal
division

Guard cells
precursor

Specialized
guard cells

SPEECHLESS

MUTE

FAMA

Figure 36.16 The development of stomatal guard cells, controlled by three genes. ©Beth Krizek

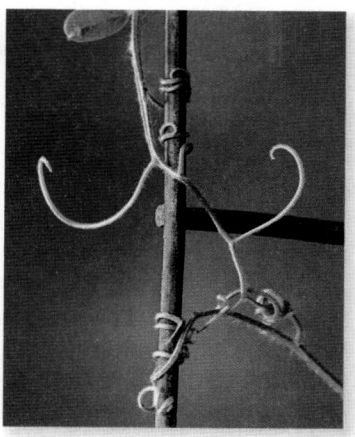
(a) Tendrils

(b) Bud scales

(c) Bracts

(d) Spines

Figure 36.17 Examples of modified leaves. **(a)** The tendrils of an American vetch plant are modified leaves that help the plant attach to a trellis. **(b)** Bud scales, such as those on this sycamore bud, are modified leaves that protect buds from winter damage. **(c)** The attractive red bracts of poinsettia are modified leaves that function like flower petals to attract pollinator insects to the small flowers. **(d)** Cactus spines, such as these on this giant saguaro, are modified leaves that function in defense. a: ©Ed Reschke/Getty Images; b: ©John Farmar; c: ©Steve Terrill/Corbis/Getty Images; d: ©Don Paulson Photography/Purestock/SuperStock

Concept Check: *Cactus leaves are so highly modified for defense that they cannot effectively accomplish photosynthesis, so how do cacti obtain organic compounds?*

leaves (**Figure 36.17b**). Poinsettia "petals" are actually modified leaves known as bracts, which are larger and more brightly colored than the flowers they surround, which helps to attract pollinators (**Figure 36.17c**). Cactus spines are actually modified leaves that have taken on a defensive role, leaving photosynthesis to the cactus stem (**Figure 36.17d**).

Stems May Contain Primary and Secondary Vascular Systems

Stems, leaves, roots, buds, flowers, and fruits all contain vascular systems composed of xylem and phloem tissues that conduct water, minerals, and organic compounds. **Herbaceous plants** such as corn and bean produce mostly primary vascular tissues. In contrast, **woody plants** produce both primary and secondary vascular tissues. A comparison of primary and secondary vascular tissues will aid in understanding their roles.

Primary Vascular Tissues   Primary vascular tissues are composed of primary xylem and phloem. Primary xylem is a complex tissue containing several cell types (see Table 36.2). These include unspecialized parenchyma cells; stiff fibers that provide structural support; and two types of cells that facilitate water transport: narrower tracheids and wider vessel elements (look ahead to Figures 39.11 and 39.12). Arranged in pipeline-like arrays, **tracheids** and **vessel elements** conduct water, along with dissolved minerals, hormones, and some other organic substances. These materials pass from one tracheid or vessel element to another through thin areas in the cell walls known as pits (**Figure 36.18**).

Mature tracheids and vessel elements are no longer living cells, and the absence of cytoplasm facilitates water flow. During development, these cells lose their cytoplasm by programmed cell death, a

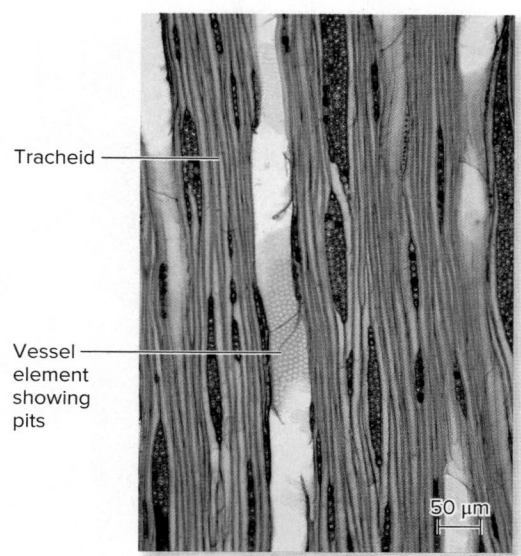
Tracheid

Vessel element showing pits

50 μm

Figure 36.18 Water-conducting cells of the xylem. In this thinly sliced portion of a stem, the lignin-impregnated walls of narrow tracheids and wider vessel elements can be distinguished. In this image, the walls of both tracheids and vessels have been stained with a red dye. ©Lee W. Wilcox

 Core Concept: Structure and Function Because lignin strengthens tracheid and vessel walls, they do not collapse as large volumes of water move through them.

process that resembles apoptosis in animals. However, the cell walls of tracheids and vessel elements don't easily break down or collapse because they are impregnated with a tough polymer known as lignin, except at pits. The rigid cell walls of tracheids and vessel elements not only foster water conduction but also help support the plant body. Like the tough plastic used in plumbing pipes, lignin provides the hydrophobic surface needed for water movement, as well as the strength to support trees weighing more than 2,000 metric tons.

In contrast to the conducting cells of xylem, mature conducting cells of phloem are alive. Phloem tissue transports organic compounds such as sugars, amino acids and proteins, hormones, RNA, and certain minerals in a watery solution. Phloem tissue includes **sieve-tube elements**, thin-walled living cells that are arranged end to end to form pipelines (**Figure 36.19**). Pores in the end walls of sieve-tube elements allow the watery solution to move from one cell to another.

Phloem tissue also includes companion cells that aid sieve-tube element metabolism, supportive fibers, and parenchyma cells (see Table 36.2). Phloem fibers are tough-walled sclerenchyma cells that are surprisingly long, 20–50 mm, and valued for their high strength. The phloem fibers of hemp (*Cannabis sativa*), flax (*Linum usitatissimum*), jute (*Corchorus capsularis*), kenaf (*Hibiscus cannabinus*), and ramie (*Boehmeria nivea*) are commercially important in the production of rope, textiles, and paper.

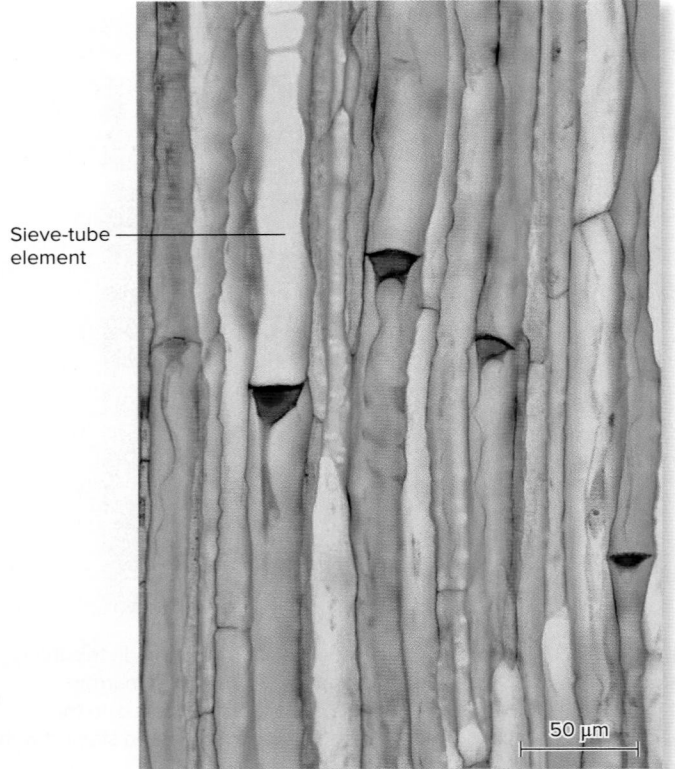

Figure 36.19 Food-conducting cells of the phloem. This thinly sliced portion of a stem shows stained, thin-walled sieve-tube elements that conduct a watery solution known as phloem sap. This solution contains sugars and other organic compounds, including amino acids and proteins, hormones, and RNA. When sieve-tube elements are damaged, which occurred when this thin slice was cut, protein plugs form. These plugs, stained red in this image, reduce loss of phloem sap, in much the same way that clotting reduces blood loss in animals. ©Lee W. Wilcox

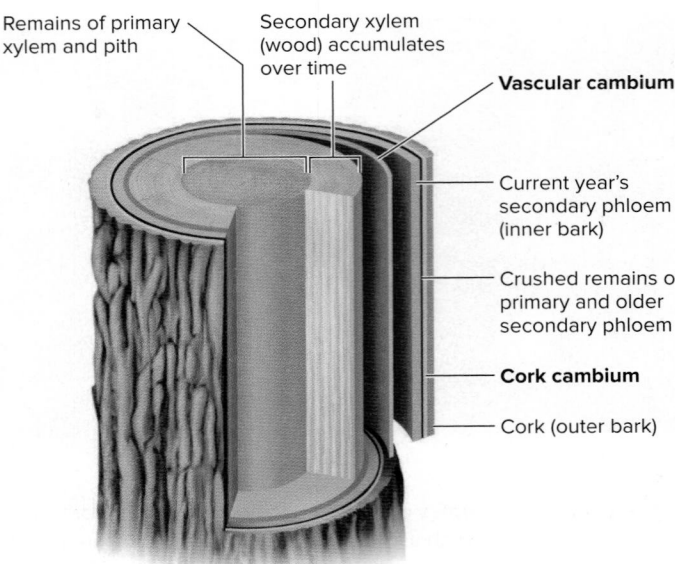

Figure 36.20 Formation of wood and bark by secondary (lateral) meristems. The vascular cambium is a thin cylinder of tissue that produces a thick cylinder of wood (secondary xylem) toward the inside of the stem and a thinner cylinder of inner bark (secondary phloem) toward the outside of the stem. The cork cambium forms an outer coating of protective cork (outer bark).

Secondary Vascular Tissues Woody plants begin life as herbaceous seedlings that possess only primary vascular systems. But as these plants mature, they produce secondary vascular tissues and bark. Secondary vascular tissues are composed of secondary xylem and secondary phloem. **Secondary xylem** is also known as **wood**, a component of plants that plays many important roles in human life (**Figure 36.20**). Wood is composed of about 25% lignin, 45% cellulose, and 25% other polysaccharides that are together known as hemicelluloses.

Secondary phloem is the **inner bark**. **Outer bark** is composed of protective layers of mostly dead cork cells that cover the outside of woody stems and roots (see Figure 36.20). Therefore, bark includes both inner bark (secondary phloem) and outer bark (cork).

Woody plants produce secondary vascular tissues by means of **secondary meristems**, also known as **lateral meristems**, which form rings of actively dividing cells that encircle the stem. The two types of secondary meristems are vascular cambium and cork cambium, which are derived from primary meristems.

The secondary meristem known as **vascular cambium** is a ring of dividing cells that produces secondary xylem to its interior and secondary phloem to its exterior (see Figure 36.20). Secondary xylem conducts most of a woody plant's water and minerals. Cell divisions that occur in secondary meristems increase the girth of woody stems. During each new growing season, the vascular cambium produces new cylinders of secondary xylem and secondary phloem.

In trees growing in temperate climates, each year's addition of new secondary xylem forms growth rings that can be observed on the cut stem surfaces (**Figure 36.21**). The growth rings of secondary xylem surround the remains of the primary xylem and a central cylinder of parenchyma cells known as the pith. If environmental conditions

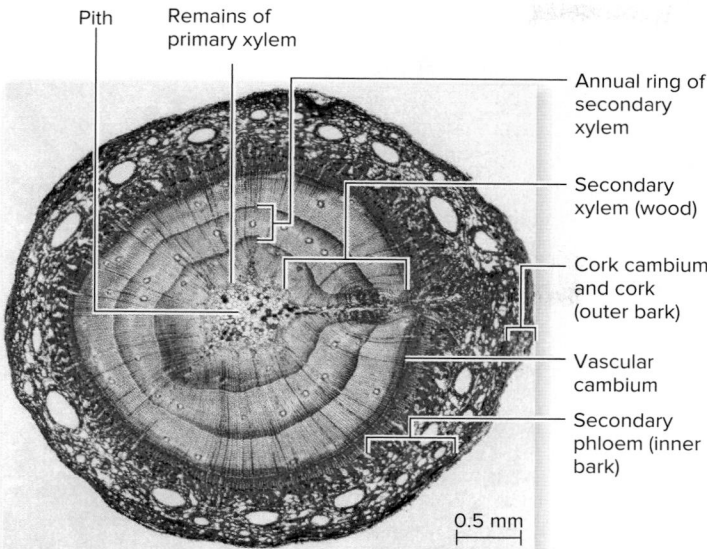

Pith   Remains of primary xylem

Annual ring of secondary xylem

Secondary xylem (wood)

Cork cambium and cork (outer bark)

Vascular cambium

Secondary phloem (inner bark)

0.5 mm

Figure 36.21 The anatomy of a woody stem. Each year, a new cylinder of wood is produced; this yearly wood production appears as annual rings on the cut surface of a woody stem. ©Lee W. Wilcox

Concept Check: *Why do tree trunks have a layer of wood (secondary xylem) that is thicker than the layer of inner bark (secondary phloem)?*

favor plant growth, the growth rings formed at that time will be wider than those formed during times of stressful conditions. Climatologists use growth ring widths in samples of old wood to deduce past climatic conditions, and archaeologists use growth ring data to determine the age of wood constructions and artifacts left by ancient cultures.

Secondary xylem may transport water for several years, but usually only the current year's production of secondary phloem is active in food transport. This is because thin-walled sieve elements typically live for only a year. Thus, only a thin layer of phloem, the inner bark, is responsible for most of the sugar transport in a large tree. Deep abrasion of tree bark may damage this thin phloem layer, disrupting a tree's food transport. If a groove is cut all the way around a tree trunk—a practice known as girdling—the tree will die because all of its functional phloem transport routes will have been interrupted.

As a young woody stem begins to increase in diameter, its thin epidermis eventually ruptures and is replaced by outer bark, which is composed of protective cork tissues. Cork is produced by a secondary meristem called the **cork cambium**, another ring of actively dividing cells. The cork cambium surrounds the secondary phloem (see Figures 36.20 and 36.21). Together, the cork cambium, layers of cork tissue produced by the cambium, and associated parenchyma cells are known as a **periderm**. The outer bark becomes thicker as woody stems accumulate multiple periderm layers. The outer bark surface is often interrupted by passages known as **lenticels** that allow inner stem tissues to accomplish gas exchange.

Cork cells are dead when mature, and their walls are layered with suberin, a material that helps to prevent both attack by microbial pathogens and water loss from the stem surface. Cork tissues also produce tannins, compounds that protect against pathogens by inactivating their proteins. The cracked surfaces of tree trunks are dead cork tissues of the outer bark. Commercial cork is sustainably harvested from the cork oak tree (*Quercus suber*) for production of

flooring material, bottle stoppers, and other items. Additional information about the structure and function of primary and secondary xylem and phloem can be found in Chapter 39.

Modified Stems Display Diverse Forms and Functions

Stems mostly grow upright because light is required for photosynthesis. But some stems, known as rhizomes, occur underground and grow horizontally. For example, potato tubers are the swollen, food-storing tips of rhizomes. Grass stems also grow horizontally, as either rhizomes just beneath the soil surface or stolons, which grow along the soil surface. The leaves and reproductive shoots of grasses grow upward from the point where they are attached to these horizontal stems. Grass blades continue to elongate from their bases even if you cut their tips off, explaining why lawns must be mowed repeatedly during the growing season. The horizontal stems of grasses are adaptations that help to protect vulnerable shoot apical meristems against natural hazards such as fire and grazing animals.

36.4 Root System Adaptations

Learning Outcomes:

1. List ways that root structure has been modified in different plants in response to different habitats.
2. **CoreSKILL »** Make a drawing that shows how branch roots develop.
3. Explain how mobile proteins influence root development.

Roots play the essential roles of absorbing water and minerals, anchoring plants in soil, and storing nutrients. The external form of roots varies among flowering plants, reflecting adaptation to particular life spans or habitats. In contrast, root internal structure is more uniform. In this section, we will first examine the internal structure and development of roots, and then consider a few examples of modified roots that have particular adaptive advantages.

Root Internal Growth and Tissue Specialization Occur in Distinct Zones

As discussed in Section 36.1, the common bean and other eudicots display an underground taproot system, whereas corn and other monocots have a fibrous root system (see Table 36.1). Studies of gene expression in the eudicot *Arabidopsis thaliana* reveal that roots are amazingly complex in their internal structure, having at least 15 distinct cell types. For our purposes, a simpler microscopic examination of root internal structure reveals three major zones: (1) a root apical meristem (RAM) protected by a root cap, (2) a zone of root elongation, and (3) a zone of maturation in which specialized cells can be observed (**Figure 36.22**).

Root Apical Meristem and Root Cap   As discussed earlier, an apical meristem occurs at the tip of each root and its branches. Like the SAM, the RAM contains stem cells, but these are organized differently in root apices. Root stem cells surround a tiny region of cells

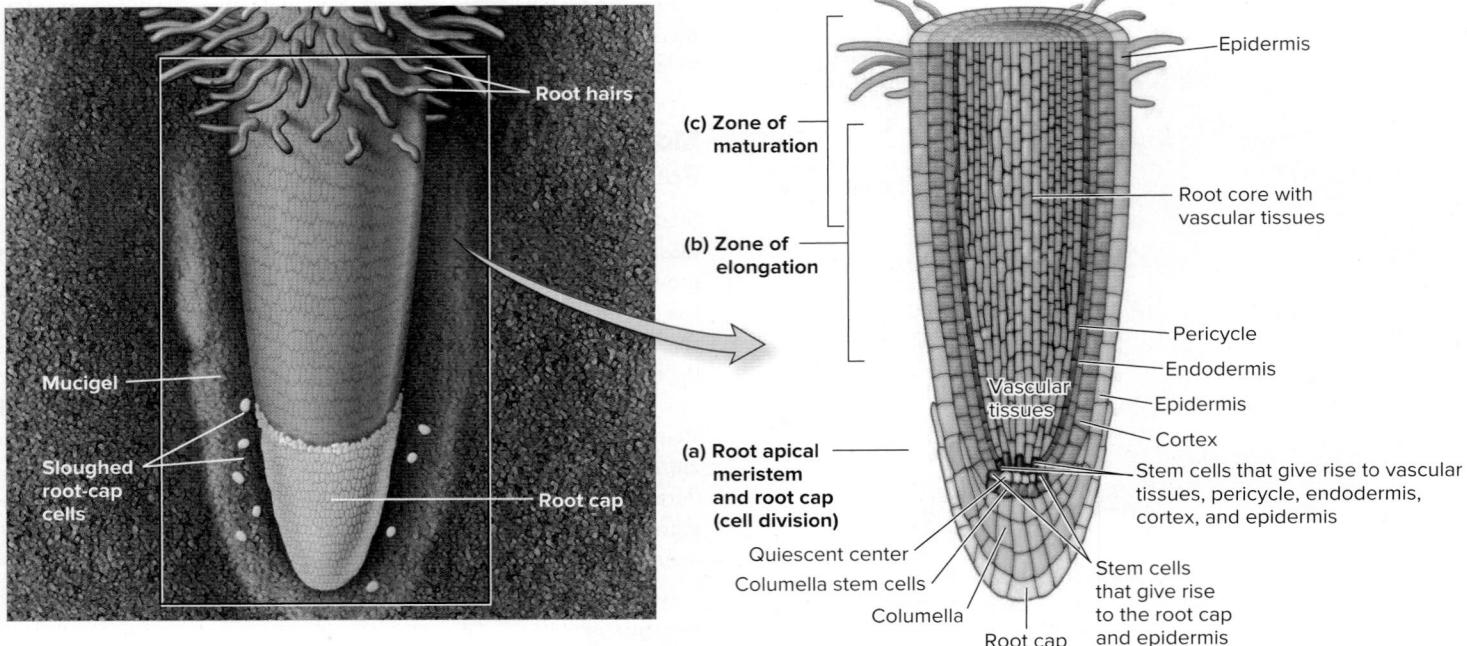

Figure 36.22 Three zones of root growth. A longitudinal view of a typical root reveals three major zones: **(a)** a root apical meristem region that includes stem cells, a quiescent zone, columella, and a root cap; **(b)** a zone of elongation; and **(c)** a zone of maturation, characterized by specialized cells and tissues including epidermal root hairs, cylinders of endodermis and pericycle tissue, and a core of vascular tissue.

that rarely divide, known as the quiescent center. Signals emanating from the quiescent center keep nearby stem cells in an undifferentiated state. Root stem cells farther away from the quiescent center produce new cells in multiple directions.

- Toward the root tip, stem cells produce columella cells that sense gravity and touch, which helps roots extend downward into the soil and around obstacles such as rocks.
- At the sides of the quiescent center, stem cells produce a protective root cap and epidermal cells. Root tip epidermal cells secrete a sticky substance called mucigel that lubricates root growth through the soil.
- Toward the shoot, stem cells generate cells that become internal root tissues.

Zones of Elongation and Maturation Above the RAM lies the **zone of elongation**, in which cells extend by water uptake, thereby dramatically increasing root length (see Figure 36.22). The root elongation zone illustrates the general principle that cell expansion in plants is not necessarily linked directly to cell division. (By contrast, animal cell expansion is more closely linked to cell division.)

Above and overlapping with the root zone of elongation is the **zone of maturation**, where most root cell differentiation and tissue specialization occur. Specialized root tissues include mature vascular tissues at the root core, an enclosing cylinder of cells known as the pericycle, another cell cylinder called the endodermis (meaning inside skin), and epidermal cells at the root surface. Relatively unspecialized parenchyma cells form a cortex that lies between the endodermis and the epidermis. Starting with the epidermis and moving

inward, we will take a closer look at these root tissues and factors that control their development.

The zone of maturation can be identified by the presence of numerous microscopic hairs that emerge from the root epidermis. **Root hairs** are specialized epidermal cells that can be as long as 1.3 cm, about the width of your little finger, but are only 10 μm in diameter, less than the width of a finger cell. Their small diameter allows root hairs to obtain water and minerals from soil pores that are too narrow for even the smallest roots to enter. Root hair plasma membranes are rich in transport proteins that use ATP to selectively absorb materials from the soil (look ahead to Figure 39.3).

The production of hairs from root epidermal cells is controlled by the activity of transcription factors that move between cells and also by cell position (**Figure 36.23**). A root hair will develop from epidermal cells lying over the junction of two cortical cells, whereas no hair will develop if an epidermal cell lies over only one cortical cell. Root hairs are so delicate that they are easily damaged by abrasion as roots grow through the soil, and they live for only 4 or 5 days. As a result, root hairs are absent from older regions above the zone of maturation. To compensate, roots must continually produce new root hairs. The average rate of root-hair production has been estimated at more than 100 million per day for some plants. One reason that gardeners use care when transplanting seedlings is to prevent extensive damage to the root hairs.

The epidermis of mature roots encloses a cylinder of parenchyma known as the root cortex (**Figure 36.24**). Much like the cells of the stem cortex, root cortex cells are often rich in starch and therefore serve as a food storage site for plants. The root cortex of some plants contains intercellular air spaces that arise as a result of programmed cell death and provide routes for oxygen diffusion within the root.

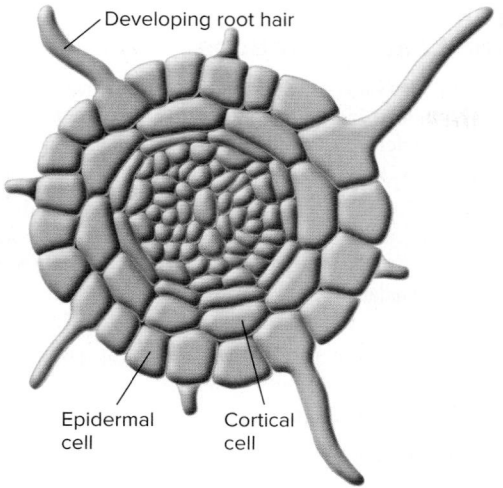

Figure 36.23 **A cross section of a root showing positional influence on root-hair development.**

Water and dissolved minerals also diffuse from the environment into roots through spaces between cortex cells, stopping only when they reach a one-cell-thick cylinder of specialized tissue known as **endodermis** (inside skin). This endodermal cell layer is an important component of the mechanism by which roots absorb selected minerals (described further in Chapter 39). Endodermal cells specialize in response to a transcription factor (called SHORT ROOT) that is synthesized in cells of the root core, then transported outward.

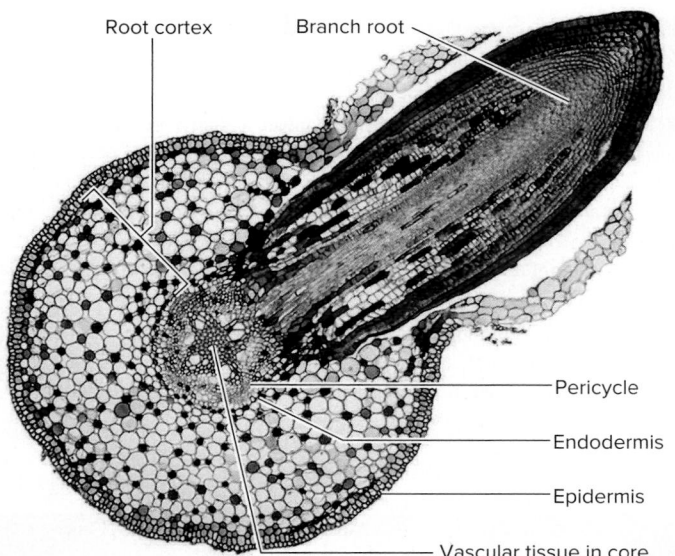

Figure 36.24 **Cross section of a mature root.** This stained light micrograph shows the epidermis and cortex of a root surrounding a central core of vascular tissue. An inner cortex layer is the endodermis, which surrounds a cylinder of meristematic pericycle tissue. The pericycle has produced a young branch (lateral) root that has grown through the cortex and the epidermis. ©Lee W. Wilcox

Concept Check: *Why must lateral roots be produced in the way shown in this figure?*

A cylinder of tissue having cell division (meristematic) capacity, known as the **pericycle**, encloses the root vascular tissue (see Figure 36.24). In response to the hormone auxin, the pericycle produces lateral branch roots that force their way through the cortex to the surface. This process differs from the way that stems produce branches by means of buds. In some roots, the pericycle generates a vascular cambium that produces wood—secondary xylem. Such woody roots also possess a cork cambium that makes a protective covering of suberin-coated cork tissue. Like woody stems, woody roots produce primary vascular tissues in their youth and secondary vascular tissues at maturity. The woody roots of trees are sometimes visible above ground.

Modified Roots Display Diverse External Forms and Functions

Plants produce several other types of roots that provide adaptive advantages in response to different habitats. For example, corn and many other plants produce supportive prop roots from the lower portions of their stems. Many tropical trees grow in such thin soils that they are vulnerable to being blown down in windstorms. Such trees often produce dramatic aboveground buttress roots that help keep them upright (**Figure 36.25a**). Many mangrove trees that grow along

(a) Buttress roots

(b) Pneumatophores

Figure 36.25 **Modified aboveground roots. (a)** Buttress roots help to keep tropical trees such as this *Pterocarpus hayesii* from toppling in windstorms. **(b)** Pneumatophores produced by mangroves are roots that extend upward into the air. These roots take up air and then transmit it to underwater roots that grow in oxygen-poor sediments.

a: ©Martin Engelmann/Getty Images; b: ©Peter E. Smith, Natural Sciences Image Library

tropical coasts produce pneumatophores (Greek meaning breath bearers), roots that grow upward into the air (**Figure 36.25b**). Functioning like snorkels, pneumatophores absorb oxygen-rich air, which diffuses to submerged roots growing in oxygen-poor sediments. This mechanism is necessary because roots require a supply of oxygen in order to produce ATP. Roots use the ATP to power their growth and the uptake of mineral nutrients (see Chapter 39).

Summary of Key Concepts

36.1 From Seed to Seed—The Life of a Flowering Plant

- Seed embryos, seedlings, and mature plants are components of the sporophyte generation in the plant sexual cycle; tiny gametophytes develop and grow within flowers (Figure 36.1).

- Plant organs are composed of tissues that contain specialized cells. The basic plant organs are roots, stems, and leaves. Shoot systems include stems and stem branches, and stems produce leaves, buds, flowers, and fruits. Root systems include one or more main roots with branches. Buds, flowers, fruits, and seeds are organ systems, composed of more than one organ (Figures 36.2, 36.3).

- The two major groups of flowering plants—eudicots and monocots—differ in the structure of their seed embryos, flowers, stems, roots, leaves, and pollen. Flowering plants may live for one year (annuals), two years (biennials), or more than two years (perennials) (Figure 36.4, Table 36.1).

36.2 How Plants Grow and Develop

- Plant growth and development features the presence of a fundamental architecture based on apical-basal polarity and radial symmetry throughout the life of a plant (Figures 36.5, 36.6).

- Plants grow by producing new cells at meristems and by controlled cell enlargement involving water uptake.

- Shoot apical meristems produce primary meristems that increase plant length and produce organs (Table 36.2).

- The simple plant tissues, containing one or two cell types, include parenchyma, collenchyma, and sclerenchyma. Complex plant tissues include the vascular tissues known as xylem and phloem, and the primary vascular tissues occur in vascular bundles (Figure 36.7).

- Leaves develop from primordia at shoot apices. Foliage leaves have internal and external structure that is adapted for photosynthetic functions (Figure 36.8).

- Meristems include stem cells that divide relatively rarely, thereby reducing the accumulation of harmful mutations. Cells that arise from stem cells may divide more frequently, producing new tissue.

- Plant cells are able to expand under conditions that result in loosening of cell-wall components, and by water uptake into vacuoles. The direction in which plant cells expand is determined by the arrangement of cellulose microfibrils in the cell wall, which is influenced by the orientation of microtubules in the nearby cytosol (Figures 36.9, 36.10, 36.11).

36.3 The Shoot System: Stem and Leaf Adaptations

- Shoots are modular systems; each module includes a node, internode, leaf, and axillary meristem or bud. An axillary bud develops in leaf axils; such buds may grow into new branches (Figure 36.12).

- Variations in leaf structure reflect adaptations that aid photosynthesis or protect against stress. For example, Sack and colleagues demonstrated that palmate leaves provide conducting system redundancy that is useful in coping with vein damage (Figures 36.13, 36.14, 36.15).

- Stomatal guard-cell differentiation is controlled by several genes (Figure 36.16).

- Leaves not only function in photosynthesis but also play other roles, including attachment, attraction, and protection (Figure 36.17).

- Herbaceous plants are those whose stems produce little or no wood and are mostly composed of primary vascular tissues. The primary vascular tissues are primary xylem and primary phloem (Figures 36.18, 36.19).

- In addition to primary tissues, woody plants such as trees and shrubs possess secondary meristems that produce wood and bark. The vascular cambium produces secondary xylem (wood) and secondary phloem (inner bark). The cork cambium produces cork tissues that form outer bark (Figures 36.20, 36.21).

- Stems occur in diverse forms that reflect adaptation to environmental conditions. Examples include grass rhizomes, which grow horizontally underground and are therefore better protected from fire and grazing animals (as well as lawnmowers).

36.4 Root System Adaptations

- The internal organization of roots is comparatively uniform, and three major zones can be recognized with the use of a microscope: the root apical meristem and root cap, a zone of cell and root elongation, and a zone of tissue maturation. Features of the mature root include epidermal root hairs that aid nutrient uptake, a food-storing cortex, an endodermis that functions in mineral selection, a pericycle that produces lateral (branch) roots (and vascular cambium in the case of woody roots), and an inner core of vascular tissue (Figures 36.22, 36.23, 36.24).

- Roots occur in multiple forms that reflect adaptation to environmental conditions. Examples of aboveground roots include prop roots, buttress roots, and pneumatophores (Figure 36.25).

Assess & Discuss

Test Yourself

1. Where would you look to find the gametophyte generation of a flowering plant?
   a. at the shoot apical meristem
   b. at the root apical meristem
   c. in seeds
   d. in flower parts
   e. Flowering plants lack a gametophyte generation.

2. What is a radicle?
    a. an embryonic leaf
    b. an embryonic stem
    c. an embryonic root
    d. a mature root system of a monocot
    e. an organism that has extreme political views

3. Which type of plant is most likely to have food-rich roots that are useful as human food?
    a. an annual
    b. a biennial
    c. a perennial
    d. a centennial
    e. plants that grow along coastal shorelines

4. Which of the following terms best describes the distinctive architecture of plants?
    a. radial symmetry and apical-basal polarity
    b. bilateral symmetry and apical-basal polarity
    c. radial symmetry and absence of apical-basal polarity
    d. bilateral symmetry and absence of apical-basal polarity
    e. absence of symmetry and absence of apical-basal polarity

5. Which is the most accurate description of how plants grow?
    a. by the addition of new cells at meristems that include stem cells
    b. by cell enlargement as the result of water uptake
    c. by both the addition of new cells and cell expansion
    d. by addition of fat cells
    e. by all of the above

6. Where would you look for leaf primordia?
    a. at a vegetative shoot tip
    b. at the root apical meristem
    c. at the vascular cambium
    d. at the cork cambium
    e. in a floral bud

7. Which leaf tissues display the greatest amount of air space?
    a. the upper epidermis
    b. the lower epidermis
    c. the palisade parenchyma
    d. the spongy parenchyma
    e. the vascular tissues

8. What are adventitious roots?
    a. roots that develop on plant cuttings that have been placed in water
    b. buttress roots that grow from tree trunks
    c. the only kinds of roots produced by monocots, because their embryonic root dies soon after seed germination
    d. any root that is produced by stem (or sometimes leaf) tissue, rather than developing directly from the embryonic root
    e. All of the above describe adventitious roots.

9. During its development, a tracheid elongates in a direction parallel to the shoot or root axis. Based on this information, what can you say about the orientation of cell-wall cellulose microfibrils and cytoplasmic microtubules in the developing tracheid?
    a. The microfibrils will be oriented perpendicularly (at right angles) to the long axis of the developing tracheid, encircling it, but the cytoplasmic microtubules will be oriented parallel to the direction in which the tracheid is elongating.
    b. Microfibrils and microtubules will both be oriented perpendicularly (at right angles) to the elongating axis of the tracheid.
    c. Microfibrils and microtubules will both be oriented parallel to the direction of tracheid elongation.
    d. Microfibrils will be oriented parallel to the direction of tracheid elongation, but microtubules will be perpendicular (at right angles) to both the microfibrils and the elongating tracheid.
    e. None of the above is correct.

10. What are examples of woody plants?
    a. trees
    b. shrubs
    c. herbaceous plants
    d. all of the above
    e. only a and b

Conceptual Questions

1. What would be the consequences if overall plant architecture were bilaterally symmetric?

2. What would be the consequences if leaves were radially symmetric (shaped like spheres or cylinders)?

3. **Core Concept: Structure and Function** Why are most tall plants woody, rather than herbaceous?

Collaborative Questions

1. Find a tree stump or a large limb that has recently been cut from a tree (or imagine doing so). Which of the following features could you locate with the unaided eye: the outer bark, the inner bark, the secondary xylem, the vascular cambium, annual rings?

2. Which physical factors would you expect to influence shoot growth most strongly? Which physical factors would you expect to influence underground root growth most strongly?

Flowering Plants: Behavior

37

Behavior of the snow buttercup. The snow buttercup (*Ranunculus adoneus*) holds its flowers above the surface of the snow. The flowers move so that they always face the Sun during the day, a behavior known as sun tracking. ©William D. Bowman

The snow buttercup (*Ranunculus adoneus*) grows in deep snowbanks in the high Rocky Mountains, with flower stems protruding above the snow's surface toward the Sun, as shown in the chapter opening photo. Amazingly, snow buttercup flowers change their position so that they face the Sun throughout the day, a process known as sun tracking. Experiments have demonstrated that sun tracking warms snow buttercup flowers, thereby favoring pollen development and germination. These processes foster fertilization, which leads to more effective seed production. In this way, sun tracking can be understood as an adaptation that increases snow buttercup reproductive fitness. Like sun-tracking solar panels, the leaves of alfalfa, lupine, soybean, common bean, cotton, and other wild and agricultural plants also track the Sun, a process that aids energy storage via photosynthesis.

Sun tracking is but one example of the many ways in which plants display behavior—that is, responses to stimuli. Plants respond not only to changes in the Sun's position, but also to day length, which is the period of daily illumination. In addition to light,

plants respond to gravity, wind, attack by animals and disease-causing microorganisms, and other environmental stimuli. This chapter provides examples of ways in which understanding plant behavior has been key to increasing agricultural productivity and protecting natural ecosystems for the benefit of humans.

We begin with a survey of the diverse types of stimuli that induce plant behavior and review how cells perceive and respond to stimuli by means of signal transduction pathways. Next, we will focus on plant hormones and other major types of mobile internal molecules that influence plant behavior. Finally, we will consider how responses to environmental stimuli foster plant survival and reproduction.

37.1 Overview of Plant Behavioral Responses

Learning Outcomes:

1. List examples of plant responses to internal and environmental stimuli.
2. Describe the three stages of cell signaling.

Behavior is defined as a response of organisms to an internal or external stimulus. Examples of plant behavior include plant movements, some types of which were described in 1880 by Charles Darwin and his son Francis in their book *The Power of Movement in Plants*. Modern time-lapse photography, which makes plant behavior more obvious to humans, reveals that most plants are constantly in motion, bending, twisting, or rotating in dancelike movements known as nutation (**Figure 37.1a**). Some plants display relatively rapid movements, illustrated by the sensitive plant (*Mimosa pudica*), whose leaves quickly fold when touched, then open more slowly (**Figure 37.1b**).

Among the many other important examples of plant behavior that occur are the following:

- Seeds germinate when they detect the presence of sufficient light and moisture for successful seedling growth.
- Plant shoots typically grow toward light and against the pull of gravity.

(a) Nutation movements   **(b) Leaf folding**

Time 0

< 1 sec

Figure 37.1 Examples of plant movements. (a) Sixteen superimposed photographs of a shoot of the honeysuckle vine *Lonicera japonica*, taken over a period of 2 hours, reveal the circular movement known as nutation. **(b)** Photographs of the sensitive plant (*Mimosa pudica*) made before and shortly after a touch reveal the rapid process of leaf folding. Even if only one leaflet is touched, electrical signals travel throughout the complex leaf, causing the entire organ to fold. The leaves will eventually unfold. a: ©Digital Photography by Ash Kaushesh, University of Central Arkansas, Conway, Arkansas 72035 USA/Image courtesy Botanical Society of America, www.botany.org St. Louis, MO 63110; b (top, bottom): ©Lee W. Wilcox

- Most roots grow toward water and in the same direction as the gravitational force. Roots can also grow around obstacles in the soil.
- Flowers, fruit, and seeds are produced only during the season(s) most favorable for reproductive success.
- Plants take protective actions when they sense attack by disease-causing microbes or hungry animals, thereby preventing excessive damage to their own bodies or those of neighboring plants.

Plant Behavior Involves Responses to Internal and External Stimuli

To gain a more complete understanding of plant behavior, we will begin by surveying the types of stimuli that cause plant responses. Most people are aware that both internal chemical signals and environmental factors influence animal behavior. Bird nesting behavior in spring, for example, involves hormonal changes triggered by seasonal conditions. Plants likewise respond to internal and environmental stimuli (**Figure 37.2**).

Internal Stimuli   Plants respond to two types of internal stimuli: internal biological clocks and mobile chemical signals. Internal biological clocks, known as **circadian rhythms**, occur not only in plants, but also in animals and other organisms. The word circadian comes from the Latin words meaning around and day. A circadian rhythm is any biological process that undergoes a consistent pattern

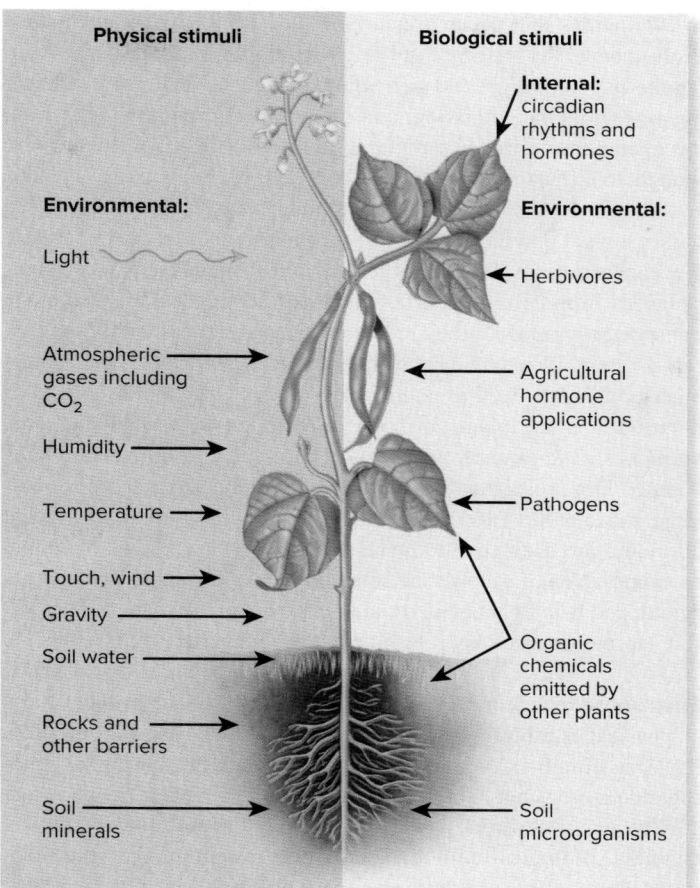

Figure 37.2 Types of plant stimuli. Plants respond to both physical and biological stimuli. Stimuli may be internal to the plant or come from the environment.

  Core Skill: Modeling The goal of this modeling challenge is to draw a model that is similar to Figure 37.2 and shows the stimuli experienced by plants in a spacecraft.

Modeling Challenge: Experiments aimed at understanding how plants respond to condition in space have been completed and continue to be performed on the International Space Station. Results of these experiments are helpful in determining how plants can be used to feed space travelers and purify their

Plant growing in the International Space Station. ©NASA Photo/Alamy Stock Photo

air and water. To design effective experiments in space requires understanding the types of environmental stimuli that plants respond to on Earth and how these environmental stimuli and plant responses might differ in space. Draw a model in the same format as Figure 37.2 that shows the stimuli that plants grown on board the International Space Station or other spacecraft would likely experience.

of oscillations that occur over a 24-hour period. Circadian rhythms evolved under the influence of Earth's rotation, which causes the regular alternation of night and day. Sun tracking, leaf movements, flower opening, fragrance emission, and many other behaviors result from the operation of circadian rhythms in plants. Circadian rhythms are thought to influence the timing of about 30% of gene activity in plants.

Plants also respond to internal chemical signals that are produced within a plant and move from one location to another, acting at very low concentrations. In plants, these chemical signals may move short distances from cell to cell via plasmodesmata or by cell membrane transporter systems, or they may move long distances within the vascular system. Plant chemical signals include transcription factors and other proteins, as well as chemically different compounds known as **hormones**. Some plant hormones are similar to particular animal hormones. One example is the plant hormone jasmonic acid, which is much like prostaglandins produced by animals. The gaseous hormone nitric oxide (NO) functions in both animals and plants. Other hormones are distinctive to plants. Even so, as in the case of animal hormones, plant hormones are often produced in response to external stimuli and help to maintain a stable internal environment (homeostasis). Hormones also play roles in plant development.

Environmental Stimuli   Plants sense and respond to many types of physical and biological environmental stimuli (see Figure 37.2). Physical stimuli in natural plant environments include light, atmospheric gases such as CO_2 and water vapor, temperature, touch, wind, gravity, soil water, rocks and other barriers to root growth, and soil minerals. Biological stimuli include herbivores (animals that consume plant parts), airborne pathogens (disease-causing microbes), organic chemicals emitted from neighboring plants, and beneficial or

harmful soil microorganisms. Crop plants also respond to applications of agricultural chemicals, which may include hormones. That plants have evolved such a broad array of sensory capacity is not surprising, because all of the listed environmental influences affect plant survival and reproduction.

Plant Responses to Environmental Stimuli   Though plants lack the specialized sense organs typical of animals, receptor molecules located in plant cells sense stimuli and cause responses. When many cells of a tissue receive and respond to the same biological or physical stimuli, entire organs or plant bodies display behavior. For example, houseplants tend to grow toward a light source such as a window. This process, known as positive **phototropism**, involves both a cellular perception of light and a growth response of stem tissue to an internal chemical signal. In general, a **tropism** is a growth response that depends on a stimulus that occurs in a particular direction. In the case of phototropism, the plant senses the direction of light and responds by changing the location of a plant hormone known as an auxin. As a result, the stem bends toward light. We will next review how plant cells more generally receive signals and transmit them intracellularly, a process known as cell signaling that occurs in all cells (refer back to Chapter 9).

Plant Cell Signaling Involves Receptors, Second Messengers, and Effectors

Cell signaling is the process in which a cell receives a physical or chemical signal, thereby switching on an intracellular pathway that leads to a cellular response (**Figure 37.3**). The process of cell signaling often involves three types of molecules: receptors that may

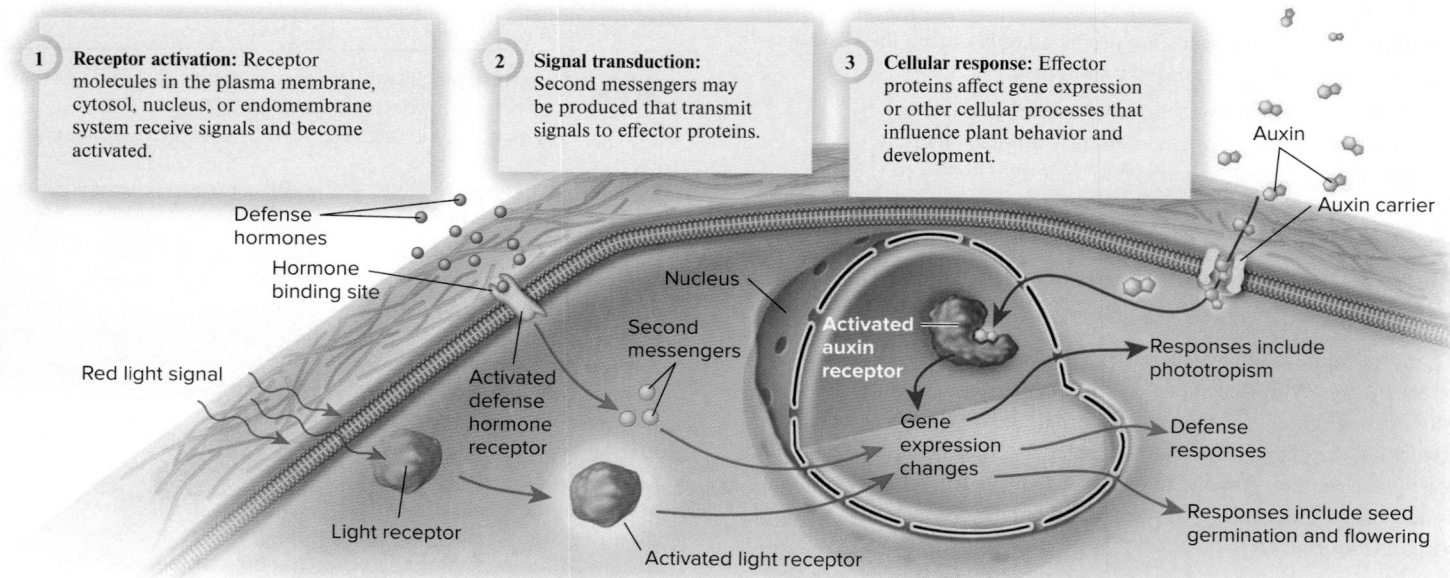

Figure 37.3 An overview of plant cell signaling. Plant cells respond to hormonal signals produced within the plant body, as well as to environmental stimuli. Three different signal transduction processes are shown here: one started by light, one started by a defense hormone having a plasma membrane receptor, and another started by an auxin having a receptor located in the nucleus.

 Core Concept: Systems Internal and environmental stimuli are received and elicit responses at the cellular level.

become activated, second messengers that transmit signals, and effectors that cause a cellular response (also refer back to Figure 9.4).

Receptors (also known as sensors) are proteins that become activated when they receive a specific type of signal (see Figure 37.3). Receptors occur in diverse cellular locations. Whereas some plant defense receptors are located within the plasma membrane, light receptors may occur in the cytosol and auxin receptors in the nucleus. Some activated receptors directly generate a response, such as an increased flow of ions across a membrane. Other activated receptors bind to signaling molecules that initiate an intracellular signaling pathway. For example, the binding of certain defense hormones to plasma membrane receptors results in the intracellular production of second messenger molecules that transmit the signal.

Second messengers transmit messages from many types of activated receptors. Cyclic AMP (cAMP), inositol triphosphate (IP_3), and calcium ions (Ca^{2+}) are major second messengers in animal and plant cells. Ca^{2+} is a particularly common second messenger in plant cells. Touch and various other stimuli cause Ca^{2+} to flow from storage sites in the lumen of the endoplasmic reticulum (ER) into the cytosol. Ca^{2+} then binds to calmodulin or other calcium-binding proteins. Ca^{2+} binding alters the structure of such proteins, causing them to interact with other cellular proteins or to alter their enzymatic function.

Effectors are molecules that directly influence cellular responses. In plants, calcium-dependent protein kinases (CDPKs) are particularly important effector molecules. The last phase of cell signaling occurs when an effector causes a cellular response, such as opening or closing an ion channel or switching the transcription of particular genes on or off. A single activated receptor can dispatch many second-messenger molecules, which, in turn, can activate scores of effectors, leading to many molecular responses within a single cell.

37.2 Plant Hormones

Learning Outcomes:

1. List some examples of plant hormones.
2. Explain how auxin functions in phototropism.
3. Explain how cytokinins, gibberellins, and ethylene are relevant to agriculture.
4. Explain how abscisic acid and brassinosteroids help plants cope with environmental stress.

Along with proteins and RNA molecules, plant hormones are chemical signals transported within the plant body. When taken up by target cells, the signals elicit responses. Here, we focus on plant hormones, about a dozen types of small molecules that are synthesized in metabolic pathways that also make amino acids, nucleotides, sterols, or secondary metabolites. Auxins, cytokinins, gibberellins, ethylene, abscisic acid, and brassinosteroids are examples of plant hormones (**Table 37.1**).

Individual plant hormones often have multiple effects, and different concentrations or combinations of hormones can produce distinct growth or developmental responses. Several plant hormones are known to act by causing the removal of gene repressors, thereby allowing gene expression to occur. This general mechanism allows hormones to cause relatively rapid responses. A closer look at the major types of plant hormones reveals their multifaceted roles.

Auxins Are the Master Plant Hormones

Plants produce several types of **auxins**, which are considered to be the master plant hormones because they influence plant structure, development, and behavior in many ways, often working with other hormones. Indoleacetic acid (IAA) is one plant auxin (see Table 37.1), but other natural and artificial compounds have similar structures and effects. In this section, we will refer to this family of related compounds simply as auxin.

Auxin exerts so many effects because it promotes the expression of thousands of genes known as **auxin-responsive genes**. Under low auxin concentrations, proteins called Aux/IAA repressors prevent plant cells from expressing these genes. The repressor proteins prevent gene expression by binding to activator proteins at gene promoters and inhibiting their function. When the auxin concentration is high enough, auxin molecules glue repressors onto a protein complex called TIR1, which causes the breakdown of the repressors. Free of the repressors, the activator proteins are no longer inhibited and enhance the expression of auxin-response genes.

Auxin Transport   The way in which auxin is transported into and out of cells is integral to its effects in plants. Auxin is produced in apical shoot tips and young leaves, and it is directionally transported from one living parenchyma cell to another. Auxin in an uncharged form (IAAH) may enter cells from intercellular spaces by means of simple diffusion. However, the negatively charged form (IAA⁻) requires the aid of a plasma membrane protein known as the **auxin influx carrier (AUX1/LAX)**. Several types of proteins, called PIN proteins, transport auxin out of cells. They are named for the pin-shaped shoot apices of plants having mutations in *PIN* genes. Because they transport auxin out of cells, PIN proteins are called **auxin efflux carriers**. They are necessary because auxin occurs as a charged ion in the cytosol that does not readily diffuse out of cells.

In shoots, AUX1/LAX is located at the apical ends of cells, whereas PIN proteins often occur at the basal ends (**Figure 37.4a**). This polar distribution of auxin carriers explains why auxin primarily flows downward in shoots and into roots, a process called **polar transport** (**Figure 37.4b**). However, the locations of auxin carriers can also change within cell plasma membranes, allowing lateral or upward transport of auxin. Differences in the presence and positions of auxin carrier proteins explain variations in auxin concentration within plants. The local auxin concentration allows plant cells to determine their position within the plant body and to respond by dividing, expanding, or specializing.

Auxin Effects   In nature, auxin influences plants throughout their lifetimes. Auxin establishes the apical-basal polarity of seed embryos, induces vascular tissue to differentiate, mediates phototropism, promotes formation of adventitious roots, and stimulates fruit development. Many of auxin's effects are also of practical importance to humans. Auxin is used to produce some types of seedless fruit, retard premature fruit drop in orchards, and stimulate root development on stem cuttings. Although we still have much to learn about auxin's function, its role in phototropism has been elucidated by a series of experiments, described next.

Table 37.1	Examples of Plant Hormones	
Type of plant hormone	**Chemical structure of an example**	**Functions***
Auxins	Indoleacetic acid (IAA) CH_2-COOH	Establish apical-basal polarity, induce vascular tissue development, mediate phototropism, promote formation of adventitious roots, inhibit leaf and fruit drop, and stimulate fruit development
Cytokinins	Zeatin $HN-CH_2-C=C$ CH_3 CH_2OH	Promote cell division, influence cell specialization and plant aging, activate secondary meristem development, promote adventitious root growth, and promote shoot development on callus
Gibberellins	Gibberellic acid	Stimulate cell division and cell elongation, stimulate stem elongation and flowering, and promote seed germination
Ethylene	Ethylene $H_2C=CH_2$	Promotes seedling growth, induces fruit ripening, plays a role in leaf and petal aging and drop, coordinates defenses against osmotic stress and pathogen attack
Abscisic acid	Abscisic acid	Slows or stops metabolism during environmental stress, induces bud and seed dormancy, prevents seed germination in unfavorable conditions, and promotes stomatal closing
Brassinosteroids	Brassinolide	Promote cell expansion, stimulate shoot elongation, retard leaf drop, stimulate xylem development, and promote stress responses

*The lists of functions are only partial lists.

The Role of Auxin in Phototropism In the 1880s, Charles Darwin and his son Francis were the first to publish results of experiments on plant phototropism. The Darwins performed their experiments on cereal seedlings, whose tips are protected by a sheath of tissue called a coleoptile. In a simple but elegant experiment, the Darwins covered either the tips or lower portions of coleoptiles with shading materials such as blackened glass tubes, left other seedlings uncovered, and removed the tips of some seedlings. They then compared how those seedlings responded to illumination from the side. The seedlings whose tips were left uncovered grew toward the light, whereas seedlings whose tips were covered or removed did not. The Darwins concluded that seedling tips transmit some "influence" to lower portions,

causing them to bend toward the light. You can probably guess what this influence was, but technology available at the time did not allow the Darwins to determine this.

Three decades later, in the 1910s, Danish botanist Peter Boysen-Jensen confirmed the Darwins' results and demonstrated that the influence was a chemical substance that diffused from the tips of the seedlings to other parts. To do this, Boysen-Jensen cut off the tips of oat seedlings and placed either a porous layer of gelatin or a nonporous material such as a sheet of the mineral mica on the cut surface. Then he replaced the tips. Oat seedlings layered with porous gelatin displayed a normal phototropic response, bending toward the light, but those layered with nonporous mica did not.

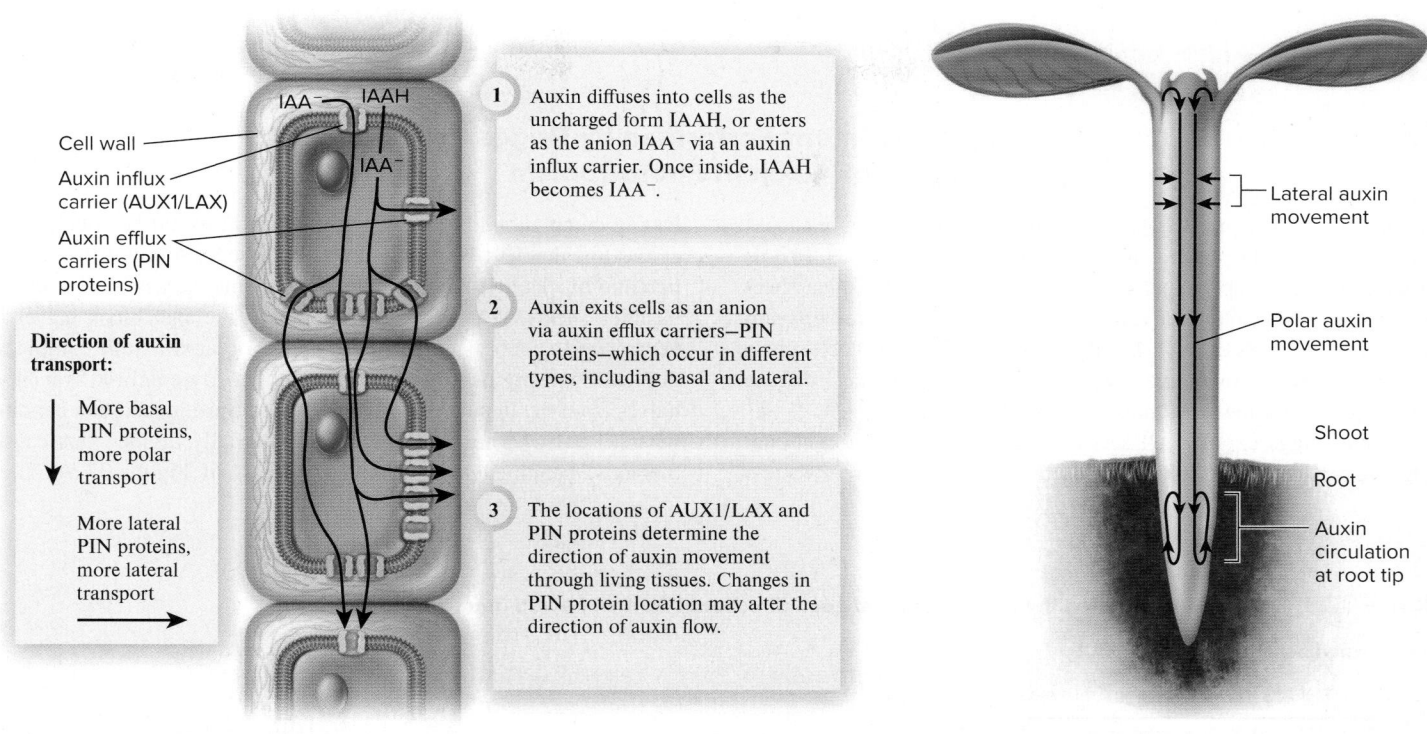

(a) **Cellular mechanism of auxin transport**

(b) **Auxin transport throughout a plant**

1. Auxin diffuses into cells as the uncharged form IAAH, or enters as the anion IAA⁻ via an auxin influx carrier. Once inside, IAAH becomes IAA⁻.

2. Auxin exits cells as an anion via auxin efflux carriers—PIN proteins—which occur in different types, including basal and lateral.

3. The locations of AUX1/LAX and PIN proteins determine the direction of auxin movement through living tissues. Changes in PIN protein location may alter the direction of auxin flow.

Figure 37.4 **Auxin transport.** **(a)** Polar and lateral auxin transport is controlled by the distribution of auxin efflux carriers located in the plasma membrane. When efflux carriers primarily occur at the basal ends of cells, auxin will flow downward. Auxin may flow laterally when auxin efflux carriers occur at the sides of cells. **(b)** In a whole plant, auxin primarily flows downward from shoot tips to root tips, where it then flows upward for a short distance.

Concept Check: *How could auxin carriers be organized to allow auxin to move upward in roots?*

Boysen-Jensen's experiment demonstrated that the phototropic substance was a diffusible chemical, but exactly which one, and how it worked, remained unknown. A series of additional experiments provided some answers.

In the 1920s, Dutch plant physiologist Frits Went named the substance discovered by Boysen-Jensen auxin (from the Greek word *auxein*, meaning to increase). Although the chemical structure of auxin was not determined until 1934, Went performed experiments that helped explain how auxin works. In a first step, Went cut the tips off oat seedlings and placed these tips onto agar blocks. Agar, a complex polysaccharide derived from red algae, forms a mesh capable of holding considerable water and dissolved compounds. Agar's permeability to auxin is similar to that of the protein gelatin used by Boysen-Jensen, but agar is much more stable at room temperature and more resistant to microbial breakdown and therefore is easier to use in laboratory experiments. In Went's experiment, the auxin diffused from cut seedling tips into these agar blocks. In the next steps, he treated decapitated seedlings in one of four ways: (1) placed auxin-laden agar blocks off-center on some, (2) placed auxin-laden blocks evenly on others, (3) placed plain agar blocks off-center on some, and (4) left some uncapped. All seedlings were then kept in the dark throughout the experiment. Only seedlings that were capped off-center with an auxin-laden block grew in the direction away from the agar block.

This experiment demonstrated that auxin application could substitute for the directional light stimulus and suggested that asymmetric auxin distribution is the mechanism by which light causes plants to bend.

Subsequently, Went and N. O. Cholodny independently proposed that light causes auxin to move to the unlit side of seedling tips, causing cells on that side to elongate more, which results in bending. But other scientists argued that bending could result if light destroys auxin on the illuminated side of a seedling. In the 1950s, American plant biologist Winslow Briggs designed two experiments to test these alternate hypotheses.

In his first experiment, which tested the hypothesis that auxin might be destroyed by light, Briggs first grew corn seedlings in the dark. Then he cut off their tips, put the tips on agar blocks, and exposed some to darkness and others to directional light. During this process, auxin from tips diffused evenly into the agar blocks. If auxin were destroyed by light, agar blocks under lighted tips should receive less auxin than blocks under tips kept in the dark. The auxin-destruction hypothesis also predicts that when agar blocks from lighted tips are placed on one side of decapitated seedlings, they should cause less bending than will blocks from tips kept in the dark. However, Briggs discovered that both types of agar blocks caused the same amount of shoot bending. This result is not consistent with the hypothesis that light destroys auxin.

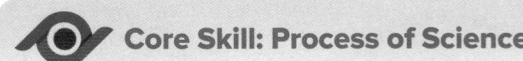

Core Skill: Process of Science

Feature Investigation | An Experiment Performed by Briggs Revealed the Role of Auxin in Phototropism

In a second experiment, Briggs tested the hypothesis that light causes auxin to move to the shaded side of seedlings (**Figure 37.5**). Briggs set shoot tips onto agar blocks (step 1) and then used a mica sheet (which is impermeable to auxin) to completely divide some tips and blocks into halves (step 2A). In other cases, he divided blocks completely but left tips incompletely divided, allowing auxin to diffuse across tips but not the block halves (step 2B).

Then Briggs exposed all sets of tips and blocks to directional light. He predicted that auxin would not be able to move across tips having complete mica barriers but that auxin would be able to move across tips that had been only partially divided. Auxin diffused from tips into blocks, but it could not diffuse evenly across blocks divided by mica sheets. When Briggs later placed the agar block halves on decapitated shoots (step 3), those receiving auxin from completely divided tips were bent by the same amount. By contrast, agar block halves from the lit side of partially divided tips induced less bending, whereas halves from the unlit side of partially divided tips caused the most bending (see the data in step 4 of Figure 37.5). These

Figure 37.5 **Briggs demonstrated the relationship between directional light and auxin function.**

Briggs experiment

HYPOTHESIS Directional light causes auxin to move to the shaded side of shoot tips.

KEY MATERIALS Corn seedlings.

	Experimental level	Conceptual level
1 Place shoot tips on agar blocks.		
2 Divide some tip/block combinations completely with a mica sheet, which prevents diffusion between the 2 halves of the tip and agar block. Divide some tip/block combinations only partially with a mica sheet. This allows auxin diffusion across the tip, but not across the agar block. Expose both to directional light.	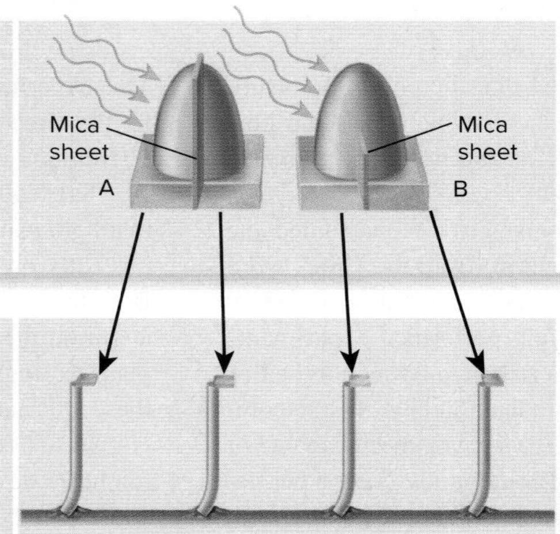 Mica sheet — A Mica sheet — B	If directional light causes auxins to move to shaded side of shoot tips, agar block in B will contain more auxin on right side.
3 Remove agar block halves from tips. Place agar halves onto right sides of shoots, which have their tips removed.		If directional light causes auxins to move laterally, the block half beneath the left side of the partially divided tip shown in B should cause the least shoot bending, whereas the block half beneath the right side of B should cause the greatest amount of bending.

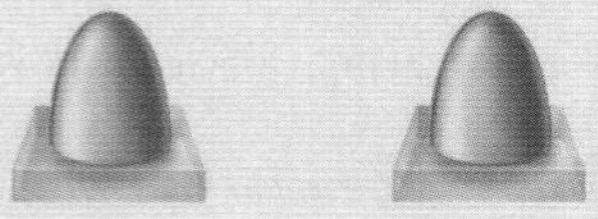

4 **THE DATA**

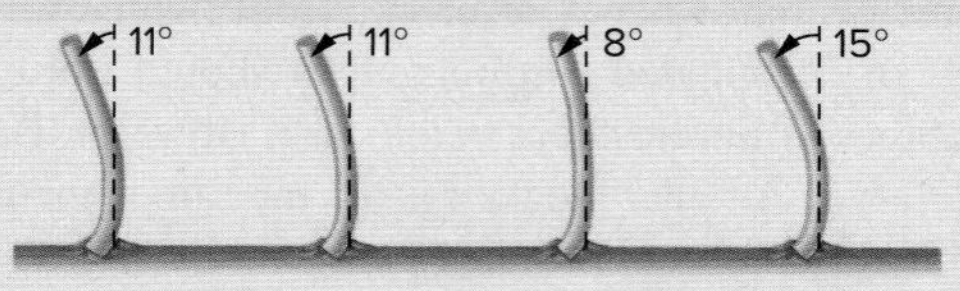

11°   11°   8°   15°

5 **CONCLUSION** In A, the mica sheets prevented auxin from moving to the shaded side of tips. In B, auxin was able to move in response to directional light. Agar block pieces from the shaded side of tips contained more auxin and therefore caused greater shoot bending. Hypothesis is correct.

6 **SOURCE** Briggs, W. R. 1963. Mediation of phototropic responses of corn coleoptiles by lateral transport of auxin. *Plant Physiology* 38(3): 237-247.

experimental results support the hypothesis that unidirectional light causes auxin to accumulate on the shaded side. Modern plant scientists would explain such auxin movement as the result of lateral transport involving PIN proteins.

How might auxin accumulation cause phototropic bending? One widely held hypothesis is that auxin accumulation on the shaded side of a plant shoot causes plasma membrane proton pumps located there to work at a faster rate. In response, the cell wall becomes more acidic, which activates expansins—proteins that break crosslinks between cellulose microfibrils and allow cells to elongate (refer back to Figure 36.10). This process might explain how auxin accumulation in cells located on the shaded side of shoot tips causes them to elongate more than do cells on the sunny side, causing the tip to bend toward the light.

Experimental Questions

1. What is the current hypothesized mechanism by which auxin accumulation causes shoot bending in response to directional light?

2. **CoreSKILL »** Figure 37.5 illustrates experiments performed with four seedling tips. Would this number really be enough to allow conclusions to be made about how such seedling tips would generally respond?

BIO TIPS

THE QUESTION *Show how Briggs tested the auxin-destruction hypothesis: that coleoptile bending in response to directional light occurs because light destroys auxin.*

T OPIC *What topic in biology does this question address?* The topic is how plants sense and respond to directional light. More specifically, the question asks you to show the procedure Briggs used to investigate the possibility that bending toward the light occurs because light destroys auxin.

I NFORMATION *What information do you know based on the question and your understanding of the topic?* You learned earlier in this chapter that phototropism in plants is initiated by directional light and followed by a growth response of stem tissue to an internal chemical signal. The signal was discovered to be the asymmetric distribution of the plant hormone auxin. The first experiment of Briggs is described in the paragraph that precedes the Feature Investigation. However, Briggs' first experiment is not illustrated.

P ROBLEM-SOLVING S TRATEGY *Make a drawing.* Creating a diagram is an excellent way to achieve understanding and communicate that understanding to others. Use the text description of Briggs's experiment to make diagrams that show how he conducted his first experiment.

ANSWER *Start by drawing two cut coleoptile tips placed onto agar blocks. Add arrows on one of the drawings that indicate how auxin is expected to flow into the agar block if the coleoptile tip is evenly illuminated. Add arrows to the other drawing to indicate how auxin is expected to flow into the agar block if directional light destroys auxin. These contrasting drawings illustrate the beginning hypothesis. Now draw diagrams that show how coleoptiles whose tips have been removed respond when agar blocks are placed on one side of them. This is the experimental test. Finally, draw these coleoptiles after they have responded by bending, which is the experimental result. Lack of a difference in bending of the experimental coleoptiles is evidence that directional light does not cause phototropism by destroying auxin.*

Cytokinins Stimulate Cell Division

Like auxins, the plant hormones known as **cytokinins** play varied and important roles throughout the lives of plants. The name of these hormones reflects their major effect—an increase in the rate of plant cytokinesis, or cell division. Root tips are major sites of cytokinin production, but shoots and seeds also make this plant hormone. Transported in the xylem to meristems and other plant parts, cytokinins bind to receptors thought to be located in the plasma membrane. At shoot and root tips, cytokinins influence meristem size, stem cell activity, and vascular tissue development. Cytokinins are also involved in root and shoot growth and branching, the production of flowers and seeds, and leaf aging.

Plant Tissue Culture In the laboratory, cytokinin and auxin are essential to cloning plants. Cloning involves a process, known as **plant tissue culture**, which is used commercially to produce thousands of identical plants having the same desirable characteristics.

- Plant tissue culture begins with pieces of stem, leaf, or root that have been removed from a plant, and have had their surfaces sterilized to prevent growth of microbes (**Figure 37.6**, step 1).

- The cleaned plant pieces are then placed into dishes containing nutrients (minerals, vitamins, and sugar) and various proportions of auxin and cytokinin. If the proportions of auxin and cytokinin are about the same (1:1), plant cells undergo division, forming a mass of white tissue known as a callus (step 2).

- If the callus is then transferred to a new dish containing the same nutrients, with auxin-to-cytokinin proportions greater than 10:1, the callus will form roots (step 3).

- After root formation has occurred, the proportion of auxin-to-cytokinin can be changed to less than 10:1. This causes the callus to develop green shoots (step 4).

- By altering the ratios of auxin and cytokinin, entire plants can be regenerated from a callus. A single callus can be divided into many pieces and each piece treated with these hormones, thereby producing many hundreds of identical new plants.

Gibberellins Stimulate Cell Division and Elongation

The **gibberellins** (such as gibberellic acid, or GA; see Table 37.1) are another group of plant hormones. Gibberellins are produced

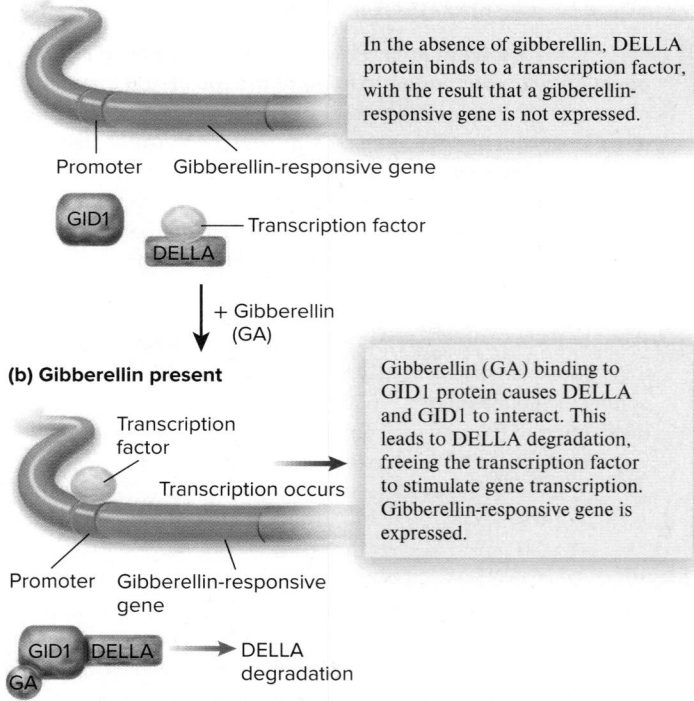

① A block of tissue is removed from a plant, and the surfaces are sterilized.

② Tissue is cultivated in dishes on nutrient media. Treatment with equal proportions of auxin and cytokinin causes formation of an undifferentiated callus.

③ Treatment with auxin-to-cytokinin ratios greater than 10:1 causes root development on many replicate plantlets.

④ Treatment with auxin-to-cytokinin ratios less than 10:1 induces shoot development on many replicate plantlets.

Plant tissue   Callus

1 : 1 auxin : cytokinin   >10 : 1 auxin : cytokinin   <10 : 1 auxin : cytokinin

Figure 37.6 The process of plant tissue culture. Plant tissue culture illustrates the effect of different proportions of auxin and cytokinin on plant organ development.

Concept Check: *How do commercial growers use plant tissue culture to produce many identical plants?*

in apical buds, roots, young leaves, and seed embryos. In addition to promoting shoot development on laboratory calluses, gibberellins interact with light and other hormones to foster seed germination and enhance stem elongation and flowering in nature. Gibberellins also retard leaf and fruit aging. These multiple effects largely arise from the hormones' stimulatory effects on cell division and elongation.

More than a hundred different forms of gibberellin have been found. Many kinds of dwarf plants are short because they produce less gibberellin than taller varieties of the same species. The dwarf strain of pea plants Mendel used in some of his breeding experiments is an example. When dwarf varieties of plants are experimentally sprayed with gibberellin, their stems grow to normal heights. However, dwarf wheat and rice crops are valued in agriculture because they can be more productive and less vulnerable to storm damage than taller varieties. Since the discovery of gibberellin, plant scientists have discovered how this plant hormone works at the molecular level and how gibberellin regulation of plant growth evolved, discussed next.

Core Concept: Evolution

Gibberellin Function Arose in a Series of Stages During Plant Evolution

In flowering plants, gibberellin works by helping to liberate repressed transcription factors. In the absence of gibberellin, certain proteins (known as DELLA proteins) bind to particular transcription factor proteins needed for the expression of gibberellin-responsive genes (**Figure 37.7a**). In this way,

(a) Gibberellin absent

In the absence of gibberellin, DELLA protein binds to a transcription factor, with the result that a gibberellin-responsive gene is not expressed.

Promoter   Gibberellin-responsive gene

GID1   — Transcription factor

DELLA

+ Gibberellin (GA)

(b) Gibberellin present

Transcription factor

Gibberellin (GA) binding to GID1 protein causes DELLA and GID1 to interact. This leads to DELLA degradation, freeing the transcription factor to stimulate gene transcription. Gibberellin-responsive gene is expressed.

Transcription occurs

Promoter   Gibberellin-responsive gene

GID1 DELLA   DELLA degradation
GA

Figure 37.7 Gibberellin works by releasing trapped transcription factors. (a) In the absence of gibberellin, DELLA binds transcription factors, and so gibberellin-responsive genes are not expressed. **(b)** When gibberellin binds to the protein GID1, GID1 can bind DELLA proteins, which causes DELLA proteins to be degraded. As a result, transcription factors that had been bound to DELLA proteins are released and can bind to gene promoters, thereby inducing gene expression.

DELLAs function as brakes that restrain cell division and expansion. When sufficient gibberellin is present, it releases the brakes by binding to a protein known as GID1 (**Figure 37.7b**). Gibberellin binding to GID1 causes DELLAs to release transcription factor proteins and fosters the destruction of DELLAs. In the absence of DELLA proteins, transcription factor proteins are able to bind to the promoter regions of gibberellin-responsive genes, allowing their expression. As a result, cell division and expansion occur, leading to growth.

In 2007, Yuki Yasumura, Nicholas Harberd, and their colleagues reported that the components of the gibberellin-DELLA mechanisms in flowering plants arose from features present in more ancient lycophyte and bryophyte lineages. Modern bryophytes and lycophytes possess GID1 as well as DELLA and the transcription factor proteins it binds, but these substances do not affect plant growth. This observation suggests that DELLA-mediated repression of plant growth evolved after the divergence of lycophytes but prior to the appearance of the first gymnosperms and flowering plants (**Figure 37.8**). Though the necessary components (DELLAs and GID1 proteins) were present earlier, only later did they assemble into a growth regulation system.

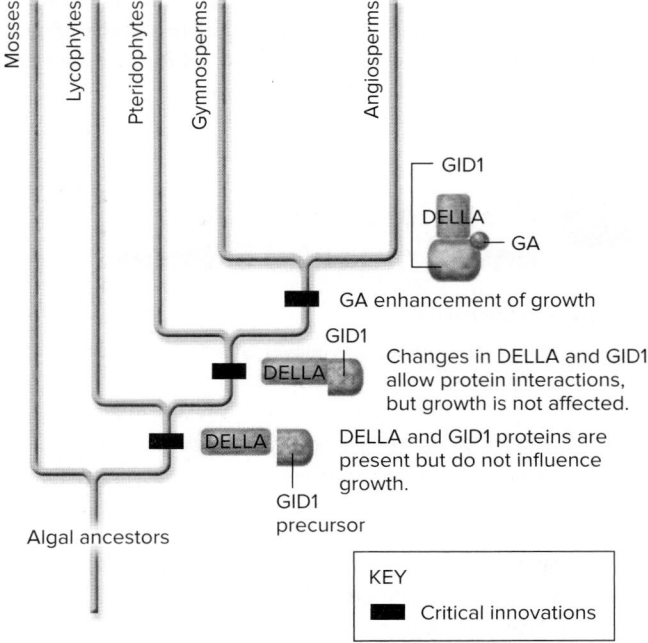

Figure 37.8 Evolution of the gibberellin-DELLA system. Although DELLA and GID1 proteins are present in a moss, they do not interact, nor does gibberellin bind to GID1. In lycophytes, GID1 interacts with DELLA, but the system does not influence growth. The growth-enhancing responses of gibberellin apparently evolved after the divergence of lycophytes.

Ethylene's Effects Include Cell Expansion

The plant hormone **ethylene** is particularly important in coordinating plant developmental and stress responses. Ethylene is a simple hydrocarbon gas produced during seedling growth, flower development, and fruit ripening (see Table 37.1). In the root tip, ethylene determines how many stem cells remain inactive in the quiescent center and how many cells undergo divisions. This hormone also plays important roles in defense against osmotic stress and pathogen attack, and leaf and petal aging and drop. As a gas, ethylene is able to diffuse through the plasma membrane and cytosol to bind to ethylene receptors localized in the endoplasmic reticulum. When activated by ethylene binding, these receptors inactivate a protein kinase known as CTR1. This action ultimately enables transcription factors to induce the transcription of various genes.

People first noticed the effects of ethylene gas on plants in the 1800s when they observed that street-side trees exposed to leaking street lanterns unexpectedly lost their leaves. A 17-year-old student in St. Petersburg, Russia, Dimitry Neljubov, performed the first experiments to explore the effects of illumination gas on plants. He exposed pea seedlings grown in the laboratory to illumination gas and noticed that the pea seedlings grew sideways rather than upward. Then he tested the individual chemical components of illumination gas for the same effect. After conducting many experiments, in 1901, Neljubov reported that ethylene was the only component of illumination gas that caused the seedlings to grow horizontally and that ethylene was effective in very low concentrations (as low as 0.06 parts per million in air). Later, scientists established that ethylene influences cell expansion, often in association with auxin. Ethylene does this by increasing the disorder of microtubules within cells, thereby causing random orientation of cell-wall microfibrils. As a result, cells exposed to ethylene tend to expand in all directions rather than elongating.

To understand how ethylene affects cell growth, researchers have exposed growing seedlings to varying concentrations of ethylene in the dark. (**Figure 37.9**). At low concentrations, ethylene prevents the seedling stem and root from elongating. At moderate concentrations, the hormone induces the stem and root to swell radially, thereby increasing in thickness. Together, these responses strengthen the seedling stem and root. At even higher concentrations, the seedling stem bends so that embryonic leaves and the delicate meristem grow horizontally rather than vertically; this is the sideways growth response that Neljubov first observed. Taken together, the three effects of ethylene on seedling growth is called the triple response.

What is the biological significance of the triple response? These experimental results provide insight regarding the growth of seedlings while they are still within the soil. The tender apical meristems of seedlings could be easily damaged during their growth through crusty soil. Ethylene helps seedlings avoid damage by thickening the stem and root. The bent portion of the stem, known as a hook, then pushes up through the soil. The hook forms as the result of an imbalance of auxin across the stem axis, which causes cells on one side of the stem to elongate faster than cells on the other side. Ethylene drives this auxin imbalance.

Knowledge of the effects of ethylene on fruit has been very useful commercially. Ripe fruit can be easily damaged during transit,

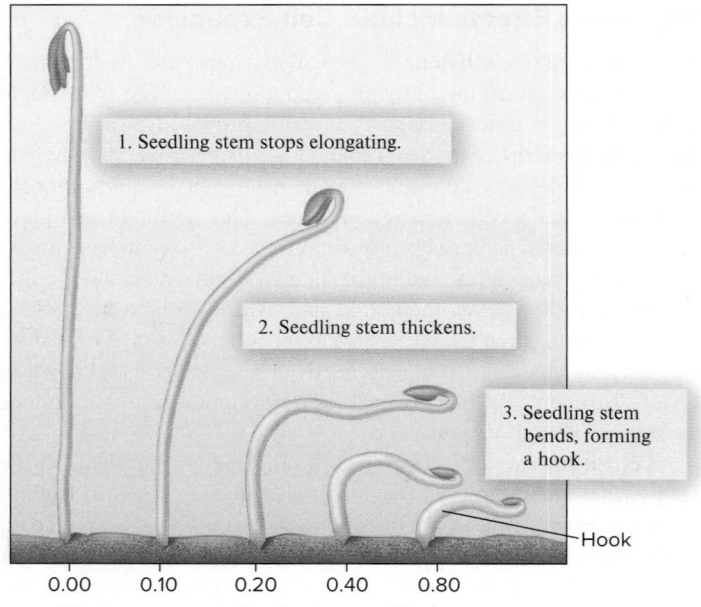

1. Seedling stem stops elongating.

2. Seedling stem thickens.

3. Seedling stem bends, forming a hook.

Hook

0.00   0.10   0.20   0.40   0.80
Ethylene concentration (parts per million)

Figure 37.9 **Seedling growth showing the triple response to ethylene.** Ethylene applications at increasing concentrations cause seedlings to cease elongation, swell radially, and bend to form a hook that can push upward through the soil. Ethylene produced naturally within seedlings causes the same response.

Concept Check: *What adaptive advantage does this seedling behavior provide?*

but tomatoes and apples can be picked before they ripen for transport with minimal damage. At their destination, such fruit can be ripened by treatment with ethylene. However, fruit that becomes overripe may exude ethylene, which hastens ripening in nearby, unripe fruit. For this reason, fruit that must be stored for extended periods is kept in ethylene-free environments.

Several Hormones Help Plants Cope with Environmental Stresses

Several plant hormones share the property of helping plants respond to environmental stresses such as flooding, drought, high salinity, cold, heat, and attack by disease-causing microorganisms and animal herbivores. These protective hormones include the major plant hormones known as **abscisic acid** and **brassinosteroids** (see Table 37.1).

Abscisic Acid Abscisic acid (ABA) was named at a time when plant biologists thought that it played a role in leaf or fruit drop, also known as abscission. Later, they discovered that ethylene actually causes leaf and fruit abscission, whereas abscisic acid slows or stops plant metabolism when growing conditions are poor.

ABA has a variety of effects on plant growth and function. For example, ABA may induce bud and seed dormancy. Dormant buds and seeds resume growth only when specific environmental signals reveal the onset of conditions suitable for survival. In preparation

for winter, ABA stimulates the formation of tough, protective scales around the buds of perennial plants. Seed coats of apple, cherry, and other plants also accumulate ABA, which prevents seeds from germinating unless temperature and moisture conditions are favorable for seedling growth. Water-stressed roots also produce ABA, which is then transported to shoots, where (together with ABA produced by water-stressed leaf mesophyll) it helps to prevent water loss from leaf surfaces by inducing leaf pores (stomata) to close.

To exert its effects, ABA binds to ABA receptors, which are soluble proteins in the cytoplasm. The binding of ABA to its receptors promotes the transcription of ABA-responsive genes, thereby leading to a cellular response.

Brassinosteroids Brassinosteroids are named after the cruciferous plant genus *Brassica* (which includes cabbage and broccoli), in which they were first identified. However, seeds, fruit, shoots, leaves, and flower buds of all types of flowering plants contain brassinosteroids. These plant hormones induce water uptake by vacuoles and influence enzymes that alter cell-wall carbohydrates, thereby fostering cell expansion. Mutations that affect brassinosteroid synthesis cause plants to exhibit dwarfism. Such plants have small, dark green cells because their tissues are unable to expand. Brassinosteroids also impede leaf drop, help grass leaves to unroll, and stimulate xylem development. They can be applied to crops to help protect plants from heat, cold, high salinity, and herbicide injury.

Brassinosteroids are chemically related to animal steroid hormones, such as human sex hormones. However, unlike animal steroid hormones, which bind to receptors in the nucleus or cytosol, brassinosteroids bind to receptors in the plasma membrane. When they bind brassinosteroids, the membrane receptors initiate a signal transduction pathway that activates transcription factors for brassinosteroid-responsive genes.

37.3 Plant Responses to Environmental Stimuli

Learning Outcomes:

1. Describe how photoreceptors allow plants to respond to light, including day length.
2. Describe how plant roots respond to gravity and touch.
3. Give examples of how plants respond to flood and drought.
4. Outline how plants protect themselves against herbivore and pathogen attacks.

Plants encounter many types of environmental challenges and behave accordingly. For example, if buried seeds were to germinate beneath soil layers too deep for light to penetrate, or beneath a cover of established plants, seedlings would not be able to obtain sufficient light for photosynthesis and would die. A related reproductive challenge for plants is to flower at times of the year that are most beneficial for achieving pollination or seed dispersal. In this section, we will examine how plants determine if there is enough light for seeds to germinate and for seedlings to grow and how they determine when to flower.

Plants Detect Light via Photoreceptors

Many activities in plants, such as photosynthesis and flowering, require the proper amount of light and must occur during the correct time of year. To sense the amount and direction of light, plants produce light sensors known as **photoreceptors**, of which there are several types. Some types of plant photoreceptors also occur in animals, whereas others are particular to plants. Each type of photoreceptor has a light-absorbing component as well as other regions that respond to light absorption by switching on signal transduction pathways. Responses by many cells in a tissue or organ cumulatively result in behaviors such as sun tracking, phototropism, flowering, and seed germination.

Blue-Light Receptors   Cryptochrome and phototropin are two types of blue-light receptors—molecules that absorb and respond to blue light. Experiments suggest that **cryptochrome** helps young seedlings determine if their environment has enough light for adequate photosynthesis. If not, seedlings continue to elongate through the soil, toward the light. Cryptochromes also function as light sensors in animals.

Phototropin is a blue-light sensor so named because one of its roles is to promote positive phototropism, the tendency of a plant to grow toward a light source. The light-activated form of this sensor has two components: a protein that has a kinase domain and a flavin pigment that can absorb blue light.

As you may recall from Chapter 9, a protein kinase domain catalyzes the attachment of phosphate to proteins. In the dark, flavin is not covalently bound to the phototropin protein and its kinase domain is inactive. However, when flavin absorbs blue light, it changes conformation and covalently binds to the protein. Flavin binding, in turn, changes the conformation of the phototropin protein, allowing it to phosphorylate itself by means of the protein kinase domain. Therefore, when a plant is exposed to directional blue light, phototropin becomes phosphorylated. Though the steps are not entirely understood, phosphorylation is thought to initiate a series of events that alters the distribution of auxin and thereby causes the plant to grow toward the light. In this way, a light signal is converted into a chemical signal that influences plant growth.

Phytochrome, the Red-Light and Far-Red-Light Receptor
Many plant growth and developmental processes are influenced by **phytochrome**, a red-light and far-red-light receptor. Phytochrome operates much like a light switch, flipping back and forth between two conformations: P_r absorbs red light, and P_{fr} absorbs only far-red light (light having a wavelength longer than that of red light) (**Figure 37.10**). When red light is abundant, as in full sunlight, P_r absorbs red light and changes to P_{fr}, which activates cellular responses such as seed germination. When left in the dark for a long period, P_{fr} slowly transforms into P_r.

The role of phytochrome as a plant "light switch" has been shown experimentally in studies of lettuce-seed germination. Researchers have found that water-soaked lettuce seeds will not germinate in darkness, but they will germinate if exposed to as little as 1 minute of red light (**Figure 37.11**). This amount of light exposure is sufficient to transform a critical amount of P_r to the active P_{fr} conformation, which stimulates germination. However, if this brief red-light treatment is followed by a few minutes of treatment with far-red light, the lettuce seeds will not germinate. This short period of far-red illumination is enough to convert seed P_{fr} back to the inactive P_r conformation.

The most recent light exposure determines whether the phytochrome occurs in the active or inactive conformation. In nature, if seeds are close enough to the surface that their phytochrome is switched on by red light, the seeds will germinate. But if seeds are buried too deeply for red light to penetrate, they will not germinate. In this way, seeds can sense if they are close enough to the surface to begin the germination process.

In the dark, phytochrome molecules in the P_r state reside in the cytosol. After exposure to red light, activated phytochrome (P_{fr})

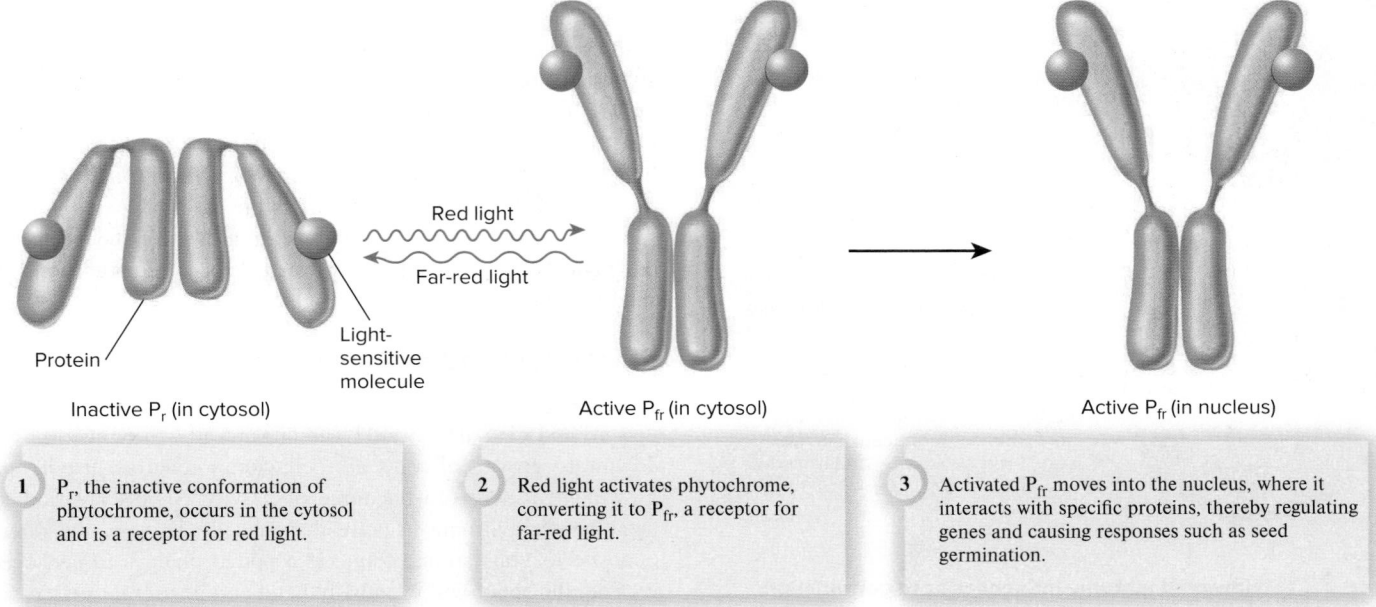

Protein

Light-sensitive molecule

Inactive P_r (in cytosol)

Red light

Far-red light

Active P_{fr} (in cytosol)

Active P_{fr} (in nucleus)

1 P_r, the inactive conformation of phytochrome, occurs in the cytosol and is a receptor for red light.

2 Red light activates phytochrome, converting it to P_{fr}, a receptor for far-red light.

3 Activated P_{fr} moves into the nucleus, where it interacts with specific proteins, thereby regulating genes and causing responses such as seed germination.

Figure 37.10 How phytochrome acts as a molecular light switch.

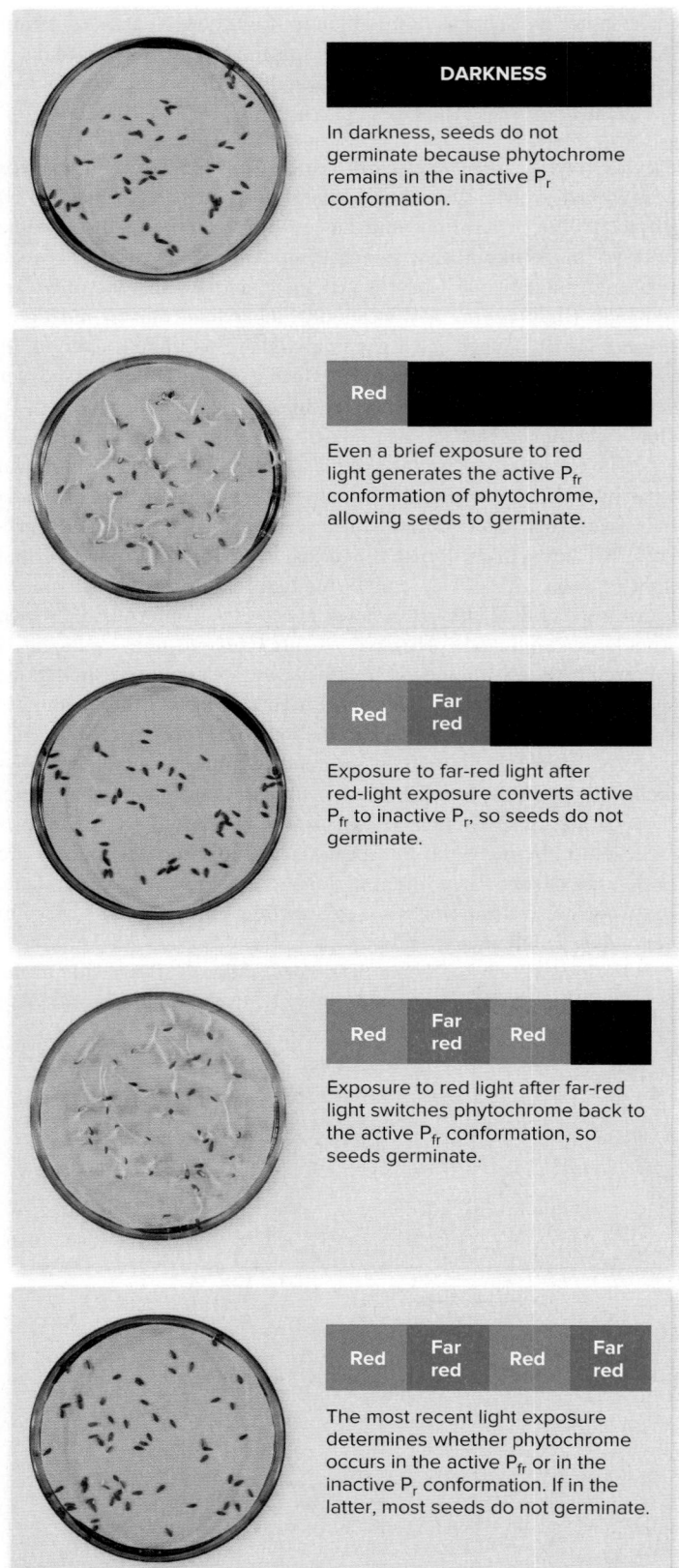

DARKNESS

In darkness, seeds do not germinate because phytochrome remains in the inactive P_r conformation.

Red

Even a brief exposure to red light generates the active P_{fr} conformation of phytochrome, allowing seeds to germinate.

Red | Far red

Exposure to far-red light after red-light exposure converts active P_{fr} to inactive P_r, so seeds do not germinate.

Red | Far red | Red

Exposure to red light after far-red light switches phytochrome back to the active P_{fr} conformation, so seeds germinate.

Red | Far red | Red | Far red

The most recent light exposure determines whether phytochrome occurs in the active P_{fr} or in the inactive P_r conformation. If in the latter, most seeds do not germinate.

Figure 37.11 How phytochrome influences seed germination.

Concept Check: *Describe the change in phytochrome that would occur if a deeply buried seed were uncovered enough to receive sunlight.*

molecules move from the cytosol to the nucleus. Within the nucleus, P_{fr} interacts with a transcription factor protein known as PIF3 (phytochrome-interacting factor 3). PIF3 binds to the regulatory elements of several phytochrome-responsive genes, functioning as a positive regulator of some of the genes and as a negative regulator of others.

Photoperiodism A plant's ability to measure and respond to the amount of light and day length is a process called **photoperiodism**, which influences the timing of dormancy and flowering. Phytochromes also play a critical role in photoperiodism. Flowering plants can be classified as long-day, short-day, or day-neutral plants. When scientists named these groups, they thought that plants measured the amount of daylight. Researchers later discovered that plants actually measure night length.

Lettuce, spinach, radish, beet, clover, gladiolus, and iris are examples of **long-day plants** because they flower in spring or early summer, when the night period is shorter (and thus the day length is longer) than a defined length (**Figure 37.12**). In contrast, asters, strawberries, dahlias, poinsettias, potatoes, soybeans, and goldenrods are examples of **short-day plants** because they flower only when the night length is longer than a defined period. Such night lengths occur in late summer, fall, or winter, when days are short. As shown in Figure 37.12, when plants are given an experimental light flash in the middle of a long dark period, the long-day plants flower but the short-day plants do not. These results indicate that both types of plants measure night length. Roses, snapdragons, cotton, carnations, dandelions, sunflowers, tomatoes, and cucumbers flower regardless of the night length, as long as day length meets the minimal requirements for plant growth, and are thus known as **day-neutral plants**.

Ornamental plant growers manipulate night length to produce flowers for market during seasons when they are not naturally available. For example, chrysanthemums are short-day plants that usually flower in the fall, but growers use light-blocking shades to increase night length in order to produce flowering plants at any season.

Shading Responses Phytochrome also mediates plant responses to shading. These responses include the extension of leaves from shady portions of a dense tree canopy into the light, and growth that allows plants to avoid being shaded by neighboring plants. These growth responses occur by the elongation of branch internodes. Leaves detect shade as an increased proportion of far-red light to red light. This means that more of the phytochrome in shaded leaves is in the inactive (P_r) conformation than is the case for leaves in the sun. Activated phytochrome (P_{fr}) inhibits the growth of shoot internodes, but phytochrome in the inactivated state does not, so branches bearing shaded leaves extend toward sunlight.

Plants Respond to Gravity and Touch

Have you ever wondered what causes plant stems to generally grow upward and roots downward? The upward growth of shoots and the downward growth of roots are behaviors known as **gravitropism**, growth in response to the force of gravity. Shoots are said to be negatively gravitropic because they usually grow in the direction opposite to gravitational force. If a potted plant is turned over on its side, the shoot will eventually bend and begin to grow vertically again (**Figure 37.13**). Most roots are said to be positively gravitropic because they grow in the same direction as the gravitational force.

Figure 37.12 Flowering and photoperiodism. Iris is a long-day plant that flowers in response to the short nights of late spring and early summer, whereas goldenrod is a short-day plant that flowers in response to the longer nights of autumn. The length of night is the critical factor, as shown by the effects of light flashes. (top left, bottom left): ©Ray Bulson/Newscom; (top right, bottom right): ©Lee W. Wilcox; (middle left): ©Garden Picture Library/Getty Images; (middle right): ©Comstock Images/Getty Images

Concept Check: *What would happen if you gave flowering plants a brief exposure to darkness in the middle of the daytime?*

Figure 37.13 Negative gravitropism in a shoot. This tomato shoot system has resumed upward growth after being placed on its side. Upward growth started about 4 hours after the plant was turned sideways; this photo was taken 20 hours later. Shoots sense gravity by means of starch-heavy statoliths present in stem tissue near the central vascular tissue. ©Lee W. Wilcox

Both roots and shoots detect gravity by means of starch-heavy plastids known as **statoliths**, which are located in specialized gravity-sensing cells called statocytes. In shoots, statocytes are located in a tissue known as the endodermis, which forms a sheath around vascular tissues. In roots, gravity-sensing cells primarily occur in the center of the root cap (**Figure 37.14**).

Gravity causes the relatively heavy statoliths to sink, which affects the levels of calcium ion second messengers that influence the direction of auxin transport. When roots are vertical, auxin moves upward equally on both sides and the root continues to elongate in the downward direction. However, a change in the direction of root growth will alter the relative position of the statoliths. For example, in a root that becomes oriented horizontally, the statoliths are pulled by gravity to the lower sides of statocytes (see right side of Figure 37.14). The change in statolith position causes more auxin to move to cells on the lower sides of roots. In roots, auxin inhibits cell elongation (in contrast to its action in shoots). Therefore, root growth slows on the lower side, while cell elongation continues normally on the upper side. This process causes the root to bend, so that it eventually grows downward again.

Recent studies suggest that gravity responses are related to touch responses, known as **thigmotropism** (from the Greek *thigma*, meaning touch). For example, when roots encounter rocks or other barriers to their downward growth in the soil, they display a touch response that temporarily supersedes their response to gravity. Such roots grow horizontally until they get around the barrier, whereupon downward growth in response to gravity resumes. Plant shoots also respond to touch; examples include vines with tendrils that wind around or clasp supporting structures. Wind also induces touch responses. In very

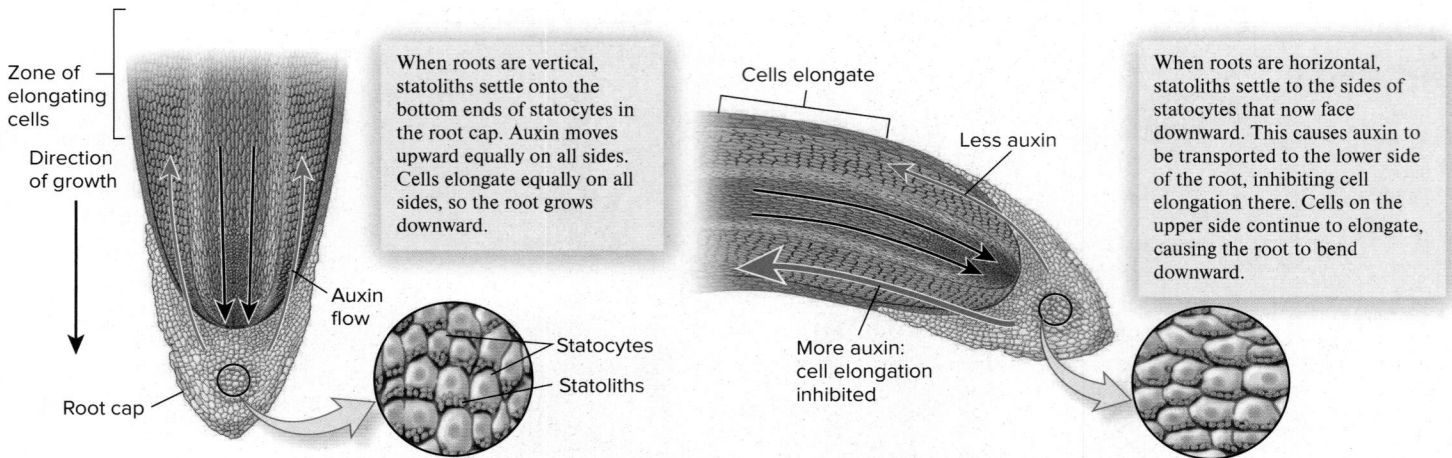

Figure 37.14 **Positive gravitropism in a root.** Root-tip cells sense gravity by means of starch-heavy statoliths present in cells at the center of the root cap.

Concept Check: *Is there any other environmental signal that roots could use to achieve downward growth?*

windy places, trees tend to be shorter than normal, giving them the advantage of being less likely to be blown over than taller trees. In the laboratory, plant scientists have simulated natural touch responses by rubbing plant stems and found that this treatment can result in shorter plants. Touch causes the release of calcium ion second messengers that influence gene expression.

More rapid responses to touch, such as leaf folding by the sensitive plant (see Figure 37.1b), are based on changes in the water content of cells within a structure known as a pulvinus (plural, pulvini), a swelling located at the base of attachment of each pair of leaflets in

complex leaves. A pulvinus consists of a thick layer of parenchyma cells that surrounds a core of vascular tissue (**Figure 37.15**). When the leaflet of a sensitive plant is touched, an electrical signal called an action potential opens ion channels in parenchyma cells near the lower surfaces of the pulvini. These cells expel potassium and chloride ions, causing water to flow out and the cells to become flattened. This bends the leaflets together, starting the leaflet-folding process. The action potential generated at the touch site also flows through the leaflet, causing many or all of the leaflets to also bend, with the result that the entire leaf folds. Reversal of this process allows the leaf to unfold.

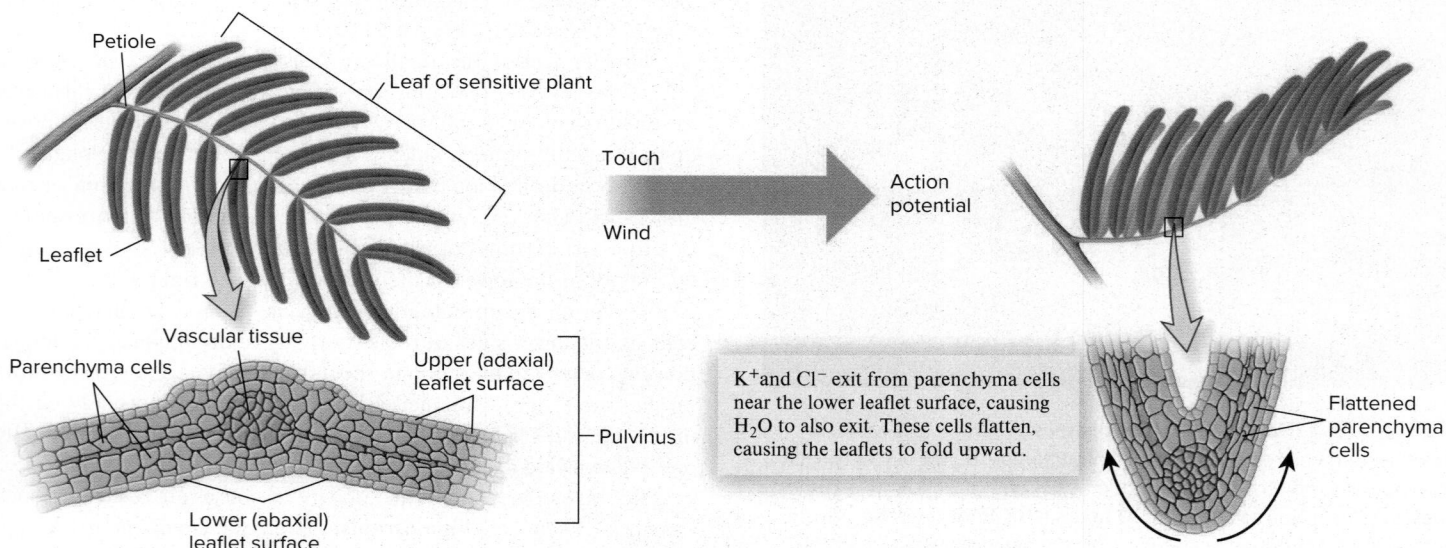

Figure 37.15 **Leaf folding in the sensitive plant: How pulvini change the positions of leaflets.** The electrical signals known as action potentials result from the rapid flow of ions through membrane ion channels. Electrical signals spread from one cell to another through plasmodesmata. Cells near the lower surface of the pulvinus respond to ion flow by losing water, causing them to flatten.

 Core Skill: Connections Action potentials are also key to the function of the nervous systems of animals (see Chapter 42).

The action of pulvini also explains some plant movements that are unrelated to touch, including sleep movements and sun tracking. Sleep movements are changes in leaf position that occur in response to day-night cycles. Sun tracking, as described at the beginning of this chapter, is the movement of leaves or flowers in response to the Sun's position.

Plants Respond to Physical Stresses Such as Flooding and Drought

Plants display many types of adaptations that help them cope with unfavorable growth conditions, such as flooding and drought. These responses are often mediated by hormones.

In most plants, roots get oxygen from air that is located in the spaces between soil particles. The major harmful effect of flooding is that too much water makes roots unable to obtain sufficient oxygen to fuel cellular respiration. Without oxygen from the air, roots cannot produce the ATP needed to absorb minerals from soil.

Many plants reduce the effects of flooding by producing **aerenchyma**, a tissue containing large, snorkel-like air channels that allow more oxygen to flow from shoots to the submerged roots (**Figure 37.16**). In some plants, aerenchyma formation is developmentally programmed. For example, aerenchyma develops in the roots of many plants native to wetland habitats even when the soil is not wet. Alternatively, aerenchyma formation may be a response to a change in environmental conditions. The roots of cultivated plants, such as corn, develop aerenchyma in response to flooding. Aerenchyma formation is regulated by the action of ethylene, which leads to programmed cell death, followed by cell collapse.

During a drought, plants are likely to receive too little water. The amount of water content in a plant is also affected by other

Vascular tissue   Air channels   Aerenchyma   Epidermis

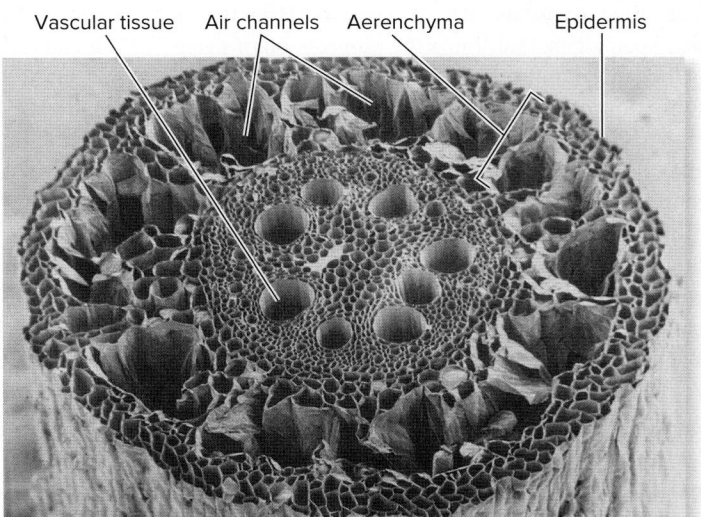

Figure 37.16 A plant response to flooding. This image of a slice of a root shows air channels within aerenchyma. Courtesy Dr. Malcolm Drew, Texas A&M University

 Core Concept: Structure and Function Air channels within aerenchyma allow air to flow from shoots to roots even when the plant is partially submerged.

environmental stresses—high salinity, heat, and cold—that reduce the amount of liquid water present in plant cells. Most plants that lose half or more of their water are unable to recover. To prevent this from happening, plants have acquired diverse adaptations that reduce water loss, such as the closure of stomata and, in extreme cases, wilting. The hormone abscisic acid triggers these responses.

Plants Respond to Biological Stresses Such as Herbivore and Pathogen Attacks

Plants are vulnerable to attack by animal herbivores and pathogens—disease-causing microorganisms. Structural features such as cuticles, epidermal trichomes, and outer bark, described in Chapter 36, help to reduce infections and herbivore attacks. These structures, together with chemical defense compounds, explain why remarkably little natural vegetation is lost to herbivore or pathogen attack. However, agricultural crops can be more vulnerable to attack than their wild counterparts. This increased vulnerability arose because some protective adaptations were lost during crop domestication as the result of genetic changes that increase edibility. For this reason, crop scientists are particularly interested in understanding plant defense, with the goal of being able to breed or genetically engineer crop plants that are better protected from pests.

Plant Responses to Herbivores   Plants produce diverse herbivore-defense compounds including secondary metabolites—terpenes and terpenoids, phenolics, and alkaloids (refer back to Figure 32.22)—and also poisonous hydrogen cyanide and other molecules. Some of these substances act directly on herbivores, making plants taste bad so that herbivores learn to avoid them. Other chemical compounds function indirectly. For example, when attacked by insect caterpillars, cruciferous plants release terpenoids that attract the bodyguard wasp (*Cotesia rubecula*), which attacks the caterpillars.

Some wounded plants can communicate with nearby plants, helping them to resist attack by herbivores (**Figure 37.17**). For example, when cutworms wound tomato plants, damaged cells release a volatile alcohol, hexenol. Nearby plants convert the hexenol into a compound that reduces the cutworms' ability to attack them.

Plants can also receive signals warning of herbivore attack from other plants by means of connecting parasitic plants. Non-photosynthetic dodders (*Cuscuta* species) (see Figure 38.20) form natural grafts to the stems of photosynthetic host plants, sometimes connecting many host plants of the same or different species. These parasite grafts allow the transmission of metabolites, proteins, mRNAs, and warning compounds from plants that have suffered herbivore attack to plants that have not yet been attacked, allowing the latter to take preemptive defensive action.

Plant Responses to Pathogen Attack   Every year, about 15% of crop production is lost to diseases caused by certain bacteria, fungi, protists, or viruses. During their evolution, plants have evolved mechanisms for detecting and responding to such microbes, but microbes can rapidly evolve new disease processes. Agricultural scientists aim to understand how pathogenic microbes attack plants and how plants are able to prevent disease, in order to develop disease-resistant crop varieties.

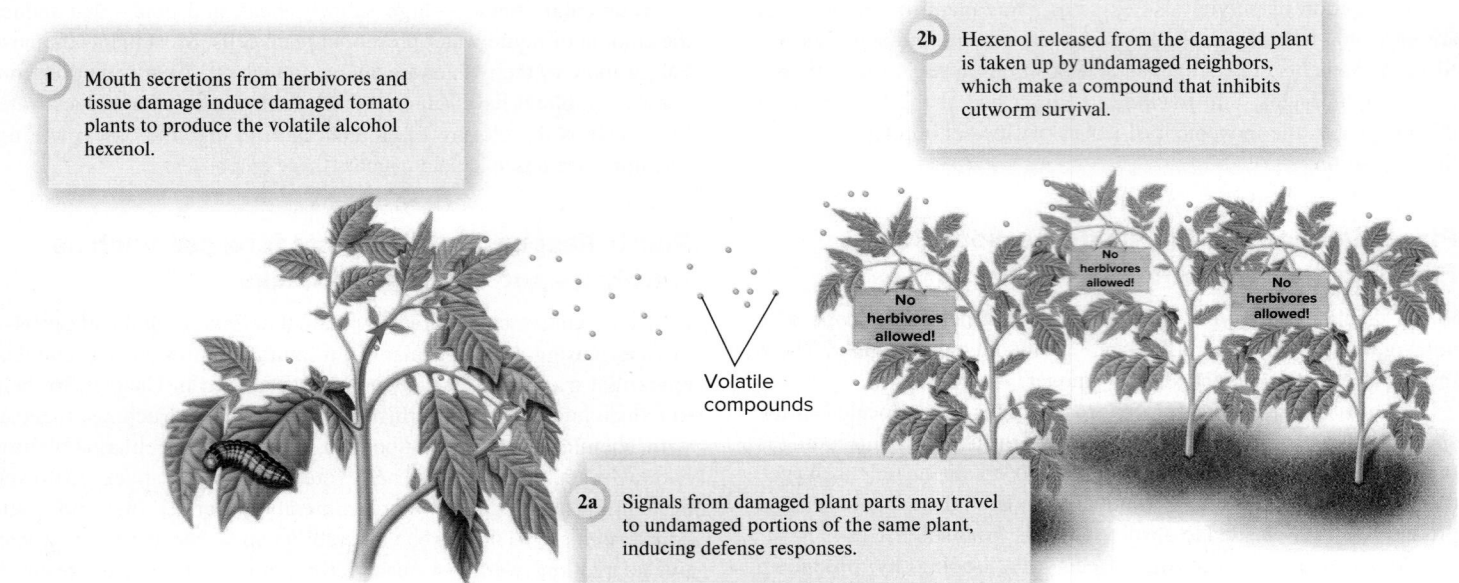

1 Mouth secretions from herbivores and tissue damage induce damaged tomato plants to produce the volatile alcohol hexenol.

2b Hexenol released from the damaged plant is taken up by undamaged neighbors, which make a compound that inhibits cutworm survival.

Volatile compounds

No herbivores allowed!

2a Signals from damaged plant parts may travel to undamaged portions of the same plant, inducing defense responses.

Figure 37.17 Plant responses to herbivore attack. (1) Leaf damage induces defensive responses such as the release of volatile compounds. **(2a)** These compounds trigger defenses in undamaged parts of the same plant. **(2b)** Such volatile compounds may also induce defenses in neighboring plants, which then become less vulnerable to herbivores.

Plant pathogens produce compounds known as **elicitors**. Such elicitors promote **virulence**, which is the ability of a pathogen to infect its host and cause disease. **Avirulence genes (*Avr* genes)** are microbial genes that encode elicitors or encode enzymes that are needed to synthesize elicitors (**Figure 37.18**, step 1). Some elicitors bind to the surface of plant cells whereas others are injected into the cytosol. For example, certain bacteria inject elicitors into plant cells by means of syringe-like systems (see Figure 27.18). Fungal pathogens often deliver elicitors into plant cells and absorb nutrients from them by means of penetration structures known as haustoria (from a Latin word, meaning to drink; see Figure 29.23).

To detect elicitors, plant species have evolved first and second lines of defense (see step 2 of Figure 37.18). The first line of defense consists of plasma membrane receptors, typically protein kinases, which specifically bind pathogen-associated elicitors. Bacterial elicitors include lipopolysaccharides, the flagellar protein flagellin, and the cell wall material peptidoglycan. Fungal elicitors include the cell wall compound chitin. A second line of defense involves receptors that bind elicitors in the cytosol. Together, these two signal detection systems allow plants to detect elicitors produced by pathogens and arm themselves against attack.

In plants, many types of **resistance genes (*R* genes)** encode receptor proteins that recognize elicitors. If a plant is genetically unable to produce a receptor that can recognize a pathogen's presence or elicitor, disease may result. By contrast, plants successfully resist disease when the product of a dominant *R* gene (a receptor) recognizes a pathogen's presence by characteristic signal compounds or its dominant *Avr* gene product (an elicitor). Diverse alleles of *R* genes occur in plant populations, providing plants with a large capacity to cope with different types of pathogens. As described next, these receptors,

together with plant responses—the hypersensitive response and systemic acquired resistance—represent the plant immune system.

The Hypersensitive Response to Pathogen Attack The binding of elicitors to receptors results in the production of chemical defense signals: hydrogen peroxide (H_2O_2), the gas nitrous oxide (NO), and mobile hormones (see steps 3 and 4 of Figure 37.18). The plant **hypersensitive response (HR)** is a local reaction to pathogen attack that limits the progression of disease. H_2O_2 can kill pathogens and also helps strengthen the cell wall by promoting the formation of cross-links in cell-wall polymers. The gaseous hormone NO works with H_2O_2 to stimulate the synthesis of hydrolytic enzymes, defensive secondary metabolites, defense hormones, and tough lignin in the cell walls of nearby tissues. NO also induces programmed cell death as a way of limiting the spread of infection. Necrotic spots are brown patches on plant organs that reveal where pathogens have attacked plants and where plant tissues have battled back. In some plants, bacterial infection causes the cells to avoid secreting sugars, which reduces food available to the pathogen. Cellular miRNAs also may help to destroy the nucleic acids of pathogenic viruses.

Systemic Acquired Resistance Defense hormones, which are made at or near a site of pathogen infection, send alarm signals to other parts of the plant, which respond by preparing defenses. Whereas the HR is a local reaction, **systemic acquired resistance (SAR)** is a defensive response of the whole plant induced by a pathogen attack (**Figure 37.19**). SAR immunizes the plant not only from the inducing pathogen, but also many others for weeks to months. Plant SAR is somewhat similar to the immune systems present in animals.

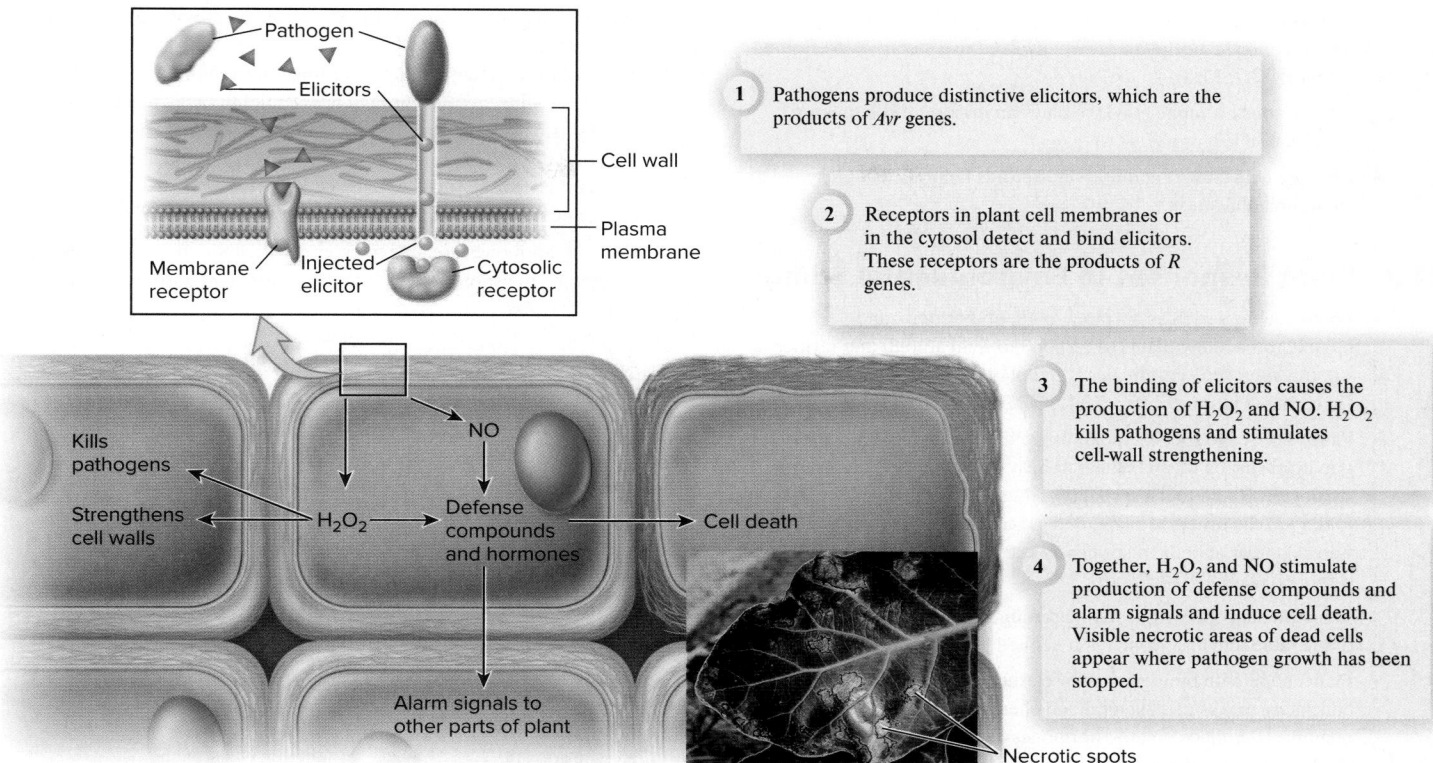

1. Pathogens produce distinctive elicitors, which are the products of *Avr* genes.

2. Receptors in plant cell membranes or in the cytosol detect and bind elicitors. These receptors are the products of *R* genes.

3. The binding of elicitors causes the production of H_2O_2 and NO. H_2O_2 kills pathogens and stimulates cell-wall strengthening.

4. Together, H_2O_2 and NO stimulate production of defense compounds and alarm signals and induce cell death. Visible necrotic areas of dead cells appear where pathogen growth has been stopped.

Figure 37.18 **Pathogen/plant interactions and the hypersensitive response to pathogen attack.** (inset): ©G. R. "Dick" Roberts/Natural Sciences Image Library

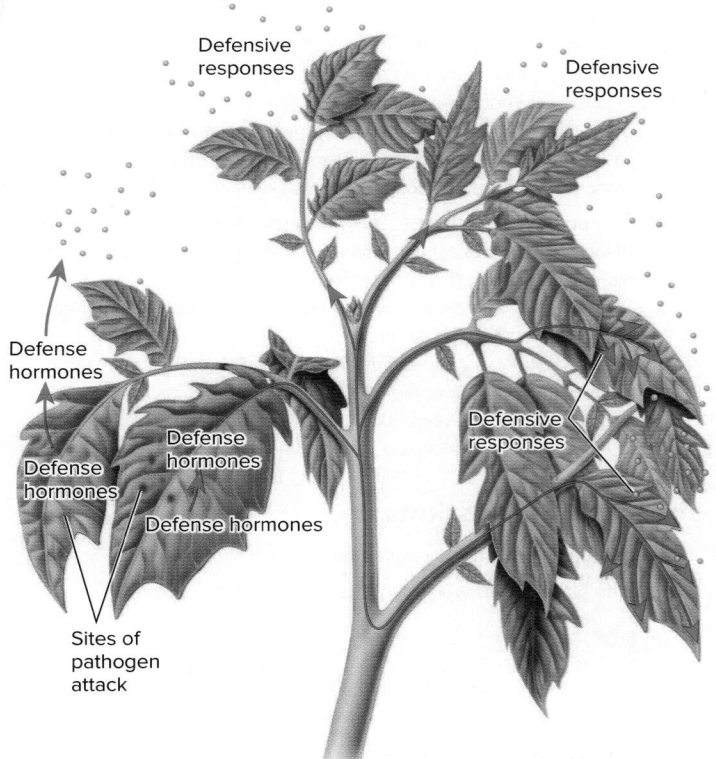

Figure 37.19 **Systemic acquired resistance to pathogen attack.**

Concept Check: *In what way is systemic acquired resistance in plants similar to the immune systems of animals?*

Summary of Key Concepts

37.1 Overview of Plant Behavioral Responses

- Plants sense and respond to diverse internal and external stimuli and thus display behavior (Figures 37.1, 37.2).

- During the process of plant cell signaling, cellular receptors respond to environmental stimuli as well as to internal hormonal signals. The process involves receptor activation, signal transduction by second messengers, and a cellular response (Figure 37.3).

- Cellular responses include changes in gene expression and ion channels that influence plant growth, development, reproduction, chemistry, and movements such as sun tracking and leaf folding.

37.2 Plant Hormones

- Plant hormones interact with environmental stimuli to control plant development, growth, and behavior (Table 37.1).

- Auxin plays an important role in many aspects of plant behavior, including phototropism, as demonstrated by the classic experiments of the Darwins, Went, Briggs, and others. Auxin can be transported downward or upward (polar transport) and sideways (lateral transport) in the plant. The positioning of auxin influx and efflux carriers determines the direction of auxin transport (Figures 37.4, 37.5).

- The major effect of cytokinins is to increase the rate of cell division. Auxin and cytokinin are used in laboratory and commercial plant tissue culture (Figure 37.6).

- Gibberellin function illustrates the general principle that plant hormones often act to release cellular brakes on gene expression.

The components of a system by which gibberellin and cell proteins interact to influence plant growth evolved in a step-by-step fashion (Figures 37.7, 37.8).

- The gaseous hormone ethylene plays an important role in seed germination (Figure 37.9).

- Abscisic acid (ABA) and brassinosteroids help plants to respond to environmental stress.

37.3   Plant Responses to Environmental Stimuli

- Photoreceptors such as cryptochrome, phototropin, and phytochrome allow plants to respond to light stimuli and influence sun tracking, seed germination, and photoperiodic control of flowering (Figures 37.10, 37.11, 37.12).

- Plant shoots and roots respond to gravity (behaviors known as gravitropism) by means of starch-heavy statoliths located within statocytes. Rapid touch responses (thigmotropism), such as leaf folding in the sensitive plant, depend on changes in the water content of cells in structures known as pulvini (Figures 37.13, 37.14, 37.15).

- Many plants cope with flooding through the production of special tissue (aerenchyma), which is regulated by ethylene (Figure 37.16).

- Plants cope with biological stresses such as herbivore and pathogen attacks by means of structural and chemical adaptations. Injured plant parts produce volatile hormones that signal other parts of the same plant and nearby plants to produce defensive responses. The hypersensitive response (HR) is a local defensive response to pathogen attack, whereas systemic acquired resistance (SAR) is a whole-plant immune response (Figures 37.17, 37.18, 37.19).

Assess & Discuss

Test Yourself

1. Examples of plant hormones include
   a. cyclic AMP, IP_3, and calcium ions.
   b. calcium, CDPKs, and DELLA proteins.
   c. auxin, cytokinin, and gibberellin.
   d. cryptochrome, phototropin, and phytochrome.
   e. statoliths, pulvini, and aerenchyma.

2. Phototropism is the
   a. production of flowers in response to a particular day length.
   b. production of flowers in response to a particular night length.
   c. growth response of a plant, organ system, or organ to directional light.
   d. growth response of a plant, organ system, or organ to gravity.
   e. growth response of a plant, organ system, or organ to touch.

3. What is the most accurate order of events during signal transduction?
   a. first, receptor activation; then, messenger signaling; and last, an effector response
   b. first, an effector response; then, messenger signaling; and last, receptor activation
   c. first, messenger signaling; then, receptor activation; and last, an effector response
   d. first, an effector response; then, receptor activation; and last, messenger signaling
   e. none of the above

4. Which of the plant hormones is known as the master plant hormone and why?
   a. cytokinin, because many plant functions require cell division
   b. gibberellins, because growth is essential to many plant responses
   c. abscisic acid, because it is necessary for leaf and fruit drop
   d. brassinosteroids, because water uptake is so fundamental to plant growth
   e. auxin, because there are many different auxin-responsive genes

5. Gaseous hormones are able to enter cells without requiring special membrane transporter. Which of the major plant hormones is a diffusible gas?
   a. auxin   d. ethylene
   b. gibberellin   e. abscisic acid
   c. cytokinin

6. Photoreceptor molecules allow plant cells to detect light of particular wavelengths. Which of these molecules is considered to be a plant photoreceptor?
   a. cryptochrome   d. a, b, and c
   b. phototropin   e. none of the above
   c. phytochrome

7. Thigmotropism is a plant response to
   a. light.   d. gravity.
   b. cold.   e. drought.
   c. touch.

8. Which response is an adaptation to flooding?
   a. geotropism   d. production of aerenchyma
   b. stomatal closure   e. opening aquaporins
   c. photoperiodism

9. What are avirulence genes?
   a. plant genes that encode proteins that prevent infection (virulence)
   b. plant genes that cause infection when the proteins they encode bind to pathogen elicitors
   c. pathogen genes that prevent the pathogens from causing plant disease
   d. pathogen genes that encode elicitors that foster disease in plants
   e. None of the above correctly describes avirulence genes.

10. How do plants defend themselves against pathogens?
    a. Plants produce resistance molecules (usually proteins) that bind pathogen elicitors, thereby preventing disease.
    b. Plants display a hypersensitive response that limits the ability of pathogens to survive and spread.
    c. Plants display systemic acquired resistance, whereby an infection induces immunity to diverse pathogens in other parts of a plant.
    d. All of the above are correct.
    e. None of the above is correct.

Conceptual Questions

1. Why can plants be said to display behavior?

2. Why do plants produce so many types of resistance (R) genes?

3. **Core Concept: Systems** Because diverse plants exude volatile compounds in response to herbivore or pathogen attack, some experts have written about "talking plants." Is there any such thing?

Collaborative Questions

1. Why are most wild plants distasteful, and some even poisonous, to people?

2. How could you increase the resistance of a crop plant species to particular types of herbivores?

Flowering Plants: Nutrition

38

Many types of fascinating carnivorous (meat-eating) plants grow abundantly in wetlands around the world, even though the soils in these places are infertile. How is this possible? Like most plants, carnivorous plants are photosynthetic and thus produce their own organic food from carbon dioxide and water, using sunlight as an energy source. These resources are abundant in wetlands, but wetland soils are low in other nutrients, such as nitrogen, that are needed for plant growth. Carnivorous plants, such as the sundews shown in the chapter opening photo, have adapted by obtaining nutrients from the bodies of trapped insects and other small animals. Carnivorous plants lure animals with enticing fragrances, brightly colored leaves, or glistening sugar-rich drops of nectar. The unsuspecting prey fall into deep, water-filled pitchers; become ensnared by gluelike mucilage; or are trapped within the walls of leafy jails whose doors suddenly snap shut. Decomposition of the animal bodies releases nutrients that plant leaves quickly absorb. Other wild and cultivated plants face similar nutritional challenges and likewise display adaptations that help them acquire sufficient resources for growth and reproduction.

This chapter focuses on plant nutrition, the processes by which plants obtain essential resources. We will begin by describing the resources needed by plants for completion of their seed-to-seed life cycle in good health. Next, we will explore the role of soil as an essential resource for plants. Last, we will examine the biological sources of plant nutrients, focusing on nutritional associations between plants and microorganisms, sources of nutrients for carnivorous plants, and the ways some plants obtain nutrients from other plants. An understanding of these topics is crucial for those who seek ways to grow more plant-derived food or biofuels for humans without causing environmental harm. Plant nutritional information is also useful to people who tend gardens or houseplants or who want to restore degraded habitats.

The tentacled leaves of the sundews (*Drosera rotundifolia and Drosera intermedia*), shown with a trapped fly, are a plant adaptation for the acquisition of nutrients. ©Dwight Kuhn

38.1 Plant Nutritional Requirements

Learning Outcomes:

1. List the major nutritional resources that most plants need for healthy growth.

2. Describe how some plants have adapted to light limitation in shady habitats.

3. **CoreSKILL »** Distinguish between plant macronutrients and micronutrients, using quantitative comparisons.

Carnivorous plants illustrate the concept that all plants—like all animals—have nutritional requirements. A **nutrient** is a substance that is metabolized by or incorporated into an organism. Photosynthetic plants require carbon dioxide (CO_2), water (H_2O), and more than a

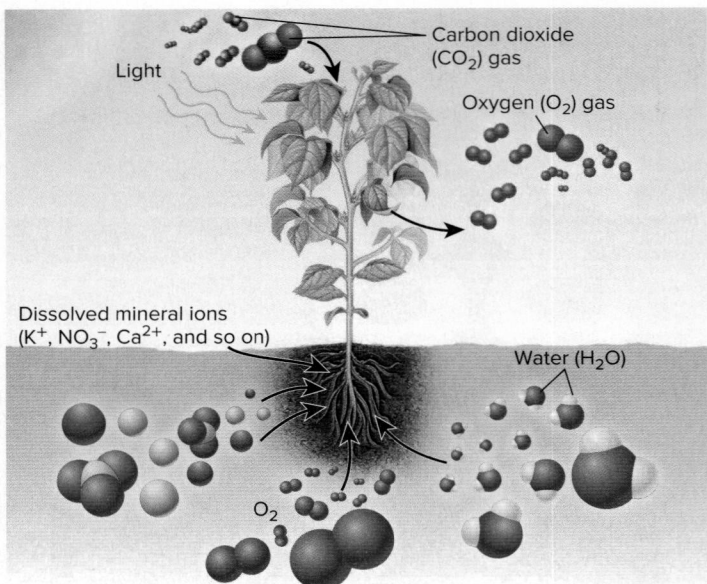

Figure 38.1 The major types of plant nutrients and their sources. Elements that are required in relatively large amounts are known as macronutrients, whereas elements required in smaller amounts are known as micronutrients. A mineral is a naturally occurring inorganic compound. Many minerals dissolve in water to form ions.

dozen elements, such as potassium (as K^+), nitrogen (in the form of NH_4^+ or NO_3^-), and calcium (as Ca^{2+}) to produce organic food by means of photosynthesis. CO_2 is primarily absorbed from air, whereas H_2O and elements are primarily taken up from soil in the form of dissolved ions (**Figure 38.1**). As is the case for animals, deficiency symptoms develop in plants that receive too little of these substances. The environmental scarcity of nutrients selects for adaptations that help plants to acquire them, illustrated by the existence of carnivorous plants.

Essential elements are chemical elements that are required by plants for survival and play many roles in plant metabolism, often functioning as enzyme cofactors (**Table 38.1**). Elements that are generally required in amounts of at least 1 g/kg of plant dry mass are known as **macronutrients**. In contrast, elements that are needed in amounts equal to or less than 0.1 g/kg of plant dry mass are known as **micronutrients**, or trace elements. Because insufficient amounts of light, carbon dioxide, water, and other mineral nutrients can limit the extent of green plant growth, these resources are known as **limiting factors**. If you were in charge of a garden, greenhouse, farm, or forest used to generate products such as wood or paper, or if you were overseeing an environmental restoration project, you would want to understand the conditions that foster or limit plant growth. In this section, we will focus on plant resource requirements, starting with light.

Light Is an Essential Resource for the Growth of Green Plants

All photosynthetic plants require light energy for the formation of the covalent bonds of organic compounds that make up the plant body. Green plants' use of light energy as an essential resource parallels animals' nutritional requirements for organic food as a source of chemical energy. Several hundred species of plants, such as the Indian

Table 38.1	Plant Essential Nutrients			
Element (chemical symbol)	Percentage of plant dry mass	Major source	Form taken up by plants	Function(s)
Macronutrients				
Carbon (C)	45	Air	CO_2	Component of all organic molecules
Oxygen (O)	45	Air, soil, water	CO_2, O_2, H_2O	Component of organic molecules
Hydrogen (H)	6	Water	H_2O	Component of all organic molecules; protons used in chemiosmosis and cotransport
Nitrogen (N)	1.5	Soil	NO_3^-, NH_4^+	Component of proteins, nucleic acids, chlorophyll, coenzymes, and alkaloids
Potassium (K)	1.0	Soil	K^+	Has essential role in cell ionic balance
Calcium (Ca)	0.5	Soil	Ca^{2+}	Component of cell walls; messenger in signal transduction
Magnesium (Mg)	0.2	Soil	Mg^{2+}	Component of chlorophyll; activates some enzymes
Phosphorus (P)	0.2	Soil	HPO_4^{2-}	Component of nucleic acids, ATP, phospholipids, and some coenzymes
Sulfur (S)	0.1	Soil	SO_4^{2-}	Component of proteins, some coenzymes, and defense compounds
Micronutrients				
Chlorine (Cl)	0.01	Soil	Cl^-	Required for water splitting in photosystem II; cell ion balance
Iron (Fe)	0.01	Soil	Fe^{3+}, Fe^{2+}	Enzyme cofactor; component of cytochromes
Manganese (Mn)	0.005	Soil	Mn^{2+}	Enzyme cofactor; required for water splitting in photosystem II
Boron (B)	0.002	Soil	$B(OH)_3$	Enzyme cofactor; component of cell walls
Zinc (Zn)	0.002	Soil	Zn^{2+}	Enzyme cofactor
Sodium (Na)	0.001	Soil	Na^+	Required to generate PEP in C_4 and CAM plants*
Copper (Cu)	0.0006	Soil	Cu^+, Cu^{2+}	Enzyme cofactor
Molybdenum (Mo)	0.00001	Soil	MoO_4^{2-}	Enzyme cofactor
Nickel (Ni)	0.000005	Soil	Ni^{2+}	Enzyme cofactor

*PEP stands for phosphoenolpyruvate; CAM stands for crassulacean acid metabolism.

Figure 38.2 **The heterotrophic flowering plant, Indian pipe (*Monotropa uniflora*).** ©Robert Ziemba/age fotostock

 Core Concept: Energy and Matter The nongreen heterotrophic plant *M. uniflora* lacks photosynthetic capacity and therefore must absorb organic compounds for use as an energy source. By contrast, nearby autotrophic green plants use sunlight as a source of energy.

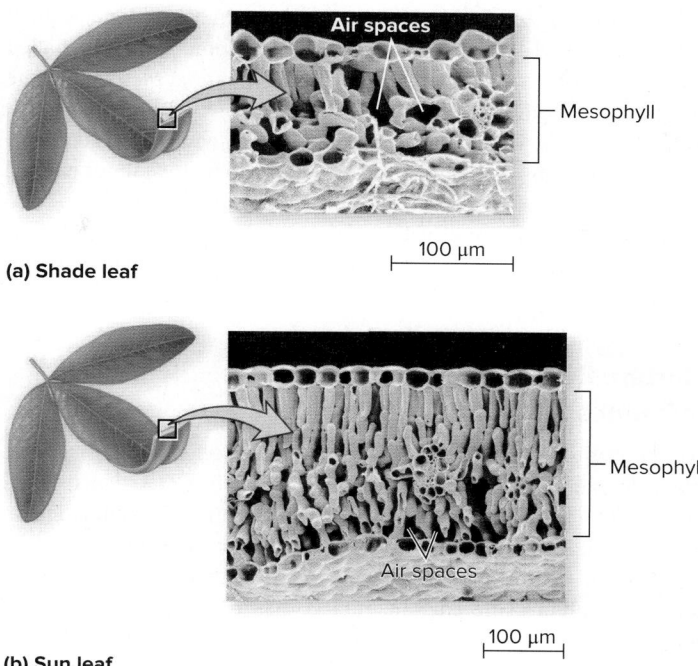

(a) Shade leaf

(b) Sun leaf

Figure 38.3 **Shade and sun leaves.** a–b: ©Raymon Donahue

 Core Concept: Structure and Function These scanning electron micrographs of cut leaves reveal the thinner mesophyll and greater number of air spaces in **(a)** shade leaves as compared with **(b)** sun leaves.

pipe (*Monotropa uniflora*), have become heterotrophic and lost their photosynthetic capacity. In heterotrophic plants, essential nutrients include absorbed organic compounds that replace light as a source of energy (**Figure 38.2**).

In nature, plants must adapt to environments with varying amounts of light and shade. For example, in forests, light availability limits the growth of tree seedlings and other small plants that are shaded by the leafy tree canopy overhead. Conversely, plants growing in deserts or on mountains often experience light so intense that it can damage the photosynthetic components. Plants have evolved adaptations that help them cope with environments that have too little or too much light.

Adaptations to Shade Plants can adapt to shading by producing thin leaves that allow some light to pass through to other leaves, producing more chlorophyll, or producing distinctive sun and shade leaves (**Figure 38.3**). Sun leaves have a thicker layer of chlorophyll-containing mesophyll and are able to harvest more of the bright sunlight that penetrates deeply into the leaf. In contrast, shade leaves have a thinner mesophyll layer, with more air spaces than do sun leaves. The arrangement of leaves on plants and stem-branching patterns also reflect adaptations that reduce shading. For example, many tropical forest trees that must compete for light with closely crowded neighbors are extremely tall, and they produce branches and leaves only at their very tops. Shorter plants native to the shady interiors of tropical rain forests are so well adapted to these moist but dim conditions that they make excellent houseplants (**Figure 38.4**).

Figure 38.4 **The tropical houseplant *Monstera deliciosa*.** *M. deliciosa* makes an attractive houseplant because its large, deep green leaves are adapted to the moist and shady conditions present in the interiors of tropical forests. ©Royal Botanical Gardens Kew

Adaptations to Excessive Light Too much light can damage plant chloroplasts by destroying an essential photosynthetic protein, called the D1 protein. To avoid damage, specific carotenoid pigments in the chloroplast absorb some of the excess light energy and dissipate it as harmless heat. Other adaptations prevent ultraviolet (UV) damage. Harmful amounts of UV radiation are absorbed by the plant's surface cuticle, as well as by carotenoid and flavonoid compounds located within leaf cells. These protective compounds are often brightly colored and, when present in large amounts, explain the attractive red or purple colors of some leaves.

Carbon Dioxide Concentration Influences Plant Growth

Although light provides the energy for plant photosynthesis, most plant dry mass originates from carbon dioxide (CO_2). Most plants obtain CO_2 gas from the atmosphere by absorption through stomata, pores that occur in the plant epidermis. Under experimental conditions, plant photosynthetic rates increase with CO_2 concentration until the Calvin cycle enzyme rubisco has become fully supplied, that is, saturated with CO_2. (To review leaf internal structure, see Figure 36.8c; to review the role of rubisco in the Calvin cycle of photosynthesis, see Figure 8.13.)

CO_2 Limitation In nature, plants are often unable to obtain enough CO_2 for maximal photosynthesis. As a result, CO_2 limits agricultural crop productivity. This is partly because the modern atmospheric concentration of CO_2 is only 390 μL/L (a small fraction of atmospheric content), whereas considerably more CO_2 would be required to maximize the rate of photosynthesis in most plants. Evidence that plant photosynthesis can be limited by CO_2 availability is provided by studies of crops grown in greenhouses, where atmospheric gas content can be controlled. When supplied with air enriched with CO_2, tomatoes, cucumbers, leafy vegetables, and some other crops can double their growth rate. In nature, plants that experience hot, dry conditions are particularly vulnerable to low CO_2 levels when their stomata close to conserve water. When stomata are closed, plants cannot absorb CO_2, which limits photosynthesis. Many plants possess structural and biochemical adaptations that help them cope with CO_2 limitation by improving CO_2 absorption.

CO_2-Absorption Adaptations Many plants that live in arid or hot environments display an adaptation known as C_4 photosynthesis, which improves productivity by aiding CO_2 absorption (refer back to Figure 8.17). About 30,000 plant species utilize C_4 photosynthesis, which is thought to have evolved from ancestral C_3 photosynthesis on more than 40 separate occasions. Today, C_4 plants dominate extensive warm grassland habitats of the world, contributing about 25% of the total terrestrial photosynthesis.

C_4 photosynthesis relies on specializations in the internal structure of leaves. In C_4 plants, the leaf mesophyll harvests light, but does not contain Calvin-cycle enzymes that bind CO_2 to form sugar. Instead, C_4 leaf mesophyll produces the enzyme phosphoenolpyruvate (PEP) carboxylase, which binds CO_2 more readily than does rubisco. PEP carboxylase adds CO_2 to PEP, a three-carbon molecule, to produce the four-carbon compound oxaloacetate. The leaves of

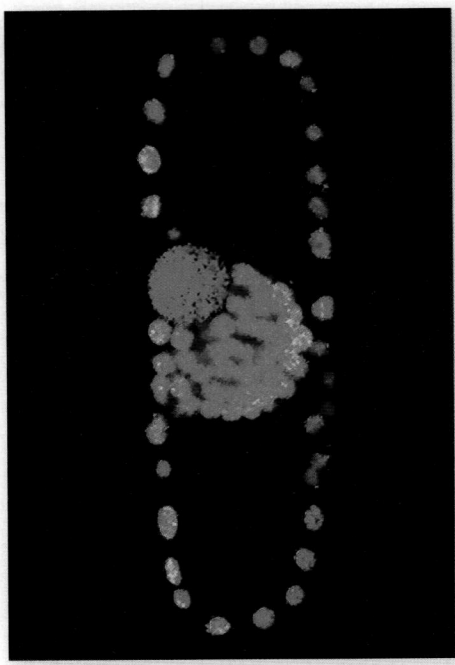

Figure 38.5 **A CO_2 absorption adaptation.** In contrast to most C_4 plants, *Bienertia cycloptera* is able to conduct C_4 photosynthesis within the confines of a single cell. In this fluorescence photograph of a *B. cycloptera* cell, the red plastids at the cell periphery function like the mesophyll cells of most C_4 plants. In contrast, the red plastids clustered near the green nucleus function much like the bundle-sheath cells of most C_4 plants. The plastids appear red because chlorophyll emits red light when it fluoresces. Confocal fluorescence micrograph courtesy Simon D.X. Chuong

Concept Check: *Which plastids should contain more of the enzyme rubisco, plastids at the cell periphery or those clustered near the nucleus?*

C_4 plants also have increased vein density, and specialized bundle-sheath cells surround each vein. In the leaves of most C_4 plants, such as maize (corn), the four-carbon compounds produced in mesophyll move through intracellular connections into the bundle-sheath cells. Within the bundle-sheath cells, enzymes release CO_2 from the C_4 compounds, and the CO_2 is incorporated into organic carbon by Calvin cycle enzymes.

Some plants native to arid regions have evolved a type of C_4 photosynthesis that occurs within a single cell. Photosynthetic cells of these plants have two types of plastids, one type containing PEP carboxylase and the other containing rubisco (**Figure 38.5**). C_4 photosynthesis is particularly valuable to plants that occur in hot, dry environments because it allows the plants to absorb sufficient CO_2 without losing too much water.

Water Is an Essential Plant Resource

Water is essential to plants for several reasons. As a nutrient, water is the source of most of the hydrogen atoms and some of the oxygen atoms in organic compounds (see Table 38.1). For example, oxygen is incorporated into organic molecules during hydrolysis reactions (refer back to Figure 3.4b). Water is also the solvent for mineral nutrients and is the main transport medium in plants, allowing movement of minerals and other solutes throughout the plant body via the vascular tissues. Cytoplasmic and vacuolar water also helps to support plants by maintaining hydrostatic pressure on the cell wall.

Though plants vary in water content, water typically makes up about 90% of the weight of living plants. Most plants die when their water content falls below half of the amount normal for that particular species. Although many types of desiccation-resistant plants display adaptations that allow them to survive for extended periods in fairly dry conditions, all plants require an adequate supply of water for active metabolism and growth.

Deficiency Syndromes Occur When Plants Receive an Inadequate Supply of Certain Nutrients

In addition to light, CO_2, and water, plants require additional elements for growth and survival (see Table 38.1). These elements occur naturally in water and soil or they can be added in the form of fertilizers. Plant biologists have quantitatively analyzed the elemental requirements of plants by growing them hydroponically, that is, by bathing plant roots in a water solution to which elements in the form of dissolved minerals are added in various combinations and amounts. Hydroponic studies reveal that when plants lack an adequate supply of an essential elemental nutrient, they display characteristic deficiency symptoms. Such symptoms include failure to reproduce, tissue death, and changes in leaf color. Yellowing of leaves, known as **chlorosis**, is a common mineral deficiency symptom, because many different elements are needed for chlorophyll production (**Figure 38.6**).

Figure 38.6 Chlorosis as a symptom of mineral deficiency. This camellia plant is suffering from an iron deficiency, as revealed by the yellow leaves, a symptom known as chlorosis. ©Geoff Kidd/SPL/Science

Concept Check: *Does chlorosis always indicate iron deficiency in plants?*

38.2 The Role of Soil in Plant Nutrition

Learning Outcomes:

1. List the benefits of soil organic matter for plant growth.
2. Explain why plants require a source of fixed nitrogen and how they obtain it.
3. Describe various plant adaptations that increase the ability to obtain phosphorus.

Soil is an essential resource for most wild and cultivated plants, providing water and other essential nutrients. For this reason, extensive loss of soil by wind and water erosion is of wide concern. Soils vary greatly in fertility, that is, their ability to support plant growth. Thus, plants of many types have had to adapt to the challenges of obtaining nutrients from poor soils. In this section, we will explore soil structure and chemistry from the perspective of plant growth and examine how plants take up nutrients from the soil.

The Physical Structure of Soils Affects Their Aeration, Water-Holding Capacity, and Fertility

Natural soils display layers, known as soil horizons (**Figure 38.7a**). The remains of plants that have recently died and other organisms form a layer of litter above the **topsoil**; the topsoil is also known as the A horizon. Many of the inorganic minerals and organic materials that enrich high-quality topsoil arise from the activities of microorganisms that decompose the litter. In this way, the minerals contained in living plants are eventually recycled to subsequent generations. Beneath the topsoil lie layers called subsoil and soil base, which are largely composed of mineral materials. Bedrock is the bottom layer that supports the soil horizons. Plant roots play an important role in conveying deep-lying minerals to the surface, thereby helping to enrich the topsoil.

Soil horizons vary in composition and thickness, depending on various factors—including climate, vegetation, bedrock type, and human influences. For example, natural grasslands produce deep, rich topsoil that is used for cropland in many regions of the world (**Figure 38.7b**). In dramatic contrast, tropical rain forests often have only thin layers of topsoil; their low-fertility soils are composed mostly of inorganic materials that are not useful to plants (**Figure 38.7c**). Farmers cope with reduced soil fertility by adding organic or inorganic fertilizers. The proportions of organic to inorganic materials and the sizes of inorganic particles are used to classify soils into different types. Soils also display variation in their amount of aeration, water-holding capacity, pH, and mineral content. All of these soil properties affect plant growth. For these reasons, we will take a closer look at soil structure and the role of fertilizers.

Soil Organic Matter   Soil organic matter, also known as humus, is largely derived from plant detritus, the dead and decaying remains of plants, although animal wastes and decayed animal bodies also contribute to the organic content of soils. Soil organic matter provides many benefits. Organic-rich soils, containing 8% or so organic matter, are less likely to erode—wash or blow away with water or wind. Soil organic matter also binds mineral nutrients, thereby fostering soil fertility, and gives soil a soft consistency that fosters plant root growth and farmers' ability to cultivate. Gardeners often produce their

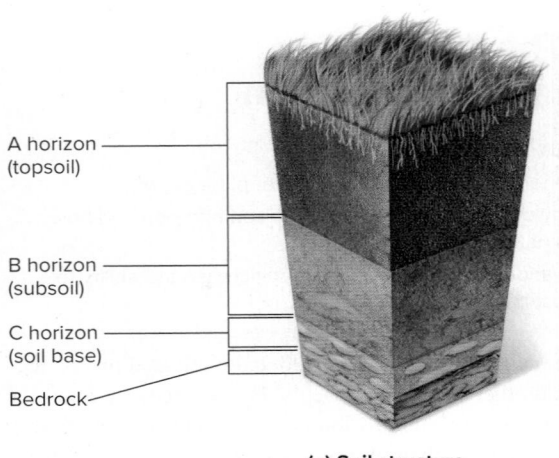

A horizon (topsoil)

B horizon (subsoil)

C horizon (soil base)

Bedrock

(a) Soil structure

(b) Thick layer of topsoil in cropland

(c) Thin layer of topsoil in rain forest

Figure 38.7 Soil horizons, the structural layers of soil. (a) Diagram showing general soil structure. **(b)** A vertical view of an agricultural soil, showing a relatively deep layer of dark topsoil. **(c)** A vertical view of a tropical rain forest soil, showing a thin layer of dark topsoil. b: Courtesy of C.A. Stiles, University of Wisconsin; c: ©Ruddy Gold/age fotostock

own organic-matter-rich compost by layering vegetable waste from the kitchen and yard waste with soil, and turning the pile occasionally to introduce the oxygen necessary for decomposition (**Figure 38.8**). Mature compost is then mixed with garden soil to improve its fertility.

Inorganic Soil Constituents Inorganic materials in soil are derived from the physical and chemical breakdown of rock, a process known as **weathering**. Rock, which is an aggregate of two or more minerals, is physically weathered by changes such as cycles of freezing and thawing. Lichens and plant roots may produce organic acids that contribute to chemical weathering of rocks. During chemical weathering, soluble salts are washed out, and minerals are hydrolyzed or oxidized. **Leaching** is the dissolution and removal of inorganic ions as water percolates through materials. Heavy rainfall can reduce the fertility of soils by leaching large amounts of nutrients from them.

The leached elements often end up in natural bodies of water, where they can foster the growth of cyanobacteria, algae, and aquatic plants.

Inorganic soil materials occur as particles that can be categorized according to their size as sand, silt, or clay (**Figure 38.9**). Sand grains range from 2 mm to 62.5 μm in diameter. Particles of silt range from 20 to 2 μm in diameter, and clay particles are even smaller. Soils can be classified according to their relative content of coarse and fine materials. For example, soils that contain 45% or more sand and 35% or less clay are classified as sandy soils. The other main types of soil are silt, clay, and loam. **Loam** contains a mixture of sand, silt, and clay and is ideal for the cultivation of most plants.

Because of their size differences, sand, silt, and clay particles confer different properties on soils. The relatively large size and irregular shapes of sand particles allow air and water to move rapidly through sandy soils, which are said to be porous (**Figure 38.10**).

Figure 38.8 Composting. Gardeners produce compost by layering small amounts of soil with vegetable waste from the kitchen and yard waste and periodically turning the pile to introduce the oxygen needed for decomposition. Compost can be used to increase the organic and mineral content of garden soils. Source: USDA

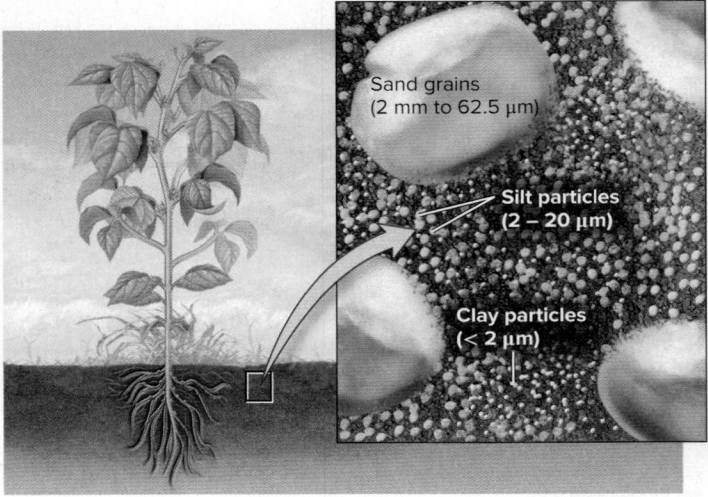

Sand grains (2 mm to 62.5 μm)

Silt particles (2 – 20 μm)

Clay particles (< 2 μm)

Figure 38.9 The relative sizes of inorganic soil components.

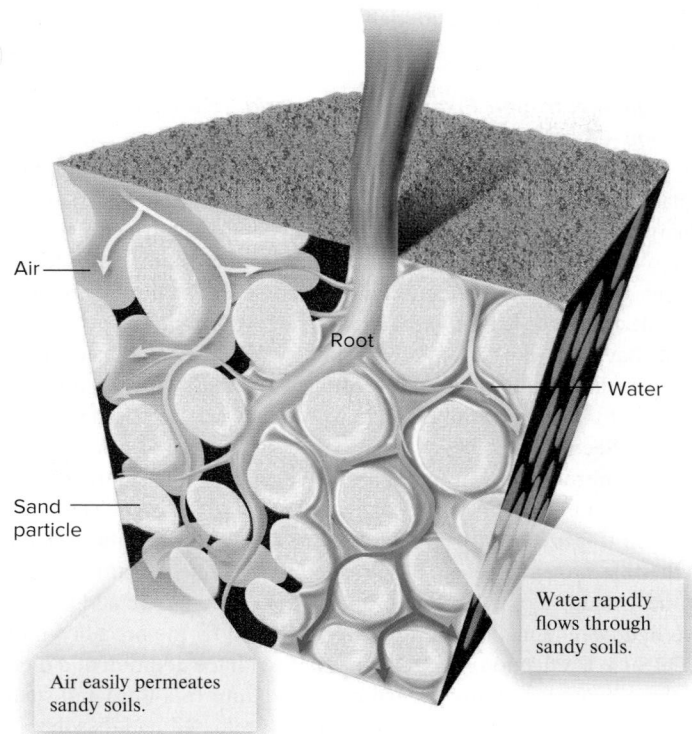

Silt and clay particles fit closely together, so soils containing larger amounts of these materials are less porous than sandy soils. Water percolates less easily through silty and clay soils, which therefore retain more ionic mineral nutrients than do sandy soils. Clay particles have negative charges on their surfaces that electrostatically bind positively charged ions (cations) such as NH_4^+, Ca^{2+}, and Fe^{2+} (**Figure 38.11a**). Cations having higher valence numbers (such as Fe^{2+}) are bound more tightly than ions having lower valence numbers.

In order to be available to plants, cations must be detached from clay particles. Hydrogen ions (H^+, protons) are able to replace mineral cations on the surfaces of clay particles in a process known as **cation exchange** (**Figure 38.11b**). Cation exchange releases cations to soil water, making them available for uptake by plant roots. However, free ions are also more easily washed out of soil. If the H^+ concentration becomes too high, large numbers of mineral ions are released and can be leached from the soil by heavy rainfall. Such leached minerals may include heavy metals such as aluminum (Al^{3+}) that would otherwise be bound in soil. Cation exchange is the mechanism by which acid rain, which adds H^+ to soil, causes loss of soil fertility and the pollution of streams with toxic substances, such as aluminum, that can harm human health.

Despite their water- and mineral-retention features, silt- and clay-rich soils may be poorly aerated and therefore unfavorable to root growth. Gardeners often mix organic materials and sand into silt or clay-rich soils to improve their aeration properties. Loam is the preferred soil for agriculture because it combines the aeration provided by sand with the mineral and water retention capacity of silt and clay. Even with a good soil mix, fertilizers may be needed to achieve maximum crop production.

Figure 38.10 The movement of air and water in sandy soil.

Concept Check: *In which type of soil is nutrient leaching more of a problem, sandy or clay soil?*

Sandy soils are well aerated, which is favorable to the growth of plant roots, which require oxygen for cellular respiration. However, sandy soils hold less water than the same volume of clay, and rapid percolation of water through sandy soils both reduces the amount of water available to the roots and leaches minerals from the soil.

The Role of Fertilizers   **Fertilizers** are soil additions that enhance plant growth by providing essential elements. The addition of fertilizer to soils can compensate for deficiencies in soil organic matter or mineral content and thus improve soil fertility. Fertilizers occur in organic and inorganic forms. Organic fertilizers are those in which

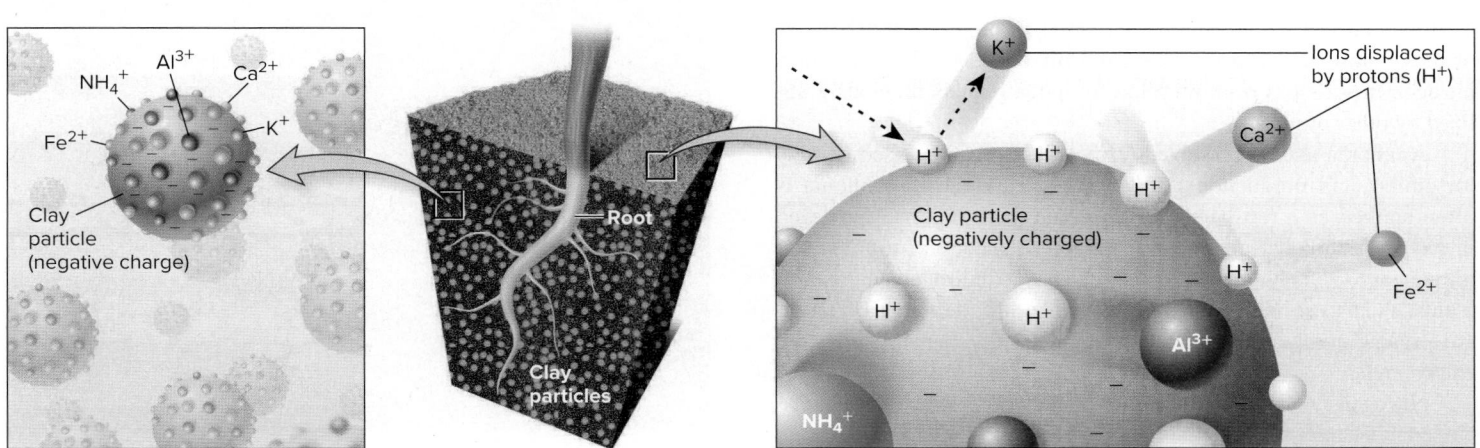

(a) Electrostatic attraction between clay particles and mineral ions

(b) Cation exchange

Figure 38.11 Cation binding and exchange. (a) Clay and organic particles in the soil display negative electrostatic surface charges that bind cations. Bound cations include not only plant mineral nutrients such as ammonium (NH_4^+) but also cations that are not plant nutrients, such as Al^{3+}. **(b)** Cation exchange occurs when protons (H^+) displace other cations, releasing them to soil water. This process makes cations more available for uptake by plant roots, but it also increases the potential for cations to leach away during rains or floods.

most of the minerals are bound to organic molecules and are thus released relatively slowly. Organic fertilizers play an important role in **organic farming**, the production of crops without the use of inorganic fertilizers, growth substances, and pesticides. Manure and compost are examples of organic fertilizers.

In contrast, inorganic fertilizers consist largely of inorganic minerals, which are immediately useful to plants but can more easily leach from soils during heavy rainfall. Nitrogen (N), phosphorus (P), and potassium (K) are the mineral nutrients that most frequently limit crop growth. For this reason, these minerals are the main components of the most common type of commercial inorganic fertilizers. Such fertilizers are available with different ratios of minerals, which are optimal for different types of plants.

Excessive application of fertilizers to fields and lawns is undesirable because minerals not taken up by plant roots are easily washed by rain into waterways, where they can fuel large growths of algae and aquatic plants that can harm other aquatic life-forms. For example, large areas of the Gulf of Mexico and other coastal regions are now known as "dead zones" because microbial decomposition of large algal populations has depleted oxygen from the water, suffocating the animal life. These large populations of algae are fostered by fertilizers that wash from farm soils into rivers, such as the Mississippi River, that drain into coastal oceans. More careful application of fertilizers and the planting of vegetation that absorbs mineral nutrients along stream and river edges can help to reduce or prevent dead zones.

Plants Require Fixed Nitrogen

Nitrogen is frequently limiting to plant growth in nature and in crop fields, because large amounts of it are required by plants to synthesize amino acids, nucleotides, and alkaloids, among many other cellular constituents. Nitrogen is the largest component of plants by mass after carbon, oxygen, and hydrogen. Although the Earth's atmosphere is 78% nitrogen gas (N_2), plants cannot utilize nitrogen in this form. To be of use to plants, soil nitrogen must occur in another form, such as ammonia (NH_3), ammonium ion (NH_4^+), or nitrate ion (NO_3^-); any of these substances is known as **fixed nitrogen**. Much of the fixed nitrogen in soils has been recycled from compounds previously utilized by other organisms.

Ammonia and its dissolved form—NH_4^+—can be used directly for amino acid production by plants, explaining why ammonia is often applied as a fertilizer to farm fields in springtime. However, in oxygen-rich soils, microorganisms oxidize much of the NH_4^+ to nitrate, so NO_3^- may be the form in which fixed nitrogen enters most plants. Plants use NH_4^+ and NO_3^- to make a wide range of essential organic compounds, including amino acids, nucleic acids, and chlorophyll.

Nitrogen flows through the environment in a nitrogen cycle, discussed in Chapter 59 (look ahead to Figure 59.15). **Nitrogen fixation** is the process by which atmospheric N_2 is combined with hydrogen to produce NH_3. New fixed nitrogen can be added to soils by the action of lightning, fire, or air pollution, as well as by biological and industrial nitrogen fixation. The nitrogen in inorganic fertilizers is produced by **industrial nitrogen fixation**, a human activity. Most of the fixed nitrogen in soils is produced by **biological nitrogen fixation**,

which is performed in nature only by certain prokaryotic organisms, as described next.

Biological Nitrogen Fixation by Bacteria   Nitrogen-fixing prokaryotic organisms include many types of cyanobacteria, which are photosynthetic organisms that occur in oceans, lakes, and other aquatic systems, as well as in surface soil crusts (**Figure 38.12**). Various types of nonphotosynthetic bacteria and archaea living in water and soil are also able to fix nitrogen. Nitrogen-fixing prokaryotic organisms often excrete a substantial amount of fixed nitrogen, and their death makes still more fixed nitrogen available to plants. Many plants have nitrogen-fixing, prokaryotic symbionts that transfer fixed nitrogen directly to plant cells. Nitrogen-fixation symbioses are so important in nature and in agriculture that they are discussed in more detail in Section 38.3.

All nitrogen-fixing prokaryotic organisms utilize relatively large amounts of ATP and an enzyme known as **nitrogenase** to fix nitrogen (**Figure 38.13**). The fixation process occurs in three steps. In the first step, a molecule of nitrogen gas (N_2) binds to nitrogenase. In the second step, the bound nitrogen is reduced by the addition of two hydrogen atoms (2 H), a reaction powered by the breakdown of ATP. Such a reduction occurs three times, with the addition of a total of three hydrogen atoms to each nitrogen atom. In a third and final step, two molecules of ammonia (NH_3) are released and dissolve in cell water to form NH_4^+. The nitrogenase enzyme is then free to bind more N_2.

Because the O_2 molecule resembles N_2, oxygen can bind to the active site of nitrogenase. Oxygen binding disables nitrogenase, thereby stopping nitrogen fixation. For this reason, many nitrogen-fixing microorganisms exist in anaerobic environments or they turn off the expression of the nitrogenase gene when oxygen is present. To increase nitrogen availability, crop scientists are working to genetically engineer nitrogen-fixation capacity into crop plants such as rice

Figure 38.12 A soil surface crust that includes nitrogen-fixing, soil-enriching cyanobacteria and lichens. Such crusts are widespread in grasslands and other arid regions. Source: Jayne Belnap, U.S. Geological Survey

Concept Check: *How might soil crusts influence the ecology and economy of regions in which grazing is important?*

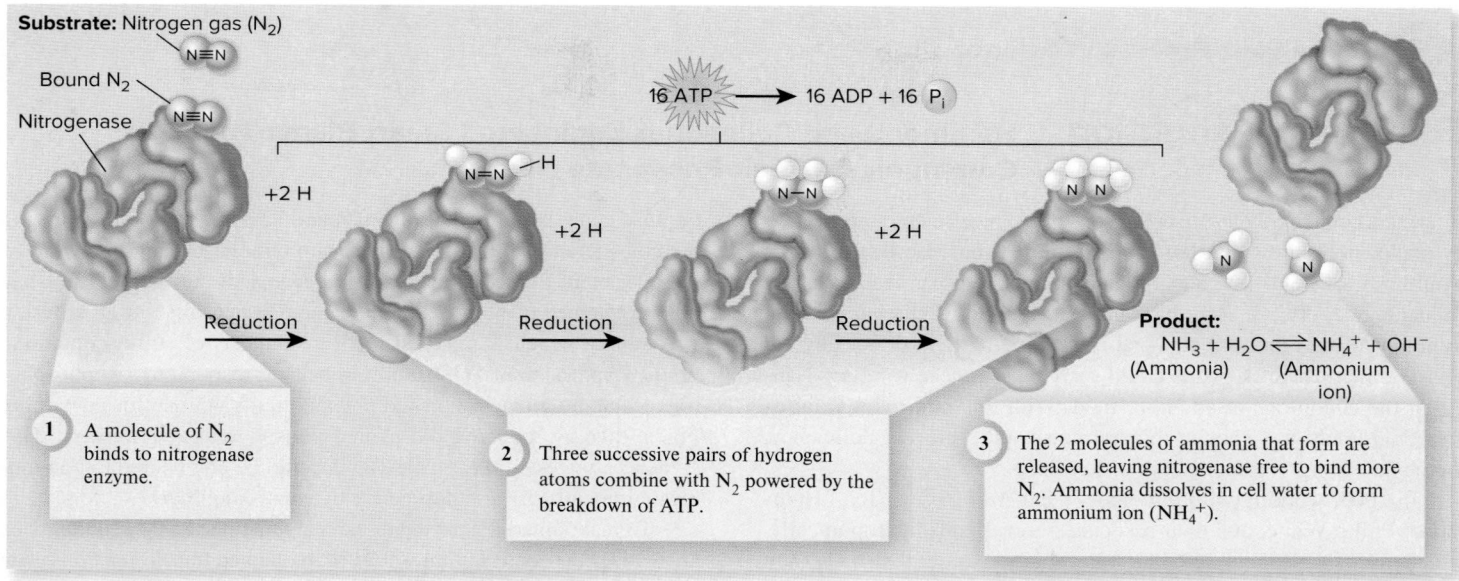

Figure 38.13 **The biological process of nitrogen fixation.**

Concept Check: *What common substance inactivates the enzyme nitrogenase by binding to its active site?*

and maize (corn). However, the vulnerability of nitrogenase to oxygen means that this enzyme may need to be altered so that it binds oxygen less readily, or plants must be engineered with some mechanism that protects nitrogenase from oxygen.

Industrial Nitrogen Fixation   Worldwide, farmers apply more than 80 million metric tons of nitrogen fertilizer per year. The fixed nitrogen found in fertilizer is produced industrially from N_2 by means of a procedure invented by German chemists Fritz Haber and Carl Bosch in 1909. The reduction of N_2 gas to NH_3 is energetically favorable at room temperature, but the activation energy is very high, so the reaction occurs extremely slowly. Using an iron catalyst, temperatures of 400–650°C (752–1,202°F), and high pressures (150–400 atmospheres), the Haber-Bosch process generates NH_3 rapidly. However, because of its high energy requirements, industrial nitrogen fixation can be costly from the perspective of many of the world's farmers. The high cost of fertilizers helps to explain why agricultural scientists are so interested in the possibility of genetically engineering biological nitrogen fixation into crop plants.

Plants Display Adaptations for Acquiring Phosphorus

Phosphorus (P) is another soil mineral that often limits plant growth. Plants obtain phosphorus from the ion known as phosphate (PO_4^{3-}), which occurs in the soil in three dissolved forms: H_3PO_4, $H_2PO_4^-$, and HPO_4^{2-}. HPO_4^{2-} (called hydrogen phosphate ion) is the form most commonly absorbed by plants. Phosphate uptake involves ATP-requiring proton cotransport, as is the case for the uptake of other anions such as nitrate (NO_3^-) and sulfate (SO_4^{2-}). The uptake of these nutrients at the root hair surface is discussed further in Chapter 39.

Although phosphorus can be abundant in soil, it is often unavailable to plants. One reason is that PO_4^{3-} forms tightly bound complexes with clay, iron and aluminum oxides, and calcium carbonate in soils. In addition, soil microbes incorporate PO_4^{3-} into organic compounds that are not taken up by plants.

Because plants need large supplies of phosphorus for a variety of cell processes, they have evolved various adaptations that increase their ability to obtain PO_4^{3-} from soil. A common adaptation for acquiring PO_4^{3-} is the symbiotic association of plant roots with various types of fungi (see Section 38.3). In addition, plants that grow in soils having low phosphorous content may produce more highly branched roots and more and longer root hairs. Plant roots also secrete protons and organic acids such as citrate and malate into the soil, which help release phosphorus from inorganic complexes. For example, the plant *Lupinus alba* releases as much as 25% of its total photosynthetic carbon into the soil as organic acids—a high price to pay but apparently one that is essential for the plant to obtain sufficient phosphorus. Plants may also secrete phosphatase enzymes from roots. These enzymes release phosphorus from organic compounds in the soil. The general process by which P, N, CO_2, and other minerals are released from organic compounds is called **mineralization**.

Farmers and gardeners apply phosphate-rich fertilizers to crop fields and gardens as a way of preventing phosphorous deficiencies, which reduce yields. Phosphorous fertilizers are obtained from phosphate-rich mineral deposits, but experts have warned that inexpensive sources of PO_4^{3-} will be exhausted within the next 90 years. Consequently, there is much interest in devising ways to maximize the efficiency by which plants are able to take up and use phosphorus. Genetic engineering to produce "smart plants" that can sense the levels of nutrients in the soil may offer some options.

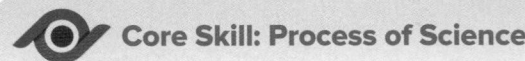

Feature Investigation | Hammond and Colleagues Engineered Smart Plants That Can Communicate Their Phosphate Needs

If farmers could apply fertilizer to crops in the precise amounts needed by plants, not only would farmers save money, but also less fertilizer would run off fields into aquatic habitats, where it can lead to harmful ecological effects. Plant biologists have used genetic engineering to produce smart plants that signal impending nutrient deficiency via a visible marker. Such plants could serve as sentinels, warning farmers of the conditions of an entire field. With this information, farmers could apply just enough mineral nutrients to prevent deficiency, thereby avoiding overapplication of fertilizers.

In 2003, working with the model plant *Arabidopsis*, John Hammond, Philip White, and their associates grew plants hydroponically, which means their roots were in a water solution rather than soil. They identified some of the genes whose expression changes when plants are transferred from nutrient solutions containing sufficient phosphorus to solutions lacking phosphorus. They found that some genes were turned on quickly after phosphorus removal, but other genes took much longer, up to 100 hours or more. This timing is important

because genes expressed between 24 and 72 hours after PO_4^{3-} removal are considered useful as phosphorous monitors. During this window of time, plant tissue levels of PO_4^{3-} decreased, but the decrease had not yet affected plant growth. One gene that met this timing criterion was *SQD1*, which is required for the synthesis of sulfur-containing lipids. Expression of *SQD1* allows plants to respond to low phosphorous levels by replacing plastid phospholipids with sulfur-containing lipids, thereby reducing the plants' phosphorous requirement. This evidence suggested that smart plants could be engineered to communicate impending PO_4^{3-} deficiency by expressing *SQD1*.

To make smart plants, the researchers first placed the reporter gene *GUS* under the control of the *SQD1* promoter and transformed this gene into *Arabidopsis* plants (**Figure 38.14**). The researchers then grew these genetically engineered plants for various time periods in hydroponic solutions of differing PO_4^{3-} levels. After different time periods, they removed leaves and chemically treated them with a compound that produces a light blue color when the *GUS* gene is expressed. Some leaves were

Figure 38.14 The experiment of Hammond and colleagues showed that plants can be engineered to communicate changes in the level of nutrients.

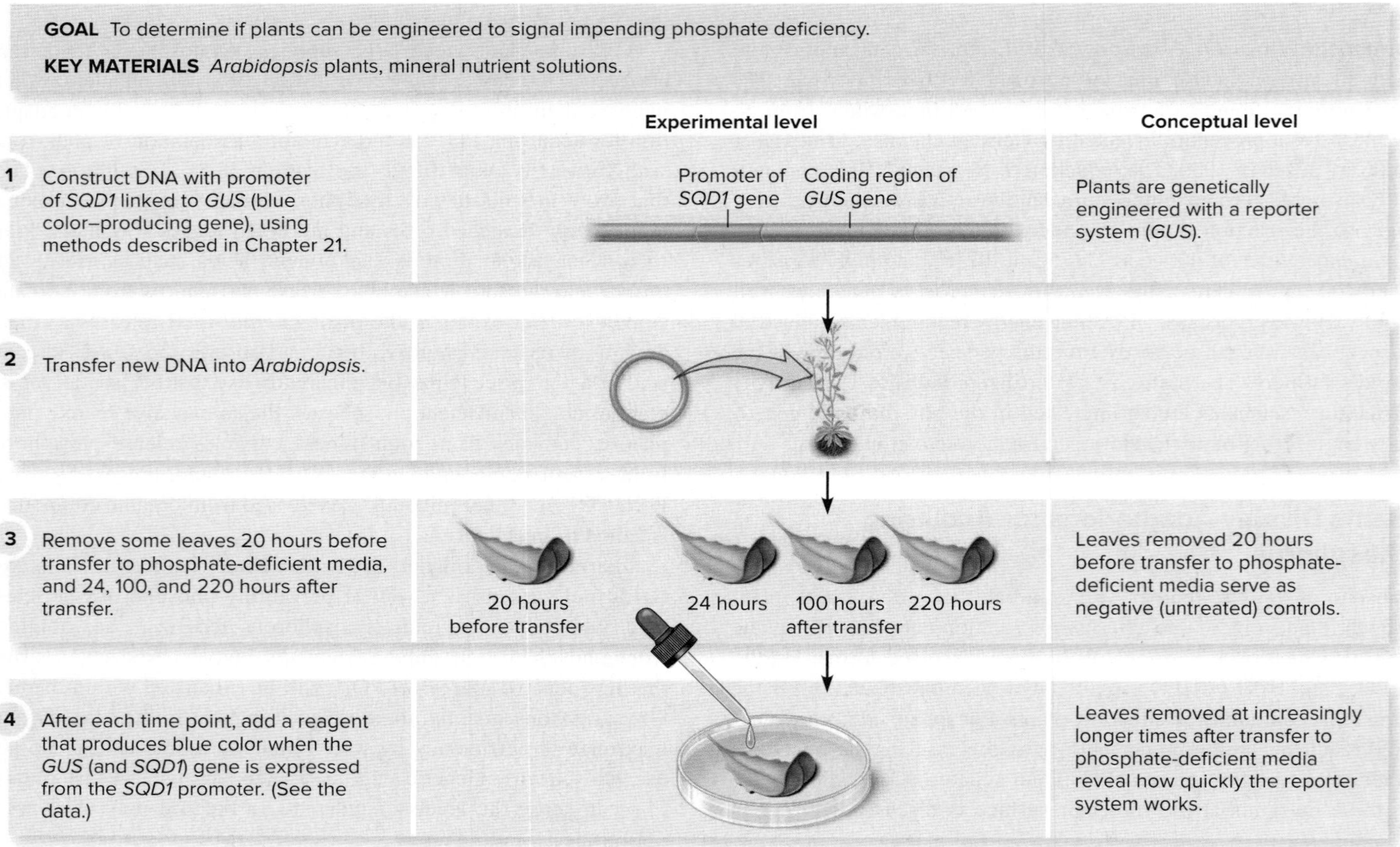

GOAL To determine if plants can be engineered to signal impending phosphate deficiency.

KEY MATERIALS *Arabidopsis* plants, mineral nutrient solutions.

	Experimental level	Conceptual level
1 Construct DNA with promoter of *SQD1* linked to *GUS* (blue color–producing gene), using methods described in Chapter 21.	Promoter of *SQD1* gene Coding region of *GUS* gene	Plants are genetically engineered with a reporter system (*GUS*).
2 Transfer new DNA into *Arabidopsis*.		
3 Remove some leaves 20 hours before transfer to phosphate-deficient media, and 24, 100, and 220 hours after transfer.	20 hours before transfer 24 hours 100 hours 220 hours after transfer	Leaves removed 20 hours before transfer to phosphate-deficient media serve as negative (untreated) controls.
4 After each time point, add a reagent that produces blue color when the *GUS* (and *SQD1*) gene is expressed from the *SQD1* promoter. (See the data.)		Leaves removed at increasingly longer times after transfer to phosphate-deficient media reveal how quickly the reporter system works.

5 **THE DATA**

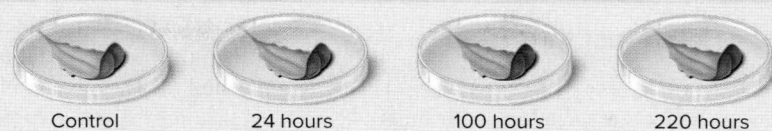

Control   24 hours   100 hours   220 hours

6 **CONCLUSION** Plants can be genetically engineered to express color signals in time for farmers to apply fertilizer sufficient to prevent nutrient deficiency.

7 **SOURCE** Hammond, J. P., et al. 2003. Changes in gene expression in Arabidopsis shoots during phosphate starvation and the potential for developing smart plants. *Plant Physiology* 132: 578–596.

removed before transfer to the phosphate-deficient solution and served as controls. Because the *GUS* gene was under the control of the *SQD1* promoter, leaves from plants that were developing PO_4^{3-} deficiency turned blue! These smart plants were able to communicate impending phosphorous deficiency in time for a farmer to apply fertilizer.

In a later and more extensive study of gene expression in *Arabidopsis*, other investigators discovered that PO_4^{3-} induces the activity of about 612 genes and represses the activity of about 254 genes. Some of these genes may encode proteins useful in monitoring plant phosphorous status. If smart plant technology can be developed for crop plants, farmers may be able to monitor and fertilize fields with much greater precision.

Experimental Questions

1. What advantage do plants obtain when the *SQD1* gene is expressed?

2. **CoreSKILL** » How were the investigators able to identify potential sentinel plants that were starting to experience phosphorous deficiency?

BIO **TIPS**   **THE QUESTION** *Explain why Hammond and colleagues sought to identify plant genes whose expression changed during the period from 24 to 72 hours after the imposition of a phosphorus limitation.*

T OPIC *What topic in biology does this question address?* The topic is plant nutrition, or more specifically, plant responses to nutrient limitation and their relevance to developing technological monitoring systems that allow more efficient applications of fertilizer to crops.

I NFORMATION *What information do you know based on the question and your understanding of the topic?* Phosphorus is an element that is essential to living things, including plants. Table 38.1 briefly reviews its role in plant nutrition. This chapter has explained how nutrients affect plant growth, and you have also learned that soil phosphorus is often bound to inorganic and organic materials that reduce its availability to plant roots. Thus, phosphorus is often applied to fields to enhance crop yields. You also know that plants (like other living organisms) respond to environmental change and that such responses include changes in gene expression.

P ROBLEM-SOLVING S TRATEGY Think about Hammond and colleagues' desire to find genes that would react to phosphorous limitation in a rather short period and whose response could be observed. Realize that a system for monitoring plant nutrient limitation needs to reveal the problem before it causes irreversible effects. Understand that farmers do not want to wait so long to apply fertilizer that crop plants will suffer in the meantime.

ANSWER *Monitoring changes in plant gene expression at different times after the onset of phosphorous limitation allowed the investigators to identify genes that could be used to reveal the point at which the plants started to respond to nutrient limitation but before they incurred serious damage.*

38.3 Biological Sources of Plant Nutrients

Learning Outcomes:

1. Explain the importance of mycorrhizal fungi to plants.
2. List the major types of prokaryotic organisms that occur in symbioses with plants, thereby helping them to acquire nitrogen.
3. Distinguish carnivorous plants from parasitic plants, giving examples.

This section focuses on several fascinating ways in which plants use other organisms as a means to obtain nutrients. Biological mechanisms by which plants obtain nutrients include maintaining symbiotic relationships with fungi or bacteria, capturing animal prey (by carnivorous plants), and serving as hosts for nonphotosynthetic plant parasites.

Mycorrhizal Associations Help Most Plants Obtain Mineral Nutrients

At least 80% of seed plants have symbiotic associations with fungi that live within the tissues of plant roots or that envelop root surfaces (Figures 30.13–30.15). These associations are termed **mycorrhizae**; the prefix *myco* refers to fungi, and *rhiza* means root, so the term literally means fungus root.

In mycorrhizal associations, soil fungi obtain organic food from the roots of photosynthetic plant hosts, and the fungi supply the plants with water and mineral nutrients. Due to the extensive mycelia that fungi produce within the soil, these fungus root associations provide an exceptionally efficient way for plants to harvest water and minerals, especially phosphate, from a much larger volume of soil than is available to roots by themselves. The presence of lush vegetation on thin, infertile tropical rain forest soils is largely due to the ability of mycorrhizae to rapidly absorb mineral nutrients released by decaying organisms and transmit the nutrients directly to plant roots (**Figure 38.15**). In many tropical rain forests, mineral nutrients occur within the bodies of living organisms, rather than accumulating in the soil where they could easily be leached away by heavy, frequent rains.

Various species of ghostly pale plants have lost their photosynthetic pigments (see Figure 38.2). Such heterotrophic plants have become dependent on organic compounds supplied by fungi that form

Figure 38.15 Nutrient acquisition via mycorrhizae.

 Core Concept: Systems In all forests, but particularly those of tropical regions, mycorrhizal fungi rapidly collect soil minerals released from decaying organisms and transport them directly to plant roots. Such efficient nutrient cycling bypasses the soil, from which mineral ions can be easily leached by heavy rainfall. This system of material movement among diverse organisms explains how lush forests can grow on thin, infertile soils.

mycorrhizal associations with a photosynthetic host, such as a nearby tree. In this process, known as mycoheterotrophy, the fungus serves as an underground conduit for the flow of organic nutrients from a green, photosynthetic plant to a heterotrophic plant. Many plant seedlings that grow in the shade of taller plants also use mycoheterotrophy to survive until they are able to obtain enough light for photosynthesis.

Plant-Bacteria Symbioses Provide Some Plants with Fixed Nitrogen

Soils contain large populations of thousands of bacterial species, many of which aid plant growth. Some soil bacteria produce plant hormones that affect root structure, others help plants to tolerate drought and other stresses, and some provide plants with nutrients, notably fixed nitrogen. In nitrogen-fixation symbioses, the plants provide organic nutrients to the bacteria, and the bacteria supply the plants with a much higher supply of fixed nitrogen than the plants could obtain from most soils. Representatives of three types of nitrogen-fixing bacteria—cyanobacteria, actinobacteria, and proteobacteria—are symbiotically associated with specific types of plants. (For more information about the characteristics of these bacterial groups, see Chapter 27.)

Plant-Cyanobacteria Symbioses   Although most cyanobacteria are themselves photosynthetic, organic compounds supplied by plant partners subsidize the high energy costs of nitrogen fixation. This subsidizing allows the cyanobacteria to fix more nitrogen than they require, secreting the excess to plant partners. Nitrogen-fixing cyanobacteria form symbioses with some bryophytes, ferns, and gymnosperms, as well as the flowering plant *Gunnera*. This plant, commonly known as the giant rhubarb or prickly rhubarb, can produce leaves almost 3 m across (**Figure 38.16**). Nitrogen-fixing symbionts are advantageous to *Gunnera* because this large plant grows in nitrogen-poor habitats, such as volcanic slopes in Hawaii. *Gunnera* harbors cyanobacteria within stems and leaf petioles. In these locations, the cyanobacteria can use cyclic electron flow to transform light energy into ATP, needed to produce fixed nitrogen. The presence of nitrogen-fixing cyanobacteria helps to explain why *Gunnera* can grow to dramatic size on poor soils.

Woody Plant–Actinobacteria Symbioses   In contrast to photosynthetic cyanobacteria, actinobacteria are heterotrophic nitrogen-fixing bacteria. The actinobacterial genus *Frankia* occurs in nodules formed on the underground roots of certain shrubs or trees, such as alder (*Alnus*) and myrtle (*Myrica*). These plants receive fixed nitrogen from their bacterial partners, which, in turn, obtain organic nutrients. Woody plants, such as shrubs of the genus *Ceanothus*, that have *Frankia* symbionts are able to grow abundantly even in places where soil nitrogen is low. This symbiosis helps to explain why *Ceanothus* covers extensive areas in mountainous regions of the western U.S.

Legume-Rhizobia Symbioses   The nitrogen-fixation symbioses most important in nature and to agriculture involve certain species of proteobacteria that are collectively known as **rhizobia** (from the Greek *rhiza*, meaning root). Rhizobia live within root cells of wild and cultivated legumes, forming legume-rhizobia symbioses. In nature, legume plants are important sources of fixed nitrogen for other plants. When legumes die, they generate soil organic matter that is enriched

Figure 38.16 *Gunnera* **growing on nitrogen-poor soil.** Nitrogen-fixing cyanobacteria that live within cavities in this plant's leaf petioles provide the plant with fixed nitrogen, which explains how such a large plant can grow on infertile soils. ©J. Hyvönen; (inset): ©Photo by Birgitta Bergman, Department of Botany, Stockholm University (Sweden)

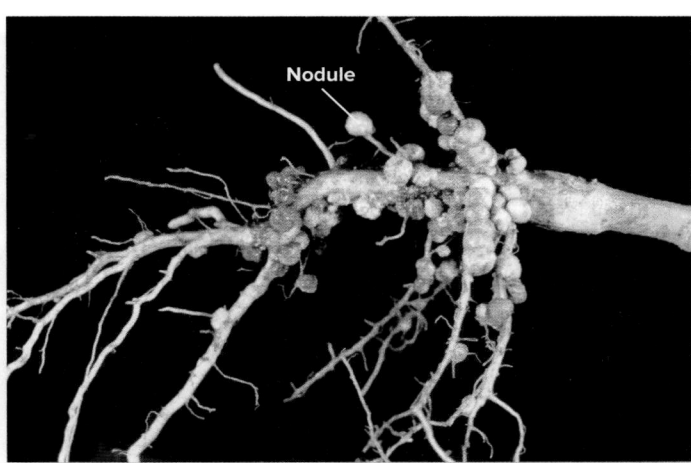

Figure 38.17 **Legume root nodules.** The cells of nodules on the roots of this soybean plant (*Glycine max*) and other legumes contain nitrogen-fixing bacteria known as rhizobia. ©Scimat/Science Source

with fixed nitrogen. Consequently, wild legumes are regarded as particularly valuable members of natural plant communities.

Important legume crops include soybeans, peas, beans, peanuts, clover, and alfalfa. Foods produced from soybeans, peas, beans, and peanuts are valued for their high protein content. Clover and alfalfa are used for animal food and to enrich fields with the fixed nitrogen needed by subsequent food crops. The value of these crops arises from their fixed-nitrogen content. The amount of ammonia produced by legume-rhizobia symbioses nearly equals the world's entire industrial production.

Core Concepts: Systems, Information

Development of Legume-Rhizobia Symbioses

Rhizobia can live independently in the soil, but are also found within lumpy **nodules** that form on legume roots (**Figure 38.17**). Different species of rhizobia preferentially form symbioses with particular plant species. Because of their agricultural importance, these legume-rhizobia symbioses have been extensively studied, and a great deal is now known about the molecular basis of their development. This information is potentially useful in efforts to genetically engineer nitrogen-fixation capacity into nonlegume crops.

Nodule development involves a series of chemical signals sent back and forth between rhizobia and their host plants (**Figure 38.18**). Legumes start this exchange by secreting particular flavonoid compounds from their roots. Recall that flavonoids are phenolic secondary metabolites that play essential roles in plant structure, reproduction, and protection (see Figure 32.22b). These flavonoids bind to receptors in the plasma membranes of compatible soil rhizobia (Figure 38.18, step 1). In response, the rhizobia typically secrete **Nod factors** (nodulation factors). Each rhizobial species produces Nod factors with distinctive structural variations that can be recognized by the preferred host species. These Nod factors function something like keys that unlock doors, allowing bacteria to enter roots via root hairs. The factors bind to receptors in the membranes of root hair cells in the host plant (step 2).

Within minutes after its membrane receptors bind Nod factors, the root hair plasma membrane allows an influx of calcium ions, and a few minutes later, root hair calcium ion concentrations start oscillating rapidly. Root hairs respond to these calcium changes by swelling at their tips and curling around the rhizobia (step 3). The rhizobia then inject infection proteins into root hairs. In response, the cell wall at the root hair tip changes so that bacterial enzymes can erode a small hole in the wall, allowing the bacterial cells to enter. The plasma membrane forms a tubular infection thread through which rhizobia move into the root cortex. The tip of the infection thread fuses with the plasma membrane of a cortex cell, then the rhizobia are released into the cell's cytoplasm, each bacterial cell enclosed by the host membrane (step 4).

Meanwhile, plants produce proteins known as **nodulins** that foster root nodule development. Within 18–30 hours after the initial infection, root cortex cells start to divide to form root nodules. Environmental conditions in developing nodules cause rhizobia to undergo changes in their structure and gene expression patterns. These modified rhizobia are known as **bacteroids** (step 5). Bacteroid respiration provides the large amounts of ATP that are necessary for nitrogen fixation.

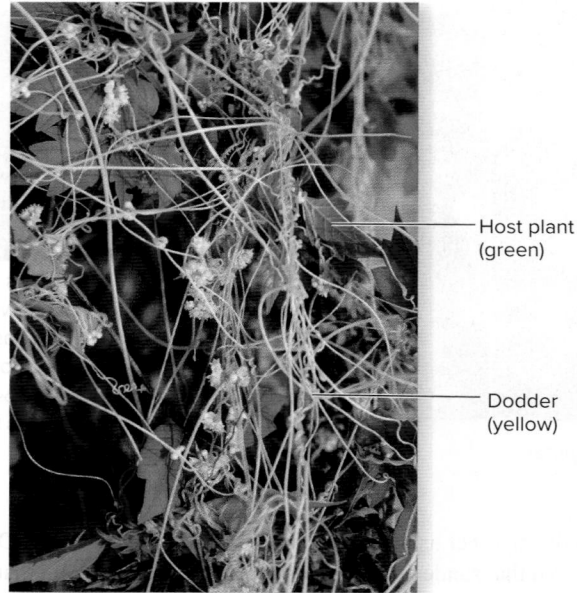

Host plant
(green)

Dodder
(yellow)

Figure 38.20 A parasitic plant. Dodder (*Cuscuta pentagona*) is
an example of a parasitic plant that obtains all of its water, minerals,
and organic compounds from one or more green plant hosts. Source:
Charles T. Bryson, USDA Agricultural Research Service, Bugwood.org

 Core Skill: Connections Look back to Figure
34.7b to see an example of a parasitic animal—a
tapeworm—and Table 34.2, which describes characteristics of tapeworms. What is similar about food
acquisition in dodder and tapeworms?

Summary of Key Concepts

38.1 Plant Nutritional Requirements

- The nutrients required by green plants are CO_2, H_2O, and several types
  of elements absorbed from soil or water (Figure 38.1, Table 38.1).

- Green plants require light energy as an essential resource for
  growth. Like animals and fungi, heterotrophic plants obtain
  chemical energy by metabolizing organic compounds absorbed
  from their environment (Figure 38.2).

- Plants display many adaptations that allow them to cope with
  insufficient or excess amounts of light and inadequate CO_2 (Figures
  38.3, 38.4, 38.5).

- Inadequate supplies of certain nutrients can limit plant growth and
  cause mineral deficiency symptoms (Figure 38.6).

38.2 The Role of Soil in Plant Nutrition

- Natural soils display layers known as soil horizons. Soils are
  composed of organic material and inorganic minerals. Soil organic
  matter is largely derived from plant detritus, animal wastes, and
  decayed animal bodies (Figures 38.7, 38.8).

- Inorganic soil components occur as particles that can be
  categorized according to their size as sand, silt, or clay. Cation
  exchange releases cations to soil water, making cations available
  for uptake by plant roots (Figures 38.9, 38.10, 38.11).

- Biological or industrial processes convert atmospheric nitrogen
  gas into fixed nitrogen that plants can utilize. Biological
  nitrogen fixation can be performed only by certain prokaryotes
  (Figures 38.12, 38.13).

- Plants display several types of adaptations to cope with phosphate
  deficiency. Genetically modified smart plants can signal impending
  phosphate deficiency (Figure 38.14).

38.3 Biological Sources of Plant Nutrients

- Mycorrhizal fungi, which are associated with the roots of most
  plants, provide plants with water, phosphorus, and other minerals
  (Figure 38.15).

- Nitrogen-fixing prokaryotes living within the tissues of some
  plants provide them with fixed nitrogen. Legume-rhizobia
  associations are particularly important in nature and in agriculture
  (Figures 38.16, 38.17, 38.18).

- Carnivorous plants obtain mineral nutrients from the digested
  bodies of trapped animals. Parasitic plants obtain water,
  minerals, and organic compounds from green plant hosts
  (Figures 38.19, 38.20).

Assess & Discuss

Test Yourself

1. Which of the following substances can limit plant growth in nature?
   a. sunlight
   b. water
   c. carbon dioxide
   d. fixed nitrogen
   e. all of the above

2. In what form do plants take up most soil minerals?
   a. as ions dissolved in water
   b. as neutral salts
   c. as mineral-clay complexes
   d. linked to particles of organic carbon
   e. None of the above describes how plants take up minerals.

3. Why do plants need sulfur?
   a. for the construction of cell walls
   b. as an essential component of chlorophyll
   c. to produce proteins and some coenzymes
   d. for all of the above
   e. for none of the above

4. Soil organic matter provides the benefit of
   a. allowing water to percolate rapidly through soil.
   b. making soil softer in consistency.
   c. increasing the aluminum content of soil.
   d. causing minerals to be leached more rapidly from soil.
   e. none of the above.

5. Which environments are conducive to heavy leaching of minerals
   from soils?
   a. those having soils that are composed primarily of sand particles
   b. those having acidic soils
   c. those impacted by acid rain
   d. regions characterized by heavy rainfall
   e. all of the above

6. Which property is *not* characteristic of clay-rich soils?
   a. high mineral nutrient retention
   b. high water retention
   c. high aeration
   d. lower amounts of sand than clay
   e. All of the above characterize clay-rich soils.

7. Which of the plants listed below is heterotrophic (has to obtain organic food from the environment)?
   a. a green houseplant
   b. a legume plant such as bean
   c. a carnivorous plant such as the sundew
   d. ghostly white *Monotropa*
   e. none of the above

8. What kinds of organisms occur in nitrogen-fixing symbioses with plants?
   a. cyanobacteria
   b. actinobacteria
   c. rhizobia
   d. all of the above
   e. none of the above

9. How do legume roots attract rhizobia?
   a. They secrete flavonoids.
   b. They secrete carotenoids.
   c. They secrete alkaloids.
   d. They secrete Nod factors.
   e. None of the above is a means of attracting rhizobia.

10. Which plant uses a passive trap to obtain animal prey as a source of mineral nutrients?
    a. the Indian pipe (*Monotropa uniflora*)
    b. the tropical pitcher plant (*Nepenthes* spp.)
    c. the Venus flytrap (*Dionaea muscipula*)
    d. dodder (*Cuscuta* spp.)
    e. all of the above

Conceptual Questions

1. Why are agricultural experts and ecologists concerned about overfertilization of crop fields?

2. Draw a diagram showing how rhizobia and legume roots communicate chemically during nodule formation.

3.  **Core Concept: Systems** How can lush tropical forests grow on relatively thin soils from which nutrients have been leached by frequent, heavy rains?

Collaborative Questions

1. Imagine that you have bought a farm and want to start growing a crop to sell at a local market. How could you go about determining if the soil needs to be fertilized and with what mineral nutrients?

2.  **Core Skill: Science and Society** Imagine that you own a large farm with a trout stream running through it. How would you protect the water quality of the stream?

Flowering Plants: Transport

39

A shade tree. The evaporation of water from plant leaves cools them and us, and even affects local and global climate.

©Barry Mason/Alamy Stock Photo

O n hot days, people naturally gravitate to the cool shade beneath trees, as shown in the chapter opening photo. But most people do not realize that trees are not only sun umbrellas. Plants actually cool the air around them as water evaporates from their surfaces. That's why grass feels cool when you walk barefoot on it, even on a hot day.

Plants benefit from this evaporation process—known as transpiration—because it cools their surfaces and enables the movement of a continuous stream of water from the soil, through roots and stems, to leaves. This evaporation process not only helps to distribute water throughout the plant body, but also aids the movement of dissolved minerals, organic compounds such as sugars and hormones, and other organic materials over long distances within plants. Transport is therefore crucial for the functions of plant growth, behavior, and nutrition, which we discussed in the preceding three chapters.

In addition, plant transport plays a critical role in Earth's global climate. On a worldwide basis, plant transpiration annually moves 3.2×10^4 billion tons of water from the soil into the atmosphere as water vapor. Plant transpiration provides important ecological services. For example, plant-produced atmospheric water vapor is the source of 30% of rain, with the rest originating from evaporation at the surfaces of oceans and freshwater bodies. Along with other atmospheric gases (including carbon dioxide and methane), water vapor also works as a greenhouse gas that helps to warm Earth's climate by absorbing the Sun's heat. Plant transport processes are also relevant to agriculture, as humans seek to improve crop productivity and the efficiency of water and nutrient use. Conservation biologists appreciate that plant transport processes are important to the preservation and restoration of natural environments.

To understand plant transport more fully, in this chapter, we first survey the materials that move through plants and the general directions of such movements. Next, we will focus more closely on water and solute uptake by plant cells. We will then examine how these materials are moved within plants over short and long distances and explore some of the plant adaptations that allow such transport to be as efficient as possible in a variety of environments. In the process, we will learn why plants are so cool!

39.1 Overview of Plant Transport

Learning Outcomes:

1. Describe how plants transport water and minerals from roots to leaves.
2. Describe how plants transport organic molecules from leaves to nonphotosynthetic parts.

In Chapters 36–38, we surveyed the structure, behavior, and nutrition of flowering plants (the angiosperms) and discussed the interdependence of plant root and shoot systems. We have seen that in most plants, the root system absorbs water and dissolved minerals from the soil and that the shoot system takes up carbon dioxide (CO_2) from the atmosphere via stomata, pores that occur in the surfaces of leaves and other aboveground structures

(**Figure 39.1**). Photosynthetic cells use these materials to produce sugar and other organic compounds needed for overall plant growth and reproduction. Nonphotosynthetic plant cells, such as those of roots and flowers, depend on organic food produced by green tissues.

The growth and survival of plants depends on a two-way transport system. Organic food is transported from photosynthetic to nonphotosynthetic parts. In most plants, this transport is generally downward from the leaves to the roots. In addition, water and minerals are transported upward from roots to shoots. Since plants can grow to sizable heights, the tallest trees being over 100 m tall, transport of materials often occurs over long distances.

The long-distance transport of water, dissolved minerals, and sugar throughout the plant body occurs within a continuous system of conducting tissues. Recall that the complex tissues of vascular plants that primarily conduct water and dissolved minerals are known as the xylem, and those that conduct mostly organic substances in a watery sap are termed the phloem. These conducting tissues are key to the ability of vascular plants to thrive in terrestrial habitats, which can sometimes be quite arid. To fully understand how plants accomplish long-distance transport, we will begin by reviewing the processes by which minerals, organic compounds, and water are taken up and move at the cellular level.

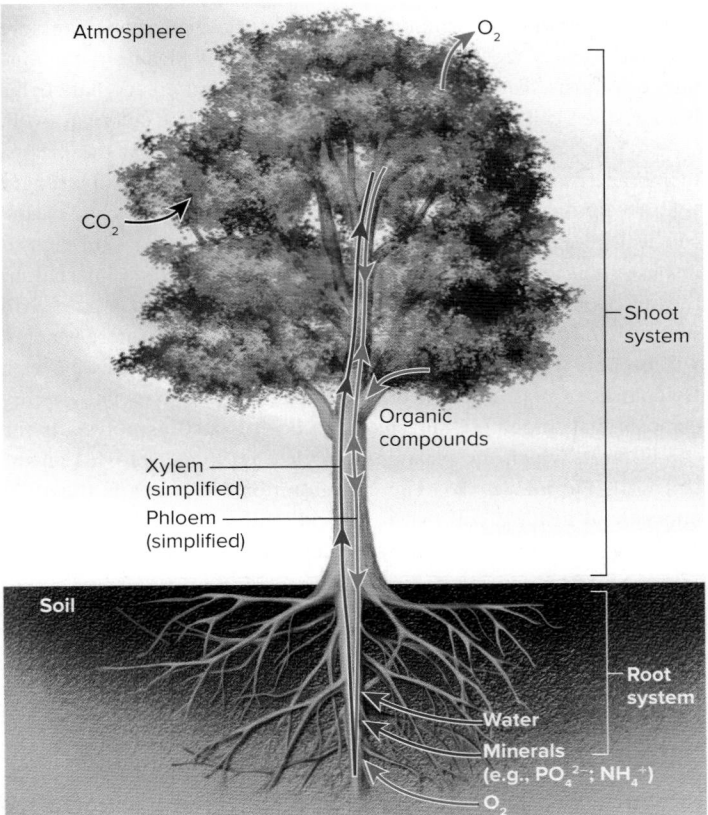

Figure 39.1 Overview of material uptake and long-distance transport processes in plants.

39.2 Uptake and Movement of Materials at the Cellular Level

Learning Outcomes:

1. Describe the differences among turgid, flaccid, and plasmolyzed plant cells.
2. **CoreSKILL** ≫ Explain how water potential and relative water content are calculated.
3. List ways in which plants cope with cellular osmotic stress.

Chapter 5 described how all cells use both passive and active processes to import or export materials. Here, we briefly review these processes, illustrating how they work in flowering plants.

Passive Transport Does Not Require the Input of Energy

Recall that water, gases, and certain small, uncharged compounds can diffuse across plasma membranes in the direction of their concentration gradients. **Passive transport** is the movement of materials into or out of cells down a concentration gradient without the expenditure of energy in the form of ATP. Passive transport across plasma membranes occurs in two ways: by simple or facilitated diffusion. **Simple diffusion** into or out of cells is the movement of molecules through a phospholipid bilayer down a concentration gradient. **Facilitated diffusion** is the transport of molecules across a plasma membrane down a concentration gradient with the aid of membrane transport proteins (**Figure 39.2a**).

The two main types of membrane transport proteins that function in facilitated diffusion are channels and transporters. **Channels** are membrane pores formed by proteins that allow movement of ions and molecules across membranes (see Figure 39.2). **Transporters** are proteins that transport molecules by binding them on one side of the membrane and then changing conformation so that the molecule is released to the other side of the membrane (refer back to Figure 5.17). Transporters increase the rate at which specific mineral ions and organic molecules are able to enter or leave plant cells and vacuoles.

Recall that osmosis is the diffusion of water across a selectively permeable membrane in response to differences in solute concentrations. In the case of plants, water moves from a solution that has a lower solute concentration (soil) to one of higher solute concentration (root cells). Osmotic water uptake into living plant cells is essential to photosynthesis, as well as to cell expansion and structural support. However, simple diffusion of water does not occur rapidly enough to supply the water needs of rapidly expanding plant cells. In this case, facilitated diffusion of water occurs through protein channels known as **aquaporins**, which occur widely in living cells. Thirty-five distinct aquaporin genes have been identified in the genome of the model plant *Arabidopsis*. Aquaporins increase the rate at which water flows into expanding plant cells and their vacuoles. Similarly, many other types of plasma membrane protein channels and transporters facilitate the diffusion of specific mineral ions and organic molecules into and out of plant cells and vacuoles.

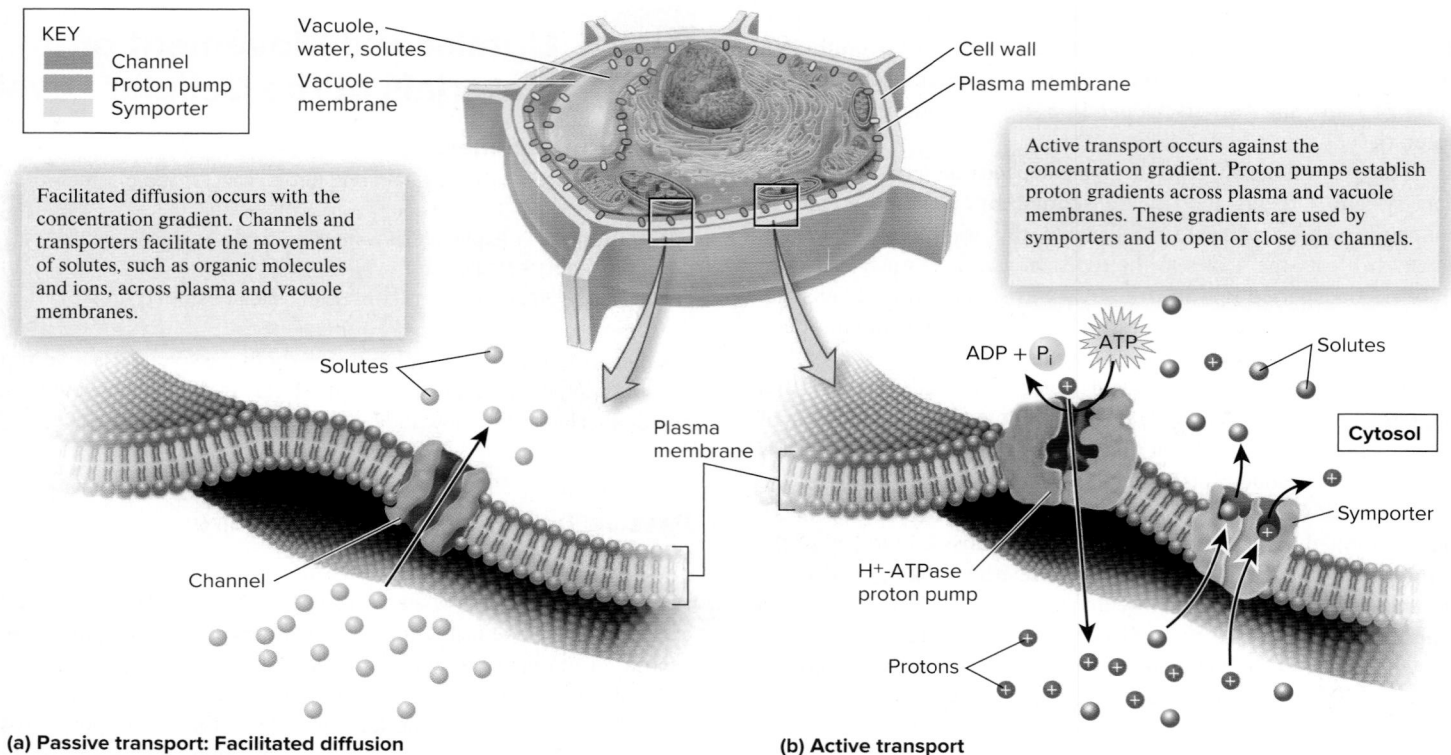

KEY
■ Channel
■ Proton pump
□ Symporter

Vacuole, water, solutes
Vacuole membrane

Cell wall
Plasma membrane

Active transport occurs against the concentration gradient. Proton pumps establish proton gradients across plasma and vacuole membranes. These gradients are used by symporters and to open or close ion channels.

Facilitated diffusion occurs with the concentration gradient. Channels and transporters facilitate the movement of solutes, such as organic molecules and ions, across plasma and vacuole membranes.

Solutes

$ADP + P_i$ ATP   Solutes

Cytosol

Plasma membrane

Symporter

Channel

H^+-ATPase proton pump

Protons

(a) Passive transport: Facilitated diffusion

(b) Active transport

Figure 39.2 **Passive and active transport.**

ATP Hydrolysis Powers Active Transport

If a substance must be transported across a plasma membrane against its concentration gradient, work must be performed, in the process known as active transport. During **active transport**, membrane transport proteins use energy to move substances against their concentration gradients. An example is the H^+-ATPase proton pump, found in the plasma membranes of plant cells, which uses ATP to pump H^+, which are protons, against a gradient (**Figure 39.2b**). This concentration gradient generates an electrical charge difference across the membrane, which is known as a **membrane potential**. Energy is released when protons pass back across the plasma membrane, in the direction of their proton gradient. This energy can then be used to power other active transport of ions or organic materials. For example, it might be used to open or close ion channels or in the functioning of a proton-solute **symporter**, a protein that transports two substances in the same direction across a membrane. Symporters are needed for the uptake of organic solutes such as sugars, amino acids, and nucleotide bases.

Active transport proteins are particularly abundant in root cell membranes (**Figure 39.3**), allowing root cells to concentrate dissolved mineral nutrients to more than 75 times their abundance in soil. As a result, soil water flows into root cells by osmosis. We next take a closer look at osmotic water movement into and out of plant cells.

Cellular Water Content Is Influenced by Solute Content and Turgor Pressure

The water content of plant cells depends on osmosis, and osmosis depends on two factors: solute content and turgor pressure.

Turgor pressure, or osmotic pressure, is the hydrostatic pressure required to stop the net flow of water across a plasma membrane due to osmosis. Turgor pressure increases as water enters plant cells, because their cell walls restrict the extent to which the cells can swell.

A plant cell whose cytosol is so full of water that the plasma membrane presses right up against the cell wall is said to be **turgid** (**Figure 39.4a**). The pressure relationship between the cytosol and cell wall resembles the way that a soccer ball's leather skin presses inward upon the air within, while at the same time the internal air presses on the ball's cover. If you add more air to a limp ball, the ball will stiffen. In the same way, if a nonturgid cell absorbs more water, it will become more rigid as the water exerts pressure on the cell wall. By contrast, a plasmolyzed cell is one that has lost so much water by osmosis that turgor pressure has also been lost. **Plasmolysis** is the condition in which the plasma membrane no longer presses on the cell wall (**Figure 39.4b**). The concentration of solutes is the same outside and inside a cell that is **flaccid**, and such a cell has a water content higher than a plasmolyzed cell but lower than a turgid cell (**Figure 39.4c**).

Water Potential Affects the Movement of Water Into and Out of Cells and a Plant's Relative Water Content

Together, solute concentration and the presence of a cell wall influence an important plant cell property known as **water potential**, the potential energy of water. Water moves from a region of higher water potential to a region of lower water potential. A good analogy is a waterfall, in which the water has high gravitational potential energy

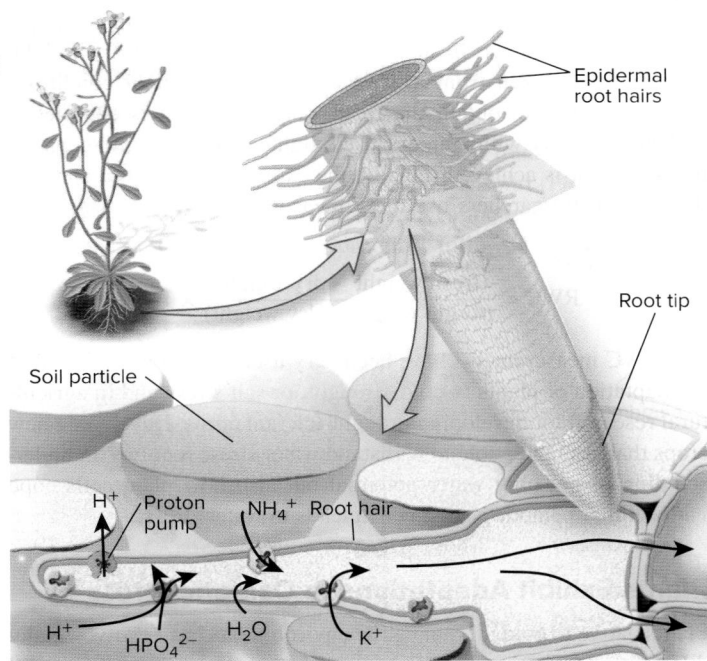

Figure 39.3 Ion uptake at root-hair membranes. The H⁺-ATPase proton pump establishes an electrochemical gradient that drives the active uptake of solutes. The resulting increase in intracellular solute concentration also drives the osmotic diffusion of water into the cell.

 Core Concept: Energy and Matter When mineral ion concentrations in the soil are lower than those within cells, root-hair plasma membranes take up nutrient ions by active transport, which requires energy in the form of ATP.

at the top. Pressure also influences water potential; a waterfall would flow upward if pressure greater than the force of gravity were applied. Solutes and some other factors also affect water potential.

Water potential is measured in pressure units known as megapascals (MPa) (a pascal is equal to 1 newton per square meter). One MPa is equal to 10 times the average air pressure at sea level, about the same pressure that occurs within an inflated bicycle tire. As another reference point, 1 MPa is several times the pressure in typical home plumbing pipes, which you experience when turning on a water faucet.

In the study of plants, the concept of water potential is used to understand the movement of water into and out of cells (cellular water potential) and between entire plants and their environment. The concept of relative water content is used to gauge the water status of whole plants or organs.

Cellular Water Potential A water potential equation can be used to predict the direction of water movement, given information about the solute concentrations inside and outside of plant cells and a measure of pressure at the cell-wall–membrane interface. In this equation, cellular water potential is symbolized by the Greek letter psi (ψ) with the subscript W for water: ψ_W. In its simplest form, total ψ_W is calculated as:

$$\psi_W = \psi_S + \psi_P$$

where ψ_S is solute potential and ψ_P is pressure potential.

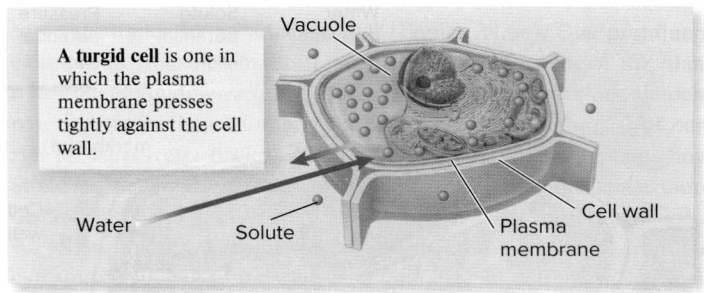

(a) Turgid cell in a hypotonic solution

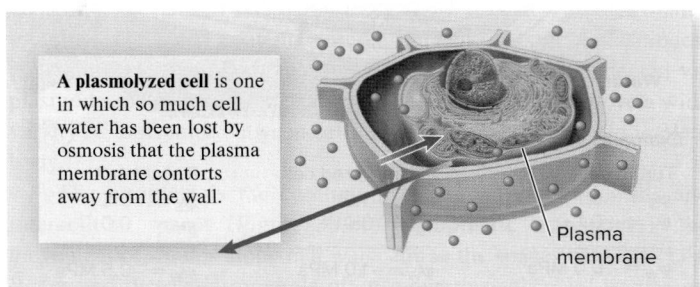

(b) Plasmolyzed cell in a hypertonic solution

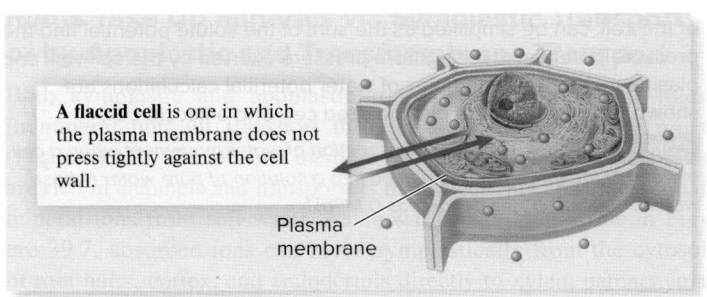

(c) Flaccid cell in an isotonic solution

Figure 39.4 Turgid, plasmolyzed, and flaccid plant cells.
(a) When the concentration of solutes inside a cell is greater than that outside (the cell is surrounded by a hypotonic solution), more water may enter the cell than will leave it. As a result, the plant cell may become swollen, or turgid. **(b)** When the concentration of solutes outside a cell is greater than within it (the cell is surrounded by a hypertonic solution), more water will leave the cell than will enter it. As a result, a plant cell will become plasmolyzed. **(c)** When a cell is bathed in an isotonic solution, it will be flaccid.

Solute potential is the component of water potential due to the presence of solute molecules. As you might expect, solute potential is proportional to the concentration of solutes in a solution. The solute potential of pure water open to the air, at sea level and room temperature, is defined as zero. When solutes are added, they interact with water molecules, thereby diluting the water and affecting its disorder. As a result, fewer free water molecules are present, which reduces the potential energy of water. Thus, in the absence of a pressure potential, water that contains solutes always has a negative solute potential. The higher the concentration of dissolved solutes, the lower (more negative) the solute potential.

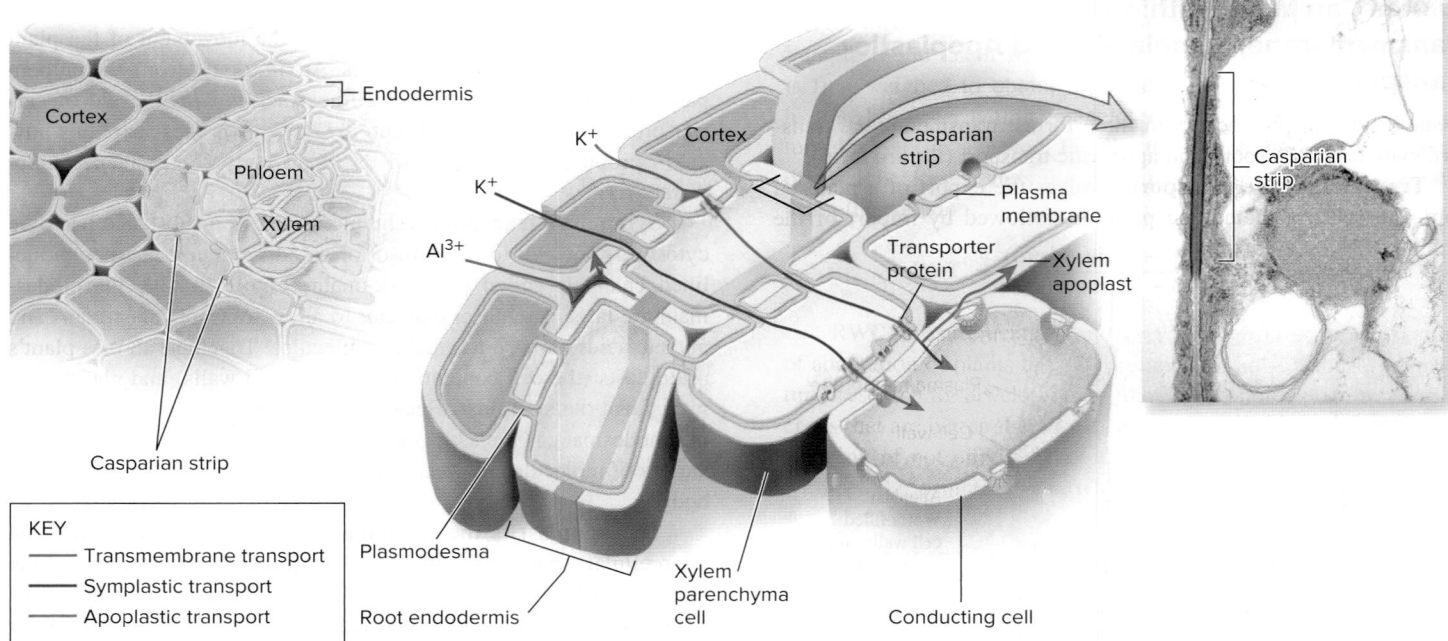

Figure 39.8 Ion transport pathways across the root endodermis. Casparian strips in endodermal cell walls prevent apoplastic transport across the root endodermis, limiting entry of harmful soil minerals such as Al^{3+} and exit of useful solutes. Mineral nutrients that are transported into the cytosol of endodermal cells are able to pass through the endodermal barrier to xylem parenchyma cells via plasmodesmata. Once past the endodermis, nutrient ions such as K^+ are moved across plasma membranes to the apoplast of the vascular tissue and are thus able to enter the xylem. Inset shows a transmission electron micrograph (TEM) of a Casparian strip in the wall of an endodermal cell. (right): ©James S. Busse

 Core Skill: Connections Look back to Figure 10.9 to see a diagram of tight junctions between adjacent cells of animal intestinal epithelium. How is the root endodermis similar in structure and function?

Apoplastic transport can also move water and dissolved minerals into root epidermal and cortex tissues. However, apoplastic movement of water and minerals stops at the **endodermis**, a term meaning inside skin. In roots, the endodermis is a thin cylinder of tissue whose close-fitting cells and specialized cell walls form a barrier to diffusion between the cortex and the central core of vascular tissue. The plant endodermis is functionally analogous to animal epithelial tissues whose cellular tight junctions likewise form diffusion barriers. Materials in the root apoplast cannot penetrate farther into the root unless endodermal cells transport them into their cytosol, a process that requires specific transporter proteins (see the green junction between the red and blue arrows in Figure 39.7).

Root endodermal cell walls possess ribbon-like strips composed of waxy, waterproof suberin and phenolic polymers. These ribbons, known as **Casparian strips**, prevent apoplastic transport of solutes through endodermal cell walls and into the root vascular tissues (**Figure 39.8**). The root endodermis thereby prevents harmful solutes (such as toxic metal ions) from moving through the apoplast to vascular tissues and being transported to the shoot. For example, aluminum ions (Al^{3+}) are commonly dissolved in soil water, but they are not plant nutrients and are highly toxic to plants. Aluminum ions can penetrate the root epidermis and cortex by moving through the apoplast, but they stop at the endodermis because they are unable to enter the cytosol of endodermal cells.

Endodermal plasma membranes possess specific channels and transporters for essential mineral nutrients (such as K^+), which allows them to enter the cytosol of root endodermal cells. By moving through endodermal cytosol, symplastically transported essential minerals are able to bypass the Casparian strips. Therefore, the root endodermis functions as a molecular filter that allows the passage of beneficial solutes.

Once solutes have moved through endodermal cells, they are transported into the apoplast of the vascular system, which includes the conducting cells of the xylem (see Figure 39.8). The endodermis prevents solutes from returning to outer root tissues or the soil, so the solute concentrations of xylem parenchyma cells rise, decreasing their cellular water potential. As a result, water flows into vascular tissues from outer root tissues and the soil. In the next section, we will see how water and solutes are transported over long distances in a plant.

39.4 Long-Distance Transport

Learning Outcomes:

1. Describe how bulk flow occurs in the xylem and phloem of flowering plants.
2. Describe how vessel elements differ from tracheids, and explain how both function in the xylem of flowering plants.
3. Summarize how the cohesion-tension theory explains long-distance water movement in plants.
4. Explain how stomata and leaf abscission help reduce transpirational water loss.

5. Describe how sieve-tube elements and companion cells work together to form a transport system.

6. **CoreSKILL** » Create a diagram showing how and why phloem sap moves from source to sink.

Plants rely on long-distance transport to move water and dissolved materials between roots and shoots and among organs. Tall trees are able to transport water and minerals to astounding heights, more than 110 m in some cases. This is possible because plants possess an extensive, branched, long-distance vascular system composed of xylem and phloem tissues. Watery solutions move through these tissues by **bulk flow**, the mass movement of liquid caused by pressure, gravity, or both. Plant conducting tissues are specialized in ways that foster bulk flow and aid plants in adapting to water stress. In this section, we will take a closer look at bulk flow and the major factors involved in long-distance transport by this process.

Bulk Flow Is Water Movement Under the Influence of Pressure and Gravity

Bulk flow (also known as mass flow) occurs when molecules of liquid all move together from one place to another as the result of differences in pressure and/or gravity. One example of bulk flow is leaching, the movement of water and dissolved minerals downward through soil layers as the result of gravity (Chapter 38). Bulk flow is one way in which mineral ions can move through soil toward plant roots. Likewise, once inside the plant, minerals and other dissolved solutes can move through xylem and phloem conducting tissues via bulk flow, which is much faster than diffusion. For example, phloem sap, which contains sugars and other dissolved solutes, moves by bulk flow up to 1 m per hour. The bulk flow of water and solutes within xylem and phloem results from differences in water pressure. However, the pressure differences originate from different processes in these two types of conducting tissues.

In xylem, the bulk flow of water and dissolved minerals is driven by **transpiration** (from the French *transpirer*, meaning to perspire), the process in which water evaporates from the aerial parts of plants, usually via the stomata of leaves (**Figure 39.9**). The extent to which

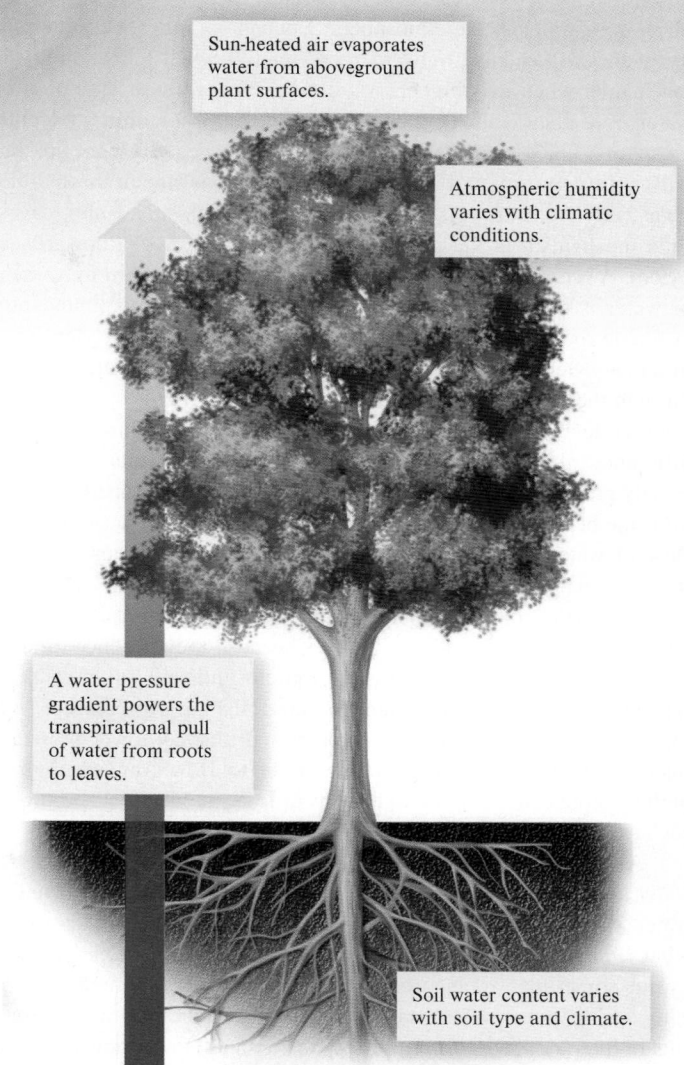

Sun-heated air evaporates water from aboveground plant surfaces.

Atmospheric humidity varies with climatic conditions.

A water pressure gradient powers the transpirational pull of water from roots to leaves.

Soil water content varies with soil type and climate.

Figure 39.9 Upward transport of water in xylem. Water pressure differences between moist soil and drier air drive the upward movement of water in plants.

 Core Skill: Modeling The goal of this modeling challenge is to show how gravity might impact plant size by influencing transport.

Modeling Challenge: Figure 39.9 is a model showing the relationship between evaporation at a tree's leaf surfaces and the water pressure gradient that occurs in the tree's water transport system (xylem), given adequate soil water availability. This model assumes constant gravity, which on Earth averages 9.8 m/s^2 (32.2 ft/s^2) for a standard latitude of 45° 32'33".

In recent years, diverse planets have been detected outside of our solar system, some occurring in orbits that might allow the existence of liquid water and life. These include three of the seven planets (labeled e, f, and g) in the TRAPPIST-1 system. Let's suppose a particular tree species on Earth attains a maximal height of 100 m. Imagine that the seeds from such trees could be transported to other planets having an orbit favorable to the presence of liquid water and to tree growth.

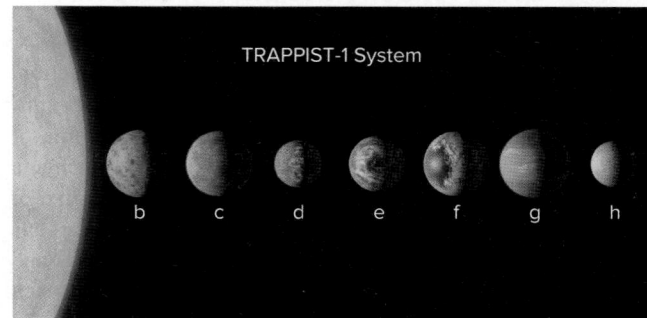

TRAPPIST-1 System

b   c   d   e   f   g   h

Source: NASA/JPL-Caltech

Sketch three trees showing differences in the maximal height that you expect to occur on three planets, one having much lower gravity than occurs on Earth, one with gravity similar to Earth's, and one with gravity much higher than Earth's. On your sketch, indicate the height of each tree and explain the differences in height.

plants lose water to the atmosphere depends on atmospheric humidity; water will diffuse outward more readily when the humidity is lower than when it is higher. As discussed later, the evaporation of water from plant cells increases the surface tension within intercellular spaces. This rise in surface tension creates a negative pressure that pulls water upward, and it moves as a continuous stream through the plant body from the soil, into roots, through stems, and into leaves. This mechanism is the primary way that water moves upward via xylem. A second mechanism that can promote the upward movement of water is related to root pressure. When soil water is abundantly available to roots, water pressure will be higher in root xylem than in shoot xylem. This positive pressure tends to push water upward through the xylem.

While the evaporation of water from leaves creates pressure differences that facilitate the upward movement of water via xylem, gravity promotes a downward movement. These two competing forces limit the heights that terrestrial plants can achieve. Because the bulk flow of water in plant xylem is affected by gravity, trees on Earth rarely exceed 100 m in height.

Bulk flow in phloem arises by a different process. Pressure builds up in the phloem sap of leaves because they produce organic solutes such as sugars as the result of photosynthesis. An increase in sap organic solutes causes water to enter, making sap pressure rise. Phloem sap that contains fewer solutes will display lower pressure. Such differences in pressure cause water to flow from regions of higher solute concentration to regions of lower solute concentrations, such as developing fruit and roots.

Although xylem serves as the primary transport system for water and minerals, and phloem for organic compounds dissolved in water, the transport functions of xylem and phloem overlap somewhat. Phloem can aid in the distribution of certain minerals, and xylem sometimes transports organic compounds. For example, in early spring, trees convert starch stored in stem parenchyma cells into sugars that are used during bud expansion and flower development. These sugars are transported in xylem sap. Maple trees produce a copious flow of sugar-rich xylem sap that people have long tapped to make maple syrup (**Figure 39.10**).

Xylem Is Adapted for Long-Distance Transport of Water and Minerals

Xylem's structure plays an essential role in its transport function. The xylem of flowering plants contains several types of specialized cells, some of which remain alive at maturity, and some of which are dead when they are fully functional. Xylem parenchyma cells are alive, but thick-walled supportive fibers may be alive or dead at maturity. Two types of specialized water-conducting cells are always dead and empty of cytosol when mature: tracheids and vessel elements. Bulk flow would be impeded by obstructions such as cytoplasm. This explains why xylem conducting cells are devoid of cytoplasm.

Together, tracheids and vessel elements are known as **tracheary elements**. During the development of tracheary elements, a secondary wall is deposited in patterns, such as spirals or rings, on the inside of the primary cell wall. This secondary wall is rich in a plastic-like polymer known as lignin. Because lignin is

Figure 39.10 **Sugar-maple tapping.** In early spring, xylem transports sugar from storage sites to the shoot buds of woody plants such as this sugar maple (*Acer saccharum*). ©Andre Jenny/Alamy Stock Photo

 Core Skill: Science and Society People tap sugar maples by boring holes into the tree trunks and collecting the xylem sap (shown here in buckets). The sap is boiled to evaporate some of the water, leaving the concentrated product—maple syrup.

resistant to compression, microbial decay, and water infiltration, it confers strength, durability, and waterproofing. Like the plumbing pipes of a building, lignin-reinforced tracheary elements do not readily collapse as water moves through them under tension. In contrast, the xylem of lignin-deficient mutant plants is more collapsible. These characteristics explain how tracheary elements contribute to structural support of the plant body as well as functioning in transport.

Tracheids Long and narrow in shape, **tracheids** typically have slanted end walls that fit together to form long tubes (**Figure 39.11a**). The end walls of tracheids are not lignified, nor are large areas of the side walls of tracheids that occur in plant tissues that are still growing. Such tracheids are extensible because they have spirals or rings of lignin that allow them to continue elongating (**Figure 39.11b**). In contrast, tracheids that develop in tissues that have already expanded have more lignin, which makes them rigid and unable to elongate any more. Tracheid walls that are extensively lignified display numerous small, lignin-free cell-wall regions known as **pits**. At such pits, the thin primary wall of the tracheid remains readily permeable to water. Water moves from one tracheid to another both vertically and laterally through pits.

Vessels and Vessel Elements Mature **vessel elements** are a second type of water-conducting cell present in xylem tissue. Vessel elements are aligned in pipeline-like structures known as **vessels** (**Figure 39.12a**). Flowering plants are distinguished from other plant groups by the abundance of vessels; nonflowering plants primarily rely on tracheids for water conduction. Vessel elements are larger in diameter and longer than tracheids, conferring greater capacity for

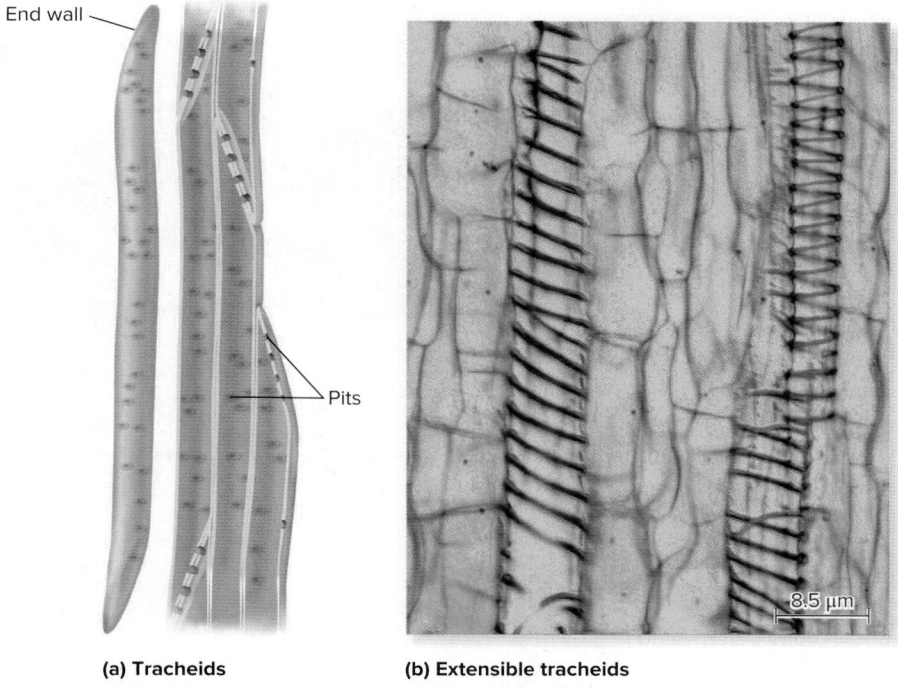

(a) Tracheids   **(b) Extensible tracheids**

Figure 39.11 **Tracheid cells in xylem tissue.** **(a)** Tracheids are long, tubular cells with slanted end walls. Water and ions move from cell to cell through the pits. **(b)** Light micrograph of extensible tracheids from the xylem of pumpkin. b: ©Astrid & Hanns-Frieder Michler/Science Source

Concept Check: *If you applied a stain specific for lignin to tracheids present in a longitudinal slice of a plant stem that is still growing in length, then observed the cells with a light microscope, what portions of the tracheids would be stained, and what parts would not be stained?*

bulk flow; they therefore represent one of the many ways in which flowering plants are particularly well adapted to life on land.

Development of vessel elements resembles that of tracheids in some ways. For example, lignified secondary walls are deposited in spirals or rings on the inside of the primary cell wall. Vessel elements also have numerous pits in their side walls. In contrast to tracheids, the end walls and some side walls of vessel elements are extensively perforated, meaning that all cell-wall material is removed from some areas (**Figure 39.12b** and **c**). This allows water to flow faster from one vessel element to another than it can flow from one tracheid to another.

Because the perforated end walls and large diameter of vessels allow them to transport more water at a faster rate than tracheids can, you might wonder why flowering plants possess two types of water-conducting cells. The answer is that vessels can be more vulnerable than tracheids to embolism, meaning blockage by air bubbles. Once an embolism forms in a vessel element, an air bubble can move through the large end-wall perforations into another element, thereby blocking the flow through an entire vessel. Just as air bubbles can cause disruption of blood circulation in people, sometimes leading to death, such bubbles also disrupt water transport in plants, sometimes severely.

An embolism can form within a xylem vessel as the result of physical damage, drought, or repeated cycles of freezing and thawing. Air bubbles form frequently during winter, because air does not dissolve

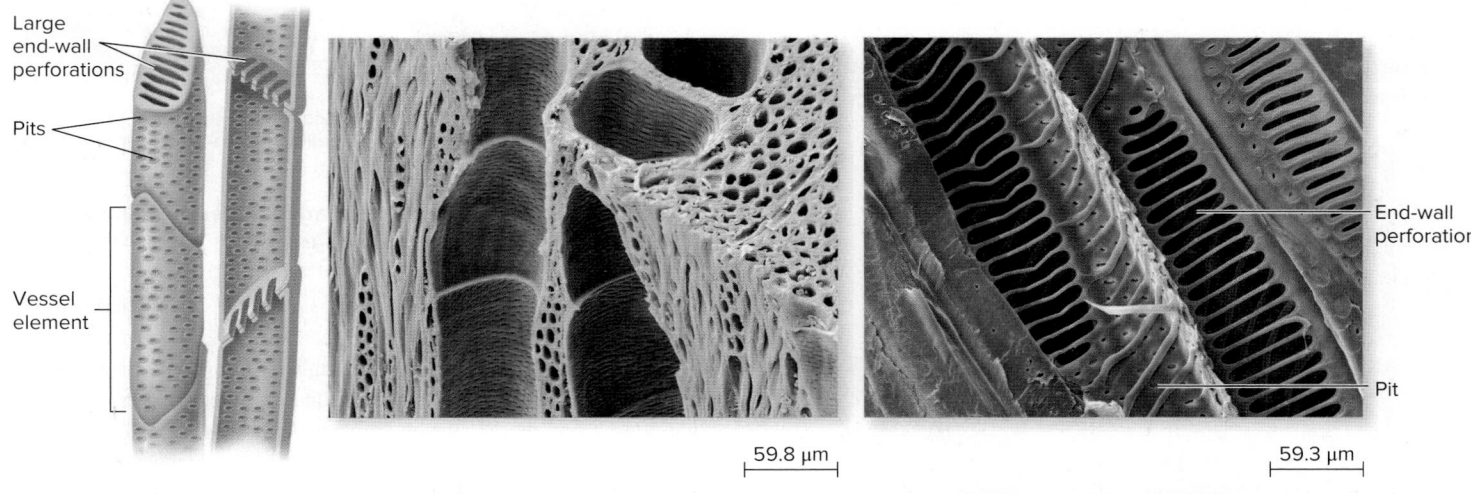

(a) Vessels made up of vessel elements   **(b) Vessel elements in a walnut tree**   **(c) Perforations in a vessel element end wall**

Figure 39.12 **Vessels composed of vessel elements in xylem tissue.** **(a)** This illustration shows the wide diameter of vessel elements with many pits and end-wall perforations. **(b)** SEM of vessels in the wood of the walnut tree (genus *Juglans*). **(c)** SEM of a perforated vessel element end wall from the tulip tree (*Liriodendron tulipifera*). b–c: ©Power and Syred/Science Source

Concept Check: *Which structural features of vessel elements explain the vulnerability of vessels to embolism, that is, blockage by air bubbles?*

in ice. By the end of a cold winter, the functional vessels of many woody plants have become almost completely blocked by air. Blocked vessels in trees often cease to function in water transport and must be replaced by new growth in the spring. Fortunately, even if vessels become blocked, water conduction can still occur via tracheids. This is because tracheid pits are so small that they do not allow air bubbles to move to other tracheids. Thus, an air bubble tends to be confined to the single tracheid in which it first formed, and water continues to flow through nearby tracheids. Tracheids thereby provide a fail-safe conduction route when vessels have become blocked by embolism.

Some plants are able to refill embolized vessels by means of a process known as **root pressure**. At night, the xylem of roots may accumulate high concentrations of ions that are not immediately transported upward to shoots. In this case, the root acts much like a cell rich in solutes, with the result that water gushes in so rapidly that it pushes upward to leaves. Evidence of this process can be observed in the early morning as droplets of water at the edges of leaves, a phenomenon known as **guttation** (**Figure 39.13**). As the water rushes upward, it can dislodge air bubbles or dissolve them, thereby reversing an embolism. Root pressure refilling has been observed to occur in nonwoody plants such as corn (*Zea mays*) and in some woody plants, including the sugar maple (*Acer saccharum*).

Cohesion-Tension Theory Explains the Role of Transpiration in Long-Distance Water Transport

As mentioned, transpiration is the process by which water is lost from the aerial parts of plants, usually via stomata on the surfaces of leaves (**Figure 39.14a**). Evaporation occurs more quickly under conditions of low humidity and/or high temperature. Transpiration is capable of pulling water via bulk flow up to the tops of the tallest trees and is the primary way in which water is transported for long distances in plants. Plants expend no energy to transport water and minerals by transpiration. Rather, the Sun's energy indirectly powers this process by generating a water pressure difference between moist soil and drier air (see Figure 39.9).

How does evaporation at plant surfaces influence long-distance water transport in the xylem? To answer this question, we must

Figure 39.13 Guttation, the result of root pressure. ©Custom Life Science Images/Alamy Stock Photo

Concept Check: *What function does root pressure serve in plants?*

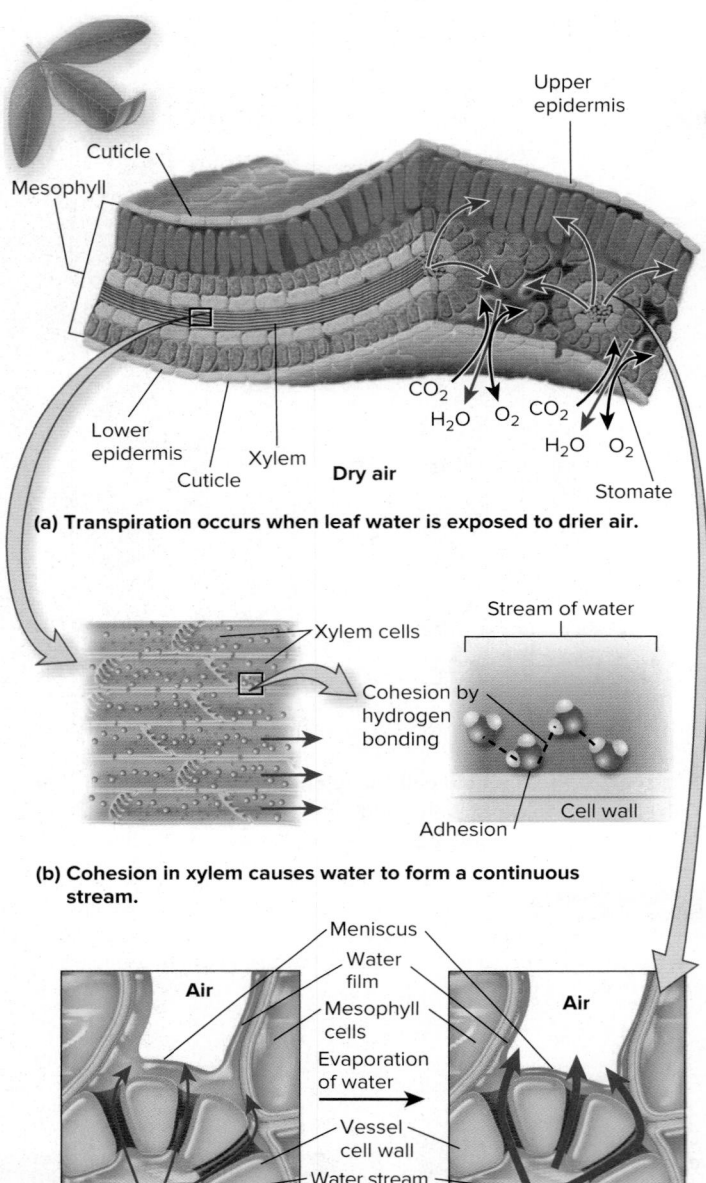

(a) Transpiration occurs when leaf water is exposed to drier air.

(b) Cohesion in xylem causes water to form a continuous stream.

(c) When water evaporates, the surface tension increases in the intercellular spaces of cells, pulling on the water stream in xylem.

Figure 39.14 The roles of transpiration, cohesion, adhesion, and tension in long-distance water transport.

consider the unique physical properties of water. Liquid water molecules are linked by hydrogen bonds (see Chapter 2). As a result, liquid water is amazingly cohesive, explaining why it tends to form continuous streams (**Figure 39.14b**). Consequently, when water molecules evaporate from plants, water films present in leaves display high surface tension. This tension causes a curved water surface known as a meniscus to form (**Figure 39.14c**); the surface tension pulls on neighboring liquid water molecules and eventually on water in the nearest vein, which is connected to the plant's entire water supply. As the result of water's cohesion and the tension exerted on water at the plant's surface, a continuous stream of water can be pulled up through the plant body from the soil, into roots, through stems, and into leaves. This explanation for long-distance water movement in plants is known as the **cohesion-tension theory**. (Recall from Chapter 1 that a scientific theory is a well-established concept, not just a hypothesis.)

Plant transpiration moves huge amounts of water from the soil to the atmosphere. About 99% of the water that enters plants via roots is generally lost as water vapor during transpiration. Each crop season, a single corn plant (*Zea mays*) loses more than 200 L of water, which is more than 100 times the corn plant's mass. A typical tree loses 400 L of water per day! On a regional and global basis, plant transpiration has enormous climate effects. For example, an estimated one-half to three-quarters of rainfall received by the Amazon tropical rain forest actually originates from plant-transpired water vapor, often visible as mist (**Figure 39.15**). Furthermore, about half of the solar heat received by Amazonian plants is dispersed to the atmosphere during transpiration. This heat dispersal has a cooling effect on regional ground temperature, which would be much higher in the absence of plant transpiration. Such cooling effects result from water's unusually high heat of vaporization, the amount of heat needed to isolate water molecules from the liquid phase and move them to the vapor phase. Most of this energy is needed to break the large numbers of hydrogen bonds that occur in liquid water. The evaporation of large amounts of water from plant surfaces effectively dissipates heat, explaining how plants cool themselves and their environments.

Although evaporation of water from plant surfaces plays an essential role in bulk flow through xylem, plants will die if they lose too much water. Plant surfaces, including those of leaves, are typically covered by a cuticle, a wax-containing layer that retards water

Figure 39.15 Plant-transpired water vapor rising as mist from a tropical rain forest. This mist visually illustrates the enormous amount of water that is transpired from the surfaces of plants into the atmosphere. Water vapor derived from plant transpiration is an important source of rainfall, and the process of evaporation cools plant surfaces and affects the local and global climate. ©Adalberto Rios Szalay/Sexto Sol/Stockbyte/Getty Images

Concept Check: *Why does evaporation of water have such a powerful cooling effect?*

loss. Only about 5% of water evaporated from plant surfaces emerges through the cuticle. More than 90% of the water that evaporates from plants is lost through stomata, surface pores that can be closed to retain water or opened to allow the entry of CO_2 needed for photosynthesis.

Plants face a constant dilemma: whether to open their stomata for CO_2 intake and suffer the effect of reduced water content or to close the stomata to retain water, thereby preventing CO_2 uptake. When the stomata are open, O_2 also exits the plant, as does water vapor when the atmospheric humidity is relatively low. Stomata are often abundantly located on the lower surfaces of leaves. Tobacco leaves, for example, possess an estimated 12,000 stomata per square centimeter of leaf surface! As described next, the regulation of stomatal opening and closing is a key way for plants to avoid excessive water loss.

Closing of Stomata Helps to Reduce Transpirational Water Loss

Depending on their environment, almost all plants experience water stress, or water deficit, which is an inadequate amount of water. Water stress is common for plants of the world's arid regions, and their growth is often limited by water availability. Even plants of moist, forested regions of the world experience water stress during drier or colder seasons, under windy conditions, or during a drought. The leaves at the tops of tall trees are generally under considerable water stress because gravity has a substantial effect on their water potential.

Earlier, we considered examples of plant cellular adaptations to deal with osmotic stress. Plants have evolved additional ways to prevent excessive loss of water by transpiration. One example is the regulation of stomatal opening and closing. Plant stomata close to conserve water under conditions of water stress and open when the stress has been relieved, allowing air exchange with the leaf's spongy mesophyll. Stomata are bordered by a pair of **guard cells**, which are sausage-shaped chloroplast-containing cells attached to one another at their ends (**Figure 39.16a**). The distinctive structural features of guard cells explain how they are able to open and close a pore.

As guard cells become fully turgid, their volume expands by 40–100%. This expansion does not occur evenly, however, because the innermost cell walls of guard cells are thicker and less extensible than are other parts of the cell walls. In addition, the guard cells expand primarily in the lengthwise direction because bands of radially oriented cellulose microfibrils prevent lateral expansion (**Figure 39.16b**). When guard cells are turgid, a stomatal pore opens between them, allowing air exchange with the leaf's spongy mesophyll. Conversely, when the guard cells lose their turgor, their volume decreases, and the stomatal pore closes.

What causes the change in turgor that opens or closes stomatal pores? In flowering plants, stomata often open early in the morning, in response to sunlight. This response makes sense, given that light, water, and carbon dioxide are all required for photosynthesis. Blue light stimulates H^+-ATPase proton pumps in guard cells, leading to the uptake of ions, especially potassium (K^+), and other solutes. As a result of increases in solute concentrations inside guard cells, osmotic water uptake occurs via plasma membrane aquaporins, resulting in cell expansion and stomatal opening (**Figure 39.17a**).

At night, the reverse process closes the stomata of flowering plants. Potassium and other solutes are pumped out of guard cells,

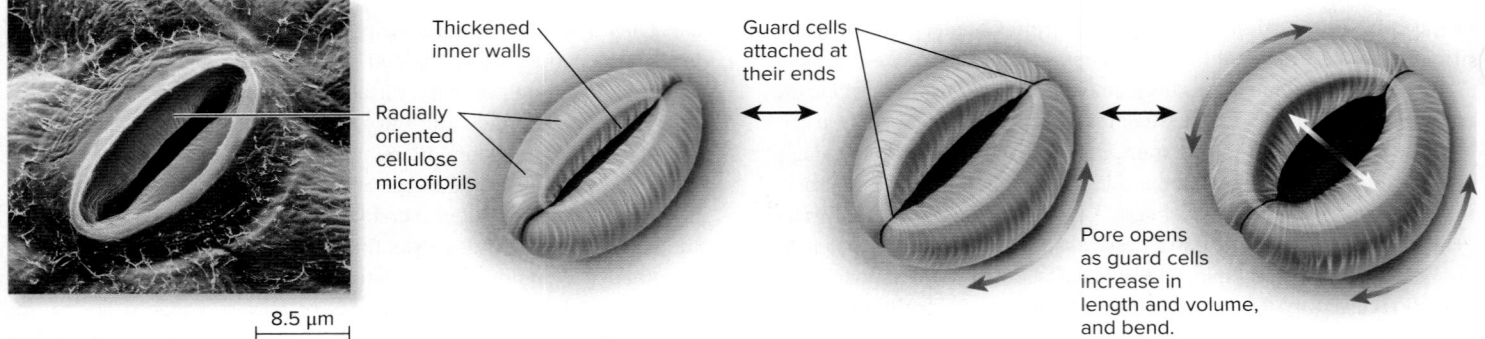

(a) **Stomatal guard cells**

8.5 μm

(b) **The roles of radial orientation of cellulose microfibrils and thickened inner walls in opening or closing guard cells**

Figure 39.16 **The structure of guard cells.** When flaccid, guard cells close stomata. Turgid guard cells produce a stomatal opening. **(a)** An SEM of a stomate in a rose leaf, showing the two guard cells bordering a partly open pore. **(b)** Thickened inner cell walls and radial orientation of cellulose microfibrils in the guard-cell walls explain why they separate when turgid, forming a pore. a: ©Andrew Syred/Science Source

Concept Check: *How could you make a physical model that would illustrate how guard-cell structure affects function?*

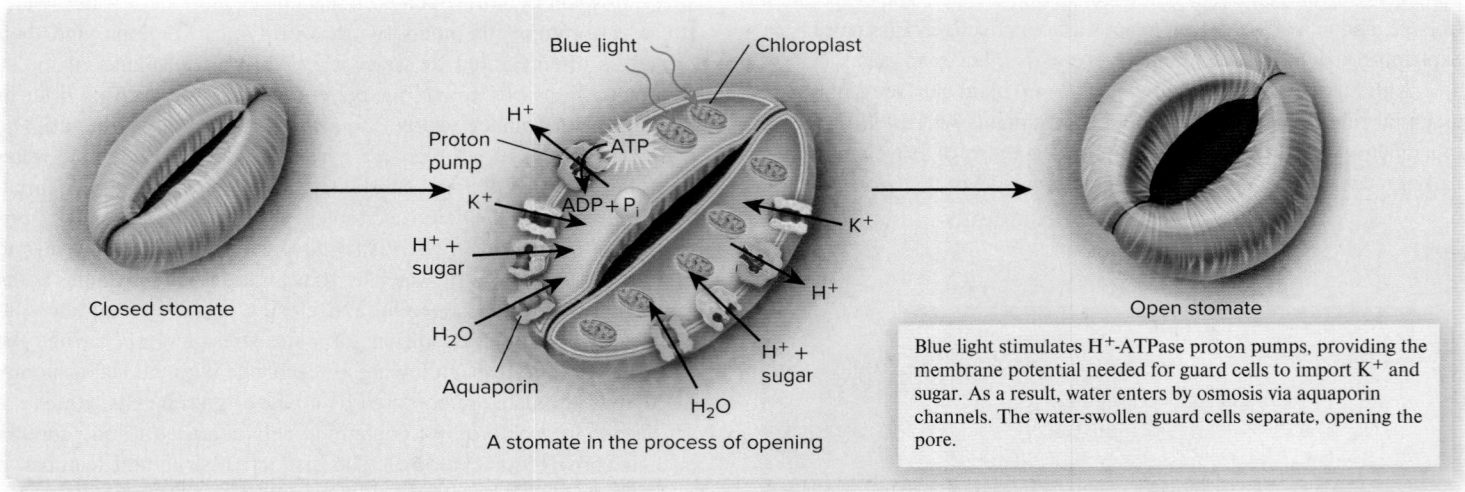

Closed stomate

Open stomate

Blue light stimulates H^+-ATPase proton pumps, providing the membrane potential needed for guard cells to import K^+ and sugar. As a result, water enters by osmosis via aquaporin channels. The water-swollen guard cells separate, opening the pore.

A stomate in the process of opening

(a) **The process of stomate opening**

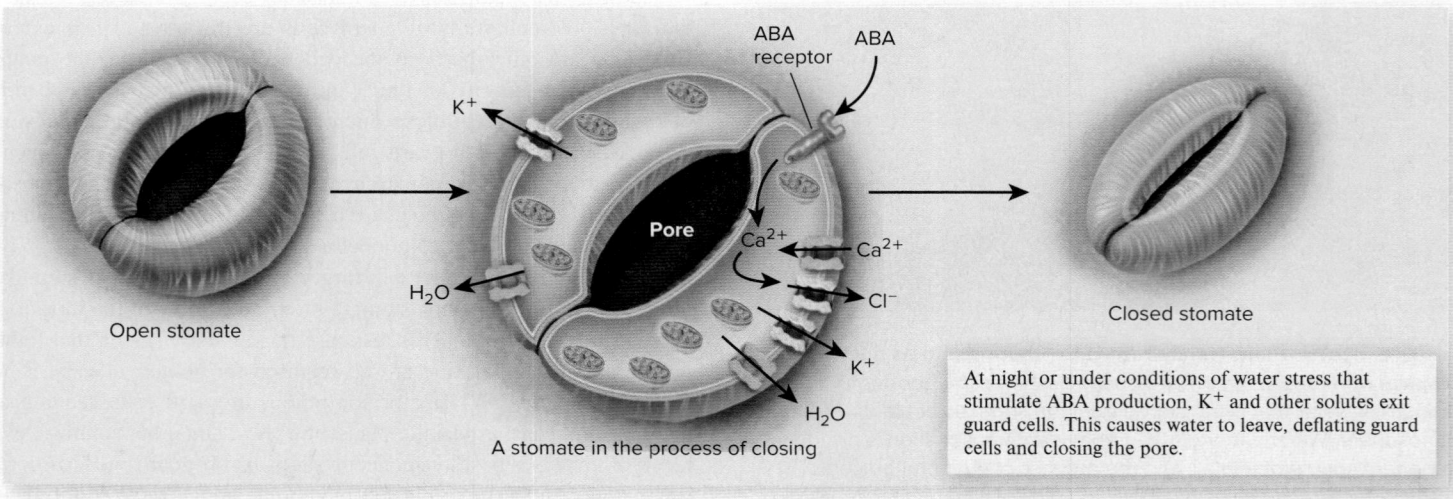

Open stomate

Pore

Closed stomate

At night or under conditions of water stress that stimulate ABA production, K^+ and other solutes exit guard cells. This causes water to leave, deflating guard cells and closing the pore.

A stomate in the process of closing

(b) **The process of stomate closing**

Figure 39.17 **How stomata of flowering plants open and close.** **(a)** Angiosperm stomata usually open in response to sunlight. **(b)** Angiosperm stomata usually close in response to lack of sunlight. They can also close during the day under conditions of water stress, which induces plants to produce more of the hormone abscisic acid (ABA). Guard-cell plasma membranes possess ABA receptors, which receive the drought signal.

causing water to exit, deflating the cells and resulting in pore closure. Flowering plants also close their stomata during the daytime under conditions of water stress, a process mediated by the stress hormone abscisic acid (ABA). Water stress causes a 50-fold increase in ABA, which is transported in the xylem sap to guard cells. ABA

then binds to a receptor, which elicits a Ca^{2+} second messenger, causing the guard cells to lose solutes and deflate (**Figure 39.17b**). An understanding of the process of stomatal closure suggests strategies by which crop plants might be genetically engineered to more effectively withstand drought, as described next.

 **Core Skill: Process of Science**

Feature Investigation | Park, Cutler, and Colleagues Genetically Engineered an ABA Receptor Protein to Foster Crop Survival During Droughts

Global climate change has increased the frequency and length of droughts that endanger agricultural production of human food. Increasing crop resistance to water stress is one way in which plant biologists are trying to improve agricultural productivity. The plant hormone abscisic acid (ABA) is key to drought response in seed plants, so agricultural biologists have been working to identify methods that farmers could use to stimulate ABA activity in crop plants.

A team of biochemists led by Sang-Youl Park and Sean Cutler hypothesized that some chemicals already approved for use in protecting crops (known as agrochemicals) might be able to bind to mutant versions of the ABA receptor and thereby activate it. To test this hypothesis, they created a large collection of *Arabidopsis* plants containing different mutations in the ABA receptor gene (known as *PYR1*). The collection included all of the 475 single substitutions that could possibly occur in the 25 amino acids at the ABA binding site.

The team then examined the responses of these mutant plants to a set of widely used agrochemicals. This process, which involved more than 7,000 individual tests of the binding of different agrochemicals to the ABA receptor, revealed that some of the mutants responded to mandipropamid, an agrochemical widely used to control pathogens called oomycetes, which are protists that cause diseases in diverse species of natural plants and crops. The researchers discovered that, in the responsive mutants, the ability of the agrochemical to fit within the ABA binding site was improved, and hydrophobic interactions and hydrogen bonding occurred between the agrochemical and the receptor.

With this fundamental information in hand, the research team next tried to determine if such mutations had applicability to crop species. To do so, the investigators created tomato plants that carried the same kind of mutations that caused the ABA receptor to recognize mandipropamid in *Arabidopsis* (**Figure 39.18**). They then

Figure 38.18 **The Park team's experiment with a genetically engineered ABA receptor protein.** (thermal images) ©Sean Cutler and Sang-Youl Park

HYPOTHESIS Tomato plants bearing a genetically engineered ABA receptor will close their stomata in response to treatment with an agrochemical.

KEY MATERIALS Genetically engineered tomato plants, wild-type (nonengineered) tomato plants, agrochemical, controlled environment culture chamber, thermal imaging equipment.

Experimental level | **Conceptual level**

1 Grow replicate wild-type (WT) and genetically engineered (E) plants of the same age together for 3 weeks.

Replicates provide reproducibility, and controlled growth conditions reduce the effects of environment.

2 Obtain thermal images before experimental treatment.

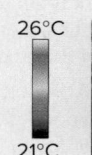

26°C
21°C WT or E

Plant temperature indicates degree of evaporation through open stomata. Blue indicates open stomata; red indicates closed stomata.

3 Treat all plants with the agrochemical.

WT plants with the agrochemical should not respond to treatment by closing their stomata, but engineered plants should do so.

4 Obtain thermal images after experimental treatment.

WT   E

26°C ▭▬▬▬▬▬ 21°C

Comparison of thermal images reveals differences in surface temperatures resulting from stomata closure.

5 **THE DATA**

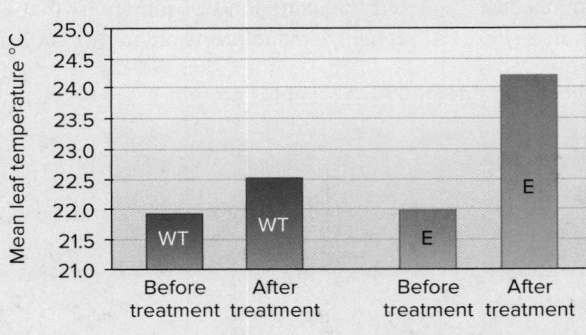

6 **CONCLUSION** Farmers might be able to use common agrochemicals to foster survival of genetically engineered crops during drought periods.

7 **SOURCE** Park, S.-Y., Peterson, F. C., Mosquna, A., Yao, J., Volkman, B.F., and Cutler, S.R. 2015. Agrochemical control of plant water use using engineered abscisic acid receptors. *Nature*. 520: 545–548.

used measurements of leaf temperature to assess the responsiveness of the ABA receptors in these plants to the agrochemical mandipropamid. A higher leaf temperature indicates stomatal closing. As seen in the data, the genetically engineered plants (E) appeared to close their stomata in response to mandipropamid. This result suggests that genetic engineering can be used to create crop varieties that farmers can treat with agrochemicals to increase drought resistance.

Experimental Questions

1. Why did the Park team grow replicate wild-type (WT) tomato plants and genetically engineered (E) tomato plants of the same age together for 3 weeks?

2. **CoreSKILL** » Why did the Park team use thermal images to compare the responses of the WT and E plants before and after experimental treatment with the agrochemical?

BIO TIPS

THE QUESTION *The data in step 5 of Figure 39.18 reveal that genetically engineered (E) tomato plants showed a higher level of response to application of an agrochemical than did wild-type (WT) plants. Did the WT plants also show any response to the experimental treatment, and if so, why might this response have occurred?*

T OPIC *What topic in biology does this question address?* The topic is leaf stomatal responses of angiosperms. More specifically, the question concerns how genetic engineering can improve a crop's ability to close its stomata when exposed to an agrochemical.

I NFORMATION *What information do you know based on the question and your understanding of the topic?* In the question, you are reminded of the data in Figure 39.18. From this chapter and Chapter 36, you know that stomata are pores that occur on plant surfaces, particularly the undersides of leaves. Figure 39.17 shows how the binding of ABA to ABA receptors causes stomatal closure, thereby reducing water loss by transpiration. From Section 9.2, you may recall that hormones bind to receptors in a very specific way to form a ligand-receptor complex.

P ROBLEM-SOLVING S TRATEGY *Interpret data. Compare and contrast.* Compare the bar graphs in step 5 of Figure 39.18 and the thermal images collected before and after the experimental treatment (in steps 2 and 4). Think about the structure of the ABA receptor in WT plants (those not genetically engineered) versus in mutant plants, and consider how the agrochemical mandipropamid might interact with the ABA receptor in these different strains.

ANSWER *Agrochemical treatment did result in a small increase in leaf temperature in WT tomato plants. This result may indicate that WT plants close at least some of their stomata in response to agrochemical treatment, though not as many as in the E plants. One explanation is that the agrochemical binds to the ABA receptor in wild-type plants, but not as well as to the ABA receptor in the engineered plants. Genetic engineering improved the ability of a particular agrochemical to fit within the receptor-binding site and activate it. For this reason, the ABA receptors of E plants bind the agrochemical more effectively than do those of WT plants. The results suggest that WT plants respond by closing some stomata, but E plants respond more strongly.*

Leaf Abscission Also Prevents Water Loss

A second way that plants can prevent water loss is by dropping their leaves, a process known as **leaf abscission**. Angiosperm trees and shrubs of seasonally cold habitats experience water stress every winter, when evaporation from plant surfaces occurs, yet soil water is frozen and therefore unavailable for uptake by roots. Desert plants also experience water stress conditions, but at less predictable times and for much of the year. Both types of plants are adapted to cope with water stress by dropping their leaves. This process lets these plants avoid very low leaf water potentials and the consequent danger

(a) Ocotillo with leaves   **(b) Ocotillo without leaves**

Figure 39.19 Leaf abscission as a drought adaptation. The ocotillo (*Fouquieria splendens*), a plant native to North American deserts, is known for its ability to respond to intermittent rain and drought by producing and dropping leaves multiple times within a year. a: ©Dan Suzio/Science Source; b: ©Matthew Heinrichs/Alamy Stock Photo

Concept Check: *Why does the ocotillo not drop its leaves at a single predictable time each year, as do temperate angiosperm trees and shrubs?*

of xylem embolism. Leaf abscission also reduces the amount of root mass that plants must produce to obtain water under arid conditions. The ocotillo (*Fouquieria splendens*) of North American deserts can produce leaves after sporadic rains and then drop all of its leaves as a direct response to drought as many as six times a year (**Figure 39.19**).

The sugar maple (*Acer saccharum*) is an example of the many types of temperate forest trees or shrubs that drop their leaves each autumn and are thus known as deciduous plants. Deciduous plants contrast with evergreen conifers, whose needle- or scale-shaped leaves are adaptations that reduce the area of leaf surface from which water can evaporate, which helps these gymnosperms cope with water stress during the cold season (refer back to Figure 32.10). The broader, thinner leaves produced by many angiosperms are well adapted for efficient light-capture, but more vulnerable to the stresses caused by cold. During their evolution, temperate zone angiosperm trees and shrubs have acquired the genetic capacity to predict the onset of cold, dry winter conditions and respond with pre-emptive leaf abscission. In contrast to the case of the ocotillo, autumn leaf drop in temperate angiosperms is not directly induced by drought.

Leaf abscission is a highly coordinated developmental process. The hormone ethylene stimulates an abscission zone to develop at the bases of leaf petioles, where they join stems (**Figure 39.20a**). The abscission zone contains two types of tissues: a separation layer of short, thin-walled cells and an underlying protective layer of cork cells (**Figure 39.20b**). The walls of the cork cells contain both water-proofing wax and phenolic polymers that retard microbial attack. As the abscission layer develops across the vein linking the petiole with the stem, this layer eventually cuts off the water supply to the leaf. Chlorophyll in the leaves degrades, revealing colorful orange and yellow carotenoid and xanthophyll pigments that were previously

25 μm

(a) LM of leaf abscission zone at the junction of a petiole and stem, stained with dyes

Petiole

Conducting tissue

Abscission zone

Stem

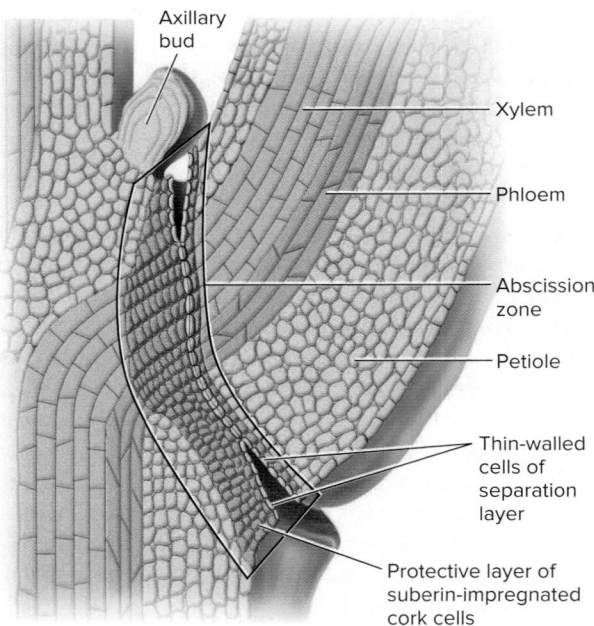

Axillary bud

Xylem

Phloem

Abscission zone

Petiole

Thin-walled cells of separation layer

Protective layer of suberin-impregnated cork cells

(b) Tissues involved in leaf abscission

Figure 39.20 Leaf abscission. Leaf abscission helps maintain plant hydration. a: ©Lee W. Wilcox

masked by the chlorophyll. In addition, some plants synthesize red and reddish-blue pigments in response to changing environmental conditions. The presence of these pigments explains colorful autumn vegetation in temperate zones. Enzymes eventually break down the cell-wall components of the separation layer, causing the petiole to break off the stem. The underlying protective layer forms a leaf scar that seals the wound, helping to protect the plant stem from water loss and pathogen attack. When environmental conditions change for the better, new branches and leaves arise from axillary buds that occur just above leaf scars (see Figure 39.20b).

Long-Distance Transport of Organic Molecules Occurs in the Phloem

Phloem plays an essential role in long-distance transport of organic molecules and some minerals in the plant body. Phloem often transports sugars from where they are produced to other sites where they are also used. Recall that primary phloem occurs in the vascular bundles of herbaceous plants and secondary phloem occurs as the inner bark of woody plants (refer back to Figure 36.20). In contrast to xylem, whose transport tissues are dead and empty of cytoplasm at maturity, mature phloem tissues remain alive and retain at least some cytoplasmic components. A closer look at phloem structure and function will help to illuminate these differences.

Phloem Structure Phloem tissues of flowering plants include supporting fibers, parenchyma cells, sieve-tube elements, and adjacent companion cells. **Sieve-tube elements** are arranged end to end to form transport pipes (**Figure 39.21**), analogous to the way that the xylem's vessel elements are aligned to form longitudinal vessels.

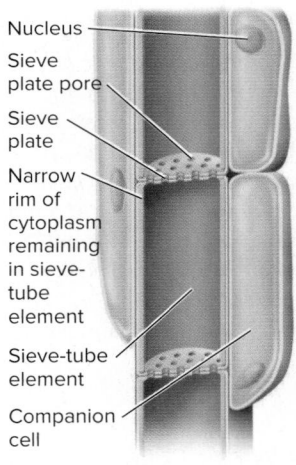

Nucleus

Sieve plate pore

Sieve plate

Narrow rim of cytoplasm remaining in sieve-tube element

Sieve-tube element

Companion cell

(a) Sieve-tube elements and companion cells

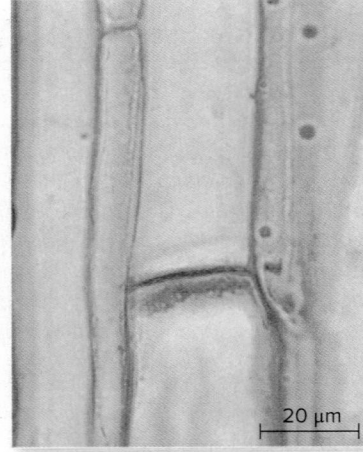

20 μm

(b) Light micrograph of phloem stained with blue dye, showing sieve-tube elements

Figure 39.21 Sieve-tube elements and companion cells of phloem. b: ©Lee W. Wilcox

 Core Skill: Connections Look back to Figure 36.16, which illustrates the development of guard cells. In what way are guard-cell development and companion-cell development similar?

Together, the sieve-tube elements and companion cells form a system for the transport of soluble organic substances made during photosynthesis. In addition, phloem sap may contain hormones such as auxin and abscisic acid, as well as many types of proteins and RNA.

Each pair, consisting of a sieve-tube element and its companion cell, has a common origin. The two cells are produced by an unequal division of a single precursor cell and are therefore linked by plasmodesmata formed at cytokinesis. The smaller of the two cells develops into a companion cell, whose name reflects its life-support function, and the larger of the two cells develops into a sieve-tube element. The sieve-tube element loses its nucleus and most of its cytoplasm in an adaptation that reduces obstruction to bulk flow. Mature sieve-tube elements retain only a thin film of cytoplasm near the cell wall that includes some endoplasmic reticulum, plastids, and mitochondria. The end walls of developing sieve-tube elements become perforated by the action of wall-digesting enzymes that enlarge existing plasmodesmata. The perforated end walls of mature sieve-tube elements are known as **sieve plates**, and the numerous perforations are known as **sieve plate pores**. Phloem sap passes through these plates from one sieve-tube element to another.

Mature sieve-tube elements are not dead. However, because they lack a nucleus, they depend on their neighboring companion cell for messenger RNAs (mRNAs) and proteins, which are supplied via plasmodesmata. For example, when a plant's conducting system is damaged, a short-term wound response occurs that involves a protein known as **P protein** (for phloem protein). Large amounts of this protein accumulate along sieve plates, preventing loss of phloem sap (**Figure 39.22**). This protein accumulation functions much like a clot that helps reduce blood loss from wounded animals. P protein also binds to the cell walls of pathogens, thereby helping to prevent infection at wounds. However, sieve-tube elements cannot produce P protein by themselves. The companion cells provide either P protein mRNA or the protein itself to sieve-tube elements. In a longer term response, plants deposit the carbohydrate callose as a sealant at the wound site.

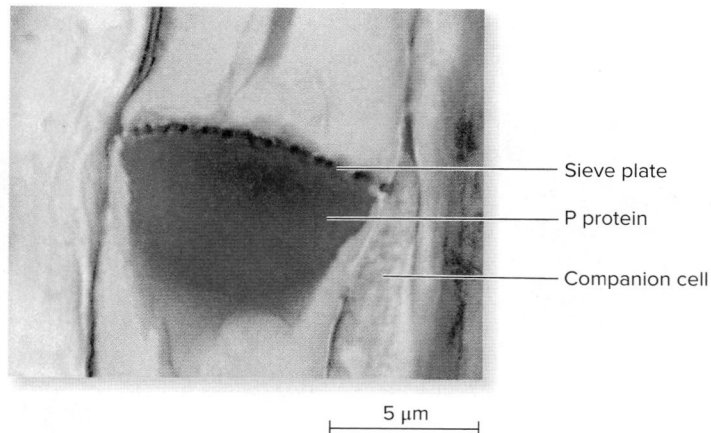

Sieve plate
P protein
Companion cell

5 μm

Figure 39.22   Phloem wound response. When phloem is damaged, the cytoplasm of a sieve-tube element surges toward the sieve plate, depositing P protein, stained red in this light micrograph. In this location, P protein helps to prevent infection and leakage of solutes. ©Lee W. Wilcox

Phloem Loading   Companion cells also play an essential role in moving sugars into sieve-tube elements for long-distance transport, a process known as **phloem loading**. Although glucose and some other monosaccharides can occur in phloem, the disaccharide sucrose is the main form in which most plants transport sugar over long distances. Plant biologists think that sucrose is less vulnerable to metabolic breakdown en route than are monosaccharides.

Two types of phloem loading occur: symplastic and partly apoplastic. Many woody plants transport sucrose from sugar-producing cells of the leaf mesophyll to companion cells and then to sieve-tube elements via plasmodesmata, a process known as symplastic phloem loading (**Figure 39.23a**). The advantage of symplastic loading is that

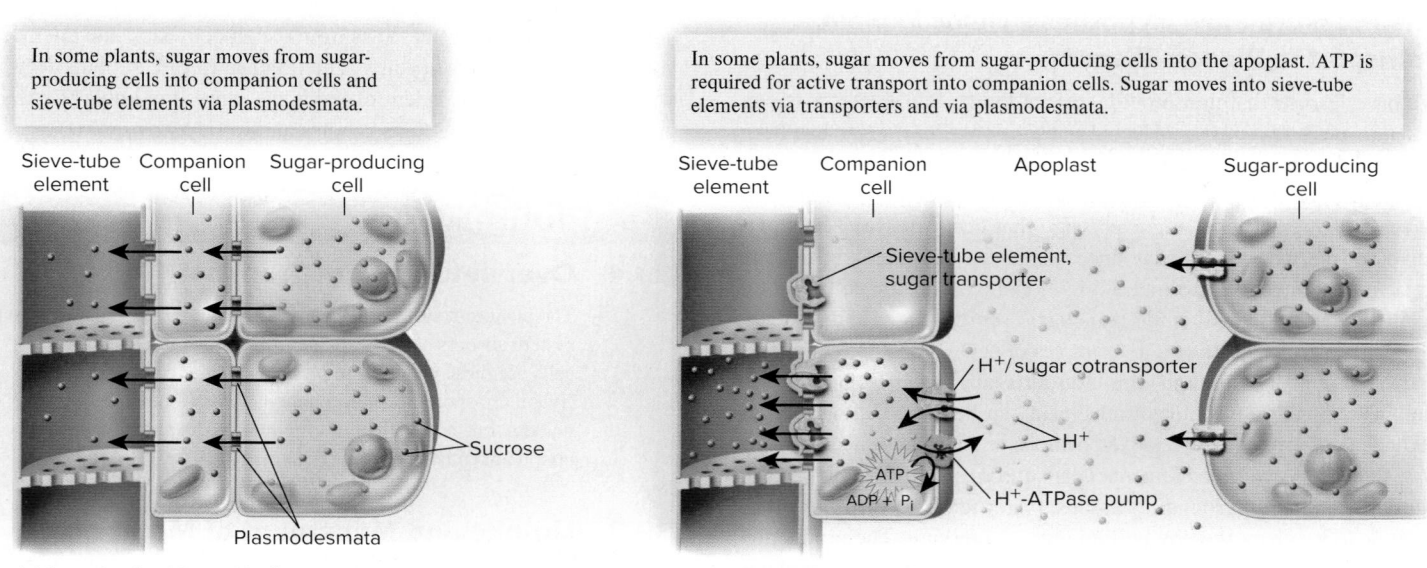

In some plants, sugar moves from sugar-producing cells into companion cells and sieve-tube elements via plasmodesmata.

Sieve-tube element | Companion cell | Sugar-producing cell

Sucrose

Plasmodesmata

(a) Symplastic phloem loading

In some plants, sugar moves from sugar-producing cells into the apoplast. ATP is required for active transport into companion cells. Sugar moves into sieve-tube elements via transporters and via plasmodesmata.

Sieve-tube element | Companion cell | Apoplast | Sugar-producing cell

Sieve-tube element, sugar transporter

H^+/sugar cotransporter

H^+

ATP
ADP + P_i

H^+-ATPase pump

(b) Partly apoplastic phloem loading

Figure 39.23   Symplastic and partly apoplastic phloem loading.

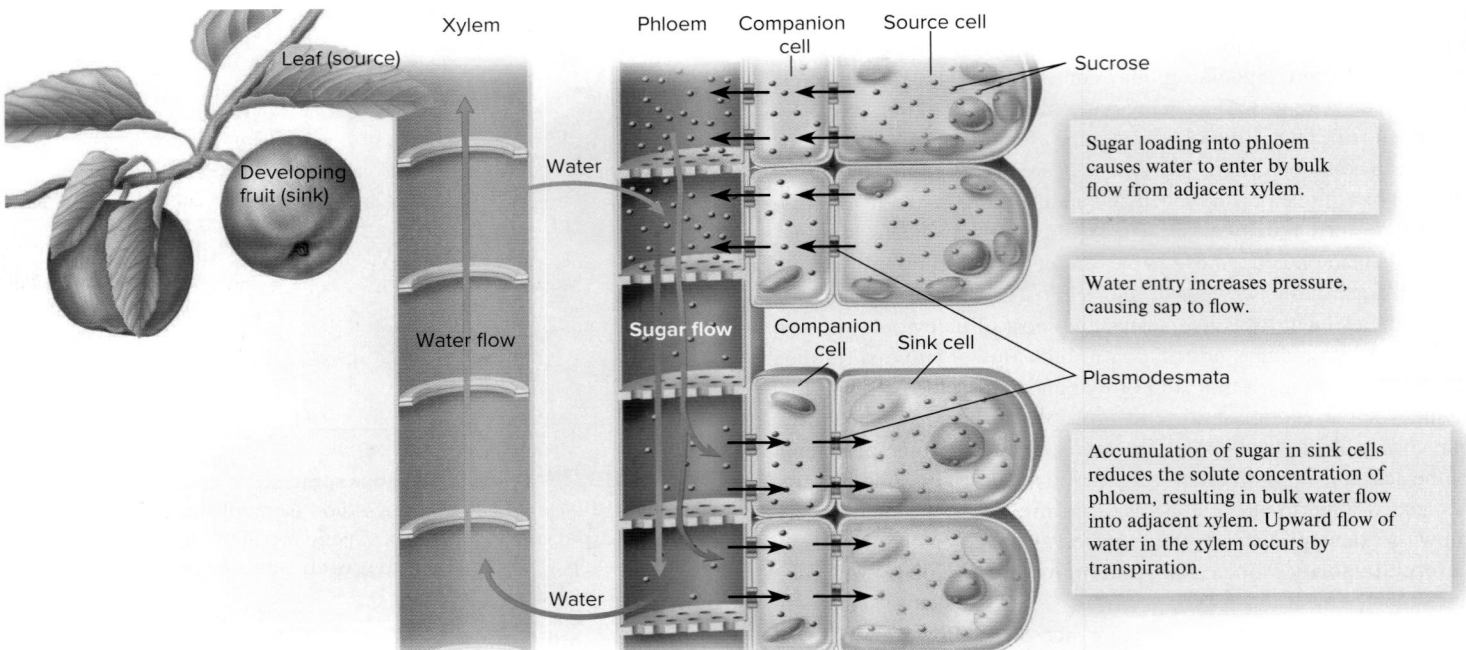

Figure 39.24 Pressure-flow hypothesis for phloem transport.

it does not require ATP; by moving through plasmodesmata, the sugar does not have to cross plasma membranes.

In contrast, most herbaceous plants, including important crop plants and the model plant *Arabidopsis,* load sugar into sieve-tube elements or companion cells from intercellular spaces, often against a concentration gradient. ATP must be used to move the sugar across a plasma membrane into a companion cell or sieve-tube element (**Figure 39.23b**). Therefore, this second type of phloem loading is partly apoplastic and partly a transmembrane process.

The Pressure-Flow Hypothesis Helps Explain Transport in Phloem Tissues

We have learned that transpiration, driven by the Sun's energy, moves water in plant xylem by cohesion and tension. Once sugar has been loaded into phloem sieve-tube elements, how does it move within the plant? The most common explanation is that phloem transport is driven by differences in turgor pressure that occur between cells of a **sugar source**, where sugar is produced, and those of a **sugar sink**, where sugar is not made, but still needed by nonphotosynthetic cells. Photosynthetic leaf mesophyll is the main sugar source. Roots and developing leaves, seeds, and fruits are examples of sugar sinks. In the process known as **translocation**, phloem transports substances from source to sink. The direction of phloem movement can be horizontal as well as vertical, depending on the relative positions of the sources and sinks.

Because sieve-tube elements near source tissues have higher solute contents than surrounding tissues, water tends to rush into them from nearby xylem, thereby building turgor pressure. The production of turgor pressure requires an intact plasma membrane. This explains why mature phloem sieve-tube elements must be alive in order to function.

In contrast to sieve-tube elements near source tissues, sieve-tube elements near sink tissues have lower solute concentrations. The resulting water pressure difference drives the bulk flow of phloem sap from source to sink tissues. This explanation for translocation is known as the **pressure-flow hypothesis** (**Figure 39.24**). At sink tissues, sugar is typically unloaded through plasmodesmata (see Figure 39.24). Because plasmodesmata are very narrow in comparison with sieve-tube elements, they slow the flow of phloem sap from sieve-tube elements into sink tissues. This reduction in flow rate helps to equalize the distribution of phloem sap, preventing delivery of too much sap to any single sink. When the solute concentration of phloem sap has been sufficiently reduced, water flows from the phloem back into the xylem, where upward transport occurs. The reliance of phloem bulk flow on water supplied by the xylem explains the close proximity of phloem and xylem tissues in vascular bundles and woody stems.

Summary of Key Concepts

39.1 Overview of Plant Transport

- The plant root system takes up water and minerals, and the shoot system absorbs carbon dioxide from the air. Photosynthetic cells use these materials to produce organic compounds. Xylem transports water and minerals from roots to shoots, and phloem transports organic compounds from photosynthetic to nonphotosynthetic tissues (Figure 39.1).

39.2 Uptake and Movement of Materials at the Cellular Level

- Facilitated diffusion is the transport of molecules across plasma membranes down a concentration gradient with the aid of membrane transport proteins, typically channels and transporters. Active transport—the transport of substances across plasma membranes against concentration gradients—usually requires ATP. Plasma membrane proton pumps use the energy released by ATP hydrolysis to move protons from the cytosol into the intercellular space, generating a membrane potential. Potential energy released by the flow of protons back into the cell can be coupled to the transport of ions and solutes (Figures 39.2, 39.3).

- Turgor pressure increases as water enters plant cells because cell walls restrict the extent to which cells can swell. A cell that is so full of water that the plasma membrane presses closely against the cell wall is turgid. A cell that contains so little water that the plasma membrane pulls away from the cell wall is plasmolyzed. A flaccid cell has a water content between these extremes (Figure 39.4).

- Solute potential and pressure potential arising from the presence of a cell wall are major factors that determine cellular water potential. Water moves from a region of higher water potential to a region of lower water potential (Figure 39.5).

- Plants display a variety of adaptations that help them cope with osmotic stress.

39.3 Tissue-Level Transport

- Tissue-level transport occurs in three forms. Transmembrane transport involves the movement of materials from one cell to another from intercellular spaces, across plasma membranes, and into the cytosol. Symplastic transport allows materials to move from one cell to another through the symplast, the cells' cytosol and plasmodesmata, without crossing plasma membranes. In apoplastic transport, water and solutes move through the apoplast, the water-filled cell walls and intercellular spaces of tissues (Figures 39.6, 39.7).

- In roots, waxy Casparian strips in cell walls of endodermal tissue function as diffusion barriers that reduce both the entry of harmful soil minerals into and the exit of useful solutes from the vascular tissues (Figure 39.8).

39.4 Long-Distance Transport

- Water and solutes move long distances by bulk flow within the xylem and phloem. Plant vascular tissues are adapted in ways that reduce resistance to bulk flow. Bulk flow of water upward in xylem is powered by the water pressure difference between moist soil and drier air, the latter resulting from solar heating. Xylem is the main conduit for water and dissolved mineral nutrients, but it may also transport certain organic compounds (Figures 39.9, 39.10).

- The water-conducting cells of xylem, tracheids and vessel elements (together known as tracheary elements), are dead and empty of cytoplasm at maturity. Pits in tracheary element walls allow water entry and exit, and narrow or constrict in response to xylem sap solute content. Vessel elements are wider than tracheids but are more vulnerable to blockage by air bubbles, or embolism. Root pressure, the effects of which include guttation, the appearance in the morning of water drops on leaf tips, helps some plants to refill embolized vessels (Figures 39.11, 39.12, 39.13).

- Transpiration is the evaporative loss of water from plant surfaces. The cohesion-tension theory proposes that as the result of water's cohesion and the tension exerted on water at the plant's surface by evaporation, a continuous stream of water is pulled up through the plant body from the soil, into roots, through stems, and into leaves, from which water is evaporated into the atmosphere (Figures 39.14, 39.15).

- Regulation of stomatal opening and closing helps plants prevent excessive water loss by transpiration. Expansion of guard cells causes stomata to open, allowing CO_2 intake. Guard-cell deflation causes pores to close, limiting water loss. Abscisic acid (ABA) stimulates stomatal closure in response to drought, a process that suggests strategies for genetically engineering crops that have greater drought tolerance. Plants under existing or predicted water stress often drop their leaves in a process known as abscission, an adaptive response that lets plants avoid very low water potentials and the threat of embolism (Figures 39.16, 39.17, 39.18, 39.19, 39.20).

- Organic solutes and minerals are transported in phloem sap as the result of osmosis. Phloem sap moves within sieve-tube elements, which are living when mature, but lack a nucleus and are thus dependent on companion cells. Phloem loading, the movement of sugars into sieve-tube elements for long-distance transport, occurs by symplastic or partly apoplastic transport (Figures 39.21, 39.22, 39.23).

- In the process known as translocation, phloem transports substances from source to sink. The pressure-flow hypothesis helps to explain translocation as a process driven by differences in turgor pressure that occur between a sugar source (for example, leaves) and a sugar sink (for example, developing fruit) (Figure 39.24).

Assess & Discuss

Test Yourself

1. An aquaporin is
   a. a channel protein that allows the influx of K^+ into cells, causing water to also flow in between the phospholipids of the plasma membrane.
   b. a type of blue-colored pore in the epidermal surfaces of plants.
   c. a protein channel in plasma membranes that facilitates the diffusion of water.
   d. a transport protein, or transporter, in plasma membranes that uses protons to cotransport water.
   e. none of the above.

2. Why is turgor pressure a property of plant cells?
   a. Plant cells possess the necessary chloroplasts.
   b. Plant cells possess a cell wall, necessary for formation of turgor.
   c. Plant cells possess mitochondria, which provide the ATP needed for turgor.
   d. All of the above are true.
   e. none of the above is true.

3. How do plant cells avoid losing too much water in very cold, dry, or saline habitats?
   a. They balance the osmotic condition of their cytosol with that of the environment.
   b. Their epidermal cells are coated with waxy cuticle.
   c. They stabilize their membranes with sugars.
   d. They produce more aquaporin water channels to take maximum advantage of available moisture.
   e. All of the above help plants avoid water loss.

4. What are ways in which plants accomplish tissue-level transport?
   a. transmembrane transport of solutes from one cell to another
   b. symplastic transport of materials from one cell to another via plasmodesmata
   c. apoplastic transport of water and dissolved solutes through cell walls and intercellular spaces
   d. All of the above are used for tissue-level transport.
   e. None of the above is used for tissue-level transport.

5. A root endodermis is
   a. an innermost layer of cortex cells that display characteristic Casparian strips.
   b. a layer of cells just inside the epidermis of a root.
   c. a layer of cells just outside the epidermis of a root.
   d. a group of specialized cells that occur within the root epidermis.
   e. none of the above.

6. Which of the following statements best explains how water enters root cells from the soil?
   a. Roots accumulate sugars from shoots, thereby increasing root cell ability to absorb water by osmosis.
   b. Roots actively pump water from the soil using the chemical energy of ATP.
   c. Water enters the spongy spaces between cells and within cell walls.
   d. Membrane-level transport of ions from soil into root hair cells increases the osmotic flow of water into them.
   e. Both c and d are correct.

7. What features of water explain how it can be drawn up a tall tree from roots to leaves?
   a. cohesion, the result of extensive hydrogen bonding
   b. adhesion, water's tendency to stick to surfaces such as the inner walls of tracheid and vessels
   c. high surface tension that develops when water evaporates from intercellular leaf spaces
   d. all of the above
   e. none of the above

8. What feature of vascular plants contributes to their ability to maintain relatively stable internal water content?
   a. a waxy surface cuticle
   b. an extensive root system that mines water from soil
   c. specialized water-conducting tracheary elements composed of dead cells
   d. epidermal pores that open and close
   e. All of the above are contributing features.

9. What structural features of guard cells underlie their ability to form an open pore in plant epidermal surfaces?
   a. thickened inner cell walls and radially oriented microfibrils
   b. thickened outer cell walls and radially oriented microfibrils
   c. thickened inner cell walls and longitudinal microfibrils
   d. thickened outer cell walls and longitudinal microfibrils
   e. uniform thickness of cell walls and randomly arranged microfibrils

10. What substances plug wounded sieve-tube elements, thereby preventing the leakage of phloem sap?
    a. X protein and callose
    b. C protein and callose
    c. P protein and callose
    d. P protein and sucrose
    e. none of the above

Conceptual Questions

1. Why is it a bad idea to overfertilize your houseplants? If the amount recommended on the package is good, wouldn't more be better?

2. Why is it a bad idea for subsistence farmers (those barely able to grow enough crops to feed themselves) to allow livestock to graze natural vegetation to the point that it disappears?

3. **Core Concept: Energy and Matter** Imagine two plants that have similar mineral nutrient concentrations in their root tissues. If one plant is planted in soil of lower mineral concentration and the other is planted in soil of higher mineral concentration, which plant will likely need to use more energy in the form of ATP to take up additional soil minerals at the root hair plasma membranes?

Collaborative Questions

1. **Core Skill: Science and Society** Take a look outside or imagine a forest or grassland. What can you deduce about the availability of soil water from the types of plants that occur?

2. Imagine that you are part of a team assigned to determine what environmental conditions best suit a new crop so that the crop can be recommended to farmers in appropriate climate regions. What features of the crop plants might you investigate?

Flowering Plants: Reproduction

40

The reproductive success of dandelions. ©Michael Roach/Alamy Stock Photo

Dandelions sometimes seem to be taking over the world, growing abundantly in open, sunny areas. Bright yellow flower heads, as shown in the chapter opening photo, are one of the secrets of dandelions' success. If you pull a dandelion flower head apart, you can see that it is actually a bouquet of 200 or so small flowers. Each flower produces a tiny, one-seeded fruit equipped with a "parachute" for effective long-distance dispersal by wind. Each dandelion plant can produce up to 5,000 fruits during its lifetime, which explains how dandelions can spread so rapidly across a landscape.

Though most flowering plants produce seeds by means of sexual reproduction, dandelions and some other plants are able to produce seeds by asexual reproduction, a process that does not involve the fusion of gametes. As a result, the traits of asexually reproducing dandelion parents and their progeny are uniform. Asexual reproduction could be very usefully applied in agriculture, because most crops reproduce only sexually. Each year many U.S. farmers buy and plant hybrid seeds that develop into mature plants having uniform and desirable trait combinations. Such farmers typically do not use seed from one year's crop to plant the next, because sexual reproduction mixes genes into diverse combinations present among the resulting seeds. For this reason, plants that grow from sexually produced seeds do not uniformly express the desirable trait combinations present in their hybrid parents. But if hybrid crop plants could be engineered to produce seed asexually, as dandelions do, farmers might be able to use seed from one crop to plant the next and continue to harvest uniformly desirable crops. Because reproduction is so important to agriculture, plant biologists aim to better understand both sexual and asexual reproduction in flowering plants.

Flowers, fruits, and seeds are essential reproductive features of the diverse types of flowering plants found in nature. This chapter begins with an overview of the reproductive cycle of flowering plants that describes how flowers, fruits, and seeds function. This overview provides essential background for a closer look at flower structure and development and some of the genes that control flower production and appearance. We will also examine the sexual reproductive processes by which plants produce gametes and accomplish fertilization, thereby producing zygotes, embryos, seeds, fruits, and seedlings. Finally, we will take a closer look at the ways in which dandelions and some other flowering plants reproduce without using the sexual process.

40.1 An Overview of Flowering Plant Reproduction

Learning Outcomes:

1. Explain how the sexual life cycle of flowering plants differs from that of earlier evolved mosses.
2. List the four organs found in many flowers and the functions of each organ.
3. Describe the phenomenon of double fertilization.
4. Describe the parts of an angiosperm seed, and explain how each part is produced and functions.

Most flowering plants display **sexual reproduction**, the process by which two gametes fuse to produce offspring that have unique combinations of genes. Flowering plants, also known as angiosperms, inherited their sexual life cycle, known as alternation of generations, from ancestors extending back to the earliest land plants (see Chapters 31 and 32). Though all plants share the same basic life cycle, flowering plants display unique reproductive features. In this section, we will first review the general features of alternation of generations and then consider more specific features of the angiosperm life cycle.

Flowering Plants Display Alternation of Generations

All groups of land plants produce two multicellular life cycle stages, in essence, two distinct plants. These two life cycle stages are the diploid, spore-producing **sporophyte** and the haploid, gamete-producing **gametophyte**. In all groups of plants, haploid spores are typically produced by diploid sporophytes via meiosis. These spores undergo mitotic cell divisions to produce multicellular gametophytes. Certain cells within the gametophytes differentiate into gametes. In contrast to meiosis in animals, plant meiosis does not directly generate the gametes.

The processes of meiosis and fertilization form the transitions between the plant sporophyte and gametophyte life stages and link them in a cycle (**Figure 40.1**). The land plant life cycle is known as **alternation of generations** because it involves the cycling between distinct sporophyte and gametophyte generations.

During the evolutionary diversification of land plants, the sporophyte generation has become larger and more complex, while the gametophyte generation has become smaller and less complex. To see this change, let's compare the life cycle stages of mosses to those of angiosperms. Mosses arose early in the history of land plants, whereas angiosperms appeared much later. During the intervening

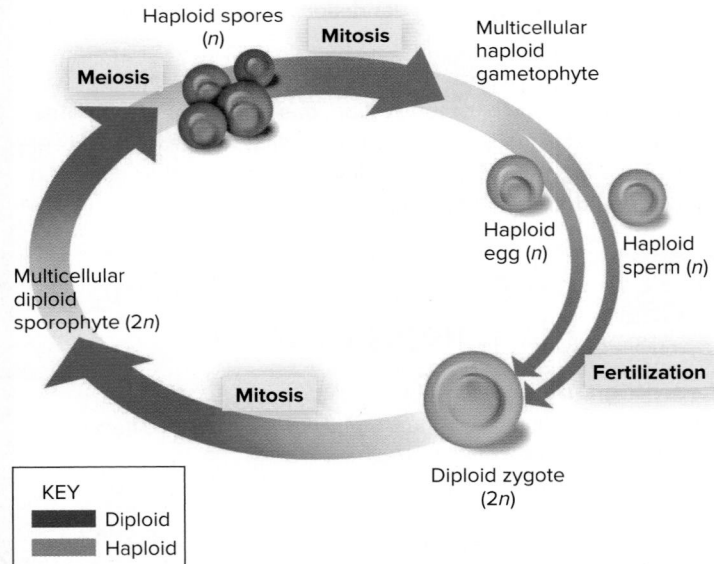

Figure 40.1 Alternation of generations, the plant life cycle.

 Core Skill: Connections Look back to Figure 32.14 to see a more detailed illustration of the flowering plant life cycle. How can you recognize and where can you find the gametophyte generation of a flowering plant?

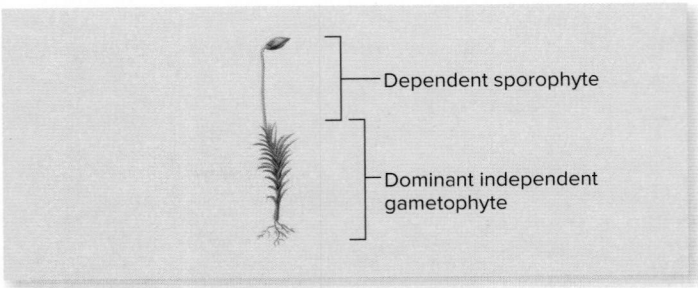

(a) Gametophyte-dominant bryophyte (moss)

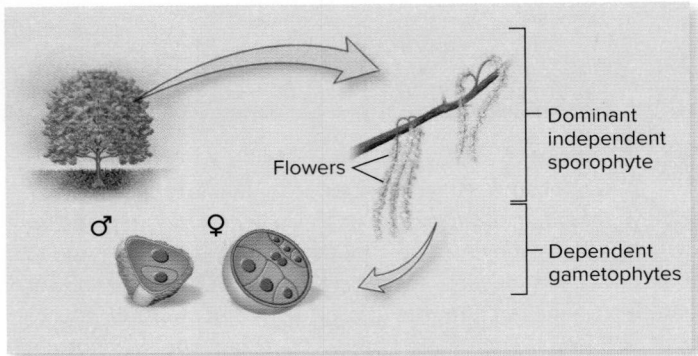

(b) Sporophyte-dominant flowering plant (oak)

Figure 40.2 Evolutionary shift in life cycle stage dominance in plants. **(a)** In mosses, the gametophyte is the dominant life cycle stage, and the sporophyte depends on the gametophyte for resources. **(b)** In flowering plants such as oak trees, the sporophyte life cycle stage is dominant. Microscopic flowering plant gametophytes develop and grow within sporophyte flowers and depend completely on sporophytes.

time, the relative sizes and dependence of the sporophyte and gametophyte generations changed dramatically. Moss sporophytes are small structures that always grow attached to larger, photosynthetic gametophytes, because moss sporophytes are incapable of independent life (**Figure 40.2a**). Moss sporophytes depend on gametophytes to supply them with essential nutrients.

In contrast, flowering plant sporophytes are notably larger and more complex than gametophytes. A tall oak tree, for example, is a single sporophyte. Oak gametophytes are few-celled, microscopic structures that develop and grow within flowers (**Figure 40.2b**). In addition, photosynthetic oak seedlings and trees grow independently, but nonphotosynthetic oak gametophytes depend completely on the sporophyte generation for their nutrition. A closer look at flower structure will provide a more complete view of angiosperm gametophyte structure and function.

Flowers Produce and Nurture Male and Female Gametophytes

The literary wit Gertrude Stein famously paraphrased Shakespeare ("a rose by any other name would smell as sweet") when she wrote, "A rose is a rose is a rose." Everyone knows that a rose is a flower, but what, exactly, is a flower? A **flower** is defined as a reproductive shoot, a stem branch that produces reproductive organs instead of leaves. Flowers are organ systems because several different organs typically occur within a flower (see Chapter 36). Flower organs are produced by shoot apical meristems much like those that generate leaves and are thought to have evolved from leaflike structures by descent with modification (refer back to Figure 32.15). Most flowering plants are classified into one of two major groups, eudicots or monocots (Chapter 32).

Most eudicot flowers contain four types of organs: sepals, petals, stamens, and carpels (**Figure 40.3**). **Sepals** often function to protect the unopened flower bud. **Petals** usually serve to attract insects or other animals for pollen transport (refer back to Figures 32.19 and 32.20). Monocot flowers typically have tepals, which are outer flower parts that are not differentiated into petals and sepals. Monocots and eudicots alike produce stamens and/or carpels at the flower's center. **Stamens** and **carpels** each produce distinctive types of spores by the process of meiosis. From these spores, tiny multicellular

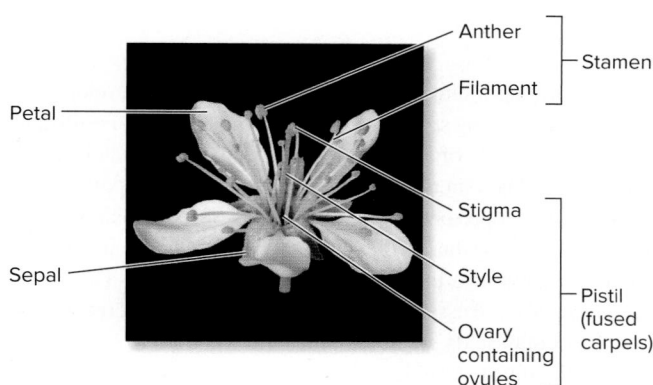

(a) Flower parts

(b) *Prunus americana* (plum)

Figure 40.3 The structure of a typical eudicot flower. b: ©Lee W. Wilcox

Concept Check: *Do all flowers have all of the structures illustrated here?*

gametophytes develop, and certain gametophytic cells become specialized gametes.

Stamens Stamens produce **male gametophytes** and foster their early development. Most stamens display an elongate **filament**, which is topped by an anther (see Figure 40.3). Filaments contain vascular tissue that delivers nutrients from the parental sporophyte to the anthers. Each **anther** is a group of four sporangia, structures in which spores are produced. Within the anther's sporangia, many diploid cells undergo meiosis, each producing four tiny, haploid spores. Because they are so small, generally 25–50 µm in diameter, the spores produced within anthers are known as **microspores**. Immature male gametophytes, known as **pollen grains**, develop from microspores. The term pollen comes from a Latin word meaning fine flour, reflecting the small size of pollen grains. Pollen grains are eventually dispersed through pores or slits in the anthers. At the time of dispersal, the pollen grain is a two- or three-celled immature male gametophyte produced by mitotic division. During a later phase of development, a mature male gametophyte produces **sperm cells**.

Carpels Carpels are vase-shaped structures that produce, enclose, and nurture **female gametophytes**. Carpels contain veins of vascular tissue that deliver nutrients from the parent sporophyte to the developing gametophytes. The term **pistil** (named for its resemblance to the pestle used to grind materials to a powder) refers to a single carpel or several fused carpels (see Figure 40.3). The topmost portion of a pistil, known as a **stigma** (Greek, meaning mark), receives pollen grains. The **style** is the middle portion of the pistil, and an ovary is at the bottom of the pistil. The **ovary** produces and nourishes one or more ovules.

An **ovule** of flowering plants consists of a spore-producing structure (a sporangium) and enclosing tissues consisting of modified leaves, known as **integuments**. Within an ovule, a diploid cell produces four haploid **megaspores** by meiosis, three of which die. The surviving megaspore generates a female gametophyte by mitosis. The female gametophytes of flowering plants typically consist of seven cells, one of which is the female gamete, the **egg**. This basic information about male and female gametophytes helps in understanding how they function to produce a young sporophyte within a seed.

Fertilization Triggers the Development of Embryonic Sporophytes, Seeds, and Fruits

In flowering plants, fertilization leads to the production of a young sporophyte that lies within a seed, completing the life cycle (**Figure 40.4**). Prior to fertilization, pollen grains released from anthers first find their way to the stigma of a compatible flower, a process known as **pollination**. Some plants display **self-pollination**, in which pollen from the anthers of a flower is transferred to the stigma of the same flower or between flowers of the same plant. **Cross-pollination**, which occurs when a stigma receives pollen from a different plant of the same species, is also common. Many flowers are attractive to insects or other animals that transport pollen, whereas oak flowers and those of some other angiosperms are adapted for pollen transport by wind. A few plants move pollen by means of water currents. Flowers are adapted for effective pollination by diverse pollination mechanisms (refer back to Table 32.2).

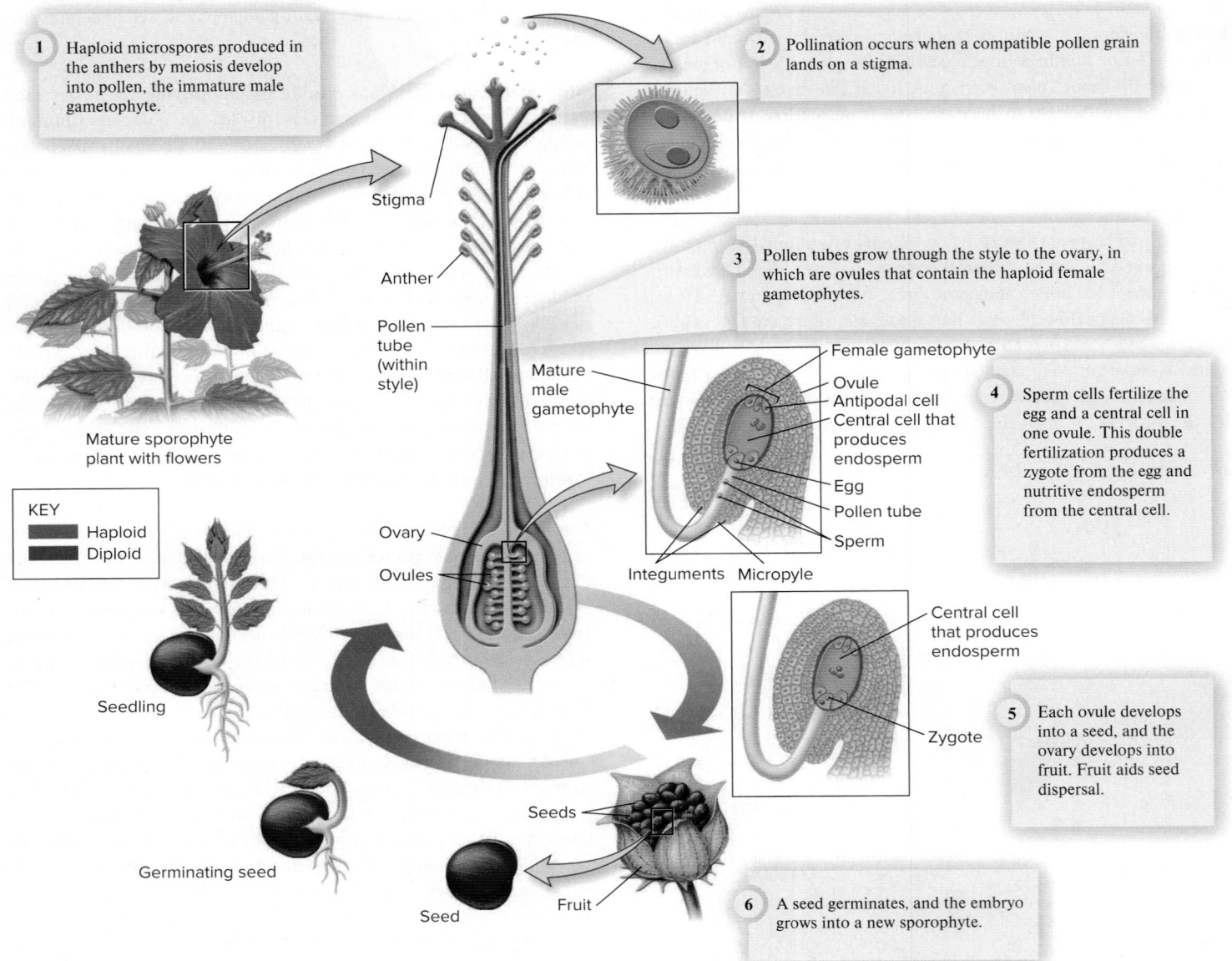

1. Haploid microspores produced in the anthers by meiosis develop into pollen, the immature male gametophyte.

2. Pollination occurs when a compatible pollen grain lands on a stigma.

3. Pollen tubes grow through the style to the ovary, in which are ovules that contain the haploid female gametophytes.

4. Sperm cells fertilize the egg and a central cell in one ovule. This double fertilization produces a zygote from the egg and nutritive endosperm from the central cell.

5. Each ovule develops into a seed, and the ovary develops into fruit. Fruit aids seed dispersal.

6. A seed germinates, and the embryo grows into a new sporophyte.

Stigma

Anther

Pollen tube (within style)

Mature sporophyte plant with flowers

KEY
Haploid
Diploid

Ovary

Ovules

Seedling

Germinating seed

Seed

Mature male gametophyte

Female gametophyte
Ovule
Antipodal cell
Central cell that produces endosperm
Egg
Pollen tube
Sperm

Integuments   Micropyle

Central cell that produces endosperm

Zygote

Seeds

Fruit

Figure 40.4 The life cycle of a flowering plant. The plant reproductive cycle is illustrated here by the eudicot hibiscus.

Concept Check: *What advantage does the hibiscus flower gain by clustering its stamens around the pistil?*

Pollen Germination   When pollen grains land on the stigma, the stigma functions as a gatekeeper, allowing only pollen of appropriate genotype to germinate. During germination, a pollen grain produces a long, thin **pollen tube** that contains two sperm cells. The pollen tube grows through the style toward the ovary. Upon reaching the ovules, the pollen tube grows through the **micropyle**, an opening in the ovule, and delivers sperm to the female gametophyte (see Figure 40.4). These sperm unite with haploid cells of the female gametophyte in the process of **fertilization**. Note that pollination and fertilization are distinct processes in flowering plants.

Double Fertilization   Angiosperms display a phenomenon known as **double fertilization**; that is, two different fertilization events occur. One of the two sperm cells delivered by a pollen tube fertilizes the egg cell,

thereby forming a diploid **zygote**. This zygote may develop by mitotic division into a young sporophyte, known as an **embryo**. Fertilization thus begins a new cycle of alternation between sporophyte and gametophyte generations. The other sperm delivered by the same pollen tube fuses with two nuclei present in one of the cells of the female gametophyte. The cell formed by this second fertilization undergoes mitosis, eventually producing a nutritive tissue known as the **endosperm**. The embryo and the endosperm are essential parts of maturing angiosperm seeds. Fertilization not only starts the development of zygotes into embryos but also triggers the transformation of ovules into seeds and ovaries into fruits. Embryo, seed, and fruit development occur at the same time.

Embryos and Seeds   An embryo is a young, multicellular, diploid sporophyte that develops from a single-celled zygote by mitosis.

Because they are not yet capable of photosynthesis, embryos depend on sporophytes for organic food and other materials. Therefore, embryo development occurs within developing seeds located in a flower ovary. Seeds develop from fertilized ovules. Each developing seed contains an embryo and nutritive endosperm tissue, enclosed and protected by a **seed coat** that develops from the ovule's integuments. When embryos and the seed coat have fully matured, they undergo drying, and the seed enters a phase of metabolic slowdown known as **dormancy**. Fully mature, dormant seeds are ready to be dispersed.

Fruit and Seed Dispersal A **fruit** is a structure that encloses and helps to disperse seeds (see Figure 40.4). Seed dispersal benefits plants by reducing competition for resources among seedlings and parental plants, and it allows plants to colonize new sites.

Fruits develop from the flower's ovary and sometimes include other flower parts. Young fruits bearing immature seeds are typically small and green. During the time that embryos and seeds are developing, the fruit also matures. The ovary wall changes into a fruit wall known as a **pericarp** (from the Greek, meaning surrounding the fruit).

Mature fruits vary greatly among plant species in size, shape, color, and water content. These variations represent adaptations for seed dispersal in different ways. For example, single-seeded dandelion fruits are dry and lightweight and bear a fluffy "parachute" derived from the flower's sepals (see the chapter opening photo). These features foster dispersal by wind. In contrast, coconut fruits feature an airy husk (the pericarp) that keeps them afloat in ocean currents so that they can be carried from one tropical shore to another. Inside the coconut fruit is a single, large seed loaded with liquid and solid endosperm, which people consume as coconut milk and coconut meat, respectively (**Figure 40.5a**). These large amounts of endosperm provide nutrients that sustain coconut seedling growth on infertile, sandy shores. Fruit variation is also extremely important to wild animals and in human agriculture. For example, most fruit crops are juicy and sweet, with relatively small seeds (**Figure 40.5b**). In nature, these features foster dispersal by birds and other animals that feed on such fruits.

Seed Germination and Seedlings If a dispersed seed encounters favorable conditions, including sufficient sunlight and water, it will undergo **germination**. During seed germination, the embryo absorbs water, becomes metabolically active, and grows out of the seed coat, producing a seedling. If the seedling obtains sufficient nutrients from the environment, it grows into a mature sporophyte capable of producing flowers. In the next section, we will focus on flower production, structure, and development.

40.2 Flower Production, Structure, and Development

Learning Outcomes:

1. List some examples of particular genes that control flower production or shape.
2. Give an example of how gene expression affects flowering time or flower appearance.
3. **CoreSKILL »** Explain recent research findings on how flowers bloom, that is, open up from a closed bud.

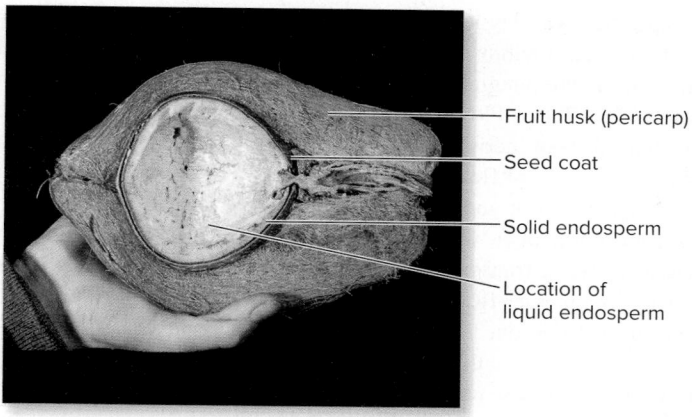

(a) Coconut fruit and seed

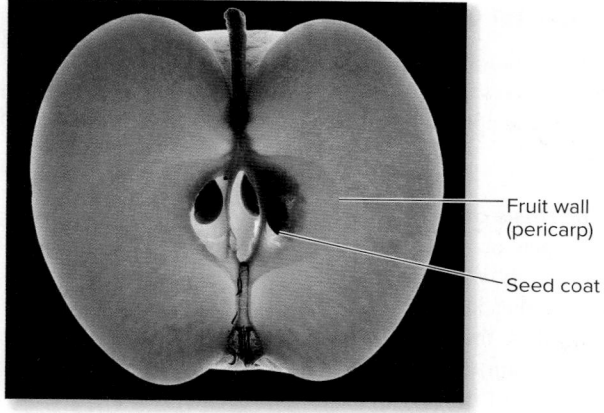

(b) Apple fruit and seed

Figure 40.5 **Fruit adaptations for seed dispersal. (a)** The coconut fruit's outer wall, called a husk, allows the fruit to float and thus disperse its seed among tropical shores. **(b)** The apple is a juicy, sweet fruit that attracts animals to consume it, thereby helping to disperse its seeds. a: ©Natural Sciences Image Library; b: ©Lee W. Wilcox

Flowers are essential sources of food for many animal pollinators. As the result of coevolutionary relationships with such animals, flowers occur in a spectacular array of colors and forms that attract particular pollinators (refer back to Table 32.2). Flowers also attract humans because we possess sensory systems much like those of animal pollinators. We give bouquets to show love and appreciation; decorate homes, workplaces, and objects with flowers; display flower arrangements on ceremonial occasions; and make perfume from flowers. Consequently, many types of flowers are grown for the florist and perfume industries. Flowers are also necessary for the production of grain and other fruit crops. For these and other reasons, biologists investigate how flower development is controlled by environmental signals and changes in gene expression.

Environmental Signals Interact with Genes to Control Flower Production

You've probably noticed that different plants flower at particular times of the year. How do plants know when to flower? Flowering time is controlled by the integration of environmental information such as temperature and day length (photoperiod) with hormonal influences and circadian rhythms (see Chapter 37). These stimuli are perceived and signals are integrated by leaves, which produce a mobile protein known as FT (for Flowering locus Time). FT protein travels in the phloem to shoot meristems and interacts with other proteins there to start the process of flower production.

Winter wheat and some other plants are planted and sprout in fall, are dormant in winter, and flower in the following spring. In these plants, a transcription factor known as FLC (for Flowering Locus C) represses flowering genes, thereby preventing flowers from appearing too soon. Exposure to cold winter conditions causes the production of a small RNA molecule that leads to the silencing of FLC, allowing these plants to flower when the appropriate day length occurs in spring. The process by which cold exposure allows plants to flower in spring is known as vernalization.

Developmental Genes Control Flower Structure

Organ identity genes specify the four basic flower organs that occur in eudicot flowers—sepals, petals, stamens, and carpels. Other genes determine flower shape, color, odor, or grouping into bunches known as inflorescences.

The Genetic Basis of Flower Organ Identity   Sepals, petals, stamens, and carpels occur in four concentric rings known as **whorls**. Sepals (collectively known as the calyx) form the outermost whorl, and petals (together known as the corolla) form an adjacent whorl. Stamens (together, the androecium) create a third whorl, and carpels (the gynoecium) form the innermost whorl (**Figure 40.6**). The **perianth** consists of the calyx plus the corolla. In monocot flowers, such as those of lilies, the perianth consists of tepals rather than petals and sepals. You may recall that *A*, *B*, *C*, and *E* genes encode transcription factors that control the production and arrangement of these whorls (refer back to Figure 20.24).

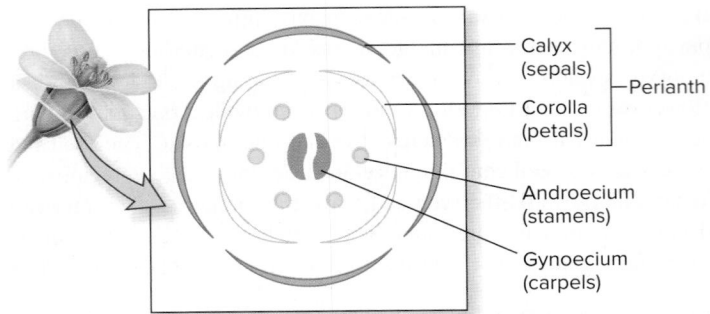

Figure 40.6 **The occurrence of eudicot flower parts in concentric whorls.**

Variation in Number of Whorls   Eudicot flowers that possess all four types of flower whorls—calyx, corolla, androecium (stamens), and gynoecium (one or more carpels)—are known as **complete flowers**. Complete monocot flowers possess tepals, androecium, and gynoecium. In contrast, flowers that lack one or more flower whorls are described as **incomplete flowers**. Flowers having both stamens and carpels are said to be **perfect flowers**, whereas flowers lacking stamens or carpels are described as **imperfect flowers**. An imperfect flower that produces only carpels is known as a carpellate flower (or pistillate flower). Imperfect flowers that produce only stamens are described as staminate flowers.

Corn produces both imperfect staminate and carpellate flowers on an individual plant (**Figure 40.7**). The flowers of corn start to develop as perfect flowers, but in carpellate flowers, the stamens stop developing. After pollination and fertilization, each carpellate flower produces one of the kernels on a cob of corn. In contrast, staminate flowers of corn, which are found in corn tassels, produce the pollen. Corn is termed **monoecious** (meaning one house) because it produces staminate and carpellate flowers on the same plant. Holly and willow also produce staminate and carpellate flowers, though on separate plants, and are examples of plants described as **dioecious** (meaning two houses).

Figure 40.7 **Imperfect flowers of corn, a monoecious plant.** **(a)** Staminate flowers lack carpels, and **(b)** carpellate flowers lack stamens, but both types of flowers occur on a single corn plant. In contrast, dioecious plants produce staminate and carpellate flowers on separate plants. These features foster cross-pollination. a: ©Scott Sinklier/age fotostock; b: ©Robert and Jean Pollock

Concept Check: *What inference can you draw from the observation that flowers of corn lack showy petals?*

(a) Staminate flowers of *Zea mays* (corn)

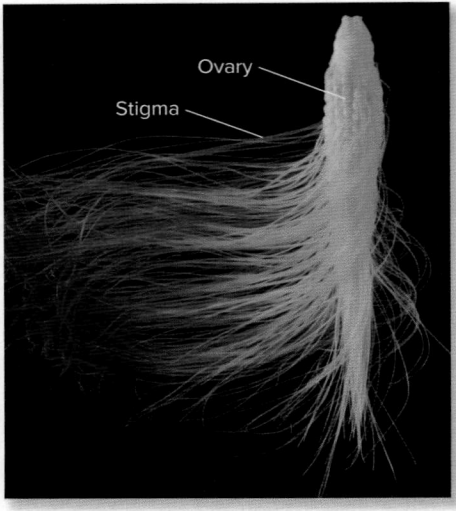

(b) Carpellate flowers of *Zea mays* (corn)

Variation in Flower Organ Number In addition to variation in whorls, flowers vary in number of organs. Eudicots and monocots commonly differ in number of flower organs (refer back to Table 36.1). Eudicot flower organs usually occur in fours or fives or a multiple of either of these numbers. By contrast, monocot flower organs typically occur in threes or a multiple of three. Some flowers possess relatively few organs. For example, a minuscule flower of the tiny floating aquatic plant *Lemna gibba* has no perianth and only two stamens.

Many plants sold for use in gardens have been bred so that the flowers produce multiple organs. Garden roses, for example, typically have many more whorls of petals than do wild roses. This change results from a mutation that causes organs that would have become stamens to instead develop into additional petals.

Variation in Flower Color Flowers and their parts may vary in color. The calyx and corolla of monocot flowers such as tulip and lily are often similar in appearance and attractive function. In contrast, eudicot flowers tend to have green, leaflike sepals (see Figure 40.3) that are quite distinct from petals, which are often colorful and fragrant. Color variations arise from differences in gene action that influence the pathways by which plants synthesize pigments.

Differences in flower color were key to recognizing one of the first cases of gene silencing in plants. Gene silencing occurs when miRNA and siRNA block gene expression (see Chapter 13). In an attempt to produce flowers of deeper color, researchers introduced an extra copy of a pigment-producing gene into petunia plants. Surprisingly, the extra gene copy sometimes produced flowers whose petals had white patches or were completely white (**Figure 40.8**). Adding the extra gene had caused the plants to produce a small-interfering RNA that not only silenced the expression of the extra gene, but also silenced the natural pigment-producing genes, causing white patches on the petals.

Variation in Flower Fragrance The fragrances of flowers result from secondary metabolites that diffuse into the air from petals and other flower organs. Recently, RNA interference (RNAi) (see Chapter 13) was used to show that petunia flowers use a transporter protein to actively transport fragrance compounds into the air. This process allows flowers to communicate with pollinator animals more effectively than if fragrances were emitted by passive diffusion alone. Plants produce chemically diverse fragrances to attract particular types of animal pollinators. Because humans possess sensory systems similar to those of many pollinators, we are also attracted to many of these fragrances.

Flower Shape Variation Resulting from Organ Fusion During their development, many flowers undergo genetically controlled fusion of whorls or fusion of the organs within a whorl. For example, pistils are often composed of two or more fused carpels. In addition, stamen filaments often partially fuse with the carpel or form a tube surrounding the pistil, a feature displayed by hibiscus flowers (see Figure 40.4). Each small dandelion flower has five petals that are fused at their sides to form a single strap-shaped structure. Some flowers have petals that are fused together to form a tube that holds nectar consumed by animal pollinators (see Figure 32.19).

Variations in Flower Symmetry and Aggregation Flower shape variation can also result from changes in symmetry. Flowers that possess radial symmetry are described as regular, actinomorphic, or polysymmetric flowers. Flowers having radial symmetry can be divided into two equal parts by more than one plane inserted through the center of the flower. In contrast, flowers that display bilateral symmetry are known as irregular, zygomorphic, or monosymmetric flowers. Flowers having bilateral symmetry can be divided into two equal parts by only a single plane inserted through the center.

Symmetry, like other flower features, is under genetic control. The production of flowers having bilateral symmetry is controlled by transcription factors such as those encoded by the *CYCLOIDEA*

(a) Normal purple petunia flowers

(b) Petunia flower affected by siRNA

Figure 40.8 Gene silencing and flower color in petunias. (a) Normal purple petunia (*Petunia hybrida*) flowers produced by the expression of all genes involved in flavonoid synthesis. **(b)** Flower of a genetically engineered plant displays petal tissues in which expression of one of the genes needed for production of purple pigment production has been silenced (suppressed) by siRNA. a: ©Michael Davis/Getty Images; b: ©Richard Jorgensen

ratio of the change in length of a material to the initial unstressed length. These measurements also enabled them to mathematically model changes in tepal shape, starting with equations that describe changes in the shapes of thin sheets (see Figure 40.11).

The biologists observed that by the end of the fourth day, each bud had absorbed one-fifth of a liter of water, increased in length by 10% and width by 20%, and turned white. The inner three tepals had become wrinkled, especially at the edges, a key clue to the mechanism underlying the blooming process. The wrinkling reflected faster growth at the edges than in the center. This difference in growth-generated strain values is large enough to cause the flower to bloom rapidly as individual tepals simultaneously reversed curvature and bent outward, a process predicted by mathematical modeling. The study revealed that flower blooming is based on a different mechanism than previously thought and illustrates the value of applying physics and mathematical models to biological phenomena.

Experimental Questions:

1. Why do you think Liang and Mahadevan used *Lilium casablanca* for their analysis of flower blooming?

2. How did time-lapse video improve data gathering in this study?

BIO TIPS   **THE QUESTION** *By employing time-lapse video, Liang and Mahadevan determined that the blooming of lily flowers resulted from faster growth of the tepals at their edges than at their centers. Consider the data from their study in step 5 of Figure 40.11. How much faster was the longitudinal growth at the edges of the tepals than the longitudinal growth at the centers?*

T **OPIC** *What topic in biology does this question address?* The topic is flowering plant reproduction, or, more specifically, how flowers bloom, that is, open fully from the bud stage. Most people have observed flowers in stages of opening, but few have watched the process from start to finish. For this reason, the physical mechanism underlying flower blooming had not been clear until this experiment was performed.

I **NFORMATION** *What information do you know based on the question and your understanding of the topic?* In the question, you are reminded of the data in Figure 40.11. From your understanding of the topic, you may recall that monocots such as lilies produce flowers whose perianth parts are known as tepals because they are not specialized into outer sepals and inner petals, as they are in eudicots. The outermost parts of the lily bud transform into petal-like tepals as the flower blooms. The investigators focused on the longitudinal (lengthwise) growth of the tepals.

P **ROBLEM-SOLVING** **S** **TRATEGY** *Interpret data.* The data are presented in the form of line graphs based on video recordings of changes in the positions of black dots marked on the surfaces of lily buds. Compare the red line showing longitudinal growth at the tepal edges to the blue line showing longitudinal growth at the tepal centers.

ANSWER *Longitudinal growth of the tepals always occurred more rapidly at the edges than at the centers, and the maximal difference was more than 4 times (a ratio of 0.45/0.1).*

40.3 Male and Female Gametophytes and Double Fertilization

Learning Outcomes:

1. Explain how gamete production in plants differs from that in animals.

2. Explain how the pistil controls pollen germination.

3. Describe the structure of the female gametophyte.

4. Outline the different fates of the two sperm cells transmitted by each pollen tube.

In animals, the cells that will undergo meiosis to produce gametes are known as the germ line, and they are set aside from other body cells during early development. By contrast, plants do not establish gamete-producing cells during early development and meiosis does not generate plant gametes. Even so, similar proteins of the Rb (retinoblastoma) family are involved in starting the process of gamete development in both animals and plants. As we have seen, plant gametes are produced by the life cycle stage known as gametophytes. In this section, we will focus on plant male and female gametophytes, gametes, and fertilization.

Pollen Grains Are Immature Male Gametophytes

Pollen grains develop within sporangia located in the anthers of stamens (see Figure 40.4). Sporangia are structures produced by all plants, within which meiosis generates spores. (Note that in plants, meiosis generates haploid spores, not haploid gametes as in animals.) Inside protective plant sporangia, diploid body cells produce a cluster of four haploid microspores, each having a thin cellulose cell wall. The development of microspores into pollen grains involves two processes that occur at the same time: (1) microspore division to produce a young male gametophyte, and (2) development of a tough pollen wall that protects the gametophyte during pollen transport. Both of these processes are completed before the anthers release pollen.

Each microspore nucleus undergoes one or two mitotic divisions to form a young male gametophyte. The first division gives rise to two specialized cells: a tube cell and a generative cell suspended within the tube cell (**Figure 40.12a**). The **generative cell** divides to produce two sperm cells, either before or (more commonly) after pollination. The **tube cell** produces the pollen tube, which delivers sperm to the female gametophyte.

A mature pollen grain has a tough wall, and each plant species produces pollen whose wall has a distinctive sculptural shape (**Figure 40.12b**). The wall, which surrounds the plasma membrane of the tube cell, is composed largely of a tough polymer known as sporopollenin. Named for its presence on the surfaces of mature spores and pollen, sporopollenin protects spores and pollen from damage.

Development of the pollen grain wall starts with deposition of a blanket of the carbohydrate callose around each cluster of four microspores after they form by meiosis. The callose blanket isolates the microspores from the influences of adjacent sporophyte tissues, thereby aiding pollen differentiation. Callose also provides a surface pattern for sporopollenin deposition and holds microspores together until an anther enzyme degrades the callose, freeing pollen grains from each other.

As pollen grains mature, anther cells secrete a pollen coat, a layer of material that covers the sporopollenin-rich pollen wall. Coat materials include additional sporopollenin, pigments that give pollen its typically yellow, orange, or brown coloration, and lipids and proteins that aid in pollen attachment to carpels. Certain of these pollen coat compounds are responsible for allergic reactions in people exposed to particular types of airborne pollen. About 10% of flowering plants are wind-pollinated, and such plants produce copious amounts of pollen.

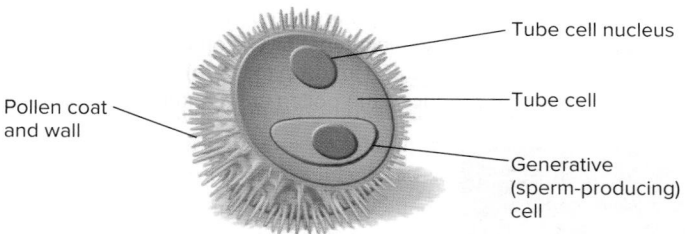

Tube cell nucleus

Tube cell

Pollen coat and wall

Generative (sperm-producing) cell

(a) A cut pollen grain showing immature male gametophyte

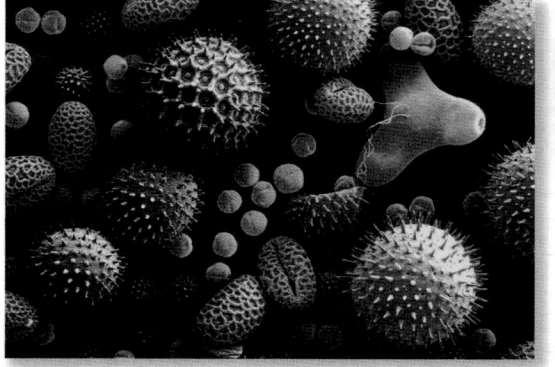

16.7 μm

(b) SEM of whole pollen grains showing distinctive sculptural shapes

Figure 40.12 Pollen grains. (a) Diagram of cut pollen grain. **(b)** SEM of whole pollen grains of different species. b: ©Phanie/Alamy Stock Photo

Concept Check: *What is the maximum number of cells in a mature male gametophyte of a flowering plant?*

For example, ragweed plants (genus *Ambrosia*), which are commonly associated with allergies, each produce an estimated 1 billion pollen grains during a year!

After Pollination, the Pistil Controls Pollen Germination

Recall that pollination is the process by which pollen is delivered to surfaces of the stigma, the uppermost part of the flower pistil. However, even if a pollen grain reaches the stigma of the right flower species, it may not be able to germinate and produce a sperm-delivery tube. The stigma and the style determine whether or not pollen grains germinate and pollen tubes grow toward ovules. How is this accomplished?

About half of plant species can serve as both mother and father to their progeny, because pollen produced by those plants is able to germinate on pistils of the same plants. Such self-pollinating plants are said to display **self-compatibility (SC)**. By contrast, plants that prevent the germination of pollen that is too genetically similar to the pistil are said to display **self-incompatibility (SI)**. Similar to human cultural practices that prevent mating between close relatives, SI helps to decrease the likelihood of recessive disorders in offspring. In many plants, SI involves the *S* gene locus, which encodes S proteins. Each locus contains genetic sequences that determine pollen compatibility traits and pistil compatibility traits. Multiple *S* alleles for both genes occur in plant populations.

Two major types of SI are known: gametophytic SI and sporophytic SI. Gametophytic SI occurs when one or more *S* genes within pollen determine compatibility by encoding S proteins located in the pollen cytosol. When the gametophyte controls compatibility, tubes may start to grow from incompatible pollen, but S proteins encoded by pistil cells enter the tubes and destroy the pollen tube RNA. This halts tube growth. In contrast, S proteins within genetically compatible pollen bind the pistil-produced proteins, thereby preventing destruction of the pollen tube RNA and allowing tube growth to continue (**Figure 40.13a**).

Sporophytic SI occurs when pollen compatibility is determined by the sporophyte that produces the pollen. This control is exerted when anthers deposit proteins into the pollen coat. When the sporophyte controls compatibility, pollen cannot germinate when S proteins in the plasma membranes of stigma cells recognize (bind) the S proteins of incompatible pollen. In this case, protein binding leads to signal transduction processes that prevent pollen germination. However, pollen can germinate if stigma proteins are unable to bind genetically distinct S proteins in its coat (Figure 40.13b).

A Female Gametophyte Develops Within Each Ovule

In flowering plants, each ovule produces a single female gametophyte that often consists of seven cells and eight nuclei (**Figure 40.14**). One of these cells is an egg cell, which lies wedged between two cells known as **synergids**. These synergids help move nutrients from the larger sporophyte to the nonphotosynthetic female gametophyte. Synergids also secrete small proteins called LURES that act as attractants for pollen tube growth. The LURES cause pollen tubes to deposit specific receptor proteins in the membranes of tube tip cells lying closest to the LURES. Then, the binding of LURES to the receptors steers pollen tube growth

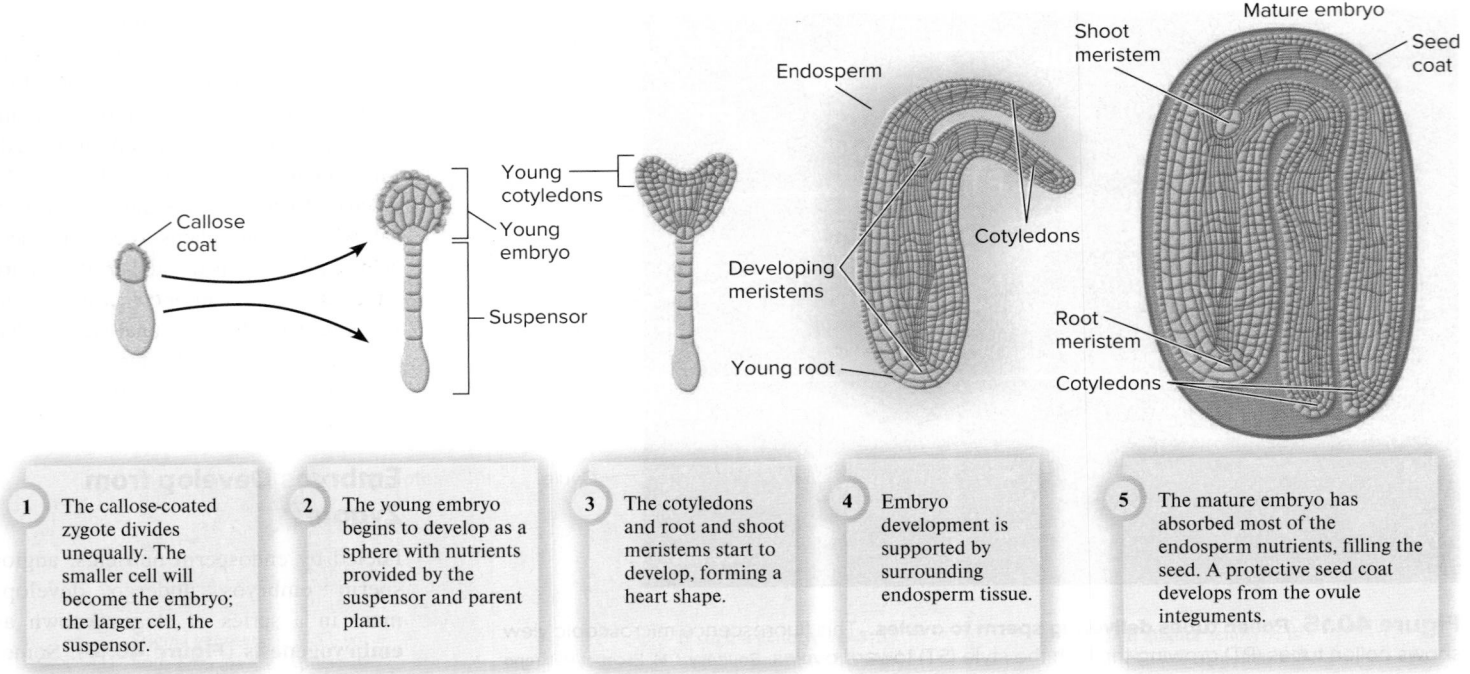

Figure 40.16 **Embryogenesis in the eudicot *Arabidopsis*.**

Concept Check: *How would the eudicot embryo differ if its TOPLESS gene were nonfunctional?*

conditions are not suitable for seedling growth. Seed maturation includes transformation of the ovule's integuments into a tough seed coat (see Figure 40.16, step 5). The seed coat restrains seedlings from growing and contains suberin, a lipid-rich material that prevents the entry of water and oxygen, thereby maintaining low seed metabolism. In addition, the coats of some seeds are darkly colored with pigments that may help to prevent damage by UV radiation or microbial attack.

A key change leading to seed dormancy is the gradual, controlled loss of water from the embryo and other seed tissues. During this process, the embryo becomes relatively dry, but is able to survive. The water content of dispersed seeds is only 5–15%. Abscisic acid (ABA) is a hormone that induces the activity of genes that help embryo tissues to survive the drying process. Some of these desiccation-tolerance genes encode proteins that form loose coils enclosing cell contents, thereby preventing damage as the cytoplasm becomes almost completely dry. When the seeds of flowering plants are dry and ready for dispersal, they are released from the plant while enclosed in a fruit or released when the fruit breaks open.

The structure of mature monocot and eudicot seeds differs. Within eudicot seeds, mature embryos often display an **epicotyl**, the portion of an embryonic stem with two tiny leaves in a first bud that is located above the point of attachment of the cotyledons (**Figure 40.17a**). The **hypocotyl** is the portion of an embryonic stem located below the point of attachment of the cotyledons. An embryonic root, the **radicle**, extends from the hypocotyl. Much of the endosperm has been absorbed into the large cotyledons. In contrast, mature monocot embryos, such as those of corn, feature an epicotyl with a first bud enclosed in a protective sheath known as the **coleoptile**. The young monocot root is enclosed within a protective envelope known as the **coleorhiza** (**Figure 40.17b**).

Fruits Develop from Ovaries and Other Flower Parts

All fruits develop from ovaries and sometimes other flower parts. They occur in diverse forms that aid seed dispersal. Some fruits are dry, whereas others are moist and juicy; some open to release seeds, and others do not. Fruits also display a wide variety of sizes, colors, and fragrances. These variations result from differences in the process of fruit development. Plant hormones, including auxins, gibberellic acid, and cytokinins, control this transformation. ABA stimulates cell expansion, and ethylene influences fruit ripening. For instance, ethylene helps to ripen nuts, a type of dry fruit, by inducing plasma membranes to rupture, causing water loss. Under the influence of plant hormones, the pericarp (ripened ovary wall) of peaches, plums, and related fruits swells and softens, and orange or red chromoplasts replace green chloroplasts. As fruits mature, the outer protective cuticle often becomes very thick, contributing to peel toughness, which helps to prevent microbe attack. In addition, many maturing fruits increase their sugar and acid content, which produces the distinctive tastes of ripe fruits. Many fruits also produce fragrant volatile compounds.

Differences in the shape, color, fragrance, and moisture content of wild fruits reflect evolutionary adaptation for effective seed dispersal. Though many fruits and seeds are dispersed by wind or water or by attaching to animal fur, others are consumed by fruit-eating animals that are attracted by the colors and fragrances. Blackberries provide a good example of fruits adapted for animal dispersal. Blackberry flowers produce many separate pistils, each containing a single ovule (**Figure 40.18a**). Following pollination and fertilization, the ovary of each pistil develops into a sweet, juicy fruitlet containing a single seed. As the individual fruitlets develop, they fuse together at the sides.

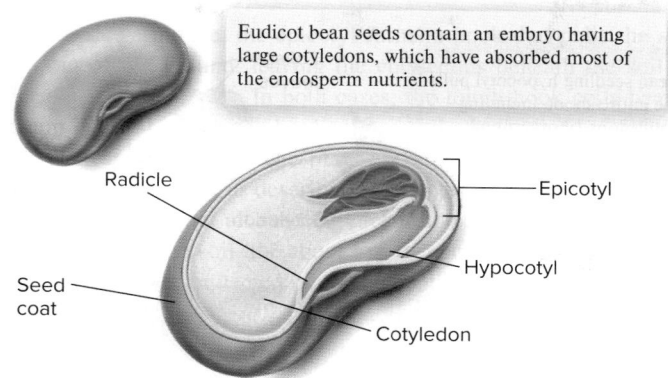

Eudicot bean seeds contain an embryo having large cotyledons, which have absorbed most of the endosperm nutrients.

(a) Eudicot bean seed, showing embryo with epicotyl, hypocotyl, and radicle

Monocot corn kernels are single-seeded fruits. The seed embryo has one cotyledon that presses against the nutritive endosperm. The embryonic shoot tip is protected by a tissue sheath—the coleoptile. The embryonic root is protected by a tissue sheath—the coleorhiza.

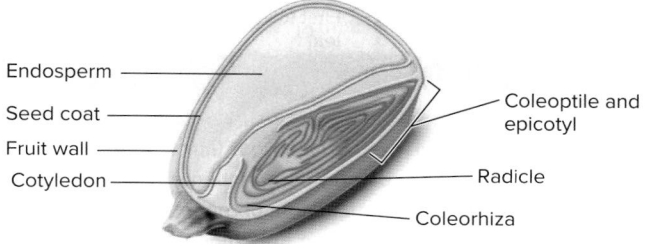

(b) Monocot corn seed, showing an embryo protected by coleoptile and coleorhiza

Figure 40.17   Structure of mature seeds and embryos. Note: You may want to look ahead to Figure 40.20a to see the relative locations of some of these structures in young seedlings.

Concept Check: *Why do mature seeds of eudicots lack extensive amounts of endosperm?*

Consequently, the many fruitlets produced by a single blackberry flower are dispersed together (**Figure 40.18b**). Attracted by the color, birds consume the whole aggregate and excrete the seeds, thereby dispersing many at a time. Many other types of fruits occur and these likewise represent adaptations that foster seed dispersal (refer back to Figure 32.21). Although a fruit is usually defined as a mature ovary containing seeds, seedless fruits such as watermelon are produced commercially by genetic modification or treatment with artificial auxin.

Environmental and Internal Factors Influence Seed Germination

Seeds vary greatly in their ability to germinate after dispersal. Small seeds such as those of dandelions and lettuces germinate quickly if light is available. Other seeds require a period of dormancy before germination occurs. Some seeds can remain dormant for amazingly long time periods. For example, a lotus (*Nelumbo nucifera*) seed collected from a lake bed in China germinated at the age of 1,300 years, as determined by radiocarbon dating. In 2005, plant scientists germinated a 2,000-year-old date seed found in Israel.

Water is generally required to rehydrate seeds so that embryos can resume their metabolic activity. Water absorption also swells seeds, helping to break the seed coat and allowing embryonic organs to emerge. In some cases, rainfall of sufficient duration to leach germination-inhibiting compounds out of seeds is required. The optimal temperature for germination of most seeds lies between 25°C and 30.25°C (77°F and 86.25°F). This explains why gardeners wait until the soil is warm before planting seeds outdoors in spring. However, some seeds need a period of cold treatment or seed coat abrasion before they will germinate. Such physical stimuli induce the activity of more than 2,000 genes associated with seed germination.

When grass seeds rehydrate, the young shoot secretes the hormone gibberellic acid from the seed cotyledon into the outermost endosperm layer, known as the aleurone. In response, the aleurone secretes digestive enzymes into the central endosperm, releasing sugars from stored starch (**Figure 40.19**). The seedling uses these sugars for growth. This

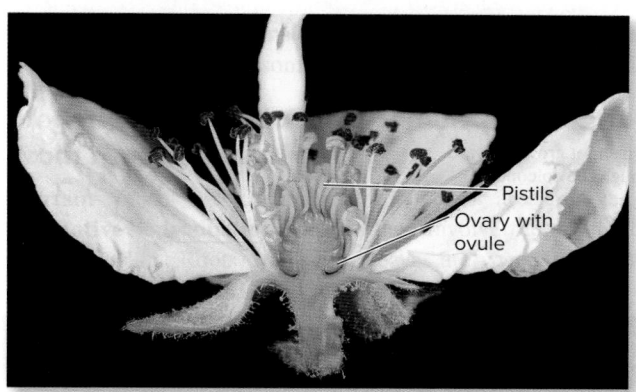

(a) *Rubus allegheniensis* (common blackberry) flower

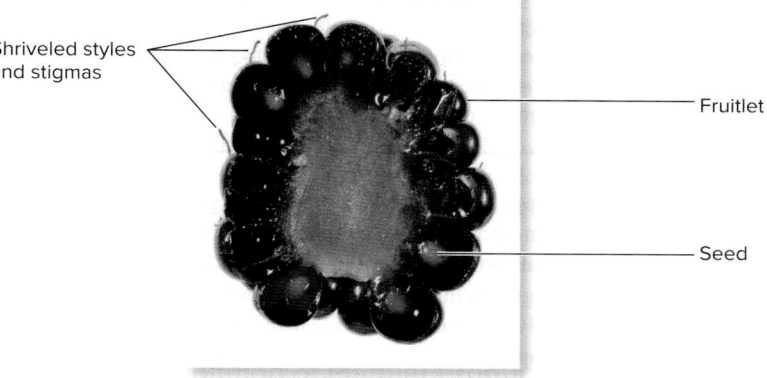

(b) Blackberry fruit

Figure 40.18   Blackberry flower and fruit. **(a)** Each of the many separate pistils in a blackberry flower is able to produce a single one-seed fruit (called a fruitlet) if fertilization occurs. **(b)** Together, the individual fruitlets of the blackberry compose an aggregate fruit that allows many seeds to be efficiently dispersed at the same time by the same animal agent. a–b: ©Lee W. Wilcox

  Core Concept: Systems The dispersal by birds of many blackberry seeds at the same time is an example of the interconnection of living systems.

UNIT VII
ANIMALS

Despite the amazing diversity of animal life, fundamental similarities link the millions of animal species. We will explore many of these similarities in this unit. The basic features of animal bodies and the maintenance of homeostasis will be introduced in Chapter 41. Chapters 42–44 will discuss major principles of nervous systems. The ability of animals to move through their environments will be covered in Chapter 45. The digestion and absorption of nutrients and the control of metabolism are the subjects of Chapters 46 and 47. Circulatory, respiratory, excretory, and endocrine systems are then covered in Chapters 48–50. The unit continues with Chapters 51–52, which focus on animal reproduction and development and immune systems, and concludes with Chapter 53, which describes the integrated responses of animals' organ systems to a life-threatening challenge to homeostasis.

 The following Core Concepts and Core Skills will be emphasized in this unit:

- *Evolution: The fundamental principles of evolution are key to understanding virtually all aspects of animal biology. This core concept is covered in several places in all the chapters. For example, we will look at the evolution of nervous systems in Chapter 43 and at an ancient family of proteins that provide immunity in animals in Chapter 52.*

- *Energy and Matter: We will see how many of the processes that achieve and maintain homeostasis require energy. For example, it takes energy to maintain blood flow (Chapter 48) and a stable concentration of sodium ions in an animal's body fluids (Chapter 49).*

- *Information: How genes play a role in determining key traits in animals will be discussed throughout this unit.*

- *Structure and Function: The relationship between structure and function in animals at the levels of cells, tissues, organs, and whole bodies will be evident throughout the unit. This core concept of animal biology is particularly relevant to our discussion of nervous systems (Chapters 42–44) and digestive systems (Chapter 46).*

- *Systems. The organ systems of animal bodies interact in many ways to maintain normal functioning of processes such as blood pressure and digestion. In Chapter 53, we will explore an integrated response to a major challenge to homeostasis.*

- *Process of Science: Most chapters have a Feature Investigation that describes a classic or recent experiment notable not only for its innovation and creativity, but also for moving the field of animal biology forward in a significant way.*

- *Modeling: Each chapter has a Modeling Challenge to help you refine this important skill.*

- *Science and Society: Most chapters include a section titled "Impact on Public Health," in which basic science from the chapter is applied to the human condition, with emphasis on how society at large is impacted by disease.*

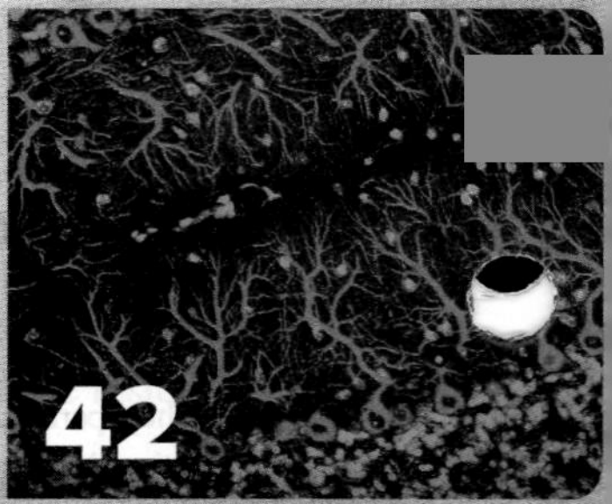

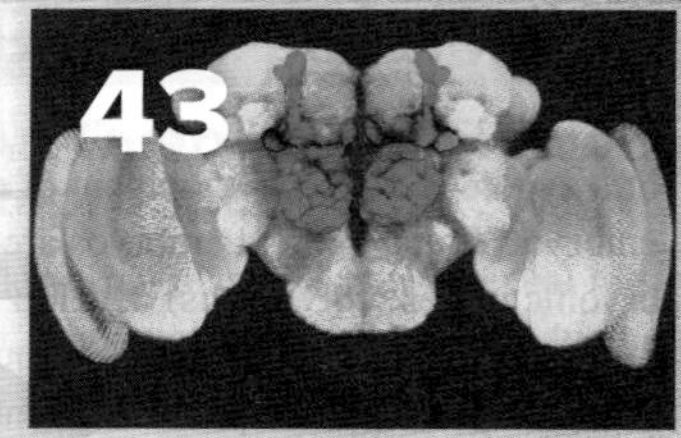

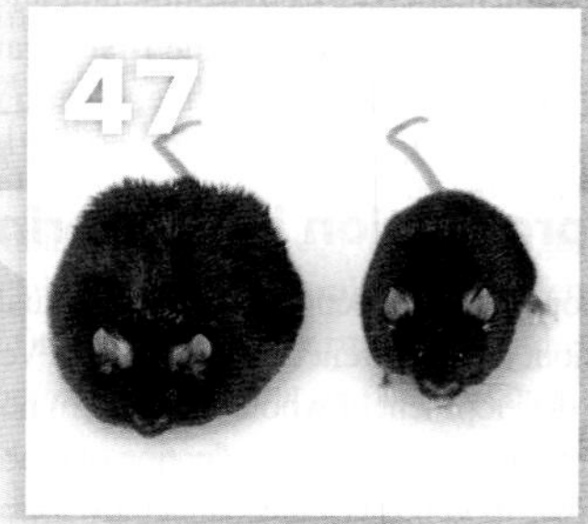

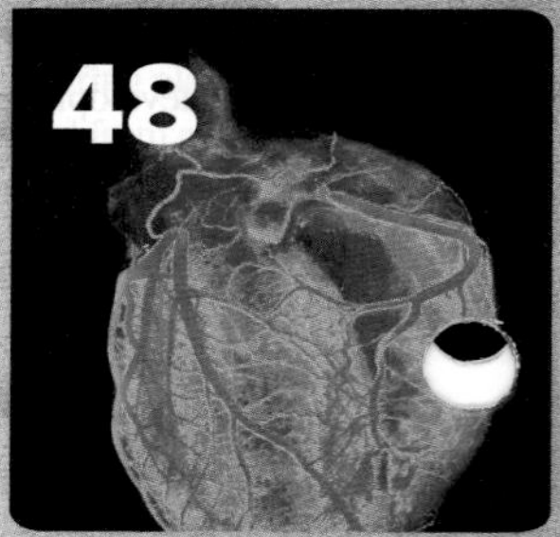

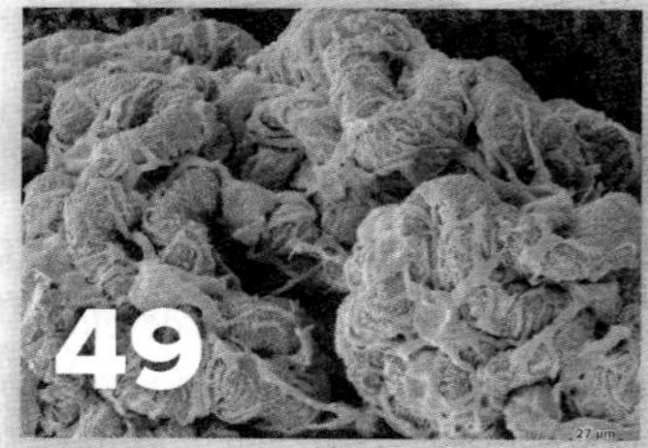

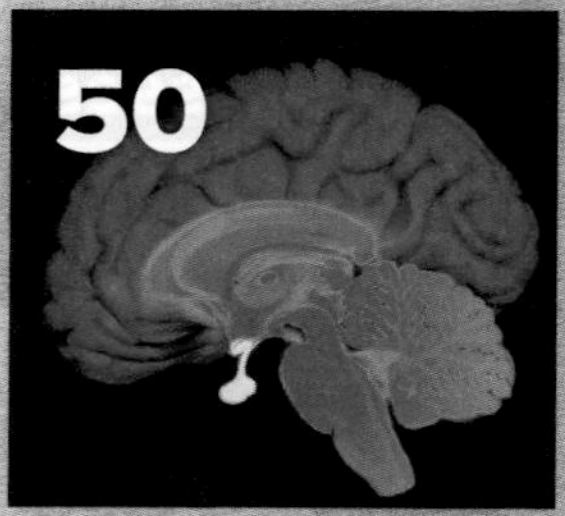

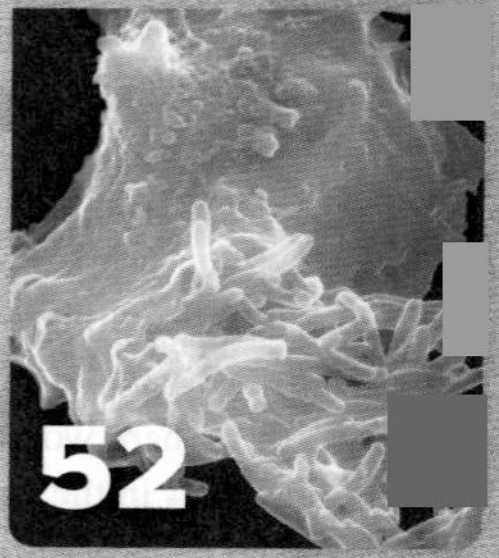

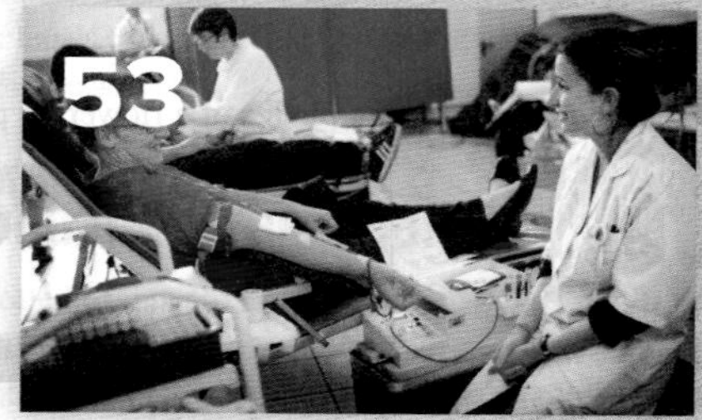

Animal Bodies and Homeostasis

41

Perspiring and drinking water are both mechanisms that help achieve homeostasis—a stable internal body environment.
©John Rowley/Getty Images

L ook at the woman in the chapter opening photo. What is happening in her body at that moment? Obviously, it is a hot day, and the woman is perspiring and thirsty; it appears that she has just been exercising outdoors. During such exertion, her body must prevent an excessive buildup of heat, because high body temperature can alter the activities of enzymes and damage cellular membranes. One way some animals, including humans, can eliminate heat from the body is to perspire. Recall from Chapter 2 that water has a high heat of vaporization, and therefore the evaporation of water from the body surface helps eliminate body heat. This benefit comes with a cost, however, because perspiration depletes some of the body's water, potentially leading to changes in ion concentrations in body fluids, blood pressure, and other critical physiological variables. Consequently, structures in the brain and other organs that are sensitive to the body's fluid level and ion concentrations trigger the sensation of thirst, and the woman drinks water to replenish what was lost through perspiration. The process through which the different aspects of an animal's internal environment (in this case, temperature and body fluids) are maintained within normal limits, even in the face of changing circumstances or external challenges, is known as **homeostasis**.

Maintenance of homeostasis is one of the fundamental principles of virtually all aspects of animal biology. Before we can fully appreciate what homeostasis means to animals and how it is achieved, however, we first need to understand some basic features of animal bodies. We begin this chapter with a discussion of the organization of cells into tissues and tissues into organs. Chapter 10 considered the organization of cells into tissues from the perspective of cell biology. Here, we look at tissues and organs from the perspective of the whole animal, examining how the properties of life arise from the complex interactions of its components. Next, we will discuss a core concept of biology that also helps us understand homeostasis, the concept that structure (form) determines function. We then link these principles together with a detailed look at what homeostasis means for different animals, how it may be challenged, and how it is restored or maintained. The final section of the chapter considers the important topic of homeostatic control of internal fluids.

41.1 Organization of Animal Bodies

Learning Outcomes:

1. List the different categories of animal tissues, providing general functions and specific examples of each.
2. Name the various organ systems found in many animals, list the components of each, and describe their general functions.

All animals share similarities in the ways in which they exchange materials with their surroundings, obtain energy from organic nutrients, synthesize complex molecules, reproduce themselves, and detect and respond to signals in their environment. Animals typically begin life as a single cell—most commonly a fertilized egg—which divides to create two cells, each of which divides in turn, resulting in four cells, and so on. If cell division were the only event

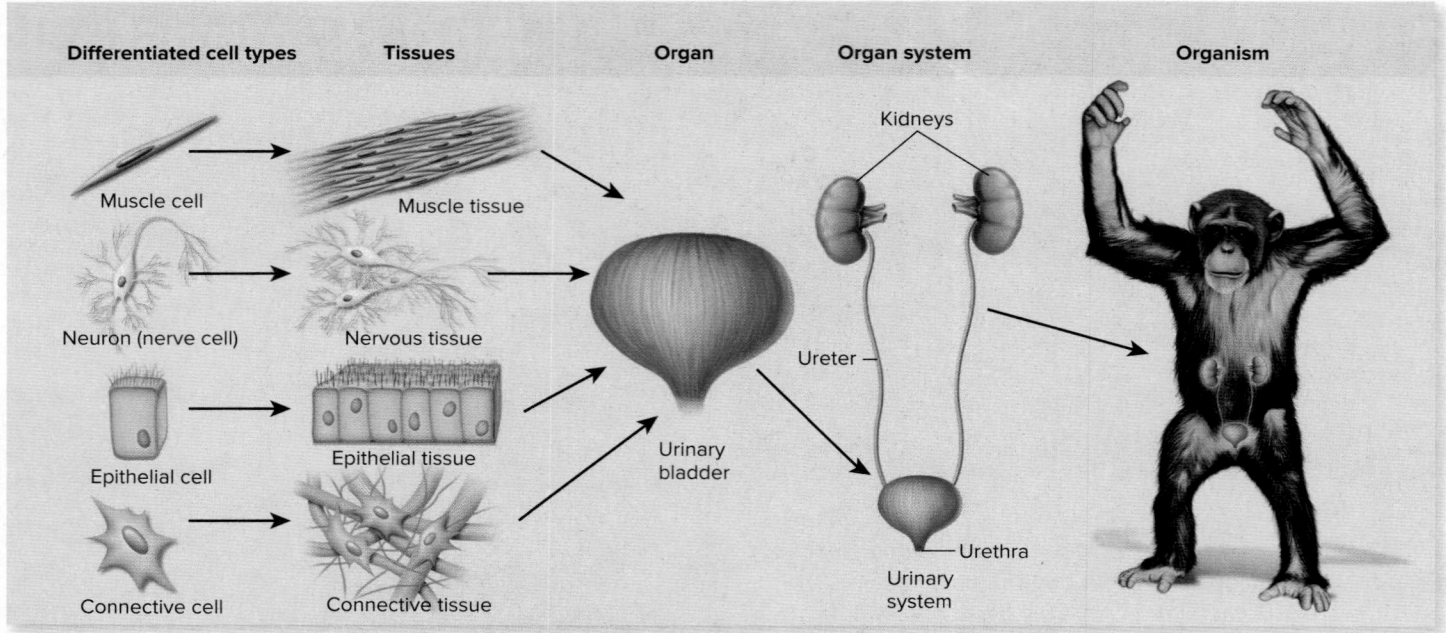

Figure 41.1 **The internal organization of cells, tissues, organs, and an organ system in a mammal.** The urinary system of mammals is part of the larger excretory system that includes all the structures that function to remove soluble wastes from animals' bodies.

 Core Concept: Systems New properties of life emerge from complex interactions. By themselves, none of the four tissues that constitute a bladder or a kidney could perform the functions of those organs, but when combined in precise ways, the result is a functional organ system capable of removing soluble wastes from the fluids of an animal's body.

occurring, the end result would be a spherical mass of identical cells. As we will see in Chapter 51, however, cells become specialized during development to perform a particular function (that is, they differentiate). Examples of differentiated cells are muscle and blood cells. As **Figure 41.1** shows for the urinary system of mammals, the cells of an animal's body are organized into progressively more complex structures, including tissues, organs, and organ systems. In this section, we will explore this organization in greater detail.

Specialized Cells Are Organized into Tissues

A **tissue** is an association of many cells that have a similar structure and function. The tissues in a typical animal's body can be classified into four types, according to their locations and the functions they perform: muscle, nervous, epithelial, and connective tissues. Within each of these functional categories, subtypes of tissues perform variations of the given function, as illustrated by the three types of muscle tissue.

Muscle Tissues **Muscle tissues** consist of cells specialized to shorten, or contract, generating the mechanical forces that may produce body movement, decrease the diameter of a tube, or exert pressure on a fluid-filled cavity. Three types of muscle tissue are found in animals: skeletal, smooth, and cardiac (**Figure 41.2**).

Skeletal muscles are generally attached to the skeleton of an animal. When skeletal muscles are stimulated by signals from the nervous system, they generate force that leads to the contraction of the muscle (see Chapter 45). Contraction of these muscles may be

under voluntary control and produce the movements required for locomotion, such as extending limbs or flapping wings.

Smooth muscles surround hollow tubes and cavities inside the body's organs, so their contraction can move the contents of those organs. For example, the contraction of smooth muscle in the stomach wall propels partially digested food into the intestines, where it can be digested. Smooth muscle also surrounds and forms part of small blood vessels and airway tubes (bronchioles). Contraction in those regions reduces blood or air flow, respectively. In the circulatory system, this contraction helps direct blood to regions of the body that most require it at any given time. In the airways of the respiratory system, it helps direct air to the healthiest parts of a lung. Contraction of all smooth muscle is involuntary—that is, it occurs without conscious control.

In the third type of muscle tissue, **cardiac muscle**, physical and electrical connections between individual cells enable many cells to contract almost simultaneously. Like smooth muscle, cardiac muscle cannot be contracted voluntarily. It is found only in the heart, where it provides the force that generates sufficient pressure to pump blood through an animal's body.

Nervous Tissues **Nervous tissues** are composed of a complex network of cells called **neurons** that are specialized to receive, generate, and conduct electrical signals from one part of an animal's body to another part (**Figure 41.3**). Depending on where it is generated in an animal's body, an electrical signal produced in one neuron may stimulate or inhibit other neurons to initiate new electrical signals,

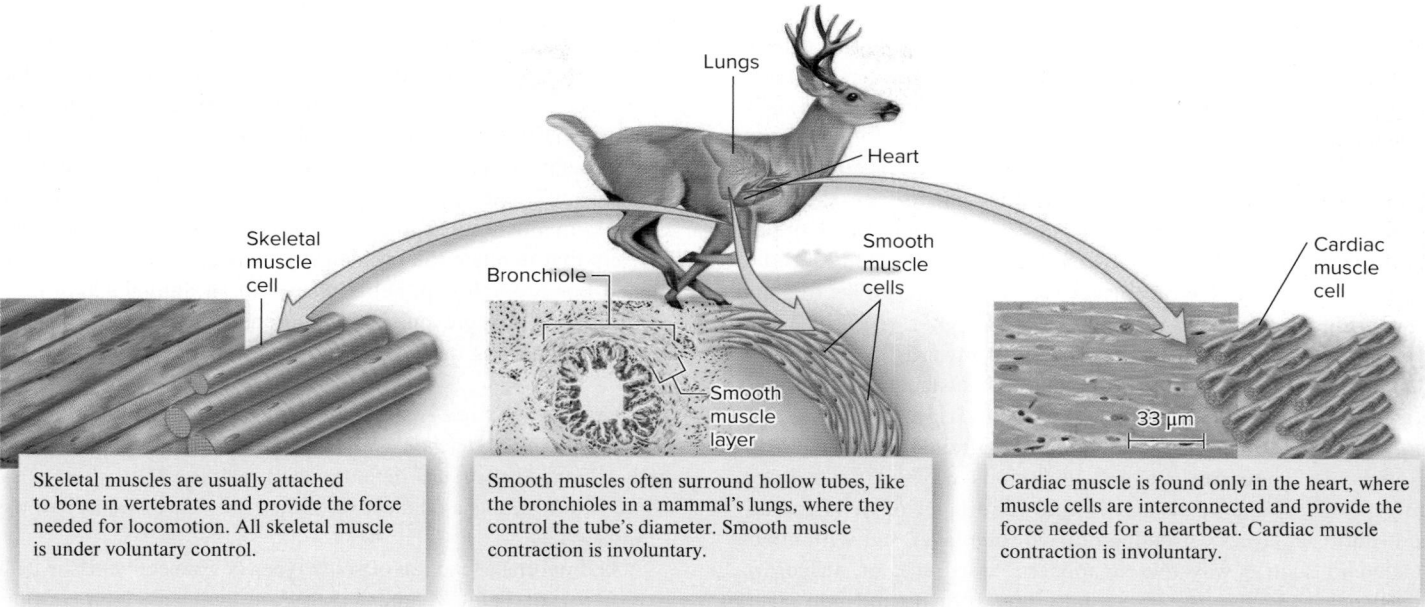

Skeletal muscle cell

Lungs

Heart

Bronchiole

Smooth muscle cells

Cardiac muscle cell

Smooth muscle layer

33 μm

Skeletal muscles are usually attached to bone in vertebrates and provide the force needed for locomotion. All skeletal muscle is under voluntary control.

Smooth muscles often surround hollow tubes, like the bronchioles in a mammal's lungs, where they control the tube's diameter. Smooth muscle contraction is involuntary.

Cardiac muscle is found only in the heart, where muscle cells are interconnected and provide the force needed for a heartbeat. Cardiac muscle contraction is involuntary.

Figure 41.2 Three types of muscle tissue: skeletal, smooth, and cardiac. All three types produce force, but they differ in their appearance and in their locations within animals' bodies. (left): ©Michael Abbey/Science Source; (middle): ©Sinclair Stammers/Science Source; (right): ©Innerspace Imaging/Science Source

 Core Skill: Modeling The goal of this modeling challenge is to draw a model showing how smooth muscle contraction affects the width of a tube such as a bronchiole.

Modeling Challenge: Smooth muscle often surrounds tubelike structures in animal bodies, where it controls the degree to which the tubes are opened. In the disease asthma, smooth muscle tissue in the small air tubes called bronchioles is sometimes in a highly contracted state. Shown below is a model of a fully opened bronchiole in a human. Draw another model of the bronchiole as you think it will appear when the person is experiencing asthmatic symptoms (contracted smooth muscle tissue). Referring to your model, explain why individuals with asthma have difficulty breathing when their symptoms flare up.

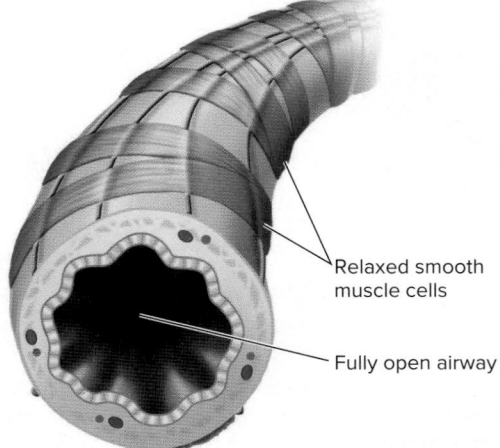

Relaxed smooth muscle cells

Fully open airway

Open bronchiole

A healthy bronchiole in a human lung. Note that the smooth muscle tissue is in a relaxed state, and the bronchiole is fully opened.

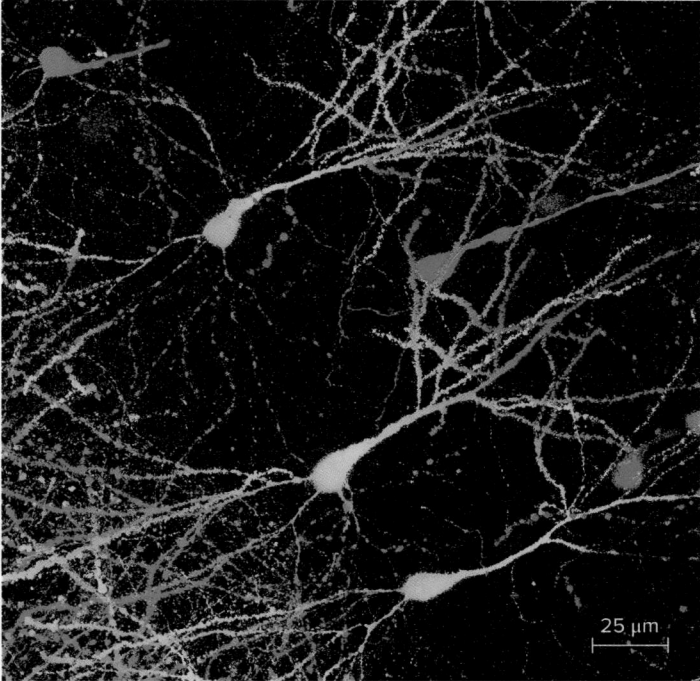

25 μm

Figure 41.3 Nervous tissue in the brain of a vertebrate. Nervous tissue consists of neurons with extensive cell-cell contacts, as shown in this confocal micrograph of a section from a human brain. The cells are labeled with fluorescent markers; different colors signify different depths in the section. ©Dr. Gopal Murti/SPL/ Science Source

 Core Concept: Systems Animals interact with their environments in many ways. These interactions largely depend on the functioning of nervous tissue, which allows animals to sense and respond to changes in the environment.

stimulate muscle cells to contract, or stimulate glandular cells to release chemicals into an animal's body fluids. Thus, nervous tissue provides a critical means of controlling diverse activities of the cells in an animal's body.

Epithelial Tissues   **Epithelial tissues** consist of sheets of densely packed cells that cover the body or individual organs and line the interiors of various cavities inside the body. Epithelial cells are specialized to protect structures and to secrete and absorb ions and organic molecules (see Chapter 10). For example, epithelial tissue can invaginate (fold inward) to form sweat glands that secrete water and ions onto the surface of an animal's skin. Epithelial cells in animals come in a variety of shapes, such as cuboidal (cube-shaped), squamous (flattened), and columnar (elongated). They are arranged in various ways to form different types of epithelial tissue: simple (one layer of cells), stratified (multiple layers), pseudostratified (one layer, but with nuclei located in such a way that it appears stratified), or, in certain cases such as in the urinary system, transitional (multiple layers with the ability to expand and contract) (**Figure 41.4**).

Regardless of their shape, organization into tissues, or location, all epithelial cells are asymmetric, or polarized. This means that one side of such a cell is anchored to or faces an extracellular matrix

(ECM) called the basal lamina, or basement membrane (see Figure 10.1); this side of the cell is called the basal or basolateral membrane. The other side, called the apical membrane, faces the internal (such as the lining of the stomach) or external (the body surface) environment of an animal. Thus, epithelial cells form boundaries between different body compartments, as discussed later in this chapter. In this way, epithelial tissues can function as selective barriers that regulate the exchange of molecules between compartments. For example, epithelial tissues in an animal's skin help to form a barrier that prevents most substances in the external environment from entering the body.

Connective Tissues   As their name implies, **connective tissues** connect, surround, anchor, and support the structures of an animal's body. Connective tissues include blood, adipose (fat-storing) tissue, bone, cartilage, loose connective tissue, and dense connective tissue (**Figure 41.5**).

An important function of some types of connective tissue cells is to form part of the ECM around cells by secreting a mixture of fibrous proteins and carbohydrates, such as glycosaminoglycans. These carbohydrates may covalently attach to proteins to form proteoglycans (refer back to Figure 10.4). In some cases, the ECM is rich in minerals. The final characteristics of any type of connective tissue are determined

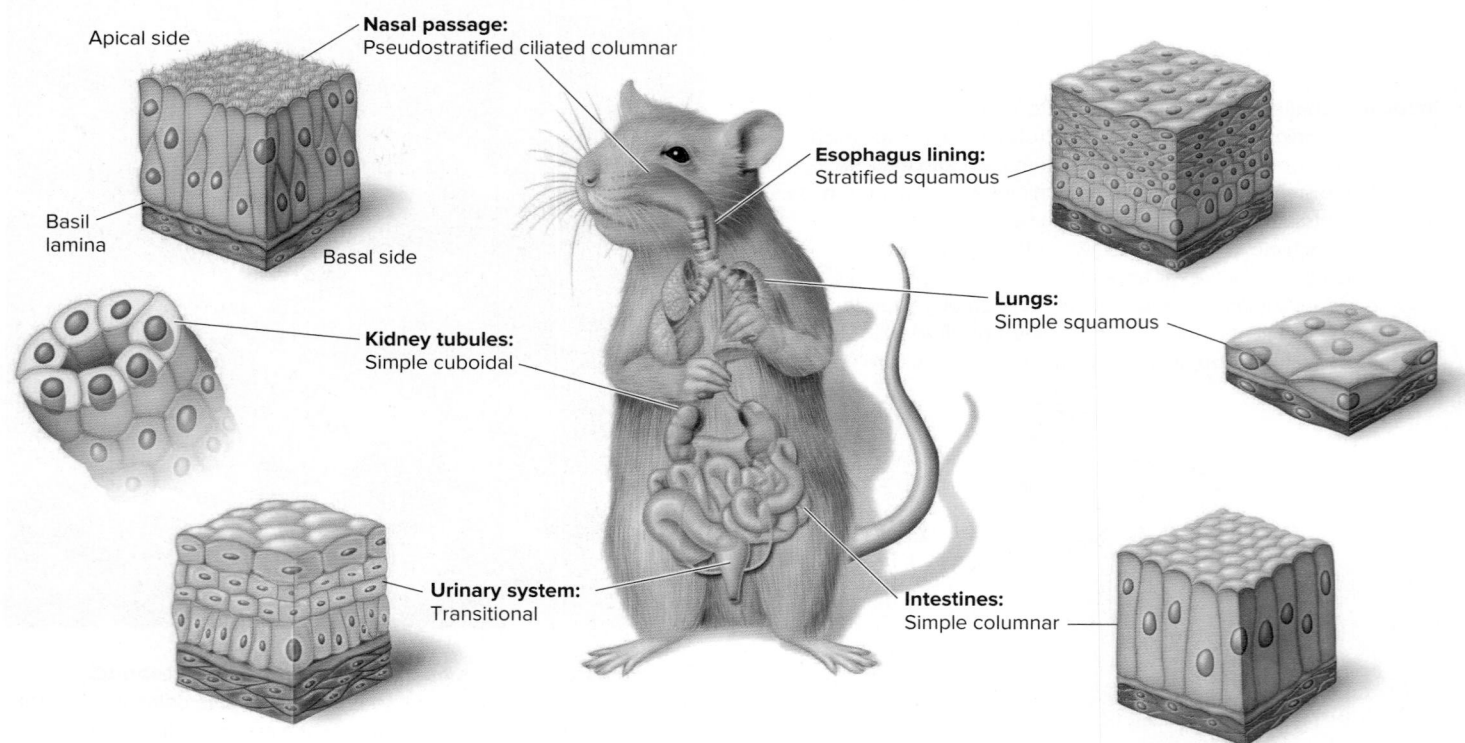

Figure 41.4   Examples of epithelial tissue. Several types of epithelial tissue are found in animals and can be distinguished by their appearance. Epithelial tissue is used to construct body coverings and the protective sheets that line and cover hollow tubes and cavities. The epithelial cells that make up epithelial tissues have an apical and basal (or basolateral) membrane; the apical side typically faces the exterior of the body or the lumen of a structure such as the intestine.

   Core Concept: Structure and Function   Note how different types of epithelial cells arranged in different ways form tissues with different functions. For example, simple cuboidal cells arranged as tubules in the kidney permit the passage of filtered body fluids, and pseudostratified ciliated columnar cells lining the nasal passage act as filters of airborne particles and debris.

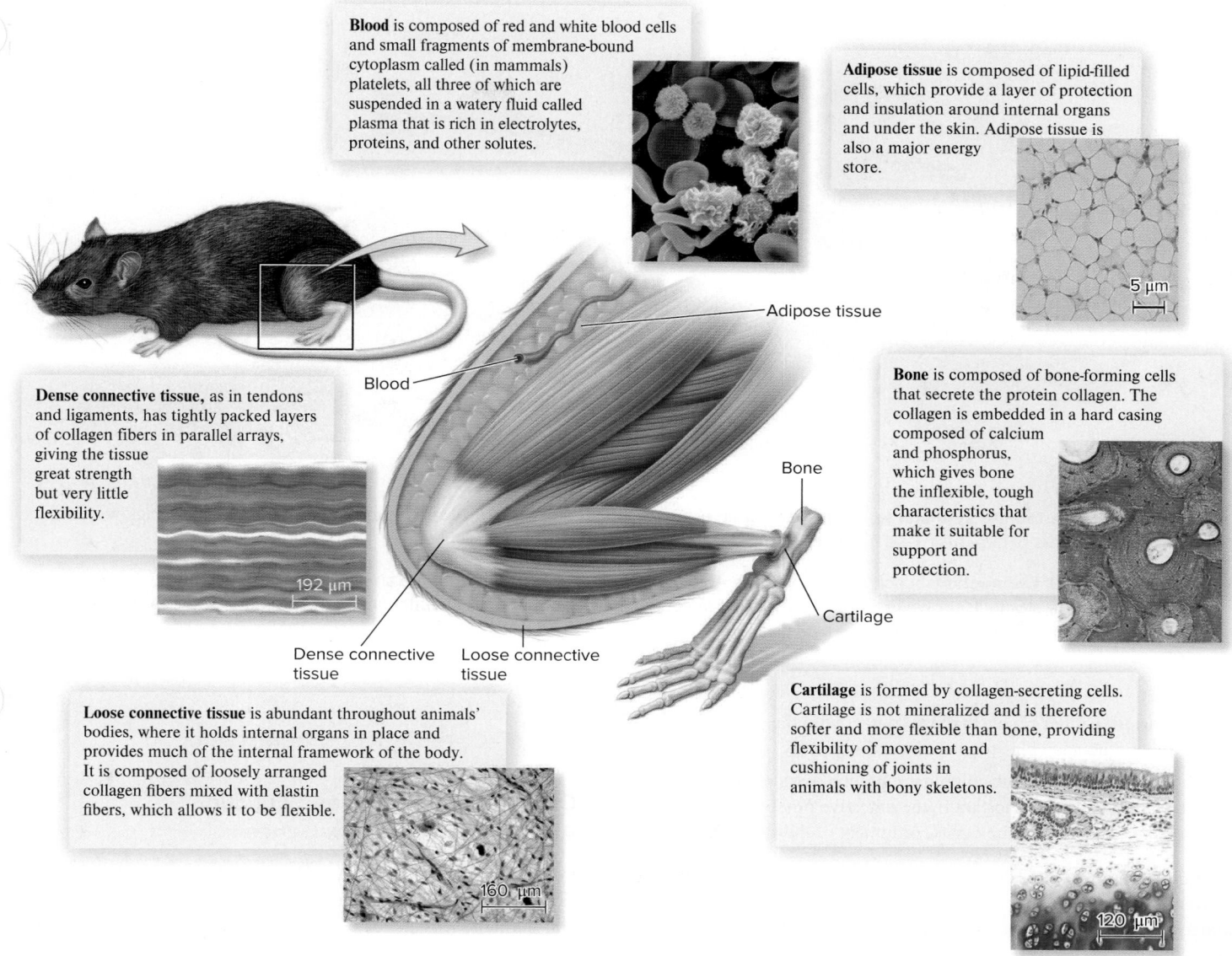

Blood is composed of red and white blood cells and small fragments of membrane-bound cytoplasm called (in mammals) platelets, all three of which are suspended in a watery fluid called plasma that is rich in electrolytes, proteins, and other solutes.

Adipose tissue is composed of lipid-filled cells, which provide a layer of protection and insulation around internal organs and under the skin. Adipose tissue is also a major energy store.

5 μm

Dense connective tissue, as in tendons and ligaments, has tightly packed layers of collagen fibers in parallel arrays, giving the tissue great strength but very little flexibility.

192 μm

Bone is composed of bone-forming cells that secrete the protein collagen. The collagen is embedded in a hard casing composed of calcium and phosphorus, which gives bone the inflexible, tough characteristics that make it suitable for support and protection.

Loose connective tissue is abundant throughout animals' bodies, where it holds internal organs in place and provides much of the internal framework of the body. It is composed of loosely arranged collagen fibers mixed with elastin fibers, which allows it to be flexible.

160 μm

Cartilage is formed by collagen-secreting cells. Cartilage is not mineralized and is therefore softer and more flexible than bone, providing flexibility of movement and cushioning of joints in animals with bony skeletons.

120 μm

Adipose tissue — Blood — Bone — Cartilage — Dense connective tissue — Loose connective tissue

Figure 41.5 Examples of connective tissue in mammals. Connective tissues connect, surround, anchor, and support other tissues and may exist as a suspension of cells (blood), clumps of cells (fat), or tough, rigid material (bone and cartilage). The samples have been stained or the micrographs have been colorized to reveal connective tissue. (blood): ©Dennis Kunkel Microscopy, Inc./Phototake; (adipose tissue): ©Ed Reschke/Getty Images; (bone): ©Innerspace Imaging/Science Source; (cartilage): ©Victor P. Eroschenko; (loose connective tissue, dense connective tissue): ©McGraw-Hill Education/Al Telser, photographer

in part by the relative proportions and types of proteins, proteoglycans, and minerals secreted into the ECM. The ECM serves several general functions, which include (1) providing a scaffold to which cells attach and organize themselves into more complex structures, (2) protecting and cushioning parts of the body, (3) providing mechanical strength, and (4) cell signaling—transmitting information to the cells that helps regulate their activity, migration, growth, and differentiation.

The proteins of the ECM consist mainly of two types. The first type is insoluble fiber-like proteins such as collagen and the rubber-band-like protein elastin; these proteins are often referred to as fibers. A second category is adhesive proteins (fibronectin and laminin) that serve to organize the protein and carbohydrate components of the ECM (refer back to Table 10.1).

Different Tissue Types Combine to Form Organs and Organ Systems

An **organ** is composed of two or more kinds of tissues arranged in various proportions and patterns, such as sheets, tubes, layers, bundles, or strips. For example, the vertebrate stomach (**Figure 41.6**) consists of the following layers:

- an outer covering of simple squamous epithelial tissue;
- connective tissue layers covering and cementing the organ together;
- layers of smooth muscle tissue, the contractions of which mechanically break up food and propel it through the stomach and into the small intestine;

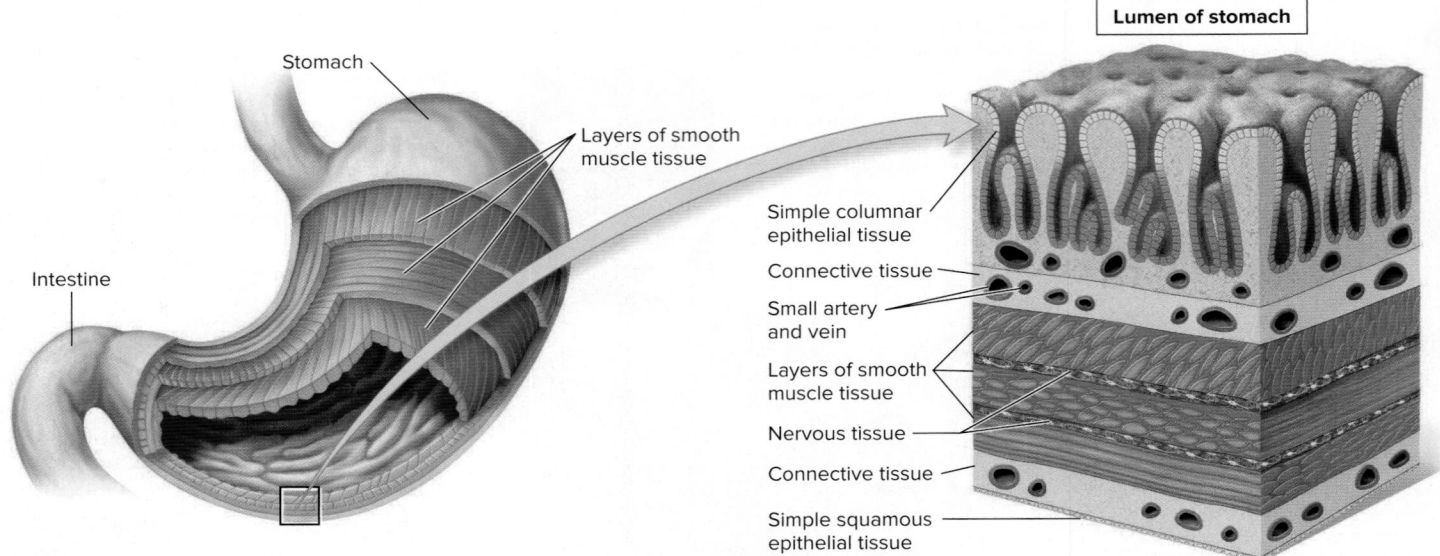

Figure 41.6 **The vertebrate stomach as an example of an organ composed of all four tissue types.** In this illustration, the thickness and appearance of the layers of nervous tissue have been considerably exaggerated for visual clarity.

 Core Skill: Connections Look ahead to Figure 46.6 and compare the structure of the small intestine shown there with the structure of the stomach shown in Figure 41.6. What can you conclude about common functions of the stomach and intestine from this comparison?

- nervous tissue that comes in close contact with the smooth muscle tissue and helps regulate its activity; and
- an inner lining of simple columnar epithelial tissue that secretes enzymes and acid (important in the digestive process) and protective mucus into the cavity, or lumen, of the stomach.

In an **organ system**, different organs work together to perform an overall function or functions. In the example just described, the stomach is part of the digestive system, along with other structures, such as the mouth, esophagus, small and large intestines, and anus. In another familiar example, the vertebrate circulatory system includes the heart, blood vessels and blood. The organ systems found in animals are described in **Table 41.1**.

Organ systems should not be considered as functioning in isolation. Instead, they frequently influence each other and depend on each other in many ways. For example, signals from the nervous, circulatory, and endocrine systems strongly influence how much water the mammalian kidney retains as it forms urine, an adaptation that can be lifesaving under certain circumstances.

The spatial arrangement of organs into organ systems is part of the overall body plan of animals. Organ systems develop at specific times and locations within the body and, in bilateral animals, along the anteroposterior body axis, as do other structures, such as limbs, tentacles, antennae, and other animal appendages. Scientists have long questioned how the layout of animal bodies is determined during the period when an embryo is developing. Remarkably, organ development in most animals appears to be under the control of a highly conserved family of body-plan genes with homologs in most animals, as described next.

 **Core Concept: Information**

Organ Development and Function Are Controlled by *Hox* Genes

In previous chapters, you have learned about a family of genes called *Hox* genes that are found in most animal phyla. In bilateral animals, *Hox* genes determine the formation of structures along the anteroposterior body axis during development. For example, we saw in Chapter 20 how these genes determine the number and position of legs and wings in *Drosophila*. *Hox* genes play a similar role in determining the spatial patterning of the vertebrate body and appendages. Recently, scientists have begun exploring the role of *Hox* genes in the development and spatial patterning of the organs that make up animals' organ systems.

By generating mutant mice that fail to express one or more *Hox* genes, researchers have discovered that these genes have the important function of determining where within the vertebrate body particular organs form. Recall from Chapter 20 (refer back to Figures 20.16 and 20.17) that mouse *Hox* genes are arranged in four clusters, designated A–D, with multiple genes per cluster. Homologous genes (for example, *HoxA-3, HoxB-3,* and *HoxD-3*) that are found within a single species are called paralogs. Such paralogs typically act in concert to regulate similar developmental processes. For example, *HoxA-3* is important for development of anterior parts of the body, including

Table 41.1	Organ Systems Found in Animals	
Organ system	**Major components***	**Major functions**
Circulatory	Contractile element (heart or vessel); distribution network (blood vessels); blood or hemolymph	Distributes solutes (nutrients, gases, wastes, and so on) to all parts of an animal's body
Digestive	Ingestion structures (mouth, mouthparts); storage structures (crop, stomach); digestive and absorptive structures (stomach, intestines); elimination structures (rectum, anus); accessory structures (pancreas, gallbladder)	Breaks complex foods into absorbable units; absorbs organic nutrients, ions, and water; eliminates solid wastes
Endocrine	All cells, tissues, organs, or glands that secrete hormones	Regulates and coordinates growth, development, metabolism, mineral balance, water balance, blood pressure, behavior, and reproduction
Excretory	All organs including respiratory structures (e.g., gills and lungs) that are involved in removing soluble wastes from the body; the vertebrate urinary system is a part of the excretory system and includes the kidneys, ureters, bladder and urethra	Eliminates soluble metabolic wastes; regulates body fluid volume and solute concentrations
Immune and lymphatic	Circulating white blood cells (leukocytes); lymph organs, lymph vessels and nodes	Defends against pathogens
Integumentary	Body surfaces (skin)	Protects from dehydration and injury; defends against pathogens; in some animals, plays a role in regulation of body temperature
Muscular-skeletal	Force-producing structures (muscles); support structures (bones, cartilage, exoskeleton); connective structures (tendons, ligaments)	Produces locomotion; generates force; propels materials through body organs; supports body
Nervous	Processing (brain); sensory structures; signal delivery (spinal cord, peripheral nerves and ganglia, sense organs)	Regulates and coordinates movement, sensation, organ functions, and learning
Reproductive	Gonads and associated structures	Produces gametes (sperm and egg); in some animals, provides nutritive environment for embryo and fetus
Respiratory	Gas-exchange sites (gills, skin, trachea, lungs)	Exchanges oxygen and carbon dioxide with the environment; regulates blood pH

*Selected examples only; these do not necessarily pertain to all animals.

the neck. When this gene is knocked out, mouse embryos show defects in neck structure. Notably, the organs within the neck—including the thymus, thyroid, and parathyroid glands—do not develop normally. When two or more paralogs of this group are knocked out, certain neck organs fail to form at all. Experimental deletion of *Hox* genes associated with other body segments does not affect the development and function of neck glands and organs. Likewise, investigators have uncovered vital roles of different *Hox* genes in lung development within the thorax and in the proper positioning and development of the vertebrate kidneys in the abdomen.

Of particular interest is the discovery that *Hox* genes are important not only for spatial patterning of organs but also for their growth, development, and function. Paralogs of *Hox* 1 and 3, for instance, help determine the final branching patterns of the airways of the lungs, the final size of the lungs, and the ability of the lungs to produce secretions that are important for breathing air after birth. Other *Hox* genes have been shown to control cell proliferation, shape changes, apoptosis, cell migration, and cell-cell adhesion within various organs. Similar results have been found in invertebrates, such as the leech, where *Hox* genes are first expressed during organ formation, and in *Drosophila*, where the final shape and size of the heart are partly controlled by *Hox* genes.

41.2 The Relationship Between Structure and Function

Learning Outcomes:

1. Provide an example of how the structure of an animal's tissues or organs can help predict the function.

2. **CoreSKILL »** Describe the quantitative relationship between the surface area of an object and its volume, and explain the importance of this relationship to animal form and function.

A key principle of biology emphasized throughout this unit is that form (structure) determines function. The appearance or structure of an animal's tissues and organs can often help us predict their functions. For example, let's compare the respiratory systems of an insect and a mammal (**Figure 41.7**). The respiratory systems of animals exchange oxygen from the environment with carbon dioxide generated by the body. Although many important differences exist between the respiratory systems of insects and mammals, notably the presence of lungs in mammals, certain structural similarities suggest that both systems serve similar functions. In both cases, for example, a series of internal branching tubes composed of epithelial and connective tissues arises from one or more openings that connect with the outside environment (the mouth and nose in the mammal, and the body surface pores called spiracles in the insect). These tubes become smaller and smaller as they continue to branch, eventually terminating in narrow structures that are only one cell thick.

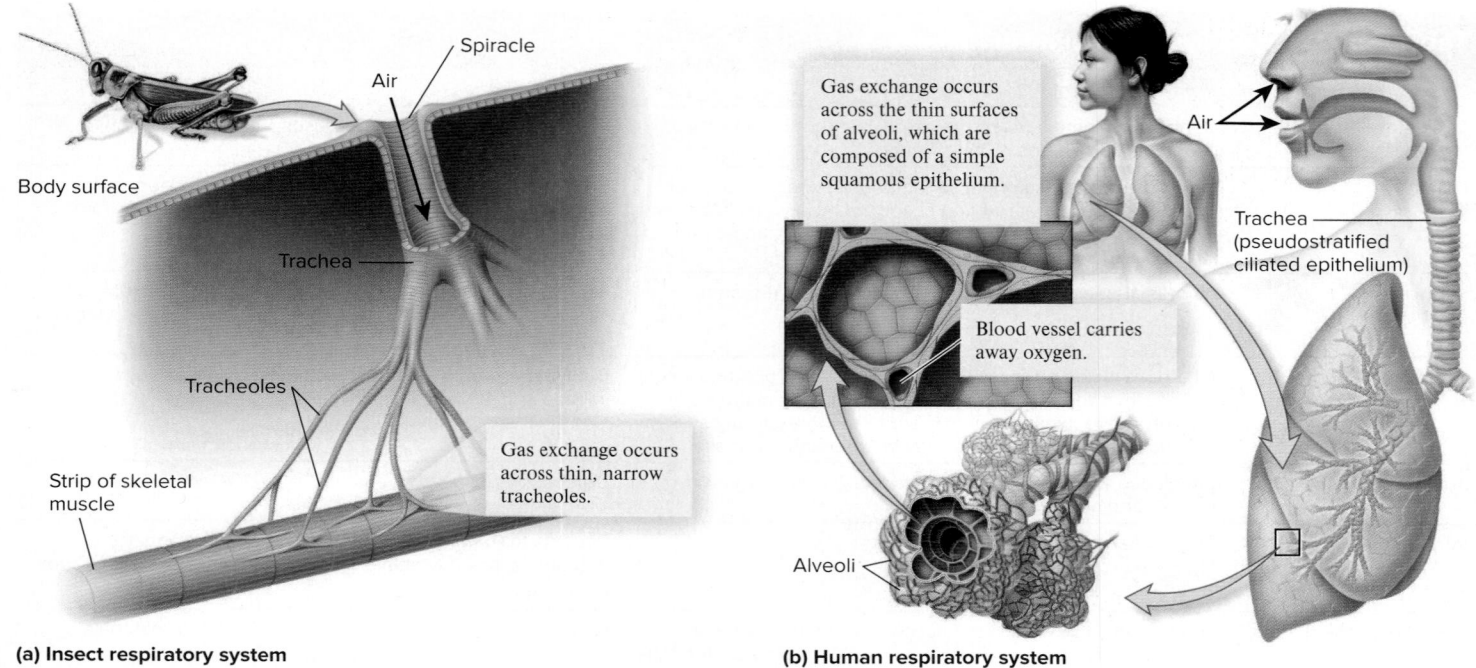

Figure 41.7 Comparison of the branching air tubes in (a) an insect and (b) a mammal. Note the similar features of highly branching, internalized hollow tubules that connect to the outside air, suggesting that these systems perform similar functions.

In both cases, these branching tubes serve as conduits for air to flow back and forth between the environment and the internal spaces of the animal. In the insect, the ends of the branching tubes (called tracheoles) are where oxygen diffuses from the air to the fluid around individual cells (and from there to intracellular fluid) (Figure 41.7a). In the mammal, the ends of the tubes form saclike structures called alveoli across which oxygen diffuses into the blood (Figure 41.7b).

If we examine the mammalian lung in greater detail, we see that the alveoli are composed of extremely thin, squamous epithelial cells. The shape of the cells provides a clue to their function. Their flat, thin structure permits rapid diffusion of gases across them. Imagine the resistance to oxygen diffusion if the cells were thick or scaly, like the cells of the body surface of many animals, for example. Therefore, both the gross and microscopic anatomy of the gas-exchange surfaces of respiratory systems facilitates their functions.

An additional structural similarity found in essentially all respiratory surfaces, including gills, is an extensive surface area. This structural similarity applies to all cells, tissues, and organs that mediate diffusion or absorption of a solute from one compartment to another or that require extensive cell-to-cell contacts. Consider, for instance, the finger-like projections of the small intestine of a human, the skin folds of some high-altitude frogs, the cellular extensions of neurons of a mouse, and the feathery antennae of a moth (**Figure 41.8**). What do these structures have in common? They all have a large surface area, which maximizes their ability to absorb nutrients (intestine), obtain oxygen by diffusion from the environment (frog skin), communicate with other cells (neurons), or detect airborne molecules (moth antennae).

The relationship between a structure's surface area and its volume is called the **surface area/volume (SA/V) ratio** (see Figure 4.12). A high SA/V ratio is ideal for exchange of heat, solutes, gases, and water across a surface without contributing greatly to the mass or volume of a body part. This concept will apply throughout this unit as we explore the ways in which animals obtain energy, regulate their metabolism and body temperature, obtain oxygen, and eliminate wastes.

A large increase in surface area of a structure, however, comes at the expense of greatly increasing volume if the shape of the structure is not changed (refer back to Figure 4.12). As a spherical object enlarges, its volume grows relatively more than its surface area, because its surface area increases by a power of 2, whereas its volume increases by a power of 3. For example, if the radius of a sphere is increased by a factor of 10, its surface area increases 100 times, but its volume increases 1,000 times.

The relationship between surface area and volume also applies to an animal's organs and could create certain disadvantages. For example, the ability to obtain sufficient oxygen from water requires a great amount of surface area on the structures that make up a fish's gills. If such structures were spherical, the gills would need to be extremely large to accomplish the needed gas exchange. The challenge of packaging an extensive surface area into a confined space is overcome by variations in shape. The gills of fish are comprised of many flattened disc- or platelike structures. Water flows over both sides of each disc (look ahead to Figure 48.17a). The flattened discs greatly increase surface area and thereby facilitate the function of gas exchange. At the same time, the flattened discs minimize the volume of the gill. Similarly, the inner surface of the human intestine in Figure 41.8a folds inward to form finger-like extensions, thereby increasing the surface area without greatly increasing the volume.

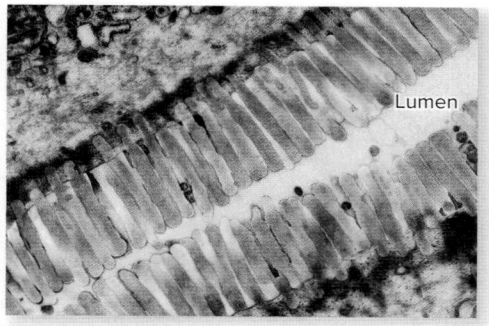

Lumen

(a) Human intestine

(b) Frog skin

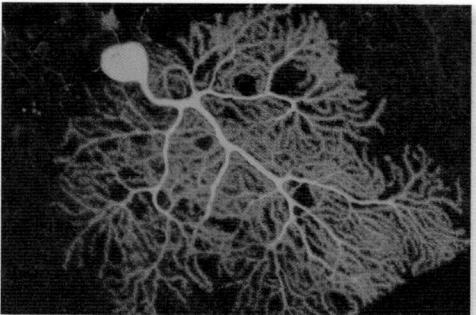

(c) Mouse brain neuron stained with a fluorescent marker

(d) Moth antennae

Figure 41.8 **Examples of structures in which extensive surface area is important for function.** A large surface area allows **(a)** high rates of transport of nutrients across the intestine of a human, **(b)** increased diffusion of oxygen across the folds of skin of a frog living at high altitude, where O_2 is less available, **(c)** extensive communication between neurons in a mouse's brain, and **(d)** detection of airborne chemicals by moth antennae. a: ©Biophoto Associates/Science Source; b: ©Dante Fenolio/Science Source; c: ©Thomas Deerinck, NCMIR/Science Source; d: ©Anthony Bannister/Science Source

Concept Check: *Is an extensive surface area important only for animals, or could it also provide advantages to other living organisms?*

41.3 General Principles of Homeostasis

Learning Outcomes:

1. Explain how the concept of homeostasis applies to the internal environment of animals.
2. List several variables that are regulated within a homeostatic range in vertebrate animals.
3. Name the four components of a homeostatic control system, and describe the importance of each to the regulation of an animal's internal environment.
4. **CoreSKILL »** Contrast negative feedback, positive feedback, and feedforward regulation, and explain how they do or do not contribute to the maintenance of homeostasis in animals.
5. Explain the importance of paracrine and hormonal signaling to homeostasis, and provide examples of each.

The environmental conditions in which animals live are rarely, if ever, constant. Animals are exposed to fluctuations in air and water temperatures, nutrient and water supplies, pH, and, in some cases, oxygen availability. Any one of these environmental changes could be harmful or even fatal if an animal is unable to respond appropriately. However, as you might expect from the incredible diversity of environments in which they exist, animals can adjust in many ways to their surroundings and thrive.

The process of maintaining a relatively stable internal environment despite changes in the external surroundings is known as homeostasis (from the Greek *homoios*, meaning similar, and *stasis*, meaning to stand still). The term was coined in the 20th century by

American physiologist Walter Cannon, but the concept itself originated in the 19th century with French physiologist Claude Bernard, who postulated that a constant *milieu interieur* (internal environment) was a prerequisite for good health.

Vertebrates Maintain Most Physiological Variables Within a Narrow Range

In vertebrates, the common physiological variables—concentrations of blood-borne solutes such as minerals, glucose, and oxygen, for example—are usually maintained within a certain range despite fluctuating external environmental conditions (**Table 41.2**). At first glance, homeostasis may appear to be a state of stable balance of physiological variables. However, this simple description cannot capture the scope of homeostasis. For example, no physiological function is constant for very long, which is why we call them variables. Some variables may fluctuate around an average value during the course of a single day yet still be considered in balance. Homeostasis is a dynamic process, not a static one.

Consider an example of a physiological variable in your own body. Normally, blood sugar (glucose) remains at fairly steady and predictable concentrations in any healthy individual. After a meal, however, the concentration of glucose in your blood can increase quickly, especially if you have just eaten something sweet. Conversely, if you skip a few meals, your blood glucose concentration may decrease slightly (**Figure 41.9**). Such fluctuations above and below the normal value might suggest that blood glucose concentration is not homeostatically controlled, but this is incorrect. Once blood glucose increases or decreases, homeostatic mechanisms restore the concentration back toward normal. In the case of glucose, the nervous and endocrine systems are primarily responsible for this quick

Table 41.2	Selected Examples of Homeostatic Variables in Animals	
Variable	Factors that influence homeostasis	Examples of functions
Minerals	Eating food; excreting wastes	
Na^+ and K^+		Establish resting membrane potentials across plasma membranes in all cells and transmit electrical signals in excitable tissues (muscles and nervous tissue)
Ca^{2+}		Important for muscle contraction; neuron function; skeleton and shell formation
Fe^{2+}		Binds and transports oxygen in blood or body fluids (some invertebrates use copper instead of iron)
Energy sources	Eating food; expending energy	
Glucose		Broken down to provide energy for use by all cells, especially brain cells
Fat		Provides an alternate source of energy, particularly for cells not in the nervous system; major component of plasma membranes
ATP		Provides energy to drive most chemical reactions and body functions; modifies function of many proteins by transferring a phosphate group to proteins
Body temperature	Rate of energy expenditure; environmental temperature; behavioral mechanisms (look ahead to Chapter 47)	Determines the rate of chemical reactions in an animal's body
pH of body fluids	Hydrogen ion transporters in cells; buffers in body fluids; rates of energy expenditure; breathing rate	Affects enzymatic activity in all cells
Other variables		
Oxygen and carbon dioxide	Movement of air or water across respiratory surfaces (for example, lungs and gills); metabolic rate	Oxygen circulates in body fluids and enters cells, where it is used during the production of ATP; carbon dioxide is a waste product that is eliminated to the environment, but it is also a key factor that regulates the rate of breathing.
Water	Drinking, eating, excretion of wastes, perspiration, osmosis across body surface (skin or gills)	Numerous biological functions including participating in chemical reactions; helping to regulate body temperature; acting as a solvent for biologically important molecules (refer back to Chapter 2)

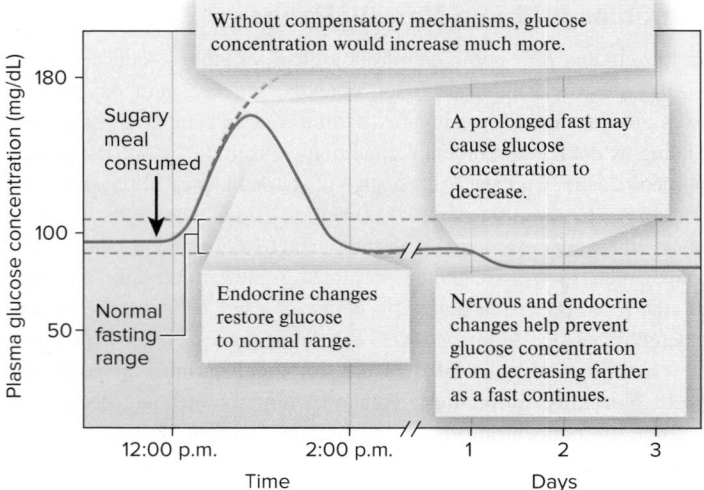

Figure 41.9 An example of a homeostatically controlled physiological variable, glucose concentration in human blood. Note that glucose concentration in the plasma may increase or decrease, depending on whether an animal has recently eaten. However, even after a sugary meal or a prolonged fast, homeostatic mechanisms either return glucose concentration to normal or enable it to remain within the range required for survival. Traditional units for glucose concentration used in the U.S. appear on the vertical axis; as a reference, a value of 100 mg/dL is equal to 5.5 mM.

adjustment, but in other examples, a wide variety of control systems may be initiated. In later chapters, we will see how every organ and tissue of an animal's body contributes to homeostasis, sometimes in multiple ways, and usually in concert with each other.

Homeostasis, then, does not imply that a given physiological function or variable is rigidly constant. Instead, homeostasis means that a variable fluctuates within a certain normal range and that once it deviates from that range, compensatory mechanisms restore the variable toward normal.

Homeostatic Control Systems Maintain the Internal Environment

The activities of cells, tissues, and organs must be regulated and coordinated with each other so that any change in the extracellular fluid—the internal environment—initiates a response to correct the change. These compensating regulatory responses are performed by homeostatic control systems. A **homeostatic control system** must have several components:

- a **set point**, which is the normal value for a controlled variable;
- a **sensor**, which monitors the level or activity of a particular variable;
- an **integrator**, which compares signals from the sensor with the set point; and
- an **effector**, which compensates for any deviation between the actual value and the set point.

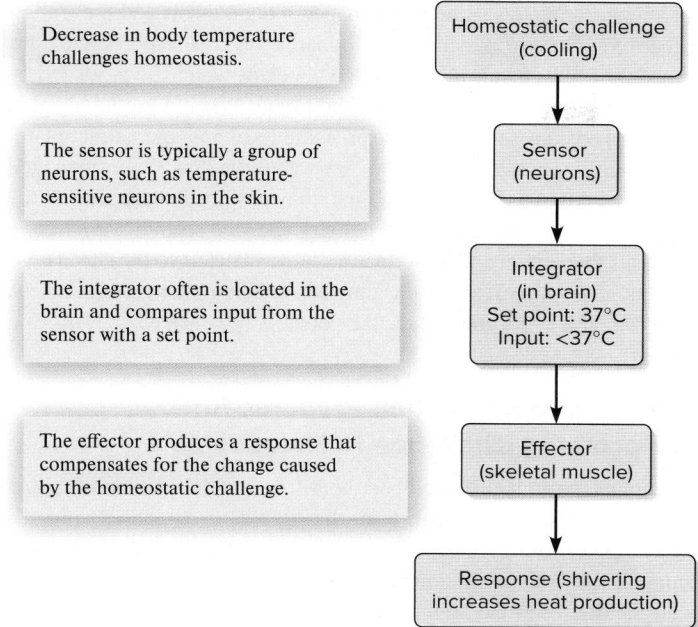

Figure 41.10   An example of a homeostatic control system. The mechanisms for responding to a decrease in body temperature are shown. Different homeostatic control systems have different sensors, integrators, and effectors.

Figure 41.10 shows an example of a homeostatic control system that regulates body temperature in mammals. This system is somewhat analogous to the heating system of a home. In that case, a sensor and integrator within the thermostat compare the actual room temperature with the set point temperature that was determined by setting the thermostat to a given temperature. If the room temperature becomes cooler than the thermostat setting, the effector (furnace) is activated and adds heat to the room. In a mammal, the sensors are temperature-sensitive neurons in the skin and brain, whereas the integrator is a collection of neurons within the brain. Signals from this part of the brain are sent along nerves to the effectors, which include skeletal muscles. If body temperature decreases, the muscles contract vigorously in response to these signals, resulting in shivering—a key way in which mammals' bodies generate heat. We will discuss other heat-conserving and heat-generating mechanisms that contribute to this important homeostatic control system in Chapter 47.

Core Skill: Modeling

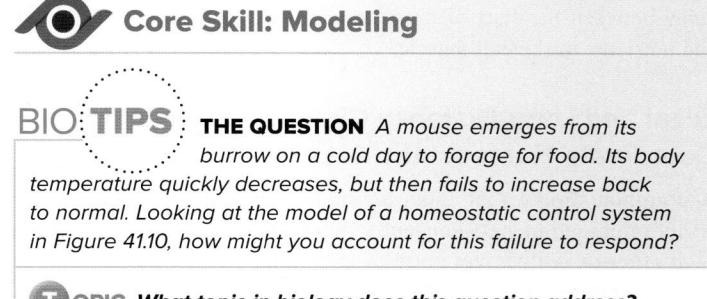

BIO TIPS   **THE QUESTION** *A mouse emerges from its burrow on a cold day to forage for food. Its body temperature quickly decreases, but then fails to increase back to normal. Looking at the model of a homeostatic control system in Figure 41.10, how might you account for this failure to respond?*

TOPIC *What topic in biology does this question address?*
The topic is homeostatic control systems. Specifically, the question asks you to explain how such a system might fail.

INFORMATION *What information do you know based on the question and your understanding of the topic?*
From the question, you know that the mouse had a homeostatic challenge and failed to respond to it. From your understanding

of the topic, you know that there are several components to any homeostatic control system.

PROBLEM-SOLVING **S**TRATEGY *Sort out the steps in a complicated process.* Figure 41.10 indicates that in a homeostatic control system that regulates body temperature in a mammal, several responses must occur in sequence for the body temperature to be maintained when the mammal is in a cold environment. These include: (1) sensing the change in the variable (body temperature), (2) comparing it to a set point in the brain, and (3) inducing a compensatory change in temperature by activating effectors (skeletal muscles). To answer the question, consider which, if any, of these responses could have failed to occur in the mouse.

ANSWER *In the mouse, any of these three responses could have failed to function properly. Perhaps the temperature-sensitive neurons were not functioning, or the brain cells responsible for comparing the input to a set point were diseased or not functioning. Finally, the output to the effectors or the effectors themselves may not have been functioning normally. Without further data, none of these possibilities can be ruled out.*

Negative Feedback Is a Key Feature of Homeostasis

As you have seen in Figure 41.10, homeostatic mechanisms can move a variable back toward its set point. Such mechanisms must be controlled so that a homeostatic response does not overcompensate. This form of regulation is termed a **negative feedback loop**, or simply negative feedback. As an example, **Figure 41.11** considers a negative feedback loop involving homeostatic changes to blood pressure. When the blood pressure of an animal decreases due to blood loss, pressure sensors in the heart and certain blood vessels detect the change in pressure and send the information to the integrator—the brain (Figure 41.11). In the brain, the signal is compared with the normal set point for blood pressure. The brain responds to the deviation from the set point in two ways. First, signals are sent along nerves to the effectors—in this case, the kidneys, heart, and blood vessels. Second, the brain stimulates the release of certain hormones into the blood; these hormones provide an additional signal to the effectors. The result is that the heart beats more rapidly and forcefully, the kidneys produce less urine and thereby retain more water in the body, and the blood vessels direct blood to the most vital organs such as the brain. These responses raise the animal's blood pressure back toward the set point.

To prevent overcompensation, that is, to prevent the blood pressure from becoming higher than normal, the return of blood pressure to its set point removes the stimulus from the sensor (see the dashed arrow in Figure 41.11). This negative feedback, in turn, shuts off further production of the hormonal and neural responses. If negative feedback did not occur, the blood pressure would not only rebound back to the set point but might continue to increase to abnormally high and possibly dangerous levels.

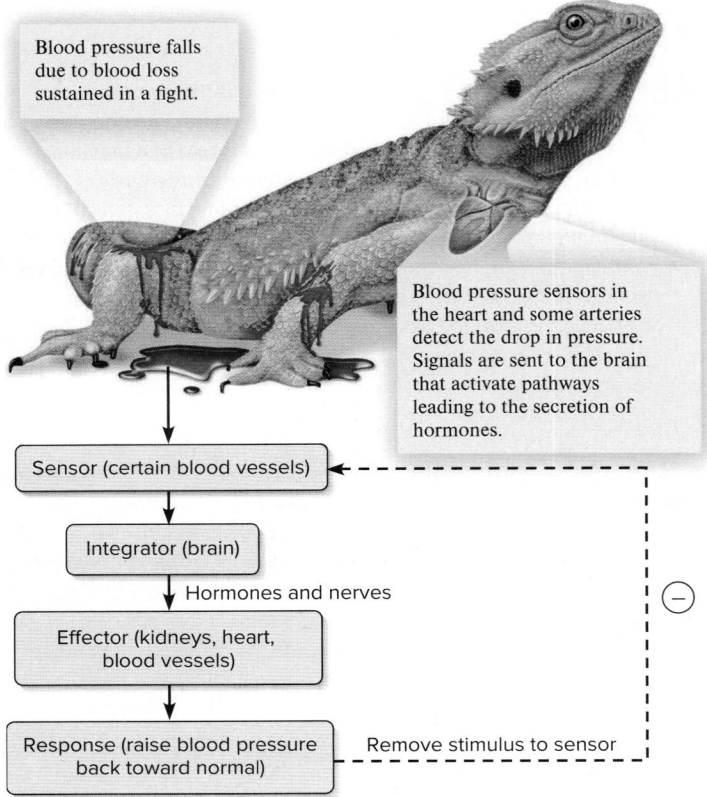

Blood pressure falls due to blood loss sustained in a fight.

Blood pressure sensors in the heart and some arteries detect the drop in pressure. Signals are sent to the brain that activate pathways leading to the secretion of hormones.

Sensor (certain blood vessels)

Integrator (brain)

Hormones and nerves

Effector (kidneys, heart, blood vessels)

Response (raise blood pressure back toward normal)

Remove stimulus to sensor

Figure 41.11 **A negative feedback loop as a mechanism by which homeostatic control systems operate.** In this example, loss of blood results in a drop in blood pressure, which could be life-threatening if not corrected. Effectors such as the kidneys, heart, and blood vessels help restore blood pressure toward normal. They do not increase blood pressure above normal, however, because of negative feedback (as denoted by the minus sign next to the dashed arrow).

 Core Skill: Connections Can negative feedback occur at levels other than the organ system level shown in this figure? Refer back to Figure 6.13 for help.

Positive Feedback Does Not Achieve Homeostasis

Thus far, we have considered homeostatic mechanisms that occur via negative feedback. A **positive feedback loop**, or simply positive feedback, accelerates or amplifies a process (think of an avalanche that begins with a small snowball rolling down a steep hill). A positive feedback loop moves a system away from homeostasis, because a change in a variable or process leads to events that amplify that change. Look again at Figure 41.10. Imagine what might happen if shivering not only generated heat, but also in some way stimulated the sensor neurons to send additional stimulatory signals to the effectors. In such a circumstance, heat production would continue without any means of stopping, leading to a dangerously high body temperature. This is contrary to the principle of homeostasis, in which large fluctuations in a variable are minimized and reversed.

One example of positive feedback occurs in the process of blood clotting in mammals (**Figure 41.12**). If an animal receives a wound that results in bleeding, as shown in Figure 41.11, various blood-borne

factors contribute to sealing the damaged blood vessels and preventing further blood loss from occurring. In mammals, this response includes the actions of fragments of cells called platelets, which are produced by the bone marrow and released into the blood. When a blood vessel is cut, damaged cells secrete chemicals in the local area that attract platelets to the site and activate them. Activated platelets seal a damaged blood vessel in two general ways. First, they physically help seal off the wound by clustering together at the injury site, and second, they secrete chemicals that attract and activate even more platelets to the site. Those platelets, in turn, secrete more chemicals, which attract more platelets, and so on. The cycle ends when the wound is fully sealed.

Feedforward Regulation Prepares for an Upcoming Challenge to Homeostasis

In animals with well-developed nervous systems, homeostasis is aided by **feedforward regulation**, the process in which an animal's body prepares for a change in some variable before it even occurs. For example, the body temperature of mammals increases slightly prior to awakening each day, which prepares the animal for the increased metabolic demands of being awake and active. A famous example of feedforward regulation, first characterized by Russian physiologist Ivan Pavlov in the 1890s, involves the changes that occur when a hungry dog smells or sees food. First, the dog starts to salivate, and its stomach begins to churn and produce acid. Salivation and activity of the stomach are important components of the digestive process, yet at this stage, the animal has not actually eaten any food. Instead, its digestive system is already preparing for the arrival of food in order to maximize digestive efficiency, speed the flow of nutrients into the blood, and minimize the time required for active cells to replenish energy stores.

In the preceding example, feedforward regulation uses sensory detectors that recognize odors and sights. Many examples of such regulation, including the example described by Pavlov, result from, or are modified by, the phenomenon called learning. The result of this process is that the nervous system learns to anticipate a homeostatic challenge. Familiar examples are the increased heart rate and breathing rate that occur just before an athletic competition—demonstrated, for example, in trained racehorses before the start of a race (**Figure 41.13**). The process of training, in which a horse's body learns to prepare for the exertion of the ensuing race, prevents any delay between the start of exercise and the adequate flow of blood and nutrients to skeletal muscle.

Local and Long-Distance Chemical Signals Coordinate Homeostatic Responses

A common thread that links all homeostatic processes together is communication between cells, whether the cells are close to each other or in different parts of an animal's body. Some homeostatic responses are highly localized, occurring only in the area of a disturbance. For example, damage to an area of skin causes cells in the injured area to release molecules that help contain the injury, prevent infections, and promote tissue repair in the immediate vicinity (see Chapter 52). Local responses provide areas of an animal's body with mechanisms for local self-regulation. It is

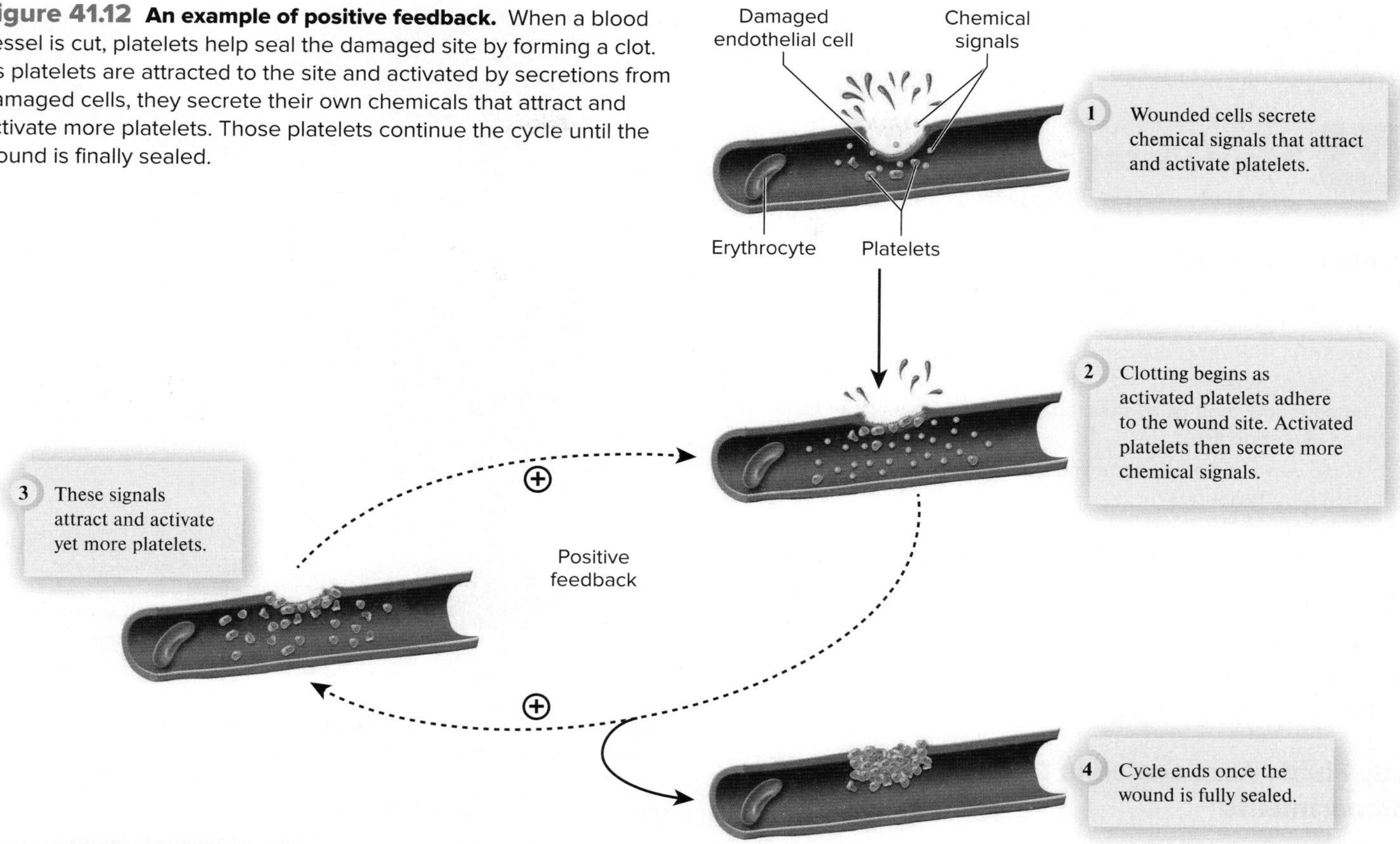

Figure 41.12 **An example of positive feedback.** When a blood vessel is cut, platelets help seal the damaged site by forming a clot. As platelets are attracted to the site and activated by secretions from damaged cells, they secrete their own chemicals that attract and activate more platelets. Those platelets continue the cycle until the wound is finally sealed.

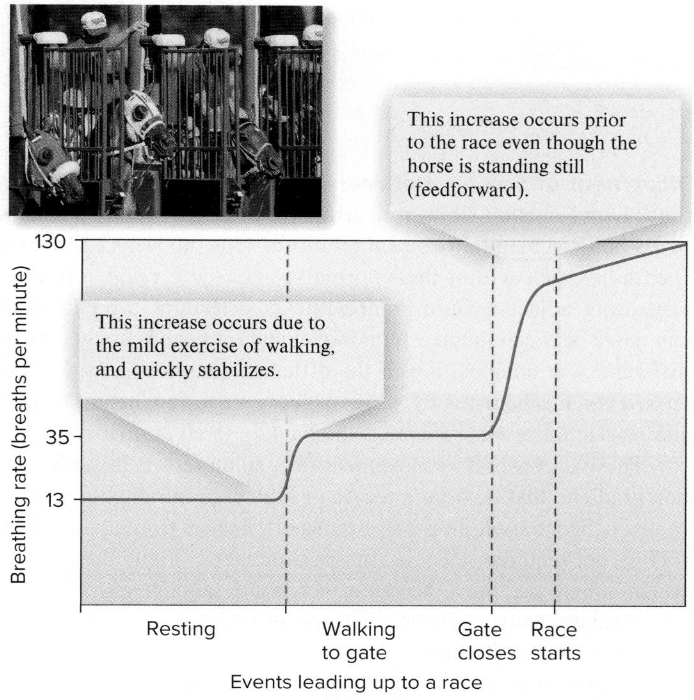

Damaged endothelial cell   Chemical signals

Erythrocyte   Platelets

1 Wounded cells secrete chemical signals that attract and activate platelets.

2 Clotting begins as activated platelets adhere to the wound site. Activated platelets then secrete more chemical signals.

3 These signals attract and activate yet more platelets.

Positive feedback

⊕

⊕

4 Cycle ends once the wound is fully sealed.

This increase occurs prior to the race even though the horse is standing still (feedforward).

This increase occurs due to the mild exercise of walking, and quickly stabilizes.

Breathing rate (breaths per minute)

130

35

13

Resting   Walking to gate   Gate closes   Race starts

Events leading up to a race

Figure 41.13 **Feedforward regulation of breathing rate in an animal trained for athletic exercise.** Feedforward regulation prepares an animal's body for an ensuing challenge or event, such as a race. ©Mitch Wojnarowicz/The Image Works

Concept Check: *What similar feedforward process might occur in an animal in nature?.*

no benefit to an animal to promote tissue repair in regions of the body that are not injured. This type of cellular communication—in which molecules are released into the extracellular fluid and act on nearby cells—is called **paracrine signaling** (refer back to Figure 9.3d).

Another example of extremely localized signaling occurs between neurons. A common way in which neurons communicate is through the release of neurotransmitters, small signaling molecules that are synthesized and stored in neurons. When a neuron releases neurotransmitters, they diffuse and then bind to receptor proteins on an adjacent neuron (or in some cases a muscle or gland cell), altering the activity of that cell. This type of cell-to-cell communication is typically very rapid, finishing within milliseconds. Consequently, neurotransmitter responses can make immediate homeostatic adjustments, like those associated with reflexes. These are just two of the many types of localized signaling that occur in animals' bodies and that will be described in subsequent chapters in this unit.

In addition to using paracrine signaling and neurotransmitter release, cells can communicate over long distances by releasing chemical messenger molecules into the blood. This type of signaling is mediated by **hormones**—chemical messengers produced by the endocrine system of animals. A hormone released in response to a homeostatic disturbance, such as the decrease in blood pressure described earlier, can influence the activities of many different cells, tissues, and organs simultaneously because the hormone is carried throughout the entire blood circulation. Some hormones act quickly—within seconds—whereas others take minutes or even hours for their effects to occur. In subsequent chapters, we will see that hormones are a key part of the regulatory processes that govern the functions of every organ system in a vertebrate's body, and they play key roles in growth, development, and reproduction in invertebrates.

41.4 Homeostatic Control of Internal Fluids

Learning Outcomes:

1. List ways in which water and ions move across cell membranes and between body fluid compartments.

2. **CoreSKILL** ≫ Predict outcomes of imbalances of water and ions on animals' function and survival.

3. Compare and contrast osmotic adaptations of freshwater fish with those of marine fish.

4. List two ways of classifying animals according to how they adapt to osmotic challenges.

Animal bodies are composed in large part of water. Dissolved in the water are many solutes, including inorganic ions such as Na⁺ and K⁺. In this section, we will first examine how water and ions are distributed in animal bodies. Next, we will explore why water and ion homeostasis is so important and consider some of the challenges that must be overcome to maintain that homeostasis.

Body Fluids Are Located in Different Fluid Compartments

Most of the water in an animal's body is contained inside its cells; this fluid is called **intracellular fluid** (from the Latin *intra*, meaning inside of). The rest of the water in the body exists outside of the cells; this fluid is called **extracellular fluid** (from the Latin *extra*, meaning outside of). Plasma membranes separate the intracellular fluid from the extracellular fluid.

In vertebrates and some invertebrates, extracellular fluid is composed of the watery (noncellular) part of blood, called **plasma**, and the fluid that fills the spaces that surround cells, called **interstitial fluid** (from the Latin *inter*, meaning between) (**Figure 41.14**). In such animals, plasma and interstitial fluid are kept separate, with plasma contained within blood vessels in a closed circulatory system. The interstitial fluid and the plasma are separated by the walls of vessels (arteries, capillaries, and veins). In many invertebrates with open circulatory systems (see Chapter 48), however, plasma and interstitial fluid are intermingled in a single fluid called hemolymph.

The locations of fluids depicted in Figure 41.14 are called body fluid compartments. In a typical vertebrate, the total water volume in the three compartments (intracellular fluid, plasma, and interstitial fluid) accounts for about two-thirds of body weight, with solids comprising the rest. Of the total body water, up to two-thirds is intracellular and one-third extracellular, with the majority of the latter located in the interstitial compartment.

The solute composition of the extracellular fluid is very different from that of the intracellular fluid. Maintaining differences in solute composition across the plasma membrane is an important way in which animal cells regulate their own activity. For example, many different proteins that are important in regulating cellular events such as mitosis, cytokinesis, and metabolism are confined to the intracellular fluid.

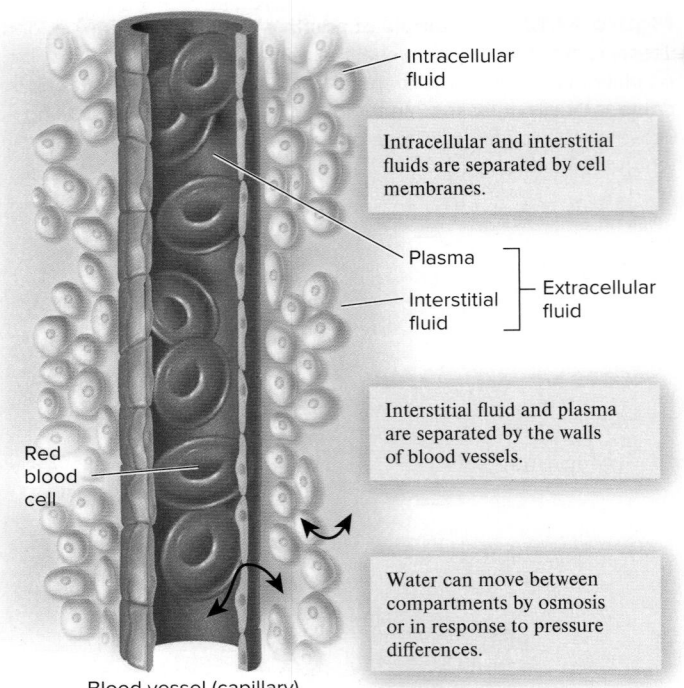

Figure 41.14 Fluid compartments in a typical vertebrate. Most of the fluid within an animal's body exists within cells (intracellular fluid). Extracellular fluid is that portion of the body's fluid that lies outside cells (interstitial fluid) or within blood vessels (plasma), such as the capillary shown here. Arrows indicate directions of water movement between adjacent compartments.

Concept Check: *What would happen to the distribution of water in an animal's body if a blood vessel was damaged and leaked its contents internally?*

Movement of Solutes Between Compartments Solutes must move between body fluid compartments in order for cells in an animal's body to maintain concentrations of ions, nutrients, and gases such as oxygen within their normal homeostatic ranges. Barriers separating adjacent fluid compartments determine which solutes can move between them. Solute movement, in turn, accounts for the differences in composition of the different compartments. We discussed the mechanisms by which solutes move in Chapter 5. Let's summarize those mechanisms, which apply to all animal cells.

Passive transport is movement of a solute down its concentration gradient, that is, from a region of high concentration to a region of low concentration. In passive transport, energy from hydrolysis of ATP is not required. Passive transport includes simple diffusion, in which substances move across a membrane without any carrier or intermediate, and facilitated diffusion in which a channel or transporter is required for diffusion to occur.

Simple diffusion is a major way in which cells gain and lose solutes. Molecules that can cross phospholipid bilayers are able to passively diffuse into or out of a cell. Examples include nonpolar molecules such as many lipids, and gases such as oxygen and carbon dioxide.

The rate of simple diffusion depends on several factors, notably the concentration gradient of the solute and the area across which it is diffusing. The rate of simple diffusion of a solute across a membrane of given thickness can be calculated using a modified form of Fick's first law of diffusion adapted for movement across a membrane:

$$J = KA(C_1 - C_2)$$

where J is the rate of simple diffusion, K is a constant that includes temperature, A is the cross-sectional area of the barrier across which diffusion is occurring, and C_1 and C_2 are the concentrations of the solute at two locations (for example, inside and outside a cell). This equation is used to determine how changes in solute concentrations, temperature, or area can influence the rate at which a substance moves across a plasma membrane. For example, breathing a gas mixture from a tank that is enriched in oxygen will increase the amount of oxygen entering the blood of a mountain climber at high altitude, where oxygen is limited. According to Fick's first law, the difference between C_1 (oxygen in the inhaled gas mixture) and C_2 (oxygen in the blood) will be increased by breathing from the tank. Therefore, we can predict that J, the rate of diffusion of oxygen into the blood, will also be increased, an important survival mechanism at very high altitudes.

Most polar molecules and ions, however, can move through a plasma membrane only with the help of a transport protein, as in facilitated diffusion. In one case, the membrane has channels that permit the solute to diffuse down its concentration gradient through the bilayer. Examples of substances that diffuse through channels are ions such as Na^+. In a second case, proteins in the membrane bind a solute and shuttle it down its concentration gradient across the lipid membrane. An example of a common solute that moves across membranes in this way is glucose. In both of these forms of diffusion, solutes move down their concentration gradients and hydrolysis of ATP is not required for their diffusion.

By contrast, in active transport, energy is required to move a solute against a concentration gradient (refer back to Figure 5.19). Typically, we will encounter this type of transport in this unit when discussing how animal cells maintain different concentrations of various ions across their plasma membranes and how such concentration differences relate to a cell's ability to function. One example of a function dependent on differences in ion concentration is the generation of electrical gradients across the membranes of muscle cells and neurons.

Movement of Water Between Compartments Water can readily move between adjacent compartments in an animal's body, because barriers such as plasma membranes tend to be highly permeable to water, due to the presence of water channels called aquaporins (see Figure 5.16). This movement depends on pressure differences in the fluids of each compartment or on differences in solute concentrations that lead to osmosis (see Chapter 5), in which water moves from a region of lower solute concentration to one of higher solute concentration.

To function properly, cells require a relatively stable internal composition, including ion and protein concentrations, cellular volume, and pH. A decrease in solute concentration outside a cell, for example, will cause water to move by osmosis from outside the cell to inside. In this case, osmosis redistributes water from the interstitial to the intracellular compartment. This movement will cause a cell to become deformed as it swells due to the influx of water. In contrast, an increase in extracellular solute concentration will lead to osmosis of water from inside the cell to outside, causing the cell to shrink. In either case, a swollen or shrunken animal cell generally is more fragile than a normal cell and will be destroyed if its membrane ruptures. **Figure 41.15** shows examples of mammalian red blood cells (known as erythrocytes) in which intracellular fluid levels have been altered. This can occur, for example, if the cells are exposed to extracellular fluids with either a higher or lower solute concentration than the fluid inside the cell. When erythrocytes swell, they may burst, a phenomenon called hemolysis. Shrinkage of erythrocytes is called crenation and is also potentially destructive (Figure 41.15, middle panel).

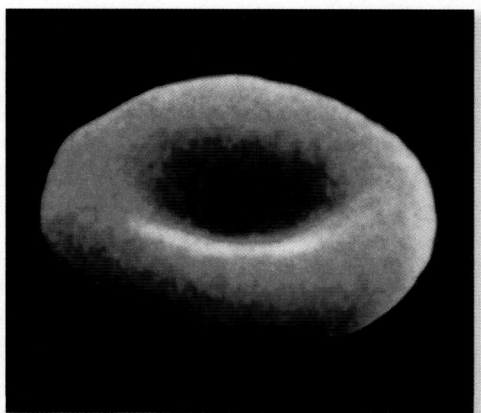
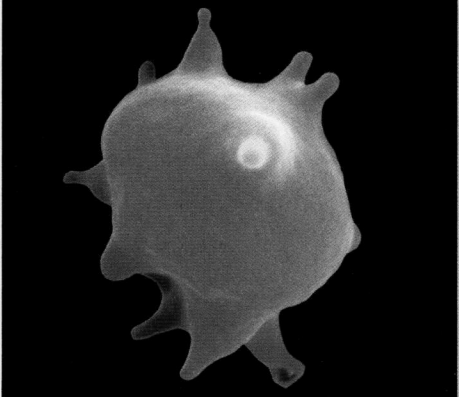
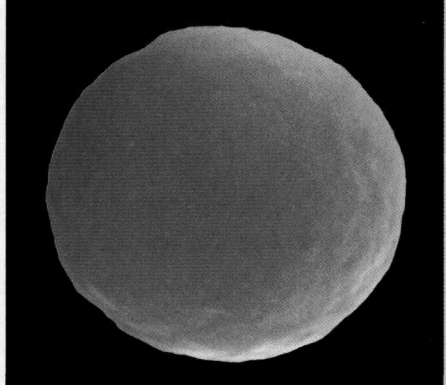

Erythrocyte in a solution of normal solute concentration

Erythrocyte that has lost intracellular fluid when placed in a solution of higher than normal solute concentration

Erythrocyte that has gained intracellular fluid when placed in a solution of lower than normal solute concentration

Figure 41.15 Changes in cell shape due to alterations in intracellular fluid volume. Alterations in intracellular fluid volume can have drastic effects on cell shape, as shown by these SEM images of erythrocytes. Large changes in shape like those in the middle and right are usually lethal for cells. Each cell is approximately 5–8 μm in diameter. (left): ©Mary Martin/Science Source; (middle, right): ©David M. Phillips/Science Source

Concept Check: *What effect will changes in intracellular fluid volume have on intracellular solute concentration?*

A Balance of Water and Ions Is Critical for Survival

Maintenance of normal levels of body water is of great importance for all animals. Not only is water the major portion of an animal's body mass, it is also the solvent that permits solutes to participate in chemical reactions. As described in Chapters 2 and 3, water itself participates in important chemical reactions, notably hydrolysis reactions. In addition, water is the transport vehicle that brings O_2 and nutrients to cells and removes wastes generated by metabolism.

When an animal's water volume is reduced below the normal range, we say the animal is dehydrated. In terrestrial animals, dehydration may occur if sufficient drinking water is not available or when water is lost by evaporation (through perspiring or panting). Dehydration can be a serious, potentially life-threatening condition. For example, because blood is roughly 50% water (plasma), blood volume tends to decrease in dehydrated animals. Decreased blood volume compromises the ability of the circulatory system to move nutrients and wastes throughout the body and to assist in the regulation of body temperature on hot days.

Ion balance is also very important for animals. A change of only a few percentage points in the extracellular fluid concentration of potassium ions (K^+), for example, can trigger changes in nerve, heart, and skeletal muscle function by altering their electrical activities. Other ions, such as calcium (Ca^{2+}), magnesium (Mg^{2+}), phosphate (PO_4^{3-}), and sulfate (SO_4^{2-}), also participate in various biological activities. Their functions include serving as cofactors for enzyme activation, participating in bone formation, forming part of the extracellular matrices around cells, and activating cellular events such as exocytosis and muscle contraction. An imbalance in any of these ions can seriously disrupt cellular activities.

The solute concentration of an aqueous solution is known as the solution's **osmolarity**, expressed in milliosmoles/liter (mOsm/L). The number of dissolved solute particles determines a solution's osmolarity. For example, a 150 mM NaCl solution has an osmolarity of 300 mOsm/L, because each NaCl molecule dissociates into two ions, one Na^+ and one Cl^- ($2 \times 150 = 300$). The value of 300 mOsm/L is well within the range of typical osmolarities of animal body fluids. Solutions with an osmolarity greater than normal are called hyperosmotic solutions; those with an osmolarity less than normal are hypo-osmotic solutions. An iso-osmotic solution is one that has the same osmolarity as a typical animal cell.

Many Exchanges of Ions and Water with the Environment Are Obligatory

Many vital processes—eliminating nitrogenous wastes, obtaining O_2 and eliminating carbon dioxide (CO_2), consuming and metabolizing food, and regulating body temperature—have the potential to disturb ion and water homeostasis. Therefore, these processes require additional energy expenditure to minimize or reverse the disturbance. Exchanges of ions and water with the environment that occur as a consequence of such vital processes are called obligatory exchanges (because the animal is obligated to make them) (**Figure 41.16**).

Exchanges Due to Elimination of Nitrogenous Wastes
When carbohydrates and fats are metabolized by animal cells, the major waste product is CO_2, which is exhaled or, in some animals, diffuses across

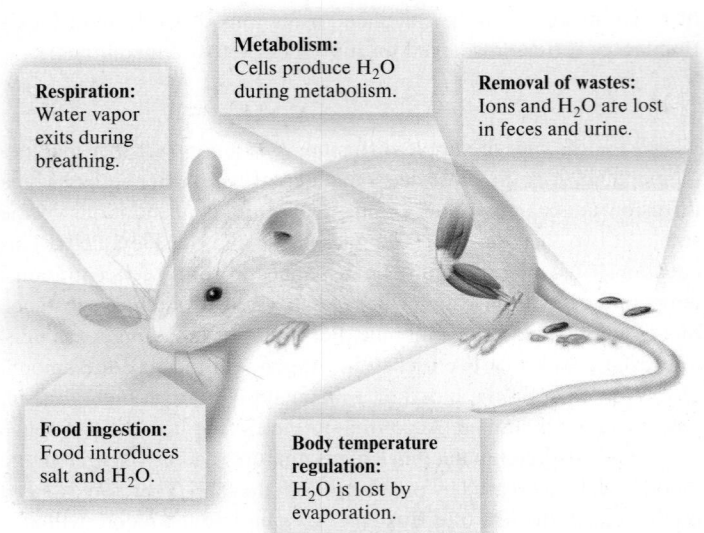

Figure 41.16 Types of obligatory ion and water exchanges in a terrestrial animal. Obligatory exchanges with the environment occur as the result of necessary life processes.

Concept Check: *Can animals completely avoid all the losses resulting from obligatory exchanges?*

the body surface. By contrast, proteins and nucleic acids contain nitrogen; when these molecules are broken down and metabolized, nitrogenous wastes are generated. Nitrogenous wastes are molecules that include nitrogen from amino groups (—NH_2). These wastes are toxic at high concentrations and must be eliminated from the body but, unlike CO_2, cannot be eliminated by exhaling or diffusion. As we will see in Chapter 49, the excretion of nitrogenous wastes is carried out by excretory organs such as kidneys and often requires body water.

Exchanges Due to Respiration
The requirements for respiration and for water and ion balance present different challenges to air- and water-breathing animals. To ventilate its lungs, an air-breathing animal moves air in and out of its airways. Water in the form of water vapor in the mouth, nasal cavity, and upper airways exits the body with each exhalation. As an animal becomes more active, it requires more O_2 and produces more CO_2. These changes are met by an increase in respiratory activity. Breathing becomes deeper and more rapid, which, in turn, increases the rate of water loss from the body. Therefore, respiration in animals with lungs is associated with significant water loss, as you can observe in cold weather when you can "see your breath."

Also, as described in Chapter 48, small, active animals with high metabolic rates usually have faster breathing rates than do larger, less active animals. Consequently, the potential for water loss due to respiration is relatively greater in small animals, particularly in endotherms (birds and mammals). A hummingbird for example, may have 15–20 times the water loss per gram of body mass than does a large goose.

In water-breathing animals, the challenge of water and ion homeostasis is more complex, because such animals move water, not air, over their respiratory organs (gills). Gills, like all respiratory organs, are thin structures with large amounts of surface area and an

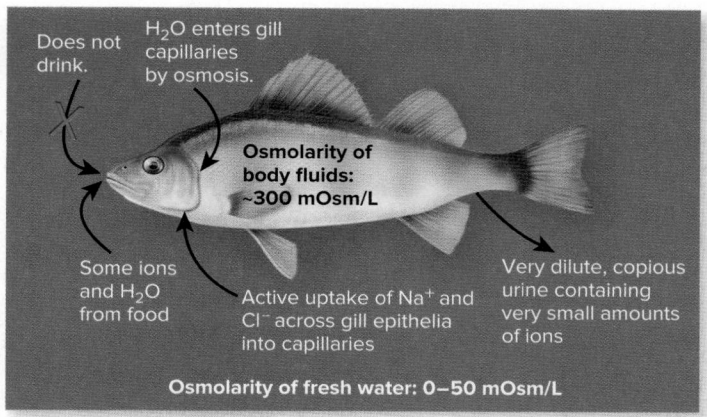

(a) Freshwater fish

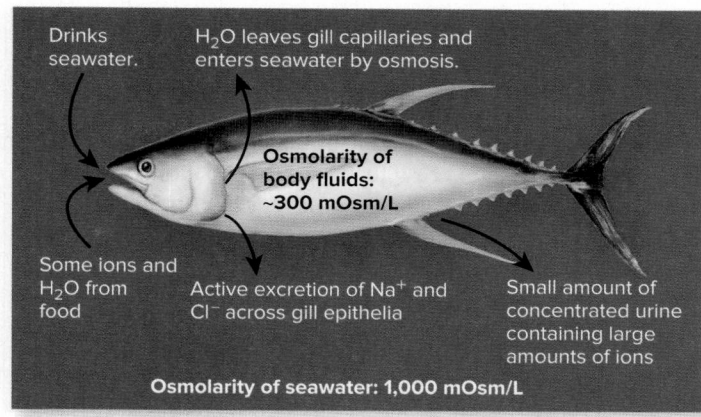

(b) Saltwater fish

Figure 41.17 Ion and water balance in water-breathers. Water breathing creates osmoregulatory challenges due to diffusion of ions and osmosis of water across gills. These challenges differ between **(a)** freshwater and **(b)** saltwater fishes and are addressed by behaviors (drinking or not drinking water), by active transport of ions across the gills, and by alterations in urine output.

 Core Concept: Energy and Matter Energy from the hydrolysis of ATP is required for all of the active transport processes illustrated in Figure 41.17. This energy is required to maintain homeostatic body fluid osmolarities despite the osmotic challenges imposed by very different environments.

extensive network of blood vessels. Although these features make gills ideal for gas exchange by diffusion between the blood and the surrounding water, they also make them ideal for ion and water movement by diffusion and osmosis, respectively.

When differences occur in ion concentration between a water-breathing animal's body fluids and the surrounding water, breathing via the gills has the potential to disrupt ion and water balance. Fishes or other water-breathing animals that live in fresh water and those that live in salt water face opposite challenges in maintaining this balance (**Figure 41.17**). The internal fluid osmolarity of most fishes is usually within the range of 225–400 mOsm/L, similar to that of most other vertebrates. Because freshwater lakes and rivers have very little ion content (usually <25 mOsm/L), this high concentration gradient for ions could promote the loss of ions from a fish's body into the fresh water. Likewise, a high osmotic gradient favors the movement of water from the lake or river into the body fluids of a freshwater fish. Freshwater fishes, therefore, gain water and lose ions when ventilating their gills (Figure 41.17a). If left uncorrected, these changes would cause a dangerous decrease in blood ion concentrations.

Freshwater fishes maintain water and ion balance via two different mechanisms. First, their kidneys are adapted to producing copious amounts of dilute urine—up to 30% of their body mass per day (an amount that would be equivalent to about 25 L per day in an average-sized human!). Second, specialized gill epithelial cells actively transport Na+ and Cl- from the surrounding water into the fish's blood. Thus, these two important ions are recaptured from the water. Freshwater fishes rarely, if ever, drink water, except for any that might be swallowed with food.

Saltwater fishes have the opposite problem. They tend to gain ions and lose water across their gills, because seawater has a much higher osmolarity (about 1,000 mOsm/L) than that of their body fluids (Figure 41.17b). The gain of ions and the loss of water from the

body are only partly offset by the kidneys, which in marine fishes produce very little urine so that as much water as possible can be retained in the body. The urine that is produced has a higher ion concentration than that of freshwater fishes. To prevent dehydration from occurring, marine fishes must drink. However, the only water available to them is the hyperosmotic seawater, which has a very high ion content. Paradoxically, therefore, marine fish drink seawater to replenish the water lost by osmosis through their gills. What does the fish do with all of the ions it ingested? The ingested ions must be eliminated, and this process is accomplished by gill epithelial cells. In contrast to the gills of freshwater fishes, which pump ions from the water into the fluids of the fish, the gills of marine fishes pump ions out of the fish and into the ocean. Thus, marine fishes drink seawater to replace the water lost through their gills by osmosis and then expend energy to transport the excess ions out of the body.

Exchanges Due to Feeding Because foods contain salts and water, eating also involves obligatory exchanges of these substances. Some plant products are over 95% water by weight, and other foods may contain high amounts of Na+ or other minerals. Therefore, the type of diet an animal consumes determines how much salt and water it ingests.

Once food has been digested and absorbed, the unusable parts of food are excreted as solid wastes. Some ions and water are lost by this route in most animals, but exceptions exist. Desert-dwelling kangaroo rats such as *Dipodomys panamintensis* produce fecal pellets that are almost completely dry, which helps these animals conserve water.

When food molecules are metabolized to provide energy that will be stored in the chemical bonds of ATP, oxygen captures electrons and combines with hydrogen ions, thereby making water (refer back to Figure 7.8). This water is sometimes called metabolic water to indicate its origin.

As noted earlier, marine fishes drink seawater. Other animals besides marine fishes may also drink seawater, either because fresh water is unavailable or because they ingest some with the food they eat. Many marine reptiles and birds also ingest seawater when consuming prey or, in some cases, when they spend prolonged periods at sea and have no access to fresh water for drinking. These animals have specialized epithelial cells that line structures called salt glands, located in groups around the nostrils, mouth, and eyes (**Figure 41.18**). Ions (notably Na^+ and Cl^-) move from the blood into the interstitial fluid, and from there, they are actively transported by the epithelial cells of the salt glands into the tubules of the gland. The ions and a small amount of fluid then collect into a central duct and are excreted as highly concentrated solutions. In general, vertebrates without salt glands cannot survive by drinking seawater, because they have no means of creating and excreting such a highly concentrated salt solution. Some marine mammals have been observed to occasionally drink small amounts of seawater, but most appear to never drink at all. These animals get their water from the food they eat.

Exchanges Due to Evaporation of Water Endotherms (animals that generate their body heat) use body water to cool off when they are active or in a hot environment. For example, sweating and panting are used to cool the body. These activities use the evaporation of water to draw heat out of the body. In the process, however, the animal loses water and, in sweat, some ions. You know from tasting sweat that it is salty, but the saltiness of sweat and that of blood are not the same. Sweat is a hypo-osmotic solution compared with blood; that is, it has a lower concentration of solutes. Thus, the fluid left behind in the body after perspiration has both a lower volume and a higher solute concentration than normal.

Other than perspiration and panting, very little water is gained or lost directly across the body surface of most terrestrial vertebrates, because their skin is impermeable to water; exceptions include amphibians. In invertebrates, the rate of water loss across the body surface depends on whether the animal is soft-bodied, like worms, or covered in a waxy, water-impermeable cuticle, like most insects.

The significance of obligatory exchanges and their effects on homeostasis was dramatically illustrated by a long-term investigation by a research team at the University of Florida, described next. Their discovery led to a revolution in our understanding of exercise physiology in humans.

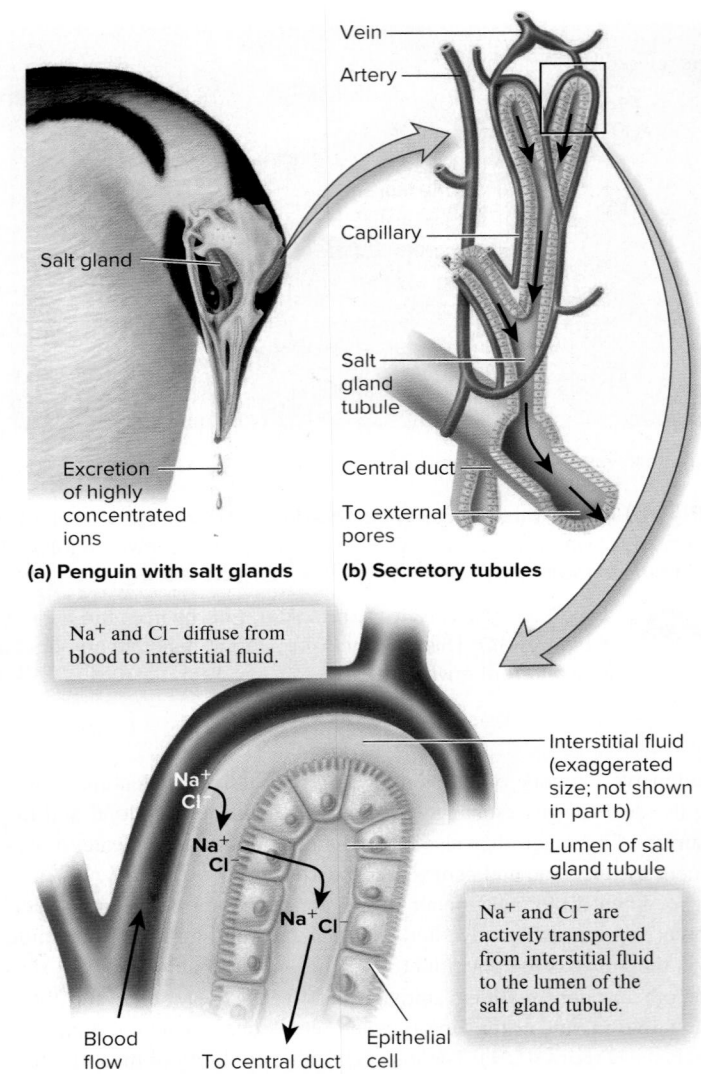

(a) Penguin with salt glands | **(b) Secretory tubules**

Na^+ and Cl^- diffuse from blood to interstitial fluid.

(c) Collection of salt solution in the tubule

Figure 41.18 Salt glands as an adaptation for marine life. Many marine birds and reptiles have salt glands, which contain a network of secretory tubules that actively transport Na^+ and Cl^- from the interstitial fluid into the tubule lumen. The viscous solution then moves through a central duct and to the outside environment through pores in the nose, around the eyes, and in other locations. The black arrows indicate direction of flow of blood or salt gland excretions.

Concept Check: *Why can't humans survive by drinking seawater?*

Feature Investigation | Cade and Colleagues Discovered Why Athletes' Performances Wane on Hot Days

On a typically hot summer day in the mid-1960s in Gainesville, Florida, the University of Florida football team was practicing in full equipment. The players were rapidly becoming dehydrated and, unbeknownst to them, the osmolarity of their body fluids was increasing as their bodies produced copious amounts of dilute sweat in an effort to maintain body temperature. The athletes became aware of two things. First, they discovered that they did not need to urinate for long periods after a strenuous practice session, and, second, their performance on the field suffered as they became increasingly fatigued and more susceptible to severe muscle cramps. Occasionally, players would require medical treatment for their symptoms. In extreme cases, athletes exercising in these conditions have been known to occasionally develop seizures—uncontrolled activity of neurons in the brain. This situation did not escape the notice of the team physicians and, notably, university faculty member and kidney specialist Robert Cade.

Many of the symptoms experienced by the players could be readily explained. The fatigue was directly related to loss of water from the body, which put a strain on the circulatory system and reduced the amount of blood flow to muscles and other organs. It was worsened by a slight decrease in blood glucose concentration during the long periods of strenuous activity without food. The muscle cramps and even the occasional seizures arose from an imbalance in extracellular ions—notably Na^+ and K^+—which are secreted out of the body by sweat glands in the process of perspiration. The resulting imbalance in extracellular fluid ion concentrations caused a change in the electrical properties of muscle cells and neurons, which triggered the spasms. Lastly, decreased urine production is one of the body's mechanisms for retaining fluid when body water is decreasing.

The key question was: How could these effects of strenuous exercise best be reversed or prevented? The answer was simple and clever. Cade and his colleagues rejected the prevailing view that drinking any fluids during heavy exercise somehow contributed to cramps and other problems. Instead, they hypothesized that the best way to maintain ion and water homeostasis in a profusely sweating person is to restore to the body exactly what was lost; that is, the person should drink a solution that resembles sweat!

The first thing Cade needed to do was analyze precisely how much Na^+, K^+, and other ions are actually present in sweat. Fortunately, he had an abundance of human sweat at his disposal to analyze. Once the players left the field, their jerseys were wrung out into a container, and the composition of the collected sweat was determined with an ion analyzer, the flame spectrophotometer shown in **Figure 41.19**. The concentrations were then compared with known values of ion concentrations in human blood. Today, we know that the composition of human sweat can change under certain conditions and can vary among people, but Cade's results were typical. The athletes' sweat contained mostly Na^+, K^+, and Cl^- at concentrations that indicated the solution was dilute compared with blood. Once Cade completed this analysis,

Figure 41.19 Cade and colleagues discovered a way to improve athletic performance and prevent ion and water imbalance during strenuous exercise.

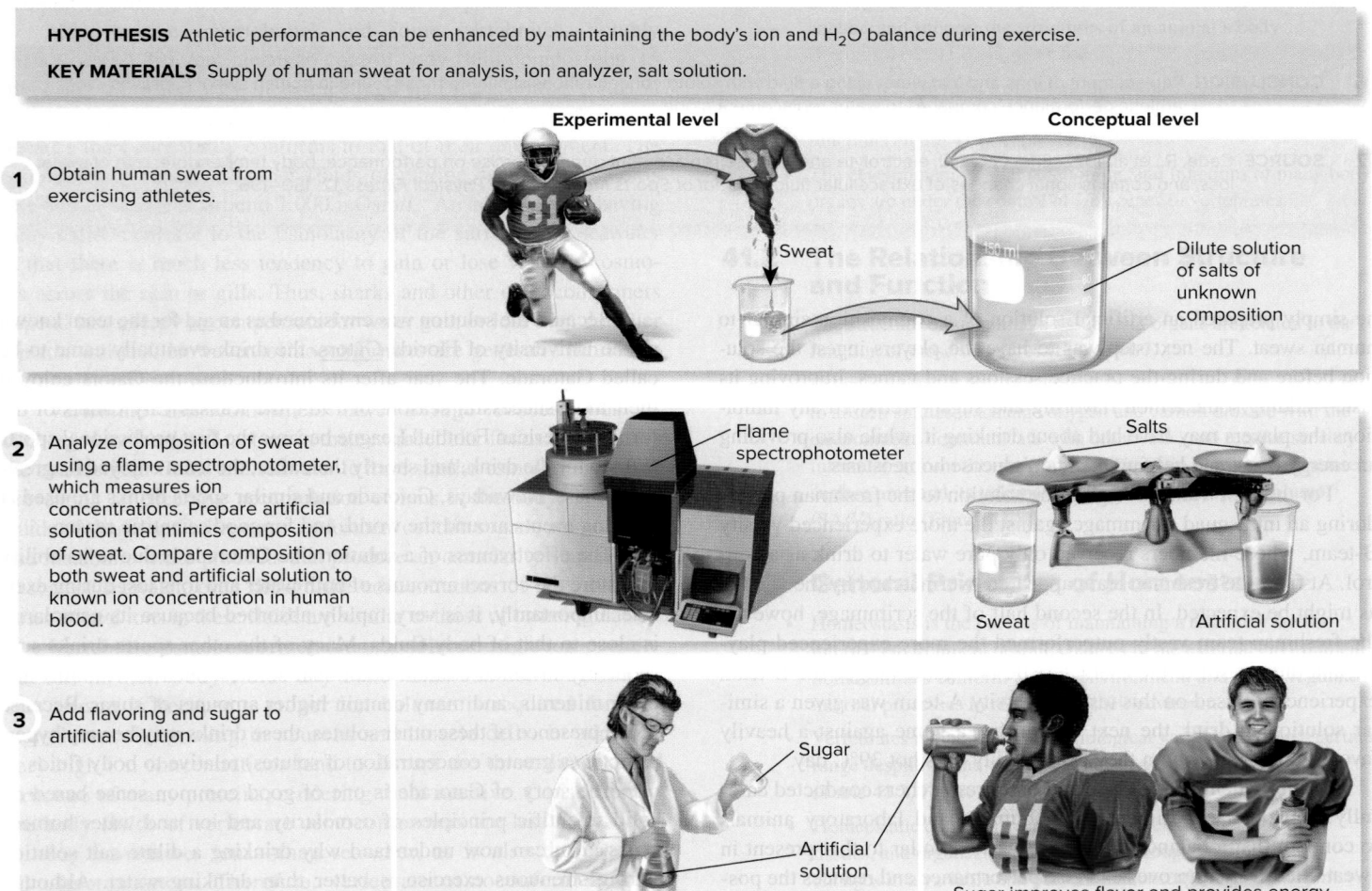

HYPOTHESIS Athletic performance can be enhanced by maintaining the body's ion and H_2O balance during exercise.

KEY MATERIALS Supply of human sweat for analysis, ion analyzer, salt solution.

Experimental level | Conceptual level

1 Obtain human sweat from exercising athletes.

Sweat

Dilute solution of salts of unknown composition

2 Analyze composition of sweat using a flame spectrophotometer, which measures ion concentrations. Prepare artificial solution that mimics composition of sweat. Compare composition of both sweat and artificial solution to known ion concentration in human blood.

Flame spectrophotometer

Salts

Sweat | Artificial solution

3 Add flavoring and sugar to artificial solution.

Sugar

Artificial solution

Sugar improves flavor and provides energy.

neurons because they transmit information from the periphery to the CNS. Many sensory neurons have a long, single axon that branches into a peripheral process and a central process, with the cell body in between (**Figure 42.3a**). This arrangement allows for the rapid transmission of a sensory signal to the CNS.

Motor Neurons **Motor neurons** transmit signals away from the CNS and elicit some type of response that depends on the type of cell receiving the signal. Motor neurons are so named because one type of response they cause is movement. In addition, motor neurons may cause other effects such as the secretion of hormones from endocrine glands. Because they send signals away from the CNS, motor neurons are also called efferent (from the Latin, meaning to carry from) neurons. Like sensory neurons, motor neurons tend to have long axons (**Figure 42.3b**), but these do not branch into two main processes.

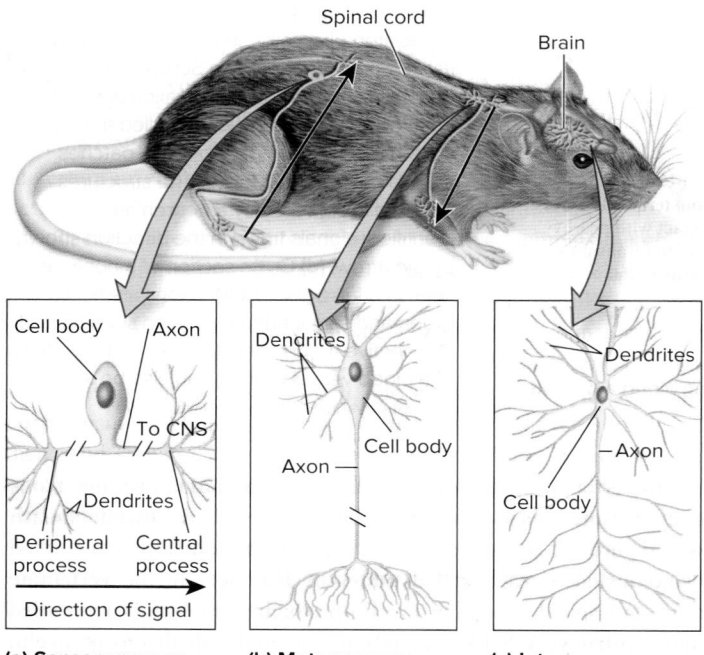

(a) Sensory neuron   **(b) Motor neuron**   **(c) Interneuron**

Figure 42.3 **Types of neurons. (a)** Vertebrate sensory neurons are afferent neurons with an axon that bypasses the cell body and projects to the CNS. **(b)** Motor neurons are efferent neurons that transmit signals away from the CNS and usually have long axons that enable them to act on distant cells. In (a) and (b), the hatch marks indicate that the axons are not to scale, but are in fact much longer. **(c)** Interneurons are usually short neurons that connect two or more other neurons within the CNS. Although short, the axons and dendrites may have extensive branches, allowing them to receive many inputs and transmit signals to many neurons.

 Core Concept: Structure and Function Cells are the simplest units of any organ system, including the nervous system. However, the structural variety and complexity of cells within an organ system can be great, as seen here. These structural differences are responsible for the different functions of neurons.

Interneurons A third type of neuron, called the **interneuron**, forms interconnections between other neurons in the CNS. The signals sent between interneurons are critical in the interpretation of information that the CNS receives, as well as the response that it may elicit. Interneurons tend to have many dendrites, and their axons are typically short and highly branched (**Figure 42.3c**). This arrangement allows interneurons to form complex connections with many other cells.

Reflex Arcs As a way to understand the interplay between sensory neurons, interneurons, and motor neurons, let's consider a simple example in which these types of neurons form interconnections with each other. Neurons transmit signals to each other through a series of connections that form a circuit. An example of a simple circuit is a **reflex arc**, which allows an organism to respond rapidly to inputs from sensory neurons and consists of only a few neurons (**Figure 42.4**). The stimulus, which is a tap below the kneecap, causes sensory neurons to send a signal to the CNS. Within the CNS, little or no interpretation of the signal occurs, because very few, if any, interneurons are involved, as in the example shown in Figure 42.4. The interneurons then transmit a signal to motor neurons, which elicit a response, in this case, a knee jerk. The response is very quick and automatic.

Reflexes are among the evolutionarily oldest and most important features of nervous systems, because they allow animals to respond quickly to potentially dangerous or otherwise important events. For instance, many vertebrates will immediately cringe, jump, leap, or take flight in response to a loud noise, which could represent sudden danger. Some animals that live in the water will reflexively dive in response to a shadow overhead, which could signify the presence of a passing shark or other predator. Many infant primates have strong grasping reflexes that help them hold onto their mother as she moves about. Other reflexes, such as the patellar tendon reflex just described, are important for postural changes and locomotion. Countless examples of useful reflexes are found in animals, and their importance is evident from the observation that they arose early in evolution and exist in nearly all animals.

42.2 Electrical Properties of Neurons and the Resting Membrane Potential

Learning Outcomes:
1. Explain the meaning of membrane potential.
2. Describe how the resting membrane potential is established and maintained.
3. Describe how an electrochemical gradient determines the direction in which an ion will move.
4. **CoreSKILL »** Write the Nernst equation, and use it to predict the direction in which different ions move across a plasma membrane.

In the late 18th century, Italian scientists Luigi Galvani and Alessandro Volta examined the ways in which frog leg muscles could be stimulated to contract. They dissected the muscles along with their associated nerves and placed them in a saline (NaCl) solution. The saline solution approximated the ion concentrations normally found in frog plasma, and helped keep the muscles and nerves alive for a short time after removal from the animal. The two scientists discovered that when they stimulated the nerve

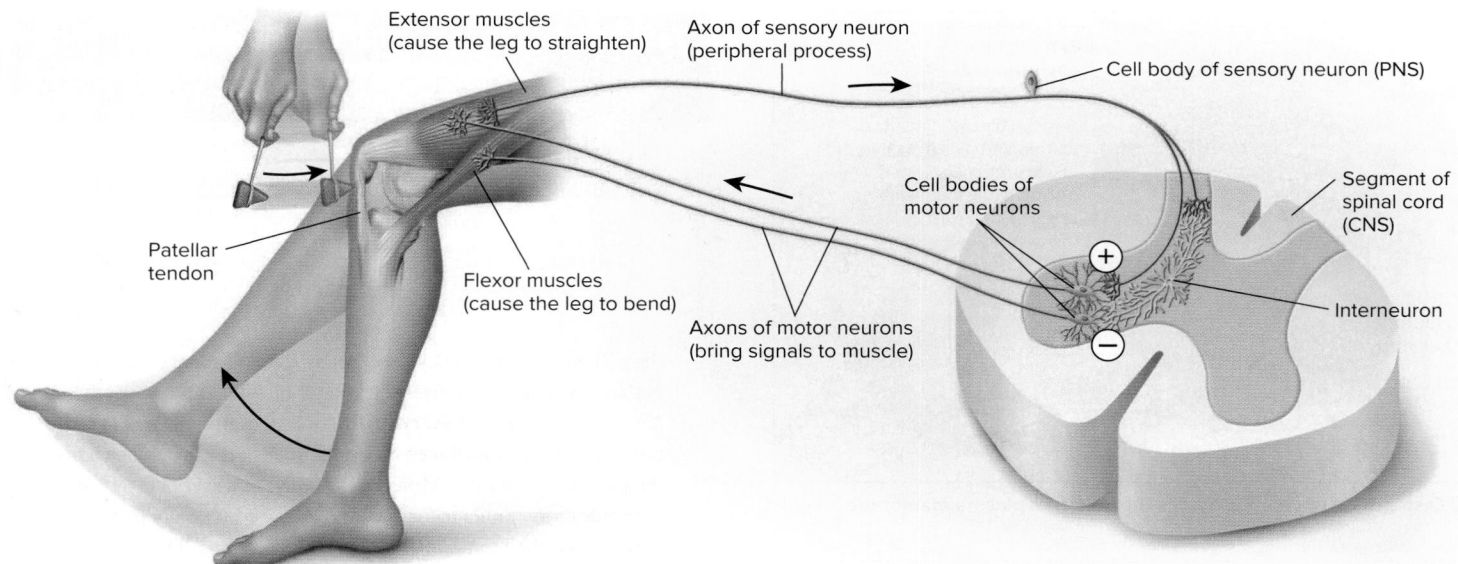

Figure 42.4   A reflex arc. The knee-jerk response is an example of a reflex arc. A tap below the kneecap (also known as the patella) stretches the patellar tendon, which acts as a stimulus for a sensory neuron. This stimulus initiates a reflex arc that activates (+) a motor neuron that causes the extensor muscle on top of the thigh to contract. At the same time, an interneuron inhibits (–) the motor neuron of the flexor muscle, causing it to relax.

Concept Check: *Animals have many types of reflexes. Once initiated, must all reflexes occur to completion, or do you think that in some cases they may be overridden or partially suppressed?*

that was attached to a muscle or directly stimulated the muscle itself with a source of electric current, the muscle contracted. They concluded that electricity was required for muscle contraction to occur, whether it originated at the nerve or the muscle itself. Eventually, Galvani postulated that electric current could somehow be generated by the nerve and muscle themselves, something he called "animal electricity."

Today, we know that Galvani's animal electricity comes from neurons, which use electrical signals to communicate with other neurons, muscle cells, or gland cells. These signals, often called nerve impulses but properly called action potentials, involve changes in the amount of electric charge across a neuron's plasma membrane. In this section, we will first examine the electrical and chemical gradients across the plasma membrane of neurons. Later, we will explore how such gradients provide a way for neurons to conduct action potentials. (In Chapter 45, we will discuss how muscle cells, too, can generate action potentials.)

Neurons Establish Differences in Ion Concentration and Electric Charge Across Their Membranes

Like all cell membranes, the plasma membrane of a neuron acts as a barrier that separates charges. Ion concentrations differ between the interior and exterior of a cell, and this sets the stage for the establishment of differences in the net charge across a membrane. Such differences in charge act as an electrical force measured in **millivolts** (mV), named after Alessandro Volta. Analogous to a battery, neurons have negative and positive poles, but these are the inside and outside surfaces, respectively, of the plasma membrane. For this reason, a neuron is said to be electrically polarized. The difference between the electric charges along the inside and outside surfaces of a cell membrane is called a potential difference, or **membrane potential**. The **resting membrane potential** refers to the membrane potential of an unstimulated cell that is not generating action potentials.

Let's begin our discussion of electrical signaling by examining how the resting membrane potential is established and maintained. When investigators first measured the resting membrane potential of neurons, they registered a voltage of about −70 mV inside the cell with respect to the outside. This means that the interior of the cell had a more negative charge than the exterior, which turns out to be typical of animal cells in their resting state. For comparison, a resting potential of −70 mV is tiny compared with the voltages used to provide electric current in a home (approximately 120 V), or even that of a small 1.5 V battery. Nonetheless, this tiny difference in charge across the membrane of a neuron is sufficient to provide the means for generating an action potential that can travel from one end of a neuron to the other, as we will see later in this chapter.

The resting membrane potential is determined by the ions located along the inner and outer surfaces of the plasma membrane (**Figure 42.5a**). Ions of opposite charges align on either side of the membrane because they are attracted to each other due to electrical forces. Negative ions within the cell are drawn to positive ions arrayed on the outer surface of the plasma membrane. Although there are more positive charges along the outside surface of a neuron and more negative charges inside, the actual number of ions that contribute to the resting membrane potential is extremely small compared with the total number of ions inside and outside the cell. **Table 42.1** lists the ions that are important in establishing the resting potential and their typical intracellular and extracellular concentrations in mammals and many other vertebrates. The ions that are critical for establishing the resting membrane potential are Na$^+$ and K$^+$ and, to a lesser extent, Cl$^-$.

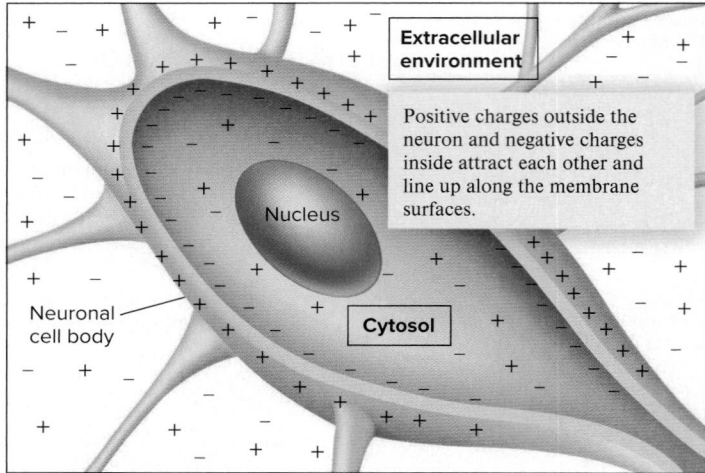

(a) Distribution of charges across the neuronal plasma membrane

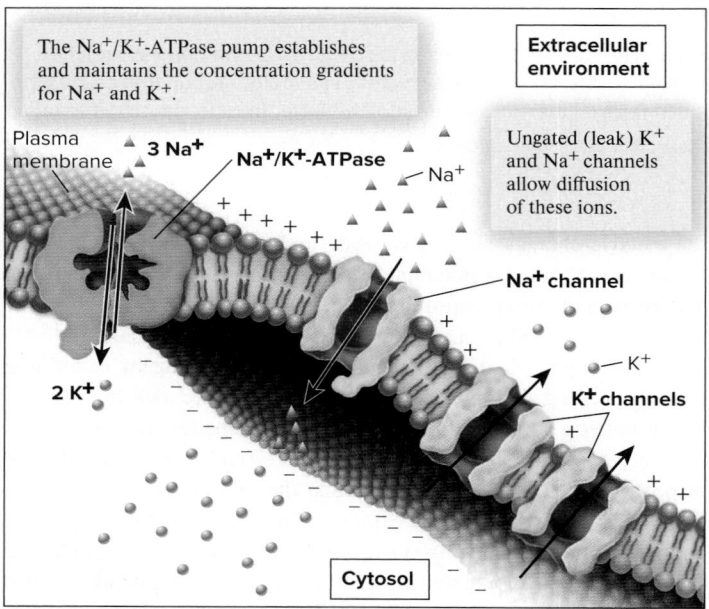

(b) Two major factors that influence the resting membrane potential

Figure 42.5 The resting membrane potential. The slight excess of negative charges inside and positive charges outside the cell membrane is shown in part **(a)**. In part **(b)**, the two major factors that contribute to this charge distribution are shown: the Na^+/K^+-ATPase pump that establishes ion concentration gradients, and ungated ion channels that permit diffusion of Na^+ and especially K^+ across the membrane.

Core Concept: Energy and Matter Animals use energy for many processes. The Na^+/K^+-ATPase pump uses the energy stored in the bonds of ATP to transport ions across the neuronal plasma membrane. Establishing and maintaining resting membrane potentials accounts for a significant fraction of the energy consumed per day in most animals.

Two factors are primarily responsible for determining the resting membrane potential (**Figure 42.5b**).

1. *Establishment of ion concentration gradients.* The Na^+/K^+-ATPase pump within the plasma membrane continually moves Na^+ out of

Table 42.1	Extracellular and Intracellular Concentrations of Ions for a Typical Mammalian Neuron	
	Concentration (mM)	
Ion	Extracellular	Intracellular
Na^+	145	15
K^+	5	150
Cl^-	110	7

the cell and K^+ into the cytosol (refer back to Figure 5.20). The Na^+/K^+-ATPase pump uses the energy of ATP to transport three Na^+ out of the cell for every two K^+ it moves into the cell. The pump therefore contributes modestly to a charge difference across the plasma membrane. More importantly, however, it establishes concentration gradients for Na^+ and K^+ by continually transporting them across the membrane in opposite directions. The charge difference and concentration gradients will determine the directions in which the ions will move by diffusion either into or out of the cell.

2. *Unequal membrane permeabilities to different ions.* The plasma membrane contains ion-specific channels that affect the permeability of the membrane to Na^+ and K^+. Ungated channels that are specific for Na^+ or K^+ influence the resting potential by allowing the passive movement of these ions. An ungated channel, sometimes referred to as a leak channel, is one that is open at rest and that does not require a stimulus such as ligand binding to open. Most neurons have about 10 to 100 times more ungated K^+ channels than ungated Na^+ channels. Therefore, at rest, the membrane is more permeable to K^+ than to Na^+. As you might predict from their concentration gradients shown in Table 42.1, Na^+ tends to diffuse into cells and K^+ diffuses out of cells through their respective channels when the cell is at rest. The greater number of leak channels for K^+, therefore, means that diffusion of K^+ makes a more significant contribution to resting membrane potential than does diffusion of Na^+, and excess positive charges exit the cell.

Now let's see how this movement of ions occurs, and how it produces the resting membrane potential.

An Electrochemical Gradient Governs the Movement of Ions Across a Membrane

The direction in which an ion diffuses depends on the **electrochemical gradient** for that ion, which is the combined effect of both an electrical and a chemical (concentration) gradient. **Figure 42.6** considers the concept of an electrochemical gradient for K^+, using two compartments separated by a semipermeable membrane that permits the diffusion of only K^+. Figure 42.6a illustrates an electrical gradient. In this case, the concentration of K^+ is equal on both sides of the membrane, but the concentrations of other ions (Na^+ and Cl^-) are unequal on opposite sides of the membrane and thereby produce an electrical gradient. Because K^+ is positively charged, it is attracted to the side of the membrane with more negative charge. Figure 42.6b shows a concentration gradient in which K^+ concentration is higher on one side than the other. In this scenario, K^+ diffuses from a region of high to low concentration. Finally, Figure 42.6c shows a balance of forces creating

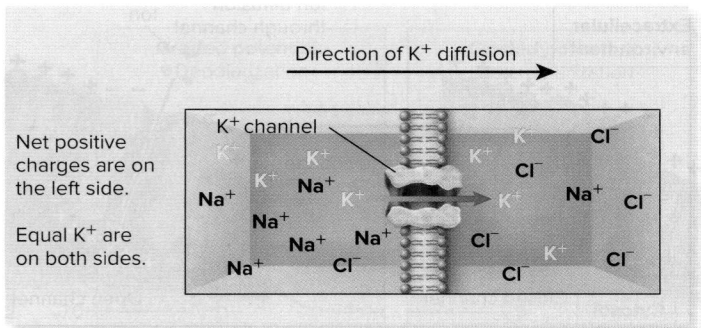

Direction of K⁺ diffusion →

Net positive charges are on the left side.

Equal K⁺ are on both sides.

(a) Electrical gradient, no concentration gradient for K⁺

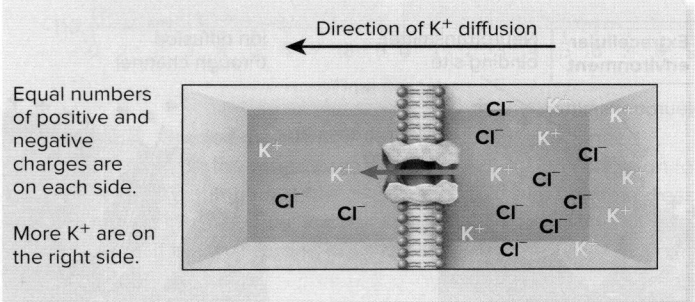

← Direction of K⁺ diffusion

Equal numbers of positive and negative charges are on each side.

More K⁺ are on the right side.

(b) Concentration gradient for K⁺, no electrical gradient

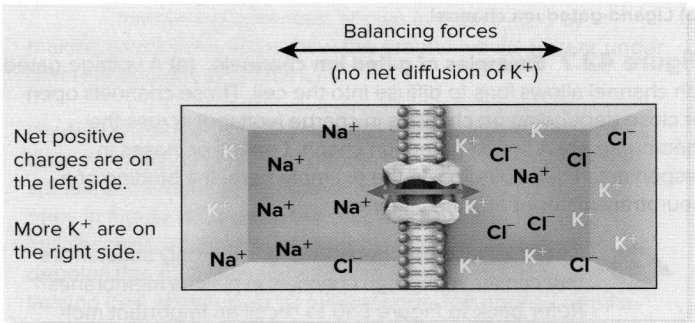

Balancing forces
(no net diffusion of K⁺)

Net positive charges are on the left side.

More K⁺ are on the right side.

(c) Electrochemical equilibrium

Figure 42.6 Electrical and chemical (concentration) gradients. This hypothetical example depicts two compartments separated by a membrane that is permeable only to K⁺. **(a)** In this example, the compartments initially contain equal concentrations of K⁺, but an electrical gradient exists due to an unequal distribution of Na⁺ and Cl⁻. Potassium ions are attracted to the higher amount of negative charge on the right side of the membrane. **(b)** In this case, there is initially no electrical gradient across the membrane, and the left compartment contains a lower concentration of K⁺ than in the right compartment. Under these conditions, K⁺ diffuses down its chemical concentration gradient from right to left. **(c)** This example illustrates opposing electrical and concentration gradients. The right compartment contains a higher concentration of K⁺, and the left side has a higher net amount of positive charge. These gradients balance each other, so no net movement of K⁺ occurs and a state of electrochemical equilibrium is reached.

  Core Skill: Connections What are some biological functions of ion electrochemical gradients in living organisms? Look back at Table 5.3 for help.

an electrochemical equilibrium. The electrical gradient favors the movement of K⁺ from left to right, but the concentration gradient favors movement from right to left. These opposing forces create an electrochemical equilibrium in which there is no net diffusion of K⁺ in either direction. In living cells, the membrane potential at which this occurs for a particular ion at a given concentration gradient is referred to as that ion's **equilibrium potential**.

With two different forces—electrical and concentration gradients—acting on a given ion, is it possible to predict the direction that ion will move across a membrane at any concentration gradient? In other words, can we compare the relative strengths of the electrical and chemical gradients and predict their net effect? By measuring the membrane potential of isolated neurons in the presence of changing concentrations of extracellular ions, scientists have deduced a mathematical formula that relates electrical and concentration gradients to each other. This formula, named the **Nernst equation** after German chemist and Nobel laureate Walther Nernst who derived it, gives the calculated equilibrium potential for an ion at any given concentration gradient. For monovalent cations such as Na⁺ and K⁺ at 37°C, the Nernst equation can be expressed as

$$E = 60 \text{ mV } \log_{10} ([X_{\text{extracellular}}]/[X_{\text{intracellular}}])$$

where E is the equilibrium potential; $[X]$ is the concentration of an ion, outside or inside the cell; and 60 mV is a value that depends on temperature, valence, and other factors. (For anions, the value is −60 mV.)

The Nernst equation allows researchers to predict when an ion is or is not in electrochemical equilibrium. To understand the usefulness of this equation, consider two examples. First, let's suppose the resting membrane potential of a neuron is found to be −88.6 mV, and the K⁺ concentrations are 5 mM outside and 150 mM inside the neuron. If we enter these concentrations into the Nernst equation, we obtain the equilibrium potential for K⁺:

$$E = 60 \text{ mV } \log_{10} (5/150) = 60 \text{ mV } (-1.48)$$

$$= -88.6 \text{ mV}$$

Under these conditions, where the calculated K⁺ equilibrium potential equals the actual resting membrane potential, K⁺ is in electrochemical equilibrium, and no net diffusion of K⁺ occurs, even when many K⁺ channels are open.

As a second example, let's suppose that the membrane potential is at a typical resting value of −70 mV and the Na⁺ concentration is 100 mM outside and 10 mM inside. If we enter these concentrations into the Nernst equation, we get

$$E = 60 \text{ mV } \log_{10} (100/10) = 60 \text{ mV } (1)$$

$$= 60 \text{ mV}$$

At a resting membrane potential of −70 mV, the value of +60 mV tells us that Na⁺ is not in electrochemical equilibrium. When the equilibrium potential for a given ion—calculated by the Nernst equation—and the actual resting membrane potential do not match, there will be a driving force for that ion to diffuse across the membrane. In this example, Na⁺ will diffuse into the cell, because both the electrical and concentration gradients favor an inward flow. However, if the membrane potential was +60 mV instead of −70 mV, Na⁺ would be in electrochemical equilibrium at those concentrations, and therefore, no net diffusion of Na⁺ would occur in either direction.

When these voltage-gated Na$^+$ channels open for 1 millisecond, they allow Na$^+$ to rapidly enter the cell, and then they become inactivated. This inactivation prevents the action potential from traveling backward (see Figure 42.10). Although the Na$^+$ channels are inactivated, K$^+$ channels are open, and the resting potential is restored. At the resting potential, the Na$^+$ channels switch from the inactivated to the closed state, in which they are once again capable of being opened by a change in voltage. The opening of K$^+$ channels also travels from the axon hillock to the axon terminals, but it causes a wave of repolarization that helps to reestablish the resting potential.

Speed of Propagation An action potential can be conducted down the axon at a speed as fast as 100 m/second or as slow as a centimeter or two per second. The speed is determined by two factors: the axon diameter and the presence or absence of myelin.

The axon diameter influences the rate at which incoming ions can spread along the inner surface of the plasma membrane. The flow of ions meets less resistance in a wide axon than it does in a thin axon, just as water moves more easily through a wide hose than a narrow one. Therefore, in a wider axon, the action potential moves faster. The very large axons of motor neurons of squids and lobsters, for example, conduct action potentials extremely rapidly, allowing the animals to move quickly when threatened.

Myelination also influences the speed at which action potentials travel along an axon. Myelinated axons conduct action potentials at a faster rate than do unmyelinated axons. Invertebrate neurons generally lack myelination, whereas vertebrate neurons may be myelinated or unmyelinated. Recall that certain glial cells (oligodendrocytes and Schwann cells) wrap around vertebrate axons to form an insulating sheath of membrane. The insulating layer of myelin reduces charge leakage across the membrane of the axon. However, this myelin sheath is not continuous (**Figure 42.11**). As described earlier (see Figure 42.2), the axons of myelinated neurons have exposed areas known as the nodes of Ranvier; these nonmyelinated regions are characterized by having many voltage-gated Na$^+$ channels. The nodes of Ranvier are the only areas of myelinated axons that have enough voltage-gated Na$^+$ channels to generate an action potential. When Na$^+$ ions diffuse into the cell at one node, the charge spreads through the cytosol and causes the opening of Na$^+$ channels at the next node, where an action potential is regenerated. This type of conduction is called **saltatory conduction** (from the Latin *saltare*, meaning to leap) because the action potential seems to jump from one node to the next. Saltatory conduction speeds up the conduction process. It takes less time for positive charges to travel from node to node than it would if action potentials were generated all along the length of the axon.

42.4 Electrical and Chemical Communication at Synapses

Learning Outcomes:

1. Describe the structural features of a synapse.
2. Distinguish between two types of potentials produced in postsynaptic cells: excitatory postsynaptic potentials (EPSPs) and inhibitory postsynaptic potentials (IPSPs).

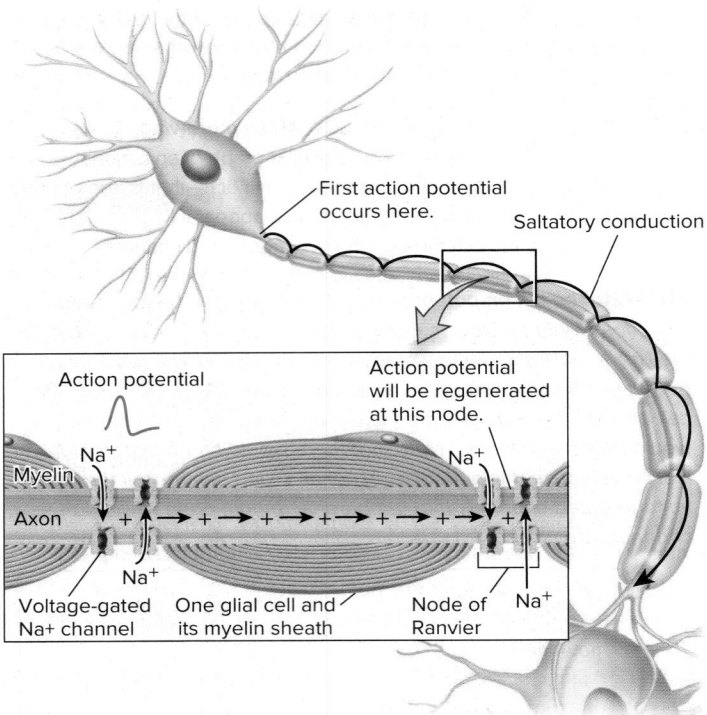

Figure 42.11 Saltatory conduction along a myelinated axon. Action potentials are generated only at the nodes of Ranvier, which lack a surrounding sheath of myelin.

Concept Check: *What is a major advantage of saltatory conduction?*

3. **CoreSKILL »** Describe the difference between spatial summation and temporal summation, and make predictions about postsynaptic potentials in a cell receiving multiple inputs from other cells.

4. List the classes of neurotransmitters, and provide brief descriptions of their generalized functions.

5. Describe the two general types of postsynaptic membrane receptors.

Neurons communicate with other cells at a **synapse**, which is a junction where an axon terminal meets another neuron, muscle cell, or gland cell. At a synapse, an electrical or chemical signal passes from an axon terminal to the next cell. A synapse includes an axon terminal of the neuron that is sending the signal, the nearby plasma membrane of the receiving cell, and in certain cases the **synaptic cleft**, or extracellular space between the two cells. The **presynaptic cell** sends the signal, and the **postsynaptic cell** receives it. A given cell may be presynaptic to one cell, and postsynaptic to another (**Figure 42.12**).

Synapses May Be Electrical or Chemical

By studying neurons from both invertebrates and vertebrates, researchers have identified two types of synapses: electrical and chemical. The first type, the **electrical synapse**, directly passes electric current from the presynaptic to the postsynaptic cell. The electrical signal passes through this type of synapse extremely rapidly, because the plasma membranes of adjacent cells are connected by gap junctions (refer back to Figure 10.11) that allow electric charge to move directly from one cell to the other. An electrical synapse does not have a synaptic

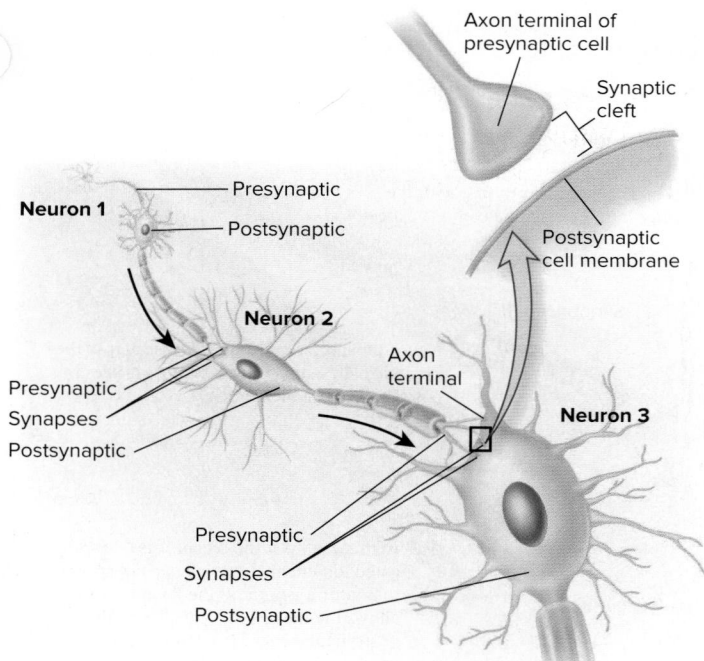

Axon terminal of presynaptic cell

Synaptic cleft

Neuron 1
Presynaptic
Postsynaptic

Postsynaptic cell membrane

Neuron 2

Axon terminal

Neuron 3

Presynaptic
Synapses
Postsynaptic

Presynaptic
Synapses
Postsynaptic

Figure 42.12 Presynaptic and postsynaptic cells. The arrows show the direction of signal transmission from one neuron to the next. Note that neuron 2 is postsynaptic with respect to neuron 1 and presynaptic with respect to neuron 3. The example shown here is a chemical synapse.

cleft, but a small intercellular gap is found between the presynaptic and postsynaptic membranes. Recent research indicates that electrical synapses are more widespread among taxa, including vertebrates, than originally thought. The most well-studied examples, however, occur in some aquatic invertebrates such as leeches. In those animals, electrical synapses occur in parts of the body where a group of neurons must fire rapidly and synchronously, such as when an animal must coordinate a number of muscles to swim or escape danger.

The second type of synapse is a **chemical synapse**, in which a neurotransmitter is released from an axon terminal and acts as a signal from the presynaptic to the postsynaptic cell. Chemical synapses appear to be more common than electrical synapses, particularly in vertebrates. Some neurons release only one type of neurotransmitter, and some neurons can release two or more different ones. Chemical synapses are slower than electrical synapses. However, unlike electrical synapses, a major advantage of these synapses is that they allow for complex modulation of the responses of postsynaptic cells, as we will see next.

At Chemical Synapses, Neurotransmitters Generate Excitatory or Inhibitory Signals in Postsynaptic Cells

Figure 42.13 shows the steps that occur when two cells communicate via a chemical synapse. An axon terminal of a presynaptic cell contains vesicles—small, membrane-enclosed packets, each containing thousands of molecules of neurotransmitter. The membranes of axon terminals contain voltage-gated Ca^{2+} channels. When an action potential arrives at an axon terminal, the voltage change from the action potential opens these channels, allowing Ca^{2+} to diffuse down

its electrochemical gradient into the cell. Calcium binds to a protein associated with the vesicle membrane. This triggers exocytosis, in which the vesicle fuses with the presynaptic membrane, thereby releasing its neurotransmitter molecules into the synaptic cleft. The neurotransmitter molecules diffuse across the 10- to 20-nm-wide synaptic cleft and bind to ligand-gated ion channels or other receptor proteins in the postsynaptic cell membrane.

The binding of neurotransmitter molecules opens or closes ligand-gated ion channels, thereby changing the membrane potential of the postsynaptic cell. In some cases, neurotransmitters directly bind to ion channels and cause the channels to open or close. In other cases, neurotransmitters bind to receptor proteins on the postsynaptic cell membrane, which leads to the accumulation of second messengers in the cytosol of the cell (see Chapter 9). These messengers, in turn, open or close ion channels by any of several mechanisms.

Some neurotransmitters are called excitatory, because they depolarize the postsynaptic membrane; the response is an **excitatory postsynaptic potential (EPSP)**. It is called excitatory because the depolarization of the postsynaptic cell membrane brings the membrane potential closer to the threshold potential that would trigger an action potential. An EPSP is a graded potential that can be caused by the opening of Na^+ channels in a neuronal membrane or by the closing of K^+ channels. In both cases, positive charges accumulate inside the cell.

By contrast, an inhibitory neurotransmitter usually hyperpolarizes the postsynaptic membrane, producing an **inhibitory postsynaptic potential (IPSP)**. This reduces the likelihood of an action potential by moving the membrane further away from threshold. An IPSP is a graded potential that can be caused by, for example, the opening of Cl^- channels. The equilibrium potential for Cl^- is typically close to or more negative than the resting membrane potential. Therefore, when Cl^- channels are opened, Cl^- moves into cells, making them more negatively charged and bringing them closer to the equilibrium potential for Cl^-. Hyperpolarization is the most common way in which neurons are inhibited.

To end the stimulation of the postsynaptic cell, neurotransmitter molecules in the synaptic cleft must be broken down by enzymes or transported back into the terminal of the presynaptic cell and repackaged into vesicles for reuse. The latter event, called reuptake, is an efficient mechanism for recapturing and reusing excess neurotransmitters that were released into the synaptic cleft. It also prevents these neurotransmitters from diffusing away from the synapse and possibly interacting with other distant cells. As we will see in the next section, drugs that block the reuptake process are used to treat people with disorders of neurotransmission, including depression.

Neurons Respond to Multiple Synaptic Inputs

A neuron may receive inputs from many synapses on its dendrites or cell body (**Figure 42.14a**), and some of these synapses may release neurotransmitters onto the neuron at the same or nearly the same time. Certain neurotransmitters are excitatory, and others are inhibitory. When do these different inputs lead to an action potential? The effect of a single synapse is usually far too weak to elicit an action potential in a postsynaptic neuron. However, when multiple EPSPs are generated at one time at many synapses along different regions of the dendrites and cell body, their depolarizations sum together. The

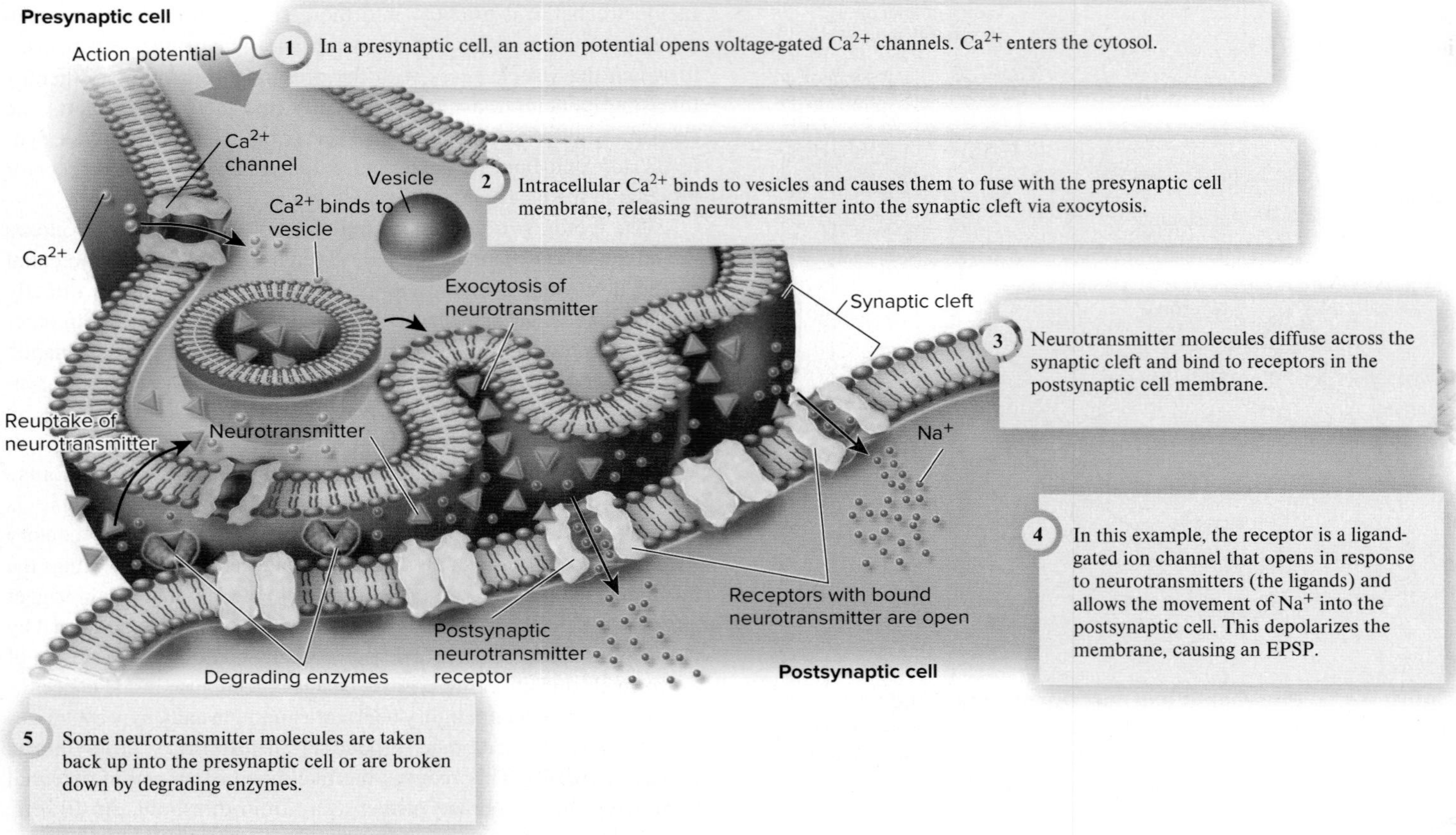

Presynaptic cell

Action potential

1 In a presynaptic cell, an action potential opens voltage-gated Ca^{2+} channels. Ca^{2+} enters the cytosol.

Ca^{2+} channel

Vesicle

Ca^{2+} binds to vesicle

2 Intracellular Ca^{2+} binds to vesicles and causes them to fuse with the presynaptic cell membrane, releasing neurotransmitter into the synaptic cleft via exocytosis.

Ca^{2+}

Exocytosis of neurotransmitter

Synaptic cleft

3 Neurotransmitter molecules diffuse across the synaptic cleft and bind to receptors in the postsynaptic cell membrane.

Reuptake of neurotransmitter

Neurotransmitter

Na^+

4 In this example, the receptor is a ligand-gated ion channel that opens in response to neurotransmitters (the ligands) and allows the movement of Na^+ into the postsynaptic cell. This depolarizes the membrane, causing an EPSP.

Receptors with bound neurotransmitter are open

Degrading enzymes

Postsynaptic neurotransmitter receptor

Postsynaptic cell

5 Some neurotransmitter molecules are taken back up into the presynaptic cell or are broken down by degrading enzymes.

(a) Events occurring at a chemical synapse

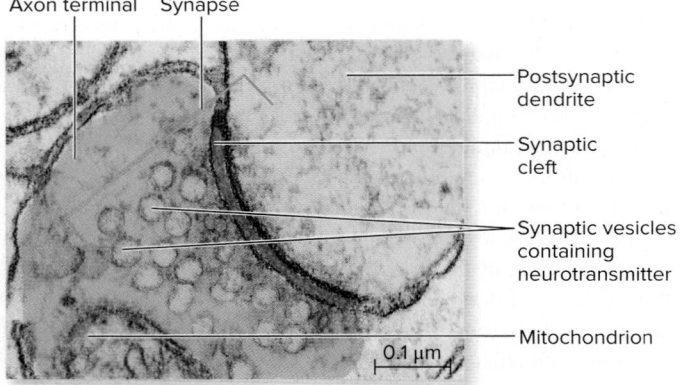

Axon terminal   Synapse

Postsynaptic dendrite

Synaptic cleft

Synaptic vesicles containing neurotransmitter

Mitochondrion

0.1 μm

(b) False-color electron micrograph of a chemical synapse

Figure 42.13 Structure and function of a chemical synapse.
(a) In response to an action potential, Ca^{2+} enters the presynaptic neuron axon terminal. This results in fusion of the vesicle with the plasma membrane, which releases neurotransmitter molecules into the synaptic cleft. The neurotransmitter molecules then bind to receptors in the plasma membrane of the postsynaptic cell. This causes ion channels to open (Na^+ in this example) or close, which, in turn, changes the membrane potential of the postsynaptic cell.
(b) False-color electron micrograph of a chemical synapse from a rat brain. b: ©McGraw-Hill Education/Al Telser, photographer

resulting larger depolarization may bring the membrane potential at the axon hillock to the threshold potential, initiating an action potential. When an action potential is initiated in this manner, the process is called **spatial summation** (**Figure 42.14b**).

Alternatively, two or more EPSPs may arrive at the same location in quick succession, such that the first EPSP has not yet decayed away when the next EPSP arrives. In that case, the depolarizations sum and may reach threshold upon arrival at the axon hillock. This process is called **temporal summation** (**Figure 42.14c**).

A third possibility is that EPSPs and IPSPs may arrive together at a postsynaptic cell. In this case, the two types of signals will cancel

each other out, and no action potential is elicited (**Figure 42.14d**). From this discussion, you might deduce that when two or more IPSPs arrive together, their hyperpolarizations might sum, too. That is exactly what happens. The membrane potential of the cell receiving multiple IPSPs moves farther away from threshold (**Figure 42.14e**).

In addition to the number of synapses that stimulate the postsynaptic membrane, the location of the synapses is also important. Synapses that occur far from the axon hillock are less effective than synapses on the cell body nearer the axon hillock.

Collectively, the various possible synaptic inputs shown in Figure 42.14a represent a major advantage of chemical synapses, allowing an animal to discern between competing signals. As one simple example, imagine a hungry fish confronted with a worm (food) and a predator (danger). IPSPs sent to hunger-sensitive neurons in the brain suppress those neurons, while other neurons that respond to danger cues receive EPSPs and thus generate action potentials that control, among other things, motor function. As a result, the fish ignores the worm and swims to safety.

Neurotransmitters Can Be Categorized According to Size or Structure

Neuroscientists have identified more than 100 different neurotransmitters in animals. Generally, neurotransmitters are categorized by size or structure (**Table 42.2**). The changing balance between excitatory and inhibitory neurotransmitters controls the state of nervous system circuits at any one time. To understand how neurotransmitters work, imagine driving a car with one foot on the gas pedal and one foot on the brake. To speed up, you could press down on the gas pedal, ease up on the brake, or both, whereas to slow down, you could do the opposite. All nervous systems operate in this way, with combined excitatory and inhibitory actions of neurotransmitters.

Next, we consider major features of the different chemical classes of neurotransmitters found in animals, which include acetylcholine,

biogenic amines, amino acids, neuropeptides, and gaseous neurotransmitters. With the exception of acetylcholine, all of these classes contain several different neurotransmitters that are similar in chemical structure but may have different functions in nervous systems.

Acetylcholine   Acetylcholine (ACh), one of the most widespread neurotransmitters in animals, is released at the synapses of **neuromuscular junctions**, where a neuron contacts a skeletal or cardiac muscle cell. It is also released at synapses within the brain and elsewhere. Acetylcholine acts as an excitatory neurotransmitter in the brain and on skeletal muscle cells and certain gland cells, but it is inhibitory when released from neurons that control cardiac muscle contraction. As we will see later, certain neurotransmitters such as ACh can exert both excitatory and inhibitory effects because they typically have more than one type of receptor to which they bind on different cells. The receptors, in turn, can be linked with different signaling mechanisms.

Biogenic Amines   The biogenic amines are compounds containing amine groups that are formed from amino acids. Common biogenic amines include the catecholamines—dopamine, norepinephrine, and epinephrine—and serotonin and histamine. The catecholamines are formed from the amino acid tyrosine, serotonin is formed from tryptophan, and histamine from histidine.

In addition to widespread physiological effects such as control of heart and lung function, catecholamines and serotonin are psychoactive; that is, they affect mood, attention, behavior, and learning. In humans, for example, abnormally high or low levels of catecholamines and serotonin have been associated with a variety of mental illnesses, including schizophrenia, attention-deficit disorder, and depression. Histamine is well known as a component of allergic reactions in people, but this is not related to its neurotransmitter functions. In the brain, neurons that produce histamine are important in modulating sleep. They are most active during waking and are nearly inactive during sleep. This explains why certain antihistamines (drugs that block the ability of histamine to bind to its receptor, thereby inhibiting its action) used to treat colds and allergies also induce drowsiness.

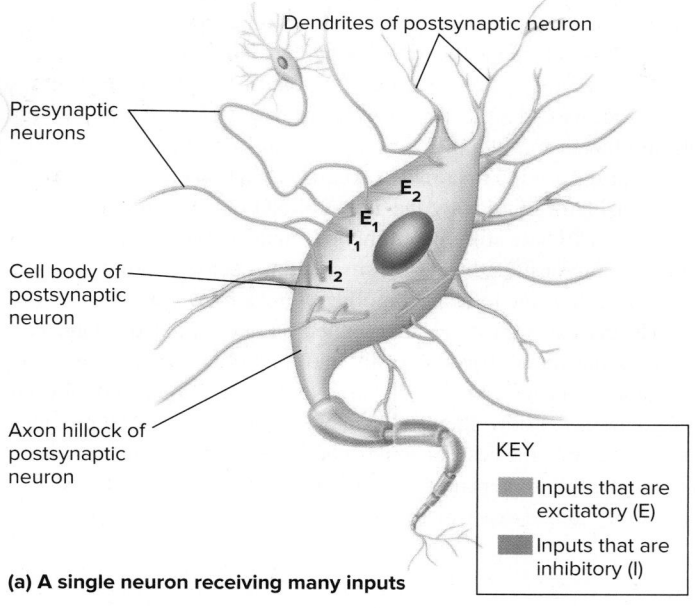

(a) A single neuron receiving many inputs

KEY
Inputs that are excitatory (E)
Inputs that are inhibitory (I)

Figure 42.14   Integration of synaptic inputs. Membrane potential changes in a postsynaptic membrane are shown under several different circumstances. When multiple excitatory (E) or inhibitory (I) inputs arrive simultaneously or nearly so, the subsequent EPSPs and IPSPs may add (summate) or cancel each other out, depending on the situation.

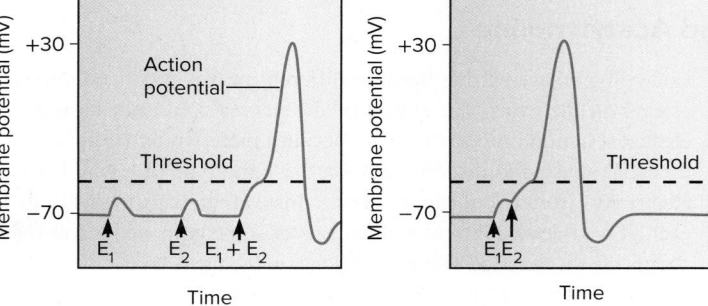

(b) Spatial summation of EPSPs

(c) Temporal summation of EPSPs

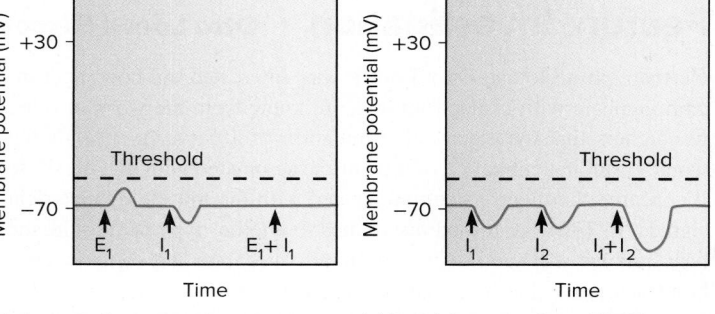

(d) Cancellation of EPSP and IPSP

(e) Spatial summation of IPSPs

Table 42.2	Classes of Neurotransmitters and Some Representative Examples and Functions
Transmitter	**Some major functions***
Acetylcholine	CNS: Stimulates the brain; important in memory, motor control, and many other functions
	PNS: Stimulates skeletal muscle at neuromuscular junctions; inhibits cardiac muscle; promotes digestion
Biogenic amines	
Catecholamines: dopamine, norepinephrine, epinephrine	CNS: Regulate mood, attention, learning, behavior
Serotonin	PNS: Stimulates cardiac muscle; improves lung function; helps animals respond to stressful situations
Histamine	CNS: Helps to maintain awake state
Amino acids	
Excitatory amino acids: glutamate, aspartate	CNS: Widespread mediators of activity in all areas of CNS; the major "on" signal of the CNS
Inhibitory amino acids: γ-aminobutyric acid (GABA), glycine	CNS: Hyperpolarize neurons; act as a "brake" on the nervous system
Neuropeptides	
Opiate peptides: endorphin	CNS: Modulate postsynaptic cell response to neurotransmitters; play a role in mood, behavior, appetite, pain perception, and many other functions
Gases	
Nitric oxide, carbon monoxide	CNS: Possible role in memory and odor sensation
	PNS: Relax smooth muscle, especially in blood vessels

*Note: CNS stands for central nervous system; PNS stands for peripheral nervous system.

Amino Acids   The amino acids glutamate, aspartate, glycine, and γ-aminobutyric acid (GABA) function as neurotransmitters. Glutamate is the most widespread excitatory neurotransmitter found in animal nervous systems, whereas GABA is the most common inhibitory neurotransmitter. GABA hyperpolarizes the postsynaptic membrane by opening Cl⁻ channels, allowing negatively charged Cl⁻ to diffuse into the cell (see Table 42.1). In this way, GABA brings neurons further away from the threshold potential required to generate an action potential, and thus it acts as the major "brake" on the CNS.

Neuropeptides   Neuropeptides are short polypeptides containing from 2 to about 15 amino acids. Like the other neurotransmitters discussed, neuropeptides can be excitatory or inhibitory. Neuropeptides are often called **neuromodulators**, because they can alter or modulate the response of the postsynaptic neuron to other neurotransmitters. For example, a neuropeptide may stimulate synthesis of receptors for another neurotransmitter, which makes a cell more responsive to that neurotransmitter. One group of neuropeptides is called the opiate peptides because opium-like drugs, such as morphine, bind to their receptors. Opiate peptides include the endorphins, a group of peptides that decrease pain and cause natural feelings of euphoria (extreme happiness and sense of invulnerability).

Gaseous Neurotransmitters   Certain gases such as nitric oxide (NO) and carbon monoxide (CO) act locally in many tissues and sometimes function as neurotransmitters. Unlike other neurotransmitters, these molecules are not sequestered into vesicles and are produced locally as required. Gaseous neurotransmitters are short-acting and influence other cells by diffusion from a presynaptic cell. In humans, NO is responsible for relaxing the smooth muscle surrounding blood vessels, including those in the penis. When a male becomes sexually aroused, NO levels increase in this tissue, dilating the vessels and increasing blood flow into the penis, producing an erection. Several drugs used to treat male sexual dysfunction enhance erections by increasing or mimicking the action of NO on smooth muscle. The functions of CO are still uncertain, but scientists think it may act as a neurotransmitter in pathways that mediate the sense of smell in some animals, such as the terrestrial mollusk *Limax maximus*.

The discovery that the actions of neurons are mediated in large part by neurotransmitters was one of the most significant achievements in the history of neuroscience. This discovery laid the foundation for our understanding of how chemical synapses function, and also provided insight regarding the basis of some neurological and muscular diseases. Amazingly, the existence of neurotransmitters was demonstrated in a remarkably simple experiment that arose from a dream, as we see next.

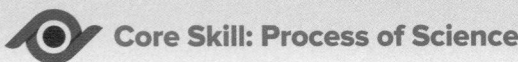 **Core Skill: Process of Science**

Feature Investigation | Otto Loewi Discovered Acetylcholine

German physiologist Otto Loewi was interested in how neurons communicate with skeletal muscle. He knew from the work of other researchers that the electrical stimulation of a nerve in a frog's leg would result in contraction of the muscle associated with that nerve, so it appeared that neurons communicated with the muscle by electrical signals. In 1921, he turned his studies to another type of muscle, the heart. As we will see in Chapter 48, all vertebrate and some invertebrate hearts receive both excitatory and inhibitory signals from different nerves that regulate the rhythm and intensity of the heartbeat.

Loewi hypothesized that because different nerves produced opposite effects on the heart, the effects of the nerves could not be a direct electrical action on heart muscle, because there would be no way for the heart muscle to discern between the same type of signal (that is, electricity) from two different nerves. Instead, perhaps the neurons in each nerve released different chemicals of some type, and it was these chemicals that exerted opposite actions on the heart.

As shown in **Figure 42.15**, Loewi removed the hearts from two frogs and placed the hearts in baths containing a solution of ions and

Figure 42.15 Loewi's experimental discovery of chemical neurotransmission.

HYPOTHESIS Neurons release chemical substances that influence the activity of the heart.

KEY MATERIALS Two frog hearts, saline solution, and stimulating and recording electrodes.

	Experimental level	Conceptual level

1 Dissect hearts from 2 frogs and place in saline solution. Heart 1 still has its vagus nerve attached.

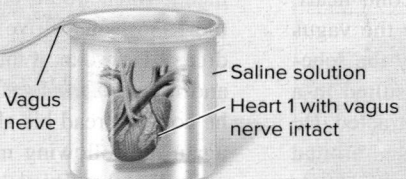

Vagus nerve

Saline solution

Heart 1 with vagus nerve intact

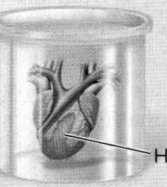

It was known that the vagus nerve has an inhibitory effect on heart activity.

Heart 2 with vagus nerve removed

2 Electrically stimulate vagus nerve of heart 1.

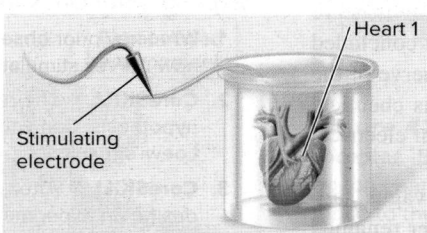

Heart 1

Stimulating electrode

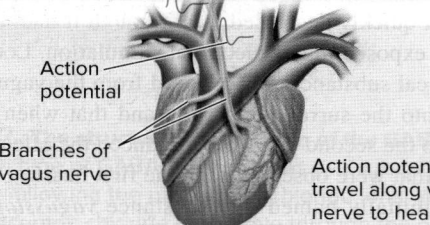

Action potential

Branches of vagus nerve

Action potentials travel along vagus nerve to heart 1.

3 Record strength and number of beats in heart 1 before and after electrical stimulation of vagus nerve. Next, remove a sample of the saline solution in and around heart 1, and transfer to heart 2. Record activity of heart 2. This was done using mercury manometers that were connected to each heart. The manometers measure pressure, which is due to the contractile force of the heart beating.

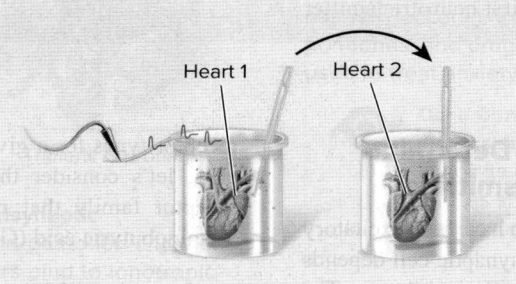

Heart 1   Heart 2

If stimulation of vagus nerve resulted in the release of chemicals onto heart 1, then these same chemicals (some of which may diffuse into the saline solution) should have an identical effect on heart 2.

4 THE DATA

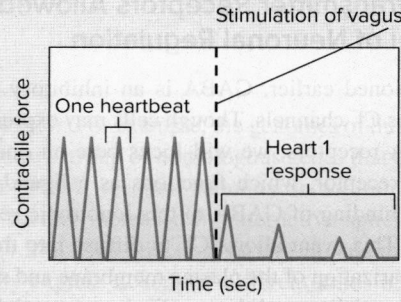

Stimulation of vagus nerve of heart 1

One heartbeat

Heart 1 response

Contractile force

Time (sec)

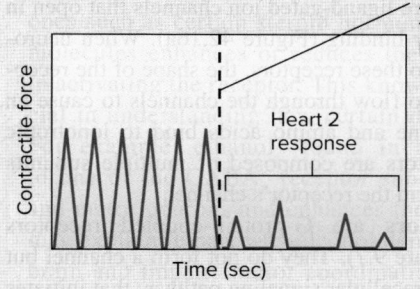

Addition of saline solution from within and around heart 1

Heart 2 response

Contractile force

Time (sec)

5 CONCLUSION Electrical stimulation causes the vagus nerve to secrete chemicals that decrease heart contractions.

6 SOURCE Loewi, O. 1921. On humoral transmission of the action of heart nerves. Pflugers archives. *European Journal of Physiology* 189: 239–242.

followed by periods of remission in which symptoms are reduced or absent. No cure is currently available, but certain drugs may slow its progression and reduce the severity of symptoms. This disease affects roughly 2.5 million people worldwide, about 75% of them women.

Summary of Key Concepts

42.1 Cellular Components of Nervous Systems

- The central nervous system (CNS) is composed of a brain and a nerve cord. The peripheral nervous system (PNS) consists of all neurons and their projections that are outside of and connect with the CNS. Nerves transmit signals between the PNS and CNS (Figure 42.1).

- The two major classes of cells in nervous systems are neurons and glia. In neurons, signals flow from dendrites to the cell body and then to the axon and axon terminal. Types of neurons include sensory neurons, motor neurons, and interneurons. A neuron's function is a reflection of its structure (Figures 42.2, 42.3).

- The most basic neural circuit is a reflex arc, which acts rapidly in response to inputs from sensory neurons and consists of only a few neurons (Figure 42.4).

42.2 Electrical Properties of Neurons and the Resting Membrane Potential

- Neuronal membranes are electrically polarized. The membrane potential is determined by the differential distribution and differential permeability of ions across the plasma membrane. The resting membrane potential is the membrane potential of a cell that is not sending electrical signals. Neurons use electrical signals to communicate with other neurons, muscle cells, or gland cells. These signals involve changes in the amount of electric charge on either side of a cell's plasma membrane (Figure 42.5, Table 42.1).

- Diffusion of ions through membrane channels occurs as a result of the concentration gradient of an ion across the membrane and the electric charge difference across the membrane. Ions move in response to an electrochemical gradient (Figure 42.6).

- The Nernst equation gives the equilibrium potential for an ion at any given concentration gradient.

42.3 Generation and Transmission of Electrical Signals Along Neurons

- Gated ion channels enable a cell to communicate by changing its membrane potential. The opening and closing of voltage-gated and ligand-gated ion channels cause two types of changes in the neuron's membrane potential—graded potentials and action potentials (Figures 42.7, 42.8).

- Graded potentials can trigger an action potential, an event that carries an electrical signal along an axon, from the axon hillock to the axon terminal. Axon diameter and myelination influence the rate of propagation of an action potential (Figures 42.9, 42.10, 42.11).

42.4 Electrical and Chemical Communication at Synapses

- In an electrical synapse, electric current is conducted from one cell to another via gap junctions. In a chemical synapse, a neurotransmitter carries the signal from the presynaptic to the postsynaptic cell. Many excitatory postsynaptic potentials (EPSPs) generated at one time can sum together and bring the membrane potential to the threshold potential, initiating an action potential (Figures 42.12, 42.13, 42.14).

- Chemical classes of neurotransmitters found in animals include acetylcholine, biogenic amines, amino acids, neuropeptides, and gaseous neurotransmitters. The discovery that the actions of neurons are mediated in large part by neurotransmitters was one of the most significant discoveries in the history of neuroscience (Table 42.2, Figure 42.15).

- The receptors of the postsynaptic neuron determine the types of signals that pass from one neuron to the other. The two major types of postsynaptic receptors are ionotropic and metabotropic (Figures 42.16, 42.17).

42.5 Impact on Public Health

- Most neurological conditions can be classified as disorders of either neurotransmission or conduction. Mood disorders caused by disrupted neurotransmission include major depressive disorder. Drugs used in the treatment of neurological disorders and many recreational and illicit drugs usually alter neurotransmission (Table 42.3).

- Some neurological conditions are caused by the inability of the axon to conduct an action potential. This occurs most commonly because axons fail to become myelinated (as in congenital hypothyroidism) or because myelinated axons become demyelinated (as in multiple sclerosis) (Figure 42.18).

Assess & Discuss

Test Yourself

1. In vertebrates, the brain and the spinal cord constitute
   a. the peripheral nervous system.
   b. the efferent division of the nervous system.
   c. the central nervous system.
   d. the autonomic nervous system.
   e. the central and peripheral nervous systems.

2. The structures of a neuron that function mainly in receiving signals from other neurons are the
   a. myelin sheaths.
   b. axons.
   c. axon terminals.
   d. dendrites.
   e. K+ channels.

3. The myelin sheath
   a. is produced by neurons in the peripheral nervous system.
   b. is formed only around neurons in the brain.
   c. is present on all neurons.
   d. is generally present around long axons in either the CNS or the PNS.
   e. significantly slows transmission along neurons.

4. Neurons that function mainly in connecting other neurons in the central nervous system are
   a. sensory neurons.
   b. efferent neurons.
   c. motor neurons.
   d. afferent neurons.
   e. interneurons.

5. The difference in charges across the plasma membrane of an unstimulated neuron is called
   a. an EPSP.
   b. the resting membrane potential.
   c. an IPSP.
   d. the graded potential.
   e. the action potential.

6. Which of the following contribute(s) to the resting membrane potential?
   a. the relative leakiness of the membrane to Na^+ and K^+
   b. active transport of ions across the membrane
   c. concentration of Na^+ and K^+ inside and outside of the cell
   d. all of the above
   e. b and c only

7. A neuron has reached a threshold potential when it has depolarized to the point where
   a. the voltage-gated Na^+ channels have become inactivated.
   b. sufficient numbers of voltage-gated Na^+ channels open to initiate a positive feedback cycle, contributing to further depolarization.
   c. voltage-gated K^+ channels close.
   d. voltage-gated Na^+ channels close.
   e. both b and c occur.

8. The speed of transmission of an action potential along an axon is influenced by
   a. the presence of myelin.
   b. an increased concentration of Ca^{2+}.
   c. the diameter of the axon.
   d. all of the above.
   e. a and c only.

9. Gap junctions are characteristic of
   a. electrical synapses.
   b. chemical synapses.
   c. acetylcholine synapses.
   d. GABA synapses.
   e. synapses between motor neurons and muscle cells.

10. The response of the postsynaptic cell at a chemical synapse is determined by
    a. the type of neurotransmitter released at the synapse.
    b. the type of receptors the postsynaptic cell has.
    c. whether or not an axon is myelinated.
    d. whether the synapse is on a dendrite or directly on the cell body of the postsynaptic cell.
    e. a and b, both.

Conceptual Questions

1. Describe the difference between graded and action potentials.

2. In certain diseases, such as kidney failure, the Na^+ concentration in the body's extracellular fluid can be altered. What effect might a high extracellular Na^+ concentration have on neurons?

3. **Core Concept: Structure and Function** How can the core concept that structure determines function be applied to neurons?

Collaborative Questions

1. Describe the difference between an electrical synapse and a chemical synapse. What advantage is provided by chemical synapses?

2. Name the parts of a neuron, and give a brief description of their major characteristics.

Neuroscience II: Evolution, Structure, and Function of the Nervous System

43

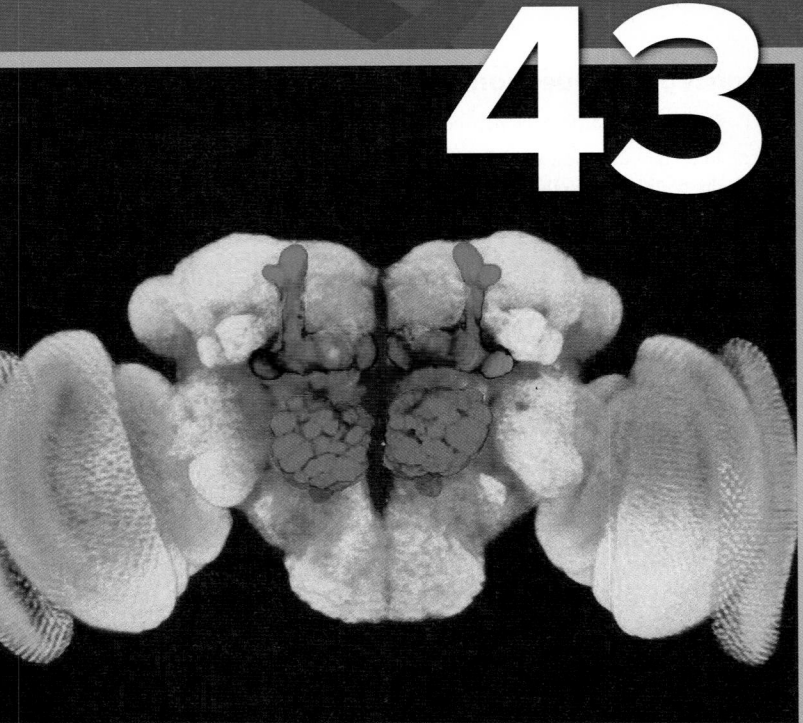

Three-dimensional reconstruction of the brain of a fruit fly. The brains of animals are organized into anatomical structures with specialized functions. For example, the green structures in this image are important for learning and memory, the purple structures for olfaction, and the large orange structures on either side for processing visual information. Courtesy Ann-Shyn Chiang, Tsing Hua Chair Professor/Brain Research Center & Institute of Biotechnology/National Tsing Hua University

It will take you approximately 2–3 seconds to read this sentence. During that time, many of the 100 billion or so neurons of your brain will have collectively fired off millions of action potentials. Some of those signals will help process the visual information reaching your eyes as you scan the lines. Others will activate centers of learning and memory to allow you to understand the meanings of the words you've read. Still other signals will help filter out extraneous inputs—such as background noise—that might distract you from your task. The complexity of the seemingly simple task of reading a single sentence indicates the enormous level of activity that goes on continually in the brain, even at rest.

The wonder of the brain lies in its incredible complexity. The human brain, for example, has several thousand miles of interconnected neurons and hundreds of trillions of synapses, resulting in a total surface area that if spread out, would cover more than four soccer fields. The brain allows us to move, think, and experience sensation and emotion. Groups of neurons also coordinate homeostatic functions such as breathing, blood circulation, and body temperature. When we examine the way that groups of neurons communicate, we begin to understand the complex mental functions of nervous systems, including learning, memory, and motivation.

Neuroscience—the study of nervous systems—is an area of intense research activity worldwide. In 2013, the administration of President Barack Obama announced the formation of the BRAIN Initiative (Brain Research through Advancing Innovative Neurotechnologies), a 10-year, federally funded effort to map the location, structure, and function of all the 100 billion or so neurons in the human brain. This initiative has the potential to revolutionize our understanding of how the human brain functions in both health and disease, and it launches a thrilling new era of neuroscience research. As one recent example, the Human Connectome Project—an international consortium of researchers at several institutions funded largely by the National Institutes of Health—has provided fascinating new insight into the organization and interconnectedness of pathways throughout the human brain.

In this chapter, we will first survey a variety of nervous systems, which allow animals to sense and respond to environmental changes. We will then examine the nervous system of humans. However, keep in mind that we still have much to learn about the organization, connectivity, and functions of nervous system structures. Our own nervous system is fascinating and mysterious, and the study of how it functions will ultimately tell us much about what makes us human.

43.1 The Evolution and Development of Nervous Systems

Learning Outcomes:

1. List the different types of nervous systems found in animals.
2. Describe the general anatomical organization of the brain in vertebrates.
3. Relate the structural changes in brain complexity that accompanied the evolution of mammals to brain function.

Animal nervous systems are the products of hundreds of millions of years of evolution. They provide advantages to animals that promote survival and reproductive success. For example, nervous systems allow animals to sense their environment and respond to changes in an appropriate way. In addition, nervous systems form connections with muscles and facilitate movement, which allows some animals to travel distances to obtain food. Likewise, nervous systems help animals avoid predation and other environmental dangers; form social bonds that enhance the chances of survival for both the individual and the group; and even perform the complex tasks of thinking, learning, remembering, and planning.

Studying the evolution and development of nervous systems helps us understand how particular nervous systems are adapted to different functions. At the structural level, the organization of nervous systems ranges from a relatively simple network of a small number of cells to the complexity of the human brain. The characteristics of an animal's nervous system determine the behaviors that it displays. In this section, we will survey some comparative features of the nervous systems of invertebrates and vertebrates.

The Evolution of Nervous Systems Gave Animals the Ability to Sense and Respond to Changes in the Environment

Precisely when nervous systems first arose and whether or not the nervous systems of most or all animals can be traced back to a common ancestor are questions of active investigation by neuroscientists. For example, recent genetic studies have uncovered remarkable similarities in the expression and activation of genes coding for proteins that regulate neuronal development across taxa in bilaterally symmetric animals. Those studies suggest that the patterning of nervous system development in these bilaterians may be traced to a common ancestor that lived more than 500 mya!

Today, all animals except sponges have a nervous system. Interestingly, though, researchers have discovered that sponges express dozens of genes that are similar to genes expressed in human neurons, particularly those that encode proteins that regulate synaptic function. The functions of the sponge genes are uncertain, but the proteins encoded by the genes interact with each other in ways that are reminiscent of human synaptic proteins. Thus, the origin of nervous systems almost certainly can be traced to genes of evolutionarily ancient organisms. As animal species evolved, these genes were modified and formed the basis of all future nervous systems.

The simplest nervous system is the **nerve net** of the radially symmetric cnidarians (jellyfish, hydras, and anemones; **Figure 43.1a**). The neurons are arranged in a network of connections between the inner and outer body layers of the animals. A characteristic feature of nerve nets is that activation of neurons in any one region leads to activation of most or all other neurons, with the excitation spreading in all directions at once. Many of these neurons stimulate contractile cells to contract. This allows the organism to move large areas of its body simultaneously, thereby coordinating simple movements such as swimming. Recent research has identified regions of specialized function in the nerve nets of some cnidarians, such as local sensory neurons in the outer body wall. These findings push the origin of specialized nervous system structures and function further back in evolutionary

time than previously thought. Some cnidarians, such as the jellyfish, have two nerve nets: one for moving tentacles and one for swimming.

Sea stars and other echinoderms also have a simple nervous system, but it is slightly more complex than that of cnidarians. A nerve ring surrounds the mouth and is connected to larger radial nerves extending into the arms (**Figure 43.1b**). This arrangement allows the mouth and arms to operate independently.

During the evolution of animals, more complex body types have been associated with **cephalization** (from the Greek *cephalo*, meaning head). This term refers to the concentration of sense organs at the anterior end of the body, forming an increasingly complex **brain** that controls sensory and motor functions of the entire body. Within the brain, neuronal pathways provide the integrative functions necessary for an animal to make more sophisticated responses to its environment. Brains are found in all vertebrates and most invertebrates, and they are usually composed of more than one anatomical and functional region with considerable complexity.

Platyhelminthes (flatworms) was the first animal phylum to evolve a brain with defined regions exhibiting many synaptic connections. In these animals, different regions of the brain appear to integrate inputs from sense organs, such as the eyes, and control motor output, such as movements involved in swimming (**Figure 43.1c**). Two nerve cords extend along the ventral surface of the animal from the anterior end to the posterior end and are connected to each other by transverse nerves.

In annelids (segmented worms), ganglia and nerves are present at each body segment, where they coordinate local sensory and motor activities (**Figure 43.1d**). Ganglia are collections of neuron cell bodies with limited processing ability, limited synapses, and few to no subdivisions like those found in a brain. Ganglia are present in most animals and often serve to coordinate local signaling in a body part.

In the simpler types of mollusks, such as the snail, the nervous system is very similar to that of the annelids. The head contains a pair of anterior ganglia; paired nerve cords extend from these ganglia and send branches to the eyes, muscular foot, and digestive system.

In arthropods, such as *Drosophila* (**Figure 43.1e** and the chapter opening photo), the brain has several subdivisions with distinct, well-defined anatomical borders and functions, such as a region devoted to learning and memory. Some mollusks, such as the squid and octopus, have complex brains with subdivisions that allow these animals to coordinate the sophisticated visual sensing and motor behaviors necessary for their predatory lifestyle (**Figure 43.1f**).

In the embryos of chordates, a dorsally located nerve cord is present that, in vertebrates, develops into the brain and **spinal cord**. The brain and spinal cord constitute the **central nervous system (CNS)** (**Figure 43.1g**). Nerves from the **peripheral nervous system (PNS)** relay signals into and out of the CNS at separate regions along the spinal cord.

Brains of Vertebrates Have Three Basic Divisions

Development of the vertebrate brain begins with the formation of a central fold in the embryo called the neural tube, or dorsal nerve cord. This hollow tube is the structure from which the entire nervous system develops (look ahead to Figure 51.19). Increased cell proliferation leads to bending and folding of the neural tube during embryonic development, resulting in bulges that become separate divisions of the nervous system. The anterior end develops into the brain, while the posterior portion becomes the spinal cord.

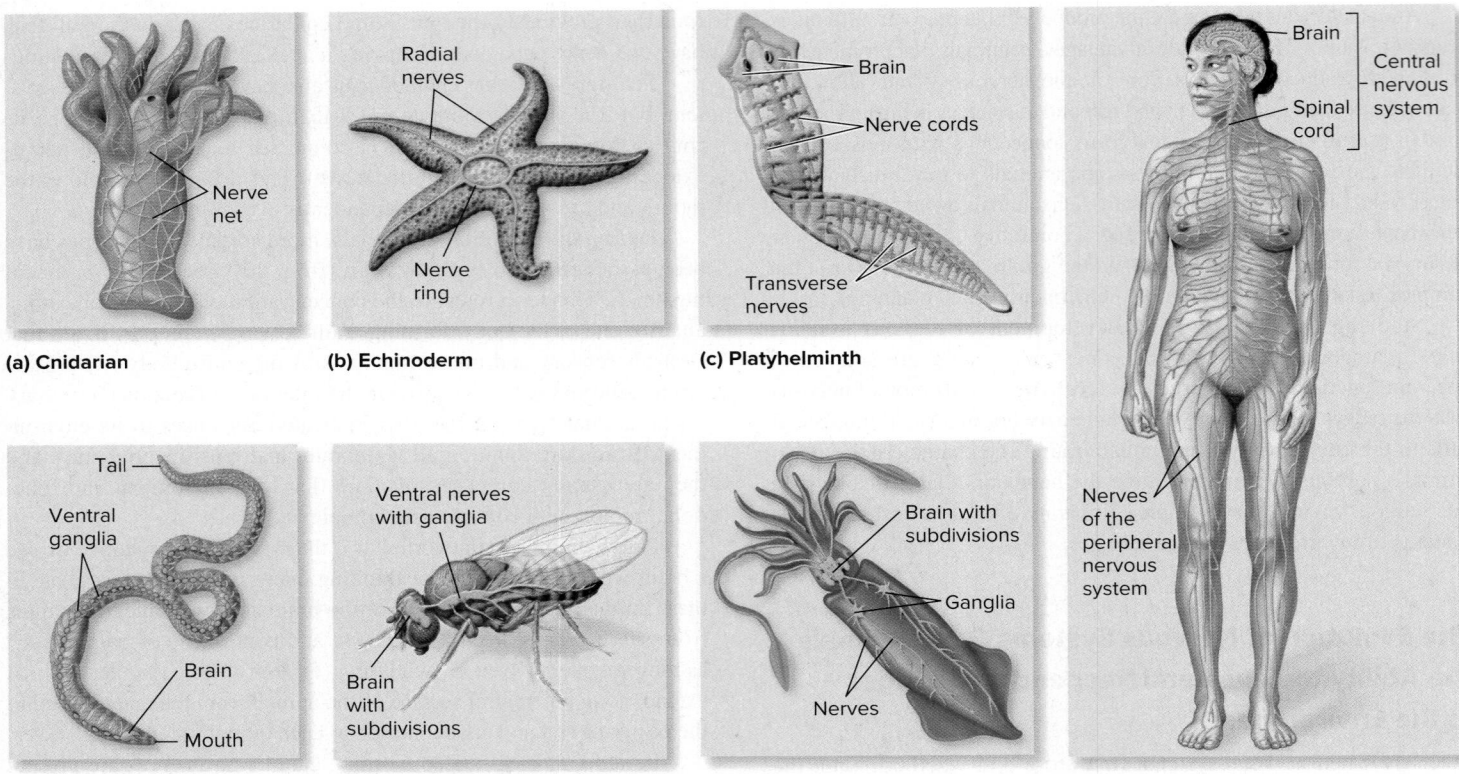

Figure 43.1 Representative nervous systems throughout the animal kingdom.

 Core Skill: Connections Nervous systems are one of the defining features of animals. In Chapter 33, you learned that several other features define animals and distinguish them from other living organisms. What are some of these features?

In vertebrates, the brain has three major anatomic divisions: **hindbrain**, **midbrain**, and **forebrain** (**Figure 43.2**). Fossils of jawless fishes that lived 400 mya show that their brains were already organized into the three basic divisions that have been retained in all modern vertebrates.

Let's look at the development of the human brain. At 4 weeks, the human embryo already exhibits the hindbrain, midbrain, and forebrain (Figure 43.2a). Just a week later, the hindbrain and forebrain have each formed two separate subdivisions (Figure 43.2b). The hindbrain subdivides into the metencephalon and the myelencephalon. The forebrain subdivides into the telencephalon and the diencephalon. The midbrain, by contrast, does not subdivide and is termed the mesencephalon. By the time the human brain is fully developed, some of these structures have further divided and specialized (Figure 43.2c; their functions will be described in Section 43.2). The development of brain subdivisions increases the capacity of the brain to perform complex, distinct functions.

Evolution of Increased Brain Complexity Involved a Larger, Highly Folded Forebrain

As evolution resulted in animals with more complex nervous systems, the size of the forebrain and its major subdivision, the **cerebrum**, also increased, making up a greater proportion of the brain. Many of the important functions of the forebrain are carried out by neurons in the

outer surface of the cerebrum called the **cerebral cortex**. Therefore, increased complexity of the brain is also correlated with an increased surface area of the cerebral cortex (see Figure 43.2). During the evolution of mammals, this increase in surface area occurred more rapidly than an expansion in the size of the skull. How could this occur? The answer is that the external surface of the forebrain in animals with increasingly complex brains is highly convoluted, forming many folds and grooves. Compare the relatively smooth-looking surface of the brain of a rat with the highly folded one of a dolphin or a primate in **Figure 43.3**.

As body size increases across the animal kingdom, you might expect that brain mass would increase proportionately—that the brain of an elephant would be proportionately larger than that of a bat, for instance. That is generally the case, with a few important exceptions (**Figure 43.4**). In particular, the masses of the human and dolphin brains are considerably greater than would be expected on the basis of body mass (note the logarithmic scale on the vertical axis).

Brain mass and the amount of folding of forebrain structures are correlated with more complex behaviors. Why is this so? As we will see in the next section, the outer surface of the brain, the cerebral cortex, plays a key role in conscious thought, reasoning, and learning. Greater size and increased folding provide more surface area to support a larger number of neurons and synapses, which, in turn, facilitates processing and interpretation of information. Even so, evidence does not suggest that people with small differences in brain size differ

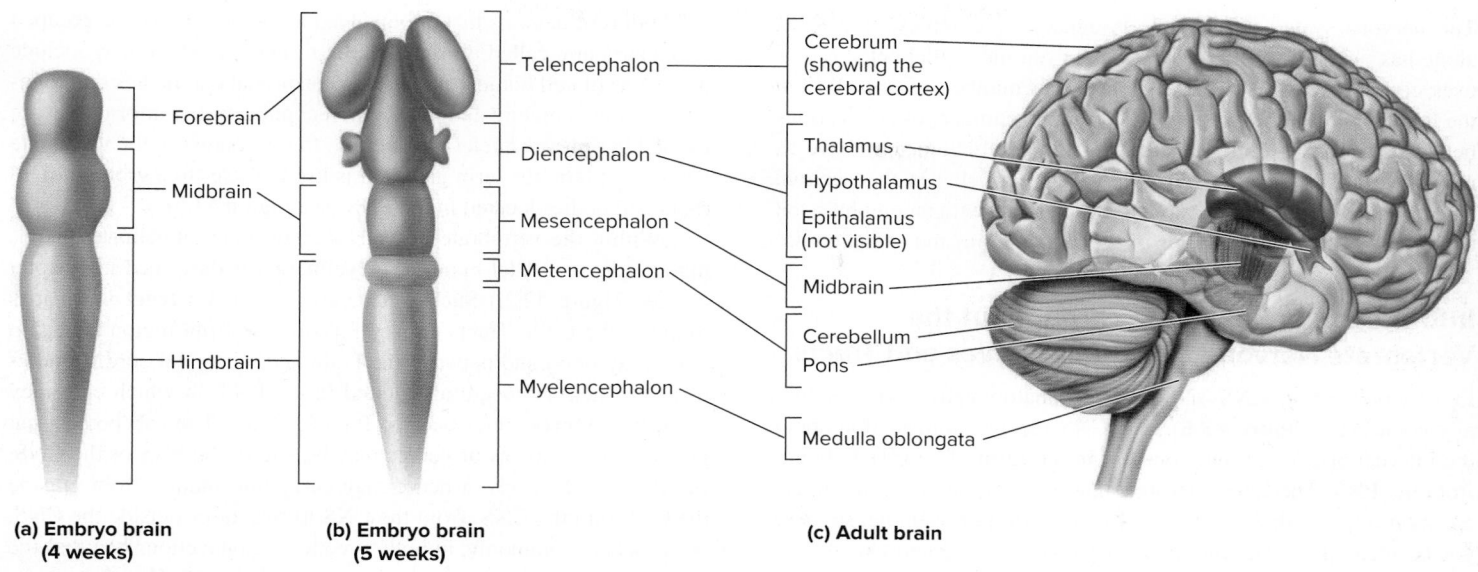

(a) **Embryo brain (4 weeks)**

(b) **Embryo brain (5 weeks)**

(c) **Adult brain**

Figure 43.2 **Development of the human brain.** Vertebrate brains begin as three major divisions, which then develop into additional subdivisions. The structures shown here that occur during embryonic development at **(a)** 4 weeks and **(b)** 5 weeks are compared with **(c)** their appearance in the adult brain. Some forebrain structures beneath the cerebrum are not shown. The functions of all of these structures will be described in Section 43.2.

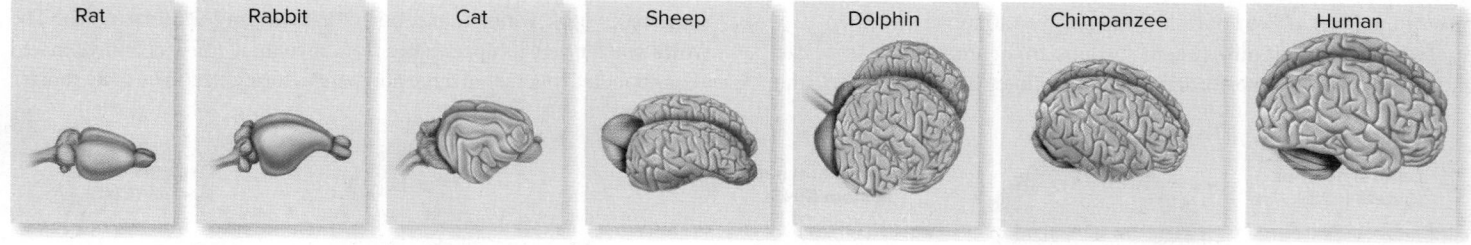

Figure 43.3 **The degree of cerebral cortex folding in different mammalian species.** The brains are not shown to scale.

👁 **Core Concept: Structure and Function** The greater amount of folding of the cerebral cortex of certain mammals increases the surface area of this part of the brain, allowing for more neuronal connections and thus more complex behaviors.

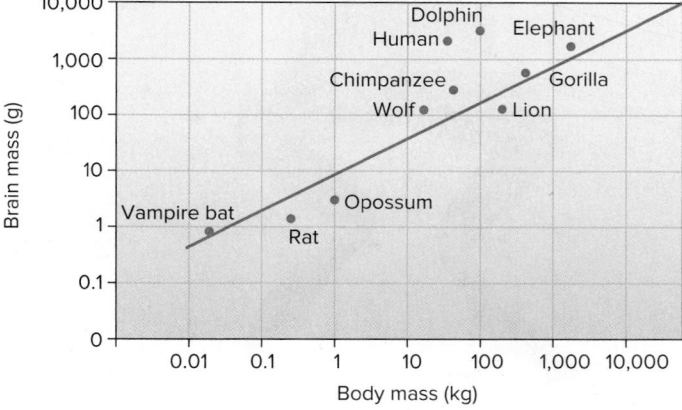

Figure 43.4 **Brain mass as a function of body mass in mammals.** For most mammals, brain mass is in proportion to body mass. However, humans and dolphins have a much greater brain mass relative to their body mass than do other mammals.

Concept Check: *Scientists have determined that the brain mass of Homo neanderthalensis (Neanderthals) was greater than that of our own. Does this mean that Neanderthals were more intelligent and capable of more complex behaviors than we are?*

in intelligence. Also, it would be wrong to assume that an animal with a small brain is profoundly limited in its behavioral repertoire. A bat with a 0.9-g brain and an elephant with a 2,500-g brain can both perform a great variety of interesting and complex behaviors, such as navigating across great distances and interacting with fellow members of their species.

43.2 Structure and Function of the Nervous Systems of Humans and Other Vertebrates

Learning Outcomes:

1. Outline the anatomical organization of the human nervous system.
2. Describe the organization of the peripheral nervous system.
3. Identify the differences between the somatic and autonomic nervous systems.
4. Briefly describe the major structures and functions of the human hindbrain, midbrain, and forebrain.

The nervous system of humans is amazingly complex—the brain alone has over 100 billion neurons and even more glial cells. Moreover, complexity is defined by more than just numbers of cells. Within the human brain, for example, are enormous numbers of connections between neurons—a single neuron in the cerebellum may have as many as 100,000 or more synapses with other cells! In this section, we will examine the vertebrate nervous system, with an emphasis on the functions of the major parts of the human brain and spinal cord.

Information Is Conveyed Throughout the Vertebrate Nervous System by Nerves and Tracts

In vertebrates, the CNS and PNS are anatomically and functionally connected (**Figure 43.5**). The CNS receives information about the internal or external environment in the form of neuronal signals from the PNS. The CNS interprets that information and may initiate a response that is then carried out by the PNS. For example, suppose you accidentally lean against a newly painted fence. Neuronal endings in your skin, which are part of the PNS, would transmit tactile (touch) information through axons that bring information directly into the spinal cord. From there, the information travels to your brain, where the sensation is analyzed and identified as something sticky. Signals are sent from your brain, down your spinal cord, and through the neurons of the PNS to your muscles, causing you to move away.

Within the nervous system, groups of neurons may associate with each other and perform a particular function. In the CNS, the cell bodies of neurons that are involved in a function may be grouped into a structure called a **nucleus** (plural, nuclei), which may include thousands of cell bodies. For instance, neuronal cell bodies that regulate body temperature and those that recognize visual information are located in separate nuclei in the brain. In the context of the vertebrate nervous system, the term ganglion is used to refer to a group of neuronal cell bodies located in the PNS (see Figure 43.5).

Within the vertebrate nervous system, many myelinated axons may occur in parallel bundles. (Myelination is described in Chapter 42; see Figure 42.2.) Such a structure is called a **tract** when it is found in the CNS. Tracts convey information from region to region within the brain and between the brain and the spinal cord. Bundles of myelinated axons are also found in the PNS, in which case they are called **nerves** (refer back to Figure 42.2d). The cell bodies that give rise to the axons of nerves may be within the PNS or the CNS. In other words, a given nerve may carry information from outside the CNS into the CNS, from the CNS to structures outside the CNS, or, as occurs commonly, in both directions. Connections between the PNS and the CNS occur at the brain or spinal cord. **Cranial nerves** are directly connected to the brain, primarily to sites within the hindbrain and midbrain. By comparison, **spinal nerves** are connections between the PNS and spinal cord (see Figure 43.5).

One of the most obvious characteristics of the CNS is that some parts look whitish, and others appear gray (**Figure 43.6**). The **white matter** gets its appearance from myelin; it consists of myelinated axons bundled together in large numbers to form tracts. The **gray matter**

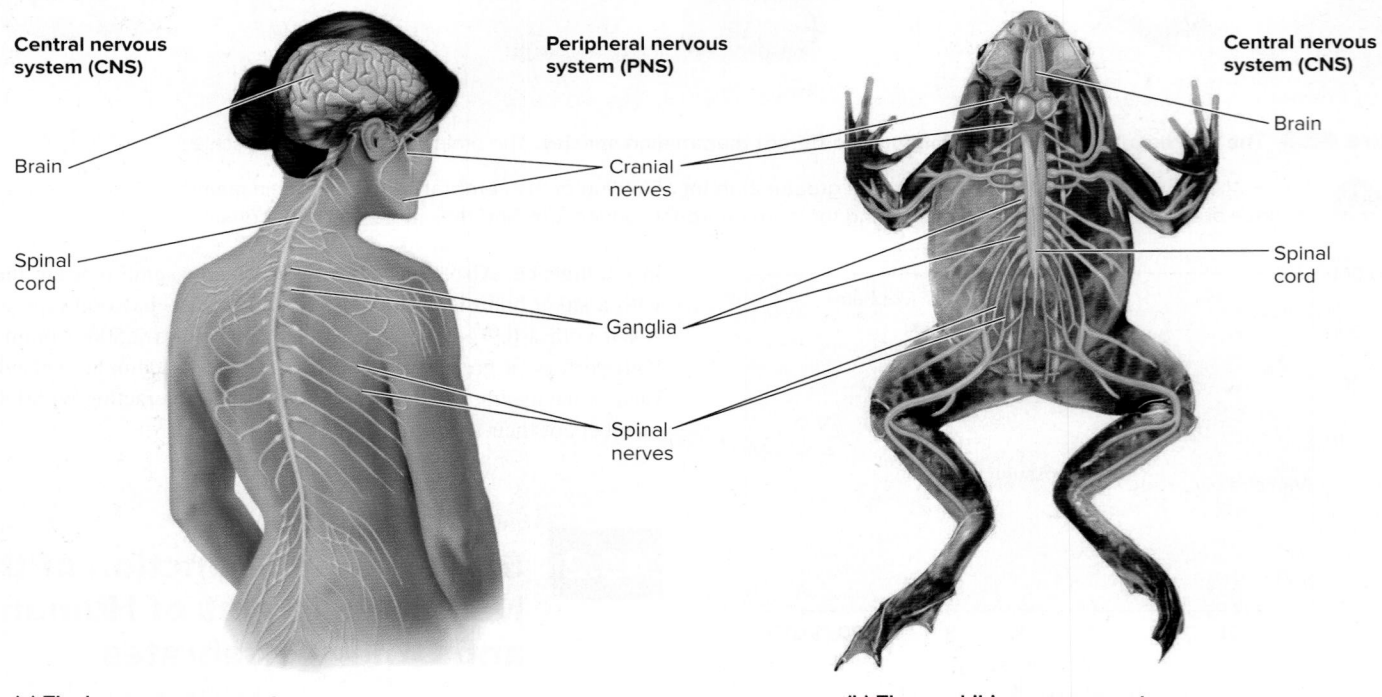

(a) The human nervous system

(b) The amphibian nervous system

Figure 43.5 Organization of the vertebrate nervous system. The CNS consists of the brain and spinal cord, both of which are encased in bone (not shown). The PNS includes cranial nerves, ganglia, and spinal nerves, which carry information to and from the CNS, and many other neurons throughout the body. Note the similarities between two widely divergent vertebrates, **(a)** humans and **(b)** frogs.

 Core Concept: Evolution The similarities between the nervous systems of these two very different-looking animals point to a common ancestor.

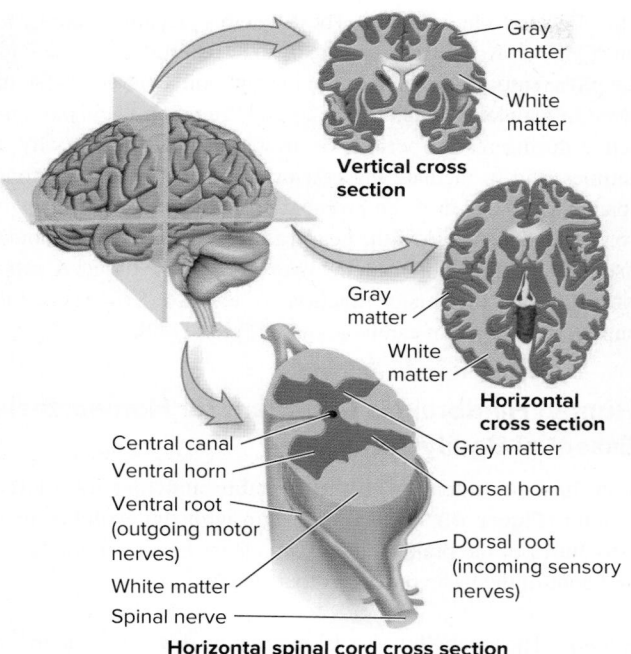

(a) Gray and white matter in the brain and spinal cord

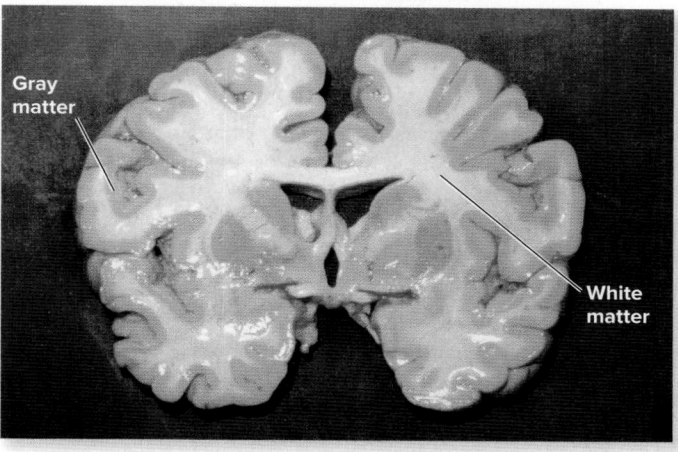

(b) Photograph of a vertical cross section of the human brain

Figure 43.6   Gray matter and white matter in the CNS. (a) The gray matter is composed of cell bodies, dendrites, and unmyelinated axons. The white matter consists of tracts of myelinated axons. **(b)** Photograph of a vertical cross section through an adult human brain. In these images, gray matter is darkened for better visibility. b: ©Biophoto Associates/Science Source

Concept Check: *Is a spinal nerve composed of axons of afferent or efferent neurons, or both?*

is darker in appearance and consists of neuronal cell bodies, dendrites, and some unmyelinated axons. The cerebral cortex is composed of gray matter that sits on top of a large collection of white matter pathways. In the spinal cord, the gray matter is located in the center and forms two dorsal extensions, or horns, and two ventral horns (Figure 43.6a). Each dorsal horn connects to a dorsal root, which is part of a spinal nerve. Dorsal roots receive incoming information from sensory (afferent) nerves of the PNS. The ventral horn connects to the ventral root, which is also part of a spinal nerve that transmits outgoing information to motor (efferent) nerves. A central canal runs through the spinal cord, carrying a nutritive and protective fluid, as described shortly.

The CNS Is Encased in Protective Structures

Unlike the PNS, the CNS is encased in protective structures including bone (the skull and vertebrae) and three layers of sheathlike membranes called **meninges** (**Figure 43.7**). The outermost membrane, the dura mater (from the Latin, meaning hard mother), is a thick protective layer that lies just inside the skull and vertebrae. The middle membrane is called the arachnoid mater (from the Latin, meaning spidery mother) because it has numerous weblike tissue connections to the innermost membrane, the pia mater (from the Latin, meaning thin mother). The pia mater is a very thin membrane that lies on the surface of the brain and spinal cord, folding with the brain's surface.

Between the arachnoid mater and pia mater is the subarachnoid space. This space is filled with **cerebrospinal fluid**, which surrounds the exterior of the brain and spinal cord and absorbs physical shocks to the brain that result from sudden movements or blows to the head. The cerebrospinal fluid contains nutrients, hormones, and other substances that are taken up by cells of the brain. The fluid is also a reservoir for metabolic waste products that are then carried away by the circulatory system. In addition to the subarachnoid space, the cerebrospinal fluid

also fills a series of connected cavities called the ventricles that lie deep within the brain and connect to the central canal that extends the length of the spinal cord (see Figure 43.6). These fluid-filled structures provide a cushion of support and protection for the CNS.

The PNS Consists of the Somatic and Autonomic Nervous Systems

The PNS of vertebrates is subdivided into two major functional and anatomical components: the somatic nervous system and the autonomic nervous system. Both divisions have sensory (afferent) nerves and motor (efferent) nerves.

Somatic Nervous System   The major functions of the **somatic nervous system** are to sense the external environment and control skeletal muscles. The afferent sensory neurons of the somatic nervous system receive stimuli, such as heat, light, odors, chemicals (in food), sounds, and touch, and transmit signals to the CNS. The efferent motor neurons of the somatic nervous system control skeletal muscles. The cell bodies of these motor neurons are located within the CNS. The axons from these cells leave the spinal cord and project directly onto skeletal muscle without any intermediary synapses along the way.

Many of the responses of the somatic nervous system can be controlled consciously. For example, we use our somatic nervous system to walk and hold a pencil. However, not all responses are voluntary. An example is a reflex arc, such as the knee-jerk response, which is automatic (refer back to Figure 42.4).

Autonomic Nervous System   The **autonomic nervous system** regulates homeostasis and organ function. For example, it is involved in regulating heart rate, blood pressure, glucose homeostasis, and the

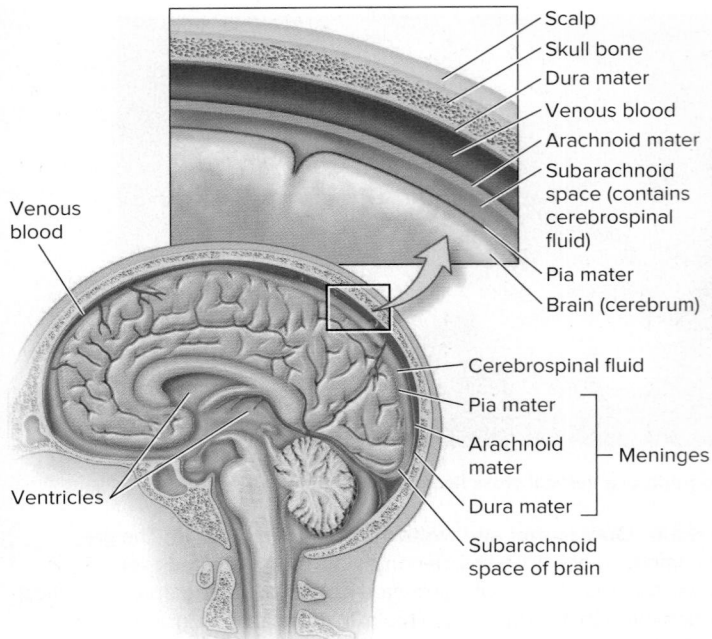

Figure 43.7 The meninges and ventricles of the CNS. The thicknesses of the meninges are exaggerated for illustrative purposes. Note that the cerebrospinal fluid encases the entire CNS and also fills the ventricles.

Concept Check: *In a procedure known as a lumbar puncture (commonly referred to as a spinal tap), physicians use a needle to withdraw a small amount of cerebrospinal fluid from the bottom of the spine to help diagnose specific illnesses. Considering that this fluid encases the brain, what effects might this procedure have on a patient?*

amount of stomach acid secreted in response to a meal. The autonomic nervous system is predominantly composed of efferent motor neurons. For the most part, the autonomic nervous system is not subject to voluntary control. For example, we usually cannot consciously change our heart rate or blood pressure.

The efferent pathways of the autonomic nervous system involve sets of two motor neurons. The cell body of the first neuron is within the CNS and synapses on a second neuron in ganglia outside the spinal cord; these ganglia, therefore, are part of the PNS. This second neuron sends its axon to an effector cell, where it alters that cell's function. These neurons control smooth muscles, cardiac muscle, and glands.

The efferent nerves of the autonomic nervous system are subdivided into the sympathetic and parasympathetic divisions (**Figure 43.8**). Both divisions of the autonomic system act on the same organs and usually have opposing actions. The **sympathetic division** is responsible for rapidly activating systems that prepare the body for danger or stress. Imagine, for example, the physiological responses that would occur if a person was hiking and came upon a grizzly bear. They are collectively called the **fight-or-flight response**, which is characterized by increased heart rate, stronger pumping action of the heart, relaxed (dilated) airways and faster breathing, inhibition of digestive activity, increased blood flow to skeletal muscles, and increased secretion into the blood of energy-supplying substances such as glucose and

fats by the liver and adipose tissue. These features prepare an animal to confront (fight) or avoid (flight) a perceived or real threat.

The **parasympathetic division** of the autonomic nervous system is involved in maintaining and restoring body functions. It is particularly active during restful periods or after a meal, which is why it is sometimes said to mediate the **rest-or-digest response**. Neurons of the parasympathetic division promote digestion and absorption of food from the intestines, slow the heart rate, and decrease the amount of fuel supplied to the blood from the liver and adipose tissue. A summary of these and other major functions of the two divisions of the autonomic nervous system can be found in Figure 43.8.

The Human Hindbrain Is Important for Homeostasis and Essential Bodily Functions

Let's now turn our attention to the structure and function of the human brain (**Figure 43.9**). We will begin with the evolutionarily oldest structures of the brain, some of which are located in the hindbrain and control the basic processes that sustain life.

Cerebellum The **cerebellum** is a large structure that sits dorsal to the rest of the hindbrain and receives sensory inputs from the cerebral cortex and the auditory and visual areas of the brain. It also receives inputs from the spinal cord and inner ears that convey information about the position of the limbs and head, respectively, and thereby helps maintain balance and coordinate hand-eye movements. In addition, the cerebellum helps control the use of multiple muscles at one time and synchronizes fine motor activities such as texting, making a jump shot in basketball, or touching the fingers to the tip of the nose with your eyes closed. When the cerebellum is damaged or injured, such as in an accident, a person finds it difficult to maintain balance and fine-tune motor functions. Although historically scientists have thought that the cerebellum does not function in learning, memory, and conscious thought, recent evidence has strongly suggested that the cerebellum may provide significant cognitive functions, the full extent of which remains to be discovered.

Pons The **pons** sits anterior to the medulla oblongata and ventral to the cerebellum. Major tracts involved in motor function pass through the pons into and out of the cerebellum, so the pons serves as a relay between the cerebellum and other areas of the brain. In addition to this integrative motor function, the pons contains nuclei that have a very important role in regulating the rate and depth of breathing. The pons is also the origin of some cranial nerves.

Medulla Oblongata The **medulla oblongata** is located between the pons and the anterior part of the spinal cord. It coordinates many processes that maintain homeostasis. It is involved in the control of heart rate, breathing, blood pressure, digestion, swallowing, and vomiting, and it is the origin of several cranial nerves.

The Human Midbrain Processes Sensory Inputs and Maintains Alertness

The midbrain lies anterior to the pons. It processes several types of sensory inputs, including vision, olfaction, and audition. It has tracts that pass this information to other parts of the brain for further processing

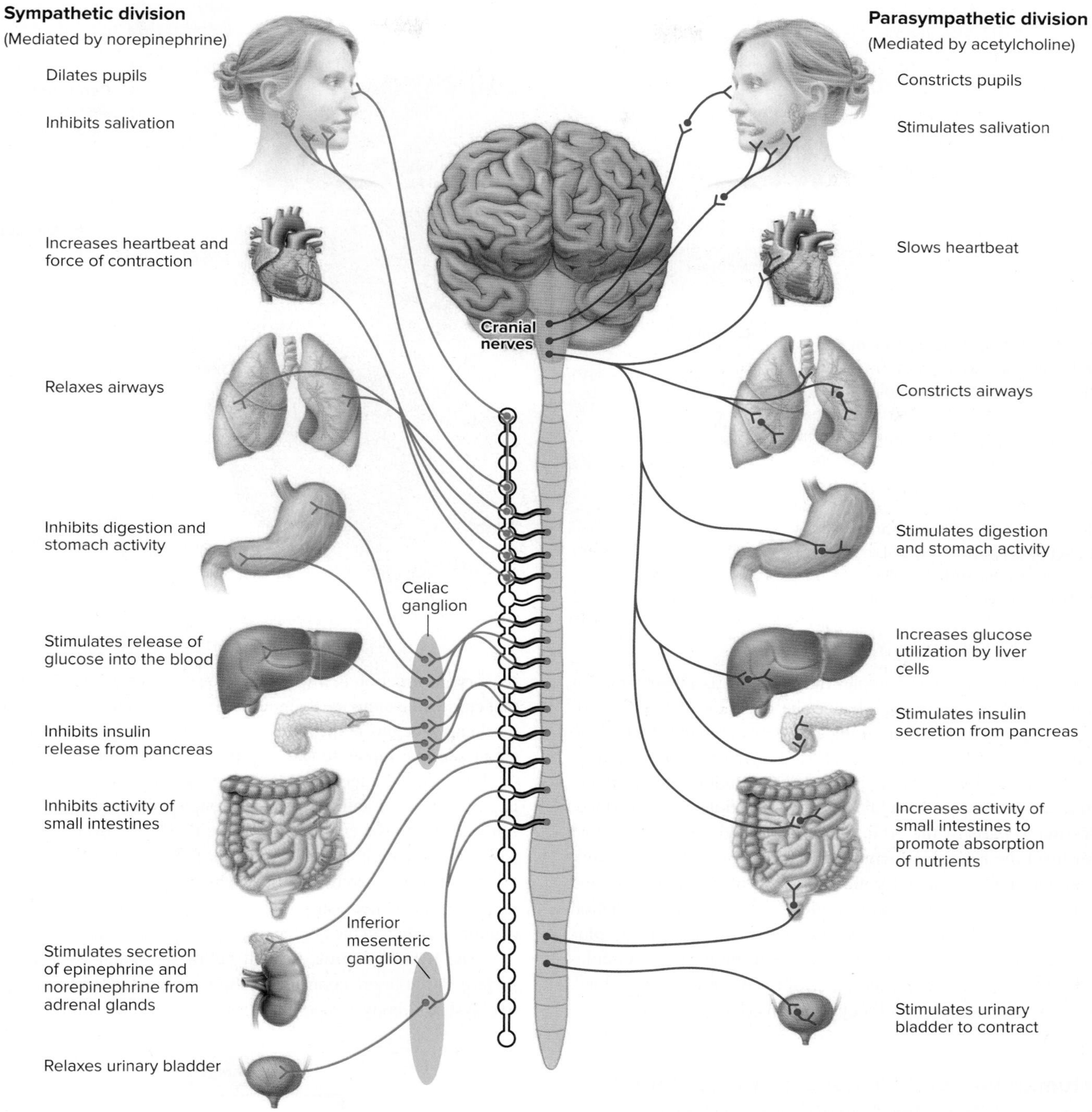

Sympathetic division
(Mediated by norepinephrine)

Dilates pupils

Inhibits salivation

Increases heartbeat and force of contraction

Relaxes airways

Inhibits digestion and stomach activity

Stimulates release of glucose into the blood

Inhibits insulin release from pancreas

Inhibits activity of small intestines

Stimulates secretion of epinephrine and norepinephrine from adrenal glands

Relaxes urinary bladder

Parasympathetic division
(Mediated by acetylcholine)

Constricts pupils

Stimulates salivation

Slows heartbeat

Constricts airways

Stimulates digestion and stomach activity

Increases glucose utilization by liver cells

Stimulates insulin secretion from pancreas

Increases activity of small intestines to promote absorption of nutrients

Stimulates urinary bladder to contract

Cranial nerves

Celiac ganglion

Inferior mesenteric ganglion

Figure 43.8 Sympathetic and parasympathetic divisions of the autonomic nervous system. For simplicity, only some of the major functions of each division are shown in this figure. The sympathetic and parasympathetic systems tend to have opposite effects, and most parts of the body receive inputs from both divisions. Nerves from the sympathetic division make connections with a chain of ganglia, most, but not all, of which are alongside the spinal cord. Nerves from the parasympathetic division make connections in ganglia near or in their targets.

 Core Concept: Systems The autonomic nervous system is important for maintaining homeostasis. Many organ systems in the body are controlled in opposite ways by the two divisions of this branch of the nervous system. Therefore, the functions of these structures can be modulated in two directions. For example, heart rate can be accelerated or slowed to match an animal's immediate metabolic requirements.

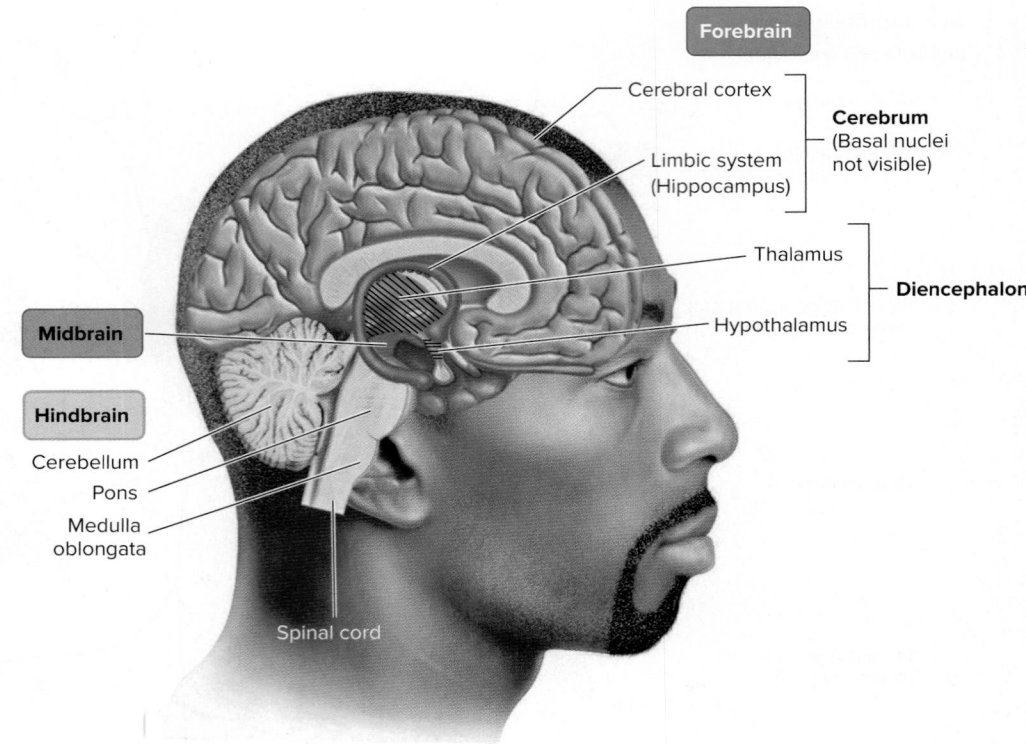

Figure 43.9 Major structures of the human brain. An overview of the brain, showing several internal structures (the basal nuclei and some other structures are not visible in this plane). The limbic system consists of the olfactory bulbs, amygdala, and hippocampus, all of which are part of the cerebrum (some neuroscientists consider parts of the thalamus and hypothalamus as part of the limbic system). The midbrain, pons, and medulla oblongata collectively comprise the brainstem.

and interpretation. As one example, the midbrain is responsible for activating neural pathways that change the diameter of the pupil of the eye in response to a change in the amount of ambient light. If the midbrain is damaged, this pupillary reflex is impaired or destroyed.

The medulla oblongata, the pons, and the midbrain collectively constitute the **brainstem**. In addition to the functions just described, all three major parts of the brainstem contain additional nuclei that together form the **reticular formation**. This interconnected network of nuclei and tracts extends throughout much of the brainstem and sends signals to many other brain regions. The reticular formation maintains and controls consciousness, alertness, and sleep, plus essential functions such as regulation of the respiratory and circulatory systems. Because of the importance of the brainstem's functions, damage to it is catastrophic and may result in coma or death.

The Human Forebrain Is Responsible for Motor, Sensory, and Complex Cognitive Functions

The human forebrain comprises the diencephalon and cerebrum (also known as the telencephalon) (**Figure 43.10**). The diencephalon is made up of the thalamus, hypothalamus, and epithalamus. The cerebrum consists of the cerebral cortex, basal nuclei, and limbic system.

Diencephalon (Thalamus, Hypothalamus, and Epithalamus) In all vertebrates including humans, the **thalamus** functions in relaying sensory information to appropriate parts of the cerebrum and, in turn, directing outputs from the cerebrum to other parts of the brain. It receives input from all sensory systems except olfaction. One type of processing performed by neurons in the thalamus is filtering out

sensory information in a way that allows us to pay attention to important cues while temporarily ignoring less important ones. This filtering mechanism begins in the reticular formation, which relays information about sensory inputs to the thalamus. Together, these brain regions permit selective attention to certain stimuli. A good example of this is a new parent's ability to sleep through a thunderstorm but awaken immediately to the cry of a baby. The thalamus also directs feedback about motor activities that it receives from the cerebellum and other structures to the cerebral cortex, which can then adjust its outgoing motor signals if necessary. Last, the thalamus is involved in the perception of pain and the degree of mental arousal in the cerebral cortex.

The **hypothalamus**, located below the thalamus at the ventral surface of the brain, controls functions of the digestive and reproductive systems, body temperature (thermoregulation), and many basic

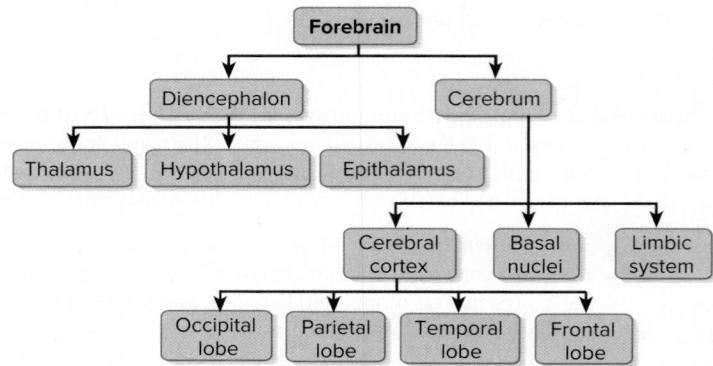

Figure 43.10 Relationships among structures that make up the human forebrain.

behaviors such as eating and drinking. This area has great importance for homeostasis and the control of behavior. Though small in size, it is composed of many nuclei, each with its own vital functions. Certain of these nuclei produce and release hormones, which travel through blood vessels to the pituitary gland located just beneath the brain. The pituitary gland, in turn, regulates hormone secretion from other glands in the body, including the thyroid, gonads, and adrenal glands. In this way, the hypothalamus acts as a link between the nervous and endocrine systems. In addition to producing hormones, the hypothalamus is sensitive to the actions of other hormones. For example, certain hormones produced by cells in the stomach, intestine, adipose tissue, gonads, and elsewhere act within the hypothalamus to facilitate feeding, drinking, sexual, and aggressive behaviors. Finally, a small pair of hypothalamic nuclei called the suprachiasmatic nuclei act as the master clock of the CNS, establishing circadian rhythms, which control behavioral, physiological, and hormonal rhythms over the 24-hour day.

The **epithalamus** is a collection of structures that have varied functions in the control of food and water intake, the integration of olfactory and visceral inputs with emotion and memory centers of the brain, and in some vertebrates, rhythmic and seasonal behaviors. One of these structures, the pineal gland, is located in the center of the brain and secretes a hormone called melatonin into the blood. Production of melatonin is regulated by the length of the light period in each day. Although still debated, melatonin has been suggested to function in daily cycles such as our sleep/wake cycle.

Cerebrum: Hemispheres   As mentioned earlier in this section, the cerebrum consists of the cerebral cortex, basal nuclei, and limbic system. One of the most recognizable features of the cerebrum, however, is its division into two halves, or **hemispheres**. Each hemisphere is connected to the other by a major tract called the **corpus callosum** (**Figure 43.11a**). In the 1950s, American neuroscientists Roger Sperry and Ronald Meyers examined the separate functions of the hemispheres in laboratory animals by performing split-brain surgeries in which they severed the corpus callosum. The animals that underwent such surgery maintained their overall health and functioning. Therefore, the surgery was thought to be safe for humans. In 1961, split-brain surgery was used for the first time to treat patients with severe epilepsy, a disorder characterized by uncontrolled electrical activity (seizures) that begins in one hemisphere and can spread via the corpus callosum to the other side. Cutting the connection between the hemispheres decreased the severity of epileptic seizures by reducing their spread.

Split-brain surgery also provided an opportunity for the researchers to make critical observations about the importance of communication between the two hemispheres. Patients who had undergone such surgery generally show normal behavior and intellectual function, because both hemispheres can function fairly independently. However, psychological tests revealed that the two sides of the brain also process different types of information. One study demonstrated that the left hemisphere produces a descriptive word for an object but does not identify certain characteristics of that object, such as its shape and texture (**Figure 43.11b**). The right hemisphere, in contrast, cannot use words to name the object but can identify other qualities. Sperry, Meyers, and other neuroscientists have concluded that the left hemisphere is involved in understanding language and producing speech in most people. Therefore, the left hemisphere is said to be

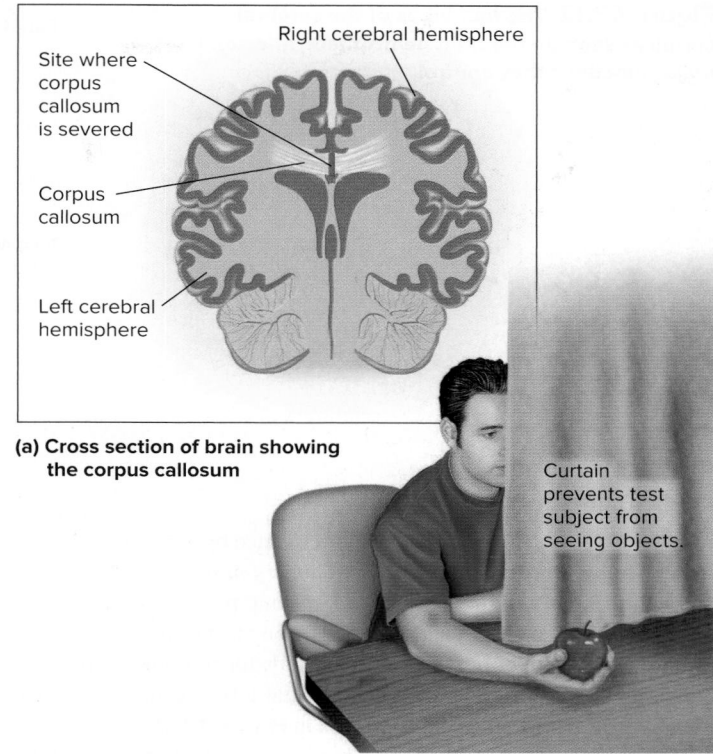

(a) Cross section of brain showing the corpus callosum

(b) Testing of split-brain patient

Figure 43.11 The hemispheres of the human brain. (a) The cerebral hemispheres and their connection by the corpus callosum. (Note: The left hemisphere controls the right side of the body, and the right hemisphere controls the left side.) **(b)** Split-brain patient being tested for hemispheric dominance. By using this apparatus, Roger Sperry and his collaborators showed that the left and right cerebral hemispheres have different capabilities. When a split-brain patient held an object in his right hand but could not see it or touch it with his left hand, he could give it a name (for example, "an apple"). When he held another object in his left hand, he could describe it (for example, "smooth"), but could not name it.

Concept Check: *With her eyes closed, a split-brain patient was given a rock to hold, and she described it as a rock. Which hand was it in?*

dominant for those functions. The right hemisphere is dominant for nonverbal memories, recognizing faces, and interpreting emotions. In 1981, Sperry received the Nobel Prize in Physiology or Medicine for his insight regarding specialization in each hemisphere of the brain.

Cerebrum: Cerebral Cortex   As mentioned earlier, the cerebral cortex is the surface layer of gray matter that covers the cerebrum (see the darkly shaded outer rim of the brain hemispheres in Figure 43.11a). Within the cortex are identifiable regions with neurons that function in sensory, motor, or other functions. Although the cerebral cortex is only a few millimeters thick, it contains about 10% of all the neurons in the human brain.

The cerebral cortex is broadly divided into four lobes in each hemisphere of the brain: the frontal, parietal, occipital, and temporal lobes named for the bones that overlie those regions during embryonic development (**Figure 43.12**). Each lobe has a number of functions,

Figure 43.12 **The four lobes of the cerebral cortex as seen on the right hemisphere, and some major functions they control.**

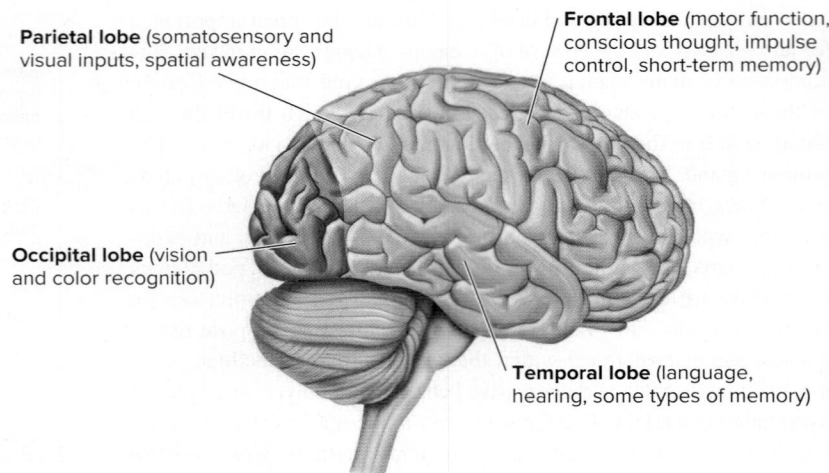

Parietal lobe (somatosensory and visual inputs, spatial awareness)

Frontal lobe (motor function, conscious thought, impulse control, short-term memory)

Occipital lobe (vision and color recognition)

Temporal lobe (language, hearing, some types of memory)

many of which are still being actively investigated by researchers. Nuclei in the **frontal lobe** are important for voluntary initiation of movement, decision making, controlling impulses, making plans, exhibiting judgment, short-term memory, and conscious thought and social awareness. The primary motor cortex, where commands for movement originate, is located at the posterior part of the frontal lobes running in a band roughly from ear to ear (see the red area in **Figure 43.13**).

Slightly posterior to the motor cortex and at the beginning of the **parietal lobe** is the region known as the somatosensory cortex (blue region in Figure 43.13). The somatosensory cortex and parietal lobe receive and interpret sensory input from somatic pathways, including touch from the surface of the body. In addition, the parietal lobe has an important role in spatial awareness, that is, our ability to use visual cues to orient ourselves in space.

The **occipital lobe** controls many aspects of visual perception and color recognition. The **temporal lobe** is necessary for language, hearing, and some types of memory.

An amazing finding is that sensory inputs enter and motor outputs exit the cerebral cortex in a pattern that forms a map of the body (see Figure 43.13). The regions of the body are represented in proportion to the amount of cortical area devoted to them. For instance, a larger part of the cerebral cortex is devoted to sensory inputs from the lips than from other areas of the face. The lips have more neuron endings and are more sensitive to touch than these other areas. Other cortical functions are also mapped in this way. For example, a map that reflects different sound frequencies (the pitch of sound) exists in the temporal lobes. The organization of the cerebral cortex may not be permanent, however, because the map may change depending on the amount of use or disuse of a given part of the body, as discussed in the Feature Investigation later in this chapter.

Cerebrum: The Basal Nuclei   The **basal nuclei** (or, as they have been historically but inaccurately referred to, basal ganglia) are a group of nuclei that surround the thalamus and lie beneath the cerebral cortex. Like the cerebellum, the basal nuclei are involved in planning, learning, and fine-tuning movements. They also function via a complex circuitry to initiate or inhibit movements.

Parkinson's disease is a relatively common neurological disorder that affects the basal nuclei. People with Parkinson's disease have

trouble initiating movement, such as beginning to move their legs when they wish to walk. They are capable of walking once movement has begun, but they move slowly with muscle tremors and a shuffling, jerky gait. These symptoms result from the gradual deterioration of dopamine-releasing neurons in an area of the midbrain called the substantia nigra, the neurons of which send axons to the basal nuclei. People in the early stages of Parkinson's disease can be treated with L-dopa, a substance that enters the blood and travels to the basal nuclei. There, axon terminals from remaining healthy cells originating in the substantia nigra take up the L-dopa and convert it into dopamine, which is then released onto cells of the basal nuclei. L-Dopa, therefore, increases the amount of dopamine in the basal nuclei and reduces the symptoms of Parkinson's disease.

Cerebrum: The Limbic System   The **limbic system** refers to a collection of evolutionarily older structures that form an inner layer at the base of the forebrain. These include structures such as the **olfactory bulbs** (which process information about smells), **amygdala**, and **hippocampus**. Some neuroscientists also consider parts of the diencephalon as part of the limbic system, because of the extensive connections between these regions. The limbic system is primarily involved in the formation and expression of emotions, and it plays an important role in learning, long-term memory, and the perception and recognition of smells. In humans, the expression of emotions occurs early in childhood before the more advanced functions of the cerebral cortex are evident. Thus, even very young babies can express fear, distress, and anger as well as bond emotionally with their parents.

Deep within the brain, the amygdala is one of the limbic system structures critical for understanding and remembering emotional situations. This structure also is involved in the ability to recognize emotional expression in others. Emotions are not unique to humans, however, and some are clearly present in other mammals. Being able to express and detect emotions imparts a selective advantage by enabling animals to establish and maintain relationships. Emotions such as fear help an animal defend itself against danger by avoiding conflict. Likewise, anger is associated with aggression, a key behavior by which many animals defend themselves or their territories.

Adjacent to the amygdala and forming a loop within the medial regions within the brain, the hippocampus is composed of several layers

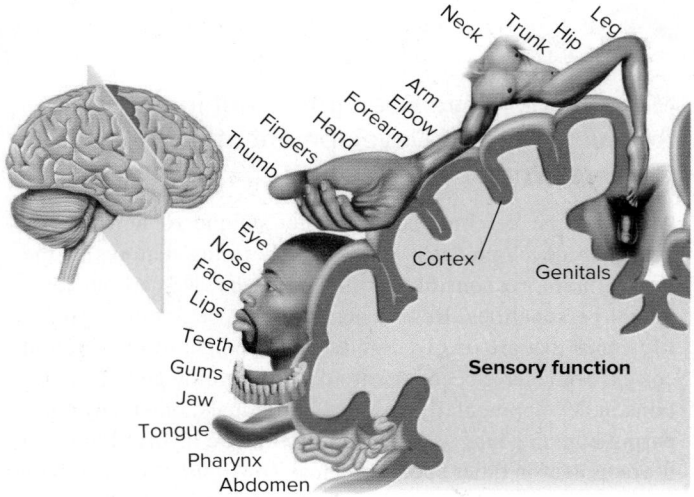

Sensory function

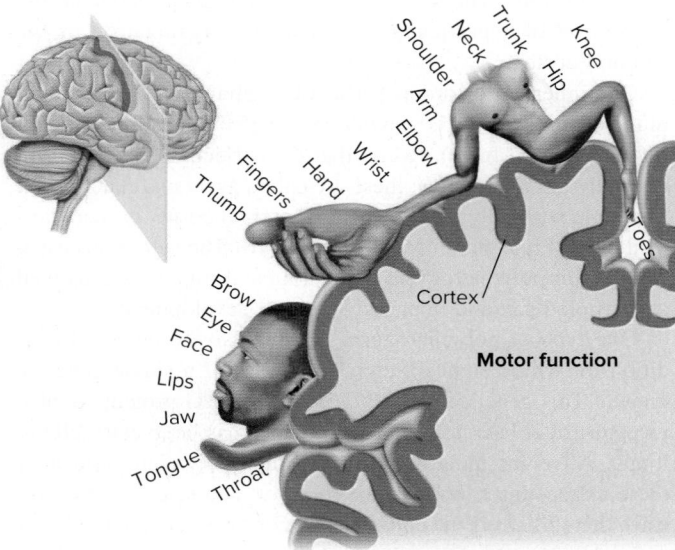

Motor function

Figure 43.13 Maps of human body parts along the cerebral cortex. These maps represent how the cortex interprets sensory information from these body parts and controls body movements of these parts (motor function). The relative sizes of body parts reflect the relative amount of cortex devoted to them. The blue region is the somatosensory cortex; the red region is the primary motor cortex.

of cells that are connected in a circuit. Its main function appears to be establishing memories for spatial locations, facts, and sequences of events. Damage to certain parts of the hippocampus in humans results in an inability to form new memories, a devastating condition that prevents recognition of other people or even an awareness of daily events.

Experiments with laboratory animals have demonstrated the importance of the hippocampus for memory and learning in other mammals. In a particularly well-studied example, rats are placed into a pool of milky water containing a hidden platform. The animals swim until they find the platform, on which they can safely stand. The time it takes to find the platform in subsequent trials is shorter as they learn and remember its whereabouts. This type of spatial

learning depends on activity in the hippocampus. Rats with parts of their hippocampus destroyed fail to improve their times with repeated trials. The hippocampus also receives extensive inputs from the olfactory bulbs, which may explain why smells are such potent triggers of memory in humans and why many animals use their sense of smell as a major way to learn and remember aspects of their environments.

Some of the major functions of the hindbrain, midbrain, and forebrain are summarized in **Table 43.1**.

Table 43.1	Major Functions of Brain Regions in Humans	
Region		**Major Functions**
Hindbrain		
	Medulla oblongata and pons	Coordinate homeostatic functions such as breathing, heart rate, digestion; form part of reticular formation that controls sleep and alertness; origins of cranial nerves
	Cerebellum	Fine-tuning of complex body movements; maintenance of balance
Midbrain		Processes visual, auditory, and olfactory sensory inputs; forms part of reticular formation
Forebrain		
Diencephalon		
	Thalamus	Routes sensory information (except olfaction) to discrete parts of cerebrum; filters irrelevant sensory information; directs outgoing motor information from cerebral cortex to spinal cord; involved in pain perception and mental arousal
	Hypothalamus	Regulates activities of gastrointestinal and reproductive systems; controls function of pituitary gland; regulates body temperature, appetite, thirst, aggressive behavior, sexual behavior, and body rhythms
	Epithalamus	Produces cerebrospinal fluid; plays a role in food and water intake; contains the pineal gland, which may regulate sleep/wake cycle and body rhythms
Cerebrum		
	Cerebral cortex	Voluntary motor control; perception of sensory inputs; attention; integration of sensory and motor information; generation of speech; decision making; impulse control; judgment; planning; conscious thought; learning; memory; and emotion
	Basal nuclei	Planning, fine-tuning, initiating, inhibiting and learning movements
	Limbic system	Formation and expression of emotions; perception of odors; learning and memory

 **Core Skill: Modeling**

BIO:**TIPS** **THE QUESTION** *Animal brains have numerous anatomical and functional structures. Many of these structures are comprised of smaller structures, which in turn contain even smaller structures. Draw a hierarchical model that describes the relationships among the larger and smaller structures of the human brain that contain the region responsible for visual perception and color recognition.*

T OPIC *What topic in biology does this question address?*
The topic is the structure of animal brains. More specifically, the question asks you to identify a hierarchy of structure in a region of the human brain.

I NFORMATION *What information do you know based on the question and your understanding of the topic?*
From the question, you know that the human brain contains numerous structures that contain smaller structures within them. The question also indicates that the region of the brain responsible for visual perception and color recognition is part of progressively larger structures. From your understanding of the topic, you may remember that the three major divisions of the brain are the forebrain, midbrain, and hindbrain, and that sensory processing (such as vision) occurs within the forebrain. You also need to recall which part of the forebrain is responsible for visual processing.

P ROBLEM-SOLVING **S** TRATEGY *Make a drawing.* Draw the major divisions of the forebrain in a hierarchy, with the forebrain at the top, and continuing down to the region responsible for visual processing. Refer to Figures 43.9 and 43.10 for help.

ANSWER *Visual processing occurs in the occipital lobe of the cerebral cortex, which is part of the cerebrum, which in turn is one of the two largest divisions of the forebrain, one of the three major divisions of the brain*

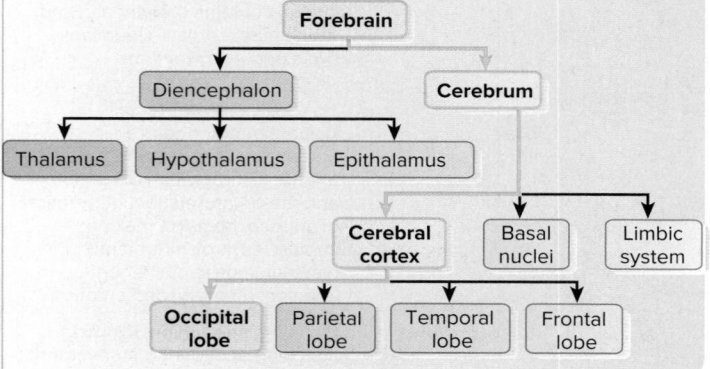

 Core Concepts: Information, Evolution

Many Genes Have Been Important in the Evolution and Development of the Cerebral Cortex

Although the cerebral cortex is not unique to humans, its extensive development is one of the defining features of the human brain, responsible for much of what we call our individual personalities. Researchers are now beginning to identify genes that are involved in the development of the cerebral cortex. Some have been identified by examining genetic mutations in developmentally disabled individuals; others, by comparing human genes with genes known to be involved in brain development in other species such as *Drosophila*. Researchers have also compared these genes in many species that show notable differences in cerebral structure. This last approach can determine whether a relationship exists between the expression of a particular gene and the organization of the cerebral cortex.

One inherited disorder that involves abnormal development of the cerebral cortex is polymicrogyria (from the Greek, meaning many small folds). Recall that the surface of the cerebrum normally has many folds; these are called gyri (singular, gyrus). In people with polymicrogyria, the cerebral cortex is characterized by multiple and unusually small gyri. The symptoms associated with polymicrogyria include mental impairment as well as disrupted gait and impaired language development.

One type of polymicrogyria is a recessively inherited condition for which eight different mutations of a single gene are known. This gene, called *GPR56*, encodes a G-protein-coupled receptor (refer back to Figure 9.7), which has large extracellular loops. All eight mutations that produce polymicrogyria alter these extracellular loops of the receptor, and scientists hypothesize that this alters the ability of the G-protein-coupled receptor to bind its ligand. Recent studies using transgenic mice have demonstrated that preventing expression of the *GPR56* gene results in decreased neurogenesis during embryonic life, whereas overexpression of the gene has the opposite effect, resulting in increased proliferation of neurons.

Several other genes, including microcephalin (*MCPH1*) (from the Greek, meaning small head) and *ASPM* (*abnormal spindle-like microcephaly-associated*), have been shown to be determinants of brain size. For example, mutations of these genes in the human population produce individuals with much smaller frontal lobes. Interestingly, the sequences of these genes in several primates, including humans, as well as in other mammals such as dogs and sheep, have shown that the proteins produced by the normal *MCPH1* and *ASPM* genes have undergone greater changes in humans and great apes than in other species. Therefore, these genes may have been under greater selection pressure in animals with larger cerebral cortexes, suggesting that the genes have played a key role in the evolution of the cerebral cortex.

43.3 Cellular Basis of Learning and Memory

Learning Outcomes:

1. Define the terms learning and memory, and describe their relationship to one another.
2. Describe how memory is related to changes in the strength of connections between neurons.
3. **CoreSKILL »** Describe the evidence that shows that the brain is capable of neurogenesis, and predict how neurogenesis might be important for human learning and memory.
4. Summarize the similarities and differences in the technologies of CT, MRI, and fMRI.

In the past few decades, an exciting advance in neuroscience has occurred—researchers have begun to understand complex behaviors, such as learning and memory, at the cellular level. Though it is difficult to separate the two concepts, **learning** can be defined as the process by which new information is acquired. Learning is an evolutionary adaptation that allows past experiences to affect ongoing and future behavior. **Memory** is the ability to retain, retrieve, and use information that was previously learned. Memory connects an animal's experiences throughout life. Our own behavior is largely controlled by what we have learned and remember from past experiences. Neuroscientists want to understand how the brain learns and how it captures memories. In this section, we will examine some current ideas about how this may be achieved at the cellular level and consider experimental approaches that researchers employ when investigating such complicated phenomena.

Learning and Memory Occur via Changes Within Neurons and in Their Connections with Each Other

Beginning in the 1960s, research along two fronts led to key insights regarding the cellular basis of memory. Norwegian neuroscientist Terje Lømo and British researcher Timothy Bliss focused their efforts on the hippocampus. As described earlier, this is a key region of the brain involved with learning and memory. Lømo and Bliss conducted experiments on anesthetized rabbits to monitor signal transmission across particular regions of the hippocampus. Their key discovery involved the effects of multiple stimuli. Experimentally, a series of short, electrical stimulations to a neuron was shown to strengthen, or potentiate, its communication at a synapse with an adjacent cell for minutes or hours. Such multiple stimuli caused neurons to communicate more readily; responses were stronger and more prolonged. This phenomenon was termed **long-term potentiation (LTP)**. LTP is the long-lasting strengthening of the connection between neurons. Later work showed that LTP occurs naturally in the hippocampus and can last from hours to days, and even years.

Austrian-born American neuroscientist Eric Kandel also was interested in learning and the formation of memory. In the 1960s, however, he took a different approach by studying a simpler organism called the California sea slug, or sea hare (*Aplysia californica*). He chose this organism for several key reasons. First, it has only about 20,000 neurons, making it easier to identify pathways that are involved in specific types of behavior. Second, some of the neurons in this organism are extremely large, which facilitated the study of action potentials via microelectrodes. In addition, the large size of the neurons made it technically simpler to inject

substances into them and study their effects. Finally, another advantage is that Kandel and colleagues could isolate proteins and mRNA from these large neurons and identify the biochemical and genetic changes that occur when the animal responds to a stimulus.

Much of Kandel's work focused on one type of learning affecting the gill-withdrawal reflex, a simple protective reflex that is thought to involve less than 100 neurons in the CNS. The gill and siphon are organs involved in respiration, located in the animal's mantle cavity and protected by muscular appendages called parapodia (**Figure 43.14a**). When the siphon is gently touched with a fine probe, the sea slug closes the siphon and retracts its gills into the mantle cavity for protection (**Figure 43.14b**). Though a reflex, this behavior is subject to learning. For example, if the touching of the siphon is accompanied with a brief electrical shock to the tail, the sea slug can learn to withdraw its gill in response to a subsequent shock without the siphon being touched. Kandel's study of the sea slug is similar in some ways to the famous conditioning experiments of Ivan Pavlov. Interestingly, a single tail shock paired with a touch of the siphon will result in conditioning that lasts for a few minutes. Amazingly, though, multiple

(a) Sea slug

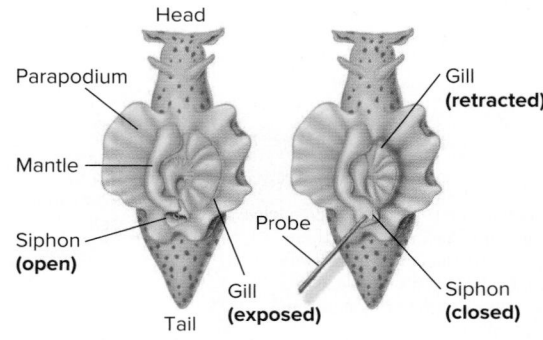

(b) Gill-withdrawal reflex

Figure 43.14   The gill-withdrawal reflex in the sea slug. (a) Photo of *Aplysia punctata* (closely related to *A. californica*) in its natural habitat; note the parapodium and tail. (b) When touched with a probe, the siphon closes and the gill retracts. In this drawing, the parapodia are moved apart for a better view of the gill. a: ©Premaphotos/Alamy Stock Photo

 Core Skill: Process of Science The use of animals such as *Aplysia* as model organisms has revealed numerous fundamentally important properties that evolved in the nervous systems of all animals. Despite the obvious differences in complexity between a sea slug and a human, much of what is learned in these relatively simple animal models is fully applicable to the function of human neurons and the nervous system.

trials over several days result in a lasting memory—a shock given 3 weeks later (without siphon touch) still results in the gill-withdrawal reflex!

Over the course of many years, the work of Kandel and colleagues revealed many clues regarding the cellular basis of learning and memory. As in vertebrates, memory in the sea slug occurs in two forms: short-term memory and long-term memory (**Figure 43.15**). Short-term

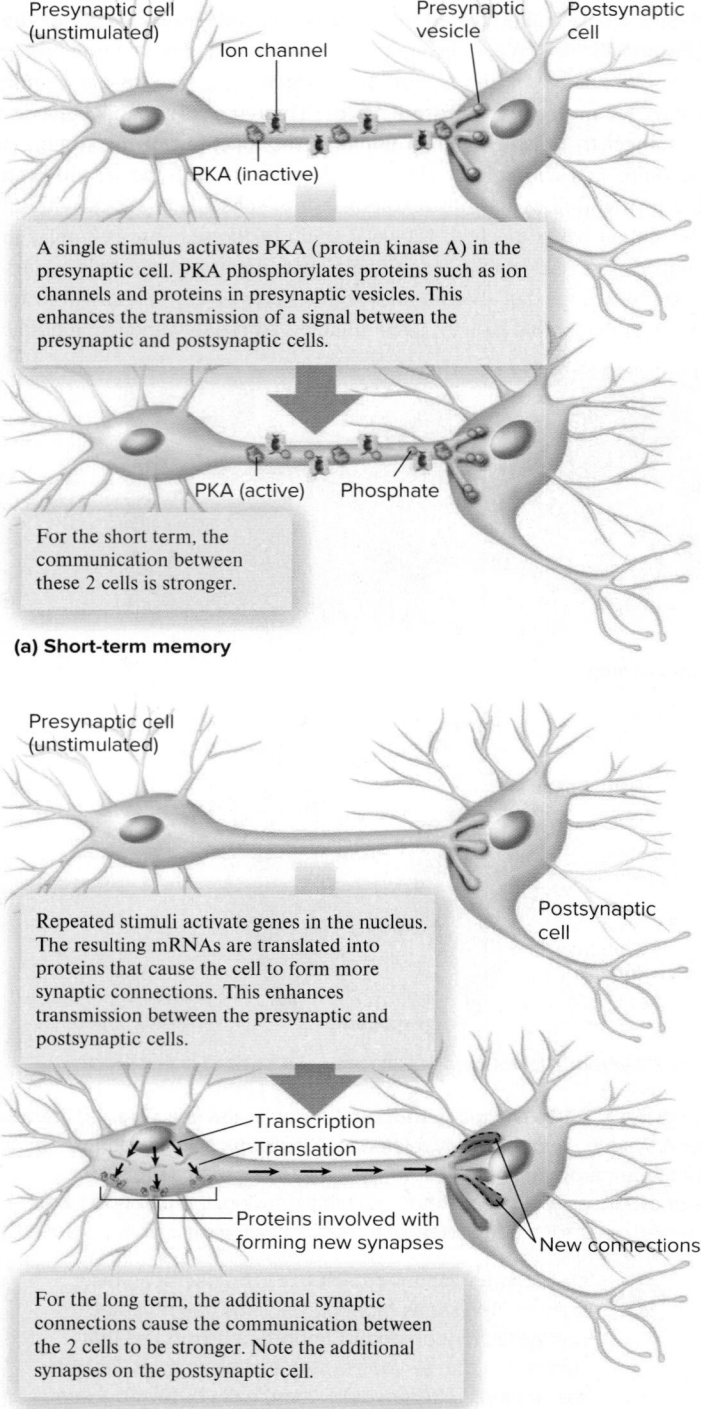

(a) **Short-term memory**

A single stimulus activates PKA (protein kinase A) in the presynaptic cell. PKA phosphorylates proteins such as ion channels and proteins in presynaptic vesicles. This enhances the transmission of a signal between the presynaptic and postsynaptic cells.

For the short term, the communication between these 2 cells is stronger.

Repeated stimuli activate genes in the nucleus. The resulting mRNAs are translated into proteins that cause the cell to form more synaptic connections. This enhances transmission between the presynaptic and postsynaptic cells.

For the long term, the additional synaptic connections cause the communication between the 2 cells to be stronger. Note the additional synapses on the postsynaptic cell.

(b) **Long-term memory**

Figure 43.15 Cellular changes associated with short-term and long-term memory in the sea slug.

memory lasts for minutes or hours. This type of memory is typically caused by a single stimulus. Kandel found that short-term memory does not require the synthesis of new proteins. Rather, a single stimulus activates intracellular second-messenger pathways that make it easier for neurons involved in a particular behavior to communicate with each other. For example, as shown in Figure 43.15a, a single stimulus may lead to the activation of protein kinases such as protein kinase A (PKA) in the presynaptic (sensory) cell. PKA, in turn, can phosphorylate proteins such as ion channels, which leads to release of an increased amount of neurotransmitter. These changes enhance the transmission of a signal between the presynaptic and postsynaptic cells.

Kandel and colleagues also discovered that repeated stimuli result in long-term memory, which lasts days or weeks. Such repeated stimuli require the synthesis of new proteins (Figure 43.15b). Long-term memory involves the activation of genes in the presynaptic cell, which leads to the synthesis of mRNA and the translation of the encoded proteins. Once made, such proteins cause the formation of additional synaptic connections. These connections also allow the presynaptic and postsynaptic cells to communicate with each other more readily. Such a change in strength of the connection between two neurons, which occurs as a result of learning, is termed **synaptic plasticity**.

Kandel's work provides a foundation for our ability to understand how learning and memory may occur at the cellular level. Short-term memory may involve changes in pre-existing cellular proteins that make it easier for neurons to communicate. Long-term memory results in protein synthesis that causes physical changes in the synapse itself, also affecting communication. Later studies by Kandel and others showed that such changes also occur in vertebrates such as the mouse. For his work on learning and memory, Kandel was awarded a share of the Nobel Prize in Physiology or Medicine in 2000.

Recently, researchers have made astonishing progress toward understanding the cellular networks that encode memories in the mammalian brain. For example, using the technique called optogenetics, in which light is used to activate ion channels in genetically altered neurons of the hippocampus of mice, investigators have for the first time mapped a cellular network that stores a specific memory, in this case, one that is associated with a stimulus that induces fear. They have even been able to induce behaviors associated with that memory by reactivating the network at a later time in response to a nonfearful stimulus! In other words, the investigators have created a false memory in mice.

Neurogenesis May Also Contribute to Learning and Memory

Until fairly recently, neuroscientists had thought that the brain of vertebrates did not produce new neurons in adulthood, that is, that the brain was incapable of **neurogenesis**, the production of new neurons by cell division. However, in 1983, a study demonstrating neurogenesis in an adult vertebrate was carried out by Argentinean biologist Fernando Nottebohm and colleagues. Their research revealed that an increase in the number of neurons in certain brain areas of the canary occurred during the mating season. In the late 1990s, evidence also revealed that the primate and human CNS, like other parts of the body, contain stem cells, cells with the potential to differentiate into a variety of cells. For example, American researchers Elizabeth Gould and Bruce McEwen demonstrated the appearance of new neurons in the hippocampus and olfactory bulbs of adult marmosets and rhesus monkeys.

In 1998, American researcher Fred Gage and Swedish physician Peter Eriksson made a key discovery: They found evidence of recent mitotic activity in neurons in the hippocampus of deceased adult cancer patients. Those patients had previously been treated with a drug called bromodeoxyuridine (BrdU) to combat their cancer. BrdU is taken up by cancerous cells, but also by any other cells that are actively dividing. Its presence in cells can be detected with special stains on sections of brain or other tissue. Gage conducted such staining procedures on the brains of the deceased patients and observed the presence of BrdU in the hippocampus, suggesting recent neurogenesis.

A key question is whether the neurogenesis observed in adult brains is involved in learning and memory. This question is hotly debated and not resolved. However, some evidence suggests that it could play a role. For example, studies have shown that the hippocampus of adult monkeys grows new neurons when the animals are placed in socially enriching environments, and the formation of these neurons slows when animals are chronically stressed. Also, other studies of rats suggested that new neurons are retained in the hippocampus in response to training in particular tasks that require hippocampus function.

Imaging Studies Help Scientists Understand the Functions of Brain Regions

Because of the enormous numbers of neurons and connections between neurons in the vertebrate brain, a key challenge in neuroscience is to understand how such complexity results in sophisticated forms of learning, memory, and responses to environmental conditions. Several imaging techniques allow doctors and researchers to examine the structure and activity level of the human brain without anesthesia or surgery. The earliest technique to be developed was computerized tomography (CT). A **CT scan** involves the use of an X-ray beam and a series of detectors that rotate around the head, producing slices of images that are reconstructed into three-dimensional images based on differences in the density of brain tissue. CT scans can easily visualize the ventricles and differences between white and gray matter, but they cannot examine the brain in great detail.

A more sensitive method, called **magnetic resonance imaging (MRI)**, was developed in the 1980s. The patient is placed in a device that contains a magnet powerful enough to generate a magnetic field many thousands of times greater than that of the Earth. This stabilizes the spinning, or resonance, of atomic nuclei (usually those of hydrogen atoms in water molecules) so that most of the nuclei align with the magnetic field. When body tissue is stimulated with a beam of radio waves, its atoms absorb the energy of the waves and the resonance of their nuclei changes, thereby altering their alignment with the magnetic field. When the radio wave pulse stops, the atoms release their energy, which is recorded by a detector. This information is analyzed by a computer, and an image is produced. MRI images allow detection of structures as small as 0.10 mm. For example, they can provide information about abnormal tissue, such as brain tumors, which respond to magnetic and radio frequency pulses differently than normal tissue. MRIs are widely used in medicine to check for injured tissue, cancers, and other abnormalities throughout the body. In 2003, American chemist Paul Lauterbur and British physicist Peter Mansfield received the Nobel Prize in Physiology or Medicine for their work in developing this technique.

With certain modifications, MRI can be used to assess the functional activity of areas within the brain. This technique, which is widely used by neuroscientists, is called **functional MRI (fMRI)**. It takes advantage of the observation that blood flow, and therefore oxygen delivery, increases to areas where neurons are more active. This increase in oxygenation is detected via fMRI. In this way, fMRI determines which neurons in particular areas of the brain are active when an individual performs certain intellectual or motor tasks (**Figure 43.16**). The principle is similar to that applied in standard MRI, except that the increased oxygen use of active tissue alters the resonance of local hydrogen atoms.

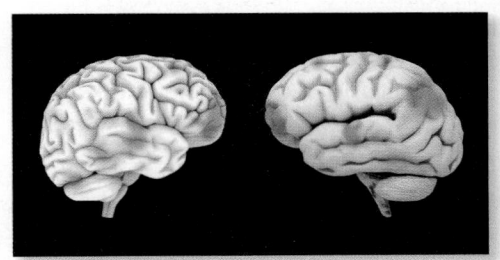

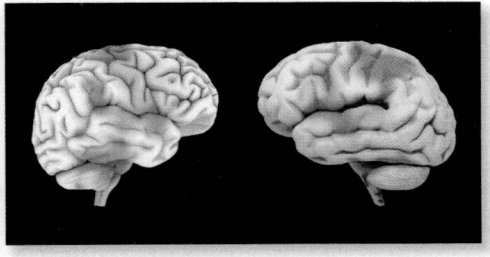

(a) Brain activity of a person thinking about a task that requires finger movements

(b) Brain activity when the same person is performing this task

Figure 43.16 **Exploring the functional activity of brain regions using fMRI scans. Red shading indicates greater O$_2$ use; both hemispheres are shown.** (brain on left): ©Science Photo Library/Alamy Stock Photo; (brain on right): ©Simone Brandt/Getty Images

---

 Core Skill: Modeling The goal of this modeling challenge is to create a model that shows the regions of the human brain that become activated by environmental stimuli, and propose experiments to identify which stimuli are activating particular regions.

Modeling Challenge: Imagine a person undergoing an fMRI procedure while viewing a video of a nature scene such as a forest, including all of the usual environmental sounds. The subject is told to think about the images and try to remember them for a brief time. Trace an image of the human brain from Figure 43.16. Next, refer back to Figure 43.12. Based on the information in Figure 43.12 make a model of the areas in the brain that you predict would be activated in an fMRI image during the test period. In your model, the areas of the brain that use more oxygen should be shaded in a color, such as orange. Then, if your model shows more than one shaded region, explain how you might redo the experiment to distinguish which regions responded to the visual images, which to auditory cues, and which to other functions such as conscious thought and short-term memory.

The use of fMRI has revealed many fascinating aspects of the activities of different brain regions, notably in people who have suffered brain damage or loss of sensory inputs. For example, individuals who are blind from birth might be predicted to have occipital lobes that are less functional or active than are those in sighted persons (recall that the occipital lobes have the major role in visual processing). However, the work of American researcher Harold Burton and others has revealed with fMRI that the occipital lobes of blind persons are active but have become adapted to other sensory functions such as tactile signals from the fingers, including those arising from Braille reading. Amazingly, this reassignment of occipital function occurs to some extent even in individuals who have lost their vision later in life. Most likely, this does not represent a new function of the occipital lobes, but rather an expansion of an existing function that remains relatively minor in sighted persons.

The plasticity of the brain revealed by the work of Burton and coworkers is not restricted to clinical situations, as just described. MRI and fMRI are also revealing differences in brain structure and function in individuals due to the types of activities in which they regularly engage, as described next.

 Core Skill: Process of Science

Feature Investigation | Gaser and Schlaug Discovered That the Sizes of Certain Brain Structures Differ Between Musicians and Nonmusicians

MRI and fMRI have been extremely useful in revealing which brain areas are involved in a particular function. They have also shown that the human brain is surprisingly adaptable. A number of studies have been carried out on musicians, because they practice a particular skill extensively throughout their lives, enabling researchers to study the effects of repeated use on brain function.

American neuroscientist Christian Gaser and German neuroscientist Gottfried Schlaug used MRI to examine the sizes of brain structures in three groups of people—professional musicians, amateur musicians, and nonmusicians. The researchers hypothesized that repeated exposure to musical training would increase the size of brain areas associated with visual, motor, and auditory skills, because each of these activities is used to read, make, and interpret music.

As shown in **Figure 43.17**, individuals were assigned to one of three groups based on their reported history of musical training: professional musicians with over 2 hours of musical practice time each day, amateur musicians who played a musical instrument regularly but not professionally (practicing about 1 hour/day), and those who never played a musical instrument regularly. After controlling for factors such as age and other characteristics, the researchers conducted MRIs on the three groups (see steps 2 and 3 of Figure 43.17). As seen in the data, brain areas involved in hearing, moving the fingers, and coordinating movements with vision and hearing were larger in professionals than in amateur musicians, and larger in amateurs than in nonmusicians. The region of the brain that controls finger movements was particularly well developed in the professional musicians, an interesting finding because all of the musicians in this study played keyboard instruments such as the piano.

In subsequent studies, Schlaug and colleagues examined the brains of people of different ages who either did or did not have musical training beginning in childhood. The researchers were able to correlate the degree of training with the sizes of different brain regions. They identified one particular region within the temporal lobes that was highly correlated with the extent of musical training in the course of one's life. This region, called the planum temporale, is believed to be especially important for recognizing and interpreting sound, identifying its source, and translating auditory signals (such as music) into motor processes (such as playing an instrument or humming a melody).

In a related study, American researchers Vincent Schmithorst and Scott Holland used fMRI to determine if musicians' brains were activated differently than nonmusicians' brains when they heard music. These researchers found that one area of the cerebral cortex

Figure 43.17 Gaser and Schlaug's study of the size of visual, motor, and auditory nuclei in the brains of musicians and nonmusicians.

HYPOTHESIS Musical training is associated with structural differences in the brain.

KEY MATERIALS Volunteer subjects with different degrees of musical training.

Experimental level	Conceptual level

1 Establish 3 groups of subjects with different musical backgrounds.

Interview subjects for musical history and assign to 1 of 3 groups.

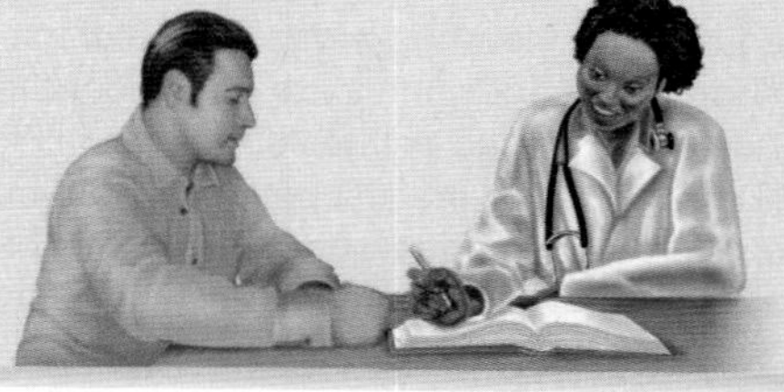

Controls (nonmusicians)
No musical training.

Amateur musicians
Play an instrument about 1 hr/day and are not employed as musicians.

Professional musicians
Employed as musicians and practice their instrument > 2 hr/day.

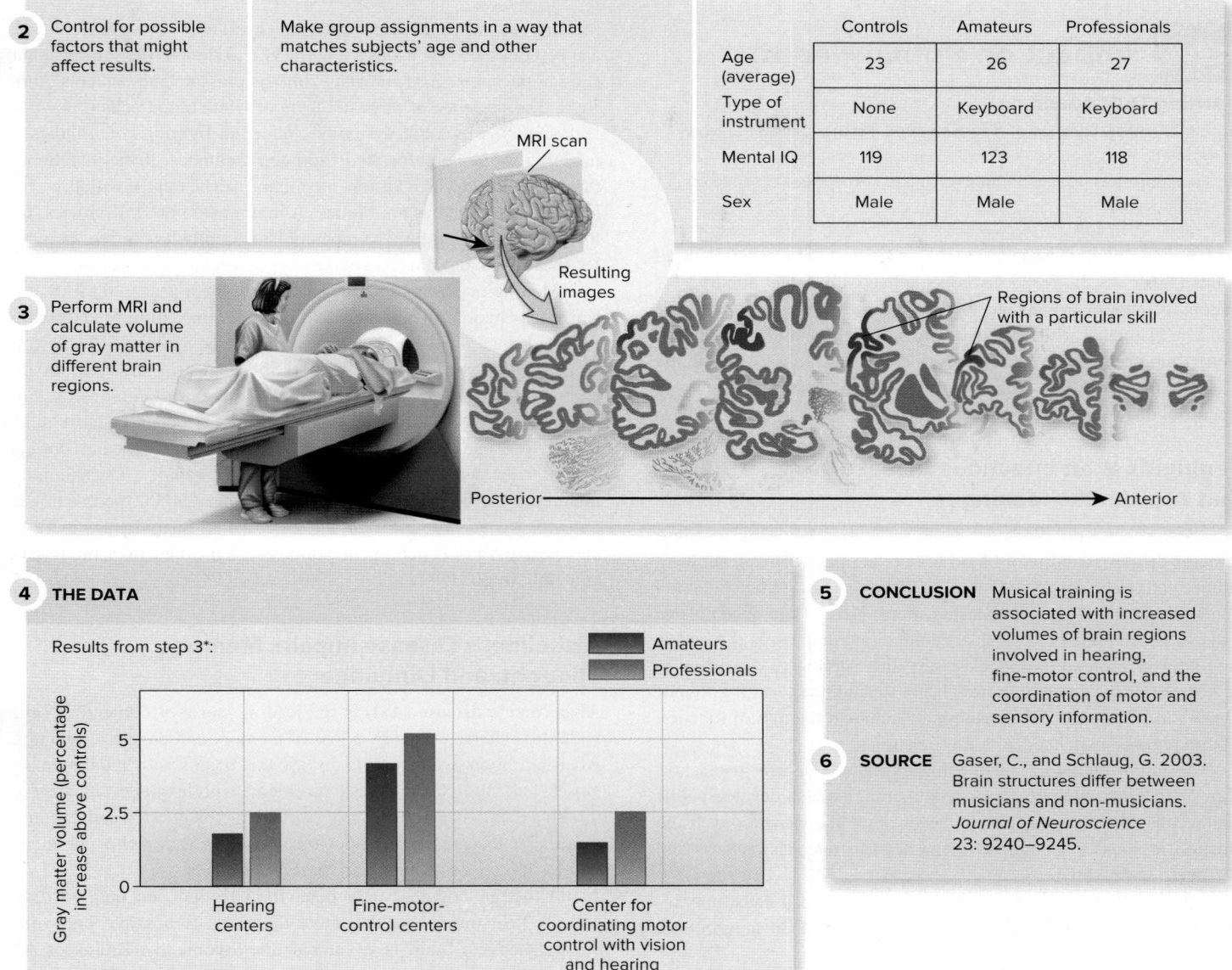

2 Control for possible factors that might affect results.

Make group assignments in a way that matches subjects' age and other characteristics.

	Controls	Amateurs	Professionals
Age (average)	23	26	27
Type of instrument	None	Keyboard	Keyboard
Mental IQ	119	123	118
Sex	Male	Male	Male

3 Perform MRI and calculate volume of gray matter in different brain regions.

MRI scan

Resulting images

Regions of brain involved with a particular skill

Posterior ——————————————→ Anterior

4 THE DATA

Results from step 3*:

Amateurs
Professionals

Gray matter volume (percentage increase above controls)

Hearing centers | Fine-motor-control centers | Center for coordinating motor control with vision and hearing

*Controls are not shown separately because the data are expressed relative to controls.

5 CONCLUSION Musical training is associated with increased volumes of brain regions involved in hearing, fine-motor control, and the coordination of motor and sensory information.

6 SOURCE Gaser, C., and Schlaug, G. 2003. Brain structures differ between musicians and non-musicians. *Journal of Neuroscience* 23: 9240–9245.

was selectively activated by melodies only in musicians. This study differed from that of Gaser and Schlaug, because Schmithorst and Holland examined the activity of brain areas as well as their sizes. Their results showed that listening to music activates certain neurons and pathways in the brains of musicians but not in nonmusicians.

The human studies of Gaser, Schlaug, Schmithorst, and Holland have not determined the underlying reason(s) for increased size of certain brain structures. One possibility is that people with increased size of these regions are more likely to become musicians. Alternatively, musical training may actually cause certain regions of the brain to grow larger and alter their neuronal pathways. In other research studies involving experimental animals, groups of animals have been randomly separated into those learning a task versus controls which do not learn the task. Such experiments have shown increases in the size of brain regions that are associated with learning and memory. The increased size may result from formation of new synapses,

growth of blood vessels to the region, and/or production of more glial cells.

Experimental Questions

1. What was the hypothesis proposed by Gaser and Schlaug? How did Gaser and Schlaug test this hypothesis? What were the results of their experiment?

2. **CoreSKILL »** How did the research of Schmithorst and Holland differ from that of Gaser and Schlaug? Were their results generally supportive of Gaser and Schlaug's hypothesis?

3. **CoreSKILL »** Based on the results described here and what you have learned in this chapter, predict general differences that might be found between the brain of a professional athlete, such as a tennis player, and that of a nonathlete. What about the brain of a person who has been deaf from birth compared to that of a person with normal hearing?

43.4 Impact on Public Health

Learning Outcomes:

1. List the broad groups of diseases affecting the human nervous system.
2. Describe the impacts of meningitis and Alzheimer's disease on public health.

Most neurological disorders can be classified into several broad groups (**Table 43.2**). These disorders collectively affect hundreds of millions of people around the world. By far, the most common are headache disorders, which affect nearly half of the world's population at one time or another. We will consider two disorders—meningitis and Alzheimer's disease—that result from very different causes and affect millions of individuals worldwide.

Meningitis Is an Infectious Disease That Attacks the Meninges

An essential response to infection is inflammation. This response increases the permeability of blood vessels in infected areas, allowing immune cells to be delivered to the site of an infection. When infection occurs within the meninges (causing **meningitis**), fluid accumulates in the subarachnoid space. This accumulation compresses the underlying brain tissue and its blood vessels, interrupting oxygen flow to the neurons of the cerebral cortex. If not treated, the resulting loss of oxygen (and nutrients) causes neuronal death and the loss of function of brain regions associated with those neurons.

The initial symptoms of meningitis include severe headaches, fever, or seizures. Many patients with meningitis also develop a stiff neck because the inflammation proceeds down the spinal cord. If the infection progresses untreated, it may lead to unconsciousness and even death within hours.

Several different viruses or bacterial species can cause meningitis. It usually results from an untreated infection in neighboring

Table 43.2	Categories of Diseases and Disorders Affecting the Human Central Nervous System
Category	**Examples**
Infectious	Meningitis, encephalitis
Neurodegenerative	Alzheimer's disease
Movement	Parkinson's disease
Seizure	Epilepsy
Sleep	Sleep apnea (brain fails to regulate breathing during sleep)
Tumors	Glioma (a tumor arising from glial cells)
Headache	Migraine (severe recurring headache)
Mood	Major depressive disorder; bipolar disorder (see Chapter 42)
Demyelinating	Multiple sclerosis (see Chapter 42)
Injury-related	Brain and spinal cord injuries due to accidents

regions, such as the sinuses behind the eyes, nose, or ears. Meningitis can be confirmed by using a long needle to sample the cerebrospinal fluid in the spinal cord and analyzing the pressure and contents of the fluid. The presence of large numbers of white blood cells (known as leukocytes), which are the body's infection-fighting cells, indicates infection in the cerebrospinal fluid and meninges. If the infection is the result of bacterial invasion, meningitis can be treated with bacteria-killing agents such as antibiotics. Antibiotics do not kill viruses, but fortunately the viral form of meningitis is usually less serious than the bacterial form and runs its course after several days or weeks.

Meningitis strikes roughly 25,000 people a year in the U.S. and can affect people of any age. Its incidence in children has greatly declined since the widespread use of a vaccine against the bacterium *Haemophilus influenzae* type b (Hib) began in the U.S. in the early 1990s. Despite the vaccine, meningitis is still a dangerous and prevalent disease worldwide, and it tends to occur in individuals living in close quarters, such as military barracks and college dormitories, where infections may spread rapidly. Occasionally, meningitis can become epidemic. For example, 250,000 people in sub-Saharan Africa were infected and 25,000 died in epidemics in 1996, and nearly 75,000 people in Southeast Asia died of a meningitis epidemic in 2004.

Alzheimer's Disease Impairs Memory, Thought, and Language

Alzheimer's disease (AD) is the leading cause of dementia worldwide. It is characterized by a loss of memory and cognitive function. AD is a progressive incurable disease that begins with small memory lapses, leading in later stages to problems with language and abstract thinking, and finally to loss of normal motor control and eventual death. The disease usually appears after age 65, though some inherited forms can strike people in their 30s and 40s.

Although cognitive and behavioral testing can help to diagnose AD, historically a definitive diagnosis is possible only after death when the brain is examined microscopically. Brains of AD patients show two major changes: plaques and neurofibrillary tangles (**Figure 43.18**). Plaques are extracellular deposits of a misfolded protein, β-amyloid, that forms large, sticky aggregates. These plaques were first noted in 1906 by German physician Alois Alzheimer, after whom the disease was named. Neurofibrillary tangles are intracellular, twisted accumulations of cytoskeletal fibers. Scientists are unsure how these changes influence intellectual function and memory. AD is also associated with the degeneration and death of neurons, particularly in the hippocampus and parietal lobes, which is why it is considered a neurodegenerative disease.

Researchers have identified variation in a few genes whose products are associated with the likelihood of developing AD later in life, but the underlying changes that result in the expression of these and other possible AD-related genes are still the subject of considerable research. Although genetics undoubtedly plays a role in AD, it is not the only possible cause. For example, when one identical twin develops AD, the other appears to be at increased risk but does not always develop the disease, even if he or she survives to very old age. Moreover, evidence suggests that severe head injuries, metabolic diseases such as diabetes, and heart and blood vessel disease may predispose a person to AD in later life.

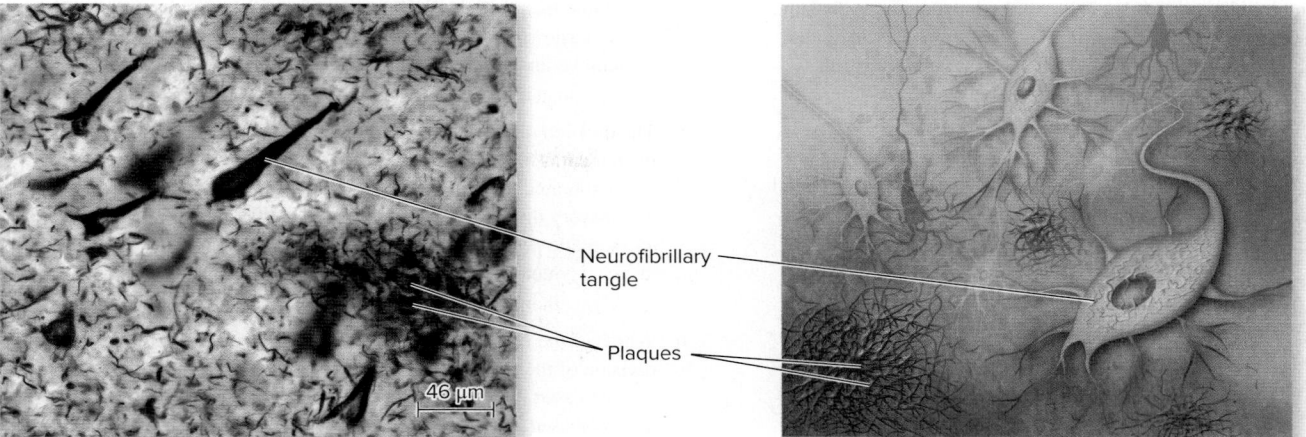

Figure 43.18 **Cellular section from the brain of a person who died from Alzheimer's disease.** The section has been stained for visualization of proteins found in plaques and neurofibrillary tangles. An illustration of plaques and tangles is shown for comparison.
(left): ©McGraw-Hill Education/Al Telser, photographer.

Currently, AD cannot be prevented or cured. However, four major clinical approaches to prevent or slow down its progression are currently being tested or employed. These approaches are designed to (1) induce a person's immune system to destroy β-amyloid as soon as it is formed, (2) prevent the formation of β-amyloid with drugs that block its synthesis, (3) prevent the accumulation of β-amyloid into large aggregates using antiaggregation drugs, or (4) restore concentrations of certain neurotransmitters that decline in concentration in the brains of people with AD. Each of these approaches holds great promise but is still unproven. Exciting recent research has demonstrated that neuronal stem cell transplants into the hippocampus of old mice can reverse the learning and memory deficits associated with a mouse model of Alzheimer's disease, providing hope for potential future therapies for humans.

Until a cure for AD is found, its impact on public health remains enormous. Currently, about 4–5 million Americans have AD, and this number is expected to grow to nearly 16 million by 2050. The prevalence of the disease is about 3% for people between the ages of 65 and 74, and 25–50% for people older than 85. Estimated costs associated with providing health care and housing for AD patients (30% of whom live in nursing homes), as well as lost productivity in the workplace, total a staggering $100 billion per year in the U.S. This number will rise substantially now that the oldest members of the population spike known as the baby boom generation are older than 70.

Summary of Key Concepts

43.1   The Evolution and Development of Nervous Systems

- All multicellular animals except sponges have a nervous system. Simple nervous systems include the nerve net of cnidarians. As animal bodies become more complex, cephalization occurs, with the formation of regionally subdivided and specialized brain that is capable of more functions (Figure 43.1).

- In all vertebrates, the three major divisions of the brain are the hindbrain, midbrain, and forebrain. Human embryos develop these divisions by 4 weeks (Figure 43.2).

- Additional folding of the brain and increased brain mass allow for expansion of regions associated with conscious thought, reasoning, and learning (Figures 43.3, 43.4).

43.2   Structure and Function of the Nervous Systems of Humans and Other Vertebrates

- In humans and other vertebrates, the brain and spinal cord are the central nervous system (CNS). The neurons and all axons outside the CNS, including the cranial and spinal nerves, constitute the peripheral nervous system (PNS). The CNS receives sensory input from the PNS, and the PNS acts on commands from the CNS (Figure 43.5).

- The gray matter of the CNS is composed of dendrites, cell bodies, and unmyelinated axons. The white matter consists of tracts of myelinated axons. The meninges are protective coverings of the CNS. Cerebrospinal fluid fills the subarachnoid space and ventricles (Figures 43.6, 43.7).

- The PNS can be subdivided into the somatic and autonomic nervous systems. The somatic nervous system senses external environmental conditions and controls skeletal muscles and skin. The autonomic nervous system senses internal body conditions and controls homeostasis. The efferent part of the autonomic nervous system is divided into two components: sympathetic (fight-or-flight response) and parasympathetic (rest-or-digest response) (Figure 43.8).

- The evolutionarily oldest structures of the brain, some of which are located in the hindbrain, control the basic processes that sustain life. These structures include the medulla oblongata, cerebellum, and pons (Figure 43.9).

- The midbrain processes several types of sensory inputs, including vision, olfaction, and audition. The medulla oblongata, the pons, and the midbrain collectively constitute the brainstem. Some nuclei of these three structures form the reticular formation, a network of nuclei and tracts that sends signals to many other brain regions (Figure 43.9).

- The forebrain is made of the thalamus, hypothalamus, epithalamus (diencephalon), and the cerebrum. The cerebrum is divided into two hemispheres. Each hemisphere is specialized to perform certain aspects of behavior and can operate independently (Figures 43.10, 43.11).

- The cerebrum consists of the basal nuclei, limbic system, and cerebral cortex. Each side of the human cerebral cortex is divided into four lobes, each of which has a number of functions (Figures 43.12, 43.13, Table 43.1).

43.3 Cellular Basis of Learning and Memory

- Learning is the process by which new information is acquired. Memory is the ability to retain, retrieve, and use information that was previously learned.

- Repeated stimuli result in long-term potentiation, in which the connections between adjacent neurons become stronger. Studies of the sea slug indicate that short-term memory is caused by a single stimulus that activates second-messenger pathways. Long-term memory is caused by repeated stimuli that activate genes, which results in stronger synaptic connections, a phenomenon called synaptic plasticity (Figures 43.14, 43.15).

- Imaging techniques such as CT scans, MRI, and fMRI allow neuroscientists and physicians to examine the structure and activity of the brain (Figures 43.16, 43.17).

43.4 Impact on Public Health

- Disorders of the human central nervous system can be placed into several broad categories (Table 43.2).

- Meningitis is a potentially life-threatening infectious disease in which the meninges become inflamed. Alzheimer's disease is a progressive disorder characterized by the formation of plaques and neurofibrillary tangles in brain tissue. Both are examples of neurological disorders with a large impact on public health (Figure 43.18).

Assess & Discuss

Test Yourself

1. A nerve net consists of
   a. bilateral neurons that extend from the head of the animal to the tail.
   b. a group of neurons that are interconnected and are activated all at once.
   c. a single nerve cord with ganglia in each body segment.
   d. a central nervous system with peripheral nerves associated with different body structures.
   e. none of the above.

2. The division of the vertebrate brain that includes the cerebellum is the
   a. hindbrain.   d. forebrain.
   b. telencephalon.   e. diencephalon.
   c. midbrain.

3. In general, the brains of more complex vertebrates
   a. are smaller.
   b. have fewer neurons but with more connections.
   c. have more folds in the cerebral cortex.
   d. use less oxygen.
   e. Both a and c are true.

4. The white matter of the CNS is composed of
   a. dendrites.   d. cell bodies.
   b. unmyelinated axons.   e. a and b only.
   c. myelinated axons.

5. The division of the nervous system that controls voluntary muscle movement is the
   a. autonomic nervous system.
   b. sensory division.
   c. somatic nervous system.
   d. parasympathetic division.
   e. sympathetic division.

6. Which of the following is *not* a response to activation of the sympathetic division of the autonomic nervous system?
   a. increased breathing rate
   b. decreased heart rate
   c. increased blood flow to the skeletal muscles
   d. increased blood glucose levels
   e. inhibition of digestion

7. The_____acts as a relay for the cerebrum.
   a. medulla   d. midbrain
   b. pons   e. thalamus
   c. hypothalamus

8. The_____is a portion of the limbic system that is important for memory formation.
   a. amygdala   d. epithalamus
   b. hippocampus   e. mesencephalon
   c. pons

9. In humans, the_____hemisphere of the cerebrum is dominant in nonverbal processing.
   a. right
   b. left
   c. The hemispheres contribute equally to nonverbal processing.

10. _____ is a progressive disease that causes a loss of memory and intellectual and emotional function.
   a. Meningitis
   b. Parkinson's disease
   c. Amnesia
   d. Alzheimer's disease
   e. Stroke

Conceptual Questions

1. One of the most important and fundamental functions of all nervous systems is the reflex, several of which were described in this chapter and in Chapter 42. Describe why reflexes are adaptive.

2. Explain the differences between white matter and gray matter.

3. **Core Concept: Systems** New properties of life emerge from complex interactions, such as those between cells. How is this principle evident in the structure and function of animal nervous systems?

Collaborative Questions

1. Discuss how the two parts of the nervous system of many animals—the central and peripheral nervous systems—interact with each other.

2. List the three major divisions of the brain of vertebrates, and briefly describe the function of each in humans.

Neuroscience III: Sensory Systems

44

Compound eyes of a robber fly (family Asilidae).
©Gustavo Mazzarollo/Moment/Getty Images

What does the world look, sound, smell, and feel like to other animals? We can never know exactly how an animal perceives its environment. Biologists can perform experiments, however, to determine the capabilities of an animal's sensory systems. For instance, researchers have examined the structure of the goldfish eye, conducted behavioral studies to determine if a goldfish can discriminate between different colors, and measured the electrical responses of neurons in the animal's visual system to different visual stimuli. From such studies, we know that goldfish and probably most animals can discriminate between light of different wavelengths.

Despite the prevalence of such abilities as light, odor, sound, taste, and touch detection across animal taxa, the sensory experience of different animals may differ radically from our own. We do not see the color patterns of flowers produced by the reflection of UV light the way honeybees do, or hear the very low frequency sounds (such as those produced by earthquakes) that elephants, whales, and alligators hear. We cannot detect the presence of chemicals using our entire body surface, the way an earthworm can as it seeks food. We cannot detect the electric field generated by excitable tissues of marine animals, although many elasmobranchs and catfish can.

Senses allow living organisms to perceive their environments. In neuroscience, a **sense** is broadly defined as a system that consists of specialized cells that detect a specific type of chemical or physical stimulus (also known as a modality) and send signals to the central nervous system (CNS) for interpretation. The senses allow animals to perceive subtle and complex aspects of their environments. They are the windows through which animals experience the world around them. The nervous systems of most animals also have the ability to sense signals arising from within the body, such as hunger or pain.

In this chapter, we will examine how nervous systems collect incoming sensory information and how membrane potentials of specialized neurons change in response to sensory inputs. We will then learn that other structures of the nervous system may modify or enhance this neural activity before sending it to the brain, where it is interpreted. Finally, we will discuss how problems with sensory systems—in particular vision and hearing deficits—can affect human health.

44.1 An Introduction to Sensation

Learning Outcomes:

1. Describe the relationship between sensory transduction and perception.
2. Explain how sensory receptors transmit the intensity of a stimulus.
3. List the classes of sensory receptors and the stimuli to which they respond.

Sensory systems convert chemical or physical stimuli from an animal's body or the external environment into a signal that causes a change in the membrane potential of sensory neurons. **Sensory transduction** is the process by which incoming stimuli are converted into neural (electrical) signals. Sensory transduction involves cellular changes, such as opening of ion channels, which cause either graded potentials or action potentials in neurons.

Perception is an awareness of sensations that are experienced. For instance, touching a hot object generates a thermal sensation, which initiates a neuronal response in the brain, giving us the perception that this stimulus is hot. Not all sensations are consciously perceived by an organism. Most of the time, for example, we are not aware of the touch of our clothing. The brain also processes sensory information in areas that do not generate conscious thought. For instance, certain neurons constantly monitor blood pressure and the concentrations of oxygen, glucose, and other substances in the blood, but we are not aware that this is occurring.

We begin our study of sensory systems by examining the specialized cells that receive sensory inputs. A **sensory receptor** is in some cases a neuron. In other cases, it may be a specialized epithelial cell that synapses with a neuron referred to as a sensory neuron. In both cases, the sensory receptor recognizes an internal or external (environmental) stimulus and initiates sensory transduction by creating graded potentials (described in Chapter 42) in itself or an adjacent cell (**Figure 44.1**). If a response is strong enough, sensory receptors initiate electrical responses to stimuli, such as chemicals, light, heat, and sound, which lead to action potentials that are sent to the CNS.

A Strong Stimulus Generates More Frequent Action Potentials

How do sensory receptors transmit the intensity of a stimulus? Let's consider an example involving weak and strong stimuli to the sense of touch (**Figure 44.2**). Sensory transduction begins when the specialized endings of a sensory receptor respond to a stimulus. Such a stimulus—in this case, the touch of a glass rod—opens ion channels that allow sodium ions (Na^+) to diffuse down their electrochemical gradient into the cell, depolarizing the sensory receptor. The amount of depolarization is directly related to the intensity of the stimulus, because a stronger stimulus opens more ion channels.

The first response of a sensory receptor is usually a graded change in the membrane potential of the cell body that is proportional to the intensity of the stimulus (see Figure 44.2). The membrane potential, known as a **receptor potential** in these cells, becomes less and less negative as the strength of the stimulus increases. When a stimulus is strong enough, it depolarizes the membrane to the threshold potential at the axon hillock and produces an action potential in a sensory neuron (refer back to Figure 42.9 for a description of the action potential).

Recall from Chapter 42 that action potentials proceed in an all-or-none manner, regardless of the nature or strength of the stimulus that elicits them. How, then, can action potentials provide information about the intensity of a stimulus? The answer is that the strength of the stimulus determines the frequency of action potentials generated. A strong stimulus generates many action potentials in a short period of time, because it can overcome the membrane's relative refractory period (see Figure 42.9). As a result, the frequency of action potentials is higher when the stimulus is strong than when it is weak. The action potentials are transmitted into the CNS and carried to the brain for interpretation. The brain interprets a higher frequency of action potentials as a more intense stimulus.

The CNS Processes Each Sense Within Its Own Pathway

Different stimuli produce different sensations because they activate specific neural pathways that are dedicated to processing only that

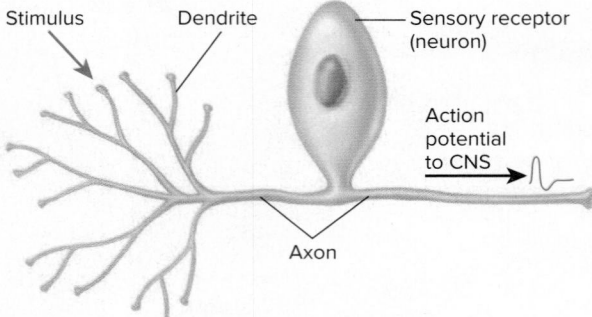

(a) A neuron as a sensory receptor

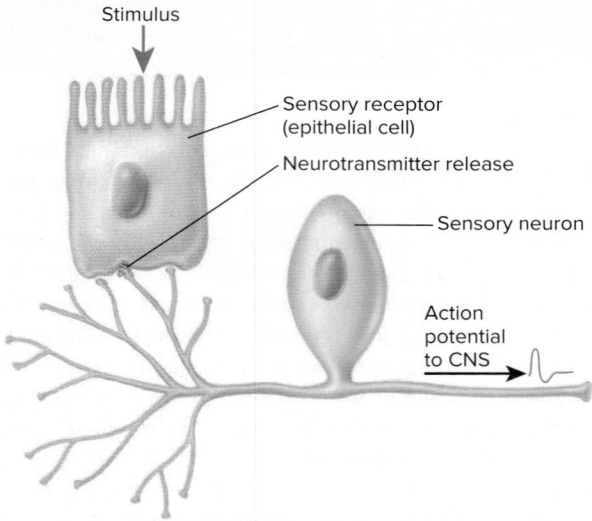

(b) A specialized epithelial cell as a sensory receptor

Figure 44.1 Sensory receptors. (a) Many sensory receptors are neurons that directly sense stimuli. **(b)** Other sensory receptors are specialized epithelial cells that sense stimuli and release neurotransmitter that stimulates nearby neurons called sensory neurons. In both cases, when stimulated, the neurons send action potentials to the CNS, where the signals are interpreted.

 Core Skill: Connections The term receptor is used in more than one way in biology. What is the difference between the sensory receptors described in this chapter and the membrane receptors described in Chapter 9?

type of stimulus. We know that we are seeing light because the signals generated by visual sensory receptors in the eye are transmitted along a neural pathway that sends action potentials into areas of the brain that are devoted to processing vision. For this reason, the brain interprets such signals as visual stimuli. The brain can separate and identify each sense because each one uses its own dedicated pathway.

Sensory receptors can be divided into general classes based on the type of stimulus, or modality, to which they respond. Each class of receptor uses a different mechanism to detect stimuli and to transmit the information to different regions of the CNS.

- **Mechanoreceptors** transduce mechanical energy such as touch, pressure, stretch, movement, and sound.

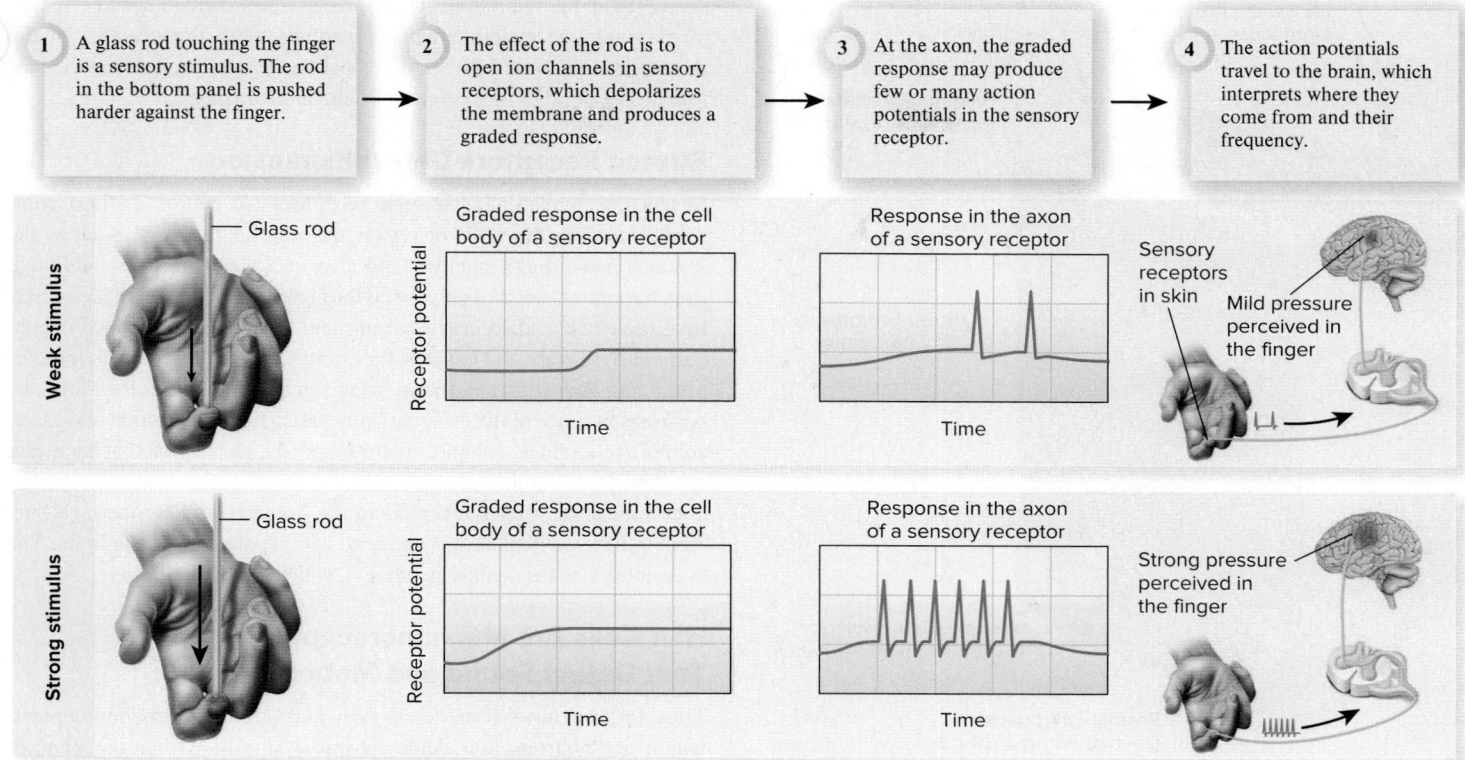

1 A glass rod touching the finger is a sensory stimulus. The rod in the bottom panel is pushed harder against the finger.

2 The effect of the rod is to open ion channels in sensory receptors, which depolarizes the membrane and produces a graded response.

3 At the axon, the graded response may produce few or many action potentials in the sensory receptor.

4 The action potentials travel to the brain, which interprets where they come from and their frequency.

Weak stimulus

Glass rod

Graded response in the cell body of a sensory receptor

Receptor potential / Time

Response in the axon of a sensory receptor

Time

Sensory receptors in skin / Mild pressure perceived in the finger

Strong stimulus

Glass rod

Graded response in the cell body of a sensory receptor

Receptor potential / Time

Response in the axon of a sensory receptor

Time

Strong pressure perceived in the finger

Figure 44.2 **Transduction of a sensory stimulus of two different intensities.** In this example, the sensory receptor is a neuron that is embedded within deformable structures composed of connective tissue. Note the faster and larger graded response following the stronger stimulus.

- **Thermoreceptors** detect cold and heat.
- **Nociceptors**, or pain receptors, detect extreme heat, cold, and pressure, as well as certain potentially damaging molecules such as acids.
- **Electromagnetic receptors** sense radiation within a portion of the electromagnetic spectrum, including visible, UV, and infrared light, as well as electrical and magnetic fields in some animals.
- **Photoreceptors** are a type of electromagnetic receptor that detect visible light.
- **Chemoreceptors** recognize specific chemical compounds in the air, water, body fluids, or food.

In most of the remaining sections of this chapter, we will examine the structures and functions of these types of sensory receptors and the organs in which they are found.

44.2 Mechanoreception

Learning Outcomes:

1. List the types of mechanoreceptors that detect touch, stretch, or movement, and describe how their structures relate to the functions of hearing and balance.
2. Describe the structure of the mammalian ear, and explain how mechanical forces move through it.

3. Give examples of adaptations for hearing in animals that inhabit different environments.
4. Describe how body position and movement are detected by sense organs.

Mechanoreceptors are cells that detect physical stimuli such as touch. Physically touching or deforming a mechanoreceptor cell opens ion channels in its plasma membrane (see Figure 44.2). As discussed in this section, some mechanoreceptors are neurons that send action potentials to the CNS in response to physical stimuli. Other mechanoreceptors are specialized epithelial cells that contain hairlike structures that bend in response to mechanical forces.

Skin Receptors Detect Touch and Pressure

Several types of receptors in the skin of many animals detect touch, deep pressure, or the bending of hairs on the skin. Some of these specialized receptors consist of neuronal dendrites covered in dense connective tissue. In mammals, these receptors are located at different depths below the surface of the skin, which makes them suitable for responding to different types of stimuli (**Figure 44.3**). For example, **Meissner corpuscles** lie just beneath the skin surface and sense touch and light pressure. They are found throughout the skin but are concentrated in areas sensitive to light touch, such as the fingertips, lips, eyelids, and genitals. In contrast, **Pacinian corpuscles** and **Ruffini corpuscles** are located much deeper beneath the surface, particularly in the soles of the feet and the palms of the hands. These corpuscles respond best to

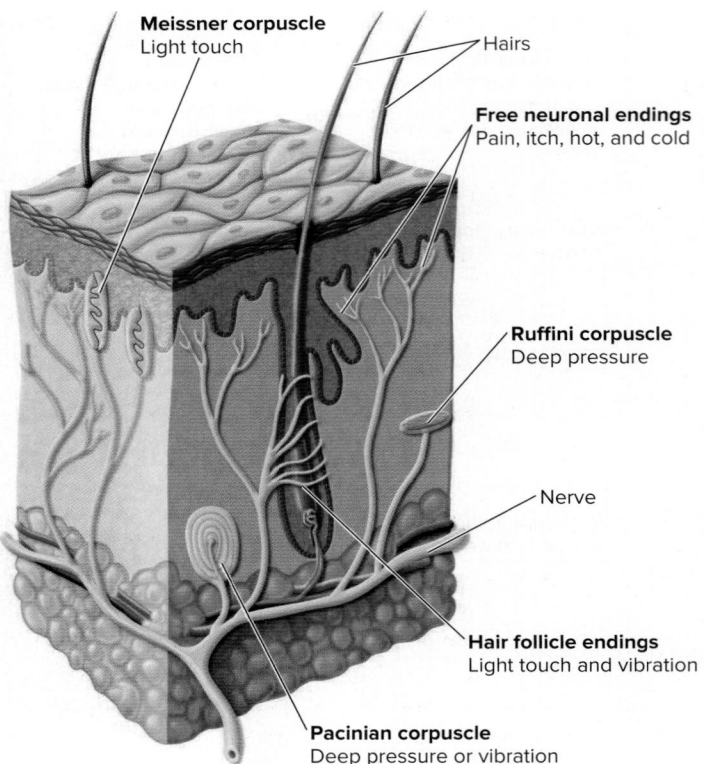

Figure 44.3 **Examples of sensory receptors in the skin of mammals.**

Concept Check: *The several types of touch receptors in the skin respond to different stimuli. What different touch sensations are you aware of?*

deep pressure or vibration. All skin corpuscles contain sensory receptor neurons that generate action potentials when the structure of the corpuscle is deformed. Other skin mechanoreceptors located in the hair follicles respond to movements of hairs and whiskers.

Stretch Receptors Detect Expansion

Mechanoreceptors called **stretch receptors** are neuron endings commonly found in the walls of organs that can be distended, such as the stomach and urinary bladder, and also in skeletal muscles. Although stretch receptors are probably found throughout the animal kingdom, they have been best studied in crustaceans and mammals. In decapod crustaceans such as crabs and lobsters, for example, stretch receptors in muscles of the tail, abdomen, and thorax relay signals to the brain regarding the positions in space of the different body parts. This information allows the animal to coordinate complex motor functions, such as walking backward or sideways. In another example, when the mammalian stomach stretches after a meal, the stretch receptors in the stomach are deformed, causing them to become depolarized and send action potentials to the brain. The brain interprets the signals as fullness, which inhibits appetite.

Hair Cells Are Mechanoreceptors That Detect Sound and Motion

Thus far, we have considered skin and stretch mechanoreceptors, which are neurons that detect physical stimuli. Other mechanoreceptors are specialized epithelial cells called **hair cells**, which have deformable projections called **stereocilia**. The stereocilia are different from true cilia (see Figure 4.17) because they do not contain motor proteins in their structure. Instead, they are displaced by movements of fluid or other physical stimuli (**Figure 44.4**). The stereocilia on hair cells allow animals to detect movements and sound waves.

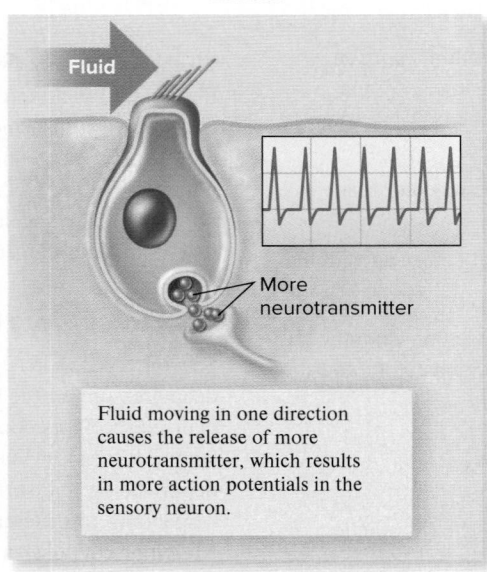
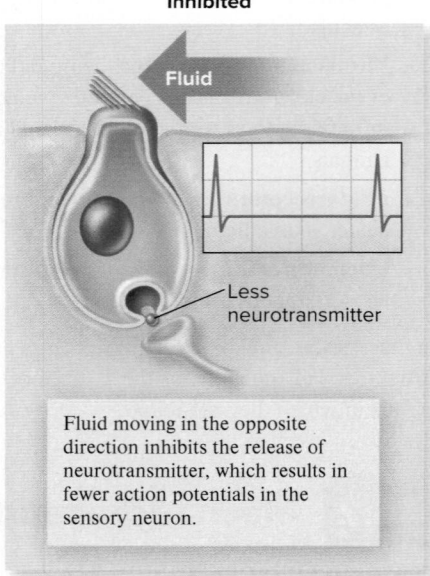

Figure 44.4 **The response of hair cells to mechanical stimulation.** The stereocilia inside these hair cells are hairlike projections of the plasma membrane that contain actin filaments.

 Core Skill: Connections How are stereocilia different from cilia, which are described in Chapter 4?

Hair cells contain ion channels that open or close when the stereocilia bend. This leads to a change in the cell's membrane potential. When the plasma membrane depolarizes, voltage-gated Ca^{2+} channels open, resulting in the release of neurotransmitter molecules from the hair cells. The neurotransmitters then bind to protein receptors in adjacent sensory neurons and may initiate action potentials that are sent to the CNS. When unstimulated, the stereocilia are not bent, and the hair cells release only a small amount of neurotransmitter onto nearby sensory neurons, resulting in a resting rate of action potentials from the sensory neurons. In the example shown in Figure 44.4, bending of the stereocilia in one direction in response to fluid movement increases the release of neurotransmitter from the hair cell, exciting the sensory receptors, whereas bending in the other direction decreases the release of the same neurotransmitter, inhibiting the sensory receptors. The result is an increase or decrease, respectively, in the rate of action potentials produced in the sensory neurons.

Hair cells provide a rich array of sensory capabilities in many animal species. For example, these cells are found in the hearing and equilibrium (balance) organs of many invertebrates and vertebrates, where they detect sound or changes in head position. They are also found along the body surface of fishes and some amphibians, where they detect external water currents, as described later.

Audition (Hearing) Involves the Detection of Sound Waves

The sense of hearing, called **audition**, is the ability to detect and interpret sound waves. This sense is critical for the survival and reproduction of many types of animals. For example, a mother seal locates her pup by hearing its calls, and a male bird sings an elaborate song to attract a mate. Hearing is also important for detecting the approach of danger—a predator, a thunderstorm, an automobile—and locating its source.

Sound travels through air or water in waves. The distance from one peak of the wave to the next peak is a **wavelength**. The number of complete wavelengths that occur in 1 second is called the **frequency** of the sound, which is measured in the number of waves per second, or hertz (Hz), after German physicist and pioneer of radio wave research, Heinrich Hertz. The length and frequency of sound waves impart certain characteristics to the stimulus. Short wavelengths have high frequencies that are perceived as a high pitch, or tone, and long wavelengths have lower frequencies and a lower pitch. The human hearing range is about 20–20,000 Hz.

The sense of hearing is present in vertebrates and arthropods, but not in other phyla. Arthropods do not appear to have more than a general sensitivity to sound, although some exceptions exist. For example, some species of moths have sound-sensitive membranes that detect the high frequencies emitted by their chief predators, bats. The sense of hearing, however, is especially well developed in many vertebrates (notably birds and mammals). We turn now to a detailed discussion of the mammalian ear and the mechanism by which it detects sound, including the importance of hair cells for hearing.

Structure of the Mammalian Ear   The mammalian ear has three main compartments: the outer, middle, and inner ears (**Figure 44.5**). The outer ear consists of the external ear, or pinna (plural, pinnae), and the auditory canal. The outer ear is separated from the middle ear by the tympanic membrane (eardrum). The middle ear contains three small bones called ossicles (named the malleus, incus, and stapes) that link movements of the eardrum with the oval window. The oval window is another membrane similar to the eardrum that separates the middle ear from the inner ear. The inner ear is composed of the **cochlea** (from the Latin, meaning snail)—a coiled chamber of bone containing hair cells and the membrane-like round window—and the vestibular system, which functions in balance, as described later.

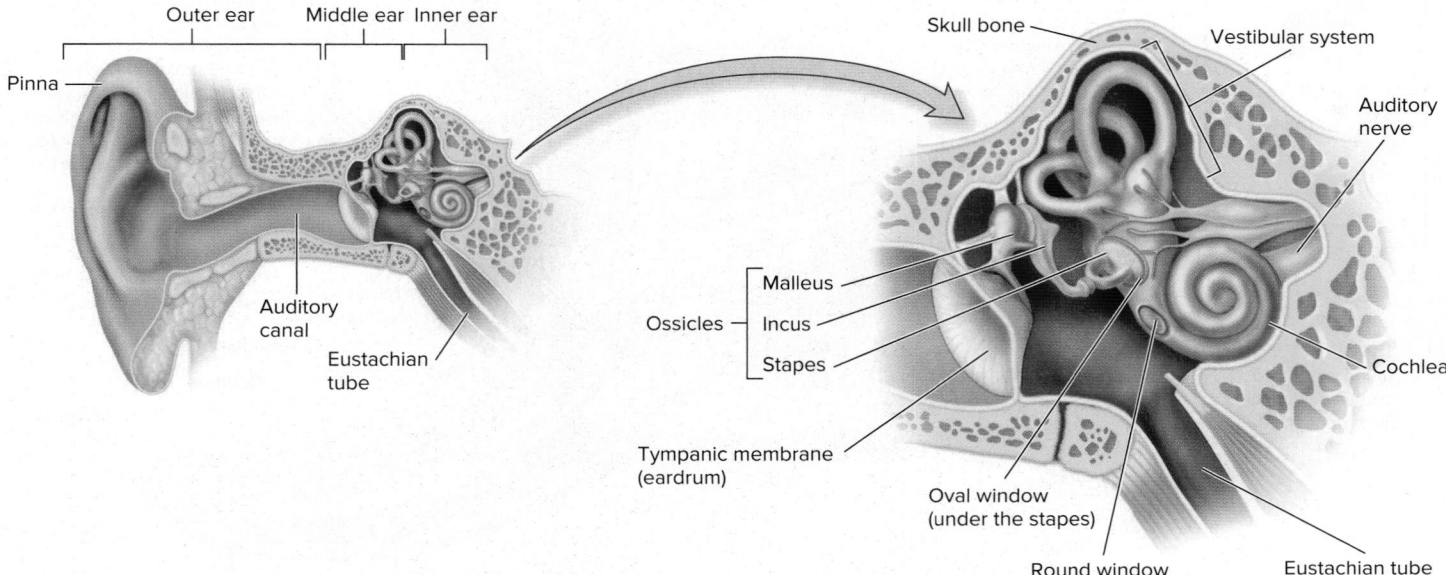

Figure 44.5 **The structure of the human ear.** The three main compartments are the outer, middle, and inner ear; the latter two are shown in more detail in the inset. (The eustachian tube shown here is a structure that connects the middle ear to the pharynx and functions to equalize air pressures in the ear.)

These structures in the inner ear generate the signals that travel via the auditory nerve to the auditory cortex of the brain.

Generation of Electrical Signals in the Mammalian Ear   To understand how mammals hear, let's first consider how mechanical forces move through the ear. Sound waves entering the outer ear cause the tympanic membrane to vibrate back and forth (**Figure 44.6**). The malleus, incus, and stapes transfer the vibration of the tympanic membrane to the oval window, causing it to vibrate against the cochlea. This vibration sends pressure waves through a fluid called perilymph. Perilymph is found within two narrow passages in the cochlea called the vestibular and tympanic canals, which are separated by a tube called the cochlear duct. The waves travel from the vestibular canal to the tympanic canal and eventually strike the round window, where they dissipate. Along the way, the waves cause the vibration of a sheath-like structure called the **basilar membrane**, which is formed from elastic fibers tensed across the cochlear duct. Sounds of very low frequency (longer wavelength) create pressure waves that take the complete route through the vestibular and tympanic canals (see the green arrows in Figure 44.6). Sounds of higher frequency (shorter wavelength) produce pressure waves that follow a different route, passing from the vestibular canal through the cochlear duct (as shown by the blue arrows in Figure 44.6). They then pass through the basilar membrane, before reaching the tympanic canal.

Within the cochlea, mechanical vibrations are transduced into electrical signals. This happens in a structure called the **organ of Corti** which rests on top of the basilar membrane. To understand how this works, we need to look at a cross section through the cochlea (**Figure 44.7**). The organ of Corti contains supporting cells and rows of hair cells. The stereocilia of the hair cells are embedded in a gelatinous

tectorial membrane. The vibration of the basilar membrane bends the stereocilia in one direction and then the other. When bent in one direction, the hair cells depolarize and release neurotransmitter, which activates adjacent sensory neurons that then send action potentials to the CNS via the auditory nerve. When bent in the other direction, the hair cells hyperpolarize and stop releasing neurotransmitter. In this way, the frequency of action potentials generated by the sensory neurons is determined by the up-and-down vibration of the basilar membrane.

The basilar membrane is lined with protein fibers that span its width. These fibers function much like the strings of a guitar. The fibers near the oval and round windows at the base of the cochlea are short and rigid, and they vibrate in response to high-frequency waves. Longer and more resilient fibers are near the other end of the cochlea and vibrate to lower-frequency waves. For this reason, hair cells closer to the oval and round windows respond to high-pitched sounds, whereas those at the opposite end are triggered by lower-pitched sounds. When we hear a great number of sound frequencies at once, such as at a musical concert, the waves traveling through the cochlea activate hair cells all along the basilar membrane in a physical representation of the music! These cells stimulate sensory neurons, which send multiple action potentials to the auditory areas of the brain for processing. The most incredible feature of this process, however, is that the mammalian ear and brain can "tune in" to all of these frequencies simultaneously.

Adaptations for Hearing Provide Survival Advantages for Animals

The range of audible pitches varies among different species of animals. As noted, humans can hear between about 20 and 20,000 Hz (conversation averages 90–300 Hz). Insectivorous bats, toothed whales, and

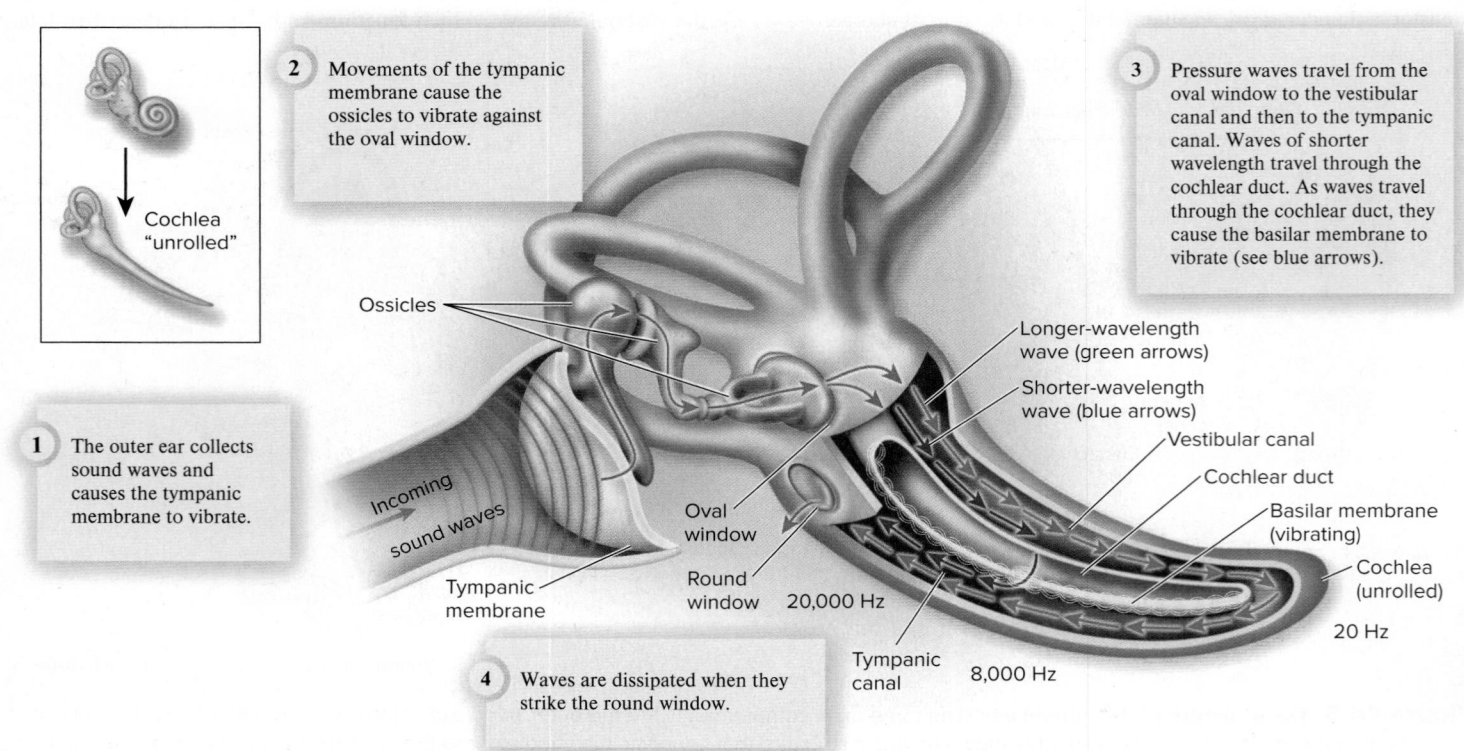

Figure 44.6 **Movement of pressure waves through the human ear.**

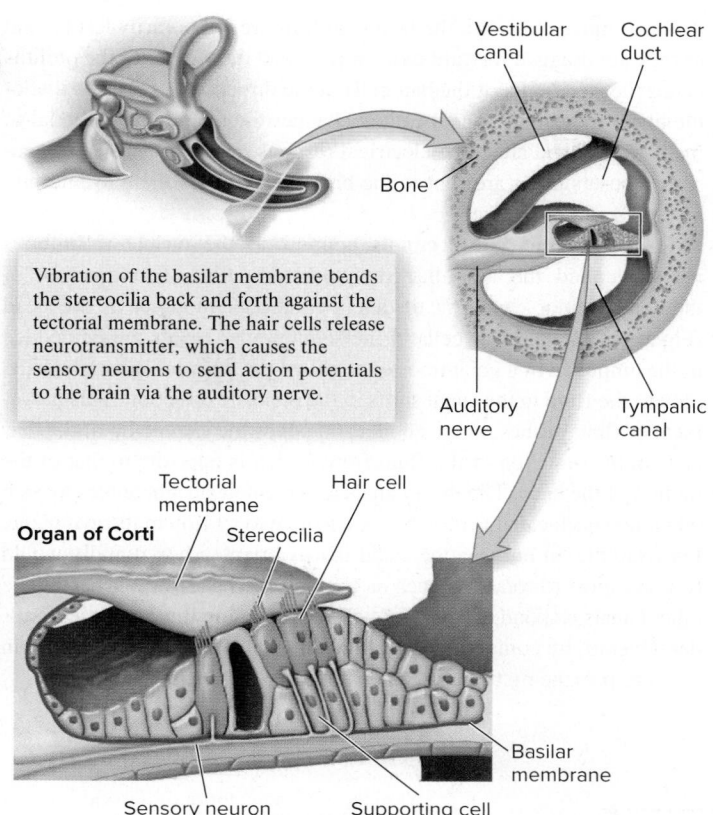

Vibration of the basilar membrane bends the stereocilia back and forth against the tectorial membrane. The hair cells release neurotransmitter, which causes the sensory neurons to send action potentials to the brain via the auditory nerve.

Organ of Corti

Figure 44.7 **Transduction of mechanical vibrations to action potentials in the organ of Corti.**

Concept Check: *What causes vibration of the basilar membrane?*

some species of moths may have the highest-frequency sensitivity (to 100,000–240,000 Hz), and baleen whales and elephants may have the lowest-frequency sensitivity (to nearly 1 Hz). These adaptations increase the animals' ability to communicate and survive. For instance, low-frequency sounds carry great distances through water or air and hearing them is especially useful for animals with large territories.

A vital feature of hearing is the ability to determine the direction from which a sound originates. For example, this ability may make the difference between a successful and an unsuccessful predator. How does an animal locate a sound? Under most circumstances, sound does not arrive at both ears simultaneously. Sound waves coming from the right, for example, excite the sensory receptors in an animal's right ear first and the left ear some milliseconds later, and therefore the brain receives action potentials from the auditory nerves of each ear at slightly different times. The brain interprets the time difference to determine the direction from which a sound came.

Animals such as owls that rely on hearing to pinpoint prey, particularly in the dark, tend to be extremely good at identifying the direction of a sound. An interesting experiment demonstrated this by outfitting owls in a dark room with small headphones. Just as in a human hearing test, sounds could be sent to either headphone or to both. If the investigator sent a high-pitched noise (that mimicked the sounds of a mouse) first to the left headphone and then a single millisecond later to the right headphone, the owl turned its head to the left, because the owl's brain perceived the sound to be coming from that direction. If

the noises reached both headphones simultaneously, the owl behaved as if the signal was coming from directly in front of its head.

Bats in the air, whales and dolphins in the sea, and shrews in underground tunnels generate high-frequency sound waves to determine the location of an object. In this phenomenon, called **echolocation**, the sound waves bounce off a distant object and return to the animal, like an echo. The time it takes for the sound to return to each ear indicates the distance and direction of the object. Echolocation is especially useful in situations where vision is limited, such as in the dark.

The Sense of Balance Is Mediated by Statocysts in Invertebrates and by the Vestibular System in Vertebrates

Let's now turn our attention to another form of mechanoreception, the sense of balance, also called equilibrium. Balance is part of a broader sense called proprioception, which is an animal's ability to sense the position, orientation, and movement of its body. Being able to sense body position is vital for the survival of animals. This is how a lobster, for example, rights itself when flipped over by a predator or how a bird maintains its balance while flying.

Statocysts   Many aquatic invertebrates have sensory organs called **statocysts** that send information to the brain about the position of the animal in space (**Figure 44.8**). Statocysts are small round structures consisting of an outer sphere of hair cells and one or more **statoliths**, which are tiny granules of sand or other dense objects. When the

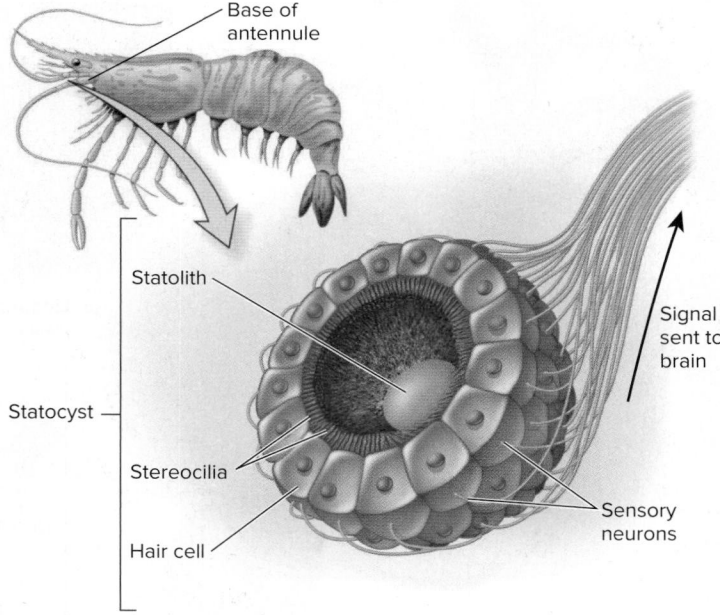

Figure 44.8 **Sensing of balance in aquatic invertebrates.** Statocysts located near the antennae consist of a sphere of sensory hair cells surrounding one or more stony statoliths. When the animal moves, gravity shifts the statolith and stimulates the hair cells beneath it.

 Core Skill: Connections Is the use of statoliths unique to animals? Look back to Figure 37.14 for help.

animal moves, gravity alters the statoliths' position. If the animal turns on its side, for example, the movement of statoliths stimulates a new set of hair cells to release neurotransmitter, generating action potentials in sensory neurons that inform the brain of the change in body position.

Several experiments have demonstrated the importance of statoliths. In one particularly dramatic example, researchers replaced the statoliths of crayfish with iron filings. Moving a magnet to different positions around the animal displaced the filings, causing the animal to change its position, and even to swim upside-down when the magnet was placed directly above its head.

The Vestibular System   The organ of balance in vertebrates, known as the **vestibular system**, is located in the inner ear next to the cochlea (**Figure 44.9**). The vestibular system is composed of a series of fluid-filled sacs and tubules, which provide information about either linear or rotational movements. The utricle and saccule, the two sacs nearest the cochlea, detect linear movements of the head (Figure 44.9a), such as those that occur when an animal runs, jumps, or changes its posture. The hair cells within these structures are embedded in a gelatinous substance that contains granules of calcium carbonate called **otoliths** (from the Latin, meaning ear stones), which are analogous to statoliths. When

the head moves forward, the heavy otoliths are temporarily left behind as they are dragged forward more slowly, and the weight of the otoliths bends the stereocilia of the hair cells in the direction opposite to that of the linear movement. This bending changes the membrane potential of the hair cells and alters the electrical responses of nearby sensory neurons. These signals are sent to the brain, which uses them to interpret how the head has moved.

Three **semicircular canals** connect to the utricle at bulbous regions called the ampullae (singular, ampulla). The function of the semicircular canals is to detect rotational motions of the head (Figure 44.9). The hair cells in the semicircular canals are embedded in the ampullae in a gelatinous cone called the **cupula**. When the head moves, the fluid in the canal shifts in the opposite direction. This movement of fluid pushes on the cupula and bends the stereocilia of the hair cells in the direction of the fluid flow, which is opposite to that of the motion of the head. The three canals are oriented at right angles to each other, and each canal is maximally sensitive to motion in its own plane. For example, in humans the canal that is oriented horizontally would respond most to rotations such as shaking the head "no," whereas the other canals respond to "yes" motions or to tipping the ear to the shoulder. Overall, by comparing the signals from the three canals, the brain can interpret the motion of the head in three dimensions.

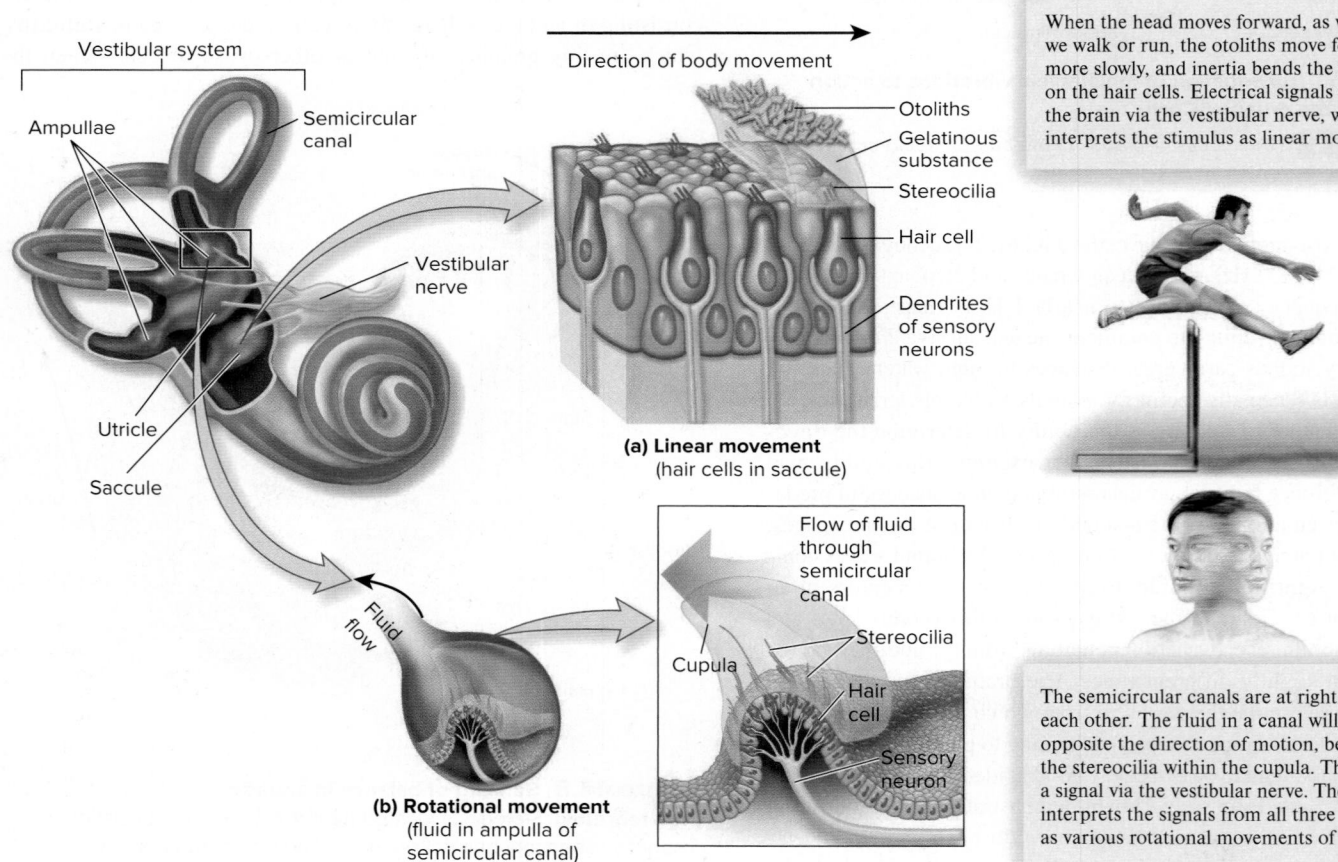

When the head moves forward, as when we walk or run, the otoliths move forward more slowly, and inertia bends the stereocilia on the hair cells. Electrical signals are sent to the brain via the vestibular nerve, which interprets the stimulus as linear motion.

The semicircular canals are at right angles to each other. The fluid in a canal will move opposite the direction of motion, bending the stereocilia within the cupula. This sends a signal via the vestibular nerve. The brain interprets the signals from all three canals as various rotational movements of the head.

Direction of body movement

Otoliths
Gelatinous substance
Stereocilia
Hair cell
Dendrites of sensory neurons

(a) Linear movement
(hair cells in saccule)

Flow of fluid through semicircular canal
Cupula
Stereocilia
Hair cell
Sensory neuron
Fluid flow

(b) Rotational movement
(fluid in ampulla of semicircular canal)

Vestibular system
Ampullae
Semicircular canal
Vestibular nerve
Utricle
Saccule

Figure 44.9   The vertebrate vestibular system.

Concept Check: *Note the orientation of the three semicircular canals with respect to each other. Why are the canals oriented in three different planes?*

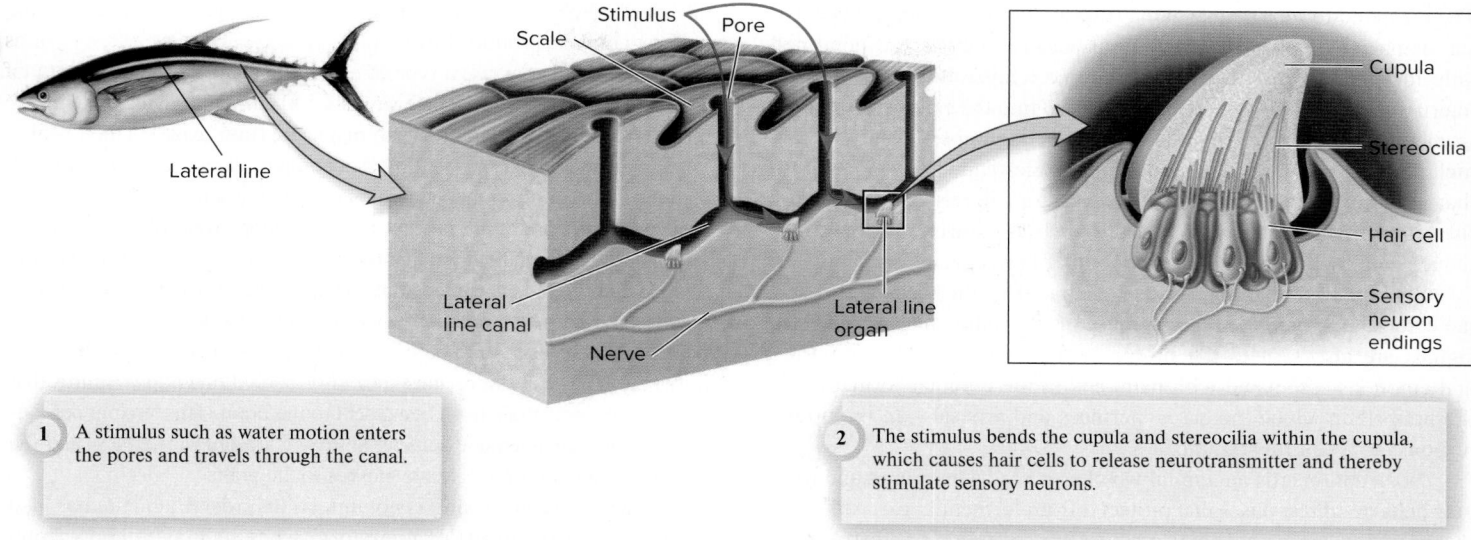

1 A stimulus such as water motion enters the pores and travels through the canal.

2 The stimulus bends the cupula and stereocilia within the cupula, which causes hair cells to release neurotransmitter and thereby stimulate sensory neurons.

Figure 44.10 Mechanoreceptors in the lateral line system of fishes that detect changes in water movement.

The vestibular system of vertebrates provides conscious information about body position and movement. It also supplies unconscious information for reflexes that maintain normal posture, control head and eye movements, and assist in locomotion. Researchers have discovered correlations between the types of locomotion in which an animal engages, and the size of its semicircular canals relative to the animal's body mass. Among primates, for example, agile animals with jerky forms of locomotion, such as leaping tarsiers, have much larger canals than do lorises, which are quadripedal and move slowly.

Mechanoreceptors in the Lateral Line System Detect Movements in Water

Fishes and some toads detect changes in their environment through a **lateral line system** (**Figure 44.10**). This sensory system has hair cells that detect changes in water currents brought about by waves, nearby moving objects, and low-frequency sounds traveling through the water. The lateral line system runs along both sides of the body and the head of the animal. Small pores let water enter into a lateral line canal. The stereocilia of hair cells of each lateral line organ protrude into a gelatinous structure called a cupula (similar to the cupula of the vertebrate vestibular system). When the cupula is moved by the water, the stereocilia bend, causing the release of neurotransmitter from the hair cell. This stimulates a response in sensory neurons at the base of the hair cells. The response provides information to the brain about changes in water movement, such as the approach of a predator.

44.3 Thermoreception and Nociception

Learning Outcome:

1. **CoreSKILL »** Distinguish between thermoreception and nociception, and propose reasons why they are vital to the safety and survival of an animal.

The perception of temperature and pain enables animals to respond effectively to potentially dangerous changes in their environments. As described in this section, these sensory stimuli are related in that their receptors are located in some of the same areas (for example, the skin; see Figure 44.3), share similar physical features, and under certain conditions result in similar perceptions.

Thermoreceptors Detect Temperature

Sensing the outside temperature is important for animals because their body temperature is affected by the external temperature. This is particularly true for ectotherms, animals whose body temperature changes with the environmental temperature. Animals can survive only if their body temperature remains within certain limits, because cell membranes and the proteins in cells function optimally only within a particular temperature range. There are two types of thermoreceptors: those that respond to hot and those that respond to cold. Both types are sensory neurons without any structural specializations or associated structures, unlike most mechanoreceptors, for example. The peripheral endings of these sensory neurons respond to cold or hot temperatures by activating or inhibiting enzymes within their plasma membranes, which alters membrane ion channels.

In addition to skin thermoreceptors that sense the outside temperature, thermoreceptors in various organs and the brains of some animals also detect changes in core body temperature. Activation of thermoreceptors triggers physiological and behavioral adjustments that help maintain homeostasis. These adjustments, described in Chapter 47, include shivering, changes in blood flow to or away from the skin, and behaviors such as seeking shade or sunlight. In addition, thermoreceptors are often linked with reflexive behaviors, such as when an animal steps on a hot surface and pulls its foot away.

Nociceptors Warn of Pain

Like thermoreceptors, nociceptors are sensory neurons with free peripheral endings in the skin and internal organs (see Figure 44.3).

They respond to local tissue damage or to stimuli that may cause tissue damage. Nociceptors are unusual because they can respond not only to external stimuli, such as extreme temperatures, but also to internal stimuli, such as molecules released into the extracellular fluid from injured cells. Damaged cells release a number of substances, including acids and small signaling molecules called prostaglandins, that cause inflammation and make nociceptors more sensitive to painful stimuli. Anti-inflammatory drugs such as aspirin and ibuprofen reduce pain by preventing the production of prostaglandins.

Signals arising from nociceptors travel to the CNS and reach the cerebrum, where the type or cause of the pain is interpreted. The signals are also sent to the limbic system, which holds memories and emotions associated with pain, and to the reticular formation in the brainstem, which increases alertness and arousal—an important response to a painful stimulus.

Nociception tells an animal whether it has been injured and triggers behavioral responses that protect it from further danger. Although in many cases we cannot know whether or how animals perceive pain, nociceptors have been identified in all classes of vertebrates and in many invertebrates.

44.4 Electromagnetic Reception

Learning Outcome:

1. Identify ways that animals use electromagnetic receptors to sense their environments.

Electromagnetic receptors detect radiation within a wide range of the electromagnetic spectrum, including those wavelengths that correspond to visible light, UV light, and infrared light, as well as electrical and magnetic stimuli. Photoreceptors are specialized electromagnetic receptors that respond to light and are described in Section 44.5. Here, we will examine the ability of some animals to sense electric and magnetic fields and also heat in the form of infrared radiation.

The ability to detect the presence of nearby prey or predators can be especially challenging in animals that inhabit low-light environments. The more ways an animal has to detect other animals, the better it can avoid danger or obtain food. One mechanism found widely in fishes is electroreception, in which specialized sensory structures detect electric fields in the environment. There are two general types of electroreception. First, many fishes living in dark waters can detect the weak electric field generated by the activity of excitable tissues such as the muscles and nerves of other animals. To do this, they use exquisitely sensitive electroreceptors located in pores in the head region. These sensory receptors are as heavily innervated as the eyes of these fishes, suggesting the importance of this sense for their survival. Sharks and rays in particular can detect even the tiny electrical signals generated by the beating hearts of prey hiding beneath a layer of sand on the ocean floor. In a second type of electroreception, some fishes generate their own electric fields with a special organ derived from excitable tissue. As a fish swims through its environment, nearby objects will disturb this field and this disturbance can be sensed by the fish. This might happen, for example, if a potential prey or predator moved close to the animal. Although electroreception is primarily found in fishes, it is not unique to them. The platypus, a mammal that lives in the murky waters of streams and ponds,

has electroreceptors on the skin of its bill that can detect very small electric currents produced by its prey.

Homing pigeons use a type of electromagnetic sensing to return to their starting points from as far away as 1,500 km. This navigational feat is made possible by small particles of magnetite (iron oxide) in their beaks, which indicate direction by acting as a compass. The magnetite particles respond to the Earth's magnetic field and alter the activity of neurons that project into the brain. In one experiment, pigeons were placed individually in large tubes and trained that food was present in only one end of the tube. When the tube was placed in a changeable magnetic field, pigeons readily learned which end contained food based solely on the magnetic polarity of the tube. In another experiment, the pigeons lost this ability when their beaks were anesthetized or cooled down, procedures that block action potentials from being sent to the brain. This finding demonstrates that their magnetic sensing ability is located in the beak and the sensations are communicated by nerves to the brain.

Magnetic field sensing is not unique to birds. Magnetite has also been found in the heads of migratory fishes such as rainbow trout. However, this probably does not entirely explain the extraordinary ability of migratory animals to navigate great distances, because other cues, such as smell and visual recognition of landmarks, also appear to play roles in this process.

Venomous snakes known as pit vipers (a group that includes copperheads and rattlesnakes) can localize prey in the dark with detectors that sense the heat emitted from animals as infrared radiation. These detectors are located in pits on each side of the head between the eyes and nostrils (**Figure 44.11**). Within the pit, a thin, nerve-rich, temperature-sensitive membrane becomes activated in response to infrared waves emitted by live animals. When the snake detects the heat of the animal, it localizes its prey by moving its head back and forth until both pits detect the same intensity of radiation. This indicates that the prey is centered in front of the snake.

Electrical, magnetic, and infrared sensing are adaptations for long-distance migration or low-light environments. When light is plentiful, however, photoreception, discussed in the next section, becomes a dominant sensory ability in many animals.

Pit—contains heat sensors

Figure 44.11 Infrared sensing. Sensory pits enable a white-lipped pit viper (*Cryptelytrops albolabris*) to detect the heat given off by its prey. ©Daniel Heuclin/Science Source

Concept Check: *What advantage does having sensory pits on both sides of the head provide to a pit viper?*

44.5   Photoreception

Learning Outcomes:

1. Describe the structure of invertebrate visual organs.
2. Describe the structure of the vertebrate (single-lens) eye, and explain how its structure is related to its ability to form images.
3. Compare and contrast the structure and function of rods and cones.
4. Describe the steps involved in the mechanisms by which photoreceptors respond to light in a single-lens eye.
5. Outline the neural pathway by which visual signals travel to reach the brain.

Although it is a form of electromagnetic reception, photoreception is such an important and widespread sense that we will cover it separately here. Visual systems employ specialized neurons called photoreceptors, which detect photons of light arriving from the Sun or other light sources or reflecting off an object. A photon is the fundamental unit of electromagnetic radiation and has the properties of both a particle and a wave. The properties of light are described in Chapter 8. In this section, we will examine the organs found in animals, usually called **eyes**, that detect light and send signals to the brain. The amazing features of these organs reflect the importance of vision in the animal world.

Eyecups and Compound Eyes Are Found in Many Invertebrates

The ability to sense light is an ancient adaptation found even in many unicellular organisms, where it may provide a selection advantage for photosynthesis or protection. Typically, such organisms may have a single eyespot that contains a small number of light-sensitive molecules, but they lack the ability to discern the direction of a light source or to interpret a visual image.

Eyecups   A slightly more sophisticated visual organ is found in free-living flatworms such as *Planaria*. These animals have two concave structures called **eyecups** (**Figure 44.12**). Each eyecup contains the endings of photoreceptor cells and a layer of pigment cells that shields the photoreceptors from one side. The left and right eyecups receive light from different directions. This allows the eyecups to detect not only the presence or absence of light, but also its direction. The nervous system compares the amount of light detected by each eyecup, and the flatworm moves toward darkness, a behavior that protects it from predators. However, this type of photoreceptor does not form visual images of the environment.

Compound Eyes   In contrast, arthropods and some annelids have image-forming **compound eyes** (**Figure 44.13a**), which consist of several hundred to more than 10,000 light detectors called **ommatidia** (singular, ommatidium) (**Figure 44.13b**). Each ommatidium makes up one facet of the eye. Within the ommatidium, a two-part **lens**—composed of an outer region called the cornea and an inner crystalline cone—focuses light onto a long central structure called a rhabdom (**Figure 44.13c**). The rhabdom is a column of light-sensitive microvilli that project from the cell membranes of the photoreceptor cells of the ommatidium (**Figure 44.13d**). The light-sensitive molecules required for vision are located in the microvilli. The extensive surface area imparted by the microvilli provides the eye with increased sensitivity to light. Pigmented cells surrounding the photoreceptor cells absorb

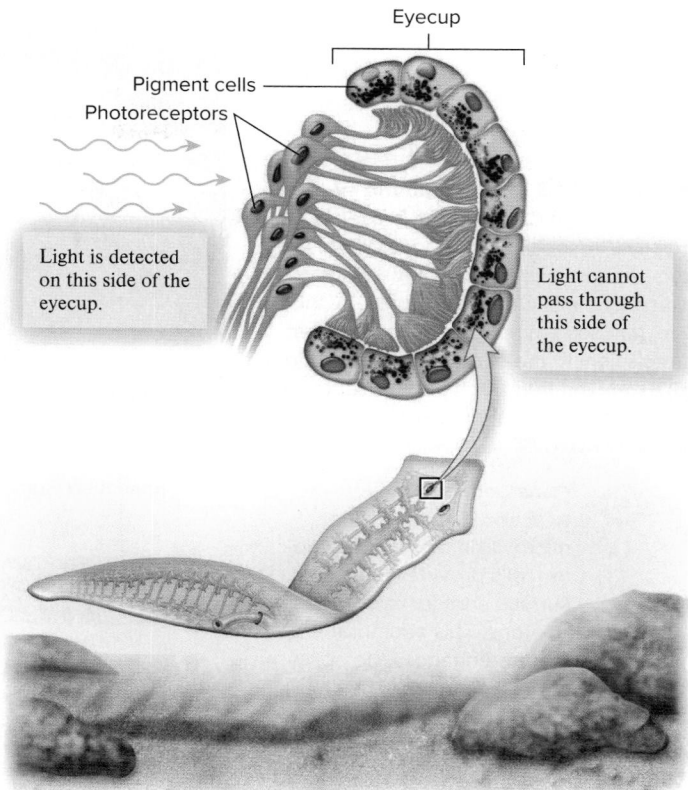

Figure 44.12   The eyecup of a flatworm. The orientation of the eyecup allows light to stimulate photoreceptors from primarily one direction. This type of visual organ senses the presence or absence of light and its direction, but does not form visual images.

excess light and thereby isolate each ommatidium from its neighbors. Thus, each ommatidium is pointed at one narrow area in space.

Each ommatidium senses the intensity and color of light. Although each ommatidium receives light from only a very narrow field, collectively they provide animals with a wide viewing area. Combining the different inputs from neighboring ommatidia, the compound eye is believed to form a mosaic-type image that the brain interprets. Animals such as bees and fruit flies, with large numbers of ommatidia, presumably have sharper vision and a wider field of vision than do those with fewer sensory cells, such as grasshoppers.

As anyone who has tried to swat a fly knows, the compound eye is extremely sensitive to movement as an object moves across successive ommatidia. This helps flying insects evade birds and other predators. Behavioral studies have shown, however, that the resolving power of even the best compound eye is considerably less than that of the single-lens eye, which we consider next.

Vertebrates and Some Invertebrates Have a Single-Lens Eye

Structure of the Single-Lens Eye   **Single-lens eyes** are found in vertebrates and also in some mollusks, such as squid, octopuses, and some snails, and in some annelids. In such eyes, different patterns of light emitted from or reflected off objects in the animal's field of view are transmitted through a small opening, or **pupil**, through a single focusing lens, to a sheetlike layer of photoreceptors in the **retina** at the back of the eye (**Figure 44.14a**). The light inputs form a

Figure 44.13 The compound eye of insects. (a) Close-up of the eyes of a fruit fly (*Drosophila melanogaster*). **(b)** Each eye has approximately 1,000 ommatidia, which form a sheet on the surface of the eye. **(c)** Each ommatidium has a lens that directs light to the photosensitive rhabdom. **(d)** Extending from each photoreceptor cell and forming the rhabdom are many light-sensitive microvilli. a: ©Omikron/Science Source

 Core Concept: Structure and Function The microvilli in the photoreceptor cells provide a large surface area for capturing photons. This structural feature enhances the ability of a photoreceptor cell to function as a light detector.

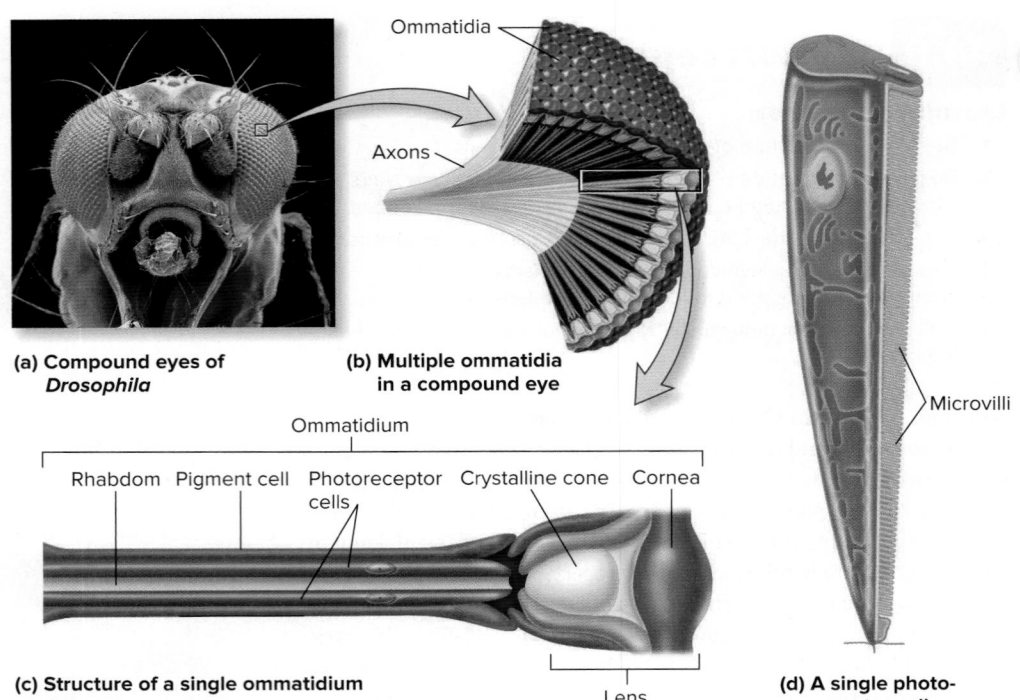

(a) Compound eyes of Drosophila

(b) Multiple ommatidia in a compound eye

Ommatidia

Axons

Ommatidium

Rhabdom   Pigment cell   Photoreceptor cells   Crystalline cone   Cornea

(c) Structure of a single ommatidium

Lens

Microvilli

(d) A single photo-receptor cell

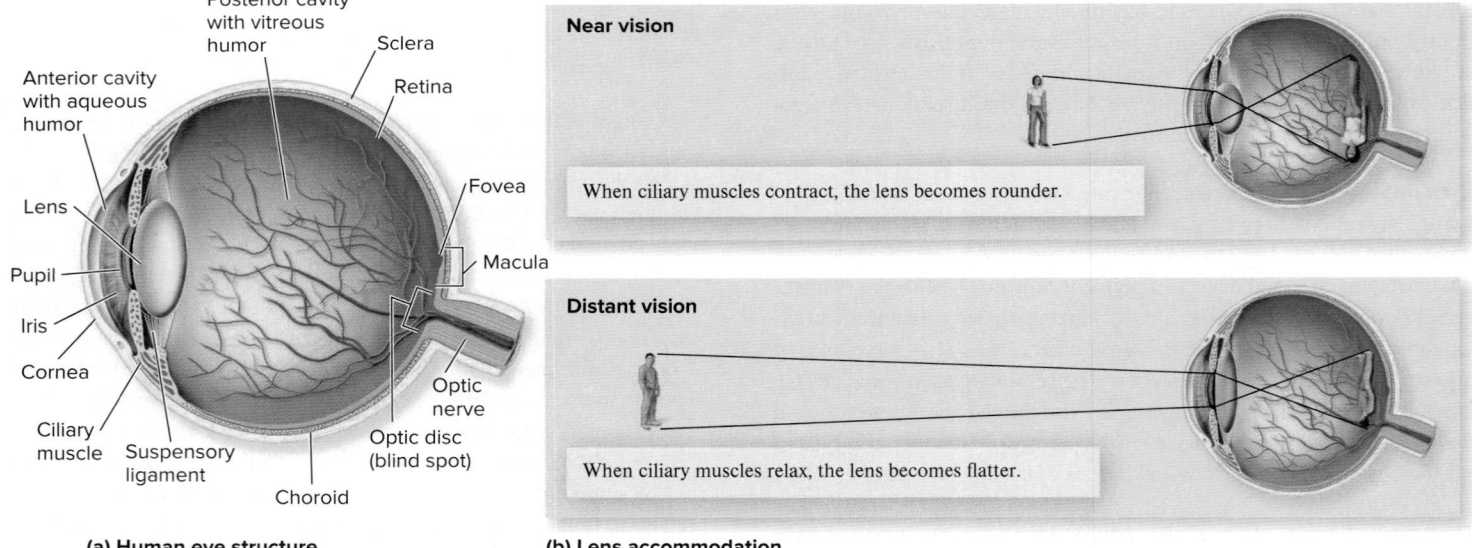

(a) Human eye structure

Posterior cavity with vitreous humor
Sclera
Anterior cavity with aqueous humor
Retina
Lens
Fovea
Pupil
Macula
Iris
Cornea
Optic nerve
Ciliary muscle
Optic disc (blind spot)
Suspensory ligament
Choroid

Near vision

When ciliary muscles contract, the lens becomes rounder.

Distant vision

When ciliary muscles relax, the lens becomes flatter.

(b) Lens accommodation

Figure 44.14 The vertebrate single-lens eye. (a) The structure of the human eye. **(b)** Changes in lens shape during accommodation. When an object is near, the ciliary muscles contract and the lens becomes rounder, causing light to bend more. When the object is far away, the ciliary muscles relax and the lens flattens. **(c)** Demonstration of the blind spot. First, position this picture in front of your face. Next, close your left eye and stare at the black spot with your right eye while you move the picture toward and away from your face. At some point, light reflecting off the plus (+) sign will fall directly on your optic disc, and it will seem to disappear. It will then reappear as you continue moving the picture.

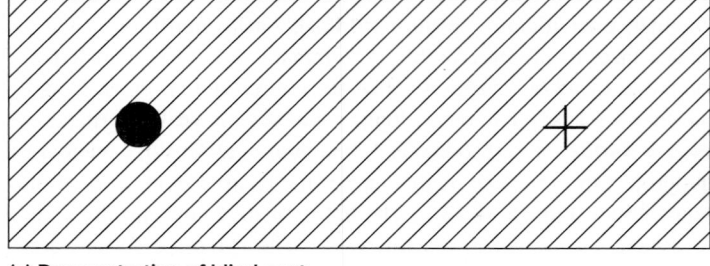

(c) Demonstration of blind spot

visual image of the environment on the retina. The activation of these photoreceptors triggers electrical changes in neurons that pass out of the eye through the **optic nerves**, which carry the signals to the brain. The brain then interprets the visual image that was transmitted.

As illustrated in Figure 44.14a, the vertebrate eye has a tough outer sheath called the sclera (the white of the eye). Between the sclera and the retina is a layer of blood vessels called the choroid. At the front of the eye, the sclera is continuous with a thin, clear layer known as the **cornea**. As in compound eyes, the cornea functions partly to focus light in single-lens eyes, and it also plays a protective role. In single-lens eyes, however, the lens plays the major role in focusing light onto photoreceptors.

Within the vertebrate eye are two cavities, the anterior and posterior cavities. The anterior cavity is the part of the eye between the lens and the cornea. Within this cavity is the **iris**—the circle of pigmented smooth muscle responsible for eye color. The anterior cavity is largely filled with a thin liquid called the aqueous humor that helps maintain eye pressure and shape, and may serve a nutritive function. The larger posterior cavity between the lens and the retina contains the thicker vitreous humor, which further helps maintain the shape of the eye.

The hole in the center of the iris is the pupil. The size of the pupil changes when the smooth muscles of the iris reflexively relax or contract to allow more or less light to enter the eye.

Light Focusing   Because light radiates in all directions from a light source, light must be bent (refracted) inward toward the photoreceptors at the back of the eye. This is accomplished by the cornea and the lens. Whenever light passes from one medium to another medium of a different density, light waves will bend (try looking at a pencil in a glass partly filled with water). The cornea, which is at the interface between the air and the aqueous humor, initially refracts the light. The light then passes through the lens, where it is refracted again and focused onto the layer of photoreceptors, the retina, at the back of the posterior chamber. The bending of the incoming light results in an upside-down and laterally inverted image on the retina, but the brain adjusts for this, and the image is perceived correctly.

The lens is adjusted to focus light that originates from different distances. In fishes and amphibians, the lens is moved forward or backward. In the avian and mammalian eye, the lens remains stationary but changes shape to become more or less round. When the lens is stretched, it flattens, and light passing through it bends less than when it is round. Contraction and relaxation of the ciliary muscles adjust the lens according to the angle at which light enters the eye, a process called **accommodation** (**Figure 44.14b**).

How does the retina form sharp images? The region on the retina directly in line with the pupil and lens is called the macula. Near the center of the macula is the **fovea**, which contains the highest density of photoreceptors for color. The fovea is responsible for the sharpness with which we and many other animals see in daylight. However, the retina also has limitations in forming images. In the eye, as mentioned, the image initiates signals that travel from the retina to the brain through neurons in the optic nerves that exit the eye. In vertebrates, the point on the retina where the optic nerve leaves the eye is called the **optic disc**. The optic disc does not have any photoreceptors, forming a blind spot where light does not activate a response (**Figure 44.14c**). Invertebrates with single-lens eyes do not have a blind spot, because the photoreceptors in their eyes are at the front of the retina. Therefore, the optic nerve does not pass through the layer of photoreceptors before leaving the eye.

Rods and Cones Are Photoreceptor Cells

Vertebrates have two types of photoreceptors with names that are derived from their shapes: rods and cones (**Figure 44.15**). **Rods** are very sensitive to low-intensity light and can respond to as little as one photon, but they do not discriminate different colors. Rods are useful mostly at night, and they send signals to the brain that generate a black-and-white visual image. **Cones** are less sensitive to low levels of light but, unlike rods, are sensitive to wavelengths of light that allow animals to perceive color.

Rods and cones are cells with three functional parts: the outer segment, the inner segment, and the synaptic terminal. The **outer segment** of the cell contains folds of membranes that form stacks like discs (**Figure 44.16**). These discs contain the pigment molecules that absorb light. The **inner segment** of the cell contains the cell nucleus and other cytoplasmic organelles. Rods and cones do not have axons but have synaptic terminals with neurotransmitter-containing vesicles, which synapse with neurons within the retina.

Nocturnal animals (those active predominantly at night) rely primarily on rod vision, though some do have limited color vision. In diurnal animals (active predominantly by day) with both rods and cones, such as humans, the rods are located around the periphery of the retina away from the fovea. Therefore, it is easiest to see low-intensity light if it comes into the eye at an angle. You can easily verify this. In early evening, before many stars are visible, look at the sky until you notice a star out of the corner of your eye. Now shift your gaze to where you thought you saw the star. You will probably not be able to locate it anymore. When you look away again so that light from the dim star enters your eye at an angle, it will reappear. This demonstrates that under low-light conditions, your vision is better when the light is directed to the part of the retina that contains only rods.

Cones are used in daylight by most diurnal vertebrate species and by some insects such as the honeybee, which can detect the

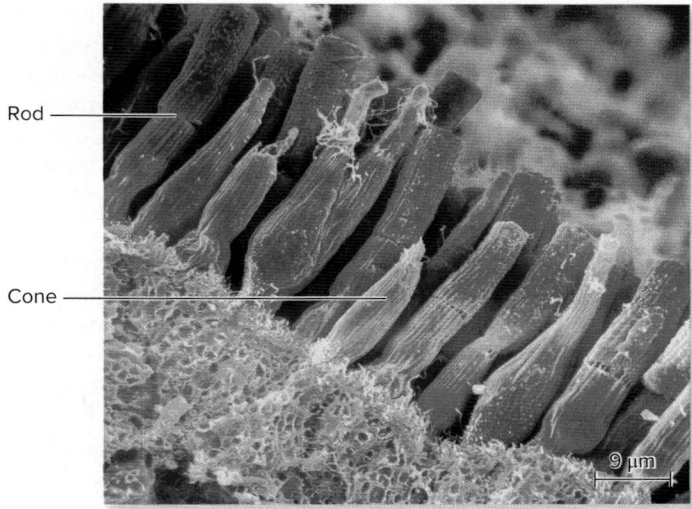

Rod

Cone

9 µm

Figure 44.15 Rod and cone photoreceptors. Rods are shown as green and cones as blue in this false-color scanning electron micrograph (SEM). ©Eye of Science/Science Source

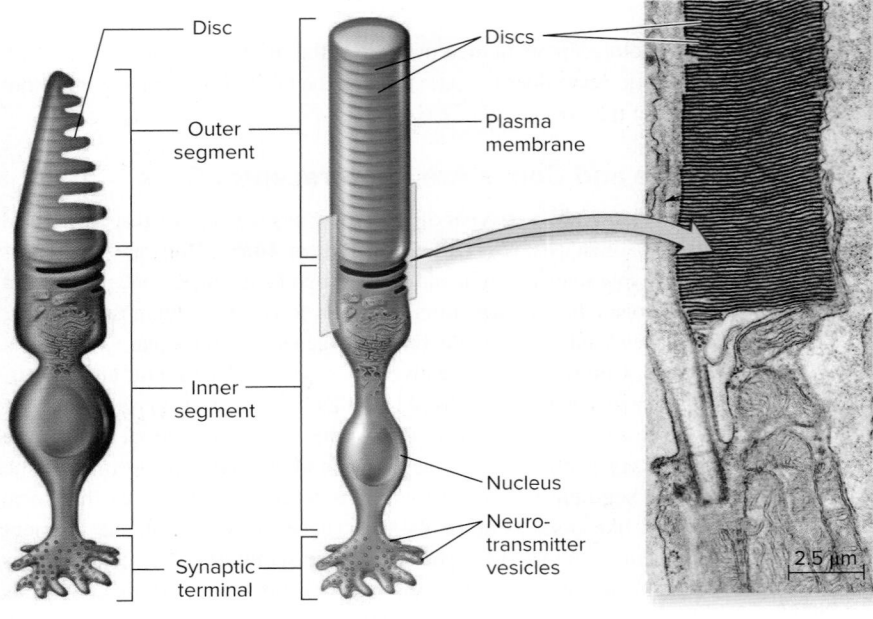

Cone cell   Rod cell

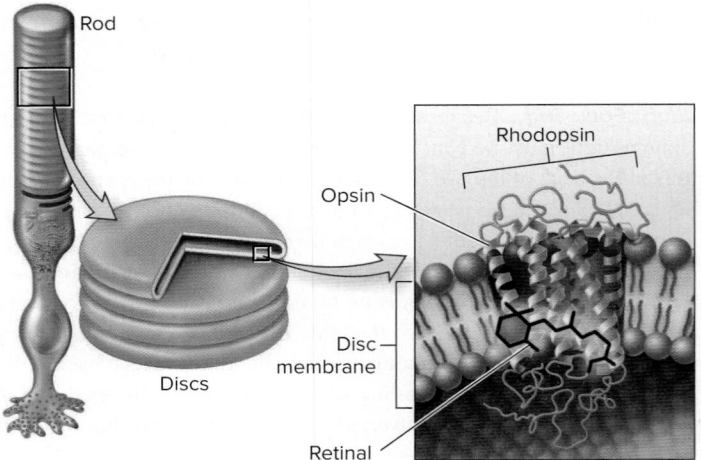

Figure 44.16 Structure of a cone and a rod. The illustration shows the structure of a cone and rod photoreceptor and the appearance of a rod in a transmission electron micrograph (TEM). Note the stacks of multiple membranous discs in the outer segments of the cells. (right): ©Don W. Fawcett/Science Source

Core Skill: Connections Refer back to Figure 44.13d. What structural similarity do the insect and vertebrate photoreceptors share?

yellow color of pollen. Compared to rods, the human retina has fewer cones, which are clustered in and around the fovea. Cones provide sharp images because of their density at the fovea. Although they are less sensitive to light than rods, this is less critical in daylight because the amount of light reaching the eyes at this time far exceeds what is needed to stimulate any photoreceptor cell.

Rods and Cones Contain Visual Pigments That Absorb Light

Visual pigments are molecules that absorb light; they are found embedded in the disc membranes of the outer segments of rods and cones. In the mid-20th century, American biologist and Nobel Laureate George Wald discovered that these pigments consist of two components bonded together. The first component is **retinal**, a derivative of vitamin A that is capable of absorbing light energy. The discovery of retinal in the visual pigment explains the need for vitamin A in the human diet and its importance in vision. The second component of visual pigments is a protein called **opsin**, of which there are several types. Opsins are examples of G-protein-coupled receptors (see Figure 9.7), which trigger a signal transduction pathway that changes the permeability of membrane channels to ions.

Rods and cones have visual pigments containing different types of opsin proteins. These pigments are named according to the type of opsin they contain. In rods, the visual pigment is named **rhodopsin** (**Figure 44.17**). Cones contain any one of several types of visual pigments called cone pigments, or **photopsins**. In humans, photopsins are composed of retinal plus one of three possible opsin proteins. Each type of opsin protein determines the wavelength of light that the retinal in a cone can absorb. For example, each cone pigment in humans responds best to red, green, or blue light. Any given cone cell makes only one type of cone pigment. Many different shades of these colors can be perceived, however, because the brain uses information about the proportion of each type of cone that was stimulated to generate perceptions of all other colors.

Figure 44.17 A visual pigment. The visual pigment rhodopsin is found within the membrane of the rod photoreceptor discs. It is composed of a transmembrane protein, opsin, that is bonded to a molecule of retinal, a derivative of vitamin A that is capable of absorbing light energy.

Core Concept: Structure and Function The stack of discs in the outer segment of a photoreceptor is an excellent example of a structural adaptation that increases surface area without significantly increasing volume, thereby allowing for greater light-capturing ability and improving the function of the cell as a sensory cell.

Core Concept: Evolution

Color Vision Is an Ancient Adaptation in Animals

Color vision requires the presence of at least two types of opsins with optimal sensitivities to light of different wavelengths. Genome analyses and behavioral and neurophysiological testing of many animals have confirmed that color vision is widespread across invertebrate and vertebrate taxa, and arose early in animal evolution. It is debatable why color vision provided a selective advantage to animals. Some investigators hypothesize that it produced more acute vision due to an overall improved contrast and was not originally related to commonly observed phenomena today, including colorful plumage displays or brightly colored flowers. Coloration in plants may have evolved in response to the color sensitivity in animals, not vice versa.

Evolutionary studies indicate that the primordial color sensitivity was to short wavelengths in the ultraviolet/blue region of visible light (refer back to Figure 8.4). From there, additional opsins evolved with sensitivities to medium and longer wavelengths. Most vertebrates have four types of color-sensitive photoreceptors. Some insects, including the butterfly *Papilio xuthus*, have up to six types of light receptors, and certain crustaceans (for example, mantis shrimp) have 12! Such animals presumably see shades of colors we cannot. A well-studied model is the honeybee, which has four color-sensitive photoreceptors that respond to wavelengths ranging from 300 nm to 600 nm (refer back to Figure 8.4). Honeybees can perceive ultraviolet light that is not seen by humans. A rainbow would appear very differently to a honeybee than it does to humans. A rainbow seen by a bee would extend past the blue edge and stop short of the red edge.

As mentioned, most vertebrates have four types of color-sensitive photoreceptors. However, most modern species of mammals are dichromatic; that is, they only have two types of opsins and therefore see a more limited color palette than do other vertebrates. One possible explanation for dichromatic vision may be related to the evolution of mammals. The earliest mammals were probably nocturnal animals. Recall that cones are less sensitive to low levels of light and therefore color vision is limited at night. For this reason, natural selection may have favored a loss of some color-sensitive photoreceptors, thereby allowing for more rods and improving night vision.

Compared with other mammals, primates are an exception to dichromatic color vision. A relatively recent gene duplication event led to the reappearance of a third opsin during the course of primate evolution, one that is sensitive to middle (green) wavelengths. The evolution of this third opsin may have imparted an advantage that allowed fruit and leaf-eating primates to better discern orange, red, and yellow fruits against a background of green leaves, but this is uncertain.

About 92% of human males and over 99% of females have trichromatic color vision. However, deviations from trichromatic color vision may result from defects in the cone pigments arising from mutations in the opsin genes. The most common is red-green color blindness, which occurs predominantly in men (1 in 12 males compared with 1 in 200 females). Individuals with red-green color blindness either lack the red or green cone pigments entirely or, more commonly, have one or both of them in an abnormal form. In one form of red-green color blindness, for example, an abnormal green pigment responds to red light as well as green, making it difficult to discriminate between the two colors.

Researchers have determined that color blindness results from a recessive mutation in one or more genes encoding the opsins. Genes encoding the red and green opsins are located on the X chromosome, but the gene encoding the blue opsin is located on a different chromosome. In males, the presence of only one X chromosome means that a single recessive allele from the mother results in red-

green color blindness, even though the mother herself may not be color blind (**Figure 44.18**). Although there is no cure or treatment for color blindness in humans, in 2009 American researcher Katherine Mancuso and colleagues were able to restore trichromatic color vision in adult squirrel monkeys who had been dichromatic (red-green color blind) since birth. This was accomplished using gene therapy in which the missing opsin gene was introduced into each eye, where it was then expressed in existing photoreceptors. Behavioral testing revealed that the monkeys could, for the first time, distinguish red and green colors. Incredibly, the visual centers of the adult brain were able to perceive this new input immediately, despite not having been "wired" for red-green signals during early life.

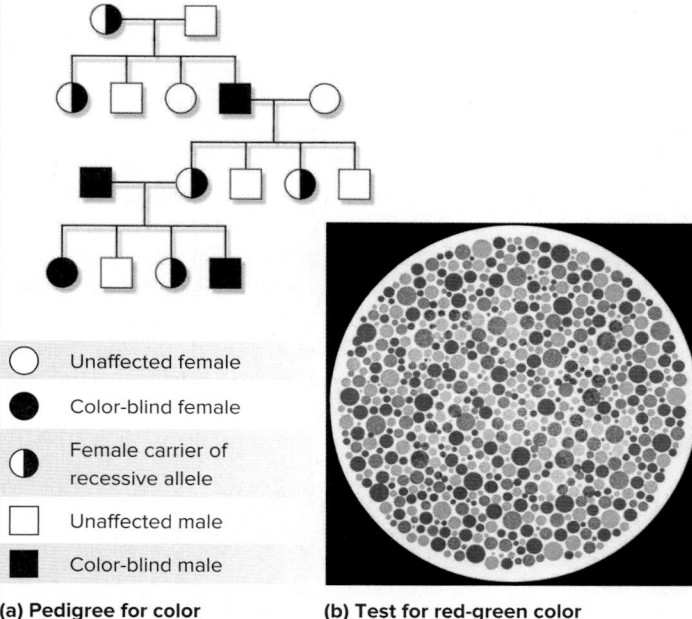

○ Unaffected female

● Color-blind female

◑ Female carrier of recessive allele

☐ Unaffected male

■ Color-blind male

(a) Pedigree for color blindness   **(b) Test for red-green color blindness**

Figure 44.18   Color blindness. (a) A pedigree for red-green color blindness showing all possible offspring. **(b)** A standard eye test to screen for red-green color blindness. People with red-green color blindness will not see the number 74 hidden in this pattern.

b: ©Steve Allen/Getty Images

Concept Check: *Why is red-green color blindness rare in females?*

 Core Skill: Modeling The goal of this modeling challenge is to make predictions about the transmission of color blindness to offspring of parents with genotypes that are different from those in the pedigree shown in Figure 44.18.

Modeling Challenge: Based on your understanding of red-green color blindness (see Figure 44.18), create a Punnett square to predict the ratios of genotypes and phenotypes of offspring from a color-blind mother and a father with normal color vision. Refer back to Section 17.1 for help in setting up a Punnett square, which is a type of model used to predict the outcomes of crosses. Let X^C represent the allele for normal color vision, and X^c the recessive allele that causes color blindness. Remember that only the X chromosome carries this gene.

Photons Change Photoreceptor Activity by Altering the Conformation of Visual Pigments

Photoreceptors differ from other sensory receptor cells because at rest in the dark their membrane is slightly depolarized, whereas in response to a light stimulus, it becomes hyperpolarized (**Figure 44.19**). In the dark, the cell membranes of the outer segments of resting cells are highly permeable to sodium ions. Na^+ diffuses into the cytosol of the cell through open Na^+ channels in the outer segment membrane. The Na^+ channels are gated by intracellular cyclic guanosine monophosphate (cGMP). In the dark, cytosolic concentrations of cGMP are high, keeping Na^+ channels open and depolarizing the cell. This depolarization results in a continuous release of the neurotransmitter glutamate from the synaptic terminal of the photoreceptor. The photoreceptor synapses with a postsynaptic cell that is the next neuron in the visual pathway. This initiates a series of events within the retina that is interpreted by the brain as an absence of light. In contrast, when exposed to light, the Na^+ channels in the outer segment membranes of the photoreceptor close. The resulting decrease in Na^+ concentration leads to a hyperpolarization of the cell. In response, the release of glutamate is stopped. This results in a series of cellular activations within the retina and brain that is interpreted as a visual image.

Let's take a more detailed look at the signal transduction pathway that allows a photoreceptor to respond to light (**Figure 44.20**). When the photoreceptor is exposed to light, the retinal within the visual pigment absorbs a photon. The energy of the photon alters the retinal from *cis*-retinal to *trans*-retinal, an isomer with a slightly different conformation due to a rotation at one of the molecule's double bonds (see Figure 44.20). This change results in retinal briefly

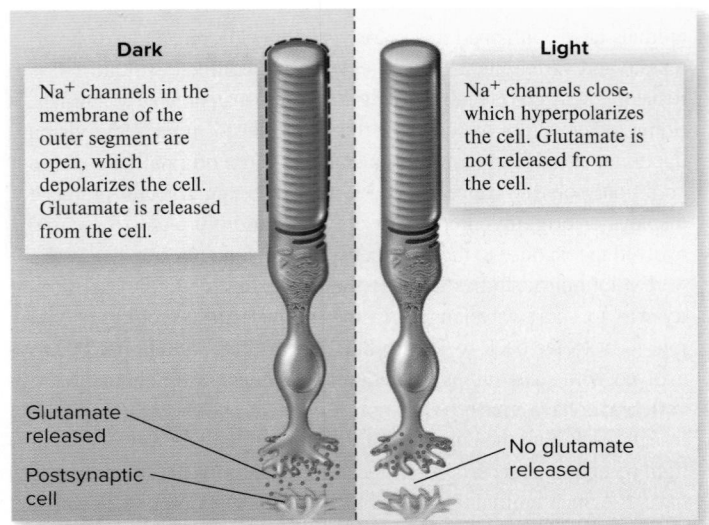

Figure 44.19 Membrane potential response of a photoreceptor to dark and light.

dissociating from the opsin protein, causing the opsin to change its three-dimensional shape and activate a G protein called transducin, located in the disc membrane. The activated transducin, in turn, activates another disc protein, the enzyme phosphodiesterase.

The action of phosphodiesterase results in the closure of Na^+ channels in the outer segment membrane. Remember that in the dark, these channels are kept open by intracellular cGMP. However, when

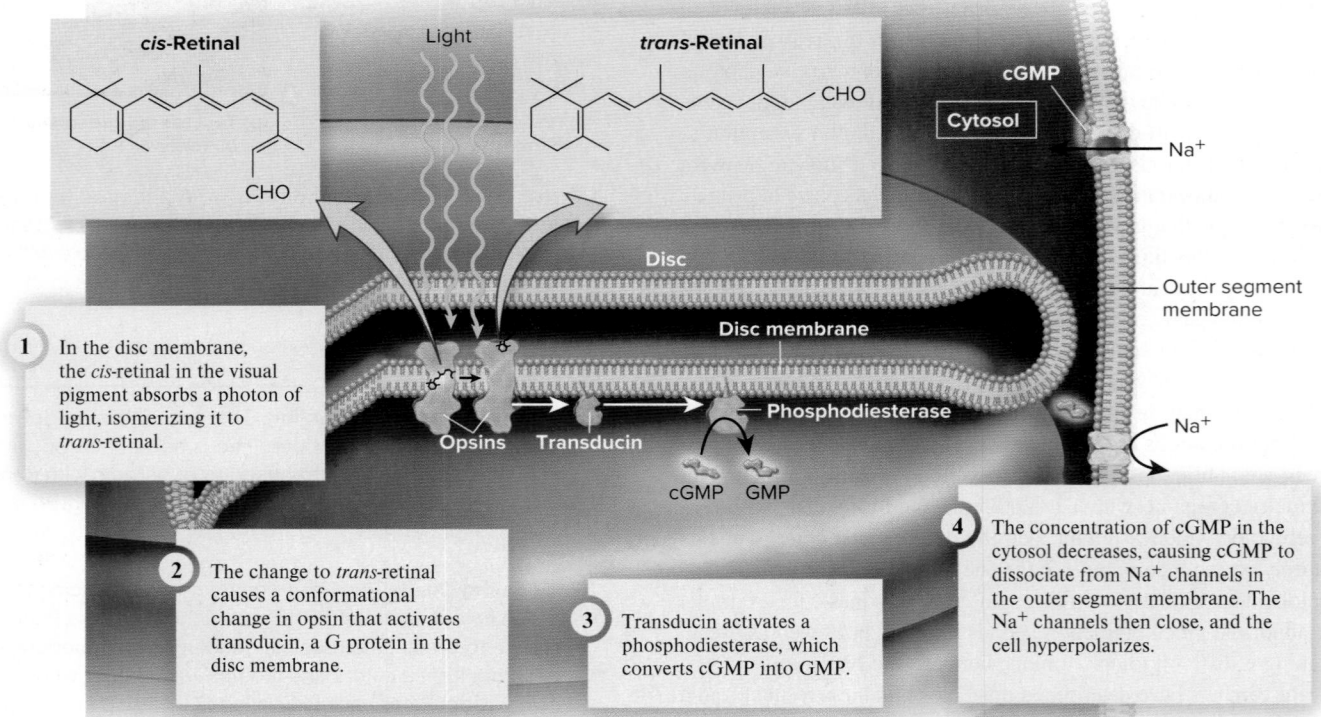

Figure 44.20 Signal transduction pathway in a photoreceptor (rod) cell in response to light.

 Core Concept: Energy and Matter The energy of light alters the configuration of the retinal molecule, causing it to isomerize. This results in a conformational change in the opsin associated with that retinal.

phosphodiesterase is activated, it decreases the concentration of cytosolic cGMP by converting that molecule to GMP. This results in the dissociation of cGMP from the channels, so the channels close, and there is no longer any net diffusion of Na$^+$ into the cell. The membrane potential of the cell becomes less positive than it was in the dark. Therefore, the response of the cell is a hyperpolarization that is proportional to the intensity of the light. The final result is a decrease in glutamate release from the photoreceptor (see Figure 44.19), ultimately leading to a visual image. The sequential activation of enzymes following activation of a single photoreceptor results in an amplification of the original signal (refer back to Figure 9.14). Because of this property, extremely low levels of light are detectable.

The Visual Image Is Refined in the Retina

Thus far, we have considered the structure of the vertebrate eye and how photoreceptors transduce light. We will now turn our attention to the neural pathway through which the visual signal travels to reach the brain. To do so, we must consider the cellular organization of the retina. The vertebrate retina has several layers of cells (**Figure 44.21**). The photoreceptors (rods and cones) form the deepest layer, closest to the

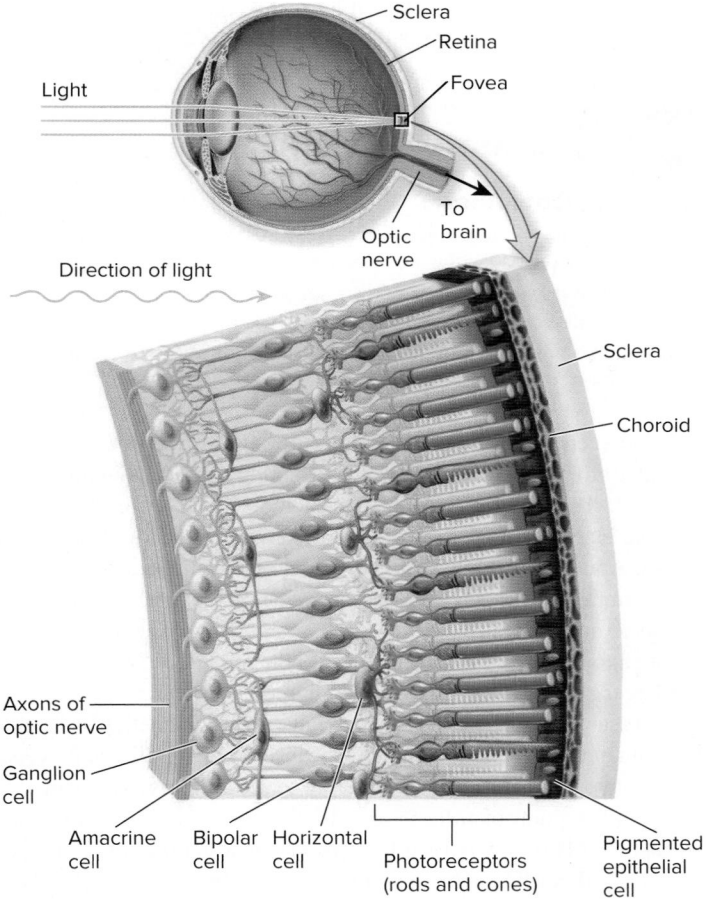

Figure 44.21 The arrangement of cells in the retina. Light passes through layers of cells before it reaches the photoreceptors. Amacrine and horizontal cells integrate the responses of the bipolar and ganglion cells. The ganglion cells generate action potentials that carry the information to the brain.

Concept Check: *With what cells do photoreceptors form synapses?*

sclera. Immediately behind the photoreceptors is a pigmented epithelium that absorbs light that missed the photoreceptors; this absorption prevents scattering of light within the retina, which could degrade the sharpness of vision. Because the photoreceptors are positioned at the back of the retina, light must pass through two transparent layers of cells before it reaches them. The middle layer contains **bipolar cells**, so named because one end (or "pole") of the cell synapses with the photoreceptors, and the other end relays responses to a top layer of cells, the **ganglion cells**. The axons of the ganglion cells extend out of the eye into the optic nerve. In addition, two other types of cells, horizontal and amacrine cells, are interspersed across the retina.

The pathway for light reception begins at the rods and cones. These photoreceptor cells release neurotransmitter molecules that affect the membrane potential of bipolar cells. The membrane potential of the bipolar cells determines the amount of neurotransmitter that they release, which, in turn, controls the membrane potential of ganglion cells. When a threshold potential is reached in ganglion cells, action potentials are sent out of the eye via the optic nerve to the brain. These signals travel along pathways that include the thalamus, brainstem, cerebellum, and the cerebral cortex. Visual information is further refined and interpreted within the vision centers of the cortex. The cortex responds to such characteristics of the visual scene as whether something is moving, how far away it is, how one color compares with another, and the nature of the image (for example, a face). The cortex does not form a picture in the brain, but forms a spatial and temporal pattern of electrical activity that is perceived as an image.

Horizontal and amacrine cells modify electrical signals as they pass from the photoreceptors to the ganglion cells. These cells adjust the signals significantly, enhancing an animal's ability to visualize a scene by emphasizing the differences between images. Horizontal cells make connections between photoreceptors and help to define the boundaries of an image. Amacrine cells are important in adjusting the eye to different light intensities and increasing the sensitivity of the eye to moving images. The ability of the retina to refine the image is especially well developed in birds and reptiles. These animals have complex retinas that process the image extensively before it is interpreted in the brain.

Vertebrate Eyes Are Adapted to Environmental Conditions and Life Histories

Many vertebrates have modifications of their visual systems that are the result of evolutionary adaptations to environmental conditions. Other adaptations have occurred as a result of behavioral requirements for obtaining food or attracting a mate. For instance, raptors can resolve images while flying at speeds close to 150 mph. In another example, cats and certain other animals have reflective surfaces at the backs of their retinas that help direct light onto photoreceptors even in low light conditions such as at night.

Differences in Eye Placement   Except for some of the ray-finned fishes, blunt-headed cetaceans, and most amphibians, vertebrate animals have some degree of **binocular (or stereoscopic) vision**. Animals with both eyes located at or near the front of the head, such as primates and raptors, have greater binocular vision, because the overlapping images coming into both eyes are processed together in the brain to form one perception (**Figure 44.22**). Binocular vision provides excellent depth perception because the images come into each eye from

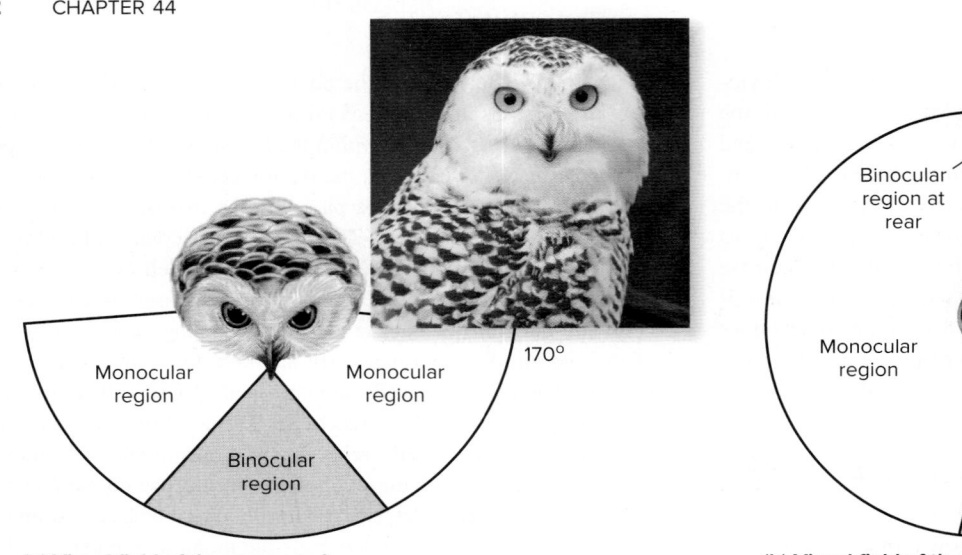

(a) Visual field of the snowy owl

(b) Visual field of the American woodcock

Figure 44.22 Examples of binocular and monocular fields of vision. Visual fields are shown for **(a)** the snowy owl (*Bubo scandiacus*) and **(b)** the American woodcock (*Scolopax minor*). Monocular regions are white; binocular regions are shaded. a: ©Enjoylife2/Getty Images; b: ©Cal Vornberger/Getty Images

slightly different angles. The brain processes those tiny differences to determine where an object is relative to other objects in its environment. Predators benefit from binocular vision because it helps them judge distance and determine the location of their prey. Binocular vision is present in predatory birds such as the snowy owl (Figure 44.22a) and mammals, particularly in arboreal animals that must judge distances between tree limbs. It is not unique to vertebrates, however. Predatory insects such as mantids also have binocular vision.

In contrast, animals with eyes on the sides of the head, such as most fishes, blunt-headed cetaceans, amphibians, herbivorous mammals, and insects, have strictly or primarily **monocular vision**. Monocular vision allows an animal to see a wide area at one time, at the cost of reduced depth perception. Many prey species have monocular vision, which may have evolved because it helps them scan for predators across a wide field of vision. The placement of the eyes in the American woodcock (*Scolopax minor*) actually permits a field of vision of 360°, most of which is monocular (Figure 44.22b). In other words, these and similar birds can see directly behind themselves, even when digging in the dirt for worms!

Vision in the Deep Sea Fishes and other deep-sea vertebrates have color vision that is limited primarily to the color blue. Light with longer wavelengths that would be seen as red or orange does not usually penetrate more than ~6 m into the water, whereas the higher-energy, shorter-wavelength light, which we perceive as blue, can penetrate to greater depths. Aquatic animals that live in the deep sea are usually capable of seeing only blue, because they generally have only one opsin, which is responsive to blue light. Deep-dwelling fishes tend to be drab-colored, because most wavelengths of light do not penetrate that far and therefore could not reflect off the surface of the fishes. Thus, there was no selection pressure for evolving bright coloration. In those deep-dwelling fishes with more than one type of opsin, the additional visual pigments detect the bioluminescence (self-generated light, like that of a firefly) produced by their own or other species.

By contrast, fishes that live near the water's surface sometimes have four or five different opsins, giving them excellent color vision. Not surprisingly, shallow water and surface-dwelling fishes are often very colorful, because light of all wavelengths penetrates shallow water. These fishes have adapted by using coloration for protection (camouflage) or for identification.

44.6 Chemoreception

Learning Outcomes:

1. **CoreSKILL »** Describe olfaction and gustation in animals, and propose reasons why these senses are advantageous.
2. Explain how olfactory receptors respond to the binding of odor molecules.
3. Outline how receptor cells within taste buds respond to the binding of food molecules.

Chemoreception includes the senses of smell (**olfaction**) and taste (**gustation**), both of which involve detecting chemicals in air, water, or food. These chemicals bind to chemoreceptors, which, in turn, initiate electrical responses in other neurons that send signals to the brain. Amazingly, the binding of a single molecule to a receptor cell can sometimes be perceived as an odor! In terrestrial vertebrates, airborne molecules that bind to olfactory receptors must be small enough to be carried in the air and into the nose. Taste molecules can be larger because they are conveyed in food and liquid.

Taste and smell are closely related. The distinction is largely meaningless for aquatic animals, because for them all chemoreception comes through the water. Even in terrestrial animals, about 80% of the perception of taste is actually due to activation of olfactory receptors. (This is why food loses its flavor when the sense of smell is impaired, such as when you have a cold.) In this section, we will explore chemoreception in invertebrates and vertebrates, focusing on insects and mammals since they provide well-studied examples.

Olfaction and Taste in Insects Involve Chemoreceptors in Sensory Hairs

Insects rely on odor and taste for finding food and mates. In insects, chemoreceptors are neurons that are located on sensory hairs on the

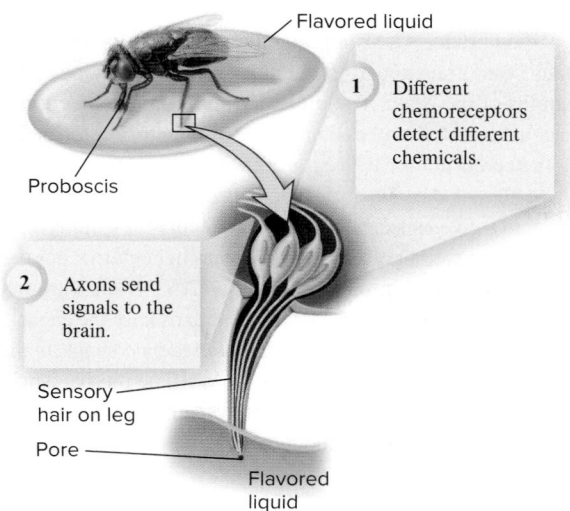

① Different chemoreceptors detect different chemicals.

② Axons send signals to the brain.

Flavored liquid

Proboscis

Sensory hair on leg

Pore

Flavored liquid

(a) Chemoreception in the blowfly

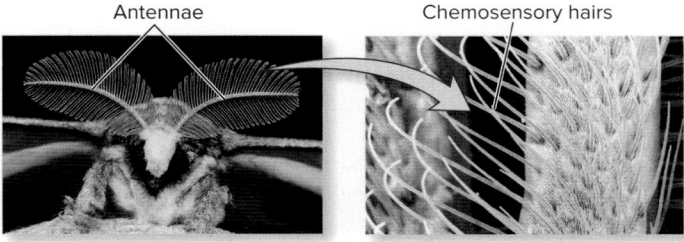

Antennae

Chemosensory hairs

(b) Chemosensory hairs on antennae of the male moth detect the odor molecules.

Figure 44.23 **Chemoreception in insects.** **(a)** Chemosensory cells of the blowfly located on the proboscis, legs, and feet sense different chemicals. **(b)** Chemosensory hairs on a male moth's antennae bind odor molecules secreted by females. b (left): ©Anthony Bannister/Science Source; b (right): Courtesy of Louisa Howard, Dartmouth College

proboscis (coiled tongue), legs, feet, and antennae. Each sensory hair on the proboscis and feet has a pore at the tip through which the substance passes. As one example, **Figure 44.23a** shows a blowfly with four separate chemoreceptors within each hair. Each of these neurons responds to different molecules. Receptors on dendrites of the chemoreceptor cells inside the pore bind to the molecules and initiate a sensory transduction pathway that opens ion channels in the membrane. This depolarizes the plasma membrane of the chemoreceptor cell and generates action potentials, which are sent to the brain for interpretation.

In certain moths, males have elaborate antennae that can sense pheromones, extremely potent signaling molecules given off by a female. The female secretes a sex-attractant pheromone into the air from an abdominal gland. The chemosensory hairs on the male's antennae (**Figure 44.23b**) can detect extremely low concentrations of the pheromone from several kilometers away. This highly sensitive detection system enables the male to locate the female in the dark or at a distance.

Mammalian Olfactory Receptors Respond to the Binding of Odor Molecules

The olfactory sensitivity of mammals varies widely depending on their supply of olfactory receptor cells, which ranges from 5 or 6 million in

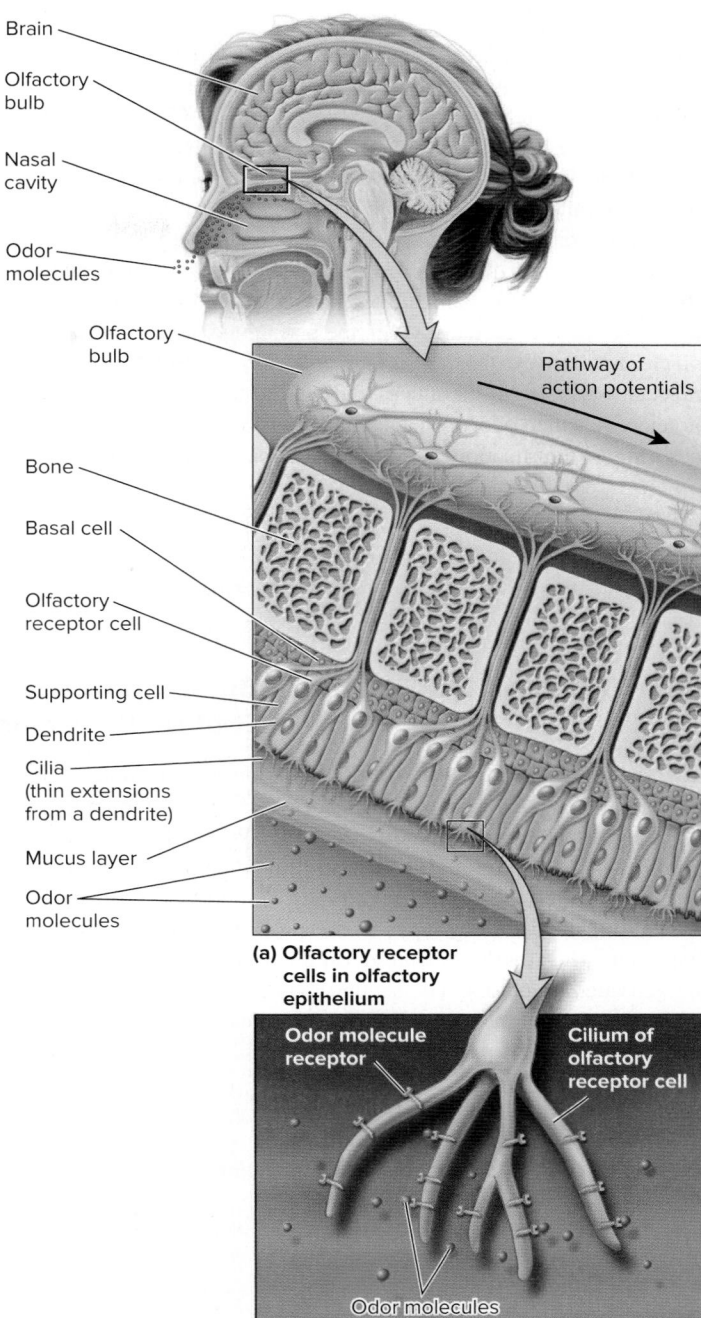

(a) Olfactory receptor cells in olfactory epithelium

(b) Cilia from dendrite with odor molecule receptors

Figure 44.24 **Olfactory structures in the human nose.** Odor molecules dissolve in a layer of mucus that coats the olfactory receptor cells. The molecules bind to protein receptors in the membranes of cilia that extend from the olfactory receptor cells. Action potentials in the olfactory receptor cells are conducted to cells in the olfactory bulb, and from there to the brain for interpretation. Basal cells periodically differentiate into new olfactory receptor cells, replacing dead or damaged cells.

humans to 100 million in rabbits and 220 million in dogs. Mammalian olfactory sensory receptors are neurons that are located in the epithelial tissue at the upper part of the nasal cavity (**Figure 44.24a**). These cells are surrounded by two additional cell types: supporting cells and basal cells. Supporting cells are located between the receptor cells and provide physical support for the olfactory receptors. The basal cells differentiate into new olfactory receptors every 30–60 days, replacing those that have died after prolonged exposure of their cell endings.

Olfactory sensory receptors have dendrites from which long, thin extensions called cilia extend into a mucous layer that covers the epithelium. Despite the superficial similarity in structure, these cells do not function like the mechanoreceptor hair cells of the auditory and vestibular systems. Unlike hair-cell stereocilia that bend, olfactory receptor cells have receptor proteins within the plasma membranes of the cilia, which provide an extensive surface area (**Figure 44.24b**). Airborne molecules dissolve in the mucus and bind to these olfactory receptor proteins. When an odor molecule binds to its receptor protein, it initiates a signal transduction pathway that ultimately opens Na$^+$ channels

in the plasma membrane. The subsequent depolarization results in action potentials being transmitted to the next series of cells located in the olfactory bulbs of the brain. The olfactory bulbs are a collection of neurons that act as an initial processing center of olfactory information and relay it to the cerebrum for further processing and interpretation.

The relative size of the olfactory bulbs correlates with the importance of olfaction to a given species. In humans, the olfactory bulbs make up only about 5% of the weight of the brain, whereas in nocturnal animals like rats and mice, they can comprise as much as 20%. Even with their relatively limited olfactory sensitivity, however, humans have the capacity to detect 10,000 or more different odors. Recent evidence suggests that this number could in principle be as high as 1 trillion! The mechanism by which mammals detect so many different odors remained a mystery until 1991, when two scientists uncovered the molecular basis of olfaction.

👁 **Core Skill: Process of Science**

Feature Investigation | Buck and Axel Discovered a Family of Olfactory Receptor Proteins That Bind Specific Odor Molecules

How does the olfactory system discriminate among thousands of different odors? American neuroscientists Linda Buck and Richard Axel set out to answer this question. When they began, two hypotheses were proposed to explain this phenomenon. One possibility was that many different types of odor molecules might bind to one or just a few types of receptor proteins, with the brain responding differently depending on the number or distribution of the activated receptors. The second hypothesis was that olfactory receptor cells can make many different types of receptor proteins, each type binding a particular odor molecule or group of structurally related odor molecules.

To begin their study, Buck and Axel made the logical assumption that olfactory receptor proteins would be highly expressed in olfactory sensory receptor cells, but not in other parts of the body. Based on previous work, they also postulated that the receptor proteins would be members of the large family of G-protein-coupled receptors (GPCRs). As shown in **Figure 44.25**, they isolated olfactory sensory receptor cells from rats and then used a homogenizer to break open the cells to release their mRNA. The mRNA was purified and then used to make complementary DNA (cDNA) using the enzyme reverse transcriptase. This generated a large collection of cDNAs, representing all of the genes that were expressed in the receptor cells at the time of mRNA collection.

Figure 44.25 Buck and Axel identified olfactory receptor proteins in olfactory receptor cells.

HYPOTHESES 1. Many different types of odor molecules bind to just a few types of receptor proteins. 2. Odor molecules are detected by many specific olfactory receptor proteins belonging to the family of G-protein-coupled receptors (GPCRs).

KEY MATERIALS Laboratory rats (*Rattus norvegicus*), PCR reagents, DNA-sequencing gels.

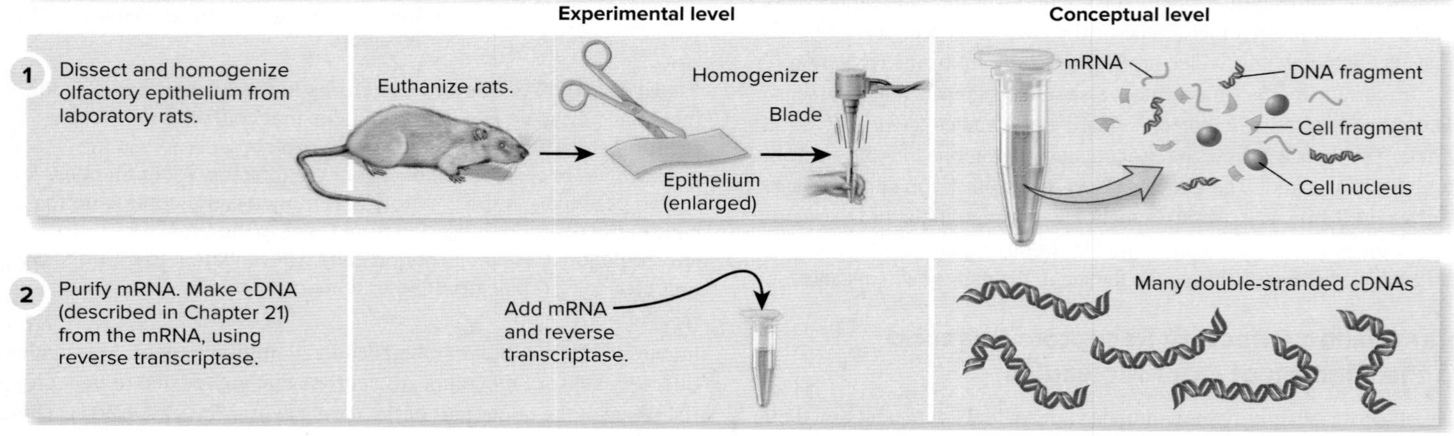

Experimental level   Conceptual level

1 Dissect and homogenize olfactory epithelium from laboratory rats.

Euthanize rats.

Homogenizer

Blade

Epithelium (enlarged)

mRNA

DNA fragment

Cell fragment

Cell nucleus

2 Purify mRNA. Make cDNA (described in Chapter 21) from the mRNA, using reverse transcriptase.

Add mRNA and reverse transcriptase.

Many double-stranded cDNAs

3 Add primers that bind specifically to genes that encode GPCRs. Subject to PCR as described in Chapter 21.

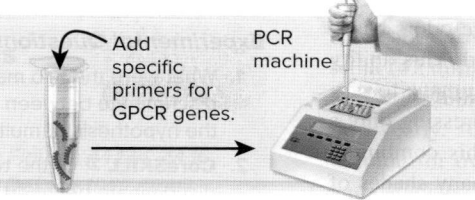

Add specific primers for GPCR genes.

PCR machine

Primers will hybridize only with cDNA that codes for proteins in the GPCR family and amplify those genes. Many different PCR products are obtained, each corresponding to a different gene.

4 Subject each PCR product to DNA sequencing, also described in Chapter 21.

Output from automated sequencing (example)

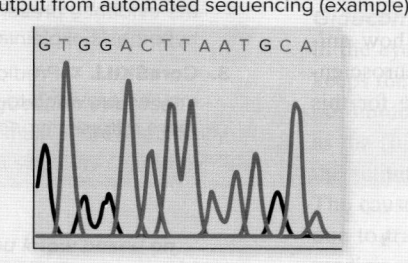

G T G G A C T T A A T G C A

Different GPCRs will have slightly different DNA sequences.

5 **THE DATA**

At least 100 different GPCRs were uniquely expressed in olfactory sensory receptor cells. Analysis of their predicted amino acid sequences revealed significant variability in the putative ligand-binding regions (transmembrane domains 3–5).

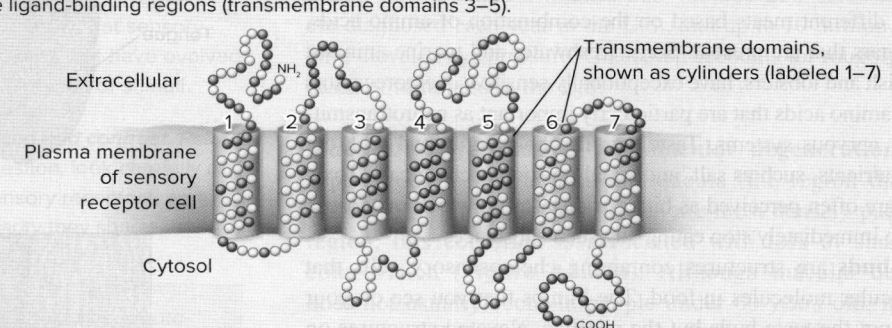

○ Amino acids that were the same in all the olfactory GPCRs.

● Amino acids that were different among the olfactory GPCRs.

Extracellular

Plasma membrane of sensory receptor cell

Cytosol

NH₂

Transmembrane domains, shown as cylinders (labeled 1–7)

COOH

6 **CONCLUSION** Olfactory receptor cells express many different receptor proteins that account for an animal's ability to detect a wide variety of odors.

7 **SOURCE** Buck, L., and Axel, R. 1991. A novel multigene family may encode odorant receptors: A molecular basis for odor recognition. *Cell* 65: 175–187.

To determine if any of these cDNAs encoded GPCRs, the researchers used primers that recognized conserved regions within previously identified genes that encoded GPCRs. A conserved region is a DNA sequence that rarely changes among different members of a gene family. The primers were used in PCR to amplify cDNAs that encoded GPCRs. This produced many PCR products that were then subjected to DNA sequencing.

As shown in the data in step 5 of Figure 44.25, Buck and Axel initially identified at least 100 different genes, each encoding a GPCR with a slightly different amino acid sequence, as predicted from the DNA sequences. Significant variability in the predicted amino acid sequences for the GPCRs was found in the putative ligand-binding region of the molecules (believed to be transmembrane domains 3–5). Further research showed that these genes were expressed only

in olfactory cells, and not in other parts of the body. These results were consistent with the second hypothesis, namely, that organisms produce a large number of distinct olfactory receptor proteins, each type binding a particular odor molecule or a group of related odor molecules.

Since these studies, researchers have determined that this family of olfactory genes in mammals is surprisingly large. In humans, roughly 400 genes encode olfactory receptor proteins. The diversity of olfactory receptor proteins is further increased by alternative splicing, which is described in Chapter 14 (refer back to Figure 14.21). Each olfactory receptor cell is thought to express only one type of GPCR that recognizes its own specific odor molecule or group of closely related molecules. Most odors that an animal encounters, however, are due to multiple chemicals that activate many different

3. _____ sense pain; _____ sense heat or cold; and _____ sense touch.
   a. Mechanoreceptors; thermoreceptors; nociceptors
   b. Nociceptors; thermoreceptors; mechanoreceptors
   c. Nociceptors; thermoreceptors; stretch receptors
   d. Mechanoreceptors; nociceptors; stretch receptors
   e. Nociceptors; photoreceptors; mechanoreceptors

4. Statocysts are sensory organs for
   a. hearing found in many invertebrates.
   b. equilibrium found in mammals.
   c. equilibrium found in many invertebrates.
   d. water current changes found in fish.
   e. hearing found in vertebrates.

5. In which process(es) are hair cells involved?
   a. balance in vertebrates and invertebrates
   b. hearing in mammals
   c. vision in animals with compound eyes
   d. heat sensing in pit vipers
   e. both a and b

6. Which statement about compound eyes is *true*?
   a. They do not contain a lens or lenslike structure.
   b. They cannot sense color.
   c. They have one ommatidium per eye.
   d. They are found in insects and also many vertebrates.
   e. They probably have less resolving power than single-lens eyes.

7. In the mammalian eye, light from near or far objects is focused on the retina when
   a. the lens moves forward or backward.
   b. the lens rounds up or flattens.
   c. the eyeball changes shape.
   d. the cornea changes shape.
   e. the retina changes shape.

8. The amount of glutamate released from photoreceptors of the vertebrate eye is highest when
   a. an animal is in full sunlight.
   b. an animal is in a completely dark place.

   c. an animal is in a dimly lit place.
   d. Na^+ channels of the photoreceptors are closed.
   e. Both a and d are true.

9. Cone pigments discriminate between different wavelengths of light due to
   a. their location in the retina.
   b. the amount of light they absorb.
   c. the type of retinal they have.
   d. the type of opsin protein they have.
   e. interactions with bipolar cells.

10. The stimulation for olfaction involves odorant molecules
    a. bending the cilia of olfactory sensory receptor cells.
    b. binding to protein receptors of olfactory sensory receptor cells.
    c. entering the cytoplasm of olfactory sensory receptor cells.
    d. opening K^+ channels of olfactory sensory receptor cells.
    e. binding to cells located in the olfactory bulbs.

Conceptual Questions

1. Distinguish between sensory transduction and perception.

2. Despite the differences in their appearances, can you identify structural and functional similarities in the compound and single-lens eyes found in animals?

3. Core Concept: Systems Which sense do you think is the least important to human survival?

Collaborative Questions

1. Discuss the several types of sensory stimuli that animals can detect, and describe some general features of the sensory receptors that are adapted for each of these stimuli.

2. Explain how the structures of the mammalian ear are adapted to detect and distinguish different frequencies of sound.

Muscular-Skeletal Systems and Locomotion

45

n 1991, Olympic athlete Mike Powell established a long-jump record of 8.95 m, roughly 5 times the height of a person. A jump of nearly 9 m sounds impressive, and it is for us, but how do humans compare with other animals? Red kangaroos can hop up to 12 m. Some tree frogs, like the one shown in the chapter opening photo, can leap distances up to 1.4 m without a running start, yet the frog is only 4.5 cm long and weighs only 8 g! This is a sensational leap for an animal that size, roughly 30 times its body length. The jumping abilities of frogs are related to their relatively large leg muscle mass, the elongation of the bones in their legs and feet, and elastic elements in the connective tissue associated with their muscle and bone. Indeed, the jumping ability of frogs makes them excellent model organisms for the study of muscle function in vertebrates.

Muscles are composed of highly specialized cells that have the ability to contract in response to stimuli. The three types of muscle tissue—skeletal, smooth, and cardiac—were introduced in Chapter 41. This chapter will explore the structure and function of skeletal muscle and the mechanism by which it controls movements, such as those required for **locomotion**, the movement of an animal from place to place.

For skeletal muscles to produce locomotion, they must exert a force on an animal's skeleton. We begin the chapter, therefore, with an overview of animal skeletons. Then we will examine the structure and function of skeletal muscle and see how the interaction of two muscle proteins, actin and myosin, produces muscle contraction. Next, we will consider various modes of locomotion in animals. We will conclude with a consideration of important bone and muscle diseases in humans.

Red-eyed tree frog (*Agalychnis callidryas*) using its muscular-skeletal system to leap from one plant to another. ©Scott Linstead/Science Source

3. List the major functions of the vertebrate skeleton.
4. Describe the composition of vertebrate bone.

When we think of the word skeleton, an image of the vertebrate system of bones usually comes to mind. However, invertebrates possess a skeleton as well, although it is not made of bone. Therefore, a broader definition of a **skeleton** is a structure that serves one or more functions related to support, protection, and locomotion. Using this definition, the two major types of skeletons found in animals are exoskeletons and endoskeletons. A third type of skeleton that broadly fits the definition is called a hydroskeleton (which will not be discussed in this chapter). This type is found in some soft-bodied invertebrates that use water pressure to propel their bodies.

Exoskeletons Are on the Outside of Animal Bodies

Arthropods have an **exoskeleton**, an external skeleton that surrounds and protects most of the body surface (**Figure 45.1a**). Exoskeletons provide support for the body, protection from the environment and predators, and protection for internal organs. The arthropod skeleton is made of a polysaccharide called chitin, and in crustaceans such as lobsters and shrimp, it is sometimes strengthened with calcium and other minerals. Exoskeletons are often tough, durable, and

45.1 Types of Animal Skeletons

Learning Outcomes:

1. Distinguish between exoskeletons and endoskeletons.
2. **CoreSKILL** » Relate the structure of an exoskeleton to its function, and propose reasons why such a skeleton provides advantages to an animal.

(a) An arthropod next to its recently shed exoskeleton

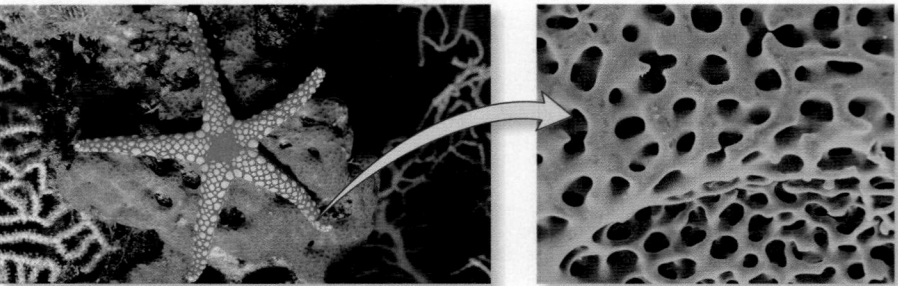

(b) Echinoderm (sea star) and (right) SEM of its endoskeleton

Figure 45.1 Types of skeletons. (a) Exoskeleton. An arthropod's skeleton covers and protects its body, but it must be periodically shed and replaced to allow growth of the animal, as shown in this photo. **(b)** Endoskeleton. Echinoderms such as the sea star (starfish) have endoskeletons of bony plates made of calcium carbonate ($CaCO_3$), shown in detail in the SEM. Vertebrate endoskeletons will be described later. a: ©Tom McHugh/Science Source; b (left): ©Georgette Douwma/Science Source; b (right): ©The Natural History Museum, London

Concept Check: *Unlike exoskeletons, endoskeletons do not provide protection for the body surface of animals. How can the lack of an external skeleton be an advantage for animals?*

segmented to allow for flexibility and movement. However, to allow growth, they must be periodically shed, regrown, and strengthened again, a process called ecdysis, or molting (see Figure 45.1a). A disadvantage of exoskeletons is that when an animal is molting, its new exoskeleton is temporarily soft, making the animal more vulnerable to predators and the environment.

Exoskeletons vary enormously in their complexity, thickness, and durability. The differences in exoskeletons are usually adaptations that enhance an animal's survival. Think, for example, of the difference between the body surfaces of a butterfly and a lobster. A butterfly's exoskeleton must be light enough for the animal to fly, whereas the thick, tough exoskeleton of the lobster provides a very effective defense against predators. Exoskeletons may seem primitive compared to the endoskeletons of vertebrates (discussed next), particularly because of the requirement for molting. Even so, arthropods are among the most successful of all animal phyla living today, having survived for hundreds of millions of years and inhabiting nearly every possible ecological niche on the planet. Clearly, exoskeletons have been advantageous for one of the planet's greatest success stories.

Endoskeletons Are Internal Support Structures

Like exoskeletons, **endoskeletons** provide support and protection. Unlike exoskeletons, however, endoskeletons are internal structures and do not protect the body surface. Some endoskeletons do, however, protect internal organs such as those in the thorax of vertebrates.

Various types of endoskeletons are found in some species of sponges and all echinoderms and vertebrates. Minerals including Ca^{2+}, Mg^{2+}, PO_4^{2-}, and CO_3^{2-} supply the hardening material that gives an endoskeleton its firm structure. The endoskeletons of sponges consist of spiky networks of proteins and minerals, while those of echinoderms are made up of mineralized platelike structures. Beneath the body surface of echinoderms, for example, arrays of mineralized plates made largely of $CaCO_3$ extend into the spines and arms that radiate from the main body (**Figure 45.1b**).

Vertebrate endoskeletons, by contrast, are composed of either cartilage (refer back to Figure 41.5), as in cartilaginous fishes (sharks,

rays, and skates), or both cartilage and bone, as in bony fishes, amphibians, reptiles, birds, and mammals.

Bone Consists of a Mixture of Organic and Mineral Components

Bone is a living, dynamic tissue with both organic and mineral components. Organic materials include cells that form bone, called osteoblasts and osteocytes, and cells that break it down, called osteoclasts. The organic part of bone is secreted by osteoblasts and osteocytes and consists largely of the protein collagen, which has a unique triple helical structure that gives bone both strength and flexibility (refer back to Figure 10.2). The mineral part of bone is composed of a crystalline mixture of primarily Ca^{2+} and PO_4^{2-} and other ions that provide rigidity. These ions must be obtained in an animal's diet, absorbed into the blood, and deposited in bone.

A proper proportion of organic and mineral components is required for normal bone function. Bone lacking sufficient mineral, for example, is easily fractured. Bone is formed at high rates during an animal's growth periods, but even in adulthood bone is continuously formed, broken down, and re-formed. The skeleton is continually changing—the one in your body right now is completely remodeled from the one that was in your body a few years ago. Similarly, the skeleton you will have a few years from now will be different from the one you have today.

The Vertebrate Skeleton Performs Several Important Functions

In the vertebrate skeleton, bones are connected in ways that allow for support, protection of internal structures, and movement. The vertebrate skeleton is often considered in two parts: the axial and appendicular skeletons (**Figure 45.2**). The axial skeleton is composed of the bones that form the main longitudinal axis of an animal's body, including the skull, vertebrae, sternum, and ribs. The appendicular skeleton consists of the limb bones and the bones that connect them to the axial skeleton. A **joint** is formed where two or more bones come together. Some joints permit free movement (for example, the joints in human shoulders).

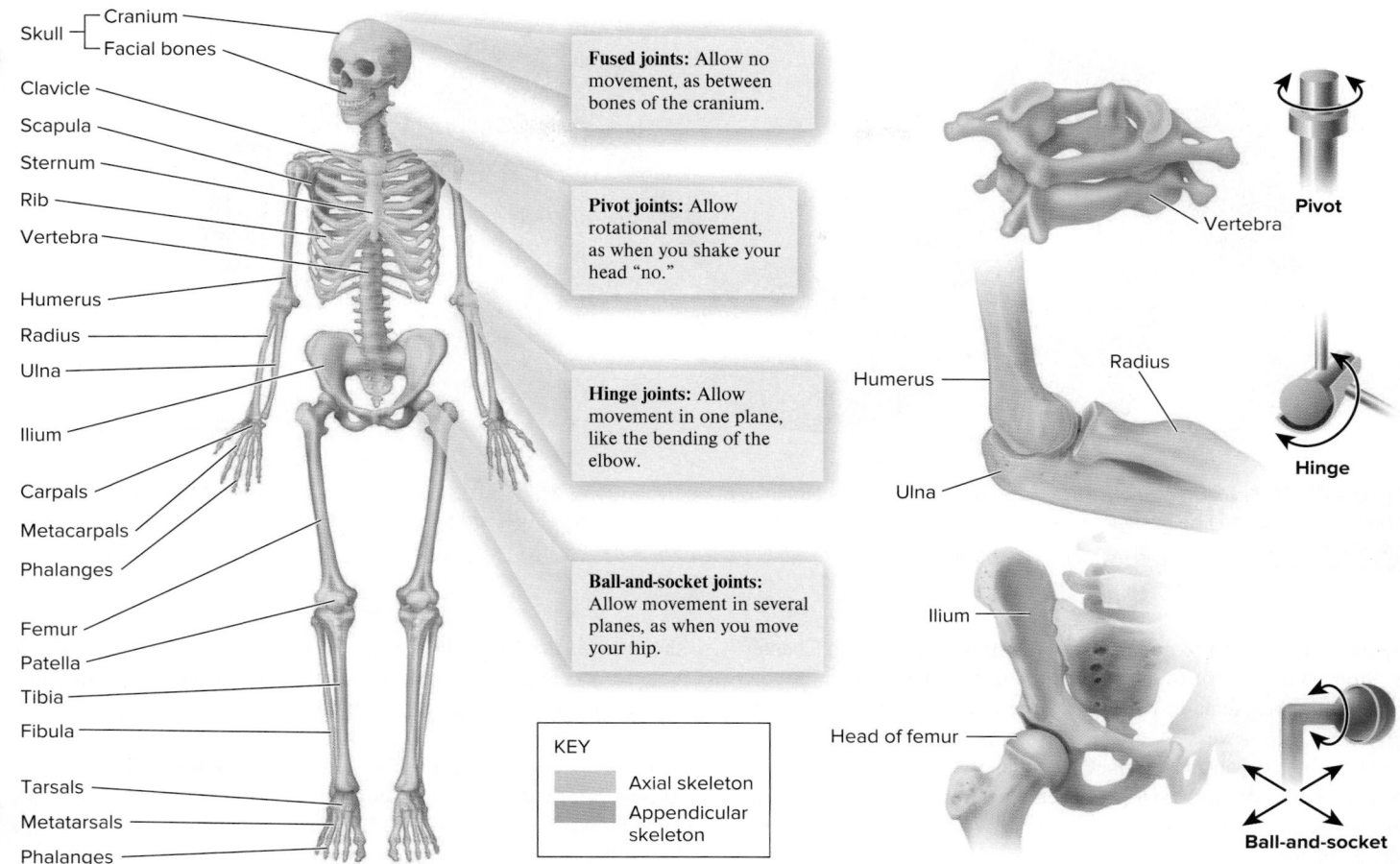

Figure 45.2 The adult human skeleton. This diagram shows the axial (beige) and appendicular (green) parts of the skeleton in an adult human, an animal with an endoskeleton. The adult human skeleton consists of 206 separate bones. Three examples of movable joints—pivot, hinge, and ball-and-socket—are shown.

Figure 45.2 illustrates three types of joints that allow different types of movements: pivot, hinge, and ball-and-socket joints. Other joints do not allow movement (fused joints like those interlocking the skull bones) or allow only limited movement (such as those of the vertebral column).

The skeleton of vertebrates serves several other functions in addition to support, protection, and movement. For example, blood cells and platelets, the latter of which help blood to clot (see Chapter 48), are formed within the soft, fatty interior (called the marrow) of certain bones including the ilia, the vertebrae, and the ends of the femurs. In addition, homeostasis of Ca^{2+} and PO_4^{2-} levels in the blood is achieved in large part through exchanges of these ions between bone and blood. For example, if dietary intake of Ca^{2+} is low, Ca^{2+} is removed from bone and added to the blood, so that all of the vital cellular activities that depend on Ca^{2+}, such as neuron signaling and muscle contraction, can continue to function normally. If dietary Ca^{2+} is restored to normal, any available excess Ca^{2+} is redeposited in bone. This Ca^{2+} cycling is under the control of hormones such as parathyroid hormone produced by the parathyroid glands (see Chapter 50). About 99% of all the Ca^{2+} in a typical vertebrate's body exists in bone. This represents a huge reservoir of Ca^{2+} for the blood.

Bones cannot move by themselves but instead provide the scaffold on which skeletal muscles cause body movement. We turn now to skeletal muscle and the mechanism by which it generates force.

45.2 Skeletal Muscle Structure and the Mechanism of Force Generation

Learning Outcomes:

1. List the three types of muscle tissue found in vertebrates, and describe where they are found in the body.
2. Describe how antagonistic muscles function at a joint.
3. Identify the structural components of a muscle down to the level of the sarcomere.
4. Explain the sliding filament mechanism of muscle contraction.
5. Explain how tropomyosin and troponin help regulate muscle contraction.
6. **CoreSKILL** » Predict how skeletal muscle contraction will be affected by changes in electrical activity in motor neurons.
7. Describe the structural features of a neuromuscular junction and the role of acetylcholine in mediating skeletal muscle excitation.

Vertebrates have three types of muscle tissue that are classified according to their structure, function, and control mechanisms. **Cardiac muscle** is found only in the heart and provides the force

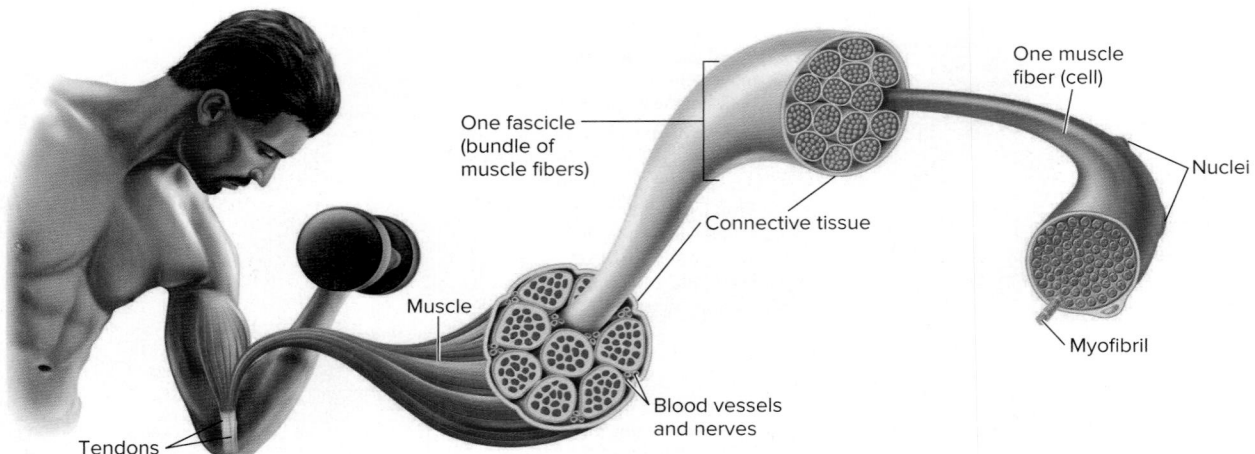

Figure 45.3 Skeletal muscle structure. Skeletal muscles attach to bone by tendons, which are bundles of collagen fibers. Each muscle consists of bundles of muscle fibers (skeletal muscle cells) bound together by connective tissue. Myofibrils are the contractile elements of muscle fibers.

Concept Check: *What would happen to the ability of a muscle to move a bone if its tendon were torn, for example, due to injury?*

required for the heart to pump blood; it will be discussed in Chapter 48. **Smooth muscle** surrounds and forms part of the lining of hollow organs and tubes, including those of the digestive tract, urinary bladder, uterus, blood vessels, and airways. Contraction of the smooth muscle in such organs may propel the contents forward or churn them up, as when the stomach contracts after a meal. In other cases, smooth muscle regulates the flow of substances by changing the tube diameter, as in the widening or narrowing of blood vessels that occurs when different parts of the body require more or less nutrients and oxygen. Smooth muscle contraction is not under voluntary control. Instead, it is controlled by the autonomic nervous system, hormones, and local chemical signals.

Skeletal muscle is found throughout the body and is directly involved in locomotion. In vertebrates, but not invertebrates, skeletal muscle is electrically excitable—it can generate action potentials in response to a stimulus (invertebrate skeletal muscle cells have graded membrane potentials but do not have action potentials). The action potentials of vertebrate skeletal muscle cells result in an increased concentration of Ca^{2+} in the cytosol, which triggers force generation. Before seeing how this is possible, however, let's begin with an overview of skeletal muscle structure and function.

A Skeletal Muscle Is a Contractile Organ That Supports and Moves Bones

A skeletal muscle such as the bicep is an organ comprised of cells—called **muscle fibers**—bound together in bundles (called fascicles) by a succession of connective tissue layers (**Figure 45.3**). Skeletal muscles are usually linked to bones by bundles of collagen fibers known as tendons. The transmission of force from contracting muscle to bone can be likened to a number of people pulling on a rope attached to a heavy object. Each person corresponds to a single muscle fiber, the rope corresponds to the tendons, and the bone is the heavy object.

Some tendons are very long, with the site of their attachment to bone far removed from the end of the muscle. For example, some of

the muscles that move the fingers are in the forearm. You can wiggle your fingers and feel the movement of the muscles in your lower arm. These muscles are connected to the finger bones by long tendons.

When the force is great enough, a bone moves as the muscle shortens. A contracting muscle exerts only a pulling force, so as the muscle attached to it via tendons shortens, the attached bones are pulled toward or away from each other. Muscles that bend a limb at a joint (that is, reduce the angle between two bones) are called **flexors**, whereas muscles that straighten a limb (increase the angle between two bones) are called **extensors**. Two or more muscles that produce oppositely directed movements at a joint are known as **antagonists**. For example, in **Figure 45.4**, we can see that contraction of the hamstrings flexes the leg at the knee joint, relaxing the quadriceps, whereas contraction of the quadriceps causes the leg to extend and the hamstrings to relax. Both antagonistic muscles exert only a pulling force when they contract; where they connect to the shin bones determines whether the leg is flexed or extended.

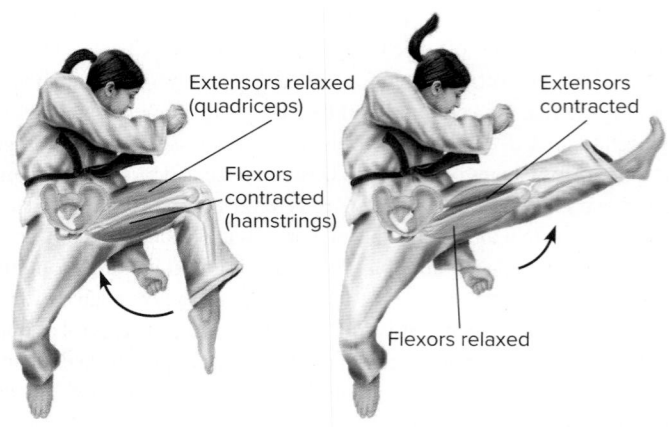

Figure 45.4 Actions of flexors and extensors. The figure shows how skeletal muscles cause flexion or extension of a limb. When the flexor muscle contracts, the extensor relaxes, and vice versa.

Muscle Fibers Contain Myofibrils Composed of Arrays of Filaments

Each skeletal muscle fiber arises from several cells that fuse to form a single mature cell with multiple nuclei (see Figure 45.3). Each fiber contains numerous cylindrical bundles known as **myofibrils** (**Figure 45.5**). Myofibrils extend from one end of the fiber to the other and are linked to the tendons at the ends of the fiber. Each myofibril contains numerous functional structures called thick and thin filaments. These filaments are arranged in a repeating pattern running the length of the myofibril. One complete unit of this repeating pattern is known as a **sarcomere** (from the Greek *sarco*, meaning muscle, and *mer*, meaning part). The **thick filaments** are composed almost entirely of the protein **myosin**. Myosin is a motor protein that hydrolyzes ATP as a source of energy. The **thin filaments**, which are about half the diameter of the thick filaments, contain the cytoskeletal protein **actin** and associated proteins. Because the arrangement of thick and thin filaments looks like a series of light and dark bands when viewed by a microscope, skeletal muscle is also known as striated muscle.

The components of a sarcomere, shown in Figure 45.5, have the following features:

- The A band is formed by the thick filaments located in the middle of each sarcomere, where their orderly parallel arrangement produces a wide, dark band. A portion of the thin filaments overlaps the thick filaments in this band.

- The Z line is a network of proteins to which thin filaments are attached. Two successive Z lines define the boundaries of one sarcomere.

- The I band lies between the A bands of two adjacent sarcomeres. Each I band contains those portions of the thin filaments that do not overlap the thick filaments, and each I band is bisected by a Z line.

- The H zone is a narrow region in the center of the A band. It corresponds to the space between the two sets of thin filaments in each sarcomere.

- The M line is in the center of the H zone and is composed of proteins that link the central regions of adjacent thick filaments.

- The spaces between overlapping thick and thin filaments are bridged by projections known as **cross-bridges**, which are regions of myosin molecules that extend from the surface of the thick filaments toward the thin filaments (see Figure 45.5).

Skeletal Muscle Shortens When Thin Filaments Slide Past Thick Filaments

Movement requires shortening of muscles to pull against attached tendons and bones. However, a muscle can generate force, or contract, without producing movement. Holding a heavy weight at a constant position, for example, requires muscle contraction, but not muscle shortening. Therefore, as used in muscle physiology, the term contraction refers to activation of the cross-bridges within muscle fibers, which initiates the generation of force. When the activating

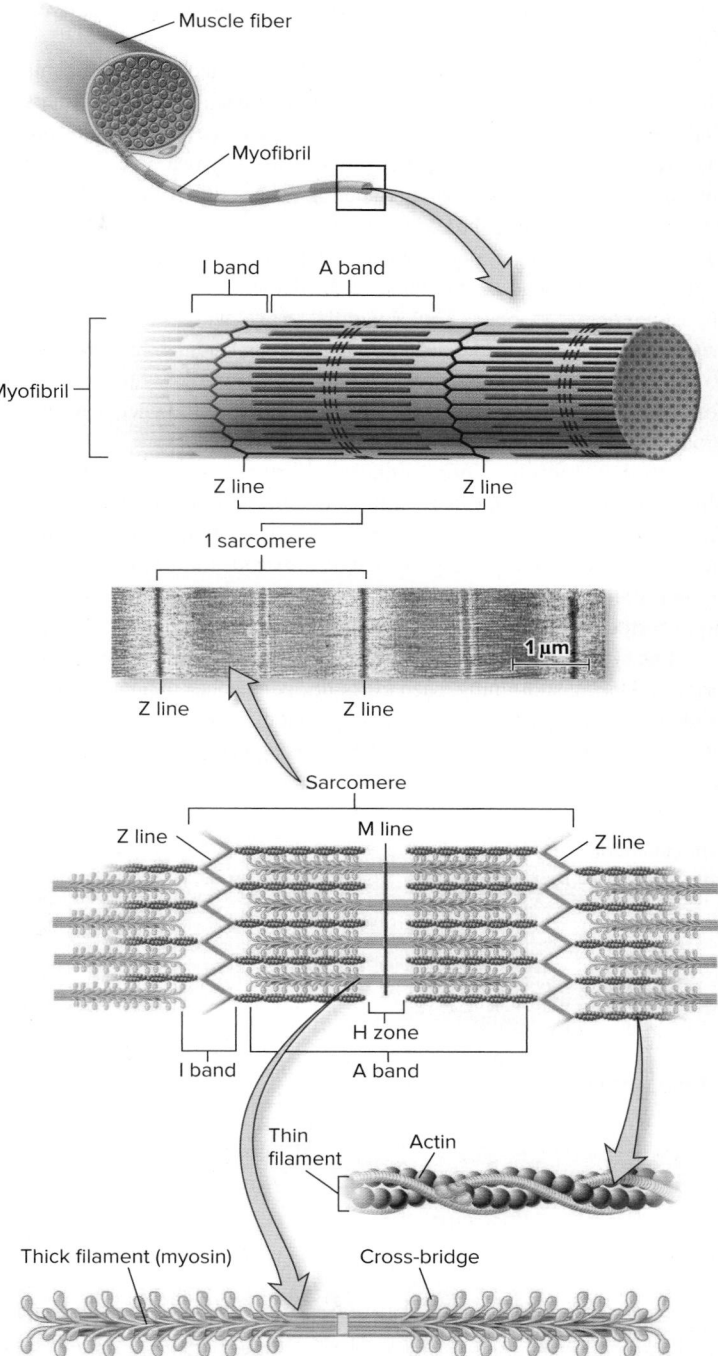

Figure 45.5 Myofibril structure. Each muscle fiber consists of numerous myofibrils containing thick and thin filaments. Their arrangement produces a striated banding pattern that can be seen with microscopy (in the inset). A myofibril is composed of repeating units called sarcomeres. ©Dr. H. E. Huxley

 Core Concept: Structure and Function A muscle (an organ) consists of many cells called fibers arranged in parallel. As the cells change their shape by shortening, the shape of the entire organ also changes; that is, the muscle contracts.

mechanisms are turned off, contractions end, allowing the muscle fiber to relax.

Let's look at how the structure of the thin and thick filaments allows them to move. In thin filaments, actin molecules form polymers that are arranged into two intertwined helical chains. These chains are closely associated with two proteins called tropomyosin and troponin that have important functions in regulating contraction (**Figure 45.6a**). Myosin proteins have a three-domain structure composed of two intertwined tails, two hinges, and two heads. The hinges are flexible regions that connect the heads to the tails. Each filament is made up of many myosin proteins associated in a parallel array, with the hinges and heads extending out to the sides, forming cross-bridges that can bind to actin. Each head contains two binding sites—one for actin and one for ATP. The hydrolysis of ATP by myosin provides the energy for the cross-bridge to move via a bending motion at the hinge.

How a muscle fiber actually shortens is known as the **sliding filament mechanism** of muscle contraction (**Figure 45.6b**). In this mechanism, the sarcomeres shorten, but neither the thick nor the thin filaments change in length. Instead, the thick filaments remain stationary while the thin filaments slide, pulling on the Z lines and shortening the sarcomere.

The sliding filament movement is propelled by the myosin cross-bridges. During shortening, each cross-bridge attaches to an actin molecule in a thin filament and moves in a motion somewhat like your fist bending at your wrist. Because of the opposing orientation of the thick

filaments, the movement of a cross-bridge forces the thin filaments toward the center of the sarcomere (the M line in the H zone), thereby narrowing the H zone and shortening the sarcomere (see Figure 45.6b). One stroke of a cross-bridge produces only a very small movement of a thin filament relative to a thick filament. As long as a muscle fiber continues to be stimulated to contract, however, each cross-bridge repeats its motion many times, resulting in continued sliding of the thin filaments. Thus, the ability of a muscle fiber to generate force and movement depends on the amount of interaction between actin and myosin.

The protein myosin was first discovered in extracts of frog leg muscle in the 1860s by German physiologist Wilhelm Kühne. We now know that eukaryotic genomes encode a family of related myosin proteins, and that at least one of them may have made a significant contribution to human evolution, as described next.

 **Core Concept: Evolution**

Myosins Are an Ancient Family of Proteins

Myosins are among the most ancient eukaryotic proteins and are found throughout the animal kingdom. Small differences in the sequences of genes that arose from a single primordial myosin gene have led to the tissue-specific expression of numerous

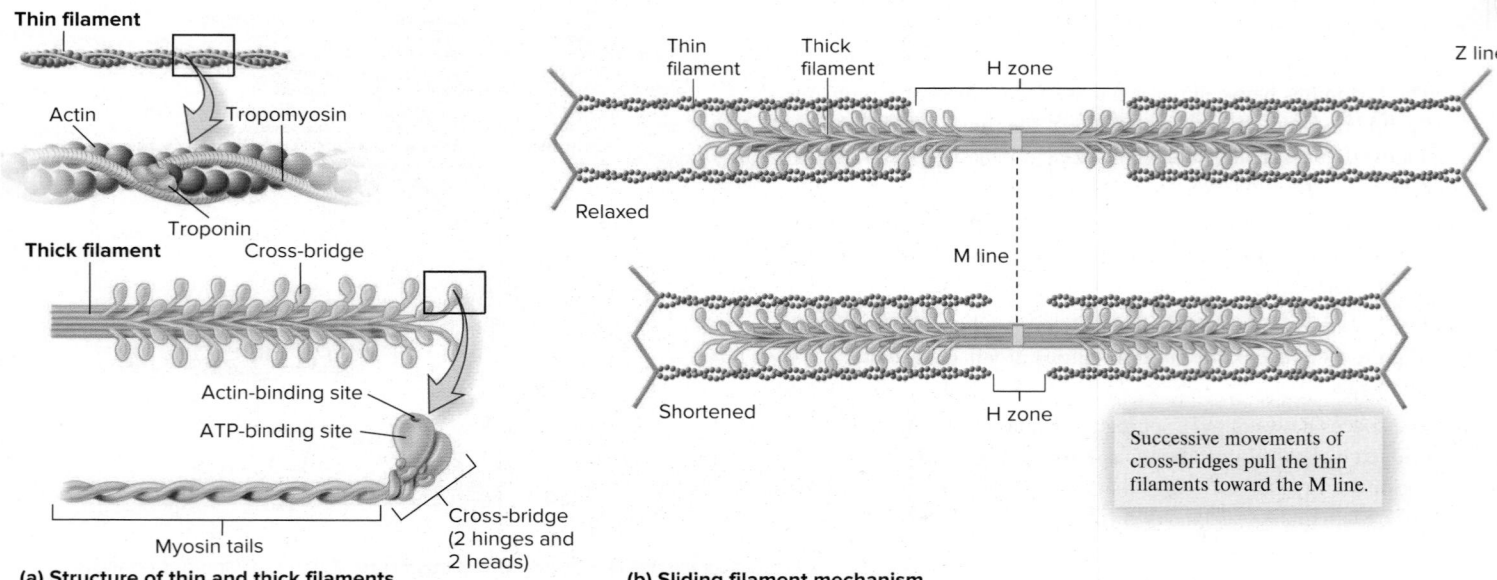

Figure 45.6 Structure and function of the thin and thick filaments. (a) Thin filaments are composed of two intertwined actin molecules and their associated proteins, tropomyosin and troponin. Thick filaments are made of the protein myosin, which has two intertwined tails, two hinges, and two heads that contain an actin-binding site and an ATP-binding site. The end of a myosin molecule that contains the actin-binding site is bent at an angle to form the cross-bridge. (b) When the cross-bridges on myosin molecules bind to actin, the thin filaments are pulled toward the M line, shortening the sarcomere. The sliding of thin filaments past the overlapping thick filaments shortens the sarcomere, but does not change the lengths of the filaments themselves.

 Core Concept: Structure and Function The precise structural arrangement of the proteins that make up thick and thin filaments gives them their function. Without this structure, actin and myosin would not produce a force that results in the shortening of the muscle cell.

different myosin proteins, each with a characteristic ability to bind actin and hydrolyze ATP. In skeletal muscle, myosin is important for generating force, but in other types of cells, various myosins function in organelle trafficking, cell locomotion, mitosis and other activities. One member of the large family of myosin genes, called *MYH16*, encodes a myosin polypeptide that is expressed mainly in the skeletal muscles of the jaw in primates. In 2004, American researcher Hansell Stedman and colleagues discovered that this gene, although present in humans, did not encode a functional polypeptide in humans because of a mutation that deleted two base pairs. This mutation was present in 100% of people tested worldwide but was not found in eight nonhuman primate species tested, including chimpanzees.

Based on genome comparisons and estimates of genetic divergence among species, the researchers estimated that the mutation occurred approximately 2.4 mya. Significantly, the genus *Homo*, with its smaller jaw and larger braincase, is also thought to have first appeared about 2.4 mya, leading Stedman to suggest that the loss of the MYH16 protein led to the smaller, less muscular jaws characteristic of modern humans (**Figure 45.7**). Because jaw muscles are attached to skull bones, massive jaw muscles may have placed a mechanical constraint on skull growth in early hominins (as well as in modern nonhuman primates). Smaller jaw-closing muscles would place less constraint on bone formation of the skull (in particular, at the areas of muscle attachment obscuring the sutures or growth plates). This in turn would prevent the early cessation of brain growth seen in the nonhuman primates. This may have eliminated a major constraint on the evolution of the larger brains seen in modern humans.

Stedman's hypothesis is compelling, given that the myosin mutation affects the jaw-closing muscles and is present only in humans. Another research group, using statistical analyses of additional gene sequences made available through the Chimpanzee Sequencing and Analysis Consortium, concluded that the mutation may have arisen earlier—perhaps 4.0–5.4 mya, before the appearance of small-jawed species of *Homo* in the fossil record. Stedman's hypothesis will require confirmation by future research. Scientists are certain that a human-specific mutation in *MYH16* arose at some point in the evolution of hominins. Whether the mutation facilitated expansion of the cranium, which in turn may have permitted enlargement of the brain, remains unknown. The hypothesis, however, does provide an intriguing piece of the puzzle of the evolution of modern humans.

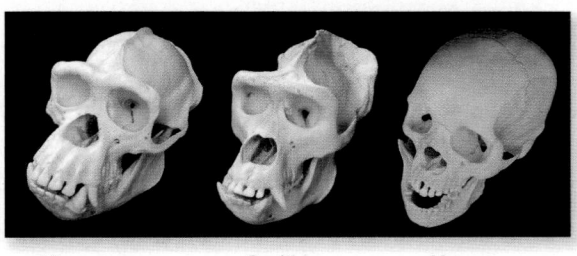

Macaque   Gorilla   Human

Figure 45.7 Comparison of jaw size and area of muscle attachment (shown in pink) in modern primates. Note: Skulls are not to scale. ©Hansell H. Stedman, M.D.

The Cross-Bridge Cycle Requires ATP and Ca²⁺

Let's now turn our attention to how actin and myosin interact to promote muscle contraction and shortening. The sequence of events that occurs between the time when a cross-bridge binds to a thin filament and when it is set to repeat the process is known as a **cross-bridge cycle**.

Cross-bridge cycling occurs when the Ca^{2+} concentration exceeds a critical threshold in the cytosol. This usually occurs when neural input results in the release of Ca^{2+} from intracellular storage sites (described in detail shortly). In other words, the contraction of skeletal muscle fibers is under nervous control.

Figure 45.8 illustrates the events that occur during the four steps of the cross-bridge cycle: (1) cross-bridge binding, (2) power stroke (moving), (3) detaching, and (4) resetting. As the cycle begins, the myosin cross-bridges are in an energized state, which is produced by the hydrolysis of their bound ATP to ADP and inorganic phosphate (P_i). The ADP and P_i remain bound to the cross-bridge until step 2. The sequence of storage and release of energy by myosin is analogous to the operation of a mousetrap: Energy is first stored in the trap by cocking the spring (ATP hydrolysis) and is then released by the springing of the trap (head binds to actin and moves in power stroke). Let's look at each step of the process more closely.

Step 1: Ca²⁺ concentration increases, triggering the cross-bridge to bind to actin. When the Ca^{2+} concentration in the cytosol increases, an energized myosin cross-bridge, along with its associated ADP and P_i, binds to an actin molecule on a thin filament.

Step 2: Release of P_i fuels the power stroke. The cross-bridge and thin filaments move. The binding of an energized myosin cross-bridge to actin in step 1 triggers the release of P_i. This release causes a conformational change in the hinge of the myosin molecule. The change in conformation causes the cross-bridge to rotate toward the M line in the H zone at the center of the sarcomere, as myosin returns to its lower energy conformation. This step is known as the **power stroke**, which moves the actin filament. At this time, ADP is released from the cross-bridge.

Step 3: ATP binds to myosin, causing the cross-bridge to detach. During the power stroke, myosin is bound very firmly to actin. After the power stroke is completed, this linkage must be broken to allow the cross-bridge to be reenergized and repeat the cycle. The binding of a new molecule of ATP to the myosin cross-bridge alters myosin's conformation and breaks the link between actin and myosin. ATP is not hydrolyzed in this step. Instead, ATP functions at this stage as an allosteric modulator of the myosin head, weakening the binding of myosin to actin and leading to their dissociation.

Step 4: ATP hydrolysis re-energizes and resets the cross-bridge. After actin and myosin dissociate, the ATP bound to myosin is hydrolyzed by the ATPase activity of myosin. This hydrolysis re-energizes myosin, causing it to reset to the position that allows actin binding. If Ca^{2+} is still available at this time, the cross-bridge can reattach to a new actin molecule in the thin filament, and the cross-bridge cycle will repeat, causing the muscle fiber to shorten further.

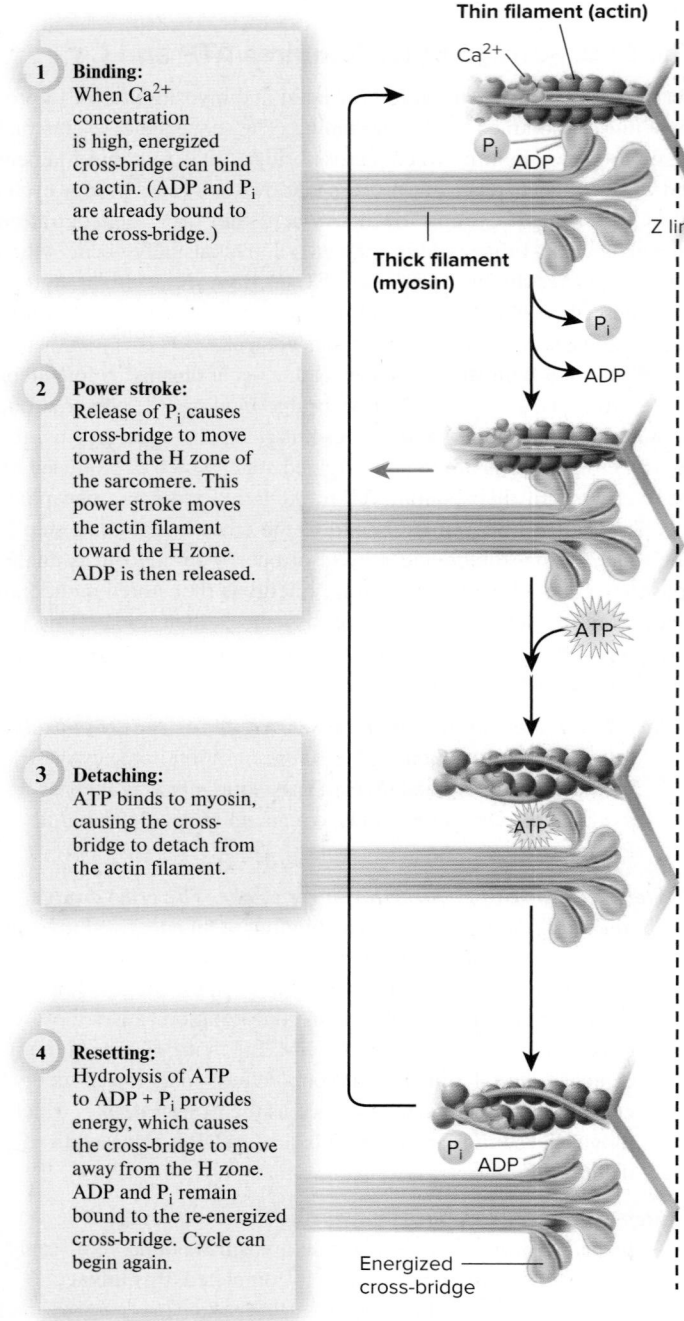

Thin filament (actin)

1 Binding:
When Ca²⁺ concentration is high, energized cross-bridge can bind to actin. (ADP and Pᵢ are already bound to the cross-bridge.)

Ca²⁺

Pᵢ
ADP

Z line

Thick filament (myosin)

Pᵢ

ADP

2 Power stroke:
Release of Pᵢ causes cross-bridge to move toward the H zone of the sarcomere. This power stroke moves the actin filament toward the H zone. ADP is then released.

ATP

3 Detaching:
ATP binds to myosin, causing the cross-bridge to detach from the actin filament.

ATP

4 Resetting:
Hydrolysis of ATP to ADP + Pᵢ provides energy, which causes the cross-bridge to move away from the H zone. ADP and Pᵢ remain bound to the re-energized cross-bridge. Cycle can begin again.

Pᵢ
ADP

Energized cross-bridge

Figure 45.8 The four steps of cross-bridge cycling in skeletal muscle.

As we have seen, ATP performs two different roles in the cross-bridge cycle. First, the energy released from ATP hydrolysis provides the energy for cross-bridge movement. Second, binding of ATP to myosin breaks the link formed between actin and myosin, allowing a new cycle to start. Although the precise mechanisms may differ slightly between vertebrates and invertebrates, biologists think that all skeletal muscle functions via steps similar to those just described.

The Regulation of Muscle Contraction by Ca²⁺ Is Mediated by Tropomyosin and Troponin

How does the presence of Ca²⁺ in the cytosol of muscle cells regulate the cycling of cross-bridges? The answer requires a closer look at the

two additional thin filament proteins mentioned earlier, tropomyosin and troponin.

Tropomyosin is a rod-shaped molecule composed of two intertwined protein subunits (**Figure 45.9a**). Tropomyosin proteins are arranged end to end along the thin filament. In the absence of Ca²⁺, they partially cover the myosin-binding site on each actin molecule, thereby preventing cross-bridges from making contact with actin. Each tropomyosin molecule is held in this blocking position by **troponin**, a smaller, globular-shaped protein with three subunits that is bound to both tropomyosin and actin. In this way, troponin and tropomyosin block access to myosin-binding sites on actin molecules in the relaxed muscle fiber.

One of the three subunits of troponin is capable of binding Ca²⁺. The binding of Ca²⁺ produces a change in the shape of troponin, which—through troponin's linkage to tropomyosin—causes tropomyosin to move away from the myosin-binding site on each actin molecule (**Figure 45.9b**). This movement allows cross-bridge cycling to occur. Conversely, release of Ca²⁺ from troponin reverses the process, blocking the myosin-binding site and turning off contractile activity.

Thus, the concentration of cytosolic Ca²⁺ determines whether or not Ca²⁺ is bound to troponin molecules, which, in turn, determines the number of actin sites available for cross-bridge binding. The cytosolic concentration of Ca²⁺, however, is very low in resting muscle. Let's see how the Ca²⁺ concentration is increased so that contraction can occur.

Ca²⁺ Concentration and Contraction of Skeletal Muscle Fibers Are Coupled with Electrical Excitation

Like neurons, vertebrate skeletal muscle cells generate and propagate action potentials in response to an appropriate stimulus. The propagation of action potentials causes an increase in the concentration of cytosolic Ca²⁺, which triggers contraction of a muscle fiber. This sequence of events by which an action potential in the plasma membrane of a muscle fiber leads to cross-bridge activity is called **excitation-contraction coupling**. The electrical activity in the plasma membrane does not act directly on the contractile proteins but instead acts as a stimulus to increase cytosolic Ca²⁺ concentration. The increased Ca²⁺ concentration continues to activate the contractile apparatus long after electrical activity in the membrane has ceased.

The source of the increased cytosolic Ca²⁺ that occurs following a muscle action potential is the muscle fiber's **sarcoplasmic reticulum**, which acts as a Ca²⁺ reservoir. The sarcoplasmic reticulum, which is a specialized form of the endoplasmic reticulum, is composed of interconnected sleevelike compartments and sacs around each myofibril (**Figure 45.10**). Separate tubular structures, the **transverse tubules (T-tubules)**, are invaginations of the plasma membrane that lie close to the sarcoplasmic reticulum. The T-tubules conduct action potentials from the outer surface of the muscle fiber to the myofibrils. An action potential causes the opening of Ca²⁺ channels in the lateral sacs of the sarcoplasmic reticulum, which allows Ca²⁺ to diffuse into the cytosol and bind to troponin, initiating cross-bridge cycling.

A contraction continues until Ca²⁺ is removed from troponin and the cytosol. This is achieved by ATP-driven Ca²⁺ transporters in the sarcoplasmic reticulum that decrease the Ca²⁺ concentration in the cytosol back to its resting concentration.

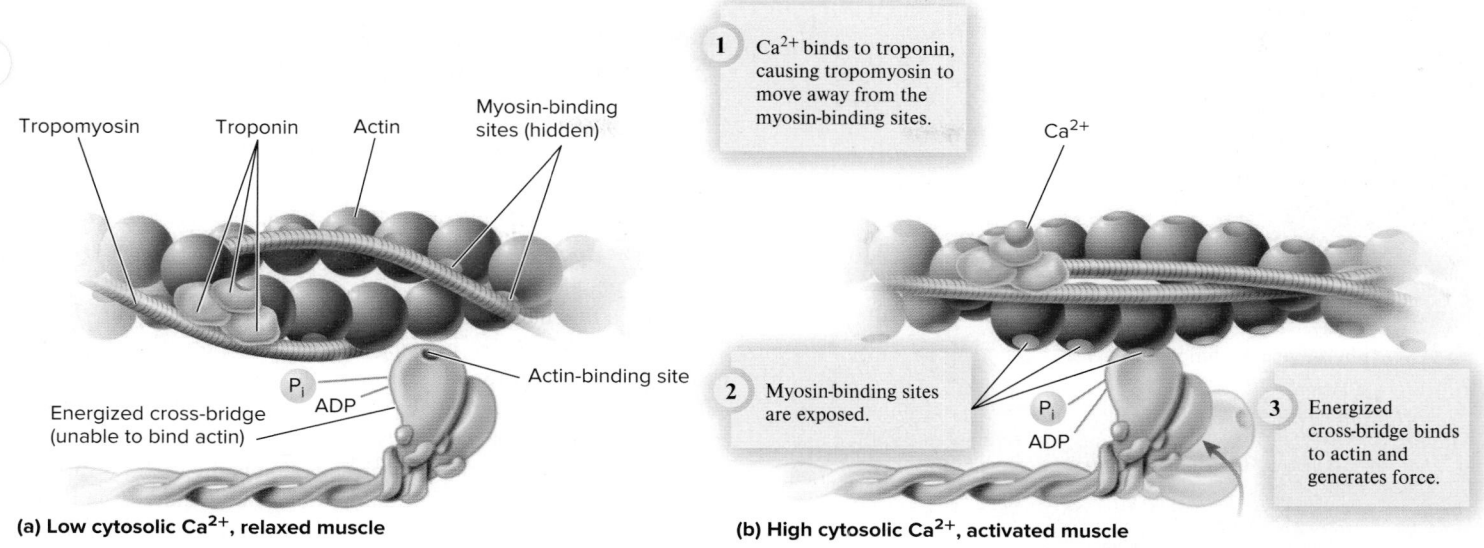

Tropomyosin   Troponin   Actin   Myosin-binding sites (hidden)

P_i   ADP

Energized cross-bridge (unable to bind actin)

Actin-binding site

(a) Low cytosolic Ca²⁺, relaxed muscle

1 Ca²⁺ binds to troponin, causing tropomyosin to move away from the myosin-binding sites.

Ca²⁺

2 Myosin-binding sites are exposed.

P_i   ADP

3 Energized cross-bridge binds to actin and generates force.

(b) High cytosolic Ca²⁺, activated muscle

Figure 45.9 Function of Ca²⁺, tropomyosin, and troponin in cross-bridge cycling. (a) When cytosolic Ca²⁺ is low, the myosin-binding sites on actin are blocked by tropomyosin. **(b)** When cytosolic Ca²⁺ increases, Ca²⁺ binds to troponin, which, in turn, causes tropomyosin to move away from the myosin-binding sites on actin.

Opening of transverse tubule to extracellular fluid

Muscle fiber plasma membrane

1 Action potentials propagate along the plasma membrane and down the transverse tubules (T-tubules).

T-tubule   Muscle fiber plasma membrane   Sarcoplasmic reticulum

T-tubule

2 The depolarization produced by the action potentials opens voltage-gated Ca²⁺ channels in the membranes of the sarcoplasmic reticulum, out of which Ca²⁺ diffuses into the cell cytosol.

Ca²⁺

Ca²⁺ (binds to troponin)

Ca²⁺

ATP   ADP + P_i

Ca²⁺ channel

Cytosol

Myofibrils

Cytosol

Mitochondrion

3 Ca²⁺ then binds to troponin in the myofibril, initiating muscle fiber contraction.

4 Ca²⁺ is then pumped back into the sarcoplasmic reticulum by ATP-driven Ca²⁺ transporters. This results in muscle fiber relaxation.

Transverse tubules

Sarcoplasmic reticulum

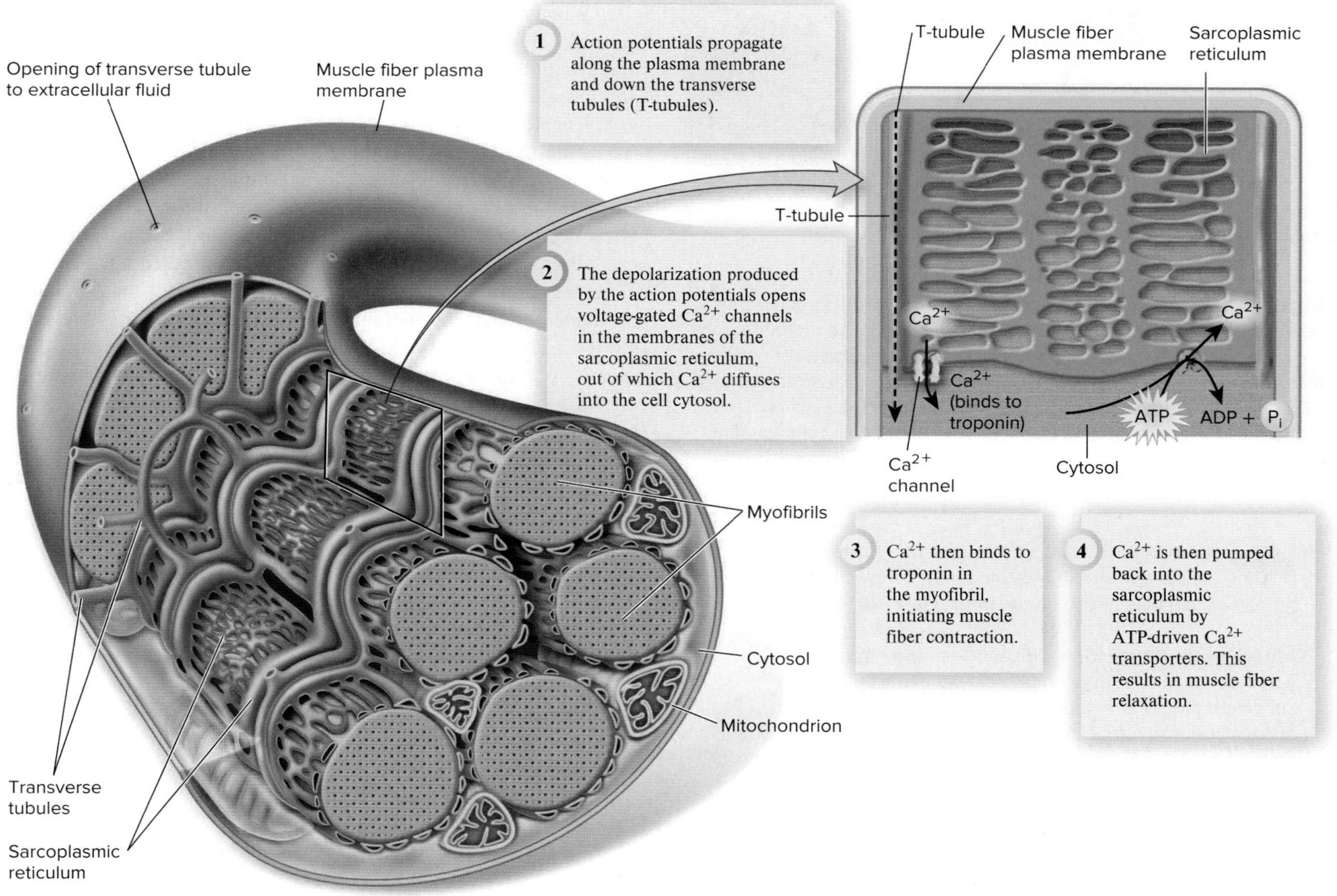

Figure 45.10 Structure and function of the sarcoplasmic reticulum, transverse tubules (T-tubles), and myofibrils in a skeletal muscle fiber.

 Core Skill: Connections What have you learned earlier about the role of voltage-gated Ca²⁺ channels in cell-to-cell communication? Look back at Figure 42.13 for help.

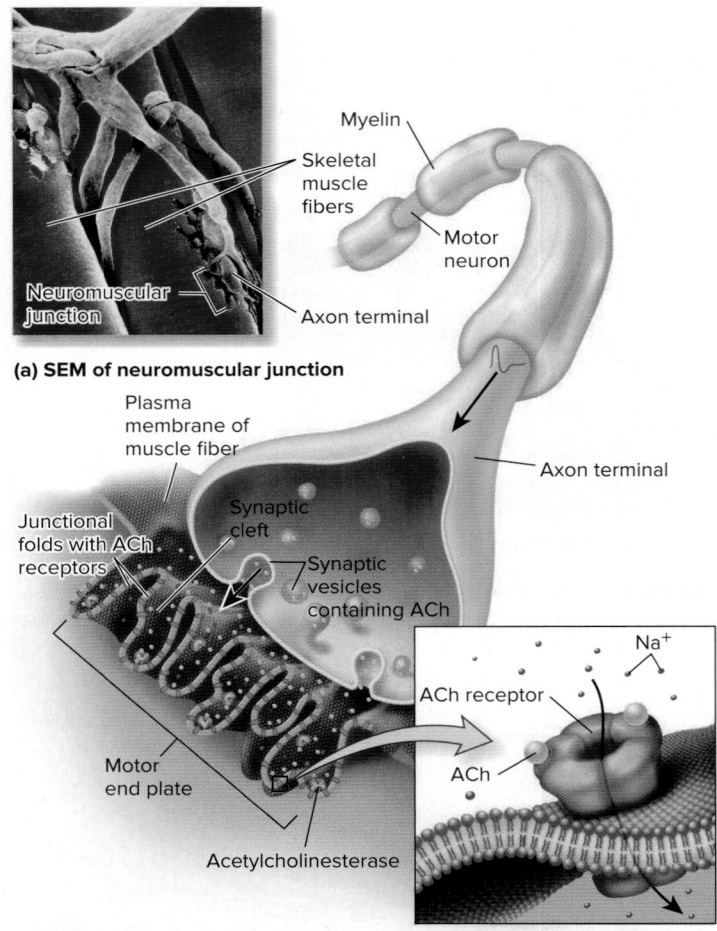

(a) SEM of neuromuscular junction

(b) Structures of, and events at, the neuromuscular junction (only part of the motor neuron is shown)

Figure 45.11 **The neuromuscular junction.** **(a)** The structure of a neuromuscular junction as seen in a colorized SEM. The motor neurons are green, and the muscle fibers are red. **(b)** Action potentials in the motor neuron cause exocytosis of ACh-containing synaptic vesicles. ACh binds to receptors in the plasma membrane in the junctional folds of the skeletal muscle fiber. This initiates Na⁺ entry and, consequently, an action potential in the muscle fiber. Excess ACh is removed by the enzyme acetylcholinesterase. a: ©Don W. Fawcett/Science Source

Electrical Stimulation of Skeletal Muscle Fibers Occurs at the Neuromuscular Junction

We have seen that an action potential in the plasma membrane of a skeletal muscle fiber is the signal that triggers contraction. The mechanism by which action potentials are initiated in a skeletal muscle fiber involves stimulation by a motor neuron. The cell bodies of these neurons are located in the central nervous system (CNS) and transmit signals from the CNS to directly control muscles.

The site where a motor neuron's axon synapses with a muscle fiber is known as a **neuromuscular junction** (**Figure 45.11**). Near the surface of the muscle fiber, the axon divides into several short processes, or terminals, containing synaptic vesicles filled with the neurotransmitter acetylcholine (ACh) (see Chapter 42). The region of the muscle fiber plasma membrane that lies directly under an axon terminal is called the **motor end plate**; it is folded into what are known as junctional folds, where the ACh receptors are located. These folds increase the total surface area available for the membrane to respond to ACh. The extracellular space between the axon terminal and the motor end plate is called the synaptic cleft.

When an action potential in a motor neuron arrives at the axon terminal, it triggers the release of stored ACh, which diffuses across the synaptic cleft and binds to receptors in the junctional folds of the muscle fiber. The ACh receptor is a ligand-gated ion channel (see Chapter 5). The binding of ACh opens the channel and causes an influx of Na⁺ into the muscle fiber, which causes the muscle fiber to depolarize, resulting in an action potential that spreads along the membrane of the muscle fiber and through the T-tubules. Most neuromuscular junctions are located near the middle of a muscle fiber, and newly generated muscle action potentials propagate from this region toward the ends of the fiber and throughout the T-tubule network. Overstimulation of a muscle fiber is prevented by the action of **acetylcholinesterase**. This enzyme breaks down excess ACh in the synaptic cleft to inactive forms that cannot bind the ACh receptor.

Now let's explore how skeletal muscle is adapted to meet the varied functional demands of vertebrates.

 Core Skill: Modeling The goal of this modeling challenge is to draw a model that shows the effects of an insecticide on the neuromuscular junction.

Modeling Challenge: Some insecticides are organic compounds that bind to and inhibit acetylcholinesterase. The simplified model of a neuromuscular junction at the right shows a neuron releasing ACh into the synaptic cleft. Draw a revised model that shows the neuromuscular junction during exposure to an insecticide. In your model, indicate where the insecticide is bound and show the relative amount of ACh in the synaptic cleft compared to the amount in the original model. Predict how the insecticide would indirectly affect Na⁺ channels in the muscle fiber's plasma membrane and, as a result, muscle function.

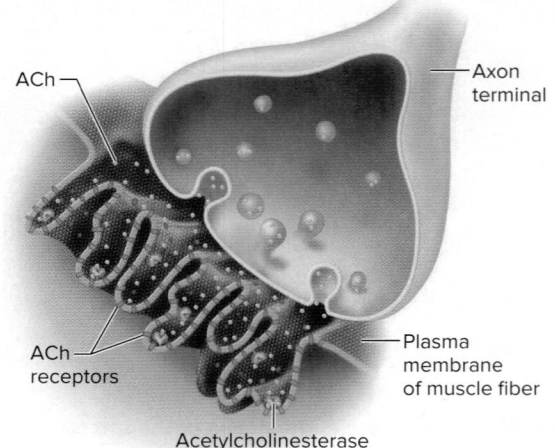

Neuromuscular junction without insecticide

Learning Outcomes:

1. Outline the general characteristics of the three types of skeletal muscle fibers.

2. **CoreSKILL** » Predict how skeletal muscles may adapt to exercise.

Animals use skeletal muscle for a wide variety of different activities, such as locomotion, stretching, chewing, breathing, and maintaining posture and balance, to name a few. Therefore, it is not surprising that not all skeletal muscle fibers share identical mechanical and metabolic characteristics. In this section, we will consider how different types of fibers can be broadly classified on the basis of their rates of shortening (as either fast or slow) and the way in which they produce the ATP required for contraction (as oxidative or glycolytic).

Skeletal Muscle Fibers Are Adapted for Different Types of Movement

Recall that there are many types of myosin, each with slightly different characteristics but all sharing an ability to hydrolyze ATP and bind actin. Different skeletal muscle fibers contain forms of myosin that differ in the maximal rates at which they can hydrolyze ATP. This, in turn, determines the maximal rates of cross-bridge cycling and muscle shortening. Fibers containing myosin with low ATPase activity are called **slow fibers**. Those containing myosin with higher ATPase activity are classified as **fast fibers**. Although the rate of cross-bridge cycling is about four times faster in fast fibers than in slow fibers, the maximal force produced by both types of cross-bridges is approximately the same.

The second means of classifying skeletal muscle fibers is based on the type of metabolic pathways available for synthesizing ATP. Fibers that contain numerous mitochondria and have a high capacity for oxidative phosphorylation are classified as **oxidative fibers**. Most of the ATP production by such fibers depends on blood flow delivering oxygen and nutrients to the muscle. Not surprisingly, therefore, these fibers are surrounded by many small blood vessels. They also contain large amounts of **myoglobin**, an oxygen-binding protein that increases the availability of oxygen in the fiber by providing an intracellular reservoir of the gas. The large amounts of myoglobin present in oxidative fibers give these fibers a dark-red color. For this reason, oxidative fibers are often referred to as red muscle fibers. The benefit of red muscle fibers is they can maintain sustained action over a long period of time without fatigue.

By contrast, **glycolytic fibers** have fewer mitochondria but possess a high concentration of the proteins involved in glycolysis (glycolytic enzymes; refer back to Figure 7.3) and large stores of glycogen, the storage form of glucose. Corresponding to their limited use of oxygen, these fibers are surrounded by relatively few blood vessels and contain little myoglobin. The lack of myoglobin is responsible for the pale color of glycolytic fibers and their designation as white muscle fibers.

On the basis of these two characteristics, three major types of skeletal muscle fibers have been distinguished:

1. **Slow-oxidative fibers** have low rates of myosin ATPase activity but have the ability to make large amounts of ATP. These fibers are useful for prolonged, regular types of movement, such as steady flight over a period of time, long-distance swimming, or the maintenance of posture. These muscles, for example, are what give the red color to the dark meat of ducks, which use the muscles for flight. Long-distance runners have a high proportion of these fibers in their leg muscles. These types of activities require muscles that do not fatigue easily.

2. **Fast-oxidative fibers** have high myosin ATPase activity and can make large amounts of ATP. Like slow-oxidative fibers, these fibers do not fatigue quickly and can be used for long-term actions. They are also particularly suited for rapid actions, such as the rapid trilling sounds made by the throat muscles in songbirds or the shaking of a rattlesnake's tail that produces a clicking sound.

3. **Fast-glycolytic fibers** have high myosin ATPase activity but cannot make as much ATP as oxidative fibers, because their source of ATP is glycolysis. These fibers are best suited for rapid, intense actions, such as a cheetah's short sprint at maximum speed. Sloths, by contrast, have few or no fast-glycolytic fibers in their leg muscles, which is not surprising given a sloth's very sedentary lifestyle. Fast-glycolytic fibers fatigue more rapidly than fast-oxidative fibers. The breast meat of chickens, for example, appears white because, unlike ducks, chickens do not fly except for very short distances and therefore do not require oxidative pectoral muscles. The fast-glycolytic muscles of chickens, however, are ideal for short flights in the air that help them quickly escape predators. When they land, chickens use slow-oxidative fibers in their leg muscles to run long distances as they continue to elude a predator.

Different muscle groups within an animal's body have different proportions of each type of fiber interspersed with one another; many activities require the action of all three types of fibers at once. This is important when you consider the wide range of animal activities related to locomotion alone, including walking, climbing, running, swimming, flying, crawling, crouching, jumping, and maintaining balance and posture. Depending on the requirements of an animal at any given moment, the motor nerve inputs can be adjusted to stimulate different ratios of fiber types. When you lift a heavy weight for a brief time, the fast-glycolytic fibers in your arm muscles are activated in large numbers. When a crab uses its pincers to grab prey, fast-glycolytic muscles snap the claws closed quickly, but then slow-oxidative fibers maintain a tight grip for as long as required. The characteristics of the three types of skeletal muscle fibers are summarized in **Table 45.1.**

Muscles Adapt to Exercise

The regularity with which a muscle is used, as well as the duration and intensity of the activity and whether it includes resistance, affects the properties of the muscle. For example, increased amounts of resistance exercise—such as weight lifting—results in hypertrophy (increase in size) of muscle fibers. Because the number of fibers in a muscle does not normally change significantly throughout adult

Table 45.1	Characteristics of the Three Types of Skeletal Muscle Fibers		
	Slow-oxidative	Fast-oxidative	Fast-glycolytic
Primary source of ATP production	Oxidative phosphorylation	Oxidative phosphorylation	Glycolysis
Mitochondria	Many	Many	Few
Blood supply	High	High	Moderate
Myoglobin content	High (red)	High (red)	Low (white)
Rate of fatigue	Slow	Intermediate	Fast
Myosin ATPase activity	Low	High	High
Rate of contraction	Slow	Fast	Fast

life, the increases in muscle size that occur with resistance exercise result primarily from increases in the size of each fiber. These fibers undergo an increase in diameter due to the increased synthesis of actin and myosin filaments, which form more myofibrils.

Exercise of relatively low intensity but long duration—popularly called aerobic exercise, including running and swimming—increases the number of mitochondria in the fibers that are required in this type of activity. In addition, the number of blood vessels around these fibers increases to supply the greater energy demands of active muscle. All of these changes increase endurance.

By contrast, short-duration, high-intensity exercise, such as weight lifting, primarily affects fast-glycolytic fibers, which are used during strong contractions. In addition, glycolytic activity is enhanced by increased synthesis of glycolytic enzymes. The results of such high-intensity exercise are the increased strength and bulging muscles of a conditioned weight lifter. Such muscles, although very powerful, have little capacity for endurance and therefore fatigue rapidly.

A decline or cessation of muscular activity results in the condition called **atrophy**, a reduction in the size of the muscle. Likewise, if the neurons to a skeletal muscle are destroyed or the neuromuscular junctions become nonfunctional, the denervated muscle fibers will become progressively smaller in diameter. This condition is known as denervation atrophy. Even with an intact nerve supply, a muscle can atrophy if it is not used for a long period of time, as when a broken limb is immobilized in a cast.

The mechanism by which changes occur in skeletal muscle during exercise is an active area of research, but recent discoveries have provided intriguing clues, an example of which is described next.

 Core Skill: Process of Science

Feature Investigation | Evans and Colleagues Activated a Gene to Produce "Marathon Mice"

In the course of investigating possible ways to reverse or prevent obesity in humans, American biologist Ron Evans and his colleagues discovered one way in which the proportions of oxidative and glycolytic fibers change in skeletal muscle. Evans was interested in a gene that encodes a transcription factor called PPAR-δ. Activation of this protein results in the expression of genes that enable skeletal muscle or other cells to more efficiently burn fat instead of glucose for energy. Evans hypothesized that mice in which PPAR-δ was chronically activated at high concentrations would lose weight due to increased fat burning, as shown in **Figure 45.12**.

To test this hypothesis, Evans created mice that carried the *PPAR-δ* gene in a modified form (see Chapter 21). The modified gene had a promoter that caused the gene to be expressed only in skeletal muscle cells. The region of the gene that encoded PPAR-δ was linked to a region of another gene that encoded a viral protein domain called VP16. This domain facilitates gene activation. The researchers expected the combination of PPAR-δ and VP16 to strongly activate genes that enable cells to preferentially metabolize fat instead of glucose for energy.

In the first part of the experiment, Evans monitored the body weights of the transgenic mice after they reached adulthood. The transgenic mice gained significantly less weight than the wild-type mice when fed high-fat diets (which normally cause mice—like humans—to gain weight), confirming Evans's hypothesis. As is sometimes the case in scientific discovery, an unexpected finding arose from this study. When Evans examined several tissues in these mice under the microscope, he observed that the skeletal muscle of the transgenic mice showed a noticeable shift from glycolytic fibers to slow-oxidative fibers. The skeletal muscle in transgenic mice appeared redder than it did in wild-type mice. It contained more myoglobin and mitochondria, and had higher concentrations of oxidative enzymes capable of providing the cells with sustained levels of ATP. These changes occurred even though the mice had not been subjected to exercise training.

Based on these observations, Evans tested a second hypothesis that the transgenic mice would have a greater capacity for prolonged exercise than wild-type mice. When the transgenic mice were challenged with an endurance exercise test, Evans discovered that they outperformed age- and weight-matched wild-type mice by a factor of nearly twofold! They could sustain a high level of activity on a miniature treadmill for nearly twice as long as wild-type mice (hence the nickname "marathon mice"). This effect occurred in transgenic mice even without prior exercise training. In other words, simply increasing the ratio of oxidative to glycolytic fibers gave the mice greater ability to sustain aerobic activity.

The results of these experiments indicate that increasing the amount of activated PPAR-δ facilitates an oxidative state in skeletal muscle fibers that somehow signals them to convert to types that are best suited for oxidative metabolism. Therefore, the switch in fiber type that occurs in exercise training may not require exercise per se, and it may be mediated in part by proteins that activate or induce *PPAR-δ* expression. These results may have important implications for enhancing physical endurance in humans, as well as for possible treatments for various muscle diseases and for prevention of obesity.

Figure 45.12 **Evans and colleagues' activation of a gene to produce "marathon mice."** (mice on treadmills): ©Mark Richards/PhotoEdit

| **HYPOTHESES** | 1. Increased expression of genes that lead to increased fat oxidation in skeletal muscle cells will prevent obesity in mice. |
| | 2. Transgenic mice have a greater capacity for prolonged exercise than do wild-type mice. |

KEY MATERIALS Mice, light and electron microscopes, motorized treadmills.

	Experimental level	Conceptual level

1 Prepare a modified gene containing a skeletal muscle–specific promoter and a coding sequence that links *VP16* and *PPAR-δ*. See Chapter 21 for gene cloning methods.

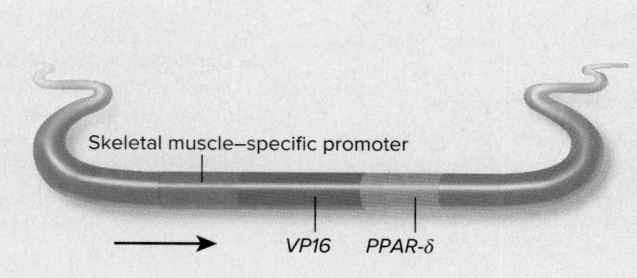

Skeletal muscle–specific promoter

VP16   *PPAR-δ*

Skeletal muscle–specific promoter ensures gene is turned on only in skeletal muscle.

VP16 encodes a domain that always activates transcription.

PPAR-δ encodes a transcription factor that specifically activates genes that allow cells to efficiently burn fat.

2 Make transgenic mice expressing the *VP16–PPAR-δ* gene.

See Chapter 21 for a discussion of gene cloning.

All of the cells will carry this gene, but only skeletal muscle cells will express the gene.

3 **Perform the following tests:**

(a) Feed wild-type control mice and transgenic mice a normal-fat diet (4%) and then switch to a high-fat diet (35%). Weigh mice weekly.

(b) Examine the muscle fibers in the mice.

(c) Test their endurance on a treadmill.

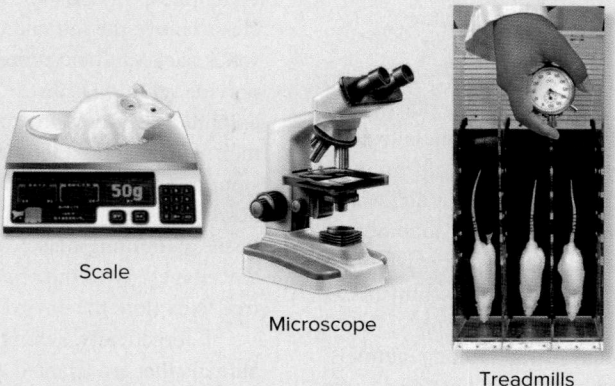

Scale

Microscope

Treadmills

(a) Eating a high-fat diet is known to cause obesity in mice and other mammals.

(b) The appearance of skeletal muscle can be examined by light and electron microscopy.

(c) The treadmills are motorized to keep mice moving until they become exhausted, at which time the treadmills are stopped.

4 **THE DATA**

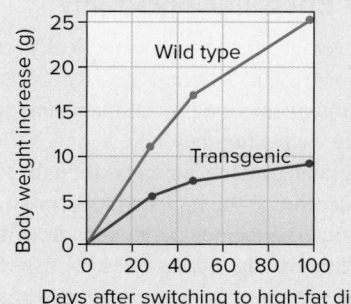

Days after switching to high-fat diet

(a) Weight gain

Characteristics of skeletal muscle in transgenic mice:

– redder than wild type
– more myoglobin
– more mitochondria
– more slow-oxidative fibers

(b) Difference in skeletal muscle

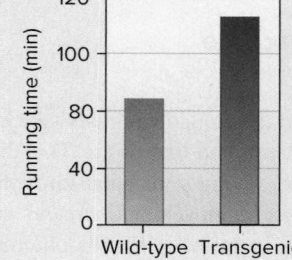

Wild-type   Transgenic

(c) Muscle endurance

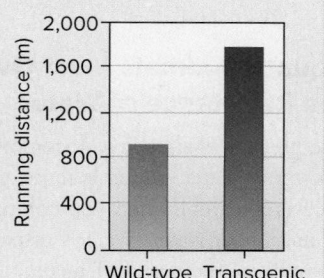

Wild-type   Transgenic

5 **CONCLUSION** PPAR-δ contributes to both weight loss and endurance in mice. The fiber-type switching associated with exercise does not require exercise, because increasing fat oxidation in skeletal muscle cells resulted in more oxidative fibers even without exercise training.

6 **SOURCE** Wang, Y.X., et al. 2004. Gene targeting turns mice into long-distance runners. *Public Library of Science Biology* 2: 322.

Experimental Questions

1. What is the normal function of the PPAR-δ protein in mice?

2. **CoreSKILL** ≫ What was the hypothesis proposed by Evans in relation to PPAR-δ and obesity? How did Evans and his colleagues test this hypothesis, and what did they observe?

3. **CoreSKILL** ≫ Assume that the mean weight of both groups of mice—wild-type and transgenic—prior to being switched to the high-fat diet was 24 g. Calculate the approximate mean weights of the two groups at the conclusion of the study. How does a diet containing 35% of its calories from fat compare to a typical human diet?

45.4 Animal Locomotion

Learning Outcomes:

1. Describe the mechanisms of animal locomotion in water, on land, and in air.
2. **CoreSKILL** ≫ Compare the quantitative differences in energy costs of swimming, running, and flying.
3. Explain how evolution has shaped the structures used for locomotion.

Locomotion, the movement of an animal from place to place, may take many forms, as described earlier. In all cases, animals experience certain constraints to locomotion. For example, all animals must overcome frictional forces (drag) generated by the air, water, or surface of the ground. In addition, all forms of locomotion require energy to provide thrust, defined as the forward motion of an animal in any environment, and/or lift, which is movement against gravity.

Although the precise mechanism may differ among animals, locomotion with few exceptions (such as the rhythmic beating of cilia in ctenophores) results from muscular contractions that exert force on one of the types of skeletons discussed at the beginning of this chapter. In this section, we will examine the similarities and differences between locomotion in water, on land, and in air.

Aquatic Animals Must Overcome the Resistance of Water

The greatest challenge to locomotion that aquatic animals face is the density of water, which is much greater than that of air. This difference is apparent when you compare waving your hand through the air and under water. Water's resistance to movement increases exponentially as the speed of locomotion increases, which is one reason why many fishes swim at relatively slow speeds. Overcoming this resistance requires considerable muscular effort. Most swimming animals, including fishes, amphibians, reptiles, diving birds, and marine mammals, have evolved streamlined bodies that reduce drag and so make swimming more efficient.

Although the density of water creates challenges to locomotion, it also provides certain benefits. An energetic advantage to swimming is that fishes and other swimmers do not need to provide as much lift to overcome gravity. Because the density of water is similar to that of an animal's body, water provides buoyancy, which helps support the animal's weight.

The mechanism of swimming is similar among many different vertebrates. Most fishes, for example, contract posterior skeletal muscles to move the tail end of the animal from side to side. This pushes water backward and propels the fish forward. Other muscles and fins provide additional thrust and enable changes in direction. Likewise, amphibians and marine reptiles rely predominantly on their hind legs, their tail, or undulations of the posterior parts of the body for propulsion through the water. Cetaceans (whales and dolphins) use up-and-down thrusts of their tail flukes to provide propulsion. Confining most of the swimming muscles to the rear of an animal's body has certain advantages. With the rear end devoted to movement, the front end is free to explore the environment, fight off aggressors, or find food.

Energetically, swimming is the "cheapest" form of locomotion in animals that are adapted to it, due to streamlining, the relatively slow speed of most swimmers, and the buoyancy of water. By contrast, terrestrial animals face considerable energetic costs associated with locomotion, as we examine next.

Locomotion on Land Is Energetically Costly

Locomotion on land is, on average, the most energetically costly means of locomotion (**Figure 45.13**). Whereas gravity is not an important factor for locomotion in swimming animals, terrestrial animals must overcome gravity each time they take a step. Of even greater importance to walking and running animals, though, is the requirement to accelerate and decelerate the limbs with every step. In essence, each step is like starting a movement from scratch, without the luxury of occasionally gliding through water or air as fishes and birds do. This challenge is even greater when an animal moves uphill or over rough terrain.

Apart from terrestrial gastropods, which move along the surface of the ground on a layer of secreted mucus, and snakes, which undulate along the ground on a portion of their ventral body surface, most

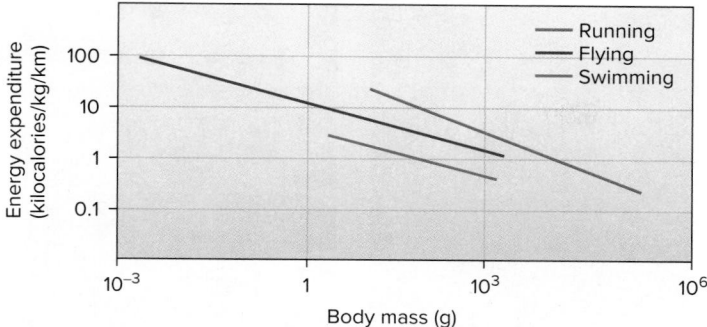

Figure 45.13 Energy costs of locomotion. The energy costs of three different modes of locomotion for animals of different sizes are shown. The vertical axis measures the energy cost as kilocalories expended per kilogram (kg) per kilometer (km). Energy costs are highest for runners compared with similarly sized fliers and swimmers. Note: Only a portion of the full range of body sizes of swimmers is shown.

terrestrial animals limit the amount of contact with the ground while moving, thereby minimizing the amount of friction they encounter. Tetrapods usually have only two feet on the ground at any time when walking, and for brief moments, an animal such as a horse galloping at full speed has all four feet off the ground.

Having fewer legs touching the ground at any one time helps increase speed but can compromise stability. Arthropods, for example, have at least six legs. This apparently provides excellent stability but reduces maximal speed (although cockroaches can attain rapid speeds by running on only two legs). At the other extreme are animals that move by jumping—fleas, certain spiders, click beetles, grasshoppers, frogs, and kangaroos.

Flying Has Evolved in Four Different Lineages

Flying is a highly successful means of locomotion and is hypothesized to have evolved in four different lineages: pterosaurs (extinct reptiles that were the first vertebrates to fly), insects, birds, and mammals (bats). Flying provides numerous advantages: Animals can escape land-based predators, scan their surroundings over great distances, and inhabit environments such as high cliffs that may be inaccessible to nonflying animals. The mechanics of flying, however, require animals to overcome gravity and air resistance, which makes flying more energetically costly than swimming but still less costly than running on land (see Figure 45.13). Many migratory birds can travel hundreds of miles daily for a week or longer. As with swimming, resistance to movement in flight is decreased by streamlined bodies. However, earthbound animals have one advantage over flying animals—they can grow to much larger sizes than animals that fly. The vast majority of flying animals have a mass between about 1 mg and 1 kg. Only a few large birds have masses exceeding 10 kg. Although this represents a wide range, it falls far short of the sizes achieved by earthbound or aquatic animals.

In flying vertebrates, lift and thrust are provided by pectoral and other muscles that move the wings. The pectoral muscles are so powerful and massive that they constitute as much as 15–20% of a bird's total body mass and up to 30% in hummingbirds, which use their wings not only to fly but also to hover. The requirement for large, strong pectoral muscles is one reason why the body mass of flying vertebrates is limited. The extinct pterosaurs would seem to be an exception because some species were known to have had wingspans of nearly 10 m. However, scientists think that these large animals were unable to generate the force required to lift their massive bodies off the ground and instead glided from trees or cliffs to fly.

In birds and bats, the wings are modifications of the forelimbs. In general, bat wings are far more maneuverable than bird wings, because unlike birds, bats have digits at the end of their forelimbs/wings. These allow bats to precisely alter the shape of their wings and perform rapid, fine-tuned changes in direction, even at high speeds. The largest birds, such as hawks and eagles, are able to glide because of the great surface area of their large wings. By using a bird's momentum to propel it forward, gliding provides a considerable energy savings. Bats and small birds, however, can glide for only very brief moments.

👁 Core Skill: Quantitative Reasoning

BIO TIPS **THE QUESTION** *Look again at Figure 45.13. Which flying animal expends more total energy over a distance of 1 km: one that weighs 1 g or another that weighs 1 kg?*

T OPIC *What topic in biology does this question address?* The topic is animal locomotion. More specifically, the question concerns the relationship of body mass to energy expenditure in flying animals.

I NFORMATION *What information do you know based on the question and your understanding of the topic?* From the question, you know you need to compare two animals that differ in body mass by a factor of 1,000 (1 g versus 1 kg) with regard to their total energy expenditure while flying an equivalent distance (1 km). From your understanding of the topic, based on Figure 45.13, you know that smaller animals expend more energy than larger ones when energy expenditure is normalized to a standard mass (such as 1 kg).

P ROBLEM-SOLVING S TRATEGY *Interpret data. Compare and contrast.* To answer this question, you must interpret the relationship between body mass and energy expenditure for flying animals (Figure 45.13). First, find the approximate energy values for flying animals with body masses of 1 g and 1 kg (1,000 g), by moving upward from those masses on the horizontal axis to the line for flying animals and then moving left from there to the vertical axis to get the energy values. Second, consider that the question asks for *total* energy expenditure. The data shown are for energy expenditure per kilogram of body mass. Thus, you must account for the fact that the animals differ in mass by a factor of 1,000.

ANSWER *A 1 g flying animal expends approximately 10 kilocalories/kg/km; because it weighs only 1 g, you must divide this value by 1,000 (there are 1,000 g in 1 kg). The result for the 1 g animal is thus 0.01 kilocalories expended over 1 km. By contrast, a 1 kg animal expends approximately 1 kilocalorie/kg/km; since the animal weighs 1 kg, there is no need to normalize the value. Therefore, the answer is that the 1-kg animal expends much more total energy flying a distance of 1 km than does the 1 g animal.*

45.5   Impact on Public Health

Learning Outcomes:

1. Describe the impacts of the bone diseases rickets and osteoporosis on public health.
2. Recognize the main symptoms and causes of muscular dystrophy.

In this chapter, we have seen how skeletal muscles and, in vertebrates, bones function together to provide animals with protection and enable them to move around in their environments. A number of diseases affect bone structure and function in humans. Bone disease may involve defects in either the mineral or organic components of bone. Poor bone formation and structure may result from inadequate nutrition, hormonal imbalances, aging, or skeletal muscle atrophy, to name just a few of the common causes.

In addition, many diseases or disorders directly affect the contraction of skeletal muscle. Some of them are temporary and not serious, such as muscle cramps, whereas others are chronic and severe, such as the disease muscular dystrophy. Also, some muscle diseases result from defects that originate in parts of the nervous system that control contraction of the muscle fibers rather than from defects that originate in the fibers themselves. One example is amyotrophic lateral sclerosis, a degenerative disease in which the destruction of motor neurons leads to skeletal muscle atrophy that may result in death from respiratory failure.

Other diseases that affect skeletal muscle function result when normal processes go awry. For example, the immune system that normally protects the body from pathogens may turn on itself, or faulty genes may produce an abnormal protein. In this section, we will look at a few of these conditions in more detail.

Rickets and Osteoporosis Affect the Bones of Millions of People

Bone diseases are fairly common, particularly among individuals older than 50. Two major abnormalities can occur in bone. The first is improper mineral deposition in bone, usually due to inadequate dietary calcium intake or inadequate absorption of Ca^{2+} from the small intestine. Without adequate minerals, bone becomes soft and easily deformed, as occurs in the weight-bearing bones of the legs of children with **rickets** (or **osteomalacia**, as it is called in adults) (**Figure 45.14a**). These disorders are best prevented or treated with vitamin D, because this vitamin is the most important factor in promoting absorption of ingested Ca^{2+} from the small intestine.

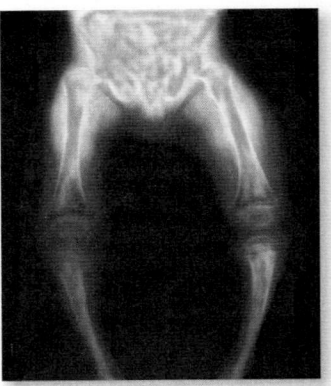
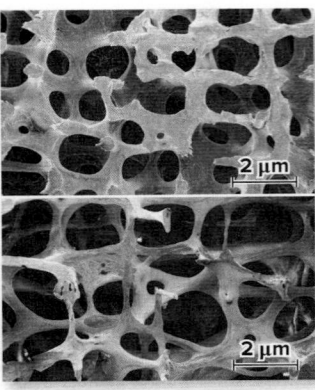
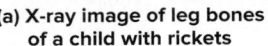

(a) X-ray image of leg bones of a child with rickets

(b) Histologic appearance of normal bone (top) and bone from a person with osteoporosis (bottom)

Figure 45.14   Human bone diseases. a: ©Dr. LR/Science Source; b: ©Tim Arnett, University College London

A second major abnormality is a more common disease called **osteoporosis**, in which both the mineral and organic portions of bone are decreased (**Figure 45.14b**). This disease, which affects four times as many women as men, occurs when the normal balance between bone formation and bone breakdown is disrupted.

One cause of osteoporosis is prolonged disuse of muscles. In ways that are not completely clear, the force produced by active skeletal muscle contractions helps maintain bone mass. When muscles are not or cannot be used—due to paralysis or long-term immobilizing illnesses—bone mass declines.

More commonly, osteoporosis may result from hormonal imbalances. Some hormones—for example, estrogen—stimulate bone formation. When estrogen concentrations decline after menopause (the time when a woman's reproductive cycles cease), bone density may decline, increasing the risk of bone fractures. Men can get osteoporosis, too, but since they typically have more bone mass to start, and do not have a pronounced drop in sex hormone concentrations like women, the onset of the disease is usually later and less severe than in women.

In contrast to estrogen, some hormones—such as parathyroid hormone (see Chapter 50)—act to demineralize bone, releasing Ca^{2+} into the extracellular fluid as part of the way in which the body normally maintains Ca^{2+} homeostasis in the blood. If such hormones are present in excess, however, they can cause enough demineralization of bone to result in osteoporosis. This may happen in rare cases when the glands that make these hormones malfunction and overproduce the hormones.

Osteoporosis can be minimized with adequate calcium and vitamin D intake and weight-bearing exercise programs. In some cases, postmenopausal women may be given estrogen to replace what their bodies are no longer producing, but this therapy is controversial due to the potential adverse effects of estrogen on cardiovascular health and possible increased risk of developing breast cancer. Osteoporosis is the most prevalent bone disease in the U.S., affecting up to 15–30 million individuals. It results in annual national expenditures of approximately $15–20 billion in hospital and other medical costs.

Muscular Dystrophy Is a Rare Genetic Disease That Causes Muscle Degeneration

The group of diseases collectively called muscular dystrophy affect 1 of every 3,500 American males; it is much less common in females. **Muscular dystrophy** is associated with the progressive degeneration of skeletal and cardiac muscle fibers, weakening the muscles and leading ultimately to death from heart failure and other causes. The signs and symptoms become evident at about 2–6 years of age, and most affected individuals do not survive beyond the age of 30.

The most common form of muscular dystrophy, called **Duchenne muscular dystrophy**, is an X-linked recessive disorder resulting from a defective gene on the X chromosome. Because females have two X chromosomes, and males only one (plus one Y), a heterozygote female with one abnormal and one normal allele will not generally develop Duchenne muscular dystrophy. If she passes the abnormal allele to a son, however, he will have the disease. The affected gene encodes a protein known as dystrophin, which is absent in patients with the disease. Dystrophin is a large protein that links cytoskeletal proteins to the plasma membrane. Scientists think it is involved in maintaining the structural integrity of the plasma membrane in muscle fibers. In the absence of dystrophin, the plasma membrane of muscle fibers is disrupted, causing extracellular fluid to enter the cell. Eventually, the cell ruptures and dies.

One focus of interest in attempts to develop a treatment for muscular dystrophy is a protein called myostatin, which is one of a large number of proteins that control muscle growth in mammals. Myostatin functions to prevent overgrowth of skeletal muscle by inhibiting maturation of stem cells into new muscle fibers and by preventing excessive growth of mature fibers. Researchers have identified animals with mutations in the gene that encodes myostatin. The mutations result in the production of an inactive protein, and such animals show astonishing muscle development (**Figure 45.15**). Whether

or not targeting the myostatin protein will lead to a treatment that can reverse muscle loss in patients with muscular dystrophy and other diseases remains to be determined.

Summary of Key Concepts

45.1 Types of Animal Skeletons

- Skeletons are structures that provide support and protection and also function in locomotion.

- Two types of skeletons are commonly found in animals. In arthropods, exoskeletons are protective external structures that must be shed to accommodate an animal's growth. Endoskeletons—found in some species of sponges and in all echinoderms and vertebrates—are internal structures that grow with an animal but do not protect its body surface (Figure 45.1).

- Vertebrate endoskeletons are considered to have two parts: axial and appendicular skeletons. A joint is formed where two or more bones of a vertebrate endoskeleton come together (Figure 45.2).

- In addition to the functions of support, protection, and locomotion, the vertebrate skeleton produces blood cells and constitutes a reservoir for ions crucial to homeostasis. A proper proportion of organic to mineral components is required for normal bone function.

45.2 Skeletal Muscle Structure and the Mechanism of Force Generation

- A skeletal muscle is a grouping of cells, called muscle fibers, bound together by connective tissue layers. Muscles that bend a limb at a joint are called flexors, whereas muscles that straighten a limb are called extensors. Two or more muscles that produce oppositely directed movements at a joint are known as antagonists (Figures 45.3, 45.4).

- Within each muscle cell are cylindrical bundles known as myofibrils, each of which contains thick filaments of myosin and thin filaments composed of actin and two other proteins, arranged in repeating units called sarcomeres. Regions of the thick filaments that extend toward the thin filaments are called cross-bridges (Figure 45.5).

- During muscle contraction, the sarcomeres shorten by a process known as the sliding filament mechanism. In muscle contraction, the thick filaments remain stationary while the thin filaments slide past them propelled by the action of cross-bridges (Figure 45.6).

- Mutations in a myosin gene expressed mainly in the jaw muscle may have allowed the human brain to become larger (Figure 45.7).

- In the cross-bridge cycle, the binding of a myosin cross-bridge to actin causes a change in the shape of the myosin molecule. As a result, the two filaments slide past each other, shortening the sarcomere and contracting the muscle fiber. Release of the cross-bridge from actin and return of myosin to its original conformation require ATP binding and hydrolysis (Figure 45.8).

- Tropomyosin and troponin, the two proteins associated with actin, play a critical role in the regulation of muscle contraction. The binding of Ca^{2+} to troponin allows tropomyosin to move away from the myosin-binding sites, initiating cross-bridge binding (Figure 45.9).

Figure 45.15 An animal with a mutation in the gene that encodes myostatin, which resulted in inactive myostatin protein and overdevelopment of skeletal muscle. McPherron, A. C., and Lee, S. 1997. Double muscling in cattle due to mutations in the myostatin gene. *PNAS* 94: 12,457-12,461.

- The concentration of cytosolic Ca^{2+} determines the number of actin sites available for cross-bridge binding. The source of the cytosolic Ca^{2+} involved in a muscle fiber's action potential is the fiber's sarcoplasmic reticulum. Transverse tubules (T-tubules) conduct action potentials from the plasma membrane at the outer surface of the muscle fiber to the interior of the cell, allowing Ca^{2+} to be released from the sarcoplasmic reticulum into the cytosol (Figure 45.10).

- Electrical stimulation of skeletal muscle occurs at a neuromuscular junction, the location where a motor neuron's axon terminal synapses with a muscle fiber (Figure 45.11).

45.3 Types of Skeletal Muscle Fibers and Their Functions

- Three major types of skeletal muscle fibers have been distinguished. Slow-oxidative fibers have low rates of myosin ATPase activity; they do not fatigue easily and are used for prolonged, regular activities. Fast-oxidative fibers have high myosin ATPase activity, do not fatigue quickly, and are particularly suited for rapid, long-term actions. Fast-glycolytic fibers have high myosin ATPase activity but cannot make as much ATP as oxidative fibers; they are best suited for rapid, short-term actions (Table 45.1).

- Increased expression of the *PPAR-δ* gene in mice results in increased slow-oxidative muscle, greater exercise endurance, and weight loss (Figure 45.12).

45.4 Animal Locomotion

- Locomotion, the movement of an animal from place to place, takes many forms, including swimming, walking, running, crawling, hopping, and flying.

- Due to streamlining, the relatively slow speed of most swimmers, and the buoyancy of water, swimming is energetically the most efficient form of locomotion. Locomotion on land is, on average, the most energetically costly means of locomotion. The energy expenditure required for flight is intermediate between those for swimming and land-based locomotion (Figure 45.13).

45.5 Impact on Public Health

- Several health conditions affect bone or muscle structure and function in humans. Rickets (osteomalacia in adults) is characterized by soft, deformed bones, usually resulting from insufficient dietary intake of calcium or inadequate absorption of Ca^{2+}. In osteoporosis, bone density is reduced when bone formation fails to keep pace with normal bone breakdown. Muscular dystrophy is an ultimately fatal genetic disease associated with the progressive degeneration of skeletal and cardiac muscle fibers (Figures 45.14, 45.15).

Assess & Discuss

Test Yourself

1. A disadvantage of an exoskeleton is that it
   a. cannot protect an animal's internal organs.
   b. must be periodically shed, leaving the animal in a vulnerable state.
   c. does not provide any flexibility for the ease of movement of an animal.
   d. is a soft, easily damaged structure.
   e. cannot protect the outside of the body surface.

2. Which, if any, of the following is *not* a function of the vertebrate skeleton?
   a. structural support
   b. protection of internal organs
   c. Ca^{2+} reserve
   d. blood cell production
   e. All of the above are functions of the vertebrate skeleton.

3. The protein that provides strength and flexibility to bone is
   a. actin.
   b. myosin.
   c. myoglobin.
   d. collagen.
   e. elastin.

4. Which of the following statements is *true*?
   a. A muscle fiber is a collection of cells embedded in connective tissue.
   b. A sarcomere contains both actin and myosin molecules arranged in a parallel fashion.
   c. The function of Ca^{2+} in contraction is to bind to tropomysin.
   d. Myofibrils are individual muscle cells.
   e. The I band of a sarcomere is the region where thin and thick filaments overlap.

5. The function of ATP during muscle contraction is to
   a. cause an allosteric change in myosin so it detaches from actin.
   b. provide the energy necessary for the movement of the cross-bridge.
   c. expose the myosin-binding sites on the thin filaments.
   d. do all of the above.
   e. do a and b only.

6. The function of Ca^{2+} in skeletal muscle contraction is to
   a. cause an allosteric change in myosin so that it detaches from actin.
   b. provide the energy necessary for the movement of the cross-bridge.
   c. expose the myosin-binding sites on the thin filaments.
   d. stimulate an action potential in the muscle fiber.
   e. do a and c only.

7. Stimulation of a muscle fiber by a motor neuron occurs at
   a. the neuromuscular junction.
   b. the transverse tubules.
   c. the myofibril.
   d. the sarcoplasmic reticulum.
   e. none of the above.

8. Muscle fibers that have a large number of mitochondria, contain large amounts of myoglobin, and exhibit low rates of ATPase activity are called _____ fibers.
   a. slow-glycolytic
   b. fast-glycolytic
   c. intermediate
   d. fast-oxidative
   e. slow-oxidative

9. Which of the following statements about movement and locomotion is *false*?
   a. Terrestrial animals and flying animals expend energy to provide lift.
   b. Swimming animals typically expend energy to provide thrust but not lift.
   c. Flexors and extensors are examples of muscles called agonists.

d. Flexors cause bending at a joint.

e. Extensors cause straightening of a limb.

10. For animals adapted to it, swimming is energetically the cheapest form of locomotion because of

a. the streamlined body forms of aquatic animals.

b. the slow speed of locomotion of many swimmers.

c. the buoyancy of water.

d. a and c only.

e. a, b, and c.

Conceptual Questions

1. Compare the structural and functional features of exoskeletons and endoskeletons and their advantages and disadvantages.

2. Describe as many types of animal locomotion as you can, and discuss the benefits and challenges presented by each in terms of energy usage.

3. **Core Concept: Energy and Matter** Explain the role of energy with regard to the mechanism by which skeletal muscle cells contract.

Collaborative Questions

1. List and briefly describe the steps in the cross-bridge cycle.

2. Discuss the three types of muscle tissues found in vertebrates, and identify distinguishing functional features of each.

d. Approximately 10% of the world's adult population is lactose-intolerant.

e. Bile is a mixture of wastes, HCO_3^-, cholesterol, and amphipathic compounds.

4. Which of the following statements is *true*?
   a. Intracellular digestion commonly occurs in vertebrates.
   b. Absorption of nutrients always requires active transport.
   c. Alimentary canals have two openings, whereas gastrovascular cavities have only one.
   d. Extracellular, but not intracellular, digestion requires hydrolytic enzymes.
   e. Most minerals are absorbed by simple diffusion.

5. To which part of the alimentary canal is the pancreas connected?
   a. esophagus   d. cecum
   b. stomach   e. large intestine
   c. small intestine

6. Which of the following statements regarding the vertebrate stomach is *false*?
   a. Its cells secrete the protease pepsin in its active form.
   b. It is a saclike organ that may have evolved to store food.
   c. Its cells secrete hydrochloric acid.
   d. It is the initial site of protein digestion.
   e. Little or no absorption of nutrients occurs there.

7. Absorption in the small intestine is increased by
   a. the many villi present on the inner surface of the small intestine.
   b. the brush border formed by microvilli on the cells of the villi.
   c. the presence of numerous transporter molecules on the epithelial cells.
   d. all of the above.
   e. a and b only.

8. In birds, the secretion of acid and pepsinogen occurs in the
   a. crop.   d. cloaca.
   b. gizzard.   e. gallbladder.
   c. proventriculus.

9. In many vertebrates, bile is produced by the _____ and stored in the _____.
   a. liver, small intestine
   b. gallbladder, liver
   c. pancreas, small intestine
   d. small intestine, gallbladder
   e. liver, gallbladder

10. Which of the following is *true* of the large intestine?
   a. It contains microorganisms that may produce useful by-products that can be absorbed.
   b. It stores and concentrates fecal material.
   c. Its cells absorb ions and water that remain in chyme after it leaves the small intestine.
   d. It varies considerably in size and may even be absent in some vertebrates.
   e. All of the above are true of the large intestine.

Conceptual Questions

1. Distinguish between digestion and absorption.

2. Explain the functions of the crop and gizzard in birds. Can you propose a reason why a crop and gizzard did not evolve in humans?

3. **Core Concept: Structure and Function** Describe the various structural adaptations of the vertebrate small intestine from the organ to the cellular level, and explain how each is related to the functions of digestion and absorption.

Collaborative Questions

1. Discuss the role of enzymes in digestion. What is their major function, and where are they produced and secreted?

2. Define nutrient. On the basis of that definition, do you consider water a nutrient? Briefly discuss the essential nutrients, vitamins, and minerals that animals must obtain through their diet.

Control of Energy Balance, Metabolic Rate, and Body Temperature

47

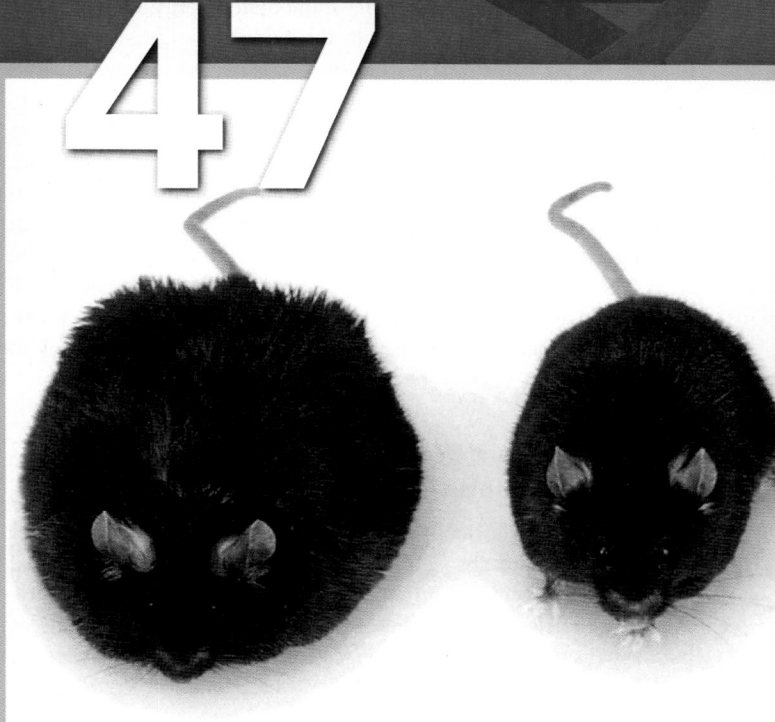

A genetically obese, leptin-deficient mouse and a wild-type mouse. ©The Rockefeller University/AP Images

In 1997, two young cousins being treated for extreme obesity were brought to the attention of researchers studying a newly discovered hormone called **leptin**. Leptin had been demonstrated to inhibit appetite in laboratory rodents. The researchers hypothesized that the children—who weighed approximately 30 kg by age 2, and in one case, 86 kg by age 9—were not producing leptin. This hypothesis was confirmed by molecular analyses and traced to a mutation in the leptin-encoding gene. Subsequently, several other individuals with mutations affecting leptin production were identified, leading in each case to extreme childhood obesity. Treatment of these individuals with leptin has proven beneficial in restoring normal body weight. Although leptin deficiency is rare and is only one of many possible causes of obesity in humans, animal models of leptin deficiency, such as the mouse shown in the chapter opening photo, represent a remarkable breakthrough in our understanding of the genetic bases of the control of appetite and metabolism. How nutrients that supply energy are processed, stored, and used by animals' bodies in times of food abundance or fasting is a focus of this chapter.

In Chapter 46, we saw that all animals require nutrients to assemble the macromolecules that make up body tissues. Some of the ingested nutrients, such as carbohydrates, lipids, and proteins, also represent a form of energy that can be used to synthesize ATP within cells. Most animals, however, do not have a constant supply of nutrients. For example, insects, cephalopods, and all vertebrates sleep or have periods of greatly reduced activity for part of the day, during which time they do not eat. In addition, environmental changes may reduce the food supply, leading to long periods of fasting. As a consequence of the irregular and sometimes unpredictable flow of nutrients into the body, animals have evolved an array of mechanisms to adequately maintain concentrations of important fuel molecules in the blood or other body fluids, even when fasting. In the first two sections of this chapter, we will explore how ingested nutrients are stored in the body for such times of need and the mechanisms by which these stores are tapped.

Metabolism refers to all the bodily activities and chemical reactions in an organism that maintain life. **Metabolic rate** is the rate at which an organism uses energy to power these reactions.

Animals may have widely different metabolic rates, which determine the amount of nutrients they require. The greater an animal's metabolic rate, the more heat it generates as a by-product of breaking down nutrients and using the energy of their chemical bonds to synthesize ATP. Some of this heat escapes to the environment, and some is used to warm an animal's body. Heat, in turn, can speed up metabolism. Metabolism and body temperature are therefore closely related, and we will examine this relationship in the next two sections of the chapter. We will also discuss energy balance, the balance between energy consumption and expenditure. The chapter will conclude with a discussion of the public health impact of human disorders associated with metabolism, including obesity.

47.1 Use and Storage of Energy

Learning Outcomes:

1. Describe the processes by which glucose, triglycerides, and amino acids are absorbed during the absorptive state.
2. Outline the two major ways that vertebrates can increase their blood glucose concentration during the postabsorptive state.
3. Define glucose sparing, and explain why it is important.

Once nutrients have been ingested, they are either used or, in many cases, stored. The handling of nutrients can be divided into two alternating phases. The **absorptive state** occurs when ingested nutrients enter the blood from the alimentary canal. The **postabsorptive state** occurs when the alimentary canal is empty of nutrients and the body's own stores must supply energy. During the absorptive state, some ingested nutrients supply the immediate energy requirements of the body. The rest are added to the body's energy stores to be called upon during the next postabsorptive state. An average meal in a human requires about 4 hours for complete absorption. Therefore, our usual three-meal-a-day pattern places us in the postabsorptive state during the late morning and afternoon and part of the night. Total-body energy stores are adequate for the average human to withstand a fast of several weeks. By contrast, some animals can barely survive a single missed meal—particularly if they have low energy reserves—because their relative metabolic requirements are much greater than our own. In this section, we will focus on nutrient absorption, use, and storage in vertebrates, with a closer look at mammals.

In the Absorptive State, Nutrients Are Absorbed and Used or Stored

The categories of nutrients that are absorbed either intact or after digestion during the absorptive state include carbohydrates, lipids, proteins, nucleic acids, vitamins, minerals, and water. We will look in depth at the first three of these; **Figure 47.1** gives an overview of what happens to these nutrients. Digested carbohydrates are absorbed as monosaccharides, including glucose (refer back to Figure 46.8).

Triglycerides are absorbed after first being digested into fatty acids and monoglycerides. Proteins are broken down into amino acids, which are then absorbed (refer back to Figure 46.9).

Absorbed Carbohydrates The chief carbohydrate monomer absorbed from the alimentary canal of vertebrates is glucose, which is one of the two major energy sources during the absorptive state (triglycerides being the other). Much of the absorbed glucose enters all cells and is enzymatically broken down, resulting in the formation of hydrogen ions, carbon dioxide, and water and, in the process, providing the energy required to synthesize ATP from ADP and inorganic phosphate (Figure 47.1a). Because skeletal muscle makes up a large fraction of body mass in most vertebrates, it is a major consumer of glucose, particularly when an animal is active. In all vertebrates, skeletal muscle also incorporates some of the glucose into the polymer glycogen, which is stored in the muscle cells for future use. If more glucose is absorbed into the blood than is required for immediate energy demands, a portion of the excess is incorporated into glycogen in the liver, and the remainder is broken down to provide substrates for synthesizing triglycerides in adipose cells. The structures of glycogen and triglycerides are described in Figures 3.7 and 3.8, respectively.

Absorbed Triglycerides Triglycerides are too large to diffuse across the plasma membranes of the intestinal epithelial cells. As described in Chapter 46 (refer back to Figure 46.10), triglycerides are digested into fatty acids and monoglycerides in the lumen of the small intestine, and then these breakdown products are resynthesized into triglycerides once they have diffused into the intestinal epithelial

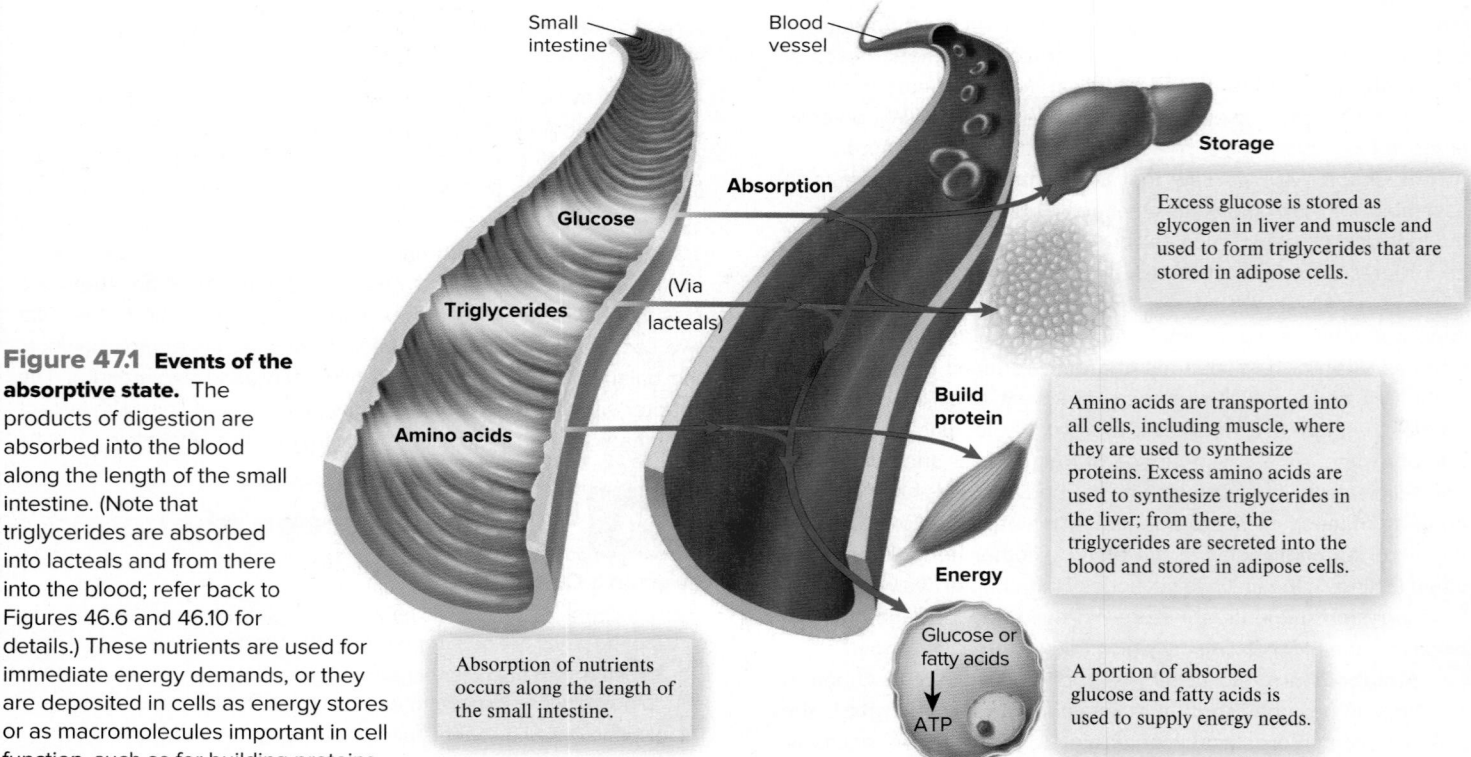

Figure 47.1 Events of the absorptive state. The products of digestion are absorbed into the blood along the length of the small intestine. (Note that triglycerides are absorbed into lacteals and from there into the blood; refer back to Figures 46.6 and 46.10 for details.) These nutrients are used for immediate energy demands, or they are deposited in cells as energy stores or as macromolecules important in cell function, such as for building proteins.

Small intestine

Blood vessel

Absorption

Storage

Glucose

(Via lacteals)

Triglycerides

Amino acids

Build protein

Energy

Excess glucose is stored as glycogen in liver and muscle and used to form triglycerides that are stored in adipose cells.

Amino acids are transported into all cells, including muscle, where they are used to synthesize proteins. Excess amino acids are used to synthesize triglycerides in the liver; from there, the triglycerides are secreted into the blood and stored in adipose cells.

Glucose or fatty acids
↓
ATP

Absorption of nutrients occurs along the length of the small intestine.

A portion of absorbed glucose and fatty acids is used to supply energy needs.

cells. The triglycerides and other ingested lipids (for example, cholesterol) are packaged into chylomicrons, which enter lymph and from there the blood. As blood moves through adipose tissue, a blood vessel enzyme called lipoprotein lipase releases the fatty acids from the triglycerides in the chylomicrons. The released fatty acids then diffuse into adipose cells to re-form triglycerides (Figure 47.1b). These triglycerides are stored in adipose cells until an animal requires additional energy.

As with glucose, some of the ingested fatty acids are not stored but are used by most organs other than the brain during the absorptive state to provide energy. The relative amounts of carbohydrate and fat used for energy during the absorptive state depend largely on the composition of a meal.

Absorbed Amino Acids Amino acids are taken up by all body cells, where they are used to synthesize proteins (Figure 47.1c). All cells require a regular supply of amino acids, because proteins are constantly being synthesized and degraded. However, unlike excess glucose and fatty acids, which are stored as glycogen and triglycerides, respectively, excess amino acids that are ingested are not stored as protein. Instead, excess amino acids are enzymatically broken down and their products are used in the synthesis of fatty acids, which then get incorporated into triglycerides. The triglycerides are then packaged and released into the blood to be taken up and stored in adipose cells. Therefore, eating large amounts of protein does not increase stores of body protein.

In the Postabsorptive State, Stored Nutrients Are Released and Used

As the postabsorptive state begins, synthesis of glycogen and triglycerides slows, and the breakdown of these substances begins. During this state, macromolecules formed during the absorptive state are broken down to supply monomers that can be used for energy. No glucose is available to be absorbed from the intestines during this time, yet the blood glucose concentration must be maintained because the cells of the central nervous system (CNS) normally rely almost entirely on glucose for energy. A large decrease in blood glucose concentration can disrupt CNS functions, ranging from subtle impairment of mental function to seizures, coma, or even death.

The events that maintain the blood glucose concentration fall into two categories: (1) reactions that provide glucose to the blood and (2) cellular use of fatty acids for energy, thus sparing glucose for the CNS. Let's look at each of these.

Production of Glucose from Glycogen and Other Sources Vertebrates can produce glucose during the postabsorptive state in two major ways: by breaking down glycogen and by synthesizing new glucose. First, the glycogen that was formed during the absorptive state can be broken back down into molecules of glucose by hydrolysis, a process known as **glycogenolysis** (**Figure 47.2a**). This process occurs primarily in the liver, from which the glucose is released into the blood, where it can travel to all cells. Skeletal muscle glycogen is

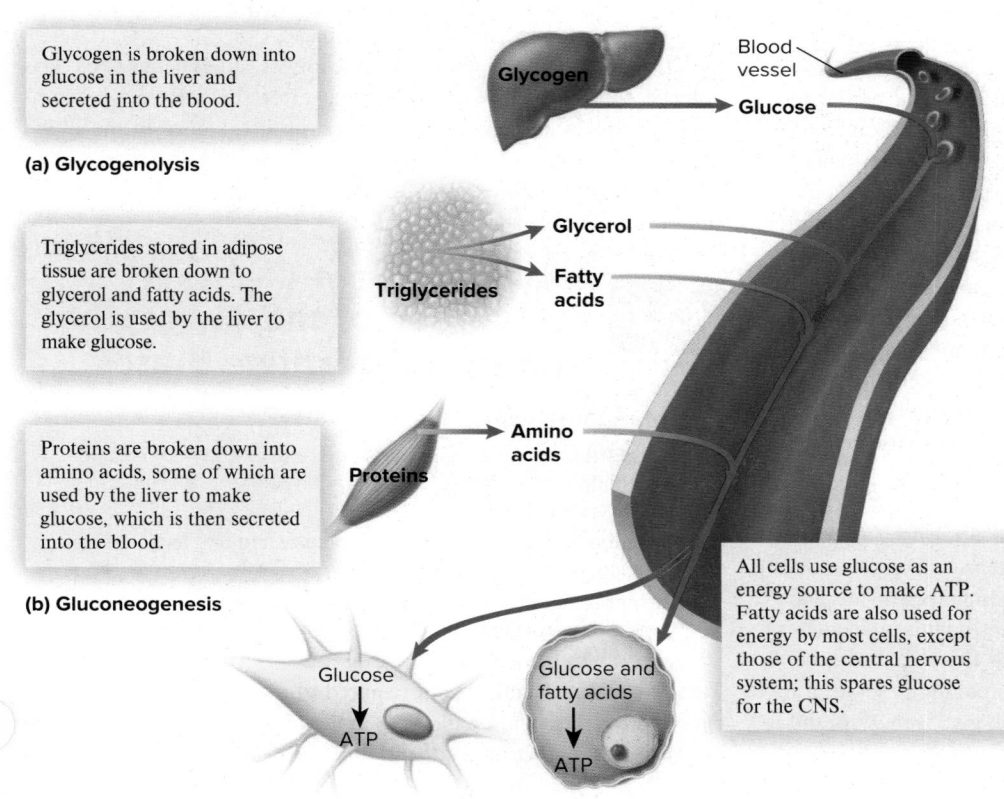

Glycogen is broken down into glucose in the liver and secreted into the blood.

(a) Glycogenolysis

Triglycerides stored in adipose tissue are broken down to glycerol and fatty acids. The glycerol is used by the liver to make glucose.

Proteins are broken down into amino acids, some of which are used by the liver to make glucose, which is then secreted into the blood.

(b) Gluconeogenesis

Glycogen

Glucose

Blood vessel

Glycerol

Fatty acids

Triglycerides

Amino acids

Proteins

Glucose

ATP

CNS

Glucose and fatty acids

ATP

All other cells

All cells use glucose as an energy source to make ATP. Fatty acids are also used for energy by most cells, except those of the central nervous system; this spares glucose for the CNS.

Figure 47.2 Events of the postabsorptive state. In the postabsorptive state, macromolecules formed and stored during the absorptive state are broken down into smaller molecules that can be released into the blood and used for energy. **(a)** This begins with glycogenolysis—the breakdown of glycogen into glucose. **(b)** In gluconeogenesis, the breakdown products of triglycerides and proteins, namely, glycerol, fatty acids, and certain amino acids, are used to synthesize glucose in the liver.

Table 47.1	Relative Changes in the Use and Generation of Energy Sources During the Absorptive and Postabsorptive States					
	Glucose absorption from alimentary canal	Glucose use by cells	Synthesis of triglycerides	Use of fatty acids for energy by cells	Breakdown of glycogen in muscle and liver	Blood concentration of glucose
Absorptive state	High	High	High	Low/moderate	Low	Normal
Postabsorptive state	Absent	Moderate (some glucose is spared for CNS use)	Low	High	High	Normal

also broken down into glucose by glycogenolysis, but this glucose is used exclusively by the muscle cells and not secreted into the blood.

The amount of liver glycogen available to provide glucose during the postabsorptive state varies among animals, but it is generally sufficient to maintain blood glucose concentration for only a brief time, such as an overnight fast. Therefore, a second mechanism for maintaining blood glucose concentration is required if the postabsorptive state continues longer. In the process of **gluconeogenesis** (literally, creation of new glucose), enzymes in the liver synthesize glucose from noncarbohydrate precursors. The glucose is then secreted into the blood (Figure 47.2b). This process occurs in all vertebrates but appears to be especially important in mammals.

A major precursor for gluconeogenesis is glycerol, which is released from triglycerides in adipose tissue by the breakdown process called **lipolysis**. In lipolysis, lipase enzymes within adipose cells hydrolyze triglycerides into fatty acids and glycerol, both of which enter the bloodstream. The fatty acids diffuse into cells, where they are used as an alternative to glucose as an energy source (except in the CNS, which continues to require primarily glucose). The glycerol is taken up by the liver, where enzymes process it by gluconeogenesis to synthesize glucose, which is then released back into the blood.

If the postabsorptive state continues for an extended period of time—as when an animal fails to find food—protein becomes an increasingly important source of blood glucose. Large quantities of protein in muscle and other tissues can be broken down to amino acids without serious tissue damage or loss of function. The amino acids enter the blood and are taken up by the liver. In the liver, the amino group is removed from each amino acid, and the remainder of the molecule is used for the synthesis of glucose by a stepwise series of enzyme-catalyzed reactions. This process, however, has limits. Continued protein loss can result in the death of cells throughout an animal's body because they depend on proteins for such vital processes as plasma membrane function, enzymatic activity, and the formation of organelles.

Lipid Metabolism by Other Tissues: Glucose Sparing Another way that glucose is made available to the organs and tissues that require it the most—such as the brain—is by having other organs and tissues decrease their dependence on glucose. They do this by increasing their use of fat as an energy supply during the postabsorptive state. This metabolic adjustment, called **glucose sparing**, reserves (or spares) the glucose produced by the liver through glycogenolysis and gluconeogenesis for use by the CNS.

The essential step in glucose sparing is lipolysis, the breakdown of adipose tissue triglycerides, which, as stated earlier, liberates fatty

acids and glycerol into the blood. In vertebrates, the circulating fatty acids are taken up and used to provide energy by almost all tissues, excluding the central nervous system, whose cells do not express the enzymes required to break down fatty acids for energy.

Of the vertebrate body's tissues and organs, the liver is unique in that most of the fatty acids entering it during the postabsorptive state are not used by that organ for energy. Instead they are processed into three small compounds collectively called **ketones**. Ketones are released into the blood during prolonged fasting. They provide an important energy source for the many cells, including those of the brain, that are able to oxidize these compounds via the citric acid cycle.

The use of fatty acids and ketones during fasting provides energy for the body, sparing the available glucose for the brain. Moreover, as just mentioned, the brain can use ketones for energy, and it does so increasingly as ketones build up in the blood during the first few days of a fast. The survival value of this phenomenon is significant. When the brain decreases its glucose requirement by using ketones, much less protein breakdown is required to supply amino acids for gluconeogenesis. Protein stores last longer, enabling the animal to survive a longer fast without serious tissue damage.

The combined effects of glycogenolysis, gluconeogenesis, and glucose sparing are so effective, that after several days of complete fasting in humans the concentration of glucose in the blood decreases by only a small percentage. **Table 47.1** summarizes the relative changes in these and other variables during the absorptive and postabsorptive states.

47.2 Regulation of the Absorptive and Postabsorptive States

Learning Outcomes:

1. **CoreSKILL** » Predict how the blood concentration of insulin will change as the blood concentration of glucose changes, and vice versa.
2. Describe how the human body regulates the use and storage of glucose.
3. Describe the effect of exercise on energy demands, and explain the mechanisms that are activated to meet those demands.

Tight control mechanisms are required to maintain homeostatic levels of energy-providing molecules in the blood. These controls come in two forms: endocrine and nervous. Cells of the endocrine system produce the blood-borne long-distance signaling molecules called hormones. Several hormones function together with signals arising from cells of the nervous system in these control mechanisms. In this section, we will see that one common function of the endocrine and nervous systems is to regulate the processes of glycogenolysis and gluconeogenesis so that glucose is made available to cells at all times.

Insulin Is a Key Regulator of Metabolism

The blood concentration of **insulin**, a polypeptide hormone made by the pancreas, increases during the absorptive state and decreases during the postabsorptive state. Insulin regulates metabolism primarily by regulating the blood glucose concentration. It does this by promoting the transport of glucose from extracellular fluid into cells, where it can be used for metabolism. Glucose is a polar molecule that cannot cross plasma membranes without the aid of a transport protein.

Insulin stimulates glucose uptake by binding to a cell-surface receptor and stimulating an intracellular signaling pathway. This pathway increases the availability of transport proteins called glucose transporters (GLUTs) in the plasma membrane (**Figure 47.3**). These GLUTs are located within preformed vesicles stored in the cytosol of cells. When these vesicles are stimulated by the insulin signaling pathway, they fuse with the plasma membrane, making more GLUTs available to transport glucose into the cell. Consequently, insulin functions to decrease the blood glucose concentration because it increases uptake of glucose into cells.

Insulin exerts its effects mainly on skeletal and cardiac muscle cells and adipose cells, because these cells have insulin receptors in their plasma membranes. However, animal cells have many types of GLUTs, but only one requires insulin for its activity, as described next.

Core Concept: Evolution

A Family of GLUT Proteins Transports Glucose in All Animal Cells

All animal cells use glucose for energy and thus require transporters to move glucose across their plasma membranes. GLUTs and the genes that encode them are evolutionarily ancient, and their structure is very similar across phyla. For example, almost 70% of the sequence of a gene that encodes a GLUT in *Drosophila* is identical to that of a gene encoding one of the GLUTs in humans. In more closely related phyla, such as birds and mammals, GLUTs are even more similar, with up to 95% of their amino acid sequences being the same. These and other considerations indicate that the GLUTs arose by accumulated mutations of a common ancestral gene. Over the course of evolution, some GLUTs acquired differences in substrate specificity (for example, some transport fructose rather than glucose) and in regulatory capacity (such as whether or not their expression is regulated by insulin).

In mammals, GLUTs make up a family of at least 14 related proteins that share similar structures but are expressed in different tissues. The different GLUTs vary in their ability to bind glucose. For example, some GLUTs have high affinity for glucose, and others have low affinity. High affinity means the protein can bind glucose even at very low concentrations of glucose. Let's look at the properties of three GLUTs, named GLUT1, GLUT3, and GLUT4. In mammals, skeletal muscle and adipose cells express the protein GLUT4, which has a low affinity for glucose, but one that is sufficient for the concentration of glucose normally

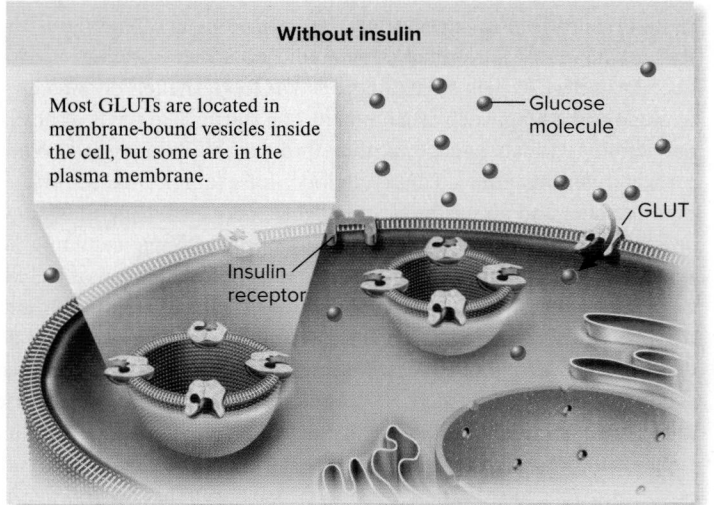

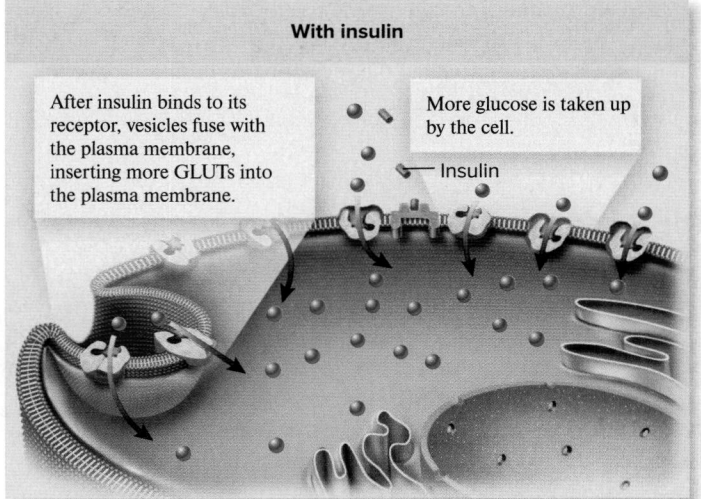

Figure 47.3 The effect of insulin on glucose transporters (GLUTs). In adipose cells and skeletal and cardiac muscle cells, the presence of insulin results in the fusion of intracellular vesicles containing GLUTs with the plasma membrane, where they facilitate glucose uptake into the cell.

 Core Skill: Connections In what other contexts does the fusion of intracellular vesicles with a cell's plasma membrane occur? (For one example, look back at Figure 5.21.)

found in mammalian blood. This is also the only GLUT whose movement to the plasma membrane requires that the cell be stimulated by insulin. Consequently, as the glucose concentration increases in the blood after a meal, the blood concentration of insulin increases. The increased insulin recruits more GLUT4 molecules from vesicles in the cytosol to the plasma membrane of skeletal muscle and adipose cells.

By comparison, GLUT1 and GLUT3 are found predominantly in the brain, where they act in concert to mediate the transport of glucose from blood vessels to the interstitial fluid of the brain, and from there into brain cells. GLUT1 and GLUT3 have much higher affinity for glucose than do other GLUTs. This means that neurons of the brain can transport glucose into their cytosol even when the concentration of glucose in the extracellular fluid is very low, a clear survival advantage for the brain. In addition, insulin is not required for GLUT1 and GLUT3 to be present in the plasma membrane, unlike the situation for GLUT4. Instead, GLUT1 and GLUT3 are always present in the plasma membranes of cells expressing them. As a result of these properties of GLUT1 and GLUT3, neurons of the brain still receive adequate energy for survival even if an animal's blood glucose concentration decreases significantly, perhaps due to disease or starvation. Insulin-dependent cells, in contrast, would not be able to take up glucose under these circumstances, thus sparing glucose for the brain.

Expressing multiple types of the same functional class of protein means that different parts of an animal's body can meet their own particular metabolic demands. Moreover, these demands may change during development. For example, high-affinity GLUTs such as GLUT1 and GLUT3 are present in high numbers in the plasma membranes of many embryonic cells, which have a greater requirement for glucose, but are present in smaller numbers during other stages of life.

Because insulin, through its actions on GLUT4, is the key regulatory molecule that controls the blood glucose concentration, it is important to understand the regulation of insulin production and release, as described next.

The Blood Glucose Concentration Is Maintained Within a Normal Range

To maintain homeostasis, the blood glucose concentration is controlled by a system of checks and balances. In the absorptive state, after a meal has been eaten, the blood glucose concentration increases; in the postabsorptive state, depending on how long it lasts, the concentration may begin to decrease. What homeostatic mechanisms keep the blood glucose concentration within a normal range?

Increased Glucose in the Blood in the Absorptive State The primary factor controlling the secretion of insulin from the pancreas is the blood glucose concentration (**Figure 47.4a**). An increase in an animal's blood glucose concentration directly stimulates cells of the pancreas to secrete insulin roughly in proportion to the amount of glucose in the blood. Later, after insulin promotes glucose uptake into its target cells, the resulting decrease in the blood glucose concentration removes the signal for insulin secretion. This is an example of a negative feedback loop, as described in Figure 41.11.

In addition to the blood glucose concentration, inputs from the nervous system to the pancreas also play a role in the regulation of insulin secretion. During a meal, signals from the parasympathetic division of the autonomic nervous system (recall the rest-or-digest response discussed in Chapter 43) stimulate the secretion of insulin into the blood.

Decreased Glucose in the Postabsorptive State Several factors act in concert to prevent blood glucose from decreasing below the normal homeostatic range, even during a short fast. Otherwise, glucose could decrease so much—a condition called hypoglycemia—that despite the high-affinity GLUT1 and GLUT3 in neuronal plasma membranes, there would not be enough glucose to keep these neurons alive.

If for any reason—such as a prolonged fast—the blood glucose concentration decreases below the normal homeostatic range for an animal, neurons within the hypothalamus in the brain that respond to changes in the extracellular concentration of glucose are activated (Figure 47.4b). Signals from the hypothalamus then stimulate the production of glucose-elevating factors. These include numerous hormones, notably **glucagon**, a protein hormone that is also secreted from the pancreas and that stimulates the processes of glycogenolysis, gluconeogenesis, and ketone synthesis in the liver. In addition, certain other hormones from various endocrine glands, as well as the neurotransmitter norepinephrine released from neurons of the sympathetic division of the autonomic nervous system, stimulate adipose tissue to release fatty acids into the blood. The fatty acids diffuse across plasma membranes and provide another source of energy for the synthesis of ATP. The overall effect is to maintain or increase the blood concentrations of glucose, fatty acids, and ketones during the postabsorptive state or during a prolonged fast.

More Energy Is Required During Physical Activity

We think of exercise as something humans do for fun or fitness, but in its broadest sense, **exercise** can be defined as any physical activity that increases an animal's metabolic rate. Generally, an animal becomes active to seek something, such as food, shelter, or a mate, or to elude something, such as a predator or a storm. The types of physical activity animals engage in, therefore, can be quite varied. When a cheetah sprints after a small antelope, for example, the activity of both predator and prey is brief and intense, perhaps lasting only a few seconds. By contrast, a tuna may never stop swimming, and a migrating bird may fly a hundred miles a day or more over a span of weeks.

For all types of activity, including exercise in humans, nutrients must be available to provide the energy required for such things as skeletal muscle contraction, increased heart and lung activity, and increased activity of the nervous system. These energy-providing nutrients include glucose and fatty acids as well as the muscle's own glycogen. The liver supplies the blood with the glucose used during exercise by breaking down its glycogen stores and by gluconeogenesis. This occurs even in the absorptive state, and thus the blood glucose concentration increases above normal when an animal is active at such times. In addition, an increase in adipose tissue lipolysis releases fatty acids into the blood, which provides an additional source of energy for the exercising muscle.

These events are mediated by the same hormones and nerves responsible for the regulation of the postabsorptive state. For example,

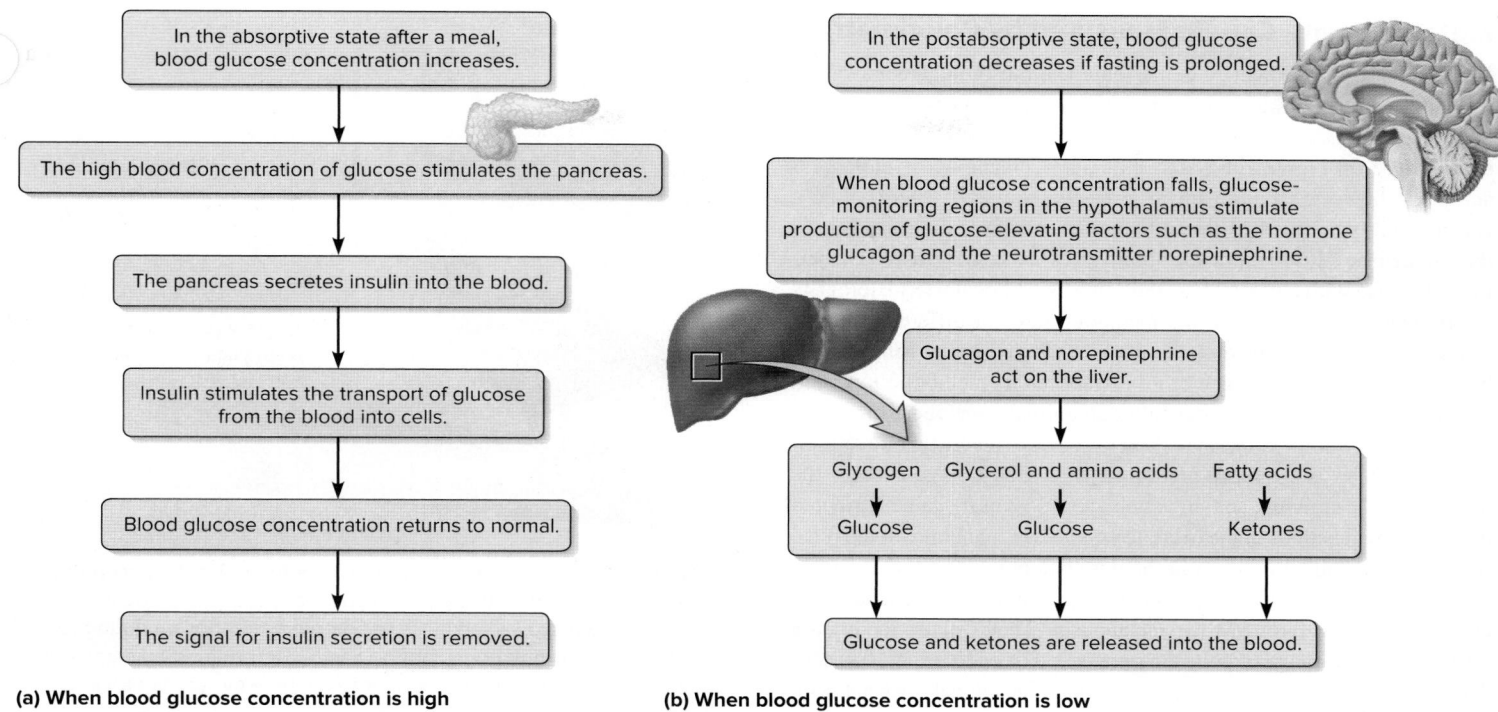

In the absorptive state after a meal, blood glucose concentration increases.

The high blood concentration of glucose stimulates the pancreas.

The pancreas secretes insulin into the blood.

Insulin stimulates the transport of glucose from the blood into cells.

Blood glucose concentration returns to normal.

The signal for insulin secretion is removed.

(a) When blood glucose concentration is high

In the postabsorptive state, blood glucose concentration decreases if fasting is prolonged.

When blood glucose concentration falls, glucose-monitoring regions in the hypothalamus stimulate production of glucose-elevating factors such as the hormone glucagon and the neurotransmitter norepinephrine.

Glucagon and norepinephrine act on the liver.

Glycogen	Glycerol and amino acids	Fatty acids
Glucose	Glucose	Ketones

Glucose and ketones are released into the blood.

(b) When blood glucose concentration is low

Figure 47.4 **The homeostatic control of blood glucose concentration within a normal range by hormones and the nervous system.**

 Core Skill: Modeling The goal of this modeling challenge is to make predictions about glucose homeostasis in a mammal whose cellular sensitivity to insulin is abnormally decreased.

Modeling Challenge: Mammals sometimes develop a disease called type 2 diabetes mellitus, in which cells that are normally sensitive to insulin no longer are able to respond properly to the hormone. Revise the model of glucose homeostasis shown in Figure 47.4a to show how glucose and insulin concentrations in the blood will be altered in a mammal with this form of diabetes. You will need to change the text in the last three boxes.

inputs from the sympathetic division to the pancreas inhibit insulin secretion during exercise. Consequently, glucose transport into muscle and adipose cells is decreased, which tends to increase the blood glucose concentration (this is part of the fight-or-flight response described in Chapter 43). Because the brain does not depend on insulin for glucose transport across neuronal membranes, as just described, more of the body's supply of glucose is available to the brain at such times, while other cells can use fatty acids for energy. Therefore, the body uses all available forms of energy in response to fasting or exercise.

47.3 | Energy Balance and Metabolic Rate

Learning Outcomes:

1. Define basal metabolic rate (BMR), and explain how it is measured.
2. **CoreSKILL** » Predict the effects of various factors on metabolic rate.
3. Describe how hormones regulate metabolic rate and appetite.

Animals have a wide range of metabolic demands that depend on numerous factors. Active animals, such as migrating birds, use energy at a greater relative rate than do inactive animals, such as hibernating mammals. Likewise, juveniles typically use energy at a greater rate relative to mature animals. Recall that the amount of energy an organism uses in a given period of time to power its metabolic requirements is called its metabolic rate.

A fundamental characteristic of energy is that it can be neither created nor destroyed, but it can be converted from one form to another (the first law of thermodynamics; see Chapter 6). The breakdown of organic molecules liberates energy in their chemical bonds, which is transferred to the bonds in ATP. This is the energy that cells harness to perform various biological activities such as muscle contraction, active transport, and molecular synthesis. We refer to these functions as work. Not all of the energy liberated from the breakdown of organic molecules is used to do work, however. Some of it appears as heat, which contributes to an animal's body temperature or is dissipated to the environment. In this section, we examine how metabolic rate is measured in animals; how metabolic rate is influenced by activity, digestion, and body mass; and how a balance is achieved between energy consumption and expenditure.

Metabolic Rate Can Be Measured by Calorimetry

The standard unit of energy is the joule (J), but biologists have historically quantified the energy of metabolism in calories. A **calorie** (equivalent to 4.184 J) is the amount of heat required to raise the temperature of 1 gram of water 1 degree Celsius. Most biological activities, however, require much greater amounts of energy than a calorie, and consequently, the more common unit of measurement is the kilocalorie (1,000 calories, abbreviated as **kcal**). (In food labeling, a Calorie with a capital C is the same as a kilocalorie.) Biologists often measure and compare the metabolic rates of different animals to learn, for example, how some animals are capable of hibernating, how an animal's body temperature influences its metabolic rate, and how hormones and other factors alter an animal's metabolism.

The most common measure used to compare the metabolic rates of different species is the **basal metabolic rate (BMR)**. The BMR is the metabolic cost of living, and, in vertebrates, most of it can be attributed to the routine functions of the heart, liver, kidneys, and brain. In the basal condition, the animal is at rest in the postabsorptive state and at a standard ambient temperature. **Endotherms** are animals that generate their own internal heat through their metabolism. They usually maintain a relatively narrow range of body temperatures. For endotherms, the standard temperature is within the range in which the animal does not need to generate additional heat (for example, by shivering) or lose excess heat (for example, by perspiration). This temperature range is called an animal's thermoneutral zone. The BMR of **ectotherms**—animals that acquire their heat from the environment—must be measured at a standard temperature for each species that approximates the average temperature that the species normally encounters. In this case, the term standard metabolic rate (SMR) is used instead of BMR, because the basal condition in ectotherms is harder to define than for endotherms.

The usual method for measuring metabolic rate, **indirect calorimetry**, is based on the principle that animals require oxygen to metabolize foodstuffs. The more fuel being metabolized—that is, the greater the metabolic rate—the more oxygen must be consumed by the animal. Measuring the rate at which a resting animal uses oxygen, therefore, provides a good estimate of BMR. Indirect calorimetry can also be used to compare the metabolic rates of an animal during rest and activity, when oxygen consumption increases (**Figure 47.5**). One limitation to this method is that a small percentage of fuel is metabolized anaerobically—that is, without oxygen—and thus indirect calorimetry underestimates the actual metabolic rate.

Activity, Digestion, and Body Mass Influence Metabolic Rate

Not all tissues in the body use oxygen and produce heat at the same rate. Some structures, such as skin, consume relatively little oxygen under resting conditions, whereas others, such as the brain, heart, and liver, have high rates of metabolism even when an animal is sleeping. Also, the metabolic rates of different tissues can vary depending on their activity. For example, the metabolism of the alimentary canal increases when food is being digested, and that of skeletal muscle increases during exercise.

Physical Activity The primary factor that increases metabolic rate is altered skeletal muscle activity. Even small increases in muscle

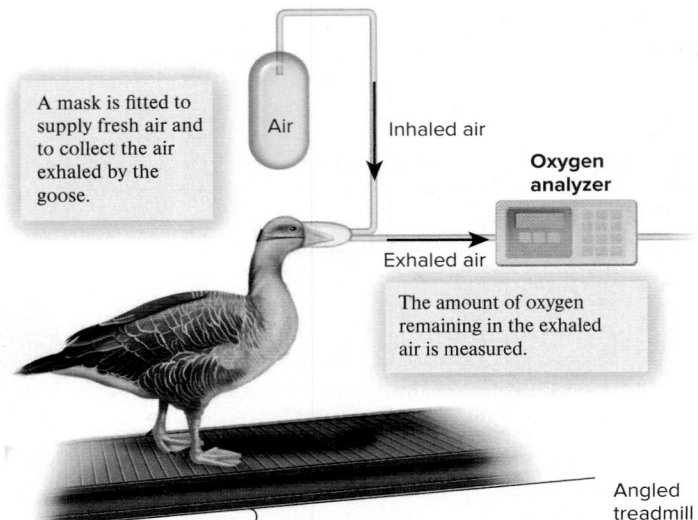

Figure 47.5 Measuring metabolic rate by indirect calorimetry. Many animals, such as this goose, can be trained to walk on a treadmill, which allows scientists to compare metabolism during rest and exercise. Oxygen consumption can be determined by sampling the air exhaled into a tightly fitting mask. One-way valves prevent inhaled and exhaled air from mixing.

In the figure:
- A mask is fitted to supply fresh air and to collect the air exhaled by the goose.
- Air
- Inhaled air
- Oxygen analyzer
- Exhaled air
- The amount of oxygen remaining in the exhaled air is measured.
- Angled treadmill

 Core Skill: Process of Science This figure illustrates how biologists can learn about general physiological principles using a variety of animal models. For example, many geese and other birds often fly for long periods at very high altitudes where oxygen availability is limited. Using experimental procedures like the one shown here allows scientists to understand how such animals can function under conditions that would be very challenging for humans. For example, the percentage of oxygen in the inhaled air can be adjusted to match that found at high altitude, or the degree of activity can be adjusted by altering the treadmill.

contraction significantly increase metabolic rate; strenuous activity increases it even more. For example, the total daily expenditure of kilocalories may vary for a healthy adult human from approximately 1,350 kcal for a small person at rest to more than 7,000 kcal for a cyclist competing in the Tour de France. Metabolic rate is also slowed during sleep, due partly to decreased muscle activity, and increased during exposure to cold temperatures, due to increased muscle activity from shivering.

Digesting Food Eating and digesting food also increase the metabolic rate. Particularly in mammals that eat meat, this may increase metabolic rate (and associated heat production) by 10–50% for a few hours after eating. You may have noticed this **food-induced thermogenesis** after consuming a large meal. Ingested protein produces the greatest effect, whereas carbohydrate and fat produce less. The increased heat is believed to result partly from the processing of the absorbed nutrients by the liver and from the energy expended by the alimentary canal in digestion and absorption. Food-induced thermogenesis is observed in nearly all vertebrates, but it is most notable in certain reptiles such as snakes that eat infrequent but very large meals. Body temperature can increase by several degrees Celsius in such animals, and persist for days and even weeks depending on the size of the meal.

Body Mass   Another factor affecting metabolic rate is body mass. In general, a large animal uses greater amounts of energy than does a small animal because the large animal has more mass and more cells, all of which consume fuel and generate heat. The metabolic rate and heat generation of an elephant are clearly greater than those of a mouse, for instance. However, when the metabolic rate of an elephant and a mouse are scaled to their respective body masses, we find that the energy expenditure per gram of body mass in a mouse is much higher than the comparable calculated value for an elephant. **Mass-specific BMR** is the amount of energy expended per gram of body mass in the resting condition.

Mass-specific BMR is a relative term that allows scientists to compare basal metabolic rates among animals of different sizes. Research has shown that the relationship between mass-specific BMR and body mass is exponential (**Figure 47.6**). One possible explanation is that the ratio of an animal's surface area to its volume or body mass is greater in smaller animals than in larger animals (refer back to Figure 4.12). Therefore, smaller animals lose heat more rapidly than larger ones. According to this hypothesis, smaller animals must generate more heat per gram of body mass than larger animals to compensate for their heat loss. However,

although this hypothesis appears to provide an explanation for the relationship between metabolism and body size in endotherms, it does not explain the observation that the same relationship exists in almost all animals, including ectotherms.

Hormones and the Nervous System Control Food Intake

When the daily amount of energy within the food that an animal consumes is equal to the amount of energy it expends, the animal's body weight remains stable. Tipping the balance in either direction causes weight gain or loss; that is, the total body mass increases or decreases. Normally, energy is stored in the form of fat in adipose tissue.

Body weight in an adult animal is usually regulated around a predetermined set point that differs among species and between individuals. Body weight is maintained by adjusting caloric intake and energy expenditure in response to changes in body weight. This mechanism usually works very precisely in those animals in which it has been studied. For example, if given the opportunity, a mammal that eats less one day will eat more the next day to compensate for the previous day's deficit. Similarly, if an animal is overfed one day, it may eat less the next day.

Short-term control of feeding generally involves a feeling of **satiety**, that is, fullness. As an animal's stomach and small intestine stretch to accommodate food, nerves send inhibitory signals from these structures to the hunger center in the hypothalamus. At the same time, the stomach and small intestine release into the blood hormones that reach the hypothalamus and suppress hunger. These satiety signals remove the sensation of hunger and set the time period before it returns again.

Long-term control of food intake is mediated by many different molecules in the brain, by hormones, and by emotional state, particularly in humans. One hormone that has received considerable attention in recent years for its ability to control appetite and metabolic rate is leptin (from the Greek *leptos*, meaning thin). Leptin has been identified in all classes of vertebrates but has been most extensively studied in mammals. In these animals, leptin is produced by adipose cells in proportion to fat mass: As more fat is stored in adipose cells, more leptin is secreted into the blood. Leptin acts on the hypothalamus to decrease appetite and increase metabolic rate (**Figure 47.7a**). In this way, the brain is made aware of how much fat is stored in the body at all times, and it can adjust appetite and metabolic rate appropriately if fat stores decline or increase. If an animal fasts for a period of time, its adipose cells shrink as they release their stored fat into the blood. The decrease in leptin secretion resulting from the decreased adipose mass results in a decrease in BMR and an increase in appetite. This may be the true evolutionary significance of leptin, namely that its disappearance from the blood lowers the BMR, consequently prolonging life during periods of starvation (**Figure 47.7b**).

Leptin was discovered in 1994, but its existence was postulated decades before that by the pioneering work of Douglas Coleman, who investigated the nature of mutations in mice that result in obesity. His observations continue to have important implications for human health today.

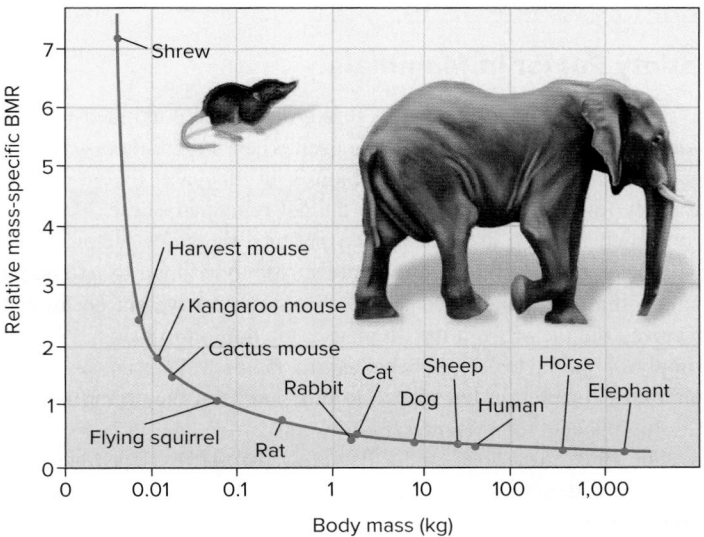

Figure 47.6 Metabolic rates of animals that differ in size. Metabolism can be scaled to body mass by measuring oxygen consumption and normalizing it to the animal's body mass (mass-specific BMR). Note that when expressed in this way, the mass-specific BMR of a shrew is greater than that of an elephant, even though the total oxygen consumption and heat output of the elephant are much greater. The values on the vertical axis are relative units of metabolism.

Concept Check: *Can the relationship between body size and metabolic rate be used to propose hypotheses about metabolic rates of extinct animals?*

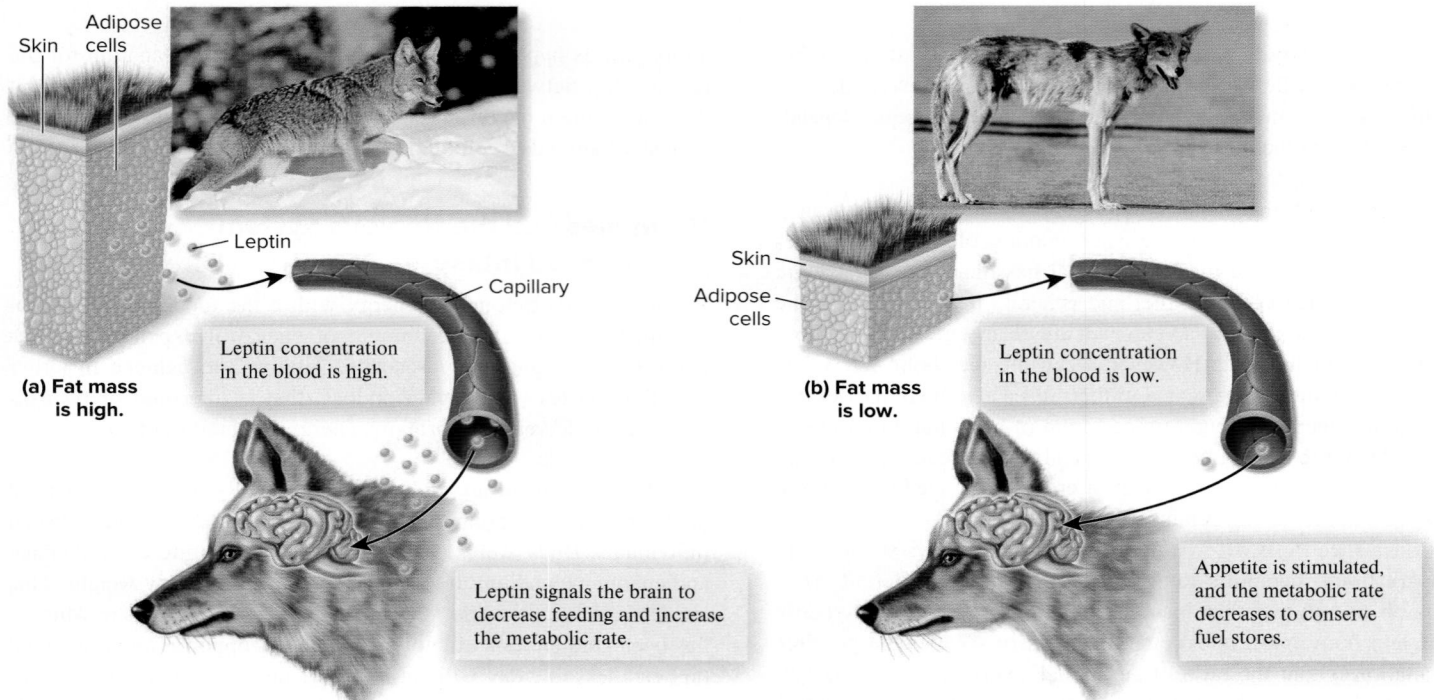

Figure 47.7 **The role of leptin in regulating appetite and metabolic rate.** In animals such as the coyote, changes in the blood leptin concentration result directly from changes in fat mass. Animals with more fat make more leptin. a: ©Paul McCormick/Getty Images; b: ©William S. Clark/ Frank Lane Picture Agency/Corbis/Getty Images

Core Skill: Process of Science

Feature Investigation | Coleman Revealed a Satiety Factor in Mammals

For many years, scientists wondered how most animals regulate their body mass around a predetermined set point, despite fluctuations in their food supply. They postulated that other parts of the body somehow communicated with the brain to signal when energy stores were above or below normal. In the 1970s, Canadian-American researcher Douglas Coleman tested this hypothesis in an experiment involving parabiosis, the surgical connection of the abdominal walls of two animals, such that the blood supply from one animal intermixes with that of the other.

Coleman used two strains of mice called ob and db mice, which carry different mutations that result in inherited forms of obesity, characterized by the excessive accumulation of body fat (an example of an ob mouse is shown in the chapter opening photo). Coleman first connected a wild-type (wt) mouse, one that lacked these mutations, with either an ob mouse or a db mouse, as shown in **Figure 47.8**. He discovered that when the circulatory system of the ob mouse was in contact with that of the wt mouse, the ob mouse ate less and gained less weight than usual. This suggested that the blood of the wt mouse contained a circulating factor that signals the brain when an animal has sufficient fat stored in its body and adjusts appetite accordingly. The ob mouse was deficient in this factor, but when exposed to it through the wt mouse's circulation, it responded in the appropriate way. The wt mouse of the parabiosis pair apparently retained a sufficient amount of the factor in its blood, because it maintained its body weight at a normal level.

Coleman noticed, however, that a db mouse continued to gain weight at an abnormally high rate even when its circulatory system was in contact with that of a wt mouse. In this case, the wt animal actually lost weight while the db animal remained obese. Coleman concluded that the db mouse must produce the same factor as the wt mouse, but for some reason, was unable to respond to it. The wt mouse that was parabiosed to the db mouse lost weight because it received the factor from the db mouse, in addition to having its own supply of the factor. Thus, whether the factor was absent as in the ob mouse, or present but unable to function as in the db mouse, the resulting phenotype was the same—obesity.

In 1994, American molecular biologist Jeffrey Friedman and coworkers identified this circulating factor as the hormone leptin. The ob mice were found to be homozygous for a mutation in the leptin gene, which produced an inactive leptin molecule, whereas db mice produced leptin but did not respond to it. The db mice were found to produce even greater amounts of leptin than wt mice, which explained why the wt mouse in Coleman's experiments lost weight when parabiosed with a db mouse. Friedman and others later showed that adipose cells produce leptin in direct proportion to the total fat mass of an animal, as stated earlier.

At first, the work of Coleman and Friedman generated considerable excitement that leptin might be useful to treat obesity in humans, but this has thus far proven difficult. Why? Recent research

Figure 47.8 Coleman's parabiosis experiments revealed a satiety factor in wild-type mice that was absent in genetically obese mice.

HYPOTHESIS Body weight is controlled by a factor that circulates in the blood. This factor is absent in strains of mice that have an inherited form of obesity.

KEY MATERIALS Two different strains of genetically obese mice, normal (wild-type) mice.

Experimental level   **Conceptual level**

1 Surgically connect the abdominal walls of a genetically obese and normal (wt; wild-type) mouse. After a few days, blood vessels from each mouse cross to the other mouse. Monitor changes in body weight. Note: 2 different strains of obese mice were tested, called ob and db mice.

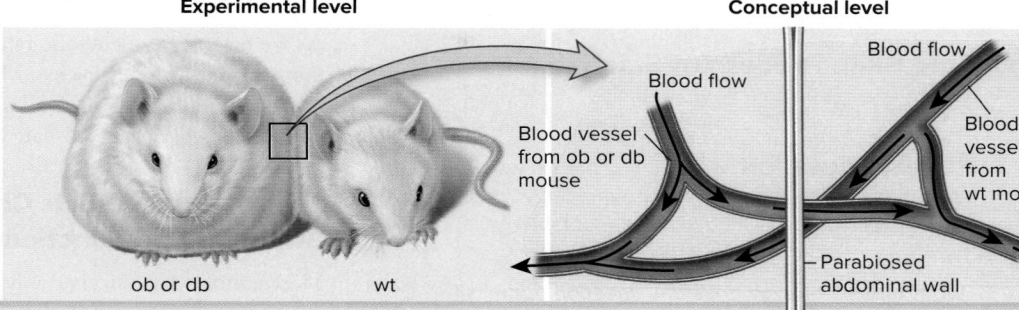

2 Feed mice a normal diet for several weeks, then visually inspect and weigh each pair.

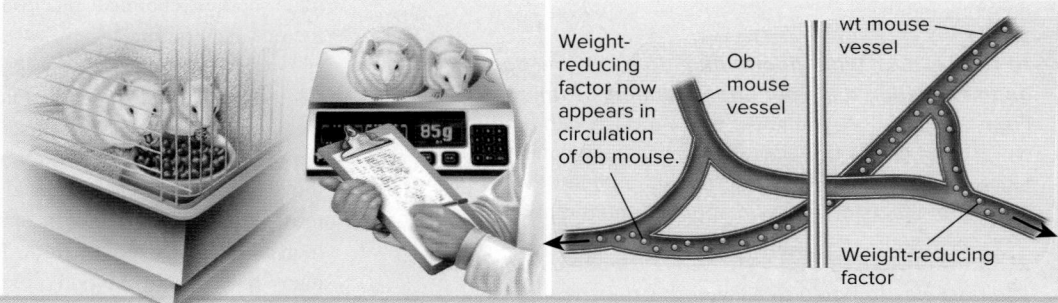

3 THE DATA

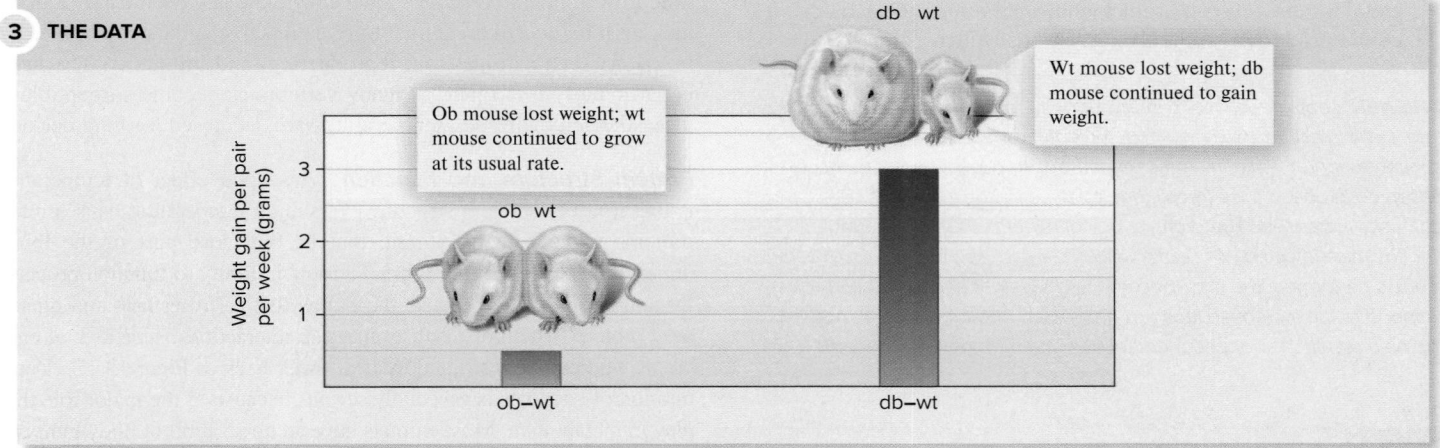

4 CONCLUSION Wild-type mice secrete a blood-borne factor that decreases body weight. The factor is absent from ob mice but present in db mice. Ob mice retain the ability to respond to the factor, unlike db mice, which cannot respond to it.

5 SOURCE Coleman, D. L. 1973. Effects of parabiosis of obese with diabetes and normal mice. *Diabetologia* 9: 294–298.

has revealed that most obese humans are more like the db mice than the ob mice. That is, they produce leptin but fail to respond adequately to it, and therefore, simply increasing the concentration of leptin in the blood may not have a significant effect on body weight. However, other studies have shown that leptin normally acts in nonobese humans in a manner much like it does in wt rodents.

As noted in the chapter introduction, researchers have identified rare individuals in whom leptin is not produced due to a mutation in the leptin gene. These individuals are extremely obese and respond well to injections of leptin, losing considerable weight. The body weight disorders of such individuals, therefore, are reminiscent of the condition in ob mice.

Experimental Questions

1. What observation led to the experiments conducted by Coleman?

2. **CoreSKILL »** How did the experimental linking of the bloodstreams of the wild-type mice and the mutant mice affect the

body weight of both strains of mutants? Why did the db mice fail to lose weight when parabiosed with the wt mice?

3. **CoreSKILL »** Predict what will happen to the respective body weights of ob and db mice if they are parabiosed to one another.

 Core Skill: Process of Science

 **THE QUESTION** *What do you predict will happen if a healthy mouse with a normal body weight is injected daily with a high dose of leptin?*

TOPIC *What topic in biology does this question address?*
The topic is the control of body weight in a mouse by the hormone leptin.

INFORMATION *What information do you know based on the question and your understanding of the topic?*
From the question, you know that a mouse with a normal body weight (not obese or underweight) will be injected daily with a high dose of leptin. From your understanding of the topic, you know the effects of leptin on appetite and metabolic rate.

PROBLEM-SOLVING **S**TRATEGY *Propose a hypothesis.*
The best way to begin to answer this question is to consider how appetite and metabolic rate are related to body weight; then you can predict what will happen if the blood concentration of leptin is experimentally increased.

ANSWER *Leptin functions to inhibit appetite and increase metabolic rate. Daily injections of a high dose of leptin will increase the blood concentration of leptin in a mouse, perhaps to a level similar to those observed in obese mice (recall that leptin secretion increases as adiposity increases). Therefore, a logical hypothesis is that normal, healthy mice injected with leptin will lose weight. When such an experiment is performed, the mice become underweight because their brains respond to the increased leptin as if the mice had an excess of body fat. As a result, their appetite decreases and metabolism increases.*

47.4 Regulation of Body Temperature

Learning Outcomes:

1. Provide examples of how changes in temperature affect chemical reactions, protein functions, and membrane structure.

2. List and define the four terms used to categorize organisms based on their source of heat and ability to maintain body temperature.

3. Identify the four main mechanisms animals use to exchange heat with the environment.

4. **CoreSKILL »** Identify several mechanisms by which animals can alter the rate of heat gain or loss, and describe some ways in which body structures facilitate these mechanisms.

As we have seen, metabolic rate and body temperature are linked. In this section, we will discuss why body temperature is important for the health and survival of all animals and consider the homeostatic mechanisms by which animals gain or lose heat.

Temperature Affects Chemical Reactions, Protein Structure and Function, and Membrane Structure

Most animals can survive only in a relatively narrow range of temperatures. Temperature has an effect on three vital features of animals' bodies: chemical reactions, protein structure and function, and membrane structure.

Chemical Reactions   Chemical reactions depend on temperature. Heat accelerates the motion of molecules, so as an animal's body temperature increases, the rates at which the molecules in its body move and contact each other also increase. Consequently, the rate of most chemical reactions in animals increases significantly with an increase in body temperature. In addition, enzymes, which catalyze many reactions in the body, including those involved in metabolism, have an optimal temperature range for their maximal catalytic function. Low temperatures slow down enzymatic and chemical reactions, making it harder for an animal to remain active and carry out internal functions such as digestion, reproduction, and immunity. The latter is particularly important, as many vertebrates become susceptible to disease when their body temperatures are decreased for long periods.

Protein Structure and Function   A second effect of temperature is that it affects protein structure. Very high temperature causes many proteins to become denatured; that is, they lose part of the three-dimensional structure that is crucial to their ability to function properly. Denaturation occurs because the bonds that form tertiary and quaternary protein structures result from weak interactions, such as hydrogen bonds, and can be disrupted by heat (refer back to Figure 3.17). Denaturation of enzymes is especially serious because of the major role they play in metabolism. Most animals have an upper limit of body temperature at which they can survive. Mammals generally have a resting body temperature of 35–38°C (95–100°F). In humans, a body temperature of 41°C (106°F) inhibits protein function and proper signaling within the nervous system, and a body temperature of 42–43°C (107–109°F) is usually fatal.

Membrane Structure   A third effect of temperature is that it affects the structures of the plasma membrane and intracellular membranes. At low temperatures, membranes become less fluid and more rigid, primarily due to changes in their phospholipids. Rigid membranes are less able to perform biological functions, such as transporting ions and binding extracellular molecules to receptors on the membrane surface. Alternatively, if the temperature becomes too high, membranes can become leaky.

Ectotherms and Endotherms May Have Fluctuating or Stable Body Temperatures

Biologists classify animals according to both the source of heat used to warm their bodies and their ability to maintain body temperature. Recall that ectotherms depend on external heat sources to warm their bodies, whereas endotherms use their own metabolically generated heat to warm themselves. **Homeotherms** have body temperatures that are maintained within a narrow range, whereas **heterotherms** have body temperatures that vary widely in response to the environmental temperature (**Figure 47.9**). Most animals can be categorized as either endotherms or ectotherms and as either homeotherms or heterotherms. Generally, birds and mammals are endothermic and homeothermic. Other vertebrates and most invertebrates are ectothermic and heterothermic.

Ectotherms are usually heterotherms because most environments on Earth have fluctuating temperatures over short periods of time. However, this is not always the case. For example, a fish living in deep ocean waters is an ectotherm but also a homeotherm because the temperature of the water—and therefore of its body—remains relatively constant for an extended period of time. Fishes that live in waters with fluctuating temperatures, by contrast, are ectothermic and heterothermic.

Even endothermic homeotherms do not have truly constant body temperatures. They have a narrow range of body temperatures that increases or decreases slightly in extreme climates, during physical activity, or during sleep. The important feature is that birds and mammals can quickly adjust the body's mechanisms for retaining or releasing heat so that body temperature remains within the optimal narrow range. This regulation provides the advantage that the body's chemical reactions are at optimal levels even when the environment imposes extreme challenges. The metabolic rate of a resting mammal, for example, is roughly six times greater than that of a comparably sized reptile. A suddenly awakened mammal is instantly capable of maximal activity

even on a winter day, but an icy-cold reptile could be at the mercy of a predator because of the time required to warm itself in order to flee.

Endothermy does have three major disadvantages, however:

1. **Requirement for larger amounts of energy.** To produce sufficient heat by metabolic processes, endotherms must consume larger amounts of food to provide the nutrients used by cells in the formation of ATP, during which heat is generated. Small endotherms with high mass-specific BMRs, such as shrews (see Figure 47.6), must eat almost continuously and may die if deprived of food for as little as a day. By contrast, many ectotherms, such as snakes, can regularly live for weeks without eating.

2. **Risk of overheating.** Endotherms have a greater risk of hyperthermia, or overheating, during periods of intense activity, even in cold weather.

3. **Loss of body fluids.** As described shortly, the prevention of overheating often requires the evaporation of bodily fluids (and thus a need for replenishment of fluid). Therefore, many endotherms are restricted to environments where fresh water is plentiful.

Animals Exchange Heat with the Environment in Four Ways

The surface of an animal's body can lose or gain heat from the external environment via four mechanisms: radiation, evaporation, convection, and conduction (**Figure 47.10**).

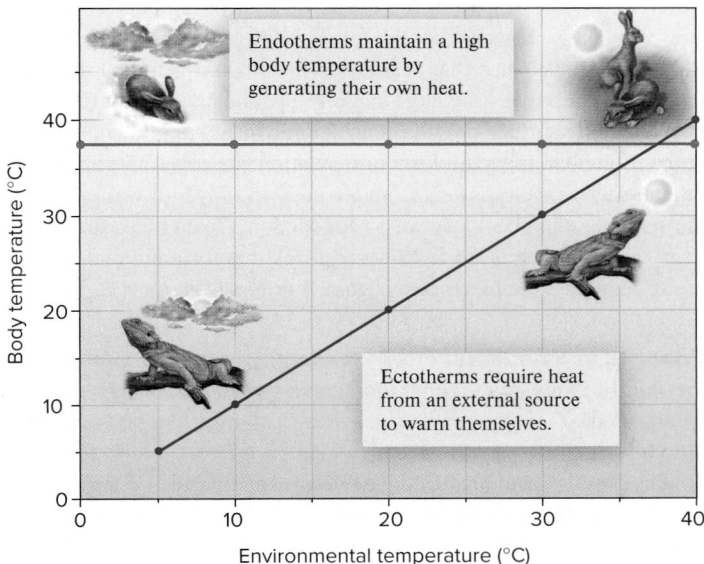

Figure 47.9 Body temperature and environmental temperature in endotherms and ectotherms. A rabbit is an endotherm but also a homeotherm because its body temperature doesn't change much. A lizard is an ectotherm but also a heterotherm because its body temperature changes considerably.

Concept Check: *Into what thermoregulatory categories do humans fit?*

Figure 47.10 Types of heat exchange. The four ways in which animals exchange heat with the environment are radiation, evaporation, convection, and conduction.

 Core Concept: Energy and Matter Heat is a form of energy and can be exchanged between an animal's body and its environment.

- **Radiation** is the emission of electromagnetic waves from the surface of an object or organism. The rate of emission is determined by the temperature of the radiating surface. Thus, if the surface of an animal's body is warmer than the environment, the body loses heat at a rate that depends on the temperature difference. If the outside temperature is warmer than body temperature, the body gains heat by radiation, for instance from sunlight. We can observe radiated heat from an animal's body with imaging devices that detect infrared light, the wavelength at which thermal energy is radiated from animal bodies (**Figure 47.11**).

- **Evaporation** is the conversion of water from the liquid to the gaseous state. Animals can lose body heat through evaporation of water from the skin and membranes lining the respiratory tract, including the surface of the tongue. A large amount of energy in the form of heat is required to transform water from liquid to gas. Whenever water vaporizes from the body's surface, the heat required to drive the process is conducted from the surface, thereby cooling the animal.

- **Convection** is the transfer of heat by the movement of air or fluid next to the body. For example, the air close to an endotherm's body is heated by conduction. Because warm air is less dense than cold air, the warm air near the body rises and carries away heat by convection. Convection is aided by creating currents of air around an animal's body. Humans may do this by sitting near fans, but other animals can create cooling air currents by other means, such as when an elephant waves its ears.

- **Conduction** is the process by which the body surface loses or gains heat through direct contact with cooler or warmer substances. The greater the temperature difference, the greater is the rate of heat transfer. Different materials have different abilities to absorb heat, however. As we saw in Chapter 2, water has a higher specific heat than air, meaning that at any temperature, water will retain greater amounts of heat than will air. Consequently, aquatic animals in water that is 10°C lose considerably more heat in a short time than terrestrial animals lose in air that is 10°C. Even on a hot day, terrestrial animals can lose heat by immersing themselves in water.

The four mechanisms of heat transfer just described can be regulated in animals in such a way that heat is retained within the body at some times and lost from the body at other times, as we see next.

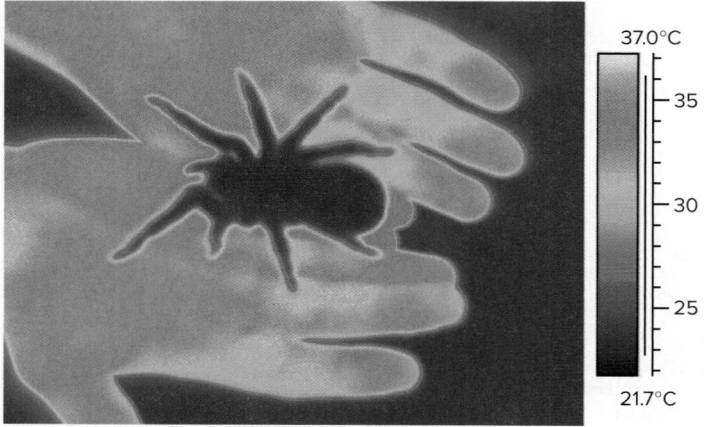

Figure 47.11 **Visualization of heat exchange in an ectotherm and an endotherm.** Thermal-imaging cameras can detect heat radiated from an animal's body. Note the warm skin of the endotherm (the human) and the cold body surface of the ectotherm (the tarantula), even though both animals are at the same environmental temperature of about 20–25°C. ©Nutscode/T Service/Science Source

 Core Skill: Communication and Collaboration
Thermal-imaging cameras have proven to be valuable for scientists attempting to gather quantitative data about large populations of endothermic animals, particularly those that are active only at night. The cameras were developed by engineers; biologists use them for census-taking and work closely with statisticians who help interpret the data. One example involves obtaining an accurate census of large colonies (up to several million individuals) of insectivorous bats in North America, many of whom have suffered enormous losses due to a fungal disease called white-nose syndrome.

Several Mechanisms Can Alter Rates of Heat Gain or Loss in Endotherms

For purposes of temperature control, think of an endotherm's body as a central core surrounded by a shell consisting of skin and subcutaneous (just below the skin) tissue. Depending on the species, the temperature of the central core of endotherms is regulated at approximately 35–42°C (95–108°F), but the temperature of the outer surface of the skin varies considerably. If the skin were a perfect insulator, the body would never lose or gain heat by conduction. The skin does not insulate completely, however, so the temperature of its surface generally is somewhere between that of the external environment and the core. Only in animals that store large amounts of subcutaneous fat (blubber) does the body surface provide considerable insulation. In endotherms without blubber, the main form of insulation is a covering of hair, fur, or feathers, which traps heat from the body in a layer of warm air near the skin, reducing heat loss due to conduction. Given these structures, then, let's take a look at four mechanisms that different endotherms use to regulate how much heat is gained or lost from their surface.

Changes in Skin Blood Flow   Rather than acting as an insulator, the skin of many endotherms functions as a heat exchanger that can be adjusted to increase or decrease heat loss from the body. Surface blood vessels of the skin dilate (widen to increase blood flow) on hot days to dissipate heat to the environment, and they constrict (get narrower to decrease blood flow) on cold days to retain body heat (**Figure 47.12**). Signals from the nervous system regulate the relaxation or contraction of the smooth muscles that control the diameter of these blood vessels. Diving birds and diving mammals are good examples of animals that use this mechanism. Ducks, seals, and walruses greatly decrease the amount of blood flowing to the skin when they dive in cold waters. This allows them to retain body heat that would otherwise be conducted into the water.

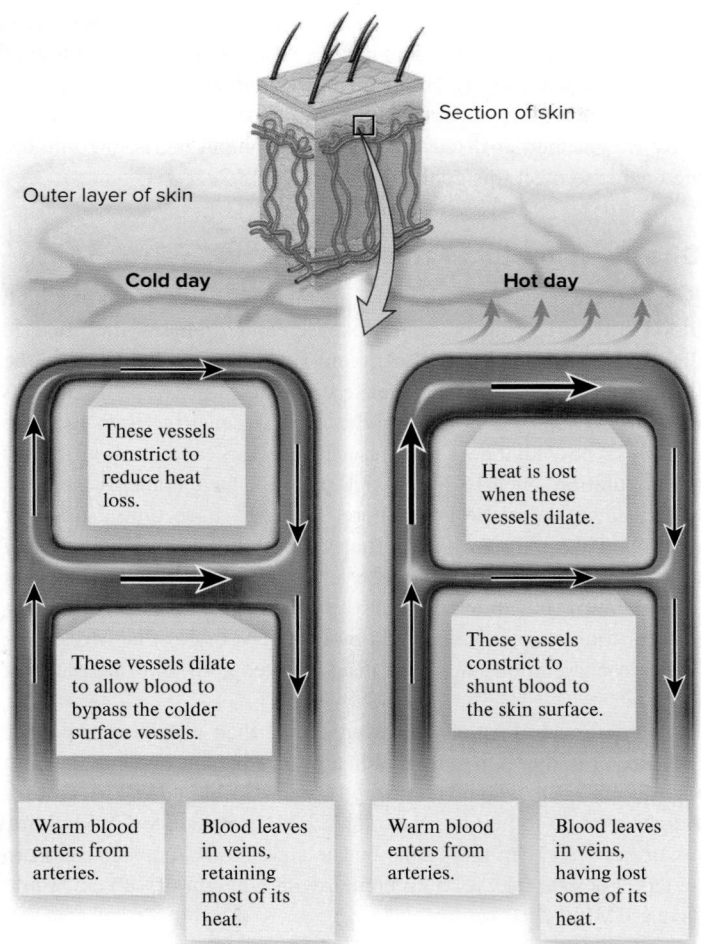

Figure 47.12 **Regulation of heat exchange in the skin.** As shown in this schematic illustration, the skin functions as a variable heat exchanger. The arrows in the blood vessels indicate the direction and relative amount of blood flow.

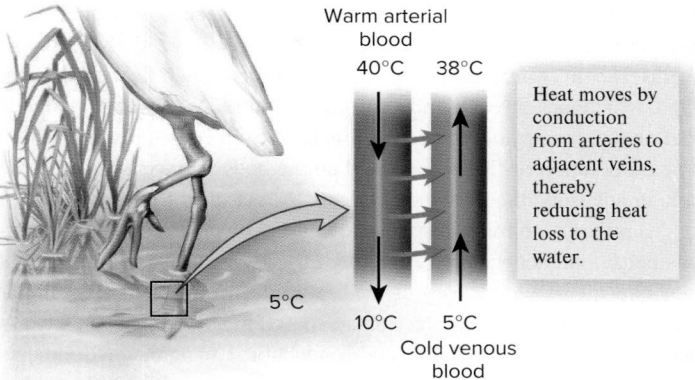

(a) Countercurrent heat exchange in the leg of an endotherm

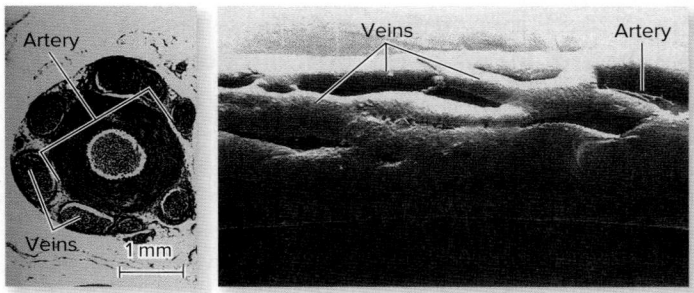

(b) Cross section and surface view of veins covering an artery

Figure 47.13 **Countercurrent exchange. (a)** Countercurrent exchange retains heat in the leg of an endotherm such as this bird. Black arrows in vessels indicate direction of blood flow. **(b)** A micrograph of the arrangement of veins surrounding an artery in a wading bird's leg. The artery is almost completely covered by overlying veins, allowing efficient heat exchange between the vessels.
b (left, right): Courtesy of Uffe Midtgård, University of Copenhagen

Countercurrent Exchange Many endotherms and ectotherms regulate heat loss to the environment through **countercurrent exchange**, in which heat is transferred between fluids flowing in opposite directions. Countercurrent exchange regulates heat loss to the environment by returning heat to the body's core and keeping the core much warmer than the extremities. In endotherms, countercurrent exchange occurs primarily in the extremities—the flippers of dolphins, for example, or the legs of birds and certain other terrestrial animals (**Figure 47.13a**). As warm blood travels from the core through arteries down a wading bird's leg, for example, heat moves by conduction from the artery to adjacent veins that carry cooler blood from the feet in the opposite direction (**Figure 47.13b**). By the time the arterial blood reaches the tip of the leg, its temperature has dropped considerably, reducing the amount of heat lost to the environment and returning the heat via the veins to the body's core.

Evaporative Heat Loss Recall that some animals lose body heat through evaporation of water from the skin and membranes lining the respiratory tract. Heat exchange in some mammals is regulated by changing the rate of water evaporation through perspiration. Nerves to the sweat glands stimulate the production of sweat, a dilute solution

containing Na^+ and Cl^-. The most important factor determining evaporation rate—and therefore heat loss—is the water vapor concentration, or humidity, of the air. The discomfort you feel on a humid day is due to the slow rate of evaporation. Your sweat glands continue to secrete, but most of the sweat simply remains on your skin and so your body temperature remains elevated, especially during exercise.

In endotherms that lack sweat glands, such as birds, or those that have very few such glands, such as dogs and cats, panting (short, rapid breaths with the mouth open) promotes evaporation of water from the tongue surface. Panting has advantages over sweating, because no ions are lost, and panting provides the air current that promotes heat exchange by convection. However, the surface area of the mouth and tongue is relatively small, which limits the rate at which heat can be eliminated. Interestingly, many reptiles also pant on hot days, suggesting that panting evolved prior to endothermy.

Behavioral Adaptations Behavioral mechanisms can also alter heat loss by radiation, conduction, and evaporation. Two such behaviors involve changing exposed surface area and changing surroundings. On hot days, birds may ruffle their feathers and raise their wings, whereas many mammals will reduce their activity and spread their limbs. These postural changes increase the surface area available for heat transfer. Terrestrial endotherms seek shade, partially immerse themselves in water, or burrow into the ground when the sun is high. Pigs, which lack sweat glands, roll in the mud to cool down. Animals that neither sweat nor pant can still benefit from evaporative heat loss. The evaporation of fluids deposited on the body surface by licking the skin or splashing the skin with water also draws heat from the body.

Similarly, animals respond to cold temperatures with numerous behavioral adaptations. Huddling in groups, curling up into a ball, hunching the shoulders, burying the head and feet in feathers, and similar maneuvers decrease the surface area exposed to a cold environment and decrease heat loss by radiation and conduction. Changing environments is also a common strategy for coping with cold. Migration from cold to warmer regions occurs in numerous species of birds and mammals.

Muscle Activity and Brown Adipose Tissue Metabolism Increase Heat Production

We have discussed how heat is gained or lost to the environment and how heat can be retained by reducing blood flow to the skin on a cold day. Body temperature, however, is a balance between these factors and heat production. Changes in muscle activity constitute a major control of heat production for temperature regulation in endotherms.

When an endotherm is in its thermoneutral zone, no significant adjustments are necessary to maintain core body temperature. When exposed to temperatures below the thermoneutral zone, however, core body temperature begins to decrease. The primary response to decreasing temperatures is to decrease the flow of blood to regions that permit conduction of heat. If this does not adequately decrease heat loss, skeletal muscle contraction is increased. This leads to shivering, which consists of rapid muscle contractions without any locomotion. Virtually all of the energy liberated by the contracting muscles appears as internal heat, a process known as **shivering thermogenesis**. Many birds that remain in cold climates during the winter shiver almost continuously.

In many mammals, chronic cold exposure also induces **nonshivering thermogenesis**, an increase in the metabolic rate and therefore heat production that is not due to increased muscle activity. Nonshivering thermogenesis occurs primarily in **brown adipose tissue** (also called brown fat), a specialized tissue in small mammals such as hibernating bats, small rodents living in cold environments, and many newborn mammals, including humans. Brown adipose tissue is responsive to hormones and signals from the nervous system, which are activated when body temperature decreases. Unlike the adipose tissue discussed previously, which stores energy in the form of fat, brown adipose tissue metabolizes fat and generates heat as a by-product.

47.5   Impact on Public Health

Learning Outcome:

1. Define body mass index (BMI), and explain how it is used to assess health risks associated with being overweight and obesity.

As we have seen, most animals, when provided adequate nutrients, maintain their body mass around a set point that is normal for their species. We rarely observe healthy animals in nature that are overweight. Generally, only domesticated animals become sufficiently sedentary that they gain excess, unnecessary weight (think of an overweight housecat). Humans, too, are prone to weight gain, particularly when living sedentary lives. Many people maintain a healthy body weight, but, as discussed in this section, an increasing number are unable to meet this goal.

Obesity Is a Global Health Issue

Excess body fat increases the risk of many diseases, including high blood pressure, cancer, heart disease, and diabetes mellitus. In diabetes mellitus, either insufficient insulin is available from the pancreas to control blood glucose concentrations (type 1 diabetes mellitus) or the cells of the body are less sensitive than usual to insulin (type 2 diabetes mellitus). In the U.S. alone, about 8% of the population—nearly 24,000,000 people—have diabetes mellitus. Of all diabetics in the U.S., more than 90% have type 2 diabetes mellitus. Compelling evidence has directly linked the incidence of this type of diabetes with being overweight. At what point does fat accumulation in humans start to pose a health risk? Historically, this question has been evaluated by research studies that investigate possible correlations between disease rates and some measure of body fat.

In ordinary practice, however, rather than obtaining a precise measure of body fat, a simple indicator of a person's potential health risk due to their weight is the **body mass index (BMI)**, a ratio of weight relative to height. A person's BMI is calculated by dividing his or her weight in kilograms by the square of his or her height in meters. For example, a 70-kg human with a height of 180 cm would have a BMI of 21.6 kg/m^2:

$$BMI = 70 \text{ kg}/(1.8)^2 \text{ m}$$
$$= 21.6 \text{ kg/m}^2$$

The BMI is not a measure of body fat. It gives an estimate of how overweight a person may be, but does not account for such things as a person's muscle development, which could also increase weight and BMI. Nonetheless, current National Institutes of Health guidelines categorize BMIs of 25 or more as overweight, that is, as having increased health risk. BMIs of 30 or greater are considered obese, with a greatly increased health risk. Data compiled by the Centers for Disease Control and Prevention in Atlanta, Georgia, and other U.S. federal agencies indicate that two-thirds or more of U.S. adults age 20–74 are now overweight or obese (**Figure 47.14**). One of the more troubling statistics is that the percentage of adults who are overweight but not obese has remained relatively unchanged since 1960, at about one-third. However, the percentage of obese adults has risen during that time from about 13% to the current level of nearly 40%. Since as recently as the early 1990s, the CDC estimates that the average body weight of Americans has risen by 10 pounds. Even more troubling, the rate of childhood obesity has also risen. In the U.S., the incidence of obesity in children age 6–11 has increased from 2–3% in 1960 to the current estimate of approximately 18.5%.

The increase in obesity is not confined to the U.S., but has become a worldwide trend. According to the World Health Organization, more than 1 billion adults globally are overweight and 300 million are obese.

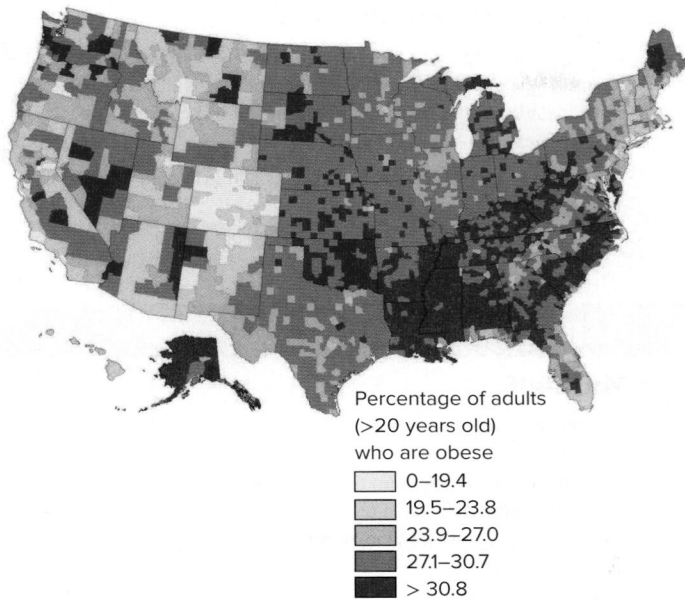

Percentage of adults
(>20 years old)
who are obese

- 0–19.4
- 19.5–23.8
- 23.9–27.0
- 27.1–30.7
- > 30.8

Figure 47.14   Obesity in U.S. adults. The Centers for Disease Control and Prevention estimate that many areas of the country experience obesity rates over 30% in adults (the darkest colored areas). Source: CDC.

 Core Skill: Science and Society Research into the causes of obesity and its consequences for human health have led to significant changes in the way we view the importance of maintaining a healthy body mass, but unfortunately obesity continues to place a significant burden on the health care systems of much of the western world.

Some studies indicate that genetic factors play an important role in obesity. Identical twins separated soon after birth and raised in different households have strikingly similar body weights as adults. Researchers hypothesize that natural selection favored the evolution of so-called thrifty genes, which boosted our ancestors' ability to store fat from each feast in order to sustain them through the next famine. Given today's abundance of high-fat and high-carbohydrate foods in many countries, what was once a survival mechanism may now be a liability.

The methods and goals of treating obesity are undergoing extensive rethinking. An increase in body fat is generally due to an excess of energy intake over energy expenditure, and overweight people have traditionally been advised to follow a low-calorie diet. However, such diets alone have limited effectiveness, because over 90% of obese people regain most or all of their lost weight within 5 years. This disturbing phenomenon may be related to the observation that metabolic rate decreases as the concentration of leptin in the blood decreases. Metabolic rate may decrease sufficiently to prevent further weight loss on a diet of as little as 1,000 kcal per day.

Research indicates that crash diets are not an effective long-term method for controlling weight. Instead, caloric intake should be set at a realistic level that can be maintained for the rest of one's life. This reduction in caloric intake should lead to a slow, steady weight loss

of no more than 1 pound per week until body weight stabilizes at a new, lower level. Most important, any program of weight loss should include increased physical activity. The exercise itself burns calories, but more importantly, it partially offsets the tendency for the metabolic rate to decrease. As a bonus, the combination of exercise and caloric restriction causes a person to lose more fat and less protein than with caloric restriction alone.

The impact of obesity on public health is enormous, accounting for many illnesses requiring hospitalization and chronic drug therapy, and well over 100,000 premature deaths per year. Its impact on the economy is far-reaching as well. The economic toll of obesity-related illnesses is felt in the loss of worker-hours in the workplace and in the costs of hospital stays, physician office visits, nursing home care, and medications. Current estimates by the Centers for Disease Control and Prevention are that as much as 20% of all U.S. health-care expenditures are directly or indirectly related to obesity! Obesity can affect society in unexpected ways. As an example, the increasing weight load of passengers forces airplanes to burn 350 million additional gallons of fuel each year, compared with just 25 years ago! This translates into nearly 4 million tons of additional pollution released into the atmosphere every year. In another recent example, for safety reasons, the U.S. Coast Guard has begun downgrading the allowable number of passengers on large state ferries due to the increasing average weight of U.S. adults.

Summary of Key Concepts

47.1   Use and Storage of Energy

- An animal's utilization of nutrients has two states: the absorptive state, during which ingested nutrients are entering the blood from the alimentary canal, and the postabsorptive state, during which the GI tract is empty of nutrients and the body's own stores must supply energy.

- Glucose and fatty acids are the two major energy sources during the absorptive state. Much of the absorbed glucose immediately enters cells and is enzymatically broken down, providing energy required to synthesize ATP. Most absorbed triglycerides are stored in adipose cells until an animal requires additional energy. Amino acids are taken up by all body cells and used to synthesize proteins (Figure 47.1).

- The events that maintain blood glucose concentration in the postabsorptive state fall into two categories: (1) the reactions of glycogenolysis and gluconeogenesis, which provide glucose to the blood, and (2) cellular use of fatty acids for energy, which spares glucose for use by the nervous system (Figure 47.2, Table 47.1).

47.2   Regulation of the Absorptive and Postabsorptive States

- Tight control mechanisms, in the form of several hormones and the nervous system, maintain homeostatic concentrations of fuel molecules in an animal's blood. The hormone insulin acts on certain cells to facilitate the diffusion of glucose from blood into the cell cytosol via glucose transporters (GLUTs). All animal cells use GLUTs to transport glucose across their plasma membranes (Figure 47.3).

- In vertebrates, an increase in blood glucose concentration in the absorptive state stimulates the cells of the pancreas to secrete insulin; a decrease in that concentration removes the signal for secretion. In the postabsorptive state, when the blood glucose concentration decreases, glucose-monitoring regions in the hypothalamus stimulate production of glucose-elevating factors such as glucagon and norepinephrine (Figure 47.4).

- Exercise or any type of physical activity increases an animal's metabolic rate. Exercise increases an animal's requirement for nutrients, including glucose and fatty acids, to provide energy.

47.3 Energy Balance and Metabolic Rate

- An animal's metabolic rate refers to the amount of energy it uses in a given period of time to power all of its metabolic requirements.
- The most common measure for comparing metabolic rates of different species is the basal metabolic rate (BMR). Most of the basal metabolism is due to the routine functions of the heart, liver, kidneys, and brain (Figure 47.5).
- Many factors affect metabolism, including skeletal muscle activity, whether an animal has recently eaten, and body mass (Figure 47.6).
- When the daily amount of energy in consumed foods equals the amount of energy expended, body weight remains stable. Tipping the balance in either direction causes weight gain or loss by increasing or decreasing total body energy content.
- Short-term control of feeding generally involves satiety signals that remove the sensation of hunger and set the time period before hunger returns again. Experiments by Coleman and Friedman investigated the hormone leptin as a satiety factor in mammals. Leptin has since been found in all classes of vertebrates (Figures 47.7, 47.8).

47.4 Regulation of Body Temperature

- Most animals can survive only in a relatively narrow temperature range that allows chemical reactions to proceed, maintains the structures of membranes, and avoids denaturing proteins.
- Animals can be classified according to their source of heat and their ability to maintain body temperature. Ectotherms depend on external heat sources to warm their bodies, whereas endotherms use their own metabolically generated heat to warm themselves. Homeotherms maintain their body temperature within a narrow range, but heterotherms have body temperatures that vary with the environmental temperature (Figure 47.9).
- The surface of an animal's body can lose or gain heat from the external environment via four mechanisms: radiation, evaporation, convection, and conduction (Figures 47.10, 47.11).
- The skin can function as a variable heat exchanger; blood vessels near the skin surface dilate to dissipate heat or constrict to retain it. Both endotherms and ectotherms regulate heat loss through countercurrent exchange, which retains heat by returning it to the body's core and keeping the core warmer than the extremities. Heat exchange can also be regulated by changing the rate of water evaporation via perspiration. Behavioral mechanisms can alter heat loss by radiation, conduction, and convection (Figures 47.12, 47.13).
- Muscle activity (shivering thermogenesis) and brown adipose tissue metabolism (nonshivering thermogenesis) increase the production of heat.

47.5 Impact on Public Health

- Excess body fat increases the risk of many diseases. A body mass index (BMI) of 25 kg/m² or more means that a person is considered overweight, and a value of 30 kg/m² gives a classification of obese (Figure 47.14).
- Obesity can have serious health risks and is treated with caloric restriction and exercise.

Assess & Discuss

Test Yourself

1. During the absorptive state, an animal is
   a. fasting.
   b. relying entirely on stored molecules for energy.
   c. absorbing nutrients from a recently ingested meal.
   d. metabolizing lipids stored in adipose tissue to supply ATP to its cells.
   e. doing both a and b.

2. Gluconeogenesis
   a. occurs when the liver synthesizes glucose from noncarbohydrate precursors.
   b. is the process by which glycogen is broken down to glucose.
   c. occurs primarily when an animal is in the absorptive state.
   d. occurs when triglycerides are being formed and stored in adipose cells.
   e. occurs primarily in skeletal muscle.

3. In the process of _____, most tissues of the vertebrate body metabolize fat instead of glucose to ensure that _____ tissue has an adequate supply of glucose.
   a. gluconeogenesis, muscle
   b. glucose sparing, epithelial
   c. glycogenolysis, nervous
   d. glucose sparing, nervous
   e. gluconeogenesis, epithelial

4. Ketones are compounds that are derived from _____ and are synthesized primarily in the _____ state.
   a. glucose, absorptive
   b. glycogen, absorptive
   c. fatty acids, postabsorptive
   d. amino acids, postabsorptive
   e. triglycerides, absorptive

5. Insulin primarily regulates the blood glucose concentration by
   a. stimulating the recruitment of GLUTs from the cytosol to the plasma membrane for transport of glucose from extracellular to intracellular fluid.
   b. stimulating gluconeogenesis.
   c. suppressing glucose uptake by muscle tissue.
   d. stimulating the release of glucose from glycogen reserves in the liver.
   e. inhibiting the synthesis of new GLUTs.

6. The rate at which an animal uses energy is called
   a. the body mass index.
   b. the animal's energy consumption.
   c. the metabolic rate.
   d. nonshivering thermogenesis.
   e. shivering thermogenesis.

7. Which factor(s) may increase metabolic rate?
   a. shivering
   b. decreased muscle activity
   c. sleeping
   d. consumption of a meal
   e. both a and d

8. Which molecule acts on brain centers to decrease appetite in mammals and other vertebrates?
   a. GLUT4
   b. glycogen
   c. leptin
   d. glucagon
   e. a ketone

9. Animals that have body temperatures that are maintained within a narrow range are
   a. endotherms.
   b. ectotherms.
   c. homeotherms.
   d. heterotherms.
   e. both b and d.

10. The rate of heat loss in a mammal is regulated by
    a. the degree of blood flow at the surface of the skin.
    b. the amount of perspiration.
    c. behavioral adaptations.
    d. air currents near the animal's body.
    e. all of the above.

Conceptual Questions

1. Explain the functions of insulin. Why do you think a hormone such as insulin is required to carry out these functions?

2. Explain how appetite is controlled by the brain. What is the benefit of having a hormone released from adipose cells in proportion to total fat mass?

3. **Core Concept: Structure and Function** How does this core concept apply to countercurrent exchange?

Collaborative Questions

1. Discuss the differences between being ectothermic and endothermic and between being heterothermic and homeothermic.

2. Discuss four ways that animals exchange heat with their environment.

have a heart but, instead, have a contractile pharynx that serves part of the same function. The pharyngeal muscles of these animals express four of the five key genes for heart development that are found in all vertebrates. Thus, the genes required for the formation of a contractile, multichambered heart arose early in the evolution of animals.

Why are some vertebrate hearts four-chambered and others are not? In a 2009 study, American researcher Benoit Bruneau and colleagues compared the expression of one of the major heart development genes, called *Tbx5*, in the hearts of amphibians, reptiles, birds, and mammals. (The *Tbx5* gene encodes Tbx5 protein, a transcription factor.) The researchers discovered that the expression of *Tbx5* became increasingly restricted to particular locations within the hearts of animals displaying greater separation of the ventricles into two chambers (**Figure 48.3**). Amphibians have two atria but only a single ventricle. In these animals, *Tbx5* was uniformly expressed throughout the developing ventricle. In lizards, in which a septum only partially divides the ventricle into two chambers, *Tbx5* expression was absent in a portion of the right half of the ventricle. In birds and mammals, with fully partitioned ventricles, Tbx5 protein was not made in the developing right ventricle, but was present in large amounts in the left ventricle. This finding suggests that a gradient of Tbx5 protein is required for the ventricle to form two chambers and thereby a complete double circulation. The investigators also showed that if *Tbx5* expression was experimentally induced in the heart of an embryonic mouse in a pattern that mimicked that seen in lizards, the mouse heart developed only three clearly defined chambers—there was no distinction between left and right ventricles!

From these and other studies, the expression of a core set of genes appears to be vital for the formation of a heart or heartlike structure, and a subset of genes, like *Tbx5,* is critical for the division of the heart into chambers. The most common congenital organ defects in humans are those associated with the heart. The relatively high incidence of heart-related birth defects makes an understanding of the genetic control of the growth and development of the heart a great concern in medicine today.

48.2 The Composition of Blood

Learning Outcomes:

1. List the four components of blood, and describe the composition and functions of each.
2. Describe the process of blood clotting in mammals.

Blood is the transport medium of animals with closed circulatory systems. It moves necessary materials—including nutrients and gases such as O_2—to all cells and takes away waste products, including CO_2 and other breakdown products of metabolism. What are the components of blood that allow it to perform its functions?

Blood Is Composed of Cells Suspended in Plasma

Blood consists of cells and, in mammals, membrane-enclosed fragments of cytosol, suspended in a solution containing dissolved nutrients, proteins, gases, and other molecules. If we collect a blood sample and spin it in a centrifuge, the blood separates into three visible layers (**Figure 48.4**). Let's take a look at each of these.

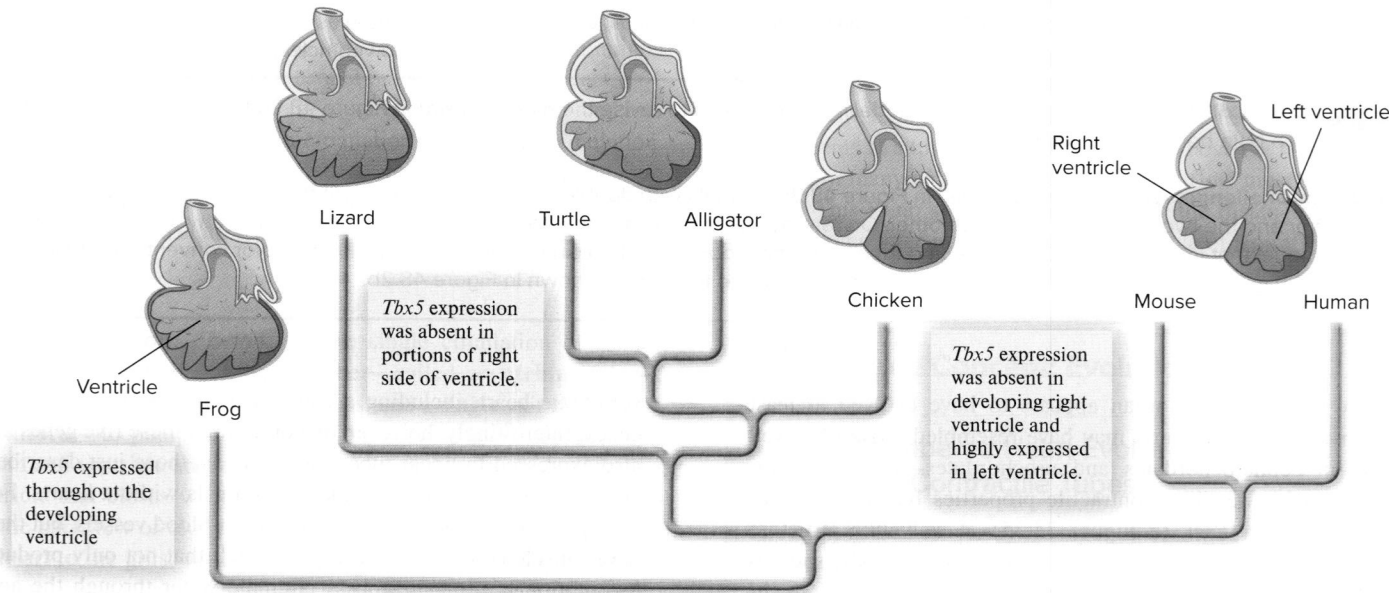

Figure 48.3 Expression of the *Tbx5* gene in embryonic vertebrate hearts. The blue color indicates where in the developing heart muscle the *Tbx5* gene was expressed. Note: Structural details have been omitted for simplicity. Source: Kazuko Koshiba-Takeuchi et al., 2009. Reptilian heart development and the molecular basis of cardiac chamber evolution. *Nature* 461: 95–98.

Figure 48.4 Components of blood. When a blood sample is centrifuged, it forms three visible layers: plasma, leukocytes, and erythrocytes. Leukocytes, shown in the scanning electron micrograph, are the white blood cells that make up part of the immune system. Erythrocytes are red blood cells, which carry oxygen. Note: The leukocyte layer is enlarged and not to scale, for illustrative purposes. (right) ©Power and Syred/Science Source

 Core Skill: Connections Leukocytes are part of the immune system of animals. Are immune defenses unique to animals? (Refer back to Figures 37.17 through 37.19 for help.)

Plasma The top layer of the centrifuged blood sample is a yellowish solution called **plasma** (see Figure 48.4). Plasma typically makes up about half of the total volume of blood in most vertebrates. It is made up of water and dissolved nutrients, oxygen, waste products of metabolism, and many other molecules released by cells, such as hormones and proteins. These proteins serve numerous functions, such as helping in the formation of blood clots, which seal off wounds to blood vessels.

Leukocytes Beneath the plasma in the centrifuged blood sample is a narrow white layer of **leukocytes**, also known as white blood cells (see Figure 48.4). Leukocytes develop from a specialized connective tissue (the marrow) of certain bones in vertebrates. Although there are several types—which we describe further in Chapter 52—all leukocytes perform vital functions that defend the body against infection and disease and thus are key components of an animal's immune system.

Erythrocytes The bottom visible layer of the centrifuged blood sample consists of **erythrocytes**, also called red blood cells because of their color (see Figure 48.4). The term **hematocrit** refers to the volume of blood (expressed as percentage) that is composed of erythrocytes, usually between 35% and 65% among vertebrates. Erythrocytes serve the critical function of transporting oxygen throughout the body. There are approximately a thousand times more erythrocytes than leukocytes in the circulation. Like leukocytes, erythrocytes are derived from cells in the bone marrow. In most vertebrates, mature erythrocytes retain their nuclei and other cellular organelles, but in all mammals (and a few species of fishes

and amphibians), the nuclei are lost upon maturation. The lack of a nucleus and many other organelles in the mammalian erythrocyte increases the cell's oxygen-carrying capacity and contributes to its characteristic biconcave shape (see Figure 48.4). The biconcave shape of the mammalian erythrocyte increases its surface area relative to the flattened disc or oval shape seen in most other vertebrates. This is believed to increase the efficiency of gas exchange between the erythrocyte and the body fluids.

Oxygen is poorly soluble in plasma. Consequently, the amount of oxygen that dissolves in plasma usually cannot support a vertebrate's basal metabolic rate, let alone more strenuous activity. Within the cytosol of erythrocytes, however, are large amounts of the protein **hemoglobin**, which can reversibly bind to oxygen. Hemoglobin greatly increases the reservoir of oxygen in the blood and enables animals to be more active. In a later section, we will consider the mechanisms by which hemoglobin binds and releases oxygen.

Platelets Vertebrate blood has a fourth component not visible in a centrifuged sample of blood, called **platelets** in mammals and thrombocytes in other vertebrates. Platelets, which are derived from bone marrow cells, are cell fragments that lack a nucleus. They serve a crucial role in the formation of blood clots that limit blood loss after injury. The formation of a blood clot requires several steps, two of which include platelets (**Figure 48.5**). First, when a blood vessel is injured, platelets secrete substances that cause them to clump together and bind to collagen fibers in the surrounding connective tissue at the wound site. This forms a plug that prevents continued blood loss. Second, other platelet secretions interact with plasma proteins to cause the precipitation from solution of a fibrous protein called

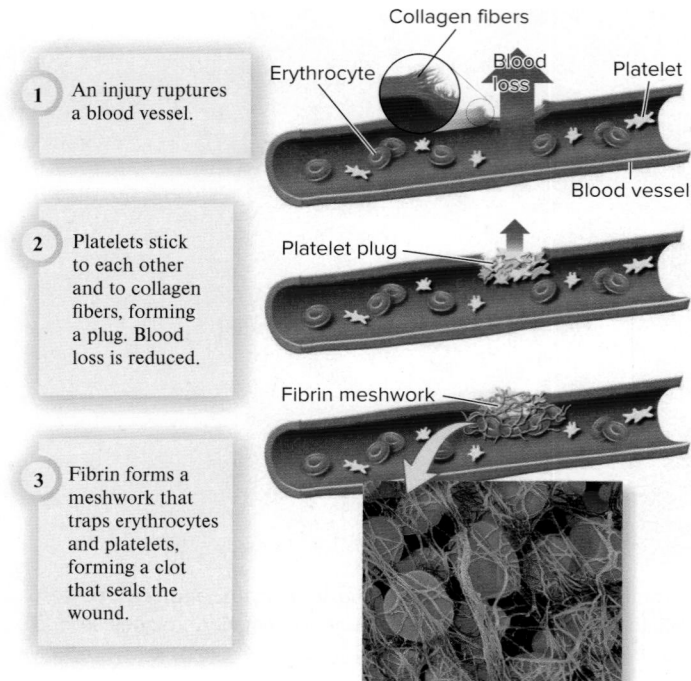

1 An injury ruptures a blood vessel.

2 Platelets stick to each other and to collagen fibers, forming a plug. Blood loss is reduced.

3 Fibrin forms a meshwork that traps erythrocytes and platelets, forming a clot that seals the wound.

Figure 48.5 **Platelets and the process of blood clot formation.** A blood clot forms in two major steps: A platelet plug reduces initial blood loss, and a fibrin clot then seals the wound. An example of a fibrin clot is shown in the scanning electron micrograph. (bottom) ©Dennis Kunkel Microscopy, Inc./Phototake

fibrin. Fibrin forms a meshwork of threadlike fibers that wrap around and between platelets and erythrocytes, enlarging and thickening the plug to form a clot. Blood clotting begins within seconds and helps prevent injured animals from losing too much blood. Eventually, the body absorbs the clot as the injured vessel heals.

48.3 The Vertebrate Heart and Its Function

Learning Outcomes:

1. Describe the structure of the vertebrate heart.
2. **CoreSKILL** ≫ Outline the sequence of events of the cardiac cycle, and draw conclusions regarding the functional relationship between electrical and contractile events.
3. **CoreSKILL** ≫ Interpret the meaning of the tracings on an electrocardiogram.

In Section 48.1, we considered some of the general features of circulatory systems in animals. In this section, we will examine the structure and function of the vertebrate heart, focusing on the human heart, which carries out a double circulation.

Vertebrate Hearts That Carry Out a Double Circulation Have Two Atria and Two Ventricles

As described earlier, animals with a double circulation, such as mammals, have a heart with a left atrium and ventricle and a right atrium

and ventricle (see Figure 48.2b) A closer look at the structure of the human heart is provided in **Figure 48.6**. The two sides of the heart are physically separated by a muscular and fibrous septum. Blood enters the atria from veins from the systemic or pulmonary circulation; the superior and inferior vena cavae return blood from the systemic circulation, and the left and right pulmonary veins return blood from the lungs. The left ventricle ejects blood into the **aorta**, which branches to other arteries that distribute the blood. The right

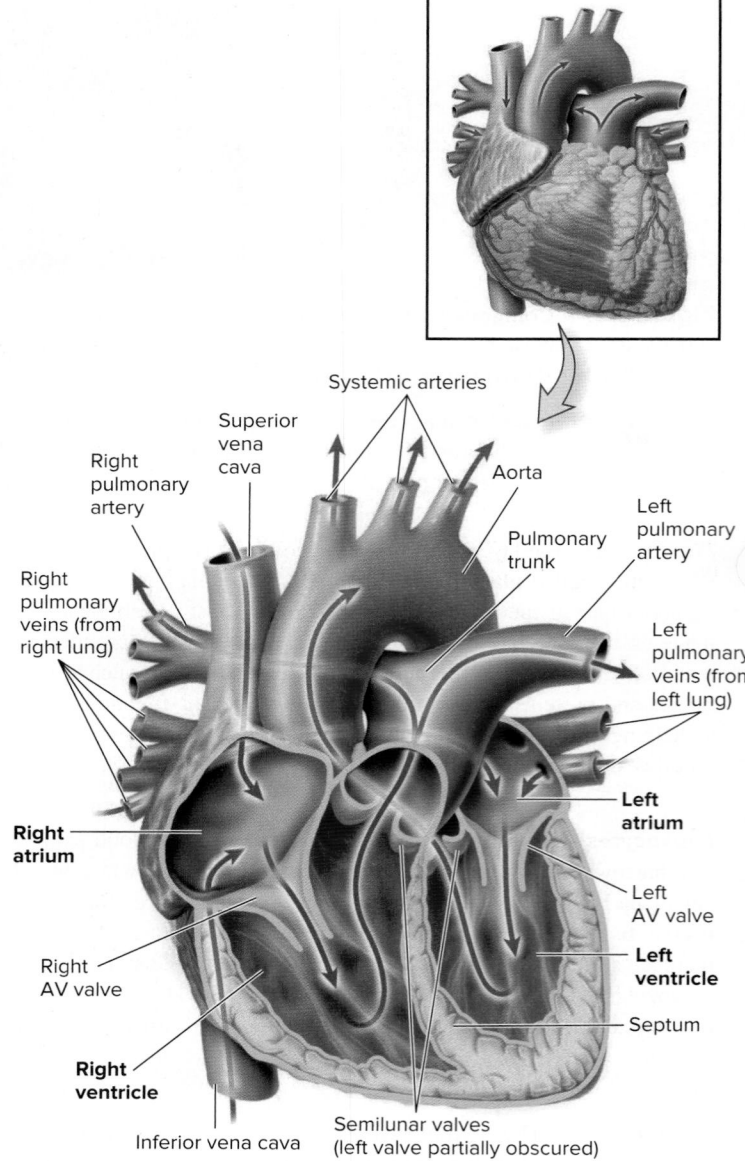

Figure 48.6 **The mammalian heart and circulation.** This cutaway illustration of a human heart shows the major blood vessels entering and leaving the heart, and the relationships of the four chambers (see the inset for the intact heart). Regions that contain oxygenated blood are shown in red, deoxygenated in blue. Note that the pulmonary veins carry oxygenated blood because they return blood from the lungs, whereas veins from the systemic circulation carry deoxygenated blood.

Concept Check: *Which vessel or vessels leading from the mammalian heart carry fully oxygenated blood?*

ventricle ejects blood into the pulmonary trunk, which divides into **pulmonary arteries** that lead to the right and left lungs.

Valves control the direction that blood flows through the heart. Blood normally can flow in only one direction through a valve. One-way valves called **atrioventricular (AV) valves** control the movement of blood between the atria and ventricles. Blood flows down a pressure gradient through the AV valves from the atria into the ventricles. One-way **semilunar valves** are found between each ventricle and the artery into which a ventricle sends blood (either the aorta or the pulmonary trunk). The right ventricle pumps deoxygenated blood to the lungs through the right semilunar valve, and the left ventricle pumps oxygenated blood to the rest of the body through the left semilunar valve.

Vertebrates Have a Myogenic Heart

What causes the heart to beat so steadily? Animals cannot consciously initiate heart contractions. The beating of the heart is initiated either by nerves or by intrinsic activity of the heart muscle cells themselves. Many arthropods, for example, have a neurogenic heart that will not beat unless it receives regular electrical impulses from the nervous system. All vertebrates, however, have a myogenic heart, in which the signaling mechanism that initiates contraction resides within the cardiac muscle itself.

In myogenic hearts, cardiac muscle is distinguished by the interconnectedness between individual cardiac muscle cells, or cardiac myocytes. Each myocyte has membrane extensions that form interlocking networks with other myocytes. Within these networks, called intercalated discs, are many gap junctions (refer back to Figure 10.11)

that electrically couple the myocytes. The large number of gap junctions permits the rapid spread of electric current from cell to cell, so that all parts of the heart are rapidly stimulated at nearly the same time. This electric current is the signal that increases the intracellular concentration of Ca^{2+} within the myocytes. Although the details are different, the increase in Ca^{2+} triggers contraction in a manner that is generally similar to skeletal muscle contraction (see Chapter 45).

Myogenic hearts are electrically excitable and generate their own action potentials. The rate and forcefulness of the beating of myogenic hearts can, however, be regulated by the nervous system. For example, the autonomic nervous system increases heart rate in vertebrates during the fight-or-flight response (see Chapter 43). Nonetheless, myogenic hearts continue to beat on their own if dissected out of an animal and placed in a nutrient bath, even with no nerves present.

Excitation of the Heart Begins in the Atria and Spreads to the Ventricles

As with skeletal muscle (see Chapter 45), contraction of the vertebrate heart cannot occur until the muscle has been electrically excited. The electrical excitation of the vertebrate heart has two phases: atrial and ventricular. In atrial excitation, electrical signals are generated within the wall of the right atrium at the **sinoatrial (SA) node**, or **pacemaker** (**Figure 48.7**). The SA node is a collection of modified myocytes that have an inherently unstable resting membrane potential. Ion channels in the membranes of these cells are opened spontaneously and allow the influx of positively charged ions into the cytosol, thereby depolarizing the cell. These depolarizations produce action potentials in the

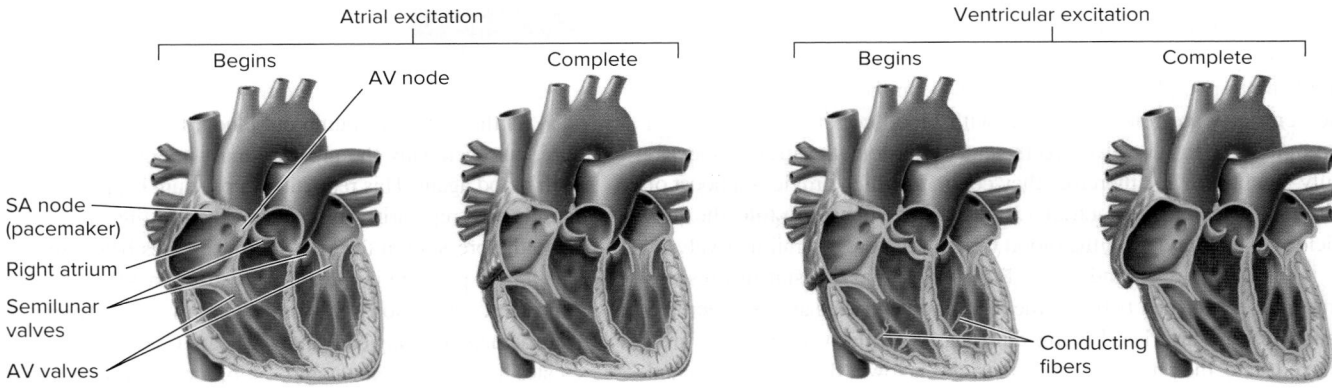

| | Atrial excitation | | Ventricular excitation | |
	Begins	Complete	Begins	Complete
AV valves	OPEN	OPEN	Beginning to close	CLOSED
Semilunar valves	CLOSED	CLOSED	CLOSED	OPEN
Phase of cardiac cycle	Diastole	Diastole	Systole beginning	Systole
Atria	Relaxed	Contracted	Beginning to relax	Relaxed
Ventricles	Relaxed	Relaxed	Beginning to contract	Contracted
Chambers with highest pressure	All are low pressure	Atria (slightly)	Ventricles	Ventricles

Figure 48.7 **Electrical activity in the mammalian heart and the events of the cardiac cycle.** The spread of electrical activity, which is shown in yellow, begins in the sinoatrial (SA) node and quickly spreads through the atria to the atrioventricular (AV) node. Branches from the AV node transmit electrical activity throughout the ventricles via conducting fibers. The atria and ventricles do not contract until they have become electrically excited. Changes in pressure gradients between the atria and ventricles, and between the ventricles and the aorta or pulmonary trunk, are the forces that open or close the two sets of heart valves. Note: The left semilunar valve is only partly visible in this orientation.

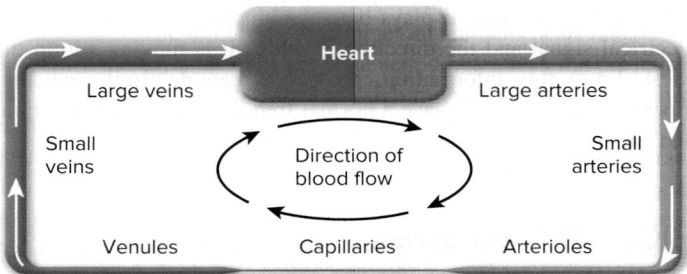

Figure 48.10 **The sequence of blood flow in a closed circulatory system.** Overview of blood flow through vessels in a closed circulatory system. Regions of gas exchange with the environment (such as the lungs), have been omitted for simplicity.

Gas and nutrient exchange occurs between the blood in the capillaries and the cells surrounding the capillaries. From capillaries, the blood then flows back to the heart through the smallest veins, called venules, to small veins and finally to large veins. In this section, we will examine the structures and functions of these vessels.

Arteries Distribute Blood to Organs and Tissues

Arteries are thick-walled vessels that consist of layers of smooth muscle and connective tissue wrapped around a single-celled inner layer of specialized epithelial cells called an endothelium. The endothelium forms a smooth lining in contact with the blood (**Figure 48.11a**). Because thick layers of tissue surround the

endothelium, most dissolved substances cannot diffuse across arteries. Instead, arteries act as conducting tubes that distribute blood leaving the heart to all the organs and tissues of an animal's body.

In vertebrates, the walls of the largest arteries, such as the aorta, also contain one or more layers of elastin, a protein with elastic properties (refer back to Figure 10.3). As the aorta stretches to accommodate blood arriving from the heart, the elastin layers also stretch. The thick layers of tissue in the aorta and other large arteries prevent them from stretching more than a small amount, however. When the heart relaxes as it readies for another beat, the elastin layers in the aorta and large arteries recoil to their original state, something like the release of a stretched rubber band. The recoiling vessels generate a force on the blood within them. This force helps prevent blood pressure from decreasing too much while the heart is refilling during diastole.

Arterioles Distribute Blood to Capillaries

As arteries carry blood away from the heart, they branch repeatedly and become smaller in diameter. Eventually, the vessels are little more than a single-celled layer of endothelium with one or two layers of smooth muscle and connective tissue (see Figure 48.11a). These are the arterioles, which deliver blood to regions of the body in proportion to metabolic demands. The adjustment of blood flow is accomplished by changing the diameter of arterioles. They widen, or dilate, in areas of high metabolic activity and narrow, or constrict, in inactive regions. Arterioles dilate when their smooth muscle cells relax and constrict when these cells contract.

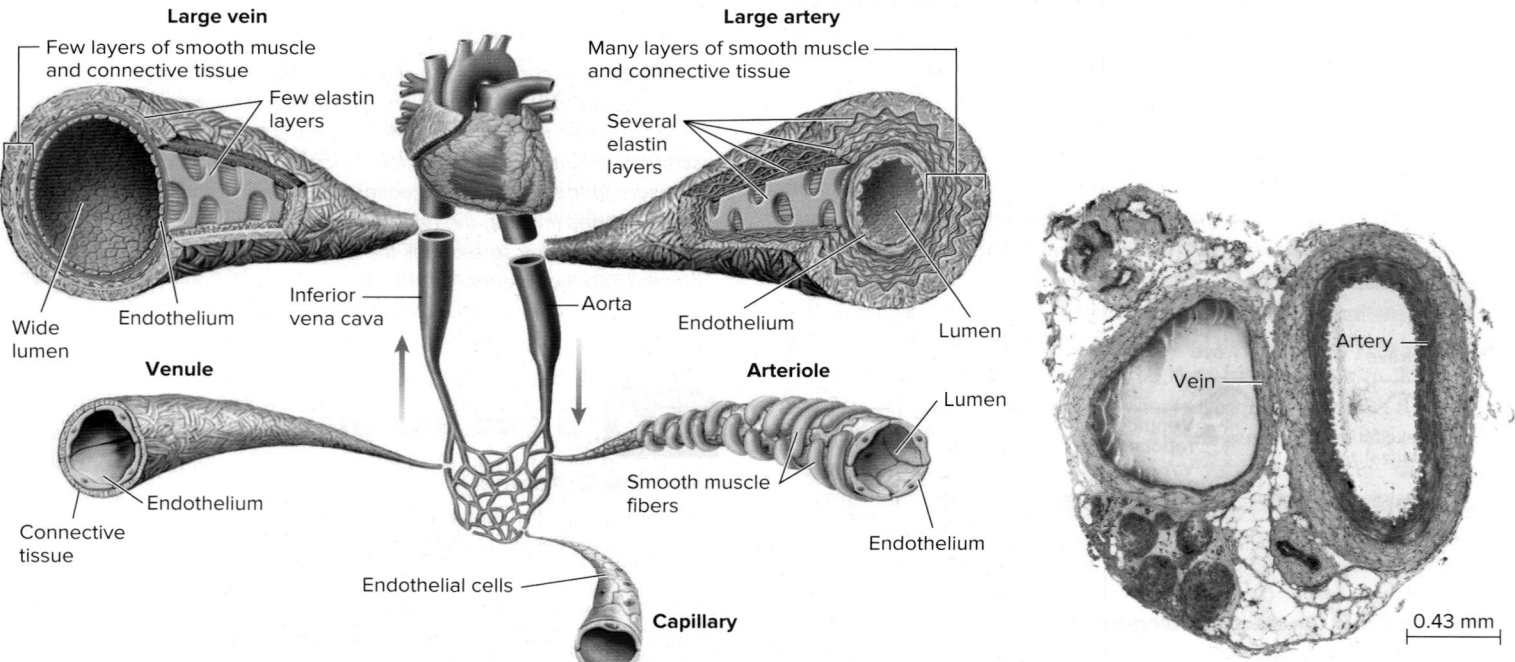

(a) The structure of blood vessels in a closed circulatory system

(b) Light micrograph of a typical artery and vein in a mammal

Figure 48.11 **Comparative features of blood vessels.** **(a)** Structures of blood vessels (not drawn to scale). **(b)** Light micrograph of a small artery near a vein. Note the differences between the two vessels in the thickness and composition of the walls. b: ©National Geographic Creative/Alamy Stock Photo

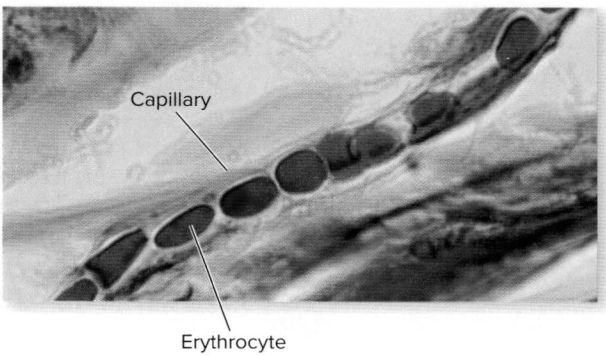

Capillary

Erythrocyte

Figure 48.12 Erythrocytes moving through a capillary. Note that the cells move along in single file, seen here through a light microscope. The diameter of the capillary is approximately 7 μm.
©Ed Reschke/Getty Images

Concept Check: *Do erythrocytes enter and exit through pores in capillaries?*

Capillaries Are the Site of Gas and Nutrient Exchange

Arterioles branch into the tiny, thin-walled capillaries. Capillaries are tubes composed of a single-celled layer of endothelium resting on a layer of extracellular matrix called a basal lamina (refer back to Figure 41.4). Capillaries are the narrowest blood vessels in animals; essentially every cell in an animal's body is near one. The diameter of a capillary is about the same as the width of erythrocytes, which move through the capillaries in single file (**Figure 48.12**).

With the exception of large proteins, most solutes readily diffuse between the plasma in a capillary and the surrounding interstitial fluid and intracellular fluid. Nutrients, hormones, and other solutes diffuse from the plasma and into cells; waste products generated by cells diffuse in the opposite direction. Gases are exchanged across capillaries between the blood and the environment via a respiratory organ, such as the lungs, and between the blood and tissues (**Figure 48.13**).

Blood enters capillaries under pressure that is created by the beating of the heart. This pressure forces some of the fluid in blood out through tiny openings in capillaries into the interstitial fluid. These openings are wide enough to permit water but not cells to leave the capillary. The movement of fluid between capillaries and interstitial fluid is important for maintaining a normal distribution of water between the body fluid compartments.

If the fluid that leaves a capillary were to remain in the interstitial fluid, the volume of plasma in the blood would decrease, and the interstitial fluid would swell. Most of the fluid that leaves at the beginning of a capillary, however, is recaptured at the capillary's end. Any excess fluid is picked up by lymphatic vessels (which will be described in Chapter 52) and eventually returned to veins.

Venules and Veins Return Blood to the Heart

Once blood travels through capillaries, picking up any substances secreted or diffusing from the cells of the body, it enters the venules, which are small, thin-walled extensions of capillaries. The venules empty into veins that return blood to the heart. The walls of veins are much thinner, less muscular, and more easily distended, or stretched, than those of arteries (see Figure 48.11a,b).

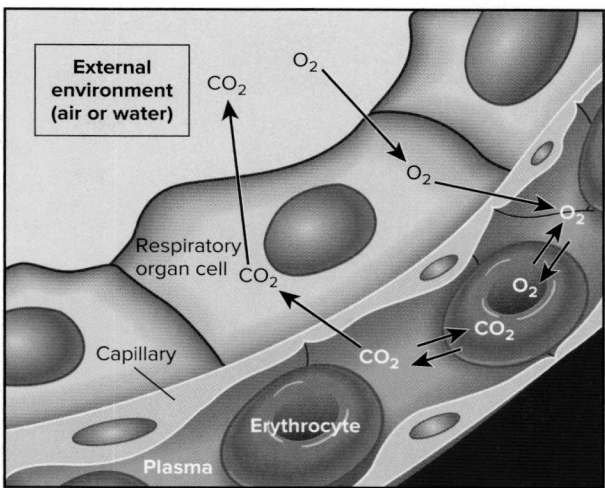

(a) Gas exchange between the environment and a respiratory organ

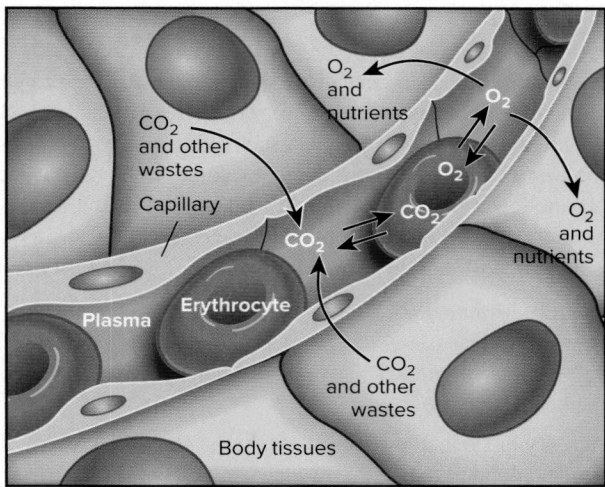

(b) Gas, nutrient, and waste exchange between the blood and tissues

Figure 48.13 Overview of gas and other solute exchange between capillaries and cells. (a) In vertebrates, oxygen (O_2) diffuses from the environment across the cells of a respiratory organ into the blood (plasma and erythrocytes); carbon dioxide (CO_2) diffuses in the opposite direction. **(b)** From the blood, O_2 and nutrients diffuse into tissue cells, where they are used during the synthesis of ATP and other activities. Cells generate CO_2 and other waste products, which diffuse out of cells and into blood. Note: Interstitial fluid is omitted for simplicity.

 Core Concepts: Systems and Energy and Matter A fundamental principle of biology is that living organisms maintain homeostasis. Keep this principle in mind as you read the rest of this chapter. The exchange of O_2 and CO_2 illustrated here is absolutely essential for all homeostatic processes in animals, in part because oxygen is required for the production of much of an animal's ATP. The ATP, in turn, provides the energy required to sustain processes that contribute to homeostasis. Two organ systems, the respiratory and circulatory systems, must function together to make this happen.

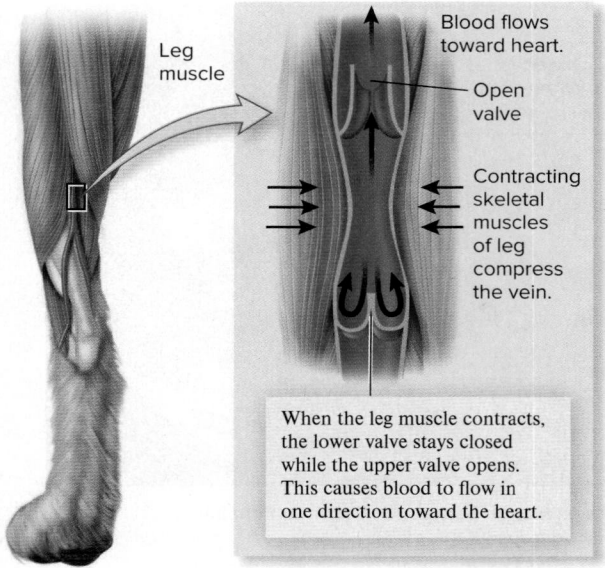

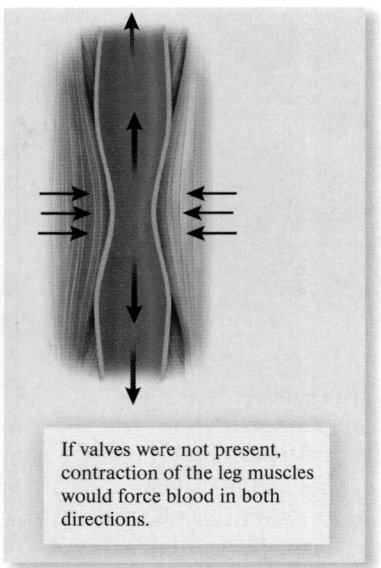

Leg muscle

Blood flows toward heart.

Open valve

Contracting skeletal muscles of leg compress the vein.

When the leg muscle contracts, the lower valve stays closed while the upper valve opens. This causes blood to flow in one direction toward the heart.

If valves were not present, contraction of the leg muscles would force blood in both directions.

(a) Vein with one-way valves

(b) Vein without valves

Figure 48.14 One-way valves in veins. (a) Valves are typically present in the veins of limbs, as shown in this dog's leg, where they assist the return of blood to the heart against the force of gravity. **(b)** Blood moving in a vein without valves would flow in both directions if the vein were compressed.

 Core Concept: Structure and Function The structure of valves in the circulatory system permits them to open in one direction only. This structure, in turn, determines the function of the valves. In this example, they facilitate the movement of blood toward the heart.

By the time blood has been distributed through all of the capillaries and reached the veins, its pressure is very low. This presents a challenge in getting blood back to the heart with such little pressure to propel it. In addition, veins can fill with considerable volumes of blood, particularly veins in the lower parts of an animal's body, such as the legs, where gravity tends to cause blood to pool. However, several factors assist the blood on its way toward the heart, even when it flows against gravity:

- Neurotransmitters released by neurons of the sympathetic nervous system stimulate contraction of smooth muscles of leg veins. This compresses the veins and helps force blood back to the heart.

- Activity of skeletal muscles in the limbs assists the return of venous blood to the heart, by squeezing the veins that travel through them (**Figure 48.14**).

- One-way valves inside veins ensure that blood returning from below the heart moves in only one direction, toward the heart (see Figure 48.14). The valves can open toward the heart, but not in the other direction. When a leg vein, for example, is compressed by the mechanisms just mentioned, the blood forces open the valves and blood moves in one direction. When the vein is relaxed, the valves close again, preventing blood from flowing backward, away from the heart. (By contrast, veins located above the heart, like those in the necks of bipeds and some quadrupeds, lack valves because gravity is sufficient to return blood toward the heart.)

Many people can easily observe the effects of gravity on venous blood flow. When the arms are held down by the sides, the veins are visible on the backs of the hands. When the arms are raised above the head, the bulging veins quickly lose blood and become less visible. When blood from the veins returns to the heart, it must travel against gravity when the arms are at a person's sides and with gravity when the arms are elevated. Blood drains from veins much more effectively when gravity works in its favor.

Relationship Among Blood Pressure, Blood Flow, and Resistance

Learning Outcomes:

1. **CoreSKILL »** Be able to relate blood pressure, blood flow, and resistance in a mathematical way.

2. Distinguish between the effects of vasodilation and vasoconstriction on blood flow.

3. **CoreSKILL »** Predict the effects of changes in resistance and cardiac output on blood pressure.

Blood pressure—the force exerted by blood on vessel walls—is responsible for blood flow, the movement of blood through the vessels. **Resistance (R)** refers to the tendency of blood vessels to slow the flow of blood through their lumens. Blood pressure varies through an animal's body in part because of differences in resistance. Such differences can be considered on a local level, as in an exercising muscle, or on a systemic level, as in the resistance the heart must overcome to pump blood throughout the entire body. In this section, we will explore the relationship among blood pressure, blood flow, and resistance.

Blood Pressure, Blood Flow, and Resistance Are Mathematically Related

The relationship among blood pressure, blood flow, and resistance is stated by Poiseuille's law, which was derived in the 1840s by Jean Marie Louis Poiseuille, a French physician and physiologist. His law is simplified here:

$$\text{Flow}(F) = \Delta\text{Pressure}(P)/\text{Resistance}(R)$$

Stated mathematically, blood flow through a blood vessel is directly proportional to the difference (Δ) in pressure of the blood between the beginning and end of the vessel, and inversely proportional to the resistance created by that vessel. The equation can be rearranged as $\Delta P = F \times R$, which demonstrates that blood pressure depends on both blood flow and resistance. Poiseuille's law applies to blood flow through a single vessel, an organ, or the entire body.

Resistance to Flow Depends on the Radius of Arterioles

A change in arteriolar resistance is the major mechanism for increasing or decreasing blood flow to a region. The relationship between arteriolar radius and resistance is not linear. Resistance is inversely proportional to the radius of the vessel raised to the fourth power: $R \propto 1/r^4$, where $\propto$ means "proportional to" and r is the radius of the arteriolar lumen. Let's consider an arteriole with a radius that increases by a factor of 2. This would occur if the smooth muscles of the arteriole relaxed sufficiently to allow the vessel to dilate and double its original radius. Because resistance is inversely proportional to the fourth power of vessel radius, an increase in radius by a factor of 2 will result in a decrease in resistance of 2^4, or 16-fold.

Vasodilation refers to an increase in blood vessel radius, and **vasoconstriction** refers to a decrease in blood vessel radius. The signals that control arteriolar radius come from three sources:

- *Local factors.* Locally, metabolic by-products such as carbon dioxide, lactic acid, and other substances secreted by metabolically active tissues cause nearby arterioles to vasodilate, thereby decreasing their resistance to blood flow. This lowering of resistance permits more blood flow to the active region, facilitating oxygen and nutrient delivery and waste removal.

- *Hormones.* Hormones secreted by glands throughout the body can also regulate arteriolar radius. For example, during the fight-or-flight response, some hormones cause the arterioles that deliver blood to the small intestine to vasoconstrict, routing blood away from the intestine and to more immediately vital areas such as the heart and skeletal muscles.

- *Nervous system.* Signals from the autonomic nervous system cause contraction or relaxation of arteriolar smooth muscle; this effect is similar to that described for hormones.

Cardiac Output and Resistance Determine Blood Pressure

Because blood vessels provide resistance to blood flow, the heart must beat forcefully enough to overcome that resistance throughout the whole body. **Cardiac output (CO)** is the amount of blood the heart pumps per unit of time, usually expressed in units of liters per minute (L/min). Poiseuille's law can be adapted to the whole body. In this case, pressure refers to arterial blood pressure (BP), flow refers to CO, and resistance refers to the total resistance provided by all the arterial vessels of the systemic circulation (**total peripheral resistance**, or **TPR**). Thus, we have BP = CO × TPR. The values of CO and TPR determine the pressure the blood exerts in the arterial vessels of a closed circulatory system.

Cardiac output depends on how often an animal's heart beats each minute, and how much blood it ejects with each beat. Each beat, or stroke, of the heart ejects an amount of blood known as the

Table 48.1	Comparative Features of Representative Mammalian Hearts*			
Animal	**Body mass (kg)**	**Heart mass (kg)**	**Stroke volume (L)**	**Heart rate (bpm)†**
Shrew††	0.0024 (2.4 g)	0.000035 (35 mg)	0.000008 (8 µl)	835
Rat	0.20	0.001	0.0002	360
Rabbit	2	0.012	0.0013	189
Small dog	5	0.030	0.007	120
Large dog	30	0.180	0.040	88
Human	75	0.380	0.075	70
Horse	450	3.50	0.90	38
Elephant	4,000	25	4.0	25
Blue whale	100,000	600	100	10

*Values are based on average body masses and resting conditions. In some cases, stroke volumes are estimates based on heart size.
†bpm = beats per minute.
††The shrew reported here is the Etruscan shrew, one of the smallest known mammals. Its heart is somewhat larger than would be predicted for its body mass. Note its heart rate; at 835 bpm, the heart beats 14 times per second!

stroke volume (SV), which is roughly proportional to the size of the heart (**Table 48.1**). Thus, if we know the stroke volume of a heart and can measure the heart rate (HR, the number of beats per minute, or bpm), we can determine the CO. Simply put, CO = SV × HR. As one example from Table 48.1, the CO of a blue whale is

$$100 \text{ L/beat} \times 10 \text{ beats/min} = 1,000 \text{ L/min}$$

To put that number in perspective, 1,000 L/min is roughly equivalent to 250 gal/min, or 25 ordinary fish aquaria!

Of course, the CO of a blue whale is far greater than that of a human, a dog, or a shrew. The heart of a typical shrew, for example, is the size of a small pea, whereas the heart of a blue whale is as large as a cow. Typically, heart size varies in proportion to body mass within a given class of vertebrates, with birds and mammals having larger hearts than similarly sized fishes, amphibians, or reptiles. Note in Table 48.1 that heart rate decreases as mammals get larger, but heart mass and stroke volume increase roughly in proportion with body mass. Smaller animals have smaller hearts and, therefore, smaller stroke volumes. However, small animals have faster heart rates than do large animals. A shrew's resting heart rate may be more than 800 bpm, whereas a blue whale's heart may beat only 10 times per minute (although the volume of blood ejected with each of those beats is enormous!). The faster heart rates of small animals give them a greater cardiac output than predicted from the size of their hearts, which helps them meet the extraordinary oxygen and nutrient demands of their relatively high metabolisms.

The greater the cardiac output and resistance to blood flow, the higher the blood pressure will be. Imagine that the circulatory system is like a faucet (the heart) connected to a garden hose (the arteries and arterioles) (**Figure 48.15**). If the faucet is fully open (analogous to maximal cardiac output) and the hose is not blocked (analogous to low resistance), the amount of water rushing through the hose will be high, and so will the water pressure, representing blood pressure (Figure 48.15a). If the faucet is only partially open, the water pressure will be lower

moved back and forth through the water. The ability to move external gills is particularly important for sessile invertebrates, which must otherwise rely on sporadic local water currents or muscular efforts of their bodies to create local currents for ventilation.

Despite the success of marine invertebrates, external gills have several limitations. First, they are unprotected and therefore are susceptible to damage from the environment. Second, because water is much denser than air, considerable energy is required to continually wave the gills back and forth through the water (think of the difference between waving your hand through air and waving it through water). Finally, their appearance and motion may draw the attention of predators.

Internal Gills By contrast, fishes have internal gills, which are covered by a bony plate called an operculum (**Figure 48.17a**, also refer back to Figure 35.6). Fish gills are confined within the opercular

cavity—the space beneath the operculum—which protects the gills and helps streamline the body.

The main support structures of gills are the gill arches, from which project gill filaments composed of numerous platelike structures called **lamellae** (**Figure 48.17b**). Blood vessels run the length of the filaments. Oxygen-poor blood travels through a vessel called the afferent vessel along one side of the filament, and oxygen-rich blood travels through another vessel called the efferent vessel along the other side. Within the lamellae are numerous capillaries, all oriented with blood flowing from the oxygen-poor vessel to the oxygen-rich one.

Water enters a fish's mouth and flows between the lamellae in the opposite direction from blood flowing through the lamellar capillaries. This arrangement of water and blood flow is an example of **countercurrent exchange** (refer back to Figure 47.13). As oxygenated water encounters the lamellae, it comes into close

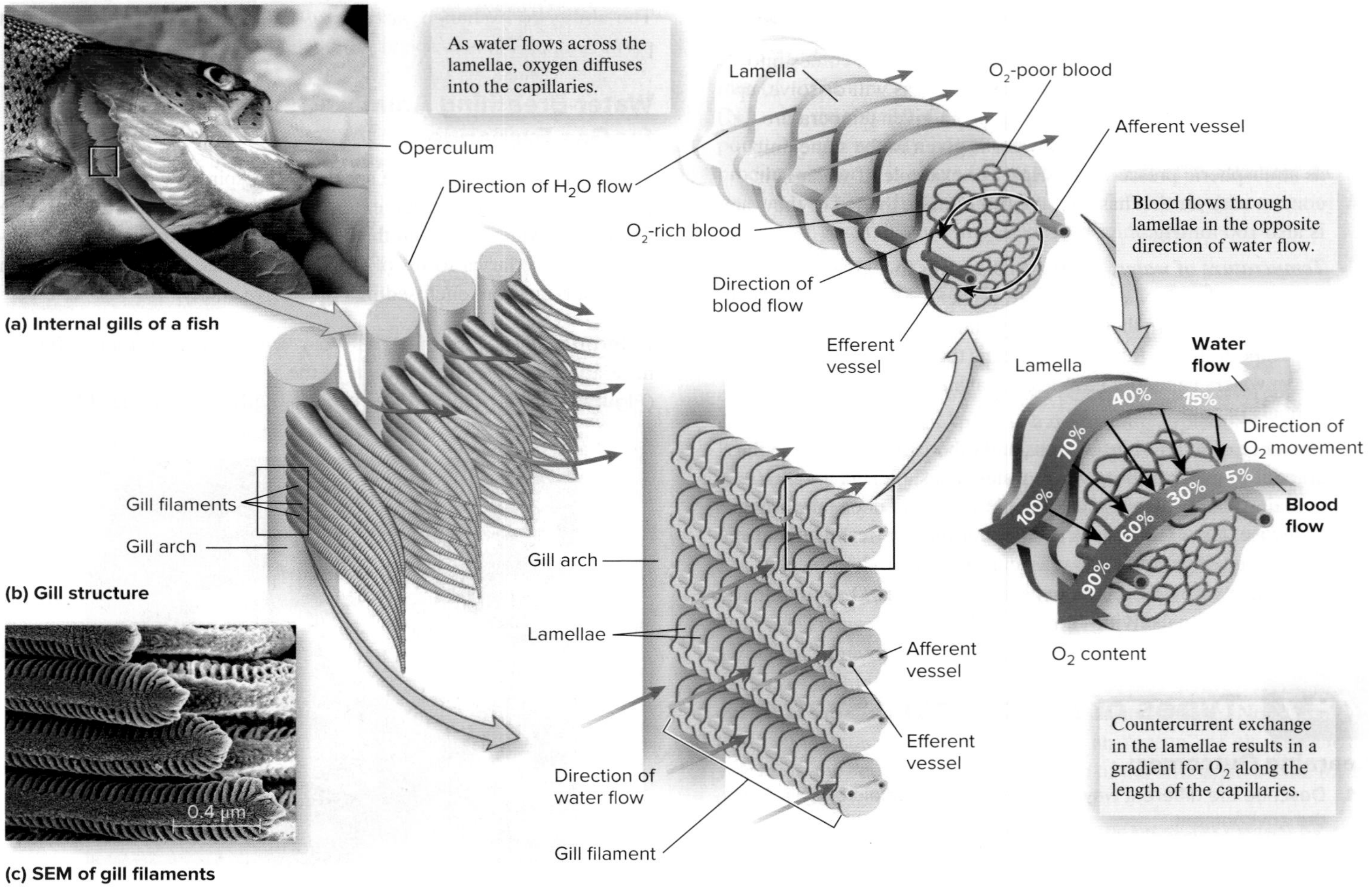

As water flows across the lamellae, oxygen diffuses into the capillaries.

Lamella

O$_2$-poor blood

(a) Internal gills of a fish

Operculum

Direction of H$_2$O flow

O$_2$-rich blood

Direction of blood flow

Afferent vessel

Blood flows through lamellae in the opposite direction of water flow.

Efferent vessel

Lamella

Water flow

Direction of O$_2$ movement

40% 15%

70%

100% 30% 5%

Blood flow

90% 60%

Gill filaments

Gill arch

(b) Gill structure

Gill arch

Lamellae

Afferent vessel

O$_2$ content

Efferent vessel

Countercurrent exchange in the lamellae results in a gradient for O$_2$ along the length of the capillaries.

Direction of water flow

Gill filament

0.4 μm

(c) SEM of gill filaments

Figure 48.17 Structure of fish gills. (a) The operculum, which has been lifted up in this photo, protects the gills underneath. **(b)** The gills are composed of gill arches, from which numerous pairs of filaments arise. Thin, platelike lamellae are arrayed along the filaments. Blood flows through the capillaries of the gill filaments in the opposite direction from water flowing between lamellae, a mechanism called countercurrent exchange. **(c)** Several filaments with their lamellae, as revealed in a scanning electron micrograph (SEM). a: ©Sarah Ahrens/Alamy Stock Photo; c: ©Electron Microscopy Unit, Royal Holloway, University of London

 Core Skill: Connections You have learned about countercurrent exchange in other contexts (for example, refer back to Figure 47.13). How does it relate to heat exchange in vertebrates?

proximity to blood in the gill capillaries. Gases such as O_2 always diffuse along a pressure gradient from a region of higher pressure to one of lower pressure. Thus, O_2 diffuses from the water into the capillaries of the lamellae. As water continues to flow across the lamellar surface, it encounters regions of capillaries that have not yet picked up O_2—in other words, even as O_2 begins to diffuse from the water into the gill capillaries, a sufficient pressure gradient remains along the lamellae to permit diffusion of more of the remaining O_2 from the water. This is an extremely efficient way to remove as much O_2 from the water as possible before the water passes out of the operculum.

Different fishes can ventilate their gills in three possible ways:

- Actively drawing water in through the mouth and out the operculum
- Swimming with the mouth open so that water continually moves across the gills
- Facing into a current of water while resting, but keeping the mouth open

Each of these ventilation mechanisms is a flow-through system—water moves only in one direction so that the gills are constantly in contact with fresh, oxygenated water. This improves gas exchange and is an important adaptation for water-breathing, considering the generally lower oxygen content of water compared to air.

Insects Use Tracheal Systems to Exchange Gases with the Air

Air-breathing probably evolved as an adaptation in aquatic animals inhabiting regions that were subject to periodic drought. One of the major mechanisms that animals evolved to breathe air is the **tracheal system** found in insects. Along the surface of an insect's body are tiny openings to the outside called **spiracles**. Arising from the spiracles are sturdy tubes called **tracheae** (singular, trachea) (**Figure 48.18**). Tracheae branch extensively into ever-smaller tubes called tracheoles, which eventually become small enough that their tips contact virtually every cell in the body. At their tips, tracheoles are filled with a small amount of fluid. Air flowing into the tracheoles comes into contact with this fluid. Oxygen from the air dissolves in the fluid, and from there it diffuses across the tracheoles and into nearby cells. Carbon dioxide diffuses in the opposite direction, from cells into the tracheoles, and from there to the environment.

When an insect's oxygen demands increase due to increased activity, muscular movements of its abdomen and thorax draw air into and out of the tracheae a little like a bellows. An insect's muscles and tracheal system match ventilation with the animal's exercise intensity and O_2 requirements. This is particularly important in flying insects, which have very great metabolic demands.

As discussed earlier, the open circulatory system of insects does not participate in gas exchange. Oxygen diffuses directly from air to trachea to tracheoles and finally to body cells. This mechanism of ventilation and O_2 delivery is very effective. The relative metabolic rate of insect flight muscles is among the highest known of any tissue

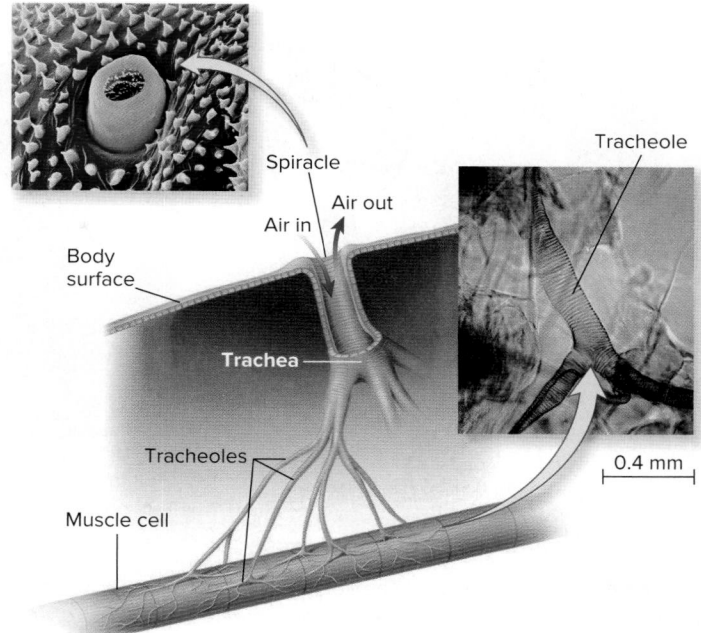

Figure 48.18 The tracheal system of insects. Air enters holes on the body surface called spiracles. Oxygen diffuses directly from the fluid-filled tracheole tips to cells that come into contact with the tips. The circulatory system plays no role in gas exchange. The micrographs show a single spiracle and a branching tracheole. (left) ©Microfield Scientific Ltd/Science Source; (right) ©Ed Reschke/Getty Images

Concept Check: *How might the structure of the respiratory system of insects be related to their relatively small size?*

in any animal, and the tracheal system supplies enough O_2 to meet those enormous demands.

Air-Breathing Vertebrates Use Lungs to Exchange Gases

Except for some amphibians such as lungless salamanders, all air-breathing terrestrial vertebrates use lungs to bring O_2 into the circulatory system and remove CO_2. **Lungs** are internal, paired structures that arise from the pharynx during embryonic life. All lungs receive deoxygenated blood from the heart and return oxygenated blood to the heart.

Most vertebrates ventilate their lungs by a process called **negative pressure filling**, in which the pressure of air in the lungs is decreased below that of the environment in order to create a pressure gradient that draws air into the lungs. Boyle's law states that the pressure and volume of a gas are inversely related (**Figure 48.19**). For example, when the volume in which a gas is contained increases, the pressure of the gas in that container decreases. By expanding its lungs (inhaling), an animal creates a pressure gradient for air to move from the atmosphere (higher pressure) into its lungs (lower pressure). When an animal exhales, the lungs become compressed, increasing the pressure of the air inside them. This increased pressure causes air to leave the lungs.

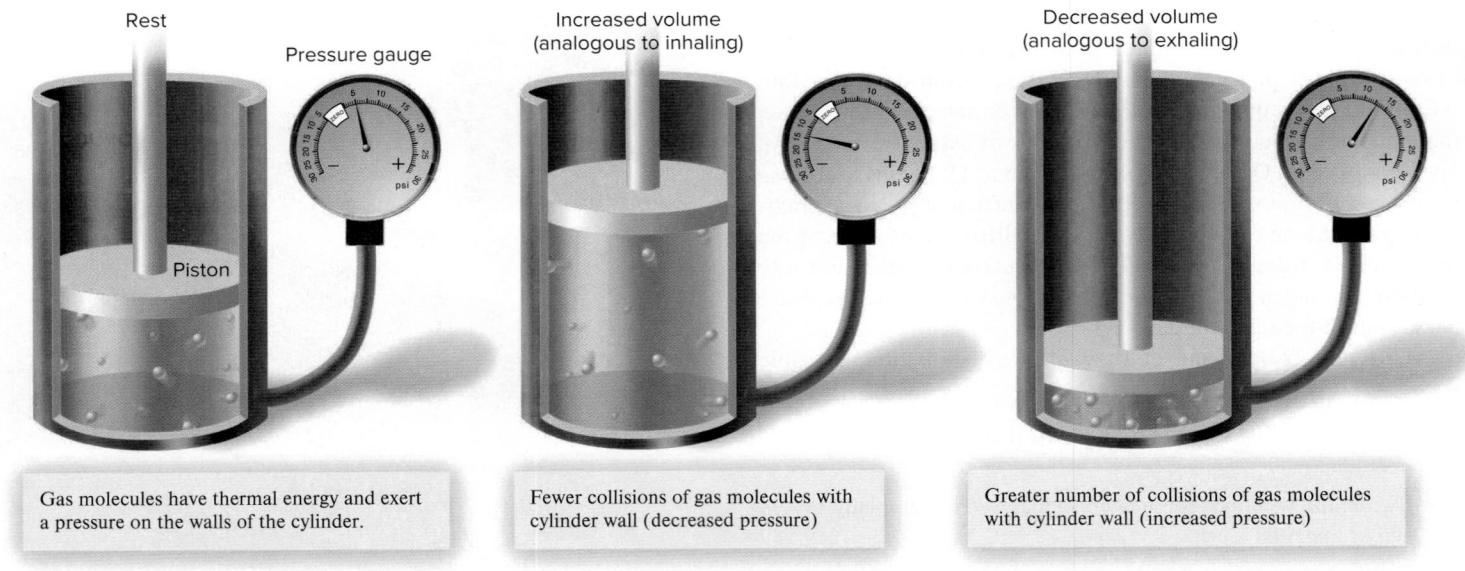

Rest	Increased volume (analogous to inhaling)	Decreased volume (analogous to exhaling)
Gas molecules have thermal energy and exert a pressure on the walls of the cylinder.	Fewer collisions of gas molecules with cylinder wall (decreased pressure)	Greater number of collisions of gas molecules with cylinder wall (increased pressure)

Pressure gauge

Piston

Figure 48.19   Boyle's law. The volume and pressure of a gas are inversely related; that is, when the volume is increased, the pressure is decreased, and vice versa. This relationship creates the gas pressure gradients that ventilate the vertebrate lungs.

Concept Check: *As lungs expand during inhalation, what happens to the pressure of the air inside them?*

48.8 Structure and Function of the Mammalian Respiratory System

Learning Outcomes:

1. Describe the components of the mammalian respiratory system and the structure of the mammalian lung.
2. Outline the process of ventilation in mammalian lungs.

In this section, we will examine in detail the structures of the mammalian respiratory system and the mechanisms by which mammals ventilate their lungs.

During Ventilation, Air Flows Through a Series of Branching Tubes

In mammals, the respiratory system includes the nose, mouth, pharynx, larynx, trachea, branching tubes, lungs, and muscles and connective tissues that encase these structures within the thoracic (chest) cavity (**Figure 48.20a**). When humans and other mammals breathe, air first enters the nose and mouth, where it is warmed and humidified. These effects protect the lungs from drying out. While in the nose, the air is partially purified as it flows over a coating of sticky mucus in the nasal cavity. The mucus and hairs in the nasal cavity trap some of the larger dust and other particles that are inhaled with air. These are then removed by the body's immune cells or swallowed.

The inhaled air from the mouth and nose converges at the back of the throat, or **pharynx**, a common passageway for air and food. From there, air passes through the **larynx**, which contains the vocal cords. Air flows from the larynx into the **trachea**, a tube that leads to the lungs.

The trachea is partially ringed by cartilage that provides rigidity and ensures that the trachea always remains open. Inhaled air flows down the trachea as it branches into two smaller tubes, called **bronchi** (singular, bronchus), which lead to each lung. The bronchi branch repeatedly into smaller and smaller tubes, eventually becoming thin-walled **bronchioles** surrounded by circular rings of smooth muscle (**Figure 48.20b**). Bronchioles can dilate or constrict in a manner analogous to that of arterioles, the small blood vessels that deliver blood to capillaries (look back at Figure 48.11).

The **alveoli** (singular, alveolus) are the saclike regions of the lungs where gas exchange occurs (**Figure 48.20c**). The alveoli are highly adapted for gas exchange and consist of two major types of cells. Gases diffuse across type I cells, whereas type II cells are secretory cells (described later). The alveoli are only one cell thick and resemble extremely thin sacs, appearing like bunches of grapes on a stem. Deoxygenated blood pumped from the right ventricle of the heart flows to the many capillaries surrounding the alveoli. Oxygen diffuses from the lumen of each alveolus across the very thin type I alveolar cells, through the interstitial space outside the cells, and into the capillaries (see Figure 48.20b). Carbon dioxide diffuses in the opposite direction. The newly oxygenated blood from the lungs then flows to the left atrium of the heart and from there enters the left ventricle, where it is pumped out through the aorta to the rest of the body.

The Pleural Sacs Protect the Lungs

The lungs are soft, delicate tissues that could easily be damaged by the surrounding bone, muscle, and connective tissue of the thorax if not protected. Each lung is encased in a **pleural sac**, a double layer of thin, moist connective tissue. Between the two layers is a microscopically thin layer of water that acts as a lubricant and makes the two tissue layers adhere to each other.

In addition to protecting the lungs, the inner pleural sac adheres to its lung, and the outer pleural sac adheres to the chest wall. In this way, movements of the chest wall result in similar movements of the lungs. This is important because the lungs are not muscular and,

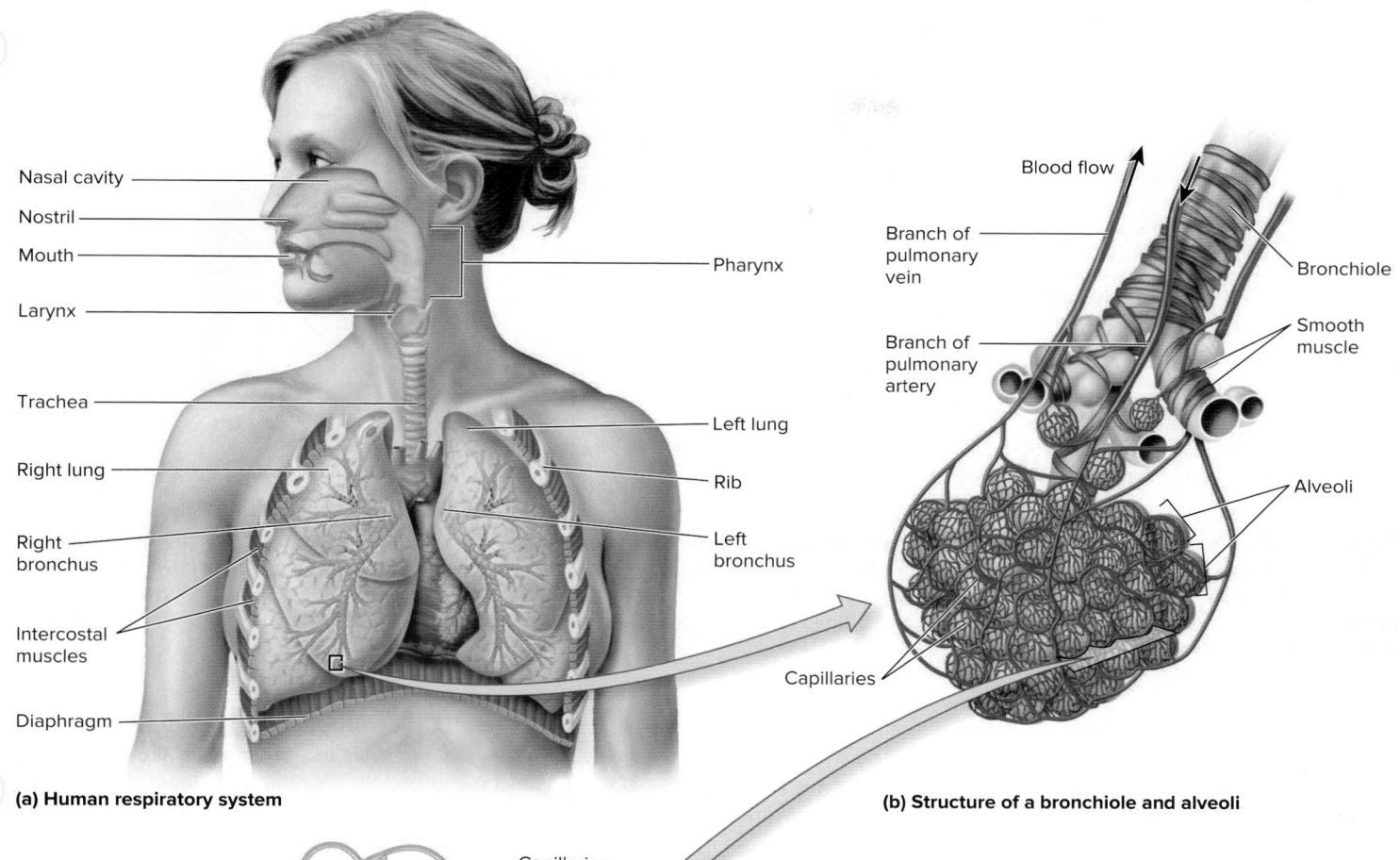

(a) Human respiratory system

Nasal cavity
Nostril
Mouth
Larynx
Trachea
Right lung
Right bronchus
Intercostal muscles
Diaphragm
Pharynx
Left lung
Rib
Left bronchus

(b) Structure of a bronchiole and alveoli

Blood flow
Branch of pulmonary vein
Branch of pulmonary artery
Bronchiole
Smooth muscle
Alveoli
Capillaries

(c) Cross section of an alveolar cluster, with enlarged region

Capillaries
Alveolus
End of one bronchiole
Direction of air flow
Alveolar air
Alveolus
Interstitium (connective tissue)
Alveolar type I cell
O_2 CO_2
Alveolar type II cell
Plasma in capillary
Erythrocyte

Figure 48.20 The mammalian respiratory system. (a) The lungs and major airways. The thoracic cavity is bounded by the ribs and intercostal muscles and the muscular diaphragm. The ribs have been partially removed to reveal underlying structures. **(b)** The bronchioles deliver air to clusters of alveoli. Smooth muscle cells around the bronchioles can cause the bronchioles to constrict (narrow) or dilate (widen). Capillaries surround the alveoli. Red represents oxygenated blood; blue represents partly deoxygenated blood. **(c)** Cross section through a cluster of alveoli. Note the single layer of alveoli cells and their close proximity to adjacent capillaries.

so, cannot inflate themselves. Instead, as we will see, the lungs are inflated by the expansion of the thoracic cavity, which results from the contraction of muscles in the thorax.

The Lungs Expand by Negative Pressure Filling

The way in which you inflate a balloon, by forcing air from your mouth into the balloon, is called positive pressure filling. Negative pressure filling, by contrast, is the mechanism by which mammals and many other vertebrates ventilate their lungs. In this process, the volume of the lungs expands, creating a decreased pressure that draws air into the lungs (see Figure 48.19). The process differs in some ways among classes of vertebrates, but in mammals, the work is provided by the intercostal muscles, which surround and connect the ribs in the chest, and a large muscle called the **diaphragm** (see Figure 48.20a), which divides the thoracic cavity from the abdomen.

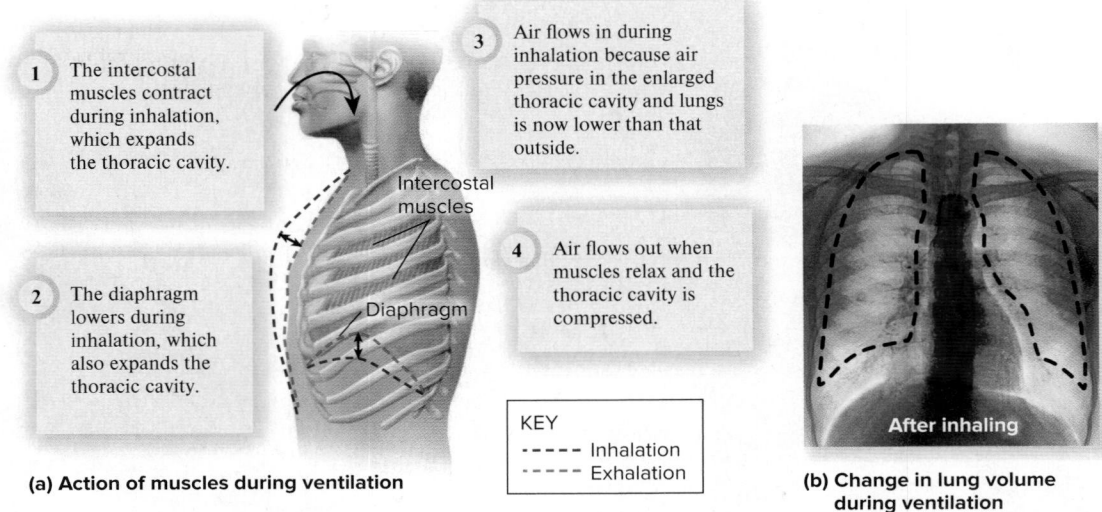

1 The intercostal muscles contract during inhalation, which expands the thoracic cavity.

2 The diaphragm lowers during inhalation, which also expands the thoracic cavity.

3 Air flows in during inhalation because air pressure in the enlarged thoracic cavity and lungs is now lower than that outside.

4 Air flows out when muscles relax and the thoracic cavity is compressed.

Intercostal muscles

Diaphragm

KEY
- - - - - Inhalation
- - - - - Exhalation

(a) Action of muscles during ventilation

After inhaling

(b) Change in lung volume during ventilation

Figure 48.21 Ventilation of the mammalian lung by negative pressure filling. (a) The intercostal muscles contract, which expands the chest cavity by moving the ribs up and out. The diaphragm also contracts, causing it to pull downward, further expanding the cavity. The muscular efforts of inhalation require energy, whereas the return to the resting state by exhaling occurs primarily by recoil. **(b)** X-ray image of the chest of an adult man after inhaling. The volume of the lungs after exhaling is superimposed using dashed lines to illustrate the relative change in lung volume. b: ©Pr. M. Brauner/Science Source

Let's follow the process when a mammal ventilates its lungs (**Figure 48.21**). At the start of a breath, the diaphragm contracts, pulling downward and enlarging the thoracic cavity. Simultaneously, the intercostal muscles contract, moving the chest upward and outward, which also helps to enlarge the thoracic cavity. Recall that the pleural sacs adhere the lungs to the chest wall, so as the chest expands, the lungs expand with it. According to Boyle's law, as the volume of the lungs increases, the pressures of the gases within them must decrease. In other words, the pressure in the lungs becomes negative with respect to the outside air. Air, therefore, flows down its pressure gradient from outside the mouth and nose, into the lungs.

Once the lungs are inflated with air, the chest muscles and diaphragm relax and recoil back to their original positions as an animal exhales. This movement compresses the lungs and forces air out of the airways. Whereas inhaling requires the expenditure of significant amounts of energy, exhaling is mostly passive and normally does not require much energy. This is possible because the lungs and chest have large numbers of elastin fibers, which, as mentioned earlier in the case of arteries, have elastic properties.

Mammals Breathe by Tidal Ventilation

When mammals exhale, air leaves via the same route that it entered during inhalation, and no new oxygen is delivered to the airways at that time. This type of breathing is called **tidal ventilation**, so named because it is like the ebb and flow of ocean tides. Tidal ventilation is less efficient than the unidirectional, flow-through system of fishes in which gills are always exposed to oxygenated water during all phases of the respiratory cycle, but is sufficient to meet the metabolic demands of terrestrial vertebrates.

As you likely know from experience, the lungs are neither fully inflated nor deflated at rest. For example, you could easily take a

larger breath than normal if you wished, or exhale more than the usual amount of air. The volume of air that is normally breathed in and out at rest is called the tidal volume, about 0.5 L in an average-sized human. Lung size and tidal volume are proportional to body size, both among humans and between species. A 6-foot-tall adult human, for example, has a larger tidal volume than a 4-foot-tall child because the adult has larger lungs. Similarly, horses have larger tidal volumes than humans, and humans have larger tidal volumes than dogs.

During exertion, the lungs can be inflated further than the resting tidal volume to provide additional oxygen. Likewise, the lungs can be deflated beyond their normal limits at rest, by exerting a strong effort during exhalation. The lungs never fully deflate, however, partly because they are held open by their adherence to the chest wall. Maintenance of partial inflation is important for a simple reason. Think again of our analogy of a balloon. It is much easier to fill a balloon that is already partly inflated than it is to inflate a completely empty balloon. The same is true of the lungs. The most difficult breath is the very first one that a newborn mammal takes—the only time its lungs are ever completely empty of air.

Surfactant Facilitates Lung Inflation by Decreasing Surface Tension

Like all cells, those that make up the lining of the alveoli are surrounded by extracellular fluid. As in the tracheoles of insects, this fluid layer is where gases dissolve. Unlike other internal body cells, however, the fluid surrounding alveolar cells comes into contact with air, creating an air/liquid interface along the inner surface of the alveoli. This results in surface tension within the alveoli.

Surface tension results from the attractive forces between water molecules at an air/liquid interface and partly explains why droplets of water form beads. This tension produces a force that tends to collapse alveoli as water molecules lining the alveolar inner surfaces are attracted to each other. If many or all of the alveoli collapsed, however, the amount of surface area available for gas exchange in the lungs would be greatly reduced. What prevents them from collapsing? The type II cells of the alveoli produce **surfactant**, a mixture of proteins and amphipathic lipids (that is, lipids with both polar and nonpolar regions), and secrete it into the alveolar lumen. Surfactant molecules dissolve in the fluid layer inside the alveoli and remain at the fluid-air interface. They are believed to increase the distance between water molecules at the fluid surface. This effect reduces surface tension in the alveolar walls, allowing them to remain open.

Surface tension is particularly important in the transition from fetal to postnatal life in mammals. Most mammalian fetuses are encased in fluid within the uterus. Consequently, their lungs do not have an air/liquid interface, and they do not start producing surfactant until the final stages of fetal development. In humans, surfactant production begins around week 26 of gestation but does not begin to approach final levels until after week 33 (normal pregnancy length is about 40 weeks). If a human baby is born prematurely (defined as prior to week 37 of gestation), sufficient surfactant may not be available, and consequently, many alveoli may collapse after birth. This condition, known as respiratory distress syndrome (RDS) of the newborn, can be partially alleviated by inserting a tube in the trachea and injecting a natural or synthetic form of surfactant. Each year in the U.S., approximately 500,000 babies are born prematurely. Of those, roughly 25,000–40,000 will be born sufficiently premature as to be diagnosed with RDS.

The discovery of surfactant and how it could be used to treat infants with RDS was among the greatest scientific achievements of the 20th century. The treatment continues to save many thousands of lives each year, as we see next.

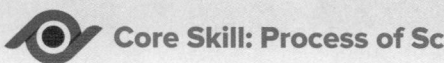

Core Skill: Process of Science

Feature Investigation | Fujiwara and Colleagues Demonstrated the Effectiveness of Administering Surfactant to Newborns with RDS

In the early part of the 20th century, researchers noted that isolated lungs from experimental animals were easier to inflate if they were first filled with fluid, which eliminated the air/liquid interface that exists in vivo. Later, investigators discovered the presence of substances in mammalian lungs (including those of humans) that had surface-active (surfactant) properties. As described earlier, surfactant is any substance that decreases surface tension in a liquid. Surfactants typically contain amphipathic molecules; that is, a portion of such a molecule is hydrophilic (soluble in water) and another portion is hydrophobic.

The hydrophilic region of a surfactant molecule dissolves in water in the alveoli fluid, while the hydrophobic region is excluded from the water and projects into the air. As mentioned, one hypothesis for how surfactants work is that by inserting themselves between water molecules at the interface between a liquid and the air, the surfactant molecules increase the distance between water molecules. Recall from Chapter 2 that each water molecule has a region of partial negative charge and another of partial positive charge. These charges produce an attractive force between water molecules. A principle of physics is that electrical forces decrease with the square of the distance between charges; thus, as surfactant increases the distance between water molecules at the surface of a liquid, the attractive forces between the water molecules decreases exponentially. This is what is meant when it is said that surface tension is decreased in the presence of surfactant.

As noted earlier, respiratory distress syndrome (RDS) is an extremely serious condition that occurs in many newborns born prematurely. In such infants, the lungs have not matured to the point that they produce sufficient amounts of surfactant to maintain a normal surface tension in the alveoli. The reason surfactant is not produced early in fetal life is there is no air/liquid interface in the fetal lungs. Instead, the lungs of fetuses are filled with amniotic fluid (the fluid in which a fetus is suspended within the uterus). Indeed, the lungs are not used for gas exchange at this time, because a fetus receives oxygen via the umbilical circulation. If a baby is born before sufficient surfactant is available, surface tension in the lungs will be too high to allow the alveoli to remain open, and they will all collapse within a few breaths of air. Recall that it is easier to inflate a balloon that is partially inflated than one that is fully deflated; in a premature infant with RDS, all of the millions of alveoli are analogous to deflated balloons. Under such conditions, it becomes impossible for a newborn to fully inflate the lungs with each breath, and he or she quickly becomes very ill. If surfactant can be administered to such babies, their chances of survival should be greatly increased because they will be better able to ventilate their lungs.

How can surfactant be administered to newborns? Prior to 1980, experiments in animals suggested that administering animal lung extracts that contained surfactant to prematurely born experimental animals improved the lung function and chances of survival of those animals. In 1980, Tetsuro Fujiwara and coworkers tested this in human newborns for the first time (**Figure 48.22**). Their hypothesis was that administering a modified form of surfactant (obtained from cows) to very premature infants with RDS would improve lung function and increase the chances that such infants would survive. Prior to the administration of surfactant, RDS was confirmed by determining the blood O_2 and CO_2 levels of the newborns. The babies were placed in ventilators with a mixture of air that was greatly enriched in O_2 during this time as part of the standard treatment for premature infants. As shown in the data in step 4 of Figure 48.22, the newborns' blood O_2 levels were lower than normal despite the oxygen-rich air they were breathing, and their CO_2 levels were also higher than normal; both measurements indicated poor lung function. The infants were then administered surfactant through a tube placed within the trachea (called an endotracheal tube). Next, their blood gases were re-examined at intervals over the next few hours. As seen in the data, the arterial P_{O_2} of each infant increased dramatically within an hour or so of surfactant administration! Other signs of improved overall health were also noted, such as heart, kidney, and gastrointestinal function (all of these organs are adversely affected when a baby has RDS and is not receiving sufficient oxygen). Within 3 hours after surfactant administration, the physicians were able to decrease the amount of oxygen supplied via the ventilator from approximately 80% to 38%, and eventually nearly to normal (which, you will recall, is 21%). In other words, by that time, the lungs of the infants were functioning almost normally, and the requirement for oxygen supplementation was greatly reduced.

Of the 12 newborns treated, 10 survived and 2 died (but from causes not directly attributable to RDS). While it is, of course, tragic that any infant failed to survive, consider that in 1979, just prior to

Figure 48.22 The pioneering study of Fujiwara and colleagues established that treatment with surfactant greatly improved the survival rate of premature infants with RDS.

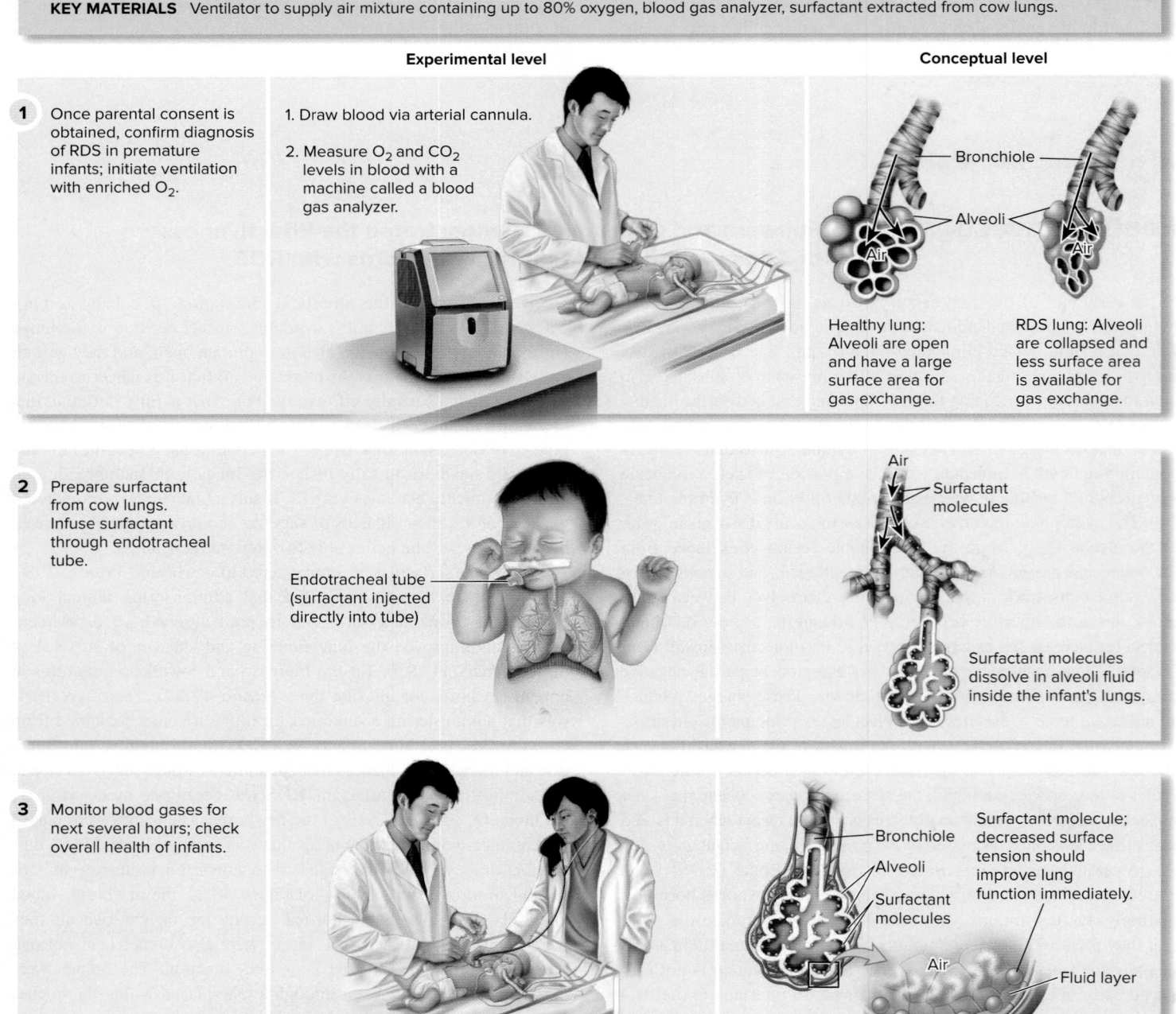

HYPOTHESIS Administration of surfactant to infants born with RDS will improve their lung function and chances for survival.

KEY MATERIALS Ventilator to supply air mixture containing up to 80% oxygen, blood gas analyzer, surfactant extracted from cow lungs.

Experimental level | Conceptual level

1 Once parental consent is obtained, confirm diagnosis of RDS in premature infants; initiate ventilation with enriched O_2.

1. Draw blood via arterial cannula.

2. Measure O_2 and CO_2 levels in blood with a machine called a blood gas analyzer.

Bronchiole

Alveoli

Air

Healthy lung: Alveoli are open and have a large surface area for gas exchange.

RDS lung: Alveoli are collapsed and less surface area is available for gas exchange.

2 Prepare surfactant from cow lungs. Infuse surfactant through endotracheal tube.

Endotracheal tube (surfactant injected directly into tube)

Air

Surfactant molecules

Surfactant molecules dissolve in alveoli fluid inside the infant's lungs.

3 Monitor blood gases for next several hours; check overall health of infants.

Bronchiole

Alveoli

Surfactant molecules

Surfactant molecule; decreased surface tension should improve lung function immediately.

Air

Fluid layer

Alveolus (portion)

4   **THE DATA**

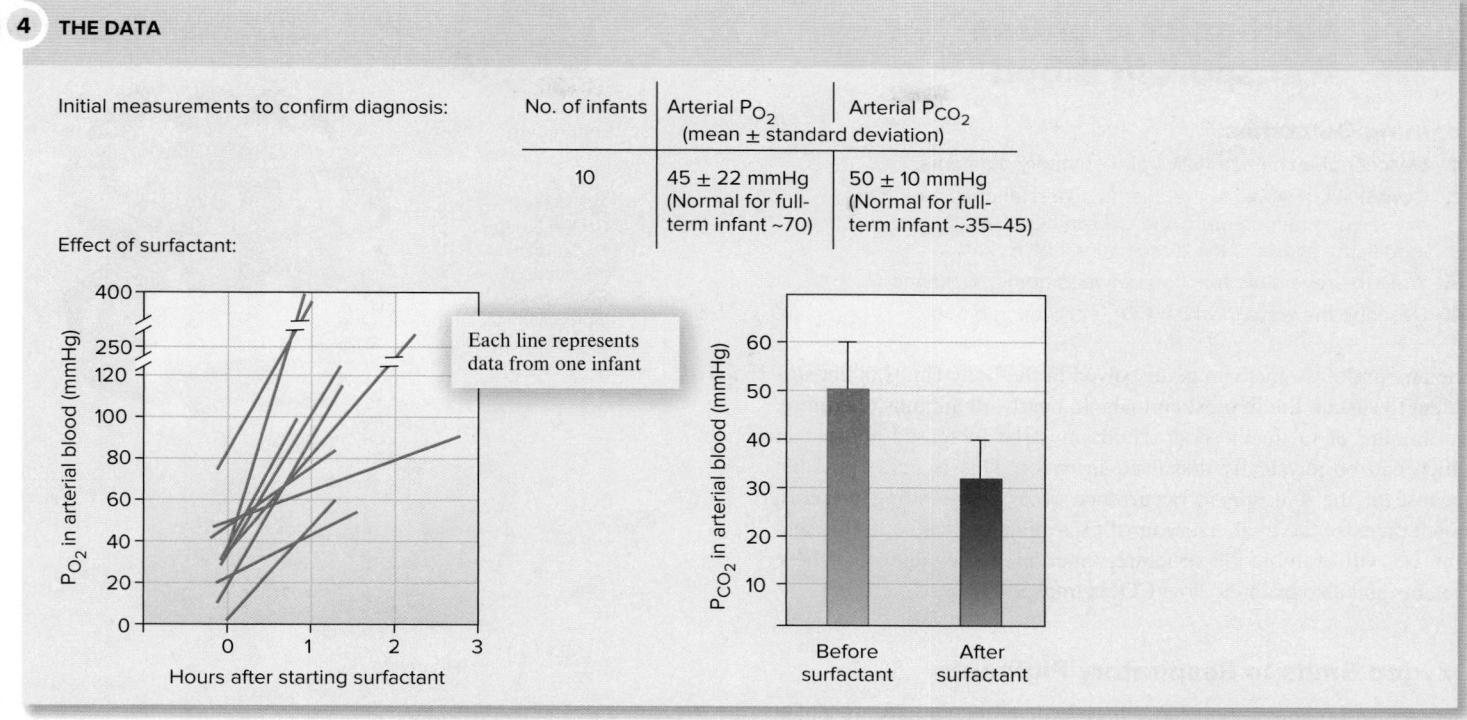

Initial measurements to confirm diagnosis:

No. of infants	Arterial P_{O_2} (mean ± standard deviation)	Arterial P_{CO_2}
10	45 ± 22 mmHg (Normal for full-term infant ~70)	50 ± 10 mmHg (Normal for full-term infant ~35–45)

Effect of surfactant:

Each line represents data from one infant

5   **CONCLUSION**   Treatment with surfactant quickly improved lung function as evidenced by greatly increased blood O_2 levels and decreased CO_2 levels, to within the normal range. Surfactant therapy improves overall health and chances for survival in premature infants.

6   **SOURCE**   Fujiwara, T. et al. 1980. Artificial surfactant therapy in hyaline-membrane disease. *The Lancet* 315: 55–59.

the advent of surfactant therapy, RDS was the second leading cause of death in infants in the U.S. Following Fujiwara's pioneering study in 1980 and subsequent improvements in the ways in which surfactant was produced and administered, RDS fell to being the fourth leading cause of death in infants by 1988, and to ninth in 2010. Prior to the 1980s, approximately 25,000 infants died from RDS in the U.S. each year. Today, despite no decrease in the number of premature births annually, fewer than 900 RDS infants do not survive. Whereas that number is still tragically high, it represents an astounding improvement, and ranks the development of the surfactant treatment among the greatest scientific achievements of modern times.

Perhaps you noticed something unusual about the experimental design in Fujiwara's study. Did you notice that there were no control groups (infants who received a vehicle solution without surfactant)? Today, the gold standard for clinical studies is a randomized control trial (RCT). However, at the time of Fujiwara's study, not all clinical experiments were controlled as they are today. In some cases, this was due to practical considerations of cost and the limited availability of subjects. In others, ethical considerations may have taken precedence, such as the immediate need to save the lives of the infants in Fujiwara's study. Nonetheless, since Fujiwara's study, the results have been replicated and expanded upon many times in

animal models and in humans using RCT protocols, and surfactant therapy is now routinely used in hospitals around the world to save countless lives.

Experimental Questions

1. **CoreSKILL** » Glucocorticoids are hormones made by the adrenal glands. They are known to stimulate surfactant production in the lungs. If a woman was told that due to complications of her pregnancy, she needed to have her baby delivered very prematurely, explain how our understanding of glucocorticoids could be used to help prevent RDS in the newborn of this woman.

2. **CoreSKILL** » Refer to the arterial blood P_{O_2} measurements for the newborns in Fujiwara's study. A normal, healthy oxygen level in a full-term (not premature) newborn is about 70 mmHg (for various reasons, this is lower than in adults). Did some of the infants in Fujiwara's study have oxygen levels much greater than 70 mmHg after surfactant therapy? Why might this be? (Hint: How were the babies treated in addition to receiving surfactant?)

3. **CoreSKILL** » Prior to treatment, arterial blood P_{O_2} levels in the newborns in this study were very low. Propose a hypothesis to explain why the newborns' blood P_{CO_2} levels were higher than normal.

48.9 Mechanisms of Gas Transport in Blood

Learning Outcomes:

1. Describe the characteristics of respiratory pigments.
2. **CoreSKILL »** Analyze the quantitative relationship between oxygen and hemoglobin, and explain how certain factors can modify the shape of the dissociation curve.
3. Write the reversible reaction between hemoglobin and O_2.
4. Describe the ways in which CO_2 is carried in blood.

The amount of O_2 that can be dissolved in the body fluids is not sufficient to sustain life in most animals. In nearly all animals, therefore, the amount of O_2 in the body fluids must be increased above that which can be physically dissolved in water. This is made possible because of the widespread occurrence of oxygen-binding proteins, which increase the total reservoir of O_2 available to cells. In this section, we will examine the structure, function, and evolution of these proteins and also examine how CO_2 is transported.

Oxygen Binds to Respiratory Pigments

The oxygen-binding proteins that have evolved in animals are called **respiratory pigments** because they have a color (blue or red). In vertebrates, the pigments are contained within erythrocytes, whereas many invertebrates have these pigments in their hemolymph. Respiratory pigments are proteins containing one or more metal atoms that bind to oxygen. In vertebrates and many marine invertebrates, the metal is typically iron (Fe^{2+}). As mentioned earlier, hemoglobin is the major iron-containing pigment and gives blood its red color. In decapod crustaceans, arachnids, and many mollusks, the metal is copper (Cu^{2+}). The copper-containing pigment **hemocyanin** gives the blood or hemolymph a bluish tint.

Hemoglobin gets its name because it is a globular protein—which refers to the shape and water solubility of a protein—and because it contains a chemical group called a heme in its core. An atom of iron is bound within the heme group. In vertebrates, hemoglobin consists of four polypeptide subunits, each with its own heme and iron atom to which a molecule of O_2 can bind. Thus, a single hemoglobin protein can bind up to four molecules of oxygen (**Figure 48.23**).

Respiratory pigments such as hemoglobin share certain characteristics that make them ideal for transporting O_2. First, they all have a high affinity for O_2. Second, the binding between the pigment and O_2 is noncovalent and reversible. The reversibility of O_2 binding allows respiratory pigments to unload O_2 to cells that require it. The reaction that describes the reversible binding of O_2 to hemoglobin (Hb) is

$$Hb + O_2 \rightleftharpoons HbO_2$$

where HbO_2 is oxyhemoglobin (hemoglobin with bound O_2), and the double arrows ($\rightleftharpoons$) indicate that the reaction is reversible.

The amount of pigment present in the blood is sufficient to provide enough O_2 to meet most oxygen demands, except for those that occur during the most strenuous exertion. In humans, for example, the presence of hemoglobin gives blood about 45 times more O_2-carrying capacity than plasma alone would have.

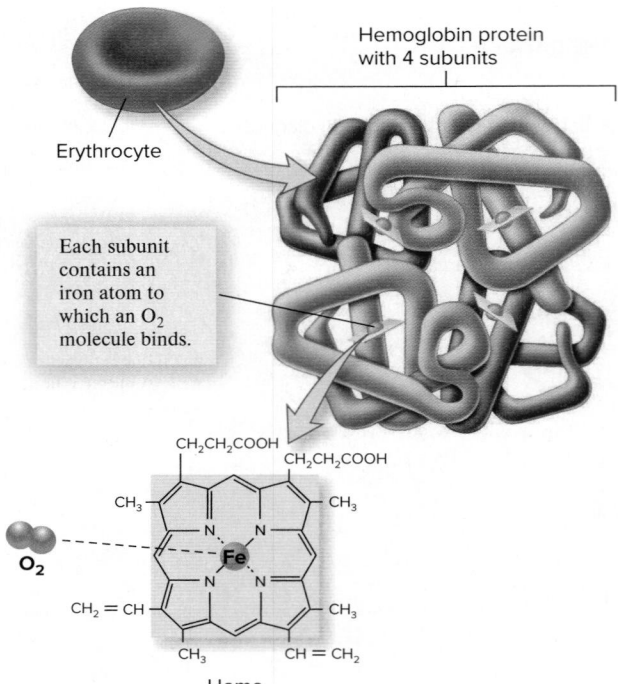

Figure 48.23 Hemoglobin. Erythrocytes contain large amounts of the protein hemoglobin. Oxygen binds reversibly to iron atoms in the heme portion of each subunit of hemoglobin.

 Core Concept: Structure and Function The precise quaternary structure of hemoglobin permits its association with heme groups, which contain the iron atoms that bind oxygen molecules.

The Amount of Oxygen Bound to Hemoglobin Depends on the P_{O_2} of Blood

The partial pressure of O_2 (P_{O_2}) in blood is a measure of its dissolved concentration. When P_{O_2} is high, more O_2 binds to hemoglobin, whereas fewer O_2 molecules will be bound when P_{O_2} is low. **Figure 48.24** shows the relationship between O_2 binding and P_{O_2}, known as an **oxygen-hemoglobin dissociation curve**, for humans. At a P_{O_2} of 100 mmHg, which is typical of the oxygenated blood leaving the lungs, nearly every hemoglobin molecule is bound to four O_2 molecules (at the far right in the graph). Under these conditions, hemoglobin is nearly 100% saturated with O_2. The P_{O_2} of blood leaving the tissue capillaries of other parts of the body is lower and depends on metabolic activity. At rest, the average P_{O_2} of blood capillaries in these other parts of the body is typically around 40 mmHg. At this P_{O_2}, hemoglobin releases some O_2 molecules, decreasing to about 75% saturation with O_2. During strenuous exercise, P_{O_2} in the capillaries drops even further (as low as 20 mmHg). Consequently, during exercise hemoglobin releases even more O_2 and becomes less saturated. In this way, hemoglobin performs its role of O_2 delivery. In the lungs, it binds O_2, and elsewhere it releases O_2 as required.

The curve in Figure 48.24 is not linear but S-shaped (sigmoidal). This shape results because the subunits of hemoglobin cooperate with each other in binding O_2. Once a molecule of O_2 binds to one subunit's iron atom, the shape of the entire hemoglobin protein changes,

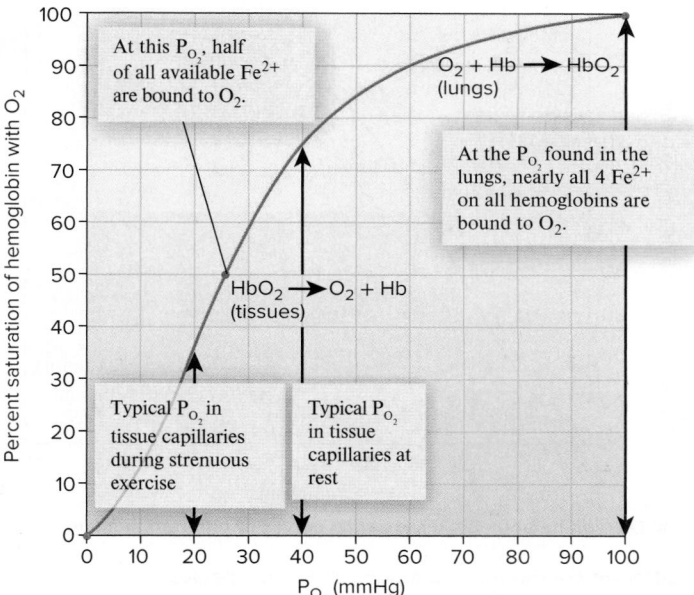

Figure 48.24   The human oxygen-hemoglobin dissociation curve. Depending on the partial pressure of oxygen (P_{O_2}), oxygen is either loaded onto hemoglobin, as in the lungs, or unloaded from hemoglobin, as in the rest of the body tissues. When P_{O_2} is high, more Fe^{2+} ions are bound to O_2, and therefore the hemoglobin is more saturated with O_2.

making it easier for a second O_2 to bind to the next subunit, and so on. Thus, the relationship between P_{O_2} and the amount of O_2 bound to hemoglobin becomes very steep in the portion of the curve that represents the pressures that occur in the tissue capillaries throughout the body. This steepness allows O_2 release from hemoglobin to be very sensitive to even small decreases in P_{O_2} generated by the diffusion of O_2 from capillaries to cells. To visualize this, follow the curve from right to left and see how hemoglobin saturation decreases as oxygen pressure decreases. In the other direction, the curve levels off at high oxygen pressures as 100% saturation is approached.

The Affinity of Hemoglobin for Oxygen Is Decreased by Factors Such as Temperature, CO_2, and pH

One of the remarkable features of the oxygen-hemoglobin binding relationship is that it is influenced by metabolic waste products such as CO_2 and H^+ and by heat (temperature). **Figure 48.25a** shows three curves, one obtained under normal resting conditions and the others in the presence of low or high levels of CO_2. Carbon dioxide binds to amino acids in the hemoglobin protein (not to the iron, as O_2 does), and when it does, it decreases the affinity of the hemoglobin for O_2. This is an example of allosteric regulation, as described in Chapter 6 (look back at Figure 6.7c). Note how an increase in CO_2 shifts the curve to the right, such that at any P_{O_2}, less O_2 is bound to hemoglobin. Another way of saying this is that at any P_{O_2}, more O_2 has been released from hemoglobin, thus becoming available to cells.

A similar shift in the curve occurs with an increase in acidity (increased H^+ concentration), because H^+ can also bind to hemoglobin

and alter its oxygen-carrying capacity; the effect of CO_2 and H^+ on the oxygen-hemoglobin dissociation curve is known as the **Bohr effect**. Elevated temperature also reduces the affinity of hemoglobin for O_2, resulting in a right-shifted curve.

Cells generate each of these products—CO_2, H^+, and heat—when they are actively metabolizing nutrients such as glucose. The metabolic products enter the surrounding capillaries and diffuse into erythrocytes, where they alter the shape of hemoglobin, causing it to release more of its O_2 than would normally occur at that P_{O_2}. This phenomenon is a way in which individual body tissues obtain more O_2 from the blood to match their higher metabolic demands. Thus, when an animal increases its physical activity, the skeletal muscles generate more CO_2, H^+, and heat than do some other tissues. Therefore, the hemoglobin in muscle capillaries releases more O_2 to muscle cells compared to the hemoglobin in the capillaries of these other tissues.

The shift in the oxygen-hemoglobin dissociation curve occurs in all classes of vertebrates (although not in all species), but it has different magnitudes in different species. Not surprisingly, perhaps, animals with relatively high metabolic rates, such as mice, show a greater Bohr effect than do animals with lower relative metabolic rates. Recall that these same waste products of metabolism also cause local vasodilation of arterioles. The more metabolically active a tissue is, therefore, the more blood flow it receives, which means more oxygen-bound hemoglobin. Moreover, the oxygen is unloaded from hemoglobin more readily due to the shift in the curve. This is an excellent example of how adaptive changes in circulatory and respiratory functions often are complementary.

Regardless of their sensitivity to CO_2 and other factors, the hemoglobins of metabolically active animals also have a lower affinity for oxygen (**Figure 48.25b**) even in the absence of a greater than normal amount of CO_2, H^+, and heat. In small, active animals, the curves are displaced to the right relative to the human curve (in other words, the hemoglobin P_{50} value is higher in small animals than it is in larger animals with lower relative metabolic rates). In contrast, larger animals with slower relative metabolic rates, such as the elephant, have curves shifted to the left compared with that of humans.

At high oxygen pressures, such as those that occur in the lungs, these shifts have little relevance because nearly all the hemoglobin is bound to oxygen at those pressures. At lower P_{O_2}, however, such as those that would occur in the capillaries of metabolically active tissues, the difference in the curves becomes significant. For example, look at the three curves at a P_{O_2} of 40 mmHg, a typical value found in tissues that are using oxygen at a resting rate. The mouse hemoglobin has less oxygen bound (its hemoglobin is less saturated) at that pressure than does the human hemoglobin, which in turn has less O_2 bound than does the elephant hemoglobin. In other words, the mouse hemoglobin has released more of its O_2 to the active tissues than have the other animal hemoglobins. The different properties of hemoglobin among species result from changes in the sequence of hemoglobin, the result of numerous evolutionary changes in the genes encoding hemoglobin subunits in vertebrates.

Carbon Dioxide Is Transported in the Blood in Three Forms

As with oxygen, only a limited amount of CO_2 physically dissolves in blood. An additional amount of CO_2 is carried bound to hemoglobin,

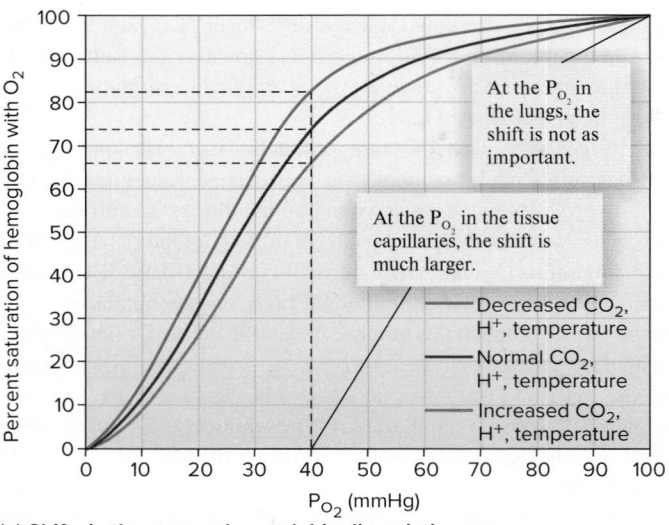

(a) Shifts in the oxygen-hemoglobin dissociation curve

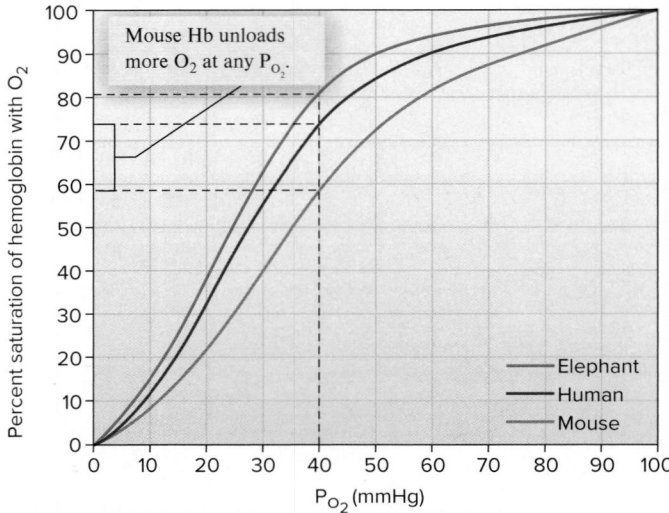

(b) Oxygen-hemoglobin dissociation curves of different animals

Figure 48.25 **Changes in oxygen-hemoglobin dissociation curves under different conditions and among different species.**
(a) Increasing or decreasing the amounts of CO_2 or H^+ (pH) and the temperature of the blood shifts the oxygen-hemoglobin dissociation curve. Metabolically active tissues generate more of these products, including heat. The change in affinity of hemoglobin for oxygen (O_2) allows different tissues to obtain O_2 in proportion to their metabolic requirements. **(b)** Oxygen-hemoglobin dissociation curves for three mammals with low (elephant), moderate (human), or high (mouse) relative metabolic rates. For any P_{O_2}, such as the one selected in the graph (40 mmHg), which is typical of the P_{O_2} of tissue capillaries, less O_2 is bound to mouse hemoglobin than to human or elephant hemoglobin, and less O_2 is bound to human hemoglobin than to elephant hemoglobin. Therefore, O_2 is unloaded from hemoglobin more readily in smaller animals.

Concept Check: *What would happen to the position of the middle curve in Figure 48.25a following infusion of an alkaline compound such as bicarbonate ions (HCO_3^-) into the blood of a resting, healthy individual?*

as noted earlier. The majority of CO_2, however, is converted into highly soluble bicarbonate ions (HCO_3^-). This conversion is achieved by the following reactions, where H_2CO_3 is a short-lived compound called carbonic acid that immediately dissociates to an H^+ and an HCO_3^-:

$$CO_2 + H_2O \rightleftharpoons H_2CO_3 \rightleftharpoons H^+ + HCO_3^-$$

Note that one H^+ is formed for every CO_2 that enters this reaction. The resulting pH change is part of what makes CO_2 a dangerous waste product, because the activities of most enzymes in an animal's body are very sensitive to changes in pH.

These reactions are readily reversible. The first step is catalyzed in both directions by the enzyme carbonic anhydrase, which is present in high amounts in erythrocytes. As you learned in Chapter 2, the concentrations of reactants and products affect the rate of a chemical reaction. For example, as tissues release CO_2 into capillaries, the forward reaction (from left to right, as written here) will be favored, and the pH of the blood will decrease because the concentration of H^+ will increase. Conversely, when CO_2 diffuses out of lung capillaries and is exhaled, the reactions will proceed from right to left, and the pH of the blood will increase as H^+ combines with HCO_3^-.

48.10 Control of Ventilation

Learning Outcome:

1. Describe the role of respiratory centers and chemoreceptors in the regulation of ventilation.

In the previous sections, we examined different ways that animals ventilate their respiratory organs. Now let's look at how the mechanisms

of breathing are controlled in mammals. Unlike the heart, lungs are neither muscles nor electrically excitable tissue. Therefore, they cannot initiate or regulate their own expansion. Nonetheless, lungs require a mechanism to rhythmically expand and recoil because animals cannot consciously control breathing at all times; for example, such control cannot be maintained during sleep. In this section, we examine the ways in which the nervous system and chemoreceptors control ventilation in mammals.

The Nervous System Contains the Control Center for Ventilation

The control center that initiates rhythmic expansion of the lungs is a collection of nuclei in the central nervous system. In mammals, these **respiratory centers** are located in the pons and medulla oblongata of the brainstem (**Figure 48.26**). Neurons within these regions rhythmically generate action potentials, somewhat analogously to the way the SA node of the heart generates a rhythm. These electrical signals travel from the brainstem through two sets of nerves. The first set stimulates the intercostal muscles, and the second set stimulates the diaphragm. When the lungs expand in response to the contraction of these muscles, stretch-sensitive neurons in the lungs and chest send signals to the respiratory centers, informing them that the lungs are inflated. The respiratory centers then temporarily turn off the stimulating signals until the animal exhales, whereupon new signals are sent to the breathing muscles.

Although the brainstem automatically generates a steady rhythm of breathing, it can be modified or overridden. For example, animals that dive underwater—including humans when we swim—can

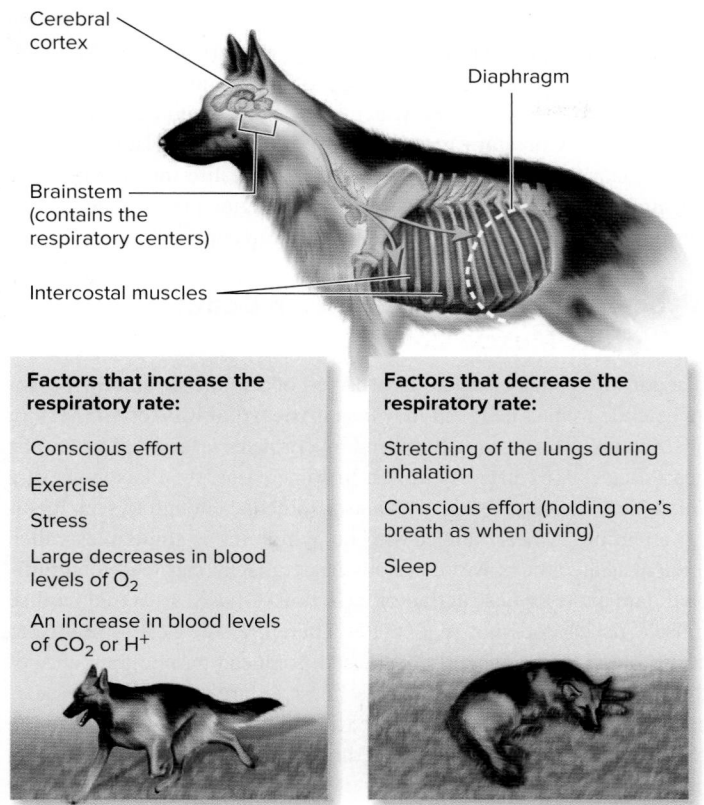

Factors that increase the respiratory rate:

Conscious effort

Exercise

Stress

Large decreases in blood levels of O_2

An increase in blood levels of CO_2 or H^+

Factors that decrease the respiratory rate:

Stretching of the lungs during inhalation

Conscious effort (holding one's breath as when diving)

Sleep

Figure 48.26 The control of breathing via respiratory centers in the mammalian brain. Neurons in the brainstem send action potentials along neurons in nerves that stimulate the intercostal muscles and diaphragm. The factors listed here can modulate the rate at which action potentials are generated and therefore the respiratory rate.

 Core Skill: Connections The brainstem of vertebrates was described in Chapter 43. What parts of the mammalian brain comprise the brainstem?

temporarily hold their breath. The respiratory centers decrease their activity during sleep and increase it during stress. In addition, increased breathing occurs in response to physical activity. At such times, a variety of neural, endocrine and metabolic factors converge on the respiratory centers to increase the rate of signals to the breathing muscles, resulting in faster and deeper breaths.

As with cardiovascular systems, respiratory activity varies with body mass, as seen for mammals in **Table 48.2**. Comparing Tables 48.1 and 48.2, we can see that in mammals, circulatory and respiratory systems evolved similarly with respect to the metabolic demands of animals of different body mass. Smaller animals have proportionally smaller lungs (as evidenced by tidal volumes) and hearts than do larger animals, but they have faster breathing rates and heart rates. These adaptations allow smaller animals to deliver oxygen to tissues at a rate sufficient for their relatively high metabolic demands.

Chemoreceptors Modulate the Activity of the Respiratory Centers

The respiratory centers are influenced by the partial pressures of oxygen and carbon dioxide in the arteries, as well as the concentration

Table 48.2	Respiratory Characteristics of Representative Mammals*			
Animal	Body mass (kg)	Tidal volume (L)	Breaths/min	P_{50} value
Shrew	0.0024	0.00003	700	37
Rat	0.20	0.0016	85	35
Dog	25	0.27	20	29
Human	75	0.50	12	26
Horse	450	6.50	9	24

*Note: All values are averages from resting animals. Tidal volume is the volume of air breathed in with each breath. Note that tidal volume increases as an animal's mass (and therefore lung size) increases. By contrast, breathing rate is higher in smaller animals. Similar relationships occur in other vertebrates, notably birds. The P_{50} value is the oxygen pressure at which an animal's hemoglobin is 50% saturated with O_2. Higher P_{50} values correspond to lower affinities of hemoglobin for O_2 (in other words, animals with high P_{50} values unload O_2 from hemoglobin more readily than do animals with low P_{50} values; see Figure 48.25).

of hydrogen ions (in other words, the pH of the blood). Recall from Chapter 44 that chemoreceptors recognize specific chemicals in the air, water, body fluids, or food. Chemoreceptors located in the aorta, carotid arteries, and the brainstem detect the circulating levels of O_2, CO_2, and H^+ and relay that information through nerves or interneurons to the respiratory centers.

If the arterial P_{O_2} decreases well below normal, as might occur at high altitude or in certain respiratory diseases, the chemoreceptors signal the respiratory centers to increase the rate and depth of breathing to increase ventilation of the lungs. The increase in ventilation brings more oxygen into the blood. Similarly, a buildup of CO_2 in the blood, which would occur if an animal's ventilation were lower than normal (again, often the result of respiratory disease), signals the respiratory centers to stimulate breathing. The increased ventilation not only brings in more O_2, but also helps eliminate more CO_2. Finally, an increased concentration of H^+ in the blood (such as during physical activity) activates chemoreceptors that signal the brain that the blood is too acidic. These signals lead to an increase in the rate of breathing, which eliminates additional CO_2, thereby allowing more H^+ to bind to HCO_3^-.

48.11 Impact on Public Health

Learning Outcomes:

1. Define hypertension and atherosclerosis, and explain their impacts on human health.
2. List the causes, symptoms, and current medical treatments for myocardial infarction (MI), or heart attack.
3. Outline the causes, symptoms, and current treatments of asthma.
4. Discuss the impact of smoking tobacco on respiratory health.

Diseases of the heart and blood vessels account for more deaths each year in the U.S. than any other cause. Why is cardiovascular disease so devastating? One reason is that damage to structures of the circulatory system often occurs slowly, over many years, and without warning symptoms until the disease has reached late stages. Cardiovascular disease not only has a dramatic impact on the health of many Americans but also has a staggering impact on the economy, including expenditures for health-care services, medications, and lost productivity.

Respiratory diseases of all kinds (including lung cancer) afflict as many as 10% of the U.S. population and result in an estimated 300,000–400,000 deaths per year, making lung disease among the top three causes of death in the U.S. The economic impact of respiratory diseases on the U.S. economy is immense, with recent estimates of up to $150 billion per year in health-related costs and lost productivity. Many of these diseases are chronic—once they appear, they last for the rest of a person's life. Lifestyle factors, such as smoking tobacco and exposure to air pollution, cause some respiratory disorders or make existing conditions worse. In this section, we will examine the nature and some common causes of cardiovascular and respiratory diseases in humans.

Hypertension and Atherosclerosis Contribute to Heart and Blood Vessel Disease

Hypertension, or high blood pressure, refers to an arterial blood pressure that is chronically above normal. The normal range of blood pressure in healthy humans varies from about 90/60 to 120/80 mmHg. Values above 120/80 mmHg are considered elevated, and a resting blood pressure of 140/90 mmHg or higher indicates hypertension. Many researchers and physicians today believe that the threshold for defining hypertension should even be lower. Hypertension has many causes, including obesity, smoking, aging, kidney disease, excess male hormones, and genetic factors, although in many cases, the cause is unknown. It can often be treated with diet and exercise and with drugs that cause vasodilation, thereby reducing total peripheral resistance.

Hypertension rarely has any noticeable symptoms, which is why it is often referred to as a "silent killer." For this reason, it is important to have blood pressure checked regularly. Without treatment, hypertension can damage arteries, contributing to the formation of **plaques**—accumulations of lipids, fibrous tissue, and smooth muscle cells—along the inner surfaces of arterial walls. Plaques may lead to **atherosclerosis**, in which plaques cause the arteries to narrow and harden (**Figure 48.27**). Large plaques may occlude (block) the lumen of an artery entirely. Arterial plaques may arise from a variety of factors in addition to hypertension, including calcium and fat deposits, and are also correlated with obesity, high blood cholesterol concentrations, and smoking.

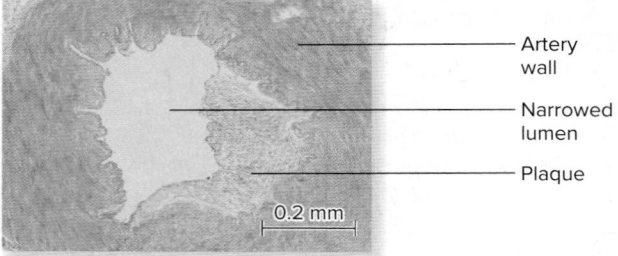

Artery wall

Narrowed lumen

Plaque

0.2 mm

Figure 48.27 An atherosclerotic plaque in a small artery. Compare this with the image of a healthy artery shown in Figure 48.11b. ©Biophoto Associates/SPL/Science Source

 Core Skill: Science and Society Heart and blood vessel disease are the leading killers among adults in the U.S. Intensive research into the causes of atherosclerosis has helped educate people about behaviors that increase the risk of this disease, such as smoking.

If plaques occlude an artery, the regions of the body supplied with blood by that artery receive less oxygen and nutrients. Although atherosclerosis is dangerous anywhere, it is especially significant if it affects the coronary arteries, which carry oxygen and nutrients to the heart muscle. **Coronary artery disease** occurs when plaques form in the coronary vessels—a condition that can be life-threatening. One warning sign of coronary artery disease is angina pectoris, chest pain during exertion due to the heart muscle being deprived of oxygen.

Myocardial Infarction Results in Death of Cardiac Muscle Cells

If a portion of heart muscle is deprived of its normal blood flow for an extended time, the result may be a **myocardial infarction (MI)**, or heart attack. This is usually caused by coronary artery disease. Some heart attacks are relatively minor. In some cases, the discomfort of a small heart attack may not even alarm someone enough to seek medical attention. A heart attack with no symptoms is sometimes called a silent heart attack. More serious heart attacks can lead to significant damage to or destruction of a portion of the heart. Dead cardiac muscle tissue does not regenerate. Therefore, the heart's ability to pump blood is permanently decreased. Reduced pumping activity of the heart can result in congestive heart failure, in which the heart cannot pump enough blood to meet the body's needs. As noted in the chapter introduction, each year in the U.S. between 1 and 1.5 million people suffer a heart attack, many of which are fatal.

Preventing a heart attack from occurring at all is obviously the best strategy for long-term health. Procedures are available that allow physicians to monitor the status of the coronary vessels in people thought to have heart disease. In the procedure called **cardiac angiography**, the coronary arteries can be visualized by injecting a dye into a person's veins and then taking an X-ray image of the chest (see the chapter opening image). The resulting image helps a physician determine if the vessels are narrowed by disease.

If a blockage is found, several common treatments can restore blood flow through a coronary artery. One is **balloon angioplasty**, in which a thin tube with a tiny, inflatable balloon at its tip is threaded through the artery to the diseased area. Inflating the balloon compresses the plaque against the arterial wall, widening the lumen. In most cases, a wire-mesh device called a stent is inserted into the artery after angioplasty has expanded it, providing a sort of lattice to hold the artery open (**Figure 48.28**). A treatment for more serious coronary artery disease is a **coronary artery bypass**, in which a small piece of healthy blood vessel is removed from one part of the body and surgically grafted onto the coronary circulation in such a way that blood bypasses the diseased region of the unhealthy artery.

Asthma Is a Disease of Hyperreactive Bronchioles

We saw previously that bronchioles resemble arterioles in that both are thin tubes with circular rings of smooth muscles that can relax or contract. In the disease **asthma**, however, the smooth muscles of the bronchioles are hyper-reactive to many stimuli and contract more than usual (**Figure 48.29**). Contraction of these muscles narrows the bronchioles, causing bronchoconstriction. This constriction makes it difficult to move air into and out of the lungs, because resistance to airflow increases when the diameter of the airways decreases

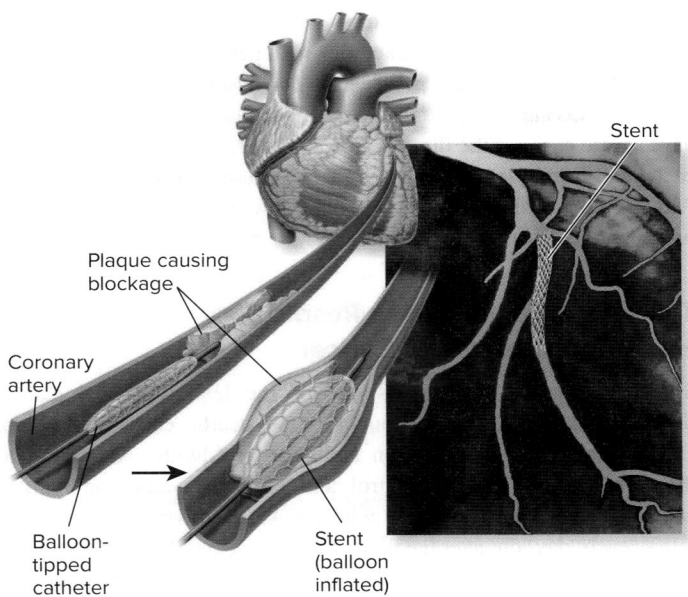

Figure 48.28 **A treatment for blocked blood vessels.** Balloon angioplasty can widen diseased arteries, followed by insertion of a stent. The inset shows a stent placed in a coronary artery of a human patient. *(inset)* ©Sovereign/ISM/Phototake

 Core Skill: Science and Society Biologists investigating the mechanisms of blood flow, heart function, and blood pressure in animals can use that knowledge to develop treatments for heart disease in humans.

(analogous to what you learned earlier about blood vessels). Often, the resistance to airflow can be so great that the movement of air creates a characteristic wheezing sound.

Asthma tends to run in families and therefore likely has a genetic basis in many individuals with the disease. Several known triggers can elicit bronchoconstriction, including exercise, cold air, and allergic reactions. The last of these—allergic reactions—is of interest because asthma is believed to be partly the result of an imbalance in the immune system, which controls inflammation and other allergic responses. During flareups of asthma, inflammation results in the secretion of a viscous, mucus-like fluid into the lumen of bronchioles and other airway tubes. This fluid inhibits airflow and worsens symptoms.

The symptoms of asthma can be alleviated by inhaling an aerosol mist containing **bronchodilators**, compounds that bind to receptors located on the plasma membranes of smooth muscle cells of bronchioles. These compounds, which are related to the neurotransmitter norepinephrine, cause bronchiolar smooth muscle cells to relax. This, in turn, allows the bronchioles to dilate (widen). To help reduce the inflammation of the lungs, the medication may also contain an adrenocortical steroid hormone with anti-inflammatory actions. Currently, there is no cure for asthma, but with regular treatment and the avoidance of known triggers, most people with this disease lead normal lives with only few restrictions.

Emphysema Causes Permanent Lung Damage

Unlike asthma, in which the major problems are periodically inflamed airways and hyper-reactive bronchioles, **emphysema** is a progressive disease that involves extensive lung damage (**Figure 48.30**).

Figure 48.29 **Comparison of healthy and asthmatic bronchioles in a human.**

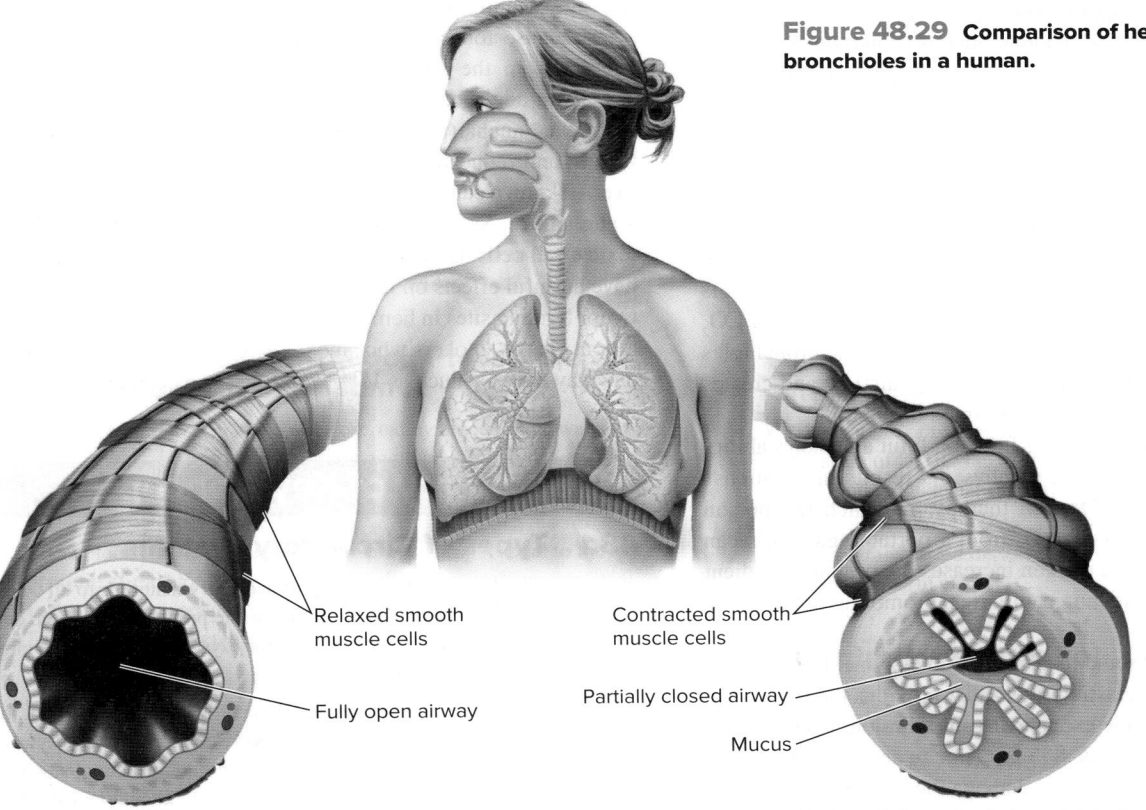

Relaxed smooth muscle cells

Fully open airway

Contracted smooth muscle cells

Partially closed airway

Mucus

Healthy bronchiole

Asthmatic bronchiole (constricted)

48.11 Impact on Public Health

- Cardiovascular disease accounts for more deaths each year in the U.S. than any other cause. Cardiovascular disorders include hypertension, atherosclerosis, coronary artery disease, angina pectoris, and myocardial infarction (heart attack) (Figure 48.27).

- Cardiovascular diagnostic techniques and treatments include cardiac angiography, balloon angioplasty, and coronary artery bypass (Figure 48.28).

- In asthma, the muscles of the bronchioles contract more than usual, increasing resistance to airflow (Figure 48.29).

- Smoking tobacco products is one of the leading global causes of death. Smoking is strongly linked to cancer, cardiovascular disease, stroke, and emphysema, in which lung tissues are severely damaged (Figure 48.30).

Assess & Discuss

Test Yourself

1. Hemolymph differs from blood in that it
   a. does not contain blood cells.
   b. is a mixed fluid found in the hemocoel.
   c. circulates through closed circulatory systems only.
   d. functions only in defense of the body and not transport.
   e. does not pass through a heart.

2. A typical hematocrit value for a human is around 42%. This means that
   a. the typical fluid portion of blood is about 42% of the total volume.
   b. the leukocytes make up 42% of the blood volume.
   c. the erythrocytes make up 42% of the blood volume.
   d. the leukocytes and erythrocytes together make up 58% of the blood volume.
   e. the erythrocytes alone make up 58% of the blood volume.

3. A major advantage of a double circulation is that
   a. blood can be pumped to the upper portions of the body by one circuit and to the lower portions of the body by the other circuit.
   b. each circuit can pump blood with differing pressures to optimize the function of each.
   c. the oxygenated blood can mix with the deoxygenated blood before being pumped to the tissues of the body.
   d. less energy is required to provide nutrients and oxygen to the tissues of the body.
   e. All of the above are advantages of a double circulation.

4. The function of erythrocytes is to
   a. transport oxygen throughout the body.
   b. defend the body against infection and disease.
   c. transport chemical signals throughout the body.
   d. secrete the proteins that form blood clots.
   e. do both a and d.

5. For blood flow through a closed circulation, which is the correct sequence of vessels beginning at the heart?
   a. arteriole, artery, capillary, vein, venule
   b. artery, capillary, arteriole, venule, vein
   c. vein, venule, capillary, arteriole, artery
   d. artery, arteriole, capillary, venule, vein
   e. artery, arteriole, capillary, vein, venule

6. Carbon dioxide is considered a harmful waste product of cellular respiration because it
   a. lowers the pH of the blood.
   b. lowers the H^+ concentration in the blood.
   c. competes with oxygen for transport in the blood.
   d. does all of the above.
   e. does a and b only.

7. The countercurrent exchange mechanism in fish gills
   a. maximizes oxygen diffusion into the bloodstream.
   b. is a less efficient mechanism for gas exchange than that used in mammalian lungs.
   c. occurs because the flow of blood is in the same direction as water flowing across the gills.
   d. facilitates diffusion of carbon dioxide into the blood of the fish.
   e. facilitates diffusion of oxygen to the environment.

8. The tracheal system of insects
   a. consists of several tracheae that connect to multiple lungs within the different segments of the body.
   b. consists of extensively branching tubes that are in close contact with all the cells of the body.
   c. allows oxygen to diffuse directly across the thin exoskeleton of the insect to the bloodstream.
   d. cannot function without constant movement of the wings to move air into and out of the body.
   e. provides oxygen that is carried through the animal's body in hemolymph.

9. Which of the following factors does *not* increase the rate of breathing by influencing the chemoreceptors?
   a. an increase in P_{CO_2} in the arterial blood
   b. an increase in P_{O_2} in the arterial blood
   c. a decrease in the pH of the arterial blood
   d. a decrease in P_{O_2} in the arterial blood
   e. an increase in the H^+ concentration in the arterial blood

10. The majority of oxygen is transported in the blood of vertebrates
    a. by binding to plasma proteins.
    b. by binding to hemoglobin in erythrocytes.
    c. as dissolved gas in the plasma.
    d. as dissolved gas in the cytoplasm in the erythrocytes.
    e. by binding to hemoglobin in the plasma.

Conceptual Questions

1. Explain the differences between closed and open circulatory systems. What advantages does a closed circulatory system provide?

2. Explain why it is an advantage for CO_2, H^+, and heat to be major factors in decreasing the affinity of hemoglobin for oxygen.

3. **Core Concepts: Structure and Function** A core concept of biology is that structure determines function. How is this concept related to what you have learned in this chapter about the hemoglobin molecule?

Collaborative Questions

1. Describe the cardiac cycle, and explain why heart valves must open in only one direction.

2. List the components of the mammalian respiratory system, and describe the major functions of each.

Excretory Systems

49

If you have ever noticed how quickly the water in an aquarium or a swimming pool becomes dirty when the filter is not functioning, you will have a good idea of the importance of filtering the soluble wastes from an animal's body fluids. The human kidneys, for example, are remarkable filtration devices. Although each one is only about the size of a computer mouse, the kidneys are able to filter blood at a rate of 150–200 L/day. Considering that a typical adult has only 5 L or so of blood, that is an astonishingly effective filtration mechanism. By the time a person reaches 50 years of age, his or her kidneys have filtered roughly 3,000,000 L of blood! As they perform this function, the kidneys not only remove soluble waste products of metabolism from the filtered blood, but also recapture from it useful substances such as sodium ions and water.

The ability of organisms to maintain homeostasis is one of the fundamental principles of biology and a common theme of the previous several chapters. Excretory systems are critical not only for removing soluble wastes from body fluids, but also for homeostasis, particularly of ion and water balance. An **excretory system** includes all of an animal's organs (such as gills, lungs, kidneys, and, in some animals, the body surface) that function to remove soluble wastes generated from metabolism. These wastes include such substances as CO_2 and the nitrogenous wastes from protein and nucleic acid metabolism.

As described in Chapter 48, the elimination of CO_2 from the body is carried out by respiratory organs such as gills and lungs, which is why these structures can also be considered part of an animal's excretory system. In this chapter, we examine how different excretory organs participate in eliminating nitrogenous and other soluble wastes from animal bodies. We then highlight some of the major features of the mammalian kidney, examine how the kidneys eliminate wastes and, in the process, regulate ion and water balance. We conclude by considering how kidney disease affects human health.

Colorized scanning electron micrograph of the filtration apparatus of a vertebrate kidney. As blood flows through bundles of capillaries known as a glomerulus (shown in blue) in the kidneys, some of the fluid in the blood leaves and enters underlying tubules called nephrons. Soluble wastes can be eliminated from the body via this mechanism. ©Steve Gschmeissner/SPL/Getty Images

49.1 Excretory Systems in Different Animal Groups

Learning Outcomes:

1. Describe the forms of nitrogenous wastes generated by animals.
2. Describe the general processes of filtration, reabsorption, secretion, and excretion.
3. Identify several invertebrate osmoregulatory organs, and compare and contrast the process of elimination in each.
4. Recognize the general structural and functional features of kidneys, which are common to all vertebrates.

into their lumens. This process, called secretion, supplements the animals that helps eliminate excess water.

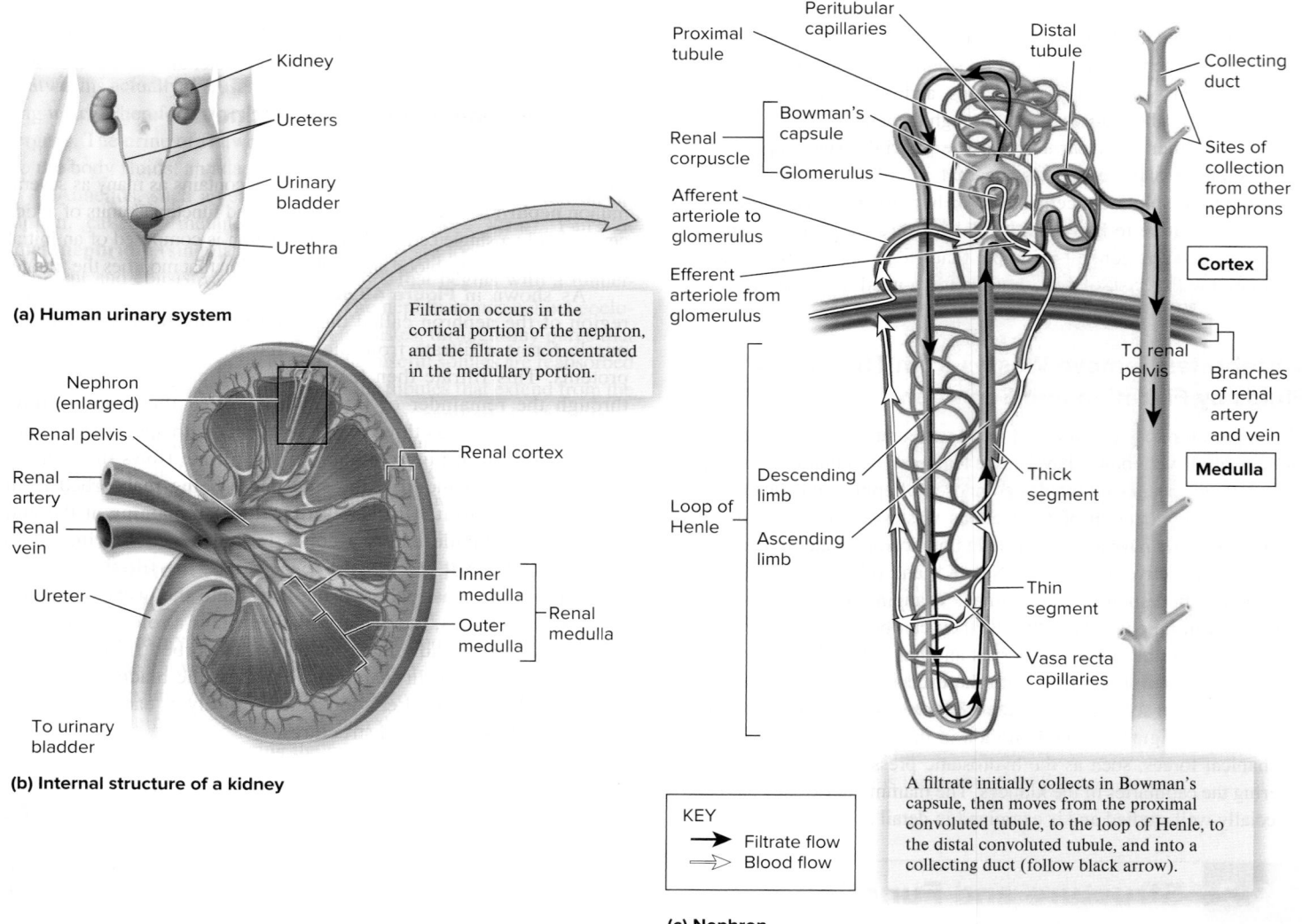

(a) Human urinary system

Filtration occurs in the cortical portion of the nephron, and the filtrate is concentrated in the medullary portion.

(b) Internal structure of a kidney

KEY
→ Filtrate flow
⇒ Blood flow

A filtrate initially collects in Bowman's capsule, then moves from the proximal convoluted tubule, to the loop of Henle, to the distal convoluted tubule, and into a collecting duct (follow black arrow).

(c) Nephron

Figure 49.6 **The mammalian urinary system, including the basic functional unit of the nephron.** **(a)** The human urinary system in a female. In the male, the urethra passes through the penis. **(b)** View of a section through a kidney, showing the locations of the major internal structures and a single nephron (enlarged; nephrons are microscopic). **(c)** Structure of a nephron. The nephron begins at Bowman's capsule, continues along the renal tubule, and empties into a collecting duct. The major segments of the renal tubule are shown (proximal tubule, loop of Henle, and distal tubule). One segment, the loop of Henle, has additional segments identified here. Many nephrons empty into a given collecting duct. Surrounding the nephron are capillaries, called peritubular capillaries in the cortex and vasa recta capillaries in the medulla.

from the proximal tubule and an ascending limb. The ascending limb has two segments—a thick segment and a thin segment—with different properties.

- The **distal tubule** arises from the thick segment of the loop of Henle. The filtrate flows from the distal tubule into a collecting duct.

Capillaries of the Nephron All along its length, each renal tubule is surrounded by capillaries. These include the peritubular capillaries in the cortex and the vasa recta capillaries in the medulla (see Figure 49.6c). Both sets of capillaries carry away reabsorbed solutes and water from the filtrate in the nephron or collecting ducts, and return them to the bloodstream.

A Filtrate Is Produced by Hydrostatic Pressure in Bowman's Capsule

Filtration begins as blood flows through the glomerulus and a portion of the plasma leaves the glomerular capillaries and filters into Bowman's capsule. Only a small portion of the plasma is filtered from the blood as it circulates through the glomerulus. Most of the plasma, therefore, exits the glomerulus by an efferent arteriole (see Figure 49.7a). Proteins and blood cells are prevented from leaving the glomerular capillaries because of the small diameter of the fenestrations and the presumed action of the filtration slits, mentioned earlier.

The rate at which the filtrate is formed in the glomeruli is called the **glomerular filtration rate (GFR)**. The GFR can be increased by dilation (widening) of the afferent arterioles. When an afferent

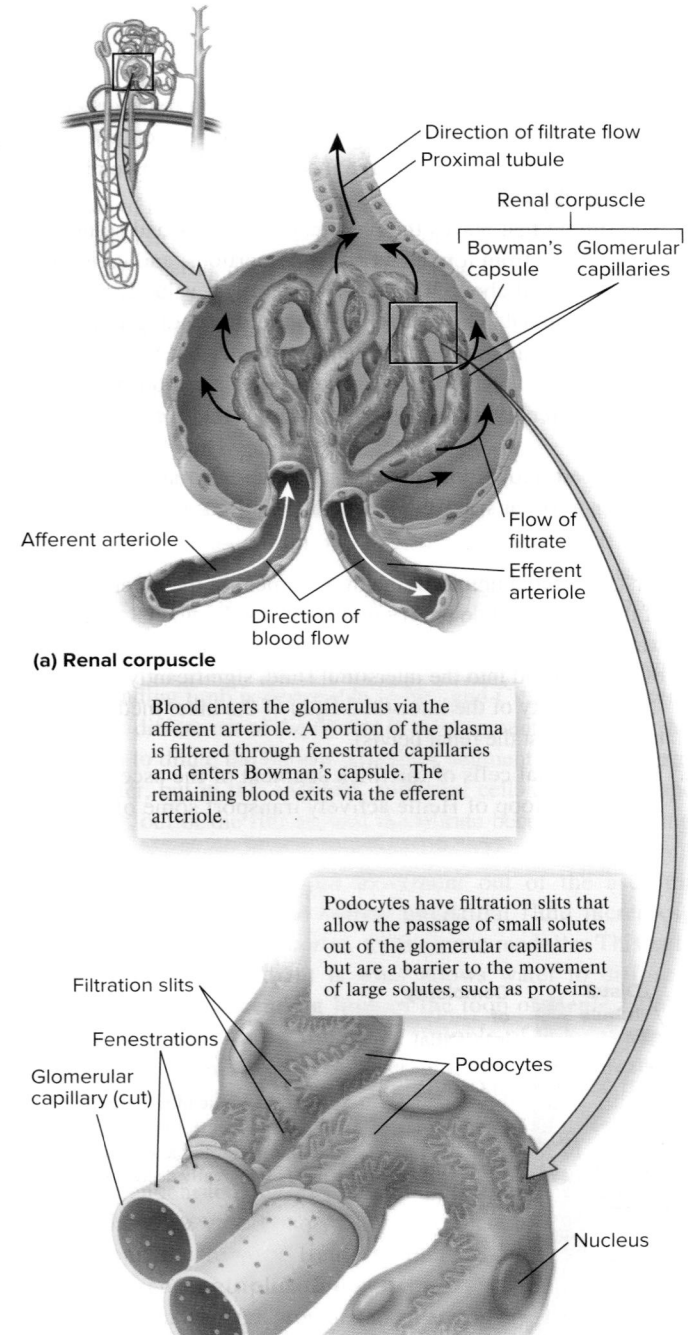

Direction of filtrate flow
Proximal tubule
Renal corpuscle
Bowman's | Glomerular
capsule | capillaries

Afferent arteriole

Flow of filtrate

Efferent arteriole

Direction of blood flow

(a) Renal corpuscle

Blood enters the glomerulus via the afferent arteriole. A portion of the plasma is filtered through fenestrated capillaries and enters Bowman's capsule. The remaining blood exits via the efferent arteriole.

Podocytes have filtration slits that allow the passage of small solutes out of the glomerular capillaries but are a barrier to the movement of large solutes, such as proteins.

Filtration slits

Fenestrations

Glomerular capillary (cut)

Podocytes

Nucleus

(b) Glomerular capillaries with podocytes

Figure 49.7 The structure and function of the renal corpuscle. **(a)** A renal corpuscle comprises Bowman's capsule and the glomerular capillaries that make up the glomerulus. It is here that the filtrate is first formed. **(b)** The glomerular capillaries are completely encased in podocytes, specialized epithelial cells that support the glomerulus and are believed to act in part as a filtration barrier.

 Core Concept: Structure and Function The structure of the capillaries in the renal glomerulus is suited to their function. Fenestrations permit the passage of plasma, but not blood cells, out of the capillaries. The structure of the podocytes is also suited to their function, in that filtration slits prevent the passage of plasma proteins into the filtrate. Damage to the structure of the podocytes might cause proteins to leak into the filtrate and be lost in the urine.

arteriole dilates, more blood enters the glomerulus, increasing the hydrostatic pressure in its capillaries and forcing more plasma through the fenestrations in the capillaries and into Bowman's capsule. This might happen, for example, when nerves or hormones signal that there is excess water in the body and that more water must be excreted in the urine.

By contrast, constriction (narrowing) of the afferent arterioles will decrease the amount of blood entering the glomerular capillaries and therefore decrease the GFR. This might occur in response to dehydration or a loss of blood due to a severe injury. In such situations, decreasing the GFR results in less urine production, which, in turn, minimizes how much water is lost from the body. The tradeoff, however, is that the blood is less effectively cleared of wastes.

Useful Solutes Are Reabsorbed from the Filtrate in the Proximal Tubule

The filtrate flows from the renal corpuscle to the proximal tubule. Unwanted substances remain in the filtrate. By contrast, anywhere from two-thirds to all of a particular useful solute is reabsorbed from the filtrate in the proximal tubule. These solutes include Ca^{2+}, Na^+, K^+, Cl^-, HCO_3^- (bicarbonate ion), and organic molecules such as glucose, vitamins, and amino acids. Some ions diffuse through channels in the membranes of the epithelial cells that form the proximal tubule. Others are actively transported across the tubule epithelium. Organic molecules generally are reabsorbed by being coupled to the transport of ions such as Na^+. The reabsorption of solutes and water is enhanced by microvilli that extend into the lumen from the apical membrane of the epithelial cells of the proximal tubule. This anatomical adaptation, called a **brush border**, creates an enormous surface area for the positioning of transporters and channels (**Figure 49.8**).

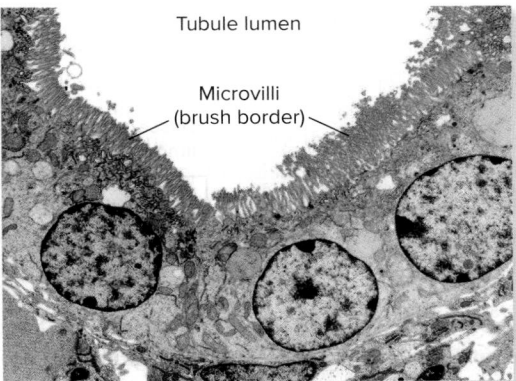

Tubule lumen

Microvilli (brush border)

Figure 49.8 Electron micrograph of cuboidal epithelial cells of the proximal tubule of a rat nephron. Note the extensive brush border of microvilli on the apical membranes of the cells. ©Steve Gschmeissner/SPL/Science Source

 Core Skill: Connections In what other organ is a brush border found (refer back to Figure 46.6)? What general conclusions can you draw about the function of such specialized epithelia?

Endocrine Systems

50

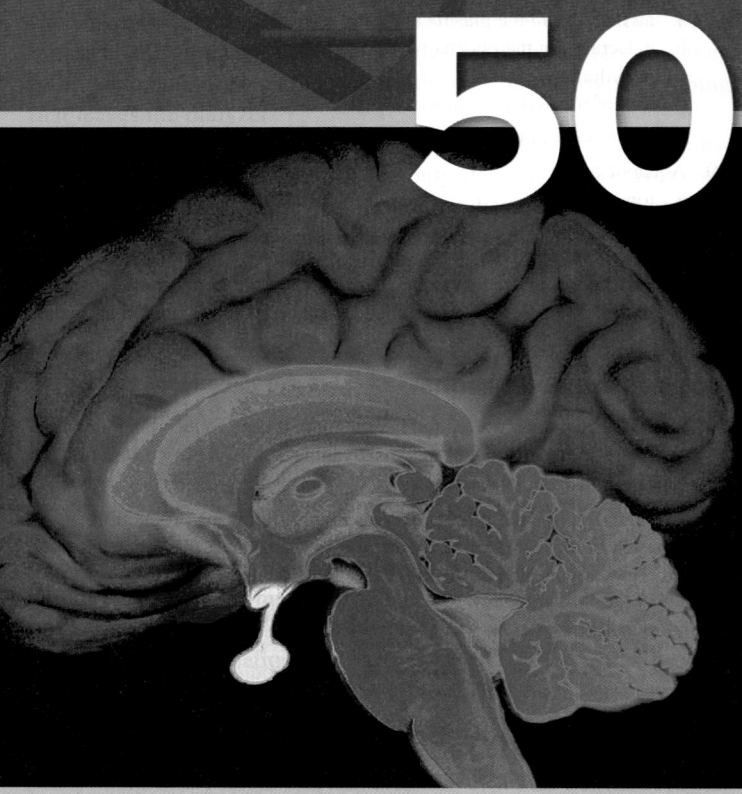

A section through a human brain, highlighting the pituitary gland and its connection to the hypothalamus (white). Both of these structures secrete numerous hormones. (Image is a three-dimensional MRI.) ©Sovereign/ISM/Phototake

A 22-year-old man was seen by his physician because of a complaint of hair loss and the appearance of severe acne over much of his face, neck, back, and shoulders. He also reported feelings of irritability and aggression. Upon examination, the man was found to have additional symptoms, including hypertension, an elevated plasma cholesterol concentration, an increased hematocrit (red blood cell count; see Chapter 48), and, alarmingly, shrunken testes. When questioned, the patient admitted that for 6 months he had been taking an oral form of the illegal drug stanozolol in an effort to improve his physique by building more muscle mass. Stanozolol is a synthetic version of a steroid hormone known as an androgen. A **hormone** is a chemical signal produced by cells that is secreted into the extracellular fluid. Unlike paracrine substances, which act on nearby cells, hormones travel through the blood or hemolymph to one or more distant target tissues to alter their functions.

In males, androgens are produced by the testes, which are reproductive organs that contain hormone-producing cells. The most well-known androgen is testosterone. As we will discuss in this chapter, in normal amounts, androgens have important functions in the physiological events associated with puberty and reproduction, including the increase in skeletal muscle mass that accompanies male puberty. This young man hoped to increase his muscle mass by consuming large amounts of a synthetic androgen that mimics testosterone. At high concentrations, however, androgens promote increased erythrocyte production, which, in turn, forces the heart to work harder and can lead to hypertension. Likewise, high concentrations of androgens increase the amount of cholesterol in the blood, promote fluid retention, damage the liver, cause hair loss, and increase the activity of the sebaceous glands. At such concentrations, androgens also strongly inhibit the activity of the testes. The body senses that sufficient androgens are already available in the blood. In response, the testes do not need to make more androgens and thus shrink in size as they become less and less active.

Fortunately, this individual was educated by his doctor about the consequences of misuse of these powerful hormones, and he discontinued the practice. Had he continued to take the synthetic androgen, all of his symptoms would have worsened, and he would have run the risk of serious and irreversible damage to his heart, liver, and other organs, while increasing his risk of cancer and other diseases.

Androgens and other hormones are found in all vertebrates and many invertebrates. Hormones are often produced in response to developmental changes, as in puberty, and to homeostatic challenges, such as a change in an animal's blood pressure or body temperature. A chief function of hormones is to counter these challenges and maintain homeostasis. Hormones affect a wide range of body functions, including gastrointestinal activity, blood pressure regulation, cholesterol balance, fluid and mineral balance, and reproduction.

Hormones are made by cells in numerous organs of an animal's body. In addition, hormone-producing cells are often found in specialized glands, called **endocrine glands**, the primary function of which is hormone synthesis and secretion. An example is the vertebrate pituitary gland highlighted in the chapter opening photo. Collectively, all the endocrine glands and other organs containing hormone-secreting cells constitute an animal's **endocrine system**.

In this chapter, we will first explore the chemical nature of hormones and their mechanisms of action. We will then discuss how the endocrine and nervous systems interact and the ways in which hormones influence such diverse functions as metabolism, growth, and reproduction. We will conclude with a discussion of how hormones affect human health, including how synthetic hormones are misused, as in the example just described.

50.1 Types of Hormones and Their Mechanisms of Action

Learning Outcomes:

1. List some of the major endocrine glands found in animals and the hormones they secrete.
2. List and give examples of the three different chemical classes of hormones, and describe some of their structural differences.
3. Describe the cellular locations of receptors for lipid-soluble hormones and receptors for water-soluble hormones.

Figure 50.1 is an overview of the major vertebrate endocrine glands and their hormones; you should take a moment and review this figure as preparation for the rest of the chapter. Throughout this chapter, we will use the human as a representative species when describing the location and appearance of vertebrate endocrine glands. All vertebrates share similar glands, although their locations and histological structures may show certain differences. We will occasionally point out important functional differences in various hormones that are present in all vertebrates. In this section, we will examine some of the general characteristics of hormones that are shared by all or most animals, including how they act and how they are controlled. Keep in mind that endocrine signaling is just one type of cell-to-cell communication. Refer back to Figure 9.3 for a review of the different types of cell-signaling mechanisms found in animals.

Hormones Are Classified According to Their Structure

Hormones fall into three broad classes: amines, polypeptides, and steroid hormones (**Table 50.1**). The amines and the polypeptides share similar chemical properties and mechanisms of action, whereas the steroid hormones act very differently from the other two classes.

The amine hormones are derived from an amino acid, either tyrosine or tryptophan. Tyrosine is the precursor for the hormones epinephrine and norepinephrine, which are produced in the adrenal medulla and are important in a vertebrate's response to stress (the fight-or-flight response; see Chapter 43). It is also the precursor for dopamine, a hormone that is made by the brain and functions in the control of the anterior pituitary gland. Tyrosine is also the molecular backbone of thyroid hormone, which is made by the thyroid gland and is an important regulator of metabolic rate, growth, and development. The major hormone derived from tryptophan is melatonin, which is produced within an endocrine gland called the pineal gland, located in the vertebrate brain. Melatonin is important in some species for controlling circadian rhythms, daily cycles of physiological or biochemical processes. In some mammals such as sheep and hamsters that breed only at certain times of year, melatonin controls seasonal cycles of reproduction.

Polypeptides are the most abundant hormones. These hormones participate in numerous body functions such as metabolism, mineral balance, growth, and reproduction. Examples include insulin and glucagon made by the pancreas, and leptin made by adipose tissue.

Amine and polypeptide hormones are generally synthesized and secreted at a steady rate or in a circadian rhythm, until an additional amount is required. In that case, transcription factors within the cell direct the increased transcription of the gene encoding the hormone in question. Conversely, when less hormone is required, gene transcription is slowed or stopped. These hormones are too large and hydrophilic to diffuse from the cytosol across the plasma membrane and then into the extracellular fluid. Instead, they are packaged into secretory vesicles in much the same way as neurotransmitters are packaged in neuron axon terminals. This packaging provides a ready means of secreting the hormones by exocytosis and establishes a reservoir of stored hormone available for immediate release when required. If a cell is stimulated to secrete more than the usual amount of a stored amine or polypeptide hormone, it also is typically stimulated to synthesize new hormone molecules to replace them.

Steroid hormones are synthesized from cholesterol, as shown in **Figure 50.2**, and thus all steroid hormones are lipids, unlike the other classes of hormones. Steroid hormones, unlike water-soluble hormones, are not packaged into secretory vesicles because a lipophilic steroid could diffuse across the lipid membrane of the vesicle. Instead, steroid hormones are made on demand, and no significant amount of them is stored.

Steroids are less soluble in water than are amines or polypeptide hormones. Due to this limited solubility, steroids are usually bound to large, soluble proteins in the blood that serve as carriers. By combining with these proteins, steroids can reach high concentrations in the blood. They can then be released from their binding proteins into the plasma in small amounts at a time. From there, they diffuse into cells.

Hormones Act Through Plasma Membrane or Intracellular Receptors

The amine and polypeptide hormones are generally water-soluble, and the steroid hormones are lipid-soluble. An exception is thyroid hormone, which is a lipophilic amine hormone. All of the other amine and polypeptide hormones are not able to cross plasma membranes

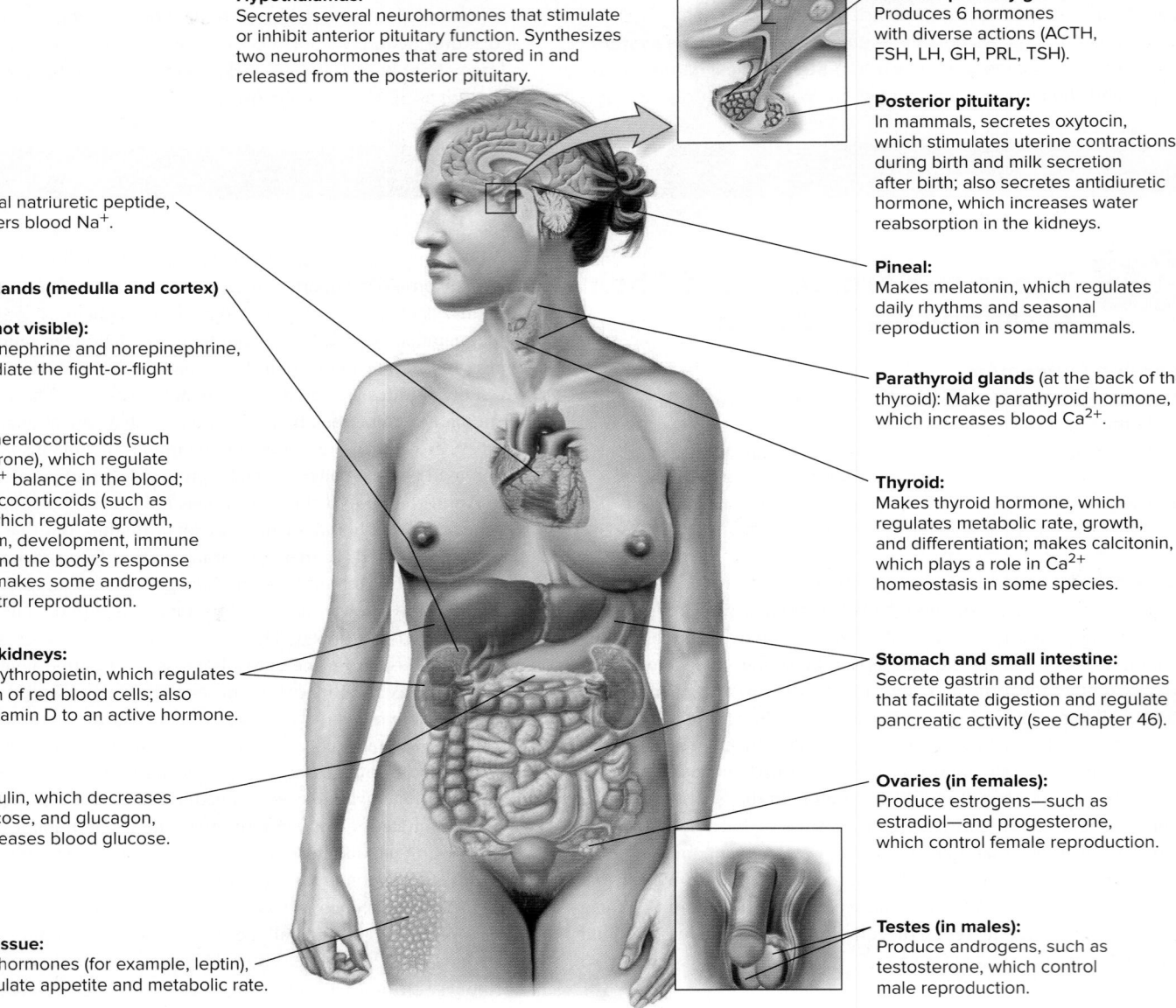

Hypothalamus:
Secretes several neurohormones that stimulate or inhibit anterior pituitary function. Synthesizes two neurohormones that are stored in and released from the posterior pituitary.

Anterior pituitary gland:
Produces 6 hormones with diverse actions (ACTH, FSH, LH, GH, PRL, TSH).

Posterior pituitary:
In mammals, secretes oxytocin, which stimulates uterine contractions during birth and milk secretion after birth; also secretes antidiuretic hormone, which increases water reabsorption in the kidneys.

Heart:
Makes atrial natriuretic peptide, which lowers blood Na^+.

Pineal:
Makes melatonin, which regulates daily rhythms and seasonal reproduction in some mammals.

Adrenal glands (medulla and cortex)

Medulla (not visible):
Makes epinephrine and norepinephrine, which mediate the fight-or-flight response.

Cortex:
Makes mineralocorticoids (such as aldosterone), which regulate Na^+ and K^+ balance in the blood; makes glucocorticoids (such as cortisol), which regulate growth, metabolism, development, immune function, and the body's response to stress; makes some androgens, which control reproduction.

Parathyroid glands (at the back of the thyroid): Make parathyroid hormone, which increases blood Ca^{2+}.

Thyroid:
Makes thyroid hormone, which regulates metabolic rate, growth, and differentiation; makes calcitonin, which plays a role in Ca^{2+} homeostasis in some species.

Liver and kidneys:
Secrete erythropoietin, which regulates production of red blood cells; also convert vitamin D to an active hormone.

Stomach and small intestine:
Secrete gastrin and other hormones that facilitate digestion and regulate pancreatic activity (see Chapter 46).

Pancreas:
Makes insulin, which decreases blood glucose, and glucagon, which increases blood glucose.

Ovaries (in females):
Produce estrogens—such as estradiol—and progesterone, which control female reproduction.

Adipose tissue:
Produces hormones (for example, leptin), which regulate appetite and metabolic rate.

Testes (in males):
Produce androgens, such as testosterone, which control male reproduction.

Figure 50.1 Overview of the vertebrate endocrine system. This figure shows many of the major endocrine glands and other structures that constitute the vertebrate endocrine system (as seen in a human) and gives the major functions of the hormones produced by those glands.

Table 50.1	Chemical Classes of Hormones			
Class	Chemical properties	Location of target cell receptors	Mechanism of action	Examples
Amines	Derived from tyrosine or tryptophan; small, water-soluble (except thyroid hormones, which are lipophilic)	Plasma membrane (except thyroid hormones, which act via intracellular receptors)	Stimulate second-messenger pathways (except thyroid hormone, which acts via changes in gene transcription)	Epinephrine, norepinephrine, dopamine, thyroid hormone, melatonin
Polypeptides	Water-soluble	Plasma membrane	Stimulate second-messenger pathways	Insulin, glucagon, leptin
Steroids	Synthesized from cholesterol; lipid-soluble	Cytosol or nucleus	Usually stimulate gene transcription directly	Aldosterone, cortisol, androgens, estrogens

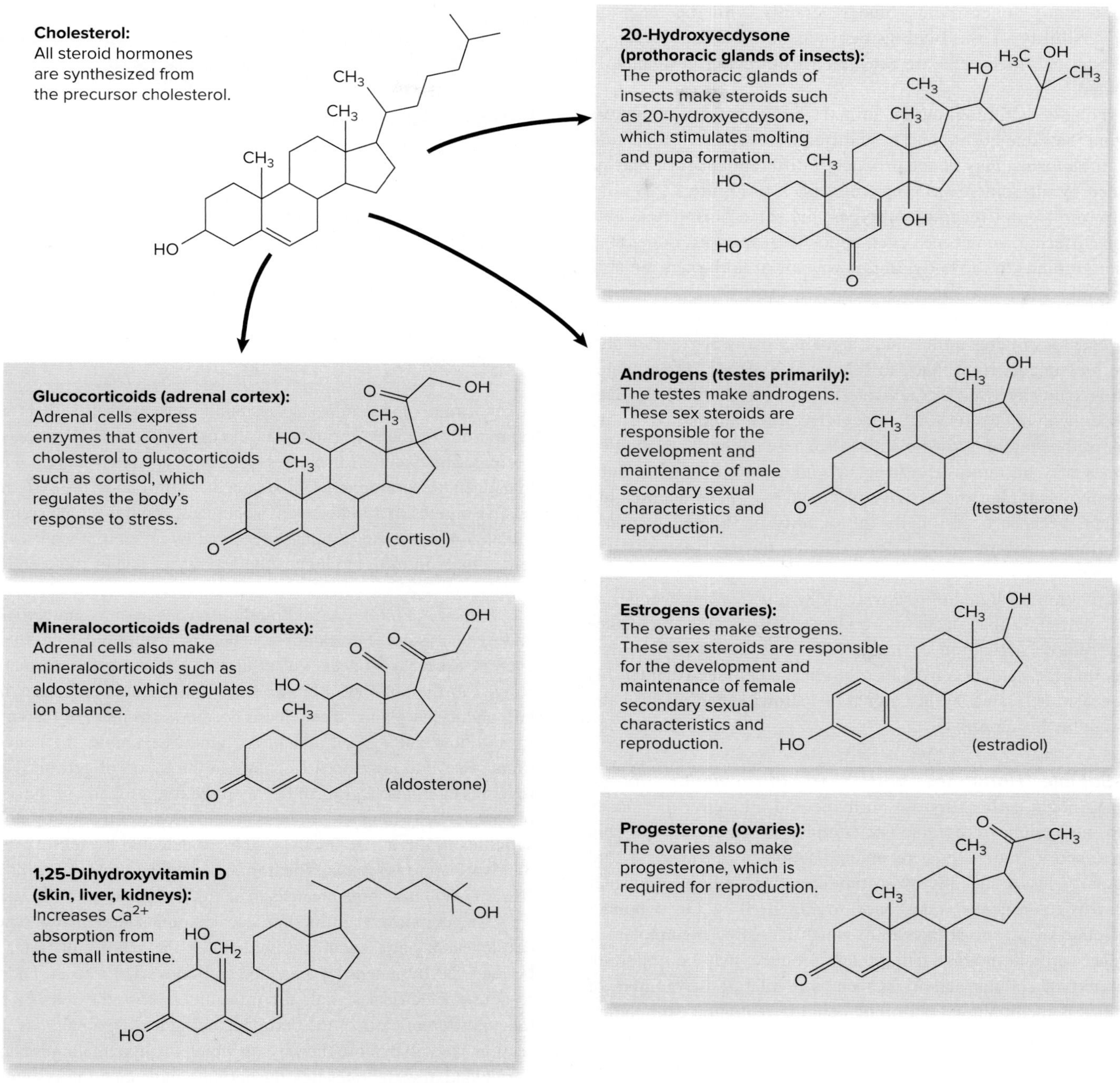

Cholesterol:
All steroid hormones are synthesized from the precursor cholesterol.

20-Hydroxyecdysone (prothoracic glands of insects):
The prothoracic glands of insects make steroids such as 20-hydroxyecdysone, which stimulates molting and pupa formation.

Glucocorticoids (adrenal cortex):
Adrenal cells express enzymes that convert cholesterol to glucocorticoids such as cortisol, which regulates the body's response to stress.

(cortisol)

Androgens (testes primarily):
The testes make androgens. These sex steroids are responsible for the development and maintenance of male secondary sexual characteristics and reproduction.

(testosterone)

Mineralocorticoids (adrenal cortex):
Adrenal cells also make mineralocorticoids such as aldosterone, which regulates ion balance.

(aldosterone)

Estrogens (ovaries):
The ovaries make estrogens. These sex steroids are responsible for the development and maintenance of female secondary sexual characteristics and reproduction.

(estradiol)

1,25-Dihydroxyvitamin D (skin, liver, kidneys):
Increases Ca^{2+} absorption from the small intestine.

Progesterone (ovaries):
The ovaries also make progesterone, which is required for reproduction.

Figure 50.2 Synthesis and functions of the major steroid hormones in animals.

 Core Concept: Structure and Function Notice how slight changes in the arrangements of side groups attached to the four-ring skeleton derived from cholesterol create products with completely different functions. Keep in mind that the three-dimensional shape of a molecule may be changed much more by such chemical modifications than is visible in a two-dimensional depiction.

and must bind to a receptor protein on the surface of a target cell. Steroid hormones and thyroid hormone, however, being lipophilic, diffuse across the target cell's plasma membranes. They bind to a receptor protein located in the cytosol or nucleus. Hormones that act through plasma membrane receptors tend to elicit fast responses (in seconds to minutes), whereas those that act via intracellular receptors generally act much more slowly (within hours), as we see next.

Water-Soluble Hormones and Their Plasma Membrane Receptors All amine and polypeptide hormones other than thyroid hormone act by binding to a receptor protein located in the plasma membrane (refer back to Figure 9.5). Only cells having the proper receptors on their surfaces can respond to these hormones. Thus, although a given hormone travels throughout the entire circulatory system, it activates only specific cells. The hormone binds noncovalently and reversibly with the receptor. The reversibility of the binding between hormone and receptor is one way in which cells are prevented from being permanently stimulated.

Among cells throughout an animal's body, different receptors may bind the same hormone. These different receptors, called subtypes, or isoforms, may be the product of different genes or may be produced by alternative splicing (refer back to Figure 14.21). By binding to different receptor subtypes, the same hormone is able to elicit differing, sometimes even opposite, responses, depending on where it binds in the body. In this way, most hormones are able to serve more than one function.

The binding of a water-soluble hormone to a plasma membrane receptor initiates intracellular signaling pathways that involve second messengers (refer back to Figures 9.12–9.14). Three major signaling pathways that are activated by water-soluble hormones are those involving cyclic AMP, diacylglycerol and inositol trisphosphate, and receptor tyrosine kinases. These signal transduction processes may be rapid, occurring in some cases within seconds, and involve changing the activity of enzymes. These features are important, because occasionally the rapidity of the cell response to a hormone may be critical, for example, during fight-or-flight conditions.

Activation of signaling pathways may also lead to changes in cellular activities that occur more slowly. These slower changes usually require activation or inhibition of genes in the nucleus, actions that are mediated by transcription factors (see Chapter 14) that are also activated by the signaling pathways initiated by the water-soluble hormones.

Lipid-Soluble Hormones and Their Intracellular Receptors As noted earlier, thyroid hormone and all steroid hormones bind to intracellular receptors. The complex of a steroid or thyroid hormone and its intracellular receptor functions as a transcriptional activator (or less frequently as an inhibitor) by binding to enhancers of particular genes (refer back to Figure 9.9). Once bound, transcription of a gene is increased, which increases the amount of that gene's protein product. The protein products may be important in a variety of cellular activities, such as regulating the number of ion pumps in membranes, controlling cell differentiation, stimulating growth, and others.

Steroids and thyroid hormone can influence several genes within a single cell or in different cells. In this way, one hormone can exert a variety of actions throughout the body. The numerous and varied physical changes that accompany puberty in mammals result from the actions of two steroid hormones—androgens in males and estrogens in females—and are among the most striking and commonly recognized examples of this kind of widespread action.

Generally, hormone concentrations in the blood remain within a relatively narrow range, but they can be increased or decreased beyond that range if required. One of the ways in which changes in hormone concentrations are initiated is through sensory input to an animal's brain. As we see next, the nervous system and endocrine system are functionally linked in many animals, including all vertebrates.

50.2 Links Between the Endocrine and Nervous Systems

Learning Outcomes:

1. Describe the anatomical connections among the hypothalamus, posterior pituitary, and anterior pituitary gland.
2. Describe the roles of the hypothalamus and anterior pituitary gland in regulation of endocrine function.
3. **CoreSKILL** » Predict what would happen to the secretion of each hormone of the anterior pituitary gland if the special blood connection between that gland and the hypothalamus was severed.
4. List some of the major functions of the hormones of the posterior pituitary.

A key feature of the endocrine system in most animals is that the concentrations of many hormones in the extracellular fluid increase and decrease in response to changes in an animal's environment. For this to happen, the hormone-producing cells of the endocrine system must receive signals that indicate environmental changes. Such signals are initiated when sensory input is received by an animal's nervous system, which, in turn, modulates the activity of one or more endocrine glands.

Sensory stimuli detected by the nervous system can activate the endocrine system. For example, when an antelope detects the presence of a nearby lioness, visual and olfactory sense information is relayed to the antelope's brain. The brain initiates responses in certain endocrine glands that release hormones to prepare the antelope for the possibility of an attack. As another example, the concentrations of several hormones fluctuate in the blood of certain fishes as they migrate back and forth between feeding grounds in the sea and freshwater spawning sites. These hormones are activated by different salinities in the environment, which are detected by sensory cells of the fish's nervous system. The hormones act to prepare the gills of the fish to handle the large changes in salinity of the water.

The common feature of these examples and many others is that a sensory cue, such as a predator or the salinity of water, must be received by a sensory receptor and converted into an endocrine response. Electrical signals are transmitted from the sensory receptors to different parts of the brain, including the hypothalamus. In this section, we will explore the ways in which the hypothalamus and pituitary gland in vertebrates link the nervous and endocrine systems. The brain/endocrine link in invertebrates will be covered in Section 50.5.

The Hypothalamus and Pituitary Gland Are Physically Connected

As described in Chapter 43, the **hypothalamus** is a collection of several nuclei that are located at the ventral surface of the vertebrate brain (**Figure 50.3a**). Neurons in these nuclei receive signals from most parts of the brain. In turn, they are connected to an endocrine gland sitting directly below the hypothalamus, called the **pituitary gland** (see the bottom part of the highlighted structure in the chapter opening photo). The pituitary gland in humans is made up of two lobes, the anterior and posterior lobes. Some vertebrate species have an

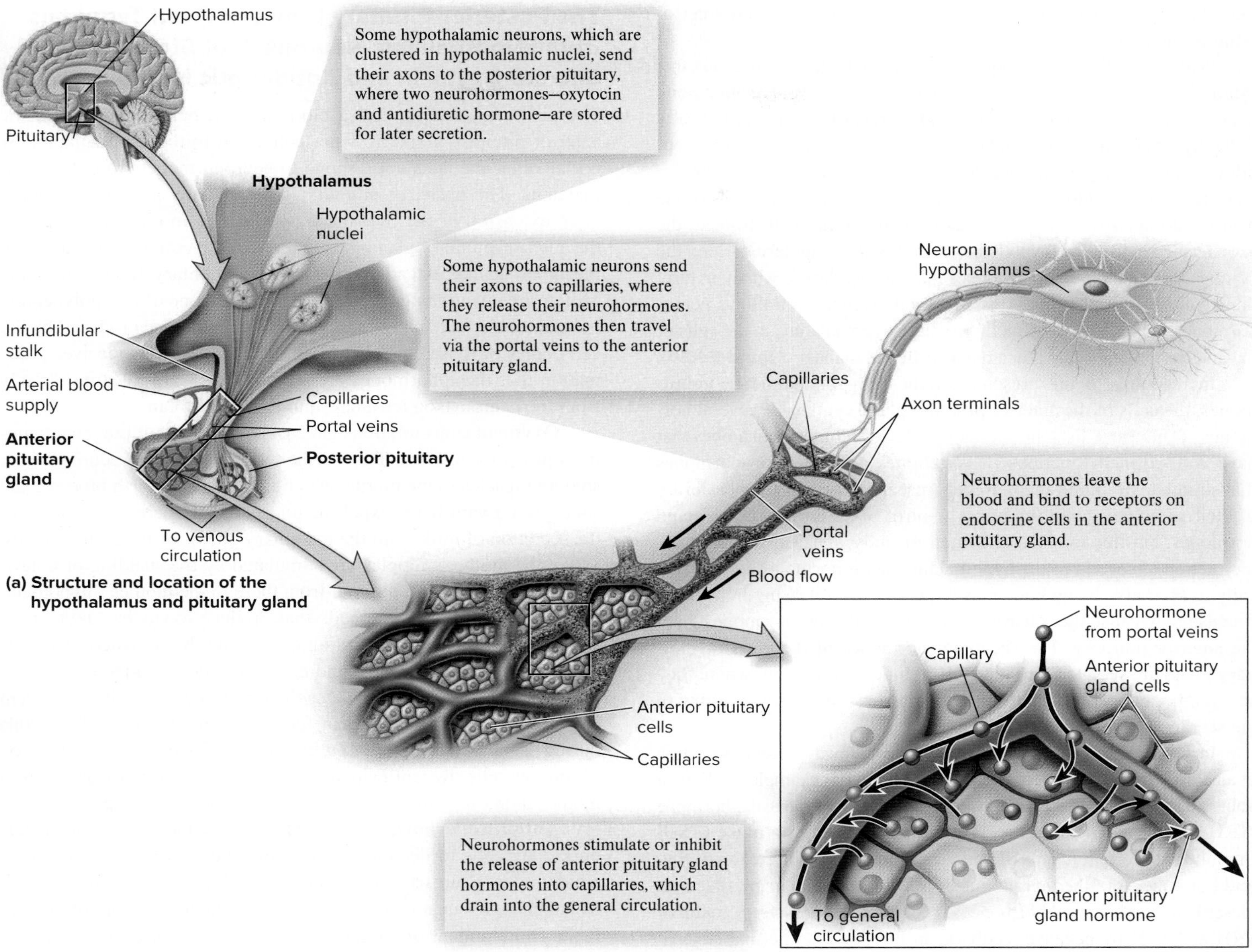

Hypothalamus

Pituitary

Some hypothalamic neurons, which are clustered in hypothalamic nuclei, send their axons to the posterior pituitary, where two neurohormones—oxytocin and antidiuretic hormone—are stored for later secretion.

Hypothalamus

Hypothalamic nuclei

Some hypothalamic neurons send their axons to capillaries, where they release their neurohormones. The neurohormones then travel via the portal veins to the anterior pituitary gland.

Neuron in hypothalamus

Infundibular stalk

Arterial blood supply

Anterior pituitary gland

Capillaries

Portal veins

Posterior pituitary

Capillaries

Axon terminals

To venous circulation

(a) Structure and location of the hypothalamus and pituitary gland

Neurohormones leave the blood and bind to receptors on endocrine cells in the anterior pituitary gland.

Portal veins

Blood flow

Anterior pituitary cells

Capillaries

Neurohormones stimulate or inhibit the release of anterior pituitary gland hormones into capillaries, which drain into the general circulation.

Neurohormone from portal veins

Capillary

Anterior pituitary gland cells

To general circulation

Anterior pituitary gland hormone

(b) Stimulation of the anterior pituitary gland by the hypothalamus

Figure 50.3 **Relationship between the hypothalamus and the pituitary gland in a human.**

 Core Skill: Connections Recall the definition of neurotransmitter from Chapter 42 and look back at Figure 42.13. What determines whether a molecule such as dopamine is considered a neurotransmitter or a hormone?

intermediate lobe that secretes hormones that function in such things as seasonal changes in coat color in certain mammals. This lobe is believed to be vestigial in many other species, including primates.

The hypothalamus and pituitary are connected by a thin piece of tissue called the **infundibular stalk** and also by a system of blood vessels called portal veins. **Portal veins** differ from ordinary veins in that they not only collect blood from capillaries—like all veins do—but they also form another set of capillaries, instead of returning the blood directly to the heart like other veins. The portal veins extend through the length of the infundibular stalk. Within the anterior lobe of the pituitary gland—often simply called the anterior pituitary gland—the portal veins empty into a second set of capillaries. This arrangement of blood vessels bypasses the general circulation and

allows the hypothalamus to communicate directly with the anterior pituitary gland. Let's now explore the nature of this communication.

The Hypothalamus and Anterior Pituitary Gland Have Integrated Functions

As described in Chapter 43, the nuclei of the vertebrate hypothalamus are vital for such diverse functions as reproduction, circadian rhythms, appetite, metabolism, and responses to stress. The hypothalamus has such wide-ranging effects in part because it acts as a master control, signaling the pituitary gland when to produce and secrete its various hormones. However, the hypothalamus communicates differently with the anterior and posterior lobes of the pituitary gland.

Let's look at the interaction between the hypothalamus and anterior pituitary gland first.

Within the different nuclei of the hypothalamus are neurons that synthesize a class of hormones called neurohormones. A **neurohormone** is any hormone that is synthesized and secreted by neurons, typically in the hypothalamus. All neurohormones are either amines or polypeptides. Although they are produced within neurons, these molecular signals are not referred to as neurotransmitters, because the endings of the neurons do not terminate in a synapse with another cell. Instead, the axon terminals from the hypothalamus end next to capillaries. Here, the neurons secrete their neurohormones into the capillaries, which, in turn, drain into the portal veins. This structural arrangement allows neurohormones to be delivered directly from the hypothalamus to the cells of the anterior pituitary gland in a quick, efficient manner (**Figure 50.3b**).

In response to the presence of these hypothalamic neurohormones, the cells of the anterior pituitary gland synthesize several hormones. **Table 50.2** lists the six major anterior pituitary hormones that have well-defined functions in vertebrates and the neurohormones that stimulate or inhibit them. Recent research suggests the possibility of dual stimulatory and inhibitory control of several pituitary gland hormones, but this remains uncertain for most species. The stimulatory action of several of the hypothalamic neurohormones led historically to their also being known as hypothalamic-releasing hormones, because they cause the release, or secretion, of other hormones from the anterior pituitary. The six major hormones of the anterior pituitary gland are secreted into the general blood circulation, where they act on other endocrine glands or structures, in some cases resulting in the secretion of yet other hormones.

In several cases, the final hormone in a pathway inhibits secretion of a neurohormone via a negative feedback loop. For example, looking at Table 50.2, we see that the neurohormone thyrotropin-releasing hormone (TRH) stimulates the secretion of thyroid-stimulating hormone (TSH) from the anterior pituitary. TSH, in turn, stimulates the secretion of thyroid hormone from the thyroid gland. In addition to its many functions (described later), thyroid hormone acts to prevent excessive secretion of TRH and TSH by negative feedback. In this way, the plasma concentrations of anterior pituitary hormones and the hormones they stimulate other glands to secrete are usually kept within an optimal range.

The Posterior Pituitary Contains Axon Terminals from Hypothalamic Neurons That Store and Secrete Oxytocin and Antidiuretic Hormone

The posterior pituitary has a blood supply, but, in contrast to the anterior pituitary gland, it is not connected to the hypothalamus by portal veins and does not respond to neurohormones from the hypothalamus. The posterior pituitary is not actually a gland but rather is an extension of the hypothalamus that lies in close contact with the anterior pituitary gland (see Figure 50.3). Axons from neurons of the hypothalamus extend into the posterior pituitary. In mammals, the axon terminals in the posterior pituitary store one of two polypeptide hormones, oxytocin or antidiuretic hormone, that are produced by the cell bodies of those neurons. When the hypothalamus receives information that these hormones are required, they are released directly from the neuron axon terminals into the bloodstream.

Oxytocin concentrations increase in the blood of pregnant mammals just prior to birth. This hormone stimulates contractions of the smooth muscles in the uterus, which facilitates the birth process, and shortly afterward helps expel the placenta. Oxytocin also stimulates the secretion of milk from the mammary glands of lactating females. When the mother's nipples are stimulated by the suckling of a newborn, neurons transmit a signal from there to the mother's hypothalamus, which stimulates the cells that produce oxytocin. Oxytocin is released from the posterior pituitary into the blood where it travels to smooth muscle cells surrounding the secretory components of the mammary glands. This stimulates the release of milk. Thus, oxytocin has two important and different functions, one during birth and one during lactation. In both cases, the hormone stimulates contraction of muscle cells. Recent evidence also supports a role of oxytocin in mother-infant bonding and prosocial behavior in some species.

Antidiuretic hormone (ADH) gets its name because it acts on kidney cells to decrease urine production—a process known as antidiuresis. (Diuresis is an increased excretion of water in the urine, as happens, for example, when you drink large amounts of fluids.) If the fluid content of an animal's body is low, for example, during dehydration or after a significant loss of blood, volume and pressure sensors in structures of the circulatory system send signals to

Table 50.2	Hormones of the Vertebrate Anterior Pituitary Gland and Hypothalamus		
Anterior pituitary gland hormone	Stimulatory neurohormone from hypothalamus	Inhibitory neurohormone from hypothalamus	Major functions
Adrenocorticotropic hormone (ACTH)	Corticotropin-releasing hormone (CRH)	None known	Stimulates adrenal cortex to make glucocorticoids
Follicle-stimulating hormone (FSH)	Gonadotropin-releasing hormone (GnRH)	None known	Stimulates germ cell development and sex steroid production in gonads
Luteinizing hormone (LH)	GnRH	None known	Stimulates release of eggs in females; stimulates sex steroid production from gonads
Growth hormone (GH)	Growth hormone-releasing hormone (GHRH)	Somatostatin	Promotes linear growth; regulates glucose and fatty acid balance in blood
Thyroid-stimulating hormone (TSH)	Thyrotropin-releasing hormone (TRH)	None known	Stimulates thyroid gland to make thyroid hormone
Prolactin (PRL)	TRH and other factors have been suggested as stimulators of PRL in some species, but this is not certain.	Dopamine	Stimulates milk formation in mammals; participates in mineral balance in other vertebrates

the hypothalamus. This results in an increase in the amount of ADH that is secreted into the blood from the posterior pituitary. ADH acts to increase the number of water-channel proteins called aquaporins that are present in the apical membranes of cells in the collecting ducts of the kidneys (refer back to Figure 49.11). Water is reabsorbed from the filtrate through these aquaporins. Minimizing the volume of water lost in the urine is an adaptation that conserves body water when necessary.

At high concentrations, ADH also increases blood pressure by stimulating vasoconstriction of blood vessels, a function that accounts for the other common name of ADH, vasopressin. Like oxytocin, therefore, ADH has more than one function. The two major functions of ADH are related in that they contribute to maintaining blood pressure and fluid levels in the body.

Oxytocin and ADH are well-studied examples of the evolution of hormones. Although these two hormones are found only in mammals, many invertebrates and all nonmammalian vertebrates secrete one or more polypeptides that are chemically similar to oxytocin and ADH but are not identical to the mammalian hormones. One of these is **vasotocin**, which combines some of the chemical structure of oxytocin and ADH. Research indicates that an ancestral vasotocin-encoding gene duplicated at some point, and then those two genes evolved into the genes for oxytocin and ADH found in mammals. Because only mammals lactate, the functions of vasotocin in birds, fishes, and other vertebrates must be different from that of oxytocin in mammals. Research has shown that vasotocin is responsible for regulating ion and water balance in the blood of nonmammalian vertebrates. The observation that members of the vasotocin/oxytocin/ADH gene family arose early in animal evolution also suggests that oxytocin and ADH may have additional, unrecognized actions that have been retained in mammals. For example, human males have oxytocin in their blood, but its role cannot be the same as in females because, of course, only females give birth and lactate. The major physiological functions of oxytocin in male humans and other animals have not been unequivocally identified.

50.3 Hormonal Control of Metabolism and Energy Balance

Learning Outcomes:

1. Explain how the structure of the thyroid gland is linked to its function (synthesis of thyroid hormone).
2. Describe the important anatomical features of the thyroid gland and the major function of thyroid hormone in adult animals.
3. List the hormones produced by the pancreas and adrenal glands, and provide a brief description of the major metabolic functions of each.
4. **Core Skill** » Identify one or more ways in which type 1 and type 2 diabetes mellitus can be distinguished if an individual shows symptoms of diabetes.

An important function of the endocrine system is to regulate an animal's metabolic rate and energy balance. Hormones are partly responsible for regulating energy balance by modulating appetite,

digestion, absorption of nutrients, and the concentration of glucose in the blood and its transport into cells. Although many hormones are involved in these processes, those from the thyroid gland, adrenal glands, pancreas, and adipose tissue have particularly important functions in vertebrates, as described in this section.

Thyroid Hormone Stimulates Metabolism

Thyroid tissue does not always form a single, distinct gland in vertebrates. In fishes, for example, thyroid tissue is scattered throughout the body. In tetrapods, it is more consolidated into paired glands in the neck or, in mammals, in a single bilobed gland straddling the trachea just below the larynx (**Figure 50.4a**). Regardless of its appearance or location, however, the thyroid consists of many small, spherical structures called follicles, each consisting of a shell of epithelial cells called follicular cells and a core of a gel-like substance called the colloid. The colloid consists primarily of large amounts of the protein thyroglobulin (TG), which plays a major role in the synthesis of thyroid hormone.

Synthesis of Thyroid Hormone Thyroid hormone is produced when thyrotropin-releasing hormone (TRH; see Table 50.2), which is made in the hypothalamus, stimulates the anterior pituitary gland to secrete thyroid-stimulating hormone (TSH) into the blood. TSH stimulates the follicular cells of the thyroid gland to begin the process of making thyroid hormone. Thyroid hormone has a negative feedback effect on the hypothalamus and anterior pituitary, preventing them from producing too much TRH and TSH, thereby keeping the circulating concentration of thyroid hormone in check.

Figure 50.4b shows the pathway leading to thyroid hormone synthesis. First, iodide—converted in the intestine from dietary iodine—diffuses from the bloodstream into the interstitial fluid, from where it is transported across the basolateral membrane of the thyroid follicular cells. The iodide then diffuses through the apical membrane and enters the colloid, where it is oxidized back to iodine and bonds to tyrosine side chains in thyroglobulin. When the thyroid follicular cells are stimulated by TSH, the apical membranes undergo endocytosis, bringing colloid with its iodinated thyroglobulin into the cell. The endocytotic vesicles fuse with lysosomes. There, lysosomal enzymes cleave the iodinated tyrosines from thyroglobulin to form **thyroxine**, also called T_4, because it contains four iodines and **triiodothyronine**, or T_3, which has three iodines. Both T_4 and T_3 then diffuse out of the follicular cells across the basolateral membrane into the blood. These molecules are carried throughout the body and diffuse into cells. Inside cells, most of the T_4 is converted by enzymes that remove one iodine, forming T_3. It is T_3 that actually binds to cellular receptor proteins. T_4 can be considered, therefore, as a circulating reservoir of the active hormone T_3. From here on, we will for simplicity refer only to T_3 as thyroid hormone.

Stimulation of Metabolism A major action of thyroid hormone in adult animals is to stimulate energy expenditure by many different cell types. This occurs in large part by increasing the number and activity of the Na^+/K^+-ATPase pumps in plasma membranes. As these pumps hydrolyze ATP, the cellular concentration of ATP decreases. This decrease releases feedback inhibition on the cell's metabolism

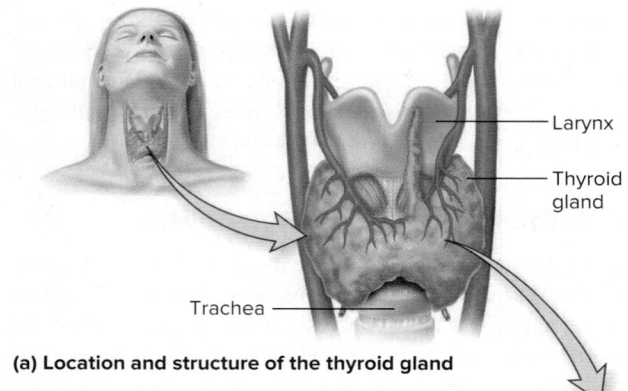

(a) Location and structure of the thyroid gland

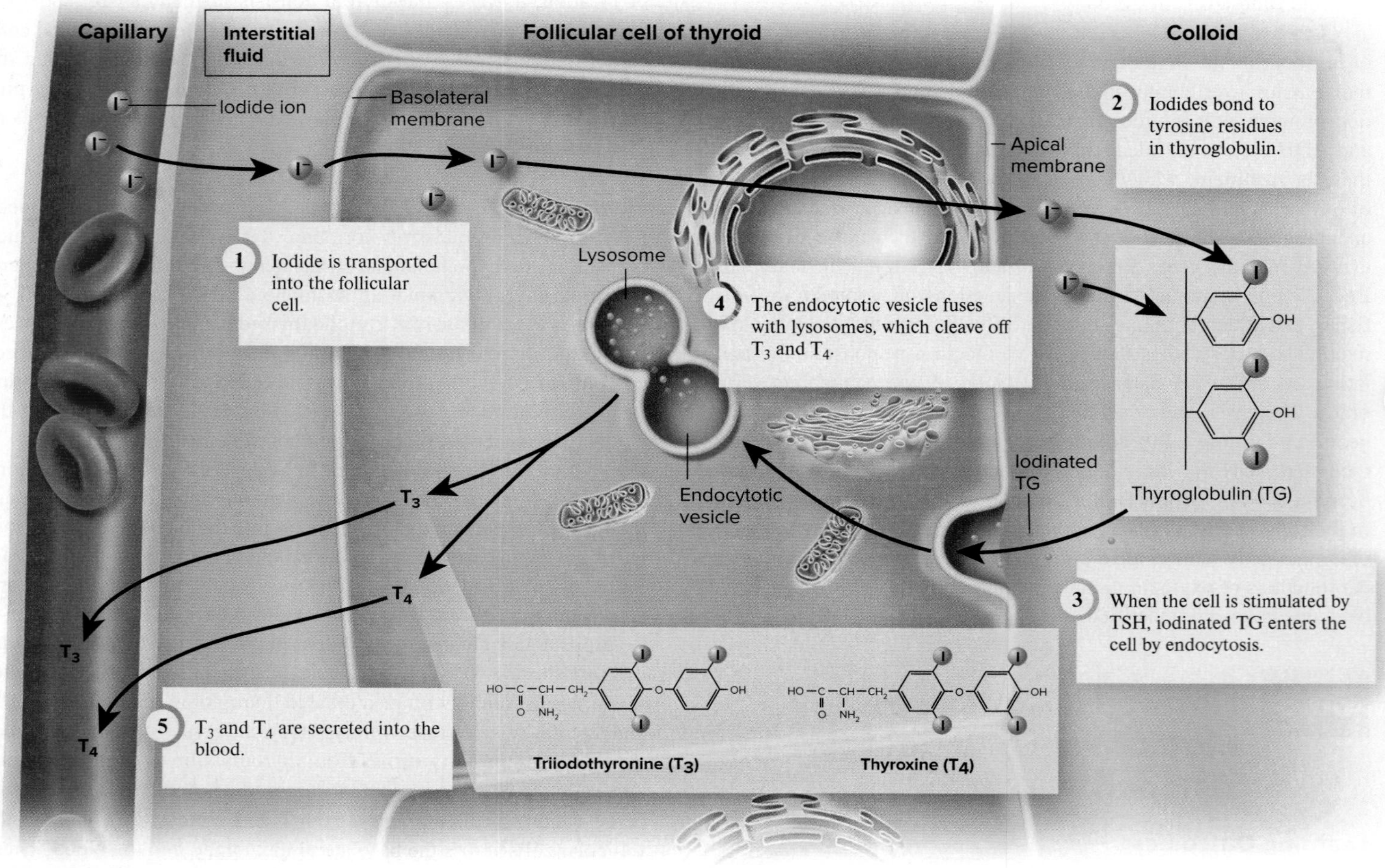

- Larynx
- Thyroid gland
- Trachea

Figure 50.4   The thyroid gland and synthesis of thyroid hormone. (a) Location and structure of the gland in a human. Vertebrates usually have thyroid tissue in the neck region, but it is not always consolidated into a single structure as shown here. **(b)** The steps involved in production of thyroid hormone. Shown is a cross section through a small part of a single follicle in a thyroid gland, with a nearby capillary (not to scale). The blood delivers iodide to the gland and picks up thyroid hormone secreted by the gland. Although T_4 and T_3 are both synthesized in the thyroid gland, T_3 is the active form of thyroid hormone. T_4 circulates in the blood and gets converted by cells to T_3.

Capillary   Interstitial fluid   **Follicular cell of thyroid**   Colloid

- I^- — Iodide ion
- Basolateral membrane

2 Iodides bond to tyrosine residues in thyroglobulin.

- Apical membrane

1 Iodide is transported into the follicular cell.

Lysosome

4 The endocytotic vesicle fuses with lysosomes, which cleave off T_3 and T_4.

Thyroglobulin (TG)

T_3

Endocytotic vesicle

T_4

Iodinated TG

3 When the cell is stimulated by TSH, iodinated TG enters the cell by endocytosis.

T_3

T_4

5 T_3 and T_4 are secreted into the blood.

Triiodothyronine (T₃)   Thyroxine (T₄)

(b) Synthesis of thyroid hormone

of glucose. As a result, glucose metabolism is increased, providing the energy required to produce more ATP. Whenever metabolism is increased, heat production is increased. Consequently, a person with a hyperactive thyroid gland (hyperthyroidism; from the Greek *hyper*, meaning over or above) generally feels warm, whereas the opposite condition (hypothyroidism; from the Greek *hypo*, meaning under or below) results in a sensation of coldness. Biologists have estimated that up to 70% of the heat produced by some endotherms is attributable solely to the actions of thyroid hormone on metabolic rate. Therefore, it is not surprising that humans with hyperthyroidism often lose weight, while weight gain is typically a problem in hypothyroidism.

Effect of Iodine Deficiency   The observation that thyroid hormone cannot be made without iodine leads to some interesting and unique consequences. The availability of iodine in the diet of most animals varies widely. As a consequence, the ability to store large amounts of thyroglobulin in the colloid of the thyroid was an important evolutionary adaptation. In this way, during times when iodine ingestion is sufficient, many thyroglobulin molecules have their tyrosine residues bound to iodines, one of the first steps in forming T_3. During times of low iodine availability, this reservoir of iodinated tyrosines in thyroglobulin molecules can be tapped. Humans, for example, have at least a 2-month supply of thyroid hormones even if dietary iodine

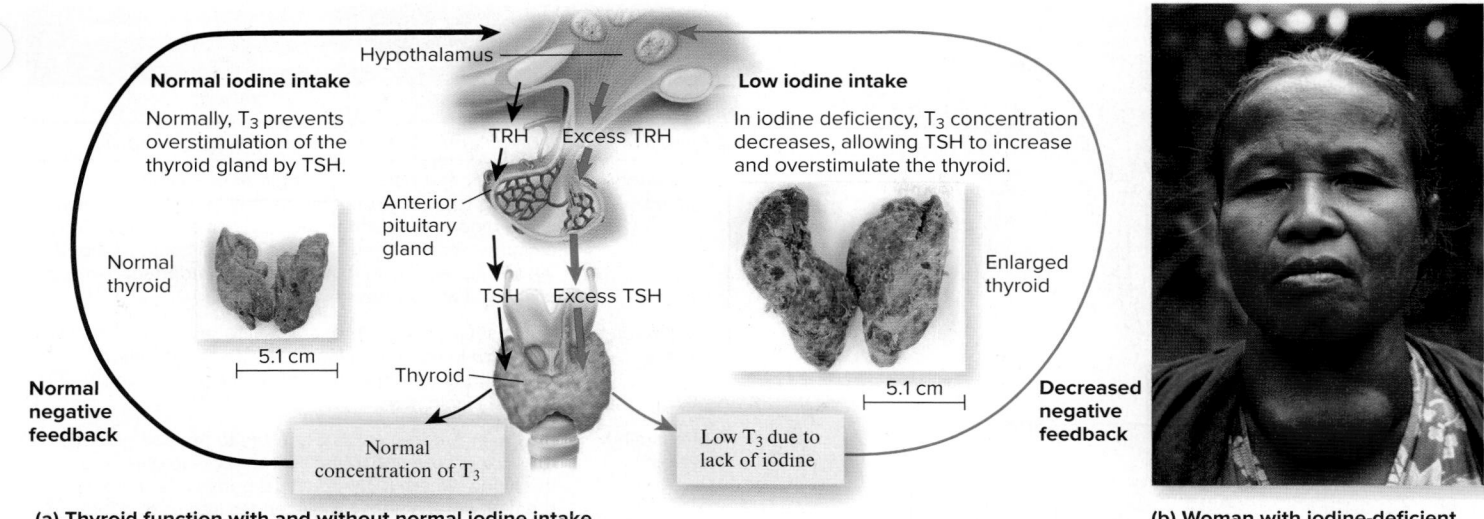

(a) Thyroid function with and without normal iodine intake

(b) Woman with iodine-deficient goiter

Figure 50.5 Consequences of inadequate iodine in the diet. (a) With normal iodine intake, as shown on the left, T_3 controls TSH secretion by negative feedback. Without adequate iodine, as shown on the right, less T_3 is synthesized, which decreases the negative feedback effect of T_3. Consequently, the TSH concentration increases and the thyroid gland enlarges. **(b)** An extreme example of an enlarged thyroid gland, or goiter, due to iodine deficiency. a (left inset, right inset): ©S. Goodwin & Dr. Max Hincke, Division of Clinical and Functional Anatomy, University of Ottawa; b: ©Bruce Coleman Inc./ AlamyStock Photo

 Core Concept: Systems Recall from Chapter 41 that a key way in which homeostasis is maintained is via negative feedback. Negative feedback participates in the control mechanisms that regulate most organ systems, including the endocrine system. Notice in Figure 50.5 how a change in dietary intake of iodine results in decreased negative feedback and subsequent over-growth of the thyroid gland.

becomes unavailable. In most industrialized countries, iodine deficiency is rarely a problem due to the introduction of iodized salt in the mid-20th century. However, in some regions of the world, it is still a major health problem.

The left side of **Figure 50.5a** shows the pattern of T_3 production from a healthy thyroid gland when iodine ingestion is adequate. The right side of the figure shows the consequences when T_3 is not produced in normal amounts, for example, due to a lack of iodine in the diet. Recall that hormones that are secreted in response to the actions of anterior pituitary gland hormones often exert a check on their own blood concentrations by negative feedback inhibition. If the plasma concentration of T_3 becomes lower than normal due to inadequate iodine ingestion, there will be less negative feedback on the hypothalamus and anterior pituitary gland, resulting in increased TRH and, consequently, TSH concentrations. The thyroid gland responds to the increased TSH by increasing the cellular machinery needed to produce more and more thyroglobulin, even though in the absence of iodine, no additional T_3 can be synthesized. What results is an overgrown gland that still lacks the resources to make T_3. This condition is known as an **iodine-deficient goiter** (**Figure 50.5b**). In humans, the problem can be alleviated either by adding iodine to the diet or by taking pills that contain thyroid hormone. Goiters are not unique to humans. Iodine deficiency is relatively common among vertebrates, and goiters are found frequently in reptiles and birds, particularly those that subsist on all-seed diets, which are generally low in iodine.

Hormones of the Adrenal Glands and Pancreas Regulate the Concentration of Energy-Yielding Molecules in the Blood

Thyroid hormone regulates an animal's metabolism. For metabolism to proceed normally, however, cells must have adequate sources of energy available, usually in the form of glucose and fatty acids. The brain, in particular, must have a constant supply of glucose because brain cells have relatively limited storage capacity for fuel. Regulation of energy availability to cells is in large part accomplished by the hormones of the adrenal glands and the pancreas.

Adrenal Glands The adrenal glands, so named because they sit on top of the kidneys (from the Latin *ad*, meaning toward, and *renis*, meaning kidney), are multifunctional glands that contain an inner region called the adrenal medulla and an outer region called the adrenal cortex (**Figure 50.6**). These two regions produce different hormones that have widespread effects in animals, including effects on metabolism (see **Table 50.3** for a summary of many of the metabolic and nonmetabolic actions of these hormones).

When an animal is fasting, the sympathetic nervous system stimulates the cells of the adrenal medulla to secrete the amine hormones epinephrine and norepinephrine. Together, these two hormones are responsible for most of the physiological reactions of the fight-or-flight response that were described in Chapter 43 and Table 9.1. These reactions include increased production of glucose by the liver

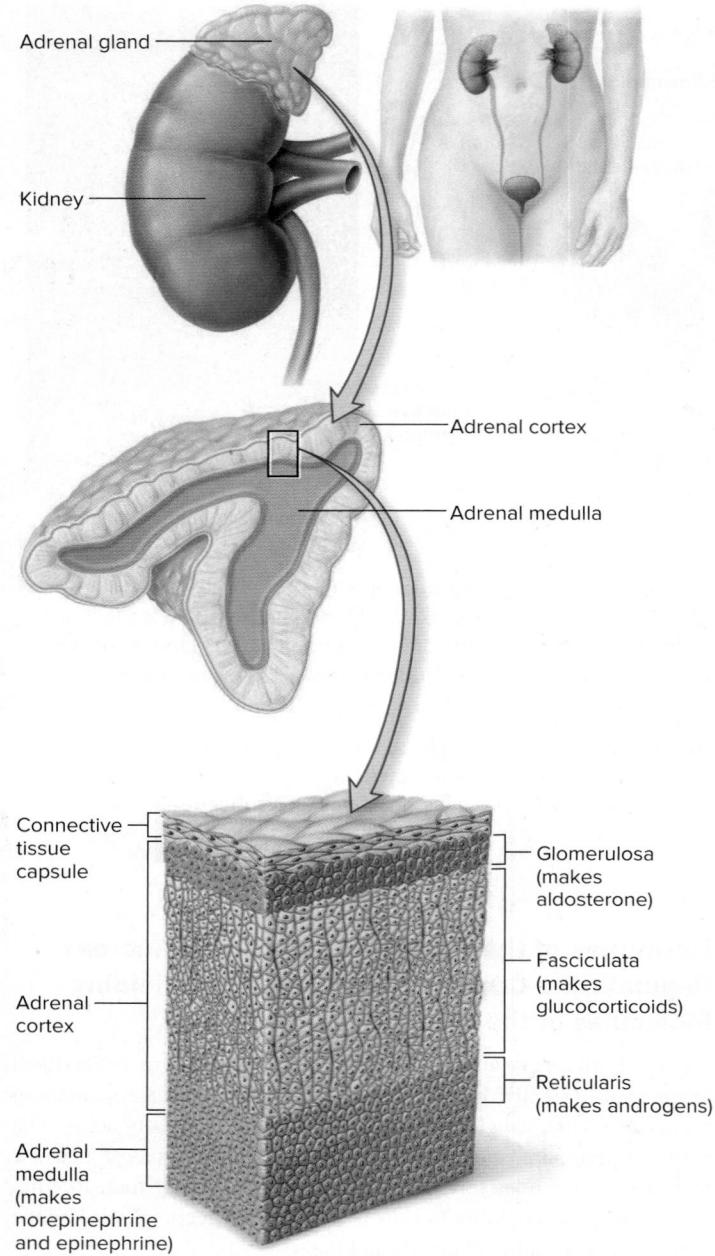

Adrenal gland

Kidney

Adrenal cortex

Adrenal medulla

Connective tissue capsule

Glomerulosa (makes aldosterone)

Fasciculata (makes glucocorticoids)

Adrenal cortex

Reticularis (makes androgens)

Adrenal medulla (makes norepinephrine and epinephrine)

Figure 50.6 **Location, structure, and function of the adrenal glands.**

Table 50.3	Major Actions of Hormones Secreted by the Adrenal Glands
Site of action	**Action(s)**
Epinephrine and norepinephrine (secreted by the adrenal medulla)	
Circulatory system	Increase heart rate and strength of heart contractions to maximize pumping of blood to all parts of the body; dilate blood vessels that enter tissues requiring more oxygen—such as skeletal muscle—and constrict blood vessels to regions of less immediate importance—such as the gut and kidneys
Respiratory system	Dilate small airways (bronchioles) to reduce resistance to airflow in mammals; increase rate and depth of breathing to maximize oxygen intake and carbon dioxide elimination
Metabolic system	Increase glycogenolysis in muscle to provide glucose for muscle cells and in the liver to provide glucose to the blood, where it can reach all body cells; increase breakdown of adipose triglycerides into usable fuel (fatty acids) that can then enter the bloodstream; stimulate secretion of glucagon, which acts on the liver to promote gluconeogenesis
Nervous system	Increase arousal and alertness; inhibit nonessential functions such as appetite
Glucocorticoids (secreted by the adrenal cortex)	
Liver	Stimulate gluconeogenesis, thus providing glucose to the blood
Adipose tissue	Stimulate breakdown of triglycerides into fatty acids and glycerol for fuel
Muscle and adipose tissue	Inhibit sensitivity to insulin, making more glucose available to brain cells, which do not require insulin to transport glucose across their plasma membranes
Bone	Inhibit bone growth and formation, because such processes require large amounts of nutrients that could be used to combat stress instead
Lungs	Stimulate lung maturation in the fetus
Immune	Suppress immune system function and reduce inflammation
Other	Regulate Na^+ and Cl^- balance in migratory fishes; stimulate nervous system development in most vertebrates; stimulate protein breakdown to provide amino acids to the liver for gluconeogenesis; inhibit reproduction

via stimulation of glycogenolysis (release of glucose from glycogen) and gluconeogenesis (synthesis of glucose from other sources) (refer back to Figure 47.2).

The outer part of the adrenal gland, the cortex, is subdivided into three zones: the glomerulosa, the fasciculata, and the reticularis (see Figure 50.6). The outer zone, the glomerulosa, is the region that makes the hormone aldosterone, which acts to maintain Na^+, K^+, and water balance (described later). The innermost cortical zone, known as the reticularis, functions in humans to make certain androgens, but its function in other animals is not as clear. The bulk of the cortex is the middle zone, the fasciculata, which produces glucocorticoid hormones such as **cortisol**.

Glucocorticoids are a group of related catabolic hormones that promote the breakdown of molecules and macromolecules. For example, they act on bone, immune, muscle, and adipose tissue to break down proteins and lipids to provide energy for the body's organs—in particular, vital organs such as the heart and brain. This source of energy is not only important for an animal that is fasting, but also for one that is facing an acute stress (traditionally defined in biology as a real or perceived threat to homeostasis), because feeding and digestion both stop during the fight-or-flight response. Consequently, internal stores become the only source of energy. These adrenal steroids are called glucocorticoids because one of their major actions is to promote gluconeogenesis in the liver during times of stress, thus providing glucose to the blood. Glucocorticoid release is stimulated by the anterior pituitary hormone adrenocorticotropic hormone (ACTH), the release of which in turn is stimulated by the neurohormone corticotropin-releasing hormone (CRH) (refer back to Table 50.2).

The actions of these two hormones are opposite with respect to each other—insulin decreases and glucagon increases blood glucose concentrations.

Maintaining homeostatic concentrations of glucose and other nutrients in the blood is a vital process that keeps cells functioning optimally. When an animal has not eaten for some time, its energy stores become depleted, and the blood glucose concentration begins to decrease. Under these conditions, glucagon is secreted into the blood, where it acts on the liver to stimulate glycogenolysis within seconds (**Figure 50.8**, right side). A second action of glucagon on the liver is particularly important for responses to prolonged fasting. In that case, glucagon stimulates gluconeogenesis. Due to the combined actions of cortisol, epinephrine, and glucagon, the concentration of glucose in the blood of a fasting animal is prevented from decreasing significantly below the normal homeostatic range.

Hormonal Changes After a Meal In contrast to fasting, after an animal eats a meal, the concentrations of glucose and other nutrients in the blood become elevated. Restoring the normal blood concentrations of glucose, fats, and amino acids is almost exclusively under the control of insulin, one of the few hormones that is absolutely essential for survival in animals. The secretion of insulin is directly stimulated by an increased concentration of glucose in the blood (Figure 50.8, left side). Once in the blood, insulin acts on plasma membrane receptors located primarily in cells of adipose and skeletal and cardiac muscle tissues to facilitate the transport of glucose across the plasma membrane into the cytosol. Glucose is then metabolized for cellular functions or used to synthesize stored energy forms such as fat.

As discussed in Chapter 47, the process of glucose transport involves the actions of proteins called glucose transporters (GLUTs; refer back to Figure 47.3). These proteins are located in cytosolic membrane-bound vesicles. The major function of insulin is to stimulate fusion of the vesicles with the plasma membrane. Once a vesicle with its GLUTs fuses with the plasma membrane, the GLUTs begin transporting glucose from the extracellular fluid into the cell. When the blood glucose concentration returns to normal, the stimulus for insulin secretion disappears, and the insulin concentration in the blood decreases. This, in turn, results in a decrease in the number of GLUTs in plasma membranes, because the GLUTs are subjected to endocytosis and thereby return to membrane vesicles in the cytosol. The action of insulin is not limited to glucose transport. It also stimulates the transport of amino acids into cells and promotes fat deposition in adipose tissue.

In the absence of sufficient insulin, as occurs in the disease **type 1 diabetes mellitus (T1DM)**, less extracellular glucose can cross plasma membranes, and consequently, glucose accumulates to a very high concentration in the blood. T1DM occurs in many mammals and other vertebrates. It is caused when the body's immune system mistakenly attacks and destroys the insulin-producing cells of the islets of Langerhans. One consequence of the disease is that muscle and adipose cells cannot receive the normal amount of glucose to produce the ATP they require. In addition, the unusually large amount of glucose in the blood overwhelms the kidneys' ability to reabsorb it from the kidney filtrate, and glucose appears in the urine. Fortunately, this form of the disease

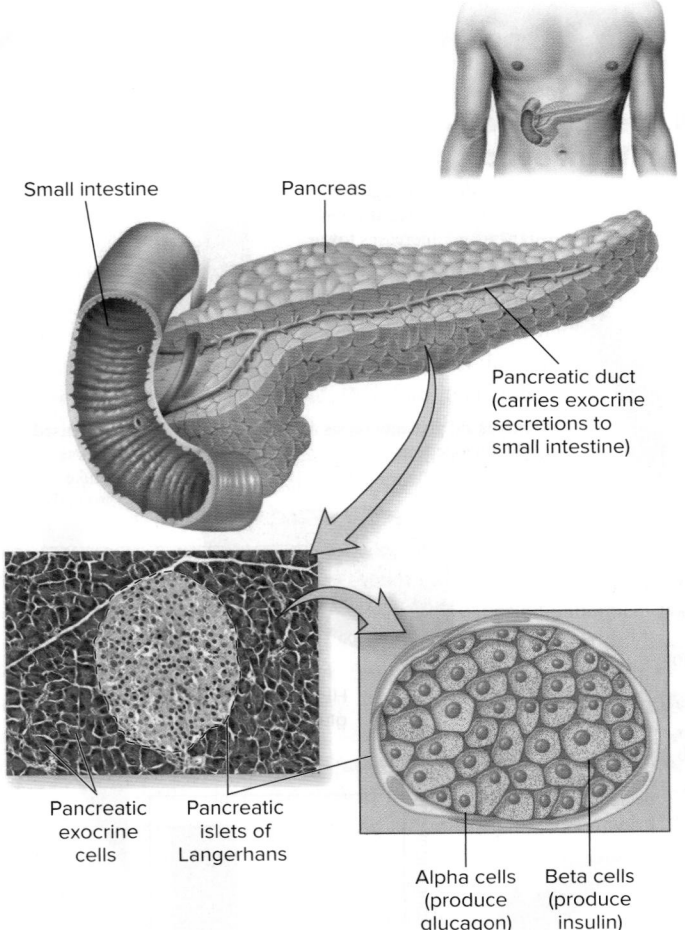

Small intestine   Pancreas

Pancreatic duct
(carries exocrine
secretions to
small intestine)

Pancreatic
exocrine
cells

Pancreatic
islets of
Langerhans

Alpha cells
(produce
glucagon)

Beta cells
(produce
insulin)

Figure 50.7 Location, appearance, and internal structure of the mammalian pancreas. Within the exocrine pancreas are scattered islets of Langerhans, which are endocrine tissue. Only the exocrine products are secreted into the intestine. The hormones from the islets of Langerhans are secreted into the blood (not shown). (bottom left): ©Cultura RM/Alamy Stock Photo

 Core Skill: Connections The pancreas contains both exocrine and endocrine tissue. Is this property ever observed in other organs? (Hint: Think about the processes associated with digestion and absorption of food described in Chapter 46.)

Pancreas The pancreas is a complex organ that is both an exocrine and endocrine gland (**Figure 50.7**). An **exocrine gland** is one in which epithelial cells secrete chemicals into a duct, which carries those molecules directly to another structure or to the outside surface of the body. Familiar examples of exocrine glands include the sweat glands and salivary glands. Most of the mass of the pancreas consists of exocrine cells. The secretions of the exocrine pancreas empty into the small intestine, where they aid digestion.

The nonexocrine portion of the pancreas consists of endocrine cells that produce polypeptide hormones. Spherical clusters of endocrine cells called **islets of Langerhans** are scattered in large numbers throughout the pancreas. Within the islets are alpha cells, which make **glucagon**, and beta cells, which make **insulin**.

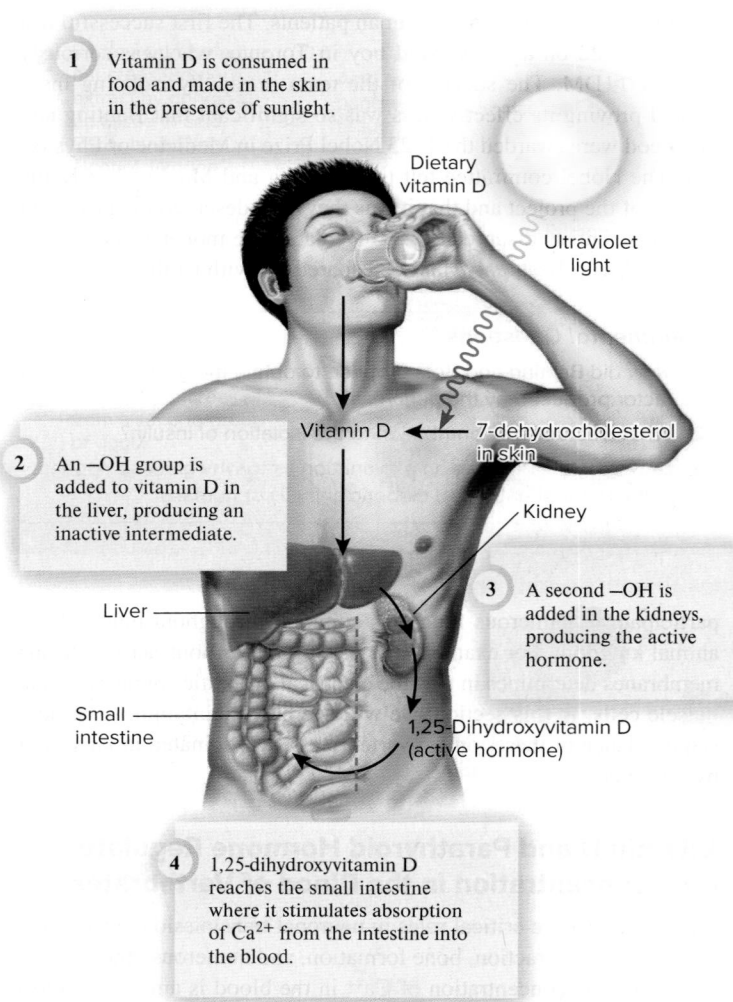

1. Vitamin D is consumed in food and made in the skin in the presence of sunlight.

Dietary vitamin D

Ultraviolet light

Vitamin D ← 7-dehydrocholesterol in skin

2. An —OH group is added to vitamin D in the liver, producing an inactive intermediate.

Kidney

Liver

Small intestine

3. A second —OH is added in the kidneys, producing the active hormone.

1,25-Dihydroxyvitamin D (active hormone)

4. 1,25-dihydroxyvitamin D reaches the small intestine where it stimulates absorption of Ca^{2+} from the intestine into the blood.

Figure 50.10   **Synthesis of the active hormone formed from vitamin D or its precursor in the skin.**

Concept Check: *Would you predict that all mammals synthesize the active form of vitamin D using the energy of sunlight?*

to activate expression of a Ca^{2+} pump in the intestinal epithelium, thereby stimulating the absorption of Ca^{2+}. The Ca^{2+} then enters the blood, which delivers the ions to tissues for such activities as building bone and maintaining nerve, muscle, and heart functions. If the active form of vitamin D is not present in the blood at a sufficient level, the bones lose Ca^{2+} and become weakened.

Parathyroid Hormone   Even when Ca^{2+} is not present in the diet, or when 1,25-dihydroxyvitamin D is not formed in normal amounts because of insufficient exposure to sunlight, the blood concentration of Ca^{2+} does not normally decrease significantly, because of a hormone called **parathyroid hormone (PTH)**. In all tetrapods, this hormone is secreted from several small glands in the neck called parathyroid glands, which in humans are located behind the thyroid gland (**Figure 50.11a**). Fishes produce parathyroid hormone from their gills and do not have parathyroid glands; recent evidence suggests that the gills of fishes and parathyroid glands of tetrapods are evolutionarily related. Cells of the parathyroid glands (or gills)

express receptors in their plasma membranes that bind extracellular Ca^{2+}. The binding of Ca^{2+} to these receptors inhibits the secretion of PTH. Thus, a decrease in the blood concentration of Ca^{2+} ends this inhibition and stimulates the cells of the parathyroid glands to secrete more PTH.

PTH acts on bone to stimulate the activity of cells that dissolve the mineral part of bone. This activity releases Ca^{2+}, which then enters the blood (**Figure 50.11b**). Typically, only a very small fraction of the total Ca^{2+} in bone is removed in this way. Therefore, besides providing a skeletal framework for the vertebrate body, bone also serves as an important reservoir of Ca^{2+}. PTH also acts to increase reabsorption of Ca^{2+} from the filtrate in the kidneys, so less Ca^{2+} is excreted in the urine. If the blood Ca^{2+} concentration increases, PTH secretion is inhibited. Without PTH, Ca^{2+} homeostasis is not possible.

Calcitonin   In addition to 1,25-dihydroxyvitamin D and PTH, another hormone called **calcitonin** functions in Ca^{2+} homeostasis in some vertebrates, notably fishes and possibly in some mammals. Calcitonin is a polypeptide produced in and secreted from cells in the thyroid gland. Its function is the opposite in many respects of that of PTH. Calcitonin promotes excretion of Ca^{2+} via the kidneys and deposition of Ca^{2+} into bone, thereby decreasing the blood Ca^{2+} concentration. This function is especially important in marine fishes, because of the high Ca^{2+} content of seawater and the entry of this ion into the body fluids of the animals when they drink (refer back to Figure 41.17).

BIO **TIPS**   **THE QUESTION** *What might happen to the blood concentrations of Ca^{2+} and parathyroid hormone (PTH) if the kidney enzyme responsible for the formation of 1,25-dihydroxyvitamin D was absent, nonfunctional, or inhibited for some reason?*

TOPIC   **What topic in biology does this question address?**
The topic is the relationship between the blood concentrations of Ca^{2+} and those of two hormones that are known to help regulate Ca^{2+} homeostasis. Specifically, how does a change in the amount of one hormone affect the blood concentrations of the other and of Ca^{2+}?

INFORMATION   **What information do you know based on the question and your understanding of the topic?**
From the question, you know that 1,25-dihydroxyvitamin D is not being produced in normal amounts. From your understanding of the topic, you may remember that this hormone acts in the small intestine to stimulate absorption of Ca^{2+} into the blood. You also know the function of PTH and that its secretion is controlled by the blood concentration of Ca^{2+}.

PROBLEM-SOLVING **S**TRATEGY   **Sort out the steps in a complicated process. Predict the outcome.** Based on your knowledge of the relationships among the blood concentrations of Ca^{2+}, 1,25-dihydroxyvitamin D, and PTH, you can predict the sequence of events that will follow a decrease in the concentration of 1,25-dihydroxyvitamin D.

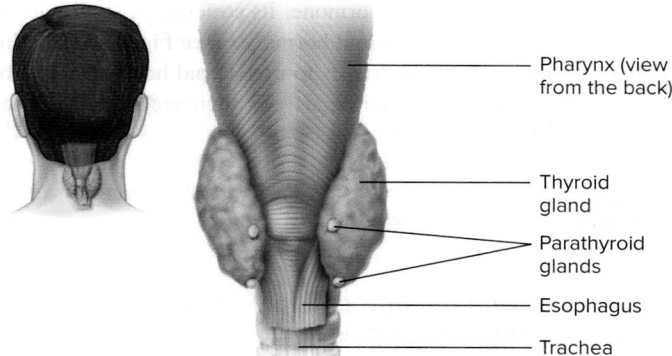

Pharynx (view from the back)

Thyroid gland

Parathyroid glands

Esophagus

Trachea

(a) Location of the parathyroid glands

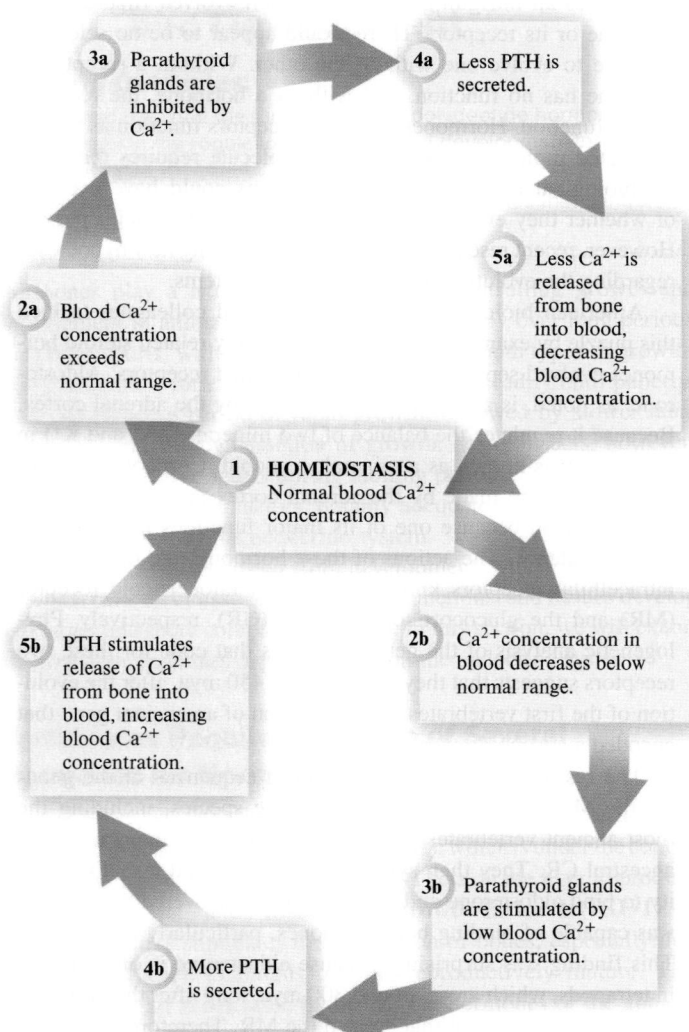

3a Parathyroid glands are inhibited by Ca^{2+}.

4a Less PTH is secreted.

5a Less Ca^{2+} is released from bone into blood, decreasing blood Ca^{2+} concentration.

2a Blood Ca^{2+} concentration exceeds normal range.

1 HOMEOSTASIS Normal blood Ca^{2+} concentration

5b PTH stimulates release of Ca^{2+} from bone into blood, increasing blood Ca^{2+} concentration.

2b Ca^{2+} concentration in blood decreases below normal range.

3b Parathyroid glands are stimulated by low blood Ca^{2+} concentration.

4b More PTH is secreted.

(b) Homeostatic control of blood Ca^{2+} concentration

Figure 50.11 The role of parathyroid hormone in calcium homeostasis. **(a)** In humans, four small parathyroid glands are located behind the thyroid. **(b)** The action of PTH: Steps 2a–5a occur when Ca^{2+} is in excess in the blood; steps 2b–5b occur when the concentration of Ca^{2+} in the blood is below normal.

Several Hormones Regulate the Extracellular Fluid Concentrations of Na⁺ and K⁺ in Vertebrates

Like Ca^{2+}, concentrations of Na^+ and K^+ in the body fluids of most animals are tightly regulated, because these ions are the basis of membrane potential formation and action potential generation (see Chapter 42), among other functions. Like Ca^{2+}, Na^+ and K^+ are ingested in the diet and excreted in the urine at rates that maintain homeostatic concentrations in the body fluids. Unlike Ca^{2+} in vertebrates, however, no large reservoirs exist in the body for Na^+ and K^+. One of the key mechanisms that regulates the concentrations of these ions in the blood is altering the rate of Na^+, K^+, and water reabsorption from the urine as it is being formed in the kidneys. This is accomplished in large part by the actions of three hormones: ADH, aldosterone, and atrial natriuretic peptide (**Figure 50.12**). All three of these hormones exert their effects on the kidneys.

The vertebrate kidney normally reabsorbs most Na^+ and K^+ from the fluid filtered through the glomeruli (refer back to Figure 49.9). However, dietary and other changes can alter the concentrations of these ions in the blood. When this happens, the kidney works to restore the ions to their normal concentrations. For example, if the blood Na^+ concentration increases above normal, the osmolarity of the blood will increase. Osmoreceptors in the brain detect this and stimulate ADH secretion from the posterior pituitary.

As mentioned earlier, ADH acts on the kidneys to reabsorb water from the forming urine. Increasing the amount of ADH available to act on the kidneys results in less water being excreted in the urine (and more being reabsorbed into the blood). In addition, the

 Core Skill: Modeling The goal of this modeling challenge is to make a model that shows the effects on Ca^{2+} homeostasis if cellular sensitivity to PTH is decreased.

Modeling Challenge: A type of endocrine disorder in many vertebrates, including mammals, occurs when target cells lose their ability to respond to a particular hormone. For example, target cells may lose their ability to express a functional receptor for a hormone. Consider the bottom part of the model in Figure 50.11b, with the steps labeled 1 through 5b. Revise that model to show how Ca^{2+} homeostasis would be affected if bone cells were unable to respond to PTH.

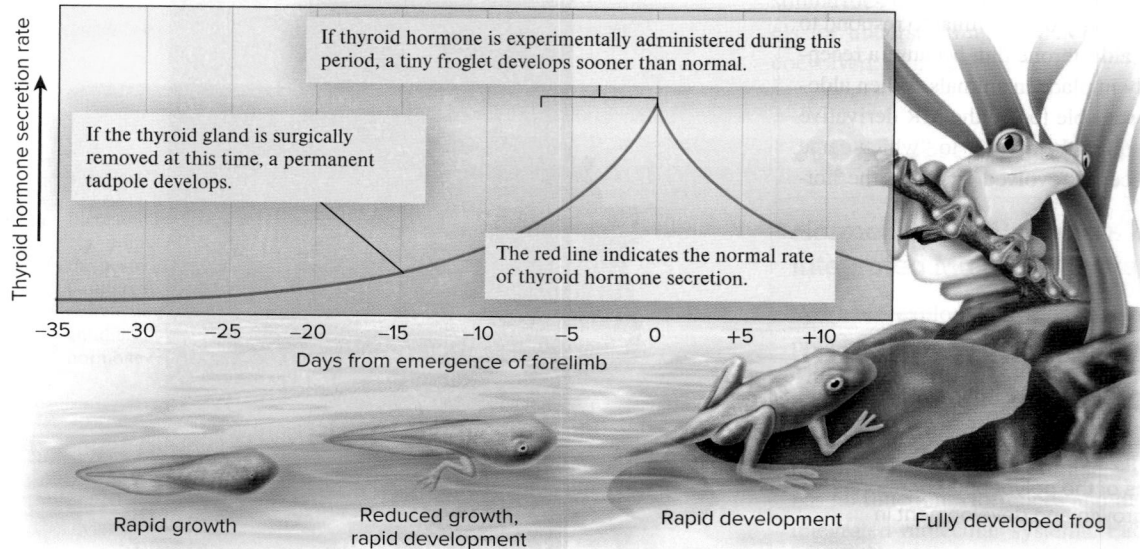

(a) The effect of thyroid hormones on tadpole development

If thyroid hormone is experimentally administered during this period, a tiny froglet develops sooner than normal.

If the thyroid gland is surgically removed at this time, a permanent tadpole develops.

The red line indicates the normal rate of thyroid hormone secretion.

Thyroid hormone secretion rate

Days from emergence of forelimb

Rapid growth   Reduced growth, rapid development   Rapid development   Fully developed frog

Stages of normal development

(b) Japanese flounder

Figure 50.14 **Effects of thyroid hormone on animal development.** **(a)** Experimental manipulation of thyroid hormone concentration can slow down or accelerate development of tadpoles. **(b)** The eyes of a bottom-dwelling flounder (*Platichthys flesus*) migrate to one side of the head during development, partly in response to thyroid hormone.
b: ©blickwinkel/Alamy Stock Photo

 Core Concept: Evolution The regulation of animal development is an ancestral function of thyroid hormone. In the course of evolution, this hormone has gained many other functions, but has retained a developmental role in all vertebrates, including humans.

As another example, thyroid hormone influences development among all vertebrates. In amphibians, thyroid hormone has a critical function in metamorphosis, notably in tadpoles, where it promotes the resorption of the tail and development of the legs (**Figure 50.14a**). This effect can be dramatically demonstrated by experimentally altering a tadpole's thyroid hormone levels. Decreasing the amount of thyroid hormone results in a tadpole that does not transform into a frog, whereas increasing the hormone causes a tadpole to undergo metamorphosis sooner than normal, resulting in a tiny froglet.

In fishes, thyroid hormone has an equally critical function in development. For example, among species of flatfish such as flounder, thyroid hormone is responsible for the characteristic change in appearance that occurs in these species as they settle into a sedentary existence on the ocean bottom. The fins and gill covers migrate to the dorsal surface facing the water; the dorsal body surface becomes pigmented; and, most remarkably, the eyes migrate to the same side

of the head so that one eye is not unused on the side facing the ocean floor (**Figure 50.14b**). Each of these metamorphic events is under the direct control of thyroid hormone.

Invertebrates Grow and Develop in Spurts Under the Control of Three Major Hormones

Like vertebrate endocrine pathways, hormonal control systems in insects and other invertebrates often involve multiple glands and neural structures acting in concert. In insects, for example, the endocrine system is critical for the growth and development of larvae and their eventual development into pupae (**Figure 50.15**). In the case of larval growth and metamorphosis, specialized neurosecretory cells in the brain periodically secrete a hormone called **prothoracicotropic hormone (PTTH)**, which then stimulates a pair of endocrine glands called the prothoracic glands. These glands,

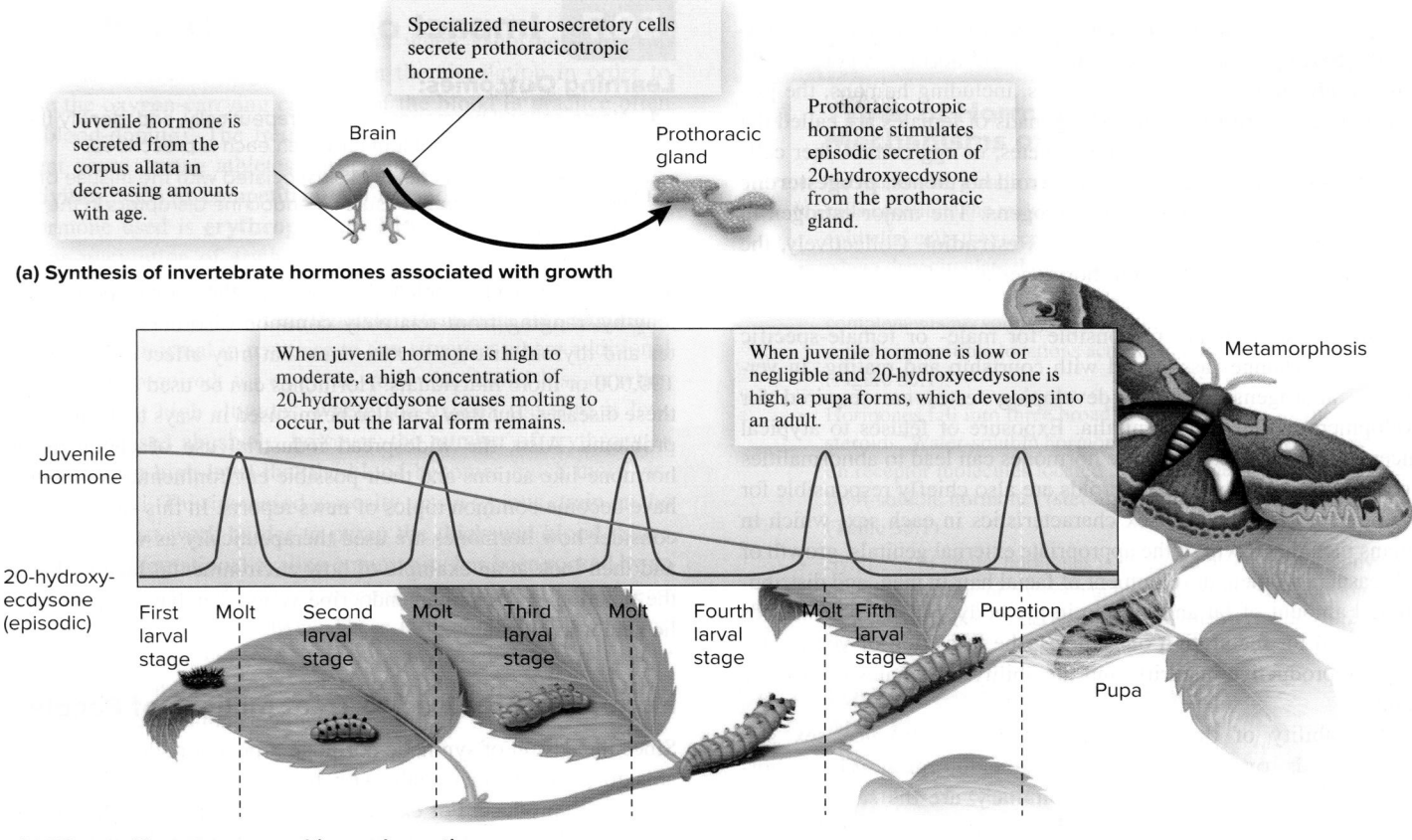

(a) **Synthesis of invertebrate hormones associated with growth**

(b) **Effects of hormones on molting and pupation**

Figure 50.15   Hormonal control of insect development.   Development of insects requires the coordinated actions of three hormones. Note: The relative concentrations and secretion patterns of 20-hydroxyecdysone and juvenile hormone in this figure are schematic and not representative of all insects.

Concept Check: *In what part of a cell do you predict the receptor for the steroid hormone 20-hydroxyecdysone is located?*

located in the thorax, synthesize and secrete into the hemolymph a steroid hormone called **20-hydroxyecdysone**. This hormone is secreted only periodically. In response to each burst of secretion, the larva undergoes a rapid development and molts (sheds its cuticle). It then begins a new developmental period until it molts again in response to another episode of secretion. The molting process is known as ecdysis, from which the name of the hormone is derived (refer back to Figure 33.13).

Throughout larval development, paired neurosecretory structures behind the brain, called the corpus allata, secrete another hormone, a protein called **juvenile hormone (JH)**. Although 20-hydroxyecdysone induces molting, JH prevents metamorphosis into an adult (hence the name juvenile, which reflects the fact that JH fosters the larval stage). As a larva progresses through different stages, however, the amount of JH it produces gradually declines until the concentration is nearly zero (see Figure 50.15). During this time, 20-hydroxyecdysone continues to be periodically secreted. The decline in JH below a certain concentration results in the transition from larva to pupa in response to a burst of 20-hydroxyecdysone. The near absence of JH is a prerequisite for the final step of metamorphosis into an adult.

50.6   Hormonal Control of Reproduction

Learning Outcomes:

1. List the vertebrate male and female sex steroids, their sites of production, and their functions in reproductive development.
2. **CoreSKILL »** Propose a mechanism by which hormones can link nutrition with reproduction.

The topic of reproduction is covered in detail in Chapter 51, but it is worth noting here that in all vertebrates and probably most invertebrates, reproduction is closely linked with endocrine function. In this section, we will briefly discuss the most common reproductive hormones and some of their major actions in male and female vertebrates.

The Gonads Secrete Sex Steroids That Influence Most Aspects of Reproduction

Hormones produced by the gonads of vertebrates have vital functions in nearly all aspects of reproduction, from reproductive behaviors to

The acrosomal reaction is followed by the **cortical reaction** (Figure 51.4b). The cytosolic Ca^{2+} concentration in eggs, as in most cells, is kept low by several mechanisms, including the transport of Ca^{2+} by an ATP-dependent pump out of the cytosol and into the endoplasmic reticulum. When the sperm binds to the egg, a small signaling molecule called inositol trisphosphate (IP_3) is released from the region of the plasma membrane nearest to the sperm entry point. IP_3 then binds to nearby sites on the endoplasmic reticulum (ER) and opens Ca^{2+} channels. Within seconds after a sperm cell binds to an egg, Ca^{2+} is released from the lumen of the ER and into the cytosol.

The release of Ca^{2+} in the cortical reaction has several important effects. First, it causes exocytosis of membrane-bound vesicles in the egg's cytosol called cortical granules. The cortical granules release enzymes and other substances that inactivate the sperm-binding proteins on the plasma membrane. At that time, also, the outer coating of the egg cell, known as the vitelline layer in sea urchins or the zona pellucida in vertebrates (see Figure 51.3), becomes hardened and begins to separate from the plasma membrane. These events create a barrier to additional sperm fusing with the egg. Additionally, the burst of cytosolic Ca^{2+} leads to the activation of molecular signaling pathways that initiate the first cell cycle and triggers an increase in protein synthesis and metabolism within the egg cell.

Shortly afterward, the nucleus of the sperm fuses with the nucleus of the egg, creating a diploid zygote. The first cell division of the zygote occurs approximately 90 minutes after fertilization in sea urchins and amphibians, but it can take up to 24 hours in mammals.

In a Given Species, Fertilization Occurs Either Outside or Inside the Female

For sperm to fertilize eggs, the two gametes must physically come into contact. In species with separate sexes, this can occur either outside or inside the female's body. When it occurs outside of the female, the process is called **external fertilization**. This type of fertilization occurs in aquatic environments, when eggs and sperm are released into the water in close enough proximity for fertilization to occur. The aqueous environment protects the gametes from drying out. Animals that reproduce by external fertilization show species-specific behaviors that help bring the eggs and sperm together. For instance, very soon after a female fish lays her eggs, a male deposits his sperm cells in the water nearby, where they spread over the clump of eggs. The fertilized eggs then develop outside the mother's body.

Although the aqueous environment protects against desiccation, eggs can be eaten by predators, washed away by currents, or subjected to potentially lethal changes in water temperature or another variable such as pH or oxygen level. Such environmental challenges have provided selection pressure for some species, including many aquatic or amphibious animals, to release very large numbers of eggs and sperm at once. For example, oysters may release several million gametes, as shown in the chapter opening photo.

In contrast to external fertilization, most terrestrial animals and some aquatic animals reproduce by **internal fertilization**, in which sperm are deposited within the reproductive tract of the female during the act called copulation. Internal fertilization protects the zygotes from desiccation, environmental hazards, and predation, and guarantees that sperm are placed and remain in very close proximity to eggs. Once fertilization occurs within the female, the zygotes then develop into offspring.

The behaviors and anatomical structures involved in achieving internal fertilization are extremely varied among species. Typically, mating involves accessory sex organs, which are reproductive structures other than the gonads. The external accessory sex organs involved in copulation include certain types of genitalia (for example, the **penis** and the **vagina** in mammals), which are used to physically join the male and female so that sperm can be deposited directly into the female's reproductive tract. A penis or analogous structure is present in most insects, reptiles, some species of birds (ratites and waterfowl), and all mammals. However, males of other vertebrate species—including most birds—that reproduce by internal fertilization lack a structure that can be inserted into the female, instead depositing sperm in the female by cloacal contact. The cloaca is a common opening for the reproductive, digestive, and excretory systems in these animals.

51.3   Human Reproductive Structure and Function

Learning Outcomes:

1. Describe the structures of the human male reproductive tract.
2. Outline the process of hormonal control of the male reproductive system.
3. Describe the structures of the human female reproductive tract.
4. Diagram the events of the ovarian cycle.
5. Outline the process of hormonal control of the reproductive cycle of the human female.
6. Explain how maternal hormones prepare the uterus to accept the embryo.

We turn now to a detailed look at the human reproductive system. For both sexes, we will begin with a description of the anatomy of the reproductive system, including the gonads and the accessory sex structures. We will then examine the hormones that control the production of the gametes and the preparation for and establishment of pregnancy.

The Human Male Reproductive Tract Is Specialized for Production and Ejaculation of Sperm

The external structures of the male reproductive tract—the genitalia—consist of the penis and the scrotum, the sac that contains the testes and holds them outside the body cavity where the temperature is better suited for spermatogenesis (**Figure 51.5**).

Each testis is composed of tightly packed **seminiferous tubules** encased in connective tissue. Surrounding the tubules are Leydig cells—endocrine cells that secrete the steroid hormone testosterone. Spermatogenesis begins at puberty and continues throughout life. It occurs all along the walls of the seminiferous tubules. Cells at the earliest stages of spermatogenesis—the spermatogonia—are located nearest the outer surface of the wall. Cells of more advanced stages are located progressively inward, so that the mature sperm are released into the tubule lumen. Cells within the seminiferous tubules are continuously

Another example of misuse occurs when a hormone is used to boost the number of erythrocytes in the circulation in order to increase the oxygen-carrying capacity of the blood (a practice often called blood-doping). The frequency of this practice has increased in recent years among athletes participating in long-distance aerobic activities, such as competitive cycling and cross-country skiing. The hormone used is **erythropoietin (EPO)**, which acts by stimulating the maturation of erythrocytes in the bone marrow and their release into the blood. EPO is primarily made by the kidneys as part of the homeostatic control of erythrocyte production. Its secretion is increased above normal in response to any situation where additional blood cells are required, for example, following blood loss or when a person lives at high altitudes, where the oxygen pressure is low. When EPO is used abusively, however, the number of erythrocytes can reach such a high level that the blood becomes much more viscous than normal. This increased viscosity puts a serious strain on the heart, which must work harder to pump the thickened blood. Since the 1990s, the international cycling community has been rocked by an alarming number of world-class European cyclists who died of heart attacks in the prime of their lives. These individuals had been using EPO to gain an unfair and, as it turns out, unwise advantage over their peers. Testing continues to detect injected EPO in the blood of some cyclists and other endurance athletes.

Synthetic Compounds May Act as Endocrine Disruptors

A recent and disturbing phenomenon is the growing prevalence of so-called **endocrine disruptors** in lakes, streams, ocean water, and soil exposed to pollution runoff. These chemicals are often derived from industrial waste and have molecular structures that in some cases sufficiently resemble estrogen to bind to estrogen receptors. They are also widespread in common household goods including nearly all plastic products. If these compounds make their way into drinking water or food, they can exert estrogen-like actions or inhibit the actions of the body's own estrogen. Such effects can lead to significant consequences for fertility and the development of embryos and fetuses.

The extent of the risk from endocrine disruptors is hotly debated, but the number of mature, functional germ cells produced in animals as diverse as mollusks and human males has declined substantially during the past 50 years in the U.S. In addition, researchers throughout the world have noted feminization of freshwater fishes downstream of wastewater facilities. For example, male fishes that were exposed to such conditions during development show increased production of proteins normally made by females bearing eggs. They also show changes in gonadal structures such that there is a resemblance to the female structures. Further research is being conducted to gain more information on the consequences of these contaminants for animal and human endocrine systems.

The U.S. Environmental Protection Agency currently lists about 10,000 chemicals that are recommended for screening or have already been documented to exert endocrine disruptive actions. Other than reproductive hormones, the hormones that are most commonly affected by different types of endocrine disruptors are thyroid hormone and, to a lesser extent, glucocorticoids.

Summary of Key Concepts

50.1 Types of Hormones and Their Mechanisms of Action

- The endocrine glands and other organs with hormone-secreting cells constitute the endocrine system. Endocrine glands contain epithelial cells that secrete hormones into the bloodstream, where they circulate throughout the body. Although slower than the electrical signaling in nervous systems, chemical signaling complements nervous system regulation through its varying actions in multiple locations across widely ranging time frames (Figure 50.1).
- Hormones fall into three broad classes: amines, polypeptides and steroids. Water-soluble hormones (amines and polypeptides) act on receptor molecules located in the plasma membrane, whereas lipid-soluble hormones (steroids) act on intracellular receptors (Table 50.1).
- Synthesis of amine hormones is mediated by enzymatic conversion of either tyrosine or tryptophan into their respective hormones. The steroid hormones are derived from cholesterol (Figure 50.2).

50.2 Links Between the Endocrine and Nervous Systems

- Sensory input from an animal's nervous system modulates the activity of certain endocrine glands and influences blood concentrations of many hormones.
- The hypothalamus in vertebrates is physically connected to the pituitary gland, which consists of anterior and posterior lobes (Figure 50.3).
- Within the hypothalamus are numerous neurons that synthesize neurohormones and stimulate the anterior pituitary. In response, the anterior pituitary gland synthesizes six different hormones that respond to the presence of hypothalamic neurohormones. They are adrenocorticotropic hormone (ACTH), follicle-stimulating hormone (FSH), luteinizing hormone (LH), growth hormone (GH), thyroid-stimulating hormone (TSH), and prolactin (PRL) (Table 50.2).
- In mammals, the neuron terminals in the posterior pituitary store and secrete one of two hormones: oxytocin or antidiuretic hormone (ADH).

50.3 Hormonal Control of Metabolism and Energy Balance

- Hormones are partly responsible for regulating energy use by cells, such as modulating appetite, digestion, absorption of nutrients, and blood concentration of glucose. Although many hormones are involved in these processes, one from the thyroid gland (T_3), three from the adrenal glands (cortisol, epinephrine, and norepinephrine), two from the pancreas (insulin and glucagon), and one from adipose tissue (leptin) have especially important functions in vertebrates.
- The thyroid gland makes T_3, which contains iodine. A major action of T_3 in adult animals is to stimulate energy consumption by many different cell types (Figures 50.4, 50.5).
- The adrenal glands produce epinephrine and norepinephrine in the medulla and glucocorticoids in the cortex; these hormones increase

the blood glucose concentration. The endocrine pancreas produces insulin and glucagon, which have opposite effects on blood glucose concentration (Figures 50.6, 50.7, Table 50.3).

- Maintaining normal glucose and other nutrient concentrations in the blood is a vital process that keeps cells functioning optimally. The combined short-term and long-term actions of insulin, glucagon, epinephrine, and cortisol help maintain normal blood glucose concentrations during fasting (Figure 50.8).

- Ground-breaking research by Banting, Best, MacLeod, and Collip isolated insulin for therapeutic use in treating diabetes mellitus (Figure 50.9).

- Adipose tissue is an important source of appetite-regulating hormones, including leptin, which acts on the hypothalamus to inhibit appetite.

50.4 Hormonal Control of Mineral Balance

- Because of the important functions that Ca^{2+} has in neuronal transmission, heart function, muscle contraction, and numerous other physiological processes, the concentration of Ca^{2+} in the blood is among the most tightly regulated variables in an animal's body. Vitamin D and parathyroid hormone, the latter produced by the parathyroid glands, regulate the blood concentration of Ca^{2+} (Figures 50.10, 50.11).

- Na^+ and K^+ play crucial roles in membrane potential formation, action potential generation, and other functions. A key mechanism that regulates blood concentrations of these ions is altering the rate of Na^+, K^+, and water reabsorption from the urine as it is being formed in the kidneys. This regulation is accomplished in large part by the actions of ADH, aldosterone, and atrial natriuretic peptide (Figure 50.12).

50.5 Hormonal Control of Growth and Development

- Hormones play a crucial role in regulating growth and development. In vertebrates, normal growth depends on a balance between growth hormone, insulin-like growth factor 1, and gonadal hormones. Thyroid hormones affect development among all vertebrates (Figures 50.13, 50.14).

- In insects, prothoracicotropic hormone, 20-hydroxyecdysone, and juvenile hormone control the growth of larvae and their development into pupae (Figure 50.15).

50.6 Hormonal Control of Reproduction

- Hormones produced by the gonads play vital roles in nearly all aspects of reproduction. The ability of the testes and ovaries to produce the sex steroids depends on the gonadotropins, which are the same in both sexes and include follicle-stimulating hormone and luteinizing hormone.

50.7 Impact on Public Health

- Hormones are used therapeutically to treat a variety of human disorders, including diabetes, infertility, growth disorders, asthma, and inflammation.

- Androgen misuse can disrupt normal hormone concentrations and cause health risks such as cardiovascular disease, skin problems,

cancer, infertility in men, and masculinizing traits in women. Blood-doping with erythropoietin can make blood dangerously thick.

- Endocrine disruptors, such as chemicals derived from industrial waste, may bind to estrogen receptors in animals' bodies. They may exert estrogen-like actions or inhibit the actions of the body's own estrogen.

Assess & Discuss

Test Yourself

1. Which is the defining feature of hormones?
   a. They are only produced in endocrine glands.
   b. They are secreted into the blood, where they may reach one or more types of distant target cells, thereby altering cell function throughout the body.
   c. They are released only by neurons.
   d. They are never released by neurons.
   e. They are secreted into ducts, where they diffuse to another nearby gland or other structure.

2. Steroid hormones are synthesized from _____ and bind to _____.
   a. proteins; membrane receptors
   b. fatty acids; membrane receptors
   c. tyrosine; intracellular receptors
   d. proteins; intracellular receptors
   e. cholesterol; intracellular receptors

3. Which of the following statements about polypeptide hormones is *false*?
   a. They bind to receptors located on the cell membrane.
   b. Most of them are lipophilic.
   c. They are the most abundant class of hormones.
   d. They normally activate second messengers.
   e. They bind reversibly to receptors.

4. Chronic deficiency of iodine in a vertebrate's diet will lead to
   a. increased secretion of TRH, decreased secretion of TSH, decreased T_3 concentration in the blood, and a goiter.
   b. decreased secretion of TRH and TSH, decreased T_3 concentration in the blood, and a goiter.
   c. increased T_3 concentration in the blood, decreased secretion of TRH and TSH, but no goiter.
   d. decreased T_3 concentration in the blood, increased secretion of TRH and TSH, and a goiter.
   e. decreased secretion of TRH, increased secretion of TSH, decreased T_3 concentration in the blood, and a goiter.

5. The hypothalamus and the pituitary gland are physically connected by
   a. arteries.
   b. the infundibular stalk and portal veins.
   c. the adrenal medulla.
   d. the spinal cord.
   e. the intermediate lobe.

6. Antidiuretic hormone (ADH)
   a. increases water reabsorption in the kidneys.
   b. regulates blood pressure by constricting arterioles.
   c. decreases the volume of urine produced by the kidneys.
   d. probably arose from the same ancestral gene as that of oxytocin.
   e. does all of the above.

7. Which of the following pairs of hormones are involved in the regulation of blood Ca^{2+} concentration in vertebrates?
   a. aldosterone and ANP
   b. insulin and glucagon

c. parathyroid hormone and 1,25-dihydroxyvitamin D
d. prolactin and oxytocin
e. thyroxine and TSH

8. In invertebrates, molting of larvae is stimulated by
   a. growth hormone.
   b. cortisol.
   c. juvenile hormone.
   d. 20-hydroxyecdysone.
   e. aldosterone.

9. Which of the following is *true* of the adrenal glands?
   a. They produce insulin.
   b. They produce hormones that control ion balance and maintain glucose homeostasis.
   c. They produce only steroid hormones.
   d. They are inhibited by the pituitary hormone ACTH.
   e. They chiefly regulate Ca^{2+} balance.

10. Endocrine disruptors are
    a. chemicals released by the nervous system to override the endocrine system.
    b. chemicals released by the male of a species to decrease the fertility of other males.
    c. drugs used to treat overactive endocrine structures.
    d. chemicals derived from industrial waste that may alter endocrine function.
    e. all of the above.

Conceptual Questions

1. What is the function of leptin, and what is the benefit to an animal of an adipose-derived signaling molecule? What function does an appetite serve in animals?

2. Distinguish between type 1 and type 2 diabetes mellitus.

3. **Core Concept: Systems** Organ systems often exert dual control over variables such as blood pressure, respiration, and growth. How do the opposing actions of insulin and glucagon maintain glucose homeostasis? When are these hormones released into the blood? What might happen to a nonfasting mammal that was injected with a high dose of glucagon?

Collaborative Questions

1. Discuss the roles of hormones in growth and development.

2. Discuss the functions of the different steroid hormones, and indicate where they are produced in the mammalian body.

Animal Reproduction and Development

51

Most animals reproduce by sexual reproduction. These oysters, shown here releasing their sperm and eggs into the water where they will combine and form new organisms, reproduce by sexual reproduction, which favors genetic variation in species. ©Robert F. Sisson/National Geographic/Getty Images

A n 18-year-old woman joined her college's cross-country track team after competing for 2 years in high school. Gradually, her training increased from about 25 km/week to a very demanding 90 km/week. Recognizing the increased ability and competitiveness of college athletes relative to those at her high school, and at the urging of her track coach, she restricted her daily food intake to become as lean as possible. As her training and diet restriction progressed, she became increasingly preoccupied with monitoring what she was eating. Eventually, her weight dropped from 59 kg to 46 kg. This was followed by the cessation of her menstrual periods for several months. Alarmed that something was wrong, she visited her physician. After a battery of tests ruled out a variety of possible causes for missing her periods, she was diagnosed with secondary amenorrhea. This is a general term for the absence of menstrual cycles in a person who had previously been cycling normally. In her case, it was clear that the cause of her condition was undernourishment combined with intense exercise. She was encouraged to receive mental health

counseling in conjunction with her parents and coach, in order to address her eating disorder, and to work with a dietitian to tailor an appropriate meal plan to support her desired level of activity.

Secondary amenorrhea is common among elite female athletes in sports and activities like cross-country track, gymnastics, and ballet, where physical activity is demanding and a lean body mass is encouraged. It is a warning sign that a person is overdoing things and needs to correct a nutritional imbalance. When a woman's body is stressed in this way, her reproductive function ceases. From a physiological perspective, this makes sense, as the likelihood of supporting a healthy pregnancy in such circumstances is greatly reduced and the body requires whatever energy is available just to survive.

This woman's case illustrates the delicate control of **reproduction**—the processes by which organisms produce offspring. The biological mechanisms that favor successful reproduction in the animal kingdom are extraordinarily diverse. Many of the observable differences in animal behavior and anatomy are the result of adaptations that increase an animal's chances of reproducing.

In this chapter, we will examine the diverse means of reproduction throughout the animal kingdom, including asexual and sexual reproduction. We will consider the control mechanisms of reproduction in mammals, including humans. We then will cover some of the general events in embryonic development and will conclude with a discussion of some key issues related to fertility in the human population today, including those that affected the young woman described in this introduction.

51.1 Overview of Sexual and Asexual Reproduction

Learning Outcomes:

1. Describe several differences between sexual and asexual reproduction.
2. **CoreSKILL »** Propose a hypothesis explaining why most animals reproduce by sexual reproduction.

Sexual reproduction is the production of a new individual by the joining of two haploid reproductive cells called gametes—typically one from each parent. This usually produces offspring that are genetically different from both parents. **Asexual reproduction** in animals occurs when offspring are produced from a single parent without the fusion of gametes. The offspring are clones of the parent organism. In this section, we will consider the processes of sexual and asexual reproduction, as well as their advantages and disadvantages.

Sexual Reproduction Occurs in Most Animals

Sexual reproduction occurs in the vast majority of animal species and involves the joining of two gametes. The gametes are spermatozoa (usually shortened to **sperm**) from the male and **egg cells**, or ova (singular, ovum), from the female. (In some species, sperm and egg cells are both produced by a single organism called a **hermaphrodite**.) When a sperm unites with an egg—the process called **fertilization**—each haploid gamete contributes its set of chromosomes to produce a diploid cell called a fertilized egg, or **zygote**. As the zygote undergoes cell divisions and begins to develop, it is called an **embryo**.

Asexual Reproduction Takes Several Forms

Asexual reproduction occurs in some invertebrates and in a small number of vertebrate species. These animals reproduce in one of three ways: budding, regeneration, or parthenogenesis. **Budding**, which is seen in cnidarians, occurs when a portion of the parent organism pinches off to form a complete, new individual (**Figure 51.1a**). In this process, cells from the parent undergo mitosis and differentiate into specific types of structures before the new individual breaks away from the parent. At any one time, a parent organism may have one, two, or multiple buds forming simultaneously. Budding continues throughout such an animal's lifetime.

Certain species of sponges, echinoderms, and worms reproduce by **regeneration**, in which a complete organism can be formed from a fragment of the animal's body. In some sea stars and starfish, for example, an arm removed by injury or predation can grow into an entirely new individual (**Figure 51.1b**). Similarly, a flatworm bisected into two pieces can regenerate into two distinct individuals.

Parthenogenesis is the development of offspring from an unfertilized egg. Animals produced by parthenogenesis are usually diploid but in some cases may be haploid. This form of asexual reproduction occurs in several invertebrate classes and in a few species of fishes and reptiles.

Sexual and Asexual Reproduction Have Advantages and Disadvantages

Asexual reproduction provides a relatively simple way for an organism to produce many copies of itself, whereas sexual reproduction usually requires two individuals to produce offspring. What are the advantages and disadvantages of each method?

Asexual reproduction has certain advantages over sexual reproduction. First, an animal can reproduce asexually even if it is isolated from others of its own species—for example, because the animal is nonmotile for much of its life or because it rarely encounters another member of its species. Second, individuals can reproduce rapidly at any time because they need not seek out, attract, and mate with an

(a) Budding

(b) Regeneration

Figure 51.1 **Examples of asexual reproduction.** **(a)** *Hydra* with a single bud. **(b)** A starfish regenerating a new body from a single arm.

a: ©Clouds Hill Imaging Ltd./Corbis/Getty Images; b: ©WaterFrame/Alamy Stock Photo

individual of the opposite sex. Asexual reproduction, therefore, is an effective way of generating large numbers of offspring. Although many kinds of animals reproduce asexually, it is more prevalent in species that live in very stable environments, where there is little selection pressure for genetic diversity in the population.

Compared with asexual reproduction, sexual reproduction is associated with unique costs. Two types of gametes (sperm and eggs) must be made (often in large numbers), males and females require specialized body parts to mate with each other, and the two sexes must be able to find each other. Yet given that the vast majority of eukaryotic species reproduce sexually, the following question has intrigued biologists since the time of Darwin: What is the advantage of sexual reproduction for the perpetuation of a species?

In the context of species survival, the major difference between asexual and sexual reproduction is that sexual reproduction allows for greater genetic variation due to genetic recombination. Only certain alleles from each parent are passed on, and when a set of genes from one parent mixes with a different set from the other parent, the offspring are never exactly like either of their parents. Thus, a key consequence of sexual reproduction is greater genetic variation within a population.

One prevalent hypothesis about the advantage of sexual reproduction is that it allows a more rapid adaptation to environmental changes than does asexual reproduction. In particular, sexual reproduction allows alleles within a species to be redistributed via crossing over and independent assortment across many generations. As a result, some offspring carry combinations of alleles that promote survival and reproduction, whereas other offspring may carry less favorable combinations. As described in Chapter 23, natural selection is the process in which certain alleles or allele combinations that promote greater reproductive success become more prevalent, whereas those that result in lower fitness become less prevalent. By comparison, the alleles of asexual organisms are not reassorted from generation to generation. As a result, it is more difficult to accumulate potentially beneficial alleles within individuals of these species. Also, as described next, sexual reproduction may facilitate elimination of harmful alleles from a population.

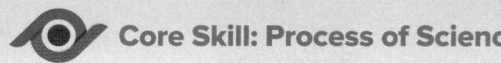 **Core Skill: Process of Science**

Feature Investigation | Paland and Lynch Provided Evidence That Sexual Reproduction May Promote the Elimination of Harmful Mutations in Populations

Evolutionary biologists have suggested that the inability of asexual species to reassort alleles may be a key disadvantage for them, compared with sexually reproducing species. To investigate this question, American researchers Susanne Paland and Michael Lynch studied the persistence of mutations in populations of *Daphnia pulex*, a freshwater organism commonly known as the water flea. The researchers chose this organism because some natural populations reproduce asexually, and others reproduce sexually.

In their experiment, shown in **Figure 51.2**, Paland and Lynch studied the sequences of several mitochondrial genes in 14 sexually reproducing and 14 asexually reproducing populations of *D. pulex*. The researchers hypothesized that asexual populations would be less able to eliminate harmful mutations. As discussed in Chapter 15, random gene mutations that change the amino acid sequence of an encoded protein are much more likely to be harmful than beneficial. Because the alleles of sexually reproducing populations can be

Figure 51.2 Paland and Lynch demonstrated the importance of sexual reproduction in reducing the frequency of harmful genetic mutations.

HYPOTHESIS Sexual reproduction allows for greater mixing of alleles of different genes and thereby may prevent the accumulation of detrimental alleles in a population.

KEY MATERIALS The researchers collected samples of *Daphnia pulex* from many natural populations. A total of 14 sexual populations and 14 asexual populations were studied.

Experimental level | Conceptual level

1 Isolate mitochondrial DNA from members of 28 populations of *D. pulex*. This involves breaking open cells and extracting the DNA (refer back to Chapter 21).

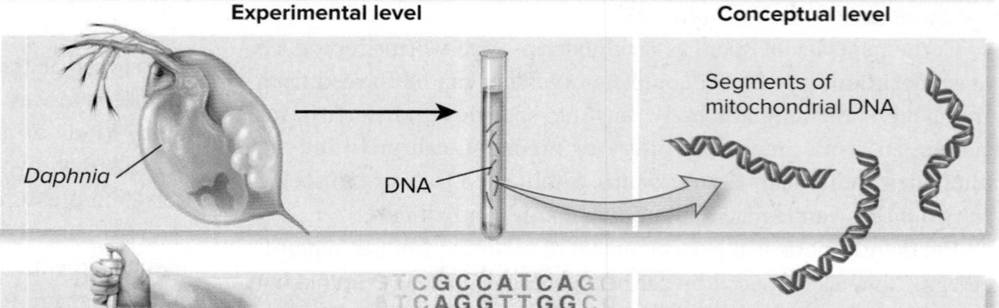

Daphnia

DNA

Segments of mitochondrial DNA

2 Amplify regions of mitochondrial genes, using PCR. Subject the regions to DNA sequencing. The techniques of PCR and DNA sequencing are described in Chapter 21 (refer back to Figures 21.6 and 21.8).

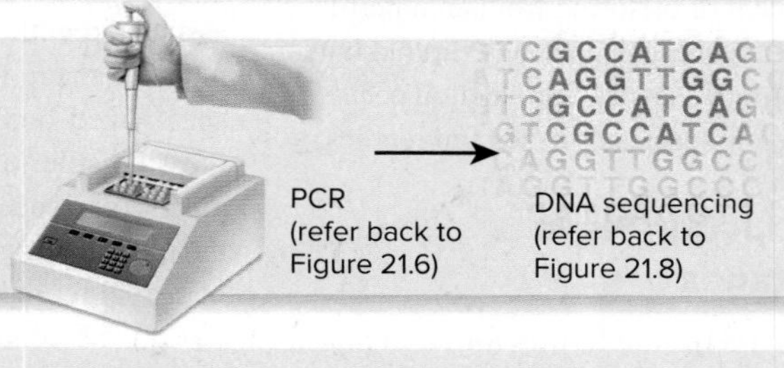

PCR (refer back to Figure 21.6)

DNA sequencing (refer back to Figure 21.8)

CGCCATCAG
CAGGTTGGC
CGCCATCAG
GTCGCCATCA
AGGTTGGCC

3 Using computer technology, align the sequences and determine the number of DNA changes that would cause amino acid substitutions. These amino acid changes were categorized as those that would be highly deleterious, moderately deleterious, mildly deleterious, or neutral for protein function. Compare the sexual and asexual populations for the persistence of these types of changes.

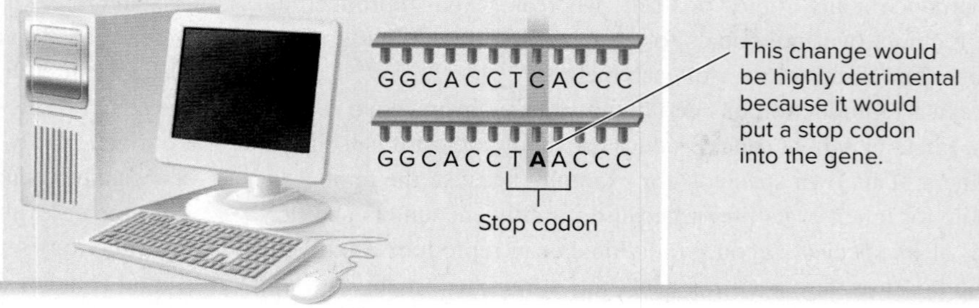

GGCACCTCACCC

GGCACCTAACCC

Stop codon

This change would be highly detrimental because it would put a stop codon into the gene.

4 **THE DATA**

Results from step 3:

Types of amino acid substitutions (The amino acid substitutions were due to rare mutations that occurred in the natural populations of *D. pulex*.)	% of total amino acid substitutions	Allowed to persist in:	
		Sexual populations	Asexual populations
Highly deleterious	73.2	No	No
Moderately deleterious	13.3	No	Yes
Mildly deleterious	4.4	Yes	Yes
Neutral	9.1	Yes	Yes

5 **CONCLUSION** Moderately deleterious mutations are less likely to persist in populations of animals that reproduce sexually.

6 **SOURCE** Paland, S., and Lynch, M. 2006. Transition to asexuality results in excess amino acid substitutions. *Science* 311: 990–992.

reassorted from generation to generation, some offspring will not inherit such detrimental alleles.

As you can see in step 4 of Figure 51.2, the researchers discovered that both the sexual and asexual populations could eliminate highly deleterious mutations. Organisms harboring such mutations probably died and did not reproduce. In addition, the sexual and asexual populations both retained mildly deleterious and neutral mutations. However, moderately deleterious mutations were eliminated from the sexual populations but not from the asexual ones. One interpretation of these data is that sexual reproduction allowed for the reassortment of beneficial and detrimental alleles, making it easier for sexually

reproducing populations to eliminate those mutations that are moderately detrimental.

Experimental Questions

1. **CoreSKILL** » How did Paland and Lynch test the hypothesis that sexual reproduction reduced the frequency of deleterious mutations in a population?

2. **CoreSKILL** » Approximately how many times more often did deleterious mutations persist in the asexually reproducing populations compared to the sexually reproducing ones?

3. What is the proposed evolutionary benefit of sexual reproduction?

51.2 Gametogenesis and Fertilization

Learning Outcomes:

1. Outline the processes of spermatogenesis and oogenesis.
2. **CoreSKILL** » Propose reasons why internal fertilization is advantageous.

The formation of gametes and the event of fertilization are common features of sexual reproduction. In this section, we will explore how most animals produce gametes and how two gametes join to form a new organism.

Sperm and Eggs Are Produced During the Process of Gametogenesis

In most species of animals, male and female gametes are formed within **gonads**—the **testes** (singular, testis) and the **ovaries** (singular, ovary). In species with separate sexes, males have testes and females have ovaries. However, some animal species are hermaphroditic, meaning that

a single individual produces sperm and egg cells. Familiar examples of hermaphroditic species include earthworms and most snails.

The formation of gametes—**gametogenesis**—begins with cells called germ cells. Germ cells multiply by mitosis, resulting in diploid cells (carrying two sets of chromosomes, denoted as 2n) called **spermatogonia** (singular, spermatogonium) and **oogonia** (singular, oogonium) (**Figure 51.3**). Some of these cells become **primary spermatocytes** or **primary oocytes** that may begin the process of meiosis. (See Chapter 16 for a review of the processes of mitosis and meiosis.) Until this point, the development of sperm and eggs is similar. From then on, gametogenesis differs between the two types of gamete.

Spermatogenesis The formation of haploid sperm from a diploid germ cell is called **spermatogenesis**. As shown in Figure 51.3a, primary spermatocytes begin this process by undergoing the first meiotic division (meiosis I) to produce two haploid (n) cells called **secondary spermatocytes**. These cells also undergo meiosis II, producing four haploid **spermatids** that eventually differentiate into mature haploid sperm cells. Gametogenesis in males, therefore, results in four gametes from each spermatogonium.

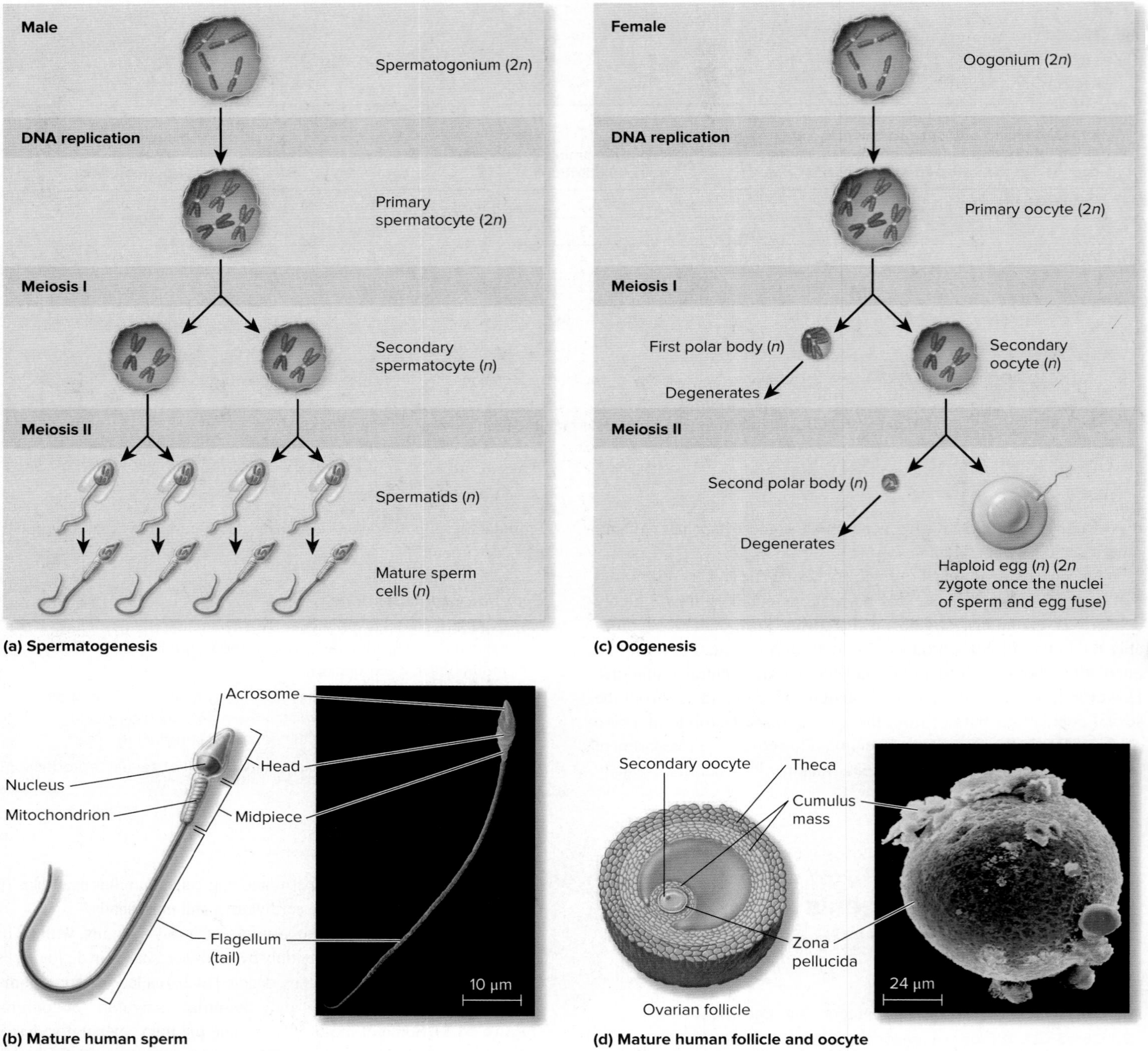

Male

Spermatogonium (2n)

DNA replication

Primary spermatocyte (2n)

Meiosis I

Secondary spermatocyte (n)

Meiosis II

Spermatids (n)

Mature sperm cells (n)

(a) Spermatogenesis

Female

Oogonium (2n)

DNA replication

Primary oocyte (2n)

Meiosis I

First polar body (n)

Degenerates

Secondary oocyte (n)

Meiosis II

Second polar body (n)

Degenerates

Haploid egg (n) (2n zygote once the nuclei of sperm and egg fuse)

(c) Oogenesis

Acrosome

Head

Nucleus

Mitochondrion

Midpiece

Flagellum (tail)

10 μm

(b) Mature human sperm

Secondary oocyte

Theca

Cumulus mass

Zona pellucida

Ovarian follicle

24 μm

(d) Mature human follicle and oocyte

Figure 51.3 Gametogenesis and gametes in human males and females. **(a)** In the process of spermatogenesis, male diploid (2n) germ cells undergo two meiotic divisions to produce mature haploid (n) sperm. **(b)** The characteristic head, midpiece, and flagellum (tail) of a mature human sperm, as seen in a drawing and accompanying scanning electron micrograph (SEM). **(c)** The process of oogenesis in females, which produces a haploid secondary oocyte that enters but does not complete meiosis II until it is fertilized. **(d)** Mature follicle and oocyte. The drawing depicts a secondary oocyte within its follicle; the SEM shows an isolated human oocyte covered by its zona pellucida and remnants of the cumulus mass. b: ©Eye of Science/Science Source; d: ©P. M. Motta & G. Familiari/Univ. La Sapienza/Science Source

 Core Concept: Structure and Function The structure of a sperm cell is a good example at the cellular level of this core concept of biology. Each of the three major structural elements of the sperm cell is suited for a particular function. When all three elements function together, the sperm is capable of fertilizing an egg.

The most striking change in each spermatocyte as it differentiates into a sperm is the formation of a flagellum, also called the tail (Figure 51.3b). The movements of the tail require energy and make the sperm motile. The sperm also has a head region, which contains the nucleus that carries the chromosomes. At the tip of the head is a special structure called the **acrosome**, which contains proteolytic enzymes that help break down the protective outer layers surrounding an egg cell. The head and tail are separated by a midpiece that typically contains as many as several dozen mitochondria, depending on the species, that produce the ATP required for tail movements.

Oogenesis   Whereas spermatogenesis produces four gametes from each primary spermatocyte, **oogenesis** results in the production of a single haploid egg from each primary oocyte (Figure 51.3c). In mammals, oogenesis begins in the ovary of a female embryo. Oogonia divide by mitosis to form primary oocytes that enter meiosis I but stop the process, remaining in an arrested state after birth. Meiosis I does not resume until puberty, the time after which a mammal first becomes capable of reproducing. Beginning at puberty, meiosis I is completed in some primary oocytes, producing from each one a haploid **secondary oocyte** plus a smaller cell, called a polar body, that eventually degenerates. Meiosis II begins in the secondary oocyte but stops at metaphase. Once the secondary oocyte is released from the ovary in the process of **ovulation**, it can become fertilized if sperm are available. Meiosis II is not complete until the oocyte is fertilized by a sperm. If the oocyte does not encounter a sperm, it never undergoes the second meiotic division. Once a haploid egg nucleus fuses with a haploid sperm nucleus, a diploid zygote is produced.

Each oocyte undergoes growth and development within an ovarian structure called a follicle. In mammals, a layer of glycoproteins called the **zona pellucida** surrounds the surface of the secondary oocyte in the follicle. In addition, a layer of cells called the cumulus mass, which provides protection and nutritive support, is outside the zona pellucida. An outer cellular layer called the theca produces hormones that control oocyte growth (Figure 51.3d). These layers have important roles in fertilization, as discussed later.

Fertilization Involves the Union of Sperm with Egg

Fertilization is the process by which the haploid male and female gametes unite and become a diploid zygote. Several important cellular and molecular processes must occur before the nuclei of the gametes can fuse. The mechanism by which the egg and sperm make contact has been studied extensively in sea urchins, and evidence suggests that a similar process occurs in humans and other mammals. Sea urchin eggs emit chemical attractants that bind to nearby sperm. This increases cellular respiration (that is, the breakdown of nutrients to synthesize ATP) within the sperm, which helps increase sperm motility. The sperm then swim toward the egg by following the concentration gradient of the attractants.

For a sperm to physically contact the egg, it must first penetrate the layers surrounding the egg's plasma membrane (**Figure 51.4**). In sea urchins, as in many animals, the sperm must penetrate a jelly-like layer consisting of glycoproteins and polysaccharides before contacting the plasma membrane of the egg. The sperm is able to do this because of the **acrosomal reaction**, in which proteases and other hydrolytic enzymes are released from the acrosome onto the jelly coat of the egg (see Figure 51.4a). These enzymes dissolve a localized region of the jelly coat, allowing the sperm head to bind to proteins in the egg's plasma membrane. Binding is followed by fusion of the sperm head membrane with the egg membrane, and shortly thereafter by penetration of the sperm head and release of its nucleus into the egg.

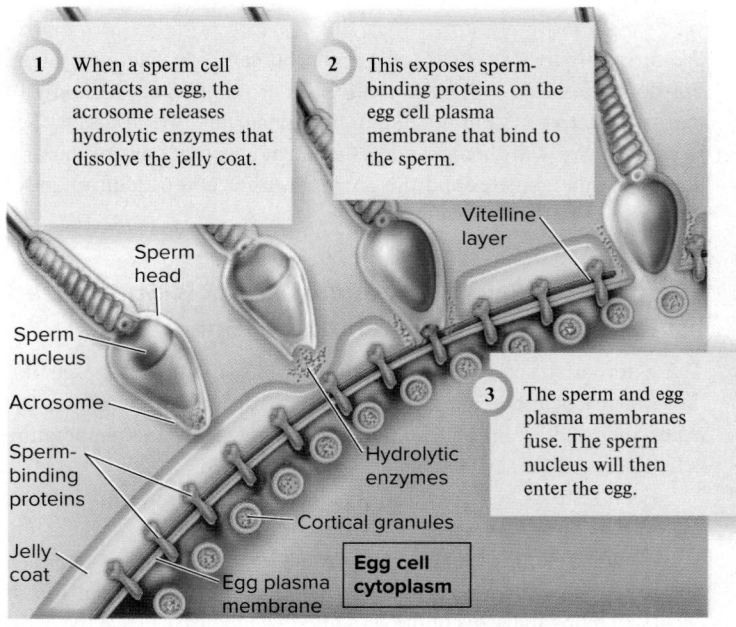

(a) Acrosomal reaction

(b) Cortical reaction

Figure 51.4 **The events during fertilization of an egg by a sperm.** **(a)** Acrosomal reaction. The contact of a sperm with an egg initiates a series of events that permits the head of the sperm to bind to the plasma membrane of the egg. **(b)** Cortical reaction. Sperm fusion leads to an increased concentration of cytosolic Ca^{2+} that ultimately causes the vitelline layer of the egg to harden, preventing additional sperm from fusing.

The acrosomal reaction is followed by the **cortical reaction** (Figure 51.4b). The cytosolic Ca^{2+} concentration in eggs, as in most cells, is kept low by several mechanisms, including the transport of Ca^{2+} by an ATP-dependent pump out of the cytosol and into the endoplasmic reticulum. When the sperm binds to the egg, a small signaling molecule called inositol trisphosphate (IP_3) is released from the region of the plasma membrane nearest to the sperm entry point. IP_3 then binds to nearby sites on the endoplasmic reticulum (ER) and opens Ca^{2+} channels. Within seconds after a sperm cell binds to an egg, Ca^{2+} is released from the lumen of the ER and into the cytosol.

The release of Ca^{2+} in the cortical reaction has several important effects. First, it causes exocytosis of membrane-bound vesicles in the egg's cytosol called cortical granules. The cortical granules release enzymes and other substances that inactivate the sperm-binding proteins on the plasma membrane. At that time, also, the outer coating of the egg cell, known as the vitelline layer in sea urchins or the zona pellucida in vertebrates (see Figure 51.3), becomes hardened and begins to separate from the plasma membrane. These events create a barrier to additional sperm fusing with the egg. Additionally, the burst of cytosolic Ca^{2+} leads to the activation of molecular signaling pathways that initiate the first cell cycle and triggers an increase in protein synthesis and metabolism within the egg cell.

Shortly afterward, the nucleus of the sperm fuses with the nucleus of the egg, creating a diploid zygote. The first cell division of the zygote occurs approximately 90 minutes after fertilization in sea urchins and amphibians, but it can take up to 24 hours in mammals.

In a Given Species, Fertilization Occurs Either Outside or Inside the Female

For sperm to fertilize eggs, the two gametes must physically come into contact. In species with separate sexes, this can occur either outside or inside the female's body. When it occurs outside of the female, the process is called **external fertilization**. This type of fertilization occurs in aquatic environments, when eggs and sperm are released into the water in close enough proximity for fertilization to occur. The aqueous environment protects the gametes from drying out. Animals that reproduce by external fertilization show species-specific behaviors that help bring the eggs and sperm together. For instance, very soon after a female fish lays her eggs, a male deposits his sperm cells in the water nearby, where they spread over the clump of eggs. The fertilized eggs then develop outside the mother's body.

Although the aqueous environment protects against desiccation, eggs can be eaten by predators, washed away by currents, or subjected to potentially lethal changes in water temperature or another variable such as pH or oxygen level. Such environmental challenges have provided selection pressure for some species, including many aquatic or amphibious animals, to release very large numbers of eggs and sperm at once. For example, oysters may release several million gametes, as shown in the chapter opening photo.

In contrast to external fertilization, most terrestrial animals and some aquatic animals reproduce by **internal fertilization**, in which sperm are deposited within the reproductive tract of the female during the act called copulation. Internal fertilization protects the zygotes from dessication, environmental hazards, and predation, and guarantees that sperm are placed and remain in very close proximity to eggs. Once fertilization occurs within the female, the zygotes then develop into offspring.

The behaviors and anatomical structures involved in achieving internal fertilization are extremely varied among species. Typically, mating involves accessory sex organs, which are reproductive structures other than the gonads. The external accessory sex organs involved in copulation include certain types of genitalia (for example, the **penis** and the **vagina** in mammals), which are used to physically join the male and female so that sperm can be deposited directly into the female's reproductive tract. A penis or analogous structure is present in most insects, reptiles, some species of birds (ratites and waterfowl), and all mammals. However, males of other vertebrate species—including most birds—that reproduce by internal fertilization lack a structure that can be inserted into the female, instead depositing sperm in the female by cloacal contact. The cloaca is a common opening for the reproductive, digestive, and excretory systems in these animals.

51.3 Human Reproductive Structure and Function

Learning Outcomes:

1. Describe the structures of the human male reproductive tract.
2. Outline the process of hormonal control of the male reproductive system.
3. Describe the structures of the human female reproductive tract.
4. Diagram the events of the ovarian cycle.
5. Outline the process of hormonal control of the reproductive cycle of the human female.
6. Explain how maternal hormones prepare the uterus to accept the embryo.

We turn now to a detailed look at the human reproductive system. For both sexes, we will begin with a description of the anatomy of the reproductive system, including the gonads and the accessory sex structures. We will then examine the hormones that control the production of the gametes and the preparation for and establishment of pregnancy.

The Human Male Reproductive Tract Is Specialized for Production and Ejaculation of Sperm

The external structures of the male reproductive tract—the genitalia—consist of the penis and the scrotum, the sac that contains the testes and holds them outside the body cavity where the temperature is better suited for spermatogenesis (**Figure 51.5**).

Each testis is composed of tightly packed **seminiferous tubules** encased in connective tissue. Surrounding the tubules are Leydig cells—endocrine cells that secrete the steroid hormone testosterone. Spermatogenesis begins at puberty and continues throughout life. It occurs all along the walls of the seminiferous tubules. Cells at the earliest stages of spermatogenesis—the spermatogonia—are located nearest the outer surface of the wall. Cells of more advanced stages are located progressively inward, so that the mature sperm are released into the tubule lumen. Cells within the seminiferous tubules are continuously

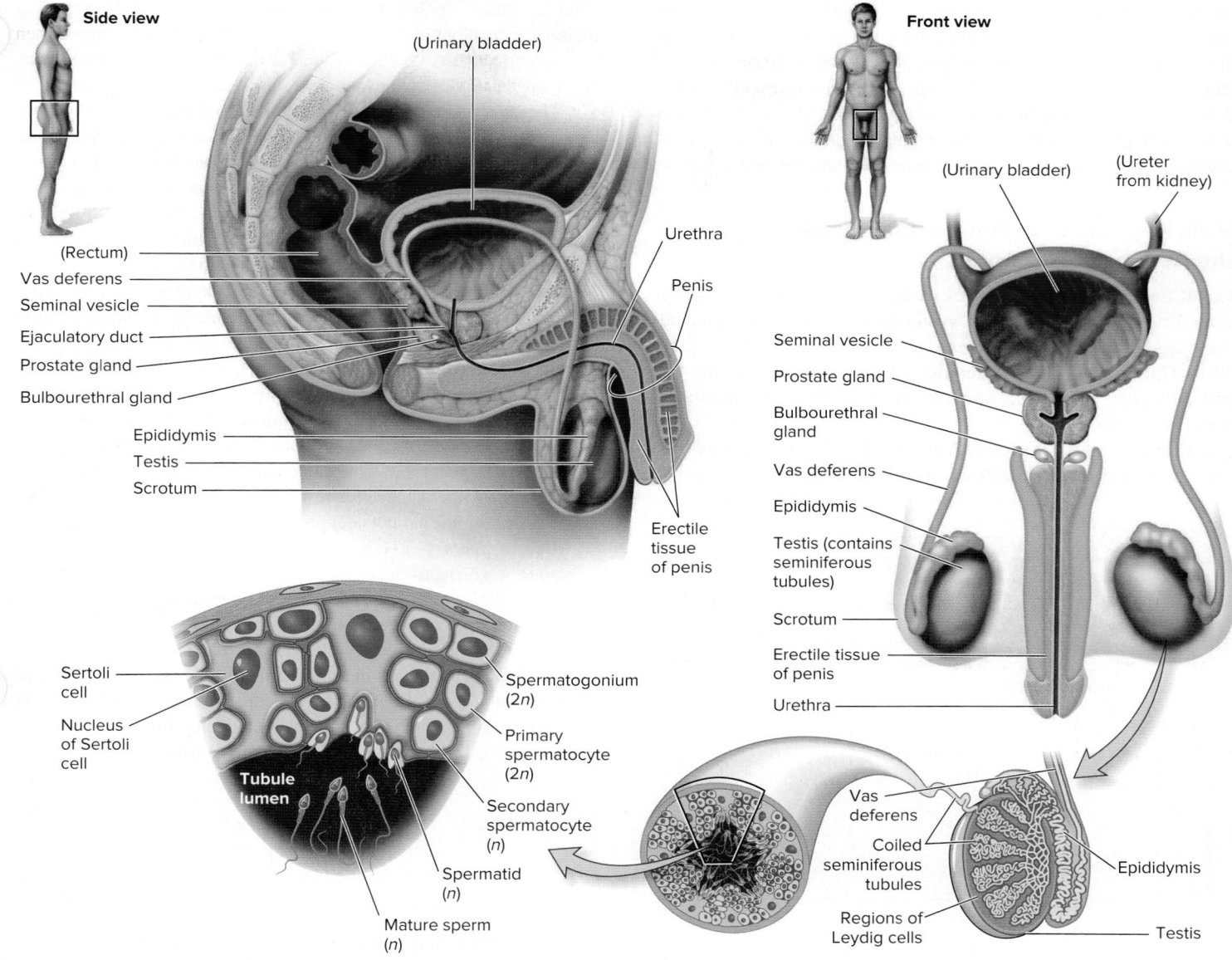

Figure 51.5 Male reproductive structures in humans. Side and front views of the male reproductive system (nonreproductive structures are identified in parentheses for orientation purposes). The enlargement (at bottom) shows the internal structure of a testis and associated structures and indicates the stages of spermatogenesis.

developing from spermatogonia into spermatocytes and eventually to sperm, so at any one time, all types of cells are present along the seminiferous tubule. Support cells, called Sertoli cells, surround the developing spermatogonia and spermatocytes, providing them with nutrients and protection and playing a role in their maturation into sperm.

Sperm moving out of the seminiferous tubules are emptied into the epididymis, a coiled, tubular structure located on the surface of the testis (see Figure 51.5). Here the sperm complete their differentiation by becoming motile and gaining the capacity to fertilize an egg.

Sperm leave the epididymis through the vas deferens, a muscular tube leading to the ejaculatory duct, which then connects to the urethra (see Figure 51.5). The urethra originates at the bladder and extends to the end of the penis. In males, the urethra not only conducts urine but also carries **semen**, a mixture containing fluid and sperm, that is released during **ejaculation**—the movement of

semen through the urethra by contraction of muscles at the base of the penis.

The liquid components of semen are important for the survival and movement of sperm through the female reproductive tract. This liquid is formed by three accessory glands that secrete substances into the urethra to mix with the sperm: the seminal vesicles, the prostate gland, and the bulbourethral glands. The seminal vesicles secrete the monosaccharide fructose, the main nutrient for sperm, as well as other factors that enhance sperm motility and survival. The prostate gland and bulbourethral glands secrete a thin, alkaline fluid that protects sperm from acidic fluids in the urethra and within the female reproductive tract.

Introduction of sperm into the female reproductive system during copulation is made possible by erection of the penis. Erection occurs when blood fills spongy erectile tissue located along the length of the penis (see Figure 51.5). Sexual arousal stimulates release of the gaseous neurotransmitter nitric oxide (NO) from parasympathetic neuron endings in the penis, which relaxes vascular smooth muscle and causes vasodilation of arteries. The pressure from the distended arteries bringing increased blood into the penis constricts nearby veins, causing a reduction in venous drainage from the penis, engorging it with blood. After ejaculation, parasympathetic signaling and NO release are decreased, causing a reversal of the vascular changes responsible for erection.

Male Reproductive Function Requires the Actions of Hormones

Recall from Chapter 50 that the hypothalamus is a structure on the ventral surface of the brain that synthesizes neurohormones, including gonadotropin-releasing hormone (GnRH) (refer back to Table 50.1). GnRH stimulates the anterior pituitary gland to release two gonadotropins: luteinizing hormone (LH) and follicle-stimulating hormone (FSH).

In males, LH stimulates the Leydig cells of the testes to produce androgens, particularly testosterone (**Figure 51.6**). Testosterone

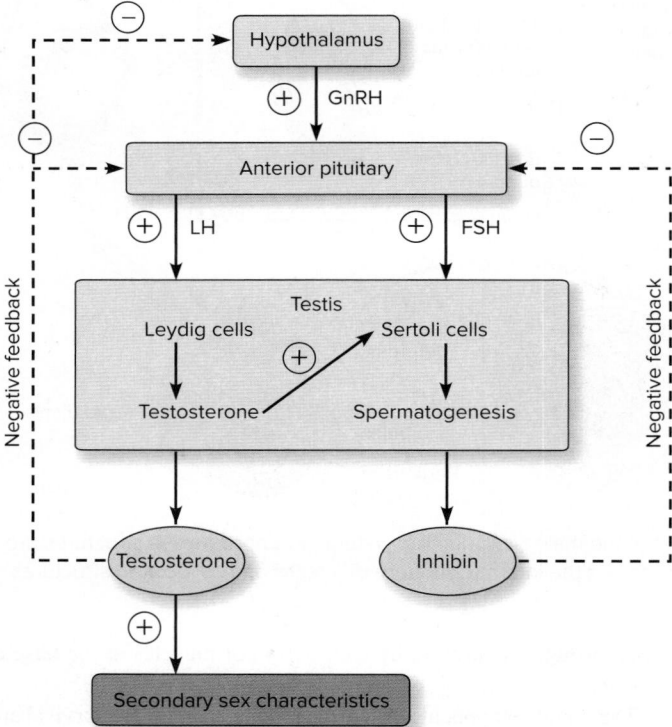

stimulates the growth of the male reproductive tract and the genitalia during development and puberty, as well as the development of male secondary sex characteristics. In humans, these include facial hair growth, increased muscle mass, and deepening of the voice.

The other pituitary gonadotropin, FSH, functions along with testosterone to stimulate spermatogenesis. FSH does this by stimulating the activity of the Sertoli cells within the seminiferous tubules (see Figures 51.5 and 51.6). The Sertoli cells provide the nutritional and structural support necessary for development of the sperm. They also respond to testosterone produced by the Leydig cells, by stimulating mitosis and meiosis of the germ cells associated with them in the tubules.

Production of sperm and testosterone is kept in check by negative feedback mechanisms that control the amount of gonadotropins produced (see Figure 51.6). Testosterone at high concentrations inhibits the secretion of GnRH from the hypothalamus, so both LH and FSH are inhibited when the blood concentration of testosterone is high. Testosterone also directly inhibits LH secretion by the anterior pituitary gland. In addition, when Sertoli cells are activated by FSH, they secrete a protein hormone called inhibin, which enters the blood and inhibits further secretion of FSH. These feedback mechanisms maintain normal concentrations of FSH and LH in the blood.

Before puberty, LH is not released in sufficient amounts to stimulate significant testicular production of testosterone, and the reproductive system is quiescent—spermatogenesis does not occur. Although the mechanisms that initiate puberty in mammals are still not completely understood, research has shown that increased GnRH production at that time initiates increased LH and FSH secretion from the pituitary. The testosterone induced by LH stimulates development of adult male characteristics. Testosterone is also responsible for an increased sex drive (libido) at this time.

 **THE QUESTION** *What will happen to spermatogenesis in a man taking supplements of testosterone to increase muscle mass and athletic performance?*

TOPIC *What topic in biology does this question address?* The topic concerns the effects of abnormally increased amounts of testosterone on spermatogenesis in men.

INFORMATION *What information do you know based on the question and your understanding of the topic?* From the question, you can assume that the testosterone supplements increase the man's plasma concentration of testosterone above the normal range. From your understanding of the topic, you may recall that the blood concentrations of testosterone and the hypothalamic hormone GnRH are linked with spermatogenesis, as shown in Figure 51.6.

PROBLEM-SOLVING **S**TRATEGY *Sort out the steps in a complicated process. Predict the outcome.* Consider the sequence of events beginning with an increase in the blood concentration of testosterone. What happens next to the concentrations of GnRH and the gonadotropins? In turn, what follows from the changes in those hormones? Based on this sequence of steps, predict what happens to sperm production.

Figure 51.6 The hormonal control of male reproduction. In response to LH, Leydig cells in the testes secrete testosterone, which, along with FSH, acts on Sertoli cells to facilitate spermatogenesis. Negative signs indicate inhibitory effects via negative feedback, and plus signs indicate stimulatory effects.

 Core Concept: Systems Organ systems, including the reproductive and endocrine systems, have regulatory mechanisms that monitor and adjust system activity. In this example, negative feedback is an important way in which the secretion of reproductive hormones is controlled.

The Female Reproductive Tract Is Specialized for Production and Fertilization of the Egg and Development of the Embryo

The female genitalia are composed of the larger, hair-covered outer folds called the labia majora and smaller, inner folds, called the labia minora, which surround the external opening of the reproductive tract (**Figure 51.7**). At the anterior part of the labia minora is the clitoris, which is erectile tissue of the same embryonic origin as the penis. Like the penis, the clitoris becomes engorged with blood during sexual arousal and is very sensitive to sexual stimulation. Unlike males, however, the openings of the reproductive tract and the urethra are separate in females. The opening of the urethra is located between the clitoris and the opening of the reproductive tract.

The external opening of the reproductive tract leads to the vagina, a tubular, smooth muscle structure into which sperm are deposited

during copulation. At the end of the vagina is the cervix, the opening to the **uterus**, a pear-shaped organ that holds and nourishes the growing embryo. It consists of an inner lining of glandular and secretory cells, called the endometrium, and a thick, muscular layer. We will discuss the functions of the uterus later in the chapter.

Oocytes develop within one of the two ovaries (see Figure 51.7), which are suspended within the abdominal cavity by connective tissue. In humans, each ovary is typically a little larger than an almond. During ovulation, a secondary oocyte is released by an ovary and is quickly drawn into a thin tube, the **oviduct** (also called the Fallopian tube), by the actions of undulating fimbriae (singular, fimbria), finger-like projections of the oviduct that extend out to the ovary.

The secondary oocyte is moved down the length of the oviduct by cilia on the oviduct's inner surface. For fertilization to take place, sperm must travel through the cervix and uterus and then into the oviduct, where fertilization typically occurs. Upon contact with a sperm, the secondary oocyte completes meiosis II, and the union of sperm and the secondary oocyte creates a fertilized egg, or zygote. The zygote undergoes several cell divisions to become a **blastocyst**, a ball of approximately 32–150 cells that enters the uterus, where embryonic development will proceed, as we will examine in detail later.

Gametogenesis in Females Is a Cyclical Process Within the Ovaries

In contrast to males, in which spermatogenesis continues throughout postpubertal life in the testes, most female mammals, including humans, appear to be born with all the primary oocytes they will ever have. At birth, each ovary in a human female has about 1 million

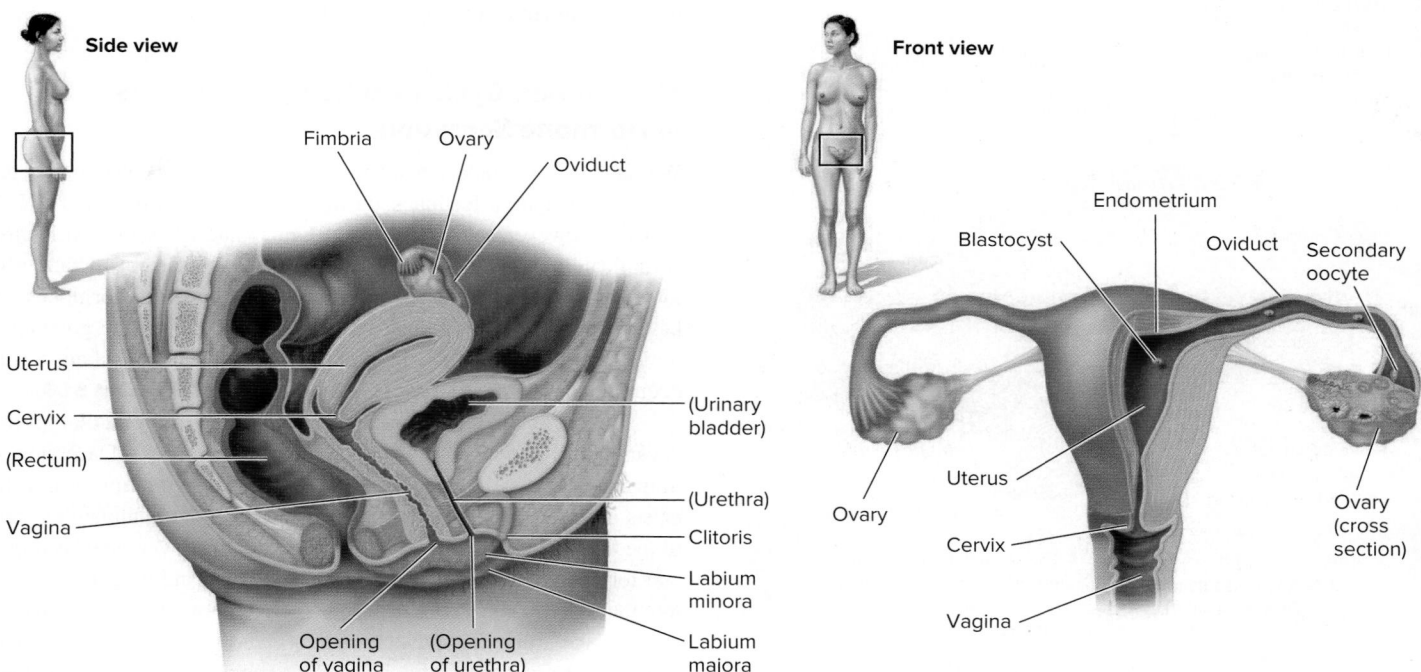

Figure 51.7 Female reproductive structure and function in humans. Side and front views of the female reproductive system (nonreproductive structures are identified in parentheses for orientation purposes). An oocyte moves from the ovary into the oviduct (or Fallopian tube), where it may be fertilized and develop into a blastocyst. Subsequently, the blastocyst enters the uterus, where it may implant in the endometrium, the inner lining of the uterus.

primary oocytes, which are arrested in prophase of meiosis I. Most of these degenerate before the onset of puberty, when each ovary contains about 200,000 primary oocytes. Other than this degeneration, the ovaries are quiescent until puberty, when they begin to show cyclical activity.

As described in Chapter 50, cells within the ovaries secrete a family of steroid hormones called estrogens. The major estrogen is **estradiol**, which has a critical role in ovulation and influences the secondary sex characteristics of females. The secondary sex characteristics, which begin to develop at puberty, include development of breasts, widening of the pelvis (an adaptation for giving birth), and a characteristic pattern of fat deposition.

The **ovarian cycle** involves the development of an ovarian follicle, the release of a secondary oocyte, and the formation and subsequent regression of the empty follicle (**Figure 51.8**). During the first week of the ovarian cycle in humans, several primary oocytes that have been maturing for several months, each within its own follicle, now begin their final maturation steps (see step 1, Figure 51.8). By the beginning of the second week, all but one of these growing follicles and their primary oocytes degenerate. The mechanisms by which one follicle becomes dominant and survives are still uncertain. The single remaining follicle continues to develop and enlarge (while a new crop of immature follicles begins their slow growth period for future ovarian cycles). During that time, the primary oocyte of the enlarging follicle completes meiosis I, becomes a secondary oocyte, and begins meiosis II (see steps 2 and 3, Figure 51.8).

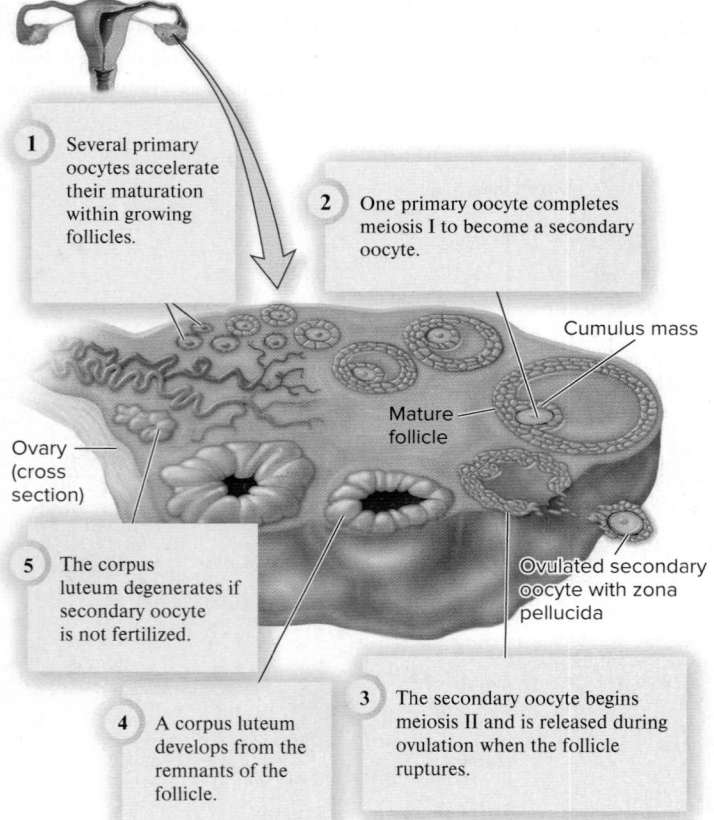

1. Several primary oocytes accelerate their maturation within growing follicles.

2. One primary oocyte completes meiosis I to become a secondary oocyte.

Cumulus mass

Mature follicle

Ovary (cross section)

5. The corpus luteum degenerates if secondary oocyte is not fertilized.

Ovulated secondary oocyte with zona pellucida

4. A corpus luteum develops from the remnants of the follicle.

3. The secondary oocyte begins meiosis II and is released during ovulation when the follicle ruptures.

Figure 51.8 Follicle and oocyte development in the ovarian cycle. Development of an oocyte and corpus luteum within the ovary are events that occur during a single ovarian cycle.

The developing secondary oocyte is surrounded by cells of the cumulus mass and theca, which protect and nurture it and secrete estradiol. The estradiol is secreted into the blood, where it functions to control the secretion of LH and FSH from the anterior pituitary gland, as we'll discuss shortly. Some estradiol is also secreted into the follicle, where it stimulates fluid secretion into the inner core of the follicle. As the follicle continues to grow, the fluid pressure inside the follicle increases, until it begins to form a bulge. Eventually, ovulation occurs as the follicle ruptures, and the secondary oocyte, the zona pellucida, and some surrounding supportive cells of the cumulus mass are released from the ovary (see step 3 of Figure 51.8).

Cells in the empty follicle subsequently undergo pronounced anatomical and physiological changes, differentiating into a structure called the **corpus luteum** (see step 4, Figure 51.8). In humans, the corpus luteum is active for approximately the second half of the ovarian cycle. It is responsible for secreting hormones that stimulate the development of the uterus required for sustaining an embryo in the event of a pregnancy. If pregnancy does not occur, the corpus luteum degenerates, and a new group of immature follicles with their primary oocytes develops (see step 5, Figure 51.8).

In humans, a typical ovarian cycle lasts approximately 28 days. As a result, of the 200,000 or so primary oocytes that were in each ovary at the onset of puberty, only about 300 to 500 secondary oocytes are ovulated over a woman's 30- to 40-year reproductive lifetime. In addition, degeneration of other primary oocytes continues at a rate of about 1000 per month throughout much of adulthood. The mechanisms that cause this cell death are still being investigated. Eventually, the oocytes become depleted and a woman stops having ovarian cycles, an event called **menopause**. The average onset of menopause in the U.S. is approximately 51 years of age. After menopause, a woman is no longer capable of ovulation.

The Ovarian Cycle Results from Changes in Hormone Secretion

We saw that in males, testosterone produced by cells in the testes exerts negative feedback on the secretion of GnRH and LH. In females, however, the regulation of GnRH and LH secretion is more complicated. Although GnRH also stimulates release of LH and FSH in females, the resulting estradiol produced by these hormones can have both negative and positive feedback effects on the gonadotropins. To understand this, let's examine the hormonal changes that occur during the ovarian cycle in a human female (**Figure 51.9**).

The first half of the ovarian cycle is called the **follicular phase**, because this is when the growth and differentiation of a cohort of immature follicles occur. The relatively low concentration of LH that exists during follicular development is sufficient to stimulate the cells of the follicle to make estradiol. The estradiol that is produced is important for enlargement and growth of the oocytes, and it is also secreted into the blood where it can influence the secretion of LH and FSH.

As the follicles develop, their secretion of estradiol gradually increases, and consequently, the concentration of estradiol in the blood begins to increase (see Figure 51.9). Another ovarian steroid, progesterone, is also secreted into the blood in very low amounts at this time. Initially, estradiol and progesterone exert a negative feedback action on the secretion of LH and FSH from the pituitary gland. As a result, LH and

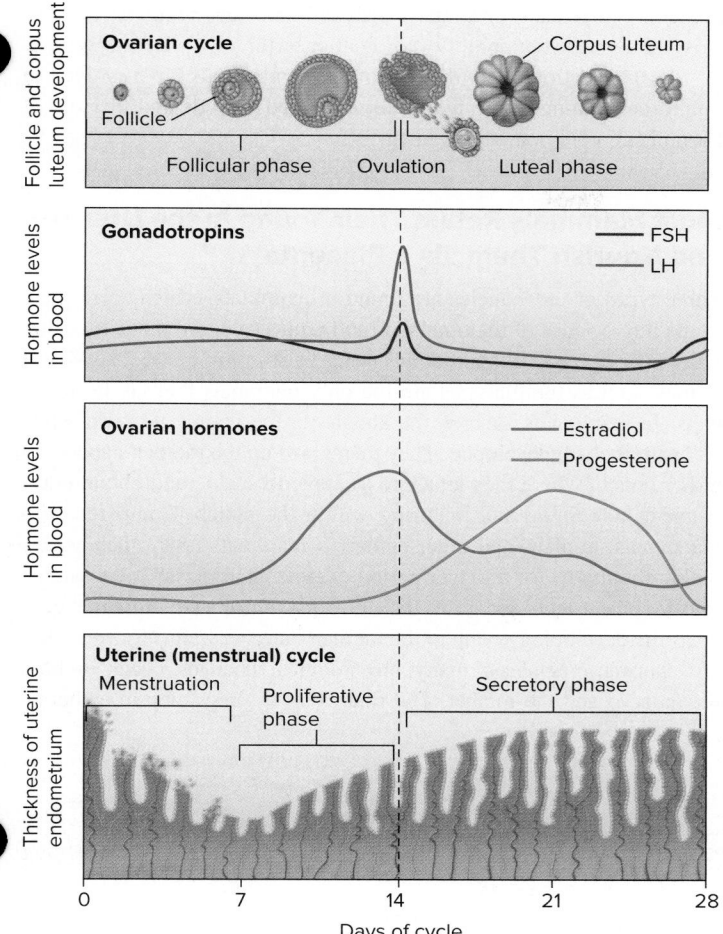

Figure 51.9 The ovarian and uterine cycles in a human female. The ovarian cycle is divided into the follicular and luteal phases. The uterine cycle is divided into menstruation and the proliferative and secretory phases.

 Core Skill: Modeling The goal of this modeling challenge is to predict the pattern of blood concentrations of LH and FSH in a woman taking a daily oral contraceptive that contains estradiol and progesterone.

Modeling Challenge: As described later in Section 51.6, a common method of preventing ovulation in women who do not wish to become pregnant is taking a daily pill that contains an estrogen, such as estradiol, and progesterone. This pill is called a contraceptive, which is any medication or device that acts to decrease the likelihood of a pregnancy. The ovarian steroids are given at a sufficient dose that they exert strong negative feedback on LH and FSH secretion, but do not exert positive feedback. In a model based on Figure 51.9, first draw the normal pattern for the blood concentrations of LH and FSH during a cycle. Then, on the same model, draw a predicted pattern for the blood levels of LH and FSH over the course of 28 days in a woman taking a contraceptive pill containing estradiol and progesterone.

FSH concentrations in the blood are kept at a relatively low level, just high enough to continue promoting follicle development. As the cycle proceeds, all but the largest of the developing follicles eventually die, as discussed earlier. As the remaining follicle nears full development and gets ready for ovulation, its production of estradiol increases, causing the blood concentration of estradiol to increase sharply. At that time, the feedback action of estradiol on LH and FSH switches from negative to positive, by mechanisms that involve increased GnRH secretion from the hypothalamus. This event results in a sudden, sharp surge in LH and FSH in the blood. The LH released from the pituitary as a result of positive feedback by estradiol induces rupture of the follicle; that is, it induces ovulation.

Ovulation marks the end of the follicular phase and the beginning of the **luteal phase** of the ovarian cycle, named after the corpus luteum. During this phase, the high concentration of LH in the blood initiates development of the corpus luteum. The corpus luteum secretes large amounts of progesterone, the dominant ovarian hormone of the luteal phase, plus some estradiol. The increasing concentration of progesterone in the blood inhibits LH and FSH secretion by negative feedback and is essential to prepare the uterus to receive and nourish the embryo. If fertilization of the secondary oocyte does not occur, the corpus luteum degenerates after 2 weeks and progesterone release decreases, allowing LH and FSH to initiate development of a new set of oocytes and their follicles. However, if fertilization does occur, the blastocyst develops a surrounding layer of cells that secrete an LH-like hormone, called **chorionic gonadotropin**, which maintains the corpus luteum and its ability to secrete progesterone. Chorionic gonadotropin is only present in pregnant women. Therefore, the detection of this hormone is the basis for some pregnancy tests.

Maternal Hormones Prepare the Uterus to Accept the Embryo

In humans, the ovarian cycle occurs in parallel with changes in the lining of the uterus during the **uterine cycle**, or **menstrual cycle**. The hormones produced by the ovarian follicle influence the development of the endometrium, the glandular inner layer of the uterus. As depicted at the bottom left of Figure 51.9, a period of bleeding called **menstruation** marks the beginning of the uterine cycle and the follicular phase of the ovarian cycle. During menstruation, the endometrium is sloughed off and released from the body.

By about the end of the first week of the menstrual cycle, the endometrium is ready to grow again in response to the newly increasing concentration of estradiol secreted by a developing follicle. This phase of the menstrual cycle, which corresponds to the latter part of the ovarian follicular phase, is called the proliferative phase (see Figure 51.9) because uterine cells begin to grow and divide. During this time, the endometrium becomes thicker and more vascularized. During the subsequent luteal phase of the ovarian cycle, progesterone from the corpus luteum initiates further endometrial growth, including the development of glands that secrete nutritive substances that sustain the embryo during its first 2 weeks in the uterus. This part of the menstrual cycle is called the secretory phase because of these glandular secretions. If fertilization does not occur, degeneration of the corpus luteum and the associated decrease in progesterone and estradiol concentrations initiate menstruation and the beginning of the next uterine cycle. If fertilization does occur, however, the blastocyst becomes embedded in the endometrium and pregnancy begins, as described in the next section.

Pregnancy and Birth in Mammals

Learning Outcomes:

1. Explain the relationship between the fetal and maternal structures of the placenta.
2. Outline the hormonal control of the birth process.

Pregnancy, or gestation, is the time during which a developing embryo or fetus grows within the uterus of the mother. Physiologically, pregnancy is considered to begin not at fertilization but when the embryo is established in the uterine lining. This occurs within days of fertilization in animals with short gestation lengths but may take weeks in large animals with long gestations.

In mammals, gestation length varies widely and is roughly related to the size of adults in a particular species. Small animals such as hamsters and mice have gestation periods of 16 to 21 days, canids have longer pregnancies of about 50 to 75 days, humans average about 268 days, and the Asian elephant carries its fetus up to 660 days. The advantages of prolonging prenatal development are twofold: The embryo is protected while it is developing in the uterus, and the offspring can be more fully developed at birth. Being more fully developed at birth is

especially important for animals such as horses and ruminants, whose survival depends on mobility shortly after birth.

In this section, we will examine how mammals have evolved to retain their young in the uterus for extended periods and the role of hormones in pregnancy and birth.

Most Mammals Retain Their Young in the Uterus and Nourish Them via a Placenta

Three types of pregnancies are found in mammals, which correspond to the three clades of mammals: prototherians (monotremes), metatherians (marsupials), and eutherians (refer back to Figure 35.25). Monotremes such as the platypus are the only mammals that lay fertilized eggs. In marsupials such as the kangaroo, the young are born while still extremely undeveloped. They then crawl up the mother's abdomen to her pouch, where they attach to a nipple to suckle and obtain nourishment, remaining and maturing within the pouch. Compared with marsupials, humans and other eutherian mammals retain their young within the uterus for a longer period of time and nourish them via the transfer of nutrients and gases through a **placenta**, a structure that connects the developing young to the mother's uterine wall (**Figure 51.10**).

During pregnancy, many physiological changes occur in both the embryo and the mother. The first event of pregnancy in eutherian

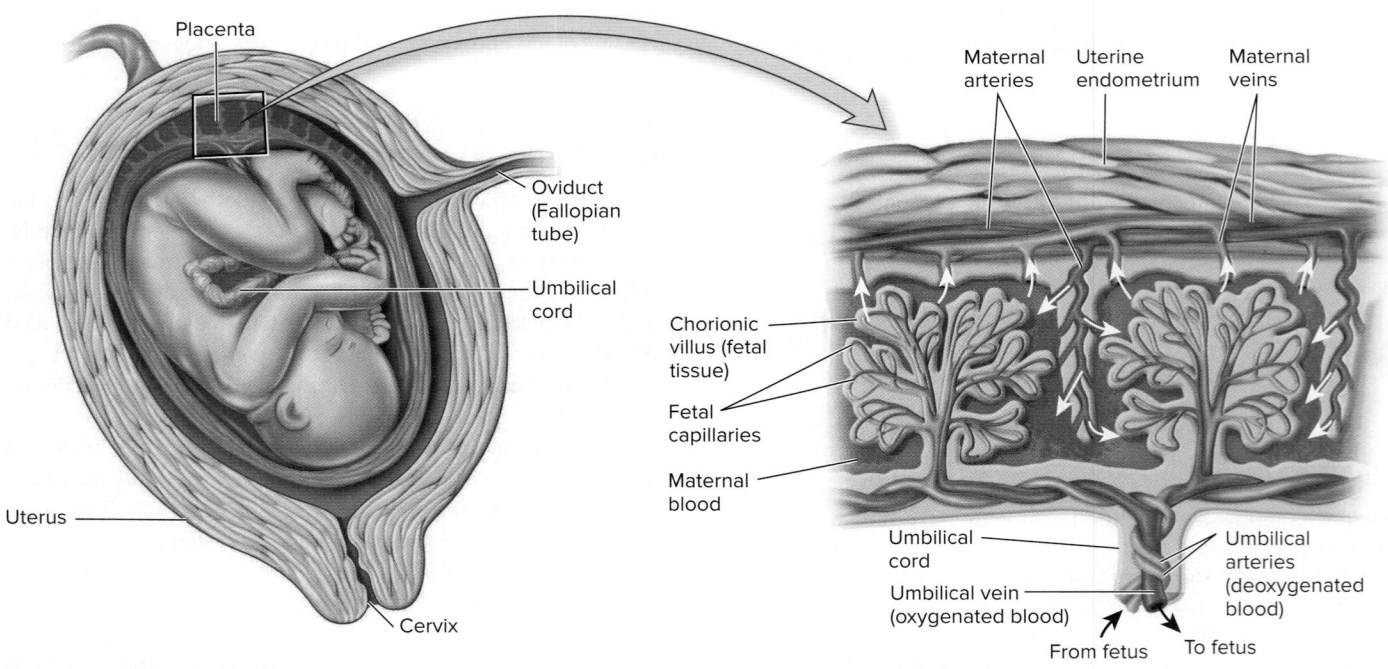

(a) Location of the placenta in the uterus

(b) Detailed view of the placenta

Figure 51.10 **The structure of the placenta.** In mammals, the placenta is composed of both maternal and embryonic or fetal tissues. **(a)** Overview of placental location and structure in the human. **(b)** Enlarged view of the placenta showing the relationship between fetal and maternal structures. Note that in humans, blood in the fetal and maternal circulations does not mix. The white arrows indicate diffusion of solutes such as nutrients and wastes; black arrows indicate direction of blood flow.

 Core Skill: Connections Note that the umbilical arteries are shown in blue to signify that they carry deoxygenated blood, and the umbilical vein is shown in red to signify it carries oxygenated blood. Normally, arteries carry oxygenated blood, and veins carry deoxygenated blood, except in the pulmonary circulation (refer back to Figure 48.2b). Why is the circulation through the placenta like that of the pulmonary circulation?

(placental) mammals is **implantation**, when the blastocyst embeds within the uterine endometrium, which typically occurs in humans around 8 to 10 days after fertilization. As mentioned earlier, the implanted blastocyst initially receives nutrients directly from endometrial glands. However, shortly after implantation, newly developing embryonic tissues merge with the endometrium to form the placenta, which remains in place and grows larger as the embryo matures into a **fetus**. (In humans, an embryo is called a fetus after the eighth week of gestation.) The placenta has a maternal portion and an embryonic or fetal portion.

The placenta is rich in blood vessels from both the mother and the fetus. The maternal and fetal sets of vessels lie in close proximity. The fetal portion of the placenta, called the chorion, contains convoluted structures called chorionic villi that provide a large surface area containing capillaries where nutrients, gases, and other solutes are exchanged. Nutrients and oxygen from the mother are carried through maternal arteries, where her blood pools in large areas of the fetal placenta surrounding the fetal capillaries. Solutes diffuse from the maternal blood into fetal capillaries, and from there flow into the umbilical vein, part of the fetal circulation. In turn, carbon dioxide and other waste products from the fetus are carried through the umbilical artery to the placenta, where they diffuse into the mother's circulation and are eventually excreted. Because of this placental organization, the maternal and fetal blood do not mix.

Prenatal development in humans is generally described as having three trimesters, each of which lasts about 3 months. At the end of the first trimester, the rudiments of the organs are present, and the developing fetus is about an inch long. The second trimester is an extremely rapid phase of growth. During the third trimester, the lungs of the fetus mature so that they are ready to function as gas-exchange organs when the fetus makes the transition to breathing air.

 **Core Concept: Evolution**

The Evolution of the Globin Gene Family Has Been Important for Internal Gestation in Mammals

As discussed in Chapter 21, genes can be duplicated, which sometimes creates gene families. Gene families have been important in the evolution of complex traits because the various members of a gene family enable the expression of complex, specialized forms and functions. An interesting example is the globin gene family in animals. Globin genes encode polypeptides that are subunits of proteins that function in oxygen binding. Hemoglobin, which is present in erythrocytes, carries oxygen throughout the body in all vertebrates and many invertebrates, delivering oxygen to all of the body's cells. In humans, the globin gene family is composed of several homologous genes that were originally derived from a single ancestral globin gene (refer back to Figure 21.14).

All of the globin polypeptides are subunits of proteins that function in oxygen binding, but the various family members tend to have specialized functions. For example, certain globin

Table 51.1	Globin Gene Expression During Mammalian Development		
Stage of development	Globin genes expressed	Hemoglobin composition	Oxygen affinity (P50)*
Embryo	ε-globin and ζ-globin	Two ε-globin and two ζ-globin subunits	5–13.5 mmHg
Fetus	γ-globin and α-globin	Two γ-globin and two α-globin subunits	19.5 mmHg
Birth to adult	β-globin and α-globin	Two β-globin and two α-globin subunits	26.5 mmHg

*P_{50} values represent the partial pressure of oxygen required to half-saturate hemoglobin (refer back to Figure 48.24): A lower P_{50} indicates a higher affinity of hemoglobin for oxygen. The value for embryos is an estimate based on in vitro experiments. All values are for human hemoglobins.

genes are expressed only during particular stages of embryonic development (refer back to Figure 14.3). This phenomenon has special importance in placental mammals, because the oxygen demands of a growing embryo and fetus are quite different from the demands of its mother. These different demands are met by the differential expression of hemoglobin genes during prenatal development.

Altogether, five globin genes—designated α, β, γ, ε, and ζ—encode the major subunits that are found in hemoglobin proteins at different developmental stages. During embryonic development, the ε-globin and ζ-globin genes are turned on, resulting in embryonic hemoglobin with a very high affinity for oxygen (**Table 51.1**). At the fetal stage, these genes are turned off, and the α-globin and γ-globin genes are turned on, producing fetal hemoglobin with slightly lower (but still high) affinity for oxygen. Finally, just before birth, expression of the γ-globin gene decreases, and the β-globin gene is turned on, resulting in adult hemoglobin, which has a lower affinity for oxygen than either the embryonic or fetal forms. The higher affinities of embryonic and fetal hemoglobins enable the embryo and fetus to remove oxygen from the mother's bloodstream and use that oxygen to meet their own metabolic demands. Therefore, the evolution of different globin genes each of which is expressed at particular stages of development enables placental mammals to develop in the uterus without breathing on their own or being exposed to atmospheric oxygen.

Birth Is Dependent on Hormones That Elicit a Positive Feedback Loop

Birth—also called parturition—is initiated by the actions of several hormones and other factors secreted by the placenta and glands of the mother (**Figure 51.11**). Toward the end of pregnancy, hormones from the fetus stimulate the placenta to start secreting large amounts of estrogens such as estradiol into the maternal circulation.

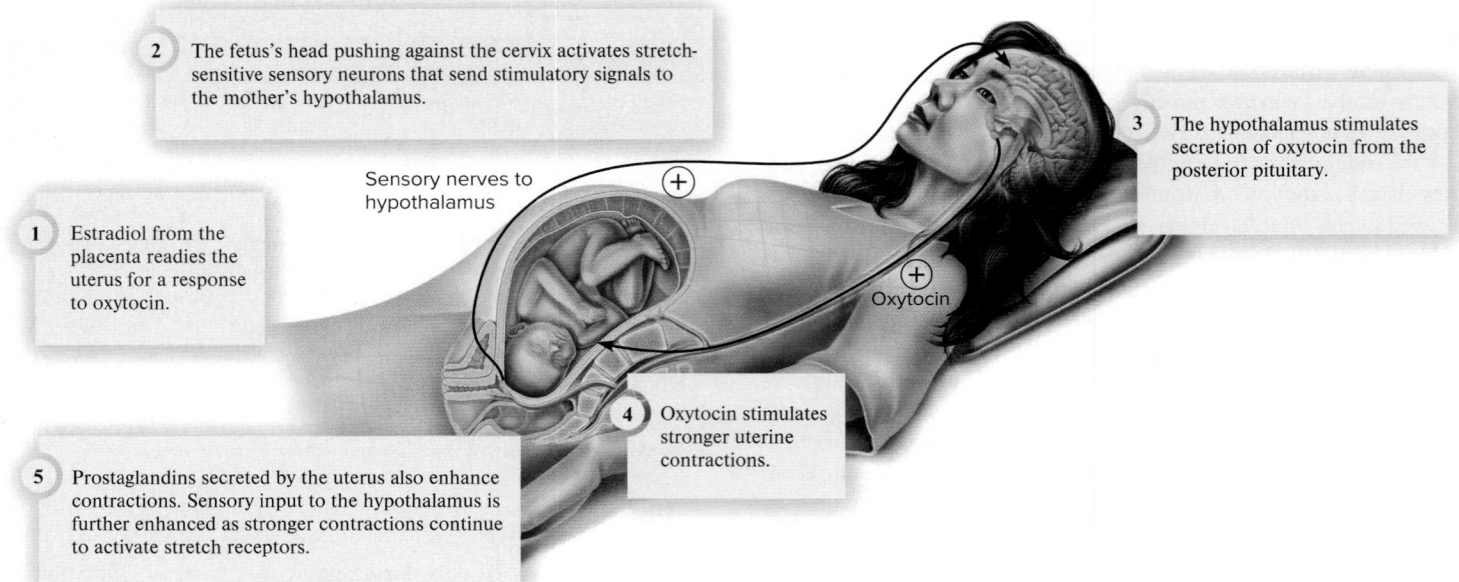

2 The fetus's head pushing against the cervix activates stretch-sensitive sensory neurons that send stimulatory signals to the mother's hypothalamus.

3 The hypothalamus stimulates secretion of oxytocin from the posterior pituitary.

Sensory nerves to hypothalamus

1 Estradiol from the placenta readies the uterus for a response to oxytocin.

Oxytocin

4 Oxytocin stimulates stronger uterine contractions.

5 Prostaglandins secreted by the uterus also enhance contractions. Sensory input to the hypothalamus is further enhanced as stronger contractions continue to activate stretch receptors.

Figure 51.11 Hormonal control of parturition. Birth relies on neural signals from the uterus and maternal hormones that act on the uterus. In response to sensory neural input arising from the push of the fetus on the cervix, the maternal posterior pituitary releases oxytocin into the blood, which stimulates uterine smooth muscle contractions. The secretion of prostaglandins by the uterus also increases the strength of the contractions. Sensory receptors in the uterus detect the more forceful contractions and signal the mother's posterior pituitary to secrete more oxytocin, thus completing a positive feedback loop that further strengthens the contractions.

 Core Skill: Connections In what other context have you learned about positive feedback in female reproduction? See Figure 51.9 for help.

Estrogens have at least two major effects on uterine tissue at this time. First, they promote the formation of gap junctions between uterine smooth muscle cells, which enables coordinated uterine contractions. Second, estrogens enhance uterine sensitivity to the hormone oxytocin.

Recall from Chapter 50 that oxytocin is a posterior pituitary hormone that stimulates contraction of uterine muscle. The high concentration of estradiol in the mother's blood near the end of pregnancy stimulates the production of oxytocin receptors in smooth muscle cells of the uterus, thereby making the uterus more sensitive to oxytocin. At the same time, the fetus usually positions itself with its head above the cervix in preparation for birth. The pressure of the fetus's head pressing on the cervix stretches the smooth muscle of the lower uterus including the cervix. This stretch is detected by neurons in these structures. Signals from the stretch-sensitive neurons are sent to the mother's hypothalamus, triggering the release of oxytocin into the blood.

Binding of oxytocin to its receptors initiates the strong uterine muscle contractions that are the hallmark of **labor**. In addition to its direct action on uterine muscle, oxytocin stimulates uterine secretion of small signaling molecules called prostaglandins that act with oxytocin to further increase the strength of the muscle contractions. The stronger contractions elicit even greater stimulation of stretch receptors, resulting in more oxytocin release from the mother's pituitary, which causes yet stronger contractions. This positive feedback loop continues until the baby is born.

Labor occurs in three stages (**Figure 51.12**). In stage one, dilation and thinning of the cervix occur, which makes it easier for the fetus to pass out of the uterus. In stage two, uterine contractions get stronger

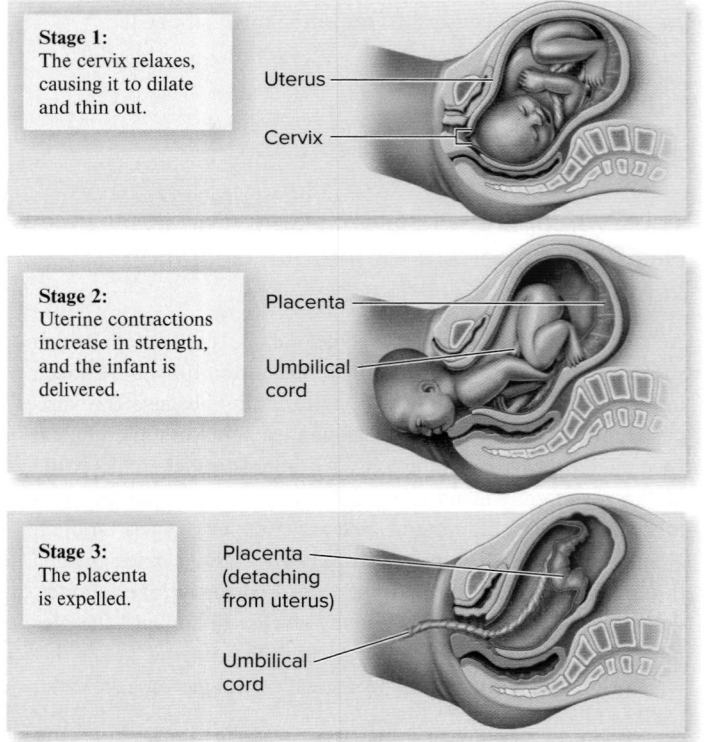

Stage 1: The cervix relaxes, causing it to dilate and thin out.

Uterus

Cervix

Stage 2: Uterine contractions increase in strength, and the infant is delivered.

Placenta

Umbilical cord

Stage 3: The placenta is expelled.

Placenta (detaching from uterus)

Umbilical cord

Figure 51.12 The three stages of labor.

Concept Check: *Many female mammals consume the placenta after giving birth. What is the benefit of this behavior?*

and more frequent. The fetus is pushed, usually headfirst, through the cervix and the vagina and out into the world. In stage three, the contractions continue for a short while. Blood vessels within the placenta and umbilical cord contract and block further blood flow, making the newborn independent from the mother. As the oxytocin-induced contractions continue for a short period, the placenta detaches from the uterine wall and is delivered a few minutes after the birth of the baby.

51.5 General Events of Embryonic Development

Learning Outcomes:

1. Describe the general events of embryonic development, and identify the end result of each.
2. Describe the process of cleavage, beginning at fertilization and leading into gastrulation.
3. **CoreSKILL »** Predict the fates of cells in a gastrula as they differentiate into the three major germ layers.
4. Outline the early development of the nervous system during neurulation.
5. Describe the migration and fates of neural crest cells.

The process by which a fertilized egg (that is, a zygote) is transformed into an animal with distinct physiological systems and body parts is called **embryonic development**. As an animal develops, cells arrange themselves in coordinated ways that lead to the establishment of a body plan. The final, adult body plan of most animals is organized along three axes: the dorsoventral axis, the anteroposterior axis, and the left-right axis. Along these axes are often separate sections, or body segments, each containing specific body parts such as a wing or leg.

To establish the correct body plan, each cell in a developing animal must receive information regarding its relative position within the body. Such information determines where a cell should move to, whether or not it should divide (or die), and what types of functions it will ultimately perform. Each cell receives the required positional information from its neighboring cells. This information is provided in a variety of ways, including intracellular and extracellular signaling molecules and by cell-to-cell contacts. A cell responds to positional information by dividing (cell division), dying (cell death, or apoptosis), or migrating from one region of the embryo to another (cell migration). Last, in the process of **cell differentiation**, different cells within a developing organism acquire specialized forms and functions, due to the expression of cell-specific genes.

Embryonic development follows a similar pattern in most animals. Most modern animals are triploblastic; that is, they develop from embryos with three distinct cell layers called the ectoderm, mesoderm, and endoderm (refer back to Figure 33.5). Triploblasts include vertebrates and most invertebrates other than sponges and cnidarians. Development in these animals can be categorized into five general events: (1) fertilization (discussed earlier; see Figure 51.4), (2) cleavage, (3) gastrulation, (4) neurulation, and (5) organogenesis (**Figure 51.13**). In this section, we will examine the key aspects of the general events of animal development beginning with cleavage. However, it should be noted that many species also have an additional event called metamorphosis, which is a transition from a feeding larval form to an adult (refer back to Figure 34.25). Metamorphosis occurs after organogenesis and facilitates the rapid growth of young organisms into mature ones. Examples of metamorphosis include the transformation of a caterpillar into a butterfly and that of a tadpole into a frog.

Cell Divisions Without Cell Growth Create a Cleavage-Stage Embryo

The initial cell cycles of embryos are unique because they involve repeated cell divisions without cell growth. The process by which

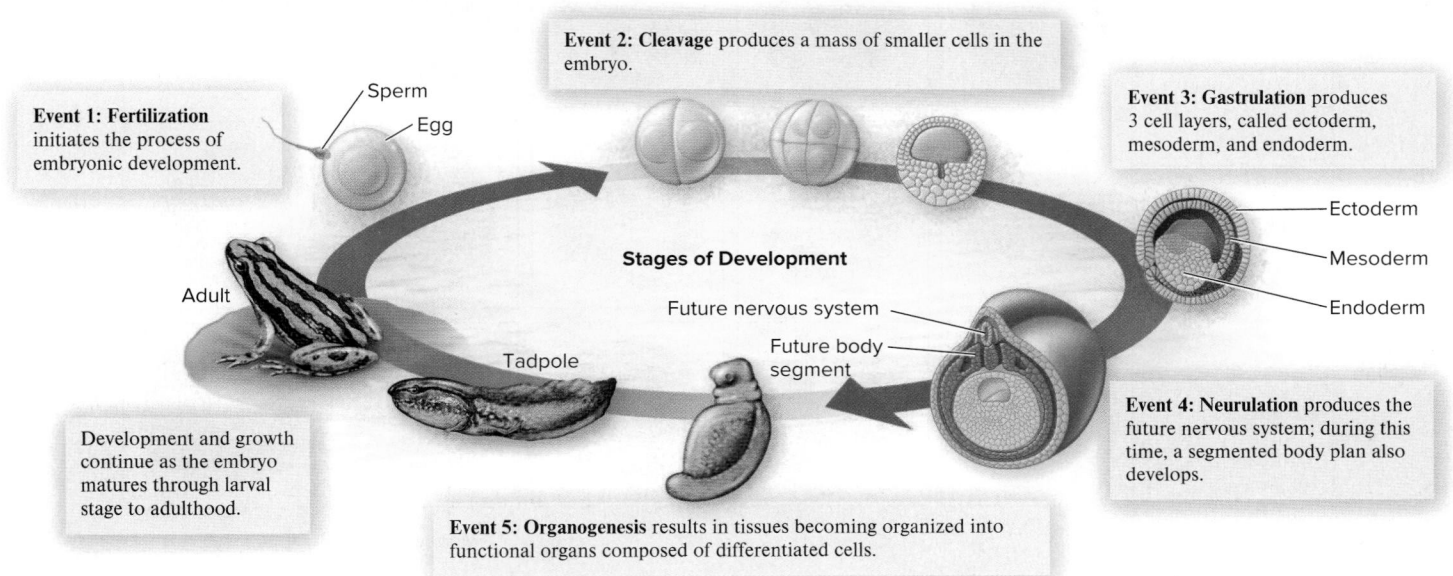

Event 1: Fertilization initiates the process of embryonic development.

Sperm

Egg

Event 2: Cleavage produces a mass of smaller cells in the embryo.

Event 3: Gastrulation produces 3 cell layers, called ectoderm, mesoderm, and endoderm.

Ectoderm

Mesoderm

Endoderm

Stages of Development

Adult

Tadpole

Future nervous system

Future body segment

Event 4: Neurulation produces the future nervous system; during this time, a segmented body plan also develops.

Development and growth continue as the embryo matures through larval stage to adulthood.

Event 5: Organogenesis results in tissues becoming organized into functional organs composed of differentiated cells.

Figure 51.13 Overview of events of embryonic development. This figure shows the general developmental events of all vertebrate embryos, using a frog as an example.

these cell cycles occur is called **cleavage**. The embryonic cells repeatedly split in two, resulting in several generations of daughter cells that are roughly half the size of the cells that gave rise to them.

In most species in which development occurs outside the mother, cell division during cleavage represents one of the fastest cell cycles found in nature. This minimizes the time in which eggs or early embryos could be eaten by predators. The cell cycle during cleavage in amphibians, for example, requires only 20 minutes. During each 20-minute cell cycle, complete genome replication, mitosis, and duplication of the nuclear envelope are followed by cytokinesis. In placental mammals, in which development occurs within the protective environment of the mother's body, cell divisions during cleavage are slower, requiring about 12 hours to complete.

The daughter cells produced during the cleavage stage of development are known as **blastomeres**. Individual blastomeres are bound together, and an outer, single-cell layer of blastomeres forms a sheet of epithelial cells that separates the embryo from its environment. After formation of the outer epithelial layer, the embryos of many animals take up water and form a cavity called a **blastocoel**. The embryo at this stage is called a **blastula**. The blastocoel provides a space into which cells will migrate to form the digestive tract and other structures of the embryo.

Animal and Vegetal Poles of Cleavage-Stage Embryos   Among triploblastic organisms, cleavage-stage embryos can vary considerably in size and appearance. This variation is in part related to whether or not the egg contains yolk and, if so, the location and amount of that yolk. Yolk is a nutrient-rich food store that is used by the developing embryo. The eggs of birds, some fishes, and some other vertebrates have large amounts of yolk. In the eggs and early embryos of these species, yolk is most concentrated toward one end—or pole—called the **vegetal pole**. Much less yolk, and much more cytoplasm, is concentrated near the

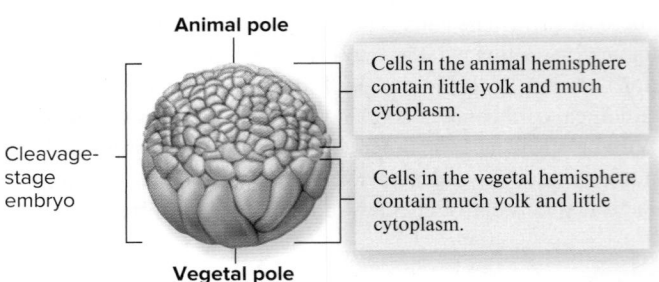

Figure 51.14 Polarity in an amphibian cleavage-stage embryo.

opposite pole, called the **animal pole** (**Figure 51.14**). These poles form the apices of the vegetal and animal hemispheres, which determine in part the future anteroposterior (head-tail) and dorsoventral (back-front or top-bottom, depending on the species) axes of the embryo.

Meroblastic Cleavage: Birds, Reptiles, and Fishes   In some species that exhibit animal and vegetal poles, the cleavage process is called **meroblastic cleavage**, or incomplete cleavage, because only the region of the embryo located within the animal hemisphere undergoes cell division (**Figure 51.15**). Instead of forming a ball of cells (a blastula), in this type of cleavage, a flattened disc of blastomeres known as a **blastoderm** develops on top of the yolk mass.

Holoblastic Cleavage: Amphibians and Mammals   In animals whose eggs have smaller amounts of yolk, cleavage during the first cell division is complete and bisects the entire zygote into two equal-sized blastomeres. This complete cleavage, or **holoblastic cleavage**, occurs in amphibians and mammals (see Figure 51.15). In amphibians, cleavage-stage embryos form a blastula, as previously noted. In mammals, however, cleavage-stage embryos undergo a process called compaction, in

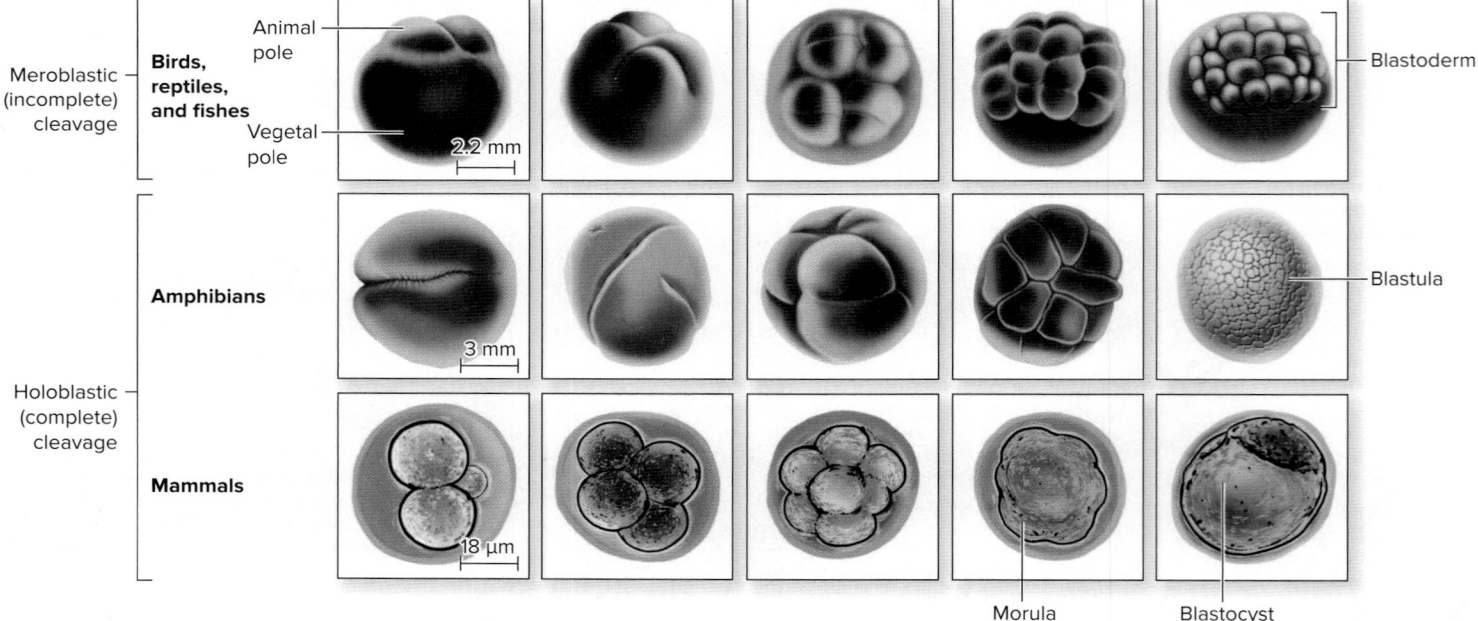

Figure 51.15 **Meroblastic and holoblastic cleavage.** Early embryos of birds, reptiles, and many fishes undergo incomplete (meroblastic) cleavage, whereas most amphibian and mammalian embryos undergo complete (holoblastic) cleavage. The amount of yolk in the egg (not visible in these illustrations) contributes to many of these morphological differences observed in various species.

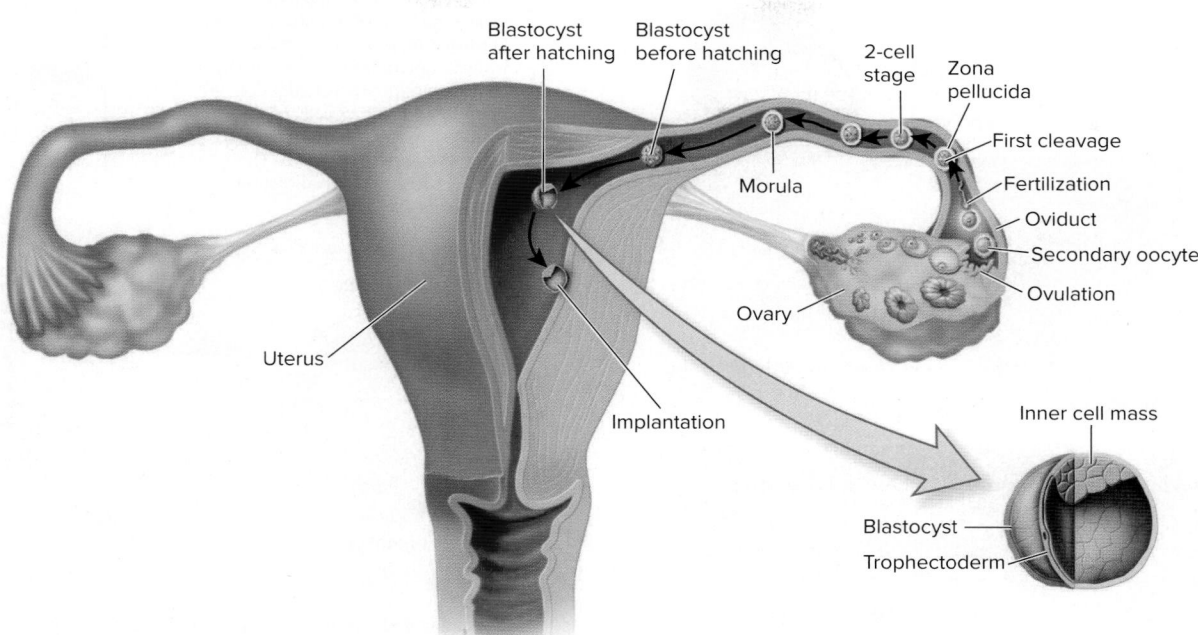

Figure 51.16 **The sites of early embryonic development in mammals.** After an ovulated secondary oocyte is fertilized, initial cleavage and development of the resulting embryo occur in the oviduct of the mother. The blastocyst hatches from the zona pellucida before implanting into the inner lining of the uterus. A blastocyst is composed of an outer epithelial layer, called the trophectoderm, which gives rise to extraembryonic tissues such as the placenta, and an inner cell mass, which develops into the embryo.

which the amount of physical contact between cells is maximized. At this stage, the embryo in these species is called a **morula**. The morula then proceeds to form a blastocyst, the mammalian counterpart of a blastula.

Cleavage and Implantation in Mammals In mammals, the events of fertilization and cleavage occur in the oviduct (**Figure 51.16**). The blastocyst has a morphological appearance that differs from that of the blastula or blastoderm in nonmammalian species, and shows no animal-vegetal polarity that is analogous to that of other chordates. The blastocyst consists of an outer epithelial layer called the **trophectoderm**, which gives rise to the placenta, and an inner layer called the inner cell mass, which develops into the embryo. Upon reaching the uterus, the blastocyst hatches from the zona pellucida, the layer of glycoproteins that surrounds the secondary oocyte and is retained up to this time to prevent premature adhesion of the blastocyst to the oviduct. The blastocyst then implants in the endometrium of the mother's uterus (see Figure 51.16). In humans, this entire process takes about 8 to 10 days.

Toward the end of cleavage, cell cycles become less synchronous, and the embryo begins to express its own genes. The embryo's shift from existing exclusively on maternal factors to developing in response to products derived from its own genome begins 6–24 hours after fertilization in vertebrates. This shift is followed by the next general event of development, called gastrulation.

Gastrulation Establishes the Three Germ Layers in the Embryo

Gastrulation is one of the most dramatic events of embryonic development in animals because of the major cell movements that occur.

During gastrulation, the hollow ball of cells that makes up a blastula or blastocyst develops into a highly organized structure called a **gastrula** (refer back to Figure 33.5). A key event is the formation of germ layers, which are primary layers of cells that form during gastrulation. In the gastrula-stage embryo, three germ layers—**ectoderm**, **mesoderm**, and **endoderm**—become clearly established. These distinct germ layers are partially differentiated tissues that occupy discrete regions of the embryo, with an outer ectoderm, a middle mesoderm, and an inner endoderm layer. Each type of germ layer eventually gives rise to different structures. The organization that emerges during gastrulation is most evident by the clear establishment of the digestive tube and body axes. Gastrulation is the first time when both the anteroposterior and dorsoventral body axes are clearly evident in the embryo.

Each germ layer gives rise to different types of cells and body structures (**Figure 51.17**). The ectoderm in the gastrula forms the epidermis and nervous system in the later embryo. The mesoderm gives rise to muscles, kidneys, blood, heart, limbs, connective tissues, and notochord; the last is a key feature of all chordates, described later in this section. The endoderm becomes the epithelial lining of the pancreas, thyroid, lungs, digestive tract, liver, and urinary bladder.

Some of the most detailed descriptions of the events in gastrulation come from the study of frog and other amphibian embryos. The major events of gastrulation are depicted in **Figure 51.18** and described next.

Invagination and Involution: Formation of Germ Layers and Archenteron Prior to gastrulation, the blastula of amphibians is enclosed in a simple, spherical epithelial cell layer. Gastrulation

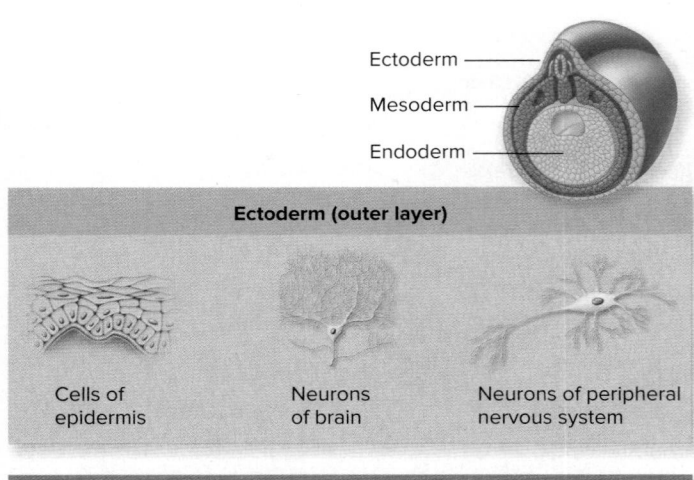

Ectoderm (outer layer)

| Cells of epidermis | Neurons of brain | Neurons of peripheral nervous system |

Mesoderm (middle layer)

| Cells of the notochord | Skeletal muscle cells | Kidney tubule cells | Red blood cells |

Endoderm (inner layer)

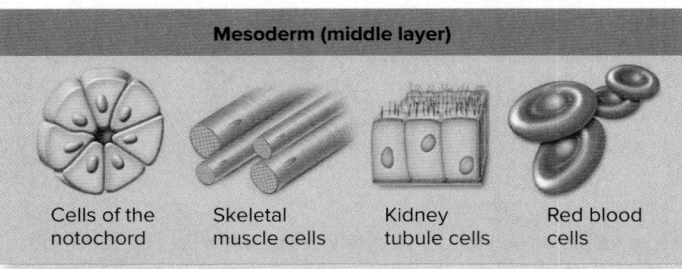

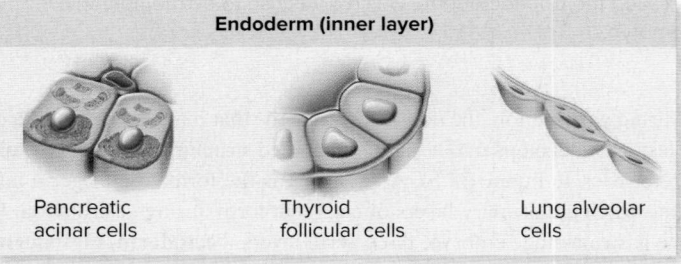

| Pancreatic acinar cells | Thyroid follicular cells | Lung alveolar cells |

Figure 51.17 Examples of cell types derived from ectoderm, mesoderm, and endoderm.

 Core Concept: Structure and Function The formation of specific cell types with different structures and functions is an example of development. Growth entails an increase in the numbers and/or size of each of these cell types.

begins when a band of epithelial cells located at the vegetal hemisphere of the blastula—called bottle cells—invaginates (pinches in), pushing cells from the outside of the embryo to the inside (see Figure 51.18, step 1). This process creates a small opening called the **blastopore**, which defines the anteroposterior axis of the animal. The initiating site of invagination becomes what is called the dorsal lip of the blastopore. This change in morphology of only a few key cells in the embryo initiates the gastrulation process in amphibians.

Once the bottle cells change their shape and push into the interior of the embryo, other cell movements occur, and together these orchestrated movements establish the mesoderm and endoderm of the organism, including its future digestive tract. Just before invagination begins, cells of the animal hemisphere spread out and move downward. When they arrive at the blastopore, they enter the opening and

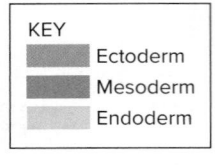

1 **Formation of the blastopore by invagination of bottle cells.**
Gastrulation is initiated by the invagination of bottle cells, which forms a blastopore. Invagination of bottle cells forces cells behind them to involute toward the future anterior end of the embryo. The curved arrows indicate directions of cell movements.

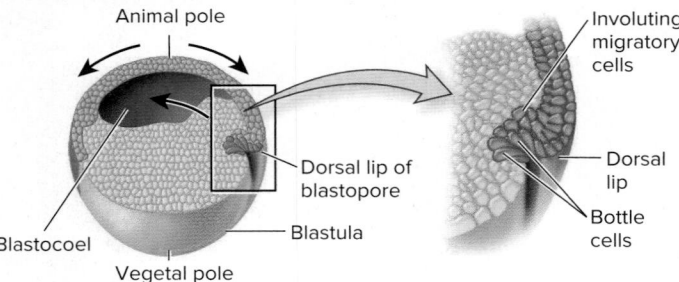

2 **Formation of the archenteron by invagination and involution.**
The cavity that begins at the blastopore expands to form the archenteron (future digestive tract). Ectoderm spreads over the embryo.

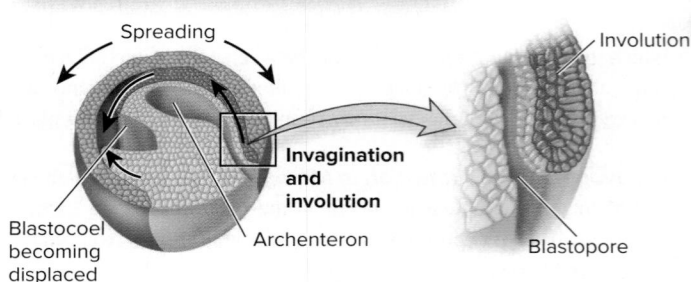

3 **Completion of gastrulation with the beginning of notochord formation.**
By the end of gastrulation, the archenteron has displaced the blastocoel and becomes closed by a yolk plug. Involution continues; some of the involuting cells become the mesoderm layer of the gastrula. The dorsal surface of the gastrula begins to thicken, and the dorsal mesoderm begins to form the notochord.

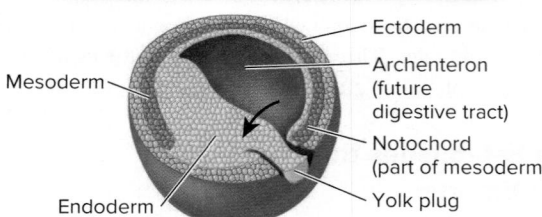

Figure 51.18 The events of gastrulation in amphibians.

subsequently migrate upward along the roof of the blastocoel, toward the animal pole of the embryo. This folding back of sheets of surface cells into the interior of the embryo is called involution (see Figure 51.18, step 2). After involution, dorsal mesodermal cells migrate toward the animal pole by crawling along the roof of the blastocoel, with endoderm following closely behind.

As the opening from the blastopore extends into the embryo, a new cavity called the **archenteron** displaces the existing blastocoel (see Figure 51.18, steps 2 and 3). The archenteron becomes the organism's future digestive tract. The blastopore opening remains sealed with a yolk-rich piece of tissue called the yolk plug until later in development. In chordates and echinoderms, the opening formed by the blastopore ultimately becomes the anus of the organism (refer back to Figure 33.6). Meanwhile, during involution, surface cells spread from the animal hemisphere to surround the entire vegetal hemisphere to become the future ectoderm. The result of these cellular rearrangements is an embryo with three distinct germ layers.

Notochord Formation A distinguishing anatomical feature that begins forming at the end of gastrulation in all chordates is the **notochord**—a structure derived from mesoderm that provides rigidity along the anteroposterior axis in the dorsal side of the gastrula (see Figure 51.18, step 3). The presence of a notochord defines the phylum Chordata. The notochord persists in the trunk and tail of fishes and amphibians. In birds and mammals, the notochord disappears by the time vertebrae have formed. By the time the notochord has formed, the dorsal ectoderm overlying the notochord begins to thicken, which initiates the next general event in development, called neurulation.

Neurulation Involves Formation of the Central Nervous System and Segmentation of the Body

By studying development in several different vertebrate species, researchers are beginning to understand some of the fundamental steps in the formation of the central nervous system (CNS)—the brain and spinal cord—in vertebrates. The multistep embryological process responsible for initiating CNS formation is called **neurulation** (**Figure 51.19**). Neurulation occurs just after gastrulation and involves the formation of the **neural tube** from ectoderm located dorsal to the notochord. All neurons and their supporting cells in the CNS originate from neural precursor cells derived from the neural tube.

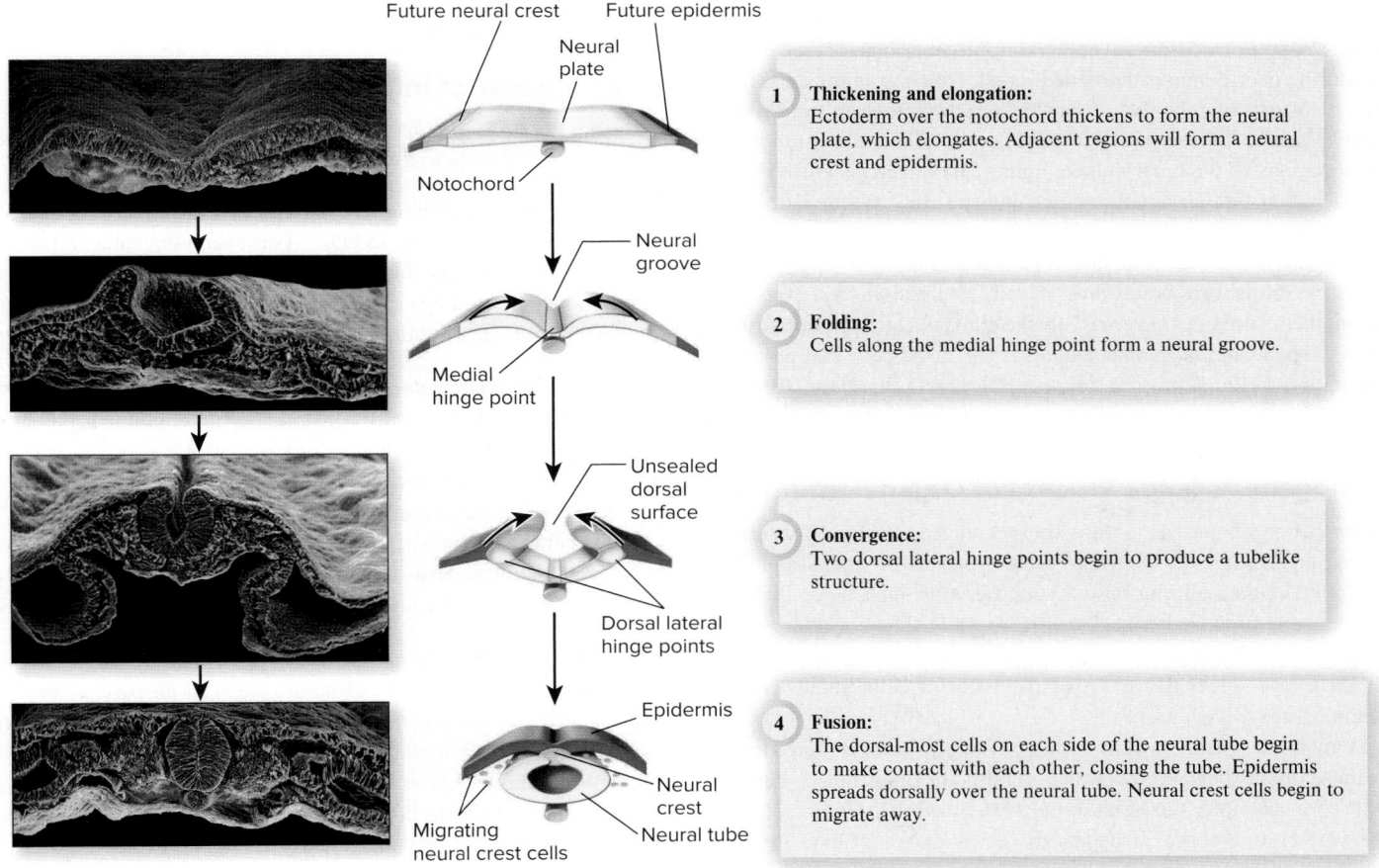

1 **Thickening and elongation:**
Ectoderm over the notochord thickens to form the neural plate, which elongates. Adjacent regions will form a neural crest and epidermis.

2 **Folding:**
Cells along the medial hinge point form a neural groove.

3 **Convergence:**
Two dorsal lateral hinge points begin to produce a tubelike structure.

4 **Fusion:**
The dorsal-most cells on each side of the neural tube begin to make contact with each other, closing the tube. Epidermis spreads dorsally over the neural tube. Neural crest cells begin to migrate away.

Figure 51.19 Neurulation and the beginning of neural crest formation in vertebrates. The major steps of neurulation are (1) thickening and elongation; (2) folding, which creates the neural groove; (3) convergence, in which the neural tube begins to take shape; and (4) fusion, in which the neural tube is completed. In a later event, cells migrate away from the neural crest to form several other structures, including the neurons of the peripheral nervous system. (1–4) Courtesy of Kathryn Tosney

Neural Tube Formation

Neurulation in vertebrates occurs in several major steps, as shown in Figure 51.19.

1. In the first step, ectoderm overlaying the notochord thickens to form the neural plate. Adjacent regions will eventually form the epidermis and a structure called the neural crest (discussed shortly). The neural plate then elongates, resulting in the formation of a single, dorsal, elongated epithelial cell layer that is aligned with the animal's anteroposterior axis.

2. Next, a column of cells along the midline of the neural plate— the medial hinge point—initiates folding of the neural plate, leading to the formation of the neural groove.

3. After folding, bilateral columns of cells in the dorsal lateral hinge points then undergo morphological changes that lead to convergence of the two sides of the neural groove and generation of a tubelike structure that is not yet sealed on the dorsal surface.

4. In the next step of neurulation, called fusion (see Figure 51.19, step 4), the dorsal-most cells on either side of the neural tube are released from adjacent ectoderm and make contact with each other, thereby closing the neural tube. At the same time, ectoderm on either side of the neural tube moves toward the centerline, then up and over the neural tube, where it forms the dorsal epidermis of the embryo.

Neural Crest Formation   Another important group of cells that arises during neurulation is the **neural crest**, which is unique to vertebrates. It consists of cells that originate from the ectoderm overlaying the dorsal surface of the newly formed neural tube and that migrate to other regions of the embryo (see Figure 51.19, step 4). Once these cells reach their final destination in the embryo, they differentiate into a variety of cell types different from those that arise from the rest of the ectoderm. All neurons and supporting cells of the peripheral nervous system in vertebrates are derived from neural crest cells. In addition, the neural crest gives rise to skeletal and cartilaginous structures in the head and face, melanocytes (specialized cells that provide pigmentation to the skin of vertebrates), the medulla of the adrenal glands, and connective tissue in numerous organs, notably the heart.

Organogenesis Is the Process of Organ Formation

As described in Chapter 41, organs are specialized structures that consist of arrangements of two or more tissue types. Most organs, such as the kidneys, contain all four tissue types: nervous, muscle, epithelial, and connective tissue (refer back to Figure 41.1). The developmental event in which cells and tissues form organs is called **organogenesis**. Each germ layer gives rise to particular types of cells found within different organs (see Figure 51.17).

Many organs begin to form during or just after neurulation. However, these organs become functional at different times during development. For example, the heart is the first functional organ to form in the vertebrate embryo. It begins to beat and pump blood by 2.5 days after fertilization in chicks, 9 days in mice, and about 22 days in humans. By contrast, the lungs of mammals do not acquire the ability to function until shortly before birth. As we saw in Chapter 41, the development of different organs in animals is controlled by genes in the embryo—notably the *Hox* genes. *Hox* genes are important

for establishing structures along the anteroposterior axis. Many of the genes controlling the processes of gastrulation, neurulation, and organogenesis encode secreted proteins or growth factors that induce cells in their local vicinity to differentiate along a specific developmental pathway. For example, the notochord produces many signaling proteins that help establish tissue patterns in the embryo. Proteins produced within it induce segment-specific expression of the *Hox* genes in subsequent stages of development.

51.6 Impact on Public Health

Learning Outcomes:

1. Explain the most common causes of human infertility.
2. Compare the different types of birth control, and explain their mechanisms of pregnancy prevention.

Approximately 5–10% of individuals of reproductive age in the U.S. are infertile; that is, they cannot reproduce. In men and women alike, this problem can be caused by a variety of factors. In this section, we discuss some of the common causes of **infertility**—the inability of a man to produce sufficient numbers or quality of sperm to impregnate a woman, or the inability of a woman to become pregnant or maintain a pregnancy. We then conclude by examining the methods in use today to prevent pregnancy.

Many Causes of Infertility Have Been Identified

As many as 75% of infertility cases have some identifiable cause, ranging from disease to toxin exposure.

Disease   Primary among the diseases that affect fertility are sexually transmitted diseases (STDs). For example, some STDs may cause blockage in the ducts of the testes, thus preventing normal sperm transport, or they can cause permanent damage to the oviducts, uterus, and surrounding tissues.

Developmental Disorders   Developmental disorders are conditions that either are present at birth or arise during childhood and adolescence. In some developmental disorders that affect fertility, inherited mutations of genes that encode enzymes involved in the biosynthesis of reproductive hormones cause abnormal expression of those genes. The result is either too much or too little of one or more of these hormones, notably estradiol or testosterone. Other developmental disorders that compromise fertility include malformations of the cervix or oviducts.

Inadequate Nutrition and Other Stressors   Adequate nutrition is required for normal growth and development of all parts of the body, including the reproductive system. Because the reproductive system is not essential for an individual's survival, it often becomes inactive when nutrients are chronically scarce—such as during starvation—and temporary infertility results. In this way, precious stores of energy in the body are preserved for vital functions, such as those of the brain and heart.

Malnutrition can also delay sexual development and puberty during late childhood and early adolescence. Undernourished children may begin puberty several years later than normal. The brains of all mammals, including humans, contain a center that monitors the body's fat stores. One of the triggers that initiate puberty may be a signal—such as the hormone leptin—from adipose tissue to the brain (see Chapter 50). Very low fat stores in undernourished girls, for example, result in decreased leptin in the blood. This low level of leptin signals the brain that the body does not contain sufficient energy to support the energetic demands of pregnancy, and thus puberty is delayed.

Starvation or poor nutrition is considered a type of stress, defined as any real or perceived threat to an animal's homeostasis. Physical and psychological forms of stress affect fertility in humans. Many nonessential functions, including the maintenance of menstrual cycles in women, can be suppressed by chronic stress. The reproductive consequences of stress are much greater in females than in males, likely because only females bear the energetic cost of pregnancy. Interestingly, from a reproduction viewpoint, the human body responds to long-term strenuous physical exercise in the same way that it responds to long-term stress. This is why many young ballerinas and gymnasts experience delayed puberty and why female long-distance runners (like the one in the chapter introduction) may have menstrual cycles that are abnormal or absent (secondary amenorrhea).

Other Causes When the causes of infertility cannot be determined, a variety of factors come under suspicion. Among these possible causes are ingestion of toxins (for example, certain heavy metals such as cadmium), tobacco smoking, marijuana use, and injuries to the gonads.

Treatments Among several currently available treatments for increasing the likelihood of pregnancy in infertile couples are hormone therapy for the woman to increase egg production and a collection of procedures known as **assisted reproductive technologies (ART)**. In the most common ART procedure, in vitro fertilization, sperm and eggs collected from a man and a woman are placed together in culture dishes. Once the sperm have fertilized the eggs and the resulting zygotes have undergone several cell divisions, one or more of the embryos are inserted into a woman's uterus with the goal that one will implant. When this procedure was first used in 1978, the children born as a result came to be known as "test-tube babies." Since then, several million children have been born using this technology.

Contraception Usually Prevents Pregnancy

The use of methods to prevent fertilization or the implantation of a fertilized egg is termed **contraception**. Methods of contraception can be either permanent or temporary.

Permanent Methods The permanent forms of contraception surgically prevent the transport of gametes through the reproductive tract (**Figure 51.20a**). **Vasectomy** is a surgical procedure in men that severs the vas deferens, thereby preventing the release of sperm at ejaculation (however, semen is still released). In women, **tubal ligation** involves the cutting and sealing of the oviducts. This procedure prevents the movement of the egg from the oviduct into the uterus. These procedures are considered permanent, because it is difficult—sometimes impossible—to reverse the surgery.

Temporary Methods Temporary methods of preventing fertilization include barrier methods, which prevent sperm from reaching an egg (**Figure 51.20b**). Barrier methods include **vaginal diaphragms**,

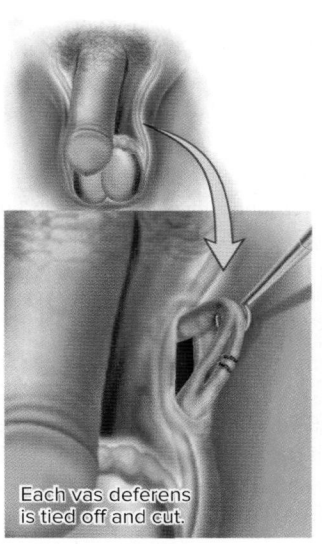
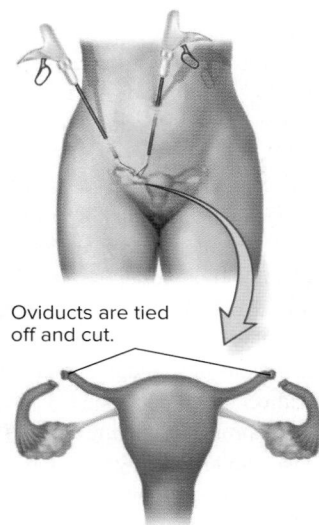

Oviducts are tied off and cut.

Each vas deferens is tied off and cut.

Vasectomy (<1.0%)
(a) Permanent methods

Tubal ligation (<1.0%)

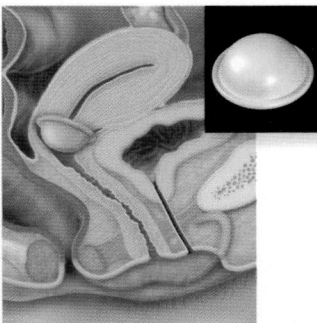
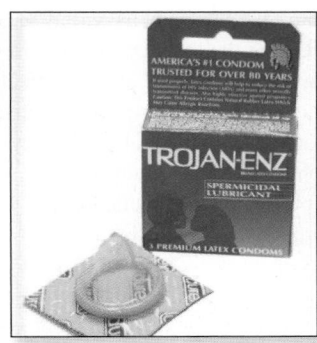

Diaphragm (5–20%)

Condoms (male) (2–15%)

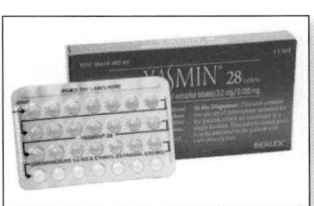
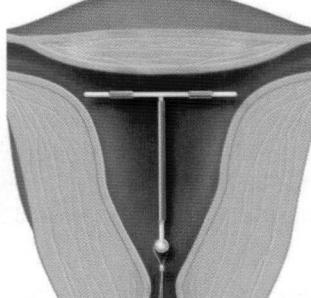

Oral contraceptive (1–2%)
(b) Temporary methods

Intrauterine device (IUD) (1–2%)

Figure 51.20 Examples of contraceptive methods. These methods may be used by men or women to **(a)** permanently or **(b)** temporarily prevent pregnancy. The estimated first-year failure rates for each method are given in parentheses (collected from data published by the U.S. Food and Drug Administration and other organizations). A failure rate of 10% means that 10 of every 100 women using that method of contraception will become pregnant in the first year of use. The large failure rate for use of condoms and diaphragms is due to improper use of these devices by many people. Female condoms are also available and have a failure rate of approximately 20%. (b diaphragm, condoms, oral contraceptive) ©McGraw-Hill Education/Jill Braaten, photographer

which are placed in the upper part of the vagina just prior to intercourse and block movement of sperm to the cervix, and **condoms**, which are sheathlike membranes worn over the penis that collect the ejaculate. In addition to their contraceptive function, condoms significantly reduce the risk of STDs such as HIV infection, syphilis, gonorrhea, chlamydia, and herpes. Other types of contraception do not reduce this risk.

Another temporary form of contraception involves synthetic hormones. Oral contraceptives (birth control pills) are synthetic forms of estradiol and progesterone, which are taken by mouth to prevent ovulation in women by inhibiting the secretion of pituitary LH and FSH and hypothalamic gonadotrophin releasing hormone (GnRH) (recall the feedback actions of estradiol and progesterone). The hormones in these pills also affect the composition of cervical mucus such that sperm cannot easily pass through it into the uterus. In addition to the oral route, hormones can be administered by injections, skin patches, and vaginal rings.

Another temporary method of contraception involves placement in the uterus of an **intrauterine device (IUD)**, a small object that prevents fertilization in part by inhibiting sperm movement and survival in the uterus. Some IUDs may also induce local inflammation in the endometrium and make it less likely that a blastocyst could implant there. Although not as widely used as other contraceptives in the U.S., IUDs are the most commonly used means of contraception by women worldwide because of their effectiveness and simplicity of use.

In addition to the contraceptive methods used before or during intercourse, any of several emergency contraception pills can be taken by a woman within 72 hours after intercourse. These pills include a high dose of progestin (a synthetic form of progesterone), a high dose of combined estrogen and progestin, and a dose of ulipristal acetate, a substance that acts on the progesterone receptor. These ingredients work to prevent ovulation or to impede the ability of sperm to reach and fertilize an egg.

Used prior to the advent of modern contraception, and still in use today by individuals who prefer not to use contraceptives, is the rhythm method, which involves abstaining from sexual intercourse near the time of ovulation. Its main drawback is the difficulty in precisely pinpointing the time of ovulation, which can occur at any time within a roughly 2-week window of the 28-day cycle. Predicting the time of ovulation is also difficult in that several of the detectable changes characteristic of the midpoint of the ovarian cycle—including a small rise in body temperature and changes in the characteristics of the cervical mucus—occur only after ovulation. These drawbacks explain why the rhythm method has a relatively high failure rate.

Summary of Key Concepts

51.1 Overview of Sexual and Asexual Reproduction

- Asexual reproduction occurs when offspring are produced from a single parent, without the fusion of genetic material from two parents (Figure 51.1).

- Sexual reproduction is the production of a new individual by the joining of two haploid gametes: a sperm from the male and an egg from the female.

- Paland and Lynch showed that sexual reproduction was more effective than asexual reproduction in eliminating deleterious mutations from populations of *Daphnia pulex* (Figure 51.2).

51.2 Gametogenesis and Fertilization

- Male and female gametes are formed within the gonads—the testes in males and the ovaries in females. Within the ovaries, each oocyte undergoes growth and development within a follicle before it leaves the ovary in a process called ovulation (Figure 51.3).

- Major events in fertilization include the acrosomal and cortical reactions (Figure 51.4).

- In external fertilization, sperm and eggs are released into an aquatic environment, where they unite. In internal fertilization, sperm are deposited within the reproductive tract of the female during copulation or by cloacal contact.

51.3 Human Reproductive Structure and Function

- Sperm production requires testosterone. Sperm move out of the seminiferous tubules and into the epididymis, which leads into the vas deferens and the ejaculatory duct. The urethra conducts semen, a mixture containing fluid and sperm, during ejaculation. The fluid components of semen are produced in the seminal vesicles, the prostate gland, and the bulbourethral glands (Figures 51.5, 51.6).

- In the ovary, primary oocytes develop into secondary oocytes. If the secondary oocyte is fertilized by a sperm, the fertilized egg undergoes several cell divisions to become a blastocyst, a ball of cells that enters the uterus (Figures 51.7, 51.8).

- In females, changes in hormone secretion produce the ovarian cycle and control the uterine (or menstrual) cycle. The cessation of ovarian cycles is called menopause (Figure 51.9).

51.4 Pregnancy and Birth in Mammals

- Pregnancy is the time during which a developing embryo or fetus grows within the uterus of the mother. Implantation is the embedding of the blastocyst within the uterine endometrium. Most mammals retain and nourish their young within the uterus via transfer of nutrients and gases through the placenta (Figure 51.10).

- The evolution of the globin gene family contributed to the ability of placental mammals to develop inside the mother's uterus (Table 51.1).

- Birth is initiated by hormones produced by the placenta and by the mother's endocrine system. Oxytocin stimulates the strong uterine muscle contractions that are the hallmark of the three-stage process called labor (Figures 51.11, 51.12).

51.5 General Events of Embryonic Development

- The process by which a fertilized egg is transformed into an organism with distinct physiological systems and body parts is called embryonic development. The process by which different cells within a developing organism acquire specialized forms and functions, due to the expression of cell-specific genes, is called cellular differentiation.

- Development in many animals, including vertebrates, involves five general events: fertilization, cleavage, gastrulation, neurulation, and organogenesis (Figure 51.13).

- Cleavage involves cell divisions without cell growth and results in daughter cells called blastomeres. Cleavage-stage embryos in triploblasts have animal and vegetal hemispheres. The hemispheres determine, in part, the future anteroposterior and dorsoventral axes of the embryo (Figure 51.14).

- Incomplete, or meroblastic, cleavage occurs in vertebrates whose eggs contain large amounts of yolk. Complete, or holoblastic, cleavage occurs in animals whose eggs have smaller amounts of yolk. In mammals, cleavage occurs in the oviduct and the blastocyst implants in the uterine wall (Figures 51.15, 51.16).

- During gastrulation, the hollow ball of cells that makes up a blastula develops into a gastrula, containing the three germ layers: endoderm, mesoderm, and ectoderm. Each germ layer gives rise to specific structures (Figures 51.17, 51.18).

- Neurulation is the multistep embryological process responsible for initiating formation of the nervous system. Neurulation involves the formation of the neural tube and neural crest (Figure 51.19).

- Organogenesis, the developmental event during which cells and tissues form organs, begins during or just after neurulation. However, organs become functional at different times during development.

51.6 Impact on Public Health

- Infertility is the inability of a man to produce sufficient numbers or quality of sperm to impregnate a woman, or the inability of a woman to become pregnant or to maintain a pregnancy. Many causes of infertility are known.

- The use of methods to prevent fertilization or implantation of a fertilized egg is termed contraception. Methods of contraception include vasectomy and tubal ligation, vaginal diaphragms, condoms, oral contraceptives, and IUDs (Figure 51.20).

Assess & Discuss

Test Yourself

1. The development of offspring from unfertilized eggs is
   a. budding.
   d. parthenogenesis.
   b. cloning.
   e. implantation.
   c. fragmentation.

2. Which is considered an advantage of sexual reproduction?
   a. necessity to locate a mate
   b. increased energy expenditure in producing gametes that may not be used in reproduction
   c. increased genetic variation
   d. decreased genetic variation
   e. both a and b

3. Spermatogonia
   a. are haploid germ cells.
   d. have flagella.
   b. are mature haploid cells.
   e. are diploid germ cells.
   c. are mature male gametes.

4. Compared with external fertilization, in internal fertilization,
   a. male gametes have a higher chance of coming into close proximity to female gametes.
   b. gametes are less protected against predation or other harmful environmental factors.
   c. gametes typically become dessicated.
   d. gametes come into contact only outside the mother's reproductive tract.
   e. Both b and c occur.

5. Which sequence correctly describes the pathway followed by sperm in mammals?
   a. epididymis→ vas deferens→ seminiferous tubules→ ejaculatory duct→ urethra
   b. seminiferous tubules→ vas deferens→ epididymis→ ejaculatory duct→ urethra
   c. vas deferens→ seminiferous tubules→ epididymis→ ejaculatory duct→ urethra
   d. seminiferous tubules→ epididymis→ vas deferens→ ejaculatory duct→ urethra
   e. epididymis→ seminiferous tubules→ ejaculatory duct→ vas deferens→ urethra

6. The fructose in semen is secreted by
   a. the epididymis.
   b. the seminiferous tubules.
   c. the seminal vesicles.
   d. the prostate gland.
   e. the bulbourethral glands.

7. A major function of FSH is to
   a. stimulate the development of the gonads during early development.
   b. stimulate spermatogenesis in males and oocyte maturation in females.
   c. increase the secretion of testosterone by the testes.
   d. regulate the secretion of the bulbourethral glands.
   e. inhibit the activity of Sertoli cells in the testes.

8. During the human ovarian cycle, ovulation is stimulated by
   a. a decrease in FSH secretion.
   b. an increase in progesterone secretion.
   c. an increase in LH secretion.
   d. the presence of semen in the vagina.
   e. a decrease in estradiol concentration in the bloodstream.

9. In vertebrates, the digestive tract forms from
   a. the blastopore.
   d. the mesoderm.
   b. the dorsal lip.
   e. both a and d.
   c. the archenteron.

10. Cells of the neural crest
    a. give rise to the central nervous system.
    b. originate from ectoderm.
    c. migrate to different areas of the body and differentiate into a variety of cells, including neurons of the peripheral nervous system.
    d. do all of the above.
    e. do b and c only.

Conceptual Questions

1. What disadvantages are associated with external fertilization, and what is one major way in which animals overcome those disadvantages?

2. How does the hypothalamus influence vertebrate reproduction?

3. **Core Concept: Matter and Energy** What are some of the energy costs associated with sexual reproduction? What outweighs those costs and accounts for the observation that most animals reproduce sexually?

Collaborative Questions

1. Describe the major events in animal development beginning with cleavage.

2. Describe the events of the ovarian and uterine cycles, and explain their relative timing.

Immune Systems

52

In an immune system response, a macrophage engulfs numerous rod-shaped bacteria (image is a false-color SEM). ©SPL/Science Source

In 2001, as many as 10 million domestic sheep and cattle had to be destroyed in England due to an epidemic of hoof-and-mouth disease, a viral disease that infected animals across the country. A similarly severe outbreak resulted in millions of diseased pigs and cattle being killed in South Korea and Japan in 2010–2011. Beginning in 2006, as many as 6 million bats in North America have died as a result of an epidemic of a fungal disease called white-nose syndrome, reducing the populations of some species by as much as 99%. Since the 1990s, thousands of gorillas and chimpanzees have died from outbreaks of the ebola virus in parts of Africa, decimating their populations. Countless numbers of crows and other birds have died from West Nile virus in recent years, a virus that, like ebola, can be transmitted to humans. These and other epidemic illnesses highlight the importance of understanding how animals protect themselves from harmful microorganisms and their secretions, as well as against other internal threats, such as cancer.

The ability of an animal to ward off these threats—an animal's **immunity**, or immune defenses—is the subject of this chapter. The cells and organs within an animal's body that contribute to immune defenses collectively constitute that animal's **immune system**. The study of immunity is called immunology. Immunologists examine the processes by which the immune system protects an animal from foreign matter, whether living or nonliving. In these processes, immune defenses recognize the body's own molecules as "self" and attack anything that is foreign, or "nonself."

The two major types of immune defenses are innate and adaptive. **Innate immunity** refers to the body's defenses that are present at birth and that act against any foreign material in much the same way, regardless of the specific identity of the invading material. Innate immunity includes a set of cellular and chemical defenses that oppose substances that breach the external barriers (skin and mucous membranes) of an animal's body. An example of an innate immune response is seen in the chapter opening image, in which a cell known as a macrophage is engulfing numerous bacteria. All animals have innate immune defenses.

In contrast, **adaptive immunity** (also called acquired immunity) develops only after an animal's body is exposed to foreign substances. This type of immunity is characterized by the ability of certain cells of the immune system to recognize a particular foreign substance and initiate a response that targets that substance specifically. Another feature distinguishing adaptive immunity is that repeated exposure to a foreign substance elicits greater and greater defense responses. In contrast, in innate immunity, each exposure to the foreign material elicits the same magnitude of defense responses. Adaptive immunity has been identified in all vertebrates except for the jawless fishes, but has not been unequivocally identified in invertebrates.

We begin the chapter with a brief overview of the different pathogens that cause disease in animals. We will then consider the mechanisms that provide animals with innate and adaptive immunity against harmful pathogens. We will conclude with a discussion of the public health implications of some immunity-related conditions in humans.

52.1 Types of Pathogens

Learning Outcome:

1. List the three main types of pathogens that elicit immune responses, and briefly describe how each damages its host organism.

An animal's immune defenses must protect against a variety of foreign materials, but most important among them are disease-causing viruses and microorganisms, or **pathogens**. Pathogens exist in nearly every ecological niche on Earth. Both terrestrial and aquatic animals, including invertebrates and vertebrates, encounter each of the three major types of pathogens: certain bacteria, viruses, and eukaryotic parasites. A fourth type of infectious agent—proteins called prions—were considered in Chapter 19 (refer back to Figure 19.8) and will not be discussed here.

Bacteria are Prokaryotes Responsible for Many Animal Diseases

As described in Chapter 27, bacteria are prokaryotic organisms that lack a true nucleus. Bacteria can either damage tissues at an open wound site on an animal or release toxins that enter the bloodstream and disrupt functions in other parts of an animal's body. Bacteria are responsible for many diseases and infections in animals and humans, including typhoid fever, strep throat, skin infections, ear infections, anthrax, plague, cholera, and food poisoning. The major ways in which bacteria gain entry into an animal's body are through direct bodily contact, open wounds, inhalation through the respiratory tract, and ingestion with food or water that has been contaminated with fecal matter. This last situation may arise because many infectious bacteria enter the intestines of animals and are excreted in feces, which may be deposited near food or water sources used by other animals.

Viruses May Cause Illness or Cancer

All viruses contain nucleic acid (DNA or RNA) within a protein coat (see Chapter 19). Unlike bacteria, viruses lack the metabolic machinery to synthesize the proteins they require to replicate themselves. Instead, they must infect a host cell and use its biochemical and genetic machinery, including nucleotides and energy sources, to make more viruses. The viral nucleic acid directs the host cell to synthesize the proteins required for the virus's replication. After entering a cell, some viruses, such as the common cold virus, multiply rapidly, kill the cell, and then infect other cells. Other viruses can lie dormant within host cells before suddenly undergoing rapid replication, which causes cell damage or death. Finally, certain viruses can transform their host cells into cancerous cells. Viruses are responsible for a great variety of illnesses, including ebola, swine fever, West Nile encephalitis, hoof-and-mouth disease, influenza, and some sexually transmitted diseases, such as that caused by the human immunodeficiency virus (HIV). Like bacterial infections, viral infections can spread rapidly among animals and can be lethal. Viruses typically enter an animal's body through the respiratory tract or through an open wound.

Eukaryotic Parasites Can Enter Animal Bodies in Several Ways and Cause Widespread Illness

Eukaryotic parasites—whether protists, fungi, or worms—damage a host by using the host's nutrients for their own growth and reproduction or by secreting toxic chemicals. In humans, parasites account for an enormous number of cases of disease annually. For example, several hundred million people are infected each year with one of the mosquito-borne protists of the genus *Plasmodium* that cause malaria. Parasitic infections may enter a host through the bite of an infected insect, as in malaria; by ingestion of food or water containing parasitic organisms, such as roundworms; or in some cases, by penetrating the skin, as with blood flukes.

52.2 Innate Immunity

Learning Outcomes:

1. Identify the general characteristics of innate defense mechanisms in animals.
2. Explain how an animal's body surface provides protection from pathogens.
3. Describe the process of phagocytosis, and explain its importance in innate immune responses.
4. List the cell types involved in innate immunity, and identify the functions of each.
5. Identify the correct sequence of the events in the inflammatory response.
6. Describe the role of Toll proteins in innate immunity.

Innate immune defenses protect against foreign cells or substances without having to recognize the invaders' specific identities. This type of defense mechanism is called innate because animals inherit the ability to perform these protective functions and because this type of immunity does not require prior exposure to invaders. Instead of distinguishing among foreign materials, innate defenses recognize some general property marking the invader as foreign, such as a particular class of carbohydrate or lipid present in the cell walls of many different kinds of microbes. For this reason, innate immunity is sometimes referred to as nonspecific immunity.

In this section, we will consider the innate immune defenses. These include the actions of phagocytic cells, the response to injury or infection known as inflammation, and various proteins secreted by cells of the immune system that facilitate the destruction of pathogens. We begin, however, with a brief look at barrier defenses that can help prevent pathogens from entering an animal's body fluids and cells.

An Animal's Body Surface Is an Initial Line of Defense

Although not part of an animal's innate immunity, an animal's initial defense against pathogens is the cellular, chemical, and anatomical barrier provided by a surface exposed to the external environment. Very few microorganisms can penetrate the intact skin or body surface of most animals, particularly the tough, thick, or scaly skin characteristic of many vertebrates or the exoskeleton of many arthropods. In addition, glands in the body surfaces of many invertebrates and vertebrates secrete a variety of antimicrobial molecules onto the body surface, including mild acids and enzymes such as lysozyme that destroy bacterial cell walls.

The mucus secreted from cells in the mucous membranes lining the respiratory and upper digestive tracts of vertebrates also contains antimicrobial molecules. More importantly, mucus is sticky—microbes that become stuck in it are prevented from penetrating the mucous membrane barrier. They are either swept up by cilia into the pharynx and then swallowed, or they are engulfed by cells that are present in both tracts. Pathogens ingested with food are often destroyed by the acidic environment of an animal's stomach.

If, however, a pathogen is able to penetrate a barrier and gain entry into an animal's internal tissues and fluids, innate defense mechanisms are activated. These mechanisms are mediated by several types of cells that reside in the body fluids and tissues, as described next.

In Innate Immunity, Phagocytic Cells Defend Against Pathogens That Enter the Body

Several different types of cells have important functions in innate immunity in vertebrates. As noted in **Figure 52.1**, some of these cell types are **phagocytes**—cells capable of phagocytosis. **Phagocytosis** is a type of endocytosis in which a cell engulfs particulate matter, which usually is then destroyed by proteases or oxidizing compounds such as hydrogen peroxide. Phagocytes are found in the body fluids, such as hemolymph and blood, and also within various tissues and organs. They are present in all classes of animals and are among the most fundamental and ancestral forms of immune defenses.

In vertebrates, most phagocytes are a type of blood cell called **leukocytes** (see Figure 52.1). All leukocytes are derived from a common type of stem cell called adult hematopoietic stem cells (refer back to Figure 20.20), which in mammals and birds are found in the bone marrow. These stem cells give rise to several types of leukocytes and other immune cells that have specialized functions. The leukocytes involved in innate immunity include the following:

- **Neutrophils** are the most abundant phagocytes. They are found in blood and some may enter tissues during inflammation. After neutrophils engulf bacteria by phagocytosis, the bacteria are destroyed within endocytotic vacuoles by proteases, oxidizing compounds, and antibacterial proteins called defensins. The production and release of neutrophils from bone marrow are greatly stimulated during the course of an infection.

- **Eosinophils** are found in the blood and in the mucosal surfaces lining the gastrointestinal, respiratory, and urinary tracts, where they fight off parasitic invasions. Eosinophils act in some cases by releasing toxic chemicals that kill parasites and in other cases by phagocytosis.

- **Monocytes** are phagocytes that circulate in the blood for a short time, after which they migrate into tissues and organs and develop into macrophages.

- **Macrophages** are strategically located where they will encounter foreign matter, for example, in epithelia in contact with the external environment, such as skin and the linings

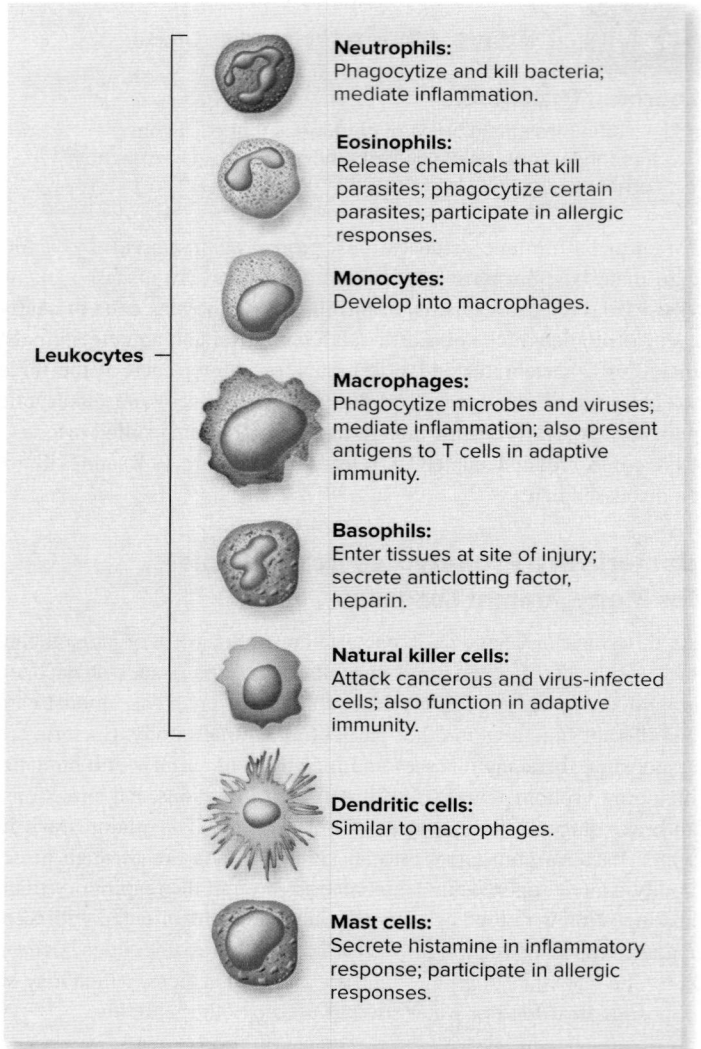

Figure 52.1 Cells involved in innate immunity in vertebrates. Six of these types of cells are leukocytes, and several are phagocytes. Some of these cells also participate in adaptive immunity; a few of those actions are included here for reference and will be described in a later section.

of respiratory and digestive tracts. Macrophages are large phagocytes capable of engulfing viruses and bacteria, as shown in the chapter opening image. As will be described later, macrophages also function in adaptive immunity.

- **Basophils** are secretory cells, not phagocytes. They secrete an anticlotting factor called heparin at the site of an infection, which helps the circulation flush out the infected site. Basophils also secrete histamine, which attracts infection-fighting cells and proteins to the site.

- **Natural killer (NK) cells** are another kind of leukocyte called lymphocytes, of which there are several types. We will discuss the other types of lymphocytes later, because they play the major role in adaptive immunity. Like macrophages, NK cells participate in both innate and adaptive immunity. These cells are part of an animal's innate defenses because they recognize general features on the surface of cancerous cells or virus-infected cells. They act by releasing chemicals into the vicinity of cancerous or virus-infected cells, thereby killing those cells.

In addition to leukocytes, two other types of cells derived from bone marrow stem cells have important functions in innate immunity. **Dendritic cells** are scattered throughout most tissues, where they perform various macrophage-like functions. **Mast cells** are found throughout connective tissues, particularly beneath the epithelial surfaces of the body. Mast cells secrete many locally acting molecules, including histamine. Histamine and other substances are involved in inflammation, a fundamental component of the innate defense mechanism, which we now examine.

Inflammation Is an Innate Response to Infection or Injury

Inflammation is an innate local response to infection or injury. The functions of inflammation are to destroy or inactivate pathogens, to clear the infected region of dead cells and other debris, and to set the stage for tissue repair. The key cellular components of this process are neutrophils, macrophages, dendritic cells, and mast cells.

The events of inflammation are induced and regulated by chemical mediators. These include a family of proteins called **cytokines** that function in both innate and adaptive immune defenses. Cytokines provide a chemical communication network that synchronizes the components of the immune response. Most cytokines are secreted by more than one type of immune cell and also by certain nonimmune cells such as fibroblasts and the endothelial cells of blood vessels.

The sequence of events in a typical inflammatory response to a bacterial infection is summarized in **Figure 52.2**. A tissue injury such as that caused by a splinter begins the inflammatory process, which results in the familiar signs and symptoms of local redness, swelling, heat, and pain.

Substances secreted into the extracellular fluid from injured tissue cells, mast cells, and neutrophils contribute to the inflammatory response. For example, histamine from mast cells and nitric oxide from endothelial cells (Figure 52.2, step 1) cause vasodilation (widening) of the small blood vessels in the infected and damaged area, which induces the vessels to leak (step 2).

These vascular changes provide two benefits. First, the increased blood flow to the inflamed area, which accounts for the redness and heat, speeds the delivery of beneficial proteins and leukocytes and increases local metabolism to facilitate healing. Second, the increased vascular permeability ensures that the plasma proteins that participate in inflammation can gain entry to the interstitial fluid. The swelling in an inflamed area also results from this increased leakiness of blood vessels.

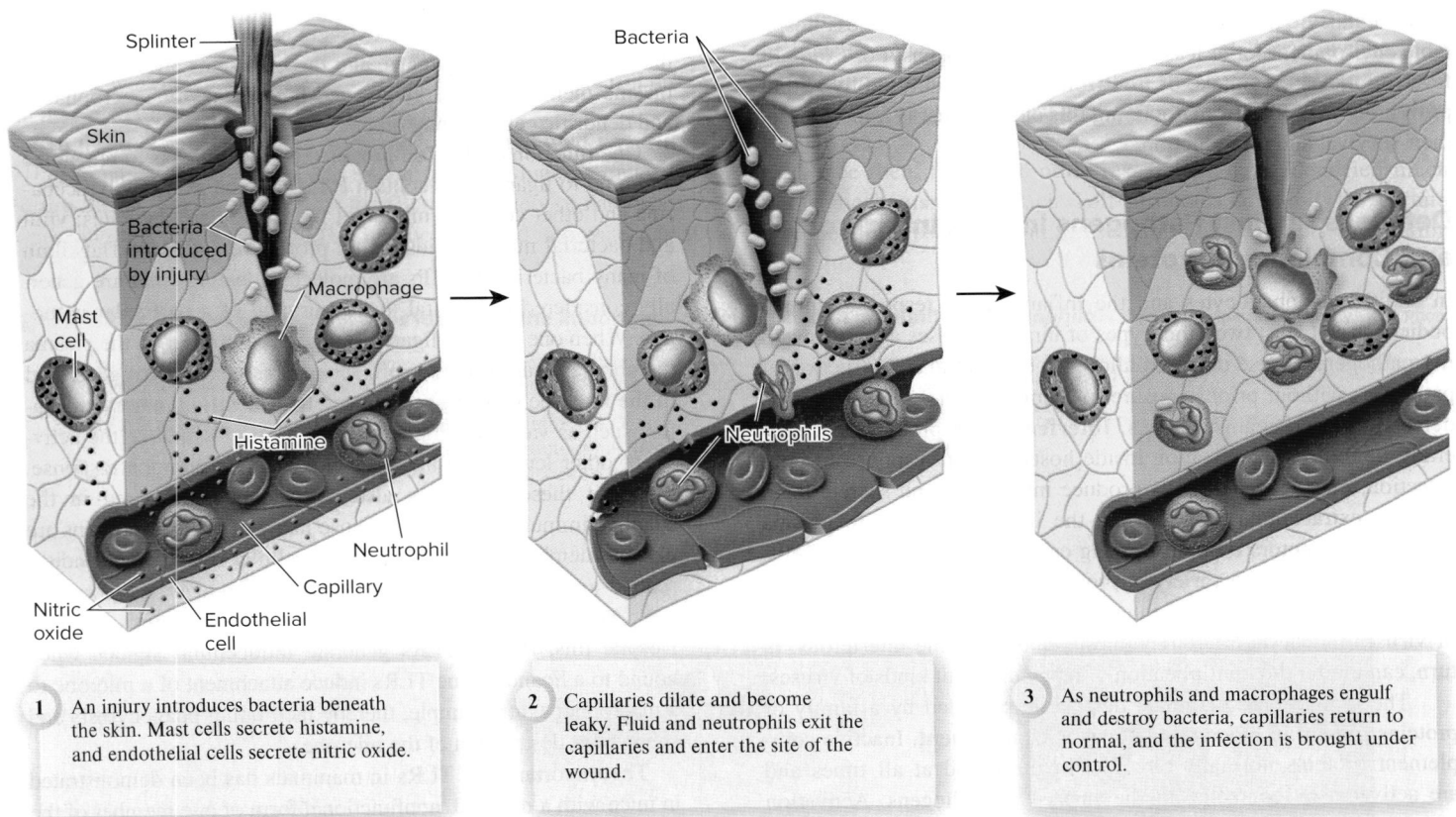

1 An injury introduces bacteria beneath the skin. Mast cells secrete histamine, and endothelial cells secrete nitric oxide.

2 Capillaries dilate and become leaky. Fluid and neutrophils exit the capillaries and enter the site of the wound.

3 As neutrophils and macrophages engulf and destroy bacteria, capillaries return to normal, and the infection is brought under control.

Figure 52.2 The events in inflammation. Shown are the initial stages of inflammation in response to a penetrating wound that introduces bacteria beneath the skin.

Concept Check: *Inflammation is often associated with swelling of the inflamed area. Could this swelling have an adaptive value?*

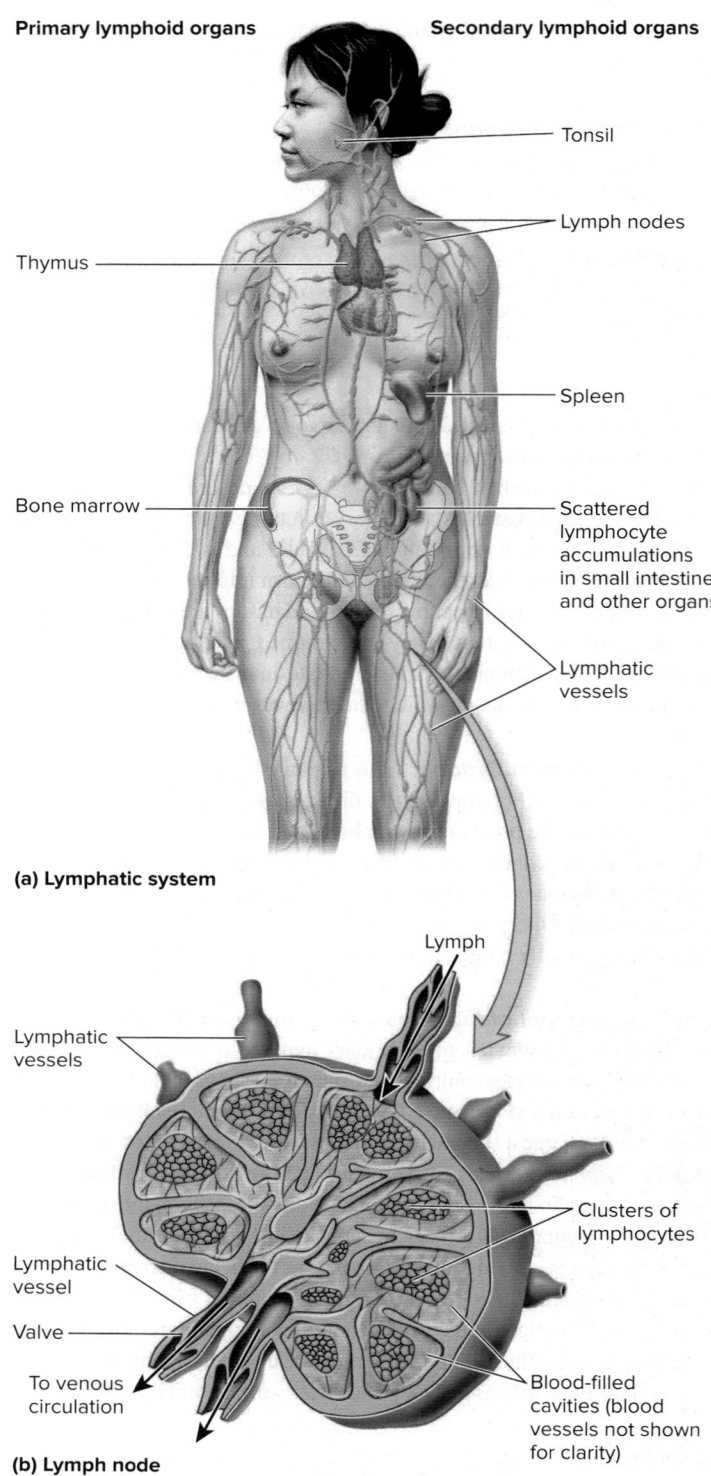

Primary lymphoid organs   **Secondary lymphoid organs**

- Tonsil
- Lymph nodes
- Thymus
- Spleen
- Bone marrow
- Scattered lymphocyte accumulations in small intestine and other organs
- Lymphatic vessels

(a) Lymphatic system

- Lymph
- Lymphatic vessels
- Lymphatic vessel
- Valve
- To venous circulation
- Clusters of lymphocytes
- Blood-filled cavities (blood vessels not shown for clarity)

(b) Lymph node

Figure 52.4   The lymphatic system in humans. (a) The major components of the human lymphatic system. Primary lymphoid organs are shown in red, and secondary lymphoid organs are shown in green. In adult humans, the primary lymphoid organs in bone are found in the sternum, ribs, parts of the skull, small regions of the femur and humerus, and, as shown here, the hip bones. **(b)** The structure of a lymph node. Lymph nodes occur along the course of lymphatic vessels, which drain lymph from tissues and return it to the venous circulation. Within a lymph node, lymph percolates through open cavities containing clusters of lymphocytes.

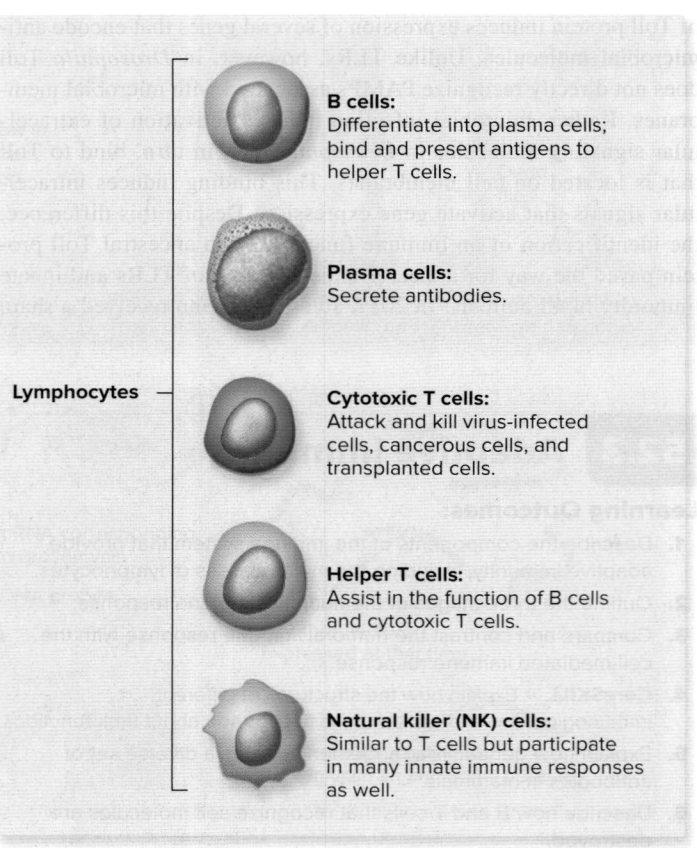

Lymphocytes

B cells:
Differentiate into plasma cells; bind and present antigens to helper T cells.

Plasma cells:
Secrete antibodies.

Cytotoxic T cells:
Attack and kill virus-infected cells, cancerous cells, and transplanted cells.

Helper T cells:
Assist in the function of B cells and cytotoxic T cells.

Natural killer (NK) cells:
Similar to T cells but participate in many innate immune responses as well.

Figure 52.5   Types of lymphocytes involved in adaptive immunity in vertebrates. Some important functions of each type of lymphocyte are noted. The shape and color conventions shown in this figure will be used throughout this chapter.

Lymphocytes Include B Cells and T Cells

Different kinds of lymphocytes participate in specific coordinated immune system responses (**Figure 52.5**). In addition to NK cells, described earlier, the two major types of lymphocytes are **B cells** and **T cells**. B cells were first observed to mature in an avian organ called the bursa of Fabricius, and therefore were named B cells. In mammals, B cells mature within bone marrow. If stimulated by antigen, some B cells differentiate further into **plasma cells**, which synthesize and secrete **antibodies**, proteins that bind to and help destroy foreign molecules, as described later.

T cells may directly kill infected, mutated, or transplanted cells. They are called T cells because they mature within the thymus gland.

 Core Concept: Systems The lymphatic system functions to protect an animal against pathogens. Like most organ systems, its function is dependent on other systems. For example, lymph arises from fluid that exits the capillaries of the circulatory system and mixes with interstitial fluid. After this fluid passes through the lymphatic vessels, it is returned to the circulatory system.

T cells that mediate defense mechanisms include two major types of lymphocytes: cytotoxic T cells and helper T cells. **Cytotoxic T cells** travel to the location of their targets, bind to the targets by recognizing an antigen, and kill the targets via secreted chemicals. In addition, responses mediated by cytotoxic T cells are directed against body cells that have become cancerous or infected by pathogens. NK cells also destroy such cells by secreting toxic chemicals.

As their name implies, **helper T cells** do not themselves function as effector cells. Instead, they assist in the activation and function of B cells and cytotoxic T cells. With only a few exceptions, B cells and cytotoxic T cells cannot function adequately unless they are stimulated by cytokines secreted from helper T cells.

An additional type of T cell that won't be considered further here is the regulatory T cell. These cells function to suppress other T cell activities and to help prevent destruction of self proteins. They serve as a check on immune activity.

Adaptive Immune Responses Include Humoral and Cell-Mediated Immunity and Occur in Three Stages

Lymphocytes function by recognizing antigens such as those found on viruses, bacteria, and the surface of cancerous cells. The ability of lymphocytes to distinguish one antigen from another has a central role in adaptive immunity. There are two types of adaptive immunity. In

humoral immunity, plasma cells secrete antibodies that bind to antigens. The adjective humoral denotes communication by way of soluble chemical messengers (the word humors was once used to refer to bodily fluids). In **cell-mediated immunity**, cytotoxic T cells directly encounter and destroy infected body cells, cancerous cells, or transplanted cells.

An adaptive immune response can usually be divided into three stages (**Figure 52.6**): recognition of antigen, activation and proliferation of lymphocytes, and attack against the recognized antigen.

Stage 1: Recognition of Antigen   During its development, each lymphocyte synthesizes a type of membrane receptor that can bind to a specific antigen. If the lymphocyte subsequently encounters that antigen, the antigen becomes bound to the receptor. This specific binding is the immunological meaning of the word recognize: Antigens that bind to a lymphocyte receptor are said to be recognized by the lymphocyte. The ability of lymphocytes to distinguish one antigen from another, therefore, is determined by the nature of their plasma membrane receptors. Each lymphocyte is specific for just one type of antigen.

Stage 2: Activation and Proliferation of Lymphocytes   In the second stage, the binding of an antigen to a receptor on a lymphocyte activates that lymphocyte. Upon activation, the lymphocyte undergoes multiple cycles of cell division. The result is the formation of

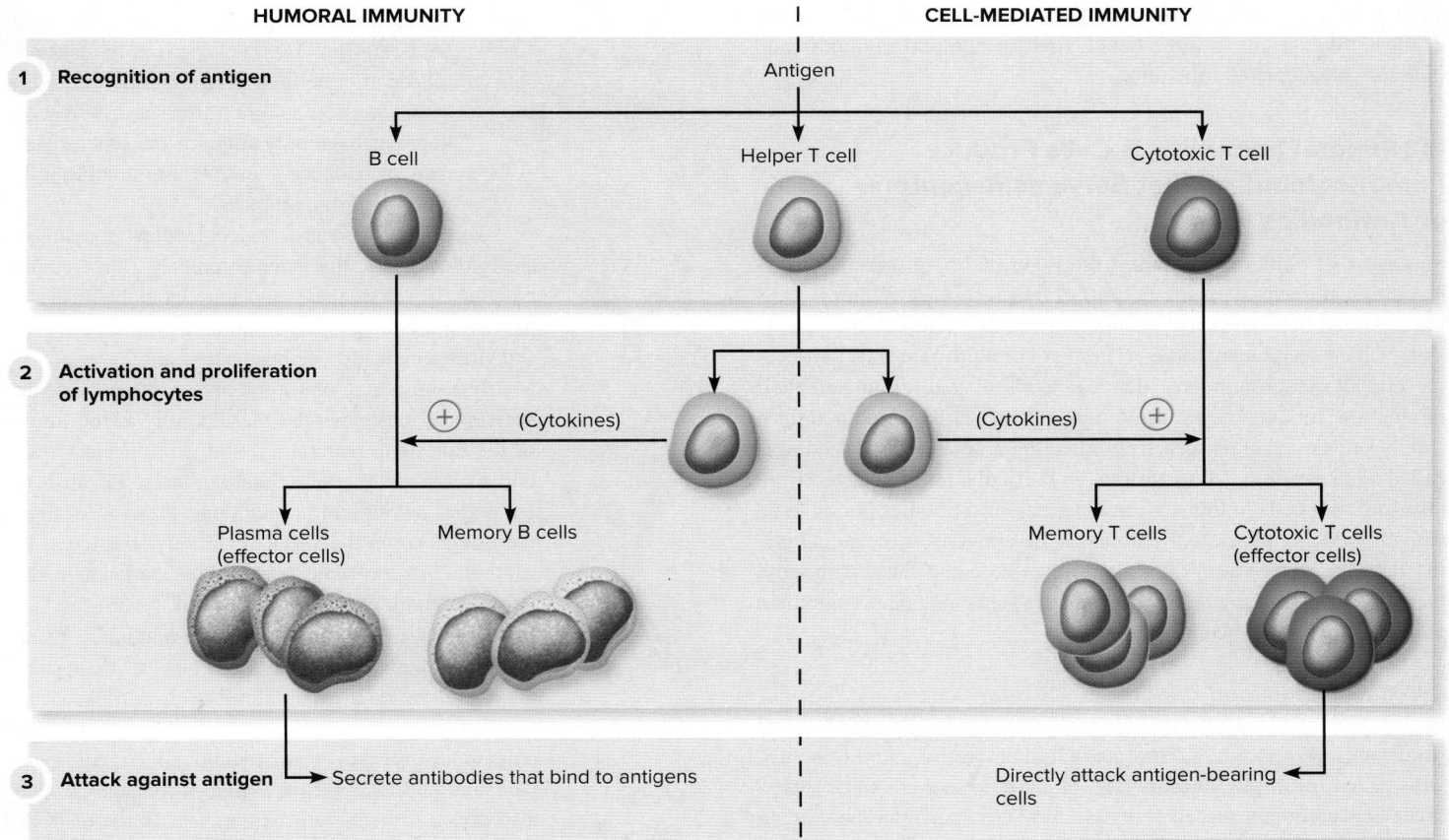

Figure 52.6 The three stages of an adaptive immune response. All three cell types in step 1 recognize the same antigen. Helper T cells secrete cytokines that activate B cells and cytotoxic T cells, as indicated by the ⊕ symbols. Both B cells and T cells undergo cell division to form clones when activated, and in both cases, some of the cloned cells are set aside as memory cells to fight off a future infection of the same type.

many identical cells called clones that express the same receptor as the receptor that first recognized the antigen. The structure of the antigen determines which individual lymphocytes will be activated to form clones. This process requires the function of helper T cells, which divide when activated and then secrete the cytokines that promote further cell division. Some of the cloned lymphocytes become **effector cells**, the plasma cells and cytotoxic T cells that carry out the attack response. Others are stored as **memory cells**, which remain poised to recognize the antigen if it returns in the future.

The size of the lymphocyte population is staggering. For example, 100 million different lymphocytes, each with the ability to recognize a unique antigen, are estimated to exist in a human's immune system. This vast population explains why our bodies are able to recognize so many different antigens as foreign and eventually destroy them.

Stage 3: Attack Against Antigen   In the third stage, the effector cells attack all antigens of the kind that initiated the immune response. Plasma cells carry out a humoral response by secreting antibodies into the blood. These antibodies then recruit and guide other molecules and cells that perform the actual attack. Activated cytotoxic T cells, by contrast, carry out cell-mediated immunity. They directly attack and kill the cells bearing the antigens.

Once the attack is successfully completed, the great majority of plasma cells and cytotoxic T cells that participated in it die by apoptosis. However, memory cells persist even after the immune response has been successfully completed, so they can recognize and fight off any future infection with the same type of antigen. Let's look at each of these three stages in more detail, first for humoral immunity and then for cell-mediated immunity.

In Humoral Immunity, B Cells Produce Immunoglobulins That Serve as Receptors or Antibodies

In stage 1 of humoral immunity (see Figure 52.6, left side), B cells recognize antigens with the help of B-cell receptors. When B cells are activated in stage 2, they proliferate and differentiate into plasma cells, which secrete antibodies. These are proteins that travel all over the body to reach antigens identical to those that stimulated their production. In some cases, the binding of an antibody to an antigen simply prevents that antigen from infecting a host cell; this action is called neutralization. Many viruses, in particular, are prevented from infecting host cells in this way. In other cases, antibodies bound to an antigen guide an attack that eliminates the antigens or the cells bearing them, a process we will discuss in more detail later. Antibody-mediated responses are the major defense against pathogens and toxin molecules in the extracellular fluid.

B-Cell Receptors and Antibodies   B-cell receptors and the antibodies secreted by plasma cells share many structural and functional similarities (**Figure 52.7**). They are both members of a family of proteins called **immunoglobulins (Ig)**. However, there are some differences between them. B-cell receptors have a transmembrane domain that anchors them in the plasma membrane of the B cell (Figure 52.7a). Antibodies are soluble proteins that are secreted from plasma cells (Figure 52.7b). Interestingly, B-cell receptors and the antibodies

made by plasma cells are encoded by the same genes. In plasma cells, the pre-mRNA is alternatively spliced, a phenomenon described in Chapter 14 (see Figure 14.21), so the transmembrane domain is not present in the protein. For this reason, the B-cell receptor in a particular B cell and secreted antibodies from the resulting plasma cells recognize the exact same antigen.

Immunoglobulin Classes and Structure   Each immunoglobulin molecule is composed of four interlinked polypeptides: two long heavy chains and two short light chains (see Figure 52.7). A hinge region that provides the molecule with flexibility separates the light chains and upper parts of the heavy chains from the lower parts of the heavy chains. One portion of an immunoglobulin chain is called the **constant region**. The amino acid sequence of the constant region is identical for all immunoglobulins of a given class and is what distinguishes the classes from each other. The constant regions are important for the binding of antibodies to immune cells and to complement proteins, and thus contribute to the eventual destruction of antigen that is bound to an antibody. A defining feature of immunoglobulins, however, is their **variable region**, which gets its name because its amino acid sequence varies among different B cells. The variable region is the site that specifically recognizes a particular antigen.

IgM
(pentamer)

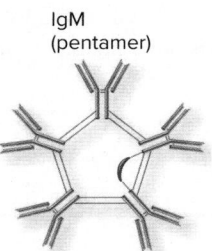

Mammals have five classes of immunoglobulins, designated IgM, IgG, IgA, IgE, and IgD. All vertebrates have IgM molecules. These pentamers (made of five Ig molecules connected by disulfide bonds and other linkages) are the first Ig class produced after antigen exposure, but their blood concentration declines afterward. Some vertebrates have only some of the other classes and also express unique immunoglobulins not found in mammals.

IgG
(monomer)

The most abundant immunoglobulins in mammals are IgM and IgG, the latter commonly called gamma globulin. Together these two immunoglobulin classes provide the bulk of specific immunity against bacteria and viruses in the extracellular fluid.

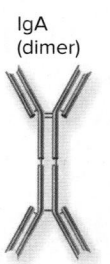

IgA
(dimer)

IgA immunoglobulins exist as dimers and are secreted as antibodies by plasma cells in the linings of the digestive, respiratory, and genitourinary tracts and in tear ducts and salivary glands. Because the antibodies are present in secretions, they act locally in the linings or on the surfaces of body structures. For example, IgA molecules secreted into saliva help keep animals' mouths relatively free of pathogens. IgA molecules are also secreted by the mammary glands of female mammals shortly after birth of their young and therefore are the major antibodies in milk.

IgE
(monomer)

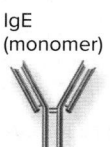

IgE immunoglobulins are monomers that participate in defenses against multicellular eukaryotic parasites and also mediate allergic responses. They also attach to mast cell membranes. When mast cell IgE molecules bind antigen, the mast cell secretes its histamine into the extracellular fluid, causing vasodilation and contributing to the allergic response. In people

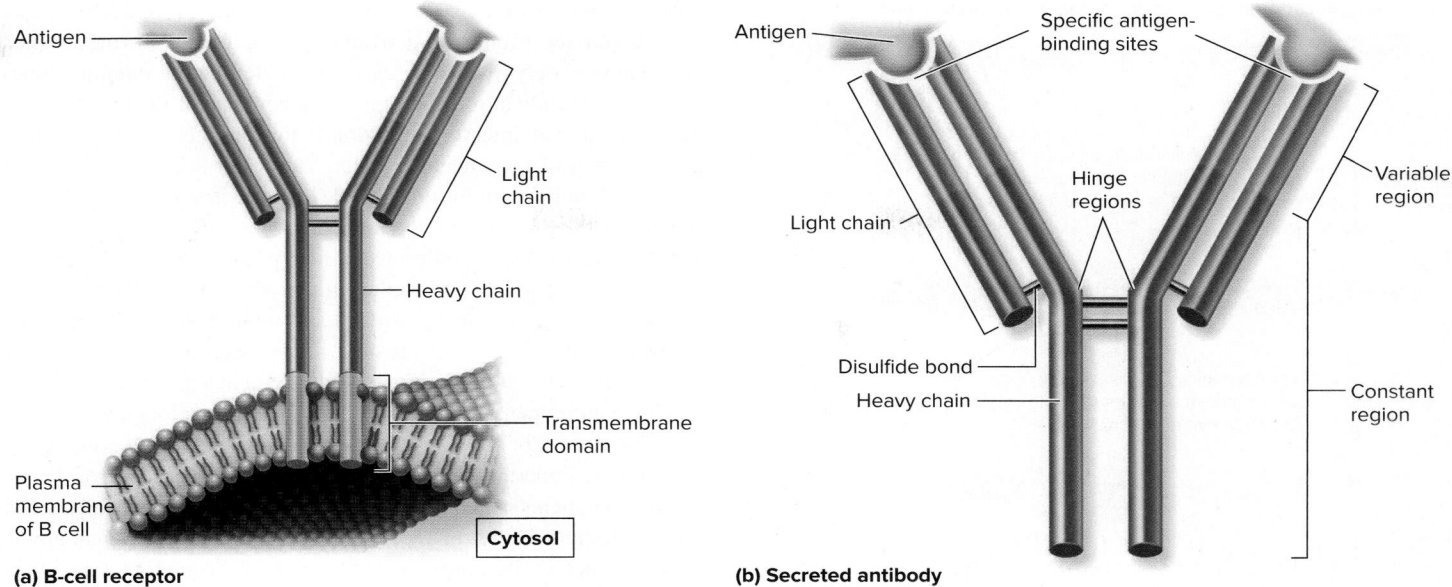

(a) B-cell receptor

(b) Secreted antibody

Figure 52.7 **Immunoglobulins.** **(a)** B-cell receptor and **(b)** secreted antibody. Immunoglobulins are composed of two heavy chains and two light chains. Disulfide bonds hold the chains together. A B-cell receptor is anchored to the plasma membrane by a transmembrane domain, whereas an antibody is secreted into the extracellular fluid. Within both types of immunoglobulins, the constant regions of the heavy and light chains (shown in blue) have identical amino acid sequences. In contrast, the antigen-binding sites formed by the light- and heavy-chain variable regions (shown in purple) have unique amino acid sequences and give each receptor or antibody its specificity for a particular antigen.

Core Skill: Modeling The goal of this modeling challenge is to make a model that depicts the binding of an immunoglobulin to an antigen that has a different structure than the one shown in Figure 52.7.

Modeling Challenge: The structures of proteins determine their functions. This is true of all immunoglobulins. Using the model of a secreted antibody shown in Figure 52.7b as a starting point, draw a new model of an antibody that binds to the antigen depicted to the right.

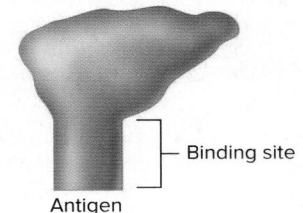

An antigen with its binding site indicated

who are particularly sensitive to allergens, this response is easily demonstrated by a pinprick injection of an antigen—such as one of the proteins associated with hay fever—into a small region under the skin, or by applying the antigen topically for an extended period of time (called patch testing). The resultant local inflammation and reddening of the skin are mediated in large part by IgE molecules.

IgD (monomer)

The functions of IgD are still unclear. However, IgD molecules are present both in blood and on the surface of B cells, and they are known to bind antigens on B cells, thus possibly contributing to B-cell activation.

The amino acid sequences of the variable regions vary widely from immunoglobulin to immunoglobulin in a given Ig class. The enormous number of variable sequences results in countless unique structures within each class of immunoglobulins. Thus, each of the five classes of immunoglobulins contains up to millions of unique molecules each capable of combining with only one specific antigen or, in some cases, with several antigens with very similar structures. How did animals evolve the ability to make all of these

different immunoglobulins? The explanation for this remarkable array was first proposed in the 1970s, as we see next.

Recombination and Immunoglobulin Structure The human genome contains about 200 genes that encode immunoglobulins. This raises an intriguing question: How can an animal such as a human produce millions of different immunoglobulin proteins if there are only 200 immunoglobulin genes? The answer is that the 200 genes undergo a unique process involving gene rearrangements. This phenomenon was discovered by Japanese scientist Susumu Tonegawa and others in the 1970s. Tonegawa was recognized for this achievement in 1987 with the Nobel Prize in Physiology or Medicine.

Along the length of a typical human immunoglobulin gene are numerous gene segments that encode a portion of the final immunoglobulin protein (**Figure 52.8**). In light chains, these gene segments are of three types, called variable, joining, and constant segments. A total of 40 variable (V) segments encode the antigen-binding site. These are next to four joining (J) segments and a single constant (C) segment. Each segment along the length of the gene is associated

Organization of gene segments in a light-chain gene

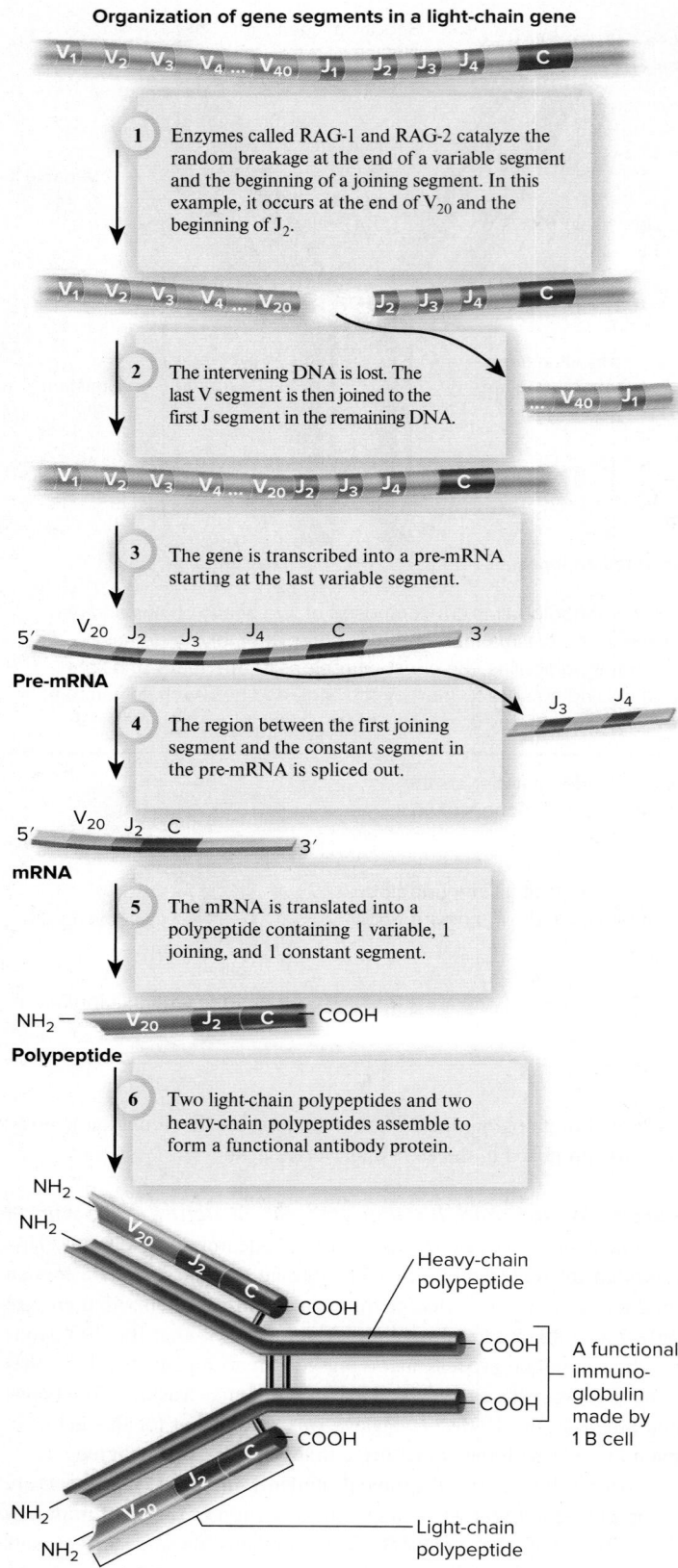

1. Enzymes called RAG-1 and RAG-2 catalyze the random breakage at the end of a variable segment and the beginning of a joining segment. In this example, it occurs at the end of V_{20} and the beginning of J_2.

2. The intervening DNA is lost. The last V segment is then joined to the first J segment in the remaining DNA.

3. The gene is transcribed into a pre-mRNA starting at the last variable segment.

Pre-mRNA

4. The region between the first joining segment and the constant segment in the pre-mRNA is spliced out.

mRNA

5. The mRNA is translated into a polypeptide containing 1 variable, 1 joining, and 1 constant segment.

Polypeptide

6. Two light-chain polypeptides and two heavy-chain polypeptides assemble to form a functional antibody protein.

Heavy-chain polypeptide

A functional immuno-globulin made by 1 B cell

Light-chain polypeptide

Figure 52.8 The mechanism of immunoglobulin diversity. Although this figure shows events for a light-chain, events similar to those depicted here also occur in the production of the heavy chains, creating even more structural diversity.

with recognition sequences that bind two enzymes, called RAG-1 and RAG-2 (for recombination-activating gene). These enzymes, which are expressed only in developing lymphocytes, cut an immunoglobulin gene randomly at the end of a V segment and at the beginning of a J segment. The intervening region is lost, and then other enzymes paste the V and J segments together. The result is a new, permanent immunoglobulin gene for that B cell. Because any V segment can be linked with any J segment, the number of possible final genes in different B cells is huge. Additionally, heavy chains also have multiple segments that are spliced together in this way, except that they have yet another segment (designated D) and more V segments, yielding an even greater number of possible heavy-chain genes. Finally, any heavy chain can combine with any light chain in a given B cell, which results in an immense number of possible immunoglobulins.

The number of possible immunoglobulins is increased even further in two more important ways within B cells. First, the joining of the V, D, and J segments is not always a precise process. Occasionally, a few nucleotides may be lost at a joining end, resulting in a different amino acid sequence in the immunoglobulin protein. Second, in a subset of activated B cells, the DNA encoding the variable antigen-binding sites of immunoglobulins undergoes a unique process known as hypermutation, which primarily produces point mutations. The result is a hypervariable region of the light and heavy chains of all immunoglobulins.

The three processes of gene recombination, imprecise joining of gene segments, and hypermutation cause each lymphocyte within an individual's body to produce a unique type of immunoglobulin. The evolution of adaptive immunity resulted in an incredibly diverse array of immunoglobulins capable of recognizing an incredibly diverse array of antigens. Nearly any foreign antigen that is taken into the body is recognized by some lymphocytes in this large population.

Activated B Cells Produce Plasma Cells That Secrete Antibodies

In stages 2 and 3 of the humoral immune response, B cells are activated and differentiate into either plasma or memory cells. The plasma cells secrete antibodies that bind the antigen that was detected (see Figure 52.6, left side). Let's take a closer look at these processes.

Clonal Selection B cells are activated by a specific antigen, with the aid of a helper T cell (a process we will discuss later). When an antigen-stimulated lymphocyte divides and replicates itself, the progeny of this lymphocyte—all of which express the same receptor—are clones. The process by which these clones are formed is called **clonal selection** (**Figure 52.9**). This term emphasizes that lymphocyte proliferation is selected by exposure to an antigen.

Antibody Destruction of Pathogens via Opsonization The antibodies secreted from the plasma cells circulate through the lymphatic system and the blood. Eventually, the antibodies combine with the antigen that initiated the immune response. These antibodies then direct the attack against the pathogen to which they are now bound. Thus, immunoglobulins have two distinct roles in humoral immune responses. First, during antigen recognition, immunoglobulins (B-cell receptors) on the surface of B cells bind to antigen brought to them. Second, immunoglobulins (antibodies) secreted by the resulting plasma cells bind to pathogens bearing the same antigens, marking them as the targets to be attacked.

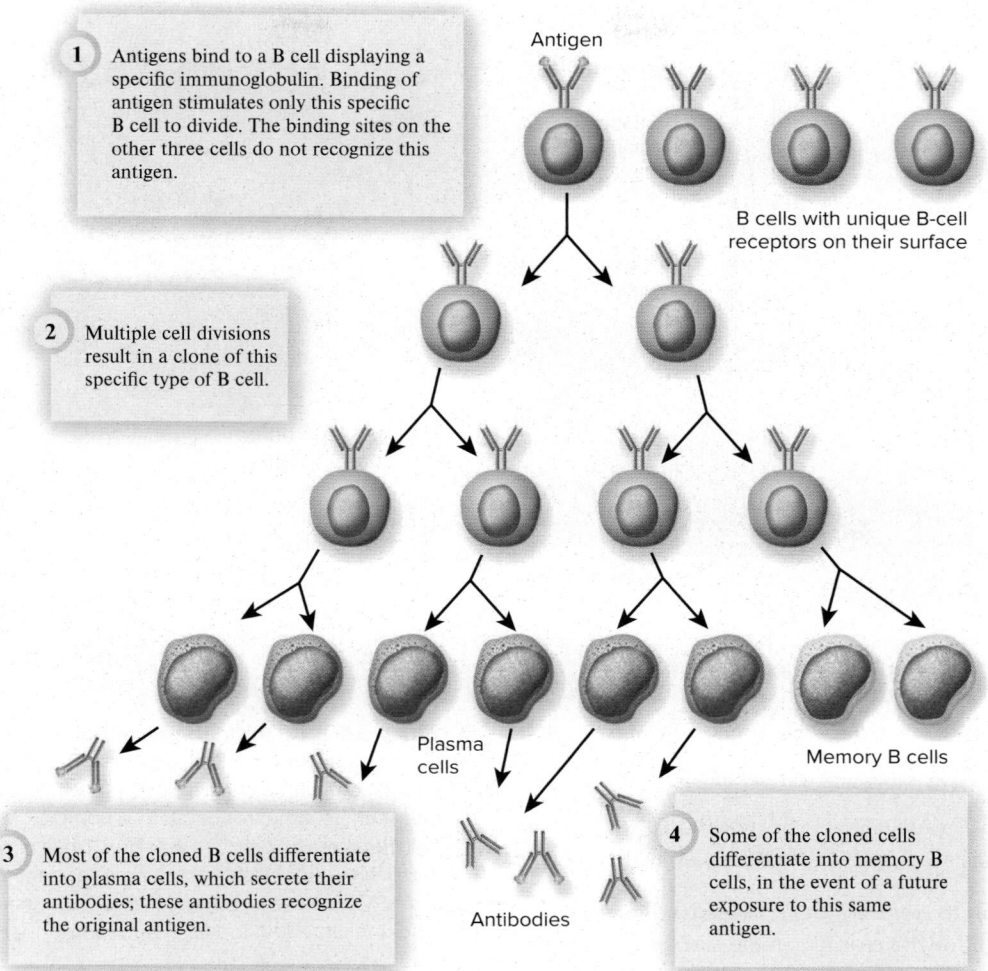

1 Antigens bind to a B cell displaying a specific immunoglobulin. Binding of antigen stimulates only this specific B cell to divide. The binding sites on the other three cells do not recognize this antigen.

Antigen

B cells with unique B-cell receptors on their surface

2 Multiple cell divisions result in a clone of this specific type of B cell.

Plasma cells

Memory B cells

3 Most of the cloned B cells differentiate into plasma cells, which secrete their antibodies; these antibodies recognize the original antigen.

Antibodies

4 Some of the cloned cells differentiate into memory B cells, in the event of a future exposure to this same antigen.

Figure 52.9 Clonal selection. In this example, a B cell with a specific immunoglobulin on its surface recognizes an antigen and is stimulated to divide into a clone of identical cells.

Instead of directly destroying the pathogens, antibodies bound to antigen on the pathogen surface inactivate the pathogens in various ways. Antibodies may physically link the pathogens to phagocytes (neutrophils and macrophages), complement proteins, or NK cells. This linkage—called **opsonization**—triggers the attack mechanism and ensures that only the pathogens, and not nearby body cells, are destroyed.

In a second mechanism, antibodies that recognize toxins produced by bacterial pathogens in the extracellular fluid bind to the toxins, thereby preventing them from harming susceptible body cells. The antibody-antigen complexes that are formed are then destroyed by phagocytes.

In a similar way, antibodies that recognize certain viral surface proteins bind to the viruses in the extracellular fluid, preventing them from attaching to the plasma membranes of potential host cells. As with bacterial toxins, the antibody-virus complexes that are formed are subsequently phagocytized.

In Cell-Mediated Immunity, T Cells Recognize Antigens Complexed with Self Proteins

In cell-mediated immunity, T cells recognize and are activated by antigens (see Figure 52.6, right side). T-cell receptors for antigens have specific regions that differ from one T cell to another. As shown

in **Figure 52.10**, they are composed of two polypeptides, each with a variable and a constant region, along with a transmembrane domain. The variable regions recognize an antigen. As in B-cell development, multiple DNA rearrangements occur during T-cell maturation, leading to millions of distinct types of T cells, each with a receptor of unique specificity. For T cells, this maturation occurs as they develop in the thymus gland.

A T-cell receptor cannot bind to an antigen unless the antigen is already complexed with a protein that is found on the surface of another cell, such as a macrophage. Such proteins are encoded by a gene family known as the **major histocompatibility complex (MHC)**, and thus the proteins are called MHC proteins. In humans, two major classes of MHC proteins are known. Class I MHC proteins are found on the surface of all human body cells except erythrocytes (that is, all nucleated cells). Class II MHC proteins are found primarily on the surface of macrophages, B cells, and dendritic cells.

The two different types of T cells have different MHC requirements. Cytotoxic T cells require that antigen be associated with class I MHC proteins, whereas helper T cells require an association with class II MHC proteins. One reason for this difference stems from the presence of different proteins on the surfaces of T cells; helper T cells can be identified by a unique membrane protein called CD4, and cytotoxic

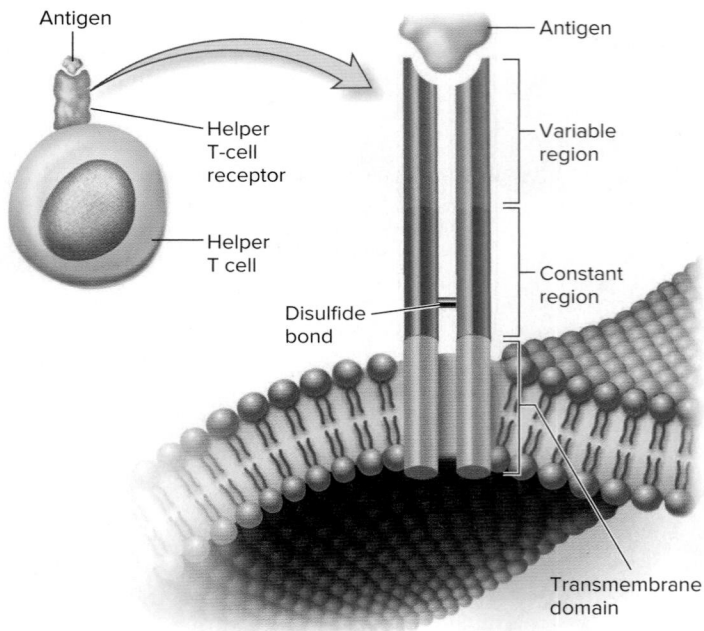

Figure 52.10 **Structure of a T-cell receptor in a plasma membrane.**

Concept Check: *What are some structural similarities between T-cell receptors and B-cell receptors?*

T cells are identified by a membrane protein known as CD8. CD4 binds to class II MHC proteins, whereas CD8 binds to class I MHC proteins.

Antigen Presentation to Helper T Cells How do foreign antigens become complexed with MHC proteins on the surface of the body's own cells? The answer involves the mechanism known as antigen presentation. As previously noted, helper T cells can bind antigen only when the antigen appears on the plasma membrane of a host cell complexed with the cell's class II MHC proteins. Cells bearing these complexes, therefore, function as **antigen-presenting cells (APCs)**. Because only macrophages, B cells, and dendritic cells express class II MHC proteins, only these cells can function as APCs for helper T cells.

Let's consider the function of macrophages as APCs for helper T cells (**Figure 52.11**). After a microbe or noncellular antigen has been phagocytized by a macrophage in an innate immune response, antigens, such as proteins, are partially broken down into smaller poly-peptide fragments by the macrophage's proteolytic enzymes within endosomes. The resulting digested fragments then bind in the endosomes to class II MHC proteins synthesized by the macrophage. Each fragment-MHC complex is then transported to the cell surface, where it is displayed on the plasma membrane. A specific helper T-cell receptor then binds this entire complex on the cell surface of the macrophage. The CD4 protein helps link the two cells. The molecule that is complexed to MHC proteins and presented to the helper T cells is not the intact antigen but instead a polypeptide fragment of the antigen—called an antigenic determinant, or **epitope**. Even so, it is customary to call this antigen presentation rather than epitope presentation.

B cells process antigen and present it to helper T cells in essentially the same way as macrophages do. The ability of B cells to present antigen to helper T cells is a second function of B cells in

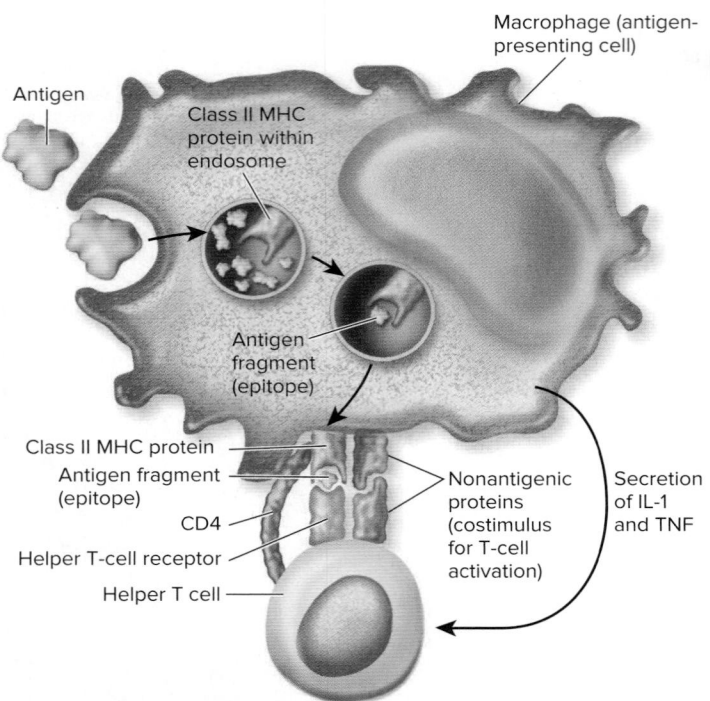

Figure 52.11 **Antigen presentation and helper T-cell activation.** In the initial events in helper T-cell activation, an antigen fragment is complexed with a class II MHC protein within an antigen-presenting cell such as a macrophage. The complex is then displayed on the cell surface and binds to a helper T-cell receptor. Also required for T-cell activation are the binding of nonantigenic proteins between the APC and the attached helper T cell, and the actions of the cytokines interleukin 1 (IL-1) and tumor necrosis factor (TNF).

response to antigenic stimulation, in addition to their differentiation into antibody-secreting plasma cells.

The binding between the helper T-cell receptor and the complex of antigen fragment and class II MHC protein on an APC is the essential antigen-specific event in helper T-cell activation. However, by itself, this specific binding does not result in T-cell activation. In addition, interactions occur between nonantigenic proteins on the surfaces of the attached helper T cell and the APC. These interactions comprise a necessary costimulus for T-cell activation (see Figure 52.11).

Finally, the antigen-dependent binding of the APC to the helper T cell plus the costimulus induces the APC to secrete large amounts of two cytokines—interleukin 1 (IL-1) and tumor necrosis factor (TNF). These molecules also stimulate the attached helper T cell.

Thus, the APC participates in the activation of a helper T cell in three ways: (1) presenting antigen, (2) providing a costimulus, and (3) secreting cytokines. Activated helper T cells then secrete additional cytokines of their own that stimulate B cells and cytotoxic T cells.

Helper T Cells and B-Cell Activation Now we can reconsider how B cells are activated by the actions of helper T cells. This process begins when a helper T cell specific for a particular antigen binds to a complex of that antigen and a class II MHC protein on an APC, activating the helper T cell. Along with other signals, this binding induces the activated helper T cell to undergo many cycles of cell division. Some of the resulting activated helper T cells then bind to B cells that display the same antigen on their surfaces. This binding, along with additional cytokines, stimulates the B cell to go through the process of clonal selection. Thus, helper T cells are so named because they help activate B cells that have bound antigen, in addition to their participation in activation of cytotoxic T cells and antigen presentation.

Antigen Presentation to Cytotoxic T Cells Unlike helper T cells, cytotoxic T cells require class I MHC proteins for activation. This distinction helps explain the major function of cytotoxic T cells—destruction of any of the body's own altered cells that have become cancerous or infected with viruses.

How do antigens that activate cytotoxic T cells arise? In viral infections, once a virus has entered a host cell, the expression of viral genes results in the synthesis of viral proteins, which are foreign to the cell. Cancer cells accumulate mutations, some of which alter the amino acid sequence of proteins. Such abnormal proteins act as antigens.

In both virus-infected and cancerous cells, cytosolic enzymes hydrolyze some of the antigenic proteins into polypeptide fragments, which are transported into the endoplasmic reticulum. There the fragments are complexed with the host cell's class I MHC proteins and then shuttled by the secretory pathway to the plasma membrane, where a cytotoxic T cell specific for the antigen/MHC protein complex can bind to it. Once binding occurs, cytotoxic T cells release chemicals that kill the infected or cancerous cell, as discussed next.

Activated Cytotoxic T Cells Kill Infected or Cancerous Cells

So far, this section has described how immune responses provide long-term defenses against bacteria, viruses, and foreign molecules that enter the body's extracellular fluid. We now examine how an animal's own cells that have become infected by viruses or transformed into cancerous cells are destroyed by cell-mediated immune responses (see Figure 52.6, right side).

What is the value of destroying virus-infected host cells? First, and most importantly, such destruction prevents cells from making more viruses. Second, for cells that already are making mature viruses, the lysis of infected cells releases the viruses into the extracellular fluid, where they can be neutralized by circulating antibody.

Functions of Cytotoxic T Cells A typical cytotoxic T-cell response triggered by viral infection of a vertebrate's body cells is summarized in **Figure 52.12**. The response triggered by a cancerous cell would be similar. A virus-infected cell produces foreign proteins, viral antigens that are processed and presented on the plasma membrane of the cell complexed with class I MHC proteins. Cytotoxic T cells specific for the particular antigen bind to the complex (Figure 52.12, step 1). As with B cells, binding to antigen alone does not cause activation of the cytotoxic T cell. Cytokines from nearby activated helper T cells are also required.

Macrophages phagocytize extracellular viruses (or, in the case of cancer, antigens released from the surface of cancerous cells) and then process and present antigen, in association with class II MHC proteins, to the helper T cells (step 2 of Figure 52.12). In addition, the macrophages provide a costimulus and also secrete IL-1 and TNF. The activated helper T cell releases IL-2 and other cytokines, which stimulate proliferation of the helper T cell.

IL-2 and other cytokines also act on the cytotoxic T cell bound to the surface of the virus-infected or cancerous cell, stimulating this attack cell to proliferate. Why is proliferation important if a cytotoxic T cell has already located and bound to its target? The answer is that there is rarely just one virus-infected or cancerous cell. By expanding the population of cytotoxic T cells capable of scanning the entire body and recognizing the particular antigen, the likelihood is greater that the other virus-infected or cancerous cells will be encountered by an appropriate cytotoxic T cell.

The cytotoxic T cells specific for that virus then find and bind to other virus-infected cells (Figure 52.12, step 3). There are two major ways in which cytotoxic T cells kill their target cells. The first way involves the release by exocytosis of secretions from the T cell. The second mechanism involves binding of a membrane protein on the T cell to surface receptors on the target cell. Both mechanisms induce apoptosis in the target cell. Let's examine the first mechanism in detail. Each cytotoxic T cell releases the contents of its secretory vesicles directly into the extracellular space between itself and the target cell to which it is bound (thereby ensuring that other nearby host cells will not be killed). These vesicles contain proteases and a protein called perforin, which is similar in structure to the proteins of the complement system's membrane attack complex. Perforin inserts into the target cell's membrane and forms pores (perforations) in it (step 4). These pores allow proteases secreted by a cytotoxic T cell to enter the attacked cell and induce apoptosis. Perforin can also cause a virus-infected cell to take up so much water that it bursts, a second way to kill it. The cytotoxic T cell is not harmed by this process and can then continue to kill other virus-infected cells (step 5).

Viruses can be eliminated from an animal's body in two ways: through the humoral actions of antibodies in body fluids and through the cell-mediated killing of virus-infected cells by cytotoxic T cells. Although cytotoxic T cells have an important role in the attack against such cells, they are not the only mechanisms. NK cells also destroy virus-infected and cancerous cells by secreting toxic chemicals. As mentioned earlier in this chapter, NK cells can recognize general features on the surface of such cells and participate in innate immunity. In addition, in a cell-mediated immune response, NK cells can be linked to such target cells by antibodies and then can destroy them by release of toxic molecules.

Summary: Example of an Adaptive Immune Response

Let's bring together our discussion of the adaptive immune system by looking in detail at one example in which a humoral immune response results in the destruction of bacteria. The sequence of events, which is quite similar to the humoral response to a virus in the extracellular fluid, is summarized in **Figure 52.13**. For this example, we consider the response in mammals, in which lymph nodes are present. Many features of the response, however, are similar in other vertebrates.

This process starts the same way as for innate responses, with the bacteria penetrating one of the body's linings through an injury and entering the interstitial fluid (Figure 52.13, step 1). The bacteria then move with lymph into the lymphatic system and are carried to lymph nodes (step 2). Within the lymph node, a macrophage and a B cell recognize the bacteria as foreign and bind to them.

As we have discussed, the process of B-cell activation usually requires the activation of helper T cells. The helper T cell binds to a

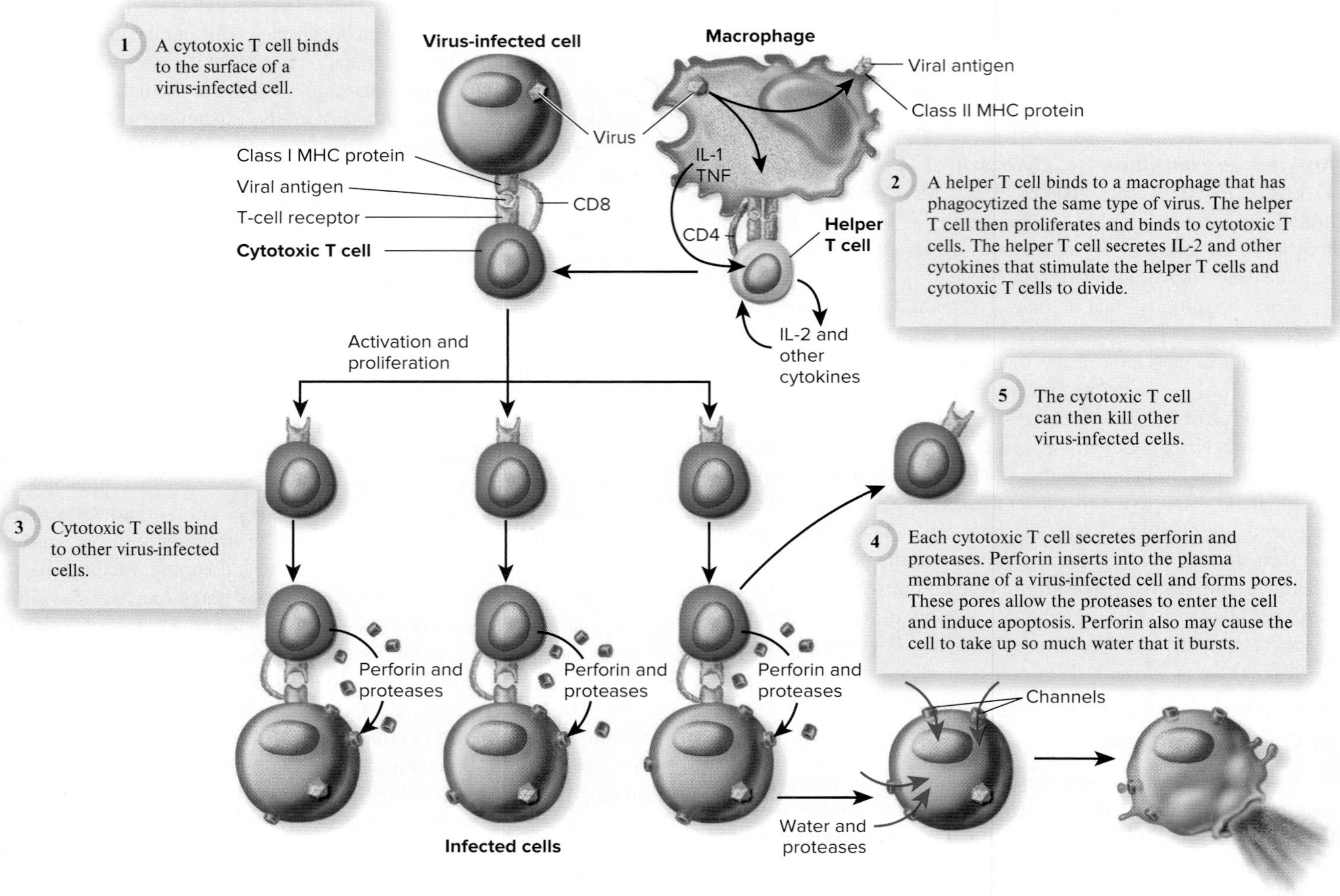

Figure 52.12 Summary of events in the killing of virus-infected cells by cytotoxic T cells. The sequence is similar for cancerous cells attacked by cytotoxic T cells.

Core Skill: Science and Society Viruses cause illness in animals and humans alike. In many cases, a viral illness can be transmitted from animals to humans. Many viral illnesses cause only temporary symptoms, such as those of the common cold. Other viruses, however, can cause very serious or life-threatening illnesses, such as the dengue virus, which infects as many as 100 million people per year and causes tens of thousands of deaths annually.

complex of processed antigen and class II MHC protein on an APC (Figure 52.13, step 3). In this case, the APC is a macrophage that has phagocytized the bacterium, hydrolyzed its proteins into polypeptide fragments, complexed the fragments with class II MHC proteins, and displayed the complexes on its surface. Once a helper T cell specific for the complex binds to it, the helper T cell becomes activated. The macrophage helps this process in two other ways: It provides a costimulus, and it secretes the cytokines IL-1 and TNF.

IL-1 and TNF stimulate the helper T cell to secrete another cytokine, IL-2. IL-2 stimulates the activated helper T cell to divide, which leads eventually to the formation of a clone of activated helper T cells (Figure 52.13, step 4). The activated helper T cells bind to B cells that display the antigen, and also secrete IL-2 and other cytokines (step 5). Some of these cytokines provide additional signals that are usually required to activate nearby antigen-bound B cells to proliferate (step 6). These cells differentiate into memory cells, which help ward off possible future attacks by the same antigen, and plasma cells, which

secrete specific antibodies (step 7). The antibodies enter the bloodstream and bind to bacterial cells, which are then destroyed (step 8).

B Cells and T Cells That Recognize Self Molecules Must Be Killed or Inhibited

As we have seen, the lymphocytes responsible for the adaptive immune response in vertebrates are very capable killers of pathogens—so capable, in fact, that it raises a question: Why don't these cells attack and kill normal self cells? In other words, how does the body distinguish between self and nonself components and develop what is called **immune tolerance**, or tolerance of its own molecules?

Recall that the huge diversity of lymphocyte receptors is ultimately the result of multiple random DNA cutting and recombination processes. It is virtually certain, therefore, that every animal possessing adaptive immune defenses will have lymphocytes with receptors that can bind to that individual's own proteins. The continued existence and functioning

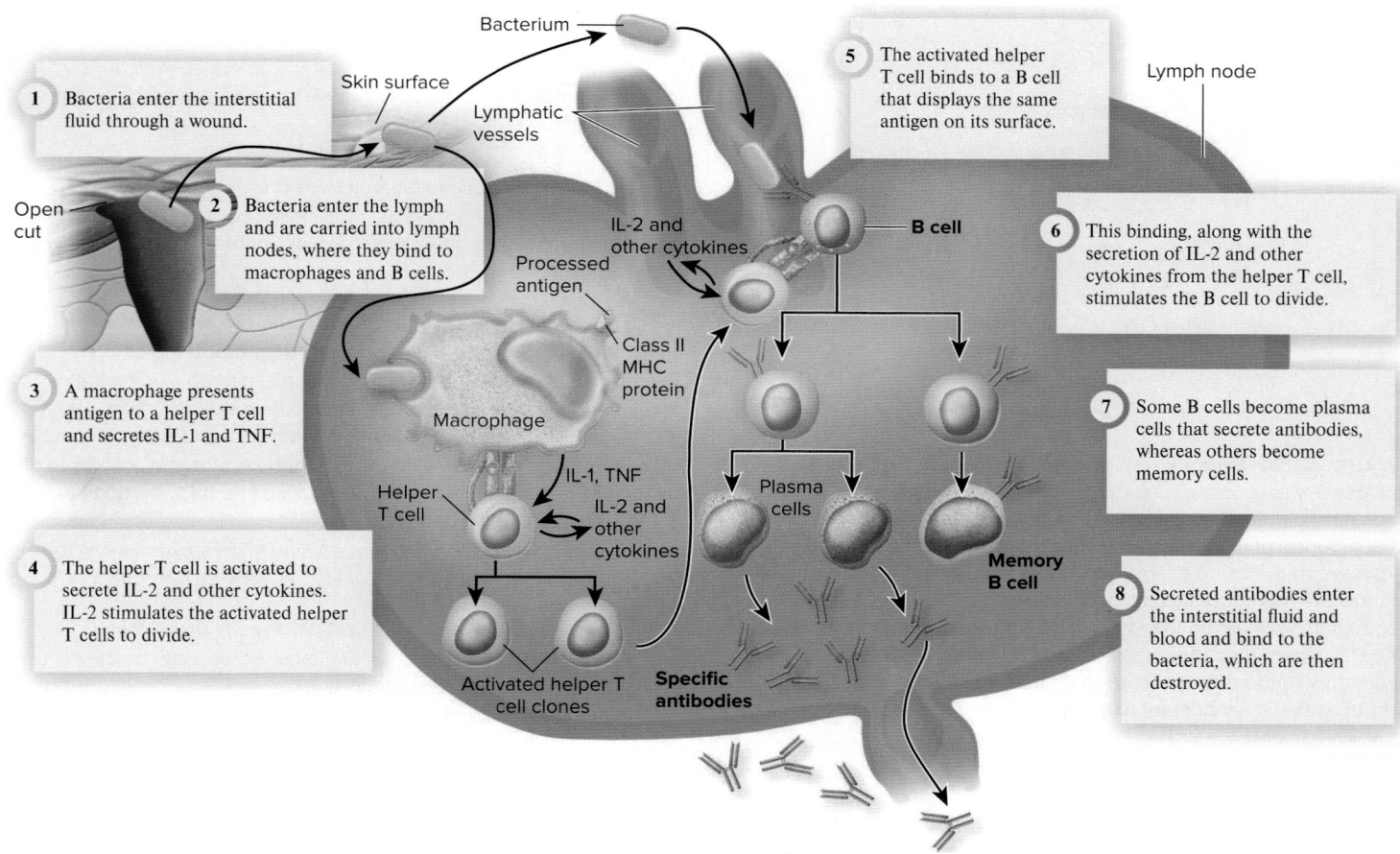

Bacterium

Skin surface

Lymphatic vessels

Lymph node

1 Bacteria enter the interstitial fluid through a wound.

Open cut

2 Bacteria enter the lymph and are carried into lymph nodes, where they bind to macrophages and B cells.

IL-2 and other cytokines

Processed antigen

Class II MHC protein

B cell

5 The activated helper T cell binds to a B cell that displays the same antigen on its surface.

6 This binding, along with the secretion of IL-2 and other cytokines from the helper T cell, stimulates the B cell to divide.

3 A macrophage presents antigen to a helper T cell and secretes IL-1 and TNF.

Macrophage

Helper T cell

IL-1, TNF

IL-2 and other cytokines

Plasma cells

Memory B cell

7 Some B cells become plasma cells that secrete antibodies, whereas others become memory cells.

4 The helper T cell is activated to secrete IL-2 and other cytokines. IL-2 stimulates the activated helper T cells to divide.

Activated helper T cell clones

Specific antibodies

8 Secreted antibodies enter the interstitial fluid and blood and bind to the bacteria, which are then destroyed.

Figure 52.13 **Summary of events in a typical humoral immune response.** Most of the events depicted occur within a lymph node.

of such lymphocytes would be disastrous, because such binding would launch an immune attack against all body cells expressing these proteins.

At least two mechanisms explain why individuals normally lack active lymphocytes that respond to self components. First, during early development in vertebrates, T cells are exposed to a wide mix of self proteins in the thymus gland. Those T cells with receptors capable of binding self proteins are destroyed by apoptosis in a process termed **clonal deletion**. The second mechanism, termed **clonal inactivation**, occurs outside the thymus gland and causes potentially self-reacting T cells to become nonresponsive. B cells undergo similar processes. The mechanisms by which these two events occur are still under investigation.

Occasionally, however, these mechanisms fail, and an animal's immune cells attack the body's own cells. When this happens, it produces an autoimmune disease. **Autoimmune diseases** are conditions in which the body's normal state of immune tolerance somehow breaks down, with the result that both humoral and cell-mediated attacks are directed against the body's own cells and tissues. A growing number of animal and human diseases are being recognized as autoimmune in origin. Examples in humans include multiple sclerosis, in which myelin around neurons is attacked; myasthenia gravis, in which the receptors for acetylcholine on skeletal muscle cells are the targets; rheumatoid arthritis, in which joints are damaged; systemic lupus erythematosus, in which numerous organs are damaged; and type 1 diabetes mellitus, in which the insulin-producing cells of

the pancreas are destroyed. Treatments for autoimmune disease range from treating the symptoms (for example, administering insulin to individuals with diabetes) to suppressing the immune system with drugs.

Immunological Memory Is an Important Feature of Adaptive Immunity

As we have learned, the magnitude of the adaptive immune response to a given antigen depends on whether or not the body has previously been exposed to that antigen. Consider, for example, the humoral immune response. In mammals, antibody production in response to the first contact with an antigen occurs slowly, over a few weeks. This response to an initial antigen exposure is termed a **primary immune response** (**Figure 52.14**). Any subsequent infection by the same pathogen elicits a rapid and heightened production of additional specific antibodies against that particular antigen, a reaction termed a **secondary immune response**.

In the case of humoral immunity, this secondary response occurs more quickly, is stronger, and lasts longer because memory B cells that were produced in the primary response are quickly stimulated to multiply and differentiate into thousands of plasma cells. These cells then produce large amounts of specific antibodies. The immune system's ability to produce this secondary response is called **immunological memory**.

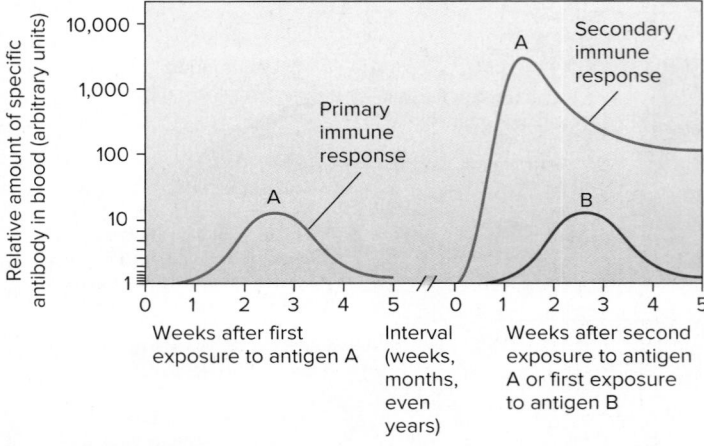

Figure 52.14 **Primary and secondary immune responses.** In a primary response, as shown on the left of this graph, an initial exposure to an antigen produces modest levels of specific antibody over a period of weeks. In a secondary response, subsequent exposure to the same antigen results in greater antibody production that occurs more rapidly and lasts longer than a primary response. (Note that the scale on the vertical axis of the graph is logarithmic.) The secondary response is specific for that antigen. During a secondary response, exposure to a different antigen for the first time produces the usual primary response.

Concept Check: *What is the advantage of a secondary immune response?*

Immunological memory explains why humans and other animals are able to fight off many illnesses, such as many common childhood diseases, after having been previously exposed to them. The adaptive response to exposure to any type of antigen is known as **active immunity**. Active immunity not only results from natural exposure to antigens, but also is the basis for exposures to antigens that occur in vaccinations. In **vaccinations**, small quantities of living, dead, or altered microbes, small quantities of toxins, or harmless antigenic molecules derived from a pathogen or its toxins are injected into the body, resulting in a primary immune response, including the production of memory cells. Subsequent natural exposure to the immunizing antigen results in a rapid, effective response that can prevent or reduce the severity of disease.

In contrast to active immunity, another type of adaptive immunity, called **passive immunity**, confers protection against disease through the direct transfer of antibodies from one individual to another. Passive immunity can occur naturally, as when IgG molecules cross the mammalian placenta to protect a fetus from various pathogens, or when a newborn mammal receives antibodies from breast milk. It can also occur artificially, as when a person is given an injection of IgG molecules shortly after being exposed to hepatitis viruses. Recent advances in the creation of highly specific and pure antibodies, called **monoclonal antibodies** because they are derived from a single clone of cells prepared in a laboratory, have paved the way for the use of passive immunity to combat certain types of cancer. Because antibodies are proteins and are eventually broken down and removed from the body, the protection afforded by the transfer of antibodies in passive immunity is relatively short-lived, usually lasting only a few weeks or months.

THE QUESTION *What might be the consequences if an animal was unable to form memory cells after being vaccinated against a particular pathogen or antigen?*

TOPIC *What topic in biology does this question address?*
The topic is memory cells. Specifically, you are asked to predict the outcome for an animal that was unable to form memory cells following a vaccination.

INFORMATION *What information do you know based on the question and your understanding of the topic?*
From the question, you know that an animal has received a vaccination to help protect it from some disease caused by a particular pathogen or antigen. From your understanding of the topic, you may recall that vaccinations rely on the processes of active immunity. You also have learned from Figure 52.14 that adaptive immunity produces a small primary response and then a larger secondary response on subsequent exposure to the same antigen.

PROBLEM-SOLVING **S**TRATEGY *Predict the outcome.*
First, consider the function of memory cells: How do they contribute to the secondary immune response? Next, predict what might happen without that contribution.

ANSWER *Artificial exposure to small quantities of a pathogen or antigen (vaccination) results in a small primary immune response, but also causes the differentiation of activated T and B cells into memory cells. These cells are activated by subsequent (natural) exposure to the same pathogen or antigen, resulting in a large secondary immune response. Without the production of memory cells, the secondary immune response would be greatly diminished, resembling the blue curve labeled B on the right side in Figure 52.14.*

52.4 Impact on Public Health

Learning Outcomes:

1. **CoreSKILL »** Predict some influences of lifestyle on immunity.
2. Explain the role of the immune system in organ transplant rejection and allergic reactions.
3. Describe the effects of HIV on a human immune system, and describe a current method of treating HIV infection.

In this section, we will consider a few ways in which the functioning of the immune system can be affected by lifestyle, medical interventions, allergies, and destruction of immune cells. Collectively, the effects of disorders of the immune system have an almost immeasurable impact on public health in terms of worker productivity, health-care resources, and the economy.

Lifestyle Has an Important Influence on Immunity

Adequate nutrition is essential for good health. Protein-calorie malnutrition in particular is the single greatest contributor to decreased resistance to infection worldwide. When adequate amino acids for synthesizing essential proteins are not available, immune function is impaired. Deficits of certain nonprotein nutrients can also lower resistance to infection.

Both stress and state of mind can affect resistance to infection and to cancer. The immune system can alter neural and endocrine function, and, in turn, neural and endocrine activity modifies immune function. For example, lymphoid tissue receives input from nerves, and immune cells have receptors for certain hormones. Conversely, immune cells release cytokines that have important effects on the brain and endocrine system. In addition, lymphocytes secrete several hormones that are also produced by endocrine glands. The multiple brain-body interactions that affect disease resistance are the subject of a field of study called psychoneuroimmunology.

Of the hormones associated with stress, the adrenal hormone cortisol has received the most attention due to its powerful suppressive effect on inflammation and adaptive immunity. Among other things, cortisol inhibits production of inflammatory mediators, reduces capillary permeability in injured areas, and suppresses the growth and activity of certain types of leukocytes. In this way, it acts as a sort of brake on the immune system, suppressing its activity. This should not be surprising, since all organ systems are generally under dual control, with stimulatory signals and inhibitory signals creating a homeostatic balance. During chronic stress or when cortisol is used to treat certain illnesses for long periods of time, however, this inhibitory action may be severe enough to cause immunosuppression. This inhibition is a key link between stress and health. Chronic stress may lead to a chronically increased concentration of cortisol in the blood that, by suppressing the body's immune responses, lowers resistance to infection.

Another feature of a person's lifestyle that appears to affect immune function is exercise. The influence of physical exercise on the body's resistance to infection and cancer has been debated for decades. Evidence now suggests that the intensity, duration, regularity, and psychological stress of the exercise all have important influences—both positive and negative—on a variety of immune functions, such as the numbers of circulating NK cells. Although evidence suggests that too much intense exercise can impair immunity, most experts currently believe that moderate exercise and physical conditioning have net beneficial effects on the immune system and on disease resistance. Recent studies suggest that exercise may be particularly beneficial in helping to ward off the onset of breast cancer, one of the most common types of cancer in women.

Organ Transplants Are Medical Procedures That Can Cause Serious Immune Reactions

Organ transplants have saved numerous lives. However, they carry the possibility of provoking immune reactions that can threaten the life of the recipient. Since the mid-20th century, organ transplants from a healthy or recently deceased donor to a recipient have become widespread. The United Network for Organ Sharing reports that approximately 28,500 organs are transplanted in the U.S. each year, with kidney (17,000), liver (6,000), heart (2,000), and lung (1,800) transplants accounting for most of these procedures. The major obstacle to successful transplantation of tissues and organs is a reaction called graft rejection, in which a person's immune system recognizes the transplant

(also called a graft) as foreign and attacks it as it would any foreign cells. Although B cells and macrophages play some role in graft rejection, cytotoxic T cells and helper T cells are mainly responsible. To minimize this possibility, transplant patients are given drugs that suppress immune function, a procedure that is associated with some risk.

Except for grafts from identical twins, the class I MHC proteins on graft cells differ from those on the recipient's cells, as do the class II MHC proteins present on macrophages in the graft. Consequently, the recipient's T cells recognize the MHC proteins in the graft as foreign, and cytotoxic T cells (with the aid of helper T cells) destroy the graft cells.

Allergies Affect the Quality of Life of Millions of People

An **allergy** (one type of a group of related immune disorders known as hypersensitivities) is a condition in which immune responses to environmental antigens cause inflammation and damage to body cells. Antigens that induce allergic reactions are called allergens. Common examples of allergens include ragweed pollen and animal dander. Most allergens themselves are relatively or completely harmless. It is the immune responses to them that cause the damage. In essence, then, allergy is immunity gone awry, for the response is of inappropriate strength and duration for the stimulus. In the U.S. alone, as many as 40 million people (about 13% of the population) suffer from allergies.

For any allergy to develop, a genetically predisposed person must first be exposed to the allergen—a process called sensitization. Subsequent exposures elicit the damaging immune responses we recognize as an allergy. Hypersensitivities can be broadly classified according to the speed of the response. Those that take up to several days to develop are considered delayed hypersensitivities. The skin rash that appears after contact with poison ivy is an example. More common are reactions considered immediate hypersensitivities, which can develop in minutes. Allergies fall into this category.

In immediate hypersensitivity, sensitization to the allergen leads to the production of specific antibodies and a clone of memory B cells. In individuals who are genetically susceptible to allergies, antigens that elicit immediate hypersensitivity reactions stimulate the production of IgE antibodies. Upon their release from plasma cells, these IgE molecules circulate throughout the body and become attached to mast cells in connective tissue (**Figure 52.15**). When the same antigen enters the body at some future time and binds with IgE that is bound to mast cells, the mast cell is stimulated to secrete many inflammatory mediators, including histamine, which then initiate an inflammatory response.

The signs and symptoms of allergies reflect both the effects of inflammatory mediators and the body site in which the binding of antigen to the IgE bound to a mast cell occurs. When, for example, a previously sensitized person inhales ragweed pollen, the antigen combines with the variable region of IgE, and the constant region of IgE binds to mast cells in the airways. The mast cells release their contents, which induce increased mucus secretion, increased blood flow, swelling of the epithelial lining, and contraction of the smooth muscle surrounding airways. These effects produce the congestion, runny nose, sneezing, and, in some persons, difficulty in breathing characteristic of hay fever. Antihistamines are drugs taken by people to block the action of histamine that is released during these allergic responses. These drugs prevent histamine from binding to its receptor

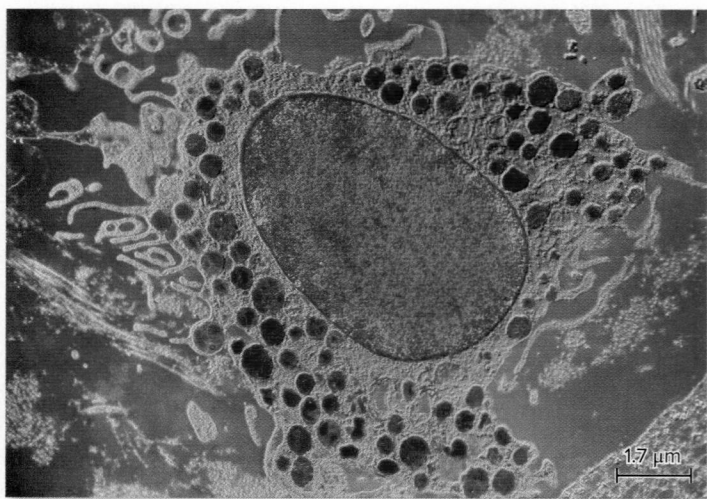

Figure 52.15 **Colorized electron micrograph of a mast cell, showing numerous secretory vesicles filled with histamine, a major mediator of allergic responses.** ©CNRI/Science Source

protein on its target cells, thereby preventing or relieving some of the symptoms of allergy.

Acquired Immunodeficiency Syndrome (AIDS) Results from HIV Infection

Acquired immunodeficiency syndrome (AIDS) is caused by the **human immunodeficiency virus (HIV)**, which weakens the immune system by preferentially killing helper T cells. HIV is a retrovirus, a virus that contains RNA as its genetic material. Once inside a helper T cell, HIV uses the enzyme reverse transcriptase to transcribe its RNA into DNA, which is then integrated into the chromosomal DNA of the host's T cells (refer back to Figure 19.4b). Later, viral replication within the T cell results in the death of the cell.

HIV infects helper T cells because the CD4 protein in their plasma membranes acts as a receptor for an HIV capsid protein. However, binding to CD4 is not sufficient to enable HIV to enter the helper T cell. Another T-cell surface protein, which normally acts as a receptor for certain cytokines, must serve as a coreceptor. Interestingly, individuals possessing a mutation in this cytokine receptor are highly resistant to HIV infection, so much research is now focused on the possible therapeutic use of chemicals that can bind to and block this coreceptor.

HIV not only directly kills helper T cells, but it also indirectly causes additional helper T-cell death by inducing cytotoxic T cells to kill HIV-infected helper T cells. In addition, by still poorly understood mechanisms, HIV causes the death of many uninfected helper T cells by apoptosis. Without adequate numbers of helper T cells, neither B cells nor cytotoxic T cells can function normally. Both humoral and cell-mediated immunity are compromised. Many individuals with AIDS die from infections and cancers that ordinarily would be readily prevented by a fully functional immune system.

AIDS, first described in 1981, has since reached pandemic proportions although its prevalence has been leveling off for several years. About 36 million people worldwide are currently living with HIV infection, and an estimated 5,000–10,000 new infections occur each day (**Figure 52.16**). The major routes of HIV transmission are (1) unprotected sexual intercourse with an infected partner; (2) transfer of contaminated blood or blood products between individuals, such as the sharing of needles among intravenous drug users, or, less commonly, as a result of a blood transfusion; (3) transfer from an infected mother to her child across the placenta or during delivery; or (4) transfer via breast milk during nursing.

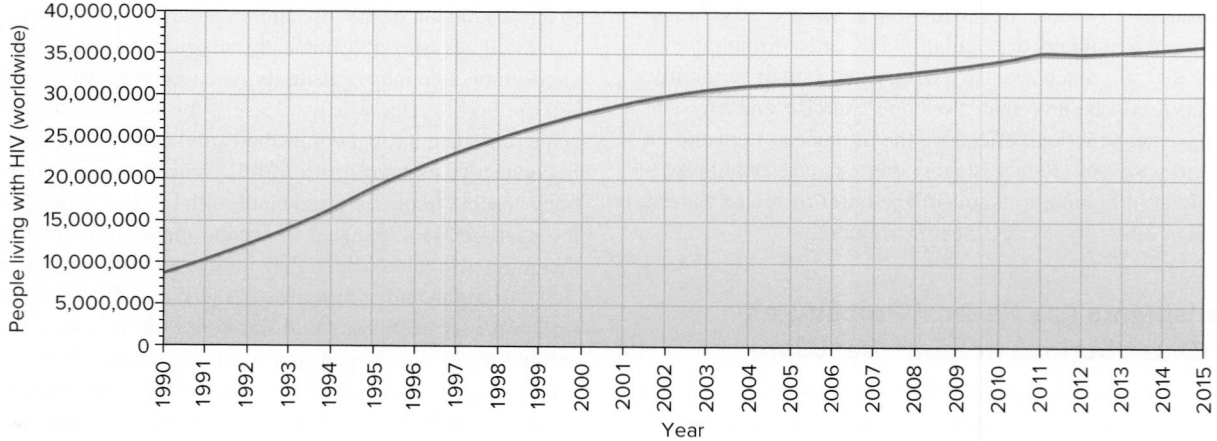

Figure 52.16 **Worldwide incidence of people living with HIV/AIDS.** Data are from the *2016 World Aids Day Report* published by UNAIDS (The Joint United Nations Programme on HIV/AIDS). Source: UNAIDS, *2016 World Aids Day Report,* Geneva: UNAIDS, 2016.

 Core Skills: Science and Society, and Communication and Collaboration Although the number of people living with HIV has not decreased, research into its causes, prevention, and treatment has greatly slowed the rate at which it is increasing in the human population (compare the slope of the curve in the early 1990s to that in recent years). These advances have arisen from a worldwide effort by scientists and policy makers. Note that the data illustrated in this figure were collected and published not in a scientific journal but by UNAIDS, which is associated with the United Nations.

The great majority of individuals now infected with HIV show no signs of AIDS. Their infections are diagnosed by the presence of anti-HIV antibodies or HIV RNA in the blood. However, if left untreated, HIV infection commonly develops into AIDS in about 10 years. During the first 5 years, killed helper T cells are typically replaced by new cells, so T-cell concentrations remain normal, and the individual remains asymptomatic. Over the next 5 years, T-cell concentrations begin to decline, until at some point, AIDS reveals itself in the form of opportunistic viral, bacterial, and fungal infections. Certain unusual cancers, such as Kaposi sarcoma, also occur with high frequency. In untreated individuals, death usually occurs within 2 years after the onset of AIDS symptoms.

Treatment for HIV-infected individuals has two components: one directed against the virus itself to delay progression of the disease, and one to prevent or treat the opportunistic infections and cancers that ultimately cause death. One current antiviral approach involves administering a combination of four drugs, known as HAART (highly active antiretroviral therapy). Two of the drugs inhibit the action of reverse transcriptase in converting viral RNA into DNA within the host cell, a third drug inhibits an HIV enzyme required for assembling new viruses, and a fourth class of drugs called fusion inhibitors prevent the virus from entering T cells. These treatments have been demonstrated to be effective in slowing the rate at which infection with HIV leads to AIDS. Unfortunately, however, the HAART regimen is associated with numerous side effects, including nausea, vomiting, diarrhea, metabolic disturbances, and liver damage. Much research is under way to find better treatments and ultimately to cure this disease. For example, drugs have been developed to block the integration of viral DNA (formed after viral RNA has been reverse transcribed into DNA) into host DNA or to increase production of new helper T cells. The possibility of using gene therapy to alter the structure of the coreceptor described earlier, thereby preventing the entry of HIV into helper T cells, is currently being investigated. Finally, the use of specific activators of a subtype of cannabinoid receptor has also shown promise as a means of inhibiting HIV replication in infected cells.

Summary of Key Concepts

- An animal's cells and organs that collectively contribute to its immunity constitute the animal's immune system.
- In innate immunity, the body's defenses are present at birth and act against foreign materials in much the same way regardless of the specific identity of the invading material. Adaptive immunity develops only after the body is exposed to foreign substances and targets those foreign substances specifically.

52.1 Types of Pathogens

- Three major types of pathogens elicit an immune response: bacteria, viruses, and eukaryotic parasites.

52.2 Innate Immunity

- An important innate defense is carried out by phagocytes—cells capable of phagocytosis. In vertebrates, most phagocytes are a type of blood cell called leukocytes. The leukocytes involved in innate immunity include neutrophils, eosinophils, monocytes, macrophages, basophils, and natural killer (NK) cells (Figure 52.1).
- Inflammation is an innate local response to infection or injury characterized by local redness, swelling, heat, and pain. The events of inflammation are induced and regulated by chemical mediators called cytokines (Figure 52.2).
- Antimicrobial proteins include interferons, which inhibit viral replication, and complement proteins, which kill microbes without prior phagocytosis. Activation of the complement proteins results in the formation of a membrane attack complex (MAC), which creates pores in the microbial plasma membrane and kills the microbe.
- Toll-like receptors (TLRs) are evolutionarily ancient proteins that recognize common molecular features of many pathogens (Figure 52.3).

52.3 Adaptive Immunity

- A foreign molecule that the host does not recognize as self and that triggers an adaptive immune response is an antigen.
- Leukocytes called lymphocytes are responsible for adaptive immune responses. Most lymphocytes reside in a group of organs and tissues that constitute the lymphatic system (Figure 52.4).
- Lymphocytes responsible for adaptive immunity are B cells and T cells. B cells differentiate into antibody-producing cells called plasma cells. T cells include cytotoxic T cells, which directly kill target cells, and helper T cells, which assist in the activation and function of B cells and cytotoxic T cells (Figure 52.5).
- Immunologists recognize two types of adaptive immunity. In humoral immunity, plasma cells secrete antibodies that bind to antigens. In cell-mediated immunity, cytotoxic T cells directly attack and destroy abnormal body cells.
- Adaptive immune responses occur in three stages: The first stage is recognition of an antigen; the second is activation and proliferation of lymphocytes; and the third is attack against the antigen (Figure 52.6).
- In humoral immunity, B cells recognize antigens with B-cell receptors. When B cells are activated, they proliferate and differentiate into plasma cells, which secrete antibodies.
- Both B-cell receptors and antibodies belong to a family of proteins called immunoglobulins. Immunoglobulins contain a constant region, which is identical for all immunoglobulins of a given Ig class, and a variable region that serves as the antigen-binding site (Figure 52.7).
- The random joining of V, D, and J domains via recombination is crucial in enabling plasma cells to produce a diverse array of antibodies capable of recognizing many different antigens. In addition, imprecise end joining and hypermutation contribute to antibody diversity (Figure 52.8).
- B cells that are activated by an antigen differentiate into plasma cells by a process called clonal selection. Antibodies combine with the antigen that activated the B cell and guide an attack that eliminates the antigen or the cells bearing it (Figure 52.9).
- Major histocompatibility complex (MHC) proteins are cellular "identity tags" that serve as genetic markers of self. Class I MHC proteins are found on the surface of all human body cells except erythrocytes. Class II MHC proteins are found only on the surface of macrophages, B cells, and dendritic cells.
- The binding between a helper T-cell receptor and an antigen bound to class II MHC proteins on an APC is essential to helper T-cell

53.1 Effects of Hemorrhage on Blood Pressure and Organ Function

Learning Outcomes:

1. Explain why a decrease in blood pressure can be dangerous.
2. **CoreSKILL** » Predict changes that may occur to an animal's blood pressure when its blood volume is increased or decreased, and explain why.

In any type of hemorrhage, no matter how small or large, one of the first responses of an animal's body is sealing the wound. This is accomplished by the clotting mechanisms described in Chapter 48 (refer back to Figure 48.5). For the purpose of our discussion, we will assume that an animal suffering a hemorrhage has normal clotting mechanisms and that they are initiated immediately following the hemorrhage and continue for some time until the wound is closed. In this section, we will focus on understanding why hemorrhage is so dangerous and how blood volume and pressure are linked.

Decreased Blood Pressure May Lead to Cell Death

Blood circulates in an animal's body under pressure, as described in Chapter 48. The source of that pressure is the beating of the heart. Blood flows through arteries when it leaves the heart and pushes against the inner surfaces of the vessels. This force is what we refer to when we measure a person's blood pressure using an arm cuff, for example. In most mammals, blood pressure is roughly similar to that of humans, but different animals face different challenges in getting blood to all parts of the body. Think of the distance blood must travel from the heart to the brain in a giraffe. Giraffes have evolved an exceptionally strong heart that moves blood up their long neck. Even in humans, the distance from the heart to the brain results in a decrease in blood pressure as the blood flows upward against gravity. You may have experienced a sense of light-headedness on occasion when standing suddenly; it takes a second or two to generate the pressure required to overcome the effect of gravity on the blood circulating to your head. This temporary light-headedness illustrates the importance of blood pressure. All cells require uninterrupted delivery of nutrients and oxygen to perform the metabolic and other activities required for optimal functioning and survival. Very active cells, such as those of the brain, are the first to show signs of malfunction if the rate of nutrient and oxygen delivery is decreased.

Because of its vital importance for cell function, let's focus for the moment on oxygen delivery. The rate of oxygen delivery to any tissue in an animal's body depends on at least four factors, which were described in detail in Chapter 48. These include

- the rate of blood flow to a region, which in turn is influenced by the degree to which vessels are dilated (widened) or constricted (narrowed);
- the number of erythrocytes in a given volume of blood;
- the percent saturation of hemoglobin in the erythrocytes; and
- the effectiveness of hemoglobin releasing its oxygen to cells.

Following a hemorrhage, the first of these factors—blood flow— is immediately affected, as blood pressure begins to decrease. Very quickly, unless compensatory events occur, this alone can be sufficient to cause widespread cell death. Adjustments to all four factors, however, can help prevent such cell death from happening.

Blood Volume and Blood Pressure Are Linked

Refer again to the chapter opening photo of a person donating blood. This procedure removes about 500 mL of blood, which is roughly 10% of the total blood volume of a typical adult human. This controlled procedure has been adapted by investigators in order to understand how an animal's body responds to a hemorrhage. For instance, using a thin, flexible, hollow tube (called a cannula) inserted into a vein of an experimental animal to withdraw carefully controlled amounts of blood, investigators can determine the relationship between the degree of hemorrhage and its effects on different organ systems. Then, investigators can monitor how these organ systems respond in an integrated, coordinated way—first, to prevent blood pressure from continuing to decrease and, second, to help restore blood volume and pressure to normal.

The results of such experiments indicate that mammals can usually cope well with a 10% hemorrhage, as humans can when donating blood. Symptoms of a 10% hemorrhage are relatively mild and, in some people, are barely noticeable. Blood pressure may remain normal or may decrease only slightly. Part of the reason that symptoms are minor can be attributed to the large volume of blood that is present in the large veins, such as those in the legs. Veins are expandable and can accommodate more blood than can arteries. This blood can serve as a reservoir for times when an animal becomes more active and requires greater cardiac output (refer back to Figures 48.10, 48.14, and 48.15). After a hemorrhage, this reservoir can also be tapped to help maintain heart function and blood pressure. However, larger hemorrhages—for example, 20% and greater of an animal's blood volume—do result in a significant decrease in blood pressure. Remarkably, though, animals may survive even such a large hemorrhage (**Figure 53.1**).

Figure 53.1 An adult zebra that survived an attack by a lioness. These deep wounds have begun healing. Note that there is no bleeding at this time. Nonetheless, these injuries would initially have caused considerable hemorrhage. The animal's homeostatic responses to the loss of blood may have helped save its life. ©Images of Africa Photobank/Alamy Stock Photo

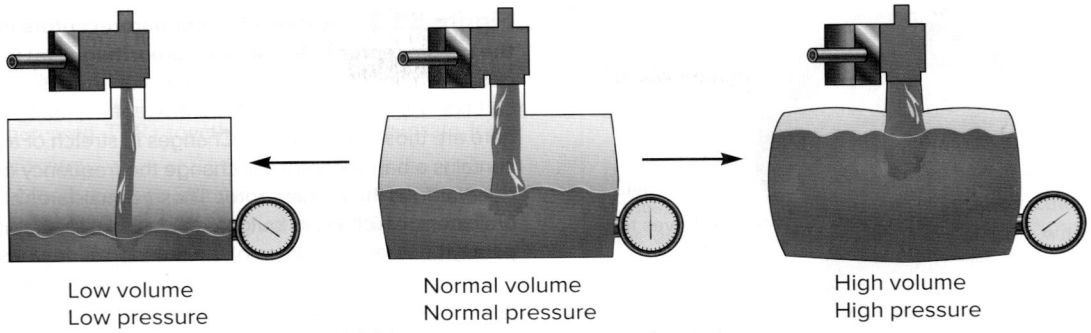

Low volume
Low pressure

Normal volume
Normal pressure

High volume
High pressure

Figure 53.2 **The relationship between blood volume and blood pressure.** In a system such as the artificial one shown here, an increase in fluid volume will increase the pressure that the fluid exerts on the walls of the chamber. In a similar way, increasing blood volume will increase the pressure of the blood in vessels such as arteries. A hemorrhage will decrease volume and thus decrease pressure.

What is the link between blood volume and blood pressure? Mammals have a closed circulatory system (refer back to Figures 48.1b and 48.2b). In such a system, volume and pressure are closely related. Look at the artificial closed system shown in **Figure 53.2**. When volume is normal, so is pressure. However, a decrease in volume decreases pressure, whereas an increase in volume causes the pressure to rise.

Recall that the blood pressure of a mammal that has lost about 10% of its blood volume does not change much. What is helping to maintain blood pressure? How is the venous reservoir of blood returned to the heart, and what other changes occur to improve circulatory function? As we will see next, numerous organ systems function together to help prevent a dangerous drop in blood pressure under these circumstances. These responses occur in two phases, one within seconds to minutes and one requiring hours to days or even weeks.

53.2 The Rapid Phase of the Homeostatic Response to Hemorrhage

Learning Outcomes:

1. Define baroreceptors, and describe where they are located in mammals.
2. **CoreSKILL** » Predict what will happen to the firing rate of baroreceptors if blood volume is increased or decreased.
3. Describe the baroreceptor reflex in mammals, its dependence on the nervous system, and the changes it induces in the function of the circulatory system.
4. Compare the distribution of blood to different organs before and after hemorrhage.
5. Explain the mechanisms that cause redistribution of blood between organs.
6. Describe how the structures of the respiratory system contribute to restoring pressure following hemorrhage.

Compensatory responses to hemorrhage occur across a timeline, and consist of both very rapid responses and more delayed responses. Although many of the responses overlap in time, those that begin within seconds can be distinguished from those that occur after hours, days or even weeks. The initial, nearly instantaneous homeostatic

response to a decrease in blood volume and pressure is mediated by the nervous system. When a hemorrhage occurs, the nervous system must receive information that blood pressure and volume are decreasing, then respond appropriately. Refer back to Figure 41.9, in which a typical homeostatic control system is described. Two key elements of such a system are a sensor, which detects a variable, and an integrator, which receives input from the sensor and compares that input to a set point (which in our example is the normal value for blood pressure). For monitoring blood volume and pressure, the sensors are located in blood vessels and the heart. The integrator is located in the brainstem. In this section, we will examine how these control elements help minimize a fall in blood pressure after a hemorrhage has occurred.

Baroreceptors Immediately Sense Changes in Blood Pressure and Initiate a Compensatory Reflex

Special pressure-sensitive regions exist within the heart and certain blood vessels in all vertebrates. For simplicity, we will focus on those that exist in the walls of certain large arteries in mammals. These include the carotid arteries in the neck, which supply blood to the brain, and the arch of the aorta, the first artery that emerges from the left ventricle. These regions contain the endings of neurons, known as **baroreceptors** (from the Greek *baros,* meaning weight or pressure), which are in constant communication with the medulla oblongata of the brainstem (**Figure 53.3a**). They mediate an important mechanism by which blood pressure is regulated in vertebrates called the **baroreceptor reflex** (**Figure 53.3b**). This response to a change in blood pressure is termed a reflex, because, like all reflexes, it is involuntary and rapid.

Let's first examine what happens if blood pressure decreases below normal, as in hemorrhage. Normally, each time the heart contracts and ejects blood, the carotid arteries and aorta are stretched, and consequently, so are the baroreceptors in those vessels. This stretching opens ion channels in the baroreceptors, depolarizing them and initiating action potentials that are sent to the brain. If the blood pressure decreases below the normal range, the arteries are less stretched, and ion channels are opened less frequently. Consequently, the baroreceptors send action potentials at a decreased frequency compared to normal. In the terminology used in Chapter 41, baroreceptors are the sensors for blood pressure, and the brainstem is the integrator. The set point for blood pressure corresponds to a baseline frequency of action

Terrestrial Biomes (continued)

Tundra

Figure 54.24j

©Bruce Coleman/Photoshot

Denali National Park in Alaska

Physical Environment: Precipitation is generally less than 25 cm per year and is often locked up as snow and unavailable for plants. Deeper water can be locked away for a large part of the year in **permafrost**, a layer of permanently frozen soil. The growing season is short, only 50–60 days. Summer temperatures are only 3–12°C, and even during the long summer days, the ground thaws to less than 1 m in depth. Midwinter temperatures average −32°C.

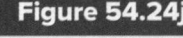

Location: Tundra (from the Finnish *tunturia*, meaning treeless plain) exists mainly in the Northern Hemisphere, north of temperate coniferous forest, because very little land area occurs in the Southern Hemisphere at the latitude where tundra would occur.

Plant Life: With so little available water, trees cannot grow. Vegetation occurs in the form of fragile, slow-growing lichens, mosses, grasses, sedges, and occasional shrubs, which grow close to the ground. Plant diversity is very low. In some places, desert conditions prevail because so little moisture falls.

Animal Life: Animals of the arctic tundra have adapted to the cold by having good insulation. Many birds, especially shorebirds and waterfowl, migrate. The fauna is much richer in summer than in winter. Many insects spend the winter at immature stages of growth, which are more resistant to cold than the adult forms. Larger animals include such herbivores as musk oxen and caribou in North America (the latter are called reindeer in Europe and Asia). Smaller animals include hares and lemmings. Common predators include arctic foxes, wolves, snowy owls, and polar bears near the coast.

Effects of Humans: Though this area is sparsely populated, mineral extraction, especially of oil, has the potential to significantly affect this biome. Ecosystem recovery from such damage would be very slow.

Mountain Ranges

Figure 54.24k

Rocky Mountains of Colorado

Physical Environment: Mountain ranges must be viewed differently from other biomes. On mountains, temperature decreases with increasing elevation through adiabatic cooling, as discussed earlier in this section. Thus, precipitation and temperature may change dramatically, depending on elevation and whether the mountainside is to windward or leeward.

Location: Mountain ranges exist in many areas of the world, but among the largest are the Himalayas in Asia, the Rockies in North America, and the Andes in South America.

©McPHOTO/age fotostock

Plant Life: A variety of biomes can be found on a single mountain range. Biome type may change from temperate forest through taiga and into tundra on an elevation gradient in the Rocky Mountains, and even from tropical forest to tundra on the highest peaks of the Andes in tropical South America. In tropical regions, daylight averages 12 hours per day throughout the year. Instead of a period of intense productivity seen in arctic tundra, vegetation in the tropical alpine tundra exhibits slow but steady rates of photosynthesis and growth all year.

Animal Life: The animals of this biome are as varied as the number of habitats it contains. Generally, more species of plants and animals are found at lower elevations than at higher ones. At higher elevations, animals such as bighorn sheep and mountain goats climb the craggy slopes and have skidproof pads on their hooves. Birds of prey, such as eagles, are frequent predators of the furry rodents found at higher elevations, including guinea pigs and marmots.

Effects of Humans: Logging and agriculture at lower elevations can cause habitat degradation. Because of the steep slopes, mountain soils are often well drained, thin, and especially susceptible to erosion following clearing for agriculture.

Aquatic Biomes Consist of Marine and Freshwater Regions

The ecology of freshwater habitats is governed largely by the unusual properties of water. Water is at its most dense at 4°C and becomes less dense as it warms or cools. At 0°C water freezes and is in its least dense state, so ice floats on unfrozen water. This explains why lakes and rivers freeze from the top down and why free-flowing water is at the bottom of a frozen lake or river (**Figure 54.25a**). From a fish's point of view, this property is advantageous, because if ice sank, all temperate lakes would freeze solid in winter, and no fish would exist in lakes outside the tropics. Oxygen content is depleted toward the bottoms of lakes by the respiration of bottom-dwelling organisms.

In the spring, ice melts, water warms and spring storms mix the water layers, creating uniform conditions of temperature and oxygen (**Figure 54.25b**). This mixing is termed the **spring overturn**. In deeper temperate lakes, in the summer, three layers are present (**Figure 54.25c**). An upper layer, called the **epilimnion**, is warmed by the sun and mixed well by the wind. Below this lies a transition zone known as the **thermocline**, where the temperature declines rapidly. Lower still is the **hypolimnion**, a cool layer too far below the surface to be much warmed and with low light levels where photosynthesis is absent and oxygen supply is low. In the fall the upper layers cool, and as their density increases they sink. Storms cause the fall overturn (**Figure 54.25d**), in which the water in the lake is thoroughly mixed and the thermocline disappears.

Coastal areas are influenced mainly by tides and waves. The gravitational pull of the Moon is 2.2 times greater than that of the Sun. As the Earth turns, each area of the globe is closer to the Moon once a day. At the equator, oceans are pulled toward the Moon at this time, creating high tides at the equator and low tides at higher latitudes. Similarly, when an ocean is on the opposite side of the Earth away from the Moon, the tide is high. This is because the Earth is itself pulled more toward the Moon at this point, leaving the water behind, causing the water to rise relative to the Earth. Thus, most areas of the Earth have two high tides per day.

Waves can range in size from small ripples to huge swells. As the wind blows, the friction between the air and the water creates small ripples. Once the ripples have formed, the wind has something to push against and the waves may increase in size. Four factors influence wave size: wind speed, fetch, duration of time of wind, and water depth. Fetch is the distance of open water over which the wind can blow. Shorter fetches in lakes reduce wave size, while long fetches of open ocean may allow the formation of 4- to 5-m waves.

Within aquatic environments, several different biome types are recognized, including distinct marine aquatic biomes (intertidal zone, coral reef, and open ocean) and freshwater biomes (lakes, rivers, and wetlands). These biomes are distinguished primarily by differences in salinity, oxygen content, depth, current strength, and availability of light (**Figure 54.26a–f**). Freshwater habitats are traditionally divided into **lentic**, or standing-water habitats (from the Latin *lenis*, meaning calm), and **lotic**, or running-water habitats (from the Latin *lotus*, meaning washed).

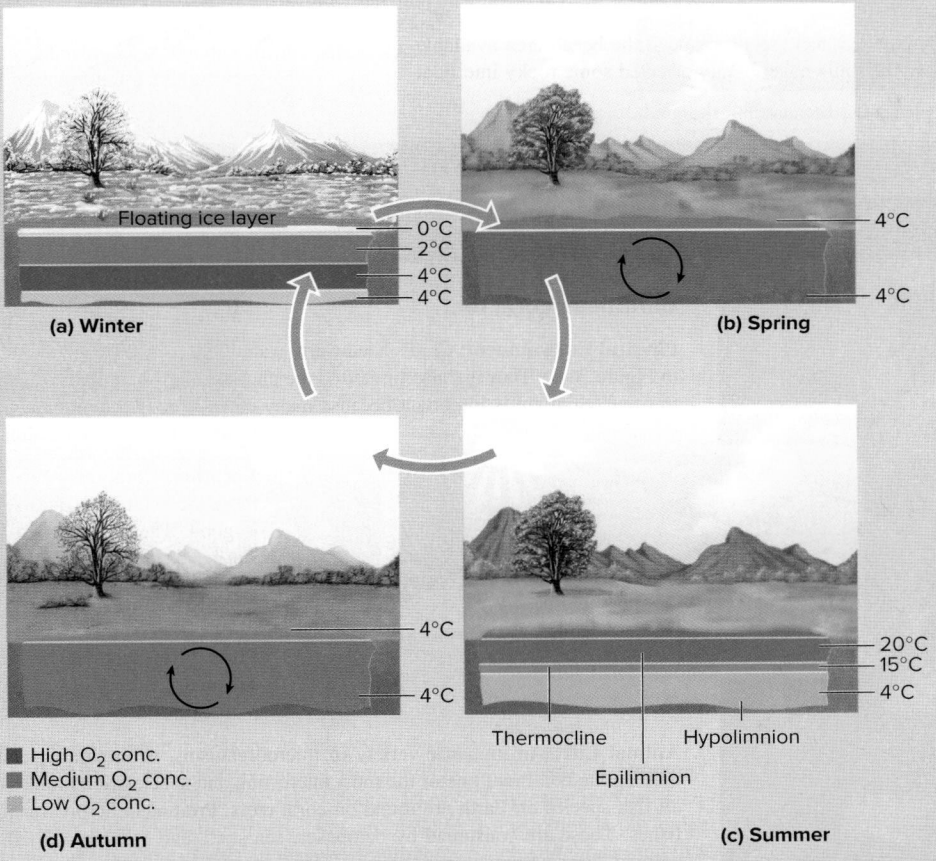

Figure 54.25 Annual cycle of a temperate lake. Cross section of a temperate lake with temperature profiles according to depth for each season. **(a)** The lake surface freezes in winter. **(b)** When the ice melts in the spring, the cold water again sinks and mixes the lake. **(c)** In the summer, the warmest water occurs at the surface, and water temperature decreases with depth. **(d)** Cold air temperatures in the fall cool the upper layers and this dense cold water sinks, thoroughly mixing the lake.

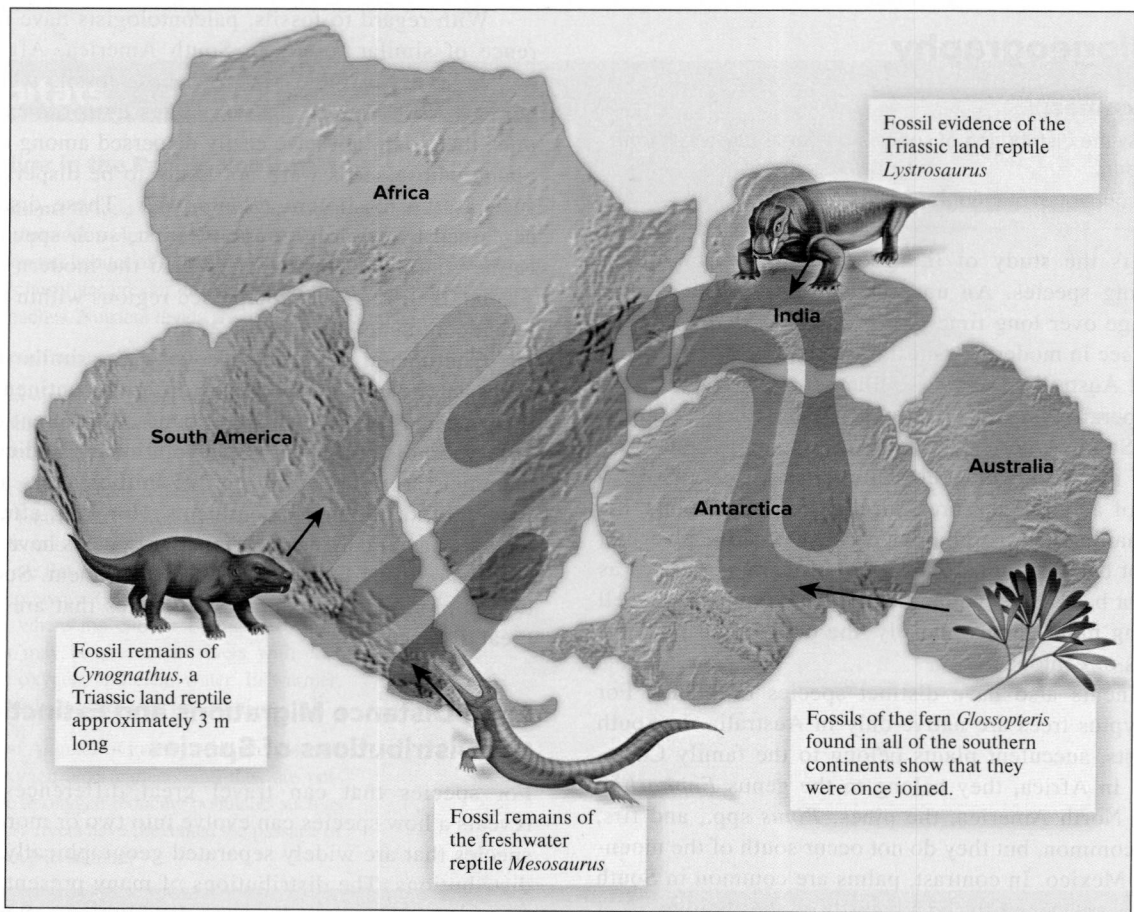

Figure 54.27 Examples of fossil plants and animals found on different continents. South America, Africa, India, Antarctica, and Australia were once united as Gondwana (refer back to Figure 26.5). The locations of the fossil remains of the four species shown here can be explained by their ranges prior to the drifting of the continents away from each other.

evolved in North America and made the reverse trek across the Bering land bridge into Eurasia; they also crossed into South America via the Central American isthmus. They have since become extinct everywhere except Asia, North Africa, and South America.

Ecologists Recognize Biogeographic Regions

In the late 19th century, British naturalist Alfred Russel Wallace was one of the earliest scientists to realize that certain plant and animal taxa were restricted to certain geographic areas of the Earth. For example, the distribution patterns of guinea pigs, anteaters, and many other groups are confined to Central and South America, from central Mexico southward. The whole area was distinct enough for Wallace to proclaim it the Neotropical region. Wallace went on to divide the world's biota into six major **biogeographic regions**: Nearctic, Palearctic, Neotropical,

Ethiopian, Oriental, and Australian (**Figure 54.29**). These regions are still widely accepted today, though debate continues about the exact locations of the boundary lines.

Biogeographical regions correspond largely to continents but more exactly to areas bounded by major barriers to dispersal, like the Himalayas and the Sahara Desert. Within these regions, areas of similar climates are often inhabited by species with similar appearance and habits but from different taxonomic groups. For example, the kangaroo rats of North American deserts, the jerboas of central Asian deserts, and the hopping mice of Australian deserts look similar and occupy similar hot, arid environments, but they arose from different lineages, belonging to the families Heteromyidae, Dipodidae, and Muridae, respectively. As noted in Chapter 22, this phenomenon, called convergent evolution, has led to the emergence of similar species that have evolved from different ancestors.

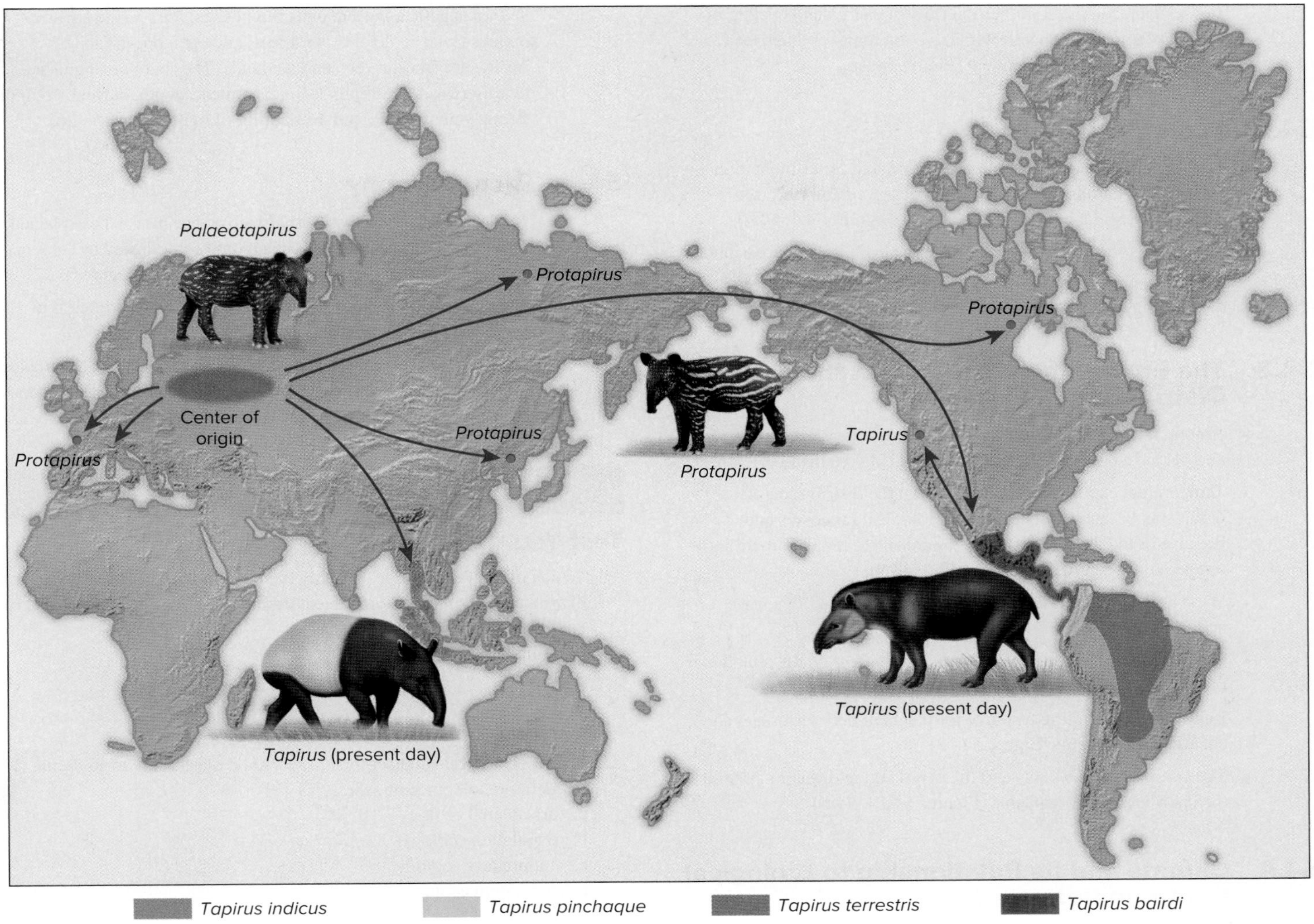

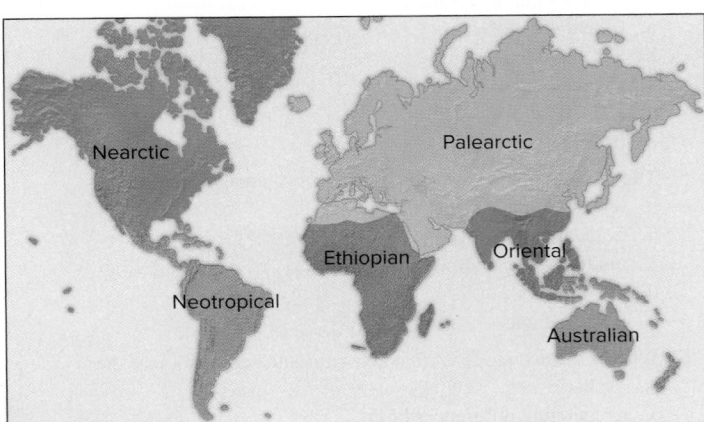

	Tapirus indicus		Tapirus pinchaque		Tapirus terrestris		Tapirus bairdi

Figure 54.28 Tapir distribution. Of the four living tapir species, three are in Central and South America and one is in Malaysia. Fossil evidence suggests a European origin of the ancestral *Paleotapirus* and a dispersal of later-evolving *Protapirus*. A more widespread distribution followed, with tapirs dying out in other regions (marked with a red dot) possibly due to climate change.

 Core Concept: Evolution Knowing that all tapir species share a common European ancestor makes it easier to explain their current distribution pattern.

Figure 54.29 The biogeographic regions proposed by Wallace. Note that the borders do not always demarcate continents.

Summary of Key Concepts

54.1   The Scale of Ecology

- Ecologists study the interactions among organisms and between organisms and their environments. The field of ecology is subdivided into broad areas of organismal, population, community, and ecosystem ecology (Figure 54.1).

- Organismal ecology considers how individuals are adapted to their environment and how the behavior of an individual organism contributes to its survival and reproductive success and the population density of the species. Population ecology explores those factors that influence a population's growth, size, and density, including species interactions such as competition, predation, and parasitism. Community ecology studies how populations of species interact and form functional communities.

Ecosystem ecology examines the flow of energy and cycling of nutrients among organisms within a community and between organisms and the environment (Figure 54.2).

54.2 Ecological Methods

- Ecological methods focus on observation and experimentation. Interactions among species are often observed and analyzed graphically, and a hypothesis is formed (Figures 54.3, 54.4).

- Ecologists test their hypotheses using well-replicated experiments. The results are often presented graphically and analyzed via a variety of statistical tests (Figure 54.5).

54.3 The Environment's Effect on the Distribution of Organisms

- Abiotic factors such as temperature, wind, water, light, salinity, and pH have powerful effects on ecological systems (Table 54.1).

- Temperature exerts important effects on the distribution of organisms because of its effect on biological processes and because of the inability of many organisms to regulate their body temperature (Figures 54.6, 54.7, 54.8, 54.9).

- Wind amplifies the effects of temperature and modifies wave action (Figure 54.10).

- The availability of water has an important effect on the abundance of organisms (Figure 54.11).

- Light can be a limiting resource for plants in both terrestrial and aquatic environments (Figure 54.12).

- The concentration of salts and the pH of soil and water can limit the distribution of organisms (Figures 54.13, 54.14).

54.4 Climate and Its Relationship to Biological Communities

- Global temperature differentials are caused by variations in incoming solar radiation and patterns of atmospheric circulation (Figures 54.15, 54.16, 54.17).

- The tilt and rotation of the Earth also affect climate, causing seasonality (Figure 54.18).

- The Coriolis force deflects the direction of northerly and southerly winds, affecting climate (Figure 54.19).

- Elevation and the proximity of a landmass to a large body of water can similarly affect climate (Figures 54.20, 54.21).

54.5 Major Biomes

- Climate has a large effect on biomes, which are major types of habitats characterized by distinctive plant and animal life (Figures 54.22, 54.23).

- Terrestrial biomes are generally named for their climate and vegetation type and include tropical rain forest, tropical deciduous forest, temperate rain forest, temperate deciduous forest, temperate coniferous forest (taiga), tropical grassland (savanna), temperate grassland (prairie), hot and cold deserts, and tundra. In mountain ranges, biome type may vary with elevation (Figure 54.24).

- Aquatic biomes are affected by tides and waves and by the fact that ice floats on water; deep lakes go through seasonal changes (Figure 54.25).

- Within aquatic environments, biomes include marine aquatic biomes (intertidal zone, coral reef, and open ocean) and freshwater lakes, rivers, and wetlands. These are distinguished by differences in salinity, oxygen content, depth, current strength (lentic versus lotic), and availability of light (Figure 54.26).

54.6 Biogeography

- The location of many fossils and living organisms can be explained by the origin of a species on one supercontinent followed by subsequent continental drift and evolution of related species (Figure 54.27).

- The current distribution patterns of some species are relics of once much broader distributions (Figure 54.28).

- Six major biogeographical regions—Nearctic, Palearctic, Neotropical, Ethiopian, Oriental, and Australian—each of which contains distinct groups of species, are widely recognized today (Figure 54.29).

Assess & Discuss

Test Yourself

1. Which of the following is probably the most important factor in the distribution of organisms in the environment?
   a. light
   b. temperature
   c. salinity
   d. water availability
   e. pH

2. Which ecological subdiscipline(s) would be most likely to study the temperature tolerance of zebras?
   a. organismal ecology
   b. population ecology
   c. community ecology
   d. ecosystem ecology
   e. both a and b

3. Physics is to engineering as ecology is to
   a. biology.
   b. environmental science.
   c. chemistry.
   d. mathematics.
   e. statistics.

4. The world's major subsidence zones occur at the latitudes
   a. 0° and 45°–55°.
   b. 30° and the poles.
   c. 0° and the poles.
   d. 20°–30° and 45°–55°.
   e. 0° and 20°–30°.

5. The most common biome type, in terms of area occupied, is
   a. open ocean.
   b. tropical rainforest.
   c. tundra.
   d. hot desert.
   e. lentic habitats.

6. What is the driving force that determines the circulation of the atmospheric air?
   a. temperature differences of the Earth
   b. winds
   c. ocean currents

d. mountain ridges

e. all of the above

7. In this biome, rainfall is between 25 cm and 100 cm and temperatures vary between –10°C in winter and 30°C in summer. Which biome is it?

a. tropical rainforest

b. tropical deciduous forest

c. savanna

d. prairie

e. temperate deciduous forest

8. What characteristic(s) (is) are commonly used to identify the terrestrial biomes of the Earth?

a. temperature

b. precipitation

c. vegetation

d. all of the above

e. a and b only

9. Young lakes are often clear and with little plant life. Such lakes are called

a. oligotrophic.

b. eutrophic.

c. lotic.

d. lentic.

e. pelagic.

10. The unique group of marsupial species found in Australia is largely a result of

a. adiabatic cooling.

b. climate.

c. continental drift and evolution.

d. rain shadows.

e. biogeographic regions.

Conceptual Questions

1. If mountains are closer to the Sun than valleys, why aren't they hotter?

2. Why are fires generally more frequent in prairies than in hotter, drier deserts?

3. **Core Concept: Systems** In most locations on Earth at about 20–30° latitude, air cools and descends, and hot deserts occur. Florida is situated between 31°N and 24°N. Why does it not support a desert biome?

Collaborative Questions

1. The so-called Telegraph Fire, near Yosemite National Park, in 2008, was one of the worst in California that year, burning more than 46 square miles covered by timber that had not burned in over 100 years. What could be done to prevent such a catastrophic fire in the park itself?

2. Based on your knowledge of biomes, identify the biome in which you live. List and describe the organisms that you have observed in your biome. Why might your observations not fit the biome predicted to occur in your area from temperature/precipitation profiles?

the wax cells and then discarding the dead larvae. Other strains are not hygienic and do not exhibit such behavior. Using genetic crosses, Rothenbuhler demonstrated that a recessive allele of one gene (*u*) controls cell uncapping and a recessive allele of a different gene (*r*) controls larval removal. Strains with the genotype, *uurr*, are hygienic strains, whereas *UURR* strains are nonhygienic. When the two strains were crossed, all the F_1 hybrids were nonhygienic (*UuRr*). When the F_1 hybrids were crossed with the hygienic strain (*uurr*), four different genotypes were produced: one-quarter of the offspring were hygienic (*uurr*), one-quarter were nonhygienic and showed neither behavior (*UuRr*), one-quarter uncapped the cells but failed to remove the larvae (*uuRr*), and one-quarter removed the larvae but only if the cells were uncapped for them (*Uurr*).

More recently, in 2004, American neuroscientist Barry Richmond and colleagues showed how the work ethic of monkeys is affected by a gene expressed in a region of the brain called the rhinal cortex. Most primates, humans and monkeys included, tend to work harder when a deadline looms. Richmond's team trained four monkeys to release a lever at the exact moment a spot on a computer screen changed color from red to green. The monkeys had to complete this task three times, but only on the third trial did they receive a food reward, regardless of how they performed on the first two trials. As an indication of how many trials were left, the monkeys could see a gray bar on the screen. As the bar became brighter, the monkeys knew they were reaching the last trial, and they worked more diligently for the reward. In the first two trials, the monkeys made more errors than in the last trial. Next, the team switched off the gene known to be involved in processing reward signals. To do this, the researchers injected a short strand of DNA into the monkeys' brains. The effects were only temporary, 10–12 weeks, but during that time the monkeys were unable to determine how many trials were left before the reward was given, and they worked vigilantly to receive the reward on every trial, making few errors even on trials one and two.

Conditioning Occurs When a Relationship Between a Stimulus and a Response Is Learned

Although many of the behavioral patterns exhibited by animals are largely innate, sometimes animals can make modifications to their behavior based on previous experience, a process that involves **learning**. Perhaps the simplest form of learning is **habituation**, in which an organism learns to ignore a repeated stimulus. For example, animals in African safari parks become habituated to the presence of vehicles containing tourists; these vehicles are neither a threat nor a benefit to them. Birds can become habituated to the presence of a scarecrow, resulting in damage to crops. Habituation can be a problem at airports, where birds eventually ignore the alarm calls designed to scare them away from the runways.

Habituation is a form of nonassociative learning, a change in response to a repeated stimulus without association with a positive or negative reinforcement. Alternatively, an association may gradually develop between a stimulus and a response. Such a change in behavior is termed **associative learning**. In associative learning, a behavior is changed or

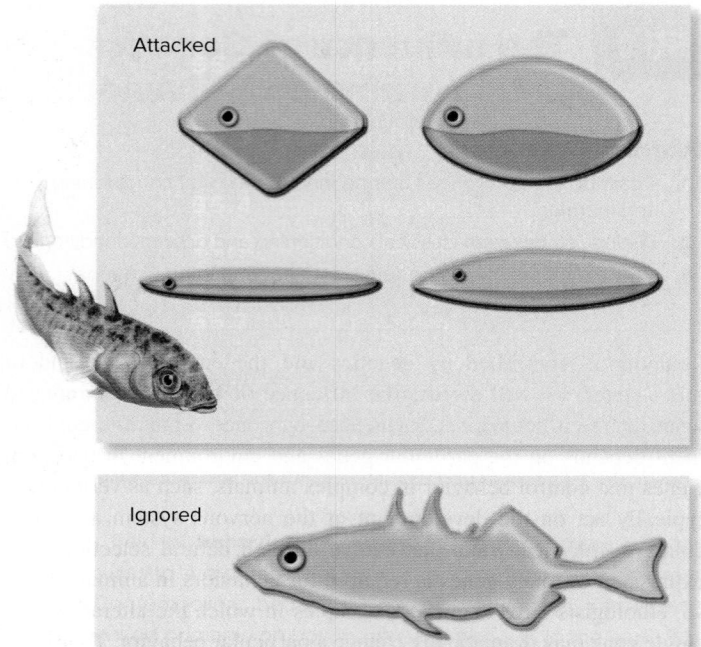

Figure 55.2   A fixed action pattern elicited by a sign stimulus. The sign stimulus for male sticklebacks to attack other males entering their territory is a red ventral surface. In experiments, male sticklebacks attacked all models that had a red underside, while ignoring a realistic model of a stickleback that lacked the red belly.

conditioned through the association. The two main types of associative learning are termed classical conditioning and operant conditioning.

In **classical conditioning**, an involuntary response comes to be associated positively or negatively with a stimulus that did not originally elicit the response. This type of learning was investigated by Russian psychologist Ivan Pavlov. In his original experiments in the 1920s, Pavlov restrained a hungry dog in a harness and presented small portions of food at regular intervals (refer back to Section 41.3). The dog would salivate whenever it smelled the food. Pavlov then began to sound a metronome when presenting the food. Eventually the dog would salivate at the sound of the metronome, whether or not the food was present. Classical conditioning is widely observed in animals. For example, many insects quickly learn to associate certain flower odors with nectar rewards and other flower odors with no rewards. In humans, the sound of a dentist's drill is enough to produce a feeling of uneasiness, tension, and sweaty palms.

In **operant conditioning**, an animal's behavior is reinforced by a consequence, either a reward or a punishment. The classic example of operant conditioning comes from the work of the American psychologist B. F. Skinner, who placed laboratory animals, usually rats, in a specially devised cage with a lever that came to be known as a Skinner box. If the rat pressed on the lever, a small amount of food would be dispensed. At the beginning of the experiment, the rat would often bump into the lever by accident, eat the food, and continue exploring its cage. Later, it would learn to associate the lever with obtaining food. Eventually, if it was hungry, the rat would almost continually press the lever. Operant conditioning, also called trial-and-error learning, is common in animals. Often it is associated with negative rather

(a) Blue jay eating monarch   **(b) Vomiting reaction**

Figure 55.3 Operant conditioning, also known as trial-and-error learning. (a) A young blue jay will eat a monarch butterfly, not knowing that it is noxious. **(b)** After the first experience of vomiting after eating a monarch, a blue jay will avoid such insects in the future.

a–b: ©L.P. Brower, Sweet Briar College

Concept Check: *What's the difference between operant conditioning and classical conditioning?*

 Core Skill: Connections Look ahead to Figure 57.9f. How might operant conditioning be related to the similar appearance of king snakes and coral snakes?

than positive reinforcement. For example, toads eventually refuse to strike at insects that sting, such as wasps and bees, and birds will learn to avoid bad-tasting butterflies (**Figure 55.3**). In humans, giving children a reward for completing homework is a positive reinforcer.

Cognitive Learning Involves Conscious Thought

Cognitive learning refers to the ability to solve problems with conscious thought and includes activities such as perception, analysis, judgment, recollection, and imagining. In the 1920s, German psychologist Wolfgang Köhler conducted a series of classic experiments with chimpanzees, and the results suggested that animals other than humans can exhibit cognitive learning. In the experiments, a chimpanzee was left in a room with bananas hanging from the ceiling and out of reach (**Figure 55.4**). Also present in the room were several wooden boxes. At first, the chimp tried in vain to jump up and grab the bananas. After a while, however, it began to arrange the boxes one on top of another underneath the fruit. Eventually, the chimp climbed the boxes and retrieved the fruit.

Many other examples of such behavior have been observed. Chimps strip leaves off twigs and use the twigs to poke into ant nests, withdrawing the twig and licking the ants off. Captive ravens have been shown to retrieve meat suspended from a branch by a string, even though they have never encountered the problem before. They pull up on the string, step on it, and then pull up on the string again, repeating the process until the meat is within reach.

Both Genetics and Learning Influence Most Behaviors

Much of the behavior we have discussed so far has been presented as either innate or learned, but the behavior we observe in nature is usually a mixture of both. Bird songs provide a good example. Many birds learn their songs as juveniles, when they hear their parents sing. If juvenile white-crowned sparrows are raised in isolation, their adult songs do not resemble the typical species-specific song (**Figure 55.5**). If they hear only the song of a different species, such as the song sparrow, they again sing a poorly developed adult song. However, if they hear the song of the white-crowned sparrow, they will learn to sing a fully developed white-crowned sparrow song. The birds are genetically programmed to learn, but they will sing the song correctly only if the appropriate instructive program is in place to guide learning.

Figure 55.4 Cognitive learning involving problem-solving ability. This chimp has devised a solution to the problem of retrieving bananas that were initially out of its reach. (all): ©Lilo Hess/The LIFE Images Collection/Getty Images

 Core Skill: Connections Look back at Figure 43.17. Does learning affect brain structure?

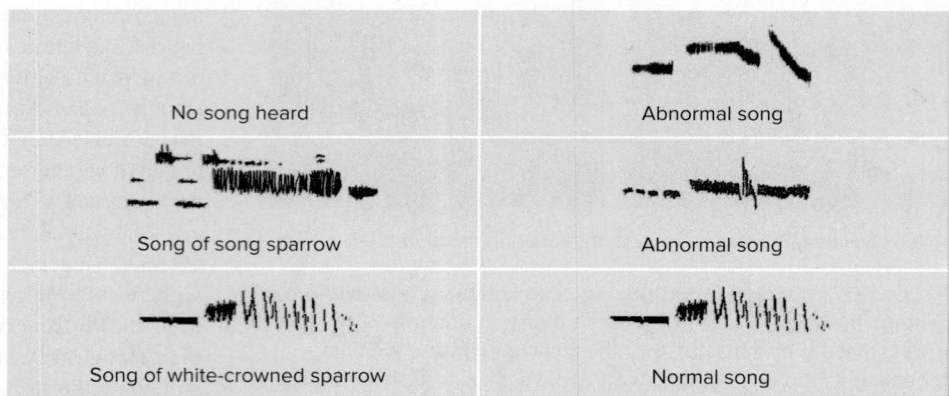

Song heard by juvenile · Song sung by juvenile

No song heard — Abnormal song

Song of song sparrow — Abnormal song

Song of white-crowned sparrow — Normal song

Figure 55.5 The interaction between genetics and learning. The lines represent the different sound frequencies produced by the birds over a short time interval. The juvenile white-crowned sparrow will sing an abnormal song if it is kept in isolation or hears only the song of a different species. However, the juvenile will sing the normal white-crowned sparrow song if exposed to it. (left): ©Robert Shantz/Alamy Stock Photo

Concept Check: *Cuckoos lay their eggs in other birds' nests, so their young are reared by parent birds of a different species. However, unlike the white-crowned sparrow, adult cuckoos always sing their own distinctive song, not that of the host species they hear as juveniles. How is this possible?*

For some types of behavior, learning can be coupled with innate behavior only during a limited time period of development, which is called a **critical period**. An example is **imprinting**. During this process, learning occurs during a brief critical period and establishes a long-lasting behavioral response to a specific object or individual, such as recognition and bonding to a parent. Imprinting was studied by Austrian ethologist Konrad Lorenz in the 1930s. Lorenz noted that young birds of some species imprint on their mother during a critical period that is usually within a few hours after hatching. This behavior serves them well, because in many species of ducks and geese, it would be hard for the mother to keep track of all her offspring as they walk or swim. After imprinting takes place, the offspring keep track of the mother.

The survival of young ducks or geese requires that they quickly learn to follow their mother's movements. Lorenz raised greylag geese from eggs, and soon after they hatched, he used himself as the model for imprinting. As a result, the young goslings imprinted on Lorenz and followed him around (**Figure 55.6**). For the rest of their life, they preferred the company of Lorenz and other humans to geese. Studies have shown that even an object as foreign as a black box, watering can, or flashing light can be imprinted on if it is the first moving object the chick sees during the critical period. In nature, if young geese are not provided with any stimulus during the critical period, they will fail to imprint on anything, and without parental care, they will almost certainly die.

Other animals imprint in different ways. Newborn shrews imprint on the scent of their mother. Mothers also can imprint on their own young within a few hours. For example, a relatively common trick used in sheep farming is to disguise a lamb whose mother has died or abandoned it by wrapping it in the fleece of another ewe's stillborn lamb. That second ewe will then care for the abandoned lamb because it smells like her own. In these situations, the innate behavior is the ability to imprint soon after birth, and the factors in the environment are the stimulus to which the imprinting is directed.

Figure 55.6 Lorenz being followed by his imprinted geese. Newborn geese follow the first object they see after hatching and later will follow that particular object only. They normally follow their mother but can be induced to imprint on humans. The first thing these young geese saw after hatching was ethologist Konrad Lorenz. ©Nina Leen/The LIFE Picture Collection/Getty Images

55.2 Local Movement and Long-Range Migration

Learning Outcomes:

1. Distinguish between kinesis and taxis, two different types of local movement.
2. Describe the three mechanisms animals use during migration.
3. **CoreSKILL »** Analyze experiments that determine whether animals learn using visual or olfactory clues.

Organisms need to find their way, both locally and over what can be extremely long distances. Locally, organisms continually need to locate sources of food, water, mates, and perhaps nesting sites. Migration involves the longer-distance seasonal movement of animals, usually between overwintering areas and summer breeding sites; these are often hundreds or even thousands of kilometers apart. Several different types of behavior may be involved in these movements.

In this section, we begin by exploring local movement and animals' use of landmarks to guide their movements. We will then consider migration and examine the possible mechanisms used by migrating animals to find their way.

Local Movement Can Involve Kinesis, Taxis, and Memory

The simplest forms of movement are mere responses to stimuli. A **kinesis** is a movement in response to a stimulus, but one that is not directed toward or away from the source of the stimulus. A simple experiment often done in classrooms is to observe the activity levels of woodlice, sometimes called sow bugs or pill bugs, in dry areas and moist areas. The woodlice move faster in drier areas, and they slow down when they reach moist environments. This behavior tends to keep them in damper areas, which they prefer in order to avoid desiccation.

A **taxis** is a more directed type of movement response, either toward (positive taxis) or away from (negative taxis) an external stimulus. Cockroaches exhibit negative phototaxis, meaning they tend to move away from light. Under low-light conditions, the photosynthetic unicellular flagellate *Euglena gracilis* shows positive phototaxis and moves toward a light source. Sea turtle hatchings are also strongly attracted to light. On emerging from their nests, they crawl toward the brightest location, traditionally the reflected moonlight on the ocean's surface. Lighted houses on the shore can disorient the hatchlings, however, and lead them to wander away from the ocean and succumb to dehydration, exhaustion, and predation. This is why beachfront property owners are requested to turn their lights down in turtle-hatching season. Male silk moths orient themselves in relation to wind direction (anemotaxis). If the air current carries the scent of a female moth, they will move upwind to locate it. Some freshwater fishes orient themselves to the currents of streams. Many fishes exhibit positive rheotaxis (from the Greek *rheos*, meaning current), in that they swim toward the oncoming water current. This taxis aids in respiration because more water passes through their gills and also helps them from being washed downstream.

Sometimes memory and landmarks may be used to aid in local movements. Dutch-born ethologist Niko Tinbergen showed how the female digger wasp uses landmarks to relocate her nests, as described next.

 Core Skill: Process of Science

Feature Investigation | Tinbergen's Experiments Showed That Digger Wasps Use Landmarks to Find Their Nests

In the sandy, dry soils of Europe, the solitary female digger wasp (*Philanthus triangulum*) digs four to five nests in which to lay her eggs. Each nest stretches obliquely down into the ground for 40–80 cm. The wasp follows the digging by performing a sequence of apparently genetically programmed events. She catches and stings a honeybee, which paralyzes it; returns to the nest; drags the bee into the nest; and lays an egg on it. The egg hatches into a larva, which feeds on the paralyzed bee. However, the larva needs to ingest five to six bees before it is fully developed. This means the wasp must catch and sting four to five more bees for each larva. She can carry only one bee at a time. After each visit, the wasp must seal the nest with soil, find a new bee, relocate the nest, open it, and add the bee.

How does the wasp relocate the nest after spending considerable time away? Niko Tinbergen observed the wasps hover and fly around the nest each time they took off. He hypothesized that they were learning the nest position by creating a mental map of the landmarks in the area.

To test his hypothesis, Tinbergen experimentally adjusted the landmarks around the burrow that the wasps might be using as cues (**Figure 55.7**). First, he put a ring of pinecones around the

Figure 55.7 **How Niko Tinbergen discovered the digger wasp's nest-locating behavior.**

Concept Check: *How would you test what type of spatial landmarks are used by female digger wasps?*

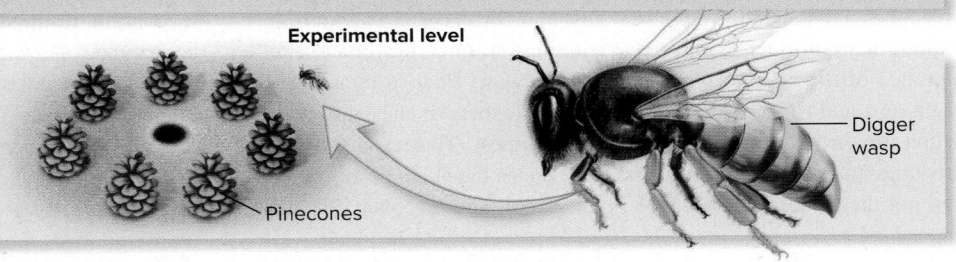

HYPOTHESIS Digger wasps (*Philanthus triangulum*) use visual landmarks to locate their nests.

STARTING LOCATION The female digger wasp excavates an underground nest, to which she returns daily, bringing food to the larvae located inside.

Experimental level

1 Place a ring of pinecones around the nest to train the wasp to associate pinecones with the nest.

Pinecones

Digger wasp

2 After the wasp leaves the nest to hunt, move the pinecones 30 cm from the real nest. The wasp returns and flies to the center of the pinecone circle instead of the real nest. Repeated experiments yield similar results (see data), indicating that the wasp uses landmarks as visual cues.

Move pinecones 30 cm from the nest.

3 To test whether it is the shape or the smell of the pinecones that elicits the response, perform the same experiment as above, except use pinecones with no scent and add 2 small pieces of cardboard coated with pine oil.

Pine oil

Cardboard

4 After the wasp leaves the nest, move the pinecones 30 cm from the nest, but leave the scented cardboard at the nest. The wasps again fly to the pinecone nest (see data), indicating that it is the arrangement of cones, not their smell, that elicits the learning.

Move pinecones 30 cm from the nest.

5 THE DATA*

Results from steps 1 and 2:

Wasp #	Number of return visits per wasp to real nest without pinecones	Number of return visits per wasp to sham nest with pinecones
1–17	0	~9

Results from steps 3 and 4:

Wasp #	Number of return visits per wasp to real nest with scented cardboard	Number of return visits per wasp to sham nest with pinecones
18–22	0	~6

*Seventeen wasps, numbered 1–17, were studied as described in steps 1 and 2. Five wasps, numbered 18–22, were studied as described in steps 3 and 4.

6 **CONCLUSION** Digger wasps remember the positions of visual landmarks and use them as aids in local movements.

7 **SOURCE** Tinbergen, N. 1951. *The study of instinct*. Clarendon Press, Oxford.

nest entrance to train the wasp to associate the pinecones with the nest. Then, when the wasp was out hunting, he moved the circle of pinecones a distance from the real nest and constructed a sham nest, making a slight depression in the sand and mimicking the covered entrance of the burrow. On returning, the wasp flew straight to the sham nest and tried to locate the entrance. Tinbergen chased it away. When it returned, it again flew to the sham nest. Tinbergen repeated this nine times, and every time the wasp chose the sham nest. Tinbergen got the same result with 16 other wasps, and not once did they choose the real nest.

Next, Tinbergen investigated the type of stimulus that might be eliciting the learning. He hypothesized that the wasps could be responding to the distinctive scent of the pinecones rather than their appearance. He trained the wasps by placing a circle of pinecones that had no scent and two small pieces of cardboard coated in pine oil around the real nest. He then moved the cones to surround a sham nest and left the scented cardboard around the real nest. The returning wasps again ignored the real nest with the scented cardboard and flew to the sham. He concluded that for the wasps, sight was apparently more important than smell in determining landmarks.

Experimental Questions

1. What observations were important for the development of Tinbergen's hypothesis explaining how digger wasps located their nests?

2. **CoreSKILL** » How did Tinbergen test the hypothesis that the wasps were using landmarks to relocate the nest? What were the results?

3. **CoreSKILL** » Did the Tinbergen experiment rule out any other cue the wasps may have been using besides the sight of pinecones?

Core Skill: Quantitative Reasoning

BIO TIPS **THE QUESTION** *Tinbergen also investigated whether digger wasps use visual and/or olfactory cues to locate their honeybee prey. He attached a number of dead bees to thread tethers so that they blew in the wind. Some of them were descented with alcohol. He also tethered bee-sized pieces of twigs to threads, and scented some of these by shaking them with dead bees. Finally, he tied dead bees to twigs, which did not move in the wind. He presented these five types of "dummies" to digger wasps and observed their behavior. The wasps either ignored the prey, hovered in place before it, pounced on or grasped it, or attempted to sting or capture it. The resultant numbers of events in 100 hours of observing are shown in the table below. Do digger wasps rely on visual or olfactory cues, or both, to locate their prey?*

Experimental treatment	Hover	Pounce or grasp	Sting or capture
Tethered bees	26	14	26
Alcohol-treated tethered bees	20	9	0
Bee-sized tethered twigs	14	3	0
Bee-sized scented, tethered twigs	34	20	9
Bees tied to twigs	0	0	0

TOPIC *What topic in biology does this question address?* The topic is animal behavior. More specifically, the question concerns how digger wasps locate suitable prey.

INFORMATION *What information do you know based on the question and your understanding of the topic?* From the question, you know that digger wasps may use visual or olfactory cues, or both, to locate their prey. From your understanding of the topic that you gained from Figure 55.7, you know that digger wasps use visual landmarks to locate their nests.

PROBLEM-SOLVING **S**TRATEGY *Interpret data.* Add two columns to the table of results, with one column labeled "Visual," which includes both accurate bee shape and movement, and the other "Olfactory," which corresponds to bee scent. Place a check mark in each of these columns if the results of the experiment indicate that digger wasps may be responding to bee shape, bee movement, or bee scent. Place a minus if they are not.

ANSWER

Experimental	Hover	Pounce or grasp	Sting or capture	Visual Bee shape/ Movement	Olfactory
Tethered bees	26	14	26	✓ / ✓	✓
Alcohol-treated tethered bees	20	9	0	✓ / ✓	–
Bee-sized tethered twigs	14	3	0	– / ✓	–
Bee-sized scented, tethered twigs	34	20	9	– / ✓	✓
Bees tied to twigs	0	0	0	– / –	✓

With regard to visual cues, an accurate bee shape was not necessary; the wasps responded to bee-sized tethered twigs. The visual cue of prey movement was very important, because bees tied to twigs did not elicit a response. The olfactory cue also appeared important, because scented bees or scented bee-sized twigs elicited a greater response compared to those that were unscented. However, the olfactory cue alone was not sufficient to elicit a response because bees tied to twigs were not recognized as prey. Taken together, a visual cue (movement) and an olfactory cue (scent) are used by digger wasps to locate their prey.

Migration Involves Long-Range Movement and More Complex Spatial Navigation

The activities of some animal species involve **migration**, which is a long-range seasonal movement. Migrations are usually linked to temperature changes, availability of food, and suitable breeding areas. For example, nearly half the bird species of North America migrate to South America to escape the cold winters and feed, returning to North America in the spring to breed. Arctic terns that breed in Arctic Canada and Asia in summer migrate to the Antarctic to feed in the winter and then return to breed. This staggering journey involves up to a 40,000-km (25,000-mile) round-trip, most of it over the open ocean, during which the birds must stay airborne for days at a time!

The monarch butterfly of North America migrates to overwinter in California, Mexico, and possibly south Florida and Cuba (**Figure 55.8**). An interesting point about the northward journey of the monarch is that it involves several generations of butterflies to complete. On their way back to the northern U.S. and Canada, the butterflies lay eggs and die. The caterpillars develop on milkweed plants, and the resultant adults continue to journey farther north.

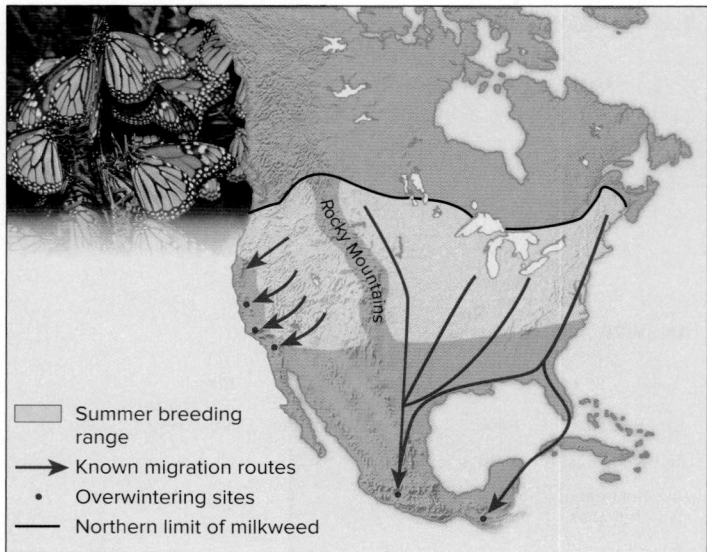

Figure 55.8 Monarch butterfly migration. Many monarch butterflies east of the Rocky Mountains migrate to a small area in Mexico to avoid the cold northern weather. Here they roost together in large numbers in fir trees (inset). Some butterflies may stay in Florida and Cuba. Butterflies west of the Rockies overwinter in mild coastal California locations. ©Jodi Jacobson/Getty Images

Concept Check: *Why is the seasonal movement of monarchs an unusual example of migration?*

This cycle happens several times in the course of the return journey. The northward and southward migrations are unique in that none of the individuals has ever been to the destinations before. Therefore, the ability to migrate must be an innate behavior.

How do migrating animals find their way? Three mechanisms may be involved: piloting, orientation, and navigation. In **piloting**, an animal moves from one familiar landmark to the next. For example, many whale species migrate between summer feeding areas and winter calving grounds. Gray whales migrate between the Bering Sea near Alaska to coastal areas of Mexico. Features of the coastline, including mountain ranges, and rivers, may aid in navigation. In **orientation**, animals have the ability to follow a compass bearing and travel in a straight line. **Navigation** involves the ability not only to follow a compass bearing but also to set or adjust it.

An experiment with starlings helps illuminate the difference between orientation and navigation (**Figure 55.9**). European starlings breed in Scandinavia and northeastern Europe and migrate in a southwest direction toward coastal France and southern England to spend the winter. Migrating starlings were captured and tagged in the Netherlands and then transported south to Switzerland and released. Juvenile birds, which had never made the trip before, flew southwest in their migration and were later recaptured in Spain. Adult birds, with more experience, returned to their normal wintering range by adjusting their course by approximately 90°. This result indicates that the adult birds can actually navigate, whereas the juveniles rely on orientation.

Many species use a combination of navigational reference points, including the position of the Sun, the stars (for nighttime travel), and

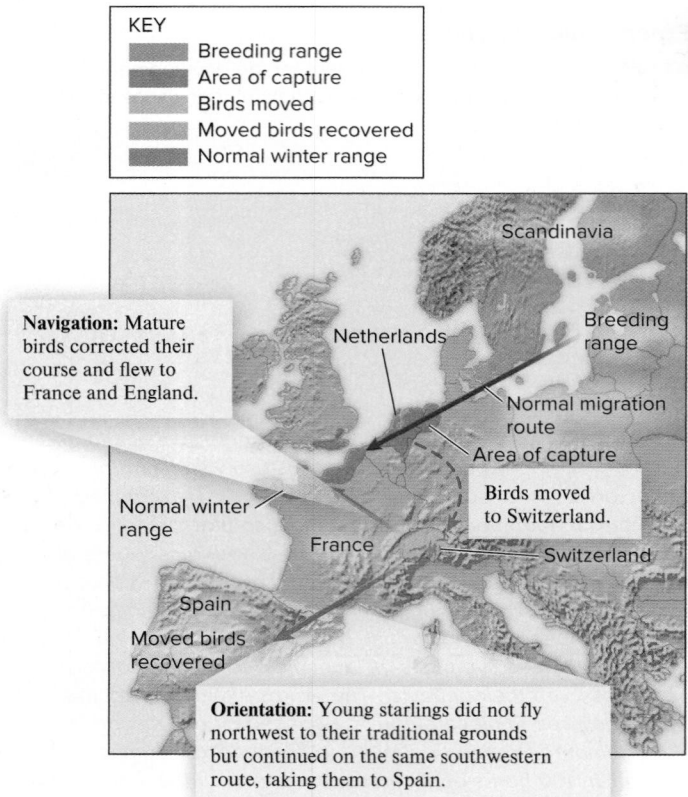

Figure 55.9 Orientation versus navigation. Starlings normally migrate from breeding grounds in Scandinavia and northeastern Europe through the Netherlands and northern Germany to overwintering sites in France and England. This involves a southwest flight. When juveniles were captured in the Netherlands and moved to Switzerland, they continued on in a southwestern direction and ended up in Spain. When adult birds were captured and moved, they changed course and flew to their normal overwintering areas.

Earth's magnetic field. Homing pigeons have magnetite in their beaks that acts as a compass to indicate direction (refer back to Section 44.4 on electromagnetic reception). Navigation by the Sun or the stars also requires the use of a timing device to compensate for the ever-changing position of these reference points. Many migrants, therefore, possess the equivalent of an internal clock. Pigeons integrate their internal clock with the position of the Sun. Researchers have altered the internal clock of pigeons by keeping them under artificial lights for certain periods of time. When the pigeons are released, they display predictable deviations in their flight. For every hour that their internal clock is shifted, the orientation of the birds shifts about 15°.

Not all examples of animal migration are well understood. Green sea turtles feed off the coast of Brazil yet swim east for 2,300 km (1,429 miles) to lay their eggs on Ascension Island, an 8-km-wide island in the center of the Atlantic Ocean between Brazil and Africa. It is not known why the turtles lay their eggs on this speck of an island or how they succeed in finding it. Perhaps fewer predators exist on Ascension than on other beaches. A combination of magnetic orientation and chemical cues may help them find it. Thus, although scientists have made many discoveries about animal navigation, much remains to be learned about how animals acquire a map sense.

Foraging Behavior and Defense of Territory

Learning Outcomes:

1. Describe and give examples of optimal foraging.
2. Explain how the risk of predation prevents optimal foraging in some species.
3. Outline the costs and benefits of defending a territory.

Food gathering, or foraging, often involves decisions about whether to remain at a resource patch and look for more food or look for a completely new patch. The analysis of these decisions is often viewed in terms of **optimality theory**, which predicts that an animal should behave in a way that maximizes the benefits of a behavior minus its costs. In this case, the benefits are the nutritional or caloric value of the food items, and the costs are the energetic or caloric costs of movement. Optimality theory can also be applied to other behavioral issues such as how large a territory to defend. Too small a territory would contain insufficient resources, such as food and mates, and too large a territory would be too energetically costly to defend. Theoretically, then, there is an optimal territory size for a given individual to defend. In this section, we will explore examples that involve optimal foraging for food and optimal defense of territory.

Optimal Foraging Entails Maximizing the Benefits and Minimizing the Costs of Food Gathering

Optimal foraging is the concept that in a given circumstance, an animal seeks to obtain the most energy possible with the least expenditure of energy. The underlying assumption of optimal foraging is that natural selection favors animals that are maximally efficient at propagating their genes and at performing all other functions that serve this purpose. In this model, the more net energy an individual gains in a limited time, the greater the reproductive success.

Shore crabs (*Carcinus maenas*) eat many different-sized mussels but tend to feed preferentially on intermediate-sized mussels, which give them the highest rate of energy return (**Figure 55.10**). Very large mussels yield more energy, but they take so long for the crab to open that they are actually less profitable, in terms of energy yield per unit time spent, than smaller sizes. Very small mussels are easy to crack open but contain so little food that they are not worth the effort. This leaves intermediate-sized mussels as the preferred size. Of course, the intermediate-sized mussels may take a longer time to locate, because more crabs are looking for them, so crabs eat some less profitable but more frequently encountered sizes of mussels. The result is that the diet consists of mussels in a range of sizes around the preferred optimal size.

In some cases, animals do not forage optimally. Many animals seek not only to maximize food intake but also to minimize the risk of predation. Some species may only dart out to take food from time to time. For example, many species of ants display this behavior because they can be attacked by parasitic flies that hover around ant colonies. Although ants are relatively quick, some of them cannot avoid these fast-flying parasites, which lay an egg on the ant's head. Once the parasite's eggs hatch, the larvae bore their way into the ant's head, eventually killing it.

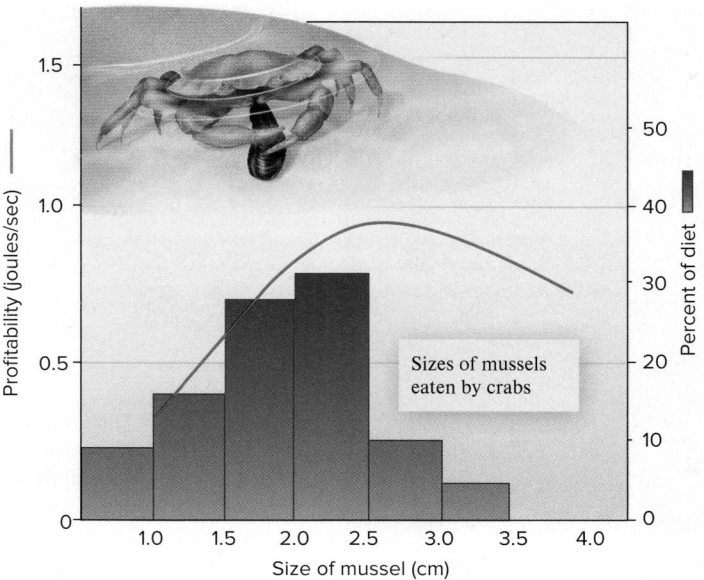

Figure 55.10 Optimal foraging behavior in shore crabs. When offered a choice of equal numbers of each size mussel, shore crabs (*Carcinus maenas*) prefer intermediate-sized mussels that provide the highest rate of energy return. Profitability is the energy yield (joules) per second of time used in breaking open the shell.

In the tropics, leafcutter ants, *Atta cephalotes*, are subject to attack by the fly *Neodohrniphora curvinervis* (**Figure 55.11a**). The larger worker ants are more likely to be attacked, because smaller workers' heads are too small to allow proper development of the parasite flies' larvae. When Matthew Orr compared the size

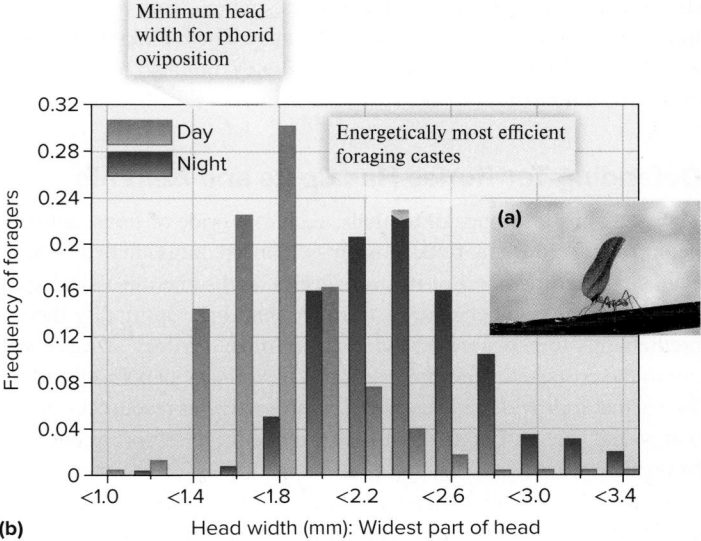

Figure 55.11 Changes in foraging strategies in the presence of parasites. (a) The tropical leafcutter ant, *Atta cephalotes*. **(b)** The most efficient leafcutter ants are larger individuals. However, larger individuals are restricted to foraging at night because of the activity of parasitic flies during the day. During the day, only small ants forage, as these are not subject to the same levels of parasitism. a: Source: Photo by Scott Bauer/USDA

(a) Golden-winged sunbird

(b) Cheetah

(c) Nesting gannets

Figure 55.12 **Differing territory sizes among animals.** **(a)** The golden-winged sunbird of East Africa (*Nectarinia reichenowi*) has a medium territory size that depends on the number of flowers it can obtain resources from and defend. **(b)** Cheetahs (*Acinonyx jubatus*) hunt over large areas and can have extensive territories. This male is urine-marking part of his territory in the southern Serengeti, near Ndutu, Tanzania. **(c)** Nesting gannets (*Morus bassanu*s) have much smaller territories, in which each bird is just beyond the pecking range of its neighbor. a: ©Tony Camacho/Science Source; b: ©Gregory G. Dimijian/Science Source; c: ©Getty Images

distributions of the leafcutter ants that foraged during the day versus those that foraged at night, he discovered a large difference in the size distributions (**Figure 55.11b**). Most foraging by larger workers is done at night, when it is too dark for the flies to see properly and their activity ceases. The lesser amount of foraging in the day is performed by smaller ants that are less susceptible to fly attack. Although the data are not shown in Figure 55.11, Orr extended the activity of *N. curvinervis* by positioning lights outside the leafcutter nests. In these cases, the foraging activities of the leafcutters were thrown into disarray. Ants were backed up around the nest, many rising on their hind legs to snap at the flies which, with the extended light, continued to try to parasitize the ants. Thus, foraging activity is influenced not only by energetic efficiency, but also by the threat of natural enemies.

Defending Territories Has Costs and Benefits

Many animals or groups of animals, such as a pride of lions, actively defend a **territory**, a fixed area in which an individual or group excludes other members of its own species, and sometimes other species, by aggressive behavior or territory marking. Optimality theory predicts that territory owners tend to optimize territory size according to the costs and benefits involved. The primary benefit of a territory is that it provides exclusive access to particular resources—food, mates, and shelter. Larger territories provide more resources but may be costly to defend.

In studies of the territorial behavior of the golden-winged sunbird (*Nectarinia reichenowi*) in East Africa, American ornithologists Frank Gill and Larry Wolf measured the energy content of nectar as the benefit of maintaining a territory and compared it to the energy costs of activities such as perching, flying, and fighting (**Figure 55.12a**). Defending the territory ensured that other sunbirds did not take nectar from available flowers, thus increasing the amount of nectar in each flower. In defending a territory, the sunbird gained 780 Calories (kilocalories) a day in extra nectar content. However,

the sunbird also spent 728 Calories in defense of the territory, yielding a net gain of 52 Calories a day and making territorial defense advantageous.

Territory size differs considerably among species. Male cheetahs defend relatively large territories, often 40 km² (about 15 square miles). These territories are usually located where densities of prey are relatively high. Males warn intruders to stay away from their territories by scent marking (**Figure 55.12b**). In contrast, territories set up solely to defend areas for mating or nesting are often relatively small. For example, male sea lions defend small areas of beach. The preferred areas contain the largest number of females and are controlled by the largest breeding bulls. The size of the territory of some nesting birds, such as gannets, is determined by how far the bird can reach to peck its neighbor without leaving its nest (**Figure 55.12c**).

55.4 Communication

Learning Outcome:

1. Give examples of how animals use chemical, auditory, visual, and tactile communication.

Communication is the use of specially designed visual, chemical, auditory, or tactile signals to modify the behavior of others. It may be used for many purposes, including defending territories, maintaining contact with offspring, courtship, and contests between males. The use of different forms of communication between organisms depends on the environment in which they live. For example, visual communication plays little role in the signals of nocturnal animals. Similarly, for animals in dense forests, sounds are of prime importance. Sound, however, is a temporary signal. Scent can last longer and is often used to mark the large territories of some mammals. In this section, we will examine the various types of communication—chemical, auditory, visual, and tactile—that occur among animals.

Chemical Communication Is Often Used to Mark Territories or Attract Mates

The chemical marking of territories is common among animals, especially among members of the canine and feline families (see Figure 55.12b). Scent trails are often used by social insects to recruit workers to help bring prey to the nest. Fire ants (genus *Solenopsis*) attack large, living prey, and many ants are needed to drag the prey back to the nest. The scout that finds the prey lays down a scent trail from the prey back to the nest. The scent excites other workers, which follow the trail to the prey. The scent marker is very volatile, and the trail effectively disappears in a few minutes to avoid mass confusion over old trails.

Animals frequently use chemicals to attract mates. Female moths attract males by powerful chemical attractants called **pheromones**. Male moths have receptors that can detect as little as a single molecule. Among social organisms, some individuals use pheromones to manipulate the behavior of others. For example, a queen bee releases pheromones that suppress the development of the reproductive system of workers, which ensures that she is the only reproductive female in the hive.

Auditory Communication Is Often Used to Attract Mates and to Deter Competitors

Many species communicate by making sounds. Because the ground can absorb sound waves, sound travels farther in the air, which is why many birds and insects perch on branches or leaves when singing. Air is on average 14 times less turbulent at dawn and dusk than during the rest of the day, so sound carries farther then, which helps explain the preference of most animals for calling at these times. Birds living near airports advance their dawn chorus to reduce overlap with aircraft noise. Some insects utilize the very plants on which they feed as a medium of song transmission. Many male leafhopper and planthopper insects vibrate their abdomens on leaves and create species-specific courtship songs that are transmitted by adjacent vegetation and are picked up by nearby females of the same species.

Although many males use auditory communication to attract females, some females use calls to attract the attention of males. Female elephant seals scream loudly when approached by a nondominant male. This sound attracts the attention of the dominant male, which drives the nondominant male away. In this way, the female is guaranteed a mating with the strongest male. Sound production can attract predators as well as mates. Some bats listen for the mating calls of male frogs to find their prey. Parasitic flies detect and locate chirping male crickets and then deposit larvae on or near them. The larvae latch onto and penetrate the cricket and eventually kill it. Sound may also be used by males during competition over females. In many animals, lower-pitched sounds come from larger males, so by calling to one another, males can gauge the size of their opponents and decide whether it is worth fighting.

Visual Communication Is Often Used in Courtship and Aggressive Displays

In courtship, animals use a vast number of visual signals to identify and select potential mates. Competition among males involving displays to attract females has led to elaborate coloration and extensive ornamentation in some species. For example, peacocks and males of many bird species have developed elaborate plumage to attract females.

Male fireflies display light flashes that are species specific with regard to number and duration of flashes (**Figure 55.13a**). Females respond with a flash of their own. Such bright flashes are also bound to attract predators. Some female fireflies use mimicry to their advantage. Female fireflies of the species *Photuris versicolor* mimic the flashing responses normally given by females of other species, such as *Photinus tanytoxus*, in order to lure the males of those species close enough to eat them!

Visual signals are also used to resolve disputes over territories or mates. Deer and antelope have antlers or horns that they use to display and spar over territory and females. Most of these matches never develop into outright fights, because the males gauge their opponent's strength by the size of these ornaments (look ahead to Figure 55.22b). Among insects, the "horns" of rhinoceros beetles and the eye stems of stalk-eyed flies send similar signals (**Figure 55.13b**).

(a) Firefly flashing

(b) Male hercules beetles fighting

Figure 55.13 Visual communication. (a) Communication between fireflies is conducted by species-specific light flashes emitted by organs located on the underside of the abdomen. **(b)** The horns of these hercules beetles provide a signal about the strength of their owners. a: ©Darwin Dale/Science Source; b: ©Taylor Weidman/LightRocket/Getty Images

 Core Concept: Evolution In both of the cases illustrated in Figure 55.13, morphological features influence animal behavior, which, in turn, affects reproductive success.

(a) Bees clustering around a recently returned scout, seen in the center vibrating her abdomen.

(b) Round dance

(c) Waggle dance: The angle of the waggle to the vertical orientation of the honeycomb corresponds to the angle of the food source from the Sun.

Figure 55.14 **Tactile communication among honeybees regarding food sources.** **(a)** Bees gather around a newly returned scout to receive information about nearby food sources. **(b)** If the food is less than 50 m away, the scout performs a round dance. **(c)** If the food is more than 50 m away, the scout performs a waggle dance, which conveys information about its location. If the dance is performed at a 30° angle to the right of the hive's vertical plane, then the food source is located at a 30° angle to the right of the Sun. a: ©Scott Camazine/Alamy Stock Photo

Tactile Communication Is Used to Strengthen Social Bonds and to Convey Information About Food

Animals often use tactile communication to establish bonds between group members. Primates frequently groom one another, and canines and felines may nuzzle and lick each other. Many insects use tactile communication to convey information on the whereabouts of food. Members of the ant genus *Leptothorax* feed on prey such as dead insects. When a scouting ant encounters such prey, it usually needs an additional worker to help bring it back to the nest. Rather than laying a scent trail, which is energetically costly, the scout ant recruits a helper and physically leads it to the food source. The helper runs in tandem with the scout, its antennae touching the scout's abdomen.

One of the most fascinating examples of tactile communication among animals is the dance of the honeybee, studied by German ethologist Karl von Frisch in the 1940s. Bees commonly live in large hives; in the case of the European honeybee (*Apis mellifera*), the hive consists of 30,000–40,000 individuals. The flowering plants on which the bees forage can be located long distances from the hive and are distributed in a patchy manner, with any given patch usually containing many flowers that store more nectar and pollen than an individual bee can carry back to the nest.

A scout bee that locates a resource patch returns to the hive and recruits more workers to join it (**Figure 55.14a**). Because the inside of the hive is dark, a visual signal will not be effective. Instead, the scout uses a tactile signal. The scout dances on the vertical side of a honeycomb, and the dance is monitored by other bees, which follow and touch her to interpret the message. If the food is relatively close to the hive, less than 50 m away, the scout performs a round dance, rapidly moving in a circle, first in one direction and then the other. The other bees know the food is relatively close at hand,

and the smell of the scout tells them what flower species to look for (**Figure 55.14b**).

If the food is more than 50 m away, the scout will perform a different type of dance, called a waggle dance. In this dance, the scout traces a figure 8, in the middle of which she waggles her abdomen and produces bursts of sound. Again, the other bees maintain contact with her. Occasionally, the scout regurgitates a small sample of nectar so the bees know the type of food source they are looking for. The truly amazing part of the waggle dance is that the angle at which the central part of the figure 8 deviates from the vertical direction of the comb represents the same angle at which the food source deviates from the point at which the Sun hits the horizon (**Figure 55.14c**). The direction is always up-to-date, because the bee adjusts the dance as the Sun moves across the sky.

55.5 Living in Groups

Learning Outcome:

1. Outline the costs and benefits of living in groups.

As we have seen, much of animal behavior is directed at other animals. Some of the more complex behavior occurs when animals live together in groups such as flocks or herds. A central concern of ecology is to explain the distribution patterns of organisms, and a very important related task is to understand the reason for variation in the degree of group living. One way to approach this question is to assess the costs and benefits involved. Although group living increases competition for food and the spread of disease, it also has benefits that compensate for the costs involved. Many of these benefits relate to locating food sources, assistance in rearing offspring, access to mates, and group defense against predators. Group living can reduce predator success in at least two ways: through increased vigilance and through protection in numbers.

Living in Large Groups May Reduce the Risk of Predation Because of Increased Vigilance

For many predators, success depends on the element of surprise. If an individual is alerted to an attack, the predator's chance of success is lowered. A wood pigeon (*Columba palumbus*) in a flock takes to the air when it spots a goshawk (*Accipiter gentilis*). Once one pigeon takes flight, the other members of the flock are alerted and follow suit. If each individual in a group occasionally scans the environment for predators, the larger the group, the less time an individual forager needs to devote to vigilance and the more time it can spend feeding. This explanation is referred to as the **many-eyes hypothesis** (**Figure 55.15**). Of course, cheating is a possibility, because some birds might never look up, relying on others to keep watch while they keep feeding. However, the individual that happens to be scanning when a predator approaches is most likely to escape, a fact that tends to discourage cheating.

Living in Groups Offers Protection by the Selfish Herd

Group living also provides protection in sheer numbers. Typically, predators take one prey animal per attack. In any given attack, an individual antelope in a herd of 100 has a 1 in 100 chance of being selected, whereas a single individual has a 1 in 1 chance. Large herds may be attacked more frequently than a solitary individual, but a herd is unlikely to attract 100 times more attacks than an individual, often because of the territorial nature of predators. Furthermore, large numbers of prey

Figure 55.15 Living in groups and the many-eyes hypothesis. The larger the number of wood pigeons, the less likely an attack will be successful.

Concept Check: *What other advantage do individuals in large groups have when the group is being attacked by a predator?*

are able to defend themselves better than single individuals, which usually choose to flee. For example, groups of nesting black-headed gulls mob a crow, thereby reducing the crow's ability to steal the gulls' eggs.

Research has shown that within a group, each individual can minimize the danger to itself by choosing the location that is as close to the center of the group as possible. This was the subject of a famous paper, "The Geometry of the Selfish Herd," by British evolutionary biologist W. D. Hamilton. The explanation of this type of defense is that predators are likely to attack prey on the periphery because they are easier to isolate visually. Many animals in herds tend to bunch close together when they are under attack, making it physically difficult for the predator to get to the center of the herd.

Overall, group size may be the result of a trade-off between the costs and benefits of group living. Although much group behavior serves to reduce predation, other complex behavior occurs in groups, including grooming behavior and behavior that appears to benefit the group at the expense of the individual. For example, a honeybee stings a potential hive predator to discourage it. The bee's stinger is barbed, and once it has penetrated the predator's skin, the bee cannot withdraw it. The bee's only means of escape is to tear away part of its abdomen, leaving the stinger behind and dying in the process. In the next section, we will explore the reasons for such apparent altruistic behavior, in which an individual incurs costs to itself for the benefit of others.

55.6 Altruism

Learning Outcomes:

1. **CoreSKILL** » Evaluate the arguments for and against the concept of group selection.
2. Describe how the concept of kin selection can explain altruistic behavior.
3. **CoreSKILL** » Predict which types of relatives are more or less likely to be the recipients of apparent altruistic acts.
4. Explain why eusociality is a form of altruism.

In Chapter 23, we learned that natural selection is a process in which certain individuals are more likely to pass on their genes, yet we see many instances in which some individuals forego reproducing altogether, apparently to benefit the group. How do ecologists explain **altruism**, a behavior that appears to benefit others at a cost to oneself? In this section, we begin by discussing whether such behavior evolved for the good of the group or for the good of the individual. As we will see, most altruistic acts serve to benefit the individual's close relatives. We will explore the concept of kin selection, which argues that acts of self-sacrifice indirectly promote the spread of an organism's genes, and see how this plays out in an extreme form in the genetics of social insect colonies. Last, we will examine reciprocal altruism, instances of altruism among nonkin.

In Nature, Selfish Behavior Is More Likely Than Altruism

One of the first attempts to explain the existence of altruism was called **group selection**, the premise that natural selection produces outcomes beneficial for the whole group or species. In 1962, British ecologist V. C.

Wynne-Edwards argued that a group containing altruists, each willing to subordinate its interests for the good of the group, would have a survival advantage over a group composed of selfish individuals. In concept, the idea of group selection seemed straightforward and logical: A group that consisted of selfish individuals would overexploit its resources and die out, but the fitness of a group with altruists would be enhanced.

In the late 1960s, the idea of group selection came under severe criticism. Leading the charge was American evolutionary biologist George C. Williams, who argued that evolution acts through the individual; that is, adaptive traits generally are selected for because they benefit the survival and reproduction of the individual rather than the group. Some of Williams's arguments against group selection follow.

Mutation   Individuals carrying mutations that allow them to readily use resources for themselves or their offspring have an advantage in a population in which individuals limit their resource use. Consider a species of bird in which a pair lays only two eggs; that is, it has a clutch size of two, and the resources are not overexploited for the good of the group. Laying two eggs ensures a replacement of the parent birds but prevents a population explosion. Suppose a mutant bird that lays three eggs arises. If the population is not overexploiting its resources, sufficient food may be available for all three young to survive. If this happens, the three-egg genotype eventually becomes more common than the two-egg genotype.

Immigration   Even in a population in which all pairs laid two eggs and no mutations occurred to increase clutch size, selfish individuals that laid more could still immigrate from other areas. In nature, populations are rarely sufficiently isolated to prevent immigration of selfish mutants from other populations.

Resource Prediction   Group selection assumes that individuals are able to assess and predict future food availability and population density within their own habitat. There is little evidence that they can. For example, it is difficult to imagine that songbirds would be able to predict the future supply of the caterpillars that they feed to their young and adjust their clutch size accordingly.

Most ecologists accept individual gain as a more plausible result of natural selection than group selection. Population size is more often controlled by competition in which individuals strive to command as much of a resource as they can. Such selfishness can cause some seemingly surprising behaviors. For example, male Hanuman langurs (*Semnopithecus entellus*) fight mothers and kill infants when they take over groups of females from other males (**Figure 55.16**). The reason for the behavior is that when they are not nursing their young, females become sexually receptive much sooner, hastening the day when the male can father his own offspring. Infanticide ensures that the male can father more offspring, and the genes governing this tendency spread by natural selection.

Apparent Altruistic Behavior in Nature Is Often Associated with Kin Selection

If individual selfishness is more common than group selection, how do we account for what appear to be examples of altruism in nature? Some propose that the answer lies in a concept known as **kin selection**, selection for behavior that lowers an individual's own fitness but enhances the reproductive success of a relative. Because

Figure 55.16 Langur monkeys fighting. Male Hanuman langurs (*Semnopithecus entellus*) may act aggressively toward mothers and even kill their young, hastening the day when the females become sexually receptive and the males can father their own offspring.
©Andrew Parkinson/Stockbyte/Getty Images

relatives share many of the same genes, altruist individuals increase the likelihood that their genes are passed along to future generations by enhancing the reproductive success of their relatives.

The probability that any two individuals will share a copy of a particular gene is a quantity, r, called the **coefficient of relatedness**. During meiosis in a diploid species, any given copy of a gene has a 50% chance of segregating into an egg or sperm. A mother and father are on average related to their children by an amount $r = 0.5$, because half of a child's genes come from its mother and half from its father. By similar reasoning, brothers or sisters are related by an amount $r = 0.5$ (they share half their mother's genes and half their father's); grandchildren and grandparents, by 0.25; and cousins, by 0.125 (**Figure 55.17**). In 1964, ecologist W. D. Hamilton realized

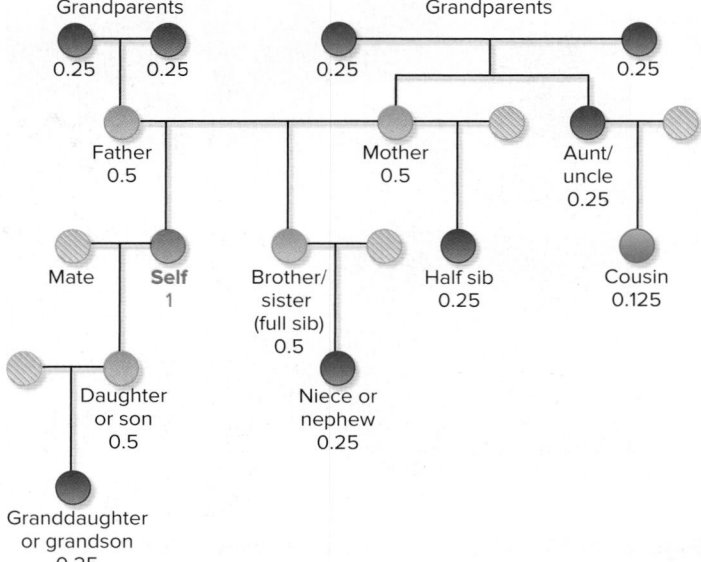

Figure 55.17 Degree of genetic relatedness to self in a diploid organism. Pink hatched circles represent completely unrelated individuals.

the implication of the coefficient of relatedness for the evolution of altruism. An organism not only can pass on its genes by having offspring, but also can pass them on via the reproductive success of siblings, nieces, nephews, and cousins. Thus, an organism has a vested interest in protecting its brothers and sisters, and even their offspring.

The term **inclusive fitness** is used to designate the total number of copies of genes passed on through one's relatives, as well as one's own reproductive output. Hamilton proposed that an altruistic gene is favored by natural selection when

$$rB > C$$

where r is the coefficient of relatedness of donor (the altruist) to the recipient, B is the benefit received by the recipient of the altruism, and C is the cost incurred by the donor. This relationship is known as **Hamilton's rule**. For example, let's suppose an altruist act caused an altruist to be killed, but saved the lives of its three sisters. If this act prevented the altruist from producing two offspring, but allowed the three sisters to produce two offspring each for a total of six, then $r = 0.5$, $B = 6$, and $C = 2$.

Let's consider a situation involving altruism within a group of insects. Many insect larvae, especially caterpillars, are soft-bodied creatures. They rely on a bad taste or toxin to deter predators and advertise this condition with bright warning colors. For example, noxious *Datana ministra* caterpillars, which feed on oaks and other trees, have bright red and yellow stripes and adopt a specific posture with head and tail ends upturned when threatened (**Figure 55.18**). After a predator kills and eats one of the caterpillars, the bright warning colors help the predator learn to avoid similar individuals in the future.

How are warning colors related to kin selection? Animals with warning colors often aggregate in kin groups because they hatch from the same egg mass. Therefore, the death of one individual is likely to benefit its siblings, which are less likely to be attacked by the same predator in the future, and thus its genes are more likely to be passed on to the next generation. This explains why the genes for bright color and a warning posture are passed on from generation to generation. Let's suppose that the death

of a caterpillar by a predator prevented that caterpillar from eventually producing 100 offspring, but saved the lives of 5 siblings, which were able to produce 100 offspring each. In this case, $r = 0.5$, $B = 500$, and $C = 100$, and the benefit ($0.5 \times 500 = 250$) is greater than the cost (100).

A common example of altruism in social animals occurs when a sentry raises an alarm call in the presence of a predator. This behavior has been observed in Belding's ground squirrels (*Spermophilus beldingi*). The squirrels feed in groups, with certain individuals acting as sentries and watching for predators. As a predator approaches, the sentry typically gives an alarm call, and the group members retreat into their burrows. Similar behavior occurs in prairie dogs (*Cynomys* spp.) (**Figure 55.19**). In drawing attention to itself, the sentry is at a higher risk of being attacked by the predator. However, in many groups, those closest to the sentry are most likely to be offspring or brothers or sisters. Thus, the altruistic act of alarm calling is thought to be favored by kin selection. Supporting this idea is the observation that most alarm calling is done by females, because they are more likely to stay in the colony where they were born and have kin nearby, whereas the males are more apt to disperse far from the colony.

Figure 55.19 Alarm calling, a possible example of kin selection. This prairie dog sentry is emitting an alarm call to warn other individuals, which are often close kin, of the presence of a predator. It is believed that by doing so, the sentry draws attention away from the others but becomes an easier target itself. ©Danita Delimont/Alamy Stock Photo

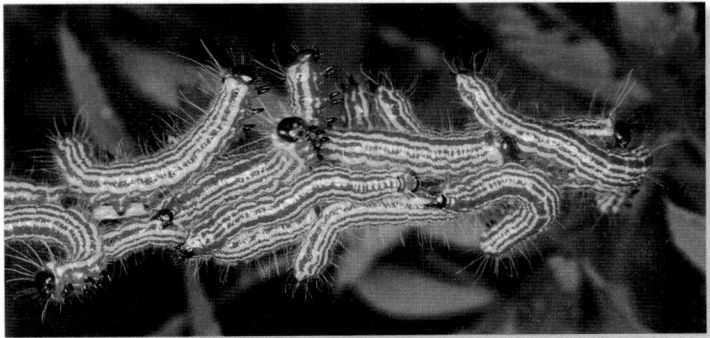

Figure 55.18 Altruistic behavior or kin selection? *Datana ministra* caterpillars exhibit a bright, striped warning pattern to advertise their bad taste to predators. ©Peter Stiling

Concept Check: *Why do D. ministra caterpillars congregate in clusters?*

 Core Concept: Evolution The similarities in DNA between kin promote behaviors whereby some animals act to save the lives of their close relatives, making it more likely to pass those genes to future generations.

therefore associated with uniparental care of young, with males contributing little. Sexual maturity is often delayed in males that fight because of the considerable time it takes to reach a sufficiently large size to compete for females.

Polygyny is influenced by the temporal or spatial distribution of breeding females and by the availability of resources. In cases when all females are sexually receptive within the same narrow period of time, little opportunity exists for a male to garner all the females for himself. When female reproductive receptivity is spread out over weeks or months, however, males have a greater opportunity to mate with more than one female. Where some critical resource is patchily distributed and in short supply, certain males may dominate the resource and breed with more than one visiting female. For example, the major source of nestling death in the lark bunting (*Calamospiza melanocorys*), which lives in North American grasslands, is overheating from too much exposure to the Sun. Prime territories are therefore those with abundant shade, and some males with shaded territories attract two females, even though the second female can expect no help from the male in the process of rearing young. Males in some exposed territories remain bachelors for the season. From the dominant male's point of view, polygyny is advantageous; from the female's point of view, there may be costs. Although by choosing dominant males, a female may be gaining access to good resources, she will have to share these resources with other females.

Sometimes males defend a group of females without commanding a resource-based territory. This pattern is more common when females naturally congregate in groups or herds, perhaps to avoid predation, as with horses, zebras, and some deer, and where space is limited, as with southern elephant seals. Usually the largest and strongest males command most of the matings, but being a dominant male is usually so exhausting that males may only manage to remain the strongest male for a year or two.

Polygynous mating can occur where neither resources nor groups of females are defended. In some instances, particularly in birds and mammals, males display in designated communal courting areas called **leks** (**Figure 55.21**). Females come to these areas specifically to find a mate, and they choose a prospective mate after the males have performed elaborate displays. Most females seek to mate with the best male, so a few of the flashiest males perform the vast majority of the matings. At a lek of the white-bearded manakin (*Manacus manacus*) of South America, one male accounted for 75% of the 438 matings even though there were as many as 10 males. A second male mated 56 times (13% of matings), but six others mated only a total of 10 times.

In Polyandrous Mating Systems, One Female Mates with Many Males

Polyandry (Greek, meaning many males), in which one female mates with several males, is rarer than polygyny. Nevertheless, it occurs in many species of mammals, birds, reptiles, and insects. In the Arctic tundra, the summer season is short but very productive, providing a bonanza of insect food for 2 months. The productivity of the breeding grounds of the spotted sandpiper (*Actitis macularia*) is so high

Figure 55.21   Male birds at a lek. Black grouse (*Tetrao tetrix*) congregate at a moorland lek in Scotland in April. Females visit the leks, and males display to them. ©Chris Knights/ardea.com

that the female becomes rather like an egg factory, laying up to five clutches of four eggs each in 40 days. Her reproductive success is limited not by food but by the number of males she can find to incubate the eggs, and females compete for males, defending territories where the males sit.

Polyandry is also seen in some species where egg predation is high, and males are needed to guard the nests. For example, in the pipefish (*Syngnathus typhle*), males have brood pouches that provide eggs with safety and a supply of oxygen- and nutrient-rich water. Females produce enough eggs to fill the brood pouches of two males and may mate with more than one male.

Mating Systems Tend to Differ in the Degree of Sexual Dimorphism

Sexual dimorphism is a pronounced difference in the morphologies of the two sexes within a species. Although males and females differ in all mating systems, the degree to which they differ tends to vary. Though exceptions occur, species that follow a monogamous mating system tend to be similar in body size and structure (**Figure 55.22a**). By comparison, sexual dimorphism is often dramatic in polygamous mating systems. In polygyny, males usually develop a much larger body size to boost success in competition over mates (**Figure 55.22b**). By comparison, in polyandry, the females are typically the larger of the sexes (see **Figure 55.22c**).

(a) Monogamous species

(b) Polygynous species

(c) Polyandrous species

Figure 55.22 Sexual dimorphism in body size and mating system. (a) In monogamous species, such as these Manchurian cranes, *Grus japonensis*, males and females do not exhibit pronounced sexual dimorphism and appear very similar. **(b)** In polygynous species, such as elk, *Cervus canadensis*, males are bigger than females, and male elk have large horns with which they engage in combat over females. **(c)** In polyandrous species, females are usually bigger, as is the case for these golden silk spiders, *Nephila clavipes*. a: ©Masahiro Iijima/ardea.com; b: ©Wildlife GmbH/Alamy Stock Photo; c: ©Millard H. Sharp/Science Source

 Core Skill: Modeling The goal of this modeling challenge is to draw a set of bar graphs illustrating the relative body sizes of males and females in different mating systems: monogamy, polygyny, and polyandry. You should be able to explain your graphical model.

Modeling Challenge: Draw a bar graph with three sets of two bars each to illustrate what you think are the relative body-size ratios of males:females in monogamous, polygynous, and polyandrous species, and explain your graph. Scale the *y*-axis from 0 to 2.0, with 1.0 representing equal body sizes for the two sexes.

Summary of Key Concepts

55.1 The Influence of Genetics and Learning on Behavior

- Behavior is usually due to the interaction of an organism's genes and the environment.

- Genetically programmed behaviors are termed innate and often involve a sign stimulus that initiates a fixed action pattern (FAP) (Figures 55.1, 55.2).

- Organisms can often make modifications to their behavior based on previous experience, a process called learning. Some forms of learning include habituation, classical conditioning, operant conditioning, and cognitive learning (Figures 55.3, 55.4).

- Much behavior is a mixture of innate and learned behaviors. A good example of this occurs in a process called imprinting, in which animals develop strong attachments that influence subsequent behavior (Figures 55.5, 55.6).

55.2 Local Movement and Long-Range Migration

- The simplest forms of local movement involve kinesis, taxis, and memory (Figure 55.7).

- Many animals undergo long-range seasonal movement called migration in order to feed or breed. They do this using three mechanisms: piloting (the ability to move from one landmark to the next), orientation (the ability to follow a compass bearing), and navigation (the ability to set, follow, and adjust a compass bearing) (Figures 55.8, 55.9).

55.3 Foraging Behavior and Defense of Territory

- Animals use complex behavior in food gathering or foraging. Optimality theory views foraging behavior as a compromise between the costs and benefits involved. The theory of optimal foraging assumes that animals modify their behavior to keep the ratio of their energy uptake to energy expenditure high. The risk of predation has an influence on foraging behavior (Figures 55.10, 55.11).

- The size of a territory, a fixed area in which an individual or group excludes other members of its own species, tends to be optimized according to the costs and benefits involved (Figure 55.12).

55.4 Communication

- Communication is a form of behavior. The use of different forms of communication between organisms depends on the environment in which they live.

- Chemical communication often involves marking territories; auditory and visual forms of communication are often used to attract mates. A fascinating form of tactile communication involves the dance of the honeybee (Figures 55.13, 55.14).

distribution further and talk in terms of **population density**—the number of organisms of a given species in a given unit area or volume. Population growth affects population density, and knowledge of both can help in making decisions about the management of species. How long will it take for a population of an endangered species to recover to a healthy level if we protect it from its most serious threats? For example, how quickly will the black-footed ferret populations increase in Wyoming? A knowledge of population growth rates and population densities would allow us to predict future ferret population sizes.

In this section, we will examine techniques that are used to measure population sizes and densities and other characteristics of populations within their habitats. We will also discuss the different reproductive strategies organisms use and see how ecologists assign individuals to different groups called age classes.

Ecologists Use Many Different Methods to Quantify Population Size and Density

The simplest method for measuring population size is to visually count the number of organisms in a given area. We can reasonably do this only if the area is small and the organisms are relatively large. For example, we can readily determine the number of gumbo limbo trees (*Bursera simaruba*) on a small island in the Florida Keys. Normally, however, population ecologists calculate the density of plants or animals in a small area and use this figure to estimate the total abundance over a larger area.

For plants, algae, or other sessile organisms such as intertidal animals, it is fairly easy to count numbers of individuals per square meter or, for larger organisms such as trees, numbers per hectare (an area of land equivalent to 2.471 acres). However, many plant individuals are clonal; that is, they grow in patches of genetically identical individuals. Rather than counting individuals, ecologists can also use the amount of ground covered by plants as an estimate of vegetation density.

Quadrats Can Be Used to Quantify Population Densities of Plants and Sessile Species Plant ecologists use a sampling device called a **quadrat**, a square frame that often, but not always, measures 50×50 cm and encloses an area of 0.25 m^2 (**Figure 56.1a**). The ecologists count the numbers of plants of a given species inside the quadrat to obtain a density estimate per square meter. For example, if you counted densities of 20, 35, 30, and 15 plants in four quadrats, you could reliably say that the density of this species was 25 individuals per 0.25 m^2, or 100/m^2. For larger plants, such as trees, a quadrat would be ineffective. To count such organisms, many ecologists perform a **line transect**, in which a long piece of string is stretched out and any tree along its length is counted. For example, to count tree species across a large area, we could lay out a 100-m line transect and count all the trees within 1 m on either side of the transect. In effect, this transect is little more than a long, thin quadrat encompassing 200 m^2. By performing five such transects, we could obtain estimates of tree density per 1,000 m^2 and then extrapolate that to a number per hectare or per island.

Traps Are Used to Study More Mobile Species Several different sampling methods exist for quantifying the population density of animals, which are more mobile than plants. Suction traps, like giant aerial vacuum cleaners, can suck flying insects from the sky. Pitfall traps set into the ground can catch species such as spiders, lizards, or beetles wandering over the surface (**Figure 56.1b**). Sweep nets can be passed over vegetation to dislodge and capture the insects feeding there. Mist nets—very fine netting spread between trees—can entangle flying birds and bats (**Figure 56.1c**). Baited snap traps, such as mouse traps, or live traps can snare terrestrial animals (**Figure 56.1d**). Population density can thus be estimated as the number of animals caught per trap or per unit area where a given number of traps are set, for example, 10 traps per 100 m^2 of habitat.

The Mark-Recapture Technique Can Be Used to Estimate Population Sizes Sometimes population biologists capture animals and then tag and release them (**Figure 56.2**). The rationale behind

(a) Quadrat **(b) Pitfall trap** **(c) Mist net** **(d) Live trap**

Figure 56.1 Sampling techniques. (a) Quadrats are frequently used to count the number of plants per unit area. **(b)** Pitfall traps set into the ground catch wandering species such as beetles and spiders. **(c)** Mist nets consist of very fine mesh to entangle birds or bats. **(d)** Baited live traps catch terrestrial animals, including this lion tamarin, *Leontopithecus rosalia*, in Brazil. a: ©Paul Glendell/Alamy Stock Photo; b: ©Nigel Cattlin/Science Source; c: Source: U.S. Fish & Wildlife Service/Donna Dewhurs; d: ©Jami Tarris/Corbis/Getty Images

Figure 56.2 **The mark-recapture technique for estimating population size.** A leg tag identifies this Red Knot (*Calidiris canutus*). Recapture, or visual relocation, of such marked animals permits estimates of population size. Source: U.S. Fish & Wildlife Service/Greg Breese

the **mark-recapture technique** is that after the tagged animals are released, they mix freely with unmarked individuals and within a short time are randomly mixed within the population. The population is resampled, and the numbers of marked and unmarked individuals are recorded. We assume that the ratio of marked to unmarked individuals in the second sample is the same as the ratio of marked individuals in the first sample to the total population size, that is:

$$\frac{\text{Number of individuals marked in first catch}}{\text{Total population size, } N} = \frac{\text{Number of marked recaptures in second catch}}{\text{Total number of second catch}}$$

Let's say we catch 50 largemouth bass in a lake and mark them with colored fin tags. A week later, we return to the lake and catch 40 fish and 5 of them were previously tagged fish. If we assume that no immigration or emigration has occurred, which is quite likely in a closed system like a lake, and that there have been no births or deaths of fish, then the total population size is given by rearranging the equation:

$$\text{Total population size, } N = \frac{\begin{array}{c}\text{Number of marked individuals in first catch}\\ \times \text{ Total number of second catch}\end{array}}{\begin{array}{c}\text{Number of marked recaptures}\\ \text{in second catch}\end{array}}$$

Using the data for the bass, we have

$$N = \frac{50 \times 40}{5} = \frac{2{,}000}{5} = 400$$

From this calculation, we estimate that the lake has a total population size of 400 largemouth bass. This information could be useful for game and fish personnel who wish to know the total size of a fish population in order to set catch limits.

However, the mark-recapture technique can have drawbacks. Some animals that have been marked may learn to avoid the traps.

Recapture rates will then be low, resulting in an overestimate of population size. Imagine that instead of 5 tagged fish out of 40 recaptured fish, we get only 2 tagged fish. Now our population size estimate is 2,000/2 = 1,000, a dramatic increase in our population size estimate. On the other hand, some animals can become "trap-happy," particularly if the traps are baited with food. This effect would result in an underestimate of the population size.

Because of the limitations of the mark-recapture technique, ecologists also use other methods to estimate population density. For some larger terrestrial or marine species, captured animals can be fitted with radio collars and followed remotely, using an antennal tracking device. Their home ranges can be determined and population estimates developed based on the area of available habitat. Unmanned aircraft systems (UAS), or drones, have emerged as a safe, low-cost method to document wildlife abundance and have been used to provide animal counts in relatively inaccessible places, including counts of walruses in rough water areas and Steller sea lions in the outer Aleutian Islands, as well as flamingoes, orangutans, and rhinoceroses. For many species with valuable pelts, ecologists can track population densities through time by examining pelt records taken from trading stations. They can also estimate relative population density by examining catch per unit effort, which is especially valuable in commercial fisheries. Ecologists can't easily expect to count the number of fishes in an area of ocean, but can count the number caught, say, per 100 hours of trawling. For frogs or birds, they can count chorusing or singing individuals.

👁 Core Skill: Quantitative Reasoning

BIO TIPS **THE QUESTION** *Suppose we capture and mark 110 Rocky Mountain goats in a population and later recapture 100 goats, 20 of which have ear tags. What is the estimate of the total population size?*

T OPIC **What topic in biology does this question address?** The topic is estimating population size, specifically, using the mark-recapture technique.

I NFORMATION **What information do you know based on the question and your understanding of the topic?** From the question, you know how many goats were marked, how many were recaptured, and how many of the recaptured goats were also marked. From your understanding of the mark-recapture technique, you may recall the formula used to estimate population size.

P ROBLEM-SOLVING **S** TRATEGY **Make a calculation.** Insert the relevant data into the formula given in the text:

$$\text{Total population size, } N = \frac{\begin{array}{c}\text{Number of marked individuals in first catch}\\ \times \text{ Total number of second catch}\end{array}}{\begin{array}{c}\text{Number of marked recaptures in second}\\ \text{catch}\end{array}}$$

$$N = \frac{110 \times 100}{20} = 550$$

ANSWER *The estimated total population size is 550 goats.*

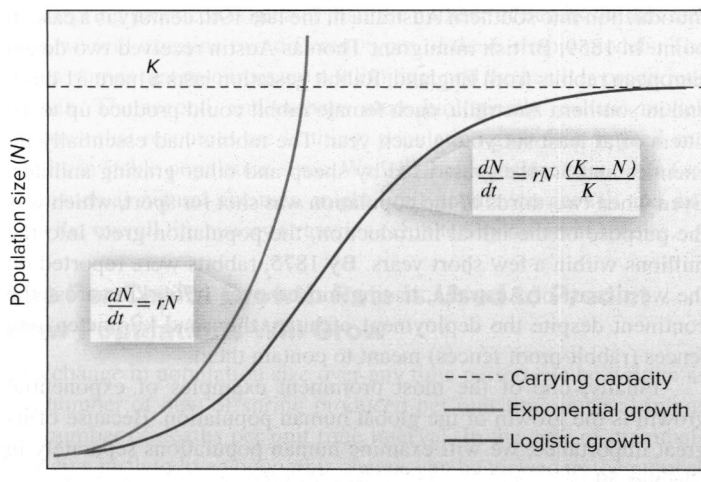

Figure 56.10 Exponential versus logistic growth. Exponential (J-shaped) growth occurs in an environment with unlimited resources, whereas logistic (S-shaped) growth occurs in an environment with limited resources.

 Core Skill: Modeling The goal of this modeling challenge is use different values for *r*, *N*, and *K* to create graphical models based on the logistic equation.

Modeling Challenge: In the growth curve for logistic growth in Figure 56.10 (see the blue line), the value for *r* is greater than 1 in the starting population (at time zero) and the value for *N* is much less than *K*. Based on the logistic equation, draw two growth curves under the following two sets of conditions: $r < 0$, $N \ll K$ and $r > 0$, $N = K$.

---

the value of *r*. With these data, the logistic equation can be used to predict changes in population size as a function of time. As seen in **Figure 56.10**, if $r > 0$ and *N* is much less than *K* for the starting population at time zero, an S-shaped growth curve results. This pattern, in which a population initially grows rapidly but then grows more slowly as *N* approaches *K*, is called **logistic growth**.

Does the logistic growth model provide a better fit to growth patterns of plants and animals in the wild than the exponential model? In some instances, such as laboratory cultures of bacteria and yeasts, the logistic growth model provides a very good fit (**Figure 56.11**). In nature, however, variations in temperature, rainfall, or resources can cause changes in carrying capacity and thus in population size. The uniform conditions of temperature, moisture, and resource levels of the laboratory do not usually exist in the outside world. In addition, time lags may occur between changes in carrying capacity and changes in reproduction. For instance, pregnant females are still likely to give birth even when resources are declining. This kind of time lag can lead to temporary overshoots of population density beyond the carrying capacity. Therefore, relatively few exact fits of the logistic growth model to population growth have been documented in the field. Instead, populations tend to fluctuate around the limits suggested by the logistic model, with frequent overshoots and undershoots.

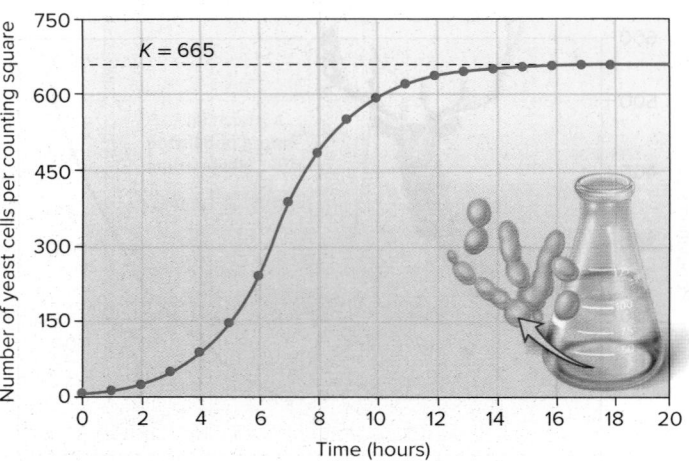

Figure 56.11 Logistic growth of yeast cells in culture. Early tests of the logistic growth curve were validated by growth of yeast cells in laboratory cultures. These populations showed the typical S-shaped growth curve.

Is the logistic model of little value because it fails to describe population growth accurately? Not really. It is a useful starting point for thinking about how populations grow, and it seems intuitively correct. However, the carrying capacity is difficult to identify for most species, and it also varies with time and according to local climate patterns. For these reasons, logistic growth is difficult to measure accurately.

Also, as we will discover, populations are affected by interactions with other species. In Chapter 57, we will examine how predators, parasites, and competitors affect population densities and explore situations in which species interactions commonly limit population growth. As described next, such population limitations are often influenced by a process known as density dependence.

Density-Dependent Factors May Regulate Population Sizes

A **density-dependent factor** is a mortality factor whose influence increases with the density of the population. Parasitism, predation, and competition are some of the many density-dependent factors that may reduce the population densities of living organisms and stabilize them at equilibrium levels. Such factors can be density-dependent when their effect depends on the density of the population; they are responsible for the deaths of relatively more individuals in a population when densities are higher and fewer individuals when densities are lower. For example, many predators develop a visual search image for a particular prey. When a prey is rare, predators tend to ignore it and kill relatively few. When a prey is common, predators key in on it and kill relatively more. In England, for example, predatory shrews kill proportionately more moth pupae in leaf litter when the pupae are common compared with when they are rare. Density-dependent mortality may also occur as population densities increase and competition for scarce resources increases, reducing offspring production or survival. Parasitism may also act in a density-dependent manner. Parasites are able to pass from host to host more easily as the host's population density increases.

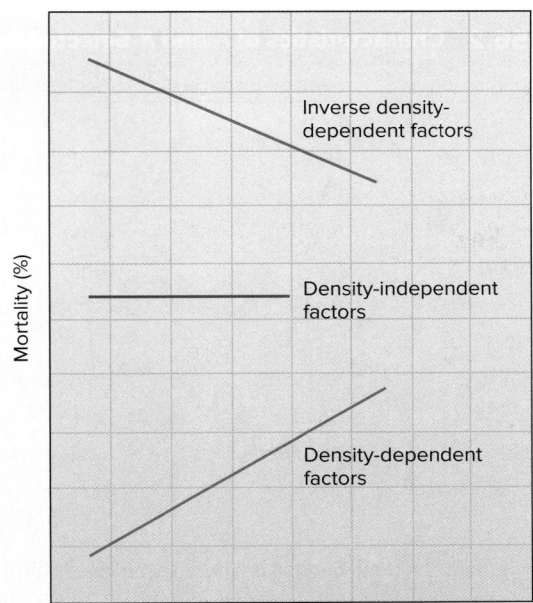

Figure 56.12 **Three ways that factors affect mortality in response to changes in population density.** For a density-dependent factor, mortality increases with population density; for a density-independent factor, mortality remains unchanged. For an inverse density-dependent factor, mortality decreases as a population increases in size.

Concept Check: *Which types of factors tend to stabilize populations at equilibrium levels?*

Density dependence can be evaluated by plotting mortality, expressed as a percentage, as a function of population density (**Figure 56.12**). If mortality increases with density, a positive slope is observed. The factor tends to have a greater effect on dense populations than on sparse ones and is clearly acting in a density-dependent manner.

A **density-independent factor** is a mortality factor whose influence is not affected by changes in population size or density. When mortality due to such a factor is plotted as a function of density, a flat line results. Physical factors are commonly density-independent, including drought, freezes, floods, and disturbances such as fire. For example, in hard freezes, the same proportion of organisms such as birds or plants are usually killed, no matter how large the population size.

Finally, a mortality factor whose influence decreases with increasing population size is considered an **inverse density-dependent factor**. In this case, a negative slope results when mortality is plotted as a function of density. For example, a territorial predator such as a lion may always kill the same number of wildebeest prey, regardless of wildebeest density. The lion is acting in an inverse density-dependent manner, because it is taking a smaller proportion of the population at higher density.

Determining which factors act in a density-dependent or density-independent fashion has large practical implications. Foresters, game managers, and conservation biologists alike are interested in

maintaining populations. For example, if a specific disease were to act in a density-dependent manner on white-tailed deer, the removal of deer predators by game managers might not result in an increase in deer population size, because proportionately more deer would be killed by disease.

Life History Strategies Incorporate Traits Relating to Survival and Competitive Ability

The population parameters we have discussed—including iteroparity versus semelparity, exponential versus logistic growth, and density-dependent versus density-independent factors—have important implications for how populations grow and for the reproductive success of populations and species. These reproductive strategies can be viewed in the context of a much larger picture of life history strategies, sets of physiological and behavioral features that incorporate not only reproductive traits but also survivorship, length of life, habitat type, and competitive ability, among other characteristics.

When comparing many different species, life history strategies follow a continuum. At the one end are species, termed **r-selected species**, that have a high rate of per capita population growth (r), but poor competitive ability. An example is a dandelion, which produces huge numbers of tiny seeds and therefore has a high value of r (**Figure 56.13a**). Weeds exist in disturbed habitats such as gaps in a forest canopy where trees have blown down, and also in areas disturbed by humans such as agricultural fields or backyard gardens. An r-selected species such as a weed grows quickly and reaches reproductive age early, devoting much energy to producing a large number of seeds that disperse widely. These weed species generally remain small, and individuals do not live long. In the animal world, insects are mostly r-selected species that produce many young and have short life cycles.

At the other end of the continuum are species, termed **K-selected species**, whose populations are relatively stable and often exist at or near the carrying capacity (K), of the environment. An example is an oak tree that exists in a mature forest (**Figure 56.13b**). Oak trees grow slowly and reach reproductive age late, having to devote much energy to growth and maintenance. A K-selected species like a tree grows large and shades out r-selected species like weeds, eventually outcompeting them. Such trees live a long time and produce seeds repeatedly every year when mature. These seeds are bigger than those of r-selected species, but do not disperse widely. Acorns contain a large food reserve that helps them grow, whereas dandelion seeds must rely on whatever nutrients they can gather from the soil where they land. Mammals, such as elephants, that grow slowly, have few young, and reach large sizes are typical of K-selected animal species. **Table 56.2** compares the general characteristics of r- and K-selected species.

In a human-dominated world, almost every life history feature of a K-selected species sets it at risk of extinction. First, K-selected species tend to be larger, so they need more habitat in which to live. For example, Florida panthers need huge tracts of land to establish their territories and hunt for deer (look ahead to Figure 60.10c). K-selected species tend to have fewer offspring, so their populations cannot recover as fast from disturbances such as fire or overhunting. California condors, for example, produce only a single chick

Table 57.2	Comparison of Feeding Characters of Sympatric and Allopatric Species				
		Measurement (mm) when		Ratio* when	
Animal (character)	Species	Sympatric	Allopatric	Sympatric	Allopatric
Weasels (skull)	Mustela erminea	50.4	46.0	1.28	1.07
	Mustela nivalis	39.3	42.9		
Mice (skull)	Apodemus flavicollis	27.0	26.7	1.09	1.04
	Apodemus sylvaticus	24.8	25.6		
Nuthatches (beak)	Sitta tephronota	29.0	25.5	1.23	1.02
	Sitta neumayer	23.5	26.0		
Galápagos finches (beak)	Geospiza fortis	12.0	10.5	1.43	1.13
	Geospiza fuliginosa	8.4	9.3		
Average ratio				1.26	1.06

*Ratio of larger to smaller character

finches Charles Darwin discovered on the Galápagos Islands (refer back to Table 22.1). When two species, *Geospiza fortis* and *Geospiza fuliginosa*, are sympatric, their beak sizes (bill depths) are different: *G. fortis* has a larger bill depth, which enables it to feed on bigger seeds, whereas *G. fuliginosa* has a smaller bill depth, which enables it to crack small seeds more efficiently. However, when these species are allopatric, that is, existing on different islands, their bills are more similar in depth. Researchers studying *Geospiza* concluded that the bill depth differences evolved in ways that minimized competition.

How great must differences between feeding characters be in order to permit coexistence? Hutchinson noted that the ratio between sizes of feeding characters when species were sympatric (and thus competed) averaged about 1.3 (**Table 57.2**). In contrast, the ratio between sizes of feeding characters when species were allopatric (and did not compete) was closer to 1.0. Hutchinson proposed that the

value of 1.3, a roughly 30% difference, could be used as an indication of the amount of difference necessary to permit two species to coexist.

The Realized Niche Is Smaller Than the Fundamental Niche Due to Competition

Most species perform best over a physiologically optimal range of conditions called the **fundamental niche**. However, if some part of the fundamental niche is occupied by competitors, the range of an organism may be limited to an area known as the **realized niche**, where the competitor is absent. Researchers have established that one of the best methods of determining an organism's fundamental niche is to temporarily remove one of the competing species and examine the effect on the other species. A now-classic example of this method involved a study of the interactions between two species of barnacles conducted on the west coast of Scotland, described next.

Core Skill: Process of Science

Feature Investigation | Connell's Experiments with Barnacle Species Revealed Each Species' Fundamental and Realized Niches

Chthamalus stellatus and *Semibalanus balanoides* (formerly known as *Balanus balanoides*) are two species of barnacles that dominate the Scottish coastline. Each organism's realized niche on the intertidal zone is well defined. *Chthamalus* occurs in the upper intertidal zone, and *Semibalanus* is restricted to the lower intertidal zone. Joseph Connell sought to determine if the range of *Chthamalus* adults would be expanded in the absence of competition from *Semibalanus* (**Figure 57.7**).

To do this, Connell obtained rocks from high on the rock face, just below the high-tide level, where only *Chthamalus* grew. These rocks already contained young and mature *Chthamalus*. He then moved the rocks into the *Semibalanus* zone, fastened them down with screws, and allowed *Semibalanus* to also colonize them. Once *Semibalanus* had colonized these rocks, he took the rocks out, removed

all the *Semibalanus* organisms from one side of the rocks with a needle, and then returned the rocks to the lower intertidal zone, screwing them down once again. As seen in the data, the mortality of *Chthamalus* on rock halves with *Semibalanus* was fairly high. On the *Semibalanus*-free halves, however, *Chthamalus* survived well.

In other studies, Connell also monitored survival of natural patches of both barnacle species where both occurred on the intertidal zone at the upper margin of the *Semibalanus* distribution. In a period of unusually low tides and warm weather, when no water reached any barnacles for several days, desiccation became a real threat to both species' survival. During this time, young *Semibalanus* suffered a 92% mortality rate, and older individuals, a 51% mortality rate. At the same time, young *Chthamalus* experienced a 62% mortality rate compared with a rate of only 2% for more-resistant older individuals. Clearly, *Semibalanus* is not

Figure 57.7 **Connell's experimental manipulation of species indicated the presence of competition.**

HYPOTHESIS *Chthamalus stellatus* is being competitively excluded from the lower intertidal zone by the species *Semibalanus balanoides*.

STARTING LOCATION The intertidal zone of the rocky shores of the Scottish coast, where the two species of barnacles occur.

Experimental level

1 Transfer rocks containing young and mature *Chthamalus* from the upper intertidal zone to the lower intertidal zone, and fasten them down in the new location with screws.

2 Allow *Semibalanus* to colonize the rocks.

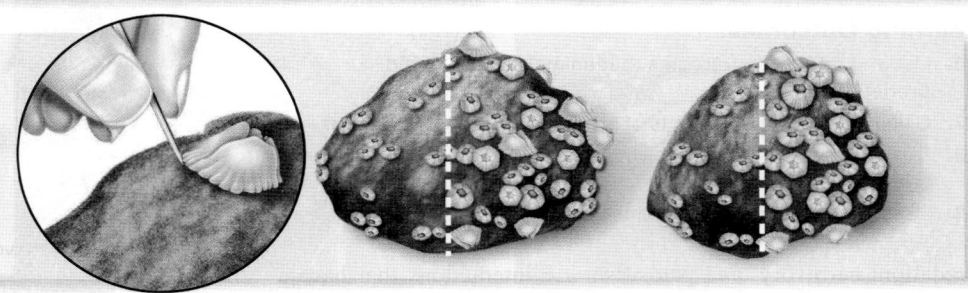

3 After the colonization period is over, remove *Semibalanus* from half of each rock with a needle (leaving the other half undisturbed). Return the rocks to the lower intertidal zone, and fasten them down once again.

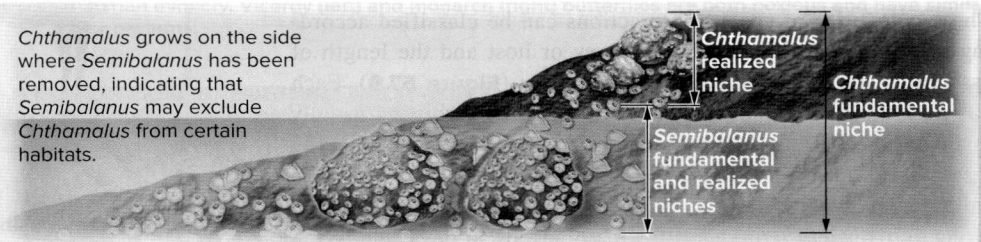

4 Monitor the survival of *Chthamalus* on both sides of the rocks.

Chthamalus grows on the side where *Semibalanus* has been removed, indicating that *Semibalanus* may exclude *Chthamalus* from certain habitats.

5 **THE DATA**

Rock No.	Side of rock	% *Chthamalus* mortality over 1 year	
		Young barnacles	**Mature barnacles**
13b	*Semibalanus* removed	35	0
	Semibalanus not removed	90	31
12a	*Semibalanus* removed	44	37
	Semibalanus not removed	95	71
14a	*Semibalanus* removed	40	36
	Semibalanus not removed	86	75

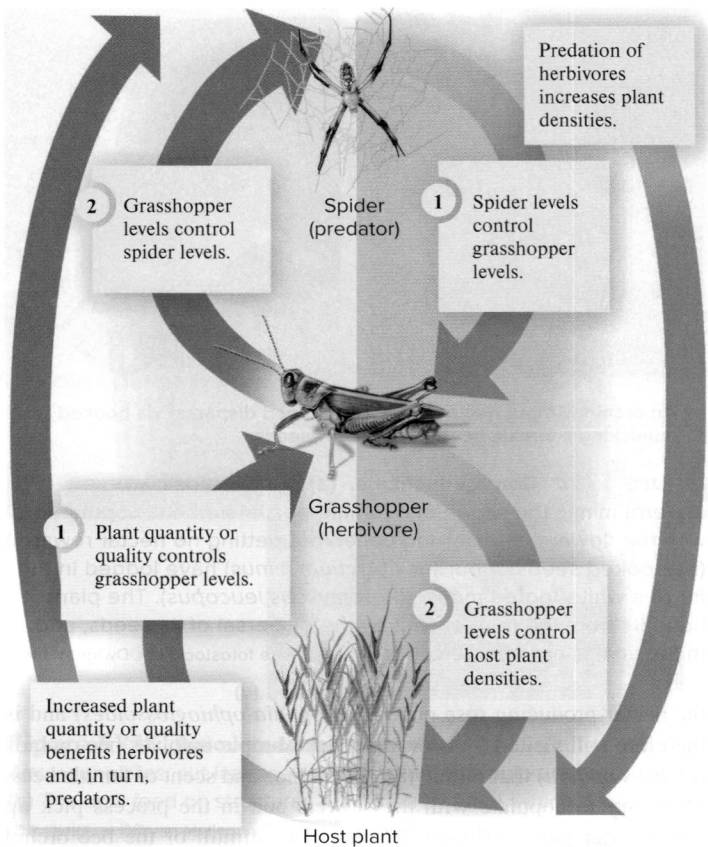

(a) Bottom-up control   (b) Top-down control

Figure 57.19 Bottom-up control versus top-down control.
(a) Bottom-up control proposes that host plant quantity or quality limits the density of herbivores, such as grasshoppers, which, in turn, sets limits on the abundance of predators, such as spiders. **(b)** Top-down control proposes that predators limit the number of herbivores, which, in turn, increases host plant density.

Concept Check: *You apply fertilizer to a bush, and this increases spider density on the bush. What type of control is occurring?*

of herbivore populations and the populations of predators that feed on them. In the example of **Figure 57.19a**, plant quantity or quality limits the density of herbivores, such as grasshoppers, which, in turn, sets limits on the abundance of predators, such as spiders. Other ecologists stress the importance of top-down factors (**Figure 57.19b**). In this case, the spiders play a major role in determining the size of grasshopper populations, which control the size of the plant population.

Current thinking is that both bottom-up and top-down control are important in affecting population sizes. Their relative importance depends on the environment and the types of species interactions that are involved. In this section, we will briefly discuss some of the evidence for bottom-up and top-down control.

Bottom-Up Control Suggests That Food Limitation Influences Population Densities

At least two lines of evidence suggest that bottom-up control is important in limiting population sizes. First, as discussed in Chapter 58, not all of the energy in food resources can be used by the consumer. For example,

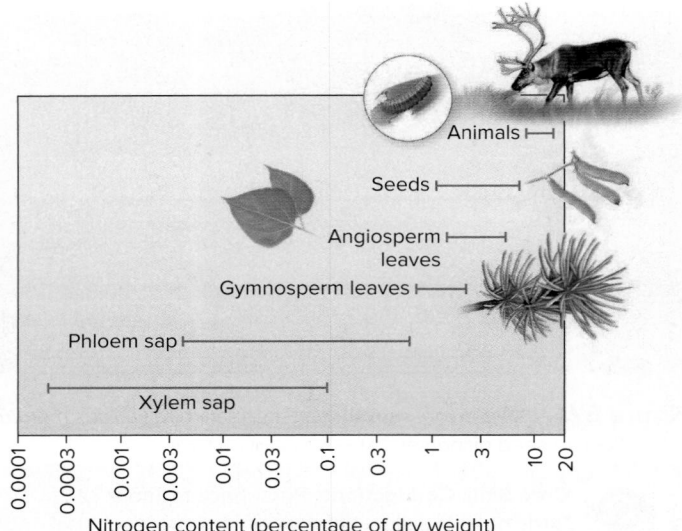

Figure 57.20 Nitrogen content of plants and animals.

when a herbivore eats plant material, some of the energy is lost in the form of heat. This phenomenon, based on the thermodynamic properties of energy transfer, suggests that the quantity and quality of plants may be limiting for the population sizes of all other species that rely on them.

Second, much evidence supports the **nitrogen-limitation hypothesis** that organisms select food in terms of the nitrogen content of the tissue. This is largely due to the different proportions of nitrogen in plants and animals (**Figure 57.20**). Animal tissue generally contains about 10 times as much nitrogen as plant tissue. For this reason, herbivores favor high-nitrogen plants. The addition of nitrogen-containing fertilizer has repeatedly been shown to benefit herbivores. Nearly 60% of 186 studies investigating the effects of fertilization on herbivores reported that increasing a plant's tissue nitrogen concentration through fertilization had strong positive effects on herbivore population sizes, survivorship, growth, and fecundity. Taken together, both lines of evidence indicate that plant densities influence herbivore densities, which in turn influence the densities of carnivores that feed on herbivores, and the carnivores that feed on other animals.

Top-Down Control Suggests That Natural Enemies Influence Population Densities

Top-down models suggest that predators control populations of their prey (ultimately, herbivores) and that these herbivores control plant populations. Supporting evidence comes from studies of predator removal and addition. Wolves, *Canus lupus*, are being reintroduced into many areas of the United States, and their populations are growing. In a 2005 study, Mark Hebblewhite and colleagues observed colonization of certain areas in Banff National Park in Canada by wolves and compared these areas to those closer to human settlements, which wolves avoid. The wolves reduced the density of elk, *Cervus elaphus*, which in turn promoted the growth of two major elk food plants: aspen, *Populus tremuloides*, and willow, *Salix* spp. (**Figure 57.21a**). Increased plant availability also increased the abundance of songbirds, especially obligate willow specialists, such as the American redstart, *Setophaga ruticilla* (**Figure 57.21b–e**). Beaver abundance also increased due to a greater availability of willow.

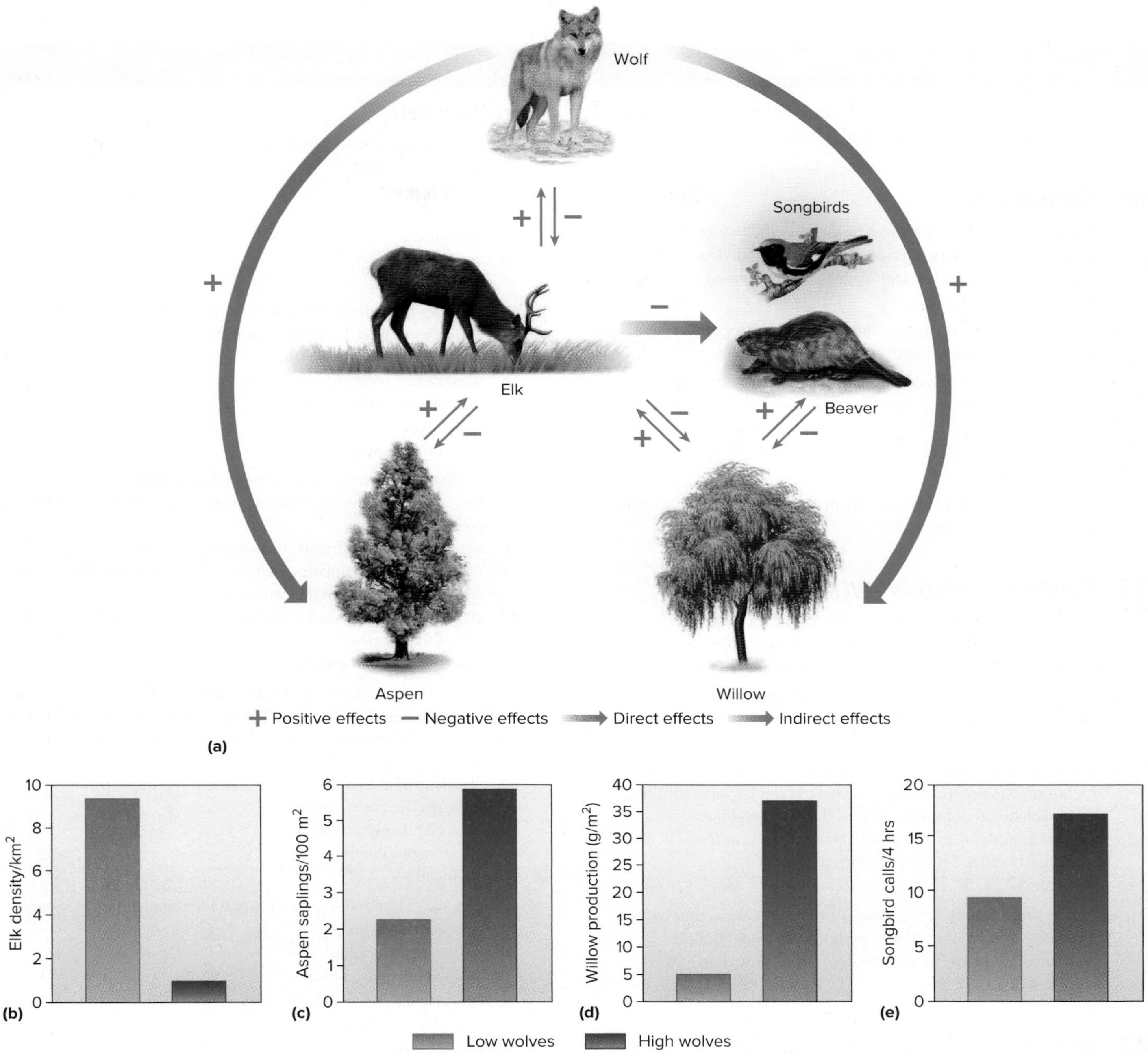

+ Positive effects   − Negative effects   ⟶ Direct effects   ⟶ Indirect effects

(a)

Figure 57.21 **Studies on wolf addition provide support for the top-down model.** **(a)** The simplified trophic interactions of wolves, elk, plants, and other organisms in Banff National Park, Canada. Increased wolf abundance caused **(b)** decreased elk abundance, **(c)** increased abundance of aspen trees and **(d)** willow trees, and **(e)** increased songbird abundance.

Core Skill: Modeling The goal of this modeling challenge is to use your understanding of top-down control to construct a simple bar graph that predicts the relative abundances of plants and herbivores under three different conditions: plants alone, plant plus herbivores, and plants plus herbivores and carnivores that prey on the herbivores.

Modeling Challenge: Let's assume that a group of plants, herbivores, and carnivores that feed on those herbivores, are subject to top-down control. An ecologist studies the relative numbers of plants in three different areas of the same size. In one area, both the herbivores and carnivores have been removed. In a second area, only the carnivores have been removed. In a third area, the plants, herbivores, and carnivores are all present. Draw a series of bar graphs that predict the relative population sizes of the plant and herbivore populations in these three different areas. The y-axis should be labeled "Relative population size," and three pairs of bars, one pair for each of the three areas, should appear along the x-axis. Within each pair of bars, the left bar should indicate the size of the plant population and the right bar should show the size of the herbivore population. Note: The y-axis does not need to have numbers on it; the goal is to predict the relative population sizes, not the actual numbers.

Summary of Key Concepts

- Species interactions can take a variety of forms that differ based on their effect on the species involved (Figure 57.1, Table 57.1).

57.1 Competition

- Competition can be categorized as intraspecific (between individuals of the same species) or interspecific (between individuals of different species), and as exploitation competition or interference competition (Figure 57.2).

- Laboratory and field experiments show that competition occurs frequently in nature (Figure 57.3).

- The competitive exclusion hypothesis states that two species with the same resource requirements cannot occupy the same niche. Resource partitioning and character displacement allow two or more species to coexist (Figures 57.4, 57.5, 57.6, 57.7, Table 57.2).

- The realized niche may be smaller than the fundamental niche due to competition (Figure 57.7).

57.2 Predation, Herbivory, and Parasitism

- Common antipredator strategies include chemical defense and aposematic coloration, camouflage, displays of intimidation, mimicry, and armor and weaponry (Figures 57.8, 57.9).

- Despite these defenses, oscillations in predator-prey cycles indicate that predators can have a large effect on prey densities (Figures 57.10).

- Plants have evolved an array of defenses against herbivores, including chemical defenses, such as secondary metabolites, and mechanical defenses, such as thorns and spines. However, herbivores can sometimes circumvent these defenses and greatly reduce plant population densities (Figures 57.11, 57.12).

- Parasitism is a long-term, usually nonlethal interaction between a parasite and its host. The experimental removal of parasites confirms that parasites can greatly reduce prey densities (Figures 57.13, 57.14).

57.3 Mutualism and Commensalism

- Mutualism is an association between two species that benefits both. In a resource-based mutualism, both species receive a benefit in the form of resources; a defensive mutualism typically involves an animal defending either a plant or herbivore; and a dispersive mutualism involves animals dispersing a plant's pollen or seeds (Figures 57.15, 57.16, 57.17).

- In a commensal relationship, one partner receives a benefit while the other is not affected (Figure 57.18).

57.4 Bottom-Up and Top-Down Control

- Bottom-up control suggests that plant quality or quantity regulates the abundance of all herbivore and predator species; top-down control suggests that the abundance of predators controls herbivore and plant densities (Figures 57.19, 57.20, 57.21).

Assess & Discuss

Test Yourself

1. A species interaction in which one species benefits but the other species is unharmed is called
   a. mutualism.
   b. amensalism.
   c. parasitism.
   d. commensalism.
   e. mimicry.

2. Two species of birds feed on similar types of insects and nest in the same species of tree. This is an example of
   a. intraspecific competition.
   b. interference competition.
   c. exploitation competition.
   d. mutualism.
   e. none of the above.

3. According to the competitive exclusion hypothesis,
   a. two species that use the exact same resources show very little competition.
   b. two species with the same niche cannot coexist.
   c. one species that competes with several different species for resources will be excluded from the community.
   d. all competition between species results in the extinction of at least one of the species.
   e. none of the above is correct.

4. In Lack's study of passerine birds in Britain, different species seem to segregate based on resource factors, such as location of prey items. This differentiation among the niches of passerine birds is known as
   a. competitive exclusion.
   b. intraspecific competition.
   c. character displacement.
   d. resource partitioning.
   e. allelopathy.

5. Divergence in morphology that is a result of competition is termed
   a. competitive exclusion.
   b. resource partitioning.
   c. character displacement.
   d. amensalism.
   e. mutualism.

6. Tapeworms have
   a. low lethality and low duration of interaction.
   b. low lethality and high duration of interaction.
   c. high lethality and low duration of interaction.
   d. high lethality and high duration of interaction.
   e. none of the above.

7. Ticks are regarded as
   a. monophagous endoparasites.
   b. monophagous ectoparasites.
   c. polyphagous endoparasites.
   d. polyphagous ectoparasites.
   d. none of the above.

8. Batesian mimicry differs from Müllerian mimicry in that
   a. in Batesian mimicry, both species possess the chemical defense.
   b. in Batesian mimicry, one species possesses the chemical defense.
   c. in Müllerian mimicry, one species has several different mimics.

d. in Müllerian mimicry, one species has several different chemical defenses.

e. in Batesian mimicry, cryptic coloration is always found.

9. Poppies are protected from herbivores by the
    a. alkaloid nicotine.
    b. alkaloid morphine.
    c. phenolic tannin.
    d. phenolic lignin.
    e. terpenoid caffeine.

10. Parasitic plants that rely solely on their host for nutrients are called
    a. hemiparasites.
    b. fungi.
    c. holoparasites.
    d. monophagous.
    e. polyphagous.

Conceptual Questions

1. Can the removal of ectoparasites from the coat of one primate by another primate (grooming) be viewed as selfish behavior, as discussed in Chapter 55? Why or why not?

2.  **Core Skill: Science and Society** Crop pests cost millions of dollars to control annually. What factors do you think might limit such losses?

Collaborative Questions

1. Explain how the reintroduction of wolves in Yellowstone National Park might be beneficial.

2. Detail several antipredator strategies that animals have evolved.

3. Can you think of examples of mimicry used by predators to catch prey rather than used by prey to avoid being eaten? Look back to Figure 55.13a and the accompanying text discussion.

Communities and Ecosystems: Ecological Organization on Large Scales

58

Mount St. Helens erupting in 1980. Ecologists have been monitoring gradual change in the species composition of the area since the disturbance. ©Gary Braasch/Corbis Historical/Getty Images

The term **ecosystem** was first used in 1935 by British plant ecologist A. G. Tansley to describe the system formed by the interaction between a community of organisms and its physical environment. **Ecosystem ecology** addresses the flow of energy and the production of **biomass**, which is the total mass of living matter in a given area, usually measured in grams or kilograms per square meter. In Section 58.5, we will explore energy flow, the movement of energy through an ecosystem. In examining energy flow, we will consider the complex networks of feeding relationships among species, which are represented by food webs. Finally, we will focus on the measurement of biomass within ecosystems.

A t 8:32 a.m. on May 18, 1980, Mount St. Helens, in the Washington Cascades, erupted. The blast felled trees over a 600-km² area, and the landslide that followed destroyed everything in its path, killing nearly 60 people. For nearly 40 years, ecologists have studied the recovery of plant and animal species in that area and noted how the appearance of some species has facilitated the recovery of others.

The assemblage of populations of different species that live in the same place at the same time is known as a **community**. **Community ecology** explores the factors that influence the number and abundance of species in a community. In this chapter, we will begin by considering patterns of species richness and diversity. We will examine why, on a global scale, the number of species is usually greatest in the tropics and declines toward the poles. Next, we will discuss why the recovery of communities following a disturbance such as a fire or a volcanic eruption tends to occur in a predictable sequence—a process termed succession—which may be determined by the balance between the rates of immigration and extinction.

58.1 Patterns of Species Richness and Species Diversity

Learning Outcomes:

1. Identify the latitudinal gradient of species richness.
2. List and describe three hypotheses for observed patterns of species richness.
3. **CoreSKILL** » Calculate the Shannon diversity index.

Community ecology is concerned with the factors that influence the number of different species in a community, or **species richness**. Globally, the number of species of most taxa varies along a latitudinal gradient, generally increasing from polar to temperate areas and reaching a maximum in the tropics. For example, the species richness of North American birds increases from Arctic Canada to Panama (**Figure 58.1**). A similar pattern exists for mammals, amphibians, reptiles, and plants. Although the latitudinal gradient of species richness is an important pattern, species richness is also influenced by topographical variation. More mountains mean more hilltops, valleys, and differing habitats. Thus, the number of birds is greater in the U.S. mountainous West. Species richness is also reduced by the peninsular effect, in which the number of species decreases as a function of distance from the main body of land.

Many hypotheses for the latitudinal gradient in species richness have been advanced. In this section, we will consider three hypotheses for patterns of species richness. The key factors are evolutionary

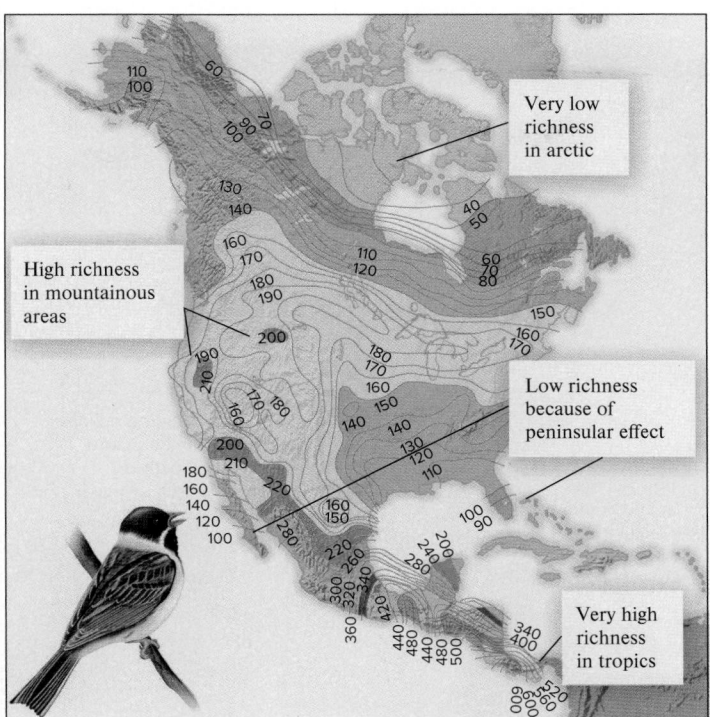

Figure 58.1 **Species richness of birds in North America.** The values indicate the numbers of different species in a given area. Contour lines show equal numbers of bird species, with colors indicating incremental changes. Note the pronounced latitudinal gradient toward the tropics and the high diversity in California, a region of considerable topographical variation and habitat diversity.

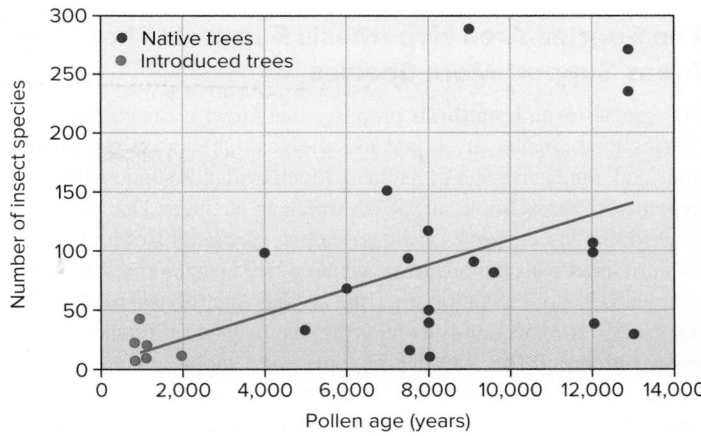

(a) Insect species richness increases on older tree species.

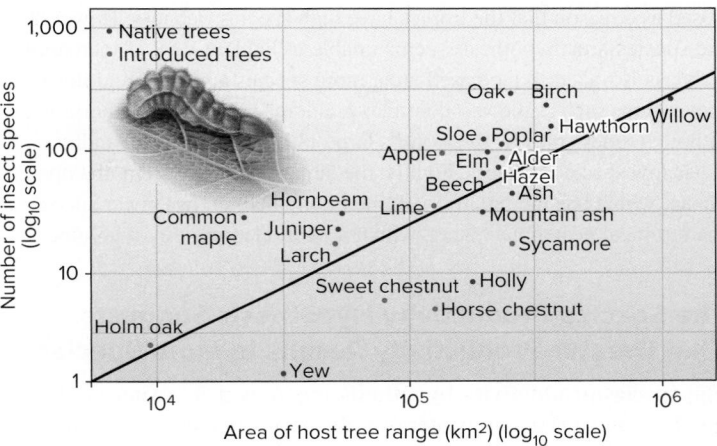

(b) Insect species richness increases on more widely occurring tree species.

Figure 58.2 **Relationship between species richness on British host trees and both evolutionary time and area.** **(a)** Insect species richness is greater on evolutionary older tree species, which supports the species-time hypothesis. **(b)** A positive correlation is also found between insect species richness and the area of the host tree's range, in square kilometers (km²), which supports the species-area hypothesis. Note the log scales in part (b).

time, area, and productivity; each factor can influence species richness to some degree. Although they are discussed separately here, these hypotheses are not mutually exclusive. All three factors can potentially contribute to patterns of species richness.

The Species-Time Hypothesis Suggests That Communities Diversify with Age

Many ecologists argue that communities diversify, or gain species, with time. Tropical communities are usually older than temperate communities, because the species in temperate regions are periodically wiped out by glaciers. The **species-time hypothesis** proposes that temperate regions have less species-rich communities than tropical ones because they are younger. According to this idea, Ice Ages have driven many species extinct in temperate regions, and it takes time for remaining species to evolve and diversify in those regions after the glaciers have retreated. More than half of the families of flowering plants have no temperate representatives.

In support of the species-time hypothesis, British ecologist H. John Birks found a significant correlation between the numbers of species of insects on various British trees and the evolutionary ages of those tree species (**Figure 58.2a**). Many of the tree species in Britain are relatively recent colonists, having appeared following the departure of the glaciers that covered most of the islands after the last Ice Age. Birks used radiocarbon dating of pollen collected from

deep lake sediments to estimate the length of time a tree species had been present in Britain. No tree species had been present for longer than 13,000 years. He then gathered information on numbers of insect species present on trees from lists provided by other experts who had been examining the insect fauna of trees in Britain for many years. The significant relationship between pollen age and the total number of insects indicated that older tree species support more insect species.

However, ecologists recognize drawbacks to the species-time hypothesis. For example, this hypothesis may help explain variations in the species richness of terrestrial organisms, but it has limited applicability to marine organisms. Although we might not expect terrestrial species, particularly plants, to redistribute themselves quickly following a glaciation—especially if there is a physical barrier, like the English Channel, to overcome—there seems to be no reason that marine organisms couldn't relatively easily shift their distribution patterns during glaciations, yet the latitudinal gradient of species richness still exists in marine habitats.

The Species-Area Hypothesis Suggests That Large Areas Support More Species

The **species-area hypothesis** proposes that larger areas contain more species than smaller areas because they can support larger populations and a greater range of habitats. Much evidence supports the area hypothesis. For example, in 1974, American ecologist Donald Strong showed that insect species richness on tree species in Britain was better correlated with the area over which a tree species could be found than with time of habitation since the last Ice Age (**Figure 58.2b**). The points cluster more tightly around the line of best fit. Even relatively newly introduced species, such as apple trees, supported a large number of insect herbivores if they were planted over a wide area. The observation that the number of species tends to increase with increasing area is called the **species-area effect**.

The large, climatically similar area of the tropics has been proposed as a reason that the tropics have high species richness. However, the species-area hypothesis seems unable to explain why, if increased richness is linked to increased area, more species are not found in certain regions such as the vast contiguous landmass of Asia. Furthermore, although tundra may be the world's largest biome in terms of landmass, it has low species richness. Finally, the largest marine system, the open ocean, which has the greatest volume of any habitat, has fewer species than tropical nearshore waters, which have a relatively small volume.

The Species-Productivity Hypothesis Suggests That Greater Productivity Results in More Species

The **species-productivity hypothesis** proposes that greater production by plants results in greater overall species richness. An increase in plant productivity, the total mass of plant material produced over time, leads to an increase in the number of herbivores and hence an increase in the number of predator, parasite, and scavenger species. Productivity itself is influenced by factors such as temperature and rainfall, because many plants grow better where it is warm and wet. For example, in 1987, Canadian biologist David Currie and colleagues showed that the species richness of trees in North America is best predicted by the **evapotranspiration rate**, the rate at which water moves into the atmosphere through the processes of evaporation from the soil and other surfaces and transpiration of plants, which are influenced by the amount of solar energy (**Figure 58.3**).

Once again, however, exceptions are observed. In 1993, American researchers Robert Latham and Robert Ricklefs showed that although patterns of tree species richness in North America support the species-productivity hypothesis, the pattern does not hold for broad comparisons between continents. For example, the temperate forests of eastern Asia support substantially higher numbers of tree species (729) than do climatically similar areas of North America (253) or Europe (124). These three areas have different evolutionary histories and different neighboring areas from which species might have invaded.

Microbial Diversity Can Be Analyzed by DNA Sequencing

An accurate determination of species richness depends on detailed knowledge of which and how many of each species are present. This

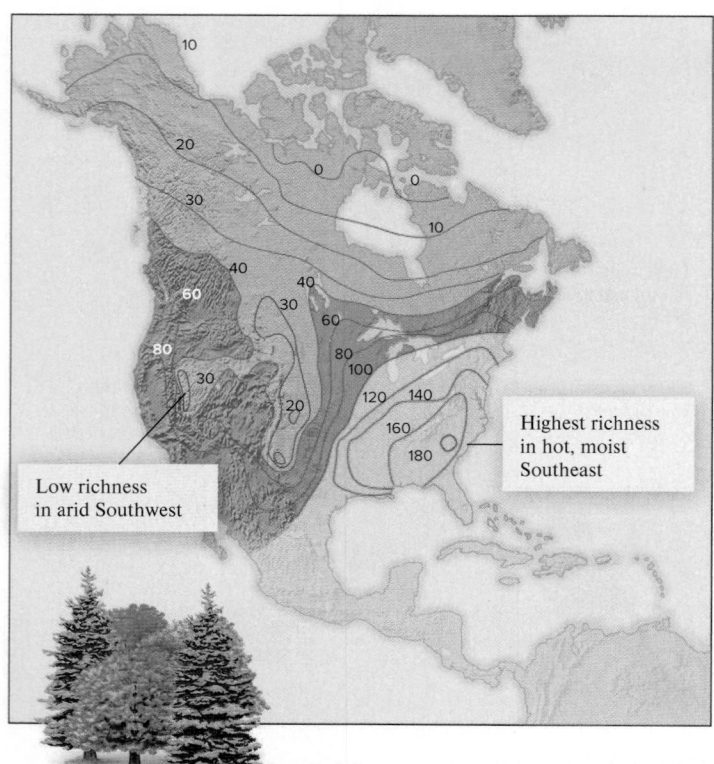

Figure 58.3   Tree species richness in North America. Contour lines show equal numbers of tree species, with colors indicating incremental changes. Tree species richness and evapotranspiration rates are highest in the Southeast.

Concept Check: *Why doesn't the species richness of trees increase in mountainous areas of the West, as is true for birds?*

information is relatively easy to determine for communities of vertebrates and some invertebrates, but it is much more difficult for microbial communities, which includes bacteria, archaea, and many species of protists and fungi. The two main obstacles for identifying microbial species are that they are very small and researchers have been unable to devise methods for growing most of them in the laboratory. These obstacles make it difficult to study the characteristics of most microbes and thereby identify new microbial species. Yet knowledge of microbial communities is of great importance, because microbes carry out vital functions such as nitrogen fixation and decomposition. As described in Chapter 30, the species richness of microbial samples can be analyzed using DNA sequencing methods (refer back to Figure 30.3).

The Shannon Diversity Index Is a Measure of Species Diversity

So far, we have discussed communities in terms of variations in species richness. However, ecologists need to take into account not only the number of species in a community but also their frequency of occurrence, or **relative abundance**. For example, consider two hypothetical communities, A and B, both with two species and 100 total individuals.

	Number of individuals of species 1	Number of individuals of species 2
Community A	99	1
Community B	50	50

Species	Abundance	p_i	$\ln p_i$	$p_i \ln p_i$
1	50	0.5	−0.693	−0.347
2	30	0.3	−1.204	−0.361
3	10	0.1	−2.302	−0.230
4	9	0.09	−2.408	−0.217
5	1	0.01	−4.605	−0.046
Total 5	100	1.00	$\sum p_i \ln p_i$	$= -1.201$

The species richness of community B equals that of community A, because they both contain two species. However, community B is considered more diverse than A because the distribution of individuals between species is more even. You would be much more likely to encounter both species in community B than in community A, where one species dominates. **Species diversity** is a measure of the diversity of an ecological community that incorporates both the number of species and their relative abundance.

To measure the species diversity of a community, ecologists calculate what is known as a diversity index. Although many different indices are available, the most widely used is the **Shannon diversity index (H_S)**, which is calculated using the formula

$$H_S = -\sum p_i \ln p_i$$

where p_i is the proportion of individuals belonging to species i in a community, ln is the natural logarithm, and Σ indicates summation. For example, for a species of which there are 50 individuals out of a total of 100 in the community, p_i is 50/100, or 0.5. The natural log of 0.5 is −0.693. For this species, $p_i \ln p_i$ is then 0.5(−0.693) = −0.347. For a hypothetical community with 5 species and 100 total individuals, the Shannon diversity index is calculated as follows:

Remember that, in the formula, the negative sign in front of the summation changes the summed value to positive, so the index calculated in the above table becomes 1.201, not −1.201.

Values of the Shannon diversity index for real communities often fall between 1.5 and 3.5, and the higher the value, the greater the diversity. **Table 58.1** calculates the diversity of two bird communities in Indonesia with similar species richness but differing species abundance. The bird communities were surveyed in a pristine unlogged forest and in a selectively logged lowland forest. To document diversity, British biologist Stuart Marsden established census stations in the two forests and recorded the type and number of all bird species for a number of 10-minute periods. A greater number of individual birds was seen in the logged areas (2,345) than in the unlogged ones (1,824), but a high proportion of the individuals in the logged areas (0.386) belonged to just one species, *Nectarinia jugularis*. Calculation of the Shannon diversity index showed a

Table 58.1	**Shannon Diversity Index for Bird Species on Logged and Unlogged Sites in Indonesia**					
	Unlogged			Logged		
Species	**N**	**p_i**	**$p_i \ln p_i$**	**N**	**p_i**	**$p_i \ln p_i$**
Nectarinia jugularis, olive-backed sunbird	410	0.225	−0.336	910	0.386	−0.367
Ducula bicolor, pied imperial pigeon	230	0.126	−0.261	220	0.093	−0.221
Philemon subcorniculatus, grey-necked friarbird	210	0.115	−0.249	240	0.102	−0.233
Nectarinia aspasia, black sunbird	190	0.104	−0.235	120	0.051	−0.152
Dicaeum vulneratum, ashy flowerpecker	185	0.101	−0.232	280	0.119	−0.253
Ducula perspicillata, white-eyed imperial pigeon	170	0.093	−0.221	180	0.076	−0.196
Phylloscopus borealis, arctic warbler	160	0.088	−0.214	140	0.059	−0.167
Eos bornea, red lory	88	0.048	−0.146	73	0.031	−0.108
Ixos affinis, golden bulbul	76	0.042	−0.133	31	0.013	−0.056
Geoffroyus geoffroyi, red-cheeked parrot	44	0.024	−0.089	54	0.023	−0.087
Rhyticeros plicatus, Papuan hornbill	24	0.013	−0.056	27	0.011	−0.050
Cacatua moluccensis, Moluccan cockatoo	12	0.007	−0.035	1	0.001	−0.007
Tanygnathus megalorynchos, great-billed parrot	9	0.005	−0.026	11	0.005	−0.026
Eclectus roratus, electus parrot	7	0.004	−0.022	0	0	0
Macropygia amboinensis, brown cuckoo-dove	6	0.003	−0.017	7	0.003	−0.017
Cacomantis sepulcralis, ruby-breasted cuckoo	3	0.002	−0.012	0	0	0
Trichoglossus haematodus, rainbow lorikeet	0	0	0	64	0.027	−0.097
Total	**1,824**	**1.0**		**2,345**	**1.0**	
Shannon diversity index			**2.284**			**2.037**

higher diversity of birds in the unlogged area, 2.284 versus 2.037, which is a sizable difference, considering the logarithmic nature of the index.

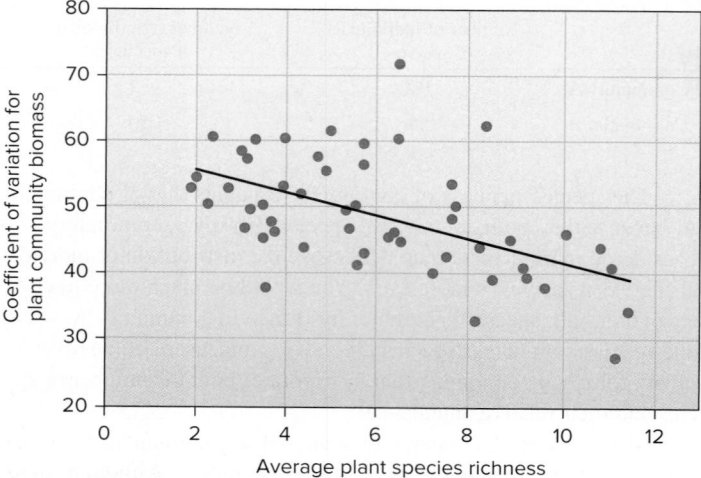

Figure 58.4 **Biomass variation and species richness.** Tilman's 11-year study of grassland plots in Minnesota revealed that year-to-year variability in community biomass was lower in species-rich plots. Each dot represents an individual plot. Only the plots from one field are graphed.

58.2 Species Richness and Community Stability

Learning Outcome:

1. Describe the diversity-stability hypothesis, and explain the evidence supporting it.

A community is often seen as stable when little to no change can be detected in the number of species and their abundances over a given time period. Such a community may also be said to be in equilibrium. Community stability is an important consideration to ecologists. A decrease in the stability of a community over time may alert ecologists to a possible problem. In this section, we will consider the relationship between species richness and community stability, using evidence from a field experiment.

The Diversity-Stability Hypothesis States That Species-Rich Communities Are More Stable Than Those with Fewer Species

The link between species richness and stability was first explicitly proposed by British ecologist Charles Elton in the 1950s. He suggested that a disturbance in a species-rich community would be cushioned by large numbers of interacting species and would not produce as drastic an effect as would a disturbance in a species-poor community. For example, an introduced predator or parasite would be more likely to cause extinctions in a species-poor community compared to a more species-rich community, where its effects would be buffered by interactions with more species. Elton argued that outbreaks of pests are often found on cultivated land or land disturbed by humans, both of which are species-poor communities with few naturally occurring species. His idea became known as the **diversity-stability hypothesis**.

However, some ecologists challenged Elton's association of diversity with stability. They pointed out many examples of introduced species that have assumed pest proportions in species-rich areas, including rabbits in Australia and pigs in North America. They also suggested that disturbed or cultivated land may suffer from pest outbreaks not because of its low number of species, but because introduced species often have no natural enemies in their new environment. In contrast, native species and their natural enemies have had long associations. For example, in Europe and North America, rabbit species and their predators, such as fox species, have coevolved based on a predator-prey relationship over the course of many generations. This relationship prevents the rabbit populations from increasing to pest proportions.

Field Studies Have Linked Stability to Richness

To test the diversity-stability hypothesis, research was needed in which the stability of communities was measured and then compared to their species richness. In 1996, American ecologist David Tilman reported the relationship between species richness and community

stability from an 11-year study of 207 grassland plots in Minnesota that varied in their species richness. At the end of every year, he measured the biomass of every plant species in each plot. He then analyzed how much this biomass varied from year to year through a statistical calculation called the coefficient of variation, which is a measure of relative variability. (It is the ratio of the standard deviation to the mean.) Less variation in biomass indicates community stability. Year-to-year variation in plant community biomass was significantly lower in plots with greater plant species richness (**Figure 58.4**). These results are consistent with the diversity-stability hypothesis—higher species richness enhances community stability.

Tilman suggested that species-rich communities are more likely to contain disturbance-resistant species that, in the event of a disturbance, could grow and compensate for the loss of disturbance-sensitive species. For example, when a change in climate such as drought decreased the abundance of competitively dominant species that thrived under normal conditions, drought-resistant species increased in mass and replaced them. Thus, declines in the number of sensitive species were compensated for by increases in other species, which acted to stabilize total community biomass.

58.3 Succession: Community Change

Learning Outcomes:

1. Distinguish between primary and secondary succession.
2. Compare and contrast facilitation, inhibition, and tolerance as mechanisms of succession.

The term **succession** describes the gradual and continuous change in species composition of a community following a disturbance. **Primary succession** refers to succession on a newly exposed site that has no biological legacy in terms of plants, animals, or microbes, such as bare ground caused by a volcanic eruption or the sediment created by the retreat of glaciers. In primary succession on land, the plants must often build up the soil, and thus a long time—even hundreds of years—may be required for the process. Only a tiny proportion of the Earth's surface is currently undergoing primary succession, including the area around Mount St. Helens and on new lava flows around the volcanoes in Hawaii and off the coast of Iceland, and behind retreating glaciers in Alaska and Canada.

Secondary succession refers to succession on a site that has previously supported life but has undergone a disturbance such as a fire, tornado, hurricane, or flood. In terrestrial areas, soil is already present. Clearing a natural forest and farming the land for several years is an example of a severe forest disturbance that does not kill all native species. Some plants and many soil bacteria, nematodes, and insects are still present. Secondary succession occurs if farming has ended. The secondary succession in abandoned farmlands can lead to a pattern of vegetation quite different from one that develops after primary succession following glacial retreat. For example, the plowing and added fertilizers, herbicides, and pesticides may have caused substantial changes in the soil of an abandoned field, allowing species that require a lot of nitrogen to colonize. These species would not be present for many years in newly created glacial soils.

American plant ecologist Frederic Clements is often viewed as the founder of successional theory. His work in the early 20th century emphasized succession as proceeding through several stages to a distinct end point, or **climax community**. Although disturbance can return a community from a later stage to an earlier stage, generally the community progresses in one direction. Clements's depiction of succession focused on a process termed facilitation, but two other mechanisms of succession—inhibition and tolerance—have since been described. In this section, we will examine the evidence for each of them.

Facilitation Assumes That Each Invading Species Creates a More Favorable Habitat for Succeeding Species

A key assumption of Clements's view of succession is that each colonizing species makes the local environment a little different, such as a little shadier or a little richer in soil nitrogen, so that it becomes more suitable for other species, which then invade and outcompete the earlier residents. This process, known as **facilitation**, continues until the most competitively dominant species have colonized, when the community is at climax. The composition of the climax community for any given region is determined by climate, soil condition, and frequency of disturbance.

Succession following the gradual retreat of Alaskan glaciers is often used as a specific example of facilitation as a mechanism of succession. Over the past 200 years, the glaciers in Glacier Bay have undergone a dramatic retreat of nearly 100 km (**Figure 58.5**). Succession in Glacier Bay has followed a distinct pattern of vegetation. As glaciers retreat, they leave moraines—deposits of stones, pulverized rock, and debris that serve as soil. In Alaska, the bare soil has a low nitrogen content and little organic matter.

In the pioneer stage, the soil is first colonized by a black crust of cyanobacteria, mosses, lichens, horsetails (*Equisetum variegatum*), with the occasional river beauty (*Epilobium latifolium*) (**Figure 58.6a**). Because the cyanobacteria are nitrogen fixers, the soil nitrogen increases a little, but soil depth and litterfall (fallen leaves, twigs, and

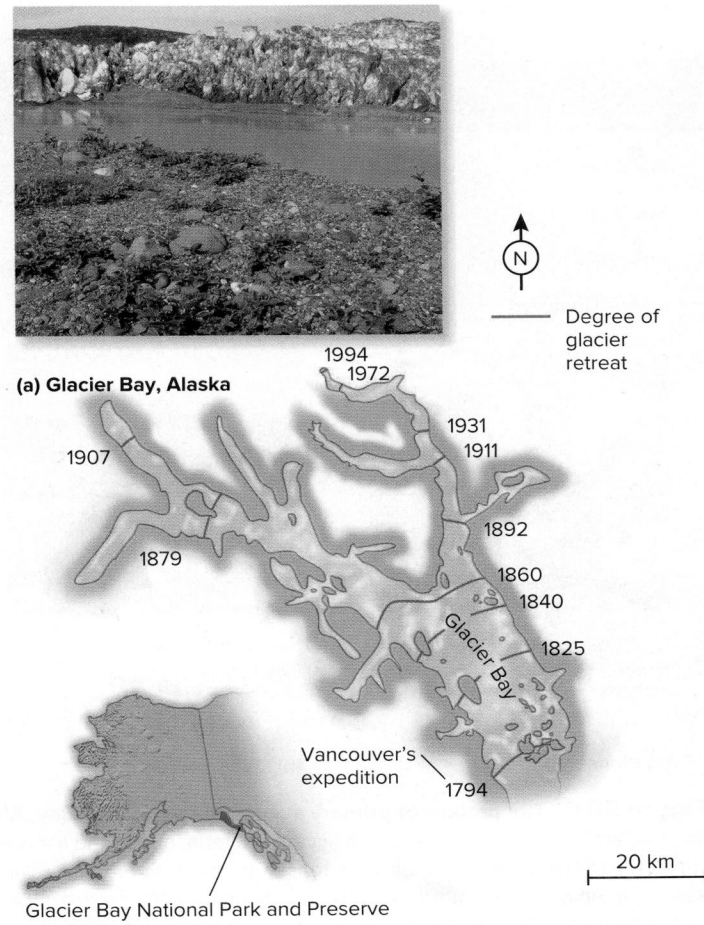

(a) Glacier Bay, Alaska

— Degree of glacier retreat

(b) Glacial retreat

Figure 58.5   The degree of glacier retreat at Glacier Bay, Alaska, since 1794. **(a)** Primary succession begins on the bare rock and soil evident at the edges of the retreating glacier. **(b)** The lines reflect the position of the glacier in 1794 and its subsequent retreat northward.
a: ©Charles D. Winters/Science Source

Concept Check: *Why might an ecologist think of walking the coastline of Glacier Bay as the equivalent of walking back in time?*

other plant material) are still minimal. At this stage, there are rare instances of seeds and seedlings of dwarf shrubs of the rose family, commonly called mountain avens (*Dryas drummondii*); alders (*Alnus sinuata*); and spruce. After about 40 years (the *Dryas* stage), mountain avens dominate the landscape (**Figure 58.6b**). Soil nitrogen increases, as does soil depth and litterfall, and alder trees begin to invade.

At about 60 years, alders form dense, close thickets (**Figure 58.6c**). Alders have nitrogen-fixing bacteria that live mutualistically in their roots and convert nitrogen from the air into a biologically useful form. Soil nitrogen dramatically increases, as does litterfall. Sitka spruce trees (*Picea sitchensis*) begin to invade at about this time. After about 75 to 100 years, the spruce trees begin to overtop the alders, shading them out. The litterfall is still high, and the large volume of needles turns the soil acidic. The shade causes competitive exclusion of many of the original understory species, including alder, and only mosses carpet the ground. At this stage, seedlings of western hemlock (*Tsuga heterophylla*) and mountain hemlock

Stage	Pioneer	*Dryas*	Alder	Spruce-hemlock
Time (years) since glacial retreat	5	40	60	200
Soil depth (cm)	5.2	7.0	8.8	15.1
Soil N (g/m²)	3.8	5.3	21.8	53.3
Soil pH	7.2	7.3	6.8	3.6
Litterfall (g/m²/yr)	1.5	2.8	277	261

Cyanobacteria
Moss
Lichens

Mountain avens
(*Dryas drummondii*)

Alder
(*Alnus sinuata*)

Spruce
(*Picea sitchensis*)
Western hemlock
(*Tsuga heterophylla*)

(a) Pioneer stage   **(b) *Dryas* stage**   **(c) Alder stage**   **(d) Spruce-hemlock stage**

Figure 58.6 **The pattern of primary succession at Glacier Bay, Alaska. (a)** The first species to colonize the bare ground following retreat of the glaciers are small species such as cyanobacteria, moss, and lichens. **(b)** Mountain avens (*Dryas drummondii*) is a flower common in the *Dryas* stage. **(c)** Soil nitrogen and litterfall increase rapidly as alder (*Alnus sinuata*) invades. Note also the appearance of a few spruce trees higher up the valley. **(d)** Sitka spruce (*Picea sitchensis*) and hemlock (*Tsuga heterophylla*) trees make up a climax spruce-hemlock forest at Glacier Bay, with moss carpeting the ground. Two hundred years ago, glaciers occupied this spot. a: ©Leon Werdinger/Alamy Stock Photo; b: ©James Hager/age fotostock; c: ©Accent Alaska.com/Alamy Stock Photo; d: ©Craig Lovell/Eagle Visions P/Newscom

(*Tsuga mertensiana*) may also occur. After 200 years, a mixed spruce-hemlock climax forest occupies the location (**Figure 58.6d**).

Other studies also provide evidence of facilitation. Early primary succession on Mount St. Helens shows that decomposition of fungi allows mosses and other fungi to colonize the soil, providing evidence of facilitation. Succession on sand dunes also supports the facilitation model; pioneer plant species stabilize the sand dunes and facilitate the establishment of subsequent plant species. The foredunes, those nearest the shoreline, are the most frequently disturbed and are maintained in a state of early succession, whereas more stable communities develop farther away from the shoreline.

Succession also occurs in aquatic communities. Although soils do not develop in marine environments, facilitation may still occur when one species enhances the quality of settling and establishment sites for another species. When experimental test plates used to measure settling rates of marine organisms were placed in Delaware Bay, researchers discovered that certain cnidarians enhanced the attachment of tunicates, and both facilitated the attachment of mussels, the dominant species in the community. In this experiment, the smooth surface of the test plates prevented many species from colonizing, but once the surface became rougher, because of the presence of the cnidarians, many other species were able to colonize. In a similar fashion, early colonizing bacteria, which create biofilms on rock surfaces, can facilitate succession of other organisms.

Inhibition Implies That Early Colonists Can Prevent Later Arrivals from Replacing Them

Although data on succession in some communities fit the facilitation model, researchers have proposed alternative hypotheses concerning how succession may operate. In the mechanism known as **inhibition**, early colonists prevent colonization by other species. For example, removing the litter of *Setaria faberi*, an early successional plant species in abandoned New Jersey farm fields, causes an increase in the biomass of a later species, *Erigeron annuus*. The release of toxic compounds from decomposing *S. faberi* litter or physical obstruction by the litter itself blocks the establishment of *E. annuus*. Without the litter present, however, *E. annuus* dominates and reduces the biomass of *S. faberi*.

Inhibition has been seen as the primary method of succession in the marine intertidal zone, where space is limited. In this habitat, early successional species are at a great advantage in maintaining possession of valuable space. In 1974, American ecologist Wayne Sousa created an environment for testing how succession works in the intertidal zone by scraping rock faces clean of all algae or putting out fresh boulders or concrete blocks. The first colonists of these areas were the green algae of the genus *Ulva*. By removing those algae from the substrate, Sousa showed that the large red alga *Chondracanthus canaliculatus* was able to colonize more quickly (**Figure 58.7**).

Figure 58.7 **Inhibition as a method of succession in the marine intertidal zone.** Removing *Ulva* from intertidal rock faces allowed colonization by *Chondracanthus canaliculatus*. The inset shows *Ulva* on a rock face with the striped shore crab *Pachygrapsus crassipes*, a herbivore. ©Wayne Sousa/University of California, Berkeley

The results of Sousa's study indicate that early colonists can inhibit rather than facilitate the invasion of subsequent colonists. Succession may eventually occur because early-colonizing species, such as *Ulva*, are more susceptible than later successional species, such as *C. canaliculatus*, to the rigors of the physical environment and to attacks by herbivores, such as crabs (*Pachygrapsus crassipes*).

Tolerance Suggests That Early Colonists Neither Facilitate Nor Inhibit Later Colonists

In 1977, researchers Joseph Connell and Ralph Slatyer proposed a third mechanism of succession, which they termed **tolerance**. In this process, any species can start the succession, but the eventual climax community is reached in a somewhat orderly fashion. The species that establish themselves and remain do not change the environment in ways that either facilitate or inhibit subsequent colonists. Species have differing tolerances to the intensity of competition as more species accumulate. Relatively competition-intolerant species are more successful early in succession, when the intensity of competition is low and resources are abundant. Relatively competition-tolerant species appear later in succession and at climax.

Connell and Slatyer found the best evidence for the tolerance model in American plant ecologist Frank Egler's earlier work on floral succession. In the 1950s, Egler showed that succession in plant communities is determined largely by species that already exist in the ground as buried seeds or old roots. Whichever species germinates first or regenerates from roots initiates the succession sequence. Germination or root regeneration, in turn, depends on the timing

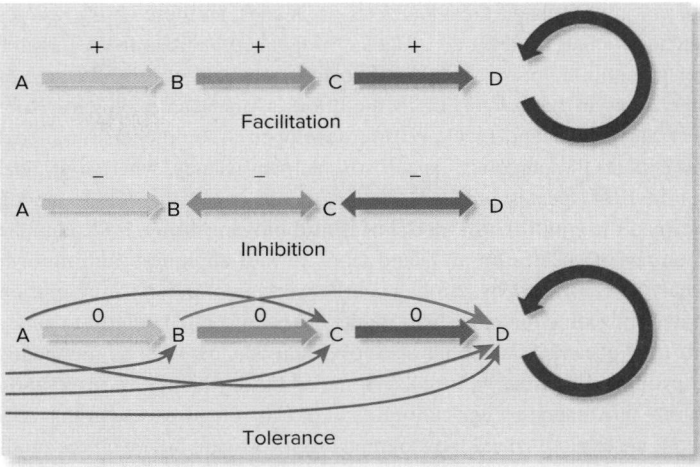

Figure 58.8 **Three models of succession.** A, B, C, and D represent four stages, with D representing the climax community. An arrow means "is replaced by," + stands for "facilitation," − stands for "inhibition," and 0 indicates no effect. The facilitation model is the classic model of succession. In the inhibition model, early-arriving species outcompete later-arriving species. The tolerance model depends on which species gets there first. The colored arrows show that succession may bypass some stages in the tolerance model.

Concept Check: *Inhibition implies that competition exists between species, with early-arriving species tending to outcompete later arrivals, at least for a while. Does competition or mutualism feature more prominently in facilitation?*

of a disturbance. For example, an early-season tree fall would promote early-germinating species to grow in the subsequent light gap, whereas a late-season tree fall would promote the growth of late-germinating species. As succession proceeds, species that are earlier in germination may be outcompeted by different species.

The Three Models of Succession Differ in How One Species Affects Colonization by a Different Species

The key distinction between the three models of succession is in the manner in which one species affects the colonization of another species. In the facilitation model, species replacement is facilitated by previous colonists; in the inhibition model, it is inhibited by the action of previous colonists; and in the tolerance model, species may be affected by previous colonists, but they do not require them (**Figure 58.8**).

58.4 Island Biogeography

Learning Outcomes:

1. **CoreSKILL »** Interpret a graph that illustrates the equilibrium model of island biogeography.
2. List the three predictions of the model, and discuss how well the evidence supports each one.

In some newly formed habitats such as volcanic islands, succession may be affected not only by facilitation, inhibition, or tolerance but also by the ability of species from neighboring areas (such as a mainland) to colonize isolated areas (such as an island). In these cases, species richness is affected by the distance of isolated habitats from a source of potential colonists from neighboring areas and also by the size of the areas to be colonized. In the 1960s, American ecologists Robert MacArthur and E. O. Wilson developed a comprehensive model to explain the process of succession on new islands, where a gradual buildup of species proceeds from a sterile beginning. Their model, termed the **equilibrium model of island biogeography**, holds that the number of species on an island tends toward an equilibrium number that is determined by the balance between two factors: immigration rates and extinction rates. This model has been applied not just to newly formed oceanic islands but also to virtual islands, such as mountains surrounded by deserts, lakes surrounded by dry land, or conservation areas surrounded by agricultural land or urban landscapes. In this section, we explore island biogeography to investigate how well the model's predictions are supported by data.

The Island Biogeography Model Suggests That During Succession, Gains in Immigration Are Balanced by Losses from Extinction

MacArthur and Wilson's model of island biogeography suggests that species repeatedly arrive on an island and either thrive or become extinct. The rate of immigration of new species is highest when no species are present on the island. As the number of species accumulates, the immigration rate decreases, since subsequent immigrants are more likely to represent species already present on the island. The rate of extinction is low at the time of first colonization, because few species are present and many have large populations. With the addition of new species, the population sizes of some species diminish, so the probability of extinction increases. Over time, the number of species tends toward an equilibrium value, $\hat{S}$, in which the rates of immigration and extinction are equal. Species may continue to arrive and go extinct, but the number of species on the island remains approximately the same.

MacArthur and Wilson reasoned that when plotted graphically, both the immigration and extinction lines would be curved, for several reasons (**Figure 58.9a**). First, species arrive on islands at different rates. Some organisms, including plants with seed-dispersal mechanisms and winged animals, are more mobile than others and arrive quickly. Other organisms arrive more slowly. This pattern causes the immigration curve to start off steep but get progressively shallower. On the other hand, extinctions rise at accelerating rates, because as later species arrive, competition increases and more species are likely to go extinct.

A strength of the island biogeography model is that it generates several testable predictions:

1. *Species-area relationships.* The number of species should increase with increasing island size (area), a concept known as the species-area effect (see Figure 58.2b). Extinction rates should be lower on larger islands because population sizes are larger and less susceptible to extinction (**Figure 58.9b**).

2. *Species-distance relationships.* The number of species should decrease with increasing distance of the island from the

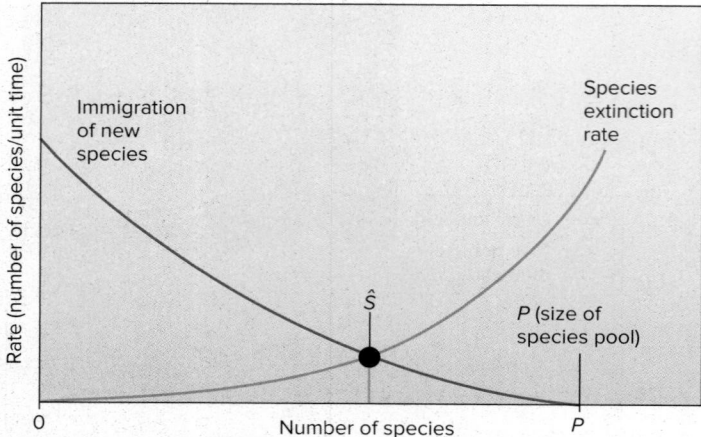

(a) Effects of immigration and extinction on species number

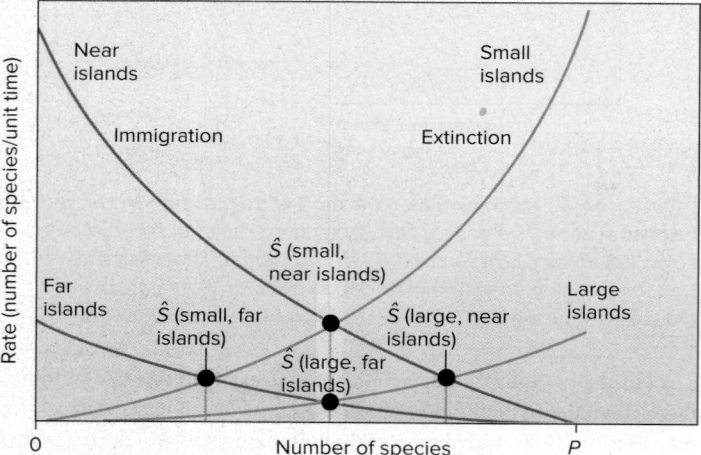

(b) Added effects of island size and proximity to the mainland on species number

Figure 58.9 MacArthur and Wilson's equilibrium model of island biogeography. **(a)** The opposing effects of immigration and extinction produce an equilibrium number of species on an island, $\hat{S}$. This number can vary from 0 species to P species, the total number of species available to colonize. **(b)** $\hat{S}$ varies according to the island's size and distance from the mainland. An increase in distance (near to far) lowers the immigration rate. An increase in island area (small to large) lowers the extinction rate.

 Core Skill: Connections Look ahead to Figure 60.8. How might the equilibrium model of island biogeography be useful in the design of nature reserves?

mainland, that is, from the **source pool**, the pool of potential species available to colonize the island. Immigration rates should be greater on islands near the source pool because species do not have as far to travel (see Figure 58.9b).

3. *Species turnover.* The turnover of species should be considerable. While the number of species on an island might remain relatively constant, the identity of the species should vary over time as new species colonize the island and others become extinct. Eventually, turnover is reduced when a

climax community is reached and it becomes difficult for new immigrants to colonize the island.

Let's examine the three predictions of the island biogeography model and see how well the data support each one.

Species-Area Relationships   The West Indies has traditionally been a key location for ecologists studying island biogeography. The physical geography and the plant and animal life of the islands are well known. Furthermore, all of the Lesser Antilles, from Anguilla in the north to Grenada in the south, enjoy a similar climate and are surrounded by deep water (**Figure 58.10a**). In 1999, Robert Ricklefs and Irby Lovette summarized the available data on the richness of species of four groups of animals—birds, bats, reptiles and amphibians, and butterflies—across 19 islands that varied in area over two orders of magnitude (13–1,510 km^2). In each case, a positive correlation occurred between area and species richness (**Figure 58.10b**).

Species-Distance Relationships   In studies of the numbers of lowland forest bird species in Polynesia, MacArthur and Wilson found that the number of species decreased with the distance from the source pool of New Guinea (**Figure 58.11**). They expressed the richness of bird species on the islands as a percentage of the number of bird species found on New Guinea. A significant decline in this percentage was observed with increasing distance. More-distant islands were inhabited by lower numbers of species than nearer islands. This research substantiated the prediction of species richness declining with increasing distance from the source pool.

Species Turnover   Studies involving species turnover on islands are difficult to perform because detailed and complete species lists are needed over long periods of time, usually many years and often decades. The lists that do exist are often compiled in a casual way and are not usually suitable for comparison with more modern data. In 1980, British researcher Francis Gilbert reviewed 25 investigations carried out to analyze turnover and found a lack of this type of rigor in nearly all of them. Furthermore, most of the observed turnover in these studies, usually less than 1% per year, or less than one species per year, appeared to be due to immigrants that never became established rather than to the extinction of well-established species. More recent studies have revealed similar findings, suggesting that the rates of turnover are low rather than high, giving little conclusive support to the third prediction of the equilibrium model of island biogeography. Even the most rigorous study, by E. O. Wilson and his student Daniel Simberloff, showed negligible turnover, as described next.

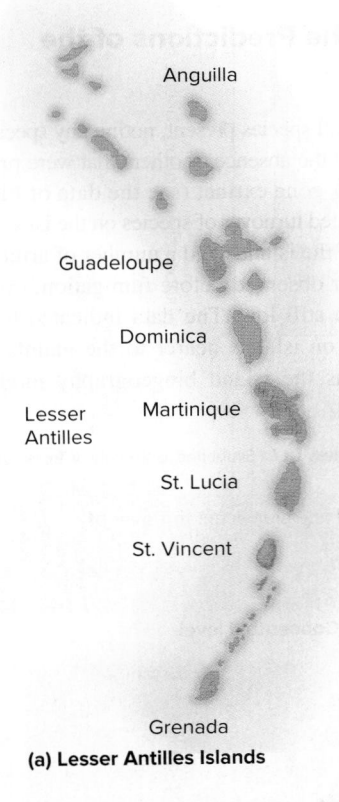

(a) **Lesser Antilles Islands**

(b) **Relationship between species richness and island size**

Figure 58.10   Species richness and island size. (a) The Lesser Antilles extend from Anguilla in the north to Grenada in the south. **(b)** On these islands, the number of bird and butterfly species increases with the area of an island. Note that these relationships are traditionally plotted on a double logarithmic scale, a so-called log-log plot, in which the horizontal axis is the logarithm to the base 10 of the area and the vertical axis is the logarithm to the base 10 of the number of species. A linear plot of the area versus the number of species would be difficult to produce because of the wide range of areas and of variation in species richness. Logarithmic scales condense this variation to manageable limits.

Concept Check: *Calculate the approximate change in bird species richness across islands in the Lesser Antilles.*

The equilibrium model of island biogeography has stimulated much research to confirm the strong effects of area and distance on species richness. However, species turnover appears to be low rather than considerable, which suggests that succession on most islands is a fairly orderly process. This conclusion means that colonization is not a random process and that the same species seem to colonize first and other species gradually appear in the same order.

The principles of island biogeography have been applied to wildlife preserves, which are essentially islands in a sea of developed land consisting of agricultural fields or urban sprawl. Conservationists have therefore utilized the model of island biogeography in the design of nature preserves, a topic we will return to in Chapter 60.

58.5 Food Webs and Energy Flow

Learning Outcomes:

1. Compare and contrast food chains and food webs, and distinguish primary producers and primary, secondary, and tertiary consumers.
2. **CoreSKILL » Calculate** the efficiency of consumers as energy transformers in two ways.
3. List and describe the different types of ecological pyramids.

We now turn our attention to ecosystem ecology, which studies the movement of energy and materials through organisms and their communities. Key factors that affect species richness are the amount of available energy and the feeding relationships among organisms. These feeding relationships can be characterized by an unbranched **food chain**—a linear depiction of energy flow, with each organism feeding on and deriving energy from the preceding organism. In this section, we will consider the unidirectional flow of energy in a food chain and also examine a food web, a more complex model of interconnected food chains. We will then explore two of the most important features of food webs—chain length and the pyramid of numbers.

The Main Trophic Levels Within Food Chains Consist of Primary Producers, Primary Consumers, and Secondary Consumers

Each level in a food chain is called a **trophic level** (from the Greek *trophos*, meaning feeder), with different species feeding at different levels. In a food-chain diagram, an arrow connects each trophic level with the one above it (**Figure 58.13**). Food chains typically consist of organisms that obtain energy in different ways. **Autotrophs** harvest light or chemical energy and store that energy in carbon compounds. Most autotrophs, which include plants, algae, and photosynthetic bacteria, use sunlight for this process. These organisms, called **primary producers**, form the base of the food chain. They produce the energy-rich organic molecules upon which nearly all other organisms depend.

Organisms that consume organic molecules from their environment to sustain life and thus receive their nutrition by eating other organisms or products of organisms are termed **heterotrophs**. Heterotrophs that obtain their food by consuming primary producers are termed **primary consumers** (also called herbivores) and include most protists, most animals, and even some plants such as mistletoe, which

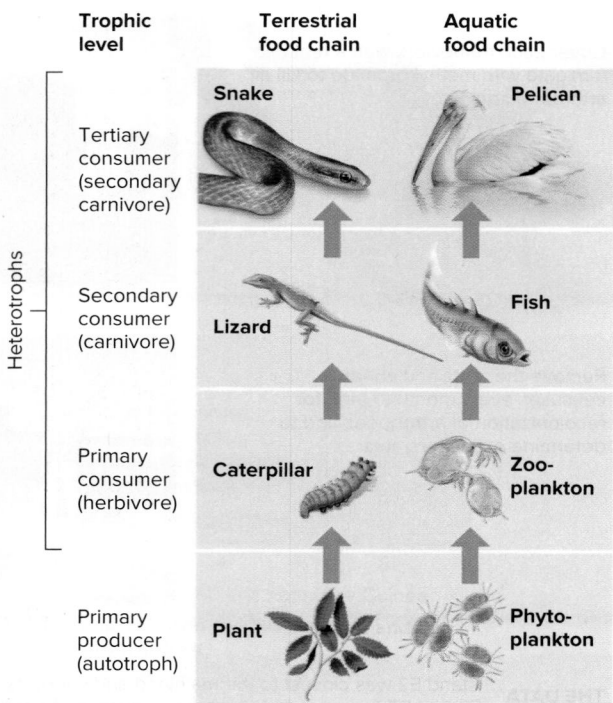

Figure 58.13 Food chains. Two examples of the flow of food energy up the trophic levels: a terrestrial food chain and an aquatic food chain.

 Core Skill: Connections In the two food chains illustrated in Figure 58.13, plants and protists (phytoplankton) are the producers. Refer back to Section 27.4. What other organisms are producers and could also support food chains?

is parasitic on other plants. Organisms that eat primary consumers are **secondary consumers** (also called carnivores). Organisms that feed on secondary consumers are **tertiary consumers** (also called secondary carnivoires), and so on. Thus, energy enters a food chain through primary producers, via photosynthesis, and is passed up the food chain to primary, secondary, and tertiary consumers (see Figure 58.13).

At each trophic level, many organisms die before they are eaten. Most energy from the first trophic level, such as plants, goes unconsumed by herbivores. Instead, unconsumed plants die and decompose in place. This material, along with dead remains of animals and waste products, is called **detritus**. Consumers that get their energy from detritus, called **detritivores**, break down dead organisms from all trophic levels. For example, carrion beetles feed on the dead bodies of other animals. Some detritivores, which do not ingest their food but feed by absorbing it on a molecular scale, are known as decomposers. The most important are fungi and bacteria. In terrestrial systems, detritivores probably consume 80–90% of plant matter, with different groups such as earthworms and fungi working in concert to extract most of the energy. Detritivores may, in turn, support a community of predators that feed on them.

In nature, feeding relationships are usually more complex than simple food chains. For example, many different herbivore species may feed on the same plant species. Also, each species of herbivore may feed on several different plant species. For instance, on the African savanna, cheetahs, lions, and hyenas all eat a variety of prey, including wildebeest, impala, and Thompson's gazelle. These herbivores, in turn, eat a variety of trees and grasses. Such relationships between plants and animals are depicted as a **food web**, a complex model of interconnected food chains in which multiple links occur among different species (**Figure 58.14**).

In Most Food Webs, Chain Lengths Are Short

Let's examine some of the characteristics of food webs in more detail. The chain length is sum of the number of links between the trophic levels involved. For example, if a lion feeds on a zebra, and a zebra feeds on grass, the chain length is two. In many food webs, chain lengths tend

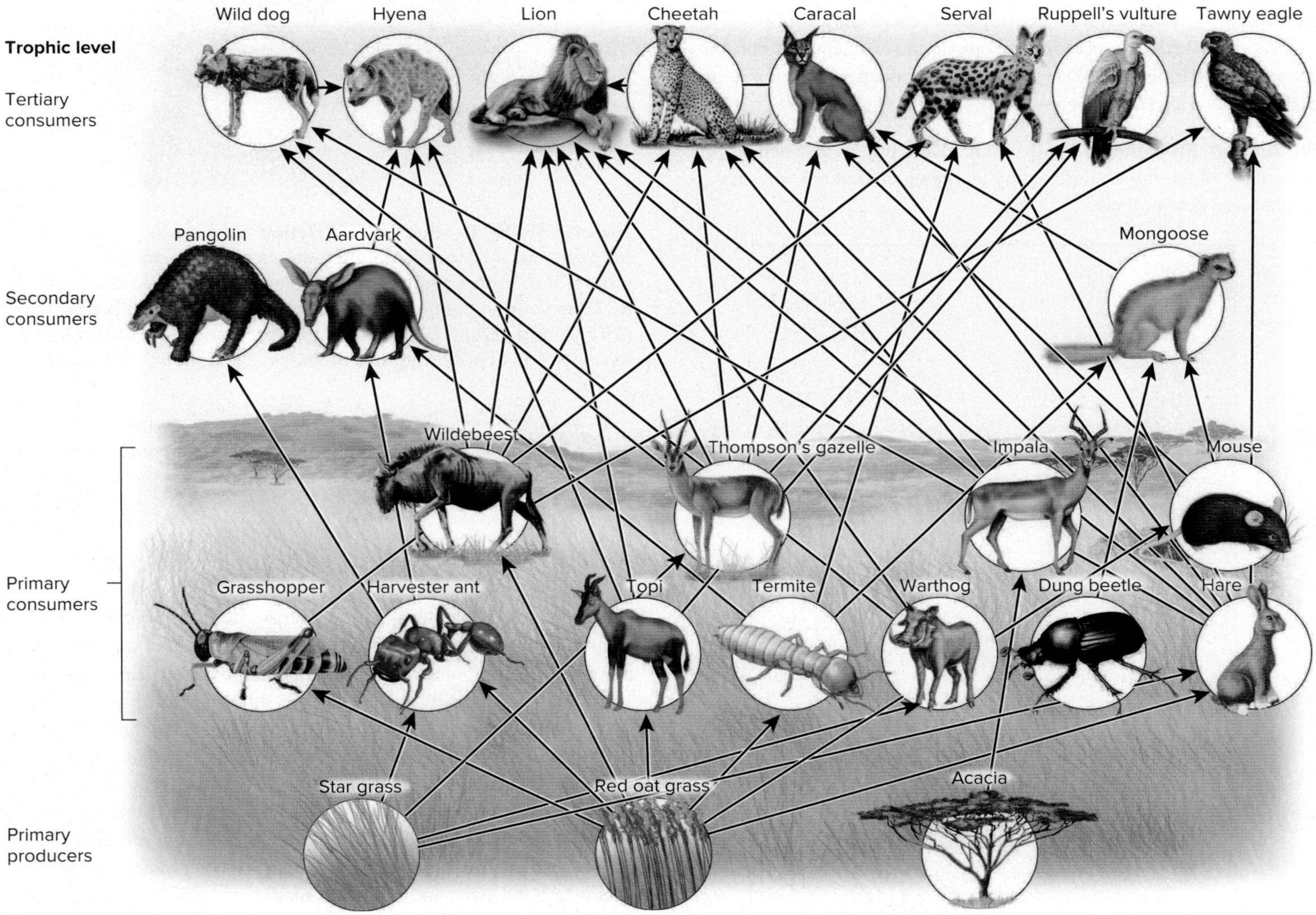

Figure 58.14 A food web depicting the feeding relationships of an African savanna ecosystem. Each trophic level is occupied by different species. Generally, each species feeds on, or is fed upon by, more than one species.

Concept Check: *At which trophic level(s) do decomposers feed?*

Core Skill: Modeling The goal of this modeling challenge is to draw a food web that depicts some of the main species that make up the food web in Banff National Park.

Modeling Challenge: Take a look back at Figure 57.21, which shows some species interactions. Beginning with this group of species, create a food web that also includes the following species: cottonwood (a tree), wheatgrass, mouse, mule deer, bison, and coyote. Remember that autotrophs, such as plants, are placed at the bottom of the food web, the herbivores are placed on the next level, and the carnivores are placed above them. The arrows point from lower trophic levels to higher trophic levels. In your food web, aspen, cottonwood, and willow are all eaten by beaver, elk, and mule deer. Wheatgrass is eaten by bison, mouse, and elk. Coyotes eat mouse and beaver, and wolves eat coyote, elk, mule deer, and bison. You may omit the songbirds from your food web.

to be short, usually five or fewer, because of two main factors. First, many organisms cannot digest all their prey. They take only the easily digestible plant leaves or animal tissue such as muscles and internal organs, leaving the hard wood or energy-rich bones behind. Second, much of the energy assimilated by animals is used in maintenance and is lost from the organism as heat. Both of these factors acting together means that, on average, only about 10% of available energy is transferred from one trophic level to another. Because energy is lost at each link, after a few links, most of the available energy has been expended and relatively little energy is available for higher trophic levels (**Figure 58.15**).

As described next, ecologists evaluate the efficiency of consumers as energy transformers in two ways: production efficiency and trophic-level transfer efficiency.

Production Efficiency **Production efficiency** is defined as the percentage of energy assimilated by an organism that becomes incorporated into new biomass.

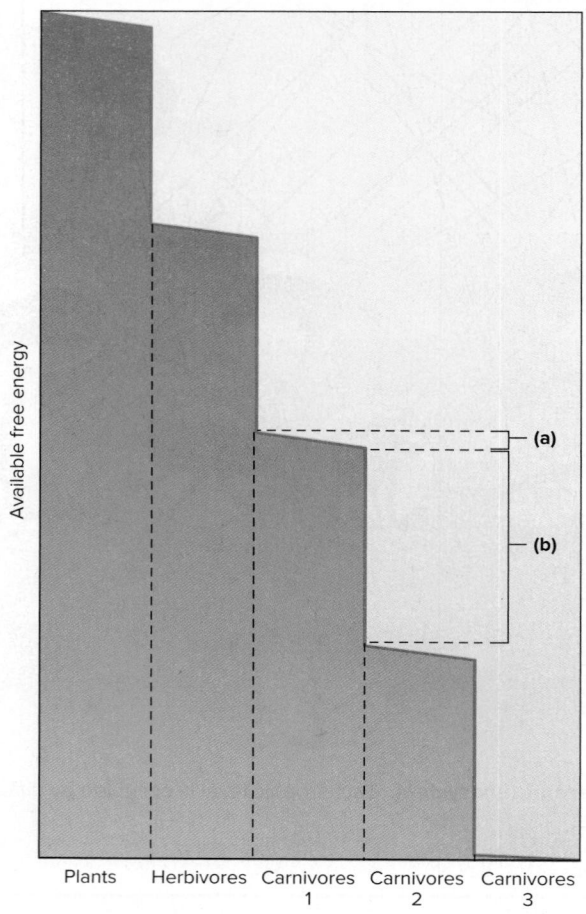

Figure 58.15 Energy flow through a food web. This graph of energy flow through a food web shows five trophic levels with four links between the trophic levels. **(a)** Energy lost as heat in a single trophic level. **(b)** Energy lost in the transfer of energy from one trophic level to another.

 Core Concept: Energy and Matter Within trophic levels, energy is lost to maintenance, and between trophic levels, energy is lost due to imperfect efficiency of transfer.

Energy derived from food 1,000 J

Growth 16 J

Feces 177 J

Cellular respiration 807 J

Figure 58.16 Production efficiency. The production efficiency of this squirrel, a mammal, is relatively low. If a mouthful of food contains 1,000 joules (J) of energy, about 807 J is used in cellular respiration to fuel metabolic processes (80.7%), and 177 J (17.7%) is lost in feces. About 16 J of the 823 J assimilated is converted into biomass, a production efficiency of 1.9%.

 Core Concept: Energy and Matter For the squirrel, maintaining a constant body temperature reduces its production efficiency.

$$\text{Production efficiency} = \frac{\text{Net productivity}}{\text{Assimilation}} \times 100$$

Here, net productivity is the energy, stored in biomass, that has accumulated over a given time span, and assimilation is the total amount of energy taken in by an organism over the same time span. Invertebrates generally have relatively high production efficiencies that average about 10–40%. Microorganisms also have relatively high production efficiencies. Vertebrates tend to have lower production efficiencies than invertebrates, because they devote more energy to sustaining their metabolism than to new biomass production (**Figure 58.16**). Even within vertebrates, much variation occurs. Fishes, which are ectotherms, typically have production efficiencies of around 10%, and birds and mammals, which are endotherms, have production efficiencies in the range of 1–2%. In large part, this difference reflects the energy cost of maintaining a constant body temperature.

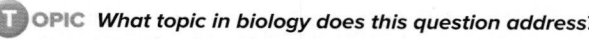

BIO·**TIPS**   **THE QUESTION** *What is the production efficiency of a caterpillar if a period of feeding delivers 1,000 J of energy of which 500 J is lost in feces, 320 J is used in cellular respiration, and 180 J goes to growth (is converted to biomass)?*

TOPIC *What topic in biology does this question address?*
The topic is the production efficiency of a consumer. More specifically, the question asks you to calculate the production efficiency of a caterpillar.

INFORMATION *What information do you know based on the question and your understanding of the topic?* From the question, you know that if a caterpillar eats food that provides 1,000 J of energy, 500 J is lost in feces, 320 J is used in cellular respiration, and 180 J is used for growth. From your understanding of the topic, you may recall that the production efficiency is calculated using this formula:

$$\text{Production efficiency} = \frac{\text{Net productivity}}{\text{Assimilation}} \times 100$$

PROBLEM-SOLVING **S**TRATEGY *Interpret data. Make a calculation.* Insert the data given in the question into the formula. Net productivity is the amount of energy used for growth, or 180 J. Assimilation is the energy used for growth plus the energy used in cellular respiration, or 320 J + 180 J = 500 J.

$$\text{Production efficiency} = \frac{180\ \text{J}}{500\ \text{J}} \times 100 = 36\%$$

ANSWER *The caterpillar's production efficiency is 36%.*

Trophic-Level Transfer Efficiency A second way to measure the efficiency of consumers as energy transformers is **trophic-level transfer efficiency**, which is the amount of energy at one trophic level that is acquired by the trophic level above and incorporated into biomass. Calculating this value provides a way of examining energy flow between trophic levels, not just energy flow for an individual species. Trophic-level transfer efficiency is calculated as follows:

$$\text{Trophic-level transfer efficiency} = \frac{\text{Production at trophic level } n}{\text{Production at trophic level } n-1} \times 100$$

For example, recall from Chapter 54 that zooplankton consists of small drifting animals that graze on microscopic photosynthetic organisms called phytoplankton. If a lake produced 14 g/m² of zooplankton (trophic level *n*) and 100 g/m² of phytoplankton (trophic level *n* − 1), the trophic-level transfer efficiency between these levels would be 14%. Trophic-level transfer efficiency tends to average around 10%, though there is much variation.

Trophic-level transfer efficiency is generally low for two reasons. First, many organisms cannot digest all of their prey. They take only the easily digestible plant leaves or animal tissue such as muscles and guts, leaving the hard wood or energy-rich bones behind. Second, much of the energy assimilated by animals is used in maintenance, so most energy is lost from the system as heat. The 10% average transfer rate of energy from one trophic level to another also necessitates short food webs of no more than four or five levels. Relatively little energy is available for the higher levels.

Ecological Pyramids Describe the Distribution of Numbers, Biomass, or Energy Between Trophic Levels

The abundance of organisms, biomass, or available energy at each trophic level of a food web can be expressed graphically as an ecological pyramid. One of the best-known ecological pyramids, described by British ecologist Charles Elton in 1927, is the **pyramid of numbers**, in which the number of individuals decreases at each trophic level, with a large

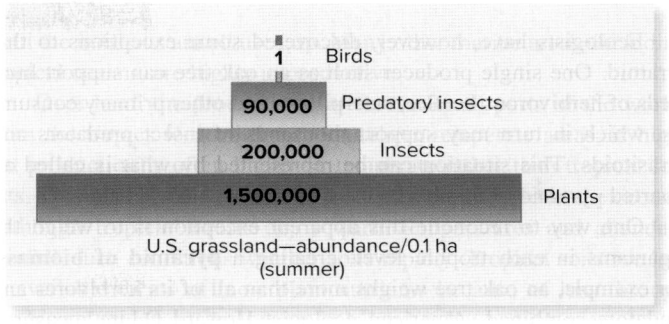

(a) Pyramid of numbers

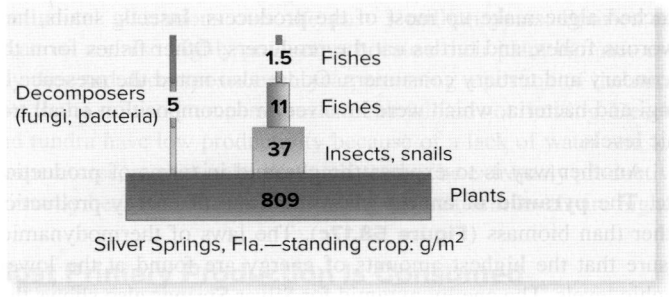

(b) Pyramid of biomass

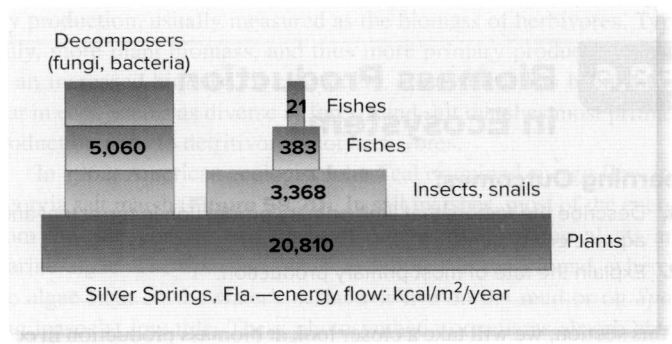

(c) Pyramid of energy

Figure 58.17 Ecological pyramids in food webs. (a) In this pyramid of numbers, the abundance of species in an American grassland decreases with increasing trophic level. **(b)** In a pyramid of biomass, the amount of biological material is represented instead of numbers of individuals. Note the presence of decomposers that decompose material at all trophic levels. **(c)** A pyramid of energy for the ecosystem of Silver Springs, Florida. Note the large energy transfers of decomposers, despite their small biomass.

number of individuals at the base and fewer individuals at the top. For example, in a grassland, there may be millions of individual plants per hectare, hundreds of thousands of insects that feed on the plants, tens of thousands of spiders feeding on the insects, and one or two birds that feed on the spiders (**Figure 58.17a**).

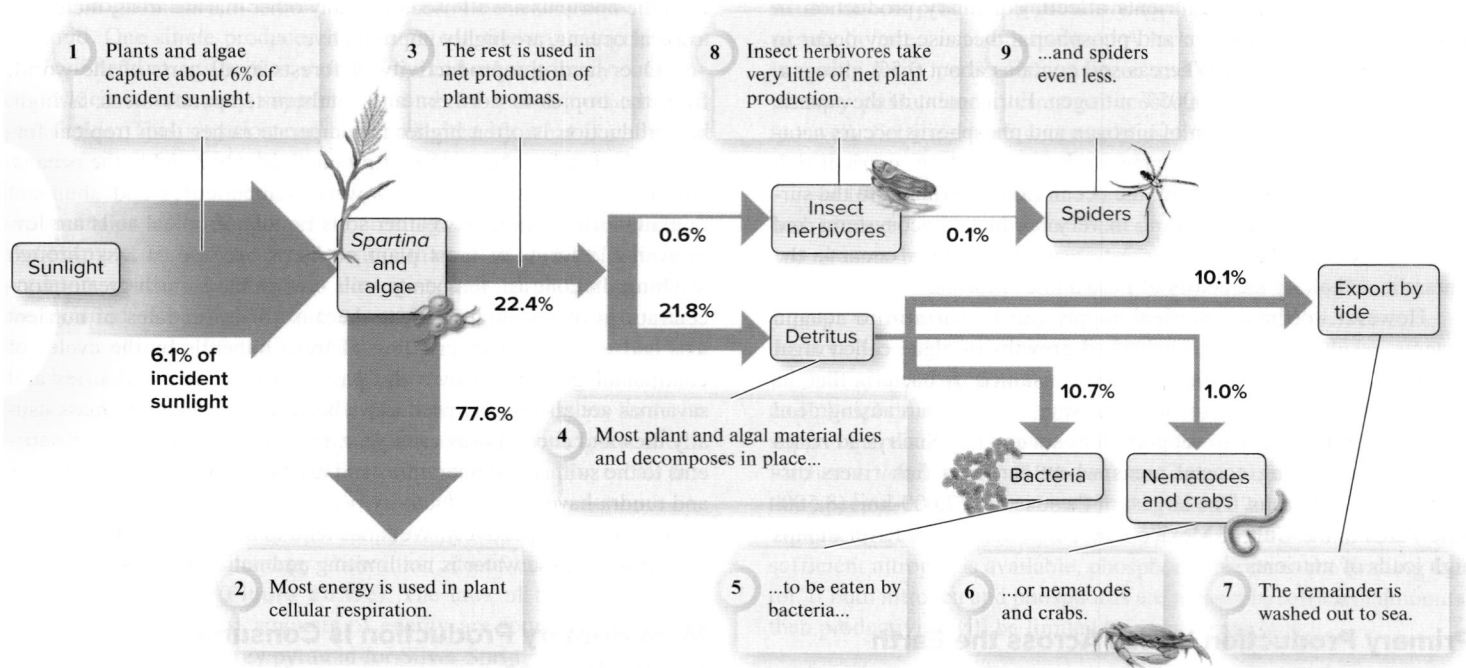

Figure 58.20 Energy-flow diagram for a Georgia salt marsh. Numbers represent the percentage of gross primary production that flows into different trophic levels or is used in plant respiration.

algal cellular respiration. The energy that is accumulated in biomass is 22.4%, and most of the biomass dies in place and rots on the muddy ground, to be consumed by bacteria. Bacteria are the major detritivores in this system, followed distantly by nematodes and crabs, which feed on tiny food particles as they sift through the mud. Some of the dead material is also removed from the system (exported) by the tide. The herbivores take very little of the plant production, around 0.6%, eating only a small proportion of the *Spartina* and none of the algae. A fraction of herbivore biomass is then consumed by spiders. Overall, if we view the species in ecosystems as transformers of energy, then plants, algae, and cyanobacteria are by far the most important organisms on the planet, other species of bacteria are next, and animals are a distant third.

Summary of Key Concepts

- The assemblage of many populations of different species in the same location is known as a community. Community ecology explores the factors that influence the number and abundance of these species. An ecosystem is the system formed between communities and their physical environment. Ecosystem ecology addresses the flow of energy and the production of biomass within ecosystems.

58.1 Patterns of Species Richness and Species Diversity

- The number of species of most taxa varies according to geographic location, generally increasing from polar areas to tropical areas (Figure 58.1).
- Different hypotheses for the variation in species richness have been advanced, including the species-time hypothesis, the

species-area hypothesis, and the species-productivity hypothesis (Figures 58.2, 58.3).

- Species diversity takes into account both species richness and species abundance. The most widely used measure of species diversity is called the Shannon diversity index (Table 58.1).

58.2 Species Richness and Community Stability

- Community stability is an important concept in ecology. The diversity-stability hypothesis maintains that species-rich communities are more stable than communities with fewer species. Tilman's field studies, which showed that year-to-year variation in plant biomass decreased with increasing species richness, established a link between diversity and stability (Figure 58.4).

58.3 Succession: Community Change

- Succession describes the gradual and continuous change in community structure over time. Primary succession refers to succession on a newly exposed site with no prior biological legacy. Secondary succession refers to succession on a site that has supported life but has undergone a disturbance (Figures 58.5, 58.6).
- Three mechanisms have been proposed for succession. With facilitation, each species facilitates, or makes the environment more suitable for, subsequent species. With inhibition, initial species inhibit later colonists. With tolerance, any species can start the succession, and species replacement is unaffected by previous colonists (Figures 58.7, 58.8).

58.4 Island Biogeography

- In the equilibrium model of island biogeography, the number of species on an island tends toward an equilibrium number determined by the balance between immigration and extinction rates (Figure 58.9).

- The model predicts that the number of species increases with increasing island size, that the number of species decreases with distance from the source pool, and that turnover is high. Support exists for the first two predictions of the model, but experiments on islands in the Florida Keys refuted the third prediction (Figures 58.10, 58.11, 58.12).

58.5 Food Webs and Energy Flow

- Ecosystem ecology studies the movement of energy and materials through organisms and their communities. Organisms that obtain energy from light or chemicals are primary producers (or autotrophs). Organisms that feed on primary producers are called primary consumers (or herbivores). Organisms that feed on primary consumers are called secondary consumers (or carnivores). Consumers that get their energy from the remains and waste products of organisms are called detritivores (Figure 58.13).

- Food webs are complex models of interconnected food chains in which multiple links occur between species. Food webs tend to have five or fewer links between top and bottom trophic levels (Figures 58.14, 58.15).

- Production efficiency measures the percentage of energy assimilated by an organism that becomes incorporated into new biomass. Trophic-level transfer efficiency measures the energy available at one trophic level that is acquired by the level above. These efficiencies can be expressed in the form of ecological pyramids, of which the best known is the pyramid of numbers (Figures 59.16, 59.17).

58.6 Biomass Production in Ecosystems

- Net primary production (NPP) is gross primary production (GPP) minus the energy released during respiration via photosynthetic organisms. NPP in terrestrial ecosystems is limited primarily by temperature and the availability of water and nutrients. In aquatic ecosystems, it is limited mainly by the availability of light and nutrients (Figures 58.18, 58.19).

- Secondary production is limited by available primary production, but most primary production goes to detritivores (Figure 58.20).

Assess & Discuss

Test Yourself

1. A community with many individuals but few different species exhibits
   a. low abundance and high species complexity.
   b. high stability.
   c. low species richness and high abundance.
   d. high species diversity.
   e. high abundance and high species richness.

2. Lake Baikal in Siberia is an ancient unglaciated temperate lake and contains 580 species of bottom-dwelling invertebrates. Great Slave Lake, a comparably sized lake that is at the same latitude in northern Canada and was once glaciated, contains only four bottom-dwelling invertebrate species. This observation supports which of the following hypotheses?
   a. species-time
   b. species-area
   c. species-productivity
   d. both a and b
   e. both b and c

3. Which evidence suggests that more diverse communities are more stable than less diverse communities?
   a. Agricultural land, with fewer species, undergoes less frequent pest outbreaks than natural prairies containing more species.
   b. In Australia, introduced rabbits frequently assume pest proportions. In Europe, coevolved predators such as foxes prevent rabbit populations from reaching pest proportions.
   c. Long-term studies of American grasslands show fields with high numbers of plant species vary less in biomass from year to year.
   d. Both a and b are correct.
   e. Both b and c are correct.

4. The process of primary succession occurs
   a. around a recently erupted volcano.
   b. on a newly plowed field.
   c. on a hillside that has suffered a mudslide.
   d. on a recently flooded riverbank.
   e. on none of the above.

5. Which of the following represent(s) secondary succession?
   a. plants growing in cracks in the pavement of a quiet street
   b. the recovery of vegetation following the 2004 Indonesian tsunami
   c. the colonization of new sand by beach plants
   d. the recovery of forests following a wildfire
   e. both b and d

6. Which is part of MacArthur and Wilson's equilibrium theory of island biogeography?
   a. Ŝ is increased by distance from the source pool.
   b. Ŝ is decreased by island size.
   c. Ŝ is a balance between immigration and extinction.
   d. Island size influences immigration rates.
   e. Distance from the source pool influences extinction rates.

7. As we learned in Chapter 27, some bacteria and archaea are able to use energy from the oxidation of sulphur, iron, or hydrogen. These organisms can be classified as
   a. heterotrophs.   d. both a and b.
   b. autotrophs.   e. both b and c.
   c. producers.

8. Which organisms are the most important consumers of energy in a Georgia salt marsh?
   a. *Spartina* grass and algae
   b. insects
   c. spiders
   d. crabs
   e. bacteria

9. Primary production in aquatic systems is limited mainly by
   a. temperature and moisture.
   b. temperature and light.
   c. temperature and nutrients.
   d. light and nutrients.
   e. light and moisture.

10. The most highly productive terrestrial ecosystems are
    a. deserts.   d. savannas.
    b. prairies.   e. tundra.
    c. forests.

Conceptual Questions

1. Forest A has 5 tree species with 100 individuals and forest B has 5 tree species with 10 individuals. What is the Shannon diversity index for both forests? Which forest has the higher diversity? What do your answers tell you about the limitations of the Shannon diversity index?

2. At what trophic level does a carrion beetle feed?

3. **Core Concept: Systems** In the nutrient-poor heathlands of Europe, scotch heather (*Calluna vulgaris*) and cross-leaved heath (*Erica tetralix*) are gradually replaced by variegated purple moor grass (*Molinia caerulea*) and wavy hair grass (*Deschampsia flexuosa*). Adding *C. vulgaris* litter or nitrogen fertilizer to the soil speeds up this process. Explain this phenomenon, and identify which mechanism of succession is supported.

Collaborative Questions

1. List some possible ecological disturbances, their likely frequency in natural communities, and the severity of their effects.

2. Calculate the species diversity (the Shannon diversity index) of the following four communities. Which community has the highest diversity? What is the maximum diversity each community could have?

Community	Species 1	Species 2	Species 3	H_S	Maximum possible diversity
1	90	10	—		
2	50	50	—		
3	80	10	10		
4	33.3	33.3	33.3		

Table header: Relative abundance of species (spanning Species 1, Species 2, Species 3)

The Age of Humans

59

Burmese python in the Florida Everglades. This species of snake was introduced into the Florida Everglades by humans and has dramatically decreased the populations of several native species. Source: Photo courtesy of National Park Service, Everglades National Park

In January 2016, British geoscientist Colin Waters and colleagues proposed formal recognition of a new geological epoch, the Anthropocene, the last and latest epoch of the Quaternary period (refer back to Figure 26.4). Some scientists have argued that the Anthropocene is a pop-culture term and a political statement, based on the word **anthropogenic**, meaning resulting from human activity, rather than a new epoch. But support is growing to embrace the Anthropocene, a term coined in the 1980s by American ecologist Eugene Stoermer and later popularized by Dutch atmospheric chemist Paul Crutzen. In the 1970s and 1980s, Crutzen showed how human pollutants can damage the ozone layer, a discovery for which he won the Nobel Prize in Chemistry in 1995, along with Mexican chemist Mario Molina and American chemist Frank Rowland.

While agreement is widespread that humans have a profound effect on the global environment, the formal recognition of a new geological time unit is subject to specific criteria. Global-scale changes must be recorded in geological stratigraphic (layered) material, usually rock, and in ice or marine sediments. Waters and colleagues noted the appearance of manufactured items in these sediments, including plastics, concrete, aluminum, and particulates from fossil-fuel combustion. Perhaps the most distinctive new identifiable items in sediments were radioactive elements from the 500 aboveground nuclear blasts that occurred between 1945 and 1963, which created globe-encircling debris.

Whether or not the Anthropocene gains wide acceptance in the scientific literature, there is no disputing the immense impacts of humans on natural systems. In this chapter, we will examine some of these impacts, which include global warming, effects on biogeochemical cycles, habitat destruction such as deforestation, the overexploitation of various species via overfishing and overhunting, and the introduction of invasive species to all corners of the globe (see the chapter opening photo of a Burmese python in the Everglades). We will begin the chapter by addressing the huge numbers of humans on the planet and our prodigious rate of population growth.

59.1 Human Population Growth

Learning Outcomes:

1. Describe how differences in age structure and human fertility across different countries affect human population growth.

2. Explain the concept of an ecological footprint.

In 2015, the world's population was estimated to be increasing at the rate of 150 people every minute: about 2 per minute in developed nations and 148 per minute in less-developed nations. In this section, we will examine human population growth trends in more detail and discuss how knowledge of the human population's age structure and fertility levels can help predict its future growth. We will then investigate the carrying capacity of the Earth for humans and explore how the concept of an ecological footprint, which measures human resource use, can help us determine this carrying capacity.

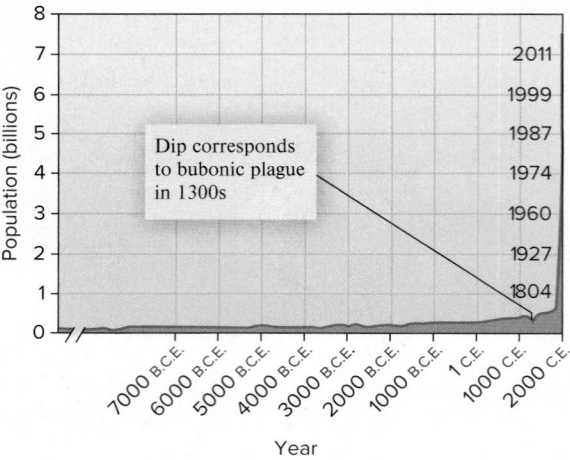

Figure 59.1 **The growth pattern of the human population through history.**

Human Populations Show Extreme Recent Growth

Until the beginning of agriculture and the domestication of animals, around 10,000 B.C.E., the average rate of human population growth was very low. With the establishment of agriculture, the world's population grew to about 300 million by 1 C.E. and to 800 million by the year 1750. Between 1750 and 2011, a relatively short period of human history, the world's human population surged from 800 million to 7 billion (**Figure 59.1**). In 2017, the number of humans was estimated at 7.5 billion. Scientists are very interested in determining when and at what size the human population will level off.

Knowledge of a Population's Age Structure Can Help Predict Its Future Growth

The age structure of a population can help to predict future population growth. In all populations, **age structure** refers to the relative numbers of individuals of each defined age group. This information is commonly displayed as a population pyramid. In West Africa, for example, children younger than age 15 make up nearly half of the population, creating a pyramid with a wide base and narrow top (**Figure 59.2a**). Even if fertility rates decline, the population is expected to significantly increase as these young people move into childbearing age. The age structure of Western Europe is much more uniform (**Figure 59.2b**). Even if the fertility rate of young women in Western Europe increases to a level higher than that of their mothers, the annual numbers of births will still be relatively low because of the low number of women of childbearing age.

Human Population Fertility Rates Vary Widely Around the World

Global population growth can be estimated by determining the **total fertility rate (TFR)**, the average number of live births a woman has during her lifetime (**Figure 59.3**). The total fertility rate differs considerably from one geographic area to another. In Africa, the total fertility rate of 4.6 in 2010 has declined substantially since the 1970s, when it was around 6.7 children per woman. In Latin America and Southeast Asia, the rates declined even more from the 1970s and are now at around 2.1. Canada and most countries in Europe have a TFR of less than 2.0. The TFR was about 1.86 in the U.S. in 2016. In Russia,

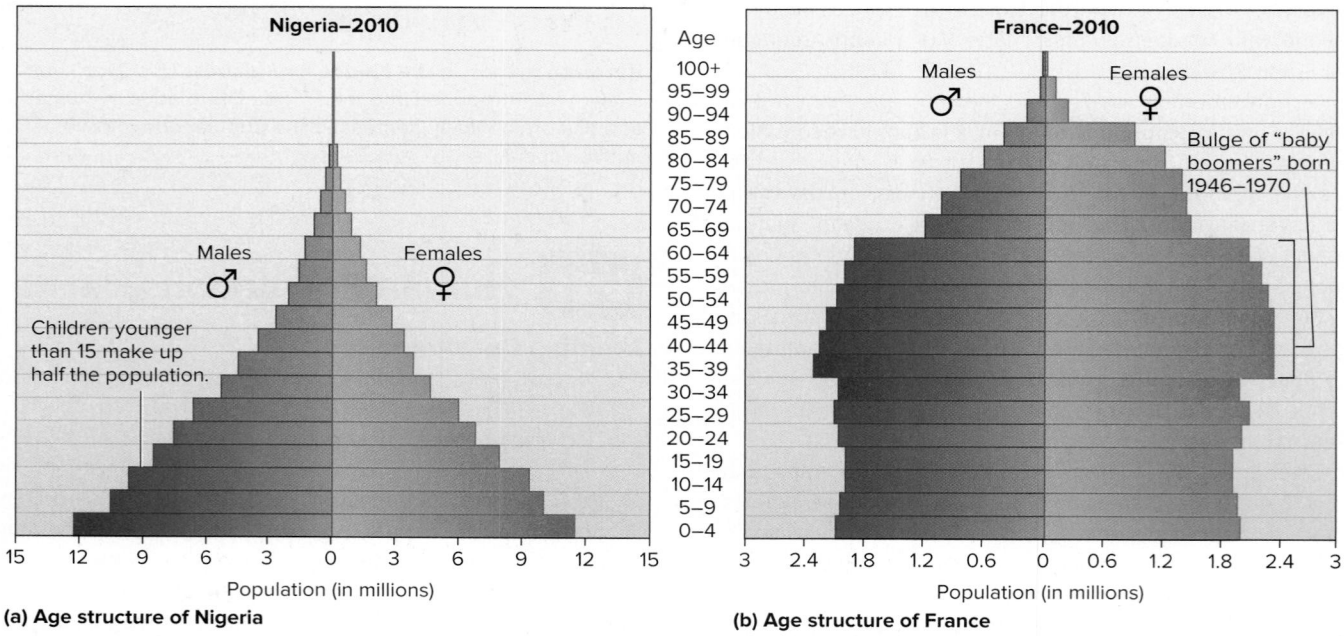

(a) Age structure of Nigeria

(b) Age structure of France

Figure 59.2 **The age structure of human populations in Nigeria and France, as of 2010.** **(a)** In developing areas of the world such as Nigeria, children comprise the most abundant age group. Population growth is rapid. **(b)** In the developed countries of Western Europe, the age structure is more evenly distributed. The bulge represents those born in the post–World War II "baby boom," when birth rates climbed due to stabilization of political and economic conditions. Population growth in developed countries is close to zero.

Concept Check: *If the population pyramid in Figure 59.2a was inverted, what would you conclude about the age structure of the population?*

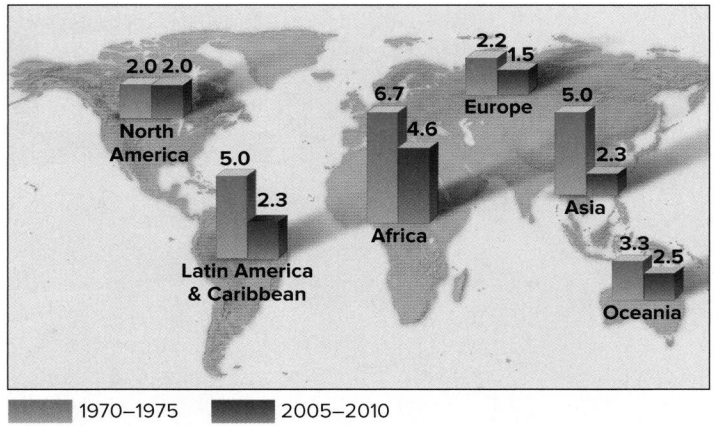

1970–1975   2005–2010

Figure 59.3 Total fertility rates (TFRs) among major regions of the world. Data refer to the average number of children born to a woman during her lifetime.

fertility rates have dropped to 1.61. In China, although the TFR is only 1.6, the population there will still continue to increase until at least 2025 because of the large number of women of reproductive age.

Although the global TFR declined from 4.47 in the 1970s to 2.42 in 2016, this is still greater than the average of 2.3 needed for zero population growth. The replacement rate is slightly higher than 2.0, the number necessary to replace a mother and father, due to natural mortality prior to reproduction. The replacement rate varies globally, from 2.1 in developed countries to between 2.5 and 3.3 in developing countries.

The wide variation in fertility rates makes it difficult to predict future population growth. A 2010 United Nations report presented world population projections to the year 2100 for three different growth scenarios: low, medium, and high (**Figure 59.4**). The three scenarios are based on three different assumptions about fertility rate. Using a low fertility rate estimate of only 1.5 children per woman, the population would reach a maximum of about 8 billion people by

2050. A more realistic assumption may be to use the fertility rate estimate of 2.0 or even 2.5; with these rates, the population would continue to rise to 10 billion or almost 16 billion, respectively.

The Concept of an Ecological Footprint Helps Estimate Carrying Capacity

Recall from Chapter 56 that carrying capacity refers to the maximum population size that can be sustained by an environment. What is the Earth's carrying capacity for the human population, and when will it be reached? Estimates vary widely. Much of the speculation on the upper boundary of the world's population size centers on lifestyle. To use a simplistic example, if everyone on the planet ate meat extensively and drove large cars, then the carrying capacity would be a lot less than if people were vegetarians and used bicycles as their main means of transportation.

In the 1990s, Swiss researcher Mathis Wackernagel and his coworkers calculated how much land is needed to support each person on Earth. Everybody has an effect on the Earth, because we consume the land's resources, including crops, wood, fossil fuels, minerals, and so on. Thus, each person has an **ecological footprint**—the amount of productive land needed to support a person. The average footprint size for everyone on the planet is about 3 hectares (1 ha = 10,000 m^2), but wide variation is found around the globe (**Figure 59.5**). The ecological footprint of the average Canadian is 7.5 hectares, and it is about 10 hectares for the average American.

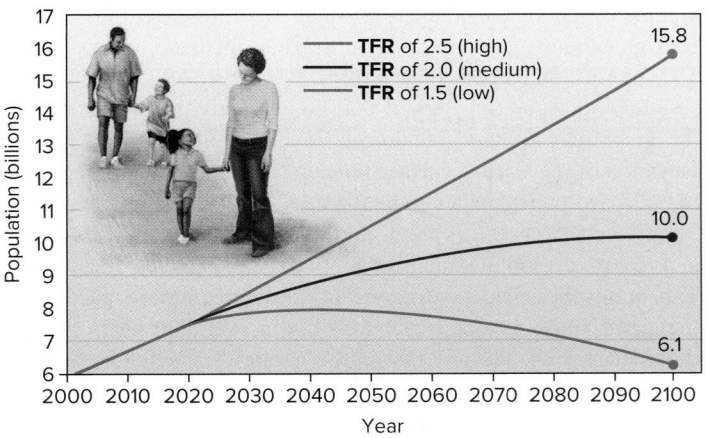

Figure 59.4 Population predictions for 2000–2100, using three different total fertility rates (TFRs).

 Core Skill: Science and Society How TFR is calculated has a great influence on assumptions about how human global population size will change over the next 80 years.

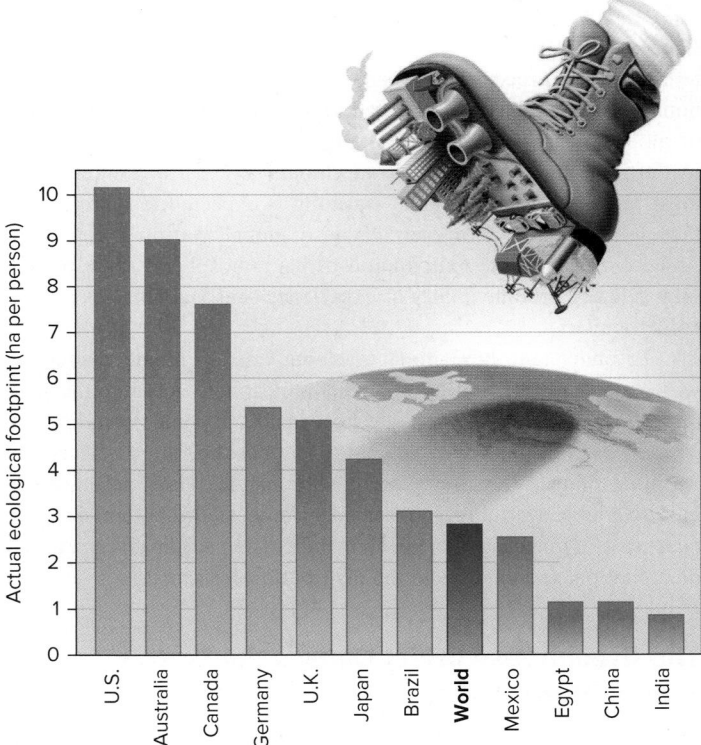

Figure 59.5 Ecological footprints of different countries. The term ecological footprint refers to the amount of productive land needed to support the average individual of that country.

Concept Check: *What is your ecological footprint?*

In most developed countries, the largest component of land use is for energy, followed by food and then forestry. Much of the land needed to provide energy serves to absorb the CO_2 emitted by the use of fossil fuels. If everyone required 10 hectares, as the average American does, we would need three Earths to provide us with the needed resources. Many people in less-developed countries use far fewer resources.

Globally, humans are already beyond the Earth's carrying capacity if we were to live in a sustainable manner. How has this happened? Many people currently live in an unsustainable manner, using more resources than can be regenerated in any given year. Furthermore, a rapidly growing human population contributes to environmental changes on a broad scale including habitat loss for wildlife, overhunting and overfishing, and pollution. As described next, pollution is thought to contribute to climate change on a global scale.

59.2 Global Warming and Climate Change

Learning Outcomes:

1. Describe how the greenhouse effect contributes to global warming.
2. Explain how global warming may affect sea levels and precipitation patterns.
3. Predict how climate change will change species distribution patterns.

Global warming refers to an increase in Earth's average surface temperature. In recent years, ecologists have been investigating how human activities have contributed to global warming. A key impact of global warming is **climate change**, which is a long-term change in Earth's climate or a change in climate in a particular region. In most regions on Earth, global warming is expected to increase surface temperatures. However, because global warming can affect ocean currents and the circulation of the atmosphere, some regions may actually become colder or experience seasonal changes such as colder winters.

To understand how global warming causes climate change, we will begin by exploring how Earth's atmosphere acts like the glass panes in a greenhouse, trapping heat inside. By understanding this process, ecologists are better able to predict the future effects of a warming Earth. We will explore how human activities have contributed to global warming and consider some of the potential consequences of climate change, which include rising sea levels, changes in precipitation, and changes in the distributions of species.

The Greenhouse Effect Causes the Earth's Temperature to Rise

The Earth is warmed by the greenhouse effect. In a greenhouse, sunlight penetrates the glass and heats the plants inside. The heat is radiated by the plants but the glass acts to trap the heat inside. Similarly, solar radiation in the form of short-wave energy passes through the atmosphere to heat the surface of the Earth. This energy is then radiated from the Earth's warmed surface into the atmosphere, but in the

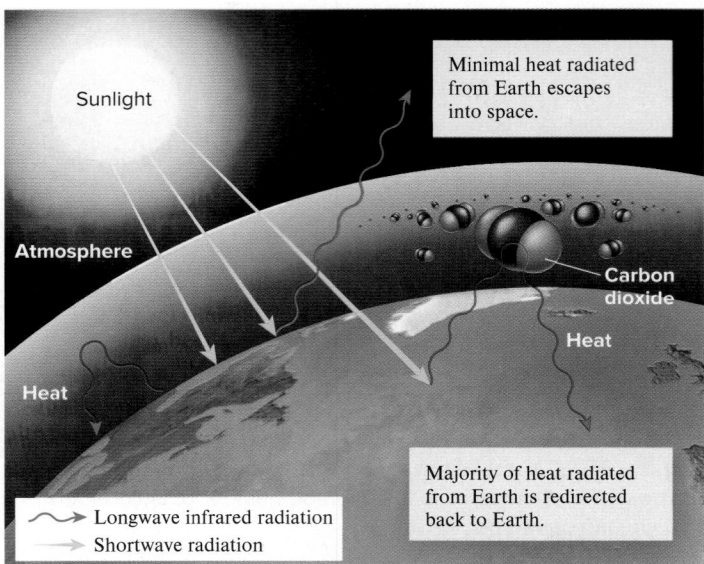

Figure 59.6 **The greenhouse effect is caused by the insulating effect of atmospheric carbon dioxide.** Solar radiation, in the form of short-wave energy, passes through the atmosphere to heat the Earth's surface. Long-wave infrared energy is radiated back into the atmosphere. Most infrared energy is redirected back to Earth by atmospheric gases, including carbon dioxide molecules, causing global temperatures to rise.

form of long-wave infrared radiation. Atmospheric gases absorb much of this infrared energy and radiate it a second time to the Earth's surface, causing its temperature to rise further (**Figure 59.6**). The greenhouse effect is important to life on Earth. Without the greenhouse effect, global temperatures would be much lower than they are, perhaps averaging only –17°C compared with the existing average of +15°C.

The greenhouse effect is caused by a small group of gases, mainly water vapor, that together make up less than 1% of the total volume of the atmosphere. After water vapor, the four most significant greenhouse gases are carbon dioxide, methane, nitrous oxide, and chlorofluorocarbons (**Table 59.1**).

Ecologists are concerned that human activities are increasing the magnitude of the greenhouse effect, resulting in the gradual elevation of the Earth's surface temperature. In particular, the burning of fossil fuels appears to be the main culprit of global warming. Fossil fuels such as oil, coal, and natural gas are high in carbon and release carbon dioxide (CO_2) into the atmosphere when burned. The atmospheric concentrations of most greenhouse gases have increased since the Industrial Revolution over 200 years ago. Of those increasing, the one that is the greatest contributor to global warming is CO_2. As Table 59.1 shows, CO_2 has a lower global warming potential per unit of gas (relative absorption) than any other major greenhouse gas, but its concentration in the atmosphere is much higher. An analysis of air trapped in glaciers shows that concentrations of atmospheric CO_2 increased from about 280 ppm (parts per million) in the pre-industrial 19th century to 400 ppm in 2015 (**Figure 59.7a**).

Since 1957, air samples have been collected directly at Mauna Loa, Hawaii, a relatively unpolluted site. The data show a 25%

Table 59.1	The Major Greenhouse Gases and Their Contribution to Global Warming			
	Carbon dioxide (CO_2)	Methane (CH_4)	Nitrous oxide (N_2O)	Chlorofluorocarbons (CFCs)
Relative absorption in ppm of increase*	1	21	310	10,000
Atmospheric concentration (ppm†)	400	1.75	0.315	0.0005
Contribution to global warming	73%	7%	19%	1%
Percent from natural sources; type of source	20–30%; volcanoes	70–90%; swamps, gas from termites and ruminants	90–100%; soils	0%
Major human-made sources	Fossil-fuel use, deforestation	Rice paddies, landfills, biomass burning, coal and gas exploitation	Cultivated soil, fossil-fuel use, automobiles, industry	Previously manufactured products (for example, aerosol propellants) but now banned in the U.S. and the E.U.

*Relative absorption is the warming potential per unit of gas.
†ppm = parts per million

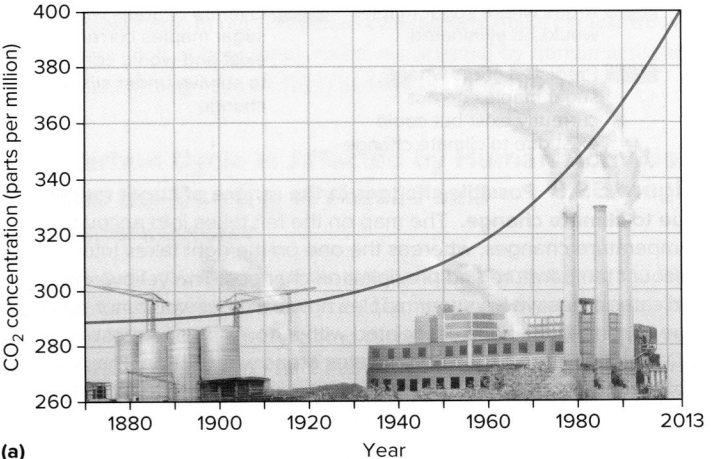

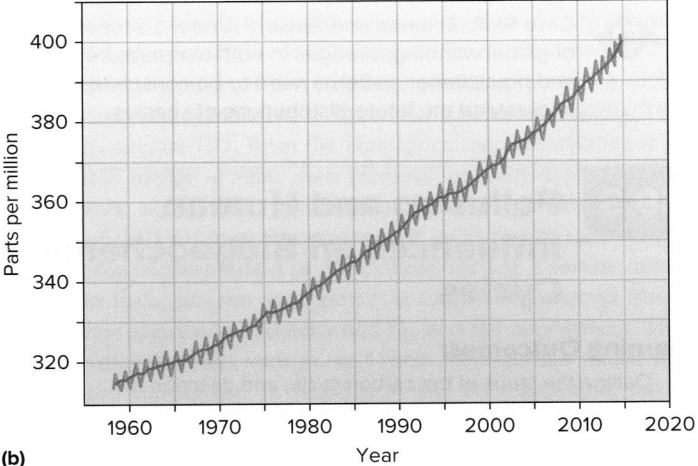

Figure 59.7 The increase of atmospheric carbon dioxide.
(a) Increases in the burning of fossil fuels have caused an increase in atmospheric CO_2 since the late 19th century. **(b)** In air samples taken directly at Mauna Loa, Hawaii, since 1957, CO_2 levels have shown consistent increases.

Concept Check: Why does the amount of CO_2 fluctuate seasonally in the graph in Figure 59.7b?

increase in atmospheric CO_2 levels in just 58 years, from 313 ppm to 400 ppm during 1957–2015 (**Figure 59.7b**). In addition, seasonal oscillations in CO_2 occur, as seen in the orange line of Figure 59.7b. These types of oscillations differ in the two hemispheres of Earth. The Northern Hemisphere, where Hawaii is located, has greater land area and plant biomass than the Southern Hemisphere. In the northern summer, more CO_2 is absorbed by plants and atmospheric CO_2 level declines slightly. In the northern winter, less CO_2 is absorbed and atmospheric CO_2 levels increase.

Global Warming Is Expected to Cause Sea Levels to Rise

To predict the effects of global warming, most scientists focus on a future point, about 2100, when the concentration of atmospheric CO_2 will have doubled—that is, increased to about 700 ppm compared with the late-20th-century level of 350 ppm. The 2014 report of the Intergovernmental Panel on Climate Change (IPCC) suggested that if greenhouse gas emissions continue to rise at the same rate, this would lead to a 2–4°C warming by about the end of this century. This increase in temperature might not seem like much, but it is comparable to the warming that ended the last Ice Age.

One consequence of global warming is its effect on sea levels due to the melting of glaciers. The term **sea level** refers to the average level for the surface of one or more of Earth's oceans. With a 2–4°C warming, sea levels are expected to rise by about 50–60 cm. Sea levels have already risen 10–25 cm over the past century, and seawater entry into coastal forests has killed trees in many areas.

An alarming problem is the long time lag between warming temperatures and the time it takes for ice to melt. Even if future temperature increases were prevented, glaciers would continue to melt for many years. For example, the ice sheets of Greenland will take hundreds of years to melt, even though the increase in temperature needed to melt them could be reached in 50–100 years. You might envision this as being similar to an ice cube on a kitchen counter—it takes a while for the ice cube to melt, even though room temperature is considerably above freezing.

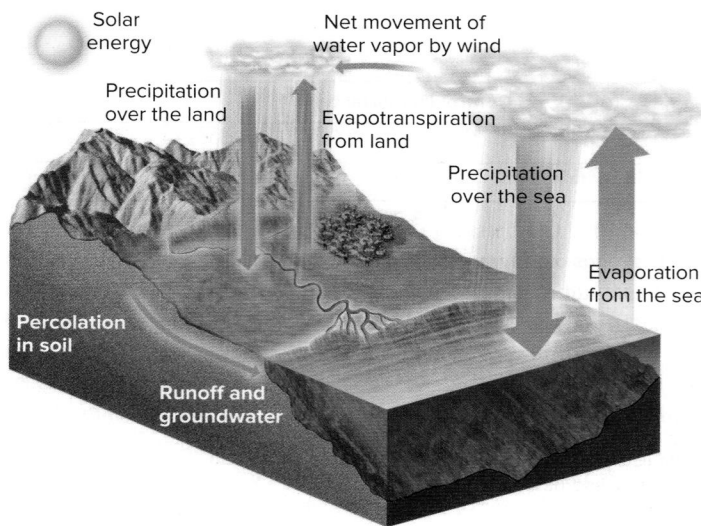

Figure 59.11 The water cycle. This cycle is primarily a physical process, not a chemical one. Solar energy drives the water cycle, causing evaporation of water from the ocean and evapotranspiration from the soil and land plants. The next step is condensation of water vapor into clouds followed by precipitation. The widths of the arrows indicate the relative contribution of each process to the cycle.

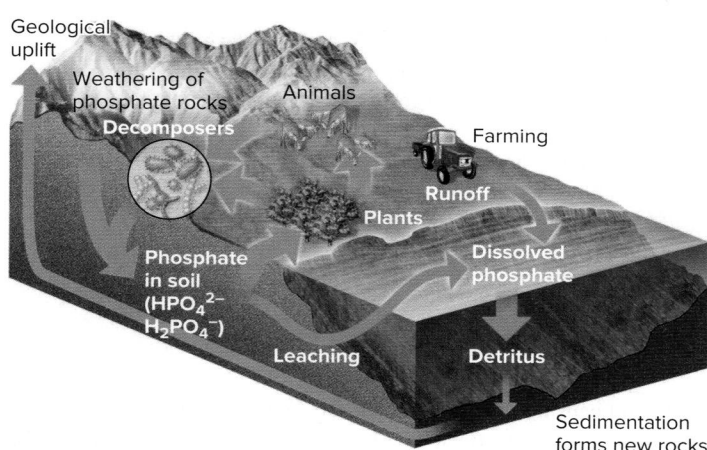

Figure 59.12 The phosphorus cycle. Unlike other major biogeochemical cycles, the phosphorus cycle does not have an atmospheric component and thus cycles only locally. The widths of the arrows indicate the relative contribution of each process to the cycle.

crust is the main storehouse for this element. Weathering and erosion of rocks release phosphorus into the soil. Plants have the metabolic means to absorb dissolved ionized forms of phosphorus, the most important of which occurs as phosphate (HPO_4^{2-} or $H_2PO_4^-$). Herbivores obtain their phosphorus only from eating plants, and carnivores obtain it by eating herbivores or other carnivores. When plants and animals excrete wastes or die, the phosphorus becomes available to decomposers, which release it back to the soil. Leaching and runoff eventually wash much phosphate into aquatic systems, where algae utilize it. Phosphate that is not taken up into the food chain settles to the ocean floor or lake bottom, forming sedimentary rock.

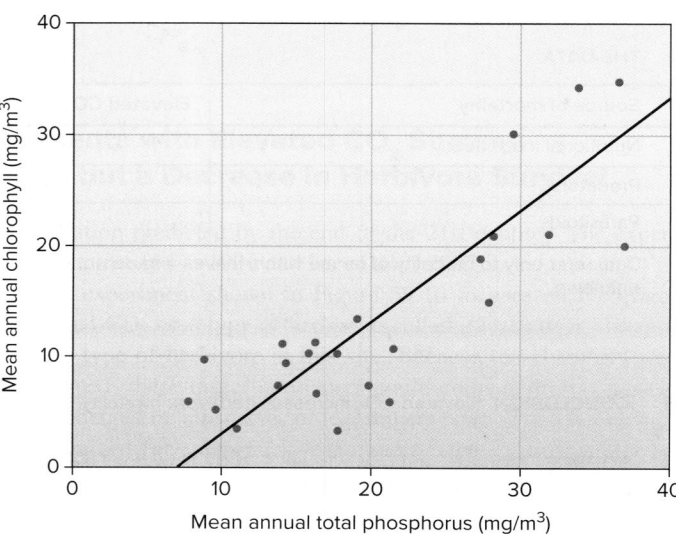

Figure 59.13 The relationship between primary production and total phosphorus concentration. As shown in this graph, primary production (measured by chlorophyll concentration) increases linearly with an increase in phosphorus. Each dot represents a different lake.

Phosphorus is commonly a limiting nutrient in aquatic ecosystems. When more phosphorus is added, the growth of algae and aquatic plants can dramatically increase. In lakes, primary production and total phosphorus concentration appear to follow a linear relationship (**Figure 59.13**). What is the consequence of high primary production? When the algae and plants die, they sink to the bottom, where bacteria decompose them and consume the dissolved oxygen in the water. Dissolved oxygen concentrations can then drop too low for fishes to breathe, killing them. The process by which elevated nutrient levels lead to an overgrowth of algae and the subsequent depletion of water oxygen concentrations is known as **eutrophication**.

Eutrophication is frequently due to the enrichment of water with nutrients derived from human activities, such as fertilizer use and sewage dumping. For example, Lake Erie became eutrophic in the 1960s due to the runoff of fertilizer rich in phosphorus from farms and to the industrial and domestic pollutants released from the many cities along its shores (**Figure 59.14a**). Fish species such as white fish and lake trout became severely depleted. The U.S. and Canada teamed together to reduce the levels of discharge by 80%, primarily through eliminating phosphorus in laundry detergents and maintaining strict controls on the phosphorus content of wastewater from sewage treatment plants. Fortunately, lake systems have great potential for recovery after phosphorus inputs are reduced, and Lake Erie has experienced fewer algal blooms, clearer water, and a restoration of fish populations (**Figure 59.14b**).

Fertilizers and Industrial Pollutants Affect the Nitrogen Cycle

Nitrogen is an essential component of proteins, nucleic acids, and chlorophyll. Because 78% of the Earth's atmosphere consists of nitrogen gas (N_2), it may seem that nitrogen should not be in short supply for organisms. However, nitrogen is often a limiting factor in

(a) Polluted (eutrophication)

(b) Cleared up

Figure 59.14 Phosphorus pollution in Lake Erie. The lake **(a)** in the 1960s, when eutrophic and polluted by industrial effluent and fertilizer runoff, and **(b)** in 2007, after eutrophication was reversed by pollution control laws. a: ©JK Enright/Alamy Stock Photo; b: ©Rolf Hicker Photography/Alamy Stock Photo

ecosystems because N_2 molecules must be broken apart before the individual nitrogen atoms can combine with other elements. Because there is a triple bond between its two nitrogen atoms, N_2 is very stable, and only certain bacteria can break it apart into usable forms such

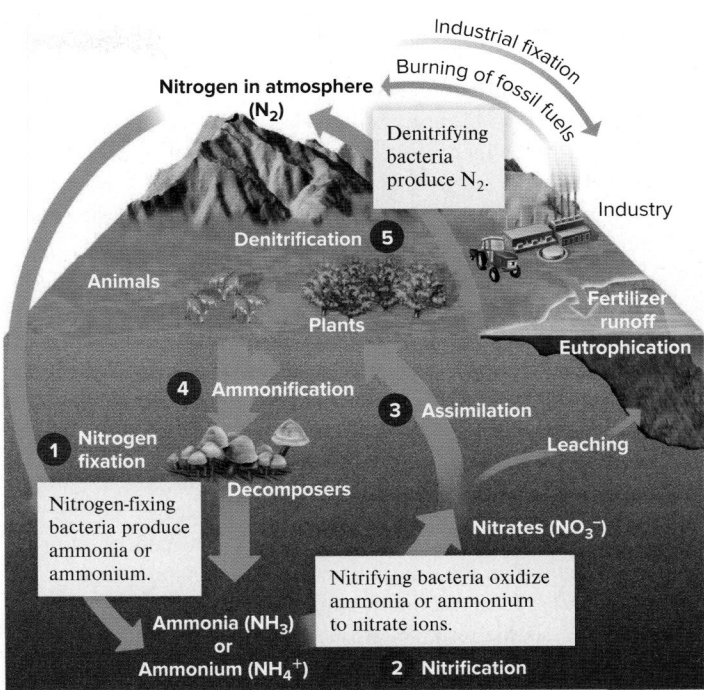

Figure 59.15 The nitrogen cycle. The five main parts of the nitrogen cycle are (1) nitrogen fixation, (2) nitrification, (3) assimilation, (4) ammonification, and (5) denitrification. The recycling of nitrogen from dead plants and animals into the soil and then back into plants is of paramount importance because this is the main pathway for nitrogen to enter the soil. The widths of the arrows indicate the relative contribution of each process to the cycle.

as ammonia (NH_3). This process, called nitrogen fixation, is a critical component of the five-part nitrogen cycle (**Figure 59.15**):

1. A few species of bacteria can accomplish **nitrogen fixation**, that is, convert atmospheric N_2 to forms usable by other organisms. The bacteria that fix nitrogen are fulfilling their own metabolic needs, but in the process, they release ammonia (NH_3) or ammonium (NH_4^+), which can be used by some plants. An important group of nitrogen-fixing bacteria, known as rhizobia, live in nodules on the roots of legumes, including peas, beans, lentils, and peanuts, and of some woody plants. Cyanobacteria are important nitrogen fixers in terrestrial and aquatic systems (refer back to Figure 38.12).

2. In the process of **nitrification**, soil bacteria convert NH_3 or NH_4^+ to nitrate (NO_3^-), a form of nitrogen commonly used by plants. Bacteria of the genera *Nitrosomonas* and *Nitrococcus* first oxidize the forms of ammonia to nitrite (NO_2^-), after which bacteria of the genus *Nitrobacter* convert NO_2^- to NO_3^-.

3. **Assimilation** is the process by which inorganic substances are incorporated into organic molecules. In the nitrogen cycle, organisms assimilate nitrogen by taking up NH_3, NH_4^+, and NO_3^- formed through nitrogen fixation and nitrification and incorporating them into organic molecules. Plants take up these forms of nitrogen through their roots, and animals assimilate nitrogen from the plant tissues they ingest.

4. Ammonia can also be formed in the soil through the decomposition of plants and animals and the release of animal waste. **Ammonification** is the conversion of organic nitrogen to NH_3 and NH_4^+. This process is carried out by bacteria and fungi. Most soils are slightly acidic, and, because of an excess of H^+, the NH_3 rapidly gains an additional H^+ to form NH_4^+. Because many soils lack nitrifying bacteria, ammonification is the most common pathway for nitrogen to enter the soil.

5. **Denitrification** is the reduction of NO_3^- to N_2. Denitrifying bacteria, which are anaerobic and use NO_3^- in their metabolism instead of O_2, perform the reverse of their nitrogen-fixing counterparts by delivering N_2 to the atmosphere. This process contributes only a relatively small amount of nitrogen to the atmosphere.

Human activities have approximately doubled the rate of nitrogen input to the nitrogen cycle. Industrial fixation of nitrogen for the production of fertilizer makes a major contribution to the pool of nitrogen-containing material in the soils and waters of agricultural regions. As with phosphorus, fertilizer runoff can cause eutrophication of rivers and lakes, and, as the resultant algae die, decomposition by bacteria depletes the oxygen level of the water, resulting in fish kills.

Excess NO_3^- in surface or groundwater systems used for drinking water is also a health hazard, particularly for infants. In the body, NO_3^- is converted to NO_2^-, which then combines with hemoglobin to form methemoglobin, a type of hemoglobin that does not carry oxygen. In infants, the production of large amounts of NO_2^- can cause methemoglobinemia, a dangerous condition in which the level of O_2 carried through the body decreases.

Finally, burning fossil fuels releases not only carbon but also nitrogen in the form of nitrous oxide (N_2O), which contributes to air pollution. N_2O can react with rainwater to form nitric acid (HNO_3), a component of acid rain, which decreases the pH of lakes and streams and increases fish mortality. The release of sulfur from the burning of fossil fuels also contributes to acid rain since the sulfur reacts with rainwater to form highly acidic sulfuric acid.

59.4 Pollution and Biomagnification

Learning Outcome:

1. Define biomagnification, and explain its relationship to pollution.

In Section 59.3, we considered how pollution generated by humans can affect biogeochemical cycles. Certain types of pollutants can also accumulate within the bodies of animals and plants. The tendency of certain chemicals to concentrate in organisms at higher trophic levels in food chains, which is called **biomagnification**, can cause health and reproductive problems for certain organisms.

The passage of dichlorodiphenyltrichloroethane (DDT), an insecticide used against mosquitoes and agricultural pests, through food chains provides a startling example of biomagnification. DDT was first synthesized by chemists in 1874. In 1939, its insecticidal properties were recognized by Paul Müller, a Swiss scientist who won the 1948 Nobel Prize in Physiology or Medicine for his discovery and subsequent research on

the uses of the chemical. The first important application of DDT was in human health programs during and after World War II, particularly as a means of controlling mosquito-borne malaria; at that time, its use in agriculture also began. The global production of DDT peaked in 1970, when 175 million kilograms of the insecticide was manufactured.

DDT has several chemical and physical properties that profoundly influence its ecological effect. First, DDT is persistent in the environment. It is not rapidly degraded to other, less toxic chemicals by microorganisms or by physical agents such as light and heat. The typical persistence in soil of DDT is about 10 years, which is two to three times longer than the persistence of many other insecticides. Another important characteristic of DDT is its low solubility in water and its high solubility in fats, or lipids. In the environment, most lipids are present in living tissue. Therefore, because of its high lipid solubility, DDT tends to concentrate in biological tissues.

Because biomagnification occurs at each step of a food chain, organisms at higher trophic levels can accumulate especially high concentrations of DDT in their lipids. A typical pattern of biomagnification is illustrated in **Figure 59.16**, which shows the relative amounts of DDT found in a Lake Michigan food chain. The highest concentration of the insecticide was found in gulls, tertiary consumers that feed on fishes, which are the secondary consumers that eat small insects. An unanticipated effect of DDT on bird species was its interference with the metabolic process of eggshell formation. The result

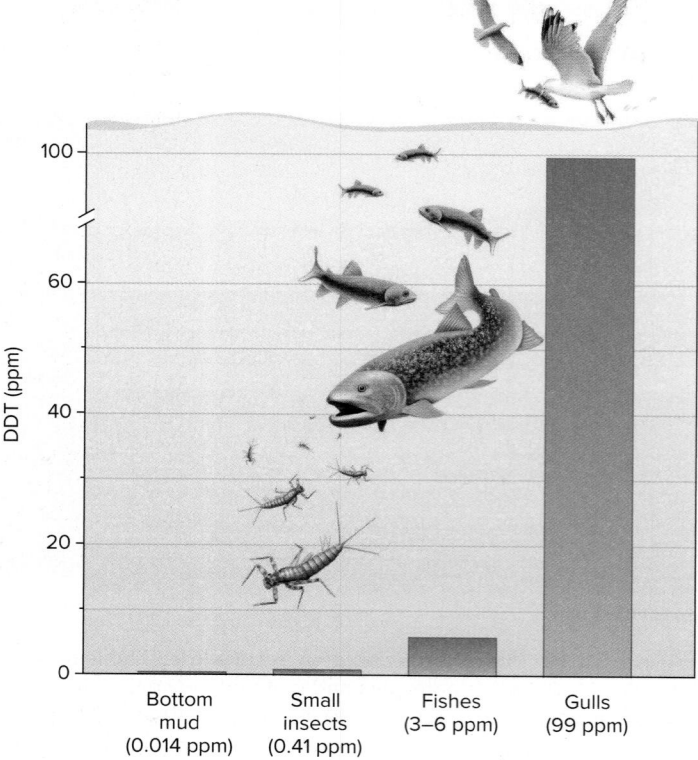

Figure 59.16 Biomagnification in a Lake Michigan food chain. The DDT tissue concentration in gulls, a tertiary consumer, was about 240 times that in the small insects sharing the same environment. The biomagnification of DDT in lipids causes its concentration to increase at each successive level in the food chain. The unit ppm is equivalent to 1 mg of DDT per kg of biological material.

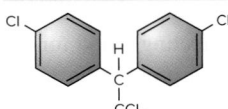

DDT (dichlorodiphenyltrichloroethane)
- Persists in environment
- High solubility in lipids
- Found in high concentrations at higher trophic levels

Figure 59.17   Thinning of eggshells caused by DDT. Ibis eggs, Texas Gulf Coast. ©George Silk/The LIFE Picture Collection/Getty Images

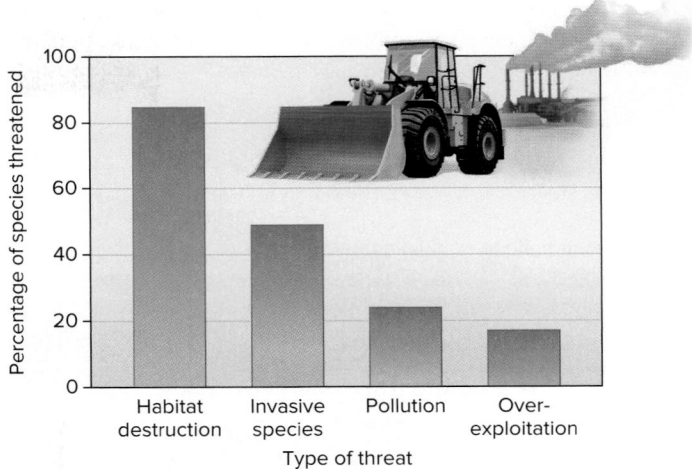

Figure 59.18   Percentages of plant and animal species threatened by various causes in the U.S. Species can suffer from multiple threats, so categories do not sum to 100%.

 Core Skill: Science and Society The effects of humans greatly increase the percentage of species threatened with extinction.

was thin-shelled eggs that often broke under the weight of incubating birds (**Figure 59.17**). DDT was responsible for a dramatic decrease in the populations of many birds due to failed reproduction. Relatively high levels of the chemical were also found to be present in some game fishes, which, as a result, became unfit for human consumption.

Because of growing awareness of the adverse effects of DDT, most industrialized countries, including the U.S., banned the use of the chemical by the early 1970s. The good news is that following the outlawing of DDT, populations of the most severely affected bird species have recovered. However, had scientists initially possessed a more thorough knowledge of how DDT accumulates in food chains, some of the damage to the bird populations might have been prevented.

Biomagnification occurs for other types of molecules that do not break down quickly in the environment and are not excreted efficiently by living organisms. Such substances include mercury, which is emitted from coal-fired power plants, and persistent organic pollutants, or POPs, that are used in herbicides and pesticides. Underwater mining of the ocean floor to extract minerals releases sulfide and selenium that can also biomagnify in food chains.

59.5   Habitat Destruction

Learning Outcomes:

1. Identify the main causes of habitat destruction by humans.
2. Explain why tropical deforestation is a particularly destructive form of habitat loss.
3. Describe how the impact of agriculture causes ecological changes.

Habitat destruction is usually a human-driven process in which a natural habitat is altered in a way that prevents it from supporting the species that were originally present. Organisms that previously occupied the habitat are displaced or unable to survive, thereby reducing biodiversity. Habitat destruction is the primary cause of species extinction, and a high percentage of existing species are threatened

by this process (**Figure 59.18**). Other human-driven practices that are threatening the survival of many species include pollution, which has already been discussed in this chapter, and overexploitation and invasive species, which are described in the last two sections.

Habitat destruction includes deforestation, conversion of habitat to agricultural land, urbanization, strip mining, quarrying, and many other forms of land modification. Urbanization, the development of cities on previously natural or agricultural areas, is the most human-dominated and fastest-growing type of land use worldwide, and it devastates the land more severely than nearly any other form of habitat destruction. Freshwater habitats have also suffered via dam construction and river channelization. Wetlands have been drained for agricultural purposes and have been filled in for urban or industrial development. In the U.S., as much as 90% of freshwater marshes have disappeared in states such as Iowa and California, though the national average is approximately 53%. In this section, we will examine the two most widespread and interrelated types of habitat destruction, at least in terms of their influence on species extinctions. These are deforestation and the conversion of land to agricultural purposes.

Deforestation by Humans Threatens the Existence of Many Species

Deforestation, the conversion of forested areas to nonforested land, is a prime cause of the extinction of species (**Figure 59.19**). About one-third of the world's land surface is covered with forests, and much of this area is at risk of deforestation.

Many species live in forests. For example, among North American terrestrial wildlife, about one-quarter of the bird species (272 species) and more than 10% of mammalian species (49 species) have an obligatory relationship with forest cover, meaning that they depend on trees for food and nesting sites. In terms of wildlife use, oaks are among the

59.3 Pollution and Human Influences on Biogeochemical Cycles

- Biogeochemical cycles involve the movement of carbon, phosphorus, nitrogen, and water between the physical environment and organisms.

- In the carbon cycle, phototrophs incorporate CO_2 from the atmosphere into their biomass; decomposition of plants and respiration recycle most of this CO_2 back to the atmosphere. Human activities, primarily the burning of fossil fuels, are causing increased amounts of CO_2 to enter the atmosphere (Figures 59.9, 59.10).

- The water cycle is a physical rather than a chemical process because it consists of essentially two phenomena: evaporation and precipitation. Climate change is altering precipitation patterns. In addition, alteration of the water cycle by dams can greatly disrupt migration of fishes such as salmon and trout (Figure 59.11).

- The phosphorus cycle lacks an atmospheric component and thus is a local cycle. An overabundance of phosphorus can cause the overgrowth of algae and subsequent depletion of oxygen levels, called eutrophication (Figures 59.12, 59.13, 59.14).

- The nitrogen cycle has five parts: nitrogen fixation, nitrification, assimilation, ammonification, and denitrification. The activities of humans, including the production and use of fertilizers, have altered the nitrogen cycle (Figure 59.15).

59.4 Pollution and Biomagnification

- Biomagnification is the tendency of certain chemicals to concentrate in higher trophic levels in food chains (Figures 59.16, 59.17).

59.5 Habitat Destruction

- Habitat destruction involves the conversion of natural habitat to agricultural land, urbanization, the draining of swamps, strip mining, dam destruction, and many other forms of land modification. It is the primary cause of species extinction and is threatening many current species (Figure 59.18).

- Deforestation—in particular, of tropical forests—threatens many species with extinction because of the high numbers of species that live in forests and the high rate of forest loss (Figures 59.19, 59.20).

- The planting of crops and the grazing of livestock are among the most important drivers of ecological change. Habitat destruction has changed huge areas of the planet into agricultural areas and rangelands for livestock (Figure 59.21; Table 59.2).

59.6 Overexploitation

- Overexploitation is the practice in which humans harvest a particular species at a rate that is unsustainable. The overexploitation of plants and animals occurs via hunting, fishing, and removing species from their native habitat. On average, humans decrease prey populations much more than natural predators do (Figure 59.22).

- Overexploitation has decreased the populations of many species and driven some of them to extinction. Examples include whales, the passenger pigeon, and many species of fishes and plants (Figures 59.23–59.27).

- The maximum sustainable yield is the largest number of individuals that can be harvested without causing long-term decreases in the population. Simple economic models suggest that populations should be harvested at levels of maximum profit, which is well below the maximum sustainable yield (Figure 59.28).

59.7 Invasive Species

- Invasive species are those species introduced into new geographic areas by humans and spread on their own without human support. Invasive species may impact native species as competitors, predators, and pathogens (Figures 59.29–59.32).

Assess & Discuss

Test Yourself

1. The average total fertility rate needed for zero population change across the world is
   a. 1.7.   d. 2.3.
   b. 1.9.   e. 2.5.
   c. 2.0.

2. Which anthropogenic gas contributes most to global warming?
   a. methane
   b. chlorofluorocarbons
   c. carbon dioxide
   d. nitrogen oxides
   e. sulfur dioxide

3. The data show that atmospheric carbon dioxide levels have increased by what percentage over the past 58 years?
   a. 1%   d. 25%
   b. 5%   e. 52%
   c. 12%

4. Eutrophication is
   a. caused by an overabundance of nitrogen, which leads to a decrease in bacteria populations.
   b. caused by an overabundance of nutrients, which leads to an increase in algal populations.
   c. usually caused by oil spills.
   d. normally seen in dry, hot regions of the world.
   e. accelerated by habitat loss.

5. Human production of fertilizers first impacts which part of the nitrogen cycle?
   a. nitrogen fixation   d. ammonification
   b. nitrification   e. denitrification
   c. assimilation

6. The concentration of certain chemicals, such as DDT, in higher trophic levels is known as
   a. eutrophication.   d. energy transfer.
   b. biomagnification.   e. turnover.
   c. biogeochemical cycling.

7. Which is *not* an example of habitat destruction?
   a. deforestation   d. draining of wetlands
   b. agriculture   e. overharvesting
   c. urbanization

8. The passenger pigeon, once the most common bird in North America, was driven to extinction by
   a. pollution.   d. invasive species.
   b. overexploitation.   e. all of the above.
   c. habitat destruction.

9. Most recorded extinctions have been caused by
   a. invasive species.   d. a and b equally.
   b. habitat destruction.   e. a, b, and c equally.
   c. overexploitation.

10. Invasive species enter an area through
    a. agricultural introductions.
    b. accidental transportation via ships.
    c. landscape plants and their pests.
    d. a and b.
    e. a, b, and c.

Conceptual Questions

1. The Earth's atmosphere consists of 78% nitrogen. Why is nitrogen a limiting nutrient?

2. Why does maximum sustainable yield occur at the midpoint of the logistic curve and not where the population is at carrying capacity?

3. **Core Skill: Science and Society** In one family, parents, who were born in 1900, have twins at age 20 but then have no more children. Their children, grandchildren, and so on behave in the same way. In another family, parents, who were also born in 1900, delay reproduction until age 33 but have triplets. Their children and grandchildren behave in the same way. Which family has the most descendants by 2000? What can you conclude?

Collaborative Questions

1. Discuss what might limit human population growth in the future.

2. As a group, try to predict what effects an atmospheric concentration of 700 ppm of CO_2 might have on the environment.

Biodiversity and Conservation Biology

60

Spix's macaw (*Cyanopsitta spixii*). Less than 100 individuals of this species are known to exist in the rain forests of Brazil.

©Patrick Pleul/dpa/picture-alliance/Newscom

I n 2009, Jeff Corwin, an American conservationist and host for programs on Animal Planet and other television networks, published a book entitled *100 Heartbeats: The Race to Save the Earth's Most Endangered Species*. The Hundred Heartbeat Club had been created earlier by biologist E. O. Wilson to highlight the plight of animal species, such as Spix's macaw (*Cyanopsitta spixii*) in Brazil (see the chapter opening photo), the Chinese river dolphin (*Lipotes vexillifer*), and the Philippine eagle (*Pithecophaga jefferyi*), that have 100 or fewer individuals left alive (and hence are that number of heartbeats away from extinction). Saving species from extinction is important in its own right, but, as we will see, conservation of biological diversity also has great economic and social value to humankind.

Biological diversity, or **biodiversity**, encompasses the genetic diversity of species, the variety of species, and the different ecosystems they form. The field of **conservation biology**

uses principles and knowledge from molecular biology, genetics, and ecology to protect and sustain biodiversity. Because it draws from nearly all chapters of this textbook, a discussion of conservation biology is a fitting way to conclude our study of biology. In this chapter, we will begin by examining the questions of what biodiversity is and why it should be conserved and exploring how much biodiversity is needed for ecosystems to function properly.

Later, we will consider what is being done to help conserve the world's endangered plant and animal life. This includes identifying global areas rich in species and establishing parks and refuges of the appropriate size, number, and connectivity. We will also discuss conservation of particularly important types of species and how to restore damaged habitats to a more natural condition. We then examine how captive-breeding programs help to build populations of rare species prior to their release back into the wild. Some programs have also used modern genetic techniques such as cloning to help breed and perhaps eventually increase populations of endangered species.

60.1 Genetic, Species, and Ecosystem Diversity

Learning Outcome:

1. List and describe the three levels of biodiversity.

Biodiversity can be examined on three levels: genetic diversity, species diversity, and ecosystem diversity. Each level of biodiversity provides valuable benefits to humanity.

Genetic diversity is the amount of genetic variation occurring within and between populations. Without such variation, populations may be unable to respond quickly to changes in environmental conditions, resulting in population decline and even extinction. Maintaining genetic variation in the wild relatives of crops may be vital to the continued success of crop-breeding programs. For example, the café marron (*Ramosmania rodriguesii*), a wild relative of the coffee plant that is native to a tiny island off the coast of

Figure 60.1 **Café marron being cultured in London's Kew Gardens.** These plants are derived from just one surviving individual found in Mauritius. ©Florapix/Alamy Stock Photo

Mauritius, was assumed to be extinct until 1979, when one surviving tree was identified. Today, cuttings from the tree are being cultured in London's Kew Gardens (**Figure 60.1**). The plant may carry genes that could allow coffee to be grown in a wider range of soils and elevations.

A second level of biodiversity is **species diversity**, the number and relative abundance of species in a community (refer back to Section 58.1). In 1973, the U.S. Endangered Species Act (ESA) was enacted, which was designed to protect both endangered and threatened species. **Endangered species** are those species that are in danger of extinction throughout all or a significant portion of their range. **Threatened species** are those species likely to become endangered in the foreseeable future. Many species are currently threatened. According to the International Union for Conservation of Nature and Natural Resources (IUCN), more than 25% of the fish species that live on coral reefs and 22% of all mammals, 12% of birds, and 31% of amphibians are threatened with extinction. In 2000, the World Wildlife Foundation placed Atlantic cod (*Gadus morhua*) on the endangered species list as a result of overfishing. Nine of 17 populations of commercially important Chinook salmon (*Oncorhynchus tshawytscha*) in California and Oregon are listed as endangered or threatened.

The last level of biodiversity is **ecosystem diversity**, the diversity of structure and function within an ecosystem. Conservation has largely focused attention on species-rich ecosystems such as tropical rain forests. Over 120 prescription drugs used to treat malaria, cancer, and other diseases were developed from rain forest plants, yet less than 1% of such plants have been tested for medicinal properties. However, some ecologists have argued that relatively species-poor ecosystems such as prairies are also highly threatened and in equal need of conservation. More than 99% of the original tallgrass prairie in the United States has been converted to agricultural land.

60.2 Biodiversity and Ecosystem Function

Learning Outcomes:

1. **CoreSKILLS »** Create graphical representations of possible relationships between biodiversity level and ecosystem function.

2. Describe experimental evidence that shows how species richness and ecosystem function are linked.

Because biodiversity affects the health of ecosystems, ecologists have explored the question of how much diversity is needed for ecosystems to function properly. In this section, we will examine several models that explore the relationship between ecosystem function and species richness and examine an experimental approach used to study this relationship.

Ecologists Have Proposed Several Models for the Relationship Between Ecosystem Function and Species Richness

Because biodiversity affects the health of ecosystems, ecologists have explored the question of how many species are needed for ecosystems to function properly. In doing so, they have described several possible relationships between ecosystem function and species richness. In the 1950s, ecologist Charles Elton proposed the **diversity-stability hypothesis**, which suggests that species-rich communities are more stable than those with fewer species (refer back to Section 58.2). If we use stability as a measure of ecosystem function, Elton's hypothesis indicates a linear correlation between ecosystem function and species richness; as the number of different species increases, ecosystem function increases proportionately (**Figure 60.2a**). Australian ecologist Brian Walker proposed an alternative to this idea, termed the **redundancy hypothesis** (**Figure 60.2b**). According to this hypothesis, ecosystem function increases rapidly at fairly low levels of species richness, but then levels off because most additional species are functionally redundant.

Two other alternative ideas relating species richness and ecosystem function have been proposed. The **keystone hypothesis** (**Figure 60.2c**) proposes that ecosystem function dramatically rises as species richness approaches its natural level. Finally, the **idiosyncratic hypothesis** suggests that although ecosystem function can change as the number of species increases or decreases, the amount and direction of change are unpredictable (**Figure 60.2d**).

Determining the correct model(s) for the relationship between ecosystem function and species richness is very important, as our understanding of the effect of species loss on ecosystem function can greatly affect the way we manage our environment. Only relatively recently has the link between ecosystem function and species richness been studied. An early and influential study, conducted by Shahid Naeem and his colleagues in laboratories in England, is described next.

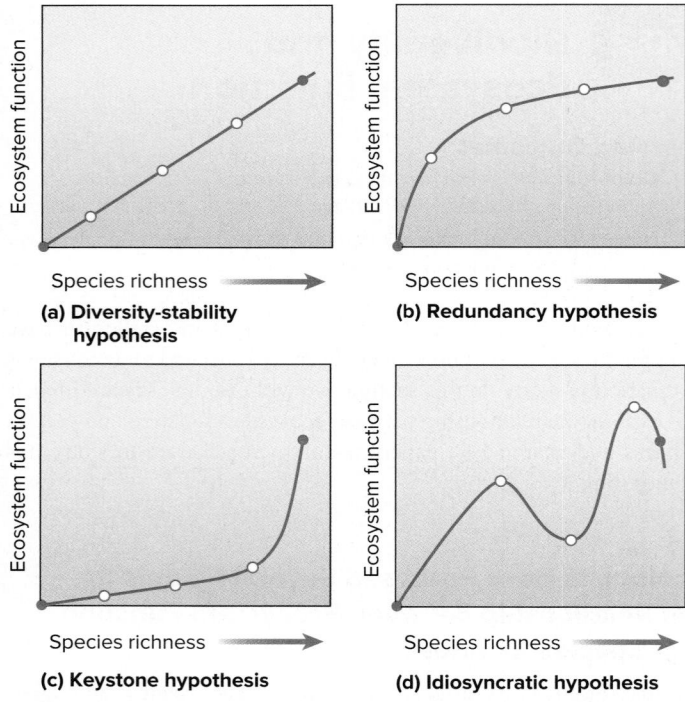

(a) Diversity-stability hypothesis

(b) Redundancy hypothesis

(c) Keystone hypothesis

(d) Idiosyncratic hypothesis

Figure 60.2 **Graphical representations of possible relationships between ecosystem function and species richness.** The two solid dots represent the end points of a continuum of species richness. The first dot is at the origin, where there are no species and no community services. The second dot represents a natural level of species richness. The relationship is strongest in **(a)** and weakest in **(d)**.

 Core Skill: Modeling The goal of this modeling challenge is to draw a graph showing a different relationship between ecosystem function and species richness, one based on the rivet hypothesis, which was proposed in 1981.

Modeling Challenge: In 1981, Paul and Ann Ehrlich proposed a relationship between ecosystem function and species richness called the rivet hypothesis. In this model, species are like the rivets on an airplane. Some species play a small but critical role in keeping the plane, the ecosystem, airborne, while other species do not, and we cannot tell beforehand which species affect the ecosystem function the most. The loss of a single rivet will probably not weaken the plane. However, the loss of few rivets would impair airworthiness. The plane could still function but not at maximum efficiency. Continuing on, the loss of a few more rivets could again be tolerated, but the loss of yet more rivets would prove critical to the airplane's function. Thus, ecosystem function declines with decreased species richness in a stepwise fashion. Draw a graph that depicts a model for the rivet hypothesis. Use the same format as those in Figure 60.2.

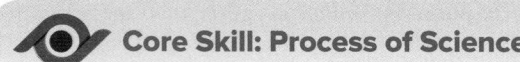 **Core Skill: Process of Science**

Feature Investigation | Ecotron Experiments Analyzed the Relationship Between Ecosystem Function and Species Richness

In the early 1990s, American ecologist Shahid Naeem and colleagues used a series of 14 environmental chambers in a facility termed the Ecotron, at Silwood Park, England, to determine how species richness affects ecosystem function. These chambers contained terrestrial communities that differed only in their level of species richness (**Figure 60.3**). The number of species in each chamber was manipulated to create high-, medium-, and low-richness ecosystems, each with four trophic levels. The trophic levels consisted of primary

Figure 60.3 **Ecotron experiments comparing species richness and ecosystem function.** (3): ©Pete Manning, Ecotron Facility, NERC Centre for Population Biology

Concept Check: *What is one of the dangers in interpreting these results?*

HYPOTHESIS Reduced species richness can lead to reduced ecosystem functioning.

STARTING LOCATION Ecotron, a controlled environment facility at the Natural Environment Research Council (NERC) Centre for Population Biology, in Silwood Park, England.

Experimental level

Conceptual level

1 Construct 14 identical experimental chambers.

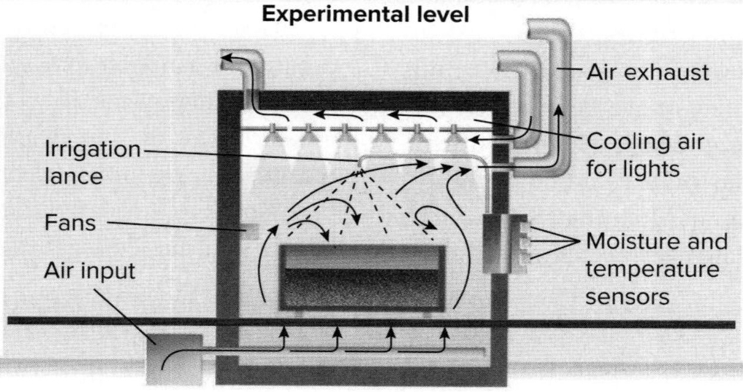

Air exhaust

Cooling air for lights

Irrigation lance

Fans

Air input

Moisture and temperature sensors

Temperature- and humidity-controlled chambers are used to control environmental conditions and allow identical starting conditions in all chambers.

2 Add different combinations of species to the 14 chambers. The species added were based on 3 types of model communities (food webs), each with 4 trophic levels but with varying degrees of species richness.

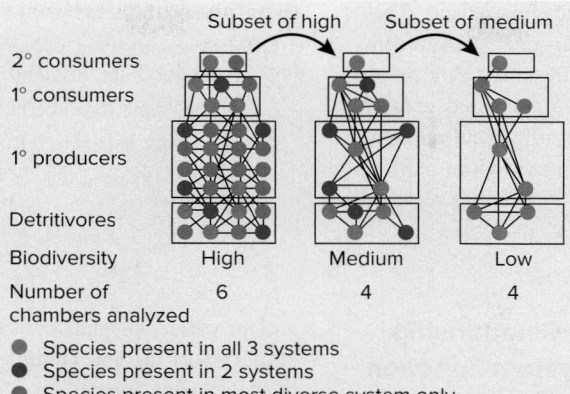

Subset of high   Subset of medium

2° consumers
1° consumers

1° producers

Detritivores

Biodiversity   High   Medium   Low
Number of   6   4   4
chambers analyzed

● Species present in all 3 systems
● Species present in 2 systems
● Species present in most diverse system only

The three diagrams to the left each represent a single chamber. Circles represent species, and lines connecting them represent biotic interactions among the species. Note that each lower-biodiversity community is a subset of its higher-diversity counterpart and that all community types have 4 trophic levels.

3 Measure and analyze a range of processes, including vegetation cover and nutrient uptake.

Measurements help determine how each different type of community functions.

4 THE DATA

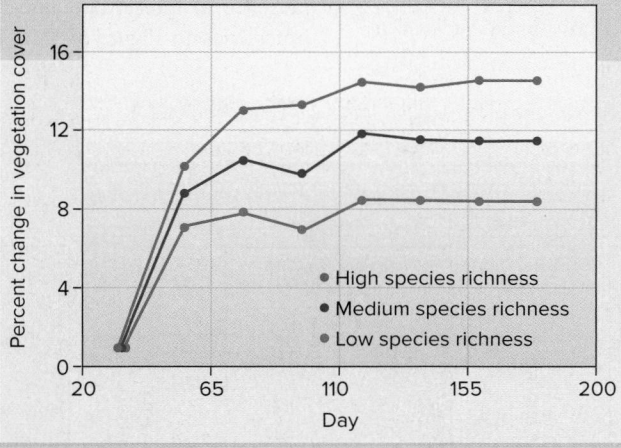

Plant productivity is linked to community diversity as measured by the percent change in vegetation cover from initial conditions.

Data reveal that low-diversity communities have lower vegetation cover and thus are less productive than high-diversity communities.

5 **CONCLUSION** Increases in species richness lead to increases in ecosystem function. In this case, increased plant species richness results in greater vegetation cover.

6 **SOURCE** Naeem, S., et al. 1994. Declining biodiversity can alter the performance of ecosystems. *Nature* 368: 734–737.

producers (annual plants), primary consumers (insects, snails, and slugs), secondary consumers (parasitoids that fed on the herbivores), and detritivores (earthworms and soil insects). The experiment ran for just over 6 months, and species were added only after the trophic level below them was established. For example, parasitoids were not added until herbivores were abundant.

Researchers monitored and analyzed a range of measures of ecosystem function, including community respiration, decomposition, nutrient retention rates, and community productivity. The data shown in step 4 of Figure 60.3 focus only on community productivity. The result was that community productivity, expressed as percent change in vegetation cover (the amount of ground covered by leaves of plants), increased as species richness increased. This productivity increase occurred because plant species of different heights could utilize light at different levels of the plant canopy. A larger ground cover also meant a larger plant biomass and greater community productivity, and increased decomposition and nutrient uptake rates. For the first time, ecologists had provided an experimental demonstration that a loss of species richness can alter or impair the functioning of an ecosystem.

Experimental Questions

1. What was the goal of Naeem and colleagues in their experiment at Silwood Park, England?

2. What was the hypothesis tested by the researchers?

3. **CoreSKILL »** How did the researchers test for ecosystem functioning?

4. **CoreSKILL »** Which relationship between species richness and ecosystem function do these results support? (Refer to Figure 60.2.)

Field Experiments Have Explored the Relationship Between Species Richness and Ecosystem Function

In the mid-1990s, David Tilman and colleagues performed experiments in the field to determine how species richness affected proper ecosystem functioning. Tilman's previous experiments had suggested that species-rich grasslands were more stable (that is, they were more resistant to the ravages of drought and recovered from drought more quickly) than species-poor grasslands (refer back to Figure 58.4). In subsequent experiments, Tilman's group sowed multiple plots, each 3 m by 3 m and having comparable soils, with seeds of 1, 2, 4, 6, 8, 12, or 24 species of prairie plants. Exactly which species were sown into each plot was determined randomly from a pool of 24 native species. The treatments were replicated 21 times, for a total of 147 plots.

The results showed that plots with more species had increased productivity, expressed as a percentage of plant cover (the amount of ground covered by leaves of plants) than plots with fewer species (**Figure 60.4a**). More species-rich plots also used more nutrients, such as nitrate (NO_3^-), than lower richness plots because a greater variety of plant root lengths could utilize nutrients at different levels of the soil (**Figure 60.4b**). Furthermore, the frequency of invasive plant species (species not originally planted in the plots) decreased with increased plant species richness (**Figure 60.4c**).

Although Tilman's results show a relationship between species richness and ecosystem function, they also suggest that most of the advantages of increasing richness come with the first 5–10 species, beyond which adding more species appears to have little to no effect. These data support the redundancy hypothesis (see Figure 60.2b).

Confirmation of the redundancy hypothesis is also observed on a larger scale. The productivity of temperate forests on different continents is roughly the same, despite different numbers of tree species being present: 729 species in East Asia, 253 in North America, and 124 in Europe. The presence of more tree species may ensure a supply of "backups," should some of the most productive species die off from insect attack or disease. This effect was seen following the demise of the American chestnut tree. Disease devastated this species, and its presence in forests dramatically decreased by the mid-20th century (refer back to Figure 59.32). The forests filled in with other species

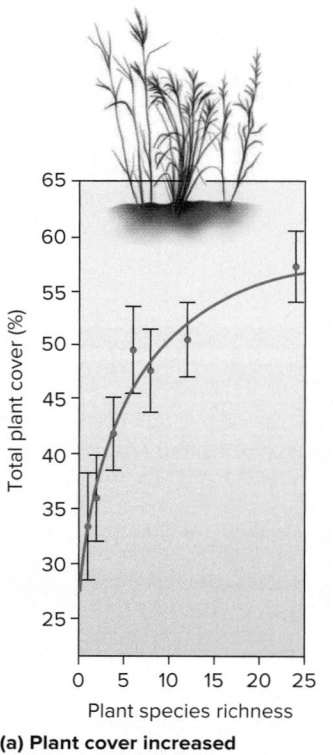

(a) Plant cover increased with more species.

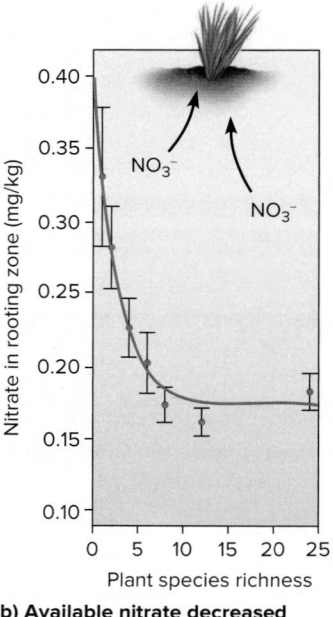

(b) Available nitrate decreased with more species.

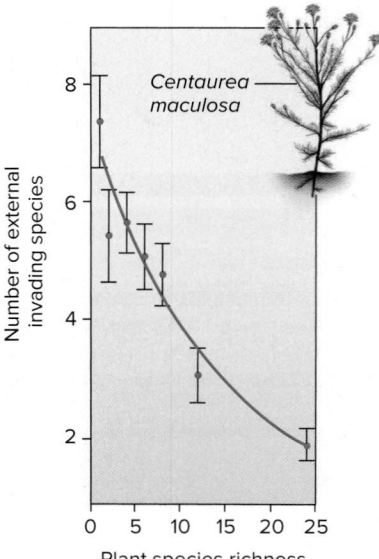

(c) Invasive species decreased with more species.

Figure 60.4 The relationship of species richness to ecosystem function.

and continued to function as before in terms of nutrient cycling and gas exchange. However, although the forests continued to function without the American chestnuts, some important changes occurred. For example, the loss of chestnuts deprived bears and other animals of an important source of food and may have affected their reproductive capacity and hence the size of their populations.

60.3 Value of Biodiversity to Human Welfare

Learning Outcomes:

1. Outline the benefits of biological diversity to human welfare.

Why should biodiversity be a concern? American biologists Paul Ehrlich and E. O. Wilson have suggested that the loss of biodiversity should be an area of great concern for at least three reasons:

1. Humans depend on plants, animals, and microorganisms for a wide range of foods, medicines, and industrial products.

2. Ecosystems provide an array of essential services, such as clean air and water.

3. Humans have an ethical responsibility to protect what are our only known living companions in the universe.

In this section, we examine some of the primary reasons why it is so important to preserve biodiversity.

Society Benefits Economically from Biodiversity

Many different sectors of society benefit from biodiversity. Three key sectors are the pharmaceutical, agricultural, and the natural products industries.

Pharmaceutical Industry The pharmaceutical industry is heavily dependent on plant, animal, fungal, and bacterial products for source material. Worldwide prescription drug sales are forecast to be $1 trillion in 2020.

An estimated 50,000–70,000 plant species are used in traditional and modern medicine. About 25% of the prescription drugs in the U.S. alone are derived from plants, and the 2015 market value of such drugs was estimated to be $374 billion, accounting for a little less than half the global pharmaceutical market. Many medicines come from plants found only in tropical rain forests. These include quinine, a drug from the bark of the cinchona tree (*Cinchona officinalis*), which is used for treating malaria, and vincristine, a drug derived from rosy periwinkle (*Catharanthus roseus*), which is a treatment for leukemia and Hodgkin's disease (**Figure 60.5a**).

Animal products have also been important to the pharmaceutical industry. For example, the venom of the gila monster (*Heloderma suspectum*), one of only two venomous lizards in the world, is being used to treat people who are resistant to conventional treatment for type 2 diabetes, a disease that may affect 30% of Americans at some point in their lives. A protein from the South American pit viper (*Bothrops jacara*) may help control human blood pressure. Tarantula venom may be helpful in treating neurological disorders such as Parkinson's disease.

Fungi and soil bacteria have provided an important reservoir of drugs. In 1928, Scottish scientist Alexander Fleming discovered that a fungus of the genus *Penicillium* produces penicillin, one of the first and most widely used antibiotics. In 1964, a group of Canadian scientists traveled to Easter Island and identified a drug produced by a soil bacterium that suppresses immune reactions in human. It is used to prevent organ rejection in transplants and as a coating on heart stents. The drug was named rapamycin after the indigenous name of Easter Island, which is Rapa Nui.

Agriculture Although humans depend on only about 20 plant species to provide 90% of the world's food, wild relatives of these crops provide a useful reservoir of genetic material for developing pest-resistant varieties or strains that can grow in marginal areas. A gene from longstamen rice (*Oryza longistaminata*), a grass species from Africa, has been integrated into the genome of commercially grown rice (*O. sativa*) to confer resistance to rice blight disease (**Figure 60.5b**). In the 1970s, infusion of genetic material from wild corn in Mexico

(a)

(b)

(c)

Figure 60.5 Societal benefits from biodiversity. **(a)** Bark of the cinchona tree (*Cinochona officinalis*), a plant found only in tropical rain forests, is used to produce quinine, an effective treatment for malaria. **(b)** A gene from longstamen rice (*Oryza longistaminata*), native to Africa, was used to reduce rice blight disease in rice, *O. sativa,* native to Asia. **(c)** Commercial fishing for salmon is an important part of the economy in the U.S. Pacific Northwest. a: ©Heather Angel/Natural Visions; b: ©Arterra Picture Library lamy Stock Photo; c: ©Joshua Roper/Alamy Stock Photo

was used to protect commercially grown U.S. corn from a leaf fungus, which had killed 15% of the crop. Lake Placid mint (*Dicerandra frutescens*), native only in central Florida, produces a powerful insect-repelling chemical that may have benefits for crop protection. Another endangered species, buffalo clover (*Trifolium stoloniferum*), has high protein content and is a perennial, making it of high potential value as a forage crop.

Natural Products Industry   Many products that are used by humans are harvested from plant species growing in their native environments. Biodiversity is important for the maintenance of those native environments. Natural plant products include wood, rubber, and dietary supplements. The forest products industry manufactures over $200 billion in products in the U.S. annually. Maple syrup, nuts, blueberries and algae are all harvested in addition to the trees themselves. Interestingly, a relatively new commercial crop is made by the flowering shrub *Parthenium argentatum*. It produces high amounts of natural rubber and grows in the deserts of the Southwest U.S., adding economic value to marginal lands.

Animals, too, have great commercial value in the natural products industry. Salmon fishing in the Pacific Northwest supports over 60,000 jobs and injects over $1 billion into the economy (**Figure 60.5c**). In the U.K., the sea fish catch is worth over $500 million annually. Exploitation of wild animals, often known as bushmeat, in Africa is a major source of animal protein for more than a billion of the world's poorest people. Game birds, especially pheasants and ducks, are often shot in North America and Europe.

Natural Ecosystems Provide Essential Services to Humans

Beyond the direct economic gains from biodiversity, humans benefit enormously from the essential services that natural ecosystems provide (**Table 60.1**). For example, forests soak up carbon dioxide, maintain soil fertility, and retain water, helping to prevent or minimize flooding. Estuaries provide water filtration and protect rivers and coastal shores from excessive erosion. *Prochlorococcus,* an abundant ocean-dwelling genus of cyanobacteria, was discovered only in 1986, yet it is estimated to produce about 20% of the oxygen we breathe. Other ecosystem functions include the maintenance of populations of natural predators to regulate pest outbreaks and of reservoirs of pollinators to pollinate crops and other plants. In addition, approximately 75% of the 100,000 chemicals released into the environment can be degraded by living organisms. The loss of biodiversity can disrupt an ecosystem's ability to carry out such functions.

In the 1990s, farmers in India began using the anti-inflammatory drug diclofenac to reduce pain and fever in their livestock. They could hardly anticipate that vultures scavenging on dead carcasses would accumulate large doses of the drug and die of renal failure. But the consequences did not stop there. Following a 97% reduction in vulture numbers over a 14-year period, the population of feral dogs exploded, because of the greater availability of uneaten carcasses. The incidence of rabies in humans increased, with estimates of an additional 48,000 people dying over the 14-year time span. The loss of the scavenging services of the vultures was estimated to cost India $24 billion.

A 2014 paper in the journal *Global Environmental Change* by economist Robert Costanza and colleagues made an attempt to calculate the monetary value of ecosystems to various economies (in 2007

Table 60.1	Examples of the World's Ecosystem Services
Service	**Example**
Atmospheric gas supply	Regulation of carbon dioxide, ozone, and oxygen levels
Climate regulation	Regulation of carbon dioxide, nitrogen dioxide, and methane levels
Disturbance regulation	Storm protection; flood control
Water regulation	Regulation of hydrological flows
Water supply	Irrigation; water for industry
Erosion control	Retention of topsoil; reduction of accumulation of sediments in lakes
Soil formation	Soil formation processes
Nutrient cycling	Nitrogen, phosphorus, and carbon cycles
Waste treatment	Sewage purification
Pollination	Pollination of crops
Biological control	Pest population regulation
Wilderness and refuges	Habitat for wildlife
Food production	Crops; livestock
Raw materials	Fossil fuels; timber
Genetic resources	Medicines; genes for plant resistance
Recreation	Ecotourism; outdoor recreation
Cultural	Aesthetic and educational value

dollars). They came to the conclusion that, at the time, the world's ecosystems were worth more than $124 trillion a year, nearly twice the gross national product of the world's economies combined ($75.2 trillion in 2007 dollars).

Ethical Reasons Underlie the Conservation of Biodiversity

Arguments can also be made against the loss of biodiversity on ethical grounds. As only one of many species on Earth, many people have argued that we have no right to destroy other species and the environment around us. John Muir, the founder of the Sierra Club, thought that natural areas had spiritual value and should be preserved rather than used as a source of natural products. This idea, which became known as the preservationist ethic, contrasts with the resource conservation ethic, which focuses on management of natural areas to allow the wisest current and future use of natural resources. In the United States, California condors (*Gymnogyps californianus*) and grizzly bears (*Ursus arctos*) have little economic value to people yet we assign them enough value that we preserve the habitats they live in. American philosopher Tom Regan suggests that animals should be treated with respect because they have a life of their own and therefore have value apart from anyone else's interests. American law professor Christopher Stone, in an influential 1972 article titled "Should Trees Have Standing?" has argued that entities such as nonhuman natural objects, like trees or lakes, should be given legal rights just as corporations are treated as individuals for certain purposes. In 1984, E. O. Wilson proposed the concept known as biophilia: Humans have innate attachments with other species and natural habitats because of our close association with them over millions of years.

60.4 Conservation Strategies

Learning Outcomes:

1. List and describe the criteria that conservation biologists use to identify areas for protection.
2. Explain how the principles of island biogeography and landscape ecology are used to create nature preserves.
3. Describe different approaches that conservation biologists use to protect individual species.
4. Define restoration ecology, and describe the approaches used to restore degraded ecosystems and populations of species.
5. Describe the advantages and disadvantages of using cloning as a conservation strategy to help save endangered species.

As discussed in Chapter 59, the activities of humans have had many negative effects that threaten biodiversity and ecosystems. The goal of conservation biologists is to manage natural resources with the aim of protecting species, their habitats, and ecosystems. In their efforts to maintain the diversity of life on Earth, these biologists are active on many fronts.

We begin this section by discussing how conservation biologists identify the global areas most in need of conservation. We will then examine some of the factors that must be considered when designing nature preserves, also called parks. These factors include the size and shape of the preserve and the ability of species to move from one nature preserve to another. In some cases, efforts are aimed at protecting species that have a great ecological impact; in others, they are aimed at protecting species, such as the panda bear, which are recognizable and garner support from humans. We will then explore the topic of **habitat restoration**—the full or partial repair or replacement of biological habitats and/or their populations that have been degraded or destroyed. Such restoration may involve captive breeding programs to reestablish populations of threatened species in the wild. Finally, we will discuss how genetic cloning may be used as an additional tool to help conserve endangered species.

Conservation Seeks to Establish Protected Areas

Currently, about 15.4% of global land area is under some form of environmental protection. More than 217,155 separate areas and 3.4% of the global ocean area are protected, with more being added daily. Conservation biologists often must make decisions regarding which habitats should be protected. Many conservation efforts have focused on saving habitats in so-called megadiversity countries, because they often have the greatest number of species. However, more recent strategies have promoted preservation of certain key areas with the highest levels of unique species or the preservation of representative areas of all types of habitat, even relatively species-poor areas.

Megadiversity Countries   One strategy of targeting areas for conservation is to identify **megadiversity countries**, those countries with the greatest numbers of species. Using the number of plants, vertebrates, and selected groups of insects as criteria, American biologist Russell Mittermeier and colleagues determined that just 17 countries are home to nearly 70% of all known species. Brazil, Indonesia, and Colombia top the list, followed by Australia, Peru, Mexico, Madagascar, China, and nine other countries. The megadiversity country approach suggests that conservation efforts should be focused on the most biologically rich countries. However, although megadiversity areas may contain the most species, they do not necessarily contain the greatest number of unique species. The mammal species list for Peru is 344, and for Ecuador, it is 271; of these, however, 208 species are common to both countries.

Areas Rich in Endemic Species   Another approach for setting conservation priorities—one adopted by the organization Conservation International—takes into account the number of species that are **endemic**; that is, they are found only in a particular place or region. This approach suggests that conservationists focus their efforts on **biodiversity hot spots**, regions that are biologically diverse and under threat of destruction. To qualify as a biodiversity hot spot, a region must meet two criteria: (1) It must contain at least 1,500 species of vascular plants as endemic species, and (2) it must have lost at least 70% of its original habitat. Vascular plants were chosen as the primary group of organisms to determine whether or not an area qualifies as a hot spot, mainly because most other terrestrial organisms depend on them to some extent.

Conservationists Norman Myers, Russell Mittermeier, and colleagues identified 34 biodiversity hot spots that together occupy a mere 2.3% of the Earth's surface but contain 150,000 endemic plant species, or 50% of the world's total (**Figure 60.6**). This approach proposes that protecting such hot spots will prevent the extinction of a larger number of endemic species than would protecting areas of a similar size elsewhere. The main argument against using hot spots as the criterion for targeting conservation efforts is that the areas richest in endemic species—tropical forests—would receive the majority of attention and funding, perhaps at the expense of protecting other areas.

Representative Habitats and Crisis Ecoregions   In a third approach to prioritizing areas for conservation, some conservation biologists have argued that we need to conserve representatives of all major habitats. Prairies are a case in point. An example is the Pampas region of South America, which is arguably the most threatened habitat on the continent because of rapid conversion of its natural grasslands to ranch land and agriculture (**Figure 60.7**). The Pampas does not compare well in richness or endemics with the rain forests, but it is a unique area that, without preservation efforts, could disappear. By selecting habitats that are most distinct from those already preserved, many areas that are threatened but not biologically rich may be preserved in addition to the less immediately threatened, but richer, tropical forests.

With regard to representative habitats, habitat loss has been most extensive in temperate grasslands and tropical and temperate deciduous forests, where, in each case, over 50% of the land has been converted to other uses, such as agriculture. At the same time, very little, less than 10%, of these habitats have been protected. Such habitats are thus termed **crisis ecoregions**.

Last of the Wild   The final approach to conservation involves preservation of regions of the world relatively untouched by humans.

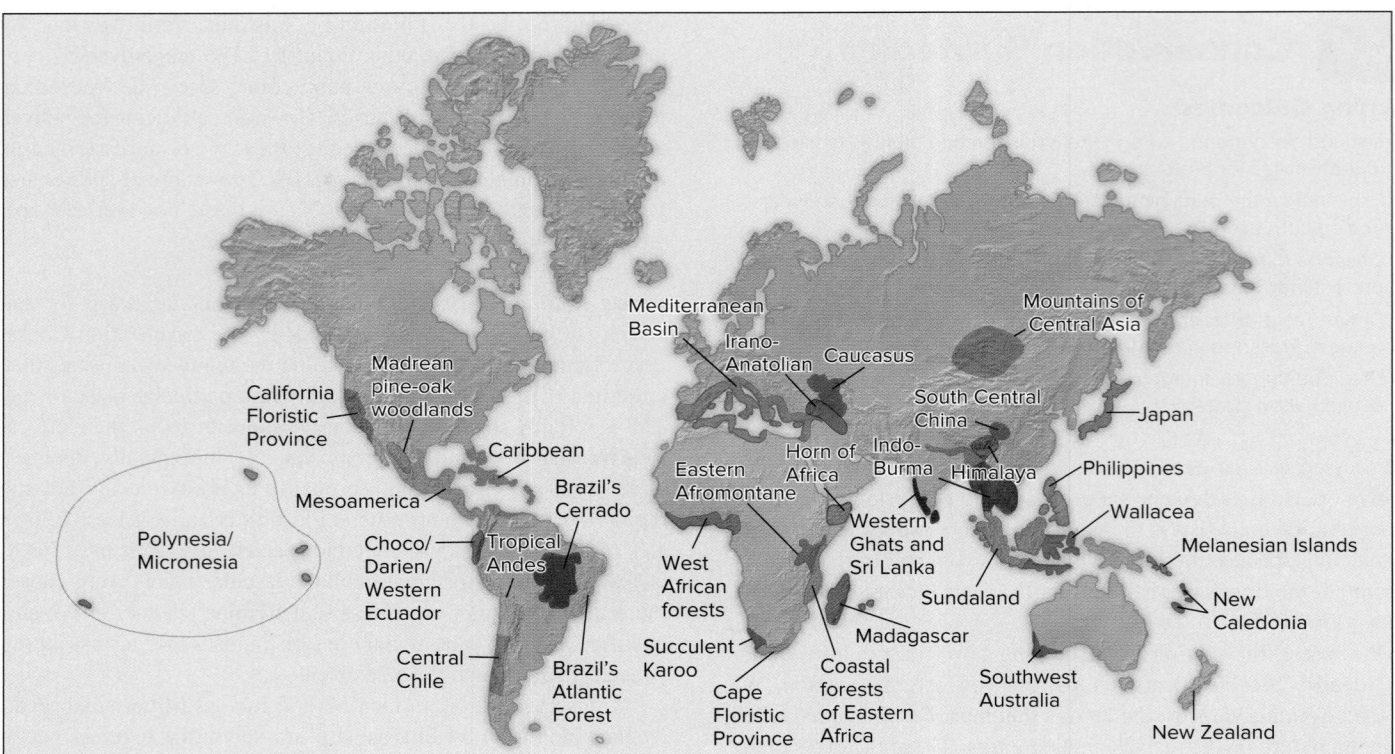

Figure 60.6 **Location of the major biodiversity hot spots.** Hot spots have high numbers of endemic species. Different colors distinguish the biodiversity hot spots.

Figure 60.7 **The Pampas, Argentina.** This habitat is not rich in species but is threatened due to conversion to ranch land and agriculture. The guanaco, shown here, is a characteristic grazer of pampas grass. ©Vicki Fisher/Alamy Stock Photo

Scientists have mapped out the extent of the human footprint on the globe. The areas of the Earth that fall within the lowest 10% of the human-affected areas have been termed the "last of the wild." Such areas, because they are relatively pristine, offer a great opportunity for conservationists because of their relatively intact communities. These wild areas include the tundra and boreal forests of Russia and Canada as well as some desert biomes and tropical forests.

Preserve Design Incorporates Principles of Island Biogeography and Landscape Ecology

After identifying areas to preserve, conservationists must determine the size, arrangement, and management of the protected land. Among the questions conservationists ask is whether one large preserve is preferable to an equivalent area composed of smaller preserves. Ecologists also need to determine whether nature preserves should be close together or far apart and whether or not they should be connected by strips of suitable habitat to allow the movement of plants and animals between them.

The Role of Island Biogeography According to the equilibrium model of island biogeography (refer back to Section 58.4), the biodiversity on an island tends toward an equilibrium number that is determined by the balance between two factors: immigration rates and extinction rates. This theory has been applied to nature preserves because, in essence, they are islands in a sea of human-altered habitat.

One question for conservationists is how large a protected area should be (**Figure 60.8a**). According to island biogeography, the number of species should increase with increasing area (the species-area effect). Thus, a larger area would mean that a larger number of species would be protected. In addition, larger preserves have other benefits. For example, they are beneficial for organisms that require

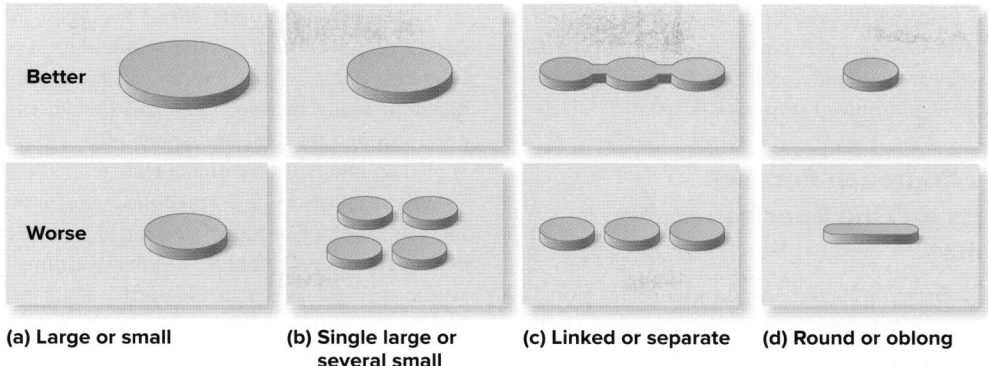

Better

Worse

(a) Large or small   **(b) Single large or several small**   **(c) Linked or separate**   **(d) Round or oblong**

Figure 60.8 **The theoretical design of nature preserves.** **(a)** A larger preserve holds more species and has low extinction rates. **(b)** A given area should be fragmented into as few pieces as possible. **(c)** Maintaining or creating corridors between fragments may also enhance dispersal. **(d)** Circular-shaped areas minimize the amount of edge effects. The labels "Better" and "Worse" refer to theoretical principles generated by the equilibrium model of island biogeography, but empirical data have not supported all the predictions.

Concept Check: *What are some of the potential risks in connecting preserved areas with movement corridors?*

large spaces, including migrating species and species with extensive territories, such as lions and tigers.

A related question is whether it is preferable to protect a single, large preserve or several smaller ones (**Figure 60.8b**). This question is called the **SLOSS debate** (for single large or several small). Proponents of a single, large preserve claim that a larger preserve is better able to protect more species and larger populations than an equal area divided into small areas. According to island biogeography, a larger block of habitat should support more species than several smaller blocks.

However, many empirical studies suggest that multiple small sites of equivalent area will contain more species, because a series of small sites is more likely to contain a broader variety of habitats than one large site. Looking at a variety of sites, American conservationists Jim Quinn and Susan Harrison concluded that animal life was richer in collections of small preserves than in a smaller number of larger ones. In their study, having more habitat types outweighed the effect of larger area size on species richness. In addition, another benefit of a series of smaller preserves is a reduction of extinction risk by a single event such as a wildfire or the spread of disease.

The Role of Landscape Ecology Landscape ecology is an area of ecology that examines the spatial arrangement of communities and ecosystems in a geographic area. Landscape ecologists have suggested that small preserves should be linked together by **movement corridors**, thin strips of land that permit the movement of species between preserved patches (**Figure 60.8c**). Such corridors ideally facilitate movements of organisms that are vulnerable to predation outside their natural habitat or have poor powers of dispersal between habitat patches. In this way, if a population in one small preserve experiences a disaster, immigrants from neighboring populations can more easily recolonize it. This avoids the need for humans to physically move new plants or animals into an area.

Several types of habitat function as movement corridors, including hedgerows (a linear patch of shrubs and small trees), which facilitate movement and dispersal of species between forest fragments (**Figure 60.9**). In China, corridors of habitat have been established to

link small, adjacent populations of giant pandas. However, some disadvantages are associated with movement corridors. Corridors also can facilitate the spread of disease, invasive species, and fire between small preserves.

Finally, nature preserves are often designed to minimize **edge effects**, the special physical conditions that exist at the boundaries, or edges, of ecosystems. Habitat edges, particularly those between a natural habitat such as a forest and developed land, are often different in physical characteristics from the habitat core. For example, the center of a forest is shaded by trees and has less wind and light than

Hedgerows

Figure 60.9 **Movement corridors.** ©Andrew Parker/Alamy Stock Photo

Concept Check: *How do these European hedgerows act as movement corridors?*

the forest edge, which is unprotected. Many forest-adapted animals therefore shy away from forest edges and prefer forest centers. For this reason, circular preserves are generally preferable to oblong ones, because the amount of edge is minimized (**Figure 60.8d**).

The Single-Species Approach Focuses Conservation Efforts on One Species in a Particular Habitat

As we have seen, many conservation biologists consider broad global issues when deciding which habitats are more important to preserve, as well as more local issues concerning the sizes, shapes, and interconnectedness of preserves. When establishing and managing nature preserves, they may take a single-species approach to their conservation efforts, which focuses on saving species that are deemed particularly important. As with habitat conservation, different approaches are used to identify the species that are most important.

Indicator Species Some conservation biologists have suggested that certain organisms can be monitored as **indicator species**, those species whose status provides information on the overall health of an ecosystem. For example, corals are good indicators of marine processes such as siltation—the accumulation of sediments transported by water. Because siltation reduces the availability of light, the abundance of many marine organisms decreases in such situations, with corals among the first to display a decline in health. Coral bleaching is also an indicator of climate change.

Polar bears (*Ursus maritimus*) are thought to be a mammalian indicator species of global climate change (**Figure 60.10a**). Most scientists are in agreement that global warming is causing the ice in the Arctic to melt earlier in the spring than in the past. Because polar bears rely on the ice to hunt for seals, the earlier breakup of the ice is leaving the bears less time to feed and build the fat that enables them to sustain themselves and their young. A U.S. Geological Survey study concluded that future reduction of Arctic ice could result in a loss of two-thirds of the world's polar bear population within 50 years. In May 2008, the polar bear was listed as a threatened species under the U.S. Endangered Species Act (ESA).

Umbrella Species **Umbrella species** are those whose habitat requirements are so large that protecting them would protect many other species existing in the same habitat. The Northern spotted owl

(a) Indicator species: polar bear

(b) Umbrella species: northern spotted owl

(c) Flagship species: Florida panther

(d) Keystone species: American beaver

Figure 60.10 Indicator, umbrella, flagship, and keystone species. **(a)** Polar bears have been called an indicator species with respect to global climate change. **(b)** The northern spotted owl is considered an umbrella species for the old-growth forest in the Pacific Northwest. **(c)** The Florida panther has become a flagship species for Florida. **(d)** The American beaver, a keystone species, creates large dams across streams, and the resultant lakes provide habitats for a great diversity of species. a: ©Robert E. Barber/Alamy Stock Photo; b: Source: John & Karen Hollingsworth/U.S. Fish & Wildlife Service; c: Source: Larry Richardson, US Fish & Wildlife Service; d: ©Wildlife/Alamy Stock Photo

(*Strix occidentalis*) of the Pacific Northwest is considered to be an important umbrella species (**Figure 60.10b**). A pair of birds needs at least 800 hectares of old-growth forest for survival and reproduction, so maintaining healthy owl populations helps to ensure survival of many other forest-dwelling species. In the southeastern U.S., the red-cockaded woodpecker (*Picoides borealis*) is often seen as that region's equivalent of the Northern spotted owl because it requires large tracts of old-growth long-leaf pine (*Pinus palustris*), including old diseased trees in which it can excavate its nests.

Flagship Species In the past, conservation resources were often allocated to a **flagship species**, a single large or instantly recognizable species. Such species were typically chosen because they were attractive and thus more readily engendered support from the public for their conservation. The concept of the flagship species, typically a charismatic vertebrate such as the American buffalo (*Bison bison*), has often been used to raise awareness for conservation in general. The giant panda (*Ailuropoda melanoleuca*) is the World Wildlife Fund's emblem for endangered species, and the Florida panther (*Puma concolor*) has become a symbol of the state's conservation campaign (**Figure 60.10c**).

Keystone Species A different conservation strategy focuses on **keystone species**, species within a community that have a role out of proportion to their abundance or biomass. The beaver, a relatively small animal, can have a dramatic impact on a community by building a dam and flooding an entire river valley (**Figure 60.10d**). The resultant lake may become a home to fish species, wildfowl, and aquatic vegetation. A decline in the number of beavers may have serious ramifications for the remaining community members, promoting fish die-offs, waterfowl loss, and the death of vegetation adapted to waterlogged soil.

American ecologist John Terborgh considers tropical palm nuts and figs to be keystone plant species because they produce fruit during otherwise fruitless times of the year and are thus critical resources for tropical forest fruit-eating animals, including primates, rodents, and many birds. Together, these fruit eaters account for as much as three-quarters of the tropical forest animal biomass. Without the fruit trees, widespread extinction of these animals could occur.

Habitat Restoration Attempts to Improve Degraded Habitats

Another aspect of conservation efforts is improving the quality of a previously degraded habitat. As noted at the beginning of this section, habitat restoration is the full or partial repair or replacement of biological habitats and/or their populations that have been degraded or destroyed. It can focus on complete restoration, rehabilitation, or replacement of a habitat, and it can involve returning species to the wild following captive breeding.

Types of Habitat Restoration In complete restoration, conservation biologists attempt to return a habitat to its composition and condition prior to the disturbance. For example, under the leadership of American ecologist Aldo Leopold, the University of Wisconsin pioneered the restoration of prairie habitats as early as 1935, converting agricultural land back to species-rich prairies (**Figure 60.11a**).

The second approach of habitat restoration aims to return the habitat to something similar to, but a little less than, full restoration, a goal called rehabilitation. In Florida, phosphate mining involves removing a layer of topsoil, mining the phosphate-rich layers, returning the topsoil, and then replanting the area. Unfortunately, species such as cogongrass (*Imperata cylindrica*), an invasive Southeast Asian species, may invade these disturbed areas. Even so, the restoration serves to revegetate the area (**Figure 60.11b**).

The third approach to repairing a habitat, termed replacement, makes no attempt to restore what was originally present but instead replaces the original ecosystem with a different one. Ecosystem replacement is particularly useful for places in which the terrain has been substantially altered by past human activities. It would be nearly impossible to re-create the original landscape of an area that was mined for stone or gravel. In these situations, however, wetlands or lakes may be created in the open pits (**Figure 60.11c**).

(a) Complete restoration

(b) Rehabilitation

(c) Ecosystem replacement

Figure 60.11 Habitat restoration. (a) The University of Wisconsin pioneered the practice of complete restoration of agricultural land to native prairies. **(b)** In Florida, complete restoration after phosphate mining is not usually possible. After topsoil is replaced, invasive species such as cogongrass often grow, resulting in habitat rehabilitation rather than complete restoration. **(c)** This old limestone mine in Crimea has been flooded to provide a valuable freshwater habitat, replacing the ecosystem that was originally present. a: ©University of Wisconsin-Madison Arboretum; b: Courtesy of DL Rockwood, School of Forest Resources and Conservation, University of Florida, Gainesville, FL; c: ©Vladimir Mulder/Shutterstock

 Core Skill: Science and Society Restoration of human-degraded habitats can lead to recovery of habitat and increased biodiversity.

- The single-species approach focuses conservation efforts on indicator species, umbrella species, flagship species, or keystone species (Figure 60.10).

- Habitat restoration seeks to repair or replace populations and their habitats. Three basic approaches to habitat restoration are complete restoration, rehabilitation, and ecosystem replacement (Figure 60.11).

- Captive breeding is propagating animals or plants outside their natural habitat and reintroducing them to the wild. Cloning of endangered species has been accomplished on a very small scale and, despite its limitations, may eventually have a role in conservation biology (Figures 60.12, 60.13).

Assess & Discuss

Test Yourself

1. Which of the following best describes an endangered species?
   a. a species that is likely to become extinct in a portion of its range
   b. a species that has disappeared in a particular community but is present in other natural environments
   c. a species that is extinct
   d. a species that is in danger of becoming extinct throughout all or a significant portion of its range
   e. Both b and d are true of endangered species.

2. In 1977, Rafael Guzman, a Mexican biologist, discovered a previously unknown wild relative of corn that is resistant to many of the viral diseases that infect domestic corn. Agriculturalists believe that crossbreeding the wild corn with domestic corn could improve current corn crops. In this case, biodiversity is important at which level?
   a. ecosystem
   b. species
   c. genetic
   d. community
   e. both a and b

3. The idea that humans have an innate attachment to other life-forms, put forth by E. O. Wilson, is known as
   a. biodiversity.
   b. biophilia.
   c. the call of the wild.
   d. biotheology.
   e. the "last of the wild."

4. The research conducted by Tilman and colleagues demonstrated that
   a. as diversity increases, productivity increases.
   b. as diversity decreases, productivity increases.
   c. areas with higher diversity demonstrate less efficient use of nutrients.
   d. increases in species richness lead to an increase in invasive species.
   e. increased diversity results in increased susceptibility to disease.

5. Which hypothesis best describes the idea that a small decline in species richness results in a large drop in ecosystem function?
   a. Diversity-stability hypothesis
   b. Redundancy hypothesis
   c. Keystone hypothesis
   d. Idiosyncratic hypothesis
   e. Community hypothesis

6. According to the equilibrium model of island biogeography, which type of preserve would contain the most species?
   a. One large park
   b. Several small parks with a combined area equal to that of a large park
   c. Several small parks connected by a movement corridor
   d. A circular park
   e. All of the above

7. Saving endangered habitats, such as the Argentine Pampas, focuses on
   a. saving genetic diversity.
   b. saving keystone species.
   c. conservation in a megadiversity country.
   d. preserving an area rich in endemic species.
   e. preserving a representative habitat.

8. Biodiversity hot spots are those areas rich in
   a. species.
   b. habitats.
   c. rare species.
   d. biodiversity.
   e. endemic species.

9. Over time, dark forms of the peppered moth (*Biston betularia*) became more common in polluted environments because predators were less able to detect them on trees darkened by soot. These moths are regarded by many as a(n)
   a. keystone species.
   b. indicator species.
   c. umbrella species.
   d. flagship species.
   e. endangered species.

10. After being used for mining, what was once a deciduous forest is replaced by grassland to be used for public recreation. This process is known as
    a. complete restoration.
    b. rehabilitation.
    c. ecosystem replacement.
    d. bioremediation.
    e. habitat repair.

Conceptual Questions

1. What is the value of increased biodiversity for human society?

2. Distinguish among the following as bases for strategies to conserve biodiversity: megadiversity countries, biodiversity hot spots, crisis ecoregions, and "last of the wild."

3.  **Core Concept: Systems** Describe how the following hypotheses link species richness with ecosystem function: diversity-stability, redundancy, keystone, and idiosyncratic.

Collaborative Questions

1. Discuss the differences between indicator species, umbrella species, flagship species, and keystone species.

2. You are called upon to design a park with maximum biodiversity in a tropical country. What are your recommendations?

Appendix A

Periodic Table of the Elements

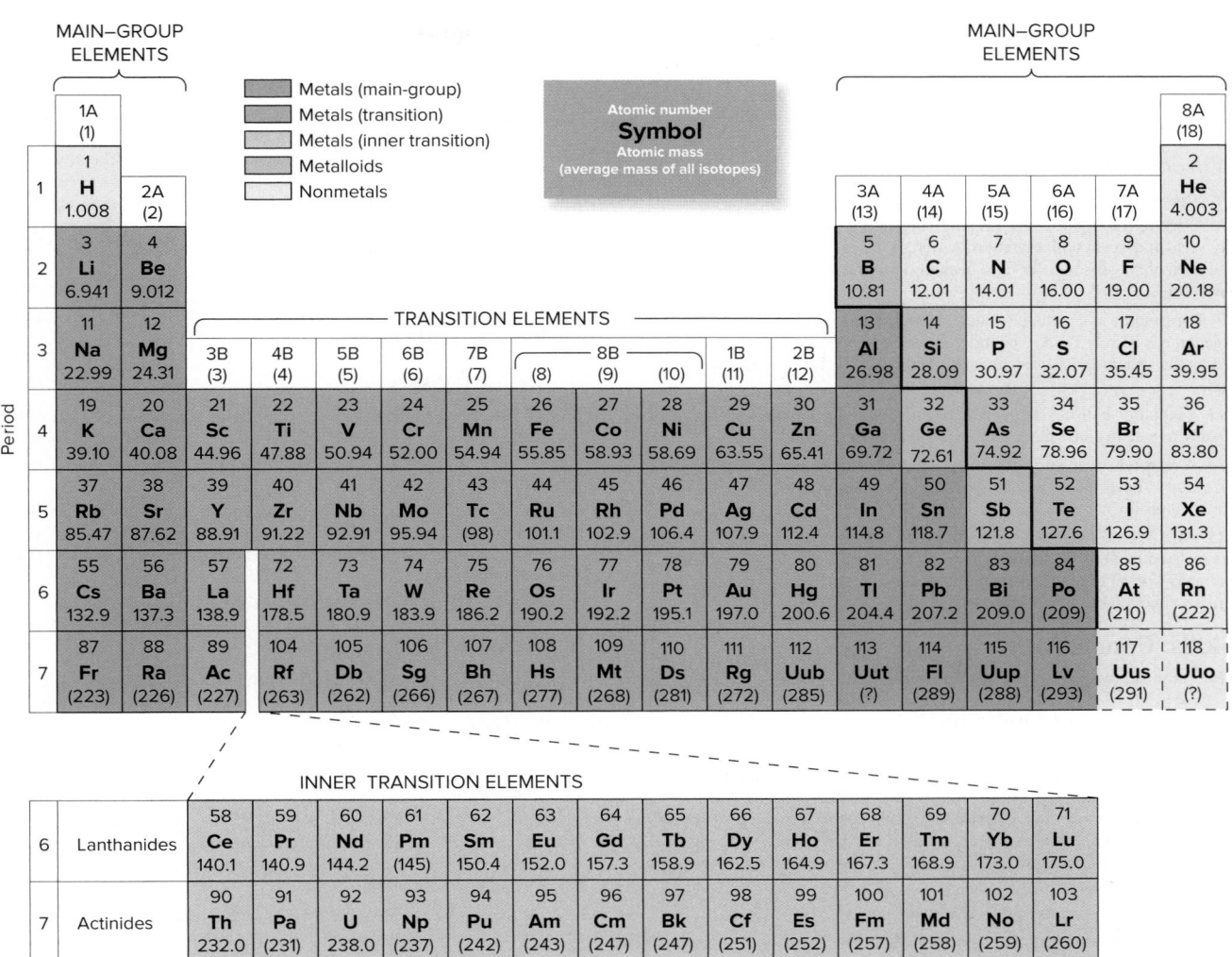

The complete Periodic Table of the Elements. Group numbers are different in some cases from those presented in Figure 2.5, because of the inclusion of transition elements. In some cases, the average atomic mass has been rounded to one or two decimal places, and in others only an estimate is given in parentheses due to the short-lived nature or rarity of those elements. The symbols and names of some of the elements between 112–118 are temporary until the chemical characteristics of these elements become better defined. Element 117 is currently not confirmed as a true element, and little is known about element 118. The International Union of Pure and Applied Chemistry (IUPAC) has recently proposed adopting the name copernicium (Cp) for element 112 in honor of scientist and astronomer Nicolaus Copernicus.

Appendix B

Answer Key

Answers to Collaborative Questions can be found on the website.

Chapter 1

Concept Checks

Figure 1.3 The herd is at the population level.

Figure 1.6 Natural selection is a process that leads to evolution.

Figure 1.8 A tree of life suggests that all living organisms evolved from a single ancestor by vertical descent with mutation. A web of life assumes that both vertical descent and horizontal gene transfer have been important mechanisms in the evolution of new species.

Figure 1.9 The genome stores the information used to make proteins. In and of itself, the genome is merely DNA. The traits of cells and organisms are largely determined by the structures and functions of the thousands of different proteins they produce.

Figure 1.11 Taxonomy helps us appreciate the unity and diversity of life. Organisms that are closely related evolutionarily are placed in smaller groups.

Figure 1.14 A researcher can compare the results from the experimental group and the control group to determine if a single variable is causing a particular outcome in the experimental group.

Figure 1.15 After the *CFTR* gene was identified by discovery-based science, researchers realized that this gene was similar to other genes that encoded proteins that were already known to be transport proteins. This provided an important clue about the likely function of the *CFTR* gene.

Core Skills: Connections

Figure 1.10 Fungi are more closely related to animals.

Feature Investigation Questions

1. In discovery-based science, a researcher does not need to have a preconceived hypothesis. Experimentation is conducted in the hope that it may have practical applications or may provide new information that will lead to a hypothesis. By comparison, hypothesis testing occurs when a researcher forms a hypothesis that makes certain predictions. Experiments are conducted to see if those predictions are correct. In this way, the hypothesis may be accepted or rejected.

2. This strategy may be described as a five-stage process:
   1. Observations are made regarding natural phenomena.
   2. These observations lead to a hypothesis that tries to explain the phenomena. A useful hypothesis is one that is testable because it makes specific predictions.
   3. Experimentation is conducted to determine if the predictions are correct.
   4. The data from the experiment are analyzed.
   5. The hypothesis is accepted or rejected.

3. In an ideal experiment, the control and experimental groups differ by only one factor. Biologists apply statistical analyses to their data to determine if the outcomes for the control and experimental groups are likely to differ because of the single variable that is different between the two groups. This provides an objective way to accept or reject a hypothesis.

Test Yourself

1. d   2. a   3. b   4. c   5. d   6. b   7. d   8. d   9. a   10. b

Conceptual Questions

1. Evolution applies only to populations, whereas the other four core concepts could apply to individuals and to populations.

2. The unity among different species occurs because modern species have evolved from a group of related ancestors. Some of the traits in those ancestors are also found in modern species, which thereby unites them. The diversity is due to the variety of environments on the Earth. Each species has evolved to occupy its own unique environment. For every species, many traits are evolutionary adaptations to survival in a specific environment. For this reason, evolution also promotes diversity.

3. Students should rephrase the concepts in their own words.

Chapter 2

Concept Checks

Figure 2.4 An electron shell is a region outside the nucleus of an atom occupied by electrons of a given energy level. More than one orbital can be found within an electron shell. An orbital may be spherical or dumbbell-shaped and contains up to two electrons.

Figure 2.11 Strand separation requires energy, because the DNA strands are held together by a large number of hydrogen bonds. Although each hydrogen bond is weak, the collective strength of such bonds in a molecule of DNA adds up to a considerable amount.

Figure 2.17 The oil will be in the centers of the soap micelles.

Core Skills: Connections

Figure 2.20 At a pH of 5.0, the H^+ concentration would be 10^{-5} M, as can be seen in Figure 2.20 and can also be calculated with the equation $pH = -\log_{10}[H^+]$. (From this information, you can also determine that the OH^- concentration must be 10^{-9} M, because the product of the H^+ and OH^- concentrations must be equal to 10^{-14} M.)

Feature Investigation Questions

1. Scientists were aware that atoms contained charged particles. Many believed that the positive charges and mass were evenly distributed throughout the atom.

2. Rutherford was testing the hypothesis that atoms are composed of positive charges evenly distributed throughout the atom. Based on this model of the structure of the atom, α particles, which are positively charged nuclei of helium atoms, should be slightly deflected as they pass through gold foil, due to the presence of positive charges spread throughout the foil.

3. Instead of showing slight deflection as they passed through the gold foil, the majority, 98%, of the α particles passed directly through the foil without deflection. Less than 2% of them showed deflection, and a much smaller percentage bounced back from the gold foil. Rutherford suggested that since most of the α particles passed unimpeded through the gold foil, most of the volume of atoms is empty space. Rutherford also proposed that the bouncing back of some of the α particles indicated that most of the positively charged particles in an atom were concentrated in a compact area. These results ran counter to the hypothesized model.

Test Yourself

1. b   2. b   3. b   4. d   5. e   6. e   7. e   8. c   9. c   10. e

Conceptual Questions

1. Covalent bonds are bonds in which atoms share electrons. A nonpolar covalent bond is one between two atoms of similar electronegativities, such as two carbon atoms. A hydrogen bond is a weak interaction that forms when a hydrogen atom in a polar molecule becomes electrically attracted to an electronegative atom. The van der Waal dispersion forces are temporary, weak interactions, resulting from random electrical forces generated by the changing distributions of electrons in the outer shells of nearby atoms. The strong attraction between two oppositely charged atoms forms an ionic bond.

2. Within limits, bonds within molecules can rotate and thereby change the molecules' shapes. This is important because it is the shape of a molecule that determines, in part, the ability of that molecule to interact with other molecules. Also, when two molecules do interact through such forces as hydrogen bonds, the shape of one or both molecules may change as a consequence. The change in shape is often part of the mechanism by which signals are sent within and between cells.

3. When two or more atoms react with each other to form a new substance, that new substance often has emergent properties that are quite different from the starting materials. A good example of emergent properties at the molecular level occurs in the formation of sodium chloride (NaCl), a solid white crystalline compound that is very important for most living organisms. In their elemental states, sodium is a soft, highly reactive metal and chlorine is a toxic gas. When they combine through ionic bonds, the two elements produce a completely new and harmless substance found in all the world's oceans and soils. Another example from this chapter is water, a liquid that is vital for all life but which is formed from two gases, hydrogen and oxygen, with very different properties.

Chapter 3

Concept Checks

Figure 3.5 One reason is that the binding of a molecule to an enzyme depends on the spatial arrangements of the atoms in that molecule. Enantiomers have different spatial relationships and are mirror images of each other. Therefore, one may bind very tightly to an enzyme and the other may not be recognized at all.

Figure 3.6 Recall from Figure 3.4 that the reverse of a dehydration reaction is a hydrolysis reaction, in which a molecule of water is added to the molecule being broken down, resulting in the formation of monomers.

Figure 3.10 Hydrogenation is the addition of hydrogens to double-bonded carbon atoms, changing them from unsaturated to saturated. This causes the resulting fat to have a higher melting point and thus be solid at room temperature.

Figure 3.14 The process would produce 71 water molecules, one less than the number of amino acids in the polypeptide.

Figure 3.18 If the primary structure of protein 1 were altered in this way, the changes would, in turn, most likely alter the secondary and tertiary structures of protein 1. Therefore, it is possible that the precise fit between proteins 1 and 2 would no longer be possible and the two proteins would lose the ability to interact.

Figure 3.23 Yes. The opposite strand must be complementary to the first strand, because A must be paired with T, and G with C. For instance, if a portion of the first strand has the sequence AATGCA, the opposite strand for that portion will be TTACGT.

Core Skills: Connections

Figure 3.7 Cellulose is believed to be the most abundant organic molecule on Earth. In addition to being part of plant cells, it is also found in many other organisms, including many protists.

Feature Investigation Questions

1. Anfinsen was testing the hypothesis that the information necessary for determining the three-dimensional shape of a protein is contained within the protein itself. In other words, the chemical characteristics of the amino acids that make up a protein determine the protein's three-dimensional shape.

2. The urea disrupts hydrogen and ionic bonds that are necessary for protein folding. The β-mercaptoethanol breaks the S—S bonds that form between certain amino acids of the same polypeptide. Both substances cause the polypeptide to unfold, disrupting the three-dimensional shape.

3. Anfinsen removed the urea and β-mercaptoethanol from the ribonuclease by size-exclusion chromatography. After removing these substances, Anfinsen discovered that the protein refolded into its proper three-dimensional shape and became functional again. This was important because the solution at that point contained only the protein and lacked any other cellular material that could possibly assist in protein folding. This demonstrated that the protein could refold itself into the functional conformation.

Test Yourself

1. b   2. e   3. e   4. a   5. c   6. b   7. e   8. d   9. b   10. b

Conceptual Questions

1. Isomers are molecules with the same chemical formula but with different structures and arrangements of their atoms. There are two major types of isomers: structural isomers and stereoisomers. Because many chemical reactions in biology depend on the actions of enzymes, which are often highly specific with respect to the spatial arrangement of atoms in a molecule, one isomer of a pair may have biological functions, and the other may not.

2. Saturated fatty acids are saturated with hydrogens and have only single (C—C) bonds, whereas unsaturated fatty acids have one or more double (C=C) bonds. The double bonds in unsaturated fatty acids alters the shape, resulting in one or more kinks in the chain. Saturated fatty acids are unkinked and are better able to stack tightly together. Fats containing saturated fatty acids have a higher melting point than those containing mostly unsaturated fatty acids; consequently, saturated fats tend to be solids at room temperatures, and unsaturated fats are usually liquids at room temperature.

3. The structures of all these macromolecules determine their functions. For example, the structure of a protein determines its three-dimensional shape. This, in turn, allows a protein to interact specifically with certain other molecules. Also, protein domains have specific structures that determine their functions. A single protein may have multiple domains, allowing that protein to perform a fairly complex function, such as activating genes in response to hormone binding. Likewise, the structures of different lipids determine such functional characteristics as male/female differences, cellular membrane formation, and energy storage. The different structures of polysaccharides determine their usefulness as energy stores or as components of plant cell walls.

Chapter 4

Concept Checks

Figure 4.2 These vents release hot gases from the interior of the Earth. Organic molecules can form in the temperature gradient between the extremely hot vent water and the cold water that surrounds the vent.

Figure 4.3 A liposome is more similar to today's cells, which are surrounded by a membrane that is composed of a phospholipid bilayer.

Figure 4.4 Chemical selection occurs when certain molecules, such as RNAs, have properties that provide advantages and therefore cause them to increase in number relative to other molecules in the same environment.

Figure 4.5 You would use an electron microscope. A light microscope does not have good enough resolution.

Figure 4.7 The primary advantage is that it gives an image of the 3-D surface of an object.

Figure 4.11 Centrioles: Not found in plant cells; their role is not entirely clear, but they are found in the centrosome, which is where microtubules are anchored. Chloroplasts: Not found in animal cells; function in photosynthesis. Cell wall: Not found in animal cells; important in cell shape. Central vacuole: Not found in animal cells; site that provides storage and regulates cell volume.

Figure 4.16 Both dynein and microtubules are anchored in place. Using ATP as a source of energy, dynein tugs on microtubules. Because the microtubules are anchored, they bend in response to the force exerted by dynein.

Figure 4.19 The nuclear matrix, located inside the nucleus, serves to organize the chromosomes into chromosome territories.

Figure 4.22 The protein is synthesized into the ER and then travels through the *cis*, medial, and *trans* Golgi before being secreted.

Figure 4.26 Of these three functions, membrane transport is probably the most important to metabolism because it determines which molecules can enter the cell

charges repel each other and prevent hemoglobin proteins from aggregating into fiber-like structures.

Figure 15.3 This trait is due to a mutation that occurred in a somatic cell, so it cannot be transmitted to the individual's offspring.

Figure 15.6 A thymine dimer is harmful because it can cause an error in DNA replication that results in a mutation.

Concept Checks

Figure 16.1 Chromosomes are readily seen when they are compacted in a dividing cell. By adding such a drug, the researchers increase the percentage of cells that are actively dividing.

Figure 16.2 Interphase consists of the G_1, S, and G_2 phases of the cell cycle.

Griffith discovered something called the transformation principle, and his experiments showed the existence of biochemical genetic information. In addition, he showed that this genetic information can move from one individual to another of the same species. In his experiments, Griffith took heat-killed type S bacteria and mixed them with living type R bacteria and injected them into

ability of cells to catalyze just one reaction in this pathway, thereby suggesting that a single gene encodes a single enzyme.

2. Each of these 20 enzymes catalyzes the attachment of a specific amino acid to a specific tRNA molecule.

3. During transcription, a DNA strand is used as a template for the synthesis of

Transformation occurs when a bacterium takes up a DNA fragment from the environment, which may have come from a dead bacterium.

Transduction occurs when a bacteriophage that has infected a bacterial cell breaks up the chromosome, and a fragment of bacterial chromosomal DNA is incorporated into a newly made bacteriophage. It then transfers this fragment of DNA to a recipient bacterial cell.

3. Horizontal gene transfer is the transfer of genes from an organism to another organism that is not the offspring of the first organism. These acquired genes sometimes promote survival and therefore may have an evolutionary advantage. Such genes may even lead to the formation of new species. From a medical perspective, an important example of horizontal gene transfer is when one bacterium acquires a resistance gene from another bacterium and becomes resistant to an antibiotic. This phenomenon is making it increasingly difficult to treat a wide variety of bacterial diseases.

Chapter 20

Concept Checks

Figure 20.3 Cell division and cell migration are common in the early stages of development, whereas cell differentiation and apoptosis are more common as tissues and organs start to form.

Figure 20.4 If apoptosis did not occur, the fingers would be webbed.

Figure 20.8 The larva would have anterior structures at both ends and would lack posterior structures such as a spiracle.

Figure 20.9 The Bicoid protein functions as a transcription factor that promotes the formation of anterior structures. Its function is highest in the anterior end of the zygote.

Figure 20.14 The last abdominal segment would have legs!

Figure 20.18 Stem cells can divide, and the daughter cells can differentiate into specific cell types.

Figure 20.20 Hematopoietic stem cells are multipotent.

Figure 20.24 The pattern would be sepal, petal, stamen, stamen.

Figure 20.23 Stem cells in plants are found in meristems, which are located at the tips of roots and shoots.

Core Skills: Connections

Figure 20.5 Some cell surface receptors recognize signals that convey positional information. After the signal binds to this type of receptor, a signal transduction pathway is activated that may cause a cell to divide, migrate, differentiate, or undergo apoptosis.

Figure 20.17 As the number of *Hox* genes increases, the body plan of the animal becomes more complex.

Feature Investigation Questions

1. The researchers were interested in the factors that cause cells to differentiate. In this particular study, they were attempting to identify the gene(s) involved in the differentiation of muscle cells.

2. Using genetic technology, the researcher compared the gene expression in cells that could differentiate into muscle cells with the gene expression in cells that could not differentiate into muscle cells. Though many genes were expressed in both, the researchers were able to identify three genes that were expressed in muscle cell lines that were not expressed in nonmuscle cell lines.

3. Again, using genetic technology, each of the candidate genes was introduced into a cell that normally did not give rise to skeletal muscle. This procedure was used to test whether or not the gene played a key role in muscle cell differentiation. If the genetically engineered cell gave rise to muscle cells, the researchers would have evidence that that particular candidate gene was involved in muscle cell differentiation. Of the three candidate genes, only one was shown to be involved in muscle cell differentiation. When the *MyoD* gene was expressed in fibroblasts, these cells differentiated into skeletal muscle cells.

Test Yourself

1. c   2. d   3. e   4. b   5. c   6. e   7. a   8. a   9. b   10. d

Conceptual Questions

1. a. This abnormality is consistent with a mutation in a segmentation gene, such as a gap gene.

   b. This abnormality is consistent with a mutation in a homeotic gene because the characteristics of a particular segment have been changed.

2. Both types of genes encode transcription factors that bind to the DNA and regulate the expression of other genes. The effects of *Hox* genes determine the characteristics of certain regions of the body, whereas the *myoD* gene is cell-specific—it causes a cell to become a skeletal muscle cell.

3. Maternal effect genes control the formation of body axes, such as the anteroposterior and dorsoventral axes. Next, the segmentation genes divide the embryo into segments, though visible segments are lost in many animal species at later stages of development. Finally, the homeotic genes determine the characteristics of each segment.

Chapter 21

Concept Checks

Figure 21.3 The insertion of chromosomal DNA into the vector disrupts the *lacZ* gene, thereby preventing the expression of β-galactosidase. The functionality of *lacZ* can be determined by providing the growth medium with a colorless compound, X-Gal, which is cleaved by β-galactosidase into a blue dye. Bacterial colonies containing recirculated vectors form blue colonies, whereas colonies containing recombinant vectors carrying a segment of chromosomal DNA will be white.

Figure 21.5 The 600-bp fragment will be closer to the bottom. Smaller pieces travel faster through the gel.

Figure 21.6 The primers are complementary to sequences at each end of the DNA region to be amplified.

Figure 21.8 If a ddNTP is added to a growing DNA strand, the strand can no longer grow because the 3′ —OH group, the site of attachment for the next nucleotide, is missing.

Figure 21.9 A fluorescent spot identifies a cDNA that is complementary to a particular DNA sequence. Because the cDNA was generated from mRNA, the fluorescence identifies a gene that has been transcribed in a particular cell type under a given set of conditions.

Figure 21.10 The sgRNA is composed of two different components of the bacterial defense system, crRNA and tracrRNA, which have been linked together.

Figure 21.12 One reason is that more complex species tend to have more genes. A second reason is that species vary with regard to the amount of repetitive DNA sequences in their genomes.

Figure 21.18 Retrotransposons. A single retrotransposon can be transcribed into multiple copies of RNA, which can be converted to DNA by reverse transcriptase, and inserted into multiple sites in the genome.

Core Skills: Connections

Figure 21.2 Plasmids are small, circular DNA molecules that exist independently of the bacterial chromosome. They have their own origin of replication. Many plasmids carry genes that convey some type of selective advantage to the host cell, such as antibiotic resistance.

Figure 21.14 The proteins produced by family members at early stages of development (embryonic and fetal stages) have a higher affinity for oxygen than the proteins produced in an adult. This allows the embryo and fetus to obtain oxygen from the mother's bloodstream.

Feature Investigation Questions

1. The goal of the experiment was to sequence the entire genome of *Haemophilus influenzae*. By conducting this experiment, the researchers would have information about genome size and the types of genes the bacterium has.

2. If you divide 20 by 4.1, this equals 4.9. The value of 4.9 represents m in the equation: $P = e^{-m}$. If you substitute 4.1 for m into the equation and solve for P, the probability P equals 0.0074 or 0.74%. Therefore, only 0.74% would be left unsequenced, which is less than 1%.

3. The researchers were successful in sequencing the entire genome of the bacterium. The genome size was determined to be 1,830,137 base pairs, with a predicted 1,743 structural genes. The researchers were also able to predict the function of many of these genes. More importantly, the results were the first complete genomic sequence of a living organism.

Test Yourself

1. d   2. b   3. b   4. b   5. c   6. e   7. e   8. a   9. c   10. e

Conceptual Questions

1. A ddNTP is missing an oxygen at the 3′ position. This prevents the further growth of a DNA strand, thereby causing chain termination.

2. a. yes

   b. No, it's only one chromosome in the nuclear genome.

   c. Yes, it's corn's nuclear genome. Corn also has a mitochondrial genome and a chloroplast genome.

   d. yes

3. The genome contains the information for the production of cellular proteins; it is a blueprint. The production of proteins is largely responsible for determining cellular characteristics, which, in turn, are largely responsible for determining an organism's traits. In addition, the genome also encodes many non-coding RNAs that perform a variety of different functions.

Chapter 22

Concept Checks

Figure 22.2 A single organism does not evolve. Populations may evolve from one generation to the next due to differences in reproductive success.

Figure 22.7 Due to a changing global climate, the island fox became isolated from the mainland species. Over time, natural selection resulted in adaptations for the population on the island and eventually resulted in a new species with characteristics that are somewhat different from those of the mainland species.

Figure 22.8 Many answers are possible. One example is the wing of a bird and the wing of a bat.

Figure 22.11 The magnitudes of traits are changing. For example, in the breeds of dogs, the lengths of legs, body size, and so on, are quite different. Artificial selection is often aimed at changing the relative sizes of body parts or the amount of something, such as oil content.

Figure 22.14 Orthologs have similar gene sequences because they are derived from the same ancestral gene. The sequences are not identical because after the species diverged, each one accumulated different random mutations that changed their sequences.

Figure 22.16 Humans have one large chromosome 2, but this chromosome is divided into two separate chromosomes in the other three species. In chromosome 3, the banding patterns among humans, chimpanzees, and gorillas are very similar, but the orangutan has a large inversion that flips the arrangement of bands in the centromeric region.

Core Skills: Connections

Figure 22.15 The three mechanisms of horizontal gene transfer between bacterial species are conjugation, transformation and transduction.

Feature Investigation Questions

1. The island has a moderate level of isolation but is located near enough to the mainland to have some migrants. The island is an undisturbed habitat, so the researchers would not have to consider the effects of human activity on the study. Finally, the island had an existing population of ground finches that would serve as the subjects of the study over many generations.

2. First, the researchers were able to show that beak depth is a genetic trait that has variation in the population. Second, the depth of the beak is an indicator of the types of seeds the birds can eat. The birds with larger beaks can eat larger and drier seeds; therefore, changes in the types of seeds available could act as a selective force on the bird population.

   During the study period, annual changes in rainfall occurred, which affected the seed sizes produced by the plants on the island. In the drier year, fewer small seeds were produced, so the birds would have to eat larger, drier seeds.

3. The researchers found that following the drought in 1977, the average beak depth in the finch population increased. This indicated that birds with larger beaks were better able to adapt to the environmental changes due to the drought and produce more offspring. This is direct evidence of the phenomenon of natural selection.

Test Yourself

1. d   2. d   3. b   4. b   5. b   6. d   7. c   8. d   9. d   10. e

Conceptual Questions

1. Some random mutations result in a phenotype with greater reproductive success. If this occurs, natural selection results in a greater proportion of such individuals in succeeding generations.

2. The process of convergent evolution produces two different species from different lineages that show similar characteristics because they occupy similar environments. An example is the long snout and tongue of both the giant anteater, found in South America, and the echidna, found in Australia. These structures enable these animals to feed on ants, but the two structures evolved independently. These observations support the idea that evolution results in adaptations to particular environments.

3. Homologous structures are two or more structures that are similar because they are derived from a common ancestor. An example is the set of bones that is found in the human arm, turtle arm, bat wing, and whale flipper. The forearms in these species have been modified to perform different functions. This supports the idea that all of these animals evolved from a common ancestor by descent with modification.

Chapter 23

Concept Checks

Figure 23.3 Over the short run, alleles that confer better fitness in the warmer climate would be favored and increase in frequency, perhaps enhancing diversity. Over the long run, however, an allele that confers high fitness in the homozygous state may become monomorphic, thereby reducing genetic diversity.

Figure 23.4 Stabilizing selection eliminates alleles that result in phenotypes that deviate significantly from the average phenotype. For this reason, it tends to decrease genetic diversity.

Figure 23.6 If malaria was eradicated, there would be no selective advantage for the heterozygote. The H^S allele would eventually be eliminated because the $H^S H^S$ homozygote has a lower fitness. Directional selection would occur.

Figure 23.7 Courtship songs are likely to be part of intersexual selection. Such traits are likely to be involved in mate choice.

Figure 23.11 The bottleneck effect tends to decrease genetic diversity. This may eliminate adaptations that promote survival and reproductive success. Therefore, the bottleneck effect makes it more difficult for a population to survive.

Figure 23.13 Migration results in gene flow, which tends to make the allele frequencies in neighboring populations more similar to each other. It also promotes genetic diversity by introducing new alleles into populations.

Core Skills: Connections

Figure 23.12 There are lots of possibilities. The idea is that you are changing one codon to another codon that specifies the same amino acid. For example, changing a codon from GGA to GGG is likely to be neutral because both codons specify glycine.

Feature Investigation Questions

1. The males of the two species of cichlids used in the experiment are distinguishable by coloration, and the researchers were testing the hypothesis that the females make mate choices based on this variable.

2. Individual females were placed in an aquarium that also contained one male from each species. The males were held in separate enclosures to limit their movement but allow the female to see each of the males. The researchers recorded the courtship behavior between the female and males and the number of positive encounters between the female and each of the different males. This procedure was conducted under normal lighting and under monochromatic lighting that obscured the coloration differences between the males of the two species. Comparing the behavior of the females under normal light conditions and monochromatic light conditions allowed the researchers to determine the importance of coloration in mate choice.

3. The researchers found that the female was more likely to select a mate from her own species in normal light conditions. However, under monochromatic light conditions, the species-specific mate choice was not observed. Females were as likely to choose males of the other species as they were males of their own species. This indicated that coloration is an important factor in mate choice in these species of fish.

2. Pathogen populations naturally display genetic variation in their susceptibility to antibiotics. When such populations are exposed to antibiotics, even if only a few cells are initially resistant, the number of resistant cells will eventually increase and such cells could come to dominate natural populations.

3. Humans and cyanobacteria. When humans pollute natural waters with high levels of fertilizers originating from sewage effluent or crop field runoff, cyanobacterial populations are able to grow large enough to produce harmful blooms.

Chapter 28

Concept Checks

Figure 28.7 After food particles are collected in a feeding groove, they are enclosed by membrane vesicles and then digested by enzymes.

Figure 28.9 The intestinal parasite *Giardia intestinalis* is transmitted from one person to another via fecal wastes, whereas the urogenital parasite *Trichomonas vaginalis* can be transmitted by sexual activity.

Figure 28.17 Flagellar hairs function like oars, helping to pull the cell through the water.

Figure 28.18 Kelps are harvested for use in the production of industrially useful materials. In addition, they nurture fishes and other wildlife of economic importance.

Figure 28.21 Genes that encode cell adhesion and extracellular matrix proteins are likely essential to modern choanoflagellates' ability to attach to surfaces, where they feed. Similar proteins are involved in the formation of multicellular tissues in animals. Evolutionary biologists would say that ancient choanoflagellates were preadapted for the later evolution of multicellular tissues in early animals.

Figure 28.24 Cysts allow protists to survive conditions that are not suitable for growth. One such condition would be the dry or cold environment outside a parasitic protist's warm, moist host tissues.

Figure 28.29 Gametes of *Plasmodium falciparum* undergo fusion to produce zygotes while in the mosquito host.

Core Skills: Connections

Figure 28.5 In sponges, amoebocytes, which move similarly to amoeboid protists, carry food to other cells.

Feature Investigation Questions

1. Natural growths of this alga were already known to resist microbial attack and breakdown.

2. This process is commonly used to release tough fossils from rock.

Test Yourself

1. c   2. a   3. b   4. b   5. e   6. b   7. e   8. d   9. b   10. c

Conceptual Questions

1. Protists are amazingly diverse, reflecting the occurrence of extensive adaptive radiation after the origin of eukaryotic cells, widespread occurrence of endosymbiosis, and adaptation to many types of moist habitats, including the tissues of animals and plants. As a result of this extensive diversity, protists cannot be classified into a single kingdom or phylum.

2. Several protists, including the apicomplexans *Cryptosporidium parvum* and *Plasmodium falciparum* and the kinetoplastids *Leishmania major* and *Trypanosoma brucei*, cause many cases of illness around the world, but few treatments are available, and organisms often evolve drug resistance. Genomic data allow researchers to identify metabolic features of these parasites that are not present in humans and are therefore good targets for development of new drugs. An example is provided by metabolic pathways of the apicoplast, a reduced plastid that is present in cells of the genus *Plasmodium*. Because the apicoplast plays essential metabolic roles in the protist but is absent from humans, drugs that disable apicoplast metabolism would kill the parasite without harming the human host.

3. Most protist cells cannot survive outside moist environments, but cysts have tough walls and dormant cytoplasm, allowing them to persist in habitats that are unfavorable for growth. While cysts play important roles in the asexual reproduction and survival of many protists, they also allow protist parasites such as *Entamoeba histolytica* (the cause of amoebic dysentery) to spread to human hosts who consume food or water that has been contaminated with cysts. Widespread contamination can cause illness or disease in thousands of people at a time.

Chapter 29

Concept Checks

Figure 29.4 Fungal hyphae growing into a substrate having a much higher solute concentration will tend to lose cell water to the substrate, a process that could inhibit fungal growth. This process explains how drying or salting foods helps to protect them from fungal degradation and thus preserves them.

Figure 29.6 You might filter the air entering the patient's room and limit the entry of visitors and materials that could introduce fungal spores from the outside environment.

Core Skills: Connections

Figure 29.7 The *Saccharomyces cerevisiae* genome is only 12 million base pairs in size, relatively small for a eukaryote.

Figure 29.10 Amanitin, by interfering with the function of RNA polymerase II, inhibits transcription in eukaryotic cells, including those of humans.

Feature Investigation Questions

1. Plants growing on soils with temperatures up to 65°C would be expected to have fungal endophytes that aid in heat stress tolerance.

2. The investigators cured some of their *Curvularia protuberata* cultures of an associated virus; then they compared the survival of plants infected with fungal endophytes that had virus versus fungal endophytes lacking virus under conditions of heat stress. Only plants infected with fungal endophytes that possessed the virus were able to survive growth on soils with a high temperature.

3. The fungus *C. protuberata* might be used to confer heat stress tolerance to crop plants, as the investigators demonstrated in tomato.

Test Yourself

1. c   2. b   3. a   4. b   5. a   6. d   7. b   8. c   9. e   10. a

Conceptual Questions

1. Fungi are like animals in being heterotrophic, having absorptive nutrition, and storing surplus organic compounds in their cells as glycogen. Fungi are like plants in having rigid cell walls and reproducing by means of walled spores that are dispersed by wind, water, or animals.

2. Toxic or hallucinogenic compounds likely help to protect the fungi from organisms that would consume them.

3. Many fungi degrade organic compounds, thereby contributing to decomposition, which recycles materials. Some fungi trap and consume the bodies of small animals, such as nematodes. Some fungi cause diseases of plants or animals, which also helps to control populations in nature.

Chapter 30

Concept Checks

Figure 30.15 Mycorrhizal fungi provide their plant partners with water and minerals absorbed from a much larger volume of soil than plant roots can exploit on their own.

Feature Investigation Questions

1. Investigators fed the experimental mice germ-free food so that microbes normally found in food would not be present, allowing the effects of the fecal transplants to be more easily detected. In this way, the investigators removed a potentially confounding factor from their experiment.

2. Microbes from healthy children enabled the mice receiving them to grow larger than mice receiving microbes from stunted children. This outcome was a first clue that the microbes directly affected child growth, a connection that was established by additional studies.

Test Yourself

1. c   2. d   3. c   4. c   5. b   6. e   7. e   8. b   9. c   10. d

Conceptual Questions

1. Ice microbiomes include colored surface films of algae that absorb solar radiation, thereby reducing the amount reflected into space. The absorption of solar radiation has a warming effect on the physical environment, but could also influence other organisms present. Soil microbiomes contain diverse prokaryotic and eukaryotic species, including nitrogen-fixing bacteria and mycorrhizal fungi that aid plant growth.

2. One example of a host is the common, abundant nearshore green alga *Cladophora*, whose microbiota include nitrogen-fixing bacteria that aid host growth and obtain oxygen and organic molecules from the host.

3. Mycorrhizal fungi, which are components of many plant root microbiomes, mobilize and transport phosphorus and other minerals to plant roots. This improves the plant's ability to obtain minerals from the environment.

Chapter 31

Concept Checks

Figure 31.5 Wind speed varies, so if the sporangium released all the spores at the same time and there were little or no wind, the spores would not travel very far and the resulting offspring might have to compete with the parent plant for scarce resources. Releasing spores gradually means that some spores may encounter strong gusts of wind that will carry them long distances, reducing competition with the parent.

Figure 31.12 During the Carboniferous period (Coal Age), atmospheric oxygen levels reached historically high levels, enough to supply the large needs of giant insects, which obtain oxygen by diffusion.

Figure 31.17 Larger sporophytes are able to capture more resources for use in producing larger numbers of progeny and therefore increase the fitness of ferns and seed plants.

Figure 31.22 Although some angiosperm seeds, such as those of corn and coconut, contain abundant endosperm, many angiosperm embryos consume most or all of the nutritive endosperm during their development.

Figure 31.24 Because the lacy integument of *R. heinzelinii* does not completely enclose the megasporangium, it probably did not function to protect the megasporangium before fertilization or act as an effective seed coat after fertilization, as do the integuments of modern seed plants. However, the lacy integument of *R. heinzelinii* might have retained the megasporangium on the parent sporophyte during the period of time when nutrients flowed from parent to developing ovule and seed. That function would prevent megasporangia from dropping off the parent plant before fertilization occurred, allow the parent plant to provide nutrients needed during embryo development, and allow seeds time to absorb and store more nutrients from the parent. Such a function would illustrate how one mutation having a positive reproductive benefit can lay the foundation for subsequent mutations that confer additional fitness. *R. heinzelinii* illustrates a first step in the multistage evolutionary process that gave rise to modern seeds.

Core Skills: Connections

Figure 31.23 Like the plant seed, the amniotic egg characteristic of many animals provides protection and nutrients to the developing embryo.

Feature Investigation Questions

1. The experimental goals were to determine the rate at which organic molecules produced by gametophyte photosynthesis were able to move into sporophytes and to investigate the effect of sporophyte size on the amount of organic molecules transferred from the gametophyte.

2. The investigators shaded sporophytes with blackened glass tubing to ensure that all of the radioactive organic molecules detected in sporophytes at the end of the experiment came originally from the gametophytes.

3. The investigators measured the amount of radioactivity in gametophytes and sporophytes, and in sporophytes of different sizes. These measurements indicated the relative amounts of labeled organic compounds that were present in different plant tissues.

Test Yourself

1. c   2. d   3. d   4. e   5. b   6. a   7. c   8. e   9. c   10. b

Conceptual Questions

1. Streptophyte algae, particularly the complex genera *Chara* and *Coleochaete*, share many features of structure, reproduction, and biochemistry with land plants. Examples include cell division similarities, plasmodesmata, and sexual reproduction by means of flagellate sperm and eggs.

2. Bryophytes are well adapted for sexual reproduction when water is available for fertilization. Their green gametophytes efficiently transfer nutrients to developing embryos, enhancing their growth into sporophytes. Their sporophytes are able to produce many genetically diverse spores as the result of meiosis and effectively disperse these spores by means of wind.

3. Vascular tissues allow tracheophytes to effectively conduct water from roots to stems and to leaves. Waxy cuticle helps prevent loss of water by evaporation through plant surfaces. Stomata allow plants to achieve gas exchange under moist conditions and help them avoid losing excess water under arid conditions.

Chapter 32

Concept Checks

Figure 32.4 The nitrogen-fixing cyanobacteria that often occur within the coralloid roots of cycads are photosynthetic organisms that require light. If coralloid roots grew underground, the cyanobacteria would not receive enough light to survive.

Figure 32.10 Ways in which conifer leaves are adapted to resist water loss include low surface area/volume ratio, needle or scale shape, thick surface coating of waxy cuticle, and stomata that are recessed and are therefore less exposed to drying winds.

Figure 32.12 Relatively wide vessels are commonly present in the water transport tissues of angiosperms and much less commonly in other plants. The vessels occasionally found in nonangiosperms are thought to have evolved independently from those of angiosperms.

Figure 32.20 A large, showy perianth would not be useful to grass plants because they are wind pollinated; such a perianth would interfere with pollination in grasses. By not producing a showy perianth, grasses increase the chances of successful pollination and save resources that would otherwise be consumed during perianth development.

Figure 32.24 The flower characteristics of *Brighamia insignis* shown in this figure (white color and deep, narrow nectar tubes) are consistent with pollination by a moth (see Table 32.2).

Core Skills: Connections

Figure 32.2 Modern forests are dominated by seed plants, gymnosperms and angiosperms, whereas nonseed plants dominated *Archaeopteris* forests.

Figure 32.8 The wind-dispersed seeds of the gymnosperm pine resemble the wind-dispersed fruits of the angiosperm maple in having winglike structures that enhance transport in air.

Feature Investigation Questions

1. The investigators obtained many samples from around the world because they wanted to increase their chances of finding as many species as possible.

2. Although cannabinoids are produced in glandular hairs that cover the plant surface, these compounds are most abundant on leaves near the flowers. Collecting such leaves reduces the chances that compounds might be missed by the analysis.

Test Yourself

1. d   2. a   3. e   4. e   5. b   6. d   7. e   8. c   9. d   10. e

Conceptual Questions

1. Refer to Figure 30.15 to see how plant biologists think stamens and pistils might have evolved from leaves that bore sporangia. Then consider how green leaves surrounding stamens and pistils might have been transformed into petals, sepals, or tepals.

2. Apple, strawberry, and cherry plants coevolved with animals that use the fleshy, sweet portion of the fruits as food and excrete the seeds, thereby dispersing them. Humans have sensory systems similar to those of the animal seed-dispersal agents and likewise are attracted by the same colors, odors, and tastes.

3. Unlike an apple flower, a sunflower is not a single flower, but rather is an inflorescence, a group of flowers. A pollinator visiting a compact inflorescence such as a sunflower head may be able to pollinate many flowers at the same time, thereby potentially producing many seeds per pollinator visit. Likewise, a seed disperser agent might be able to disperse more seeds per plant.

Chapter 33

Core Skills: Connections

Figure 33.5 A shared derived character.

Figure 33.10 Yellow.

Feature Investigation Questions

1. The researchers sequenced the complete gene that encodes small subunit rRNA from a variety of representative phyla of animals to determine their phylogenetic relationships, particularly the relationships of arthropods to other phyla.

2. The results indicated a monophyletic clade containing arthropods and nematodes. This clade was called the Ecdysozoa. The results of this study indicated that nematodes are more closely related to arthropods than was previously believed.

3. The fruit fly, *Drosophila melanogaster*, and the nematode, *Caenorhabditis elegans*, have been widely studied to understand early development. Under the traditional phylogeny, these two species were not considered to be closely related, so similarities in development were assumed to have arisen early in animal evolution. With the closer relationship indicated by this study, these similarities may have evolved after the divergence of the Ecdysozoan clade. This puts into question the applicability of studies of these organisms to the understanding of human biology.

Test Yourself

1. b   2. c   3. e   4. c   5. c   6. d   7. d   8. d   9. b   10. e

Conceptual Questions

1. See Figure below.

2. The coelom cushioned the internal organs in fluid, preventing injury from external forces. In addition, the coelom enabled the internal organs to grow and move independently of the outer body wall. Finally, in some invertebrates, the coelom acts as a hydrostatic skeleton that supports the body and permits movement.

3. They are paraphyletic since the group contains a common ancestor but not all of its descendants.

Chapter 34

Concept Checks

Figure 34.3 Sponges aren't eaten by other organisms because they produce toxic chemicals and contain needle-like silica spicules that are hard to digest.

Figure 34.4 The dominant life stages are jellyfish: medusa; sea anemone: polyp; Portuguese man-of-war: polyp (in a large floating colony).

Figure 34.5 Cnidocytes are not reused. New ones form to replace the discharged ones.

Figure 34.6 Having no specialized respiratory or circulatory system, flatworms obtain oxygen by diffusion. A flattened shape ensures that no cells are too far from the body surface.

Figure 34.10 The lophophore functions as (1) a ciliary feeding device and (2) a respiratory organ.

Figure 34.11 Technically, the hearts of most mollusks pump hemolymph into vessels and then into tissues. The hemolymph collects in open, fluid-filled cavities called sinuses, which flow into the gills and then back to the heart. This is known as an open circulatory system. Only closed circulatory systems pump blood, as occurs in the cephalopods.

Figure 34.15 Some advantages of segmentation are organ duplication, minimization of body distortion during movement, and specialization of some segments.

Figure 34.17 An annelid is segmented and possesses a true coelom, whereas a nematode is unsegmented and has a pseudocoelom. In addition, nematodes molt, but annelids do not.

Figure 34.21 All arachnids have a body consisting of two tagmata: a cephalothorax and an abdomen. Insects have three tagmata: head, thorax, and abdomen.

Figure 34.24 Two other key insect adaptations are the development of wings and an exoskeleton that reduced water loss and aided in the colonization of land.

Figure 34.30 In embryonic development, deuterostomes show radial cleavage and indeterminate cleavage, and the blastopore becomes the anus. (In protostomes, cleavage is spiral and determinate, and the blastopore becomes the mouth.)

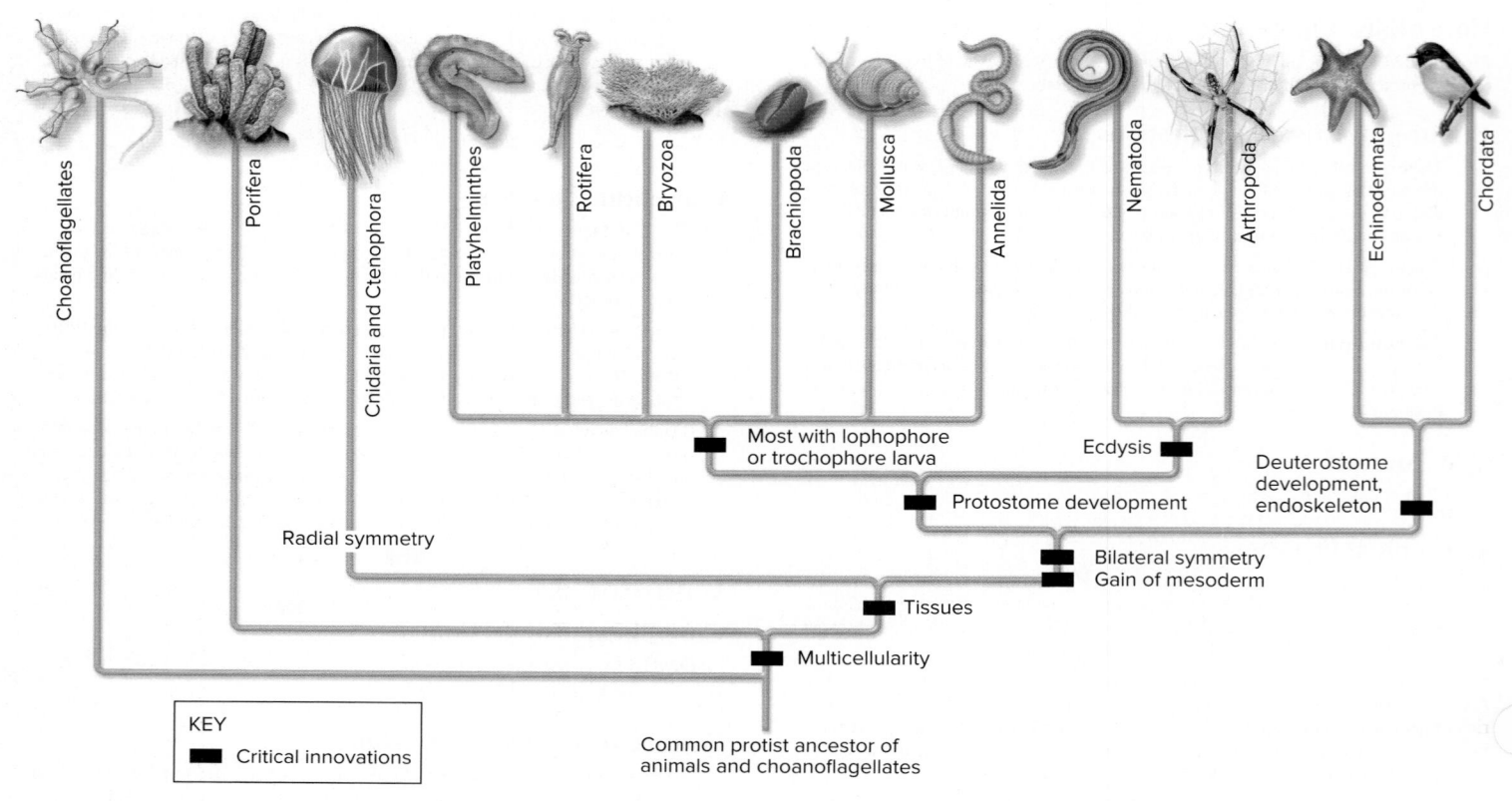

Choanoflagellates · Porifera · Cnidaria and Ctenophora · Platyhelminthes · Rotifera · Bryozoa · Brachiopoda · Mollusca · Annelida · Nematoda · Arthropoda · Echinodermata · Chordata

Most with lophophore or trochophore larva

Ecdysis

Deuterostome development, endoskeleton

Protostome development

Bilateral symmetry
Gain of mesoderm

Radial symmetry

Tissues

Multicellularity

KEY
■ Critical innovations

Common protist ancestor of animals and choanoflagellates

Core Skills: Connections

Figure 34.19 Because most species can excrete urine that is isoosmotic or hyperosmotic to the body fluids.

Figure 34.27 These organs, called statocysts, are located at the base of the antennules.

Feature Investigation Questions

1. The researchers tested the hypothesis that an octopus can learn by observing the behavior of another octopus.

2. The results indicated that the observer learned by watching the training of the other octopus. The observer was much more likely to choose the same color ball that the demonstrator was trained to attack. These results support the hypothesis that octopuses can learn by observing the behavior of others.

3. The untrained octopuses had no prior exposure to the demonstrators. The results indicated that these octopuses were as likely to attack the white ball as the red ball. No preference for either color was indicated. The untrained octopuses acted as a control. This is an important factor to ensure that the results from the trials using observers indicate a response to learning and not an existing preference for a certain color.

Test Yourself

1. b   2. d   3. d   4. d   5. b   6. c   7. b   8. a   9. c   10. b

Conceptual Questions

1. The five main feeding methods used by invertebrate animals are (1) suspension feeding, (2) decomposition, (3) herbivory, (4) predation, and (5) parasitism. Suspension feeding is usually used to filter out food particles from the water. A great many phyla, including sponges, rotifers, bryozoans, brachiopods, some mollusks, some echinoderms and tunicates, are filter feeders. Decomposers usually feed on dead material such as animal carcasses or dead leaves. For example, many fly and beetle larvae feed on dead animals, and earthworms consume dead leaves from the surface of the Earth. Earthworms and crabs also sift through soil or mud, eating the substrate and digesting the soil-dwelling bacteria, protists, and dead organic material. Herbivores eat plants or algae and are especially common in the arthropoda. Adult moths and butterflies also consume nectar. Snails are also common plant feeders. Predators feed on other animals, killing their prey, and may be active hunters or sit-and-wait predators. Many scorpions and spiders actively pursue their prey, whereas web-spinning spiders ambush their prey using webs. Parasites also feed on other animals but do not normally kill their hosts. Endoparasites, which includes flukes, tapeworms, and nematodes, live inside their hosts. Ectoparasites (ticks and lice) live on the outside of their hosts.

2. Gametes would dry out on land, and internal fertilization prevents this from happening. Also, water facilitates the movement of gametes, reducing the need for internal fertilization.

3. Complete metamorphosis has four stages: egg, larva, pupa, and adult. The larval stage is often spent in an entirely different habitat from that of the adult, and larval and adult forms utilize different food sources. Incomplete metamorphosis has only three stages: egg, nymph, and adult. Young insects, called nymphs, look like miniature adults when they hatch from their eggs.

Chapter 35

Concept Checks

Figure 35.1 Vertebrates (but not invertebrates) usually possess a (1) notochord; (2) dorsal hollow nerve chord; (3) pharyngeal slits; (4) postanal tail, exhibited by all chordates; (5) vertebral column; (6) cranium; and (7) endoskeleton of cartilage or bone.

Figure 35.7 Ray-finned fishes (but not sharks) have a (1) bony skeleton; (2) mucus-covered skin; (3) swim bladder; and (4) operculum covering the gills.

Figure 35.8 Both lungfishes and coelocanths are Sarcopterygii, having lobe fins.

Figure 35.11 The advantages for animals that moved onto land included an oxygen-rich environment and a bonanza of food in the form of terrestrial plants and the insects that fed on them.

Figure 35.13 No. Caecilians and some salamanders give birth to live young.

Figure 35.14 Besides the amniotic egg, other critical innovations in amniotes are thoracic breathing; internal fertilization; a thicker, less permeable skin; and more efficient kidneys.

Figure 35.16 Snakes evolved from tetrapod ancestors but subsequently lost their limbs. Some species have tiny vestigial limbs.

Figure 35.20 Adaptations in birds to reduce body weight for flight include a light-weight skull, reduction of organ size (including smaller gonads outside of breeding season), and a lack of a urinary bladder and teeth. Also female birds have one ovary and can carry relatively few eggs.

Core Skills: Connections

Figure 35.5 No, an examination of Figure 35.1 shows that "fishy" organisms include an ancestral population and some of its descendants, but not all of them. The "fish" are thus a paraphyletic group. To be a monophyletic group, the fish would have to include the tetrapods as well. Therefore, there is no true monophyletic group that corresponds to the popular name "fish."

Figure 35.17 Both crocodilians and birds and mammals have four-chambered hearts and care for their young.

Figure 35.26 None. The bloodstreams of fetus and mother are brought into close contact in the placenta, but they do not mix.

Feature Investigation Questions

1. The researchers were interested in determining the role of *Hox* genes in controlling limb development in mice.

2. The researchers bred mice that were homozygous for certain mutations in specific *Hox* genes. This allowed the researchers to determine the function of individual genes.

3. The researchers found that homozygous mutants developed limbs of shorter length compared to limbs of the wild-type mice. The reduced length was due to the lack of development of particular bones in the limb, specifically, the radius, ulna, and some carpels. These results indicated that simple mutations in a few genes could lead to dramatic changes in limb development.

Test Yourself

1. b   2. e   3. d   4. e   5. a   6. d   7. d   8. c   9. c   10. a

Conceptual Questions

1. Both vertebrates and arthropods have external limbs that move when the attached muscles contract or relax. The difference is that arthropods have external skeletons, with the muscles attached internally, whereas vertebrates have internal skeletons with the muscles attached externally.

2. Endothermy (warm-bloodedness) probably evolved independently in both birds and mammals. If the common ancestor of reptiles and birds were endothermic, the chances are that all reptiles would be endothermic.

3. Probably. Both birds and reptiles lay amniotic eggs and possess scales, though these only cover the legs in birds. Birds and crocodilians also share a four-chambered heart. Finally, birds share many skeletal similarities with certain dinosaurs.

Chapter 36

Concept Checks

Figure 36.8 Having stomata located on the darker and cooler lower epidermis helps reduce water loss from the leaf.

Figure 36.12 A twig having five sets of bud scale scars is likely to be approximately 6 years old.

Figure 36.17 Cactus stems are green and photosynthetic; they play the role served by the leaves of most plants and make the organic compounds.

Figure 36.21 A woody stem such as a tree trunk builds up a thicker layer of wood than inner bark in part because older tracheids and vessel element walls are not lost during shedding of bark, which is the case for secondary phloem. In addition, plants typically produce a greater volume of xylem than phloem tissue per year, in part because vessel elements are relatively wide. A large volume of water-conducting tissue helps plants maintain a large amount of internal water.

Figure 36.24 Lateral roots are produced from internal meristematic tissue because roots do not produce axillary buds like those from which shoot branches develop. Internal production of branch roots helps to prevent them from shearing off as the root tip grows through abrasive soil.

Core Skills: Connections

Figure 36.5 Apical-basal polarity of the plant body resembles anterior-posterior polarity in the animal body.

Figure 36.9 Plant cells often possess a large vacuole, whereas vacuoles in animal cells are relatively small.

Figure 36.11 There is no difference among eukaryotes with respect to the structure of microtubules.

Feature Investigation Questions

1. The advantages of using natural plants include the opportunity to avoid influencing plants with unnatural environmental factors, such as artificial light, and the exposure of all experimental plants to similar growth conditions. In addition, the investigators studied the leaves of some large trees, which would be hard to accommodate in a greenhouse.

2. Pinnately veined leaves were splinted to prevent their breaking, since they were cut at the single main vein, which has both support and conducting functions.

3. The researchers measured leaf water conduction at two or more places on each leaf because the effect of cutting a vein might have affected some portions of leaves more than others.

Test Yourself

1. d   2. c   3. b   4. a   5. c   6. a   7. d   8. e   9. b   10. e

Conceptual Questions

1. If overall plant architecture were bilaterally symmetrical, plants would be shaped like higher animals, with a distinct front (ventral surface) and back (dorsal surface). Bilaterally symmetrical plants would have a reduced ability to deploy branches and leaves in a way that would fill available lighted space and would thus be unable to take optimal photosynthetic advantage of their habitats.

2. If leaves were generally radially symmetrical (shaped like spheres or cylinders), they would not have the maximal ability to absorb sunlight, and they would not be able to optimally disperse excess heat from their surfaces.

3. Although tall herbaceous plants exist (palms and bamboo are examples), the additional support and water-conducting capacity that are provided by secondary xylem allow woody plants to grow tall.

Chapter 37

Concept Checks

Figure 37.4 Auxin efflux carriers could be located on the upper sides of root cells, thereby allowing auxin to move upward in roots.

Figure 37.6 Once a callus has been formed from a single plant having desirable characteristics using plant tissue culture, the callus can be divided into many small calluses. A grower can transfer these to separate containers having the appropriate hormone mixtures to induce root and shoot growth, then transplant the young plant clones to soil. In this way, the grower can produce many identical plants.

Figure 37.9 The triple response of a seedling to internally produced ethylene serves to protect the delicate apical meristem from damage as the seedling pushes upward through the soil.

Figure 37.11 The inactive conformation of phytochrome would absorb the red light in the sunlight, thereby converting the molecule into the active conformation.

Figure 37.12 Exposing plants to brief periods of darkness during the daytime will have no effect on flowering because flowering is determined by night length.

Figure 37.14 Yes, just as shoots exhibit negative gravitropism in upward growth, roots are capable of using negative phototropism to grow downward, because light decreases with depth in the soil.

Figure 37.19 The immunity effect is relatively long-lasting in both cases.

Feature Investigation Questions

1. Hypothetically, auxin enhances the rate at which cell membrane proton pumps acidify the plant cell wall, thereby allowing cells to extend. Although the evidence for acid effects on cell-wall extension is strong, the molecular basis of possible auxin effects on proton pumps is not as yet clear.

2. A small number of seedling tips could display atypical responses for a variety of reasons. The investigators actually performed the experiment with many replicate seedling tips (coleoptiles), in order to gain confidence that the responses are general.

Test Yourself

1. c   2. c   3. a   4. e   5. d   6. d   7. c   8. d   9. d   10. d

---

BioTIPS page 762

HYPOTHESIS Light destroys auxin on lit side of shoot tips, causing unequal auxin distribution. Unlit side should grow more than lit side.

STARTING MATERIALS Corn seedlings.

	Experimental level	Conceptual level

1 Collect auxin into agar blocks from:
A dark-grown tips
B tips grown with directional light

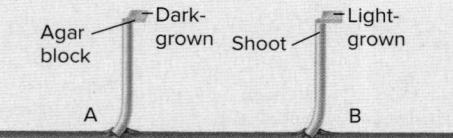

Dark-grown tip — Auxin diffusion — Directional light-grown tip   A   B

If light destroys auxin on one side, less auxin will enter the block. (Light)

2 Place agar blocks on right side of decapitated shoots.

Agar block — Dark-grown — Shoot — Light-grown   A   B

If the block on the right side has less auxin, it will cause less bending.

3 THE DATA

Dark-grown 26°   Light-grown 26°
A   B

4 CONCLUSION

Similar bending demonstrates that light did not destroy auxin in the directionally lit shoot tip. If it had, less auxin would have been present in the agar block in B, and the degree of bending would have been less. The hypothesis described under conceptual level (above) is incorrect.

within plant roots and/or mycorrhizal fungi that harvest minerals from decaying organisms and transport the minerals to plant root tissues.

Chapter 39

Concept Checks

Figure 39.5 When placed in pure water, a turgid cell having a water potential of 1.0 will lose water, because 1 is greater than 0. When placed in pure water, a plasmolyzed cell having a water potential of –1.0 MPa will gain water. When placed in pure water, a flaccid cell having a water potential of –0.5 MPa will gain water. This is because water moves from a region of higher water potential to a region of lower water potential, and 0 is greater than –0.5.

Figure 39.11 You would likely see stained rings or helical ribbons extending up the insides of the walls of extensible tracheids. You would not see staining at the ends of tracheids, where they connect to form long tubes.

Figure 39.12 The large perforations in vessel element end walls allow an air bubble to extend from one element to another, thereby clogging a vessel and preventing water flow through it. In contrast, the much smaller pores in the end walls of tracheids do not allow water to flow as efficiently as it does through vessels, but these smaller pores also retard the movement of air bubbles. As a result, an air bubble will be confined to a single tracheid where it can do little harm.

Figure 39.13 Root pressure can help to reverse an embolism, thereby restoring water flow through the plant xylem.

Figure 39.15 The evaporation of water has a powerful cooling effect because it dissipates heat so effectively. Water has the highest heat of vaporization of any known liquid.

Figure 39.16 You could model a stomatal guard cell with an elongate balloon by partially inflating it, then attaching thick tape along one side to represent thickened inner walls and circles of string or thin tape to represent radial cellulose, then adding more air to the balloon. The balloon should curve as it expands, just as a guard cell does when the stomatal pore opens. Two such balloons could be used to model both guard cells and the stomatal pore.

Figure 39.19 In the ocotillo's desert habitat, times of drought and availability of water sufficient to support the development and photosynthetic function of leaves do not occur as predictably as in temperate forests. For this reason, ocotillo leaf abscission is not amenable to the evolution of genetic mechanisms that allow leaf drop to be precisely timed in anticipation of the onset of drought.

Core Skills: Connections

Figure 39.8 Tight junctions in the intestinal epithelium of animals and Casparian strips in walls of endodermal cells of plant roots both form a tight seal, preventing movement of materials from one location to another.

Figure 39.21 Stomatal guard cell and phloem companion cell development both begin with an unequal cell division.

Feature Investigation Questions

1. Replicates provide reproducibility, and controlled growth conditions reduce the effects of environment.
2. Leaf temperature indicates degree of evaporation through open stomata.

Test Yourself

1. c   2. b   3. e   4. d   5. a   6. e   7. d   8. e   9. a   10. c

Conceptual Questions

1. In the case of plant fertilizers, more is not better, because the ion concentration of overfertilized soil may become so high as to draw water from plant cells. In this case, the cells would be bathed in a hypertonic solution and would likely lose water to the solution. If plant cells lose too much water, they will die.
2. When the natural vegetation is removed, transpiration stops, so water is not transported from the ground to the atmosphere, where it may be an important contributor to local rainfall. Extensive removal of plants actually changes local climates in ways that reduce agricultural productivity and human survival.
3. When mineral ion concentrations in the soil are lower than those within root cells, root-hair plasma membranes take up nutrient ions by active transport, which requires energy in the form of ATP. So the plant rooted in soil of lower mineral concentration will likely expend more ATP during nutrient uptake.

Conceptual Questions

1. Behavior is defined as the response of a living thing to a stimulus. Therefore, because plants display many kinds of responses to diverse stimuli, they display behavior.
2. Many kinds of disease-causing bacteria and fungi occur in nature, and these organisms evolve very quickly, producing diverse elicitors. Thus, plants must maintain various types of resistance genes, each having many alleles.
3. Talking implies a conversation with "listeners" who detect a message and respond to it. Thus, plants that exude volatile compounds that attract enemies of herbivores could be interpreted as "talking" to those enemies. The message is "Hey, you guys, there's food for you over here." In addition, research has revealed that some plants near those under attack respond to volatile compounds by building up defenses. "Talking" to other plants does not enhance the "talker's" fitness. But the ability to "listen" enhances the "listener's" fitness, because it can take preemptive actions to prevent attack.

Chapter 38

Concept Checks

Figure 38.5 Plastids that are clustered near the nucleus should have more rubisco than plastids at the periphery.

Figure 38.6 Chlorosis is not always a sign of iron deficiency; it can be a symptom of a deficiency of any of several mineral nutrients, including zinc in corn.

Figure 38.10 Mineral leaching occurs more readily in sandy soils than in clay soils.

Figure 38.12 Soil crusts containing nitrogen-fixing cyanobacteria increase soil fertility, fostering the growth of larger plants that stabilize soils against erosion and provide forage for animals.

Figure 38.13 Oxygen, which makes up 21% of Earth's present atmosphere, can bind to the active site of nitrogenase, thereby inactivating it.

Core Skills: Connections

Figure 38.20 Both the tapeworm and the dodder obtain organic food from a host, an animal or a plant, respectively.

Feature Investigation Questions

1. *SDQ1* expression is induced by phosphorus deficiency. This gene fosters replacement of plastid phospholipids with sulfur-containing lipids, thereby reducing the plant's phosphorus requirement.
2. They used genetic engineering techniques to place a reporter gene under the control of the *SQD1* promoter, so that when *SQD1* was expressed, the reporter gene was expressed also. After growing plants in nutrient solutions containing various levels of phosphorus, they removed sample leaves and treated them with a compound that turns blue when the reporter gene is expressed. When they saw blue leaves, the investigators could infer (1) that the plants from which those leaves had been taken were beginning to experience phosphorus deficiency and (2) that application of fertilizer at this point could prevent damage to the plants.

Test Yourself

1. e   2. a   3. c   4. b   5. e   6. c   7. d   8. d   9. a   10. b

Conceptual Questions

1. Agricultural experts are concerned that adding excess fertilizer to crop fields increases the costs of crop production. Ecologists are concerned that excess fertilizers will wash from crop fields into natural waters and cause harmful overgrowths of cyanobacteria, algae, and aquatic plants. Methods for closely monitoring crop nutrient needs so that only the appropriate amount of fertilizer is applied would help to allay both groups' concerns.
2. Use Figure 38.18 as a reference. A first arrow could be drawn from a root to rhizobia in the soil, and the arrow labeled "flavonoids." A second arrow could be drawn from rhizobia to roots and labeled "Nod factors." A third arrow from rhizobia to roots could be labeled "infection proteins." A fourth arrow from roots to rhizobia could be labeled "nodulins" and the resulting nodule environmental conditions, which influence the formation of bacterioids. A fifth arrow could represent the flow of fixed nitrogen from bacterioids to plant. A sixth arrow could represent the flow of organic compounds from plant to bacterioids.
3. Tropical plants often partner with microbes that provide essential mineral nutrients. Such partnerships include nitrogen-fixing bacteria that may live

Conceptual Questions

1. All animals with nervous systems have reflexes, which allow rapid behavioral responses to changes in the environment. When a cnidarian senses a tactile stimulus, its nerve net responds immediately and the animal reflexively contracts nearly all of its muscles, making the animal a smaller target. This behavior protects the animal from predators. When you hear a loud, unexpected, and frightening sound (such as a firecracker), you hunch your shoulders and slightly lower your head; this reflex protects you from danger by minimizing exposure of your neck and head to danger. Dilation of the pupils of the eyes in darkness, and constriction of the pupils in bright light, are reflexes that help us see in the dark and protect our retinas in bright light. Reflexes are particularly adaptive because they occur rapidly, typically with very few synapses involved, and without the need for conscious thought.

2. White matter consists of the myelinated axons that are bundled together in large tracts in the central nervous system and which connect different CNS regions. The lipid-rich myelin gives the tracts a whitish appearance. In contrast, gray matter consists of the cell bodies, dendrites, and some unmyelinated axons of neurons in the CNS.

3. The activities of animal nervous systems are replete with examples of new properties emerging from complex interactions. For example, you learned about reflexes in this chapter, which are behaviors that emerge from interactions between individual neurons that form communication circuits between the peripheral and central nervous systems. You also learned about "higher" functions of nervous systems, such as conscious thought, which also emerges from the interactions between many individual cells, each of which is in communication with up to hundreds of thousands of other cells. Individually, the cells cannot "think," but networked together in elaborate ways, they enable a person to think, remember, plan ahead, and interpret the environment.

Chapter 44

Concept Checks

Figure 44.3 To think about the touch sensations you are aware of, let's take the example of sitting in a chair reading this textbook while holding it on your lap. You are aware of the constant weight of the book, the brush of the pages on your fingertips as you turn a page, a gentle breeze that may be circulating in your environment, the deep pressure from regularly adjusting your posture in your chair, an itch you may have on your skin, and the heat or cold of the room. Even a simple exercise such as this one is filled with stimuli of numerous types and durations.

Figure 44.7 Waves of fluid (perilymph) movement caused by sound pressure on the tympanic membrane result in vibration of the basilar membrane.

Figure 44.9 The orientation of the canals permits animals to detect circular or angular movement of the head in three different planes. The fluid in a canal that is oriented in the same plane as the plane of movement will respond maximally to the movement. For example, the canal that is oriented horizontally will show the greatest response to horizontal movements, while the other two canals will not respond as much. Overall, by comparing the signals from the three canals, the brain can interpret the motion in three dimensions.

Figure 44.11 By comparing the intensity of signals from both sides of its head, a pit viper can determine the direction from which the heat is coming and thus localize its prey.

Figure 44.18 Because red-green color blindness is caused by a sex-linked recessive gene, males require only a single defective allele on an X chromosome, whereas females require two defective alleles, one on each X chromosome.

Figure 44.21 Photoreceptors synapse with bipolar cells, which in turn form synapses with ganglion cells.

Figure 44.26 Salt is a vital nutrient needed to maintain plasma membrane potentials and fluid balance in animals' bodies. Sugar provides glucose and other monosaccharides, important energy-yielding compounds. Sour (acidic) foods, like citrus fruits, provide nutrients and important antioxidants (vitamin C, for example) that protect against disease. Bitter substances are often toxic, and their bad taste discourages animals from eating them.

Core Skills: Connections

Figure 44.1 The term sensory receptor refers to a type of cell that can respond to a particular type of stimulus. The term membrane receptor refers to a protein within a cell membrane that binds a ligand, thereby generating signals that initiate a cellular response.

Figure 44.4 Cilia are cell extensions that contain in their internal structure microtubules and motor proteins that cause them to beat, or move, in a coordinated fashion. Stereocilia are membrane projections that are not motile, but instead are deformed by the movements of surrounding fluids.

Figure 44.8 Statoliths are also found in the roots and shoots of plants. They serve as a gravity-detection mechanism that results in roots growing downward and shoots upward.

Figure 44.16 The microvilli of the photoreceptor in the compound eye of insects and the outer segments of the rod and cone in the vertebrate eye share membrane adaptations that increase their surface area, making them better able to detect photons.

Feature Investigation Questions

1. One possibility is that many different types of odor molecules might bind to one or just a few types of receptor proteins, with the brain responding differently depending on the number or distribution of the activated receptors. The second hypothesis is that organisms can make a large number of receptor proteins, each type binding a particular odor molecule or group of odor molecules. According to this hypothesis, it is the *type* of receptor protein, and not the number or distribution of receptors, that is important for olfactory sensing.

   The researchers extracted mRNA molecules from the olfactory receptor cells of the nasal epithelium of rats. They then used this mRNA to identify genes that encoded G-protein-coupled receptors.

2. The results of the experiment conducted by Buck and Axel support the hypothesis that animals discriminate between different odors based on having a variety of receptor proteins that recognize different odor molecules. Current research suggests that each olfactory receptor cell has a single type of receptor protein that is specific to particular odor molecules. Because most odors are due to multiple chemicals that activate many different types of odor receptor proteins, the brain detects odors based on the combination of the activated receptor proteins. Odor seems to be discriminated by many olfactory receptor proteins, which are in the membrane of separate olfactory receptor cells.

3. Among other things, animals use odors to detect potential sources of food, shelter, mates, and danger. Discerning between the odors of food versus potentially toxic material is key to the survival of many animals (think, for example, how we recognize fresh milk and spoiled milk). Many animals also use olfaction in finding shelter; some birds, for example, can distinguish the odors produced by particular beneficial plants that they use to build their nests. These plants have natural pathogen-killing properties and help maintain a healthier nest site. Odor preference also plays an important role in animals finding mates via the release of pheromones, particularly animals that live in dark environments such as nocturnal animals. The ability to discern the odors of different predators even when the predator may not be close enough to hear, or may not be in sight, is a huge survival advantage for many animals, who generally can differentiate such odors from those of nonthreatening species.

Test Yourself

1. d   2. c   3. b   4. c   5. e   6. e   7. b   8. b   9. d   10. b

Conceptual Questions

1. Sensory transduction is the process by which incoming stimuli are converted into neural signals. An example is the generation of signals in the retina when a photon of light strikes a photoreceptor.

   Perception is an awareness of the sensations that are experienced. An example is realizing what a particular visual image is.

2. Structurally, single-lens and compound eyes both have a lens, photoreceptors, light-absorbing pigmented cells, and structures with extensive surface areas. Functionally, both types of eye are capable of sensing the intensity of light, as well as distinguishing between wavelengths of light (color). In both cases, also, information from the eye is sent to the brain.

3. Of the various senses, the sense of olfaction (smell) is least important for the survival of humans. As diurnal animals, we rely largely on our visual sense. Sounds are a critical way to learn about impending danger, such as a car horn, but also provide our major means of communication. Other senses, such as the ability to sense pain, have acutely important functions from time to time. Olfaction, though often a pleasurable sense and at times a protective one (think of the smell of spoiled food), nonetheless provides little survival advantage to us. In fact, many people spend much of their lives with greatly diminished olfactory abilities, whether from chronic allergies or other problems, and are not hindered in any significant way. The story is very different for animals such as nocturnal mammals, which rely very heavily on olfaction to find food, locate mates, and avoid predators.

Chapter 45

Concept Checks

Figure 45.1 In addition to not needing to shed their skeletons periodically, animals with endoskeletons can use their skin as an efficient means of heat transfer (and, to an extent in amphibians, water transfer). In addition, the body surface of such animals is often a highly sensitive sensory organ.

Figure 45.3 If a tendon is torn, the attachment of a muscle to a bone is reduced or lost. Therefore, when that muscle contracts, it will not be able to move the bone, at least not as much as usual.

Core Skills: Connections

Figure 45.10 Voltage-gated Ca^{2+} channels exist in the terminals of all axons that communicate by chemical signaling (neurotransmitter release). In those cases, depolarization of the axon terminal opens Ca^{2+} channels, allowing Ca^{2+} to enter the terminal and trigger exocytosis of stored vesicles containing neurotransmitter molecules.

Feature Investigation Questions

1. PPAR-δ is a transcription factor that regulates the expression of genes that enable cells to more efficiently burn fat instead of glucose for energy.

2. Evans hypothesized that if PPAR-δ were highly activated in mice, the mice would lose weight because of the high level of fat metabolism. Evans and his coworkers developed transgenic mice with highly activated PPAR-δ. Then they fed the transgenic mice and a group of wild-type mice high-fat diets. They then compared the weights of the two groups of mice to determine if the change in PPAR-δ activity affected weight. The weights of the transgenic mice were considerably lower than those of the wild-type mice. These results supported the hypothesis that highly activated PPAR-δ would lead to lower weight gain due to fat metabolism. Interestingly, the researchers also discovered that the transgenic mice could perform prolonged exercise for a much longer time than the wild-type mice. The muscle tissue of the transgenic mice was more specialized for long-term exercise.

3. Based on the mean body weight prior to the switch in diet, the wild-type and transgenic mice should weigh approximately 49–50 g and 33–34 g, respectively, at the conclusion of the study. Current dietary recommendations suggest that people consume no more than about 30% of their daily calories from fat, and that most of that fat should be in the form of unsaturated fat. According to the Centers for Disease Control and Prevention, the average consumption of fat in the U.S. amounts to roughly 33% of daily calories; however, that is an average and many individuals consume far more fat than that each day.

Test Yourself

1. b   2. e   3. d   4. b   5. e   6. c   7. a   8. e   9. c   10. e

Conceptual Questions

1. Exoskeletons are on the outside of an animal's body, and endoskeletons are inside the body. Both function in support and protection, but only exoskeletons protect an animal's outer surface. Exoskeletons must be shed when an animal grows, whereas endoskeletons grow with an animal.

2. Animals can fly, glide, swim, walk, hop, jump, crawl, and be moved by water or air currents. For animals adapted to it, swimming and flying are energetically less costly than moving on land. In all cases, however, friction due to contact with land or drag due to the resistance of water or air requires energy to overcome.

3. The use of energy released by the hydrolysis of ATP is fundamental to skeletal muscle function and locomotion. Recall that ATP must be hydrolyzed during the cross-bridge cycle for skeletal muscle cells to shorten. Energy is also used to maintain calcium ion balance in the sarcoplasmic reticulum and is expended in all forms of locomotion. The amount of energy expended by animals during locomotion reflects how well they are adapted to the environment in which they must move.

Chapter 46

Concept Checks

Figure 46.4 Sauropod dinosaurs were herbivores that probably had a gizzard-type structure in which stones helped to grind up coarse vegetation. Such stones would have become smooth after months or even years of tumbling around in the gizzard. Some of these sauropods are known to have lacked the sort of grinding teeth characteristic of modern mammalian herbivores, and thus a gizzard would have functioned in their digestion much as it does in modern birds.

Figure 46.7 A gallbladder stores bile and releases it precisely when it is needed, in response to a meal, which is particularly useful for animals that consume large or infrequent meals. In the absence of a gallbladder, bile flows into the intestine continuously and cannot be increased to match the amount or timing of food intake.

Core Skills: Connections

Figure 46.8 Transmembrane transport processes such as facilitated diffusion and secondary active transport are not unique to animals, and one or more types occur in virtually all cells.

Figure 46.11 CCK inhibits stomach activity. This is an example of negative feedback. The arrival of chyme in the small intestine stimulates secretion of CCK, which promotes digestion. At the same time, CCK inhibits contraction of the smooth muscles of the stomach so that the entry of chyme into the small intestine is slowed down. This allows time for controlled digestion and absorption of nutrients in the small intestine, and prevents the intestine becoming overfilled with chyme. Simultaneously, CCK inhibits acid production by the stomach so that the pH of the small intestine does not become dangerously low before bicarbonate ions are able to neutralize it.

Feature Investigation Questions

1. The surprising observations that some people with gastritis or ulcers have living bacteria (*H. pylori*) in their stomachs and that administering bacteria-killing compounds provided some relief from the symptoms led to the hypothesis that *H. pylori* infection is a cause of ulcers in humans.

2. The results did support the hypothesis. However, the results also clearly indicated that not all ulcers are due to *H. pylori* infection.

3. A combined treatment with bismuth and an antibiotic seems to be the most effective treatment. It is apparent, however, that even in individuals with continued *H. pylori* infections, some ulcers will heal on their own. In the absence of bismuth-antibiotic therapy, though, the likelihood of a recurrence of a new ulcer is much greater.

Test Yourself

1. d   2. e   3. d   4. c   5. c   6. a   7. d   8. c   9. e   10. e

Conceptual Questions

1. Digestion is the breaking down of large molecules into smaller ones by the action of enzymes and acid. Absorption is the transport of ions and small molecules, including those that do not require digestion, across the epithelial cells of the alimentary canal and from there into the extracellular fluid of an animal.

2. The crop is a dilation of the esophagus, which stores and softens food. The gizzard contains swallowed pebbles that help pulverize food. Both of these functions are adaptations that assist digestion in birds, which do not have teeth and therefore do not chew food. Humans, like many animals, can chew food before swallowing.

3. The small intestine contains layers of smooth muscle whose contractions help mix the contents of the intestine; this mixing facilitates digestion by bringing enzymes and food molecules into contact. Tight junctions along the apical membranes of the epithelium prevent enzymes from leaking out of the intestine. The surface area available for absorption is greatly increased by the folding of the epithelium to form villi and by the presence of microvilli, making up the brush border. The epithelial cells have digestive enzymes on their apical membranes; this ensures that the final steps of digestion will release products at the cell surface, where they can be quickly absorbed. The small intestine also contains neurons that, when activated by stretching of the intestine, signal the stomach to temporarily relax so that the intestine can process chyme in small amounts.

Chapter 47

Concept Checks

Figure 47.6 Nearly all animals today show a similar relationship between body mass and metabolic rate, and there is no reason why that should not always have been true. Thus, the tiny 1-foot-tall ancestral horse *Eohippus* most likely had a higher BMR than do today's larger horses.

Figure 47.9 Humans are homeothermic endotherms. We maintain our body temperature within a very narrow range, and we supply our own body heat.

Core Skills: Connections

Figure 47.3 Exocytosis involves the fusion of intracellular vesicles with the plasma membrane, resulting in the release of the vesicle contents into the extracellular fluid. See Figure 5.21 for a general description and Figure 42.13 for a specific example unique to animal cells.

Feature Investigation Questions

1. Scientists were interested in knowing how animals regulate their body mass around a particular level, even though many animals experience changes in food supply throughout the year. This observation seemed to indicate that a mechanism existed within the body that monitored when fuel stores were higher or lower than normal and that initiated changes in behavior and metabolism to compensate.

2. The ob mice lost weight and ate less during the experimental procedure. This confirmed that something in the bloodstream of the wild-type mice was regulating body weight but was missing in the ob mice. When the unknown factor crossed into the bloodstream of the ob mice, it caused them to lose weight. In another group of parabiosed mice, however, the wild-type mice lost weight, but the db mice did not. Coleman concluded that these obese mice were not able to respond to the chemical signal that regulates body weight, even though they made the signal themselves and it was active in their parabiosed wild-type partners. It is now known that db mice produce leptin and ob mice do not; however, db mice are not sensitive to leptin and consequently they failed to lose weight in Coleman's experiment.

3. When parabiosed, leptin from db mice will enter the circulation of ob mice. The ob mice will lose weight as a consequence. The db mice will continue to gain weight because they remain insensitive to leptin.

Test Yourself

1. c   2. a   3. d   4. c   5. a   6. c   7. e   8. c   9. c   10. e

Conceptual Questions

1. Insulin acts on adipose and skeletal muscle cells to facilitate the diffusion of glucose from extracellular fluid into the cells' cytosol. This is accomplished by increasing the translocation of proteins called glucose transporters (GLUTs) from the cytosol to sites within the plasma membrane of insulin-sensitive cells. Insulin also inhibits glycogenolysis and gluconeogenesis in the liver, which decreases the amount of glucose secreted into the blood by the liver. Insulin is required for glucose transport because like many other polar molecules, glucose cannot move across the lipid bilayer of a plasma membrane by simple diffusion. The inhibitory effects of insulin on liver function help to ensure that liver glycogen stores will be spared for the postabsorptive period.

2. Appetite is controlled by a satiety center in the brain that receives signals from the stretched stomach and intestines after a meal. When digestion and absorption are complete, the stomach and intestines return to their original size, and the brain no longer perceives that the animal feels "full." In addition, appetite is controlled by leptin, a hormone secreted by adipose cells in direct proportion to the amount of fat stored in an animal's body. When leptin concentrations in the blood are high, appetite is suppressed. When leptin concentrations are low, as occurs when an animal is losing weight, appetite is increased. The presence of a hormone that is released into the blood in proportion to fat mass in the body allows the brain to monitor the amount of energy stored in the body. A decrease in the concentration of leptin in the blood, for example, is the mechanism that communicates to the brain that fat stores are lower than normal. This initiates the sensation of hunger, which encourages an animal to seek food.

3. Countercurrent exchange is a mechanism for retaining body heat. The physical arrangement (structure) of arteries and veins in an animal's body can contribute to the very important function of thermoregulation. As warm blood travels through arteries down a bird's leg, for example, heat moves by conduction from the artery to adjacent veins carrying cooler blood in the other direction, toward the heart. By the time the arterial blood reaches the tip of the leg, its temperature has dropped considerably, decreasing the amount of heat loss to the environment, while the heat is returned to the body's core via the warmed veins.

Chapter 48

Concept Checks

Figure 48.1 Open circulatory systems evolved prior to closed systems. However, this does not mean that open systems are in some way "primitive" compared to closed circulatory systems. It is better to think of open systems as being ideally suited to the needs of those animals that have them. Arthropods are an incredibly successful order of animals, having the greatest number of species and inhabiting virtually every ecological niche on Earth. Clearly, their type of circulatory system has not hindered the success of arthropods.

Figure 48.6 The aorta and all arteries branching from it carry oxygenated blood.

Figure 48.8 The left and right ventricles pump blood through the semilunar valves into the aorta and the pulmonary trunk, respectively.

Figure 48.12 No, erythrocytes never leave the blood vessels unless a vessel is cut.

Figure 48.18 Several factors probably limit insect body size, but the respiratory system most likely is one of them. If an insect grew to the size of a human, for example, the trachea and tracheoles would be so large and extensive that there would be little room for any other internal organs in the body! Also, the mass of the animal's body

and the forces generated during locomotion would probably collapse the tracheoles. Finally, diffusion of oxygen from the surface of the body to the deepest regions of a human-sized insect would take far too long to support the metabolic demands of internal structures.

Figure 48.19 As the lungs expand, the pressure within them decreases, as defined by Boyle's law. This permits air to flow into the lungs.

Figure 48.25 An increase in the blood concentration of HCO_3^- would favor the reaction $HCO_3^- + H^+ \rightarrow H_2CO_3 \rightarrow CO_2 + H_2O$. This would reduce the H^+ concentration of the blood, thereby raising the pH; the CO_2 formed as a result would be exhaled. These changes would shift the hemoglobin curve to the left of the usual position.

Core Skills: Connections

Figure 48.4 Immune defenses are found in most living organisms. Many bacteria produce antibacterial secretions that kill other bacteria. Plants, as shown in Figures 37.17 through 37.19, have a wide array of pathogen-fighting mechanisms.

Figure 48.17 Countercurrent exchange is an efficient means of heat transfer between arteries and veins, such as those near the skin surface of the legs of a wading bird. Heat from the descending arteries is transferred to surrounding veins, which return the warm blood to the heart, preventing heat loss through the skin to the water.

Figure 48.26 The brainstem includes the midbrain, pons, and medulla oblongata. See Figure 43.9 for an illustration of the major parts of the human brain.

Feature Investigation Questions

1. Since glucocorticoids stimulate production of surfactant by lung tissues, injections of glucocorticoids to a pregnant woman should induce surfactant production by the lungs of the fetus. This indeed happens; the glucocorticoids cross into the fetal circulation from the mother, and stimulate surfactant in the fetus. Once born, even though the baby is premature, its lungs are relatively more mature and are able to remain open.

2. The oxygen levels achieved after surfactant therapy were all improved compared to the pre-treatment levels, but some babies actually had far higher values than is normal for a healthy baby. This was because at first all the babies were being ventilated with a mixture of gas that was very high in oxygen (much higher than is found in air); when their lung function improved, this mixture resulted in very high blood oxygen levels until the oxygen mixture was reduced. The differences in outcomes between babies likely reflected the degree of overall health of the individual babies; some were born slightly less prematurely than others.

3. Blood CO_2 levels were increased in the sick infants because lung ventilation is important not just for obtaining O_2, but for eliminating CO_2. If ventilation is compromised in any person, for any reason, blood levels of CO_2 inevitably increase.

Test Yourself

1. b   2. c   3. b   4. a   5. d   6. a   7. a   8. b   9. b   10. b

Conceptual Questions

1. *Closed circulatory system:* In a closed circulatory system, the blood is contained within tubes called blood vessels and is transported by a pump called the heart. All of the nutrients and oxygen that tissues require are delivered directly to them by the blood vessels. Advantages of a closed circulatory system are that different parts of an animal's body can receive blood flow in proportion to each part's metabolic requirements at any given time. Due to its efficiency, a closed circulatory system allows organisms to become larger.

    Open circulatory system: In an open circulatory system, the organs are bathed in hemolymph that ebbs and flows into and out of the heart(s) and body cavity, rather than having blood directed to all cells by increasingly smaller vessels. As in a closed circulatory system, there are a pump and blood vessels, but these two structures are less developed and less complex than those in a closed circulatory system. Partly as a result, the sizes of organisms such as mollusks and arthropods are generally relatively small, although exceptions do exist.

2. Carbon dioxide, hydrogen ions, and heat are produced by metabolism; the more active a cell is, the more of these products it generates. Because these products, in turn, reduce the ability of hemoglobin to bind oxygen (in other words facilitate the unloading of oxygen), more active regions of an animal's body obtain more oxygen in proportion to their metabolic demand at that time.

3. Hemoglobin is a protein with quaternary structure (see Chapter 3) in which the different subunits cooperate to bind up to a total of four oxygen molecules. It is the structure of the subunits and their relationship to each other that contributes to their ability to bind O_2 and to the nonlinear relationship of the oxygen-hemoglobin dissociation curve. In addition, however, interactions

of hemoglobin with other molecules, such as CO_2, change the structure of hemoglobin in such a way that its properties change. Under such conditions, hemoglobin is less able to bind O_2 and consequently it releases the gas. Any molecule that binds to hemoglobin will alter its structure and change its properties; these revert to the original state once the bound molecules are released. A particularly dramatic example of the relationship between the structure and function of hemoglobin is that which occurs in sickle cell disease, due to a mutation that changes the structure of the protein.

Chapter 49

Concept Checks

Figure 49.2 Secretion of substances into the tubules is advantageous because it increases the amounts of the substances that are removed from the body by the excretory organs. The increase in amounts is important, because many substances that get secreted are potentially toxic. Filtration, though efficient, is limited by the volume of fluid that can leave the capillaries and enter the excretory tubule.

Core Skills: Connections

Figure 49.8 A brush border composed of microvilli is also present along the epithelial cell layer of the vertebrate small intestine (as shown in Figure 46.6). In the intestine, the brush border serves to increase the absorption of nutrients. In both the intestine and the proximal tubules of nephrons, therefore, a brush border provides extensive surface area for the transport of substances between a lumen and the epithelial cells (and from there to extracellular fluid).

Figure 49.10 Epithelial cells like those in the distal tubule and cortical collecting duct can distribute proteins between the apical and basolateral sides of the plasma membrane. In this way, the Na^+/K^+-ATPase pumps that are stimulated by aldosterone are present and active only on one side of the cells, the basolateral surfaces. If the pumps were activated on the apical surfaces of the cells, aldosterone would not be able to promote reabsorption of Na^+ and water, because Na^+ would also be transported from the cells into the lumen.

Figure 49.13 Countercurrent exchange is important in heat regulation in endotherms, in oxygen diffusion from the water into the blood across the gills of fishes, and in solute and water reabsorption in the loop of Henle in the mammalian kidney.

Test Yourself

1. e   2. e   3. a   4. c   5. c   6. e   7. d   8. a   9. e   10. b

Conceptual Questions

1. Nitrogenous wastes are the breakdown products of the metabolism of proteins and nucleic acids. They can be ammonia and ammonium ions, urea, or uric acid. The predominant type of waste excreted depends in part on an animal's environment. For example, aquatic animals typically excrete ammonia and ammonium ions, whereas many terrestrial animals excrete primarily urea and uric acid. Urea and uric acid are less toxic than the other types but require energy to be synthesized. Urea and uric acid also result in less water being excreted, an adaptation that is especially useful for organisms that must conserve water, such as many terrestrial species.

2. The three processes are filtration, reabsorption, and secretion. During filtration, an organ acts like a sieve or filter, removing some of the water and small solutes from the blood, interstitial fluid, or hemolymph, while excluding blood cells and large solutes such as proteins. Reabsorption is the process whereby epithelial cells of an excretory organ recapture useful solutes that were filtered. Secretion is the process whereby epithelial cells of an excretory organ transport unneeded or harmful solutes from the blood to the excretory tubules for elimination. Some substances such as glucose and amino acids are reabsorbed but not secreted, while some other substances such as toxic compounds are not reabsorbed and are secreted. Still other substances, namely proteins, are not filtered at all.

3. The respiratory system eliminates CO_2, the major waste product of metabolism produced by animals. The digestive system eliminates certain solid wastes from ingested food. The urinary system eliminates soluble wastes other than CO_2.

Chapter 50

Concept Checks

Figure 50.10 Not all mammals use the energy of sunlight to synthesize vitamin D. Many animals, such as those that inhabit caves or that are strictly nocturnal, rarely are exposed to sunlight. Some of these animals get their vitamin D from dietary sources.

How others maintain Ca^{2+} balance without dietary or sunlight-derived active vitamin D remains uncertain.

Figure 50.12 Na^+ and K^+ balance is of vital importance for most animals because of the critical role these ions play in nervous system and muscle function. It is more the rule than the exception that such important physiological variables are under multiple layers of control. This control grants a high degree of fine-tuning capability so that these ions—and other similarly important substances—rarely exceed or fall below the normal range of concentration for a given animal.

Figure 50.13 The great height of the twin on the left clearly indicates that his condition arose prior to puberty.

Figure 50.15 Because 20-hydroxyecdysone is a steroid hormone, you would predict that its receptor would be intracellular. All steroid hormones interact with receptors located either in the cytosol or, more commonly, in the nucleus. The hormone-receptor complex then acts to promote or inhibit transcription of one or more genes. The receptor for 20-hydroxyecdysone is indeed found in cell nuclei.

Core Skills: Connections

Figure 50.3 When dopamine is secreted from an axon terminal into a synapse, from which it diffuses into a postsynaptic cell, it is considered a neurotransmitter. When it is secreted from an axon terminal into the extracellular fluid, from which it diffuses into the blood, it is considered a hormone.

Figure 50.7 In addition to the pancreas, certain other organs in an animal's body may contain both exocrine and endocrine tissue or cells. For example, you learned in Chapters 46 and 47 that the vertebrate alimentary canal is composed of several types of secretory cells. Some of these cells release hormones into the blood that regulate the activities of the pancreas and other structures, such as the gallbladder. Other cells of the alimentary canal secrete exocrine products such as acids or mucus into the lumen of the canal that directly aid in digestion or act as a protective coating, respectively.

Feature Investigation Questions

1. Banting and Best based their procedure on a condition that results when the pancreatic duct is blocked. The exocrine cells will deteriorate in a pancreas that has an obstructed duct; however, the islet cells are not affected. The researchers proposed to experimentally replicate the condition to isolate the cells suspected of secreting the glucose-lowering factor. From these cells, they assumed they would be able to extract the substance of interest without contamination or degradation due to exocrine products.

2. The extracts obtained by Banting and Best did contain insulin, the glucose-lowering factor, but were of low strength and purity. Collip developed a procedure to obtain a more purified extract with a higher concentration of insulin.

3. Normally, the concentration of glucose in a mammal's blood is never high enough to exceed the ability of the kidneys to reabsorb it all from the filtrate (refer back to Chapter 49 for details about filtration). However, like all transport processes, reabsorption of glucose from the kidney filtrate has a finite capacity that depends on the number of transporter molecules and their inherent rate of activity. In untreated diabetes, the blood concentration of glucose becomes so high that it exceeds the capacity of the kidney nephrons to fully reabsorb it from the filtrate. Consequently, some glucose appears in the urine.

Test Yourself

1. b   2. e   3. b   4. d   5. b   6. e   7. c   8. d   9. b   10. d

Conceptual Questions

1. Leptin acts in the hypothalamus to reduce appetite and increase metabolic rate. Because adipose tissue is typically the most important and abundant source of stored energy in an animal's body, the ability to relay information to the appetite and metabolism centers of the brain about the amount of available adipose tissue is a major benefit. In this way, the brain's centers can indirectly monitor the minute-to-minute energy status in the body. A decrease in leptin, for example, indicates a decrease in adipose tissue—as might occur during a fast. Removal of the leptin signal causes appetite to increase and metabolism to decrease, thereby conserving energy. The presence of an appetite and the subjective sensations associated with hunger motivate an animal to seek food at the expense of other activities, such as seeking shelter, finding a mate, and so on.

2. Type 1 diabetes mellitus is characterized by insufficient production of insulin due to the immune system destroying the insulin-producing cells of the pancreas. In type 2 diabetes mellitus, insulin is still produced by the pancreas (at least for a time), but adipose and muscle cells do not respond normally to the insulin.

3. Insulin acts to lower blood glucose concentrations, for example, after a meal, whereas glucagon elevates blood glucose, for example, during fasting. Insulin acts by stimulating the insertion of glucose transporters (GLUTs) into the cell membrane of muscle and fat cells. Glucagon acts by stimulating glycogenolysis in the liver. If a high dose of glucagon were injected into an mammal, including a human, the blood concentration of glucagon would increase rapidly. This would stimulate increased glycogenolysis, resulting in blood glucose concentrations that were above normal.

Chapter 51

Concept Checks

Figure 51.12 Pregnancy and subsequent lactation require considerable energy and, therefore, nutrient ingestion. Consuming the placenta provides the female with a rich supply of protein and other important nutrients.

Core Skills: Connections

Figure 51.10 In addition to its other functions, the placenta must serve the function of the lungs for the fetus. Arteries always carry blood away from the heart; veins carry blood to the heart. Blood leaving the heart of the fetus and traveling through arteries to the placenta is deoxygenated. As blood leaves the placenta and returns to the heart, the blood has become oxygenated as oxygen diffuses from the maternal blood into fetal blood. That oxygenated blood then gets pumped from the fetal heart through other arteries to the rest of the fetus's body.

Figure 51.11 Positive feedback also occurs during ovulation in the ovarian cycle (see Figure 51.9). Stimulation of an ovarian follicle by LH causes growth of the follicle and the release of estradiol, which further stimulates LH, which causes more follicle activity, and so on until ovulation occurs.

Feature Investigation Questions

1. Using *Daphnia pulex*, Paland and Lynch compared the accumulation of mito-chondrial mutations between sexually reproducing populations and asexually reproducing populations.

2. Of all the mutations observed in the populations, 17.7% were either moderately or mildly deleterious and all of these persisted in the asexually reproducing species, whereas only 4.4% persisted in sexually reproducing species. Thus, populations of asexually reproducing species were about four times more likely to retain a deleterious mutation.

3. Sexual reproduction allows for mixing of the different alleles of genes with each generation, thereby increasing genetic variation within the population. This increased variation could prevent the accumulation of deleterious alleles in the population.

Test Yourself

1. d   2. c   3. e   4. a   5. d   6. c   7. b   8. c   9. c   10. e

Conceptual Questions

1. External fertilization results in exposure of gametes to predation and other environmental dangers. Many animals have evolved the ability to lay enormous numbers of eggs to compensate for these dangers.

2. Cells of the hypothalamus produce two important hormones that regulate reproduction. GnRH stimulates the anterior pituitary gland to release two gonadotropic hormones, LH and FSH. These two hormones regulate the production of gonadal hormones and development of gametes in both sexes. In addition, increased secretion of GnRH contributes to the initiation of puberty. The mammalian hypothalamus also produces oxytocin, a hormone that is stored in the posterior pituitary gland and that acts to stimulate uterine contractions during labor and milk release during lactation.

3. Sexual reproduction requires that males and females of a species produce different gametes and that these gametes come into contact with each other. Thus, males and females must expend energy to locate mates. Also, the production of very large numbers of gametes may be necessary to increase the likelihood that the eggs are fertilized. These costs are outweighed by the genetic diversity afforded by sexual reproduction.

Chapter 52

Concept Checks

Figure 52.2 Although swelling is one of the most obvious manifestations of inflammation, it has no significant adaptive value of its own. It is a consequence of fluid leaking out of blood vessels into the interstitial space. It can, however, contribute to pain sensations, because the buildup of fluid may cause distortion of connective tissue structures such as tendons and ligaments. Pain, while obviously unpleasant, is an important signal that alerts many animals to an injury and serves as a reminder to protect the injured site.

Figure 52.10 Both B-cell and T-cell receptors have transmembrane domains, a constant region, and a variable region that binds a specific antigen.

Figure 52.14 Because an animal may encounter the same type of pathogen many times during its life, having a secondary immune response means that future infections will be fought off much more efficiently.

Feature Investigation Questions

1. The amino acid sequence of Toll protein shared similarities with a portion of a protein known to be involved in immune responses in vertebrates. In addition, activation of Toll protein and the vertebrate immune protein (a cytokine receptor) resulted in the generation of some of the same intracellular signals. These findings suggested that in addition to its characterized role in embryonic development, Toll may also be important in immune functions in flies.

2. No, Toll protein is not a receptor that recognizes pathogen-associated molecular patterns (PAMPs) expressed on microbial surfaces, and thus it is distinguishable from Toll-like receptors in vertebrates. Toll is, however, a transmembrane protein that binds to extracellular signals; these signals arise, however, not from the microbes themselves but rather from proteins that are endogenous to flies and that are generated during infections.

3. Yes, the results of the survival study clearly implicated Toll as a protein required for the induction of antimicrobial proteins and the ability to withstand fungal infection. Thus, the investigators' hypothesis was supported.

Test Yourself

1. e   2. b   3. c   4. c   5. a   6. e   7. b   8. a   9. d   10. b

Conceptual Questions

1. Innate immunity is present at birth and is found in all animals. These defenses recognize general, conserved features common to a wide array of pathogens and include internal defenses involving phagocytes and other cells. Adaptive immunity develops *after* an animal has been exposed to a *particular* antigen. The responses include humoral and cell-mediated defenses. Adaptive immunity appears to be largely restricted to vertebrates. Unlike innate immunity, in adaptive immunity, the response to an antigen is greatly increased if an animal is exposed to that antigen again at some future time.

2. Bacteria are single-celled prokaryotes that lack a true nucleus but are capable of reproducing on their own. Viruses are nucleic acids packaged in a protein coat; they require a host cell to reproduce. Eukaryotic parasites include certain fungi, protists and worms.

3. An immunoglobulin consists of four interlinked polypeptides, two heavy chains and two light chains, held together by disulfide bonds. Each immunoglobulin contains within its structure a constant region that is the same from one molecule to another within a given immunoglobulin class, and a variable region. The amino acid sequence of the variable region is what distinguishes one immunoglobulin from another and allows that region to specifically bind a particular antigen.

Chapter 53

Concept Checks

Figure 53.6 Most of these receptors are located in or associated with blood vessels supplying the brain, a vital organ that among other functions controls many of the compensatory responses to changes in blood pressure or blood oxygen levels. Other receptors are located in the aorta, the first major vessel to leave the heart. Thus, blood pressure and gases are monitored in the general circulation and also specifically in the circulation entering the brain.

Core Skills: Connections

Figure 53.3 Stretch-sensitive receptors are widespread in animal bodies. The familiar knee-jerk response is a reflex triggered by the stretch of receptors located in tendons in the knee. Other examples include stretch receptors in muscles that provide feedback information on an animal's posture and movement, receptors in the stomach that relay a sense of fullness when the stomach is stretched after eating, and receptors in the urinary bladder that signal when the bladder is full.

Figure 53.11 Positive feedback also occurs during the ovarian cycle in mammals at the time of ovulation (see Figure 51.9) and during the process of birth in mammals (see Figure 51.11).

Feature Investigation Questions

1. Muscular movements help propel blood from veins in the limbs back to the heart. The increased venous return helps restore blood pressure by providing additional blood for the heart to pump. It is also possible that the unusually large decrease in pressure that occurred in the denervated dogs upon standing activated other, slower mechanisms that increased blood pressure independently of the two sets of baroreceptors described here. For example, although it was not described in the chapter, most animals including mammals have additional sets of baroreceptors in other organs that appear to play a smaller role in the control of blood pressure.

2. By testing the animals in a quiet, isolated room, the investigators reduced the possibility of other complicating variables that might cause a change in blood pressure. For example, stressful sounds or smells, or the sight of unfamiliar investigators might activate neural pathways associated with fight-or-flight responses, and these could raise blood pressure independently of baroreceptor input.

3. To ascertain the relative contributions of different baroreceptors to the responses shown by the animals in this experiment, the investigators could denervate the carotid or aortic baroreceptors independently, leaving the other set intact. This would allow a direct comparison of the effectiveness of each set of baroreceptors.

Test Yourself

1. b 2. d 3. a 4. c 5. a 6. c 7. e 8. e 9. c 10. e

Conceptual Questions

1. Animals in nature are confronted with many types of homeostatic challenges that often require integrated responses by multiple organ systems. For example, a bird flying at a high altitude over a mountain range faces the challenge of obtaining sufficient oxygen from the air. In such a situation, a bird might increase its breathing rate, adjust its cardiac output, or both; indeed, both of these changes and several others do occur. Similarly, fish that migrate between fresh and salt water, such as salmon, alter the function of their respiratory and urinary systems to help compensate for the changes in ion and water movement across the gills due to moving from one environment to another. Yet another common example of a challenge to homeostasis is starvation, during which the nervous, endocrine, urinary, and digestive systems will help maintain glucose homeostasis by processes such as gluconeogenesis.

2. Light-headedness can occur in some people when donating blood, which is essentially a carefully controlled hemorrhage. Initially, as the homeostatic processes described in this chapter are just beginning, there is a period of instability with respect to blood pressure control. While lying or sitting down, this is rarely noticeable, but when the person stands, gravity counteracts the movement of blood through limb veins back to the heart, causing a sudden decrease in pressure. Fainting does not usually occur, however, because the baroreceptor reflex responds immediately to this sudden change in pressure, and within seconds the heart rate and cardiac output are increased due to the actions of the sympathetic nervous system. The phenomenon of light-headedness can actually happen any time a person stands up after reclining, even under ordinary circumstances, but it is more noticeable when a person's blood volume is reduced such as after donating blood.

3. All of the homeostatic responses to hemorrhage described in this chapter require energy. Increasing the activity of any muscle, including that of the heart and the respiratory muscles, requires a considerable increase in expenditure of energy (ATP). Activity of the nervous system, so vital to the compensatory response to hemorrhage, requires continual ATP production and hydrolysis to maintain ion concentration gradients across the plasma membrane of neurons; without the maintenance of these gradients, there could be no flow of current along a neuron. Many of the transport processes in the kidneys also require ATP to drive the ion pumps that move ions across membranes and that create osmotic gradients for the movement of water.

Chapter 54

Concept Checks

Figure 54.6 Cold water suppresses the ability of the coral-building organisms to secrete their calcium carbonate shell.

Figure 54.9 In some areas when fire is prevented, fuel, in the form of old leaves and branches, can accumulate. When a fire eventually occurs, it can be so large and hot that it destroys everything in its path, even reaching high into the tree canopy.

Figure 54.14 Acid soils are low in essential plant and animal nutrients such as calcium and nitrogen and are lethal to some soil microorganisms that are important in decomposition and nutrient cycling.

Figure 54.16 This band is due to increasing cloudiness and rain in the tropics, which maintain fairly constant temperatures across a relatively wide latitudinal range.

Figure 54.22 Soil conditions can also influence biome type. Nutrient-poor soils, for example, may support vegetation different from that of the surrounding area.

Figure 54.23 Taiga.

Core Skills: Connections

Figure 54.13 Plants cannot readily absorb salty water because of its highly negative water potential.

Feature Investigation Questions

1. Most believed that invasive species succeed in new environments because of the lack of natural enemies and that diseases and predators present in the original environment controlled the growth of the population. When a species is introduced into a novel environment, the natural enemies are usually absent. This allows for an unchecked increase in the population of the invasive species.

2. Callaway and Aschehoug were able to demonstrate through a controlled experiment that the presence of *C. diffusa*, an invasive species, reduced the biomass of three other native species of grasses by releasing allelochemicals. Similar experiments using species of grasses that are found in the native region of *C. diffusa* indicated that these species have evolved defenses against the allelochemicals.

3. The activated charcoal helped to remove the allelochemical(s) from the soil. The researchers conducted this experiment to provide further evidence that the chemical(s) released by *C. diffusa* was reducing the biomass of the native Montana grasses. With the removal of the chemical(s) by the addition of the charcoal, the researchers observed an increase in biomass of the native Montana grasses compared with the experiments lacking the charcoal.

4. Researchers could measure the biomass of *C. diffusa*. Because *C. diffusa* is invasive in the U.S., effects of native North American grasses on *C. diffusa* would be expected to be weak. Conversely, *C. diffusa* is not invasive in Eurasia so strong effects of Eurasian grasses on *C. diffusa* should be observed, and this is what researchers found.

Test Yourself

1. b 2. a 3. b 4. b 5. a 6. a 7. d 8. d 9. a 10. c

Conceptual Questions

1. Mountains are cooler than valleys because of adiabatic cooling. Air at higher altitudes expands because of decreased pressure. As it expands, air cools, at a rate of 10°C for every 1,000 m in elevation. As a result, mountain tops can be much cooler than the plains or valleys that surround them.

2. First, lightning strikes from electrical storms are usually more frequent in prairies than in deserts. Second, the vegetation in a prairie is more continuous and the biomass more extensive than in a desert, so fires burn more frequently and for longer periods.

3. Florida is a peninsula that is surrounded by the Atlantic Ocean and the Gulf of Mexico. Differential heating between the land and the sea creates onshore sea breezes on both the east and west coasts. These breezes often drive clouds across the whole peninsula, bringing heavy rain.

Chapter 55

Concept Checks

Figure 55.3 In operant conditioning a behavior is reinforced by a reward or punishment. In classical conditioning, an involuntary response comes to be associated with a stimulus that did not originally elicit the response, as with Pavlov's dogs salivating at the sound of a metronome.

Figure 55.5 The ability to sing the same distinctive song must be considered innate behavior because the cuckoo has had no opportunity to learn its song from its parents.

Figure 55.7 Tinbergen manipulated pinecones, but not all digger wasp nests are surrounded by pinecones. You could manipulate branches, twigs, stones, and leaves to determine the necessary size and dimensions of objects that digger wasps use as landmarks.

Figure 55.8 Monarch migration is an unusual example because the return trip involves several different generations: One generation overwinters in Mexico, but these individuals lay eggs and die on the return journey, and their offspring continue the return trip.

Figure 55.15 The individuals in the center of the group are less likely to be attacked than those on the edge of the group. This advantage is referred to as the geometry of the selfish herd.

Figure 55.18 All the larvae in the group are likely to be the progeny of one egg mass from one adult female moth. The death of one caterpillar in the cluster teaches a predator to avoid preying on caterpillars with that warning pattern and thus benefits the caterpillar's close kin.

Core Skills: Connections

Figure 55.3 Prey species converge on the color patterns displayed by toxic, bad-tasting, or dangerous species to reinforce predators' avoidance of them.

Figure 55.4 According to studies of humans and other animals, learning a task increases the size of brain regions that are associated with learning and memory.

Feature Investigation Questions

1. Tinbergen observed the activity of digger wasps as they prepared to leave the nest. Each time, the wasp hovered and flew around the nest for a period of time before leaving. Tinbergen suggested that during this time, the wasp was making a mental map of the nest site. He hypothesized that the wasp was using characteristics of the nest site, particularly landmarks, to help relocate it.

2. Tinbergen placed pinecones around the nest of the wasps. When the wasps left the nest, he removed the pinecones from the nest site and set them up in the same pattern a distance away, constructing a sham nest. For each trial, the wasps would go directly to the sham nest, which had the pinecones around it. This indicated to Tinbergen that the wasps identified the nest based on the pinecone landmarks.

3. No, but Tinbergen also conducted an experiment to determine if the wasps were responding to the visual cue of the pinecones or the chemical cue of the pinecone scent. The results of this experiment indicated that the wasps responded to the visual cue of the pinecones and not their scent.

Test Yourself

1. d   2. d   3. d   4. c   5. c   6. d   7. b   8. c   9. a   10. c

Conceptual Questions

1. The donation of the male's body to the female is the ultimate nuptial gift. It is possible that this meal enables the females to produce more eggs. In this way, the male benefits because its genes will be passed on to future generations.

2. Certainty of paternity influences degree of parental care. With internal fertilization, certainty of paternity is relatively low. With external fertilization, eggs and sperm are deposited together, and paternity is more certain. This explains why males of some species, such as mouth-breeding cichlid fish, are more likely to engage in parental care.

3. Alarm calling calls attention to the caller, so if no relatives are present, females bolt into their warren to escape a predator. However, daughters and sisters are kin and may pass on copies of a female's genes, so alarm calls are frequently made when these relatives are present.

Chapter 56

Concept Checks

Figure 56.3 In a half-empty classroom, the distribution is often clumped because friends sit together.

Figure 56.6 (a) type III, (b) type II

Figure 56.12 Only density-dependent factors have this stabilizing tendency.

Core Skills: Connections

Figure 56.3 Uniform. Territorial marking is likely to keep cheetahs well separated from each other.

Figure 56.13 It has lost the ability to produce viable seeds but it makes thousands of fully formed plantlets, borne on its leaves.

Feature Investigation Questions

1. It became apparent that the sheep population was declining. Some individuals thought that the decline in the population was due to the negative effect of increased wolf predation on population growth. This idea led to the suggestion of culling the wolf population to reduce the level of predation on the sheep.

2. The survivorship curve is similar to a typical type I survivorship curve, which would suggest that survival is high among young and reproductively active members of the population and that mortality rates are higher for older members of the population. One difference between the actual survivorship curve and a typical type I curve is that the mortality rate of very young sheep was higher in the actual curve and then leveled off after the second year. This suggests that very young and older sheep are at greater risk from predation.

3. It was concluded that wolf predation was not the primary reason for the drop in the sheep population. It appeared that wolves prey on the vulnerable members of the population and not on the healthy, reproductively active members. The Park Service determined that several cold winters may have had a more important effect on the sheep population than wolf predation did. Based on these conclusions, the Park Service ended its wolf-control program.

Test Yourself

1. b   2. e   3. b   4. c   5. c   6. b   7. b   8. c   9. d   10. c

Conceptual Questions

1. It increases. Instead of recapturing 5 tagged fish, you will recapture only 4. Population size is now estimated as $50 \times 40/4 = 2,000/4 = 500$. Your population size estimate has increased to 500 when, in fact, it is more likely that 400 fish occur in the lake.

2. When population sizes are low ($N = 100$), $(K - N)/K$ is so small that growth is low.

$$\frac{dN}{dt} = (0.1)(100) \times \frac{(1,000 - 100)}{1,000}$$

$$\frac{dN}{dt} = 9$$

At medium values of N, $(K - N)/K$ is closer to a value of 1, and population growth is relatively large. If $K = 1,000$, $N = 500$, and $r = 0.1$, then

$$\frac{dN}{dt} = (0.1)(500) \times \frac{(1,000 - 100)}{1,000}$$

$$\frac{dN}{dt} = 25$$

By comparing these two examples with that shown in Section 56.3, we see that growth is small at high and low values of N and is greatest at immediate values of N. Growth is greatest when $N = K/2$. However, when expressed as a percentage, growth is greatest at low population sizes. Where $N = 100$, percentage growth $= 9/100 = 9\%$. Where $N = 500$, percentage growth $= 25/500 = 5\%$, and where $N = 900$, percentage growth $= 9/100 = 1\%$.

3. In the ponds that dry out, species would tend to be semelparous, producing all their offspring in a single reproductive event while water is present. In the permanently wet ponds, species would be iteroparous, reproducing repeatedly over the course of a lifetime.

Collaborative Questions

2. a) $\lambda = 1,200 / 1,000 = 1.2$
   b) After 5 years, $N_5 = N_0\lambda^5$
   $$= (1,000)(1.2)^5$$
   $$= 2,488$$

Chapter 57

Concept Checks

Figure 57.2 Individual vultures often fight one another over small carcasses. These interactions constitute intraspecific interference competition.

Figure 57.6 In 1974, Tom Schoener examined segregation in a more wide-ranging literature review of over 80 species, including slime molds, mollusks, and insects, as well as birds. He found segregation by habitat occurred in the majority of the examples, 55%. The second most common form of segregation was by food type, 40%.

Figure 57.8 Omnivores, such as bears, can feed on both plant material, such as berries, and animals, such as salmon. Thus, omnivores may act as either predators or herbivores, depending on what they are feeding on.

Figure 57.9 Batesian mimicry has a positive effect for the mimic, and the model is unaffected, so it is a +/0 relationship, like commensalism. Müllerian mimicry has a positive effect on both species, so it is a +/+ relationship, like mutualism.

Figure 57.11 Invertebrate herbivores can eat around mechanical defenses; therefore, chemical defenses are probably most effective against these herbivores.

Figure 57.16 It's an example of facultative mutualism, because both species can live without the other.

Figure 57.19 Fertilizer increases plant quality and hence herbivore density, which, in turn, increases the density of spiders. This is bottom-up control.

Core Skills: Connections

Figure 57.9 Most mollusks are heavily armored. However, sea slugs have lost their shells. These species are aposematically colored, advertising a poisonous body. In addition, some octopuses are poisonous, and most can eject an inky chemical "smokescreen."

Figure 57.11 Red hot chili peppers.

Figure 57.13 Dodder, *Cuscuta pentagona*, is another important parasitic plant.

Figure 57.17 Red.

Feature Investigation Questions

1. The two species of barnacles can be found in the same intertidal zone, but there is a distinct difference between the realized niches of these species. *Chthamalus stellatus* is found only in the upper intertidal zone. *Semibalanus balanoides* is found only in the lower tidal zone.

2. Connell moved rocks with young *Chthamalus* from the upper intertidal zone into the lower intertidal zone to allow *Semibalanus* to colonize the rocks. After the rocks were colonized by *Semibalanus*, he removed *Semibalanus* from one side of each rock and returned the rocks to the lower intertidal zone. This procedure allowed Connell to observe the growth of *Chthamalus* in the presence and the absence of *Semibalanus.*

3. Connell observed that *Chthamalus* was more resistant to desiccation than *Semibalanus*. Though *Semibalanus* was the better competitor in the lower intertidal zone, that species was at a disadvantage in the upper intertidal zone when water levels were low. This fact allowed *Chthamalus* to flourish and outcompete *Semibalanus* in a different region of the intertidal zone.

Test Yourself

1. d   2. c   3. b   4. d   5. c   6. b   7. d   8. b   9. b   10. c

Conceptual Questions

1. Yes, it is possible that by removing parasites from a neighbor, a primate may be reducing the likelihood of the parasite spreading to infect it. You scratch my back, I'll scratch yours, and together we will both be better off.

2. There are at least three factors that might limit losses due to pest damage to crops. First, plants possess an array of defensive chemicals, including alkaloids, phenolics, and terpenes. Second, many herbivore populations are reduced by the action of natural enemies. Third, the low nutritive value of plants ensures that herbivore populations remain low and unlikely to affect plant populations. While we can't easily increase the levels of defensive chemicals in many crop plants or reduce their nutritive value, we can introduce more natural enemies of plant pests. We see evidence for this in the use of biological controls.

Chapter 58

Concept Checks

Figure 58.3 The species richness of trees doesn't increase in the mountainous areas of the West because rainfall in the western U.S. is low compared to that in the East.

Figure 58.5 Walking from the current edge of the glacier to the mouth of the inlet, an ecologist is walking backward in ecological time to communities that originated hundreds of years ago.

Figure 58.8 Competition features more prominently. Although early colonists tend to make the habitat more favorable for later colonists, it is the later colonists who outcompete the earlier ones, and this fuels species change.

Figure 58.10 At first glance, the change looks small, but the data are plotted on a log scale. On this scale, an increase in bird richness from 1.2 to 1.6 equals an increase from 16 to 40 species, a change of over 100%.

Figure 58.14 It depends on the trophic level of their food, whether dead vegetation or dead animals. Many decomposers feed at multiple trophic levels.

Core Skills: Connections

Figure 58.9 The model helps conservationists design the best shaped and optimally placed nature reserves in a "sea" of developed land.

Figure 58.13 Cyanobacteria.

Feature Investigation Questions

1. Simberloff and Wilson were testing the three predictions of the equilibrium theory of island biogeography. One prediction suggested that the number of species should increase with increasing island size. Another prediction suggested that the number of species should decrease with increasing distance of the island from the source pool. Finally, the researchers were testing the prediction that the turnover of species on islands should be considerable.

2. Simberloff and Wilson used the information gathered from the species survey to determine whether the same types of species recolonized the islands or the colonizing species were random.

3. Island distance to the mainland affected species richness with near islands having higher numbers of species than distant islands. However, species turnover was low on all islands and was unaffected by island distance from the mainland.

Test Yourself

1. c   2. a   3. c   4. a   5. e   6. c   7. e   8. a   9. d   10. c

Conceptual Questions

1. The value of the Shannon diversity index is 1.609 for both forests. By this measure, diversity is equal in the two forests. The index is unable to discriminate between communities that have different species abundances but the same relative proportions of species. An observer would be more likely to encounter a variety of trees in forest A than in forest B.

2. Carrion beetles are decomposers. They feed on dead animals such as mice, at trophic level 3 or 4. Mice generally feed on vegetative material (trophic level 1) or crawling arthropods (trophic level 2), so mice themselves feed at trophic level 2 or 3.

3. *C. vulgaris* litter enriches the soil with nitrogen, facilitating the growth of the grasses. Adding fertilizer also increases soil nitrogen. The mechanism of succession operating in this case is facilitation.

Chapter 59

Concept Checks

Figure 59.2 The conclusion would be that were very few juveniles in the population and many mature adults. The population would be in decline.

Figure 59.5 Many different ecological footprint calculators are available on the Internet. Does altering inputs such as type of transportation, amount of meat eaten, or amount of waste generated make a difference?

Figure 59.7 Hawaii lies north of the equator. The Northern Hemisphere has greater land area and plant biomass than the Southern Hemisphere, so in the northern summer more CO_2 is used up by plants and atmospheric CO_2 level declines slightly. In the northern winter, less CO_2 is absorbed and atmospheric CO_2 levels increase.

Figure 59.9 The greatest stores are in rocks and fossil fuels.

Core Skills: Connections

Figure 59.9 The other three elements are oxygen, hydrogen, and nitrogen. Therefore, the water and nitrogen cycles are very important to humans.

Feature Investigation Questions

1. The researchers wanted to learn the effects of increased carbon dioxide levels on the forest ecosystem: the effects on primary production as well as on other trophic levels in the ecosystem.

2. By increasing the carbon dioxide levels in only half of the chambers, the researchers were maintaining the control treatment necessary in all scientific studies.

By maintaining equal numbers of control and experimental treatments, the researchers could compare data to determine what effects the experimental treatment had on the ecosystem.

3. $t_{14} = 5.667$, $P < 0.001$; $x_1 = 10.00$, s.d $= 2.93$; $x_2 = 3.20$, s.d $= 1.72$

Test Yourself

1. d 2. c 3. d 4. b 5. a 6. b 7. e 8. b 9. b 10. e

Conceptual Questions

1. Nitrogen molecules have a triple bond, making them hard to break apart. Only a few species of bacteria can break apart atmospheric nitrogen and fix nitrogen. The excess ammonia, NH_3, or ammonium, NH_4^+, that they produce in this way gradually accumulates and can be used by plants.

2. Maximum sustainable yield represents the number of individuals that can be removed from a population without affecting population growth. This is rather like removing the interest from a bank account and not touching the principal. Maximal sustainable yield occurs at the steepest point of the growth curve, which is at the midpoint of the logistic curve.

3. The family whose members have triplets has 27 descendants in 2000, compared to 32 for the family whose members have twins. Delaying reproduction can slow population growth.

Chapter 60

Concept Checks

Figure 60.3 It is possible that the results are driven by what is known as a sampling effect. As the numbers of species in the community increase, so does the likelihood of including a "superspecies," a species with exceptionally large individuals that would use up resources. In communities with higher diversity, care has to be taken that increased species richness is driving the results, not the increased likelihood of including a superspecies.

Figure 60.8 Corridors might also promote the movement of invasive species or the spread of fire between areas.

Figure 60.9 The hedgerows act as habitat corridors because they permit species movement between forest fragments.

Feature Investigation Questions

1. The researchers hoped to replicate terrestrial communities that differed only in their level of species richness. This would allow the researchers to determine the relationship between species richness and ecosystem function.

2. The hypothesis was that ecosystem function was directly related to species richness. If species richness increased, the hypothesis suggested that ecosystem function should increase.

3. The researchers tested for ecosystem functioning by monitoring community respiration, decomposition, nutrient retention rates, and productivity. All of these indicate the efficiency of nutrient production and use in the ecosystem.

4. The redundancy hypothesis.

Test Yourself

1. d 2. c 3. b 4. a 5. c 6. a 7. e 8. e 9. b 10. c

Conceptual Questions

1. Increased species diversity increases ecosystem function. Ecosystem functions such as nutrient cycling, regulation of atmospheric gases, pollination of crops, pest regulation, water purity, storm protection, and sewage purification are all likely to be increased by increased species diversity. In addition, increased plant species diversity increases likely availability of new medicines for humans.

2. Megadiversity countries are those with the greatest number of species. Biodiversity hot spots conserve the greatest numbers of endemic species. Crisis ecoregions are those areas of the Earth which represent distinct biome types, such as temperate grasslands and tropical deciduous forests, but have undergone substantial habitat loss. "Last of the wild" areas are relatively pristine areas such as much tundra and taiga, deserts, and some tropical rainforests.

3. The diversity-stability hypothesis suggests a linear correlation between species richness and ecosystem function; as diversity increases, ecosystem function increases proportionately. The redundancy hypothesis suggests that ecosystem function increases rapidly at lower levels of species richness but then levels off, as additional species are functionally redundant. The keystone hypothesis suggests that ecosystem function is low at low levels of species richness and only rises substantially as species richness approaches high levels. The idiosyncratic hypothesis suggests that there is no predictable relationship between species richness and ecosystem function.

Glossary

1000 Genomes Project An international research effort to establish the level of human genetic variation.

20-hydroxyecdysone A hormone produced by the prothoracic glands of arthropods that stimulates molting.

30-nm fiber Nucleosome units organized into a more compact structure that is 30 nm in diameter.

5′ cap The 7-methylguanosine structure at the 5′ end of most mature mRNAs in eukaryotes.

A

ABC model A model for flower development in which three classes of genes, called *A*, *B*, and *C*, govern the formation of sepals, petals, stamens, and carpels. More recently, a fourth class, called the *E* genes, was found to be required for this process.

abiotic The term used to describe interactions between organisms and their nonliving environment.

abscisic acid One of several plant hormones that help a plant cope with environmental stress.

absolute refractory period The period during an action potential when the inactivation gate of the voltage-gated sodium channel is closed; during this time, it is impossible to generate another action potential.

absorption spectrum A diagram that depicts the wavelengths of electromagnetic radiation that are absorbed by a pigment.

absorption The process in which ions, water, and small molecules diffuse or are transported out of the alimentary canal into an animal's body fluids.

absorptive nutrition The process whereby an organism uses enzymes to digest organic materials and absorbs the resulting small food molecules into its cells.

absorptive state One of two alternating phases in the utilization of nutrients; occurs when ingested nutrients enter the blood from the gastrointestinal tract. The other phase is the postabsorptive state.

accommodation In the vertebrate eye, the process in which contraction and relaxation of the ciliary muscles adjust the lens according to the angle at which light enters the eye.

acetylcholinesterase An enzyme located on membranes of postsynaptic cells that respond to the neurotransmitter acetylcholine, such as in muscle fibers in a neuromuscular junction; breaks down excess acetylcholine released into the synaptic cleft.

acid hydrolase A hydrolytic enzyme found in lysosomes that functions at acidic pH and uses a molecule of water to break a covalent bond.

acid rain Precipitation with a pH of less than 5.6; results from the burning of fossil fuels.

acid A molecule that releases hydrogen ions (H⁺) in solution.

acidic A solution that has a pH below 7.

acoelomate An animal that lacks a fluid-filled body cavity.

acquired antibiotic resistance The common phenomenon in which a previously susceptible strain of bacteria becomes resistant to a specific antibiotic.

acquired immunodeficiency syndrome (AIDS) A disease caused by the human immunodeficiency virus (HIV) that weakens the immune system of infected individuals.

acrocentric A chromosome in which the centromere is near one end.

acromegaly A condition in which a person's growth hormone level is abnormally elevated after puberty, causing many bones to thicken and enlarge.

acrosomal reaction An event in fertilization in which enzymes released from a sperm's acrosome break down the outer layers of an egg cell, allowing the entry of the sperm cell's nucleus into the egg cell.

acrosome A special structure at the tip of a sperm's head containing proteolytic enzymes that help break down the protective outer layers of the egg cell at fertilization.

actin filament A thin type of protein filament composed of actin proteins that forms part of the cytoskeleton and supports the plasma membrane; plays a key role in cell strength, shape, and movement.

actin A cytoskeletal protein, found in the thin filaments of myofibrils.

action potential An electrical signal along a cell's plasma membrane; occurs in animal neuron axons and muscle cells and in some plant cells.

action spectrum The rate of photosynthesis plotted as a function of the wavelength of light.

activation energy An initial input of energy in a chemical reaction that allows the molecules to get close enough to cause a rearrangement of bonds.

activator A transcription factor that binds to DNA and increases the rate of transcription.

active immunity An animal's ability to fight off a pathogen to which it has been previously exposed. Active immunity can develop as a result of natural infection or artificial immunization.

active site The location in an enzyme where a chemical reaction takes place.

active transport The transport of a substance across a membrane from an area of low concentration to one of higher concentration with the aid of a transport protein; requires an input of energy.

adaptations Changes in populations of living organisms that are the result of natural selection and that increase their ability to survive and reproduce in their environment.

adaptive immunity A specific immune defense that develops only after an animal is exposed to a foreign substance; believed to be unique to vertebrates.

adaptive radiation The process whereby a single ancestral species evolves into a wide array of descendant species that differ greatly in their habitat, form, or behavior.

adenine (A) A purine base found in DNA and RNA.

adenosine triphosphate (ATP) A molecule that is a common energy source for all cells.

adenylyl cyclase An enzyme in the plasma membrane that synthesizes cAMP from ATP.

adherens junction A mechanically strong type of cell junction between animal cells that is organized into bands. The cells are connected to each other via cadherins, and the cadherins are linked to actin filaments on the inside of the cells.

adhesion The ability of two different substances to bind to each other; the ability of water to be attracted to, and thereby adhere to, a surface that is not electrically neutral.

adiabatic cooling The process in which increasing elevation produces a decrease in air temperature due to lowered air pressure.

adventitious root A root that is produced on the surfaces of stems (and sometimes leaves) of vascular plants; also, roots that develop at the bases of stem cuttings.

aerenchyma Spongy plant tissue with large air spaces.

aerobic respiration A type of cellular respiration in which O_2 is consumed and CO_2 is released.

aerotolerant anaerobe A microorganism that does not use oxygen but is not poisoned by it either.

afferent arteriole Blood vessel that carries blood into a glomerulus of the vertebrate kidney.

affinity The degree of attraction between an enzyme and its substrate(s).

aflatoxins Fungal toxins that cause liver cancer and are a major health concern worldwide.

age structure The relative numbers of individuals of each defined age group in a population.

age-specific fertility rate The rate of offspring production for females of a certain age; used to calculate how a population grows.

akinete A thick-walled, food-filled cell produced by certain bacteria or protists that enables them to survive unfavorable conditions in a dormant state.

aldosterone A steroid hormone made by the adrenal glands that regulates salt and water balance in vertebrates.

algae (singular, **alga**) A term that applies to about 10 phyla of protists, including mostly photosynthetic and some nonphotosynthetic species; often also includes cyanobacteria.

alimentary canal In animals, the single elongated tube of a digestive system, with an opening at either end through which food and eventually wastes pass from one end to the other.

alkaline A solution with a pH above 7.

allantois One of the four extraembryonic membranes in the amniotic egg. It serves as a disposal sac for metabolic wastes.

allele frequency The number of copies of a particular allele in a population divided by the total number of alleles for that gene in that population.

allele A variant form of a gene.

allelochemical A powerful plant chemical, often a root exudate, that kills other plant species.

allelopathy The suppression of growth of one species due to the release of toxic chemicals by another species.

allergy Hypersensitivity reaction to an environmental antigen (an allergen) that is otherwise a harmless or relatively harmless substance.

allopatric speciation A form of speciation that occurs when a population becomes geographically isolated from other populations and evolves into one or more new species.

allopatric The term used to describe species occurring in different geographic areas.

alloploid An organism having at least one set of chromosomes from two or more different species.

allosteric site A site on an enzyme where a molecule can bind noncovalently and affect the enzyme's function.

alternation of generations The phenomenon that occurs in plants and some protists in which the life cycle alternates between multicellular diploid organisms, called sporophytes, and multicellular haploid organisms, called gametophytes.

alternative splicing The splicing of pre-mRNA in more than one way to allow the production of two or more different polypeptides from the same gene.

altruism Behavior that appears to benefit others at a cost to oneself.

alveolus (plural, **alveoli**) 1. Saclike structures in the lungs where gas exchange occurs. 2. Saclike cellular features of the protists known as alveolates.

Alzheimer's disease (AD) The leading worldwide cause of dementia; characterized by a loss of memory and intellectual and emotional function.

GLOSSARY

AM *See* arbuscular mycorrhizae.

amensalism One-sided competition between species, in which the interaction is detrimental to one species but not to the other.

Ames test A test that helps ascertain whether or not an agent is a mutagen by using a strain of a bacterium, *Salmonella typhimurium*.

amino acid Any of the monomers that are linked to form a protein. Amino acids have a common structure in which a carbon atom, called the α-carbon, is linked to an amino group (—NH$_2$) and a carboxyl group (—COOH), as well as to a hydrogen atom and a side chain that distinguishes the particular amino acid.

aminoacyl site (A site) One of three sites for tRNA binding in the ribosome during translation; the other two are the peptidyl site (P site) and the exit site (E site). The A site is where incoming tRNA molecules bind to the mRNA (except for the initiator tRNA).

aminoacyl tRNA *See* charged tRNA.

aminoacyl-tRNA synthetase An enzyme that catalyzes the attachment of amino acids to tRNA molecules.

ammonification The conversion of organic nitrogen to NH$_3$ and NH$_4^+$ during the nitrogen cycle.

amnion The innermost of the four extraembryonic membranes in the amniotic egg. It protects the developing embryo in a fluid-filled sac called the amniotic cavity.

amniotes A group of tetrapods with amniotic eggs that includes turtles, lizards, snakes, crocodiles, birds, and mammals.

amniotic egg A type of egg produced by amniotes that contains the developing embryo and the four separate extraembryonic membranes that it produces: the amnion, the yolk sac, the allantois, and the chorion.

amoeba (plural, **amoebae**) A protist that moves by pseudopodia, which involves extending cytoplasm into filaments or lobes.

amoebocyte A mobile cell within a sponge's mesophyl that absorbs food from choanocytes, digests it, and carries the nutrients to other cells.

amphibian An ectothermic, vertebrate animal that metamorphoses from a water-breathing to an air-breathing form but must return to the water to reproduce.

amphipathic Refers to molecules containing a hydrophobic (water-fearing) region and a hydrophilic (water-loving) region.

amplicon analysis A comparison of amplicons (amplified sequences) present in a particular DNA sample to reference sequences in a database.

amplicon Any gene region for which many copies have been made (amplified) from a DNA sample with the use of specific primer sequences in polymerase chain reaction (PCR).

ampulla (plural, **ampullae**) 1. A muscular sac at the base of each tube foot of an echinoderm; used to store water. 2. A bulge in the walls of the semicircular canals of the mammalian inner ear; important for sensing circular motions of the head.

amygdala An area of the limbic system of the vertebrate forebrain known to be critical for understanding and remembering emotional situations.

amylase A digestive enzyme in saliva and the pancreas involved in the digestion of carbohydrates.

anabolic reaction A metabolic pathway that involves the synthesis of larger molecules from smaller precursor molecules. Such reactions usually require an input of energy.

anabolism A metabolic pathway that results in the synthesis of cellular molecules and macromolecules; requires an input of energy.

anaerobic respiration The breakdown of organic molecules in the absence of oxygen by using a final electron acceptor that is something other than oxygen.

anaerobic Refers to an environment that lacks oxygen or a process that occurs in the absence of oxygen; a form of metabolism that does not require oxygen.

anagenesis The pattern of speciation in which a single species is transformed into a different species over the course of many generations.

analogous structure A structure that is the result of convergent evolution. Such structures have arisen independently, two or more times, because species have occupied similar types of environments on Earth.

anaphase The phase of mitosis during which the sister chromatids separate from each other and move to opposite poles; the poles themselves also move farther apart.

anatomy The study of the structures of living things.

anchoring junction A type of junction between animal cells that attaches cells to each other and to the extracellular matrix (ECM).

androgens Steroid hormones produced by the male testes (and, to a lesser extent, the adrenal glands) that affect most aspects of male reproduction.

aneuploidy Alteration of the number of a particular chromosome present in an organism or cell, so the total number of chromosomes is not an exact multiple of a set.

angiosperm A flowering plant. The term means enclosed seed, which reflects the presence of seeds within fruits.

animal pole In triploblast organisms, the pole of the egg with less yolk and more cytoplasm.

Animalia A eukaryotic kingdom of the domain Eukarya.

animals Multicellular heterotrophs with cells that lack cell walls. Most animals have nerves, muscles, the capacity to move at some point in their life cycle, and the ability to reproduce sexually, with sperm fusing directly with eggs.

anion An ion that has a net negative charge.

annual A plant that dies after producing seed during its first year of life.

antagonist Two or more muscles that produce oppositely directed movements at a joint.

anterior Refers to the end of an animal where the head is found.

anteroposterior axis In bilateral animals, one of the three axes along which the adult body pattern is organized; the others are the dorsoventral axis and the left-right axis.

anther The uppermost part of a flower stamen, consisting of a cluster of four sporangia that produce and release pollen.

antheridia Spherical or elongate gametangia that produce sperm in plants.

anthropogenic Caused by humans or their activities; the term comes from the Greek *anthropogenes*, meaning "born of man," and is often applied to environmental pollution originating from human activity.

anthropoidea A group of primates that includes the monkeys and the hominoidea; these species are larger-brained, diurnal, and have opposable thumbs.

antibiotic A chemical, usually made by microorganisms, that inhibits the growth of certain other microorganisms.

antibody A protein secreted by plasma cells that is part of the immune response; antibodies travel all over the body to reach antigens identical to those that stimulated their production, combine with these antigens, and then guide an attack that eliminates the antigens or the cells bearing them.

anticodon A three-base sequence in tRNA that is complementary to a codon in mRNA.

antidiuretic hormone (ADH) A polypeptide hormone secreted by the posterior pituitary that acts on kidney cells to decrease urine production.

antigen Any foreign molecule that the host does not recognize as self and that triggers a specific immune response.

antigen-presenting cells (APCs) Cells of a vertebrate's acquired immune system that complex antigen with class II MHC proteins, leading to helper T cell activation.

antiparallel The arrangement in DNA where one strand runs in the 5′ to 3′ direction and the other strand is oriented in the 3′ to 5′ direction.

antiporter A type of transporter that binds two or more ions or molecules and transports them in opposite directions across a membrane.

anus The opening at the posterior end of the alimentary canal through which solid wastes are expelled.

aorta In vertebrates, a large blood vessel that exits a ventricle of the heart and leads to the systemic circulation.

apical meristem In plants, a group of actively dividing cells at a growing tip.

apical region The region of a plant seedling that produces the leaves and flowers.

apical-basal polarity An architectural feature of plants in which they display an upper, apical pole and a lower, basal pole; the shoot apical meristem occurs at the apical pole, and the root apical meristem occurs at the basal pole.

apical-basal-patterning genes A category of genes that are important in early stages of plant development during which the apical and basal axes are formed.

apomixis A natural asexual reproductive process in which plant fruits and seeds are produced within flowers in the absence of fertilization.

apoplast The continuum of water-filled cell walls and intercellular spaces in a plant.

apoplastic transport The movement of solutes along cell walls and in the spaces between cells.

apoptosis Programmed cell death.

apoptosome A complex of proteins that promotes apoptosis via the intrinsic pathway by activating caspases.

aposematic coloration Warning coloration that advertises an organism's unpalatable taste.

aquaporin A transport protein in the form of a channel that allows the rapid diffusion of water across the cell membrane.

aqueous solution A solution made with water.

aquifer An underground water supply.

arbuscular mycorrhizae Associations between plant cells, often root cells of vascular plants, and fungi that form highly branched hyphae.

Archaea One of the three domains of life; the other two are Bacteria and Eukarya.

archaea When not capitalized, refers to a species within the domain Archaea.

archegonia (singular, **archegonium**) Flask-shaped gametangia that each enclose a single egg cell in plants.

archenteron A cavity formed in an animal embryo during gastrulation that will become the organism's digestive tract.

area hypothesis The proposal that larger areas contain more species than smaller areas because they can support larger populations and a greater range of habitats.

artery A blood vessel that carries blood away from the heart.

artificial selection *See* selective breeding.

asci (singular, **ascus**) Fungal sporangia shaped like sacs that produce and release sexual ascospores.

ascocarp The type of fruiting body produced by ascomycete fungi.

ascomycetes A phylum of fungi that produce sexual spores in saclike asci located at the surfaces of fruiting bodies known as ascocarps.

ascospore   The type of sexual spore produced by fungi in the phylum Ascomycota.

aseptate   The condition of not being partitioned into smaller cells; usually refers to fungal cells.

asexual reproduction   A reproductive strategy that occurs when offspring are produced from a single parent, without the fusion of gametes from two parents. The offspring are therefore clones of the parent.

assimilation   During the nitrogen cycle, the process by which plants and animals incorporate the NH_3, NH_4^+, and NO_3^- formed through nitrogen fixation and nitrification.

assisted reproductive technologies (ART)   A collection of procedures used to produce a pregnancy by artificial mechanisms.

association   A statistical result in which changes in two variables follow a pattern.

associative learning   A change in behavior due to the development of an association between a stimulus and a response.

asthma   A disease in which the smooth muscles around the bronchioles contract more than usual, decreasing airflow in the lungs.

AT/GC rule   Refers to the phenomenon that an A in one DNA strand always hydrogen-bonds with a T in the opposite strand, and a G in one strand always hydrogen-bonds with a C.

atherosclerosis   The condition in which plaques cause the arteries to narrow and harden and large plaques may occlude (block) the lumen of an artery.

atmospheric pressure   The pressure exerted by the gases in the air on the body surfaces of animals.

atom   The smallest functional unit of matter that forms all chemical substances and cannot be further broken down into other substances by ordinary chemical or physical means.

atomic mass   An atom's mass relative to the mass of other atoms. By convention, the most common form of carbon, which has six protons and six neutrons, is assigned an atomic mass of exactly 12.

atomic nucleus   The center of an atom; contains protons and neutrons.

atomic number   The number of protons in an atom.

ATP synthase   An enzyme that utilizes the energy stored in a H^+ electrochemical gradient for the synthesis of ATP via chemiosmosis.

ATP-dependent chromatin remodeling complex   A collection of proteins that alters chromatin structure.

atrial natriuretic peptide (ANP)   A polypeptide hormone secreted from the atria of the heart whenever blood levels of sodium increase; ANP causes a loss of Na^+ in the urine (natriuresis) by decreasing sodium reabsorption in the renal tubules.

atrioventricular (AV) node   Specialized cardiac cells in most vertebrates that sit near the junction of the atria and ventricles and conduct the electrical events from the atria to the ventricles.

atrioventricular (AV) valve   A one-way valve into a ventricle of the vertebrate heart through which blood moves from an atrium.

atrium   In the heart, a chamber to collect blood from the tissues.

atrophy   A reduction in the size of a structure, such as a muscle.

audition   The ability to detect and interpret sound waves; present in vertebrates and arthropods.

autoimmune disease   In humans and many other vertebrates, a disorder in which the body's normal state of immune tolerance breaks down, with the result that immune responses are directed against the body's own cells and tissues.

autonomic nervous system   The division of the peripheral nervous system that regulates homeostasis and organ function.

autophagosome   A double-membrane structure enclosing cellular material destined to be degraded; produced by the process of autophagy.

autophagy   A process whereby cellular material, such as a worn-out organelle, becomes enclosed in a double membrane and is degraded.

autosomes   All of the chromosomes found in the cell nucleus of eukaryotes except for the sex chromosomes.

autotomy   In echinoderms, the ability to detach a body part, such as a limb, that will later regenerate.

autotroph   An organism that has metabolic pathways that use energy from either inorganic molecules or light to make organic molecules.

auxin efflux carrier   One of several types of PIN proteins, which transport auxin out of plant cells.

auxin influx carrier (AUX1/LAX)   A plasma membrane protein that transports auxin into plant cells.

auxin-responsive genes   Plant genes that are regulated by the hormone auxin.

auxins   A group of plant hormones; considered to be "master" plant hormones because they influence plant structure, development, and behavior in many ways.

avirulence gene (*Avr* gene)   A gene in a plant pathogen that encodes a virulence-enhancing elicitor, which causes plant disease.

axillary bud   A bud that occurs in the axil, the upper angle where a twig or leaf emerges from a stem.

axillary meristem   A meristem produced in the axil, the upper angle where a twig or leaf emerges from a stem. Axillary meristems generate axillary buds, which can produce flowers or branches.

axon hillock   The part of the axon closest to the cell body; typically where an action potential begins.

axon terminal   The end of an axon, which conveys electrical or chemical messages to other cells.

axon   An extension of the plasma membrane of a neuron that is involved in sending signals to neighboring cells.

axoneme   An internal structure of eukaryotic flagella and cilia that contains microtubules, the motor protein dynein, and linking proteins.

B

B cell   A type of lymphocyte that participates in acquired immune responses.

bacilli (singular, **bacillus**)   Rod-shaped prokaryotic cells.

backbone   The linear arrangement of phosphates and sugar molecules in a DNA or RNA strand.

Bacteria   One of the three domains of life; the other two are Archaea and Eukarya.

bacterial colony   A clone of genetically identical cells formed from a single bacterium by repeated cell divisions.

bacteriophage   A virus that infects bacteria.

bacteroid   A modified bacterial cell of the type known as rhizobia present in mature root nodules of some plants.

balanced polymorphism   The phenomenon in which two or more alleles are kept in balance and maintained in a population over the course of many generations.

balancing selection   A type of natural selection that maintains genetic diversity in a population.

balloon angioplasty   A common treatment to restore blood flow through an artery. A thin tube with a tiny, inflatable balloon at its tip is threaded through the artery to the diseased area; inflating the balloon compresses the plaque against the arterial wall, widening the lumen.

baroreceptor reflex   The rapid, involuntary compensatory response of vertebrates to a change in blood pressure; the pressure is detected by *baroreceptors*, which signal the brainstem to initiate changes in the activity of autonomic neurons. This, in turn, influences the function of structures of the circulatory system in such a way as to correct for a deviation of blood pressure beyond the normal range.

baroreceptor   A pressure-sensitive region within the walls of certain arteries that contains the endings of nerve cells; these regions sense and help to maintain blood pressure in the normal range for an animal.

Barr body   A highly condensed X chromosome present in the cells of female mammals.

basal body   A site at the base of flagella or cilia from which microtubules grow. Basal bodies are anchored on the cytosolic side of the plasma membrane.

basal metabolic rate (BMR)   The metabolic rate of an animal under resting conditions, in a postabsorptive state, and at a standard temperature.

basal nuclei   Clusters of neuronal cell bodies in the vertebrate forebrain that surround the thalamus and lie beneath the cerebral cortex; involved in planning and learning movements.

basal region   The region of a plant seedling that produces the roots.

basal transcription   A low level of transcription resulting from the action of the core promoter alone.

base pair   The structure in which two bases in opposite strands of DNA are held together by hydrogen bonding to each other.

base substitution   A mutation that involves the substitution of a single base in the DNA for another base.

base   1. A molecule that when dissolved in water lowers the H^+ concentration. 2. A component of nucleotides that is a single or double ring of carbon and nitrogen atoms.

basidia   Club-shaped cells that produce sexual spores in the fruiting bodies of basidiomycete fungi.

basidiocarp   The type of fruiting body produced by fungi in the phylum Basidiomycota.

basidiomycetes   A phylum of fungi whose sexual spores are produced on the surfaces of club-shaped structures (basidia).

basidiospore   A sexual spore of fungi in the phylum Basidiomycota.

basilar membrane   A component of the mammalian ear that vibrates back and forth in response to sound and bends the stereocilia in one direction and then the other.

basophil   A type of leukocyte that secretes the anticlotting factor heparin at the site of an infection, which helps flush out the infected site; basophils also secrete histamine, which attracts infection-fighting cells and proteins.

Batesian mimicry   The mimicry of an unpalatable species (the model) by a palatable one (the mimic).

behavior   The observable response of an organism to an external or internal stimulus.

behavioral ecology   A subdiscipline of organismal ecology that focuses on how the behavior of an individual organism contributes to its survival and reproductive success, which, in turn, eventually affects the population density of the species.

benign tumor   A precancerous mass of abnormal cells.

bidirectional replication   The process in which DNA replication proceeds outward from the origin in opposite directions.

biennial   A plant that does not reproduce during the first year of life but may reproduce within the following year.

Bilateria   Bilaterally symmetric animals.

bile salts   A group of substances produced in the liver that solubilize dietary fat and increase its accessibility to digestive enzymes.

bile   A substance produced by the liver that contains bicarbonate ions, cholesterol, phospholipids, a number

cycle. Its function is dependent on the binding of a cyclin.

cyst   A unicellular or multicellular structure that often has a thick, protective wall and can remain dormant through periods of unfavorable climate or low food availability.

cytogenetics   The field of genetics that involves the microscopic examination of chromosomes.

cytokines   A family of proteins that function in both innate and acquired immune defenses by providing a chemical communication network that synchronizes the components of the immune response.

cytokinesis   The division of the cytoplasm to produce two distinct daughter cells.

cytokinin   A type of plant hormone that promotes cell division.

cytosine (C)   A pyrimidine base found in DNA and RNA.

cytoskeleton   In eukaryotes, a network within the cytosol consisting of three different types of protein filaments called microtubules, intermediate filaments, and actin filaments.

cytosol   The region of a eukaryotic cell that is inside the plasma membrane and outside the organelles.

cytotoxic T cell   A type of lymphocyte that travels to the location of its target, binds to the target by combining with an antigen on it, and directly kills the target via secreted chemicals.

D

dalton (Da)   A measure of atomic mass. One dalton equals one-twelfth the mass of a carbon atom.

daughter strand   The newly made strand in DNA replication.

day-neutral plant   A plant that flowers regardless of the night length, as long as day length meets the minimal requirements for plant growth.

deafness   Hearing loss, usually caused by damage to the hair cells within the cochlea.

death receptor   A type of cell surface receptor found in eukaryotic cells that can promote apoptosis when it becomes activated.

decomposer   An organism that gets its energy from the remains and waste products of other organisms.

defecation   The expulsion of feces that occurs through the anus of an animal's digestive canal.

defensive mutualism   A mutually beneficial interaction often involving an animal defending a plant or herbivore in return for food or shelter.

deforestation   The conversion of forested areas by humans to nonforested land.

degenerate   The characteristic of the genetic code that more than one codon can specify the same amino acid.

dehydration reaction   A type of condensation reaction in which a molecule of water is lost.

deletion   A type of mutation in which a segment of chromosomal material has been removed.

demographic transition   The shift in birth and death rates accompanying human societal development.

demography   The study of birth rates, death rates, age distributions, and the sizes of populations.

dendrite   A treelike extension of the plasma membrane of a neuron that receives electrical signals from other neurons.

dendritic cell   A type of cell derived from bone marrow stem cells that plays an important role in innate immunity; these cells are scattered throughout most tissues, where they perform various macrophage-like functions.

denitrification   The reduction of nitrate (NO_3^-) to gaseous nitrogen (N_2).

density-dependent factor   A mortality factor whose influence increases with the density of the population.

density-independent factor   A mortality factor whose influence is not affected by changes in population density.

deoxynucleoside triphosphates   Individual nucleotides with three phosphate groups.

deoxyribonucleic acid (DNA)   One of two types of nucleic acids; the other is ribonucleic acid (RNA). A DNA molecule consists of two strands of nucleotides coiled around each other to form a double helix, held together by hydrogen bonds according to the AT/GC rule.

deoxyribose   A five-carbon sugar found in DNA.

depolarization   The change in the membrane potential that occurs when a cell membrane becomes less polarized, that is, less negative inside the cell relative to the surrounding fluid.

dermal tissue   The covering on various parts of a plant.

desertification   The process by which an area becomes more desert-like, usually as a result of overstocking with domestic animals that can greatly reduce grass coverage through overgrazing.

desmosome   A mechanically strong type of cell junction between animal cells that typically occurs in spotlike rivets.

determinate cleavage   In animals, a characteristic of protostome development in which the fate of each embryonic cell is determined very early.

determinate growth   Growth that is of limited duration, such as the growth of flowers or of animal bodies.

determined   Refers to a cell that has committed to become a particular cell type.

detritivore   An organism that gets its energy from consuming detritus.

detritus   Unconsumed plants that die and decompose, along with the dead remains of animals and animal waste products.

deuterostome   An animal whose development exhibits radial, indeterminate cleavage and in which the blastopore becomes the anus; includes echinoderms and vertebrates.

development   In biology, a series of changes in the state of a cell, tissue, organ, or organism; the underlying process that gives rise to the structures and functions of living organisms.

developmental genetics   A field of study aimed at understanding how gene expression controls the process of development.

diaphragm   A large muscle that subdivides the thoracic cavity from the abdomen in mammals; contraction of the diaphragm enlarges the thoracic cavity during inhalation.

diarrhea   A common intestinal disorder arising from ingested microbes or other causes; usually runs its course within one or two days but, in serious cases, can require hospitalization.

diastole   The first phase of the cardiac cycle, in which the ventricles fill with blood coming from the atria through the open AV valves.

dideoxy chain-termination method   A method for determining the sequence of bases in DNA that utilizes dideoxynucleotide triphosphates as reagents.

dideoxy sequencing   *See* dideoxy chain-termination method.

differential gene regulation   The phenomenon in which the expression of genes differs under various environmental conditions and in specialized cell types.

digestion   The process of breaking down nutrients in food into smaller molecules that can be absorbed across the intestinal epithelia and directly used by cells.

digestive system   In animals, the long tube through which food is processed. In a vertebrate, this system consists of the alimentary canal plus several associated structures.

dihybrid   Refers to an offspring that is a hybrid with respect to two traits.

dikaryotic mycelium   A fungal body that is made of cells that each possess two genetically distinct nuclei.

dimorphic fungi   Fungi that exist in two different morphological forms.

dinosaur   A term, meaning terrible lizard, used to describe some of the extinct reptiles preserved as fossils.

dioecious   Refers to plants that produce staminate and carpellate flowers on separate plants.

diploblastic   Having two distinct germ layers—ectoderm and endoderm—but not mesoderm.

diploid   Containing two sets of chromosomes; designated as $2n$.

diploid-dominant species   Species in which the diploid organism is the multicellular organism in the life cycle. Animals are an example.

direct repair   A type of DNA repair in which an enzyme finds an incorrect structure in the DNA and directly restores the correct structure.

directional selection   A pattern of natural selection that favors individuals at one extreme of a phenotypic distribution.

directionality   In a DNA or RNA strand, refers to the orientation of the sugar molecules within that strand. Can be 5′ to 3′ or 3′ to 5′.

disaccharide   A carbohydrate composed of two monosaccharides.

discovery science   The collection and analysis of data without the need for a preconceived hypothesis; also called discovery-based science.

discovery-based science   The collection and analysis of data without the need for a preconceived hypothesis; also called discovery science.

discrete trait   A trait with clearly defined phenotypic variants.

dispersion   The extent to which individuals in a population are clustered together or spread out.

dispersive mechanism   In this incorrect model for DNA replication, segments of parental DNA and newly made DNA are interspersed in both strands following the replication process.

dispersive mutualism   A mutually beneficial interaction often involving plants and pollinators that disperse their pollen, and plants and fruit eaters that disperse the plant's seeds.

dissociation constant   An equilibrium constant for the formation and dissociation of a ligand and a protein, such as a receptor or an enzyme.

distal tubule   The segment of the renal tubule through which fluid flows into one of the many collecting ducts in the kidney.

disulfide bridge   Covalent chemical bond formed between two sulfhydryl groups on cysteine side chains in a protein; important in the tertiary structure of proteins.

diversifying selection   A pattern of natural selection that favors the survival of two or more different genotypes that produce different phenotypes.

diversity-stability hypothesis   The proposal that species-rich communities are more stable than those with fewer species.

DNA (deoxyribonucleic acid)   The genetic material that provides a blueprint for the organization, development, and function of living things.

DNA helicase   An enzyme that uses ATP to separate DNA strands during DNA replication.

DNA library   A collection of recombinant vectors, each containing a particular fragment of DNA from a given organism.

DNA ligase   An enzyme that catalyzes the formation of a covalent bond between nucleotides in adjacent DNA fragments to complete the replication process.

DNA methylation   A process in which methyl groups are attached to cytosines in DNA.

DNA methyltransferase   An enzyme that attaches methyl groups to bases in DNA.

DNA microarray   A technology used to monitor the expression of thousands of genes simultaneously.

DNA polymerase   An enzyme responsible for covalently linking nucleotides together during DNA replication.

DNA primase   An enzyme that synthesizes a primer for DNA replication.

DNA replication   The process by which DNA is copied. The original DNA strands are used as templates for the synthesis of new DNA strands

DNA sequencing   A procedure used to determine the base sequence of DNA.

DNA supercoiling   A process that compacts a chromosome through twisting of the DNA molecule to form additional coils.

DNA topoisomerase   An enzyme that alleviates DNA supercoiling during DNA replication.

DNA transposon   A type of transposable element that moves as a DNA molecule.

DNase   An enzyme that digests DNA.

domain   1. A defined region of a protein with a distinct structure and function. 2. One of the three major categories of life: Bacteria, Archaea, and Eukarya.

domestication   A process that involves artificial selection of plants or animals for traits desirable to humans.

dominant species   A species that has a large effect in a community because of its high abundance or high biomass.

dominant   Refers to the trait that is displayed in a heterozygote.

dormancy   A phase of metabolic slowdown in a plant or a seed.

dorsal hollow nerve cord   A hollow tract of nervous tissue that lies dorsal to the notochord and alimentary canal and which in vertebrates develops into the spinal cord and brain.

dorsal   Refers to the upper side of an animal.

dorsoventral axis   In bilateral animals, one of the three axes along which the adult body pattern is organized; the others are the anteroposterior axis and the left-right axis.

dosage compensation   The phenomenon in which the expression of X-linked genes is equalized between males and females; in mammals, the inactivation of one X chromosome in the female reduces the number of expressed copies (doses) of X-linked genes from two to one.

double bond   A bond that occurs when the atoms of a molecule share two pairs of electrons.

double fertilization   In angiosperms, the process in which two different fertilization events occur, producing both a zygote and the first cell of a nutritive endosperm tissue.

double helix   Two strands of DNA hydrogen-bonded with each other. In a DNA double helix, two DNA strands are twisted together to form a structure that resembles a spiral staircase.

Down syndrome   A human disorder caused by the inheritance of three copies of chromosome 21.

droplet organelle   An organelle that is not surrounded by a membrane but exists as a droplet formed by liquid-liquid phase separation.

Duchenne muscular dystrophy   An inherited, X-linked recessive disorder of humans causing muscle weakness and muscle degeneration.

duodenum   The first part of the vertebrate small intestine, arising from the stomach.

duplication   A type of mutation in which a section of a chromosome occurs two or more times.

dynamic instability   The oscillation of a single microtubule between growing and shortening phases; important in many cellular activities, including the sorting of chromosomes during cell division.

E

Ecdysis   The process by which an animal molts, or breaks out of its old exoskeleton, and secretes a newer, larger one.

Ecdysozoa   A clade of molting animals that encompasses the arthropods and nematodes.

echolocation   The phenomenon in which certain species listen for echoes of high-frequency sound waves in order to determine the distance and location of an object.

ecological footprint   The amount of productive land needed to support each person on Earth.

ecological species concept   An approach used to distinguish species; considers a species within its native environment and states that each species occupies its own ecological niche.

ecology   The study of interactions among organisms and between organisms and their environments.

ecosystem diversity   The diversity of structure and function within an ecosystem.

ecosystem   The biotic community of organisms in an area, as well as the abiotic environment affecting that community.

ecosystems ecology   The study of the flow of energy and cycling of nutrients among organisms within a community and between organisms and the environment.

ecotypes   Genetically distinct populations adapted to their local environments.

ectoderm   In animals, the outermost layer of cells formed during gastrulation that covers the surface of the embryo and differentiates into the epidermis and nervous system.

ectomycorrhizae   Beneficial associations between temperate forest trees and soil fungi that coat their roots.

ectoparasite   A parasite that lives on the outside of the host's body.

ectotherm   An animal that largely depends on the environment to warm its body.

ectothermic   Dependent on external heat as the main source of body heat.

edge effect   A special physical condition that exists at the boundary, or edge, of an area of habitat.

effective number of species   The number of equally abundant species needed to obtain the same diversity index as that observed in a dataset of interest in which all species are not equally abundant. It is a measure of diversity that converts values from species diversity indices into equivalent numbers of species.

effective population size   The number of individuals that contribute genes to future populations, often smaller than the actual population size.

effector cell   A cloned lymphocyte that carries out the attack response during an acquired immune response.

effector   A molecule that directly influences a cellular response; in a homeostatic control system in animals, a structure that compensates for a deviation of a physiological variable from its set point.

efferent arteriole   A blood vessel that carries blood away from a glomerulus of the vertebrate kidney.

egestion   In animals, the process of eliminating undigested material from the body.

egg cells   Female haploid gametes in species that reproduce sexually.

egg   The mature female gamete; also called an ovum.

ejaculation   The movement of semen through the urethra by contraction of muscles at the base of the penis.

elastin   A protein that makes up elastic fibers in the extracellular matrix of animals.

electrical synapse   A synapse that directly passes electric current from the presynaptic to the postsynaptic cell via gap junctions.

electrocardiogram (ECG or EKG)   A record of the electrical impulses generated by the cells of the heart during the cardiac cycle.

electrochemical gradient   The combined effect of both an electrical and a chemical gradient across a membrane; determines the direction in which ions will move.

electrogenic pump   A pump that generates an electrical gradient across a membrane.

electromagnetic receptor   A sensory receptor in animals that detects radiation within a wide range of the electromagnetic spectrum, including visible, ultraviolet, and infrared light, as well as electrical and magnetic fields in some animals.

electromagnetic spectrum   All possible wavelengths of electromagnetic radiation, from relatively short wavelengths (gamma rays) to much longer wavelengths (radio waves).

electron microscope   A microscope that uses an electron beam for illumination.

electron shell   The region around an atom's nucleus where electrons reside; larger atoms have more electron shells than smaller atoms.

electron transport chain (ETC)   A group of protein complexes and small organic molecules within the inner membranes of mitochondria and chloroplasts and the plasma membrane of prokaryotes. The components accept and donate electrons to each other in a linear manner and produce an H^+ electrochemical gradient.

electron   A negatively charged particle found in orbitals around an atomic nucleus.

electronegativity   A measure of an atom's ability to attract electrons in a bond with another atom.

element   A pure substance composed of only one kind of atom.

elicitor   A protein produced by bacterial and fungal pathogens that promotes virulence.

elongation factor   A protein that is needed for polypeptide synthesis during the elongation stage of translation.

elongation   The second stage in transcription or translation, where RNA strands or polypeptides are made, respectively.

embryo   The early stages of development in a multicellular organism during which the organization of the organism is largely established.

embryogenesis   The process by which embryos develop from single-celled zygotes by mitotic divisions.

embryonic development   The process by which a fertilized egg is transformed into an organism with distinct physiological systems and body parts.

embryonic germ cell (EG cell)   A cell in the early mammalian embryo that later gives rise to sperm or egg cells. These cells are pluripotent.

embryonic stem cell (ES cell)   A cell in the early mammalian embryo that can differentiate into almost every cell type of the body. These cells are pluripotent.

embryophytes   The land plants.

emerging virus   A virus that has arisen recently or has recently shown a greater probability of causing infection.

emphysema   A progressive disease characterized by a loss of elastic recoil ability of the lungs, usually resulting from chronic tobacco smoking.

empirical thought   Thought that relies on observation to form an idea or hypothesis, rather than trying to understand life from a nonphysical or spiritual point of view.

emulsification A process during digestion that disrupts large lipid droplets into many tiny droplets, thereby increasing their total surface area and providing greater exposure to lipase action.

enantiomer One of a pair of stereoisomers that exist as mirror images.

endangered species Those species that are in danger of extinction throughout all or a significant portion of their range.

endemic Refers to species that are naturally found only in a particular place or region.

endergonic Refers to chemical reactions that require an addition of free energy and do not proceed spontaneously.

endocrine disruptor A chemical found in polluted water and soil that resembles a natural hormone; a common example are chemicals that resemble estrogen and can bind to estrogen receptors in animals.

endocrine glands Structures that contain epithelial cells that secrete hormones into the bloodstream, where they circulate throughout the body.

endocrine system All the endocrine glands and other organs containing hormone-secreting cells.

endocytosis A process in which the plasma membrane invaginates, or folds inward, to form a vesicle that brings substances into the cell.

endoderm In animals, the innermost layer of cells formed during gastrulation; lines the gut and gives rise to many internal organs.

endodermis In vascular plants, a thin cylinder of root tissue that forms a barrier between the root cortex and the central core of vascular tissue.

endomembrane system A network of membranes that includes the nuclear envelope, the endoplasmic reticulum, Golgi apparatus, lysosomes, vacuoles, peroxisomes, and plasma membrane.

endomycorrhizae Partnerships between plants and fungi in which the fungal hyphae grow into the spaces between root cell walls and plasma membranes.

endoparasite A parasite that lives inside the host's body.

endoplasmic reticulum (ER) A convoluted network of membranes in a cell's cytoplasm that forms flattened, fluid-filled tubules, or cisternae.

endoskeleton An internal hard skeleton covered by soft tissue; present in echinoderms and vertebrates.

endosperm A nutritive tissue that increases the efficiency with which food is stored and used in the seeds of flowering plants.

endospore A structure with a tough coat that is produced inside of certain bacteria and then released when the enclosing bacterial cell dies and breaks down.

endosporic gametophyte A plant gametophyte that grows within the confines of microspore or megaspore walls.

endosymbiosis theory A theory that mitochondria and chloroplasts originated from bacteria that took up residence within primordial eukaryotic cells.

endosymbiosis A symbiotic relationship in which the smaller species (the symbiont) lives inside the larger species (the host).

endosymbiotic Describes a relationship in which one organism (the endosymbiont) lives inside another (the host).

endotherm An animal that generates most of its body heat by metabolic processes.

endothermic Capable of generating body heat through metabolism.

energy flow The movement of energy through an ecosystem.

energy intermediate A molecule such as ATP or NADH that stores energy and is used to drive endergonic reactions in cells.

energy The ability to promote change or do work.

enhancer A regulatory element in eukaryotes that increases the rate of transcription when bound by an activator protein.

enthalpy (*H*) The total energy of a system.

entomology The scientific study of insects.

entropy The degree of disorder of a system.

environmental science The application of ecology to real-world problems.

enzyme A protein that acts as a catalyst to speed up a chemical reaction in a cell.

enzyme-linked receptor A receptor found in all living species that typically has two important domains: an extracellular domain, which binds a signaling molecule, and an intracellular domain, which has a catalytic function.

enzyme-substrate complex The structure produced by binding an enzyme and its substrate(s).

eosinophil A type of phagocyte found in large numbers in mucosal surfaces lining the gastrointestinal, respiratory, and urinary tracts, where they fight off parasitic infections.

epicotyl The portion of an embryonic plant stem with two tiny leaves in a first bud; located above the point of attachment of the cotyledons.

epidermis A layer of dermal tissue on the surfaces of leaves, stems, and roots that helps protect a plant from damage.

epigenetic inheritance An epigenetic change that is passed from parent to offspring. An example is genomic imprinting.

epigenetics The study of mechanisms that lead to changes in gene expression that can be passed from cell to cell and are reversible, but do not involve a change in the sequence of DNA.

epilimnion The upper layer of water in a lake, usually warm and containing high levels of dissolved oxygen.

epimutation A heritable change in gene expression that does not alter the sequence of DNA.

episome A plasmid or viral genome that can integrate into a host chromosome or can replicate independently.

epistasis A gene interaction in which the alleles of one gene mask the expression of the alleles of another gene.

epithalamus A region of the vertebrate forebrain that includes the pineal gland.

epithelial tissue In animals, a sheet of densely packed cells that covers the body, covers individual organs, or lines the walls of various cavities inside the body.

epitope An antigenic determinant; the polypeptide fragment of an antigen that is complexed to an MHC protein and presented to a helper T cell.

equilibrium model of island biogeography A model that explains the process of succession on new islands, proposing that the number of species on an island tends toward an equilibrium number that is determined by the balance between immigration rates and extinction rates.

equilibrium potential The membrane potential at which the flow of an ion is at equilibrium, with no net movement in either direction.

equilibrium 1. In a chemical reaction, occurs when the rate of the forward reaction is balanced by the rate of the reverse reaction. 2. In a population, the situation in which the population size stays the same.

ER lumen A single compartment enclosed by the ER membrane.

ER signal sequence A sorting signal in a polypeptide that is usually located near the N-terminus and is recognized by SRP (signal recognition particle), allowing the polypeptide to be directed to the ER membrane.

erythrocyte A cell that serves the critical function of transporting oxygen throughout an animal's body; also known as a red blood cell.

erythropoietin (EPO) A hormone made by the liver and kidneys in response to any situation where additional red blood cells are required.

esophagus In animals, the tubular structure that forms a pathway from the pharynx to the stomach.

essential amino acid An amino acid that is required in the diet of many animals.

essential element In plants, a chemical element that is required for metabolism, sometimes by functioning as an enzyme cofactor.

essential fatty acid An unsaturated fatty acid, such as linoleic acid, that cannot be synthesized by animal cells and must therefore be consumed in the diet.

essential nutrient In animals, a compound that cannot be synthesized from any ingested or stored precursor molecule and so must be obtained in the diet in its complete form. In plants, those substances needed to complete reproduction while avoiding the symptoms of nutrient deficiency.

estradiol The major estrogen in many vertebrates, including humans.

estrogens Steroid hormones produced by the ovaries that affect most aspects of female reproduction.

ethology Scientific studies of animal behavior.

ethylene A plant hormone that is particularly important in coordinating plant developmental and stress responses.

euchromatin The less condensed regions of a chromosome; areas that are capable of gene transcription.

eudicots One of the two largest lineages of flowering plants in which the embryo possesses two seed leaves.

Eukarya One of the three domains of life; the other two are Bacteria and Archaea.

eukaryote A member of the domain Eukarya. The distinguishing feature of eukaryotes is cell compartmentalization, including a cell nucleus; eukaryotes include protists, fungi, plants, and animals.

eukaryotic Refers to organisms having cells with internal compartments that serve various functions; includes all members of the domain Eukarya.

euphyll A leaf with branched veins.

euploid Refers to an organism that has a chromosome number that is a multiple of a chromosome set ($1n$, $2n$, $3n$, etc.).

eusociality An extreme form of altruism in social insects in which the vast majority of females, known as workers, do not reproduce. Instead, they help one reproductive female (the queen) raise offspring.

eustele In plants, a ring of vascular tissue arranged around a central pith of nonvascular tissue; typical of progymnosperms, gymnosperms, and angiosperms.

eutherian A placental mammal; a member of the clade Eutheria.

eutrophic Waters that contain relatively high levels of nutrients such as phosphate or nitrogen and typically exhibit high levels of primary productivity and low levels of biodiversity.

eutrophication The process by which elevated nutrient levels in a body of water lead to an overgrowth of algae or aquatic plants and a subsequent depletion of water oxygen concentrations when these photosynthesizers decay.

evaporation The conversion of water from the liquid to the gaseous state at normal temperatures. Animals use evaporation as a means of losing excess body heat.

evapotranspiration rate The rate at which water moves into the atmosphere through the processes of evaporation from the soil and other surfaces and transpiration of plants.

evo-devo *See* evolutionary developmental biology.

evolution A heritable change in a population of organisms from one generation to the next.

evolutionarily conserved The term used to describe homologous DNA sequences that are very similar or identical between different species.

evolutionary developmental biology The field of biology that compares the development of different organisms in an attempt to understand relationships between organisms and the mechanisms that bring about evolutionary change; referred to as evo-devo.

evolutionary lineage concept An approach used to distinguish species; states that a species is derived from a single distinct lineage and has its own evolutionary tendencies and historical fate.

excitation-contraction coupling The sequence of events by which an action potential in the plasma membrane of a muscle fiber leads to cross-bridge activity.

excitatory postsynaptic potential (EPSP) The response to an excitatory neurotransmitter that depolarizes the postsynaptic membrane; the depolarization brings the membrane potential closer to the threshold potential that would trigger an action potential.

excretion In animals, the process of expelling waste or harmful materials from the body.

excretory system All of an animal's organs (such as gills, lungs, kidneys, and, in some animals, the body surface) that function to remove soluble wastes generated from metabolism.

excurrent siphon A structure in a tunicate used to expel water from the body

exercise Any physical activity that increases an animal's metabolic rate.

exergonic Refers to chemical reactions that release free energy and occur spontaneously.

exocrine gland A gland in which epithelial cells secrete chemicals into a duct, which carries those molecules directly to another structure or to the outside surface of the body.

exocytosis A process in which material inside a cell is packaged into vesicles and excreted into the extracellular environment.

exon A portion of RNA that is found in the mature mRNA molecule after splicing is finished.

exoskeleton An external skeleton made primarily of chitin that surrounds and protects most of the body surface of animals such as insects.

expansin A protein that occurs in the plant cell wall and fosters cell enlargement.

experimental group The sample in an experiment that is subjected to some type of variation that does not occur for the control group.

exploitation competition Competition in which organisms compete indirectly through the consumption of a limited resource.

exponential growth Rapid population growth that occurs when the per capita growth rate remains above zero.

extant Refers to a species that is still in existence.

extensor A muscle that straightens a limb at a joint.

external fertilization Fertilization that occurs in aquatic environments, when eggs and sperm are released into the water in close enough proximity for fertilization to occur.

extinct Refers to a species that existed in the past, but has died out.

extinction The end of the existence of a species or a group of species.

extracellular fluid The fluid in an organism's body that is outside of the cells.

extracellular matrix (ECM) A network of material that is secreted from animal cells and forms a complex meshwork outside of cells. The ECM provides strength, support, and organization.

extranuclear inheritance In eukaryotes, the transmission of genes that are located outside the cell nucleus.

extremophile An organism that occurs primarily in extreme habitats.

extrinsic pathway One of two different pathways for apoptosis that involves the activation of death receptors.

eye The visual organ in animals that detects light and sends signals to the brain.

eyecup A visual organ in flatworms that detects light and its direction but does not form an image.

F

F factor A fertility factor, or type of bacterial plasmid that plays a role in bacterial conjugation.

F_1 generation The first generation of offspring in a genetic cross.

F_2 generation The second generation of offspring in a genetic cross.

facilitated diffusion A mechanism of passive transport in which a transport protein provides a passageway for a substance to cross a membrane from an area of higher concentration to one of lower concentration.

facilitation A mechanism for succession in which a species facilitates or makes the local environment more suitable for subsequent species.

facultative anaerobe A microorganism that can use oxygen in aerobic respiration, obtain energy via anaerobic fermentation, or use inorganic chemical reactions to obtain energy.

facultative mutualism An interaction between mutualistic species that is beneficial but not essential to the survival and reproduction of either species.

falsifiable Refers to a hypothesis that can be shown to be incorrect based on additional observations or experimentation.

family In taxonomy, a subdivision of an order.

fast fiber A skeletal muscle fiber containing myosin with higher ATPase activity.

fast-glycolytic fiber A skeletal muscle fiber that has high myosin ATPase activity but cannot make as much ATP as an oxidative fiber because its source of ATP is glycolysis; best suited for rapid, intense actions.

fast-oxidative fiber A skeletal muscle fiber that has high myosin ATPase activity and can make large amounts of ATP; used for long-term actions.

fate The ultimate morphological features that a cell or a group of cells will adopt.

feedback inhibition A type of regulation in which the product of a metabolic pathway inhibits an enzyme that acts early in the pathway, thus preventing the overaccumulation of the product.

feedforward regulation The process by which an animal's body begins preparing for a change in some variable before it even occurs.

female gametophyte A haploid multicellular plant generation that produces one or more eggs but does not produce sperm cells.

female-enforced monogamy hypothesis The hypothesis that a male is monogamous due to various actions employed by his female mate.

fermentation The breakdown of organic molecules to produce energy without any net oxidation of an organic molecule.

fertilization The union of two gametes, such as an egg cell with a sperm cell, to form a zygote.

fertilizer A soil addition that enhances plant growth by providing essential elements.

fetus The maturing embryo after the eighth week of gestation in humans.

fever An increase in an animal's body temperature, typically due to infection.

fiber A type of tough-walled plant cell that provides support.

fibrous root system The root system of monocots, which consists of multiple adventitious roots that grow from the stem base.

fight-or-flight response The response of vertebrates to real or perceived danger; associated with increased activity of the sympathetic branch of the autonomic nervous system.

filament 1. The elongate portion of a flower's stamen; contains vascular tissue that delivers nutrients from parental sporophytes to anthers. 2. In fishes, a part of the gills.

filtrate In the process of filtration in an excretory system, the material that passes through the filter and enters the excretory organ for either further processing or excretion.

filtration The passive removal of water and small solutes from the blood during the production of urine.

finite rate of increase In ecology, the ratio of a population size from one year to the next.

fitness The relative likelihood that a genotype will contribute to the gene pool of the next generation as compared with other genotypes.

fixed action pattern (FAP) An animal behavior that, once initiated, will continue until completed.

fixed nitrogen Atmospheric nitrogen that has been combined with another element into a substance that can be used by plants. An example is ammonia, NH_3.

flaccid Refers to a plant cell in which the concentration of solutes is the same as that in the external fluid environment. A flaccid cell has a water content higher than a plasmolyzed cell, but lower than a turgid cell.

flagella (singular, **flagellum**) Relatively long cell appendages that facilitate cellular movement or the movement of extracellular fluids.

flagellate A protist that uses one or more flagella to move in water or cause water motions useful in feeding.

flagship species A single large or instantly recognizable species.

flame cell A cell that exists primarily to maintain osmotic balance between an organism's body and surrounding fluids; present in flatworms.

flexor A muscle that bends a limb at a joint.

flower A reproductive shoot; a short stem branch bearing reproductive organs instead of leaves.

flowering plants The angiosperms, which produce ovules within the protective ovaries of flowers. The ovules develop into seeds, and the ovaries develop into fruits, which function in seed dispersal.

fluidity A property of biological membranes in which individual molecules remain in close association yet have the ability to move rotationally or laterally within the plane of the membrane. Membranes are semifluid.

fluid-mosaic model The accepted model of a biological membrane; its basic framework is the semifluid phospholipid bilayer with a mosaic of proteins. Carbohydrates may be attached to the lipids or proteins.

focal adhesion A mechanically strong type of cell junction that connects an animal cell to the extracellular matrix (ECM).

follicle-stimulating hormone (FSH) A gonadotropin that stimulates follicle development.

follicular phase The first half of the human ovarian cycle, in which a cohort of immature follicles begin to grow and differentiate.

food chain A linear depiction of energy flow between organisms, with each organism feeding on and deriving energy from the preceding organism.

food web A complex model of interconnected food chains in which there are multiple links among different species.

food-induced thermogenesis A rise in an animal's metabolic rate and heat production for a few hours after eating.

foot In mollusks, a muscular structure usually used for movement.

knowledge The awareness and understanding of information.

Koch's postulates A series of steps used to determine whether a particular organism causes a specific disease.

K-selected species A species whose life history strategy shows a low rate of per capita population growth but good competitive ability.

L

labor The strong rhythmic contractions of the uterus that serve to deliver a fetus during childbirth.

lac repressor A repressor protein that regulates the *lac* operon.

***lac* operon** An operon in the genome of *E. coli* that contains the genes for the proteins that allow the bacterium to metabolize lactose.

lacteal A lymphatic vessel in the center of each intestinal villus; lipids are absorbed by the lacteals, which eventually empty into the circulatory system.

lagging strand During DNA replication, a DNA strand made as a series of small Okazaki fragments that are subsequently connected to each other to form a continuous strand.

lamellae (singular, **lamella**) Platelike structures in the internal gills of fishes that branch from structures called filaments; gas exchange occurs here.

larva A free-living organism that is morphologically very different from the embryo and adult.

larynx The segment of the respiratory tract that contains the vocal cords.

latent The term used to describe a prophage or provirus that remains inactive for a long time.

lateral line system Microscopic sensory organs in fishes and some toads that allows them to detect movement in surrounding water.

lateral meristem *See* secondary meristem.

leaching The dissolution and removal of inorganic ions as water percolates through materials such as soil.

leading strand During DNA replication, a DNA strand made in the same direction that the replication fork is moving. The strand is synthesized as one long continuous molecule.

leaf abscission The process by which a leaf drops after the formation of an abscission zone.

leaf primordia Small outgrowths that occur at the sides of a shoot apical meristem and develop into young leaves.

leaf vein In plants, a bundle of vascular tissue in a leaf.

leaflet 1. Half of a phospholipid bilayer. 2. A portion of a compound leaf.

learning The ability of an animal to make modifications to a behavior based on previous experience; the process by which new information is acquired.

leaves Flattened plant organs that emerge from stems and typically function in photosynthesis.

left-right axis In bilaterally symmetric animals, the left and right sides of the body.

leghemoglobin A protein found in legume plants that helps to regulate local oxygen concentrations around rhizobial bacteroids in root nodules.

legume A member of the pea (bean) family; also the distinctive fruit of such a plant.

lek A designated communal courting area used by certain species of animals.

lens 1. A structure of the eye that focuses light. 2. The glass components of a light microscope or the electromagnetic parts of an electron microscope that allow the production of magnified images of microscopic structures.

lentic Refers to a freshwater habitat characterized by standing water.

lenticels Passages in the outer bark of a woody plant stem that allow inner stem tissues to accomplish gas exchange.

leptin A hormone produced by adipose cells in proportion to fat mass; controls appetite and metabolic rate.

leukocyte A cell that develops from the marrow of certain bones of vertebrates; all leukocytes (also known as white blood cells) perform vital functions that defend the body against infection and disease.

lichen A complex mutualistic association between fungi and other microbes, including photosynthetic green algae or cyanobacteria.

Liebig's law of the minimum The principle that states that species' biomass or abundance is limited by the scarcest factor.

life cycle The sequence of events that characterize the steps of development of the individuals of a given species.

life table A table that provides data on the numbers of living individuals in various age classes in a population and their relative fertilities.

ligand An ion or molecule that binds to a protein, such as an enzyme or a receptor.

ligand·receptor complex The structure formed when a ligand and its receptor bind noncovalently to each other.

ligand-gated ion channel A type of cell surface receptor that binds a ligand and functions as an ion channel. Ligand binding either opens or closes a channel.

light microscope A microscope that utilizes light for illumination.

light reactions The first of two stages in the process of photosynthesis. During the light reactions, photosystem II and photosystem I absorb light energy and produce ATP, NADPH, and O_2.

light-harvesting complex A component of photosystem II and photosystem I composed of several dozen pigment molecules that are anchored to proteins in the thylakoid membrane of a chloroplast. The role of these complexes is to absorb photons of light.

lignin A tough polymer that adds strength and decay resistance to cell walls of tracheids, vessel elements, and other cells of plants.

limbic system In the vertebrate forebrain, the areas involved in the formation and expression of emotions; also plays a role in learning, memory, and the perception of smells.

limiting factor A factor whose amount or concentration limits the rate of a biological process or a chemical reaction.

line transect A sampling technique used by plant ecologists in which the number of plants located along a length of string are counted.

lineage A series of species that forms a line of descent.

linear electron flow In the light reactions of photosynthesis, the movement of electrons from PSII to PSI and ultimately to $NADP^+$ to form NADPH.

linkage group A group of genes that usually stay together during meiosis.

linkage The phenomenon in which two genes close together on the same chromosome are transmitted as a unit.

lipase The major fat-digesting enzyme, secreted by the pancreas.

lipid raft In a membrane, a group of lipids, sometimes including associated proteins, that float together as a unit in a larger sea of lipids.

lipid A molecule composed predominantly of hydrogen and carbon atoms. Lipids are nonpolar and therefore very insoluble in water. They include fats (triglycerides), phospholipids, waxes, and steroids.

lipid-anchored protein A type of integral membrane protein that is attached to the membrane via a lipid molecule.

lipid-exchange protein A protein that extracts a lipid from one membrane, diffuses through the cell, and inserts the lipid into another membrane.

lipolysis The enzymatic breakdown of triglycerides into fatty acids and either monoglycerides or glycerol.

lipopolysaccharides Lipids with covalently bound polysaccharides; prevalent in the thin, outer envelope that encloses the cell walls of Gram-negative bacteria.

liposome A vesicle surrounded by a phospholipid bilayer.

liquid-liquid phase separation The phenomenon in which aggregated solutes, such as proteins and RNA molecules, separate from the bulk solvent, and form a droplet.

liver An organ in vertebrates that performs diverse metabolic functions and is the site of bile production.

liverworts A phylum of bryophytes; formally called Hepatophyta.

loam A type of soil that contains a mixture of sand, silt, and clay and is ideal for plant cultivation.

lobe-finned fishes Fishes in which the fins are part of the body; the fins are supported by skeletal extensions of the pectoral and pelvic areas.

locomotion The movement of an animal from place to place.

locus The physical location of a gene on a chromosome.

logistic equation An equation that relates the growth of a population to the carrying capacity, K, of its environment.

logistic growth The pattern in which the growth of a population typically slows down as the population size approaches the carrying capacity.

long-day plant A plant that flowers in spring or early summer, when the night period is shorter (and thus the day length is longer) than a defined period.

long-term potentiation (LTP) The long-lasting strengthening of the connection between neurons that is believed to be part of the mechanism of learning and memory.

loop domain In bacteria, a chromosomal segment that is folded into a loop by attachment to proteins; a means of compacting a bacterial chromosome.

loop of Henle A segment of the renal tubule of the kidney containing a sharp hairpin-like loop that contributes to reabsorption of ions and water and that consists of a descending limb coming from the proximal tubule and an ascending limb leading to the distal tubule.

lophophore A horseshoe-shaped crown of tentacles used for feeding in several invertebrate species.

Lophotrochozoa A clade of animals that encompasses the mollusks, annelids, and several other phyla; they are distinguished by two morphological features: the lophophore, a crown of tentacles used for feeding, and the trochophore larva, a distinct larval stage.

lotic Refers to a freshwater habitat characterized by running water.

lumen The internal space or hollow cavity of an organelle or an organ, such as the endoplasmic reticulum, the stomach, or a blood vessel.

lung In terrestrial vertebrates, internal paired structures used to bring O_2 into the circulatory system and remove CO_2.

lungfishes The Dipnoi; fish with primitive lungs that live in oxygen-poor freshwater swamps and ponds.

luteal phase The phase of the human ovarian cycle that begins after ovulation and during which a corpus luteum is formed.

luteinizing hormone (LH) A gonadotropin that controls the production of sex steroids in both males and females.

lycophyll A relatively small leaf having a single unbranched vein; produced by lycophytes.

lycophytes Members of a phylum (Lycopodiophyta) of vascular land plants whose leaves are lycophylls.

lymphatic system A system of vessels along with a group of organs and tissues where most leukocytes reside. The lymphatic vessels collect excess interstitial fluid and return it to the blood.

lymphocyte A type of leukocyte that is responsible for specific immunity; may be either a B cell or a T cell.

lysogenic cycle A type of viral reproductive cycle consisting of integration of phage DNA into that of a bacterium, prophage replication, and excision.

lysosome A small organelle found in animal cells that contains acid hydrolases that degrade molecules and macromolecules.

lytic cycle A type of viral reproductive cycle in which the production and release of new phages lyses the host cell.

M

M phase The phase of the cell cycle consisting of the sequential events of mitosis and cytokinesis.

macroalgae Photosynthetic protists that can be seen with the unaided eye; also known as seaweeds.

macroevolution Evolutionary changes that produce new species and groups of species.

macromolecule Many molecules bonded together to form a polymer. Carbohydrates, proteins, and nucleic acids (for example, DNA and RNA) are important macromolecules found in living organisms.

macronutrient An element required by plants in amounts of at least 1 g/kg of plant dry matter.

macroparasite A parasite that lives in a host but releases infective juvenile stages outside the host's body.

macrophage A large phagocyte capable of engulfing viruses and bacteria.

macular degeneration An eye condition in which photoreceptor cells in and around the macula (which contains the fovea of the retina) are lost; one of the leading causes of blindness in the U.S.

madreporite A sievelike plate on the surface of an echinoderm through which water enters the water vascular system.

magnetic resonance imaging (MRI) An imaging method that relies on the use of magnetic fields and radio waves to visualize the internal structure of an organism's body.

magnification The ratio between the size of an image produced by a microscope and the object's actual size.

major depressive disorder A neurological disorder characterized by feelings of despair and sadness, resulting from an imbalance in neurotransmitter levels in the brain.

major groove A wider groove that spirals around the DNA double helix; provides a location where a protein can bind to a particular sequence of bases and affect the expression of a gene.

major histocompatibility complex (MHC) A gene family that encodes the plasma membrane self proteins that must be complexed with an antigen for T-cell recognition to occur.

male gametophyte A haploid multicellular plant life cycle stage that produces sperm.

male-assistance hypothesis A hypothesis to explain the existence of monogamy that maintains that males remain with females to help them rear their offspring.

malignant tumor A growth of cells that has progressed to the cancerous stage.

Malpighian tubules Delicate projections from the digestive tract of insects and some other taxa that function as an excretory organ.

mantle cavity The chamber in a mollusk mantle that houses delicate gills.

mantle In mollusks, a fold of skin draped over the visceral mass that secretes a shell in those species that form shells.

many-eyes hypothesis The idea that increased group size decreases predators' success because of increased detection of predators.

map distance The distance between genes along chromosomes, which is calculated as the number of recombinant offspring divided by the total number of offspring times 100.

map unit (mu) A unit of distance on a chromosome equivalent to a 1% recombination frequency.

marker genes Genes that mark, or indicate, the occurrence of particular metabolic functions in organisms.

mark-recapture technique The capture and tagging of animals so they can be released and recaptured, allowing an estimate of population size.

marsupial A member of a group of seven mammalian orders and about 280 species found in the clade Metatheria.

mass extinction An event in which many species become extinct at the same time.

mass-specific BMR The amount of energy expended per gram of body mass in the resting condition.

mast cell A type of cell derived from bone marrow stem cells that occurs throughout connective tissues and plays an important role in innate immunity.

mastax The circular muscular pharynx in the mouth of rotifers.

mate-guarding hypothesis The hypothesis that a male is monogamous to prevent his mate from being fertilized by other males.

maternal effect gene A gene for which only the mother's gene product affects the phenotype of the resulting offspring.

maternal inheritance A phenomenon in which offspring inherit particular genes only from the female parent (through the egg).

matrotrophy In plants, the phenomenon in which zygotes remain enclosed within gametophyte tissues, where they are sheltered and fed.

matter Anything that has mass and takes up space.

mature mRNA In eukaryotes, transcription produces a longer RNA, called pre-mRNA, which undergoes certain modifications before it exits the nucleus; mature mRNA is the final functional product.

maximum likelihood One method used to evaluate a phylogenetic tree based on an evolutionary model.

maximum sustainable yield (MSY) The largest number of individuals that can be removed without causing long-term decreases in the population.

mean fitness of the population The average reproductive success of members of a population.

mechanoreceptor A sensory receptor in animals that transduces mechanical energy such as pressure, touch, stretch, movement, and sound.

mediator A large protein complex that plays a role in initiating transcription at the core promoter of protein-encoding genes in eukaryotes.

medulla oblongata The part of the vertebrate hindbrain that coordinates many processes that maintain homeostasis, such as breathing.

medusa A type of cnidarian body form that is motile and usually floats mouth down.

megadiversity countries Those countries with the greatest numbers of species; used in targeting areas for conservation.

megaspore In seed plants and some seedless plants, a large spore that produces a female gametophyte within the spore wall.

meiosis I The first division of meiosis in which homologous chromosomes are separated into different cells.

meiosis II The second division of meiosis in which sister chromatids are separated into different cells.

meiosis The process by which haploid cells are produced from a cell that was originally diploid.

Meissner corpuscle A specialized receptor that senses touch and light pressure and lies just beneath the skin surface of an animal.

membrane attack complex (MAC) A multi-unit protein formed by the activation of complement proteins; the complex creates water channels in the microbial plasma membrane and causes the microbe to swell and burst.

membrane potential The difference between the electric charges outside and inside a cell; also called a potential difference (or voltage).

membrane transport The movement of ions or molecules across a biological membrane.

membrane vesicle A small sphere enclosed by a membrane.

memory cell A cloned lymphocyte that remains poised to recognize a returning antigen; a component of acquired immunity.

memory The ability to retain, retrieve, and use previously learned information.

Mendelian inheritance The inheritance patterns of genes that segregate and assort independently.

Mendel's law of independent assortment The alleles of different genes assort independently of each other during the process that gives rise to gametes.

Mendel's law of segregation The two alleles of a gene separate (segregate) from each other during the process that gives rise to gametes, so every gamete receives only one allele.

meninges Three layers of sheathlike membranes that cover and protect the brain and spinal cord.

meningitis A potentially life-threatening infectious disease in which the meninges become inflamed.

menopause The event during which a woman permanently stops having ovarian cycles.

menstrual cycle The cyclical changes that occur in the uterus in parallel with the ovarian cycle in a female mammal; also called the uterine cycle.

menstruation A period of bleeding at the beginning of the uterine cycle in a female mammal.

meristem In plants, a region of undifferentiated cells (stem cells) that produces new tissue by cell division.

meroblastic cleavage An incomplete type of cell cleavage in which only the region of the egg containing cytoplasm at the animal pole undergoes cell division; occurs in birds and some fishes.

merozygote A bacterial cell that contains an F′ factor.

mesoderm In animals, a layer of cells formed during gastrulation that develops between the ectoderm and endoderm; gives rise to the skeleton, muscles, and much of the circulatory system.

mesoglea A gelatinous substance between the epidermis and the gastrodermis in cnidarians.

mesohyl A gelatinous, protein-rich matrix in between the choanocytes and the epithelial cells of a sponge.

mesophyll The internal tissue of a plant leaf; the site of photosynthesis.

messenger RNA (mRNA) RNA that contains the information to specify a polypeptide with a particular amino acid sequence.

metabolic cycle A biochemical cycle in which particular molecules enter while others leave; the process is cyclical because it involves a series of organic molecules that are regenerated with each turn of the cycle.

metabolic pathway In living cells, a coordinated series of chemical reactions in which each step is catalyzed by a specific enzyme.

metabolic rate The total energy expenditure of an organism per unit of time.

metabolism The sum of all bodily activities and chemical reactions that occur within an organism. Also, a specific set of chemical reactions occurring at the cellular level.

metabolome Collection of information about the types and abundances of molecules, such as sugars and fatty acids, produced by metabolism in a single organism.

metabotropic receptor A G-protein-coupled receptor that initiates a signaling pathway in response to a neurotransmitter. One of two types of postsynaptic receptors, the other being an ionotropic receptor.

metacentric Refers to a chromosome in which the centromere is near the middle.

metagenome The genomes of all the organisms present in a sample.

metagenomics A field of study that seeks to identify and analyze the collective microbial genomes contained in a community of organisms, including those not easily cultured in the laboratory.

meta-metabolome Collection of information about the types and abundances of molecules, such as sugars and fatty acids, produced by metabolism by an entire microbiome.

metamorphosis The process in which a pupal or juvenile organism changes into a mature adult with very different characteristics.

metanephridia Excretory filtration organs found in a variety of invertebrates, including annelids.

metaphase plate A plane halfway between the poles of the spindle apparatus on which the sister chromatids align during metaphase in mitosis.

metaphase The phase of mitosis during which the chromosomes are aligned along the metaphase plate.

metaproteome All the proteins produced by all the members of a microbiome.

metastasis The process by which cancer cells spread from their original location to distant parts of the body.

metatranscriptome A collection of all the mRNAs present in an environmental sample, that is, all of the mRNAs produced by all of the organisms sampled from a particular place at a particular time.

methanogens Several groups of anaerobic archaea that convert CO_2, methyl groups, or acetate to methane, and release it from their cells.

methanotroph An aerobic bacterium that consumes methane.

methyl-CpG-binding protein A protein that binds methylated DNA sequences and inhibits transcription.

micelle A sphere formed from the aggregation of long amphipathic molecules when they are mixed with water. The polar regions are on the surface and in contact with water and the nonpolar regions are in the center.

microbiome A particular assemblage of microbes (including their genes) that are associated with a defined environment.

microbiota Collections of microbial life cataloged by amplicon analysis.

microcystin A type of toxin produced by some cyanobacteria, including the genus *Microcystis*.

microevolution Changes in a population's gene pool, such as changes in allele frequencies, from generation to generation.

microfilament *See* actin filament.

micrograph An image taken with the aid of a microscope.

micronutrient An element required by plants in amounts equal to or less than 0.1 g/kg of plant dry matter; also known as a trace element.

microparasite A parasite that multiplies within its host, usually within the cells.

micropyle A small opening in the integument of a seed plant ovule through which a pollen tube grows.

microRNAs (miRNAs) Small RNA molecules, typically 22 nucleotides in length, that are transcribed from endogenous eukaryotic genes and silence the expression of specific mRNAs by inhibiting translation.

microscope A magnification tool that enables researchers to visualize the structures and inner workings of cells.

microspore In seed plants and some seedless plants, a relatively small spore that produces a male gametophyte within the spore wall.

microtubule A type of hollow protein filament composed of tubulin proteins that is part of the cytoskeleton and is important for cell shape, organization, and movement.

microvilli Small projections of the plasma membranes of epithelial cells in the small intestine and many other absorptive cells.

midbrain One of three major divisions of the vertebrate brain; the other two divisions are the hindbrain and the forebrain.

middle lamella An extracellular layer in plants composed primarily of carbohydrate; cements adjacent plant cell walls together.

migration Long-range seasonal movement of animals in order to feed or breed.

mimicry The resemblance of an organism (the mimic) to another organism (the model).

mineral An inorganic ion required by a living organism for normal cellular functioning.

mineralization The general process by which phosphorus, nitrogen, CO_2, and other minerals are released from organic compounds.

minor groove A groove that spirals around the DNA double helix but is smaller than the major groove.

missense mutation A base substitution that changes a single amino acid in a polypeptide.

mitochondrial genome The chromosome found in mitochondria.

mitochondrial matrix A compartment inside the inner membrane of a mitochondrion.

mitochondrial pathway *See* intrinsic pathway.

mitochondrion A semiautonomous organelle found in eukaryotic cells that supplies most of a cell's ATP.

mitosis In eukaryotes, the process in which nuclear division results in two nuclei, each of which receives the same complement of chromosomes.

mitotic cell division A process whereby a eukaryotic cell divides to produce two new cells that are genetically identical to the original cell.

mitotic spindle The structure responsible for organizing and sorting the chromosomes during mitosis; also called the mitotic spindle apparatus.

mixotroph An organism that is able to use photoautotrophy as well as phagotrophy or osmotrophy to obtain organic nutrients.

model organism An organism studied by many different researchers so that they can compare their results and determine scientific principles that apply more broadly to other species.

model-based learning An educational approach in which students evaluate or generate models as a way to enhance their understanding of scientific concepts and improve their critical-thinking skills.

moderately repetitive sequence A DNA sequence that is repeated a few hundred to several thousand times in a genome.

molar A term used to describe a solution's molarity; a 1 molar solution contains 1 mole of a solute dissolved in enough water to make 1 L of solution.

molarity The number of moles of a solute dissolved in 1 L of water.

mole The amount of any substance that contains the same number of particles as there are atoms in exactly 12 g of carbon.

molecular biology A field of study spawned largely by genetic technology that allows researchers to study the structure and function of the molecules of life.

molecular clock A method for estimating evolutionary time; based on the observation that neutral mutations occur at a relatively constant rate.

molecular evolution The process of evolution at the level of genes and proteins.

molecular formula A representation of a molecule that consists of the chemical symbols for all of the atoms present and subscripts that indicate how many of those atoms are present.

molecular homologies Similarities at the molecular level that indicate that living species evolved from a common ancestor or interrelated group of ancestors.

molecular mass The sum of the atomic masses of all atoms in a molecule.

molecular systematics A field of study that involves the analysis of genetic data, such as DNA and amino acid sequences, to identify and study genetic homologies and construct phylogenetic trees.

molecule Two or more atoms that are connected by chemical bonds.

monoclonal antibodies Antibodies of a specific type that are derived from a single clone of cells.

monocots One of the two largest lineages of flowering plants in which the embryo possesses a single seed leaf.

monocular vision A type of vision in animals that have eyes on the sides of the head; the animal sees a wide area at one time, though depth perception is reduced.

monocyte A type of phagocyte that circulates in the blood for only a few days, after which it enters an organ or tissue and develops into a macrophage.

monoecious Refers to plants that produce carpellate and staminate flowers on the same plant.

monogamy A mating system in which each individual mates exclusively with one partner over at least a single breeding cycle.

monohybrid The F_1 offspring, also called single-trait hybrids, of true-breeding parents that differ with regard to a single character.

monomer An organic molecule that can be used to form a larger molecule (polymer) consisting of many repeating units of the monomer.

monomorphic gene A gene that exists predominantly as a single allele in a population.

monophagous The term used to describe parasites that feed on one or a few closely related species.

monophyletic group A group of species, a taxon, that is a clade.

monosaccharide A simple sugar, such as a pentose or hexose.

monotreme A member of the mammalian order Monotremata, which consists of five species found in Australia and New Guinea: the duck-billed platypus and four species of echidna.

morphogen A molecule that imparts positional information and promotes developmental changes at the cellular level.

morphology The structure or form of a body part or an entire organism.

morula An early stage in a mammalian embryo in which physical contact between cells is maximized by compaction.

mosaic An individual with somatic regions that are genetically different from each other.

mosses A phylum of bryophytes; formally called Bryophyta.

motility The ability of a cell to move or change position within its environment.

motor end plate The region of a skeletal muscle cell that lies beneath an axon terminal at the neuromuscular junction.

motor neuron A neuron that sends signals away from the central nervous system and elicits some type of response from a gland, muscle or other structure.

motor protein   A type of cellular protein that uses ATP as a source of energy to promote movement; consists of three domains called the head, hinge, and tail.

movement corridor   Thin strips of habitat that may permit the movement of individuals between larger habitat patches.

mRNA   *See* messenger RNA.

Müllerian mimicry   A type of mimicry in which two or more noxious species converge to look the same, thus reinforcing the basic distasteful design.

multicellular   Describes an organism consisting of more than one cell, particularly when cell-to-cell adherence and signaling processes and cellular specialization can be demonstrated.

multiple alleles   The phenomenon in which a gene has three or more alleles in a natural population.

multiple sclerosis (MS)   A disease in which the patient's own body attacks and destroys myelin as if it were a foreign substance; impairs the function of myelinated neurons that control movement, speech, memory, and emotion.

multipotent   Refers to a stem cell that can differentiate into several cell types, but far fewer than a pluripotent cell can.

muscle fiber   Individual cell within a muscle.

muscle tissue   Bundles of muscle fibers (cells) that are specialized to contract when stimulated and thus generate a force that facilitates movement or exerts pressure .

muscular dystrophy   A group of diseases associated with progressive degeneration of skeletal and cardiac muscle fibers.

mutagen   An agent known to cause mutation.

mutant allele   An allele that has been altered by mutation.

mutation   A heritable change in the genetic material of an organism.

mutation   A heritable change in the genetic material.

mutualism   A symbiotic interaction in which both species benefit.

mycelium   A fungal body composed of microscopic branched filaments known as hyphae.

mycorrhizae (singular, **mycorrhiza**)   Associations between the hyphae of certain fungi and the roots of seed plants.

myelin sheath   In the nervous system, an insulating layer made up of specialized glial cells wrapped around the axons.

myocardial infarction (MI)   The death of cardiac muscle cells, which can occur if a region of the heart is deprived of blood for an extended time.

myofibril   Rodlike collection of myofilaments within a muscle fiber (cell); contains thick and thin filaments.

myoglobin   An oxygen-binding protein that provides an intracellular reservoir of oxygen for muscle fibers.

myosin   A motor protein found abundantly in muscle cells and also in other cell types.

N

NAD⁺   Nicotinamide adenine dinucleotide; an organic molecule that functions as an energy intermediate. It combines with two electrons and H⁺ to form NADH.

NADPH   Nicotinamide adenine dinucleotide phosphate; an energy intermediate that provides the energy and electrons to drive the Calvin cycle during photosynthesis.

natural killer (NK) cell   A type of leukocyte that participates in both innate and acquired immunity; recognizes general features on the surface of cancer cells or any virus-infected cells.

natural selection   The process that eliminates those individuals that are less likely to survive and reproduce in a particular environment, while allowing other individuals with traits that confer greater reproductive success to increase in numbers.

nauplius   The first larval stage in a crustacean.

navigation   A mechanism of migration that involves the ability not only to follow a compass bearing but also to set or adjust it.

negative control   Transcriptional regulation by repressor proteins.

negative feedback loop   A homeostatic mechanism in animals in which a change in the variable being regulated brings about responses that move the variable in the opposite direction.

negative frequency-dependent selection   A pattern of natural selection in which the fitness of a genotype decreases when its frequency becomes higher; the result is balanced polymorphism.

negative pressure filling   The process by which reptiles, birds, and mammals ventilate their lungs.

nekton   Free-swimming animals in the open ocean that can swim against currents to locate food.

nematocyst   In a cnidarian, a powerful capsule with an inverted coiled and barbed thread that functions to immobilize small prey.

nephron   One of several million single-cell-thick tubules that are the functional units of the mammalian kidney.

Nernst equation   The formula that gives the equilibrium potential for an ion at any given concentration gradient: $E = 60$ mV $\log_{10}([X_{\text{extracellular}}]/[X_{\text{intracellular}}])$.

nerve net   Interconnected neurons with no central control organ.

nerve   A structure found in the peripheral nervous system that is composed of multiple myelinated axons bound by connective tissue; carries information to or from the central nervous system.

nervous system   Coordinated circuits of cells that sense internal and environmental changes and transmit signals that enable an animal to respond in an appropriate way.

nervous tissue   Networks of cells (neurons) that receive, generate, and conduct electrical signals throughout an animal's body.

net primary production (NPP)   Gross primary production minus the energy lost in plant cellular respiration.

net reproductive rate   The population growth rate per generation.

neural crest   In vertebrates, a group of embryonic cells derived from ectoderm that disperse throughout the embryo and contribute to the development of the skeleton and other structures, including peripheral nerves.

neural tube   In chordates, a structure formed from ectoderm located dorsal to the notochord; all neurons and their supporting cells in the central nervous system originate from neural precursor cells derived from the neural tube.

neurogenesis   The production of new neurons by cell division.

neurohormone   A hormone made in and secreted by neurons whose cell bodies are in the hypothalamus.

neuromodulator   Another term for a neuropeptide, which is a neurotransmitter that can alter or modulate the response of a postsynaptic neuron to other neurotransmitters.

neuromuscular junction   The contact point between an axon terminal of a motor neuron and a skeletal or cardiac muscle fiber.

neuron   A highly specialized cell found in nervous systems of animals that communicates with other cells by electrical or chemical signals.

neuroparasitology   The study of how parasites control the nervous systems of their hosts.

neuroscience   The scientific study of nervous systems.

neurulation   The embryological process responsible for initiating central nervous system formation.

neutral theory of evolution   Theory proposing that most genetic variation in a population is due to the accumulation of neutral mutations that have attained high frequencies in the population via genetic drift.

neutral variation   Changes in genes and proteins that result from genetic drift and do not have an effect on reproductive success.

neutron   A neutral particle found in the nucleus of an atom.

neutrophil   A phagocyte that is the most abundant type of leukocyte; neutrophils engulf bacteria by endocytosis.

niche   The unique set of habitat resources a species requires as well as its effect on the ecosystem.

nitrification   The conversion by soil bacteria of ammonia (NH_3) or ammonium (NH_4^+) to nitrate (NO_3^-), a form of nitrogen commonly used by plants.

nitrogen fixation   A specialized metabolic process in which certain prokaryotes use the enzyme nitrogenase to convert inert atmospheric nitrogen gas (N_2) into ammonia (NH_3); also, the industrial process by which humans produce NH_3 fertilizer from N_2.

nitrogenase   An enzyme used in the biological process of fixing nitrogen.

nitrogen-limitation hypothesis   The proposal that organisms select food based on its nitrogen content.

nociceptor   A sensory receptor in animals that responds to extreme heat, cold, and pressure, as well as to certain molecules such as acids; also known as a pain receptor.

Nod factor   Nodulation factor; a substance produced by nitrogen-fixing bacteria in response to flavonoids secreted from the roots of potential host plants. Nod factors bind to receptors in plant root membranes, starting a process that allows the bacteria to invade roots.

node   1. The region of a plant stem from which one or more leaves, branches, or buds emerge. 2. The branch points in a phylogenetic tree.

nodes of Ranvier   Exposed areas along the axons of myelinated neurons that contain many voltage-gated Na^+ channels and are the sites of regeneration of action potentials.

nodule   A small swelling on a plant root that contains nitrogen-fixing bacteria.

nodulin   One of several plant proteins that foster root nodule development.

non-coding RNA (ncRNA)   An RNA molecule that does not encode the amino acid sequence of a polypeptide.

noncompetitive inhibitor   A molecule that binds noncovalently to an enzyme at a location that is outside the active site and inhibits the enzyme's function.

non-Darwinian evolution   The idea that much of the modern variation in gene sequences is explained by neutral variation rather than adaptive variation.

nondisjunction   An event in which the chromosomes do not separate properly during cell division.

nonpolar covalent bond   A strong bond formed between two atoms of similar electronegativities in which electrons are shared between the atoms.

nonrandom mating   The phenomenon that occurs when individuals choose their mates based on their genotypes or phenotypes.

nonrecombinant   An offspring whose combination of traits has not changed from the true-breeding parental generation.

nonsense mutation   A mutation that changes a normal codon into a stop codon; this causes translation to be terminated earlier than expected, producing a truncated polypeptide.

phenotype The characteristics of an organism that are the result of the expression of its genes.

pheromone A powerful chemical attractant used to manipulate the behavior of others.

phloem loading The process of conveying sugars to sieve-tube elements for long-distance transport.

phloem A specialized conducting tissue in a plant's stem.

phoresy A form of commensalism in which individuals of one species use individuals of a second species for transportation.

phosphodiester linkage Refers to a double linkage (two phosphoester bonds) that holds together adjacent nucleotides in DNA and RNA strands.

phosphodiesterase An enzyme that breaks a bond in cAMP to form AMP.

phospholipid bilayer The basic framework of a biological membrane, consisting of two layers of phospholipids.

phospholipid A type of lipid that is similar in structure to a triglyceride, but with the third hydroxyl group of glycerol linked to a phosphate group instead of a fatty acid; a key component of biological membranes.

phosphorylation The attachment of a phosphate to a molecule.

photic zone A fairly narrow zone close to the surface of an aquatic environment, where light is sufficient to allow photosynthesis to occur.

photoautotroph An organism that uses the energy from light to make organic molecules from inorganic sources.

photoheterotroph An organism that is able to use light energy to generate ATP but must take in organic compounds from the environment as a source of carbon.

photon One of the discrete particles that make up light. A photon is massless and travels in a wavelike pattern.

photoperiodism A plant's ability to measure and respond to the amount of light and day length; used as a way of detecting seasonal change.

photophosphorylation The process by which the light reactions of photosynthesis produce ATP.

photopsin Any of several types of visual pigments in the cone cells of the vertebrate eye.

photoreceptor A specialized sensory receptor in an animal that responds to visible light energy; in plants, molecules that respond to light.

photorespiration The metabolic process occurring in C_3 plants when the enzyme rubisco combines with O_2 instead of CO_2 and produces only one molecule of 3PG instead of two, thereby reducing photosynthetic efficiency.

photosynthesis The process whereby light energy is captured by plant, algal, or photosynthetic bacterial cells and is used to synthesize organic molecules from CO_2 and H_2O (or H_2S).

photosystem I (PSI) A distinct complex of proteins and pigment molecules in chloroplasts that absorbs light during the light reactions of photosynthesis.

photosystem II (PSII) A distinct complex of proteins and pigment molecules in chloroplasts that absorbs light and also generates oxygen from water during the light reactions of photosynthesis.

phototropin The main blue-light sensor involved in positive phototropism in plants.

phototropism The tendency of a plant to grow toward a light source.

phylogenetic tree A diagram that describes the evolutionary relationships among various species, based on the information available to and gathered by systematists.

phylogeny The evolutionary history of a species or group of species.

phylum (plural, **phyla**) In taxonomy, a subdivision of a kingdom.

physical mutagen A physical agent, such as ultraviolet light, that causes mutations.

physical systems Physical environments, such as oceans, ice, fresh waters, and soils, that serve as habitats for microbiomes.

physiological ecology A subdiscipline of organismal ecology that investigates how organisms are physiologically adapted to their environment and how the environment impacts the distribution of species.

physiology The study of the functions of living things.

phytochrome A red-light and far-red-light receptor in plants.

phytoplankton Microscopic photosynthetic protists that float in water or actively move through it.

pigment A molecule that can absorb light energy.

pili (singular, **pilus**) Threadlike surface appendages that allow bacteria to attach to each other during conjugation or to move across surfaces.

piloting A mechanism of migration in which an animal moves from one familiar landmark to the next.

pinnate A type of leaf vein pattern in which veins appear feather-like.

pinocytosis A type of endocytosis that involves the formation of membrane vesicles from the plasma membrane as a way for cells to internalize the extracellular fluid.

pistil A flower structure that may consist of a single carpel or multiple, fused carpels and is differentiated into stigma, style, and ovary.

pit A thin-walled circular area in a plant cell wall where secondary wall materials such as lignin are absent and through which water moves.

pituitary giant A person who has a tumor of the GH-secreting cells of the anterior pituitary gland and thus produces excess GH during childhood and, if untreated, during adulthood; the person can grow very tall before growth ceases after puberty.

pituitary gland A multilobed endocrine gland sitting directly below the hypothalamus of the brain.

placenta A structure in humans and other eutherian mammals that connects the developing young to the mother's uterine wall and allows the transfer of nutrients and gases.

placental transfer tissues In plants, nutritive tissues that aid in the transfer of nutrients from maternal parent to embryo.

plant tissue culture A laboratory process to produce thousands of identical plants having the same desirable characteristics.

plant A multicellular eukaryotic organism that is usually photosynthetic (having plastids), primarily lives on land, and has cells with a cell wall containing cellulose.

Plantae A eukaryotic kingdom of the domain Eukarya.

plaques 1. Deposits of lipids, fibrous tissue, and smooth muscle cells that may develop inside arterial walls. 2. A bacterial biofilm that may form on the surfaces of teeth.

plasma cell A cell that synthesizes and secretes antibodies.

plasma membrane The biological membrane that separates the internal contents of a cell from its external environment.

plasma The fluid part of blood that contains water and dissolved solutes.

plasmid A small circular piece of DNA that exists separately from the bacterial chromosome in many strains of bacteria; plasmids are also found in some eukaryotic cells, such as yeast, and can be used as vectors in cloning experiments.

plasmodesma (plural, **plasmodesmata**) A membrane-lined, ER-containing channel that connects the cytoplasm of adjacent plant cells.

plasmogamy The fusion of the cytoplasm between two gametes.

plasmolysis The shrinkage of algal or plant cytoplasm that occurs when water leaves the cell by osmosis,

with the result that the plasma membrane no longer presses on the cell wall.

plastid A general name given to organelles found in plant and algal cells that are bound by two or more membranes and contain DNA and large amounts of either chlorophyll (in chloroplasts), carotenoids (in chromoplasts), or starch (in amyloplasts).

platelets Cell fragments in the blood of mammals that play a crucial role in the formation of blood clots.

pleiotropy The phenomenon in which a mutation in a single gene can have multiple effects on an individual's phenotype.

pleural sac A double layer of thin, moist connective tissue that encases each lung.

pluripotent Refers to the ability of embryonic stem cells to differentiate into almost every cell type of the body.

point mutation A mutation that affects only a single base pair within DNA or that involves the addition or deletion of a single base pair to a DNA sequence.

polar covalent bond A covalent bond between two atoms that have different electronegativities; the shared electrons are closer to the nucleus of the atom of higher electronegativity than to the nucleus of the atom of lower electronegativity. This distribution of the shared electrons around the atoms creates a polarity, or difference in electric charge, across the molecule.

polar transport The process whereby auxin flows primarily downward in shoots.

pole A structure of the spindle apparatus defined by each centrosome.

pollen grain The immature male gametophyte of a seed plant.

pollen tube In seed plants, a long, thin tube produced by a pollen grain that delivers sperm to the ovule.

pollen In seed plants, tiny male gametophytes enclosed by sporopollenin-containing microspore walls.

pollination syndromes The pattern of coevolved traits between particular types of flowers and their specific pollinators.

pollination The process in which pollen grains are transported to an angiosperm flower or a gymnosperm cone primarily by means of wind or animal pollinators.

pollinator An animal that carries pollen between angiosperm flowers or cones of gymnosperms.

poly A tail A string of adenine nucleotides at the 3′ end of most mature mRNAs in eukaryotes.

polyandry A mating system in which one female mates with several males, but males mate with only one female.

polycistronic mRNA An mRNA that contains the coding sequences for two or more protein-encoding genes.

polygenic Refers to a trait for which several or many genes contribute to the outcome.

polygyny A mating system in which one male mates with several females in a single breeding season, but females mate with only one male.

polymer A large molecule formed by linking many smaller molecules called monomers.

polymerase chain reaction (PCR) A technique to make many copies of a gene in vitro; primers are used that flank the region of DNA to be amplified.

polymorphic gene A gene that commonly exists as two or more alleles in a population.

polymorphism The presence of two or more variations of a character (trait) within a population.

polyp A type of cnidarian body form that is sessile and occurs mouth up.

polypeptide A molecule consisting of a linear sequence of amino acids; the term denotes structure.

polyphagous Parasites that feed on many host species.

polyphyletic group A group of species that consists of members of several evolutionary lines and does not include the most recent common ancestor of the included lineages.

polyploid Refers to an organism or cell that has three or more sets of chromosomes.

polyploidy The condition in which a cell or organism has three or more sets of chromosomes.

polysaccharide A long carbohydrate polymer formed of many monosaccharides linked together.

polysome The complex of a single mRNA and multiple ribosomes.

pons The part of the vertebrate hindbrain that, along with the cerebellum, has an integrative motor function; it also plays a role in regulating breathing.

population density The number of organisms of a given species in a given unit area or volume.

population ecology The study of how populations grow and what factors promote or limit growth.

population genetics The study of genes and genotypes in a population.

population A group of individuals of the same species that occupy the same environment and (for sexually reproducing organisms) can interbreed with one another.

portal vein A vein that not only collects blood from capillaries—like all veins—but also forms another set of capillaries, as opposed to returning the blood directly to the heart.

positional information Information regarding a cell's location relative to other cells that is conveyed by morphogens and cell-to-cell contacts.

positive control Transcriptional regulation by activator proteins.

positive feedback loop In animals, a mechanism that accelerates or amplifies a process, leading to what is sometimes called an explosive system.

postabsorptive state One of two alternating phases in the utilization of nutrients; occurs when the gastrointestinal tract is empty of nutrients and the body's own stores must supply energy. The other phase is the absorptive state.

postanal tail A defining characteristic of all chordate embryos; a tail of variable length that extends posterior to the anal opening.

posterior Refers to the rear (tail) end of an animal.

postsynaptic cell The cell that receives the electrical or chemical signal sent from a neuron.

post-translational sorting The uptake of proteins into the nucleus, mitochondria, chloroplasts, or peroxisomes that occurs after the protein is completely made in the cytosol (that is, completely translated).

postzygotic isolating mechanism A mechanism that prevents interbreeding by blocking the development of a viable and fertile individual after fertilization has taken place.

potential energy The energy that a substance possesses due to its structure or location.

power stroke In muscle, a conformation change in the myosin cross-bridge that results in binding between myosin and actin and the movement of the actin filament.

prebiotic soup The medium formed by the slow accumulation of organic molecules in the early oceans over a long period of time prior to the existence of life.

predation An interaction in which the action of a predator results in the death of its prey.

prediction An expected outcome based on a hypothesis that can be shown to be correct or incorrect through observation or experimentation.

pregnancy The time during which a developing embryo or fetus grows within the uterus of the mother; also known as gestation.

preinitiation complex The assembled structure consisting of RNA polymerase II and transcription factors (GTFs) at the TATA box prior to transcription of eukaryotic protein-encoding genes.

pre-mRNA In eukaryotes, the mRNA transcript before any biochemical modifications are made to it.

pressure potential The component of water potential due to hydrostatic pressure.

pressure-flow hypothesis Explains sugar translocation in plants as a process driven by differences in turgor pressure between cells of a sugar source, where sugar is produced, and cells of a sugar sink, where sugar is consumed.

presynaptic cell The neuron that sends an electrical or chemical signal to another cell.

prezygotic isolating mechanism A mechanism that blocks interbreeding by preventing the formation of a zygote.

primary active transport A type of transport that involves pumps that directly use energy to transport a solute against a gradient.

primary cell wall In plants, a relatively thin and flexible cell wall that is synthesized first between two newly made daughter cells.

primary consumer An organism that obtains its food by eating primary producers; also called a herbivore.

primary electron acceptor The molecule to which a high-energy electron from an excited pigment molecule such as P680* is transferred during photosynthesis.

primary endosymbiosis The process by which a eukaryotic host cell acquires prokaryotic endosymbionts. Mitochondria and the plastids of green and red algae are examples of organelles that originated via primary endosymbiosis.

primary growth Plant growth that occurs from primary meristems and produces primary tissues and organs of diverse types.

primary immune response The immune response to an initial exposure to an antigen.

primary meristem A meristematic tissue that increases plant length and produces new organs.

primary oocyte In animals, a cell that undergoes meiosis to begin the process of egg production.

primary plastid A plastid that originated from a prokaryote as the result of primary endosymbiosis.

primary producers Autotrophs such as plants, algae, and photosynthetic bacteria that use sunlight and form the basis of the food chain.

primary production Production by autotrophs, normally green plants.

primary spermatocyte In animals, a cell that undergoes meiosis to begin the process of sperm production.

primary structure The linear sequence of amino acids of a polypeptide; one of four levels of protein structure.

primary succession Succession on newly exposed sites that were not previously occupied by soil and vegetation.

primary vascular tissue Plant tissue composed of xylem and phloem; a conducting tissue of nonwoody plants.

principle of parsimony The concept that the preferred hypothesis is the one that is the simplest.

principle of species individuality A view of the nature of a community in which each species is distributed according to its physiological needs and population dynamics; most communities intergrade continuously, and competition does not create distinct vegetational zones.

prion An infectious protein that causes disease by inducing the abnormal folding of other protein molecules.

probability The chance that an event will have a particular outcome.

probiotic treatment The introduction of one or more microbial strains into the microbiome of a host organism, usually to improve health.

proboscis The coiled tongue of a butterfly or moth, which can be uncoiled, enabling the insect to drink nectar from flowers.

processivity The characteristic of DNA polymerase that keeps it from falling off the template stand as it is synthesizing a new daughter strand.

producer An organism that synthesizes the organic compounds used by other organisms for food.

product rule The probability that two or more independent events will occur is equal to the product of their individual probabilities.

product The end result of a chemical reaction.

production efficiency The percentage of energy assimilated by an organism that becomes incorporated into new biomass.

productivity hypothesis The proposal that greater production by plants results in greater overall species richness.

progesterone A hormone secreted by the female ovaries that plays a key role in pregnancy.

progymnosperms An extinct group of plants having wood but not seeds, which evolved before the gymnosperms.

prokaryotic cell Refers to a cell lacking a membrane-enclosed nucleus and cell compartmentalization; includes the cells from all members of the domains Bacteria and Archaea.

prokaryotic Refers to organisms having cells lacking a membrane-enclosed nucleus and cell compartmentalization; includes all members of the domains Bacteria and Archaea.

prometaphase The phase of mitosis during which the nuclear envelope completely fragments into vesicles and the mitotic spindle is fully formed.

promiscuous In ecology, a term for animals that have many different sexual mates.

promoter A sequence of DNA within a gene that controls when and where transcription begins.

proofreading The ability of DNA polymerase to identify a mismatched nucleotide and remove it from the daughter strand.

prophage The DNA of a phage that has become integrated into a bacterial chromosome.

prophase The phase of mitosis during which the chromosomes condense and the nuclear membrane begins to vesiculate.

proplastid A type of unspecialized structure from which a plastid is derived.

prosthetic group A small molecule that is permanently attached to the surface of an enzyme and aids in the enzyme's function.

protease An enzyme that cuts proteins into smaller polypeptides.

proteasome A protein complex that provides the primary pathway for protein degradation in archaea and eukaryotic cells.

protein kinase cascade The sequential activation of multiple protein kinases.

protein kinase An enzyme that transfers a phosphate group from ATP to a specific amino acid in a protein.

protein phosphatase An enzyme responsible for removing phosphate groups from proteins.

protein subunit An individual polypeptide within a functional protein; most functional proteins are composed of two or more polypeptides.

protein A functional unit composed of one or more polypeptides. Each polypeptide is composed of a linear sequence of amino acids.

protein-encoding gene A gene that serves as a template to make an mRNA molecule that contains the information to specify a polypeptide with a particular

sclerenchyma A rigid plant ground tissue composed of tough-walled fibers and sclereids.

sea level The average level for the surface of one or more of Earth's oceans.

second messengers Small molecules or ions that relay signals inside the cell after an extracellular signaling molecule (a first messenger) has activated a cell surface receptor.

secondary active transport A type of membrane transport that involves the utilization of a pre-existing gradient to drive the active transport of another solute.

secondary cell wall A thick rigid plant cell wall that is synthesized and deposited between the plasma membrane and the primary cell wall after a plant cell matures and has stopped increasing in size.

secondary consumer An organism that eats primary consumers; also called a carnivore.

secondary endosymbiosis A process that occurs when a eukaryotic host cell acquires a eukaryotic endosymbiont having a primary plastid.

secondary growth Plant growth that occurs from secondary meristems and increases the girth of woody plant stems and roots.

secondary immune response An immediate and heightened production of additional specific antibodies against the particular antigen that previously elicited a primary immune response.

secondary meristem A meristem in woody plants forming a ring of actively dividing cells that encircle the stem.

secondary metabolite Molecules that are produced by secondary metabolism.

secondary oocyte In animals, the large haploid cell that is produced when a primary oocyte completes meiosis I during oogenesis.

secondary phloem The inner bark of a woody plant.

secondary plastid A plastid that has originated by the endosymbiotic incorporation of a eukaryotic cell containing a primary plastid into a eukaryotic host cell.

secondary production The measure of production of heterotrophs and decomposers.

secondary spermatocytes In animals, the haploid cells produced when a primary spermatocyte undergoes meiosis I during spermatogenesis.

secondary structure The bending or twisting of a region of a protein into an α helix or β sheet; one of four levels of protein structure.

secondary succession Succession on a site that has previously supported life but has undergone a disturbance.

secondary xylem In plants, a type of secondary vascular tissue that is also known as wood.

secretin A hormone released by cells of the small intestine in vertebrates; stimulates release of bicarbonate ions from the pancreas into the small intestine.

secretion 1. The export of a substance from a cell. 2. In the production of urine, the process in which some solutes are actively transported into the tubules of the excretory organ; this supplements the amount of a solute that would normally be removed by filtration alone.

secretory pathway A pathway for the movement of larger substances, such as carbohydrates and proteins, from the ER to the outside of a cell.

secretory vesicle A membrane vesicle carrying different types of materials that fuses with the cell's plasma membrane to release the contents extracellularly.

seed coat A hard, tough covering that develops from the ovule's integuments and protects a plant embryo.

seed plant The informal name for gymnosperms and angiosperms.

seed A reproductive structure having specialized tissues that enclose a plant embryo; produced by gymnosperms and flowering plants, usually as the result of sexual reproduction.

segmentation gene A gene that controls the segmentation pattern of an animal embryo.

segmentation The organization of an animal's body into clearly defined regions.

segment-polarity gene A type of segmentation gene; a mutation in this gene causes portions of segments to be missing and cause adjacent regions to become mirror images of each other.

selectable marker A gene whose presence can allow organisms (such as bacteria) to grow under a certain set of conditions. For example, an antibiotic-resistance gene is a selectable marker that allows bacteria to grow in the presence of the antibiotic.

selective breeding Programs and procedures designed to modify traits in domesticated species.

selective permeability The property of membranes that allows the passage of certain ions or molecules but not others.

selective serotonin reuptake inhibitors (SSRIs) Drugs used to treat major depressive disorder that act by increasing concentrations of serotonin in the brain.

self-compatibility (SC) The reproductive state of plants that can serve as both mother and father to their progeny.

self-fertilization Fertilization that involves the union of a female gamete and male gamete from the same individual.

self-incompatibility (SI) Reproductive state of a plant that prevents the germination of pollen that is genetically too similar to its pistil.

self-pollination The process in which pollen from the anthers of a flower is transferred to the stigma of the same flower or between flowers of the same plant.

self-splicing The phenomenon in which an rRNA or a tRNA catalyzes the removal of its own intron(s).

semelparity A reproductive pattern in which organisms produce all of their offspring in a single reproductive event.

semen A mixture containing fluid and sperm that is released during ejaculation.

semicircular canal Structures of the vertebrate ear that can detect a range of motions of the head.

semiconservative mechanism The correct model for DNA replication; double-stranded DNA is half conserved following replication, resulting in new double-stranded DNA containing one parental strand and one daughter strand.

semifluid A property of biological membranes in which movement of membrane components occurs only in two dimensions.

semilunar valve One-way valve into the aorta or pulmonary trunk through which blood is pumped from the left or right ventricle, respectively.

seminiferous tubule A tightly packed tubule in the testis, where spermatogenesis takes place.

sense A system in an animal that consists of specialized cells that respond to a specific type of chemical or physical stimulus and send signals to the central nervous system, where the signals are received and interpreted.

sensor A structure such as a sensory receptor or a nucleus in the brain that detects a signal in a homeostatic control system.

sensory neuron A neuron that detects or senses information from the outside world, such as light, sound, touch, and heat; sensory neurons also detect internal body conditions such as blood pressure and body temperature.

sensory receptor In animals, a specialized cell whose function is to receive sensory inputs.

sensory transduction The process by which incoming stimuli are converted into neural signals.

sepal A flower structure that is often green and is part of the outer layer of a bud.

septum (plural, septa) A cross wall; examples include the cross walls that divide the hyphae of most fungi into many small cells and the structure that separates the old and new chambers of a nautilus.

set point The normal value for a controlled variable, such as blood pressure, in an animal.

setae Chitinous bristles in the integument of many invertebrates.

sex chromosomes A distinctive pair of chromosomes that are different in males and females of some species and determine the sex of an individual.

sex pili Hairlike structures made by bacterial F^+ cells that bind specifically to F^- cells.

sex-linked gene A gene that is found on one sex chromosome but not on the other.

sexual dimorphism A pronounced difference in the morphologies of the two sexes within a species.

sexual reproduction A process in which two haploid gametes unite in a fertilization event to produce a cell called a zygote.

sexual selection A type of natural selection that is directed at certain traits of sexually reproducing species that make it more likely for individuals to find or choose a mate and/or engage in successful reproduction.

Shannon diversity index (*HS*) A means of measuring the diversity of a community, using the formula $H_S = -\Sigma p_i \ln p_i$.

shared derived character A character that is shared by two or more species or taxa and originated in their most recent common ancestor.

shared primitive character A character that is shared by two or more different taxa and inherited from ancestors older than their last common ancestor.

shattering The process by which ears of wild grain crops break apart and disperse seeds.

shell A tough, protective covering on an amniotic egg that is impermeable to water and prevents the embryo from drying out.

shivering thermogenesis Rapid muscle contractions in an animal, without any locomotion, in order to raise body temperature.

shock A condition in which the vertebrate circulatory system cannot provide sufficient delivery of blood containing oxygen and nutrients to the vital organs of the body, resulting in cell death and decreased function of those organs.

shoot apical meristem (SAM) The region of rapidly dividing cells at the tip of a plant shoot.

shoot system The collection of plant organs produced by shoot apical meristems.

shoot The portion of a plant consisting of stems and leaves.

short stature A condition characterized by stunted growth; formerly called pituitary dwarfism.

short-day plant A plant that flowers only when the night length is longer than a defined period.

shotgun DNA sequencing A strategy for sequencing an entire genome by randomly sequencing many different DNA fragments.

sickle cell disease A disease due to a mutation in a hemoglobin gene that results in sickle-shaped red blood cells that are less able to move smoothly through capillaries and can block blood flow, resulting in pain and cell death of the surrounding tissue.

sieve plate pore One of many perforations in a plant's sieve plate.

sieve plate The perforated end wall of a mature sieve-tube element.

sieve-tube elements A component of the phloem tissues of flowering plants; thin-walled cells arranged end to end to form pipes.

sigma factor   A protein that recognizes the promoter in a bacterial gene and binds RNA polymerase to the promoter.

sign stimulus   In animals, a trigger that initiates a fixed action pattern of behavior.

signal recognition particle (SRP)   A protein-RNA complex that recognizes the ER signal sequence of a polypeptide, pauses translation, and directs the ribosome to the ER to complete translation.

signal transduction pathway   A group of proteins that convert an initial signal to a different signal inside a cell.

signal   Regarding cell communication, an agent that influences the properties of cells.

silencer   A regulatory element in eukaryotes that prevents transcription of a given gene when bound by a repressor protein.

silent mutation   A gene mutation that does not alter the amino acid sequence of the polypeptide, even though the base sequence has changed.

simple diffusion   When a substance moves across a membrane from a region of high concentration to a region of lower concentration by passing directly through the phospholipid bilayer.

simple Mendelian inheritance   The inheritance pattern of traits affected by a single gene that is found in two variants, one of which is completely dominant over the other.

simple translocation   A type of mutation in which a single piece of chromosome is attached to another chromosome.

single-factor cross   A cross in which an experimenter follows the variants of only one character.

single-lens eye   Type of eye found in vertebrates and some invertebrates that has only one lens, as opposed to compound eyes with many lenses.

single-nucleotide polymorphism (SNP)   A type of genetic variation in a population in which a particular gene sequence varies at a single nucleotide.

single-strand binding protein   A protein that binds to both of the single strands of parental DNA and prevents them from re-forming a double helix during DNA replication.

sinoatrial (SA) node   A collection of modified cardiac cells in the right atrium of most vertebrates that spontaneously and rhythmically generates action potentials that spread across the entire atria; also known as the pacemaker of the heart.

sister chromatids   The two duplicated chromatids that are still joined to each other after DNA replication.

skeletal muscle   A type of muscle tissue that is attached by tendons to bones in vertebrates and to the exoskeleton of invertebrates.

skeleton   A structure that serves one or more functions related to support, protection, and locomotion.

sliding filament mechanism   The process by which a muscle fiber shortens during muscle contraction.

SLOSS debate   In conservation biology, the debate over whether it is preferable to protect one single, large preserve or several smaller ones.

slow fiber   A skeletal muscle fiber containing myosin with low ATPase activity.

slow-oxidative fiber   A skeletal muscle fiber that has a low rate of myosin ATPase activity but has the ability to make large amounts of ATP; used for prolonged, regular movement.

small effector molecule   A molecule that affects gene transcription by binding to a regulatory transcription factor, causing a conformational change in that protein.

small intestine   In vertebrates, the part of the alimentary canal that leads from the stomach to the large intestine (or to the anus or cloaca in animals that lack a large intestine) and that carries out nearly all digestion of food and absorption of food nutrients and water.

small-interfering RNAs (siRNAs)   RNA molecules that are usually from outside sources and are processed to a small size (22 nucleotides). They are usually a perfect match to pre-existing mRNAs and cause their degradation.

smooth endoplasmic reticulum (smooth ER)   The part of the ER whose outer surface is not studded with ribosomes. This region is continuous with the rough ER and functions in diverse metabolic processes such as detoxification, carbohydrate metabolism, accumulation of calcium ions (Ca^{2+}), and synthesis and modification of lipids.

smooth muscle   A type of muscle tissue that surrounds and forms part of the lining of hollow organs and tubes in vertebrate bodies; it is not under conscious control.

solute potential   The component of water potential due to the presence of solute molecules.

solute   A substance dissolved in a liquid.

solution   A liquid that contains one or more dissolved solutes.

solvent   The liquid in which a solute is dissolved.

somatic cell   The type of cell that constitutes all cells of an animal or plant body except those that give rise to gametes.

somatic embryogenesis   The production of plant embryos from body (somatic) cells.

somatic nervous system   The division of the peripheral nervous system that senses external environmental conditions and controls skeletal muscles.

sorting signal   A short amino acid sequence in a protein that directs the protein to its correct location in a cell; also known as a traffic signal.

source pool   The pool of species on the mainland that is available to colonize an island.

spatial summation   Occurs when two or more postsynaptic potentials are generated at one time along different regions of the dendrites and their depolarizations and hyperpolarizations sum together to initiate an action potential.

speciation   The formation of new species.

species concept   A way of defining the concept of a species and/or of providing an approach to distinguish one species from another

species diversity   A measure of biological diversity that incorporates both the number of species in an area and the relative distribution of individuals among species.

species interactions   The various ways in which a species can interact with other species, such as predation, competition, parasitism, mutualism, and commensalism; part of the study of population ecology.

species richness   The numbers of species in a community.

species   In taxonomy, a subdivision of a genus. Each species is a group of related organisms that share a distinctive set of attributes in nature and (for sexually reproducing species) are capable of interbreeding.

species-area effect   The relationship between the amount of available area and the number of species present.

species-area hypothesis   The proposal that larger areas contain more species than smaller ones because they can support larger populations and a greater range of habitats.

species-productivity hypothesis   The proposal that greater production by plants results in greater overall species richness.

species-time hypothesis   The proposal that temperate regions have less species-rich communities than tropical ones because they are younger.

specific heat   The amount of energy required to raise the temperature of 1 gram of a substance by 1°C.

sperm   Refers to a male gamete that is generally smaller than the female gamete (egg).

spermatids   In animals, haploid cells produced when the secondary spermatocytes undergo meiosis II; these cells eventually differentiate into sperm cells.

spermatogenesis   Gametogenesis in a male animal, resulting in the production of sperm.

spermatogonium (plural, spermatogonia)   In animals, a diploid germ cell that gives rise to the male gamete, the sperm.

spermatophytes   All of the living and extinct phyla of seed-producing plants.

spicules   Needle-like structures that are made of protein, calcium carbonate, or silica and form lattice-like skeletons in sponges, possibly helping to reduce predation.

spinal cord   In chordates, the structure that connects the brain to all areas of the body and together with the brain constitutes the central nervous system.

spinal nerve   A nerve that connects the peripheral nervous system and the spinal cord.

spiracle   One of several pairs of pores on the body surface of insects through which air enters and exits the body.

spiral cleavage   A mechanism of animal development in which the planes of cell cleavage are oblique to the axis of the embryo.

spirilli   Rigid, spiral-shaped prokaryotic cells.

spirochaetes   Flexible, spiral-shaped prokaryotic cells.

spliceosome   A complex of several subunits known as snRNPs that removes introns from eukaryotic pre-mRNA.

splicing   The process in which introns are removed from an RNA molecule, such as a pre-mRNA, and the remaining exons are connected to each other.

spongin   A tough protein that lends skeletal support to a sponge.

spongocoel   A central cavity in the body of a sponge.

spongy parenchyma   Photosynthetic ground tissue of the plant leaf mesophyll that contains rounded cells separated by abundant air spaces.

spontaneous mutation   A mutation resulting from some abnormality in a biological process.

sporangia (singular, sporangium)   Structures that produce and disperse the spores of plants, fungi, or protists.

spore   A haploid, typically single-celled reproductive structure of fungi and plants. A spore is able to grow into a new fungal mycelium or plant gametophyte in a suitable location.

sporophyte   The diploid generation of plants or multicellular protists that have a sporic life cycle; this generation produces haploid spores by the process of meiosis.

sporopollenin   A tough material found in the walls of plant spores that helps to prevent cellular damage during transport in air.

spring overturn   The mixing of lake water as ice melts and storms churn up water from the bottom.

stabilizing selection   A pattern of natural selection that favors the survival of individuals with intermediate phenotypes.

stamen   A flower organ that produces the male gametophytes, pollen.

standing crop   The total biomass in an ecosystem at any one point in time.

starch   A polysaccharide composed of repeating glucose units that is produced by the cells of plants and some algal protists.

Starling forces   The forces that influence the movement of water into and out of capillaries in animals; they are the osmotic imbalance between the plasma and the interstitial fluid and the hydrostatic pressure of the blood entering and exiting the capillary.

start codon   A three-base sequence—usually AUG—that specifies the first amino acid in a polypeptide.

statocyst   An organ of equilibrium found in many invertebrate species.

statolith   1. Tiny granules of sand or other dense objects located in a statocyst that aid equilibrium in many invertebrates. 2. In plants, a starch-heavy plastid that allows both roots and shoots to detect gravity.

stem cell   A cell that divides in such a way that one daughter cell can remain a stem cell and the other can differentiate into a specialized cell type. Stem cells supply the cells that constitute the bodies of all animals and plants.

stem   A plant organ that contains vascular tissue and produces buds, leaves, branches, and reproductive structures.

stereocilia   Deformable projections from epithelial cells called hair cells that are bent by movements of fluid or other stimuli.

stereoisomers   Isomers with identical bonding relationships, but different spatial positioning of their atoms.

sternum   The breastbone of a vertebrate.

steroid   A lipid containing four interconnected rings of carbon atoms; functions as a hormone in animals and plants.

stigma   In a flower, the topmost portion of the pistil, which receives and recognizes pollen of the appropriate species or genotype.

stomach   A saclike organ in some animals that most likely evolved as a means of storing food; it partially digests some of the macromolecules in food and regulates the rate at which its contents empty into the small intestine.

stomata (singular, stoma or stomate)   Pores on plant surfaces that can be closed to retain water or open to allow the entry of CO_2 (needed for photosynthesis) and the exit of O_2 and water vapor.

stop codon   One of three three-base sequences—UAA, UAG, and UGA—that signals the end of translation; also called a termination codon or codon.

strain   Within a given species, a lineage that has genetic differences compared to another lineage.

strand   A structure of DNA (or RNA) formed by the covalent linkage of nucleotides in a linear manner.

strepsirrhini   Smaller species of primates, including bush babies, lemurs, and pottos.

streptophyte algae   The green algae that are closely related to land plants (embryophytes).

streptophyte   Land pants (embryophytes) and their close relatives among the green algae.

stretch receptor   A type of mechanoreceptor found widely in an animal's organs and muscle tissues that can be distended.

stroke volume (SV)   The amount of blood ejected with each beat, or stroke, of the heart.

stroma   The fluid-filled region of the chloroplast between the thylakoid membrane and the inner membrane.

stromatolite   A layered calcium carbonate structure generally produced by cyanobacteria living in an aquatic environment.

strong acid   An acid that completely dissociates into ions when added to water.

structural formula   A type of chemical formula for molecules in which each covalent bond is represented by a line indicating a pair of shared electrons.

structural isomers   Isomers that contain the same atoms but in different bonding relationships.

style   In a flower, the elongate portion of the pistil through which the pollen tube grows.

stylet   A sharp, piercing organ in the mouth of nematodes and some insects.

submetacentric   Refers to a chromosome in which the centromere is off center.

subsidence zones   Areas of high pressure that are the sites of the world's tropical deserts because the subsiding air is relatively dry, having released all of its moisture over the equator.

subspecies   A subdivision of a species; this designation is used when two or more geographically restricted groups of the same species differ, but not enough to warrant their placement into separate species.

substrate   1. The reactant molecules that bind to an enzyme at the active site and participate in a chemical reaction. 2. The organic compounds such as soil or rotting wood that fungi use as food.

substrate-level phosphorylation   A method of synthesizing ATP that occurs when an enzyme directly transfers a phosphate from an organic molecule to ADP.

succession   The gradual and continuous change in species composition of a community over time.

sugar sink   The plant tissues or organs in which more sugar is consumed than is produced by photosynthesis.

sugar source   The plant tissues or organs that produce more sugar than they consume in respiration.

supergroup   One of the seven subdivisions of the domain Eukarya.

surface area-to-volume (SA/V) ratio   The ratio between a structure's surface area and the volume in which the structure is contained.

surface tension   A measure of how difficult it is to break the interface between a liquid and air.

surfactant   A mixture of proteins and amphipathic lipids produced in type II alveolar cells that prevents the collapse of the alveoli by reducing surface tension in the lungs.

survivorship curve   A graphical plot of the numbers of surviving individuals for each age class in a population.

suspensor   A short chain of cells at the base of an early angiosperm embryo that provides anchorage and nutrients.

swim bladder   A gas-filled, balloon-like structure that helps a fish remain buoyant in the water even when it is completely stationary.

symbiosis   An intimate association between two or more organisms of different species.

sympathetic division   The division of the autonomic nervous system that is responsible for rapidly activating body systems to provide immediate energy in response to danger or stress.

sympatric speciation   A form of speciation that occurs when members of a species that initially occupy the same habitat within the same range diverge into two or more different species even though there are no physical barriers to interbreeding.

sympatric   The term used to describe species occurring in the same geographic area.

symplast   All of a plant's protoplasts (the cell contents without the cell walls) and plasmodesmata.

symplastic transport   The movement of a substance from the cytosol of one cell to the cytosol of an adjacent cell via membrane-lined channels called plasmodesmata.

symplesiomorphy   *See* shared primitive character.

symporter   A type of transporter that binds two or more ions or molecules and transports them in the same direction across a membrane; also called a cotransporter.

synapomorphy   *See* shared derived character.

synapse   A junction where an axon terminal meets another neuron, a muscle cell, or a gland cell and through which an electrical or chemical signal passes.

synapsis   The process of forming a bivalent.

synaptic cleft   The extracellular space between a neuron and a receiving cell.

synaptic plasticity   A change in strength of the connection between two neurons, which occurs as a result of learning.

synergids   In the female gametophyte of a flowering plant, the two cells adjacent to the egg cell that help to import nutrients from maternal sporophyte tissues.

synthetic microbiomes   Microbiomes generated by mixing cultures of beneficial microbial species.

systematics   The study of biological diversity and evolutionary relationships among species, both extant and extinct.

systemic acquired resistance (SAR)   A whole-plant defensive response to a pathogen attack.

systemic circulation   The circuit of a double circulation in which blood is pumped from the left side of an animal's heart to the body to drop off O_2 and nutrients and pick up CO_2 and wastes. The blood then returns to the right side of the heart.

systems biology   A field of study in which researchers investigate living organisms in terms of their underlying networks—groups of structural and functional connections—rather than their individual molecular components.

systole   The second phase of the cardiac cycle, in which the ventricles contract and eject the blood through the open semilunar valves.

T

T cells   A type of lymphocyte that directly kills infected, mutated, or transplanted cells.

tagmata   Functional units composed of fused body segments.

taproot system   The root system of eudicots, consisting of one main root with many branch roots.

taste buds   Structures located in the mouth and tongue of vertebrates that contain the sensory cells, supporting cells, and associated neuronal endings that contribute to taste sensation.

TATA box   One of three features found in promoters of many protein-encoding genes in eukaryotes; the others are the transcriptional start site and regulatory elements.

taxis   A directed movement in response to a stimulus, either toward or away from the stimulus.

taxon   A group of species that are evolutionarily related to each other. In taxonomy, each species is placed into several taxons that form a hierarchy from large (domain) to small (genus).

taxonomy   The field of biology that is concerned with the theory, practice, and rules of classifying living and extinct species and also viruses.

telocentric   Refers to a chromosome in which the centromere is at the end.

telomerase   An enzyme that catalyzes the replication of the telomere.

telomere   A region at the ends of eukaryotic chromosomes where a specialized form of DNA replication occurs.

telophase   The phase of mitosis during which the chromosomes decondense and the nuclear membrane re-forms.

temperate phage   A bacteriophage that can follow either a lysogenic or a lytic cycle.

template strand   The DNA strand that is used as a template for RNA synthesis or DNA replication.

temporal lobe   One of four lobes of the cerebral cortex of human brain; necessary for language, hearing, and some types of memory.

temporal summation   Occurs when two or more postsynaptic potentials arrive at the same location in a dendrite in quick succession and their depolarizations and hyperpolarizations sum together to initiate an action potential.

tepal   A flower perianth part that cannot be distinguished by appearance as a petal or a sepal.

termination codon   *See* stop codon.

termination   The final stage of transcription, in which the RNA dissociates from the DNA, or of translation, in which the polypeptide is released from the ribosome.

terminator   A sequence of DNA within a gene that specifies the end of transcription.

territory   A fixed area in which an individual or group excludes other members of its own species, and sometimes other species, by aggressive behavior or territory marking.

tertiary consumer   An organism that feeds on secondary consumers; also called a secondary carnivore.

tertiary endosymbiosis   The acquisition by eukaryotic protist host cells of plastids from cells that possess secondary plastids.

tertiary plastid   A plastid acquired by the incorporation into a host cell of an endosymbiont having a secondary plastid.

tertiary structure   The three-dimensional shape of a single polypeptide; one of four levels of protein structure.

testable   Refers to a hypothesis that can be accepted or rejected based on experimentation.

testcross   (1) A cross to determine if an individual with a dominant phenotype is a homozygote or a heterozygote. (2) Also, a cross to determine if two different genes are linked.

testis (plural, testes)   In animals, the male gonad, where sperm are produced.

testosterone   The primary androgen in many vertebrates, including humans.

tetraploid   Refers to an organism or cell that has four sets of chromosomes.

tetrapod   A vertebrate animal having four legs or leglike appendages.

thalamus   A region of the vertebrate forebrain that plays a major role in relaying sensory information to appropriate parts of the cerebrum and, in turn, sending outputs from the cerebrum to other parts of the brain.

theory   In biology, a broad explanation of some aspect of the natural world that is substantiated by a large body of evidence. Biological theories incorporate observations, hypothesis testing, and the laws of other disciplines such as chemistry and physics. A theory makes valid predictions.

thermocline   The thin transitional zone in a lake that separates the epilimnion from the hypolimnion

thermodynamics   The study of energy interconversions.

thermoreceptor   A sensory receptor in animals that responds to cold and heat.

theropods   A group of bipedal saurischian dinosaurs.

thick filament   A section of the repeating pattern in a myofibril composed almost entirely of the motor protein myosin.

thigmotropism   Touch responses in plants.

thin filament   A section of the repeating pattern in a myofibril that contains the cytoskeletal protein actin, as well as two other proteins—troponin and tropomyosin—that play important roles in regulating contraction.

thoracic breathing   Breathing in which coordinated contractions of muscles expand the rib cage, creating a negative pressure to suck air in and then forcing it out later; used by amniotes.

thoraco-abdominal pump   In mammals, the mechanical effect of breathing movements on the return of blood from veins in the abdomen to the thorax where the

heart is located; increased depth and rate of breathing results in pressure differences between the two body compartments that favors flow of blood into the chest; also called the respiratory pump.

threatened species   Those species that are likely to become endangered in the foreseeable future.

threshold concentration   The concentration above which a morphogen exerts its effects but below which it is ineffective.

threshold potential   The membrane potential, typically around −55 to −50 mV, which is sufficient to trigger an action potential in an electrically excitable cell such as a neuron.

thylakoid lumen   The fluid-filled compartment within a thylakoid.

thylakoid membrane   A membrane within the chloroplast that forms many flattened, fluid-filled tubules that enclose a single, convoluted compartment. It contains chlorophyll and is the site where the light-dependent reactions of photosynthesis occurs.

thylakoid   A flattened, fluid-filled tubule found in cyanobacterial cells and the chloroplasts of photosynthetic protists and plants; the location of the light reactions of photosynthesis.

thymine (T)   A pyrimidine base found in DNA.

thymine dimer   A site in DNA where two adjacent thymine bases become covalently crosslinked to each other; may cause a mutation when the DNA strand is replicated.

thyroxine (T$_4$)   A weakly active thyroid hormone that contains iodine and helps regulate metabolic rate; it is converted by cells into the more active triiodothyronine (T$_3$).

tidal ventilation   A type of breathing in mammals in which the lungs are inflated with air and then the chest muscles and diaphragm relax and recoil back to their original positions as an animal exhales. During exhalation, air leaves via the same route that it entered during inhalation, and no new oxygen is delivered to the airways at that time.

tight junction   A type of junction between animal cells that forms a tight seal between adjacent cells and thereby prevents material from leaking between the cells.

tissue   A part of an animal or plant consisting of a group of cells having a similar structure and function, for example, muscle tissue.

tolerance   A mechanism for succession in which any species can start the succession, but the eventual climax community is reached in a somewhat orderly fashion; early species neither facilitate nor inhibit subsequent colonists.

Toll-like receptors (TLRs)   Receptor proteins that recognize nonspecific antigens in microbes; a key part of the innate immune response.

topsoil   The uppermost layer of a soil.

torus (plural, tori)   The nonporous, flexible central region of a conifer pit that functions like a valve.

total fertility rate   The average number of live births a female has during her lifetime.

total peripheral resistance (TPR)   The sum of all the resistance in all the arterial vessels of the systemic circulation.

totipotent   Refers to the ability of a fertilized egg to produce all of the cell types in the adult organism or the ability of unspecialized plant cells to regenerate an adult plant.

toxins   Compounds that have adverse physiological effects in living organisms; often produced by various protist and plant species.

trace element   An element that is essential for normal growth and function of living organisms but is required in extremely small quantities.

trachea   1. A sturdy tube arising from the spiracles of an insect's body; involved in respiration. 2. The name of the tube leading to the lungs of air-breathing vertebrates.

tracheal system   The respiratory system of insects, consisting of a series of finely branched air tubes called tracheae; air enters and exits the tracheae through spiracles, which are pores on the body surface.

tracheary elements   Water-conducting cells in plants that, when mature, are always dead and empty of cytosol; include tracheids and vessel elements.

tracheid   A type of dead, lignified plant cell in xylem that conducts water, along with dissolved minerals and hormones; also provides structural support.

tracheophytes   A term used to describe vascular plants.

tract   A parallel bundle of myelinated axons in the central nervous system.

traffic signal   *See* sorting signal.

trait   An identifiable characteristic; usually refers to a variant.

transcription factor   A protein that influences the ability of RNA polymerase to transcribe genes.

transcription   The process that produces an RNA copy of a gene.

transcriptional start site   The site in a eukaryotic promoter where transcription begins.

transcriptome   A collection of all the mRNA sequences produced by a single organism under defined conditions.

transduction   A type of gene transfer between bacteria in which a virus infects a bacterial cell and then a newly made virus subsequently transfers some of that cell's DNA to another bacterium.

***trans*-effect**   In both prokaryotes and eukaryotes, a form of genetic regulation that can occur even though two DNA segments are not physically adjacent. The action of the lac repressor on the *lac* operon is a *trans*-effect.

transepithelial transport   The process of moving molecules across an epithelium, such as across the intestinal cells of animals.

transfer RNA (tRNA)   An RNA that carries amino acids and is used to translate mRNA into polypeptides.

transformation   A type of gene transfer between bacteria in which a segment of DNA from the environment is taken up by a competent cell and incorporated into the bacterial chromosome.

transition state   In a chemical reaction, a state in which the original bonds have stretched to their limit; once this state is reached, the reaction can proceed to the formation of products.

transitional form   An organism that provides a link between earlier and later forms in evolution.

translation   The process of synthesizing a specific polypeptide on a ribosome.

translocation   1. A type of mutation in which one segment of a chromosome becomes attached to a different chromosome. 2. A process in plants in which phloem transports substances from a source to a sink.

transmembrane gradient   A situation in which the concentration of a solute is higher on one side of a membrane than on the other.

transmembrane protein   A protein that has one or more regions that are physically embedded in the hydrophobic region of a membrane's phospholipid bilayer.

transmembrane transport   The export of material from one cell into the intercellular space and then into an adjacent cell.

transmission electron microscopy (TEM)   A type of microscopy in which a beam of electrons is transmitted through a biological sample to form an image on a photographic plate or screen.

GLOSSARY

transpiration The process by which water evaporates from the aerial parts of plants, usually via the stomata of leaves.

transport protein A transmembrane protein that provides a passageway for the movement of ions and hydrophilic molecules across the phospholipid bilayer.

transporter A transmembrane protein that binds a solute and undergoes a conformational change to allow the movement of the solute across a membrane; also called a carrier.

transposable element (TE) A segment of DNA that can move from one site to another within a genome.

transposase An enzyme that facilitates transposition.

transposition The process in which a short segment of DNA, a transposable element, moves to a new site in a genome.

transverse tubules (T-tubules) Invaginations of the plasma membrane of skeletal muscle fibers that open to the extracellular fluid and conduct action potentials from the outer surface of the fibers to the myofibrils.

trichome A projection, often hairlike, from the epidermal tissue of a plant that offers protection from excessive light, ultraviolet radiation, extreme air temperature, or attack by herbivores.

triglyceride A molecule composed of three fatty acids linked by ester bonds to a molecule of glycerol; also known as a triacylglycerol.

triiodothyronine (T_3) A thyroid hormone that contains iodine and helps regulate metabolic rate.

triplet A group of three bases that functions as a codon.

triploblastic Having three distinct germ layers: endoderm, ectoderm, and mesoderm.

triploid Refers to an organism or cell that has three sets of chromosomes.

trochophore larva A distinct larval stage of many invertebrate phyla.

trophectoderm The outer layer of cells in a developing mammalian blastocyst; continuous with the ectoderm layer.

trophic level Each feeding level in a food chain.

trophic-level transfer efficiency The amount of energy at a trophic level that is acquired by the trophic level above and incorporated into biomass.

tropism In plants, a growth response that is dependent on a stimulus that occurs in a particular direction.

tropomyosin A rod-shaped protein that plays an important role in regulating muscle contraction.

troponin A small globular-shaped protein that plays an important role in regulating muscle contraction through its ability to bind Ca^{2+}.

trp **operon** An operon of *E. coli* that encodes enzymes required to make the amino acid tryptophan, a building block of cellular proteins.

true-breeding line A strain that continues to exhibit the same trait after several generations of self-fertilization or inbreeding.

trypsin A protease involved in the breakdown of proteins in the small intestine.

tubal ligation A means of contraception that involves the cutting and sealing of a woman's oviducts, thereby preventing movement of a fertilized egg into the uterus.

tube cell In a seed plant, one of the cells resulting from the division of a microspore; produces the pollen tube to deliver sperm to the female gametophyte.

tube feet Echinoderm structures that function in movement, gas exchange, feeding, and excretion.

tumor An abnormal overgrowth of cells.

tumor-suppressor gene A gene that when normal (that is, not mutant) encodes a protein that prevents cancer; however, when a mutation eliminates its function, cancer may occur.

tunic A nonliving structure that encloses a tunicate, made of protein and a cellulose-like material called tunicin.

turgid Refers to a plant cell whose cytosol is so full of water that the plasma membrane presses right up against the cell wall; as a result, a turgid cell is firm or swollen.

turgor pressure *See* osmotic pressure.

two-factor cross A cross in which an experimenter simultaneously follows the inheritance of two different characters.

type 1 diabetes mellitus (T1DM) A disease in which the pancreas does not produce sufficient insulin; as a result, extracellular glucose cannot cross plasma membranes, and glucose accumulates to very high concentrations in the blood.

type 2 diabetes mellitus (T2DM) A disease in which the pancreas produces sufficient insulin, but the cells of the body lose much of their ability to respond to insulin.

U

ubiquitin A small protein in eukaryotic cells that is covalently attached to an unwanted protein, which directs the protein to a proteasome for degradation.

ulcer An erosion of the wall of the alimentary canal; typically occurs in the lower esophagus, stomach, or duodenum.

ultimate cause The reason a particular behavior evolved, in terms of its effect on reproductive success.

umbrella species A species whose habitat requirements are so large that protecting it would protect many other species existing in the same habitat.

uniform A pattern of dispersion within a population in which individuals maintain a certain minimum distance between themselves to produce an evenly spaced distribution.

uniporter A type of transporter that binds a single ion or molecule and transports it across a membrane.

unipotent Refers to a stem cell found in an adult organism that can produce daughter cells that differentiate into only one cell type.

unsaturated fatty acid A fatty acid that contains one or more C=C double bonds.

unsaturated The property of certain lipids that contain one or more C=C double bonds.

upwelling In the ocean, a process that carries mineral nutrients from the bottom waters to the surface.

uracil (U) A pyrimidine base found in RNA.

urea A nitrogenous waste commonly produced in many terrestrial species, including mammals.

uremia A condition characterized by the retention of urea and other waste products in the blood; typically results from kidney disease.

uric acid A nitrogenous waste produced by birds, insects, and most reptiles.

urine The part of the filtrate formed in the kidney that remains after all reabsorption of solutes and water is complete.

uterine cycle *See* menstrual cycle.

uterus A small, pear-shaped organ capable of enlarging and specialized for carrying a developing fetus in female mammals.

V

vaccination The injection into the body of small quantities of weakened or dead pathogens, resulting in the development of immunity to those pathogens without causing disease.

vacuole Specialized compartments found in eukaryotic cells that function in storage, the regulation of cell volume, and degradation.

vagina The birth canal of female mammals; also functions to receive sperm during copulation.

vaginal diaphragm A barrier method of preventing fertilization in which a diaphragm is placed in the upper part of the vagina just prior to intercourse; blocks movement of sperm to the cervix.

valence electron An electron in the outermost shell of an atom that is available to share with other atoms. Such electrons allow atoms to form chemical bonds with each other.

van der Waals dispersion forces Attractive forces between molecules in close proximity to each other, caused by the variations in the distribution of electron density around individual atoms.

variable region A unique domain within an immunoglobulin that serves as the antigen-binding site.

vasa recta capillaries Capillaries surrounding the renal tubules in the medulla of the kidney.

vascular bundle A cluster of primary plant vascular tissues that appears round or oval in cross section.

vascular cambium A secondary meristematic tissue of seed plants that produces both wood and inner bark.

vascular plants A broad category of plants distinguished by internal water and nutrient-conducting (vascular) tissues that also provide structural support

vascular tissue A complex plant tissue composed of interconnected cells that form conducting vessels for water, minerals, and organic compounds.

vasectomy A surgical procedure in men that severs the vas deferens, thereby preventing the release of sperm at ejaculation.

vasoconstriction A decrease in blood vessel radius; an important mechanism for directing blood flow away from specific regions of the body.

vasodilation An increase in blood vessel radius; an important mechanism for directing blood flow to specific regions of the body.

vasotocin A peptide hormone that is responsible for regulating salt and water balance in the blood of nonmammalian vertebrates.

vector A type of DNA that acts as a carrier of a DNA segment that is to be cloned.

vegetal pole In triploblast organisms, the pole of the egg where the yolk is most concentrated.

vegetative growth The production of new nonreproductive tissues by the shoot apical meristem and root apical meristem during seedling development and growth of mature plants.

vegetative reproduction A form of asexual reproduction that involves nonreproductive parts of plants.

vein 1. In animals, a blood vessel that returns blood to the heart. 2. In plants, a bundle of vascular tissue in a leaf.

veliger In mollusks, a free-swimming larva that has a rudimentary foot, shell, and mantle.

venation Leaf vein patterns.

ventilation The process of bringing oxygenated water or air into contact with a respiratory organ such as gills or lungs.

ventral Refers to the lower side of an animal.

ventricle In the heart, a chamber that pumps blood out of the heart.

vernalization The process in which certain species of plants require an exposure to cold temperatures in order to flower.

vertebrae Interlocking bony or cartilaginous structures forming a column that provides support and also protects the nerve cord, which lies within the column's tubelike structure.

vertebrate An animal with a backbone.

vertical evolution A type of evolution in which genetic changes occur in a series of related species that form a lineage; species evolve from pre-existing species by the accumulation of mutations.

vessel element A type of plant cell in xylem that conducts water, along with dissolved structure made up hormones, and certain balance in vertebrates.

vessel In a plant anatomical feature that has of a[n] ...tion but resembles a structure of a ...cestor.

... Comma-shaped prokaryotic cells.

...i (singular, **villus**) Finger-like projections extending from the inner surface into the lumen of the vertebrate small intestine; these are specializations that aid in digestion and absorption.

viral envelope A structure enclosing a viral capsid that consists of a membrane derived from the plasma membrane of the host cell and embedded with virally encoded spike glycoproteins.

viral genome The genetic material of a virus.

viral reproductive cycle The series of steps that results in the production of new viruses during a viral infection.

viral vector A type of vector used in cloning experiments that is derived from a virus.

viroid An RNA molecule that infects plant cells.

virulence The ability of a pathogen to infect its host and cause disease.

virulent phage A bacteriophage that follows only the lytic cycle.

virus A small infectious particle that consists of nucleic acid enclosed in a protein coat. Some viruses also have a viral envelope derived from the plasma membrane of the host cell.

visceral mass In mollusks, a structure that rests atop the foot and contains the internal organs.

vitamin D A vitamin that is converted into a hormone in the body; regulates the calcium level in the body through an effect on intestinal transport of calcium ions.

vitamin An organic nutrient that serves as an enzyme for a metabolic or biosynthetic reaction develop

viviparous Refers to an animal whose embryos develop within the uterus, receiving nourishment from the mother via a placenta.

V$_{max}$ The maximal velocity, or rate, of an enzyme-catalyzed reaction.

volt A unit of measurement of potential difference in charge (electrical force), such as the difference between the interior and exterior of a cell.

voltage-gated ion channels Ion channels that open and close in response to changes in voltage across a cell membrane.

W

water potential The potential energy of water.

water vascular system A network of canals in which water pressure generated by the contraction of muscles enables extension and contraction of the tube feet, allowing echinoderms to move slowly.

water The liquid form of H_2O.

wavelength The distance from one peak to the next in a sound wave or light wave.

weak acid An acid that only partially dissociates into ions when added to water.

weathering The physical and chemical breakdown of rock.

white matter Brain tissue that consists of myelinated axons that are bundled together in large numbers to form tracts.

whole metagenomic sequencing (WMS) Base sequencing of all of the DNA present in a sample.

whorls In a flower, concentric rings of sepals and petals (or tepals), stamens, and carpels.

wild-type allele A prevalent allele in a population.

wood A secondary plant tissue composed of numerous pipelike arrays of empty, water-conducting cells whose walls are strengthened by an exceptionally tough polymer known as lignin.

woody plant A type of plant that produces both primary and secondary vascular tissues.

X

X inactivation center (Xic) A short region on the X chromosome known to play a critical role in X inactivation.

X-chromosome inactivation (XCI) A process that causes an X chromosome to become highly compacted and silences the genes that it carries.

X-linked gene A gene found on the X chromosome but not on the Y.

xylem A specialized conducting tissue in plants that transports water, minerals, and some organic compounds.

Y

yeast A unicellular fungus that may reproduce by budding.

yield The number of individuals harvested in a given unit of time.

yolk sac One of the four extraembryonic membranes in the amniotic egg. The yolk sac encloses a stockpile of nutrients, in the form of yolk, for the developing embryo.

Z

Z scheme A model depicting the series of energy changes of an electron during the light reactions of photosynthesis. The electron absorbs light energy twice, resulting in an energy curve with a zigzag shape.

zero population growth The situation in which no changes in population size occur.

zombie parasite A parasite that infects its host and is then able to control that host's behavior.

zona pellucida The glycoprotein covering that surrounds a mature oocyte.

zone of elongation The area above the root apical meristem of a plant where cells extend by water uptake, thereby dramatically increasing root length.

zone of maturation The area above the zone of elongation in a plant root where most root cell differentiation and tissue specialization occur.

zooplankton Aquatic organisms drifting in the open ocean or fresh water; includes minute animals consisting of some worms, copepods, tiny jellyfish, and the small larvae of invertebrates and fishes.

zygospore A dark-pigmented, thick-walled, multinucleate spore that matures within the zygosporangium of zygomycete fungi during sexual reproduction.

zygote A diploid cell formed by the fusion of two haploid gametes.

Z

On the Cover

Giraffes are currently classified as a single species, *Giraffa camelopardalis*. However, a research study published in 2016 has challenged this concept. Scientists collected DNA samples from 190 giraffes across Africa. By comparing these DNA samples, the researchers concluded that giraffes should be classified as four distinct species as described in Chapter 1. While not all experts agree with this conclusion, the work illustrates how our perception of biological diversity can change as we gather more information.

Your grades. Your time. Make the most of it.

You want to achieve the best grades possible with the limited time you have to study. McGraw-Hill Connect helps you do just that. Connect is your personalized digital learning assistant that makes earning better grades and managing time easier, quicker, and more convenient than ever.

Students who access Connect sooner, do better.*
Activate your Connect subscription today!

11%

Average increase in student scores when using Connect on day 1 vs. day 14 of class

85%

of students pass their courses using Connect compared to **72%** of students not using Connect

Source: The Impact of Connect on Student Success. McGraw-Hill Connect® Effectiveness Study 2016

If you need a hand getting started with Connect, or at any step along the way, we're standing by—ready to help.

SUPPORT AT every step

mhhe.com/collegesmarter
800.331.5094

ISBN 978-1-260-48790-9
MHID 1-260-48790-3

EAN

9 781260 487909

mheducation.com/highered

Exploring Psychology, Eleventh Edition in Modules

DAVID G. MYERS

HOPE COLLEGE
HOLLAND, MICHIGAN

C. NATHAN DEWALL

UNIVERSITY OF KENTUCKY
LEXINGTON, KENTUCKY

worth publishers
Macmillan Learning
New York

Senior Vice President, Content Strategy: Charles Linsmeier
Program Director, Social Sciences: Shani Fisher
Executive Program Manager: Carlise Stembridge
Development Manager, Social Sciences: Christine Brune
Development Editors: Nancy Fleming, Trish Morgan, Danielle Slevens
Associate Editor: Katie Pachnos
Editorial Assistant: Anna Munroe
Executive Marketing Manager: Katherine Nurre
Marketing Assistant: Chelsea Simens
Director of Media Editorial & Assessment, Social Sciences: Noel Hohnstine
Executive Media Editor, Psychology: Laura Burden
Media Editorial Assistant: Stephanie Matamoros
Supplements Editor: Betty Probert
Director, Content Management Enhancement: Tracey Kuehn
Senior Managing Editor: Lisa Kinne
Senior Content Project Manager: Won McIntosh
Director of Digital Production: Keri deManigold
Senior Media Project Manager: Chris Efstratiou
Media Project Manager: Eve Conte
Senior Workflow Supervisor: Susan Wein
Senior Photo Editor: Robin Fadool
Photo Researcher: Donna Ranieri
Director of Design, Content Management: Diana Blume
Design Services Manager: Natasha Wolfe
Design Manager, Cover: John Callahan
Interior Design: Charles Yuen
Art Manager: Matthew McAdams
Interior Illustrations: Evelyn Pence
Composition: Lumina Datamatics, Inc.
Printing and Binding: LSC Communications
Cover Photo: PeopleImages/E+/Getty Images

Library of Congress Control Number: 2018948564

ISBN-13: 978-1-319-10417-7

ISBN-10: 1-319-10417-7

© 2019, 2016, 2014, 2011 by Worth Publishers

Printed in the United States of America

1 2 3 4 5 6   23 22 21 20 19 18

First printing

David Myers' royalties from the sale of this book are assigned to the David and Carol Myers Foundation, which exists to receive and distribute funds to other charitable organizations.

Worth Publishers
One New York Plaza
Suite 4500
New York, NY 10004-1562
www.macmillanlearning.com

[DM] For Carlise Stembridge, once my marketing manager, now my executive program manager, and always my supportive and encouraging friend.

[ND] For Roy Baumeister, who showed me the joy of writing, the value of hard work, and the gift of curiosity.

About the Authors

David Myers received his B.A. in chemistry from Whitworth University, and his psychology Ph.D. from the University of Iowa. He has spent his career at Hope College in Michigan, where he has taught dozens of introductory psychology sections. Hope College students have invited him to be their commencement speaker and voted him "outstanding professor."

His research and writings have been recognized by the Gordon Allport Intergroup Relations Prize, an Honored Scientist award from the Federation of Associations in Behavioral & Brain Sciences, an Award for Service on Behalf of Personality and Social Psychology, a Presidential Citation from APA Division 2, election as an American Association for the Advancement of Science Fellow, and three honorary doctorates.

With support from National Science Foundation grants, Myers' scientific articles have appeared in three dozen scientific periodicals, including *Science, American Scientist, Psychological Science,* and the *American Psychologist*. In addition to his scholarly and textbook writing, he digests psychological science for the general public. His writings have appeared in four dozen magazines, from *Today's Education* to *Scientific American*. He also has authored five general audience books, including *The Pursuit of Happiness* and *Intuition: Its Powers and Perils*.

David Myers has chaired his city's Human Relations Commission, helped found a thriving assistance center for families in poverty, and spoken to hundreds of college, community, and professional groups worldwide.

Drawing on his experience, he also has written articles and a book (*A Quiet World*) about hearing loss, and he is advocating a transformation in American assistive listening technology (see HearingLoop.org). For his leadership, he has received awards from the American Academy of Audiology, the hearing industry, and the Hearing Loss Association of America.

David and Carol Myers met and married while undergraduates, and have raised sons Peter and Andrew, and a daughter, Laura. They have one grandchild, Allie (seen on page 128).

Nathan DeWall is professor of psychology and director of the Social Psychology Lab at the University of Kentucky. He received his bachelor's degree from St. Olaf College, a master's degree in social science from the University of Chicago, and a master's degree and Ph.D. in social psychology from Florida State University. DeWall received the College of Arts and Sciences Outstanding Teaching Award, which recognizes excellence in undergraduate and graduate teaching. The Association for Psychological Science identified DeWall as a "Rising Star" early in his career for "making significant contributions to the field of psychological science." He is in the top 1 percent of all cited scientists in psychology and psychiatry on the Institute for Scientific Information list, according to the Web of Science.

DeWall conducts research on close relationships, self-control, and aggression. With funding from the National Institutes of Health, the National Science Foundation, and the John Templeton Foundation, he has published over 200 scientific articles and chapters. DeWall's research awards include the SAGE Young Scholars Award from the Foundation for Personality and Social Psychology, the Young Investigator Award from the International Society for Research on Aggression, and the Early Career Award from the International Society for Self and Identity. His research has been covered by numerous media outlets, including Good Morning America, *The Wall Street Journal, Newsweek, The Atlantic Monthly, The New York Times, The Los Angeles Times, Harvard Business Review, USA Today*, National Public Radio, the BBC, and *The Guardian*. He has lectured nationally and internationally, including in Hong Kong, China, the Netherlands, England, Greece, Hungary, Sweden, Australia, and France.

Nathan is happily married to Alice DeWall and is the proud father of Beverly "Bevy" and Ellis. He enjoys playing with his two golden retrievers, Finnegan and Atticus. In his spare time, he writes novels, watches sports, tends his chickens, and runs and runs and runs. He has braved all climates—from the snowy trails of Michigan to the scorching sands of the Sahara Desert—to complete over 1000 miles' worth of ultramarathons—including the Badwater 135 in 2017 (dubbed "the World's toughest foot race").

Brief Contents

Motivation and Emotion 347

Stress, Health, and Human Flourishing 383

Social Psychology 415

Personality 461

Psychological Disorders 493

Therapy 535

Contents

Personality 461

Psychological Disorders 493

Therapy 535

Instructor Preface:

Engage Your Students So They Retain Psychology

Psychology is fascinating, and so relevant to our everyday lives. Psychology's insights enable students to be more successful in their courses, more tuned-in as friends and partners, more effective as co-workers, and wiser as parents. And helping students to think more like psychological scientists will arm them with the critical thinking skills they need to challenge our post-truth world. As teachers, we want both to *engage* students and to help them *retain* what they learn. In this new edition, we've inserted "Engage" icons to flag the instances throughout the text where we've offered hands-on opportunities for students to try out the concepts (**FIGURE 1**). We've also inserted "Retain" icons to indicate places where students can connect concepts and test their understanding.

This new edition and its resources will be particularly useful in helping you employ *active learning* in your classes. The text is newly available in an engaging, professionally-produced **Audiobook** version. **LaunchPad** offers engaging and effective Concept Practice exercises, videos, and tutorials. LaunchPad's **Immersive Learning activities** include "How Would You Know?" research activities and "Assess Your Strengths" research-based self-assessments. Students love **LearningCurve** adaptive quizzing in LaunchPad because of its game-like format and the way it boosts their course performance. You will appreciate the way LearningCurve helps students come to class better prepared. We also offer numerous **active learning classroom activities** in our *Instructor's Resources*, and a robust collection of **iClicker questions** to help you engage your class. And our simplest and most affordable new student solution is **Achieve Read & Practice**, which contains the eBook and adaptive quizzing only.

Just as introductory psychology *teachers* differ, introductory psychology *resources* differ. They vary in quality, effectiveness, and ease of use. With help from Worth Publishers, we've heard from hundreds of psychology instructors like you who have told us about their needs and concerns, and about the challenges faced by their students. Here are nine frequently mentioned issues, and how we've responded with this *Exploring Psychology, Eleventh Edition in Modules* text and resources.

① "It's very important that I teach my students to think critically, and help them understand that psychology is a science."

Teaching Critical Thinking Is the Foundation of These Resources

We love to write in a way that gets students thinking and keeps their minds active. Students will see how psychological science can help them evaluate competing ideas and highly publicized claims ranging from intuition, subliminal persuasion, and ESP to using only 10 percent of our brain, alternative therapies, and repressed and recovered memories. We help students build the scientific literacy skills they will need to separate intuitive fiction from empirical fact.

In *Exploring Psychology, Eleventh Edition in Modules* and its resources, students have many opportunities to learn and practice their critical thinking skills:

- *"To teach critical thinking"* has been the first of the "Eight Guiding Principles" that have guided our work on this text from its inception. (See p. xxiv.)

- *Modules 1 and 2 take a critical thinking approach to introducing students to psychology's research methods.* Understanding the weak points of our everyday thinking and common sense helps students see the need for psychological science. Critical thinking is introduced as a key term on page 3.

- NEW *"Thinking Critically About . . ." infographics* appear throughout the text. In class testing, students have applauded this visual tool for thinking critically about key psychological concepts (parenting styles, gender bias, sexual aggression, group polarization, introversion, lifestyle changes, and more). See **FIGURE 2** for an example. I [DM] created new *"Thinking Critically About . . ." Infographic Activities* for LaunchPad—with assessment questions targeting higher Bloom's taxonomy levels to teach and reinforce critical thinking.

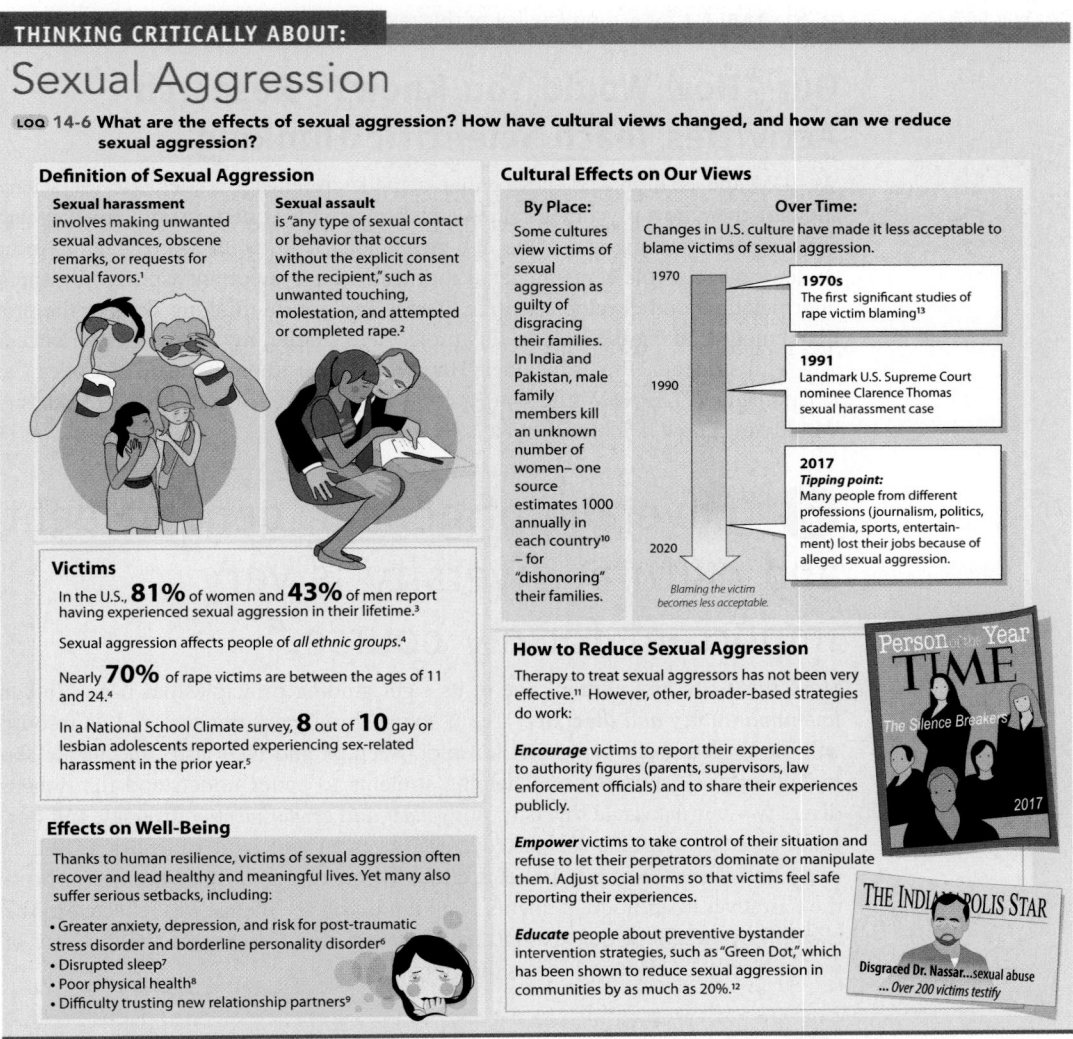

THINKING CRITICALLY ABOUT:

Sexual Aggression

LOQ 14-6 **What are the effects of sexual aggression? How have cultural views changed, and how can we reduce sexual aggression?**

Definition of Sexual Aggression

Sexual harassment involves making unwanted sexual advances, obscene remarks, or requests for sexual favors.[1]

Sexual assault is "any type of sexual contact or behavior that occurs without the explicit consent of the recipient," such as unwanted touching, molestation, and attempted or completed rape.[2]

Victims

In the U.S., **81%** of women and **43%** of men report having experienced sexual aggression in their lifetime.[3]

Sexual aggression affects people of *all ethnic groups*.[4]

Nearly **70%** of rape victims are between the ages of 11 and 24.[4]

In a National School Climate survey, **8** out of **10** gay or lesbian adolescents reported experiencing sex-related harassment in the prior year.[5]

Effects on Well-Being

Thanks to human resilience, victims of sexual aggression often recover and lead healthy and meaningful lives. Yet many also suffer serious setbacks, including:

- Greater anxiety, depression, and risk for post-traumatic stress disorder and borderline personality disorder[6]
- Disrupted sleep[7]
- Poor physical health[8]
- Difficulty trusting new relationship partners[9]

Cultural Effects on Our Views

By Place:
Some cultures view victims of sexual aggression as guilty of disgracing their families. In India and Pakistan, male family members kill an unknown number of women– one source estimates 1000 annually in each country[10] – for "dishonoring" their families.

Over Time:
Changes in U.S. culture have made it less acceptable to blame victims of sexual aggression.

1970 — **1970s** The first significant studies of rape victim blaming[13]

1990 — **1991** Landmark U.S. Supreme Court nominee Clarence Thomas sexual harassment case

2017 *Tipping point:* Many people from different professions (journalism, politics, academia, sports, entertainment) lost their jobs because of alleged sexual aggression.

2020 — *Blaming the victim becomes less acceptable.*

How to Reduce Sexual Aggression

Therapy to treat sexual aggressors has not been very effective.[11] However, other, broader-based strategies do work:

Encourage victims to report their experiences to authority figures (parents, supervisors, law enforcement officials) and to share their experiences publicly.

Empower victims to take control of their situation and refuse to let their perpetrators dominate or manipulate them. Adjust social norms so that victims feel safe reporting their experiences.

Educate people about preventive bystander intervention strategies, such as "Green Dot," which has been shown to reduce sexual aggression in communities by as much as 20%.[12]

Person of the Year **TIME** *The Silence Breakers* 2017

THE INDIANAPOLIS STAR
Disgraced Dr. Nassar...sexual abuse ... Over 200 victims testify

1. McDonald, 2012; U.S.E.E.O.C., 2018. 2. U.S.D.O.J., 2018. 3. Stop Street Harassment, 2018. 4. Black et al., 2011. 5. GLSEN, 2012. 6. Choudhary et al., 2012; Krahé & Berger, 2017; Snipes et al., 2017; Zanarini et al., 1997. 7. Krakow et al., 2001, 2002. 8. Schuyler et al., 2017; Zinzow et al., 2011. 9. Muldoon et al., 2016; Starzynski et al., 2017. 10. HBVA, 2018. 11. Grønnerød et al., 2015. 12. Coker et al., 2017. 13. Burt, 1980.

FIGURE 2

SAMPLE "THINKING CRITICALLY ABOUT" INFOGRAPHIC FROM MODULE 14

- *Psychological Science in a Post-Truth World* is a new section in Module 2 that will help your students understand why we are so vulnerable to believing untruths and how we can use critical thinking and a scientific mindset to build a real-truth world. This message is supported by my [DM's] new tutorial animation, *"Thinking Critically in Our Post-Truth World"* in LaunchPad.

- *Detective-style stories* throughout the text get students thinking critically about psychology's key research questions. In Module 26, for example, we present as a puzzle the history of discoveries about where and how language happens in the brain. We guide students through the puzzle, showing them how researchers put all the pieces together.

- *Critical examinations of pop psychology* spark interest and provide lessons in thinking critically about everyday topics. For example, Module 18 scrutinizes ESP, and Module 24 explores the controversy over the alleged repression of painful memories.

See **TABLE 1** for a complete list of this text's coverage of critical thinking topics.

Our "How Would You Know?" Research Activities Teach Scientific Thinking

We [DM and ND] created these online activities to engage students in the scientific process, showing them how psychological research begins with a question, and how key decision points can alter the meaning and value of a psychological study. In a fun, interactive environment, students play the role of researcher as they learn about important aspects of research design and interpretation, and develop scientific literacy and critical thinking skills in the process. I [ND] have enjoyed taking the lead on this project and sharing my research experience and enthusiasm with students. Topics include: "How Would You Know If a Cup of Coffee Can Warm Up Relationships?," "How Would You Know If People Can Learn to Reduce Anxiety?," and "How Would You Know If Schizophrenia Is Inherited?"

2 "Coverage of gender, gender-identity, and cultural diversity is very important for my course."

Since this text's first edition, one of its eight guiding principles has been *"To convey respect for human unity and diversity"* (see p. xxv). Throughout this text and its resources, students will see evidence of our human kinship. We [DM and ND] also care deeply about celebrating all forms of diversity, and helping students to better understand the dimensions of our diversity—our *individual* diversity, our *gender* and *gender-identity* diversity, and our *cultural* and *ethnic* diversity. **TABLE 2** lists the coverage of gender and gender identity. **TABLE 3** provides the integrated coverage of cultural and ethnic diversity. Significant coverage is presented within the narrative. In addition, students of all kinds will see themselves reflected in the photos and examples throughout the text and its resources, which showcase the diversity of individuals within North America and across the globe.

3 "We need to minimize cost to the student."

Students deserve the highest quality educational resources at an affordable cost. Macmillan Learning has made a big effort to reduce production costs for our texts, which has allowed them to significantly reduce costs to students—especially for loose-leaf and digital options,

TABLE 1

Critical Thinking and Scientific Inquiry Critical thinking coverage and in-depth stories of psychology's process of scientific inquiry can be found on the following pages:

Thinking Critically About . . . infographics:

The Scientific Attitude, p. 4

Correlation and Causation, p. 26

Using More Than 10 Percent of Our Brain, p. 62

Tolerance and Addiction, p. 102

Parenting Styles—Too Hard, Too Soft, Too Uncaring, and Just Right?, p. 139

Gender Bias in the Workplace, p. 164

Sexual Aggression, p. 170

Subliminal Sensation and Subliminal Persuasion, p. 193

The Effects of Viewing Media Violence, p. 263

Can Memories of Childhood Sexual Abuse Be Repressed and Then Recovered?, p. 293

The Fear Factor, p. 302

Cross-Sectional and Longitudinal Studies, p. 332

The Challenges of Obesity and Weight Control, p. 365

Lie Detection, p. 374

Stress and Health, p. 393

The Internet as Social Amplifier, p. 432

The Stigma of Introversion, p. 476

ADHD—Normal High Energy or Disordered Behavior?, p. 498

Therapeutic Lifestyle Change, p. 559

Critical Examinations of Pop Psychology:

The need for psychological science, pp. 15–17

Perceiving order in random events, p. 16

Do we use only 10 percent of our brain?, p. 62

Has the concept of "addiction" been stretched too far?, p. 102

Near-death experiences, p. 108

How much credit or blame do parents deserve?, p. 139

Critiquing the evolutionary perspective, pp. 185–186

Sensory restriction, p. 213

Can hypnosis be therapeutic? Alleviate pain?, p. 224

Is there extrasensory perception?, p. 229–230

Do other species have language?, pp. 317–318

Do violent video games teach social scripts for violence?, pp. 444–445

How valid is the Rorschach test?, pp. 467–468

Is Freud credible?, pp. 468–470

Is repression a myth?, p. 469

Is psychotherapy effective?, pp. 550–552

Evaluating alternative therapies, pp. 552–555

Thinking Critically With Psychological Science:

"Critical thinking" introduced as a key term, p. 3

The limits of intuition and common sense, p. 15

Psychological science in a post-truth world, pp. 18–19

The scientific method, pp. 19–30

Correlation and causation, p. 26

Exploring cause and effect, pp. 24–29

Random assignment, p. 29

Independent and dependent variables, pp. 28–29

Choosing the right research design, p. 29–30

The evolutionary perspective on human sexuality, pp. 192–195

Statistical reasoning, pp. A-1–A-9

Describing data, pp. A-1–A-6

Regression toward the mean, pp. A-5–A-6

Making inferences, pp. A-6–A-8

Scientific Detective Stories:

Is breast milk better than formula?, pp. 27–28

Our divided brain, pp. 65–67

Twin and adoption studies, pp. 70–73

Why do we sleep?, pp. 91–92

Why we dream, pp. 97–99

How a child's mind develops, pp. 125–126

What determines sexual orientation?, pp. 179–182

How do we see in color?, pp. 203–205

Parallel processing, p. 206

How can hypnosis provide pain relief?, p. 224

How are memories constructed?, pp. 269–274

How do we store memories in our brain?, pp. 275–279

Do other species exhibit language?, pp. 317–318

Aging and intelligence, pp. 373–374

Why do we feel hunger?, pp. 361–363

Why—and in whom—does stress contribute to heart disease?, pp. 391–392

How and why is social support linked with health?, pp. 399–401

The pursuit of happiness: Who is happy, and why?, pp. 407–412

Why do people fail to help in emergencies?, pp. 418–419

Self-esteem versus self-serving bias, pp. 487–489

What causes major depressive disorder and bipolar disorder?, pp. 518–519

Do prenatal viral infections increase the risk of schizophrenia?, pp. 525–526

Is psychotherapy effective?, pp. 550–552

---

including the new, simplified *Achieve Read & Practice* with eBook and adaptive quizzing only. See MacmillanLearning.com/Catalog/page/affordable-solutions.

In my [ND's] recent course, *I required only the LaunchPad key—giving students access to the eBook and full online resources.* Students had the option of also purchasing a loose-leaf version of the text. The result? In addition to loving the text and online resources, *9 in 10 students said they felt that the price was fair.*

You may be interested in customizing print or digital resources as a way to save costs for your students, to provide materials for your course that match your syllabus more closely, or to add your own or other Macmillan resources to your course. We were pleased to learn that our custom options are now available for even the smallest of courses via a new "Worth Select" program, which is part of Macmillan's broad Curriculum Solutions program.

TABLE 2

The Psychology of Gender, Gender Identity, and Sexuality Coverage of the psychology of gender, gender identity, and sexuality can be found on the following pages:

Absolute thresholds, p. 192

ADHD, p. 498

Adulthood: physical changes, pp. 151–153

Aggression, pp. 441, 443
    father absence, p. 443
    pornography, p. 444
    rape, pp. 440, 444

Alcohol:
    and alcohol use disorder, p. 103
    and sexual aggression, p. 103
    use, pp. 103–104

Altruism, pp. 452–455

Androgyny, p. 169

Antisocial personality disorder, pp. 530–531

Attraction, pp. 447–452

Attractiveness, pp. 448–450

Autism spectrum disorder, p. 131

Biological sex/gender, pp. 165–171

Bipolar disorder, pp. 515–516

Body image, pp. 531–533

Color vision, pp. 203–204

Dating, p. 448

Depression, pp. 504, 515, 517, 518, 520
    learned helplessness, p. 520

Dream content, pp. 96–97

Drug use:
    biological influences, pp. 110–111
    psychological/social-cultural influences, pp. 111–113

Eating disorders, pp. 531–533

Emotion-detecting ability, pp. 377–378

Empathy, p. 378

Empty nest, p. 157

Father care, pp. 135–136

Father presence, p. 178

Freud's views:
    evaluating, pp. 468–470
    identification/gender identity, pp. 464–465

Oedipus/Electra complexes, p. 464
    penis envy, p. 466

Fundamental attribution error, pp. 416–417

Gender:
    and child raising, p. 169
    bias in the workplace, p. 164
    definition, p. 162
    development, pp. 162–171
    prejudice, p. 437
    roles, pp. 168–171
    similarities/differences, pp. 162–165

Gendered brain, pp. 164, 177, 180–182

Generalized anxiety disorder, p. 507

Generic pronoun "he," p. 320

Grief, pp. 159–160

Group polarization, pp. 431–432

Happiness, p. 411

Hearing loss, p. 218

Hormones and:
    aggression, p. 441
    sexual behavior, pp. 173–174
    sexual development, pp. 141–142, 165–167
    testosterone-replacement therapy, pp. 173–174

Intelligence, pp. 340–341

bias, p. 343
    stereotype threat, p. 344

Leadership: transformational, p. B-10

Losing weight, p. 366

Love, pp. 156–157, 451–452

Marriage, pp. 156–157, 400

Maturation, pp. 141–142

Menarche, p. 141

Menopause, p. 151

Midlife crisis, p. 155

Obedience, p. 426

Obesity:
    health risks, p. 365

Observational learning:
    sexually violent media, p. 263
    media influence, p. 262

Ostracism, p. 354

Pain sensitivity, p. 222

Paraphilias, pp. 174–175

Perceptual set, p. 196

Pornography, pp. 176–177

Prejudice, pp. 304, 437

Psychological disorders, rates of, pp. 503–505

PTSD: development of, pp. 509–510

Rape, pp. 440, 444

Religiosity and life expectancy, pp. 404–406

REM sleep, arousal in, p. 89

Romantic love, p. 451

Rumination, pp. 520–521

Savant syndrome, pp. 324–325

Schizophrenia, p. 524

Self-injury, p. 500

Sense of smell, pp. 226–227

Sex reassignment, pp. 167–168

Sex: definition, p. 162

Sexual abuse, pp. 180, 468

Sexual attraction, pp. 166–167, 173–174, 178–179, 447–450

Sexual dysfunctions, p. 175

Sexual fantasies, p. 177

Sexual orientation, pp. 178–182

Sexuality:
    adolescent, pp. 166–167
    evolutionary explanation, pp. 183–186
    external stimuli, pp. 176–177
    imagined stimuli, p. 177
    Sexualization of girls, pp. 177–178

Sexually transmitted infections, p. 175

Sleep, p. 87

Social connectedness, p. 163

Social networking, p. 355

Stereotype threat, pp. 343–344

Stereotyping, pp. 165, 196, 435, 438–439

Stress and:
    AIDS, pp. 390, 401, 406
    depression, p. 391
    health, and sexual abuse, pp. 400–401
    heart disease, pp. 391–392
    immune system, pp. 388–390
    response to, pp. 386–388

Suicide, p. 500

Teratogens: alcohol consumption, p. 120

Transgender, pp. 170–171

Women in psychology's history, pp. 6–7

See also Modules 14 and 15.

TABLE 3

The Psychology of Culture, Ethnicity, and Race Coverage of culture, ethnicity, and race may be found on the following pages:

Adolescence, p. 141

Adulthood, emerging, pp. 149–150

Aggression, pp. 163, 442–445

and video games, pp. 263, 443–445

AIDS, pp. 390

Anger, pp. 393–394

Animal research ethics, p. 31

Attraction: matchmaking, p. 448

Attractiveness, pp. 447–450

Attribution: political effects of, pp. 416–417

Behavioral effects of culture, pp. 9–10, 421–422

Body ideal, pp. 365, 532–533

Body image, pp. 532–533

Categorization, p. 342

Conformity, pp. 423–425

Corporal punishment practices, p. 249

Cultural norms, pp. 169, 421

Culture:

context effects, pp. 196–197

definition, p. 421

experiencing other, p. 307

variation over time, p. 422

Culture and the self, pp. 489–491

Culture shock, p. 385

Deaf culture, pp. 64, 67, 312–314, 316–317

Development:

adolescence, p. 141

attachment, pp. 134–135

child raising, pp. 138–140

cognitive development, p. 130

moral development, pp. 143–145

parenting styles, pp. 138–140

social development, pp. 146–147

Drug use, pp. 111–113

Emotion:

emotion-detecting ability, pp. 375–377

expressing, pp. 378–380

Enemy perceptions, pp. 456–457

Fear, pp. 301–302

Flow, p. B-1

Fundamental attribution error, pp. 416–417

Gender:

cultural norms, pp. 162, 168–169

equality, p. 185

roles, pp. 168–169

social power, p. 163

Grief, expressing, pp. 159–160

Happiness, pp. 407–408, 411, 416–417

Hindsight bias, pp. 16–17

History of psychology, pp. 5–7

Homosexuality, views on, pp. 178–179

Human diversity/kinship, pp. 9–10, 76, 421–422, 459

Identity: forming social, p. 146

Individualism/collectivism, pp. 489–491

Intelligence, pp. 329, 340–344

and nutrition, pp. 343–344, 359

bias, pp. 343–344

Down syndrome, p. 331

Language, pp. 312–313, 319–320

critical periods, p. 315

bilingualism, pp. 319–320

universal grammar, pp. 312–313

Leadership style, cultural influences on, pp. B-11–B-12

Leaving the nest, pp. 149–150

Life satisfaction, pp. 409–410

Life span and well-being, pp. 158–159

Management styles, pp. B-11–B-12

Marriage, pp. 156–157, 451–452

Memory, encoding, pp. 271–272

Menopause, p. 151

Mental illness rate, pp. 503–505

Morality, development of, pp. 143–145

Motivating achievement, pp. 358, B-9

Motivation: hierarchy of needs, pp. 351, 354, 357–358

Need to belong, pp. 352–355

Neurotransmitters: curare, p. 44

Normality, perceptions of, p. 494

Obedience, pp. 425–428

Obesity, pp. 364–366

Observational learning: television and aggression, pp. 262–263

Organ donation, p. 305

Pace of life, p. 23

Pain: perception of, pp. 223, 354–355

Parent and peer relationships, pp. 147–149

Participative management, p. B-11

Peacemaking:

conciliation, p. 459

contact, p. 457

cooperation, pp. 457–458

Personality, pp. 477–479

Power of individuals, pp. 428–429

Prejudice, pp. 32, 438, 435–441

belief systems, p. 438

explicit, p. 435

gender, p. 437

implicit, p. 436

LGBTQ, p. 437

racial and ethnic, p. 436

Prejudice prototypes, p. 304

Psychological disorders:

amok, p. 496

cultural norms, pp. 494–496

dissociative identity disorder, pp. 528–529

eating disorders, pp. 496, 531–533

schizophrenia, pp. 496, 525

suicide, p. 500

susto, p. 496

taijin-kyofusho, p. 496

Psychotherapy:

culture and values in, pp. 556

EMDR training, p. 554

Puberty and adult independence, pp. 149–150

Self-esteem, pp. 350–351

Self-serving bias, pp. 487–489

Sex drive, p. 183

Sexual activity: middle and late adulthood, p. 151

Sexual orientation, p. 178

Similarities, pp. 76–77

Sleep patterns, pp. 91–92

Social clock, p. 155

Social-cultural perspective, pp. 10–11

Social loafing, p. 430

Social networking, pp. 355–356

Spirituality, pp. 404–405

Stress:

adjusting to a new culture, p. 385

health consequences, pp. 385, 389–390, 392–394

racism and, p. 386

social support and, p. 399

Taste preferences, pp. 363–364

Teen pregnancy, pp. 177–178,

Testing bias, pp. 343–344

See also Modules 35, 36, and 37.

④ **"My administrators are eager to see results—better learning outcomes and improved retention of students."**

Our Online Resources May Improve Retention of Students

Students love LaunchPad, and especially the LearningCurve adaptive quizzing engine. When Macmillan Learning asked the thousands of psychology students using LearningCurve in the spring of 2017, 86 percent rated it either "Good" or "Excellent."

When I [ND] taught introductory psychology recently, I asked my students at the end of the course what they liked best about the class. Most answered "LaunchPad!" I've enjoyed using these resources in my classes, because they allow me to engage my students so successfully. In fact, at my institution (University of Kentucky), I've been involved in efforts to improve retention of students. In my own class, I have found that assigning something in LaunchPad on the first day of class, and heavily relying on LaunchPad throughout the term, seems to improve retention in my large (~350-student) classes.

Researchers have begun to do efficacy studies with our online materials, and initial results have been promising. Our Learning Science Team, led by Dr. Adam Black (an award-winning researcher and digital innovation specialist), has several exciting projects underway. (See MacmillanLearning.com/Catalog/page/LearningScience for more information.) Stay tuned as we continue to learn more (and let us know if you'd like to participate).

Our Resources Help Address APA Learning Goals and Outcomes

In 2011, the American Psychological Association (APA) approved the ***Principles for Quality Undergraduate Education in Psychology.*** These broad-based principles and their associated recommendations are a guide to producing "psychologically literate citizens who apply the principles of psychological science at work and at home." (See apa.org/education/undergrad/principles.aspx.)

APA's more specific ***2013 Learning Goals and Outcomes***, from their *Guidelines for the Undergraduate Psychology Major,* Version 2.0, were designed to gauge progress in students graduating with psychology majors. (See apa.org/ed/precollege/about/psymajor-guidelines.pdf.) Many psychology departments use these goals and outcomes to help establish their own benchmarks for departmental assessment purposes. **TABLE 4** outlines the way *Exploring Psychology, Eleventh Edition in Modules* can help you and your department address the APA's Learning Goals and Outcomes. In addition, all of the Test Bank items for this text are coded for the APA Outcomes.

⑤ **"Active learning is essential—I need materials that will help me engage students."**

Our Materials Engage Students With Active Learning

We've found that engaged students who are learning actively tend to be successful students. They do better in the course and are more likely to stay in school.

NEW Ask Yourself Questions

For this new edition, we've added *Ask Yourself* questions periodically in the text margins to help students relate the material to their own lives. When students make the material meaningful, it also becomes more enjoyable and memorable (**FIGURE 3**).

Scattered throughout this book, students will also find interesting and informative notes and quotes from researchers and others that will encourage them to be active learners and to apply their new knowledge to everyday life.

  (ASK YOURSELF)

Were you surprised to learn that psychology is a science? How would you explain that if someone else now asked you about this?

FIGURE 3

SAMPLE "ASK YOURSELF" QUESTION

TABLE 4

Exploring Psychology, Eleventh Edition in Modules **Corresponds to 2013 APA Learning Goals**

Relevant Feature from *Exploring Psychology, Eleventh Edition in Modules*	Knowledge Base in Psychology	Scientific Inquiry and Critical Thinking	Ethical and Social Responsibility in a Diverse World	Communication	Professional Development
Text content	•	•	•	•	•
"Thinking Critically About" infographic features	•	•	•		•
Learning Objective Questions previewing text sections	•	•		•	
Retrieve It self-tests throughout text	•	•		•	
Experience the Testing Effect tests in the text, and Chapter Quizzes online	•	•		•	
"Try this"-style activities integrated throughout	•	•		•	•
Video Activities online	•	•	•		•
Psychology at Work appendix	•	•	•		•
Career Fields in Psychology appendix in the text, with Pursuing a Psychology Career online	•		•		•
Learning Curve formative quizzing online, with personalized study plan	•	•	•	•	•
"How Would You Know?" research activities online	•	•	•	•	•
Assess Your Strengths self-assessment feature online	•	•	•	•	•
PsychSim6 online tutorials	•	•	•		•
Concept Practice activities online	•	•			

Engage

Engage icons mark the many active learning opportunities throughout the text. We often encourage students to imagine themselves as participants in experiments. In Module 35, for example, students take the perspective of participants in a Solomon Asch conformity experiment and, later, in one of Stanley Milgram's obedience experiments. We've also asked students to join the fun by taking part in activities they can try along the way. For example, in Module 16, students try out a quick sensory adaptation activity. In Module 32, they try matching expressions to faces and test the effects of different facial expressions on themselves.

LaunchPad

It has been a joy for me [ND] to teach introductory psychology with this book and its resources. The online materials make it easy to engage students effectively starting on Day 1 of the class when I make a LaunchPad assignment. With immediate engagement, and active learning throughout the course, most students become hooked on psychology and stay in my class. This book and its resources help me not only to *engage* students, but also to *retain* them.

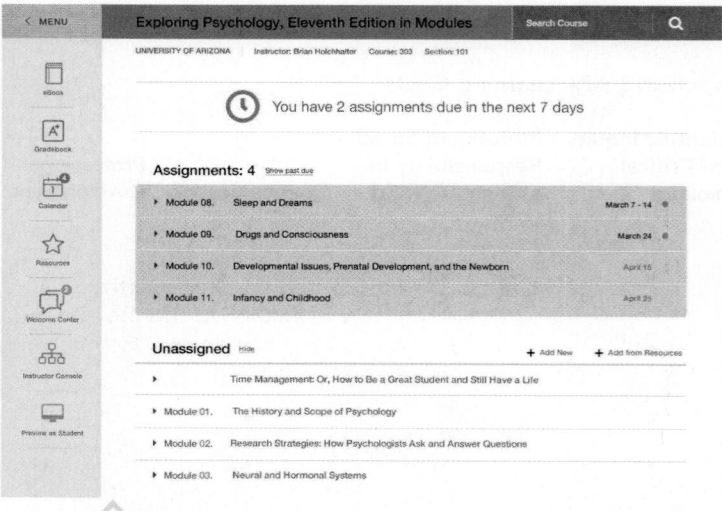

FIGURE 4

SAMPLE FROM LAUNCHPAD

LaunchPad (LaunchPadWorks.com) facilitates active learning as it solves key challenges (see **FIGURE 4**). In combination with the meticulously created text, these online resources give students everything they need to prepare for class and exams, while giving you, the instructor, everything *you* need to quickly set up a course, shape the content to your syllabus, craft presentations and lectures, assign and assess homework, and guide the progress of individual students and the class as a whole.

- Our **NEW eBook** can now go with any student, anywhere. It is fully mobile-compatible and meets accessibility standards.

- Our **NEW Audiobook** has been professionally produced (a real voice—the first of its kind for introductory psychology!) and personalized with an opening and closing message from us [DM and ND]. As an avid audiobook listener, I [ND] know the value of being able to listen to a book as I walk across campus, while I exercise, or as I am on my way to pick up my kids from the babysitter. Students can fit reading assignments into their busy lives or catch up while they're on the go. And some students just prefer to learn this way, with a professional voice bringing the text's narrative to life.

- **LearningCurve's game-like quizzing** motivates students and adapts to their needs based on their performance. It is the perfect tool to get students to engage before class, and review after. Additional reporting tools and metrics will help you assess the progress of individual students and the class as a whole.

- **iClicker offers active learning simplified, and now includes the REEF mobile app (iClicker.com).** iClicker's simple, flexible tools in LaunchPad help you give students a voice and facilitate active learning in the classroom. Students can use iClicker remotes, or the REEF mobile app on their phone, tablet, or laptop to participate more meaningfully. LaunchPad includes a robust collection of iClicker questions for each module—readily available for use in your class.

- **The NEW Concept Practice collection** offers 120 dynamic, interactive mini-tutorials that teach and reinforce the course's foundational ideas. Each brief activity (only five minutes to complete) addresses one or two concepts, in a consistent format—review, practice, quiz, and conclusion.

- The **Topic Tutorials: PsychSim6,** Thomas Ludwig's (Hope College) award-winning interactive psychology simulations, were designed for the mobile web. PsychSim immerses students in the world of psychological research, placing them in the role of scientist or participant in activities that highlight important concepts, processes, and experimental approaches.

- In the significantly revised **Assess Your Strengths** activities, students apply what they are learning from the text to their own lives and experiences by considering key "strengths." Each activity starts with a personalized video introduction from us [DM and ND], explaining how that strength ties in to the content of the modules. Next, students assess themselves on the strength (critical thinking, quality of sleep, self-control, relationship strength, belonging, hope, and more) using scales developed by researchers across psychological science. After showing students their results, we offer tips for nurturing that strength in their own lives. Finally, students take a quiz to help solidify their learning.

- I [DM] have created 19 new **"Thinking Critically About…" Infographic Activities**—designed to teach and reinforce critical thinking skills.

- **LMS integration** into your school's system is readily available. Check with your local sales representative for details.

- **The Video Assignment Tool** makes it easy to assign and assess video-based activities and projects, and provides a convenient way for students to submit video coursework.

- The **Gradebook** gives a clear window on performance for the whole class, for individual students, and for individual assignments.

- A **streamlined interface** helps students manage their schedule of assignments, while *social commenting tools* let them connect with classmates, and learn from one another. 24/7 help is a click away, accessible from a link in the upper right corner in LaunchPad.

- We [DM and ND] curated **optional pre-built units,** which can be used as is or customized. Or choose not to use them and build your course from scratch.

- Our **Instructor's Resources** have long been considered the "gold standard" in the field. They include lecture and classroom activity suggestions—with a new grid identifying the *Active Learning Instructor's Resources* (those that work well for think-pair-share, small group, and large group activities), *Lecture Guides* (summarizing key text discussions and connecting instructor's resources with text learning objectives), the best *Test Banks* in the industry (carefully authored, and professionally edited and tightly coordinated with the text by the same fabulous supplements editor since the first edition), and nice starter PowerPoint sets with textbook graphics.For this new edition, you will see that we've offered callouts from the text pages to especially pertinent, helpful online resources. (See **FIGURE 5** for a sample.)

LaunchPad For an interactive, animated explanation of this process, engage online with **Concept Practice: Action Potentials.**

FIGURE 5

SAMPLE CALLOUT TO LAUNCHPAD ONLINE RESOURCES FROM MODULE 3

Achieve Read & Practice

Achieve Read & Practice is the marriage of our LearningCurve adaptive quizzing and our mobile, accessible eBook in one, easy-to-use and affordable product **(FIGURE 6)**. New, built-in analytics make it easier than ever for instructors to track student progress and intervene to help students succeed. Instructors who class-tested Achieve Read & Practice were surprised by its truly easy interface, and pleased with their course results. In a study of 227 students at 6 institutions, instructors found a significant improvement in the proportion of students who stayed on track with the assigned reading, and they found that students who retook quizzes (a helpful feature of Achieve Read & Practice) earned higher grades in the course. (Access the full report at MacmillanLearning.com/Catalog/Page/LearningScience.)

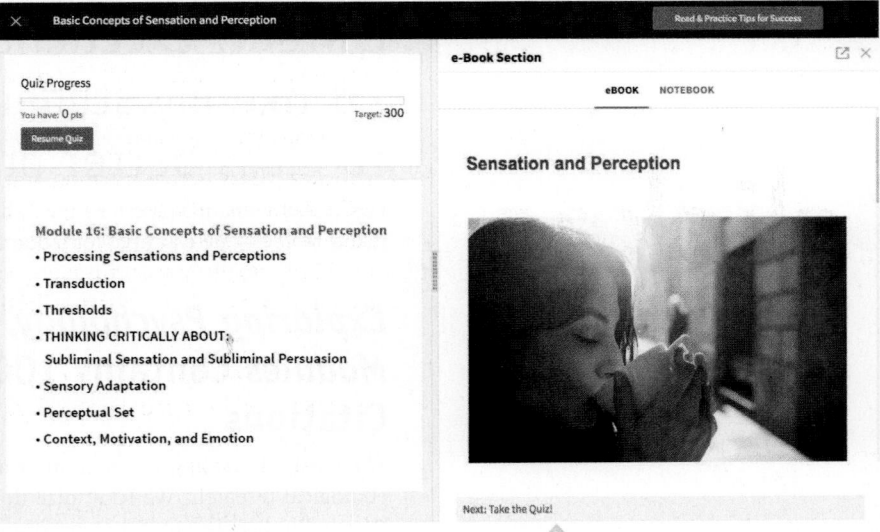

FIGURE 6

SAMPLE FROM ACHIEVE READ & PRACTICE

The Macmillan Community Will Engage You, Too!

The *Macmillan Community* (Community.Macmillan.com) was created *by* instructors *for* instructors. This is an ideal forum for interacting with fellow educators—including Macmillan authors **(FIGURE 7)**. Join ongoing conversations about everything from course prep and presentations to assignments and assessments, to teaching with media, keeping pace with—and influencing—new directions in your field. The Community offers exclusive access to classroom resources, blogs (including my [DM's] TalkPsych.com), webinars, and professional development opportunities. Our mission is to provide the highest quality educational resources to

FIGURE 7

SAMPLE FROM MACMILLAN COMMUNITY (COMMUNITY .MACMILLAN.COM)

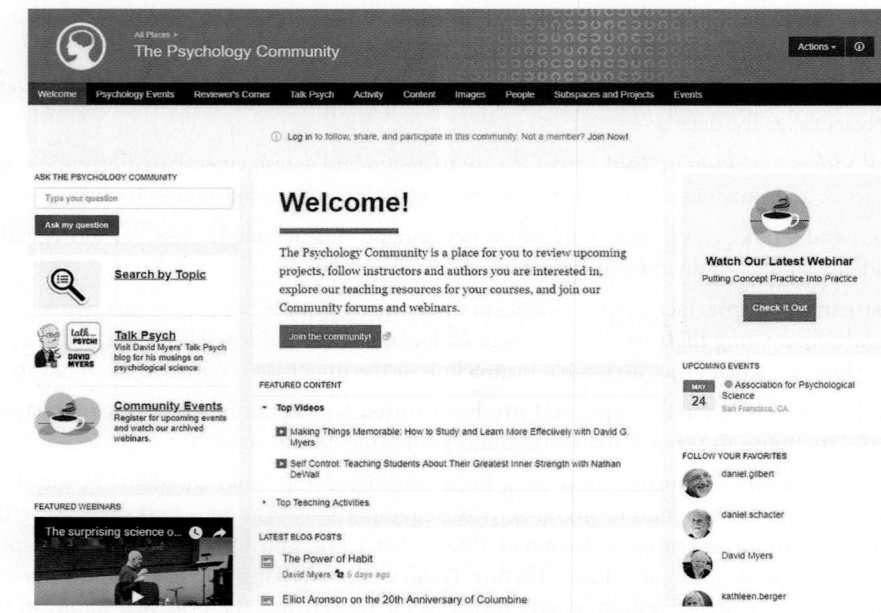

instructors and students. By participating in the Macmillan Community, you will join a group of enthusiastic educators who have unmatched access to high-quality resources and a forum to further your understanding of how to implement them.

6 "I need especially reliable, current, excellent materials, and I'd like my students to come to class better prepared."

Especially at the introductory level, high quality, cohesive, connected materials—text, assessment, review—are essential for students' success.

Exploring Psychology, Eleventh Edition in Modules Contains 1000+ New Research Citations

The work of creating our text and online resources begins as we stay current with new psychological research. We scrutinize dozens of scientific periodicals and science news sources. Worth Publishers commissions numerous reviews, and we receive countless emails from instructors and students. These sources feed our reporting on psychology's most important, thought-provoking, and student-relevant new discoveries. Part of the pleasure that sustains this work is learning something new every day! Each new edition is an adventure down the ever-changing road of psychological science. Every topic is inspected closely and painstakingly updated. This time around, it's been particularly fun to watch all of the developments in neuroscience (**TABLE 5**) and in behavior genetics (**TABLE 6**). The end result is more than 1000 new citations for this edition. See MacmillanLearning.com for our lengthy list of significant *Content Changes*.

TABLE 5

Neuroscience In addition to the coverage found in Modules 3, 4, and 5, **neuroscience** can be found on the following pages:

TABLE 6

Behavior Genetics and Evolutionary Psychology In addition to the coverage found in Module 6, **behavior genetics** is covered on the following pages:

Abuse, intergenerational transmission of, p. 262

Adaptability, pp. 58–59

Aggression, pp. 441–445

intergenerational transmission of, p. 262

Autism spectrum disorder, pp. 130–132

Behavior genetics perspective, pp. 8-9, 12

Biological perspective, p. 38

Brain plasticity, p. 39

Continuity and stages, p. 117

Deprivation of attachment, pp. 136–138

Depth perception, pp. 208–210

Development, pp. 116–117

Drives and incentives, p. 349

Drug use, pp. 110–113

Eating disorders, pp. 531–533

Epigenetics, pp. 120, 138, 496, 511–512, 519, 527

Happiness, pp. 411–412

Hunger and taste preference, pp. 363–364

Intelligence:

Down syndrome, p. 331

genetic and environmental influences, pp. 336–339

Learning, pp. 254–257

Motor development, p. 124

Nature-nurture, p. 8

twins, p. 9

Obesity and weight control, pp. 365–366

Optimism, pp. 398–399

Pain, pp. 221–223

Parenting styles, pp. 138–140

Perception, pp. 213–214

Personality traits, pp. 475–479

Psychological disorders and:

ADHD, pp. 497–498

anxiety-related disorders, pp. 510–512

biopsychosocial approach, pp. 495–496

bipolar disorder and major depressive disorder, pp. 518–521

depressed thinking, p. 521

obsessive-compulsive disorder, pp. 510–512

personality disorders, pp. 530–531

posttraumatic stress disorder, pp. 509–512

schizophrenia, pp. 524–527

suicide, pp. 500–501

violent behavior, pp. 502–503

Reward deficiency syndrome, p. 56

Romantic love, pp. 156–157

Sexual dysfunctions, p. 175

Sexual orientation, pp. 179–182

Sexuality, pp. 172–174

Sleep patterns, pp. 90–91

Smell, pp. 225–227

Stress, personality, and illness, pp. 388–393

benefits of exercise, pp. 401–402

Traits, gay-straight differences, pp. 182–183

In addition to the coverage found in Module 6, the **evolutionary perspective** is covered on the following pages:

Aging, pp. 161–162

Anger, pp. 393–394

Anxiety-related disorders, pp. 511–512

Biological predispositions:

in learning, pp. 254–255

in operant conditioning, p. 256

Brainstem, pp. 53–54

Classical conditioning, pp. 254–255

Consciousness, p. 80

Darwin, Charles, pp. 5, 9

Depression and light exposure therapy, pp. 554–555

Emotion, effects of facial expressions and, pp. 380–382

Emotional expression, pp. 378–380

Evolutionary perspective, defined, pp. 11, 12

Fear, p. 302

Feature detection, p. 205

Fight or flight, p. 386

Gene-environment interaction, pp. 73–75

Hearing, p. 216

Hunger and taste preference, pp. 363–364

Instincts, pp. 348–349

Intelligence, pp. 327–328, 340–343

Language, pp. 312–317

Love, pp. 156–157

Math and spatial ability, p. 340

Mating preferences, pp. 184–185

Menopause, p. 151

Need to belong, pp. 352–353

Obesity, p. 365

Overconfidence, pp. 303–304

Perceptual adaptation, pp. 213–214

Sensation, p. 190

Sensory adaptation, pp. 194–195

Sexual orientation, pp. 179–182

Sexuality, pp. 173–174, 179–180, 183–186

Sleep, pp. 86, 91–92

Smell, p. 226

Taste, pp. 225–227

Eight Principles Have Always Guided This Text's Creation

We follow eight guiding principles that have animated all of my [DM's] texts since their first editions.

Facilitating the Learning Experience

1. ***To teach critical thinking*** By presenting research as intellectual detective work, we illustrate an inquiring, analytical mindset. Whether students are studying development, cognition, or social behavior, they will be drawn into critical reasoning. They will discover how an empirical approach can help them evaluate competing ideas and claims for highly publicized

phenomena—ranging from extrasensory perception and alternative therapies to group differences in intelligence and repressed and recovered memories. (See pp. xii–xiv for more information about critical thinking in this text.)

2. **To integrate principles and applications** Throughout, we relate the findings of basic research to their applications and implications. Knowledge is power when we harness it to bring about positive change in the world. Where psychology can illuminate pressing human issues—overcoming prejudice, pursuing happiness, moving past conflict to peace—we have not hesitated to shine its light. The new "Ask Yourself" questions integrated throughout the text help students continue to make personally meaningful what they are learning. And our online "Assess Your Strengths" activities invite students to apply important concepts to their own lives, and to learn ways to develop personal strengths. As the author of an early book devoted to the scientific study of happiness, *The Pursuit of Happiness* (Myers, 1992), I [DM] have a special place in my heart for understanding and cultivating human strengths. Throughout the text we integrate coverage of *positive psychology* (see **TABLE 7**).

3. **To reinforce learning at every step** Everyday examples and thought-provoking questions encourage students to process the material actively. Concepts presented earlier are frequently applied and later reinforced. For instance, in Module 2, students learn that much of our information processing occurs outside of our conscious awareness. Subsequent modules drive home this concept. Self-testing opportunities throughout the text and online resources help students learn and retain important concepts and terminology.

Demonstrating the Science of Psychology

4. **To teach the process of inquiry** We strive to show students not just the outcome of research, but how the research process works. Throughout, the narrative excites the reader's curiosity. It invites students to imagine themselves as participants in classic experiments. Several modules introduce research stories as mysteries that progressively unravel as one clue after another falls into place. Our online "Immersive Learning: How Would You Know?" activities allow students to play the role of the researcher in thinking about research questions and how psychological scientists attempt to answer them.

5. **To be as up-to-date as possible** Few things dampen students' interest as quickly as the sense that they are reading stale news. While keeping psychology's classic studies and concepts, we also present the discipline's most important recent developments. In this edition, 1173 references are dated 2015–2018. Likewise, new photos and new everyday examples are drawn from today's world.

6. **To put facts in the service of concepts** Our intention is not to overwhelm students with facts, but to reveal psychology's major concepts—to teach students how to think, and to offer psychological ideas worth thinking about. While writing, we keep in mind a simple question: *What does an educated person need to know?* Learning Objective Questions and Retrieve It questions throughout each module help students focus on the most important concepts. Online Concept Practice and TopicTutorial activities help ensure student understanding of key points.

Promoting Big Ideas and Broadened Horizons

7. **To enhance comprehension by providing continuity** Many modules have a significant issue or theme that links subtopics, forming a thread that ties the module together. The Learning modules convey the idea that bold thinkers can serve as intellectual pioneers. The Thinking, Language, and Intelligence modules raise the issue of human rationality and irrationality. The Psychological Disorders modules raise empathy for, and understanding of, troubled lives. Other threads, such as cognitive neuroscience, dual processing, and cultural, gender, and gender-identity diversity weave throughout the whole book. Although we [DM and ND] occupy separate bodies, we write with a unified voice. (We also have a similar sense of humor.) Our singleness of purpose and our editing of each other give students a familiar companion who will help guide them through psychology's interconnected roads.

8. **To convey respect for human unity and diversity** Throughout the book, readers will see evidence of our human kinship—our shared biological heritage, our common mechanisms

TABLE 7

Examples of Positive Psychology

Coverage of positive psychology topics can be found in the following modules:	
Topic	**Module**
Altruism/compassion	12, 25, 37, 38, 46
Coping	34
Courage	37
Creativity	22, 25, 29, 38
Emotional Intelligence	27, 37
Empathy	11, 21, 32, 35, 44
Flow	Appendix B
Gratitude	34
Happiness/Life Satisfaction	13, 29, 34, 44, 46
Humility	1
Humor	34, 35
Justice	35
Leadership	35, 39
Love	13, 15, 29, 37, 39, 44
Morality	12
Optimism	34, 38
Personal control	34
Resilience	11, 33, 46
Self-discipline	12, 29, 39
Self-efficacy	39
Self-esteem	29, 38, 39
Spirituality	34, 35
Toughness (grit)	27, 29
Wisdom	1, 25, 34, 35, 39

of seeing and learning, hungering and feeling, loving and hating. They will also better understand the dimensions of our diversity—our individual diversity in development and aptitudes, temperament and personality, and disorder and health; and our cultural diversity in attitudes and expressive styles, child raising and care for the elderly, and life priorities.

Our Resources Are Carefully Designed to Help Students Learn, and Care About Their Learning

We and our team work hard to create top-quality resource materials. To encourage students to read, we communicate psychology's story with crisp writing, vivid storytelling, and occasional humor. We get help from our editors, who work with us line by line. Similar care is devoted to the Instructor's Resources and assessment materials. Our text modules for this new edition went through eight drafts, and all other resources also went through multiple drafts. This creative process requires our daily focus, as we collect and create new information that will expand students' minds and enlarge their hearts. Working through what is often over *one thousand* edits and comments in a given group of modules can be daunting! But in the end it gives students the best chance at success in this life-relevant course. With the support of Worth Publishers, our author and editorial team has no rival in its investment of time and energy.

Students Love This Book

Students seem to appreciate the effort. They read the book! We get a stream of wonderfully encouraging, and sometimes funny, letters from appreciative students. Here are two examples:

> "Mr. Myers: I have been reading . . . your Psychology textbook. . . . The way you write and explain makes me feel like we're buddies."
>
> —FROM AN ANONYMOUS STUDENT

> "Your text goes above and beyond; your command of language, the . . . witty remarks and puns, the frequent inclusion of concrete psychological experiments pertaining to the . . . subject. I often found myself nodding my head while reading along, as I felt like the information I was taking in was substantiated with real life applications."
>
> —FROM A STUDENT AT SANTA MONICA COLLEGE

Students also love the online learning resources. We hear repeatedly that students benefit from the LearningCurve formative quizzing system and use it both to explore new concepts and to test their understanding.

⑦ "My students need truly effective learning tools they will use."

Our Pedagogy Follows Best Practices From Learning and Memory Research

Students want to do well in this course, and we all want to give them the best possible chance of doing so. How can we best enhance student success? We can use findings from psychological science to teach psychological science. Researchers have found that "Achievement is . . . strongly associated with the stimulation of meaningful learning by presenting information in a clear way, relating it to the students, and using conceptually demanding learning tasks" (Schneider & Preckel, 2017). So, for starters, we write and rewrite our materials under scrutiny from each other and our team of editors—ensuring that each sentence is clear and compelling, and that our student readers will readily relate psychology's concepts to their lives.

Our learning system also harnesses the *testing effect*, which documents the benefits of actively retrieving information through regular testing with *immediate feedback* (**FIGURE 8**). Thus, our LearningCurve system, which has been *very* popular with students, offers an adaptive quizzing program that provides a personalized study plan. In the text, each module offers

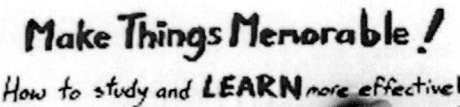

Make Things Memorable!
How to study and **LEARN** more effectively.
With David G. Myers, author

FIGURE 8

HOW TO LEARN AND REMEMBER
For a 5-minute animated guide to more effective studying, visit tinyurl.com/HowToRemember.

🔒 **RETRIEVE IT** • • •   *ANSWERS IN APPENDIX E*

RI-2 Using sound as your example, explain how these concepts differ: *absolute threshold*, *subliminal stimulation*, and *difference threshold*.

FIGURE 9

SAMPLE OF RETRIEVE IT FEATURE

Retrieve It questions interspersed throughout (**FIGURE 9**). Creating these *desirable difficulties* for students along the way optimizes the testing effect, as does immediate feedback via answers that are available for checking.

Each main section of text begins with a numbered question that establishes a *learning objective* and directs student reading. The Review found at the end of each module repeats these questions as a further self-testing opportunity (with answers in the Complete Module Reviews appendix). The Review section also offers a page-referenced list of **Terms and Concepts to Remember**, and **Experience the Testing Effect** questions in multiple formats to promote optimal retention.

These features enhance the Survey-Question-Read-Retrieve-Review (SQ3R) format. "The Overview of Modules" feature allows students to *survey* what's to come. Main sections begin with a learning objective *question* that encourages students to *read* actively. Periodic Retrieve It sections and the Module Review (with repeated Learning Objective Questions, Key Terms list, and Experience the Testing Effect questions) encourage students to test themselves by *retrieving* what they know and *reviewing* what they don't. (See Figure 9 for a Retrieve It sample.)

key terms Students will also find complete definitions of each important term in a page corner near the term's introduction in the narrative.

8 "I have a lot of nursing and premed students. I need a book that maps well onto the new MCAT's psychology section."

Since 2015, the Medical College Admission Test (MCAT) has devoted 25 percent of its questions to the "Psychological, Social, and Biological Foundations of Behavior," with most of those questions coming from the psychological science taught in introductory psychology courses. From 1977 to 2014, the MCAT focused on biology, chemistry, and physics. Thereafter, reported the *Preview Guide for MCAT 2015*, the exam also recognizes "the importance of socio-cultural and behavioral determinants of health and health outcomes." The exam's new psychology section beautifully matches this text's topics. For example, see **TABLE 8**, which outlines the precise correlation between this text's coverage of Emotion and Stress, and the corresponding portion of the MCAT exam. In addition, our Test Bank questions are keyed to MCAT topics. To improve their MCAT preparation, I [ND] regularly teach premedical students an intensive course covering the topics that appear in this text. For a complete pairing of the new MCAT psychology topics with this book's contents, see MacmillanLearning.com.

9 "I am eager to use more digital resources but uncertain how to proceed, and in need of assistance in this process."

With up to 350 students in my [ND's] classes, I, too, worried about switching to LaunchPad a few years ago. I spent some extra time the first semester learning about all of the available resources, but it was worth it. LaunchPad has saved me time and allowed me to do things that I thought were impossible with so many students. For example, I now offer a first-day-of-class, gradable assignment in LaunchPad to get students immediately engaged. I also use frequent quizzes throughout the course, which helps my students and me to track their learning progress. LaunchPad has helped make my course a success. *Assigning* materials shows that I value these resources, and I've been delighted to see a significant improvement in student retention rates since I started using LaunchPad.

The best way to get started is to visit LaunchPadWorks.com and consult with your Macmillan Learning representative.

TABLE 8

Sample MCAT Correlation With *Exploring Psychology, Eleventh Edition in Modules*

MCAT 2015 Content Category 6C: Responding to the world	*Exploring Psychology, Eleventh Edition in Modules* Correlations	Page Numbers
Emotion	Emotion: Introduction to Emotion, Expressing Emotion, Experiencing Emotion	367–382
Three components of emotion (i.e., cognitive, physiological, behavioral)	Emotion: Arousal, Behavior, and Cognition	367–368
Universal emotions (e.g., fear, anger, happiness, surprise, joy, disgust, and sadness)	Culture and Emotional Expression—including the universal emotions	378–380
	The Basic Emotions	372
Adaptive role of emotion	Emotion as the body's adaptive response	367–368
Theories of emotion	*Emotions and the Autonomic Nervous System*	372–373
James-Lange theory	*James-Lange Theory: Arousal Comes Before Emotion*	368
Cannon-Bard theory	*Cannon-Bard Theory: Arousal and Emotion Occur Simultaneously*	368–369
Schachter-Singer theory	*Schachter and Singer Two-Factor Theory: Arousal + Label = Emotion*	369
The role of biological processes in perceiving emotion	Emotions and the Autonomic Nervous System; The Physiology of Emotions	372–374
Brain regions involved in the generation and experience of emotions	Emotions and the Autonomic Nervous System; The Physiology of Emotions	372–374
The role of the limbic system in emotion	The Physiology of Emotions—including the brain's pathways for emotions	373–374
	Emotions and the Autonomic Nervous System	372–373
	The Physiology of Emotions	372–374
Emotion and the autonomic nervous system	*Emotions and the Autonomic Nervous System*	372–373
Physiological markers of emotion (signatures of emotion)	The Physiology of Emotions	373–374
Stress	Stress and Illness	383–394
The nature of stress	Stress: Some Basic Concepts	383–388
Appraisal	Stress appraisal	384
Different types of stressors (i.e., cataclysmic events, personal)	*Stressors—Things That Push Our Buttons*	385–386
Effects of stress on psychological functions	*The Stress Response System*	386–388
Stress outcomes/response to stressors	The Stress Response System	386–388
Physiological	The Stress Response System	386–388
Emotional	Stress and Vulnerability to Disease	388–394
Behavioral	*Stress and Heart Disease—Type A/B, anger management*	391–392
	Coping With Stress	395–401
	Posttraumatic Stress Disorder (PTSD)	509–510
	The Stress Response System	386–388
	Coping With Stress	395–401
Managing stress (e.g., exercise, relaxation techniques, spirituality)	Reducing Stress—aerobic exercise, relaxation/meditation, faith communities	401–406

In Appreciation

"Nothing we ever do, however virtuous, can be accomplished alone."

~ Reinhold Niebuhr, 1952

Our authoring is a collective enterprise. Aided by input from thousands of instructors and students over the years, this has become a better, more effective, more accurate book than two authors alone (these authors at least) could write. Our indebtedness continues to the innumerable researchers who have been so willing to share their time and talent to help us accurately report their research, and to the hundreds of instructors who have taken the time to offer feedback. We empathize with long-time *Atlantic* writer James Fallows' observation that "In this business you spend most of your time talking with people who *know more* about a given subject than you do. That is in hopes of eventually being able to explain it to people who know less."

Our gratitude extends to the colleagues who contributed criticism, corrections, and creative ideas related to the content and effectiveness of this new edition and its resources. For their expertise and encouragement, and the gift of their time to the teaching of psychology, we thank the reviewers and consultants listed here.

Christopher Adalio
University of California, Berkeley

Stephanie Afful
Lindenwood University

Lauren Bates
Colorado State University

Barbara Beaver
University of Wisconsin–Whitewater

Michael Brislawn
Olympic College

Amy Buckingham
Red Rocks Community College

Candace Cresap-Blomquist
Bay de Noc Community College

Jennifer Dale
Community College of Aurora

Myra Darty
North Idaho College

Scott Debb
Norfolk State University

Kyle De Young
University of Wyoming

Christyn Dolbier
East Carolina University

Angela Dortch
Ivy Tech Community College

Charles Dufour
University of Maine

Rebecca Ewing
Western New Mexico University

Rebecca Foushee
Lindenwood University

Matt Gray
University of Wyoming

Christine Henderson
SUNY Orange/Orange County Community College

Katie Hodgin
Colorado State University

Kathy Howard
Harding University

Regina Hughes
Collin College

Amy Kausler
Jefferson College

Joanna Key
Gwinnett Technical College

Kimberly Knesting-Lund
University of Wisconsin–Whitewater

Ken Luke
Tyler Junior College

Pamela Lundeberg
Colorado State University

Sharmin Maswood
Elizabethtown College

Nicole McCray
University of Montana

Corinne McNamara
Kennesaw State University

Kelly O'Dell
Community College of Aurora

Maeve O'Donnell
Colorado State University

Lawrence Patihis
University of Southern Mississippi

Michael Rader
Johnson County Community College

Julia Ramey
University of Arkansas–Pulaski Technical College

Edie Sample
Metropolitan Community College

Christopher Stanzione
Georgia Institute of Technology

Kim Stark
University of Central Missouri

Brianna Stinebaugh
Towson University

Daniel Storage
University of Denver

Rose Suggett
Southeast Community College

William Travis Suits
Seminole State College of Florida

Russell Warne
Utah Valley University

Brandon Whittington
Jefferson College

Chrysalis Wright
University of Central Florida

Kevin Zabel
Western New England University

We appreciate the guidance offered by the following teaching psychologists, who reviewed and offered helpful feedback on the development of our significantly revised "Assess Your Strengths" online activities.

Malinde Althaus
Inver Hills Community College

TaMetryce Collins
Hillsborough Community College, Brandon

Lisa Fosbender
Gulf Coast State College

Kelly Henry
Missouri Western State University

Brooke Hindman
Greenville Technical College

Natalie Kemp
University of Mount Olive

David Payne
Wallace Community College

Tanya Renner
Kapi'olani Community College

Lillian Russell
Alabama State University, Montgomery

Amy Williamson
Moraine Valley Community College

And we'd like to offer special thanks to the reviewers and consultants who helped us shape the new Thinking Critically About: Sexual Aggression infographic feature in Module 14:

Christia Brown
University of Kentucky

Ann Coker
University of Kentucky

Jane Dickie
Hope College

Sara Dorer
Hope College

Claire Renzetti
University of Kentucky

At Worth Publishers a host of people played key roles in creating this eleventh edition.

Executive Program Manager Carlise Stembridge has been a valued team leader, thanks to her dedication, creativity, and sensitivity. Carlise oversees, encourages, and guides our author-editor team, and she serves as an important liaison with our colleagues in the field.

Noel Hohnstine and Laura Burden expertly coordinated creation of the media resources. Betty Probert efficiently edited and produced the Test Bank questions (working with Chrysalis Wright, University of Central Florida), Instructor's Resources, and Lecture Guides and, in the process, helped fine-tune the whole book. Katie Pachnos and Anna Munroe provided terrific support in commissioning and organizing the multitude of reviews, coordinating our development and production schedules, and providing editorial guidance. Lee McKevitt did a splendid job of laying out each page. Robin Fadool and Donna Ranieri worked together to locate the myriad photos. Art Manager Matt McAdams managed the updating of our art program, and worked with artist Evelyn Pence to create the wonderful new "Thinking Critically About" infographics.

Senior Content Project Manager Won McIntosh and Senior Workflow Supervisor Susan Wein masterfully kept the book to its tight schedule, and Design Services Manager Natasha Wolfe skillfully directed creation of the beautiful new design.

Christine Brune, chief editor for the last three decades, is a wonder worker. She offers just the right mix of encouragement, gentle admonition, attention to detail, and passion for excellence. An author could not ask for more. Development editors Nancy Fleming, Trish Morgan, and Danielle Slevens amazed us with their meticulous focus, impressive knowledge, and helpful editing—and with kindred spirits to our own. And Deborah Heimann did an excellent job with the copyediting. After their several thousand hours of world-class skill invested in guiding and shaping this book, we fully appreciate Helen Keller's comment that "Alone we can do so little. Together we can do so much."

To achieve our goal of supporting the teaching of psychology, these resources not only must be authored, reviewed, edited, and produced, but also made available to teachers of psychology. For their exceptional success in doing that, our author team is grateful to Macmillan Learning's professional sales and marketing team. We are especially grateful to Executive Marketing Manager Kate Nurre, Marketing Manager Clay Bolton, and Learning Solutions Specialists Robyn Burnett and Elizabeth Chaffin Woosley for tirelessly working to inform our teaching colleagues of our efforts to assist their teaching, and for the joy of working with them.

At Hope College, the supporting team members for this edition included Kathryn Brownson, who researched countless bits of information and edited and proofed hundreds of pages. Kathryn is a knowledgeable and sensitive adviser on many matters. Sara Neevel, our longtime manuscript developer and friend, did advance work before we were saddened by her untimely death, leaving us so grateful for her life and her gifts. At the University of Kentucky, Lorie Hailey has showcased a variety of indispensable qualities, including a sharp eye and a strong work ethic.

Again, I [DM] gratefully acknowledge the editing assistance and mentoring of my writing coach, poet Jack Ridl, whose influence resides in the voice you will be hearing in the pages that follow. He, more than anyone, cultivated my delight in dancing with the language, and taught me to approach writing as a craft that shades into art. Likewise, I [ND] am grateful to my intellectual hero and mentor, Roy Baumeister, who taught me how to hone my writing and embrace the writing life. I'm also indebted to John Tierney, who has offered unending support and served as a role model of how to communicate to a general audience.

And we have enjoyed our ongoing work with each other. It has been a joy for me [DM] to continue working with Nathan on this project. This is our sixth book together. Nathan's fresh insights and contributions continue to enrich this book as we work together on each module—every day, every month, every year. With support from our wonderful editors, this is a team project. In addition to our work together on the textbook, Nathan and I contribute to the monthly "Teaching Current Directions in Psychological Science" column in the *APS Observer* (tinyurl.com/MyersDeWall). I [DM] also blog at TalkPsych.com, where I share exciting new findings, everyday applications, and observations on all things psychology.

Finally, our gratitude extends to the many students and instructors who have written to offer suggestions, or just an encouraging word. It is for them, and those about to begin their study of psychology, that we have done our best to introduce the field we love.

*   *   *

DAVID
MYERS

The day this book went to press was the day we started gathering information and ideas for the next edition. Your input will influence how this book continues to evolve. So, please, do share your thoughts.

David G. Myers

@DavidGMyers

Hope College

Holland, Michigan 49422-9000 USA

DavidMyers.org

Nathan DeWall

@cndewall

University of Kentucky

Lexington, Kentucky 40506-0044 USA

NathanDeWall.com

Student Preface:

Time Management—How to Be a Great Student and Still Have a Life

Richard O. Straub, University of Michigan, Dearborn

How Are You Using Your Time Now?

Design a Better Schedule

Plan the Term

Plan Your Week

More Tips for Effective Scheduling

The Importance of Playing Offense

Make Every Minute of Your Study Time Count

Use SQ3R to Help You Master This Text

Take Useful Class Notes

Create a Study Space That Helps You Learn

Set Specific, Realistic Daily Goals

Don't Forget About Rewards!

Do You Need to Revise Your New Schedule?

Are You Doing Well in Some Courses But Not in Others?

Have You Received a Poor Grade on a Test?

Are You Trying to Study Regularly for the First Time and Feeling Overwhelmed?

Desislava Draganova/Alamy

We all face challenges in our schedules. This might be your first time living outside of your parents' home, leaving you unsure how to juggle your school and social commitments. Some of you may be taking night classes, others squeezing in an online course between jobs or after putting children to bed at night. Some of you may be veterans using military benefits to jump-start a new life. Whatever your situation, the transition from your previous life situation to this one presents some challenges.

How can you balance all of your life's demands and be successful? Time management. Manage the time you have so that you can find the time you need.

In this section, I will outline a simple, four-step process for improving the way you make use of your time.

1. Keep a time-use diary to understand how you are using your time. You may be surprised at how much time you're wasting.

2. Design a new schedule for using your time more effectively.

3. Make the most of your study time so that your new schedule will work for you.

4. If necessary, refine your new schedule, based on what you've learned.

How Are You Using Your Time Now?

Although everyone gets 24 hours in the day and seven days in the week, we fill those hours and days with different obligations and interests. If you are like most people, you probably use your time wisely in some ways, and not so wisely in others. Answering the questions in

TABLE 1

Study Habits Survey

Answer the following questions, writing *Yes* or *No* for each line.

1. Do you usually set up a schedule to budget your time for studying, work, recreation, and other activities? _____

2. Do you often put off studying until time pressures force you to cram? _____

3. Do other students seem to study less than you do, but get better grades? _____

4. Do you usually spend hours at a time studying one subject, rather than dividing that time among several subjects? _____

5. Do you often have trouble remembering what you have just read in a textbook? _____

6. Before reading a chapter in a textbook, do you skim through it and read the section headings? _____

7. Do you try to predict test questions from your class notes and reading? _____

8. Do you usually try to summarize in your own words what you have just finished reading? _____

9. Do you find it difficult to concentrate for very long when you study? _____

10. Do you often feel that you studied the wrong material for a test? _____

Thousands of students have participated in similar surveys. Students who are fully realizing their academic potential usually respond as follows: (1) yes, (2) no, (3) no, (4) no, (5) no, (6) yes, (7) yes, (8) yes, (9) no, (10) no.
Do your responses fit that pattern? If not, you could benefit from improving your time management and study habits.

TABLE 1 can help you find trouble spots—and hopefully more time for the things that matter most to you.

The next thing you need to know is how you *actually* spend your time. To find out, record your activities in a *time-use diary* for one week. Be realistic. Take notes on how much time you spend attending class, studying, working, commuting, meeting personal and family needs, preparing and eating meals, socializing (don't forget texting, social networking, and gaming), exercising, and anything else that occupies your time, including life's small practical tasks, which can take up plenty of your time. As you record your activities, take notes on how you are feeling at various times of the day. When does your energy slump, and when do you feel most energetic?

Design a Better Schedule

Take a good look at your time-use diary. Where do you think you may be wasting time? Do you spend a lot of time commuting, for example? If so, could you use that time more productively? If you take public transportation, commuting is a great time to read and test yourself for review. You can access the eBook anywhere, anytime! Or you may want to take advantage of the *new Audiobook*.

Did you remember to include time for meals, personal care, work schedules, family commitments, and other fixed activities?

How much time do you sleep? In the battle to meet all of life's daily commitments and interests, we tend to treat sleep as optional. Do your best to manage your life so that you can get enough sleep to feel rested. It's hard to achieve your goals if you don't have the energy to complete them. You will feel better and be healthier, and you will also do better academically and in relationships with your family and friends. (You will read more about this in Module 8.)

Are you dedicating enough time for focused study? Take a last look at your notes to see if any other patterns pop out. Now it's time to create a new and more efficient schedule.

LWA/The Image Bank/Getty Images

Plan the Term

Before you draw up your new schedule, think ahead. If your course is not already online—complete with a schedule of assignments, activities, quizzes, and exams for the term—use your phone's calendar feature, or buy a portable calendar. Enter the dates of all exams and assignments. Also be sure to track your own long-range personal plans, including work and family commitments. Keep your personal calendar up-to-date, refer to it often, and change it as needed. Through this process, you will develop a regular schedule that will help you achieve success.

Plan Your Week

To pass those exams, meet those deadlines, and keep up with your life outside of class, you will need to convert your long-term goals into a daily schedule. Be realistic—you will be living with this routine for the entire school term. Here are some more things to add to your personal calendar.

1. Enter your class times, work hours, and any other fixed obligations. Be thorough. Allow plenty of time for such things as commuting, meals, and laundry.

2. Set up a study schedule for each course. Remember what you learned about yourself in the study habits survey (Table 1) and your time-use diary.

3. After you have budgeted time for studying, fill in slots for other obligations, exercise, fun, and relaxation.

More Tips for Effective Scheduling

There are a few other things you will want to keep in mind when you set up your schedule.

Spaced study is more effective than massed study. If you need 3 hours to study one subject, for example, it's best to divide that into shorter periods spaced over several days.

Alternate subjects, but avoid interference. Alternating the subjects you study in any given session will keep you fresh and will, surprisingly, increase your ability to remember what you're learning in each different area. Studying similar topics back-to-back, however, such as two different foreign languages, could lead to interference in your learning. (You will hear more about this in Module 24.)

Determine the amount of study time you need to do well in each course. The time you need depends on the difficulty of your courses and the effectiveness of your study methods. Ideally, you would spend at least 1 to 2 hours studying for each hour spent in class. Increase your study time slowly by setting weekly goals that will gradually bring you up to the desired level.

Create a schedule that makes sense. Tailor your schedule to meet the demands of each course. For the course that emphasizes lecture notes, plan a daily review of your notes soon after each class. If you are evaluated for class participation (for example, in a language course), allow time for a review just before the class meets. Schedule study time for your most difficult (or least motivating) courses during hours when you are the most alert and distractions are fewest.

Schedule open study time. Life can be unpredictable. Emergencies and new obligations can throw off your schedule. Or you may simply need some extra time for a project or for review in one of your courses. Try to allow for some flexibility in your schedule each week.

The Importance of Playing Offense

We can't control everything. Car troubles, family problems, and work challenges happen. Sometimes it seems as if we have to play "defense" against the demands and problems that can pile up, leaving us stressed out and unable to achieve our goals. There is a solution: Play "offense" against your environment. Set out with a plan for each day, rather than just letting the day happen to you. You will then have a lot more control over how you spend your time. Establishing routines and making decisions in advance actually conserves energy, as it spares us from some of our daily decision making. If we know we are going to study two hours in the morning before class, we won't waste time and energy weighing the pros and the cons of that choice over breakfast each day.

Earlier, I recommended that in your time-use diary you track the times you feel most energetic. Keep that in mind as you plan your days. Try to match your high-energy times with your most challenging schoolwork and projects. And don't forget to replenish your energy along the way with meals, rest, and social time.

Following these guidelines will help you find a schedule that works for you!

Make Every Minute of Your Study Time Count

Gary S Chapman/The Image Bank/Getty Images

How do you study from a textbook? We've learned a lot about effective study techniques from cognitive psychologists. To get the most out of your text, avoid simply reading and rereading in a passive manner. That method may cause you to remember the wrong things—the catchy stories but not the main points that show up later in test questions. And it's clearer than ever that taking effective class notes is essential. Here are some tips that will help you get the most from your text resources and your class.

Use SQ3R to Help You Master This Text

David Myers and Nathan DeWall organized this text by using a system called SQ3R (Survey, Question, Read, Retrieve, Review). Using SQ3R can help you to understand what you read, and to retain that information longer.

Applying SQ3R may feel at first as though it's taking more time and effort to "read" a module, but with practice, these steps will become automatic.

Survey

You will hear more about SQ3R in Module 2.

Before you read a module, survey its key parts. Scan the headings. Note that main sections have numbered Learning Objective Questions to help you focus. Pay attention to words set in bold type.

Surveying gives you the big picture of a module's content and organization. Understanding the module's logical sections will help you break your work into manageable pieces in your study sessions.

Question

To show you care about your education, continually ask questions. Doing so signals that you're engaged, curious, and motivated to work hard. Questioning starts while you're reading. As you survey, don't limit yourself to the numbered Learning Objective Questions that appear throughout the module. Jotting down additional questions of your own will cause you to look at the material in a new way. (You might, for example, scan this section's headings and ask "What does 'SQ3R' mean?") Information becomes easier to remember when you make it personally meaningful. Trying to answer your questions while reading will keep you in an active learning mode.

Read

As you read, keep your questions in mind and actively search for the answers. If you come to material that seems to answer an important question that you haven't jotted down, stop and write down that new question.

Be sure to read everything. Don't skip photo or art captions, graphs, tables, or quotes. An idea that seems vague when you read about it may become clear when you see it in a graph or table. Keep in mind that instructors sometimes base their test questions on figures and tables. And take advantage of the "Thinking Critically About" infographic features that will help you learn about key concepts.

Retrieve

When you have found the answer to one of your questions, look away and mentally recite the question and its answer. Then write the answer next to the question in your own words. Trying to explain something in your own words will help you figure out where there are gaps in your understanding. These kinds of opportunities to practice *retrieving* develop the skills you will need when you are taking exams. If you study without ever putting your book and notes aside, you may develop false confidence about what you know. With the material available, you may be able to recognize the correct answer to your questions. But will you be able to recall it later, when you take an exam without having your mental props in sight?

Test your understanding as often as you can. Testing yourself is part of successful learning, because the act of testing forces your brain to work at remembering, thus establishing the memory more permanently (so you can find it later for the exam!). Use the self-testing opportunities throughout each module, including the periodic Retrieve It items. Also take advantage of the self-testing that is available in the online resources (LaunchPadWorks.com).

Review

After working your way through the module, read over your questions and your written answers. Take an extra few minutes to create a brief written summary covering all of your questions and answers. At the end of each module, you should take advantage of three important opportunities for self-testing and review—a list of that module's Learning Objective Questions for you to try answering before checking Appendix D (Complete Module Reviews), a list of that module's key terms for you to try to define before checking the referenced page, and a set of Experience the Testing Effect test questions that cover all of that module's key concepts (with answers in Appendix E).

Take Useful Class Notes

Good notes will boost your understanding and retention. Are yours thorough? Do they form a sensible outline of what you learned in each class? If not, you may need to make some changes.

Keep Each Course's Notes Separate and Organized

Keeping all your notes for a course in one location will allow you to easily find answers to questions. Three options are (1) separate notebooks for each course, (2) clearly marked sections in a shared ring binder, or (3) carefully organized folders if you opt to take notes electronically. For the print options, removable pages will allow you to add new information and weed out past mistakes. Choosing notebook pages with lots of space, or using mark-up options in electronic files, will allow you to add comments when you review and revise your notes after class.

Use an Outline Format

Use roman numerals for major points, letters for supporting arguments, and so on. (See **FIGURE 1** for a sample.) Creating an outline from what you've learned in class will help you to put the information in context and to see the key takeaway points.

Clean Up Your Notes After Class

Try to reorganize your notes soon after class. Expand or clarify your comments and clean up any unclear phrases while the material is fresh in your mind. Write important questions in the margin, or by using an

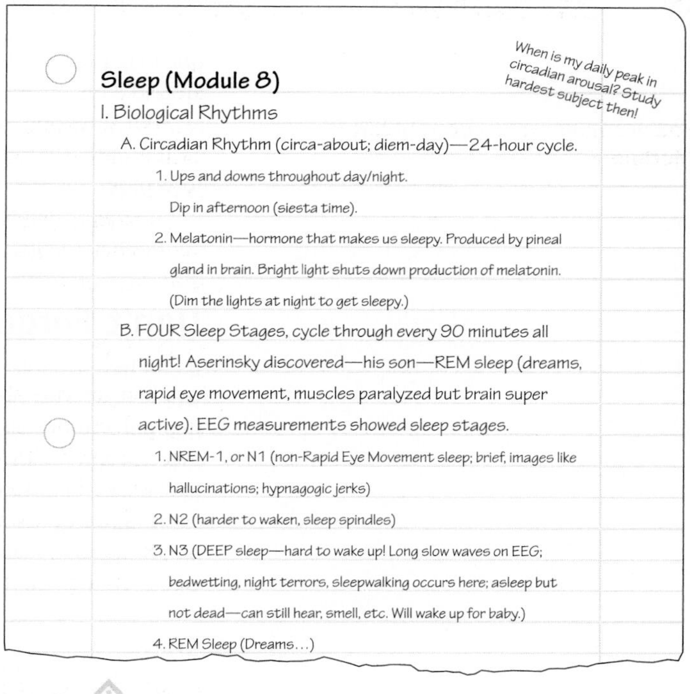

Sleep (Module 8)

When is my daily peak in circadian arousal? Study hardest subject then!

I. Biological Rhythms

    A. Circadian Rhythm (circa-about; diem-day)—24-hour cycle.

        1. Ups and downs throughout day/night.

        Dip in afternoon (siesta time).

        2. Melatonin—hormone that makes us sleepy. Produced by pineal gland in brain. Bright light shuts down production of melatonin. (Dim the lights at night to get sleepy.)

    B. FOUR Sleep Stages, cycle through every 90 minutes all night! Aserinsky discovered—his son—REM sleep (dreams, rapid eye movement, muscles paralyzed but brain super active). EEG measurements showed sleep stages.

        1. NREM-1, or N1 (non-Rapid Eye Movement sleep; brief, images like hallucinations; hypnagogic jerks)

        2. N2 (harder to waken, sleep spindles)

        3. N3 (DEEP sleep—hard to wake up! Long slow waves on EEG; bedwetting, night terrors, sleepwalking occurs here; asleep but not dead—can still hear, smell, etc. Will wake up for baby.)

        4. REM Sleep (Dreams…)

FIGURE 1

SAMPLE CLASS NOTES IN OUTLINE FORM Here is a sample from a student's notes taken in outline form from a class that was focused on sleep.

electronic markup feature, next to notes that answer them. (For example: "What are the sleep stages?") This will help you when you review your notes before a test.

Create a Study Space That Helps You Learn

It's easier to study effectively if your work area is well designed.

Organize Your Space

Work at a desk or table, not on your bed or a comfy chair that will tempt you to nap.

Minimize Distractions

Turn the TV off, turn off your phone and its notifications, and close distracting windows on your computer. If you must listen to music to mask outside noise, play soft instrumentals, not vocal selections that will draw your mind to the lyrics.

Ask Others to Honor Your Quiet Time

Tell roommates, family, and friends about your new schedule. Try to find a study place where you are least likely to be disturbed. Quiet places do exist. Sometimes you just need to do a little detective work to find them.

Set Specific, Realistic Daily Goals

The simple note "7–8 p.m.: Study Psychology" is too broad to be useful. Instead, break your studying into manageable tasks. For example, you will want to subdivide large reading assignments. If you aren't used to studying for long periods, start with relatively short periods of concentrated study, with breaks in between. In this text, for example, you might decide to read one major section before each break. Limit your breaks to 5 or 10 minutes to stretch or move around a bit.

Your attention span is a good indicator of whether you are pacing yourself successfully. At this early stage, it's important to remember that you're in training. If your attention begins to wander, get up immediately and take a short break. It is better to study effectively for 15 minutes and then take a break than to fritter away 45 minutes out of your study hour. As your endurance develops, you can increase the length of study periods.

Don't Forget About Rewards!

If you have trouble studying regularly, giving yourself a reward may help. What kind of reward works best? That depends on what you enjoy. You might start by making a list of 5 or 10 things that put a smile on your face. Spending time with a loved one, taking a walk or going for a bike ride, relaxing with a magazine or novel, or watching a favorite show can provide immediate rewards for achieving short-term study goals.

To motivate yourself when you're having trouble sticking to your schedule, allow yourself an immediate reward for completing a specific task. If running makes you smile, change your shoes, grab a friend, and head out the door! You deserve a reward for a job well done.

Do You Need to Revise Your New Schedule?

What if you've lived with your schedule for a few weeks, but you aren't making progress toward your academic and personal goals? What if your studying hasn't paid off in better grades? Don't despair and abandon your program, but do take a little time to figure out what's gone wrong.

Are You Doing Well in Some Courses But Not in Others?

Perhaps you need to shift your priorities a bit. You may need to allow more study time for chemistry, for example, and less time for some other course.

Have You Received a Poor Grade on a Test?

Did your grade fail to reflect the effort you spent preparing for the test? This can happen to even the hardest-working student, often on a first test with a new instructor. This common experience can be upsetting. "What do I have to do to get an A?" "The test was unfair!" "I studied the wrong material!"

Try to figure out what went wrong. Analyze the questions you missed, dividing them into two categories: class-based questions and text resource-based questions. How many questions did you miss in each category? If you find far more errors in one category than in the other, you'll have some clues to help you revise your schedule. Depending on the pattern you've found, you can add extra study time to the review of class notes, or to studying the text resources.

Are You Trying to Study Regularly for the First Time and Feeling Overwhelmed?

Perhaps you've set your initial goals too high. Remember, the point of time management is to identify a regular schedule that will help you achieve success. Like any skill, time management takes practice. Accept your limitations and revise your schedule to work slowly up to where you know you need to be—perhaps adding 15 minutes of study time per day.

* * *

I hope that these suggestions help make you more successful academically, and that they enhance the quality of your life in general. Having the necessary skills makes any job a lot easier and more pleasant. Let me repeat my warning not to attempt to make too drastic a change in your lifestyle immediately. Good habits require time and self-discipline to develop. Once established, they can last a lifetime.

🔒 REVIEW STUDENT PREFACE: TIME MANAGEMENT—HOW TO BE A GREAT STUDENT AND STILL HAVE A LIFE

1. **How Are You Using Your Time Now?**
    - Identify your areas of weakness.
    - Keep a time-use diary.
    - Record the time you actually spend on activities.
    - Record your energy levels to find your most productive times.

2. **Design a Better Schedule**
    - Decide on your goals for the term and for each week.
    - Enter class times, work times, social times (for family and friends), and time needed for other obligations and for practical activities.
    - Tailor study times to avoid interference and to meet each course's needs.
    - Play offense with your schedule, so that you take control and use your energy efficiently.

3. **Make Every Minute of Your Study Time Count**
    - Use the SQ3R system (survey, question, read, retrieve, review) to master material covered in your text.
    - Take careful notes (in outline form) that will help you recall and rehearse what you learned in class.
    - Try to eliminate distractions to your study time, and ask friends and family to help you focus on your work.
    - Set specific, realistic daily goals to help you focus on each day's tasks.
    - When you achieve your daily goals, reward yourself with something that you value.

4. **Do You Need to Revise Your New Schedule?**
    - Allocate extra study time for courses that are more difficult, and a little less time for courses that are easy for you.
    - Analyze your test results to help determine a more effective balance in how you spend your study time.
    - Make sure your schedule is not too ambitious. Gradually establish a schedule that will be effective for the long term.

Thinking Critically With Psychological Science

Klaus Vedfelt/Getty Images

From news and media portrayals, you might think that psychologists analyze personality, offer counseling, dispense child-raising advice, examine crime scenes, and testify in court. Do they? *Yes*—and much more. Consider some of psychology's questions that you may wonder about:

- Have you ever found yourself reacting to something as one of your biological parents would—perhaps in a way you vowed you *never* would—and then wondered how much of your personality you inherited? ***To what extent do genes predispose our individual personality differences? To what extent do home and community environments shape us?***

- Have you ever worried about how to act among people of a different culture, race, gender identity, or sexual orientation? ***How are we alike as members of the human family? How do we differ?***

- Have you ever awakened from a nightmare and wondered why you had such a crazy dream? ***Why do we dream?***

- Have you ever played peekaboo with a 6-month-old and wondered why the baby finds your disappearing/reappearing act so delightful? ***What do babies actually perceive and think?***

- Have you ever wondered what fosters school and work success? ***Does inborn intelligence explain why some people get richer, think more creatively, or relate more sensitively? Or does gritty effort, and a belief that we can grow smarter, matter more?***

- Have you ever become depressed or anxious and wondered whether you'll ever feel "normal"? *What triggers our bad moods—and our good ones? What's the line between a normal mood swing and a psychological disorder?*

As we will see in Modules 1 and 2, psychology is a science that seeks to answer such questions about us all—how and why we think, feel, and act as we do. ▶

A SMILE IS A SMILE THE WORLD AROUND Throughout this book, you will see examples not only of our cultural and gender diversity but also of the similarities that define our shared human nature. People in different cultures vary in when and how often they smile, but a naturally happy smile *means* the same thing anywhere in the world.

MODULE 1 The History and Scope of Psychology

PSYCHOLOGY IS A SCIENCE

LEARNING OBJECTIVE QUESTION (LOQ)

1-1   How is psychology a science?

To assist your learning, numbered Learning Objective Questions appear at the beginning of major sections. You can test your understanding by trying to answer the question before, and then again after, you read the section.

Underlying all science is, first, a passion to explore and understand without misleading or being misled. Some questions (*Is there life after death?*) are beyond science. Answering them in any way requires a leap of faith. With many other ideas (*Can some people demonstrate ESP?*), the proof is in the pudding. Let the facts speak for themselves.

Magician James Randi has used this **empirical approach** when testing those claiming to see glowing auras around people's bodies:

Randi: Do you see an aura around my head?

Aura seer: Yes, indeed.

Randi: Can you still see the aura if I put this magazine in front of my face?

Aura seer: Of course.

Throughout the text, important concepts are **boldfaced.** As you study, you can find these terms with their definitions nearby and in the Glossary at the end of the book.

Randi: Then if I were to step behind a wall barely taller than I am, you could determine my location from the aura visible above my head, right?

Randi once told me [DM] that no aura seer had yet agreed to take this simple test.

No matter how sensible-seeming or how wild an idea, the smart thinker asks: *Does it work?* When put to the test, do the data support its predictions? Subjected to such scrutiny, crazy-sounding ideas sometimes find support. More often, science becomes society's garbage disposal, sending crazy-sounding ideas to the waste heap, atop previous claims of perpetual motion machines, miracle cancer cures, and out-of-body travels into centuries past. To sift reality from fantasy and fact from fiction therefore requires a scientific attitude: being skeptical but not cynical, open-minded but not gullible.

empirical approach an evidence-based method that draws on observation and experimentation.

critical thinking thinking that does not blindly accept arguments and conclusions. Rather, it examines assumptions, appraises the source, discerns hidden biases, evaluates evidence, and assesses conclusions.

Putting a scientific attitude into practice requires not only curiosity and skepticism but also *humility*—awareness of our own vulnerability to error and openness to surprises and new perspectives. What matters is not my opinion or yours, but the truths revealed by our questioning and testing. If people or other animals don't behave as our ideas predict, then so much the worse for our ideas. This humble attitude was expressed in one of psychology's early mottos: "The rat is always right." (See Thinking Critically About: The Scientific Attitude.)

CRITICAL THINKING

LOQ 1-3   How does critical thinking feed a scientific attitude, and smarter thinking for everyday life?

The scientific attitude—curiosity + skepticism + humility—prepares us to think harder and smarter. This thinking style, called **critical thinking,** examines assumptions, appraises the source, discerns hidden biases, evaluates evidence, and assesses conclusions. Whether reading a research report or an online opinion, or listening to news or a talk show, critical thinkers ask questions: *How do they know that? What is this person's agenda? Is the conclusion based on an anecdote, or on evidence? Does the evidence justify a cause-effect conclusion? What alternative explanations are possible?* By thinking hard, critical thinkers arrive at the smart conclusion.

Critical thinkers wince when people make factual claims based on gut intuition: "I *feel like* climate change is [or isn't] happening." "I *feel like* self-driving cars are more [or less] dangerous." "I *feel like* my candidate is more honest." Such beliefs (commonly mislabeled as feelings) may or may not be true. Critical thinkers are open to the possibility that they (or you) might be wrong. Sometimes, they know, the best evidence confirms our intuitions. Sometimes it challenges them and beckons us to a different way of thinking.

Historians of science tell us that these three attitudes—curiosity, skepticism, and humility—helped make modern science possible. Some deeply religious people may view critical thinking and scientific inquiry, including psychology's, as a threat. Yet many of the leaders of the scientific revolution, including Copernicus and Newton, were deeply religious people acting on the idea that "in order to love and honor God, it is necessary to fully appreciate the wonders of his handiwork" (Stark, 2003a,b).

Critical inquiry can lead us to surprising findings. Other modules illustrate some examples from psychological science: Massive losses of brain tissue early in life may have minimal long-term effects. Within days, newborns can recognize their mother's odor. After brain damage, a person may be able to learn new skills yet be unaware of such learning. Diverse groups—men and women, old and young, rich and middle class, those with and without disabilities—report roughly comparable levels of personal happiness. The more people use critical thinking, the better they separate intuitive fiction from empirical fact (Bensley et al., 2014).

Critical inquiry sometimes debunks popular presumptions, as we may also see in other modules. For example, evidence indicates that sleepwalkers are *not* acting out their dreams. Our past experiences are *not* all recorded verbatim in our brains; with brain stimulation or hypnosis, one *cannot* simply replay and relive long-buried or repressed memories. Opposites tend *not* to attract. Most people do *not* suffer from unrealistically low self-esteem, and high self-esteem is *not* all good. In these instances and many others, what psychological scientists have learned is not what is widely believed.

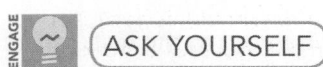

ASK YOURSELF

Were you surprised to learn that psychology is a science? How would you explain that if someone else now asked you about this?

From a tongue-in-cheek Twitter feed: "The problem with quotes on the internet is that you never know if they're true." —Abraham Lincoln

"My deeply held belief is that if a god anything like the traditional sort exists, our curiosity and intelligence are provided by such a god. We would be unappreciative of those gifts . . . if we suppressed our passion to explore the universe and ourselves." —Carl Sagan, *Broca's Brain*, 1979

THINKING CRITICALLY ABOUT:

The Scientific Attitude

Three basic attitudes helped make modern science possible.

LOQ 1-2   What are the three key elements of the scientific attitude, and how do they support scientific inquiry?

1 CURIOSITY:

Does it work?

When put to the test, can its predictions be confirmed?

Can some people read minds?

Are stress levels related to health and well-being? ○

○ No one has yet been able to demonstrate extrasensory mind-reading.

○ Many studies have found that higher stress relates to poorer health.

2 SKEPTICISM:

What do you mean?

How do you know?

Sifting reality from fantasy requires a healthy skepticism—an attitude that is not cynical (doubting everything), but also not gullible (believing everything).

Do our facial expressions and body postures affect how we actually feel? ○

Do parental behaviors determine their children's sexual orientation— or not? ○

○ Our facial expressions and body postures can affect how we feel.

○ Module 15 explains that there is not a relationship between parental behaviors and their children's sexual orientation.

3 HUMILITY:

Researchers must be willing to be surprised and follow new ideas. People and other animals don't always behave as our ideas and beliefs would predict.

The rat is always right.

RETAIN 🔒 Study Tip: Memory research reveals a *testing effect:* We retain information much better if we actively retrieve it by self-testing and rehearsing. (More on this in Module 2.) To bolster your learning and memory, take advantage of the *Retrieve It* self-tests you'll find throughout this text.

Psychology's critical inquiry can also identify effective policies. To deter crime, should we invest money in lengthening prison sentences or increase the likelihood of arrest? To help people recover from a trauma, should counselors help them relive it, or not? To increase voting, should we tell people about the low turnout problem, or emphasize that their peers are voting? When put to critical thinking's test—and contrary to common practice—the second option in each case wins (Shafir, 2013). Thinking critically can—and sometimes does—change the world.

🔒 **RETRIEVE IT • • •**   *ANSWERS IN APPENDIX E*

RI-1 Describe what's involved in critical thinking.

LIFE AFTER STUDYING PSYCHOLOGY
The study of psychology, and its critical thinking strategies, have helped prepare people for varied occupations, as illustrated by Facebook founder Mark Zuckerberg (who studied psychology and computer science while in college) and actress and film producer Natalie Portman (who majored in psychology and co-authored a scientific article in college—and on one of her summer breaks was filmed for *Star Wars: Episode I*).

PSYCHOLOGICAL SCIENCE IS BORN

LOQ 1-4   What were some important milestones in psychology's early development?

To be human is to be curious about ourselves and the world around us. Before 300 B.C.E., the Greek naturalist and philosopher Aristotle theorized about learning and memory, motivation and emotion, perception and personality. Today we chuckle at some of his guesses, like his suggestion that a meal makes us sleepy by causing gas and heat to collect around the source of our personality, the heart. But credit Aristotle with asking the right questions.

PSYCHOLOGY'S FIRST LABORATORY Philosophers' thinking about thinking continued until the birth of psychology, as we know it, on a December day in 1879, in a small, third-floor room at Germany's University of Leipzig. There, two young men were helping an austere, middle-aged professor, Wilhelm Wundt, create an experimental apparatus. Their machine measured the time it took for people to press a telegraph key after hearing a ball hit a platform (Hunt, 1993). Curiously, people responded in about one-tenth of a second when asked to press the key as soon as the sound occurred—and in about two-tenths of a second when asked to press the key as soon as they were consciously aware of perceiving the sound. (To be aware of one's awareness takes a little longer.) Wundt was seeking to measure "atoms of the mind"—the fastest and simplest mental processes. So began the first psychological laboratory, staffed by Wundt and by psychology's first graduate students.

PSYCHOLOGY'S FIRST SCHOOLS OF THOUGHT Before long, this new science of psychology became organized into different branches, or schools of thought, each promoted by pioneering thinkers. Two early schools were **structuralism** and **functionalism**. Much as chemists developed the periodic table to classify chemical elements, so psychologist Edward Bradford Titchener aimed to classify and understand elements of the mind's structure. He engaged people in self-reflective *introspection* (looking inward), training them to report elements of their experience as they looked at a rose, listened to a metronome, smelled a scent, or tasted a substance. What were their immediate sensations, their images, their feelings? And how did these relate to one another? Alas, structuralism's technique of introspection proved somewhat unreliable. It required smart, verbal people, and its results varied from person to person and experience to experience. As introspection waned, so did structuralism. Hoping to assemble the mind's structure from simple elements was rather like trying to understand a car by examining its disconnected parts.

Philosopher-psychologist William James thought it would be more fruitful to go beyond labeling our inward thoughts and feelings by considering their evolved *functions*. Smelling is what the nose does; thinking is what the brain does. But *why* do the nose and brain do these things? Under the influence of evolutionary theorist Charles Darwin, James assumed that thinking, like smelling, developed because it was *adaptive*—it helped our ancestors survive and reproduce. Consciousness serves a function. It enables us to

WILHELM WUNDT (1832–1920) Wundt established the first psychology laboratory at the University of Leipzig, Germany.

Throughout the book, information sources are cited in parentheses, with researchers' names and the date the research was published. Every citation can be found in the end-of-book References section, with complete documentation that follows American Psychological Association (APA) style.

structuralism an early school of thought promoted by Wundt and Titchener; used introspection to reveal the structure of the human mind.

functionalism an early school of thought promoted by James and influenced by Darwin; explored how mental and behavioral processes function—how they enable the organism to adapt, survive, and flourish.

EDWARD BRADFORD TITCHENER (1867–1927) Titchener used introspection to search for the mind's structural elements.

WILLIAM JAMES (1842–1910) AND MARY WHITON CALKINS (1863–1930) James was a legendary teacher-writer who authored an important 1890 psychology text. He mentored Calkins, who became a pioneering memory researcher and the first woman to be president of the American Psychological Association.

consider our past, adjust to our present, and plan our future. To explore the mind's adaptive functions, James studied down-to-earth emotions, memories, willpower, habits, and moment-to-moment streams of consciousness. James' writings included a textbook of the new science of psychology. More than a century later, people still read his *Principles of Psychology* (1890) and marvel at the brilliance and elegance with which he introduced psychology to the educated public.

PSYCHOLOGY'S FIRST WOMEN James' legacy stems from his Harvard mentoring as well as from his writing. In 1890—thirty years before American women had the right to vote—he admitted Mary Whiton Calkins into his graduate seminar over the objections of Harvard's president (Scarborough & Furumoto, 1987). When Calkins joined, the other students (all men) dropped out. So James tutored her alone. Later, she finished all of Harvard's Ph.D. requirements, outscoring all the male students on the qualifying exams. Alas, Harvard denied her the degree she had earned, offering her instead a degree from Radcliffe College, its undergraduate "sister" school for women. Calkins resisted the unequal treatment and refused the degree. She nevertheless went on to become a distinguished memory researcher and, in 1905, the first female president of the American Psychological Association (APA).

MARGARET FLOY WASHBURN (1871–1939) The first woman to receive a psychology Ph.D., Washburn synthesized animal behavior research in *The Animal Mind* (1908).

The honor of being the first official female psychology Ph.D. later fell to Margaret Floy Washburn, who also wrote an influential book, *The Animal Mind*, and became the second female APA president in 1921. But Washburn's gender barred doors for her, too. Although her thesis was the first foreign study Wundt published in his psychology journal, she could not join the all-male organization of experimental psychologists founded

ADDRESSING DIVERSITY DEFICIENCIES At this 1964 meeting of the Society of Experimental Psychologists, Eleanor Gibson was easy to spot among the many male members, all in a sea of white faces. By contrast, women now are 55 percent of Association for Psychological Science members and 75 percent of psychology graduate students. People of color have made enormous contributions to the field (see, for example, coverage of Kenneth Clark and Mamie Phipps Clark in Module 2), and psychology's diversity continues to grow. (For more on the history of these changes, see the Historical Timeline at the very beginning of this book).

by Titchener, her own graduate adviser (Johnson, 1997). What a different world from the recent past—1997 to 2017—when women were 10 of the 20 elected presidents of the science-oriented Association for Psychological Science. In the United States, Canada, and Europe, women now earn most psychology doctorates.

🔒 **RETRIEVE IT • • •**   *ANSWERS IN APPENDIX E*

RI-2 What event defined the start of scientific psychology?

RI-3 Why did introspection fail as a method for understanding how the mind works?

RI-4 The school of _____ used introspection to define the mind's makeup; _____ focused on how mental processes enable us to adapt, survive, and flourish.

PSYCHOLOGICAL SCIENCE MATURES

LOQ 1-5   How did behaviorism, Freudian psychology, and humanistic psychology further the development of psychological science?

In psychology's early days, many psychologists shared with English essayist C. S. Lewis the view that "there is one thing, and only one in the whole universe which we know more about than we could learn from external observation." That one thing, Lewis said, is ourselves: "We have, so to speak, inside information" (1960, pp. 18–19). Wundt and Titchener focused on inner sensations, images, and feelings. James also engaged in introspective examination of the stream of consciousness and emotion, hoping to understand their adaptive functions. For these and other early pioneers, *psychology* was defined as "the science of mental life."

BEHAVIORISM   That definition endured until the 1920s, when the first of two provocative American psychologists challenged it. John B. Watson, and later B. F. Skinner, dismissed introspection and redefined *psychology* as "the scientific study of observable behavior." After all, they said, science is rooted in observation: What you cannot observe and measure, you cannot scientifically study. You cannot observe a sensation, a feeling, or a thought, but you *can* observe and record people's *behavior* as they are *conditioned*—as they respond to and learn in different situations. Many agreed, and **behaviorism** was one of psychology's two major forces well into the 1960s.

FREUDIAN (PSYCHOANALYTIC) PSYCHOLOGY   The second major force was Sigmund Freud's *psychoanalytic psychology,* which emphasized the ways our unconscious mind and childhood experiences affect our behavior. (In other modules, we'll look more closely at Freud's ideas.)

behaviorism the view that psychology (1) should be an objective science that (2) studies behavior without reference to mental processes. Most psychologists today agree with (1) but not with (2).

B. F. SKINNER (1904–1990) This leading behaviorist rejected introspection and studied how consequences shape behavior.

JOHN B. WATSON (1878–1958) AND ROSALIE RAYNER (1898–1935) Working with Rayner, Watson championed psychology as the scientific study of behavior. In a controversial study on a baby who became famous as "Little Albert," he and Rayner showed that fear could be learned.

SIGMUND FREUD (1856–1939) The controversial ideas of this famed personality theorist and therapist have influenced humanity's self-understanding.

humanistic psychology a historically significant perspective that emphasized human growth potential.

cognitive psychology the study of mental processes, such as occur when we perceive, learn, remember, think, communicate, and solve problems.

cognitive neuroscience the interdisciplinary study of the brain activity linked with cognition (including perception, thinking, memory, and language).

psychology the science of behavior and mental processes.

nature–nurture issue the longstanding controversy over the relative contributions that genes and experience make to the development of psychological traits and behaviors. Today's science sees traits and behaviors arising from the interaction of nature and nurture.

ASK YOURSELF

How would you have defined *psychology* before taking this class?

natural selection the principle that inherited traits that better enable an organism to survive and reproduce in a particular environment will (in competition with other trait variations) most likely be passed on to succeeding generations.

evolutionary psychology the study of the evolution of behavior and the mind, using principles of natural selection.

behavior genetics the study of the relative power and limits of genetic and environmental influences on behavior.

culture the enduring behaviors, ideas, attitudes, values, and traditions shared by a group of people and transmitted from one generation to the next.

HUMANISTIC PSYCHOLOGY As the behaviorists had rejected the early 1900's definition of *psychology*, other groups rejected the behaviorists' definition. In the 1960s, **humanistic psychologists,** led by Carl Rogers and Abraham Maslow, found both behaviorism and Freudian psychology too limiting. Rather than focusing on conditioned responses or childhood memories, the humanistic psychologists focused on our needs for love and acceptance and on environments that nurture or limit personal growth.

🔒 **RETRIEVE IT • • •**   *ANSWERS IN APPENDIX E*

RI-5 From the 1920s through the 1960s, the two major forces in psychology were _____ and _____ psychology.

CONTEMPORARY PSYCHOLOGY

LOQ 1-6   How has contemporary psychology focused on cognition, on biology and experience, on culture and gender, and on human flourishing?

Simultaneous with humanistic psychology's emergence, psychologists in the 1960s pioneered a *cognitive revolution*. This led the field back to its early interest in how our mind processes and retains information. **Cognitive psychology** today continues its scientific exploration of how we perceive, process, and remember information, and of how thinking and emotion interact in anxiety, depression, and other disorders. The marriage of cognitive psychology (the science of mind) and neuroscience (the science of brain) gave birth to **cognitive neuroscience.** This specialty, with researchers in many disciplines, studies the brain activity underlying mental activity.

Today's psychology builds on the work of many earlier scientists and schools of thought. To encompass psychology's concern with observable behavior *and* with inner thoughts and feelings, we now define **psychology** as the *science of behavior and mental processes*. Let's unpack this definition. *Behavior* is anything an organism *does*—any action we can observe and record. Yelling, smiling, blinking, sweating, talking, tweeting, and questionnaire marking are all observable behaviors. *Mental processes* are our internal, subjective experiences—our sensations, perceptions, dreams, thoughts, beliefs, and feelings.

The key word in psychology's definition is *science*. Psychology is less a set of findings than a way of asking and answering questions. Our aim, then, is not merely to report results but also to show you how psychologists play their game. You will see how researchers evaluate conflicting opinions and ideas. And you will learn how all of us, whether scientists or simply curious people, can think harder and smarter when experiencing and explaining the events of our lives.

Psychology—the science of behavior and mental processes—has roots in many disciplines and countries. The young science of psychology developed from the more established fields of philosophy and biology. Wundt was both a philosopher and a physiologist. James was an American philosopher. Freud was an Austrian physician. Ivan Pavlov, who pioneered the study of learning, was a Russian physiologist. Jean Piaget, the last century's most influential observer of children, was a Swiss biologist. These "Magellans of the mind," as psychology historian Morton Hunt (1993) called them—illustrate the diversity of psychology's origins.

Like those pioneers, today's estimated 1+ million psychologists are citizens of many lands (Zoma & Gielen, 2015). The International Union of Psychological Science has 82 member nations, from Albania to Zimbabwe. Psychology is *growing* and it is *globalizing*. The story of psychology is being written in many places, with interests ranging from the study of nerve cell activity to the study of international conflicts. Contemporary psychology, shaped by many forces, is particularly influenced by our understanding of biology and experience, culture and gender, and human flourishing.

Evolutionary Psychology and Behavior Genetics

Are our human traits present at birth, or do they develop through experience? The debate over this huge **nature–nurture issue** is ancient. Greek philosopher Plato (428–348 B.C.E.) assumed that we inherit character and intelligence and that certain ideas are inborn. Aristotle (384–322 B.C.E.) countered that there is nothing in the mind that does not first come in from the external world through the senses.

A NATURE-MADE NATURE–NATURE EXPERIMENT Identical twins have the same genes. This makes them ideal participants in studies designed to shed light on hereditary and environmental influences on personality, intelligence, and other traits. Fraternal twins have different genes but often share a similar environment. Twin studies provide a wealth of findings—described in other modules—showing the importance of both nature and nurture.

More insight into nature's influence on behavior arose after a 22-year-old seafaring voyager, Charles Darwin, pondered the incredible species variation he encountered, including tortoises on one island that differed from those on nearby islands. Darwin's 1859 *On the Origin of Species* explained this diversity by proposing the evolutionary process of **natural selection:** From among chance variations, nature selects traits that best enable an organism to survive and reproduce in a particular environment. Darwin's principle of natural selection is still with us 150+ years later as biology's organizing principle. Evolution also has become an important principle for twenty-first-century psychology. This would surely have pleased Darwin, who believed his theory explained not only animal structures (such as a polar bear's white coat) but also animal behaviors (such as the emotional expressions associated with human lust and rage).

The nature–nurture issue recurs throughout this text as today's psychologists explore the relative contributions of biology and experience. They ask, for example, how are we humans *alike* because of our common biology and evolutionary history? That's the focus of **evolutionary psychology.** And how do we individually *differ* because of our differing genes and environments? That's the focus of **behavior genetics.**

We can, for example, ask: Are gender differences biologically predisposed or socially constructed? Is children's grammar mostly innate or formed by experience? How are intelligence and personality differences influenced by heredity, and by environment? Are sexual behaviors more "pushed" by inner biology or "pulled" by external incentives? Should we treat psychological disorders—depression, for example—as disorders of the brain, disorders of thought, or both?

Over and over again we will see that in contemporary science, the nature–nurture tension dissolves: *Nurture works on what nature provides.* Our species is biologically endowed with an enormous capacity to learn and adapt. Moreover, every psychological event (every thought, every emotion) is simultaneously a biological event. Thus, depression can be both a brain disorder *and* a thought disorder.

CHARLES DARWIN (1809–1882) Darwin argued that natural selection shapes behaviors as well as bodies.

🔒 RETRIEVE IT • • •   *ANSWERS IN APPENDIX E*

RI-6 How did the cognitive revolution affect the field of psychology?

RI-7 What is natural selection?

RI-8 What is contemporary psychology's position on the nature–nurture issue?

ENGAGE   (ASK YOURSELF)

Think of one of your own unique traits. How do you think that trait was influenced by nature and nurture?

Cross-Cultural and Gender Psychology

What can we learn about people in general from psychological studies done in one time and place—often with participants from what some psychologists have called the WEIRD cultures (Western, Educated, Industrialized, Rich, and Democratic [Henrich et al., 2010])? As we will see time and again, **culture**—shared ideas and behaviors that one generation passes on to the next—matters. Our culture shapes our behavior. It influences our standards of promptness and frankness, our attitudes toward premarital sex and varying body shapes, our tendency to be casual or formal, our willingness to make eye contact, our conversational distance, and much, much more. Being aware of such differences, we can restrain our assumptions that others will think and act as we do.

"All people are the same; only their habits differ." —Confucius, 551–479 B.C.E.

ENGAGE **CULTURE AND KISSING** Kissing crosses cultures. Yet how we do it varies. Imagine yourself kissing someone on the lips. Do you tilt your head right or left? In Western cultures, in which people read from left to right, about two-thirds of couples kiss right, as in William and Kate's famous kiss, and in Auguste Rodin's sculpture, *The Kiss.* In one study, 77 percent of Hebrew- and Arabic-language right-to-left readers kissed tilting left (Shaki, 2013).

Mark Cuthbert/Getty Images

Hemis/Alamy

ENGAGE (ASK YOURSELF)

How have your cultural experiences influenced your development?

ENGAGE  **LaunchPad** Our online learning tools will help you excel in this course. Take advantage of adaptive quizzing, interactive simulations, "How Would You Know?" research activities, and "Assess Your Strengths" personal self-assessments. For more information, see LaunchPadWorks.com.

 **LaunchPad** For an excellent tour of psychology's roots, view the 9.5-minute **Video: The History of Psychology**.

It is also true, however, that our shared biological heritage unites us as a universal human family. The same underlying processes guide people everywhere. Some examples:

- People diagnosed with specific learning disorder (formerly called dyslexia) exhibit the same brain malfunction whether they are Italian, French, or British (Paulesu et al., 2001).

- Variation in languages may impede communication across cultures. Yet all languages share deep principles of grammar, and people from different corners of the world can communicate with a smile or a frown.

- People in different cultures vary in feelings of loneliness (Lykes & Kemmelmeier, 2014). But across cultures, loneliness is magnified by shyness, low self-esteem, and being unmarried (Jones et al., 1985; Rokach et al., 2002).

We are each in certain respects like all others, like some others, and like no other. Studying people of all races and cultures helps us discern our similarities and our differences, our human kinship and our diversity.

You will see throughout this book that one's socially defined *gender* (as well as one's biologically defined sex) matters, too. Researchers report gender differences in what we dream, in how we express and detect emotions, and in our risk for alcohol use disorder, depression, and eating disorders. Gender differences fascinate us, and studying them is potentially beneficial. For example, many researchers have observed that women carry on conversations more readily to build relationships, while men talk more to give information and advice (Tannen, 2001). Understanding these differences can help us prevent conflicts and misunderstandings in everyday interactions.

But again, psychologically as well as biologically, women and men are overwhelmingly similar. Whether female or male, we learn to walk at about the same age. We experience the same sensations of light and sound. We remember vivid emotional events and forget mundane details. We feel the same pangs of hunger, desire, and fear. We exhibit similar overall intelligence and well-being.

The point to remember: Even when specific attitudes and behaviors vary by gender or across cultures, as they often do, the underlying processes are much the same.

Positive Psychology

Psychology's first hundred years focused on understanding and treating troubles, such as abuse and anxiety, depression and disease, prejudice and poverty. Much of today's psychology continues the exploration of such challenges. Without slighting the need to repair damage and cure disease, Martin Seligman and others (2002, 2005, 2011) have called for more research on *human flourishing*. These psychologists call their approach **positive psychology.** They believe that happiness is a by-product of a pleasant, engaged, and meaningful life. Thus, positive psychology uses scientific methods to explore the building of a "good life" that engages our skills, and a "meaningful life" that points beyond ourselves.

Psychology's Three Main Levels of Analysis

LOQ 1-7   What are psychology's levels of analysis and related perspectives?

Each of us is a complex system that is part of a larger social system. But each of us is also composed of smaller systems, such as our nervous system and body organs, which are composed of still smaller systems—cells, molecules, and atoms.

These tiered systems suggest different **levels of analysis,** which offer complementary outlooks. Consider horrific school shootings. Have they occurred because the shooters have brain disorders or genetic tendencies that cause them to be violent? Because they have observed brutality and mayhem in the media or played violent video games? Because they live in a gun-toting society? Such perspectives are complementary because "everything is related to everything else" (Brewer, 1996). Together, different levels of analysis form a

Biological influences:
- genetic *predispositions* (genetically influenced traits)
- genetic *mutations* (random errors in gene replication)
- natural selection of adaptive traits and behaviors passed down through generations
- genes responding to the environment

Psychological influences:
- learned fears and other learned expectations
- emotional responses
- cognitive processing and perceptual interpretations

Behavior or mental process

Social-cultural influences:
- presence of others
- cultural, societal, and family expectations
- peer and other group influences
- compelling models (such as in the media)

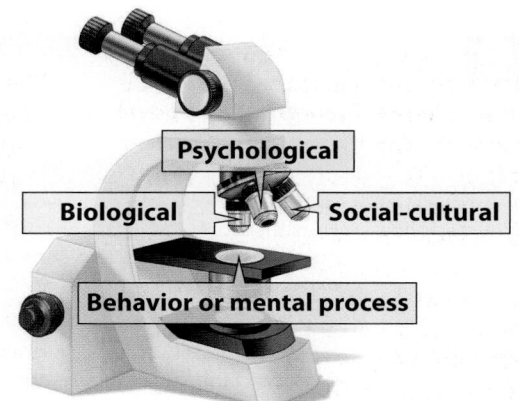

FIGURE 1.1

BIOPSYCHOSOCIAL APPROACH This integrated viewpoint incorporates various levels of analysis and offers a more complete picture of any given behavior or mental process.

biopsychosocial approach, which considers the influences of biological, psychological, and social-cultural factors (**FIGURE 1.1**).

Each level of analysis offers a perspective for looking at a behavior or mental process, yet each by itself is incomplete. Each perspective described in **TABLE 1.1** asks different questions and has its limits, but together they complement one another. Consider, for example, how they shed light on anger:

- Someone working from a **neuroscience perspective** might study brain circuits that cause us to be red in the face and "hot under the collar."

- Someone working from an **evolutionary perspective** might analyze how anger facilitated the survival of our ancestors' genes.

- Someone working from a **behavior genetics perspective** might study how heredity and experience influence our individual differences in temperament.

- Someone working from a **psychodynamic perspective** might view an outburst as an outlet for unconscious hostility.

- Someone working from a **behavioral perspective** might attempt to determine what triggers aggressive acts.

- Someone working from a **cognitive perspective** might study how our interpretation of a situation affects our anger and how our anger affects our thinking.

- Someone working from a **social-cultural perspective** might explore how expressions of anger vary across cultural contexts.

The point to remember: Like two-dimensional views of a three-dimensional object, each of psychology's perspectives is helpful. But each by itself fails to reveal the whole picture.

positive psychology the scientific study of human flourishing, with the goals of discovering and promoting strengths and virtues that help individuals and communities to thrive.

levels of analysis the differing complementary views, from biological to psychological to social-cultural, for analyzing any given phenomenon.

biopsychosocial approach an integrated approach that incorporates biological, psychological, and social-cultural levels of analysis.

ENGAGE 💡 (ASK YOURSELF)

Which of psychology's theoretical perspectives do you find most interesting? Why?

🔒 **RETRIEVE IT • • •**   *ANSWERS IN APPENDIX E*

RI-9 What advantage do we gain by using the biopsychosocial approach in studying psychological events?

RI-10 The _____-_____ perspective in psychology focuses on how behavior and thought differ from situation to situation and from culture to culture, while the _____ perspective emphasizes observation of how we respond to and learn in different situations.

JUERGEN SCHWARZ/AFP/Getty Images

TABLE 1.1

Psychology's Theoretical Perspectives

Perspective	Focus	Sample Questions	Examples of Subfields Using This Perspective
Neuroscience	How the body and brain enable emotions, memories, and sensory experiences	How do pain messages travel from the hand to the brain? How is blood chemistry linked with moods and motives?	Biological; cognitive; clinical
Evolutionary	How the natural selection of traits has promoted the survival of genes	How does evolution influence behavior tendencies?	Biological; developmental; social
Behavior genetics	How our genes and our environment influence our individual differences	To what extent are psychological traits such as intelligence, personality, sexual orientation, and vulnerability to depression products of our genes? Of our environment?	Personality; developmental; legal/forensic
Psychodynamic	How behavior springs from unconscious drives and conflicts	How can someone's personality traits and disorders be explained by unfulfilled wishes and childhood traumas?	Clinical; counseling; personality
Behavioral	How we learn observable responses	How do we learn to fear particular objects or situations? What is the most effective way to alter our behavior, say, to lose weight or stop smoking?	Clinical; counseling; industrial-organizational
Cognitive	How we encode, process, store, and retrieve information	How do we use information in remembering? Reasoning? Solving problems?	Cognitive neuroscience; clinical; counseling; industrial-organizational
Social-cultural	How behavior and thinking vary across situations and cultures	How are we affected by the people around us, and by our surrounding culture?	Developmental; social; clinical; counseling

Psychology's Subfields

LOQ 1-8   What are psychology's main subfields?

Picturing a chemist at work, you may envision a laboratory scientist surrounded by test tubes and high-tech equipment. Picture a psychologist at work and you would be right to envision

- a white-coated scientist probing a rat's brain.
- an intelligence researcher measuring how quickly an infant shows boredom by looking away from a familiar picture.
- an executive evaluating a new "healthy lifestyles" training program for employees.
- a researcher at a computer analyzing "big data" from social media status updates or Google searches.
- a therapist actively listening to a depressed client's thoughts.
- a traveling academic visiting another culture and collecting data on variations in human values and behaviors.
- a teacher or writer sharing the joy of psychology with others.

"I'm a social scientist, Michael. That means I can't explain electricity or anything like that, but if you ever want to know about people I'm your man."

The New Yorker Collection, 1986, J.B. Handelsman from cartoonbank.com

The cluster of subfields we call psychology is a meeting ground for different disciplines. Thus, it's a perfect home for those with wide-ranging interests. In its diverse activities, from biological experimentation to cultural comparisons, psychology is united by a common quest: *describing and explaining behavior and the mind underlying it.*

Some psychologists conduct **basic research** that builds psychology's knowledge base. We will meet a wide variety of such researchers, including *biological psychologists* exploring the links between brain and mind; *developmental psychologists* studying our changing abilities from womb to tomb; *cognitive psychologists* experimenting with how we perceive, think, and solve problems; *personality psychologists* investigating our persistent traits; and *social psychologists* exploring how we view and affect one another.

Ted Fitzgerald/AP Images

These and other psychologists also may conduct **applied research,** tackling practical problems. *Industrial-organizational psychologists,* for example, use psychology's concepts and methods in the workplace to help organizations and companies select and train employees, boost morale and productivity, design products, and implement systems.

Psychology is a science, but it is also a profession that helps people have healthier relationships, overcome anxiety or depression, and raise thriving children. **Counseling psychologists** help people to cope with challenges and crises (including academic, vocational, and relationship issues) and to improve their personal and social functioning. **Clinical psychologists** assess and treat people with mental, emotional, and behavior disorders. Both counseling and clinical psychologists administer and interpret tests, provide counseling and therapy, and sometimes conduct basic and applied research. By contrast, **psychiatrists,** who also may provide psychotherapy, are medical doctors licensed to prescribe drugs and otherwise treat physical causes of psychological disorders.

Rather than seeking to change people to fit their environment, **community psychologists** work to create social and physical environments that are healthy for all (Bradshaw et al., 2009; Trickett, 2009). To prevent bullying, for example, they might consider ways to improve the culture of the school and neighborhood, and how to increase bystander intervention (Polanin et al., 2012).

With perspectives ranging from the biological to the social, and with settings ranging from the laboratory to the clinic to the office, psychology relates to many fields. Psychologists teach in medical schools, business schools, law schools, and theological seminaries, and they work in hospitals, factories, and corporate offices. They engage in interdisciplinary studies, such as psychobiography (the study of the lives and personalities of public figures), psycholinguistics (the study of language and thinking), and psychoceramics (the study of crackpots).[1]

Psychology also influences culture. And psychology deepens our appreciation for how we humans perceive, think, feel, and act. By so doing it can enrich our lives and enlarge

basic research pure science that aims to increase the scientific knowledge base.

applied research a scientific study that aims to solve practical problems.

counseling psychology a branch of psychology that assists people with problems in living (often related to school, work, or marriage) and in achieving greater well-being.

clinical psychology a branch of psychology that studies, assesses, and treats people with psychological disorders.

psychiatry a branch of medicine dealing with psychological disorders; practiced by physicians who sometimes provide medical (for example, drug) treatments as well as psychological therapy.

community psychology a branch of psychology that studies how people interact with their social environments and how social institutions affect individuals and groups.

---

1. Confession: I [DM] wrote the last part of this sentence on April Fool's Day.

LAURENT/GLUCK/AGE Fotostock

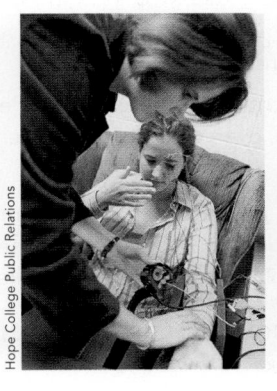

Hope College Public Relations

Scott J. Ferrell/Getty Images

📖 **LaunchPad** Want to learn more? See Appendix C, Career Fields in Psychology, at the end of this book, and go to our online **Pursuing a Psychology Career** resource to learn about the many interesting options available to those with bachelor's, master's, and doctoral degrees in psychology. To review and test your understanding of psychology's perspectives and subfields, engage online with **Concept Practice: Psychology's Current Perspectives** and **Concept Practice: Psychology's Subfields.**

our vision. Through this book we hope to help guide you toward that end. As educator Charles Eliot said a century ago: "Books are the quietest and most constant of friends, and the most patient of teachers."

🔒 **RETRIEVE IT • • •**   *ANSWERS IN APPENDIX E*

RI-11 Match the specialty (I through III) with the description (a through c).

I. Clinical psychology   a. works to create social and physical environments that are healthy for all.

II. Psychiatry   b. studies, assesses, and treats people with psychological disorders but usually does not provide medical therapy.

III. Community psychology   c. is a branch of medicine dealing with psychological disorders.

🔒 **REVIEW** THE HISTORY AND SCOPE OF PSYCHOLOGY

⟩⟩ Learning Objectives

TEST YOURSELF Answer these repeated Learning Objective Questions on your own (before checking the answers in Appendix D) to improve your retention of the concepts (McDaniel et al., 2009, 2015).

1-1 How is psychology a science?

1-2 What are the three key elements of the scientific attitude, and how do they support scientific inquiry?

1-3 How does critical thinking feed a scientific attitude, and smarter thinking for everyday life?

1-4 What were some important milestones in psychology's early development?

1-5 How did behaviorism, Freudian psychology, and humanistic psychology further the development of psychological science?

1-6 How has contemporary psychology focused on cognition, on biology and experience, on culture and gender, and on human flourishing?

1-7 What are psychology's levels of analysis and related perspectives?

1-8 What are psychology's main subfields?

⟩⟩ Terms and Concepts To Remember

TEST YOURSELF Write down the definition yourself, then check your answer on the referenced page.

empirical approach, **p. 2**

critical thinking, **p. 2**

structuralism, **p. 5**

functionalism, **p. 5**

behaviorism, **p. 7**

humanistic psychology, **p. 8**

cognitive psychology, **p. 8**

cognitive neuroscience, **p. 8**

psychology, **p. 8**

nature–nurture issue, **p. 8**

natural selection, **p. 8**

evolutionary psychology, **p. 8**

behavior genetics, **p. 8**

culture, **p. 8**

positive psychology, **p. 11**

levels of analysis, **p. 11**

biopsychosocial approach, **p. 11**

basic research, **p. 13**

applied research, **p. 13**

counseling psychology, **p. 13**

clinical psychology, **p. 13**

psychiatry, **p. 13**

community psychology, **p. 13**

⟩⟩ Experience the Testing Effect

TEST YOURSELF Answer the following questions on your own first, then check your answers in Appendix E.

1. As scientists, psychologists

   a. keep their methods private so others will not repeat their research.

   b. assume the truth of articles published in leading scientific journals.

   c. reject evidence that competes with traditional findings.

   d. are willing to ask questions and to reject claims that cannot be verified by research.

2. How can critical thinking help you evaluate claims in the media, even if you're not a scientific expert on the issue?

3. In 1879, in psychology's first experiment, _____ and his students measured the time lag between hearing a ball hit a platform and pressing a key.

4. William James would be considered a(n) _____. Wilhelm Wundt and Edward Titchener would be considered _____.

   a. functionalist; structuralists
   b. structuralist; functionalists
   c. evolutionary theorist; structuralists
   d. functionalist; evolutionary theorists

5. In the early twentieth century, _____ redefined psychology as "the science of observable behavior."

   a. John B. Watson   c. William James
   b. Abraham Maslow   d. Sigmund Freud

6. Nature is to nurture as

   a. personality is to intelligence.
   b. biology is to experience.
   c. intelligence is to biology.
   d. psychological traits are to behaviors.

7. "Nurture works on what nature provides." Describe what this means, using your own words.

8. Which of the following is true regarding gender differences and similarities?

   a. Differences between the genders outweigh any similarities.
   b. Despite some gender differences, the underlying processes of human behavior are the same.

   c. Both similarities and differences between the genders depend more on biology than on environment.
   d. Gender differences are so numerous that it is difficult to make meaningful comparisons.

9. Martin Seligman and other researchers who explore various aspects of human flourishing refer to their field of study as _____ _____.

10. A psychologist treating emotionally troubled adolescents at a local mental health agency is most likely to be a(n)

    a. research psychologist.
    b. psychiatrist.
    c. industrial-organizational psychologist.
    d. clinical psychologist.

11. A mental health professional with a medical degree who can prescribe medication is a _____.

12. A psychologist conducting basic research to expand psychology's knowledge base may

    a. design a computer screen with limited glare and assess the effect on computer operators' eyes after a day's work.
    b. treat older people who are overcome by depression.
    c. observe 3- and 6-year-olds solving puzzles and analyze differences in their abilities.
    d. interview children with behavioral problems and suggest treatments.

Continue testing yourself with 📖 **LearningCurve** or 📖 **Achieve Read & Practice** to learn and remember most effectively.

---

② Research Strategies: How Psychologists Ask and Answer Questions

THE NEED FOR PSYCHOLOGICAL SCIENCE

LOQ 2-1   How does our everyday thinking sometimes lead us to a wrong conclusion?

Some people suppose that psychology is mere common sense—documenting and dressing in jargon what people already know: "You get paid for using fancy methods to prove what my grandmother knows?" Indeed, Grandma's intuition is often right. As the baseball great Yogi Berra (1925–2015) once said, "You can observe a lot by watching." (We have Berra to thank for other gems, such as "Nobody ever goes there any more—it's too crowded," and "If the people don't want to come out to the ballpark, nobody's gonna stop 'em.") Because we're all behavior watchers, it would be surprising if many of psychology's

hindsight bias the tendency to believe, after learning an outcome, that one would have foreseen it. (Also known as the *I-knew-it-all-along phenomenon.*)

"Those who trust in their own wits are fools." —Proverbs 28:26

"Life is lived forwards, but understood backwards." —Philosopher Søren Kierkegaard, 1813–1855

"Anything seems commonplace, once explained." —Dr. Watson to Sherlock Holmes

findings had *not* been foreseen. Many people believe that love breeds happiness, for example, and they are right (we have what researchers call a deep "need to belong").

But sometimes Grandma's common sense, informed by countless casual observations, is wrong. In other modules, we will see how research has overturned popular ideas—that familiarity breeds contempt, that dreams predict the future, and that most of us use only 10 percent of our brain. We will also see how research has surprised us with discoveries about how the brain's chemical messengers control our moods and memories, about other animals' abilities, and about the effects of stress on our capacity to fight disease.

Other things seem like commonsense truth only because we so often hear them repeated. Mere repetition of statements—whether true or false—makes them easier to process and remember, and thus more true-seeming (Dechêne at al., 2010; Fazio et al., 2015). Easy-to-remember misconceptions ("Zinc prevents the common cold") can therefore overwhelm hard truths. This power of familiar, hard-to-erase falsehoods is a lesson well known to political manipulators, and kept in mind by critical thinkers.

Three roadblocks to critical thinking—*hindsight bias, overconfidence,* and *perceiving patterns in random events*—help illustrate why we cannot rely solely on common sense.

Did We Know It All Along? Hindsight Bias

Consider how easy it is to draw the bull's-eye *after* the arrow strikes. After the stock market drops, people say it was "due for a correction." After the athletic match, we credit the coach if a "gutsy play" wins the game, and fault the coach for the "stupid play" if it doesn't. After a war or an election, its outcome usually seems obvious. Although history may therefore seem like a series of inevitable events, the actual future is seldom foreseen. No one's diary recorded, "Today the Hundred Years War began."

This **hindsight bias** (also known as the *I-knew-it-all-along phenomenon*) is easy to demonstrate by giving half the members of a group some purported psychological finding and giving the other half an opposite result. Tell the first group, for example, "Psychologists have found that separation weakens romantic attraction. As the saying goes, 'Out of sight, out of mind.'" Ask them to imagine why this might be true. Most people can, and after hearing an explanation, nearly all will then view this true finding as unsurprising.

Tell the second group the opposite: "Psychologists have found that separation strengthens romantic attraction. As the saying goes, 'Absence makes the heart grow fonder.'" People given this untrue result can also easily imagine it, and most will also see it as unsurprising. When opposite findings both seem like common sense, there is a problem.

Such errors in people's recollections and explanations show why we need psychological research. It's not that common sense is usually wrong. Rather, common sense describes, after the fact, what *has* happened better than it predicts what *will* happen.

More than 800 scholarly papers have shown hindsight bias in people young and old from across the world (Roese & Vohs, 2012). As physicist Niels Bohr reportedly jested, "Prediction is very difficult, especially about the future."

HINDSIGHT BIAS When drilling its Deepwater Horizon oil well in 2010, BP employees took shortcuts and ignored warning signs, without intending to harm any people, the environment, or their company's reputation. *After* the resulting Gulf oil spill and the death of 11 employees, with the benefit of 20/20 hindsight, the foolishness of those judgments became obvious.

Overconfidence

We humans tend to think we know more than we do. Asked how sure we are of our answers to factual questions (*Is Boston north or south of Paris?*), we tend to be more confident than correct.[2] Or consider these three anagram solutions (from Goranson, 1978):

WREAT   ⟶   WATER
ETRYN   ⟶   ENTRY
GRABE   ⟶   BARGE

About how many seconds do you think it would have taken you to unscramble each of these? Knowing the answer tends to make us overconfident. (Surely the solution would take only 10 seconds or so?) In reality, the average problem solver spends 3 minutes, as you also might, given a similar anagram without the solution: OCHSA.[3]

Are we any better at predicting social behavior? Psychologist Philip Tetlock (1998, 2005) collected more than 27,000 expert predictions of world events, such as the future of South Africa or whether Quebec would separate from Canada. His repeated finding: These predictions, which experts made with 80 percent confidence on average, were right less than 40 percent of the time. Only about 2 percent of people do an excellent job predicting social behavior. Tetlock and science writer Dan Gardner (2016) call them "superforecasters." What is a superforecaster's defining feature? A lack of overconfidence. Faced with a difficult prediction, a superforecaster "gathers facts, balances clashing arguments, and settles on an answer."

🔒 RETRIEVE IT • • •
ANSWERS IN APPENDIX E

RI-1 Why, after friends start dating, do we often feel that we *knew* they were meant to be together?

Perceiving Order in Random Events

We're born with an eagerness to make sense of our world. People see a face on the Moon, hear Satanic messages in music, or perceive the Virgin Mary's images on a grilled cheese sandwich. Even in random data, we often find patterns, because—here's a curious fact of life—*random sequences often don't look random* (Falk et al., 2009; Nickerson, 2002, 2005). Flip a coin 50 times and you may be surprised at the streaks of heads and tails—much like supposed "hot" and "cold" streaks in basketball shooting and baseball hitting. In actual random sequences, patterns and streaks (such as repeating digits) occur more often than people expect (Oskarsson et al., 2009). That also makes it hard for people to generate random-like sequences. When embezzlers try to simulate random digits when deciding how much to steal, their nonrandom patterns can alert fraud experts (Poundstone, 2014).

Why do we search for order in random events? For most people, a random, unpredictable world is unsettling (Tullett et al., 2015). To relieve stress, people often make connections between random events (Ma et al., 2017). Making sense of our world helps us stay calm and get on with daily living.

Some happenings, such as winning the lottery twice, seem so extraordinary that we find it difficult to conceive an ordinary, chance-related explanation. "But with a large enough sample," said statisticians Persi Diaconis and Frederick Mosteller (1989), "any outrageous thing is likely to happen." An event that happens to but 1 in 1 billion people every day occurs about 7 times a day, more than 2500 times a year.

The point to remember: Hindsight bias, overconfidence, and our tendency to perceive patterns in random events tempt us to overestimate our intuition. But scientific inquiry can help us sift reality from illusion.

📱 **LaunchPad** Play the role of a researcher using scientific inquiry to think smarter about random hot streaks in sports. Engage online with **Immersive Learning: How Would You Know If There Is a "Hot Hand" in Basketball?**

---

2. Boston is south of Paris.
3. The anagram solution: CHAOS.

Do you have a hard time believing you may be overconfident? Could overconfidence be at work in that self-assessment?

Fun anagram solutions from Wordsmith (wordsmith.org):
Snooze alarms = Alas! No more z's
Dormitory = dirty room
Slot machines = cash lost in 'em

Overconfidence in history:
"We don't like their sound. Groups of guitars are on their way out." —Decca Records, in turning down a recording contract with the Beatles in 1962

"Computers in the future may weigh no more than 1.5 tons. " —Popular Mechanics, 1949

"They couldn't hit an elephant at this distance." —General John Sedgwick just before being killed during a U.S. Civil War battle, 1864

"The telephone may be appropriate for our American cousins, but not here, because we have an adequate supply of messenger boys." —British expert group evaluating the invention of the telephone

"The really unusual day would be one where nothing unusual happens." —Statistician Persi Diaconis (2002)

BIZARRE-LOOKING, PERHAPS. But actually no more unlikely than any other number sequence.

PSYCHOLOGICAL SCIENCE IN A POST-TRUTH WORLD

LOQ 2-2 Why are we so vulnerable to believing untruths?

In 2017, the Oxford English Dictionary's word of the year was *post-truth*—describing a modern culture where people's emotions and personal beliefs often override their acceptance of objective facts. "Never," says psychology and law professor Dan Kahan (2015), "have human societies *known so much* . . . but *agreed so little* about what they collectively know."

Consider two examples of widely shared misinformation:

Belief: *U.S. crime rate is rising.* Every recent year, 7 in 10 Americans have told Gallup that there is more crime "than there was a year ago" (Swift, 2016).

Fact: For several decades, both violent and property crime rates have been *falling*. In 2015, the violent crime rate was less than half the 1990 rate (BJS, 2017; Statista, 2017).

Belief: *Many immigrants are criminals.* Memorable incidents feed this narrative. Stories of an immigrant murdering, burglarizing, or lying spread through social networks and news outlets.

Fact: Most immigrants are not criminals. Compared with native-born Americans, immigrants are 44 percent *less* likely to be imprisoned (CATO, 2017).

Political party bias has distorted Americans' thinking.

"*I'm sorry, Jeannie, your answer was correct, but Kevin shouted his incorrect answer over yours, so he gets the points.*"

- **Was unemployment up, and the stock market down under U.S. Democratic President Barack Obama?** At the end of 2016, 67 percent of Republican voters believed that unemployment increased during the Obama years, and only 41 percent said the stock market had risen (PPP, 2016). In reality, the U.S. unemployment rate during the Obama years dropped nearly in half, and the stock market more than doubled (BLS, 2017; Vardi, 2017).

- **Did inflation rise under U.S. Republican President Ronald Reagan?** At the end of the Reagan presidency, more than half of strong Democrats believed inflation had worsened under Reagan. In actuality, it had plummeted—from 13 to 4 percent (Gelman, 2009).

Indeed, psychologist Peter Ditto and his colleagues (2015) report that researchers have found "partisan bias in both liberals and conservatives, and at virtually identical levels." American Democrats discriminate against Republican candidates for college scholarships as much as Republicans discriminate against identically qualified Democratic candidates (Iyengar & Westwood, 2015). So, no Americans can smugly think, "Yes but that doesn't apply to *me*."

U.S. Democrats and Republicans share concern about failures to separate fact from fiction. In his farewell address, President Obama (2017) warned that without a "common baseline of facts," democracy is threatened: "We become so secure in our bubbles that we start accepting only information, whether it's true or not, that fits our opinions instead of basing our opinions on the evidence that is out there." Republican Senator John McCain (2017) similarly expressed alarm about "the growing inability, and even unwillingness, to separate truth from lies."

So why do post-truth era people so often, in the words of psychologist Tom Gilovich (1991), "know what isn't so?"

"*Falsehood flies, and truth comes limping after it.*" —Jonathan Swift, 1710

False news Some misinformation gets fed to us intentionally. It's "lies in the guise of news" (Kristof, 2017). And false news persists. In one analysis of 126,000 stories tweeted by 3 million people, falsehoods—especially false political news—"diffused significantly farther, faster, deeper, and more broadly than the truth" (Vosoughi et al., 2018).

Repetition In experiments, statements become more believable when they are repeated (Dechêne et al., 2010). What we hear over and over—perhaps a made-up smear of a political opponent—gets remembered and comes to seem true (Fazio et al., 2015).

Availability of powerful examples In the media, "if it bleeds it leads." Gruesome violence—a horrific murder, a mass killing, a plane crash—gets reported, with vivid images that implant in our memory and color our judgments. No wonder Americans grossly overestimate their risk of been victimized by crime, terror, and plane crashes.

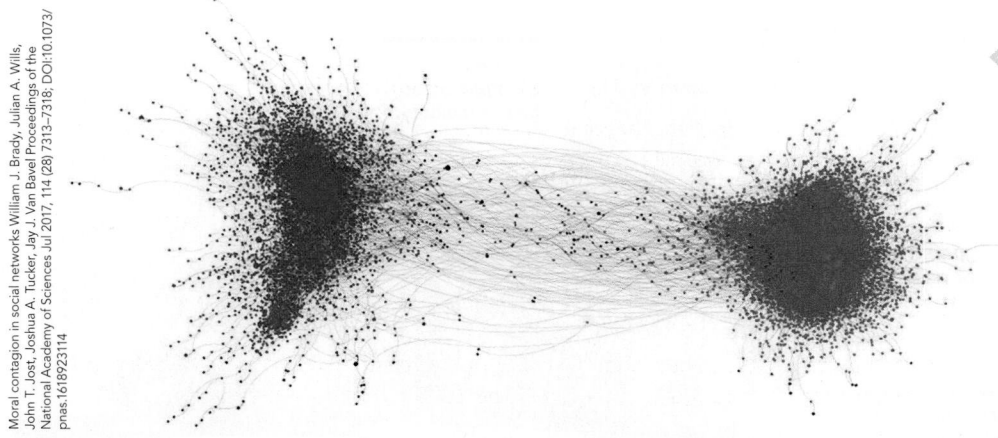

Moral contagion in social networks William J. Brady, Julian A. Wills, John T. Jost, Joshua A. Tucker, Jay J. Van Bavel Proceedings of the National Academy of Sciences Jul 2017, 114 (28) 7313–7318; DOI:10.1073/pnas.1618923114

←⋯ **FIGURE 2.1**

THE MEETING OF LIKE MINDS On social media, most people discuss contentious issues, such as gun control, same-sex marriage, and climate change, only with like-minded others. In one Twitter analysis, users overwhelmingly sent messages to, and retweeted messages from, those who shared their liberal (blue) or conservative (red) ideology (Brady et al., 2017).

Group identity and the echo chamber of the like-minded Our social identities matter. Feeling good about our groups helps us feel good about ourselves. On social media we tend to friend people who think as we do (see **FIGURE 2.1**). We often read news sources that affirm our views and demonize news sources that do not.

The good news is that we can build a real-truth world by embracing critical thinking and a scientific mindset. By seeking information with curiosity, skepticism, and humility, we can usually know what really is so.

🔲 **LaunchPad** To experience my [DM's] animated walk through some important, scientific thinking strategies, view the 3.5 minute **Video: Thinking Critically in a "Post-Truth" World.**

THE SCIENTIFIC METHOD

At the foundation of all science is a scientific attitude that combines *curiosity, skepticism,* and *humility.* Psychologists arm their scientific attitude with the *scientific method*—a self-correcting process for evaluating ideas with observation and analysis. Psychological science welcomes hunches and plausible-sounding theories. And it puts them to the test. If a theory works—if the data support its predictions—so much the better for that theory. If the predictions fail, psychological scientists revise or reject the theory.

Constructing Theories

LOQ 2-3   How do theories advance psychological science?

In everyday conversation, we often use *theory* to mean "mere hunch." Someone might, for example, discount evolution as "only a theory"—as if it were mere speculation. In science, a **theory** *explains* behaviors or events by offering ideas that *organize* observations. By using deeper principles to organize isolated facts, a theory summarizes and simplifies. As we connect the observed dots, a coherent picture emerges.

A theory of how sleep affects memory, for example, helps us organize countless sleep-related observations into a short list of principles. Imagine that we observe over and over that people with good sleep habits tend to answer questions correctly in class and do well at test time. We might therefore theorize that sleep improves memory. So far so good: Our principle neatly summarizes a list of observations about the effects of a good night's sleep.

Yet no matter how reasonable a theory may sound—and it does seem reasonable to suggest that sleep boosts memory—we must put it to the test. A good theory produces testable *predictions,* called **hypotheses.** Such predictions specify what results would support the theory and what results would disconfirm it. To test our theory about sleep effects on memory, we might hypothesize that when sleep deprived, people will remember less from the day before. To test that hypothesis, we might assess how well people remember course materials they studied either before a good night's sleep or before a shortened night's sleep (**FIGURE 2.2**). The results will either support our theory or lead us to revise or reject it.

Our theories can bias our observations. Having theorized that better memory springs from more sleep, we may see what we expect: We may perceive sleepy people's comments as less accurate. The urge to see what we expect is ever-present, both inside and outside the laboratory, as when people's views of climate change influence their interpretation of local weather events.

theory an explanation using an integrated set of principles that organizes observations and predicts behaviors or events.

hypothesis a testable prediction, often implied by a theory.

FIGURE 2.2

THE SCIENTIFIC METHOD A self-correcting process for asking questions and observing nature's answers.

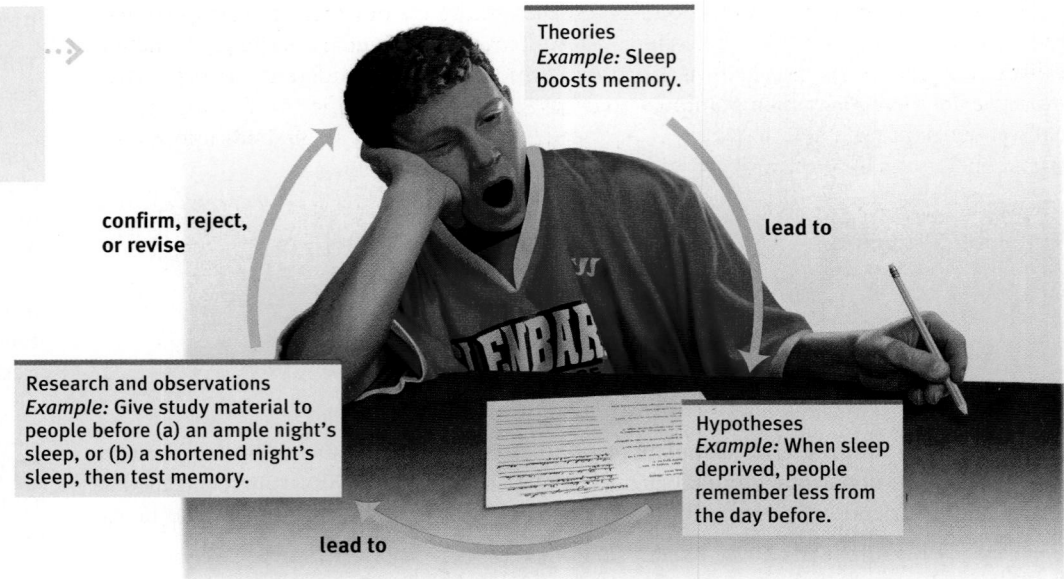

Theories
Example: Sleep boosts memory.

lead to

Hypotheses
Example: When sleep deprived, people remember less from the day before.

lead to

Research and observations
Example: Give study material to people before (a) an ample night's sleep, or (b) a shortened night's sleep, then test memory.

confirm, reject, or revise

operational definition a carefully worded statement of the exact procedures (operations) used in a research study. For example, *human intelligence* may be operationally defined as what an intelligence test measures.

replication repeating the essence of a research study, usually with different participants in different situations, to see whether the basic finding can be reproduced.

meta-analysis a statistical procedure for analyzing the results of multiple studies to reach an overall conclusion.

case study a descriptive technique in which one individual or group is studied in depth in the hope of revealing universal principles.

"Failure to replicate is not a bug; it is a feature. It is what leads us along the path—the wonderfully twisty path—of scientific discovery." —Lisa Feldman Barrett, "Psychology Is Not in Crisis," 2015

For more information about statistical methods that psychological scientists use in their work, see Appendix A, Statistical Reasoning in Everyday Life.

As a check on their own biases, psychologists report their research with precise, measureable **operational definitions** of procedures and concepts. *Sleep deprived,* for example, might be defined as "X hours less" than the person's natural sleep. Using these carefully worded statements, others can **replicate** (repeat) the original observations with different participants, materials, and circumstances. If they get similar results, confidence in the finding's reliability grows. The first study of hindsight bias aroused psychologists' curiosity. Now, after many successful replications with different people and questions, we feel sure of the phenomenon's power. Replication is confirmation.

Replication is an essential part of good science. In psychology, replication efforts have produced mixed results. One cluster of replications brought encouraging news: Only 2 of 13 experiments failed to replicate (Klein et al., 2014). But then when 270 psychologists together redid 100 psychological studies, the results were disheartening: Only 36 percent of the results were replicated (Open Science Collaboration, 2015). (None of the nonreproducible findings appears in this text.) However, another team of scientists found that most of the failed replications did not accurately recreate the original study. "The reproducibility of psychological science" is actually "quite high," they concluded (Gilbert et al., 2016). Still others argue that certain research topics and amount of researcher experience can affect replication success (Bench et al., 2017; Van Bavel et al., 2016). Despite the differing findings, most researchers agree that psychological science benefits from more replications and from greater transparency as researchers increasingly disclose their detailed methods and data (Gilmore & Adolph, 2017; Nosek et al., 2015; Open Science Collaboration, 2017).

Other fields, including genetics, behavioral neuroscience, and brain imaging, also have nonreplicated findings (Baxter & Burwell, 2017; Carter et al., 2017; Eklund et al., 2016). Especially when based on a small sample, a single failure to replicate itself needs replication (Maxwell et al., 2015). In all scientific fields, replication either confirms findings, or enables us to revise our understanding.

Psychological and medical science also harness the power of **meta-analysis.** Meta-analysis is a procedure for statistically synthesizing a body of scientific evidence. By combining the results of many studies, researchers avoid the problem of small samples and arrive at a bottom-line result.

In the end, our theory will be useful if it (1) *organizes* observations and (2) implies *predictions* that anyone can use to check the theory or to derive practical applications. (Does people's sleep predict their retention?) Eventually, our research may (3) stimulate further research that leads to a revised theory that better organizes and predicts.

As we will see next, we can test our hypotheses and refine our theories using *descriptive* methods (which describe behaviors, often through case studies, surveys, or naturalistic observations), *correlational* methods (which associate different factors), and *experimental* methods (which manipulate factors to discover their effects). To think critically about popular psychology claims, we need to understand these methods and know what conclusions they allow.

🔒 **RETRIEVE IT • • •**   *ANSWERS IN APPENDIX E*

RI-2 What does a good theory do?

RI-3 Why is replication important?

Description

LOQ 2-4   How do psychologists use case studies, naturalistic observations, and surveys to observe and describe behavior, and why is random sampling important?

The starting point of any science is description. In everyday life, we all observe and describe people, often drawing conclusions about why they think, feel, and act as they do. Professional psychologists do much the same, though more objectively and systematically, through

- *case studies* (in-depth analyses of individuals or groups).

- *naturalistic observations* (recording the natural behavior of many individuals).

- *surveys* and interviews (asking people questions).

THE CASE STUDY Among the oldest research methods, the **case study** examines one individual or group in depth in the hope of revealing things true of us all. Some examples:

- *Brain damage.* Much of our early knowledge about the brain came from case studies of individuals who suffered a particular impairment after damage to a certain brain region.

- *Children's minds.* Jean Piaget taught us about children's thinking after carefully observing and questioning only a few children.

- *Animal intelligence.* Studies of various animals, including only a few chimpanzees, have revealed their capacity for understanding and language.

Intensive case studies are sometimes very revealing, and they often suggest directions for further study.

But atypical individual cases may mislead us. Both in our everyday lives and in science, unrepresentative information can lead to mistaken conclusions. Indeed, anytime a researcher mentions a finding (*Smokers die younger: 95 percent of men over 85 are nonsmokers*) someone is sure to offer a contradictory anecdote (*Well, I have an uncle who smoked two packs a day and lived to be 89*). Dramatic stories and personal experiences (even psychological case examples) command our attention and are easily remembered. Journalists understand that and often begin their articles with compelling stories. Stories move us. But stories can mislead. Which of the following do you find more memorable? (1) "In one study of 1300 dream reports concerning a kidnapped child, only 5 percent correctly envisioned the child as dead" (Murray & Wheeler, 1937). (2) "I know a man who dreamed his sister was in a car accident, and two days later she died in a head-on collision!" Numbers can be numbing, but *the plural of anecdote is not evidence*. A single story of someone who supposedly changed from gay to straight is not evidence that sexual orientation is a choice. As psychologist Gordon Allport (1954, p. 9) said, "Given a thimbleful of [dramatic] facts we rush to make generalizations as large as a tub."

The point to remember: Individual cases can suggest fruitful ideas. What's true of all of us can be glimpsed in any one of us. But to find those general truths, we must employ other research methods.

📺 **LaunchPad** See the **Video: Case Studies** for an animated tutorial.

Skye Hohmann/Alamy

FREUD AND LITTLE HANS Sigmund Freud's case study of 5-year-old Hans' extreme fear of horses led Freud to his theory of childhood sexuality. He conjectured that Hans felt unconscious desire for his mother, feared castration by his rival father, and then transferred this fear into his phobia about being bitten by a horse. Today's psychological science discounts Freud's theory of childhood sexuality but does agree that much of the human mind operates outside our conscious awareness.

RI-4 We cannot assume that case studies always reveal general principles that apply to all of us. Why not?

"'Well my dear,' said Miss Marple, 'human nature is very much the same everywhere, and of course, one has opportunities of observing it at closer quarters in a village'." –Agatha Christie, *The Tuesday Club Murders*, 1933

NATURALISTIC OBSERVATION A second descriptive method records responses in natural environments. These **naturalistic observations** range from watching chimpanzee societies in the jungle, to videotaping and analyzing parent-child interactions in different cultures, to recording racial differences in students' self-seating patterns in a school lunchroom.

Naturalistic observation has mostly been "small science"—science that can be done with pen and paper rather than fancy equipment and a big budget (Provine, 2012). But new technologies, such as smart-phone apps, body-worn sensors, and social media, are enabling "big data" observations. Using such tools, researchers can track people's location, activities, and opinions—without interference. Want to keep track of how often people go to the gym, a cafe, or the library? All you need is access to their phone's global positioning system (GPS) (Harari et al., 2016). The billions of people on Facebook, Twitter, and Google have also created a huge new opportunity for big-data naturalistic observation. One research team studied the ups and downs of human moods by counting positive and negative words in 504 million Twitter messages from 84 countries (Golder & Macy, 2011). As **FIGURE 2.3** shows, people seem happier on weekends, shortly after waking, and in the evenings. (Are late Saturday evenings often a happy time for you, too?) Another study found that negative emotion (especially anger-related) words in 148 million tweets from 1347 U.S. counties predicted the counties' heart disease rates better than other predictors such as smoking and obesity rates (Eichstaedt et al., 2015). Google data—on the words people search and the questions they ask—can pinpoint a geographical area's level of racism and depression (Stephens-Davidowitz, 2017).

Like the case study, naturalistic observation does not *explain* behavior. It *describes* it. Nevertheless, descriptions can be revealing. We once thought, for example, that only humans use tools. Then naturalistic observation revealed that chimpanzees sometimes insert a stick in a termite mound and withdraw it, eating the stick's load of termites. Such unobtrusive naturalistic observations paved the way for later studies of animal thinking, language, and emotion, which further expanded our understanding of our fellow animals. Thanks to researchers' observations, we know that chimpanzees and baboons use deception: Psychologists repeatedly saw one young baboon pretending to have been attacked by another as a tactic to get its mother to drive the other baboon away from its food (Byrne & Whiten, 1988; Whiten & Byrne, 1988).

Naturalistic observations also illuminate human behavior. Here are two findings you might enjoy:

FIGURE 2.3
TWITTER MESSAGE MOODS, BY TIME AND BY DAY This illustrates how, without knowing anyone's identity, big data enable researchers to study human behavior on a massive scale. It now is also possible to associate people's moods with, for example, their locations or with the weather, and to study the spread of ideas through social networks. (Data from Golder & Macy, 2011.)

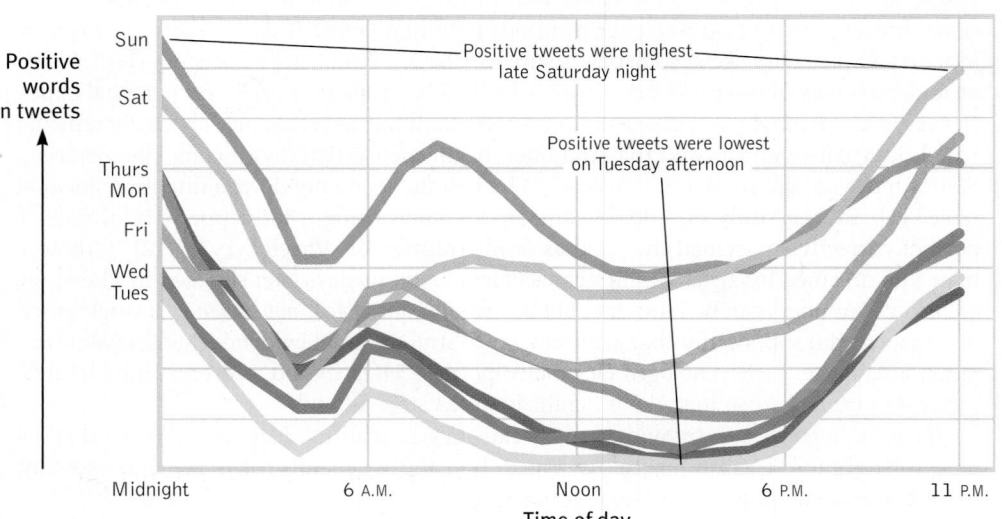

- *A funny finding* We humans laugh 30 times more often in social situations than in solitary situations (Provine, 2001). (Have you noticed how seldom you laugh when alone?)

- *Culture and the pace of life* Naturalistic observation also enabled Robert Levine and Ara Norenzayan (1999) to compare the pace of life—walking speed, accuracy of public clocks, and so forth—in 31 countries. Their conclusion: Life is fastest paced in Japan and Western Europe and slower paced in economically less-developed countries.

Naturalistic observation offers interesting snapshots of everyday life, but it does so without controlling for all the factors that may influence behavior. It's one thing to observe the pace of life in various places, but another to understand what makes some people walk faster than others. Nevertheless, descriptions can be revealing: The starting point of any science is description.

THE SURVEY A **survey** looks at many cases in less depth, asking people to report their behavior or opinions. Questions about everything from sexual practices to political opinions are put to the public. In recent surveys:

- Compared with those born in the 1960s and 1970s, twice as many millennials born in the 1990s reported having no sexual partners since age 18 (Twenge et al., 2017).

- 1 in 5 people across 22 countries report believing that alien beings have come to Earth and now walk among us disguised as humans (Ipsos, 2010).

- 68 percent of all humans—some 4.6 billion people—say that religion is important in their daily lives (Diener et al., 2011).

But asking questions is tricky, and the answers often depend on how questions are worded and how respondents are chosen.

A NATURAL OBSERVER "Observations, made in the natural habitat," noted chimpanzee observer Jane Goodall (1998), "helped to show that the societies and behavior of animals are far more complex than previously supposed."

LaunchPad See the **Video: Naturalistic Observation** for a helpful tutorial animation.

RETRIEVE IT • • •   *ANSWERS IN APPENDIX E*

AN EAR FOR NATURALISTIC OBSERVATION Psychologists Matthias Mehl and James Pennebaker have used electronically activated recorders (EARs) to sample naturally occurring slices of daily life.

Courtesy of Matthias Mehl

RI-5 What are the advantages and disadvantages of naturalistic observation, such as Mehl and his colleagues used in this study?

naturalistic observation a descriptive technique of observing and recording behavior in naturally occurring situations without trying to manipulate and control the situation.

survey a descriptive techni… ing the self-reported at… of a particular group, … ing a representative, … group.

WORDING EFFECTS Even subtle changes in the order or wording of questions can have major effects. People are much more approving of "aid to the needy" than of "welfare," of "affirmative action" than of "preferential treatment," of "not allowing" televised pornography than of "censoring" it, of "gun safety" laws than of "gun control" laws, and of "revenue enhancers" than of "taxes." Because wording is such a delicate matter, critical thinkers will reflect on how the phrasing of a question might affect people's expressed opinions.

RANDOM SAMPLING In everyday thinking, we tend to generalize from samples we observe, especially vivid cases. An administrator who reads (a) a statistical summary of a professor's student evaluations and (b) the vivid comments of two irate students may be influenced as much by the biased sample of two unhappy students as by the many favorable evaluations in the statistical summary. The temptation to succumb to the *sampling bias*—to generalize from a few vivid but unrepresentative cases—is nearly irresistible.

So how do you obtain a *representative sample*? Say you want to learn how students at your college or university feel about a proposed tuition increase. It's often not possible to survey the whole group. How then could you choose a group that would represent the total student body? Typically, you would seek a **random sample,** in which every person in the entire **population** has an equal chance of being included in the sample group. You might number the names in the general student listing and then use a random number generator to pick your survey participants. (Sending each student a questionnaire wouldn't work because the conscientious people who returned it would not be a random sample.) Large representative samples are better than small ones, but a smaller representative sample of 100 is better than a larger unrepresentative sample of 500.

Political pollsters sample voters in national election surveys just this way. Using some 1500 randomly sampled people, drawn from all areas of a country, they can provide a remarkably accurate snapshot of the nation's opinions. Without random sampling, large samples—including unrepresentative call-in phone samples and TV or website polls—often give misleading results.

The point to remember: Before accepting survey findings, think critically. Consider the sample. The best basis for generalizing is from a representative sample. You cannot compensate for an unrepresentative sample by simply adding more people.

> **🔒 RETRIEVE IT • • •**   *ANSWERS IN APPENDIX E*
>
> **RI-6** What is an unrepresentative sample, and how do researchers avoid it?

Correlation

LOQ 2-5   What does it mean when we say two things are correlated, and what are positive and negative correlations?

Describing behavior is a first step toward predicting it. Naturalistic observations and surveys often show us that one trait or behavior tends to coincide with another. In such cases, we say the two **correlate.** A statistical measure (the **correlation coefficient**) helps us figure how closely two things vary together, and thus how well either one *predicts* the other. Knowing how much aptitude test scores *correlate* with school success tells us how well the scores *predict* school success.

A *positive correlation* (above 0 to +1.00) indicates a *direct* relationship, meaning that two things increase together or decrease together. For example, height and weight are positively correlated.

A *negative correlation* (below 0 to –1.00) indicates an *inverse* relationship: As one thing increases, the other decreases. The weekly number of hours spent in TV watching and video gaming correlates negatively with grades. Negative correlations could go as low as –1.00, which means that, like people on opposite ends of a teeter-totter, one set of scores goes down precisely as the other goes up.

Though informative, psychology's correlations usually explain only part of the variation among individuals. As we will see, there is a positive correlation between parents'

With very large samples, estimates become quite reliable. *E* is estimated to represent 12.7 percent of the letters in written English. *E,* in fact, is 12.3 percent of the 925,141 letters in Melville's *Moby-Dick,* 12.4 percent of the 586,747 letters in Dickens' *A Tale of Two Cities,* and 12.1 percent of the 3,901,021 letters in 12 of Mark Twain's works (*Chance News,* 1997).

random sample a sample that fairly represents a population because each member has an equal chance of inclusion.

population all those in a group being studied, from which samples may be drawn. (*Note:* Except for national studies, this does not refer to a country's whole population.)

correlation a measure of the extent to which two factors vary together, and thus of how well either factor predicts the other.

correlation coefficient a statistical index of the relationship between two things (from –1.00 to +1.00).

abusiveness and their children's later abusiveness when they become parents. But this does not mean that most abused children become abusive. The correlation simply indicates a statistical relationship: Most abused children do not grow into abusers, but nonabused children are even less likely to become abusive. Correlations point us toward predictions, but usually imperfect ones.

Other times correlations can lead us astray. Just because two things vary together doesn't mean they cause each other. Consider the strong positive correlation ($r = +0.79$) between chocolate consumption in 23 countries and their number of Nobel laureates (Messerli, 2012). Eating more chocolate will not cause a country to have more Nobel laureates. But for whatever reason, chocolate-loving countries have knowledge-loving Nobel laureates.

The point to remember: A correlation coefficient helps us see the world more clearly by revealing the extent to which two things relate. But correlational research, although it helpfully reveals relationships, cannot explain them. See Thinking Critically About: Correlation and Causation.

LaunchPad For an animated tutorial on correlations, engage online with **Concept Practice: Positive and Negative Correlations.** See also the **Video: Correlational Studies** for another helpful tutorial animation.

🔒 **RETRIEVE IT** • • •   *ANSWERS IN APPENDIX E*

RI-7 Indicate whether each association is a positive correlation or a negative correlation.

a. The more husbands viewed internet pornography, the worse their marital relationships (Muusses et al., 2015). _____

b. The less sexual content teens saw on TV, the less likely they were to have sex (Collins et al., 2004). _____

c. The longer children were breast-fed, the greater their later academic achievement (Horwood & Fergusson, 1998). _____

d. The more income rose among a sample of poor families, the fewer psychiatric symptoms their children experienced (Costello et al., 2003). _____

Experimentation

LOQ 2-7 What are the characteristics of experimentation that make it possible to isolate cause and effect?

Happy are they, remarked the Roman poet Virgil, "who have been able to perceive the causes of things." How might psychologists sleuth out the causes in correlational studies, such as the correlation between breast feeding and intelligence?

EXPERIMENTAL MANIPULATION Some researchers (not all) have found that breast-fed infants develop higher childhood intelligence scores than do bottle-fed babies—an average 3 test-point difference in a review of 17 studies (Horta et al., 2015; von Stumm & Plomin, 2015; Walfisch et al., 2014). Moreover, the longer infants breast-feed, the higher their later intelligence test scores (Jedrychowski et al., 2012; Victora et al., 2015).

What do such findings mean? Do the nutrients of mother's milk contribute to brain development? Or do smarter mothers have smarter children? (Breast-fed children tend to be healthier and higher achieving than other children. But their bottle-fed siblings, born and raised in the same families, tend to be similarly healthy and high achieving [Colen & Ramey, 2014].) Even big data from a million or a billion mothers and their offspring couldn't tell us. To find answers to such questions—to isolate cause and effect—researchers must **experiment.** Experiments enable researchers to isolate the effects of one or more factors by (1) *manipulating the factors of interest* and (2) *holding constant (controlling) other factors.* To do so, they often create an **experimental group,** in which people receive the treatment, and a contrasting **control group** that does not receive the treatment. To minimize any preexisting differences between the two groups, researchers **randomly assign** people to the two conditions. Random assignment—whether with a random numbers table or flip of the coin—effectively equalizes the two groups. If one-third of the volunteers for

experiment a research method in which an investigator manipulates one or more factors (independent variables) to observe the effect on some behavior or mental process (the dependent variable). By *random assignment* of participants, the experimenter aims to control other relevant factors.

experimental group in an experiment, the group exposed to the treatment, that is, to one version of the independent variable.

control group in an experiment, the group *not* exposed to the treatment; contrasts with the experimental group and serves as a comparison for evaluating the effect of the treatment.

random assignment assigning participants to experimental and control groups by chance, thus minimizing preexisting differences between the different groups.

THINKING CRITICALLY ABOUT:

Correlation and Causation

LOQ 2-6 Why do correlations enable prediction but not cause-effect explanation?

Mental illness *correlates* with smoking—meaning that those who experience mental illness are also more likely to be smokers.[1] Does this tell us anything about what *causes* mental illness or smoking? **NO.**

There may be something about smoking that leads to mental illness.

Those with mental illness may be more likely to smoke.

OR

There may be some *third variable*, such as a stressful home life, for example, that triggers *both* smoking and mental illness.

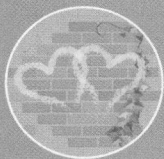

So, then, how would you interpret these recent findings:
  a) sexual hook-ups correlate with college women's experiencing depression, and
  b) *delaying* sexual intimacy correlates with positive outcomes such as greater relationship satisfaction and stability?[2]

Possible explanations:

1. Sexual restraint	→ Better mental health and stronger relationships
2. Depression	→ People being more likely to hook up
3. Some third factor, such as lower impulsivity	→ Sexual restraint, psychological well-being, and better relationships

Correlations do help us predict. Consider: Self-esteem correlates negatively with (and therefore predicts) depression. The lower people's self-esteem, the greater their risk for depression.

Possible interpretations:

1. Low self-esteem	→ Depression
2. Depression	→ Low self-esteem
3. Some third factor, such as distressing events or biological predisposition	→ Both low self-esteem and depression

You try it!
A survey of over 12,000 adolescents found that the more teens feel loved by their parents, the less likely they are to behave in unhealthy ways—having early sex, smoking, abusing alcohol and drugs, exhibiting violence.[3] What are three possible ways we could interpret that finding?[4]

The point to remember: **Correlation does not prove causation.**

Correlation suggests a possible cause-effect relationship but does not prove it. Remember this principle and you will be wiser as you read and hear news of scientific studies.

1. Belluck, 2013. 2. Fielder et al., 2013; Willoughby et al., 2014. 3. Resnick et al., 1997. 4. *ANSWERS:* a. Parental love may produce healthy teens. b. Well-behaved teens may feel more parental love and approval. c. Some third factor, such as income or neighborhood, may influence both parental love AND teen behaviors.

Nancy Brown/Getty Images

🔒 **RETRIEVE IT • • •**   *ANSWERS IN APPENDIX E*

RI-8 Length of marriage positively correlates with hair loss in men. Does this mean that marriage causes men to lose their hair (or that balding men make better husbands)?

an experiment can wiggle their ears, then about one-third of the people in each group will be ear wigglers. So, too, with ages, attitudes, and other characteristics, which will be similar in the experimental and control groups. Thus, if the groups differ at the experiment's end, we can surmise that the treatment had an effect. (Note the difference between random *sampling*—which creates a representative survey sample—and random *assignment,* which equalizes the experimental and control groups.)

To experiment with breast feeding, one research team randomly assigned some 17,000 Belarus newborns and their mothers either to a control group given normal pediatric care, or to an experimental group that promoted breast feeding, thus increasing expectant mothers' breast intentions (Kramer et al., 2008). At 3 months of age, 43 percent of the experimental group infants were being exclusively breast-fed, as were 6 percent in the control group. At age 6, when nearly 14,000 of the children were restudied, those who had been in the breast-feeding-promotion group had intelligence test scores averaging 6 points higher than their control condition counterparts.

With parental permission, one British research team directly experimented with breast milk. They randomly assigned 424 hospitalized premature infants either to formula feedings or to breast-milk feedings (Lucas et al., 1992). Their finding: On intelligence tests taken at age 8, those nourished with breast milk scored significantly higher than those who were formula-fed. Breast was best.

No single experiment is conclusive, of course. But randomly assigning participants to one feeding group or the other effectively eliminated all factors except nutrition. If test performance changes when we vary infant nutrition, then we infer that nutrition matters.

Lane Oatey/Getty Images

The point to remember: Unlike correlational studies, which uncover naturally occurring relationships, an experiment manipulates a factor to determine its effect.

PROCEDURES AND THE PLACEBO EFFECT Consider, then, how we might assess therapeutic interventions. Our tendency to seek new remedies when we are ill or emotionally down can produce misleading testimonies. If three days into a cold we start taking zinc tablets and find our cold symptoms lessening, we may credit the pills rather than the cold naturally subsiding. In the 1700s, bloodletting *seemed* effective. People sometimes improved after the treatment; when they didn't, the practitioner inferred the disease was too advanced to be reversed. So, whether or not a remedy is truly effective, enthusiastic users will probably endorse it. To determine its effect, we must control for other factors.

And that is precisely how new drugs and new methods of psychological therapy are evaluated. Investigators randomly assign participants in these studies to research groups. One group receives a treatment (such as an antidepressant medication). The other group receives a pseudotreatment—an inert *placebo* (perhaps a pill with no drug in it). The participants are often *blind* (uninformed) about what treatment, if any, they are receiving. If the study is using a **double-blind procedure,** neither the participants nor those who administer the drug and collect the data will know which group is receiving the treatment.

In double-blind studies, researchers check a treatment's actual effects apart from the participants' and the staff's belief in its healing powers. Just *thinking* you are getting a treatment can boost your spirits, relax your body, and relieve your symptoms. This **placebo effect** is well documented in reducing pain, depression, anxiety, and auditory hallucinations in schizophrenia (Dollfus et al., 2016; Kirsch, 2010). Athletes have run faster when given a supposed performance-enhancing drug (McClung & Collins, 2007). Decaf-coffee drinkers have reported increased vigor and alertness—when they thought their brew had caffeine in it (Dawkins et al., 2011). People have felt better after receiving a phony mood-enhancing drug (Michael et al., 2012). And the more expensive the placebo, the more "real" it seems to us—a fake pill that costs $2.50 works better than one costing 10 cents (Waber et al., 2008). To know how effective a therapy really is, researchers must control for a possible placebo effect.

RETAIN Recall that in a well-done survey, *random sampling* is important. In an experiment, *random assignment* is equally important.

LaunchPad See the **Video: Random Assignment** for a tutorial animation.

double-blind procedure an experimental procedure in which both the research participants and the research staff are ignorant (blind) about whether the research participants have received the treatment or a placebo. Commonly used in drug-evaluation studies.

placebo [pluh-SEE-bo; Latin for "I shall please"] **effect** experimental results caused by expectations alone; any effect on behavior caused by the administration of an inert substance or condition, which the recipient assumes is an active agent.

"If I don't think it's going to work, will it still work?"

independent variable in an experiment, the factor that is manipulated; the variable whose effect is being studied.

confounding variable in an experiment, a factor other than the factor being studied that might influence a study's results.

dependent variable in an experiment, the outcome that is measured; the variable that may change when the independent variable is manipulated.

A similar experiment on a drug approved to increase women's sexual arousal produced a result described as, um, anticlimactic—an additional "half of one satisfying sexual encounter a month" (Ness, 2016; Tavernise, 2016).

"[We must guard] against not just racial slurs, but . . . against the subtle impulse to call Johnny back for a job interview, but not Jamal."
—U.S. President Barack Obama, Eulogy for Clementa Pinckney, June 26, 2015

RI-9 What measures do researchers use to prevent the *placebo effect* from confusing their results?

INDEPENDENT AND DEPENDENT VARIABLES Here is an even more potent example: The drug Viagra was approved for use after 21 clinical trials. One trial was an experiment in which researchers randomly assigned 329 men with erectile disorder to either an experimental group (Viagra takers) or a control group (placebo takers given an identical-looking pill). The procedure was double-blind—neither the men nor the person giving them the pills knew what they were receiving. The result: At peak doses, 69 percent of Viagra-assisted attempts at intercourse were successful, compared with 22 percent for men receiving the placebo (Goldstein et al., 1998). Viagra performed.

This simple experiment manipulated just one factor: the drug (Viagra versus no Viagra). We call this experimental factor the **independent variable** because we can vary it *independently* of other factors, such as the men's age, weight, and personality. Other factors that can potentially influence a study's results are called **confounding variables.** Random assignment controls for possible confounding variables.

Experiments examine the effect of one or more independent variables on some measurable behavior, called the **dependent variable** because it can vary *depending* on what takes place during the experiment. Both variables are given precise *operational definitions,* which specify the procedures that manipulate the independent variable (the exact drug dosage and timing in this study) or measure the dependent variable (the men's responses to questions about their sexual performance). These definitions answer the "What do you mean?" question with a level of precision that enables others to replicate the study. (See **FIGURE 2.4** for the British breast milk experiment's design.)

Let's pause to check your understanding using a simple psychology experiment: To test the effect of perceived ethnicity on the availability of rental housing, Adrian Carpusor and William Loges (2006) sent identically worded email inquiries to 1115 Los Angeles-area landlords. The researchers varied the ethnic connotation of the sender's name and tracked the percentage of positive replies (invitations to view the apartment in person). "Patrick McDougall," "Said Al-Rahman," and "Tyrell Jackson" received, respectively, 89 percent, 66 percent, and 56 percent invitations. In this experiment, what was the independent variable? What was the dependent variable?[4]

Experiments can also help us evaluate social programs. Do early childhood education programs boost impoverished children's chances for success? What are the effects of different antismoking campaigns? Do school sex-education programs reduce teen pregnancies? To answer such questions, we can experiment: If an intervention is welcomed but resources are scarce, we could use a lottery to randomly assign some people (or regions) to experience the new program and others to a control condition. If later the two groups differ, the intervention's effect will be supported (Passell, 1993).

---

4. The independent variable, which the researchers manipulated, was the implied ethnicity of the applicants' names. The dependent variable, which the researchers measured, was the rate of positive responses from the landlords.

FIGURE 2.4

EXPERIMENTATION To discern causation, psychologists control for confounding variables by randomly assigning some participants to an experimental group, others to a control group. Measuring the dependent variable (later intelligence test score) will determine the effect of the independent variable (type of milk).

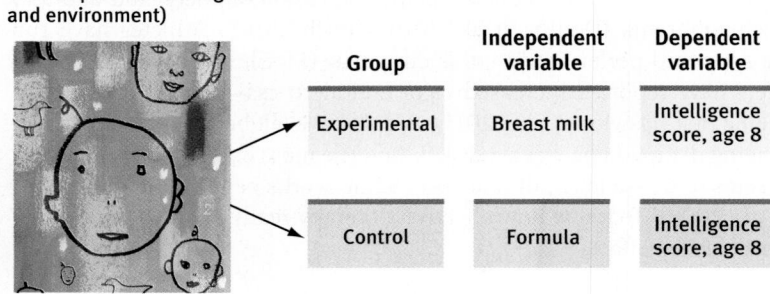

Random assignment
(controlling for other confounding variables such as parental intelligence and environment)

Group	Independent variable	Dependent variable
Experimental	Breast milk	Intelligence score, age 8
Control	Formula	Intelligence score, age 8

R. Michael Wertz

Let's recap. A *variable* is anything that can vary (infant nutrition, intelligence, TV exposure—anything within the bounds of what is feasible and ethical). Experiments aim to *manipulate* an *independent* variable, *measure* a *dependent* variable, and control *confounding* variables. An experiment has at least two different conditions: an *experimental condition* and a *comparison* or *control condition*. *Random assignment* works to minimize preexisting differences between the groups before any treatment effects occur. In this way, an experiment tests the effect of at least one independent variable (what we manipulate) on at least one dependent variable (the outcome we measure).

> **LaunchPad** See the **Videos: Experiments** and **Confounding Variables** for helpful tutorial animations.

🔒 RETRIEVE IT • • •

ANSWERS IN APPENDIX E

RI-10 By using *random assignment*, researchers are able to control for _____ _____, which are other factors besides the independent variable(s) that may influence research results.

RI-11 Match the term (I through III) with the description (a through c).

I. Double-blind procedure   a. helps researchers generalize from a small set of survey responses to a larger population.

II. Random sampling   b. helps minimize preexisting differences between experimental and control groups.

III. Random assignment   c. controls for the placebo effect; neither researchers nor participants know who receives the real treatment.

RI-12 Why, when testing a new drug to control blood pressure, would we learn more about its effectiveness from giving it to half the participants in a group of 1000 than to all 1000 participants?

Research Design

LOQ 2-8   How would you know which research design to use?

Throughout this book, you will read about amazing psychological science discoveries. But how do we know fact from fiction? How do psychological scientists choose research methods and design their studies in ways that provide meaningful results? Understanding how research is done—how testable questions are developed and studied—is key to appreciating all of psychology. **TABLE 2.1** compares the features of psychology's main research methods. Other modules explain additional research designs, including *twin studies* and *cross-sectional* and *longitudinal research*.

In psychological research, no questions are off limits, except untestable (or unethical) ones: Does free will exist? Are people born evil? Is there an afterlife? Psychologists can't test those questions. But they *can* test whether free will beliefs, aggressive personalities, and a belief in life after death influence how people think, feel, and act (Dechesne et al., 2003; Shariff et al., 2014; Webster et al., 2014).

 TABLE 2.1

Comparing Research Methods

Research Method	Basic Purpose	How Conducted	What Is Manipulated	Weaknesses
Descriptive	To observe and record behavior	Do case studies, naturalistic observations, or surveys	Nothing	No control of variables; single cases may be misleading
Correlational	To detect naturally occurring relationships; to assess how well one variable predicts another	Collect data on two or more variables; no manipulation	Nothing	Cannot specify cause and effect
Experimental	To explore cause and effect	Manipulate one or more factors; use random assignment	The independent variable(s)	Sometimes not feasible; results may not generalize to other contexts; not ethical to manipulate certain variables

ASK YOURSELF

If you could conduct a study on any psychological question, which would you choose? How would you do it?

To help you build your understanding, your critical thinking, and your *scientific literacy skills,* we created online Immersive Learning research activities. In these "How Would You Know?" activities, you get to play the role of the researcher, making choices about the best ways to test interesting questions. Some examples: How Would You Know If Having Children Relates to Being Happier?, How Would You Know If a Cup of Coffee Can Warm Up Relationships?, and How Would You Know If People Can Learn to Reduce Anxiety?

LaunchPad To review and test your understanding of research methods, engage online with **Concept Practice: Psychology's Research Methods** and **The Language of Experiments,** and the interactive **Topic Tutorial: PsychSim6, Understanding Psychological Research.** For a 9.5-minute video synopsis of psychology's scientific research strategies, see the **Video: Research Methods.**

LaunchPad See the **Video: Research Ethics** for a helpful tutorial animation.

Having chosen their question, psychologists then select the most appropriate research design—*experimental, correlational, case study, naturalistic observation, twin study, longitudinal,* or *cross-sectional*—and determine how to set it up most effectively. They consider how much money and time are available, ethical issues, and other limitations. For example, it wouldn't be ethical for a researcher studying child development to use the experimental method and randomly assign children to loving versus punishing homes.

Next, psychological scientists decide how to measure the behavior or mental process being studied. For example, researchers could measure aggressive behavior by measuring participants' willingness to blast a stranger with supposed intense noise.

Researchers want to have confidence in their findings, so they carefully consider confounding variables—factors other than those being studied that may affect their interpretation of results.

Psychological research is a creative adventure. Researchers *design* each study, *measure* target behaviors, *interpret* results, and learn more about the fascinating world of behavior and mental processes along the way.

Predicting Everyday Behavior

LOQ 2-9   How can simplified laboratory conditions illuminate everyday life?

When you see or hear about psychological research, do you ever wonder whether people's behavior in the lab will predict their behavior in real life? Does detecting the blink of a faint red light in a dark room say anything useful about flying a plane at night? After viewing a violent, sexually explicit film, does an aroused man's increased willingness to push buttons that he thinks will deliver a noise blast to a woman really say anything about whether viewing violent pornography makes a man more likely to abuse a woman?

Before you answer, consider: The experimenter *intends* the laboratory environment to be a simplified reality—one that simulates and controls important features of everyday life. Just as a wind tunnel lets airplane designers re-create airflow forces under controlled conditions, a laboratory experiment lets psychologists re-create psychological forces under controlled conditions.

An experiment's purpose is not to re-create the exact behaviors of everyday life, but to test *theoretical principles* (Mook, 1983). In aggression studies, deciding whether to push a button that delivers a noise blast may not be the same as slapping someone in the face, but the principle is the same. It is the *resulting principles—not the specific findings—that help explain everyday behaviors.*

When psychologists apply laboratory research on aggression to actual violence, they are applying theoretical principles of aggressive behavior, principles refined through many experiments. Similarly, it is the principles of the visual system, developed from experiments in artificial settings (such as looking at red lights in the dark), that researchers apply to more complex behaviors such as night flying. And many investigations show that principles derived in the laboratory typically generalize to the everyday world (Mitchell, 2012).

The point to remember: Psychological science focuses less on specific behaviors than on revealing general principles that help explain many behaviors.

PSYCHOLOGY'S RESEARCH ETHICS

LOQ 2-10   Why do psychologists study animals, and what ethical guidelines safeguard human and animal research participants? How do psychologists' values influence psychology?

We have reflected on how a scientific approach can restrain biases. We have seen how case studies, naturalistic observations, and surveys help us describe behavior. We have also noted that correlational studies assess the association between two factors, showing how well one predicts another. We have examined the logic that underlies experiments, which use control conditions and random assignment of participants to isolate the causal effects of an independent variable on a dependent variable.

Yet, even knowing this much, you may still be approaching psychology with a mixture of curiosity and apprehension. So before we plunge in, let's entertain some common questions about psychology's ethics and values.

Protecting Research Participants

STUDYING AND PROTECTING ANIMALS Many psychologists study nonhuman animals because they find them fascinating. They want to understand how different species learn, think, and behave. Psychologists also study animals to learn about people. We humans are not *like* animals; we *are* animals, sharing a common biology. Animal experiments have therefore led to treatments for human diseases—insulin for diabetes, vaccines to prevent polio and rabies, transplants to replace defective organs.

Humans are complex. But some of the same processes by which we learn are present in rats, monkeys, and even sea slugs. The simplicity of the sea slug's nervous system is precisely what makes it so revealing of the neural mechanisms of learning. Ditto for the honeybee, which resembles us humans in how it learns to cope with stress (Dinges et al., 2017).

Sharing such similarities, should we not respect our animal relatives? The animal protection movement protests the use of animals in psychological, biological, and medical research.

Out of this heated debate, two issues emerge. The basic one is whether it is right to place the well-being of humans above that of other animals. In experiments on stress and cancer, is it right that mice get tumors in the hope that people might not? Should some monkeys be exposed to an HIV-like virus in the search for an AIDS vaccine? Humans raise and slaughter 56 billion animals a year—a rate expected to double by 2050 (Worldwatch Institute, 2017). Is our use and consumption of other animals as natural as the behavior of carnivorous hawks, cats, and whales?

For those who give human life top priority, a second question emerges: What safeguards should protect the well-being of animals in research? One survey of animal researchers gave an answer. Some 98 percent supported government regulations protecting primates, dogs, and cats, and 74 percent also supported regulations providing for the humane care of rats and mice (Plous & Herzog, 2000). Many professional associations and funding agencies already have such guidelines. British Psychological Society (BPS) guidelines call for housing animals under reasonably natural living conditions, with companions for social animals (Lea, 2000). American Psychological Association (APA) guidelines state that researchers must provide "humane care and healthful conditions" and that testing should "minimize discomfort" (APA, 2012). The European Parliament also mandates standards for animal care and housing (Vogel, 2010). Most universities screen research proposals, often through an animal care ethics committee, and laboratories are regulated and inspected.

Animals have themselves benefited from animal research. One Ohio team of research psychologists measured stress hormone levels in samples of millions of dogs brought each year to animal shelters. They devised handling and stroking methods to reduce stress and ease the dogs' transition to adoptive homes (Tuber et al., 1999). Other studies have helped improve care and management in animals' natural habitats. By revealing our behavioral kinship with animals and the remarkable intelligence of chimpanzees, gorillas, and other animals, experiments have also led to increased empathy and protection for them. At its best, a psychology concerned for humans and sensitive to animals serves the welfare of both.

STUDYING AND PROTECTING HUMANS What about human participants? Does the image of white-coated scientists seeming to deliver electric shocks trouble you? Actually, most psychological studies are free of such stress. Blinking lights, flashing words, and pleasant social interactions are more common. Moreover, psychology's experiments are mild compared with the stress and humiliation often inflicted in reality TV "experiments." In two episodes of *The Bachelor*, a man dumped his new fiancee—on camera—for a woman who earlier had been runner-up (Collins, 2009; Bonos, 2018).

Occasionally, though, researchers do temporarily stress or deceive people, but only when they believe it is essential to a justifiable end, such as understanding and controlling violent behavior or studying mood swings. Some experiments won't work if participants know everything beforehand. (Wanting to be helpful, the participants might try to confirm the researcher's predictions.)

The ethics codes of the APA and Britain's BPS urge researchers to (1) obtain potential participants' **informed consent** to take part, (2) protect participants from greater-than-usual harm and discomfort, (3) keep information about individual participants confidential, and (4) fully **debrief** people (explain the research afterward, including any temporary deception). As with nonhuman animals, most university ethics committees have guidelines that screen research proposals and safeguard participants' well-being.

informed consent giving potential participants enough information about a study to enable them to choose whether they wish to participate.

debriefing the postexperimental explanation of a study, including its purpose and any deceptions, to its participants.

"Rats are very similar to humans except that they are not stupid enough to purchase lottery tickets." —Dave Barry, July 2, 2002

"Please do not forget those of us who suffer from incurable diseases or disabilities who hope for a cure through research that requires the use of animals." —Psychologist Dennis Feeney (1987)

"The greatness of a nation can be judged by the way its animals are treated." —Mahatma Gandhi, 1869–1948

ANIMAL RESEARCH BENEFITING ANIMALS Psychologists have helped zoos enrich animal environments, such as by reducing the "learned helplessness" of captivity by giving animals more choices (Kurtycz, 2015; Weir, 2013). Thanks partly to research on the benefits of novelty, control, and stimulation, these gorillas are enjoying an improved quality of life in New York's Bronx Zoo.

MARY ALTAFFER/AP Images

🔒 **RETRIEVE IT** • • •

ANSWERS IN APPENDIX E

RI-13 How are animal subjects and human research participants protected?

FIGURE 2.5

WHAT DO YOU SEE? Our expectations influence what we perceive. Did you see a duck or a rabbit? Show some friends this image with the rabbit photo covered up and see if they are more likely to perceive a duck instead. (Inspired by Shepard, 1990.)

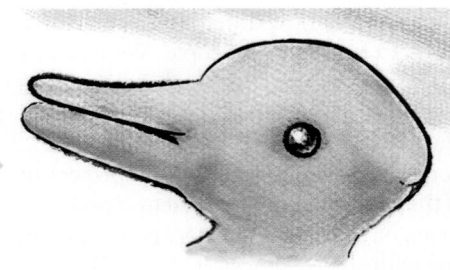

"There can be no peace until they renounce their Rabbit God and accept our Duck God."

 (ASK YOURSELF)

What other questions or concerns do you have about psychology?

Values in Psychology

Values affect what we study, how we study it, and how we interpret results. Researchers' values influence their choice of topics. Should we study worker productivity or worker morale? Sex discrimination or gender differences? Conformity or independence? Values can also color "the facts"—our observations and interpretations; sometimes we see what we want or expect to see (**FIGURE 2.5**).

Even the words we use to describe traits and tendencies can reflect our values. In psychology and in everyday speech, labels describe and labels evaluate: One person's *rigidity* is another's *consistency*. One person's *undocumented worker* is another's *illegal alien*. One person's *faith* is another's *fanaticism*. One country's *enhanced interrogation techniques* become *torture* when practiced by its enemies. Our labeling someone as *firm* or *stubborn*, *careful* or *picky*, *discreet* or *secretive* reveals our own attitudes.

Popular applications of psychology also contain hidden values. If you defer to "professional" guidance about how to live—how to raise children, how to achieve self-fulfillment, how to respond to sexual feelings, how to get ahead at work—you are accepting value-laden advice. A science of behavior and mental processes can help us reach our goals. But it cannot decide what those goals should be.

If some people see psychology as merely common sense, others have a different concern—that it is becoming dangerously powerful. Might psychology be used to manipulate people?

Knowledge, like all power, can be used for good or evil. Nuclear power has been used to light up cities—and to demolish them. Persuasive power has been used to educate people—and to deceive them. Although psychology does have the power to deceive, its purpose is to enlighten. Every day, psychologists explore ways to enhance learning, creativity, and compassion. Psychology speaks to many of our world's great problems—war, overpopulation, inequality, prejudice, family crises, crime—all of which involve attitudes and behaviors. Psychology also speaks to our deepest longings—for nourishment, for love, for happiness. Psychology cannot address all of life's great questions, but it speaks to some mighty important ones.

PSYCHOLOGY SPEAKS In making its historic 1954 school desegregation decision, the U.S. Supreme Court cited the expert testimony and research of psychologists Kenneth Clark and Mamie Phipps Clark (1947). The Clarks reported that, when given a choice between Black and White dolls, most African-American children chose the White doll, which seemingly indicated internalized anti-Black prejudice.

USE PSYCHOLOGY TO BECOME A STRONGER PERSON—AND A BETTER STUDENT

LOQ 2-11 How can psychological principles help you learn, remember, and thrive?

Throughout this text, we will offer evidence-based suggestions that you can use to live a happy, effective, flourishing life, including the following:

- *Get a full night's sleep.* Unlike sleep-deprived people, who live with fatigue and gloomy moods, well-rested people live with greater energy, alertness, and productivity.

- *Make space for exercise.* Aerobic activity not only increases health and energy, it also is an effective remedy for mild to moderate depression and anxiety.

- *Set long-term goals, with daily aims.* Successful people take time each day to work toward their goals, such as exercising or sleeping more, or eating more healthfully. Over time, they often find that their daily practice becomes a habit.

- *Have a growth mindset.* Rather than seeing their abilities as fixed, successful people view their mental abilities as like a muscle—something that grows stronger with effortful use.

- *Prioritize relationships.* We humans are social animals. We flourish when connected in close relationships. We are both happier and healthier when supported by (and supporting) caring friends.

Psychology's research also shows how we can learn and retain information. Many students assume that the way to cement new learning is to reread. What helps even more—and what this book therefore encourages—is repeated self-testing and rehearsal of previously studied material. Memory researchers Henry Roediger and Jeffrey Karpicke (2006) call this phenomenon the **testing effect.** (It is also sometimes called the *retrieval practice effect* or *test-enhanced learning*.) They note that "testing is a powerful means of improving learning, not just assessing it." In one study, English-speaking students recalled the meaning of 20 previously learned Lithuanian words better if tested repeatedly than if they spent the same time restudying the words (Ariel & Karpicke, 2017). Repetitive testing's rewards also make it reinforcing: Students who used repetitive testing once more often used it later when learning new material. Many other studies, including in college classrooms, confirm that *frequent quizzing and self-testing boosts students' retention* (Cho et al., 2017; Foss & Pirozzolo, 2017; Trumbo et al., 2016).

As you will see in the Memory modules, to master information you must *actively process it.* In one digest of 225 studies, students engaged in active learning showed the highest examination performance in science, technology, engineering, and mathematics (STEM) (Freeman et al., 2014). So don't treat your mind like your stomach, something to be filled passively. Treat it more like a muscle that grows stronger with exercise. Countless experiments reveal that people learn and remember best when they put material in their own words, rehearse it, and then retrieve and review it again.

The **SQ3R** study method incorporates these principles (McDaniel et al., 2009; Robinson, 1970). SQ3R is an acronym for its five steps: *Survey, Question, Read, Retrieve,*[5] *Review.*

To study a module, first *survey,* taking a bird's-eye view. Scan each module's headings, and notice how the module is organized.

Before you read each main section, try to answer its numbered Learning Objective *Question* (for this section: "How can psychological principles help you learn, remember, and thrive?"). Roediger and Bridgid Finn (2010) have found that "trying and failing to retrieve the answer is actually helpful to learning." Those who test their understanding *before* reading, and discover what they don't yet know, will learn and remember better.

testing effect enhanced memory after retrieving, rather than simply rereading, information. Also referred to as a *retrieval practice effect* or *test-enhanced learning*.

SQ3R a study method incorporating five steps: *Survey, Question, Read, Retrieve, Review.*

"If you read a piece of text through twenty times, you will not learn it by heart so easily as if you read it ten times while attempting to recite it from time to time and consulting the text when your memory fails." —Francis Bacon, *Novum Organum,* 1620

---

5. Also sometimes called "Recite."

Then *read,* actively searching for the answer to the question. At each sitting, read only as much of the module (usually a single main section) as you can absorb without tiring. Read actively and critically. Ask questions. Take notes. Make the ideas your own: How does what you've read relate to your own life? Does it support or challenge your assumptions? How convincing is the evidence? Write out what you know. "Writing is often a tool for learning," said one group of researchers (Arnold et al., 2017).

Having read a section, *retrieve* its main ideas. "Active retrieval promotes meaningful learning," says Karpicke (2012). So *test yourself.* This will not only help you figure out what you know, the testing itself will help you learn and retain the information more effectively. Even better, test yourself repeatedly. To facilitate this, we offer periodic *Retrieve It* self-tests throughout each module (see, for example, the questions at the end of this section). After answering these questions for yourself, you can check your answers, and then reread as needed.

Finally, *review:* Read over any notes you have taken, again with an eye on the module's organization, and quickly review the whole module. Write or say what a concept is before rereading to check your understanding.

Survey, question, read, retrieve, review. We have organized this book to facilitate your use of the SQ3R study system. Each group of modules begins with an outline that aids your *survey.* Headings and Learning Objective *Questions* suggest issues and concepts you should consider as you *read.* The material is organized into sections of readable length. The Retrieve It questions will challenge you to retrieve what you have learned, and thus *retain* it better. The end-of-module *Review* is set up as a self-test, with the collected Learning Objective Questions and key terms listed, along with Experience the Testing Effect questions in a variety of formats. In the eBook, answer-checking is a click away. In the printed text, answers may be found in Appendix D and Appendix E.

Four additional study tips may further boost your learning:

Distribute your study time. One of psychology's oldest findings is that *spaced practice* promotes better retention than does massed practice. You'll remember material better if you space your time over several study periods—perhaps one hour a day, six days a week—rather than cram it into one week-long or all-night study blitz. For example, rather than trying to read an entire module in a single sitting, read just one main section and then turn to something else. *Interleaving* your study of psychology with your study of other subjects boosts long-term retention and protects against overconfidence (Kornell & Bjork, 2008; Taylor & Rohrer, 2010).

Spacing your study sessions requires a disciplined approach to managing your time. At the beginning of this text, Richard O. Straub explains time management in a helpful preface.

Learn to think critically. Whether you are reading or in class, note people's assumptions and values. What perspective or bias underlies an argument? Evaluate evidence. Is it anecdotal? Or is it based on informative experiments? Assess conclusions. Are there alternative explanations?

Process class information actively. Listen for a lecture's main ideas and sub-ideas. *Write them down.* Ask questions during and after class. In class, as in your private study, process the information actively and you will understand and retain it better. As psychologist William James urged a century ago, *"No reception without reaction, no impression without . . . expression."* Make the information your own. Engage with the Ask Yourself questions found periodically throughout each module to relate what you read to your own life. Tell someone else about it. (As any teacher will confirm, to teach is to remember.)

Also, take notes *by hand.* Handwritten notes, in your own words, typically engage more active processing, with better retention, than does verbatim note-taking on laptops (Mueller & Oppenheimer, 2014).

Overlearn. Psychology tells us that overlearning improves retention. We are prone to overestimating how much we know. You may understand a module as you read it, but that feeling of familiarity can be deceptively comforting. By using the Retrieve It and Experience the Testing Effect questions as well as our online learning opportunities, you can test your knowledge and *overlearn* in the process.

MORE LEARNING TIPS To learn more about the testing effect and the SQ3R method, view the 5-minute animation, "Make Things Memorable," at tinyurl.com/ HowToRemember.

Memory experts Elizabeth Bjork and Robert Bjork (2011, p. 63) offer simple, scientifically supported advice for how to improve your retention and your grades:

> Spend less time on the input side and more time on the output side, such as summarizing what you have read from memory or getting together with friends and asking each other questions. Any activities that involve testing yourself—that is, activities that require you to retrieve or generate information, rather than just representing information to yourself—will make your learning both more durable and flexible. (p. 63)

ENGAGE (ASK YOURSELF)

Of all of these helpful principles, which ones seem most relevant and important for improving your own life and studies?

🔒 **RETRIEVE IT • • •**   *ANSWERS IN APPENDIX E*

RI-14 The _____ _____ describes the enhanced memory that results from repeated retrieval (as in self-testing) rather than from simple rereading of new information.

RI-15 What does the acronym SQ3R stand for?

🔒 **REVIEW** RESEARCH STRATEGIES: HOW PSYCHOLOGISTS ASK AND ANSWER QUESTIONS

⟶ Learning Objectives

TEST YOURSELF Answer these repeated Learning Objective Questions on your own (before checking the answers in Appendix D) to improve your retention of the concepts (McDaniel et al., 2009, 2015).

2-1 How does our everyday thinking sometimes lead us to a wrong conclusion?

2-2 Why are we so vulnerable to believing untruths?

2-3 How do theories advance psychological science?

2-4 How do psychologists use case studies, naturalistic observations, and surveys to observe and describe behavior, and why is random sampling important?

2-5 What does it mean when we say two things are correlated, and what are positive and negative correlations?

2-6 Why do correlations enable prediction but not cause-effect explanation?

2-7 What are the characteristics of experimentation that make it possible to isolate cause and effect?

2-8 How would you know which research design to use?

2-9 How can simplified laboratory conditions illuminate everyday life?

2-10 Why do psychologists study animals, and what ethical guidelines safeguard human and animal research participants? How do psychologists' values influence psychology?

2-11 How can psychological principles help you learn, remember, and thrive?

⟶ Terms and Concepts to Remember

TEST YOURSELF Write down the definition yourself, then check your answer on the referenced page.

hindsight bias, **p. 16**

theory, **p. 19**

hypothesis, **p. 19**

operational definition, **p. 20**

replication, **p. 20**

meta-analysis, **p. 20**

case study, **p. 20**

naturalistic observation, **p. 23**

survey, **p. 23**

random sample, **p. 24**

population, **p. 24**

correlation, **p. 24**

correlation coefficient, **p. 24**

experiment, **p. 25**

experimental group, **p. 25**

control group, **p. 25**

random assignment, **p. 25**

double-blind procedure, **p. 27**

placebo [pluh-SEE-bo] effect, **p. 27**   dependent variable, **p. 28**   testing effect, **p. 33**
independent variable, **p. 28**   informed consent, **p. 31**   SQ3R, **p. 33**
confounding variable, **p. 28**   debriefing, **p. 31**

⊙→ Experience the Testing Effect

TEST YOURSELF Answer the following questions on your own first, then check your answers in Appendix E.

1. _____ _____ refers to our tendency to perceive events as obvious or inevitable after the fact.

2. Theory-based predictions are called _____.

3. Which of the following is NOT one of the *descriptive* methods psychologists use to observe and describe behavior?
   a. A case study
   b. Naturalistic observation
   c. Correlational research
   d. A phone survey

4. For your survey, you need to establish a group of people who represent the country's entire adult population. To do this, you will need to question a _____ sample of the population.

5. A study finds that the more childbirth training classes women attend, the less pain medication they require during childbirth. This finding can be stated as a _____ (positive/negative) correlation.

6. Knowing that two events are correlated provides
   a. a basis for prediction.
   b. an explanation of why the events are related.
   c. proof that as one increases, the other also increases.
   d. an indication that an underlying third factor is at work.

7. Here are some recently reported correlations, with interpretations drawn by journalists. Knowing just these correlations, can you come up with other possible explanations for each of these?
   a. Alcohol use is associated with violence. (One interpretation: Drinking triggers or unleashes aggressive behavior.)
   b. Educated people live longer, on average, than less-educated people. (One interpretation: Education lengthens life and enhances health.)
   c. Teens engaged in team sports are less likely to use drugs, smoke, have sex, carry weapons, and eat junk food than are teens who do not engage in team sports. (One interpretation: Team sports encourage healthy living.)
   d. Adolescents who frequently see smoking in movies are more likely to smoke. (One interpretation: Movie stars' behavior influences impressionable teens.)

8. To explain behaviors and clarify cause and effect, psychologists use _____.

9. To test the effect of a new drug on depression, we randomly assign people to control and experimental groups. Those in the control group take a pill that contains no medication. This pill is a _____.

10. In a double-blind procedure,
    a. only the participants know whether they are in the control group or the experimental group.
    b. experimental and control group members will be carefully matched for age, sex, income, and education level.
    c. neither the participants nor the researchers know who is in the experimental group or control group.
    d. someone separate from the researcher will ask people to volunteer for the experimental group or the control group.

11. A researcher wants to determine whether noise level affects workers' blood pressure. In one group, she varies the level of noise in the environment and records participants' blood pressure. In this experiment, the level of noise is the _____ _____.

12. The laboratory environment is designed to
    a. exactly re-create the events of everyday life.
    b. re-create psychological forces under *controlled* conditions.
    c. re-create psychological forces under *random* conditions.
    d. minimize the use of animals and humans in psychological research.

13. In defending their experimental research with animals, psychologists have noted that
    a. animals' physiology and behavior can tell us much about our own.
    b. animal experimentation sometimes helps animals as well as humans.
    c. animals are fascinating creatures and worthy of study.
    d. all of these statements are correct.

Continue testing yourself with 📖 **LearningCurve** or 📖 **Achieve Read & Practice** to learn and remember most effectively.

The Biology of Behavior

PeopleImages/Getty Images

A Chinese transplant surgeon, Xiaoping Ren, is building an international team that hopes to undertake a really, really bold medical venture—a full-body transplant (Kean, 2016; Tatlow, 2016). Wang Huanming, who is paralyzed from the neck down, volunteered to become one of ten volunteers for this mind-boggling experiment. What would Wang have to do? Have his fully-functioning head transferred to a brain-dead person's still-functioning body.

Ignore for the moment the experiment's serious ethical issues, including the near-certainty that the surgery will end Wang's life (Kean, 2016). And ignore the seeming impossibility of precisely connecting the head-to-spinal-cord nerves. Imagine, just imagine, that the procedure could work. With the same brain and a new body, would Wang still be Wang? After recovering, to whose home should he return? If the old Wang was once a skilled musician, would the new Wang conceivably retain that skill—or would that depend on the muscle memories stored in the new body? And if he (assuming the new body was male) later had a child, whom should the birth certificate list as the father?

Most of us twenty-first-century people (you, too?) presume that, even with a new body, Wang would still be Wang. We presume that our brain, designed by our genes and sculpted by our experience, provides our identity and enables our mind. No brain, no mind.

We are, indeed, living brains, but more. We are bodies alive. No principle is more central to today's psychology, or to this book, than this: *Everything psychological is simultaneously biological.* Your every idea, every mood, every urge is a biological happening.

"You're certainly a lot less fun since the operation."

You love, laugh, and cry with your body. To think, feel, or act without a body would be like running without legs. Without your body—your genes, your nervous system, your hormones, your appearance—you truly would be nobody. Moreover, your body and your brain influence and are influenced by your experience.

In Modules 3 through 5, we explore the mind's biology. We start small and build from the bottom up—from nerve cells up to the brain. In Module 6, we will consider how our behavior and environment can influence our biology from the top down. Life changes us. You've heard it before and you'll hear it again: *Nurture works on what nature provides.* ▶

3 Neural and Hormonal Systems

MODULE

BIOLOGY, BEHAVIOR, AND MIND

LEARNING OBJECTIVE QUESTION (LOQ)

3-1   Why are psychologists concerned with human biology?

Our understanding of how the brain gives birth to the mind has come a long way. The ancient Greek physician, Hippocrates, correctly located the mind in the brain. His contemporary, the philosopher Aristotle, believed the mind was in the heart, which pumps warmth and vitality to the body. The heart remains our symbol for love, but science has long since overtaken philosophy on this issue: It's your brain, not your heart, that falls in love.

In the early 1800s, German physician Franz Gall proposed that *phrenology,* studying bumps on the skull, could reveal a person's mental abilities and character traits. At one point, Britain had 29 phrenological societies, and phrenologists traveled North America giving skull readings (Dean, 2012; Hunt, 1993). Using a false name, humorist Mark Twain put one famous phrenologist to the test. "He found a cavity [and] startled me by saying that that cavity represented the total absence of the sense of humor!" Three months later, Twain sat for a second reading, this time identifying himself. Now "the cavity was gone, and in its place was . . . the loftiest bump of humor he had ever encountered in his life-long experience!" (Lopez, 2002). The "science" of phrenology remains known today as a reminder of our need for critical thinking and scientific analysis. Phrenology did at least succeed in focusing attention on the *localization of function*—the idea that various brain regions have particular functions.

Today, we are living in a time Gall could only dream about. **Biological psychologists** use advanced technologies to study the links between biological (genetic, neural, hormonal) processes and psychological processes. They and other researchers working from a biological perspective are announcing discoveries about the interplay of our biology and our behavior and mind at an exhilarating pace. Within little more than the past century, researchers seeking to understand the biology of the mind have discovered that

- our adaptive brain is wired by our experiences.
- among the body's cells are nerve cells that conduct electricity and "talk" to one another by sending chemical messages across a tiny gap that separates them.
- specific brain systems serve specific functions (though not the functions Gall supposed).
- we integrate information processed in these different brain systems to construct our experience of sights and sounds, meanings and memories, pain and passion.

We have also realized that we are each a system composed of subsystems that are in turn composed of even smaller subsystems. Tiny cells organize to form body organs.

These organs form larger systems for digestion, circulation, and information processing. And those systems are part of an even larger system—the individual, who in turn is a part of a family, culture, and community. Thus, we are *biopsychosocial* systems. To understand our behavior, we need to study how these biological, psychological, and social-cultural systems work and interact. Let's begin with the brain's ability to rewire itself as it adapts to experience.

🔒 **RETRIEVE IT • • •**   *ANSWERS IN APPENDIX E*

RI-1 What do phrenology and biological psychology have in common?

THE POWER OF PLASTICITY

LOQ 3-2   How do biology and experience interact in neural plasticity?

Your brain is sculpted not only by your genes but also by your life. Under the surface of your awareness, your brain is constantly changing, building new pathways as it adjusts to little mishaps and new experiences. This neural change is called **plasticity.** Although plasticity is strongest in childhood, it continues throughout life (Gutchess, 2014).

To see plasticity at work, consider London's taxi driver trainees, who spend years learning and remembering the city's 25,000 street locations and connections. For the half who pass the difficult final test, big rewards are in store: not only a better income but also an enlarged hippocampus, one of the brain's memory centers that processes spatial memories. London's bus drivers, who navigate a smaller set of roads, gain no similar neural rewards (Maguire et al., 2000, 2006).

We also see plasticity in well-practiced pianists, who have a larger-than-usual auditory cortex area (a sound-processing region) that encodes piano sounds (Bavelier et al., 2000; Pantev et al., 1998). After years of practice, the brains of ballerinas and jugglers reflect other changes related to improved performance (Draganski et al., 2004; Hänggi et al., 2010; Herholz & Zatorre, 2012). Your brain, too, is a work in progress. It changes with the focus and practice you're devoting to the ideas, skills, and people you care about the most. The brain you were born with is not the brain you will die with.

Plasticity is part of what makes the human brain unique (Gómez-Robles et al., 2015). More than for any other species, our brain is designed to change, and thus to adapt to our changing world.

NEURAL COMMUNICATION

For scientists, it is a happy fact of nature that the information systems of humans and other animals operate similarly. This similarity allows researchers to study relatively simple animals to discover how our neural systems operate. Cars differ, but all have engines, accelerators, steering wheels, and brakes. A space alien could study any one of them and grasp the operating principles. Likewise, animals differ, yet their nervous systems operate similarly.

Neurons

LOQ 3-3   What are *neurons*, and how do they transmit information?

Our body's neural information system is complexity built from simplicity. Its building blocks are **neurons,** or nerve cells. Throughout life, new neurons are born and unused neurons wither away (O'Leary et al., 2014; Shors, 2014). To fathom our thoughts and actions, our memories and moods, we must first understand how neurons work and communicate.

Neurons differ, but all are variations on the same theme (**FIGURE 3.1**). Each consists of a **cell body** and its branching fibers. The often bushy **dendrite** fibers receive and integrate information, conducting it toward the cell body (Stuart & Spruston, 2015). From there, the cell's single lengthy **axon** fiber passes the message through its terminal branches to other neurons or to muscles or glands (see **FIGURE 3.2**). Dendrites listen. Axons speak.

Volker Correll Photography

THE MIND'S EYE Daniel Kish, who is completely blind, enjoys going for walks in the woods. To stay safe, he uses echolocation—the same navigation method used by bats and dolphins. Blind echolocation experts such as Kish engage the brain's visual centers to navigate their surroundings (Thaler et al., 2011, 2014). Although Kish is blind, his flexible brain helps him to "see."

biological psychology the scientific study of the links between biological (genetic, neural, hormonal) and psychological processes. Some biological psychologists call themselves *behavioral neuroscientists, neuropsychologists, behavior geneticists, physiological psychologists,* or *biopsychologists.*

plasticity the brain's ability to change, especially during childhood, by reorganizing after damage or by building new pathways based on experience.

neuron a nerve cell; the basic building block of the nervous system.

cell body the part of a neuron that contains the nucleus; the cell's life-support center.

dendrites a neuron's often bushy, branching extensions that receive and integrate messages, conducting impulses toward the cell body.

axon the neuron extension that passes messages through its branches to other neurons or to muscles or glands.

myelin [MY-uh-lin] **sheath** a fatty tissue layer segmentally encasing the axons of some neurons; enables vastly greater transmission speed as neural impulses hop from one node to the next.

glial cells (glia) cells in the nervous system that support, nourish, and protect neurons; they may also play a role in learning, thinking, and memory.

action potential a neural impulse; a brief electrical charge that travels down an axon.

FIGURE 3.1
A MOTOR NEURON

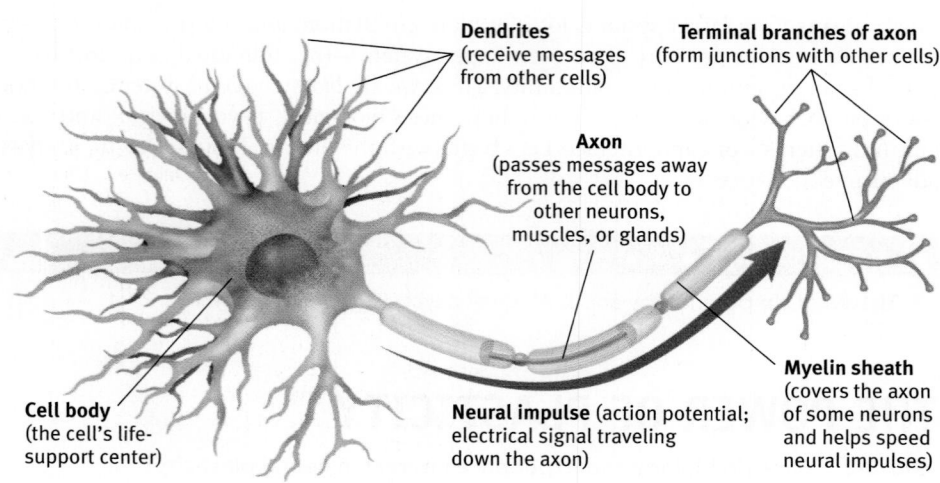

Dendrites (receive messages from other cells)

Terminal branches of axon (form junctions with other cells)

Axon (passes messages away from the cell body to other neurons, muscles, or glands)

Cell body (the cell's life-support center)

Neural impulse (action potential; electrical signal traveling down the axon)

Myelin sheath (covers the axon of some neurons and helps speed neural impulses)

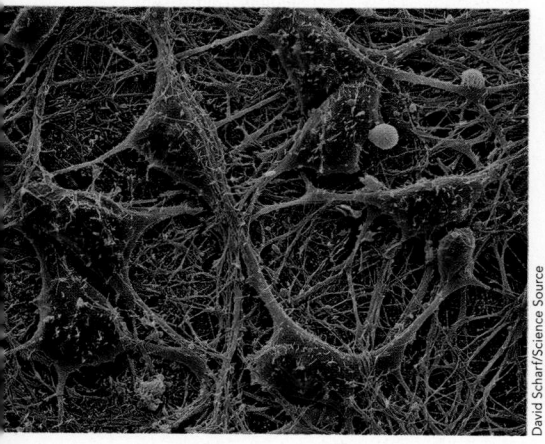

David Scharf/Science Source

FIGURE 3.2
NEURONS COMMUNICATING

When we learn about neurons, we often see them one at a time to learn their parts. But our billions of neurons exist in a vast and densely interconnected web. One neuron's terminal branches send messages to neighboring dendrites. Read on to learn more about this complex and fascinating electrochemical communication process.

 ENGAGE (ASK YOURSELF)

Does it surprise you to learn that despite your brain's complexity, your reaction time is slower than a computer's? What does this suggest regarding which tasks might be more readily performed by computers rather than humans?

Unlike the short dendrites, axons may be very long, projecting several feet through the body. A human neuron carrying orders to a leg muscle, for example, has a cell body and axon roughly on the scale of a basketball attached to a 4-mile-long rope. Much as home electrical wire is insulated, some axons are encased in a **myelin sheath,** a layer of fatty tissue that insulates them and speeds their impulses. As myelin is laid down up to about age 25, neural efficiency, judgment, and self-control grow (Fields, 2008). If the myelin sheath degenerates, *multiple sclerosis* results: Communication to muscles slows, with eventual loss of muscle control.

Supporting our billions of nerve cells are spidery **glial cells** ("glue cells"). Neurons are like queen bees; on their own they cannot feed or sheathe themselves. Glial cells are worker bees. They provide nutrients and insulating myelin, guide neural connections, and clean up after neurons send messages to one another. Glia also play a role in learning, thinking, and memory. By "chatting" with neurons they participate in information transmission and memory (Fields, 2011, 2013; Martín et al., 2015).

In more complex animal brains, the proportion of glia to neurons increases. A postmortem analysis of Albert Einstein's brain did not find more or larger-than-usual neurons, but it did reveal a much greater concentration of glial cells than found in an average Albert's head (Fields, 2004). Einstein's glial cells likely kept his brain abuzz with activity.

The Neural Impulse

Neurons transmit messages when stimulated by our senses or by neighboring neurons. A neuron sends a message by firing an impulse, called the **action potential**—a brief electrical charge that travels down its axon.

Depending on the type of fiber, a neural impulse travels at speeds ranging from a sluggish 2 miles (3 kilometers) per hour to more than 200 miles (320 kilometers) per hour. But even its top speed is 3 million times slower than that of electricity through a wire. We measure brain activity in milliseconds (thousandths of a second) and computer activity in nanoseconds (billionths of a second). Thus, unlike the nearly instantaneous reactions of a computer, your reaction to a sudden event, such as a child darting in front of your car, may take a quarter-second or more. Your brain is vastly more complex than a computer but slower at executing simple responses. And if you were an elephant—whose round-trip message travel time from a yank on the tail to the brain and back to the tail is 100 times longer than that of a tiny shrew—your reflexes would be slower yet (More et al., 2010).

Like batteries, neurons generate electricity from chemical events. In the neuron's chemistry-to-electricity process, *ions* (electrically charged atoms) are exchanged. The fluid outside an axon's membrane has mostly positively charged sodium ions. A resting axon's fluid interior (which includes both large, negatively charged protein ions and smaller, positively charged potassium ions) has a mostly negative charge. Like a tightly guarded facility, the axon's surface is selective about what it allows through its gates.

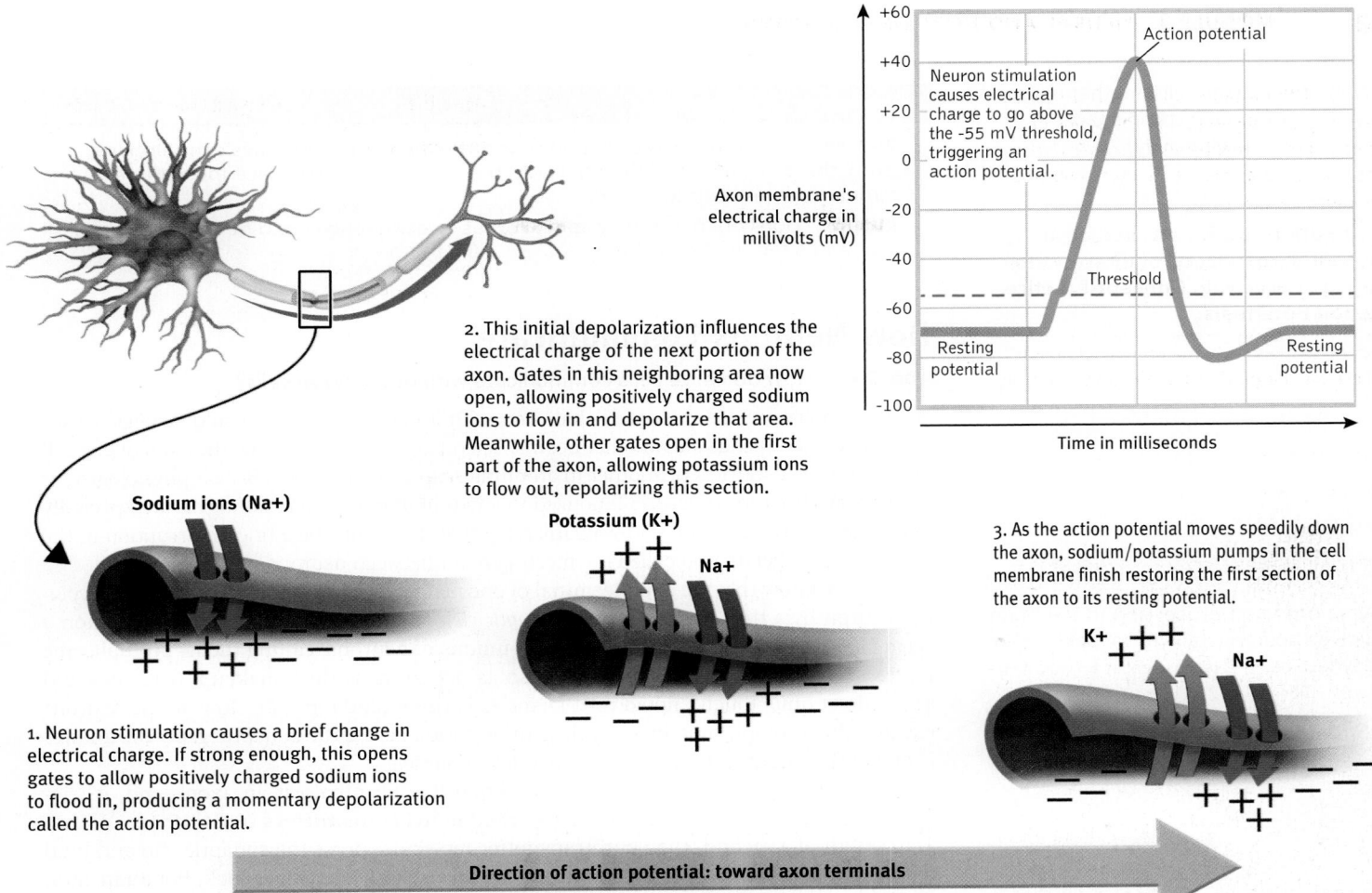

1. Neuron stimulation causes a brief change in electrical charge. If strong enough, this opens gates to allow positively charged sodium ions to flood in, producing a momentary depolarization called the action potential.

2. This initial depolarization influences the electrical charge of the next portion of the axon. Gates in this neighboring area now open, allowing positively charged sodium ions to flow in and depolarize that area. Meanwhile, other gates open in the first part of the axon, allowing potassium ions to flow out, repolarizing this section.

3. As the action potential moves speedily down the axon, sodium/potassium pumps in the cell membrane finish restoring the first section of the axon to its resting potential.

Sodium ions (Na+)

Potassium (K+)

Na+

K+ Na+

Axon membrane's electrical charge in millivolts (mV)

+60
+40
+20
0
-20
-40
-60
-80
-100

Action potential

Neuron stimulation causes electrical charge to go above the -55 mV threshold, triggering an action potential.

Threshold

Resting potential

Resting potential

Time in milliseconds

Direction of action potential: toward axon terminals

We say the axon's surface is *selectively permeable.* This positive-outside/negative-inside state is called the *resting potential.*

When a neuron fires, the first section of the axon opens its gates, rather like a storm sewer cover flipping open, and positively charged sodium ions (attracted to the negative interior) flood in through the now-open channels. The loss of the inside/outside charge difference, called *depolarization,* causes the next section of axon channels to open, and then the next, like a line of falling dominos. This temporary inflow of positive ions is the neural impulse—the action potential. Each neuron is itself a miniature decision-making device performing complex calculations as it receives signals from hundreds, even thousands, of other neurons. The mind boggles when imagining this electrochemical process repeating up to 100 or even 1000 times a second. But this is just the first of many astonishments.

Most neural signals are *excitatory,* somewhat like pushing a neuron's gas pedal. Some are *inhibitory,* more like pushing its brake. If excitatory signals exceed the inhibitory signals by a minimum intensity, or **threshold** (**FIGURE 3.3**), the combined signals trigger an action potential. (Think of it this way: If the excitatory party animals outvote the inhibitory party poopers, the party's on.) The action potential then travels down the axon, which branches into junctions with hundreds or thousands of other neurons or with the body's muscles and glands.

Neurons need short breaks (a tiny fraction of an eyeblink). During a resting pause called the **refractory period,** subsequent action potentials cannot occur until the axon returns to its resting state. Then the neuron can fire again.

Increasing the level of stimulation above the threshold will not increase the neural impulse's intensity. The neuron's reaction is an **all-or-none response:** Like guns, neurons either fire or they don't. How, then, do we detect the intensity of a stimulus? How do we distinguish a gentle touch from a big hug? A strong stimulus can trigger *more* neurons to fire, and to fire more often. But it does not affect the action potential's strength or speed. Squeezing a trigger harder won't make a bullet go faster.

FIGURE 3.3

ACTION POTENTIAL Bodily sensations and actions—detecting a hug or kicking a soccer ball—happen when our neurons are stimulated enough that their membrane's electrical charge reaches a threshold (−55 mV in this example—see graph). This prompts each of those neurons to "fire" an impulse—an action potential—which travels down its axon (see numbered drawings) and transmits a message to other neurons, muscles, or glands.

threshold the level of stimulation required to trigger a neural impulse.

refractory period in neural processing, a brief resting pause that occurs after a neuron has fired; subsequent action potentials cannot occur until the axon returns to its resting state.

all-or-none response a neuron's reaction of either firing (with a full-strength response) or not firing.

"What one neuron tells another neuron is simply how much it is excited."
—Francis Crick, *The Astonishing Hypothesis*, 1994

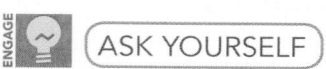 **LaunchPad** For an interactive, animated explanation of this process, engage online with **Concept Practice: Action Potentials.**

"All information processing in the brain involves neurons 'talking to' each other at synapses." —Neuroscientist Solomon H. Snyder, 1984

ENGAGE

🔋 (ASK YOURSELF)

Why was the discovery of neurons' communication mechanism so important?

synapse [SIN-aps] the junction between the axon tip of the sending neuron and the dendrite or cell body of the receiving neuron. The tiny gap at this junction is called the *synaptic gap* or *synaptic cleft.*

neurotransmitters chemical messengers that cross the synaptic gap between neurons. When released by the sending neuron, neurotransmitters travel across the synapse and bind to receptor sites on the receiving neuron, thereby influencing whether that neuron will generate a neural impulse.

reuptake a neurotransmitter's reabsorption by the sending neuron.

🔒 RETRIEVE IT • • •   *ANSWERS IN APPENDIX E*

RI-2 When a neuron fires an action potential, the information travels through the axon, the dendrites, and the cell body, but not in that order. Place these three structures in the correct order.

RI-3 How does our nervous system allow us to experience the difference between a slap and a tap on the back?

How Neurons Communicate

LOQ 3-4   How do nerve cells communicate with other nerve cells?

Neurons interweave so intricately that even with a microscope, you would struggle to see where one neuron ends and another begins. Scientists once believed that the axon of one cell fused with the dendrites of another in an uninterrupted fabric. Then British physiologist Sir Charles Sherrington (1857–1952) noticed that neural impulses were taking an unexpectedly long time to travel a neural pathway. Inferring that there must be a brief interruption in the transmission, Sherrington called the meeting point between neurons a **synapse.**

We now know that the axon terminal of one neuron is in fact separated from the receiving neuron by a tiny *synaptic gap* (or *synaptic cleft*). Spanish anatomist Santiago Ramón y Cajal (1852–1934) marveled at these near-unions of neurons, calling them "protoplasmic kisses." "Like elegant ladies air-kissing so as not to muss their makeup, dendrites and axons don't quite touch," noted poet Diane Ackerman (2004, p. 37). How do the neurons execute this protoplasmic kiss, sending information across the synaptic gap? The answer is one of the important scientific discoveries of our age.

When an action potential reaches the knob-like terminals at an axon's end, it triggers the release of chemical messengers, called **neurotransmitters** (FIGURE 3.4). Within 1/10,000th of a second, the neurotransmitter molecules cross the synaptic gap and bind to receptor sites on the receiving neuron—as precisely as a key fits a lock. For an instant, the neurotransmitter unlocks tiny channels at the receiving site, and electrically charged atoms flow in, exciting or inhibiting the receiving neuron's readiness to fire. The excess neurotransmitters finally drift away, are broken down by enzymes, or are reabsorbed by the sending neuron—a process called **reuptake.** Some antidepressant medications partially block the reuptake of mood-enhancing neurotransmitters.

🔒 RETRIEVE IT • • •   *ANSWERS IN APPENDIX E*

RI-4 What happens in the *synaptic gap*?

RI-5 What is *reuptake*? What two other things can happen to excess neurotransmitters after a neuron reacts?

How Neurotransmitters Influence Us

LOQ 3-5   How do neurotransmitters influence behavior, and how do drugs and other chemicals affect neurotransmission?

In their quest to understand neural communication, researchers have discovered several dozen neurotransmitters and almost as many new questions: Are certain neurotransmitters found only in specific places? How do neurotransmitters affect our moods, memories, and mental abilities? Can we boost or diminish these effects through drugs or diet?

Other modules explore neurotransmitter influences on hunger and thinking, depression and euphoria, addictions and therapy. For now, let's glimpse how neurotransmitters influence our motions and emotions.

One of the best-understood neurotransmitters, *acetylcholine (ACh),* plays a role in learning and memory. It is also the messenger at every junction between motor neurons (which carry information from the brain and spinal cord to the body's tissues) and skeletal muscles. When ACh is released to our muscle cell receptors, the muscle contracts. If ACh transmission is blocked, as happens during some kinds of anesthesia and with some poisons, the muscles cannot contract and we are paralyzed.

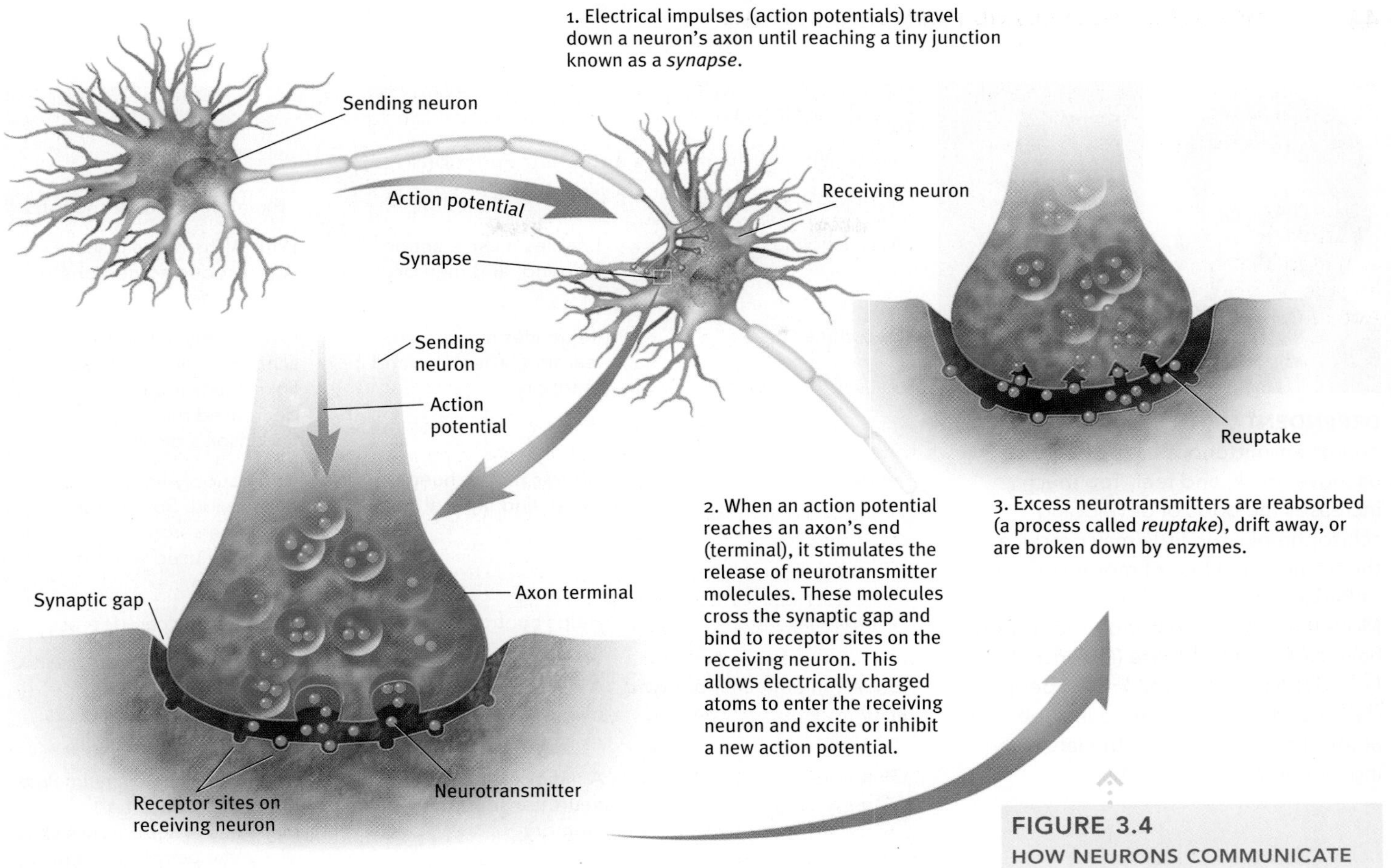

1. Electrical impulses (action potentials) travel down a neuron's axon until reaching a tiny junction known as a *synapse*.

Sending neuron

Action potential

Receiving neuron

Synapse

Sending neuron

Action potential

Synaptic gap

Axon terminal

Receptor sites on receiving neuron

Neurotransmitter

Reuptake

2. When an action potential reaches an axon's end (terminal), it stimulates the release of neurotransmitter molecules. These molecules cross the synaptic gap and bind to receptor sites on the receiving neuron. This allows electrically charged atoms to enter the receiving neuron and excite or inhibit a new action potential.

3. Excess neurotransmitters are reabsorbed (a process called *reuptake*), drift away, or are broken down by enzymes.

FIGURE 3.4
HOW NEURONS COMMUNICATE

Candace Pert and Solomon Snyder (1973) made an exciting discovery about neurotransmitters when they attached a harmless radioactive tracer to morphine, an opiate drug that elevates mood and eases pain. As the researchers tracked the morphine in an animal's brain, they noticed it was binding to receptors in areas linked with mood and pain sensations. But why would the brain have these "opiate receptors"? Why would it have a chemical lock, unless it also had a key—a natural painkiller—to open it?

Researchers soon confirmed that the brain does indeed produce its own naturally occurring opiates. Our body releases several types of neurotransmitter molecules similar to morphine in response to pain and vigorous exercise. These **endorphins** (short for *endo*genous [produced within] m*orphine*) help explain good feelings such as the "runner's high," the painkilling effects of acupuncture, and the indifference to pain in some severely injured people (Boecker et al., 2008; Fuss et al., 2015). But once again, new knowledge led to new questions.

HOW DRUGS AND OTHER CHEMICALS ALTER NEUROTRANSMISSION If natural endorphins lessen pain and boost mood, why not increase this effect by flooding the brain with artificial opiates, thereby intensifying the brain's own "feel-good" chemistry? Because it would disrupt the brain's chemical balancing act. When flooded with opiate drugs such as heroin and morphine, the brain, to maintain its chemical balance, may stop producing its own natural opiates. When the drug is withdrawn, the brain may then be deprived of any form of opiate, causing intense discomfort. For suppressing the body's own neurotransmitter production, nature charges a price.

Drugs and other chemicals affect brain chemistry, often by either exciting or inhibiting neurons' firing. **Agonist** molecules increase a neurotransmitter's action. Some agonists may increase the production or release of neurotransmitters, or block reuptake in the synapse. Other agonists may be similar enough to a neurotransmitter to bind to its receptor and mimic its excitatory or inhibitory effects. Some opiate drugs are agonists and produce a temporary "high" by amplifying normal sensations of arousal or pleasure.

Antagonists decrease a neurotransmitter's action by blocking production or release. Botulin, a poison that can form in improperly canned food, causes paralysis by blocking ACh release. (Small injections of botulin—Botox—smooth wrinkles by paralyzing the

Physician Lewis Thomas, on the endorphins: "There it is, a biologically universal act of mercy. I cannot explain it, except to say that I would have put it in had I been around at the very beginning, sitting as a member of a planning committee." —*The Youngest Science*, 1983

ENGAGE

ASK YOURSELF

Can you recall a time, perhaps after a workout, when you felt the effects of endorphins? How would you describe these feelings?

endorphins [en-DOR-fins] "morphine within"—natural, opiate-like neurotransmitters linked to pain control and to pleasure.

agonist a molecule that increases a neurotransmitter's action.

antagonist a molecule that inhibits or blocks a neurotransmitter's action.

DEPENDENT UPON DOPAMINE The neurotransmitter dopamine helps us move, think, and feel. Too much increases the odds of developing schizophrenia; too little may produce the tremors and loss of motor control of Parkinson's disease (NIH, 2016). More than 10 million people worldwide have Parkinson's disease (Parkinson's Foundation, 2018). Well-known people diagnosed with the disease include actor Michael J. Fox and the late boxing legend Muhammad Ali.

"When it comes to the brain, if you want to see the action, follow the neurotransmitters." —Neuroscientist Floyd Bloom, 1993

🔒 📖 **LaunchPad** For an illustrated review of neural communication, visit **Topic Tutorial: PsychSim6, Neural Messages.**

🔒 **TABLE 3.1**

Some Neurotransmitters and Their Functions

Neurotransmitter	Function	Examples of Malfunctions
Acetylcholine (ACh)	Enables muscle action, learning, and memory	With Alzheimer's disease, ACh-producing neurons deteriorate.
Dopamine	Influences movement, learning, attention, and emotion	Oversupply linked to schizophrenia. Undersupply linked to tremors and decreased mobility in Parkinson's disease.
Serotonin	Affects mood, hunger, sleep, and arousal	Undersupply linked to depression. Some drugs that raise serotonin levels are used to treat depression.
Norepinephrine	Helps control alertness and arousal	Undersupply can depress mood.
GABA (gamma-aminobutyric acid)	A major inhibitory neurotransmitter	Undersupply linked to seizures, tremors, and insomnia.
Glutamate	A major excitatory neurotransmitter; involved in memory	Oversupply can overstimulate the brain, producing migraines or seizures (which is why some people avoid MSG, monosodium glutamate, in food).
Endorphins	Neurotransmitters that influence the perception of pain or pleasure	Oversupply with opiate drugs can suppress the body's natural endorphin supply.

underlying facial muscles.) These antagonists are enough like the natural neurotransmitter to occupy its receptor site and block its effect, but are not similar enough to stimulate the receptor (rather like foreign coins that fit into, but won't operate, a vending machine). Curare, a poison some South American Indians have applied to hunting-dart tips, occupies and blocks ACh receptor sites on muscles, producing paralysis in their prey.

See **TABLE 3.1** for an overview of key neurotransmitters and the specific behaviors and emotions they affect.

🔒 **RETRIEVE IT • • •**   *ANSWERS IN APPENDIX E*

RI-6 Curare poisoning paralyzes its victims by blocking ACh receptors involved in muscle movements. Morphine mimics endorphin actions. Which is an agonist, and which is an antagonist?

RI-7 Serotonin, dopamine, and endorphins are all chemical messengers called _____.

THE NERVOUS SYSTEM

LOQ 3-6   What are the functions of the nervous system's main divisions, and what are the three main types of neurons?

Neurons communicating with neurotransmitters make up our body's **nervous system,** a communication network that takes in information from the world and the body's tissues, makes decisions, and sends back information and orders to the body's tissues (**FIGURE 3.5**).

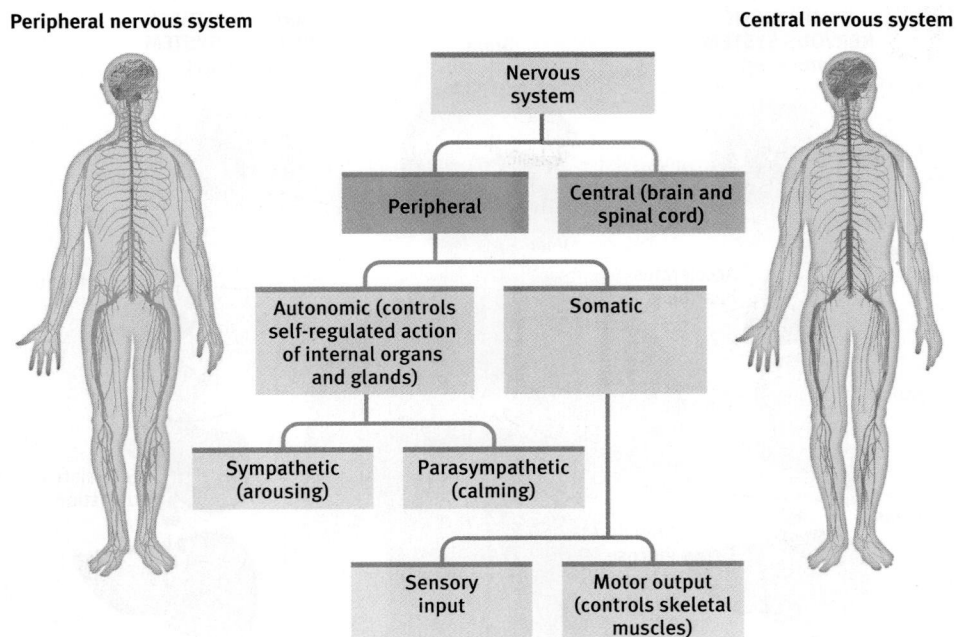

Peripheral nervous system

Central nervous system

FIGURE 3.5

THE FUNCTIONAL DIVISIONS OF THE HUMAN NERVOUS SYSTEM

A quick overview: The brain and spinal cord form the **central nervous system (CNS),** the body's decision maker. The **peripheral nervous system (PNS)** is responsible for gathering information and for transmitting CNS decisions to other body parts. **Nerves,** electrical cables formed from bundles of axons, link the CNS with the body's sensory receptors, muscles, and glands. The optic nerve, for example, bundles a million axons into a single cable carrying the messages from the eye to the brain (Mason & Kandel, 1991).

Information travels in the nervous system through three types of neurons. **Sensory neurons** carry messages from the body's tissues and sensory receptors inward (thus, they are *afferent*) to the brain and spinal cord for processing. **Motor neurons** (which are *efferent*) carry instructions from the central nervous system outward to the body's muscles and glands. Between the sensory input and motor output, information is processed via **interneurons.** Our complexity resides mostly in these interneurons. Our nervous system has a few million sensory neurons, a few million motor neurons, and billions and billions of interneurons.

> ## 🔒 RETRIEVE IT • • •
> ANSWERS IN APPENDIX E
>
> **RI-8** Match the type of neuron (I–III) to its description (a–c).
>
> | Type: | Description: |
> |---|---|
> | I. Motor neurons | a. Carry incoming messages from sensory receptors to the CNS. |
> | II. Sensory neurons | b. Communicate within the CNS and process information between incoming and outgoing messages. |
> | III. Interneurons | c. Carry outgoing messages from the CNS to muscles and glands. |

The Peripheral Nervous System

Our peripheral nervous system has two components—somatic and autonomic. Our **somatic nervous system** enables voluntary control of our skeletal muscles. As you reach the end of this page, your somatic nervous system will report to your brain the current state of your skeletal muscles and carry instructions back, triggering a response from your hand so you can read on.

Our **autonomic nervous system (ANS)** controls our glands and our internal organ muscles. The ANS influences functions such as glandular activity, heartbeat, and

nervous system the body's speedy, electrochemical communication network, consisting of all the nerve cells of the peripheral and central nervous systems.

central nervous system (CNS) the brain and spinal cord.

peripheral nervous system (PNS) the sensory and motor neurons that connect the central nervous system (CNS) to the rest of the body.

nerves bundled axons that form neural cables connecting the central nervous system with muscles, glands, and sense organs.

sensory (afferent) neurons neurons that carry incoming information from the body's tissues and sensory receptors to the brain and spinal cord.

motor (efferent) neurons neurons that carry outgoing information from the brain and spinal cord to the muscles and glands.

interneurons neurons within the brain and spinal cord; they communicate internally and process information between the sensory inputs and motor outputs.

somatic nervous system the division of the peripheral nervous system that controls the body's skeletal muscles. Also called the *skeletal nervous system.*

autonomic [aw-tuh-NAHM-ik] **nervous system (ANS)** the part of the peripheral nervous system that controls the glands and the muscles of the internal organs (such as the heart). Its sympathetic division arouses; its parasympathetic division calms.

FIGURE 3.6
THE DUAL FUNCTIONS OF THE AUTONOMIC NERVOUS SYSTEM
The autonomic nervous system controls the more autonomous (or self-regulating) internal functions. Its sympathetic division arouses and expends energy. Its parasympathetic division calms and conserves energy, allowing routine maintenance activity. For example, sympathetic stimulation accelerates heartbeat, whereas parasympathetic stimulation slows it.

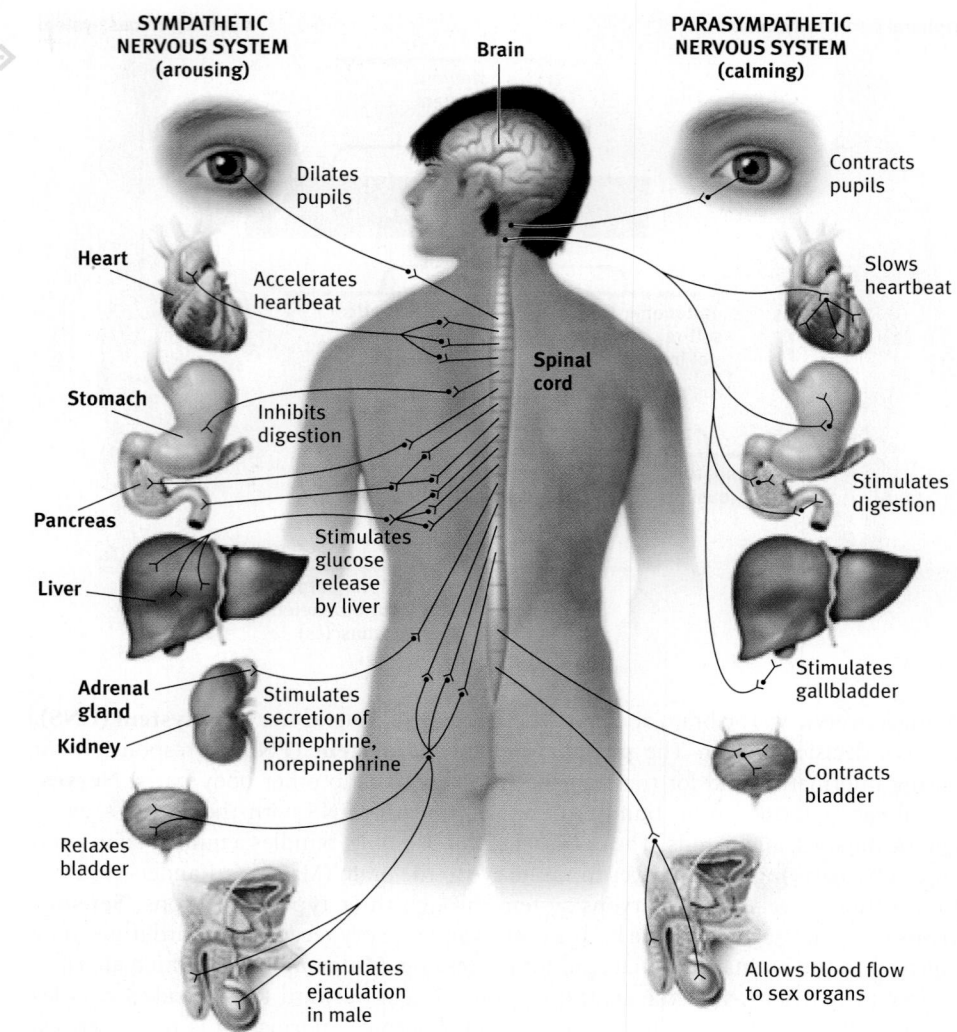

SYMPATHETIC NERVOUS SYSTEM (arousing)

PARASYMPATHETIC NERVOUS SYSTEM (calming)

Brain

Dilates pupils

Contracts pupils

Heart

Accelerates heartbeat

Slows heartbeat

Spinal cord

Stomach

Inhibits digestion

Stimulates digestion

Pancreas

Stimulates glucose release by liver

Liver

Stimulates gallbladder

Adrenal gland

Stimulates secretion of epinephrine, norepinephrine

Kidney

Contracts bladder

Relaxes bladder

Stimulates ejaculation in male

Allows blood flow to sex organs

sympathetic nervous system the division of the autonomic nervous system that arouses the body, mobilizing its energy.

parasympathetic nervous system the division of the autonomic nervous system that calms the body, conserving its energy.

ENGAGE

(ASK YOURSELF)

Think back to a time when you felt your sympathetic nervous system kick in at a stressful moment. What was your body preparing you for? Were you able to sense your parasympathetic nervous system's response when the challenge had passed?

digestion. (*Autonomic* means "self-regulating.") Like an automatic pilot, this system may be consciously overridden, but usually it operates on its own (autonomously).

The autonomic nervous system's subdivisions serve two important functions (**FIGURE 3.6**). The **sympathetic nervous system** arouses and expends energy. If something alarms or challenges you (such as a longed-for job interview), your sympathetic nervous system will accelerate your heartbeat, raise your blood pressure, slow your digestion, raise your blood sugar, and cool you with perspiration, making you alert and ready for action. When the stress subsides (the interview is over), your **parasympathetic nervous system** will produce the opposite effects, conserving energy as it calms you. The sympathetic and parasympathetic nervous systems work together to keep us in a steady internal state called *homeostasis*.

I [DM] recently experienced my ANS in action. Before sending me into an MRI machine for a shoulder scan, the technician asked if I had issues with claustrophobia. "No, I'm fine," I assured her, with perhaps a hint of macho swagger. Moments later, as I found myself on my back, stuck deep inside a coffin-sized box and unable to move, my sympathetic nervous system had a different idea. Claustrophobia overtook me. My heart began pounding, and I felt a desperate urge to escape. Just as I was about to cry out for release, I felt my calming parasympathetic nervous system kick in. My heart rate slowed and my body relaxed, though my arousal surged again before the 20-minute confinement ended. "You did well!" the technician said, unaware of my ANS roller-coaster ride.

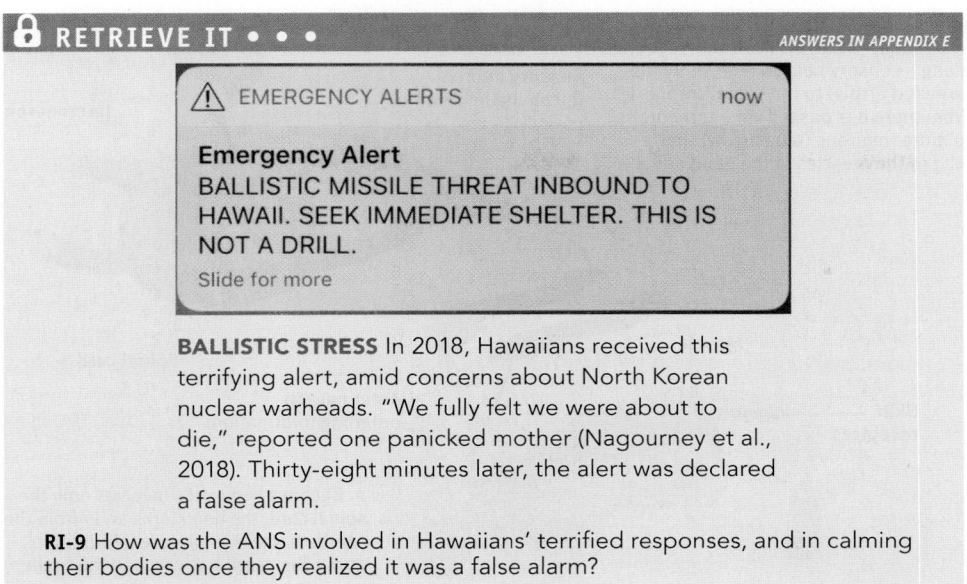

⚠ EMERGENCY ALERTS   now

Emergency Alert
BALLISTIC MISSILE THREAT INBOUND TO
HAWAII. SEEK IMMEDIATE SHELTER. THIS IS
NOT A DRILL.
Slide for more

BALLISTIC STRESS In 2018, Hawaiians received this
terrifying alert, amid concerns about North Korean
nuclear warheads. "We fully felt we were about to
die," reported one panicked mother (Nagourney et al.,
2018). Thirty-eight minutes later, the alert was declared
a false alarm.

RI-9 How was the ANS involved in Hawaiians' terrified responses, and in calming
their bodies once they realized it was a false alarm?

The Central Nervous System

From neurons "talking" to other neurons arises the complexity of the central nervous
system's brain and spinal cord.

It is the brain that enables our humanity—our thinking, feeling, and acting. Tens
of billions of neurons, each communicating with thousands of other neurons, yield
an ever-changing wiring diagram. By one estimate—projecting from neuron counts
in small brain samples—our brain has some 86 billion neurons (Azevedo et al., 2009;
Herculano-Houzel, 2012).

Rather like individual pixels combining to form a picture, the brain's individual
neurons cluster into work groups called *neural networks*. To understand why, Stephen
Kosslyn and Olivier Koenig (1992, p. 12) have invited us to "think about why cities exist;
why don't people distribute themselves more evenly across the countryside?" Like people
networking with people, neurons network with nearby neurons with which they can
have short, fast connections.

The other part of the CNS, the *spinal cord,* is a two-way information highway connecting the peripheral nervous system and the brain. Ascending neural fibers send up
sensory information, and descending fibers send back motor-control information. The
neural pathways governing our **reflexes,** our automatic responses to stimuli, illustrate
the spinal cord's work. A simple spinal reflex pathway is composed of a single sensory
neuron and a single motor neuron. These often communicate through an interneuron.
The knee-jerk response, for example, involves one such simple pathway. A headless warm
body could do it.

Another neural circuit enables the pain reflex (**FIGURE 3.7**). When your finger touches
a flame, neural activity (excited by the heat) travels via sensory neurons to interneurons
in your spinal cord. These interneurons respond by activating motor neurons leading to
the muscles in your arm. Because the simple pain-reflex pathway runs through the spinal
cord and right back out, your hand jerks away from the candle's flame *before* your brain
receives and responds to the information that causes you to feel pain. That's why it feels as
if your hand jerks away not by your choice, but on its own.

Information travels to and from the brain by way of the spinal cord. Were the top of
your spinal cord severed, you would not feel pain from your paralyzed body below. Nor
would you feel pleasure. With your brain literally out of touch with your body, you would
lose all sensation and voluntary movement in body regions with sensory and motor
connections to the spinal cord below its point of injury. You would exhibit the knee-jerk
response without feeling the tap. To produce bodily pain or pleasure, the sensory information must reach the brain.

*"The body is made up of millions and
millions of crumbs."*

reflex a simple, automatic response to
a sensory stimulus, such as the knee-jerk
response.

FIGURE 3.7
A SIMPLE REFLEX

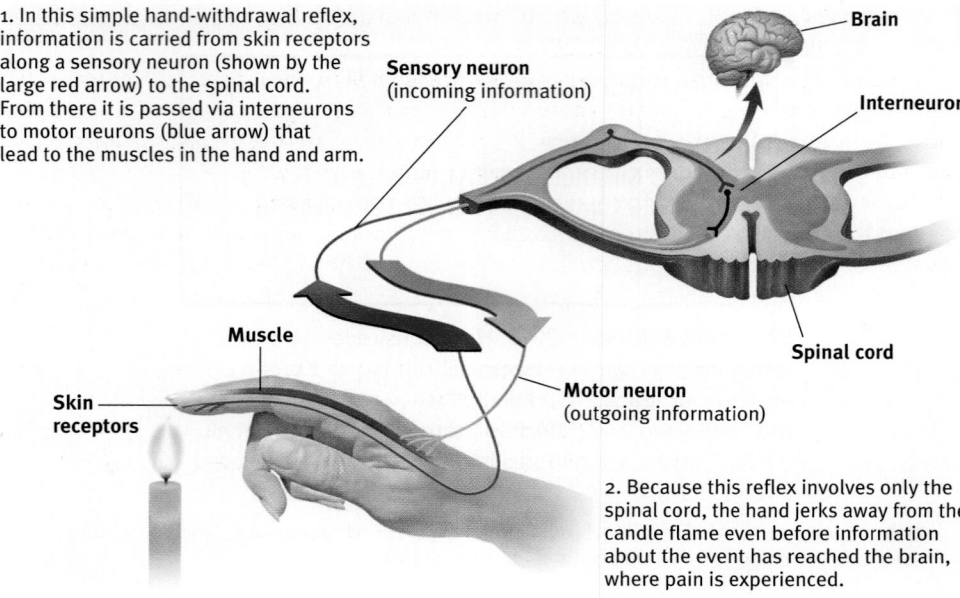

1. In this simple hand-withdrawal reflex, information is carried from skin receptors along a sensory neuron (shown by the large red arrow) to the spinal cord. From there it is passed via interneurons to motor neurons (blue arrow) that lead to the muscles in the hand and arm.

Brain

Sensory neuron (incoming information)

Interneuron

Muscle

Spinal cord

Skin receptors

Motor neuron (outgoing information)

2. Because this reflex involves only the spinal cord, the hand jerks away from the candle flame even before information about the event has reached the brain, where pain is experienced.

endocrine [EN-duh-krin] **system** the body's "slow" chemical communication system; a set of glands that secrete hormones into the bloodstream.

hormones chemical messengers that are manufactured by the endocrine glands, travel through the bloodstream, and affect other tissues.

adrenal [ah-DREEN-el] **glands** a pair of endocrine glands that sit just above the kidneys and secrete hormones (epinephrine and norepinephrine) that help arouse the body in times of stress.

pituitary gland the endocrine system's most influential gland. Under the influence of the hypothalamus, the pituitary regulates growth and controls other endocrine glands.

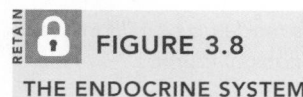

FIGURE 3.8
THE ENDOCRINE SYSTEM

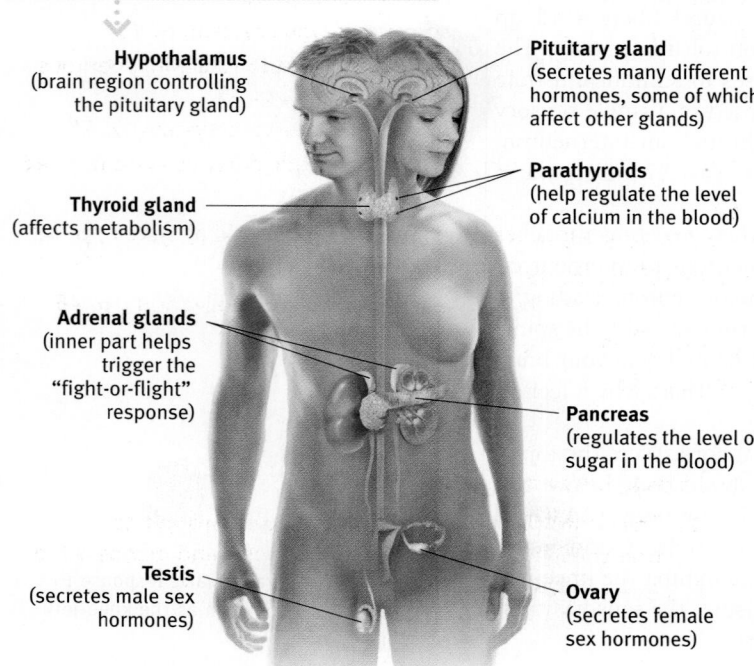

Hypothalamus (brain region controlling the pituitary gland)

Pituitary gland (secretes many different hormones, some of which affect other glands)

Parathyroids (help regulate the level of calcium in the blood)

Thyroid gland (affects metabolism)

Adrenal glands (inner part helps trigger the "fight-or-flight" response)

Pancreas (regulates the level of sugar in the blood)

Testis (secretes male sex hormones)

Ovary (secretes female sex hormones)

THE ENDOCRINE SYSTEM

LOQ 3-7   How does the endocrine system transmit information and interact with the nervous system?

So far, we have focused on the body's speedy electrochemical information system. Interconnected with your nervous system is a second communication system, the **endocrine system** (FIGURE 3.8). The endocrine system's glands secrete another form of chemical messengers, **hormones,** which travel through the bloodstream and affect other tissues, including the brain. When hormones act on the brain, they influence our interest in sex, food, and aggression.

Some hormones are chemically identical to neurotransmitters (the chemical messengers that diffuse across a synapse and excite or inhibit an adjacent neuron). The endocrine system and nervous system are therefore close relatives: Both produce molecules that act on receptors elsewhere. Like many relatives, they also differ. The speedier nervous system zips messages from eyes to brain to hand in a fraction of a second. Endocrine messages trudge along in the bloodstream, taking several seconds or more to travel from the gland to the target tissue. If the nervous system transmits information with text-message speed, the endocrine system delivers an old-fashioned letter.

But slow and steady sometimes wins the race. Endocrine messages tend to outlast the effects of neural messages. Have you ever felt angry long after the cause of your angry feelings was resolved (say, your friend apologized for her rudeness)? You may have experienced an "endocrine hangover" from lingering emotion-related hormones.

In a moment of danger, the ANS orders the **adrenal glands** on top of the kidneys to release *epinephrine* and *norepinephrine* (also called *adrenaline* and *noradrenaline*). These hormones increase heart rate, blood pressure, and blood sugar, providing a surge of energy. When the emergency passes, the hormones—and the feelings—linger a while.

The most influential endocrine gland is the **pituitary gland,** a pea-sized structure located in the core of the brain, where it is controlled by an adjacent brain area, the *hypothalamus* (more on that shortly). Among the hormones released by the pituitary is a growth hormone that stimulates physical development. Another is *oxytocin*, which enables social bonding (De Dreu et al., 2010; Marsh et al., 2017; Pfundmair et al., 2017).

Pituitary secretions also direct other endocrine glands to release their hormones. The pituitary, then, is a *master gland* (whose own master is the hypothalamus). For example, under the brain's influence, the pituitary triggers your sex glands to release sex hormones. These in turn influence your brain and behavior (Goetz et al., 2014).

This feedback system (brain ⟶ pituitary ⟶ other glands ⟶ hormones ⟶ body and brain) reveals the intimate connection of the nervous and endocrine systems. The nervous system directs endocrine secretions, which then affect the nervous system. Conducting and coordinating this whole electrochemical orchestra is that flexible maestro we call the brain.

ASK YOURSELF

Do you remember feeling the lingering effects of a hormonal response, such as anger, after some particularly aggravating event? How did it feel? How long did it last?

🔒 **RETRIEVE IT • • •**   *ANSWERS IN APPENDIX E*

RI-10 Why is the pituitary gland called the "master gland"?

RI-11 How are the nervous and endocrine systems alike, and how do they differ?

🔒 REVIEW NEURAL AND HORMONAL SYSTEMS

⟶ Learning Objectives

TEST YOURSELF Answer these repeated Learning Objective Questions on your own (before checking the answers in Appendix D) to improve your retention of the concepts (McDaniel et al., 2009, 2015).

3-1 Why are psychologists concerned with human biology?

3-2 How do biology and experience interact in neural plasticity?

3-3 What are *neurons*, and how do they transmit information?

3-4 How do nerve cells communicate with other nerve cells?

3-5 How do neurotransmitters influence behavior, and how do drugs and other chemicals affect neurotransmission?

3-6 What are the functions of the nervous system's main divisions, and what are the three main types of neurons?

3-7 How does the endocrine system transmit information and interact with the nervous system?

⟶ Terms and Concepts to Remember

TEST YOURSELF Write down the definition yourself, then check your answer on the referenced page.

biological psychology, **p. 39**

plasticity, **p. 39**

neuron, **p. 39**

cell body, **p. 39**

dendrites, **p. 39**

axon, **p. 39**

myelin [MY-uh-lin] sheath, **p. 40**

glial cells (glia), **p. 40**

action potential, **p. 40**

threshold, **p. 41**

refractory period, **p. 41**

all-or-none response, **p. 41**

synapse [SIN-aps], **p. 42**

neurotransmitters, **p. 42**

reuptake, **p. 42**

endorphins [en-DOR-fins], **p. 43**

agonist, **p. 43**

antagonist, **p. 43**

nervous system, **p. 45**

central nervous system (CNS), **p. 45**

peripheral nervous system (PNS), **p. 45**

nerves, **p. 45**

sensory (afferent) neurons, **p. 45**

motor (efferent) neurons, **p. 45**

interneurons, **p. 45**

somatic nervous system, **p. 45**

autonomic [aw-tuh-NAHM-ik] nervous system (ANS), **p. 45**

sympathetic nervous system, **p. 46**

parasympathetic nervous system, **p. 46**

reflex, **p. 47**

endocrine [EN-duh-krin] system, **p. 48**

hormones, **p. 48**

adrenal [ah-DREEN-el] glands, **p. 48**

pituitary gland, **p. 48**

⟶ Experience the Testing Effect

TEST YOURSELF Answer the following questions on your own first, then check your answers in Appendix E.

1. What do psychologists mean when they say the brain is "plastic"?

2. The neuron fiber that passes messages through its branches to other neurons or to muscles and glands is the _____.

3. The tiny space between the axon of one neuron and the dendrite or cell body of another is called the
   a. axon terminal.
   c. synaptic gap.
   b. branching fiber.
   d. threshold.

4. Regarding a neuron's response to stimulation, the intensity of the stimulus determines
   a. whether or not an impulse is generated.
   b. how fast an impulse is transmitted.
   c. how intense an impulse will be.
   d. whether reuptake will occur.

5. In a sending neuron, when an action potential reaches an axon terminal, the impulse triggers the release of chemical messengers called _____ .

6. Endorphins are released in the brain in response to
   a. morphine or heroin.
   b. pain or vigorous exercise.
   c. the all-or-none response.
   d. all of the above.

7. The autonomic nervous system controls internal functions, such as heart rate and glandular activity. The word *auto-nomic* means
   a. calming.
   c. self-regulating.
   b. voluntary.
   d. arousing.

8. The sympathetic nervous system arouses us for action and the parasympathetic nervous system calms us down. Together, the two systems make up the _____ nervous system.

9. The neurons of the spinal cord are part of the _____ nervous system.

10. The most influential endocrine gland, known as the "master gland," is the
    a. pituitary.
    c. thyroid.
    b. hypothalamus.
    d. pancreas.

11. The _____ _____ secrete(s) epineph-rine and norepinephrine, helping to arouse the body during times of stress.

Continue testing yourself with 📚 **LearningCurve** or 📖 **Achieve Read & Practice** to learn and remember most effectively.

---

④ Tools of Discovery, Older Brain Structures, and the Limbic System

The mind seeking to understand the brain—that is among the ultimate scientific challenges. And so it will always be. To paraphrase cosmologist John Barrow, a brain simple enough to be fully understood is too simple to produce a mind able to understand it.

When you think *about* your brain, you're thinking *with* your brain—by releasing billions of neurotransmitter molecules across trillions of synapses. Indeed, say neuroscientists, *the mind is what the brain does.*

"I am a brain, Watson. The rest of me is a mere appendix." —Sherlock Holmes, in Arthur Conan Doyle's "The Adventure of the Mazarin Stone," 1921

THE TOOLS OF DISCOVERY: HAVING OUR HEAD EXAMINED

LOQ 4-1   How do neuroscientists study the brain's connections to behavior and mind?

For most of human history, scientists had no tools high powered yet gentle enough to reveal a living brain's activity. Early case studies helped localize some brain functions. Damage to one side of the brain often caused numbness or paralysis on the opposite side, suggesting that the body's right side is wired to the brain's left side, and vice versa.

Damage to the back of the brain disrupted vision, and damage to the left-front part of the brain produced speech difficulties. Gradually, these early explorers were mapping the brain.

Now, within a lifetime, a new generation of neural mapmakers is charting the known universe's most amazing organ. Scientists can selectively **lesion** (destroy) tiny clusters of normal or defective brain cells, observing any effect on brain function. Today's neuroscientists can also stimulate various brain parts—electrically, chemically, or magnetically—and note the effect. Depending on the stimulated brain part, people may—to name a few examples—giggle, hear voices, turn their head, feel themselves falling, or have an out-of-body experience (Selimbeyoglu & Parvizi, 2010).

Scientists can even snoop on the messages of individual neurons. With tips small enough to detect the electrical pulse in a single neuron, modern electrodes can, for example, now detect exactly where the information goes in a rat's brain when someone tickles its belly (Ishiyama & Brecht, 2017). They can also eavesdrop on the chatter of billions of neurons and see color representations of the brain's energy-consuming activity.

Right now, your mental activity is emitting telltale electrical, metabolic, and magnetic signals that would enable neuroscientists to observe your brain at work. Electrical activity in your brain's billions of neurons sweeps in regular waves across its surface. An **EEG (electroencephalogram)** is an amplified readout of such waves. Researchers record the brain waves through a shower-cap-like hat that is filled with electrodes covered with a conductive gel.

A related technique, **MEG (magnetoencephalography)**, measures magnetic fields from the brain's natural electrical activity. Participants sit underneath a head coil that resembles a hair salon hairdryer. While participants complete activities, tens of thousands of neurons create electrical pulses, which in turn create magnetic fields. The speed and strength of the magnetic fields enable researchers to understand how certain tasks influence brain activity.

"You must look into people, as well as at them," advised Lord Chesterfield in a 1746 letter to his son. Newer neuroimaging techniques give us that Superman-like ability to see inside the living brain. One such tool, the **PET (positron emission tomography) scan** (FIGURE 4.1), depicts brain activity by showing each brain area's consumption of its chemical fuel, the sugar glucose. Active neurons gobble glucose. Our brain, though only about 2 percent of our body weight, consumes 20 percent of our calorie intake. After a person receives temporarily radioactive glucose, the PET scan can track the gamma rays released by this "food for thought" as a task is performed. Rather like weather radar showing rain activity, PET-scan "hot spots" show the most active brain areas as the person does mathematical calculations, looks at images of faces, or daydreams.

In **MRI (magnetic resonance imaging)** brain scans, the person's head is put in a strong magnetic field, which aligns the spinning atoms of brain molecules. Then, a radiowave pulse momentarily disorients the atoms. When the atoms return to their normal spin, they emit signals that provide a detailed picture of soft tissues, including the brain.

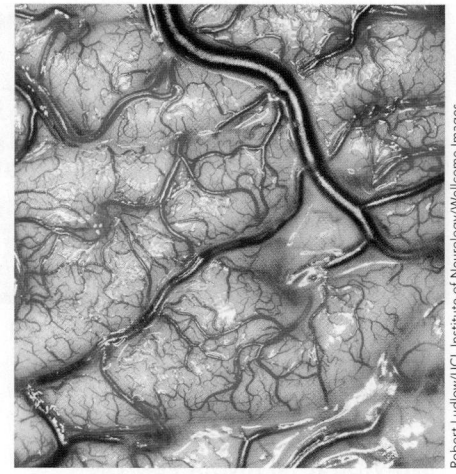

A LIVING HUMAN BRAIN EXPOSED Today's neuroscience tools enable us to "look under the hood" and glimpse the brain at work, enabling the mind.

lesion [LEE-zhuhn] tissue destruction. A brain lesion is a naturally or experimentally caused destruction of brain tissue.

EEG (electroencephalogram) an amplified recording of the waves of electrical activity sweeping across the brain's surface. These waves are measured by electrodes placed on the scalp.

MEG (magnetoencephalography) a brain-imaging technique that measures magnetic fields from the brain's natural electrical activity.

PET (positron emission tomography) scan a visual display of brain activity that detects where a radioactive form of glucose goes while the brain performs a given task.

MRI (magnetic resonance imaging) a technique that uses magnetic fields and radio waves to produce computer-generated images of soft tissue. MRI scans show brain anatomy.

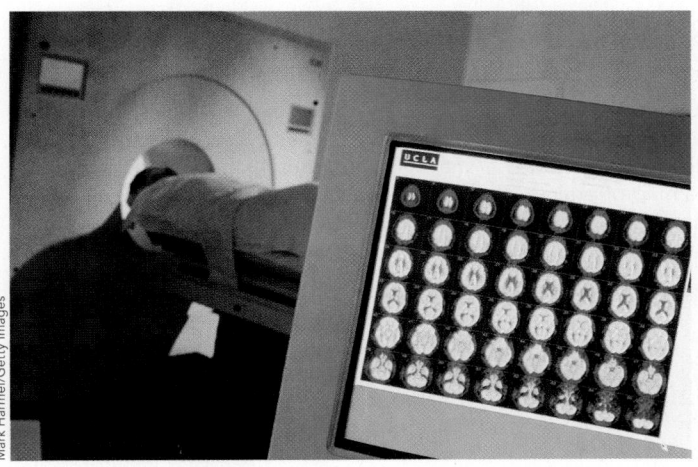

FIGURE 4.1

THE PET SCAN To obtain a PET scan, researchers inject volunteers with a low and harmless dose of a short-lived radioactive sugar. Detectors around the person's head pick up the release of gamma rays from the sugar, which has concentrated in active brain areas. A computer then processes and translates these signals into a map of the brain at work.

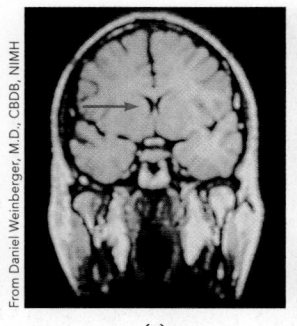 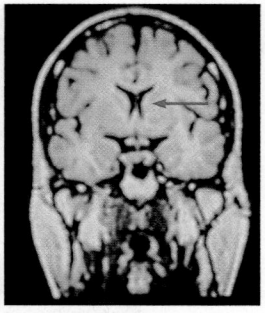

From Daniel Weinberger, M.D., CBDB, NIMH

(a)   (b)

FIGURE 4.2

MRI SCAN OF A HEALTHY INDIVIDUAL (a) AND A PERSON WITH SCHIZOPHRENIA (b) Note the enlarged ventricle, the fluid-filled brain region at the tip of the arrow in the brain of the person with schizophrenia (b).

MRI scans have revealed a larger-than-average neural area in the left hemisphere of musicians who display perfect pitch (Schlaug et al., 1995). They have also revealed enlarged *ventricles*—fluid-filled brain areas (marked by the red arrows in **FIGURE 4.2**)—in some patients who have schizophrenia, a disabling psychological disorder.

A special application of MRI—**fMRI (functional MRI)**—can reveal the brain's functioning as well as its structure. Where the brain is especially active, blood goes. By comparing successive MRI scans, researchers can watch as specific brain areas activate, showing increased oxygen-laden blood flow. As a person looks at a scene, for example, the fMRI machine detects blood rushing to the back of the brain, which processes visual information. See **TABLE 4.1** to compare these imaging techniques.

Such snapshots of the brain's activity provide new insights into how the brain divides its labor. A mountain of recent fMRI studies suggests which brain areas are most active when people feel pain or rejection, listen to angry voices, think about scary things, feel happy, or become sexually excited. The technology enables a very crude sort of mind reading. One neuroscience team scanned 129 people's brains as they did eight different mental tasks (such as reading, gambling, or rhyming). Later, they were able, with 80 percent accuracy, to identify which of these mental activities their participants had been doing (Poldrack et al., 2009).

You've seen the pictures—of colorful brains with accompanying headlines, such as "your brain on music." Hot brains make hot news (Bowers, 2016; Fine, 2010). In one study, students rated scientific explanations as more believable and interesting when they contained neuroscience (Fernandez-Duque et al., 2015). But "neuroskeptics" caution against overblown claims about any ability to predict customer preferences, detect lies, and foretell crime (Rose & Rose, 2016; Satel & Lilienfeld, 2013; Schwartz et al., 2016).

RETAIN 🔒 **TABLE 4.1**

Types of Neural Measures

Name	How Does It Work?	Sample Finding
EEG (Electroencephalogram)	Electrodes placed on the scalp measure electrical activity in neurons.	Symptoms of depression and anxiety correlate with increased activity in the right frontal lobe, a brain area associated with behavioral withdrawal and negative emotion (Thibodeau et al., 2006).
MEG (Magnetoencephalography)	A head coil records magnetic fields from the brain's natural electrical currents.	Soldiers with posttraumatic stress disorder (PTSD), compared with those who do not have PTSD, show stronger magnetic fields in the visual cortex when they view trauma-related images (Todd et al., 2015).
PET (Positron emission tomography)	Tracks where a temporarily radioactive form of glucose goes while the brain of the person given it performs a task.	Monkeys with an anxious temperament have brains that use more glucose in regions related to fear, memory, and expectations of reward and punishment (Fox et al., 2015).
MRI (Magnetic resonance imaging)	People sit or lie down in a chamber that uses magnetic fields and radio waves to provide a map of brain structure.	People with a history of violence tend to have smaller frontal lobes, especially in regions that aid moral judgment and self-control (Glenn & Raine, 2014).
fMRI (Functional magnetic resonance imaging)	Measures blood flow to brain regions by comparing continuous MRI scans.	Years after surviving a near plane crash, passengers who viewed material related to their trauma showed greater activation in the brain's fear, memory, and visual centers than when they watched footage related to the 9/11 terrorist attacks (Palombo et al., 2015).

Neuromarketing, neurolaw, neuropolitics, and neurotheology are often neurohype. Imaging techniques illuminate brain structure and activity, and sometimes help us test different theories of behavior (Mather et al., 2013). But given that all human experience is brain-based, it's no surprise that different brain areas become active when one listens to a lecture or lusts for a lover.

Today's techniques for peering into the thinking, feeling brain are doing for psychology what the microscope did for biology and the telescope did for astronomy. Europe's Human Brain Project promises $1 billion for brain computer modeling. The PsychENCODE project enables researchers to examine differences between the brains of healthy people and those with various disorders, such as autism spectrum disorder, bipolar disorder, and schizophrenia (Akbarian et al., 2015). The $40 million Human Connectome Project seeks "neural pathways [that] will reveal much about what makes us uniquely human and what makes every person different from all others" (2013; Gorman, 2014; Smith et al., 2015). It harnesses the power of *diffusion spectrum imaging*, a type of MRI technology that maps long-distance brain fiber connections (Jarbo & Verstynen, 2015) (**FIGURE 4.3**). Such efforts have led to the creation of a new brain map with 100 neural centers not previously described (Glasser et al., 2016). This truly is the golden age of brain science.

LaunchPad To check your understanding of brain scans and their functions, engage online with **Concept Practice: Scanning the Brain.**

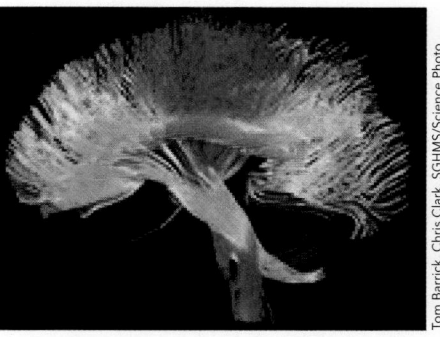

FIGURE 4.3

BEAUTIFUL BRAIN CONNECTIONS The Human Connectome Project is using cutting-edge methods to map the brain's interconnected network of neurons. Scientists created this multicolored "symphony" of neural fibers transporting water through different brain regions.

Tom Barrick, Chris Clark, SGHMS/Science Photo Library/Science Source

RETRIEVE IT • • •   *ANSWERS IN APPENDIX E*

RI-1 Match the scanning technique (I–III) with the correct description (a–c).

Technique:	Description:
I. fMRI scan	a. tracks radioactive glucose to reveal brain *activity*.
II. PET scan	b. tracks successive images of brain tissue to show brain *function*.
III. MRI scan	c. uses magnetic fields and radio waves to show brain *anatomy*.

OLDER BRAIN STRUCTURES

LOQ 4-2 What structures make up the brainstem, and what are the functions of the brainstem, thalamus, reticular formation, and cerebellum?

An animal's capacities come from its brain structures. In primitive animals, such as sharks, a not-so-complex brain primarily regulates basic survival functions: breathing, resting, and feeding. In lower mammals, such as rodents, a more complex brain enables emotion and greater memory. In advanced mammals, such as humans, a brain that processes more information enables increased foresight as well.

The brain's increasing complexity arises from new brain systems built on top of the old, much as Earth's landscape covers the old with the new. Digging down, one discovers the fossil remnants of the past—brainstem components performing for us much as they did for our distant ancestors. Let's start with the brain's base and work up to the newer systems.

imageBROKER/Alamy

The Brainstem

The **brainstem** is the brain's oldest and innermost region. Its base is the **medulla,** the slight swelling in the spinal cord just after it enters the skull (**FIGURE 4.4**). Here lie the controls for your heartbeat and breathing. As some brain-damaged patients in a vegetative state illustrate, we need no higher brain or conscious mind to orchestrate our heart's pumping and lungs' breathing. The brainstem handles those tasks. Just above the medulla sits the *pons,* which helps coordinate movements and control sleep.

LaunchPad For an introductory 12.5-minute overview of the brain, see the **Video: The Central Nervous System—Spotlight on the Brain.**

fMRI (functional MRI) a technique for revealing blood flow and, therefore, brain activity by comparing successive MRI scans. fMRI scans show brain function as well as structure.

brainstem the oldest part and central core of the brain, beginning where the spinal cord swells as it enters the skull; the brainstem is responsible for automatic survival functions.

medulla [muh-DUL-uh] the base of the brainstem; controls heartbeat and breathing.

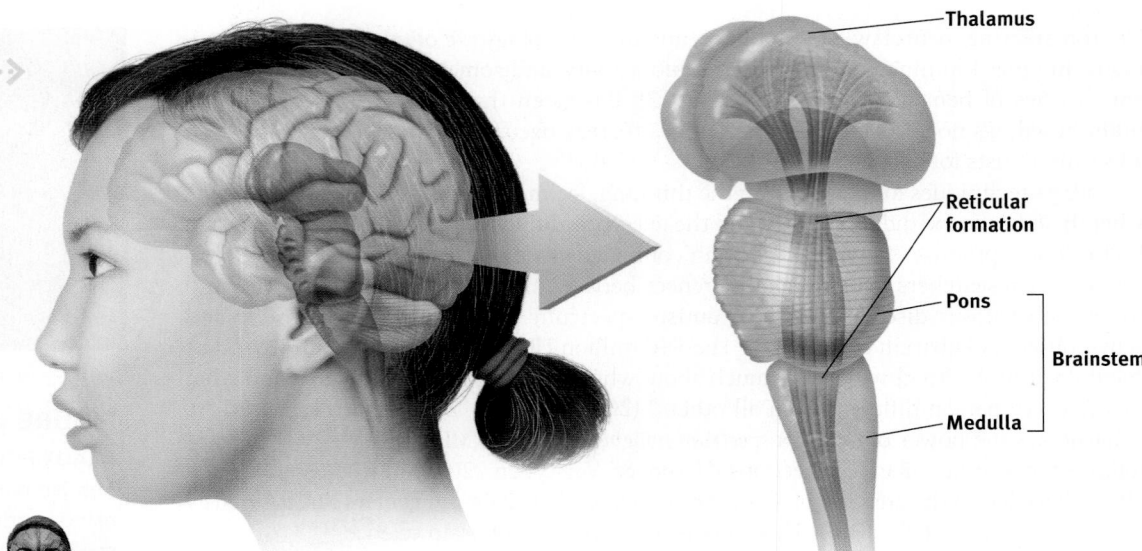

FIGURE 4.4
THE BRAINSTEM AND THALAMUS The brainstem, including the pons and medulla, is an extension of the spinal cord. The thalamus is attached to the top of the brainstem. The reticular formation passes through both structures.

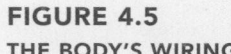

FIGURE 4.5
THE BODY'S WIRING

thalamus [THAL-uh-muss] the brain's sensory control center, located on top of the brainstem; it directs messages to the sensory receiving areas in the cortex and transmits replies to the cerebellum and medulla.

reticular formation a nerve network that travels through the brainstem into the thalamus and plays an important role in controlling arousal.

cerebellum [sehr-uh-BELL-um] the "little brain" at the rear of the brainstem; functions include processing sensory input, coordinating movement output and balance, and enabling nonverbal learning and memory.

If a cat's brainstem is severed from the rest of the brain above it, the animal will still breathe and live—and even run, climb, and groom (Klemm, 1990). But cut off from the brain's higher regions, it won't *purposefully* run or climb to get food.

The brainstem is a crossover point, where most nerves to and from each side of the brain connect with the body's opposite side (**FIGURE 4.5**). This peculiar cross-wiring is but one of the brain's many surprises.

🔒 **RETRIEVE IT • • •**   *ANSWERS IN APPENDIX E*

RI-2 The _____ is a crossover point where nerves from the left side of the brain are mostly linked to the right side of the body, and vice versa.

The Thalamus

Sitting atop the brainstem is the **thalamus,** a pair of egg-shaped structures that act as the brain's sensory control center (see Figure 4.4). The thalamus receives information from all the senses except smell, and routes that information to higher brain regions that deal with seeing, hearing, tasting, and touching. The thalamus also receives some of the higher brain's replies, which it then directs to the medulla and to the cerebellum. Think of the thalamus as being to sensory information what London is to England's trains: a hub through which traffic passes en route to various destinations.

The Reticular Formation

Inside the brainstem, between your ears, lies the **reticular** ("netlike") **formation,** a neuron network extending from the spinal cord right up through the thalamus. As the spinal cord's sensory input flows up to the thalamus, some of it travels through the reticular formation, which filters incoming stimuli and relays important information to other brain areas. Have you multitasked today? You can thank your reticular formation (Wimmer et al., 2015).

The reticular formation also controls arousal, as Giuseppe Moruzzi and Horace Magoun discovered in 1949. Electrically stimulating a sleeping cat's reticular formation almost instantly produced an awake, alert animal. When Magoun *severed* a cat's reticular formation without damaging nearby sensory pathways, the effect was equally dramatic: The cat lapsed into a coma from which it never awakened.

The Cerebellum

Extending from the rear of the brainstem is the baseball-sized **cerebellum,** meaning "little brain," which is what its two wrinkled halves resemble (**FIGURE 4.6**). The cerebellum enables nonverbal learning and skill memory. It also helps us judge time, modulate our emotions, and discriminate sounds and textures (Bower & Parsons, 2003). And (with assistance from the pons) it coordinates voluntary movement. When a soccer player masterfully controls the ball, give the player's cerebellum some credit. Under alcohol's influence, coordination suffers. And if you injured your cerebellum, you would have difficulty walking, keeping your balance, or shaking hands. Your movements would be jerky and exaggerated. Gone would be any dreams of being a dancer or guitarist.

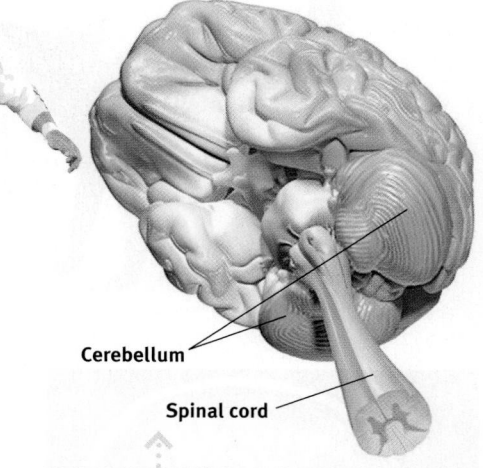

* * *

Note: These older brain functions all occur without any conscious effort. This illustrates another of our recurring themes: *Our brain processes most information outside of our awareness.* We are aware of the *results* of our brain's labor—say, our current visual experience—but not *how* we construct the visual image. Likewise, whether we are asleep or awake, our brainstem manages its life-sustaining functions, freeing our newer brain regions to think, talk, dream, or savor a memory.

🔒 RETRIEVE IT • • •   *ANSWERS IN APPENDIX E*

RI-3 In what brain region would damage be most likely to (a) disrupt your ability to jump rope? (b) disrupt your ability to hear? (c) leave you in a coma? (d) cut off the very breath and heartbeat of life?

Cerebellum

Spinal cord

FIGURE 4.6

THE BRAIN'S ORGAN OF AGILITY Hanging at the back of the brain, the cerebellum coordinates our voluntary movements, as when soccer star Cristiano Ronaldo controls the ball.

THE LIMBIC SYSTEM

LOQ 4-3 What are the limbic system's structures and functions?

We've considered the brain's oldest parts, but we've not yet reached its newest and highest regions, the *cerebral hemispheres* (the two halves of the brain). Between the oldest and newest brain areas lies the **limbic system** (*limbus* means "border"). This system contains the *amygdala,* the *hypothalamus,* and the *hippocampus* (**FIGURE 4.7**).

The Amygdala

Research has linked the **amygdala,** two lima-bean-sized neural clusters, to aggression and fear. In 1939, psychologist Heinrich Klüver and neurosurgeon Paul Bucy surgically removed a rhesus monkey's amygdala, turning the normally ill-tempered animal into the most mellow of creatures. So, too, with human patients. Those with amygdala lesions often display reduced arousal to fear- and anger-arousing stimuli (Berntson et al., 2011). One such woman, patient S. M., has been called "the woman with no fear," even if being threatened with a gun (Feinstein et al., 2013).

What then might happen if we electrically stimulated the amygdala of a normally placid domestic animal, such as a cat? Do so in one spot and the cat prepares to attack, hissing with its back arched, its pupils dilated, its hair on end. Move the electrode only slightly within the amygdala, cage the cat with a small mouse, and now it cowers in terror.

These and other experiments have confirmed the amygdala's role in fear and rage. Monkeys and humans with amygdala damage become less fearful of strangers (Harrison et al., 2015). Other studies link criminal behavior with amygdala dysfunction (Boccardi et al., 2011; da Cunha-Bang et al., 2017; Ermer et al., 2012a). But we must be careful. The brain is not neatly organized into structures that correspond to our behavior categories. The amygdala is engaged with other mental phenomena as well. And when we feel afraid or act aggressively, there is neural activity in many areas of our brain—not just the amygdala. If you destroy a car's battery, it's true that you won't be able to start the engine. Yet the battery is merely one link in an integrated system.

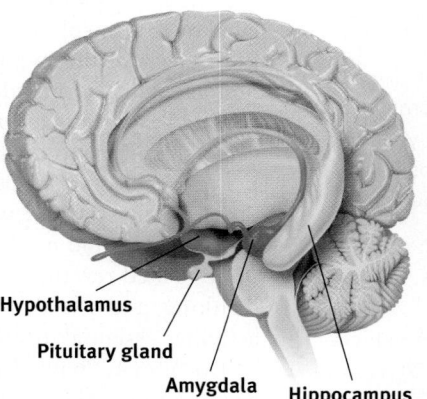

Hypothalamus

Pituitary gland

Amygdala   **Hippocampus**

FIGURE 4.7

THE LIMBIC SYSTEM This neural system sits between the brain's older parts and its cerebral hemispheres. The limbic system's hypothalamus controls the nearby pituitary gland.

limbic system neural system (including the *amygdala, hypothalamus,* and *hippocampus*) located below the cerebral hemispheres; associated with emotions and drives.

amygdala [uh-MIG-duh-la] two lima-bean-sized neural clusters in the limbic system; linked to emotion.

GK Hart/Vikki Hart/Getty Images

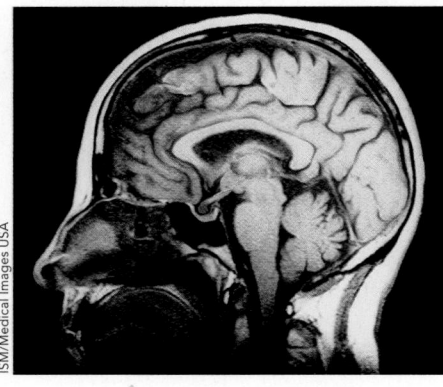

ISM/Medical Images USA

FIGURE 4.8

THE HYPOTHALAMUS This small but important structure, colored yellow/orange in this MRI scan, helps keep the body's internal environment in a steady state.

"If you were designing a robot vehicle to walk into the future and survive, . . . you'd wire it up so that behavior that ensured the survival of the self or the species—like sex and eating—would be naturally reinforcing." —Candace Pert (1986)

ENGAGE

ASK YOURSELF

Why do you think our brain evolved into so many interconnected structures with varying functions?

🔒 **RETRIEVE IT • • •**   *ANSWERS IN APPENDIX E*

RI-4 Electrical stimulation of a cat's amygdala provokes angry reactions. Which *autonomic nervous system* division is activated by such stimulation?

The Hypothalamus

Just below *(hypo)* the thalamus is the **hypothalamus** (FIGURE 4.8), an important link in the command chain governing bodily maintenance. Some neural clusters in the hypothalamus influence hunger; others regulate thirst, body temperature, and sexual behavior. Together, they help maintain a steady *(homeostatic)* internal state.

To monitor your body state, the hypothalamus tunes into your blood chemistry and any incoming orders from other brain parts. For example, picking up signals from your brain's cerebral cortex that you are thinking about sex, your hypothalamus will secrete hormones. These hormones will in turn trigger the adjacent "master gland" of the endocrine system, your pituitary (see Figure 4.7), to influence your sex glands to release *their* hormones. These hormones will intensify the thoughts of sex in your cerebral cortex. (Note the interplay between the nervous and endocrine systems: The brain influences the endocrine system, which in turn influences the brain.)

A remarkable discovery about the hypothalamus illustrates how progress in science often occurs—when curious, open-minded investigators make an unexpected observation. Two young McGill University neuropsychologists, James Olds and Peter Milner (1954), were trying to implant an electrode in a rat's reticular formation when they made a magnificent mistake: They placed the electrode incorrectly (Olds, 1975). Curiously, as if seeking more stimulation, the rat kept returning to the location where it had been stimulated by this misplaced electrode. On discovering that they had actually placed the device in a region of the hypothalamus, Olds and Milner realized they had stumbled upon a brain center that provides pleasurable rewards (Olds, 1975).

Later experiments located other such regions. Just how rewarding are these reward centers? Enough to cause rats to self-stimulate these brain regions more than 1000 times per hour. In other species, including dolphins and monkeys, researchers later discovered other limbic system reward centers, such as the *nucleus accumbens* in front of the hypothalamus (Hamid et al., 2016). Animal research has also revealed both a general dopamine-related reward system and specific centers associated with the pleasures of eating, drinking, and sex. Animals, it seems, come equipped with built-in systems that reward activities essential to survival.

Do humans have limbic centers for pleasure? To calm violent patients, one neurosurgeon implanted electrodes in such areas. Stimulated patients reported mild pleasure; unlike Olds' rats, however, they were not driven to a frenzy (Deutsch, 1972; Hooper & Teresi, 1986). Moreover, newer research reveals that stimulating the brain's "hedonic hotspots" (its reward circuits) produces more *desire* than pure enjoyment (Kringelbach & Berridge, 2012).

Some researchers believe that substance use disorders may stem from malfunctions in natural brain systems for pleasure and well-being (Balodis & Potenza, 2015). People genetically predisposed to this *reward deficiency syndrome* may crave whatever provides that missing pleasure or relieves negative feelings (Blum et al., 1996).

The Hippocampus

The **hippocampus**—a seahorse-shaped brain structure—processes conscious, explicit memories and decreases in size and function as we grow older. Humans who lose their hippocampus to surgery or injury also lose their ability to form new memories of facts and events (Clark & Maguire, 2016). Those who survive a hippocampal brain tumor in childhood struggle to remember new information in adulthood (Jayakar et al., 2015). National Football League players who experience one or more loss-of-consciousness concussions may later have a shrunken hippocampus and poor memory (Strain et al., 2015). Hippocampus size and function decrease as we grow older, which furthers cognitive decline. The Memory modules discuss how our two-track mind uses the hippocampus to process our memories.

Elise Amendola/AP Images

HAS PROFESSIONAL FOOTBALL DAMAGED PLAYERS' BRAINS? When researchers analyzed the brains of 111 deceased National Football League players, 99 percent showed signs of degeneration related to frequent head trauma (Mez et al., 2017). In 2017, NFL player Aaron Hernandez (#81) committed suicide while imprisoned for murder. An autopsy demonstrated that his brain, at age 27, was already showing advanced degeneration (Kilgore, 2017). Will today's more protective gear and rules protect players' brains?

hypothalamus [hi-po-THAL-uh-muss] a neural structure lying below *(hypo)* the thalamus; it directs several maintenance activities (eating, drinking, body temperature), helps govern the endocrine system via the pituitary gland, and is linked to emotion and reward.

hippocampus a neural center located in the limbic system; helps process explicit (conscious) memories—of facts and events—for storage.

* * *

FIGURE 4.9 locates the brain areas we've discussed, as well as the *cerebral cortex*—the body's ultimate control and information-processing center.

RETAIN 🔒 📖 **LaunchPad** To review and assess your understanding, engage online with **Concept Practice: The Limbic System.**

🔒 **RETRIEVE IT • • •**   *ANSWERS IN APPENDIX E*

RI-5 What are the three key structures of the limbic system, and what functions do they serve?

RETAIN 🔒 **FIGURE 4.9**

BRAIN STRUCTURES AND THEIR FUNCTIONS

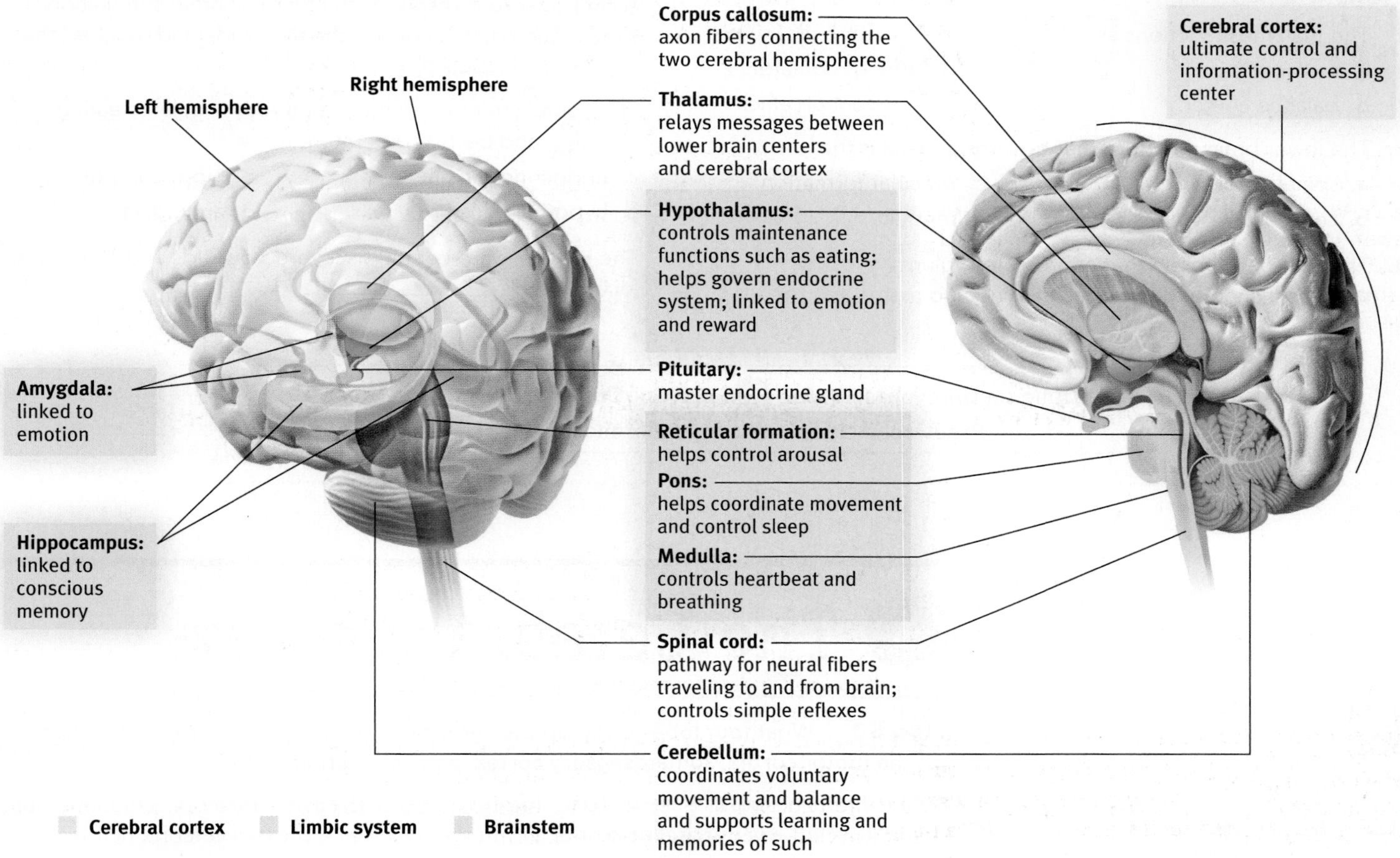

Left hemisphere

Right hemisphere

Corpus callosum: axon fibers connecting the two cerebral hemispheres

Thalamus: relays messages between lower brain centers and cerebral cortex

Hypothalamus: controls maintenance functions such as eating; helps govern endocrine system; linked to emotion and reward

Pituitary: master endocrine gland

Reticular formation: helps control arousal

Pons: helps coordinate movement and control sleep

Medulla: controls heartbeat and breathing

Spinal cord: pathway for neural fibers traveling to and from brain; controls simple reflexes

Cerebellum: coordinates voluntary movement and balance and supports learning and memories of such

Cerebral cortex: ultimate control and information-processing center

Amygdala: linked to emotion

Hippocampus: linked to conscious memory

◼ **Cerebral cortex**   ◼ **Limbic system**   ◼ **Brainstem**

🔒 REVIEW   TOOLS OF DISCOVERY, OLDER BRAIN STRUCTURES, AND THE LIMBIC SYSTEM

⤳ Learning Objectives

TEST YOURSELF Answer these repeated Learning Objective Questions on your own (before checking the answers in Appendix D) to improve your retention of the concepts (McDaniel et al., 2009, 2015).

4-1 How do neuroscientists study the brain's connections to behavior and mind?

4-2 What structures make up the brainstem, and what are the functions of the brainstem, thalamus, reticular formation, and cerebellum?

4-3 What are the limbic system's structures and functions?

⤳ Terms and Concepts to Remember

TEST YOURSELF Write down the definition yourself, then check your answer on the referenced page.

lesion [LEE-zhuhn], **p. 51**

EEG (electroencephalogram), **p. 51**

MEG (magnetoencephalography), **p. 51**

PET (positron emission tomography) scan, **p. 51**

MRI (magnetic resonance imaging), **p. 51**

fMRI (functional MRI), **p. 53**

brainstem, **p. 53**

medulla [muh-DUL-uh], **p. 53**

thalamus [THAL-uh-muss], **p. 54**

reticular formation, **p. 54**

cerebellum [sehr-uh-BELL-um], **p. 54**

limbic system, **p. 55**

amygdala [uh-MIG-duh-la], **p. 55**

hypothalamus [hi-po-THAL-uh-muss], **p. 57**

hippocampus, **p. 57**

⤳ Experience the Testing Effect

TEST YOURSELF Answer the following questions on your own first, then check your answers in Appendix E.

1. The part of the brainstem that controls heartbeat and breathing is the
   - a. cerebellum.
   - b. medulla.
   - c. cortex.
   - d. thalamus.

2. The thalamus functions as a
   - a. memory bank.
   - b. balance center.
   - c. breathing regulator.
   - d. sensory control center.

3. The lower brain structure that governs arousal is the
   - a. spinal cord.
   - b. cerebellum.
   - c. reticular formation.
   - d. medulla.

4. The part of the brain that coordinates voluntary movement and enables nonverbal learning and memory is the _____.

5. Two parts of the limbic system are the amygdala and the
   - a. cerebral hemispheres.
   - b. hippocampus.
   - c. thalamus.
   - d. pituitary.

6. A cat's ferocious response to electrical brain stimulation would lead you to suppose the electrode had touched the _____.

7. The neural structure that most directly regulates eating, drinking, and body temperature is the
   - a. endocrine system.
   - b. hypothalamus.
   - c. hippocampus.
   - d. amygdala.

8. The initial reward center discovered by Olds and Milner was located in the _____.

Continue testing yourself with 📖 **LearningCurve** or ≈ **Achieve Read & Practice** to learn and remember most effectively.

---

⑤ The Cerebral Cortex

LOQ 5-1   What four lobes make up the cerebral cortex, and what are the functions of the motor cortex, somatosensory cortex, and association areas?

Older brain networks sustain basic life functions and enable memory, emotions, and basic drives. Newer neural networks within the *cerebrum*—the two cerebral hemispheres contributing 85 percent of the brain's weight—form specialized work teams that enable our perceiving, thinking, and speaking. Like other structures above the brainstem (including the thalamus, hippocampus, and amygdala), the cerebral hemispheres come as a pair. Covering those hemispheres, like bark on a tree, is the **cerebral cortex,** a thin surface layer of interconnected neural cells. In our brain's evolutionary history, the cerebral cortex—our brain's thinking crown—is a relative newcomer.

As we move up the ladder of animal life, the cerebral cortex expands, tight genetic controls relax, and the organism's adaptability increases. Frogs and other small-cortex amphibians operate extensively on preprogrammed genetic instructions. The larger cortex of mammals offers increased capacities for learning and thinking, enabling them to adapt to ever-changing environments. What makes us distinctively human mostly arises from the complex functions of our cerebral cortex.

RETAIN 🔒 The people who first dissected and labeled the brain used the language of scholars—Latin and Greek. Their words are actually attempts at graphic description: For example, *cortex* means "bark," *cerebellum* is "little brain," and *thalamus* is "inner chamber."

🔒 **RETRIEVE IT • • •**   *ANSWERS IN APPENDIX E*

RI-1 Which area of the human brain is most similar to that of less complex animals? Which part of the human brain distinguishes us most from less complex animals?

STRUCTURE OF THE CORTEX

If you opened a human skull, exposing the brain, you would see a wrinkled organ, shaped somewhat like an oversized walnut. Without these wrinkles, a flattened cerebral cortex would require triple the area—roughly that of a large pizza. The brain's left and right hemispheres are filled mainly with axons connecting the cortex to the brain's other regions. The cerebral cortex—that thin surface layer—contains some 20 to 23 billion of the brain's nerve cells and 300 trillion synaptic connections (de Courten-Myers, 2005). Being human takes a lot of nerve.

ENGAGE 💡 Each hemisphere's cortex is subdivided into four *lobes,* separated by prominent *fissures,* or folds (**FIGURE 5.1**). Starting at the front of your brain and moving over the top, there are the **frontal lobes** (behind your forehead), the **parietal lobes** (at the top and to the rear), and the **occipital lobes** (at the back of your head). Reversing direction and moving forward, just above your ears, you find the **temporal lobes.** Each of the four lobes carries out many functions, and many functions require the interplay of several lobes.

FUNCTIONS OF THE CORTEX

More than a century ago, surgeons found damaged cortical areas during autopsies of people who had been partially paralyzed or speechless. This rather crude evidence did not prove that specific parts of the cortex control complex functions like movement or speech. A laptop with a broken power cord might go dead, but we would be fooling ourselves if we thought we had "localized" the internet in the cord.

cerebral [seh-REE-bruhl] **cortex** the intricate fabric of interconnected neural cells covering the cerebral hemispheres; the body's ultimate control and information-processing center.

frontal lobes the portion of the cerebral cortex lying just behind the forehead; involved in speaking and muscle movements and in making plans and judgments.

parietal [puh-RYE-uh-tuhl] **lobes** the portion of the cerebral cortex lying at the top of the head and toward the rear; receives sensory input for touch and body position.

occipital [ahk-SIP-uh-tuhl] **lobes** the portion of the cerebral cortex lying at the back of the head; includes areas that receive information from the visual fields.

temporal lobes the portion of the cerebral cortex lying roughly above the ears; includes the auditory areas, each receiving information primarily from the opposite ear.

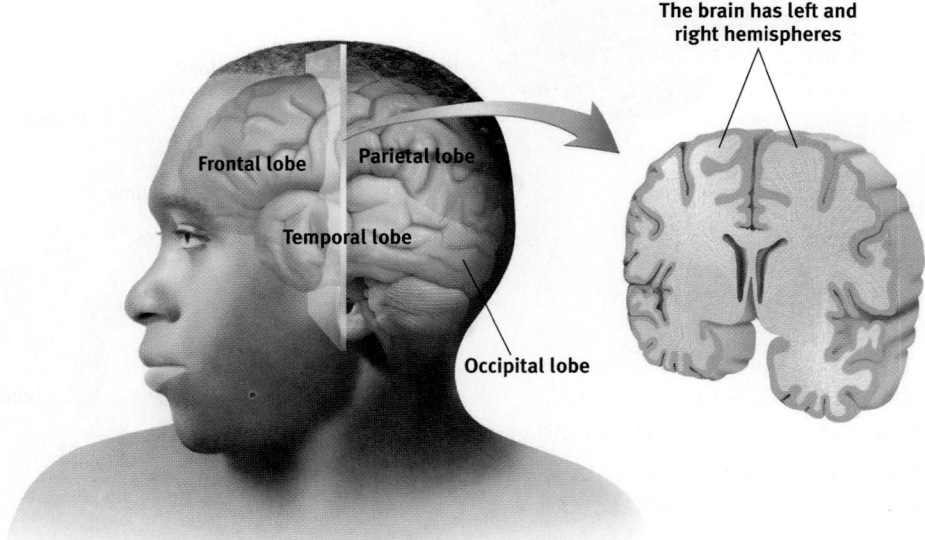

The brain has left and right hemispheres

Frontal lobe   Parietal lobe

Temporal lobe

Occipital lobe

FIGURE 5.1

THE CORTEX AND ITS BASIC SUBDIVISIONS

Motor Functions

Scientists had better luck in localizing simpler brain functions. For example, in 1870, German physicians Gustav Fritsch and Eduard Hitzig made an important discovery: Mild electrical stimulation to parts of an animal's cortex made parts of its body move. The effects were selective: Stimulation caused movement only when applied to an arch-shaped region at the back of the frontal lobe, running roughly ear-to-ear across the top of the brain. Moreover, stimulating parts of this region in the left or right hemisphere caused movements of specific body parts on the *opposite* side of the body. Fritsch and Hitzig had discovered what is now called the **motor cortex.**

MAPPING THE MOTOR CORTEX Lucky for brain surgeons and their patients, the brain has no sensory receptors. Knowing this, in the 1930s, Otfrid Foerster and Wilder Penfield were able to map the motor cortex in hundreds of wide-awake patients by stimulating different cortical areas and observing the body's responses. They discovered that body areas requiring precise control, such as the fingers and mouth, occupy the greatest amount of cortical space (**FIGURE 5.2**). In one of his many demonstrations of motor behavior mechanics, Spanish neuroscientist José Delgado stimulated a spot on a patient's left motor cortex, triggering the right hand to make a fist. Asked to keep the fingers open during the next stimulation, the patient, whose fingers closed despite his best efforts, remarked, "I guess, Doctor, that your electricity is stronger than my will" (Delgado, 1969, p. 114).

More recently, scientists were able to predict a monkey's arm motion a tenth of a second *before* it moved—by repeatedly measuring motor cortex activity preceding specific arm movements (Gibbs, 1996). Such findings have opened the door to research on brain-controlled computer technology.

FIGURE 5.2

MOTOR CORTEX AND SOMATOSENSORY CORTEX TISSUE DEVOTED TO EACH BODY PART As you can see from this classic though inexact representation, the amount of cortex devoted to a body part in the motor cortex (in the frontal lobes) or in the somatosensory cortex (in the parietal lobes) is not proportional to that body part's size. Rather, the brain devotes more tissue to sensitive areas and to areas requiring precise control. Thus, the fingers have a greater representation in the cortex than does the upper arm.

🔒 **RETRIEVE IT • • •**   ANSWERS IN APPENDIX E

RI-2 Try moving your right hand in a circular motion, as if cleaning a table. Then start your right foot doing the same motion, synchronized with your hand. Now reverse the right foot's motion, but not the hand's. Finally, try moving the *left* foot opposite to the right hand.

a. Why is reversing the right foot's motion so hard?

b. Why is it easier to move the left foot opposite to the right hand?

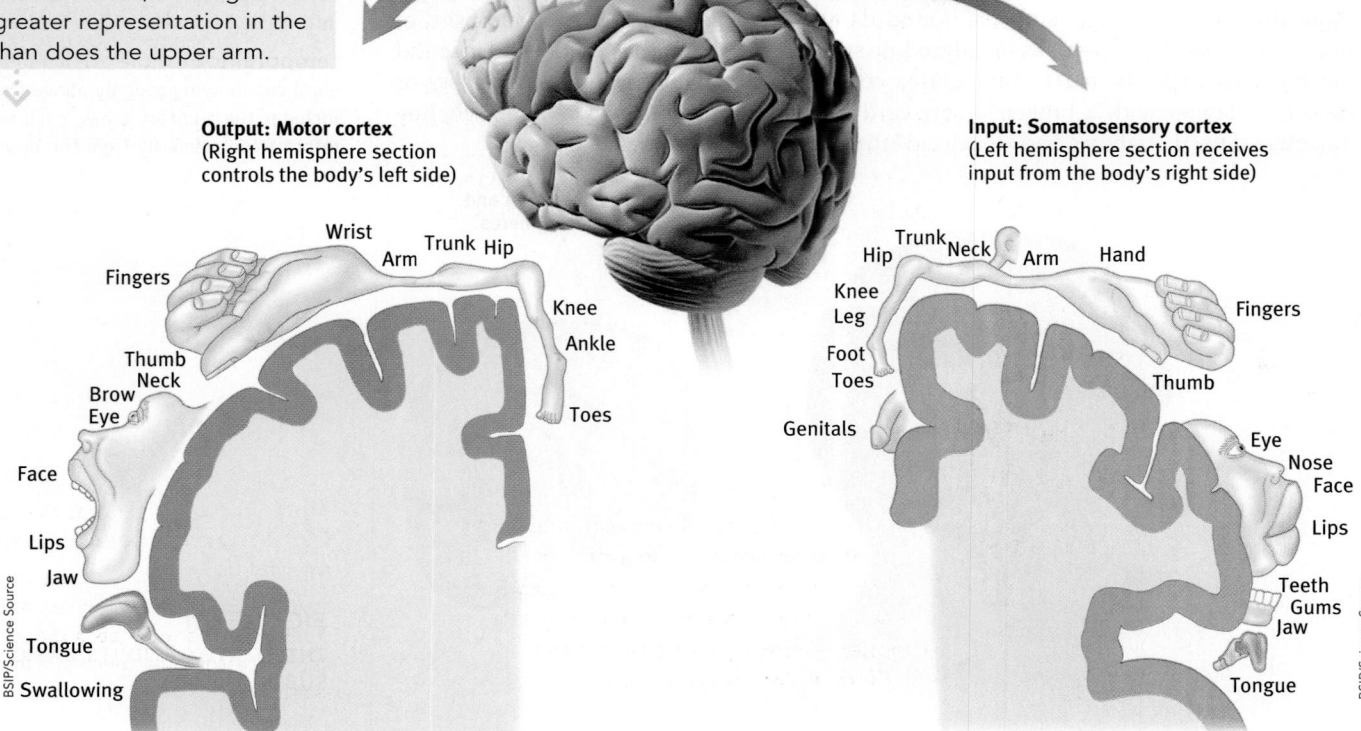

Output: Motor cortex
(Right hemisphere section controls the body's left side)

Input: Somatosensory cortex
(Left hemisphere section receives input from the body's right side)

BSIP/Science Source

BRAIN-MACHINE INTERFACES What might happen if researchers implant a device to detect motor cortex activity in humans? Could such devices help people with paralysis learn to command a cursor to write email or work online? Clinical trials are now under way with people who have severe paralysis or have lost a limb (Andersen et al., 2010; Nurmikko et al., 2010). The first patient, a 25-year-old man with paralysis, was able to mentally control a TV, draw shapes on a computer screen, and play video games—all thanks to an aspirin-sized chip with 100 microelectrodes recording activity in his motor cortex (Hochberg et al., 2006). Since then, others with paralysis who have received implants have learned to direct robotic arms with their thoughts (Clausen et al., 2017).

Sensory Functions

If the motor cortex sends messages out to the body, where does the cortex receive incoming messages? Penfield identified a cortical area—at the front of the parietal lobes, parallel to and just behind the motor cortex—that specializes in receiving information from the skin senses, such as touch and temperature, and from the movement of body parts. We now call this area the **somatosensory cortex.** Stimulate a point on the top of this band of tissue and a person may report being touched on the shoulder; stimulate some point on the side and the person may feel something on the face.

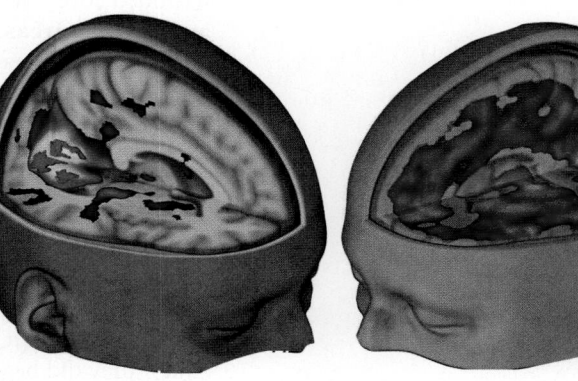

(a)   (b)

Imperial College London

ENGAGE The more sensitive the body region, the larger the somatosensory cortex area devoted to it (see Figure 5.2). Your supersensitive lips project to a larger brain area than do your toes, which is one reason we kiss rather than touch toes. Rats have a large area of the brain devoted to their whisker sensations, and owls to their hearing sensations.

Scientists have identified additional areas where the cortex receives input from senses other than touch. Any visual information you are receiving now is going to the visual cortex in your occipital lobes, at the back of your brain (**FIGURES 5.3** and **5.4**). If you have normal vision, you might see flashes of light or dashes of color if stimulated in your occipital lobes. (In a sense, we *do* have eyes in the back of our head!) Having lost much of his right occipital lobe to a tumor removal, a friend of mine [DM's] was blind to the left half of his field of vision. Visual information travels from the occipital lobes to other areas that specialize in tasks such as identifying words, detecting emotions, and recognizing faces.

Any sound you now hear is processed by your auditory cortex in your temporal lobes (just above your ears; see Figure 5.4). Most of this auditory information travels a circuitous route from one ear to the auditory receiving area above your opposite ear. If stimulated in your auditory cortex, you might hear a sound. Researchers studying fMRI scans of people with schizophrenia have found active auditory areas in the temporal lobes during the false sensory experience of auditory *hallucinations* (Lennox et al., 1999). Even the phantom ringing sound experienced by people with hearing loss is—if heard in one ear— associated with activity in the temporal lobe on the brain's opposite side (Muhlnickel, 1998).

FIGURE 5.3

SEEING WITHOUT EYES The psychoactive drug LSD often produces vivid *hallucinations.* Why? It dramatically increases communication between the visual cortex (in the occipital lobe) and other brain regions. (a) This fMRI (functional MRI) scan shows a research participant with closed eyes who has been given a placebo. (b) In this fMRI, the same person is under the influence of LSD (color represents increased blood flow) (Carhart-Harris et al., 2016; Cormier, 2016).

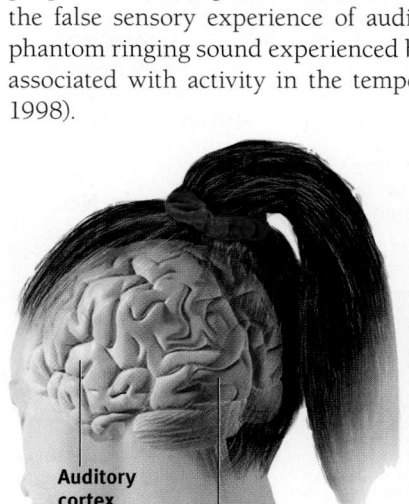

Auditory cortex

Visual cortex

FIGURE 5.4

THE VISUAL CORTEX AND AUDITORY CORTEX The visual cortex in the occipital lobes at the rear of your brain receives input from your eyes. The auditory cortex in your temporal lobes—above your ears—receives information from your ears.

motor cortex an area at the rear of the frontal lobes that controls voluntary movements.

somatosensory cortex an area at the front of the parietal lobes that registers and processes body touch and movement sensations.

association areas areas of the cerebral cortex that are not involved in primary motor or sensory functions; rather, they are involved in higher mental functions such as learning, remembering, thinking, and speaking.

🔒 RETRIEVE IT • • •   *ANSWERS IN APPENDIX E*

RI-3 Our brain's _____ cortex registers and processes body touch and movement sensations. The _____ cortex controls our voluntary movements.

Association Areas

So far, we have pointed out small cortical areas that either receive sensory input or direct muscular output. Together, these occupy about one-fourth of the human brain's thin, wrinkled cover. What, then, goes on in the remaining vast regions of the cortex? In these **association areas**, neurons are busy with higher mental functions—many of the tasks that make us human.

Electrically probing an association area won't trigger any observable response. So, unlike the somatosensory and motor areas, association area functions cannot be neatly mapped. Does this mean we don't use them? See Thinking Critically About: Using More Than 10 Percent of Our Brain.

Association areas are found in all four lobes. The *prefrontal cortex* in the forward part of the frontal lobes enables judgment, planning, social interactions, and processing of new memories (de la Vega et al., 2016; Silwa & Frehwald, 2017). People with damaged frontal lobes may have high intelligence test scores and great cake-baking skills. Yet they would not be able to plan ahead to *begin* baking a cake for a birthday party (Huey et al., 2006). And if they did begin to bake, they might forget the recipe (MacPherson et al., 2016).

Frontal lobe damage also can alter personality and remove a person's inhibitions. Consider the classic case of railroad worker Phineas Gage. One afternoon in 1848, Gage, then 25 years old, was using a tamping iron to pack gunpowder into a rock. A spark ignited the gunpowder, shooting the rod up through his left cheek and out the top of his skull, leaving his frontal lobes damaged (**FIGURE 5.5**). To everyone's amazement, Gage was immediately able to sit up and speak, and after the wound healed, he returned to work. But having lost some of the neural tracts that enabled his frontal lobes to control

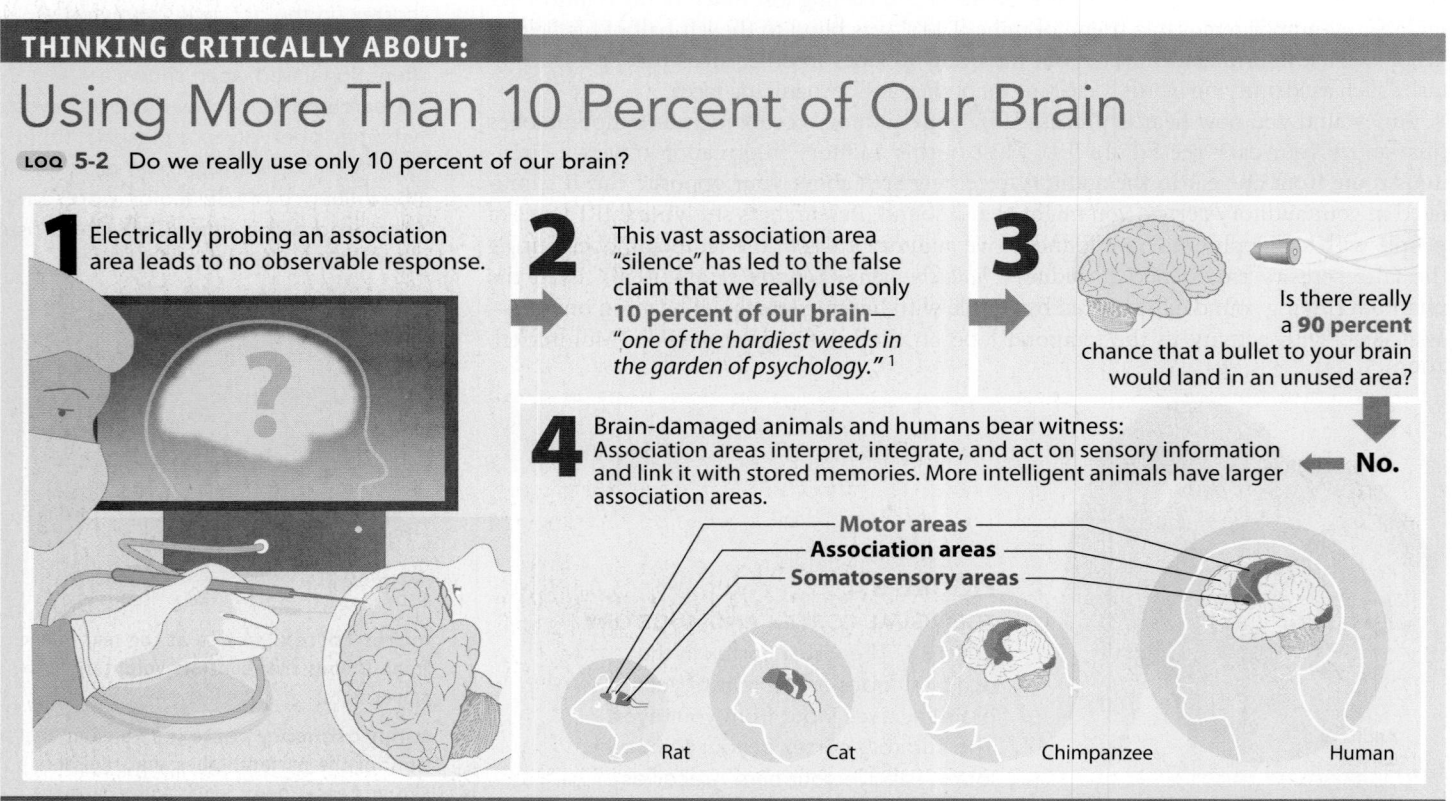

THINKING CRITICALLY ABOUT:

Using More Than 10 Percent of Our Brain

LOQ 5-2 Do we really use only 10 percent of our brain?

1 Electrically probing an association area leads to no observable response.

2 This vast association area "silence" has led to the false claim that we really use only **10 percent of our brain**— *"one of the hardiest weeds in the garden of psychology."* [1]

3 Is there really a **90 percent** chance that a bullet to your brain would land in an unused area?

→ **No.**

4 Brain-damaged animals and humans bear witness: Association areas interpret, integrate, and act on sensory information and link it with stored memories. More intelligent animals have larger association areas.

Motor areas
Association areas
Somatosensory areas

Rat   Cat   Chimpanzee   Human

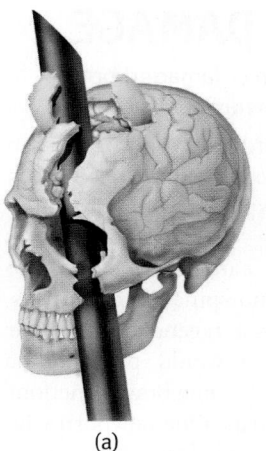

(a)

Warren Anatomical Museum in the Francis A. Countway Library of Medicine. Gift of Jack and Beverly Wilgus

(b)

FIGURE 5.5

A BLAST FROM THE PAST (a) Phineas Gage's skull was kept as a medical record. Using measurements and modern neuroimaging techniques, researchers have reconstructed the probable path of the rod through Gage's brain (Van Horn et al., 2012). (b) This photo shows Gage after his accident. (The image has been reversed to show the features correctly. Early photos, including this one, were actually mirror images.)

his emotions, the affable, soft-spoken man was now irritable, profane, and dishonest (Van Horn et al., 2012). This person, said his friends, was "no longer Gage." His mental abilities and memories were intact, but for the next few years his personality was not. (Gage later lost his railroad job, but over time, he adapted to his injury and found work as a stage-coach driver [Macmillan & Lena, 2010].)

Studies of others with damaged frontal lobes have revealed similar impairments. Not only do they become less inhibited (without the frontal lobe brakes on their impulses), but their moral judgments also seem unrestrained. Cecil Clayton lost 20 percent of his left frontal lobe in a 1972 sawmill accident. Thereafter, his intelligence test score dropped to an elementary school level and he displayed increased impulsivity. In 1996, he fatally shot a deputy sheriff. In 2015, when he was 74, the State of Missouri executed him (Williams, 2015).

Would you advocate pushing one person in front of a runaway trolley to save five others? Most people would not, but those with damage to the frontal lobe are often untroubled by such ethical dilemmas (Koenigs et al., 2007). The frontal lobes help steer us away from violent actions (Molenberghs et al., 2015; Yang & Raine, 2009). With their frontal lobes ruptured, people's moral compass seems to disconnect from their behavior.

Association areas also perform other mental functions. The parietal lobes, parts of which were large and unusually shaped in Einstein's normal-weight brain, enable mathematical and spatial reasoning (Burrell, 2015; Ibos & Freedman, 2014). On the underside of the right temporal lobe, another association area enables us to recognize faces. If a stroke or head injury destroyed this area of your brain, you would still be able to describe facial features and to recognize someone's gender and approximate age, yet be strangely unable to identify the person as, say, Miley Cyrus, or even your grandmother.

Nevertheless, complex mental functions don't reside in any one place. During a complex task, a brain scan shows many islands of brain activity working together—some running automatically in the background, and others under conscious control (Chein & Schneider, 2012). Your memory, language, and attention result from *functional connectivity*—communication among distinct brain areas and neural networks (Knight, 2007). Ditto for religious experience. More than 40 distinct brain regions become active in different religious states, such as prayer and meditation, indicating that there is no simple "God spot" (Fingelkurts & Fingelkurts, 2009). *The point to remember:* Our mental experiences arise from coordinated brain activity.

LaunchPad See the **Video: Case Studies** for a helpful tutorial animation.

MISSING FRONTAL LOBE BRAKES With part of his left frontal lobe (in this downward-facing brain scan) lost to injury, Cecil Clayton became more impulsive and killed a deputy sheriff. Nineteen years later, his state executed him for this crime.

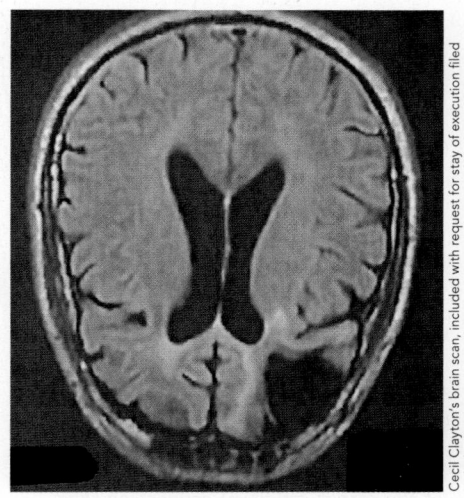

Cecil Clayton's brain scan, included with request for stay of execution filed with the Supreme Court, showing a missing portion of his frontal lobe.

🔒 **RETRIEVE IT** • • •   *ANSWERS IN APPENDIX E*

RI-4 Why are association areas important?

RETAIN 🔒 **LaunchPad** Check your understanding of the parts of the brain by engaging online with **Concept Practice: Brain Areas Within the Head.**

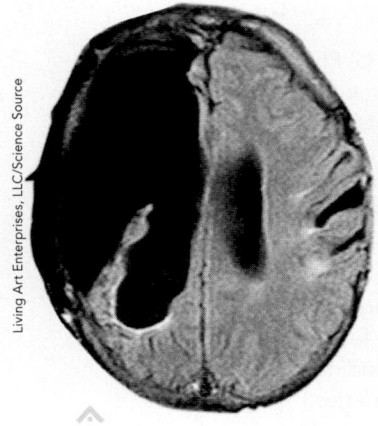

FIGURE 5.6

BRAIN WORK IS CHILD'S PLAY
This 6-year-old had surgery to end her life-threatening seizures. Although most of an entire hemisphere was removed (see MRI of hemispherectomy), her remaining hemisphere compensated by putting other areas to work. One Johns Hopkins medical team reflected on the child hemisherectomies they had performed. Although use of the opposite arm was compromised, the team reported being "awed" by how well the children had retained their memory, personality, and humor (Vining et al., 1997). The younger the child, the greater the chance that the remaining hemisphere can take over the functions of the one that was surgically removed (Choi, 2008; Danelli et al., 2013).

plasticity the brain's ability to change, especially during childhood, by reorganizing after damage or by building new pathways based on experience.

neurogenesis the formation of new neurons.

corpus callosum [KOR-pus kah-LOW-sum] the large band of neural fibers connecting the two brain hemispheres and carrying messages between them.

split brain a condition resulting from surgery that isolates the brain's two hemispheres by cutting the fibers (mainly those of the corpus callosum) connecting them.

RESPONSES TO DAMAGE

LOQ 5-3   To what extent can a damaged brain reorganize itself, and what is *neurogenesis*?

Our brain displays an extraordinary **plasticity**—an ability to change in response to experiences, both good and bad. Here we will explore the brain's ability to modify itself after damage.

Most brain-damage effects can be traced to two hard facts: (1) Severed brain and spinal cord neurons, unlike cut skin, usually do not regenerate. (If your spinal cord were severed, you would probably be permanently paralyzed.) And (2) some brain functions seem preassigned to specific areas. One newborn who suffered damage to temporal lobe facial recognition areas was never able to recognize faces (Farah et al., 2000). But there is good news: Some neural tissue can *reorganize* in response to damage.

Plasticity may also occur after serious damage, especially in young children (Kolb, 1989; see also **FIGURE 5.6**). The brain's plasticity is good news for those with vision or hearing loss. Blindness or deafness makes unused brain areas available for other uses (Amedi et al., 2005). If a blind person uses one finger to read Braille, the brain area dedicated to that finger expands as the sense of touch invades the visual cortex that normally helps people see (Barinaga, 1992; Sadato et al., 1996).

Plasticity also helps explain why some studies have found that deaf people who learned sign language before another language have enhanced peripheral and motion-detection vision (Bosworth & Dobkins, 1999; Shiell et al., 2014). In deaf people whose native language is sign, the temporal lobe area normally dedicated to hearing waits in vain for stimulation. Finally, it looks for other signals to process, such as those from the visual system used to see and interpret signs.

Similar reassignment may occur when disease or damage frees up other brain areas normally dedicated to specific functions. If a slow-growing left hemisphere tumor disrupts language (which resides mostly in the left hemisphere), the right hemisphere may compensate (Thiel et al., 2006). If a finger is amputated, the somatosensory cortex that received its input will begin to receive input from the adjacent fingers, which then become more sensitive (Oelschläger et al., 2014). So what do you suppose was the sexual intercourse experience of one patient whose lower leg had been amputated? "I actually experience my orgasm in my [phantom] foot. [Note that in Figure 5.2, the toes region is adjacent to the genitals.] And there it's much bigger than it used to be because it's no longer just confined to my genitals" (Ramachandran & Blakeslee, 1998, p. 36).

Although the brain often attempts self-repair by reorganizing existing tissue, it sometimes attempts to mend itself through **neurogenesis**—producing new neurons. Researchers have found baby neurons deep in the brains of adult mice, birds, monkeys, and humans (He & Jin, 2016; Jessberger et al., 2008). These neurons may then migrate elsewhere and form connections with neighboring neurons (Aimone et al., 2010; Egeland et al., 2015; Gould, 2007).

Master stem cells that can develop into any type of brain cell have also been discovered in the human embryo. If mass-produced in a lab and injected into a damaged brain, might neural stem cells turn themselves into replacements for lost brain cells? Researchers at universities and biotech companies continue to break new ground on how to produce stem cells that resemble functioning human neurons (Lu et al., 2016; Paşca et al., 2015). Such stem cell research not only helps treat the diseased or damaged brain, but also aids understanding of brain development, memory, and other basic psychological processes (Mariani et al., 2012; Sun et al, 2015; Zhang et al., 2016). Might surgeons someday be able to rebuild damaged brains, much as we reseed damaged lawns? Stay tuned. In the meantime, we can all benefit from natural promoters of neurogenesis, such as exercise, sleep, and nonstressful but stimulating environments (Iso et al., 2007; Pereira et al., 2007; Sexton et al., 2016).

THE DIVIDED BRAIN

LOQ 5-4   What do split brains reveal about the functions of our two brain hemispheres?

Our brain's look-alike left and right hemispheres serve differing functions. This *lateralization* is apparent after brain damage. Research spanning more than a century has shown that left hemisphere accidents, strokes, and tumors can impair reading, writing, speaking, arithmetic reasoning, and understanding. Similar right hemisphere damage has less visibly dramatic effects. Does this mean that the right hemisphere is just along for the ride? Many believed this was the case until the 1960s, when a fascinating chapter in psychology's history began to unfold: Researchers found that the "minor" right hemisphere was not so limited after all.

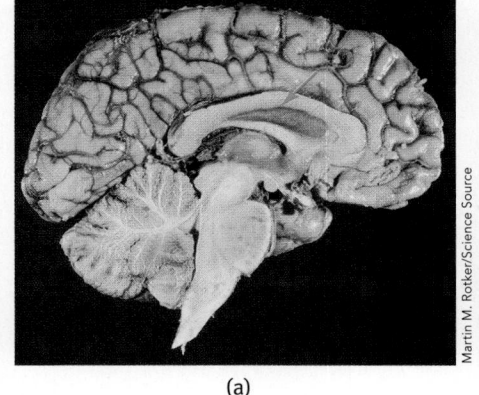

(a)

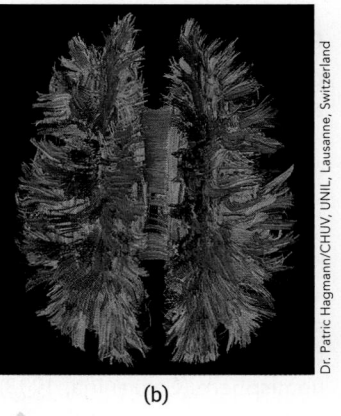

(b)

Splitting the Brain

In 1961, Los Angeles neurosurgeons Philip Vogel and Joseph Bogen speculated that major epileptic seizures were caused by an amplification of abnormal brain activity bouncing back and forth between the two cerebral hemispheres, which work together as a whole system. If so, they wondered, could they end this biological tennis match by severing the **corpus callosum,** the wide band of axon fibers connecting the two hemispheres and carrying messages between them (**FIGURE 5.7**)? Vogel and Bogen knew that psychologists Roger Sperry, Ronald Myers, and Michael Gazzaniga had divided cats' and monkeys' brains in this manner, with no serious ill effects.

So the surgeons operated. The result? The seizures all but disappeared. The patients with these **split brains** were surprisingly normal, their personality and intellect hardly affected. Waking from surgery, one even joked that he had a "splitting headache" (Gazzaniga, 1967). By sharing their experiences, these patients have greatly expanded our understanding of interactions between the intact brain's two hemispheres.

To appreciate these findings, we need to focus for a minute on the peculiar nature of our visual wiring, illustrated in **FIGURE 5.8**. Note that each eye receives sensory information from the entire visual field. But in each eye, information from the left half of your field of vision goes to your right hemisphere, and information from the right half of your visual field goes to your left hemisphere, which usually controls speech. Information received by either hemisphere is quickly transmitted to the other across the corpus callosum. In a person with a severed corpus callosum, this information-sharing does not take place.

Knowing these facts, Sperry and Gazzaniga could send information to a patient's left or right hemisphere. As the person stared at a spot, they flashed a stimulus to its right or left. They could do this with you, too, but in your intact brain, the hemisphere receiving the information would instantly pass the news to the other side. Because the split-brain surgery had cut the communication lines between the hemispheres, the researchers could, with these patients, quiz each hemisphere separately.

In an early experiment, Gazzaniga (1967) asked split-brain patients to stare at a dot as he flashed

FIGURE 5.7

THE CORPUS CALLOSUM This large band of neural fibers connects the two brain hemispheres. (a) To photograph this half brain, a surgeon separated the hemispheres by cutting through the corpus callosum (see blue arrow) and lower brain regions. (b) This high-resolution diffusion spectrum image, showing a top-facing brain from above, reveals brain neural networks within the two hemispheres, and the corpus callosum neural bridge between them.

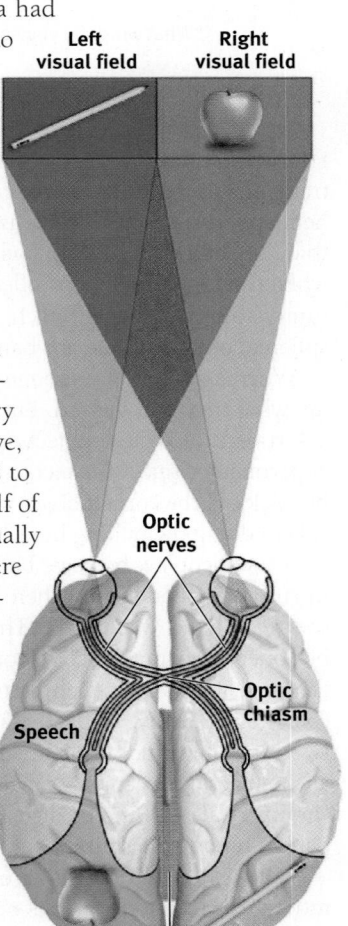

Left visual field

Right visual field

Optic nerves

Optic chiasm

Speech

Visual area of left hemisphere

Corpus callosum

Visual area of right hemisphere

FIGURE 5.8

THE INFORMATION HIGHWAY FROM EYE TO BRAIN

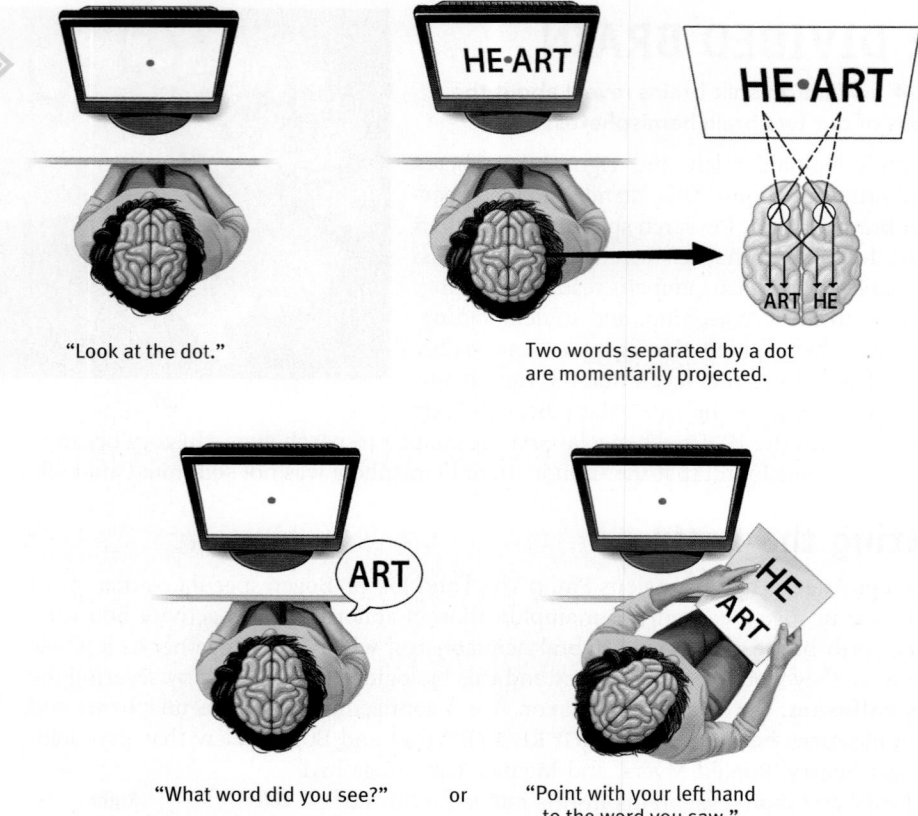

FIGURE 5.9

ONE SKULL, TWO MINDS When an experimenter flashes the word HEART across the visual field, a woman with a split brain verbally reports seeing the portion of the word transmitted to her left hemisphere. However, if asked to indicate with her left hand what she saw, she points to the portion of the word transmitted to her right hemisphere (Gazzaniga, 1983).

"Look at the dot."

HE·ART

Two words separated by a dot are momentarily projected.

ART HE

"What word did you see?"   or   "Point with your left hand to the word you saw."

HE·ART on a screen (**FIGURE 5.9**). Thus, HE appeared in their left visual field (which transmits to the right hemisphere) and ART in the right field (which transmits to the left hemisphere). When he then asked them to *say* what they had seen, the patients reported that they had seen ART. But when asked to *point* to what they had seen, they were startled when their left hand (controlled by the right hemisphere) pointed to HE. Given an opportunity to express itself, each hemisphere indicated what it had seen. The right hemisphere (controlling the left hand) intuitively knew what it could not verbally report.

When a picture of a spoon was flashed to their right hemisphere, the patients could not *say* what they had viewed. But when asked to *identify* what they had viewed by feeling an assortment of hidden objects with their left hand, they readily selected the spoon. If the experimenter said, "Correct!" the patient might reply, "What? Correct? How could I possibly pick out the correct object when I don't know what I saw?" It is, of course, the left hemisphere doing the talking here, bewildered by what the nonverbal right hemisphere knows.

A few people who have had split-brain surgery have been for a time bothered by the unruly independence of their left hand. It seemed the left hand truly didn't know what the right hand was doing. The left hand might unbutton a shirt while the right hand buttoned it, or put grocery store items back on the shelf after the right hand put them in the cart. It was as if each hemisphere was thinking "I've half a mind to wear my green (blue) shirt today." Indeed, said Sperry (1964), split-brain surgery leaves people "with two separate minds." With a split brain, both hemispheres can comprehend and follow an instruction to copy—*simultaneously*—different figures with the left and right hands (Franz et al., 2000; see also **FIGURE 5.10**). (Reading these reports, can you imagine a patient enjoying a solitary game of "rock, paper, scissors"—left versus right hand?)

"Do not let your left hand know what your right hand is doing." —Matthew 6:3

When the "two minds" are at odds, the left hemisphere does mental gymnastics to rationalize reactions it does not understand. If a patient follows an order ("Walk") sent to the right hemisphere, a strange thing happens. The left hemisphere, unaware of the order, doesn't know why the patient begins walking. But if asked, the patient doesn't reply, "I don't know." Instead, the left hemisphere improvises—"I'm going into the house to get a Coke." Gazzaniga (2006), who described these patients as "the most fascinating

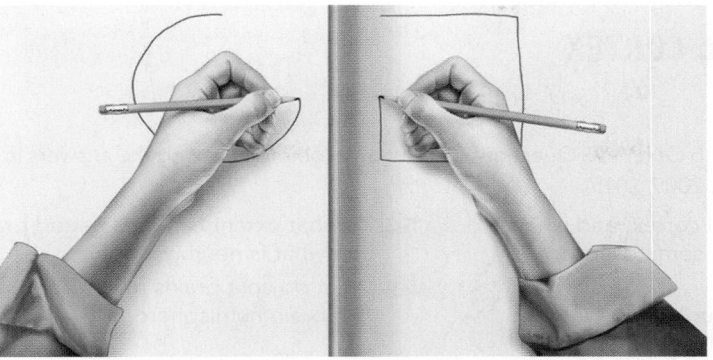

ENGAGE

FIGURE 5.10

TRY THIS! People who have had split-brain surgery can simultaneously draw two different shapes.

people on earth," realized that the conscious left hemisphere resembles an "interpreter" that instantly constructs explanations. The brain, he concluded, often runs on autopilot; it acts first and then explains itself.

> 🔒 **RETRIEVE IT** • • •   *ANSWERS IN APPENDIX E*
>
> **RI-5** (1) If we flash a red light to the right hemisphere of a person with a split brain, and flash a green light to the left hemisphere, will each observe its own color? (2) Will the person be aware that the colors differ? (3) What will the person verbally report seeing?

ENGAGE 💡 📶 **LaunchPad** Have you ever been asked if you are "left-brained" or "right-brained"? Consider this popular misconception by engaging online with **Immersive Learning: How Would You Know If People Can Be "Left-Brained" or "Right-Brained"?**

Right-Left Differences in the Intact Brain

So, what about the 99.99+ percent of us with undivided brains? Does each of *our* hemispheres also perform distinct functions? The short answer is *Yes*. When a person performs a *perceptual* task, a brain scan often reveals increased activity (brain waves, blood flow, and glucose consumption) in the *right* hemisphere. When the person speaks or does a math calculation, activity usually increases in the *left* hemisphere.

A dramatic demonstration of hemispheric specialization happens before some types of brain surgery. To locate the patient's language centers, the surgeon injects a sedative into the neck artery feeding blood to the left hemisphere, which usually controls speech. Before the injection, the patient is lying down, arms in the air, chatting with the doctor. Can you predict what happens when the drug puts the left hemisphere to sleep? Within seconds, the person's right arm falls limp. If the left hemisphere is controlling language, the patient will be speechless until the drug wears off. If the drug is injected into the artery to the right hemisphere, the *left* arm will fall limp, but the person will still be able to speak.

To the brain, language is language, whether spoken or signed. Just as hearing people usually use the left hemisphere to process spoken language, deaf people use the left hemisphere to process sign language (Corina et al., 1992; Hickok et al., 2001). Thus, a left hemisphere stroke disrupts a deaf person's signing, much as it would disrupt a hearing person's speaking (Corina, 1998).

Although the left hemisphere is skilled at making quick, literal interpretations of language, the right hemisphere excels at *making inferences* (Beeman & Chiarello, 1998; Bowden & Beeman, 1998; Mason & Just, 2004). It also *helps us modulate our speech* to make meaning clear—as when we say "Let's eat, Grandpa" instead of "Let's eat Grandpa" (Heller, 1990). The right hemisphere also *helps orchestrate our self-awareness*. People who suffer partial paralysis will sometimes stubbornly deny their impairment—mysteriously claiming they can move a paralyzed limb—if the damage is to the right hemisphere (Berti et al., 2005).

Simply looking at the two hemispheres, so alike to the naked eye, who would suppose they each contribute uniquely to the harmony of the whole? Yet a variety of observations—of people with split brains, of people with normal brains, and even of other species' brains—converge beautifully, leaving little doubt that we have unified brains with specialized parts (Hopkins & Cantalupo, 2008; MacNeilage et al., 2009).

How does the brain's intricate networking emerge? How does our *heredity*—the legacy of our ancestral history—conspire with our experiences to organize and "wire" the brain? To that we turn next.

Brain scans show that, like humans, dogs usually process words with their left hemisphere and intonation with a right hemisphere region. One study demonstrated that giving praise was ineffective if what the dogs heard didn't match *how* it was spoken (Andics et al., 2016).

RETAIN 🔒 📶 **LaunchPad** For a helpful animated review of this research, see **Topic Tutorial: PsychSim6, Hemispheric Specialization.**

🔒 REVIEW THE CEREBRAL CORTEX

⟫ Learning Objectives

TEST YOURSELF Answer these repeated Learning Objective Questions on your own (before checking the answers in Appendix D) to improve your retention of the concepts (McDaniel et al., 2009, 2015).

5-1 What four lobes make up the cerebral cortex, and what are the functions of the motor cortex, somatosensory cortex, and association areas?

5-2 Do we really use only 10 percent of our brain?

5-3 To what extent can a damaged brain reorganize itself, and what is *neurogenesis*?

5-4 What do split brains reveal about the functions of our two brain hemispheres?

⟫ Terms and Concepts to Remember

TEST YOURSELF Write down the definition yourself, then check your answer on the referenced page.

cerebral [seh-REE-bruhl] cortex, **p. 59**

frontal lobes, **p. 59**

parietal [puh-RYE-uh-tuhl] lobes, **p. 59**

occipital [ahk-SIP-uh-tuhl] lobes, **p. 59**

temporal lobes, **p. 59**

motor cortex, **p. 61**

somatosensory cortex, **p. 61**

association areas, **p. 62**

plasticity, **p. 64**

neurogenesis, **p. 64**

corpus callosum [KOR-pus kah-LOW-sum], **p. 64**

split brain, **p. 64**

⟫ Experience the Testing Effect

TEST YOURSELF Answer the following questions on your own first, then check your answers in Appendix E.

1. If a neurosurgeon stimulated your right motor cortex, you would most likely
   a. see light.
   b. hear a sound.
   c. feel a touch on the right arm.
   d. move your left leg.

2. How do different neural networks communicate with one another to let you respond when a friend greets you at a party?

3. Which of the following body regions has the greatest representation in the somatosensory cortex?
   a. Upper arm
   b. Toes
   c. Lips
   d. All regions are equally represented.

4. Judging and planning are enabled by the _____ lobes.

5. The "uncommitted" areas that make up about three-fourths of the cerebral cortex are called _____ _____.

6. The flexible brain's ability to respond to damage is especially evident in the brains of
   a. split-brain patients.
   b. young adults.
   c. young children.
   d. right-handed people.

7. An experimenter flashes the word HERON across the visual field of a man whose corpus callosum has been severed. HER is transmitted to his right hemisphere and ON to his left hemisphere. When asked to indicate what he saw, the man says he saw _____ but his left hand points to _____.

8. Studies of people with split brains and brain scans of those with undivided brains indicate that the left hemisphere excels in
   a. processing language.
   b. visual perceptions.
   c. making inferences.
   d. neurogenesis.

9. Damage to the brain's right hemisphere is most likely to reduce a person's ability to
   a. recite the alphabet rapidly.
   b. make inferences.
   c. understand verbal instructions.
   d. solve arithmetic problems.

Continue testing yourself with 📘 **LearningCurve** or 📖 **Achieve Read & Practice** to learn and remember most effectively.

⬛6 Genetics, Evolutionary Psychology, and Behavior

BEHAVIOR GENETICS: PREDICTING INDIVIDUAL DIFFERENCES

LOQ 6-1 What are *chromosomes, DNA, genes,* and the human *genome?* How do behavior geneticists explain our individual differences?

Our shared brain architecture predisposes some common behavioral tendencies. Whether we live in the Arctic or the tropics, we sense the world, develop language, and feel hunger through identical mechanisms. We prefer sweet tastes to sour. We divide the color spectrum into similar colors. And we feel drawn to behaviors that produce and protect offspring.

Our human family shares not only a common biological heritage—cut us and we bleed—but also common social behaviors. Whether named Gonzales, Nkomo, Smith, or Wong, we start fearing strangers at about eight months, and as adults we prefer the company of those with attitudes and attributes similar to our own. As members of one species, we affiliate, conform, return favors, punish offenses, organize hierarchies of status, and grieve a child's death. A visitor from outer space could drop in anywhere and find humans dancing and feasting, singing and worshiping, playing sports and games, laughing and crying, living in families and forming groups. We are the leaves of one tree.

But in important ways, we also are each unique. We are each a one-of-a-kind package of looks, language, personality, interests, and cultural background. What causes our striking diversity? How much of it is shaped by our differing genes, and how much by our **environment**—by every external influence, from maternal nutrition while in the womb to social support while nearing the tomb? How does our **heredity** interact with our experiences to create both our universal human nature and our individual and social diversity? Such questions intrigue **behavior geneticists.**

Genes: Our Codes for Life

Barely more than a century ago, few would have guessed that every cell nucleus in your body contains the genetic master code for your entire body. It's as if every room in Dubai's Burj Khalifa (the world's tallest building) contained a book detailing the architect's plans for the entire structure. The plans for your own book of life run to 46 chapters—23 donated by your mother's egg and 23 by your father's sperm. Each of these 46 chapters, called a **chromosome,** is composed of a coiled chain of the molecule **DNA (deoxyribonucleic acid). Genes,** small segments of the giant DNA molecules, form the words of those chapters (**FIGURE 6.1**). Altogether, you have some 20,000 genes, which are either active (*expressed*) or inactive. Environmental events "turn on" genes, rather like hot water enabling a tea bag to express its flavor. When turned on, genes provide the code for creating *protein molecules,* our body's building blocks.

Genetically speaking, every other human is nearly your identical twin. Human **genome** researchers have discovered the common sequence within human DNA. This shared genetic profile is what makes us humans, rather than tulips, bananas, or chimpanzees.

The occasional variations found at particular gene sites in human DNA fascinate geneticists and psychologists. Slight person-to-person variations from the common pattern give clues to our uniqueness—why one person has a disease that another does not, why one person is tall and another short, why one is anxious and another calm.

Most of our traits have complex genetic roots. How tall you are, for example, reflects the size of your face, vertebrae, leg bones, and so forth—each of which may be influenced

environment every nongenetic influence, from prenatal nutrition to the people and things around us.

heredity the genetic transfer of characteristics from parents to offspring.

behavior genetics the study of the relative power and limits of genetic and environmental influences on behavior.

chromosomes threadlike structures made of DNA molecules that contain the genes.

DNA (deoxyribonucleic acid) a complex molecule containing the genetic information that makes up the chromosomes.

genes the biochemical units of heredity that make up the chromosomes; segments of DNA capable of synthesizing proteins.

genome the complete instructions for making an organism, consisting of all the genetic material in that organism's chromosomes.

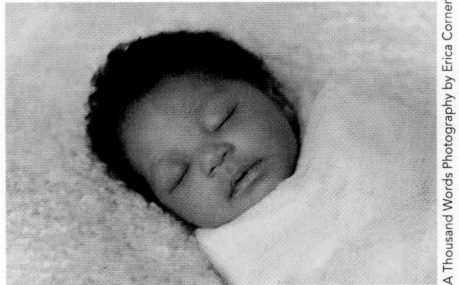

THE NURTURE OF NATURE Parents everywhere wonder: Will my baby grow up to be peaceful or aggressive? Plain or attractive? Successful or struggling at every step? What comes built in, and what is nurtured—and how? Research reveals that nature and nurture together shape our development— every step of the way.

"Your DNA and mine are 99.9 percent the same. . . . At the DNA level, we are clearly all part of one big worldwide family." —Francis Collins, Human Genome Project director, 2007

"We share half our genes with the banana." —Evolutionary biologist Robert May, president of Britain's Royal Society, 2001

THE LIFE CODE The nucleus of every human cell contains chromosomes, each of which is made up of two strands of DNA connected in a double helix. Genes are DNA segments that, when expressed (turned on), direct the development of proteins that influence a person's individual development.

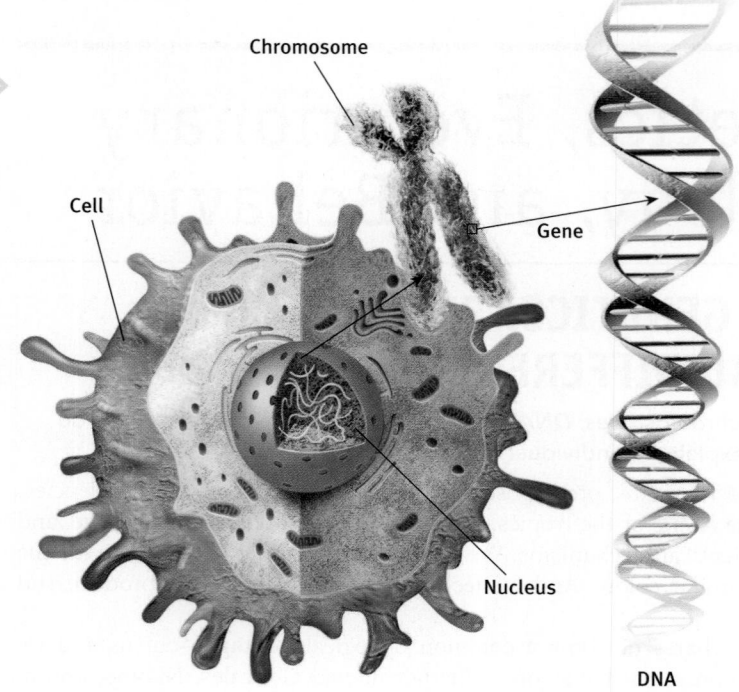

"Thanks for almost everything, Dad."

by different genes interacting with your specific environment. Traits such as intelligence, happiness, and aggressiveness are similarly influenced by many genes. Indeed, one of the big take-home findings of today's behavior genetics is that there is no single smart gene, gay (or straight) gene, or schizophrenia gene. Rather, our differing traits are influenced by "many genes of small effect" (Okbay et al., 2016; Plomin et al., 2016).

So, our many genes help explain both our shared human nature and our human diversity. But—another take-home finding—knowing our heredity tells only part of our story. To form us, environmental influences interact with our genetic predispositions.

🔒 RETRIEVE IT • • •

RI-1 Put the following cell structures in order from smallest to largest: nucleus, gene, chromosome.

Twin and Adoption Studies

LOQ 6-2   How do twin and adoption studies help us understand the effects and interactions of nature and nurture?

To scientifically tease apart the influences of environment and heredity, behavior geneticists could wish for two types of experiments. The first would control heredity while varying the home environment. The second would control the home environment while varying heredity. Although such experiments with human infants would be unethical, nature has done this work for us.

IDENTICAL VERSUS FRATERNAL TWINS **Identical (monozygotic) twins** develop from a single fertilized egg that splits. Thus they are *genetically* identical—nature's own human clones (**FIGURE 6.2**). Indeed, they are clones who share not only the same genes but the same conception and uterus, and usually the same birth date and cultural history.

Fraternal (dizygotic) twins develop from two separate fertilized eggs. Although they share a prenatal environment, they are genetically no more similar than ordinary siblings.

Shared genes can translate into shared experiences. A person whose identical twin has *autism spectrum disorder,* for example, has about a 3 in 4 risk of being similarly diagnosed. If the affected twin is fraternal, the co-twin has about a 1 in 3 risk (Ronald & Hoekstra, 2011). To study the effects of genes and environments, several thousand medical and psychological researchers have studied nearly 15 million identical and fraternal twin pairs (Polderman et al., 2015).

📺 **LaunchPad** See the **Video: Twin Studies** for a helpful tutorial animation.

identical (monozygotic) twins individuals that develop from a single fertilized egg that splits in two, creating two genetically identical organisms.

fraternal (dizygotic) twins individuals that develop from separate fertilized eggs. They are genetically no closer than ordinary siblings, but they share a prenatal environment.

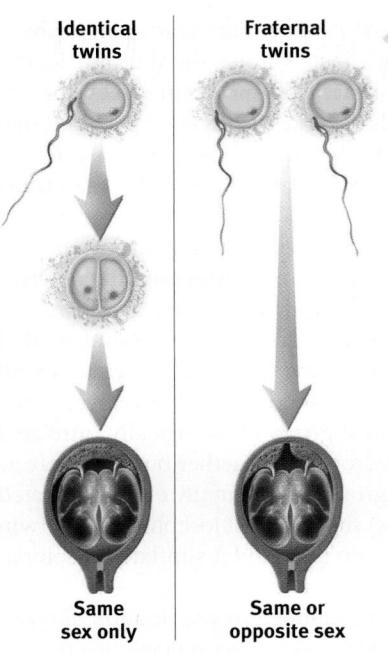

Identical
twins

Fraternal
twins

FIGURE 6.2

SAME FERTILIZED EGG, SAME GENES; DIFFERENT EGGS, DIFFERENT GENES Identical twins develop from a single fertilized egg, fraternal twins from two.

Same
sex only

Same or
opposite sex

Are genetically identical twins also *behaviorally* more similar than fraternal twins? Studies of thousands of twin pairs have found that identical twins are much more alike in *extraversion* (outgoingness) and *neuroticism* (emotional instability) than are fraternal twins (Kandler et al., 2011; Laceulle et al., 2011; Loehlin, 2012).

Identical twins, more than fraternal twins, look alike. So, do people's responses to their looks account for their similarities? *No.* In a clever approach, researcher (and twin) Nancy Segal (2013; Segal et al., 2013) compared personality similarity between identical twins and unrelated look-alike pairs. Only the identical twins reported similar personalities. Other studies have shown that identical twins whose parents treated them alike (for example, dressing them identically) were not psychologically more alike than other identical twins (Kendler et al., 1994; Loehlin & Nichols, 1976). In explaining individual differences, genes matter.

SEPARATED TWINS Imagine the following science fiction experiment: A mad scientist decides to separate identical twins at birth, then raise them in differing environments. Better yet, consider a *true* story:

In 1979, some time after divorcing, Jim Lewis awoke next to his second wife. Determined to make this marriage work, Jim made a habit of leaving love notes around the house. As he lay in bed he thought about others he had loved, including his son, James Alan, and his faithful dog, Toy.

Jim enjoyed spending part of the day in his basement woodworking shop building furniture, picture frames, and other items, including a white bench now circling a tree in his front yard. Jim also liked to drive his Chevy, watch stock-car racing, and drink Miller Lite beer.

What was extraordinary about Jim Lewis, however, was that at that same moment (we are not making this up) there existed another man—also named Jim—for whom all these things (right down to the dog's name) were also true.[1] This other Jim—Jim Springer—just happened, 38 years earlier, to have been his womb-mate. Thirty-seven days after their birth, these genetically identical twins were separated, adopted, and raised with no contact or knowledge of each other's whereabouts until the day Jim Lewis received a call from his genetic clone (who, having been told he had a twin, set out to find him).

One month later, the brothers became the first of many separated twin pairs tested by University of Minnesota psychologist Thomas Bouchard and his colleagues (Miller, P., 2012).

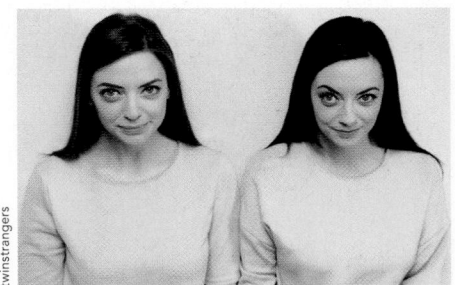

twinstrangers

DO LOOK-ALIKES ACT ALIKE? Genetically unrelated look-alikes, such as these doppelgangers, tend not to have notably similar personalities (Segal, 2013).

Twins Lorraine and Levinia Christmas, driving to deliver Christmas presents to each other near Flitcham, England, collided (Shepherd, 1997).

---

1. Actually, this description of the two Jims errs in one respect: Jim Lewis named his son James Alan. Jim Springer named his James Allan.

Bouchard's famous twin research was, appropriately enough, conducted in Minneapolis, the "Twin City" (with St. Paul) and home to the Minnesota Twins baseball team.

The brothers' voice intonations and inflections were so similar that, hearing a playback of an earlier interview, Jim Springer guessed, "That's me." Wrong—it was Jim Lewis. Given tests measuring their personality, intelligence, heart rate, and brain waves, the Jim twins—despite 38 years of separation—were virtually as alike as the same person tested twice. Both married women named Dorothy Jane Scheckelburger. Okay, the last item is a joke. But as Judith Rich Harris (2006) has noted, it would hardly be weirder than some other reported similarities.

Aided by media publicity, Bouchard (2009) and his colleagues located and studied 74 pairs of identical twins raised apart. They continued to find similarities not only of tastes and physical attributes but also of personality, abilities, attitudes, interests, and fears.

Stories of startling twin similarities have not impressed critics, who remind us that "the plural of *anecdote* is not *data*." They note that if any two strangers were to spend hours comparing their behaviors and life histories, they would probably discover many coincidental similarities. If researchers created a control group of biologically unrelated pairs of the same age, sex, and ethnicity, who had not grown up together but who were as similar to one another in economic and cultural background as are many of the separated twin pairs, wouldn't these pairs also exhibit striking similarities (Joseph, 2001)? Twin researchers have replied that separated fraternal twins do not exhibit similarities comparable with those of separated identical twins.

The impressive data from personality assessments are clouded by the reunion of many of the separated twins some years before they were tested. Adoption agencies also tend to place separated twins in similar homes. Despite these criticisms, the striking twin-study results helped shift scientific thinking toward a greater appreciation of genetic influences.

If genetic influences help explain individual differences, can the same be said of trait differences *between* groups? Not necessarily. Individual differences in height and weight, for example, are highly heritable; yet nutrition (an environmental factor) rather than genetic influences explains why, as a group, today's adults are taller and heavier than those of a century ago. The two groups differ, but not because human genes have changed in a mere century's eyeblink of time. Ditto aggressiveness, a genetically influenced trait. Today's peaceful Scandinavians differ from their more aggressive Viking ancestors, despite carrying many of the same genes.

BIOLOGICAL VERSUS ADOPTIVE RELATIVES For behavior geneticists, nature's second real-life experiment—adoption—creates two groups: *genetic relatives* (biological parents and siblings) and *environmental relatives* (adoptive parents and siblings). For personality or any other given trait, we can therefore ask whether adopted children are more like their biological parents, who contributed their genes, or their adoptive parents, who contribute a home environment. And while sharing that home environment, do adopted siblings come to share traits?

The stunning finding from studies of hundreds of adoptive families is that, apart from identical twins, people who grow up together—whether biologically related or not—do not much resemble one another in personality (McGue & Bouchard, 1998; Plomin, 2011; Rowe, 1990). In personality traits such as extraversion and agreeableness, for example, people who have been adopted are more similar to their *biological* parents than their caregiving adoptive parents.

The finding is important enough to bear repeating: The normal range of environments shared by a family's children has little discernible impact on their personalities. Two adopted children raised in the same home are no more likely to share personality traits with each other than with the child down the block.

Heredity shapes other primates' personalities, too. Macaque monkeys raised by foster mothers exhibited social behaviors that resembled their biological, rather than foster, mothers (Maestripieri, 2003).

The genetic leash may limit the family environment's influence on personality, but it does not mean that adoptive parenting is a fruitless venture. As an adoptive parent, I [ND] especially find it heartening to know that parents do influence their children's attitudes, values, manners, politics, and faith (Kandler & Riemann, 2013). This was dramatically illustrated by separated identical twins Jack Yufe, a Jew, and Oskar Stöhr, a member

(ASK YOURSELF)

Do you know of any biological siblings who, despite having been raised in the same home, have very different personalities? (Are *you* one of these siblings, perhaps?) Knowing what you do of their lives and upbringing, what do you think contributed to these differences?

ADOPTION MATTERS Country music singer Faith Hill and late Apple founder Steve Jobs both benefited from one of the biggest gifts of love: adoption.

of Germany's Hitler Youth. After later reuniting, Oskar mused to Jack: "If we had been switched, I would have been the Jew, and you would have been the Nazi" (Segal, 2005, p. 70). Parenting—and the cultural environments in which parents place children—matters!

Moreover, child neglect and abuse and even parental divorce are rare in adoptive homes. (Adoptive parents are carefully screened; biological parents are not.) So it is not surprising that studies have shown that, despite a slightly greater risk of psychological disorder, most adopted children thrive, especially when adopted as infants (Loehlin et al., 2007; van IJzendoorn & Juffer, 2006; Wierzbicki, 1993). Seven in eight adopted children have reported feeling strongly attached to one or both adoptive parents. As children of self-giving parents, they have grown up to be more self-giving and altruistic than average (Sharma et al., 1998). Many scored higher than their biological parents and raised-apart biological siblings on intelligence tests, and most grew into happier and more stable adults (Kendler et al., 2015b; van IJzendoorn et al., 2005). In one Swedish study, children adopted as infants grew up with fewer problems than were experienced by children whose biological mothers initially registered them for adoption but then decided to raise the children themselves (Bohman & Sigvardsson, 1990). *The bottom line:* Regardless of personality differences between adoptive family members, most adopted children benefit from adoption.

Siblings so different: Hermann Goering was outgoing, loved crowds, and became Hitler's right-hand man and founder of the Nazi Gestapo. His younger brother Albert Goering was quiet and reclusive, and worked to save Jews that brother Hermann's regime was killing (Brennan, 2010).

🔒 **RETRIEVE IT** • • •   *ANSWERS IN APPENDIX E*

RI-2 How do researchers use twin and adoption studies to learn about psychological principles?

Gene-Environment Interaction

LOQ 6-3   How do heredity and environment work together?

Among our similarities, the most important—the behavioral hallmark of our species—is our enormous adaptive capacity. Some human traits, such as having two eyes, develop the same way in virtually every environment. But other traits are expressed only in particular environments. Go barefoot for a summer and you will develop toughened, callused feet—a biological adaptation to friction. Meanwhile, your shod neighbor will remain a tenderfoot. The difference between the two of you is an effect of environment. But it is the product of a biological mechanism—adaptation.

Genes and environment—nature and nurture—work together, like two hands clapping. Genes are *self-regulating*. Rather than acting as blueprints that lead to the same result no matter the context, genes react. An African butterfly that is green in summer turns brown in fall, thanks to a temperature-controlled genetic switch. The same genes that produce green in one situation produce brown in another.

GENETIC SPACE EXPLORATION In 2015, Scott Kelly (on the left) and Mark Kelly (on the right) embarked on a twin study that was literally out of this world. Scott spent 340 days orbiting the planet in the International Space Station. His identical twin, Mark, remained on Earth. Both twins underwent the same physical and psychological testing. The study results will help scientists understand how genes and environment—in outer space and on Earth—interact.

Derek Storm/Splash News/Newscom

FIGURE 6.3

EPIGENETICS INFLUENCES GENE EXPRESSION Beginning in the womb, life experiences lay down epigenetic marks—often organic methyl molecules—that can influence the expression of any gene in the DNA segment they affect. (Research from Champagne, 2010.)

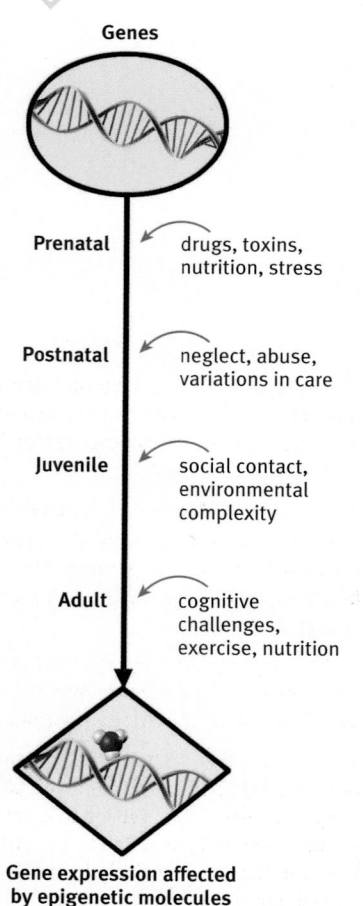

Genes

Prenatal — drugs, toxins, nutrition, stress

Postnatal — neglect, abuse, variations in care

Juvenile — social contact, environmental complexity

Adult — cognitive challenges, exercise, nutrition

Gene expression affected by epigenetic molecules

To say that genes and experience are *both* important is true. But more precisely, they **interact.** Imagine two babies, one genetically predisposed to be attractive, sociable, and easygoing, the other less so. Assume further that the first baby attracts more affectionate and stimulating care and so develops into a warmer and more outgoing person. As the two children grow older, the more naturally outgoing child may seek more activities and friends that encourage further social confidence.

What has caused their resulting personality differences? Neither heredity nor experience act alone. Environments trigger gene activity. And our genetically influenced traits *evoke* significant responses in others. Thus, a child's impulsivity and aggression may evoke an angry response from a parent or teacher, who reacts warmly to well-behaved children in the family or classroom. In such cases, the child's nature and the adult's nurture interact. Gene and scene dance together.

Identical twins not only share the same genetic predispositions, they also seek and create similar experiences that express their shared genes (Kandler et al., 2012). This helps explain why identical twins raised in different families have recalled their parents' warmth as remarkably similar—almost as similar as if they had been raised by the same parents (Plomin et al., 1988, 1991, 1994). Fraternal twins have more differing recollections of their early family life—even if raised in the same family. "Children experience us as different parents, depending on their own qualities," noted Sandra Scarr (1990).

Recall that genes can be either active (expressed, as the hot water activates the tea bag) or inactive. **Epigenetics** (meaning "in addition to" or "above and beyond" genetics) studies the molecular mechanisms by which environments can trigger or block genetic expression. Our experiences create *epigenetic marks,* which are often organic methyl molecules attached to part of a DNA strand (**FIGURE 6.3**). If a mark instructs the cell to ignore any gene present in that DNA segment, those genes will be "turned off"—they will prevent the DNA from producing the proteins coded by that gene. As one geneticist explained, "Things written in pen you can't change. That's DNA. But things written in pencil you can. That's epigenetics" (Reed, 2011).

Environmental factors such as diet, drugs, and stress can affect the epigenetic molecules that regulate gene expression. Mother rats normally lick their infants. Deprived of this licking in experiments, infant rats had more epigenetic molecules blocking access to their brain's "on" switch for developing stress hormone receptors. When stressed, those animals had above-average levels of free-floating stress hormones and were more stressed (Champagne et al., 2003; Champagne & Mashoodh, 2009).

Epigenetics provides a mechanism by which the effects of childhood trauma, poverty, or malnutrition may last a lifetime (Nugent et al., 2016; Peter et al., 2016; Swartz et al., 2016). Child abuse may leave its fingerprints in a person's genome. Moreover, it now appears that some epigenetic changes are passed down to future generations. In one study, Holocaust trauma survivors shared epigenetic alterations with their offspring (Yehuda et al., 2016).

Epigenetics research may solve some scientific mysteries, such as why only one member of an identical twin pair may develop a genetically influenced mental disorder (Spector, 2012). Epigenetics can also help explain why identical twins may look slightly different. Researchers studying mice have found that in utero exposure to certain chemicals can cause genetically identical twins to have different-colored fur (Dolinoy et al., 2007).

So, if Beyoncé and Jay Z's daughter, Blue Ivy, grows up to be a popular recording artist, should we attribute her musical talent to her "superstar genes"? To her growing up in a musically rich environment? To high expectations? The best answer seems to be "All of the above." From conception onward, we are the product of a cascade of interactions between our genetic predispositions and our surrounding environments (McGue, 2010). Our genes affect how people react to and influence us. Forget nature *versus* nurture; think nature *via* nurture.

📺 **LaunchPad** For a 7-minute explanation of genes and environment, watch the **Video: Behavior Genetics.**

🔒 **RETRIEVE IT • • •**   *ANSWERS IN APPENDIX E*

RI-3 Match the following terms (I–II) to the correct explanation (a–b).

Term:
I. Epigenetics

II. Behavior genetics

Explanation:
a. Study of the relative effects of our genes and our environment on our behavior.

b. Study of environmental factors that affect how our genes are *expressed*.

EVOLUTIONARY PSYCHOLOGY: UNDERSTANDING HUMAN NATURE

LOQ 6-4   How do evolutionary psychologists use natural selection to explain behavior tendencies?

Behavior geneticists explore the genetic and environmental roots of human differences. **Evolutionary psychologists** instead focus mostly on what makes us so much alike as humans. They use Charles Darwin's principle of **natural selection** to understand the roots of behavior and mental processes. The idea, simplified, is this:

- Organisms' varied offspring compete for survival.

- Certain biological and behavioral variations increase organisms' reproductive and survival chances in their particular environment.

- Offspring that survive are more likely to pass their genes to ensuing generations.

- Thus, over time, population characteristics may change.

To see these principles at work, let's consider a straightforward example in foxes.

Natural Selection and Adaptation

A fox is a wild and wary animal. If you capture a fox and try to befriend it, be careful: If the timid fox cannot flee, it may snack on your fingers. Russian scientist Dmitry Belyaev wondered how our human ancestors had domesticated dogs from their equally wild wolf forebears. Might he, within a comparatively short stretch of time, accomplish a similar feat by transforming the fearful fox into a friendly fox?

To find out, Belyaev set to work with 30 male and 100 female foxes. From their offspring he selected and mated the tamest 5 percent of males and 20 percent of females. (He measured tameness by the foxes' responses to attempts to feed, handle, and stroke them.) Over more than 30 generations of foxes, Belyaev and his successor, Lyudmila Trut, repeated that simple procedure. Forty years and 45,000 foxes later, they had a new breed of foxes that, in Trut's (1999) words, were "docile, eager to please, and unmistakably domesticated. . . . Before our eyes, 'the Beast' has turned into 'beauty,' as the aggressive behavior of our herd's wild [ancestors] entirely disappeared." So friendly and eager for human contact were these animals, so inclined to whimper to attract attention and to lick people like affectionate dogs, that the cash-strapped institute seized on a way to raise funds—marketing its friendly foxes as house pets.

Eric Isselée/Shutterstock

LASTING EFFECTS Canadian Senator Murray Sinclair, seen here with Prime Minister Justin Trudeau, was honored for an in-depth report on the devastating effects of Canada's long running residential school program that removed Aboriginal Canadian children from their families. As psychologist Susan Pinker (2015) observed, the epigenetic effects of forced family separation "can play out, not only in the survivors of residential schools but in subsequent generations."

Adrian Wyld/The Canadian Press via AP

interaction the interplay that occurs when the effect of one factor (such as environment) depends on another factor (such as heredity).

epigenetics "above" or "in addition to" *(epi)* genetics; the study of the molecular mechanisms by which environments can influence genetic expression (without a DNA change).

evolutionary psychology the study of the evolution of behavior and the mind, using principles of natural selection.

natural selection the principle that inherited traits that better enable an organism to survive and reproduce in a particular environment will (in competition with other trait variations) most likely be passed on to subsequent generations.

mutation a random error in gene replication that leads to a change.

Does the same process work with naturally occurring selection? Does natural selection explain our human tendencies? Nature has indeed selected advantageous variations from the new gene combinations produced at each human conception plus the **mutations** (random errors in gene replication) that sometimes result. But the tight genetic leash that predisposes a dog's retrieving, a cat's pouncing, or a bird's nesting is looser on humans. The genes selected during our ancestral history provide more than a long leash; they give us a great capacity to learn and therefore to *adapt* to life in varied environments, from the tundra to the jungle. Genes and experience together wire the brain. Our adaptive flexibility in responding to different environments contributes to our *fitness*—our ability to survive and reproduce.

> 🔒 **RETRIEVE IT • • •**   *ANSWERS IN APPENDIX E*
>
> **RI-4** How are Belyaev and Trut's breeding practices similar to, and how do they differ from, the way natural selection normally occurs?

Evolutionary Success Helps Explain Similarities

Our similarities arise from our shared human genome, our common genetic profile. How did we develop our genetic kinship?

OUR GENETIC LEGACY At the dawn of human history, our ancestors faced certain questions: Who is my ally, who is my foe? With whom should I mate? What food should I eat? Some individuals answered those questions more successfully than others. For example, women who experienced nausea in the critical first three months of pregnancy were genetically predisposed to avoid certain bitter, strongly flavored, and novel foods. Avoiding such foods had survival value, since they are the very foods most often toxic to prenatal development (Profet, 1992; Schmitt & Pilcher, 2004). Early humans disposed to eat nourishing rather than poisonous foods survived to contribute their genes to later generations. Those who deemed leopards "nice to pet" often did not.

Similarly successful were those whose mating helped them produce and nurture offspring. Over generations, the genes of individuals not disposed to mate or nurture tended to be lost from the human gene pool. As success-enhancing genes continued to be selected, behavioral tendencies and learning capacities emerged that prepared our Stone Age ancestors to survive, reproduce, and send their genes into the future, and into you.

Count yourself fortunate: Despite high infant mortality and rampant disease in past millennia, not one of your countless ancestors died childless.

As heirs to this prehistoric legacy, we are genetically predisposed to behave in ways that promoted our ancestors' surviving and reproducing. But in some ways, we are biologically prepared for a world that no longer exists. We love the taste of sweets and fats, nutrients that prepared our physically active ancestors to survive food shortages. But few of us now hunt and gather our food; instead, we find sweets and fats in fast-food outlets and vending machines. Our natural dispositions, rooted deep in history, are mismatched with today's junk-food and often inactive lifestyle.

EVOLUTIONARY PSYCHOLOGY TODAY Darwin's theory of evolution has become one of biology's fundamental organizing principles and lives on in the *second Darwinian revolution*: the application of evolutionary principles to psychology. In concluding *On the Origin of Species,* Darwin (1859, p. 346) anticipated this, foreseeing "open fields for far more important researches. Psychology will be based on a new foundation."

Those who are troubled by an apparent conflict between scientific and religious accounts of human origins may find it helpful to consider that different perspectives on life can be complementary. For example, the scientific account attempts to tell us when and how; religious creation stories usually aim to tell about an ultimate who and why. As Galileo explained to the Grand Duchess Christina, "The Bible teaches how to go to heaven, not how the heavens go."

Elsewhere in this text, we address questions that intrigue evolutionary psychologists: Why do infants start to fear strangers about the time they become mobile? Why do so many more people have phobias about spiders, snakes, and heights than about more dangerous threats, such as guns and electricity? And why do we fear safe air travel so much more than dangerous driving?

* * *

We know from our correspondence and from surveys that some readers are troubled by the naturalism and evolutionism of contemporary science. (A note to readers from other nations: In the United States there is a wide gulf between scientific and lay thinking about evolution.) "The idea that human minds are the product of evolution is . . .

unassailable fact," declared a 2007 editorial in *Nature,* a leading science journal. In *The Language of God,* Human Genome Project director Francis Collins (2006, pp. 141, 146), a self-described evangelical Christian, compiled the "utterly compelling" evidence that led him to conclude that Darwin's big idea is "unquestionably correct." Yet Gallup poll-sters report that 42 percent of U.S. adults believe that humans were created "pretty much in their present form" within the last 10,000 years (Newport, 2014). Many people who dispute the scientific story worry that a science of behavior (and evolutionary science in particular) will destroy our sense of the beauty, mystery, and spiritual significance of the human creature. For those concerned, we offer some reassuring thoughts.

When Isaac Newton explained the rainbow in terms of light of differing wavelengths, the British poet John Keats feared that Newton had destroyed the rainbow's mysterious beauty. Yet, as evolutionary biologist Richard Dawkins (1998) noted in *Unweaving the Rainbow,* Newton's analysis led to an even deeper mystery—Einstein's theory of special relativity. Nothing about Newton's optics need diminish our appreciation for the dramatic elegance of a rainbow arching across a brightening sky.

When Galileo assembled evidence that Earth revolved around the Sun, not vice versa, he did not offer irrefutable proof for his theory. Rather, he offered a coherent explanation for a variety of observations, such as the changing shadows cast by the Moon's moun-tains. His explanation eventually won the day because it described and explained things in a way that made sense, that hung together. Darwin's theory of evolution likewise is a coherent view of natural history. It offers an organizing principle that unifies various observations.

Many people of faith find the scientific idea of human origins congenial with their spirituality. In the fifth century, St. Augustine (quoted by Wilford, 1999) wrote, "The universe was brought into being in a less than fully formed state, but was gifted with the capacity to transform itself from unformed matter into a truly marvelous array of structures and life forms." Some 1600 years later, Pope Francis in 2015 welcomed a science-religion dialogue, saying, "Evolution in nature is not inconsistent with the notion of creation, because evolution requires the creation of beings that evolve."

Meanwhile, many people of science are awestruck at the emerging understanding of the universe and the human creature. It boggles the mind—the entire universe popping out of a point some 14 billion years ago, and instantly inflating to cosmological size. Had the energy of this Big Bang been the tiniest bit less, the universe would have collapsed back on itself. Had it been the tiniest bit more, the result would have been a soup too thin to support life. Astronomer Sir Martin Rees has described *Just Six Numbers* (1999), any one of which, if changed ever so slightly, would produce a cosmos in which life could not exist. Had gravity been a tad stronger or weaker, or had the weight of a carbon proton been a wee bit different, our universe just wouldn't have worked.

What caused this almost-too-good-to-be-true, finely tuned universe? Why is there something rather than nothing? How did it come to be, in the words of Harvard-Smithso-nian astrophysicist Owen Gingerich (1999), "so extraordinarily right, that it seemed the universe had been expressly designed to produce intelligent, sentient beings"? On such matters, a humble, awed, scientific silence is appropriate, suggested philosopher Ludwig Wittgenstein: "Whereof one cannot speak, thereof one must be silent" (1922, p. 189).

Rather than fearing science, we can welcome its enlarging our understanding and awakening our sense of awe. In *The Fragile Species,* Lewis Thomas (1992) described his utter amazement that Earth in time gave rise to bacteria and eventually to Bach's Mass in B Minor. In a short 4 billion years, life on Earth has come from nothing to struc-tures as complex as a 6-billion-unit strand of DNA and the incomprehensible intricacy of the human brain. Atoms no different from those in a rock somehow formed dynamic entities that produce extraordinary, self-replicating, information-processing systems—us (Davies, 2007). Although we appear to have been created from dust, over eons of time, the end result is a priceless creature, one rich with potential beyond our imagining.

🔒 REVIEW GENETICS, EVOLUTIONARY PSYCHOLOGY, AND BEHAVIOR

⊚⟫ Learning Objectives

TEST YOURSELF Answer these repeated Learning Objective Questions on your own (before checking the answers in Appendix D) to improve your retention of the concepts (McDaniel et al., 2009, 2015).

6-1 What are *chromosomes, DNA, genes,* and the human *genome*? How do behavior geneticists explain our individual differences?

6-2 How do twin and adoption studies help us understand the effects and interactions of nature and nurture?

6-3 How do heredity and environment work together?

6-4 How do evolutionary psychologists use natural selection to explain behavior tendencies?

⊚⟫ Terms and Concepts to Remember

TEST YOURSELF Write down the definition yourself, then check your answer on the referenced page.

environment, **p. 69**

heredity, **p. 69**

behavior genetics, **p. 69**

chromosomes, **p. 69**

DNA (deoxyribonucleic acid), **p. 69**

genes, **p. 69**

genome, **p. 69**

identical (monozygotic) twins, **p. 70**

fraternal (dizygotic) twins, **p. 70**

interaction, **p. 75**

epigenetics, **p. 75**

evolutionary psychology, **p. 75**

natural selection, **p. 75**

mutation, **p. 76**

⊚⟫ Experience the Testing Effect

TEST YOURSELF Answer the following questions on your own first, then check your answers in Appendix E.

1. The threadlike structures made largely of DNA molecules are called _____.

2. A small segment of DNA that codes for particular proteins is referred to as a _____.

3. When the mother's egg and the father's sperm unite, each contributes
   a. one chromosome pair.
   b. 23 chromosomes.
   c. 23 chromosome pairs.
   d. 25,000 chromosomes.

4. Fraternal twins result when
   a. a single egg is fertilized by a single sperm and then splits.
   b. a single egg is fertilized by two sperm and then splits.
   c. two eggs are fertilized by two sperm.
   d. two eggs are fertilized by a single sperm.

5. _____twins share the same DNA.

6. Adoption studies seek to understand genetic influences on personality. They do this mainly by
   a. comparing adopted children with nonadopted children.
   b. evaluating whether adopted children's personalities more closely resemble those of their adoptive parents or their biological parents.
   c. studying the effect of prior neglect on adopted children.
   d. studying the effect of children's age at adoption.

7. Epigenetics is the study of the molecular mechanisms by which _____ trigger or block genetic expression.

8. Behavior geneticists are most interested in exploring _____ (commonalities/differences) in our behaviors. Evolutionary psychologists are most interested in exploring _____ (commonalities/differences).

9. Evolutionary psychologists are most likely to focus on
   a. how individuals differ from one another.
   b. the social consequences of learned behaviors.
   c. the natural selection of traits that helped our ancestors survive and reproduce.
   d. twin and adoption studies.

Continue testing yourself with 📖 **LearningCurve** or 📖 **Achieve Read & Practice** to learn and remember most effectively.

Consciousness and the Two-Track Mind

Consciousness can be a funny thing. It offers us weird experiences, as when entering sleep or leaving a dream. And sometimes it leaves us wondering who is really in control. After zoning me [DM] out with nitrous oxide, my dentist tells me to turn my head to the left. My conscious mind resists: "No way," I silently say. "You can't boss me around!" Whereupon my robotic head, ignoring my conscious mind, turns obligingly under the dentist's control.

Then there are those times when consciousness seems to split. Sometimes, my [ND's] mind wanders while singing portions of the *Moana* soundtrack daily with my toddler daughter. When reading *Green Eggs and Ham* to one of my [DM's] preschoolers for the umpteenth time, my obliging mouth could say the words while my mind flitted in and out of the story. And if a friend interrupts you mid-text to ask what you're doing for lunch, it's not a problem. Your thumbs complete their keyboard dance as you suggest getting tacos.

What do such experiences tell us? Does the mind's wandering while singing, reading, or texting reveal a split in consciousness? And what exactly is *consciousness* (Module 7)? How do our states of consciousness play out in our sleep and dreams (Module 8)? And was that drug-induced dental episode akin to people's experiences with other mood- and perception-altering *psychoactive drugs* (Module 9)? ▶

Roz Chast The New Yorker Collection/The Cartoon Bank

MODULE 7 Consciousness: Some Basic Concepts

Every science has concepts so fundamental they are nearly impossible to define. Biologists agree on what is alive but not on precisely what *life* is. In physics, *matter* and *energy* elude simple definition. To psychologists, *consciousness* is similarly a fundamental yet slippery concept.

DEFINING CONSCIOUSNESS

LEARNING OBJECTIVE QUESTION (LOQ)

7-1   What is the place of consciousness in psychology's history?

At its beginning, *psychology* was "the description and explanation of states of consciousness" (Ladd, 1887). But during the first half of the twentieth century, the difficulty of scientifically studying consciousness led many psychologists—including those in the emerging school of *behaviorism*—to turn to direct observations of behavior. By the 1960s, psychology had nearly lost consciousness and was defining itself as "the science of behavior." Consciousness was likened to a car's speedometer: "It doesn't make the car go, it just reflects what's happening" (Seligman, 1991, p. 24).

"Psychology must discard all reference to consciousness." —Behaviorist John B. Watson (1913)

After 1960, psychology began regaining consciousness. Neuroscience advances linked brain activity to sleeping, dreaming, and other mental states. Researchers began studying consciousness altered by drugs, hypnosis, and meditation. (There is more on hypnosis in Module 18, and on meditation in Module 34.) Psychologists of all persuasions were affirming the importance of *cognition,* or mental processes.

Most psychologists today define **consciousness** as our subjective awareness of ourselves and our environment (Feinberg & Mallatt, 2016):

- This awareness allows us to assemble information from many sources as we reflect on our past, adapt to our present, and plan for our future. First-year college and university students may think back to their high school years, adjust to the ups and downs of academic life, and look ahead to their life beyond graduation.

- Conscious awareness focuses our attention when we learn a complex concept or behavior. When learning to drive, we focus on the car and the traffic. With practice, driving becomes semi-automatic, freeing us to focus our attention elsewhere.

- Over time, we flit between different *states of consciousness,* including normal waking awareness and various altered states (**FIGURE 7.1**).

INSADCO Photography/Alamy

FIGURE 7.1

ALTERED STATES OF CONSCIOUSNESS In addition to normal, waking awareness, consciousness comes to us in altered states, including daydreaming, drug-induced hallucinating, and meditating.

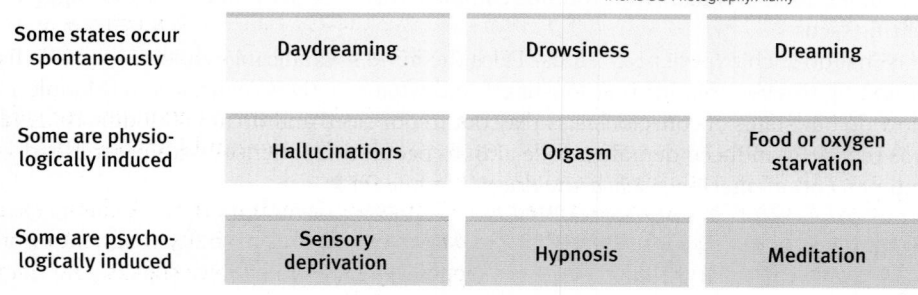

Some states occur spontaneously	Daydreaming	Drowsiness	Dreaming
Some are physiologically induced	Hallucinations	Orgasm	Food or oxygen starvation
Some are psychologically induced	Sensory deprivation	Hypnosis	Meditation

COGNITIVE NEUROSCIENCE

Today's science explores the biology of consciousness. Scientists now assume, in the words of neuroscientist Marvin Minsky (1986, p. 287), that "the mind is what the brain does."

Evolutionary psychologists presume that consciousness offers a reproductive advantage (Barash, 2006; Murdik et al., 2011). By considering consequences and reading others' intentions, consciousness helps us to cope with novel situations, act in ways that further our long-term goals, and foster relationships through sacrificing our self-interest (Mrkva, 2017). Even so, that leaves us with what researchers call the "hard problem": How do brain cells jabbering to one another create our awareness of the taste of toast, the idea of infinity, the feeling of fright? The question of how consciousness arises from the material brain is one of life's deepest mysteries. Such questions are at the heart of **cognitive neuroscience**—the interdisciplinary study of the brain activity linked with our mental processes.

A stunning demonstration of consciousness appeared in brain scans of a noncommunicative patient—a 23-year-old woman who had been in a car accident and showed no outward signs of conscious awareness (Owen, 2014; Owen et al., 2006). When researchers asked her to *imagine* playing tennis, fMRI scans revealed activity in a brain area that normally controls arm and leg movements (**FIGURE 7.2**). Even in a motionless body, the researchers concluded, the brain—and the mind—may still be active. A follow-up analysis of 42 behaviorally unresponsive patients revealed 13 more who also showed meaningful, though diminished, brain responses to questions (Stender et al., 2014).

Conscious experience arises from synchronized activity across the brain (Chennu et al., 2014). If a stimulus activates enough brain-wide coordinated neural activity—as strong signals in one brain area trigger activity elsewhere—it crosses a threshold for consciousness. A weaker stimulus—perhaps a word flashed too briefly to be consciously perceived—may trigger localized visual cortex activity that quickly fades. A stronger stimulus will engage other brain areas, such as those involved with language, attention, and memory. Such reverberating activity (detected by brain scans) is a telltale sign of conscious awareness (Boly et al., 2011; Silverstein et al., 2015). For example, awareness of your body involves communication between several brain areas (Blanke, 2012; Olivé et al., 2015). How the synchronized activity produces awareness—how matter makes mind—remains a mystery.

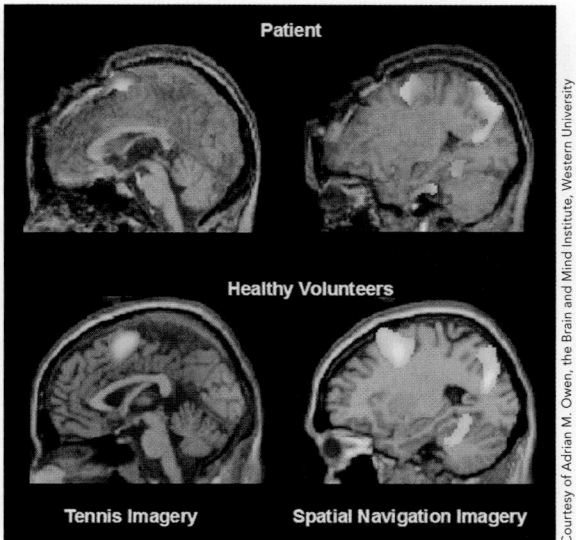

Courtesy of Adrian M. Owen, the Brain and Mind Institute, Western University

FIGURE 7.2

EVIDENCE OF AWARENESS?
When asked to imagine playing tennis or navigating her home, a noncommunicative patient's brain (top) exhibited activity similar to a healthy person's brain (bottom). Researchers wonder if such fMRI scans might enable a "conversation" with some unresponsive patients, by instructing them, for example, to answer yes to a question by imagining playing tennis (top and bottom left), and no by imagining walking around their home (top and bottom right).

🔒 **RETRIEVE IT • • •**   *ANSWERS IN APPENDIX E*

RI-1 Those working in the interdisciplinary field called _____ _____ study the brain activity associated with the mental processes of perception, thinking, memory, and language.

SELECTIVE ATTENTION

LOQ 7-2   How does selective attention direct our perceptions?

Through **selective attention,** our awareness focuses, like a flashlight beam, on a minute aspect of all that we experience. We may think we can fully attend to a conversation or a class lecture while checking and returning text messages. Actually, our consciousness focuses on but one thing at a time.

By one estimate, our five senses take in 11,000,000 bits of information per second, of which we consciously process about 40 (Wilson, 2002). Yet our mind's unconscious track intuitively makes great use of the other 10,999,960 bits.

What captures our limited attention? Things we deem important. A classic example of selective attention is the *cocktail party effect*—your ability to attend to only one voice within a sea of many. But what happens when another voice speaks your name?

consciousness our subjective awareness of ourselves and our environment.

cognitive neuroscience the interdisciplinary study of the brain activity linked with cognition (including perception, thinking, memory, and language).

selective attention the focusing of conscious awareness on a particular stimulus.

"Has a generation of texters, surfers, and twitterers evolved the enviable ability to process multiple streams of novel information in parallel? Most cognitive psychologists doubt it."
—Steven Pinker, "Not at All," 2010

"I wasn't texting. I was building this ship in a bottle."

☒ LaunchPad Watch the thought-provoking **Video: Automatic Skills—Disrupting a Pilot's Performance.**

inattentional blindness failing to see visible objects when our attention is directed elsewhere.

change blindness failing to notice changes in the environment; a form of *inattentional blindness.*

Your cognitive radar, operating on your mind's other track, instantly brings that unattended voice into consciousness. This effect might have prevented an embarrassing and dangerous situation in 2009, when two Northwest Airlines pilots "lost track of time." Focused on their laptops and in conversation, they ignored alarmed air traffic controllers' attempts to reach them and overflew their Minneapolis destination by 150 miles. If only the controllers had known and spoken the pilots' names.

Selective Attention and Accidents

Have you, like 60 percent of American drivers, read or sent a text message or viewed a phone map while driving in the last month (Gliklich et al., 2016)? Such digital distraction can have tragic consequences (Stavrinos et al., 2017). Why do digital devices make us dangerous drivers? Our selective attention shifts back and forth between the road and its digital competition. Indeed, our attention shifts more often than we realize. One study left people in a room for 28 minutes with full internet and television access. On average, participants guessed their attention switched 15 times during the 28-minute session. But they were not even close. Eye-tracking revealed eight times that many attentional switches—120 on average (Brasel & Gips, 2011).

Rapid toggling between activities is today's great enemy of sustained, focused attention. When we switch attentional gears, especially when we shift to complex tasks like noticing and avoiding cars around us, we pay a toll—a slight and sometimes fatal delay in coping (Rubenstein et al., 2001). When a driver attends to a conversation, activity in brain areas vital to driving decreases an average of 37 percent (Just et al., 2008). To stay safe, drivers should limit external distractions and keep their eyes on the road (Mackenzie & Harris, 2017).

Texting or phone chatting accompanies about 28 percent of traffic accidents (NSC, 2010; Pew, 2011). One video cam study of teen drivers found that driver distraction from passengers or phones occurred right before 58 percent of their crashes (AAA, 2015). Talking with passengers makes the risk of an accident 1.6 times higher than normal. Talking on a cell phone (even with a hands-free set) makes the risk 4 times higher than normal—equal to the risk of drunk driving (McEvoy et al., 2005, 2007). And while talking is distracting, texting wins the danger game. One 18-month video cam study tracked the driving habits of long-haul truckers. When they were texting, their risk of a collision increased 23 times (Olson et al., 2009)! Many European countries and most American states and Canadian provinces now ban texting while driving (CBC News, 2014; Rosenthal, 2009). So the next time you're behind the wheel, put the brakes on your texts. Your passengers and fellow drivers will thank you.

Inattentional Blindness

At the level of conscious awareness, we are "blind" to all but a tiny sliver of visual stimuli. Ulric Neisser (1979) and Robert Becklen and Daniel Cervone (1983) demonstrated this **inattentional blindness** dramatically by showing people a 1-minute video of basketball players, three in black shirts and three in white shirts, tossing a ball. Researchers told the viewers to press a key every time they saw a black-shirted player pass the ball. Most viewers were so intent on their task that they failed to notice a young woman carrying an umbrella saunter across the screen midway through the video (**FIGURE 7.3**). Watching a later replay, viewers were astonished to see her (Mack & Rock, 2000). This inattentional blindness is a by-product of what we are really good at: focusing attention on some part of our environment.

In a repeat of the experiment, smart-aleck researchers sent a gorilla-suited assistant through a swirl of players (Simons & Chabris, 1999). During its 5- to 9-second cameo appearance, the gorilla paused and thumped its chest. But the gorilla did not steal the show: Half the conscientious pass-counting viewers failed to see it. Psychologists like to have fun, and have continued to do so with the help of invisible gorillas. When 24 radiologists were looking for cancer nodules in lung scans, 20 of them missed the gorilla superimposed in the upper right (**FIGURE 7.4**)—though, to their credit, their focus enabled them to discover the much tinier cancer tissue (Drew et al., 2013). The point of these purposeful pranks: Attention is powerfully selective. Your conscious mind is in one place at a time.

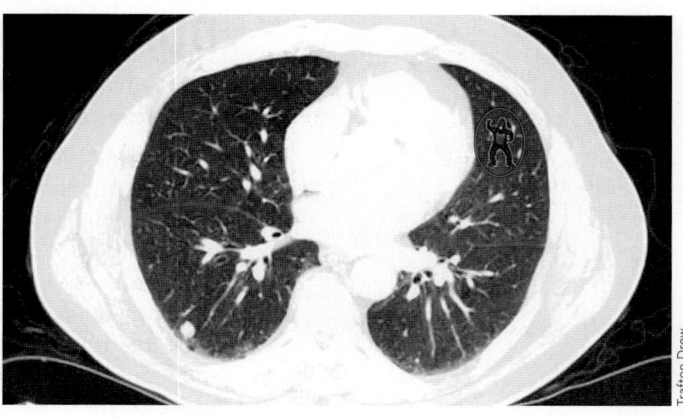

FIGURE 7.3

INATTENTIONAL BLINDNESS Viewers who were attending to basketball tosses among the black-shirted players usually failed to notice the umbrella-toting woman sauntering across the screen (Neisser, 1979).

FIGURE 7.4

THE INVISIBLE GORILLA STRIKES AGAIN When repeatedly exposed to the gorilla in the upper right (which we've circled in red) while searching for much tinier cancer nodules, radiologists usually failed to see it (Drew et al., 2013).

LaunchPad For more on the limits of our attention, engage online with **Concept Practice: Selective Attention and Multitasking**.

ENGAGE **ASK YOURSELF**

Can you recall a recent time when, as your attention focused on one thing, you were oblivious to something else (perhaps to pain, to someone's approach, or to background music)?

Given that most people miss someone in a gorilla suit while their attention is riveted elsewhere, imagine the fun that others can have by manipulating our selective attention. Misdirect people's attention and they will miss the hand slipping into the pocket. "Every time you perform a magic trick, you're engaging in experimental psychology," says magician Teller (2009), a master of mind-messing methods. Clever thieves know this, too. One Swedish psychologist was surprised in Stockholm by a woman suddenly exposing herself; only later did he realize that he had been pickpocketed, outwitted by thieves who understood the limits of our selective attention (Gallace, 2012).

In other experiments, people exhibited a form of inattentional blindness called **change blindness.** Participants in laboratory experiments failed to notice that, after a brief visual interruption, a big Coke bottle had disappeared, a railing had risen, clothing had changed color—and construction workers had changed places (**FIGURE 7.5**) (Chabris & Simons, 2010; Resnick et al., 1997). Out of sight, out of mind.

FIGURE 7.5

CHANGE BLINDNESS While a man (in red) provides directions to another (a), two experimenters rudely pass between them carrying a door (b). During this interruption, the original worker switches places with another person wearing different-colored clothing (c). Most people, focused on their direction giving, do not notice the switch (Simons & Levin, 1998).

🔒 RETRIEVE IT • • •   *ANSWERS IN APPENDIX E*

RI-2 Explain two attentional principles that magicians may use to fool us.

(a)

(b)

(c)

DUAL PROCESSING: THE TWO-TRACK MIND

LOQ 7-3   What is the *dual processing* being revealed by today's cognitive neuroscience?

Discovering which brain regions become active with a particular conscious experience strikes many people as interesting, but not mind blowing. If everything psychological is simultaneously biological, then our ideas, emotions, and spirituality must all, somehow, be embodied. What *is* mind blowing to many of us is evidence that we have, so to speak, two minds, each supported by its own neural equipment.

At any moment, we are aware of little more than what's on the screen of our consciousness. But as we've seen, beneath the surface, unconscious information processing occurs simultaneously on many parallel tracks. When we look at a bird flying, we are consciously aware of the result of our cognitive processing ("It's a hummingbird!") but not of our subprocessing of the bird's color, form, movement, and distance. One of the grand ideas of recent cognitive neuroscience is that much of our brain work occurs off stage, out of sight. Perception, memory, thinking, language, and attitudes all operate on two independent levels—a conscious, deliberate "high road," and an unconscious, automatic "low road" (Wang, Y., et al., 2017). The high road is reflective, the low road intuitive (Evans & Stanovich, 2013; Kahneman, 2011). Today's researchers call this **dual processing.** We know more than we know we know.

If you are a driver, consider how you move into the right lane. Drivers know this unconsciously but cannot accurately explain it (Eagleman, 2011). Most say they would bank to the right, then straighten out—a procedure that would actually steer them off the road. In reality, an experienced driver, after moving right, automatically reverses the steering wheel just as far to the left of center, and only then returns to the center position. The lesson: The human brain is a device for converting conscious into unconscious knowledge.

Or consider this story, which illustrates how science can be stranger than science fiction. During my sojourns at Scotland's University of St Andrews, I [DM] came to know cognitive neuroscientists David Milner and Melvyn Goodale (2008). They studied a local woman, D. F., who suffered brain damage when overcome by carbon monoxide, leaving her unable to recognize and discriminate objects visually. Consciously, D. F. could see nothing. Yet she exhibited **blindsight**—she acted *as though* she could see. Asked to slip a postcard into a vertical or horizontal mail slot, she could do so without error. Asked the width of a block in front of her, she was at a loss, but she could grasp it with just the right finger-thumb distance.

How could this be? Don't we have one visual system? Goodale and Milner knew from animal research that the eye sends information simultaneously to different brain areas, which support different tasks (Weiskrantz, 2009, 2010). Sure enough, a scan of D. F.'s brain activity revealed normal activity in the area concerned with reaching for, grasping, and navigating objects, but damage in the area concerned with consciously recognizing objects. (See another example in **FIGURE 7.6**.)

How strangely intricate is this thing we call vision, conclude Goodale and Milner in their aptly titled book, *Sight Unseen* (2004). We may think of our vision as a single system that controls our visually guided actions. Actually, it is a dual-processing system (Foley et al., 2015). A *visual perception track* enables us "to think about the world"—to recognize things and to plan future actions. A *visual action track* guides our moment-to-moment movements.

The dual-track mind also appeared in a patient who lost all of his left visual cortex, leaving him blind to objects and faces presented on the right side of his field of vision. He nevertheless could sense the emotion expressed in faces that he did not consciously perceive (de Gelder, 2010). The same is true of normally sighted people whose visual cortex has been disabled with magnetic stimulation. Such findings suggest that brain areas below the cortex process emotion-related information.

People often have trouble accepting that much of our everyday thinking, feeling, and acting operates outside our conscious awareness (Bargh & Chartrand, 1999). Some "80 to 90 percent of what we do is unconscious," says Nobel laureate and memory expert Eric Kandel (2008). We are understandably inclined to believe that our intentions and deliberate choices rule our lives. But they don't. Consciousness, though enabling us to exert

FIGURE 7.6

WHEN THE BLIND CAN "SEE" In this compelling demonstration of blindsight and the two-track mind, researcher Lawrence Weiskrantz trailed a blindsight patient down a cluttered hallway. Although told the hallway was empty, the patient meandered around all the obstacles without any awareness of them.

voluntary control and to communicate our mental states to others, is but the tip of the information-processing iceberg. Just ask the volunteers who chose a card after watching a magician shuffle through the deck (Olson et al., 2015). In nearly every case, the magician swayed participants' decisions by subtly allowing one card to show for longer—but 91 percent of participants believed they had made the choice on their own. Being intensely focused on an activity (such as reading this module, we hope) increases your total brain activity no more than 5 percent above its baseline rate. Even when you rest, activity whirls inside your head (Raichle, 2010).

Unconscious parallel processing is faster than conscious sequential processing, but both are essential. **Parallel processing** enables your mind to take care of routine business. **Sequential processing** is best for solving new problems, which requires your focused attention on one thing at a time. Try this: If you are right-handed, move your right foot in a smooth counterclockwise circle and write the number 3 repeatedly with your right hand—at the same time. Try something equally difficult: Tap a steady beat three times with your left hand while tapping four times with your right hand. Both tasks require conscious attention, which can be in only one place at a time. If time is nature's way of keeping everything from happening at once, then consciousness is nature's way of keeping us from thinking and doing everything at once.

dual processing the principle that information is often simultaneously processed on separate conscious and unconscious tracks.

blindsight a condition in which a person can respond to a visual stimulus without consciously experiencing it.

parallel processing processing many aspects of a stimulus or problem at once.

sequential processing processing one aspect of a stimulus or problem at a time; generally used to process new information or to solve difficult problems.

🔒 **RETRIEVE IT • • •**   *ANSWERS IN APPENDIX E*

RI-3 What are the mind's two tracks, and what is *dual processing*?

🖰 **LaunchPad** To think further about conscious awareness and decision making, engage online with **Topic Tutorial: PsychSim6, Who's in Charge?**

🔒 **REVIEW** CONSCIOUSNESS: SOME BASIC CONCEPTS

⟫ Learning Objectives

TEST YOURSELF Answer these repeated Learning Objective Questions on your own (before checking the answers in Appendix D) to improve your retention of the concepts (McDaniel et al., 2009, 2015).

7-1 What is the place of consciousness in psychology's history?

7-2 How does selective attention direct our perceptions?

7-3 What is the *dual processing* being revealed by today's cognitive neuroscience?

⟫ Terms and Concepts to Remember

TEST YOURSELF Write down the definition yourself, then check your answer on the referenced page.

consciousness, **p. 81**

cognitive neuroscience, **p. 81**

selective attention, **p. 81**

inattentional blindness, **p. 82**

change blindness, **p. 82**

dual processing, **p. 85**

blindsight, **p. 85**

parallel processing, **p. 85**

sequential processing, **p. 85**

⟫ Experience the Testing Effect

TEST YOURSELF Answer the following questions on your own first, then check your answers in Appendix E.

1. Failure to see visible objects because our attention is occupied elsewhere is called _____ _____.

2. We register and react to stimuli outside of our awareness by means of _____ processing. When we devote

deliberate attention to stimuli, we use _____ processing.

3. Inattentional blindness is a product of our _____ attention.

Continue testing yourself with 🖰 **LearningCurve** or 🖰 **Achieve Read & Practice** to learn and remember most effectively.

sleep a periodic, natural loss of consciousness—as distinct from unconsciousness resulting from a coma, general anesthesia, or hibernation. (Adapted from Dement, 1999.)

circadian [ser-KAY-dee-an] **rhythm** our biological clock; regular bodily rhythms (for example, of temperature and wakefulness) that occur on a 24-hour cycle.

REM (R) sleep rapid eye movement sleep; a recurring sleep stage during which vivid dreams commonly occur. Also known as *paradoxical sleep,* because the muscles are relaxed (except for minor twitches) but other body systems are active.

alpha waves the relatively slow brain waves of a relaxed, awake state.

"I love to sleep. Do you? Isn't it great? It really is the best of both worlds. You get to be alive and unconscious."
—Comedian Rita Rudner, 1993

Some students sleep like the fellow who stayed up all night to see where the Sun went. (Then it dawned on him.)

8 Sleep and Dreams

LOQ 8-1   What is *sleep*?

Sleep—the irresistible tempter to whom we inevitably succumb. Sleep—the equalizer of presidents and peasants. Sleep—sweet, renewing, mysterious sleep. While sleeping, we may feel "dead to the world," but we are not. Although the roar of my [ND's] neighborhood garbage truck leaves me undisturbed, my baby's cry will shatter my sleep. Even when you are deeply asleep, your perceptual window is open a crack. You move around on your bed, but you manage not to fall out. The sound of your name can also cause your unconscious body to perk up. EEG recordings confirm that the brain's auditory cortex responds to sound stimuli even during sleep (Kutas, 1990). And when you sleep, as when awake, you process most information outside your conscious awareness.

By recording the brain waves and muscle movements of sleeping participants, and by observing and occasionally waking them, researchers are solving some of sleep's deepest mysteries. Perhaps you can anticipate some of their discoveries. Are the following statements true or false?

1. When people dream of performing some activity, their limbs often move in concert with the dream.

2. Older adults sleep more than young adults.

3. Sleepwalkers are acting out their dreams.

4. Sleep experts recommend treating insomnia with an occasional sleeping pill.

5. Some people dream every night; others seldom dream.

All these statements (adapted from Palladino & Carducci, 1983) are *false.* To see why, read on.

BIOLOGICAL RHYTHMS AND SLEEP

Like the ocean, life has its rhythmic tides. Over varying time periods, our bodies fluctuate, and with them, our minds. Let's look more closely at two of those biological rhythms—our 24-hour biological clock and our 90-minute sleep cycle.

Circadian Rhythm

LOQ 8-2   How do our biological rhythms influence our daily functioning?

The rhythm of the day parallels the rhythm of life—from our waking at a new day's birth to our nightly return to what Shakespeare called "death's counterfeit." Our bodies roughly synchronize with the 24-hour cycle of day and night thanks to an internal biological clock called the **circadian rhythm** (from the Latin *circa,* "about," and *diem,* "day"). As morning nears, body temperature rises; it then peaks during the day, dips for a time in early afternoon (when many people take siestas), and begins to drop again in the evening. Thinking is sharpest and memory most accurate as we approach our daily peak in circadian arousal. Have you ever pulled an all-nighter? Perhaps you recall feeling groggiest in the middle of the night but with a sense of new alertness with the arrival of your normal wake-up time.

Age and experience can alter our circadian rhythm. Most 20-year-olds are evening-energized "owls," with performance improving across the day (May & Hasher, 1998). Most older adults experience more fragile sleep and are morning-loving "larks." For our ancestors (and for today's hunter-gatherers), a grandparent who awakened easily and early helped protect the family from predators (Samson et al., 2017).

Eric Isselée/Shutterstock

By mid-evening, when the night has hardly begun for many young adults, retirement homes are typically quiet. After about age 20 (slightly earlier for women), we begin to shift from being owls to being larks (Roenneberg et al., 2004). Age is one influence, but in general night owls tend to be smart and creative (Giampietro & Cavallera, 2007). Morning types tend to do better in school, take more initiative, be more punctual, and be less vulnerable to depression (Preckel et al., 2013; Randler, 2008, 2009; Werner et al., 2015).

Peter Chadwick/Science Source

Sleep Stages

LOQ 8-3   What is the biological rhythm of our sleeping and dreaming stages?

Sooner or later, sleep overtakes us all, and consciousness fades as different parts of our brain's cortex stop communicating (Massimini et al., 2005). Yet the sleeping brain remains active and has its own biological rhythm.

About every 90 minutes, you cycle through distinct sleep stages. This fact came to light when 8-year-old Armond Aserinsky went to bed one night in 1952. His father, Eugene, a University of Chicago graduate student, needed to test an electroencephalograph he had repaired that day (Aserinsky, 1988; Seligman & Yellen, 1987). Placing electrodes near Armond's eyes to record the rolling eye movements then believed to occur during sleep, Aserinsky watched the machine go wild, tracing deep zigzags on the graph paper. Could the machine still be broken? As the night proceeded and the activity recurred, Aserinsky realized that the periods of fast, jerky eye movements were accompanied by energetic brain activity. Awakened during one such episode, Armond reported having a dream. Aserinsky had discovered what we now know as **REM sleep** (rapid *eye* movement sleep; also called *R sleep*).

Similar procedures used with thousands of volunteers showed the cycles were a normal part of sleep (Kleitman, 1960). To appreciate these studies, imagine yourself as a participant. As the hour grows late, you feel sleepy and yawn in response to reduced brain metabolism. (Yawning, which is also socially contagious, stretches your neck muscles and increases your heart rate, which increases your alertness [Moorcroft, 2003].) When you are ready for bed, a researcher comes in and tapes electrodes to your scalp (to detect your brain waves), your chin (to detect muscle tension), and just outside the corners of your eyes (to detect eye movements) (**FIGURE 8.1**). Other devices may record your heart rate, respiration rate, and genital arousal.

When you are in bed with your eyes closed, the researcher in the next room sees on the EEG the relatively slow **alpha waves** of your awake but relaxed state (**FIGURE 8.2**). As you adapt to all this equipment, you grow tired and, in an unremembered moment, slip into sleep (**FIGURE 8.3**). This transition is marked by the slowed breathing and the irregular brain waves of what the American Academy of Sleep Medicine classifies as *NREM-1* (or *N1*) sleep (Silber et al., 2007).

ENGAGE (ASK YOURSELF)

Would you consider yourself a night owl or a morning lark? When do you usually feel most energetic? What time of day works best for you to study?

Dolphins, porpoises, and whales sleep with one side of their brain at a time (Miller et al., 2008).

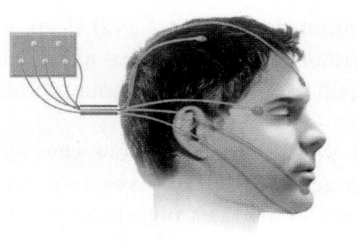
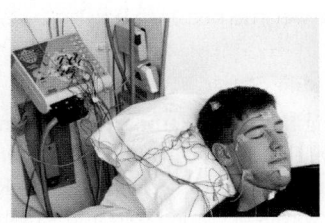

Hank Morgan/Science Source

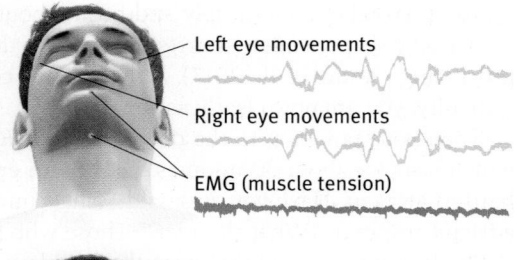
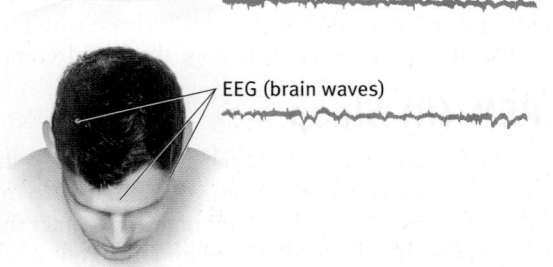

Left eye movements

Right eye movements

EMG (muscle tension)

EEG (brain waves)

FIGURE 8.1

MEASURING SLEEP ACTIVITY Sleep researchers measure brain-wave activity, eye movements, and muscle tension with electrodes that pick up weak electrical signals from the brain, eyes, and facial muscles (Dement, 1978).

hallucinations false sensory experiences, such as seeing something in the absence of an external visual stimulus.

delta waves the large, slow brain waves associated with deep sleep.

FIGURE 8.2

BRAIN WAVES AND SLEEP STAGES
The beta waves of an alert, waking state and the regular alpha waves of an awake, relaxed state differ from the slower, larger delta waves of deep N3 sleep. Although the rapid REM (R) sleep waves resemble the near-waking N1 sleep waves, the body is more internally aroused during REM sleep than during NREM sleep (the N1, N2, and N3 stages).

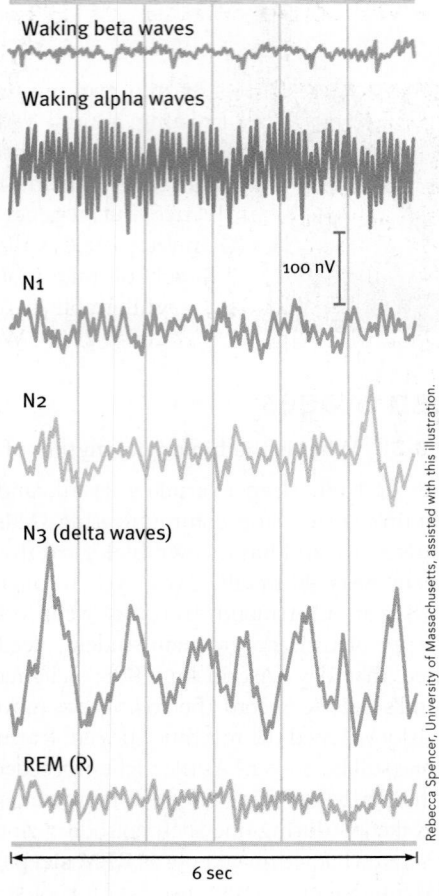

Waking beta waves

Waking alpha waves

100 nV

N1

N2

N3 (delta waves)

REM (R)

6 sec

Rebecca Spencer, University of Massachusetts, assisted with this illustration.

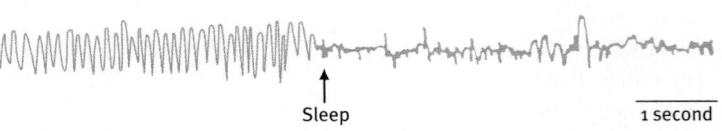

Sleep

1 second

FIGURE 8.3

THE MOMENT OF SLEEP We seem unaware of the moment we fall into sleep, but someone watching our brain waves could tell (Dement, 1999).

"My problem has always been an overabundance of alpha waves."

Sidney Harris/Science Cartoons Plus

ENGAGE To catch your own hypnagogic experiences, you might use your alarm's snooze function.

LaunchPad To better understand EEG readings and their relationship to consciousness, sleep, and dreams, experience the tutorial and simulation of **Topic Tutorial: PsychSim6, EEG and Sleep Stages.**

In one of his 15,000 research participants, William Dement (1999) observed the moment the brain's perceptual window to the outside world slammed shut. Dement asked this sleep-deprived young man with eyelids taped open to press a button every time a strobe light flashed in his eyes (about every 6 seconds). After a few minutes, the young man missed one. Asked why, he said, "Because there was no flash." But there was a flash. He missed it because (as his brain activity revealed) he had fallen asleep for 2 seconds, missing not only the flash 6 inches from his nose but also the awareness of the abrupt moment of entry into sleep.

During this brief N1 sleep you may experience fantastic images resembling **hallucinations**—sensory experiences that occur without a sensory stimulus. You may have a sensation of falling (when your body may suddenly jerk) or of floating weightlessly. These *hypnagogic* (also called *hypnic*) sensations may later be incorporated into your memories. People who claim they were abducted by aliens—often shortly after getting into bed—commonly recall being floated off (or pinned down on) their beds (Clancy, 2005; McNally, 2012).

You then relax more deeply and begin about 20 minutes of *NREM-2 (N2)* sleep, with its periodic *sleep spindles*—bursts of rapid, rhythmic brain-wave activity that aid memory processing (Studte et al., 2017). Although you could still be awakened without too much difficulty, you are now clearly asleep.

Then you transition to the deep sleep of *NREM-3 (N3)*. During this slow-wave sleep, which lasts for about 30 minutes, your brain emits large, slow **delta waves** and you are hard to awaken. Have you ever said, "That thunder was so loud last night!" only to have a friend respond, "What thunder?" Those who missed the storm may have been in delta sleep. (It is at the end of this stage that children may wet the bed.)

REM (R) Sleep

About an hour after you first fall asleep, a strange thing happens. Rather than continuing in deep slumber, you ascend from your initial sleep dive. Returning through N2 (where you'll ultimately spend about half your night), you enter the most intriguing sleep phase—REM (R) sleep **(FIGURE 8.4)**. For about 10 minutes, your brain waves become rapid and saw-toothed, more like those of the nearly awake N1 sleep. But unlike N1, during REM sleep your heart

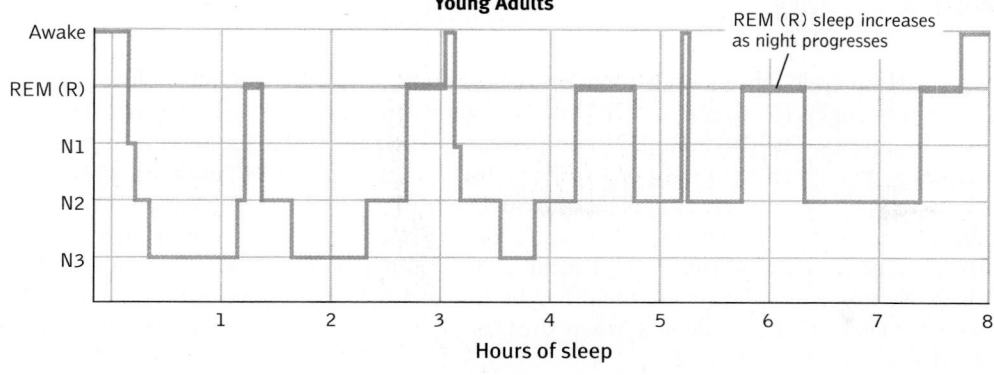

Young Adults

REM (R) sleep increases as night progresses

Hours of sleep

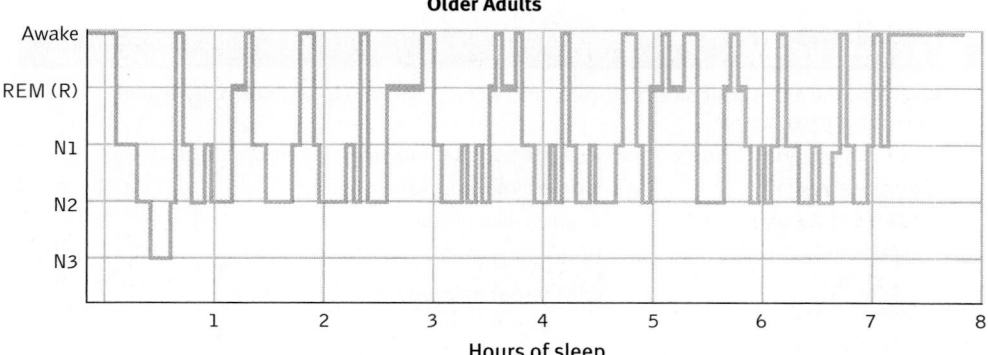

Older Adults

Hours of sleep

FIGURE 8.4

THE STAGES IN A TYPICAL NIGHT'S SLEEP People pass through a multistage sleep cycle several times each night, with the periods of deep sleep diminishing and REM (R) sleep periods increasing in duration. As people age, sleep becomes more fragile, with awakenings common among older adults (Kamel & Gammack, 2006; Neubauer, 1999).

rate rises, your breathing becomes rapid and irregular, and every half-minute or so your eyes dart around in momentary bursts of activity behind closed lids. These eye movements announce the beginning of a dream—often emotional, usually story-like, and richly hallucinatory. Dreams aren't real, but REM sleep tricks your brain into responding as if they were (Andrillon et al., 2015). Because anyone watching a sleeper's eyes can notice these REM bursts, it is amazing that science was ignorant of REM sleep until 1952.

Except during very scary dreams, your genitals become aroused during REM sleep. You may have an erection or increased vaginal lubrication and clitoral engorgement, regardless of whether the dream's content is sexual (Karacan et al., 1966). Men's common "morning erection" stems from the night's last REM period, often just before waking. In young men, sleep-related erections outlast REM periods, lasting 30 to 45 minutes on average (Karacan et al., 1983; Schiavi & Schreiner-Engel, 1988). A typical 25-year-old man therefore has an erection during nearly half his night's sleep, a 65-year-old man for one-quarter. Many men troubled by occasional erectile difficulties have sleep-related erections, suggesting the problem is not between their legs.

During REM sleep, your brain's motor cortex is active, but your brainstem blocks its messages. This leaves your muscles relaxed, so much so that, except for an occasional finger, toe, or facial twitch, you are essentially paralyzed. Moreover, you cannot easily be awakened. REM sleep is thus sometimes called *paradoxical sleep:* The body is internally aroused, with waking-like brain activity, yet asleep and externally calm. We spend about 600 hours a year experiencing some 1500 dreams, or more than 100,000 dreams over a typical lifetime—dreams swallowed by the night but not acted out, thanks to REM's protective paralysis.

People rarely snore during dreams. When REM starts, snoring stops.

Horses, which spend 92 percent of each day standing and can sleep standing, must lie down for REM sleep (Morrison, 2003).

🔒 **RETRIEVE IT • • •**   *ANSWERS IN APPENDIX E*

Uriel Sinai/Getty Images

RI-1 Why would communal sleeping provide added protection for those whose safety depends upon vigilance, such as these soldiers?

The sleep cycle repeats itself about every 90 minutes for younger adults (with shorter, more frequent cycles for older adults). As the night wears on, deep N3 sleep grows shorter and disappears. The REM and N2 sleep periods get longer (see Figure 8.4). By morning, we have spent 20 to 25 percent of an average night's sleep—some 100 minutes—in REM sleep. In sleep lab studies, 37 percent of participants have reported rarely or never having dreams that they "can remember the next morning" (Moore, 2004). Yet even they, more than 80 percent of the time, could recall a dream after being awakened during REM sleep. Neuroscientists have also identified brain regions that are active during dreaming, which enables them to identify when dreaming occurs, whether during or outside of REM sleep (Sicarli et al., 2017).

🔒 RETRIEVE IT • • •   *ANSWERS IN APPENDIX E*

RI-2 What are the four sleep stages, and in what order do we normally travel through those stages?

RI-3 Can you match the cognitive experience (a–c) with the sleep stage (I–III)?

Sleep Stage:	Cognitive experience:
I. N1	a. story-like dream
II. N3	b. fleeting images
III. REM (R)	c. minimal awareness

What Affects Our Sleep Patterns?

LOQ 8-4 How do biology and environment interact in our sleep patterns?

True or false? "Everyone needs 8 hours of sleep." *False.* Newborns often sleep two-thirds of their day, most adults no more than one-third (with some thriving on fewer than 6 hours nightly, others racking up 9 or more). But there is more to our sleep differences than age. Some are awake between nightly sleep periods—sometimes called "first sleep" and "second sleep" (Randall, 2012). And some find that a 15-minute midday nap is as effective as another hour of nighttime sleep (Horne, 2011).

Sleep patterns are genetically influenced, and researchers are tracking the sleep-regulating genes in humans and animals (Hayashi et al., 2015; Mackenzie et al., 2015). Sleep patterns are also culturally influenced. Canadian, American, British, German, and Japanese adults average 7 hours of sleep on workdays and 7 to 8 hours on other days (NSF, 2013). Earlier school start times, more extracurricular activities, and fewer parent-set bedtimes lead American adolescents to get less sleep than their Australian counterparts (Short et al., 2013). Thanks to modern lighting, shift work, and social media diversions, many who might have gone to bed at 9:00 P.M. in days past are now up until 11:00 P.M. or later. With sleep, as with waking behavior, biology and environment interact.

Being bathed in (or deprived of) light disrupts our 24-hour biological clock (Czeisler et al., 1999; Dement, 1999). Whether for work or play, bright light affects our sleepiness by activating light-sensitive retinal proteins. This signals the brain's **suprachiasmatic nucleus (SCN)** to decrease production of *melatonin,* a sleep-inducing hormone (Chang et al., 2015; Gandhi et al., 2015) (**FIGURE 8.5**). (A 2017 Nobel Prize was awarded for research on the molecular biology that runs our biological clock.)

Night-shift workers may experience a chronic state of *desynchronization.* As a result, they become more likely to develop fatigue, stomach problems, heart disease, and, for women, breast cancer (Knutsson & Bøggild, 2010; Lin et al., 2015; Puttonen et al., 2009). Curiously—given that our ancestors' body clocks were attuned to the rising and setting Sun of the 24-hour day—many of today's young adults adopt something closer to a 25-hour day, by staying up too late to get 8 hours of sleep. Approximately 90 percent of Americans report using a light-emitting electronic device one hour before going to sleep (Chang et al., 2015). Such artificial light delays sleep.

Sleep often eludes those who stay up late and sleep in on weekends, and then go to bed earlier on Sunday to prepare for the week ahead (Oren & Terman, 1998). Like New

suprachiasmatic nucleus (SCN) a pair of cell clusters in the hypothalamus that controls circadian rhythm. In response to light, the SCN causes the pineal gland to adjust melatonin production, thus modifying our feelings of sleepiness.

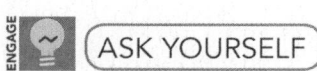

ASK YOURSELF

How does your need for sleep compare with that of others you know? Do you see age-related differences among your friends and family?

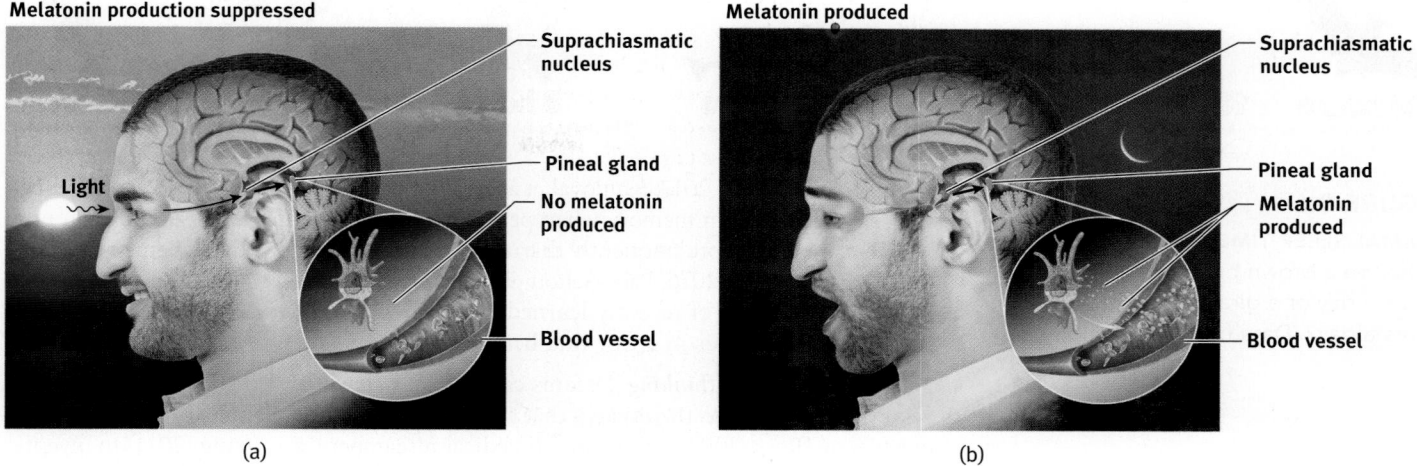

Melatonin production suppressed

Suprachiasmatic nucleus

Light

Pineal gland

No melatonin produced

Blood vessel

(a)

Melatonin produced

Suprachiasmatic nucleus

Pineal gland

Melatonin produced

Blood vessel

(b)

Yorkers readjusting after a trip to California, they experience "social jet lag." For North Americans who fly to Europe and need to be up when their circadian rhythm cries *"SLEEP,"* bright light (spending the next day outdoors) helps reset the biological clock (Czeisler et al., 1986, 1989; Eastman et al., 1995).

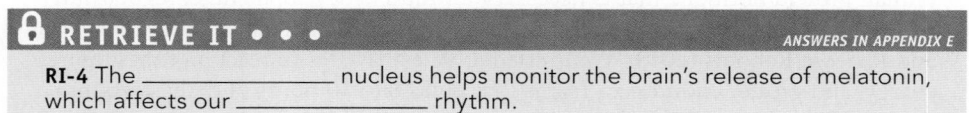

🔒 **RETRIEVE IT** • • •   *ANSWERS IN APPENDIX E*

RI-4 The _____ nucleus helps monitor the brain's release of melatonin, which affects our _____ rhythm.

WHY DO WE SLEEP?

LOQ 8-5 What are sleep's functions?

So, our sleep patterns differ from person to person and from culture to culture. But why do we have this need for sleep? Psychologists offer five possible reasons:

1. ***Sleep protects.*** When darkness shut down the day's hunting, gathering, and travel, our distant ancestors were better off asleep in a cave, out of harm's way. Those who didn't wander around dark cliffs were more likely to leave descendants. This fits a broader principle: A species' sleep pattern tends to suit its ecological niche (Siegel, 2009). Animals with the greatest need to graze and the least ability to hide tend to sleep less. Animals also sleep less, with no ill effects, during times of mating and migration (Siegel, 2012). (For a sampling of animal sleep times, see **FIGURE 8.6**.)

2. ***Sleep helps us recuperate.*** Sleep helps restore the immune system and repair brain tissue. Sleep gives resting neurons time to repair themselves, while pruning or weakening unused connections (Ascády & Harris, 2017; Ding et al., 2016; Li et al., 2017). Bats and other animals with high waking metabolism burn a lot of calories, producing *free radicals,* molecules that are toxic to neurons. Sleep sweeps away this toxic waste (Xie et al., 2013). Think of it this way: When consciousness leaves your house, workers come in to clean, saying "Good night. Sleep tidy."

3. ***Sleep helps restore and rebuild our fading memories of the day's experiences.*** To sleep is to strengthen. Sleep *consolidates* our memories by replaying recent learning and strengthening neural connections (Pace-Schott et al., 2015; Yang et al., 2014). It reactivates recent experiences stored in the hippocampus and shifts them for permanent storage elsewhere in the cortex (Racsmány et al., 2010; Urbain et al., 2016). Adults, children, and infants trained to perform tasks therefore recall them better after a night's sleep, or even after a short nap, than after several hours awake (Friedrich et al.,

FIGURE 8.5

THE BIOLOGICAL CLOCK (a) Light striking the retina signals the suprachiasmatic nucleus (SCN) to suppress the pineal gland's production of the sleep hormone melatonin. (b) At night, the SCN quiets down, allowing the pineal gland to release melatonin into the bloodstream.

A circadian disadvantage: One study of more than 24,000 Major League Baseball games found that teams who had crossed three time zones before playing a series had a nearly 60 percent chance of losing their first game (Winter et al., 2009). A follow-up study replicated this effect in the National Basketball Association and National Hockey League (Roy & Forest, 2017).

"Sleep faster, we need the pillows."
—Yiddish proverb

"Corduroy pillows make headlines."
—Anonymous

20 hours
Kruglov Orda/Shutterstock

16 hours
Andrew D. Myers

12 hours
Utekhina Anna/Shutterstock

10 hours
Steffen Foerster/Shutterstock

8 hours
Rubberball Productions/Getty Images

4 hours
Eric Isselée/Shutterstock

2 hours
pandapa/Shutterstock

FIGURE 8.6

ANIMAL SLEEP TIME Would you rather be a brown bat and sleep 20 hours a day or a giraffe and sleep 2 hours a day? (Data from NIH, 2010.)

2015; Horváth et al., 2017; Sandoval et al., 2017; Seehagen et al., 2015). Even bad experiences linger more in memory when people sleep on them (Liu et al., 2016).

Older adults' more frequently disrupted sleep also disrupts their memory consolidation (Boyce et al., 2016; Pace-Schott & Spencer, 2011). After sleeping well, older people remember more of recently learned material (Drummond, 2010). Sleep, it seems, strengthens memories in a way that being awake does not.

4. ***Sleep feeds creative thinking.*** Dreams can inspire noteworthy artistic and scientific achievements, such as the dreams that clued chemist August Kekulé to the structure of benzene (Ross, 2006) and inspired medical researcher Carl Alving (2011) to invent the vaccine patch. More commonplace is the boost that a complete night's sleep gives to our thinking and learning. After working on a task, then sleeping on it, people solve difficult problems more insightfully than do those who stay awake (Barrett, 2011; Sio et al., 2013). They also are better at spotting connections among novel pieces of information (Ellenbogen et al., 2007; Whitehurst et al., 2016). To think smart and see connections, it often pays to ponder a problem just before bed and then sleep on it.

5. ***Sleep supports growth.*** During slow-wave sleep, the pituitary gland releases a human growth hormone that is necessary for muscle development. A regular full night's sleep can also "*dramatically* improve your athletic ability," report James Maas and Rebecca Robbins (2010). Well-rested athletes have faster reaction times, more energy, and greater endurance. Teams that build 8 to 10 hours of daily sleep into their training show improved performance.

Given all the benefits of sleep, it's no wonder that sleep loss hits us so hard.

🔒 **RETRIEVE IT • • •**   *ANSWERS IN APPENDIX E*

RI-5 What are five proposed reasons for our need for sleep?

SLEEP DEPRIVATION AND SLEEP DISORDERS

LOQ 8-6   How does sleep loss affect us, and what are the major sleep disorders?

When our body yearns for sleep but does not get it, we begin to feel terrible. Trying to stay awake, we will eventually lose. In the tiredness battle, sleep always wins.

Effects of Sleep Loss

Modern sleep patterns leave us not only sleepy but drained of energy and our sense of well-being. Some researchers see today's tiredness as a "Great Sleep Recession" (Keyes et al., 2015). After several 5-hour nights, we accumulate a sleep debt that cannot be satisfied by one long sleep. "The brain keeps an accurate count of sleep debt for at least two weeks," reported sleep researcher William Dement (1999, p. 64).

Obviously, then, we need sleep. Sleep commands roughly one-third of our lives—some 25 years, on average. Allowed to sleep unhindered, most adults will sleep at least 9 hours a night (Coren, 1996). With that much sleep, we awaken refreshed, sustain better moods, and perform more efficiently and accurately. The U.S. Navy and the National Institutes of Health have demonstrated the benefits of unrestricted sleep in experiments in which volunteers spent 14 hours daily in bed for at least a week. For the first few days, the volunteers averaged 12 hours of sleep or more per day, apparently paying off a sleep debt that averaged 25 to 30 hours. That accomplished, they then settled back to 7.5 to 9 hours nightly and felt energized and happier (Dement, 1999). In one Gallup survey, 63 percent of

In 1989, Michael Doucette was named America's Safest Driving Teen. In 1990, while driving home from college, he fell asleep at the wheel and collided with an oncoming car, killing both himself and the other driver. Michael's driving instructor later acknowledged never having mentioned sleep deprivation and drowsy driving (Dement, 1999).

adults who reported getting the sleep they needed also reported being "very satisfied" with their personal life (as did only 36 percent of those needing more sleep) (Mason, 2005).

College and university students are especially sleep deprived; 69 percent in one national survey reported "feeling tired" or "having little energy" on at least several days during the last two weeks (AP, 2009). Less sleep also predicts more conflicts in friendships and romantic relationships (Gordon & Chen, 2014; Tavernier & Willoughby, 2014). Tiredness triggers testiness. In another survey, 28 percent of high school students acknowledged falling asleep in class at least once a week (NSF, 2006). The going needn't get boring before students start snoring.

Sleep loss is also a predictor of depression (Baglioni et al., 2016). Researchers who studied 15,500 12- to 18-year-olds found that those who slept 5 or fewer hours a night had a 71 percent higher risk of depression than their peers who slept 8 hours or more (Gangwisch et al., 2010). This link does not appear to reflect an effect of depression on sleep. When children and youth are followed through time, sleep loss predicts depression rather than vice versa (Gregory et al., 2009). Moreover, REM sleep's processing of emotional experiences helps protect against depression (Walker & van der Helm, 2009). After a good night's sleep, we often do feel better the next day. And that may help to explain why parentally enforced bedtimes predict less depression, and why pushing back school start time leads to improved adolescent sleep, alertness, and mood (Morgenthaler et al., 2016; Winsler et al., 2015). Thus, the American Academy of Pediatrics (2014) advocates delaying adolescents' school start times to "allow students the opportunity to achieve optimal levels of sleep (8.5–9.5 hours)."

Sleep-deprived students often function below their peak. And they know it: Four in five teens and three in five 18- to 29-year-olds wish they could get more sleep on weekdays (Mason, 2003, 2005). "Sleep deprivation has consequences—difficulty studying, diminished productivity, tendency to make mistakes, irritability, fatigue," noted Dement (1999, p. 231). Yet teens who stagger glumly out of bed in response to an unwelcome alarm, yawn through morning classes, and feel half-depressed much of the day may feel energized at 11:00 P.M., heedless of the next day's looming sleepiness (Carskadon, 2002).

Lack of sleep can also make you gain weight. Sleep deprivation

- increases *ghrelin,* a hunger-arousing hormone, and decreases its hunger-suppressing partner, *leptin* (Shilsky et al., 2012).

- decreases metabolic (energy use) rate (Buxton et al., 2012).

- increases *cortisol,* a stress hormone that stimulates the body to make fat.

- enhances limbic brain responses to the mere sight of food and decreases cortical responses that help us resist temptation (Benedict et al., 2012; Greer et al., 2013; St-Onge et al., 2012).

Thus, children and adults who sleep less are heavier than average, and in recent decades people have been sleeping less and weighing more (Shiromani et al., 2012; Suglia et al., 2014). Moreover, experimental sleep deprivation increases appetite and eating; our tired brain finds fatty foods more enticing (Fang et al., 2015; Hanlon et al., 2016). So, sleep loss helps explain the weight gain common among sleep-deprived students (Hull et al., 2007).

Sleep also affects our physical health. When infections do set in, we typically sleep more, boosting our immune cells. Sleep deprivation can suppress the immune cells that battle viral infections and cancer (Möller-Levet et al., 2013; Motivala & Irwin, 2007; Opp & Krueger, 2015). In one experiment, when researchers exposed volunteers to a cold virus, those who had averaged less than 5 hours sleep a night were 4.5 times more likely to develop a cold than those who slept more than 7 hours a night (Prather et al., 2015). Sleep's protective effect may help explain why people who sleep 7 to 8 hours a night tend to outlive those who are chronically sleep deprived, and why older adults who have no difficulty falling or staying asleep tend to live longer than their sleep-deprived agemates (Dew et al., 2003; Parthasarathy et al., 2015; Scullin & Bliwise, 2015).

Sleep deprivation slows reactions and increases errors on visual attention tasks similar to those involved in screening airport baggage, performing surgery, and reading X-rays (Caldwell, 2012; Lim & Dinges, 2010). Slow responses can also spell disaster for those operating equipment, piloting, or driving. After 2017 U.S. Navy warship collisions, one prescribed remedy was "more sleep" for the captains (Schmitt, 2017). Drowsy driving

"Maybe 'Bring Your Pillow To Work Day' wasn't such a good idea."

LaunchPad To see whether you are one of the many sleep-deprived students, engage online with the **Immersive Learning** self-assessment activity **Assess Your Strengths: Are You Sleep Deprived? How Can You Improve Your Sleep?**

"Remember to sleep because you have to sleep to remember." —James B. Maas and Rebecca S. Robbins, *Sleep for Success,* 2010

Sleep stealers "You wake up in the middle of the night and grab your smartphone to check the time—it's 3 A.M.—and see an alert. Before you know it, you fall down a rabbit hole of email and Twitter. Sleep? Forget it." —Nick Bilton, "Disruptions: For a Restful Night, Make Your Smartphone Sleep on the Couch," 2014

94

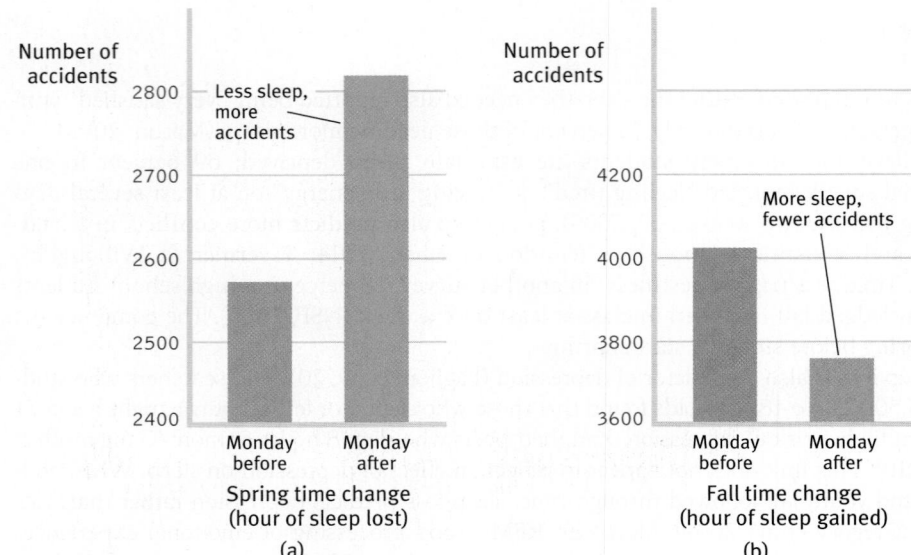

FIGURE 8.7

LESS SLEEP = MORE ACCIDENTS
(a) On the Monday after the spring time change, when people lose one hour of sleep, accidents increased, as compared with the Monday before. (b) In the fall, traffic accidents normally increase because of greater snow, ice, and darkness, but they diminished after the time change. (Data from Coren, 1996.)

"So shut your eyes
Kiss me goodbye
And sleep
Just sleep."
—My Chemical Romance, "Sleep"

ENGAGE 💡 📱 **LaunchPad** Consider how researchers have addressed these issues by engaging online with **Immersive Learning: How Would You Know If Sleep Deprivation Affects Academic Performance?**

has also contributed to an estimated 1 in 6 American traffic accidents (AAA, 2010) and to some 30 percent of Australian highway deaths (Maas, 1999). One 2-year study examined the driving accidents of more than 20,000 Virginia 16- to 18-year-olds in two major cities. In one city, the high schools started 75 to 80 minutes later than in the other. The late starters had about 25 percent fewer crashes (Vorona et al., 2011). When sleepy frontal lobes confront an unexpected situation, misfortune often results.

Stanley Coren capitalized on what is, for many North Americans, a semi-annual sleep-manipulation experiment—the "spring forward" to daylight saving time and "fall back" to standard time. Searching millions of Canadian and American records, Coren found that accidents increased immediately after the spring-forward time change, which shortens sleep (**FIGURE 8.7**).

FIGURE 8.8 summarizes the effects of sleep deprivation. But there is good news! Psychologists have discovered a treatment that strengthens memory, increases concentration, boosts mood, moderates hunger, reduces obesity, fortifies the immune system, and lessens the risk of fatal accidents. Even better news: The treatment feels good, it can be self-administered, and it's free! If you are a typical university-age student, often going to bed near 2:00 A.M. and dragged out of bed 6 hours later by the dreaded alarm, the

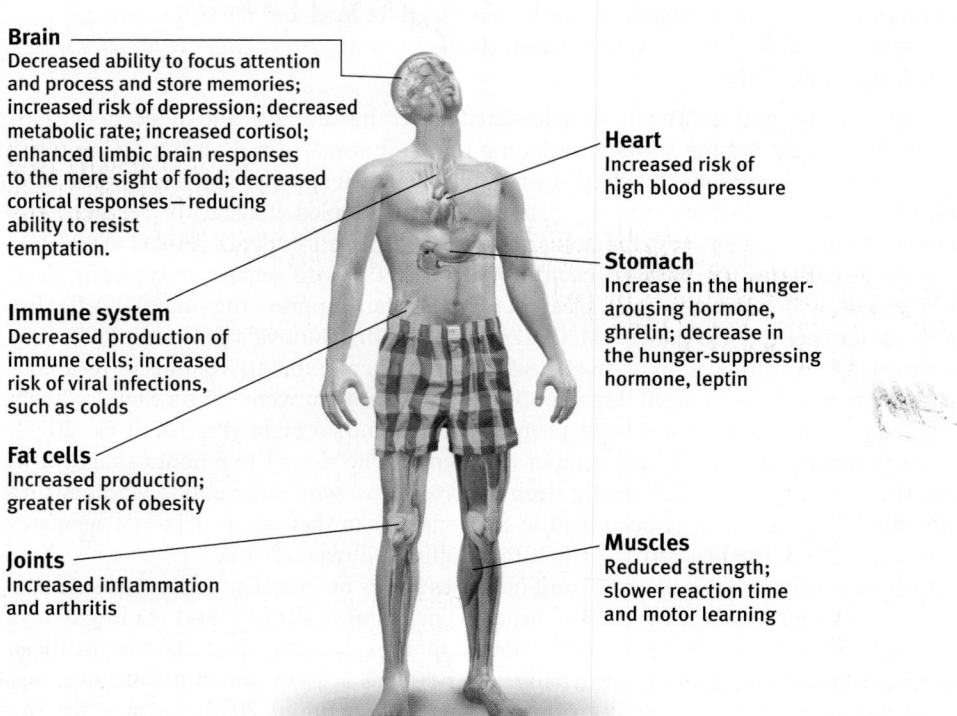

 **FIGURE 8.8**

HOW SLEEP DEPRIVATION AFFECTS US

TABLE 8.1

Get a Better Night's Sleep: Natural Sleep Aids

- Exercise regularly but not in the late evening. (Late afternoon is best.)
- Avoid caffeine after early afternoon, and avoid food and drink near bedtime. The exception would be a glass of milk, which provides raw materials for the manufacture of serotonin, a neurotransmitter that facilitates sleep.
- Relax before bedtime, using dimmer light.
- Sleep on a regular schedule (rise at the same time even after a restless night) and avoid long naps.
- Hide time displays so you aren't tempted to check repeatedly.
- Reassure yourself that temporary sleep loss causes no great harm.
- Focus your mind on nonarousing, engaging thoughts, such as song lyrics or vacation travel (Gellis et al., 2013).
- Manage stress. Realize that for any stressed organism, being vigilant is natural and adaptive. Less stress = better sleep.

insomnia recurring problems in falling or staying asleep.

narcolepsy a sleep disorder characterized by uncontrollable sleep attacks. The sufferer may lapse directly into REM sleep, often at inopportune times.

sleep apnea a sleep disorder characterized by temporary cessations of breathing during sleep and repeated momentary awakenings.

night terrors a sleep disorder characterized by high arousal and an appearance of being terrified; unlike nightmares, night terrors occur during N3 sleep, within two or three hours of falling asleep, and are seldom remembered.

ASK YOURSELF

What have you learned about sleep that you could apply to yourself?

treatment is simple. Each night, try to add 15 minutes to your sleep until you feel more like a rested and energized student than a zombie. For some additional tips on getting better quality sleep, see **TABLE 8.1**.

Major Sleep Disorders

Do you have trouble sleeping when anxious or excited? Most of us do. An occasional loss of sleep is nothing to worry about. But for those who have a major sleep disorder—**insomnia, narcolepsy, sleep apnea**, sleepwalking *(somnambulism)*, sleeptalking, or **night terrors**—trying to sleep can be a nightmare. (See **TABLE 8.2** for a summary of these disorders).

DID BRAHMS NEED HIS OWN LULLABIES? Cranky, overweight, and nap-prone, classical composer Johannes Brahms exhibited common symptoms of sleep apnea (Margolis, 2000).

TABLE 8.2

Sleep Disorders

Disorder	Rate	Description	Effects
Insomnia	1 in 10 adults; 1 in 4 older adults	Ongoing difficulty falling or staying asleep.	Chronic tiredness. Reliance on sleeping pills and alcohol, which reduce REM sleep and lead to tolerance—a state in which increasing doses are needed to produce an effect.
Narcolepsy	1 in 2000 adults	Sudden attacks of overwhelming sleepiness.	Risk of falling asleep at a dangerous moment. Narcolepsy attacks usually last less than 5 minutes, but they can happen at the worst and most emotional times. Everyday activities, such as driving, require extra caution.
Sleep apnea	1 in 20 adults	Stopping breathing repeatedly while sleeping.	Fatigue and depression (as a result of slow-wave sleep deprivation). Associated with obesity (especially among men).
Sleepwalking and sleeptalking	1–15 in 100 in the general population for sleepwalking (NSF, 2016); about half of young children for sleeptalking (Reimão & Lefévre, 1980)	Doing normal waking activities (sitting up, walking, speaking) while asleep. Sleeptalking can occur during any sleep stage. Sleepwalking happens in N3 sleep.	Few serious concerns. Sleepwalkers return to their beds on their own or with the help of a family member, rarely remembering their trip the next morning.
Night terrors	1 in 100 adults; 1 in 30 children	Appearing terrified, talking nonsense, sitting up, or walking around during N3 sleep; different from nightmares.	Doubling of a child's heart and breathing rates during the attack. Luckily, children remember little or nothing of the fearful event the next day. As people age, night terrors become more and more rare.

"Sleep is like love or happiness. If you pursue it too ardently it will elude you."
—Wilse Webb, *Sleep: The Gentle Tyrant*, 1992

off the mark.com   by Mark Parisi

LET ME GET THIS STRAIGHT, IT'S BEEN TWO CONSECUTIVE HOURS SINCE YOU'VE SLEPT?

WHEN CATS EXPERIENCE INSOMNIA

Mark Parisi/offthemark.com

"I do not believe that I am now dreaming, but I cannot prove that I am not." —Philosopher Bertrand Russell (1872–1970)

About 1 in 10 adults, and 1 in 4 older adults, complain of insomnia—persistent problems in either falling or staying asleep (Irwin et al., 2006). The result is tiredness and increased risk of depression (Baglioni et al., 2016). From middle age on, awakening occasionally during the night becomes the norm, not something to fret over or treat with medication (Vitiello, 2009). Ironically, insomnia becomes worse when we fret about it. In laboratory studies, people with insomnia do sleep less than others. But they typically overestimate how long it takes them to fall asleep and underestimate how long they actually have slept (Harvey & Tang, 2012). Even if we have been awake only an hour or two, we may *think* we have had very little sleep because it's the waking part we remember.

The most common quick fixes for true insomnia—sleeping pills and alcohol—typically aggravate the problem, reducing REM sleep and leaving the person with next-day blahs. Such aids can also lead to *tolerance*—a state in which increasing doses are needed to produce an effect.

🔒 **RETRIEVE IT • • •**   ANSWERS IN APPENDIX E

RI-6 A well-rested person would be more likely to have _____ (trouble concentrating/quick reaction times) and a sleep-deprived person would be more likely to _____ (gain weight/fight off a cold).

DREAMS

LOQ 8-7   What do we dream, and what functions have theorists proposed for dreams?

Now playing at an inner theater near you: the premiere of a sleeping person's vivid dream. This never-before-seen mental movie features captivating characters wrapped in a plot so original and unlikely, yet so intricate and so seemingly real, that the viewer later marvels at its creation.

Unlike daydreams, REM **dreams** are vivid, emotional, and often bizarre (Loftus & Ketchum, 1994). Waking from one, we may wonder how our brain can so creatively, colorfully, and completely construct this alternative world. In the shadowland between our dreaming and waking consciousness, we may even wonder for a moment which is real. Awakening from a nightmare, a 4-year-old may be sure there is a bear in the house.

Discovering the link between REM sleep and dreaming ushered in a new era in dream research. Instead of relying on someone's hazy recall hours later, researchers could catch dreams as they happened, awakening people during or within 3 minutes of a REM sleep period to hear a vivid account.

What We Dream

We spend 6 years of our life in dreams, many of which are anything but sweet. For both women and men, 8 in 10 dreams are marked by at least one negative event or emotion (Domhoff, 2007). Common themes include repeatedly failing in an attempt to do something; being attacked, pursued, or rejected; or experiencing misfortune (Hall et al., 1982). Dreams with sexual imagery occur less often than you might think. In one study, only 1 in 10 dreams among young men and 1 in 30 among young women had sexual content (Domhoff, 1996).

More commonly, a dream's story line incorporates traces of previous days' nonsexual experiences and preoccupations (Nikles et al., 2017):

- *Trauma and dreams* After suffering a trauma, people commonly report nightmares, which help extinguish daytime fears (Levin & Nielsen, 2007, 2009). One sample of Americans recording their dreams during September, 2001 reported an increase in threatening dreams following the 9/11 terrorist attacks (Propper et al., 2007). Compared with Palestinian children living in a peaceful town in Galilee, those living in the conflict-ridden Gaza Strip more often dreamed of aggression (Punamäki & Joustie, 1998).

- *Musicians' dreams* Compared with nonmusicians, musicians report twice as many dreams of music (Uga et al., 2006).

- *Blind people's dreams* Studies in four countries have found blind people mostly dreaming of using their nonvisual senses (Buquet, 1988; Taha, 1972; Vekassy, 1977). But even natively blind people sometimes "see" in their dreams (Bértolo, 2005). Likewise, people born paralyzed below the waist sometimes dream of walking, standing, running, or cycling (Saurat et al., 2011; Voss et al., 2011).

- *Media experiences and dreams* In a study of 1287 Turkish people, "participants who consumed violent media tended to have violent dreams, and participants who consumed sexual media tended to have sexual dreams" (Van den Bulck et al., 2016).

Our two-track mind continues to monitor our environment while we sleep. Sensory stimuli—a particular odor or a phone's ringing—may be instantly and ingeniously woven into the dream story. In a classic experiment, researchers lightly sprayed cold water on dreamers' faces (Dement & Wolpert, 1958). Compared with sleepers who did not get the cold-water treatment, these people were more likely to dream about a waterfall, a leaky roof, or even about being sprayed by someone.

So, could we learn a foreign language by hearing it played while we sleep? If only. While sleeping, we can learn to associate a sound with a mild electric shock (and to react to the sound accordingly). We can also learn to associate a particular sound with a pleasant or unpleasant odor (Arzi et al., 2012). But we do not remember recorded information played while we are soundly asleep (Eich, 1990; Wyatt & Bootzin, 1994). In fact, anything that happens during the 5 minutes just before we fall asleep is typically lost from memory (Roth et al., 1988). This explains why sleep apnea patients, who repeatedly awaken with a gasp and then immediately fall back to sleep, do not recall the episodes. Ditto someone who awakens momentarily, sends a text message, and the next day can't remember doing so. It also explains why dreams that momentarily awaken us are mostly forgotten by morning. To remember a dream, get up and stay awake for a few minutes.

Why We Dream

Dream theorists have proposed several explanations of why we dream, including these five:

To satisfy our own wishes. In 1900, in his landmark book *The Interpretation of Dreams*, Sigmund Freud offered what he thought was "the most valuable of all the discoveries it has been my good fortune to make." He proposed that dreams provide a psychic safety valve that discharges otherwise unacceptable feelings. He viewed a dream's **manifest content** (the apparent and remembered story line) as a censored, symbolic version of its **latent content,** the unconscious drives and wishes (often erotic) that would be threatening if expressed directly. Thus, a gun might be a disguised representation of a penis.

Freud considered dreams the key to understanding our inner conflicts. However, his critics say it is time to wake up from Freud's dream theory, which they regard as a scientific nightmare. Seth Stephens-Davidowitz (2017) analyzed whether phallic-shaped foods "sneak into our dreams with unexpected frequency." His answer: They do not. In dreams, bananas are the second most common fruit. They also are the second most consumed fruit. Cucumbers are the seventh most dreamt vegetable, and the seventh most consumed vegetable. Thus, "there is no reason to believe any of Freud's specific claims about dreams and their purposes," observed dream researcher William Domhoff (2003).

Some contend that even if dreams are symbolic, they could be interpreted any way one wished. Others maintain that dreams hide nothing: A dream about a gun is a dream about a gun. Legend has it that even Freud, who loved to smoke cigars, acknowledged that "sometimes, a cigar is just a cigar." Freud's wish-fulfillment theory of dreams has in large part given way to other theories.

To file away memories. The *information-processing* perspective proposes that dreams may help sift, sort, and fix the day's experiences in our memory. Some studies support this view. When tested the day after learning a task, those who had been deprived of both slow-wave and REM sleep did not do as well as those who had slept undisturbed (Stickgold, 2012). Other studies showed similar memory lapses for new material among people who were awakened every time they began REM sleep (Empson & Clarke, 1970; Karni & Sagi, 1994).

dream a sequence of images, emotions, and thoughts passing through a sleeping person's mind.

manifest content according to Freud, the symbolic, remembered story line of a dream (as distinct from its latent, or hidden, content).

latent content according to Freud, the underlying meaning of a dream (as distinct from its manifest content).

A popular sleep myth: If you dream you are falling and hit the ground (or if you dream of dying), you die. Unfortunately, those who could confirm these ideas are not around to do so. Many people, however, have had such dreams and are alive to report them.

"Follow your dreams, except for that one where you're naked at work." —Attributed to comedian Henny Youngman

"When people interpret [a dream] as if it were meaningful and then sell those interpretations, it's quackery." —Sleep researcher J. Allan Hobson (1995)

(a) Learning.

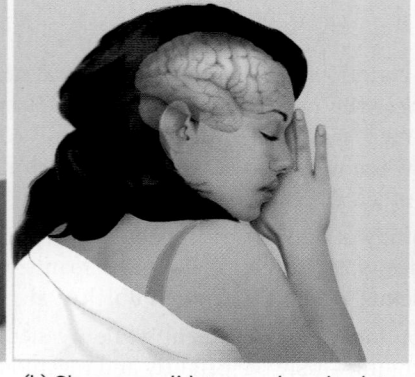

(b) Sleep consolidates our learning into long-term memory.

(c) Learning is retained.

FIGURE 8.9

A SLEEPING BRAIN IS A WORKING BRAIN

Brain scans confirm the link between REM sleep and memory. The brain regions that were active as rats learned to navigate a maze, or as people learned to perform a visual-discrimination task, became active again later during REM sleep (Louie & Wilson, 2001; Maquet, 2001). So precise were these activity patterns that scientists could tell where in the maze the rat would be if awake. To sleep, perchance to remember.

This is important news for students, many of whom, observed researcher Robert Stickgold (2000), suffer from a kind of sleep bulimia—sleep deprived on weekdays and binge sleeping on the weekend. "If you don't get good sleep and enough sleep after you learn new stuff, you won't integrate it effectively into your memories," he warned. That helps explain why high school students with high grades slept about 25 minutes longer each night than their lower-achieving classmates (Wolfson & Carskadon, 1998; see **FIGURE 8.9**). Sacrificing sleep time to study actually *worsens* academic performance, by making it harder the next day to understand class material or do well on a test (Gillen-O'Neel et al., 2013).

To develop and preserve neural pathways. Perhaps dreams, or the brain activity associated with REM sleep, serve a *physiological* function, providing the sleeping brain with periodic stimulation. This theory makes developmental sense. Stimulating experiences preserve and expand the brain's neural pathways. Infants, whose neural networks are fast developing, spend much of their abundant sleep time in REM sleep (**FIGURE 8.10**).

Rapid eye movements also stir the liquid behind the cornea; this delivers fresh oxygen to corneal cells, preventing their suffocation.

To make sense of neural static. Other theories propose that dreams erupt from *neural activation* spreading upward from the brainstem (Antrobus, 1991; Hobson, 2003, 2004, 2009). According to the *activation-synthesis theory,* dreams are the brain's attempt to synthesize random neural activity. Much as a neurosurgeon can produce hallucinations by stimulating different parts of a patient's cortex, so can stimulation originating within the brain. As Freud might have expected, PET scans of sleeping people also reveal increased activity in the emotion-related limbic system (in the amygdala) during emotional dreams (Schwartz, 2012). In contrast, frontal lobe regions responsible for inhibition and logical

FIGURE 8.10

SLEEP ACROSS THE LIFE SPAN As we age, our sleep patterns change. During our first few months, we spend progressively less time in REM sleep. During our first 20 years, we spend progressively less time asleep. (Data from Snyder & Scott, 1972.)

swissmacky/Shutterstock

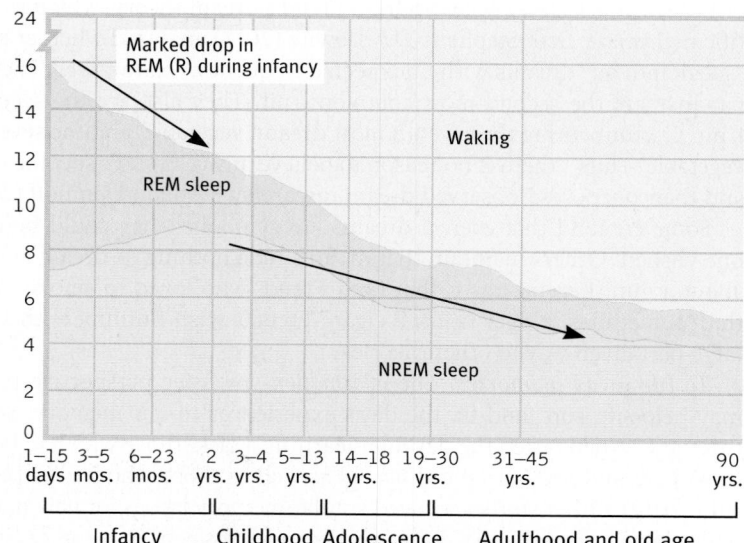

thinking seem to idle, which may explain why our dreams are less inhibited than we are when awake (Maquet et al., 1996). Add the limbic system's emotional tone to the brain's visual bursts and—Voila!—we dream. Damage either the limbic system or the visual centers active during dreaming, and dreaming itself may be impaired (Domhoff, 2003).

To reflect cognitive development. Some dream researchers prefer to see dreams as part of brain maturation and cognitive development (Domhoff, 2010, 2011; Foulkes, 1999). For example, prior to age 9, children's dreams seem more like a slide show and less like an active story in which the dreamer is an actor. Dreams overlap with waking cognition and feature coherent speech. They *simulate reality* by drawing on our concepts and knowledge. They engage brain networks that also are active during daydreaming—and so may be viewed as intensified mind-wandering, enhanced by visual imagery (Fox et al., 2013). Unlike the idea that dreams arise from bottom-up brain activation, the cognitive perspective emphasizes our mind's top-down control of our dream content (Nir & Tononi, 2010).

TABLE 8.3 compares these major dream theories. Although today's sleep researchers debate dreams' functions—and some are skeptical that dreams serve any function—there is one thing they agree on: We need REM sleep. Deprived of it by repeated awakenings, people return more and more quickly to the REM stage after falling back to sleep. When finally allowed to sleep undisturbed, they literally sleep like babies—with increased REM sleep, a phenomenon called **REM rebound.** Most other mammals also experience REM rebound, suggesting that the causes and functions of REM sleep are deeply biological. (That REM sleep occurs in mammals—and not in animals such as fish, whose behavior is less influenced by learning—fits the information-processing theory of dreams.)

So does this mean that because dreams serve physiological functions and extend normal cognition, they are psychologically meaningless? Not necessarily. Every psychologically meaningful experience involves an active brain. We are once again reminded of a basic principle: *Biological and psychological explanations of behavior are partners, not competitors.*

Dreams are a fascinating altered state of consciousness. But they are not the only altered state. As we will see next, drugs also alter conscious awareness.

REM rebound the tendency for REM sleep to increase following REM sleep deprivation.

Question: Does eating spicy foods cause us to dream more?
Answer: A spicy food that causes you to awaken more increases your chance of recalling a dream (Moorcroft, 2003).

ASK YOURSELF

Which explanation for why we dream makes the most sense to you? How well does it explain your own dreams?

TABLE 8.3

Dream Theories

Theory	Explanation	Critical Considerations
Freud's wish-fulfillment	Dreams provide a "psychic safety valve"—expressing otherwise unacceptable feelings; dreams contain manifest (remembered) content and a deeper layer of latent content (a hidden meaning).	Lacks any scientific support; dreams may be interpreted in many different ways.
Information-processing	Dreams help us sort out the day's events and consolidate our memories.	But why do we sometimes dream about things we have not experienced and about past events?
Physiological function	Regular brain stimulation from REM sleep may help develop and preserve neural pathways.	This does not explain why we experience *meaningful* dreams.
Activation-synthesis	REM sleep triggers neural activity that evokes random visual memories, which our sleeping brain weaves into stories.	The individual's brain is weaving the stories, which still tells us something about the dreamer.
Cognitive development	Dream content reflects dreamers' level of cognitive development—their knowledge and understanding. Dreams simulate our lives, including worst-case scenarios.	Does not propose an adaptive function of dreams.

RETRIEVE IT • • •   *ANSWERS IN APPENDIX E*

RI-7 What five theories propose explanations for why we dream?

🔒 REVIEW   SLEEP AND DREAMS

⟶ Learning Objectives

TEST YOURSELF Answer these repeated Learning Objective Questions on your own (before checking the answers in Appendix D) to improve your retention of the concepts (McDaniel et al., 2009, 2015).

8-1 What is *sleep*?

8-2 How do our biological rhythms influence our daily functioning?

8-3 What is the biological rhythm of our sleeping and dreaming stages?

8-4 How do biology and environment interact in our sleep patterns?

8-5 What are sleep's functions?

8-6 How does sleep loss affect us, and what are the major sleep disorders?

8-7 What do we dream, and what functions have theorists proposed for dreams?

⟶ Terms and Concepts to Remember

TEST YOURSELF Write down the definition yourself, then check your answer on the referenced page.

sleep, **p. 86**

circadian [ser-KAY-dee-an] rhythm, **p. 86**

REM (R) sleep, **p. 86**

alpha waves, **p. 86**

hallucinations, **p. 88**

delta waves, **p. 88**

suprachiasmatic nucleus (SCN), **p. 90**

insomnia, **p. 95**

narcolepsy, **p. 95**

sleep apnea, **p. 95**

night terrors, **p. 95**

dream, **p. 97**

manifest content, **p. 97**

latent content, **p. 97**

REM rebound, **p. 99**

⟶ Experience the Testing Effect

TEST YOURSELF Answer the following questions on your own first, then check your answers in Appendix E.

1. Our body temperature tends to rise and fall in sync with a biological clock, which is referred to as _____.

2. During the NREM-1 (N1) sleep stage, a person is most likely to experience
   a. sleep spindles.
   b. hallucinations.
   c. night terrors or nightmares.
   d. rapid eye movements.

3. The brain emits large, slow delta waves during _____ sleep.

4. As the night progresses, what happens to the REM (R) stage of sleep?

5. Which of the following is NOT one of the reasons that have been proposed to explain why we need sleep?
   a. Sleep has survival value.
   b. Sleep helps us recuperate.
   c. Sleep rests the eyes.
   d. Sleep plays a role in the growth process.

6. What is the difference between narcolepsy and sleep apnea?

7. In interpreting dreams, Freud was most interested in their
   a. information-processing function.
   b. physiological function.
   c. manifest content, or story line.
   d. latent content, or hidden meaning.

8. How has *activation-synthesis* been used to explain why we dream?

9. "For what one has dwelt on by day, these things are seen in visions of the night" (Menander of Athens [342–292 B.C.E.], *Fragments*). How might we use the information-processing perspective on dreaming to interpret this ancient Greek quote?

10. The tendency for REM sleep to increase following REM sleep deprivation is referred to as _____.

Continue testing yourself with 📘 **LearningCurve** or ≋ **Achieve Read & Practice** to learn and remember most effectively.

Drugs and Consciousness

TOLERANCE AND ADDICTION IN SUBSTANCE USE DISORDERS

LOQ 9-1   What are *substance use disorders?*

Let's imagine a day in the life of a legal-drug user. It begins with a wake-up energy drink. By midday, several cigarettes have calmed frazzled nerves before an appointment at the plastic surgeon's office for wrinkle-smoothing Botox injections. An afternoon latté provides a needed boost to get through the day, with a beer at home for relaxation. A diet pill before dinner helps curb the appetite. Later, two Advil PMs help offset those stimulating effects. And if performance needs enhancing, there are beta blockers for onstage performers, Viagra for middle-aged and older men, and Adderall for students hoping to focus their concentration.

Such substances are **psychoactive drugs**—chemicals that change perceptions and moods. Most of us manage to use some psychoactive drugs in moderation and without disrupting our lives. But sometimes, drug use crosses the line between moderation and **substance use disorder (TABLE 9.1).** A drug's overall effect depends not only on its biological effects but also on the user's expectations, which vary with social and cultural contexts (Gu et al., 2015; Ward, 1994). If one culture assumes that a particular drug produces euphoria (or aggression or sexual arousal) and another does not, each culture

---

TABLE 9.1

When Is Drug Use a Disorder? According to the American Psychiatric Association, a person may be diagnosed with *substance use disorder* when drug use continues despite significant life disruption. Resulting brain changes may persist after quitting use of the substance (thus leading to strong cravings when exposed to people and situations that trigger memories of drug use). The severity of substance use disorder varies from *mild* (two to three of the indicators listed below) to *moderate* (four to five indicators) to *severe* (six or more indicators). (*Source:* American Psychiatric Association, 2013.)

Diminished Control

1. Uses more substance, or for longer, than intended.

2. Tries unsuccessfully to regulate use of substance.

3. Spends much time acquiring, using, or recovering from effects of substance.

4. Craves the substance.

Diminished Social Functioning

5. Use disrupts commitments at work, school, or home.

6. Continues use despite social problems.

7. Causes reduced social, recreational, and work activities.

Hazardous Use

8. Continues use despite hazards.

9. Continues use despite worsening physical or psychological problems.

Drug Action

10. Experiences tolerance (needing more substance for the desired effect).

11. Experiences withdrawal when attempting to end use.

---

psychoactive drug a chemical substance that alters perceptions and moods.

substance use disorder a disorder characterized by continued substance craving and use despite significant life disruption and/or physical risk.

Tolerance and Addiction

LOQ 9-2 What roles do tolerance and addiction play in substance use disorders, and how has the concept of *addiction* changed?

Tolerance

With continued use of alcohol and some other drugs (but not marijuana), users develop **tolerance** as their brain chemistry adapts to offset the drug effect (*neuroadaptation*). To experience the same effect, users require larger and larger doses, which increase the risk of becoming *addicted* and developing a *substance use disorder*.

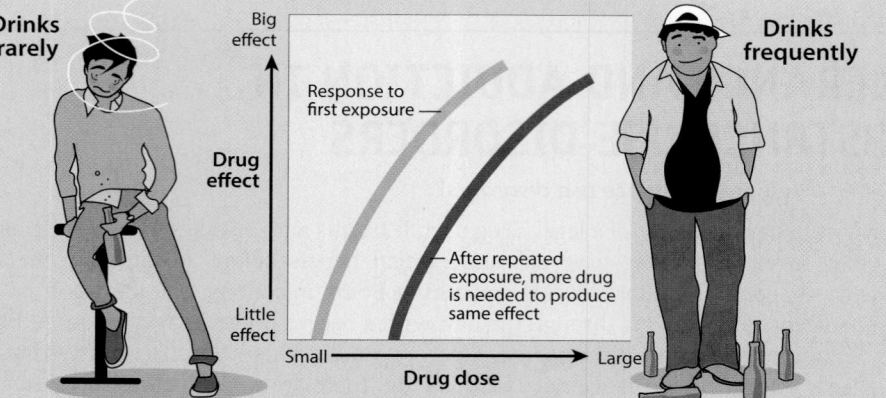

Drinks rarely

Drinks frequently

Big effect

Drug effect

Little effect

Response to first exposure

After repeated exposure, more drug is needed to produce same effect

Small ——— Drug dose ——→ Large

Addiction

Caused by ever-increasing doses of most psychoactive drugs (including prescription painkillers). Prompts user to crave the drug, to continue use despite adverse consequences, and to struggle when attempting to **withdraw** from it. These behaviors suggest a *substance use disorder*. Once in the grip of addiction, people *want* the drug more than they *like* the drug.[1]

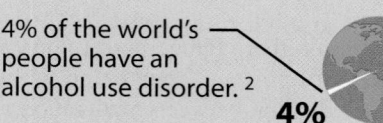

4% of the world's people have an alcohol use disorder.[2]

4%

The lifetime odds of getting hooked after using various drugs:

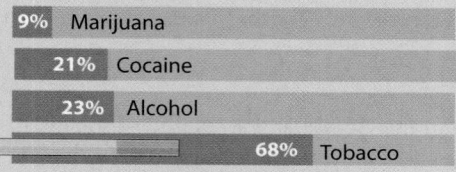

9% Marijuana
21% Cocaine
23% Alcohol
68% Tobacco

Source: National Epidemiologic Survey on Alcohol and Related Conditions [3]

Therapy or group support, such as from Alcoholics Anonymous, may help. It also helps to believe that addictions are controllable and that people can change. Many people do voluntarily stop using addictive drugs, without any treatment. Most ex-smokers have kicked the habit on their own.[4]

Behavior Addictions

Psychologists try to avoid using "addiction" to label driven, excessive behaviors such as eating, work, sex, and accumulating wealth.

I'm ADDICTED to cheeseburgers!

Yet some behaviors can become compulsive and dysfunctional—similar to problematic alcohol and drug use. [5]

• Behavior addictions include *gambling disorder*.
• *Internet gaming disorder* has been proposed "for further study."[6] Some internet users display an apparent inability to resist logging on and staying on, even when this excessive use impairs their work and relationships. [7]

Psychological and drug therapies may be "highly effective" for problematic internet use.[8]

1. Berridge et al., 2009; Robinson & Berridge, 2003. 2. WHO, 2014b. 3. Lopez-Quintero et al., 2011. 4. Newport, 2013b. 5. Gentile, 2009; Griffiths, 2001; Hoeft et al., 2008. 6. American Psychiatric Association, 2013.; Wittek et al., 2016; Wu et al., 2016. 7. Cheng & Li, 2014; Ko et al., 2005. 8. Winkler et al., 2013.

may find its expectations fulfilled. We'll take a closer look at these interacting forces in the use and potential abuse of particular psychoactive drugs. But first, to consider what contributes to the disordered use of various substances, see Thinking Critically About: Tolerance and Addiction.

tolerance the diminishing effect with regular use of the same dose of a drug, requiring the user to take larger and larger doses before experiencing the drug's effect.

withdrawal the discomfort and distress that follow discontinuing an addictive drug or behavior.

🔒 **RETRIEVE IT** • • •

ANSWERS IN APPENDIX E

RI-1 What is the process that leads to drug tolerance?

RI-2 Can someone become "addicted" to shopping?

TYPES OF PSYCHOACTIVE DRUGS

The three major categories of psychoactive drugs are *depressants, stimulants,* and *hallucinogens.* All do their work at the brain's synapses, stimulating, inhibiting, or mimicking the activity of the brain's own chemical messengers, the neurotransmitters.

Depressants

LOQ 9-3   What are *depressants,* and what are their effects?

Depressants are drugs such as alcohol, barbiturates (tranquilizers), and opiates that calm neural activity and slow body functions.

ALCOHOL True or false? Alcohol is a depressant in large amounts but a stimulant in small amounts. *False.* In any amount, alcohol is a depressant. Low doses of alcohol may, indeed, enliven a drinker, but they do so by acting as a *disinhibitor*—they slow brain activity that controls judgment and inhibitions. Alcohol is an equal-opportunity drug: It increases (disinhibits) helpful tendencies, as when tipsy restaurant patrons leave extravagant tips and social drinkers bond in groups (Fairbairn & Sayette, 2014; Lynn, 1988). And it increases harmful tendencies, as when sexually aroused men become more disposed to sexual aggression. When drinking, both men and women are more disposed to casual sex (Claxton et al., 2015; Johnson & Chen, 2015). *The bottom line:* The urges you would feel if sober are the ones you will more likely act upon when intoxicated. And that helps us understand why, among 18- to 24-year old Americans, there are each year more than 1800 alcohol-related deaths and nearly 700,000 alcohol-related assaults, including some 97,000 sexual assaults (NIH, 2015).

The prolonged and excessive drinking that characterizes **alcohol use disorder** can shrink the brain and contribute to premature death (Kendler et al., 2016; **FIGURE 9.1**). Girls and young women (who have less of a stomach enzyme that digests alcohol) can become addicted to alcohol more quickly than boys and young men do, and they are at risk for lung, brain, and liver damage at lower consumption levels (CASA, 2003).

SLOWED NEURAL PROCESSING Alcohol slows sympathetic nervous system activity. Larger doses cause reactions to slow, speech to slur, and skilled performance to deteriorate. Paired with sleep deprivation, alcohol is a potent sedative. Add these physical effects to lowered inhibitions, and the result can be deadly. Worldwide, several hundred thousand lives are lost each year in alcohol-related accidents and violent crime. As blood-alcohol levels rise and judgment falters, people's qualms about drinking and driving lessen. When drunk, people aren't aware of how drunk they are (Moore et al., 2016). In experiments, virtually all drinkers who had insisted when sober that they would not drive under the influence later decided to drive home from a bar, even when given a Breathalyzer test and told they were intoxicated (Denton & Krebs, 1990; MacDonald et al., 1995). Alcohol can also be life threatening when heavy drinking follows an earlier period of moderate drinking, which depresses the vomiting response. People may poison themselves with an overdose that their bodies would normally throw up.

MEMORY DISRUPTION Alcohol can disrupt memory formation, and heavy drinking can have long-term effects on the brain and cognition. In rats, at a developmental period corresponding to human adolescence, binge drinking contributes to nerve cell death and reduces the birth of new nerve cells. It also impairs the growth of synaptic connections (Crews et al., 2006, 2007). In humans, heavy drinking may lead to blackouts, in which drinkers are unable to recall people they met the night before or what they said or did while intoxicated. These blackouts result partly from the way alcohol suppresses REM sleep, which helps fix the day's experiences into permanent memories.

REDUCED SELF-AWARENESS In one experiment, those who consumed alcohol (rather than a placebo beverage) were doubly likely to be caught mind-wandering during a reading task, yet were *less*

depressants drugs (such as alcohol, barbiturates, and opiates) that reduce neural activity and slow body functions.

alcohol use disorder (popularly known as *alcoholism*) alcohol use marked by tolerance, withdrawal, and a drive to continue problematic use.

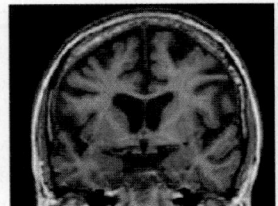 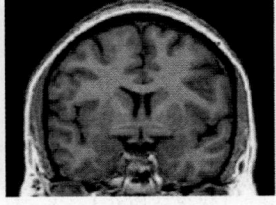

Scan of woman with alcohol use disorder
(a)

Scan of woman without alcohol use disorder
(b)

FIGURE 9.1

DISORDERED DRINKING SHRINKS THE BRAIN MRI scans show brain shrinkage in women with alcohol use disorder (a) compared with women in a control group (b).

DRINKING DISASTER DEMO
Firefighters reenacted the trauma of an alcohol-related car accident, providing a memorable demonstration for these high school students. Alcohol consumption leads to feelings of invincibility, which become especially dangerous behind the wheel of a car.

barbiturates drugs that depress central nervous system activity, reducing anxiety but impairing memory and judgment.

opiates opium and its derivatives, such as morphine and heroin; depress neural activity, temporarily lessening pain and anxiety.

stimulants drugs (such as caffeine, nicotine, and the more powerful cocaine, amphetamines, methamphetamine, and Ecstasy) that excite neural activity and speed up body functions.

amphetamines drugs (such as methamphetamine) that stimulate neural activity, causing accelerated body functions and associated energy and mood changes.

nicotine a stimulating and highly addictive psychoactive drug in tobacco.

likely to notice that they zoned out (Sayette et al., 2009). Sometimes we mind-wander to give our brains a break, but unintentional zoning out—while driving, for example—can cause later regret, especially if we've endangered ourselves or others (Seli et al., 2016). Alcohol not only reduces self-awareness, it also produces a sort of "myopia" by focusing attention on an arousing situation (say, a provocation) and distracting it from normal inhibitions and future consequences (Giancola et al., 2010; Hull & Bond, 1986; Steele & Josephs, 1990).

Reduced self-awareness may help explain why people who want to suppress their awareness of failures or shortcomings are more likely to drink than are those who feel good about themselves. Losing a business deal, a game, or a romantic partner sometimes elicits a drinking binge.

EXPECTANCY EFFECTS As with other drugs, expectations influence behavior. Expectations help explain why adolescents—presuming that alcohol will lift their spirits—sometimes drink when they're upset and alone. Solitary drinking actually does not boost mood, but it does increase the likelihood of developing a substance use disorder (Creswell et al., 2014; Fairbairn & Sayette, 2014).

Simply *believing* we're consuming alcohol can cause us to act out alcohol's presumed influence (Christiansen et al., 2016; Moss & Albery, 2009). In a classic experiment, researchers gave Rutgers University men (who had volunteered for a study on "alcohol and sexual stimulation") either an alcoholic or a nonalcoholic drink (Abrams & Wilson, 1983). (Both had strong tastes that masked any alcohol.) After watching an erotic movie clip, the men who *thought* they had consumed alcohol were more likely to report having strong sexual fantasies and feeling guilt free. Being able to *attribute* their sexual responses to alcohol released their inhibitions—whether or not they had actually consumed any alcohol.

So, alcohol's effect lies partly in that powerful sex organ, the mind. Fourteen "intervention studies" have educated college drinkers about that very point (Scott-Sheldon et al., 2014). Most participants have come away with lower positive expectations of alcohol and reduced their drinking the ensuing month.

BARBITURATES Like alcohol, the **barbiturate** drugs, which are *tranquilizers*, depress nervous system activity. Barbiturates such as Nembutal, Seconal, and Amytal are sometimes prescribed to induce sleep or reduce anxiety. In larger doses, they can impair memory and judgment. If combined with alcohol—as sometimes happens when people take a sleeping pill after an evening of heavy drinking—the total depressive effect on body functions can be lethal.

OPIATES The **opiates**—opium and its derivatives—also depress neural functioning. Opiates include *heroin* and its medically prescribed substitute, *methadone*. They also include pain-relief *narcotics* such as codeine, OxyContin, and morphine (and its much more powerful synthetic counterpart, fentanyl). As blissful pleasure replaces pain and anxiety, the user's pupils constrict, breathing slows, and lethargy sets in. Those who become addicted to this short-term pleasure may pay a long-term price: a gnawing craving for another fix, a need for progressively larger doses (as tolerance develops), and the extreme discomfort of withdrawal. When repeatedly flooded with an artificial opiate, the brain eventually stops producing *endorphins,* its own opiates. If the artificial opiate is then withdrawn, the brain will lack the normal level of these painkilling neurotransmitters. An alarming number of Americans have become unable or unwilling to tolerate this state and have paid an ultimate price—death by overdose. Between 2013 and 2016, the U.S. rate of overdose deaths from synthetic opioids more than quadrupled to 20,000 per year, with another 44,000 annual deaths due to other opioids (CDC, 2017). The opioid crisis is "a major problem," declared U.S. President Trump (2017) in announcing a government initiative to stop opioid abuse.

🔒 **RETRIEVE IT • • •**   *ANSWERS IN APPENDIX E*

RI-3 Alcohol, barbiturates, and opiates are all in a class of drugs called
_____.

Stimulants

LOQ 9-4   What are *stimulants*, and what are their effects?

A **stimulant** excites neural activity and speeds up body functions. Pupils dilate, heart and breathing rates increase, and blood sugar levels rise, causing a drop in appetite. Energy and self-confidence also rise.

Stimulants include caffeine, nicotine, and the more powerful cocaine, **amphetamines,** methamphetamine ("speed"), and Ecstasy. People use stimulants to feel alert, lose weight, or boost mood or athletic performance. Some students resort to stimulants in hopes of boosting their academic performance, despite the fact that they may offer only small benefit (Ilieva et al., 2015). Stimulants can also be addictive, as you may know if you are one of the many who use caffeine daily in your coffee, tea, soda, or energy drinks. Cut off from your usual dose, you may crash into fatigue, headaches, irritability, and depression (Silverman et al., 1992). A mild dose of caffeine typically lasts three or four hours, which—if taken in the evening—may impair sleep.

NICOTINE   Tobacco products deliver highly addictive **nicotine.** Imagine that cigarettes were harmless—except, once in every 25,000 packs, an occasional innocent-looking one was filled with dynamite instead of tobacco. Not such a bad risk of having your head blown off. But with 250 million packs a day consumed worldwide, we could expect more than 10,000 gruesome daily deaths (more than three times the 9/11 terrorist fatalities each and every day)—surely enough to have cigarettes banned everywhere.[1]

The lost lives from these dynamite-loaded cigarettes approximate those from today's actual cigarettes. A teen-to-the-grave smoker has a 50 percent chance of dying from the habit, and each year, tobacco kills nearly 5.4 million of its 1.3 billion customers worldwide. (Imagine the outrage if 25 loaded jumbo jets crashed today, let alone tomorrow and every day thereafter.) By 2030, annual tobacco deaths are expected to increase to 8 million. That means that *1 billion* twenty-first-century people may be killed by tobacco (WHO, 2012).

Tobacco products include cigarettes, cigars, chewing tobacco, pipe tobacco, snuff, and—most recently—e-cigarettes. Inhaling e-cigarette vapor ("vaping") gives users a jolt of nicotine without cancer-causing tar. As a result, their sale has boomed: Between 2013 and 2014, youth e-cigarette use tripled (Das et al., 2016). But there is a downside: E-cigarettes deliver toxic chemicals and can increase one's chances of using conventional cigarettes (Barrington-Trimis et al., 2016; Farsalinos et al., 2014).

Smoke a cigarette and nature will charge you 12 minutes—ironically, just about the length of time you spend smoking it (*Discover*, 1996). (Researchers don't yet know how e-cigarette smoking affects life expectancy.) Smokers die, on average, at least a decade before nonsmokers (Jha et al., 2013). Eliminating smoking would increase life expectancy more than any other preventive measure.

Tobacco products are as powerfully and quickly addictive as heroin and cocaine. Attempts to quit even within the first weeks of smoking often fail (DiFranza, 2008). As with other addictions, smokers develop *tolerance,* and quitting causes withdrawal symptoms, including craving, insomnia, anxiety, irritability, and distractibility. Nicotine-deprived smokers trying to focus on a task experience a tripled rate of mind-wandering (Sayette et al., 2010). When not craving a cigarette, they tend to underestimate the power of such cravings (Sayette et al., 2008).

All it takes to relieve this aversive state is a single puff on a cigarette. Within 7 seconds, a rush of nicotine will signal the central nervous system to release a flood of neurotransmitters (**FIGURE 9.2**). Epinephrine and norepinephrine will diminish appetite and boost alertness and mental efficiency. Dopamine and opioids will temporarily calm anxiety and reduce sensitivity to pain (Ditre et al., 2011; Gavin, 2004). No wonder ex-smokers will sometimes, under stress, return to smoking—as did some 1 million Americans after the 9/11 terrorist attacks (Pesko, 2014). Ditto for people with major depressive disorder, who are more likely than others to see their efforts to quit go up in smoke (Zvolensky et al., 2015).

Vasca/Shutterstock

ENGAGE   (ASK YOURSELF)

Have you ever relied on caffeinated drinks to stay awake for a late-night study session, and then struggled to fall asleep afterward? How do you think this pattern affects next-day performance in class or at work? How might you plan your study sessions to avoid this?

"Smoking cures weight problems . . . eventually." —Comedian writer Steven Wright

For HIV patients who smoke, the virus is now much less lethal than the smoking (Helleberg et al., 2013).

---

1. This analogy, adapted here with world-based numbers, was suggested by mathematician Sam Saunders, as reported by K. C. Cole (1998).

FIGURE 9.2

WHERE THERE'S SMOKE . . . : THE PHYSIOLOGICAL EFFECTS OF NICOTINE Nicotine reaches the brain within 7 seconds, twice as fast as intravenous heroin. Within minutes, the amount in the blood soars.

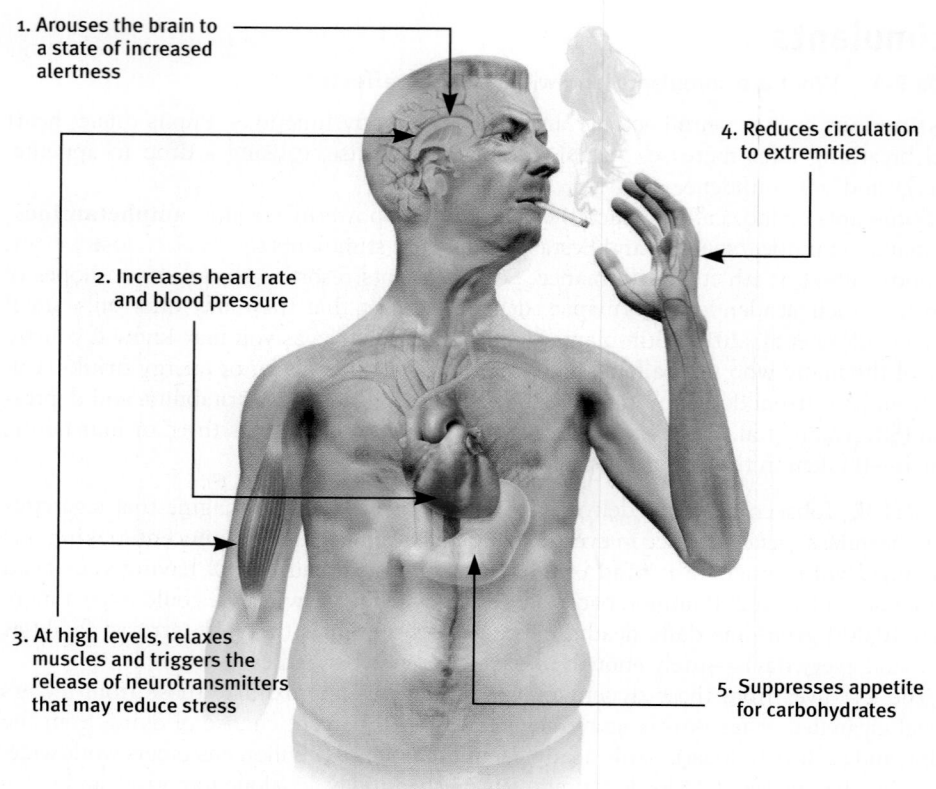

1. Arouses the brain to a state of increased alertness

4. Reduces circulation to extremities

2. Increases heart rate and blood pressure

3. At high levels, relaxes muscles and triggers the release of neurotransmitters that may reduce stress

5. Suppresses appetite for carbohydrates

cocaine a powerful and addictive stimulant derived from the coca plant; produces temporarily increased alertness and euphoria.

methamphetamine a powerfully addictive drug that stimulates the central nervous system, with accelerated body functions and associated energy and mood changes; over time, appears to reduce baseline dopamine levels.

Ecstasy (MDMA) a synthetic stimulant and mild hallucinogen. Produces euphoria and social intimacy, but with short-term health risks and longer-term harm to serotonin-producing neurons and to mood and cognition.

Humorist Dave Barry (1995) recalling why he smoked his first cigarette the summer he turned 15: "Arguments against smoking: 'It's a repulsive addiction that slowly but surely turns you into a gasping, gray-skinned, tumor-ridden invalid, hacking up brownish gobs of toxic waste from your one remaining lung.' Arguments for smoking: 'Other teenagers are doing it.' Case closed! Let's light up!"

(ASK YOURSELF)

Think of a friend or family member who is addicted to nicotine. What do you think would be most effective to say to that person to convince them to try to quit?

These rewards keep people smoking, even among the 3 in 4 smokers who wish they could stop (Newport, 2013b). Each year, fewer than 1 in 7 who want to quit will be able to resist. Even those who know they are committing slow-motion suicide may be unable to stop (Saad, 2002).

Nevertheless, repeated attempts seem to pay off. The worldwide smoking rate—25 percent among men and 5 percent among women—is down about 30 percent since 1990 (GBD, 2017). Half of all Americans who have ever smoked have quit, sometimes aided by a nicotine replacement drug and with encouragement from a counselor or support group. Some researchers argue that it is best to quit abruptly—to go "cold turkey" (Lindson-Hawley et al., 2016). Others suggest that success is equally likely whether smokers quit abruptly or gradually (Fiore et al., 2008; Lichtenstein et al., 2010). For those who endure, the acute craving and withdrawal symptoms gradually dissipate over the ensuing 6 months (Ward et al., 1997). After a year's abstinence, only 10 percent will relapse in the next year (Hughes, 2010). These nonsmokers may live not only healthier but also happier lives. Smoking correlates with higher rates of depression, chronic disabilities, and divorce (Doherty & Doherty, 1998; Edwards & Kendler, 2012; Vita et al., 1998). Healthy living seems to add both years to life and life to years. Awareness of nonsmokers' better health and happiness has contributed to U.S. high school seniors' increasing disapproval (87 percent) of smoking a pack or more a day, and also to a plunge in their smoking rate, from 37 percent in 1997 to 10 percent in 2017 (Johnston et al., 2018).

RETRIEVE IT • • •

ANSWERS IN APPENDIX E

RI-4 What withdrawal symptoms should your friend expect when she finally decides to quit smoking?

COCAINE **Cocaine** is a powerfully addictive stimulant derived from the coca plant. The recipe for Coca-Cola originally included a coca extract, creating a cocaine tonic for tired elderly people. Between 1896 and 1905, Coke was indeed "the real thing." But no longer. Cocaine is now snorted, injected, or smoked (sometimes as *crack cocaine,* a

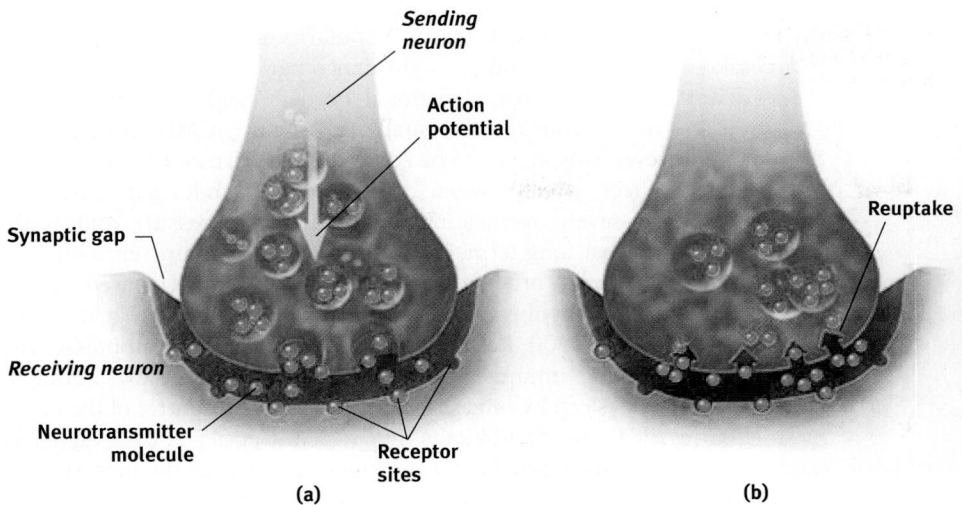

Sending neuron

Action potential

Synaptic gap

Receiving neuron

Neurotransmitter molecule

Receptor sites

(a)

Neurotransmitters carry a message from a sending neuron across a synapse to receptor sites on a receiving neuron.

(b)

The sending neuron normally reabsorbs excess neurotransmitter molecules, a process called *reuptake*.

Reuptake

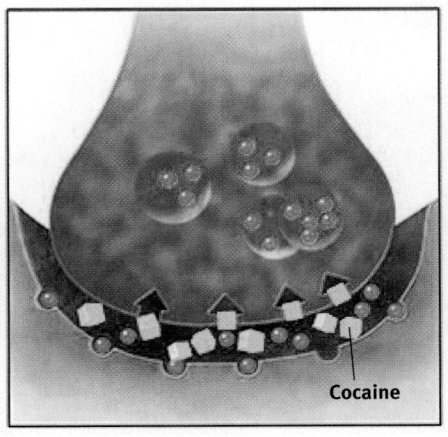

Cocaine

(c)

By binding to the sites that normally reabsorb neurotransmitter molecules, cocaine blocks reuptake of dopamine, norepinephrine, and serotonin (Ray & Ksir, 1990). The extra neurotransmitter molecules therefore remain in the synapse, intensifying their normal mood-altering effects and producing a euphoric rush. When the cocaine level drops, the absence of these neurotransmitters produces a crash.

FIGURE 9.3
COCAINE EUPHORIA AND CRASH

"Cocaine makes you a new man. And the first thing that new man wants is more cocaine." —Comedian George Carlin (1937–2008)

faster-working crystallized form that produces a briefer but more intense high, followed by a more intense crash). Cocaine enters the bloodstream quickly, producing a rush of euphoria that depletes the brain's supply of the neurotransmitters dopamine, serotonin, and norepinephrine (**FIGURE 9.3**). Within the hour, a crash of agitated depression follows as the drug's effect wears off. After several hours, the craving for more wanes, only to return several days later (Gawin, 1991).

In situations that trigger aggression, ingesting cocaine may heighten reactions. Caged rats fight when given foot shocks, and they fight even more when given cocaine *and* foot shocks. Likewise, humans who voluntarily ingest high doses of cocaine in laboratory experiments impose higher shock levels on a presumed opponent than do those receiving a placebo (Licata et al., 1993). Cocaine use may also lead to emotional disturbances, suspiciousness, convulsions, cardiac arrest, or respiratory failure.

Cocaine use is powerfully rewarding (Keramati et al., 2017). Its psychological effects vary with the dosage and form consumed, but the situation and the user's expectations and personality also play a role. Given a placebo, cocaine users who *thought* they were taking cocaine often had a cocaine-like experience (Byck & Van Dyke, 1982).

In national surveys, 2.7 percent of American twelfth graders and 6 percent of British 18- to 24-year-olds reported having tried cocaine during the past year (ACMD, 2009; Johnston et al., 2018).

METHAMPHETAMINE Amphetamines stimulate neural activity. As body functions speed up, the user's energy rises and mood soars. Amphetamines are the parent drug for the highly addictive **methamphetamine**, which is chemically similar but has greater effects (NIDA, 2002, 2005). Methamphetamine triggers the release of the neurotransmitter dopamine, which stimulates brain cells that enhance energy and mood, leading to 8 hours or so of heightened energy and euphoria. Its aftereffects may include irritability, insomnia, hypertension, seizures, social isolation, depression, and occasional violent outbursts (Homer et al., 2008). Over time, methamphetamine may reduce baseline dopamine levels, leaving the user with depressed functioning.

ECSTASY Ecstasy, a street name for **MDMA** (methylenedioxymethamphetamine, also known in its powder form as *Molly*), is both a stimulant and a mild hallucinogen. As an amphetamine derivative, Ecstasy triggers dopamine release, but its major effect is releasing stored serotonin and blocking its reuptake, thus prolonging serotonin's feel-good flood (Braun, 2001). Users feel the effect about a half-hour after taking an Ecstasy pill. For 3 or 4 hours, they experience high energy, emotional elevation, and (given a social context) connectedness with those around them ("I love everyone").

DRAMATIC DRUG-INDUCED DECLINE
In the 18 months between these two mug shots, this woman's methamphetamine addiction led to obvious physical changes.

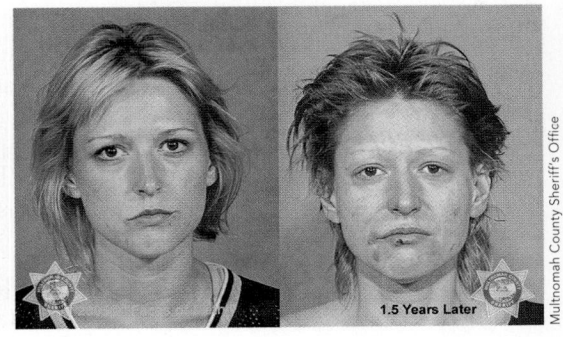

1.5 Years Later

Multnomah County Sheriff's Office

THE HUG DRUG MDMA, known as Ecstasy and often taken at clubs, produces a euphoric high and feelings of intimacy. But repeated use can destroy serotonin-producing neurons, impair memory, and permanently deflate mood.

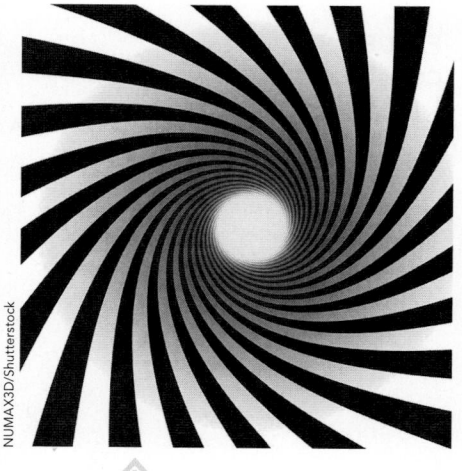

FIGURE 9.4

NEAR-DEATH VISION OR HALLUCINATION? Psychologist Ronald Siegel (1977) reported that people under the influence of hallucinogenic drugs often see "a bright light in the center of the field of vision. . . . The location of this point of light create[s] a tunnel-like perspective." This is very similar to others' near-death experiences.

Synthetic marijuana (*K2*, also called *Spice*) mimics THC. Its harmful side effects can include agitation and hallucinations (Fattore, 2016; Sherif et al., 2016).

During the 1990s, Ecstasy's popularity soared as a "club drug" taken at nightclubs and all-night dance parties (Landry, 2002). The drug's popularity crosses national borders, with an estimated 60 million tablets consumed annually in Britain (ACMD, 2009). There are, however, reasons not to be ecstatic about Ecstasy. One is its dehydrating effect, which—when combined with prolonged dancing—can lead to severe overheating, increased blood pressure, and death. Another is that long-term, repeated leaching of brain serotonin can damage serotonin-producing neurons, leading to decreased output and increased risk of permanently depressed mood (Croft et al., 2001; McCann et al., 2000; Roiser et al., 2005). Ecstasy also suppresses the disease-fighting immune system, impairs memory, slows thought, and disrupts sleep by interfering with serotonin's control of the circadian clock (Laws & Kokkalis, 2007; Schilt et al., 2007; Wagner et al., 2012). Ecstasy delights for the night but dispirits the morrow.

Hallucinogens

LOQ 9-5   What are *hallucinogens*, and what are their effects?

Hallucinogens distort perceptions and evoke sensory images in the absence of sensory input (which is why these drugs are also called *psychedelics*, meaning "mind-manifesting"). Some, such as LSD and MDMA (Ecstasy), are synthetic. Others, including psilocybin and the mild hallucinogen marijuana, are natural substances.

Whether provoked to hallucinate by drugs, loss of oxygen, or extreme sensory deprivation, the brain hallucinates in basically the same way (Siegel, 1982). The experience typically begins with simple geometric forms, such as a lattice, cobweb, or spiral. The next phase consists of more meaningful images; some may be superimposed on a tunnel or funnel, others may be replays of past emotional experiences. Brain scans of people on an LSD trip reveal that their visual cortex becomes hypersensitive and strongly connected to their brain's emotion centers (Carhart-Harris et al., 2016). As the hallucination peaks, people frequently feel separated from their body and experience dreamlike scenes. Their sense of self dissolves, which also dissolves the border between themselves and the external world (Lebedev et al., 2015).

These sensations are strikingly similar to the **near-death experience,** an altered state of consciousness reported by about 10 to 15 percent of those revived from cardiac arrest (Agrillo, 2011; Greyson, 2010; Parnia et al., 2014). Many describe visions of tunnels (**FIGURE 9.4**), bright lights, a replay of old memories, and out-of-body sensations (Siegel, 1980). These experiences can later enhance spirituality and promote feelings of personal growth (Khanna & Greyson, 2014, 2015). Given that oxygen deprivation and other insults to the brain are known to produce hallucinations, it is difficult to resist wondering whether a brain under stress manufactures the near-death experience. During epileptic seizures and migraines, people may experience similar hallucinations of geometric patterns (Billock & Tsou, 2012). So have solitary sailors and polar explorers while enduring monotony, isolation, and cold (Suedfeld & Mocellin, 1987). The philosopher-neuroscientist Patricia Churchland (2013, p. 70) surmises that such experiences represent "neural funny business."

LSD Chemist Albert Hofmann created—and on one Friday afternoon in April 1943 accidentally ingested—**LSD** (lysergic acid diethylamide). The result—"an uninterrupted stream of fantastic pictures, extraordinary shapes with intense, kaleidoscopic play of colors"—reminded him of a childhood mystical experience that had left him longing for another glimpse of "a miraculous, powerful, unfathomable reality" (Siegel, 1984; Smith, 2006).

The emotions of an LSD (or *acid*) trip range from euphoria to detachment to panic. Users' current mood and expectations (their "high hopes") color the emotional experience, but the perceptual distortions and hallucinations have some commonalities.

MARIJUANA   The straight dope on marijuana: Marijuana leaves and flowers contain **THC** (delta-9-tetrahydrocannabinol). Whether smoked (getting to the brain in about 7 seconds) or eaten (traveling at a slower, unpredictable rate), THC produces a mix of effects.

It is usually classified as a mild hallucinogen because it amplifies sensitivity to colors, sounds, tastes, and smells. But like the depressant alcohol, marijuana relaxes, disinhibits, and may produce a euphoric high. Both alcohol and marijuana impair the motor coordination, perceptual skills, and reaction time necessary for safely operating an automobile or other machine. "THC causes animals to misjudge events," reported Ronald Siegel (1990, p. 163). "Pigeons wait too long to respond to buzzers or lights that tell them food is available for brief periods; and rats turn the wrong way in mazes."

Marijuana and alcohol also differ. The body eliminates alcohol within hours. THC and its by-products linger in the body for more than a week, which means that regular users experience less abrupt withdrawal and may achieve a high with smaller-than-usual drug amounts. This is the opposite of typical tolerance, in which repeat users need larger doses to feel the same effect.

After considering more than 10,000 scientific reports, the U.S. National Academies of Sciences, Engineering, and Medicine (2017) concluded that marijuana use

- alleviates chronic pain and chemotherapy-related nausea,

- is not associated with tobacco-related cancers, such as lung cancer,

- is predictive of increased risk of traffic accidents, chronic bronchitis, psychosis, social anxiety disorder, and suicidal thoughts, and

- likely contributes to impaired attention, learning, and memory, and possibly to academic underachievement.

A marijuana user's experience can vary with the situation. If the person feels anxious or depressed, marijuana may intensify the feelings. The more often the person uses marijuana, especially during adolescence, the greater the risk of anxiety, depression, or addiction (Bambico et al., 2010; Hurd et al., 2013; Volkow et al., 2016).

Some countries and U.S. states have passed laws legalizing marijuana possession. Greater legal acceptance helps explain why Americans' marijuana use nearly doubled between 2013 and 2016, from 7 to 13 percent (McCarthy, 2016).

* * *

Despite their differences, the psychoactive drugs summarized in **TABLE 9.2** (with the exception of marijuana) share a common feature: They trigger negative aftereffects that offset their immediate positive effects and grow stronger with repetition. This helps explain both tolerance and withdrawal.

hallucinogens psychedelic ("mind-manifesting") drugs, such as LSD, that distort perceptions and evoke sensory images in the absence of sensory input.

near-death experience an altered state of consciousness reported after a close brush with death (such as cardiac arrest); often similar to drug-induced hallucinations.

LSD *(lysergic acid diethylamide)* a powerful hallucinogenic drug; also known as *acid*.

THC the major active ingredient in marijuana; triggers a variety of effects, including mild hallucinations.

LaunchPad To review the basic psychoactive drugs and their actions, and to play the role of experimenter as you administer drugs and observe their effects, visit **Topic Tutorial: PsychSim6, Your Mind on Drugs.**

TABLE 9.2
A Guide to Selected Psychoactive Drugs

Drug	Type	Pleasurable Effects	Negative Aftereffects
Alcohol	Depressant	Initial high followed by relaxation and disinhibition	Depression, memory loss, organ damage, impaired reactions
Heroin	Depressant	Rush of euphoria, relief from pain	Depressed physiology, agonizing withdrawal
Caffeine	Stimulant	Increased alertness and wakefulness	Anxiety, restlessness, and insomnia in high doses; uncomfortable withdrawal
Nicotine	Stimulant	Arousal and relaxation, sense of well-being	Heart disease, cancer
Cocaine	Stimulant	Rush of euphoria, confidence, energy	Cardiovascular stress, suspiciousness, depressive crash
Methamphetamine	Stimulant	Euphoria, alertness, energy	Irritability, insomnia, hypertension, seizures
Ecstasy (MDMA)	Stimulant; mild hallucinogen	Emotional elevation, disinhibition	Dehydration, overheating, depressed mood, impaired cognitive and immune functioning
LSD	Hallucinogen	Visual "trip"	Risk of panic
Marijuana (THC)	Mild hallucinogen	Enhanced sensation, relief of pain, distortion of time, relaxation	Impaired learning and memory, increased risk of psychological disorders

🔒 **RETRIEVE IT • • •**   *ANSWERS IN APPENDIX E*

"How strange would appear to be this thing that men call pleasure! And how curiously it is related to what is thought to be its opposite, pain! . . . Wherever the one is found, the other follows up behind." (Plato, *Phaedo*, fourth century B.C.E.)

RI-5 How does this pleasure-pain description apply to the repeated use of psychoactive drugs?

INFLUENCES ON DRUG USE

LOQ 9-6   Why do some people become regular users of consciousness-altering drugs?

Drug use by North American youth increased during the 1970s. Then, with increased drug education and a more realistic and deglamorized media depiction of taking drugs, drug use declined sharply (except for a small rise in the mid-1980s). After the early 1990s, the cultural antidrug voice softened, and some drugs for a time were again glamorized in music and films. Consider these historical trends in the use of marijuana:

- In the University of Michigan's annual survey of 15,000 U.S. high school seniors, the proportion who said there is "great risk" in regular marijuana use rose from 35 percent in 1978 to 79 percent in 1991, then retreated to 29 percent in 2017 (Johnston et al., 2018).

- After peaking in 1978, marijuana use by U.S. high school seniors declined through 1992, then rose and held steady until beginning to trend back up in 2017 (see **FIGURE 9.5**). Canadian use among 15- to 24-year-olds has been similarly trending upward since 2012 (CCSA, 2017). European teen drug use is lower, but with trends mirroring those in North America: rising marijuana and declining cigarette and alcohol use (Wadley & Lee, 2016).

For some adolescents, occasional drug use represents thrill seeking. Yet why do some teens, but not others, become regular drug users? In search of answers, researchers have engaged biological, psychological, and social-cultural levels of analysis.

U.S. high school seniors reporting drug use

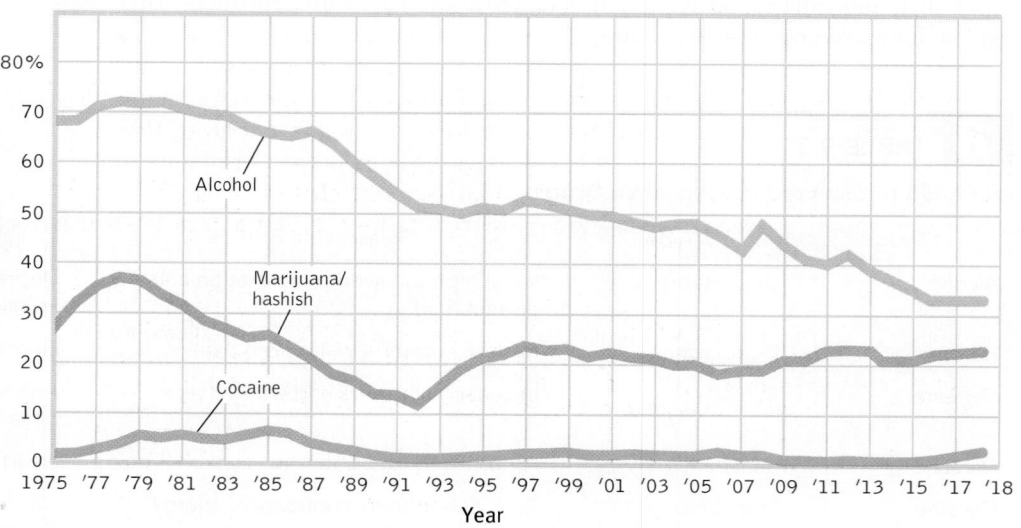

FIGURE 9.5

TRENDS IN DRUG USE The percentage of U.S. high school seniors who said they had used alcohol, marijuana, or cocaine during the past 30 days largely declined from the late 1970s to 1992, when it partially rebounded for a few years. (Data from Johnston et al., 2018; Miech et al., 2016.)

Biological Influences

Some people may be biologically vulnerable to particular drugs. For example, heredity influences some aspects of substance use problems, especially those appearing by early adulthood (Crabbe, 2002):

- If an identical rather than fraternal twin is diagnosed with alcohol use disorder, the other twin is at increased risk for alcohol problems (Kendler et al., 2002). In marijuana use, too, identical twins more closely resemble each other than do fraternal twins.

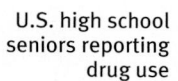 **LaunchPad** See the **Video: Twin Studies** for a helpful tutorial animation about this type of research design.

- Researchers have identified genes associated with alcohol use disorder, and they are seeking genes that contribute to tobacco addiction (Stacey et al., 2012). These culprit genes seemingly produce deficiencies in the brain's natural dopamine reward system: While triggering temporary dopamine-produced pleasure, the addictive drugs disrupt normal dopamine balance. Studies of how drugs reprogram the brain's reward systems raise hopes for anti-addiction drugs that might block or blunt the effects of alcohol and other drugs (Miller, 2008; Wilson & Kuhn, 2005).

- Biological influences on drug use extend to other drugs as well. One study tracked 18,115 Swedish adoptees. Those with drug-abusing biological parents were at doubled risk of drug abuse, indicating a genetic influence—a finding confirmed in another Swedish study of 14,000+ twins and 1.3 million other siblings. But then those with drug-abusing adoptive siblings also had a doubled risk of drug abuse, indicating an environmental influence (Kendler et al., 2012; Maes et al., 2016). So, what might those environmental influences be?

Psychological and Social-Cultural Influences

Throughout this text, we see that biological, psychological, and social-cultural factors interact to produce behavior. So, too, with problematic drug use (**FIGURE 9.6**). One psychological factor that has appeared in studies of youth and young adults is the feeling that life is meaningless and directionless (Newcomb & Harlow, 1986). This feeling is common among school dropouts who subsist without job skills, without privilege, and with little hope.

Sometimes the psychological influence is obvious. Many heavy users of alcohol, marijuana, and cocaine have experienced significant stress or failure and are depressed. Girls with a history of depression, eating disorders, or sexual or physical abuse are at increased risk for substance addiction. So are youth undergoing school or neighborhood transitions (CASA, 2003; Logan et al., 2002). Undergraduates who have not yet achieved a clear identity are also at greater risk (Bishop et al., 2005). By temporarily dulling the pain of self-awareness, psychoactive drugs may offer a way to avoid coping with depression, anger, anxiety, or insomnia. The relief may be temporary, but behavior is often controlled more by its immediate consequences than by its later ones.

Smoking and vaping usually begin during early adolescence. (If you are in college or university, and the cigarette manufacturers haven't yet made you their devoted customer, they almost surely never will.) Adolescents, self-conscious and often thinking the world is watching their every move, are vulnerable to smoking's allure. They may first light up to imitate glamorous celebrities, to project a mature image, to handle stress, or to get the social reward of acceptance by other smokers (Cin et al., 2007; DeWall & Pond, 2011; Tickle et al., 2006). Mindful of these tendencies, cigarette companies have effectively modeled smoking with themes that appeal to youths:

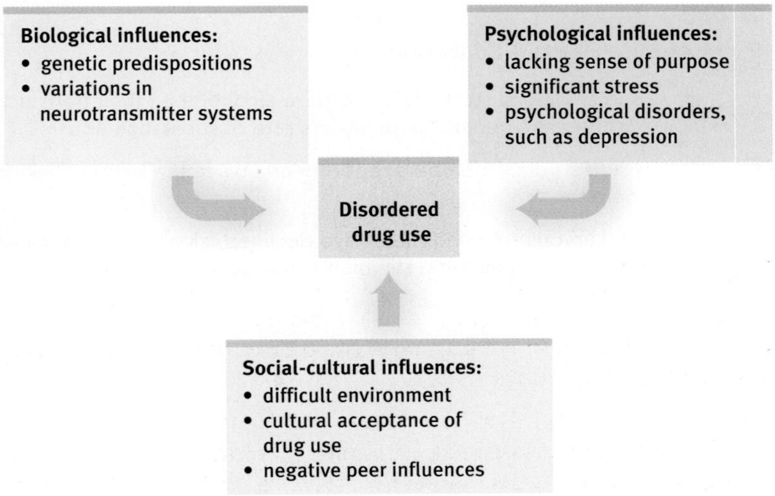

Warning signs of alcohol use disorder:
- Drinking binges (five drinks for men and four for women over two hours)
- Craving alcohol
- Use results in unfulfilled work, school, or home tasks
- Failing to honor a resolve to drink less
- Continued use despite health risk
- Avoiding family or friends when drinking

Biological influences:
- genetic predispositions
- variations in neurotransmitter systems

Psychological influences:
- lacking sense of purpose
- significant stress
- psychological disorders, such as depression

Disordered drug use

Social-cultural influences:
- difficult environment
- cultural acceptance of drug use
- negative peer influences

FIGURE 9.6
LEVELS OF ANALYSIS FOR DISORDERED DRUG USE The biopsychosocial approach enables researchers to investigate disordered drug use from complementary perspectives.

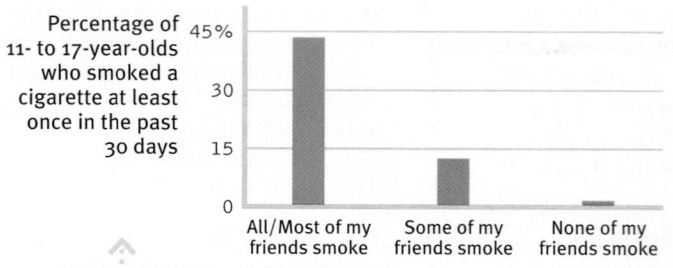

Percentage of 11- to 17-year-olds who smoked a cigarette at least once in the past 30 days

45%

30

15

0

All/Most of my friends smoke | Some of my friends smoke | None of my friends smoke

FIGURE 9.7

PEER INFLUENCE Kids don't smoke if their friends don't (Philip Morris, 2003). A correlation-causation question: Does the close link between teen smoking and friends' smoking reflect peer influence? Teens seeking similar friends? Or both?

NIC-A-TEEN Virtually nobody starts smoking past the vulnerable teen years. Eager to hook customers whose addiction will give them business for years to come, cigarette companies target teens. Portrayals of smoking by popular actors—such as Scarlett Johansson in *Hail, Caesar!*—tempt teens to imitate.

attractiveness, independence, adventure-seeking, social approval (Surgeon General, 2012).

Rates of drug use vary across cultural and ethnic groups. One survey of European teens found that lifetime marijuana use ranged from 5 percent in Norway to more than eight times that in the Czech Republic (Romelsjö et al., 2014). Independent U.S. government studies of drug use in households and among high schoolers nationwide reveal that African-American teens have sharply lower rates of drinking, smoking, and cocaine use (Johnston et al., 2007). Alcohol and other drug addiction rates have also been low among actively religious people, with extremely low rates among Orthodox Jews, Mormons, Mennonites, and the Amish (DeWall et al., 2014; Salas-Wright et al., 2012).

Typically, teens who start smoking also have friends who smoke, who suggest its pleasures and offer them cigarettes (Rose et al., 1999). Among teens whose parents and best friends are nonsmokers, the smoking rate is close to zero (Moss et al., 1992; also see **FIGURE 9.7**). Similarly, if an adolescent's friends use drugs, the odds are that he or she will, too. If the friends do not, the opportunity may not even arise. Whether in cities or rural areas, peers throw the parties and provide (or don't provide) the drugs. Teens who come from happy families, who do not begin drinking before age 15, and who do well

Pictorial Press Ltd/Alamy

in school tend not to use drugs, largely because they rarely associate with those who do (Bachman et al., 2007; Hingson et al., 2006; Odgers et al., 2008).

Adolescents' expectations—what they *believe* friends are doing and favoring— also influence their behavior (Vitória et al., 2009). One study surveyed sixth graders in 22 U.S. states. How many believed their friends had smoked marijuana? About 14 percent. How many of those friends acknowledged doing so? Only 4 percent (Wren, 1999). University students are not immune to such misperceptions: Drinking dominates social occasions partly because students overestimate their peers' enthusiasm for

alcohol and underestimate their views of its risks (Prentice & Miller, 1993; Self, 1994) (**TABLE 9.3**). When students' overestimates of peer drinking are corrected, alcohol use often subsides (Moreira et al., 2009).

TABLE 9.3

Facts About "Higher" Education

- College and university students drink more alcohol than their nonstudent peers and exhibit 2.5 times the general population's rate of substance abuse.

- Fraternity and sorority members report nearly twice the binge-drinking rate of nonmembers.

- Since 1993, campus smoking rates have declined, alcohol use has been steady, and abuse of prescription opioids, stimulants, tranquilizers, and sedatives has increased, as has marijuana use.

Source: NCASA, 2007.

People whose beginning use of drugs was influenced by their peers are more likely to stop using when friends stop or their social network changes (Chassin & MacKinnon, 2015; Kandel & Raveis, 1989). One study that followed 12,000 adults over 32 years found that smokers tend to quit in clusters (Christakis & Fowler, 2008). Within a social network, the odds of a person quitting increased when a spouse, friend, or co-worker stopped smoking. Similarly, most soldiers who engaged in problematic drug use while in Vietnam ceased after returning home (Robins et al., 1974).

As always with correlations, the traffic between friends' drug use and our own may be two-way: Our friends influence us. Social networks matter. But we also select as friends those who share our likes and dislikes.

What do the findings on drug use suggest for drug prevention and treatment programs? Three channels of influence seem possible:

SNAPSHOTS at jasonlove.com

Once upon a time, peer pressure caused Bob to start smoking.

Twenty years later, it forces him to quit.

© Jason Love

- Educate young people about the long-term costs of a drug's temporary pleasures.

- Help young people find other ways to boost their self-esteem and discover their purpose in life.

- Attempt to modify peer associations or to "inoculate" youth against peer pressures by training them in refusal skills.

People rarely abuse drugs if they understand the physical and psychological costs, feel good about themselves and the direction their lives are taking, and are in a peer group that disapproves of using drugs. These educational, psychological, and social-cultural factors may help explain why 26 percent of U.S. high school dropouts, but only 6 percent of those with a postgraduate education, report smoking (CDC, 2011).

"Substance use disorders don't discriminate; they affect the rich and the poor; they affect all ethnic groups. This is a public health crisis, but we do have solutions." —U.S. Surgeon General Vivek Murthy, November 2016

🔒 RETRIEVE IT • • •

ANSWERS IN APPENDIX E

RI-6 Why do tobacco companies try so hard to get customers hooked as teens?

RI-7 Studies have found that people who begin drinking in their early teens are much more likely to develop alcohol use disorder than those who begin at age 21 or after. What possible explanations might there be for this correlation?

🔒 REVIEW   DRUGS AND CONSCIOUSNESS

⟫ Learning Objectives

TEST YOURSELF Answer these repeated Learning Objective Questions on your own (before checking the answers in Appendix D) to improve your retention of the concepts (McDaniel et al., 2009, 2015).

9-1 What are *substance use disorders*?

9-2 What roles do tolerance and addiction play in substance use disorders, and how has the concept of *addiction* changed?

9-3 What are *depressants*, and what are their effects?

9-4 What are *stimulants*, and what are their effects?

9-5 What are *hallucinogens*, and what are their effects?

9-6 Why do some people become regular users of consciousness-altering drugs?

⟫ Terms and Concepts to Remember

TEST YOURSELF Write down the definition yourself, then check your answer on the referenced page.

psychoactive drug, **p. 101**

substance use disorder, **p. 101**

tolerance, **p. 102**

withdrawal, **p. 102**

depressants, **p. 103**

alcohol use disorder, **p. 103**

barbiturates, **p. 104**

opiates, **p. 104**

stimulants, **p. 104**

amphetamines, **p. 104**

nicotine, **p. 104**

cocaine, **p. 106**

methamphetamine, **p. 106**

Ecstasy (MDMA), **p. 106**

hallucinogens, **p. 109**

near-death experience, **p. 109**

LSD, **p. 109**

THC, **p. 109**

⟫ Experience the Testing Effect

TEST YOURSELF Answer the following questions on your own first, then check your answers in Appendix E.

1. After continued use of a psychoactive drug, the drug user needs to take larger doses to get the desired effect. This is referred to as _____.

2. The depressants include alcohol, barbiturates,
   a. and opiates.
   b. cocaine, and morphine.
   c. caffeine, nicotine, and marijuana.
   d. and amphetamines.

3. Why might alcohol make a person more helpful *or* more aggressive?

4. Long-term use of Ecstasy can
   a. depress sympathetic nervous system activity.
   b. deplete the brain's supply of epinephrine.
   c. deplete the brain's supply of dopamine.
   d. damage serotonin-producing neurons.

5. Near-death experiences are strikingly similar to the experiences evoked by _____ drugs.

6. Use of marijuana
   a. impairs motor coordination, perception, reaction time, and memory.
   b. inhibits people's emotions.
   c. leads to dehydration and overheating.
   d. stimulates brain cell development.

7. An important psychological contributor to drug use is
   a. inflated self-esteem.
   b. the feeling that life is meaningless and directionless.
   c. genetic predispositions.
   d. overprotective parents.

Continue testing yourself with 📖 **LearningCurve** or 📖 **Achieve Read & Practice** to learn and remember most effectively.

Developing Through the Life Span

Life is a journey, from womb to tomb. So it is for me [DM], and so it will be for you. My story, and yours, began when a man and a woman together contributed 20,000+ genes to an egg that became a unique person. Those genes coded the protein building blocks that, with astonishing precision, formed our bodies and predisposed our traits. My grandmother handed down to my mother a rare hearing-loss pattern, which she, in turn, gave to me (the least of her gifts). My father was an amiable extravert, and sometimes I forget to stop talking (although as a child, my talking was impeded by embarrassing stuttering, for which Seattle Public Schools provided speech therapy).

Along with my parents' nature, I also received their nurture. Like you, I was born into a particular family and culture, with its own way of viewing the world. My values have been shaped by a family culture filled with talking and laughter, by a religious culture that speaks of love and justice, and by an academic culture that encourages critical thinking (asking, *What do you mean? How do you know?*).

We are formed by our genes and by our contexts, so our stories will differ. But in many ways we are each like nearly everyone else on Earth. Being human, you and I have a need to belong. My mental video library, which began after age 4, is filled with scenes of social attachment. Over time, my attachments to parents loosened as peer friendships grew. After lacking confidence to date in high school, I fell in love with a college class-mate and married at age 20. Natural selection predisposes us to survive and perpetuate our genes. Sure enough, two years later a child entered our lives and I experienced a new form of love that surprised me with its intensity.

115

developmental psychology a branch of psychology that studies physical, cognitive, and social change throughout the life span.

But life is marked by change. That child and his brother now live 2000 miles away, and their sister has found her calling in South Africa. The tight rubber bands linking parent and child have loosened, as yours likely have as well.

Change also marks most vocational lives, which for me transitioned from a teen working in the family insurance agency, to a premed chemistry major and hospital aide, to (after discarding my half-completed medical school applications) a psychology professor and author. I predict that in 10 years you, too, will be doing things you do not currently anticipate.

Stability also marks our development: Our life situations change, but we experience a continuous self. When I look in the mirror I do not see the person I once was, but I feel like the person I have always been. I am the same person who, as a late teen, played basketball and discovered love. A half-century later, I still play basketball and still love (with less passion but more security) the life partner with whom I have shared life's griefs and joys.

We experience a continuous self, but that self morphs through stages—for me, growing up, raising children, enjoying a career, and, eventually, life's final stage, which will demand my presence. As I wend my way through this cycle of life and death, I am mindful that life's journey is a continuing process of development, seeded by nature and shaped by nurture, animated by love and focused by work, begun with wide-eyed curiosity and completed, for those blessed to live to a good old age, with peace and never-ending hope.

Across the life span, we grow from newborn to toddler, from toddler to teenager, and from teenager to mature adult. At each stage of life there are physical, cognitive, and social milestones. We begin with prenatal development and the newborn (Module 10). Then we'll turn our attention to infancy and childhood (Module 11), adolescence (Module 12), and adulthood (Module 13). ▶

⓾ Developmental Issues, Prenatal Development, and the Newborn

DEVELOPMENTAL PSYCHOLOGY'S MAJOR ISSUES

LEARNING OBJECTIVE QUESTION (LOQ)

10-1 What three issues have engaged developmental psychologists?

Researchers find human development interesting for the same reasons most of the rest of us do—they want to understand more about how we've become our current selves, and how we may change in the years ahead. **Developmental psychology** examines our physical, cognitive, and social development across the life span, with a focus on three major issues:

1. *Nature and nurture:* How does our genetic inheritance (our *nature*) interact with our experiences (our *nurture*) to influence our development? How have your nature and your nurture influenced *your* life story?

2. *Continuity and stages:* What parts of development are gradual and continuous, like riding an escalator? What parts change abruptly in separate stages, like climbing rungs on a ladder?

3. *Stability and change:* Which of our traits persist through life? How do we change as we age?

"Nature is all that a man brings with him into the world; nurture is every influence that affects him after his birth." —Francis Galton, *English Men of Science*, 1874

Nature and Nurture

The unique gene combination created when our mother's egg engulfed our father's sperm helped form us, as individuals. Genes predispose both our shared humanity and our individual differences.

But our experiences also shape us. Our families and peer relationships teach us how to think and act. Even differences initiated by our nature may be amplified by our nurture. We are not formed by either nature or nurture, but by the interaction between them. Biological, psychological, and social-cultural forces interact.

Mindful of how others differ from us, however, we often fail to notice the similarities stemming from our shared biology. Regardless of our culture, we humans share the same life cycle. We speak to our infants in similar ways and respond similarly to their coos and cries (Bornstein et al., 1992a,b). Although ethnic groups have differed in some ways, including average school achievement, the differences are "no more than skin deep." To the extent that family structure, peer influences, and parental education predict behavior in one of these ethnic groups, they do so for the others as well. Compared with the person-to-person differences within groups, between-group differences are small.

Continuity and Stages

Do adults differ from infants as a giant redwood differs from its seedling—a difference created by gradual, cumulative growth? Or do they differ as a butterfly differs from a caterpillar—a difference of distinct stages?

Researchers who emphasize experience and learning typically see development as a slow, continuous shaping process. Those who emphasize biological maturation tend to see development as a sequence of genetically predisposed stages or steps: Although progress through the various stages may be quick or slow, everyone passes through the stages in the same order.

Are there clear-cut stages of psychological development, as there are physical stages such as walking before running? The *stage theories* we will consider—of Jean Piaget on cognitive development, Lawrence Kohlberg on moral development, and Erik Erikson on psychosocial development—propose developmental stages (summarized in **FIGURE 10.1**). But as we will also see, some research casts doubt on the idea that life proceeds through neatly defined age-linked stages.

Although many modern developmental psychologists do not identify as stage theorists, the stage concept remains useful. The human brain does experience growth spurts during childhood and puberty that correspond roughly to Piaget's stages (Thatcher et al., 1987). And stage theories contribute a developmental perspective on the whole life span by suggesting how people of one age think and act differently when they arrive at a later age.

Stages of the life cycle.

FIGURE 10.1

COMPARING THE STAGE THEORIES[1]

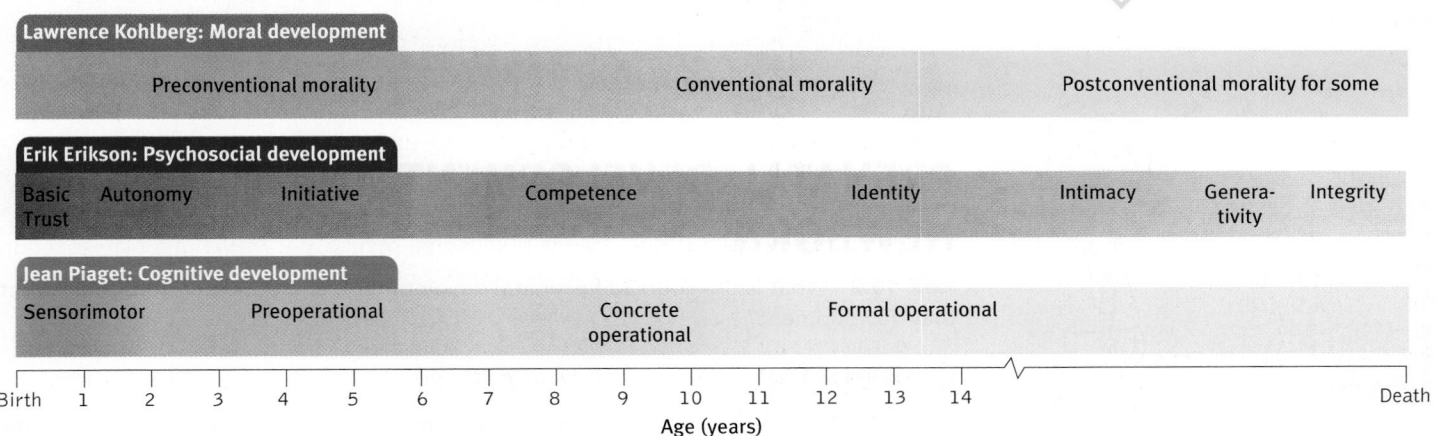

1. With thanks to Dr. Sandra Gibbs, Muskegon Community College, for inspiring this illustration.

(a)

(b)

SMILES PREDICT MARITAL STABILITY
In one study of 306 U.S. college alums, 1 in 4 with yearbook expressions like the one in photo (a) later divorced, as did only 1 in 20 with smiles like the one in photo (b) (Hertenstein et al., 2009).

"At 70, I would say the advantage is that you take life more calmly. You know that 'this, too, shall pass'!" —Eleanor Roosevelt, 1954

"When I look at myself in the first grade and I look at myself now, I'm basically the same. The temperament is not that different." —Donald J. Trump to his biographer in *Never Enough*, 2015

"As at 7, so at 70." —Jewish proverb

(ASK YOURSELF)

Are you the same person you were as a preschooler? As an 8-year-old? As a 12-year-old? How do you differ? How are you the same?

As adults grow older, there is continuity of self.

Stability and Change

As we follow lives through time, do we find more evidence for stability or change? If reunited with a long-lost grade-school friend, do we instantly realize that "it's the same old Andy"? Or do long-ago friends now seem like strangers? (At least one acquaintance of mine [DM's] would choose the second option. At his 40-year college reunion, he failed to recognize a former classmate. The understandably appalled classmate was his first wife!)

We experience both stability and change. Some of our characteristics, such as *temperament*, are very stable. One research team that studied 1000 people from ages 3 to 38 was struck by the consistency of temperament and emotionality across time (Moffitt et al., 2013; Slutske et al., 2012). Out-of-control 3-year-olds were the most likely to engage in teen smoking, adult criminal behavior, or out-of-control gambling. Researchers have also confirmed stability of moods when following 174 Scots across 63 years—from age 14 to 77 (Harris et al., 2016). Other studies report that the children who are repeatedly cruel to animals often become violent adults, and, on a happier note, that the widest smilers in childhood and college photos are, years later, the ones most likely to enjoy enduring marriages (Hensley et al., 2017; Hertenstein et al., 2009).

We cannot, however, predict all aspects of our future selves based on our early life. Our social attitudes, for example, are much less stable than our temperament, especially during the impressionable late adolescent years (Krosnick & Alwin, 1989; Rekker et al., 2015). Older children and adolescents learn new ways of coping. Although delinquent children have elevated rates of later problems, many confused and troubled children blossom into mature, successful adults (Moffitt et al., 2002; Roberts et al., 2013; Thomas & Chess, 1986). Life is a process of becoming. Our present struggles may lay the foundation for a happier tomorrow.

In some ways, we *all* change with age. Most shy, fearful toddlers begin opening up by age 4, and most people become more conscientious, stable, agreeable, and self-confident in the years after adolescence (Lucas & Donnellan, 2009; Shaw et al., 2010; Van den Akker et al., 2014). Risk-prone adolescents tend to become more cautious adults (Mata et al., 2016). Indeed, many irresponsible 18-year-olds have matured into 40-year-old business or cultural leaders. (If you are the former, you aren't done yet.)

Life requires *both* stability and change. Stability provides our identity. Change gives us our hope for a brighter future, allowing us to adapt and grow with experience.

🔒 **RETRIEVE IT** • • •   *ANSWERS IN APPENDIX E*

RI-1 Developmental researchers who consider how biological, psychological, and social-cultural forces interact are focusing on _____ and _____.

RI-2 Developmental researchers who emphasize learning and experience are supporting _____; those who emphasize biological maturation are supporting _____.

RI-3 What findings in psychology support (1) the stage theory of development and (2) the idea of stability in personality across the life span?

PRENATAL DEVELOPMENT AND THE NEWBORN

LOQ 10-2 What is the course of prenatal development, and how do *teratogens* affect that development?

Conception

ENGAGE Nothing is more natural than a species reproducing itself. And nothing is more wondrous. For you, the process started inside your *grandmother*—as an egg formed inside a developing female inside of her. (Your mother was born with all the immature

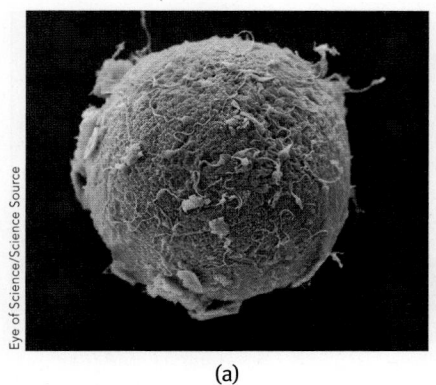

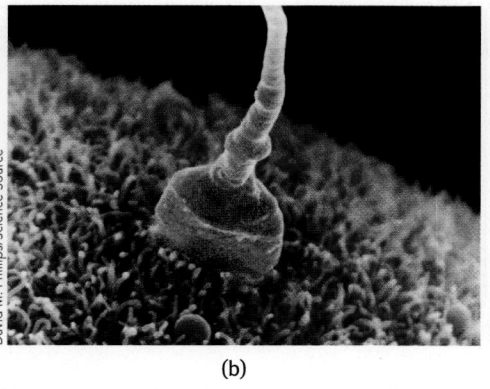

(a)   (b)

FIGURE 10.2

LIFE IS SEXUALLY TRANSMITTED (a) Sperm cells surround an egg. (b) As one sperm penetrates the egg's jellylike outer coating, a series of chemical events begins that will cause sperm and egg to fuse into a single cell. If all goes well, that cell will subdivide again and again to emerge 9 months later as a 37-trillion-cell human being.

eggs she would ever have.) Your father, in contrast, began producing sperm cells nonstop at *puberty*—in the beginning at a rate of more than 1000 sperm during the second it takes to read this phrase.

Some time after puberty, your mother's ovary released a mature egg—a cell roughly the size of the period that ends this sentence. Like space voyagers approaching a huge planet, some 250 million deposited sperm began their frantic race upstream, approaching a cell 85,000 times their own size. The small number reaching the egg released digestive enzymes that ate away the egg's protective coating (**FIGURE 10.2a**). The one winning sperm penetrated the coating and was welcomed in (Figure 10.2b), the egg's surface blocking out the others. Before half a day elapsed, the egg nucleus and the sperm nucleus fused: The two became one.

Consider it your most fortunate of moments. Among 250 million sperm, the one needed to make you, in combination with that one particular egg, won the race. And so it was for innumerable generations before us. If any one of our ancestors had been conceived with a different sperm or egg, or died before conceiving, or not chanced to meet their partner or. . . . The mind boggles at the improbable, unbroken chain of events that produced us.

Prenatal Development

How many fertilized eggs, called **zygotes,** survive beyond the first 2 weeks? Fewer than half (Grobstein, 1979; Hall, 2004). But for us, good fortune prevailed. One cell became 2, then 4—each just like the first—until this cell division had produced some 100 identical cells within the first week. Then the cells began to differentiate—to specialize in structure and function ("I'll become a brain, you become intestines!").

About 10 days after conception, the zygote attaches to the mother's uterine wall, beginning approximately 37 weeks of the closest human relationship. The zygote's inner cells become the **embryo** (**FIGURE 10.3a**). Many of its outer cells become the *placenta,* the life-link that transfers nutrients and oxygen from mother to embryo. Over the next 6 weeks, the embryo's organs begin to form and function. The heart begins to beat.

By 9 weeks after conception, an embryo looks unmistakably human (Figure 10.3b). It is now a **fetus** (Latin for "offspring" or "young one"). During the sixth month, organs such as the stomach have developed enough to give the fetus a good chance of surviving and thriving if born prematurely.

At each prenatal stage, genetic and environmental factors affect our development. By the sixth month, the fetus is responsive to sound. Microphone readings taken inside the uterus reveal that the fetus is exposed to the sound of its mother's muffled voice (Ecklund-Flores, 1992; Hepper, 2005). Immediately after emerging from their underwater world, newborns prefer their mother's voice to another woman's, or to their father's (DeCasper et al., 1986, 1994; Lee & Kisilevsky, 2014).

They also prefer hearing their mother's language. In one study, day-old American and Swedish newborns paused more in their pacifier sucking when listening to familiar vowels from their mother's language (Moon et al., 2013). After repeatedly hearing a fake word (*tatata*) in the womb, Finnish newborns' brain waves displayed recognition when hearing the word after birth (Partanen et al., 2013). If their mother spoke two languages during

zygote the fertilized egg; it enters a 2-week period of rapid cell division and develops into an embryo.

embryo the developing human organism from about 2 weeks after fertilization through the second month.

fetus the developing human organism from 9 weeks after conception to birth.

 ENGAGE Care to guess your body's total number of cells?[2]

---

2. ANSWER: By one careful estimate, the average human has 37.2 trillion cells (Bianconi et al., 2013).

FIGURE 10.3

PRENATAL DEVELOPMENT (a) The embryo grows and develops rapidly. At 40 days, the spine is visible and the arms and legs are beginning to grow. (b) By the start of the ninth week, when the fetal period begins, facial features, hands, and feet have formed. (c) As the fetus enters the sixteenth week, its 3 ounces could fit in the palm of your hand.

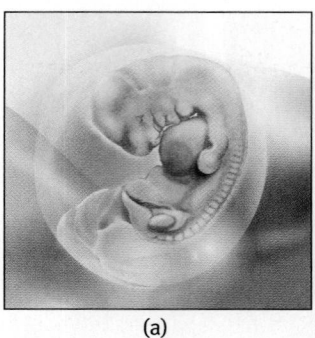 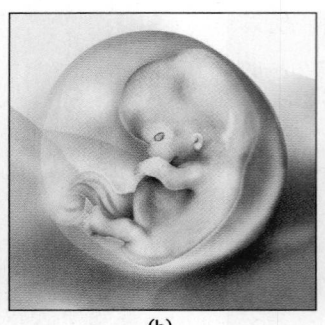 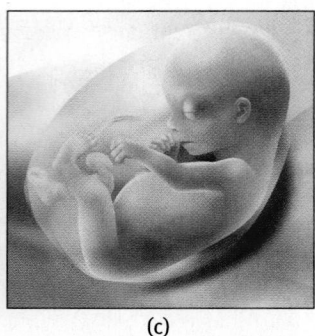

(a)   (b)   (c)

teratogens (literally, "monster makers") agents, such as chemicals and viruses, that can reach the embryo or fetus during prenatal development and cause harm.

fetal alcohol syndrome (FAS) physical and cognitive abnormalities in children caused by a pregnant woman's heavy drinking. In severe cases, signs include a small, out-of-proportion head and abnormal facial features.

Prenatal development

Zygote: Conception to 2 weeks
Embryo: 2 to 9 weeks
Fetus: 9 weeks to birth

"You shall conceive and bear a son. So then drink no wine or strong drink."
—Judges 13:7

LaunchPad For an interactive review of prenatal development, see **Topic Tutorial: PsychSim6, Conception to Birth.** See also the 8-minute **Video: Prenatal Development.**

pregnancy, newborns displayed interest in both (Byers-Heinlein et al., 2010). And just after birth, the melodic ups and downs of newborns' cries bear the tuneful signature of their mother's native tongue (Mampe et al., 2009). Babies born to French-speaking mothers tended to cry with the rising intonation of French; babies born to German-speaking mothers cried with the falling tones of German. Would you have guessed? The learning of language begins in the womb.

In the two months before birth, fetuses demonstrate learning in other ways, as when they adapt to a vibrating, honking device placed on their mother's abdomen (Dirix et al., 2009). Like people who adapt to the sound of trains in their neighborhood, fetuses get used to the honking. Moreover, four weeks later, they recall the sound (as evidenced by their blasé response, compared with the reactions of those fetuses not previously exposed).

Sounds are not the only environmental factors that impact fetal development. In addition to transferring nutrients and oxygen from mother to fetus, the placenta screens out many harmful substances. But some slip by. **Teratogens,** agents such as viruses and drugs, can damage an embryo or fetus. This is one reason pregnant women are advised not to drink alcoholic beverages or smoke cigarettes or marijuana (Saint Louis, 2017). A pregnant woman never drinks or smokes alone. When alcohol enters her bloodstream and that of her fetus, it reduces activity in both their central nervous systems. Alcohol use during pregnancy may prime the woman's offspring to like alcohol and may put them at risk for heavy drinking and alcohol use disorder during their teen years. In experiments, when pregnant rats drank alcohol, their young offspring later displayed a liking for alcohol's taste and odor (Youngentob & Glendinning, 2009; Youngentob et al. 2007).

Even light drinking or occasional binge drinking can affect the fetal brain (Braun, 1996; Marjonen et al., 2015). Persistent heavy drinking puts the fetus at risk for a dangerously low birth weight, birth defects, future behavior problems, and lower intelligence. For 1 in about 700 children, the effects are visible as **fetal alcohol syndrome (FAS),** the most serious of all fetal alcohol spectrum disorders, marked by lifelong physical and mental abnormalities (May et al., 2014). The fetal damage may occur because alcohol has an *epigenetic effect:* It leaves chemical marks on DNA that switch genes abnormally on or off (Liu et al., 2009). Smoking during pregnancy also leaves epigenetic scars that weaken infants' ability to handle stress (Stroud et al., 2014).

If a pregnant woman experiences extreme stress, the stress hormones flooding her body may indicate a survival threat to the fetus and produce an earlier delivery (Glynn & Sandman, 2011). Some stress in early life prepares us to cope with later adversity. But substantial prenatal stress exposure, including famine or malnourishment, puts a child at increased risk for health problems such as hypertension, heart disease, obesity, and psychiatric disorders (Barker, 2012).

🔒 RETRIEVE IT • • •   ANSWERS IN APPENDIX E

RI-4 The first two weeks of prenatal development is the period of the _____. The period of the _____ lasts from 9 weeks after conception until birth. The time between those two prenatal periods is considered the period of the _____.

The Competent Newborn

LOQ 10-3 What are some newborn abilities, and how do researchers explore infants' mental abilities?

Babies come with apps preloaded. Having survived prenatal hazards, we as newborns came equipped with automatic reflex responses ideally suited for our survival. We withdrew our limbs to escape pain. If a cloth over our face interfered with our breathing, we turned our head from side to side and swiped at it.

New parents are often in awe of the coordinated sequence of reflexes by which their baby gets food. When something touches their cheek, babies turn toward that touch, open their mouth, and vigorously *root* for a nipple. Finding one, they automatically close on it and begin *sucking*. (Failing to find satisfaction, the hungry baby may cry—a behavior parents find highly unpleasant, and very rewarding to relieve.) Other adaptive reflexes include the *startle* reflex (when arms and legs spring out, quickly followed by fist clenching and loud crying) and the surprisingly strong *grasping* reflex, both of which may have helped infants stay close to their caregivers.

The pioneering American psychologist William James presumed that newborns experience a "blooming, buzzing confusion," an assumption few people challenged until the 1960s. Then scientists discovered that babies can tell you a lot—if you know how to ask. To ask, you must capitalize on what babies can do—gaze, suck, and turn their heads. So, equipped with eye-tracking machines and pacifiers wired to electronic gear, researchers set out to answer parents' age-old questions: What can my baby see, hear, smell, and think?

Consider how researchers exploit **habituation**—decreased responding with repeated stimulation. We saw this earlier when fetuses adapted to a vibrating, honking device placed on their mother's abdomen. The novel stimulus gets attention when first presented. With repetition, the response weakens. This seeming boredom with familiar stimuli gives us a way to ask infants what they see and remember.

As newborns, we prefer sights and sounds that facilitate social responsiveness. We turn our heads in the direction of human voices. We gaze longer at a drawing of a facelike image (**FIGURE 10.4**). Even late-stage fetuses look more at face-like patterns in red lights shined through the womb (Reid et al., 2017). As young infants, we also prefer to look at objects 8 to 12 inches away, which—wonder of wonders—just happens to be about the distance between a nursing infant's eyes and its mother's (Maurer & Maurer, 1988). Our brain's default settings help us connect socially.

Within days after birth, our brain's neural networks were stamped with the smell of our mother's body. Week-old nursing babies, placed between a gauze pad from their mother's bra and one from another nursing mother, have usually turned toward the smell of their own mother's pad (MacFarlane, 1978). What's more, that smell preference lasts. One experiment capitalized on the fact that some nursing mothers in a French maternity ward used a chamomile-scented balm to prevent nipple soreness (Delaunay-El Allam et al., 2010). Twenty-one months later, their toddlers preferred playing with chamomile-scented toys! Their peers who had not sniffed the scent while breast-feeding showed no such preference. (This makes us wonder: Will these children grow up to become devoted chamomile tea drinkers?) Such studies reveal the remarkable abilities with which we enter our world.

"I felt like a man trapped in a woman's body. Then I was born." —Comedian Chris Bliss

habituation decreasing responsiveness with repeated stimulation. As infants gain familiarity with repeated exposure to a stimulus, their interest wanes and they look away sooner.

FIGURE 10.4
NEWBORNS' PREFERENCE FOR FACES When shown these two stimuli with the same elements, Italian newborns spent nearly twice as many seconds looking at the face-like image (Johnson & Morton, 1991). Canadian newborns—average age 53 minutes in one study—displayed the same apparently inborn preference to look toward faces (Mondloch et al., 1999).

PREPARED TO FEED AND EAT Humans and other animals are predisposed to respond to their offspring's cries for nourishment, even if they are in the middle of a 314-mile ultramarathon, as I [ND] was when my 18-month-old Bevy decided that only Daddy could feed her.

🔒 **RETRIEVE IT** • • •   *ANSWERS IN APPENDIX E*

RI-5 Infants' _____ to repeated stimulation helps developmental psychologists study what infants can learn and remember.

🔒 REVIEW DEVELOPMENTAL ISSUES, PRENATAL DEVELOPMENT, AND THE NEWBORN

⟫ Learning Objectives

TEST YOURSELF Answer these repeated Learning Objective Questions on your own (before checking the answers in Appendix D) to improve your retention of the concepts (McDaniel et al., 2009, 2015).

10-1 What three issues have engaged developmental psychologists?

10-2 What is the course of prenatal development, and how do *teratogens* affect that development?

10-3 What are some newborn abilities, and how do researchers explore infants' mental abilities?

⟫ Terms and Concepts to Remember

TEST YOURSELF Write down the definition yourself, then check your answer on the referenced page.

developmental psychology, **p. 116**

zygote, **p. 119**

embryo, **p. 119**

fetus, **p. 119**

teratogens, **p. 120**

fetal alcohol syndrome (FAS), **p. 120**

habituation, **p. 121**

⟫ Experience the Testing Effect

TEST YOURSELF Answer the following questions on your own first, then check your answers in Appendix E.

1. The three major issues that interest developmental psychologists are nature/nurture, stability/change, and _____/_____.

2. Although development is lifelong, there is stability of personality over time. For example,
   a. most personality traits emerge in infancy and persist throughout life.
   b. temperament tends to remain stable throughout life.
   c. few people change significantly after adolescence.
   d. people tend to undergo greater personality changes as they age.

3. Body organs first begin to form and function during the period of the _____; within 6 months, during the period of the _____, organs are sufficiently functional to provide a good chance of surviving and thriving.
   a. zygote; embryo
   b. zygote; fetus
   c. embryo; fetus
   d. placenta; fetus

4. Chemicals that the placenta isn't able to screen out that may harm an embryo or fetus are called _____.

Continue testing yourself with 🞄 **LearningCurve** or 🞄 **Achieve Read & Practice** to learn and remember most effectively.

··

maturation biological growth processes that enable orderly changes in behavior, relatively uninfluenced by experience.

"It is a rare privilege to watch the birth, growth, and first feeble struggles of a living human mind." —Annie Sullivan, in Helen Keller's *The Story of My Life*, 1903

11 Infancy and Childhood

As a flower unfolds in accord with its genetic instructions, so do we. **Maturation**—the orderly sequence of biological growth—decrees many of our commonalities. Babies first stand, then walk. Toddlers first use nouns, then adjectives. Severe deprivation or abuse can slow development, but genetic growth patterns are inborn. Maturation (nature) sets the basic course of development; experience (nurture) adjusts it. Genes and scenes interact.

PHYSICAL DEVELOPMENT

LOQ 11-1 During infancy and childhood, how do the brain and motor skills develop?

Brain Development

Our formative nurture began at conception, with the prenatal environment in the womb. Nurture continued outside the womb, where our early experiences fostered brain development.

In your mother's womb, your developing brain formed nerve cells at the explosive rate of nearly one-quarter million per minute. On the day you were born, you had most of the brain cells you would ever have. However, the wiring among these cells—your nervous system—was immature: After birth, these neural networks had a wild growth spurt branching and linking in patterns that would eventually enable you to walk, talk, and remember (**FIGURE 11.1**). This rapid development helps explain why infant brain size increases rapidly in the early days after birth (Holland et al., 2014).

From ages 3 to 6, the most rapid brain growth was in your frontal lobes, which enable rational planning. During those years, your brain required vast amounts of energy (Kuzawa et al., 2014). This energy-intensive process caused rapid progress in your ability to control your attention and behavior (Garon et al., 2008; Thompson-Schill et al., 2009). Frontal lobe development continues into adolescence and beyond.

The brain's association areas—those linked with thinking, memory, and language—were the last cortical areas to develop. As they did, your mental abilities surged (Chugani & Phelps, 1986; Thatcher et al., 1987). Fiber pathways supporting agility, language, and self-control proliferated into puberty. Under the influence of adrenal hormones, tens of billions of synapses formed and organized, while a use-it-or-lose-it *pruning* process shut down unused links (Paus et al., 1999; Thompson et al., 2000).

Your genes dictate your overall brain architecture, rather like the lines of a coloring book, but experience fills in the details (Kenrick et al., 2009). So how do early experiences leave their "fingerprints" in the brain? Mark Rosenzweig, David Krech, and their colleagues (1962) opened a window on that process when they raised some young rats in solitary confinement, and others in a communal playground that simulated a natural environment. When the researchers later analyzed the rats' brains, those living in the enriched environment had usually developed a heavier and thicker brain cortex (**FIGURE 11.2**). So great are the effects that, shown brief video clips of the rats, you could tell from their activity and curiosity whether their environment had been impoverished or enriched (Renner & Renner, 1993). After 60 days in the enriched environment, the rats' brain weights increased 7 to 10 percent and the number of synapses mushroomed by about 20 percent (Kolb & Whishaw, 1998).

Such results have motivated improvements in environments for laboratory, farm, and zoo animals—and for children in institutions. Stimulation by touch or massage also benefits infant rats and premature babies (Field et al., 2007; Sarro et al., 2014). "Handled" infants of both species develop faster neurologically and gain weight more rapidly. Preemies who have had skin-to-skin contact with their mothers sleep better, experience less stress, and show better cognitive development 10 years later (Feldman et al., 2014).

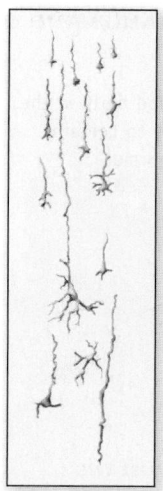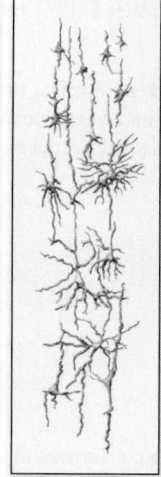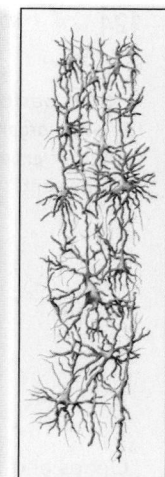

Newborn   3 months   15 months

FIGURE 11.1

INFANT BRAIN DEVELOPMENT In humans, the brain is immature at birth. As the child matures, the neural networks grow increasingly complex.

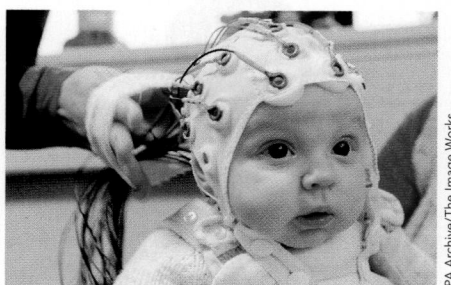

THE BABY EXPERIMENT This "electrode cap" allows researchers to detect changes in brain activity triggered by different stimuli.

FIGURE 11.2

EXPERIENCE AFFECTS BRAIN DEVELOPMENT Mark Rosenzweig, David Krech, and their colleagues (1962) raised rats either alone in an environment without playthings, or with other rats in an environment enriched with playthings changed daily. In 14 of 16 repetitions of this basic experiment, rats in the enriched environment developed significantly more cerebral cortex (relative to the rest of the brain's tissue) than did those in the impoverished environment.

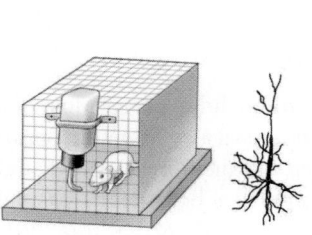  

Impoverished   **Impoverished**   **Enriched**   **Enriched**
environment   **rat brain cell**   **environment**   **rat brain cell**

critical period an optimal period early in the life of an organism when exposure to certain stimuli or experiences produces normal development.

"Genes and experiences are just two ways of doing the same thing—wiring synapses." —Joseph LeDoux, *The Synaptic Self* (2002)

PHYSICAL DEVELOPMENT Sit, crawl, walk, run—the sequence of these motor development milestones is the same around the world, though babies reach them at varying ages.

Juice Images/JupiterImages/Getty Images

In the eight years following the 1994 launch of a U.S. Back to Sleep educational campaign, the number of infants sleeping on their stomach dropped from 70 to 11 percent—and sudden unexpected infant deaths fell significantly (Braiker, 2005).

"*Someday we'll look back at this time in our lives and be unable to remember it.*"

Nature and nurture interact to sculpt our synapses. Brain maturation provides us with an abundance of neural connections. Experiences—sights and smells, touches and tastes, music and movement—activate and strengthen some neural pathways while others weaken from disuse. Like forest pathways, popular tracks are broadened and less-traveled ones gradually disappear. The result by puberty is a massive loss of unemployed connections.

Here at the juncture of nurture and nature is the biological reality of early childhood learning. During early childhood—while excess connections are still on call—youngsters can most easily master such skills as the grammar and accent of another language. We seem to have a **critical period** for some skills. Lacking any exposure to spoken, written, or signed language before adolescence, a person will never master any language. Likewise, lacking visual experience during the early years, a person whose vision is restored by cataract removal will never achieve normal perceptions (Gregory, 1978; Wiesel, 1982). Without that early visual stimulation, the brain cells normally assigned to vision will die during the pruning process or be diverted to other uses. The maturing brain's rule: Use it or lose it.

Although normal stimulation during the early years is critical, the brain's development does not end with childhood. Thanks to the brain's amazing *plasticity,* our neural tissue is ever changing and reorganizing in response to new experiences. New neurons also are born. If a monkey pushes a lever with the same finger many times a day, brain tissue controlling that finger changes to reflect the experience. Human brains work similarly. Whether learning to keyboard, skateboard, or navigate London's streets, we perform with increasing skill as our brain incorporates the learning (Ambrose, 2010; Maguire et al., 2000).

Motor Development

The developing brain enables physical coordination. Skills emerge as infants exercise their maturing muscles and nervous system. With occasional exceptions, the motor development sequence is universal. Babies roll over before they sit unsupported, and they usually crawl before they walk. These behaviors reflect not imitation but a maturing nervous system; blind children, too, crawl before they walk.

Genes guide motor development. In the United States, 25 percent of all babies walk by 11 months of age, 50 percent within a week after their first birthday, and 90 percent by age 15 months (Frankenburg et al., 1992). Identical twins typically begin walking on nearly the same day (Wilson, 1979). Maturation—including the rapid development of the cerebellum at the back of the brain—creates our readiness to learn walking at about age 1. The same is true for other physical skills, including bowel and bladder control. Before necessary muscular and neural maturation, neither pleading nor punishment will produce successful toilet training. You can't rush a child's first flush.

Still, nurture may amend what nature intends. In some regions of Africa, the Caribbean, and India, caregivers frequently massage and exercise babies, which can accelerate the process of learning to walk (Karasik et al., 2010). The recommended infant *back to sleep position* (putting babies to sleep on their backs to reduce crib-death risk) has been associated with somewhat later crawling but not with later walking (Davis et al., 1998; Lipsitt, 2003).

🔒 **RETRIEVE IT • • •**   *ANSWERS IN APPENDIX E*

RI-1 The biological growth process called _____ explains why most children begin walking by about 12 to 15 months.

Brain Maturation and Infant Memory

ENGAGE Can you recall your first day of preschool or your third birthday party? Most of us *consciously* recall little from before age 4. Mice and monkeys also forget their early life, as rapid neuron growth disrupts the circuits that stored old memories (Akers et al., 2014). But as children mature, this *infantile amnesia* wanes, and they become increasingly capable of remembering experiences, even for a year or more (Bauer & Larkina, 2014; Morris et al., 2010). The brain areas underlying memory, such as the hippocampus and frontal lobes, continue to mature during and after adolescence (Luby et al., 2016; Murty et al., 2016).

Despite consciously recalling little from our early years, our brain was processing and storing information. While finishing her doctoral work in psychology, Carolyn Rovee-Collier observed nonverbal infant memory in action. Her colicky 2-month-old, Benjamin, could be calmed by moving a crib mobile. Weary of hitting the mobile, she strung a cloth ribbon connecting the mobile to Benjamin's foot. Soon, he was kicking his foot to move the mobile. Thinking about her unintended home experiment, Rovee-Collier realized that, contrary to popular opinion in the 1960s, babies can learn. To know for sure that her son wasn't just a whiz kid, she repeated the experiment with other infants (Rovee-Collier, 1989, 1999). Sure enough, they, too, soon kicked more when hitched to a mobile, both on the day of the experiment and the day after. If, however, she hitched them to a different mobile the next day, the infants showed no learning, indicating that they remembered the original mobile and recognized the difference. Moreover, when tethered to the familiar mobile a month later, they remembered the association and again began kicking (**FIGURE 11.3**).

Traces of forgotten childhood languages may also persist. One study tested English-speaking British adults who had no conscious memory of the Hindi or Zulu they had spoken as children. Yet, up to age 40, they could relearn subtle sound contrasts in these languages that other English speakers could *not* learn (Bowers et al., 2009). Chinese adoptees living in Canada since age 1 process Chinese sounds as do native speakers, even if they have no conscious recollection of Chinese words (Pierce et al., 2014). Again, our two-track mind is at work: What the conscious mind does not know and cannot express in words, the nervous system and unconscious mind somehow remember.

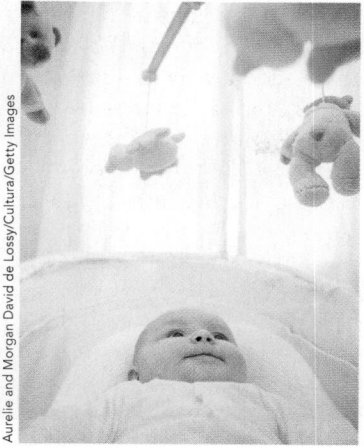

Aurelie and Morgan David de Lossy/Cultura/Getty Images

FIGURE 11.3

INFANT AT WORK Babies only 3 months old learned that kicking moves a mobile, and they retained that learning for a month (Rovee-Collier, 1989, 1997).

ENGAGE **ASK YOURSELF**

What do you regard as your earliest memory? Now that you know about infantile amnesia, has your opinion changed about the accuracy of that memory?

cognition all the mental activities associated with thinking, knowing, remembering, and communicating.

schema a concept or framework that organizes and interprets information.

assimilation interpreting our new experiences in terms of our existing schemas.

accommodation adapting our current understandings (schemas) to incorporate new information.

COGNITIVE DEVELOPMENT

LOQ 11-2 From the perspectives of Piaget, Vygotsky, and today's researchers, how does a child's mind develop?

ENGAGE Somewhere on your life journey, you became conscious. When was that? And once conscious, how did your mind grow? Jean Piaget [pee-ah-ZHAY] was a pioneering developmental psychologist who spent his life searching for the answers to such questions. He studied children's developing **cognition**—all the mental activities associated with thinking, knowing, remembering, and communicating. His interest in children's cognitive development began in 1920, when he was in Paris developing questions for children's intelligence tests. While administering the tests, Piaget became intrigued by children's wrong answers, which were often strikingly similar among same-age children. Where others saw childish mistakes, Piaget saw intelligence at work. Such accidental discoveries are among the fruits of psychological science.

A half-century spent with children convinced Piaget that a child's mind is not a miniature model of an adult's. Thanks partly to his careful observations, we now understand that children reason differently than adults, in "wildly illogical ways" (Brainerd, 1996).

Piaget's studies led him to believe that a child's mind develops through a series of stages, in an upward march from the newborn's simple reflexes to the adult's abstract reasoning power. Thus, an 8-year-old can comprehend things a toddler cannot, such as the analogy that "getting an idea is like having a light turn on in your head."

Piaget's core idea was that our intellectual progression reflects an unceasing struggle to make sense of our experiences. To this end, the maturing brain builds **schemas**—concepts or mental molds into which we pour our experiences.

To explain how we use and adjust our schemas, Piaget proposed two more concepts. First, we **assimilate** new experiences—we interpret them in terms of our current understandings (schemas). Having a simple schema for *dog,* for example, a toddler may call all four-legged animals *dogs.* But as we interact with the world, we also adjust, or **accommodate,** our schemas to incorporate information provided by new experiences.

JEAN PIAGET (1896–1980) "If we examine the intellectual development of the individual or of the whole of humanity, we shall find that the human spirit goes through a certain number of stages, each different from the other" (1930).

Bill Anderson/Science Source

FIGURE 11.4
A CHANGING MARRIAGE SCHEMA
A generation ago, most people had a schema of marriage as a union between a man and a woman. The Netherlands was the first country to change its marriage laws to accommodate same-sex marriage (in 2001). Today, more than 20 other countries have also legalized same-sex marriage.

Image Ideas/Getty Images

Christian L Birmele

ASK YOURSELF

Can you recall a time when you misheard some song lyrics because you assimilated them into your own schema? (For hundreds of examples of this phenomenon, visit kissthisguy.com.)

sensorimotor stage in Piaget's theory, the stage (from birth to nearly 2 years of age) during which infants know the world mostly in terms of their sensory impressions and motor activities.

object permanence the awareness that things continue to exist even when not perceived.

FIGURE 11.5

OBJECT PERMANENCE Infants younger than 6 months seldom understand that things continue to exist when they are out of sight. But for this older infant, out of sight is definitely not out of mind.

Thus, the child soon learns that the original *dog* schema is too broad and accommodates by refining the category. By adulthood we have built countless schemas, ranging from *cats* and *dogs* to our concept of *love* (**FIGURE 11.4**).

Piaget's Theory and Current Thinking

Piaget believed that children construct their understanding of the world while interacting with it. Their minds experience spurts of change, followed by greater stability as they move from one cognitive plateau to the next, each with distinctive characteristics that permit specific kinds of thinking. In Piaget's view, cognitive development consisted of four major stages—*sensorimotor, preoperational, concrete operational,* and *formal operational.*

SENSORIMOTOR STAGE In the **sensorimotor stage,** from birth to nearly age 2, babies take in the world through their senses and actions—through looking, hearing, touching, mouthing, and grasping. As their hands and limbs begin to move, they learn to make things happen.

Very young babies seem to live in the present: Out of sight is out of mind. In one test, Piaget showed an infant an appealing toy and then flopped his beret over it. Before the age of 6 months, the infant acted as if the toy ceased to exist. Young infants lack **object permanence**—the awareness that objects continue to exist when not perceived. By 8 months, infants begin exhibiting memory for things no longer seen. If you hide a toy, the infant will momentarily look for it (**FIGURE 11.5**). Within another month or two, the infant will look for it even after being restrained for several seconds.

So does object permanence in fact blossom suddenly at 8 months, much as tulips blossom in spring? Today's researchers believe object permanence unfolds gradually, and they see development as more continuous than Piaget did. Even young infants will at least momentarily look for a toy where they saw it hidden a second before (Wang et al., 2004).

© Doug Goodman/Science Source

Researchers also believe Piaget and his followers underestimated young children's competence. Young children think like little scientists. They test ideas, make causal inferences, and learn from statistical patterns (Gopnik et al., 2015). Consider these simple experiments:

- **Baby physics:** Like adults staring in disbelief at a magic trick (the *"Whoa!"* look), infants look longer at and explore an unexpected, impossible, or unfamiliar scene—a car seeming to pass through a solid object, a ball stopping in midair, or an object violating object permanence by magically disappearing (Baillargeon, 2008; Shuwairi & Johnson, 2013; Stahl & Feigenson, 2015). Why do infants show this visual bias? Because impossible events violate infants' expectations (Baillargeon et al., 2016).

- **Baby math:** Karen Wynn (1992, 2000, 2008) showed 5-month-olds one or two objects (**FIGURE 11.6a**). Then she hid the objects behind a screen, and visibly removed or added one (Figure 11.6d). When she lifted the screen, the infants sometimes did a double take, staring longer when shown a wrong number of objects (Figure 11.6f). But were they just responding to a greater or smaller *mass* of objects, rather than a change in *number* (Feigenson et al., 2002)? Later experiments showed that babies' number sense extends to larger numbers, to ratios, and to such things as drumbeats and motions (Libertus & Brannon, 2009; McCrink & Wynn, 2004; Spelke et al., 2013). If accustomed to a Daffy Duck puppet jumping three times on stage, they showed surprise if it jumped only twice.

Clearly, infants are smarter than Piaget appreciated. Even as babies, we had a lot on our minds.

(a) Objects placed in case

(b) Screen comes up

(c) Empty hand enters

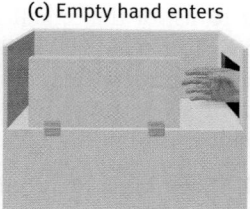

(d) One object removed

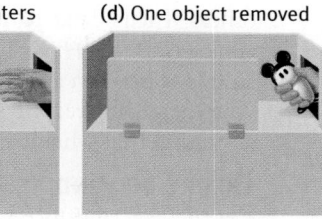

PREOPERATIONAL STAGE Piaget believed that until about age 6 or 7, children are in a **preoperational stage**—able to represent things with words and images but too young to perform *mental operations* (such as imagining an action and mentally reversing it). For a 5-year-old, the milk that seems "too much" in a tall, narrow glass may become just right if poured into a short, wide glass. Focusing only on the height dimension, this child cannot perform the operation of mentally pouring the milk back. Before about age 6, said Piaget, children lack the concept of **conservation**—the principle that quantity remains the same despite changes in shape (**FIGURE 11.7**).

📺 **LaunchPad** For quick video examples of children being tested for conservation, visit **Concept Practice: Piaget and Conservation.**

PRETEND PLAY Symbolic thinking and *pretend play* appear at an earlier age than Piaget supposed. Judy DeLoache (1987) showed children a model of a room and hid a miniature stuffed dog behind its miniature couch. The 2½-year-olds easily remembered where to find the miniature toy, but they could not use the model to locate an actual stuffed dog

preoperational stage in Piaget's theory, the stage (from about 2 to 6 or 7 years of age) during which a child learns to use language but does not yet comprehend the mental operations of concrete logic.

conservation the principle (which Piaget believed to be a part of concrete operational reasoning) that properties such as mass, volume, and number remain the same despite changes in the forms of objects.

FIGURE 11.6

BABY MATH Shown a numerically impossible outcome, 5-month-old infants stare longer (Wynn, 1992).

Then either: possible outcome

(e) Screen drops revealing 1 object

or: impossible outcome

(f) Screen drops revealing 2 objects

FIGURE 11.7

PIAGET'S TEST OF CONSERVATION This visually focused preoperational child does not yet understand the principle of conservation. When the milk is poured into a tall, narrow glass, it suddenly seems like "more" than when it was in the shorter, wider glass. In another year or so, she will understand that the amount stays the same.

Bianca Moscatelli/Worth Publishers

David Myers

EGOCENTRISM IN ACTION "Look, Granddaddy, a match!" So said my [DM's] granddaughter, Allie, at age 4, when showing me two memory game cards with matching pictures—that faced her.

"The curse of knowledge is the single best explanation I know of why good people write bad prose. It simply doesn't occur to the writer that her readers don't know what she knows."
—Psychologist Steven Pinker, *The Sense of Style*, 2014

Use your finger to trace a capital E on your forehead. When Adam Galinsky and his colleagues (2006) invited people to do that (as you can, with a friend), they were more egocentric—less likely to draw it from the perspective of someone looking at them—if they were first made to feel powerful. Other studies confirm that feeling powerful reduces people's sensitivity to how others see, think, and feel.

egocentrism in Piaget's theory, the preoperational child's difficulty taking another's point of view.

theory of mind people's ideas about their own and others' mental states—about their feelings, perceptions, and thoughts, and the behaviors these might predict.

concrete operational stage in Piaget's theory, the stage of cognitive development (from about 7 to 11 years of age) during which children gain the mental operations that enable them to think logically about concrete events.

behind a couch in a real room. Three-year-olds—only 6 months older—usually went right to the actual stuffed animal in the real room, showing they *could* think of the model as a symbol for the room. Although Piaget did not view the stage transitions as abrupt, he probably would have been surprised to see symbolic thinking at such an early age.

EGOCENTRISM Piaget taught us that preschool children are **egocentric:** They have difficulty perceiving things from another's point of view. They are like the person who, when asked by someone across a river, "How do I get to the other side?" answered "You're *on* the other side." Asked to "show Mommy your picture," 2-year-old Gabriella holds the picture up facing her own eyes. Three-year-old Gray makes himself "invisible" by putting his hands over his eyes, assuming that if he can't see his grandparents, they can't see him. Children's conversations also reveal their egocentrism, as one young boy demonstrated (Phillips, 1969, p. 61):

"Do you have a brother?"
"Yes."
"What's his name?"
"Jim."
"Does Jim have a brother?"
"No."

Like Gabriella, TV-watching preschoolers who block your view of the TV assume that you see what they see. They simply have not yet developed the ability to take another's viewpoint. Even adolescents egocentrically overestimate how much others are noticing them (Lin, 2016). And adults may overestimate the extent to which others share our opinions, knowledge, and perspectives. We assume that something will be clear to others if it is clear to us, or that email recipients will "hear" our "just kidding" intent (Epley et al., 2004; Kruger et al., 2005). Perhaps you can recall asking someone to guess a simple tune such as "Happy Birthday" as you clapped or tapped it out. With the tune in your head, it seemed so obvious! But you suffered the egocentric *curse of knowledge*, assuming that what was in your head was also in someone else's.

THEORY OF MIND When Little Red Riding Hood realized her "grandmother" was really a wolf, she swiftly revised her ideas about the creature's intentions and raced away. Preschoolers, although still egocentric, develop this ability to infer others' mental states when they begin forming a **theory of mind** (Premack & Woodruff, 1978). The theory of mind concept was first used to describe chimpanzees' seeming ability to read others' intentions. Later, psychologists aimed to identify when humans develop a theory of mind.

As the ability to take another's perspective gradually develops, preschoolers come to understand what made a playmate angry, when a sibling will share, and what might make a parent buy a toy. They begin to tease, empathize, and persuade. And when making decisions, they use their understanding of how their actions will make others feel (Repacholi et al., 2016). Children who have an advanced ability to understand others' minds tend to be helpful and well-liked (Imuta et al., 2016; Slaughter et al., 2015).

Between about ages 3 and 4½, children worldwide come to realize that others may hold false beliefs (Callaghan et al., 2005; Rubio-Fernández & Geurts, 2013; Sabbagh et al., 2006). Jennifer Jenkins and Janet Astington (1996) showed Canadian children a Band-Aid box and asked them what was inside. Expecting Band-Aids, the children were surprised to discover that the box actually contained pencils. Asked what a child who had never seen the box would think was inside, 3-year-olds typically answered "pencils." By age 4 to 5, the children's theory of mind had leapt forward, and they anticipated their friends' false belief that the box would hold Band-Aids. Children with *autism spectrum disorder* have difficulty understanding that another's state of mind differs from their own.

CONCRETE OPERATIONAL STAGE By about age 7, said Piaget, children enter the **concrete operational stage.** Given concrete (physical) materials, they begin to grasp operations such as conservation. Understanding that change in form does not mean change in quantity, they can mentally pour milk back and forth between glasses of different shapes. They also enjoy jokes that use this new understanding:

Mr. Jones went into a restaurant and ordered a whole pizza for his dinner. When the waiter asked if he wanted it cut into 6 or 8 pieces, Mr. Jones said, "Oh, you'd better make it 6, I could never eat 8 pieces!" (McGhee, 1976)

RETAIN 🔒 **TABLE 11.1**

Piaget's Stages of Cognitive Development

Typical Age Range	Stage and Description	Key Milestones
Birth to nearly 2 years	*Sensorimotor* Experiencing the world through senses and actions (looking, hearing, touching, mouthing, and grasping)	• Object permanence • Stranger anxiety
About 2 to 6 or 7 years	*Preoperational* Representing things with words and images; using intuitive rather than logical reasoning	• Pretend play • Egocentrism
About 7 to 11 years	*Concrete operational* Thinking logically about concrete events; grasping concrete analogies and performing arithmetical operations	• Conservation • Mathematical transformations
About 12 through adulthood	*Formal operational* Reasoning abstractly	• Abstract logic • Potential for mature moral reasoning

Image Source/Getty Images

PRETEND PLAY

Piaget believed that during the concrete operational stage, children become able to comprehend mathematical transformations and conservation. When my [DM's] daughter, Laura, was 6, I was astonished at her inability to reverse simple arithmetic. Asked, "What is 8 plus 4?" she required 5 seconds to compute "12," and another 5 seconds to then compute 12 minus 4. By age 8, she could answer a reversed question instantly.

FORMAL OPERATIONAL STAGE By about age 12, our reasoning expands from the purely concrete (involving actual experience) to encompass abstract thinking (involving imagined realities and symbols). As children approach adolescence, said Piaget, they can ponder hypothetical propositions and deduce consequences: *If* this, *then* that. Systematic reasoning, what Piaget called **formal operational** thinking, is now within their grasp.

ENGAGE 💡 Although full-blown logic and reasoning await adolescence, the rudiments of formal operational thinking begin earlier than Piaget realized. Consider this simple problem:

If John is in school, then Mary is in school. John is in school. What can you say about Mary?

Formal operational thinkers have no trouble answering correctly. But neither do most 7-year-olds (Suppes, 1982). **TABLE 11.1** summarizes the four stages in Piaget's theory.

An Alternative Viewpoint: Lev Vygotsky and the Social Child

As Piaget was forming his theory of cognitive development, Russian psychologist Lev Vygotsky was also studying how children think and learn. Where Piaget emphasized how the child's mind grows through interaction with the physical environment, Vygotsky emphasized how the child's mind grows through interaction with the *social* environment. If Piaget's child was a young scientist, Vygotsky's was a young apprentice. By giving children new words and mentoring them, parents, teachers, and other children provide what we now call a temporary **scaffold** from which children can step to higher levels of thinking (Renninger & Granott, 2005; Wood et al., 1976). Children learn best when their social environment presents them with something in the sweet spot between too easy and too difficult.

Language, an important ingredient of social mentoring, provides the building blocks for thinking, noted Vygotsky (who was born the same year as Piaget, but died prematurely of tuberculosis). By age 7, children increasingly think in words and use words to solve problems. They do this, Vygotsky said, by internalizing their culture's language and relying on inner speech (Fernyhough, 2008). Parents who say *"No, no, Bevy!"* when pulling their child's hand away from a cup of hot coffee are giving her a self-control tool. When Bevy later needs to resist temptation, she may likewise think, *"No, no, Bevy!"*

formal operational stage in Piaget's theory, the stage of cognitive development (normally beginning about age 12) during which people begin to think logically about abstract concepts.

scaffold a framework that offers children temporary support as they develop higher levels of thinking.

LEV VYGOTSKY (1896–1934)
Vygotsky, pictured here with his daughter, was a Russian developmental psychologist. He studied how a child's mind feeds on the language of social interaction.

James V. Wertsch/Washington University

Second graders who muttered to themselves while doing math problems grasped third-grade math better the following year (Berk, 1994). Whether out loud or inaudibly, talking to themselves helps children control their behavior and emotions and master new skills. (It helps adults, too. Adults who motivate themselves using self-talk—"You can do it!"—experience better performance [Kross et al., 2014].)

"It's too late, Roger—they've seen us." Roger has not outgrown his early childhood egocentrism.

🔒 **RETRIEVE IT • • •**   *ANSWERS IN APPENDIX E*

RI-2 Object permanence, pretend play, conservation, and abstract logic are developmental milestones for which of Piaget's stages, respectively?

RI-3 Label each of the following developmental phenomena (I–VI) with the correct cognitive developmental stage: (a) sensorimotor, (b) preoperational, (c) concrete operational, or (d) formal operational.

I. Thinking about abstract concepts, such as "freedom."

II. Enjoying imaginary play (such as dress-up).

III. Understanding that physical properties stay the same even when objects change form.

IV. Having the ability to reverse math operations.

V. Understanding that something is not gone for good when it disappears from sight, as when Mom "disappears" behind the shower curtain.

VI. Having difficulty taking another's point of view (as when blocking someone's view of the TV).

Reflecting on Piaget's Theory

What remains of Piaget's ideas about the child's mind? Plenty—enough to merit his being singled out by *Time* magazine as one of the twentieth century's 20 most influential scientists and thinkers, and his being rated in a survey of British psychologists as the last century's greatest psychologist (*Psychologist,* 2003). Piaget identified significant cognitive milestones and stimulated worldwide interest in how the mind develops. His emphasis was less on the ages at which children typically reach specific milestones than on their sequence. Studies around the globe, from aboriginal Australia to Algeria to North America, have confirmed that human cognition unfolds basically in the sequence Piaget described (Lourenco & Machado, 1996; Segall et al., 1990).

However, today's researchers see development as more continuous than did Piaget. By detecting the beginnings of each type of thinking at earlier ages, they have revealed conceptual abilities Piaget missed. Moreover, they see formal logic as a smaller part of cognition than he did. Today, as part of our own cognitive development, we are adapting Piaget's ideas to accommodate new findings.

IMPLICATIONS FOR PARENTS AND TEACHERS Future parents and teachers, remember this: Young children are incapable of adult logic. Preschoolers who block one's view of the TV simply have not learned to take another's viewpoint. What seems simple and obvious to us—getting off a seesaw will cause a friend on the other end to crash—may be incomprehensible to a 3-year-old. Also remember that children are not passive receptacles waiting to be filled with knowledge. Better to build on what they already know, engaging them in concrete demonstrations and stimulating them to think for themselves. Finally, accept children's cognitive immaturity as adaptive. It is nature's strategy for keeping children close to protective adults and providing time for learning and socialization (Bjorklund & Green, 1992).

Autism Spectrum Disorder

LOQ 11-3   What is *autism spectrum disorder?*

Autism spectrum disorder (ASD) is a cognitive and social-emotional disorder that is marked by social deficiencies and repetitive behaviors. Once believed to affect 1 in 2500 children (and referred to simply as *autism*), ASD is now diagnosed in 1 in 68 American

---

"Assessing the impact of Piaget on developmental psychology is like assessing the impact of Shakespeare on English literature." —Developmental psychologist Harry Beilin (1992)

"Childhood has its own way of seeing, thinking, and feeling, and there is nothing more foolish than the attempt to put ours in its place." —Philosopher Jean-Jacques Rousseau, 1798

📺 **LaunchPad** For a 7-minute synopsis of Piaget's concepts, see the **Video: Cognitive Development.**

autism spectrum disorder (ASD) a disorder that appears in childhood and is marked by significant deficiencies in communication and social interaction, and by rigidly fixated interests and repetitive behaviors.

children by age 8. Rates range from 1 in 34 in the studied area of New Jersey to only 1 in 77 in Arkansas. Outside the U.S., rates also vary, from 1 in 38 in South Korea to 1 in 100 in Britain (CDC, 2014c; Kim et al., 2011; NAS, 2011). The increase in ASD diagnoses has been offset by a decrease in the number of children with a "cognitive disability" or "learning disability," which suggests a relabeling of children's disorders (Gernsbacher et al., 2005; Grinker, 2007; Shattuck, 2006).

The underlying source of ASD's symptoms seems to be poor communication among brain regions that normally work together to let us take another's viewpoint. From age 2 months on, children normally spend more and more time looking into others' eyes; those who later develop ASD do so less and less (Baron-Cohen, 2017; Moriuchi et al., 2017). People with ASD are said to have an *impaired theory of mind* (Rajendran & Mitchell, 2007; Senju et al., 2009). Mind reading that most of us find intuitive (*Is that face conveying a smirk or a sneer?*) is difficult for those with ASD. They have difficulty inferring and remembering others' thoughts and feelings, appreciating that playmates and parents might view things differently, and understanding that their teachers know more than they do (Boucher et al., 2012; Frith & Frith, 2001; Knutsen et al., 2015). Partly for such reasons, a national survey of parents and school staff reported that 46 percent of adolescents with ASD had suffered the taunts and torments of bullying—about four times the 11 percent rate for other children (Sterzing et al., 2012). Children with ASD do make friends, but their peers often find such relationships emotionally unsatisfying (Mendelson et al., 2016).

ASD has differing levels of severity. Some (those diagnosed with what used to be called *Asperger syndrome*) generally function at a high level. They have normal intelligence, often accompanied by exceptional skill or talent in a specific area, but deficient social and communication skills and a tendency to become distracted by irrelevant stimuli (Remington et al., 2009). Those at the spectrum's more severe end struggle to use language.

Biological factors, including genetic influences and abnormal brain development, contribute to ASD (Colvert et al., 2015; Makin, 2015; Tick et al., 2015). Studies suggest that the prenatal environment matters, especially when altered by maternal infection and inflammation, psychiatric drug use, or stress hormones (NIH, 2013; Wang, 2014). Childhood vaccinations do *not* contribute to ASD (Taylor et al., 2014). Based on a fraudulent 1998 study—"the most damaging medical hoax of the last 100 years" (Flaherty, 2011)— some parents were misled into thinking that the childhood MMR vaccine increased risk of ASD. The unfortunate result was a drop in vaccination rates and an increase in cases of measles and mumps. Some unvaccinated children suffered long-term harm or even death. Unvaccinated children also place at risk other children who are too young to be fully vaccinated.

ASD afflicts about three boys for every girl (Loomes et al., 2017). Psychologist Simon Baron-Cohen (2010) believes this is because boys more often than girls are "systemizers." They tend to understand things according to rules or laws, as in mathematical and mechanical systems. Girls, he contends, are more often predisposed to be "empathizers." They tend to excel at reading facial expressions and gestures (van Honk et al., 2011). Whether male or female, those with ASD are systemizers who have more difficulty reading facial expressions (Baron-Cohen at al., 2015).

Numerous studies verify biology's influence. If one identical twin is diagnosed with ASD, the chances are 50 to 70 percent that the co-twin will be as well (Tick et al., 2015). A younger genetic sibling of a child with ASD also is at a heightened risk (Sutcliffe, 2008). No one "autism gene" accounts for the disorder. Rather, many genes—with more than 400 identified so far—appear to contribute (Krishnan et al., 2016; Yuen et al., 2016). Random genetic mutations in sperm cells may also play a role. As men age, these mutations become more frequent, which may help explain why an over-40 man has a much higher risk of fathering a child with ASD than does a man under 30 (Wu et al., 2017).

Researchers are also sleuthing ASD's telltale signs in the brain's structure. Several studies have revealed "underconnectivity"—fewer-than-normal fiber tracts connecting the front of the brain to the back (Picci et al., 2016). With underconnectivity, there is less of the whole-brain synchrony that, for example, integrates visual and emotional information.

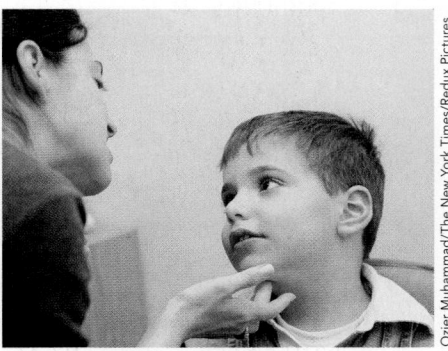

AUTISM SPECTRUM DISORDER This speech-language pathologist is helping a boy with ASD learn to form sounds and words. ASD is marked by deficient social communication and difficulty grasping others' states of mind.

"AUTISM" CASE NUMBER 1 In 1943, Donald Gray Triplett, an "odd" child with unusual gifts and social deficits, was the first person to receive the diagnosis of "autism." (After a 2013 change in the diagnosis manual, his condition is now called *autism spectrum disorder.*) In 2016, at age 82, Triplett was still living in his family home and Mississippi town, where he often played golf (Atlas, 2016).

(a)

 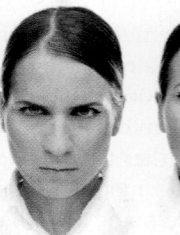 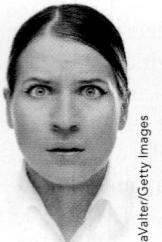

(b)

FIGURE 11.8

TRANSPORTED INTO A WORLD OF EMOTION A research team at Cambridge University's Autism Research Centre introduced children with ASD to emotions experienced and displayed by (a) toy vehicles and (b) human faces. Children matched the correct face with the story ("The neighbor's dog has bitten people before. He is barking at Louise. Point to the face that shows how Louise is feeling"). (The graph shows data for two trials.)

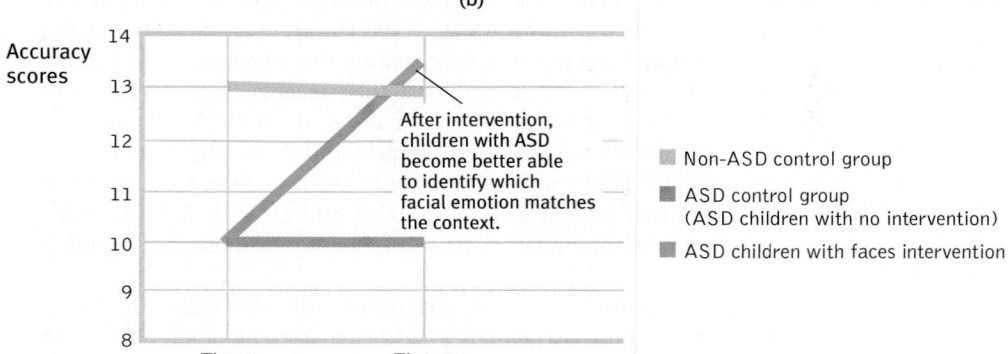

Biology's role in ASD also appears in the brain's functioning. People without ASD often yawn after seeing others yawn. And as they view and imitate another's smiling or frowning, they feel something of what the other is feeling. Not so among those with ASD, who are less imitative and show less activity in brain areas involved in mirroring others' actions (Edwards, 2014; Yang & Hoffman, 2015). When people with ASD watch another person's hand movements, for example, their brain displays less-than-normal mirroring activity (Oberman & Ramachandran, 2007; Théoret et al., 2005). Scientists are exploring and debating this idea that the brains of people with ASD have "broken mirrors" (Gallese et al., 2011). And they are exploring whether treatment with oxytocin, the hormone that promotes social bonding, might improve social understanding in those with ASD (Gordon et al., 2013; Lange & McDougle, 2013).

Seeking to "systemize empathy," Baron-Cohen and his Cambridge University colleagues (2007; Golan et al., 2010) collaborated with Britain's National Autistic Society and a film production company. Knowing that television shows with vehicles have been popular among kids with ASD, they created animations with toy vehicle characters in a pretend boy's bedroom, grafting emotion-conveying faces onto toy trams, trains, and tractors (**FIGURE 11.8**). After the boy leaves for school, the characters come to life and have experiences that lead them to display various emotions (see TheTransporters.com). The children were surprisingly able to generalize what they had learned to a new, real-life context. By the intervention's end, their previously deficient ability to recognize emotions on real faces now equaled that of children without ASD.

🔒 **RETRIEVE IT • • •**   *ANSWERS IN APPENDIX E*

RI-4 What does *theory of mind* have to do with autism spectrum disorder?

SOCIAL DEVELOPMENT

LOQ 11-4 How do parent-infant attachment bonds form?

From birth, most babies are social creatures, developing an intense attachment to their caregivers. Infants come to prefer familiar faces and voices, then to coo and gurgle when given a parent's attention. After about 8 months, soon after object permanence emerges and children become mobile, a curious thing happens: They develop **stranger anxiety.**

They may greet strangers by crying and reaching for familiar caregivers: "No! Don't leave me!" Children this age have schemas for familiar faces; when they cannot assimilate the new face into these remembered schemas, they become distressed (Kagan, 1984). Once again, we see an important principle: *The brain, mind, and social-emotional behavior develop together.*

Origins of Attachment

One-year-olds typically cling tightly to a parent when they are frightened or expect separation. Reunited after being apart, they often shower the parent with smiles and hugs. This striking parent-infant **attachment** bond is a powerful survival impulse that keeps infants close to their caregivers. Infants normally become attached to those—typically their parents—who are comfortable and familiar. For many years, psychologists reasoned that infants became attached to those who satisfied their need for nourishment. But an accidental finding overturned this explanation.

BODY CONTACT During the 1950s, University of Wisconsin psychologists Harry Harlow and Margaret Harlow bred monkeys for their learning studies. To equalize experiences and to isolate any disease, they separated the infant monkeys from their mothers shortly after birth and raised them in individual cages, each including a cheesecloth baby blanket (Harlow et al., 1971). Then came a surprise: When their soft blankets were taken to be washed, the monkeys became distressed.

The Harlows recognized that this intense attachment to the blanket contradicted the idea that attachment derives from an association with nourishment. But how could they show this more convincingly? To pit the drawing power of a food source against the contact comfort of the blanket, they created two artificial mothers. One was a bare wire cylinder with a wooden head and an attached feeding bottle, the other a cylinder wrapped with terry cloth.

When raised with both, the monkeys overwhelmingly preferred the comfy cloth mother (**FIGURE 11.9**). Like other infants clinging to their live mothers, the monkey babies would cling to their cloth mothers when anxious. When exploring their environment, they used her as a *secure base,* as if attached to her by an invisible elastic band that stretched only far before pulling them back. Researchers soon learned that other qualities—rocking, warmth, and feeding—made the cloth mother even more appealing.

Human infants, too, become attached to parents who are soft and warm and who rock, feed, and pat. Much parent-infant emotional communication occurs via touch, which can be either soothing (snuggles) or arousing (tickles) (Hertenstein et al., 2006). Indeed, when asked to describe the ideal mother, people across the globe agreed that she "shows affection by touching" (Mesman et al., 2015). Such parental affection not only feels good, it aids brain development and later cognitive performance (Davis et al., 2017).

Human attachment also consists of one person providing another with a secure base from which to explore and a safe haven when distressed. As we mature, our secure base and safe haven shift—from parents to peers and partners (Cassidy & Shaver, 1999). But at all ages we are social creatures. We gain strength when someone offers, by words and actions, a safe haven: "I will be here. I am interested in you. Come what may, I will support you" (Crowell & Waters, 1994).

FAMILIARITY Contact is one key to attachment. Another is familiarity. In many animals, attachments based on familiarity form during a *critical period*—an optimal period when certain events must take place to facilitate proper development (Bornstein, 1989).

stranger anxiety the fear of strangers that infants commonly display, beginning by about 8 months of age.

attachment an emotional tie with another person; shown in young children by their seeking closeness to their caregiver and showing distress on separation.

Science Source

◄⋯ **FIGURE 11.9**

THE HARLOWS' MONKEY MOTHERS Psychologists Harry Harlow and Margaret Harlow raised monkeys with two artificial mothers—one a bare wire cylinder with a wooden head and an attached feeding bottle, the other a cylinder with no bottle but covered with foam rubber and wrapped with terry cloth. The Harlows' discovery surprised many psychologists: The infants much preferred contact with the comfortable cloth mother, even while feeding from the wire nourishing mother.

IMPRINTING Konrad Lorenz (1937) explored this rigid attachment process. He wondered: What would ducklings do if he was the first moving creature they observed? What they did was follow him around: Everywhere that Konrad went, the ducks were sure to go. Although baby birds imprint best to their own species, they also will imprint on a variety of moving objects—an animal of another species, a box on wheels, or a bouncing ball (Colombo, 1982; Johnson, 1992). Once formed, this attachment is difficult to reverse.

Humans seem to have a critical period for language. Goslings, ducklings, and chicks have a critical period for attachment, called **imprinting,** which falls in the hours shortly after hatching, when the first moving object they see is normally their mother. From then on, the young fowl follow her, and her alone.

Children—unlike ducklings—do not imprint. However, they do become attached to what they've known. *Mere exposure* to people and things fosters fondness. Children like to reread the same books, rewatch the same movies, reenact family traditions. They prefer to eat familiar foods, live in the same familiar neighborhood, attend school with the same old friends. Familiarity is a safety signal. Familiarity breeds content.

🔒 **RETRIEVE IT** • • •   *ANSWERS IN APPENDIX E*

RI-5 What distinguishes imprinting from attachment?

Attachment Differences

LOQ 11-5 How have psychologists studied attachment differences, and what have they learned?

What accounts for children's attachment differences? To answer this question, Mary Ainsworth (1979) designed the *strange situation* experiment. She observed mother-infant pairs at home during their first six months. Later she observed the 1-year-old infants in a strange situation (usually a laboratory playroom) with and without their mothers. Such research has shown that about 60 percent of infants and young children display *secure attachment* (Moulin et al., 2014). In their mother's presence they play comfortably, happily exploring their new environment. When she leaves, they become distressed; when she returns, they seek contact with her.

Other infants show *insecure attachment,* marked either by anxiety or avoidance of trusting relationships. These infants are less likely to explore their surroundings; they may even cling to their mother. When she leaves, they either cry loudly and remain upset or seem indifferent to her departure and return (Ainsworth, 1973, 1989; Kagan, 1995; van IJzendoorn & Kroonenberg, 1988).

Ainsworth and others found that sensitive, responsive mothers—those who noticed what their babies were doing and responded appropriately—had infants who exhibited secure attachment (De Wolff & van IJzendoorn, 1997). Insensitive, unresponsive mothers—mothers who attended to their babies when they felt like doing so but ignored them at other times—often had infants who were insecurely attached. The Harlows' monkey studies, with unresponsive artificial mothers, produced even more striking effects. When put in strange situations without their artificial mothers, the deprived infants were terrified (**FIGURE 11.10**).

Although remembered by some as the researcher who tortured helpless monkeys, Harry Harlow defended his methods: "Remember, for every mistreated monkey there exist a million mistreated children," he said, expressing the hope that his research would sensitize people to child abuse and neglect. "No one who knows Harry's work could ever argue that babies do fine without companionship, that a caring mother doesn't matter," noted Harlow biographer Deborah Blum (2011, pp. 292, 307). "And since we . . . didn't fully believe that before Harry Harlow came along, then perhaps we needed—just once—to be smacked really hard with that truth so that we could never again doubt."

So, caring parents matter. But is attachment style the *result* of parenting? Or are other factors also at work?

TEMPERAMENT AND ATTACHMENT How does **temperament**—a person's characteristic emotional reactivity and intensity—affect attachment style? Twin and developmental studies reveal that heredity affects temperament, and temperament affects attachment style (Picardi et al., 2011; Raby et al., 2012).

As most parents will tell you after having their second child, babies differ even before gulping their first breath. Some babies are noticeably *difficult*—irritable, intense, and

FIGURE 11.10

SOCIAL DEPRIVATION AND FEAR In the Harlows' experiments, monkeys raised with inanimate surrogate mothers were overwhelmed when placed in strange situations without that source of emotional security. (Today there is greater oversight and concern for animal welfare, which would regulate this type of study.)

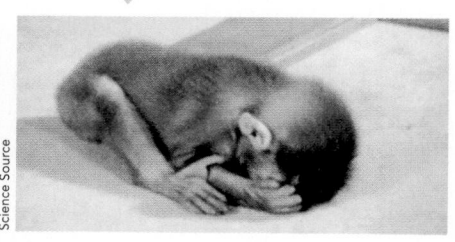

unpredictable. Others are *easy*—cheerful, relaxed, and predictably feeding and sleeping (Chess & Thomas, 1987). Identical twins, more than fraternal twins, often have similar temperaments (Fraley & Tancredy, 2012; Kandler et al., 2013). And differences in temperament appear in physiological differences. Anxious, inhibited infants have high and variable heart rates and a reactive nervous system. When facing new or strange situations, they become more physiologically aroused (Kagan & Snidman, 2004; Roque et al., 2012).

Temperament differences typically persist. The most emotionally reactive newborns tend also to be the most reactive 9-month-olds (Wilson & Matheny, 1986; Worobey & Blajda, 1989). Emotionally intense preschoolers tend to become relatively intense young adults (Larsen & Diener, 1987). In one study of more than 900 New Zealanders, emotionally reactive and impulsive 3-year-olds developed into somewhat more impulsive, aggressive, and crime-prone adults (Caspi et al., 2016).

Parenting studies that neglect such inborn differences, noted Judith Harris (1998), do the equivalent of "comparing foxhounds reared in kennels with poodles reared in apartments." To separate the effects of nature and nurture on attachment, we would need to vary parenting while controlling temperament. (Pause and think: If you were the researcher, how might you do this?)

Dutch researcher Dymphna van den Boom's solution was to randomly assign 100 temperamentally difficult 6- to 9-month-olds to either an experimental group, in which mothers received personal training in sensitive responding, or to a control group, in which they did not. At 12 months of age, 68 percent of the experimental group were securely attached, as were only 28 percent of the control group infants. Other studies confirm that intervention programs can increase parental sensitivity and, to a lesser extent, infant attachment security (Bakermans-Kranenburg et al., 2003; Van Zeijl et al., 2006). Such "positive parenting" interventions seem to be especially beneficial for children with difficult temperaments (Slagt et al., 2016).

As many of these examples indicate, researchers have more often studied mother care than father care, but fathers are more than just mobile sperm banks. Despite the widespread attitude that "fathering a child" means impregnating, and "mothering" means nurturing, nearly 100 studies worldwide have shown that a father's love and acceptance are comparable with a mother's love in predicting an offspring's health and well-being (Rohner & Veneziano, 2001; see also **TABLE 11.2**). Fathers matter.

In one large British study following 7259 children from birth to adulthood, those whose fathers were most involved in parenting (through outings, reading to them, and taking an interest in their education) tended to achieve more in school, even after controlling for other factors such as parental education and family wealth (Flouri & Buchanan, 2004). Girls with involved fathers are also less likely to engage in risky sexual behavior or to befriend those who do (DelPriore et al., 2017). Increasing nonmarital births and the greater instability of cohabiting versus married partnerships has, however, meant more father-absent families (Hymowitz et al., 2013). In Europe and the United States,

imprinting the process by which certain animals form strong attachments during early life.

temperament a person's characteristic emotional reactivity and intensity.

LaunchPad Play the role of a researcher studying temperament and personality by engaging online with **Immersive Learning: How Would You Know If Personality Runs in Our Genes?**

TABLE 11.2
Dual Parenting Positives

- *Active dads are caregiving more.* Today's co-parenting fathers are more engaged, with a doubling in the weekly hours spent with their children, compared with fathers in 1965 (Livingston & Parker, 2011).

- *Couples that share housework and child care are happier in their relationships and less divorce prone* (Wilcox & Marquardt, 2011).

- *Dual parenting supports children.* After controlling for other factors, children average better life outcomes "if raised by both parents" (Taylor, 2014).

- *Parents' gender and sexual orientation do not affect children's well-being.* The American Academy of Pediatrics (2013) reports that what matters is competent, secure, nurturing parents. The American Sociological Association (2013) concurs: Parental stability and resources matter, but "whether a child is raised by same-sex or opposite-sex parents has no bearing on a child's well-being."

FIGURE 11.11

INFANTS' DISTRESS OVER SEPARATION FROM PARENTS In an experiment, infants were left by their mothers in an unfamiliar room. Regardless of whether the infant had experienced day care, the percentage who cried when the mother left peaked at about 13 months of age (Kagan, 1976).

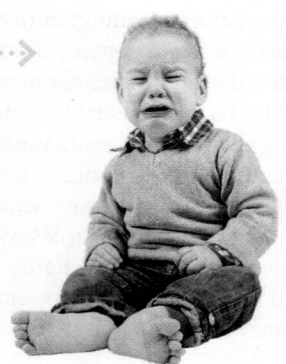

Jouke van Keulen/Shutterstock

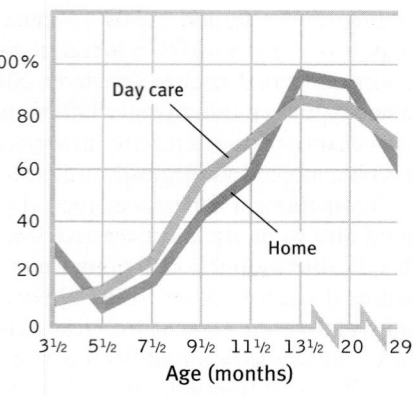

for example, children born to married parents are (compared to cohabiting parents) about half as likely to experience their parents' separation, which often entails diminished father care (Brown et al., 2016; Wilcox & DeRose, 2017). Even after controlling for parents' income, education, and race, children co-parented by two married parents experience a lower rate of school problems (Zill & Wilcox, 2017).

Children's anxiety over separation from parents peaks at around 13 months, then gradually declines (**FIGURE 11.11**). This happens whether they live with one parent or two, are cared for at home or in day care, live in North America, Guatemala, or the Kalahari Desert. Does this mean our need for and love of others also fades away? Hardly. Our capacity for love grows, and our pleasure in touching and holding those we love never ceases.

ATTACHMENT STYLES AND LATER RELATIONSHIPS Developmental theorist Erik Erikson (1902–1994), working with his wife, Joan Erikson (1902–1997), believed that securely attached children approach life with a sense of **basic trust**—a sense that the world is predictable and reliable. He attributed basic trust not to environment or inborn temperament, but to early parenting. He theorized that infants blessed with sensitive, loving caregivers form a lifelong attitude of trust rather than fear.

Many researchers now believe that our early attachments form the foundation for our adult relationships (Birnbaum et al., 2006; Fraley et al., 2013). People who report secure relationships with their parents tend to enjoy secure friendships (Gorrese & Ruggieri, 2012). Students leaving home to attend college or university—another kind of "strange situation"— tend to adjust well if securely attached to parents (Mattanah et al., 2011). Children with sensitive, responsive mothers tend to flourish socially and academically (Raby et al., 2014).

Feeling insecurely attached to others may take one of two main forms (Fraley et al., 2011). One is *anxious attachment,* in which people constantly crave acceptance but remain alert to signs of possible rejection. The other is *avoidant attachment,* in which people experience discomfort getting close to others and use avoidant strategies to maintain distance from others. In romantic relationships, an anxious attachment style creates constant concern over rejection, leading people to cling to their partners. An avoidant style decreases commitment and increases conflict (DeWall et al., 2011; Overall et al., 2015).

Adult attachment styles can also affect relationships with one's own children. But say this for those (nearly half of all people) who exhibit wary, insecure attachments: Anxious or avoidant tendencies have helped our groups detect or escape dangers (Ein-Dor et al., 2010).

Deprivation of Attachment

LOQ 11-6 How does childhood neglect or abuse affect children's attachments?

If secure attachment fosters social trust, what happens when circumstances prevent a child's forming any attachments? In all of psychology, there is no sadder research literature. Babies locked away at home under conditions of abuse or extreme neglect are often withdrawn, frightened, even speechless. The same is true of those raised in institutions without the stimulation and attention of a regular caregiver, as was tragically illustrated

---

For some people, a perceived relationship with God functions as do other attachments, by providing a secure base for exploration and a safe haven when threatened (Granqvist et al., 2010; Kirkpatrick, 1999).

ENGAGE (ASK YOURSELF)

How would you describe the style of your parents or primary caregivers? How do you think this has affected your attachment style or your other traits and behaviors?

ENGAGE **LaunchPad** To consider how your own attachment style may be affecting your current relationships, engage online with **Immersive Learning: Assess Your Strengths— What Is Your Attachment Style?**

during the 1970s and 1980s in Romania. Having decided that economic growth for his impoverished country required more human capital, Nicolae Ceaușescu, Romania's Communist dictator, outlawed contraception, forbade abortion, and taxed families with fewer than five children. The birthrate skyrocketed. But unable to afford the children they had been coerced into having, many families had to leave them at government-run orphanages with untrained and overworked staff. Child-to-caregiver ratios often were 15 to 1, so the children were deprived of healthy attachments with at least one adult. When tested after Ceaușescu's 1989 execution, these socially deprived children had lower intelligence scores, reduced brain development, abnormal stress responses, and quadruple the rate of attention-deficit/hyperactivity disorder (ADHD) found in children assigned to quality foster care settings (Bick et al., 2015; Kennedy et al., 2016; McLaughlin et al., 2015; Nelson et al., 2014). Dozens of other studies across 19 countries have shown that orphaned children tend to fare better on later intelligence tests if raised in family homes. This is especially so for those placed at an early age (van IJzendoorn et al., 2008, 2017).

Most children growing up under adversity (such as the surviving children of the Holocaust and victims of childhood sexual abuse) are *resilient;* they withstand the trauma and become well-adjusted adults (Clancy, 2010; Helmreich, 1992; Masten, 2001). And hardship short of trauma often boosts mental toughness (Seery, 2011). Moreover, although enduring the hardship of growing up poor puts children at risk for some social pathologies, growing up rich puts them at risk for other problems. Affluent children are at elevated risk for substance abuse, eating disorders, anxiety, and depression (Lund & Dearing, 2012; Luthar et al., 2013). So when you face adversity, consider the possible silver lining. Your coping may strengthen your resilience—your tendency to bounce back and go on to lead a better life.

But many who experience enduring abuse don't bounce back so readily. The Harlows' monkeys raised in total isolation, without even an artificial mother, bore lifelong scars. As adults, when placed with other monkeys their age, they either cowered in fright or lashed out in aggression. When they reached sexual maturity, most were incapable of mating. If artificially impregnated, females often were neglectful, abusive, even murderous toward their first-born. Another primate experiment confirmed the abuse-breeds-abuse phenomenon in rhesus monkeys: 9 of 16 females who had been abused by their mothers became abusive parents, as did *none* of the females raised by a nonabusive mother (Maestripieri, 2005).

In humans, too, the unloved may become the unloving. Most abusive parents—and many condemned murderers—have reported being neglected or battered as children (Kempe & Kempe, 1978; Lewis et al., 1988). Some 30 percent of people who have been abused later abuse their children—a rate lower than that found in the primate study, but four times the U.S. national rate of child abuse (Dumont et al., 2007; Kaufman & Zigler, 1987).

Although most abused children do *not* later become violent criminals or abusive parents, extreme early trauma may nevertheless leave footprints on the brain (Teicher and Samson, 2016). Like battle-stressed soldiers, abused children's brains respond to angry faces with heightened activity in threat-detecting areas (McCrory et al., 2011). In conflict-plagued homes, even sleeping infants' brains show heightened reactivity to hearing angry speech (Graham et al., 2013). As adults, these children exhibit stronger startle responses (Jovanovic et al., 2009). If repeatedly threatened and attacked while young, normally placid golden hamsters grow up to be cowards when caged with same-sized hamsters, or bullies when caged with weaker ones (Ferris, 1996). Such animals show changes in the brain chemical serotonin, which calms aggressive impulses. A similarly sluggish serotonin response has been found in abused children who become aggressive teens and adults. By sensitizing the stress response system, early stress can permanently heighten reactions to later stress and increase stress-related disease (Fagundes & Way, 2014; van Zuiden et al., 2012; Wei et al., 2012). Child abuse can also leave *epigenetic* marks—chemical tags—that can alter normal gene expression (Lutz et al., 2017; Romens et al., 2015).

basic trust according to Erik Erikson, a sense that the world is predictable and trustworthy; said to be formed during infancy by appropriate experiences with responsive caregivers.

"Out of the conflict between trust and mistrust, the infant develops hope, which is the earliest form of what gradually becomes faith in adults." —Erik Erikson (1983)

THE DEPRIVATION OF ATTACHMENT In this 1980s Romanian orphanage, the 250 children between ages one and five outnumbered caregivers 15 to 1.

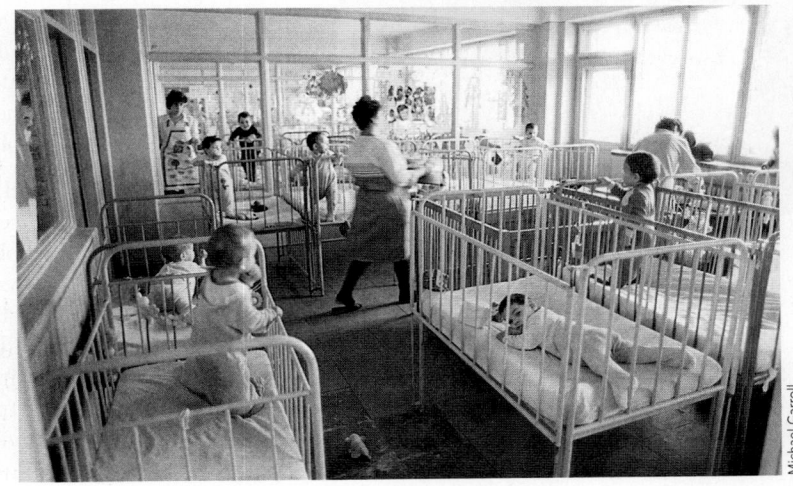

Michael Carroll

"What is learned in the cradle, lasts to the grave." —French proverb

Such findings help explain why young children who have survived severe or prolonged physical abuse, childhood sexual abuse, bullying, or wartime atrocities are at increased risk for health problems, psychological disorders, substance abuse, criminality, and, for women, earlier death (Chen et al., 2016; Lereya et al., 2015; Whitelock et al., 2013; Wolke et al., 2013). In one national study of 43,093 adults, 8 percent reported experiencing physical abuse at least fairly often before age 18 (Sugaya et al., 2012). Among these, 84 percent had experienced at least one psychiatric disorder. Moreover, the greater the abuse, the greater the odds of anxiety, depression, substance use disorder, and attempted suicide. Abuse victims are at especially heightened risk for depression if they carry a gene variation that spurs stress-hormone production (Bradley et al., 2008). As we will see again and again, behavior and emotion arise from a particular environment interacting with particular genes. Nature *and* nurture matter.

We adults also suffer when our attachment bonds are severed. Whether through death or separation, a break produces a predictable sequence. Agitated preoccupation with the lost partner is followed by deep sadness and, eventually, the beginnings of emotional detachment and a return to normal living (Hazan & Shaver, 1994). Newly separated couples who have long ago ceased feeling affection are sometimes surprised at their desire to be near the former partner. Detaching is a process, not an event.

Parenting Styles

LOQ 11-7   What are the four main parenting styles?

Some parents spank; others reason. Some are strict; others are lax. Some show little affection; others liberally hug and kiss. How do parenting-style differences affect children?

The most heavily researched aspect of parenting has been how, and to what extent, parents seek to control their children. Parenting styles can be described as a combination of two traits: how responsive and how demanding parents are (Kakinami et al., 2015). Investigators have identified four parenting styles (Baumrind, 1966, 1967; Steinberg, 2001):

1. *Authoritarian* parents are *coercive*. They impose rules and expect obedience: "Don't interrupt." "Keep your room clean." "Don't stay out late or you'll be grounded." "Why? Because I said so."

2. *Permissive* parents are *unrestraining*. They make few demands, set few limits, and use little punishment.

3. *Negligent* parents are *uninvolved*. They are neither demanding nor responsive. They are careless, inattentive, and do not seek a close relationship with their children.

4. *Authoritative* parents are *confrontive*. They are both demanding and responsive. They exert control by setting rules, but, especially with older children, they encourage open discussion and allow exceptions.

For more on parenting styles and their associated outcomes, see Thinking Critically About: Parenting Styles.

Parents who struggle with conflicting advice should also remember that *all advice reflects the advice-giver's values.* For parents who prize unquestioning obedience or whose children live in dangerous environments, an authoritarian style may have the desired effect. For those who value children's sociability and self-reliance, authoritative firm-but-open parenting is advisable.

CULTURE AND CHILD RAISING Child-raising practices reflect not only individual values, but also cultural values that vary across time and place. Should children be independent or obedient? If you live in a Westernized culture, you likely prefer independence. "You are responsible for yourself," families and schools tell their children. "Follow your conscience. Be true to yourself. Discover your gifts." Some Western parents go further, telling their children, "You are more special than other children" (Brummelman et al., 2015). (Not surprisingly, these children tend to have inflated self-views years later.) In the past, Western cultural values placed greater priority on obedience, respect, and sensitivity to others (Alwin, 1990; Remley, 1988). "Be true to your traditions," parents then taught their children. "Be loyal to your heritage and country. Show respect toward your parents and other superiors." Cultures change.

Stephen H. Reehl

CULTURES VARY Parents everywhere care about their children, but raise and protect them differently depending on the surrounding culture. In big cities, parents keep their children close. In smaller, close-knit communities, such as Scotland's Orkney Islands' town of Stromness, social trust has enabled parents to park their toddlers outside shops.

Parenting Styles—
Too Hard, Too Soft, Too Uncaring, and Just Right?

LOQ 11-8 What outcomes are associated with each parenting style?

Researchers have identified four parenting styles,[1] which have been associated with varying outcomes.

1 **Authoritarian parents** ↗↙

Children with less social skill and self-esteem, and a brain that over-reacts when they make mistakes [2]

2 **Permissive parents** ↗↙

Children who are more aggressive and immature [3]

HOWEVER, Correlation ≠ Causation!

What other factors might explain this parenting-competence link?

• Children's traits may influence parenting. Parental warmth and control vary somewhat from child to child, even in the same family.[6] Maybe socially mature, agreeable, easygoing children evoke greater trust and warmth from their parents? Twin studies have supported this possibility.[7]

• Some underlying third factor may be at work. Perhaps, for example, competent parents and their competent children share genes that predispose social competence. Twin studies have also supported this possibility. [8]

3 **Negligent parents** ↗↙

Children with poor academic and social outcomes [4]

4 **Authoritative parents** ↗↙

Children with the highest self-esteem, self-reliance, self-regulation, and social competence [5]

1. Kakinami et al., 2015. 2. Meyer et al., 2015. 3. Luyckx et al., 2011. 4. Pinquart, 2015; Steinberg et al., 1994. 5. Baumrind, 1996, 2013; Buri et al.,1988; Coopersmith, 1967; Sulik et al., 2015. 6. Holden & Miller, 1999; Klahr & Burt, 2014. 7. Kendler, 1996. 8. South et al., 2008.

Children across time and place have thrived under various child-raising systems. Many North Americans now give children their own bedrooms and entrust them to day care. Upper-class British parents traditionally handed off routine caregiving to nannies, then sent their 10-year-olds away to boarding school. These children generally grew up to be pillars of British society.

Asians and Africans more often live in cultures that value emotional closeness. Infants and toddlers may sleep with their mothers and spend their days close to a family member (Morelli et al., 1992; Whiting & Edwards, 1988). These cultures encourage a strong sense of *family self*—a feeling that what shames the child shames the family, and what brings honor to the family brings honor to the self.

LaunchPad See the **Video: Correlational Studies** for a helpful tutorial animation about correlational research design.

In traditional African Gusii society, babies nursed freely but spent most of the day on their mother's or siblings' back—with lots of body contact but little face-to-face and language interaction. Ditto for members of some rural villages in Senegal, whose cultural traditions discourage caregivers' talking with young children. Encouraging Senegalese caregivers to talk with children improved the children's language development one year later (Weber et al., 2017). But are the language improvements worth the cost of disrupting cultural traditions? What might appear as a lack of interaction to many Westerners might, to these Gusii and Senegalese parents, seem far preferable to the lesser body contact experienced by babies pushed in strollers and left in playpens (Small, 1997).

Such diversity in child raising cautions us against presuming that our culture's way is the only way to raise children successfully. One thing is certain, however: Whatever our culture, the investment in raising a child buys many years of joy and love, but also of worry and irritation. Yet for most people who become parents, a child is one's legacy—one's personal investment in the human future. To paraphrase psychiatrist Carl Jung, we reach backward into our parents and forward into our children, and through their children into a future we will never see, but about which we must therefore care.

"You are the bows from which your children as living arrows are sent forth." —Kahlil Gibran, *The Prophet*, 1923

🔒 RETRIEVE IT • • •

ANSWERS IN APPENDIX E

RI-6 The four parenting styles may be described as "too hard, too soft, too uncaring, and just right." Which parenting style goes with each of these descriptions, and how do children benefit from the "just right" style?

🔒 REVIEW INFANCY AND CHILDHOOD

⤳ Learning Objectives

TEST YOURSELF Answer these repeated Learning Objective Questions on your own (before checking the answers in Appendix D) to improve your retention of the concepts (McDaniel et al., 2009, 2015).

11-1 During infancy and childhood, how do the brain and motor skills develop?

11-2 From the perspectives of Piaget, Vygotsky, and today's researchers, how does a child's mind develop?

11-3 What is *autism spectrum disorder*?

11-4 How do parent-infant attachment bonds form?

11-5 How have psychologists studied attachment differences, and what have they learned?

11-6 How does childhood neglect or abuse affect children's attachments?

11-7 What are the four main parenting styles?

11-8 What outcomes are associated with each parenting style?

⤳ Terms and Concepts to Remember

TEST YOURSELF Write down the definition yourself, then check your answer on the referenced page.

maturation, **p. 122**

critical period, **p. 124**

cognition, **p. 125**

schema, **p. 125**

assimilation, **p. 125**

accommodation, **p. 125**

sensorimotor stage, **p. 126**

object permanence, **p. 126**

preoperational stage, **p. 127**

conservation, **p. 127**

egocentrism, **p. 128**

theory of mind, **p. 128**

concrete operational stage, **p. 128**

formal operational stage, **p. 129**

scaffold, **p. 129**

autism spectrum disorder (ASD), **p. 130**

stranger anxiety, **p. 133**

attachment, **p. 133**

imprinting, **p. 135**

temperament, **p. 135**

basic trust, **p. 137**

⤳ Experience the Testing Effect

TEST YOURSELF Answer the following questions on your own first, then check your answers in Appendix E.

1. Stroke a newborn's cheek and the infant will root for a nipple. This illustrates
   a. a reflex.
   b. nurture.
   c. a preference.
   d. continuity.

2. Between ages 3 and 6, the human brain experiences the greatest growth in the _____ lobes, which enable rational planning and aid memory.

3. Which of the following is true of motor-skill development?
   a. It is determined solely by genetic factors.
   b. The sequence, but not the timing, is universal.
   c. The timing, but not the sequence, is universal.
   d. It is determined solely by environmental factors.

4. Why can't we consciously recall learning to walk?

5. Use Piaget's first three stages of cognitive development to explain why young children are not just miniature adults in the way they think.

6. Although Piaget's stage theory continues to inform our understanding of children's thinking, many researchers believe that

    a. Piaget's stages begin earlier and development is more continuous than he realized.

    b. children do not progress as rapidly as Piaget predicted.

    c. few children progress to the concrete operational stage.

    d. there is no way of testing much of Piaget's theoretical work.

7. An 8-month-old infant who reacts to a new babysitter by crying and clinging to his father's shoulder is showing
_____ _____.

8. In a series of experiments, the Harlows found that monkeys raised with artificial mothers tended, when afraid, to cling to their cloth mother, rather than to a wire mother holding the feeding bottle. Why was this finding important?

Continue testing yourself with 📖 **LearningCurve** or 📖 **Achieve Read & Practice** to learn and remember most effectively.

---

12 Adolescence

adolescence the transition period from childhood to adulthood, extending from puberty to independence.

puberty the period of sexual maturation, during which a person becomes capable of reproducing.

LOQ 12-1 How is *adolescence* defined, and how do physical changes affect developing teens?

Many psychologists once believed that childhood sets our traits. Today's developmental psychologists see development as lifelong. As this *life-span perspective* emerged, psychologists began to look at how maturation and experience shape us not only in infancy and childhood, but also in adolescence and beyond. **Adolescence**—the years spent morphing from child to adult—starts with the physical beginnings of sexual maturity and ends with the social achievement of independent adult status. In some cultures, where teens are self-supporting, this means that adolescence hardly exists.

G. Stanley Hall (1904), one of the first psychologists to describe adolescence, believed that the tension between biological maturity and social dependence creates a period of "storm and stress." It's a time when teens crave social acceptance, but often feel socially disconnected. Three in four U.S. friendships started in seventh grade dissolve by the time adolescents complete eighth grade (Hartl et al., 2015). Indeed, after age 30, many who grow up in independence-fostering Western cultures look back on their teenage years as a time they would not want to relive—a time when their peers' social approval was imperative, their sense of direction in life was in flux, and their feeling of alienation from their parents was deepest (Arnett, 1999; Macfarlane, 1964). But for others, adolescence is a time of vitality without the cares of adulthood, a time of rewarding friendships, heightened idealism, and a growing sense of life's exciting possibilities.

PHYSICAL DEVELOPMENT

Adolescence begins with **puberty,** the time when we mature sexually. Puberty follows a surge of hormones, which may intensify moods and which trigger a series of bodily changes outlined in the Sex, Gender, and Sexuality modules.

The Timing of Puberty

Just as in the earlier life stages, the *sequence* of physical changes in puberty (for example, breast buds and visible pubic hair before *menarche*—the first menstrual period) is far more predictable than their *timing*. Some girls start their growth spurt at 9, some boys as late as age 16. How do girls and boys experience early maturation?

For boys, early maturation has mixed effects. Boys who are stronger and more athletic during their early teen years tend to be more popular, self-assured, and independent,

At a five-year high school reunion, former best friends may be surprised at their divergence; a decade or more later, they may have trouble sustaining a conversation.

though also more at risk for alcohol use, delinquency, and premature sexual activity (Conley & Rudolph, 2009; Copeland et al., 2010; Lynne et al., 2007). For girls, early maturation can be a challenge (Mendle et al., 2007). If a young girl's body and hormone-fed feelings are out of sync with her emotional maturity and her friends' physical development and experiences, she may begin associating with older adolescents, suffer teasing or sexual harassment, and experience increased *rumination* with anxiety or depression (Alloy et al., 2016; Ge & Natsuaki, 2009; Weingarden & Renshaw, 2012).

The Teenage Brain

An adolescent's brain is a work in progress. Until puberty, brain cells increase their connections, like trees growing more roots and branches. Then, during adolescence, comes a selective *pruning* of unused neurons and connections (Blakemore, 2008). What we don't use, we lose.

As teens mature, their frontal lobes also continue to develop. The continuing growth of *myelin,* the fatty tissue that forms around axons and speeds neurotransmission, enables better communication with other brain regions (Whitaker et al., 2016). These developments bring improved judgment, impulse control, and long-term planning.

Maturation of the frontal lobes nevertheless lags behind that of the emotional limbic system. Puberty's hormonal surge and limbic system development help explain teens' occasional impulsiveness, risky behaviors, and emotional storms—slamming doors and turning up the music (Casey and Caudle, 2013; Casey et al., 2008; Fuhrmann et al., 2015). No wonder younger teens (whose unfinished frontal lobes aren't yet fully equipped for making long-term plans and curbing impulses) may succumb to the tobacco corporations. Teens actually don't underestimate the risks of smoking—or fast driving or unprotected sex. They just, when reasoning from their gut, weigh the immediate benefits more heavily (Reyna & Farley, 2006; Steinberg, 2007, 2010). Teens find rewards more exciting than adults do. They are like a car with a forceful accelerator but an incompletely developed brake pedal (**FIGURE 12.1**).

So, when Junior drives recklessly and struggles academically, should his parents reassure themselves that "he can't help it; his frontal cortex isn't yet fully grown"? They can take hope: Brain changes underlie teens' new self-consciousness about what others are thinking as well as their valuing of risky rewards (Barkley-Levenson & Galván, 2014; Somerville et al., 2013). And the brain with which Junior begins his teens differs from the brain with which he will end his teens. Unless he slows his brain development with heavy drinking—leaving him prone to impulsivity and addiction—his frontal lobes will continue maturing until about age 25 (Crews et al., 2007; Giedd, 2015). They will also become better connected with the limbic system, enabling better emotion regulation (Cohen et al., 2016; Steinberg, 2012).

In 2004, the American Psychological Association (APA) joined seven other medical and mental health associations in filing U.S. Supreme Court briefs arguing against the death penalty for 16- and 17-year-olds. The briefs documented the teen brain's immaturity "in areas that bear upon adolescent decision making." Brain scans of young teens reveal that frontal lobe immaturity is most evident among juvenile offenders and drug users (Shannon et al., 2011; Whelan et al., 2012). Thus, teens are "less guilty by reason of adolescence," suggested psychologist Laurence Steinberg and law professor Elizabeth Scott (2003; Steinberg et al., 2009). In 2005, by a 5-to-4 margin, the Court concurred, declaring juvenile death penalties unconstitutional. In 2012, the APA offered similar arguments against sentencing juveniles to life without parole (Banville, 2012; Steinberg, 2013). Once again, the Court, by a narrow 5-to-4 vote, concurred.

"Young man, go to your room and stay there until your cerebral cortex matures."

"Be afraid to try new things!"

ENGAGE How will you look back on your life 10 years from now? Are you making choices that someday you will recollect with satisfaction?

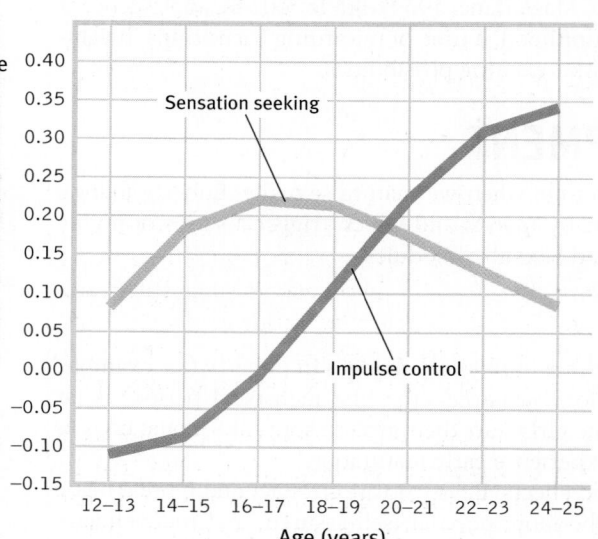

FIGURE 12.1

IMPULSE CONTROL LAGS REWARD SEEKING Surveys of more than 7000 American 12- to 24-year-olds reveal that sensation seeking peaks in the mid-teens, with impulse control developing more slowly as frontal lobes mature. (National Longitudinal Study of Youth and Children and Young Adults survey data presented by Steinberg, 2013.)

COGNITIVE DEVELOPMENT

LOQ 12-2 How did Piaget, Kohlberg, and later researchers describe adolescent cognitive and moral development?

During the early teen years, reasoning is often self-focused. Adolescents may think their private experiences are unique, something parents just could not understand: "But, Mom, *you* don't really know how it feels to be in love" (Elkind, 1978). Capable of thinking about their own thinking, and about other people's thinking, they also begin imagining what others are thinking about *them*. (They might worry less if they understood their peers' similar self-absorption.) Gradually, though, most begin to reason more abstractly.

Developing Reasoning Power

When adolescents achieve the intellectual summit that Jean Piaget called *formal operations,* they apply their new abstract reasoning tools to the world around them. They may think about what is ideally possible and compare that with the imperfect reality of their society, their parents, and themselves. They may debate human nature, good and evil, truth and justice. Their sense of what's fair changes from simple equality to equity—to what's proportional to merit (Almås et al., 2010). Having left behind the concrete images of early childhood, they may search for spirituality and a deeper meaning of life (Boyatzis, 2012; Elkind, 1970). Reasoning hypothetically and deducing consequences also enables adolescents to detect inconsistencies and spot hypocrisy in others' reasoning, sometimes leading to heated debates with parents and silent vows never to lose sight of their own ideals (Peterson et al., 1986).

Samuel Corum/Anadolu Agency/Getty Images

Developing Morality

Two crucial tasks of childhood and adolescence are discerning right from wrong and developing character—the psychological muscles for controlling impulses. Children learn to empathize with others, an ability that continues to develop in adolescence. To be a moral person is to *think* morally and *act* accordingly. Jean Piaget and Lawrence Kohlberg proposed that moral reasoning guides moral actions. A more recent view builds on psychology's game-changing new recognition that much of our functioning occurs not on the "high road" of deliberate, conscious thinking but on the "low road," unconscious and automatic.

MORAL REASONING Piaget (1932) believed that children's moral judgments build on their cognitive development. Agreeing with Piaget, Lawrence Kohlberg (1981, 1984) sought to describe the development of *moral reasoning,* the thinking that occurs as we consider right and wrong. Kohlberg posed moral dilemmas (for example, whether a person should

"When the pilot told us to brace and grab our ankles, the first thing that went through my mind was that we must all look pretty stupid." —Jeremiah Rawlings, age 12, after surviving a 1989 plane crash in Sioux City, Iowa

FED UP WITH FIREARMS After a 2018 mass shooting at a Parkland, Florida high school, student survivors started the #NeverAgain movement to demand U.S. gun law reform. Hundreds of thousands of teens have since participated in school walkouts (shown here), and marches, demonstrating their ability to think logically about abstract topics and to voice their ideals. According to Piaget, these teens are in the final cognitive stage, formal operations.

"I helped a so-called friend commit armed robbery and murder. . . . I was just 17 years old. . . . Been in prison for over 20 years . . . longer than I was ever free. . . . I am among the 300 plus "Juvenile Lifers" in Michigan prisons. I learned and matured a lot since my time incarcerated. I experience great remorse and regret over the tragedy that I ashamedly participated in. But I salvage this experience by learning and growing from it." —M. H., Michigan prison inmate, personal correspondence, 2015

 TABLE 12.1

Kohlberg's Levels of Moral Thinking Kohlberg posed moral dilemmas, such as: "Is it okay to steal medicine to save a loved one?"

Level (approximate age)	Focus	Example of Moral Reasoning
Preconventional morality (before age 9)	Self-interest; obey rules to avoid punishment or gain concrete rewards.	"If you save your loved one, you'll be a hero."
Conventional morality (early adolescence)	Uphold laws and rules to gain social approval or maintain social order.	"If you steal the medicine, everyone will think you're a criminal."
Postconventional morality (adolescence and beyond)	Actions reflect belief in basic rights and self-defined ethical principles.	"People have a right to live."

MORAL REASONING Some Houston, Texas residents faced a moral dilemma in 2017 when Hurricane Harvey caused disastrous flooding. Should they risk their lives to try to rescue family, friends, and neighbors in dangerously flooded areas? Their reasoning likely reflected different levels of moral thinking, even if they behaved similarly.

Luke Sharrett/Bloomberg via Getty Images

steal medicine to save a loved one's life) and asked children, adolescents, and adults whether the action was right or wrong. His analysis of their answers led him to propose three basic levels of moral thinking: *preconventional, conventional,* and *postconventional* (**TABLE 12.1**). Kohlberg claimed these levels form a moral ladder. As with all stage theories, the sequence is unvarying. We begin on the bottom rung and rise to varying heights; at the post-conventional level, we may place others' comfort above our own (Crockett et al., 2014). Infants recognize right and wrong, preferring moral over immoral action (Cowell & Decety, 2015). Preschoolers, typically identifying with their cultural group, conform to and enforce its moral norms (Haun et al., 2014; Schmidt & Tomasello, 2012). When those norms reward kind actions, preschoolers help others (Carragan & Dweck, 2014). Kohlberg's critics have noted that his postconventional stage is culturally limited, appearing mostly among people from large societies that prize individualism (Barrett et al., 2016; Eckensberger, 1994; Miller & Bersoff, 1995).

 RETRIEVE IT • • •   *ANSWERS IN APPENDIX E*

RI-1 According to Kohlberg, _____ morality focuses on self-interest, _____ morality focuses on self-defined ethical principles, and _____ morality focuses on upholding laws and social rules.

RI-2 How has Kohlberg's theory of moral reasoning been criticized?

MORAL INTUITION Psychologist Jonathan Haidt [pronounced HITE] (2002, 2012) believes that much of our morality is rooted in *moral intuitions*—"quick gut feelings, or affectively laden intuitions." According to this intuitionist view, the mind makes moral judgments in much the same way that it makes aesthetic judgments—quickly and automatically. Feelings of disgust or of elation trigger moral reasoning, says Haidt.

One woman recalled traveling through her snowy neighborhood with three young men as they passed "an elderly woman with a shovel in her driveway. . . . [O]ne of the guys . . . asked the driver to let him off there. . . . [M]y mouth dropped in shock as I realized that he was offering to shovel her walk for her." Witnessing this unexpected goodness triggered elevation: "I felt like jumping out of the car and hugging this guy. I felt like singing and running, or skipping and laughing. I felt like saying nice things about people" (Haidt, 2000).

"Could human morality really be run by the moral emotions," Haidt wonders, "while moral reasoning struts about pretending to be in control?" Consider the desire to punish. Laboratory games reveal that the desire to punish wrongdoing is mostly driven not by reason (such as an objective calculation that punishment deters crime) but rather by emotional reactions, such as moral outrage and the pleasure of revenge (Chester & DeWall, 2016; Darley, 2009). After the emotional fact, moral reasoning—our mind's press secretary—aims to convince us and others of the logic of what we have intuitively felt.

This intuitionist perspective on morality finds support in a study of moral paradoxes. Imagine seeing a runaway trolley headed for five people. All will certainly be killed unless you throw a switch that diverts the trolley onto another track, where it will kill one person. Should you throw the switch? Most say *Yes.* Kill one, save five.

Now imagine the same dilemma, except that your opportunity to save the five requires you to push a large stranger onto the tracks, where he will die as his body stops the trolley. The logic is the same—kill one, save five?—but most say *No.* Seeking to understand why, researchers used brain imaging to spy on people's neural responses as they contemplated such dilemmas. Only the body-pushing type of moral dilemma activated the brain's emotion areas (Greene et al., 2001). Thus, our moral judgments provide another example of the two-track mind—of dual processing (Feinberg et al., 2012). Moral reasoning, centered in one brain area, says throw the switch. Our intuitive moral emotions, rooted in other brain areas, override reason when saying *don't* push the man. We may liken our moral cognition to our phone's camera settings. Usually, we rely on the default settings. Yet sometimes we use reason to manually override those settings and make adjustments (Greene, 2010).

MORAL ACTION Our moral thinking and feeling surely affect our moral talk. But sometimes talk is cheap and emotions are fleeting. Morality involves *doing* the right thing, and what we do also depends on social influences. As political theorist Hannah Arendt (1963) observed, many Nazi concentration camp guards during World War II were ordinary "moral" people who were corrupted by a powerfully evil situation.

Today's character education programs tend to focus on the whole moral package—thinking, feeling, and *doing* the right thing. In service-learning programs, teens have tutored, cleaned up their neighborhoods, and assisted older adults. The result? The teens' sense of competence and desire to serve has increased, their school absenteeism and dropout rates have dropped, and their violent behavior has diminished (Andersen, 1998; Heller, 2014; Piliavin, 2003). Moral action feeds moral attitudes.

A big part of moral development is the self-discipline needed to restrain one's own impulses—to delay small gratifications now to enable bigger rewards later. In one of psychology's best-known experiments, Walter Mischel (2014) gave 4-year-olds a choice between one marshmallow now, or two marshmallows when he returned a few minutes later. The children who delayed gratification went on to have higher college completion rates and incomes, and less often suffered addiction.

A newer and larger study found that a 4-year-old's single act of willpower only modestly predicted the child's long-term academic success, especially after controlling for other factors (Watts et al., 2018). The larger point remains: Our capacity to *delay gratification*—to decline small rewards now for bigger rewards later—is basic to our future academic, vocational, and social success (Daly et al., 2015; Funder & Block, 1989; Sawyer et al., 2015). A preference for large-later rather than small-now rewards minimizes one's risk of problem gambling, smoking, and delinquency (Callan et al., 2011; Ert et al., 2013; Lee et al., 2017).

What enables our ability to delay gratification? Brain scans reveal a larger prefrontal cortex among adolescents who excel at delaying gratification, which may also help explain their better academic performance (Wang, Y., et al., 2017). An analysis of 36 species yielded similar results: Animals with larger brains showed a better ability to delay gratification (MacLean et al., 2014). But a bigger brain is not the only factor that enhances this ability. Our beliefs about willpower, our motivation, and our cultural views also play a role (Berkman et al., 2017; Job et al., 2010; Lamm et al., 2017). *The bottom line:* This is an ability worth cultivating. Delaying gratification—living with one eye on the future—fosters flourishing.

"This might not be ethical. Is that a problem for anybody?"

"It is a delightful harmony when doing and saying go together." —Michel Eyquem de Montaigne (1533–1592)

"The best time to plant a tree was 20 years ago. The second best time is now." —Chinese proverb

SOCIAL DEVELOPMENT

LOQ 12-3 What are the social tasks and challenges of adolescence?

Theorist Erik Erikson (1963) contended that each stage of life has its own *psychosocial task,* a crisis that needs resolution. Young children wrestle with issues of *trust,* then *autonomy* (independence), then *initiative.* School-age children strive for *competence,* feeling able and productive. The adolescent's task is to synthesize past, present, and future possibilities into a clearer sense of self (**TABLE 12.2**). Adolescents wonder, "Who am I as an individual? What do I want to do with my life? What values should I live by? What do I believe in?" Erikson called this quest the adolescent's *search for identity.*

Competence vs. inferiority

Intimacy vs. isolation

TABLE 12.2

Erikson's Stages of Psychosocial Development

Stage (approximate age)	Issue	Description of Task
Infancy (to 1 year)	Trust vs. mistrust	If needs are dependably met, infants develop a sense of basic trust.
Toddlerhood (1 to 3 years)	Autonomy vs. shame and doubt	Toddlers learn to exercise their will and do things for themselves, or they doubt their abilities.
Preschool (3 to 6 years)	Initiative vs. guilt	Preschoolers learn to initiate tasks and carry out plans, or they feel guilty about their efforts to be independent.
Elementary school (6 years to puberty)	Competence vs. inferiority	Children learn the pleasure of applying themselves to tasks, or they feel inferior.
Adolescence (teen years into 20s)	Identity vs. role confusion	Teenagers work at refining a sense of self by testing roles and then integrating them to form a single identity, or they become confused about who they are.
Young adulthood (20s to early 40s)	Intimacy vs. isolation	Young adults struggle to form close relationships and to gain the capacity for intimate love, or they feel socially isolated.
Middle adulthood (40s to 60s)	Generativity vs. stagnation	Middle-aged people discover a sense of contributing to the world, usually through family and work, or they may feel a lack of purpose.
Late adulthood (late 60s and up)	Integrity vs. despair	Reflecting on their lives, older adults may feel a sense of satisfaction or failure.

Forming an Identity

To refine their sense of identity, adolescents in individualist cultures usually try out different "selves" in different situations. They may act out one self at home, another with friends, and still another at school or online. If two situations overlap—as when a teenager brings new friends home—the discomfort can be considerable (Klimstra et al., 2015). The teen often wonders, "Which self should I be? Which is the real me?" The eventual resolution is a self-definition that unifies the various selves into a consistent and comfortable sense of who one is—an **identity.**

For both adolescents and adults, group identities are often formed by how we differ from those around us. When living in Britain, I [DM] become conscious of my Americanness. When spending time in Hong Kong, I [ND] become conscious of my minority White race. For international students, for those of a minority ethnic or religious group, for gay and transgender people, or for people with a disability, a **social identity** often forms around their distinctiveness.

Erikson noticed that some adolescents forge their identity early, simply by adopting their parents' values and expectations. Other adolescents may adopt the identity of a particular peer group—jocks, preps, geeks, band kids, debaters. Traditional, collectivist cultures teach adolescents who they are, rather than encouraging them to decide on their own. Bicultural adolescents form complex identities as they integrate multiple group memberships and their feelings about them (Marks et al., 2011).

Most young people do develop a sense of contentment with their lives. A question: Which statement best describes you? "I would choose my life the way it is right now" or "I wish I were somebody else"? When American teens answered, 81 percent picked the first, and 19 percent the second (Lyons, 2004). Reflecting on their existence, 75 percent of American collegians say they "discuss religion/spirituality" with friends, "pray," and agree that "we are all spiritual beings" and "search for meaning/purpose in life" (Astin et al., 2004; Bryant & Astin, 2008). This would not surprise Stanford

"Somewhere between the ages of 10 and 13 (depending on how hormone-enhanced their beef was), children entered adolescence, a.k.a. 'the de-cutening.'" —Jon Stewart et al., *Earth (The Book)*, 2010

Nine times out of ten, it's all about peer pressure.

psychologist William Damon and his colleagues (2003), who have contended that a key task of adolescence is to achieve a purpose—a desire to accomplish something personally meaningful that makes a difference to the world beyond oneself.

Several studies indicate that self-esteem typically falls during the early to mid-teen years, and, for girls, depression scores often increase. But then self-image rebounds during the late teens and twenties, and self-esteem gender differences become small (Zuckerman et al., 2016). Late adolescence is also a time when agreeableness and emotional stability scores increase (Klimstra et al., 2009).

ENGAGE 💡 📖 **LaunchPad** For an interactive self-assessment of your own identity, see **Topic Tutorial: PsychSim6, Who Am I?**

These are the years when many people in industrialized countries begin exploring new opportunities by attending college or working full time. Many college seniors have achieved a clearer identity and a more positive self-concept than they had as first-year students (Waterman, 1988). Those who have achieved a clear sense of identity are less prone to alcohol misuse (Bishop et al., 2005).

Erikson contended that adolescent identity formation (which continues into adulthood) is followed in young adulthood by a developing capacity for **intimacy,** the ability to form emotionally close relationships. When Mihaly Csikszentmihalyi [chick-SENT-me-hi] and Jeremy Hunter (2003) used a beeper to sample the daily experiences of American teens, they found them unhappiest when alone and happiest when with friends. Romantic relationships, which tend to be emotionally intense, are reported by some two in three North American 17-year-olds, but by fewer in collectivist countries such as China (Collins et al., 2009; Li et al., 2010). Those who enjoy high-quality (intimate, supportive) relationships with family and friends tend also to enjoy similarly high-quality romantic relationships in adolescence, which set the stage for healthy adult relationships. Such relationships are, for most of us, a source of great pleasure.

Parent and Peer Relationships

LOQ 12-4 How do parents and peers influence adolescents?

As adolescents in Western cultures seek to form their own identities, they begin to pull away from their parents (Shanahan et al., 2007). The preschooler who can't be close enough to her mother, who loves to touch and cling to her, becomes the 14-year-old who wouldn't be caught dead holding hands with Mom. The transition occurs gradually, but this period is typically a time of diminishing parental influence and growing peer influence. As children, we more readily recognize adult than other children's faces; by adolescence, we display superior recognition for our peers' faces (Picci & Scherf, 2016). Puberty alters attachments and primes perceptions.

As Aristotle long ago recognized, we humans are "the social animal." At all ages, but especially during childhood and adolescence, we seek to fit in with our groups (Harris, 1998, 2002). Teens who start smoking typically have friends who model smoking, suggest its pleasures, and offer cigarettes (Rose et al., 1999, 2003). Part of this peer similarity may result from a *selection effect,* as kids seek out peers with similar attitudes and interests. Those who smoke (or don't) may select as friends those who also smoke (or don't). Put two teens together and their brains become hypersensitive to reward (Albert et al., 2013). This increased activation helps explain why teens take more driving risks when with friends than they do alone (Chein et al., 2011).

By adolescence, parent-child arguments occur more often, usually over mundane things—household chores, bedtime, homework (Tesser et al., 1989). Conflict during the transition to adolescence tends to be greater with first-born than with second-born children, and greater with mothers than with fathers (Burk et al., 2009; Shanahan et al., 2007).

For a minority of parents and their adolescents, differences lead to real splits and great stress (Steinberg & Morris, 2001). But most disagreements are at the level of harmless bickering. With sons, the issues often are behavior problems, such as acting out or

WHO SHALL I BE TODAY? By varying the way they look, adolescents try out different "selves." Although we eventually form a consistent and stable sense of identity, the self we present may change with the situation.

"Self-consciousness, the recognition of a creature by itself as a 'self,' [cannot] exist except in contrast with an 'other,' a something which is not the self."
—C. S. Lewis, *The Problem of Pain*, 1940

"She says she's someone from your past who gave birth to you, and raised you, and sacrificed everything so you could have whatever you wanted."

identity our sense of self; according to Erikson, the adolescent's task is to solidify a sense of self by testing and integrating various roles.

social identity the "we" aspect of our self-concept; the part of our answer to "Who am I?" that comes from our group memberships.

intimacy in Erikson's theory, the ability to form close, loving relationships; a primary developmental task in young adulthood.

hygiene; for daughters, the issues commonly involve relationships, such as dating and friendships (Schlomer et al., 2011). In a survey of nearly 6000 adolescents in 10 countries—from Australia to Bangladesh to Turkey—most said they like their parents (Offer et al., 1988). "We usually get along but . . . ," adolescents often report (Galambos, 1992; Steinberg, 1987).

Positive parent-teen relations and positive peer relations often go hand in hand. High school girls who had the most affectionate relationships with their mothers tended also to enjoy the most intimate friendships with girlfriends (Gold & Yanof, 1985). And teens who felt close to their parents have tended to be healthy and happy and to do well in school (Resnick et al., 1997). Of course, we can state this correlation the other way: Misbehaving teens are more likely to have tense relationships with parents and other adults.

Although heredity does much of the heavy lifting in forming individual temperament and personality differences, parents and peers influence teen's behaviors and attitudes. When with peers, teens discount the future and focus more on immediate rewards (O'Brien et al., 2011). Most teens are herd animals, talking, dressing, and acting more like their peers than their parents. What their friends are, they often become, and what "everybody's doing," they often do. Teens' social media use illustrates the power of peer influence. Compared to photos with few likes, teens prefer photos with many other likes. Moreover, when viewing many-liked photos, teens' brains become more active in areas associated with reward processing and imitation (Sherman et al., 2016). Liking and doing what everybody else likes and does feels good.

Part of what everybody's doing is networking—a lot. Teens rapidly adopt social media. U.S. teens typically send 30 text messages daily and average 145 Facebook friends (Lenhart, 2015b). They tweet, post videos to Snapchat, and share pictures on Instagram. Online communication stimulates intimate self-disclosure—both for better (support groups) and for worse (online predators and extremist groups) (Subrahmanyam & Greenfield, 2008; Valkenburg & Peter, 2009; Wilson et al., 2012).

Both online and face-to-face, for those who feel excluded and bullied by their peers, the pain is acute. Most excluded "students suffer in silence. . . . A small number act out in violent ways against their classmates" (Aronson, 2001). The pain of exclusion also persists. In one large study, those who were bullied as children showed poorer physical health and greater psychological distress 40 years later (Takizawa et al., 2014). Peer approval matters.

"I'm fourteen, Mom, I don't do hugs."

ASK YOURSELF

What are the most positive and the most negative things you remember about your own adolescence? Who do you credit or blame more—your parents or your peers?

HOW MUCH CREDIT OR BLAME DO PARENTS DESERVE? In procreation, a woman and a man shuffle their gene decks and deal a life-forming hand to their child-to-be, who is then subjected to countless influences beyond their control. Parents, nonetheless, feel enormous satisfaction in their children's successes or guilt and shame over their failures. They beam over the child who wins trophies and titles. They wonder where they went wrong with the child who is repeatedly in trouble.

Freudian psychiatry and psychology encouraged such ideas by blaming problems from asthma to schizophrenia on "bad mothering." Believing that parents shape their offspring as a potter molds clay, many people praise parents for their children's virtues and blame them for their children's vices, and for the psychological harm that toxic parents presumably inflict on their fragile children. No wonder having and raising children can seem so risky.

But do parents really produce wounded future adults by being (take your pick from the toxic-parenting lists) overbearing—or uninvolved? Pushy—or indecisive? Overprotective—or distant? Should we then blame our parents for our failings, and ourselves for our children's failings? Or does talk of wounding fragile children through normal parental mistakes trivialize the brutality of real abuse?

Parents do matter. But parenting wields its largest effects at the extremes: the abused children who become abusive, the deeply loved but firmly handled who become self-confident and socially competent. The power of the family environment also appears in the remarkable academic and vocational successes of many children of people who leave their home countries, such as those of refugees who fled war-torn Vietnam and Cambodia—successes attributed to close-knit, supportive, even demanding families (Caplan et al., 1992). Asian-Americans and European-Americans often differ in their parenting expectations. An Asian-American

"First, I did things for my parents' approval, then I did things for my parents' disapproval, and now I don't know why I do things."

mother may push her children to do well, but usually not in a way that strains their relationship (Fu & Markus, 2014). Having a supportive "Tiger Mother"—one who pushes her children and works alongside them—tends to motivate children (whose culture prepares them to expect such pushing) to work harder. European-Americans, however, might see this as going overboard and undermining children's motivation (Deal, 2011).

Yet in personality measures, shared environmental influences from the womb onward typically account for less than 10 percent of children's differences. In the words of behavior geneticists Robert Plomin and Denise Daniels (1987; Plomin, 2011), "Two children in the same family are [apart from their shared genes] as different from one another as are pairs of children selected randomly from the population." To developmental psychologist Sandra Scarr (1993), this implied that "parents should be given less credit for kids who turn out great and blamed less for kids who don't." So, knowing that children's personalities are not easily sculpted by parental nurture, perhaps parents can relax and love their children for who they are.

> 🔒 **RETRIEVE IT** • • •   *ANSWERS IN APPENDIX E*
>
> **RI-3** What is the *selection effect,* and how might it affect a teen's decision to join sports teams at school?

EMERGING ADULTHOOD

LOQ 12-5 What is *emerging adulthood?*

In the Western world, adolescence now roughly corresponds to the teen years. At earlier times, and in other parts of the world today, this slice of life has been much smaller (Baumeister & Tice, 1986). Shortly after sexual maturity, young people would assume adult responsibilities and status. The event might be celebrated with an elaborate initiation—a public rite of passage. The new adult would then work, marry, and have children.

When schooling became compulsory in many Western countries, independence was put on hold until after graduation. Adolescents are now taking more time to establish themselves as adults. In the United States, for example, the average age at first marriage has increased more than 5 years since 1960 (to 29 for men, 27 for women). In 1960, three in four women and two in three men had, by age 30, finished school, left home, become financially independent, married, and had a child. In the early twenty-first century, fewer than half of 30-year-old women and one-third of men were meeting these five milestones (Henig, 2010). In 2016, 15 percent of 25- to 35-year-old Americans—double the 1981 proportion—were living in their parents' home (Fry, 2017).

Together, later independence and earlier sexual maturity have widened the once-brief interlude between biological maturity and social independence (**FIGURE 12.2**). In prosperous communities, the time from 18 to the mid-twenties is an increasingly not-yet-settled phase of life, now often called **emerging adulthood** (Arnett, 2006, 2007; Reitzle, 2006).

emerging adulthood a period from about age 18 to the mid-twenties, when many in Western cultures are no longer adolescents but have not yet achieved full independence as adults.

"Men resemble the times more than they resemble their fathers." —Ancient Arab proverb

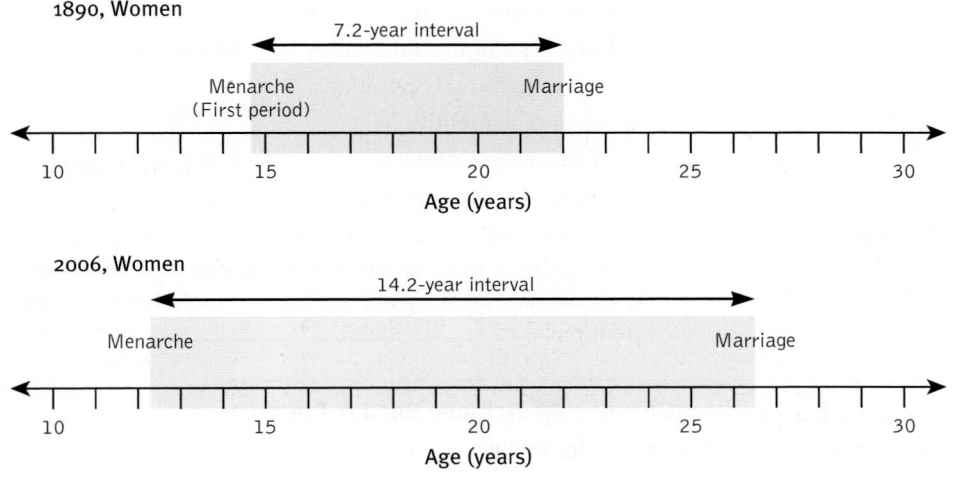

FIGURE 12.2

THE TRANSITION TO ADULTHOOD IS BEING STRETCHED FROM BOTH ENDS In the 1890s, the average interval between a woman's first menstrual period and marriage, which typically marked a transition to adulthood, was about 7 years. By 2006 in industrialized countries, that gap had widened to about 14 years (Finer & Philbin, 2014; Guttmacher Institute, 1994). Although many adults are unmarried, later marriage combines with prolonged education and earlier menarche to help stretch out the transition to adulthood.

ASK YOURSELF

What do you think makes a person an adult? Do you feel like an adult? Why or why not?

"I just don't know what to do with myself in that long stretch after college but before social security."

No longer adolescents, these emerging adults, having not yet assumed full adult responsibilities and independence, feel "in between." After high school, those who enter the job market or go to college may be managing their own time and priorities. Yet they may be doing so from their parents' home, unable to afford their own place and perhaps still emotionally dependent as well. Recognizing today's more gradually emerging adulthood, the U.S. government now allows dependent children up to age 26 to remain on their parents' health insurance (Cohen, 2010).

🔒 **RETRIEVE IT • • •**   *ANSWERS IN APPENDIX E*

RI-4 Match the psychosocial development stage (I–VIII) with the issue that Erikson believed we wrestle with at that stage (a–h).

I.	Infancy	a.	Generativity vs. stagnation
II.	Toddlerhood	b.	Integrity vs. despair
III.	Preschool	c.	Initiative vs. guilt
IV.	Elementary school	d.	Intimacy vs. isolation
V.	Adolescence	e.	Identity vs. role confusion
VI.	Young adulthood	f.	Competence vs. inferiority
VII.	Middle adulthood	g.	Trust vs. mistrust
VIII.	Late adulthood	h.	Autonomy vs. shame and doubt

🔒 REVIEW ADOLESCENCE

⟫ Learning Objectives

TEST YOURSELF Answer these repeated Learning Objective Questions on your own (before checking the answers in Appendix D) to improve your retention of the concepts (McDaniel et al., 2009, 2015).

12-1 How is *adolescence* defined, and how do physical changes affect developing teens?

12-2 How did Piaget, Kohlberg, and later researchers describe adolescent cognitive and moral development?

12-3 What are the social tasks and challenges of adolescence?

12-4 How do parents and peers influence adolescents?

12-5 What is *emerging adulthood*?

⟫ Terms and Concepts to Remember

TEST YOURSELF Write down the definition yourself, then check your answer on the referenced page.

adolescence, **p. 141**

puberty, **p. 141**

identity, **p. 147**

social identity, **p. 147**

intimacy, **p. 147**

emerging adulthood, **p. 149**

⟫ Master the Material

TEST YOURSELF Answer the following questions on your own first, then check your answers in Appendix E.

1. Adolescence is marked by the onset of
   a. an identity crisis.
   b. puberty.
   c. moral reasoning.
   d. parent-child conflict.

2. According to Piaget, a person who can think logically about abstractions is in the _____ _____ stage.

3. In Erikson's stages, the primary task during adolescence is
   a. attaining formal operations.
   b. forging an identity.
   c. developing a sense of intimacy with another person.
   d. living independent of parents.

4. Some developmental psychologists refer to the period that occurs in some Western cultures from age 18 to the mid-twenties and beyond (up to the time of full adult independence) as _____ _____.

Continue testing yourself with 📚 **LearningCurve** or 📚 **Achieve Read & Practice** to learn and remember most effectively.

Adulthood

13

The unfolding of our lives continues across the life span. It is, however, more difficult to generalize about adulthood stages than about life's early years. If you know that James is a 1-year-old and Jamal is a 10-year-old, you could say a great deal about each child. Not so with adults who differ by a similar number of years. The boss may be 30 or 60; the marathon runner may be 20 or 50; the 19-year-old may be a parent who supports a child or a child who receives an allowance. Yet our life courses are in some ways similar. Physically, cognitively, and especially socially, we differ at age 50 from our 25-year-old selves. In the discussion that follows, we recognize these differences and use three terms: *early adulthood* (roughly twenties and thirties), *middle adulthood* (to age 65), and *late adulthood* (the years after 65). Within each of these stages, people will vary widely in physical, psychological, and social development.

PHYSICAL DEVELOPMENT

LOQ 13-1   What physical changes occur during middle and late adulthood?

Like the declining daylight after the summer solstice, our physical abilities—muscular strength, reaction time, sensory keenness, and cardiac output—all begin an almost imperceptible decline in our mid-twenties. Athletes are often the first to notice. Baseball players peak at about age 27—with 60 percent of Most Valuable Player awardees since 1985 coming within 2 years of that age (Silver, 2012). But most of us—especially those of us whose daily lives do not require top physical performance—hardly perceive the early signs of decline.

Physical Changes in Middle Adulthood

Athletes over 40 know all too well that physical decline gradually accelerates. During early and middle adulthood, physical vigor has less to do with age than with a person's health and exercise habits. Many physically fit 50-year-olds run 4 miles with ease, while sedentary 25-year-olds find themselves huffing and puffing up two flights of stairs.

Aging also brings a gradual decline in fertility, especially for women. For a 35- to 39-year-old woman, the chance of getting pregnant after a single act of intercourse is half that of a woman 19 to 26 (Dunson et al., 2002). Men experience a gradual decline in sperm count, testosterone level, and speed of erection and ejaculation. Women experience **menopause** as menstrual cycles end, usually within a few years of age 50. Some may experience distress, as do some men who experience declining virility and physical capacities. But most people age without such problems.

With age, sexual activity lessens. Nevertheless, most men and women remain capable of satisfying sexual activity, and most express satisfaction with their sex life. This was true of 70 percent of Canadians surveyed (ages 40 to 64) and 75 percent of Finns (ages 65 to 74) (Kontula & Haavio-Mannila, 2009; Wright, 2006). In other surveys, 75 percent of respondents reported being sexually active into their eighties. It seems that, for most older people, life's "sexual wisdom" sustains sexual satisfaction even as sexual frequency subsides (Schick et al., 2010). In an American Association of Retired Persons sexuality survey, it was not until age 75 or older that most women and nearly half of men reported little sexual desire (DeLamater, 2012; DeLamater & Sill, 2005). As Alex Comfort (2002, p. 226) jested, "The things that stop you having sex with age are exactly the same as those that stop you riding a bicycle (bad health, thinking it looks silly, no bicycle)."

Physical Changes in Late Adulthood

Is old age "more to be feared than death" (Juvenal, *The Satires*)? Or is life "most delightful when it is on the downward slope" (Seneca, *Epistulae ad Lucilium*)? What is it like to grow old?

menopause the time of natural cessation of menstruation; also refers to the biological changes a woman experiences as her ability to reproduce declines.

ENGAGE   (ASK YOURSELF)

Imagining the future, how do you think you might change? How might you stay the same?

ENGAGE   How old does a person have to be before you think of him or her as old? Depends on who you ask. For 18- to 29-year-olds, 67 was old. For those 60 and over, old was 76 (Yankelovich Partners, 1995).

ADULT ABILITIES VARY WIDELY
George Blair was, at age 92, the world's oldest barefoot water skier. He is shown here in 2002 when he first set the record, at age 87. (He died in 2013 at age 98.)

"Happy fortieth. I'll take the muscle tone in your upper arms, the girlish timbre of your voice, your amazing tolerance for caffeine, and your ability to digest french fries. The rest of you can stay."

"For some reason, possibly to save ink, the restaurants had started printing their menus in letters the height of bacteria." —Dave Barry, *Dave Barry Turns Fifty*, 1998

SUITING UP FOR OLD AGE A long life is a gift. To reach old age, it takes good genes, a nurturing environment, and a little luck. New technology allows you to put yourself in your elders' shoes. In these special suits, younger people can hear, see, and move as if they were 85 years old.

SENSORY ABILITIES, STRENGTH, AND STAMINA Although physical decline begins in early adulthood, we are not usually acutely aware of it until later in life, when the stairs get steeper, the print gets smaller, and other people seem to mumble more. Muscle strength, reaction time, and stamina diminish in late adulthood. As a lifelong basketball player, I [DM] find myself increasingly not racing for that loose ball. But even diminished vigor is sufficient for normal activities.

With age, visual sharpness diminishes, as does distance perception and adaptation to light-level changes. The eye's pupil shrinks and its lens becomes less transparent, reducing the amount of light reaching the retina: A 65-year-old retina receives only about one-third as much light as its 20-year-old counterpart (Kline & Schieber, 1985). Thus, to see as well as a 20-year-old when reading or driving, a 65-year-old needs three times as much light—a reason for buying cars with untinted windshields. This also explains why older people sometimes ask younger people, "Don't you need better light for reading?"

The senses of smell, hearing, and touch also diminish. In Wales, teens' loitering around a convenience store has been discouraged by a device that emits an aversive high-pitched sound almost no one over 30 can hear (Lyall, 2005).

HEALTH As people age, they care less about what their bodies look like and more about how their bodies function. For those growing older, there is both bad and good news about health. The bad news: The body's disease-fighting immune system weakens, making older adults more susceptible to life-threatening ailments such as cancer and pneumonia. The good news: Thanks partly to a lifetime's accumulation of antibodies, people over 65 suffer fewer short-term ailments, such as common flu and cold viruses. One study found they were half as likely as 20-year-olds and one-fifth as likely as preschoolers to suffer upper respiratory flu each year (National Center for Health Statistics, 1990).

THE AGING BRAIN Up to the teen years, we process information with greater and greater speed (Fry & Hale, 1996; Kail, 1991). But compared with teens and young adults, older people take a bit more time to react, to solve perceptual puzzles, even to remember names (Bashore et al., 1997; Verhaeghen & Salthouse, 1997). At video games, most 70-year-olds are no match for a 20-year-old. This processing lag can also have deadly consequences (Aichele et al., 2016). As **FIGURE 13.1** indicates, fatal accident rates per mile driven increase sharply after age 75. By age 85, they exceed the 16-year-old level. Older drivers appear to focus well on the road ahead, but attend less to vehicles approaching from the side (Pollatsek et al., 2012). Nevertheless, because older people drive less, they account for fewer than 10 percent of crashes (Coughlin et al., 2004).

Brain regions important to memory begin to atrophy during aging (Fraser et al., 2015; Ritchie et al., 2015). The blood-brain barrier also breaks down beginning in the hippocampus, which furthers cognitive decline (Montagne et al., 2015). No wonder older adults feel even older after taking a memory test: It's like "aging 5 years in 5 minutes," joked one research team (Hughes et al., 2013). In early adulthood, a small, gradual net loss of brain cells begins, contributing by age 80 to a brain-weight reduction of 5 percent or so. We know that our frontal lobes help us override undesirable urges—their slow development (not fully mature

FIGURE 13.1

AGE AND DRIVER FATALITIES
Slowing reactions contribute to increased accident risks among those 75 and older, and older adults' greater fragility increases their risk of death when accidents happen (NHTSA, 2000). Would you favor driver exams based on performance, not age, to screen out those whose slow reactions or sensory impairments indicate accident risk?

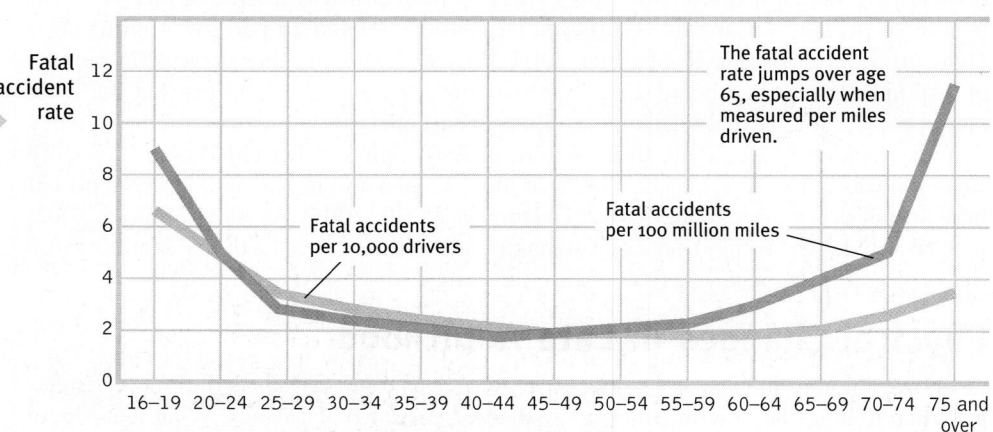

until about age 25) helps account for teen impulsivity. Late in life, some of that impulsiveness often returns as those same frontal lobes begin to atrophy, seemingly explaining older people's occasional blunt questions ("Have you put on weight?") or inappropriate comments (von Hippel, 2007, 2015). But good news: There is still some plasticity in the aging brain, which partly compensates for what it loses by recruiting and reorganizing neural networks (Park & McDonough, 2013). During memory tasks, for example, the left frontal lobes are especially active in young adult brains, while older adult brains use both left and right frontal lobes.

EXERCISE AND AGING And more good news: Exercise slows aging, as shown in studies of identical twin pairs in which only one twin exercised (Iso-Markku et al., 2016; Rottensteiner et al., 2015). Midlife and older adults who do more exercising and less TV watching tend to be mentally quick older adults (Hoang et al., 2016). Physical exercise not only enhances muscles, bones, and energy and helps prevent obesity and heart disease, it maintains the *telomeres* that protect the chromosome ends and even appears to slow the progression of Alzheimer's disease (Kivipelto & Håkansson, 2017; Loprinzi et al., 2015; Smith et al., 2014).

Exercise also stimulates brain cell development and neural connections, thanks perhaps to increased oxygen and nutrient flow (Erickson et al., 2013; Fleischman et al., 2015; Pereira et al., 2007).

Sedentary older adults randomly assigned to aerobic exercise programs exhibit enhanced memory, sharpened judgment, and reduced risk of severe cognitive decline (Raji et al., 2016; Smith, 2016). In aging brains, exercise reduces brain shrinkage (Gow et al., 2012). It promotes neurogenesis (the birth of new nerve cells) in the hippocampus, a brain region important for memory (Erickson, 2009; Pereira et al., 2007). And it increases the cellular mitochondria that help power both muscles and brain cells (Steiner et al., 2011). We are more likely to rust from disuse than to wear out from overuse. Fit bodies support fit minds.

COGNITIVE DEVELOPMENT
Aging and Memory

LOQ 13-2 How does memory change with age?

Among the most intriguing developmental psychology questions is whether adult cognitive abilities, such as memory, intelligence, and creativity, parallel the gradually accelerating decline of physical abilities.

As we age, we remember some things well. Looking back in later life, adults asked to recall the one or two most important events over the last half-century tend to name events from their teens or twenties (Conway et al., 2005; Rubin et al., 1998). They also display this "reminiscence bump" when asked to name their all-time favorite music, movies, and athletes (Janssen et al., 2012). Whatever people experience around this time of life—the Vietnam war, the 9/11 terrorist attacks, the election of the first Black U.S. president—becomes pivotal (Pillemer, 1998; Schuman & Scott, 1989). Our teens and twenties hold so many memorable "firsts"—first kiss, first job, first day at college or university, first meeting our romantic partner.

Early adulthood is indeed a peak time for some types of learning and remembering. In one test of recall, people watched video clips as 14 strangers said their names, using a common format: "Hi, I'm Larry" (Crook & West, 1990). Then those strangers reappeared and gave additional details. For example, they said, "I'm from Philadelphia," providing more visual *and* voice cues for remembering the person's name. As **FIGURE 13.2** shows, after a second and third replay of the introductions, everyone remembered more names, but younger adults consistently surpassed older adults. How well older people remember depends in part on the task. In another experiment, when asked to *recognize* 24 words they had earlier tried to memorize, older adults showed no memory decline. When asked to *recall* that information without clues, however, the decline was greater (**FIGURE 13.3**).

In our capacity to learn and remember, as in other areas of development, we show individual differences. Younger adults vary in their abilities to learn and remember, but 70-year-olds vary much more. "Differences between the most and least able 70-year-olds

Most stairway falls taken by older people occur on the top step, precisely where the person typically descends from a window-lit hallway into the darker stairwell (Fozard & Popkin, 1978). Our knowledge of aging could be used to design environments that would reduce such accidents (National Research Council, 1990).

"I've been working out for six months, but all my gains have been in cognitive function."

"I am still learning." —Michelangelo, 1560, at age 85

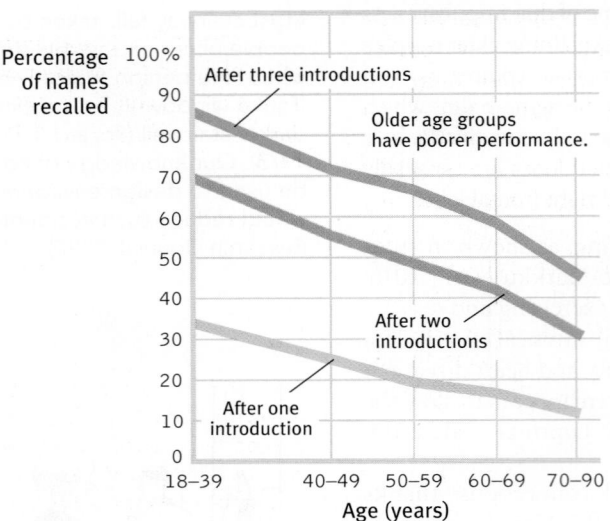

FIGURE 13.2

TESTS OF RECALL Recalling new names introduced once, twice, or three times is easier for younger adults than for older ones. (Data from Crook & West, 1990.)

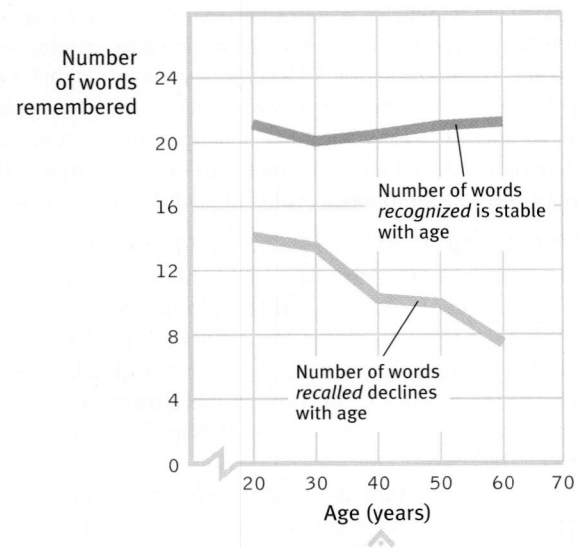

FIGURE 13.3

RECALL AND RECOGNITION IN ADULTHOOD In this experiment, the ability to *recall* new information declined during early and middle adulthood, but the ability to *recognize* new information did not. (Data from Schonfield & Robertson, 1966.)

become much greater than between the most and least able 50-year-olds," reports Oxford researcher Patrick Rabbitt (2006). Some 70-year-olds perform below nearly all 20-year-olds; other 70-year-olds match or outdo the average 20-year-old.

No matter how quick or slow we are, remembering seems also to depend on the type of information we are trying to retrieve. If the information is meaningless—nonsense syllables or unimportant events—then the older we are, the more errors we are likely to make. If the information is *meaningful,* older people's rich web of existing knowledge will help them to hold it. But they may take longer than younger adults to *produce* the words and things they know. Older adults also more often experience tip-of-the-tongue forgetting (Ossher et al., 2012). Quick-thinking game show winners are usually young or middle-aged adults (Burke & Shafto, 2004).

Maintaining Mental Abilities

Psychologists who study the aging mind debate whether "brain fitness" computer-based training programs can build mental muscles and stave off cognitive decline. Our brains remain plastic throughout life (Gutchess, 2014). So, can exercising our brains on a "cognitive treadmill"—with memory, visual tracking, and problem-solving exercises—avert losing our minds? "At every point in life, the brain's natural plasticity gives us the ability to improve . . . function," said one neuroscientist-entrepreneur (Merzenich, 2007). One analysis of cognitive training programs showed that they consistently improved scores on tests related to their training (Simons et al., 2016).

Based on such findings, some computer game makers have been marketing daily brain-exercise programs for older adults. But other researchers, after reviewing all the available studies, advise caution (Melby-Lervåg et al., 2016). One team of experts reported "extensive evidence that brain-training interventions improve performance on the trained tasks, less evidence that such interventions improve performance on closely related tasks, and little evidence that training enhances performance on distantly related tasks or that training improves everyday cognitive performance" (Simons et al., 2016, p. 103). As researcher Zach Hambrick (2014) explains, "Play a video game and you'll get better at that video game, and maybe at very similar video games"—but not at driving a car or filling out your tax return.

cross-sectional study research that compares people of different ages at the same point in time.

longitudinal study research that follows and retests the same people over time.

social clock the culturally preferred timing of social events such as marriage, parenthood, and retirement.

In 2016, the maker of one prominent brain-training program, Lumosity, was fined $2 million for deceiving customers about the program's supposed benefits. "Lumosity preyed on consumers' fears about age-related cognitive decline," said the Federal Trade Commission's Jessica Rich (FTC, 2016). "But Lumosity simply did not have the science to back up its ads."

In other modules, we will explore another dimension of cognitive development: intelligence. As we will see, **cross-sectional studies** and **longitudinal studies** have identified mental abilities that do and do not change as people age. Age is less a predictor of memory and intelligence than is proximity to death. Knowing whether someone is 8 months or 8 years from a natural death, regardless of age, gives a clue to that person's mental ability. In the last three or four years of life and especially as death approaches, negative feelings and cognitive decline typically increase (Vogel et al., 2013; Wilson et al., 2007). Researchers call this near-death drop *terminal decline* (Backman & MacDonald, 2006). Our goals also shift: We're driven less to learn and more to connect socially (Carstensen, 2011).

SOCIAL DEVELOPMENT

LOQ 13-3 What themes and influences mark our social journey from early adulthood to death?

Many differences between younger and older adults are created by significant life events. A new job means new relationships, new expectations, and new demands. Marriage brings the joy of intimacy and the stress of merging two lives. The three years surrounding the birth of a child bring increased life satisfaction for most parents (Dyrdal & Lucas, 2011). The death of a loved one creates an irreplaceable loss. Do these adult life events shape a sequence of life changes?

Adulthood's Ages and Stages

As people enter their forties, they undergo a transition to middle adulthood, a time when they realize that life will soon be mostly behind instead of ahead of them. Some psychologists have argued that for many the *midlife transition* is a crisis, a time of great struggle, regret, or even feeling struck down by life. The popular image of the midlife crisis—an early-forties man who forsakes his family for a younger romantic partner and a hot sports car—is more a myth than reality. Unhappiness, job dissatisfaction, marital dissatisfaction, divorce, anxiety, and suicide do *not* surge during the early forties (Hunter & Sundel, 1989; Mroczek & Kolarz, 1998). Divorce, for example, is most common among those in their twenties, suicide among those in their seventies and eighties. One study of emotional instability in nearly 10,000 men and women found "not the slightest evidence" that distress peaks anywhere in the midlife age range (McCrae & Costa, 1990).

For the 1 in 4 adults who report experiencing a life crisis, the trigger is not age but a major event, such as illness, divorce, or job loss (Lachman, 2004). Some middle-aged adults describe themselves as a "sandwich generation," simultaneously supporting their aging parents and their emerging adult children or grandchildren (Riley & Bowen, 2005).

Life events trigger transitions to new life stages at varying ages. The **social clock**—the definition of "the right time" to leave home, get a job, marry, have children, or retire—varies from era to era and culture to culture. The once-rigid sequence has loosened; the social clock still ticks, but people feel freer about being out of sync with it.

Even *chance events* can have lasting significance, by deflecting us down one road rather than another. Albert Bandura (1982, 2005) recalls the ironic true story of a book editor who came to one of Bandura's lectures on the "Psychology of Chance Encounters and Life Paths"—and ended up marrying the woman who happened to sit next to him. The sequence that led to my [DM's] authoring this book (which was not my idea) began with my being seated near, and getting to know, a distinguished colleague at an international conference. The road to my [ND's] co-authoring this book began in a similarly unplanned manner: After stumbling on an article about my professional life, DM invited me to visit his college. There, we began a conversation that resulted in our collaboration. Chance events can change our lives.

LaunchPad See the **Video: Longitudinal and Cross-Sectional Studies** for a helpful tutorial animation.

"The sudden knowledge of the fragility of his life narrowed his focus and altered his desires. . . . It made him visit with his grandchildren more often, put in an extra trip to see his family in India, and tamp down new ventures." —Atul Gawande, *Being Mortal: Medicine and What Matters in the End*, 2014, describing his father's terminal condition and the way it changed his perspective

"The important events of a person's life are the products of chains of highly improbable occurrences." —Joseph Traub, "Traub's Law," 2003

LOVE Intimacy, attachment, commitment—love by whatever name—is central to healthy and happy adulthood.

Adulthood's Commitments

Two basic aspects of our lives dominate adulthood. Erik Erikson called them *intimacy* (forming close relationships) and *generativity* (being productive and supporting future generations). Sigmund Freud (1935/1960) put this more simply: The healthy adult, he said, is one who can *love* and *work*.

LOVE We typically flirt, fall in love, and commit—one person at a time. "Pair-bonding is a trademark of the human animal," observed anthropologist Helen Fisher (1993). From an evolutionary perspective, relatively monogamous pairing makes sense: Parents who cooperated to nurture their children to maturity were more likely to have their genes passed along to posterity than were parents who didn't.

Adult bonds of love are most satisfying and enduring when marked by a similarity of interests and values, a sharing of emotional and material support, and intimate self-disclosure. And for better or for worse, our standards have risen over the years: We now hope not only for an enduring bond, but also for a mate who is a wage earner, caregiver, intimate friend, and warm and responsive lover (Finkel, 2017). There also appears to be "vow power." Straight and gay relationships sealed with commitment more often endure (Balsam et al., 2008; Rosenfeld, 2014). Such bonds are especially likely to last when couples marry after age 20 and are well educated. Compared with their counterparts of 30 years ago, people in Western countries *are* better educated and marrying later (Wolfinger, 2015). These trends may help explain why the American divorce rate, which surged from 1960 to 1980, has since slightly declined. Canadian divorce rates since the 1980s have followed a similar pattern (Statistics Canada, 2011).

Historically, couples have met at school, on the job, or through friends and family. Thanks to the internet, many couples now meet online—as have nearly a quarter of heterosexual couples and some two-thirds of same-sex couples in one recent national survey (**FIGURE 13.4**).

Might test-driving life together minimize divorce risk? In Europe, Canada, and the United States, those who live together before marriage (and especially before engagement) have had *higher* rates of divorce and marital dysfunction than those who did not (Goodwin et al., 2010; Jose et al., 2010; Manning & Cohen, 2012; Stanley et al., 2010). Three factors contribute. First, those who live together tend to be initially less committed to the ideal of enduring marriage. Second, they may become even less marriage-supporting while living together. Third, it's more awkward to break up with a cohabiting partner than with a dating partner, leading some cohabiters to marry someone "they otherwise would have left behind" (Stanley & Rhoades, 2016a,b).

Although there is more variety in relationships today, the institution of marriage endures. Ninety-five percent of Americans have either married or want to (Newport & Wilke, 2013). In Western countries, what counts as a "very important" reason to marry? Among Americans, 31 percent say financial stability, and 93 percent say love (Cohn, 2013). And marriage is a predictor of happiness, sexual satisfaction, income, and physical and mental health (Scott et al., 2010). National Opinion Research Center surveys of more than

FIGURE 13.4

THE CHANGING WAY AMERICANS MEET THEIR PARTNERS A national survey of 2452 straight couples and 462 gay and lesbian couples reveals the increasing role of the internet. (Data from Rosenfeld, 2013; Rosenfeld & Thomas, 2012.)

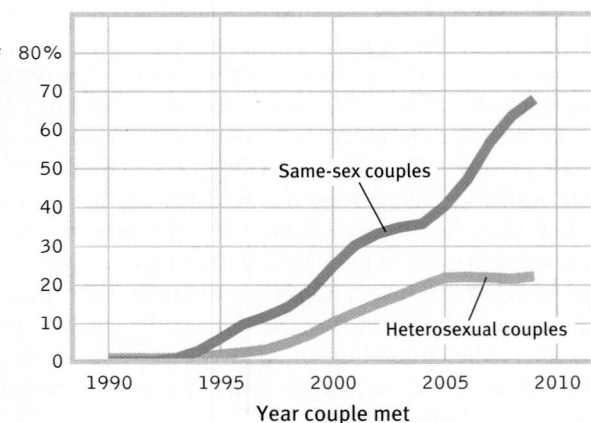

50,000 heterosexual Americans between 1972 and 2014 reveal that 40 percent of married adults, and only 23 percent of unmarried adults, have reported being "very happy." Lesbian couples, too, report greater well-being than those who are single (Peplau & Fingerhut, 2007; Wayment & Peplau, 1995). Moreover, neighborhoods with high marriage rates typically have low rates of social pathologies such as crime, delinquency, and emotional disorders among children (Myers & Scanzoni, 2005).

Relationships that last are not always devoid of conflict. Some couples fight but also shower each other with affection. Other couples never raise their voices yet also seldom praise each other or nuzzle. Both styles can last. After observing the interactions of 2000 couples, John Gottman (1994) reported one indicator of marital success: at least a five-to-one ratio of positive to negative interactions. Stable marriages provide five times more instances of smiling, touching, complimenting, and laughing than of sarcasm, criticism, and insults. So, if you want to predict which couples will stay together, don't pay attention to how passionately they are in love. The pairs who make it are more often those who refrain from putting down their partners. To prevent a cancerous negativity, successful couples learn to fight fair (to state feelings without insulting) and to steer conflict away from chaos with comments like "I know it's not your fault" or "I'll just be quiet for a moment and listen."

Often, love bears children. For most people, this most enduring of life changes is a happy event—one that adds meaning, joy, and occasional stress (Nelson et al., 2013; Witters, 2014). "I feel an overwhelming love for my children unlike anything I feel for anyone else," said 93 percent of American mothers in a national survey (Erickson & Aird, 2005). Many fathers feel the same. A few weeks after the birth of my first child I [DM] was suddenly struck by a realization: "So *this* is how my parents felt about me!"

When children begin to absorb time, money, and emotional energy, satisfaction with the marriage itself may decline (Doss et al., 2009). This is especially likely among employed women who, more than they expected, may also carry the burden of doing more chores at home. Putting effort into creating an equitable relationship can thus pay double dividends: greater satisfaction, which breeds better parent-child relations (Erel & Burman, 1995).

Eventually, children leave home. This departure is a significant and sometimes difficult event. But for most people, an empty nest is a happy place (Adelmann et al., 1989; Gorchoff et al., 2008). Many parents experience a "postlaunch honeymoon," especially if they maintain close relationships with their children (White & Edwards, 1990). As Daniel Gilbert (2006) said, "The only known symptom of 'empty nest syndrome' is increased smiling."

WORK For many adults, the answer to "Who are you?" depends a great deal on the answer to "What do you do?" For women and men, choosing a career path is difficult, especially during bad economic times. Even in the best of times, few students in their first two years of college or university can predict their later careers.

In the end, happiness is about having work that fits your interests and provides you with a sense of competence and accomplishment. It is having a close, supportive companion, or family and friends, who notice and cheer your accomplishments (Gable et al., 2006). And for some, it includes having children who love you and whom you love and feel proud of.

ENGAGE What do you think? Does marriage correlate with happiness because marital support and intimacy breed happiness, because happy people more often marry and stay married, or both?

"Our love for children is so unlike any other human emotion. I fell in love with my babies so quickly and profoundly, almost completely independently of their particular qualities. And yet 20 years later I was (more or less) happy to see them go—I had to be happy to see them go. We are totally devoted to them when they are little and yet the most we can expect in return when they grow up is that they regard us with bemused and tolerant affection." —Developmental psychologist Alison Gopnik, "The Supreme Infant," 2010

"To understand your parents' love, bear your own children." —Chinese proverb

ENGAGE **LaunchPad** Play the role of a researcher exploring the connection between parenting and happiness by engaging online with **Immersive Learning: How Would You Know If Having Children Relates to Being Happier?**

Hill Street Studios/Getty Images

© Jose Luis Pelaez Inc/Blend Images/Corbis

JOB SATISFACTION AND LIFE SATISFACTION Work can provide us with a sense of identity and competence, and opportunities for accomplishment. Perhaps this is why challenging and interesting occupations enhance people's happiness. For more on work, including discovering your own strengths, see Appendix B: Psychology at Work.

Well-Being Across the Life Span

LOQ 13-4   How does our well-being change across the life span?

To live is to grow older. This moment marks the oldest you have ever been and the youngest you will henceforth be. That means we all can look back with satisfaction or regret, and forward with hope or dread. When asked what they would have done differently if they could relive their lives, people's most common answer has been "taken my education more seriously and worked harder at it" (Kinnier & Metha, 1989; Roese & Summerville, 2005). Other regrets—"I should have told my father I loved him," "I regret that I never went to Europe"—have also focused less on mistakes made than on the things one *failed* to do (Gilovich & Medvec, 1995).

But prior to the very end, the over-65 years are not notably unhappy. Self-esteem remains stable (Wagner et al., 2013). The Gallup Organization asked 658,038 people worldwide to rate their lives on a ladder from 0 ("the worst possible life") to 10 ("the best possible life"). Age—from 15 to over 90 years—gave no clue to life satisfaction (Morrison et al., 2014). Positive feelings, supported by enhanced emotional control, tend to grow after midlife, and negative feelings subside (Stone et al., 2010; Urry & Gross, 2010). Compared with younger Chinese and American adults, for example, older adults are *more* attentive to positive news (Isaacowitz, 2012; Wang et al., 2015a).

Compared with teens and young adults, older adults do, however, tend to have a smaller social network, with fewer friendships and greater loneliness (Luhmann & Hawkley, 2016; Wagner et al., 2016). Like people of all ages, older adults are happiest when not alone (**FIGURE 13.5**). Older adults experience fewer problems in their relationships—less attachment anxiety, stress, and anger (Chopik et al., 2013; Fingerman & Charles, 2010; Stone et al., 2010). With age, we become more stable and more accepting (Carstensen et al., 2011; Shallcross et al., 2013).

The aging brain may help nurture these positive feelings. Brain scans of older adults show that the amygdala, a neural processing center for emotions, responds less actively to negative events (but not to positive events) (Mather et al., 2004). Brain-wave reactions to negative images also diminish with age (Kisley et al., 2007). As we reach the later chapters of our lives, our brain enables a contented culmination (Mather, 2016).

Moreover, at all ages, the bad feelings we associate with negative events fade faster than do the good feelings we associate with positive events (Walker et al., 2003). This

"When you were born, you cried and the world rejoiced. Live your life in a manner so that when you die the world cries and you rejoice." —Native American proverb

"Still married after all these years? No mystery. We are each other's habit, And each other's history."

—Judith Viorst, "The Secret of Staying Married," 2007

"At 20 we worry about what others think of us. At 40 we don't care what others think of us. At 60 we discover they haven't been thinking about us at all." —Anonymous

FIGURE 13.5

HUMANS ARE SOCIAL CREATURES Both younger and older adults report greater happiness when spending time with others. (Note this correlation could also reflect happier people being more social.) (Gallup survey data reported by Crabtree, 2011.)

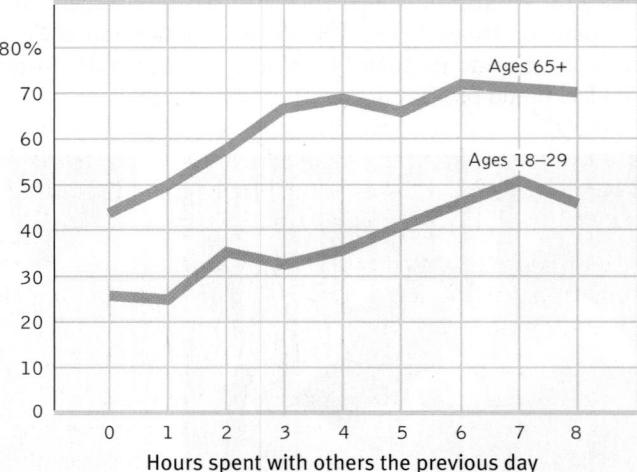

Percentage of Americans reporting a lot of stress-free enjoyment and happiness the previous day

Hours spent with others the previous day

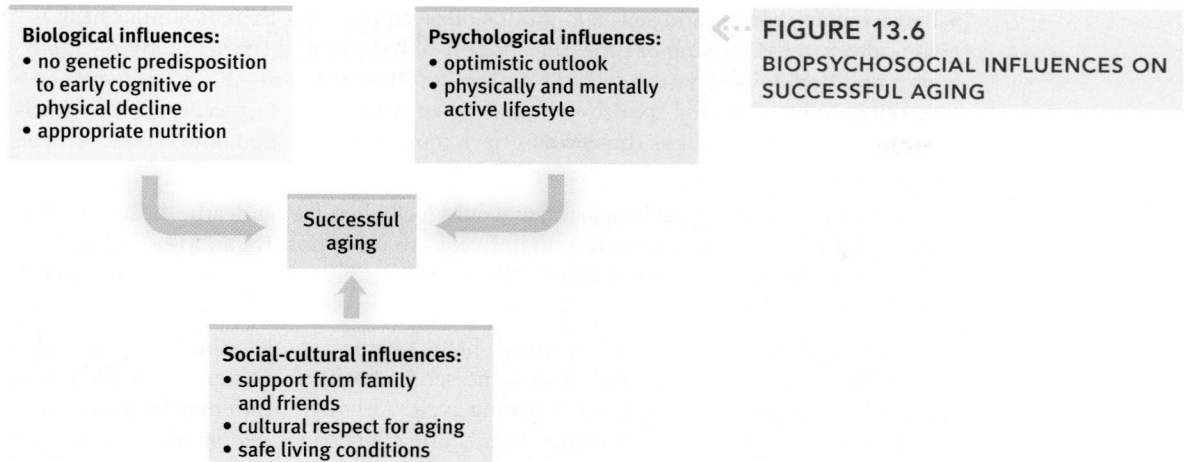

FIGURE 13.6
BIOPSYCHOSOCIAL INFLUENCES ON SUCCESSFUL AGING

leaves most older people with the comforting feeling that life, on balance, has been mostly good. Thanks to biological, psychological, and social-cultural influences, more and more people flourish into later life (**FIGURE 13.6**).

"The best thing about being 100 is *no peer pressure.*" —Lewis W. Kuester, 2005, on turning 100

🔒 **RETRIEVE IT** • • •   *ANSWERS IN APPENDIX E*

RI-2 What are some of the most significant challenges and rewards of growing old?

Death and Dying

LOQ 13-5 A loved one's death triggers what range of reactions?

Warning: If you begin reading the next paragraph, you will die.

But of course, if you hadn't read this, you would still die in due time. "Time is a great teacher," noted the nineteenth-century composer Hector Berlioz, "but unfortunately it kills all its pupils." Death is our inevitable end. We enter the world with a wail, and usually leave it in silence.

Most of us will also cope with the deaths of relatives and friends. For most people, the most difficult separation they will experience is the death of a partner—a loss suffered by four times more women than men. Maintaining everyday engagements and relationships increases resilience in the face of such a loss (Infurna & Luthar, 2016a). But for some, grief is severe, especially when a loved one's death comes suddenly and before its expected time on the social clock. I [ND] experienced this firsthand when a tragic accident claimed the life of my 60-year-old mother. Such tragedies may trigger a year or more of memory-laden mourning that eventually subsides to a mild depression (Lehman et al., 1987).

For some, the loss is unbearable. One Danish long-term study of more than 1 million people found that about 17,000 of them had suffered the death of a child under 18. In the 5 years following that death, 3 percent of them had a first psychiatric hospitalization, a 67 percent higher rate than among other parents (Li et al., 2005).

Reactions to a loved one's death range more widely than most suppose. Some cultures encourage public weeping and wailing; others hide grief. Within any culture, individuals differ. Given similar losses, some people grieve hard and long, others less so (Ott et al., 2007). Contrary to popular misconceptions, however:

"Love—why, I'll tell you what love is: It's you at 75 and her at 71, each of you listening for the other's step in the next room, each afraid that a sudden silence, a sudden cry, could mean a lifetime's talk is over." —Brian Moore, *The Luck of Ginger Coffey*, 1960

- Terminally ill and bereaved people do not go through identical predictable stages, such as denial before anger (Friedman & James, 2008; Nolen-Hoeksema & Larson, 1999).

- Those who express the strongest grief immediately do not purge their grief more quickly (Bonanno & Kaltman, 1999; Wortman & Silver, 1989). But grieving parents who try to protect their partner by "staying strong" and not discussing their child's death may actually prolong the grieving (Stroebe et al., 2013).

- Bereavement therapy and self-help groups offer support, but there is similar healing power in the passing of time, the support of friends, and the act of giving support and help to others (Baddeley & Singer, 2009; Brown et al., 2008; Neimeyer & Carrier, 2009). Grieving spouses who talk often with others or receive grief counseling adjust about as well as those who grieve more privately (Bonanno, 2004; Stroebe et al., 2005).

- Compared to what people *imagine* they would feel when facing death, those actually facing imminent death due to terminal illness are more positive and less sad and despairing. In the researchers' words, "Dying is unexpectedly positive" (Goranson et al., 2017).

Facing death with dignity and openness helps people complete the life cycle with a sense of life's meaningfulness and unity—the sense that their existence has been good and that life and death are parts of an ongoing cycle. Although death may be unwelcome, life itself can be affirmed even at death. This is especially so for people who review their lives not with despair but with what Erik Erikson called a sense of *integrity*—a feeling that one's life has been meaningful and worthwhile.

🔒 REVIEW ADULTHOOD

⟩ Learning Objectives

TEST YOURSELF Answer these repeated Learning Objective Questions on your own (before checking the answers in Appendix D) to improve your retention of the concepts (McDaniel et al., 2009, 2015).

13-1 What physical changes occur during middle and late adulthood?

13-2 How does memory change with age?

13-3 What themes and influences mark our social journey from early adulthood to death?

13-4 How does our well-being change across the life span?

13-5 A loved one's death triggers what range of reactions?

⟩ Terms and Concepts to Remember

TEST YOURSELF Write down the definition yourself, then check your answer on the referenced page.

menopause, **p. 151**

cross-sectional study, **p. 154**

longitudinal study, **p. 154**

social clock, **p. 154**

⟩ Experience the Testing Effect

TEST YOURSELF Answer the following questions on your own first, then check your answers in Appendix E.

1. By age 65, a person would be most likely to experience a cognitive decline in the ability to
   a. recall and list all the important terms and concepts in a module.
   b. select the correct definition in a multiple-choice question.
   c. recall their own birth date.
   d. practice a well-learned skill, such as knitting.

2. How do cross-sectional and longitudinal studies differ?

3. Freud defined the healthy adult as one who is able to love and work. Erikson agreed, observing that the adult struggles to attain intimacy and _____.

4. Contrary to what many people assume,
   a. older people are significantly less happy than adolescents are.
   b. we become less happy as we move from our teen years into midlife.
   c. positive feelings tend to grow after midlife.
   d. those whose children have recently left home—the empty nesters—have the lowest level of happiness of all groups.

Continue testing yourself with 📖 **LearningCurve** or 📖 **Achieve Read & Practice**
to learn and remember most effectively.

Sex, Gender, and Sexuality

Image Source/Alamy Stock Photo

Cultures change, and their ideas about gender change, too. Several decades apart, this text's two authors had similar experiences with different outcomes.

In 1972, as the young chair of our psychology department, I [DM] was proud to make the announcement: We had concluded our search for a new colleague. We had found just who we were looking for—a bright, warm, enthusiastic woman about to receive her Ph.D. in developmental psychology. The vote was unanimous. Alas, our elderly chancellor rejected our recommendation. "As a mother of a preschooler," he said, "she should be home with her child, *not* working full time." No amount of pleading or arguing (for example, that it might be possible to parent a child while employed) could change his mind. So, with a heavy heart, I drove to her city to explain, face to face, my embarrassment in being able to offer her only a temporary position.

This case ended well. She accepted the temporary position and quickly became a beloved, tenured colleague who went on to found our college's women's studies program. Today, she and I marvel at the swift transformation in our culture's thinking about gender.

In 2011, I [ND] experienced something quite different. We, too, were concluding our search for a new colleague. Our department faculty had assessed several candidates, and the top two vote-getters were a man and a woman. Our faculty hiring committee would make the final choice. Before they announced their decision, a senior committee member spoke out. "Look around the table. We're all men. We need to consider that." The accomplished woman was offered the position.

In Module 14, we'll look at some of the ways nature and nurture interact to form our unique gender identities. We'll see what researchers tell us about how alike we are as males and females, and how and why we differ. In Module 15, we'll gain insight about the psychology and biology of sexual attraction and intimacy. As part of the journey, we'll see how evolutionary psychologists explain our sexuality. ▶

14 Gender Development

LEARNING OBJECTIVE QUESTION (LOQ)

14-1   How does the meaning of *gender* differ from the meaning of *sex*?

We humans share an irresistible urge to organize our worlds into simple categories. Among the ways we classify people—as tall or short, dull or smart, cheerful or churlish—one stands out. Immediately after your birth (or before), everyone wanted to know, "Boy or girl?" Your parents may have offered clues with pink or blue clothing. Their answer described your **sex,** your biological status, defined by your chromosomes and anatomy. For most people, those biological traits help define their assigned **gender,** their culture's expectations about what it means to be a man or a woman.

Simply said, your body defines your sex; your mind defines your gender. But your mind's understanding of gender arises from the interplay between your biology and your experiences (Eagly & Wood, 2013). Before we consider that interplay in more detail, let's take a closer look at some ways that males and females are both similar and different.

HOW ARE WE ALIKE? HOW DO WE DIFFER?

LOQ 14-2   What are some ways in which males and females tend to be alike and to differ?

Whether male or female, each of us receives 23 chromosomes from our mother and 23 from our father. Of those 46 chromosomes, 45 are *unisex*—the same for males and females. Both men and women needed to survive, reproduce, and avoid predators, and so today we are in most ways alike. Survival for both men and women involved traveling long distances, and in today's ultramarathons men and women often have similar finishing times. Identify yourself as male or female and you give no clues to your vocabulary, happiness, or ability to see, learn, and remember. Males and females, on average, have comparable creativity and intelligence and feel the same emotions and longings (Hyde, 2014). Our "opposite" sex is, in reality, our very similar sex.

But in some areas, males and females do differ, and differences command attention. Some oft-noted differences (like the difference in self-esteem shown in **FIGURE 14.1**) are actually quite modest (Zell et al., 2015). Others are more striking. The average girl enters puberty about a year earlier than the average boy, and her life expectancy is 5 years longer. She expresses emotions more freely, smiling and crying more, and, in Facebook updates, more often expresses "love" and being "sooo excited!!!" (Fischer & LaFrance, 2015; Schwartz et al., 2013). She can detect fainter odors, receives offers of help more often, and can become sexually re-aroused sooner after orgasm. She also has twice the risk of developing depression and anxiety, and 10 times the risk of developing an eating disorder. Yet the average man is 4 times more likely to die by suicide or to develop an alcohol use disorder. His "more likely" list also includes autism spectrum disorder, color-deficient vision, and attention-deficit/hyperactivity disorder (ADHD). And as an adult, he is more at risk for antisocial personality disorder. Male or female, each has its own heightened risks.

Gender similarities and differences appear throughout this book, but for now let's take a closer look at three gender differences. Although individuals vary widely, the *average* male and female differ in aggression, social power, and social connectedness.

Pink and blue baby outfits illustrate how cultural norms vary and change. "The generally accepted rule is pink for the boy and blue for the girl," declared the *Earnshaw's Infants' Department* in 1918 (Frassanito & Pettorini, 2008). "Pink being a more decided and stronger color is more suitable for the boy, while blue, which is more delicate and dainty, is prettier for the girls."

sex in psychology, the biologically influenced characteristics by which people define *male* and *female*.

gender in psychology, the socially influenced characteristics by which people define *boy*, *girl*, *man*, and *woman*.

aggression any physical or verbal behavior intended to harm someone physically or emotionally.

relational aggression an act of aggression (physical or verbal) intended to harm a person's relationship or social standing.

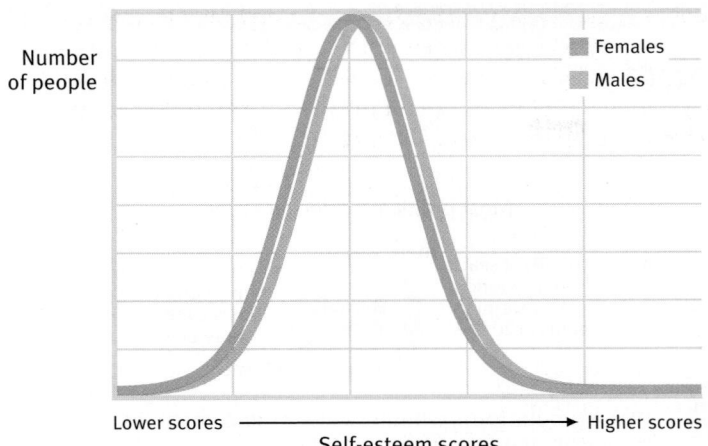

Number of people

Lower scores ——————→ Higher scores
Self-esteem scores

Females
Males

FIGURE 14.1

MUCH ADO ABOUT A SMALL DIFFERENCE IN SELF-ESTEEM These two normal distributions differ by the approximate magnitude (0.21 standard deviation) of the sex difference in self-esteem, averaged over all available samples (Hyde, 2005). Moreover, such comparisons illustrate differences between the *average* female and male. The variation *among* individual females or *among* individual males greatly exceeds this difference.

Aggression

To a psychologist, **aggression** is any physical or verbal behavior intended to hurt someone physically or emotionally (Bushman & Huesmann, 2010). Think of examples of aggressive people. Are most of them men? Likely yes. Men generally admit to more aggression, especially extreme physical violence (Wölfer & Hewstone, 2015; Yount et al., 2017). In romantic relationships between men and women, minor acts of physical aggression, such as slaps, are roughly equal, but the most violent acts are mostly committed by men (Archer, 2000; Johnson, 2008).

Laboratory experiments confirm a gender difference in aggression. Men have been more willing to blast people with what they believed was intense and prolonged noise (Bushman et al., 2007). And outside the laboratory, men—worldwide—commit more violent crime (Antonaccio et al., 2011; Caddick & Porter, 2012; Frisell et al., 2012). They also take the lead in hunting, fighting, warring, and supporting war (Liddle et al., 2012; Wood & Eagly, 2002, 2007).

Here's another question: Think of examples of people harming others by passing along hurtful gossip, or by shutting someone out of a social group or situation. Were most of those people men? Perhaps not. Those behaviors are acts of **relational aggression,** and women are slightly more likely than men to commit them (Archer, 2004, 2007, 2009).

Social Power

ENGAGE — Imagine you've walked into a job interview and are taking your first look at the two interviewers. The unsmiling person on the left oozes self-confidence and independence, maintaining steady eye contact. The person on the right gives you a warm, welcoming smile but makes less eye contact and seems to expect the other interviewer to take the lead.

Which interviewer is male?

If you said the person on the left, you're not alone. Around the world, from Nigeria to New Zealand, people have perceived gender differences in power (Williams & Best, 1990). For more on this topic, see Thinking Critically About: Gender Bias in the Workplace.

Social Connectedness

Whether male or female, we all have a need to belong, though we may satisfy this need in different ways (Baumeister, 2010). Males tend to be *independent.* Even as children, males typically form large play groups that brim with activity and competition, with little intimate discussion (Rose & Rudolph, 2006). As adults, men enjoy side-by-side activities, and their conversations often focus on problem solving (Tannen, 1990; Wright, 1989). When asked a difficult question—"Do you have any idea why the sky is blue?"—men are more likely than women to hazard answers than to admit they don't know, a phenomenon researchers have called the *male answer syndrome* (Giuliano et al., 1998).

DEADLY RELATIONAL AGGRESSION Sladjana Vidovic was a high school student who died by suicide after suffering constant relational aggression by bullies.

Amy Sancetta/AP Images

"I said, 'I wonder what it means,' not 'Tell me what it means.'"

Will McPhail/The Cartoon Bank/Condé Nast Publications

THINKING CRITICALLY ABOUT:

Gender Bias in the Workplace

LOQ 14-3 What factors contribute to gender bias in the workplace?

Differences in PERCEPTION

Among politicians who seem power-hungry, women are less successful than men.[1]

"She's so aggressive!"

"He's so take-charge!"

Most political leaders are men:

Men held 77% of seats in the world's governing parliaments in 2018.[2]

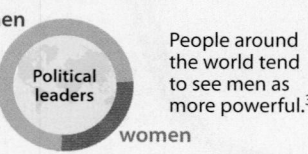
men — Political leaders — women

People around the world tend to see men as more powerful.[3]

When groups form, whether as juries or companies, leadership tends to go to males.[4]

Differences in COMPENSATION

Women in traditionally male occupations have received less than their male colleagues.[5]

Medicine U.S. salary disparity between male and female physicians:[6]

$150,053 **women** $211,526 **men**

Academia **Female** research grant applicants have received lower "quality of researcher" ratings and have been less likely to be funded.[7] (But as we will see, gender attitudes and roles are changing.)

Differences in FAMILY-CARE RESPONSIBILITY

U.S. mothers still do nearly **twice** as much child care as **fathers**.[8] In the workplace, women are less often driven by money and status, compromise more, and more often opt for reduced work hours.[9]

What else contributes to WORKPLACE GENDER BIAS?

Social norms

In most societies, men place more importance on power and achievement, and are socially dominant.[10]

Leadership styles

Men are more *directive*, telling people what to do and how to do it.

Women are more *democratic*, welcoming others' input in decision making.[11]

Interaction styles

Men are more likely to offer opinions.[12]

Women are more likely to express support.[12]

Everyday behavior

Men are more likely to talk assertively, interrupt, initiate touches, and stare.[13]

Women smile and apologize more than men.[13]

Yet GENDER ROLES VARY WIDELY across place and time.

Women are increasingly represented in leadership (now 50% of Canada's cabinet ministers) and in the workforce. In 1963, the Harvard Business School admitted its first women students. Among its Class of 2016, 41% were women.[14] In 1960, women were 6% of U.S. medical students. Today they are about half.[15]

1. Okimoto & Brescoll, 2010. 2. IPU, 2018. 3. Williams & Best, 1990. 4. Colarelli et al., 2006. 5. Willett et al., 2015. 6. Census Bureau, 2014. 7. van der Lee & Ellemers, 2015. 8. CEA, 2014; Parker & Wang, 2013; Pew, 2015. 9. Nikolova & Lamberton, 2016; Pinker, 2008. 10. Gino et al., 2015; Schwartz & Rubel-Lifschitz, 2009. 11. Eagly & Carli, 2007; van Engen & Willemsen, 2004. 12. Aries, 1987; Wood, 1987. 13. Leaper & Ayres, 2007; Major et al., 1990; Schumann & Ross, 2010. 14. Peck, 2015. 15. AAMC, 2014.

Scans of more than 1400 brains show no striking sex differences: "Human brains cannot be categorized into two distinct classes—male brain/female brain" (Joel et al., 2015). Brain scans do, however, suggest that a woman's brain, more than a man's, is wired in a way that enables social relationships (Ingalhalikar et al., 2013). This helps explain why females tend to be more *interdependent*. In childhood, girls usually play in small groups, often with one friend. They compete less and imitate social relationships more (Maccoby, 1990; Roberts, 1991). Teen girls spend more time with friends and less time alone (Wong & Csikszentmihalyi, 1991). In late adolescence, they spend more time on social networking sites, and average twice as many text messages per day as boys

EVERY MAN FOR HIMSELF, OR "TEND AND BEFRIEND"? Sex differences in the way we interact with others begin to appear at a very young age.

(Lenhart, 2015a; Pryor et al., 2007, 2011). Girls' and women's friendships are more intimate, with more conversation that explores relationships (Maccoby, 2002). In one analysis of 10 million Facebook posts, women's status updates were as assertive as men's, but used warmer words, while men more often swore or expressed anger (Park et al., 2016). An analysis of over 700 million Facebook words found women also used more family-related words, whereas men used more work-related words (Schwartz et al., 2013).

When searching for understanding from someone who will share their worries and hurts, people usually turn to women. Both men and women have reported that their friendships with women are more intimate, enjoyable, and nurturing (Kuttler et al., 1999; Rubin, 1985; Sapadin, 1988). And how do women cope with stress? Compared with men, women are more likely to turn to others for support. They are said to *tend and befriend* (Tamres et al., 2002; Taylor, 2002).

Gender differences in both social connectedness and power are greatest in late adolescence and early adulthood—the prime years for dating and mating. By their teen years, girls become less assertive and more flirtatious, and boys appear more dominant and less expressive (Chaplin, 2015). In adulthood, after the birth of a first child, attitude and behavior differences often peak. Mothers especially may express more traditionally female attitudes and behaviors (Ferriman et al., 2009; Katz-Wise et al., 2010). By age 50, most parenting-related gender differences subside. Men become less domineering and more empathic, and women—especially those with paid employment—become more assertive and self-confident (Kasen et al., 2006; Maccoby, 1998). Worldwide, fewer women than men work full-time for an employer (19 percent versus 33 percent). But, similar to men, women are more satisfied with their lives when employed rather than unemployed (Ryan, 2016).

So, although women and men are more alike than different, there are some behavior differences between the average woman and man. Are such differences dictated by our biology? Shaped by our cultures and other experiences? Do we vary in the extent to which we are male or female? Read on.

Question: Why does it take 200 million sperm to fertilize one egg?
Answer: Because they won't stop for directions.

"In the long years liker must they grow; The man be more of woman, she of man." —Alfred Lord Tennyson, *The Princess,* 1847

🔒 **RETRIEVE IT ● ● ●**   *ANSWERS IN APPENDIX E*

RI-1 _____ (Men/Women) are more likely to commit relational aggression, and _____ (men/women) are more likely to commit physical aggression.

THE NATURE OF GENDER: OUR BIOLOGICAL SEX

LOQ 14-4 How do sex hormones influence prenatal and adolescent sexual development, and what is an *intersex* condition?

In most physical ways—regulating heat with sweat, preferring energy-rich foods, growing calluses where the skin meets friction—men and women are similar. When looking for a mate, men and women also prize many of the same traits—someone who is kind, honest, and intelligent. But in some mating-related domains, say evolutionary psychologists, guys

X chromosome the sex chromosome found in both males and females. Females typically have two X chromosomes; males typically have one. An X chromosome from each parent produces a female child.

Y chromosome the sex chromosome typically found only in males. When paired with an X chromosome from the mother, it produces a male child.

testosterone the most important male sex hormone. Both males and females have it, but the additional testosterone in males stimulates the growth of the male sex organs during the fetal period, and the development of the male sex characteristics during puberty.

puberty the period of sexual maturation, when a person becomes capable of reproducing.

primary sex characteristics the body structures (ovaries, testes, and external genitalia) that make sexual reproduction possible.

secondary sex characteristics non-reproductive sexual traits, such as female breasts and hips, male voice quality, and body hair.

spermarche [sper-MAR-key] the first ejaculation.

menarche [meh-NAR-key] the first menstrual period.

act like guys whether they're chimpanzees or elephants, rural peasants or corporate presidents (Geary, 2010).

Biology does not *dictate* gender. But in two ways, biology influences our gender psychology:

- *Genetically*—males and females have differing *sex chromosomes*.
- *Physiologically*—males and females have differing concentrations of *sex hormones*, which trigger other anatomical differences.

These two influences began to form you long before you were born.

Prenatal Sexual Development

Six weeks after you were conceived, you and someone of the other sex looked much the same. Then, as your genes kicked in, your biological sex—determined by your twenty-third pair of chromosomes (the two sex chromosomes)—became more apparent. Whether you are male or female, your mother's contribution to that chromosome pair was an **X chromosome.** From your father, you received the 1 chromosome out of 46 that is not unisex—either another X chromosome, making you female, or a **Y chromosome,** making you male.

About seven weeks after conception, a single gene on the Y chromosome throws a master switch, which triggers the testes to develop and to produce **testosterone,** the main *androgen* (male hormone) that promotes male sex organ development. (Females also have testosterone, but less of it.)

Later, during the fourth and fifth prenatal months, sex hormones bathe the fetal brain and influence its wiring. Different patterns for males and females develop under the influence of the male's greater testosterone and the female's ovarian hormones (Hines, 2004; Udry, 2000). If, however, females are prenatally exposed to unusually high levels of male hormones, they tend to grow up with more male-typical activity interests (Endendijk et al., 2016). Prenatal hormones help sculpt what we love to do.

Adolescent Sexual Development

A flood of hormones triggers another period of dramatic physical change during adolescence, when boys and girls enter **puberty.** In this two-year period of rapid sexual maturation, pronounced male-female differences emerge. A variety of changes begin at about age 11 in girls and at about age 12 in boys, though the subtle beginnings of puberty, such as enlarging testes, appear earlier (Herman-Giddens et al., 2012). A year or two before the physical changes are visible, boys and girls often feel the first stirrings of sexual attraction (McClintock & Herdt, 1996).

Girls' slightly earlier entry into puberty can at first propel them to greater height than boys of the same age (**FIGURE 14.2**). But boys catch up when they begin puberty, and by age 14, they are usually taller than girls. During these growth spurts, the

Pubertal boys may not at first like their sparse beard. (But then it grows on them.)

FIGURE 14.2

HEIGHT DIFFERENCES Throughout childhood, boys and girls are similar in height. At puberty, girls surge ahead briefly, but then boys typically overtake them at about age 14. (Data from Tanner, 1978.)

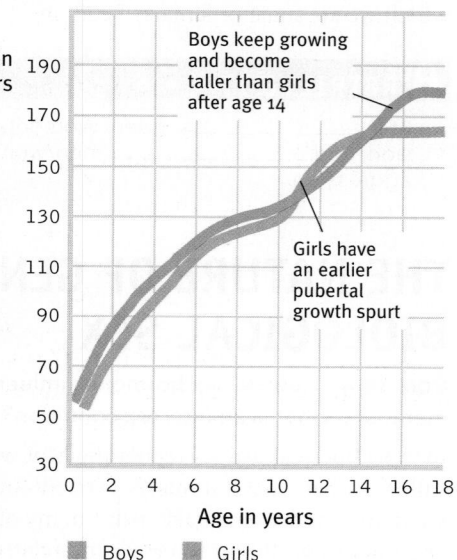

Height in centimeters

Boys keep growing and become taller than girls after age 14

Girls have an earlier pubertal growth spurt

Age in years

Boys   Girls

Marili Forastieri/Getty Images

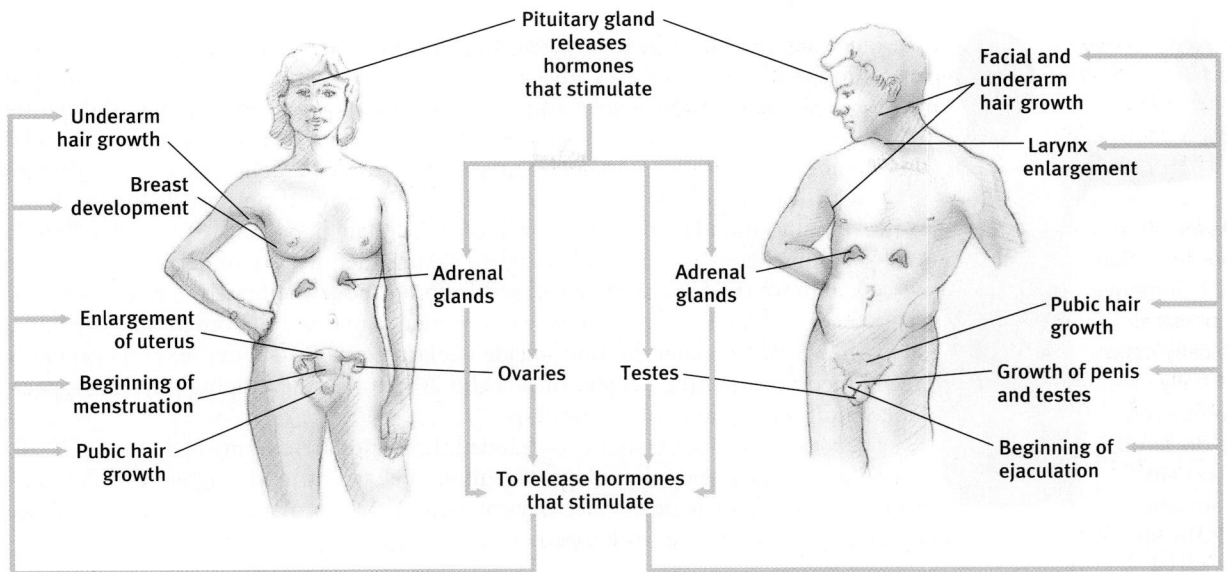

FIGURE 14.3

BODY CHANGES AT PUBERTY At about age 11 in girls and age 12 in boys, a surge of hormones triggers a variety of visible physical changes.

primary sex characteristics—the reproductive organs and external genitalia—develop dramatically. So do the nonreproductive **secondary sex characteristics.** Girls develop breasts and larger hips. Boys' facial hair begins growing and their voices deepen. Pubic and underarm hair emerges in both girls and boys (**FIGURE 14.3**).

For boys, puberty's landmark is the first ejaculation, which often occurs first during sleep (as a "wet dream"). This event, called **spermarche,** usually happens by about age 14.

In girls, the landmark is the first menstrual period, **menarche,** usually within a year of age 12½ (Anderson et al., 2003). Scientists have identified nearly 250 genes that predict when girls experience menarche (Day et al., 2017). But environment matters, too. Early menarche is more likely following stresses related to father absence, sexual abuse, insecure attachments, or a history of a mother's smoking during pregnancy (Rickard et al., 2014; Shrestha et al., 2011; Sung et al., 2016). Girls in various countries are developing breasts and reaching puberty earlier today than in the past, a phenomenon variously attributed to increased body fat, increased hormone-mimicking chemicals in the diet, and increased stress related to family disruption (Biro et al., 2010, 2012; Ellis et al., 2012; Herman-Giddens, 2013). But the good news is that a secure child-mother attachment can provide a buffer against childhood stresses, including those related to early puberty (Sung et al., 2016). Remember: *Nature and nurture interact.*

Girls prepared for menarche usually view it as a positive life transition (Chang et al., 2009). Males report mostly positive emotional reactions to spermarche (Fuller & Downs, 1990).

LaunchPad For a 7-minute discussion of sexual development, see the **Video: Gender Development.**

🔒 **RETRIEVE IT • • •**　　　　　　　　　*ANSWERS IN APPENDIX E*

RI-2 Prenatal sexual development begins about _____ weeks after conception. Adolescence is marked by the onset of _____.

Sexual Development Variations

Nature may blur the biological line between males and females. People with **intersex** conditions may be born with unusual combinations of male and female chromosomes, hormones, and anatomy. For example, a genetic male may be born with two or more X chromosomes as well as a Y chromosome (*Klinefelter syndrome*), often resulting in sterility and small testes. Genetic females born with only one X chromosome (*Turner syndrome*) may not have menstrual periods, develop breasts, or be able to have children without reproductive assistance. Such individuals may struggle with their gender identity.

In the past, medical professionals often recommended *sex-reassignment surgery* to create an unambiguous sex identity for some children with these conditions. One study reviewed 14 cases of genetic boys who had undergone early surgery and been raised as girls. Of those cases, 6 had later identified as male, 5 were living as females, and 3 reported an unclear male or female identity (Reiner & Gearhart, 2004).

intersex a condition present at birth due to unusual combinations of male and female chromosomes, hormones, and anatomy; possessing biological sexual characteristics of both sexes.

"I AM WHO I AM." Dramatic improvements in South African track star Caster Semenya's race times prompted the International Association of Athletics Federations to undertake sex testing in 2009. Semenya was reported to have physical characteristics not typically male or female. She was officially cleared to continue competing as a woman. Semenya declared, "God made me the way I am and I accept myself. I am who I am" (*YOU*, 2009). In 2016, she won an Olympic gold medal.

Michael Dalder/SEMENYA Reuters/Newscom

New Yorker Collection, 2001. Barbara Smaller from cartoonbank.com

"Sex brought us together, but gender drove us apart."

THE GENDERED TSUNAMI In Sri Lanka, Indonesia, and India, the gendered division of labor helps explain the excess of female deaths from the 2004 tsunami. In some villages, 80 percent of those killed were women, who were mostly at home while the men were more likely to be at sea fishing or doing outdoor chores (Oxfam, 2005).

Dinodia/The Image Works

In one famous case, a little boy lost his penis during a botched circumcision. His parents followed a psychiatrist's advice to raise him as a girl rather than as a damaged boy. So, with male chromosomes and hormones and a female upbringing, did nature or nurture form this child's gender identity? Although raised as a girl, "Brenda" Reimer was not like most other girls. "She" didn't like dolls. She tore her dresses with rough-and-tumble play. At puberty she wanted no part of kissing boys. Finally, Brenda's parents explained what had happened, which led Brenda immediately to reject the assigned female identity. He underwent surgery to remove the breasts he developed from hormone therapy. He cut his hair and chose a male name, David. He eventually married a woman and became a stepfather. Sadly, he later died by suicide (Colapinto, 2000). Today, experts generally recommend postponing surgery until a child's naturally developing physical appearance and gender identity become clear.

The bottom line: "Sex matters," concluded the National Academy of Sciences (2001). Sex-related genes and physiology "result in behavioral and cognitive differences between males and females." Yet environmental factors matter, too, as we will see next. Nature and nurture work together.

THE NURTURE OF GENDER: OUR CULTURE AND EXPERIENCES

LOQ 14-5 How do gender roles and gender identity differ?

For many people, biological sex and gender coexist in harmony. Biology draws the outline, and culture paints the details. The physical traits that define a newborn as male or female are the same worldwide. But the gender traits that define how men (or boys) and women (or girls) *should* act, interact, or feel about themselves differ across time and place (Zentner & Eagly, 2015).

Gender Roles

Cultures shape our behaviors by defining how we ought to behave in a particular social position, or **role.** We can see this shaping power in **gender roles**—the social expectations that guide our behavior as men or women.

In just a thin slice of history, gender roles worldwide have undergone an extreme makeover. At the beginning of the twentieth century, only one country in the world—New Zealand—granted women the right to vote (Briscoe, 1997). By 2015, all countries granted that right. A century ago, American women could not vote in national elections, serve in the military, or divorce a husband without cause. And if a woman worked for pay, she would more likely have been a seamstress than a surgeon. Now, nearly half the workforce is female (DOL, 2015). In the STEM fields (science, technology, engineering, and mathematics), men still hold most faculty positions and receive greater financial research support (Ceci et al., 2014; Sege et al., 2015; Sheltzer & Smith, 2014). But signs point to increases in supply and demand for women in the STEM fields. For example, U.S. women, compared with men, earn more college degrees and higher college grades, and show equal competence at STEM-related activities, such as writing computer code (Keiser et al., 2016; Terrell et al., 2017). When researchers invited U.S. professors to recommend candidates for STEM positions, most said they preferred hiring the highly talented women over the equally talented men (Williams & Ceci, 2015). This is good news for budding female scientists and engineers, who benefit from having capable and motivated female mentors (Dennehy & Dasgupta, 2017).

Gender roles also vary from one place to another. Nomadic societies of food-gathering people have had little division of labor by sex. Boys and girls receive much the same upbringing. In agricultural societies, where women typically work in the nearby fields and men roam while herding livestock, cultures have shaped children to assume more distinct gender roles (Segall et al., 1990; Van Leeuwen, 1978).

Take a minute to check your own gender expectations. Would you agree that "When jobs are scarce, men should have more rights to a job?" In the United States, Britain, and Spain, barely over 12 percent of adults agree. In Nigeria, Pakistan, and India, about 80 percent of adults agree (Pew, 2010). We're all human, but my, how our views differ. Northern European countries offer the greatest gender equity, Middle Eastern and North African countries the least (UN, 2015a).

Expectations about gender roles also factor into cultural attitudes about **sexual aggression.** In the United States, 2017 marked the beginning of a massive cultural shift in such attitudes, as a number of famous and powerful men—in politics, movie-making, broadcasting, sports, academia—faced credible accusations. (See Thinking Critically About: Sexual Aggression.)

How Do We Learn Gender?

A *gender role* describes how others expect us to think, feel, and act. Our **gender identity** is our personal sense of being male, female, or, occasionally, some combination of the two. How do we develop that personal viewpoint?

Social learning theory assumes that we acquire our identity in childhood, by observing and imitating others' gender-linked behaviors and by being rewarded or punished for acting in certain ways. ("Tatiana, you're such a good mommy to your dolls"; "Big boys don't cry, Armand.") But some critics think there's more to gender identity than imitating parents and being repeatedly rewarded for certain responses. They point out that **gender typing**—taking on a traditional male or female role—varies from child to child (Tobin et al., 2010).

Parents do help to transmit their culture's views on gender. In one analysis of 43 studies, parents with traditional gender views were more likely to have gender-typed children who shared their culture's expectations about how males and females should act (Tenenbaum & Leaper, 2002). When fathers share equally in housework, their daughters develop higher aspirations for work outside the home (Croft et al., 2014).

But no matter how much parents encourage or discourage traditional gender behavior, children may drift toward what feels right to them. Some organize themselves into "boy worlds" and "girl worlds," each guided by their understanding of the rules. Others conform to these rules more flexibly. Still others seem to prefer **androgyny:** a blend of male and female roles feels right to them. Androgyny has benefits. As adults, androgynous people are more adaptable. They are more flexible in their actions and in their career choices (Bem, 1993). From childhood onward, they tend to be more resilient and self-accepting, and they experience less depression (Lam & McBride-Chang, 2007; Mosher & Danoff-Burg, 2008; Pauletti et al., 2017).

Feelings matter, but so does how we think. Early in life, we all form *schemas,* or concepts that help us make sense of our world. Our *gender schemas* organize our experiences of male-female characteristics and help us think about our gender identity, about who we are (Bem, 1987, 1993; Martin et al., 2002).

As young children, we were "gender detectives" (Martin & Ruble, 2004). Before our first birthday, we knew the difference between a male and female voice or face (Martin et al., 2002). After we turned 2, language forced us to label the world in terms of gender. English classifies people as *he* and *she.* Other languages classify objects as masculine ("*le train*") or feminine ("*la table*").

Once children grasp that two sorts of people exist—and that they are of one of these two sorts—they search for clues about gender. In every culture, people communicate their gender in many ways. Their *gender expression* drops hints not only in their language but also in their clothing, interests, and possessions. Having picked up such clues, 3-year-olds may divide the human world in half. They will then like their own kind better and seek them out for play. "Girls," they may decide, are the ones who watch *My Little Pony* and have long hair. "Boys" watch *Transformers* and don't wear dresses. Armed with their newly collected "proof," they then adjust their behaviors to fit their concept of gender. These stereotypes are most rigid at about age 5 or 6. If the new neighbor is a girl, a 6-year-old boy may assume he cannot share her interests. For young children, gender looms large.

In 2018, women were 23.4 percent of legislators in the world's national parliaments (IPU, 2018).

"You cannot put women and men on an equal footing. It is against nature."
—Turkish President Recep Tayyip Erdoğan

role a set of expectations (norms) about a social position, defining how those in the position ought to behave.

gender role a set of expected behaviors, attitudes, and traits for males or for females.

sexual aggression any physical or verbal behavior of a sexual nature that is intended to harm someone physically or emotionally. Can be expressed as either *sexual harassment* or *sexual assault.*

gender identity our sense of being male, female, or some combination of the two.

social learning theory the theory that we learn social behavior by observing and imitating and by being rewarded or punished.

gender typing the acquisition of a traditional masculine or feminine role.

androgyny displaying both traditional masculine and feminine psychological characteristics.

"We need to keep changing the attitude that raises our girls to be demure and our boys to be assertive, that criticizes our daughters for speaking out and our sons for shedding a tear." —U.S. President Barack Obama, 2016

THE SOCIAL LEARNING OF GENDER Children observe and imitate parental models.

Courtesy of David Myers

THINKING CRITICALLY ABOUT:

Sexual Aggression

LOQ 14-6 What are the effects of sexual aggression? How have cultural views changed, and how can we reduce sexual aggression?

Definition of Sexual Aggression

Sexual harassment involves making unwanted sexual advances, obscene remarks, or requests for sexual favors.[1]

Sexual assault is "any type of sexual contact or behavior that occurs without the explicit consent of the recipient," such as unwanted touching, molestation, and attempted or completed rape.[2]

Victims

In the U.S., **81%** of women and **43%** of men report having experienced sexual aggression in their lifetime.[3]

Sexual aggression affects people of *all ethnic groups*.[4]

Nearly **70%** of rape victims are between the ages of 11 and 24.[4]

In a National School Climate survey, **8** out of **10** gay or lesbian adolescents reported experiencing sex-related harassment in the prior year.[5]

Effects on Well-Being

Thanks to human resilience, victims of sexual aggression often recover and lead healthy and meaningful lives. Yet many also suffer serious setbacks, including:

• Greater anxiety, depression, and risk for post-traumatic stress disorder and borderline personality disorder[6]
• Disrupted sleep[7]
• Poor physical health[8]
• Difficulty trusting new relationship partners[9]

Cultural Effects on Our Views

By Place:
Some cultures view victims of sexual aggression as guilty of disgracing their families. In India and Pakistan, male family members kill an unknown number of women— one source estimates 1000 annually in each country[10] – for "dishonoring" their families.

Over Time:
Changes in U.S. culture have made it less acceptable to blame victims of sexual aggression.

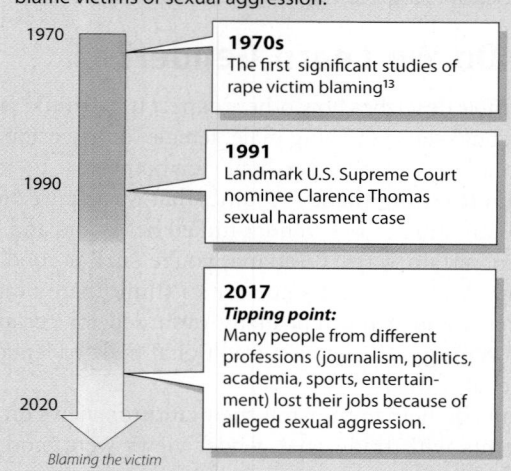

1970

1970s
The first significant studies of rape victim blaming[13]

1990

1991
Landmark U.S. Supreme Court nominee Clarence Thomas sexual harassment case

2017
Tipping point:
Many people from different professions (journalism, politics, academia, sports, entertainment) lost their jobs because of alleged sexual aggression.

2020

Blaming the victim becomes less acceptable.

How to Reduce Sexual Aggression

Therapy to treat sexual aggressors has not been very effective.[11] However, other, broader-based strategies do work:

Encourage victims to report their experiences to authority figures (parents, supervisors, law enforcement officials) and to share their experiences publicly.

Empower victims to take control of their situation and refuse to let their perpetrators dominate or manipulate them. Adjust social norms so that victims feel safe reporting their experiences.

Educate people about preventive bystander intervention strategies, such as "Green Dot," which has been shown to reduce sexual aggression in communities by as much as 20%.[12]

Disgraced Dr. Nassar...sexual abuse ... Over 200 victims testify

1. McDonald, 2012; U.S.E.E.O.C., 2018. 2. U.S.D.O.J., 2018. 3. Stop Street Harassment, 2018. 4. Black et al., 2011. 5. GLSEN, 2012. 6. Choudhary et al., 2012; Krahé & Berger, 2017; Snipes et al., 2017; Zanarini et al., 1997. 7. Krakow et al., 2001, 2002. 8. Schuyler et al., 2017; Zinzow et al., 2011. 9. Muldoon et al., 2016; Starzynski et al., 2017. 10. HBVA, 2018. 11. Grønnerød et al., 2015. 12. Coker et al., 2017. 13. Burt, 1980.

transgender an umbrella term describing people whose gender identity or expression differs from that associated with their birth-designated sex.

For someone who identifies as **transgender**, gender identity differs from what's typical for that person's birth-designated sex (APA, 2010; Bockting, 2014). Even as 5- to 12-year-olds, transgender children typically view themselves in terms of their expressed gender rather than their birth-designated sex (Olson et al., 2015). From childhood onward, a person may feel like a male in a female body, or a female in a male body. Brain scans reveal that those who seek medical sex-reassignment have some neural tracts that differ from those whose gender identity matches their birth-designated sex (Kranz et al., 2014;

Van Kesteren et al., 1997). Biologist Robert Sapolsky (2015) explains: "It's not that [these] individuals think they are a different gender than they actually are. It's that they [are] stuck with bodies that are a different gender from who they actually are."

In most countries, it's not easy being transgender. In a national survey of lesbian, gay, bisexual, and transgender Americans, 71 percent saw "some" or "a lot" of social acceptance for gay men, and 85 percent said the same for lesbians. But only 18 percent saw similar acceptance for transgender people, who number about 1.4 million in the United States (Flores et al., 2016; Sandstrom, 2015). And that is the experience of transgender people—46 percent of whom, in a survey of 27,175 transgender Americans, reported being verbally harassed in the last year (James et al., 2016). The psychiatric profession no longer considers gender nonconformity as a mental disorder, and thus no longer labels transgender people as having a "gender identity disorder." But some transgender people (not surprisingly, given the social disapproval) may experience profound distress and be diagnosed with *gender dysphoria*.

Transgender people may attempt to align their outward appearance and everyday lives with their internal gender identity. Such affirming of one's internal gender identity can help transgender people avoid depression and low self-esteem (Glynn et al., 2017). Note that *gender identity* is distinct from *sexual orientation* (the direction of one's sexual attraction). Transgender people may be sexually attracted to people of the other gender, the same gender, or both genders, or to no one at all. Your sexual orientation, as some say, is who you fantasize going to bed *with*; your gender identity is who you go to bed *as*.

BOYS WILL BE BOYS Chaz Bono, writer, musician, advocate, and actor, is the transgender son of famous singer and actress Cher and author of the book *Family Outing*.

Axelle/Bauer-Griffin/Getty Images

Colin McPherson/Getty Images

"MY FATHER . . . IS . . . A WOMAN." So said Mark Morris (2015) of his famous parent, the transgender Welsh writer Jan Morris. After gender reassignment surgery in 1973, Jan Morris was forced by law to divorce Mark's mother. "They continued to live together in a remarkably strong marital bond," until remarrying when same-sex marriages became legal in Britain.

🌊 **LaunchPad** For a 6.5-minute exploration of one pioneering transgender person's journey, see the **Video: Renée Richards—A Long Journey.**

ENGAGE 💡 (ASK YOURSELF)

How gender-typed are you? What has influenced your feelings of masculinity, femininity, or some combination of the two?

🔒 **RETRIEVE IT** • • •   *ANSWERS IN APPENDIX E*

RI-3 What are gender roles, and what do their variations tell us about our human capacity for learning and adaptation?

🔒 **REVIEW** GENDER DEVELOPMENT

⟶ Learning Objectives

TEST YOURSELF Answer these repeated Learning Objective Questions on your own (before checking the answers in Appendix D) to improve your retention of the concepts (McDaniel et al., 2009, 2015).

14-1 How does the meaning of *gender* differ from the meaning of *sex*?

14-2 What are some ways in which males and females tend to be alike and to differ?

14-3 What factors contribute to gender bias in the workplace?

14-4 How do sex hormones influence prenatal and adolescent sexual development, and what is an *intersex* condition?

14-5 How do gender roles and gender identity differ?

14-6 What are the effects of sexual aggression? How have cultural views changed, and how can we reduce sexual aggression?

⊙ Terms and Concepts to Remember

TEST YOURSELF Write down the definition yourself, then check your answer on the referenced page.

sex, **p. 162**

gender, **p. 162**

aggression, **p. 162**

relational aggression, **p. 162**

X chromosome, **p. 166**

Y chromosome, **p. 166**

testosterone, **p. 166**

puberty, **p. 166**

primary sex characteristics, **p. 166**

secondary sex characteristics, **p. 166**

spermarche [sper-MAR-key], **p. 166**

menarche [meh-NAR-key], **p. 166**

intersex, **p. 167**

role, **p. 169**

gender role, **p. 169**

sexual aggression, **p. 169**

gender identity, **p. 169**

social learning theory, **p. 169**

gender typing, **p. 169**

androgyny, **p. 169**

transgender, **p. 170**

⊙ Experience the Testing Effect

TEST YOURSELF Answer the following questions on your own first, then check your answers in Appendix E.

1. In psychology, _____ is the biologically in-fluenced characteristics by which people define male and female. The socially influenced characteristics by which people define boy, girl, man and woman is _____.

2. Females and males are very similar, but one way they differ is that
   a. females are more physically aggressive than males.
   b. males are more democratic than females in their leader-ship roles.
   c. as children, females tend to play in small groups, while males tend to play in large groups.
   d. females are more likely to die by suicide.

3. A fertilized egg will develop into a male if it receives a/n _____ chromosome from its father.

4. Primary sex characteristics relate to _____; secondary sex characteristics refer to _____.
   a. spermarche; menarche
   b. breasts and facial hair; ovaries and testes

   c. emotional maturity; hormone surges
   d. reproductive organs; nonreproductive traits

5. On average, girls begin puberty at about the age of _____, boys at about the age of _____.

6. A person born with sexual anatomy that differs from typical male or female anatomy may be considered to have a(n) _____ condition.

7. *Gender role* refers to our
   a. personal sense of being male or female.
   b. culture's expectations about the "right" way for males and females to behave.
   c. assigned birth sex—our chromosomes and anatomy.
   d. unisex characteristics.

8. Our sense of being male, female, or some combi-nation of the two is known as our _____ _____.

Continue testing yourself with  **LearningCurve** or ⋙ **Achieve Read & Practice** to learn and remember most effectively.

In one British survey of 18,876 people, and in other surveys since, about 1 percent acknowledge being asexual, having "never felt sexually attracted to anyone at all" (Bogaert, 2004, 2015). People identifying as asexual are, however, nearly as likely as others to report masturbating, noting that it feels good, reduces anxiety, or "cleans out the plumbing."

⑮ Human Sexuality

As you've probably noticed, we can hardly talk about gender without talking about our sexuality. For all but the tiny fraction of us considered **asexual,** dating and mating become a high priority from puberty on. Biologist Alfred Kinsey (1894–1956) pioneered the study of human sexuality (Kinsey et al., 1948, 1953). Kinsey and his colleagues' find-ings ignited debate and controversy, but they also motivated future scientific research devoted to understanding male and female sexual behavior. Our sexual feelings and behaviors reflect both physiological and psychological influences.

THE PHYSIOLOGY OF SEX

Sex is not like hunger, because it is not an actual *need*. (Without it, we may feel like dying, but we will not.) Yet sex is a part of life. Had this not been so for all of your biological ancestors, you would not be alive and reading these words. Sexual motivation is nature's clever way of making people procreate, thus enabling our species' survival. Life is sexually transmitted.

Hormones and Sexual Behavior

LOQ 15-1 How do hormones influence human sexual motivation?

Among the forces driving sexual behavior are the *sex hormones*. The main male sex hormone is **testosterone.** The main female sex hormones are the **estrogens,** such as *estradiol*. Sex hormones influence us at several points in the life span:

- During the prenatal period, they direct our development as males or females.

- During puberty, a sex hormone surge ushers us into adolescence.

- After puberty and well into the late adult years, sex hormones facilitate sexual behavior.

In most mammals, nature neatly synchronizes sex with fertility. Females become sexually receptive (in nonhumans, "in heat") when their estrogens peak at ovulation, and researchers can cause female animals to become receptive by injecting them with estrogens. Male hormone levels are more constant, and hormone injection does not so easily affect the sexual behavior of male animals. Nevertheless, male hamsters that have had their testosterone-making testes surgically removed will gradually lose much of their interest in receptive females. They gradually regain it if injected with testosterone (Piekarski et al., 2009).

Hormones do influence human sexual behavior, but more loosely. Researchers are exploring and debating whether women's mate preferences change across the menstrual cycle, especially at ovulation, when both estrogens and testosterone rise (Gildersleeve et al., 2014; Haselton & Gildersleeve, 2011, 2016; Wood et al., 2014a). Some evidence suggests that, among women with mates, sexual desire rises slightly at ovulation—a change that men can sometimes detect in women's behaviors and voices (Haselton & Gildersleeve, 2011, 2016).

Women have much less testosterone than men do. But more than other mammalian females, women are responsive to their testosterone level (Davison & Davis, 2011; van Anders, 2012). If a woman's natural testosterone level drops, as happens with removal of the ovaries or adrenal glands, her sexual interest may wane. And as experiments with surgically or naturally menopausal women have demonstrated, testosterone-replacement therapy can often restore diminished sexual activity, arousal, and desire (Braunstein et al., 2005; Buster et al., 2005; Petersen & Hyde, 2011).

In human males with abnormally low testosterone levels, testosterone-replacement therapy often increases sexual desire and also energy and vitality (Khera et al., 2011). But normal fluctuations in testosterone levels, from man to man and hour to hour, have little effect on sexual drive (Byrne, 1982). Indeed, male hormones sometimes vary in *response* to sexual stimulation (Escasa et al., 2011). In one study, Australian skateboarders' testosterone surged in the presence of an attractive female, contributing to riskier moves and more crash landings (Ronay & von Hippel, 2010). Thus, sexual arousal can be a *cause* as well as a consequence of increased testosterone levels.

Large hormonal surges or declines affect sexual desire in shifts that tend to occur at two predictable points in the life span, and sometimes at an unpredictable third point:

1. **The pubertal surge in sex hormones triggers the development of sex characteristics and sexual interest.** If puberty's hormonal surge is precluded—as it was during the 1600s and 1700s for prepubertal boys who were castrated to preserve their soprano voices for Italian opera—sex characteristics and sexual desire do not develop normally (Peschel & Peschel, 1987).

"It is a near-universal experience, the invisible clause on one's birth certificate stipulating that one will, upon reaching maturity, feel the urge to engage in activities often associated with the issuance of more birth certificates." —Science writer Natalie Angier, 2007

asexual having no sexual attraction toward others.

testosterone the most important male sex hormone. Both males and females have it, but the additional testosterone in males stimulates the growth of the male sex organs during the fetal period, and the development of the male sex characteristics during puberty.

estrogens sex hormones, such as estradiol, that contribute to female sex characteristics and are secreted in greater amounts by females than by males. Estrogen levels peak during ovulation. In nonhuman mammals, this promotes sexual receptivity.

2. *In later life, sex hormone levels fall.* Women experience menopause as their estrogen levels decrease; males experience a more gradual change. Sex remains a part of life, but as hormone levels decline, sexual fantasies and intercourse decline as well (Leitenberg & Henning, 1995).

3. *For some, surgery or drugs may cause hormonal shifts.* When adult men were castrated, their sex drive typically fell as testosterone levels declined sharply (Hucker & Bain, 1990). Male sex offenders who took Depo-Provera, a drug that reduces their testosterone level to that of a prepubertal boy, similarly lost much of their sexual urge (Bilefsky, 2009; Money et al., 1983).

To summarize: We might compare human sex hormones, especially testosterone, to the fuel in a car. Without fuel, a car will not run. But if the fuel level is minimally adequate, adding more fuel to the gas tank won't change how the car runs. The analogy is imperfect, because hormones and sexual motivation interact. However, it correctly suggests that biology is a necessary but incomplete explanation of human sexual behavior. The hormonal fuel is essential, but so are the psychological stimuli that turn on the engine, keep it running, and shift it into high gear.

🔒 **RETRIEVE IT • • •**   *ANSWERS IN APPENDIX E*

RI-1 The primary male sex hormone is _____. The primary female sex hormones are the _____.

The Sexual Response Cycle

LOQ 15-2 What is the human *sexual response cycle,* and how do sexual dysfunctions and paraphilias differ?

The scientific process often begins with careful observations of complex behaviors. When gynecologist-obstetrician William Masters and his collaborator Virginia Johnson (1966) applied this process to human sexual intercourse in the 1960s, they made headlines. They recorded the physiological responses of volunteers who came to their lab to masturbate or have intercourse. (The volunteers, 382 women and 312 men, were a somewhat atypical sample, consisting only of people able and willing to display arousal and orgasm while scientists observed.) Masters and Johnson reported observing more than 10,000 sexual "cycles." Their description of the **sexual response cycle** identified four stages:

1. *Excitement* The genital areas become engorged with blood, causing a woman's clitoris and a man's penis to swell. A woman's vagina expands and secretes lubricant; her breasts and nipples may enlarge.

2. *Plateau* Excitement peaks as breathing, pulse, and blood pressure rates continue to increase. A man's penis becomes fully engorged—to an average length of 5.6 inches among 1661 men who measured themselves for condom fitting (Herbenick et al., 2014). Some fluid—frequently containing enough live sperm to enable conception—may appear at its tip. A woman's vaginal secretion continues to increase, and her clitoris retracts. Orgasm feels imminent.

3. *Orgasm* Muscle contractions appear all over the body and are accompanied by further increases in breathing, pulse, and blood pressure rates. The pleasurable feeling of sexual release is much the same for both sexes. One panel of experts could not reliably distinguish between descriptions of orgasm written by men and those written by women (Vance & Wagner, 1976). In another study, PET scans showed that the same subcortical brain regions were active in men and women during orgasm (Holstege et al., 2003a,b).

4. *Resolution* The body gradually returns to its unaroused state as the genital blood vessels release their accumulated blood. This happens relatively quickly if orgasm has occurred, relatively slowly otherwise. (It's like the nasal tickle that goes away rapidly if you have sneezed, slowly otherwise.) Men then enter a **refractory period** that lasts from a few minutes to a day or more, during which they are incapable of another orgasm. A woman's much shorter refractory period may enable her, if restimulated during or soon after resolution, to have more orgasms.

A nonsmoking 50-year-old male has about a 1-in-a-million chance of a heart attack during any hour. This increases to merely 2-in-a-million in the two hours during and following sex (with no increase for those who exercise regularly). Compared with risks associated with heavy exertion or anger, this risk seems not worth losing sleep (or sex) over (Jackson, 2009; Muller et al., 1996).

RETAIN 🔒 There is also a *refractory period* in neural processing—the brief resting pause that occurs after a neuron has fired.

Sexual Dysfunctions and Paraphilias

Masters and Johnson sought not only to describe the human sexual response cycle but also to understand and treat the inability to complete it. **Sexual dysfunctions** are problems that consistently impair sexual arousal or functioning at any point in this cycle. Some involve sexual motivation, especially lack of sexual energy and arousability. For men, others include **erectile disorder** (inability to have or maintain an erection) and *premature ejaculation*. For women, the problem may be pain or **female orgasmic disorder** (distress over infrequently or never experiencing orgasm). In separate surveys of some 3000 Boston women and 32,000 other American women, about 4 in 10 reported a sexual problem, such as orgasmic disorder or low desire, but only about 1 in 8 reported that this caused personal distress (Lutfey et al., 2009; Shifren et al., 2008). Most women who have experienced sexual distress have related it to their emotional relationship with their partner during sex (Bancroft et al., 2003).

Psychological and medical therapies can help men and women with sexual dysfunctions (Frühauf et al., 2013). In behaviorally oriented therapy, for example, men learn ways to control their urge to ejaculate, and women are trained to bring themselves to orgasm. Starting with the introduction of Viagra in 1998, erectile disorder has been routinely treated by taking a pill. Researchers have struggled to develop reliable drug treatments for *female sexual interest/arousal disorder.*

Sexual dysfunction involves problems with arousal or sexual functioning. People with **paraphilias** (mostly men) do experience sexual desire, but they direct it in unusual ways (Baur et al., 2016). The American Psychiatric Association (2013) only classifies such behavior as disordered if

- a person experiences distress from an unusual sexual interest *or*
- it entails harm or risk of harm to others.

The serial killer Jeffrey Dahmer had *necrophilia,* a sexual attraction to corpses. Those with *exhibitionism* derive pleasure from exposing themselves sexually to others, without consent. People with the paraphilic disorder *pedophilia* experience sexual arousal toward children who haven't entered puberty.

Sexually Transmitted Infections

LOQ 15-3 How can sexually transmitted infections be prevented?

Every day, more than 1 million people worldwide acquire a *sexually transmitted infection* (*STI*; also called *STD*, for *sexually transmitted disease*) (WHO, 2013). Common STIs include chlamydia, gonorrhea, herpes simplex virus (HSV), and human papillomavirus (HPV) infection. "Compared with older adults," reports the Centers for Disease Control and Prevention (CDC, 2016b), "sexually active adolescents aged 15–19 years and young adults aged 20–24 years are at higher risk." Teenage girls, for example, are at heightened risk given their not yet fully mature anatomy and lower levels of protective antibodies (Dehne & Riedner, 2005; Guttmacher Institute, 1994).

Condoms offer only limited protection against certain skin-to-skin STIs, such as herpes, but they do reduce other risks (NIH, 2001). The effects were clear when Thailand promoted condom use by commercial sex workers. Over a four-year period, as condom use soared from 14 to 94 percent, the annual number of bacterial STIs plummeted from 410,406 to 27,362 (WHO, 2000). When used by people with an infected partner, condoms also have been 80 percent effective in preventing transmission of *HIV* (*human immunodeficiency virus*—the virus that causes **AIDS**) (Weller & Davis-Beaty, 2002; WHO, 2003). Although HIV can be transmitted by other means, such as needle sharing during drug use, its sexual transmission is most common. Half of all humans with HIV (and one fourth of Americans with HIV) are women. Because the virus is spread more easily from men to women, women's proportion of the worldwide AIDS population is growing.

Just over half of Americans with AIDS are between ages 30 and 49 (CDC, 2013). AIDS' long incubation period means that many were infected in their teens and twenties. In 2012, the death of 1.6 million people with AIDS worldwide left behind countless grief-stricken loved ones, including millions of orphaned children (UNAIDS, 2013).

LaunchPad To explore the stories of participants in a drug therapy program for sexual dysfunctions, see the 6-minute **Video: Sexual Dysfunctions and Their Treatments.**

sexual response cycle the four stages of sexual responding described by Masters and Johnson—excitement, plateau, orgasm, and resolution.

refractory period in human sexuality, a resting period that occurs after orgasm, during which a person cannot achieve another orgasm.

sexual dysfunction a problem that consistently impairs sexual arousal or functioning at any point in the sexual response cycle.

erectile disorder inability to develop or maintain an erection due to insufficient blood flow to the penis.

female orgasmic disorder distress due to infrequently or never experiencing orgasm.

paraphilias sexual arousal from fantasies, behaviors, or urges involving nonhuman objects, the suffering of self or others, and/or nonconsenting persons.

AIDS (acquired immune deficiency syndrome) a life-threatening, sexually transmitted infection caused by the *human immunodeficiency virus (HIV)*. AIDS depletes the immune system, leaving the person vulnerable to infections.

social script a culturally modeled guide for how to act in various situations.

In Sub-Saharan Africa, home to two-thirds of those with HIV, medical treatment to extend life and care for the dying is sapping needed resources.

Having sex with one person means also partnering with that person's past partners—any one of whom might have unknowingly transmitted an STI. Hence, the first step in preventing STIs is knowing one's status, and sharing it with one's sexual partner.

> 🔒 **RETRIEVE IT • • •**   *ANSWERS IN APPENDIX E*
>
> **RI-2** Someone who is distressed by impaired sexual arousal may be diagnosed with a _____ _____. Exhibitionism would be considered a _____.

THE PSYCHOLOGY OF SEX

LOQ 15-4 How do external and imagined stimuli contribute to sexual arousal?

Biological factors powerfully influence our sexual motivation and behavior. Yet the wide variations over time, across place, and among individuals document the great influence of psychological factors as well (**FIGURE 15.1**). Thus, despite the shared biology that underlies sexual motivation, the 281 reasons study participants expressed for having sex ranged widely—from "to get closer to God" to "to get my boyfriend to shut up" (Buss, 2008; Meston & Buss, 2007).

External Stimuli

Men and women become aroused when they see, hear, or read erotic material (Heiman, 1975; Stockton & Murnen, 1992). In men more than in women, *feelings* of sexual arousal closely mirror their (more obvious) physical genital responses (Chivers et al., 2010).

People may find sexual arousal either pleasing or disturbing. (Those who wish to control their arousal often limit their exposure to arousing materials, just as those wishing to avoid overeating limit their exposure to tempting food cues.) With repeated exposure to any stimulus, including an erotic stimulus, the emotional response lessens, or *habituates*. During the 1920s, when Western women's hemlines rose to the knee, an exposed leg made hearts flutter. Today, many would barely notice.

Can exposure to sexually explicit material have adverse effects? Research indicates that it can, in three ways.

- *Believing rape is acceptable* Depictions of women being sexually coerced—and appearing to enjoy it—have increased viewers' belief in the false idea that women want to be overpowered, and have increased male viewers' expressed willingness to hurt women and to commit rape after viewing such scenes (Allen et al., 1995, 2000; Foubert et al., 2011; Zillmann, 1989).

- *Reducing satisfaction with a partner's appearance or with a relationship* After viewing images or erotic films of sexually attractive women and men, people have judged an average person, their own partner, or their spouse as less attractive. And they have found their own relationship less satisfying (Kenrick & Gutierres, 1980; Lambert et al., 2012). Perhaps reading or watching erotica's unlikely scenarios creates expectations that few men and women can fulfill.

- *Desensitization* Some studies have found that extensive online pornography exposure desensitizes young men to normal sexuality, thus contributing to erectile problems, lowered sexual desire, and diminished brain activation in response to sexual images. "Porn is messing with your manhood," argue Philip Zimbardo and colleagues (2016). In one brain-imaging study, men who frequently watched pornography had smaller-sized brain regions that aid sexual pleasure (Kühn & Gallinat, 2014).

Digital Vision/Getty Images

FIGURE 15.1

BIOPSYCHOSOCIAL INFLUENCES ON SEXUAL MOTIVATION Compared with our motivation for eating, our sexual motivation is less influenced by biological factors. Psychological and social-cultural factors play a bigger role.

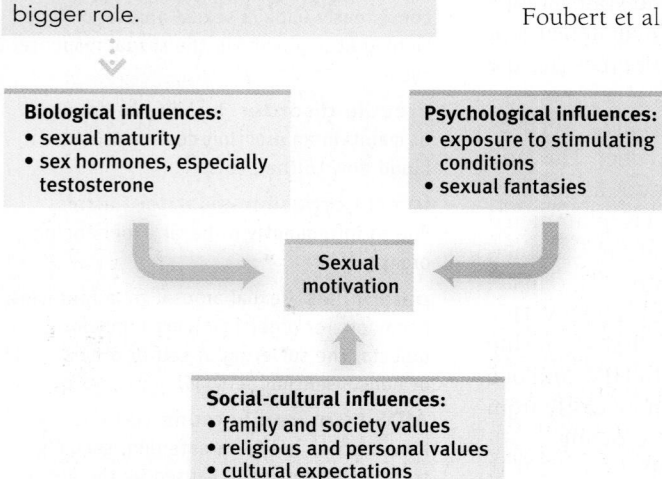

Biological influences:
- sexual maturity
- sex hormones, especially testosterone

Psychological influences:
- exposure to stimulating conditions
- sexual fantasies

Sexual motivation

Social-cultural influences:
- family and society values
- religious and personal values
- cultural expectations
- media

Imagined Stimuli

The brain, it has been said, is our most significant sex organ. The stimuli inside our heads—our imagination—can influence sexual arousal and desire. Lacking genital sensation because of a spinal-cord injury, people can still feel sexual desire (Willmuth, 1987).

Both men and women (about 95 percent of each) report having sexual fantasies, which for a few women can, by themselves, produce orgasms (Komisaruk & Whipple, 2011). Men, regardless of sexual orientation, tend to have more frequent, more physical, and less romantic fantasies (Schmitt et al., 2012). They also prefer less personal and faster-paced sexual content in books and videos (Leitenberg & Henning, 1995). Fantasizing about sex does *not* indicate a sexual problem or dissatisfaction. If anything, sexually active people have more sexual fantasies.

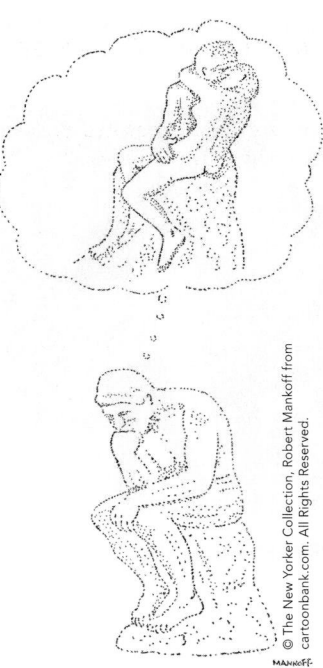

🔒 RETRIEVE IT • • •
ANSWERS IN APPENDIX E

RI-3 What factors influence our sexual motivation and behavior?

Sexual Risk Taking and Teen Pregnancy

LOQ 15-5 What factors influence teenagers' sexual behaviors and use of contraceptives?

Sexual attitudes and behaviors vary dramatically across cultures and eras. "Sex between unmarried adults" is "morally unacceptable," agree 97 percent of Indonesians and 6 percent of Germans (Pew, 2014b). And thanks to decreased sexual activity and increased protection, American teen pregnancy rates are declining (CDC, 2016b; Twenge et al., 2016b). What environmental factors contribute to teen pregnancy?

COMMUNICATION ABOUT BIRTH CONTROL Many teenagers are uncomfortable discussing contraception with parents, partners, and peers. But teens who talk freely and openly with their parents and with their partner in an exclusive relationship are more likely to use contraceptives (Aspy et al., 2007; Milan & Kilmann, 1987).

IMPULSIVITY Among sexually active 12- to 17-year-old American girls, 72 percent said they regretted having had sex (Reuters, 2000). If passion overwhelms intentions (either to use contraceptives or to delay having sex), unplanned sexual activity may result in pregnancy (Ariely & Loewenstein, 2006; MacDonald & Hynie, 2008).

ALCOHOL USE Among late teens and young adults, most sexual hook-ups (casual encounters outside of a relationship) occur after alcohol use, often without knowing consent (Fielder et al., 2013; Garcia et al., 2013; Johnson & Chen, 2015). Those who use alcohol prior to sex are less likely to use condoms (Kotchick et al., 2001). By depressing the brain centers that control judgment, inhibition, and self-awareness, alcohol disarms normal restraints—a phenomenon well known to sexually coercive people.

MASS MEDIA Perceived peer norms influence teens' sexual behavior (Lyons et al., 2015; van de Bongardt et al., 2015). Teens attend to other teens, who, in turn, are influenced by popular media. Media help write the **social scripts** that affect our perceptions and actions. The more sexual content adolescents and young adults view or read (even when controlling for other predictors of early sexual activity), the more likely they are to perceive their peers as sexually active, to develop sexually permissive attitudes, and to experience early intercourse (Escobar-Chaves et al., 2005; Kim & Ward, 2012; Parkes et al., 2013). One study asked more than a thousand 12- to 14-year-olds what movies they had seen, and then after age 18 asked them about their sexual experiences (O'Hara et al., 2012). After controlling for various adolescent and family characteristics, the more the adolescents viewed movies with high sexual content, the greater was their sexual risk taking—with earlier first sex, more partners, and inconsistent condom use.

KEEPING ABREAST OF HYPERSEXUALITY An analysis of the 60 top-selling video games found 489 characters, 86 percent of whom were males (like most of the game players). The female characters were much more likely than the male characters to be "hypersexualized"—partially nude or revealingly clothed, with large breasts and tiny waists (Downs & Smith, 2010). Such depictions can lead to unrealistic expectations about sexuality and contribute to the early sexualization of girls. The American Psychological Association suggests countering this by teaching girls to "value themselves for who they are rather than how they look" (APA, 2007).

"Condoms should be used on every conceivable occasion." –Anonymous

FATHER PRESENCE

ASK YOURSELF

What strategies might be effective for reducing teen pregnancy?

Several factors predict sexual restraint:

- *High intelligence* Teens with high rather than average intelligence test scores more often delayed sex, partly because they considered possible negative consequences and were more focused on future achievement than on here-and-now pleasures (Harden & Mendle, 2011).

- *Religious engagement* Actively religious teens more often reserve sexual activity for adulthood or long-term relationships (Hull et al., 2011; Schmitt & Fuller, 2015; Štulhofer et al., 2011).

- *Father presence* In studies that followed hundreds of New Zealand and U.S. girls from age 5 to 18, having Dad around has reduced the risk of teen pregnancy and of sexual activity before age 16 (Ellis et al., 2003). These associations held even after adjusting for other influences, such as poverty. Close family attachments—as in families that eat together and where parents know their teens' activities and friends—also predict later sexual initiation (Coley et al., 2008).

- *Service learning participation* Several experiments have found that American teens volunteering as tutors or teachers' aides, or participating in community projects, had lower pregnancy rates than did comparable teens randomly assigned to control conditions (Kirby, 2002; O'Donnell et al., 2002). Researchers are unsure why. Does service learning promote a sense of personal competence, control, and responsibility? Does it encourage more future-oriented thinking? Or does it simply reduce opportunities for unprotected sex? (After-school activities and later school start times also reduced unplanned pregnancies [Bryan et al., 2016; Steinberg, 2015].)

🔒 **RETRIEVE IT • • •**   *ANSWERS IN APPENDIX E*

RI-4 Which THREE of the following five factors contribute to unplanned teen pregnancies?

a. Alcohol use

b. Higher intelligence level

c. Father absence

d. Mass media models

e. Participating in service learning programs

SEXUAL ORIENTATION

LOQ 15-6 What has research taught us about sexual orientation?

We express the *direction* of our sexual interest in our **sexual orientation**—which usually is our enduring sexual attraction toward members of our own sex (*homosexual orientation*) or the other sex (*heterosexual orientation*). Other variations include an attraction to both sexes (*bisexual orientation*). Cultures vary in their attitudes toward same-sex attractions. "Should society accept homosexuality?" *Yes*, say 88 percent of Spaniards and 1 percent of Nigerians, with women everywhere being more accepting than men (Pew, 2013a). Yet whether a culture condemns or accepts same-sex unions, heterosexuality is most common and homosexuality and bisexuality exist. In most African countries, same-sex relationships are illegal. Yet the ratio of lesbian, gay, or bisexual people "is no different from other countries in the rest of the world," reports the Academy of Science of South Africa (2015). What is more, same-sex activity spans human history.

Sexual Orientation: The Numbers

How many people are exclusively homosexual? According to more than a dozen national surveys in Europe and the United States, about 3 or 4 percent of men and 2 percent of women (Chandra et al., 2011; Herbenick et al., 2010; Savin-Williams et al., 2012). When the U.S. National Center for Health Statistics asked 34,557 Americans about their sexual identity, they found that all but 3.4 percent answered "straight," with 1.6 percent answering "gay" or "lesbian" and 0.7 percent saying "bisexual" (Ward et al., 2014). In a follow-up

sexual orientation an enduring sexual attraction toward members of one's own sex (*homosexual* orientation), the other sex (*heterosexual* orientation), or both sexes (*bisexual* orientation).

survey, 1.6 percent of women and 2.3 percent of men anonymously reported feeling "mostly" or "only" same-sex attraction (Copen et al., 2016). A larger number of adults—13 percent of women and 5 percent of men—report some same-sex sexual contact during their lives (Chandra et al., 2011).

In less tolerant places, people are more likely to hide their sexual orientation. About 3 percent of California men express a same-sex preference on Facebook, for example, as do only about 1 percent in Mississippi. Yet about 5 percent of Google pornography searches in both states are for gay porn. And Craigslist ads for males seeking "casual encounters" with other men tend to be at least as common in less tolerant states, where there are also more Google searches for "gay sex" and "Is my husband gay?" (MacInnis & Hodson, 2015; Stephens-Davidowitz, 2013).

What does it feel like to have same-sex attractions in a majority heterosexual culture? If you are heterosexual, imagine how you would feel if you were socially isolated for openly admitting or displaying your feelings. How would you react if you overheard people making crude jokes about heterosexual people, or if most movies, TV shows, and advertisements portrayed (or implied) homosexuality? And how would you answer if your family members were pleading with you to change your heterosexual "life-style" and to enter into a homosexual marriage?

Facing such reactions, some individuals struggle with their sexual attractions, especially during adolescence and if feeling rejected by parents or harassed by peers. If lacking social support, nonheterosexual teens express greater anxiety and depression, and an increased risk of contemplating and attempting suicide (Becker et al., 2014; Lyons, 2015; Wang et al., 2012, 2015b). They may at first try to ignore or deny their desires, hoping they will go away. But they don't. They may try to change their orientation through psychotherapy, willpower, or prayer. But the feelings typically persist, as do those of heterosexual people—who are similarly incapable of change (Haldeman, 1994, 2002; Myers & Scanzoni, 2005).

Today's psychologists view sexual orientation as neither willfully chosen nor willfully changed. Sexual orientation in some ways is like handedness: Most people are one way, some the other. A very few are truly ambidextrous. Regardless, the way one is endures. "Efforts to change sexual orientation are unlikely to be successful and involve some risk of harm," declared a 2009 American Psychological Association report. Recognizing this, in 2016, Malta became the first European country to outlaw the controversial practice of "conversion therapy," which aims to change people's gender identities or sexual orientations. Several U.S. states have likewise banned conversion therapy with minors.

Sexual orientation is especially persistent for men. Women's sexual orientation tends to be less strongly felt and, for some women, is more fluid and changing (Dickson et al., 2013; Norris et al., 2015). In general, men are sexually simpler. Men's lesser sexual variability is apparent in many ways (Baumeister, 2000). Across time, across cultures, across situations, and across differing levels of education, religious observance, and peer influence, men's sexual drive and interests are less flexible and varying than are women's. Women, for example, more often prefer to alternate periods of high sexual activity with periods of almost none (Mosher et al., 2005). Baumeister calls this flexibility *erotic plasticity*.

Origins of Sexual Orientation

So, our sexual orientation seems to be something we do not choose and (especially for males) cannot change. Where, then, do these preferences come from? See if you can anticipate the conclusions that have emerged from hundreds of research studies by responding *Yes* or *No* to the following questions:

1. Is homosexuality linked with a child's problematic relationships with parents, such as with a domineering mother and an ineffectual father, or a possessive mother and a hostile father?

2. Does homosexuality involve a fear or hatred of people of the other sex, leading individuals to direct their desires toward members of their own sex?

3. Is sexual orientation linked with sex hormone levels?

4. As children, were most homosexuals molested, seduced, or otherwise sexually victimized by an adult homosexual?

In tribal cultures in which homosexual behavior is expected of all boys before marriage, most men are heterosexual (Hammack, 2005; Money, 1987). As this illustrates, homosexual *behavior* does not always indicate a homosexual *orientation*.

DRIVEN TO SUICIDE In 2010, Rutgers University student Tyler Clementi jumped off this bridge after his roommate secretly filmed, shared, and tweeted about Clementi's intimate encounter with another man. Reports then surfaced of other gay teens who had reacted in a similarly tragic fashion after being taunted. Since 2010, Americans—especially those under 30—have been increasingly supportive of those with same-sex orientations.

STAN HONDA/Getty Images

The answer to all these questions has been *No* (Storms, 1983). In a search for possible environmental influences on sexual orientation, Kinsey Institute investigators interviewed nearly 1000 homosexuals and 500 heterosexuals. They assessed nearly every imaginable psychological cause of homosexuality—parental relationships, childhood sexual experiences, peer relationships, dating experiences (Bell et al., 1981; Hammersmith, 1982). Their findings: Homosexuals are no more likely than heterosexuals to have been smothered by maternal love or neglected by their father. In one national survey of nearly 35,000 adults, those with a same-sex attraction were somewhat more likely to report having experienced child sexual abuse. But 86 percent of the men and 75 percent of the women with same-sex attraction reported no such abuse (Roberts et al., 2013).

And consider this: If "distant fathers" were more likely to produce homosexual sons, then shouldn't boys growing up in father-absent homes more often be gay? (They are not.) And shouldn't the rising number of such homes have led to a noticeable increase in the gay population? (It has not.) Most children raised by gay or lesbian parents grow up straight (Gartrell & Bos, 2010). And they grow up with health and emotional well-being similar to (and sometimes better than) children with straight parents (Bos et al., 2016; Farr, 2017; Miller et al., 2017).

The bottom line from a half-century's theory and research: If there are environmental factors that influence sexual orientation after we're born, we do not yet know what they are. The lack of evidence for environmental causes of homosexuality has motivated researchers to explore possible biological influences. They have considered these possibilities:

- Same-sex behaviors in other species,
- Gay-straight brain differences,
- Genetic influences, and
- Prenatal influences.

SAME-SEX ATTRACTION IN OTHER SPECIES In Boston's Public Gardens, caretakers solved the mystery of why a much-loved swan couple's eggs never hatched. Both swans were female. In New York City's Central Park Zoo, penguins Silo and Roy spent several years as devoted same-sex partners. Same-sex sexual behaviors have also been observed in several hundred other species, including grizzlies, gorillas, monkeys, flamingos, and owls (Bagemihl, 1999). Among rams, for example, some 7 to 10 percent display same-sex attraction by shunning ewes and seeking to mount other males (Perkins & Fitzgerald, 1997). Homosexual behavior seems a natural part of the animal world.

GAY-STRAIGHT BRAIN DIFFERENCES Researcher Simon LeVay (1991) studied sections of the hypothalamus (a brain structure linked to emotion) taken from deceased heterosexual and homosexual people. As a gay scientist, LeVay wanted to do "something connected with my gay identity." To avoid biasing the results, he did a *blind study,* not knowing which donors were gay. For nine months he peered through his microscope at a cell cluster that varied in size among donors. Then, one morning, he broke the code: One cell cluster was reliably larger in heterosexual men than in women and homosexual men. "I was almost in a state of shock," LeVay said (1994). "I took a walk by myself on the cliffs over the ocean. I sat for half an hour just thinking what this might mean."

It should not surprise us that brains differ with sexual orientation. Remember, *everything psychological is simultaneously biological.* But when did the brain difference begin? At conception? During childhood or adolescence? Did experience produce the difference? Or was it genes or prenatal hormones (or genes activating prenatal hormones)?

LeVay does not view this cell cluster as an "on-off button" for sexual orientation. Rather, he believes it is an important part of a brain pathway that is active during sexual behavior. He agrees that sexual behavior patterns could influence the brain's anatomy. (Neural pathways in our brain do grow stronger with use.) In fish, birds, rats, and humans, brain structures vary with experience—including sexual experience (Breedlove, 1997). But LeVay believes it more likely that brain anatomy influences sexual orientation. His hunch seems confirmed by the discovery of a similar difference between

"There is no sound scientific evidence that sexual orientation can be changed." —UK Royal College of Psychiatrists, 2009

📺 **LaunchPad** See the **Video: Naturalistic Observation** for a helpful tutorial animation.

JULIET AND JULIET Boston's beloved swan couple, "Romeo and Juliet," were discovered actually to be, as are many other animal partners, a same-sex pair.

The Boston Globe/Getty Images

male sheep that do and don't display same-sex attraction (Larkin et al., 2002; Roselli et al., 2002, 2004). Moreover, such differences seem to develop soon after birth, and perhaps even before birth (Rahman & Wilson, 2003).

Since LeVay's discovery, other researchers have reported additional gay-straight brain activity differences. One is an area of the hypothalamus that governs sexual arousal (Savic et al., 2005). When straight women were given a whiff of a scent derived from men's sweat (which contains traces of male hormones), this area became active. Gay men's brains responded similarly to the men's scent. Straight men's brains did not. They showed the arousal response only to a female hormone sample. In a similar study, lesbians' responses differed from those of straight women (Kranz & Ishai, 2006; Martins et al., 2005). Researcher Qazi Rahman (2015) sums it up: Compared with heterosexuals, "gay men appear, on average, more 'female typical' in brain pattern responses and lesbian women are somewhat more 'male typical.'"

GENETIC INFLUENCES Evidence indicates that "about a third of variation in sexual orientation is attributable to genetic influences" (Bailey et al., 2016). A same-sex orientation does tend to run in families. And identical twins are somewhat more likely than fraternal twins to share a homosexual orientation (Alanko et al., 2010; Långström et al., 2010). But because sexual orientations differ in many identical twin pairs, especially female twins, we know that other factors besides genes are also at work—including, it appears, epigenetic marks that help distinguish gay and straight identical twins (Balter, 2015).

By altering a single gene in fruit flies, experimenters have created female fruit flies that pursued other females during courtship, and males that pursued other males (Demir & Dickson, 2005; Dickson, 2005). With humans, it's likely that multiple genes, possibly in interaction with other influences, shape sexual orientation. A genome-wide study of 409 pairs of gay brothers identified sexual orientation links with areas of two chromosomes, one maternally transmitted (Sanders et al., 2015).

Researchers have speculated about possible reasons why "gay genes" might exist in the human gene pool, given that same-sex couples cannot naturally reproduce. One possible answer is kin selection. Evolutionary psychologists remind us that many of our genes also reside in our biological relatives. Perhaps, then, gay people's genes live on through their supporting the survival and reproductive success of their relatives.

A *fertile females theory* suggests that maternal genetics may also be at work (Bocklandt et al., 2006). Homosexual men tend to have more homosexual relatives on their mother's side than on their father's (Camperio-Ciani et al., 2004, 2009, 2012; VanderLaan et al., 2012; VanderLaan & Vasey, 2011). And the relatives on the mother's side also produce more offspring than do the maternal relatives of heterosexual men. Perhaps the genes that dispose some women to conceive more children with men also dispose some men to be attracted to men (LeVay, 2011). Thus, the decreased reproduction by gay men appears to be offset by the increased reproduction by their maternal extended family.

PRENATAL INFLUENCES Twins share not only genes, but also a prenatal environment. Recall that in the womb, sex hormones direct our development as male or female. Two sets of findings indicate that the prenatal environment matters.

First, in humans, a critical period for fetal brain development seems to be the second trimester (Ellis & Ames, 1987; Garcia-Falgueras & Swaab, 2010; Meyer-Bahlburg, 1995). Exposure to the hormone levels typically experienced by female fetuses during this period may predispose a person (female or male) later to become attracted to males. When pregnant sheep were injected with testosterone during a similar critical period, their female offspring later showed homosexual behavior (Money, 1987).

Second, the mother's immune system may play a role in the development of sexual orientation. Men with older brothers are somewhat more likely to be gay—about one-third more likely for each additional older brother (Blanchard, 2004, 2008a,b, 2014; Bogaert, 2003). If the odds of homosexuality are roughly 2 percent among first sons, they would rise to about 2.6 percent among second sons, 3.5 percent for third sons, and so on for each additional older brother (Bailey et al., 2016). This is called the *older-brother* or *fraternal birth-order effect* (see **FIGURE 15.2**).

"Gay men simply don't have the brain cells to be attracted to women." –Simon LeVay, *The Sexual Brain*, 1993

LaunchPad See the **Video: Twin Studies** for a helpful tutorial animation.

FIGURE 15.2

THE OLDER BROTHER EFFECT Researcher Ray Blanchard (2008a) offers these approximate curves depicting a man's likelihood of homosexuality as a function of the number of biological (not adopted) older brothers he has. This correlation has been found in several studies, but only among right-handed men (as about 9 in 10 men are).

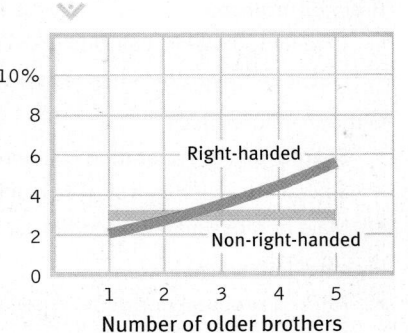

182   MODULE 15 | HUMAN SEXUALITY

"Modern scientific research indicates that sexual orientation is . . . partly determined by genetics, but more specifically by hormonal activity in the womb." —Glenn Wilson and Qazi Rahman, *Born Gay: The Psychobiology of Sex Orientation*, 2005

ENGAGE **ASK YOURSELF**

Has learning more about what contributes to sexual orientation influenced your views? If so, in what ways?

LaunchPad For an 8-minute overview of the biology of sexual orientation, see the **Video: Homosexuality and the Nature–Nurture Debate.**

Note that the scientific question is not "What causes homosexuality?" (or "What causes heterosexuality?") but "What causes differing sexual orientations?" In pursuit of answers, psychological science compares the backgrounds and physiology of people whose sexual orientations *differ*.

The reason for this curious effect is unclear. But the explanation does seem biological. The effect does not occur among adopted brothers (Bogaert, 2006). Researchers suspect the mother's immune system may have a defensive response to substances produced by male fetuses. After each pregnancy with a male fetus, the maternal antibodies may become stronger and may prevent the fetal brain from developing in a typical male pattern.

Gay-Straight Trait Differences

Comparing the traits of gay and straight people is akin to comparing the heights of men and women. The average man is taller than most women, but many women are taller than most men. And just as knowing someone's height doesn't specify their sex, neither does knowing someone's traits tell you their sexual orientation. Yet on several traits, the average homosexual female or male is intermediate between straight females and males (**TABLE 15.1**; see also LeVay, 2011; Rahman & Koerting, 2008; Rieger et al., 2016).

Gay-straight spatial abilities also differ. On mental rotation tasks such as the one illustrated in **FIGURE 15.3**, straight men tend to outscore straight women (Boone & Hegarty, 2017). Scores of gays and lesbians tend to fall between those of straight men and women (Rahman & Koerting, 2008; Rahman et al., 2004). But straight women and gays have both outperformed straight men at remembering objects' spatial locations in memory game tasks (Hassan & Rahman, 2007).

* * *

ENGAGE   Taken together, the brain, genetic, and prenatal findings offer strong support for a biological explanation of sexual orientation (LeVay, 2011; Rahman & Koerting, 2008). If you see sexual orientation as inborn—as shaped by biological and prenatal influences—then you likely favor "equal rights for homosexual and bisexual people" (Bailey et al., 2016). People who see same-sex attraction as a lifestyle choice often oppose equal rights for nonheterosexual people. To justify his signing a 2014 bill that made some homosexual acts punishable by life in prison, the president of Uganda, Yoweri Museveni, declared that homosexuality is not inborn but rather is a matter of "choice" (Balter, 2014; Landau et al., 2014). Stay tuned for whether the new biological research can encourage care and compassion for people of all sexual orientations.

TABLE 15.1
Biological Correlates of Sexual Orientation

Gay-straight trait differences

Sexual orientation is part of a package of traits. Studies—some in need of replication—indicate that homosexuals and heterosexuals differ in the following biological and behavioral traits:

• spatial abilities	• occupational preferences	• face structure and birth size/weight
• fingerprint ridge counts	• relative finger lengths	• sleep length
• auditory system development	• gender nonconformity	• physical aggression
• handedness	• age of onset of puberty in males	• walking style

On average (the evidence is strongest for males), results for gays and lesbians fall between those of straight men and straight women. Three biological influences—brain, genetic, and prenatal—may contribute to these differences.

Brain differences

• One hypothalamic cell cluster is smaller in women and gay men than in straight men.

• Gay men's hypothalamus reacts as does straight women's to the smell of men's sex-related hormones.

Genetic influences

• Shared sexual orientation is higher among identical twins than among fraternal twins.

• Sexual attraction in fruit flies can be genetically manipulated.

• Male homosexuality often appears to be transmitted from the mother's side of the family.

Prenatal influences

• Altered prenatal hormone exposure may lead to homosexuality in humans and other animals.

• Men with several older biological brothers are more likely to be gay, possibly due to a maternal immune-system reaction.

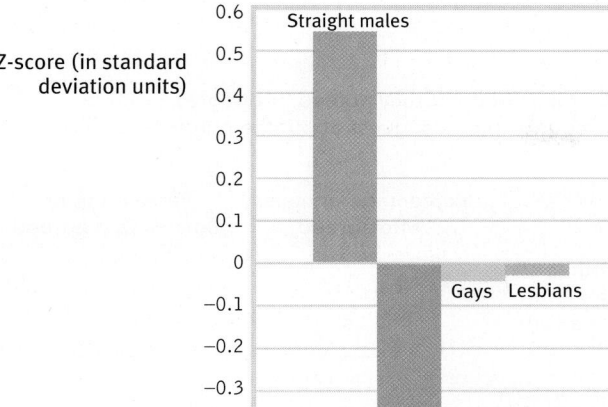

Z-score (in standard deviation units)

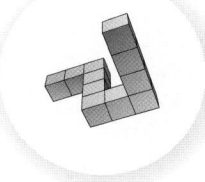

Original

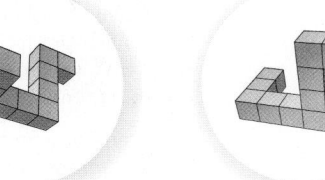

(a) (b)

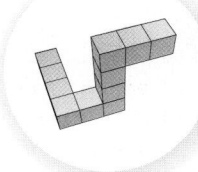

(c)

🔒 RETRIEVE IT • • •

ANSWERS IN APPENDIX E

RI-5 Which THREE of the following five factors have researchers found to have an effect on sexual orientation?

a. A domineering mother

b. The size of a certain cell cluster in the hypothalamus

c. Prenatal hormone exposure

d. A distant or ineffectual father

e. For right-handed men, having multiple older biological brothers

---

ENGAGE

💡 FIGURE 15.3

SPATIAL ABILITIES AND SEXUAL ORIENTATION Which of the three figures can be rotated to match the Original figure?[1] Straight males tend to find this type of mental rotation task easier than do straight females, with gays and lesbians falling in between (see graph) (Rahman et al., 2004).

AN EVOLUTIONARY EXPLANATION OF HUMAN SEXUALITY

LOQ 15-7 How might an evolutionary psychologist explain male-female differences in sexuality and mating preferences?

Having faced many similar challenges throughout history, males and females have adapted in similar ways: We eat the same foods, avoid the same dangers, and perceive, learn, and remember similarly. It is only in those domains where we have faced differing adaptive challenges—most obviously in behaviors related to reproduction—that we differ, say evolutionary psychologists.

Male-Female Differences in Sexuality

And differ we do. Consider sex drives. Both men and women are sexually motivated, some women more so than many men. Yet, on average, who thinks more about sex? Hooks up more often? Masturbates more often? Views more pornography? The answers worldwide: *men, men, men,* and *men* (Baumeister et al., 2001; Hall et al., 2017; Lippa, 2009; Petersen & Hyde, 2010). No surprise, then, that in one BBC survey of more than 200,000 people in 53 nations, men everywhere more strongly agreed that "I have a strong sex drive" and "It doesn't take much to get me sexually excited" (Lippa, 2008).

And there are other sexuality differences between males and females (Hyde, 2005; Petersen & Hyde, 2010; Regan & Atkins, 2007). To see if you can predict some of these differences in Americans, take the quiz in **TABLE 15.2**.

Many gender similarities and differences transcend sexual orientation. Compared with lesbians, gay men (like straight men) report more responsiveness to visual sexual stimuli, and more concern with their partner's physical attractiveness (Bailey et al., 1994; Doyle, 2005; Schmitt, 2007; Sprecher et al., 2013). Gay male couples also report having sex more often than do lesbian couples (Peplau & Fingerhut, 2007). And (also like straight men) gay men report more interest in uncommitted sex (Schmitt, 2003).

📺 **LaunchPad** To listen to experts discuss evolutionary psychology and sex differences, see the 4-minute **Video: Evolutionary Psychology and Sex Differences.**

"It's not that gay men are oversexed; they are simply men whose male desires bounce off other male desires rather than off female desires." —Steven Pinker, *How the Mind Works*, 1997

---

1. Answer: Figure (c).

TABLE 15.2

Predict the Responses

Researchers asked samples of U.S. adults whether they agreed or disagreed with the following statements. For each item, give your best guess about the percentage who agreed with the statement.[2]

Statement	Percentage of males who agreed	Percentage of females who agreed
1. If two people really like each other, it's all right for them to have sex even if they've known each other for a very short time.	_____	_____
2. I can imagine myself being comfortable and enjoying "casual" sex with different partners.	_____	_____
3. Affection was the reason I first had intercourse.	_____	_____
4. I think about sex every day, or several times a day.	_____	_____
5. Pornography is "morally acceptable."	_____	_____

Information from Bailey et al., 2000; Dugan, 2015; Laumann et al., 1994; Pryor et al., 2005.

Natural Selection and Mating Preferences

Natural selection is nature selecting traits and appetites that contribute to survival and reproduction. Evolutionary psychologists use this principle to explain how men and women differ more in the bedroom than in the boardroom. Our natural yearnings, they say, are our genes' way of reproducing themselves. "Humans are living fossils—collections of mechanisms produced by prior selection pressures" (Buss, 1995).

Why do women tend to be choosier than men when selecting sexual partners? Women have more at stake. To send her genes into the future, a woman must—at a minimum—conceive and protect a fetus growing inside her body for up to nine months, and may often nurse for an extended period following birth. No surprise then, that heterosexual women prefer partners who will offer their joint offspring support and protection—stick-around dads over likely cads. Heterosexual women are attracted to tall men with slim waists and broad shoulders—all signs of reproductive success (Mautz et al., 2013). And they prefer men who seem mature, dominant, bold, and affluent (Conroy-Beam et al., 2015; Fales et al., 2016; Lukaszewski et al., 2016). One study of hundreds of Welsh pedestrians asked people to rate a driver pictured at the wheel of a humble Ford Fiesta or a swanky Bentley. Men said a female driver was equally attractive in both cars. Women, however, found a male driver more attractive if he was in the luxury car (Dunn & Searle, 2010).

The data are in, say evolutionists: Men pair widely; women pair wisely. And what traits do straight men find desirable? Some, such as a woman's smooth skin and youthful shape, cross place and time, and they convey health and fertility (Buss, 1994). Mating with such women might increase a man's chances of sending his genes into the future. And sure enough, men feel most attracted to women whose waist is roughly a third narrower than their hips—a sign of future fertility (Lewis et al., 2015; Perilloux et al., 2010). Even blind men show this preference for women with a low waist-to-hip ratio (Karremans et al., 2010). Men are most attracted to women whose ages in the ancestral past (when ovulation began later than today) would be associated with peak fertility (Kenrick et al., 2009). Thus, teen boys are most excited by a woman several years older

2. ANSWERS: (1) males, 58 percent; females, 34 percent. (2) males, 48 percent; females, 12 percent. (3) males, 25 percent; females, 48 percent. (4) males, 54 percent; females, 19 percent. (5) males, 43 percent; females, 25 percent.

than themselves, mid-twenties men prefer women around their own age, and older men prefer younger women. This pattern consistently appears across European singles ads, Indian marital ads, and marriage records from North and South America, Africa, and the Philippines (Singh, 1993; Singh & Randall, 2007).

There is a principle at work here, say evolutionary psychologists: Nature selects behaviors that increase genetic success. As mobile gene machines, we are designed to prefer whatever worked for our ancestors in their environments. They were genetically predisposed to act in ways that produce children, grandchildren, and beyond. Had they not been, we wouldn't be here. As carriers of their genetic legacy, we are similarly predisposed.

Critiquing the Evolutionary Perspective

LOQ 15-8 What are the key criticisms of evolutionary explanations of human sexuality, and how do evolutionary psychologists respond?

Most psychologists agree that natural selection prepares us for survival and reproduction. But critics say there is a weakness in evolutionary psychology's explanation of our mating preferences. Let's consider how an evolutionary psychologist might explain the findings in a startling study (Clark & Hatfield, 1989), and how a critic might object.

In this experiment, someone posing as a stranger approached people of the other sex and remarked, "I have been noticing you around campus. I find you to be very attractive." The "stranger" then asked a question, which was sometimes "Would you go to bed with me tonight?" What percentage of men and women do you think agreed? An evolutionary explanation of sexuality would predict that women would be choosier than men in selecting their sexual partners. In fact, not a single woman agreed—but 70 percent of the men did. A repeat of this study in France produced a similar result (Guéguen, 2011). The research seemed to support an evolutionary explanation.

Or did it? Critics note that evolutionary psychologists start with an effect—in this case, the survey result showing that men were more likely to accept casual sex offers—and work backward to explain what happened. What if research showed the opposite effect? If men refused an offer for casual sex, might we not reason that men who partner with one woman for life make better fathers, whose children more often survive?

Other critics ask why we should try to explain today's behavior based on decisions our distant ancestors made thousands of years ago. Don't cultural expectations also bend the genders? Alice Eagly and Wendy Wood (1999; Eagly, 2009) point to the smaller behavioral differences between men and women in cultures with greater gender equality. Such critics believe that *social learning theory* offers a better, more immediate explanation for these results. We all learn *social scripts*—our culture's guide to how people should act in certain situations. By watching and imitating others in their culture, women may learn that sexual encounters with strangers can be dangerous, and that casual sex may not offer much sexual pleasure (Conley, 2011). This alternative explanation of the study's effects proposes that women react to sexual encounters in ways that their modern culture teaches them. And men's reactions may reflect their learned social scripts: "Real men" take advantage of every opportunity to have sex.

A third criticism focuses on the social consequences of accepting an evolutionary explanation. Are heterosexual men truly hardwired to have sex with any woman who approaches them? If so, does it mean that men have no moral responsibility to remain faithful to their partners? Does this explanation excuse men's *sexual aggression*—"boys will be boys"—because of our evolutionary history?

Evolutionary psychologists agree that much of who we are is *not* hardwired. "Evolution forcefully rejects a genetic determinism," insisted one research team (Confer et al., 2010). Genes are not destiny. And evolutionary psychologists remind us that men and women, having faced similar adaptive problems, are far more alike than different. Natural selection has prepared us to be flexible. We humans have a great capacity for learning and social progress. We adjust and respond to varied environments. We adapt and survive, whether we live in the Arctic or the desert.

THE MATING GAME Evolutionary psychologists are not surprised that older men, and not just George Clooney (pictured with his wife, Amal Clooney, who is 16 years younger), often prefer younger women whose features suggest fertility.

Guillaume Horcajuelo/Epa/REX/Shutterstock

LaunchPad To observe an experiment showing men's and women's attitudes toward casual sex, see the **Video: Openness to Casual Sex—A Study of Men Versus Women.**

LaunchPad For an interactive demonstration of evolutionary psychology and mating preferences, visit **Topic Tutorial: PsychSim6, Dating and Mating.**

MGP/Getty Images

Evolutionary psychologists also agree with their critics that some traits and behaviors, such as suicide, are hard to explain in terms of natural selection (Barash, 2012; Confer et al., 2010). But they ask us to remember evolutionary psychology's scientific goal: to explain behaviors and mental traits by offering testable predictions using principles of natural selection (Lewis et al., 2017). We may, for example, predict that people are more likely to perform favors for those who share their genes or can later return those favors. Is this true? (The answer is *Yes*.) And evolutionary psychologists remind us that studying how we *came to be* need not dictate how we *ought to be*. Understanding our tendencies can help us overcome them.

🔒 **RETRIEVE IT • • •**   *ANSWERS IN APPENDIX E*

RI-6 How do evolutionary psychologists explain male-female differences in sexuality?

RI-7 What are the three main criticisms of the evolutionary explanation of human sexuality?

SEX AND HUMAN RELATIONSHIPS

LOQ 15-9 What role do social factors play in our sexuality?

Human sexuality research does not aim to define the personal meaning of sex in our own lives. We could know every available fact about sex—that the initial spasms of male and female orgasm come at 0.8-second intervals, that female nipples expand 10 millimeters at the peak of sexual arousal, that systolic blood pressure rises some 60 points and respiration rate reaches 40 breaths per minute—but fail to understand the human significance of sexual intimacy.

Surely one significance of such intimacy is its expression of our profoundly social nature. In one national study that followed participants to age 30, later first sex predicted greater satisfaction in one's marriage or partnership (Harden, 2012). Another study asked 2035 married people when they started having sex (while controlling for education, religious engagement, and relationship length). Those whose relationship first developed to a deep commitment, and then included sex, not only reported greater relationship satisfaction and stability but also better sex than those who had sex very early in their relationship (Busby et al., 2010; Galinsky & Sonenstein, 2013). For both men and women, but especially for women, sex is more satisfying (with less regret and more orgasms) for those in a committed relationship, rather than a brief sexual hook-up (Armstrong et al., 2012; Garcia et al., 2012, 2013). Partners who share regular meals are more likely than one-time dinner companions to understand what seasoning touches suit each other's food tastes; so, too, with the touches of loyal partners who share a bed.

Sex is a socially significant act. Men and women can achieve orgasm alone, yet most people find greater satisfaction—and experience a much greater surge in *prolactin*, the hormone associated with sexual satisfaction and satiety—after intercourse and orgasm with their loved one (Brody & Tillmann, 2006). Thanks to their overlapping brain reward areas, sexual desire and love feed each other (Cacioppo et al., 2012). Sex at its human best is life uniting and love renewing.

Increased sex ≠ more happiness
Among married couples, more frequent sex correlates with happiness. So, would systematically increasing sexual frequency *cause* people to be happier? Alas, heterosexual married couples randomly assigned to double their intercourse frequency over three months became slightly *less* happy (Loewenstein et al., 2015).

REFLECTIONS ON THE NATURE AND NURTURE OF SEX, GENDER, AND SEXUALITY

LOQ 15-10 How do nature, nurture, and our own choices influence gender roles?

Our ancestral history helped form us as a species. Where there is variation, natural selection, and heredity, there will be evolution. Our genes form us. This is a great truth about human nature.

But our culture and experiences also form us. If their genes and hormones predispose males to be more physically aggressive than females, culture can amplify this gender difference through norms that reward macho men and gentle women. If men are encouraged toward roles that demand physical power, and women toward more nurturing roles, each may act accordingly. By exhibiting the actions expected of those who fill such roles, men and women shape their own traits. Presidents in time typically become more presidential, servants more servile. Gender roles similarly shape us.

In many modern cultures, gender roles are merging. Brute strength has become less important for power and status (think "philanthrocapitalists" Priscilla Chan and Mark Zuckerberg). From 1965 to 2016, women soared from 9 percent to 47 percent of U.S. medical students (AAMC, 2014, 2016). In 1965, U.S. married women devoted eight times as many hours to housework as did their husbands; by 2012, this gap had shrunk to less than twice as many (Parker & Wang, 2013; Sayer, 2016). Such swift changes signal that biology does not fix gender roles.

If nature and nurture jointly form us, are we "nothing but" the product of nature and nurture? Are we rigidly determined?

We *are* the product of nature and nurture, but we are also an open system. Genes are all-pervasive but not all-powerful. People may reject their evolutionary role as transmitters of genes and choose not to reproduce. Culture, too, is all-pervasive but not all-powerful. People may defy peer pressures and resist social expectations.

Moreover, we cannot excuse our failings by blaming them solely on bad genes or bad influences. In reality, we are both creatures and creators of our worlds. So many things about us—including our gender roles—are the products of our genes and environments. Yet the stream that runs into the future flows through our present choices. Our decisions today design our environments tomorrow. We are its architects. Our hopes, goals, and expectations influence our destiny. And that is what enables cultures to vary and to change. Mind matters.

CULTURE MATTERS As this exhibit at San Diego's Museum of Man illustrates, children learn their culture. A baby's foot can step into any culture.

San Diego Museum of Man, photograph by Rose Tyson

ENGAGE  ASK YOURSELF

Based on what you've learned so far, how would you say that genes, the brain, hormones, and environment work together to influence sexual behavior?

🔒 REVIEW HUMAN SEXUALITY

⟶ Learning Objectives

TEST YOURSELF Answer these repeated Learning Objective Questions on your own (before checking the answers in Appendix D) to improve your retention of the concepts (McDaniel et al., 2009, 2015).

15-1 How do hormones influence human sexual motivation?

15-2 What is the human *sexual response cycle,* and how do sexual dysfunctions and paraphilias differ?

15-3 How can sexually transmitted infections be prevented?

15-4 How do external and imagined stimuli contribute to sexual arousal?

15-5 What factors influence teenagers' sexual behaviors and use of contraceptives?

15-6 What has research taught us about sexual orientation?

15-7 How might an evolutionary psychologist explain male-female differences in sexuality and mating preferences?

15-8 What are the key criticisms of evolutionary explanations of human sexuality, and how do evolutionary psychologists respond?

15-9 What role do social factors play in our sexuality?

15-10 How do nature, nurture, and our own choices influence gender roles?

⟿ Terms and Concepts to Remember

TEST YOURSELF Write down the definition yourself, then check your answer on the referenced page.

asexual, **p. 173**

testosterone, **p. 173**

estrogens, **p. 173**

sexual response cycle, **p. 175**

refractory period, **p. 175**

sexual dysfunction, **p. 175**

erectile disorder, **p. 175**

female orgasmic disorder, **p. 175**

paraphilias, **p. 175**

AIDS (acquired immune deficiency syndrome), **p. 175**

social script, **p. 176**

sexual orientation, **p. 178**

⟿ Experience the Testing Effect

TEST YOURSELF Answer the following questions on your own first, then check your answers in Appendix E.

1. A striking effect of hormonal changes on human sexual behavior is the
   a. end of sexual desire in men over 60.
   b. sharp rise in sexual interest at puberty.
   c. decrease in women's sexual desire at the time of ovulation.
   d. increase in testosterone levels in castrated males.

2. In describing the sexual response cycle, Masters and Johnson noted that
   a. a plateau phase follows orgasm.
   b. people experience a refractory period during which they cannot experience orgasm.
   c. the feeling that accompanies orgasm is stronger in men than in women.
   d. testosterone is released equally in women and men.

3. What is the difference between sexual dysfunctions and paraphilias?

4. Using condoms during sex _____ (does/doesn't) reduce the risk of getting HIV and _____ (does/doesn't) fully protect against skin-to-skin STIs.

5. An example of an external stimulus that might influence sexual behavior is
   a. the level of testosterone in the bloodstream.
   b. the onset of puberty.
   c. a sexually explicit film.
   d. an erotic fantasy or dream.

6. Which factors have researchers thus far found to be *unrelated* to the development of our sexual orientation?

7. How do evolutionary psychologists use the principle of *natural selection* to explain differences in mating preferences in men and women?

Continue testing yourself with 🔖 **LearningCurve** or 🔖 **Achieve Read & Practice**
to learn and remember most effectively.

Sensation and Perception

Superstudio/Getty Images

"I have perfect vision," explains writer and teacher Heather Sellers. Her vision may be perfect, but her perception is not. In her memoir, *You Don't Look Like Anyone I Know,* she tells of awkward moments resulting from her lifelong *prosopagnosia*—face blindness (Sellers, 2010).

In college, on a date at the Spaghetti Station, I returned from the bathroom and plunked myself down in the wrong booth, facing the wrong man. I remained unaware he was not my date even as my date (a stranger to me) accosted Wrong Booth Guy, and then stormed out. . . . I do not recognize myself in photos or videos. I can't recognize my stepsons in the soccer pick-up line; I failed to determine which husband was mine at a party, in the mall, at the market.

To avoid being perceived as snobby or aloof, Sellers sometimes fakes recognition. She often smiles at people she passes, in case she knows them. Or she pretends to know the person with whom she is talking. (Similarly, those of us with hearing loss often fake hearing.) But, Sellers points out, there is an upside: When encountering someone who previously irritated her, she typically feels no ill will—she doesn't recognize the person.

Unlike Sellers, most of us have a functioning area on the underside of our brain's right hemisphere that helps us recognize a familiar human face as soon as we detect it—in only one-seventh of a second (Jacques & Rossion, 2006; Rossion & Boremanse, 2011).

sensation the process by which our sensory receptors and nervous system receive and represent stimulus energies from our environment.

sensory receptors sensory nerve endings that respond to stimuli.

perception the process of organizing and interpreting sensory information, enabling us to recognize meaningful objects and events.

bottom-up processing analysis that begins with the sensory receptors and works up to the brain's integration of sensory information.

top-down processing information processing guided by higher-level mental processes, as when we construct perceptions drawing on our experience and expectations.

This remarkable ability illustrates a broader principle. *Nature's sensory gifts enable each animal to obtain essential information.* Other examples:

- Human ears are most sensitive to sound frequencies that include human voices, especially a baby's cry.
- Frogs, which feed on flying insects, have cells in their eyes that fire only in response to small, dark, moving objects. A frog could starve to death knee-deep in motionless flies. But let one zoom by and the frog's "bug detector" cells snap awake. (As Kermit the Frog said, "Time's fun when you're having flies.")
- Male silkworm moths' odor receptors can detect one-billionth of an ounce of chemical sex attractant per second, released by a female one mile away (Sagan, 1977). That is why there continue to be silkworms.

In these modules, we'll look more closely at what psychologists have learned about how we sense and perceive our world. Module 16 begins by considering some basic principles that apply to all our senses. In Module 17, we take a close look at sensory and perceptual processes in vision. Module 18 reviews our nonvisual senses. ▶

16 Basic Concepts of Sensation and Perception

How do we create meaning from the blizzard of sensory stimuli that bombards our body 24 hours a day? Meanwhile, in a silent, cushioned, inner world, our brain floats in utter darkness. By itself, it sees nothing. It hears nothing. It feels nothing. *So, how does the world out there get in?* To phrase the question scientifically: How do we construct our representations of the external world? How do a campfire's flicker, crackle, and smoky scent activate neural connections? And how, from this living neurochemistry, do we create our conscious experience of the fire's motion and temperature, its aroma and beauty? In search of answers, let's examine the basics of sensation and perception.

PROCESSING SENSATIONS AND PERCEPTIONS

LEARNING OBJECTIVE QUESTION (LOQ)

16-1 What are *sensation* and *perception?* What do we mean by *bottom-up processing* and *top-down processing?*

Heather Sellers' curious mix of "perfect vision" and face blindness illustrates the distinction between *sensation* and *perception*. When she looks at a friend, her **sensation** is normal: Her **sensory receptors** detect the same information yours would, and her nervous system transmits that information to her brain. Her **perception**—the processes by which her brain organizes and interprets sensory input—is *almost* normal. Thus, she may recognize people from their hair, gait, voice, or particular physique, just not from their face. Her experience is much like the struggle any human would have trying to recognize a specific penguin.

Under normal circumstances, sensation and perception blend into one continuous process.

- **Bottom-up processing** starts at your sensory receptors and works up to higher levels of processing.
- **Top-down processing** constructs perceptions from this sensory input by drawing on your experience and expectations.

As your brain absorbs the information in **FIGURE 16.1**, bottom-up processing enables your sensory systems to detect the lines, angles, and colors that form the flower and leaves. Using top-down processing, you interpret what your senses detect.

FIGURE 16.1

WHAT'S GOING ON HERE? Our sensory and perceptual processes work together to help us sort out complex images, including the hidden couple in Sandro Del-Prete's drawing, *The Flowering of Love.*

© Sandro Del-Prete/www.sandrodelprete.com

TRANSDUCTION

LOQ 16-2 What three steps are basic to all our sensory systems?

Every second of every day, our sensory systems perform an amazing feat: They convert one form of energy into another. Vision processes light energy. Hearing processes sound waves. All our senses

- *receive* sensory stimulation, often using specialized receptor cells.
- *transform* that stimulation into neural impulses.
- *deliver* the neural information to our brain.

The process of converting one form of energy into another that our brain can use is called **transduction.** Transduction is rather like translation—of a physical energy such as light waves into the brain's electrochemical language. How do we see? Hear? Feel pain? Taste? Smell? Keep our balance? In each case, one of our sensory systems receives, transforms, and delivers the information to our brain.

Let's explore some strengths and weaknesses in our ability to detect and interpret stimuli in the vast sea of energy around us.

> **🔒 RETRIEVE IT • • •**   *ANSWERS IN APPENDIX E*
>
> **RI-1** What is the rough distinction between *sensation* and *perception*?

THRESHOLDS

LOQ 16-3 How do *absolute thresholds* and *difference thresholds* differ?

At this moment, we are being struck by X-rays and radio waves, ultraviolet and infrared light, and sound waves of very high and very low frequencies. To all of these we are blind and deaf. Other animals with differing needs detect a world that lies beyond our experience. Migrating birds stay on course aided by an internal magnetic compass. Bats and dolphins locate prey using sonar, bouncing echoing sound off objects. Bees navigate on cloudy days by detecting invisible (to us) polarized light.

Our senses open the shades just a crack, allowing us a restricted awareness of this vast sea of energy. But for our needs, this is enough.

Absolute Thresholds

To some kinds of stimuli we are exquisitely sensitive. Standing atop a mountain on an utterly dark, clear night, most of us could see a candle flame atop another mountain 30 miles away. We could feel the wing of a bee falling on our cheek. We could smell a single drop of perfume in a three-room apartment (Galanter, 1962).

German scientist and philosopher Gustav Fechner (1801–1887) studied the edge of our awareness of these faint stimuli, which he called an **absolute threshold**—the minimum stimulation necessary to detect a particular light, sound, pressure, taste, or odor 50 percent of the time. To test your absolute threshold for sounds, a hearing specialist would send tones, at varying levels, into each of your ears and record whether you could hear each tone (**FIGURE 16.2**). The test results would show the point where, for any sound frequency, half the time you could detect the sound and half the time you could not. That 50-50 point would define your absolute threshold.

Detecting a weak stimulus, or signal (such as a hearing-test tone), depends not only on its strength but also on our psychological state— our experience, expectations, motivation, and alertness. **Signal detection theory** predicts when we will detect weak signals (measured

transduction conversion of one form of energy into another. In sensation, the transforming of stimulus energies, such as sights, sounds, and smells, into neural impulses our brain can interpret.

absolute threshold the minimum stimulus energy needed to detect a particular stimulus 50 percent of the time.

signal detection theory a theory predicting how and when we detect the presence of a faint stimulus *(signal)* amid background stimulation *(noise)*. Assumes there is no single absolute threshold and that detection depends partly on a person's experience, expectations, motivation, and alertness.

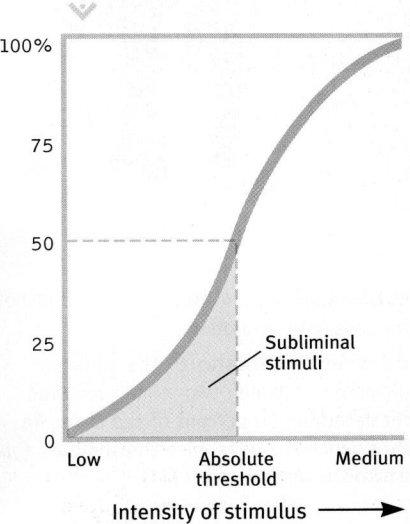

FIGURE 16.2

ABSOLUTE THRESHOLD Can I detect this sound? An *absolute threshold* is the intensity at which a person can detect a stimulus half the time. Hearing tests locate these thresholds for various frequencies.

SIGNAL DETECTION When reading mammograms, health professionals seek to detect the presence of a faint cancer stimulus (*signal*) amid background stimulation (*noise*), and without raising false alarms. New 3D ultrasound breast imaging technologies aim to clarify the signal and reduce the rate of false alarms.

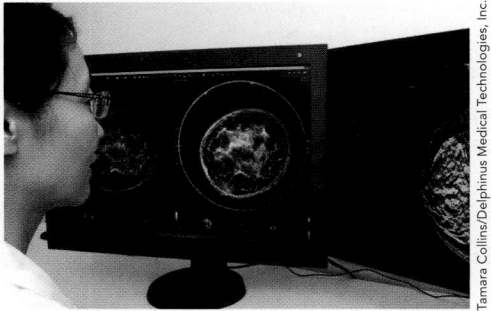

Tamara Collins/Delphinus Medical Technologies, Inc.

as our ratio of "hits" to "false alarms"). Signal detection theorists seek to understand why people respond differently to the same stimuli, and why the same person's reactions vary as circumstances change.

Stimuli you cannot consciously detect 50 percent of the time are **subliminal**—below your absolute threshold (Figure 16.2). One experiment using subliminal stimuli illustrated the deep reality of sexual orientation. As people gazed at the center of a screen, a photo of a nude person was flashed on one side and a scrambled version of the photo on the other side (Jiang et al., 2006). Because the nude images were immediately masked by a colored checkerboard, viewers consciously perceived nothing but flashes of color and so were unable to state on which side the nude had appeared. To test whether this unseen image had unconsciously attracted their attention, the experimenters then flashed a geometric figure on one side or the other. This, too, was quickly followed by a masking stimulus that interrupts the brain's processing before conscious perception (Herring et al., 2013; Van den Bussche et al., 2009). When asked to give the figure's angle, straight men guessed more accurately when it appeared where a nude *woman* had been a moment earlier (**FIGURE 16.3**). Gay men (and straight women) guessed more accurately when the geometric figure replaced a nude *man*. As other experiments confirm, we can evaluate a stimulus even when we are not consciously aware of it—and even when we are unaware of our evaluation (Ferguson & Zayas, 2009). So can we be *controlled* by subliminal messages? For more on that question, see Thinking Critically About: Subliminal Sensation and Subliminal Persuasion.

FIGURE 16.3

THE HIDDEN MIND After an image of a nude man or woman was flashed on a screen, then masked before it could be consciously perceived, people's attention was unconsciously drawn to images in a way that reflected their sexual orientation (Jiang et al., 2006).

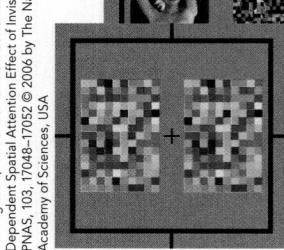

Y. Jiang et al., "A Gender- and Sexual Orientation-Dependent Spatial Attention Effect of Invisible Images," PNAS, 103, 17048–17052 © 2006 by The National Academy of Sciences, USA

📎 **LaunchPad** For a helpful tutorial animation about this type of research method, see the **Video: Experiments.**

Difference Thresholds

To function effectively, we need absolute thresholds low enough to allow us to detect important sights, sounds, textures, tastes, and smells. We also need to detect small differences among stimuli. A musician must detect minute discrepancies when tuning an instrument. Parents must detect the sound of their own child's voice amid other children's voices. Even after I [DM] had spent two years in Scotland, all sheep *baa*s sounded alike to my ears. But not to their mother's, as I observed. After shearing, each ewe would streak directly to the *baa* of *her* lamb amid the chorus of other distressed lambs.

The **difference threshold** (or the *just noticeable difference [jnd]*) is the minimum stimulus difference a person can detect half the time. That detectable difference increases with the size of the stimulus. If we listen to our music at 40 decibels, we might barely detect an added 5 decibels (the jnd). But if we increase the volume to 110 decibels, we probably won't detect an additional 5-decibel change.

In the late 1800s, Ernst Weber described this with a principle so simple and so widely applicable that

Eric Isselée/Shutterstock

subliminal below one's absolute threshold for conscious awareness.

difference threshold the minimum difference between two stimuli required for detection 50 percent of the time. We experience the difference threshold as a *just noticeable difference* (or *jnd*).

⚡ ENGAGE **THE DIFFERENCE THRESHOLD** In this computer-generated copy of the Twenty-third Psalm, each line of the typeface increases slightly. How many lines are required for you to experience a just noticeable difference?

> The LORD is my shepherd;
>   I shall not want.
> He maketh me to lie down
>   in green pastures:
>   he leadeth me
>   beside the still waters.
> He restoreth my soul:
>   he leadeth me
>   in the paths of righteousness
>   for his name's sake.
> Yea, though I walk through the valley
>   of the shadow of death,
>   I will fear no evil:
>   for thou art with me;
>   thy rod and thy staff
>   they comfort me.
> Thou preparest a table before me
>   in the presence of mine enemies:
>   thou anointest my head with oil,
>   my cup runneth over.
> Surely goodness and mercy
>   shall follow me
>   all the days of my life:
>   and I will dwell
>   in the house of the LORD
>   for ever.

Subliminal Sensation and Subliminal Persuasion

LOQ 16-4 How are we affected by subliminal stimuli?

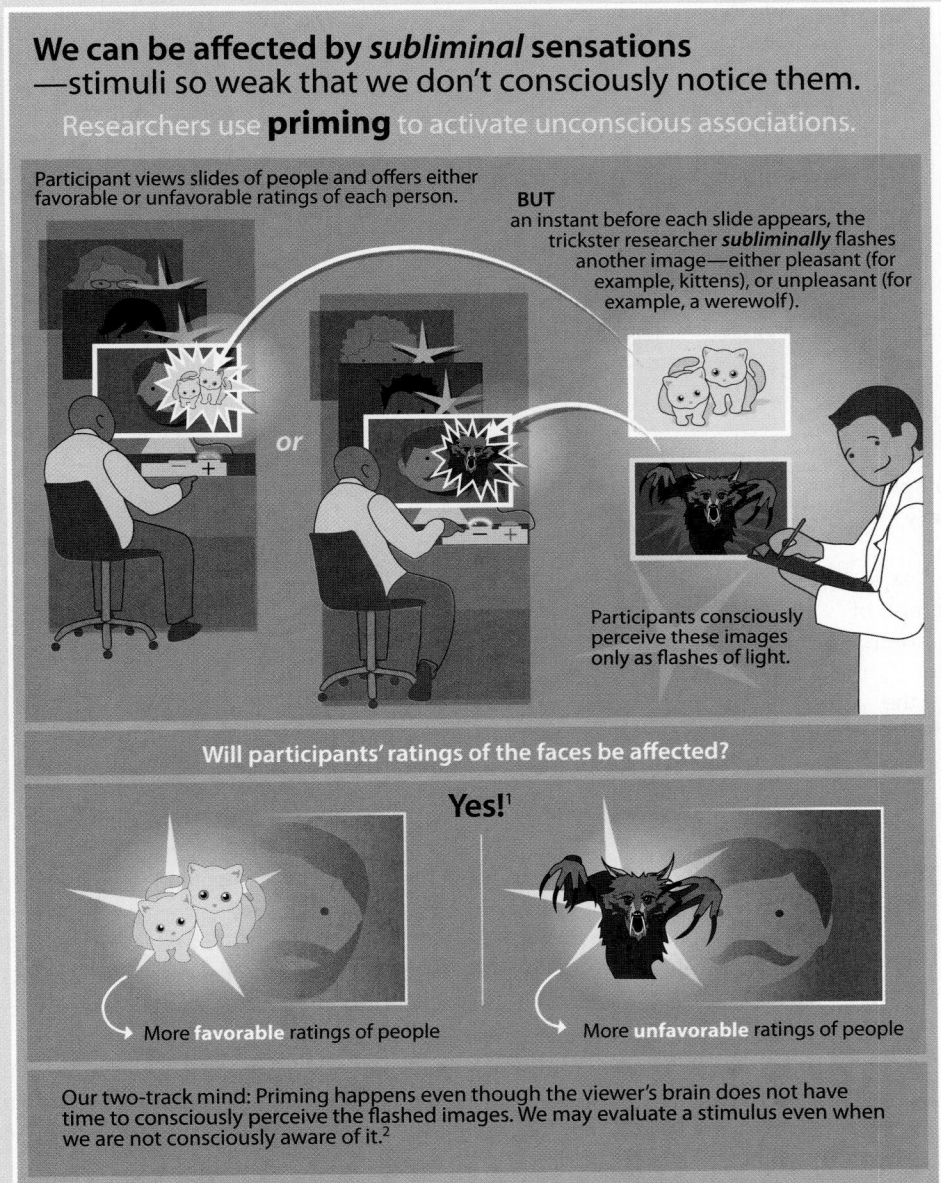

We can be affected by *subliminal* sensations
—stimuli so weak that we don't consciously notice them.

Researchers use **priming** to activate unconscious associations.

Participant views slides of people and offers either favorable or unfavorable ratings of each person.

BUT
an instant before each slide appears, the trickster researcher *subliminally* flashes another image—either pleasant (for example, kittens), or unpleasant (for example, a werewolf).

Participants consciously perceive these images only as flashes of light.

Will participants' ratings of the faces be affected?

Yes![1]

→ More **favorable** ratings of people

→ More **unfavorable** ratings of people

Our two-track mind: Priming happens even though the viewer's brain does not have time to consciously perceive the flashed images. We may evaluate a stimulus even when we are not consciously aware of it.[2]

So, we can be *primed,* but **can we be *persuaded* by subliminal stimuli**, for example to lose weight, stop smoking, or improve our memory?

Quiz 100%

Audio and video messages subliminally (without recipients' conscious awareness) announce:

"I am thin,"
"Cigarette smoke tastes bad,"
and
"I do well on tests. I have total recall of information."

Results from 16 experiments[3] showed no powerful, enduring influence on behavior. Not one of the recordings helped more than a placebo, which works only because we believe it will.

1. Krosnick et al., 1992.   2. Ferguson & Zayas, 2009.   3. Greenwald et al., 1991, 1992.

we still refer to it as **Weber's law:** For an average person to perceive a difference, two stimuli must differ by a constant minimum *percentage* (not a constant *amount*). The exact percentage varies, depending on the stimulus. Two lights, for example, must differ in intensity by 8 percent. Two objects must differ in weight by 2 percent. And two tones must differ in frequency by only 0.3 percent (Teghtsoonian, 1971).

🔒 **RETRIEVE IT** • • •   *ANSWERS IN APPENDIX E*

RI-2 Using sound as your example, explain how these concepts differ: *absolute threshold, subliminal stimulation,* and *difference threshold.*

priming the activation, often unconsciously, of certain associations, thus predisposing one's perception, memory, or response.

Weber's law the principle that, to be perceived as different, two stimuli must differ by a constant minimum percentage (rather than a constant amount).

sensory adaptation diminished sensitivity as a consequence of constant stimulation.

perceptual set a mental predisposition to perceive one thing and not another.

SENSORY ADAPTATION

LOQ 16-5 What is the function of sensory adaptation?

Sitting down on the bus, you are overwhelmed by your seatmate's heavy perfume. You wonder how she endures it, but within minutes you no longer notice. **Sensory adaptation** has come to your rescue. When constantly exposed to an unchanging stimulus, we become less aware of it because our nerve cells fire less frequently. (To experience sensory adaptation, roll up your sleeve. You will feel it—but only for a few moments.)

Why, then, if we stare at an object without flinching, does it *not* vanish from sight? Because, unnoticed by us, our eyes are always moving. This continual flitting from one spot to another ensures that stimulation on the eyes' receptors continually changes (**FIGURE 16.4**).

FIGURE 16.4

THE JUMPY EYE Our gaze jumps from one spot to another every third of a second or so, as eye-tracking equipment illustrated as a person looked at this photograph of Edinburgh's Princes Street Gardens (Henderson, 2007). The circles represent visual fixations, and the numbers indicate the time of fixation in milliseconds (300 milliseconds = 3/10ths of a second).

© John M. Henderson

"We need above all to know about changes; no one wants or needs to be reminded 16 hours a day that his shoes are on." —Neuroscientist David Hubel (1979)

What if we actually could stop our eyes from moving? Would sights seem to vanish, as odors do? To find out, psychologists have devised ingenious instruments that maintain a constant image on the eye's inner surface. Imagine that we have fitted a volunteer, Mary, with such an instrument—a miniature projector mounted on a contact lens (**FIGURE 16.5a**). When Mary's eye moves, the image from the projector moves as well. So everywhere that Mary looks, the scene is sure to go.

If we project images through this instrument, what will Mary see? At first, she will see the complete image. But within a few seconds, as her sensory system begins to fatigue, things get weird. Bit by bit, the image vanishes, only to reappear and then disappear—often in fragments (Figure 16.5b).

Although sensory adaptation reduces our sensitivity, it offers an important benefit: freedom to focus on informative changes in our environment. Technology companies

FIGURE 16.5

SENSORY ADAPTATION: NOW YOU SEE IT, NOW YOU DON'T! (a) A projector mounted on a contact lens makes the projected image move with the eye. (b) Initially, the person sees the stabilized image. But thanks to sensory adaptation, her eye soon becomes accustomed to the unchanging stimulus. Rather than the full image, she begins to see fragments fading and reappearing.

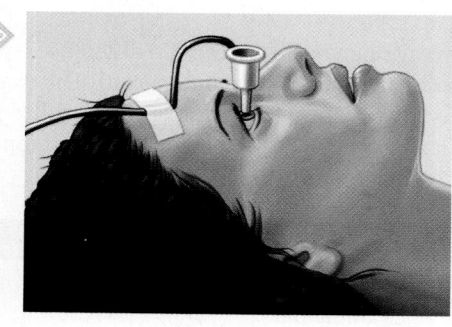

(a)

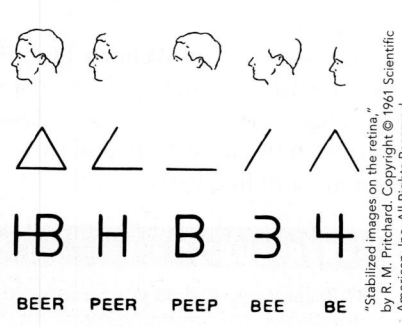

BEER   PEER   PEEP   BEE   BE

(b)

understand the attention-grabbing power of changing stimulation: New tweets, likes, snapchats, breaking news stories, and other background chatter popping up on our phones are hard to ignore. "There's always another hashtag to click on," one of Instagram's founding engineers told psychologist Adam Alter (2017). "Then it takes on its own life, like an organism, and people can become obsessive." If we're performing other tasks, these intrusions can harm our performance (Stothart et al., 2015).

Sensory adaptation even influences our perception of emotions. By creating a 50-50 morphed blend of an angry face and a scared face (**FIGURE 16.6b**), researchers showed that our visual system adapts to a static facial expression (as in Figure 16.6a or Figure 16.6c) by becoming less responsive to it (Butler et al., 2008). The effect is created by our brain, not our retinas. We know this because the illusion also works when we view either image (a) or (c) with one eye, and image (b) with the other eye.

The point to remember: Our sensory system is alert to novelty; bore it with repetition and it frees our attention for more important things. We see this principle again and again: *We perceive the world not exactly as it is, but as it is useful for us to perceive it.*

ASK YOURSELF

What types of sensory adaptation have you experienced in the last 24 hours?

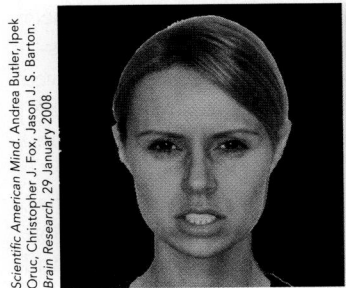
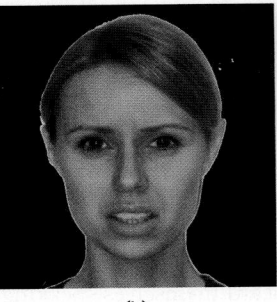
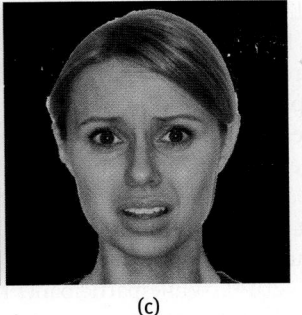

(a)   (b)   (c)

Scientific American Mind, Andrea Butler, Ipek Oruc, Christopher J. Fox, Jason J. S. Barton. Brain Research, 29 January 2008.

 FIGURE 16.6

EMOTION ADAPTATION Gaze at the angry face in image (a) for 20 to 30 seconds, then look at the face in image (b)—looks scared, yes? Then gaze at the scared face in image (c) for 20 to 30 seconds, before returning to the image (b) face—now looks angry, yes? (From Butler et al., 2008.)

🔒 **RETRIEVE IT** • • •   *ANSWERS IN APPENDIX E*

RI-3 Why is it that after wearing shoes for a while, you cease to notice them (until questions like this draw your attention back to them)?

 # PERCEPTUAL SET

LOQ 16-6 How do our expectations, contexts, motivation, and emotions influence our perceptions?

To see is to believe. As we less fully appreciate, to believe is to see. Through experience, we come to expect certain results. Those expectations may give us a **perceptual set**—a set of mental tendencies and assumptions that affects, top-down, what we hear, taste, feel, and see.

Consider **FIGURE 16.7**: Is image (b) an old or young woman? What we see in such a drawing can be influenced by first looking at either image (a) or image (b), which are both unambiguous versions (Boring, 1930). Likewise, in **FIGURE 16.8**, our expectations affect our perception.

The New Yorker Collection, 2002, Leo Cullum from cartoonbank.com

(a)   (b)   (c)

W. E. Hill, 1915

 FIGURE 16.7

PERCEPTUAL SET Show a friend either image (a) or image (c). Then show image (b) and ask, "What do you see?" Whether your friend reports seeing an old woman's face or young woman's profile may depend on which of the other two drawings was viewed first. In each of those images, the meaning is clear, and it will establish perceptual expectations.

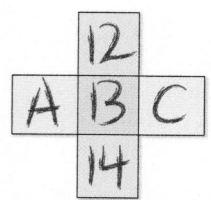

There
Are Two
Errors in The
The Title Of
This Book
—Title of a book by Robert M. Martin, 2011

In the note above, did you perceive what you expected in this title—and miss the errors? If you are still puzzled, see explanation below.[1]

"We hear and apprehend only what we already half know." —Henry David Thoreau, *Journal*, 1860

FIGURE 16.8

BELIEVING IS SEEING
What do you perceive? Is this Nessie, the Loch Ness monster, or a log?

Keystone/Getty Images

Everyday examples abound of perceptual set—of "mind over mind." In 1972, a British newspaper published unretouched photographs of a "monster" in Scotland's Loch Ness—"the most amazing pictures ever taken," stated the paper. If this information creates in you the same expectations it did in most of the paper's readers, you, too, will see the monster in a similar photo in Figure 16.8. But when a skeptical researcher approached the original photos with different expectations, he saw a curved tree limb—as had others the day that photo was shot (Campbell, 1986). What a difference a new perceptual set makes.

Perceptual set also affects what we hear—"stuffy nose" or "stuff he knows"? Consider the kindly airline pilot who, on a takeoff run, looked over at his sad co-pilot and said, "Cheer up." Expecting to hear the usual "Gear up," the co-pilot promptly raised the wheels—before they left the ground (Reason & Mycielska, 1982). Or ask the little boy who loved the prelude to U.S. baseball games when people rose to sing to him: "Jose, can you see?" Or tell people about a couple who suffered from their experience with some bad sects and (depending on what's on their mind) they may hear something quite different (bad sex).

Now consider this odd question: If you said one thing but heard yourself saying another, what would you think you said? To find out, a clever Swedish research team invited people to name a font color, such as saying "gray" when the word *green* appeared in a gray font (Lind et al., 2014). While participants heard themselves speaking over a noise-canceling headset, the wily experimenters occasionally substituted the participant's own previously recorded voice, such as saying "green" instead of "gray." Surprisingly, people usually missed the switch—and experienced the inserted word as self-produced. Again, hearing was believing.

Our expectations can also influence our taste perceptions. In one experiment, preschool children, by a 6-to-1 margin, thought french fries tasted better when served in a McDonald's bag rather than a plain white bag (Robinson et al., 2007). Another experiment invited campus bar patrons at the Massachusetts Institute of Technology to sample free beer (Lee et al., 2006). When researchers added a few drops of vinegar to a brand-name beer and called it "MIT brew," the tasters preferred it—unless they had been told they were drinking vinegar-laced beer. In that case, they expected, and usually experienced, a worse taste.

What determines our perceptual set? Through experience we form concepts, or *schemas,* that organize and interpret unfamiliar information. Our preexisting schemas for monsters and tree trunks influence how we apply top-down processing to interpret ambiguous sensations.

In everyday life, stereotypes about gender (another instance of perceptual set) can color perception. Without the obvious cues of pink or blue, people will struggle over whether to call the new baby "he" or "she." But told an infant is "David," people (especially children) have perceived "him" as bigger and stronger than when the same infant was called "Diana" (Stern & Karraker, 1989). Some differences, it seems, exist merely in the eyes of their beholders.

🔒 RETRIEVE IT • • •

ANSWERS IN APPENDIX E

RI-4 Does *perceptual set* involve bottom-up or top-down processing? Why?

CONTEXT, MOTIVATION, AND EMOTION

Perceptual set influences how we interpret stimuli. But our immediate context, and the motivation and emotion we bring to a situation, also affect our interpretations.

CONTEXT Social psychologist Lee Ross invited us to recall our own perceptions in different contexts: "Ever notice that when you're driving you hate pedestrians,

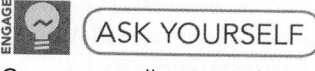
1. The title's first error is its repeated "The." Its ironic second error is its misstatement that there are two errors, when there is only one.

 FIGURE 16.9

CULTURE AND CONTEXT EFFECTS What is above the woman's head? In one classic study, most rural East Africans questioned said the woman was balancing a metal box or can on her head (a typical way to carry water at that time). They also perceived the family as sitting under a tree. Westerners, used to running water and box-like houses with corners, were more likely to perceive the family as being indoors, with the woman sitting under a window (Gregory & Gombrich, 1973).

the way they saunter through the crosswalk, almost daring you to hit them, but when you're walking you hate drivers?" (Jaffe, 2004).

Some other examples of the power of context:

- When holding a gun, people become more likely to perceive another person as gun-toting—a phenomenon that has led to the shooting of some unarmed people who were actually holding their phone or wallet (Witt & Brockmole, 2012).

- Imagine hearing a noise interrupted by the words "eel is on the wagon." Likely, you would actually perceive the first word as *wheel*. Given "eel is on the orange," you would more likely hear *peel*. In each case, the context creates an expectation that, top-down, influences our perception (Grossberg, 1995).

- Cultural context helps inform our perceptions, so it's not surprising that people from different cultures view things differently, as in **FIGURE 16.9**.

- How is the woman in **FIGURE 16.10** feeling? The context provided in **FIGURE 16.11** will leave no doubt.

MOTIVATION Motives give us energy as we work toward a goal. Like context, they can bias our interpretations of neutral stimuli:

- Desirable objects, such as a water bottle viewed by a thirsty person, seem closer than they really are (Balcetis & Dunning, 2010). This perceptual bias energizes our going for it.

- A to-be-climbed hill can seem steeper when we are carrying a heavy backpack, and a walking destination further away when we are feeling tired (Burrow et al., 2016; Philbeck & Witt, 2015; Proffitt, 2006a,b). Going on a diet can lighten our biological "backpack" (Taylor-Covill & Eves, 2016). When heavy people lose weight, hills and stairs no longer seem so steep.

- A softball appears bigger when you are hitting well, as researchers observed after asking players to choose a circle the size of the ball they had just hit well or poorly (Witt & Proffitt, 2005). There's also a reciprocal phenomenon: Seeing a target as bigger—as happens when athletes focus directly on a target—improves performance (Witt et al., 2012).

EMOTION Other clever experiments have demonstrated that emotions can shove our perceptions in one direction or another:

- Hearing sad music can predispose people to perceive a sad meaning in spoken homophonic words—*mourning* rather than *morning*, *die* rather than *dye*, *pain* rather than *pane* (Halberstadt et al., 1995).

- A hill seems less steep to people who feel others understand them (Oishi et al., 2013).

Craig Klomparens/Hope College

 FIGURE 16.10

WHAT EMOTION IS THIS? (See Figure 16.11.)

"When you're hitting the ball, it comes at you looking like a grapefruit. When you're not, it looks like a black-eyed pea." —Former Major League Baseball player George Scott

HEARING HYPE Why do people pay millions of dollars for old Italian violins? They believe the sound quality is unmatched. Unfortunately, a recent study showed that, under blind conditions, listeners generally preferred the sound of inexpensive, modern violins over expensive, old Italian violins (Fritz et al., 2017).

- When angry, people more often perceive neutral objects as guns (Baumann & DeSteno, 2010).

- When made to feel mildly upset by subliminal exposure to a scowling face, people perceive a neutral face as less attractive and less likeable (Anderson et al., 2012).

Emotions and motives color our *social* perceptions, too. People more often perceive solitary confinement, sleep deprivation, and cold temperatures as "torture" when experiencing a small dose of such themselves (Nordgren et al., 2011). Spouses who feel loved and appreciated perceive less threat in stressful marital events—"He's just having a bad day" (Murray et al., 2003).

The point to remember: Much of what we perceive comes not just from what's "out there," but also from what's behind our eyes and between our ears. Through top-down processing, our experiences, assumptions, expectations—and even our context, motivation, and emotions—can shape and color our views of reality.

FIGURE 16.11 CONTEXT MAKES CLEARER The Hope College volleyball team celebrates its national championship winning moment.

🔒 REVIEW BASIC CONCEPTS OF SENSATION AND PERCEPTION

⤵ Learning Objectives

TEST YOURSELF Answer these repeated Learning Objective Questions on your own (before checking the answers in Appendix D) to improve your retention of the concepts (McDaniel et al., 2009, 2015).

16-1 What are *sensation* and *perception*? What do we mean by *bottom-up processing* and *top-down processing*?

16-2 What three steps are basic to all our sensory systems?

16-3 How do *absolute thresholds* and *difference thresholds* differ?

16-4 How are we affected by subliminal stimuli?

16-5 What is the function of sensory adaptation?

16-6 How do our expectations, contexts, motivation, and emotions influence our perceptions?

⤵ Terms and Concepts to Remember

TEST YOURSELF Write down the definition yourself, then check your answer on the referenced page.

sensation, **p. 190**

sensory receptors, **p. 190**

perception, **p. 190**

bottom-up processing, **p. 190**

top-down processing, **p. 190**

transduction, **p. 191**

absolute threshold, **p. 191**

signal detection theory, **p. 191**

subliminal, **p. 192**

difference threshold, **p. 192**

priming, **p. 193**

Weber's law, **p. 193**

sensory adaptation, **p. 194**

perceptual set, **p. 194**

⤵ Experience the Testing Effect

TEST YOURSELF Answer the following questions on your own first, then check your answers in Appendix E.

1. Sensation is to _____ as perception is to
   _____.

   a. absolute threshold; difference threshold

   b. bottom-up processing; top-down processing

   c. interpretation; detection

   d. grouping; priming

2. The process by which we organize and interpret sensory information is called _____.

3. Subliminal stimuli are
   a. too weak to be processed by the brain.
   b. consciously perceived more than 50 percent of the time.
   c. strong enough to affect our behavior at least 75 percent of the time.
   d. below our absolute threshold for conscious awareness.

4. Another term for *difference threshold* is the

   _____ _____ _____ .

5. Weber's law states that for a difference to be perceived, two stimuli must differ by
   a. a fixed or constant energy amount.
   b. a constant minimum percentage.

   c. a constantly changing amount.
   d. more than 7 percent.

6. Sensory adaptation helps us focus on
   a. visual stimuli.
   b. auditory stimuli.
   c. constant features of the environment.
   d. important changes in the environment.

7. Our perceptual set influences what we perceive. This mental tendency reflects our
   a. experiences, assumptions, and expectations.
   b. sensory adaptation.
   c. priming ability.
   d. difference thresholds.

Continue testing yourself with ▲ **LearningCurve** or ▲ **Achieve Read & Practice** to learn and remember most effectively.

⒘ Vision: Sensory and Perceptual Processing

LIGHT ENERGY AND EYE STRUCTURES

LOQ 17-1 What are the characteristics of the energy that we see as visible light? What structures in the eye help focus that energy?

Our eyes receive light energy and **transduce** (transform) it into neural messages. From this neural input, our brain—in one of life's greatest wonders—then creates what we consciously see. How does such a taken-for-granted yet extraordinary thing happen?

The Stimulus Input: Light Energy

When you look at a bright red tulip, the stimuli striking your eyes are not particles of the color red but pulses of electromagnetic energy that your visual system *perceives* as red. What we see as visible light is but a thin slice of the wide spectrum of electromagnetic energy, ranging from imperceptibly short gamma waves to the long waves of radio transmission (**FIGURE 17.1**). Other portions are visible to other animals. Bees, for instance, cannot see what we perceive as red but can see ultraviolet light.

Light travels in waves, and the shape of those waves influences what we see. Light's **wavelength** is the distance from one wave peak to the next (**FIGURE 17.2a**). Wavelength determines **hue,** the color we experience, such as a tulip's red petals or green leaves. A light wave's *amplitude*, or height, determines its **intensity**—the amount of energy the wave contains. Intensity influences brightness (Figure 17.2b).

To understand *how* we transform physical energy into color and meaning, we need to know more about vision's window—the eye.

The Eye

Light enters the eye through the *cornea*, which bends light to help provide focus (**FIGURE 17.3**). The light then passes through the *pupil*, a small adjustable opening. Surrounding the pupil and controlling its size is the *iris*, a colored muscle that dilates or constricts in response to light intensity. Each iris is so distinctive that an iris-scanning machine can confirm your identity.

transduction conversion of one form of energy into another. In sensation, the transforming of stimulus energies, such as sights, sounds, and smells, into neural impulses our brain can interpret.

wavelength the distance from the peak of one light wave or sound wave to the peak of the next. Electromagnetic wavelengths vary from the short gamma waves to the long pulses of radio transmission.

hue the dimension of color that is determined by the wavelength of light; what we know as the color names *blue, green,* and so forth.

intensity the amount of energy in a light wave or sound wave, which influences what we perceive as brightness or loudness. Intensity is determined by the wave's amplitude (height).

FIGURE 17.1

THE WAVELENGTHS WE SEE What we see as light is only a tiny slice of a wide spectrum of electromagnetic energy, which ranges from gamma rays as short as the diameter of an atom to radio waves over a mile long. The wavelengths visible to the human eye (shown enlarged) extend from the shorter waves of blue-violet light to the longer waves of red light.

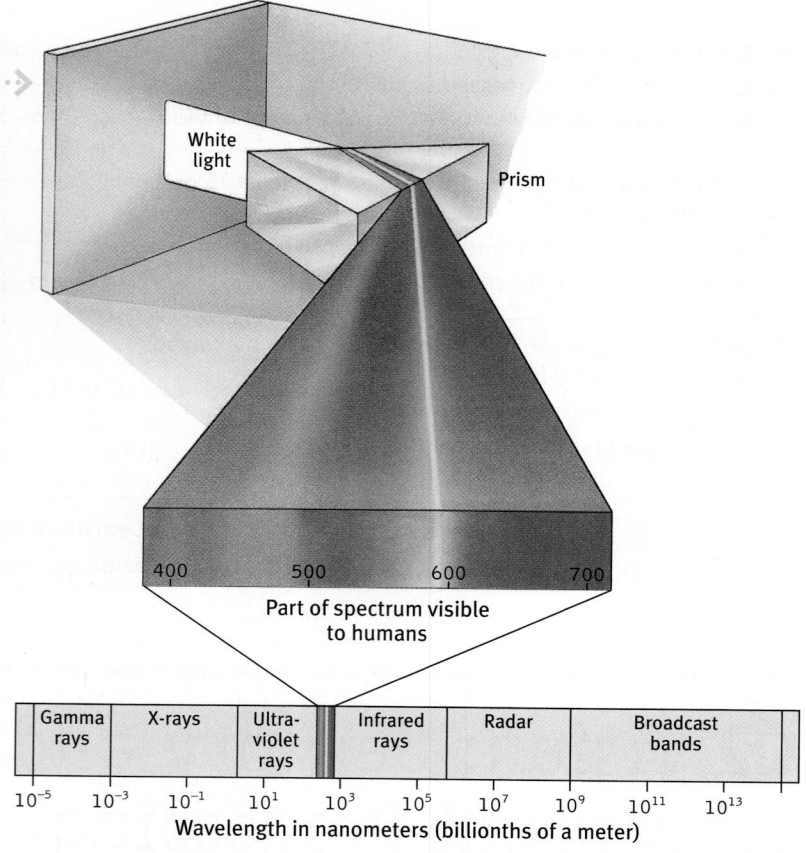

FIGURE 17.2

THE PHYSICAL PROPERTIES OF WAVES (a) Waves vary in *wavelength* (the distance between successive peaks). *Frequency*, the number of complete wavelengths that can pass a point in a given time, depends on the wavelength. The shorter the wavelength, the higher the frequency. Wavelength determines the perceived *color* of light. (b) Waves also vary in amplitude (the height from peak to trough). Wave *amplitude* influences the perceived *brightness* of colors.

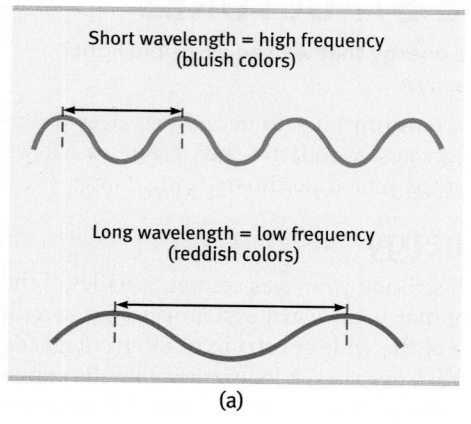
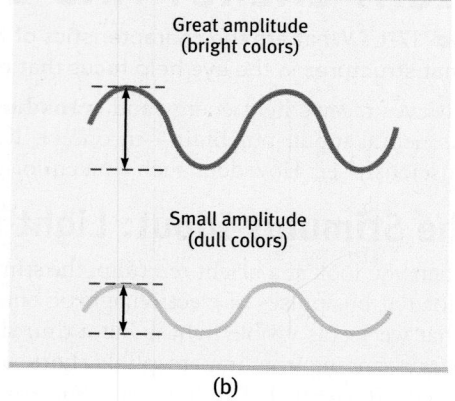

(a)   (b)

FIGURE 17.3

THE EYE Light rays reflected from a candle pass through the cornea, pupil, and lens. The curvature and thickness of the lens change to bring nearby or distant objects into focus on the retina. Rays from the top of the candle strike the bottom of the retina, and those from the left side of the candle strike the right side of the retina. The candle's image on the retina thus appears upside down and reversed.

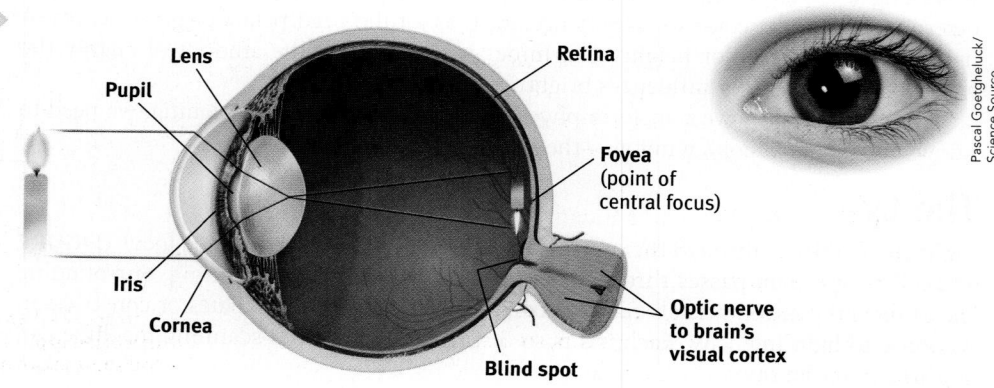

Pascal Goetgheluck/ Science Source

The iris responds to your cognitive and emotional states. Imagine a sunny sky and your iris will constrict, making your pupil smaller; imagine a dark room and it will dilate (Laeng & Sulutvedt, 2014). The iris also constricts when you feel disgust or you are about to answer *No* to a question (de Gee et al., 2014; Goldinger & Papesh, 2012). And when you're feeling amorous, your telltale dilated pupils and resulting dark eyes subtly signal your interest.

After passing through your pupil, light hits the transparent *lens* in your eye. The lens then focuses the light rays into an image on your **retina,** a multilayered tissue on the eyeball's sensitive inner surface. To focus the rays, the lens changes its curvature and thickness, in a process called **accommodation.** If the lens focuses the image on a point in front of the retina, you see near objects clearly but not distant objects. This nearsightedness—*myopia*—can be remedied with glasses, contact lenses, or surgery.

For centuries, scientists knew that an image of a candle passing through a small opening will cast an inverted mirror image on a dark wall behind. If the image passing through the pupil casts this sort of upside-down image on the retina, as in Figure 17.3, how can we see the world right side up? Eventually, the answer became clear: The retina doesn't "see" a whole image. Rather, its millions of receptor cells convert particles of light energy into neural impulses and forward those to the brain. *There,* the impulses are reassembled into a perceived, upright-seeming image. And along the way, visual information processing percolates through progressively more abstract levels, all at astonishing speed. Consider: As a baseball pitcher's fastball approaches home plate, the light signals work their way from the batter's retina to the visual cortex, which then informs the motor cortex, which then sends out orders to contract the muscles—all within the 4/10ths of a second that the ball is in flight.

retina the light-sensitive inner surface of the eye, containing the receptor rods and cones plus layers of neurons that begin the processing of visual information.

accommodation the process by which the eye's lens changes shape to focus near or far objects on the retina.

rods retinal receptors that detect black, white, and gray, and are sensitive to movement; necessary for peripheral and twilight vision, when cones don't respond.

cones retinal receptors that are concentrated near the center of the retina and that function in daylight or in well-lit conditions. Cones detect fine detail and give rise to color sensations.

optic nerve the nerve that carries neural impulses from the eye to the brain.

blind spot the point at which the optic nerve leaves the eye, creating a "blind" spot because no receptor cells are located there.

INFORMATION PROCESSING IN THE EYE AND BRAIN

The Eye-to-Brain Pathway

LOQ 17-2 How do the rods and cones process information, and what is the path information travels from the eye to the brain?

Imagine that you could follow behind a single light-energy particle after it entered your eye. First, you would thread your way through the retina's sparse outer layer of cells. Then, reaching the back of your eye, you would encounter its buried receptor cells, the **rods** and **cones** (**FIGURE 17.4**). There, you would see the light energy trigger chemical changes. That chemical reaction would spark neural signals in nearby *bipolar cells.* You could then watch the bipolar cells activate neighboring *ganglion cells,* whose axons twine together like the strands of a rope to form the **optic nerve.** After a momentary stopover at the thalamus, the information would fly on to the final destination, your visual cortex, in the occipital lobe at the back of your brain.

The optic nerve is an information highway from the eye to the brain. This nerve can send nearly 1 million messages at once through its nearly 1 million ganglion fibers. (The auditory nerve, which enables hearing, carries much less information through its mere 30,000 fibers.) We pay a small price for this high-speed connection, however. Your eye has a **blind spot,** with no receptor cells, where the optic nerve leaves the eye (**FIGURE 17.5**). Close one eye and you won't see a black hole, however. Without seeking your approval, your brain fills in the hole.

FIGURE 17.4
THE RETINA'S REACTION TO LIGHT

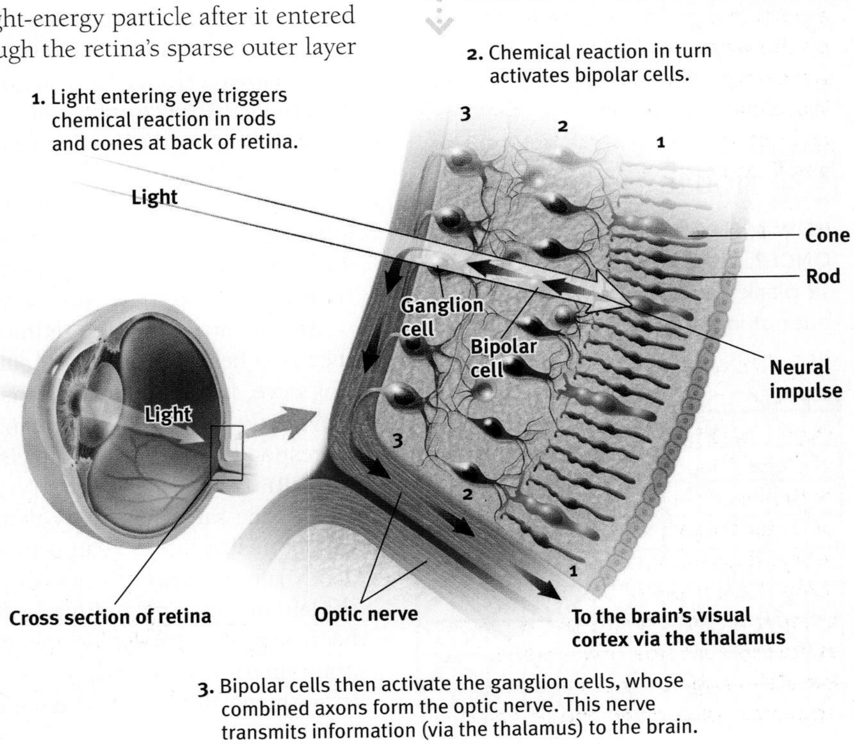

2. Chemical reaction in turn activates bipolar cells.

1. Light entering eye triggers chemical reaction in rods and cones at back of retina.

Light

Cone

Rod

Ganglion cell

Bipolar cell

Neural impulse

Light

Cross section of retina

Optic nerve

To the brain's visual cortex via the thalamus

3. Bipolar cells then activate the ganglion cells, whose combined axons form the optic nerve. This nerve transmits information (via the thalamus) to the brain.

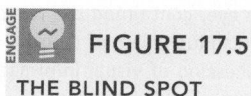

ENGAGE

FIGURE 17.5

THE BLIND SPOT

🔒 RETRIEVE IT • • •

RI-1 There are no receptor cells where the optic nerve leaves the eye. This creates a blind spot in your vision. To demonstrate, close your left eye, look at the spot above, and move your face away until one of the cars disappears. (Which one do you predict it will be?) Repeat with your right eye closed—and note that now the other car disappears. Can you explain why?

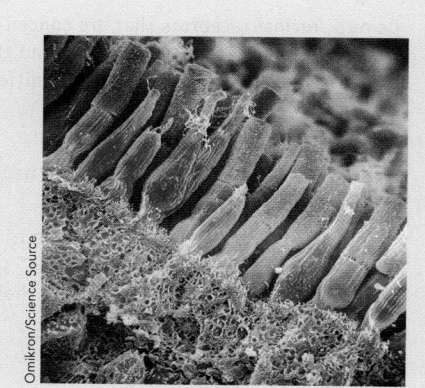

Omikron/Science Source

RETAIN

🔒 **TABLE 17.1**

Receptors in the Human Eye: Rod-Shaped Rods and Cone-Shaped Cones

	Cones	Rods
Number	6 million	120 million
Location in retina	Center	Periphery
Sensitivity in dim light	Low	High
Color sensitivity	High	Low
Detail sensitivity	High	Low

Rods and cones are our eyes' light-sensitive *photoreceptors*. They differ in where they're found and what they do (**TABLE 17.1**). *Cones* cluster in and around the **fovea,** the retina's area of central focus (Figure 17.3). Many cones have their own hotline to the brain: One cone transmits its message to a single bipolar cell, which relays the message to the visual cortex (where a large area receives input from the fovea). These direct connections preserve the cones' precise information, making them better able to detect fine detail. Although cones can detect white, they also enable you to perceive color (Sabesan et al., 2016). But in dim light, they become unresponsive, so you see no colors.

ENGAGE Unlike cones, which cluster in the center of your retina, *rods* are located around the retina's outer regions. Rods remain sensitive in dim light, and they enable black-and-white vision. Rods have no hotline to the brain. If cones are soloists, rods perform as a chorus. Several rods pool their faint energy output and funnel it onto a single bipolar cell, which sends the combined message to your brain. Cones and rods each provide a special sensitivity—cones to detail and color, and rods to faint light and peripheral motion. Stop for a minute and experience this rod-cone difference. Pick a word in this sentence and stare directly at it, focusing its image on the cones in your fovea. Notice that words a few inches off to the side appear blurred? Their image is striking your retina's outer regions, where rods predominate. Thus, when you drive or bike, rods help you detect a car in your peripheral vision well before you perceive its details. And in **FIGURE 17.6**, which has 12 black dots, you can see barely two at a time, with your brain filling in the less distinct peripheral input (Kitaoka, 2016, adapting Ninio & Stevens, 2000).

When you enter a darkened theater or turn off the light at night, your pupils dilate to allow more light to reach your retina. Your eyes adapt, but fully adapting typically takes 20 minutes or more. This period of dark adaptation matches the average natural twilight transition between the Sun's setting and darkness. How wonderfully made we are.

At the entry level, the retina's neural layers don't just pass along electrical impulses; they also help to encode and analyze sensory information. (The third neural layer in a frog's eye, for example, contains those "bug detector" cells that fire only in response to moving fly-like stimuli.) In human eyes, any given retinal area relays its information to a corresponding location in the visual cortex, in the occipital lobe at the back of your brain (**FIGURE 17.7**).

ENGAGE

FIGURE 17.6

HOW MANY DOTS CAN YOU SEE AT ONCE? Look at or near any of the 12 black dots and you can see them, but not in your peripheral vision.

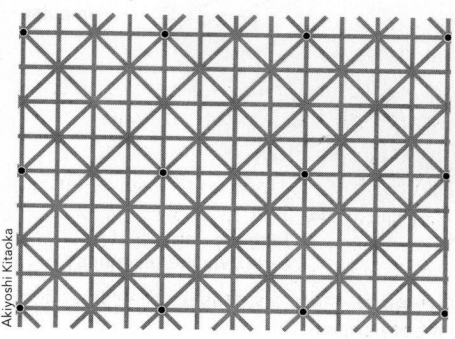

Akiyoshi Kitaoka

ENGAGE The same sensitivity that enables retinal cells to fire messages can lead them to misfire, as you can demonstrate. Turn your eyes to the left, close them, and then gently rub the right side of your right eyelid with your fingertip. Note the patch of light to the left, moving as your finger moves. Why do you see light? Why at the left? This happens because your retinal cells are so responsive that even pressure triggers them. But your brain interprets their firing as light. Moreover, it interprets the light as coming from the left—the normal direction of light that activates the right side of the retina.

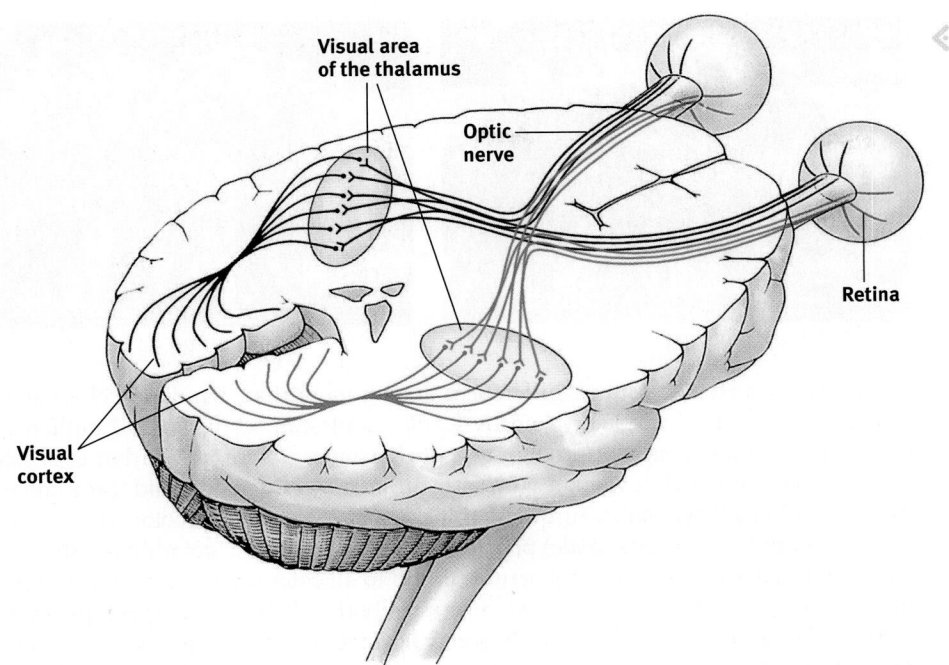

Visual area
of the thalamus

Optic
nerve

Retina

Visual
cortex

FIGURE 17.7

PATHWAY FROM THE EYES TO THE VISUAL CORTEX Ganglion axons forming the optic nerve run to the thalamus, where they synapse with neurons that run to the visual cortex.

Kruglov_Orda/Shutterstock

🔒 **RETRIEVE IT** • • •   *ANSWERS IN APPENDIX E*

RI-2 Some nocturnal animals, such as toads, mice, rats, and bats, have impressive night vision thanks to having many more _____ (rods/cones) than _____ (rods/cones) in their retinas. These creatures probably have very poor _____ (color/black-and-white) vision.

RI-3 Cats are able to open their _____ much wider than we can, which allows more light into their eyes so they can see better at night.

Color Processing

LOQ 17-3 How do we perceive color in the world around us?

We talk as though objects possess color: "A tomato is red." Recall the old question, "If a tree falls in the forest and no one hears it, does it make a sound?" We can ask the same of color: If no one sees the tomato, is it red?

The answer is *No*. First, the tomato is everything *but* red, because it *rejects* (reflects) the long wavelengths of red. Second, the tomato's color is our mental construction. As Sir Isaac Newton (1704) noted, "The [light] rays are not colored." Like all aspects of vision, our perception of color resides not in the object itself but in the theater of our brain, as evidenced by our dreaming in color.

One of vision's most basic and intriguing mysteries is how we see the world in color. How, from the light energy striking the retina, does our brain construct our experience of such a multitude of colors?

Modern detective work on the mystery of color vision began in the nineteenth century, when Hermann von Helmholtz built on the insights of an English physicist, Thomas Young. They knew that any color can be created by combining the light waves of three primary colors—red, green, and blue. So Young and von Helmholtz formed a hypothesis: The eye must therefore have three corresponding types of color receptors.

Years later, researchers confirmed the **Young-Helmholtz trichromatic (three-color) theory.** By measuring the response of various cones to different color stimuli, they confirmed that the retina does indeed have three types of color receptors, each especially sensitive to the wavelengths of red, green, and blue. When light stimulates combinations of these cones, we see other colors. For example, the retina has no separate receptors especially sensitive to yellow. But when red and green wavelengths stimulate both red-sensitive and green-sensitive cones, we see yellow.

ENGAGE 💡 **ASK YOURSELF**

Consider your activities in the last hour. Which of them relied on your rods? Which relied on your cones? How would these activities be different—or impossible—without these cells' different abilities?

"Only mind has sight and hearing; all things else are deaf and blind."
—Epicharmus, *Fragments*, 550 B.C.E.

fovea the central focal point in the retina, around which the eye's cones cluster.

Young-Helmholtz trichromatic (three-color) theory the theory that the retina contains three different types of color receptors—one most sensitive to red, one to green, one to blue—which, when stimulated in combination, can produce the perception of any color.

FIGURE 17.8

COLOR-DEFICIENT VISION The photo in image (a) shows how people with red-green deficiency perceived a 2015 Buffalo Bills versus New York Jets football game. "For the 8 percent of Americans like me that are red-green colorblind, this game is a nightmare to watch," tweeted one fan. "Everyone looks like they're on the same team," said another. The photo in image (b) shows how the game looked for those with normal color vision.

(a)

(b)

BEN SOLOMON/The New York Times/Redux Pictures

opponent-process theory the theory that opposing retinal processes (red-green, blue-yellow, white-black) enable color vision. For example, some cells are stimulated by green and inhibited by red; others are stimulated by red and inhibited by green.

feature detectors nerve cells in the brain's visual cortex that respond to specific features of the stimulus, such as shape, angle, or movement.

By one estimate, we can see differences among more than 1 million color variations (Neitz et al., 2001). Some lucky (mostly female) souls can see up to 100 million colors thanks to a genetic condition known as *tetrachromatic color vision* (Jordan et al., 2010). Asked to look at a leaf, a woman with tetrachromatic color vision said, "You might see dark green but I'll see violet, turquoise, blue. It's like a mosaic of color" (Ossola, 2014). Some other unlucky (mostly male) people—about 1 in 50—are "colorblind." Most people with color-deficient vision are not actually blind to all colors. They simply lack functioning red- or green-sensitive cones, or sometimes both. Their vision—perhaps unknown to them, because their lifelong vision *seems* normal—is monochromatic (one-color) or dichromatic (two-color) instead of trichromatic, making it impossible to distinguish the red and green in **FIGURE 17.8** (Boynton, 1979). Dogs, too, lack receptors for the wavelengths of red, giving them only limited, dichromatic color vision (Neitz et al., 1989).

But why do people blind to red and green often still see yellow? And why does yellow appear to be a pure color and not a mixture of red and green, the way purple is of red and blue? As physiologist Ewald Hering—a contemporary of von Helmholtz—noted, trichromatic theory leaves some parts of the color vision mystery unsolved.

Hering found a clue in *afterimages.* Stare at a green square for a while and then look at a white sheet of paper, and you will see red, green's *opponent color.* Stare at a yellow square and its opponent color, blue, will appear on the white paper. (To experience this, try the flag demonstration in **FIGURE 17.9**.) Hering formed another hypothesis: Color vision must involve two *additional* color processes, one responsible for red-versus-green perception, and one for blue-versus-yellow perception.

Indeed, a century later, researchers also confirmed Hering's hypothesis, now called the **opponent-process theory.** This concept is tricky, but here's the gist: Color vision depends on three sets of opposing retinal processes—*red-green, blue-yellow,* and *white-black.* As impulses travel to the visual cortex, some neurons in both the retina and the thalamus are turned "on" by red but turned "off" by green. Others are turned on by green but off by red (DeValois & DeValois, 1975). Like red and green marbles sent down a narrow tube, "red" and "green" messages cannot both travel at once. Red and green are thus opponents, so we see either red or green, not a reddish-green mixture. But red and blue travel in separate channels, so we *can* see a reddish-blue magenta.

So how does opponent-process theory help us understand negative afterimages, as in the flag demonstration? Here's the answer (for the green changing to red): First, you stared at green bars, which tired your green response. Then you stared at a white area. White contains all colors, including red. Because you had tired your green response, only the red part of the green-red pairing fired normally.

FIGURE 17.9

AFTERIMAGE EFFECT Stare at the center of the flag for a minute and then shift your eyes to the dot in the white space beside it. What do you see? (After tiring your neural response to black, green, and yellow, you should see their opponent colors.) Stare at a white wall and note how the size of the flag grows with the projection distance.

RETAIN

The present solution to the mystery of color vision is therefore roughly this: *Color processing occurs in two stages.*

1. The retina's red, green, and blue cones respond in varying degrees to different color stimuli, as the Young-Helmholtz trichromatic theory suggested.

2. The cones' responses are then processed by opponent-process cells, as Hering's theory proposed.

🔒 **RETRIEVE IT** • • •   *ANSWERS IN APPENDIX E*

RI-4 What are two key theories of color vision? Are they contradictory or complementary? Explain.

Feature Detection

LOQ 17-4 Where are feature detectors located, and what do they do?

Scientists once likened the brain to a movie screen on which the eye projected images. Then along came David Hubel and Torsten Wiesel (1979), who showed that our visual processing deconstructs visual images and then reassembles them. Hubel and Wiesel received a Nobel Prize for their work on **feature detectors,** nerve cells in the occipital lobe's visual cortex that respond to a scene's specific visual features—to particular edges, lines, angles, and movements.

Using microelectrodes, they had discovered that some neurons fired actively when cats were shown lines at one angle, while other neurons responded to lines at a different angle. They surmised that these specialized neurons, now known as feature detectors, receive information from individual ganglion cells in the retina. Feature detectors pass this specific information to other cortical areas, where teams of cells (*supercell clusters*) respond to more complex patterns.

For biologically important objects and events, monkey brains (and surely ours as well) have a "vast visual encyclopedia" distributed as specialized cells (Perrett et al., 1990, 1992, 1994). These cells respond to one type of stimulus, such as a specific gaze, head angle, posture, or body movement. Other supercell clusters integrate this information and fire only when the cues collectively indicate the direction of someone's attention and approach. This instant analysis, which aided our ancestors' survival, also helps a soccer player anticipate where to strike the ball, and a driver to anticipate a pedestrian's next movement.

One temporal lobe area by your right ear (**FIGURE 17.10**) enables you to perceive faces and, thanks to a specialized neural network, to recognize them from varied viewpoints (Connor, 2010). If stimulated in this *fusiform face area,* you might spontaneously see faces—as did the participant who reported to an experimenter that "You just turned into someone else. Your face metamorphosed" (Koch, 2015). If this face recognition region were damaged, you might recognize other forms and objects, but not familiar faces.

When researchers temporarily disrupt the brain's face-processing areas with magnetic pulses, people are unable to recognize faces. But they can still recognize other objects, such as houses, because the brain's face perception occurs separately from its object perception (McKone et al., 2007; Pitcher et al., 2007). Thus, functional MRI (fMRI) scans have shown different brain areas activating when people viewed varied objects (Downing et al., 2001). Brain activity is so specific that, with the help of brain scans, researchers can tell whether people are "looking at a shoe, a chair, or a face, based on the pattern of their brain activity" (Haxby, 2001).

ENGAGE

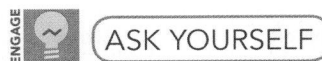

ASK YOURSELF

Does it surprise you to learn that colors don't "live" in the objects we perceive—that in fact, these objects are everything *but* the color we experience? If someone had asked you "Is grass green?" before you read this section, how would you have responded?

RETAIN

🔒 📺 **LaunchPad** For an interactive review of these color vision principles, visit **Topic Tutorial: PsychSim6, Colorful World.**

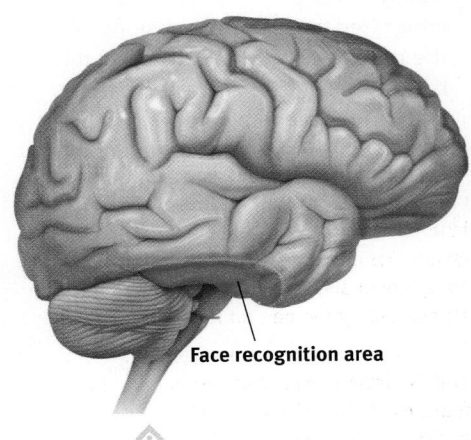

Face recognition area

FIGURE 17.10

FACE RECOGNITION PROCESSING In social animals such as humans, a large right temporal lobe area (shown here in a right-facing brain) is dedicated to the crucial task of face recognition.

SUPERCELLS SCORE In this 2017 National Hockey League game, Alex Ovechkin (in red) instantly processed visual information about the positions and movements of three opponents. By using his pattern-detecting supercells, Ovechkin somehow managed to get the puck into the net.

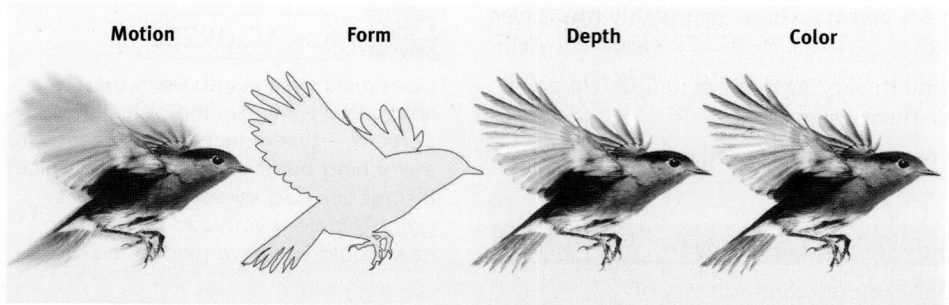

Motion	Form	Depth	Color

FIGURE 17.11

PARALLEL PROCESSING Studies of patients with brain damage suggest that the brain delegates the work of processing motion, form, depth, and color to different areas. After taking a scene apart, the brain integrates these subdimensions into the perceived image. How does the brain do this? The answer to this *binding problem* (how does the brain bind multiple sensory inputs into a single perception?) is the Holy Grail of vision research.

"I am . . . wonderfully made." —King David, Psalm 139:14

Parallel Processing

LOQ 17-5   How does the brain use parallel processing to construct visual perceptions?

Our brain achieves these and other remarkable feats by **parallel processing:** doing many things at once. To analyze a visual scene, the brain divides it into subdimensions—motion, form, depth, color—and works on each aspect simultaneously (**FIGURE 17.11**). We then construct our perceptions by integrating (*binding*) the separate but parallel work of these different visual teams (Livingstone & Hubel, 1988).

To recognize a face, your brain integrates information projected by your retinas to several visual cortex areas and compares it with stored information, thus enabling your fusiform face area to recognize the face: *Grandmother!* Scientists have debated whether this stored information is contained in a single cell or, more likely, distributed over a network of cells that build a facial image bit by bit. Some supercells—actually nicknamed *"grandmother cells"*—do appear to respond very selectively to 1 or 2 faces in 100 (Bowers, 2009; Quiroga et al., 2013). The whole face recognition process requires tremendous brain power: 30 percent of the cortex (10 times the brain area devoted to hearing).

Destroy or disable a neural workstation for a visual subtask, and something peculiar results, as happened to "Mrs. M." (Hoffman, 1998). After a stroke damaged areas near the rear of both sides of her brain, she could not perceive motion. People in a room seemed "suddenly here or there but I [had] not seen them moving." Pouring tea into a cup was a challenge because the fluid appeared frozen—she could not perceive it rising in the cup.

After stroke or surgery has damaged the brain's visual cortex, others have experienced *blindsight.* Shown a series of sticks, they report seeing nothing. Yet when asked to guess whether the sticks are vertical or horizontal, their visual intuition typically offers the correct response. When told, "You got them all right," they are astounded. There is, it seems, a second "mind"—a parallel processing system—operating unseen. These separate visual systems for perceiving and for acting illustrate once again the astonishing dual processing of our two-track mind.

🔁 **LaunchPad** For a 4-minute depiction of a blindsight patient, see the **Video— Blindsight: Seeing Without Awareness.**

* * *

Think about the wonders of visual processing. As you read these words, the letters reflect light rays onto your retina, which triggers a process that sends formless nerve impulses to several areas of your brain, which integrate the information and decode meaning. The amazing result: We have transferred information across time and space, from our minds to your mind (**FIGURE 17.12**). That all of this happens instantly, effortlessly, and continuously is indeed awesome. As Roger Sperry (1985) observed, the "insights of science give added, not lessened, reasons for awe, respect, and reverence."

RETAIN 🔒 ## FIGURE 17.12

A SIMPLIFIED SUMMARY OF VISUAL INFORMATION PROCESSING

Tom Walker/ Getty Images

| Scene | → | **Retinal processing:** Receptor rods and cones → bipolar cells → ganglion cells | → | **Feature detection:** Brain's detector cells respond to specific features—edges, lines, and angles | → | **Parallel processing:** Brain cell teams process combined information about motion, form, depth, and color | → | **Recognition:** Brain interprets the constructed image based on information from stored images— it's a tiger! |

RI-5 What is the rapid sequence of events that occurs when you see and recognize a friend?

PERCEPTUAL ORGANIZATION

LOQ 17-6 How did the Gestalt psychologists understand perceptual organization, and how do figure-ground and grouping principles contribute to our perceptions?

It's one thing to understand how we see colors and shapes. But how do we organize and interpret those sights so that they become *meaningful* perceptions—a rose in bloom, a familiar face, a sunset?

Early in the twentieth century, a group of German psychologists noticed that people who are given a cluster of sensations tend to organize them into a **gestalt,** a German word meaning a "form" or a "whole." As we look straight ahead, we cannot separate the perceived scene into our left and right fields of view (each as seen with one eye closed). Our conscious perception is, at every moment, a seamless scene—an integrated whole.

Consider **FIGURE 17.13:** The individual elements of this figure, called a *Necker cube,* are really nothing but eight blue circles, each containing three converging white lines. When we view these elements all together, however, we see a cube that sometimes reverses direction. This phenomenon nicely illustrates a favorite saying of Gestalt psychologists: *In perception, the whole may exceed the sum of its parts.*

Over the years, the Gestalt psychologists demonstrated many principles we use to organize our sensations into perceptions (Wagemans et al., 2012a,b). Underlying all of them is a fundamental truth: *Our brain does more than register information about the world.* Perception is not just opening a shutter and letting a picture print itself on the brain. We filter incoming information and *construct* perceptions. Mind matters.

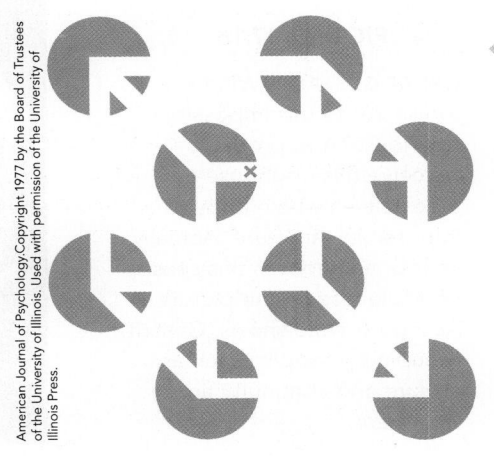

American Journal of Psychology. Copyright 1977 by the Board of Trustees of the University of Illinois. Used with permission of the University of Illinois Press.

Form Perception

Imagine designing a video-computer system that, like your eye-brain system, could recognize faces at a glance. What abilities would it need?

FIGURE AND GROUND To start with, the system would need to perceive **figure-ground**—to separate faces from their backgrounds. In our eye-brain system, this is our first perceptual task—perceiving any object (the *figure*) as distinct from its surroundings (the *ground*). As you read, the words are the figure; the white space is the ground. This perception applies to our hearing, too. As you hear voices at a party, the one you attend to becomes the figure; all others are part of the ground. Sometimes the same stimulus can trigger more than one perception. In **FIGURE 17.14,** the figure-ground relationship continually reverses. First we see the vase, then the faces, but we always organize the stimulus into a figure seen against a ground.

GROUPING Having discriminated figure from ground, we (and our video-computer system) must also organize the figure into a *meaningful*

---

parallel processing processing many aspects of a stimulus or problem at once.

gestalt an organized whole. Gestalt psychologists emphasized our tendency to integrate pieces of information into meaningful wholes.

figure-ground the organization of the visual field into objects (the *figures*) that stand out from their surroundings (the *ground*).

💡 **FIGURE 17.13**

A NECKER CUBE What do you see: circles with white lines, or a cube? If you stare at the cube, you may notice that it reverses location, moving the tiny X in the center from the front edge to the back. At times, the cube may seem to float forward, with circles behind it. At other times, the circles may become holes through which the cube appears, as though it were floating behind them. There is far more to perception than meets the eye. (From Bradley et al., 1976.)

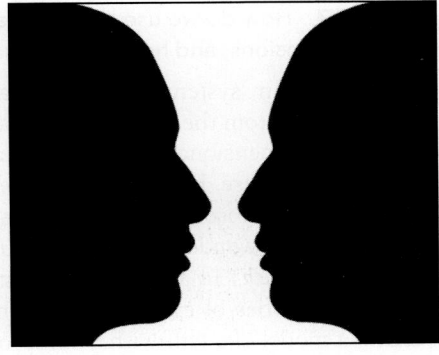

FIGURE 17.14
REVERSIBLE FIGURE AND GROUND

FIGURE 17.15

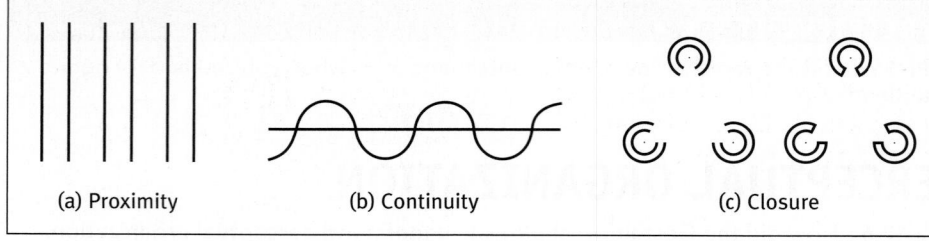

(a) Proximity   (b) Continuity   (c) Closure

THREE PRINCIPLES OF GROUPING
(a) Thanks to *proximity*, we group nearby figures together. We see not six separate lines, but three sets of two lines. (b) Through *continuity*, we perceive smooth, continuous patterns rather than discontinuous ones. This pattern could be a series of alternating semicircles, but we perceive it as two continuous lines—one wavy, one straight. (c) Using *closure*, we fill in gaps to create a complete, whole object. Thus we assume that the circles on the left are complete but partially blocked by the (illusory) triangle. Add nothing more than little line segments to close off the circles and your brain stops constructing a triangle.

form. Some basic features of a scene—such as color, movement, and light-dark contrast—we process instantly and automatically (Treisman, 1987). Our minds bring order and form to other stimuli by following certain rules for **grouping**, also identified by the Gestalt psychologists. These rules, which we apply even as infants and even in our touch perceptions, illustrate how the perceived whole differs from the sum of its parts (Gallace & Spence, 2011; Quinn et al., 2002; Rock & Palmer, 1990). See **FIGURE 17.15** for three examples. Such principles usually help us construct reality. Sometimes, however, they lead us astray, as when we look at the doghouse in **FIGURE 17.16**.

 FIGURE 17.16

GREAT GESTALT! What's the secret to this impossible doghouse? You probably perceive this doghouse as a gestalt—a whole (though impossible) structure. Actually, your brain imposes this sense of wholeness on the picture. As Figure 17.20 shows, Gestalt grouping principles such as closure and continuity are at work here.

Photo by Walter Wick. Reprinted by permission from GAMES Magazine © 1983 PCS Games Limited Partnership

🔒 RETRIEVE IT • • •   *ANSWERS IN APPENDIX E*

RI-6 In terms of perception, a band's lead singer would be considered _____ (figure/ground), and the other musicians would be considered _____ (figure/ground).

RI-7 What do we mean when we say that, in perception, "the whole may exceed the sum of its parts"?

grouping the perceptual tendency to organize stimuli into coherent groups.

depth perception the ability to see objects in three dimensions although the images that strike the retina are two-dimensional; allows us to judge distance.

visual cliff a laboratory device for testing depth perception in infants and young animals.

binocular cue a depth cue, such as retinal disparity, that depends on the use of two eyes.

retinal disparity a binocular cue for perceiving depth. By comparing retinal images from the two eyes, the brain computes distance—the greater the disparity (difference) between the two images, the closer the object.

Depth Perception

LOQ 17-7 How do we use binocular and monocular cues to perceive the world in three dimensions, and how do we perceive motion?

Our eye-brain system performs many remarkable feats, among which is **depth perception**. From the two-dimensional images falling on our retinas, we somehow organize three-dimensional perceptions that let us estimate the distance of an oncoming car or a faraway house. How do we acquire this ability? Are we born with it? Do we learn it?

As Eleanor Gibson picnicked on the rim of the Grand Canyon, her scientific curiosity kicked in. She wondered: *Would a toddler peering over the rim perceive the dangerous drop-off and draw back?* To answer that question and others, Gibson and Richard Walk (1960) designed a series of experiments in their Cornell University laboratory using a **visual cliff**—a model of a cliff with a "drop-off" area that was actually covered by sturdy glass.

They placed 6- to 14-month-old infants on the edge of the "cliff" and had the infants' mothers coax them to crawl out onto the glass (**FIGURE 17.17**). Most infants refused to do so, indicating that they could perceive depth.

Had they *learned* to perceive depth? Learning appears also to be part of the human story, because crawling, no matter when it begins, seems to increase infants' wariness of heights (Adolph et al., 2014; Campos et al., 1992). But depth perception is also partly innate. Mobile newborn animals—even those with no visual experience (including young kittens, a day-old goat, and newly hatched chicks)—also refuse to venture across the visual cliff. Thus, biology prepares us to be wary of heights, and experience amplifies that fear.

If we were to build the ability to perceive depth into our video-computer system, what rules might enable it to convert two-dimensional images into a single three-dimensional perception? A good place to start would be the depth cues our brain receives from information supplied by one or both of our eyes.

ENGAGE 💡 **BINOCULAR CUES** People who see with two eyes perceive depth thanks partly to **binocular cues.** Here's an example: With both eyes open, hold two pens or pencils in front of you and touch their tips together. Now do so with one eye closed. A more difficult task, yes?

We use binocular cues to judge the distance of nearby objects. One such cue is *convergence,* the inward angle of the eyes focusing on a near object. Another is **retinal disparity.** Because your eyes are about 2 inches apart, your retinas receive slightly different images of the world. By comparing these two images, your brain can judge how close an object is to you. The greater the disparity (difference) between the two retinal images, the closer the object. Try it. Hold your two index fingers, with the tips about half an inch apart, directly in front of your nose, and your retinas will receive quite different views. If you close one eye and then the other, you can see the difference. (Bring your fingers close and you can create a finger sausage, as in **FIGURE 17.18.**) At a greater distance—say, when you hold your fingers at arm's length—the disparity is smaller.

FIGURE 17.17

VISUAL CLIFF Eleanor Gibson and Richard Walk devised this miniature cliff with a glass-covered drop-off to determine whether crawling infants and newborn animals can perceive depth. Even when coaxed, infants are reluctant to venture onto the glass over the cliff.

📺 **LaunchPad** See the **Video: Experiments** for a helpful tutorial animation about this type of research method.

🔒 **RETAIN** 📺 **LaunchPad** Check your understanding of these cues by engaging online with **Concept Practice: Depth Cues.**

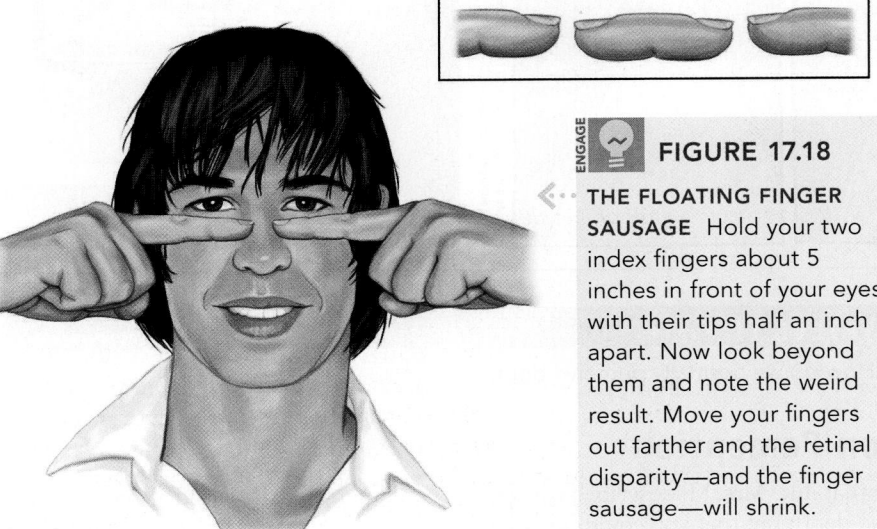

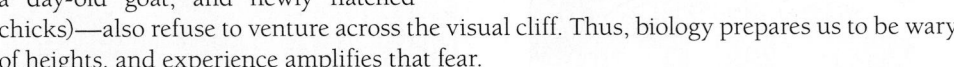

ENGAGE 💡 **FIGURE 17.18**

THE FLOATING FINGER SAUSAGE Hold your two index fingers about 5 inches in front of your eyes, with their tips half an inch apart. Now look beyond them and note the weird result. Move your fingers out farther and the retinal disparity—and the finger sausage—will shrink.

"I can't go on living with such lousy depth perception."

monocular cue a depth cue, such as interposition or linear perspective, available to either eye alone.

We could easily include retinal disparity in our video-computer system. Moviemakers sometimes film a scene with two cameras placed a few inches apart. Viewers then watch the film through glasses that allow the left eye to see only the image from the left camera, and the right eye to see only the image from the right camera. The resulting effect, as 3-D movie fans know, mimics or exaggerates normal retinal disparity giving the perception of depth.

MONOCULAR CUES How do we judge whether a person is 10 or 100 meters away? Retinal disparity won't help us here, because there won't be much difference between the images cast on our right and left retinas. At such distances, we depend on **monocular cues** (depth cues available to each eye separately). See **FIGURE 17.19** for some examples.

RETAIN

🔒 **FIGURE 17.19**

MONOCULAR DEPTH CUES

Image courtesy of Shaun P. Vecera, Ph.D., adapted from stimuli that appeared in Vecera et al. 2002

RELATIVE HEIGHT We perceive objects higher in our field of vision as farther away. Because we assume the lower part of a figure-ground illustration is closer, we perceive it as figure (Vecera et al., 2002). Invert this illustration and the black will become ground, like a night sky.

RELATIVE SIZE If we assume two objects are similar in size, *most* people perceive the one that casts the smaller retinal image as farther away.

Philip Mugridge/Alamy

INTERPOSITION If one object partially blocks our view of another, we perceive it as closer.

RELATIVE MOTION As we move, objects that are actually stable may appear to move. If while riding on a bus you fix your gaze on some point—say, a house—the objects beyond the fixation point will appear to move with you. Objects in front of the point will appear to move backward. The farther an object is from the fixation point, the faster it will seem to move.

LIGHT AND SHADOW Shading produces a sense of depth consistent with our assumption that light comes from above. If you invert this illustration, the hollow will become a hill.

© George V. Kelvin

LINEAR PERSPECTIVE Parallel lines appear to meet in the distance. The sharper the angle of convergence, the greater the perceived distance.

Rhymes with Oranges ©2010 Hilary B. Price. Distributed by King Features Syndicate, Inc.

DIRECTION OF PASSENGER'S MOTION →

🔒 **RETRIEVE IT • • •**　　　　　　　　*ANSWERS IN APPENDIX E*

RI-8 How do we normally perceive depth?

Motion Perception

Imagine that, like Mrs. M. described earlier, you could perceive the world as having color, form, and depth but that you could not see motion. Not only would you be unable to bike or drive, you would have trouble writing, eating, and walking.

Normally your brain computes motion based partly on its assumption that shrinking objects are retreating (not getting smaller) and enlarging objects are approaching. But sometimes our brain is tricked into believing what it is not seeing. When large and small objects move at the same speed, the large objects appear to move more slowly. Thus, trains seem to move slower than cars, and jumbo jets seem to land more slowly than little jets.

Our brain also perceives a rapid series of slightly varying still images as continuous movement—a phenomenon called *stroboscopic movement*. As film animators know well, a super-fast slide show of 24 still images a second will create an illusion of movement. We construct that motion in our head, just as we construct movement in blinking marquees and holiday lights. We perceive two adjacent stationary lights blinking on and off in quick succession as one single light jumping back and forth. Lighted signs exploit this **phi phenomenon** with a succession of lights that creates the impression of, say, a moving arrow.

Perceptual Constancy

LOQ 17-8   How do perceptual constancies help us construct meaningful perceptions?

So far, we have noted that our video-computer system must perceive objects as we do—as having a distinct form and location. Its next task is to recognize objects without being deceived by changes in their color, brightness, shape, or size—a *top-down* process called **perceptual constancy.** Regardless of the viewing angle, distance, and illumination, we can identify people and things in less time than it takes to draw a breath. This feat, which challenges even advanced computers, would be a monumental challenge for a video-computer system.

COLOR AND BRIGHTNESS CONSTANCIES Our experience of color depends on an object's *context*. This would be clear if you viewed an isolated tomato through a paper tube over the course of a day. As the light—and thus the tomato's reflected wavelengths—changed, the tomato's color would also seem to change. But if you discarded the paper tube and viewed the tomato as one item in a salad bowl, its perceived color would remain essentially constant. This perception of consistent color we call *color constancy.*

Though we take color constancy for granted, this ability is truly remarkable. A blue poker chip under indoor lighting reflects wavelengths that match those reflected by a sunlit gold chip (Jameson, 1985). Yet bring a goldfinch indoors and it won't look like a bluebird. The color is not in the bird's feathers. We see color thanks to our brain's computations of the light reflected by an object *relative to the objects surrounding it.* **FIGURE 17.21** dramatically illustrates the ability of a blue object to appear very different in three different contexts. Yet we have no trouble seeing these disks as blue. Nor does knowing the truth—that these disks are identically colored—diminish our perception that they are quite different. Because we construct our perceptions, we can simultaneously accept alternative objective and subjective realities.

phi phenomenon an illusion of movement created when two or more adjacent lights blink on and off in quick succession.

perceptual constancy perceiving objects as unchanging (having consistent color, brightness, shape, and size) even as illumination and retinal images change.

Photo by Walter Wick. Reprinted from GAMES Magazine ©1983
PCS Games Limited Partnership

FIGURE 17.20

THE SOLUTION Another view of the impossible doghouse in Figure 17.16 reveals the secrets of this illusion. From the photo angle in Figure 17.16, the grouping principles of closure and continuity lead us to perceive the boards as continuous.

"From there to here, from here to there, funny things are everywhere." — Dr. Seuss, *One Fish, Two Fish, Red Fish, Blue Fish,* 1960

R. Beau Lotto/Lottolab

(a)

(b)

FIGURE 17.21

COLOR DEPENDS ON CONTEXT
(a) Believe it or not, these three blue disks are identical in color.
(b) Remove the surrounding context and see what results.

FIGURE 17.22

RELATIVE LUMINANCE Because of its surrounding context, we perceive Square A as lighter than Square B. But believe it or not, they are identical. To channel comedian Richard Pryor, "Who you gonna believe: me, or your lying eyes?" If you believe your lying eyes—actually, your lying brain—you can photocopy (or screen-capture and print) the illustration, then cut out the squares and compare them. (Information from Edward Adelson.)

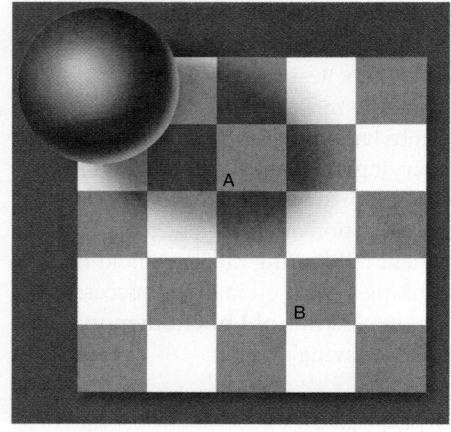

"Sometimes I wonder: Why is that Frisbee getting bigger? And then it hits me." —Anonymous

LaunchPad To experience more visual illusions, and to understand what they reveal about how you perceive the world, visit **Topic Tutorial: PsychSim6, Visual Illusions.**

FIGURE 17.23

SHAPE CONSTANCY A door casts an increasingly trapezoidal image on our retinas as it opens. Yet we still perceive it as rectangular.

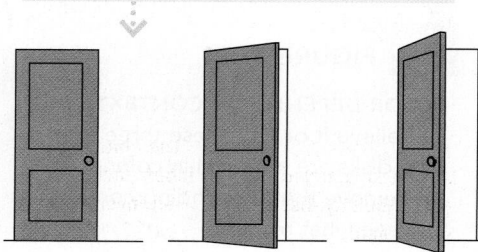

Brightness constancy (also called *lightness constancy*) similarly depends on context. We perceive an object as having a constant brightness even as its illumination varies. This perception of constancy depends on *relative luminance*—the amount of light an object reflects *relative to its surroundings* (**FIGURE 17.22**). White paper reflects 90 percent of the light falling on it; black paper, only 10 percent. Although a black paper viewed in sunlight may reflect 100 times more light than does a white paper viewed indoors, it will still look black (McBurney & Collings, 1984). But try viewing sunlit black paper through a narrow tube so nothing else is visible and it may look gray, because in bright sunshine it reflects a fair amount of light. View it without the tube and it is again black, because it reflects much less light than the objects around it.

This principle—that we perceive objects not in isolation but in their environmental context—matters to artists, interior decorators, and clothing designers. Our perception of the color and brightness of a wall or of a streak of paint on a canvas is determined not just by the paint in the can but by the surrounding colors. The take-home lesson: *Context governs our perceptions.*

SHAPE AND SIZE CONSTANCIES Thanks to *shape constancy,* we perceive the form of familiar objects, such as the door in **FIGURE 17.23**, as constant even while our retinas receive changing images of them. Our brain manages this feat because visual cortex neurons rapidly learn to associate different views of an object (Li & DiCarlo, 2008).

Thanks to *size constancy,* we perceive an object as having an unchanging size, even while our distance from it varies. We assume a car is large enough to carry people, even when we see its tiny image from two blocks away. This assumption also illustrates the close connection between perceived *distance* and perceived *size.* Perceiving an object's distance gives us cues to its size. Likewise, knowing its general size—that the object is a car—provides us with cues to its distance.

Even in size-distance judgments, however, we consider an object's context. This interplay between perceived size and perceived distance helps explain several well-known illusions, including the *Moon illusion:* The Moon looks up to 50 percent larger when near the horizon than when high in the sky. Can you imagine why?

For at least 22 centuries, scholars have wondered (Hershenson, 1989). One reason is that monocular cues to objects' distances make the horizon Moon appear farther away. If it's farther away, our brain assumes, it must be larger than the Moon high in the night sky (Kaufman & Kaufman, 2000). But again, if you use a paper tube to take away the distance cue, the horizon Moon will immediately seem smaller.

Perceptual illusions reinforce a fundamental lesson: Perception is not merely a projection of the world onto our brain. Rather, our sensations are disassembled into information bits that our brain then reassembles into its own functional model of the external world. During this reassembly process, our assumptions—such as the usual relationship between distance and size—can lead us astray. *Our brain constructs our perceptions.*

* * *

Form perception, depth perception, motion perception, and perceptual constancies illuminate how we organize our visual experiences. Perceptual organization applies to our other senses, too. Listening to an unfamiliar language, we have trouble hearing where one word stops and the next one begins. Listening to our own language, we automatically hear distinct words. This, too, reflects perceptual organization. But it is more, for we even organize a string of letters—THEDOGATEMEAT—into words that make an intelligible phrase, more likely "The dog ate meat" than "The do gate me at" (McBurney & Collings, 1984). This process involves not only the organization we've been discussing, but also interpretation—discerning meaning in what we perceive.

PERCEPTUAL INTERPRETATION

Philosophers have debated whether our perceptual abilities should be credited to our nature or our nurture. To what extent do we *learn* to perceive? German philosopher Immanuel Kant (1724–1804) maintained that knowledge comes from our *inborn* ways of organizing sensory experiences. Indeed, we come equipped to process sensory information. But British philosopher John Locke (1632–1704) argued that through our experiences we also *learn* to perceive the world. Indeed, we learn to link an object's distance with its size. So, just how important is experience? How radically does it shape our perceptual interpretations?

Experience and Visual Perception

LOQ 17-9 What does research on restored vision, sensory restriction, and perceptual adaptation reveal about the effects of experience on perception?

RESTORED VISION AND SENSORY RESTRICTION Writing to John Locke, William Molyneux wondered whether "a man *born* blind, and now adult, taught by his *touch* to distinguish between a cube and a sphere" could, if made to see, visually distinguish the two. Locke's answer was *No,* because the man would never have *learned* to see the difference. Molyneux's hypothetical case has since been put to the test with people who, though blind from birth, later gained sight (Gandhi et al., 2017; Gregory, 1978; Huber et al., 2015; von Senden, 1932). Most were born with cataracts—clouded lenses that allowed them to see only diffused light, rather as a sighted person might see a foggy image through a Ping-Pong ball sliced in half. After cataract surgery, the patients could distinguish figure from ground, could differentiate colors, and could distinguish faces from nonfaces—suggesting that these aspects of perception are innate. But much as Locke supposed, they often could not visually recognize objects that were familiar by touch.

Seeking to gain more control than is provided by clinical cases, researchers have outfitted infant kittens and monkeys with goggles through which they could see only diffuse, unpatterned light (Wiesel, 1982). After infancy, when their vision was restored, these animals behaved much like the humans born with cataracts. They could distinguish color and brightness, but not the form of a circle from that of a square. Their eyes had not degenerated; their retinas still relayed signals to their visual cortex. But lacking stimulation, their brain's cortical cells had not developed normal connections. Thus, the animals remained functionally blind to shape. Surgery on children in India reveals that those who are blind from birth can benefit from removal of cataracts, and the younger they are, the more they will benefit. But their visual acuity (sharpness) may never be normal (Chatterjee, 2015; Gandhi et al., 2014). For normal sensory and perceptual development, there is a *critical period*—an optimal period when exposure to certain stimuli or experiences is required.

Once this critical period has passed, sensory restrictions later in life do no permanent harm. When researchers cover an adult animal's eye for several months, its vision will be unaffected after the eye patch is removed. When surgeons remove cataracts that develop during late adulthood, most people are thrilled at the return to normal vision.

PERCEPTUAL ADAPTATION Given a new pair of glasses, we may feel slightly disoriented, even dizzy. Within a day or two, we adjust. Our **perceptual adaptation** to changed visual input makes the world seem normal again. But imagine a far more dramatic new pair of glasses—one that shifts the apparent location of objects 40 degrees to the left. When you first put them on and toss a ball to a friend, it sails off to the left. Walking forward to shake hands with someone, you veer to the left.

Could you adapt to this distorted world? Not if you were a baby chicken. When fitted with such lenses, baby chicks continue to peck where food grains *seem* to be (Hess, 1956; Rossi, 1968). But we humans adapt to distorting lenses quickly. Within a few minutes your throws would again be accurate, your stride on target. Remove the lenses and you would experience an aftereffect: At first your throws would err in the *opposite* direction, sailing off to the right; but again, within minutes you would readapt.

ENGAGE

"Let us then suppose the mind to be, as we say, white paper void of all characters, without any ideas: How comes it to be furnished? . . . To this I answer, in one word, from EXPERIENCE." —John Locke, *An Essay Concerning Human Understanding*, 1690

LEARNING TO SEE At age 3, Mike May lost his vision in an explosion. Decades later, after a new cornea restored vision to his right eye, he got his first look at his wife and children. Alas, although signals were now reaching his visual cortex, it lacked the experience to interpret them. May could not recognize expressions, or faces, apart from features such as hair. Yet he can see an object in motion and has learned to navigate his world and to marvel at such things as dust floating in sunlight (Abrams, 2002; Gorlick, 2010; Huber et al., 2015).

Marcio Jose Sanchez/AP Images

perceptual adaptation the ability to adjust to changed sensory input, including an artificially displaced or even inverted visual field.

PERCEPTUAL ADAPTATION "Oops, missed," thought researcher Hubert Dolezal as he attempted a handshake while viewing the world through inverting goggles. Yet, believe it or not, kittens, monkeys, and humans can adapt to an inverted world.

Courtesy of Hubert Dolezal

Indeed, given an even more radical pair of glasses—one that literally turns the world upside down—you could still adapt. Psychologist George Stratton (1896) experienced this. He invented, and for eight days wore, optical headgear that flipped left to right *and* up to down, making him the first person to experience a right-side-up retinal image while standing upright. The ground was up, the sky was down.

At first, when Stratton wanted to walk, he found himself searching for his feet, which were now "up." Eating was nearly impossible. He became nauseated and depressed. But he persisted, and by the eighth day he could comfortably reach for an object and, if his hands were in view, could walk without bumping into things. When Stratton finally removed the headgear, he readapted quickly.

So did research participants who wore such gear in later experiments—while riding a motorcycle, skiing the Alps, or flying an airplane (Dolezal, 1982; Kohler, 1962). By actively moving about in their topsy-turvy world, they adapted to their new context and learned to coordinate their movements.

So, do we learn to perceive the world? In part we do, as we constantly adjust to changed sensory input. Research on critical periods teaches us that early nurture sculpts what nature has provided. In less dramatic ways, nurture continues to do so throughout our lives. Experience guides, sustains, and maintains the brain pathways that enable our perception.

ENGAGE

ASK YOURSELF

Consider someone you know who has a visual disability (could be yourself). What sort of disrupted visual process causes that disability?

🔒 REVIEW VISION: SENSORY AND PERCEPTUAL PROCESSING

⟩⟩ Learning Objectives

TEST YOURSELF Answer these repeated Learning Objective Questions on your own (before checking the answers in Appendix D) to improve your retention of the concepts (McDaniel et al., 2009, 2015).

17-1 What are the characteristics of the energy that we see as visible light? What structures in the eye help focus that energy?

17-2 How do the rods and cones process information, and what is the path information travels from the eye to the brain?

17-3 How do we perceive color in the world around us?

17-4 Where are feature detectors located, and what do they do?

17-5 How does the brain use parallel processing to construct visual perceptions?

17-6 How did the Gestalt psychologists understand perceptual organization, and how do figure-ground and grouping principles contribute to our perceptions?

17-7 How do we use binocular and monocular cues to perceive the world in three dimensions, and how do we perceive motion?

17-8 How do perceptual constancies help us construct meaningful perceptions?

17-9 What does research on restored vision, sensory restriction, and perceptual adaptation reveal about the effects of experience on perception?

⟩⟩ Terms and Concepts to Remember

TEST YOURSELF Write down the definition yourself, then check your answer on the referenced page.

transduction, **p. 199**

wavelength, **p. 199**

hue, **p. 199**

intensity, **p. 199**

retina, **p. 201**

accommodation, **p. 201**

rods, **p. 201**

cones, **p. 201**

optic nerve, **p. 201**

blind spot, **p. 201**

fovea, **p. 203**

Young-Helmholtz trichromatic (three-color) theory, **p. 203**

opponent-process theory, **p. 204**

feature detectors, **p. 204**

parallel processing, **p. 207**

gestalt, **p. 207**

figure-ground, **p. 207**

grouping, **p. 208**

depth perception, **p. 208**

visual cliff, **p. 208**

binocular cue, **p. 208**

retinal disparity, **p. 208**

monocular cue, **p. 210**

phi phenomenon, **p. 211**

perceptual constancy, **p. 211**

perceptual adaptation, **p. 213**

⊙→ Experience the Testing Effect

TEST YOURSELF Answer the following questions on your own first, then check your answers in Appendix E.

1. The characteristic of light that determines the color we experience, such as blue or green, is _____.

2. The amplitude of a light wave determines our perception of
   a. brightness.
   b. color.
   c. meaning.
   d. distance.

3. The blind spot in your retina is located where
   a. there are rods but no cones.
   b. there are cones but no rods.
   c. the optic nerve leaves the eye.
   d. the bipolar cells meet the ganglion cells.

4. Cones are the eye's receptor cells that are especially sensitive to _____ light and are responsible for our _____ vision.
   a. bright; black-and-white
   b. dim; color
   c. bright; color
   d. dim; black-and-white

5. Two theories together account for color vision. The Young-Helmholtz trichromatic theory shows that the eye contains _____, and Hering's theory accounts for the nervous system's having _____.
   a. opposing retinal processes; three pairs of color receptors
   b. opponent-process cells; three types of color receptors
   c. three pairs of color receptors; opposing retinal processes
   d. three types of color receptors; opponent-process cells

6. What mental processes allow you to perceive a lemon as yellow?

7. The cells in the visual cortex that respond to certain lines, edges, and angles are called _____ _____.

8. The brain's ability to process many aspects of an object or a problem simultaneously is called _____ _____.

9. In listening to a concert, you attend to the solo instrument and perceive the orchestra as accompaniment. This illustrates the organizing principle of
   a. figure-ground.
   b. shape constancy.
   c. grouping.
   d. depth perception.

10. Our tendencies to fill in the gaps and to perceive a pattern as continuous are two different examples of the organizing principle called
    a. interposition.
    b. depth perception.
    c. shape constancy.
    d. grouping.

11. The visual cliff experiments suggest that
    a. infants have not yet developed depth perception.
    b. crawling human infants and very young animals perceive depth.
    c. we have no way of knowing whether infants can perceive depth.
    d. unlike other species, humans are able to perceive depth in infancy.

12. Depth perception underlies our ability to
    a. group similar items in a gestalt.
    b. perceive objects as having a constant shape or form.
    c. judge distances.
    d. fill in the gaps in a figure.

13. Two examples of _____ depth cues are interposition and linear perspective.

14. Perceiving a tomato as consistently red, despite lighting shifts, is an example of
    a. shape constancy.
    b. perceptual constancy.
    c. a binocular cue.
    d. continuity.

15. After surgery to restore vision, adults who had been blind from birth had difficulty
    a. recognizing objects by touch.
    b. recognizing objects by sight.
    c. distinguishing figure from ground.
    d. distinguishing between bright and dim light.

16. In experiments, people have worn glasses that turned their visual fields upside down. After a period of adjustment, they learned to function quite well. This ability is called _____ _____.

Continue testing yourself with 📖 **LearningCurve** or 📖 **Achieve Read & Practice**
to learn and remember most effectively.

audition the sense or act of hearing.

frequency the number of complete wavelengths that pass a point in a given time (for example, per second).

pitch a tone's experienced highness or lowness; depends on frequency.

middle ear the chamber between the eardrum and cochlea containing three tiny bones (malleus, incus, and stapes) that concentrate the vibrations of the eardrum on the cochlea's oval window.

cochlea [KOHK-lee-uh] a coiled, bony, fluid-filled tube in the inner ear; sound waves traveling through the cochlear fluid trigger nerve impulses.

inner ear the innermost part of the ear, containing the cochlea, semicircular canals, and vestibular sacs.

18 The Nonvisual Senses

HEARING

Like our other senses, our hearing, or **audition,** helps us adapt and survive. Hearing provides information and enables relationships. Hearing humanizes us; people seem more thoughtful, competent, and likable when we hear their words than when we read their words (Schroeder & Epley, 2015, 2016). And hearing is pretty spectacular. It lets us communicate invisibly—shooting unseen air waves across space and receiving the same from others. Hearing loss is therefore an invisible disability. To not catch someone's name, to not grasp what someone is asking, and to miss the hilarious joke is to be deprived of what others know, and sometimes to feel excluded. As a person with hearing loss, I [DM] know the feeling, and can understand why adults with significant hearing loss experience a doubled risk of depression (Li et al., 2014).

Most of us, however, can hear a wide range of sounds, and the ones we hear best are those in the range of the human voice. With normal hearing, we are remarkably sensitive to faint sounds, such as a child's whimper. (If our ears were only slightly more sensitive, we would hear a constant hiss from the movement of air molecules.) Our distant ancestors' survival depended on this keen hearing when hunting or being hunted.

We are also remarkably attuned to sound variations. Among thousands of possible voices, we easily recognize an unseen friend's. Moreover, hearing is fast. "It might take you a full second to notice something out of the corner of your eye, turn your head toward it, recognize it, and respond to it," notes auditory neuroscientist Seth Horowitz (2012). "The same reaction to a new or sudden sound happens at least 10 times as fast." A fraction of a second after such events stimulate your ear's receptors, millions of neurons have simultaneously coordinated in extracting the essential features, comparing them with past experience, and identifying the stimulus (Freeman, 1991). For hearing as for our other senses, we wonder: How do we do it?

The Stimulus Input: Sound Waves

LOQ 18-1 What are the characteristics of air pressure waves that we hear as sound?

Draw a bow across a violin, and you will unleash the energy of sound waves. Air molecules, each bumping into the next, create waves of compressed and expanded air, like the ripples on a pond circling out from a tossed stone. As we swim in our ocean of moving air molecules, our ears detect these brief air pressure changes.

Like light waves, sound waves vary in shape (**FIGURE 18.1**). The height, or *amplitude,* of sound waves determines their perceived *loudness.* Their length, or **frequency,** determines the **pitch** we experience. Long waves have low frequency—and low pitch. Short waves have high frequency—and high pitch. Sound waves produced by a violin are much shorter and faster than those produced by a cello or a bass guitar.

FIGURE 18.1

THE PHYSICAL PROPERTIES OF WAVES (a) Waves vary in *wavelength* (the distance between successive peaks). *Frequency*, the number of complete wavelengths that can pass a point in a given time, depends on the wavelength. The shorter the wavelength, the higher the frequency. Wavelength determines the *pitch* of sound. (b) Waves also vary in *amplitude* (the height from peak to trough). Wave amplitude influences sound *intensity*.

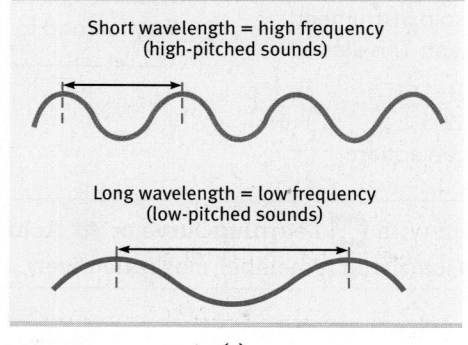

(a)

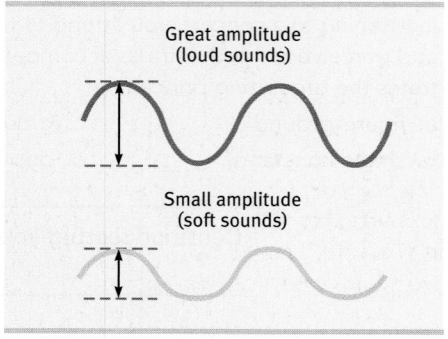

(b)

We measure sounds in *decibels,* with zero decibels representing the absolute threshold for hearing. Every 10 decibels correspond to a tenfold increase in sound intensity. Thus, normal conversation (60 decibels) is 10,000 times more intense than a 20-decibel whisper. And a temporarily tolerable 100-decibel passing subway train is 10 billion times more intense than the faintest detectable sound. If prolonged, exposure to sounds above 85 decibels can produce hearing loss. Tell that to basketball fans at the University of Kentucky who, in 2017, broke the Guinness World Record for the noisiest indoor stadium at 126 decibels (WKYT, 2017). Hear today, gone tomorrow.

Zdorov Kirill Vladimirovich/
Shutterstock

sbarabu/Shutterstock

THE SOUNDS OF MUSIC
A violin's short, fast waves create a high pitch. The longer, slower waves of a cello or bass create a lower pitch. Differences in the waves' height, or amplitude, also create differing degrees of loudness.

The Ear

LOQ 18-2 How does the ear transform sound energy into neural messages?

How does vibrating air trigger nerve impulses that your brain can decode as sounds? The process begins when sound waves strike your *eardrum,* causing this tight membrane to vibrate (**FIGURE 18.2**).

In your **middle ear,** a piston made of three tiny bones—the *hammer* (malleus), *anvil* (incus), and *stirrup* (stapes)—picks up the vibrations and transmits them to the **cochlea,** a snail-shaped tube in the **inner ear.**

The incoming vibrations then cause the cochlea's membrane-covered opening (the *oval window*) to vibrate, jostling the fluid inside the cochlea. This motion causes ripples in the *basilar membrane,* bending the *hair cells* lining its surface, rather like wheat stalks bending in the wind.

The hair cell movements in turn trigger impulses in the adjacent nerve cells, whose axons converge to form the *auditory nerve.* The auditory nerve carries the neural messages

FIGURE 18.2

HEAR HERE: HOW WE TRANSFORM SOUND WAVES INTO NERVE IMPULSES THAT OUR BRAIN INTERPRETS (a) The outer ear funnels sound waves to the eardrum. The bones of the middle ear (hammer, anvil, and stirrup) amplify and relay the eardrum's vibrations through the oval window into the fluid-filled cochlea. (b) As shown in this detail of the middle and inner ear, the resulting pressure changes in the cochlear fluid cause the basilar membrane to ripple, bending the hair cells on its surface. Hair cell movements trigger impulses at the base of the nerve cells, whose fibers converge to form the auditory nerve. That nerve sends neural messages to the thalamus and on to the auditory cortex.

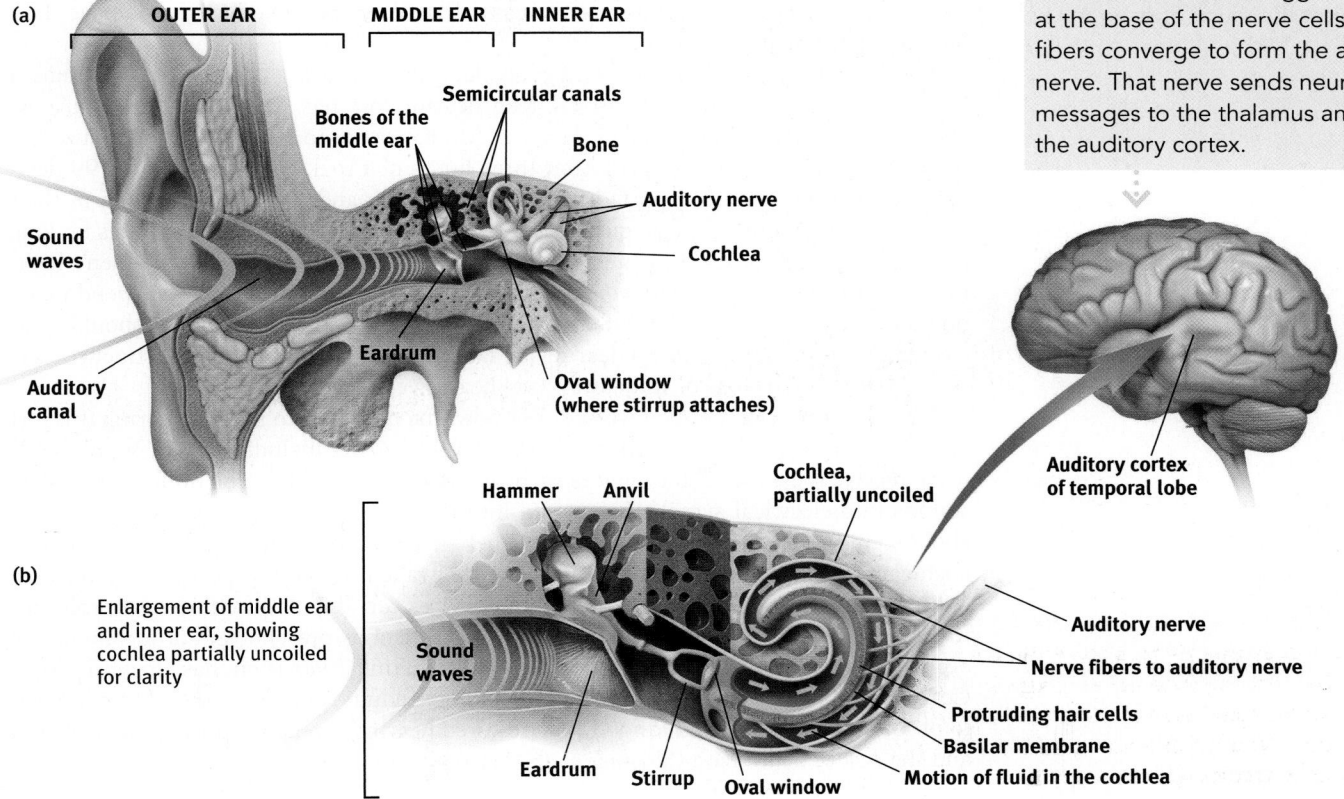

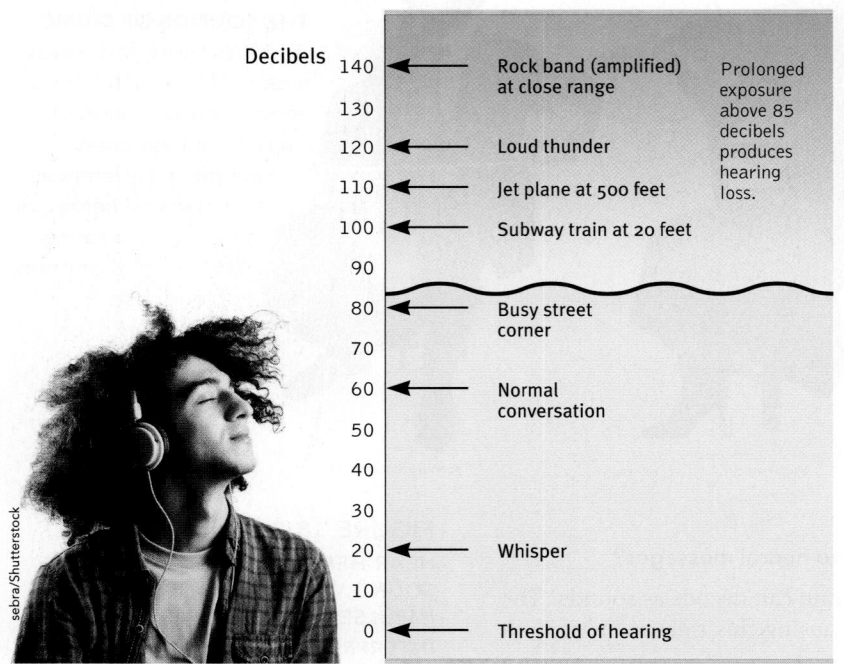

Decibels		
140	←	Rock band (amplified) at close range
130		
120	←	Loud thunder
110	←	Jet plane at 500 feet
100	←	Subway train at 20 feet
90		
80	←	Busy street corner
70		
60	←	Normal conversation
50		
40		
30		
20	←	Whisper
10		
0	←	Threshold of hearing

Prolonged exposure above 85 decibels produces hearing loss.

FIGURE 18.3

THE INTENSITY OF SOME COMMON SOUNDS One study of 3 million Germans found professional musicians with almost four times the normal rate of noise-induced hearing loss (Schink et al., 2014). Some modern headphones block out environmental noise, reducing the need to blast the music at dangerous volumes.

to the thalamus and then on to the *auditory cortex* in the brain's temporal lobe. From vibrating air, to tiny moving bones, to fluid waves, to electrical impulses to the brain: Voila! You hear.

Perhaps the most intriguing part of the hearing process is the hair cells—"quivering bundles that let us hear" thanks to their "extreme sensitivity and extreme speed" (Goldberg, 2007). A cochlea has 16,000 of them, which sounds like a lot until we compare that with an eye's 130 million or so photoreceptors. But consider a hair cell's responsiveness. Deflect the tiny bundles of *cilia* on its tip by only the width of an atom—imagine—and the alert hair cell, thanks to a special protein at its tip, will trigger a neural response (Corey et al., 2004).

Damage to the cochlea's hair cell receptors or the auditory nerve can cause **sensorineural hearing loss** (or nerve deafness). With auditory nerve damage, people may hear sound but have trouble discerning what someone is saying (Liberman, 2015).

Occasionally, disease damages hair cell receptors, but more often the culprits are biological changes linked with heredity and aging, and prolonged exposure to ear-splitting noise or music. Sensorineural hearing loss is more common than **conduction hearing loss,** which is caused by damage to the mechanical system—the eardrum and middle ear bones—that conducts sound waves to the cochlea.

The cochlea's hair cells have been likened to carpet fibers. Walk around on them and they will spring back. But leave a heavy piece of furniture on them and they may never rebound. As a general rule, any noise we cannot talk over (loud machinery, fans screaming at a sports event, music blasting at maximum volume) may be harmful, especially if prolonged and repeated (Roesser, 1998) (**FIGURE 18.3**). And if our ears ring after exposure to such experiences, we have been bad to our unhappy hair cells. As pain alerts us to possible bodily harm, ringing of the ears alerts us to possible hearing damage. It is hearing's equivalent of bleeding.

Worldwide, 1.23 billion people are challenged by hearing loss (Global Burden of Disease, 2015). Since the early 1990s, teen hearing loss has risen by a third and now affects 1 in 5 teens (Shargorodsky et al., 2010). Exposure to loud music, both live and through headphones, is a culprit: After three hours of a rock concert averaging 99 decibels, 54 percent of teens reported not hearing as well, and 1 in 4 had ringing in their ears. Teen boys more than teen girls or adults blast themselves with loud volumes for long periods (Zogby, 2006). Males' greater noise exposure may help explain why men's hearing tends to be less acute than women's. But regardless of gender, those who spend many hours in a loud nightclub, behind a power mower, or above a jackhammer should wear earplugs, or they risk needing a hearing aid later. "Condoms or, safer yet, abstinence," say sex educators. "Earplugs or walk away," say hearing educators.

Nerve deafness cannot be reversed. For now, the only way to restore hearing is a sort of bionic ear—a **cochlear implant.** Some 50,000 people, including some 30,000 children, receive these electronic devices each year (Hochmair, 2013). The implants translate sounds into electrical signals that, wired into the cochlea's nerves, convey information about sound to the brain (**FIGURE 18.4**). When given to deaf kittens and human infants, cochlear implants have seemed to trigger an "awakening" of the pertinent brain area (Klinke et al., 1999; Sireteanu, 1999). These devices can help children become proficient in oral communication (especially if they receive them as preschoolers or ideally before age 1) (Dettman et al., 2007; Schorr et al., 2005). Hearing, like vision, has a *critical period.* Cochlear implants can help restore hearing for most adults, but only if their brain learned to process sound during childhood. The restored hearing can also reduce social isolation and the risk of depression (Mosnier et al., 2015).

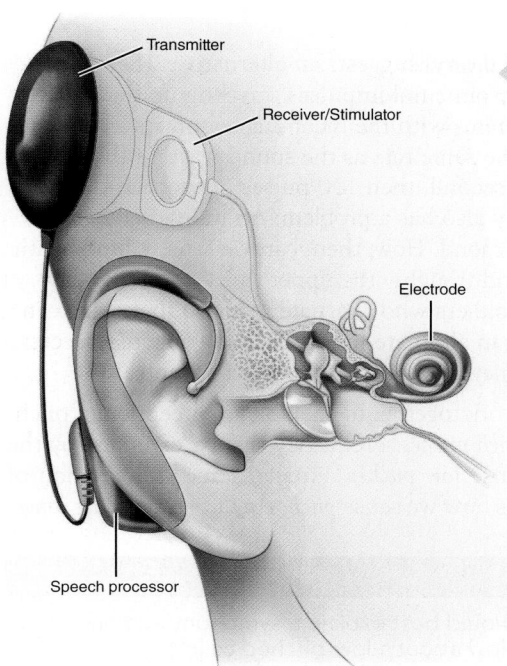

Transmitter

Receiver/Stimulator

Electrode

Speech processor

FIGURE 18.4

HARDWARE FOR HEARING Cochlear implants work by translating sounds into electrical signals that are transmitted to the cochlea and, via the auditory nerve, relayed to the brain.

🔒 RETRIEVE IT • • •

ANSWERS IN APPENDIX E

RI-1 The amplitude of a sound wave determines our perception of _____ (loudness/pitch).

RI-2 The longer the sound waves are, the _____ (lower/higher) their frequency and the _____ (higher/lower) their pitch.

Perceiving Loudness, Pitch, and Location

LOQ 18-3 How do we detect loudness, discriminate pitch, and locate sounds?

RESPONDING TO LOUD AND SOFT SOUNDS How do we detect loudness? If you guessed that it's related to the intensity of a hair cell's response, you'd be wrong. Rather, a soft, pure tone activates only the few hair cells attuned to its frequency. Given louder sounds, neighboring hair cells also respond. Thus, your brain interprets loudness from the *number* of activated hair cells.

If a hair cell loses sensitivity to soft sounds, it may still respond to loud sounds. This helps explain another surprise: Really loud sounds may seem loud to people with or without normal hearing. As a person with hearing loss, I [DM] used to wonder what really loud music must sound like to people with normal hearing. Now I realize it sounds much the same; where we differ is in our perception of soft sounds.

HEARING DIFFERENT PITCHES How do we know whether a sound is the high-frequency, high-pitched chirp of a bird or the low-frequency, low-pitched roar of a truck? Current thinking on how we discriminate pitch combines two theories.

- **Place theory** presumes that we hear different pitches because different sound waves trigger activity at different places along the cochlea's basilar membrane. Thus, the brain determines a sound's pitch by recognizing the specific place (on the membrane) that is generating the neural signal. When Nobel laureate-to-be Georg von Békésy (1957) cut holes in the cochleas of guinea pigs and human cadavers and looked inside with a microscope, he discovered that the cochlea vibrated, rather like a shaken bedsheet, in response to sound. High frequencies produced large vibrations near the beginning of the cochlea's membrane. Low frequencies vibrated more of the membrane and were not so easily localized. So, there is a problem: Place theory can explain how we hear high-pitched sounds but not low-pitched sounds.

sensorineural hearing loss hearing loss caused by damage to the cochlea's receptor cells or to the auditory nerves; the most common form of hearing loss, also called *nerve deafness.*

conduction hearing loss a less common form of hearing loss, caused by damage to the mechanical system that conducts sound waves to the cochlea.

cochlear implant a device for converting sounds into electrical signals and stimulating the auditory nerve through electrodes threaded into the cochlea.

place theory in hearing, the theory that links the pitch we hear with the place where the cochlea's membrane is stimulated.

frequency theory in hearing, the theory that the rate of nerve impulses traveling up the auditory nerve matches the frequency of a tone, thus enabling us to sense its pitch. (Also called *temporal theory*.)

🔒 🌐 **LaunchPad** For an interactive review of how we perceive sound, visit **Topic Tutorial: PsychSim6, The Auditory System.** For an animated test of your knowledge, engage online with **Concept Practice: The Auditory Pathway.**

• **Frequency theory** (also called *temporal theory*) suggests an alternative: The brain reads pitch by monitoring the frequency of neural impulses traveling up the auditory nerve. The whole basilar membrane vibrates with the incoming sound wave, triggering neural impulses to the brain at the same rate as the sound wave. If the sound wave has a frequency of 100 waves per second, then 100 pulses per second travel up the auditory nerve. But frequency theory also has a problem: An individual neuron cannot fire faster than 1000 times per second. How, then, can we sense sounds with frequencies above 1000 waves per second (roughly the upper third of a piano keyboard)? Enter the *volley principle:* Like soldiers who alternate firing so that some can shoot while others reload, neural cells can alternate firing. By firing in rapid succession, they can achieve a *combined frequency* above 1000 waves per second.

So, place theory and frequency theory work together to enable our perception of pitch. Place theory best explains how we sense *high pitches*. Frequency theory, extended by the volley principle, also explains how we sense *low pitches*. Finally, some combination of place and frequency theories likely explains how we sense *pitches in the intermediate range*.

> 🔒 **RETRIEVE IT • • •**   *ANSWERS IN APPENDIX E*
>
> **RI-3** Which theory of pitch perception would best explain a symphony audience's enjoyment of a high-pitched piccolo? How about a low-pitched cello?

LOCATING SOUNDS Why don't we have one big ear—perhaps above our one nose? "All the better to hear you with," as the wolf said to Little Red Riding Hood. Thanks to the placement of our two ears, we enjoy stereophonic ("three-dimensional") hearing. Two ears are better than one for at least two reasons (**FIGURE 18.5**). If a car to your right honks, your right ear will receive a more *intense* sound, and it will receive the sound slightly *sooner* than your left ear.

Because sound travels 761 miles per hour and human ears are but 6 inches apart, the intensity difference and the time lag are extremely small. A just noticeable difference in the direction of two sound sources corresponds to a time difference of just 0.000027 second! Lucky for us, our supersensitive auditory system can detect such minute differences—and locate the sound (Brown & Deffenbacher, 1979; Middlebrooks & Green, 1991).

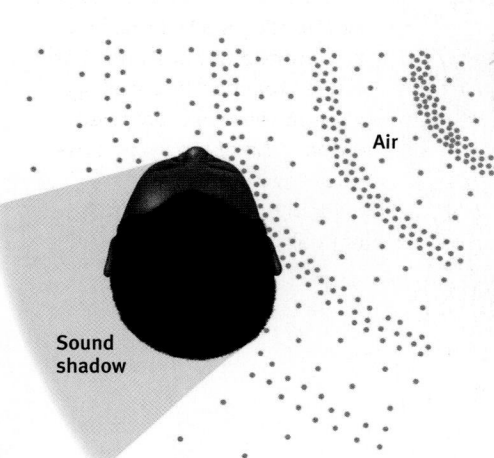

Air

Sound shadow

FIGURE 18.5

HOW WE LOCATE SOUNDS Sound waves strike one ear sooner and more intensely than the other. From this information, our nimble brain can compute the sound's location. As you might therefore expect, people who lose all hearing in one ear often have difficulty locating sounds.

THE OTHER SENSES

Sharks and dogs rely on their outstanding sense of smell, aided by large smell-related brain areas. Our human brain allocates more real estate to seeing and hearing. But extraordinary happenings also occur within our other senses. Without our senses of touch, taste, smell, and body position and movement, we humans would be seriously hampered, and our capacities for enjoying the world would be greatly diminished.

Touch

LOQ 18-4 How do we sense touch?

Touch, our tactile sense, is vital. Right from the start, touch aids our development. Infant rats deprived of their mother's grooming produce less growth hormone and have a lower metabolic rate—a good way to keep alive until the mother returns, but a reaction that stunts growth if prolonged. Infant monkeys that are allowed to see, hear, and smell—but not touch—their mother become desperately unhappy (Suomi et al., 1976). Premature human babies gain weight faster and go home sooner if they are stimulated by hand massage (Field et al., 2006). As adults, we still yearn to touch—to kiss, to stroke, to snuggle.

Humorist Dave Barry was perhaps right to jest that your skin "keeps people from seeing the inside of your body, which is repulsive, and it prevents your organs from falling onto the ground." But skin does much more. Touching various spots on the skin with a soft hair, a warm or cool wire, and the point of a pin reveals that some spots are especially sensitive to *pressure*, others to *warmth*, others to *cold*, still others to *pain*. Our "sense of touch" is actually a mix of these four basic and distinct skin senses, and our other skin sensations are variations of pressure, warmth, cold, and pain. For example, stroking adjacent pressure spots creates a tickle. Repeated gentle stroking of a pain spot creates an itching sensation. Touching adjacent cold and pres-s●re spots triggers a sense of wetness (which you can experience by touching dry, cold metal).

Touch sensations involve more than tactile stimulation, however. A self-administered tickle produces less somatosensory cortex activation than does the same tickle from something or someone else (Blakemore et al., 1998). Likewise, a sensual leg caress evokes a different somatosensory cortex response when a heterosexual man believes it comes from an attractive woman rather than a man (Gazzola et al., 2012). Such responses reveal how quickly cognition influences our brain's sensory response.

THE PRECIOUS SENSE OF TOUCH
As William James wrote in his *Principles of Psychology* (1890), "Touch is both the alpha and omega of affection."

Pain

LOQ 18-5 What biological, psychological, and social-cultural influences affect our experience of pain? How do placebos, distraction, and hypnosis help control pain?

Be thankful for occasional pain. Pain is your body's way of telling you something has gone wrong. By drawing your attention to a burn, a break, or a sprain, pain orders you to change your behavior—"Stay off that turned ankle!" The rare people born without the ability to feel pain may experience severe injury or even death before early adulthood. Without the discomfort that makes us occasionally shift position, their joints can fail from excess strain. Without the warnings of pain, infections can run wild and injuries can accumulate (Neese, 1991).

More numerous are those who live with chronic pain, which is rather like an alarm that won't shut off. Persistent backaches, arthritis, headaches, and cancer-related pain prompt two questions: What is pain? How might we control it?

UNDERSTANDING PAIN Our experience of pain reflects both *bottom-up* sensations and *top-down* cognition. Pain is a biopsychosocial phenomenon (Hadjistavropoulos et al., 2011). As such, pain experiences vary widely, from group to group and from person to person. Viewing pain from many perspectives can help us better understand how to cope with it and treat it (**FIGURE 18.6**).

"PAIN IS A GIFT." So said a doctor studying Ashlyn Blocker, who has a rare genetic muta-tion that prevents her from feeling pain. At birth, she didn't cry. As a child, she ran around for two days on a broken ankle. She has put her hands on a hot machine and burned the flesh off. And she has reached into boiling water to retrieve a dropped spoon. "Everyone in my class asks me about it, and I say, 'I can feel pressure, but I can't feel pain.' *Pain!* I cannot feel it!"

Jeff Riedel/Contour/Getty Images

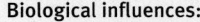

Biological influences:
• activity in spinal cord's large and small fibers
• genetic differences in endorphin production
• the brain's interpretation of CNS activity

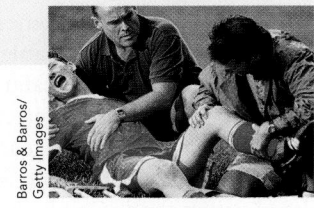

Barros & Barros/Getty Images

Psychological influences:
• attention to pain
• learning based on experience
• expectations

Halfpoint/Shutterstock

Social-cultural influences:
• presence of others
• empathy for others' pain
• cultural expectations

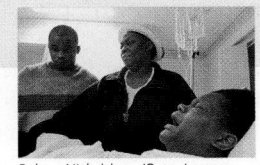

Robert Nickelsberg/Getty Images

Personal experience of pain

FIGURE 18.6
BIOPSYCHOSOCIAL APPROACH TO PAIN Our experience of pain is much more than the neural messages sent to our brain.

FIGURE 18.7

THE PAIN CIRCUIT Sensory receptors (*nociceptors*) respond to potentially damaging stimuli by sending an impulse to the spinal cord, which passes the message to the brain, which interprets the signal as pain.

BIOLOGICAL INFLUENCES Pain is a physical event produced by your senses. But pain differs from some of your other sensations. No one type of stimulus triggers pain the way light triggers vision. And no specialized receptors process pain signals, the way your retina receptors react to light rays. Instead, sensory receptors called *nociceptors*—mostly in your skin but also in your muscles and organs—detect hurtful temperatures, pressure, or chemicals (**FIGURE 18.7**).

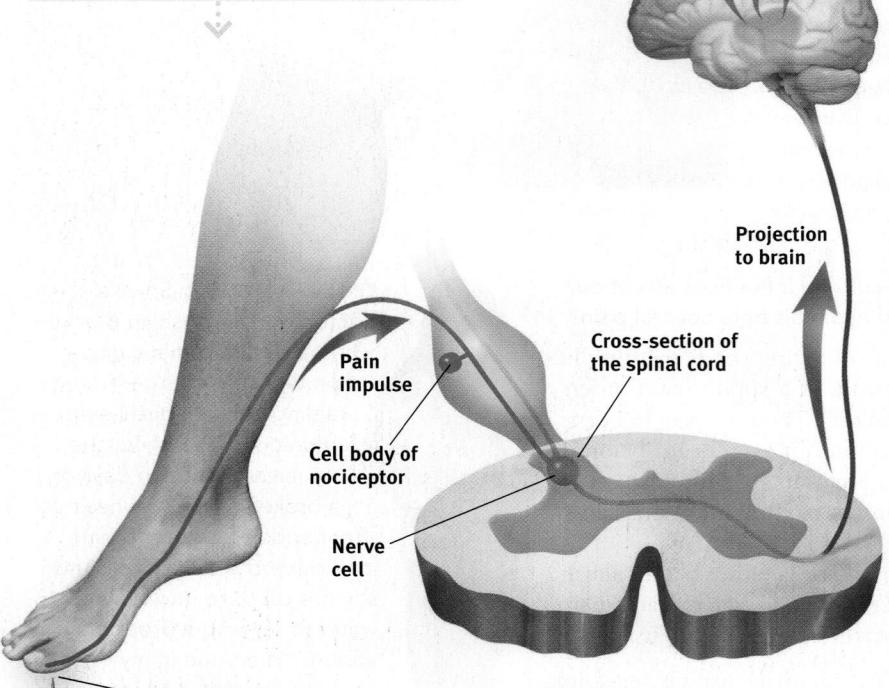

Projection to brain

Pain impulse

Cross-section of the spinal cord

Cell body of nociceptor

Nerve cell

Tissue injury

Your experience of pain depends in part on the genes you inherited and on your physical characteristics (Gatchel et al., 2007; Reimann et al., 2010). Women are more sensitive to pain than men are (their senses of hearing and smell also tend to be more sensitive) (Ruau et al., 2012; Wickelgren, 2009).

No pain theory can explain all available findings. One useful model, **gate-control theory,** was proposed by psychologist Ronald Melzack and biologist Patrick Wall (1965, 1983; Melzack & Katz, 2013, with support from Foster et al., 2015). This theory suggests that the spinal cord contains a neurological "gate" that controls the transmission of pain messages to the brain.

Small spinal cord nerve fibers conduct most pain signals. Melzack and Wall theorized that when tissue is injured, the small fibers activate and open the gate. The pain signals can then travel to your brain, and you feel pain. But large-fiber activity (stimulated by massage, electric stimulation, or acupuncture) can close the gate, blocking pain signals. Brain-to-spinal-cord messages can also close the gate. Thus, chronic pain can be treated both by gate-closing stimulation, such as massage, and by mental activity, such as distraction (Wall, 2000).

gate-control theory the theory that the spinal cord contains a neurological "gate" that blocks pain signals or allows them to pass on to the brain. The "gate" is opened by the activity of pain signals traveling up small nerve fibers and is closed by activity in larger fibers or by information coming from the brain.

But pain is not merely a physical phenomenon of injured nerves sending impulses to a definable brain or spinal cord area—like pulling on a rope to ring a bell. The brain can also create pain, as it does in *phantom limb sensations* after a limb amputation. Without normal sensory input, the brain may misinterpret and amplify spontaneous but irrelevant central nervous system activity. As the dreamer may see with eyes closed, so 7 in 10 such people may feel pain or movement in nonexistent limbs (Melzack, 1992, 2005). Some may even try to lift a cup with a phantom hand, or step off a bed onto a phantom leg. Even those born without a limb sometimes perceive sensations from the absent arm or leg. The brain, Melzack (1998) has surmised, comes prepared to anticipate "that it will be getting information from a body that has limbs."

Phantoms may haunt other senses, too. People with hearing loss often experience the sound of silence: *tinnitus,* the phantom sound of ringing in the ears that's accompanied by auditory brain activity (Sedley et al., 2015). Those who lose vision to glaucoma, cataracts, diabetes, or macular degeneration may experience phantom sights—nonthreatening hallucinations (Ramachandran & Blakeslee, 1998). Others who have nerve damage in the systems for tasting and smelling have experienced phantom tastes or smells, such as ice water that seems sickeningly sweet or fresh air that reeks of rotten food (Goode, 1999). The point to remember: *We feel, see, hear, taste, and smell with our brain, which can sense even without functioning senses.*

PSYCHOLOGICAL INFLUENCES One powerful influence on our perception of pain is the attention we focus on it. Athletes, focused on winning, may perceive pain differently and play through it.

We also seem to edit our *memories* of pain, which often differ from the pain we actually experienced. In experiments, and after painful experiences such as medical procedures or childbirth, people overlook a pain's duration. Their memory

William Haefeli/The Cartoon Bank/Conde Nast Publications

"I'd know my tinnitus anywhere and this isn't it."

snapshots instead record two factors: their pain's *peak* moment (which can lead them to recall variable pain, with peaks, as worse [Chajut et al., 2014; Stone et al., 2005]), and how much pain they felt at the *end*. In one experiment, people immersed one hand in painfully cold water for 60 seconds, and then the other hand in the same painfully cold water for 60 seconds followed by a slightly less painful 30 seconds more (Kahneman et al., 1993). Which experience would you expect they recalled as most painful?

Curiously, when asked which trial they would prefer to repeat, most preferred the 90-second trial, with more net pain—but less pain at the end. Physicians have used this principle with patients undergoing colon exams—lengthening the discomfort by a minute but lessening its intensity at the end (Kahneman, 1999). Patients experiencing this taper-down treatment later recalled the exam as less painful than did those whose pain ended abruptly. (If, as a painful root canal is ending, the oral surgeon asks if you'd rather go home or to have a few more minutes of milder discomfort, there's a case to be made for prolonging your hurt.)

The end of an experience can color our memory of pleasures, too. In one simple experiment, some people, on receiving a fifth and last piece of chocolate, were told it was their "next" one. Others, told it was their "last" piece, liked it better and also rated the whole experiment as being more enjoyable (O'Brien & Ellsworth, 2012). Endings matter.

SOCIAL-CULTURAL INFLUENCES Pain is a product of our attention, our expectations, and also our culture (Gatchel et al., 2007; Reimann et al., 2010). Not surprisingly, then, our perception of pain varies with our social situation and our cultural traditions. We tend to perceive more pain when others seem to be experiencing pain (Symbaluk et al., 1997). This may help explain the apparent social aspects of pain, as when groups of Australian keyboard operators during the mid-1980s suffered outbreaks of severe pain while typing or performing other repetitive work—without any discernible physical abnormalities (Gawande, 1998). Sometimes the pain in sprain is mainly in the brain—literally. When people felt empathy for another's pain, their own brain activity partly mirrored the activity of the actual brain in pain (Singer et al., 2004).

CONTROLLING PAIN If pain is where body meets mind—if it is both a physical and a psychological phenomenon—then it should be treatable both physically and psychologically. Depending on the symptoms, pain control therapies may include drugs, surgery, acupuncture, electrical stimulation, massage, exercise, hypnosis, relaxation training, meditation, and thought distraction.

When in pain we also benefit from our own built-in pain controls. Our brain releases a natural painkiller—*endorphins*—in response to severe pain or even vigorous exercise. Thus, when we are distracted from pain and soothed by endorphin release, the pain we experience may be greatly reduced. Sports injuries may go unnoticed until the after-game shower. People who carry a gene that boosts the availability of endorphins are less bothered by pain, and their brain is less responsive to pain (Zubieta et al., 2003). Others, who carry a mutated gene that disrupts pain circuit neurotransmission, may be unable to experience pain (Cox et al., 2006). Such discoveries point the way toward future pain medications that mimic these genetic effects.

PLACEBOS Even *placebos* can help, by dampening the central nervous system's attention and responses to painful experiences—mimicking painkilling drugs (Eippert et al., 2009; Wager & Atlas, 2013). After being injected in the jaw with a stinging saltwater solution, men in one experiment received a placebo they had been told would relieve the pain. It did—they immediately felt better. "Nothing" worked. The men's belief in the fake painkiller triggered their brain to respond by dispensing endorphins, as revealed by activity in an area that releases natural painkilling opiates (Scott et al., 2007; Zubieta et al., 2005). "Believing becomes reality," noted one commentator (Thernstrom, 2006), as "the mind unites with the body."

DISTRACTION Have you ever had a health care professional suggest that you focus on a pleasant image ("*Think of a warm, comfortable environment*") or perform some task ("*Count backward by 3's*")? Drawing attention away from the painful stimulation is an effective way to activate brain pathways that inhibit pain and increase pain tolerance (Edwards et al., 2009).

NOT PAYING ATTENTION TO PAIN After a tackle in the first half of a competitive game, Mohammed Ali Khan (here playing for BK Häcken in white) said he "had a bit of pain" but thought it was "just a bruise." With his attention focused on the game, he played on. In the second half he was surprised to learn from an attending doctor that his leg was broken.

ACUPUNCTURE: A JAB WELL DONE This acupuncturist is attempting to help this woman gain relief from back pain by using needles on points of the patient's hand.

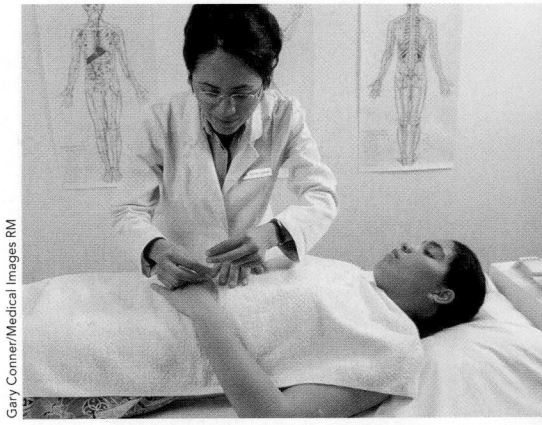

"Pain is increased by attending to it."
—Charles Darwin, *The Expression of Emotions in Man and Animals*, 1872

DISSOCIATION OR SOCIAL INFLUENCE? This hypnotized woman being tested by famous researcher Ernest Hilgard showed no pain when her arm was placed in an ice bath. But asked to press a key if some part of her felt the pain, she did so. To Hilgard (1986, 1992), this was evidence of dissociation, or divided consciousness. The social influence perspective, however, maintains that people responding this way are caught up in playing the role of "good subject."

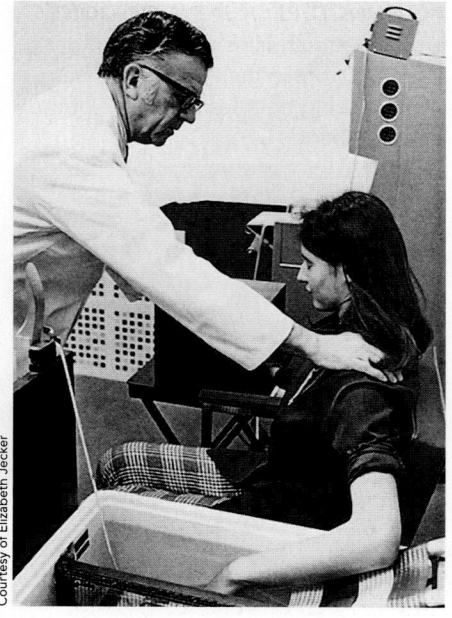

Courtesy of Elizabeth Jecker

For burn victims receiving excruciating wound care, an even more effective distraction is escaping into a computer-generated 3-D world. Functional MRI (fMRI) scans have revealed that playing in the virtual reality reduces the brain's pain-related activity (Hoffman, 2004). Because pain is in the brain, diverting the brain's attention may bring relief.

HYPNOSIS Better yet, research suggests, maximize pain relief by combining a placebo with distraction (Buhle et al., 2012) and amplifying their effects with **hypnosis.** Imagine you are about to be hypnotized. The hypnotist invites you to sit back, fix your gaze on a spot high on the wall, and relax. You hear a quiet, low voice suggest, "Your eyes are growing tired. . . . Your eyelids are becoming heavy . . . now heavier and heavier. . . . They are beginning to close. . . . You are becoming more deeply relaxed. . . . Your breathing is now deep and regular. . . . Your muscles are becoming more and more relaxed. . . . Your whole body is beginning to feel like lead." After a few minutes of this *hypnotic induction,* you may experience hypnosis. Words will have changed your brain.

Hypnotists have no magical mind-control power; they merely focus people's attention on certain images or behaviors. To some extent, we are all open to suggestion. But highly hypnotizable people—such as the 20 percent who can carry out a suggestion not to react to an open bottle of smelly ammonia—are especially suggestible and imaginative (Barnier & McConkey, 2004; Silva & Kirsch, 1992). Their brain also displays altered activity when under hypnosis (Jiang et al., 2016).

Can hypnosis relieve pain? *Yes.* When unhypnotized people put their arm in an ice bath, they felt intense pain within 25 seconds (Elkins et al., 2012; Jensen, 2008). When hypnotized people did the same after being given suggestions to feel no pain, they indeed reported feeling little pain. As some dentists know, light hypnosis can reduce fear, thus reducing hypersensitivity to pain. Hypnosis has also lessened some forms of chronic and disability-related pain (Adachi et al., 2014; Bowker & Dorstyn, 2016).

In surgical experiments, hypnotized patients have required less medication, recovered sooner, and left the hospital earlier than unhypnotized control patients (Askay & Patterson, 2007; Hammond, 2008; Spiegel, 2007). Nearly 10 percent of us can become so deeply hypnotized that even major surgery can be performed without anesthesia. Half of us can gain at least some pain relief from hypnosis. The surgical use of hypnosis has flourished in Europe, where one Belgian medical team has performed more than 5000 surgeries with a combination of hypnosis, local anesthesia, and a mild sedative (Song, 2006).

Psychologists have proposed two explanations for how hypnosis works:

- *Social influence theory* contends that hypnosis is a by-product of normal social and mental processes (Lynn et al., 1990, 2015; Spanos & Coe, 1992). In this view, hypnotized people, like actors caught up in a role, begin to feel and behave in ways appropriate for "good hypnotic subjects." They may allow the hypnotist to direct their attention and fantasies away from pain.

- *Dissociation theory* proposes that hypnosis is a special dual-processing state of **dissociation**—a split between different levels of consciousness. Dissociation theory seeks to explain why, when no one is watching, hypnotized people may carry out **posthypnotic suggestions** (which are made during hypnosis but carried out after the person is no longer hypnotized) (Perugini et al., 1998). It also offers an explanation for why people hypnotized for pain relief may show brain activity in areas that receive sensory information, but not in areas that normally process pain-related information (Rainville et al., 1997).

Selective attention may also play a role in hypnotic pain relief. Brain scans show that hypnosis increases activity in frontal lobe attention systems (Oakley & Halligan, 2013). So, while hypnosis does not block sensory input itself, it may block our attention to those stimuli. This helps explain why injured soldiers, caught up in battle, may feel little or no pain until they reach safety.

🔒 **RETRIEVE IT • • •**   *ANSWERS IN APPENDIX E*

RI-4 Which of the following has NOT been proven to reduce pain?
a. Distraction   b. Hypnosis   c. Phantom limb sensations   d. Endorphins

Taste

LOQ 18-6 In what ways are our senses of taste and smell similar, and how do they differ?

Like touch, *gustation*—our sense of taste—involves several basic sensations. Taste's sensations were once thought to be *sweet, sour, salty,* and *bitter,* with all others stemming from mixtures of these four (McBurney & Gent, 1979). Then, as investigators searched for specialized nerve fibers for the four taste sensations, they encountered a receptor for what we now know is a fifth—the savory, meaty taste of *umami,* best experienced as the flavor enhancer monosodium glutamate (MSG).

Tastes exist for more than our pleasure (see **TABLE 18.1**). Pleasureful tastes attracted our ancestors to energy- or protein-rich foods that enabled their survival. Aversive tastes deterred them from new foods that might be toxic. We see the inheritance of this biological wisdom in today's 2- to 6-year-olds, who are typically fussy eaters, especially when offered new meats or bitter-tasting vegetables, such as spinach and brussels sprouts (Cooke et al., 2003). Meat and plant toxins were both potentially dangerous sources of food poisoning for our ancestors, especially for children. Given repeated small tastes of disliked new foods, however, most children begin to accept them (Wardle et al., 2003). We come to like what we eat. Compared with breast-fed babies, German babies bottle-fed vanilla-flavored milk grew up to be adults with a striking preference for vanilla flavoring (Haller et al., 1999).

Taste is a chemical sense. Inside each little bump on the top and sides of your tongue are 200 or more taste buds, each containing a pore that catches food chemicals and releases neurotransmitters (Roper & Chaudhari, 2017). In each taste bud pore, 50 to 100 taste receptor cells project antenna-like hairs that sense food molecules. Some receptors respond mostly to sweet-tasting molecules, others to salty-, sour-, umami-, or bitter-tasting ones. Each receptor transmits its message to a matching partner cell in your brain's temporal lobe (Barretto et al., 2015). It doesn't take much to trigger a taste response. If a stream of water is pumped across your tongue, the addition of a concentrated salty or sweet taste for but one-tenth of a second will get your attention (Kelling & Halpern, 1983). When a friend asks for "just a taste" of your soft drink, you can squeeze off the straw after a mere instant.

Taste receptors reproduce themselves every week or two, so if you burn your tongue it hardly matters. However, as you grow older, the number of taste buds decreases, as does taste sensitivity (Cowart, 1981). (No wonder adults enjoy strong-tasting foods that children resist.) Smoking and alcohol use accelerate these declines. Those who have lost their sense of taste have reported that food tastes like "straw" and is hard to swallow (Cowart, 2005).

There's more to taste than meets the tongue. Expectations can influence taste. When told a sausage roll was "vegetarian," nonvegetarian people judged it decidedly inferior to its identical partner labeled "meat" (Allen et al., 2008). In another experiment, hearing that a wine cost $90 rather than its real $10 price made it taste better and triggered more activity in a brain area that responds to pleasant experiences (Plassmann et al., 2008). Contrary to Shakespeare's presumption (in *Romeo and Juliet*) that "a rose by any other name would smell as sweet," labels matter. And speaking of smell . . .

Smell

Inhale, exhale. Between birth's first inhale and death's last exhale, about 500 million breaths of life-sustaining air will bathe your nostrils in a stream of scent-laden molecules. The resulting experience of smell (**olfaction**) is strikingly intimate. With every breath, you inhale something of whatever or whoever it is you smell.

Smell, like taste, is a chemical sense. We smell something when molecules of a substance carried in the air reach a tiny cluster of receptor cells at the top of each nasal cavity (**FIGURE 18.8**). These 20 million olfactory receptors, waving like sea anemones on a reef, respond selectively—to the aroma of a cake baking, to a wisp of smoke, to a friend's fragrance. Instantly, they alert the brain through their axon fibers.

Being part of an old, primitive sense, olfactory neurons bypass the brain's sensory control center, the thalamus. Eons before our cerebral cortex had fully evolved, our

hypnosis a social interaction in which one person (the hypnotist) suggests to another (the subject) that certain perceptions, feelings, thoughts, or behaviors will spontaneously occur.

dissociation a split in consciousness, which allows some thoughts and behaviors to occur simultaneously with others.

posthypnotic suggestion a suggestion, made during a hypnosis session, to be carried out after the subject is no longer hypnotized; used by some clinicians to help control undesired symptoms and behaviors.

olfaction our sense of smell.

Lauren Burke/Getty Images

TABLE 18.1

The Survival Functions of Basic Tastes

Taste	Indicates
Sweet	Energy source
Salty	Sodium essential to physiological processes
Sour	Potentially toxic acid
Bitter	Potential poisons
Umami	Proteins to grow and repair tissue

Impress your friends with your new word for the day: People unable to see are said to experience blindness. People unable to hear experience deafness. People unable to smell experience *anosmia.* The 1 in 7500 people born with anosmia not only have trouble cooking and eating, but also are somewhat more prone to depression, accidents, and relationship insecurity (Croy et al., 2012, 2013).

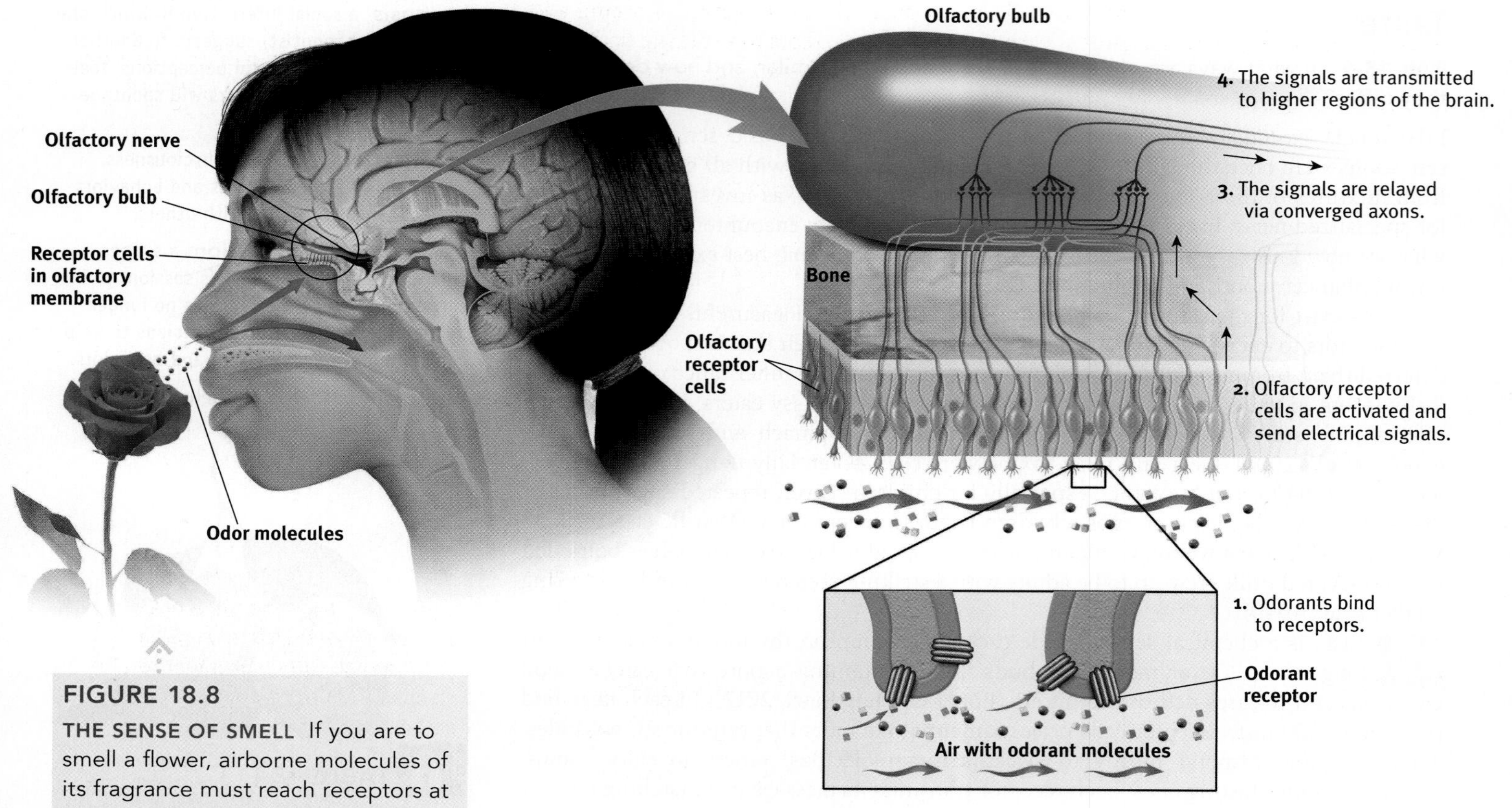

Olfactory bulb

4. The signals are transmitted to higher regions of the brain.

3. The signals are relayed via converged axons.

Olfactory nerve

Olfactory bulb

Receptor cells in olfactory membrane

Bone

Olfactory receptor cells

2. Olfactory receptor cells are activated and send electrical signals.

Odor molecules

1. Odorants bind to receptors.

Odorant receptor

Air with odorant molecules

FIGURE 18.8

THE SENSE OF SMELL If you are to smell a flower, airborne molecules of its fragrance must reach receptors at the top of your nose. Sniffing swirls air up to the receptors, enhancing the aroma. The receptor cells send messages to the brain's olfactory bulb, and then onward to the temporal lobe's primary smell cortex and to the parts of the limbic system involved in memory and emotion.

THE NOSE KNOWS Humans have some 20 million olfactory receptors. A blood-hound has 220 million (Herz, 2007).

mammalian ancestors sniffed for food—and for predators. They also smelled molecules called *pheromones*, secreted by other members of their species. Some pheromones serve as sexual attractants.

Odor molecules come in many shapes and sizes—so many, in fact, that it takes many different receptors to detect them. A large family of genes designs the 350 or so receptor proteins that recognize particular odor molecules (Miller, 2004). Linda Buck and Richard Axel (1991) discovered (in work for which they received a 2004 Nobel Prize) that these receptor proteins are embedded on the surface of nasal cavity neurons. As a key slips into a lock, so odor molecules slip into these receptors. Yet we don't seem to have a distinct receptor for each detectable odor. Odors trigger combinations of receptors, in patterns that are interpreted by the olfactory cortex. As the English alphabet's 26 letters can combine to form many words, so odor molecules bind to different receptor arrays, producing at least 1 trillion odors that we could potentially discriminate (Bushdid et al., 2014). Neuroscientists have identified complex combinations of olfactory receptors that trigger different neural networks, allowing us to distinguish between delightful and disagreeable odors (Zou et al., 2016).

Aided by smell, a mother fur seal returning to a beach crowded with pups will find her own. Human mothers and nursing infants also quickly learn to recognize each other's scents (McCarthy, 1986).

The brain knows what the nose doesn't like (Cook et al., 2017; Zou et al., 2016). When mice sniff a predator's scent, their brain instinctively sends signals to stress-related neurons (Kondoh et al., 2016). But a smell's appeal—or lack of it—also depends on learned associations (Herz, 2001). In the United States, people associate the smell of wintergreen with candy and gum, and they tend to like it. In Great Britain, wintergreen often is associated with medicine, and people find it less appealing. Odors also evoked unpleasant emotions when researchers frustrated Brown University students with a rigged computer game in a scented room (Herz et al., 2004). Later, if exposed to the same odor while working on a verbal task, the students' frustration was rekindled and they gave up sooner than others exposed to a different odor or no odor.

Although important, our sense of smell is less acute than our senses of seeing and hearing. Looking out across a garden, we see its forms and colors in exquisite detail and hear a variety of birds singing, yet we smell little of it without sticking our nose into the blossoms. Compared with how we experience and remember sights and sounds, smells are primitive and harder to describe and recall (Richardson & Zucco, 1989; Zucco, 2003).

We might struggle to recall odors by name, but we have a remarkable capacity to recognize long-forgotten odors and their associated memories (Engen, 1987; Schab, 1991). Our brain's circuitry helps explain why certain odors—the smell of the sea, the scent of a perfume, or an aroma of a favorite relative's kitchen—can bring to mind a happy time. Other odors remind us of traumatic events—childhood physical abuse, tragedy on the battlefield—activating brain regions related to fear (Kadohisa, 2013). Indeed, a hotline runs between the brain area receiving information from the nose and the brain's ancient limbic centers associated with memory and emotion (**FIGURE 18.9**). Thus, when put in a foul-smelling room, people have expressed harsher judgments of immoral acts (such as lying or keeping a found wallet) (Inbar et al., 2011; Schnall et al., 2008). Exposed to a fishy smell, people became more suspicious (Lee et al., 2015). And when riding on a train car with the citrus scent of a cleaning product, people have left behind less trash (de Lange et al., 2012).

Gender, age, and physical condition influence our ability to identify scents. Women tend to have a better sense of smell, but for all of us, the sense of smell peaks in early adulthood and gradually declines thereafter (Doty, 2001; Wickelgren, 2009; Wysocki & Gilbert, 1989).

🔒 RETRIEVE IT • • •   *ANSWERS IN APPENDIX E*

RI-5 How does our system for sensing smell differ from our sensory systems for touch and taste?

Body Position and Movement

LOQ 18-7   How do we sense our body's position and movement?

Millions of position and motion sensors in muscles, tendons, and joints all over your body provide constant feedback to your brain, enabling your sense of **kinesthesia,** which keeps you aware of your body parts' position and movement. Twist your wrist one degree and your brain receives an immediate update.

You can momentarily imagine being without sight or sound. Close your eyes or plug your ears, and experience the dark silence. But what would it be like to live without touch or kinesthesia—without being able to sense the positions of your limbs when you wake during the night? Ian Waterman of Hampshire, England, knows. In 1972, at age 19, Waterman contracted a rare viral infection that destroyed the nerves enabling his sense of light touch and of body position and movement. People with this condition report feeling disembodied, as though their body is dead, not real, not theirs (Sacks, 1985). With prolonged practice, Waterman learned to walk and eat—by visually focusing on his limbs and directing them accordingly. But if the lights went out, he would crumple to the floor (Azar, 1998).

Vision interacts with kinesthesia for you, too. Stand with your right heel in front of your left toes. Easy. Now close your eyes and try again. Did you wobble?

A companion **vestibular sense** monitors your head's (and thus your body's) position and movement. The biological gyroscopes for this sense of equilibrium are two structures in your inner ear. The first, your fluid-filled *semicircular canals,* look like a three-dimensional pretzel (Figure 18.2a). The second structure is the pair of calcium-crystal–filled *vestibular sacs.* When your head rotates or tilts, the movement of these organs stimulates hair-like receptors, which send nerve signals to your cerebellum at the back of your brain, enabling you to sense your body position and maintain your balance.

If you twirl around and then come to an abrupt halt, neither the fluid in your semicircular canals nor your kinesthetic receptors will immediately return to their neutral state.

🔒 📷 LaunchPad Test your understanding of how we smell by engaging online with **Concept Practice: Sense of Smell.**

"There could be a stack of truck tires burning in the living room, and I wouldn't necessarily smell it. Whereas my wife can detect a lone spoiled grape two houses away." —Dave Barry, 2005

FIGURE 18.9

TASTE, SMELL, AND MEMORY Information from the taste buds (yellow arrow) travels to an area between the frontal and temporal lobes of the brain. It registers in an area not far from where the brain receives information from our sense of smell, which interacts with taste. The brain's circuitry for smell (red area) also connects with areas involved in memory storage, which helps explain why a smell can trigger a memory.

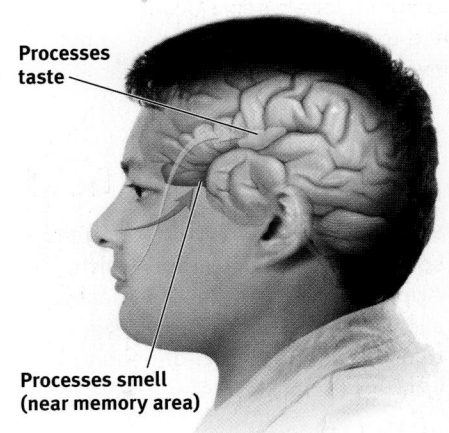

Processes taste

Processes smell (near memory area)

kinesthesia [kin-ehs-THEE-zhuh] our movement sense—our system for sensing the position and movement of individual body parts.

vestibular sense our sense of balance— our sense of body movement and position that enables our sense of balance.

BODIES IN SPACE Each of these high school competitive cheer team members can thank her inner ears for the information that enables her brain to monitor her body's position so expertly.

sensory interaction the principle that one sense may influence another, as when the smell of food influences its taste.

embodied cognition the influence of bodily sensations, gestures, and other states on cognitive preferences and judgments.

extrasensory perception (ESP) the controversial claim that perception can occur apart from sensory input; includes telepathy, clairvoyance, and precognition.

FIGURE 18.10

SENSORY INTERACTION Seeing the speaker forming the words, which Apple's FaceTime video-chat feature allows, makes those words easier to understand for hard-of-hearing listeners (Knight, 2004).

The dizzy aftereffect fools your brain with the sensation that you're still spinning. This illustrates a principle that underlies perceptual illusions: *Mechanisms that normally give us an accurate experience of the world can, under certain conditions, fool us.* Understanding how we get fooled provides clues to how our perceptual system works.

One little-known fact about your vestibular sense: It is super speedy. If you slip, your vestibular sensors automatically and instantly order your skeletal response, well before you have consciously decided how to right yourself.

ENGAGE   Try this: Hold one of your thumbs in front of your face then move it rapidly right to left and back. Notice how your thumb blurs (your vision isn't fast enough to track it). Now hold your thumb still and swivel your head from left to right. Surprise! Your thumb stays clear—because your vestibular system, which is monitoring your head position, speedily moves the eyes. Head moves right, eyes move left. Vision is fast, but the vestibular sense is faster.

🔒 RETRIEVE IT • • •   *ANSWERS IN APPENDIX E*

RI-6 Where are the kinesthetic receptors and the vestibular sense receptors located?

SENSORY INTERACTION

LOQ 18-8 How does *sensory interaction* influence our perceptions, and what is *embodied cognition*?

We have seen that vision and kinesthesia interact. Actually, none of our senses acts alone. All of them—seeing, hearing, tasting, smelling, touching—eavesdrop on one another, and our brain blends their inputs to interpret the world (Rosenblum, 2013). This is **sensory interaction** at work. One sense can influence another.

ENGAGE   Consider how smell sticks its nose into the business of taste. Hold your nose, close your eyes, and have someone feed you various foods. A slice of apple may be indistinguishable from a chunk of raw potato. A piece of steak may taste like cardboard. Without their smells, a cup of cold coffee may be hard to distinguish from a glass of red wine. A big part of taste is right under your nose.

Thus, to savor a taste, we normally breathe the aroma through our nose. Like smoke rising in a chimney, food molecules rise into your nasal cavity. This is why food tastes bland when you have a bad cold. Smell can also change our perception of taste: A drink's strawberry odor enhances our perception of its sweetness. Even touch can influence taste. Depending on its texture, a potato chip "tastes" fresh or stale (Smith, 2011). Smell + texture + taste = flavor. Yet perhaps you have noticed: Despite smell's contribution, flavor feels located in the mouth, not in the nose (Stevenson, 2014).

Vision and hearing may similarly interact. A weak flicker of light that we have trouble perceiving becomes more visible when accompanied by a short burst of sound (Kayser, 2007). The reverse is also true: We can hear soft sounds more easily if they are paired with a visual cue. If I [DM], as a person with hearing loss, watch a video with on-screen captions, I have no trouble hearing the words I am seeing. But if I then decide I don't need the captions and turn them off, I will quickly realize I do need them. The eyes guide the ears (**FIGURE 18.10**).

So our senses interact. But what happens if they disagree? What if our eyes *see* a speaker form one sound but our ears *hear* another sound? Surprise: Our brain may perceive a third sound that blends both inputs. Seeing the mouth movements for *ga* while hearing *ba* we may perceive *da*. This phenomenon is known as the *McGurk effect,* after Scottish psychologist Harry McGurk, who, with his assistant John MacDonald, discovered the effect (1976). For all of us, lip reading is part of hearing.

We have seen that our perceptions have two main ingredients: Our bottom-up sensations and our top-down cognitions (such as expectations, attitudes, thoughts, and memories). In everyday life, sensation and perception are two points on a continuum. It's not surprising, then, that the brain circuits processing our physical sensations sometimes interact with brain circuits responsible for cognition. The result is **embodied cognition.** We think from within a body. Some examples from playful experiments:

- *Physical warmth may promote social warmth.* After holding a warm drink rather than a cold one, people were more likely to rate someone more warmly, feel closer to them, and behave more generously (IJzerman & Semin, 2009; Williams & Bargh, 2008). Have hot tea with Jose and iced tea with his identical twin Juan, and you may perceive Jose to be a warmer person.

- *Pose your fingers, prime your mind.* After using their fingers to show a number (2, 3, or 4), people more quickly identified that same number when they heard it (Sixtus et al., 2017). Numbers made with fingers make thoughts of numbers linger.

- *Judgments of others may also mimic body sensations.* Sitting at a wobbly desk and chair makes others' relationships, or even one's own romantic relationship, seem less stable (Forest et al., 2015: Kille et al., 2013).

ASK YOURSELF

When have you experienced a feeling that you think could be explained by embodied cognition?

LaunchPad Are you wondering how researchers test these kinds of questions? Play the role of researcher by engaging online with **Immersive Learning: How Would You Know If a Cup of Coffee Can Warm Up Relationships?**

As we attempt to decipher our world, our brain blends inputs from multiple channels. But in a few select individuals, the brain circuits for two or more senses become joined in a phenomenon called *synesthesia,* where the stimulation of one sense (such as hearing sound) triggers an experience of another (such as seeing color). Early in life, "exuberant neural connectivity" produces some arbitrary associations among the senses, which later are normally—but not always—pruned (Wagner & Dobkins, 2011). Thus, hearing music may activate color-sensitive cortex regions and trigger a sensation of color (Brang et al., 2008; Hubbard et al., 2005). Seeing the number 3 may evoke a taste or color sensation (Ward, 2003). People with synesthesia experience such sensory shifts.

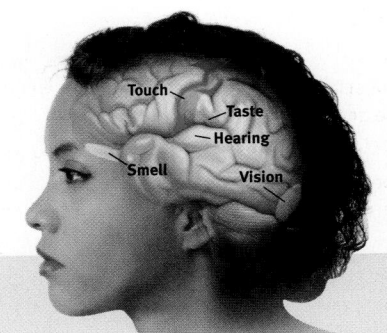

* * *

For a summary of our sensory systems, see **TABLE 18.2**.

TABLE 18.2

Summarizing the Senses

Sensory System	Source	Receptors	Key Brain Areas
Vision	Light waves striking the eye	Rods and cones in the retina	Occipital lobes
Hearing	Sound waves striking the outer ear	Cochlear hair cells (cilia) in the inner ear	Temporal lobes
Touch	Pressure, warmth, cold, harmful chemicals	Receptors (including pain-sensitive *nociceptors*), mostly in the skin, which detect pressure, warmth, cold, and pain	Somatosensory cortex
Taste	Chemical molecules in the mouth	Basic taste receptors for sweet, sour, salty, bitter, and umami	Frontal temporal lobe border
Smell	Chemical molecules breathed in through the nose	Millions of receptors at top of nasal cavities	Olfactory bulb
Body position—kinesthesia	Any change in position of a body part, interacting with vision	Kinesthetic sensors in joints, tendons, and muscles	Cerebellum
Body movement—vestibular sense	Movement of fluids in the inner ear caused by head/ body movement	Hair-like receptors in the ears' semicircular canals and vestibular sacs	Cerebellum

ESP—PERCEPTION WITHOUT SENSATION?

LOQ 18-9   What are the claims of *ESP,* and what have most research psychologists concluded after putting these claims to the test?

The river of perception is fed by streams of sensation, cognition, and emotion. If perception is the product of these three sources, what can we say about **extrasensory perception (ESP)**, which claims that perception can occur apart from sensory input? Are there indeed people—any people—who can read minds, see through walls, or foretell the future? Nearly half of Americans have agreed there are (AP, 2007; Moore, 2005).

LaunchPad Do you think you might have ESP? Test your skills by engaging online with **Immersive Learning: Assess Your Strengths—ESP and Critical Thinking.**

WHEN PSYCHICS PROPOSE

Will you marry me, live happily for 3 years, become bored, pretend to be taking a pottery class but actually be having an affair, then agree to go to marriage counseling to stay together for the sake of our hyperactive son, Derrick?

A headline you've never seen: "Psychic wins lottery."

If ESP is real, we would need to overturn the scientific understanding that we are creatures whose minds are tied to our physical brains and whose perceptual experiences of the world are built of sensations. The most testable and, for this discussion, most relevant ESP claims are

- *telepathy:* mind-to-mind communication.
- *clairvoyance:* perceiving remote events, such as a house on fire in another state.
- *precognition:* perceiving future events, such as an unexpected death in the next month.

Closely linked is *psychokinesis,* or "mind moving matter," such as levitating a table or influencing the roll of a die. (The claim, also called *telekinesis,* is illustrated by the wry request, "Will all those who believe in psychokinesis please raise my hand?")

Most research psychologists and scientists have been skeptical that paranormal phenomena exist. But in several reputable universities, **parapsychology** researchers perform scientific experiments searching for possible ESP phenomena (Storm et al., 2010a,b; Turpin, 2005). Before seeing how they conduct their research, let's consider some popular beliefs.

Premonitions or Pretensions?

Can psychics see into the future? Although one might wish for a psychic stock forecaster, the tallied forecasts of "leading psychics" reveal meager accuracy. During the 1990s, the tabloid psychics were all wrong in predicting surprising events. (Madonna did not become a gospel singer, the Statue of Liberty did not lose both its arms in a terrorist blast, Queen Elizabeth did not abdicate her throne to enter a convent.) And the psychics have missed big-news events. Where were the psychics on 9/10 when we needed them? Why, despite a $50 million reward, could no psychics help locate Osama bin Laden after 9/11? And why, when the Chilean government consulted four psychics after a mine collapse trapped 33 miners in 2010, did those psychics sorrowfully decide "They're all dead" (Kraul, 2010)? Imagine their surprise when all 33 miners were rescued 69 days later.

After Amanda Berry went missing in Cleveland in 2003, her distraught and desperate mother turned to a famed TV psychic detective for answers. "She's not alive, honey," the psychic told the devastated mom, who died without living to see her daughter rescued in 2013 (Radford, 2013). According to one analysis, this result brought that psychic's record on 116 missing person and death cases to 83 unknown outcomes, 33 incorrect, and zero mostly correct. To researcher Ryan Shaffer (2013), that's the record of a "psychic defective."

The psychic visions offered to police departments have been no more accurate than guesses made by others (Nickell, 1994, 2005; Radford, 2010; Reiser, 1982). But their sheer volume does increase the odds of an occasional correct guess, which psychics can then report to the media. Such visions can sound amazingly correct when later retrofitted to match events. Nostradamus, a sixteenth-century French psychic, explained in an unguarded moment that his ambiguous prophecies "could not possibly be understood till they were interpreted after the event and by it."

Are everyday people's "visions" any more accurate than the psychics' predictions? Do our dreams foretell the future, or do they only seem to do so when we recall or reconstruct them in light of what has already happened? Are our remembered visions merely revisions? After famed aviator Charles Lindbergh's baby son was kidnapped and murdered in 1932, but before the body was discovered, two Harvard psychologists invited people to report their dreams about the child (Murray & Wheeler, 1937). How many visionaries replied? 1300. How many accurately envisioned the child dead? Five percent. How many also correctly anticipated the body's location—buried among trees? Only 4. Although this number was surely no better than chance, to those 4 dreamers, the accuracy of their apparent precognitions must have seemed uncanny.

Given the countless events in the world each day, and given enough days, some stunning coincidences are sure to occur. By one careful estimate, chance alone would predict that more than a thousand times per day, someone on Earth will think of another person and then, within the next five minutes, learn of that person's death (Charpak & Broch, 2004). Thus, when explaining an astonishing event, we should "give chance a chance" (Lilienfeld, 2009). With enough time and people, the improbable becomes inevitable.

parapsychology the study of paranormal phenomena, including ESP and psychokinesis (also called *telekinesis*).

Putting ESP to Experimental Test

When faced with claims of mind reading or out-of-body travel or communication with the dead, how can we separate fiction from strange-but-true fact? Psychological science offers a simple answer: *Test them to see if they work.* If they do, so much the better for the ideas. If they don't, so much the better for our skepticism.

Both believers and skeptics agree that what parapsychology needs is a reproducible phenomenon and a theory to explain it. Parapsychologist Rhea White (1998) spoke for many in saying that "the image of parapsychology that comes to my mind, based on nearly 44 years in the field, is that of a small airplane [that] has been perpetually taxiing down the runway of the Empirical Science Airport since 1882 . . . its movement punctuated occasionally by lifting a few feet off the ground only to bump back down on the tarmac once again. It has never taken off for any sustained flight."

How might we test ESP claims in a controlled, reproducible experiment? An experiment differs from a staged demonstration. In the laboratory, the experimenter controls what the "psychic" sees and hears. On stage, the psychic controls what the audience sees and hears.

Daryl Bem, a respected social psychologist, once quipped that "a psychic is an actor playing the role of a psychic" (1984). Yet this one-time skeptic reignited hopes for replicable evidence of ESP with nine experiments that seemed to show people anticipating future events (2011). In one, when an erotic scene was about to appear on a screen in one of two randomly selected positions, Cornell University participants guessed the right placement 53.1 percent of the time (beating 50 percent by a small but statistically significant margin).

Despite the paper having survived critical reviews by a top-tier journal, critics scoffed. Some found the methods "badly flawed" (Alcock, 2011) or the statistical analyses "biased" (Wagenmakers et al., 2011). Others predicted the results could not be replicated by "independent and skeptical researchers" (Helfand, 2011).

Anticipating such skepticism, Bem has made his research materials available to anyone who wishes to replicate his studies. Multiple attempts have met with minimal success and continuing controversy (Bem et al., 2014; Galak et al., 2012; Ritchie et al., 2012; Wagenmakers, 2014). Regardless, science is doing its work:

- It has been open to a finding that challenges its own assumptions.
- Through follow-up research, it has assessed the reliability and validity of that finding.

And that is how science sifts crazy-sounding ideas, leaving most on the historical waste heap while occasionally surprising us.

For 19 years, one skeptic, magician James Randi, offered $1 million "to anyone who proves a genuine psychic power under proper observing conditions" (Randi, 1999; Thompson, 2010). French, Australian, and Indian groups have made similar offers of up to 200,000 euros (CFI, 2003). Large as these sums are, the scientific seal of approval would be worth far more. To refute those who say there is no ESP, one need only produce a single person who can demonstrate a single, reproducible ESP event. (To refute those who say pigs can't talk would take but one talking pig.) So far, no such person has emerged.

* * *

To feel awe, mystery, and a deep reverence for life, we need look no further than our own perceptual system and its capacity for organizing formless nerve impulses into colorful sights, vivid sounds, and evocative smells. As Shakespeare's Hamlet recognized, "There are more things in Heaven and Earth, Horatio, than are dreamt of in your philosophy." Within our ordinary sensory and perceptual experiences lies much that is truly extraordinary—surely much more than has so far been dreamt of in our psychology.

Courtesy of Claire Cole

TESTING PSYCHIC POWERS IN THE BRITISH POPULATION Psychologists created a "mind machine" to see if people could influence or predict a coin toss (Wiseman & Greening, 2002). Using a touch-sensitive screen, visitors to British festivals were given four attempts to call heads or tails, playing against a computer that kept score. By the time the experiment ended, nearly 28,000 people had predicted 110,959 tosses—with 49.8 percent correct.

"A person who talks a lot is sometimes right." —Spanish proverb

"At the heart of science is an essential tension between two seemingly contradictory attitudes—an openness to new ideas, no matter how bizarre or counterintuitive they may be, and the most ruthless skeptical scrutiny of all ideas, old and new." —Carl Sagan (1987)

🔒 **RETRIEVE IT** • • •   *ANSWERS IN APPENDIX E*

RI-7 If an ESP event occurred under controlled conditions, what would be the next best step to confirm that ESP really exists?

⟫ Learning Objectives

TEST YOURSELF Answer these repeated Learning Objective Questions on your own (before checking the answers in Appendix D) to improve your retention of the concepts (McDaniel et al., 2009, 2015).

18-1 What are the characteristics of air pressure waves that we hear as sound?

18-2 How does the ear transform sound energy into neural messages?

18-3 How do we detect loudness, discriminate pitch, and locate sounds?

18-4 How do we sense touch?

18-5 What biological, psychological, and social-cultural influences affect our experience of pain? How do placebos, distraction, and hypnosis help control pain?

18-6 In what ways are our senses of taste and smell similar, and how do they differ?

18-7 How do we sense our body's position and movement?

18-8 How does *sensory interaction* influence our perceptions, and what is *embodied cognition*?

18-9 What are the claims of *ESP*, and what have most research psychologists concluded after putting these claims to the test?

⟫ Terms and Concepts to Remember

TEST YOURSELF Write down the definition yourself, then check your answer on the referenced page.

audition, **p. 216**

frequency, **p. 216**

pitch, **p. 216**

middle ear, **p. 216**

cochlea [KOHK-lee-uh], **p. 216**

inner ear, **p. 216**

sensorineural hearing loss, **p. 219**

conduction hearing loss, **p. 219**

cochlear implant, **p. 219**

place theory, **p. 219**

frequency theory, **p. 220**

gate-control theory, **p. 222**

hypnosis, **p. 225**

dissociation, **p. 225**

posthypnotic suggestion, **p. 225**

olfaction, **p. 225**

kinesthesia, **p. 227**

vestibular sense, **p. 227**

sensory interaction, **p. 228**

embodied cognition, **p. 228**

extrasensory perception (ESP), **p. 228**

parapsychology, **p. 230**

⟫ Experience the Testing Effect

TEST YOURSELF Answer the following questions on your own first, then check your answers in Appendix E.

1. The snail-shaped tube in the inner ear, where sound waves are converted into neural activity, is called the _____.

2. What are the basic steps in transforming sound waves into perceived sound?

3. _____ theory explains how we hear high-pitched sounds, and _____ theory, extended by the _____ principle, explains how we hear low-pitched sounds.

4. The sensory receptors that are found mostly in the skin and that detect hurtful temperatures, pressure, or chemicals are called _____.

5. The gate-control theory of pain proposes that
   a. special pain receptors send signals directly to the brain.
   b. pain is a property of the senses, not of the brain.
   c. small spinal cord nerve fibers conduct most pain signals, but large-fiber activity can close access to those pain signals.
   d. pain can often be controlled and managed effectively through the use of relaxation techniques.

6. How does the biopsychosocial approach explain our experience of pain? Provide examples.

7. We have specialized nerve receptors for detecting which five tastes? How did this ability aid our ancestors?

8. _____ is your sense of body position and movement. Your _____ _____ specifically monitors your head's movement, with sensors in the inner ear.

9. Why do you feel a little dizzy immediately after a roller-coaster ride?

10. A food's aroma can greatly enhance its taste. This is an example of
    a. olfaction.
    b. synesthesia.
    c. kinesthesia.
    d. sensory interaction.

11. Which of the following ESP phenomena is supported by solid, replicable scientific evidence?
    a. Telepathy
    b. Clairvoyance
    c. Precognition
    d. None of these phenomena

Continue testing yourself with 📖 **LearningCurve** or 📖 **Achieve Read & Practice**
to learn and remember most effectively.

Learning

MODULES 19–21

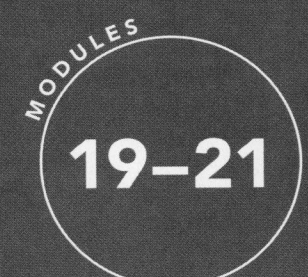

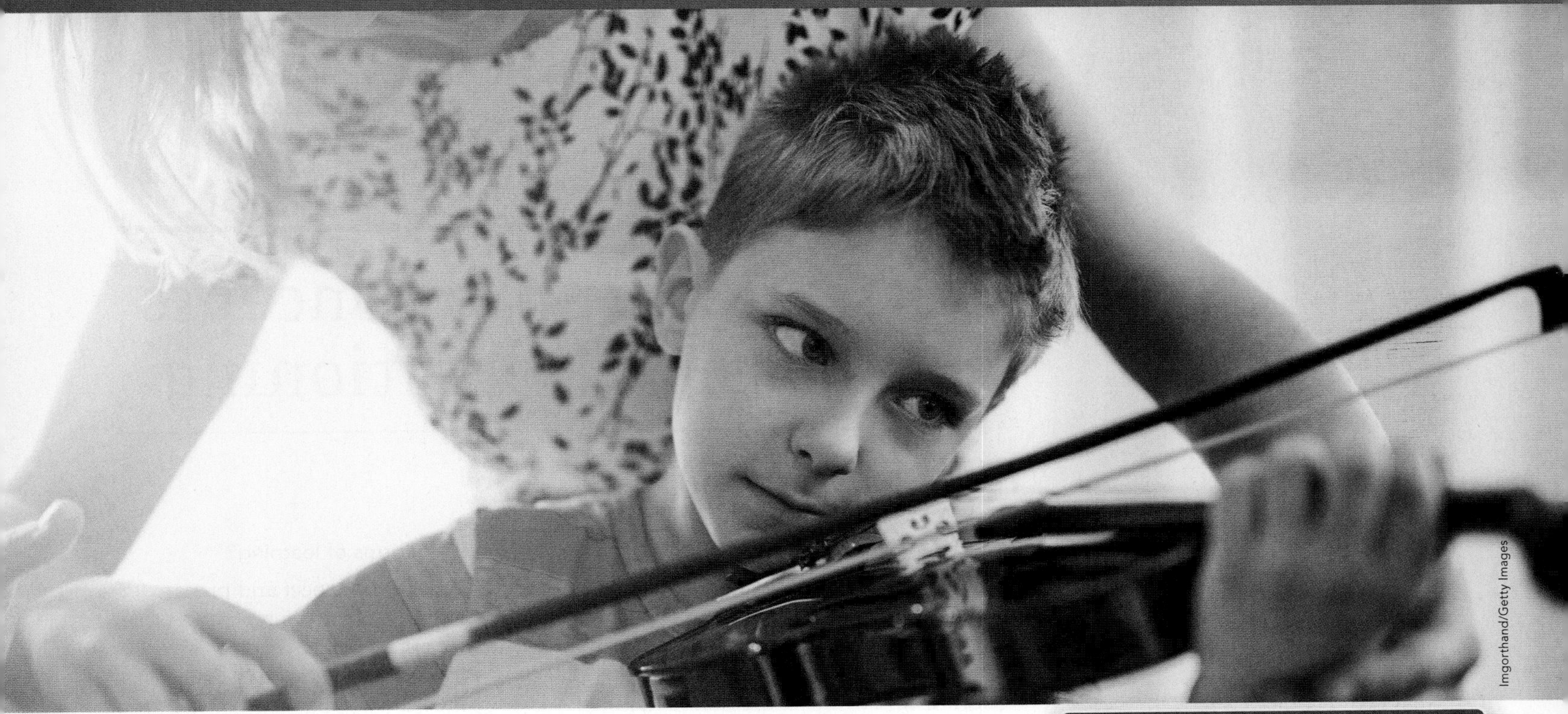

Imgorthand/Getty Images

OVERVIEW OF MODULES

In the early 1940s, University of Minnesota graduate students Marian Breland and Keller Breland witnessed the power of a new learning technology. Their mentor, B. F. Skinner, would become famous for *shaping* rat and pigeon behaviors by delivering well-timed rewards as the animals inched closer and closer to a desired behavior. Impressed by Skinner's results, the Brelands began shaping the behavior of cats, chickens, parakeets, turkeys, pigs, ducks, and hamsters (Bailey & Gillaspy, 2005). They eventually formed Animal Behavior Enterprises and spent the next half-century training more than 15,000 animals from 140 species. Their efforts helped pave the way for training animals to help humans, including police officers and people with vision loss or seizure disorders.

Like other animals, humans learn from experience. Indeed, nature's most important gift may be our *adaptability*—our capacity to learn new behaviors that help us cope with our changing world. We can learn how to build grass huts or snow shelters, submarines or space stations, and thereby adapt to almost any environment.

Oprah Winfrey is a living example of adaptability. Growing up in poverty with her grandmother, Winfrey wore dresses made of potato sacks. She was a constant target of racism. Beginning at age nine, she was molested by several family members, leading her to run away from home at age 13. She became pregnant at age 14, but her son died shortly after birth.

To overcome such tremendous adversity, Winfrey learned how to adapt to new situations. She joined her high school speech team and used this talent to win a college scholarship. After graduating, she moved to Chicago and took over as the host of a struggling talk show, transforming it into the most popular show in America. "Education," Winfrey said, "is the key to unlocking the world, a passport to freedom."

Winfrey shows us how learning breeds hope. What is learnable we can potentially teach—a fact that encourages parents, educators, coaches, and animal trainers. What has been learned we can potentially change by new learning—an assumption that underlies counseling, psychotherapy, and rehabilitation programs. No matter how unhappy, unsuccessful, or unloving we are, that need not be the end of our story.

No topic is closer to the heart of psychology than *learning*. Psychologists study infants' learning, and the learning of visual perceptions, of a drug's expected effect, and of gender roles. They also consider how learning shapes our thoughts and language, our motivations and emotions, our personalities and attitudes. Here in Modules 19–21 we examine the heart of learning: classical conditioning, operant conditioning, the effects of biology and cognition on learning, and learning by observation. ▶

⒆ Basic Learning Concepts and Classical Conditioning

HOW DO WE LEARN?

LEARNING OBJECTIVE QUESTION (LOQ)

19-1 How do we define *learning*, and what are some basic forms of learning?

By **learning**, we humans adapt to our environments. We learn to expect and prepare for significant events such as food or pain (*classical conditioning*). We learn to repeat acts that bring rewards and to avoid acts that bring unwanted results (*operant conditioning*). We learn new behaviors by observing events and people, and through language, we learn things we have neither experienced nor observed (*cognitive learning*). But *how* do we learn?

One way we learn is by *association*. Our mind naturally connects events that occur in sequence. Suppose you see and smell freshly baked bread, eat some, and find it satisfying. The next time you see and smell fresh bread, you will expect that eating it will again be satisfying. So, too, with sounds. If you associate a sound with a frightening consequence, hearing the sound alone may trigger your fear. As one 4-year-old exclaimed after watching a TV character get mugged, "If I had heard that music, I wouldn't have gone around the corner!" (Wells, 1981).

Learned associations also feed our habitual behaviors (Wood et al., 2014b). Habits can form when we repeat behaviors in a given context—sleeping in a certain posture in bed, biting our nails in class, eating popcorn in a movie theater. As behavior becomes linked with the context, our next experience of the context will evoke our habitual response. Especially when our willpower is depleted, as when we're mentally fatigued, we tend to fall back on our habits (Neal et al., 2013). That's true of both good habits (eating fruit) and bad (overindulging in alcohol) (Graybiel & Smith, 2014). To increase our self-control, and to connect our resolutions with positive outcomes, the key is forming "beneficial habits" (Galla & Duckworth, 2015).

How long does it take to form a beneficial habit? To find out, one British research team asked 96 university students to choose some healthy behavior (such as running before dinner or eating fruit with lunch), to do it daily for 84 days, and to record whether the behavior felt automatic (something they did without thinking and would find it hard not to do). On average, behaviors became habitual after about 66 days (Lally et al., 2010). Is there something you'd like to make a routine or essential part of your life?

---

learning the process of acquiring through experience new and relatively enduring information or behaviors.

associative learning learning that certain events occur together. The events may be two stimuli (as in classical conditioning) or a response and its consequence (as in operant conditioning).

stimulus any event or situation that evokes a response.

respondent behavior behavior that occurs as an automatic response to some stimulus.

operant behavior behavior that operates on the environment, producing a consequence.

Two related events:

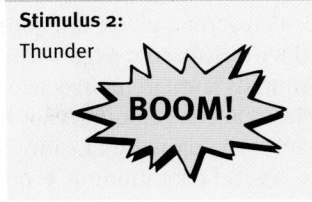

Stimulus 1:
Lightning

Stimulus 2:
Thunder

BOOM!

Response:
Startled reaction; wincing

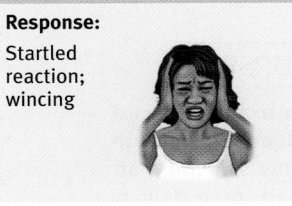

FIGURE 19.1
CLASSICAL CONDITIONING

Result after repetition:

Stimulus:
Lightning

Response:
Anticipation of booming thunder; wincing

Just do it every day for two months, or a bit longer for exercise, and you likely will find yourself with a new habit. This happened for both of us—with a midday workout [DM] or late afternoon run [ND] having long ago become an automatic daily routine.

Other animals also learn by association. Disturbed by a squirt of water, the sea slug *Aplysia* protectively withdraws its gill. If the squirts continue, as happens naturally in choppy water, the withdrawal response diminishes. But if the sea slug repeatedly receives an electric shock just after being squirted, its protective response to the squirt instead grows stronger. The animal has associated the squirt with the impending shock.

Complex animals can learn to associate their own behavior with its outcomes. An aquarium seal will repeat behaviors, such as slapping and barking, that prompt people to toss it a herring.

By linking two events that occur close together, both sea slugs and seals are exhibiting **associative learning**. The sea slug associates the squirt with an impending shock; the seal associates slapping and barking with a herring treat. Each animal has learned something important to its survival: anticipating the immediate future.

This process of learning associations is *conditioning*. It takes two main forms:

- In *classical conditioning,* we learn to associate two stimuli and thus to anticipate events. (A **stimulus** is any event or situation that evokes a response.) We learn that a flash of lightning signals an impending crack of thunder; when lightning flashes nearby, we start to brace ourselves (**FIGURE 19.1**). We associate stimuli that we do not control, and we respond automatically (exhibiting **respondent behavior**).

- In *operant conditioning,* we learn to associate a response (our behavior) and its consequence. Thus, we (and other animals) learn to repeat acts followed by good results (**FIGURE 19.2**) and avoid acts followed by bad results. These associations produce **operant behaviors** (which operate on the environment to produce consequences).

"Watch your thoughts, they become words;
watch your words, they become actions;
watch your actions, they become habits;
watch your habits, they become character;
watch your character, for it becomes your destiny."

—Attributed to nineteenth-century fugitive cowboy Frank Outlaw, 1977

ENGAGE Most of us would be unable to name the order of the songs on our favorite album or playlist. Yet, hearing the end of one piece cues (by association) an anticipation of the next. Likewise, when singing your national anthem, you associate the end of each line with the beginning of the next. (Pick a line out of the middle and notice how much harder it is to recall the *previous* line.)

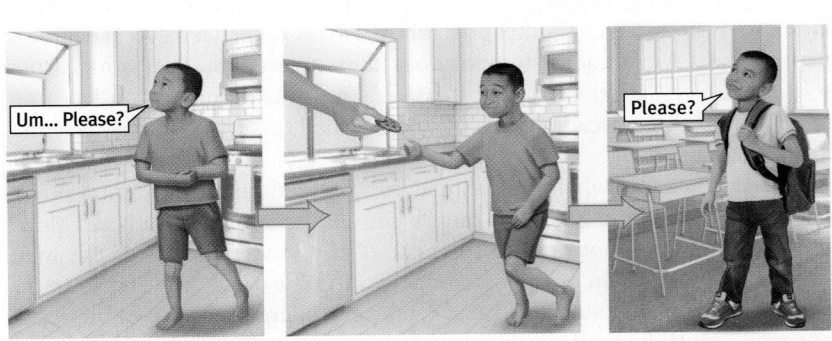

"Um... Please?"   "Please?"

(a) Response: Being polite   **(b)** Consequence: Getting a treat   **(c)** Behavior strengthened

FIGURE 19.2
OPERANT CONDITIONING

ASK YOURSELF

Can you remember examples from your childhood of learning through *classical conditioning* (salivating at the sound or smell of some delicious food cooking in the kitchen?), *operant conditioning* (deciding not to repeat a behavior because you disliked its consequence?), and *cognitive learning* (repeating or avoiding what you watched someone else do)?

IVAN PAVLOV "Experimental investigation. . . should lay a solid foundation for a future true science of psychology" (1927).

cognitive learning the acquisition of mental information, whether by observing events, by watching others, or through language.

classical conditioning a type of learning in which we link two or more stimuli; as a result, to illustrate with Pavlov's classic experiment, the first stimulus (a tone) comes to elicit behavior (drooling) in anticipation of the second stimulus (food).

behaviorism the view that psychology (1) should be an objective science that (2) studies behavior without reference to mental processes. Most research psychologists today agree with (1) but not with (2).

neutral stimulus (NS) in classical conditioning, a stimulus that elicits no response before conditioning.

unconditioned response (UR) in classical conditioning, an unlearned, naturally occurring response (such as salivation) to an unconditioned stimulus (US) (such as food in the mouth).

unconditioned stimulus (US) in classical conditioning, a stimulus that unconditionally—naturally and automatically—triggers an unconditioned response (UR).

To simplify, we will explore these two types of associative learning separately. Often, though, they occur together, as on one Japanese cattle ranch, where the clever rancher outfitted his herd with electronic pagers which he called from his cell phone. After a week of training, the animals learned to associate two stimuli—the beep of their pager and the arrival of food (classical conditioning). But they also learned to associate their hustling to the food trough with the pleasure of eating (operant conditioning), which simplified the rancher's work. Classical conditioning + operant conditioning did the trick.

Conditioning is not the only form of learning. Through **cognitive learning** we acquire mental information that guides our behavior. *Observational learning,* one form of cognitive learning, lets us learn from others' experiences. Chimpanzees, for example, sometimes learn behaviors merely by watching other chimpanzees perform them. If one animal sees another solve a puzzle and gain a food reward, the observer may perform the trick more quickly. So, too, in humans: We look and we learn.

🔒 RETRIEVE IT • • •

ANSWERS IN APPENDIX E

RI-1 Why are habits, such as having something sweet with that cup of coffee, so hard to break?

CLASSICAL CONDITIONING

LOQ 19-2 What is behaviorism's view of learning?

For many people, the name Ivan Pavlov (1849–1936) rings a bell. His early twentieth-century experiments—now psychology's most famous research—are classics, and the phenomenon he explored we justly call **classical conditioning**.

Pavlov's work laid the foundation for many of psychologist John B. Watson's ideas. In searching for laws underlying learning, Watson (1913) urged his colleagues to discard reference to inner thoughts, feelings, and motives. The science of psychology should instead study how organisms respond to stimuli in their environments, said Watson: "Its theoretical goal is the prediction and control of behavior. Introspection forms no essential part of its methods." Simply said, psychology should be an objective science based on observable behavior.

This view, which Watson called **behaviorism**, influenced North American psychology, especially during the first half of the twentieth century. Pavlov and Watson came to share both a disdain for "mentalistic" concepts (such as consciousness) and a belief that the basic laws of learning were the same for all animals—whether dogs or humans. Few researchers today agree that psychology should ignore mental processes, but most do agree that classical conditioning is a basic form of learning by which all organisms adapt to their environment.

Pavlov's Experiments

LOQ 19-3 Who was Pavlov, and what are the basic components of classical conditioning?

Pavlov was driven by a lifelong passion for research. After setting aside his initial plan to follow his father into the Russian Orthodox priesthood, Pavlov earned a medical degree at age 33 and spent the next two decades studying dogs' digestive system. This work earned him, in 1904, Russia's first Nobel Prize. But it was his novel experiments on learning, which consumed the last three decades of his life, that earned this feisty, intense scientist his place in history (Todes, 2014).

Pavlov's new direction came when his creative mind seized on an incidental observation: Without fail, putting food in a dog's mouth caused the animal to salivate. Moreover, the dog began salivating not only to the taste of the food, but also to the mere sight of the food, or the food dish, or the person delivering the food, or even the sound of that person's approaching footsteps. At first, Pavlov considered these "psychic secretions" an annoyance—until he realized they pointed to a simple but fundamental form of learning.

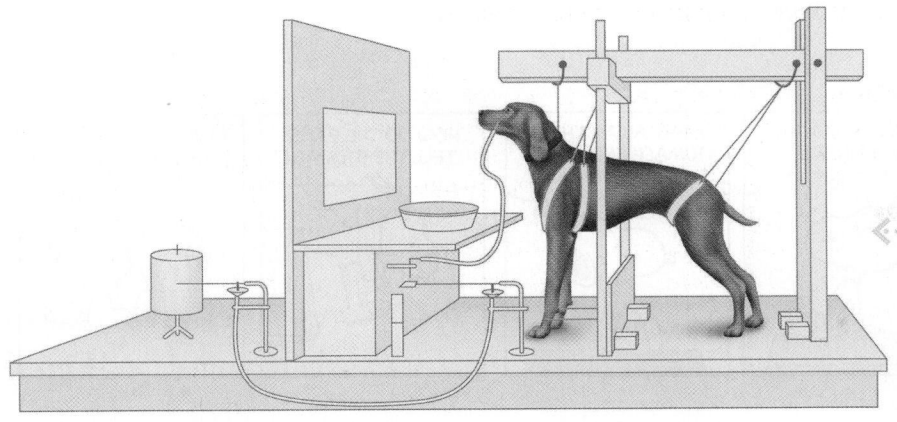

FIGURE 19.3

PAVLOV'S DEVICE FOR RECORDING SALIVATION A tube in the dog's cheek collects saliva, which is measured in a cylinder outside the chamber.

Pavlov and his assistants tried to imagine what the dog was thinking and feeling as it drooled in anticipation of the food. This only led them into fruitless debates. So, to explore the phenomenon more objectively, they experimented. To eliminate other possible influences, they isolated the dog in a small room, secured it in a harness, and attached a device to divert its saliva to a measuring instrument (**FIGURE 19.3**). From the next room, they presented food—first by sliding in a food bowl, later by blowing meat powder into the dog's mouth at a precise moment. They then paired various **neutral stimuli (NS)**—events the dog could see or hear but didn't associate with food—with food in the dog's mouth. If a sight or sound regularly signaled the arrival of food, would the dog learn the link? If so, would it begin salivating in anticipation of the food?

The answers proved to be *Yes* and *Yes*. Just before placing food in the dog's mouth to produce salivation, Pavlov sounded a tone. After several pairings of tone and food, the dog, now anticipating the meat powder, began salivating to the tone alone. In later experiments, a buzzer,[1] a light, a touch on the leg, even the sight of a circle set off the drooling. (This procedure works with people, too. When hungry young Londoners viewed abstract figures before smelling peanut butter or vanilla, their brain soon responded in anticipation to the abstract images alone [Gottfried et al., 2003].)

A dog does not learn to salivate in response to food in its mouth. Rather, food in the mouth automatically, *unconditionally,* triggers a dog's salivary reflex (**FIGURE 19.4**). Thus, Pavlov called this drooling an **unconditioned response (UR)**. And he called the food an **unconditioned stimulus (US)**.

---

1. The "buzzer" (English translation) was perhaps the bell people commonly associate with Pavlov (Tully, 2003). Pavlov used various stimuli, but some have questioned whether he used a bell.

FIGURE 19.4

PAVLOV'S CLASSIC EXPERIMENT Pavlov presented a neutral stimulus (a tone) just before an unconditioned stimulus (food in mouth). The neutral stimulus then became a conditioned stimulus, producing a conditioned response.

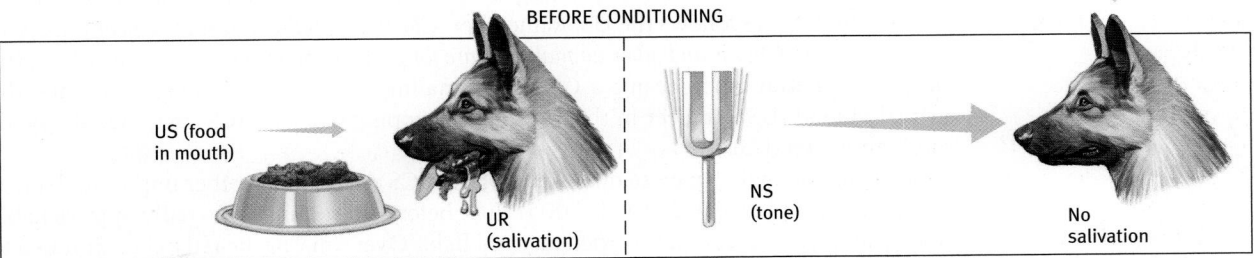

BEFORE CONDITIONING

US (food in mouth) → UR (salivation)

An unconditioned stimulus (US) produces an unconditioned response (UR).

NS (tone) → No salivation

A neutral stimulus (NS) produces no salivation response.

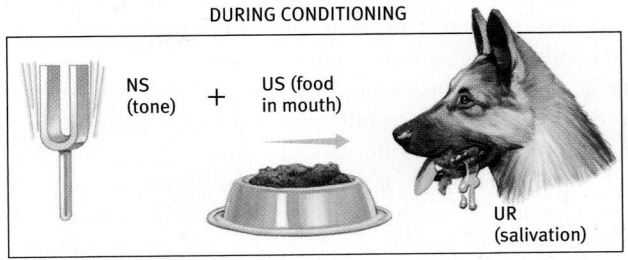

DURING CONDITIONING

NS (tone) + US (food in mouth) → UR (salivation)

The US is repeatedly presented just after the NS. The US continues to produce a UR.

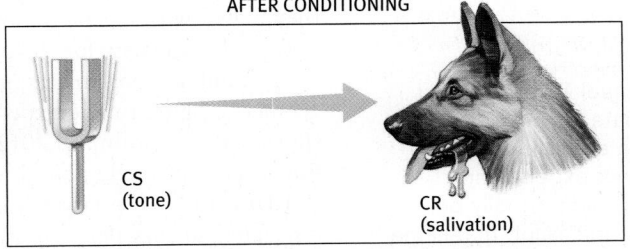

AFTER CONDITIONING

CS (tone) → CR (salivation)

The previously neutral stimulus alone now produces a conditioned response (CR), thereby becoming a conditioned stimulus (CS).

conditioned response (CR) in classical conditioning, a learned response to a previously neutral (but now conditioned) stimulus (CS).

conditioned stimulus (CS) in classical conditioning, an originally neutral stimulus that, after association with an unconditioned stimulus (US), comes to trigger a conditioned response (CR).

acquisition in classical conditioning, the initial stage, when one links a neutral stimulus and an unconditioned stimulus so that the neutral stimulus begins triggering the conditioned response. In operant conditioning, the strengthening of a reinforced response.

extinction the diminishing of a conditioned response; occurs in classical conditioning when an unconditioned stimulus (US) does not follow a conditioned stimulus (CS); occurs in operant conditioning when a response is no longer reinforced.

spontaneous recovery the reappearance, after a pause, of an extinguished conditioned response.

generalization the tendency, once a response has been conditioned, for stimuli similar to the conditioned stimulus to elicit similar responses. (In operant conditioning, generalization occurs when responses learned in one situation occur in other, similar situations.)

PEANUTS

Peanuts reprinted with permission of United Features Syndicate

Salivation in response to a tone, however, is learned. It is *conditional* upon the dog's associating the tone with the food. Thus, we call this response the **conditioned response (CR)**. The stimulus that used to be neutral (in this case, a previously meaningless tone that now triggers salivation) is the **conditioned stimulus (CS)**. Distinguishing these two kinds of stimuli and responses is easy: Conditioned = learned; *unconditioned* = *unlearned.*

If Pavlov's demonstration of associative learning was so simple, what did he do for the next three decades? What discoveries did his research factory publish in his 532 papers on salivary conditioning (Windholz, 1997)? He and his associates explored five major conditioning processes: *acquisition, extinction, spontaneous recovery, generalization,* and *discrimination.*

🔒 RETRIEVE IT • • •   *ANSWERS IN APPENDIX E*

RI-2 An experimenter sounds a tone just before delivering an air puff that causes your eye to blink. After several repetitions, you blink to the tone alone. What is the NS? The US? The UR? The CS? The CR?

ACQUISITION

LOQ 19-4 In classical conditioning, what are the processes of *acquisition, extinction, spontaneous recovery, generalization,* and *discrimination?*

Acquisition is the initial learning of an association. Pavlov and his associates wondered: How much time should elapse between presenting the NS (the tone, the light, the touch) and the US (the food)? In most cases, not much—half a second usually works well.

What do you suppose would happen if the food (US) appeared before the tone (NS) rather than after? Would conditioning occur? Not likely. Conditioning usually won't occur when the NS follows the US. Remember: *Classical conditioning is biologically adaptive because it helps humans and other animals prepare for good or bad events.* To Pavlov's dogs, the originally neutral tone became a CS after signaling an important biological event—the arrival of food (US). To deer in the forest, the snapping of a twig (CS) may signal a predator's approach (US).

Research on male Japanese quail shows how a CS can signal another important biological event (Domjan, 1992, 1994, 2005). Just before presenting a sexually approachable female quail, the researchers turned on a red light. Over time, as the red light continued to herald the female's arrival, the light alone caused the male quail to become excited. They developed a preference for their cage's red light district, and when a female appeared, they mated with her more quickly and released more semen and sperm (Matthews et al., 2007). This capacity for classical conditioning supports reproduction.

In humans, too, objects, smells, and sights associated with sexual pleasure—even a geometric figure in one experiment—can become conditioned stimuli for sexual arousal (Byrne, 1982; Hoffman, 2012). Onion breath does not usually produce sexual arousal. But when repeatedly paired with a passionate kiss, it can become a CS and do just that (**FIGURE 19.5**). The larger lesson: *Conditioning helps an animal survive and reproduce—by responding to cues that help it gain food, avoid dangers, locate mates, and produce offspring* (Hollis, 1997). Learning makes for yearning.

ENGAGE

💡 **ASK YOURSELF**

Psychologist Michael Tirrell recalled coming to associate his girlfriend's onion breath with arousal. Can you remember ever experiencing something that would normally be neutral (or even unpleasant) that came to mean something special?

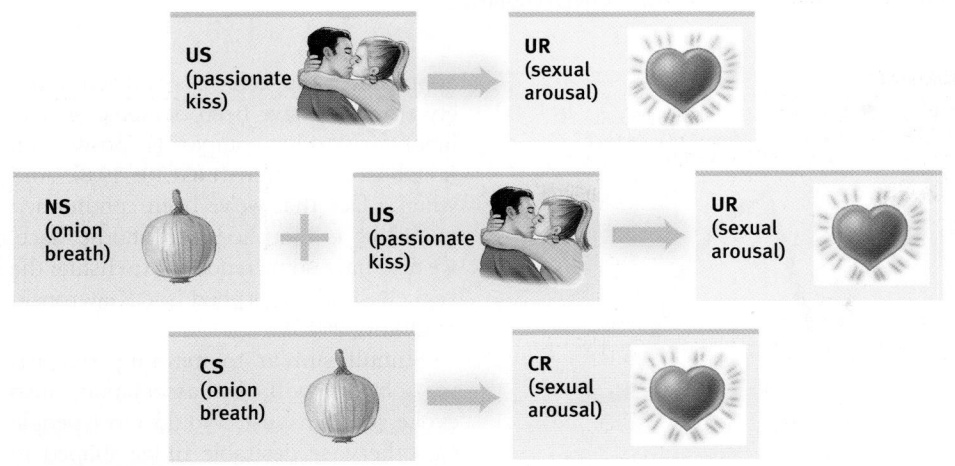

EXTINCTION AND SPONTANEOUS RECOVERY What would happen, Pavlov wondered, if, after conditioning, the CS occurred repeatedly without the US? If the tone sounded again and again, but no food appeared, would the tone still trigger salivation? The answer was mixed. The dogs salivated less and less, a reaction known as **extinction**. Extinction is the diminished responding that occurs when the CS (tone) no longer signals an impending US (food). But a different picture emerged when Pavlov allowed several hours to elapse before sounding the tone again. After the delay, the dogs would again begin salivating to the tone (**FIGURE 19.6**). This **spontaneous recovery**—the reappearance of a (weakened) CR after a pause—suggested to Pavlov that extinction was suppressing the CR rather than eliminating it.

RETAIN 🔒 Remember:

NS = **N**eutral **S**timulus
US = **U**nconditioned **S**timulus
UR = **U**nconditioned **R**esponse
CS = **C**onditioned **S**timulus
CR = **C**onditioned **R**esponse

🔒 **RETRIEVE IT** • • •

ANSWERS IN APPENDIX E

RI-3 If the aroma of a baking cake sets your mouth to watering, what is the US? The CS? The CR?

RI-4 The first step of classical conditioning, when an NS becomes a CS, is called _____. When a US no longer follows the CS, and the CR becomes weakened, this is called _____.

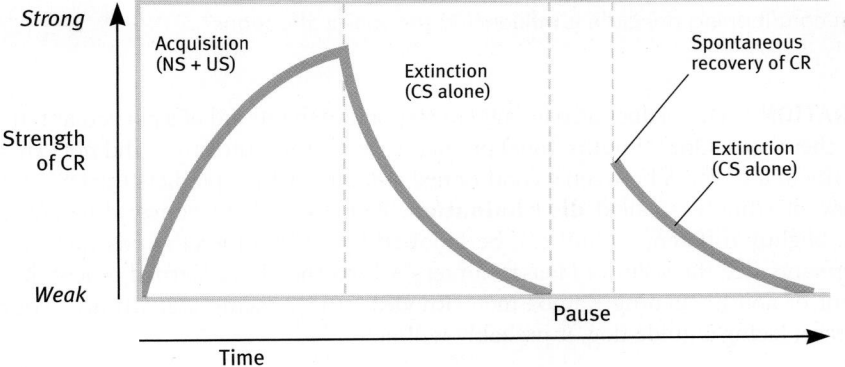

FIGURE 19.6

IDEALIZED CURVE OF ACQUISITION, EXTINCTION, AND SPONTANEOUS RECOVERY The rising curve shows the CR rapidly growing stronger as the NS becomes a CS due to repeated pairing with the US *(acquisition)*. The CR then weakens rapidly as the CS is presented alone *(extinction)*. After a pause, the (weakened) CR reappears *(spontaneous recovery)*.

GENERALIZATION Pavlov and his students noticed that a dog conditioned to the sound of one tone also responded somewhat to the sound of a new and different tone. Likewise, a dog conditioned to salivate when rubbed would also drool a bit when scratched (Windholz, 1989) or when touched on a different body part (**FIGURE 19.7**). This tendency to respond to stimuli similar to the CS is called **generalization** (or *stimulus generalization*).

Generalization can be adaptive, as when toddlers who learn to fear moving cars also become afraid of moving trucks and motorcycles. And generalized fears can linger. For two months after being in a car collision, sensitized young drivers are less vulnerable to repeat collisions (O'Brien et al., 2017). Years after being tortured, one Argentine writer reported still flinching with fear at the sight of black shoes—his first glimpse of his torturers as they

FIGURE 19.7

GENERALIZATION Pavlov demonstrated generalization by attaching miniature vibrators to various parts of a dog's body. After conditioning salivation to stimulation of the thigh, he stimulated other areas. The closer a stimulated spot was to the dog's thigh, the stronger the conditioned response. (Data from Pavlov, 1927.)

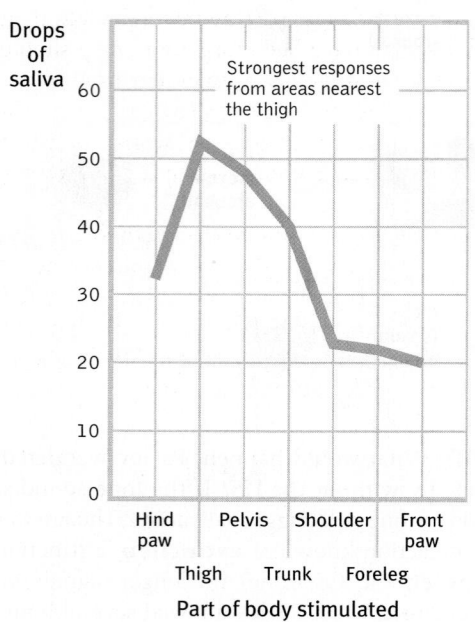

Drops of saliva

Strongest responses from areas nearest the thigh

Part of body stimulated

Hind paw · Pelvis · Shoulder · Front paw

Thigh · Trunk · Foreleg

approached his cell. Generalized anxiety reactions have been demonstrated in laboratory studies comparing abused with nonabused children (**FIGURE 19.8**). And when a face that we've been conditioned to dislike is morphed into another face, we also have some tendency to dislike the vaguely similar morphed face (Gawronski & Quinn, 2013).

Stimuli similar to naturally disgusting objects will, by association, also evoke some disgust. Would most people eat otherwise desirable fudge shaped to resemble dog feces? Or drink sanitary, filtered water that had been collected from a toilet? *No* and *No.* Both situations cause people to feel repulsed (Rozin et al., 1986, 2015). These examples show how people's emotional reactions to one stimulus can generalize to similar stimuli.

🔒 **RETRIEVE IT** • • •   *ANSWERS IN APPENDIX E*

"I don't care if she's a tape dispenser. I love her."

RI-5 What conditioning principle is influencing the snail's affections?

DISCRIMINATION Pavlov's dogs also learned to respond to the sound of a particular tone and *not* to other tones. One stimulus (tone) predicted the US, and the others did not. This learned ability to *distinguish* between a conditioned stimulus (which predicts the US) and other, irrelevant stimuli is called **discrimination**. Being able to recognize differences is adaptive. Slightly different stimuli can be followed by vastly different consequences. Kenyan elephants flee the scent of Maasai hunters, whom they have learned to fear, but not the scent of nonthreatening Kamba men (Rhodes, 2017). Facing a guard dog, your heart may race; facing a guide dog, it probably will not.

Pavlov's Legacy

LOQ **19-5** Why does Pavlov's work remain so important?

What remains today of Pavlov's ideas? A great deal. Most psychologists now agree that classical conditioning is a basic form of learning. Modern neuroscience has also supported Pavlov's ideas—by identifying neural circuits that link a conditioned stimulus (warning signal) with an impending unconditioned stimulus (threat) (Harnett et al., 2016). Judged with today's knowledge of the interplay of our biology, psychology, and social-cultural environment, some of Pavlov's ideas were incomplete. But if we see further than Pavlov did, it is because we stand on his shoulders.

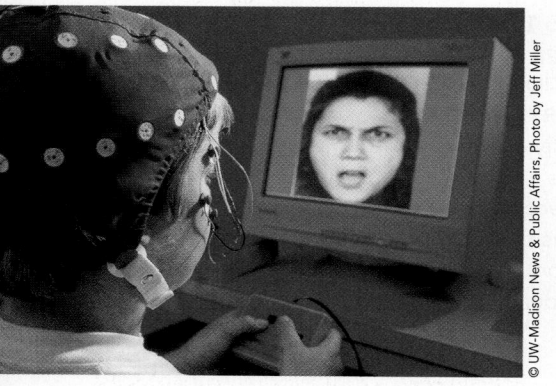

FIGURE 19.8

CHILD ABUSE LEAVES TRACKS IN THE BRAIN Abused children's sensitized brains react more strongly to angry faces (Pollak et al., 1998). This generalized anxiety response may help explain their greater risk of psychological disorder.

Why does Pavlov's work remain so important? If he had merely taught us that old dogs can learn new tricks, his experiments would long ago have been forgotten. Why should we care that dogs can be conditioned to salivate to the sound of a tone? The importance lies first in this finding: *Many other responses to many other stimuli can be classically conditioned in many other organisms*—in fact, in every species tested, from earthworms to fish to dogs to monkeys to people (Schwartz, 1984). Thus, classical conditioning is one way that virtually all organisms learn to adapt to their environment.

Second, *Pavlov showed us how a process such as learning can be studied objectively*. He was proud that his methods involved virtually no subjective judgments or guesses about what went on in a dog's mind. The salivary response is a behavior measurable in cubic centimeters of saliva. Pavlov's success therefore suggested a scientific model for how the young discipline of psychology might proceed—by isolating the basic building blocks of complex behaviors and studying them with objective laboratory procedures.

🔒 **RETRIEVE IT • • •**   *ANSWERS IN APPENDIX E*

RI-6 In horror movies, sexually arousing images of women are sometimes paired with violence against women. Based on classical conditioning principles, what might be an effect of this pairing?

APPLICATIONS OF CLASSICAL CONDITIONING

LOQ 19-6 What have been some applications of Pavlov's work to human health and well-being? How did Watson apply Pavlov's principles to learned fears?

In many areas of psychology, including consciousness, motivation, emotion, health, psychological disorders, and therapy, Pavlov's principles are used to influence human health and well-being. Three examples:

- *Drug cravings.* Former drug users often feel a craving when they are again in the drug-using context—with people or in places they associate with previous highs. Thus, drug counselors advise their clients to steer clear of people and settings that may trigger these cravings (Siegel, 2005).

- *Food cravings.* Classical conditioning makes dieting difficult. Sugary substances evoke sweet sensations. Researchers have conditioned healthy volunteers to experience cravings after only one instance of eating a sweet food (Blechert et al., 2016). Eating one cookie can create hunger for another. People who struggle with their weight often have eaten unhealthy foods thousands of times, leaving them with strongly conditioned responses to eat the very foods that will keep them in poor health (Hill, 2007).

- *Immune responses.* Classical conditioning even works on the body's disease-fighting immune system. When a particular taste accompanies a drug that influences immune responses, the taste by itself may come to produce an immune response (Ader & Cohen, 1985).

Pavlov's work also provided a basis for Watson's (1913) idea that human emotions and behaviors, though biologically influenced, are mainly a bundle of conditioned responses. Working with an 11-month-old, Watson and his graduate student Rosalie Rayner (1920; Harris, 1979) showed how specific fears might be conditioned. Like most infants, "Little Albert" feared loud noises but not white rats. Watson and Rayner presented a white rat and, as Little Albert reached to touch it, struck a hammer against a steel bar just behind his head. After seven repeats of seeing the rat and hearing the frightening noise, Albert burst into tears at the mere sight of the rat. Five days later, he reportedly generalized this startled fear reaction to the sight of a rabbit, a dog, and even a furry coat. Although a modern reanalysis questions Watson's evidence for Albert's conditioning, the case remains legendary (Powell & Schmaltz, 2017).

For years, people wondered what became of Little Albert. Sleuthing by Russell Powell and his colleagues (2014) found a well-matched child of one of the hospital's wet nurses.

discrimination in classical conditioning, the learned ability to distinguish between a conditioned stimulus and similar stimuli that do not signal an unconditioned stimulus. (In operant conditioning, the ability to distinguish responses that are reinforced from similar responses that are not reinforced.)

ENGAGE

💡 ⧉ **LaunchPad** Play the role of experimenter in classical conditioning research by visiting **Topic Tutorial: PsychSim6, Classical Conditioning.** And review Pavlov's classic work by watching a 3-minute re-creation of Pavlov's lab in the **Video: Pavlov's Discovery of Classical Conditioning.**

JOHN B. WATSON Watson (1924) admitted to "going beyond my facts" when offering his famous boast: "Give me a dozen healthy infants, well-formed, and my own specified world to bring them up in and I'll guarantee to take any one at random and train him to become any type of specialist I might select—doctor, lawyer, artist, merchant-chief, and, yes, even beggar-man and thief, regardless of his talents, penchants, tendencies, abilities, vocations, and race of his ancestors."

The child, William Albert Barger, went by Albert B.—precisely the name used by Watson and Rayner. This Albert, who died in 2007, was an easygoing person, though, perhaps coincidentally, he had an aversion to dogs. He died without ever knowing of his early life in a hospital residence or his role in psychology's history.

People also wondered what became of Watson. After losing his Johns Hopkins professorship over an affair with Rayner (whom he later married), he joined an advertising agency as the company's resident psychologist. There, he used his knowledge of associative learning to conceive many successful advertising campaigns, including one for Maxwell House that helped make the "coffee break" an American custom (Hunt, 1993).

The treatment of Little Albert would be unethical by today's standards. Also, some psychologists had difficulty repeating Watson and Rayner's findings with other children. Nevertheless, Little Albert's learned fears led many psychologists to wonder whether each of us might be a walking warehouse of conditioned emotions. If so, might extinction procedures or new conditioning help us change our unwanted responses to emotion-arousing stimuli?

One patient, who for 30 years had feared entering an elevator alone, did just that. Following his therapist's advice, he forced himself to enter 20 elevators a day. Within 10 days, his fear had nearly vanished (Ellis & Becker, 1982). In the Therapy modules, there are more examples of how psychologists use behavioral techniques such as *counterconditioning* to treat emotional disorders and promote personal growth.

📺 **LaunchPad** See the **Video: Research Ethics** for a helpful tutorial animation.

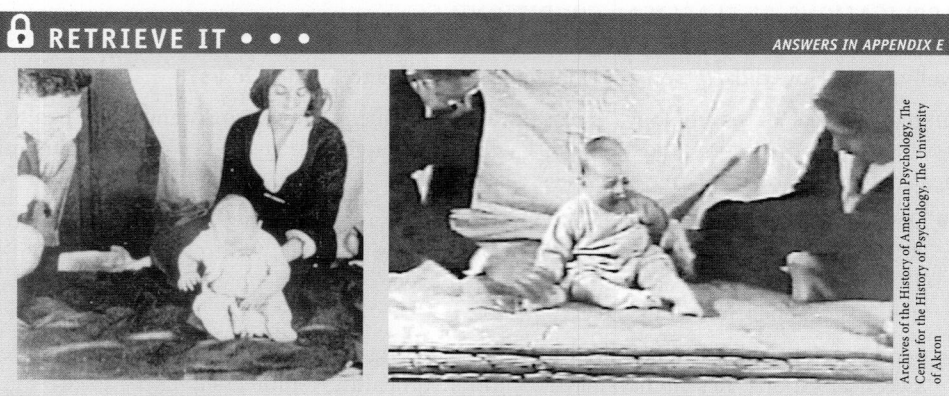

🔒 RETRIEVE IT • • •   *ANSWERS IN APPENDIX E*

Archives of the History of American Psychology, The Center for the History of Psychology, The University of Akron

RI-7 In Watson and Rayner's experiments, "Little Albert" learned to fear a white rat after repeatedly experiencing a loud noise as the rat was presented. In these experiments, what was the US? The UR? The NS? The CS? The CR?

🔒 REVIEW BASIC LEARNING CONCEPTS AND CLASSICAL CONDITIONING

⟫ Learning Objectives

TEST YOURSELF Answer these repeated Learning Objective Questions on your own (before checking the answers in Appendix D) to improve your retention of the concepts (McDaniel et al., 2009, 2015).

19-1 How do we define *learning*, and what are some basic forms of learning?

19-2 What is behaviorism's view of learning?

19-3 Who was Pavlov, and what are the basic components of classical conditioning?

19-4 In classical conditioning, what are the processes of *acquisition, extinction, spontaneous recovery, generalization,* and *discrimination*?

19-5 Why does Pavlov's work remain so important?

19-6 What have been some applications of Pavlov's work to human health and well-being? How did Watson apply Pavlov's principles to learned fears?

⟫ Terms and Concepts to Remember

TEST YOURSELF Write down the definition yourself, then check your answer on the referenced page.

learning, **p. 234**

associative learning, **p. 234**

stimulus, **p. 234**

respondent behavior, **p. 234**

operant behavior, **p. 234**

cognitive learning, **p. 236**

⟶ Experience the Testing Effect

TEST YOURSELF Answer the following questions on your own first, then check your answers in Appendix E.

1. Learning is defined as "the process of acquiring through experience new and relatively enduring _____ or _____."

2. Two forms of associative learning are classical conditioning, in which the organism associates _____, and operant conditioning, in which the organism associates _____.

   a. two or more responses; a response and consequence
   b. two or more stimuli; two or more responses
   c. two or more stimuli; a response and consequence
   d. two or more responses; two or more stimuli

3. In Pavlov's experiments, the tone started as a neutral stimulus, and then became a(n) _____ stimulus.

4. Dogs have been taught to salivate to a circle but not to a square. This process is an example of _____.

5. After Watson and Rayner classically conditioned Little Albert to fear a white rat, the child later showed fear in response to a rabbit, a dog, and a furry coat. This illustrates

   a. extinction.
   b. generalization.
   c. spontaneous recovery.
   d. discrimination between two stimuli.

6. "Sex sells!" is a common saying in advertising. Using classical conditioning terms, explain how sexual images in advertisements can condition your response to a product.

Continue testing yourself with 📖 **LearningCurve** or 📖 **Achieve Read & Practice** to learn and remember most effectively.

⟲ 20 Operant Conditioning

LOQ 20-1 What is *operant conditioning*?

It's one thing to classically condition a dog to salivate to the sound of a tone, or a child to fear moving cars. But to teach an elephant to **learn** to walk on its hind legs or a child to say *please*, we turn to operant conditioning.

Classical conditioning and operant conditioning are both forms of **associative learning**, yet their differences are straightforward:

- *Classical conditioning* forms associations between **stimuli** (a CS and the US it signals). It also involves **respondent behavior**—automatic responses to a stimulus (such as salivating in response to meat powder, and later in response to a tone).

- In **operant conditioning**, organisms associate their own actions with consequences. Actions followed by reinforcers increase; those followed by punishers often decrease. Behavior that *operates* on the environment to *produce* rewarding or punishing stimuli is called **operant behavior.**

🔒 RETRIEVE IT • • •
ANSWERS IN APPENDIX E

RI-1 With classical conditioning, we learn associations between events we _____ (do/do not) control. With operant conditioning, we learn associations between our behavior and _____ (resulting/random) events.

learning the process of acquiring through experience new and relatively enduring information or behaviors.

associative learning learning that certain events occur together. The events may be two stimuli (as in classical conditioning) or a response and its consequence (as in operant conditioning).

stimulus any event or situation that evokes a response.

respondent behavior behavior that occurs as an automatic response to some stimulus.

operant conditioning a type of learning in which a behavior becomes more likely to recur if followed by a reinforcer or less likely to recur if followed by a punisher.

operant behavior behavior that operates on the environment, producing consequences.

SKINNER'S EXPERIMENTS

LOQ 20-2 Who was Skinner, and how is operant behavior reinforced and shaped?

B. F. Skinner (1904–1990) was a college English major and aspiring writer who, seeking a new direction, enrolled as a graduate student in psychology. He went on to become modern behaviorism's most influential and controversial figure. Skinner's work elaborated on what psychologist Edward L. Thorndike (1874–1949) called the **law of effect:** Rewarded behavior tends to recur (**FIGURE 20.1**). Using Thorndike's law of effect as a starting point, Skinner developed a behavioral technology that revealed principles of *behavior control.* By shaping pigeons' natural walking and pecking behaviors, for example, Skinner was able to teach pigeons such unpigeon-like behaviors as walking in a figure 8, playing Ping-Pong, and keeping a missile on course by pecking at a screen target.

FIGURE 20.1

CAT IN A PUZZLE BOX Thorndike used a fish reward to entice cats to find their way out of a puzzle box through a series of maneuvers. The cats' performance tended to improve with successive trials, illustrating Thorndike's *law of effect.* (Data from Thorndike, 1898.)

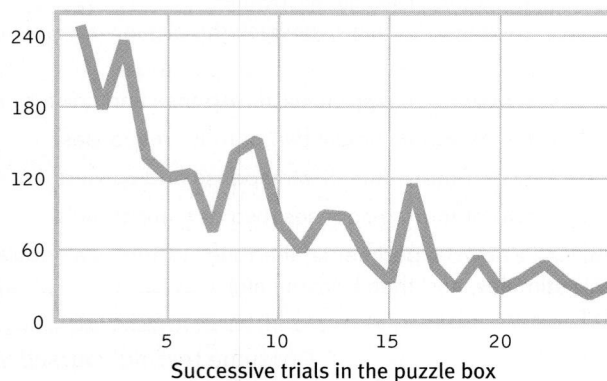

FIGURE 20.2

A SKINNER BOX Inside the box, the rat presses a bar for a food reward. Outside, measuring devices (not shown here) record the animal's accumulated responses.

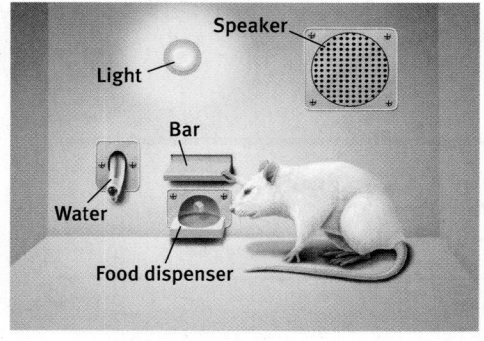

For his pioneering studies, Skinner designed an **operant chamber,** popularly known as a *Skinner box* (**FIGURE 20.2**). The box has a bar (a lever) that an animal presses—or a key (a disc) the animal pecks—to release a reward of food or water. It also has a device that records these responses. This creates a stage on which rats and other animals act out Skinner's concept of **reinforcement:** any event that strengthens (increases the frequency of) a preceding response. What is reinforcing depends on the animal and the conditions. For people, it may be praise, attention, or a paycheck. For hungry and thirsty rats, food and water work well. Skinner's experiments have done far more than teach us how to pull habits out of a rat. They have explored the precise conditions that foster efficient and enduring learning.

law of effect Thorndike's principle that behaviors followed by favorable consequences become more likely, and that behaviors followed by unfavorable consequences become less likely.

operant chamber in operant conditioning research, a chamber (also known as a *Skinner box*) containing a bar or key that an animal can manipulate to obtain a food or water reinforcer; attached devices record the animal's rate of bar pressing or key pecking.

reinforcement in operant conditioning, any event that *strengthens* the behavior it follows.

shaping an operant conditioning procedure in which reinforcers guide behavior toward closer and closer approximations of the desired behavior.

Shaping Behavior

Imagine that you wanted to condition a hungry rat to press a bar. Like Skinner, you could tease out this action with **shaping,** gradually guiding the rat's actions toward the desired behavior. First, you would watch how the animal naturally behaves, so that you could build on its existing behaviors. You might give the rat a bit of food each time it approaches the bar. Once the rat is approaching regularly, you would give the food only when it moves close to the bar, then closer still. Finally, you would require it to touch the bar to get food. By rewarding *successive approximations,* you reinforce only those responses that are ever-closer to the final desired behavior. By making rewards contingent on desired behaviors, researchers and animal trainers gradually shape complex behaviors. We can also readily shape our own behavior. For example, let's say you want to get in shape to run your first 5K race. You set up a daily running plan and treat yourself to a cookie once you've worked up to running 1 mile without stopping, then again when you can run 1.5 miles, and so on for every additional half mile—rewarding successive approximations of your target behavior.

Shaping can also help us understand what nonverbal organisms can perceive. Can a dog distinguish red and green? Can a baby hear the difference between lower- and higher-pitched tones? If we can shape them to respond to one stimulus and not to another, then we know they can perceive the difference. Such experiments have even shown that some nonhuman animals can form concepts. When experimenters reinforced pigeons for pecking after seeing a human face, but not after seeing other images, the pigeons' behavior showed that they could recognize human faces (Herrnstein & Loveland, 1964). In this experiment, the human face was a *discriminative stimulus*. Like a green traffic light, discriminative stimuli signal that a response will be reinforced. After being trained to discriminate among classes of events or objects—flowers, people, cars, chairs—pigeons were usually able to identify the category in which a new pictured object belonged (Bhatt et al., 1988; Wasserman, 1993). They have even been trained to discriminate between the music of Bach and Stravinsky (Porter & Neuringer, 1984).

Skinner noted that we continually reinforce and shape others' everyday behaviors, though we may not mean to do so. Isaac's nagging annoys his dad, for example, but consider how Dad typically responds:

ISAAC: *Could you take me to the mall?*

DAD: *(Continues reading paper.)*

ISAAC: *Dad, I need to go to the mall.*

DAD: *Uh, yeah, in a few minutes.*

ISAAC: *DAAAAD! The mall!*

DAD: *Show me some manners! Okay, where are my keys . . .*

Isaac's nagging is reinforced, because he gets something desirable—a trip to the mall. Dad's response is reinforced, because it gets rid of something aversive—Isaac's nagging.

Or consider a teacher who sticks gold stars on a wall chart beside the names of children scoring 100 percent on spelling tests. As everyone can then see, some children consistently do perfect work. The others, who may have worked harder than the academic all-stars, get no rewards. The teacher would be better advised to apply the principles of operant conditioning—to reinforce all spellers for gradual improvements (successive approximations toward perfect spelling of words they find challenging).

Types of Reinforcers

LOQ 20-3 How do positive and negative reinforcement differ, and what are the basic types of reinforcers?

Until now, we've mainly been discussing **positive reinforcement**, which strengthens responding by *presenting* a typically *pleasurable* stimulus immediately after a response. But, as the nagging Isaac story illustrates, there are two basic kinds of reinforcement (**TABLE 20.1**). **Negative reinforcement** strengthens a response by *reducing or removing* something negative. Isaac's nagging was *positively* reinforced, because Isaac got something desirable—a trip to the mall. His dad's response (doing what Isaac wanted) was *negatively* reinforced, because it ended an aversive event—Isaac's nagging. Similarly, taking aspirin may relieve your headache, and hitting *snooze* will silence your irritating alarm. These welcome results provide negative reinforcement and increase the odds that you will repeat these behaviors. For those with drug addiction, the negative reinforcement

Will Burgess/Reuters/Newscom

REINFORCERS VARY WITH CIRCUMSTANCES What is reinforcing (a heat lamp) to one animal (a cold meerkat) may not be to another (an overheated child). What is reinforcing in one situation (a cold snap at the Taronga Zoo in Sydney) may not be in another (a sweltering summer day). Reinforcers also vary among humans. Food that is reinforcing to one person (chocolate) might not be to another person (a vanilla-lover).

Levenson RM, Krupinski EA, Navarro VM, Wasserman EA (2015) Pigeons (Columba livia) as Trainable Observers of Pathology and Radiology Breast Cancer Images. PLoS ONE

BIRD BRAINS SPOT TUMORS After being rewarded with food when correctly spotting breast tumors, pigeons became as skilled as humans at discriminating cancerous from healthy tissue (Levenson et al., 2015). Other animals have been shaped to sniff out land mines or locate people amid rubble (La Londe et al., 2015).

ENGAGE (ASK YOURSELF)

Can you recall a time when a teacher, coach, family member, or employer helped you learn something by shaping your behavior in little steps until you achieved your goal?

positive reinforcement increasing behaviors by presenting positive reinforcers. A positive reinforcer is any stimulus that, when *presented* after a response, strengthens the response.

negative reinforcement increasing behaviors by stopping or reducing aversive stimuli. A negative reinforcer is any stimulus that, when *removed* after a response, strengthens the response. (*Note:* Negative reinforcement is not punishment.)

TABLE 20.1

Ways to Increase Behavior

Operant Conditioning Term	Description	Examples
Positive reinforcement	Add a desirable stimulus	Pet a dog that comes when you call it; pay someone for work done.
Negative reinforcement	Remove an aversive stimulus	Take painkillers to end pain; fasten seatbelt to end loud beeping.

of ending withdrawal pangs can be a compelling reason to resume using (Baker et al., 2004). Note that *negative reinforcement is not punishment.* (Some friendly advice: Repeat the italicized words in your mind.) Rather, negative reinforcement—psychology's most misunderstood concept—*removes* a punishing (aversive) event. Think of negative reinforcement as something that provides relief—from that nagging teen, bad headache, or annoying alarm clock.

Sometimes negative and positive reinforcement coincide. Imagine a worried student who, after goofing off and getting a bad exam grade, studies harder for the next exam. This increased effort may be *negatively* reinforced by reduced anxiety, and *positively* reinforced by a better grade. We reap the rewards of escaping the aversive stimulus, which increases the chances that we will repeat our behavior. *The point to remember:* Whether it works by reducing something aversive, or by providing something desirable, *reinforcement is any consequence that strengthens behavior.*

RETRIEVE IT • • •

ANSWERS IN APPENDIX E

RI-2 How is operant conditioning at work in this cartoon?

PRIMARY AND CONDITIONED REINFORCERS Getting food when hungry or having a painful headache go away is innately satisfying. These **primary reinforcers** are unlearned. **Conditioned reinforcers**, also called *secondary reinforcers*, get their power through learned association with primary reinforcers. If a rat in a Skinner box learns that a light reliably signals a food delivery, the rat will work to turn on the light. The light has become a conditioned reinforcer. Our lives are filled with conditioned reinforcers—money, good grades, a pleasant tone of voice—each of which has been linked with more basic rewards.

IMMEDIATE AND DELAYED REINFORCERS Let's return to the imaginary shaping experiment in which you were conditioning a rat to press a bar. Before performing this "wanted" behavior, the hungry rat will engage in a sequence of "unwanted" behaviors—scratching, sniffing, and moving around. If you present food immediately after any one of these behaviors, the rat will likely repeat that rewarded behavior. But what if the rat presses the bar while you are distracted, and you delay giving the reinforcer? If the delay lasts longer than about 30 seconds, the rat will not learn to press the bar. It will have moved on to other incidental behaviors, such as scratching, sniffing, and moving, and one of these behaviors will instead get reinforced. Delays also decrease human learning. Students learn class material better when they complete frequent quizzes that provide them with immediate feedback (Healy et al., 2017).

---

primary reinforcer an innately reinforcing stimulus, such as one that satisfies a biological need.

conditioned reinforcer a stimulus that gains its reinforcing power through its association with a primary reinforcer; also known as a *secondary reinforcer.*

reinforcement schedule a pattern that defines how often a desired response will be reinforced.

continuous reinforcement schedule reinforcing the desired response every time it occurs.

partial (intermittent) reinforcement schedule reinforcing a response only part of the time; results in slower acquisition of a response but much greater resistance to extinction than does continuous reinforcement.

fixed-ratio schedule in operant conditioning, a reinforcement schedule that reinforces a response only after a specified number of responses.

variable-ratio schedule in operant conditioning, a reinforcement schedule that reinforces a response after an unpredictable number of responses.

fixed-interval schedule in operant conditioning, a reinforcement schedule that reinforces a response only after a specified time has elapsed.

But unlike rats, humans *can* respond to delayed reinforcers: the paycheck at the end of the week, the good grade at the end of the term, the trophy at the end of the sports season. Indeed, to function effectively we must learn how to master the difficult task of delaying gratification. In one of psychology's most famous studies, some 4-year-olds showed this ability. In choosing a piece of candy or a marshmallow, these impulse-controlled children preferred having a big one tomorrow to munching on a small one right away. Learning to control our impulses in order to achieve more valued rewards is a big step toward maturity and can later protect us from committing an impulsive crime (Åkerlund et al., 2016; Logue, 1998a,b). Children who delay gratification have tended to become socially competent and high-achieving adults (Mischel, 2014).

To our detriment, small but immediate pleasures (the enjoyment of watching late-night TV, for example) are sometimes more alluring than big but delayed rewards (feeling rested for a big exam tomorrow). For many teens, the immediate gratification of risky, unprotected sex in passionate moments prevails over the delayed gratifications of safe sex or saved sex. And for many people, the immediate rewards of today's gas-guzzling vehicles, air travel, and air conditioning prevail over the bigger future consequences of global climate change, rising seas, and extreme weather.

"Oh, not bad. The light comes on, I press the bar, they write me a check. How about you?"

Reinforcement Schedules

LOQ 20-4 How do different reinforcement schedules affect behavior?

In most of our examples, the desired response has been reinforced every time it occurs. But **reinforcement schedules** vary. With **continuous reinforcement**, learning occurs rapidly, which makes it the best choice for mastering a behavior. But extinction also occurs rapidly. When reinforcement stops—when we stop delivering food after the rat presses the bar—the behavior soon stops (is *extinguished*). If a normally dependable candy machine fails to deliver a chocolate bar twice in a row, we stop putting money into it (although a week later we may exhibit *spontaneous recovery* by trying again).

Real life rarely provides continuous reinforcement. Salespeople do not make a sale with every pitch. But they persist because their efforts are occasionally rewarded. This persistence is typical with **partial (intermittent) reinforcement schedules**, in which responses are sometimes reinforced, sometimes not. Learning is slower to appear, but *resistance to extinction* is greater than with continuous reinforcement. Imagine a pigeon that has learned to peck a key to obtain food. If you gradually phase out the food delivery until it occurs only rarely, in no predictable pattern, the pigeon may peck 150,000 times without a reward (Skinner, 1953). Slot machines reward gamblers in much the same way—occasionally and unpredictably. And like pigeons, slot players keep trying, time and time again. With intermittent reinforcement, hope springs eternal.

Lesson for parents: Partial reinforcement also works with children. *Occasionally* giving in to children's tantrums for the sake of peace and quiet intermittently reinforces the tantrums. This is the very best procedure for making a behavior persist.

Skinner (1961) and his collaborators compared four schedules of partial reinforcement and their effects on behavior.

Fixed-ratio schedules reinforce behavior after a set number of responses. Coffee shops may reward us with a free drink after every 10 purchased. Once conditioned, rats may be reinforced on a fixed ratio of, say, one food pellet for every 30 responses. Once conditioned, animals will pause only briefly after a reinforcer before returning to a high rate of responding (**FIGURE 20.3**).

Variable-ratio schedules provide reinforcers after a seemingly unpredictable number of responses. This unpredictable reinforcement is what slot-machine players and fly fishers experience, and it's what makes gambling and fly fishing so hard to extinguish even when they don't produce the desired results. Because reinforcers increase as the number of responses increases, variable-ratio schedules produce high rates of responding.

Fixed-interval schedules reinforce the first response after a fixed time period. Animals on this type of schedule tend to respond more frequently as the anticipated time for reward draws near. People check more frequently for the mail as delivery time approaches. A hungry child jiggles the Jell-O more often to see if it has set. Pigeons peck keys more rapidly as the time for reinforcement draws nearer (see Figure 20.3).

"The charm of fishing is that it is the pursuit of what is elusive but attainable, a perpetual series of occasions for hope." —Scottish author John Buchan (1875–1940)

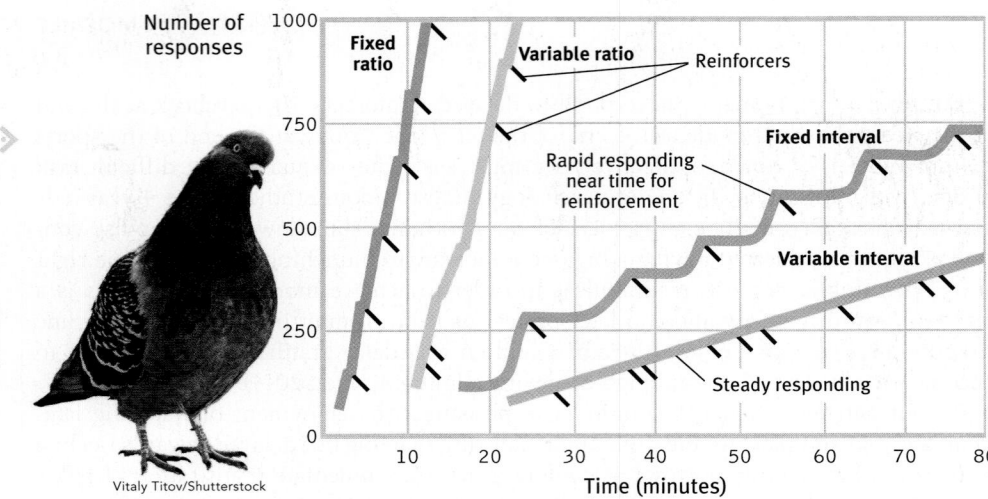

Vitaly Titov/Shutterstock

FIGURE 20.3

INTERMITTENT REINFORCEMENT SCHEDULES Skinner's (1961) laboratory pigeons produced these response patterns to each of four reinforcement schedules. (Reinforcers are indicated by diagonal marks.) For people, as for pigeons, reinforcement linked to number of responses (a *ratio* schedule) produces a higher response rate than reinforcement linked to amount of time elapsed (an *interval* schedule). But the predictability of the reward also matters. An unpredictable *(variable)* schedule produces more consistent responding than does a predictable *(fixed)* schedule. (Data from Skinner, 1961.)

Variable-interval schedules reinforce the first response after *varying* time intervals. At unpredictable times, a food pellet rewarded Skinner's pigeons for persistence in pecking a key. Like the longed-for message that finally rewards persistence in checking our phone, variable-interval schedules tend to produce slow, steady responding. This makes sense, because there is no knowing when the waiting will be over (**TABLE 20.2**).

In general, response rates are higher when reinforcement is linked to the number of responses (a ratio schedule) rather than to time (an interval schedule). But responding is more consistent when reinforcement is unpredictable (a variable schedule) than when it is predictable (a fixed schedule). Animal behaviors differ, yet Skinner (1956) contended that the reinforcement principles of operant conditioning are universal. It matters little, he said, what response, what reinforcer, or what species you use. The effect of a given reinforcement schedule is pretty much the same: "Pigeon, rat, monkey, which is which? It doesn't matter. . . . Behavior shows astonishingly similar properties."

TABLE 20.2

Schedules of Partial Reinforcement

	Fixed	**Variable**
Ratio	*Every so many:* reinforcement after every *nth* behavior, such as buy 10 coffees, get 1 free, or pay workers per product unit produced	*After an unpredictable number:* reinforcement after a random number of behaviors, as when playing slot machines or fly fishing
Interval	*Every so often:* reinforcement for behavior after a fixed time, such as Tuesday discount prices	*Unpredictably often:* reinforcement for behavior after a random amount of time, as when checking our phone for a message

RETRIEVE IT • • •   *ANSWERS IN APPENDIX E*

RI-3 People who send spam email are reinforced by which schedule? Home bakers checking the oven to see if the cookies are done are reinforced on which schedule? Donut shops that offer a free donut after every 10 donuts purchased are using which reinforcement schedule?

Punishment

LOQ 20-5 How does punishment differ from negative reinforcement, and how does punishment affect behavior?

Reinforcement increases a behavior; **punishment** does the opposite. A *punisher* is any consequence that *decreases* the frequency of a preceding behavior (**TABLE 20.3**). Swift and sure punishers can powerfully restrain unwanted behavior. The rat that is shocked after touching a forbidden object and the child who is burned by touching a hot stove will learn not to repeat those behaviors.

variable-interval schedule in operant conditioning, a reinforcement schedule that reinforces a response at unpredictable time intervals.

punishment an event that tends to *decrease* the behavior that it follows.

TABLE 20.3

Ways to Decrease Behavior

Type of Punisher	Description	Examples
Positive punishment	Administer an aversive stimulus.	Spray water on a barking dog; give a traffic ticket for speeding.
Negative punishment	Withdraw a rewarding stimulus.	Take away a misbehaving teen's driving privileges; revoke a rude person's chat room access.

Criminal behavior, much of it impulsive, is also influenced more by swift and sure punishers than by the threat of severe sentences (Darley & Alter, 2013). Thus, when Arizona introduced an exceptionally harsh sentence for first-time drunk drivers, the drunk-driving rate changed very little. But when Kansas City police started patrolling a high crime area to increase the swiftness and sureness of punishment, that city's crime rate dropped dramatically.

What do punishment studies imply for parenting? One analysis of over 160,000 children found that physical punishment rarely corrects unwanted behavior (Gershoff & Grogan-Kaylor, 2016). Many psychologists note five major drawbacks of physical punishment (Finkenauer et al., 2015; Gershoff, 2002; Marshall, 2002).

1. *Punished behavior is suppressed, not forgotten. This temporary state may (negatively) reinforce parents' punishing behavior.* The child swears, the parent swats, the child stops swearing in their parents' presence, so the parents believe the punishment successfully stopped the behavior. No wonder spanking is a hit with so many parents— with 68 percent of American adults believing that a child sometimes needs a "good hard spanking" (Smith et al., 2017).

2. *Physical punishment does not replace the unwanted behavior.* Physical punishment may reduce or even eliminate unwanted behavior, but it does not provide direction for appropriate behavior. A child who is spanked for screaming in the car may stop yelling but continue to throw her food or steal her brother's toys.

3. *Punishment teaches discrimination among situations.* In operant conditioning, *discrimination* occurs when an organism learns that certain responses, but not others, will be reinforced. Did the punishment effectively end the child's swearing? Or did the child simply learn that while it's not okay to swear around the house, it's okay elsewhere?

4. *Punishment can teach fear.* In operant conditioning, *generalization* occurs when an organism's response to similar stimuli is also reinforced. A punished child may associate fear not only with the undesirable behavior but also with the person who delivered the punishment or the place it occurred. Thus, children may learn to fear a punishing teacher and try to avoid school, or may become more anxious (Gershoff et al., 2010). For such reasons, most European countries and 31 U.S. states now ban hitting children in schools and child-care institutions (EndCorporalPunishment.org). As of 2017, 51 countries outlaw hitting by parents. A large survey in Finland, the second country to pass such a law, revealed that children born after the law passed were, indeed, less often slapped and beaten (Österman et al., 2014).

5. *Physical punishment may increase aggression by modeling violence as a way to cope with problems.* Studies find that spanked children are at increased risk for aggression (MacKenzie et al., 2013). We know, for example, that many aggressive delinquents and abusive parents come from abusive families (Straus & Gelles, 1980; Straus et al., 1997).

Some researchers question this logic. Physically punished children may be more aggressive, they say, for the same reason that people who have undergone psychotherapy are more likely to suffer depression—because they had preexisting problems that triggered the treatments (Ferguson, 2013a; Larzelere, 2000; Larzelere et al., 2004). So, does spanking cause misbehavior, or does misbehavior trigger spanking? Correlations don't hand us an answer.

LaunchPad See the **Video: Correlational Studies** for a helpful tutorial animation.

The debate continues. Some researchers note that frequent spankings predict future aggression—even when studies control for preexisting bad behavior (Taylor et al., 2010). Other researchers believe that lighter spankings pose less of a problem (Baumrind et al., 2002; Larzelere & Kuhn, 2005). That is especially so if physical punishment is used only as a backup for milder disciplinary tactics, and if it is combined with a generous dose of reasoning and reinforcing.

Parents of delinquent youths are often unaware of how to achieve desirable behaviors without screaming, hitting, or threatening their children with punishment (Patterson et al., 1982). Training programs can help transform dire threats ("You clean up your room this minute or no dinner!") into positive incentives ("You're welcome at the dinner table after you get your room cleaned up"). Stop and think about it. Aren't many threats of punishment just as forceful, and perhaps more effective, when rephrased positively? Thus, "If you don't get your homework done, there'll be no car" could be phrased more positively as. . . .

In classrooms, too, teachers can give feedback by saying, "No, but try this . . ." and "Yes, that's it!" Such responses reduce unwanted behavior while reinforcing more desirable alternatives. Remember: *Punishment tells you what not to do; reinforcement tells you what to do.* Thus, punishment trains a particular sort of morality—one focused on prohibition (what *not* to do) rather than positive obligations (Sheikh & Janoff-Bulman, 2013).

What punishment often teaches, said Skinner, is how to avoid it. Most psychologists now favor an emphasis on reinforcement: Notice people doing something right and affirm them for it.

B. F. SKINNER "I am sometimes asked, 'Do you think of yourself as you think of the organisms you study?' The answer is yes. So far as I know, my behavior at any given moment has been nothing more than the product of my genetic endowment, my personal history, and the current setting" (1983).

"A pat on the back, though only a few vertebrae removed from a kick in the pants, is miles ahead in results."
—Attributed to publisher Bennett Cerf (1898–1971)

🔒 **RETRIEVE IT • • •**   *ANSWERS IN APPENDIX E*

RI-4 Fill in the blanks with one of the following terms: positive reinforcement (PR), negative reinforcement (NR), positive punishment (PP), and negative punishment (NP). We have provided the first answer (PR) for you.

Type of Stimulus	Give It	Take It Away
Desired (for example, a teen's use of the car)	1. PR	2.
Undesired/aversive (for example, an insult)	3.	4.

SKINNER'S LEGACY

LOQ 20-6 Why did Skinner's ideas provoke controversy, and how might his operant conditioning principles be applied at school, in sports, at work, in parenting, and for self-improvement?

B. F. Skinner stirred a hornet's nest with his outspoken beliefs. He repeatedly insisted that external influences, not internal thoughts and feelings, shape behavior. He argued that brain science isn't needed for psychological science, saying that "a science of behavior is independent of neurology" (Skinner, 1938/1966, pp. 423–424). And he urged people to use operant conditioning principles to influence others' behavior at school, work, and home. Knowing that behavior is shaped by its results, he argued that we should use rewards to evoke more desirable behavior.

Skinner's critics objected, saying that he dehumanized people by neglecting their personal freedom and by seeking to control their actions. Skinner's reply: External consequences already haphazardly control people's behavior. Why not administer those consequences toward human betterment? Wouldn't reinforcers be more humane than the punishments used in homes, schools, and prisons? And if it is humbling to think that our history has shaped us, doesn't this very idea also give us hope that we can shape our future?

Applications of Operant Conditioning

Psychologists apply operant conditioning principles to help people with a variety of challenges, from moderating high blood pressure to gaining social skills. Reinforcement techniques have also been used in schools, sports, workplaces, and homes, and these principles can support our self-improvement as well (Flora, 2004).

ENGAGE 🔆 📖 **LaunchPad** Simulate operant conditioning and shaping by visiting **Topic Tutorial: PsychSim6, Operant Conditioning** and also **Topic Tutorial: PsychSim6, Shaping.**

AT SCHOOL More than 50 years ago, Skinner and others worked toward a day when "machines and textbooks" would shape learning in small steps, by immediately reinforcing correct responses. Such machines and texts, they said, would revolutionize education and free teachers to focus on each student's special needs. "Good instruction demands two things," said Skinner (1989). "Students must be told immediately whether what they do is right or wrong and, when right, they must be directed to the step to be taken next."

Skinner might be pleased to know that many of his ideals for education are now possible. Teachers used to find it difficult to pace material to each student's rate of learning, and to provide prompt feedback. Online adaptive quizzing, such as the LearningCurve and Achieve Read & Practice systems available with this text, do both. Students move through quizzes at their own pace, according to their own level of understanding. And they get immediate feedback on their efforts, including personalized study plans.

IN SPORTS The key to shaping behavior in athletic performance, as elsewhere, is first reinforcing small successes and then gradually increasing the challenge. Golf students can learn putting by starting with very short putts, and eventually, as they build mastery, stepping back farther and farther. Novice batters can begin with half swings at an oversized ball pitched from 10 feet away, giving them the immediate pleasure of smacking the ball. As the hitters' confidence builds with their success and they achieve mastery at each level, the pitcher gradually moves back and eventually introduces a standard baseball and pitching distance. Compared with children taught by conventional methods, those trained by this behavioral method have shown faster skill improvement (Simek & O'Brien, 1981, 1988).

AT WORK Knowing that reinforcers influence productivity, many organizations have invited employees to share the risks and rewards of company ownership. Others have focused on reinforcing a job well done. Rewards are most likely to increase productivity if the desired performance is both well-defined and achievable. The message for managers? *Reward specific, achievable behaviors, not vaguely defined "merit."*

Operant conditioning also reminds us that reinforcement should be *immediate.* IBM legend Thomas Watson understood. When he observed an achievement, he wrote the employee a check on the spot (Peters & Waterman, 1982). But rewards need not be material, or lavish. An effective manager may simply walk the floor and sincerely affirm people for good work, or write notes of appreciation for a completed project. As Skinner said, "How much richer would the whole world be if the reinforcers in daily life were more effectively contingent on productive work?"

IN PARENTING As we have seen, parents can learn from operant conditioning practices. Parent-training researchers remind us that by saying, "Get ready for bed" and then caving in to protests or defiance, parents reinforce such whining and arguing (Wierson & Forehand, 1994). Exasperated, they may then yell or gesture menacingly. When the child, now frightened, obeys, that reinforces the parents' angry behavior. Over time, a destructive parent-child relationship develops.

To disrupt this cycle, parents should remember that basic rule of shaping: *Notice people doing something right and affirm them for it.* Give children attention and other reinforcers when they are behaving *well.* Target a specific behavior, reward it, and watch it increase. When children misbehave or are defiant, don't yell at them or hit them. Simply explain the misbehavior and take away the iPad, remove a misused toy, or give a brief time-out.

TO CHANGE YOUR OWN BEHAVIOR Finally, we can use operant conditioning in our own lives. To reinforce your own desired behaviors (perhaps to improve your study habits) and extinguish the undesired ones (to stop smoking, for example), psychologists suggest taking these steps:

1. *State a realistic goal in measurable terms and announce it.* You might, for example, aim to boost your study time by an hour a day. To increase your commitment and odds of success, share that goal with friends.

2. *Decide how, when, and where you will work toward your goal.* Take time to plan. Those who specify how they will implement goals become more focused on those goals and more often fulfill them (Gollwitzer & Oettingen, 2012).

LaunchPad Operant conditioning principles may be used to help us achieve our goals. What else affects our goal achievement? To find out, engage online with the **Immersive Learning** activity, **Assess Your Strengths: How Might Your Willingness to Think of the Future Affect Your Ability to Achieve Long-Term Goals?**

"I wrote another five hundred words. Can I have another cookie?"

ASK YOURSELF

Think of a bad habit of yours or of a friend. How could you or your friend use operant conditioning to break it?

3. *Monitor how often you engage in your desired behavior.* You might log your current study time, noting under what conditions you do and don't study. (When we began writing textbooks, we each logged our time and were amazed to discover how much we were wasting.)

4. *Reinforce the desired behavior.* People's persistence toward long-term goals, such as New Year's resolutions to study or exercise more, is powered mostly by immediate rewards (Woolley & Fishbach, 2017). So to increase your study time, give yourself a reward (a snack or some activity you enjoy) only after you finish your extra hour of study. Agree with your friends that you will join them for weekend activities only if you have met your realistic weekly studying goal.

5. *Reduce the rewards gradually.* As your new behaviors become more habitual, give yourself a mental pat on the back instead of a cookie.

LaunchPad Conditioning principles may also be applied in clinical settings. Play the role of a researcher exploring these applications by engaging online with **Immersive Learning: How Would You Know If People Can Learn to Reduce Anxiety?**

🔒 RETRIEVE IT • • •   ANSWERS IN APPENDIX E

RI-5 Ethan constantly misbehaves at preschool even though his teacher scolds him repeatedly. Why does Ethan's misbehavior continue, and what can his teacher do to stop it?

CONTRASTING CLASSICAL AND OPERANT CONDITIONING

LOQ 20-7   How does operant conditioning differ from classical conditioning?

Both classical and operant conditioning are forms of *associative learning*. Both involve *acquisition, extinction, spontaneous recovery, generalization,* and *discrimination*. But these two forms of learning also differ. Through classical (Pavlovian) conditioning, we associate different stimuli we do not control, and we respond automatically (*respondent behaviors*) (**TABLE 20.4**). Through operant conditioning, we associate our own behaviors—which act on our environment to produce rewarding or punishing stimuli (*operant behaviors*)—with their consequences.

As we shall next see, our biology and cognitive processes influence both classical and operant conditioning.

"O! This learning, what a thing it is."
—William Shakespeare, *The Taming of the Shrew, 1597*

🔒 TABLE 20.4

Comparison of Classical and Operant Conditioning

	Classical Conditioning	Operant Conditioning
Basic idea	Learning associations between events we do not control.	Learning associations between our behavior and its consequences.
Response	Involuntary, automatic.	Voluntary, operates on environment.
Acquisition	Associating events; NS is paired with US and becomes CS.	Associating a response with a consequence (reinforcer or punisher).
Extinction	CR decreases when CS is repeatedly presented alone.	Responding decreases when reinforcement stops.
Spontaneous recovery	The reappearance, after a rest period, of an extinguished CR.	The reappearance, after a rest period, of an extinguished response.
Generalization	The tendency to respond to stimuli similar to the CS.	Responses learned in one situation occurring in other, similar situations.
Discrimination	Learning to distinguish between a CS and other stimuli that do not signal a US.	Learning that some responses, but not others, will be reinforced.

RI-6 Salivating in response to a tone paired with food is a(n) _____ behavior; pressing a bar to obtain food is a(n) _____ behavior.

🔒 REVIEW　OPERANT CONDITIONING

⟫ Learning Objectives

TEST YOURSELF Answer these repeated Learning Objective Questions on your own (before checking the answers in Appendix D) to improve your retention of the concepts (McDaniel et al., 2009, 2015).

20-1 What is *operant conditioning*?

20-2 Who was Skinner, and how is operant behavior reinforced and shaped?

20-3 How do positive and negative reinforcement differ, and what are the basic types of reinforcers?

20-4 How do different reinforcement schedules affect behavior?

20-5 How does punishment differ from negative reinforcement, and how does punishment affect behavior?

20-6 Why did Skinner's ideas provoke controversy, and how might his operant conditioning principles be applied at school, in sports, at work, in parenting, and for self-improvement?

20-7 How does operant conditioning differ from classical conditioning?

⟫ Terms and Concepts to Remember

TEST YOURSELF Write down the definition yourself, then check your answer on the referenced page.

learning, **p. 243**
associative learning, **p. 243**
stimulus, **p. 243**
respondent behavior, **p. 243**
operant conditioning, **p. 243**
operant behavior, **p. 243**
law of effect, **p. 244**
operant chamber, **p. 244**
reinforcement, **p. 244**

shaping, **p. 244**
positive reinforcement, **p. 245**
negative reinforcement, **p. 245**
primary reinforcer, **p. 246**
conditioned reinforcer, **p. 246**
reinforcement schedule, **p. 246**
continuous reinforcement schedule, **p. 246**

partial (intermittent) reinforcement schedule, **p. 246**
fixed-ratio schedule, **p. 246**
variable-ratio schedule, **p. 246**
fixed-interval schedule, **p. 246**
variable-interval schedule, **p. 248**
punishment, **p. 248**

⟫ Experience the Testing Effect

TEST YOURSELF Answer the following questions on your own first, then check your answers in Appendix E.

1. Thorndike's law of effect was the basis for _____'s work on operant conditioning and behavior control.

2. One way to change behavior is to reward natural behaviors in small steps, as the organism gets closer and closer to a desired behavior. This process is called _____.

3. Your dog is barking so loudly that it's making your ears ring. You clap your hands, the dog stops barking, your ears stop ringing, and you think to yourself, "I'll have to do that when he barks again." The end of the barking was for you a
   a. positive reinforcer.
   b. negative reinforcer.
   c. positive punishment.
   d. negative punishment.

4. How could your psychology instructor use negative reinforcement to encourage your attentive behavior during class?

5. Reinforcing a desired response only some of the times it occurs is called _____ reinforcement.

6. A restaurant is running a special deal. After you buy four meals at full price, you will get a free appetizer. This is an example of a _____-_____ schedule of reinforcement.
   a. fixed-ratio
   b. variable-ratio
   c. fixed-interval
   d. variable-interval

7. The partial reinforcement schedule that reinforces a response after unpredictable time periods is a _____-_____ schedule.

8. A medieval proverb notes that "a burnt child dreads the fire." In operant conditioning, the burning would be an example of a
   a. primary reinforcer.
   b. negative reinforcer.
   c. punisher.
   d. positive reinforcer.

Continue testing yourself with 📖 **LearningCurve** or 📖 **Achieve Read & Practice** to learn and remember most effectively.

learning the process of acquiring through experience new and relatively enduring information or behaviors.

preparedness a biological predisposition to learn associations, such as between taste and nausea, that have survival value.

21 Biology, Cognition, and Learning

From drooling dogs, running rats, and pecking pigeons we have learned much about the basic processes of **learning**. But conditioning principles don't tell us the whole story. Today's learning theorists recognize that learning is the product of the interaction of biological, psychological, and social-cultural influences (**FIGURE 21.1**).

FIGURE 21.1
BIOPSYCHOSOCIAL INFLUENCES ON LEARNING Our learning results not only from environmental experiences, but also from cognitive and biological influences.

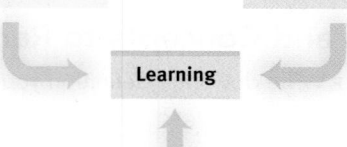

Biological influences:
- genetic predispositions
- unconditioned responses
- adaptive responses
- neural mirroring

Psychological influences:
- previous experiences
- predictability of associations
- generalization
- discrimination
- expectations

Learning

Social-cultural influences:
- culturally learned preferences
- motivation, affected by presence of others
- modeling

BIOLOGICAL CONSTRAINTS ON CONDITIONING

LOQ 21-1 How do biological constraints affect classical and operant conditioning?

Ever since Charles Darwin, scientists have assumed that all animals share a common evolutionary history and thus share commonalities in their makeup and functioning. Ivan Pavlov and John Watson, for example, believed the basic laws of learning were essentially similar in all animals. So it should make little difference whether one studied pigeons or people. Moreover, it seemed that any natural response could be conditioned to any neutral stimulus.

Biological Limits on Classical Conditioning

In 1956, learning researcher Gregory Kimble proclaimed, "Just about any activity of which the organism is capable can be conditioned and . . . these responses can be conditioned to any stimulus that the organism can perceive" (p. 195). Twenty-five years later, he humbly acknowledged that "half a thousand" scientific reports had proven him wrong (Kimble, 1981). More than the early behaviorists realized, an animal's capacity for conditioning is limited by biological constraints. For example, each species' predispositions *prepare* it to learn the associations that enhance its survival—a phenomenon called **preparedness**. Environments are not the whole story. Biology matters.

John Garcia was among those who challenged the prevailing idea that all associations can be learned equally well. While researching the effects of radiation on laboratory animals, Garcia and Robert Koelling (1966) noticed that rats began to avoid drinking water from the plastic bottles in radiation chambers. Could classical conditioning be the culprit? Might the rats have linked the plastic-tasting water (a CS) to the sickness (UR) triggered by the radiation (US)?

JOHN GARCIA As the laboring son of California farmworkers, Garcia attended school only in the off-season during his early childhood years. After entering junior college in his late twenties, and earning his Ph.D. in his late forties, he received the American Psychological Association's Distinguished Scientific Contribution Award "for his highly original, pioneering research in conditioning and learning." He was also elected to the National Academy of Sciences.

To test their hunch, Garcia and Koelling exposed the rats to a particular taste, sight, or sound (CS) and later also to radiation or drugs (US) that led to nausea and vomiting (UR). Two startling findings emerged: First, even if sickened as late as several hours after tasting a particular novel flavor, the rats thereafter avoided that flavor. This appeared to violate the widely held belief that for conditioning to occur, the US must immediately follow the CS.

Second, the sickened rats developed aversions to tastes but not to sights or sounds. This contradicted the behaviorists' idea that any perceivable stimulus could serve as a CS. But it made adaptive sense. For rats, the easiest way to identify tainted food is to taste it; if sickened after sampling a new food, they thereafter avoid it. This response, called *taste aversion,* makes it difficult to eradicate a population of "bait-shy" rats by poisoning.

Humans, too, seem biologically prepared to learn some associations rather than others. If you become violently ill four hours after eating contaminated oysters, you will probably develop an aversion to the *taste* of oysters more readily than to the sight of the associated restaurant, its plates, the people you were with, or the music you heard there. (In contrast, birds, which hunt by sight, appear biologically primed to develop aversions to the *sight* of tainted food [Nicolaus et al., 1983].)

Garcia and Koelling's taste-aversion research is but one instance in which psychological experiments that began with the discomfort of some laboratory animals ended by enhancing the welfare of many others. In one conditioned taste-aversion study, coyotes and wolves were tempted into eating sheep carcasses laced with a sickening poison. Thereafter, they developed an aversion to sheep meat; two wolves later penned with a live sheep seemed actually to fear it (Gustavson et al., 1974, 1976). These studies not only saved the sheep from their predators, but also saved the sheep-shunning coyotes and wolves from angry ranchers and farmers who had wanted to destroy them. Similar applications have prevented baboons from raiding African gardens, raccoons from attacking chickens, and ravens and crows from feeding on crane eggs. In all these cases, research helped preserve both the prey and their predators, all of which occupy an important ecological niche (Dingfelder, 2010; Garcia & Gustavson, 1997).

Such research supports Darwin's principle that natural selection favors traits that aid survival. Our ancestors who readily learned taste aversions were unlikely to eat the same toxic food again and were more likely to survive and leave descendants. Nausea, like anxiety, pain, and other bad feelings, serves a good purpose. Like a car's low-fuel warning light, each alerts the body to a threat (Davidson & Riley, 2015; Neese, 1991).

Our preparedness to associate a CS with a US that follows predictably and immediately is adaptive. Causes often do immediately precede effects. But as we saw in the taste-aversion findings, our predisposition to associate an effect with a preceding event can trick us. When chemotherapy triggers nausea and vomiting more than an hour following treatment, cancer patients may, over time, develop classically conditioned nausea (and sometimes anxiety) to the sights, sounds, and smells associated with the clinic (**FIGURE 21.2**) (Hall, 1997). Merely returning to the clinic's waiting room or seeing the nurses can provoke these conditioned feelings (Burish & Carey, 1986; Davey, 1992). Under normal circumstances, such revulsion to sickening stimuli would be adaptive.

TASTE AVERSION If you became violently ill after eating oysters, you would probably have a hard time eating them again. Their smell and taste would have become a CS for nausea. This learning occurs readily because our biology prepares us to learn taste aversions to toxic foods.

"Once bitten, twice shy." —G. F. Northall, *Folk-Phrases,* 1894

ANIMAL TASTE AVERSION As an alternative to killing wolves and coyotes that preyed on sheep, some ranchers have sickened the animals with lamb laced with a drug to create a taste aversion.

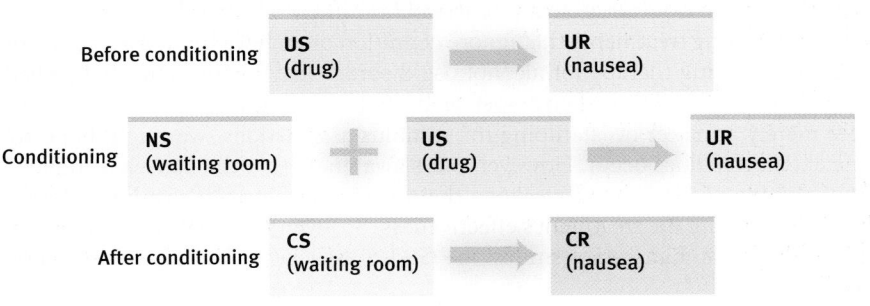

Before conditioning	US (drug)	→	UR (nausea)	
Conditioning	NS (waiting room) + US (drug)	→	UR (nausea)	
After conditioning	CS (waiting room)	→	CR (nausea)	

FIGURE 21.2
NAUSEA CONDITIONING IN CANCER PATIENTS

NATURAL ATHLETES Animals can most easily learn and retain behaviors that draw on their biological predispositions, such as horses' inborn ability to move around obstacles with speed and agility.

For more information on animal behavior, see books by (we are not making this up) Robin Fox and Lionel Tiger.

🔒 **RETRIEVE IT • • •**   *ANSWERS IN APPENDIX E*

RI-1 How did Garcia and Koelling's taste-aversion studies help disprove Gregory Kimble's early claim that "just about any activity of which the organism is capable can be conditioned . . . to any stimulus that the organism can perceive"?

Biological Limits on Operant Conditioning

Nature also constrains each species' capacity for operant conditioning. Science fiction writer Robert Heinlein (1907–1988) said it well: "Never try to teach a pig to sing; it wastes your time and annoys the pig."

We most easily learn and retain behaviors that reflect our biological predispositions. Thus, using food as a reinforcer, you could easily condition a hamster to dig or to rear up, because these are among the animal's natural food-searching behaviors. But you won't be so successful if you use food as a reinforcer to shape face washing and other hamster behaviors that aren't normally associated with food or hunger (Shettleworth, 1973). Similarly, you could easily teach pigeons to flap their wings to avoid being shocked, and to peck to obtain food: Fleeing with their wings and eating with their beaks are natural pigeon behaviors. However, pigeons would have a hard time learning to peck to avoid a shock, or to flap their wings to obtain food (Foree & LoLordo, 1973). The principle: *Biological constraints predispose organisms to learn associations that are naturally adaptive.*

In the early years of their work, animal trainers Marian Breland and Keller Breland presumed that operant principles would work on almost any response an animal could make. But they, too, learned about biological constraints. In one act, pigs trained to pick up large wooden "dollars" and deposit them in a piggy bank began to drift back to their natural ways. They dropped the coin, pushed it with their snouts as pigs are prone to do, picked it up again, and then repeated the sequence—delaying their food reinforcer. This **instinctive drift** occurred as the animals reverted to their biologically predisposed patterns.

📱 **LaunchPad** To learn more about biology's influence on learning, engage online with **Concept Practice: Biologically Adaptive Associations.**

COGNITION'S INFLUENCE ON CONDITIONING

LOQ 21-2 How do cognitive processes affect classical and operant conditioning?

Cognition and Classical Conditioning

"All brains are, in essence, anticipation machines." —Daniel C. Dennett, *Consciousness Explained*, 1991

In their dismissal of "mentalistic" concepts such as consciousness, Pavlov and Watson underestimated the importance of not only biological constraints such as preparedness and instinctive drift, but also the effects of cognitive processes (thoughts, perceptions, expectations). The early behaviorists believed that rats' and dogs' learned behaviors could be reduced to mindless mechanisms, so there was no need to consider cognition. But Robert Rescorla and Allan Wagner (1972) showed that an animal can learn the *predictability* of an event. If a shock always is preceded by a tone, and then may also be preceded by a light that accompanies the tone, a rat will react with fear to the tone but not to the light. Although the light is always followed by the shock, it adds no new information; the tone is a better predictor. The more predictable the association, the stronger the conditioned response. It's as if the animal learns an *expectancy,* an awareness of how likely it is that the US will occur.

Classical conditioning treatments that ignore cognition often have limited success. For example, people receiving therapy for alcohol use disorder may be given alcohol spiked with a nauseating drug. Will they then associate alcohol with sickness? If classical conditioning were merely a matter of "stamping in" stimulus associations, we might hope so, and to some extent this does occur. However, one's awareness that the nausea is induced by the drug, not the alcohol, often weakens the association between drinking alcohol and feeling sick, reducing the treatment's effectiveness. So, even in classical conditioning, it is—especially with humans—not simply the CS-US association but also the thought that counts.

Cognition and Operant Conditioning

B. F. Skinner acknowledged the biological underpinnings of behavior and the existence of private thought processes. Nevertheless, many psychologists criticized him for discounting cognition's importance.

A mere eight days before dying of leukemia in 1990, Skinner stood before the American Psychological Association convention. In this final address, he still resisted the growing belief that cognitive processes have a necessary place in the science of psychology and even in our understanding of conditioning. He viewed "cognitive science" as a throwback to early twentieth-century introspectionism. For Skinner, thoughts and emotions were behaviors that follow the same laws as other behaviors.

Nevertheless, the evidence of cognitive processes cannot be ignored. For example, animals on a *fixed-interval reinforcement schedule* respond more and more frequently as the time approaches when a response will produce a reinforcer. Although a strict behaviorist would object to talk of "expectations," the animals behave as if they expected that repeating the response would soon produce the reward.

Evidence of cognitive processes has also come from studying rats in mazes. Rats exploring a maze, given no obvious rewards, seem to develop a **cognitive map**, a mental representation of the maze. When an experimenter then places food in the maze's goal box, these rats run the maze as quickly as other rats that were previously reinforced with food for this result. Like people sightseeing in a new town, the exploring rats seemingly experienced **latent learning** during their earlier tours. That learning became apparent only when there was some incentive to demonstrate it. Children, too, may learn from watching a parent but demonstrate the learning only much later, as needed. *The point to remember:* There is more to learning than associating a response with a consequence; there is also cognition. In the Thinking, Language, and Intelligence modules, we will encounter more striking evidence of animals' cognitive abilities in solving problems and in using aspects of language.

Will & Deni McIntyre/Science Source

TABLE 21.1 compares the biological and cognitive influences on classical and operant conditioning.

"Bathroom? Sure, it's just down the hall to the left, jog right, left, another left, straight past two more lefts, then right, and it's at the end of the third corridor on your right."

LATENT LEARNING Animals, like people, can learn from experience, with or without reinforcement. In a classic experiment, rats in one group repeatedly explored a maze, always with a food reward at the end. Rats in another group explored the maze with no food reward. But once given a food reward at the end, rats in the second group thereafter ran the maze as quickly as (and even faster than) the always-rewarded rats (Tolman & Honzik, 1930).

TABLE 21.1

Biological and Cognitive Influences on Conditioning

	Classical Conditioning	Operant Conditioning
Biological influences	Natural predispositions constrain what stimuli and responses can easily be associated.	Organisms most easily learn behaviors similar to their natural behaviors; unnatural behaviors instinctively drift back toward natural ones.
Cognitive influences	Organisms develop an expectation that a CS signals the arrival of a US.	Organisms develop an expectation that a response will be reinforced or punished; they also exhibit latent learning, without reinforcement.

instinctive drift the tendency of learned behavior to gradually revert to biologically predisposed patterns.

cognitive map a mental representation of the layout of one's environment. For example, after exploring a maze, rats act as if they have learned a cognitive map of it.

latent learning learning that occurs but is not apparent until there is an incentive to demonstrate it.

🔒 **RETRIEVE IT** • • •   *ANSWERS IN APPENDIX E*

RI-2 Instinctive drift and latent learning are examples of what important idea?

LEARNING BY OBSERVATION

LOQ 21-3 What is *observational learning?*

Cognition supports **observational learning** (also called *social learning*), in which higher animals, especially humans, learn without direct experience, by watching and imitating others. A child who sees his sister burn her fingers on a hot stove learns not to touch it. We learn our native languages and various other specific behaviors by observing and imitating others, a process called **modeling**.

ALBERT BANDURA "The Bobo doll follows me wherever I go. The photographs are published in every introductory psychology text and virtually every undergraduate takes introductory psychology. I recently checked into a Washington hotel. The clerk at the desk asked, 'Aren't you the psychologist who did the Bobo doll experiment?' I answered, 'I am afraid that will be my legacy.' He replied, 'That deserves an upgrade. I will put you in a suite in the quiet part of the hotel'" (2005). A recent analysis of citations, awards, and textbook coverage identified Bandura—shown here receiving a 2016 U.S. National Medal of Science from President Obama—as the world's most eminent psychologist (Diener et al., 2014).

Picture this scene from an experiment by Albert Bandura, the pioneering researcher of observational learning (Bandura et al., 1961): A preschool child is working on a drawing, while an adult in another part of the room builds with Tinkertoys. As the child watches, the adult gets up and for nearly 10 minutes pounds, kicks, and throws around the room a large inflated Bobo doll, yelling, "Sock him in the nose. . . . Hit him down. . . . Kick him."

The child is then taken to another room filled with appealing toys. Soon the experimenter returns and tells the child she has decided to save these good toys "for the other children." She takes the now-frustrated child to a third room containing a few toys, including a Bobo doll. Left alone, what does the child do?

Compared with children not exposed to the adult model, those who viewed the model's actions were more likely to lash out at the doll. Observing the aggressive outburst apparently lowered their inhibitions. But *something more* was also at work, for the children imitated the very acts they had observed and used the very words they had heard (**FIGURE 21.3**).

LaunchPad For 3 minutes of classic footage, see the **Video: Bandura's Bobo Doll Experiment.**

That "something more," Bandura suggested, was this: By watching models, we experience *vicarious reinforcement* or *vicarious punishment,* and we learn to anticipate a behavior's consequences in situations like those we are observing. We are especially likely to learn from people we perceive as similar to ourselves, or as successful, or as admirable. fMRI scans show that when people observe someone winning a reward (and especially when

FIGURE 21.3
THE FAMOUS BOBO DOLL EXPERIMENT Notice how the children's actions directly imitate the adult's.

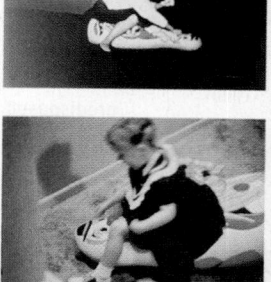

it's someone likable and similar to themselves), their own brain reward systems activate, much as if they themselves had won the reward (Mobbs et al., 2009). When we identify with someone, we experience their outcomes vicariously. Even our learned fears may extinguish as we observe another safely navigating the feared situation (Golkar et al., 2013). Lord Chesterfield (1694–1773) had the idea: "We are, in truth, more than half what we are by imitation."

Bandura's work provides an example of how basic research "pursued for its own sake" can have a broader purpose. "The Bobo Doll studies," he reflected (2016), "provided the principles for unforeseen global applications 25 years later." Insights derived from his research have been used not only to restrain televised violence, but also to offer social models that have helped reduce unplanned childbearing, protect against AIDS, and promote environmental conservation.

Mirrors and Imitation in the Brain

LOQ 21-4 How may observational learning be enabled by neural mirroring?

In 1991, on a hot summer day in Parma, Italy, a lab monkey awaited its researchers' return from lunch. The researchers had implanted wires next to its motor cortex, in a frontal lobe brain region that enabled the monkey to plan and enact movements. The monitoring device would alert the researchers to activity in that region of the monkey's brain. When the monkey moved a peanut into its mouth, for example, the device would buzz. That day, as one of the researchers reentered the lab, ice cream cone in hand, the monkey stared at him. As the researcher raised the cone to lick it, the monkey's monitor buzzed—as if the motionless monkey had itself moved (Blakeslee, 2006; Iacoboni, 2008, 2009).

The same buzzing had been heard earlier, when the monkey watched humans or other monkeys move peanuts to their mouths. The flabbergasted researchers had, they believed, stumbled onto a previously unknown type of neuron (Rizzolatti et al., 2002, 2006). These presumed **mirror neurons**, they argued, provide a neural basis for everyday imitation and observational learning. When a monkey grasps, holds, or tears something, these neurons fire. And they likewise fire when the monkey observes another doing so. When one monkey sees, its neurons mirror what another monkey does. (For a debate regarding the importance of mirror neurons, which are sometimes overblown in the popular press, see Gallese et al., 2011; Hickok, 2014.)

Imitation is widespread in other species. Primates observe and imitate all sorts of novel tool use behaviors, such as how to crack nuts using stone hammers (Fragaszy et al., 2017). These types of behaviors are then transmitted from generation to generation within their local culture (Hopper et al., 2008; Whiten et al., 2007). In one study, researchers trained vervet monkeys to prefer either blue or pink corn by soaking one color in a disgusting-tasting solution (van de Waal et al., 2013). Four to six months later, after a new generation of monkeys was born, the adults stuck with whatever color they had learned to prefer—and, on observing them, so did all but one of 27 infant monkeys. Moreover,

observational learning learning by observing others.

modeling the process of observing and imitating a specific behavior.

mirror neurons frontal lobe neurons that some scientists believe fire when we perform certain actions or observe another doing so. The brain's mirroring of another's action may enable imitation and empathy.

MIRROR NEURONS AT WORK?

"Your back is killing me!"

ANIMAL SOCIAL LEARNING (a) Whacking the water, which drives prey fish into a clump and thus boosts feeding, has spread among humpback whales through social learning (Allen et al., 2013). (b) Likewise, monkeys learn to prefer whatever color corn they observe other monkeys eating.

(a)

(b)

Meltzoff, A. N., Kuhl, P. K., Movellan, J & Sejnowski, T. J. (2009). Foundations for a new science of learning. Science, 325, 284–288.

FIGURE 21.4

IMITATION This 12-month-old infant sees an adult look left, and immediately follows her gaze (Meltzoff et al., 2009).

"This instinct to humiliate, when it's modeled by someone in the public platform, by someone powerful, it filters down into everybody's life, because it . . . gives permission for other people to do the same thing."
—Meryl Streep, U.S. Golden Globe Award speech, 2017

"Children need models more than they need critics." —Joseph Joubert, *Pensées,* 1842

when blue- (or pink-) preferring males migrated to the other group, they switched preferences and began eating as the other group did. Monkey see, monkey do.

In humans, imitation is pervasive. Our catchphrases, fashions, ceremonies, foods, traditions, morals, and fads all spread by one person copying another. Children, and even infants, are natural imitators (Marshall & Meltzoff, 2014). By 8 to 16 months, infants imitate various novel gestures (Jones, 2007). By 12 months (**FIGURE 21.4**), they look where an adult is looking (Meltzoff et al., 2009). And by 14 months, children imitate acts modeled on TV (Meltzoff, 1988; Meltzoff & Moore, 1989, 1997). Even as 2½-year-olds, when many of their mental abilities are near those of adult chimpanzees, young humans surpass chimps at social tasks such as imitating another's solution to a problem (Herrmann et al., 2007). Children see, children do.

So strong is the human predisposition to learn from watching adults that 2- to 5-year-old children *overimitate.* Whether living in urban Australia or rural Africa, they copy even irrelevant adult actions. Before reaching for a toy in a plastic jar, they will first stroke the jar with a feather if that's what they have observed (Lyons et al., 2007). Or, imitating an adult, they will wave a stick over a box and then use the stick to push on a knob that opens the box—when all they needed to do to open the box was to push on the knob (Nielsen & Tomaselli, 2010).

Humans, like monkeys, have brains that support empathy and imitation. Researchers cannot insert experimental electrodes in human brains, but they can use fMRI scans to see brain activity associated with performing and with observing actions. So, is the human capacity to simulate another's action and to share in another's experience due to specialized mirror neurons? Or is it due to distributed brain networks? That issue is under debate (Fox et al., 2016; Gallese et al., 2011; Hickok, 2014; Iacoboni, 2008, 2009; Spaulding, 2013). Regardless, children's brains do enable their empathy and their ability to infer another's mental state, an ability known as *theory of mind.*

Our brain's response to observing others makes emotions contagious. Our brain simulates and vicariously experiences what we observe. So real are these mental instant replays that we may misremember an action we have observed as one we have performed (Lindner et al., 2010). But through these reenactments, we grasp others' states of mind. Observing others' postures, faces, voices, and writing styles, we unconsciously synchronize our own to theirs—which helps us feel what they are feeling (Bernieri et al., 1994; Ireland & Pennebaker, 2010). Imitation helps us gain friends, leading us to mimic those we like (Chartrand & Lakin, 2013). We find ourselves yawning when they yawn, smiling when they smile, laughing when they laugh.

Seeing a loved one's pain, our faces mirror the other's emotion. But as **FIGURE 21.5** shows, so do our brains. In this fMRI scan, the pain imagined by an empathic romantic partner triggered some of the same brain activity experienced by the loved one who actually had the pain (Singer et al., 2004). Observing others' pain also releases our body's natural painkillers, thus calming our distress and enabling our helping (Haaker et al., 2017). Even fiction reading may trigger such activity, as we mentally simulate (and vicariously experience) the feelings and actions described (Mar & Oatley, 2008; Speer et al., 2009). Students who read *Harry Potter*—the bestselling kid wizard series that masterfully modeled tolerance—reported less prejudice against immigrants, refugees, and gay people (Vezzali et al., 2015).

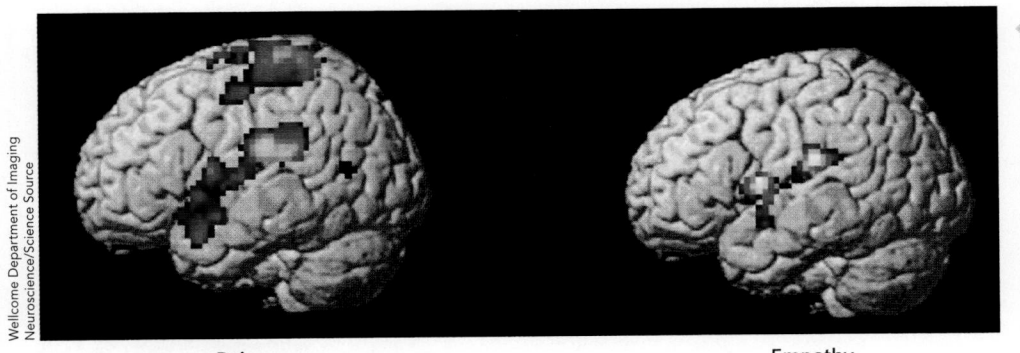

Pain   Empathy

FIGURE 21.5
EXPERIENCED AND IMAGINED PAIN IN THE BRAIN Brain activity related to actual pain is mirrored in the brain of an observing loved one. Empathy in the brain shows up in emotional brain areas, but not in the somatosensory cortex, which receives the physical pain input.

Applications of Observational Learning

LOQ 21-5 What is the impact of prosocial modeling and of antisocial modeling?

The big news from Bandura's studies and the mirror-neuron research is that we look, we mentally imitate, and we learn. Models—in our family, our neighborhood, or the media we consume—may have effects, good and bad.

PROSOCIAL EFFECTS The good news is that people's modeling of **prosocial** (positive, helpful) **behaviors** can have prosocial effects. Many business organizations effectively use *behavior modeling* to help new employees learn communication, sales, and customer service skills (Taylor et al., 2005). Trainees gain these skills faster when they are able to observe the skills being modeled effectively by experienced workers (or actors simulating them).

People who exemplify nonviolent, helpful behavior can also prompt similar behavior in others. After observing someone helping (assisting a woman with dropped books), people become more helpful, such as by assisting someone who dropped a dollar (Burger et al., 2015). India's Mahatma Gandhi and America's Martin Luther King, Jr., both drew on the power of modeling, making nonviolent action a powerful force for social change in both countries (Matsumoto et al., 2015). The media offer models. For example, one research team found that across seven countries, viewing prosocial TV, movies, and video games boosted later helping behavior (Prot et al., 2014).

Parents are also powerful models. European Christians who risked their lives to rescue Jews from the Nazis usually had a close relationship with at least one parent who modeled a strong moral or humanitarian concern; this was also true for U.S. civil rights activists in the 1960s (London, 1970; Oliner & Oliner, 1988). The observational learning of morality begins early. Socially responsive toddlers who readily imitated their parents tended to become preschoolers with a strong internalized conscience (Forman et al., 2004).

Models are most effective when their actions and words are consistent. To encourage children to read, read to them and surround them with books and people who read. To increase the odds that your children will practice your religion, worship and attend religious activities with them. Sometimes, however, models say one thing and do another. Many parents seem to operate according to the principle "Do as I *say*, not as I do."

A MODEL CAREGIVER This girl is learning orphan-nursing skills, as well as compassion, by observing her mentor in this Humane Society program. As the sixteenth-century proverb states, "Example is better than precept."

prosocial behavior positive, constructive, helpful behavior. The opposite of antisocial behavior.

CHILDREN SEE, CHILDREN DO? Children who often experience physical punishment tend to display more aggression.

David Strickler/The Image Works

Experiments suggest that children learn to do both (Rice & Grusec, 1975; Rushton, 1975). Exposed to a hypocrite, they tend to imitate the hypocrisy—by doing what the model did and saying what the model said.

> 🔒 **RETRIEVE IT • • •**   ANSWERS IN APPENDIX E
>
> **RI-3** Jason's parents and older friends all drive over the speed limit, but they advise him not to. Juan's parents and friends drive within the speed limit, but they say nothing to deter him from speeding. Will Jason or Juan be more likely to speed?

ANTISOCIAL EFFECTS The bad news is that observational learning may also have *antisocial effects*. This helps us understand why abusive parents might have aggressive children, why children who are lied to become more likely to cheat and lie, and why many men who beat their wives had wife-battering fathers (Hays & Carver, 2014; Stith et al., 2000). Critics note that such aggressiveness could be genetic. But with monkeys, we know it can be environmental. In study after study, young monkeys separated from their mothers and subjected to high levels of aggression grew up to be aggressive themselves (Chamove, 1980). The lessons we learn as children are not easily replaced as adults, and they are sometimes visited on future generations.

TV shows, movies, and online videos are sources of observational learning. While watching, children may learn that bullying is an effective way to control others, that free and easy sex brings pleasure without later misery or disease, or that men should be tough and women gentle. And they have ample time to learn such lessons. During their first 18 years, most children in developed countries spend more time watching TV than they spend in school. The average teen watches more than 4 hours a day; the average adult, 3 hours (Robinson & Martin, 2009; Strasburger et al., 2010).

Viewers are learning about life from a peculiar storyteller, one that reflects the culture's mythology rather than its reality. Between 1998 and 2006, prime-time violence on TV reportedly increased 75 percent (PTC, 2007). An analysis of more than 3000 network and cable programs aired during one closely studied year revealed that nearly 6 in 10 featured violence, that 74 percent of the violence went unpunished, that 58 percent did not show the victims' pain, that nearly half the incidents involved "justified" violence, and that nearly half involved an attractive perpetrator. These conditions define the recipe for the *violence-viewing effect* described in many studies and recognized by a near-consensus of media researchers (Bushman et al., 2015; Donnerstein, 1998, 2011).

In 2012, a well-armed man targeted young children and their teachers in a horrifying mass shooting at Connecticut's Sandy Hook Elementary School. Was the American media correct in wondering whether the killer was influenced by the violent video games found stockpiled in his home? (See Thinking Critically About: The Effects of Viewing Media Violence.)

"The problem with television is that the people must sit and keep their eyes glued to a screen: The average American family hasn't time for it. Therefore the showmen are convinced that . . . television will never be a serious competitor of [radio] broadcasting." —*The New York Times*, 1939

ENGAGE Screen time's greatest effect may stem from what it displaces. Children and adults who spend several hours a day in front of a screen spend that many fewer hours in other pursuits—talking, studying, playing, reading, or socializing face-to-face with friends. What would you have done with your extra time if you had spent even half as many hours in front of a screen? How might you be different as a result?

ENGAGE   (ASK YOURSELF)

Who has been a significant role model for you? What did you learn from observing this person? For whom are you a role model?

THINKING CRITICALLY ABOUT:

The Effects of Viewing Media Violence

LOQ 21-6   What is the violence-viewing effect?

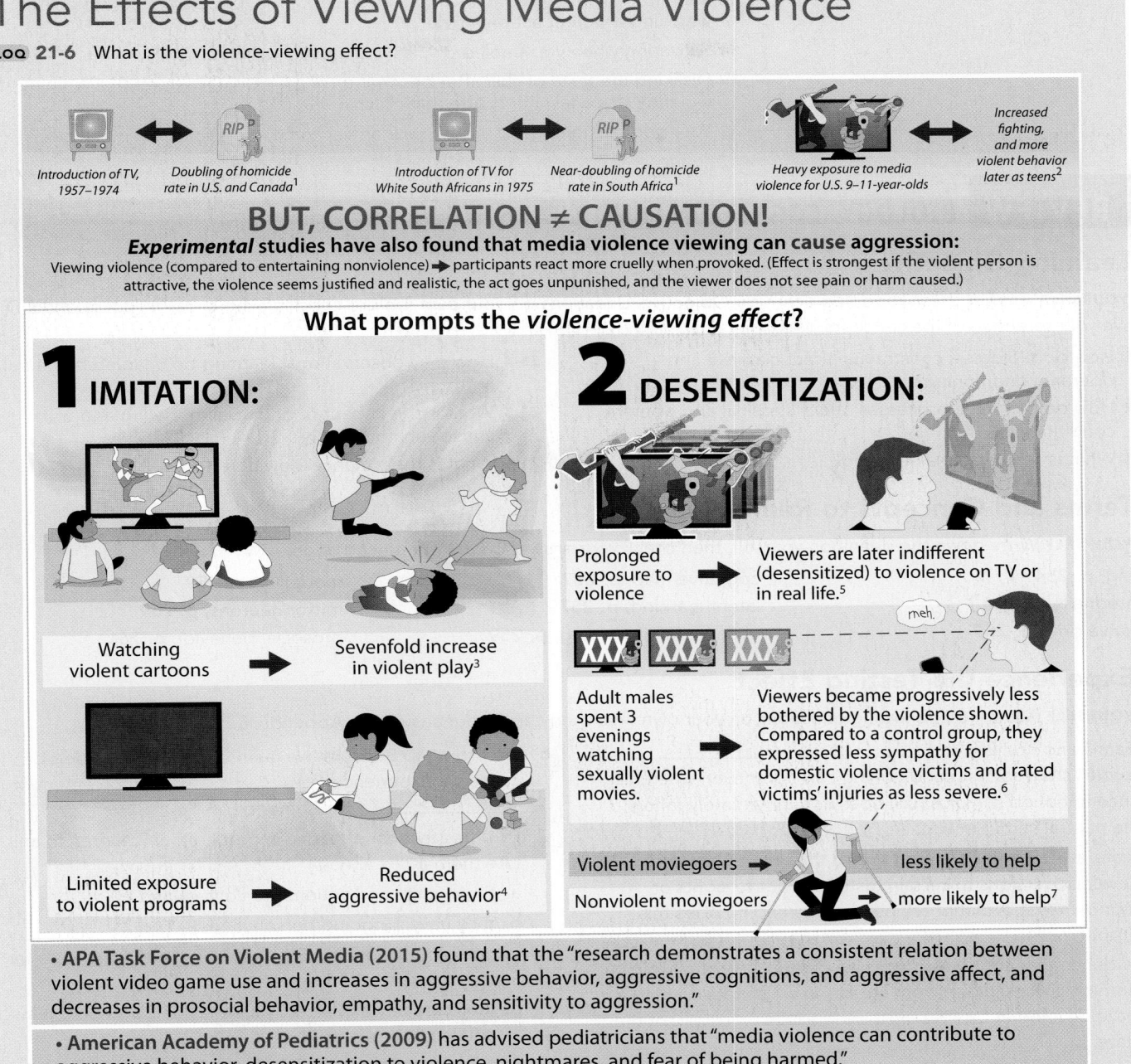

BUT, CORRELATION ≠ CAUSATION!

Experimental studies have also found that media violence viewing can **cause** aggression:

Viewing violence (compared to entertaining nonviolence) ➤ participants react more cruelly when provoked. (Effect is strongest if the violent person is attractive, the violence seems justified and realistic, the act goes unpunished, and the viewer does not see pain or harm caused.)

What prompts the *violence-viewing effect*?

1 IMITATION:

Watching violent cartoons ➤ Sevenfold increase in violent play[3]

Limited exposure to violent programs ➤ Reduced aggressive behavior[4]

2 DESENSITIZATION:

Prolonged exposure to violence ➤ Viewers are later indifferent (desensitized) to violence on TV or in real life.[5]

Adult males spent 3 evenings watching sexually violent movies. ➤ Viewers became progressively less bothered by the violence shown. Compared to a control group, they expressed less sympathy for domestic violence victims and rated victims' injuries as less severe.[6]

Violent moviegoers ➤ less likely to help

Nonviolent moviegoers ➤ more likely to help[7]

• **APA Task Force on Violent Media (2015)** found that the "research demonstrates a consistent relation between violent video game use and increases in aggressive behavior, aggressive cognitions, and aggressive affect, and decreases in prosocial behavior, empathy, and sensitivity to aggression."

• **American Academy of Pediatrics (2009)** has advised pediatricians that "media violence can contribute to aggressive behavior, desensitization to violence, nightmares, and fear of being harmed."

1. Centerwall, 1989.   2. Boxer at al., 2009; Gentile et al., 2011; Gentile & Bushman, 2012.   3. Boyatzis et al., 1995.   4. Christakis et al., 2013.   5. Fanti et al., 2009; Rule & Ferguson, 1986.   6. Mullin & Linz, 1995.   7. Bushman & Anderson, 2009.

* * *

Bandura's work—like that of Ivan Pavlov, John Watson, B. F. Skinner, and thousands of others who advanced our knowledge of learning principles—illustrates the impact that can result from single-minded devotion to a few well-defined problems and ideas. These researchers defined the issues and impressed on us the importance of learning. As their legacy demonstrates, intellectual history is often made by people who risk going to extremes in pushing ideas to their limits (Simonton, 2000).

🔒 **RETRIEVE IT • • •**

ANSWERS IN APPENDIX E

RI-4 Match the examples (I–V) to the appropriate underlying learning principle (a–e):

I. Knowing the way from your bed to the bathroom in the dark	a. Classical conditioning
II. Your little brother getting in a fight after watching a violent action movie	b. Operant conditioning
III. Salivating when you smell brownies in the oven	c. Latent learning
IV. Disliking the taste of chili after becoming violently sick a few hours after eating chili	d. Observational learning
V. Your dog racing to greet you on your arrival home	e. Biological predispositions

🔒 REVIEW BIOLOGY, COGNITION, AND LEARNING

⌁ Learning Objectives

TEST YOURSELF Answer these repeated Learning Objective Questions on your own (before checking the answers in Appendix D) to improve your retention of the concepts (McDaniel et al., 2009, 2015).

21-1 How do biological constraints affect classical and operant conditioning?

21-2 How do cognitive processes affect classical and operant conditioning?

21-3 What is *observational learning*?

21-4 How may observational learning be enabled by neural mirroring?

21-5 What is the impact of prosocial modeling and of antisocial modeling?

21-6 What is the violence-viewing effect?

⌁ Terms and Concepts to Remember

TEST YOURSELF Write down the definition yourself, then check your answer on the referenced page.

learning, **p. 254**

preparedness, **p. 254**

instinctive drift, **p. 257**

cognitive map, **p. 257**

latent learning, **p. 257**

observational learning, **p. 259**

modeling, **p. 259**

mirror neurons, **p. 259**

prosocial behavior, **p. 261**

⌁ Experience the Testing Effect

TEST YOURSELF Answer the following questions on your own first, then check your answers in Appendix E.

1. Garcia and Koelling's _____-_____ studies showed that conditioning can occur even when the unconditioned stimulus (US) does not immediately follow the neutral stimulus (NS).

2. Taste-aversion research has shown that some animals develop aversions to certain tastes but not to sights or sounds. What evolutionary psychology finding does this support?

3. Evidence that cognitive processes play an important role in learning comes in part from studies in which rats running a maze develop a _____ _____ of the maze.

4. Rats that explored a maze without any reward were later able to run the maze as well as other rats that had received food rewards for running the maze. The rats that had learned without reinforcement demonstrated _____ _____.

5. Children learn many social behaviors by imitating parents and other models. This type of learning is called _____ _____.

6. According to Bandura, we learn by watching models because we experience _____ reinforcement or _____ punishment.

7. Parents are most effective in getting their children to imitate them if
   a. their words and actions are consistent.
   b. they have outgoing personalities.
   c. one parent works and the other stays home to care for the children.
   d. they carefully explain why a behavior is acceptable in adults but not in children.

8. Some scientists believe that the brain has _____ neurons that enable empathy and imitation.

9. Most experts agree that repeated viewing of media violence
   a. makes all viewers significantly more aggressive.
   b. has little effect on viewers.
   c. is a risk factor for viewers' increased aggression.
   d. makes viewers angry and frustrated.

Continue testing yourself with 📚 **LearningCurve** or 📚 **Achieve Read & Practice** to learn and remember most effectively.

Memory

MODULES 22–24

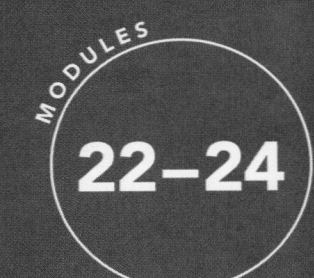

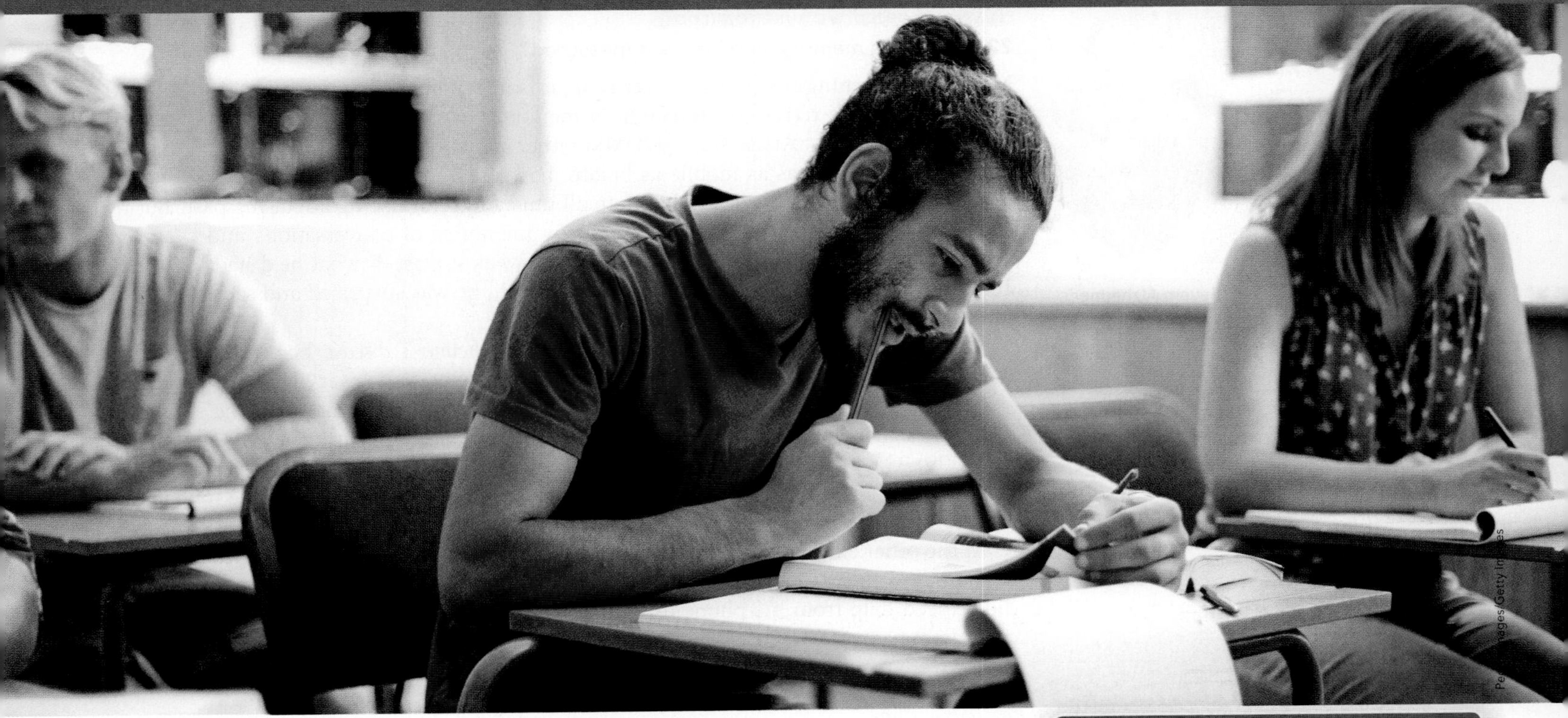

Be thankful for memory. We take it for granted, except when it malfunctions. But it is our memory that accounts for time and defines our life. It is our memory that enables us to recognize family, speak our language, and find our way home. It is our memory that enables us to enjoy an experience and then mentally replay and enjoy it again. It is our memory that enables us to build histories with those we love. And it is our memory that occasionally pits us against those whose offenses we cannot forget. Our shared memories help bind us together as Irish or Icelandic, Syrian or Samoan.

In large part, we are what we remember. Without memory—our storehouse of accumulated learning—there would be no savoring of past joys, no guilt or anger over painful recollections. We would instead live in an enduring present, each moment fresh. Each person would be a stranger, every language foreign, every task—dressing, cooking, biking—a new challenge. You would even be a stranger to yourself, lacking that continuous sense of self that extends from your distant past to your momentary present.

Researchers study memory from many perspectives. Module 22 introduces the measuring, modeling, and encoding of memories. Module 23 examines how memories are stored and retrieved. Module 24 explores what happens when our memories fail us, and looks at ways to improve memory. ▶

OVERVIEW OF MODULES

22 Studying and Encoding Memories

STUDYING MEMORY

LEARNING OBJECTIVE QUESTION (LOQ)

22-1 What is *memory*, and how is it measured?

Memory is learning that persists over time; it is information that has been acquired and stored and can be retrieved. Research on memory's extremes has helped us understand how memory works. At age 92, my [DM's] father suffered a small stroke that had but one peculiar effect. He was as mobile as before. His genial personality was intact. He knew us and enjoyed poring over family photo albums and reminiscing about his past. But he had lost most of his ability to lay down new memories of conversations and everyday episodes. He could not tell me what day of the week it was, or what he'd had for lunch. Told repeatedly of his brother-in-law's recent death, he was surprised and saddened each time he heard the news.

Some disorders slowly strip away memory. *Alzheimer's disease* begins as difficulty remembering new information, progressing to an inability to do everyday tasks. Complex speech becomes simple sentences; family members and close friends become strangers; the brain's memory centers, once strong, become weak and wither away (Desikan et al., 2009). Over several years, someone with Alzheimer's may become unknowing and unknowable. Lost memory strikes at the core of our humanity, leaving people robbed of a sense of joy, meaning, and companionship.

At the other extreme are people who win gold medals in memory competitions. When two-time World Memory Champion Feng Wang was a 21-year-old college student, he didn't need help from his phone to remember his friends' numbers. The average person can parrot back a string of about 7—maybe even 9—digits. Feng could repeat up to 200, if they were read about 1 second apart in an otherwise silent room (Ericsson et al., 2017). At one competition, he even memorized 300 digits!

Amazing? Yes, but consider your own impressive memory. You remember countless faces, places, and happenings; tastes, smells, and textures; voices, sounds, and songs. In one study, students listened to snippets—a mere four-tenths of a second—from popular songs. How often did they recognize the artist and song? More than 25 percent of the time (Krumhansl, 2010). We often recognize songs as quickly as we recognize a familiar voice.

So, too, with faces and places. Imagine viewing more than 2500 slides of faces and places for 10 seconds each. Later, you see 280 of these slides, paired with others you've never seen. Actual participants recognized 90 percent of the slides they had viewed in the first round (Haber, 1970). In a follow-up experiment, people exposed to 2800 images for only 3 seconds each spotted the repeats with 82 percent accuracy (Konkle et al., 2010). Look for a target face in a sea of faces and you later will recognize other faces from the scene as well (Kaunitz et al., 2016). Some super-recognizers display an extraordinary ability to recognize faces. Eighteen months after viewing a video of an armed robbery, one such police officer spotted and arrested the robber walking on a busy street (Davis et al., 2013). And it's not just humans who have shown remarkable memory for faces. Sheep remember faces, too (**FIGURE 22.1**). And so has at least one fish species—as demonstrated by their spitting at familiar faces to trigger a food reward (Newport et al., 2016).

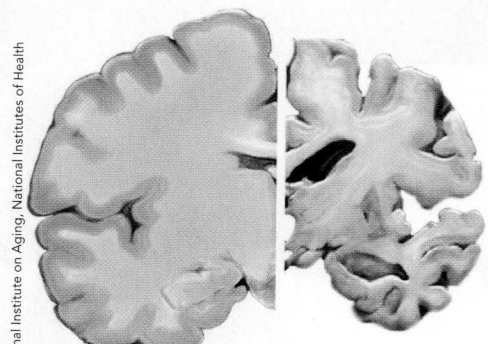

National Institute on Aging, National Institutes of Health

Healthy brain   **Severe Alzheimer's disease**

EXTREME FORGETTING Alzheimer's disease severely damages the brain, and in the process strips away memory.

ENGAGE

ASK YOURSELF

Imagine having an injury or disorder that significantly impaired your memory. Now, imagine having a record-setting ability to remember, like Feng Wang. How would each condition affect your daily routine?

Eric Isselee/Shutterstock

FIGURE 22.1

OTHER ANIMALS ALSO DISPLAY FACE SMARTS After food rewards are repeatedly associated with some sheep faces, but not with others, sheep remember those food-associated faces for two years (Kendrick & Feng, 2011).

ENGAGE How do we humans accomplish such memory feats? How does our brain pluck information from the world around us and tuck it away for later use? How can we remember things we have not thought about for years, yet forget the name of someone we just met? How are memories stored in our brain? Why will you be likely, later in this module, to misrecall this sentence: *"The angry rioter threw the rock at the window"*? Here and in the other Memory modules, we'll consider these fascinating questions and more.

"If any one faculty of our nature may be called *more* wonderful than the rest, I do think it is memory." —Jane Austen, *Mansfield Park*, 1814

Measuring Retention

To a psychologist, evidence that learning persists includes these three *retention measures:*

- **recall**—*retrieving* information that is not currently in your conscious awareness but that was learned at an earlier time. A fill-in-the-blank question tests your recall.

- **recognition**—*identifying* items previously learned. A multiple-choice question tests your recognition.

- **relearning**—*learning something more quickly* when you learn it a second or later time. When you study for a final exam or engage a language used in early childhood, you will relearn the material more easily than you did initially.

ENGAGE Long after you cannot recall most of the people in your high school graduating class, you may still be able to recognize their yearbook pictures and spot their names in a list of names. In one experiment, people who had graduated 25 years earlier could not recall many of their old classmates. But they could *recognize* 90 percent of their pictures and names (Bahrick et al., 1975). If you are like most students, you, too, could probably recognize more names of Snow White's seven dwarfs than you could recall (Miserandino, 1991).

Our recognition memory is impressively quick and vast. "Is your friend wearing a new or old outfit?" "Old." "Is this five-second movie clip from a film you've ever seen?" "Yes." "Have you ever seen this person before?" "No." Before the mouth can form our answer to any of millions of such questions, the mind knows, and knows that it knows.

Our response speed when recalling or recognizing information indicates memory strength, as does our speed at *relearning.* Pioneering memory researcher Hermann Ebbinghaus (1850–1909) showed this over a century ago, using nonsense syllables. He randomly selected a sample of syllables, practiced them, and tested himself. To get a feel for his experiments, rapidly read aloud, eight times over, the following list (from Baddeley, 1982), then look away and try to recall the items:

JIH, BAZ, FUB, YOX, SUJ, XIR, DAX, LEQ, VUM, PID, KEL, WAV, TUV, ZOF, GEK, HIW.

The day after learning such a list, Ebbinghaus could recall few of the syllables. But they weren't entirely forgotten. As **FIGURE 22.2** portrays, the more frequently he repeated the list aloud on Day 1, the less time he required to relearn the list on Day 2. Additional rehearsal (*overlearning*) of verbal information increases retention—especially when practice is distributed over time. For students, this means that it helps to rehearse course material even after you know it. Better to rehearse and overlearn than relax and remember too little.

The point to remember: Tests of recognition and of time spent relearning demonstrate that we remember more than we can recall.

REMEMBERING THINGS PAST Even if Taylor Swift and Bruno Mars had not become famous, their high school classmates would most likely still recognize them in these photos.

memory the persistence of learning over time through the encoding, storage, and retrieval of information.

recall a measure of memory in which the person must retrieve information learned earlier, as on a fill-in-the-blank test.

recognition a measure of memory in which the person identifies items previously learned, as on a multiple-choice test.

relearning a measure of memory that assesses the amount of time saved when learning material again.

encoding the process of getting information into the memory system—for example, by extracting meaning.

storage the process of retaining encoded information over time.

retrieval the process of getting information out of memory storage.

parallel processing processing many aspects of a stimulus or problem at once.

sensory memory the immediate, very brief recording of sensory information in the memory system.

short-term memory activated memory that holds a few items briefly, such as digits of a phone number while calling, before the information is stored or forgotten.

long-term memory the relatively permanent and limitless storehouse of the memory system. Includes knowledge, skills, and experiences.

FIGURE 22.2
EBBINGHAUS' RETENTION CURVE
Ebbinghaus found that the more times he practiced a list of nonsense syllables on Day 1, the less time he required to relearn it on Day 2. Speed of relearning is one measure of memory retention. (Data from Baddeley, 1982.)

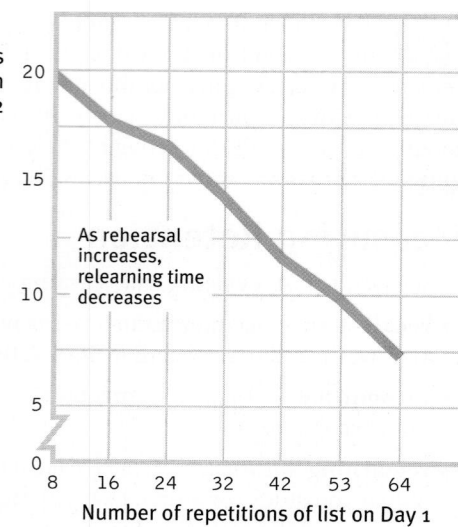

Number of repetitions of list on Day 1

ENGAGE

(ASK YOURSELF)

What has your memory system encoded, stored, and retrieved today?

🔒 **RETRIEVE IT** • • •   *ANSWERS IN APPENDIX E*

RI-1 Multiple-choice questions test our _____. Fill-in-the-blank questions test our _____.

RI-2 If you want to be sure to remember what you're learning for an upcoming test, would it be better to use *recall* or *recognition* to check your memory? Why?

Memory Models

LOQ 22-2 How do psychologists describe the human memory system?

Architects make virtual house models to help clients imagine their future homes. Similarly, psychologists create memory models that, even if imperfect, are useful. Such models help us think about how our brain forms and retrieves memories. History offers us multiple memory models: Memory is like a wax tablet (Aristotle), a "mystic writing pad" (Freud), a house, a library, or the once-commonplace videotape or telephone switchboard (Roediger, 1980). Today's *information-processing model* likens human memory to computer operations. Thus, to remember any event, we must

- get information into our brain, a process called **encoding.**

- retain that information, a process called **storage.**

- later get the information back out, a process called **retrieval.**

Like all analogies, computer models have their limits. Our memories are less literal and more fragile than a computer's. Most computers also process information sequentially, even while alternating between tasks. Our agile brain processes many things simultaneously (some of them unconsciously) by means of **parallel processing.** To focus on multitrack processing, one information-processing model, *connectionism*, views memories as products of interconnected neural networks. Specific memories arise from particular activation patterns within these networks. Every time you learn something new, your brain's neural connections change, forming and strengthening pathways that allow you to interact with and learn from your constantly changing environment.

To explain our memory-forming process, Richard Atkinson and Richard Shiffrin (1968, 2016) proposed a three-stage model:

1. We first record to-be-remembered information as a fleeting **sensory memory.**

2. From there, we process information into **short-term memory,** where we encode it through *rehearsal.*

3. Finally, information moves into **long-term memory** for later retrieval.

This model has since been updated (**FIGURE 22.3**) with important newer concepts, including *working memory* and *automatic processing.*

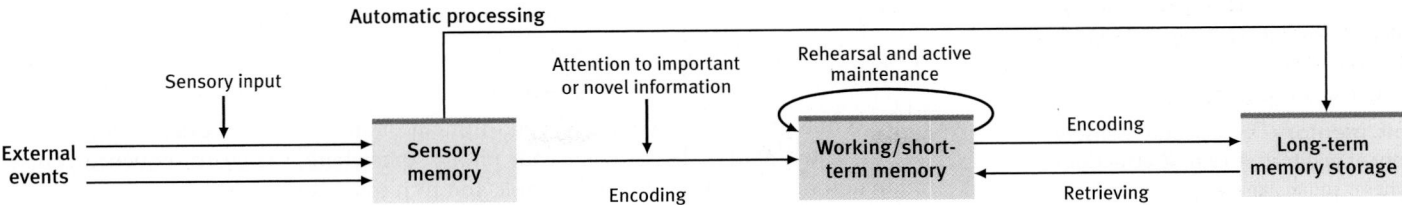

WORKING MEMORY Alan Baddeley and others (Baddeley, 2002; Barrouillet et al., 2011; Engle, 2002) extended Atkinson and Shiffrin's initial view of short-term memory as a space for briefly storing recent thoughts and experiences. This stage is not just a temporary shelf for holding incoming information. It's an active scratchpad where your brain actively processes information by making sense of new input and linking it with long-term memories. It also works in the opposite direction, by processing already stored information. Whether we hear "eye-scream" as *ice cream* or *I scream* depends on how the context and our experience guide our interpreting and encoding of the sounds. To emphasize the active processing that takes place in this middle stage, psychologists use the term **working memory.** Right now, you are using your working memory to link the information you're reading with your previously stored information (Cowan, 2010, 2016; Kail & Hall, 2001).

For most of you, what you are reading enters working memory through vision. You might also repeat the information using auditory rehearsal. As you integrate these memory inputs with your existing long-term memory, your attention is focused. In Baddeley's (2002) model, a *central executive* coordinates this focused processing.

Without focused attention, information often fades. If you think you can look something up later, you attend to it less and forget it more quickly. In one experiment, people read and typed new bits of trivia they would later need, such as "An ostrich's eye is bigger than its brain." If they knew the information would be available online, they invested less energy and remembered it less well (Sparrow et al., 2011; Wegner & Ward, 2013). Online, out of mind.

FIGURE 22.3

A MODIFIED THREE-STAGE PROCESSING MODEL OF MEMORY Atkinson and Shiffrin's classic three-step model helps us to think about how memories are processed, but today's researchers recognize other ways long-term memories form. For example, some information slips into long-term memory via a "back door," without our consciously attending to it (*automatic processing*). And so much active processing occurs in the short-term memory stage that many now prefer the term *working memory*.

🔒 **RETRIEVE IT • • •**   *ANSWERS IN APPENDIX E*

RI-3 How does the *working memory* concept update the classic Atkinson-Shiffrin three-stage information-processing model?

RI-4 What are two basic functions of working memory?

📺 **LaunchPad** For a 14-minute explanation and demonstration of our memory systems, see the **Video: Models of Memory.**

ENCODING MEMORIES

Dual-Track Memory: Effortful Versus Automatic Processing

LOQ 22-3 How do explicit and implicit memories differ?

Atkinson and Shiffrin's model focuses on how we process our **explicit memories**—the facts and experiences we can consciously know and "declare" (thus, also called *declarative memories*). We encode explicit memories through conscious **effortful processing.** But behind the scenes, other information skips the conscious encoding track and barges directly into storage. This **automatic processing,** which happens without our awareness, produces **implicit memories** (also called *nondeclarative memories*).

Our two-track mind, then, helps us encode, retain, and recall information through both effortful and automatic tracks. Let's begin by seeing how automatic processing assists the formation of implicit memories.

Automatic Processing and Implicit Memories

LOQ 22-4 What information do we process automatically?

Our implicit memories include *procedural* memory for automatic skills (such as how to ride a bike) and classically conditioned *associations* among stimuli. If attacked by a dog in childhood, years later you may, without recalling the conditioned association, automatically tense up as a dog approaches.

working memory a newer understanding of short-term memory that adds conscious, active processing of incoming sensory information, and of information retrieved from long-term memory.

explicit memory retention of facts and experiences that we can consciously know and "declare." (Also called *declarative memory*.)

effortful processing encoding that requires attention and conscious effort.

automatic processing unconscious encoding of incidental information, such as space, time, and frequency, and of well-learned information, such as word meanings.

implicit memory retention of learned skills or classically conditioned associations independent of conscious recollection. (Also called *nondeclarative memory*.)

iconic memory a momentary sensory memory of visual stimuli; a photographic or picture-image memory lasting no more than a few tenths of a second.

echoic memory a momentary sensory memory of auditory stimuli; if attention is elsewhere, sounds and words can still be recalled within 3 or 4 seconds.

chunking organizing items into familiar, manageable units; often occurs automatically.

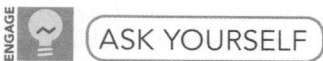 **ASK YOURSELF**

Does it surprise you to learn how much of your memory processing is automatic? What might life be like if *all* memory processing were effortful?

Without conscious effort you also automatically process information about

- **space.** While studying, you often encode the place where certain material appears; later, when you want to retrieve the information, you may visualize its location.

- **time.** While going about your day, you unintentionally note the sequence of its events. Later, realizing you've left your phone somewhere, the event sequence your brain automatically encoded will enable you to retrace your steps.

- **frequency.** You effortlessly keep track of how many times things happen, as when you realize, "This is the third time I've run into her today!"

Our two-track mind engages in impressively efficient information processing. As one track automatically tucks away routine details, the other track is free to focus on conscious, effortful processing. Mental feats such as vision, thinking, and memory may seem to be single abilities, but they are not. Rather, we split information into different components for separate and simultaneous processing.

Effortful Processing and Explicit Memories

Automatic processing happens effortlessly. When you see words in your native language, perhaps on the side of a delivery truck, you can't help but read them and register their meaning. *Learning* to read wasn't automatic. You may recall working hard to pick out letters and connect them to certain sounds. But with experience and practice, your reading became automatic. Imagine now learning to read sentences in reverse:

.citamotua emoceb nac gnissecorp luftroffE

At first, this requires effort, but after enough practice, you would also perform this task much more automatically. We develop many skills in this way: driving, texting, and speaking a new language.

SENSORY MEMORY

LOQ 22-5 How does sensory memory work?

Sensory memory (recall Figure 22.3) feeds our active working memory. For example, our mind records momentary images, echoes of sounds, and strong scents. How much of this page could you sense and recall with less exposure than a lightning flash? In one experiment, people viewed three rows of three letters each, for only one-twentieth of a second (**FIGURE 22.4**). After the nine letters disappeared, they could recall only about half of them.

Was it because they had insufficient time to glimpse them? *No.* People actually *could* see and recall all the letters, but only momentarily. Rather than ask them to recall all nine letters at once, researcher George Sperling sounded a high, medium, or low tone immediately *after* flashing the nine letters. This tone directed participants to report only the letters of the top, middle, or bottom row, respectively. Now they rarely missed a letter, showing that all nine letters were momentarily available for recall.

Sperling's experiment demonstrated **iconic memory,** a fleeting sensory memory of visual stimuli. For a few tenths of a second, our eyes register a picture-image memory of a scene, and we can recall any part of it in amazing detail. But delaying the tone signal by more than half a second caused the image to fade and memory to suffer. We also have an impeccable, though fleeting, memory for auditory stimuli, called **echoic memory** (Cowan, 1988; Lu et al., 1992). Picture yourself becoming distracted by a text message while you sit in class. If your mildly irked professor tests you by asking, "What did I just say?" you can recover the last few words from your mind's echo chamber. Auditory echoes tend to linger for 3 or 4 seconds.

SHORT-TERM MEMORY CAPACITY

LOQ 22-6 What is our short-term memory capacity?

Recall that short-term memory refers to what we can briefly retain. The related idea of working memory also includes our active processing, as our brain makes sense of incoming information and links it with stored memories. What are the limits of what we can hold in this middle, short-term stage?

FIGURE 22.4

TOTAL RECALL—BRIEFLY When George Sperling (1960) flashed a group of letters similar to this for one-twentieth of a second, people could recall only about half the letters. But when signaled to recall a particular row immediately after the letters had disappeared, they could do so with near-perfect accuracy.

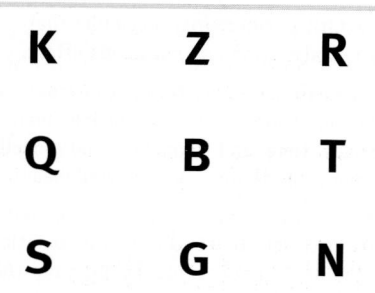

George Miller (1956) proposed that we can store about seven pieces of information (give or take two) in short-term memory. Miller's magical number seven is psychology's contribution to the list of magical sevens—the seven wonders of the world, the seven seas, the seven deadly sins, the seven colors of the rainbow, the seven musical scale notes, the seven days of the week—seven magical sevens. Other researchers have confirmed that we can, if nothing distracts us, recall about seven digits. But the number varies by task; we tend to remember about six letters and only about five words (Baddeley et al., 1975; Cowan, 2015). And how quickly do our short-term memories disappear? To find out, Lloyd Peterson and Margaret Peterson (1959) asked people to remember three-consonant groups, such as *CHJ*. To prevent rehearsal, the researchers asked them, for example, to start at 100 and begin counting aloud backward by threes. After 3 seconds, people recalled the letters only about half the time; after 12 seconds, they seldom recalled them at all (**FIGURE 22.5**). Without the active processing that we now understand to be a part of our working memory, short-term memories have a limited life.

Working-memory capacity varies, depending on age and other factors. Young adults tend to have greater working-memory capacity—the ability to juggle multiple items while processing information—than do children and older adults. This helps young adults to better retain information after sleeping and to solve problems creatively (De Dreu et al., 2012; Fenn & Hambrick, 2012; Wiley & Jarosz, 2012). But whatever our age, we do better and more efficient work when focused, without distractions, on one task at a time. *The bottom line:* It's probably a bad idea to try to stream videos, text your friends, and write a psychology paper all at the same time, with your attention switching between them (Willingham, 2010)!

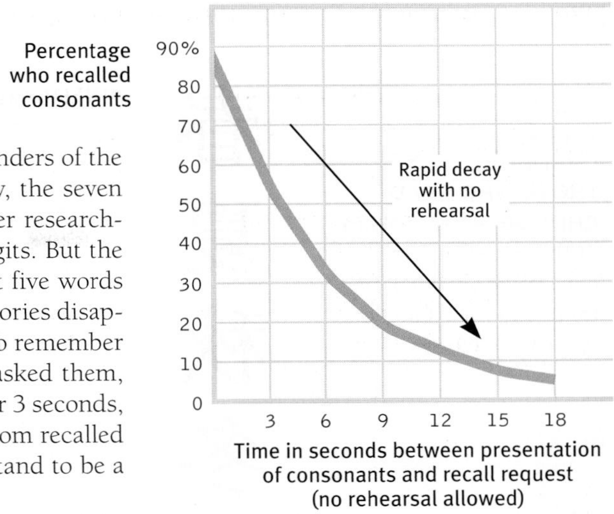

FIGURE 22.5
SHORT-TERM MEMORY DECAY Unless rehearsed, verbal information may be quickly forgotten. (Data from Peterson & Peterson, 1959; see also Brown, 1958.)

ENGAGE **LaunchPad** For a review of memory stages and a test of your own short-term memory capacity, visit **Topic Tutorial: PsychSim6, Short-Term Memory.**

RETRIEVE IT • • • *ANSWERS IN APPENDIX E*

RI-5 What is the difference between *automatic* and *effortful* processing, and what are some examples of each?

RI-6 At which of Atkinson-Shiffrin's three memory stages would *iconic* and *echoic* memory occur?

After Miller's 2012 death, his daughter recalled his best moment of golf: "He made the one and only hole-in-one of his life at the age of 77, on the seventh green . . . with a seven iron. He loved that" (quoted by Vitello, 2012).

ENGAGE RETAIN

EFFORTFUL PROCESSING STRATEGIES

LOQ 22-7 What are some effortful processing strategies that can help us remember new information?

Several effortful processing strategies boost our ability to form new memories. Later, when we try to retrieve a memory, these strategies can make the difference between success and failure.

CHUNKING Glance for a few seconds at the first set of letters (row 1) in **FIGURE 22.6**, then look away and try to reproduce what you saw. Impossible, yes? But you can easily reproduce set 2, which is no less complex. Similarly, you will probably remember sets 4 and 6 more easily than the same elements in sets 3 and 5. As this demonstrates, **chunking** information—organizing items into familiar, manageable units—enables us to recall it more easily. Try remembering 43 individual numbers and letters. It would be impossible, unless chunked into, say, seven meaningful chunks, such as "Try remembering 43 individual numbers and letters." ☺

Chunking usually occurs so naturally that we take it for granted. If you are a native English speaker, you can reproduce perfectly the 150 or so line segments that make up the words in the three phrases of set 6 in Figure 22.6. It would astonish someone unfamiliar with the language. Similarly amazing is a Chinese reader's ability to glance at **FIGURE 22.7** and reproduce all the strokes, or a varsity basketball player's recall of all the players' positions after a 4-second peek at a basketball play (Allard & Burnett, 1985). We all remember information best when we can organize it into personally meaningful arrangements.

RETAIN **FIGURE 22.6**
CHUNKING EFFECTS Organizing information into meaningful units, such as letters, words, and phrases, helps us recall it more easily (Hintzman, 1978).

1. 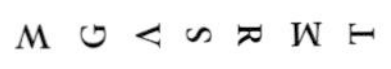

2. W G V S R M T

3. VRESLI UEGBN GSORNW CDOUL LWLE NTOD WTO
4. SILVER BEGUN WRONGS CLOUD WELL DONT TWO

5. SILVER BEGUN WRONGS CLOUD DONT TWO
HALF MAKE WELL HAS A
EVERY IS RIGHT A DONE LINING

6. WELL BEGUN IS HALF DONE
EVERY CLOUD HAS A SILVER LINING
TWO WRONGS DONT MAKE A RIGHT

FIGURE 22.7

AN EXAMPLE OF CHUNKING—FOR THOSE WHO READ CHINESE After looking at these characters, can you reproduce them exactly? If so, you can read Chinese.

春夏秋冬

MNEMONICS To help encode lengthy passages and speeches, ancient Greek scholars and orators developed **mnemonics.** Many of these memory aids use vivid imagery, because we are particularly good at remembering mental pictures. We more easily remember concrete, visualizable words than we do abstract words (Akpinar & Berger, 2015). (When we quiz you later, which three of these words—*bicycle, void, cigarette, inherent, fire, process*—will you most likely recall?) If you still recall the rock-throwing rioter sentence, it is probably not only because of the meaning you encoded but also because the sentence painted a mental image.

Memory whizzes understand the power of such systems. Star performers in the World Memory Championships do not usually have exceptional intelligence, but rather are superior at using mnemonic strategies (Maguire et al., 2003b). Frustrated by his ordinary memory, science writer Joshua Foer wanted to see how much he could improve it. After a year of intense practice, he won the U.S. Memory Championship by memorizing a pack of 52 playing cards in under two minutes. How did Foer do it? He added vivid new details to memories of a familiar place—his childhood home. Each card, presented in any order, could then match up with the clear picture in his head. As the test subject of his own wild memory experiment, he learned the power of painting pretty pictures in his mind (Foer, 2011).

When combined, chunking and mnemonic techniques can be great memory aids for unfamiliar material. Want to remember the colors of the rainbow in order of wavelength? Think of the mnemonic ROY G. BIV (*red, orange, yellow, green, blue, indigo, violet*). Need to recall the names of North America's five Great Lakes? Just remember HOMES (*Huron, Ontario, Michigan, Erie, Superior*). In each case, we chunk information into a more familiar form by creating a word (called an *acronym*) from the first letters of the to-be-remembered items.

HIERARCHIES When people develop expertise in an area, they often process information in *hierarchies* composed of a few broad concepts divided and subdivided into narrower concepts and facts.

Organizing knowledge in hierarchies helps us retrieve information efficiently, as Gordon Bower and his colleagues (1969) demonstrated by presenting words either randomly or grouped into categories. When the words were organized into categories, recall was two to three times better. Such results show the benefits of organizing what you study—of giving special attention to module headings, and, in this text, to numbered Learning Objective questions. Taking lecture and textbook notes in outline format—a type of hierarchical organization—may also prove helpful.

DISTRIBUTED PRACTICE We retain information better when our encoding is distributed over time. Experiments have consistently revealed the benefits of this **spacing effect** (Cepeda et al., 2006; Soderstrom et al., 2016). *Massed practice* (cramming) can produce speedy short-term learning and a feeling of confidence. But to paraphrase memory researcher Hermann Ebbinghaus (1885), those who learn quickly also forget quickly. *Distributed practice* produces better long-term recall. After you've studied long enough to master the material, further study at that time becomes inefficient. Better to spend that extra reviewing time later—a day later if you need to remember something 10 days hence, or a month later if you need to remember something 6 months hence (Cepeda et al., 2008). The spacing effect is one of psychology's most reliable findings, and it extends to motor skills and online game performance, too (Stafford & Dewar, 2014). Memory researcher Henry Roediger (2013) sums it up: "Hundreds of studies have shown that distributed practice leads to more durable learning."

One effective way to distribute practice is *repeated* self-testing, a phenomenon that Roediger and Jeffrey Karpicke (2006) have called the **testing effect.** Testing does more than assess learning and memory: It improves them (Brown et al., 2014; Pan et al., 2015; Trumbo et al., 2016). Testing also protects our memory from the harmful effects of stress, which usually impairs memory retrieval (Smith et al., 2016). In this textbook, the Retrieve It questions and Review sections, including the Experience the Testing Effect questions, offer opportunities to improve learning and memory. Better to practice retrieval (as any exam will demand) than to merely reread material

"The mind is slow in unlearning what it has been long in learning." —Roman philosopher Seneca, 4 B.C.E.–65 C.E.

(which may lull you into a false sense of mastery). Roediger (2013) explains, "Two techniques that students frequently report using for studying—highlighting (or underlining) text and rereading text—[have been found] ineffective." Happily, "retrieval practice (or testing) is a powerful and general strategy for learning." As another memory expert explained, "What we recall becomes more recallable" (Bjork, 2011). No wonder daily online quizzing improves introductory psychology students' course performance (Batsell et al., 2017; Pennebaker et al., 2013).

The point to remember: Spaced study and self-assessment beat cramming and rereading. Practice may not make perfect, but smart practice—occasional rehearsal with self-testing—makes for lasting memories.

LEVELS OF PROCESSING

LOQ 22-8 What are the levels of processing, and how do they affect encoding?

Memory researchers have discovered that we process verbal information at different levels, and that depth of processing affects our long-term retention. **Shallow processing** encodes on an elementary level, such as a word's letters or, at a more intermediate level, a word's sound. Thus, we may type *there* when we mean *their, write* when we mean *right,* and *two* when we mean *too.* **Deep processing** encodes *semantically,* based on the meaning of the words. The deeper (more meaningful) the processing, the better our retention.

In one classic experiment, researchers Fergus Craik and Endel Tulving (1975) flashed words at viewers. Then they asked them questions that would elicit different levels of processing. To experience the task yourself, rapidly answer the following sample questions:

Sample Questions to Elicit Different Levels of Processing	Word Flashed	Yes	No
Most shallow: Is the word in capital letters?	CHAIR	_____	_____
Shallow: Does the word rhyme with train?	Brain	_____	_____
Deep: Would the word fit in this sentence? The girl put the _____ on the table.	Doll	_____	_____

Which type of processing would best prepare you to recognize the words at a later time? In Craik and Tulving's experiment, the deeper, semantic processing triggered by the third question yielded a much better memory than did the shallower processing elicited by the second question or the very shallow processing elicited by the first question (which was especially ineffective).

MAKING MATERIAL PERSONALLY MEANINGFUL If new information is neither meaningful nor related to our experience, we have trouble processing it. Imagine being asked to remember the following recorded passage:

> The procedure is actually quite simple. First you arrange things into different groups. Of course, one pile may be sufficient depending on how much there is to do. . . . After the procedure is completed, one arranges the materials into different groups again. Then they can be put into their appropriate places. Eventually they will be used once more and the whole cycle will then have to be repeated. However, that is part of life.

When some students heard the paragraph you have just read, without a meaningful context, they remembered little of it (Bransford & Johnson, 1972). When others were told the paragraph described washing clothes (something meaningful), they remembered much more of it—as you probably could now after rereading it.

Can you repeat the sentence about the rioter that we gave you at this module's beginning ("The angry rioter threw . . .")? Perhaps, like those in an experiment by William

LaunchPad For suggestions on how to apply the *testing effect* to your own learning, watch my [DM's] 5-minute **Video: Make Things Memorable** in LaunchPad or at: tinyurl.com/HowToRemember.

mnemonics [nih-MON-iks] memory aids, especially those techniques that use vivid imagery and organizational devices.

spacing effect the tendency for distributed study or practice to yield better long-term retention than is achieved through massed study or practice.

testing effect enhanced memory after retrieving, rather than simply rereading, information. Also sometimes referred to as a *retrieval practice effect* or *test-enhanced learning.*

shallow processing encoding on a basic level, based on the structure or appearance of words.

deep processing encoding semantically, based on the meaning of the words; tends to yield the best retention.

Brewer (1977), you recalled the sentence by the meaning you encoded when you read it (for example, "The angry rioter threw the rock *through* the window") and not as it was written ("The angry rioter threw the rock *at* the window"). Referring to such mental mismatches, some researchers have likened our minds to theater directors who, given a raw script, imagine the finished stage production (Bower & Morrow, 1990). Asked later what we heard or read, we recall not the literal text but what we encoded. Thus, studying for an exam, you may remember your lecture notes rather than the lecture itself.

We can avoid some of these mismatches by rephrasing what we see and hear into meaningful terms. From his experiments on himself, Ebbinghaus estimated that, compared with learning nonsense material, learning meaningful material required one-tenth the effort. As memory researcher Wayne Wickelgren (1977, p. 346) noted, "The time you spend thinking about material you are reading and relating it to previously stored material is about the most useful thing you can do in learning any new subject matter."

Psychologist-actor team Helga Noice and Tony Noice (2006) have described how actors inject meaning into the daunting task of learning "all those lines." They do it by first coming to understand the flow of meaning: "One actor divided a half-page of dialogue into three [intentions]: 'to flatter,' 'to draw him out,' and 'to allay his fears.'" With this meaningful sequence in mind, the actor more easily remembered the lines.

Most people excel at remembering personally relevant information. Asked how well certain adjectives describe someone else, we often forget them; asked how well the adjectives describe us, we often remember them. This tendency, called the *self-reference effect*, is especially strong in members of individualist Western cultures (Symons & Johnson, 1997; Wagar & Cohen, 2003). Information deemed "relevant to me" is processed more deeply and remains more accessible. In contrast, members of collectivist Eastern cultures remember self-relevant and family-relevant information equally well (Sparks et al., 2016).

The point to remember: The amount remembered depends both on the time spent learning and on your making it meaningful for deep processing.

ENGAGE · In the discussion of mnemonics, we gave you six words and told you we would quiz you about them later. How many of these words can you now recall? Of these, how many are high-imagery words? How many are low-imagery?[1]

🔒 RETRIEVE IT • • •   *ANSWERS IN APPENDIX E*

RI-7 Which strategies are better for long-term retention: cramming and rereading material, or spreading out learning over time and repeatedly testing yourself?

RI-8 If you try to make the material you are learning personally meaningful, are you processing at a shallow or a deep level? Which level leads to greater retention?

---

1. bicycle, void, cigarette, inherent, fire, process.

🔒 REVIEW STUDYING AND ENCODING MEMORIES

⟩⟩ Learning Objectives

TEST YOURSELF Answer these repeated Learning Objective Questions on your own (before checking the answers in Appendix D) to improve your retention of the concepts (McDaniel et al., 2009, 2015).

22-1 What is *memory*, and how is it measured?

22-2 How do psychologists describe the human memory system?

22-3 How do explicit and implicit memories differ?

22-4 What information do we process automatically?

22-5 How does sensory memory work?

22-6 What is our short-term memory capacity?

22-7 What are some effortful processing strategies that can help us remember new information?

22-8 What are the levels of processing, and how do they affect encoding?

⟩⟩ Terms and Concepts to Remember

TEST YOURSELF Write down the definition yourself, then check your answer on the referenced page.

memory, **p. 267**

recall, **p. 267**

recognition, **p. 267**

relearning, **p. 267**

encoding, **p. 268**

storage, **p. 268**

retrieval, **p. 268**

parallel processing, **p. 268**

sensory memory, **p. 268**

(⤜⤚) Experience the Testing Effect

TEST YOURSELF Answer the following questions on your own first, then check your answers in Appendix E.

1. A psychologist who asks you to write down as many objects as you can remember having seen a few minutes earlier is testing your _____.

2. The psychological terms for taking in information, retaining it, and later getting it back out are _____, _____, and _____.

3. The concept of working memory
   a. clarifies the idea of short-term memory by focusing on the active processing that occurs in this stage.
   b. splits short-term memory into two substages—sensory memory and iconic memory.
   c. splits short-term memory into two types—implicit and explicit memory.
   d. clarifies the idea of short-term memory by focusing on space, time, and frequency.

4. Sensory memory may be visual (_____ memory) or auditory (_____ memory).

5. Our short-term memory for new information is limited to about _____ digits.

6. Memory aids that use visual imagery or other organizational devices (such as acronyms) are called _____.

Continue testing yourself with 📖 **LearningCurve** or 📖 **Achieve Read & Practice** to learn and remember most effectively.

㉓ Storing and Retrieving Memories

MEMORY STORAGE

LOQ 23-1 What is the capacity of long-term memory? Are our long-term memories processed and stored in specific locations?

In Arthur Conan Doyle's *A Study in Scarlet,* Sherlock Holmes offers a popular theory of memory capacity:

> I consider that a man's brain originally is like a little empty attic, and you have to stock it with such furniture as you choose. . . . It is a mistake to think that that little room has elastic walls and can distend to any extent. Depend upon it, there comes a time when for every addition of knowledge you forget something that you knew before.

Contrary to Holmes' "memory model," our brain is *not* like an attic, which once filled can store more items only if we discard old ones. Our capacity for storing long-term memories is essentially limitless. One research team, after studying the brain's neural connections, estimated its storage capacity as "in the same ballpark as the World Wide Web" (Sejnowski, 2016).

Retaining Information in the Brain

I [DM] marveled at my aging mother-in-law, a retired pianist and organist. At age 88, her blind eyes could no longer read music. But let her sit at a keyboard and she would flaw-lessly play any of hundreds of hymns, including ones she had not thought of for 20 years. Where did her brain store those thousands of sequenced notes?

semantic memory explicit memory of facts and general knowledge; one of our two conscious memory systems (the other is *episodic memory*).

episodic memory explicit memory of personally experienced events; one of our two conscious memory systems (the other is *semantic memory*).

hippocampus a neural center located in the limbic system; helps process explicit (conscious) memories—of facts and events—for storage.

memory consolidation the neural storage of a long-term memory.

"Our memories are flexible and superimposable, a panoramic blackboard with an endless supply of chalk and erasers." —Elizabeth Loftus and Katherine Ketcham, *The Myth of Repressed Memory*, 1994

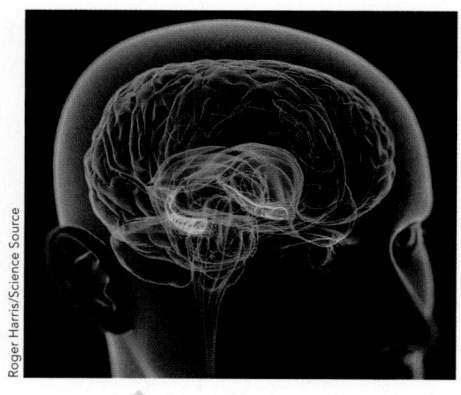

Roger Harris/Science Source

FIGURE 23.1

THE HIPPOCAMPUS Explicit memories for facts and episodes are processed in the hippocampus (orange structures) and fed to other brain regions for storage.

HIPPOCAMPUS HERO Among animals, one contender for champion memorist would be a mere birdbrain—the Clark's Nutcracker—which during winter and spring can locate up to 6000 caches of pine seed it had previously buried (Shettleworth, 1993).

For a time, some surgeons and memory researchers marveled at patients' apparently vivid memories triggered by brain stimulation during surgery. Did this prove that our whole past, not just well-practiced music, is "in there," in complete detail, just waiting to be relived? On closer analysis, the seeming flashbacks appeared to have been invented, not a vivid reliving of long-forgotten experiences (Loftus & Loftus, 1980). In a further demonstration that memories do not reside in single, specific spots, psychologist Karl Lashley (1950) trained rats to find their way out of a maze, then surgically removed pieces of their brain's cortex and retested their memory. No matter which small brain section he removed, the rats retained at least a partial memory of how to navigate the maze. Memories *are* brain-based, but the brain distributes the components of a memory across a network of locations. These specific locations include some of the circuitry involved in the original experience: Some brain cells that fire when we experience something fire again when we recall it (Miller, G., 2012; Miller et al., 2013).

The point to remember: Despite the brain's vast storage capacity, we do not store information as libraries store their books, in single, precise locations. Instead, brain networks encode, store, and retrieve the information that forms our complex memories.

EXPLICIT MEMORY SYSTEM: THE FRONTAL LOBES AND HIPPOCAMPUS

LOQ 23-2 What roles do the frontal lobes and hippocampus play in memory processing?

Explicit, conscious memories are either **semantic** (facts and general knowledge) or **episodic** (experienced events). The network that processes and stores new explicit memories for these facts and episodes includes your frontal lobes and hippocampus. When you summon up a mental encore of a past experience, many brain regions send input to your *prefrontal cortex* (the front part of your frontal lobes) for working memory processing (de Chastelaine et al., 2016; Michalka et al., 2015). The left and right frontal lobes process different types of memories. Recalling a password and holding it in working memory, for example, would activate the left frontal lobe. Calling up a visual party scene would more likely activate the right frontal lobe.

Cognitive neuroscientists have found that the **hippocampus,** a temporal lobe neural center located in the limbic system, can be likened to a "save" button for explicit memories (**FIGURE 23.1**). As children mature, their hippocampus grows, enabling them to construct detailed memories (Keresztes et al., 2017). Brain scans reveal activity in the hippocampus and nearby brain networks as people form explicit memories of names, images, and events (Terada et al., 2017; Wang et al., 2014).

Damage to this structure therefore disrupts the formation and recall of explicit memories. If their hippocampus is severed, chickadees and other birds will continue to cache food in hundreds of places, but later be unable to find them (Kamil & Cheng, 2001; Sherry & Vaccarino, 1989). With left-hippocampus damage, people have trouble remembering verbal information, but they have no trouble recalling visual designs and locations. With right-hippocampus damage, the problem is reversed (Schacter, 1996).

Subregions of the hippocampus also serve different functions. One part is active as people and mice learn social information (Okuyama et al., 2016; Zeineh et al., 2003). Another part is active as memory champions engage in spatial mnemonics (Maguire et al., 2003a). The rear area, which processes spatial memory, grows bigger as London cabbies navigate the city's complicated maze of streets (Woolett & Maguire, 2011).

Memories are not permanently stored in the hippocampus. Instead, the hippocampus acts as a loading dock where the brain registers and temporarily holds the elements of a to-be-remembered episode—its smell, feel, sound, and location. Then, like older files shifted to a basement storeroom, memories migrate to the cortex for storage. This storage process is called **memory consolidation.**

Sleep supports memory consolidation. In one experiment, students who learned material in a study/sleep/restudy condition remembered material better, both a week and six months later, than those who studied in the morning and restudied in the evening without intervening sleep (Mazza et al., 2016). During deep sleep, the hippocampus

Tim Zurowski/All Canada Photos/Getty Images

processes memories for later retrieval. After a training experience, the greater one's hippocampus activity during sleep, the better the next day's memory will be (Peigneux et al., 2004; Whitehurst et al., 2016). Researchers have watched the hippocampus and brain cortex displaying simultaneous activity rhythms during sleep, as if they were having a dialogue (Euston et al., 2007; Mehta, 2007). They suspect that the brain is replaying the day's experiences as it transfers them to the cortex for long-term storage (Squire & Zola-Morgan, 1991). When our learning is distributed over days rather than crammed into a single day, we experience more sleep-induced memory consolidation. And that helps explain the *spacing effect* (the improved retention demonstrated after distributed rather than massed study).

IMPLICIT MEMORY SYSTEM: THE CEREBELLUM AND BASAL GANGLIA

LOQ 23-3 What roles do the cerebellum and basal ganglia play in memory processing?

Your hippocampus and frontal lobes are processing sites for your *explicit* memories. But you could lose those areas and still, thanks to automatic processing, lay down *implicit* memories for skills and newly conditioned associations. Joseph LeDoux (1996) recounted the story of a brain-damaged patient whose amnesia left her unable to recognize her physician as, each day, he shook her hand and introduced himself. One day, she yanked her hand back, for the physician had pricked her with a tack in his palm. The next time he returned to introduce himself she refused to shake his hand but couldn't explain why. Having been classically conditioned, she just wouldn't do it. Implicitly, she felt what she could not explain.

The *cerebellum* plays a key role in forming and storing the implicit memories created by classical conditioning. With a damaged cerebellum, people cannot develop certain conditioned reflexes, such as associating a tone with an impending puff of air—and thus do not blink in anticipation of the puff (Daum & Schugens, 1996; Green & Woodruff-Pak, 2000). Implicit memory formation needs the cerebellum.

The *basal ganglia,* deep brain structures involved in motor movement, facilitate formation of our procedural memories for skills (Mishkin, 1982; Mishkin et al., 1997). The basal ganglia receive input from the cortex, but do not return the favor of sending information back to the cortex for conscious awareness of procedural learning. If you have learned how to ride a bike, thank your basal ganglia.

Our implicit memory system, enabled partly by these more ancient brain areas, helps explain why the reactions and skills we learned during infancy reach far into our future. Yet as adults, our *conscious* memory of our first four years is largely blank, an experience called *infantile amnesia.* In one study, events children experienced and discussed with their mothers at age 3 were 60 percent remembered at age 7 but only 34 percent remembered at age 9 (Bauer et al., 2007). Two influences contribute to infantile amnesia: First, we index much of our explicit memory with a command of language that young children do not possess. Second, the hippocampus is one of the last brain structures to mature, and as it does, more gets retained (Akers et al., 2014).

🔒 **RETRIEVE IT • • •**   *ANSWERS IN APPENDIX E*

RI-1 Which parts of the brain are important for *implicit* memory processing, and which parts play a key role in *explicit* memory processing?

RI-2 Your friend has experienced brain damage in an accident. He can remember how to tie his shoes but has a hard time remembering anything you tell him during a conversation. How can implicit versus explicit information processing explain what's going on here?

THE AMYGDALA, EMOTIONS, AND MEMORY

LOQ 23-4 How do emotions affect our memory processing?

Our emotions trigger stress hormones that influence memory formation. When we are excited or stressed, these hormones make more glucose energy available to fuel brain activity, signaling the brain that something important is happening. Moreover, stress hormones focus memory. Stress provokes the *amygdala* (two limbic system, emotion-processing clusters) to initiate a memory trace that boosts activity in the brain's memory-forming areas (Buchanan, 2007; Kensinger, 2007) (**FIGURE 23.2**). It's as if the amygdala says, "Brain, encode this moment for future reference!" The result? Emotional arousal can sear certain events into the brain, while disrupting memory for irrelevant events that occur around the same time (Brewin et al., 2007; McGaugh, 2015).

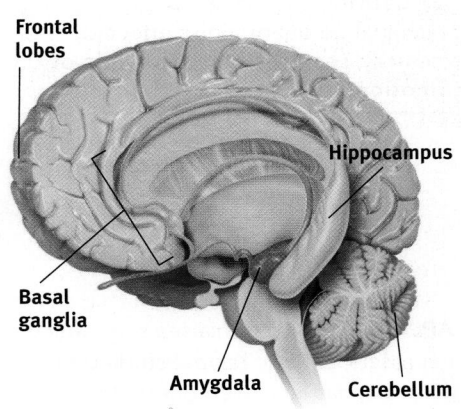

Frontal lobes

Hippocampus

Basal ganglia

Amygdala

Cerebellum

RETAIN 🔒 **FIGURE 23.2**

REVIEW KEY MEMORY STRUCTURES IN THE BRAIN
Frontal lobes and *hippocampus:* explicit memory formation
Cerebellum and *basal ganglia:* implicit memory formation
Amygdala: emotion-related memory formation

flashbulb memory a clear memory of an emotionally significant moment or event.

long-term potentiation (LTP) an increase in a cell's firing potential after brief, rapid stimulation; a neural basis for learning and memory.

Significantly stressful events can form unforgettable memories. After a traumatic experience—a school shooting, a house fire, a rape—vivid recollections of the horrific event may intrude again and again. It is as if they were burned in: "Stronger emotional experiences make for stronger, more reliable memories," noted James McGaugh (1994, 2003). Such experiences even strengthen recall for relevant, immediately preceding events (Dunsmoor et al., 2015). This makes adaptive sense: Memory helps us anticipate the future and alerts us to potential dangers. Emotional events produce tunnel vision memory. They focus our attention and recall on high-priority information, and reduce our recall of irrelevant details (Mather & Sutherland, 2012). Whatever rivets our attention gets well recalled, at the expense of the surrounding context.

Emotion-triggered hormonal changes help explain why we long remember exciting or shocking events, such as our first kiss or our whereabouts when learning of a loved one's death. In a 2006 Pew survey, 95 percent of American adults said they could recall exactly where they were or what they were doing when they first heard the news of the 9/11 terrorist attacks. This perceived clarity of memories of surprising, significant events (where were you when learning that Donald Trump was elected U.S. president?) leads some psychologists to call them **flashbulb memories.**

The people who experienced a 1989 San Francisco earthquake had perfect recall of where they had been and what they were doing (verified by their recorded thoughts within a day or two of the quake). Others' memories for the circumstances under which they merely *heard* about the quake were more prone to errors (Neisser et al., 1991; Palmer et al., 1991).

Our flashbulb memories are noteworthy for their vividness and our confidence in them. But as we relive, rehearse, and discuss them, even these memories may come to err. With time, some errors crept into people's 9/11 recollections (compared with their reports taken right afterward). Mostly, however, people's memories of 9/11 remained consistent over the next two to three years (Conway et al., 2009; Hirst et al., 2009).

Dramatic experiences remain clear in our memory in part because we rehearse them (Hirst & Phelps, 2016). We think about them and describe them to others. Memories of personally important experiences also endure (Storm & Jobe, 2012; Talarico & Moore, 2012). Compared with non-Catholics, devout Catholics recalled better the resignation of Pope Benedict XVI (Curci et al., 2015). Ditto for baseball fans' memories of their team's championship games (Breslin & Safer, 2011). When their team won, fans enjoyed recalling and recounting the victory, leading to longer-lasting memories.

ENGAGE Which is more important—your experiences or your memories of them?

LaunchPad For an 8-minute examination of emotion's effect on memory, see the **Video: The Role of Emotion.**

Synaptic Changes

LOQ 23-5 How do changes at the synapse level affect our memory processing?

As you now think and learn about memory processes, your brain is changing. Given increased activity in particular pathways, neural interconnections are forming and strengthening.

The quest to understand the physical basis of memory—how information becomes embedded in brain matter—has sparked study of the synaptic meeting places where neurons communicate with one another via their neurotransmitter messengers. Eric Kandel and James Schwartz (1982) observed synaptic changes during learning in the neurons of the California sea slug, *Aplysia,* a simple animal with a mere 20,000 or so unusually large and accessible nerve cells. A sea slug can be classically conditioned (with mild electric shock) to reflexively withdraw its gills when squirted with water, much as a soldier traumatized by combat might jump at the sound of a firecracker. When learning occurs, Kandel and Schwartz discovered, the slug releases more of the neurotransmitter *serotonin* into certain neurons. These cells' synapses then become more efficient at transmitting signals. Experience and learning can increase—even double—the number of synapses, even in slugs (Kandel, 2012).

In experiments with people, rapidly stimulating certain memory-circuit connections has increased their sensitivity for hours or even weeks to come. The sending neuron now needs less prompting to release its neurotransmitter, and more connections exist between neurons. This increased efficiency of potential neural firing, called **long-term potentiation (LTP),** provides a neural basis for learning and remembering associations (Lynch, 2002; Whitlock et al., 2006) (**FIGURE 23.3**). Several lines of evidence confirm that LTP is a physical basis for memory:

APLYSIA The California sea slug, which neuroscientist Eric Kandel studied for 45 years, has increased our understanding of the neural basis of learning and memory.

- Drugs that block LTP interfere with learning (Lynch & Staubli, 1991).

- Drugs that mimic what happens during learning increase LTP (Harward et al., 2016).

- Rats given a drug that enhanced LTP learned a maze with half the usual number of mistakes (Service, 1994).

After LTP has occurred, passing an electric current through the brain won't disrupt old memories. But the current will wipe out very recent memories. Such is the experience both of laboratory animals and of severely depressed people given *electroconvulsive therapy (ECT)*. A blow to the head can do the same. Football players and boxers momentarily knocked unconscious typically have no memory of events just before the knockout (Yarnell & Lynch, 1970). Their working memory had no time to consolidate the information into long-term memory before the lights went out.

Recently, I [DM] did a little test of memory consolidation. While on an operating table for a basketball-related tendon repair, I was given a face mask and soon could smell the anesthesia gas. "So how much longer will I be with you?" I asked the anesthesiologist. My last moment of memory was her answer: "About 10 seconds." My brain spent that 10 seconds consolidating a memory for her 2-second answer, but could not tuck any further memory away before I was out cold.

Some memory-biology explorers have helped found companies that are competing to develop memory-altering drugs. The target market for memory-boosting drugs includes millions of people with memory-destroying Alzheimer's disease, millions more with *mild cognitive impairment* that often becomes Alzheimer's, and countless millions who would love to turn back the clock on age-related memory decline. Meanwhile, students already have one safe and free memory enhancer: effective study techniques followed by adequate *sleep!*

Some of us may wish for memory-*blocking* drugs that, when taken after a traumatic experience, might blunt intrusive memories (Adler, 2012; Kearns et al., 2012). In one experiment, victims of car accidents, rapes, and other traumas received, for 10 days following their horrific event, either one such drug, propranolol, or a placebo. When tested three months later, half the placebo group but none of the drug-treated group showed signs of stress (Pitman & Delahanty, 2005; Pitman et al., 2002).

FIGURE 23.4 summarizes the brain's two-track memory processing and storage system for implicit (automatic) and explicit (effortful) memories. *The bottom line:* Learn something and you change your brain a little.

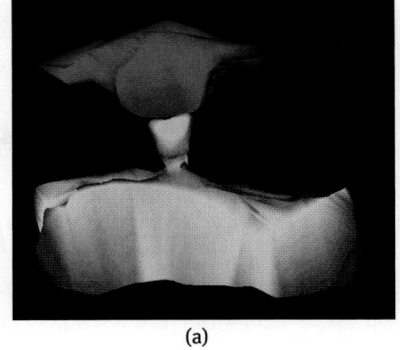

(a)   (b)

From N. Toni et al., Nature, 402, Nov. 25, 1999. Dominique Muller

FIGURE 23.3

DOUBLED RECEPTOR SITES An electron microscope image (a) shows just one receptor site (gray) reaching toward a sending neuron before long-term potentiation. Image (b) shows that, after LTP, the receptor sites have doubled. This means the receiving neuron has increased sensitivity for detecting the presence of the neurotransmitter molecules that may be released by the sending neuron (Toni et al., 1999).

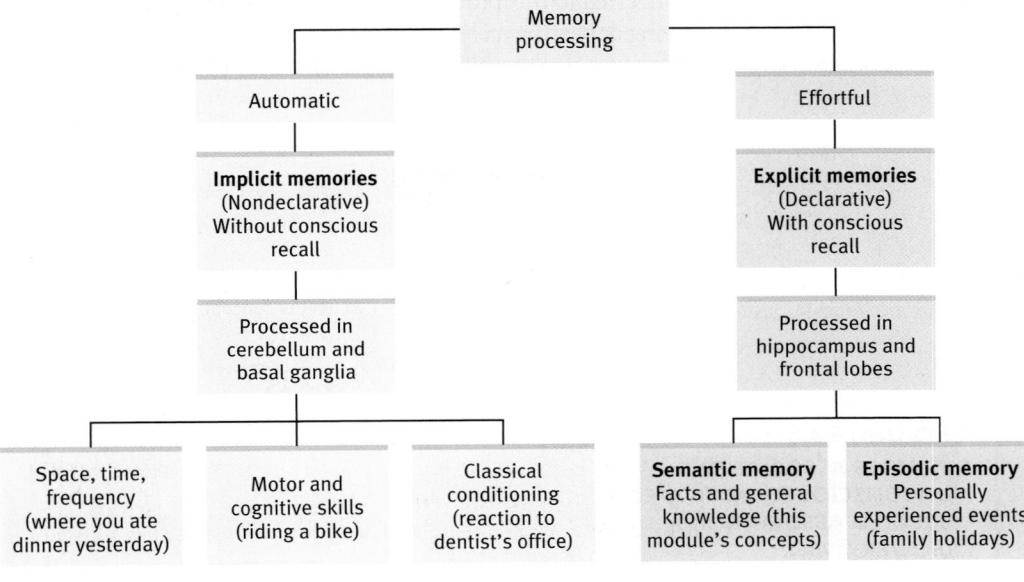

Memory processing

Automatic — Effortful

Implicit memories (Nondeclarative) Without conscious recall

Explicit memories (Declarative) With conscious recall

Processed in cerebellum and basal ganglia

Processed in hippocampus and frontal lobes

Space, time, frequency (where you ate dinner yesterday)

Motor and cognitive skills (riding a bike)

Classical conditioning (reaction to dentist's office)

Semantic memory Facts and general knowledge (this module's concepts)

Episodic memory Personally experienced events (family holidays)

FIGURE 23.4

OUR TWO MEMORY SYSTEMS

priming the activation, often unconsciously, of particular associations in memory.

encoding specificity principle the idea that cues and contexts specific to a particular memory will be most effective in helping us recall it.

mood-congruent memory the tendency to recall experiences that are consistent with one's current good or bad mood.

"Memory is not like a container that gradually fills up; it is more like a tree growing hooks onto which memories are hung." —Peter Russell, *The Brain Book*, 1979

📺 **LaunchPad** For an 8-minute synopsis of how we access what's stored in our brain, see the **Video: Memory Retrieval.**

🔒 **RETRIEVE IT** • • •   *ANSWERS IN APPENDIX E*

RI-3 Which brain area responds to stress hormones by helping to create stronger memories?

RI-4 Increased efficiency at the synapses is evidence of the neural basis of learning and memory. This is called _____-_____ _____.

MEMORY RETRIEVAL

After the magic of brain encoding and storage, we still have the daunting task of retrieving the information. What triggers retrieval?

Retrieval Cues

LOQ 23-6 How do external cues, internal emotions, and order of appearance influence memory retrieval?

Imagine a spider suspended in the middle of her web, held up by the many strands extending outward from her in all directions to different points. If you were to trace a pathway to the spider, you would first need to locate an anchor point and then follow the strand down into the web.

The process of retrieving a memory follows a similar principle, because memories are held in storage by a web of associations, each piece of information interconnected with others. When you encode into memory a target piece of information, such as the name of the person sitting next to you in class, you associate with it other bits of information about your surroundings, mood, seating position, and so on. These bits can serve as *retrieval cues* that you can later use to access the information. The more retrieval cues you have, the better your chances of finding a route to the suspended memory. To remember to do something (say, to write a note tomorrow), one effective strategy is to mentally associate the act with a cue (perhaps a pen left in the middle of your desk) (Rogers & Milkman, 2016).

The best retrieval cues come from associations we form at the time we encode a memory—smells, tastes, and sights that can evoke our memory of the associated person or event. To call up visual cues when trying to recall something, we may mentally place ourselves in the original context. After losing his sight, British scholar John Hull (1990, p. 174) described his difficulty recalling such details:

> I knew I had been somewhere, and had done particular things with certain people, but where? I could not put the conversations . . . into a context. There was no background, no features against which to identify the place. Normally, the memories of people you have spoken to during the day are stored in frames which include the background.

PRIMING Often our associations are activated without our awareness. Philosopher-psychologist William James referred to this process, which we call **priming,** as the "wakening of associations." After seeing or hearing *rabbit,* we are later more likely to spell the spoken word *hair/hare* as *h-a-r-e,* even if we don't recall seeing or hearing *rabbit* (**FIGURE 23.5**).

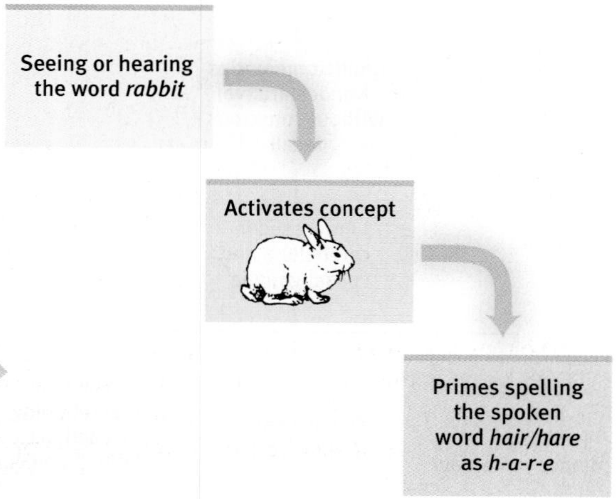

FIGURE 23.5
PRIMING ASSOCIATIONS UNCONSCIOUSLY ACTIVATES RELATED ASSOCIATIONS (BOWER, 1986).

Seeing or hearing the word *rabbit*

Activates concept

Primes spelling the spoken word *hair/hare* as *h-a-r-e*

Priming is often "memoryless memory"—an implicit, invisible memory, without your conscious awareness. If you see a poster of a missing child, you may then unconsciously be primed to interpret an ambiguous adult-child interaction as a possible kidnapping (James, 1986). Although you no longer have the poster in mind, it predisposes your interpretation.

Priming can influence behaviors as well (Herring et al., 2013). Adults and children primed with money-related words and materials were less likely to help another person when asked (Gasiorowska et al., 2016; Vohs et al., 2006). In such cases, money may prime our materialism and self-interest rather than the social norms that encourage us to help (Ariely, 2009).

CONTEXT-DEPENDENT MEMORY Have you noticed? Putting yourself back in the context where you earlier experienced something can prime your memory retrieval. Remembering, in many ways, depends on our environment (Palmer, 1989). When you visit your childhood home or neighborhood, old memories surface. When scuba divers listened to a word list in two different settings (either 10 feet underwater or sitting on the beach), they recalled more words when later tested in the same place where they first heard the list (Godden & Baddeley, 1975).

By contrast, experiencing something outside the usual setting can be confusing. Have you ever run into a former teacher in an unusual place, such as at the store or park? Perhaps you felt a glimmer of recognition, but struggled to realize who it was and how you were acquainted. The **encoding specificity principle** helps us understand how cues *specific* to an event or person will most effectively trigger that memory. In new settings, you may not have the memory cues needed for speedy face recognition. Our memories are *context-dependent,* and are affected by the cues we have associated with that context.

In several experiments, Carolyn Rovee-Collier (1993) found that a familiar context could activate memories even in 3-month-olds. After infants learned that kicking would make a crib mobile move (via a connecting ribbon from their ankle), the infants kicked more when tested again in the same crib than when in a different context.

STATE-DEPENDENT MEMORY Closely related to context-dependent memory is *state-dependent memory.* What we learn in one state—be it drunk or sober—may be more easily recalled when we are again in that state. What people learn when drunk they don't recall well in any state (alcohol disrupts memory storage). But they recall it slightly better when again drunk. Someone who hides money when drunk may forget the location until drunk again.

Our mood states provide an example of memory's state dependence. Emotions that accompany good or bad events become retrieval cues (Gaddy & Ingram, 2014). Thus, our memories are somewhat **mood congruent.** If you've had a bad evening—your plans with friends fell through, your favorite jeans have disappeared, your internet went out 10 minutes before the end of the show—your gloomy mood may facilitate recalling other bad times. Being depressed sours memories by priming negative associations, which we then use to explain our current mood. In many experiments, people put in a buoyant mood—whether under hypnosis or just by the day's events (a World Cup soccer victory for German participants in one study)—recall the world through rose-colored glasses (DeSteno et al., 2000; Forgas et al., 1984; Schwarz et al., 1987). They recall their behaviors as competent and effective, other people benevolent, happy events more frequent.

Have you ever noticed that your mood influences your perceptions of family members? In one study, adolescents' ratings of parental warmth in one week gave little clue to how they would rate their parents six weeks later (Bornstein et al., 1991). When teens were down, their parents seemed cruel; as their mood brightened, their parents morphed from devils into angels. We may nod our heads knowingly. Yet, in a good or bad mood, we persist in attributing to reality our own changing judgments, memories, and interpretations. In a bad mood, we may read someone's look as a glare and feel even worse. In a good mood, we may encode the same look as interest and feel even better. Moods magnify.

Mood effects on retrieval help explain why our moods persist. When happy, we recall happy events and therefore see the world as a happy place, which helps prolong our good mood. When depressed, we recall sad events, which darkens our interpretations of current events. For those of us predisposed to depression, this process can help maintain a vicious, dark cycle.

"I can't remember what we're arguing about, either. Let's keep yelling, and maybe it will come back to us."

"When a feeling was there, they felt as if it would never go; when it was gone, they felt as if it had never been; when it returned, they felt as if it had never gone." —George MacDonald, *What's Mine's Mine,* 1886

ENGAGE  (ASK YOURSELF)

What sort of mood have you been in lately? How has your mood colored your memories, perceptions, and expectations?

FIGURE 23.6

THE SERIAL POSITION EFFECT Immediately after Pope Francis made his way through this receiving line of special guests, he would probably have recalled the names of the last few people best *(recency effect)*. But later he may have been able to recall the first few people best *(primacy effect)*.

Vincenzo Pinto/AFP/Getty Images

serial position effect our tendency to recall best the last *(recency effect)* and first *(primacy effect)* items in a list.

ENGAGE

LaunchPad For a simulated experiment showing the probability of recalling a specific item from a list, engage online with **Concept Practice: The Serial Position Effect.**

ENGAGE

SERIAL POSITION EFFECT Another memory-retrieval quirk, the **serial position effect,** explains why we may have large holes in our memory of a list of recent events. Imagine it's your first day in a new job, and your manager is introducing co-workers. As you meet each person, you silently repeat everyone's name, starting from the beginning. As the last person smiles and turns away, you feel confident you'll be able to greet your new co-workers by name the next day.

Don't count on it. Because you have spent more time rehearsing the earlier names than the later ones, those are the names you'll probably recall more easily the next day. In experiments, when people viewed a list of items (words, names, dates, even experienced odors or tastes) and immediately tried to recall them in any order, they fell prey to the serial position effect (Daniel & Katz, 2017; Reed, 2000). They briefly recalled the last items especially quickly and well (a *recency effect*), perhaps because those last items were still in working memory. But after a delay, when their attention was elsewhere, their recall was best for the first items (a *primacy effect;* see **FIGURE 23.6**).

🔒 RETRIEVE IT • • •

ANSWERS IN APPENDIX E

RI-5 What is *priming*?

RI-6 When we are tested immediately after viewing a list of words, we tend to recall the first and last items best, which is known as the _____ _____ effect.

🔒 REVIEW   STORING AND RETRIEVING MEMORIES

⟫ Learning Objectives

TEST YOURSELF Answer these repeated Learning Objective Questions on your own (before checking the answers in Appendix D) to improve your retention of the concepts (McDaniel et al., 2009, 2015).

23-1 What is the capacity of long-term memory? Are our long-term memories processed and stored in specific locations?

23-2 What roles do the frontal lobes and hippocampus play in memory processing?

23-3 What roles do the cerebellum and basal ganglia play in memory processing?

23-4 How do emotions affect our memory processing?

23-5 How do changes at the synapse level affect our memory processing?

23-6 How do external cues, internal emotions, and order of appearance influence memory retrieval?

⤵ Terms and Concepts to Remember

TEST YOURSELF Write down the definition yourself, then check your answer on the referenced page.

semantic memory, **p. 276**

episodic memory, **p. 276**

hippocampus, **p. 276**

memory consolidation, **p. 276**

flashbulb memory, **p. 278**

long-term potentiation (LTP), **p. 278**

priming, **p. 280**

encoding specificity principle, **p. 280**

mood-congruent memory, **p. 280**

serial position effect, **p. 282**

⤵ Experience the Testing Effect

TEST YOURSELF Answer the following questions on your own first, then check your answers in Appendix E.

1. The hippocampus seems to function as a
   a. temporary processing site for explicit memories.
   b. temporary processing site for implicit memories.
   c. permanent storage area for emotion-based memories.
   d. permanent storage area for iconic and echoic memories.

2. Hippocampus damage typically leaves people unable to learn new facts or recall recent events. However, they may be able to learn new skills, such as riding a bicycle, which is an _____ (explicit/implicit) memory.

3. Long-term potentiation (LTP) refers to
   a. emotion-triggered hormonal changes.
   b. the role of the hippocampus in processing explicit memories.
   c. an increase in a cell's firing potential.
   d. aging people's potential for learning.

4. Specific odors, visual images, emotions, or other associations that help us access a memory are examples of _____ _____.

5. When you feel sad, why might it help to look at pictures that reawaken some of your best memories?

6. When tested immediately after viewing a list of words, people tend to recall the first and last items more readily than those in the middle. When retested after a delay, they are most likely to recall
   a. the first items on the list.
   b. the first and last items on the list.
   c. a few items at random.
   d. the last items on the list.

Continue testing yourself with ☒ **LearningCurve** or ≈ **Achieve Read & Practice** to learn and remember most effectively.

㉔ Forgetting, Memory Construction, and Improving Memory

FORGETTING

LOQ 24-1 Why do we forget?

Amid all the applause for memory—all the efforts to understand it, all the books on how to improve it—have any voices been heard in praise of forgetting? William James (1890, p. 680) was such a voice: "If we remembered everything, we should on most occasions be as ill off as if we remembered nothing." To discard the clutter of useless or out-of-date information—where we parked the car yesterday, our old phone number, restaurant orders already cooked and served—is surely a blessing (Nørby, 2015). The Russian journalist and memory whiz Solomon Shereshevsky, who had merely to listen while other reporters

"Oh, is that today?"

THE WOMAN WHO CAN'T FORGET
Jill Price remembers every day of her life since age 14 in incredible detail, including both the joys and the hurts. Researchers have identified enlarged brain areas in people with super memory (Ally et al., 2013; LePort et al., 2012).

"Amnesia seeps into the crevices of our brains, and amnesia heals." —Joyce Carol Oates, "Words Fail, Memory Blurs, Life Wins," 2001

FIGURE 24.1

WHEN DO WE FORGET? Forgetting can occur at any memory stage. When we process information, we filter, alter, or lose much of it.

scribbled notes, was haunted by his junk heap of memories (Luria, 1968). They dominated his consciousness. He had difficulty thinking abstractly—generalizing, organizing, evaluating. After reading a story, he could recite it but would struggle to summarize its gist.

A more recent case of a life overtaken by memory is Jill Price, whose experience has been studied by a University of California at Irvine research team, along with several dozen other cases of "highly superior autobiographical memory" (McGaugh & LePort, 2014; Parker et al., 2006). Price compares her memory to "a running movie that never stops. It's like a split screen. I'll be talking to someone and seeing something else. . . . Whenever I see a date flash on the television (or anywhere for that matter) I automatically go back to that day and remember where I was, what I was doing, what day it fell on, and on and on and on and on. It is nonstop, uncontrollable, and totally exhausting." Jill, and others like her, are prone to having their minds fill up with information that, once it enters memory storage, never leaves (Patihis, 2016). A good memory is helpful, but so is the ability to forget. If a memory-enhancing pill ever becomes available, it had better not be *too* effective.

 More often, however, our unpredictable memory dismays and frustrates us. Memories are quirky. My [DM's] own memory can easily call up such episodes as that wonderful first kiss with the woman I love, or trivial facts like the air mileage from London to Detroit. Then it abandons me when I discover I have failed to encode, store, or retrieve a student's name, or where I left my sunglasses. See how you do with remembering this sentence when we ask you about it later: *The fish attacked the swimmer.*

As we process information, we sift, change, or lose most of it (**FIGURE 24.1**).

Information bits

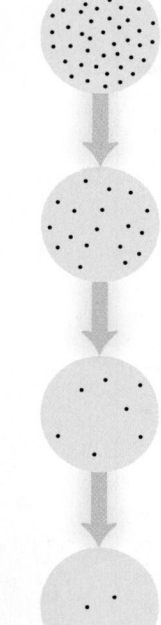

Sensory memory
The senses momentarily register amazing detail.

Working/short-term memory
A few items are both noticed and encoded.

Long-term storage
Some items are altered or lost.

Retrieval from long-term memory
Depending on interference, retrieval cues, moods, and motives, some things get retrieved, some don't.

Forgetting and the Two-Track Mind

For some, memory loss is severe and permanent. Consider Henry Molaison (or H. M., as he was known until his 2008 death). Surgeons removed much of his hippocampus in order to stop persistent seizures. This resulted "in severe disconnection of the remaining hippocampus" from the rest of the brain (Annese et al., 2014). For his remaining 55 years, Molaison was unable to form new conscious memories. He was, as before his surgery, intelligent and did daily crossword puzzles. Yet, reported neuroscientist Suzanne Corkin (2005, 2013), "I've known H. M. since 1962, and he still doesn't know who I am." For about 20 seconds during a conversation he could keep something in mind. When distracted, he would lose what was just said or what had just occurred. Without the neural tissue for turning new information into long-term memories, he never could name the current president of the United States (Ogden, 2012).

Molaison suffered from **anterograde amnesia**—he could recall his past, but he could not form new memories. (Those who cannot recall their past—the old information stored in long-term memory—suffer from **retrograde amnesia**.)

Neurologist Oliver Sacks (1985, pp. 26–27) described another patient, Jimmie, who had anterograde amnesia resulting from brain damage. Jimmie had no memories—thus, no sense of elapsed time—beyond his injury in 1945.

When Jimmie gave his age as 19, Sacks set a mirror before him: "Look in the mirror and tell me what you see. Is that a 19-year-old looking out from the mirror?"

Jimmie turned ashen, gripped the chair, cursed, then became frantic: "What's going on? What's happened to me? Is this a nightmare? Am I crazy? Is this a joke?"

When his attention was diverted to some children playing baseball, his panic ended, the dreadful mirror forgotten.

Sacks showed Jimmie a photo from *National Geographic*. "What is this?" he asked.

"It's the Moon," Jimmie replied.

"No, it's not," Sacks answered. "It's a picture of the Earth taken from the Moon."

"Doc, you're kidding! Someone would've had to get a camera up there!"

"Naturally."

"Hell! You're joking—how the hell would you do that?" Jimmie's wonder was that of a bright young man from the 1940s, amazed by his travel back to the future.

Careful testing of these unique people reveals something even stranger: Although incapable of recalling new facts or anything they have done recently, Molaison, Jimmie, and others with similar conditions can learn nonverbal tasks. Shown hard-to-find figures in pictures (in the *Where's Waldo?* series), they can quickly spot them again later. They can find their way to the bathroom, though without being able to tell you where it is. They can learn to read mirror-image writing or do a jigsaw puzzle, and they have even learned complicated *procedural* job skills (Schacter, 1992, 1996; Xu & Corkin, 2001). They can be classically conditioned. However, *they do all these things with no awareness of having learned them.* "Well, this is strange," Molaison said, after demonstrating his nondeclarative memory of skillful mirror tracing. "I thought that would be difficult. But it seems as though I've done it quite well" (Shapin, 2013).

Molaison and Jimmie lost their ability to form new explicit memories, but their automatic processing ability remained intact. Like Alzheimer's patients, whose *explicit* memories for new people and events are lost, they could form new *implicit* memories (Lustig & Buckner, 2004). These patients can learn *how* to do something, but they will have no conscious recall of learning their new skill. Such sad case studies confirm that we have two distinct memory systems, controlled by different parts of the brain.

For most of us, forgetting is a less drastic process. Let's consider some of the reasons we forget.

Encoding Failure

Much of what we sense we never notice, and what we fail to encode, we will never remember (**FIGURE 24.2**). English novelist and critic C. S. Lewis (1967, p. 107) described the enormity of what we never encode:

> [We are] bombarded every second by sensations, emotions, thoughts . . . nine-tenths of which [we] must simply ignore. The past [is] a roaring cataract of billions upon billions of such moments: Any one of them too complex to grasp in its entirety, and the aggregate beyond all imagination. . . . At every tick of the clock, in every inhabited part of the world, an unimaginable richness and variety of "history" falls off the world into total oblivion.

Age can affect encoding efficiency. The brain areas that jump into action when young adults encode new information are less responsive in older adults. This slower encoding helps explain age-related memory decline (Grady et al., 1995).

But no matter how young we are, we selectively attend to few of the myriad sights and sounds continually bombarding us. Consider: You have surely seen the Apple computer logo thousands of times. Can you draw it? In one study, only 1 of 85 UCLA students (including 52 Apple users) could do so accurately (Blake et al., 2015). Without encoding effort, many potential memories never form.

anterograde amnesia an inability to form new memories.

retrograde amnesia an inability to retrieve information from one's past.

"Waiter, I'd like to order, unless I've eaten, in which case bring me the check."

LaunchPad For a helpful tutorial animation about this type of research method, see the **Video: Case Studies.**

```
External     →   Sensory    Attention   Working/    Encoding   Long-term
events       →   memory      ────→      short-term  ────→      memory
                                        memory                  storage
                                           │
                                           ↓
                                    Encoding failure
                                    leads to forgetting
```

FIGURE 24.2

FORGETTING AS ENCODING FAILURE We cannot remember what we have not encoded.

FIGURE 24.3

EBBINGHAUS' FORGETTING CURVE
After learning lists of nonsense syllables, such as *YOX* and *JIH*, Ebbinghaus studied how much he retained up to 30 days later. He found that memory for novel information fades quickly, then levels off. (Data from Ebbinghaus, 1885.)

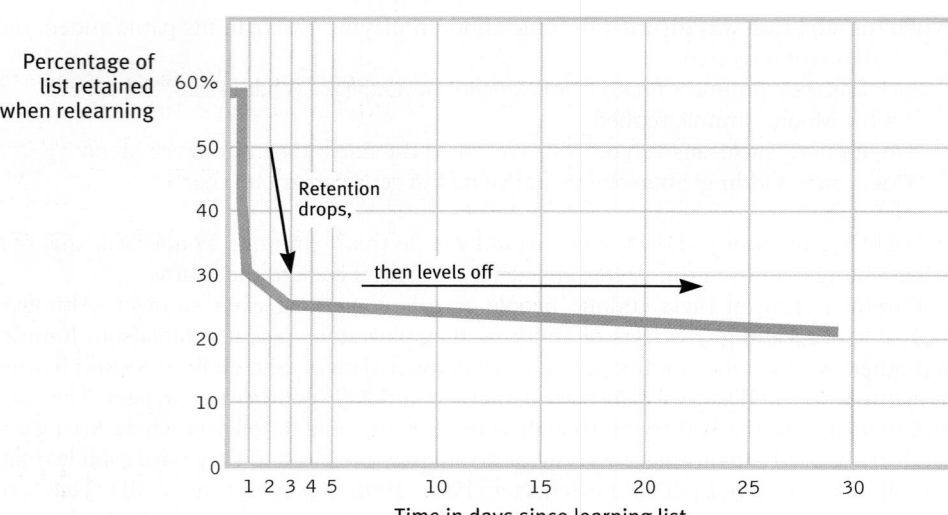

FIGURE 24.4

THE FORGETTING CURVE FOR SPANISH LEARNED IN SCHOOL
Compared with people just completing a Spanish course, those 3 years out of the course remembered much less (on a vocabulary recognition test). Compared with the 3-year group, however, those who studied Spanish even longer ago did not forget much more. (Data from Bahrick, 1984.)

Storage Decay

Even after encoding something well, we sometimes later forget it. To study the durability of stored memories, pioneering memory researcher Hermann Ebbinghaus (1885) learned lists of nonsense syllables and measured how much he retained when relearning each list, from 20 minutes to 30 days later. The result, confirmed by later experiments, was his famous forgetting curve: *The course of forgetting is initially rapid, then levels off with time* (**FIGURE 24.3**; Wixted & Ebbesen, 1991). Harry Bahrick (1984) found a similar forgetting curve for Spanish vocabulary learned in school. Compared with those just completing a high school or college Spanish course, people 3 years out of school had forgotten much of what they had learned (**FIGURE 24.4**). However, what people remembered then, they still remembered 25 and more years later. Their forgetting had leveled off.

One explanation for these forgetting curves is a gradual fading of the physical memory trace. Cognitive neuroscientists are getting closer to solving the mystery of the physical storage of memory and are increasing our understanding of how memory storage could decay. Like books you can't find in your campus library, memories may be inaccessible for many reasons. Some were never acquired (not encoded). Others were discarded (stored memories decay). And others are out of reach because we can't retrieve them.

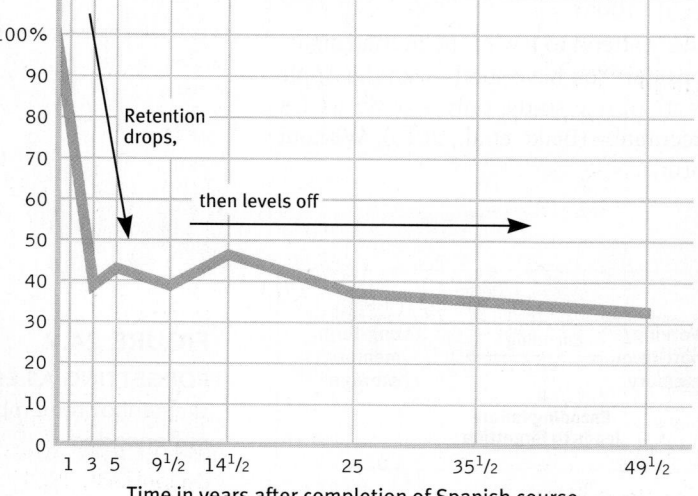

Retrieval Failure

Often, forgetting is not memories faded, but memories unretrieved. We store in long-term memory what's important to us or what we've rehearsed. But sometimes important events defy our attempts to access them (**FIGURE 24.5**). How frustrating when a name lies poised on the tip of our tongue, just beyond reach. Given retrieval cues ("*It begins with an M*"), we may easily retrieve the elusive memory. Retrieval problems contribute to the occasional memory failures of older adults, who more frequently are frustrated by tip-of-the-tongue forgetting (Abrams, 2008; Salthouse & Mandell, 2013).

Deaf persons fluent in sign language experience a parallel "tip of the fingers" phenomenon (Thompson et al., 2005).

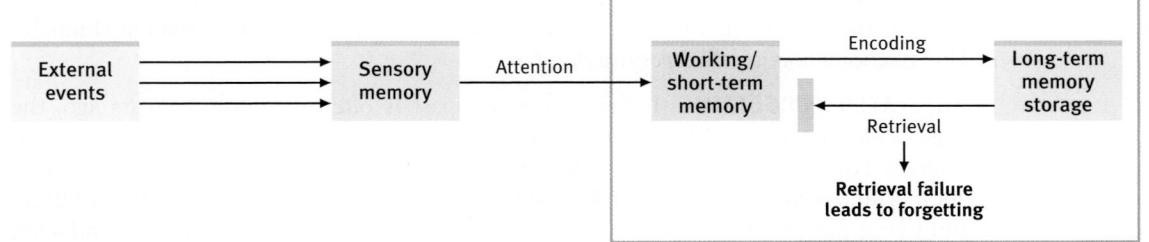

◄-- **FIGURE 24.5**

RETRIEVAL FAILURE Sometimes even stored information cannot be accessed, which leads to forgetting.

ENGAGE Do you recall the gist of the sentence about the attacked swimmer that we asked you to remember? If not, does the word *shark* serve as a retrieval cue? Experiments show that *shark* (likely what you visualized) more readily retrieves the image you stored than does the sentence's actual word, *fish* (Anderson et al., 1976). (The sentence was *The fish attacked the swimmer.*)

Retrieval problems occasionally stem from interference and even from motivated forgetting.

INTERFERENCE As you collect more and more information, your mental attic never fills, but it does get cluttered. Your brain tries to keep things tidy: Using a new password weakens your memory of competing old passwords (Wimber et al., 2015). But sometimes the clutter wins, and new and old learning collide. **Proactive** *(forward-acting)* **interference** occurs when prior learning disrupts your recall of new information. If you buy a new combination lock, your well-rehearsed old combination may interfere with your retrieval of the new one.

Retroactive *(backward-acting)* **interference** occurs when new learning disrupts recall of old information. If someone sings new lyrics to the tune of an old song, you may have trouble remembering the original words. It is rather like a second stone tossed in a pond, disrupting the waves rippling out from the first.

Information presented in the hour before sleep suffers less retroactive interference because the opportunity for interfering events is minimized (Mercer, 2015). Researchers John Jenkins and Karl Dallenbach (1924) first discovered this in a now-classic experiment. Day after day, two people each learned some nonsense syllables, then tried to recall them after up to eight hours of being awake or asleep at night. As **FIGURE 24.6** shows,

proactive interference the forward-acting disruptive effect of older learning on the recall of *new* information.

retroactive interference the backward-acting disruptive effect of newer learning on the recall of *old* information.

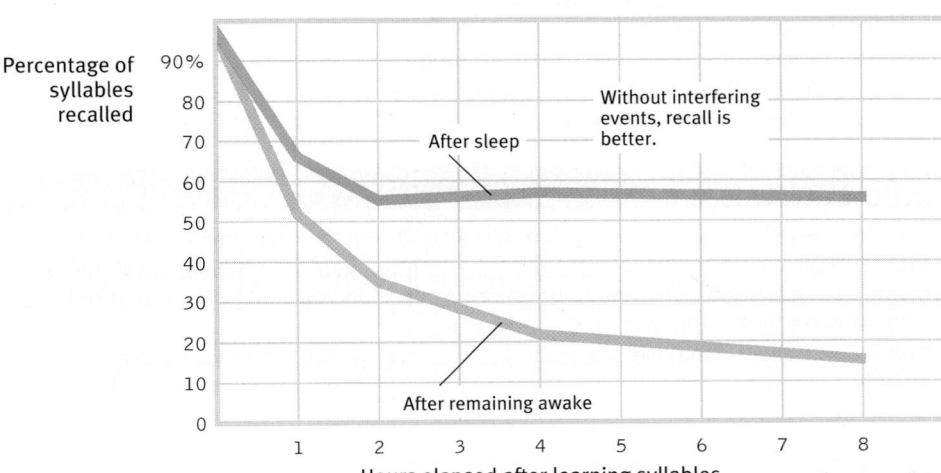

◄-- **FIGURE 24.6**

RETROACTIVE INTERFERENCE More forgetting occurred when a person stayed awake and experienced other new material. (Data from Jenkins & Dallenbach, 1924.)

LaunchPad To experience a demonstration and explanation of interference effects on memory, visit **Topic Tutorial: PsychSim6, Forgetting.**

Peter Johansky/Photolibrary/Getty Images

forgetting occurred more rapidly after being awake and involved with other activities. The investigators surmised that "forgetting is not so much a matter of the decay of old impressions and associations as it is a matter of interference, inhibition, or obliteration of the old by the new" (1924, p. 612).

The hour before sleep is a good time to commit information to memory (Scullin & McDaniel, 2010), though information presented in the *seconds* just before sleep is seldom remembered (Wyatt & Bootzin, 1994). If you're considering learning *while* sleeping, forget it. We have little memory for information played aloud in the room during sleep, although the ears do register it (Wood et al., 1992).

Old and new learning do not always compete with each other, of course. Previously learned information (Latin) often facilitates our learning of new information (French). This phenomenon is called *positive transfer*.

MOTIVATED FORGETTING To remember our past is often to revise it. Years ago, the huge cookie jar in my [DM's] kitchen was jammed with freshly baked chocolate chip cookies. Still more were cooling across racks on the counter. Twenty-four hours later, not a crumb was left. Who had taken them? During that time, my wife, three children, and I were the only people in the house. So while memories were still fresh, I conducted a little memory test. Andy admitted wolfing down as many as 20. Peter thought he had eaten 15. Laura guessed she had stuffed her then-6-year-old body with 15 cookies. My wife, Carol, recalled eating 6, and I remembered consuming 15 and taking 18 more to the office. We sheepishly accepted responsibility for 89 cookies. Still, we had not come close; there had been 160.

Why do our memories fail us? This happens in part because memory is an "unreliable, self-serving historian" (Tavris & Aronson, 2007, p. 6). Consider one study, in which researchers told some participants about the benefits of frequent toothbrushing. Those individuals then recalled (more than others did) having frequently brushed their teeth in the preceding two weeks (Ross et al., 1981).

So why were my family and I so far off in our estimates of the cookies we had eaten? Was it an *encoding* problem? (Did we just not notice what we had eaten?) Was it a storage problem? (Might our memories of cookies, like Ebbinghaus' memory of nonsense syllables, have melted away almost as fast as the cookies themselves?) Or was the information still intact but not *retrievable* because it would be embarrassing to remember?[1]

Sigmund Freud might have argued that our memory systems self-censored this information. He proposed that we **repress** painful or unacceptable memories to protect our self-concept and to minimize anxiety. But the repressed memory lingers, he believed, and can be retrieved by some later cue or during therapy. Repression was central to Freud's psychoanalytic theory and remains a popular idea. Indeed, an American study revealed that 81 percent of university students, and 60 to 90 percent of therapists (depending on their perspective), believe "traumatic memories are often repressed" (Patihis et al., 2014a,b). However, most memory researchers think repression rarely, if ever, occurs. People succeed in forgetting unwanted neutral information (yesterday's parking place), but it's harder to forget emotional events (Payne & Corrigan, 2007). Trauma releases stress hormones that cause people to pay attention and remember a threat (Quaedflieg & Schwabe, 2017). Thus, we may have intrusive memories of the very same traumatic experiences we would most like to forget.

RETRIEVE IT • • •   *ANSWERS IN APPENDIX E*

RI-1 What are three ways we forget, and how does each of these happen?

RI-2 You will experience less _____ (proactive/retroactive) interference if you learn new material in the hour before sleep than you will if you learn it before turning to another subject.

RI-3 Freud believed that we _____ unacceptable memories to minimize anxiety.

---

1. One of my cookie-scarfing sons, on reading this in his father's textbook years later, confessed he had fibbed "a little."

MEMORY CONSTRUCTION ERRORS

LOQ 24-2 How do misinformation, imagination, and source amnesia influence our memory construction? How do we decide whether a memory is real or false?

Nearly two-thirds of Americans agree: "Human memory works like a video camera, accurately recording the events we see and hear so that we can review and inspect them later" (Simons & Chabris, 2011). Actually, memory is not so precise. Even people with exceptional memories, such as Jill Price, sometimes make mistakes (Johnson, 2017; Patihis et al., 2013). Like scientists who infer a dinosaur's appearance from its remains, we infer our past from stored information plus what we later imagined, expected, saw, and heard. We don't just retrieve memories, we reweave them. Our memories are like Wikipedia pages, capable of constant revision. When we "replay" a memory, we often replace the original with a slightly modified version, rather like what happens in the telephone game, as a whispered message gets progressively altered when passed from person to person (Hardt et al., 2010). Memory researchers call this **reconsolidation.** So, in a sense, said Joseph LeDoux (2009), "your memory is only as good as your last memory. The fewer times you use it, the more pristine it is." This means that, to some degree, "all memory is false" (Bernstein & Loftus, 2009b).

Despite knowing all this, I [DM] recently rewrote my own past. It happened at an international conference, where memory researcher Elizabeth Loftus (2012) was demonstrating how memory works. Loftus showed us a handful of individual faces that we were to identify later, as if in a police lineup. Then she showed us some pairs of faces, one face we had seen earlier and one we had not, and asked us to identify the one we had seen. But one pair she had slipped in included *two* new faces, one of which was rather *like* a face we had seen earlier. Most of us understandably but wrongly identified this face as one we had previously seen. To climax the demonstration, she showed us the originally seen face and the previously chosen wrong face, and asked us to choose the original face we had seen. Most of us picked the wrong face! As a result of our memory reconsolidation, we— an audience of psychologists who should have known better—had replaced the original memory with a false memory.

Clinical researchers have experimented with memory reconsolidation. People recalled a traumatic or negative experience and then had the reconsolidation of that memory disrupted, with a drug or brief, painless electroconvulsive shock (Kroes et al., 2014; Lonergan et al., 2013; Treanor et al., 2017). Someday it might become possible to erase your memory of a specific traumatic experience—by reactivating your memory and then disrupting its storage in this way. Would you wish for this? If brutally assaulted, would you welcome having your memory of the attack and its associated fears deleted?

DO PEOPLE VIVIDLY REMEMBER—OR REPRESS—TRAUMATIC EXPERIENCES? Imagine yourself several hours into Flight AT236 From Toronto to Lisbon. A fractured fuel line begins leaking. Soon the engines go silent and primary electrical power is lost. In the eerie silence, the pilots instruct you and the other terrified passengers to don life jackets, and, when hearing the countdown to ocean impact, to assume a brace position. After minutes of descent the pilot declares above the passengers' screams and prayers, "About to go into the water." Death awaits.

But no! "We have a runway! We have a runway! Brace! Brace! Brace!" The plane makes a hard landing at an Azores airbase, averting death for you and the 305 other passengers and crew.

Among the passengers thinking "I'm going to die" was psychologist Margaret Mckinnon. Seizing the opportunity, she tracked down 15 of her fellow passengers to test their trauma memories. Did they repress the experience? To the contrary, all exhibited vivid, detailed memories. With trauma comes not repression, but, far more often, "robust" memory (Mckinnon et al., 2015).

repression in psychoanalytic theory, the basic defense mechanism that banishes from consciousness anxiety-arousing thoughts, feelings, and memories.

reconsolidation a process in which previously stored memories, when retrieved, are potentially altered before being stored again.

Misinformation and Imagination Effects

In more than 200 experiments involving more than 20,000 people, Loftus has shown how eyewitnesses reconstruct their memories after a crime or accident. In one important study, two groups of people watched a film clip of a traffic accident and then answered questions about what they had seen (Loftus & Palmer, 1974). Those asked, "About how fast were the cars going when they *smashed* into each other?" gave higher speed estimates than those asked, "About how fast were the cars going when they *hit* each other?" A week later, when asked whether they recalled seeing any broken glass, people who had heard *smashed* were more than twice as likely to report seeing glass fragments (**FIGURE 24.7**). In fact, the film showed no broken glass.

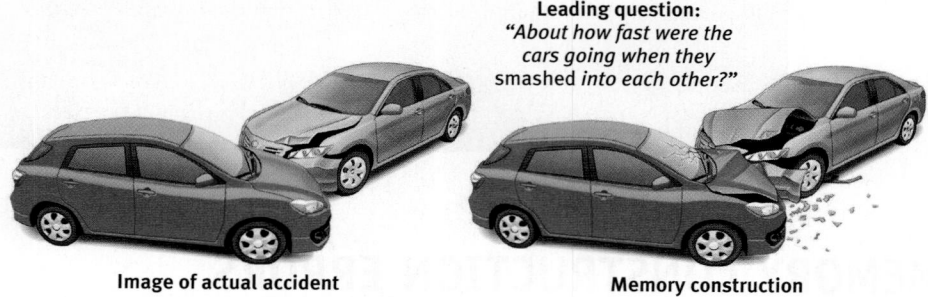

Leading question:
"About how fast were the cars going when they smashed into each other?"

Image of actual accident   Memory construction

FIGURE 24.7

MEMORY CONSTRUCTION In this experiment, people viewed a film clip of a car accident. Those who later were asked a leading question recalled a more serious accident than they had witnessed (Loftus & Palmer, 1974).

"Memory is insubstantial. Things keep replacing it. Your batch of snapshots will both fix and ruin your memory. . . . You can't remember anything from your trip except the wretched collection of snapshots." —Annie Dillard, "To Fashion a Text," 1988

In many follow-up experiments around the world, others have witnessed an event, received or not received misleading information about it, and then taken a memory test. The repeated result is a **misinformation effect:** People may misremember when exposed to subtly misleading information, despite feeling confident (Loftus et al., 1992). Across studies, about half of people show some vulnerability to the misinformation effect (Brewin & Andrews, 2017; Scoboria et al., 2017). A yield sign becomes a stop sign, hammers become screwdrivers, Coke cans become peanut cans, breakfast cereal becomes eggs, and a clean-shaven man morphs into a man with a mustache.

So powerful is the misinformation effect that it can influence later attitudes and behaviors (Bernstein & Loftus, 2009a). One experiment falsely suggested to some Dutch university students that, as children, they became ill after eating spoiled egg salad (Geraerts et al., 2008). After absorbing that suggestion, they were less likely to eat egg-salad sandwiches, both immediately and four months later.

Even repeatedly *imagining* nonexistent actions and events can create false memories. In one study, Canadian university students were asked to recall two events from their past. One event actually happened; the other was a false event that involved committing a crime, such as assaulting someone with a weapon. Initially, none of the lawful students remembered breaking the law. But after repeated interviewing, 70 percent reported a detailed false memory of having committed the crime (Shaw & Porter, 2015). Telling lies can likewise change people's memory for the truth; fibbing feeds false memories (Otgaar & Baker, 2018).

Digitally altered photos have also produced this *imagination inflation*. In experiments, researchers have altered photos from a family album to show some family members

WAS ALEXANDER HAMILTON A U.S. PRESIDENT? Sometimes our mind tricks us into misremembering dates, places, and names. This often happens because we misuse familiar information. In one study, many people mistakenly recalled Alexander Hamilton—the subject of a popular Broadway musical whose face also appears on the U.S. $10 bill—as a U.S. president (Roediger & DeSoto, 2016).

Evan Agostini/Invision/AP Photos

"LYIN' BRIAN"? OR A VICTIM OF FALSE MEMORY? In 2015, *NBC Nightly News* anchor Brian Williams recounted a story about traveling in a military helicopter that was hit with a rocket-propelled grenade. But the event never happened as he described. The public branded him a liar, leading his bosses to fire him. Several memory researchers, including psychologist Christopher Chabris, had a different opinion: "I think a lot of people don't appreciate the extent to which false memories can happen even when we are extremely confident in the memory" (2015).

taking a hot-air balloon ride. After viewing these photos (rather than photos showing just the balloon), children reported more false memories and indicated high confidence in those memories. When interviewed several days later, they reported even richer details of their false memories (Strange et al., 2008; Wade et al., 2002).

In British and Canadian university surveys, nearly one-fourth of students have reported autobiographical memories that they later realized were not accurate (Foley, 2015; Mazzoni et al., 2010). I [DM] empathize. For decades, my cherished earliest memory was of my parents getting off the bus and walking to our house, bringing my baby brother home from the hospital. When, in middle age, I shared that memory with my father, he assured me they did *not* bring their newborn home on the Seattle Transit System. The human mind, it seems, comes with built-in Photoshopping software. The moral: Don't believe everything you remember.

Source Amnesia

What is the frailest part of a memory? Its source. We may recognize someone but have no idea where we have seen the person. We may remember learning something on social media but be uncertain whether it was real or false news. We may dream an event and later be unsure whether it really happened. We may tell a friend some gossip, only to learn we got the news from the friend. Famed child psychologist Jean Piaget was startled as an adult to learn that a vivid, detailed memory from his childhood—a nursemaid's thwarting his kidnapping—was utterly false. He apparently constructed the memory from repeatedly hearing the story (which his nursemaid, after undergoing a religious conversion, later confessed had never happened). In attributing his "memory" to his own experiences, rather than to his nursemaid's stories, Piaget exhibited **source amnesia** (also called *source misattribution*). Misattribution is at the heart of many false memories. Authors, songwriters, and stand-up comedians sometimes suffer from it. They think an idea came from their own creative imagination, when in fact they are unintentionally plagiarizing something they earlier read or heard.

Even preschoolers experience source amnesia. In one study, preschoolers interacted with "Mr. Science," who engaged them in activities such as blowing up a balloon with baking soda and vinegar (Poole & Lindsay, 1995, 2001). Three months later, on three successive days, their parents read them a story describing some things the children had experienced with Mr. Science and some they had not. When a new interviewer asked what Mr. Science had done with them—"Did Mr. Science have a machine with ropes to pull?"—4 in 10 children spontaneously recalled him doing things that had happened only in the story.

Source amnesia also helps explain **déjà vu** (French for "already seen"). Two-thirds of us have experienced this fleeting, eerie sense that "I've been in this exact situation before." The key to déjà vu seems to be familiarity with a stimulus without a clear idea of where we encountered it before (Brown & Marsh, 2009; Cleary, 2008). Normally, we experience a feeling of *familiarity* (thanks to temporal lobe processing) before we consciously remember details (thanks to hippocampus and frontal lobe processing). When these functions

"It isn't so astonishing, the number of things I can remember, as the number of things I can remember that aren't so." —Author Mark Twain, 1835–1910

misinformation effect occurs when misleading information has corrupted one's memory of an event.

source amnesia faulty memory for how, when, or where information was learned or imagined. (Also called *source misattribution*.) Source amnesia, along with the misinformation effect, is at the heart of many false memories.

déjà vu that eerie sense that "I've experienced this before." Cues from the current situation may unconsciously trigger retrieval of an earlier experience.

Patrick Andrade/Polaris Images/Newscom

"Do you ever get that strange feeling of vujà dé? Not déjà vu; vujà dé. It's the distinct sense that, somehow, something just happened that has never happened before. Nothing seems familiar. And then suddenly the feeling is gone. Vujà dé."
—Comedian George Carlin, in *Funny Times*, December 2001

(and brain regions) are out of sync, we may experience a feeling of familiarity without conscious recall. Our amazing brains try to make sense of such an improbable situation, and we get an eerie feeling that we're reliving some earlier part of our life. Our source amnesia forces us to do our best to make sense of an odd moment.

Discerning True and False Memories

Since memory is reconstruction as well as reproduction, we can't be sure whether a memory is real by how real it feels. Much as perceptual illusions may seem like real perceptions, unreal memories *feel* like real memories. Because the misinformation effect and source amnesia happen outside our awareness, it is hard to separate false memories from real ones (Schooler et al., 1986). Perhaps you can recall describing a childhood experience to a friend and filling in memory gaps with reasonable guesses and assumptions. We all do it, and after more retellings, those guessed details—now absorbed into our memories—may feel as real as if you had actually experienced them (Roediger et al., 1993). False memories, like fake diamonds, seem so real.

False memories can be persistent. Imagine that we were to read aloud a list of words such as *candy, sugar, honey,* and *taste.* Later, we ask you to recognize the presented words from a larger list. If you are at all like the people tested by Henry Roediger and Kathleen McDermott (1995), you would err three out of four times—by falsely remembering a nonpresented similar word, such as *sweet.* We more easily remember the gist than the words themselves.

False memories are socially contagious. When we hear others falsely remember events, we tend to make the same memory mistakes (Roediger et al., 2001). Your Facebook friend may misremember a shy classmate acting rude, leading you to also mistakenly remember the classmate negatively. It's easy to see how false news, whether it comes from bloggers, social media, or politicians, can spread and become false memories.

Memory construction also helps explain why some people have been sent to prison for crimes they never committed. Of 351 people who were later proven not guilty by DNA testing, 70 percent had been convicted because of faulty eyewitness identification (Innocence Project, 2015; Smalarz & Wells, 2015). It explains why "hypnotically refreshed" memories of crimes so easily incorporate errors, some of which originate with the hypnotist's leading questions (*Did you hear loud noises?*). It explains why dating partners who fell in love have *over*estimated their first impressions of one another (*It was love at first sight*), while those who broke up *under*estimated their earlier liking (*We never really clicked*) (McFarland & Ross, 1987). And it explains why people asked how they felt 10 years ago about marijuana or gender issues recalled attitudes closer to their current views than to the views they had actually reported a decade earlier (Markus, 1986). People tend to recall having always felt as they feel today (Mazzoni & Vannucci, 2007). As George Vaillant (1977, p. 197) noted after following adult lives through time, "It is all too common for caterpillars to become butterflies and then to maintain that in their youth they had been little butterflies. Maturation makes liars of us all." Memory construction errors also seem to be at work in many "recovered" memories of childhood abuse. See Thinking Critically About: Can Memories of Childhood Sexual Abuse Be Repressed and Then Recovered?

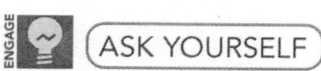 ASK YOURSELF

Think of a memory you frequently recall. How might you have changed it without conscious awareness?

LaunchPad To participate in a simulated experiment on false memory formation, and to review related research, visit **Topic Tutorial: PsychSim6, Can You Trust Your Memory?**

Children's Eyewitness Recall

LOQ 24-4 How reliable are young children's eyewitness descriptions?

If memories can be sincere, yet sincerely wrong, how can jurors decide cases in which children's memories of sexual abuse are the only evidence? "It would be truly awful to ever lose sight of the enormity of child abuse," observed Stephen Ceci (1993). Yet Ceci and Maggie Bruck's (1993, 1995) studies of children's memories have made them aware of how easily children's memories can be molded. For example, they asked 3-year-olds to show on anatomically correct dolls where a pediatrician had touched them. Of the children who had not received genital examinations, 55 percent pointed to either genital or anal areas.

In other experiments, the researchers studied the effect of suggestive interviewing techniques (Bruck & Ceci, 1999, 2004). In one study, children chose a card from a deck of possible happenings, and an adult then read the card to them. For example, "Think real hard, and tell me if this ever happened to you. Can you remember going to the

THINKING CRITICALLY ABOUT:

Can Memories of Childhood Sexual Abuse Be Repressed and Then Recovered?

LOQ 24-3 Why have reports of repressed and recovered memories been so hotly debated?

Two Possible Tragedies:

1. People doubt childhood sexual abuse survivors who tell their secret.

2. Innocent people are falsely accused, as therapists prompt "recovered" memories of childhood sexual abuse:

"Victims of sexual abuse often have your symptoms. So maybe you were abused and *repressed* the memory. Let's see if I can help you recover the memory, by digging back and visualizing your trauma."

Well-intentioned therapist

Misinformation effect and **source amnesia:** Adult client may form image of threatening person. → With *rehearsal* (repeated therapy sessions), the image grows more vivid. → Client is stunned, angry, and ready to confront or sue the remembered abuser. → Accused person is equally stunned and vigorously denies the long-ago accusation.

Professional organizations (including the American Medical, American Psychological, and American Psychiatric Associations) are working to find sensible common ground to resolve psychology's "memory war": [1]

- **Childhood sexual abuse happens** and can leave its victims at risk for problems ranging from sexual dysfunction to depression.[2] But there is no "survivor syndrome"—no group of symptoms that lets us spot victims of sexual abuse.[3]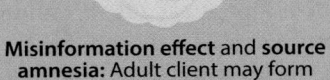

- **Injustice happens.** Innocent people have been falsely convicted. And guilty people have avoided punishment by casting doubt on their truth-telling accusers.

- **Forgetting happens.** Children abused when very young may not have understood the meaning of their experience or remember it. Forgetting long-ago good and bad events is an ordinary part of everyday life.

- **Recovered memories are common.** Cued by a remark or an experience, we may recover pleasant or unpleasant memories of long-forgotten events. But does the unconscious mind *forcibly* repress painful experiences, and can these experiences be *recovered* by therapist-aided techniques?[4] Memories that surface naturally are more likely to be true.[5]

- **Memories of events before age 4 are unreliable.** *Infantile amnesia* results from not yet developed brain pathways. Most psychologists therefore doubt "recovered" memories of abuse during infancy.[6] The older a child was when suffering sexual abuse, and the more severe the abuse, the more likely it is to be remembered.[7]

- **Memories "recovered" under hypnosis are especially unreliable.**

- **Memories, whether real or false, can be emotionally upsetting.** What was born of mere suggestion can become, like an actual event, a stinging memory that drives bodily stress.[8]

Psychologists question whether *repression* ever occurs. (We will learn more in other modules about this concept—the cornerstone of Freud's theory and of so much popular psychology.)

Traumatic experiences (witnessing a loved one's murder, being terrorized by a hijacker or rapist, losing everything in a natural disaster) → **TYPICALLY LEAD TO** → **vivid, persistent, haunting memories**[9]

The Royal College of Psychiatrists Working Group on Reported Recovered Memories of Child Sexual Abuse advised that "when memories are 'recovered' after long periods of amnesia, particularly when extraordinary means were used to secure the recovery of memory, there is a high probability that the memories are false."[10]

1. Patihis et al., 2014a. 2. Freyd et al., 2007. 3. Kendall-Tackett et al., 1993. 4. McNally & Geraerts, 2009. 5. Geraerts et al., 2007. 6. Gore-Felton et al., 2000; Knapp & VandeCreek, 2000. 7. Goodman et al., 2003. 8. McNally, 2003, 2007. 9. Porter & Peace, 2007. 10. Brandon et al., 1998.

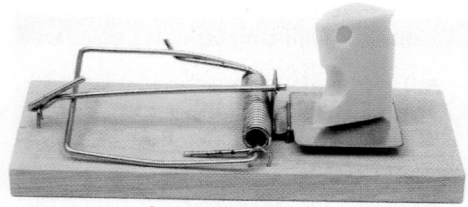

Darren Matthews/Alamy

LaunchPad Consider how researchers have studied these issues by engaging online with **Immersive Learning: How Would You Know If People's Memories Are Accurate?**

Like children (whose frontal lobes have not fully matured), older adults—especially those whose frontal lobe functioning has declined—are more susceptible than young adults to false memories. This makes older adults more vulnerable to scams, as when a repair person overcharges by falsely claiming, "I told you it would cost x, and you agreed to pay" (Jacoby et al., 2005; Jacoby & Rhodes, 2006; Roediger & Geraci, 2007; Roediger & McDaniel, 2007).

hospital with a mousetrap on your finger?" In interviews, the same adult repeatedly asked children to think about several real and fictitious events. After 10 weeks of this, a new adult asked the same question. The stunning result: 58 percent of preschoolers produced false (often vivid) stories regarding one or more events they had never experienced (Ceci et al., 1994). Here's one:

> My brother Colin was trying to get Blowtorch [an action figure] from me, and I wouldn't let him take it from me, so he pushed me into the wood pile where the mousetrap was. And then my finger got caught in it. And then we went to the hospital, and my mommy, daddy, and Colin drove me there, to the hospital in our van, because it was far away. And the doctor put a bandage on this finger.

Given such detailed stories, professional psychologists who specialize in interviewing children could not reliably separate the real memories from the false ones. Nor could the children themselves. The above child, reminded that his parents had told him several times that the mousetrap incident never happened—that he had imagined it—protested, "But it really did happen. I remember it!" Unfortunately, this type of error is common. In one analysis of eyewitness data from over 20,000 participants, children regularly identified innocent suspects as guilty (Fitzgerald & Price, 2015). "[The] research," said Ceci (1993), "leads me to worry about the possibility of false allegations. It is not a tribute to one's scientific integrity to walk down the middle of the road if the data are more to one side."

Children can, however, be accurate eyewitnesses. When questioned about their experiences in neutral words they understand, children often accurately recall what happened and who did it (Brewin & Andrews, 2017; Goodman, 2006). When interviewers have used less suggestive, more effective techniques, even 4- to 5-year-old children have produced more accurate recall (Holliday & Albon, 2004; Pipe et al., 2004). Children are especially accurate when they haven't talked with involved adults prior to the interview and when their disclosure was made in a first interview with a neutral person who asked nonleading questions.

RETRIEVE IT • • •

ANSWERS IN APPENDIX E

RI-4 What—given the commonness of source amnesia—might life be like if we remembered all our waking experiences and all our dreams?

RI-5 Imagine being a jury member in a trial for a parent accused of sexual abuse based on a recovered memory. What insights from memory research should you share with the rest of the jury?

IMPROVING MEMORY

LOQ 24-5 How can you use memory research findings to do better in this and other courses?

Biology's findings benefit medicine. Botany's findings benefit agriculture. So, too, can memory researchers' findings benefit education. Here, for easy reference, is a summary of some research-based suggestions that can help you remember information when you need it. The SQ3R—*Survey, Question, Read, Retrieve, Review*—study technique used in this book incorporates several of these strategies:

Rehearse repeatedly. To master material, remember the *spacing effect* and use *distributed (spaced) practice.* To learn a concept, give yourself many separate study sessions. Take advantage of life's little intervals—riding a bus, walking across campus, waiting for class to start. New memories are weak; exercise them and they will strengthen. To memorize specific facts or figures, research has shown that you should "rehearse the name or number you are trying to memorize, wait a few seconds, rehearse again, wait a little longer, rehearse again, then wait longer still and rehearse yet again. The waits should be as long as possible without losing the information" (Landauer, 2001). Reading complex material with minimal rehearsal yields little retention. Producing information—saying, writing, or typing it—beats silently reading it (a phenomenon called the *production effect*) (MacLeod & Bodner, 2017). Rehearsal and critical reflection help even more. As the *testing effect* has shown, it pays to study actively. Taking lecture notes by hand, which requires summarizing material in your own words, leads to better retention than does verbatim laptop note taking. "The pen is mightier than the keyboard," note researchers Pam Mueller and Daniel Oppenheimer (2014).

Make the material meaningful. You can build a network of retrieval cues by taking notes in your own words, and then increase these cues by forming as many associations as possible. Apply the concepts to your own life. Form images. Understand and organize information. Relate the material to what you already know or have experienced. As William James (1890) suggested, "Knit each new thing on to some acquisition already there." Mindlessly repeating someone else's words without taking the time to really understand what they mean won't supply many retrieval cues. On an exam, you may find yourself stuck when a question uses phrasing different from the words you memorized.

Activate retrieval cues. Remember the importance of *context-dependent* and *state-dependent memory*. Mentally re-create the situation and the mood in which your original learning occurred. Jog your memory by allowing one thought to cue the next.

Use mnemonic devices. Make up a story that incorporates *vivid images* of the items. *Chunk* information into acronyms. Create rhythmic rhymes (such as "*i* before *e*, except after *c*").

Minimize proactive and retroactive interference. Study before sleep. Do not schedule back-to-back study times for topics that are likely to interfere with each other, such as Spanish and French.

Sleep more. During sleep, the brain reorganizes and *consolidates* information for long-term memory. Sleep deprivation disrupts this process (Frenda et al., 2014; Lo et al., 2016). Even 10 minutes of waking rest enhances memory of what we have read (Dewar et al., 2012). So, after a period of hard study, you might just sit or lie down for a few minutes before tackling the next subject.

Test your own knowledge, both to rehearse it and to find out what you don't yet know. The testing effect is real, and it is powerful. Don't be lulled into overconfidence by your ability to *recognize* information. Test your *recall* using the periodic Retrieve It items and the numbered Learning Objective and Experience the Testing Effect questions in the Review sections. Outline sections using a blank page. Define the terms and concepts listed at each section's end before turning back to their definitions. Take practice tests; the online resources that accompany many textbooks, including this one, are a good source for such tests.

© Sigrid Olsson/PhotoAlto/Corbis

THINKING AND MEMORY Actively thinking as we read, by rehearsing and relating ideas, and by making the material personally meaningful, yields the best retention.

Laptop distraction? In one study of university introductory psychology students, the average student spent one-third of the class hour browsing online. More time spent online predicted poorer exam performance, even after controlling for aptitude and expressed interest (Ravizza et al., 2017).

ENGAGE · 💡 (ASK YOURSELF)

Which three of these study and memory strategies will be most important for you to employ to improve your own learning and retention?

ENGAGE · 💡 📕 **LaunchPad** Evaluate your own memory skills by engaging online with **Immersive Learning: Assess Your Strengths—How Might You Improve Your Memory?**

🔒 **RETRIEVE IT • • •**   *ANSWERS IN APPENDIX E*

RI-6 Which memory strategies can help you study smarter and retain more information?

🔒 **REVIEW** FORGETTING, MEMORY CONSTRUCTION, AND IMPROVING MEMORY

⟶ Learning Objectives

TEST YOURSELF Answer these repeated Learning Objective Questions on your own (before checking the answers in Appendix D) to improve your retention of the concepts (McDaniel et al., 2009, 2015).

24-1 Why do we forget?

24-2 How do misinformation, imagination, and source amnesia influence our memory construction? How do we decide whether a memory is real or false?

24-3 Why have reports of repressed and recovered memories been so hotly debated?

24-4 How reliable are young children's eyewitness descriptions?

24-5 How can you use memory research findings to do better in this and other courses?

⟨⋅⟩ Terms and Concepts to Remember

TEST YOURSELF Write down the definition yourself, then check your answer on the referenced page.

anterograde amnesia, **p. 285**

retrograde amnesia, **p. 285**

proactive interference, **p. 287**

retroactive interference, **p. 287**

repression, **p. 289**

reconsolidation, **p. 289**

misinformation effect, **p. 291**

source amnesia, **p. 291**

déjà vu, **p. 291**

⟨⋅⟩ Experience the Testing Effect

TEST YOURSELF Answer the following questions on your own first, then check your answers in Appendix E.

1. When forgetting is due to encoding failure, information has not been transferred from
   a. the environment into sensory memory.
   b. sensory memory into long-term memory.
   c. long-term memory into short-term memory.
   d. short-term memory into long-term memory.

2. Ebbinghaus' "forgetting curve" shows that after an initial decline, memory for novel information tends to
   a. increase slightly.
   b. decrease slightly.
   c. decrease greatly.
   d. level off.

3. The hour before sleep is a good time to memorize information, because going to sleep after learning new material minimizes _____ interference.

4. Freud proposed that painful or unacceptable memories are blocked from consciousness through a mechanism called _____.

5. One reason false memories form is our tendency to fill in memory gaps with our reasonable guesses and assumptions, sometimes based on misleading information. This tendency is an example of
   a. proactive interference.
   b. the misinformation effect.
   c. retroactive interference.
   d. the forgetting curve.

6. Eliza's family loves to tell the story of how she "stole the show" as a 2-year-old, dancing at her aunt's wedding reception. Even though she was so young, Eliza says she can recall the event clearly. How is this possible?

7. We may recognize a face at a social gathering but be unable to remember how we know that person. This is an example of _____ _____.

8. When a situation triggers the feeling that "I've been here before," you are experiencing _____ _____.

9. Children can be accurate eyewitnesses if
   a. interviewers give the children hints about what really happened.
   b. a neutral person asks nonleading questions soon after the event.
   c. the children have a chance to talk with involved adults before the interview.
   d. interviewers use precise technical and medical terms.

10. Psychologists involved in the study of memories of abuse tend to *disagree* with each other about which of the following statements?
    a. Memories of events that happened before age 4 are not reliable.
    b. We tend to repress extremely upsetting memories.
    c. Memories can be emotionally upsetting.
    d. Sexual abuse happens.

Continue testing yourself with 📘 **LearningCurve** or 📖 **Achieve Read & Practice** to learn and remember most effectively.

Thinking, Language, and Intelligence

Thomas Barwick/Getty Images

Throughout history, we humans have both celebrated our wisdom and bemoaned our foolishness. The poet T. S. Eliot was struck by "the hollow men . . . Headpiece filled with straw." But Shakespeare's Hamlet extolled the human species as "noble in reason! . . . infinite in faculties! . . . in apprehension how like a god!" Throughout this text, we likewise marvel at both our abilities and our errors.

We study the human brain—three pounds of wet tissue the size of a small cabbage, yet containing staggeringly complex circuitry. We appreciate the amazing abilities of newborns. We marvel at our visual system, which converts physical stimuli into nerve impulses, distributes them for parallel processing, and reassembles them into colorful perceptions. We ponder our memory's enormous capacity, and the ease with which our two-track mind processes information, with and without our awareness. Little wonder that our species has had the collective genius to invent the camera, the car, and the computer; to unlock the atom and crack the genetic code; to travel out to space and into our brain's depths.

Yet we also see that in some other ways we are less than noble in reason. Our species is kin to the other animals, influenced by the same principles that produce learning in rats and pigeons. We note that we not-so-wise humans are easily deceived by perceptual illusions, pseudopsychic claims, and false memories.

In Modules 25 through 28, we encounter further instances of these two aspects of the human condition—the rational and the irrational. We will consider thinking and how we use—and sometimes ignore or misuse—information about the world around us. We will look at our gift for language and why and how it develops. We will consider a century's research on intelligence—what it is and how (and why) we measure it. And we will reflect on how deserving we are of our species name, *Homo sapiens*—wise human. ▶

MODULE 25 Thinking

CONCEPTS

LEARNING OBJECTIVE QUESTION (LOQ)

25-1 What is *cognition*, and what are the functions of concepts?

Psychologists who study **cognition** focus on the mental activities associated with thinking, knowing, remembering, and communicating information. One of these activities is forming **concepts**—mental groupings of similar objects, events, ideas, or people. The concept *chair* includes many items—a baby's high chair, a reclining chair, a dentist's chair—all for sitting. Concepts simplify our thinking. Imagine life without them. We could not ask a child to "throw the ball" because there would be no concept of *throw* or *ball*. Instead of saying, "They were angry," we would have to describe expressions, intensities, and words. Concepts such as *ball* and *anger* give us much information with little cognitive effort.

We often form our concepts by developing a **prototype**—a mental image or best example of a category (Rosch, 1978). People more quickly agree that "a crow is a bird" than that "a penguin is a bird." For most of us, the crow is the birdier bird; it more closely resembles our *bird* prototype. Similarly, for people in modern multiethnic Germany, Caucasian Germans are more prototypically German (Kessler et al., 2010). When something closely matches our prototype of a concept—such as *bird* or *German*—we more readily recognize it as an example of the concept.

When we categorize people, we mentally shift them toward our category prototypes. Such was the experience of Belgian students who viewed ethnically blended faces. When viewing a blended face in which 70 percent of the features were Caucasian and 30 percent were Asian, the students categorized the face as Caucasian (**FIGURE 25.1**). Later, as their memory shifted toward the Caucasian prototype, they were more likely to remember an 80 percent Caucasian face than the 70 percent Caucasian face they had actually seen (Corneille et al., 2004). Likewise, if shown a 70 percent Asian face, they later remembered a more prototypically Asian face. So, too, with gender: People who viewed 70 percent male faces categorized them as male (no surprise there) and then later misremembered them as even more prototypically male (Huart et al., 2005).

Move away from our prototypes, and category boundaries may blur. Is a tomato a fruit? Is a 16-year-old female a girl or a woman? Is a whale a fish or a mammal? Because a whale fails to match our *mammal* prototype, we are slower to recognize it as a mammal. Similarly, when symptoms don't fit one of our disease prototypes, we are slow to perceive an illness (Bishop, 1991). People whose heart attack symptoms (shortness of breath, exhaustion, a dull

"Attention, everyone! I'd like to introduce the newest member of our family."

FIGURE 25.1

CATEGORIZING FACES INFLUENCES RECOLLECTION Shown a face that was 70 percent Caucasian, people tended to classify the person as Caucasian and to recollect the face as more Caucasian than it was. (Re-creation of experiment courtesy of Olivier Corneille.)

90% CA   80% CA   70% CA   60% CA   50%/50%   60% AS   70% AS   80% AS   90% AS

weight in the chest) don't match their *heart attack* prototype (sharp chest pain) may not seek help. And when behaviors don't fit our *discrimination* prototypes—of White against Black, male against female, young against old—we often fail to notice prejudice. People more easily detect male prejudice against females than female against males or female against females (Cunningham et al., 2009; Inman & Baron, 1996). Although concepts speed and guide our thinking, they don't always make us wise.

PROBLEM SOLVING: STRATEGIES AND OBSTACLES

LOQ 25-2 What cognitive strategies assist our problem solving, and what obstacles hinder it?

One tribute to our rationality is our problem-solving skill. What's the best route around this traffic jam? How should we handle a friend's criticism? How, without our keys, can we get in the house?

Some problems we solve through *trial and error.* Thomas Edison tried thousands of light bulb filaments before stumbling upon one that worked. For other problems, we use **algorithms,** step-by-step procedures that guarantee a solution. But step-by-step algorithms can be laborious and exasperating. To find a word using the 10 letters in *SPLOYOCHYG,* for example, you could try each letter in each of the 10 positions—907,200 permutations in all. Rather than give you a computing brain the size of a beach ball, nature resorts to **heuristics,** simpler thinking strategies. Thus, you might reduce the number of options in the *SPLOYOCHYG* example by grouping letters that often appear together (*CH* and *GY*) and excluding rare letter combinations (such as YY). By using heuristics and then applying trial and error, you may hit on the answer. Have you guessed it?[1]

Sometimes we puzzle over a problem and the pieces suddenly fall together in a flash of **insight**—an abrupt, true-seeming, and often satisfying solution (Topolinski & Reber, 2010). Ten-year-old Johnny Appleton had one of these Aha! moments and solved a problem that had stumped construction workers: how to rescue a young robin from a narrow 30-inch-deep hole in a cement-block wall. Johnny's solution: Slowly pour in sand, giving the bird enough time to keep its feet on top of the constantly rising pile (Ruchlis, 1990).

Brain scans (EEGs or fMRIs) show bursts of activity associated with sudden flashes of insight (Kounios & Beeman, 2014). In one study, researchers asked people to think of a word that forms a compound word or phrase with each of three other words in a set (such as *pine, crab,* and *sauce*) and to press a button to sound a bell when they knew the answer. (Need a hint? The word is a fruit.[2]) A sudden Aha! insight led to about half the solutions. Before the Aha! moment, the problem solvers' frontal lobes (involved in focusing attention) were active. At the instant of discovery, there was a burst of activity in the right temporal lobe, just above the ear (**FIGURE 25.2**).

Insight strikes suddenly, with no prior sense of "getting warmer" or feeling close to a solution (Knoblich & Oellinger, 2006; Metcalfe, 1986). When the answer pops into mind (*apple!*), we feel a happy sense of satisfaction. The joy of a joke may similarly lie in our sudden comprehension of an unexpected ending or a double meaning: "You don't need a parachute to skydive. You only need a parachute to skydive twice." Groucho Marx was a master at this: "I once shot an elephant in my pajamas. How he got in my pajamas I'll never know."

Insightful as we are, other cognitive tendencies may lead us astray. **Confirmation bias,** for example, leads us to seek evidence *for* our ideas more

cognition all the mental activities associated with thinking, knowing, remembering, and communicating.

concept a mental grouping of similar objects, events, ideas, or people.

prototype a mental image or best example of a category. Matching new items to a prototype provides a quick and easy method for sorting items into categories (as when comparing feathered creatures to a prototypical bird, such as a crow).

algorithm a methodical, logical rule or procedure that guarantees solving a particular problem. Contrasts with the usually speedier—but also more error-prone—use of *heuristics.*

heuristic a simple thinking strategy that often allows us to make judgments and solve problems efficiently; usually speedier but also more error-prone than an *algorithm.*

insight a sudden realization of a problem's solution; contrasts with strategy-based solutions.

confirmation bias a tendency to search for information that supports our preconceptions and to ignore or distort contradictory evidence.

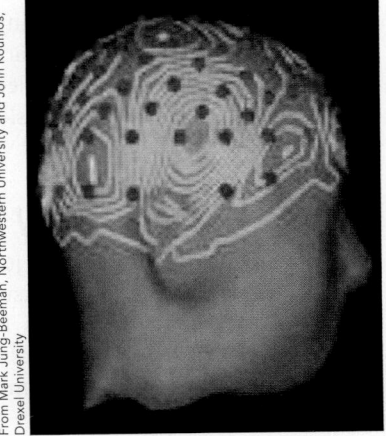

From Mark Jung-Beeman, Northwestern University and John Kounios, Drexel University

FIGURE 25.2

THE AHA! MOMENT A burst of right temporal lobe activity accompanied insight solutions to word problems (Jung-Beeman et al., 2004). The red dots designate EEG electrodes. The light gray lines show the distribution of high-frequency activity accompanying insight. The insight-related activity is centered in the right temporal lobe (yellow area).

---

1. Answer to SPLOYOCHYG anagram: PSYCHOLOGY.

2. The word is *apple*: pineapple, crabapple, applesauce.

"The human understanding, when any proposition has been once laid down . . . forces everything else to add fresh support and confirmation." —Francis Bacon, *Novum Organum*, 1620

eagerly than *against* them (Klayman & Ha, 1987; Skov & Sherman, 1986). In a now-classic experiment, Peter Wason (1960) gave British university students a set of three numbers (*2-4-6*) and told them the series was based on a rule. Their task was to guess the rule. (It was simple: any three ascending numbers.) Before submitting answers, students generated their own three-number sets, and Wason told them whether their sets conformed to his rule. Once *certain* they had the rule, they could announce it. The result? Most students formed a wrong idea (*"Maybe it's counting by twos"*) and then searched only for confirming evidence (by testing *6-8-10, 100-102-104,* and so forth). Seldom right but never in doubt.

"Ordinary people," said Wason (1981), "evade facts, become inconsistent, or systematically defend themselves against the threat of new information relevant to the issue." Thus, having formed a belief—that vaccines cause (or do not cause) autism spectrum disorder, that people can (or cannot) change their sexual orientation, that gun control fails (or does not fail) to save lives—we prefer information that supports our belief. And once we get hung up on an incorrect view of a problem, it's hard to approach it from a different angle. This obstacle to problem solving is called **fixation,** an inability to come to a fresh perspective. See if fixation prevents you from solving the matchstick problem in **FIGURE 25.3.** (For the solution, see **FIGURE 25.4.**)

A prime example of fixation is **mental set,** our tendency to approach a problem with the mindset of what has worked for us previously. Indeed, solutions that worked in the past often do work on new problems. Consider:

Given the sequence *O-T-T-F-?-?-?,* what are the final three letters?

Most people have difficulty recognizing that the three final letters are *F*(ive), *S*(ix), and *S*(even). But solving this problem may make the next one easier:

Given the sequence *J-F-M-A-?-?-?,* what are the final three letters? (If you don't get this one, ask yourself what month it is.)

As a *perceptual set* predisposes what we perceive, a mental set predisposes how we think. Sometimes this can be an obstacle to problem solving, as when our mental set from our past experiences with matchsticks predisposes us to arrange them in two dimensions.

FORMING GOOD (AND BAD) DECISIONS AND JUDGMENTS

LOQ 25-3 What is *intuition,* and how can the representativeness and availability heuristics influence our decisions and judgments?

When making each day's hundreds of judgments and decisions (*Should I take a jacket? Can I trust this person? Should I shoot the basketball or pass to the player who's hot?*), we seldom take the time and effort to reason systematically. We just follow our **intuition,** our fast, automatic, unreasoned feelings and thoughts. After interviewing policy makers in government, business, and education, social psychologist Irving Janis (1986) concluded that they "often do not use a reflective problem-solving approach. How do they usually arrive at their decisions? If you ask, they are likely to tell you . . . they do it mostly *by the seat of their pants.*"

Two Quick But Risky Shortcuts

When we need to make snap judgments, heuristics enable quick thinking without conscious awareness, and they usually serve us well (Gigerenzer, 2015). But as research by cognitive psychologists Amos Tversky and Daniel Kahneman (1974) on the *representativeness* and *availability heuristics* has shown, these intuitive mental shortcuts can lead even the smartest people into dumb decisions.[3]

"The heart has its reasons which reason does not know." —Blaise Pascal, *Pensées*, 1670

FIGURE 25.3

THE MATCHSTICK PROBLEM How would you arrange six matches to form four equilateral triangles?

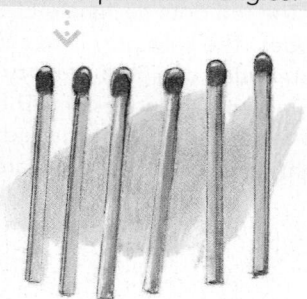

---

3. Tversky and Kahneman's joint work on decision making received a 2002 Nobel Prize; sadly, only Kahneman was alive to receive the honor. As Kahneman wrote in a vignette for my [DM's] *Social Psychology* text, "Amos and I shared the wonder of together owning a goose that could lay golden eggs—a joint mind that was better than our separate minds."

Carsten Rehder/KIEL/European Pressphoto Agency/Newscom

"In creating these problems, we didn't set out to fool people. All our problems fooled us, too." —Amos Tversky (1985)

"Intuitive thinking [is] fine most of the time. . . . But sometimes that habit of mind gets us in trouble." —Daniel Kahneman (2005b)

fixation in cognition, the inability to see a problem from a new perspective; an obstacle to problem solving.

mental set a tendency to approach a problem in one particular way, often a way that has been successful in the past.

intuition an effortless, immediate, automatic feeling or thought, as contrasted with explicit, conscious reasoning.

representativeness heuristic estimating the likelihood of events in terms of how well they seem to represent, or match, particular prototypes; may lead us to ignore other relevant information.

availability heuristic estimating the likelihood of events based on their availability in memory; if instances come readily to mind (perhaps because of their vividness), we presume such events are common.

THE REPRESENTATIVENESS HEURISTIC To judge the likelihood of something by intuitively comparing it to particular prototypes is to use the **representativeness heuristic**. Imagine someone who is short, slim, and likes to read poetry. Is this person more likely to be an Ivy League university English professor or a truck driver (Nisbett & Ross, 1980)?

Many people guess English professor—because the person better fits their prototype of nerdy professor than of truck driver. In doing so, they fail to consider the base rate number of Ivy League English professors (fewer than 400) and truck drivers (3.5 million in the United States alone). Thus, even if the description is 50 times more typical of English professors than of truck drivers, the fact that there are about 7000 times more truck drivers means that the poetry reader is many times more likely to be a truck driver.

Some prototypes have social consequences. Consider the reaction of some non-Arab travelers soon after 9/11, when a young male of Arab descent boarded their plane. The young man fit (represented) their "terrorist" prototype, and the representativeness heuristic kicked in. His presence evoked anxiety among his fellow passengers—even though nearly 100 percent of those who fit this prototype are peace-loving citizens.

Or consider the questions one mother of two Black and three White teens asked other parents, "Do store personnel follow your children when they are picking out their Gatorade flavors? They didn't follow my White kids. . . . When your kids trick-or-treat dressed as a ninja and a clown, do they get asked who they are with and where they live, door after door? My White kids didn't get asked. Do your kids get pulled out of the TSA line time and again for additional screening? My White kids didn't" (Roper, 2016). If people have a prototype—a stereotype—of delinquent Black teens, they may unconsciously use the representativeness heuristic when judging individuals. The result, even if unintended, is racism.

THE AVAILABILITY HEURISTIC The **availability heuristic** operates when we estimate the commonality of an event *based on its mental availability*. Anything that makes information pop into mind—its vividness, recency, or distinctiveness—can make it seem commonplace. Casinos entice us to gamble by broadcasting wins with noisy bells and flashing lights. The big losses are soundlessly invisible.

The availability heuristic can also distort our judgments of risks. Dramatic air crashes or horrific terrorist attacks capture attention and strike unwarranted fears. If people from a particular ethnic or religious group commit a terrorist act, as seen in pictures of innocent people about to be beheaded, our readily available memory of the dramatic event may shape our impression of the whole group. Terrorists aim to evoke excessive terror. If terrorists were to kill 1000 people in the United States this year, Americans would be

"Kahneman and his colleagues and students have changed the way we think about the way people think." —American Psychological Association President Sharon Brehm, 2007

AVAILABILITY HEURISTIC With scenes from terrorist attacks flooding people's minds, 27 percent of Americans recently identified terrorism as their biggest worry—up from 8 percent just before the 2015 Paris attacks—and 38 percent said terrorist threats made them less likely to attend large events (Reinhart, 2017; Reuters, 2015). This hijacking of our rationality by fears of terrorist guns and trucks (when other risks, such as driving or influenza, kill so many more) illustrates how we often fear the wrong things.

CHRISTOPHE PETIT TESSON/European Pressphoto Agency/Newscom

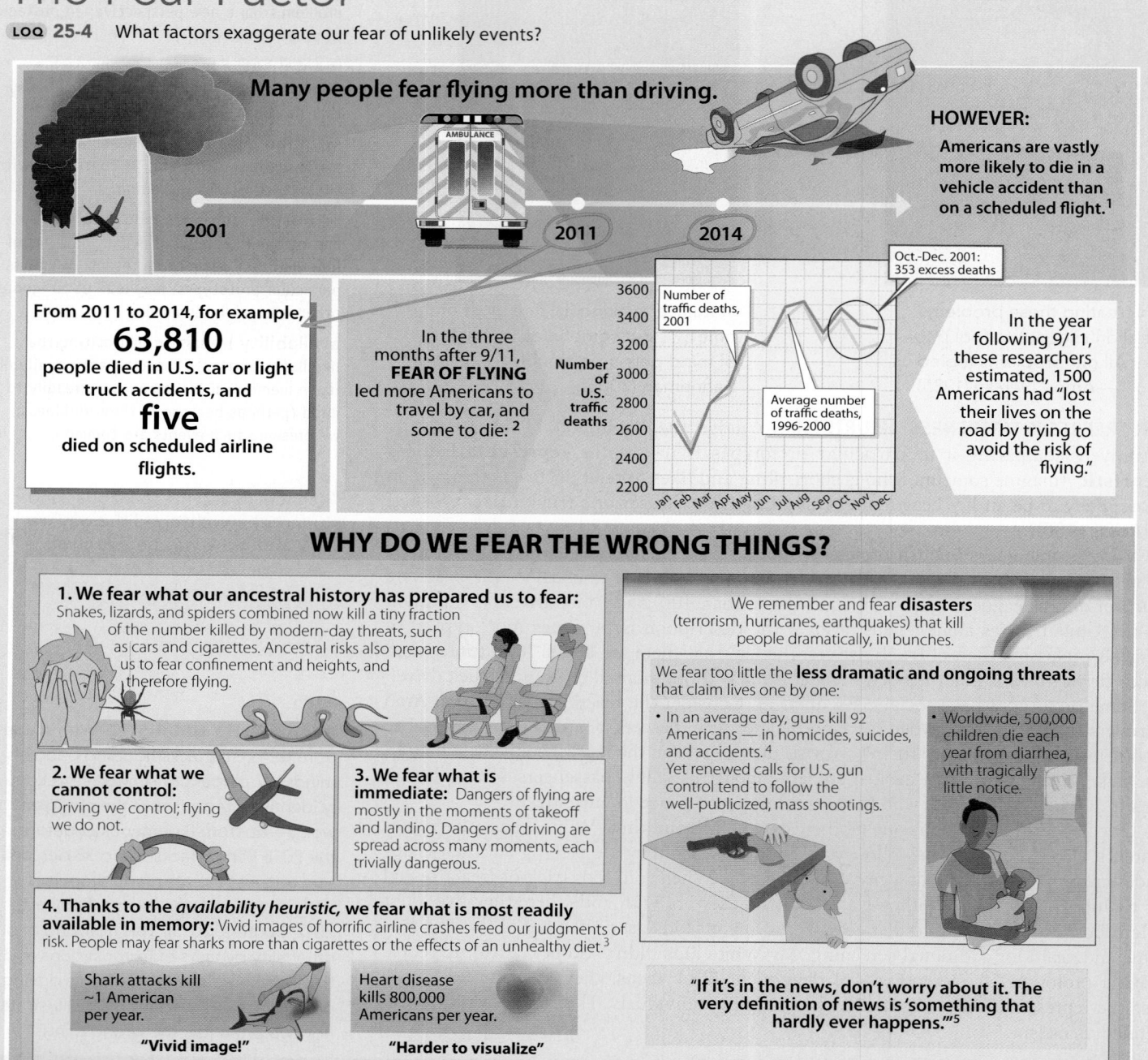

THINKING CRITICALLY ABOUT:
The Fear Factor

LOQ 25-4 What factors exaggerate our fear of unlikely events?

Many people fear flying more than driving.

2001   2011   2014

HOWEVER: Americans are vastly more likely to die in a vehicle accident than on a scheduled flight.[1]

From 2011 to 2014, for example, **63,810** people died in U.S. car or light truck accidents, and **five** died on scheduled airline flights.

In the three months after 9/11, **FEAR OF FLYING** led more Americans to travel by car, and some to die:[2]

Number of U.S. traffic deaths (graph): Number of traffic deaths, 2001; Average number of traffic deaths, 1996-2000; Oct.-Dec. 2001: 353 excess deaths. (Jan–Dec, 2200–3600)

In the year following 9/11, these researchers estimated, 1500 Americans had "lost their lives on the road by trying to avoid the risk of flying."

WHY DO WE FEAR THE WRONG THINGS?

1. We fear what our ancestral history has prepared us to fear: Snakes, lizards, and spiders combined now kill a tiny fraction of the number killed by modern-day threats, such as cars and cigarettes. Ancestral risks also prepare us to fear confinement and heights, and therefore flying.

2. We fear what we cannot control: Driving we control; flying we do not.

3. We fear what is immediate: Dangers of flying are mostly in the moments of takeoff and landing. Dangers of driving are spread across many moments, each trivially dangerous.

4. Thanks to the *availability heuristic*, we fear what is most readily available in memory: Vivid images of horrific airline crashes feed our judgments of risk. People may fear sharks more than cigarettes or the effects of an unhealthy diet.[3]

Shark attacks kill ~1 American per year. "Vivid image!"

Heart disease kills 800,000 Americans per year. "Harder to visualize"

We remember and fear **disasters** (terrorism, hurricanes, earthquakes) that kill people dramatically, in bunches.

We fear too little the **less dramatic and ongoing threats** that claim lives one by one:

- In an average day, guns kill 92 Americans — in homicides, suicides, and accidents.[4] Yet renewed calls for U.S. gun control tend to follow the well-publicized, mass shootings.
- Worldwide, 500,000 children die each year from diarrhea, with tragically little notice.

"If it's in the news, don't worry about it. The very definition of news is 'something that hardly ever happens.'"[5]

1. National Safety Council, 2017. 2. Gaissmater & Gigerenzer, 2012; Gigerenzer, 2004, 2006. 3. Daley, 2011. 4. Xu et al., 2016. 5. Schneier, 2007.

mighty afraid. Yet they would have reason to be 30 times more afraid of homicidal, suicidal, and accidental death by guns, which take more than 30,000 lives annually. In 2015 and again in 2016, feared foreign terrorists shot and killed fewer Americans than did armed toddlers (Ingraham, 2016; LaCapria, 2015). The bottom line: *We often fear the wrong things.* (See Thinking Critically About: The Fear Factor.)

"Don't believe everything you think."
—Bumper sticker

🔒 RETRIEVE IT • • •

ANSWERS IN APPENDIX E

RI-1 Why can news be described as "something that hardly ever happens"? How does knowing this help us assess our fears?

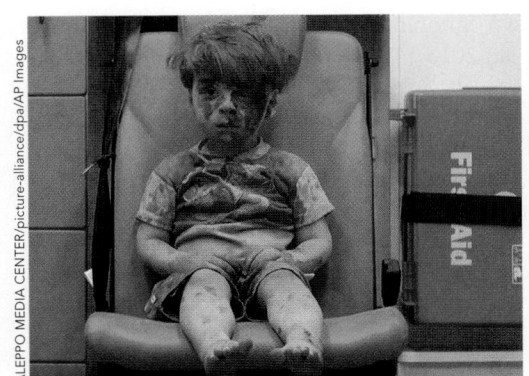

THE POWER OF A VIVID EXAMPLE
The unforgettable (cognitively available) photo of 5-year-old Omran Daqneesh—dazed after being pulled from the rubble of yet another air strike in Aleppo, Syria—did more than an armload of statistics to awaken Western nations to the plight of Syrian migrants fleeing violence.

overconfidence the tendency to be more confident than correct—to overestimate the accuracy of our beliefs and judgments.

 ASK YOURSELF

What do you fear? Are some of those fears out of proportion to statistical risk? Are there other areas of your life where you need to take more precautions?

To offer a vivid depiction of climate change, Cal Tech scientists created an interactive map of global temperatures over the past 120 years. (See tinyurl.com/TempChange.)

Meanwhile, the lack of available images of future climate change disasters—which some scientists regard as "Armageddon in slow motion"—has left most people unconcerned (Pew, 2014a). What's more cognitively available than slow climate change is our recently experienced local weather, which tells us nothing about long-term planetary trends (Egan & Mullin, 2012; Kaufmann et al., 2017; Zaval et al., 2014). Unusually hot local weather increases people's worry about global climate warming, while a recent cold day reduces their concern and overwhelms less memorable scientific data (Li et al., 2011). As Stephen Colbert (November 18, 2014) tweeted, "Global warming isn't real because it was cold today! Also great news: World hunger is over because I just ate."

Over 40 nations have sought to harness the positive power of vivid, memorable images by putting eye-catching warnings and graphic photos on cigarette packages (Riordan, 2013). This campaign has worked because we reason emotionally (Huang et al., 2013). We overfeel and underthink (Slovic, 2007). In one study, Red Cross donations to Syrian refugees were 55 times greater in response to the publication of an iconic photo of a child killed, than in response to statistics describing the hundreds of thousands of other refugee deaths (Slovic et al., 2017). Dramatic outcomes make us gasp; probabilities we hardly grasp.

Overconfidence

LOQ 25-5 How are our decisions and judgments affected by overconfidence, belief perseverance, and framing?

Sometimes our judgments and decisions go awry simply because we are more confident than correct. Across various tasks, people overestimate their performance (Metcalfe, 1998). If 60 percent of people correctly answer a factual question, such as "Is absinthe a liqueur or a precious stone?" they will typically average 75 percent confidence (Fischhoff et al., 1977). (It's a licorice-flavored liqueur.) This tendency to overestimate the accuracy of our knowledge and judgments is **overconfidence.**

It is overconfidence that drives stockbrokers and investment managers to market their ability to outperform stock market averages—which, as a group, they cannot (Malkiel, 2016). A purchase of stock X, recommended by a broker who judges this to be the time to buy, is usually balanced by a sale made by someone who judges this to be the time to sell. Despite their confidence, buyer and seller cannot both be right. And it is overconfidence that so often leads us to succumb to a *planning fallacy*—overestimating our future leisure time and income (Zauberman & Lynch, 2005). Students and others often expect to finish assignments ahead of schedule (Buehler et al., 1994, 2002). In fact, such projects generally take about twice the predicted time. Anticipating how much more time we will have next month, we happily accept invitations. And believing we'll surely have more money next year, we take out loans or buy on credit.

Overconfidence—the bias that Kahneman (2015), if given a magic wand, would most like to eliminate—can also feed extreme political views. One research team tested 743 intelligence analysts' ability to predict future events—predictions that typically are overconfident. Those whose predictions most often failed tended to be inflexible and closed-minded (Mellers et al., 2015). Ordinary citizens with a shallow understanding of complex proposals, such as cap-and-trade or a flat tax, may also express strong views. Sometimes the less we know, the more definite we sound. Asking such people to explain the details

FIGURE 25.4

SOLUTION TO THE MATCHSTICK PROBLEM To solve this problem, you must view it from a new perspective, breaking the fixation of limiting solutions to two dimensions.

Hofstadter's Law: It always takes longer than you expect, even when you take into account Hofstadter's Law.
—Douglas Hofstadter, *Gödel, Escher, Bach: The Eternal Golden Braid*, 1979

of these policies exposes them to their own ignorance, which in turn leads them to express more moderate views (Fernbach et al., 2013). To confront one's own ignorance is to become wiser.

Nevertheless, overconfidence can have adaptive value. Believing that their decisions are right and they have time to spare, self-confident people tend to live more happily. They make tough decisions more easily, and they seem competent (Anderson et al., 2012). Given prompt and clear feedback, we can also learn to be more realistic about the accuracy of our judgments (Fischhoff, 1982). That's true of weather forecasters: Extensive feedback has enabled them to estimate their forecast accuracy ("a 60 percent chance of rain"). The wisdom to know when we know a thing and when we do not is born of experience.

Belief Perseverance

Our overconfidence is startling. Equally so is our **belief perseverance**—our tendency to cling to our beliefs in the face of contrary evidence. A classic study of belief perseverance engaged people with opposing views of capital punishment (Lord et al., 1979). After studying two supposedly new research findings, one supporting and the other refuting the claim that the death penalty deters crime, each side was more impressed by the study supporting its own beliefs. And each readily disputed the other study. Thus, showing the pro- and anti-capital-punishment groups the *same* mixed evidence actually *increased* their disagreement. Rather than using evidence to draw conclusions, they used their conclusions to assess evidence—a phenomenon also known as *motivated reasoning.* In other studies and in everyday life, people have similarly welcomed belief-supporting evidence—about climate change, same-sex marriage, or politics—while discounting challenging evidence (Friesen et al., 2015; Sunstein et al., 2016). Often, prejudice persists. Beliefs persevere.

To rein in belief perseverance, a simple remedy exists: *Consider the opposite.* When the same researchers repeated the capital-punishment study, they asked some participants to be "as *objective* and *unbiased* as possible" (Lord et al., 1984). The plea did nothing to reduce biased evaluations of evidence. They also asked another group to consider "whether you would have made the same high or low evaluations had exactly the same study produced results on the *other* side of the issue." Having imagined and pondered *opposite* findings, these people became much less biased.

Once beliefs form and get justified, it takes more compelling evidence to change them than it did to create them. Having explained to ourselves why candidate X or Y will be a better commander-in-chief, we then tend to ignore evidence undermining our belief. As an old Chinese proverb says, "Two-thirds of what we see is behind our eyes."

The Effects of Framing

Framing—the way we present an issue—can be a powerful tool of persuasion, as psychologists and economists have together learned. As a young scholar, behavioral economist Richard Thaler worked closely with cognitive psychologists Amos Tversky and Daniel Kahneman at Stanford University. Thaler and others have shown how the framing of options can influence—or as they say—**nudge** people toward beneficial decisions (Bohannon, 2016; Benartzi et al., 2017; Thaler & Sunstein, 2008).

- *Saving for retirement.* U.S. companies once required employees who wanted to contribute to a retirement plan to choose a lower take-home pay, which few people did. Thanks to a new law, they can now automatically enroll their employees in the plan but allow them to opt out. Either way, the decision to contribute is the employee's. But under the new "opt-out" arrangement, enrollments in one analysis of 3.4 million workers soared from 59 to 86 percent (Rosenberg, 2010). Britain's 2012 change to an opt-out framing similarly led to 5 million more retirement savers (Halpern, 2015).

- *Choosing to live or die.* Imagine two surgeons explaining the risk of an upcoming surgery. One explains that during this type of surgery, 10 percent of people die. The other explains that 90 percent survive. The information is the same. The effect

PREDICT YOUR OWN BEHAVIOR
When will you finish reading this module?

belief perseverance clinging to one's initial conceptions after the basis on which they were formed has been discredited.

framing the way an issue is posed; how an issue is worded can significantly affect decisions and judgments.

nudge a framing of choices by which governments and companies can, without coercion or altered incentives, encourage people to make choices that support their health, retirement savings, and well-being.

is not. In real-life surveys, patients and physicians overwhelmingly say the risk is greater when they hear that 10 percent *die* (Marteau, 1989; McNeil et al., 1988; Rothman & Salovey, 1997).

- **Becoming an organ donor.** In many European countries as well as in the United States, people renewing their driver's license can decide whether to be organ donors. In some countries, the default option is *Yes,* but people can opt out. Nearly 100 percent of the people in opt-out countries have agreed to be donors. In countries where the default option is *No,* most do *not* agree to be donors (Hajhosseini et al., 2013; Johnson & Goldstein, 2003).

The point to remember: Framing can nudge our attitudes and decisions.

The Perils and Powers of Intuition

LOQ 25-6 How do smart thinkers use intuition?

"The problem is I can't tell the difference between a deeply wise, intuitive nudge from the Universe and one of my own bone-headed ideas!"

The perils of intuition can persist even when people are offered extra pay for thinking smart, even when they are asked to justify their answers, and even among expert physicians, clinicians, and U.S. federal intelligence agents (Reyna et al., 2014; Shafir & LeBoeuf, 2002; Stanovich et al., 2013). Very smart people can make not-so-smart judgments.

So, are our heads indeed "filled with straw," as T. S. Eliot suggested? Good news: Cognitive scientists are also revealing intuition's powers:

Throughout this book you will see examples of smart intuition. In brief,

- **Intuition is recognition born of experience.** It is implicit (unconscious) knowledge— what we've recorded in our brains but can't fully explain (Chassy & Gobet, 2011; Gore & Sadler-Smith, 2011). We see this ability to size up a situation and react in an eyeblink in chess masters playing speed chess, as they intuitively know the right move (Burns, 2004). We see it in the smart and quick judgments of experienced nurses, firefighters, art critics, and car mechanics. We see it in skilled athletes who react *without thinking.* Indeed, conscious thinking may disrupt well-practiced movements, leading skilled athletes to choke under pressure, as when shooting free throws (Beilock, 2010). And we would see this instant intuition in you, too, for anything in which you have developed knowledge based on experience.

- **Intuition is usually adaptive, enabling quick reactions.** Our fast and frugal heuristics let us intuitively assume that fuzzy-looking objects are far away—which they usually are, except on foggy mornings. Our learned associations surface as gut feelings, right or wrong. Seeing a stranger who looks like someone who has harmed or threatened us in the past, we may automatically react with distrust. Newlyweds' implicit attitudes toward their new spouses likewise predict their future marital happiness (McNulty et al., 2013).

- **Intuition is huge.** Unconscious, automatic influences are constantly affecting our judgments (Custers & Aarts, 2010). Consider: Most people guess that the more complex the choice, the smarter it is to make decisions rationally rather than intuitively (Inbar et al., 2010). Actually, in making complex decisions, we sometimes benefit by letting our brain work on a problem without consciously thinking about it (Strick et al., 2010, 2011). In one series of experiments, three groups of people read complex information (for example, about apartments or soccer matches). Those in the first group stated their preference immediately after reading information about four possible options. The second group, given several minutes to analyze the information, made slightly smarter decisions. But wisest of all, in several studies, were those in the third group, whose attention was distracted for a time, enabling their minds to engage in automatic, unconscious processing of the complex information. The practical lesson: Letting a problem incubate while we attend to other things can pay dividends (Dijksterhuis & Strick, 2016). Facing a difficult decision involving lots of facts, we're wise to gather all the information we can, and then say, "Give me some time *not* to think about this, even to sleep on it." Thanks to our ever-active brain, nonconscious thinking (reasoning, problem solving, decision making, planning) can be surprisingly astute (Creswell et al., 2013; Hassin, 2013; Lin & Murray, 2015).

Critics note that some studies have not found the supposed power of unconscious thought, and they remind us that deliberate, conscious thought also furthers smart thinking (Newell, 2015; Nieuwenstein et al., 2015; Phillips et al., 2016). In challenging situations, superior decision makers, including chess players, take time to think (Moxley et al., 2012). And with many sorts of problems, deliberative thinkers are aware of the intuitive option, but know when to override it (Mata et al., 2013).

 Consider:

1. A bat and a ball together cost 110 cents. The bat costs 100 cents more than the ball. How much does the ball cost?

2. Emily's father has three daughters. The first two are named April and May. What is the third daughter's name?

Most people's intuitive responses—10 cents and June—are wrong, and a few moments of deliberate thinking reveals why.[4]

The bottom line: Our two-track mind makes sweet harmony as smart, critical thinking listens to the creative whispers of our vast unseen mind and then evaluates evidence, tests conclusions, and plans for the future.

THINKING CREATIVELY

LOQ 25-7 What is *creativity*, and what fosters it?

Creativity is the ability to produce ideas that are both novel and valuable (Hennessey & Amabile, 2010). Consider Princeton mathematician Andrew Wiles' incredible, creative moment. Pierre de Fermat, a seventeenth-century mischievous genius, had challenged mathematicians of his day to match his solutions to various number theory problems. His most famous challenge—*Fermat's last theorem*—baffled the greatest mathematical minds, even after a $2 million prize (in today's dollars) was offered in 1908 to whoever first created a proof.

Wiles had pondered Fermat's theorem for more than 30 years and had come to the brink of a solution. One morning, out of the blue, the final "incredible revelation" struck him. "It was so indescribably beautiful; it was so simple and so elegant. I couldn't understand how I'd missed it. . . . It was the most important moment of my working life" (Singh, 1997, p. 25).

Creativity like Wiles' is supported by a certain level of *aptitude* (ability to learn). Those who score exceptionally high in quantitative aptitude as 13-year-olds, for example, are later more likely to create published or patented work (Park et al., 2008; Robertson et al., 2010). Yet there is more to creativity than aptitude, or what intelligence tests reveal. Indeed, brain activity associated with intelligence differs from that associated with creativity (Jung & Haier, 2013; Shen et al., 2017) Aptitude tests (such as the SAT) require **convergent thinking**—an ability to provide a single correct answer.

Creativity tests (*How many uses can you think of for a brick?*) require expansive, **divergent thinking**—the ability to consider many different options and to think in novel ways. Injury to certain areas of the frontal lobes can leave reading, writing, and arithmetic skills intact but destroy imagination (Kolb & Whishaw, 2006).

Robert Sternberg and his colleagues believe creativity has five components (Sternberg, 1988, 2003; Sternberg & Lubart, 1991, 1992):

1. *Expertise*—well-developed knowledge—furnishes the ideas, images, and phrases we use as mental building blocks. "Chance favors only the prepared mind," observed Louis Pasteur. The more blocks we have, the more chances we have to combine them in novel ways. Wiles' well-developed knowledge put the needed theorems and methods at his disposal.

CREATIVE WOMEN Researcher Sally Reis (2001) found that notably creative women, such as Nobel laureate geneticist Barbara McClintock, were typically "intelligent, hard working, imaginative, and strong willed" as girls. In her acceptance speech for the 2013 Nobel Prize for Literature, author Alice Munro, shown here, described story writing creativity as hard work: "The part that's hardest is when you go over the story and realize how bad it is. You know, the first part, excitement, the second, pretty good, but then you pick it up one morning and you think, 'what nonsense,' and that is when you really have to get to work."

PETER MUHLY/Getty Images

4. The first answer is 5 cents. The bat would then cost $1.05, for a $1.10 total. If the ball cost the intuitive answer of 10 cents, the bat would then have to cost $1.10 (for a bat-and-ball total of $1.20, not $1.10). The second answer is Emily. If you answered incorrectly, don't feel bad—so do many other people (Frederick, 2005; Thomson & Oppenheimer, 2016).

2. **Imaginative thinking skills** provide the ability to see things in novel ways, to recognize patterns, and to make connections. Having mastered a problem's basic elements, we can redefine or explore it in a new way. Wiles' imaginative solution combined two partial solutions.

3. **A venturesome personality** seeks new experiences, tolerates ambiguity and risk, and perseveres in overcoming obstacles. Wiles said he labored in near-isolation from the mathematics community partly to stay focused and avoid distraction. Such determination is an enduring trait.

4. **Intrinsic motivation** is the quality of being driven more by interest, satisfaction, and challenge than by external pressures (Amabile & Hennessey, 1992). Creative people focus less on extrinsic motivators—meeting deadlines, impressing people, or making money—than on the pleasure and stimulation of the work itself. As Wiles noted, "I was so obsessed by this problem that . . . I was thinking about it all the time—[from] when I woke up in the morning to when I went to sleep at night" (Singh & Riber, 1997).

5. **A creative environment** sparks, supports, and refines creative ideas. Wiles stood on the shoulders of others and collaborated with a former student. A study of the careers of 2026 prominent scientists and inventors revealed that the most eminent were mentored, challenged, and supported by their colleagues (Simonton, 1992). Creativity-fostering environments support innovation, team building, and communication (Hülsheger et al., 2009). They also minimize anxiety and foster contemplation (Byron & Khazanchi, 2011). While on a retreat in a monastery, Jonas Salk solved a problem that led to the polio vaccine. Later, when he designed the Salk Institute, he provided contemplative spaces where scientists could work without interruption (Sternberg, 2006).

ENGAGE For those seeking to boost the creative process, research offers some ideas:

- **Develop your expertise.** Ask yourself what you care about and most enjoy. Follow your passion by broadening your knowledge base and becoming an expert at something.

- **Allow time for incubation.** Think hard on a problem, but then set it aside and come back to it later. For those with enough knowledge—the needed mental building blocks—a period of inattention to a problem ("sleeping on it") allows for automatic processing to form associations (Zhong et al., 2008).

- **Set aside time for the mind to roam freely.** Creativity springs from "defocused attention" (Simonton, 2012a,b). So detach from attention-grabbing television, social networking, and video gaming. Jog, go for a long walk, or meditate. Serenity seeds spontaneity.

- **Experience other cultures and ways of thinking.** Living abroad sometimes sets the creative juices flowing. Controlled studies show that students who have spent time abroad and embraced their host culture are more adept at working out creative solutions to problems (Lee et al., 2012; Tadmor et al., 2012). Even getting out of your neighborhood and exposing yourself to multicultural experiences fosters flexible thinking (Kim et al., 2013; Ritter et al., 2012).

For a summary of some key ideas from this section, see **TABLE 25.1**.

IMAGINATIVE THINKING Cartoonists often display creativity as they see things in new ways or make unusual connections.

creativity the ability to produce new and valuable ideas.

convergent thinking narrowing the available problem solutions to determine the single best solution.

divergent thinking expanding the number of possible problem solutions; creative thinking that diverges in different directions.

A CREATIVE ENVIRONMENT

"For the love of God, is there a doctor in the house?"

🔒 TABLE 25.1

Comparing Cognitive Processes and Strategies

Process or Strategy	Description	Powers	Perils
Algorithm	Methodical rule or procedure	Guarantees solution	Requires time and effort
Heuristic	Simple thinking shortcut, such as the availability heuristic (which estimates likelihood based on how easily events come to mind)	Lets us act quickly and efficiently	Puts us at risk for errors
Insight	Sudden Aha! reaction	Provides instant realization of solution	May not happen
Confirmation bias	Tendency to search for support for our own views and ignore contradictory evidence	Lets us quickly recognize supporting evidence	Hinders recognition of contradictory evidence
Fixation	Inability to view problems from a new angle	Focuses thinking	Hinders creative problem solving
Intuition	Fast, automatic feelings and thoughts	Is based on our experience; huge and adaptive	Can lead us to overfeel and underthink
Overconfidence	Overestimating the accuracy of our beliefs and judgments	Allows us to be happy and to make decisions easily	Puts us at risk for errors
Belief perseverance	Ignoring evidence that proves our beliefs are wrong	Supports our enduring beliefs	Closes our mind to new ideas
Framing	Wording a question or statement so that it evokes a desired response	Can influence others' decisions	Can produce a misleading result
Creativity	Ability to innovate valuable ideas	Produces new insights and products	May distract from structured, routine work

🔒 RETRIEVE IT • • •

ANSWERS IN APPENDIX E

RI-2 Match the process or strategy listed below (I–X) with the description (a–j).

I. Algorithm

II. Intuition

III. Insight

IV. Heuristic

V. Fixation

VI. Confirmation bias

VII. Overconfidence

VIII. Creativity

IX. Framing

X. Belief perseverance

a. Inability to view problems from a new angle; focuses thinking but hinders creative problem solving

b. Methodological rule or procedure that guarantees a solution but requires time and effort

c. Your fast, automatic, effortless feelings and thoughts based on your experience; huge and adaptive but can lead you to overfeel and underthink

d. Simple thinking shortcut that enables quick and efficient decisions but puts us at risk for errors

e. Sudden Aha! reaction that instantly reveals the solution

f. Tendency to search for support for your own views and to ignore contradictory evidence

g. Holding on to your beliefs even after they are proven wrong; closing your mind to new ideas

h. Overestimating the accuracy of your beliefs and judgments; allows you to be happier and to make decisions more easily, but puts you at risk for errors

i. Wording a question or statement so that it evokes a desired response; can mislead people and influence their decisions

j. The ability to produce novel and valuable ideas

DO OTHER SPECIES SHARE OUR COGNITIVE SKILLS?

LOQ 25-8   What do we know about thinking in other species?

Other animals are surprisingly smart (de Waal, 2016). In her 1908 book, *The Animal Mind*, pioneering psychologist Margaret Floy Washburn argued that animal consciousness and intelligence can be inferred from their behavior. In 2012, neuroscientists convening at the University of Cambridge added that animal consciousness can also be inferred from their brains: "Nonhuman animals, including all mammals and birds," possess the *neural networks* "that generate consciousness" (Low et al., 2012). Consider, then, what animal brains can do.

USING CONCEPTS AND NUMBERS By touching screens in quest of a food reward, black bears have learned to sort pictures into animal and nonanimal categories, or concepts (Vonk et al., 2012). The great apes—a group that includes chimpanzees and gorillas—also form concepts, such as *cat* and *dog*. After monkeys have learned these concepts, certain frontal lobe neurons in their brain fire in response to new "cat-like" images, others to new "dog-like" images (Freedman et al., 2001). Even pigeons—mere bird-brains—can sort objects (pictures of cars, cats, chairs, flowers) into categories. Shown a picture of a never-before-seen chair, pigeons will reliably peck a key that represents *chairs* (Wasserman, 1995).

DISPLAYING INSIGHT Psychologist Wolfgang Köhler (1925) showed that humans are not the only creatures to display insight. He placed a piece of fruit and a long stick outside the cage of a chimpanzee named Sultan, beyond his reach. Inside the cage, Köhler placed a short stick, which Sultan grabbed, using it to try to reach the fruit. After several failed attempts, the chimpanzee dropped the stick and seemed to survey the situation. Then suddenly (as if thinking "Aha!"), Sultan jumped up and seized the short stick again. This time, he used it to pull in the longer stick—which he then used to reach the fruit. Apes have even exhibited foresight by storing a tool they could use to retrieve food the next day (Mulcahy & Call, 2006). (For one example of a chimpanzee's use of foresight, see **FIGURE 25.5a**.) And apes have displayed an ability to read others' minds—by anticipating where a human will look for an object, even if it's no longer there (Krupenye et al., 2016).

Birds, too, have displayed insight. One experiment, by (yes) Christopher Bird and Nathan Emery (2009), brought to life an Aesop fable in which a thirsty crow is unable to reach the water in a partly filled pitcher. See the crow's solution in Figure 25.5b. Other crows have fashioned wire or sticks for extracting food, such as insects in rotting logs (Rutz et al., 2016). Ravens are similarly adept at inventive tool use, and can plan hours ahead for future events (Kabadayi & Osvath, 2017).

TRANSMITTING CULTURE Like humans, other species invent behaviors and transmit cultural patterns to their observing peers and offspring (Boesch-Achermann & Boesch, 1993). Dolphins form coalitions, cooperatively hunt, and learn tool use from one another

ANIMAL COGNITION IN ACTION Alex, an African Grey parrot, was able to categorize and name objects (Pepperberg, 2009, 2012, 2013). Among his jaw-dropping numerical skills was the ability to comprehend numbers up to 8. He could speak the number of objects. He could add two small clusters of objects and announce the sum. He could indicate which of two numbers was greater. And he gave correct answers when shown various groups of objects. Asked, for example, "What color four?" (meaning "What's the color of the objects of which there are four?"), he could speak the answer.

(a)   (b)

FIGURE 25.5

ANIMAL TALENTS (a) One male chimpanzee in Sweden's Furuvik Zoo was observed every morning collecting stones into a neat little pile, which later in the day he used as ammunition to pelt visitors (Osvath & Karvonen, 2012). (b) Crows studied by Christopher Bird and Nathan Emery (2009) quickly learned to raise the water level in a tube and nab a floating worm by dropping in stones. Other crows have used twigs to probe for insects, and bent strips of metal to reach food.

(Bearzi & Stanford, 2010). In Shark Bay, Western Australia, one small group of dolphins learned to use marine sponges as protective nose guards when probing the sea floor for fish (Krützen et al, 2005).

Forest-dwelling chimpanzees select different tools for different purposes—a heavy stick for making holes, a light, flexible stick for fishing for termites, or a pointed stick for roasting marshmallows. (Just kidding: They don't roast marshmallows, but they have surprised us with their sophisticated tool use [Sanz et al., 2004]). Researchers have found at least 39 local customs related to chimpanzee tool use, grooming, and courtship (Claidière & Whiten, 2012; Whiten & Boesch, 2001). One group may slurp termites directly from a stick, another group may pluck them off individually. One group may break nuts with a stone hammer, while their neighbors use a wooden hammer. One chimpanzee discovered that tree moss could absorb water for drinking from a waterhole, and within six days seven other observant chimpanzees began doing the same (Hobaiter et al., 2014). These transmitted behaviors, along with differing communication and hunting styles, are the chimpanzee version of cultural diversity.

OTHER COGNITIVE SKILLS A baboon in an 80-member troop can distinguish every other member's voice (Jolly, 2007). Great apes, dolphins, and elephants recognize themselves in a mirror, demonstrating self-awareness. Elephants also display their abilities to learn, remember, discriminate smells, empathize, cooperate, teach, and spontaneously use tools (Byrne et al., 2009). Chimpanzees have shown altruism, cooperation, and group aggression. Like humans, they will purposefully kill their neighbor to gain land, and they grieve over dead relatives (Anderson et al., 2010; Biro et al., 2010; Mitani et al., 2010).

* * *

Thinking about other species' abilities brings us back to our initial question: How deserving are we of the label *Homo sapiens*—wise human? Let's pause to give our species some midterm grades. On decision making and risk assessment, our smart but error-prone species might rate a B-. On problem solving, where humans are inventive yet vulnerable to confirmation bias and fixation, we would probably receive a better mark, perhaps a B+. And on cognitive efficiency and creativity, our quick (though sometimes faulty) heuristics and divergent thinking would surely earn us an A.

ENGAGE What time is it now? When we asked you (in the section on overconfidence) to estimate how quickly you would finish this module, did you underestimate or overestimate?

🔒 REVIEW | THINKING

⤷ Learning Objectives

TEST YOURSELF Answer these repeated Learning Objective Questions on your own (before checking the answers in Appendix D) to improve your retention of the concepts (McDaniel et al., 2009, 2015).

25-1 What is *cognition,* and what are the functions of concepts?

25-2 What cognitive strategies assist our problem solving, and what obstacles hinder it?

25-3 What is *intuition,* and how can the representativeness and availability heuristics influence our decisions and judgments?

25-4 What factors exaggerate our fear of unlikely events?

25-5 How are our decisions and judgments affected by overconfidence, belief perseverance, and framing?

25-6 How do smart thinkers use intuition?

25-7 What is *creativity,* and what fosters it?

25-8 What do we know about thinking in other species?

⤷ Terms and Concepts to Remember

TEST YOURSELF Write down the definition yourself, then check your answer on the referenced page.

cognition, **p. 299**

concept, **p. 299**

prototype, **p. 299**

algorithm, **p. 299**

heuristic, **p. 299**

insight, **p. 299**

confirmation bias, **p. 299**

fixation, **p. 301**

mental set, **p. 301**

intuition, **p. 301**

representativeness heuristic, **p. 301**

availability heuristic, **p. 301**

overconfidence, **p. 303**

belief perseverance, **p. 304**

framing, **p. 304**

nudge, **p. 304**

creativity, **p. 307**

convergent thinking, **p. 307**

divergent thinking, **p. 307**

⟶ Experience the Testing Effect

TEST YOURSELF Answer the following questions on your own first, then check your answers in Appendix E.

1. A mental grouping of similar things is called a _____.

2. The most systematic procedure for solving a problem is a(n) _____.

3. Oscar describes his political beliefs as "strongly liberal," but he is interested in exploring opposing viewpoints. How might he be affected by confirmation bias and belief perseverance?

4. A major obstacle to problem solving is fixation, which is a(n)
   a. tendency to base our judgments on vivid memories.
   b. tendency to wait for insight to occur.
   c. inability to view a problem from a new perspective.
   d. rule of thumb for judging the likelihood of an event in terms of our mental image of it.

5. Terrorist attacks made Americans more fearful of being victimized by terrorism than of other, greater threats. Such exaggerated fear after dramatic events illustrates the _____ heuristic.

6. When consumers respond more positively to ground beef described as "75 percent lean" than to the same product labeled "25 percent fat," they have been influenced by _____.

7. Which of the following is NOT a characteristic of a creative person?
   a. Expertise
   b. Extrinsic motivation
   c. A venturesome personality
   d. Imaginative thinking skills

8. In the early twentieth century, some psychologists noted that animal consciousness can be inferred from their behavior. In the early twenty-first century, other scientists argued that animal consciousness can be inferred from their brain's _____ _____.

Continue testing yourself with 📘 **LearningCurve** or 📖 **Achieve Read & Practice** to learn and remember most effectively.

MODULE 26 Language and Thought

language our spoken, written, or signed words and the ways we combine them to communicate meaning.

Imagine an alien species that could pass thoughts from one head to another merely by pulsating air molecules in the space between them. Perhaps these weird creatures could inhabit a future science fiction movie? Actually, we are those creatures. When we speak, our brain and voice apparatus transmit air-pressure waves that we send banging against another's eardrum—enabling us to transfer thoughts from our brain into theirs. As cognitive psychologist Steven Pinker (1998) noted, we sometimes sit for hours "listening to other people make noise as they exhale, because those hisses and squeaks contain *information*." And thanks to all those funny sounds created from the air pressure waves we send out, we get people's attention. We get them to do things. And we maintain relationships (Guerin, 2003). Depending on how you vibrate the air, you may get a scowl or a kiss.

Language is more than vibrating air—it is our spoken, written, or signed words, and the ways we combine them to communicate meaning. When I [DM] created this paragraph, my fingers on a keyboard generated electronic binary numbers that were translated into the squiggles in front of you. When transmitted by reflected light rays into your retina, these squiggles trigger formless nerve impulses that travel to several areas of your brain, which integrate the information, compare it to stored information, and decode meaning. Thanks to language, information is moving from my mind to yours. Many animals know little more than what they sense. Thanks to language, we comprehend much that we've never seen and that our distant ancestors never knew.

Let's begin our study of language by examining some of its components.

LANGUAGE TRANSMITS KNOWLEDGE Whether spoken, written, or signed, language—the original wireless communication—enables mind-to-mind information transfer, and with it the transmission of civilization's accumulated knowledge across generations.

M. Spencer Green/AP Photo

STEVE INVALIDATES HIS WEDDING VOWS THROUGH THE CLEVER USE OF HOMOPHONES.

"Eye dew."

J.C. Duffy The New Yorker Collection/
The Cartoon Bank

LANGUAGE STRUCTURE

LOQ 26-1   What are the structural components of a language?

Consider how we might go about inventing a language. For a spoken language, we would need three building blocks:

- **Phonemes** are the smallest distinctive sound units in a language. To say *bat,* English speakers utter the phonemes *b, a,* and *t.* (Phonemes aren't the same as letters. *That* also has three phonemes—*th, a,* and *t.*) English uses about 40 phonemes; other languages use anywhere from half to more than twice that many. As a general rule, consonant phonemes carry more information than do vowel phonemes. *The treth ef thes stetement shed be evedent frem thes bref demenstretien.*

- **Morphemes** are the smallest language units that carry meaning. In English, a few morphemes are also phonemes—the article *a,* for instance. But most morphemes combine two or more phonemes. The word *readers,* for example, contains three morphemes: "read," "er" (signaling that we mean "one who reads"), and "s" (signaling that we mean not one, but multiple readers). Every word in a language contains one or more morphemes.

- **Grammar** is a language's set of rules that enable people to communicate. Grammatical rules guide us in deriving meaning from sounds (*semantics*) and ordering words into sentences (*syntax*).

Like life constructed from the genetic code's simple alphabet, language is complexity built of simplicity. In English, for example, 40 or so phonemes can be combined to form more than 100,000 morphemes, which alone or in combination produce the 600,000 variations of past and present words in the *Oxford English Dictionary.* Using those words, we can then create an infinite number of sentences, most of which (like this one) are original.

We humans have an astonishing knack for language. With remarkable efficiency, we sample tens of thousands of words in our memory, effortlessly assemble them with near-perfect syntax, and spew them out, three words a second (Vigliocco & Hartsuiker, 2002). Seldom do we form sentences in our minds before speaking them. Rather, we organize them on the fly as we speak. And while doing all this, we adapt our utterances to our social and cultural context. We also follow norms for speaking (*How far apart should we stand?*) and listening (*Is it OK to interrupt?*). Given how many ways there are to mess up, it's amazing that we master this social dance. How and when does it happen?

phoneme in a language, the smallest distinctive sound unit.

morpheme in a language, the smallest unit that carries meaning; may be a word or a part of a word (such as a prefix).

grammar in a language, a system of rules that enables us to communicate with and understand others. *Semantics* is the language's set of rules for deriving meaning from sounds, and *syntax* is its set of rules for combining words into grammatically sensible sentences.

🔒 **RETRIEVE IT • • •**   *ANSWERS IN APPENDIX E*

RI-1 How many morphemes are in the word *cats?* How many phonemes?

LANGUAGE ACQUISITION AND DEVELOPMENT

To Steven Pinker (1990), language is "the jewel in the crown of cognition." Without sight or hearing, you could still have friends and a job. But without language, could you have these things? If you were able to retain only one cognitive ability, make it language, suggested researcher Lera Boroditsky (2009). "Language is so fundamental to our experience, so deeply a part of being human, that it's hard to imagine life without it."

Language Acquisition: How Do We Learn Language?

LOQ 26-2   How do we acquire language, and what is *universal grammar?*

Linguist Noam Chomsky has argued language is an unlearned human trait, separate from other parts of human cognition. He theorized that a built-in predisposition to learn grammar rules, which he called *universal grammar,* helps explain why preschoolers pick up language so readily and use grammar so well. It happens so naturally—as naturally as birds learn to fly—that training hardly helps.

"The secret to our ancestors' survival was probably our use of language to develop new modes of cooperation."
—David Grinspoon, "Can Humans Outsmart Extinction?," 2016

CREATING A LANGUAGE Brought together as if on a desert island (actually a school), Nicaragua's young deaf children over time drew upon sign gestures from home to create their own Nicaraguan Sign Language, complete with words and intricate grammar. Our biological predisposition for language does not create language in a vacuum. But activated by a social context, nature and nurture work creatively together (Osborne, 1999; Sandler et al., 2005; Senghas & Coppola, 2001).

Other researchers note that children learn grammar as they discern patterns in the language they hear (Ibbotson & Tomasello, 2016). And even Chomsky agrees that we are not born with a built-in *specific* language or *specific* set of grammatical rules. The world's languages are structurally very diverse—more so than the universal grammar idea implies (Bergen, 2014). But all human languages—and there are more than 6000 of them—have nouns, verbs, and adjectives as grammatical building blocks, and order and utter words in some common ways (Blasi et al., 2016; Futrell et al., 2015). Whatever language we experience as children, whether spoken or signed, we will readily learn its specific grammar and vocabulary (Bavelier et al., 2003). And no matter what language we learn, we start speaking it mostly in nouns (*kitty, da-da*) rather than in verbs and adjectives (Bornstein et al., 2004). Biology and experience work together.

🔒 RETRIEVE IT • • •   *ANSWERS IN APPENDIX E*

RI-2 What was the premise of researcher Noam Chomsky's work in language development?

Language Development: When Do We Learn Language?

LOQ 26-3 What are the milestones in language development, and when is the critical period for acquiring language?

ENGAGE Make a quick guess: How many words of your native language did you learn between your first birthday and your high school graduation? Although you use only 150 words for about half of what you say, you probably learned about 60,000 words (Bloom, 2000; McMurray, 2007). That averages (after age 2) nearly 3500 words each year, or nearly 10 each day! How you did it—how those 3500 words could so far outnumber the roughly 200 words your schoolteachers consciously taught you each year—is one of the great human wonders.

Could you even now state the rules of syntax (the correct way to string words together to form sentences) for the language(s) you speak fluently? Most of us cannot. Yet before you were able to add 2 + 2, you were creating your own original sentences and applying these rules. As a preschooler, you comprehended and spoke with a facility that would put to shame college students struggling to learn a new language.

RECEPTIVE LANGUAGE Children's language development moves from simplicity to complexity. Infants start without language (*in fantis* means "not speaking"). Yet by 4 months of

A NATURAL TALENT Human infants come with a remarkable capacity to soak up language. But the particular language they learn will reflect their unique interactions with others.

age, babies can recognize differences in speech sounds (Stager & Werker, 1997). They can also read lips: We know this because in experiments, babies have preferred looking at a face that matches a sound—an "ah" coming from wide open lips and an "ee" from a mouth with corners pulled back (Kuhl & Meltzoff, 1982). Recognizing such differences marks the beginning of the development of babies' *receptive language,* their ability to understand what is said to and about them.

Infants' language comprehension greatly outpaces their language production. Even at 6 months, long before speaking, many infants recognize object names (Bergelson & Swingley, 2012, 2013). At 7 months and beyond, they grow in their power to do what adults find difficult when listening to an unfamiliar language: to segment spoken sounds into individual words.

PRODUCTIVE LANGUAGE Long after the beginnings of receptive language, babies' *productive language,* their ability to produce words, matures. Before nurture molds babies' speech, nature enables a wide range of possible sounds in the **babbling stage,** beginning around 4 months. Many of these spontaneously uttered sounds are consonant-vowel pairs formed by simply bunching the tongue in the front of the mouth (*da-da, na-na, ta-ta*) or by opening and closing the lips (*ma-ma*), both of which babies do naturally for feeding (MacNeilage & Davis, 2000). Babbling does not imitate the adult speech babies hear—it includes sounds from various languages. From this early babbling, a listener could not identify an infant as being, say, French, Korean, or Ethiopian.

By about 10 months old, infants' babbling has changed so that a trained ear can identify the household language (de Boysson-Bardies et al., 1989). Deaf infants who observe their deaf parents signing begin to babble more with their hands (Petitto & Marentette, 1991). Without exposure to other languages, babies lose their ability to do what we (believe it or not) cannot—to discriminate and produce sounds and tones outside our native language (Kuhl et al., 2014; Meltzoff et al., 2009; Pallier et al., 2001). Thus, by adulthood, those who speak only English cannot discriminate certain sounds in Japanese speech. Nor can Japanese adults with no training in English hear the difference between the English *r* and *l*. For a Japanese-speaking adult, "*la-la-ra-ra*" may sound like the same syllable repeated.

Around their first birthday, most children enter the **one-word stage.** They have already learned that sounds carry meanings, and if repeatedly trained to associate, say, *fish* with a picture of a fish, 1-year-olds will look at a fish when a researcher says, "Fish, fish! Look at the fish!" (Schafer, 2005). They begin to use sounds—usually only one barely recognizable syllable, such as *ma* or *da*—to communicate meaning. But family members learn to understand, and gradually the infant's language conforms more to the family's language. Across the world, baby's first words are often nouns that label objects or people (Tardif et al., 2008). At this one-word stage, a single inflected word ("*Doggy!*") may communicate a sentence ("*Look at the dog out there!*").

At about 18 months, children's word learning explodes from about a word per week to a word per day. By their second birthday, most have entered the **two-word stage** (TABLE 26.1). They start uttering two-word sentences in **telegraphic speech.** Like yesterday's telegrams that charged by the word (TERMS ACCEPTED. SEND MONEY), a 2-year-old's speech contains mostly nouns and verbs ("*Want juice*"). Also like telegrams, their speech follows rules of syntax, arranging words in a sensible order. English-speaking children typically place adjectives before nouns—*white house* rather than *house white.* Spanish reverses this order, as in *casa blanca.*

Moving out of the two-word stage, children quickly begin uttering longer phrases (Fromkin & Rodman, 1983). By early elementary school, they understand complex sentences and begin to enjoy the humor conveyed by double meanings: "You never starve in the desert because of all the sand-which-is there."

"Got idea. Talk better. Combine words. Make sentences."

Sidney Harris

DON'T MEANS DON'T—NO MATTER HOW YOU SAY IT! Deaf children of deaf-signing parents and hearing children of hearing parents have much in common. They develop language skills at about the same rate, and they are equally effective at opposing parental wishes and demanding their way.

George Ancona

RETAIN

TABLE 26.1

Summary of Language Development

Month (approximate)	Stage
4	Babbles many speech sounds ("ah-goo")
10	Babbling resembles household language ("ma-ma")
12	One-word speech ("Kitty!")
24	Two-word speech ("Get ball.")
24+	Rapid development into complete sentences

🔒 RETRIEVE IT • • •

ANSWERS IN APPENDIX E

RI-3 What is the difference between *receptive* and *productive* language, and when do children normally hit these milestones in language development?

CRITICAL PERIODS Some children—such as those who received a cochlear implant to enable hearing, or those who are adopted by a family in another country—get a late start on learning a particular language. For these late bloomers, language development follows the same sequence, although usually at a faster pace (Ertmer et al., 2007; Snedeker et al., 2007). But there is a limit on how long language learning can be delayed. Childhood seems to represent a *critical* (or "sensitive") *period* for mastering certain aspects of language before the language-learning window closes (Hernandez & Li, 2007; Lenneberg, 1967). In one study, Korean language exposure in just the first months of life enabled Korean adoptees in the Netherlands to do what others could not—to readily learn the consonant sounds of their forgotten language (Choi et al., 2017). Some of what was forgotten was unconsciously retained.

Later-than-usual exposure—at age 2 or 3—unleashes the idle language capacity of a child's brain, producing a rush of language. But by about age 7, those who have not been exposed to either a spoken or a signed language gradually lose their ability to master *any* language. And children exposed to low-quality language—such as 4-year-olds in class-rooms with 3-year-olds, or some children from impoverished homes—often display less language skill (Ansari et al., 2015; Hirsh-Pasek et al., 2015).

Thanks to the shared human ability to learn language, even Europeans and Native Australia–New Zealand populations—groups that have been geographically separated for 50,000 years—can readily learn each other's languages (Chater et al., 2009). But if we learn a new language as adults, we will usually speak it with the accent of our native language, and we will also have difficulty mastering the new grammar. In one experiment, U.S. immigrants from South Korea and China considered 276 English sentences (*"Yesterday the hunter shoots a deer"*) and decided whether they were grammatically correct or incorrect (Johnson & Newport, 1991). All had been in the United States for approximately 10 years: Some had arrived in early childhood, others as adults. As **FIGURE 26.1** reveals, those who learned their second language early learned it best. The older we are when moving to a new country, the harder it is to learn its language and to absorb its culture (Cheung et al., 2011; Hakuta et al., 2003). Cognitive psychologist Stephen Kosslyn (2008) summed it up nicely: "Children can learn multiple languages without an accent and with good grammar, if they are exposed to the language before puberty. But after puberty, it's very difficult to learn a second language so well." Similarly, when I [ND] first went to Japan, I was told not even to bother trying to bow, that there were something like a dozen different bows and I was always going to "bow with an accent."

🔒 RETRIEVE IT • • •

ANSWERS IN APPENDIX E

RI-4 Why is it so difficult to learn a new language in adulthood?

babbling stage beginning around 4 months, the stage of speech development in which an infant spontaneously utters various sounds at first unrelated to the household language.

one-word stage the stage in speech development, from about age 1 to 2, during which a child speaks mostly in single words.

two-word stage beginning about age 2, the stage in speech development during which a child speaks mostly in two-word statements.

telegraphic speech the early speech stage in which a child speaks like a telegram—"go car"—using mostly nouns and verbs.

FIGURE 26.1

OUR ABILITY TO LEARN A NEW LANGUAGE DIMINISHES WITH AGE
Ten years after coming to the United States, Asian immigrants took an English grammar test. Although there is no sharply defined critical period for second language learning, those who arrived before age 8 understood American English grammar as well as native speakers did. Those who arrived later did not. (Data from Johnson & Newport, 1991.)

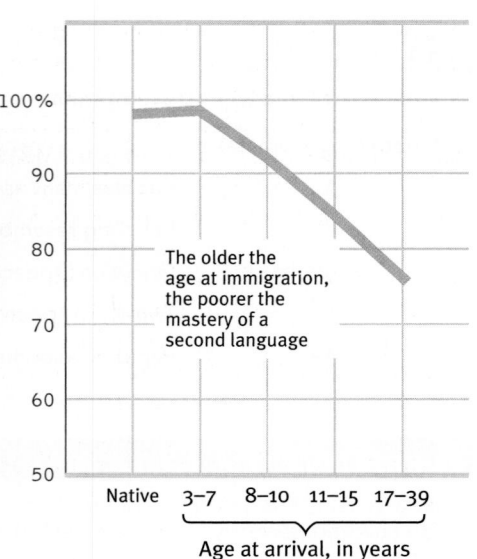

Percentage correct on grammar test

The older the age at immigration, the poorer the mastery of a second language

Native 3–7 8–10 11–15 17–39
Age at arrival, in years

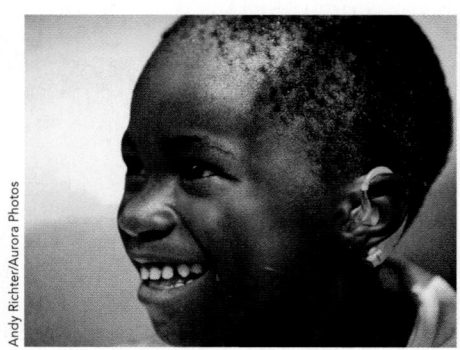

HEARING IMPROVED A boy in Malawi experiences new hearing aids.

Deafness and Language Development

The impact of early experiences is evident in language learning in prelingually (before learning language) deaf children born to hearing-nonsigning parents. These children typically do not experience language during their early years. Natively deaf children who learn sign language after age 9 never learn it as well as those who learned it early in life (Mayberry et al., 2002). Those who learn to sign as teens or adults are like immigrants who learn a second language after childhood: They can master basic words and learn to order them, but they never become as fluent as native signers in producing and comprehending subtle grammatical differences (Newport, 1990). As a flower's growth will be stunted without nourishment, so, too, children will typically become linguistically stunted if isolated from language during the critical period for its acquisition.

THE BRAIN AND LANGUAGE

LOQ 26-4 What brain areas are involved in language processing and speech?

We think of speaking and reading, or writing and reading, or singing and speaking as merely different examples of the same general ability—language. But consider this curious finding: Damage to any of several cortical areas can produce **aphasia**, impairment of language. Even more curious, some people with aphasia can speak fluently but cannot read (despite good vision). Others can comprehend what they read but cannot speak. Still others can write but not read, read but not write, read numbers but not letters, or sing but not speak. These cases suggest that language is complex, and that different brain areas must serve different language functions.

Indeed, in 1865, French physician Paul Broca confirmed a fellow physician's observation that after damage to an area of the left frontal lobe (later called **Broca's area**) a person would struggle to *speak* words, yet could still sing familiar songs and comprehend speech. A decade later, German investigator Carl Wernicke discovered that after damage to a specific area of the left temporal lobe (**Wernicke's area**), people were unable to *understand* others' words and could speak only meaningless words. Asked to describe a picture that showed two boys stealing cookies behind a woman's back, one patient responded: "Mother is away her working her work to get her better, but when she's looking the two boys looking the other part. She's working another time" (Geschwind, 1979).

Today's neuroscience has confirmed brain activity in Broca's and Wernicke's areas during language processing (**FIGURE 26.2**). For people with aphasia, electrical stimulation

aphasia impairment of language, usually caused by left hemisphere damage either to Broca's area (impairing speaking) or to Wernicke's area (impairing understanding).

Broca's area helps control language expression—an area of the frontal lobe, usually in the left hemisphere, that directs the muscle movements involved in speech.

Wernicke's area a brain area involved in language comprehension and expression; usually in the left temporal lobe.

of Broca's area can help restore speaking abilities (Marangolo et al., 2016). But we also now know that the brain's processing of language is complex. Broca's area coordinates the brain's processing of language in other areas as well (Flinker et al., 2015; Tremblay & Dick, 2016). Although you experience language as a single, unified stream, fMRI scans would show that your brain is busily multitasking and networking. Different neural networks are activated by nouns and verbs (or objects and actions); by different vowels; by stories of visual versus motor experiences; by who spoke and what was said; and by many other stimuli (Perrachione et al., 2011; Shapiro et al., 2006; Speer et al., 2009). Moreover, if you're lucky enough to be natively fluent in two languages, your brain processes them in similar areas (Kim et al., 2017). But your brain doesn't use the same areas if you learned a second language after the first or if you sign rather than speak your second language (Berken et al., 2015; Kovelman et al., 2014).

The point to remember: In processing language, as in other forms of information processing, the brain operates by dividing its mental functions—speaking, perceiving, thinking, remembering—into subfunctions. Your conscious experience of reading this page *seems* indivisible, but, thanks to your parallel processing, many different neural networks are pooling their work to give the word strings coherence and meaning (Fedorenko et al., 2016). *E pluribus unum*: Out of many, one.

RETAIN ENGAGE 🔒💡 📖 **LaunchPad** To review research on left and right hemisphere language processing—and to test your own processing speed—see **Topic Tutorial: PsychSim6, Dueling Hemispheres.**

🔒 **RETRIEVE IT • • •**   *ANSWERS IN APPENDIX E*

RI-5 _____ _____ is one part of the brain that, if damaged, might impair your ability to speak words. Damage to _____ _____ might impair your ability to understand language.

DO OTHER SPECIES HAVE LANGUAGE?

LOQ 26-5 What do we know about other species' capacity for language?

Humans have long and proudly proclaimed that language sets us above all other animals. "When we study human language," asserted Chomsky (1972), "we are approaching what some might call the 'human essence,' the qualities of mind that are, so far as we know, unique [to humans]." Is it true that humans, alone, have language?

Some animals display basic language processing. Pigeons can learn the difference between words and nonwords, but they could never read this book (Scarf et al., 2016). Other animals show impressive comprehension and communication. Various monkey species sound different alarm cries for different predators, such as a barking call for a leopard, a cough for an eagle, and a chuttering for a snake. Hearing the leopard alarm, vervets climb the nearest tree. Hearing the eagle alarm, they rush into the bushes. Hearing the snake chutter, they stand up and scan the ground (Byrne, 1991; Clarke et al., 2015; Coye et al., 2015). To indicate such things as a type of threat—an eagle, a leopard, a falling tree, a neighboring group—monkeys will combine 6 different calls into a 25-call sequence (Balter, 2010). But are such communications language?

In the late 1960s, psychologists Allen Gardner and Beatrix Gardner (1969) aroused enormous scientific and public interest with their work with Washoe, a young chimpanzee. Building on chimpanzees' natural tendencies for gestured communication, they taught Washoe sign language. After four years, Washoe could use 132 signs; by her life's end in 2007, she was using 250 signs (Metzler, 2011; Sanz et al., 1998).

During the 1970s, more and more reports came in. Some chimpanzees were stringing signs together to form sentences. Washoe, for example, signed "You me go out, please." Some word combinations seemed creative—saying *water bird* for "swan" or *apple-which-is-orange* for "orange" (Patterson, 1978; Rumbaugh, 1977).

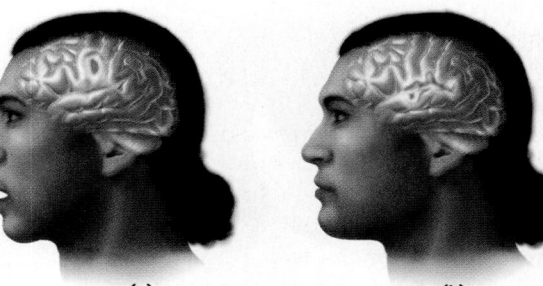

(a)
Speaking words
(Broca's area and the motor cortex)

(b)
Hearing words
(Wernicke's area and the auditory cortex)

FIGURE 26.2
BRAIN ACTIVITY WHEN SPEAKING AND HEARING WORDS

"It is the way systems interact and have a dynamic interdependence that is—unless one has lost all sense of wonder—quite awe-inspiring." —Simon Conway Morris, "The Boyle Lecture," 2005

TALKING HANDS Human language appears to have evolved from gestured communications (Corballis, 2002, 2003; Pollick & de Waal, 2007). Even today, gestures are naturally associated with spontaneous speech, and similarly so for blind and sighted speakers of a given language (Özçaliskan et al., 2016). Both gesture and speech communicate, and when they convey the same rather than different information (as they do in baseball's sign language), we humans understand faster and more accurately (Hostetter, 2011; Kelly et al., 2010). Outfielder William Hoy, the first deaf player to join the major leagues (1892), reportedly helped invent hand signals for "Strike!," "Safe!" (shown here), and "Yerr out!" (Pollard, 1992). Referees in all sports now use invented signs, and fans are fluent in sports sign language.

Jim Cummins/Getty Images

COMPREHENDING CANINE Border collie Rico had a vocabulary of 200 human words. If asked to retrieve a toy with a name he had never heard, Rico would pick out a new toy from a group of familiar items (Kaminski et al., 2004). Hearing that name for the second time four weeks later, Rico more often than not would retrieve the same toy. Another border collie, Chaser, has set an animal record by learning 1000 object names (Pilley, 2013). Like a 3-year-old child, she can also categorize them by function and shape. She can "fetch a ball" or "fetch a doll."

BUT IS THIS LANGUAGE? Chimpanzees' ability to express themselves in American Sign Language (ASL) raises questions about the very nature of language. Here, the trainer is asking, "What is this?" The sign in response is "Baby." Does the response constitute language?

ENGAGE

(ASK YOURSELF)

Can you think of a time when you believed an animal was communicating with you? How might you put that to a test?

But by the late 1970s, other psychologists were growing skeptical. Were the chimps language champs or were the researchers chumps? Consider, said the skeptics:

- Ape vocabularies and sentences are simple, rather like those of a 2-year-old child. And unlike speaking or signing children, apes gain their limited vocabularies only with great difficulty (Wynne, 2004, 2008).

- Chimpanzees can make signs or push buttons in a sequence to get a reward. But pigeons, too, can peck a sequence of keys to get grain (Straub et al., 1979). The apes' signing might be nothing more than aping their trainers' signs and learning that certain arm movements produce rewards (Terrace, 1979).

- When information is unclear, we are prone to *perceptual set*—a tendency to see what we want or expect to see. Interpreting chimpanzee signs as language may have been little more than the trainers' wishful thinking (Terrace, 1979). When Washoe signed *water bird,* she may have been separately naming *water* and *bird.*

- "Give orange me give eat orange me eat orange . . ." is a far cry from the exquisite syntax of a 3-year-old (Anderson, 2004; Pinker, 1995). Rules of syntax in human language govern the order of words in sentences. So to a child, "You tickle" and "Tickle you" communicate different ideas. A chimpanzee, lacking these rules of syntax, might use the same sequence of signs for both phrases.

Controversy can stimulate progress, and in this case, it triggered more evidence of other species' abilities to think and communicate. Kanzi, a bonobo with a reported 384-word vocabulary, could understand syntax in spoken English (Savage-Rumbaugh et al., 1993, 2009). Kanzi, who appears to have the receptive language ability of a human 2-year-old, has responded appropriately when asked, "Can you show me the light?" and "Can you bring me the [flash]light?" and "Can you turn the light on?" Given stuffed animals and asked—for the first time—to "make the dog bite the snake," he put the snake to the dog's mouth.

So, how should we interpret such studies? Are humans the only language-using species? If by *language* we mean an ability to communicate through a meaningful sequence of symbols, then apes are indeed capable of language. But if we mean a verbal or signed expression of complex grammar, most psychologists would now agree that humans alone possess language. Moreover, humans, alone, have a version of a gene (*FOXP2*) that helps enable the lip, tongue, and vocal cord movements of human speech (Lieberman, 2013). Humans with a mutated form of this gene have difficulty speaking words.

One thing is certain: Studies of animal language and thinking have moved psychologists toward a greater appreciation of other species' remarkable abilities (Friend, 2004; Rumbaugh & Washburn, 2003; Wilson et al., 2015). In the past, many psychologists doubted that other species could plan, form concepts, count, use tools, or show compassion (Thorpe, 1974). Today, thanks to animal researchers, we know better. Other species exhibit insight, show family loyalty, communicate with and care for one another, and transmit cultural patterns across generations. Working out what this means for the moral rights of other animals is an unfinished task.

📺 **LaunchPad** For examples of intelligent communication and problem solving among orangutans, elephants, and killer whales, see the 6-minute **Video: How Intelligent Are Animals?** See also **Video: Case Studies** for a helpful tutorial animation on this type of research method.

🔒 **RETRIEVE IT** • • •   *ANSWERS IN APPENDIX E*

RI-6 If your dog barks at a stranger at the door, does this qualify as language? What if the dog yips in a telltale way to let you know she needs to go out?

THINKING AND LANGUAGE

LOQ 26-6 What is the relationship between thinking and language, and what is the value of thinking in images?

Thinking and language—which comes first? This is one of psychology's great chicken-and-egg questions. Do our ideas come first and then the words to name them? Or are our thoughts conceived in words and therefore unthinkable without them?

Language Influences Thinking

Linguist Benjamin Lee Whorf (1956) contended that "language itself shapes a [person's] basic ideas." The Hopi, who have no past tense for their verbs, could not readily *think* about the past, he said. Today's psychologists believe that a strong form of Whorf's idea—**linguistic determinism**—is too extreme. We all think about things for which we have no words. (Can you think of a shade of blue you cannot name?) And we routinely have *unsymbolized* (wordless, imageless) thoughts, as when someone, watching two men carry a load of bricks, wondered whether the men would drop them (Heavey & Hurlburt, 2008; Hurlburt et al., 2013).

A weaker version of linguistic determinism—**linguistic relativism**—recognizes that our words influence our thinking (Gentner, 2016). To those who speak two dissimilar languages, such as English and Japanese, it seems obvious that a person may think differently in different languages (Brown, 1986). Unlike English, which has a rich vocabulary for self-focused emotions such as anger, Japanese has more words for interpersonal emotions such as sympathy (Markus & Kitayama, 1991). Many bilingual individuals report having different senses of self—that they feel like different people—depending on which language they are using (Matsumoto, 1994; Pavlenko, 2014). In one series of studies with bilingual Israeli Arabs (who spoke both Arabic and Hebrew), participants thought differently about their social world, with differing automatic associations with Arabs and Jews, depending on which language the testing session used (Danziger & Ward, 2010).

Depending on which emotion they want to express, bilingual people will often switch languages. "When my mom gets angry at me, she'll speak in Mandarin," explained one Chinese-American student. "If she's really mad, she'll switch to Cantonese" (Chen et al., 2012). Bilingual individuals may even reveal different personality profiles when taking the same test in two languages, with their differing cultural associations (Chen & Bond, 2010; Dinges & Hull, 1992). When China-born, bilingual University of Waterloo students were asked to describe themselves in English, their responses fit typical Canadian profiles, expressing mostly positive self-statements and moods. When responding in Chinese, the same students gave typically Chinese self-descriptions, reporting more agreement with Chinese values and roughly equal positive and negative self-statements and moods (Ross et al., 2002). Similar attitude and personality changes have been shown when bicultural, bilingual people shift between the cultural frames associated with Spanish and English, or Arabic and English (Ogunnaike et al., 2010; Ramírez-Esparza et al., 2006). "Learn a new language and get a new soul," says a Czech proverb. When responding in their second language, bilingual people's moral judgments also reflect less emotion—they respond with more "head" than "heart" (Costa et al., 2014).

So our words do *influence* our thinking (Boroditsky, 2011). Words define our mental categories. In Brazil, the isolated Piraha people have words for the numbers 1 and 2, but numbers above that are simply "many." Thus, if shown 7 nuts in a row, they find it difficult to lay out the same number from their own pile (Gordon, 2004).

Words also influence our thinking about colors. Whether we live in New Mexico, New South Wales, or New Guinea, we *see* colors much the same, but we use our native language to *classify* and *remember* them (Davidoff, 2004; Roberson et al., 2004, 2005). Imagine viewing three colors and calling two of them "yellow" and one of them "blue." Later you would likely recall the yellows as being more similar. But if you speak the language of Papua New Guinea's Berinmo tribe, which has words for two different shades of yellow, you would more speedily perceive and better recall the variations between the two yellows. And if your language is Russian, which has distinct names for various

linguistic determinism Whorf's hypothesis that language determines the way we think.

linguistic relativism the idea that language has an influence on the way we think.

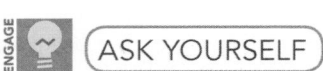
ASK YOURSELF

Consider a language you began to learn *after* learning your first language. How did your learning this other language differ from learning your first language? Does speaking it feel different?

CULTURE AND COLOR In Papua New Guinea, Berinmo children have words for different shades of "yellow," which might enable them to spot and recall yellow variations more quickly. Here and everywhere, "the languages we speak profoundly shape the way we think, the way we see the world, the way we live our lives," noted psychologist Lera Boroditsky (2009).

"All words are pegs to hang ideas on." —Henry Ward Beecher, *Proverbs from Plymouth Pulpit*, 1887

📱 **LaunchPad** Play the role of a researcher studying the benefits of learning more than one language by engaging online with **Immersive Learning: How Would You Know If There Is a Bilingual Advantage?**

shades of blue, such as *goluboy* and *siniy,* you might recall the yellows as more similar and remember the blue better. Words matter.

Perceived differences grow as we assign different names. On the color spectrum, blue blends into green—until we draw a dividing line between the portions we call "blue" and "green." Although equally different on the color spectrum, two different items that share the same color name (as the two "blues" do in **FIGURE 26.3**, contrast B) are harder to distinguish than two items with different names ("blue" and "green," as in Figure 26.3, contrast A) (Özgen, 2004). Likewise, two places seem closer and more vulnerable to the same natural disaster if labeled as in the same state rather than at an equal distance in adjacent states (Burris & Branscombe, 2005; Mishra & Mishra, 2010). Tornadoes don't know about state lines, but people do.

Given words' subtle influence on thinking, we do well to choose our words carefully. Is "A child learns language as *he* interacts with *his* caregivers" any different from "Children learn language as *they* interact with *their* caregivers"? Many studies have found that it is. When hearing the generic *he* (as in "the artist and his work") people are more likely to picture a male (Henley, 1989; Ng, 1990). If *he* and *his* were truly gender free, we shouldn't skip a beat when hearing that "man, like other mammals, nurses his young."

To expand language is to expand the ability to think. Young children's thinking develops hand in hand with their language (Gopnik & Meltzoff, 1986). Indeed, it is very difficult to think about or conceptualize certain abstract ideas (*commitment, freedom,* or *rhyming*) without language! And what is true for preschoolers is true for everyone: *It pays to increase your word power.* That's why most textbooks, including this one, introduce new words—to teach new ideas and new ways of thinking.

Increased word power helps explain what McGill University researcher Wallace Lambert has called the *bilingual advantage* (1992; Lambert et al., 1993). In some studies (though not all), bilingual people have exhibited skill at inhibiting one language while using the other (Bialystok et al., 2015; de Bruin et al., 2015a,b). And thanks to their well-practiced "executive control" over language, they also more readily inhibit their attention to irrelevant information (Bak et al., 2014; Bialystok, 2017; Kroll et al., 2014). Bilingual children also exhibit enhanced social skill, by being better able to shift to understand another's perspective (Fan et al., 2015). The bilingual advantage even extends to aging by preserving healthy brain functioning later in life (Li et al., 2017).

Bilingual people's switching between different languages does, however, take a moment (Kleinman & Gollan, 2016; Palomar-García et al., 2015). That's a phenomenon I [DM] failed to realize before speaking to bilingual Chinese colleagues in Beijing. While I spoke in English, my accompanying slides were in Chinese. Alas, I later learned, the translated slides required constant "code switching" from my spoken words, thus making it *hard* for my audience to process both.

Lambert helped devise a Canadian program that has, since 1981, immersed millions of English-speaking children in French (Statistics Canada, 2013). Not surprisingly, the children attain a natural French fluency unrivaled by other methods of language teaching. Moreover, compared with similarly capable children in control groups, they do so without detriment to their English fluency, and with increased aptitude scores, creativity, and appreciation for French-Canadian culture (Genesee & Gándara, 1999; Lazaruk, 2007).

Whether we are in the linguistic minority or majority, language links us to one another. Language also connects us to the past and the future. "To destroy a people," goes a saying, "destroy their language."

FIGURE 26.3

LANGUAGE AND PERCEPTION When people view blocks of equally different colors, they perceive those with different names as more different. Thus the "green" and "blue" in contrast A may appear to differ more than the two equally different blues in contrast B (Özgen, 2004).

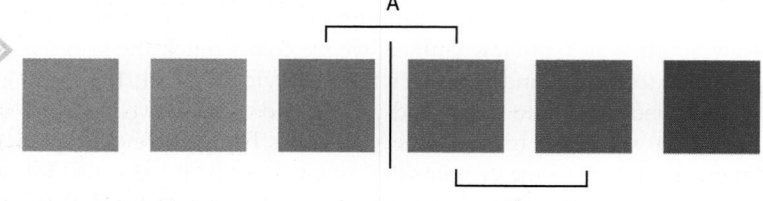

RI-7 Benjamin Lee Whorf's controversial hypothesis, called _____ _____, suggested that we cannot think about things unless we have words for those concepts or ideas.

Thinking in Images

When you are alone, do you talk to yourself? Is "thinking" simply conversing with yourself? Words do convey ideas. But sometimes ideas precede words. To turn on the cold water in your bathroom, in which direction do you turn the handle? To answer, you probably thought not in words but with *implicit* (nondeclarative, procedural) memory—a mental picture of how you do it.

Indeed, we often think in images. Artists think in images. So do composers, poets, mathematicians, athletes, and scientists. Albert Einstein reported that he achieved some of his greatest insights through visual images and later put them into words. Pianist Liu Chi Kung harnessed the power of thinking in images. One year after placing second in the 1958 Tchaikovsky piano competition, Liu was imprisoned during China's cultural revolution. Soon after his release, after seven years without touching a piano, he was back on tour. Critics judged Liu's musicianship as better than ever. How did he continue to develop without practice? "I did practice," said Liu, "every day. I rehearsed every piece I had ever played, note by note, in my mind" (Garfield, 1986).

For someone who has learned a skill, such as ballet dancing, even *watching* the activity will activate the brain's internal simulation of it (Calvo-Merino et al., 2004). So, too, will *imagining* a physical experience, which activates some of the same neural networks that are active during the actual experience (Grèzes & Decety, 2001). Small wonder, then, that mental practice has become a standard part of training for Olympic athletes (Blumenstein & Orbach, 2012; Ungerleider, 2005).

One experiment on mental practice and basketball free-throw shooting tracked the University of Tennessee women's team over 35 games (Savoy & Beitel, 1996). During that time, the team's free-throw accuracy increased from approximately 52 percent in games following standard physical practice, to some 65 percent after mental practice. Players had repeatedly imagined making free throws under various conditions, including being "trash-talked" by their opposition. In a dramatic conclusion, Tennessee won the national championship game in overtime, thanks in part to their free-throw shooting.

Mental rehearsal can also help you achieve an academic goal, as researchers demonstrated with two groups of introductory psychology students facing a midterm exam one week later (Taylor et al., 1998). (Students who were not engaged in any mental rehearsal formed a control group.) The first group spent five minutes each day visualizing themselves scanning the posted grade list, seeing their A, beaming with joy, and feeling proud. This daily *outcome simulation* had little effect, adding only 2 points to their exam-score average. The second group spent five minutes each day visualizing themselves effectively studying—reading their text, going over notes, eliminating distractions, declining an offer to go out. This daily *process simulation* paid off: The group began studying sooner, spent more time at it, and beat the others' average score by 8 points.

🔒 *The point to remember:* It's better to spend your fantasy time planning *how* to reach your goal than to focus on your desired destination.

💡 📕 **LaunchPad** To experience your own thinking as (a) manipulating words and (b) manipulating images, see **Topic Tutorial: PsychSim6, My Head Is Spinning!**

* * *

What, then, should we say about the relationship between thinking and language? As we have seen, language influences our thinking. But if thinking did not also affect language, there would never be any new words. And new words and new combinations of old words express new ideas. The basketball term *slam dunk* was coined after the act itself had

"When we see a person walking down the street talking to himself, we generally assume that he is mentally ill. But we all talk to ourselves continuously—we just have the good sense of keeping our mouths shut. . . . It's as though we are having a conversation with an imaginary friend possessed of infinite patience. Who are we talking to?" —Sam Harris, "We Are Lost in Thought," 2011

💡 ENGAGE (**ASK YOURSELF**)

How could you use mental practice to improve your performance in some area of your life?

FIGURE 26.4

THE INTERPLAY OF THOUGHT AND LANGUAGE The traffic runs both ways between thinking and language. Thinking affects our language, which affects our thought.

Thinking

Language

Jupiterimages/Getty Images

become fairly common. *Blogs* became part of our language after "web logs" appeared. So, let us say that *thinking affects our language, which then affects our thought* (**FIGURE 26.4**).

Psychological research on thinking and language mirrors the mixed impressions of our species by those in fields such as literature and religion. The human mind is simultaneously capable of striking intellectual failures and of striking intellectual power. Misjudgments are common and can have disastrous consequences. So we do well to appreciate our capacity for error. Yet our ingenuity at problem solving and our extraordinary power of language mark humankind as (in Shakespeare's words), almost "infinite in faculties."

🔒 **RETRIEVE IT • • •**   *ANSWERS IN APPENDIX E*

RI-8 What is mental practice, and how can it help you to prepare for an upcoming event?

🔒 REVIEW LANGUAGE AND THOUGHT

⟫ Learning Objectives

TEST YOURSELF Answer these repeated Learning Objective Questions on your own (before checking the answers in Appendix D) to improve your retention of the concepts (McDaniel et al., 2009, 2015).

26-1 What are the structural components of a language?

26-2 How do we acquire language, and what is *universal grammar*?

26-3 What are the milestones in language development, and when is the critical period for acquiring language?

26-4 What brain areas are involved in language processing and speech?

26-5 What do we know about other species' capacity for language?

26-6 What is the relationship between thinking and language, and what is the value of thinking in images?

⟫ Terms and Concepts to Remember

TEST YOURSELF Write down the definition yourself, then check your answer on the referenced page.

language, **p. 311**

phoneme, **p. 312**

morpheme, **p. 312**

grammar, **p. 312**

babbling stage, **p. 315**

one-word stage, **p. 315**

two-word stage, **p. 315**

telegraphic speech, **p. 315**

aphasia, **p. 316**

Broca's area, **p. 316**

Wernicke's area, **p. 316**

linguistic determinism, **p. 319**

linguistic relativism, **p. 319**

⟫ Experience the Testing Effect

TEST YOURSELF Answer the following questions on your own first, then check your answers in Appendix E.

1. Children reach the one-word stage of speech development at about
   a. 4 months.
   b. 6 months.
   c. 1 year.
   d. 2 years.

2. The three basic building blocks of language are _____, _____, and _____.

3. When young children speak in short phrases using mostly verbs and nouns, this is referred to as _____ _____.

4. According to Chomsky, humans have a built-in predisposition to learn grammar rules; he called this trait _____ _____.

5. Most researchers agree that apes can

    a. communicate through symbols.

    b. reproduce most human speech sounds.

    c. master language in adulthood.

    d. surpass a human 3-year-old in language skills.

Continue testing yourself with ≋ **LearningCurve** or ≋ **Achieve Read & Practice** to learn and remember most effectively.

---

27 Intelligence and Its Assessment

MODULE

imageBROKER/Alamy

In and beyond psychology, few topics have sparked more debate than the intelligence controversy: Does each of us have an inborn general mental capacity (intelligence)? Can we quantify this capacity as a meaningful number? How much does intelligence vary within and between groups, and why? And can we measure intelligence without bias?

WHAT IS INTELLIGENCE?

LOQ 27-1 How do psychologists define *intelligence,* and what are the arguments for *g?*

In many studies, *intelligence* has been defined as whatever *intelligence tests* measure, which has tended to be school smarts. But intelligence is not a quality like height or weight, which has the same meaning to everyone worldwide. People assign this term to the qualities that enable success in their own time and culture (Sternberg & Kaufman, 1998). In Cameroon's equatorial forest, *intelligence* may reflect understanding the medicinal qualities of local plants. In a North American high school, it may reflect mastering difficult concepts in calculus or chemistry. In both places, **intelligence** is the ability to learn from experience, solve problems, and use knowledge to adapt to new situations.

You probably know some people with talents in science, others who excel in the humanities, and still others gifted in athletics, art, music, or dance. You may also know a talented artist who is stumped by the simplest math problem, or a brilliant math student who struggles when discussing literature. Are all these people intelligent? Could you rate their intelligence on a single scale? Or would you need several different scales?

Is Intelligence One General Ability?

Charles Spearman (1863–1945) believed we have one **general intelligence** (often shortened to **g**) that is at the heart of all of our intelligent behavior, from navigating the sea to excelling in school. He granted that people often have special, outstanding abilities. But he noted that those who score high in one area, such as verbal intelligence, typically score higher than average in other areas, such as spatial or reasoning ability.

Spearman's (1904) belief stemmed in part from his work with *factor analysis,* a statistical procedure that identifies clusters of related items. In this view, mental abilities are much like physical abilities: Athleticism is not one thing, but many. The ability to run fast is distinct from the eye-hand coordination required to throw a ball on target. Yet there remains some tendency for good things to come packaged together—for running speed and throwing accuracy to correlate. So, too, with intelligence. Several distinct

HANDS-ON HEALING The socially constructed concept of intelligence varies from culture to culture. This natural healer in Cameroon displays intelligence in his knowledge about medicinal plants and his understanding of the needs of the people he is helping.

"g is one of the most reliable and valid measures in the behavioral domain . . . and it predicts important social outcomes such as educational and occupational levels far better than any other trait." —Behavior geneticist Robert Plomin (1999)

intelligence the ability to learn from experience, solve problems, and use knowledge to adapt to new situations.

general intelligence (g) according to Spearman and others, underlies all mental abilities and is therefore measured by every task on an intelligence test.

savant syndrome a condition in which a person otherwise limited in mental ability has an exceptional specific skill, such as in computation or drawing.

abilities tend to cluster together and to correlate enough to define a general intelligence factor. Distinct brain networks enable distinct abilities, with *g* explained by their coordinated activity (Cole et al., 2015; Hampshire et al., 2012). The result is a chorus of actions orchestrated from distributed mental resources (Carroll & Bright, 2016; Lee et al., 2015).

Theories of Multiple Intelligences

LOQ 27-2 How do Gardner's and Sternberg's theories of multiple intelligences differ, and what criticisms have they faced?

Other psychologists, particularly since the mid-1980s, have sought to extend the definition of *intelligence* beyond the idea of academic smarts. One prominent theory based on the work of Raymond Cattell, John Horn, and John Carroll—the *Cattell-Horn-Carroll (CHC) theory*—affirmed a general intellectual ability factor, but also identified more specific abilities, such as reading and writing ability, memory capacity, and processing speed (Schneider & McGrew, 2012). Other psychologists have also offered theories of varied intelligence domains.

GARDNER'S MULTIPLE INTELLIGENCES Howard Gardner has identified eight *relatively independent intelligences,* including the verbal and mathematical aptitudes assessed by standardized tests (**FIGURE 27.1**).

Thus, the computer programmer, the poet, the street-smart adolescent, and the basketball team's play-making point guard exhibit different kinds of intelligence (Gardner, 1998). Gardner (1999a) has also proposed a ninth possible intelligence—*existential intelligence*—the ability "to ponder large questions about life, death, existence."

Gardner (1983, 2006, 2011; Davis et al., 2011) views these intelligence domains as multiple abilities that come in different packages. Brain damage, for example, may destroy one ability but leave others intact. And consider people with **savant syndrome,** who have an island of brilliance but often score low on intelligence tests and may have limited or no language ability (Treffert, 2010). Some can compute complicated calculations

ISLANDS OF GENIUS: SAVANT SYNDROME After a brief helicopter ride over Singapore followed by five days of drawing, British savant artist Stephen Wiltshire accurately reproduced an aerial view of the city from memory.

RETAIN 🔒 **FIGURE 27.1**

GARDNER'S EIGHT INTELLIGENCES Gardner has also proposed existential intelligence (the ability to ponder deep questions about life) as a ninth possible intelligence.

NATURALIST • LINGUISTIC • LOGICAL-MATHEMATICAL • MUSICAL • SPATIAL • BODILY-KINESTHETIC • INTRAPERSONAL • INTERPERSONAL

almost instantly, or identify the day of the week of any given historical date, or render incredible works of art or music (Miller, 1999).

About four in five people with savant syndrome are male, and many also have *autism spectrum disorder (ASD),* a developmental disorder. The late memory whiz Kim Peek (who did not have ASD) inspired the movie *Rain Man.* In 8 to 10 seconds, he could read and remember a page. During his lifetime, he memorized 9000 books, including Shakespeare's works and the Bible. He could provide GPS-like travel directions within any major U.S. city. Yet he could not button his clothes, and he had little capacity for abstract concepts. Asked by his father at a restaurant to lower his voice, he slid down in his chair to lower his voice box. Asked for Lincoln's Gettysburg Address, he responded, "227 North West Front Street. But he only stayed there one night—he gave the speech the next day" (Treffert & Christensen, 2005).

📲 **LaunchPad** To witness extraordinary savant ability in music, see the **Video: Savant Musical Skills.**

STERNBERG'S THREE INTELLIGENCES Robert Sternberg (1985, 2011) agrees with Gardner that there is more to success than traditional intelligence and that we have multiple intelligences. But Sternberg's *triarchic theory* proposes three, not eight or nine, intelligences:

- *Analytical (academic problem-solving) intelligence* is assessed by intelligence tests, which present well-defined problems having a single right answer. Such tests predict school grades reasonably well and vocational success more modestly.

- *Creative intelligence* is demonstrated in innovative smarts: the ability to adapt to new situations and generate novel ideas.

- *Practical intelligence* is required for everyday tasks that may be poorly defined and may have multiple solutions.

Gardner and Sternberg differ in some areas, but they agree on two important points: Multiple abilities can contribute to life success, and differing varieties of giftedness bring both spice to life and challenges for education. Trained to appreciate such variety, many teachers have applied multiple intelligence theories in their classrooms.

CRITICISMS OF MULTIPLE INTELLIGENCE THEORIES Wouldn't it be nice if the world were so fair that a weakness in one area would be compensated by genius in another? Alas, say critics, the world is not fair (Ferguson, 2009; Scarr, 1989). Research using factor analysis confirms that there *is* a general intelligence factor; g matters (Johnson et al., 2008). It predicts performance on various complex tasks and in various jobs (Gottfredson, 2002a,b, 2003a,b; see also **FIGURE 27.2**). And extremely high cognitive-ability scores predict exceptional achievements, such as doctoral degrees and publications (Kuncel & Hezlett, 2010).

Even so, "success" is not a one-ingredient recipe. It also helps to have the luck of an advantaged home and school, and to have been born in a time and place where your talents matter. And though high intelligence will help you get into a profession (via schools and training programs), it won't make you successful once there. Success is a combination of talent and *grit:* Those who become highly successful tend also to be conscientious, well connected, and doggedly energetic. K. Anders Ericsson and others report a *10-year rule:* A common ingredient of expert performance in chess, dance, sports, computer programming, music, and medicine is "about 10 years of intense, daily practice" (Ericsson, 2002; Ericsson & Pool, 2016; Simon & Chase, 1973). Becoming a

SPATIAL INTELLIGENCE GENIUS In 1998, World Checkers Champion Ron "Suki" King of Barbados set a new record by simultaneously playing 385 players in 3 hours and 44 minutes. Thus, while his opponents often had hours to plot their game moves, King could only devote about 35 seconds to each game. Yet he still managed to win all 385 games!

STREET SMARTS This child selling candy on the streets of Manaus, Brazil, is developing practical intelligence at a very young age.

 ASK YOURSELF

The concept of multiple intelligences assumes that the analytical school smarts measured by traditional intelligence tests are important, but that other abilities are also important. Different people have different gifts. What are yours?

FIGURE 27.2

SMART AND RICH? Jay Zagorsky (2007) tracked 7403 participants in the U.S. National Longitudinal Survey of Youth across 25 years. As shown in this illustrative scatterplot, their intelligence scores correlated +.30, a moderate positive correlation, with their later income.

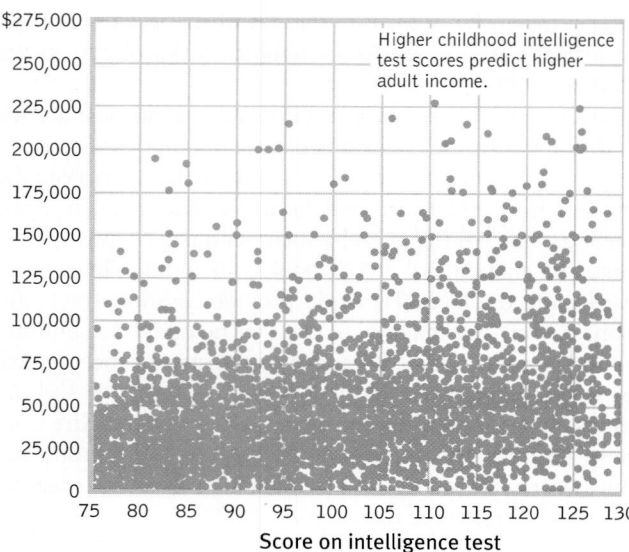

Annual income

Higher childhood intelligence test scores predict higher adult income.

Score on intelligence test

The procrastinator's motto: "Hard work pays off later; laziness pays off now."

"You have to be careful, if you're good at something, to make sure you don't think you're good at other things that you aren't necessarily so good at. . . . Because I've been very successful at [software development] people come in and expect that I have wisdom about topics that I don't." —Microsoft co-founder Bill Gates (1998)

professional musician or an elite athlete requires, first, native ability (Macnamara et al., 2014, 2016). But it also requires years of practice—about 11,000 hours on average, and a *minimum* of 3000 hours (Campitelli & Gobet, 2011). The recipe for success is a gift of nature plus a whole lot of nurture.

🔒 **RETRIEVE IT • • •**   ANSWERS IN APPENDIX E

RI-1 How does the existence of savant syndrome support Gardner's theory of multiple intelligences?

Emotional Intelligence

LOQ 27-3 What are the four components of emotional intelligence?

Social intelligence is the know-how involved in understanding social situations and managing yourself successfully (Cantor & Kihlstrom, 1987). Psychologist Edward Thorndike first proposed the concept in 1920, noting that "the best mechanic in a factory may fail as a foreman for lack of social intelligence" (Goleman, 2006, p. 83).

A critical part of social intelligence, **emotional intelligence,** consists of four abilities (Mayer et al., 2002, 2012, 2016):

- *Perceiving* emotions (recognizing them in faces, music, and stories)
- *Understanding* emotions (predicting them and how they may change and blend)
- *Managing* emotions (knowing how to express them in varied situations)
- *Using* emotions to enable adaptive or creative thinking

Emotionally intelligent people are both socially aware and self-aware. They avoid being hijacked by overwhelming depression, anxiety, or anger. They can read others' emotional cues and know what to say to soothe a grieving friend, encourage a workmate, and manage a conflict. They can delay gratification in pursuit of long-range rewards. Thus, emotionally intelligent people more often succeed in relationship, career, and parenting situations where academically smarter but less emotionally intelligent people might fail (Cherniss, 2010a,b; Czarna et al., 2016; Miao et al., 2016). They also tend to be happy and healthy (Sánchez-Álvarez et al., 2016; Schutte et al., 2007, 2016). Aware of these benefits, school-based programs have sought to increase teachers' and students' emotional intelligence (Castillo-Gualda et al., 2017; Nathanson et al., 2016).

"You're wise, but you lack tree smarts."

Some scholars, however, are concerned that emotional intelligence stretches the intelligence concept too far (Visser et al., 2006). Howard Gardner (1999b) includes interpersonal and intrapersonal intelligences as two of his multiple intelligences. But he notes that we should respect emotional sensitivity, creativity, and motivation as important but different. Stretch *intelligence* to include everything we prize and the word will lose its meaning.

* * *

For a summary of these theories of intelligence, see **TABLE 27.1**.

 LaunchPad Engage online with **Concept Practice: Theories of Intelligence** to review these different approaches to intelligence.

TABLE 27.1

Comparing Theories of Intelligence

Theory	Summary	Strengths	Other Considerations
Spearman's general intelligence (g)	A basic intelligence predicts our abilities in varied academic areas.	Different abilities, such as verbal and spatial, do have some tendency to correlate.	Human abilities are too diverse to be encapsulated by a single general intelligence factor.
Gardner's multiple intelligences	Our abilities are best classified into eight or nine independent intelligences, which include a broad range of skills beyond traditional school smarts.	Intelligence is more than just verbal and mathematical skills. Other abilities are equally important to our human adaptability.	Should all our abilities be considered *intelligences*? Shouldn't some be called less vital *talents*?
Sternberg's triarchic theory	Our intelligence is best classified into three areas that predict real-world success: analytical, creative, and practical.	These three domains can be reliably measured.	These three domains may be less independent than Sternberg thought and may actually share an underlying *g* factor.
Emotional intelligence	Social intelligence is an important indicator of life success. Emotional intelligence is a key aspect, consisting of perceiving, understanding, managing, and using emotions.	These four components predict social success and emotional well-being.	Does this stretch the concept of intelligence too far?

ASSESSING INTELLIGENCE

LOQ 27-4 What is an *intelligence test,* and how do achievement and aptitude tests differ?

An **intelligence test** assesses people's mental aptitudes and compares them with those of others, using numerical scores. How do psychologists design such tests, and what makes them credible?

In your lifetime, you've taken dozens of mental ability tests, which can be categorized into two general categories:

- **Achievement tests,** which are intended to *reflect* what you have learned. Your final exam will measure what you learned in this class.
- **Aptitude tests,** which are intended to *predict* your ability to learn some new skill. If you took a college entrance exam, it was designed to predict your ability to do college work.

Let's consider why psychologists created and used such tests of mental abilities.

What Do Intelligence Tests Test?

LOQ 27-5 When and why were intelligence tests created, and how do today's tests differ from early intelligence tests?

Barely more than a century ago, psychologists began designing tests to assess people's mental abilities. Modern intelligence testing traces its birth to early-twentieth-century France.

emotional intelligence the ability to perceive, understand, manage, and use emotions.

intelligence test a method for assessing an individual's mental aptitudes and comparing them with those of others, using numerical scores.

achievement test a test designed to assess what a person has learned.

aptitude test a test designed to predict a person's future performance; *aptitude* is the capacity to learn.

 ASK YOURSELF

What achievement or aptitude tests have you taken? In your opinion, how well did these tests assess what you'd learned or predict what you were capable of learning?

ALFRED BINET (1857–1911) "Some recent philosophers have given their moral approval to the deplorable verdict that an individual's intelligence is a fixed quantity, one which cannot be augmented. We must protest and act against this brutal pessimism" (Binet, 1909, p. 141).

"The IQ test was invented to predict academic performance, nothing else. If we wanted something that would predict life success, we'd have to invent another test completely."
—Social psychologist Robert Zajonc (1984b)

Mrs. Randolph takes mother's pride too far.

ALFRED BINET: PREDICTING SCHOOL ACHIEVEMENT With a new French law that required all children to attend school, officials knew that some children, including many newcomers to Paris, would struggle and need special classes. But how could the schools make fair judgments about children's learning potential? Teachers might assess children who had little prior education as slow learners. Or they might sort children into classes on the basis of their social backgrounds. To minimize such bias, France's minister of public education gave psychologist Alfred Binet the task of designing fair tests.

Binet and his student, Théodore Simon, began by assuming that all children follow the same course of intellectual development but that some develop more rapidly (Nicolas & Levine, 2012). A "dull" child should score much like a typical younger child, and a "bright" child like a typical older child. Thus, their goal became measuring each child's **mental age,** the level of performance typically associated with a certain chronological age. The average 8-year-old, for example, has a mental age of 8. An 8-year-old with a below-average mental age (perhaps performing at the level of a typical 6-year-old) would struggle with schoolwork considered normal for 8-year-olds.

Binet and Simon tested a variety of reasoning and problem-solving questions on Binet's two daughters, and then on "bright" and "backward" Parisian schoolchildren. Items answered correctly could then predict how well other French children would handle their schoolwork. Binet hoped his test would be used to improve children's education, but he also feared it would be used to label children and limit their opportunities (Gould, 1981).

🔒 **RETRIEVE IT • • •**   ANSWERS IN APPENDIX E

RI-2 What did Binet hope to achieve by establishing a child's mental age?

LEWIS TERMAN: MEASURING INNATE INTELLIGENCE After Binet's death in 1911, others adapted his tests for use as a numerical measure of intelligence. Stanford University professor Lewis Terman (1877–1956) tried the Paris-developed questions and age norms with California kids. Adapting some of Binet's original items, adding others, and establishing new age norms, Terman extended the upper end of the test's range from age 12 to "superior adults." He also gave his revision the name today's version retains—the **Stanford-Binet.**

From such tests, German psychologist William Stern derived the famous **intelligence quotient,** or **IQ.** The IQ was simply a person's mental age divided by chronological age and multiplied by 100 to get rid of the decimal point. Thus, an average child, whose mental age (8) and chronological age (8) are the same, has an IQ of 100. But an 8-year-old who answers questions at the level of a typical 10-year-old has an IQ of 125:

$$IQ = \frac{\text{mental age of 10}}{\text{chronological age of 8}} \times 100 = 125$$

The original IQ formula worked fairly well for children but not for adults. (Should a 40-year-old who does as well on the test as an average 20-year-old be assigned an IQ of only 50?) Most current intelligence tests, including the Stanford-Binet, no longer compute an IQ in this manner (though the term *IQ* still lingers in everyday vocabulary as shorthand for "intelligence test score"). Instead, they represent the test-taker's performance *relative to the average performance* (which is arbitrarily set at 100) of others the same age. Most people—about 68 percent of those taking an intelligence test)—fall between 85 and 115.

Terman inferred that intelligence tests revealed a mental capacity present from birth. He also assumed that some ethnic groups were naturally more intelligent than others. And he supported the controversial *eugenics* movement—the much-criticized nineteenth-century movement that proposed measuring human traits and using the results to encourage only smart and fit people to reproduce.

With Terman's help, the U.S. government developed new tests to evaluate both newly arriving immigrants and World War I army recruits—the world's first mass administration of an intelligence test. To some psychologists, the results indicated the inferiority of people not sharing their Anglo-Saxon heritage. Such findings were part of the cultural climate that led to a 1924 immigration law that reduced Southern and Eastern immigration quotas to be less than a fifth of those for Northern and Western Europe.

Binet probably would have been horrified that his test had been adapted and used to draw such conclusions. Indeed, such sweeping judgments became an embarrassment to most of those who championed testing. Even Terman came to appreciate that test scores reflected not only people's innate mental abilities but also their education, native language, and familiarity with the culture assumed by the test. Abuses of the early intelligence tests serve to remind us that science can be value-laden. Behind a screen of scientific objectivity, ideology sometimes lurks.

DAVID WECHSLER: TESTING SEPARATE STRENGTHS Psychologist David Wechsler created what is now the most widely used individual intelligence test, the **Wechsler Adult Intelligence Scale (WAIS).** There is a version for school-age children (the *Wechsler Intelligence Scale for Children [WISC]*), and another for preschool children (Evers et al., 2012). The 2008 WAIS edition (with a new version anticipated in 2020) consists of 15 subtests, including:

- *Similarities*—reasoning the commonality of two objects or concepts ("In what way are wool and cotton alike?")
- *Vocabulary*—naming pictured objects, or defining words ("What is a guitar?")
- *Block design*—visual abstract processing ("Using the four blocks, make one just like this.")
- *Letter-number sequencing*—on hearing a series of numbers and letters ("R-2-C-1-M-3"), repeating the numbers in ascending order, and then the letters in alphabetical order

The WAIS yields both an overall intelligence score and separate scores for verbal comprehension, perceptual reasoning, working memory, and processing speed. In such ways, this test helps realize Binet's aim: to identify those who could benefit from special educational opportunities for improvement.

MATCHING PATTERNS Block-design puzzles test visual abstract processing ability. Wechsler's individually administered intelligence test comes in forms suited for adults and children.

ENGAGE **LaunchPad** To learn more about the promise and perils of intelligence testing, watch the **Video: Locking Away the "Feebleminded"— A Shameful History.** And to test your own performance on simulated WAIS subtasks, see **Concept Practice: Wechsler Intelligence Tasks.**

> ## 🔒 RETRIEVE IT • • •
> *ANSWERS IN APPENDIX E*
>
> **RI-3** What is the IQ of a 4-year-old with a mental age of 5?
>
> **RI-4** An employer with a pool of applicants for a single available position is interested in testing each applicant's potential. To determine that, she should use an _____ (achievement/aptitude) test. That same employer wishing to test the effectiveness of a new, on-the-job training program would be wise to use an _____ (achievement/aptitude) test.

Three Tests of a "Good" Test

LOQ 27-6 What is a *normal curve,* and what does it mean to say that a test has been *standardized* and is *reliable* and *valid?*

To be widely accepted, a psychological test must be *standardized, reliable,* and *valid.* The Stanford-Binet and Wechsler tests meet these requirements.

WAS THE TEST STANDARDIZED? The number of questions you answer correctly on an intelligence test would reveal almost nothing. To know how well you performed, you would need some basis for comparison. That's why test-makers give new tests to a representative sample of people. The scores from this pretested group become the basis for future comparisons. If you then take the test following the same procedures, your score will be meaningful when compared with others. This process is called **standardization.** To keep the average score near 100, the Stanford-Binet and Wechsler scales are periodically restandardized. If you recently took the WAIS, Fourth Edition, your performance was compared with the standardization sample who took the test during 2007, not to David Wechsler's initial 1930s sample.

mental age a measure of intelligence test performance devised by Binet; the level of performance typically associated with children of a certain chronological age. Thus, a child who does as well as an average 8-year-old is said to have a mental age of 8.

Stanford-Binet the widely used American revision (by Terman at Stanford University) of Binet's original intelligence test.

intelligence quotient (IQ) defined originally as the ratio of mental age *(ma)* to chronological age *(ca)* multiplied by 100 (thus, IQ = *ma/ca* × 100). On contemporary intelligence tests, the average performance for a given age is assigned a score of 100.

Wechsler Adult Intelligence Scale (WAIS) the WAIS and its companion versions for children are the most widely used intelligence tests; they contain verbal and performance (nonverbal) subtests.

standardization defining uniform testing procedures and meaningful scores by comparison with the performance of a pretested group.

FIGURE 27.3

THE NORMAL CURVE Scores on aptitude tests tend to form a normal, or bell-shaped, curve around an average score. For the Wechsler scale, for example, the average score is 100.

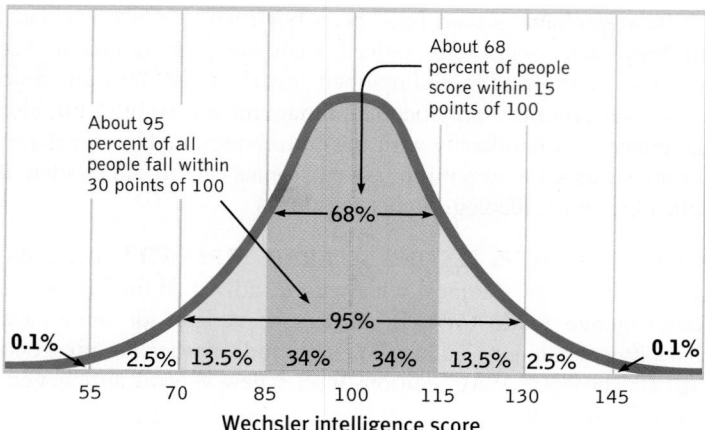

Number of scores

About 95 percent of all people fall within 30 points of 100

About 68 percent of people score within 15 points of 100

68%

95%

0.1%   2.5% 13.5%   34%   34% 13.5% 2.5%   0.1%

55   70   85   100   115   130   145

Wechsler intelligence score

If we construct a graph of test-takers' scores, the scores typically form a bell-shaped pattern called the *bell curve, or* **normal curve.** For many human attributes—including height, weight, and mental aptitude—the curve's highest point is the average score. On an intelligence test, we give this average score a value of 100 (**FIGURE 27.3**). Moving out from the average, toward either extreme, we find fewer and fewer people. For both the Stanford-Binet and Wechsler tests, a person's score indicates whether that person's performance fell above or below the average. A performance higher than all but 2.5 percent of all scores earns an intelligence score of 130. A performance lower than 97.5 percent of all scores earns an intelligence score of 70.

IS THE TEST RELIABLE? Knowing where you stand in comparison to a standardization group still won't say much about your intelligence unless the test has **reliability.** A reliable test gives consistent scores, no matter who takes the test or when they take it. To check a test's reliability, researchers test people many times. They may split the test in half (*split-half*: agreement of odd-question scores and even-question scores), test with alternative forms of the test, or retest with the same test (*test-retest*). The higher the *correlation* between the two scores, the higher the test's reliability. The tests we have considered—the Stanford-Binet, the WAIS, and the WISC—are very reliable after early childhood (with *correlation coefficients* of about +.9). In retests, sometimes decades later, people's scores generally are similar to the first score (Lyons et al., 2017).

📺 **LaunchPad** Watch the **Video: Correlational Studies** for a helpful tutorial animation.

IS THE TEST VALID? High reliability does not ensure a test's **validity**—the extent to which the test actually measures or predicts what it promises. Imagine using a tape measure with faulty markings. If you use it to measure people's heights, your results will be very reliable. No matter how many times you measure, people's heights will be the same. But your faulty height results will not be valid.

We expect intelligence tests to have **predictive validity:** They should predict future performance, and to some extent they do. The predictive power of aptitude tests is fairly strong in the early school years (Roth et al., 2015). But later it weakens.

🔒 **RETRIEVE IT • • •**

ANSWERS IN APPENDIX E

RI-5 What are the three criteria that a psychological test must meet in order to be widely accepted? Explain.

RI-6 Correlation coefficients were used in this section. Here's a quick review: Correlations do not indicate cause-effect, but they do tell us whether two things are associated in some way. A correlation of –1.00 represents perfect _____ (agreement/disagreement) between two sets of scores: As one score goes up, the other score goes _____ (up/down). A correlation of _____ represents no association. The highest correlation, +1.00, represents perfect _____ (agreement/disagreement): As the first score goes up, the other score goes _____ (up/down).

Extremes of Intelligence

LOQ 27-7 What are the traits of those at the low and high intelligence extremes?

One way to glimpse the validity and significance of any test is to compare people who score at the two extremes of the normal curve. The two groups should differ noticeably, and on intelligence tests, they do.

THE LOW EXTREME **Intellectual disability** (formerly called *mental retardation*) is a developmental condition that is apparent before age 18, sometimes with a known physical cause. (*Down syndrome*, for example, is a disorder of varying intellectual and physical severity caused by an extra copy of chromosome 21 in the person's genetic makeup.) To be diagnosed with an intellectual disability, a person must meet two criteria:

1. An intelligence test score indicating performance that is in the lowest 3 percent of the general population, or about 70 or below (Schalock et al., 2010).

2. Difficulty adapting to the normal demands of independent living, as expressed in three areas, or skills: *conceptual* (language, reading, and concepts of money, time, and number); *social* (interpersonal skills, being socially responsible, following basic rules and laws, avoiding being victimized); and *practical* (health and personal care, occupational skill, and travel). In mild forms, intellectual disability, like normal intelligence, results from a combination of genetic and environmental factors (Reichenberg et al., 2016).

For some, intelligence test scores can mean life or death. In the United States (one of the only industrialized countries with the death penalty), fewer people are now eligible for execution. Why? Because in 2002, the U.S. Supreme Court ruled that the execution of people with an intellectual disability—defined as a test score below 70—is "cruel and unusual punishment." For Teresa Lewis, that cutoff was high stakes. Lewis, a "dependent personality" with limited intellect (a reported test score of 72), allegedly agreed to a plot in which two men killed her husband and stepson in exchange for a split of a life insurance payout (Eckholm, 2010). The State of Virginia executed Lewis in 2010. If only she had scored 69.

In 2014, the U.S. Supreme Court recognized the imprecision and arbitrariness of a fixed cutoff score of 70. And it required states with death row inmates who have scored just above 70 to consider other evidence. Thus Ted Herring, who had scored 72 and 74 on intelligence tests—but without knowing that summer follows spring or how to transfer between buses—was taken off Florida's death row (Alvarez & Schwartz, 2014).

> 🔒 **RETRIEVE IT • • •**   *ANSWERS IN APPENDIX E*
>
> **RI-7** Why do psychologists NOT diagnose an intellectual disability based solely on a person's intelligence test score?

THE HIGH EXTREME In one famous project begun in 1921, Lewis Terman studied more than 1500 California schoolchildren with IQ scores over 135. Terman's high-scoring children (later called the "Termites") were—like those in later studies—healthy, well adjusted, and unusually successful academically (Friedman & Martin, 2012; Koenen et al., 2009; Lubinski, 2009, 2016). When restudied over the next seven decades, most people in Terman's group had attained high levels of education (Austin et al., 2002; Holahan & Sears, 1995). Many were doctors, lawyers, professors, scientists, and writers, though none were Nobel Prize winners.

Other studies have followed the lives of precocious youths who had aced the math SAT at age 13—by scoring in the top 1 percent of their age group. By their fifties, these 1650 math whizzes had secured 681 patents (Lubinski et al., 2014). Another group of 13-year-old verbal aptitude high scorers were, by age 38, twice as likely as the math aces to have become humanities professors or written a novel (Kell et al., 2013). About 1 percent of Americans earn doctorates. But for the 12- and 13-year-olds who scored in the top 1 in 10,000 among those of their age taking the SAT, about 4 in 10 had done so (Kell et al., 2013; Makel et al., 2016). One of psychology's whiz kids was Jean Piaget, who by age 15 was publishing scientific articles on mollusks and who went on to become

normal curve the bell-shaped curve that describes the distribution of many physical and psychological attributes. Most scores fall near the average, and fewer and fewer scores lie near the extremes.

reliability the extent to which a test yields consistent results, as assessed by the consistency of scores on two halves of the test, on alternative forms of the test, or on retesting.

validity the extent to which a test measures or predicts what it is supposed to. (See also *predictive validity*.)

predictive validity the success with which a test predicts the behavior it is designed to predict; it is assessed by computing the correlation between test scores and the criterion behavior. (Also called *criterion-related validity*.)

intellectual disability a condition of limited mental ability, indicated by an intelligence test score of 70 or below and difficulty adapting to the demands of life. (Formerly referred to as *mental retardation*.)

"Zach is in the gifted-and-talented-and-you're-not class."

Terman did test two future Nobel laureates in physics, but they failed to score above his gifted sample cutoff (Hulbert, 2005).

Among the high-scoring whiz kids in national searches for precocious youth were Google co-founder Sergey Brin, Facebook's Mark Zuckerberg, and musician Stefani Germanotta (Lady Gaga) (Clynes, 2016). Another became a professional poker player with $100,000+ annual earnings (Lubinski, 2016).

the twentieth century's most famous developmental psychologist (Hunt, 1993). Children with extraordinary academic gifts are sometimes more isolated, shy, and in their own worlds (Winner, 2000). But most thrive.

INTELLIGENCE ACROSS THE LIFE SPAN

What happens to our intellectual muscles as we age? Do they gradually decline, as does our body strength? Or do they remain constant? To see how psychologists track intelligence across the lifetime, see Thinking Critically About: Cross-Sectional and Longitudinal Studies. The quest for answers to such questions illustrates psychology's self-correcting process.

Stability or Change?

LOQ 27-9   How stable are intelligence test scores over the life span?

What can we predict from a child's early-life intelligence scores? Will a precocious 2-year-old mature into a talented college student and a brilliant senior citizen? Maybe—or maybe not. For most children, casual observation and intelligence tests before age 3 only modestly predict their future aptitudes (Humphreys & Davey, 1988; Tasbihsazan et al., 2003). Even Albert Einstein was once thought "slow"—as he was in learning to talk (Quasha, 1980).

By age 4, however, children's performance on intelligence tests begins to predict their adolescent and adult scores. The consistency of scores over time increases with the age of the child (Tucker-Drob & Briley, 2014). By age 11, the stability becomes impressive, as Ian Deary and his colleagues (2004, 2009b, 2013) discovered when they retested the same **cohort**—the same group of people—over a period of years. Their amazing longitudinal

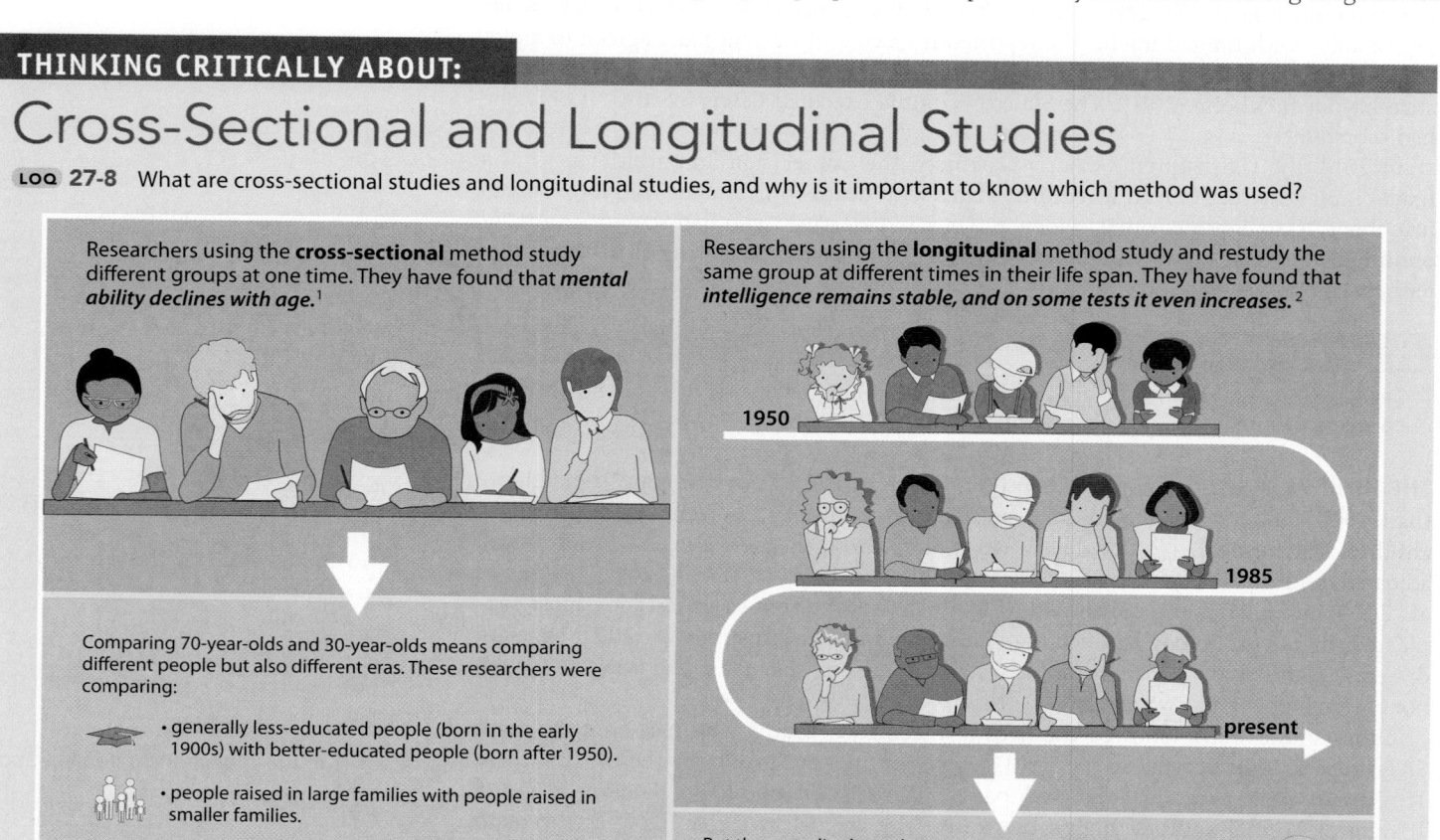

THINKING CRITICALLY ABOUT:
Cross-Sectional and Longitudinal Studies

LOQ 27-8   What are cross-sectional studies and longitudinal studies, and why is it important to know which method was used?

Researchers using the **cross-sectional** method study different groups at one time. They have found that *mental ability declines with age.*[1]

Comparing 70-year-olds and 30-year-olds means comparing different people but also different eras. These researchers were comparing:

- generally less-educated people (born in the early 1900s) with better-educated people (born after 1950).
- people raised in large families with people raised in smaller families.
- people from less-affluent families with people from more-affluent families.

Researchers using the **longitudinal** method study and restudy the same group at different times in their life span. They have found that *intelligence remains stable, and on some tests it even increases.*[2]

1950

1985

present

But these studies have their own issue. Participants who survive to the end may be the healthiest and brightest people. When researchers adjust for loss of participants, they find an intelligence decline, especially after age 85.[3]

RIP

1. Wechsler, 1972. 2. Salthouse, 2010, 2014; Schaie & Geiwitz, 1982. 3. Brayne et al., 1999.

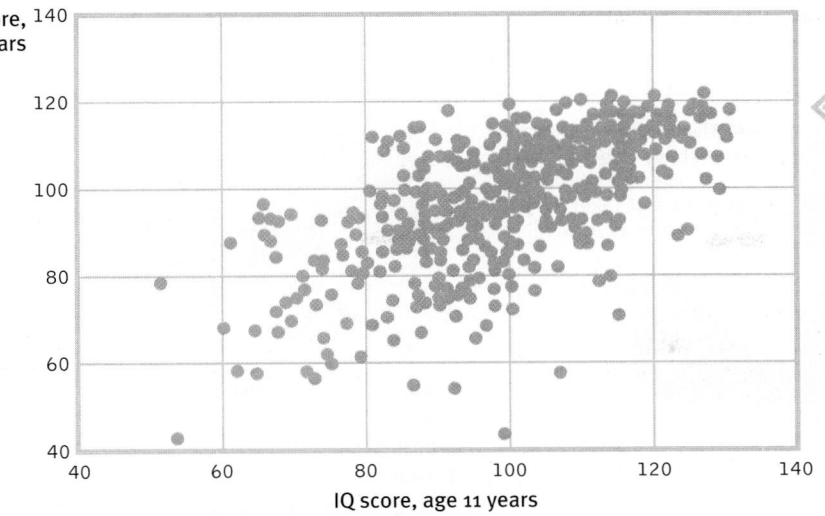

IQ score, age 80 years (y-axis, ranging 40 to 140)
IQ score, age 11 years (x-axis, ranging 40 to 140)

FIGURE 27.4

INTELLIGENCE ENDURES When Ian Deary and his colleagues retested 80-year-old Scots, using an intelligence test they had taken as 11-year-olds, their scores across seven decades correlated +0.66, as shown here. (Data from Deary et al., 2004.) When 106 survivors were again retested at age 90, the correlation with their age 11 scores was +0.54 (Deary et al., 2013).

studies have been enabled by their country, Scotland, doing something no nation has done before or since. On June 1, 1932, essentially every child in the country born in 1921—87,498 children around age 11—took an intelligence test. The aim was to identify working-class children who would benefit from further education. Sixty-five years later to the day, Patricia Whalley, the wife of Deary's co-worker, Lawrence Whalley, discovered the test results on dusty storeroom shelves at the Scottish Council for Research in Education, not far from Deary's Edinburgh University office. "This will change our lives," Deary replied when Whalley told him the news.

And so it has, with dozens of studies of the stability and the predictive capacity of these early test results. One of Deary's studies, for example, retested 542 survivors—now turn-of-the-millennium 80-year-olds—using the same intelligence test they had taken as 11-year-olds in 1932. The result? The correlation between the two sets of scores—after nearly 70 years of varied life experiences—was striking (**FIGURE 27.4**). Ditto when 106 survivors were retested at age 90 (Deary et al., 2013). Another study that followed Scots born in 1936 from ages 11 to 70 confirmed the remarkable stability of intelligence, independent of life circumstance (Johnson et al., 2010).

Children and adults who are more intelligent tend to live healthier and longer lives (Calvin et al., 2017). Why might this be the case? Deary (2008) has proposed four possible explanations:

1. Intelligence facilitates more education, better jobs, and a healthier environment.

2. Intelligence encourages healthy living: less smoking, better diet, more exercise.

3. Prenatal events or early childhood illnesses can influence both intelligence and health.

4. A "well-wired body," as evidenced by fast reaction speeds, perhaps fosters both intelligence and longevity.

LaunchPad Play the role of a researcher studying these issues by engaging online with **Immersive Learning: How Would You Know If Intelligence Changes With Age?**

"Whether you live to collect your old-age pension depends in part on your IQ at age 11." —Ian Deary, "Intelligence, Health, and Death," 2005

Women scoring in the highest 25 percent on the Scottish national intelligence test at age 11 tended to live longer than those who scored in the lowest 25 percent. "On average," reports Deary (2016), "a girl with a 30-point disadvantage in IQ on this 45-minute test at age 11 was half as likely to be alive" 65 years later.

Aging and Intelligence

LOQ 27-10 How does aging affect crystallized and fluid intelligence?

Does intelligence increase, decrease, or remain constant as we age? The answer depends on the type of intellectual performance we measure:

- **Crystallized intelligence**—our accumulated knowledge as reflected in vocabulary and analogies tests—*increases* up to old age.

- **Fluid intelligence**—our ability to reason speedily and abstractly, as when solving novel logic problems—*decreases* beginning in the twenties and thirties, slowly up to age 75 or so, then more rapidly, especially after age 85 (Cattell, 1963; Deary & Ritchie, 2016; Salthouse, 2009; 2013).

cohort a group of people sharing a common characteristic, such as being from a given time period.

cross-sectional study research that compares people of different ages at the same point in time.

longitudinal study research that follows and retests the same people over time.

crystallized intelligence our accumulated knowledge and verbal skills; tends to increase with age.

fluid intelligence our ability to reason speedily and abstractly; tends to decrease with age, especially during late adulthood.

FIGURE 27.5

WITH AGE, WE LOSE AND WE WIN. Studies reveal that word power grows with age, while fluid intelligence declines. (Data from Salthouse, 2010.)

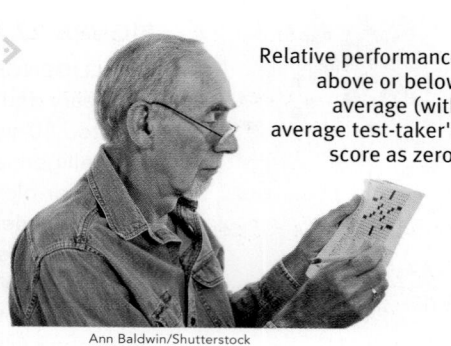
Ann Baldwin/Shutterstock

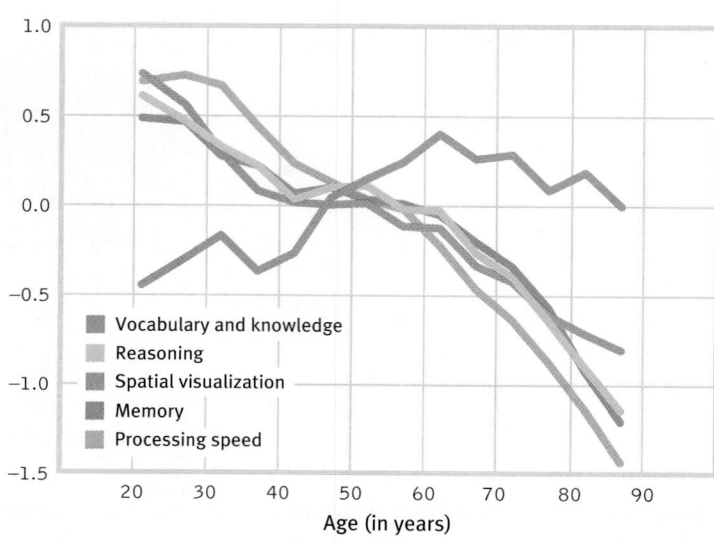

Relative performance above or below average (with average test-taker's score as zero)

- Vocabulary and knowledge
- Reasoning
- Spatial visualization
- Memory
- Processing speed

Age (in years)

"Knowledge is knowing a tomato is a fruit; wisdom is not putting it in a fruit salad." —Anonymous

© Randy Glasbergen

"We're looking for someone with the wisdom of a 50-year-old, the experience of a 40-year-old, the drive of a 30-year-old, and the payscale of a 20-year-old."

"In youth we learn, in age we understand." —Marie Von Ebner-Eschenbach, *Aphorisms*, 1883

With age we lose and we win. We lose recall memory and processing speed, but we gain vocabulary and knowledge (**FIGURE 27.5**). Fluid intelligence may decline, but older adults' social-reasoning skills increase, as shown by an ability to take multiple perspectives, to appreciate knowledge limits, and to offer helpful wisdom in times of social conflict (Grossman et al., 2010). Decisions also become less distorted by negative emotions such as anxiety, depression, and anger (Blanchard-Fields, 2007; Carstensen & Mikels, 2005).

Age-related cognitive differences help explain why older adults are less likely to embrace new technologies (Charness & Boot, 2009; Pew, 2017). These cognitive differences also help explain why mathematicians and scientists produce much of their most creative work during their late twenties or early thirties, when fluid intelligence is at its peak (Jones et al., 2014). In contrast, authors, historians, and philosophers tend to produce their best work in their forties, fifties, and beyond—after accumulating more knowledge (Simonton, 1988, 1990). Poets, for example, who depend on fluid intelligence, reach their peak output earlier than prose authors, who need the deeper knowledge reservoir that accumulates with age. This finding holds in every major literary tradition, for both living and dead languages.

🔒 RETRIEVE IT • • •   *ANSWERS IN APPENDIX E*

RI-8 Researcher A wants to study how intelligence changes over the life span. Researcher B wants to study the intelligence of people who are now at various life stages. Which researcher should use the cross-sectional method, and which the longitudinal method?

LaunchPad Watch the **Video: Longitudinal and Cross-Sectional Studies** for a helpful tutorial animation.

🔒 REVIEW   INTELLIGENCE AND ITS ASSESSMENT

⟫ Learning Objectives

TEST YOURSELF Answer these repeated Learning Objective Questions on your own (before checking the answers in Appendix D) to improve your retention of the concepts (McDaniel et al., 2009, 2015).

27-1 How do psychologists define *intelligence*, and what are the arguments for *g*?

27-2 How do Gardner's and Sternberg's theories of multiple intelligences differ, and what criticisms have they faced?

27-3 What are the four components of emotional intelligence?

27-4 What is an *intelligence test*, and how do achievement and aptitude tests differ?

27-5 When and why were intelligence tests created, and how do today's tests differ from early intelligence tests?

27-6 What is a *normal curve*, and what does it mean to say that a test has been *standardized* and is *reliable* and *valid*?

27-7 What are the traits of those at the low and high intelligence extremes?

27-8 What are cross-sectional studies and longitudinal studies, and why is it important to know which method was used?

27-9 How stable are intelligence test scores over the life span?

27-10 How does aging affect crystallized and fluid intelligence?

⟿ Terms and Concepts to Remember

TEST YOURSELF Write down the definition yourself, then check your answer on the referenced page.

⟿ Experience the Testing Effect

TEST YOURSELF Answer the following questions on your own first, then check your answers in Appendix E.

1. Charles Spearman suggested we have one _____ _____ underlying success across a variety of intellectual abilities.

2. The existence of savant syndrome seems to support
   a. Sternberg's distinction among three types of intelligence.
   b. criticism of multiple intelligence theories.
   c. Gardner's theory of multiple intelligences.
   d. Thorndike's view of social intelligence.

3. Sternberg's three types of intelligence are _____, _____, and _____.

4. Emotionally intelligent people tend to
   a. seek immediate gratification.
   b. understand their own emotions but not those of others.
   c. understand others' emotions but not their own.
   d. succeed in their careers.

5. The IQ of a 6-year-old with a measured mental age of 9 would be
   a. 67.
   b. 133.
   c. 86.
   d. 150.

6. The Wechsler Adult Intelligence Scale (WAIS) is best able to tell us
   a. what part of an individual's intelligence is determined by genetic inheritance.
   b. whether the test-taker will succeed in a job.
   c. how the test-taker compares with other adults in vocabulary and arithmetic reasoning.
   d. whether the test-taker has specific skills for music and the performing arts.

7. The Stanford-Binet, the Wechsler Adult Intelligence Scale, and the Wechsler Intelligence Scale for Children yield consistent results, for example on retesting. In other words, these tests have high _____.

8. Use the concepts of crystallized and fluid intelligence to explain why writers tend to produce their most creative work later in life, while scientists often hit their peak much earlier.

9. Which of the following is NOT a possible explanation for the fact that more intelligent people tend to live longer, healthier lives?
   a. Intelligence facilitates more education, better jobs, and a healthier environment.
   b. Intelligence encourages a more health-promoting lifestyle.
   c. Intelligent people have slower reaction times, so are less likely to put themselves at risk.
   d. Prenatal events or early childhood illnesses could influence both intelligence and health.

Continue testing yourself with ⟿ **LearningCurve** or ⟿ **Achieve Read & Practice** to learn and remember most effectively.

28 Genetic and Environmental Influences on Intelligence

"I told my parents that if grades were so important they should have paid for a smarter egg donor."

Intelligence runs in families. But why? Are our intellectual abilities mostly inherited? Or are they molded by our environment? Few issues in psychology arouse so much passion. Let's examine some of the evidence, focusing on these questions:

• What do twin and adoption studies tell us about how heredity and experience influence intelligence?

• Can extreme environmental influences amplify or diminish intelligence?

• What intelligence test score similarities and differences exist among groups, and what accounts for those differences?

HEREDITY AND INTELLIGENCE

LOQ 28-1 What is *heritability*, and what do twin and adoption studies tell us about the nature and nurture of intelligence?

Heritability is the portion of variation among people in a group that we can attribute to genes. Estimates of the heritability of intelligence—the extent to which intelligence test score variation within a group can be attributed to genetic variation—range from 50 to 80 percent (Madison et al., 2016; Plomin et al., 2016). Does this mean that we can assume that 50 percent of *your* intelligence is due to your genes, and the rest to your environment? *No.* Heritability never applies to an individual, only to *why people in a group differ from one another.*

The heritability of intelligence varies from study to study. To see why, consider humorist Mark Twain's fantasy of raising boys in barrels until age 12, feeding them through a hole. Let's take his joke a step further and say we'll give all those boys an intelligence test at age 12. Since their *environments* were all equal, any difference in their test scores could only be due to heredity—thus, heritability would be 100 percent. But what if a mad scientist cloned 100 boys and raised them in drastically different environments (some in barrels and others in mansions)? In this case, *heredity* would be equal, so any test-score differences could only be due to environment. The environmental effect would be 100 percent, and heritability would be zero.

In real life, we can't clone people to study the effects of heredity and environment. But nature has done that work for us. Identical twins share the same genes. Do they also share the same mental abilities? As you can see from **FIGURE 28.1**, which summarizes many studies, the answer is clearly *Yes.* Even when adopted by two different families, their intelligence test scores are very similar. When raised together, their scores are nearly as similar as those of the same person taking the same test twice (Haworth et al., 2009; Lykken, 2006; Plomin et al., 2016). Identical twins also exhibit substantial similarity (and heritability) in specific talents, such as music, math, and sports.

Scans reveal that identical twins' brains have similar gray- and white-matter volume, and the areas associated with verbal and spatial intelligence are virtually the same (Deary et al., 2009a; Thompson et al., 2001). Their brains also show similar activity while doing mental tasks (Koten et al., 2009).

Although genes matter, there is no known "genius" gene. When 200 researchers pooled their data on 126,559 people, all the gene variations analyzed accounted for only about 2 percent of the differences in educational achievement (Rietveld et al., 2013, 2014). Others have replicated this modest effect (Belsky et al., 2016). One follow-up British study, using

heritability the proportion of variation among individuals in a group that we can attribute to genes. The heritability of a trait may vary, depending on the range of populations and environments studied.

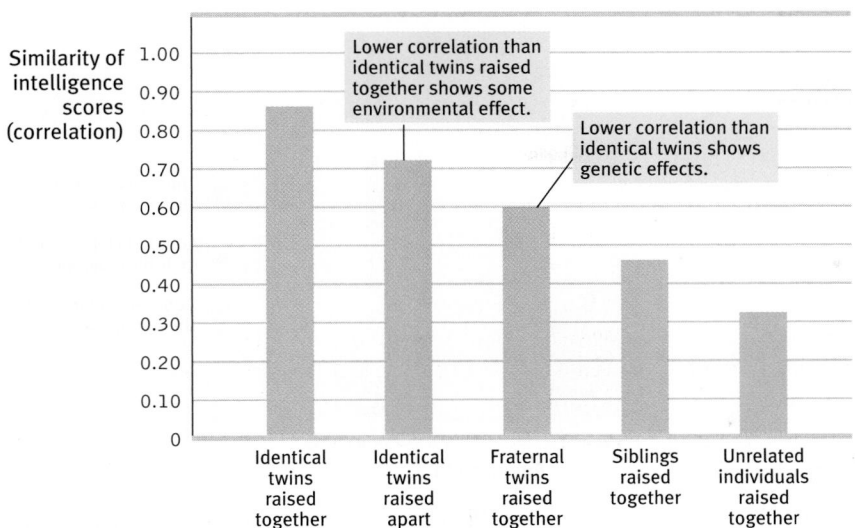

FIGURE 28.1

INTELLIGENCE: NATURE AND NURTURE The most genetically similar people have the most similar intelligence scores. Remember: 1.00 indicates a perfect correlation; zero indicates no correlation at all. (Data from McGue et al., 1993.)

a new genetic method, found genes that together predicted 9 percent of school achievement variation at age 16 (Selzam et al., 2016). This much seems clear: Like height, intelligence is *polygenetic,* involving many genes (Johnson, 2010). More than 50 specific gene variations together account for 5 percent of our individual height differences, leaving the rest yet to be discovered. What matters for intelligence (as for height, personality, sexual orientation, schizophrenia, or just about any human trait) is the combination of many genes—including 52 intelligence-linked genes identified in one pooling of findings from nearly 80,000 people (Sniekers et al., 2017).

ENVIRONMENT AND INTELLIGENCE

Fraternal twins are genetically no more alike than other siblings, but they usually share an environment and are often treated similarly. Their intelligence test scores are also more alike than are the scores of two other siblings (see Figure 28.1). So environment does have some effect. Adoption studies help us assess the influence of environment. Seeking to untangle genes and environment, researchers have compared the intelligence test scores of adopted children with those of their

- *biological parents* (who provided their genes).
- *adoptive parents* (who provided their home environment).
- *adoptive siblings* (who shared that home environment).

Several studies suggest that a shared environment exerts a modest influence on intelligence test scores.

- Adoption from poverty into middle-class homes enhances children's intelligence test scores (Nisbett et al., 2012). One large Swedish study looked at this effect among children adopted into wealthier families with more educated parents. The adopted children's test scores were higher, by an average of 4.4 points, than those of their not-adopted biological siblings (Kendler et al., 2015a).
- Adoption of mistreated or neglected children also enhances their intelligence scores (Almas et al., 2017).
- The intelligence scores of "virtual twins"—same-age, unrelated siblings adopted as infants and raised together—correlate at a level higher than chance: +0.28 (Segal et al., 2012).

So during childhood, adoptive siblings' test scores correlate modestly. What do you think happens as the years go by and adopted children settle in with their adoptive families? Would you expect the family-environment effect to grow stronger and the genetic-legacy effect to shrink?

"Selective breeding has given me an aptitude for the law, but I still love fetching a dead duck out of freezing water."

FIGURE 28.2

IN VERBAL ABILITY, WHOM DO ADOPTED CHILDREN RESEMBLE? As the years went by in their adoptive families, children's verbal ability scores became more like their *biological* parents' scores. (Data from Plomin & DeFries, 1998.)

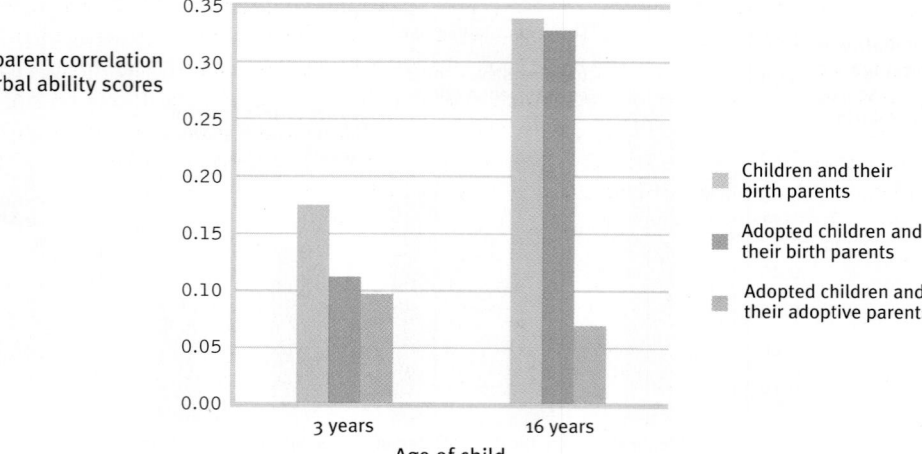

Child-parent correlation in verbal ability scores

- Children and their birth parents
- Adopted children and their birth parents
- Adopted children and their adoptive parents

Age of child

If you said *Yes*, behavior geneticists have a stunning surprise for you. Adopted children's intelligence test scores resemble those of their biological parents much more than their adoptive families (Loehlin, 2016). And over time, adopted children's verbal ability scores become even more like those of their biological parents **(FIGURE 28.2)**. Mental similarities between adopted children and their adoptive families wane with age (McGue et al., 1993). Who would have guessed?

Genetic influences become more apparent as we accumulate life experience. Identical twins' similarities, for example, continue or increase into their eighties. In one massive study of 11,000 twin pairs in four countries, the heritability of general intelligence (*g*) increased from 41 percent in middle childhood to 55 percent in adolescence to 66 percent in young adulthood (Haworth et al., 2010). Thus, report Ian Deary and his colleagues (2009a, 2012), the heritability of general intelligence increases from "about 30 percent" in early childhood to "well over 50 percent in adulthood."

ENGAGE

📖 **LaunchPad** For a helpful tutorial animation, watch the **Video: Twin Studies.** Then try to predict the correlation of intelligence scores in **Concept Practice: Studying Twins and Adopted Children.**

🔒 **RETRIEVE IT • • •**   *ANSWERS IN APPENDIX E*

RI-1 A check on your understanding of heritability: If environments become more equal, the heritability of intelligence will

a. increase.   b. decrease.   c. be unchanged.

GENE-ENVIRONMENT INTERACTIONS

LOQ 28-2 How can environmental influences affect cognitive development?

Genes and experience together weave the fabric of intelligence. *Epigenetics* studies the microbiology of this nature–nurture meeting place. With all our abilities—whether mental or physical—our genes shape the experiences that shape us. If you have a natural aptitude for sports, you will probably play more often than others (getting more practice, coaching, and experience). Or, if you have a natural aptitude for academics, you will more likely stay in school, read books, and ask questions—all of which will increase your brain power. The same would be true for your identical twin—who might, not just for genetic reasons, also become a star performer. In gene-environment interactions, small genetic advantages can trigger social experiences that multiply our original skills.

Sometimes, however, environmental conditions work in reverse, depressing physical or cognitive development. Severe deprivation leaves footprints on the brain, as J. McVicker Hunt (1982) observed in a destitute Iranian orphanage. The typical child Hunt observed there could not sit up unassisted at age 2 or walk at age 4. The little care infants received was not in response to their crying, cooing, or other behaviors, so the children developed little sense of personal control over their environment. They were instead becoming passive "glum lumps." Extreme deprivation was crushing native intelligence—a finding confirmed by other studies of children raised in poorly run orphanages in Romania and elsewhere (Nelson et al., 2009, 2013; van IJzendoorn et al., 2008).

DEVASTATING NEGLECT Some Romanian orphans, such as this child in the Leaganul Pentru Copii orphanage in 1990, had minimal interaction with caregivers, and suffered delayed development.

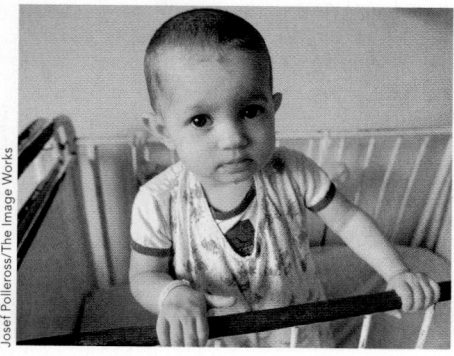

Josef Polleross/The Image Works

Aware of both the dramatic effects of early experiences and the impact of early intervention, Hunt began a training program for Iranian caregivers, teaching them to play language-fostering games with 11 infants. They imitated the babies' babbling. They engaged them in vocal follow-the-leader. And, finally, they taught the infants sounds from the Persian language. The results were dramatic. By 22 months of age, the infants could name more than 50 objects and body parts. They so charmed visitors that most were adopted—an unprecedented success for the orphanage.

Hunt's findings are an extreme case of a more general finding: The poor environmental conditions that accompany poverty can depress cognitive development and produce stresses that impede cognitive performance (Heberle & Carter, 2015; Tuerk, 2005). And this may help explain another finding: Where environments vary widely, as they do among children of less-educated parents, environmental differences are more predictive of intelligence scores (Tucker-Drob & Bates, 2016). Like a computer that slows when running multiple operations, impoverished people's worries and distractions consume cognitive bandwidth and can diminish their thinking capacity. On tests of cognitive functioning, sugar cane farmers in India scored better after being paid for their harvest—when their money worries dropped (Mani et al., 2013).

If extreme conditions—sensory deprivation, social isolation, poverty—can slow normal brain development, could the reverse also be true? Could an "enriched" environment amplify normal development and give children a superior intellect? Most experts are doubtful (Bruer, 1999; DeLoache et al., 2010; Reichert et al., 2010). There is no environmental recipe for fast-forwarding a normal infant into a genius. All babies should have normal exposure to sights, sounds, and speech. Beyond that, Sandra Scarr's (1984) verdict still is widely shared: "Parents who are very concerned about providing special educational lessons for their babies are wasting their time."

More encouraging results come from intensive, post-babyhood preschool programs (Dodge et al., 2017; Garcia et al., 2016; Tucker-Drob, 2012). Across a number of experiments, intelligence scores also rise with nutritional supplements to pregnant mothers and newborns (3.5 points), with quality preschool experiences (4 points), and with interactive reading programs (6 points) (Protzko et al., 2013).

"It is our choices . . . that show what we truly are, far more than our abilities." —Professor Dumbledore to Harry Potter in J. K. Rowling's *Harry Potter and the Chamber of Secrets*, 1999

Growth Mindset

Schooling and intelligence interact, and both enhance later income (Ceci & Williams, 1997, 2009). But what we accomplish with our intelligence depends also on our own beliefs and motivation. One analysis of 72,431 undergraduates found that study motivation and study skills rivaled aptitude and previous grades as predictors of academic achievement (Credé & Kuncel, 2008). Motivation can even affect intelligence test performance. Four dozen studies show that, when promised money for doing well, adolescents score higher on such tests (Duckworth et al., 2011).

These observations would not surprise psychologist Carol Dweck (2012a,b, 2015). She reports that believing intelligence is changeable fosters a *growth mindset,* a focus on learning and growing. Dweck teaches young teens to adopt a growth mindset. She and her team explain that the brain is like a muscle, growing stronger with use as neuron connections grow. Receiving praise for *effort* and for tackling challenges, rather than for being smart or accomplished, helps teens understand the link between hard work and success (Gunderson et al., 2013). Although a growth mindset doesn't alter intelligence, it can make children and youth more resilient when others frustrate them (Paunesku et al., 2015; Yeager et al., 2013, 2014, 2016a).

More than 300 studies confirm that ability + opportunity + motivation = success in fields from sports to science to music (Ericsson et al., 2007). High school students' math proficiency and college students' grades reflect their aptitude but also their self-discipline, their belief in the power of effort, and a curious "hungry mind" (Murayama et al., 2013; Richardson et al., 2012;

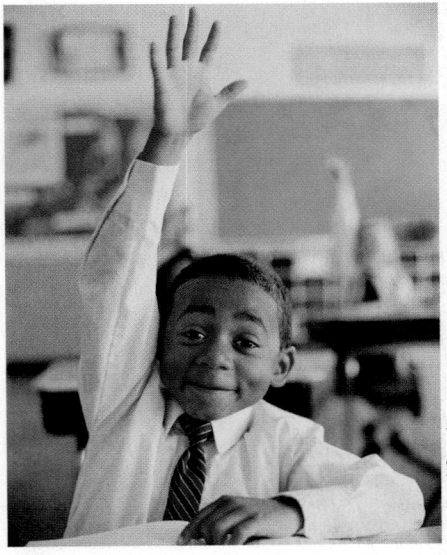

A HUNGRY MIND

Dave Nagel/Getty Images

U.S. SPELLING CHAMPS Nihar Janga, 11, and Jairam Hathwar, 13, celebrate their co-winning the 2016 Scripps National Spelling Bee. What were Nihar and Jairam's winning words? "Gesellschaft" and "Feldenkrais."

Alex Wong/Getty Images

ASK YOURSELF

Are you working to the potential reflected in your standardized test scores? What, other than your aptitude, is affecting your school performance?

von Stumm et al., 2011). And consider: Between 2008 and 2016, youth of South-Asian heritage won all nine U.S. national spelling bee contests—an incredible achievement likely influenced by a cultural belief that strong effort will bring success (Rattan et al., 2012; Shankar, 2016).

Some researchers caution that applying growth mindset findings in large-scale interventions with at-risk students can have a downside: the social cost of blaming struggling individuals for their circumstances (Ikizer & Blanton, 2016). Sometimes people need more than the power of positive thinking to overcome their harsh conditions.

GROUP DIFFERENCES IN INTELLIGENCE TEST SCORES

If there were no group differences in aptitude scores, psychologists would have less debate over hereditary and environmental influences. But there are group differences. What are they? And what shall we make of them?

Gender Similarities and Differences

LOQ 28-3 How and why do the genders differ in mental ability scores?

In science, as in everyday life, differences, not similarities, excite interest. In worldwide studies, men estimate their own intelligence higher than do women (Furnham, 2016). Yet compared with their anatomical and physiological differences, men and women's intelligence differences are minor. In that 1932 testing of all Scottish 11-year-olds, for example, girls' average intelligence score was 100.6 and boys' was 100.5 (Deary et al., 2003). So far as *g* is concerned, boys and girls, men and women, are the same.

Yet most people find differences more newsworthy. In cultures where both boys and girls benefit from schooling, girls outpace boys in spelling, verbal fluency, and locating objects (Voyer & Voyer, 2014). They are better emotion detectors and are more sensitive to touch, taste, and color (Halpern et al., 2007). In math computation and overall math performance, girls and boys hardly differ (Else-Quest et al., 2010; Hyde & Mertz, 2009; Lindberg et al., 2010).

On complex math problems, boys outperform girls. But the most reliable male edge appears in spatial ability tests like the one shown in **FIGURE 28.3** (Maeda & Yoon, 2013; Palejwala & Fine, 2015). (To solve the problem, you must quickly rotate three-dimensional objects in your mind.) Males' mental ability scores (and brains) also vary more than females'. Worldwide, boys outnumber girls at both the low and high extremes (Ball et al., 2017; Brunner et al., 2013). Boys, for example, are more often found in special education classes, but also among those scoring very high on the SAT math test.

Psychologist Steven Pinker (2005) has argued the evolutionary perspective—that biology affects gender differences in life priorities (women's somewhat greater interest in people versus men's in money and things), in risk-taking (with men more reckless), and in math reasoning and spatial abilities. Such differences are, he noted, observed across cultures, stable over time, influenced by prenatal hormones, and observed in genetic boys raised as girls.

© Punch Limited

"That's an excellent suggestion, Miss Triggs. Perhaps one of the men would like to suggest it."

Give females long-term testosterone therapy (for female-to-male sex reassignment) and their brain language-processing areas become, after losing some gray matter, more male-like (Hahn et al., 2016).

Which one of the options below matches the Original?

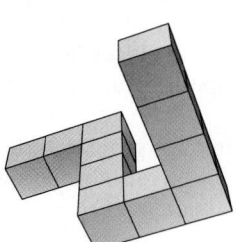

Original

(a)

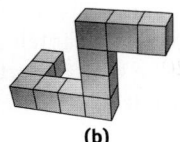
(b)

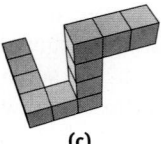
(c)

 **FIGURE 28.3**

THE MENTAL ROTATION TEST This illustrates the type of items found on a spatial abilities test. See answer below.[5]

But social expectations and opportunities also construct gender by shaping interests and abilities (Crawford et al., 1995; Eccles et al., 1990). In Asia and Russia, teen girls have outperformed boys in an international science exam; in North America and Britain, boys have scored higher (Fairfield, 2012). More gender-equal cultures, such as Sweden and Iceland, exhibit little of the gender math gap found in gender-unequal cultures, such as Turkey and Korea (Guiso et al., 2008; Kane & Mertz, 2012). And since the 1970s, as gender equity has increased in the United States, the boy-to-girl ratio among 12- to 14-year-olds with very high SAT math scores (above 700) has declined from 13 to 1 to 3 to 1 (Nisbett et al., 2012; Makel et al. 2016).

Maryam Mirzakhani/Getty Images

MINDING THE MATH GAP In 2014, Iranian math professor Maryam Mirzakhani (1977–2017) became the first woman to win math's most admired award, the Fields Medal. What was her advice to people who want to know more about math? Practice patience. "The beauty of mathematics," Mirzakhani said, "only shows itself to more patient followers" (*The Guardian*, 2014).

Racial and Ethnic Similarities and Differences

LOQ 28-4 How and why do racial and ethnic groups differ in mental ability scores?

Fueling the group-differences debate are two other disturbing but scientifically agreed-upon facts:

- Racial and ethnic groups differ in their average intelligence test scores.
- High-scoring people (and groups) are more likely to attain high levels of education and income.

Larry Williams/Getty Images

---

5. The correct answer is *c*.

There are many group differences in average intelligence test scores. New Zealanders of European descent outscore native Maori New Zealanders. Israeli Jews outscore Israeli Arabs. Most Japanese outscore most Burakumin, a stigmatized Japanese minority. And White Americans have outscored Black Americans. This Black-White difference appears to have diminished somewhat in recent years, especially among children (Dickens & Flynn, 2006; Nisbett et al., 2012).

One more agreed-upon fact is that *group* differences provide little basis for judging individuals. Worldwide, women outlive men by four years, but knowing that you are male or female won't tell us how long you will live.

We have seen that heredity contributes to *individual* differences in intelligence. But group differences in a heritable trait may be entirely environmental, as in our earlier boys-in-barrels versus boys-in-mansions example. Consider one of nature's experiments: Allow some children to grow up hearing their culture's dominant language, while others, born deaf, do not. Then give both groups an intelligence test rooted in the dominant language. The result? No surprise. Those with expertise in the dominant language will score higher than those who were born deaf (Braden, 1994; Steele, 1990; Zeidner, 1990).

Might the racial and ethnic gaps be similarly environmental? Consider:

Genetics research reveals that under the skin, we humans are remarkably alike. Despite some racial variation, such as in health risks, the average genetic difference between two Icelandic villagers or between two Kenyans greatly exceeds the group difference between Icelanders and Kenyans (Cavalli-Sforza et al., 1994; Rosenberg et al., 2002). Moreover, looks can deceive. Light-skinned Europeans and dark-skinned Africans are genetically closer than are dark-skinned Africans and dark-skinned Aboriginal Australians.

Race is not a neatly defined biological category. Many social scientists see race primarily as a social construction without well-defined physical boundaries, as each race blends seamlessly into the race of its geographical neighbors (Helms et al., 2005; Smedley & Smedley, 2005). In one genetic analysis of more than 160,000 people living in the United States, most with less than 28 percent African ancestry said they were White; those with more than 28 percent mostly said they were African-American (Byrc et al., 2015). Moreover, with increasingly mixed ancestries, more and more people defy neat racial categorization and self-identify as multiracial (Pauker et al., 2009).

Within the same populations, there are generation-to-generation differences in test scores. Test scores of today's better-fed, better-educated, and more test-prepared populations exceed the scores of 1930's populations (Flynn, 2012; Pietschnig & Voracek, 2015; Trahan et al., 2014). The scores of the two generations differ by a greater margin than the intelligence test score of the average U.S. White today exceeding that of the average U.S. Black. One research review noted that the average intelligence test performance of today's sub-Saharan Africans is the same as that of British adults in 1948 (Wicherts et al., 2010). No one credits genetics for such generation-to-generation differences.

Schools and culture matter. Countries whose economies create a large wealth gap between rich and poor tend also to have a large rich-versus-poor intelligence test score gap (Nisbett, 2009). In China and Turkey, people in poorer regions have the lowest scores, and those in wealthier regions have the highest (Lynn et al., 2015, 2016). Moreover, educational policies (such as kindergarten attendance, school discipline, and instructional time per year) predict national differences in intelligence and knowledge tests (Lynn & Vanhanen, 2012; Rindermann & Ceci, 2009). Math achievement, aptitude test differences, and especially grades may reflect conscientiousness more than competence (Poropat, 2014). Asian students, who have outperformed North American students on such tests, have also spent 30 percent more time in school and much more time in and out of school studying math (Geary et al., 1996; Larson & Verma, 1999; Stevenson, 1992). Women in college and university

WORLD SCRABBLE CHAMPS In 2015, Team Nigeria was the top country in the World Scrabble Championship. Five of its six members finished among the top 50 contestants, including Wellington Jighere, center, the individual world Scrabble champion.

PIUS UTOMI EKPEI/Getty Images

similarly outperform equally able men, thanks partly to their greater conscientiousness (Keiser et al., 2016).

In different eras, different ethnic groups have experienced golden ages—periods of remarkable achievement. Twenty-five hundred years ago, it was the Greeks and the Egyptians, then the Romans. In the eighth and ninth centuries, genius seemed to reside in the Arab world. Five hundred years ago, the Aztec Indians and the peoples of Northern Europe were the superachievers. Today, many people notice Asian technological genius and Jewish cultural success. Cultures rise and fall over centuries; the gene pool changes more slowly.

"Do not obtain your slaves from Britain, because they are so stupid and so utterly incapable of being taught." —Cicero, 106–43 B.C.E.

🔒 **RETRIEVE IT • • •**   *ANSWERS IN APPENDIX E*

RI-2 The heritability of intelligence scores will be greater in a society marked by equal opportunity than in a society of peasants and aristocrats. Why?

THE QUESTION OF BIAS

LOQ 28-5 Are intelligence tests biased or unfair? What is *stereotype threat,* and how does it affect test-takers' performance?

Knowing there are group differences in intelligence test scores leads us to wonder whether those differences are built into the tests. Is intelligence testing a constructive way to guide people toward suitable opportunities? Or is it a potent, discriminatory weapon camouflaged as science? In short, are intelligence tests biased? The answer depends on which of two very different definitions of bias we use.

The *scientific* meaning of *bias* hinges solely on a test's validity—on whether it predicts future behavior for all groups of test-takers, not just for some. For example, if the SAT accurately predicted the college achievement of women but not that of men, then the test would be biased. In this scientific meaning of the term, the near-consensus among psychologists has been that the major U.S. aptitude tests are *not* biased (Berry & Zhao, 2015; Neisser et al., 1996; Wigdor & Garner, 1982). The tests' predictive validity is roughly the same, regardless of gender, race, ethnicity, or socioeconomic level. If an intelligence test score of 95 predicts slightly below-average grades, that rough prediction usually applies equally to all.

But in everyday language we may consider a test "biased" if it is unfair—if test scores will be influenced by the test-taker's cultural experience. This in fact happened to Eastern

stereotype threat a self-confirming concern that one will be evaluated based on a negative stereotype

European immigrants in the early 1900s. Lacking the experience to answer questions about their new culture, many were classified as "feebleminded."

If we use "biased" in this popular sense, then yes, intelligence tests may be considered unfair (even if scientifically unbiased). Why? Because they measure the test-takers' developed abilities, which reflect, in part, their education and experiences. Some researchers therefore recommend creating culture-neutral questions—such as assessing people's ability to learn novel words, sayings, and analogies—to enable *culture-fair* aptitude tests (Fagan & Holland, 2007, 2009).

Other researchers believe that blaming a test for a group's lower scores is like blaming a messenger for bad news. Why blame the tests for exposing unequal experiences and opportunities? If, because of malnutrition, people were to suffer stunted growth, would you blame the measuring stick that reveals it? If unequal past experiences predict unequal future achievements, a valid aptitude test will detect such inequalities.

As you have seen in so many contexts throughout this text, expectations and attitudes influence perceptions and behaviors. For intelligence test makers, expectations can introduce bias. And for intelligence test takers, they can become self-fulfilling prophecies.

🔒 **RETRIEVE IT • • •**   *ANSWERS IN APPENDIX E*

RI-3 What is the difference between a test that is culturally "biased" and a test that is scientifically biased?

Test-Takers' Expectations

"Math class is tough!" — "Teen Talk" talking Barbie doll (introduced July 1992, recalled October 1992)

When Steven Spencer and his colleagues (1997) gave a difficult math test to equally capable men and women, women did not do as well—except when they had been led to expect that women usually do as well as men on the test. Otherwise, something affected their performance. There was a "threat in the air" (Spencer et al., 2016). And with Claude Steele and Joshua Aronson, Spencer (2002) again observed this self-fulfilling **stereotype threat** when Black students performed worse after being reminded of their race just before taking verbal aptitude tests. Follow-up experiments have confirmed that negatively stereotyped minorities and women may have unrealized academic potential (Grand, 2016; Nguyen & Ryan, 2008; Walton & Spencer, 2009). If, when taking an intelligence test or performing a work-related task, you are worried that your group or "type" often doesn't do well, your self-doubts and self-monitoring may hijack your working memory and impair your performance (Hutchison et al., 2013). Such thoughts and worries about what others are thinking about you can be distracting. For such reasons, stereotype threat may impair attention, performance, and learning (Inzlicht & Kang, 2010; Rydell et al., 2010). Remove the threat—by labeling the assessment a "warm-up" exercise rather than a "test"—and stereotyped minorities often perform better (Taylor & Walton, 2011).

Stereotype threat helps explain why Blacks have scored higher when tested by Blacks than when tested by Whites (Danso & Esses, 2001; Inzlicht & Ben-Zeev, 2000). It implies a possible effect of non-Black teachers having lower expectations for Black students than do Black teachers (Gershenson et al., 2016). And it gives us insight into why women have scored higher on math tests with no male test-takers present, and why women's online chess performance drops sharply when they *think* they are playing a male opponent (Maass et al., 2008). From such studies, Steele (1995, 2010) has concluded that telling students they probably won't succeed (as is sometimes implied by remedial "minority support" programs) can function as a stereotype and erode performance.

Other research teams have demonstrated benefits of self-affirmation exercises (Cohen & Sherman, 2014; Goyer et al., 2017; Harackiewicz et al., 2014, 2016). When challenged to believe in their potential, increase their sense of belonging, or focus on intelligence as malleable, disadvantaged university students have earned markedly higher grades and have had lower dropout rates (Tibbetts et al., 2016; Yeager et al., 2016b).

* * *

Perhaps, then, our goals for tests of mental abilities should be threefold. First, we should realize the benefits that intelligence-testing pioneer Alfred Binet foresaw—to enable schools to recognize who might profit most from early intervention. Second, we must remain alert to Binet's wish that intelligence test scores not be misinterpreted as literal measures of a person's worth and potential. Third, we must remember that the competence that general intelligence tests sample is important; it helps enable success in some life paths. Without such tests, those who decide on jobs and admissions would rely more on other considerations, such as personal opinion. But these tests reflect only one important aspect of personal competence (Stanovich et al., 2013, 2014a,b). Our rationality, practical intelligence, and emotional intelligence matter, too, as do other forms of creativity, talent, and character.

The point to remember: There are many ways of being successful: Our differences are variations of human adaptability. Life's great achievements result not only from "can do" abilities (and fair opportunity) but also from "will do" motivation. Competence + Diligence → Accomplishment.

"Almost all the joyful things of life are outside the measure of IQ tests."
—Madeleine L'Engle, *A Circle of Quiet,* 1972

"[Einstein] showed that genius equals brains plus tenacity squared." —Walter Isaacson, "Einstein's Final Quest," 2009

🔒 RETRIEVE IT • • •

ANSWERS IN APPENDIX E

RI-4 What psychological principle helps explain why women tend to perform more poorly when they believe their online chess opponent is male?

🔗 **LaunchPad** To explore how you perceive your own intelligence, engage online with **Immersive Learning: Assess Your Strengths—What Is Your Theory of Intelligence, and How Is That Affecting Your Success?**

🔒 REVIEW GENETIC AND ENVIRONMENTAL INFLUENCES ON INTELLIGENCE

Learning Objectives

TEST YOURSELF Answer these repeated Learning Objective Questions on your own (before checking the answers in Appendix D) to improve your retention of the concepts (McDaniel et al., 2009, 2015).

28-1 What is *heritability,* and what do twin and adoption studies tell us about the nature and nurture of intelligence?

28-2 How can environmental influences affect cognitive development?

28-3 How and why do the genders differ in mental ability scores?

28-4 How and why do racial and ethnic groups differ in mental ability scores?

28-5 Are intelligence tests biased or unfair? What is *stereotype threat,* and how does it affect test-takers' performance?

Terms and Concepts to Remember

TEST YOURSELF Write down the definition yourself, then check your answer on the referenced page.

heritability, **p. 336**

stereotype threat, **p. 344**

Experience the Testing Effect

TEST YOURSELF Answer the following questions on your own first, then check your answers in Appendix E.

1. To say that the heritability of intelligence is about 50 percent means that 50 percent of
   a. an individual's intelligence is due to genetic factors.
   b. the similarities between two groups of people are attributable to genes.
   c. the variation in intelligence within a group of people is attributable to genetic factors.
   d. an individual's intelligence is due to each parent's genes.

2. The strongest support for heredity's influence on intelligence is the finding that
   a. identical twins, but not other siblings, have nearly identical intelligence test scores.
   b. the correlation between intelligence test scores of fraternal twins is not higher than that for other siblings.
   c. mental similarities between adopted siblings increase with age.
   d. children in impoverished families have similar intelligence scores.

3. The environmental influence that has the clearest, most profound effect on intellectual development is
   a. exposing normal infants to enrichment programs before age 1.
   b. growing up in an economically disadvantaged home or neighborhood.
   c. being raised in conditions of extreme deprivation.
   d. being an identical twin.

4. _____ _____ can lead to poor performance on tests by undermining test-takers' belief that they can do well on the test.

Continue testing yourself with 📖 **LearningCurve** or 〰 **Achieve Read & Practice** to learn and remember most effectively.

Motivation and Emotion

Flashpop/Getty Images

How well I [DM] remember asking my first discussion question in a new introductory psychology class. Several hands rose, along with one left foot. The foot belonged to Chris Klein, who was the unlikeliest person to have made it to that class. At birth, Chris suffered oxygen deprivation that required 40 minutes of CPR. "One doctor wanted to let him go," recalled his mother.

The result was severe cerebral palsy. With damage to the brain area that controls muscle movement, Chris is unable to control his constantly moving hands. He cannot feed, dress, or care for himself. And he cannot speak. But what Chris can control are his keen mind and left foot. With that blessed foot, he operates the joystick on his motorized wheelchair. Using his left big toe, he can type sentences, which his communication system can store, send, or speak. And Chris is motivated, very motivated.

When Chris was a high school student in suburban Chicago, three teachers doubted he would be able to leave home for college. Yet he persisted, and, with much support, attended my school, Hope College. Five years later, as his left foot drove him across the stage to receive his diploma, his admiring classmates honored his achievement with a spontaneous standing ovation.

Today, Chris is an inspirational speaker for schools, churches, and community events, giving "a voice to those that have none, and a helping hand to those with disabilities." He is writing a book, *Lessons from the Big Toe*. And he has found love and married.

Few of us face Chris Klein's challenges. But we all seek to direct our energy in ways that will produce satisfaction and success. We are moved by our feelings along the way,

347

A MOTIVATED MAN: CHRIS KLEIN To see and hear Chris presenting his story, visit tinyurl.com/ChrisPsychStudent.

and we inspire them in others. We are pushed by social motives, such as affiliation and achievement (Module 29), and biological ones, such as hunger (Module 30). We feel hope and happiness, sadness and pain, tenderness and triumph. Chris Klein's fierce will to live, learn, and love highlights the close ties between our own *motivations* and *emotions* (Modules 31 and 32), which energize, direct, and enrich our lives.

29 Basic Motivational Concepts, Affiliation, and Achievement

MOTIVATIONAL CONCEPTS

LEARNING OBJECTIVE QUESTION (LOQ)

29-1 How do psychologists define *motivation?* From what perspectives do they view motivated behavior?

Our **motivations** arise from the interplay between nature (the bodily "push") and nurture (the "pulls" from our personal experiences, thoughts, and culture). That is usually, but not always, for the better. When our bodies tell us we're hungry, we respond by eating foods we have learned to trust and enjoy. But when our motivations get hijacked, our lives go awry. Those with *substance use disorder,* for example, may find their cravings for an addictive substance override their longings for sustenance, safety, and social support.

In their attempts to understand motivated behavior, psychologists have viewed it from four perspectives:

- *Instinct theory* (now replaced by the *evolutionary perspective*) focuses on genetically predisposed behaviors.
- *Drive-reduction theory* focuses on how we respond to inner pushes and outer pulls.
- *Arousal theory* focuses on finding the right level of stimulation.
- *Abraham Maslow's hierarchy of needs* focuses on the priority of some needs over others.

Instincts and Evolutionary Theory

To qualify as an **instinct**, a complex behavior must have a fixed pattern throughout a species and be unlearned (Tinbergen, 1951). Such unlearned behaviors include *imprinting* in birds and the return of salmon to their birthplace. A few human behaviors, such as infants' innate reflexes to root for a nipple and suck, exhibit unlearned fixed patterns. But many more are directed by both physiological needs and psychological wants.

SAME MOTIVE, DIFFERENT WIRING The more complex the nervous system, the more adaptable the organism. Both humans and weaverbirds satisfy their need for shelter in ways that reflect their inherited capacities. Human behavior is flexible; we can learn whatever skills we need to build a house. The bird's behavior pattern is fixed; it can build only this kind of nest.

Although instincts cannot explain most human motives, the underlying assumption endures in *evolutionary psychology:* Genes do predispose some species-typical behavior. Psychologists might apply this perspective, for example, to explain animals' biological predispositions, and the influence of evolution on our taste preferences, helping behaviors, and romantic attractions.

Drives and Incentives

In addition to our predispositions, we have *drives.* **Physiological needs** (such as for food or water) create an aroused, motivated state—a drive (such as hunger or thirst)—that pushes us to reduce the need. **Drive-reduction theory** explains that, with few exceptions, when a physiological need increases, so does our psychological drive to reduce it.

Drive reduction is one way our bodies strive for **homeostasis** (literally "staying the same")—the maintenance of a steady internal state. For example, our body regulates its temperature in a way similar to a room's thermostat. Both systems operate through feedback loops: Sensors feed room temperature to a control device. If the room's temperature cools, the control device switches on the furnace. Likewise, if our body's temperature cools, our blood vessels constrict (to conserve warmth) and we feel driven to put on more clothes or seek a warmer environment (**FIGURE 29.1**).

Not only are we *pushed* by our need to reduce drives, we also are *pulled* by **incentives**—positive or negative environmental stimuli that lure or repel us. Such stimuli increase our dopamine levels, causing our underlying drives (such as for food or sex) to become active impulses (Hamid et al., 2016). And the more those impulses are satisfied and reinforced, the stronger the drive may become: As Roy Baumeister (2015) noted, "Getting begets wanting." Thus, our learning influences our motives. Depending on our learning, the aroma of good food, whether roasted peanuts or toasted ants, can motivate our behavior. So can the sight of those we find attractive or threatening.

When there is both a need and an incentive, we feel strongly driven. The food-deprived person who smells pizza baking may feel a strong hunger drive, and the baking pizza may become a compelling incentive. For each motive, we can therefore ask, "How is it pushed by our inborn physiological needs and pulled by learned incentives in the environment?"

FIGURE 29.1

DRIVE-REDUCTION THEORY Drive-reduction motivation arises from *homeostasis*—an organism's natural tendency to maintain a steady internal state. Thus, if we are water deprived, our thirst drives us to drink to restore the body's normal state.

Arousal Theory

We are much more than calm homeostatic systems, however. Some motivated behaviors actually *increase* rather than decrease arousal. Well-fed animals will leave their shelter to explore and gain information, seemingly in the absence of any need-based drive. Curiosity drives monkeys to monkey around trying to figure out how to unlock a latch that opens nothing, or how to open a window that allows them to see outside their room (Butler, 1954). It drives newly mobile infants to investigate every accessible corner of the house. It drove students, in one experiment, to click on pens to see whether they did or didn't deliver an electric shock (Hsee & Ruan, 2016). It drives the scientists whose work this text discusses. And it drives explorers and adventurers such as mountaineer George Mallory. Asked why he wanted to climb Mount Everest, Mallory famously answered, "Because it's there." Sometimes uncertainty brings excitement, which amplifies motivation (Shen et al., 2015). Those who, like Mallory, enjoy high arousal are most likely to seek out intense music, novel foods, and risky behaviors and careers (Roberti et al., 2004; Zuckerman, 1979, 2009). Although they have been called *sensation-seekers,* risk takers may also be motivated to master their emotions and actions (Barlow et al., 2013).

So, human motivation aims not to eliminate arousal but to seek optimum levels of arousal. Having all our biological needs satisfied, we feel driven to experience stimulation and we hunger for information. Lacking stimulation, we feel bored and look for a way to increase arousal. If left alone, most people prefer to do something—even, when given no other option, to self-administer mild electric shocks (Wilson et al., 2014). Why might

motivation a need or desire that energizes and directs behavior.

instinct a complex behavior that is rigidly patterned throughout a species and is unlearned.

physiological need a basic bodily requirement.

drive-reduction theory the idea that a physiological need creates an aroused state (a drive) that motivates an organism to satisfy the need.

homeostasis a tendency to maintain a balanced or constant internal state; the regulation of any aspect of body chemistry, such as blood glucose, around a particular level.

incentive a positive or negative environmental stimulus that motivates behavior.

DRIVEN BY CURIOSITY Young monkeys and children are fascinated by the unfamiliar. Their drive to explore maintains an optimum level of arousal and is one of several motives that do not fill any immediate physiological need.

ASK YOURSELF

Does boredom ever motivate you to do things just to figure out something new? When was the last time that happened, and what did you find?

people seek to increase their arousal? Moderate arousal and even anxiety can be motivating—leading to higher levels of math achievement, for example (Wang et al., 2015c). However, given too much stimulation or stress, we look for ways to decrease arousal. In one experiment, people felt less stress when they cut back checking email to three times a day rather than being continually accessible (Kushlev & Dunn, 2015).

Two early twentieth-century psychologists studied the relationship of arousal to performance and identified the **Yerkes-Dodson law:** *moderate arousal leads to optimal performance* (Yerkes & Dodson, 1908). When taking an exam, it pays to be moderately aroused—alert but not trembling with nervousness. (If already anxious, it's better not to become further aroused with caffeine.) Between bored low arousal and anxious hyperarousal lies a flourishing life. But optimal arousal levels depend on the task, with more difficult tasks requiring lower arousal for best performance (Hembree, 1988).

🔒 **RETRIEVE IT • • •**   *ANSWERS IN APPENDIX E*

RI-1 Performance peaks at lower levels of arousal for difficult tasks, and at higher levels for easy or well-learned tasks. (1) How might this phenomenon affect marathon runners? (2) How might this phenomenon affect anxious test-takers facing a difficult exam?

A Hierarchy of Needs

Some needs take priority over others. At this moment, with your needs for air and water hopefully satisfied, other motives—such as your desire to learn and achieve—are energizing and directing your behavior. Let your need for water go unsatisfied, however, and your thirst will preoccupy you. Deprived of air, you'd instantly find your thirst disappear.

LaunchPad To test your understanding of the hierarchy of needs, engage online with **Concept Practice: Building Maslow's Hierarchy**

Abraham Maslow (1970) described these priorities as a **hierarchy of needs** (FIGURE 29.2). At the base of this pyramid are our physiological needs, such as for food and water. Only if these needs are met are we prompted to meet our need for safety, and then to satisfy our needs to give and receive love and to enjoy self-esteem. Beyond this, said Maslow (1971), lies the need for *self-actualization*—to realize our full potential.

Near the end of his life, Maslow proposed that some of us also reach a level of *self-transcendence*. At the self-actualization level, we seek to realize our own potential. At the self-transcendence level, we strive for meaning, purpose, and communion in a way that is transpersonal—beyond the self (Koltko-Rivera, 2006). Maslow's contemporary, psychiatrist Viktor Frankl (1962), a Nazi concentration camp survivor, concurred that the search for meaning is an important human motive: "Life is never made unbearable by circumstances, but only by lack of meaning and purpose."

ASK YOURSELF

Consider your own experiences in relation to Maslow's hierarchy of needs. Have you ever experienced hunger or thirst that displaced your concern for other, higher-level needs? Do you usually feel safe? Loved? Confident? How often do you feel you are able to address what Maslow called "self-actualization" needs? What about "self-transcendence" needs?

"Do you feel your life has an important purpose or meaning?" When Gallup asked this of people in 132 countries, 91 percent answered *Yes* (Oishi & Diener, 2014). People sense meaning when they experience their life as having *purpose* (goals), *significance* (value), and *coherence* (sense)—sentiments that may be nourished by strong social connections, a religious faith, an orderly world, and social status (King et al., 2016; Martela & Steger, 2016). Moreover, meaning matters: People's sense of life's meaning predicts their psychological and physical well-being, and their capacity to delay gratification (Heine et al., 2006; Van Tongeren et al., 2018).

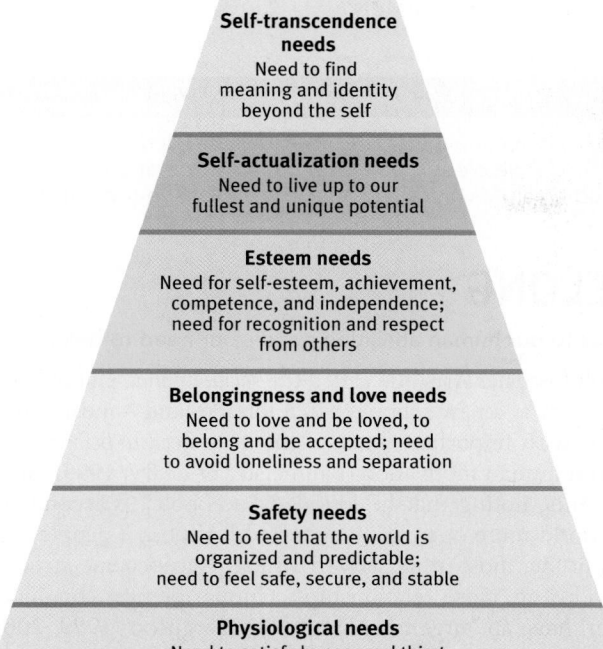

FIGURE 29.2

MASLOW'S HIERARCHY OF NEEDS Reduced to semistarvation by their rulers, inhabitants of Suzanne Collins' fictional nation, Panem, hunger for food and survival. *Hunger Games* heroine Katniss Everdeen (played in the movie by Jennifer Lawrence, shown here) expresses higher-level needs for actualization and transcendence, and in the process inspires the nation.

The order of Maslow's hierarchy is not universally fixed: People have starved themselves, for example, to make a political statement. Culture also influences our priorities: Self-esteem matters most in individualist nations, whose citizens tend to focus more on personal achievements than on family and community identity (Oishi et al., 1999). And, while agreeing with Maslow's basic levels of need, today's psychologists add that gaining and retaining mates, parenting offspring, and desiring social status are also universal human motives (Anderson et al., 2015; Kenrick et al., 2010).

Nevertheless, the simple idea that some motives are more compelling than others provides a framework for thinking about motivation. Worldwide life-satisfaction surveys support this basic idea (Oishi et al., 1999; Tay & Diener, 2011). In poorer nations that lack easy access to money and the food and shelter it buys, financial satisfaction more strongly predicts feelings of well-being. In wealthy nations, where most are able to meet their basic needs, social connections better predict well-being.

With these classic motivation theories in mind (**TABLE 29.1**), let's now take a closer look at two specific, higher-level motives: the *need to belong* and the *need to achieve*. As you read about these motives, watch for ways that incentives (the psychological "pull") interact with physiological needs (the biological "push").

"Hunger is the most urgent form of poverty." —Alliance to End Hunger, 2002

TABLE 29.1

RETAIN

Classic Motivation Theories

Theory	Its Big Idea
Instincts and evolutionary theory	There is a genetic basis for unlearned, species-typical behavior (such as birds building nests or infants rooting for a nipple).
Drive-reduction theory	Physiological needs (such as hunger and thirst) create an aroused state that drives us to reduce the need (for example, by eating or drinking).
Arousal theory	Our need to maintain an optimal level of arousal motivates behaviors that meet no physiological need (such as our yearning for stimulation and our hunger for information).
Maslow's hierarchy of needs	We prioritize survival-based needs and then social needs more than the needs for esteem and meaning.

Yerkes-Dodson law the principle that performance increases with arousal only up to a point, beyond which performance decreases.

hierarchy of needs Maslow's pyramid of human needs, beginning at the base with physiological needs that must first be satisfied before people can fulfill their higher-level safety needs and then psychological needs.

THE NEED TO BELONG

LOQ 29-2 What evidence points to our human affiliation need—our need to belong?

We are what the ancient Greek philosopher Aristotle called the *social animal.* Cut off from friends or family—alone in prison or at a new school or in a foreign land—most people feel keenly their lost connections with important others. This deep *need to belong*—our **affiliation need**—seems a central human motivation (Baumeister & Leary, 1995). Mark Zuckerberg (2012) understands this, noting that he founded Facebook "to accomplish a social mission—to make the world more open and connected." Although people vary in their wish for privacy and solitude, most of us seek to affiliate—to become strongly attached to certain others in enduring, close relationships. Human beings, contended personality theorist Alfred Adler, have an "urge to community" (Ferguson, 1989, 2001, 2010).

The Benefits of Belonging

Social bonds boosted our early ancestors' chances of survival. Adults who formed attachments were more likely to survive and reproduce, and to co-nurture their offspring to maturity. Attachment bonds motivated caregivers to keep children close, calming them and protecting them from threats (Esposito et al., 2013). Indeed, to be "wretched" literally means, in its Middle English origin *(wrecched),* to be without kin nearby.

Cooperating with friends and acquaintances also enhanced survival. In solo combat, our ancestors were not the toughest predators. But as hunters, they learned that six hands were better than two. As food gatherers, they gained protection from two-footed and four-footed enemies by traveling in groups. Those who felt a need to belong survived and reproduced most successfully, and their genes now predominate. Our innate need to belong drives us to befriend people who cooperate and to avoid those who exploit (Feinberg et al., 2014). People in every society on Earth belong to groups and prefer and favor "us" over "them." Having a social identity—feeling part of a group—boosts people's health and well-being (Allen et al., 2015; Greenaway et al., 2015, 2016).

Do you have close friends—people with whom you freely disclose your ups and downs? Having someone who rejoices with us over good news helps us feel better about both the news and the friendship (Reis et al., 2010). Such companionship creates connection and cooperation (Canavello & Crocker, 2017). A stranger's grateful thank-you can warm our heart (Williams & Bartlett, 2015). And close friends can literally make us feel warm, as if we are holding a soothing cup of warm tea (Inagaki & Eisenberger, 2013). The need to belong runs deeper, it seems, than any need to be rich. One study found that very happy university students were distinguished not by their money but by their "rich and satisfying close relationships" (Diener & Seligman, 2002).

The need to belong colors our thoughts and emotions. We spend a great deal of time thinking about actual and hoped-for relationships. Falling in mutual love, people have been known to feel their cheeks ache from their irrepressible grins. Asked, "What is necessary for your happiness?" or "What is it that makes your life meaningful?" most people have mentioned—before anything else—close, satisfying relationships with family, friends, or romantic partners (Berscheid, 1985). Happiness hits close to home.

💡 Consider: What was your most satisfying moment in the past week? Researchers asked that question of American and South Korean university students, then asked them to rate how much that moment had satisfied various needs (Sheldon et al., 2001). In both countries, the peak moment had satisfied self-esteem and relatedness-belonging needs. According to **self-determination theory,** we strive to satisfy three needs: *competence,* *autonomy* (a sense of personal control), and *relatedness* (Deci & Ryan, 2012; Ryan &

Photodisc/Getty Images

"We must love one another or die."
—W. H. Auden, "September 1, 1939"

Deci, 2000). Fulfilling these motives increases our health, improves our performance, and boosts our self-esteem (Cerasoli et al., 2016; Deci & Ryan, 2009; Guertin et al., 2017). Indeed, self-esteem is a gauge of how valued and accepted we feel (Leary, 2012).

Small wonder, then, that our social behavior so often aims to increase our feelings of belonging. To gain acceptance, we generally conform to group standards. We monitor our behavior, hoping to make a good impression. We spend billions on clothes, cosmetics, and diet and fitness aids—all motivated by our search for love and acceptance.

Thrown together in groups at school, at work, or at camp, we behave like magnets, moving closer, forming bonds. Parting, we feel distress. We promise to call, to write, to return for reunions. By drawing a sharp circle around "us," the need to belong feeds both deep attachments to those inside the circle (loving families, faithful friendships, and team loyalty) and hostilities toward those outside (teen gangs, ethnic rivalries, and fanatic nationalism). Feelings of love activate brain reward and safety systems. In one experiment, deeply in love university students exposed to heat felt less pain when looking at their beloved's picture (Younger et al., 2010). Pictures of our loved ones activate a brain region—the prefrontal cortex—that dampens feelings of physical pain (Eisenberger et al., 2011). Love is a natural painkiller.

Even when bad relationships end, people suffer. In one 16-nation survey, and in repeated U.S. surveys, separated and divorced people have been half as likely as married people to say they are "very happy" (Inglehart, 1990; NORC, 2016a). Is that simply because happy people more often marry and stay married? A national study following British lives through time revealed that, even after controlling for premarital life satisfaction, "the married are still more satisfied, suggesting a causal effect" of marriage (Grover & Helliwell, 2014). Divorce also predicts earlier mortality. Data from more than 600 million (!) people in 24 countries reveal that, compared with married people, separated and divorced people are at greater risk for early death (Shor et al., 2012). "If you're in a happy marriage, you will tend to live longer," says data scientist Lyle Ungar (2014). "[A happy marriage] is perhaps as important as not smoking, which is to say: huge."

Children who move through a series of foster homes or through repeated family relocations know the fear of being alone. After repeated disruption of budding relationships, they may have difficulty forming deep attachments (Oishi & Schimmack, 2010b). The evidence is clearest at the extremes. Children who grow up in institutions without a sense of belonging to anyone, or who are locked away at home and severely neglected often become withdrawn, frightened, even speechless.

No matter how secure our early years were, we all experience anxiety, loneliness, jealousy, or guilt when something threatens or dissolves our social ties. Much as life's best moments occur when close relationships begin—making a new friend, falling in love, having a baby—life's worst moments happen when close relationships end (Beam et al., 2016). Bereaved, we may feel life is empty or pointless, and we may overeat to fill that emptiness (Yang et al., 2016). Even the first months of living on campus can be distressing (English et al., 2017). But our need to belong usually pushes us to form new social connections (Oishi et al., 2013).

For immigrants and refugees moving alone to new places, the stress and loneliness can be depressing. After years of placing individual families in isolated communities, U.S. immigration policies began to encourage *chain migration* (Pipher, 2002). The second Syrian refugee family settling in a town generally has an easier adjustment than the first.

Social isolation can put us at risk for mental decline and ill health (Cacioppo et al., 2015). Lonely older adults, for example, make more doctor visits and are at greater risk of dementia (Gerst-Emerson & Jayawardhana, 2015; Holwerda et al., 2014). Social isolation can hurt our health as much as physical inactivity and diabetes do (Yang et al., 2016). But if feelings of acceptance and connection increase sufficiently, so will self-esteem, positive feelings, and physical health (Blackhart et al., 2009; Holt-Lunstad et al., 2010; Li & Kanazawa, 2016). The World Health Organization (2017b) lists social connection to family, friends, and community as a "determinant of health." A socially connected life is often a happy and healthy life.

affiliation need the need to build relationships and to feel part of a group.

self-determination theory the theory that we feel motivated to satisfy our needs for competence, autonomy, and relatedness.

ENGAGE 🔗 LaunchPad To improve your own relationships, try the online **Immersive Learning: Assess Your Strengths—How Strong Is Your Relationship, and How Might You Increase Its Strength?**

THE NEED TO CONNECT Six days a week, women from the Philippines work as domestic helpers in thousands of Hong Kong households. On Sundays, they throng to the central business district to picnic, dance, sing, talk, and laugh. "Humanity could stage no greater display of happiness," reported one observer (*Economist*, 2001).

VINCENT YU/AP Images

ENDURING THE PAIN OF OSTRACISM
White cadets at the United States Military Academy at West Point ostracized Henry Flipper for years, hoping he would drop out. He persevered in spite of their cruelty and in 1877 became the first African-American West Point graduate.

"How can we subject prisoners to unnecessary solitary confinement, knowing its effects, and then expect them to return to our communities as whole people? It doesn't make us safer. It's an affront to our common humanity." —U.S. President Barack Obama, 2016

> **ENGAGE** 🔆 📖 **LaunchPad** To consider your own need to belong, try the online **Immersive Learning: Assess Your Strengths—How Strong Is Your Need to Belong, and How Can You Strengthen Your Feelings of Belonging?**

The Pain of Being Shut Out

Can you recall feeling excluded, ignored, or shunned? Perhaps your texts went unanswered, or you were unfriended or ignored online. Perhaps others gave you the silent treatment, avoided you, looked away, mocked you, or shut you out in some other way. Or perhaps you have felt excluded when among people speaking an unfamiliar language (Dotan-Eliaz et al., 2009). All these experiences are instances of **ostracism**—of social exclusion (Williams, 2007, 2009). Worldwide, humans use many forms of ostracism—exile, imprisonment, solitary confinement—to punish, and therefore control, social behavior. For children, even a brief time-out in isolation can be punishing. Asked to describe personal episodes that made them feel especially *bad* about themselves, people will—about four times in five—describe a broken or painful social relationship (Pillemer et al., 2007).

Being shunned threatens one's need to belong (Vanhalst et al., 2015; Wirth et al., 2010). "It's the meanest thing you can do to someone, especially if you know they can't fight back. I never should have been born," said Lea, a lifelong victim of the silent treatment by her mother and grandmother. Like Lea, people often respond to ostracism with initial efforts to restore their acceptance, with depressed moods, and finally with withdrawal. Prisoner William Blake (2013) has spent more than a quarter-century in solitary confinement. "I cannot fathom how dying any death could be harder and more terrible than living through all that I have been forced to endure," he observed. To many, social exclusion is a sentence worse than death.

To experience ostracism is to experience real pain, as social psychologists Kipling Williams and his colleagues were surprised to discover in their studies of exclusion on social media (Gonsalkorale & Williams, 2006). Such ostracism, they discovered, takes a toll: It elicits increased activity in brain areas, such as the *anterior cingulate cortex,* that also respond to physical pain (Lieberman & Eisenberger et al., 2015; Rotge et al., 2015).

When people view pictures of romantic partners who caused their heart to break, their brain and body begin to ache (Kross et al., 2011). That helps explain another surprising finding: The pain reliever acetaminophen (as in Tylenol) lessens *social* as well as physical pain (DeWall et al., 2010). Across cultures, people use the same words (for example, *hurt, crushed*) for social pain and physical pain (MacDonald & Leary, 2005). Psychologically, we seem to experience social pain with the same emotional unpleasantness that marks physical pain.

Pain, whatever its source, focuses our attention and motivates corrective action. Rejected and unable to remedy the situation, people may relieve stress by seeking new friends, eating calorie-laden comfort foods, or strengthening their religious faith (Aydin et al., 2010; Maner et al., 2007; Sproesser et al., 2014). Or they may turn hostile. Ostracism breeds disagreeableness, which leads to further ostracism (Hales et al., 2016).

SOCIAL ACCEPTANCE AND REJECTION Successful participants on the reality TV show *Survivor* form alliances and gain acceptance among their peers. The rest receive the ultimate social punishment as they are "voted off the island."

In one series of experiments, researchers told some students (who had taken a personality test) that they were "the type likely to end up alone later in life," or that people they had met didn't want them in a group that was forming (Gaertner et al., 2008; Twenge et al., 2001).[1] They told other students that they would have "rewarding relationships throughout life," or that "everyone chose you as someone they'd like to work with." Those who were excluded became much more likely to engage in self-defeating behaviors and to act in disparaging or aggressive ways against those who had excluded them (blasting them with noise, for example). "If intelligent, well-adjusted, successful . . . students can turn aggressive in response to a small laboratory experience of social exclusion," noted the research team, "it is disturbing to imagine the aggressive tendencies that might arise from . . . chronic exclusion from desired groups in actual social life." Indeed, as Williams (2007) has observed, ostracism "weaves through case after case of school violence."

> ## 🔒 RETRIEVE IT • • •
> *ANSWERS IN APPENDIX E*
>
> **RI-3** How have students reacted in studies where they were made to feel rejected and unwanted? What helps explain these results?

Connecting and Social Networking

LOQ 29-3 How does social networking influence us?

As social creatures, we live for connection. Researcher George Vaillant (2013) was asked what he had learned from studying 238 Harvard University men from the 1930s to the end of their lives. He replied, "Happiness is love." A South African Zulu saying captures the idea: *Umuntu ngumuntu ngabantu*—"a person is a person through other persons."

 MOBILE NETWORKS AND SOCIAL MEDIA Look around and see humans connecting: talking, tweeting, texting, posting, chatting, social gaming, emailing. Walking across campus, you may see students glued to their phones, making little eye contact with passersby (or perhaps that's you?). Today have you observed more students engaging with each other face-to-face, or silently checking their phones, as one research team's phone app counted students doing 56 times a day (Elias et al., 2016)? The changes in how we connect have been fast and vast:

- *Mobile phones:* At the end of 2016, 95 percent of the world's 7.5 billion people lived in an area covered by a mobile-cellular network (ITU, 2016).

- *Texts:* The typical U.S. teen sends 30 texts a day (Lenhart, 2015b). Half of 18- to 29-year-olds check their phone multiple times per hour, and "can't imagine . . . life without [it]" (Newport, 2015; Saad, 2015).

- *The internet:* Worldwide in 2015, 68 percent of adults have used the internet (Poushter, 2016).

- *Social networking:* Among 2014's entering American college students, 94 percent were using social networking sites (Eagan et al., 2014). With one's friends online, it's hard not to be: Check in or miss out.

THE NET RESULT: SOCIAL EFFECTS OF SOCIAL NETWORKING By connecting like-minded people, the internet serves as a social amplifier. In times of social crisis or personal stress, it provides information and supportive connections. But it also enables people to compare their lives with others, which can create envy and be depressing (Verduyn et al., 2017). Gaining a large number of likes does activate the brain's reward centers (Blease, 2015; Sherman et al., 2016). And the internet can function as a matchmaker (as I [ND] can attest: I met my wife online). Dating websites aren't for everyone, and their algorithms might have limitations (Joel et al., 2017). But dating websites can widen the pool of potential matches, making it easier to find a desirable partner.

"If no one turned around when we entered, answered when we spoke, or minded what we did, but if every person we met 'cut us dead,' and acted as if we were non-existing things, a kind of rage and impotent despair would ere long well up in us."
—William James, *Principles of Psychology*, 1890/1950, pp. 293–294

💡 ENGAGE (ASK YOURSELF)

Have there been times when you felt out of the loop with family and friends, or even ostracized by them? How did you respond?

Drew Panckeri The New Yorker Collection/ The Cartoon Bank

ostracism deliberate social exclusion of individuals or groups.

---

1. The researchers later *debriefed* and reassured the participants.

"Look, until there's a Tinder for Pandas, we have to meet the old-fashioned way: being locked in a room together by scientists."

"The women on these dating sites don't seem to believe I'm a prince."

Online networking is double-edged: Nature has designed us for face-to-face relationships, and those who spend hours online are *less* likely to know and draw help from their real-world neighbors. But it does help us connect with friends, stay in touch with extended family, and find support when facing challenges (Pew, 2009; Pinker, 2014; Rainie et al., 2011). When used in moderation, social networking predicts longer life (Hobbs et al., 2016).

DOES ELECTRONIC COMMUNICATION STIMULATE HEALTHY SELF-DISCLOSURE? *Self-disclosure* is sharing ourselves—our joys, worries, and weaknesses—with others. Confiding can be a healthy way of coping with day-to-day challenges. When communicating electronically, rather than face-to-face, we often are less focused on others' reactions. We are less self-conscious, and thus less inhibited. Sometimes this is taken to an extreme, as when bullies hound a victim, hate groups post messages promoting bigotry, or people send photos of themselves they later regret. More often, however, the increased self-disclosure serves to deepen friendships (Valkenburg & Peter, 2009).

DOES SOCIAL NETWORKING PROMOTE NARCISSISM? **Narcissism** is self-esteem gone wild. Narcissistic people are self-important, self-focused, and self-promoting. To measure your narcissistic tendencies, you might rate your agreement with personality test items such as "I like to be the center of attention" and "If I ruled the world it would be a better place." People who agree with these statements tend to have high narcissism scores—and they are especially active on social networking sites (Liu & Baumeister, 2016). They collect more superficial "friends." They offer more staged, glamorous photos. They retaliate more against negative comments. And, not surprisingly, they *seem* more narcissistic to strangers (Buffardi & Campbell, 2008; Weiser, 2015).

For narcissists, social networking sites are more than a gathering place; they are a feeding trough. In one study, college students were *randomly assigned* either to edit and explain their online profiles for 15 minutes, or to use that time to study and explain a Google Maps routing (Freeman & Twenge, 2010). After completing their tasks, all were tested. Who then scored higher on a narcissism measure? Those who had spent the time focused on themselves.

LaunchPad See the **Video: Random Assignment** for a helpful tutorial animation.

MAINTAINING BALANCE AND FOCUS It will come as no surprise that excessive online socializing and gaming have correlated with lower grades and with increased anxiety and depression (Brooks, 2015; Lepp et al., 2014; Walsh et al., 2013). In one U.S. survey, 47 percent of the heaviest users of the internet and other media were receiving mostly C grades or lower, as were just 23 percent of the lightest users (Kaiser Family Foundation, 2010). In another national survey, young adults who used seven or more social media platforms were three times more likely to be depressed or anxious than those who used two or fewer (Primack et al., 2016).

In today's world, it can be challenging to maintain a healthy balance between our real-world and online time. Experts offer some practical suggestions:

- *Monitor your time.* Keep a log of how you use your time. Then ask yourself, "Does my time use reflect my priorities? Am I spending more time online than I intended? Is my time online interfering with my school or work performance or my relationships?"

- *Monitor your feelings.* Ask yourself, "Am I emotionally distracted by my online interests? When I disconnect and move to another activity, how do I feel? Have family or friends commented on this?"

- *Hide from your incessantly posting online friends when necessary.* And in your own postings, practice the golden rule. Ask yourself, "Is this something I'd care about if someone else posted it?"

- *When studying, get in the practice of checking your phone and email less often.* Selective attention—the flashlight of your mind—can be in only one place at a time. When we try to do two things at once, we don't do either one of them very

narcissism excessive self-love and self-absorption.

well (Willingham, 2010). If you want to study or work productively, resist the temptation to be always available. Disable sound alerts, vibration, and pop-ups. (To reduce internet distraction, I [DM] am working on this module in a coffee shop without Wi-Fi.)

- **Refocus by taking a nature walk.** People learn better after a peaceful walk in a park, which—unlike a walk on a busy street—refreshes our capacity for focused attention (Berman et al., 2008). Connecting with nature boosts our spirits and sharpens our minds (Zelenski & Nisbet, 2014).

As psychologist Steven Pinker (2010) said, "The solution is not to bemoan technology but to develop strategies of self-control, as we do with every other temptation in life."

"It keeps me from looking at my phone every two seconds."

🔒 **RETRIEVE IT • • •**   *ANSWERS IN APPENDIX E*

RI-4 Social networking tends to _____ (strengthen/weaken) your relationships with people you already know and _____ (increase/decrease) your self-disclosure.

ENGAGE 💡 (ASK YOURSELF)

Do your connections on social media increase your sense of belonging, or do they make you feel lonelier? At busy times, what strategies do you use to maintain balance and focus?

ACHIEVEMENT MOTIVATION

LOQ 29-4 What is *achievement motivation,* and what are some ways to encourage achievement?

Some motives seem to have little obvious survival value. Billionaires may be motivated to make ever more money, reality TV stars to attract ever more social media followers, politicians to achieve ever more power, daredevils to seek ever greater thrills. Motives vary across cultures. In an individualist culture, employees may work to receive an "employee of the month" award; in a collectivist culture, they may strive to join a company's hardest-working team. Such motives seem not to diminish when they are fed. The more we achieve, the more we may need to achieve. Psychologist Henry Murray (1938) defined **achievement motivation** as a desire for significant accomplishment, for mastering skills or ideas, for control, and for attaining a high standard.

Thanks to their persistence and eagerness for challenge, people with high achievement motivation do accomplish more. They tend to have greater financial success, healthy social relationships, good physical health, and emotional well-being (Steptoe & Wardle, 2017). One famous study followed the lives of 1528 California children whose intelligence test scores were in the top 1 percent. Forty years later, researchers compared those who were most and least successful professionally. What did the researchers discover? A motivational difference. The most successful were more ambitious, energetic, and persistent. As children, they had more active hobbies. As adults, they participated in more groups and sports (Goleman, 1980). Gifted children are able learners. Accomplished adults are tenacious doers. Most of us are energetic doers when starting and when finishing a project. It's easiest—have you noticed?—to get stuck in the middle. That's when high achievers keep going (Bonezzi et al., 2011).

In some studies of both secondary school and university students, self-discipline has surpassed intelligence test scores in predicting school performance, attendance, and graduation honors. For school performance, "discipline outdoes talent," concluded researchers Angela Duckworth and Martin Seligman (2005, 2006).

Discipline focuses and refines talent. By their early twenties, top violinists have accumulated thousands of lifetime practice hours—in fact, double the practice time of other violin students aiming to be teachers (Ericsson 2001, 2006, 2007). A study of outstanding scholars, athletes, and artists found that all were highly motivated and self-disciplined, willing to dedicate hours every day to the pursuit of their goals (Bloom, 1985). But as young Mozart composing at age 8 illustrates, native talent matters, too (Hambrick & Meinz, 2011; Ruthsatz & Urbach, 2012). In sports, music, and chess, people's practice-time differences, while significant, account for a third or less of their performance differences (Hambrick et al., 2014a,b; Macnamara et al., 2014, 2016; Ullén et al., 2016). High achievers benefit from passion and perseverance, but the superstars among them are also distinguished by their extraordinary natural talent.

"Genius is 1% inspiration and 99% perspiration." —Thomas Edison (1847–1931)

achievement motivation a desire for significant accomplishment, for mastery of skills or ideas, for control, and for attaining a high standard.

CALUM'S ROAD: WHAT GRIT CAN ACCOMPLISH Having spent his life on the Scottish island of Raasay, farming a small patch of land, tending its lighthouse, and fishing, Malcolm ("Calum") MacLeod (1911–1988) felt anguished. His local government repeatedly refused to build a road that would enable vehicles to reach his north end of the island. With the once-flourishing population there having dwindled to two—MacLeod and his wife—he responded with heroic determination. One spring morning in 1964, MacLeod, then in his fifties, gathered an ax, a chopper, a shovel, and a wheelbarrow. By hand, he began to transform the existing footpath into a 1.75-mile road (Miers, 2009).

"With a road," a former neighbor explained, "he hoped new generations of people would return to the north end of Raasay," restoring its culture (Hutchinson, 2006). Day after day he worked through rough hillsides, along hazardous cliff faces, and over peat bogs. Finally, 10 years later, he completed his supreme achievement. The road, which the government has since surfaced, remains a visible example of what vision plus determined grit can accomplish. It bids us each to ponder: What "roads"—what achievements— might we, with sustained effort, build in the years before us?

From Calum's Road by Roger Hutchinson, reproduced courtesy of Birlinn Ltd.

Duckworth (2016) has a name for passionate dedication to an ambitious, long-term goal: **grit.** When combined with self-control (regulating one's attention and actions in the face of temptation), gritty goal-striving can produce great achievements. Researchers have begun to sleuth the neural and genetic markers of grit (Nemmi et al., 2016; Rimfeld et al., 2016). As the saying goes, "If you want to look good in front of thousands, you have to outwork thousands in front of nobody."

Although intelligence is distributed like a bell curve, achievements are not. This tells us that achievement involves much more than raw ability. That is why it pays to know how best to engage people's motivations to achieve. Promising people a reward for an enjoyable task can backfire. Excessive rewards can destroy **intrinsic motivation**—the desire to perform a behavior effectively for its own sake. In experiments, children have been promised a payoff for playing with an interesting puzzle or toy. Later, they played with the toy *less* than did unpaid children (Deci et al., 1999; Tang & Hall, 1995). Likewise, rewarding children with toys or candy for reading diminishes the time they spend reading (Marinak & Gambrell, 2008). It is as if they think, "If I have to be bribed into doing this, it must not be worth doing!"

To sense the difference between intrinsic motivation and **extrinsic motivation** (behaving in certain ways that gain external rewards or avoid threatened punishment), think about your experience in this course. Like most students, you probably want to earn a high grade. But what motivates your actions to achieve your goal? Do you feel pressured to finish this reading before a deadline? Are you worried about your grade? Eager for the credits that will count toward graduation? If *Yes*, then you are extrinsically motivated (as, to some extent, all students must be). Do you also find the material interesting? Does learning it make you feel more competent? If there were no grade at stake, might you be curious enough to want to learn the material for its own sake? If *Yes*, intrinsic motivation also fuels your efforts.

Students who focus on learning (intrinsic reward) often get good grades and graduate (extrinsic rewards). Doctors who focus on healing (intrinsic reward) generally make a good living (extrinsic reward). Indeed, research suggests that people who focus on their work's meaning and significance not only do better work but ultimately earn more extrinsic rewards (Wrzesniewski et al., 2014).

Extrinsic rewards work well when people perform tasks that don't naturally inspire complex, creative thinking (Hewett & Conway, 2015). They're also effective when used to signal a job well done (rather than to bribe or control someone) (Boggiano et al., 1985). "Most improved player" awards, for example, can boost feelings of competence and increase enjoyment of a sport. Rightly administered, rewards can improve performance and spark creativity (Eisenberger & Aselage, 2009; Henderlong & Lepper, 2002). And the rewards that often follow academic achievement, such as access to scholarships and a variety of jobs, can have long-lasting benefits.

Organizational psychologists seek ways to engage and motivate ordinary people doing ordinary jobs (see Appendix B: Psychology at Work). Indeed, each of us can adopt some research-based strategies for achieving our goals:

1. *Do make that resolution.* Challenging goals motivate achievement (Harkin et al., 2016). Concrete goals—"finish that psychology paper by Tuesday"—direct attention and motivate persistence.

2. *Announce the goals to friends or family.* We're more likely to follow through after making a public commitment.

grit in psychology, passion and perseverance in the pursuit of long-term goals.

intrinsic motivation the desire to perform a behavior effectively for its own sake.

extrinsic motivation the desire to perform a behavior to receive promised rewards or avoid threatened punishment.

3. ***Develop an implementation plan.*** An action strategy should specify when, where, and how we will progress toward our goal. People who flesh out goals with detailed plans become more focused and more likely to succeed (Gollwitzer & Oettingen, 2012). Better to center on small steps—the day's running goal, say—than to fantasize about the marathon.

4. ***Create short-term rewards that support long-term goals.*** Although delayed rewards motivate us to set goals, immediate rewards best predict our persistence toward them (Woolley & Fishbach, 2017).

5. ***Monitor and record progress.*** If striving for more exercise, use a wearable fitness tracker such as Fitbit. It's even more motivating when progress is shared rather than kept secret (Harkin et al., 2016).

6. ***Create a supportive environment.*** When trying to eat healthily, keep junk food out of the cupboards. Decrease portion sizes. When focusing on a project, hole up in the library. When sleeping, stash the phone. Such "situational self-control strategies" prevent tempting impulses (Duckworth et al., 2016).

7. ***Transform the hard-to-do behavior into a must-do habit.*** Habits form when we repeat behaviors in a given context. As our behavior becomes linked with the context, our next experience of that context evokes our habitual response. To increase our self-control, to connect our resolutions with positive outcomes, the key is forming "beneficial habits" (Galla & Duckworth, 2015). Do something every day for about two months and it will become an ingrained habit.

To achieve important life goals, we often know what to do. We *know* that a full night's sleep boosts our alertness, energy, and mood. We *know* that exercise lessens depression and anxiety, sculpts our body, and strengthens our heart and mind. We *know* that what we put into our body—junk food or balanced nutrition, addictive substances or clean air—affects our health and longevity. Alas, as T. S. Eliot foresaw, "Between the idea/And the reality . . . Falls the Shadow." Nevertheless, by taking these seven steps—resolving, announcing, planning, rewarding, monitoring, controlling, and persistently acting—we can create a bridge between the idea and the reality.

ENGAGE **ASK YOURSELF**

What goal would you like to achieve? How might you use the seven strategies offered in this section to meet that goal?

🔒 **RETRIEVE IT • • •**   *ANSWERS IN APPENDIX E*

RI-5 What have researchers found to be an even better predictor of school performance than intelligence test scores?

🔒 **REVIEW** BASIC MOTIVATIONAL CONCEPTS, AFFILIATION, AND ACHIEVEMENT

⤳ Learning Objectives

TEST YOURSELF Answer these repeated Learning Objective Questions on your own (before checking the answers in Appendix D) to improve your retention of the concepts (McDaniel et al., 2009, 2015).

29-1 How do psychologists define *motivation*? From what perspectives do they view motivated behavior?

29-2 What evidence points to our human affiliation need—our need to belong?

29-3 How does social networking influence us?

29-4 What is *achievement motivation*, and what are some ways to encourage achievement?

⤳ Terms and Concepts to Remember

TEST YOURSELF Write down the definition yourself, then check your answer on the referenced page.

motivation, **p. 349**

instinct, **p. 349**

physiological need, **p. 349**

drive-reduction theory, **p. 349**

homeostasis, **p. 349**

incentive, **p. 349**

Yerkes-Dodson law, **p. 351**

hierarchy of needs, **p. 351**

affiliation need, **p. 353**

self-determination theory, **p. 353**

ostracism, **p. 355**

narcissism, **p. 356**

achievement motivation, **p. 357**

grit, **p. 358**

intrinsic motivation, **p. 358**

extrinsic motivation, **p. 358**

⟳ Experience the Testing Effect

TEST YOURSELF Answer the following questions on your own first, then check your answers in Appendix E.

1. Today's evolutionary psychology shares an idea that was an underlying assumption of instinct theory. This idea is that
   a. physiological needs arouse psychological states.
   b. genes predispose species-typical behavior.
   c. physiological needs increase arousal.
   d. external needs energize and direct behavior.

2. An example of a physiological need is _____. An example of a psychological drive is _____.
   a. hunger; a "push" to find food
   b. a "push" to find food; hunger
   c. curiosity; a "push" to reduce arousal
   d. a "push" to reduce arousal; curiosity

3. Danielle walks into a friend's kitchen, smells cookies baking, and begins to feel very hungry. The smell of baking cookies is a(n) _____ (incentive/drive).

4. _____ theory attempts to explain behaviors that do NOT reduce physiological needs.

5. With a challenging task, such as taking a difficult exam, performance is likely to peak when arousal is
   a. very high.   c. very low.
   b. moderate.   d. absent.

6. According to Maslow's hierarchy of needs, our most basic needs are physiological, including the need for food and water; just above these are _____ needs.
   a. safety   c. belongingness
   b. self-esteem   d. self-transcendence

7. Which of the following is NOT evidence supporting the view that humans are strongly motivated by a need to belong?
   a. Students who rated themselves as "very happy" also tended to have satisfying close relationships.
   b. Social exclusion—such as exile or solitary confinement—is considered a severe form of punishment.
   c. As adults, adopted children tend to resemble their biological parents.
   d. Children who are extremely neglected become withdrawn, frightened, and speechless.

8. What are some ways to manage our social networking time successfully?

9. If we want to increase our chance of success in achieving a new goal, such as stopping smoking, we _____ (should/should not) announce the goal publicly, and we _____ (should/should not) share with others our progress toward achieving that goal.

Continue testing yourself with ⊞ **LearningCurve** or ⊞ **Achieve Read & Practice** to learn and remember most effectively.

㉚ Hunger

Those who have tried to restrict their eating know that physiological influences are powerful. This was vividly demonstrated when Ancel Keys and his research team (1950) studied semistarvation among volunteers, who participated as an alternative to military service. After feeding 200 men normally for three months, researchers halved the food intake for 36 of them. These semistarved men became listless and apathetic as their bodies conserved energy. Eventually, their body weights stabilized about 25 percent below their starting weights.

Consistent with Abraham Maslow's idea of a needs hierarchy, the men became food obsessed. They talked food. They daydreamed food. They collected recipes, read cookbooks, and feasted their eyes on delectable forbidden food. Preoccupied with their unmet basic need, they lost interest in sex and social activities. As one man reported, "If we see a show, the most interesting part of it is contained in scenes where people are eating. I couldn't laugh at the funniest picture in the world, and love scenes are completely dull." The semistarved men's preoccupations illustrate how powerful motives can hijack our consciousness.

When you are hungry, thirsty, fatigued, or sexually aroused, little else may seem to matter. In studies, people in a motivational "hot" state (from fatigue, hunger, or sexual arousal) have easily recalled such feelings in their own past and have perceived them

"Nobody wants to kiss when they are hungry." —Journalist Dorothy Dix (1861–1951)

"Nature often equips life's essentials—sex, eating, nursing—with built-in gratification." —Frans de Waal, "Morals Without God?" 2010

HUNGER HIJACKS THE MIND World War II survivor Louis Zamperini (protagonist of the book and movie *Unbroken*, shown here) went down with his plane over the Pacific Ocean. He and two other crew members drifted for 47 days, subsisting on an occasional bird or a fish. To help pass time, the hunger-driven men recited recipes or recalled their mothers' home cooking.

as driving forces in others' behavior (Nordgren et al., 2006, 2007). (Interestingly, there is a parallel effect of our current good or bad mood on our memories of good or bad moods.) In another experiment, people were given money to bid for foods. When hungry, people *over*bid for snacks they were told they could eat later when they would be full. When full, people *under*bid for snacks they were told they could eat later when they would be hungry (Fisher & Rangel, 2014). It's hard to imagine what we're not feeling! Grocery shop with an empty stomach and you are more likely to see those jelly-filled doughnuts as just what you've always loved and will be wanting tomorrow. *Motives matter mightily.*

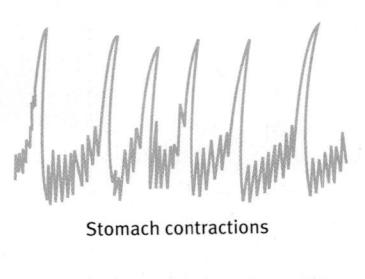

"Never hunt when you're hungry."

THE PHYSIOLOGY OF HUNGER

LOQ 30-1 What physiological factors produce hunger?

"The full person does not understand the needs of the hungry." —Irish proverb

Deprived of a normal food supply, Keys' semistarved volunteers were clearly hungry. But what precisely triggers hunger? Is it the pangs of an empty stomach? So it seemed to A. L. Washburn. Working with Walter Cannon, Washburn agreed to swallow a balloon attached to a recording device (Cannon & Washburn, 1912) (**FIGURE 30.1**). When inflated to fill his stomach, the balloon transmitted his stomach contractions. Washburn supplied information about his *feelings* of hunger by pressing a key each time he felt a hunger pang. The discovery: Whenever Washburn felt hungry, he was indeed having stomach contractions.

Can hunger exist without stomach pangs? To answer that question, researchers removed some rats' stomachs and created a direct path to their small intestines (Tsang, 1938). Did the rats continue to eat? Indeed they did. Some hunger similarly persists in humans whose ulcerated or cancerous stomachs have been removed. So the pangs of an empty stomach are not the *only* source of hunger. What else might trigger hunger?

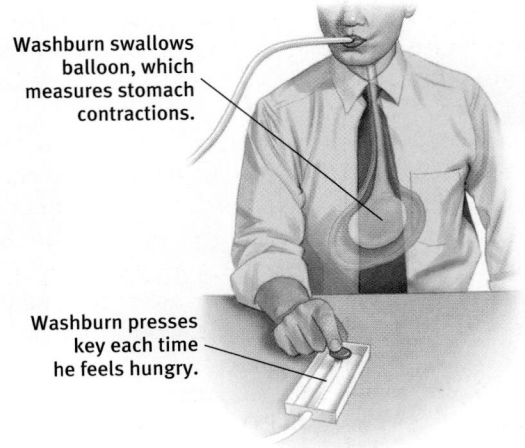

Washburn swallows balloon, which measures stomach contractions.

Washburn presses key each time he feels hungry.

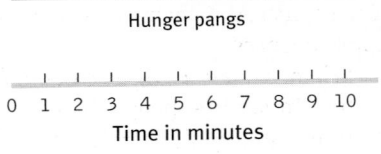

Stomach contractions

Hunger pangs

0 1 2 3 4 5 6 7 8 9 10
Time in minutes

FIGURE 30.1

MONITORING STOMACH CONTRACTIONS (Information from Cannon, 1929.)

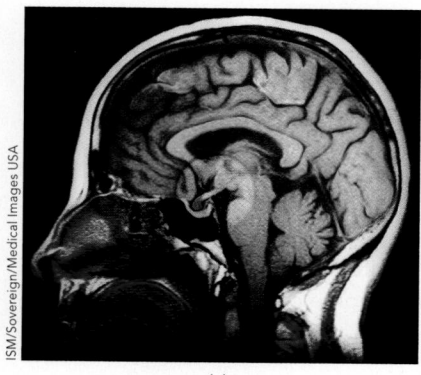

(a)   (b)

FIGURE 30.2

THE HYPOTHALAMUS (a) The hypothalamus (colored orange) performs various body maintenance functions, including control of hunger. Blood vessels supply the hypothalamus, enabling it to respond to our current blood chemistry as well as to incoming neural information about the body's state. (b) The fat mouse on the left has nonfunctioning receptors in the appetite-suppressing part of the hypothalamus.

 LaunchPad For an interactive and visual tutorial on the brain and eating, visit **Topic Tutorial: PsychSim6, Hunger and the Fat Rat.**

Body Chemistry and the Brain

Somehow, somewhere, your body is keeping tabs on the energy it takes in and the energy it uses. If this weren't true, you would be unable to maintain a stable body weight. A major source of energy in your body is the blood sugar **glucose.** If your blood glucose level drops, you won't consciously feel the lower blood sugar, but your stomach, intestines, and liver will signal your brain to motivate eating. Your brain, which is automatically monitoring your blood chemistry and your body's internal state, will then trigger hunger.

How does the brain integrate these messages and sound the alarm? The work is done by several neural areas, some housed deep in the brain within the hypothalamus, a neural traffic intersection (**FIGURE 30.2**). For example, one neural network (called the *arcuate nucleus*) has a center that secretes appetite-stimulating hormones. When stimulated electrically, well-fed animals begin to eat. If the area is destroyed, even starving animals have no interest in food. Another neural center secretes appetite-suppressing hormones. When electrically stimulated, animals will stop eating. Destroy this area and animals can't stop eating and will become obese (see Figure 30.2b) (Duggan & Booth, 1986; Hoebel & Teitelbaum, 1966).

Blood vessels connect the hypothalamus to the rest of the body, so it can respond to our current blood chemistry and other incoming information. One of its tasks is monitoring levels of appetite hormones, such as *ghrelin,* a hunger-arousing hormone secreted by an empty stomach. During bypass surgery for severe *obesity,* surgeons seal off or remove part of the stomach. The remaining stomach then produces much less ghrelin, reducing the person's appetite and making food less enticing (Ammori, 2013; Lemonick, 2002; Scholtz et al., 2013). Other appetite hormones include *orexin, insulin, leptin,* and *PYY;* **FIGURE 30.3** describes how they influence your feelings of hunger.

You can also blame your brain for weight regain (Cornier, 2011). The interaction of appetite hormones and brain activity suggests that the body has some sort of "weight thermostat." When semistarved rats fall below their normal weight, this system signals

FIGURE 30.3

THE APPETITE HORMONES
Increases appetite
- *Ghrelin:* Hormone secreted by empty stomach; sends "I'm hungry" signals to the brain.
- *Orexin:* Hunger-triggering hormone secreted by hypothalamus.

Decreases appetite
- *Insulin:* Hormone secreted by pancreas; controls blood glucose.
- *Leptin:* Protein hormone secreted by fat cells; when abundant, causes brain to increase metabolism and decrease hunger.
- *PYY:* Digestive tract hormone; sends "I'm *not* hungry" signals to the brain.

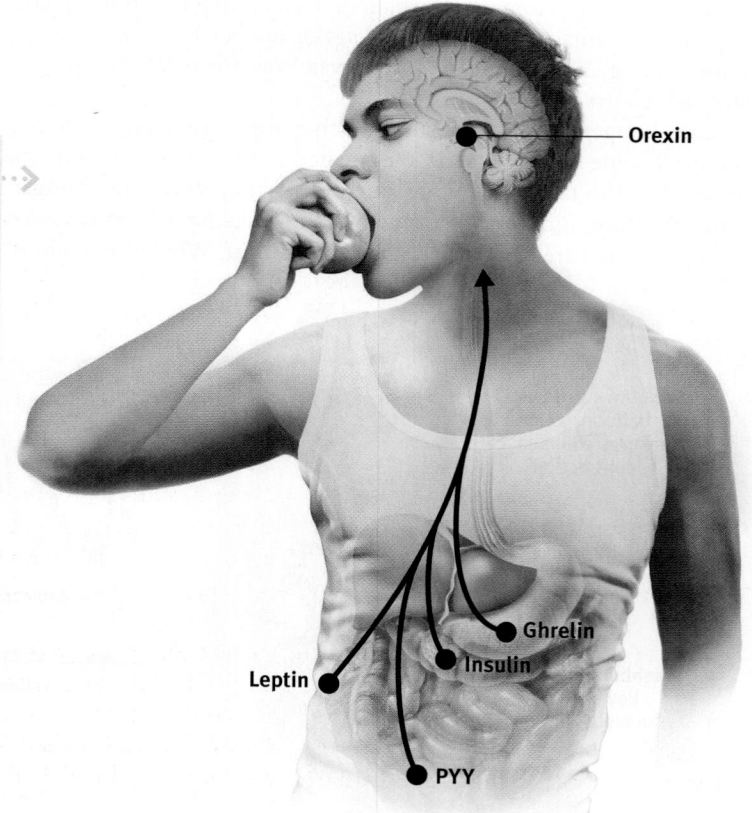

the body to restore the lost weight. It's as though fat cells cry out "Feed me!" and grab glucose from the bloodstream (Ludwig & Friedman, 2014). Hunger increases and energy output decreases. In this way, rats (and humans) tend to hover around a stable weight, or **set point,** influenced in part by heredity (Keesey & Corbett, 1984).

We humans (and other species, too) vary in our **basal metabolic rate,** the resting rate of energy expenditure for maintaining basic body functions. But we share a common response to decreased food intake: Our basal metabolic rate drops, as it did for participants in Keys' experiment. After 24 weeks of semistarvation they stabilized at three-quarters of their normal weight, even though they were taking in only *half* their previous calories. How did they achieve this dieter's nightmare? They reduced their energy expenditure, partly because they were less active, but partly because their basal metabolic rate dropped by 29 percent.

Some researchers have suggested that the idea of a biologically *fixed* set point is too rigid to explain some things. One thing it doesn't address is that slow, sustained changes in body weight can alter a person's set point (Assanand et al., 1998). Another is that when we have unlimited access to a wide variety of tasty foods, we tend to overeat and gain weight (Raynor & Epstein, 2001). And set points don't explain why psychological factors influence hunger. For all these reasons, some prefer the looser term *settling point* to indicate the level at which a person's weight settles in response to caloric intake and energy use. As we will see next, these factors are influenced by environment as well as biology.

🔒 **RETRIEVE IT • • •**   *ANSWERS IN APPENDIX E*

RI-1 Hunger occurs in response to _____ (low/high) blood glucose and _____ (low/high) levels of ghrelin.

THE PSYCHOLOGY OF HUNGER

LOQ 30-2 What cultural and situational factors influence hunger?

Our internal hunger is pushed by our physiology—our body chemistry and brain activity. Yet there is more to hunger than meets the stomach. This was strikingly apparent when researchers tested two patients who had no memory for events occurring more than a minute ago (Rozin et al., 1998). If offered a second lunch 20 minutes after eating a normal lunch, both patients readily consumed it . . . and usually a third meal offered 20 minutes after they finished the second. This suggests that one part of our decision to eat is our memory of the time of our last meal. As time passes, we think about eating again, and those thoughts trigger feelings of hunger.

Taste Preferences: Biology and Culture

Body cues and environmental factors together influence not only the *when* of hunger, but also the *what*—our taste preferences. When feeling tense or depressed, do you tend to take solace in high-calorie foods, as has been found in ardent football fans after a big loss (Cornil & Chandon, 2013)? The carbohydrates in pizza, chips, and sweets help boost levels of the neurotransmitter serotonin, which has calming effects. When stressed, both rats and many humans find it extra rewarding to scarf chocolate cookies (Artiga et al., 2007; Sproesser et al., 2014).

Our preferences for sweet and salty tastes are genetic and universal, but conditioning can intensify or alter those preferences. People given highly salted foods may develop a liking for excess salt (Beauchamp, 1987). People sickened by a food may develop an aversion to it. (The frequency of children's illnesses provides many chances for them to learn to avoid certain foods.)

Our culture teaches us that some foods are delicious but others are not. Many Japanese people enjoy *nattō,* a fermented soybean dish, which smell expert Rachel Herz (2012) reports "smells like the marriage of ammonia and a tire fire." Asians, she adds, are often repulsed by what many Westerners love—"the rotted bodily fluid of an ungulate" (a.k.a. cheese, some varieties of which have the same bacteria and odor as stinky feet).

"Never get a tattoo when you're drunk and hungry."

glucose the form of sugar that circulates in the blood and provides the major source of energy for body tissues. When its level is low, we feel hunger.

set point the point at which your "weight thermostat" may be set. When your body falls below this weight, increased hunger and a lowered metabolic rate may combine to restore lost weight.

basal metabolic rate the body's resting rate of energy output.

AN ACQUIRED TASTE People everywhere learn to enjoy the fatty, bitter, or spicy foods common in their culture. For these Alaska Natives, but not for most other North Americans, whale blubber is a tasty treat. For Peruvians, roasted guinea pig is similarly delicious.

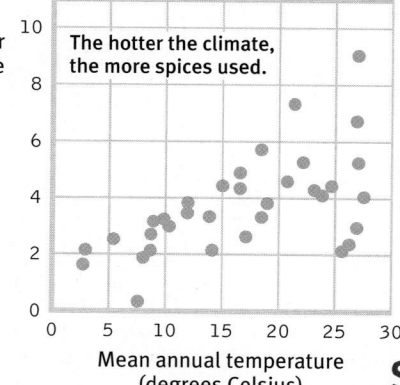

FIGURE 30.4

HOT CULTURES LIKE HOT SPICES
Countries with hot climates, in which food historically spoiled more quickly, feature recipes with more bacteria-inhibiting spices (Sherman & Flaxman, 2001). India averages nearly 10 spices per meat recipe; Finland, 2 spices.

ENGAGE
(ASK YOURSELF)

Do you usually eat only when your body sends hunger signals? How much does the sight or smell of delicious food tempt you even when you're full?

But there is biological wisdom to many of our taste preferences. For example, in hot climates (where foods spoil more quickly) recipes often include spices that inhibit bacteria growth (**FIGURE 30.4**). Pregnancy-related food dislikes—and the nausea associated with them—peak about the tenth week, when the developing embryo is most vulnerable to toxins.

Rats tend to avoid unfamiliar foods (Sclafani, 1995). So do we, especially those that are animal-based. This *neophobia* (dislike of unfamiliar things) surely was adaptive for our ancestors by protecting them from potentially toxic substances. We can overcome harmless food dislikes by repeatedly trying small samples of an unfamiliar food or drink. In experiments, this tends to increase people's appreciation for the new taste (Pliner, 1982; Pliner et al., 1993).

Situational Influences on Eating

To a surprising extent, situations also control our eating—a phenomenon psychologists have called the *ecology of eating*. Here are four situational influences you may have noticed but underestimated:

- *Friends and food* Do you eat more when eating with others? Most of us do (Herman et al., 2003; Hetherington et al., 2006). After a party, you may realize you've over-eaten. This happens because the presence of others tends to amplify our natural behavior tendencies. (Psychologists call this *social facilitation*.)

- *Serving size is significant* Investigators studied the effects of portion size by offering people varieties of free snacks (Geier et al., 2006). For example, in an apartment building's lobby, they laid out full or half pretzels, big or little Tootsie Rolls, or a small or large serving scoop with a bowl of M&M'S. Their consistent result: Offered a supersized portion, people put away more calories. Larger portions induce bigger bites, which may increase intake by decreasing oral exposure time (Herman et al., 2015). Children also eat more when using adult-sized (rather than child-sized) dishware (DiSantis et al., 2013). Portion size matters.

- *Selections stimulate* Food variety also stimulates eating. Offered a dessert buffet, people eat more than they do when choosing a portion from one favorite dessert. For our early ancestors, variety was healthy. When foods were abundant and varied, eating more provided a wide range of vitamins and minerals and produced protective fat for winter cold or famine. When a bounty of varied foods was unavailable, eating less extended the food supply until winter or famine ended (Polivy et al., 2008; Remick et al., 2009).

- *Nudging nutrition* One research team quadrupled carrots taken by offering school-children carrots before they picked up other foods in a lunch line (Redden et al., 2015). Such "nudges" support U.S. President Barack Obama's 2015 executive order to use "behavioral science insights to serve the American people."

* * *

To consider how hunger and other factors affect our risks for **obesity**, see Thinking Critically About: The Challenges of Obesity and Weight Control. And for tips on shedding unwanted weight, see **TABLE 30.1**.

obesity defined as a body mass index (BMI) measurement of 30 or higher, which is calculated from our weight-to-height ratio. (Overweight individuals have a BMI of 25 or higher.)

🔒 **RETRIEVE IT • • •**   *ANSWERS IN APPENDIX E*

RI-2 After an 8-hour hike without food, your long-awaited favorite dish is placed in front of you, and your mouth waters in anticipation. Why?

THINKING CRITICALLY ABOUT:

The Challenges of Obesity and Weight Control

LOQ 30-3 How does obesity affect physical and psychological health, and what factors are involved in weight management?

A Growing Problem

Obesity is associated with:
- **physical health risks**, including diabetes, high blood pressure, heart disease, gallstones, arthritis, and certain types of cancer. [1]

- **increased depression**, especially among women. [2]
- **bullying**, outranking race and sexual orientation as the biggest reason for youth bullying in Western cultures. [3]

Percentage Overweight in 195 Countries Studied [4]

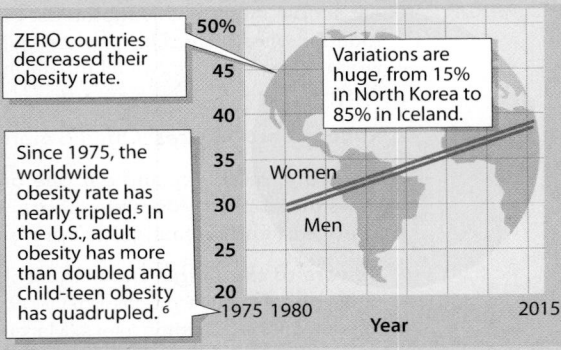

ZERO countries decreased their obesity rate.

Variations are huge, from 15% in North Korea to 85% in Iceland.

Since 1975, the worldwide obesity rate has nearly tripled.[5] In the U.S., adult obesity has more than doubled and child-teen obesity has quadrupled. [6]

Women
Men
Year (1975 1980 — 2015)

Body Mass Index (BMI)

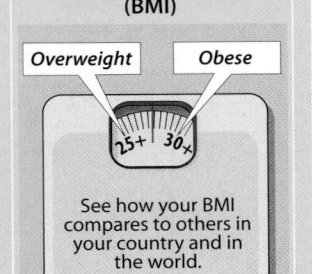

Overweight | Obese
25+ | 30+

See how your BMI compares to others in your country and in the world.

tinyurl.com/GiveMyBMI

How Did We Get Here?

Does obesity reflect a simple lack of willpower, as some people presume? [7]
No. Many factors contribute to obesity.

PHYSIOLOGY FACTORS

Storing fat was adaptive.
- This ideal form of stored energy carried our ancestors through periods of famine. People in impoverished places still find heavier bodies attractive, as plumpness signals affluence and status. [8]
- In food-rich countries, the drive for fat has become dysfunctional. [9]

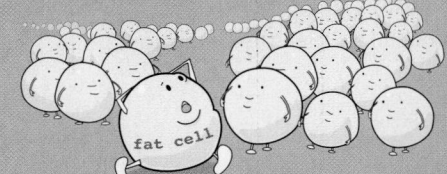

fat cell

Set point and metabolism matter.
- Fat (lower metabolic rate than muscle) requires less food intake to maintain than it did to gain.
- If weight drops below *set point/settling point*, the brain triggers ⬆ hunger and ⬇ metabolism.
- Body perceives STARVATION; adapts by burning fewer calories. Most dieters in the long run regain what they lose on weight-loss programs.[10]
- 30 weeks of competition on *The Biggest Loser* ➡ 6 years later ➡ Only 1 of 14 contestants kept the weight off. On average they regained 70% of what they lost and were still struggling with lessened caloric burn from their slowed metabolism. [11]

Genes influence us.
- Lean people seem naturally disposed to move about, burning more calories than energy-conserving overweight people, who tend to sit still longer. [12]
- Adoptive siblings' body weights are uncorrelated with one another or with their adoptive parents, instead resembling their biological parents' weight. [13]
- Identical twins have closely similar weights, even if raised apart. [14] Much lower *fraternal* twin weight correlation suggests genes explain 2/3 of our varying body mass. [15]
- More than 100 genes have been identified as each affecting weight in some small way. [16]

ENVIRONMENTAL FACTORS

- **Sleep loss** makes us more vulnerable to obesity. [17]

Increasing — Sleep deprivation — Decreasing

Ghrelin—appetite-stimulating stomach hormone   **Leptin**— reports body fat to the brain

- **Social influences:** Our own odds of becoming obese triple if a close friend becomes obese. [18]
- **Food and activity levels:** Worldwide, we eat more and move less, with 31% of adults (including 43% of Americans and 25% of Europeans) now sedentary—averaging <20 minutes per day of moderate activity such as walking. [19]

NOTE: With weight, as with intelligence and other characteristics, there can be high levels of *heritability* (genetic influence on individual differences) without heredity explaining *group* differences. Genes mostly determine why one person today is heavier than another. Environment mostly determines why people today are heavier than their counterparts 50 years ago.

1. Kitahara et al., 2014. 2. de Wit et al., 2010; Luppino et al., 2010. 3. Puhl et al., 2015. 4. GBD, 2017. 5. NCD, 2016. 6. Flegal et al., 2010, 2012, 2016. 7. NORC, 2016b. 8. Furnham & Baguma, 1994; Nettle et al., 2017; Swami, 2015. 9. Hall, 2016. 10. Mann et al., 2015. 11. Fothergill et al., 2016. 12. Levine et al., 2005. 13. Grilo & Pogue-Geile, 1991. 14. Hjelmborg et al., 2008; Plomin et al., 1997. 15. Maes et al., 1997. 16. Akiyama et al., 2017. 17. Keith et al., 2006; Nedeltcheva et al., 2010; Taheri, 2004; Taheri et al., 2004. 18. Christakis & Fowler, 2007. 19. Hallal et al., 2012.

"Remember when we used to have to fatten the kids up first?"

RETAIN

TABLE 30.1

Waist Management

People struggling with obesity should seek medical evaluation and guidance. For others who wish to lose weight, researchers have offered these tips:

- ***Begin only if you feel motivated and self-disciplined.*** Permanent weight loss usually requires a lifelong change in eating habits combined with increased exercise.

- ***Exercise and get enough sleep.*** Especially when supported by 7 to 8 hours of sleep a night, exercise empties fat cells, builds muscle, speeds up metabolism, helps lower your settling point, and reduces stress and stress-induced craving for carbohydrate-rich comfort foods (Bennett, 1995; Ruotsalainen et al., 2015; Thompson et al., 1982). Among *Biggest Loser* competitors, exercise predicted less weight regain (Kerns et al., 2017).

- ***Minimize exposure to tempting food cues.*** Food shop on a full stomach. Keep tempting foods out of the house, and tuck away special-occasion foods.

- ***Limit variety and eat healthy foods.*** Given more variety, people consume more. So eat simple meals with vegetables, fruits, and whole grains. Healthy fats, such as those found in olive oil and fish, help regulate appetite (Taubes, 2001, 2002). Water- and vitamin-rich veggies can fill the stomach with few calories. Better crispy greens than Krispy Kremes.

- ***Reduce portion sizes.*** Offered more, people consume more.

- ***Don't starve all day and eat one big meal at night.*** This common eating pattern slows metabolism. Moreover, those who eat a balanced breakfast are, by late morning, more alert and less fatigued (Spring et al., 1992).

- ***Beware of the binge.*** Drinking alcohol or feeling anxious or depressed can unleash the urge to eat (Herman & Polivy, 1980). And men especially should note that eating slowly can lead to eating less (Martin et al., 2007).

- ***Before eating with others, decide how much you want to eat.*** Eating with friends can distract us from monitoring our own eating (Ward & Mann, 2000).

- ***Remember, most people occasionally lapse.*** A lapse need not become a collapse.

- ***Chart your progress online.*** Those who record and disclose their progress toward a goal more often achieve it (Harkin et al., 2016).

- ***Connect to a support group.*** Join with others, either face-to-face or online, to share goals and progress updates (Freedman, 2011).

LaunchPad For a 7-minute review of hunger, see the **Video: Hunger and Eating.**

RETRIEVE IT • • •

ANSWERS IN APPENDIX E

RI-3 Why can two people of the same height, age, and activity level maintain the same weight, even if one of them eats much less than the other does?

REVIEW HUNGER

Learning Objectives

TEST YOURSELF Answer these repeated Learning Objective Questions on your own (before checking the answers in Appendix D) to improve your retention of the concepts (McDaniel et al., 2009, 2015).

30-1 What physiological factors produce hunger?

30-2 What cultural and situational factors influence hunger?

30-3 How does obesity affect physical and psychological health, and what factors are involved in weight management?

Terms and Concepts to Remember

TEST YOURSELF Write down the definition yourself, then check your answer on the referenced page.

glucose, **p. 363**

set point, **p. 363**

basal metabolic rate, **p. 363**

obesity, **p. 365**

⤳ Experience the Testing Effect

TEST YOURSELF Answer the following questions on your own first, then check your answers in Appendix E.

1. Journalist Dorothy Dix once remarked, "Nobody wants to kiss when they are hungry." How does Maslow's hierarchy of needs support her statement?

2. According to the concept of _____ _____, our body maintains itself at a particular weight level.

3. Which of the following is a genetically predisposed response to food?
   a. An aversion to eating cats and dogs
   b. An interest in novel foods
   c. A preference for sweet and salty foods
   d. An aversion to carbohydrates

4. Blood sugar provides the body with energy. When it is _____ (low/high), we feel hungry.

5. The rate at which your body expends energy while at rest is referred to as the _____ _____ rate.

6. Obese people find it very difficult to lose weight permanently. This is due to several factors, including the fact that
   a. dieting triggers neophobia.
   b. the set point of obese people is lower than average.
   c. with dieting, metabolism increases.
   d. there is a genetic influence on body weight.

7. Sanjay recently adopted the typical college diet, increasing his intake of processed foods and sugar. He knows he may gain weight, but he figures it's no big deal because he can simply lose it in the future. How would you evaluate Sanjay's plan?

Continue testing yourself with 📖 **LearningCurve** or ≈ **Achieve Read & Practice** to learn and remember most effectively.

---

³¹ Theories and Physiology of Emotion

EMOTION: AROUSAL, BEHAVIOR, AND COGNITION

LOQ 31-1 How do arousal, expressive behavior, and cognition interact in emotion?

Motivated behavior is often connected to powerful emotions. My [DM's] own need to belong was unforgettably disrupted one day. I went to a huge store and brought along Peter, my toddler first-born child. As I set Peter down on his feet for a moment so I could do some paperwork, a passerby warned, "You'd better be careful or you'll lose that boy!" Not more than a few breaths later, I turned and found no Peter beside me.

With mild anxiety, I looked around one end of the store aisle. No Peter in sight. With slightly more anxiety, I peered around the other side. No Peter there, either. Now, with my heart accelerating, I circled the neighboring counters. Still no Peter anywhere. As anxiety turned to panic, I began racing up and down the store aisles. He was nowhere to be found. The alerted store manager used the public-address system to ask customers to assist in looking for a missing child. Soon after, I passed the customer who had warned me. "I told you that you were going to lose him!" he now scolded. With visions of kidnapping (strangers routinely adored that beautiful child), I braced for the unthinkable possibility that my negligence had caused me to lose what I loved above all else, and that I might have to return home and face my wife after losing our only child.

But then, as I passed the customer service counter yet again, there he was, having been found and returned by some obliging customer. In an instant, the arousal of terror spilled into ecstasy. Clutching my son, with tears suddenly flowing, I found myself unable to speak my thanks and stumbled out of the store awash in grateful joy.

Courtesy of David Myers

Emotions are subjective. But they are real, says researcher Lisa Feldman Barrett (2012, 2013): "My experience of anger is not an illusion. When I'm angry, I feel angry. That's real." Where do our emotions come from? Why do we have them? What are they made of?

Emotions are our body's adaptive response. They support our survival. When we face challenges, emotions focus our attention and energize our actions (Cyders & Smith, 2008). Our heart races. Our pace quickens. All our senses go on high alert. Receiving unexpected good news, we may find our eyes tearing up. We raise our hands triumphantly. We feel exuberance and a newfound confidence. Yet negative and prolonged emotions can harm our health.

As my panicked search for Peter illustrates, **emotions** are a mix of:

- *bodily arousal* (heart pounding).
- *expressive behaviors* (quickened pace).
- *conscious experience* (Is this a kidnapping?) *and feelings* (panic, fear, joy).

The puzzle for psychologists is figuring out how these three pieces fit together. To do that, the first researchers of emotion considered two big questions:

1. A chicken-and-egg debate: Does your bodily arousal come *before* or *after* your emotional feelings? (Did I first notice my racing heart and faster step, and then feel terror about losing Peter? Or did my sense of fear come first, stirring my heart and legs to respond?)

2. How do *thinking* (cognition) and *feeling* interact? Does cognition always come before emotion? (Did I think about a kidnapping threat before I reacted emotionally?)

The psychological study of emotion began with the first question: How do bodily responses relate to emotions? Two of the earliest emotion theories offered different answers.

James-Lange Theory: Arousal Comes Before Emotion

Common sense tells most of us that we cry because we are sad, lash out because we are angry, tremble because we are afraid. But to pioneering psychologist William James, this commonsense view of emotion had things backward. Rather, "We feel sorry because we cry, angry because we strike, afraid because we tremble" (1890, p. 1066). To James, emotions result from attention to our bodily activity. James' idea was also proposed by Danish physiologist Carl Lange, and so is called the **James-Lange theory.** James and Lange would have guessed that I noticed my racing heart and then, shaking with fright, felt the whoosh of emotion—that my feeling of fear *followed* my body's response.

Cannon-Bard Theory: Arousal and Emotion Occur Simultaneously

Physiologist Walter Cannon (1871–1945) disagreed with the James-Lange theory. Does a racing heart signal fear or anger or love? The body's responses—heart rate, perspiration, and body temperature—are too similar, and they change too slowly, to *cause* the different emotions, said Cannon. He, and later another physiologist, Philip Bard, concluded that our bodily responses and experienced emotions occur separately but simultaneously. So, according to the **Cannon-Bard theory,** my heart began pounding *as* I experienced fear. The emotion-triggering stimulus traveled to my sympathetic nervous system, causing my body's arousal. *At the same time,* it traveled to my brain's cortex, causing my awareness of my emotion. My pounding heart did not cause my feeling of fear, nor did my feeling of fear cause my pounding heart.

But are they really independent of each other? The Cannon-Bard theory has been challenged by studies of people with severed spinal cords, including a survey of 25 World War II soldiers (Hohmann, 1966). Those with *lower-spine injuries,* who had lost sensation only in their legs, reported little change in their emotions' intensity. Those with *high spinal cord injury,* who could feel nothing below the neck, did report changes. Some reactions were much less intense than before the injuries. Anger, one man with a high spinal cord injury confessed, "just doesn't have the heat to it that it used to. It's a mental kind

Not only emotion, but most psychological phenomena (vision, sleep, memory, sex, and so forth) can be approached these three ways—physiologically, behaviorally, and cognitively.

JOY EXPRESSED According to the James-Lange theory, we don't just smile because we share our teammates' joy. We also share the joy because we are smiling with them.

of anger." Other emotions, those expressed mostly in body areas above the neck, were felt *more* intensely. These men reported increases in weeping, lumps in the throat, and getting choked up when saying good-bye, worshiping, or watching a touching movie. Such evidence has led some researchers to view feelings as "mostly shadows" of our bodily responses and behaviors (Damasio, 2003). Brain activity underlies our emotions and our emotion-fed actions (Davidson & Begley, 2012).

But our emotions also involve cognition (Averill, 1993; Barrett, 2006). Here we arrive at psychology's second big emotion question: How do thinking and feeling interact? Whether we fear the man behind us on a dark street depends entirely on whether or not we interpret his actions as threatening.

> ## 🔒 RETRIEVE IT • • •
> *ANSWERS IN APPENDIX E*
>
> **RI-1** According to the Cannon-Bard theory, (a) our *physiological response* to a stimulus (for example, a pounding heart), and (b) the *emotion we experience* (for example, fear) occur _____ (simultaneously/sequentially). According to the James-Lange theory, (a) and (b) occur _____ (simultaneously/ sequentially).

Schachter-Singer Two-Factor Theory: Arousal + Label = Emotion

LOQ 31-2 To experience emotions, must we consciously interpret and label them?

Stanley Schachter and Jerome Singer (1962) demonstrated that how we *appraise* (interpret) our experiences also matters. Our physical reactions *and our thoughts* (perceptions, memories, and interpretations) together create emotion. In their **two-factor theory,** emotions have two ingredients: physical arousal and cognitive appraisal. An emotional experience, they argued, requires a conscious interpretation of arousal.

Consider how arousal spills over from one event to the next. Imagine arriving home after an invigorating run and finding a message that you got a longed-for job. With arousal lingering from the run, would you feel more elated than if you heard this news after staying awake all night studying?

To explore this *spillover effect,* Schachter and Singer injected college men with the hormone epinephrine, which triggers feelings of arousal. But the trickster researchers told one group of men that the drug would just help test their eyesight. Picture yourself as a participant: After receiving the injection, you go to a waiting room, where you find yourself with another person (actually an accomplice of the experimenters) who is acting either euphoric or irritated. As you observe this person, you begin to feel your heart race, your body flush, and your breathing become more rapid. If you had been in the group who were told to expect these effects from the injection, what would you feel? In the actual experiment, these volunteers felt little emotion—because they correctly attributed their arousal to the drug. But if you had been told the injection would help assess your eyesight, what would you feel? Perhaps you would react as this group of participants did. They "caught" the apparent emotion of the other person in the waiting room. They became happy if the accomplice was acting euphoric, and testy if the accomplice was acting irritated.

This discovery—that a stirred-up state can be experienced as one emotion or another, depending on how we interpret and label it—has been replicated in dozens of experiments and continues to influence modern emotion research (MacCormack & Lindquist, 2016; Reisenzein, 1983; Sinclair et al., 1994). As Daniel Gilbert (2006) noted, "Feelings that one interprets as fear in the presence of a sheer drop may be interpreted as lust in the presence of a sheer blouse."

The point to remember: Arousal fuels emotion; cognition channels it.

emotion a response of the whole organism, involving (1) physiological arousal, (2) expressive behaviors, and (3) conscious experience.

James-Lange theory the theory that our experience of emotion is our awareness of our physiological responses to an emotion-arousing stimulus.

Cannon-Bard theory the theory that an emotion-arousing stimulus simultaneously triggers (1) physiological responses and (2) the subjective experience of emotion.

two-factor theory the Schachter-Singer theory that to experience emotion one must (1) be physically aroused and (2) cognitively label the arousal.

THE SPILLOVER EFFECT Arousal from a soccer match can fuel anger, which can descend into rioting or other violent confrontations.

OLEG POPOV/REUTERS/Newscom

LaunchPad For a 4-minute demonstration of the relationship between arousal and cognition, see the **Video: Emotion = Arousal Plus Interpretation.**

🔒 **RETRIEVE IT** • • •   *ANSWERS IN APPENDIX E*

RI-2 According to Schachter and Singer, two factors lead to our experience of an emotion: (1) physiological arousal and (2) _____ appraisal.

Zajonc, LeDoux, and Lazarus: Does Cognition Always Precede Emotion?

But is the heart always subject to the mind? Must we *always* interpret our arousal before we can experience an emotion? Robert Zajonc [ZI-yence] (1923–2008) didn't think so. He contended that we actually have many emotional reactions apart from, or even before, our conscious interpretation of a situation (1980, 1984a). Perhaps you can recall liking something or someone immediately, without knowing why.

Even when people repeatedly view stimuli flashed too briefly for them to interpret, they come to prefer those stimuli (Kunst-Wilson & Zajonc, 1980). Unaware of having previously seen them, they nevertheless like them. We also have an acutely sensitive automatic radar for emotionally significant information; even a subliminally flashed stimulus can prime us to feel better or worse about a follow-up stimulus (Murphy et al., 1995; Zeelenberg et al., 2006).

Neuroscientists are charting the neural pathways of emotions (Ochsner et al., 2009). Our emotional responses can follow two different brain pathways. Some emotions (especially more complex feelings such as hatred and love) travel a "high road." A stimulus following this path would travel (by way of the thalamus) to the brain's cortex (**FIGURE 31.1a**). There, it would be analyzed and labeled before the response command is sent out, via the amygdala (an emotion-control center).

But sometimes our emotions (especially simple likes, dislikes, and fears) take what Joseph LeDoux (2002, 2015) has called the more direct "low road," a neural shortcut that bypasses the cortex. Following the low road, a fear-provoking stimulus would travel from the eye or ear (again via the thalamus) directly to the amygdala (Figure 31.1b). This short-cut enables our greased-lightning emotional response before our intellect intervenes. Like speedy reflexes (that also operate separately from the brain's thinking cortex), the amygdala's reactions are so fast that we may be unaware of what's transpired (Dimberg et al., 2000). A cortex-produced conscious fear experience then occurs as we become aware that our brain has detected danger (LeDoux & Brown, 2017).

The amygdala sends more neural projections up to the cortex than it receives back, which makes it easier for our feelings to hijack our thinking than for our thinking to rule our feelings (LeDoux & Armony, 1999). Thus, in the forest, we can jump at the sound

FIGURE 31.1

THE BRAIN'S PATHWAYS FOR EMOTIONS In the two-track brain, sensory input may be routed (a) to the cortex (via the thalamus) for analysis and then transmission to the amygdala; or (b) directly to the amygdala (via the thalamus) for an instant emotional reaction.

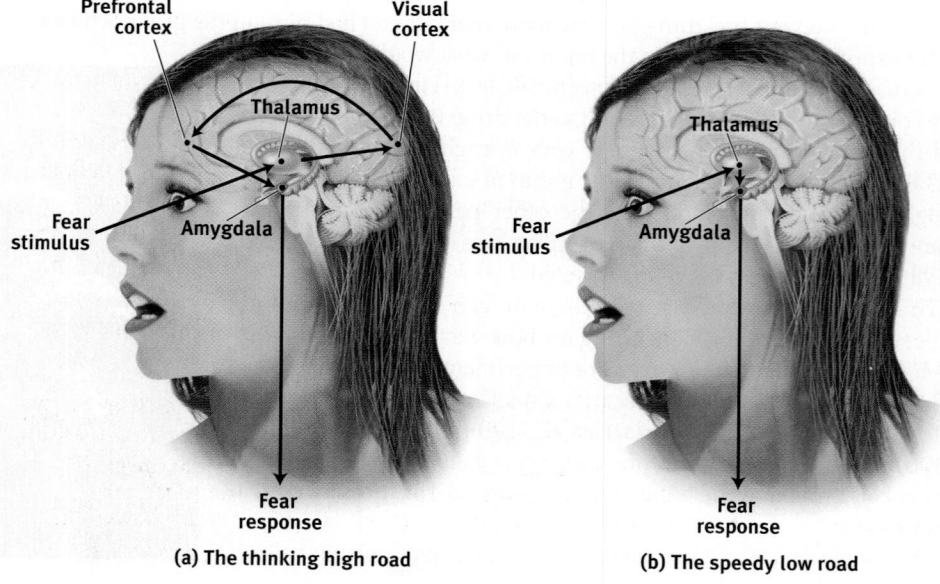

(a) The thinking high road

(b) The speedy low road

TABLE 31.1

Summary of Emotion Theories

Theory	Explanation of Emotions	Example
James-Lange	Emotions arise from our awareness of our specific bodily responses to emotion-arousing stimuli.	We observe our heart racing after a threat and then feel afraid.
Cannon-Bard	Emotion-arousing stimuli trigger our bodily responses and simultaneous subjective experience.	Our heart races at the same time that we feel afraid.
Schachter-Singer two-factor	Our experience of emotion depends on two factors: general arousal and a conscious cognitive label.	We may interpret our arousal as fear or excitement, depending on the context.
Zajonc's; LeDoux's	Some embodied responses happen instantly, without conscious appraisal.	We automatically feel startled by a sound in the forest before labeling it as a threat.
Lazarus'	Cognitive appraisal ("Is it dangerous or not?")—sometimes without our awareness—defines emotion.	The sound is "just the wind."

of rustling bushes nearby, leaving it to our cortex to decide later whether the sound was made by a snake or by the wind. Such experiences support Zajonc's and LeDoux's belief that *some* of our emotional reactions involve no deliberate thinking.

Emotion researcher Richard Lazarus (1991, 1998) conceded that our brain processes vast amounts of information without our conscious awareness, and that some emotional responses do not require *conscious* thinking. Much of our emotional life operates via the automatic, speedy low road. But he wondered: How would we *know* what we are reacting to if we did not in some way appraise the situation? The appraisal may be effortless and we may not be conscious of it, but it is still a mental function. To know whether a stimulus is good or bad, the brain must have some idea of what it is (Storbeck et al., 2006). Thus, said Lazarus, emotions arise when we *appraise* an event as harmless or dangerous. We appraise the sound of the rustling bushes as the presence of a threat. Later, we realize that it was "just the wind."

So, let's sum up (see also **TABLE 31.1**). As Zajonc and LeDoux have demonstrated, some simple emotional responses involve no conscious thinking (**FIGURE 31.2**). When I [ND] see a big spider trapped behind glass, I experience fear, even though I *know* the spider can't hurt me. Such responses are difficult to alter by changing our thinking. Within a fraction of a second, we may automatically perceive one person as more likable or trustworthy than another (Willis & Todorov, 2006). This instant appeal can even influence our political decisions, if we vote (as many people do) for the candidate we *like* over the candidate who expresses positions closer to our own (Westen, 2007).

But other emotions—including depressive moods and complex feelings such as hatred and love—are greatly affected by our conscious and unconscious information processing: our memories, expectations, and interpretations. For these emotions, we have more conscious control. When we feel emotionally overwhelmed, we can change our interpretations (Gross, 2013). Such *reappraisal* often reduces distress and the corresponding amygdala response (Buhle et al., 2014; Denny et al., 2015). Reappraisal not only reduces stress, it also helps students achieve higher exam scores (Jamieson et al., 2016). Don't stress about your stress. Embrace it, and approach your next exam with this mindset: "Stress evolved to help maintain my focus and solve problems." Although the emotional low road functions automatically, the thinking high road allows us to retake some control over our emotional life. *The bottom line:* Together, automatic emotion and conscious thinking weave the fabric of our emotional lives.

FIGURE 31.2

TWO PATHWAYS FOR EMOTIONS
Zajonc and LeDoux emphasized that some emotional responses are immediate, before any conscious appraisal. Lazarus, Schachter, and Singer emphasized that our appraisal and labeling of events also determine our emotional responses.

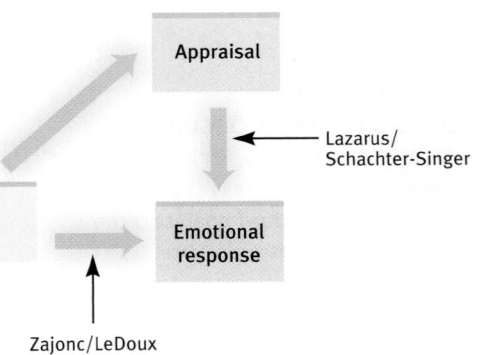

RETRIEVE IT • • •

ANSWERS IN APPENDIX E

RI-3 Emotion researchers have disagreed about whether emotional responses occur in the absence of cognitive processing. How would you characterize the approach of each of the following researchers: Zajonc, LeDoux, Lazarus, Schachter, and Singer?

EMBODIED EMOTION

Whether you are falling in love or grieving a death, you need little convincing that emotions involve the body. Feeling without a body is like breathing without lungs. Some physical responses are easy to notice. Other emotional responses we experience without awareness. Before examining our physical responses to specific emotions, consider another big question: How many distinct emotions are there?

The Basic Emotions

LOQ 31-3 What are some of the basic emotions?

When surveyed, most emotion scientists agreed that anger, fear, disgust, sadness, and happiness are basic human emotions (Ekman, 2016). Carroll Izard (1977) isolated 10 basic emotions (joy, interest-excitement, surprise, sadness, anger, disgust, contempt, fear, shame, and guilt), most present in infancy (**FIGURE 31.3**). Others believe that pride and love are also basic emotions (Shaver et al., 1996; Tracy & Robins, 2004). Izard has argued that other emotions are combinations of these 10, with love, for example, being a mixture of joy and interest-excitement. But are these emotions biologically distinct? Does our body know the difference between fear and anger?

Emotions and the Autonomic Nervous System

LOQ 31-4 What is the link between emotional arousal and the autonomic nervous system?

In a crisis, the *sympathetic division* of your *autonomic nervous system (ANS)* mobilizes your body for action (**FIGURE 31.4**). It triggers your adrenal glands to release the stress hormones epinephrine (adrenaline) and norepinephrine (noradrenaline). To provide energy, your liver pours extra sugar into your bloodstream. To help burn the sugar, your respiration increases to supply needed oxygen. Your heart rate and blood pressure increase. Your digestion slows, diverting blood from your internal organs to your muscles. With blood sugar driven into the large muscles, running becomes easier. Your pupils

FIGURE 31.3

SOME NATURALLY OCCURRING INFANT EMOTIONS To identify the emotions generally present in infancy, Carroll Izard analyzed the facial expressions of infants.

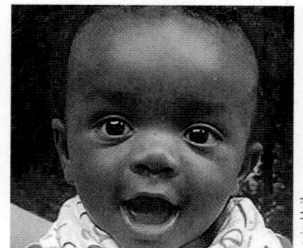
(a) Joy (mouth forming smile, cheeks lifted, twinkle in eye)

(b) Anger (brows drawn together and downward, eyes fixed, mouth squarish)

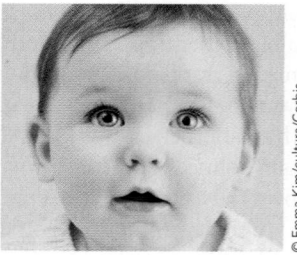
(c) Interest (brows raised or knitted, mouth softly rounded, lips may be pursed)

(d) Disgust (nose wrinkled, upper lip raised, tongue pushed outward)

(e) Surprise (brows raised, eyes widened, mouth rounded in oval shape)

(f) Sadness (brow's inner corners raised, mouth corners drawn down)

(g) Fear (brows level, drawn in and up, eyelids lifted, mouth corners retracted)

Sympathetic division (arousing)		Parasympathetic division (calming)
Pupils dilate	EYES	Pupils contract
Decreases	SALIVATION	Increases
Perspires	SKIN	Dries
Increases	RESPIRATION	Decreases
Accelerates	HEART	Slows
Inhibits	DIGESTION	Activates
Secrete stress hormones	ADRENAL GLANDS	Decrease secretion of stress hormones
Reduced	IMMUNE SYSTEM FUNCTIONING	Enhanced

dilate, letting in more light. To cool your stirred-up body, you perspire. If wounded, your blood would clot more quickly.

When the crisis passes, the *parasympathetic division* of your ANS gradually calms your body, as stress hormones slowly leave your bloodstream. After your next crisis, think of this: Without any conscious effort, your body's response to danger is wonderfully coordinated and adaptive—preparing you to *fight* or *flee.* So, do the different emotions have distinct arousal fingerprints?

 LaunchPad To review and then check your understanding of the ANS in action, engage online with **Concept Practice: The Autonomic Nervous System.**

The Physiology of Emotions

LOQ 31-5 Do different emotions activate different physiological and brain-pattern responses?

 Imagine conducting an experiment measuring the physiological responses of emotion. In each of four rooms, you have someone watch a movie: In the first, the person views a horror film; in the second, an anger-provoking film; in the third, a sexually arousing film; in the fourth, a boring film. From the control center, you monitor each person's perspiration, pupil size, breathing, and heart rate. Could you tell who is frightened? Who is angry? Who is sexually aroused? Who is bored?

With training, you could probably pick out the bored viewer. But discerning physiological differences among fear, anger, and sexual arousal is much more difficult (Barrett, 2006). Different emotions can share common biological signatures.

A single brain region can also serve as the seat of seemingly different emotions. Consider the broad emotional portfolio of the *insula,* a neural center deep inside the brain. The insula is activated when we experience various negative social emotions, such as lust, pridefulness, and disgust. In brain scans, it becomes active when people bite into some disgusting food, smell disgusting food, think about biting into a disgusting cockroach, or feel moral disgust over a sleazy business exploiting a saintly widow (Sapolsky, 2010). Similar multitasking regions are found in other brain areas.

Yet our varying emotions *feel* different to us, and they often *look* different to others. We may appear "paralyzed with fear" or "ready to explode." Fear and joy prompt a similar increased heart rate, but they stimulate different facial muscles. During fear, your brow muscles tense.

FIGURE 31.4

EMOTIONAL AROUSAL Like a crisis control center, the autonomic nervous system arouses the body in a crisis and calms it when danger passes.

"Fear lends wings to his feet." —Virgil, *Aeneid,* 19 B.C.E.

 ASK YOURSELF

Can you think of a recent time when you noticed your body's reactions to an emotionally charged situation, such as a difficult social setting, or perhaps a test or game you had been worrying about in advance? How would you describe your sympathetic nervous system's responses?

SCARY THRILLS Elated excitement and panicky fear involve similar physiological arousal, which allows us to flip rapidly between the two emotions.

polygraph a machine used in attempts to detect lies that measures emotion-linked changes in perspiration, heart rate, and breathing.

"No one ever told me that grief felt so much like fear. I am not afraid, but the sensation is like being afraid. The same fluttering in the stomach, the same restlessness, the yawning. I keep on swallowing." —C. S. Lewis, *A Grief Observed*, 1961

ENGAGE

LaunchPad To see how skilled you are at lie detection, visit **Topic Tutorial: PsychSim6, Catching Liars.**

During joy, muscles in your cheeks and under your eyes pull into a smile (Witvliet & Vrana, 1995).

Some of our emotions also have distinct brain circuits (Panksepp, 2007). Observers watching fearful faces showed more amygdala activity than did other observers who watched angry faces (Whalen et al., 2001). Brain scans and EEG recordings show that emotions also activate different areas of the brain's cortex. When you experience negative emotions such as disgust, your right prefrontal cortex tends to be more active than the left. Depression-prone people, and those with generally negative perspectives, have also shown more right frontal lobe activity (Harmon-Jones et al., 2002).

Positive moods tend to trigger more left frontal lobe activity. People with positive personalities—exuberant infants and alert, energized, and persistently goal-directed adults—have also shown more activity in the left frontal lobe than in the right (Davidson, 2000; Urry et al., 2004).

To sum up, we can't easily see differences in emotions from tracking heart rate, breathing, and perspiration. But facial expressions and brain activity can vary from one emotion to another. So, do we, like Pinocchio, give off telltale signs when we lie? For more on that question, see Thinking Critically About: Lie Detection.

🔒 **RETRIEVE IT** • • •   *ANSWERS IN APPENDIX E*

RI-4 How do the two divisions of the autonomic nervous system affect our emotional responses?

THINKING CRITICALLY ABOUT:

Lie Detection

LOQ 31-6   How effective are polygraphs in using body states to detect lies?

Polygraphs measure emotion-linked autonomic arousal, as reflected in changed breathing, heart rate, and perspiration. Can we use these results to detect lies?

In the last 20 years, have you ever taken something that didn't belong to you?

Did you ever steal anything from your previous employer?

No!

Uh, no.

EEG

Many people tell a little white lie in response to this *control question*, prompting elevated arousal readings that give the examiner a baseline for comparing responses to other questions.

EEG

This person shows greater arousal in response to the *critical question* than she did to the control question, so the examiner may infer she is lying.

But is it true that *only a thief becomes nervous when denying a theft*?

1. We have similar bodily arousal in response to anxiety, irritation, and guilt. So, is she really guilty, or just anxious?

2. Many innocent people *do* get tense and nervous when accused of a bad act. (Many rape victims, for example, have "failed" these tests because they had strong emotional reactions while telling the truth about the rapist.[1])

About one-third of the time, polygraph test results are *just wrong*.[2]

Innocent people

Guilty people

⚪ Judged innocent by polygraph   ⚫ Judged guilty by polygraph

If these polygraph experts had been the judges, more than one-third of the innocent would have been declared guilty, and nearly one-fourth of the guilty would have gone free.

The CIA and other U.S. agencies have spent millions of dollars testing tens of thousands of employees. Yet the U.S. National Academy of Sciences (2002) has reported that "no spy has ever been caught [by] using the polygraph."

The Concealed Information Test is more effective. Innocent people are seldom wrongly judged to be lying.

Questions focus on specific crime-scene details known only to the police and the guilty person.[3] (If a camera and computer had been stolen, for example, only a guilty person should react strongly to the brand names of the stolen items.)

---

1. Lykken, 1991. 2. Kleinmuntz & Szucko, 1984. 3. Ben-Shakhar & Elaad, 2003; Verschuere & Meijer, 2014; Vrij & Fisher, 2016.

⤳ Learning Objectives

TEST YOURSELF Answer these repeated Learning Objective Questions on your own (before checking the answers in Appendix D) to improve your retention of the concepts (McDaniel et al., 2009, 2015).

31-1 How do arousal, expressive behavior, and cognition interact in emotion?

31-2 To experience emotions, must we consciously interpret and label them?

31-3 What are some of the basic emotions?

31-4 What is the link between emotional arousal and the autonomic nervous system?

31-5 Do different emotions activate different physiological and brain-pattern responses?

31-6 How effective are polygraphs in using body states to detect lies?

⤳ Terms and Concepts to Remember

TEST YOURSELF Write down the definition yourself, then check your answer on the referenced page.

emotion, **p. 369**

James-Lange theory, **p. 369**

Cannon-Bard theory, **p. 369**

two-factor theory, **p. 369**

polygraph, **p. 374**

⤳ Experience the Testing Effect

TEST YOURSELF Answer the following questions on your own first, then check your answers in Appendix E.

1. The _____-_____ theory of emotion maintains that a physiological response happens BEFORE we know what we are feeling.

2. Assume that after spending an hour on a treadmill, you receive a letter saying that your scholarship application has been approved. The two-factor theory of emotion would predict that your physical arousal will

   a. weaken your happiness.
   b. intensify your happiness.
   c. transform your happiness into relief.
   d. have no particular effect on your happiness.

3. Zajonc and LeDoux have maintained that some emotional reactions occur before we have had the chance to consciously label or interpret them. Lazarus noted the importance of how we appraise events. These psychologists differ in the emphasis they place on _____ in emotional responses.

   a. physical arousal
   b. the hormone epinephrine
   c. cognitive processing
   d. learning

4. What does a polygraph measure, and why are its results questionable?

Continue testing yourself with 📘 **LearningCurve** or 📖 **Achieve Read & Practice** to learn and remember most effectively.

---

³²⁽ᴹᴼᴰᵁᴸᴱ⁾ Expressing and Experiencing Emotion

Expressive behavior implies emotion. Dolphins, with smiles seemingly plastered on their faces, appear happy. To decipher people's emotions we read their bodies, listen to their voice tones, and study their faces. Does nonverbal language vary with culture—or is it universal? And do our expressions influence our experienced emotions?

"Your face, my thane, is a book where men may read strange matters." — Lady Macbeth to her husband, in William Shakespeare's *Macbeth*

DETECTING EMOTION IN OTHERS

LOQ 32-1 How do we communicate nonverbally?

To Westerners, a firm handshake conveys an outgoing, expressive personality (Chaplin et al., 2000). A gaze communicates intimacy, while darting eyes may signal anxiety (Kleinke, 1986; Perkins et al., 2012). When two people are passionately in love, they typically spend

A SILENT LANGUAGE OF EMOTION
Hindu classic dance uses the face and body to effectively convey 10 different emotions (Hejmadi et al., 2000).

time—quite a bit of time—gazing into each other's eyes (Bolmont et al., 2014; Rubin, 1970). Would such gazes stir these feelings between strangers? To find out, researchers have asked unacquainted (and presumed heterosexual) male-female pairs to gaze intently for 2 minutes either at each other's hands or into each other's eyes. After separating, the eye gazers reported feeling a tingle of attraction and affection (Kellerman et al., 1989).

Our brain is an amazing detector of subtle expressions, helping most of us read nonverbal cues well. We are adept at detecting a hint of a smile (Maher et al., 2014). Shown 10 seconds of video from the end of a speed-dating interaction, people can often tell whether one person is attracted to the other (Place et al., 2009). Signs of status are also easy to spot. When shown someone with arms raised, chest expanded, and a slight smile, people—from Canadian undergraduates to Fijian villagers—perceive that person as experiencing pride and having high status (Tracy et al., 2013). Even glimpsing a face for one-tenth of a second has enabled viewers to judge people's attractiveness or trustworthiness, or to rate politicians' competence and predict their voter support (Willis & Todorov, 2006). "First impressions . . . occur with astonishing speed," note Christopher Olivola and Alexander Todorov (2010).

We also excel at detecting nonverbal threats. We readily sense subliminally presented negative words, such as *snake* or *bomb* (Dijksterhuis & Aarts, 2003). A single, angry face will "pop out" of a crowd (Pinkham et al., 2010). Experience can sensitize us to particular emotions, as shown by experiments using a series of faces (like those in **FIGURE 32.1**) that morph from anger to fear (or sadness). Viewing such faces, physically abused children are much quicker than other children to spot the signals of anger. Shown a face that is 50 percent fear and 50 percent anger, those with a history of being abused are more likely to perceive anger than fear. Their perceptions become sensitively attuned to glimmers of danger that nonabused children miss.

Hard-to-control facial muscles can reveal signs of emotions, even ones you are trying to conceal. Lifting just the inner part of your eyebrows, which few people do consciously, reveals distress or worry. Eyebrows raised and pulled together signal fear. Raised cheeks and activated muscles under the eyes suggest a natural smile. A feigned smile, such as one we make for a photographer, is often frozen in place for several seconds, then suddenly switched off (**FIGURE 32.2**). Genuine happy smiles tend to be briefer but to fade less abruptly (Bugental, 1986). If you have the urge to hide your happiness, remember that genuine smiles cause others to perceive us as trustworthy, authentic, and attractive (Gunnery & Ruben, 2016). Let your smile shine.

Despite our brain's emotion-detecting skill, we find it difficult to discern deceit. The behavioral differences between liars and truth tellers are too minute for most people to detect (Hartwig & Bond, 2011). In one digest of many studies, people were just 54 percent accurate in discerning truth from lies—barely better than a coin toss (Bond & DePaulo, 2006). Moreover, virtually no one—save perhaps police professionals in high-stakes situations—beats chance by much, not even when detecting children's lies (Gongola et al., 2017; O'Sullivan et al., 2009; ten Brinke et al., 2016).

Some of us more than others are sensitive to the physical cues of various emotions. In one study, people named the emotion displayed in brief film clips. The clips showed portions of a person's emotionally expressive face or body, sometimes accompanied by a garbled voice (Rosenthal et al., 1979). For example, after a 2-second scene revealing only the face of an upset woman, the researchers asked whether the woman was criticizing someone for being late or was talking about her divorce. Given such "thin slices," some people were much better emotion detectors than others. Introverts tend to excel at reading others' emotions, while extraverts are generally easier to read (Ambady et al., 1995).

FIGURE 32.1

EXPERIENCE INFLUENCES HOW WE PERCEIVE EMOTIONS Viewing the morphed middle face, evenly mixing anger with fear, physically abused children were more likely than nonabused children to perceive the face as angry (Pollak & Kistler, 2002; Pollak & Tolley-Schell, 2003).

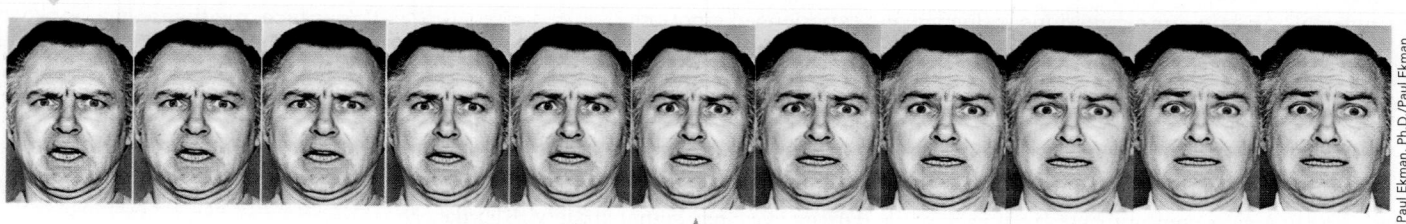

Gestures, facial expressions, and voice tones, which are absent in written communication, convey important information. The difference was clear when study participants in one group heard 30-second recordings of people describing their marital separations. Participants in the other group read a script of the recording. Those who heard the recording were better able to predict people's current and future adjustment (Mason et al., 2010). Just hearing a stranger say "hello" is enough to give listeners some clue to the speaker's personality. Researcher Phil McAleer and his colleagues (2014) call this "the Jerry Maguire effect," after the movie in which Renée Zellweger says to Tom Cruise, "You had me at hello."

The absence of expressive emotion can make for ambiguous emotion in electronic communications. To partly remedy that, we often embed cues to emotion 😊 in our messages. Without the vocal nuances that signal whether our statement is serious, kidding, or sarcastic, we are in danger of what developmental psychologist Jean Piaget called *egocentrism,* by failing to perceive how others interpret our "just kidding" message (Kruger et al., 2005).

GENDER, EMOTION, AND NONVERBAL BEHAVIOR

LOQ 32-2 How do the genders differ in their ability to communicate nonverbally?

Do women have greater sensitivity than men to nonverbal cues, as so many believe? After analyzing 176 studies, Judith Hall and her colleagues (2016) concluded that, when given thin slices of behavior, women generally do surpass men at reading people's emotional cues. The female advantage emerges early in development. Female infants, children, and adolescents have outperformed males in many studies (McClure, 2000).

Women's nonverbal sensitivity helps explain their greater emotional literacy. When invited to describe how they would feel in certain situations, men tend to describe simpler emotional reactions (Barrett et al., 2000). You might like to try this yourself: Ask some people how they might feel when saying good-bye to friends after graduation. Research suggests men are more likely to say, simply, "I'll feel bad," and women to express more complex emotions: "It will be bittersweet; I'll feel both happy and sad."

Women's skill at decoding others' emotions may also contribute to their greater emotional responsiveness and expressiveness, especially for positive emotions (Fischer & LaFrance, 2015; McDuff et al., 2017). In studies of 23,000 people from 26 cultures, women more than men reported themselves open to feelings (Costa et al., 2001). Girls also express stronger emotions than boys do, hence the extremely strong perception that emotionality is "more true of women"—a perception expressed by nearly 100 percent of 18- to 29-year-old Americans (Chaplin & Aldao, 2013; Newport, 2001).

One exception: Quickly—imagine an angry face. What gender is the person? If you are like 3 in 4 Arizona State University students, you imagined a male (Becker et al., 2007). And when a gender-neutral face was made to look angry, most people perceived it as male. If the face was smiling, they were more likely to perceive it as female (**FIGURE 32.3**). Anger strikes most people as a more masculine emotion.

(a)   (b)

Paul Ekman, Ph.D./Paul Ekman Group, LLC.

FIGURE 32.2

WHICH OF RESEARCHER PAUL EKMAN'S SMILES IS FEIGNED, WHICH NATURAL? Smile (b) engages the facial muscles of a natural smile.

SIPRESS

David Sipress

"Now, that wasn't so hard, was it?"

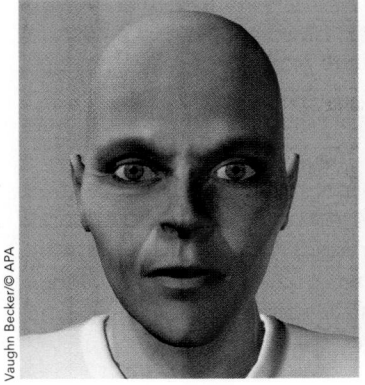 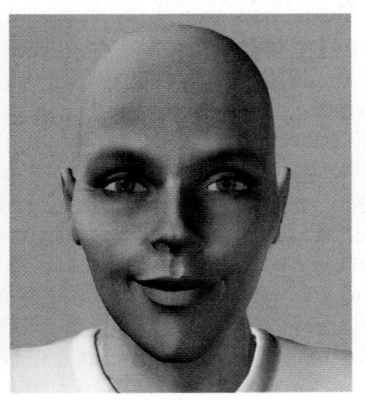

Vaughn Becker/© APA

FIGURE 32.3

MALE OR FEMALE? Researchers manipulated a gender-neutral face. People were more likely to see it as male when it wore an angry expression and female when it wore a smile (Becker et al., 2007).

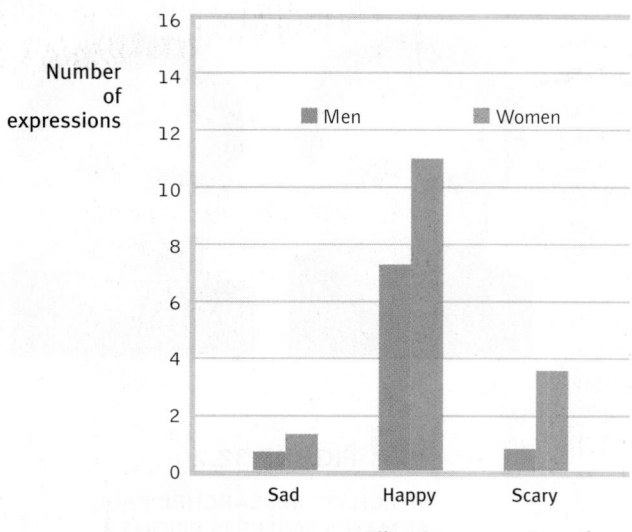

FIGURE 32.4

GENDER AND EXPRESSIVENESS
Male and female film viewers did not differ dramatically in self-reported emotions or physiological responses. But the women's faces showed much more emotion. (Data from Kring & Gordon, 1998.)

UNIVERSAL EMOTIONS No matter where on Earth you live, you have no trouble recognizing the joy experienced by Chicago Cubs fans over their 2016 World Series victory following a 108-year wait.

The perception of women's emotionality also feeds—and is fed by—people's attributing women's emotionality to their disposition and men's to their circumstances: "She's emotional" versus "He's having a bad day" (Barrett & Bliss-Moreau, 2009). Many factors influence our attributions, including cultural norms (Mason & Morris, 2010). Nevertheless, there are some gender differences in descriptions of emotional experiences. When surveyed, women are far more likely than men to describe themselves as empathic. If you have *empathy,* you identify with others. You consider things from their point of view. You imagine being in their skin. You appraise a situation as they do, rejoicing with those who rejoice and weeping with those who weep (Wondra & Ellsworth, 2015). Fiction readers, who immerse themselves in the lives of their favorite characters, report higher empathy levels and indeed are more often women (Mar et al., 2009; Tepper, 2000). But physiological measures, such as heart rate while seeing another's distress, reveal a much smaller gender gap (Eisenberg & Lennon, 1983; Rueckert et al., 2010).

Females are also more likely to *express* empathy—to display more emotion when observing others' emotions. As **FIGURE 32.4** shows, this gender difference was clear when male and female students watched film clips that were sad (children with a dying parent), happy (slapstick comedy), or frightening (a man nearly falling off the ledge of a tall building) (Kring & Gordon, 1998). Women also tend to experience emotional events, such as viewing pictures of mutilation, more deeply and with more brain activation in areas sensitive to emotion. And they remember the scenes better three weeks later (Canli et al., 2002).

🔒 RETRIEVE IT • • •   *ANSWERS IN APPENDIX E*

RI-1 _____ (Women/Men) report experiencing emotions more deeply, and they tend to be more adept at reading nonverbal behavior.

CULTURE AND EMOTION

LOQ 32-3 How are gestures and facial expressions understood within and across cultures?

The meaning of *gestures* varies from culture to culture. U.S. President Richard Nixon learned this after making the North American "A-OK" sign before a welcoming crowd of Brazilians, not realizing it was a crude insult in that country. The importance of cultural definitions of gestures was again demonstrated in 1968, when North Korea publicized photos of supposedly happy officers from a captured U.S. Navy spy ship. In the photo, three men had raised their middle finger, telling their captors it was a "Hawaiian good luck sign" (Fleming & Scott, 1991).

Do *facial expressions* also have different meanings in different cultures? To find out, two investigative teams showed photographs of various facial expressions to people in different parts of the world and asked them to guess the emotion (Ekman, 1994, 2016; Izard, 1977, 1994). You can try this matching task yourself by pairing the six emotions with the six faces in **FIGURE 32.5**.

Regardless of your cultural background, you probably did pretty well. A smile's a smile the world around. Ditto for sadness. Other emotional expressions are less universally recognized (Crivelli et al., 2016a; Jack et al., 2012). But there is no culture where people frown when they are happy.

Facial expressions do convey some nonverbal accents that provide clues to one's culture (Crivelli et al., 2016b; Marsh et al., 2003). Thus, data from 182 studies have shown slightly enhanced accuracy when people judged emotions from their own culture (Elfenbein & Ambady, 2002; Laukka et al., 2016). Still, the telltale signs of emotion generally cross cultures. The world over, children cry when distressed, shake their heads when defiant, and smile when they are happy. So, too, with blind children who have never seen a face (Eibl-Eibesfeldt, 1971). People blind from birth spontaneously exhibit the common facial expressions associated with such emotions as joy, sadness, fear, and anger (Galati et al., 1997).

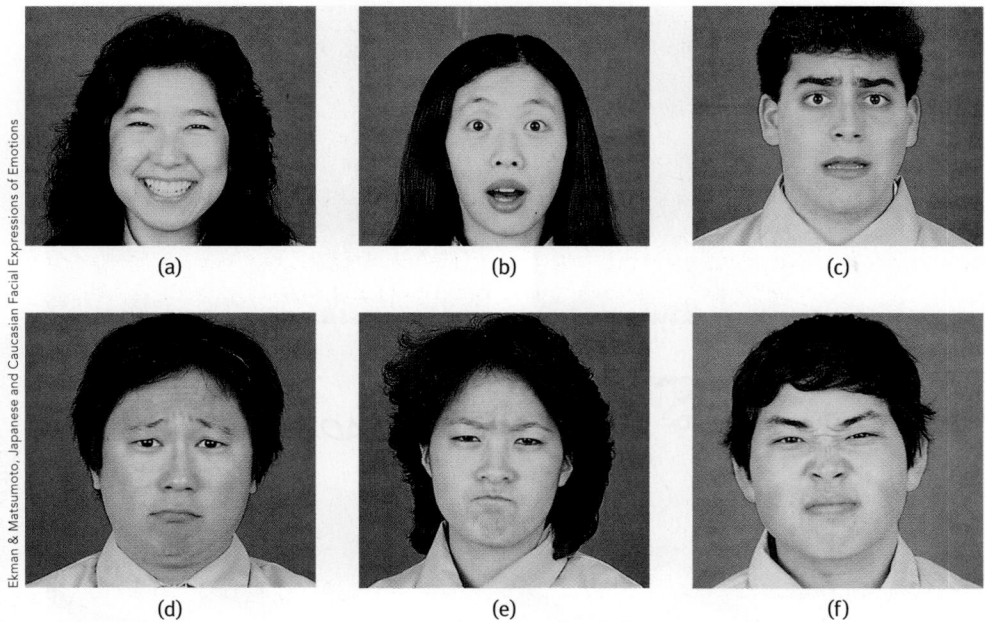

(a)   (b)   (c)

(d)   (e)   (f)

FIGURE 32.5

CULTURE-SPECIFIC OR CULTURALLY UNIVERSAL EXPRESSIONS? As people of differing cultures, do our faces speak differing languages? Which face expresses disgust? Anger? Fear? Happiness? Sadness? Surprise? (From Matsumoto & Ekman, 1989.)[1]

Do these shared emotional categories reflect shared *cultural* experiences, such as movies and TV shows seen around the world? Apparently not. Paul Ekman and Wallace Friesen (1971) asked isolated people in New Guinea to respond to such statements as, "Pretend your child has died." When North American undergraduates viewed the recorded responses, they easily read the New Guineans' facial reactions.

So we can say that facial muscles speak a universal language. This discovery would not have surprised Charles Darwin (1809–1882), who argued that in prehistoric times, before our ancestors communicated in words, they communicated threats, greetings, and submission with facial expressions. Their shared expressions helped them survive (Hess & Thibault, 2009). In confrontations, for example, a human sneer retains elements of an animal baring its teeth in a snarl. Emotional expressions may enhance our survival in other ways, too. Surprise raises the eyebrows and widens the eyes, enabling us to take in more information. Disgust wrinkles the nose, closing it from foul odors.

Smiles are social as well as emotional events. Euphoric Olympic gold-medal winners typically don't smile when they are awaiting their award ceremony. But they wear broad grins when interacting with officials and when facing the crowd and cameras (Fernández-Dols & Ruiz-Belda, 1995).

Although we share a universal facial language for some emotions, it has been adaptive for us to interpret faces in particular contexts (**FIGURE 32.6**). People judge an angry face set in a frightening situation as afraid. They judge a fearful face set in a painful situation as pained (Carroll & Russell, 1996). Movie directors harness this phenomenon by creating scenes and soundtracks that amplify our perceptions of particular emotions.

Cultures share a facial language, but they differ in how *much* emotion they express. Those that encourage individuality, as in Western Europe, Australia, New Zealand, and North America, display visible emotions (van Hemert et al., 2007). Those that encourage people to adjust to others, as in Japan and China, often have less visible emotional displays (Matsumoto et al., 2009; Tsai et al., 2007). In Japan, people infer emotion more from the surrounding context. Moreover, the mouth, often so expressive in North Americans, conveys less emotion than do the telltale eyes (Masuda et al., 2008; Yuki et al., 2007). Compared with their counterparts in China, where calmness is emphasized, European-American leaders express excited smiles six times more frequently in their official photos (**FIGURE 32.7**) (Tsai et al., 2006, 2016). If we're happy and we know it, our culture will surely teach us how to show it.

"For news of the heart, ask the face."
—Guinean proverb

LaunchPad For a 4-minute demonstration of our universal facial language, see the **Video: Emotions and Facial Expression.**

While weightless, astronauts' internal bodily fluids move toward their upper body and their faces become puffy. This makes nonverbal communication more difficult, especially among multinational crews (Gelman, 1989).

---

1. (a) happiness, (b) surprise, (c) fear, (d) sadness, (e) anger, (f) disgust.

FIGURE 32.6

WE READ FACES IN CONTEXT
Whether we perceive the man as (a) disgusted or (b) angry depends on which body his face appears on (Aviezer et al., 2008). Tears on a woman's face in (c) make her expression seem sadder than in (d) (Provine et al., 2009).

Cultural differences also exist *within* nations. The Irish and their Irish-American descendants have tended to be more expressive than the Scandinavians and their Scandinavian-American descendants (Tsai & Chentsova-Dutton, 2003). And that reminds us of a familiar lesson: Like most psychological events, emotion is best understood not only as a biological and cognitive phenomenon, but also as a social-cultural phenomenon.

🔒 RETRIEVE IT • • •   *ANSWERS IN APPENDIX E*

RI-2 Are people more likely to differ culturally in their interpretations of facial expressions, or of gestures?

FIGURE 32.7

CULTURE AND SMILING Former U.S. Vice President Joe Biden's broad smile and Chinese President Xi Jinping's more reserved one illustrate a cultural difference in facial expressiveness.

"Whenever I feel afraid
I hold my head erect
And whistle a happy tune."
—Richard Rodgers and Oscar Hammerstein,
The King and I, 1958

THE EFFECTS OF FACIAL EXPRESSIONS

LOQ 32-4 How do our facial expressions influence our feelings?

As William James (1890) struggled with feelings of depression and grief, he came to believe that we can control emotions by going "through the outward movements" of any emotion we want to experience. "To feel cheerful," he advised, "sit up cheerfully, look around cheerfully, and act as if cheerfulness were already there."

Studies of emotional effects of facial expressions support what James predicted. Expressions not only communicate emotion, they also amplify and regulate it. In *The Expression of the Emotions in Man and Animals,* Charles Darwin (1872) contended that "the free expression by outward signs of an emotion intensifies it. . . . He who gives way to violent gestures will increase his rage."

Want to test Darwin's hypothesis? Try this: Fake a big grin. Now scowl. Can you feel the "smile therapy" difference? Participants in dozens of experiments have felt a difference. Researchers subtly induced students to make a frowning expression by asking them to "contract these muscles" and "pull your brows together" (supposedly to help the researchers attach facial electrodes) (Laird, 1974, 1984; Laird & Lacasse, 2014).

The results? The students reported feeling a little angry, as do people who are naturally frowning (by squinting) when facing the Sun (Marzoli et al., 2013). So, too, for other basic emotions. For example, people reported feeling more fear than anger, disgust, or sadness when made to construct a fearful expression: "Raise your eyebrows. And open your eyes wide. Move your whole head back, so that your chin is tucked in a little bit, and let your mouth relax and hang open a little" (Duclos et al., 1989).

This **facial feedback effect** has been found many times, in many places, for many basic emotions (**FIGURE 32.8**). Just activating one of the smiling muscles by holding a pen in the teeth (rather than gently between the lips, which produces a neutral expression) makes stressful situations less upsetting (Kraft & Pressman, 2012). A hearty smile—made not just with the mouth but with raised cheeks that crinkle the eyes—enhances positive feelings even more when you are reacting to something pleasant or funny (Soussignan, 2001). When happy we smile, and when smiling we become happier. Although some researchers question the reliability of the facial feedback effect (Wagenmakers et al., 2016), many others have replicated it (Strack, 2016).

So, your face is more than a billboard that displays your feelings; it also feeds your feelings. Scowl and the whole world scowls back. No wonder some depressed patients reportedly felt better after Botox injections paralyzed their frowning muscles (Parsaik et al., 2016). Four months after treatment, they continued to report lower depression levels. Botox paralysis of the frowning muscles slows people's reading of sadness- or anger-related sentences, and it slows activity in emotion-related brain circuits (Havas et al., 2010; Hennenlotter et al., 2008).

ENGAGE Other researchers have observed a broader **behavior feedback effect** (Carney et al., 2015; Flack, 2006). You can duplicate the participants' experience: Walk for a few minutes with short, shuffling steps, keeping your eyes downcast. Now walk around taking long strides, with your arms swinging and your eyes looking straight ahead. Can you feel your mood shift? Going through the motions awakens the emotions.

You can use your understanding of feedback effects to become more empathic: Let your own face mimic another person's expression. Acting as another acts helps us feel what another feels (Vaughn & Lanzetta, 1981). Losing this ability to mimic others can leave us struggling to make emotional connections, as one social worker with Moebius

A request from your authors: Smile often as you read this book.

🔒 RETRIEVE IT • • •   *ANSWERS IN APPENDIX E*

FIGURE 32.8

HOW TO MAKE PEOPLE SMILE WITHOUT TELLING THEM TO SMILE Do as Kazuo Mori and Hideko Mori (2009) did with students in Japan: Attach rubber bands to the sides of the face with adhesive bandages, and then run them either over the head or under the chin.

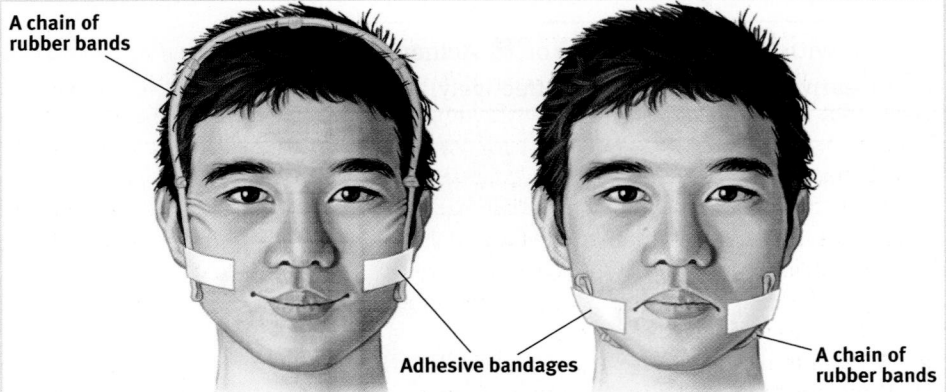

A chain of rubber bands

Adhesive bandages

A chain of rubber bands

RI-3 (1) Based on the *facial feedback effect*, how might students report feeling when the rubber bands raise their cheeks as though in a smile? (2) How might students report feeling when the rubber bands pull their cheeks downward?

facial feedback effect the tendency of facial muscle states to trigger corresponding feelings such as fear, anger, or happiness.

behavior feedback effect the tendency of behavior to influence our own and others' thoughts, feelings, and actions.

syndrome, a rare facial paralysis disorder, discovered while working with Hurricane Katrina refugees: When people made a sad expression, "I wasn't able to return it. I tried to do so with words and tone of voice, but it was no use. Stripped of the facial expression, the emotion just dies there, unshared" (Carey, 2010).

Our natural mimicry of others' emotions helps explain why emotions are contagious (Dimberg et al., 2000; Neumann & Strack, 2000; Peters & Kashima, 2015). Positive, upbeat Facebook posts create a ripple effect, leading Facebook friends to also express more positive emotions (Kramer, 2012).

* * *

We have seen how our motivated behaviors, triggered by the forces of nature and nurture, frequently go hand in hand with significant emotional responses. Our often-adaptive psychological emotions likewise come equipped with physical reactions. Nervous about an important encounter, we feel stomach butterflies. Anxious over public speaking, we frequent the bathroom. Smoldering over a family conflict, we get a splitting headache. As this text's discussion of stress and health shows, negative emotions and the prolonged high arousal that may accompany them can tax the body and harm our health.

ENGAGE

ASK YOURSELF

Imagine one situation in which you would like to change the way you feel. How could you do so by altering your facial expressions or the way you carry yourself?

🔒 REVIEW EXPRESSING AND EXPERIENCING EMOTION

⤵ Learning Objectives

TEST YOURSELF Answer these repeated Learning Objective Questions on your own (before checking the answers in Appendix D) to improve your retention of the concepts (McDaniel et al., 2009, 2015).

32-1 How do we communicate nonverbally?

32-2 How do the genders differ in their ability to communicate nonverbally?

32-3 How are gestures and facial expressions understood within and across cultures?

32-4 How do our facial expressions influence our feelings?

⤵ Terms and Concepts to Remember

TEST YOURSELF Write down the definition yourself, then check your answer on the referenced page.

facial feedback effect, **p. 381**   behavior feedback effect, **p. 381**

⤵ Experience the Testing Effect

TEST YOURSELF Answer the following questions on your own first, then check your answers in Appendix E.

1. When people are induced to assume fearful expressions, they often report feeling a little fear. This response is known as the _____ _____ effect.

2. Aiden has a bad cold and finds himself shuffling to class with his head down. How might his posture, as well as his cold, affect his emotional well-being?

Continue testing yourself with 📘 **LearningCurve** or 📗 **Achieve Read & Practice** to learn and remember most effectively.

Stress, Health, and Human Flourishing

Thomas Barwick/Getty Images

S ir Ranulph Fiennes, called "the world's greatest living explorer" by Guinness World Records, has experienced significant stress—much of it self-imposed. He has persevered through what should have been impossible Arctic expeditions and grueling long-distance athletic endeavors. Yet he has thrived.

Just before Fiennes' birth, his father died in WWII, which was a particularly difficult time to grow up fatherless. As an adult adventurer, Fiennes tried to walk solo to the North Pole, but his sleds fell through the ice. He pulled them out by hand and later sawed off his own frostbitten fingertips. Years later, as he was preparing to run seven marathons on seven continents in seven days, he experienced a heart attack and had double bypass surgery. Then his beloved wife of 33 years died of cancer. And when he tried to become the oldest Briton to climb Mount Everest, he had to quit near the summit when having another heart attack.

Despite those setbacks, Fiennes chose to press on with his relentless, can-do spirit. With his upbeat nature, Fiennes' presence could light up a room. He did finally achieve his goal of running seven marathons on seven continents in seven days, and of becoming the oldest Briton to summit Mount Everest. He remarried and has enjoyed parenting his daughter. And in 2015, at age 71, he finished a 6-day, 156-mile running race across the Sahara desert. After the race, he described his exhausting ordeal as "more hellish than hell" (Silverman, 2015). (After completing the same race in 2017, I [ND] know what he means.) And yet Fiennes is already planning for his next big challenge.

OVERVIEW OF MODULES

33 Stress and Illness
Stress: Some Basic Concepts
Stress and Vulnerability to Disease
THINKING CRITICALLY ABOUT:
Stress and Health

34 Health and Happiness
Coping With Stress
Reducing Stress
Happiness

ENGAGE How often do you experience *stress* in your daily life? Do you feel differently about stressors that seem imposed on you (deadlines, assignments, tragic events) than about the stress you impose on yourself (adventures, challenges, happy changes)? As we will see, our interpretation of events affects our experience of those events and whether we even consider them "stressful."

Fiennes' life, and yours, embodies what Modules 33 and 34 explore: the difficulty of unwanted stress, the important ways we are affected by our interpretation of events, how we cope with stress and setbacks, and the possibilities for a happy, flourishing life. ▶

EXTREME STRESS From the audio recording of a 911 caller reporting Ben Carpenter's distress: "You are not going to believe this. There is a semitruck pushing a guy in a wheelchair on Red Arrow highway!"

MODULE 33 Stress and Illness

Stress often strikes without warning. Imagine being 21-year-old Ben Carpenter, who experienced the world's wildest and fastest wheelchair ride. As he crossed a street, the light changed and a semitruck moved into the intersection. When they bumped, Ben's wheelchair handles got stuck in the truck's grille. The driver, who hadn't seen Ben and couldn't hear his cries for help, took off down the highway, pushing the wheelchair at 50 miles per hour until reaching his destination two miles away. "It was very scary," said Ben.

In this section, we take a closer look at stress—what it is and how it affects our health and well-being. Let's begin with some basic terms.

STRESS: SOME BASIC CONCEPTS

LEARNING OBJECTIVE QUESTION (LOQ)

33-1 How does our appraisal of an event affect our stress reaction, and what are the three main types of stressors?

Stress is the process of appraising and responding to a threatening or challenging event (**FIGURE 33.1**). But stress is a slippery concept. We sometimes use the word informally to describe threats or challenges ("Ben was under a lot of stress"), and at other times our responses ("Ben experienced acute stress"). To a psychologist, the terrifying truck ride was a *stressor*. Ben's physical and emotional responses were a *stress reaction*. And the process by which he related to the threat was *stress*. Stress arises less from events themselves than from how we appraise them (Lazarus, 1998). One person, alone in a house, ignores its creaking sounds and experiences no stress; someone else suspects an intruder and becomes alarmed. One person regards a new job as a welcome challenge; someone else appraises it as risking failure.

When short-lived, or when perceived as challenges, stressors can have positive effects. A momentary stress can mobilize the immune system for fending off infections and healing wounds (Segerstrom, 2007). Stress also arouses and motivates us to conquer problems.

FIGURE 33.1

STRESS APPRAISAL The events of our lives flow through a psychological filter. How we appraise an event influences how much stress we experience and how effectively we respond.

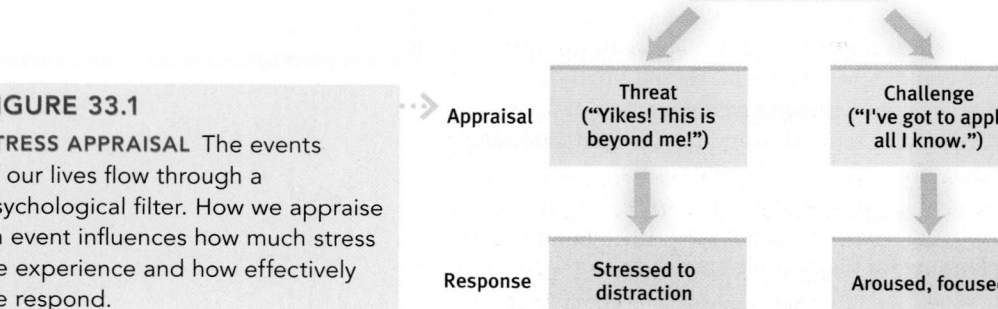

Stressful event
(tough math test)

Appraisal

Threat
("Yikes! This is beyond me!")

Challenge
("I've got to apply all I know.")

Response

Stressed to distraction

Aroused, focused

Championship athletes, successful entertainers, motivated students, and great teachers and leaders all thrive and excel when aroused by a challenge (Blascovich & Mendes, 2010; Wang et al., 2015a). In games and athletic contests, the stress of not knowing who will win makes the competition enjoyable (Abuhamdeh et al., 2015). Having conquered cancer or rebounded from a lost job, some people emerge with stronger self-esteem and a deepened spirituality and sense of purpose. Indeed, experiencing some stress early in life builds *resilience* (Seery, 2011). Adversity can produce growth.

But extreme or prolonged stress can harm us. Stress can trigger risky decisions and unhealthy behaviors (Cohen et al., 2016; Starcke & Brand, 2016). When facing stress, people may smoke or drink. And stress can affect health directly, making us more vulnerable to disease. Pregnant women with overactive stress systems tend to have shorter pregnancies, which pose health risks for their infants (Guardino et al., 2016).

So there is an interplay between our head and our health. Psychological states are physiological events that influence other parts of our physiological system. Just pausing to *think* about biting into an orange wedge—the sweet, tangy juice from the pulpy fruit flooding across your tongue—can trigger salivation. We'll explore that interplay shortly, but first, let's look more closely at stressors and stress reactions.

Stressors—Things That Push Our Buttons

Stressors fall into three main types: catastrophes, significant life changes, and daily hassles (including social stress). All can be toxic.

CATASTROPHES Catastrophes are large-scale disasters such as earthquakes, floods, wildfires, and storms. After such events, damage to emotional and physical health can be significant. In the four months after Hurricane Katrina, New Orleans' suicide rate reportedly tripled (Saulny, 2006). And in surveys taken in the three weeks after the 9/11 terrorist attacks, 58 percent of Americans said they were experiencing greater-than-average arousal and anxiety (Silver et al., 2002). In the New York City area, people were especially likely to report such symptoms, and sleeping pill prescriptions rose by a reported 28 percent (HMHL, 2002; NSF, 2001). Extensively watching 9/11 television footage predicted worse health outcomes two to three years later (Silver et al., 2013). A similar uptick in health issues, from heart problems to suicides, immediately followed the 2011 terrorist attacks in Norway (Strand et al., 2016).

For those who respond to catastrophes by relocating to another country, the stress may be twofold. The trauma of uprooting and family separation may combine with the challenges of adjusting to a new culture's language, ethnicity, climate, and social norms (Pipher, 2002; Williams & Berry, 1991). In the first half-year, before their morale begins to rebound, newcomers often experience culture shock and deteriorating well-being (Markovizky & Samid, 2008). This *acculturative stress* declines over time, especially when people engage in meaningful activities and connect socially (Bostean & Gillespie, 2017; Kim et al., 2012). In years to come, such relocations may become increasingly common due to climate change.

SIGNIFICANT LIFE CHANGES Life transitions—leaving home, having a loved one die, taking on student debt, losing a job, getting divorced—are often keenly felt. Even happy events, such as graduating or getting married, can be stressful life transitions. Many of these changes happen during young adulthood. One survey asked 15,000 Canadian adults whether they were "trying to take on too many things at once." It found the highest stress levels among young adults (Statistics Canada, 1999). When 650,000 Americans were asked if they had experienced a lot of stress "yesterday," young adults likewise reported the most stress (Newport & Pelham, 2009).

Some psychologists study the health effects of life changes by following people over time. Others compare the life challenges experienced by those who have (or have not) suffered a health problem, such as a heart attack. In such studies, those recently widowed, fired, or divorced have been more vulnerable to disease (Dohrenwend et al., 1982; Sbarra et al., 2015; Strully, 2009). One Finnish study of 96,000 widowed people found that the survivor's risk of death doubled in the week following a partner's death (Kaprio et al., 1987). A cluster of crises—losing a job, home, and partner—puts one even more at risk.

stress the process by which we perceive and respond to certain events, called *stressors,* that we appraise as threatening or challenging.

"Too many parents make life hard for their children by trying, too zealously, to make it easy for them." —German author Johann Wolfgang von Goethe (1749–1832)

© Julien Tack

SEISMIC STRESS Unpredictable large-scale events, such as the catastrophic earthquake that devastated Haiti in 2010 (aftermath shown here), trigger significant levels of stress-related ills. When an earthquake struck Los Angeles in 1994, sudden-death heart attacks increased fivefold. Most occurred in the first two hours after the quake and near its center and were unrelated to physical exertion (Muller & Verrier, 1996).

general adaptation syndrome (GAS)
Selye's concept of the body's adaptive
response to stress in three phases—alarm,
resistance, exhaustion.

DAILY HASSLES AND SOCIAL STRESS Events don't have to remake our lives to cause stress. Stress also comes from *daily hassles*—dead cell phones, aggravating housemates, and too many things to do (Lazarus, 1990; Pascoe & Richman, 2009; Ruffin, 1993). We might have to give a public speech or do difficult math problems (Balodis et al., 2010; Dickerson & Kemeny, 2004) (**FIGURE 33.2**). Some people shrug off such hassles; others cannot. This is especially the case for those who wake up each day facing housing problems, unreliable child care, budgets that won't stretch to the next payday, and poor health. Such stressors add up and take a toll on health and well-being (DeLongis et al., 1982, 1988; Piazza et al., 2013; Sin et al., 2015).

Daily pressures may be compounded by prejudice against our gender identity, sexual orientation, or ethnicity, which—like other stressors—can have both psychological and physical consequences (Lick et al., 2013; Pascoe & Richman, 2009; Schetter et al., 2013). Thinking that some of the people you encounter each day will dislike, distrust, or doubt you makes daily life stressful. When prolonged, such stress takes a toll on our health. For many African-Americans, for example, the stress of racial discrimination can lead to unhealthy blood pressure levels and sleep deprivation, which can reduce academic achievement (Levy et al., 2016). In the aftermath of the 2016 U.S. presidential election, 7 in 10 African-Americans and nearly 6 in 10 Asian- and Hispanic-Americans said the outcome was a source of stress for them (APA, 2017).

The Stress Response System

LOQ 33-2 How do we respond and adapt to stress?

Medical interest in stress dates back to Hippocrates (460–377 B.C.E.). Centuries later, Walter Cannon (1929) confirmed that the stress response is part of a unified mind-body system. He observed that extreme cold, lack of oxygen, and emotion-arousing events all trigger an outpouring of the adrenal stress hormones epinephrine (adrenaline) and norepinephrine (noradrenaline) from the core of the adrenal glands. When alerted by any of a number of brain pathways, the sympathetic nervous system arouses us, preparing the body for the wonderfully adaptive response that Cannon called *fight or flight*. It increases heart rate and respiration, diverts blood from digestion to the skeletal muscles, dulls feelings of pain, and releases sugar and fat from the body's stores. By fighting or fleeing, we increase our chances of survival.

Canadian scientist Hans Selye's (1936, 1976) 40 years of research on stress extended Cannon's findings. His studies of animals' reactions to various stressors, such as electric shock and surgery, helped make stress a major concept in both psychology and medicine. Selye proposed that the body's adaptive response to stress is so general that, like a single burglar alarm, it sounds, no matter what intrudes. He named this response the **general adaptation syndrome (GAS),** and he saw it as a three-phase process. Let's say you suffer a physical or an emotional trauma:

- In *Phase 1,* you have an *alarm reaction,* as your sympathetic nervous system is suddenly activated. Your heart rate zooms. Blood is diverted to your skeletal muscles. You feel the faintness of shock. With your resources mobilized, you are now ready to fight back.

- During *Phase 2, resistance,* your temperature, blood pressure, and respiration remain high. Your adrenal glands pump hormones into your bloodstream. You are fully engaged, summoning all your resources to meet the challenge. As time passes, with no relief from stress, your body's reserves dwindle.

- You have reached *Phase 3, exhaustion.* With exhaustion, you become more vulnerable to illness or even, in extreme cases, collapse and death.

Selye's basic point: Although the human body copes well with temporary stress, prolonged stress can damage it. Severe childhood stress gets under the skin, leading to greater adult stress. Three examples: In one two-decade study, severely stressed Welsh children were three times more likely to develop heart disease as adults (Ashton

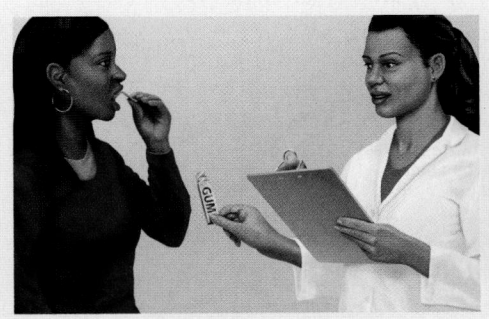

Participants chew gum so that collecting saliva is easy.

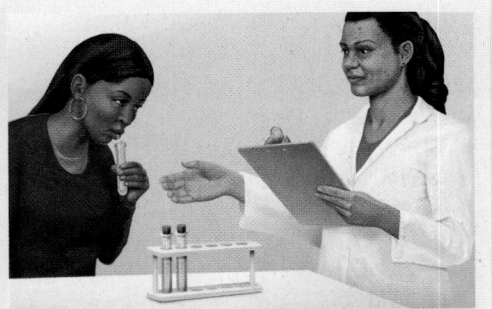

Researcher takes a saliva sample from each participant at the beginning of the experiment to measure levels of the stress hormone, cortisol.

Participant gives simulated job interview speech to a critical panel.

What is 1223 minus 17?

Next, the participant is asked to compute difficult math problems out loud.

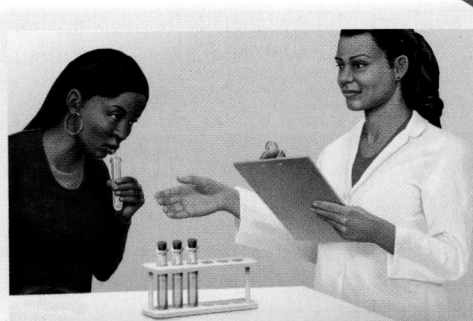

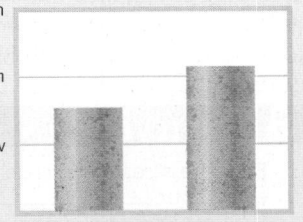

High

Cortisol (stress hormone) levels   Medium

Low

Beginning of experiment   After social stress

(Balodis et al., 2010; Dickerson & Kemeny, 2004)

Measuring cortisol in participants' saliva before and after tells us that although they enter the lab experiencing some stress, that level goes up 40 percent after they experience social stress.

Research team thanks and *debriefs* the participant—explaining the purpose of the experiment and the role she played.

FIGURE 33.2

STUDYING STRESS Most people experience stress when giving a public speech. To study stress, researchers re-create this type of situation. At the end, they *debrief* and reassure each participant.

FIGURE 33.3

SELYE'S GENERAL ADAPTATION SYNDROME Due to the ongoing conflict, Syria's White Helmets (volunteer rescuers) are perpetually in "alarm reaction" mode, rushing to pull victims from the rubble after each fresh attack. As their resistance depletes, they risk exhaustion.

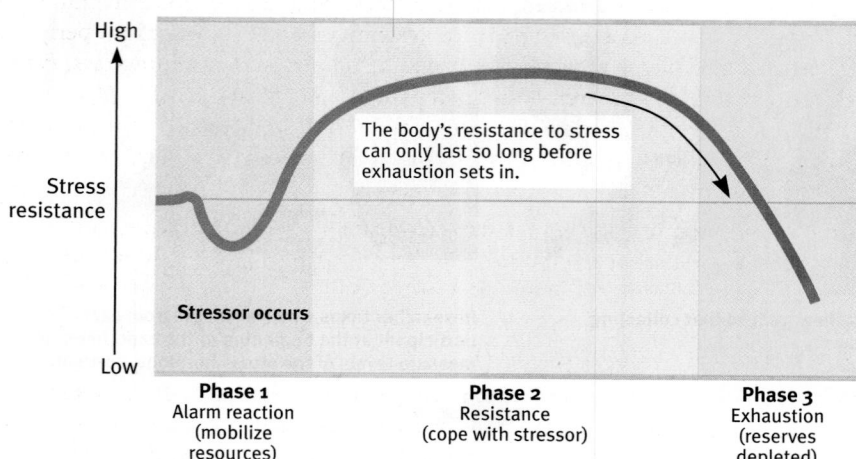

The body's resistance to stress can only last so long before exhaustion sets in.

Stressor occurs

Phase 1	Phase 2	Phase 3
Alarm reaction (mobilize resources)	Resistance (cope with stressor)	Exhaustion (reserves depleted)

"We sleep afraid, we wake up afraid, and leave our homes afraid." —15-year-old girl's Facebook post, describing her family's daily life in war-torn Yemen (al-Asaadi, 2016)

"You may be suffering from what's known as full-nest syndrome."

et al., 2016). Syria's civil war has taken a toll on the health of its refugees (Al Ibraheem et al., 2017). And former prisoners of war, who experienced constant stress and suffering, develop shorter *telomeres* protecting the chromosome ends. That may explain why, compared with noncaptive soldiers, former war prisoners tend to die sooner (Solomon et al., 2014, 2017). (See **FIGURE 33.3**.)

We respond to stress in other ways, too. One response is common after a loved one's death: Withdraw. Pull back. Conserve energy. Faced with an extreme disaster, such as a ship sinking, some people become paralyzed by fear. Another response, found often among women, is to give and receive support—what's called the **tend-and-befriend response** (Lim & DeSteno, 2016; Taylor, 2006; Taylor et al., 2000).

Facing stress, men more often than women tend to withdraw socially, turn to alcohol, or become emotionally insensitive (Bodenmann et al., 2015). Women more often respond to stress by nurturing and banding together.

🔒 RETRIEVE IT • • •   *ANSWERS IN APPENDIX E*

RI-1 The stress response system: When alerted to a negative, uncontrollable event, our _____ nervous system arouses us. Heart rate and respiration _____ (increase/decrease). Blood is diverted from digestion to the skeletal _____. The body releases sugar and fat. All this prepares the body for the _____ - _____ - _____ response.

STRESS AND VULNERABILITY TO DISEASE

LOQ 33-3   How does stress make us more vulnerable to disease?

It often pays to spend our resources in fighting or fleeing an external threat. But we do so at a cost. When stress is momentary, the cost is small. When stress persists, the cost may be greater, in the form of lowered resistance to infections and other threats to mental and physical well-being.

To study how stress—and healthy and unhealthy behaviors—influence health and illness, psychologists and physicians created the interdisciplinary field of *behavioral medicine,* integrating behavioral and medical knowledge. **Health psychology** provides psychology's contribution to behavioral medicine. A branch of health psychology called **psychoneuroimmunology** focuses on mind-body interactions (Kiecolt-Glaser, 2009). This awkward name makes sense when said slowly: Your thoughts and feelings (*psycho*) influence your brain (*neuro*), which influences the endocrine hormones that affect your disease-fighting *immune* system. And this subfield is the study (*ology*) of those interactions. If you've ever had a stress headache, or felt your blood pressure rise with anger, you don't need to be convinced that our psychological states have physiological effects. Stress can even leave you less able to fight off disease because your nervous and endocrine systems influence your immune system (Sternberg, 2009). You can think of your immune system as a complex surveillance system. When it functions properly, it keeps you healthy by isolating and destroying bacteria, viruses, and other invaders. Four types of cells are active in these search-and-destroy missions (**FIGURE 33.4**).

Your age, nutrition, genetics, body temperature, and stress all influence your immune system's activity. If it doesn't function properly, your immune system can err in two directions:

1. Responding too strongly, the immune system may attack the body's own tissues, causing an allergic reaction or a self-attacking disease such as lupus, multiple sclerosis, or some forms of arthritis. Women, who are immunologically stronger than men, are more susceptible to self-attacking diseases (Nussinovitch & Schoenfeld, 2012; Schwartzman-Morris & Putterman, 2012).

2. Underreacting, the immune system may allow a bacterial infection to flare, a dormant virus to erupt, or cancer cells to multiply. To protect transplanted organs, which the recipient's body treats as foreign invaders, surgeons may deliberately suppress the patient's immune system.

Stress can also trigger immune suppression by reducing the release of disease-fighting lymphocytes. This has been observed when animals were stressed by physical restraints, unavoidable electric shocks, noise, crowding, cold water, social defeat, or separation from their mothers (Maier et al., 1994). One study monitored immune responses in 43 monkeys over six months (Cohen et al., 1992). Half were left in stable groups. The rest were stressed by being housed with new roommates—3 or 4 new monkeys each month. By the end of the experiment, the socially disrupted monkeys had weaker immune systems.

Human immune systems react similarly. Three examples:

- ***Surgical wounds heal more slowly in stressed people.*** In one experiment, dental students received punch wounds (precise small holes punched in the skin). Compared with wounds placed during summer vacation, those placed three days before a major exam healed 40 percent more slowly (Kiecolt-Glaser et al., 1998). In other studies, marriage conflict has also slowed punch-wound healing (Kiecolt-Glaser et al., 2005).

tend-and-befriend response under stress, people (especially women) often provide support to others (tend) and bond with and seek support from others (befriend).

health psychology a subfield of psychology that provides psychology's contribution to behavioral medicine.

psychoneuroimmunology the study of how psychological, neural, and endocrine processes together affect the immune system and resulting health.

Intruders!

Is it a bacterial infection?

Is it a cancer cell, virus, or other "foreign substance"?

Is it some other harmful intruder, or perhaps a worn-out cell needing to be cleaned up?

Are there diseased cells (such as those infected by viruses or cancer) that need to be cleaned out?

Possible Responses:

Send in: *B lymphocytes,* which fight bacterial infections. (This one is shown in front of a macrophage.)

Send in: *T lymphocytes,* which attack cancer cells, viruses, and foreign substances

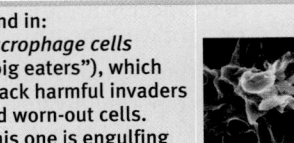

Send in: *macrophage cells* ("big eaters"), which attack harmful invaders and worn-out cells. (This one is engulfing tuberculosis bacteria.)

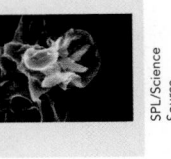

Send in: *natural killer cells* (NK cells), which attack diseased cells. (These two are attacking a cancer cell.)

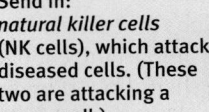

FIGURE 33.4

A SIMPLIFIED VIEW OF IMMUNE RESPONSES
Four types of cells carry out the work of our immune system:

- *B lymphocytes* (white blood cells) release antibodies that fight bacterial infections.
- *T lymphocytes* (white blood cells) attack cancer cells, viruses, and foreign substances.
- *Macrophage cells* ("big eaters") identify, pursue, and ingest harmful invaders and worn-out cells.
- *Natural killer cells* (NK cells) attack diseased cells (such as those infected by viruses or cancer).

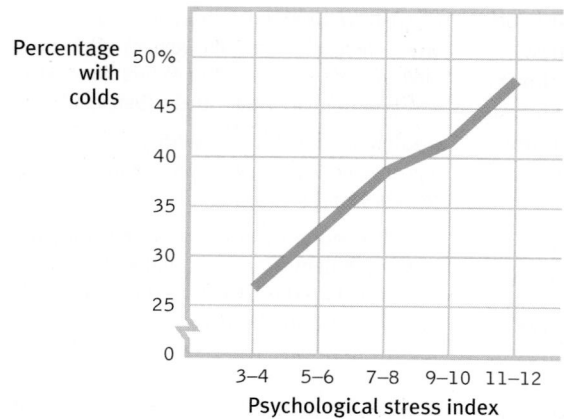

Percentage with colds (y-axis): 50%, 45, 40, 35, 30, 25, 0
Psychological stress index (x-axis): 3–4, 5–6, 7–8, 9–10, 11–12

Laurent/Yakou/Science Source

FIGURE 33.5

STRESS AND COLDS People with the highest life stress scores were also most vulnerable when exposed to an experimentally delivered cold virus (Cohen et al., 1991).

"I didn't give myself cancer." —Mayor Barbara Boggs Sigmund (1939–1990), Princeton, New Jersey

When organic causes of illness are unknown, it is tempting to invent psychological explanations. Before the germ that causes tuberculosis was discovered, personality explanations of TB were popular (Sontag, 1978).

- *Stressed people are more vulnerable to colds.* Major life stress increases the risk of a respiratory infection (Pedersen et al., 2010). When researchers dropped a cold virus into people's noses, 47 percent of those living stress-filled lives developed colds (**FIGURE 33.5**). Among those living relatively free of stress, only 27 percent did. In follow-up research, the happiest and most relaxed people were likewise markedly less vulnerable to an experimentally delivered cold virus (Cohen et al., 2003, 2006; Cohen & Pressman, 2006).

- *Stress can hasten the course of disease.* As its name tells us, *AIDS (acquired immune deficiency syndrome)* is an immune disorder, caused by the *human immunodeficiency virus (HIV)*. Stress cannot give people AIDS. But an analysis of 33,252 participants from around the world found that stress and negative emotions sped the transition from HIV infection to AIDS. And stress predicted a faster decline in those with AIDS (Chida & Vedhara, 2009). The greater the stress that HIV-infected people experienced, the faster their disease progressed.

The stress effect on immunity makes physiological sense. It takes energy to track down invaders, produce swelling, and maintain fevers. Thus, when diseased, your body reduces its muscular energy output by decreasing activity (and increasing sleep). Stress does the opposite. It creates a competing energy need. During an aroused fight-or-flight reaction, your stress responses divert energy from your disease-fighting immune system and send it to your muscles and brain. This increases your vulnerability to illness. *The point to remember:* Stress does not make us sick, but it does alter our immune functioning, which leaves us less able to resist infection.

🔒 **RETRIEVE IT • • •**   *ANSWERS IN APPENDIX E*

RI-2 The field of _____ studies mind-body interactions, including the effects of psychological, neural, and endocrine functioning on the immune system and overall health.

RI-3 What general effect does stress have on our health?

Stress and Cancer

Stress does not create cancer cells. But in a healthy, functioning immune system, lymphocytes, macrophages, and NK cells search out and destroy cancer cells and cancer-damaged cells. If stress weakens the immune system, might this weaken a person's ability to fight off cancer? To explore a possible stress-cancer connection, experimenters have implanted tumor cells in rodents or given them *carcinogens* (cancer-producing substances). They then exposed some rodents to uncontrollable stress, such as inescapable shocks, that weakened their immune systems (Sklar & Anisman, 1981). Stressed rodents, compared with their unstressed counterparts, developed cancer more often, experienced tumor growth sooner, and grew larger tumors.

Does this stress-cancer link also hold with humans? The results are generally the same (Lutgendorf & Andersen, 2015). Some studies find that people are at increased risk for cancer within a year after experiencing significant stress or bereavement (Chida et al., 2008; Steptoe et al., 2010). In one large Swedish study, the risk of colon cancer was 5.5 times greater among people with a history of workplace stress than among those who reported no such problems. This difference was not due to group differences in age, smoking, drinking, or physical characteristics (Courtney et al., 1993). Not all studies, however, have found a link between stress and human cancer (Coyne et al., 2010; Petticrew et al., 1999, 2002). Concentration camp survivors and former prisoners of war, for example, do not have elevated cancer rates. One danger in overstating the link between emotions and cancer is that some patients may then blame themselves for their illness.

It's important enough to repeat: *Stress does not create cancer cells.* At worst, it may affect their growth by weakening the body's natural defenses against multiplying malignant cells (Lutgendorf et al., 2008; Nausheen et al., 2010; Sood et al., 2010). Although a relaxed, hopeful state may enhance these defenses, we should be aware of the thin line that divides science from wishful thinking. The powerful biological processes at work in advanced cancer are not likely to be completely derailed by avoiding stress or maintaining a relaxed but determined spirit (Anderson, 2002). And that explains why research consistently indicates that psychotherapy does not extend cancer patients' survival (Coyne et al., 2007, 2009; Coyne & Tennen, 2010).

Stress and Heart Disease

LOQ 33-4 Why are some of us more prone than others to coronary heart disease?

Imagine a world where you wake up each day, eat your breakfast, and check the news. Among the headlines, you see that four 747 jumbo jet airplanes crashed again yesterday, killing another 1642 passengers. You finish your breakfast, grab your bag, and head to class. It's just an average day.

Replace airline crashes with **coronary heart disease,** the United States' leading cause of death, and you have reentered reality. About 610,000 Americans die annually from heart disease (CDC, 2016a). High blood pressure and a family history of the disease increase the risk. So do smoking, obesity, an unhealthy diet, physical inactivity, and a high cholesterol level.

Stress and personality also play a big role in heart disease. The more psychological trauma people experience, the more their bodies generate *inflammation*, which is associated with heart and other health problems, including depression (Haapakoski et al., 2015; O'Donovan et al., 2012). Plucking a hair and measuring its level of cortisol (a stress hormone) can help indicate whether a child has experienced prolonged stress or predict whether an adult will have a future heart attack (Karlén et al., 2015; Pereg et al., 2011; Vliegenthart et al., 2016). Even cortisol in a fingernail clipping can indicate people's prior stress exposure (Izawa et al., 2017).

THE EFFECTS OF PERSONALITY, PESSIMISM, AND DEPRESSION In a classic study, Meyer Friedman, Ray Rosenman, and their colleagues tested the idea that stress increases vulnerability to heart disease by measuring the blood cholesterol level and clotting speed of 40 U.S. male tax accountants at different times of year (Friedman & Ulmer, 1984). From January through March, the test results were completely normal. But as the accountants began scrambling to finish their clients' tax returns before the April 15 filing deadline, their cholesterol and clotting measures rose to dangerous levels. In May and June, with the deadline past, the measures returned to normal. For these men, stress predicted heart attack risk.

So, are some of us at high risk of stress-related coronary heart disease? To answer this question, the researchers launched a *longitudinal study* of more than 3000 healthy men, aged 35 to 59. The researchers first interviewed each man for 15 minutes, noting his work and eating habits, manner of talking, and other behavior patterns. Those who seemed the most reactive, competitive, hard-driving, impatient, time-conscious, super-motivated, verbally aggressive, and easily angered they called **Type A.** The roughly equal number who were more easygoing they called **Type B.**

Nine years later, 257 men had suffered heart attacks, and 69 percent of them were Type A. Moreover, not one of the "pure" Type Bs—the most mellow and laid-back of their group—had suffered a heart attack.

As often happens in science, this exciting discovery provoked enormous public interest. After that initial honeymoon period, researchers wanted to know more. Was the finding reliable? If so, what was the toxic component of the Type A profile: Time-consciousness? Competitiveness? Anger?

More than 700 studies have explored possible psychological correlates or predictors of cardiovascular health (Chida & Hamer, 2008; Chida & Steptoe, 2009). These reveal that Type A's toxic core is negative emotions—especially the anger associated with an aggressively reactive temperament. When challenged, our active sympathetic nervous system redistributes blood flow to our muscles, pulling it away from our internal organs. The liver, which normally removes cholesterol and fat from the blood, can't do its job. Thus, excess cholesterol and fat may continue to circulate in the blood and later get deposited around the heart. Hostility also correlates with other risk factors, such as smoking, drinking, and obesity (Bunde & Suls, 2006). Our mind and heart interact.

LaunchPad For a 7-minute demonstration of the links between stress, cancer, and the immune system, see the **Video: Fighting Cancer— Mobilizing the Immune System.**

coronary heart disease the clogging of the vessels that nourish the heart muscle; the leading cause of death in many developed countries.

Type A Friedman and Rosenman's term for competitive, hard-driving, impatient, verbally aggressive, and anger-prone people.

Type B Friedman and Rosenman's term for easygoing, relaxed people.

LaunchPad See the **Video: Longitudinal and Cross-Sectional Studies** for a helpful tutorial animation about these types of research studies.

In both India and the United States, Type A bus drivers are literally hard-driving: They brake, pass, and honk their horns more often than their more easygoing Type B colleagues (Evans et al., 1987).

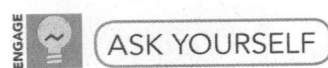 ASK YOURSELF

Do you think you are Type A, Type B, or somewhere in between? In what ways has this been helpful to you, and in what ways has this been a challenge?

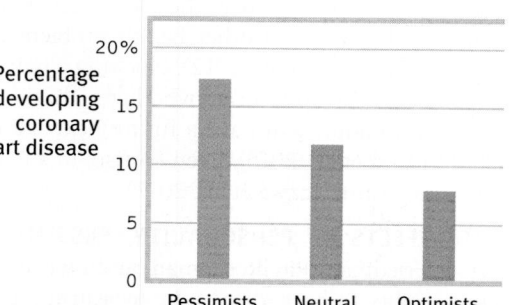
© PhotoSpin, Inc/Alamy

Hundreds of other studies of young and middle-aged men and women confirm that people who react with anger over little things are the most coronary-prone. In Western cultures, suppressing negative emotions only heightens the risk (Kitayama et al., 2015; Kupper & Denollet, 2007). Rage "seems to lash back and strike us in the heart muscle" (Spielberger & London, 1982).

Pessimism seems to be similarly toxic (Pänkäläinen et al., 2016). One longitudinal study followed 1306 initially healthy men who a decade earlier had scored as optimists, pessimists, or neither (Kubzansky et al., 2001). Even after adjusting for other risk factors such as smoking, pessimists were more than twice as likely as optimists to develop heart disease (**FIGURE 33.6**). Happy and consistently satisfied people tend to be healthy and to outlive their unhappy peers (Diener et al., 2017; Gana et al., 2016; Martín-María et al., 2017). People with big smiles tend to have extensive social networks, which predict longer life (Hertenstein, 2009). Having a happy spouse also predicts better health. Happy you, healthy me (Chopik & O'Brien, 2017).

FIGURE 33.6
PESSIMISM AND HEART DISEASE A Harvard School of Public Health team found pessimistic men at doubled risk of developing heart disease over a 10-year period. (Data from Kubzansky et al., 2001.)

Percentage developing coronary heart disease

Pessimists	~17%
Neutral	~11%
Optimists	~7%

Many studies show that depression can likewise be lethal (Wulsin et al., 1999). In one study, nearly 4000 English adults (ages 52 to 79) provided mood reports from a single day. Compared with those in a good mood, those in a depressed mood were twice as likely to be dead five years later (Steptoe & Wardle, 2011). In a U.S. survey of 164,102 adults, those who had experienced a heart attack were twice as likely to report also having been depressed at some point in their lives (Witters & Wood, 2015). And in the years following a heart attack, people with high scores for depression were four times more likely than their low-scoring counterparts to develop further heart problems (Frasure-Smith & Lesperance, 2005). Depression is disheartening.

A BROKEN HEART? The day after the death of her beloved daughter, Carrie Fisher (right), actress Debbie Reynolds (left) also died. People wondered: Might grief-related depression and stress hormones have contributed to Reynolds' stroke (Carey, 2016)?

LaunchPad To play the role of a researcher studying these issues, engage online with **Immersive Learning: How Would You Know If Stress Increases Risk of Disease?**

STRESS AND INFLAMMATION Depressed people tend to smoke more and exercise less (Whooley et al., 2008). But stress itself is also disheartening: Work stress, involuntary job loss, and trauma-related stress symptoms increase heart disease risk (Allesøe et al., 2010; Gallo et al., 2006; Kubzansky et al., 2009; Slopen et al., 2010).

Both heart disease and depression may result when chronic stress triggers blood vessel inflammation (Miller & Blackwell, 2006; Mommersteeg et al., 2016). As the body focuses its energies on fleeing or fighting a threat, stress hormones boost the production of proteins that contribute to inflammation. Persistent inflammation can lead to asthma or clogged arteries and can worsen depression.

In many ways stress can affect our health. (See Thinking Critically About: Stress and Health.) The stress-illness connection is a price we pay for the benefits of stress. Stress invigorates our lives by arousing and motivating us. An unstressed life would hardly be challenging, productive, or even safe.

Jason LaVeris/Getty Images

Stress and Health

LOQ 33-5 So, does stress *cause* illness?

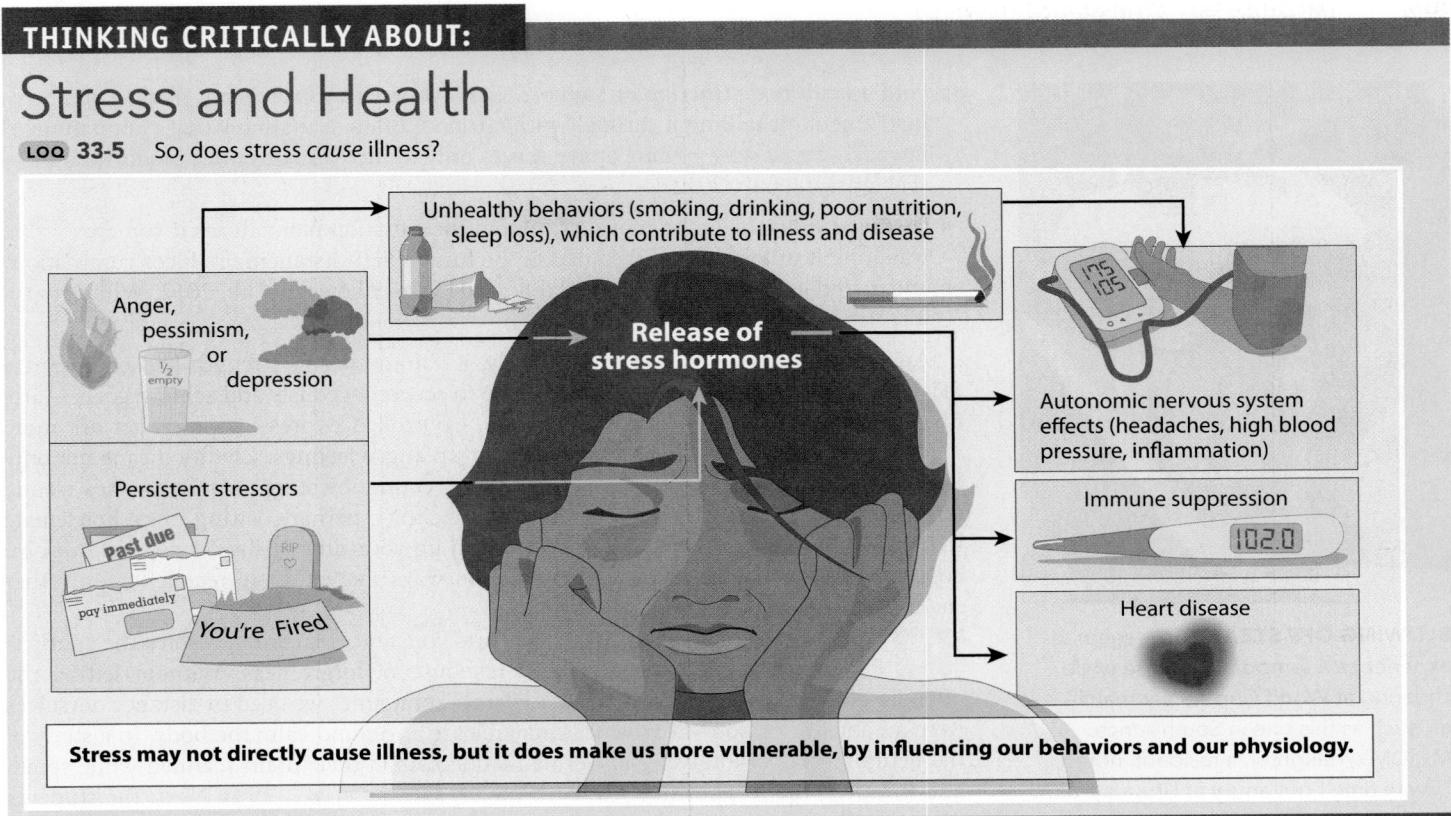

Unhealthy behaviors (smoking, drinking, poor nutrition, sleep loss), which contribute to illness and disease

Anger, pessimism, or depression

½ empty

Persistent stressors

Past due

pay immediately

RIP

You're Fired

Release of stress hormones

Autonomic nervous system effects (headaches, high blood pressure, inflammation)

Immune suppression

102.0

Heart disease

Stress may not directly cause illness, but it does make us more vulnerable, by influencing our behaviors and our physiology.

Anger Management

LOQ 33-6 What are the causes and consequences of anger?

When we face a threat or challenge, fear triggers flight but anger triggers fight—each at times an adaptive behavior. Yet chronic hostility, as in the Type A personality, is linked to heart disease. How, then, can we manage our anger?

Individualist cultures encourage people to vent their rage. Such advice is seldom heard in cultures where people's identity is centered more on the group. People who keenly sense their *inter*dependence see anger as a threat to group harmony (Markus & Kitayama, 1991). In Tahiti, for instance, people learn to be considerate and gentle. In Japan, from infancy on, angry expressions are less common than in Western cultures, where in recent politics and on social media anger seems all the rage.

The Western vent-your-anger advice presumes that aggressive action or fantasy enables emotional release, or **catharsis.** Expressing anger can indeed be *temporarily* calming if it does not leave us feeling guilty or anxious (Geen & Quanty, 1977; Hokanson & Edelman, 1966).

However, catharsis usually fails to cleanse our rage. More often, expressing anger breeds more anger. For one thing, it may provoke further retaliation, causing a minor conflict to escalate into a major confrontation. For another, expressing anger can magnify anger. As *behavior feedback* research demonstrates, *acting* angry can make us *feel* angrier (Flack, 2006; Snodgrass et al., 1986). Anger's backfire potential appeared in a study of people who were asked to wallop a punching bag while ruminating about a person who had recently angered them (Bushman, 2002). Later, when given a chance for revenge, those who vented their anger became even more aggressive.

Angry outbursts that temporarily calm us may also become reinforcing and therefore habit forming. If stressed managers find they can temporarily drain off some of their tension by berating an employee, then the next time they feel irritated and tense they may be more likely to explode again.

What are some better ways to manage anger? Experts offer three suggestions:

ENGAGE

• **Wait.** Doing so will reduce your physiological arousal. "What goes up must come down," noted Carol Tavris (1982). "Any emotional arousal will simmer down if you just wait long enough."

"Venting to reduce anger is like using gasoline to put out a fire." —Psychologist Brad Bushman, 2002

catharsis in psychology, the idea that "releasing" aggressive energy (through action or fantasy) relieves aggressive urges.

BLOWING OFF STEAM Fans seem to experience a *temporary* release while cheering at World Cup soccer matches, such as this one in South Africa. My [DM's] daughter, a resident, noted, "Every time I got angry at Uruguay, blowing that vuvuzela and joining the chorus of dissent released something in me."

"Anger will never disappear so long as thoughts of resentment are cherished in the mind." —The Buddha, 500 B.C.E.

• *Find a healthy distraction or support.* Calm yourself by exercising, playing an instrument, or talking it through with a friend. Brain scans show that ruminating inwardly about why you are angry serves only to increase amygdala blood flow (Fabiansson et al., 2012).

• *Distance yourself.* Try to move away from the situation mentally, as if you are watching it unfold from a distance or the future. Self-distancing reduces rumination, anger, and aggression (Kross & Ayduk, 2011; Mischkowski et al., 2012; White et al., 2015).

Anger is not always wrong. Used wisely, it communicates strength and competence (Tiedens, 2001). Anger also motivates people to act courageously and achieve goals (Aarts & Custers, 2012; Halmburger et al., 2015). Controlled expressions of anger are more adaptive than either hostile outbursts or pent-up angry feelings. Civility means not only keeping silent about trivial irritations but also communicating important ones clearly and assertively. A nonaccusing statement of feeling—perhaps letting one's housemate know that "I get irritated when I have to clean up your dirty dishes"—can help resolve conflicts. Anger that expresses a grievance in ways that promote reconciliation rather than retaliation can benefit a relationship.

What if someone's behavior really hurts you, and you cannot resolve the conflict? Research commends the age-old response of forgiveness. Without letting the offender off the hook or inviting further harm—sometimes we need to distance ourselves from an abusive person—forgiveness may release anger and calm the body. In a study of the neural effects of forgiveness, German students had their brain scanned while someone thwarted their opportunity to earn money (Strang et al., 2014). Next, the students were asked whether or not they forgave the wrongdoer. Forgiveness increased blood flow to brain regions that help people understand their own emotions and make socially appropriate decisions.

🔒 **RETRIEVE IT • • •**   ANSWERS IN APPENDIX E

RI-4 Which component of the Type A personality has been linked most closely to coronary heart disease?

RI-5 Which one of the following is an effective strategy for reducing angry feelings?
a. Retaliate verbally or physically.
b. Wait or "simmer down."
c. Express anger in action or fantasy.
d. Review the grievance silently.

* * *

Traditionally, people have thought about their health only when something goes wrong and they visit a physician for diagnosis and treatment. That, say health psychologists, is like ignoring a car's maintenance and going to a mechanic only when the car breaks down. Health maintenance begins with implementing strategies that prevent illness by alleviating stress, managing anger, and enhancing well-being.

🔒 **REVIEW** STRESS AND ILLNESS

⊙ Learning Objectives

TEST YOURSELF Answer these repeated Learning Objective Questions on your own (before checking the answers in Appendix D) to improve your retention of the concepts (McDaniel et al., 2009, 2015).

33-1 How does our appraisal of an event affect our stress reaction, and what are the three main types of stressors?

33-2 How do we respond and adapt to stress?

33-3 How does stress make us more vulnerable to disease?

33-4 Why are some of us more prone than others to coronary heart disease?

33-5 So, does stress *cause* illness?

33-6 What are the causes and consequences of anger?

⟶ Terms and Concepts to Remember

TEST YOURSELF Write down the definition yourself, then check your answer on the referenced page.

stress, **p. 385**

general adaptation syndrome (GAS),
   p. 386

tend-and-befriend response, **p. 389**

health psychology, **p. 389**

psychoneuroimmunology, **p. 389**

coronary heart disease, **p. 391**

Type A, **p. 391**

Type B, **p. 391**

catharsis, **p. 393**

⟶ Experience the Testing Effect

TEST YOURSELF Answer the following questions on your own first, then check your answers in Appendix E.

1. Selye's general adaptation syndrome (GAS) consists of an alarm reaction followed by _____, then _____.

2. When faced with stress, women are more likely than men to show a _____-and-_____ response.

3. The number of short-term illnesses and stress-related psychological disorders was higher than usual in the months following an earthquake. Such findings suggest that
   a. daily hassles have adverse health consequences.
   b. experiencing a very stressful event increases a person's vulnerability to illness.
   c. the amount of stress a person feels is directly related to the number of stressors experienced.
   d. daily hassles don't cause stress, but catastrophes can be toxic.

4. Which of the following is NOT one of the three main types of stressors?
   a. Catastrophes
   b. Significant life changes
   c. Daily hassles
   d. Pessimism

5. Stress can suppress the immune system by prompting a decrease in the release of _____, the immune cells that ordinarily attack bacteria, viruses, cancer cells, and other foreign substances.

6. Research has shown that people are at increased risk for cancer a year or so after experiencing depression, helplessness, or bereavement. In describing this link, researchers are quick to point out that
   a. accumulated stress causes cancer.
   b. anger is the negative emotion most closely linked to cancer.
   c. stress does not create cancer cells, but it weakens the body's natural defenses against them.
   d. feeling optimistic about chances of survival increases the likelihood of a cancer patient's recovery.

7. A Chinese proverb warns, "The fire you kindle for your enemy often burns you more than him." How is this true of Type A individuals?

Continue testing yourself with 📘 **LearningCurve** or 📗 **Achieve Read & Practice** to learn and remember most effectively.

㉞ Health and Happiness

COPING WITH STRESS

LOQ 34-1 In what two ways do people try to alleviate stress?

Stressors—events that we appraise as threatening or challenging—are unavoidable. This fact, coupled with the fact that persistent stress correlates with heart disease, depression, and lowered immunity, gives us a clear message: We need to learn to **cope** with the stress in our lives, alleviating it with emotional, cognitive, or behavioral methods.

Some stressors we address directly, with **problem-focused coping.** If our impatience leads to a family fight, we may go directly to that family member to work things out. We tend to use problem-focused strategies when we feel a sense of control over a situation and think we can change the circumstances, or at least change ourselves to deal with the circumstances more capably. We turn to **emotion-focused coping** when we believe

coping alleviating stress using emotional, cognitive, or behavioral methods.

problem-focused coping attempting to alleviate stress directly—by changing the stressor or the way we interact with that stressor.

emotion-focused coping attempting to alleviate stress by avoiding or ignoring a stressor and attending to emotional needs related to our stress reaction.

personal control our sense of controlling our environment rather than feeling helpless.

learned helplessness the hopelessness and passive resignation an animal or person learns when unable to avoid repeated aversive events.

external locus of control the perception that chance or outside forces beyond our personal control determine our fate.

internal locus of control the perception that we control our own fate.

we cannot change a situation. If, despite our best efforts, we cannot get along with that family member, we may relieve stress by reaching out to friends for support and comfort. Sometimes our emotion-focused coping can harm our health, such as when we respond by eating comforting but fattening foods. When challenged, some of us tend to respond with cool problem-focused coping, others with emotion-focused coping (Connor-Smith & Flachsbart, 2007). Our feelings of personal control, our explanatory style, and our supportive connections all influence our ability to cope successfully.

Perceived Loss of Control

LOQ 34-2 How does a perceived lack of control affect health?

Picture the scene: Two rats receive simultaneous shocks. Only one of them can turn a wheel to stop the shocks. The helpless rat, but not the wheel turner, becomes more susceptible to ulcers and lowered immunity to disease (Laudenslager & Reite, 1984). In humans, too, uncontrollable threats trigger the strongest stress responses (Dickerson & Kemeny, 2004).

Any of us may feel helpless, hopeless, and depressed after experiencing a series of bad events beyond our **personal control.** Martin Seligman and his colleagues have shown that for some animals and people, a series of uncontrollable events creates a state of **learned helplessness,** with feelings of passive resignation (**FIGURE 34.1**). In one series of experiments, dogs were strapped in a harness and given repeated shocks, with no opportunity to avoid them (Seligman & Maier, 1967). Later, when placed in another situation where they *could* escape the punishment by simply leaping a hurdle, the dogs displayed learned helplessness; they cowered as if without hope. Other dogs that had been able to escape the first shocks reacted differently. They had learned they were in control and easily escaped the shocks in the new situation (Seligman & Maier, 1967). People have shown similar patterns of learned helplessness (Abramson et al., 1978, 1989; Seligman, 1975).

Perceiving a loss of control, we become more vulnerable to ill health. This is a special problem for the elderly, who are particularly susceptible to health problems and also perceive the greatest loss of control (Drewelies et al., 2017). In a famous study of elderly nursing home residents, those who perceived the least amount of control over their activities declined faster and died sooner than those given more control (Rodin, 1986). Workers able to adjust office furnishings and control interruptions and distractions in their work environment have experienced less stress (O'Neill, 1993). Such findings help explain why British executives have tended to outlive those in clerical or laboring positions, and why Finnish workers with low job stress have been less than half as likely to die of stroke or heart disease as those with a demanding job and little control. The more control workers have, the longer they live (Bosma et al., 1997, 1998; Kivimaki et al., 2002; Marmot et al., 1997).

Increasing control—allowing prisoners to move chairs and to control room lights and the TV, having workers participate in decision making, allowing people to personalize their work space—has noticeably improved health and morale (Humphrey et al., 2007; Ng et al., 2012; Ruback et al., 1986). In the case of nursing home residents, 93 percent of those who were encouraged to exert more control became more alert, active, and happy (Rodin, 1986). As researcher Ellen Langer concluded, "Perceived control is basic to human functioning" (1983, p. 291).

Control also helps explain a link between economic status and longevity (Jokela et al., 2009). In one study of 843 grave markers in an old cemetery in Glasgow, Scotland, those with the costliest, highest pillars (indicating the most affluence) tended to have lived the longest (Carroll et al., 1994). Likewise, American presidents, who are generally wealthy and well-educated, have had above-average life spans (Olshansky, 2011). Across cultures, high economic status predicts a lower risk of heart and respiratory diseases (Sapolsky,

FIGURE 34.1

LEARNED HELPLESSNESS When animals and people experience no control over repeated bad events, they often learn helplessness.

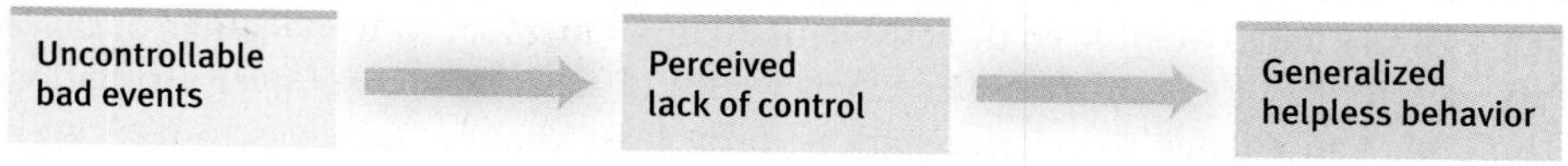

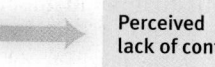 Uncontrollable bad events → Perceived lack of control →  Generalized helpless behavior

2005). Wealthy parents also tend to have wealthy, healthy children (Savelieva et al., 2016). With higher economic status come reduced risks of low birth weight, infant mortality, smoking, and violence. Even among other primates, individuals at the bottom of the social pecking order have been more likely than their higher-status counterparts to become sick when exposed to a cold-like virus (Cohen et al., 1997).

Why does perceived loss of control predict health problems? Because losing control provokes an outpouring of stress hormones. When rats cannot control shock or when humans or other primates feel unable to control their environment, stress hormone levels rise, blood pressure increases, and immune responses drop (Rodin, 1986; Sapolsky, 2005). Captive animals experience more stress and are more vulnerable to disease than their wild counterparts (Roberts, 1988). Human studies confirm that stress increases when we lack control. The greater nurses' workload, the higher their cortisol level and blood pressure—but only among nurses who reported little control over their environment (Fox et al., 1993). The crowding in high-density neighborhoods, prisons, and college and university dorms is another source of diminished feelings of control—and of elevated levels of stress hormones and blood pressure (Fleming et al., 1987; Ostfeld et al., 1987).

Thomas Cordy/The Palm Beach Post/ZUMAPRESS.com

HAPPY TO HAVE CONTROL Working alongside Habitat for Humanity volunteers, this family helped build their own new home.

INTERNAL VERSUS EXTERNAL LOCUS OF CONTROL If experiencing a loss of control can be stressful and unhealthy, do people who generally *perceive* they have control of their lives enjoy better health? Consider your own perceptions of control. Do you believe that your life is beyond your control? That getting a good job depends mainly on being in the right place at the right time? Or do you more strongly believe that you control your own fate? That being a success is a matter of hard work? Did your parents influence your feelings of control? Did your culture?

Hundreds of studies have compared people who differ in their perceptions of control. On one side are those who have what psychologist Julian Rotter called an **external locus of control**—the perception that chance or outside forces control their fate. In one study of more than 1200 Israeli individuals exposed to missile attacks, those with an external locus of control experienced the most *posttraumatic stress* symptoms (Hoffman et al., 2016). On the other side are those who perceive an **internal locus of control,** who believe they control their own destiny. In study after study, the "internals" have achieved more in school and work, acted more independently, enjoyed better health, and felt less depressed than did the "externals" (Lefcourt, 1982; Ng et al., 2006). In longitudinal research on more than 7500 people, those who had expressed a more internal locus of control at age 10 exhibited less obesity, lower blood pressure, and less distress at age 30 (Gale et al., 2008). Compared with nonleaders, military and business leaders have lower-than-average levels of stress hormones and report less anxiety, thanks to their greater sense of control (Sherman et al., 2012).

Compared with their parents' generation, today's young Americans more often express an external locus of control (Twenge et al., 2004). This shift may help explain an associated increase in rates of depression and other psychological disorders in young people (Twenge et al., 2010b).

Another way to say that we believe we are in control of our own life is to say we have *free will*. Studies show that people who believe they have free will learn better, perform better at work, and behave more helpfully (Job et al., 2010; Stillman et al., 2010). They tend to enjoy making decisions, oppose behavior-restricting government regulations, and favor punishing rule breakers (Clark et al., 2014; Feldman et al., 2014; Hannikainen et al., 2016). Belief in free will also predicts another type of control known as *willpower* or *self-control*—an important related topic we turn to next.

ENGAGE

ASK YOURSELF

How much control do you have over your life? What changes could you make to increase your sense of control?

🔒 **RETRIEVE IT • • •**   *ANSWERS IN APPENDIX E*

RI-1 To cope with stress when we feel in control of our world, we tend to use _____ (emotion/problem) -focused strategies. To cope with stress when we believe we cannot change a situation, we tend to use _____ (emotion/problem) -focused strategies.

LatitudeStock - Brian Fairbrother/Getty Images

EXTREME SELF-CONTROL Our ability to exert self-control increases with practice, and some of us have practiced more than others! A number of performing artists make their living as very convincing human statues, as does this actress performing on The Royal Mile in Edinburgh, Scotland.

BUILDING SELF-CONTROL

LOQ 34-3 Why is self-control important, and can our self-control be depleted?

When we have a sense of personal control over our lives, we are more likely to develop **self-control**—the ability to control impulses and delay short-term gratification for longer-term rewards. Self-control predicts good health, higher income, and better school performance (Bub et al., 2016; Keller et al., 2016; Moffitt et al., 2011). In studies of American, Asian, and New Zealander children, self-control outdid intelligence test scores in predicting future academic and life success (Duckworth & Seligman, 2005; Poulton et al., 2015; Wu et al., 2016).

Strengthening self-control is an important key to coping effectively with stress. Doing so requires attention and energy—similar to strengthening a muscle. It's easy to form bad habits, but it takes hard work to break them. With frequent practice in overcoming unwanted urges, people have strengthened their self-control, as seen in their improved self-management of anger, dishonesty, smoking, and impulsive spending (Beames et al., 2017; Wang, J., et al., 2017a).

Researchers disagree about the factors that deplete self-control. Self-control varies over time. Like a muscle, it tends to weaken after use, recover after rest, and grow stronger with exercise (Baumeister & Vohs, 2016). Does exercising willpower temporarily deplete the mental energy we need for self-control on other tasks (see Grillon et al., 2015; Luethi et al., 2016; Vohs et al., 2012 versus Hagger et al., 2016)? In one famous experiment, hungry people who had spent some of their willpower resisting the temptation to eat chocolate chip cookies then abandoned a tedious task sooner than did others (Baumeister et al., 1998a). While some researchers debate the reliability of this "depletion effect," the big lesson of self-control remains: Develop self-discipline, and your self-control can help you lead a healthier, happier, and more successful life (Tuk et al., 2015). The next time you face the temptation of studying versus partying, remember that delaying a little fun now can lead to bigger future rewards.

LaunchPad Test your own self-control with **Immersive Learning: Assess Your Strengths—How Much Self-Control Do You Have, and Why Is This Worth Working to Increase?**

Explanatory Style: Optimism Versus Pessimism

LOQ 34-4 How does an optimistic outlook affect health and longevity?

In *The How of Happiness* (2008), social psychologist Sonja Lyubomirsky tells the true story of Randy. By any measure, Randy has lived a hard life. His dad and best friend both died by suicide. Growing up, his mother's boyfriend treated him poorly. Randy's first wife was unfaithful, and they divorced. Despite these misfortunes, Randy has a sunny disposition. He remarried and enjoys being the stepfather to three boys. His work is rewarding. Randy says he survived his life challenges by seeing the "silver lining in the cloud."

Randy's story illustrates how our outlook—what we expect from the world—influences how we cope with stress. Pessimists expect things to go badly (Aspinwall & Tedeschi, 2010; Carver et al., 2010; Rasmussen et al., 2009). When bad things happen, pessimists knew it all along. They attribute their poor performance to a basic lack of ability ("I can't do this") or to situations enduringly beyond their control ("There is nothing I can do about it"). Optimists, such as Randy, expect to have more control, to cope better with stressful events, and to enjoy better health (Aspinwall & Tedeschi, 2010; Boehm & Kubzansky, 2012; Hernandez et al., 2015). During a semester's final month, students previously identified as optimistic reported less fatigue and fewer coughs, aches, and pains than did their more pessimistic counterparts. And during the stressful first few weeks of law school, those who were optimistic ("It's unlikely that I will fail") enjoyed better moods and stronger immune systems (Segerstrom et al., 1998). Optimists also respond to stress with smaller increases in blood pressure, and they recover more quickly from heart bypass surgery.

Optimistic students have also tended to get better grades because they often respond to setbacks with the hopeful attitude that effort, good study habits, and self-discipline make a difference (Noel et al., 1987; Peterson & Barrett, 1987). When dating couples wrestle

self-control the ability to control impulses and delay short-term gratification for greater long-term rewards.

with conflicts, optimists and their partners see each other as engaging constructively, and they then tend to feel more supported and satisfied with the resolution and with their relationship (Srivastava et al., 2006). Optimism relates to well-being and success in many places, including China and Japan (Qin & Piao, 2011). Realistic positive expectations fuel motivation and success (Oettingen & Mayer, 2002).

Consider the consistency and startling magnitude of the optimism and positive emotions factor in several other studies:

- When one research team followed 70,021 nurses over time, they discovered that those scoring in the top quarter on optimism were nearly 30 percent less likely to have died than those scoring in the bottom quarter (Kim et al., 2017). Even greater optimism-longevity differences have been found in studies of Finnish men and American Vietnam War veterans (Everson et al., 1996; Phillips et al., 2009).

- A famous study followed up on 180 Catholic nuns who had written brief autobiographies at about 22 years of age and had thereafter lived similar lifestyles. Those who had expressed happiness, love, and other positive feelings in their autobiographies lived an average 7 years longer than their more dour counterparts (Danner et al., 2001). By age 80, some 54 percent of those expressing few positive emotions had died, as had only 24 percent of the most positive-spirited.

- Optimists not only live long lives, but they maintain a positive view as they approach the end of their lives. One study followed more than 68,000 American women, ages 50 to 79 years, for nearly two decades (Zaslavsky et al., 2015). As death grew nearer, the optimistic women tended to feel more life satisfaction than did the pessimistic women.

Optimism runs in families, so some people truly are born with a sunny, hopeful outlook. If one identical twin is optimistic, the other often will be as well (Bates, 2015; Mosing et al., 2009). One genetic marker of optimism is a gene that enhances the social-bonding hormone *oxytocin,* which in humans is released, for example, by cuddling, massage, and breast feeding (Campbell, 2010; Saphire-Bernstein et al., 2011).

The good news is that all of us, even the most pessimistic, can learn to become more optimistic. Compared with a control group of pessimists who simply kept diaries of their daily activities, pessimists in a skill-building group—who learned ways of seeing the bright side of difficult situations and of viewing their goals as achievable—reported lower levels of depression (Sergeant & Mongrain, 2014). Optimism is the light bulb that can brighten anyone's mood.

Social Support

LOQ 34-5 How does social support promote good health?

Social support—feeling liked and encouraged by intimate friends and family—promotes both happiness and health. In massive investigations, some following thousands of people for several years, close relationships have predicted happiness and health in both individualist and collectivist cultures (Brannan et al., 2013; Gable et al., 2012; Rueger et al., 2016). People are less likely to die early if supported by close relationships (Shor et al., 2013). When Brigham Young University researchers combined data from 70 studies of 3.4 million people worldwide, they confirmed a striking effect of social support (Holt-Lunstad et al., 2015, 2017). Compared with those who had ample social connections, those who were socially isolated or felt lonely had a 30 percent greater death rate during the 7-year study period. Social isolation's association with risk of death is equivalent to that of smoking (Holt-Lunstad et al., 2010).

To combat social isolation, we need to do more than collect lots of acquaintances. We need people who genuinely care about us (Cacioppo et al., 2014; Hawkley et al., 2008). Some fill this need by connecting with friends, family, co-workers, members of a faith community, or other support groups. Others connect in positive, happy, supportive marriages. One seven-decade-long study found that at age 50, healthy

POSITIVE EXPECTATIONS OFTEN MOTIVATE EVENTUAL SUCCESS:

"We just haven't been flapping them hard enough."

"The optimist proclaims we live in the best of all possible worlds; and the pessimist fears this is true." —James Branch Cabell, *The Silver Stallion,* 1926

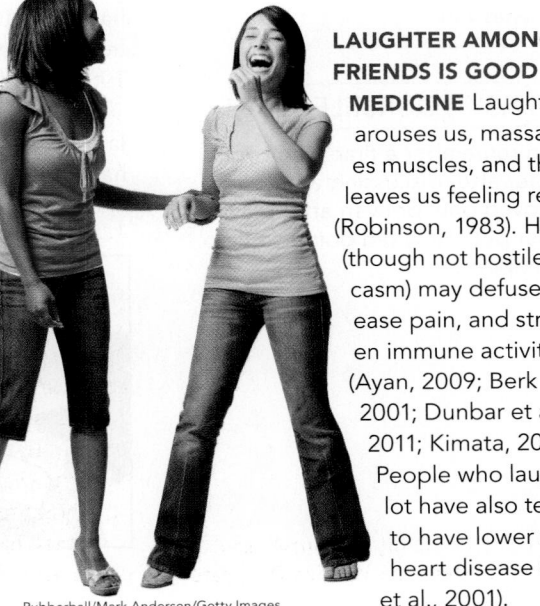

LAUGHTER AMONG FRIENDS IS GOOD MEDICINE Laughter arouses us, massages muscles, and then leaves us feeling relaxed (Robinson, 1983). Humor (though not hostile sarcasm) may defuse stress, ease pain, and strengthen immune activity (Ayan, 2009; Berk et al., 2001; Dunbar et al., 2011; Kimata, 2001). People who laugh a lot have also tended to have lower rates of heart disease (Clark et al., 2001).

Rubberball/Mark Andersen/Getty Images

aging was better predicted by a good marriage than by a low cholesterol level (Vaillant, 2002). On the flip side, divorce predicts poor health. In one analysis of 600 million people in 24 countries, separated and divorced people were more likely to die early (Shor et al., 2012). But it's less marital status than marital *quality* that predicts health—to about the same extent as a healthy diet and physical activity do (Robles, 2015; Smith & Baucom, 2017).

What explains the link between social support and health? Are middle-aged and older adults who live alone more likely to smoke, be obese, and have high cholesterol—and therefore to have a doubled risk of heart attacks (Nielsen et al., 2006)? Or are healthy people simply more sociable? Possibly. But research suggests that social support does have health benefits.

Social support calms us and reduces blood pressure and stress hormones (Baron et al., 2016; Hostinar et al., 2014; Uchino et al., 1996, 2017). To see if social support might calm people's response to threats, one research team subjected happily married women, while lying in an fMRI machine, to the threat of electric shock to an ankle (Coan et al., 2006). During the experiment, some women held their husband's hand. Others held the hand of an unknown person or no hand at all. While awaiting the occasional shocks, women holding their husband's hand showed less activity in threat-responsive areas. This soothing benefit was greatest for those reporting the highest-quality marriages. People with supportive marriages also had below-average stress hormone levels 10 years later (Slatcher et al., 2015). Even animal support, such as a companionable pet, helps buffer stress (Siegel, 1990).

Social support fosters stronger immune functioning. Volunteers in studies of resistance to cold viruses showed this effect (Cohen, 2004; Cohen et al., 1997). Healthy volunteers inhaled nasal drops laden with a cold virus and were quarantined and observed for five days. (In these experiments, the more than 600 participants were well-paid volunteers.) Age, race, sex, and health habits being equal, those with close social ties were least likely to catch a cold. People whose daily life included frequent hugs likewise experienced fewer cold symptoms and less symptom severity (Cohen et al., 2015). The cold fact: The effect of social ties is nothing to sneeze at!

Close relationships give us an opportunity for "open heart therapy"—a chance to confide painful feelings (Frattaroli, 2006). Talking about a long-ago stressful event can temporarily arouse us, but in the long run it calms us (Lieberman et al., 2007; Mendolia & Kleck, 1993; Niles et al., 2015). In one study, 33 Holocaust survivors spent two hours recalling their experiences, many in intimate detail never before disclosed (Pennebaker et al., 1989). In the weeks following, most watched a video of their recollections and showed it to family and friends. Those who were most self-disclosing had the most improved health 14 months later. In another study, of surviving spouses of people who had committed suicide or died in car accidents, those who bore their grief alone had more health problems than those who could share it with others (Pennebaker & O'Heeron, 1984). Confiding is good for the body and the soul.

Suppressing emotions can be detrimental to physical health. When psychologist James Pennebaker (1985) surveyed more than 700 undergraduate women, those who had experienced a traumatic sexual experience in childhood reported more headaches and stomach ailments than those who had experienced other traumas—possibly because

"Woe to one who is alone and falls and does not have another to help."
—Ecclesiastes 4:10

ENGAGE (ASK YOURSELF)

Can you remember a time when you felt better after discussing a problem with a loved one, or even after playing with your pet? How did doing so help you to cope?

survivors of sexual abuse are less likely to confide in others. Another study, of 437 Australian ambulance drivers, supported the ill effects of suppressing one's emotions after witnessing traumas (Wastell, 2002).

Even writing about personal traumas in a diary can help (Burton & King, 2008; Kállay, 2015; Lyubomirsky et al., 2006). In an analysis of 633 trauma victims, writing therapy was as effective as psychotherapy in reducing psychological trauma (van Emmerik et al., 2013). In another experiment, volunteers who wrote trauma diaries had fewer health problems during the ensuing 4 to 6 months (Pennebaker, 1990). As one participant explained, "Although I have not talked with anyone about what I wrote, I was finally able to deal with it, work through the pain instead of trying to block it out. Now it doesn't hurt to think about it."

If we are aiming to exercise more, drink less, quit smoking, or attain a healthy weight, our social ties can tug us away from or toward our goal. If you are trying to achieve some goal, think about whether your social network will help or hinder you.

Photos.com/Getty Images

PETS ARE FRIENDS, TOO Pets can provide social support. Having a pet may increase the odds of survival after a heart attack, relieve depression among people with AIDS, and lower blood pressure and other coronary risk factors (Allen, 2003; McConnell et al., 2011; Wells, 2009). To lower blood pressure, pets are no substitute for effective drugs and exercise. But for people who enjoy animals, and especially for those who live alone, pets are a healthy pleasure (Reis et al., 2017).

REDUCING STRESS

Having a sense of control, developing more optimistic thinking, and building social support can help us *experience* less stress and thus improve our health. Moreover, these factors interrelate: People who are upbeat about themselves and their future have tended also to enjoy health-promoting social ties (Stinson et al., 2008). But sometimes we cannot alleviate stress and simply need to *manage* our stress. Aerobic exercise, relaxation, meditation, and active spiritual engagement may help us gather inner strength and lessen stress effects.

Aerobic Exercise

LOQ 34-6 How effective is aerobic exercise as a way to manage stress and improve well-being?

Aerobic exercise is sustained, oxygen-consuming exertion—such as jogging, swimming, or biking—that increases heart and lung fitness. It's hard to find bad things to say about exercise. Estimates vary, but moderate exercise adds to your quantity of life— about seven hours longer life for every exercise hour (Lee et al., 2017; Zahrt & Crum, 2017)—*and* your quality of life, with more energy, better mood, and stronger relationships (Flueckiger et al., 2016; Hogan et al., 2015).

Exercise helps fight heart disease by strengthening the heart, increasing blood flow, keeping blood vessels open, and lowering both blood pressure and the blood pressure reaction to stress (Ford, 2002; Manson, 2002). Compared with inactive adults, people who exercise suffer about half as many heart attacks (Evenson et al., 2016; Visich & Fletcher, 2009). Dietary fat contributes to clogged arteries, but exercise makes our muscles hungry for those fats and helps clean them out of our arteries (Barinaga, 1997). In one study of over 650,000 American adults, walking 150 minutes per week predicted living seven years longer than nonexercisers (Moore et al., 2012). A follow-up study of 1.44 million Americans and Europeans found that exercise predicted "lower risks of many cancer types" (Moore et al., 2016). Scottish mail carriers, who spend their days walking, have lower heart disease risk than Scottish mail office workers (Tigbe et al., 2017). Regular exercise in later life also predicts better cognitive functioning and reduced risk of neurocognitive disorder and Alzheimer's disease (Kramer & Erickson, 2007).

Does exercise also boost the spirit? In a 21-country survey of university students, physical exercise was a strong and consistent predictor of life satisfaction (Grant et al., 2009). Americans, Canadians, and Britons who do aerobic exercise at least three times a week manage stress better, exhibit more self-confidence, have more vigor, and feel less depressed and fatigued than their inactive peers (Rebar et al., 2015; Smits et al., 2011).

off the mark .com   by Mark Parisi

PHARMACY

ASK ABOUT OUR ANTI-DEPRESSANTS

offthemark.com   ©2007 MARK PARISI DIST. BY UFS INC.

Mark Parisi/Off the Mark/Atlantic Feature Syndicate

aerobic exercise sustained exercise that increases heart and lung fitness; also helps alleviate depression and anxiety.

Paik Photography/Alamy

FIGURE 34.2

AEROBIC EXERCISE REDUCES MILD DEPRESSION (Data from McCann & Holmes, 1984.)

Depression score

- No-treatment group
- Relaxation treatment group — Relaxation reduced depression.
- Aerobic exercise group — Exercise reduced depression more.

Evaluation before treatment — Evaluation after treatment

THE MOOD BOOST When energy or spirits are sagging, few things reboot the day better than exercising, as I [DM] can confirm from my noontime biking and basketball, and as I [ND] can confirm from my running.

Kathryn Brownson

Alice DeWall

Going from active exerciser to couch potato can increase the likelihood of depression—by 51 percent in two years for the women in one study (Wang et al., 2011). Among people with depression, getting off the couch and into a more physically active life reduces depressive symptoms (Kvam et al., 2016; Snippe et al., 2016). "Exercise has a large and significant antidepressant effect," concluded one digest of 25 controlled studies (Schuch et al., 2016a).

But we could state this observation another way: Stressed and depressed people exercise less. These findings are correlations, and cause and effect are unclear. To sort out cause and effect, researchers experiment. They *randomly assign* stressed, depressed, or anxious people either to an aerobic exercise group or to a control group. Next, they measure whether aerobic exercise (compared with a control activity not involving exercise) produces a change in stress, depression, anxiety, or some other health-related outcome. One classic experiment randomly assigned mildly depressed female college students to three groups. One-third participated in a program of aerobic exercise. Another third took part in a program of relaxation exercises. The remaining third (the control group) formed a no-treatment group (McCann & Holmes, 1984). As **FIGURE 34.2** shows, 10 weeks later, the women in the aerobic exercise program reported the greatest decrease in depression. Many had, quite literally, run away from their troubles.

Dozens of other experiments and longitudinal studies confirm that exercise prevents or reduces depression and anxiety (Catalan-Matamoros et al., 2016; Harvey et al., 2018; Stubbs et al., 2017). When experimenters randomly assigned depressed people to an exercise group, an antidepressant group, or a placebo pill group, exercise diminished depression as effectively as antidepressants—and with longer-lasting effects (Hoffman et al., 2011).

LaunchPad See the **Video: Random Assignment** for a helpful tutorial animation about this important part of effective research design.

Vigorous exercise provides a substantial and immediate mood boost (Watson, 2000). Even a 10-minute walk stimulates 2 hours of increased well-being by raising energy levels and lowering tension (Thayer, 1987, 1993). Exercise works its magic in several ways. It increases arousal, thus counteracting depression's low arousal state. It produces toned muscles, which filter a depression-causing toxin (Agudelo et al., 2014). It enables muscle relaxation and sounder sleep. Like an antidepressant drug, it orders up mood-boosting chemicals from our body's internal pharmacy—neurotransmitters such as norepinephrine, serotonin, and the endorphins (Jacobs, 1994; Salmon, 2001). Exercise also fosters *neurogenesis*. In mice, exercise causes the brain to produce a molecule that stimulates the production of new, stress-resistant neurons (Hunsberger et al., 2007; Reynolds, 2009; van Praag, 2009).

On a simpler level, the sense of accomplishment and improved physique and body image that often accompany a successful exercise routine may enhance one's self-image, leading to a better emotional state. Frequent exercise is like a drug that prevents and treats disease, increases energy, calms anxiety, and boosts mood—a drug we would all take, if available. Yet few people (only 1 in 4 in the United States) do it (Mendes, 2010).

Relaxation and Meditation

LOQ 34-7 In what ways might relaxation and meditation influence stress and health?

Knowing the damaging effects of stress, could we learn to counteract our stress responses by altering our thinking and lifestyle? In the late 1960s, psychologists began experimenting with *biofeedback,* a system of recording, amplifying, and feeding back information about subtle physiological responses, many controlled by the autonomic nervous system. Biofeedback instruments mirror the results of a person's own efforts, enabling the person to learn which techniques do (or do not) control a particular physiological response. After a decade of study, however, the initial claims for biofeedback seemed overblown and oversold (Miller, 1985). In 1995, a National Institutes of Health panel declared that biofeedback works best on tension headaches.

Simple methods of relaxation, which require no expensive equipment, produce many of the results biofeedback once promised. Figure 34.2 pointed out that aerobic exercise reduces depression. But did you notice in that figure that depression also decreased among women in the relaxation treatment group? More than 60 studies have found that relaxation procedures can also help alleviate headaches, hypertension, anxiety, and insomnia (Nestoriuc et al., 2008; Stetter & Kupper, 2002).

Such findings would not surprise Meyer Friedman, Ray Rosenman, and their colleagues. They tested relaxation in a program designed to help *Type A* heart attack survivors (hard-driving people who are more prone to heart attacks than their relaxed *Type B* peers) reduce their risk of future attacks. They randomly assigned hundreds of middle-aged men to one of two groups. The first group received standard advice from cardiologists about medications, diet, and exercise habits. The second group received similar advice, but they also were taught ways of modifying their lifestyles. They learned to slow down and relax by walking, talking, and eating more slowly. They learned to smile at others and laugh at themselves. They learned to admit their mistakes, to take time to enjoy life, and to renew their religious faith. The training paid off (**FIGURE 34.3**). During the next three years, the lifestyle modification group had half as many repeat heart attacks as did the first group. This, wrote the exuberant Friedman, was an unprecedented, spectacular reduction in heart attack recurrence. A smaller-scale British study spanning 13 years similarly showed a halved death rate among high-risk people trained to alter their thinking and lifestyle (Eysenck & Grossarth-Maticek, 1991). After suffering a heart attack at age 55, Friedman started taking his own behavioral medicine—and lived to age 90 (Wargo, 2007).

Time may heal all wounds, but relaxation can help speed that process. In one study, surgery patients were randomly assigned to two groups. Both groups received standard treatment, but the second group also experienced a 45-minute relaxation exercise and

FURRY FRIENDS FOR FINALS WEEK Some schools bring cuddly critters on campus for finals week as a way to help students relax and bring disruptive stress levels down. This student at Emory University is relaxing with dogs and puppies. Other schools offer petting zoos or encourage instructors to bring in their own pets that week.

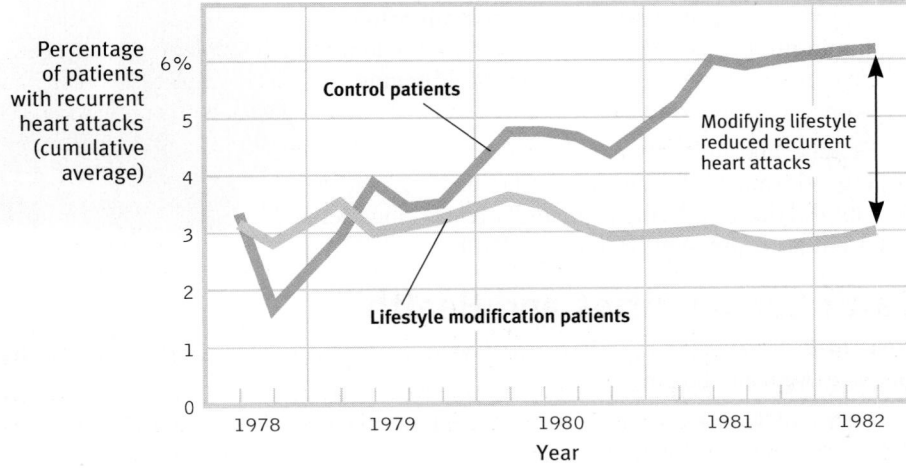

FIGURE 34.3

RECURRENT HEART ATTACKS AND LIFESTYLE MODIFICATION The San Francisco Recurrent Coronary Prevention Project offered counseling from a cardiologist to survivors of heart attacks. Those who were also guided in modifying their Type A lifestyle suffered fewer repeat heart attacks. (Data from Friedman & Ulmer, 1984.)

mindfulness meditation a reflective practice in which people attend to current experiences in a nonjudgmental and accepting manner.

"Sit down alone and in silence. Lower your head, shut your eyes, breathe out gently, and imagine yourself looking into your own heart. . . . As you breathe out, say 'Lord Jesus Christ, have mercy on me.' . . . Try to put all other thoughts aside. Be calm, be patient, and repeat the process very frequently." —Gregory of Sinai, died 1346

And then there are the mystics who seek to use the mind's power to enable novocaine-free cavity repair. Their aim: transcend dental medication.

received relaxation recordings to use before and after surgery. A week after surgery, patients in the relaxation group reported lower stress and showed better wound healing (Broadbent et al., 2012).

Meditation is a modern practice with a long history. In many world religions, meditation has been used to reduce suffering and improve awareness, insight, and compassion. Numerous studies have confirmed the psychological benefits of different types of meditation (Goyal et al., 2014; Rosenberg et al., 2015; Sedlmeier et al., 2012). One type, **mindfulness meditation**, has found a new home in stress management programs. If you were taught this practice, you would relax and silently attend to your inner state, without judging it (Brown et al., 2016; Kabat-Zinn, 2001). You would sit down, close your eyes, and mentally scan your body from head to toe. Zooming in on certain body parts and responses, you would remain aware and accepting. You would also pay attention to your breathing, attending to each breath as if it were a material object.

Practicing mindfulness may lessen anxiety and depression (Goyal et al., 2014). In one study of 1140 people, some received mindfulness-based therapy for several weeks. Others did not. Levels of anxiety and depression were lower among those who received the therapy (Hofmann et al., 2010). Mindfulness practices have also been linked with improved sleep, interpersonal relationships, and immune system functioning (Gong et al., 2016; Rosenkranz et al., 2013; Sedlmeier et al., 2012; Tang et al., 2007). Just a few minutes of daily mindfulness meditation is enough to improve concentration and decision making (Hafenbrack et al., 2014; Rahl et al., 2016).

Some researchers caution that mindfulness may be over-hyped (Coronado-Montoya et al., 2016; Van Dam et al., 2018). But the positive results make us wonder: What's going on in the brain as we practice mindfulness? Correlational and experimental studies offer three explanations. Mindfulness

- *strengthens connections among regions in our brain.* The affected regions are those associated with focusing our attention, processing what we see and hear, and being reflective and aware (Berkovich-Ohana et al., 2014; Ives-Deliperi et al., 2011; Kilpatrick et al., 2011).

- *activates brain regions associated with more reflective awareness* (Davidson et al., 2003; Way et al., 2010). When labeling emotions, mindful people show less activation in the amygdala, a brain region associated with fear, and more activation in the prefrontal cortex, which aids emotion regulation (Creswell et al., 2007; Gotink et al., 2016).

- *calms brain activation in emotional situations.* This lower activation was clear in one study in which participants watched two movies—one sad, one neutral. Those in the control group, who were not trained in mindfulness, showed strong differences in brain activation when watching the two movies. Those who had received mindfulness training showed little change in brain response to the two movies (Farb et al., 2010). Emotionally unpleasant images also trigger weaker electrical brain responses in mindful people than in their less mindful counterparts (Brown et al., 2013). A mindful brain is strong, reflective, and calm.

Exercise and meditation are not the only routes to healthy relaxation. Massage helps relax both premature infants and those suffering pain, and it relaxes muscles and helps reduce depression (Hou et al., 2010).

Djomas/Shutterstock

Faith Communities and Health

LOQ 34-8 What is the *faith factor,* and what are some possible explanations for the link between faith and health?

A wealth of studies—some 1800 of them in the twenty-first century's first decade alone—has revealed another curious correlation: the *faith factor* (Koenig et al., 2012). Religiously active people tend to live longer than those who are not religiously active. One

AlisaNata/Shutterstock   Getty Images/Fuse   Sura Nualpradid/Shutterstock   casejustin/Shutterstock

Georgios Kollidas/Alamy   Georgios Kollidas/Shutterstock   ppart/Shutterstock

such study compared the death rates for 3900 people living in two Israeli communities. The first community contained 11 religiously orthodox collective settlements; the second contained 11 matched, nonreligious collective settlements (Kark et al., 1996). Over a 16-year period, "belonging to a religious collective was associated with a strong protective effect" not explained by age or economic differences. In every age group, religious community members were about half as likely to have died as were their nonreligious counterparts. This difference is roughly comparable to the gender difference in mortality. A more recent study followed 74,534 nurses over 20 years. When controlling for various health risk factors, those who attended religious services more than weekly were a third less likely to have died than were nonattenders (Li et al., 2016).

How should we interpret such findings, given that we cannot experiment by randomly assigning people to be religiously engaged or not? Correlations are not cause-effect statements, and they leave many factors uncontrolled (Sloan, 2005; Sloan et al., 1999, 2000, 2002). Here is another possible interpretation: Women are more religiously active than men, and women outlive men. Might religious involvement merely reflect this gender-longevity link? Apparently not. One 8-year National Institutes of Health study followed 92,395 women, ages 50 to 79. After controlling for many factors, researchers found that women attending religious services at least weekly experienced an approximately 20 percent reduced risk of death during the study period (Schnall et al., 2010). Moreover, the association between religious involvement and life expectancy is also found among men (Benjamins et al., 2010; McCullough et al., 2000; McCullough & Laurenceau, 2005). A 28-year study that followed 5286 Californians found that, after controlling for age, gender, ethnicity, and education, frequent religious attenders were 36 percent less likely to have died in any year (**FIGURE 34.4**). In another 8-year controlled study of more than 20,000 people (Hummer et al., 1999), this effect translated into a life expectancy of 83 years for those frequently attending religious services and only 75 years for nonattenders.

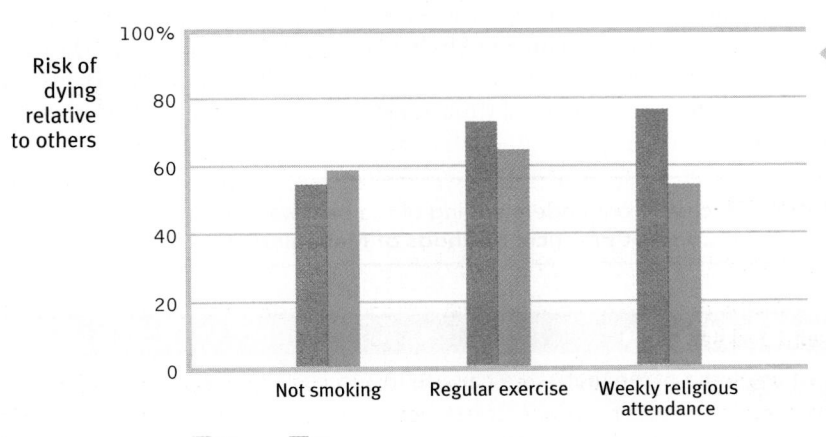

Risk of dying relative to others

Men   Women

FIGURE 34.4

PREDICTORS OF LONGER LIFE: NOT SMOKING, FREQUENT EXERCISE, AND REGULAR RELIGIOUS ATTENDANCE One 28-year study followed 5286 Alameda, California, adults (Oman et al., 2002; Strawbridge, 1999; Strawbridge et al., 1997). Controlling for age and education, the researchers found that not smoking, regular exercise, and religious attendance all predicted a lowered risk of death in any given year. Women attending weekly religious services, for example, were only 54 percent as likely to die in a typical study year as were nonattenders.

FIGURE 34.5

POSSIBLE EXPLANATIONS FOR THE CORRELATION BETWEEN RELIGIOUS INVOLVEMENT AND HEALTH/ LONGEVITY

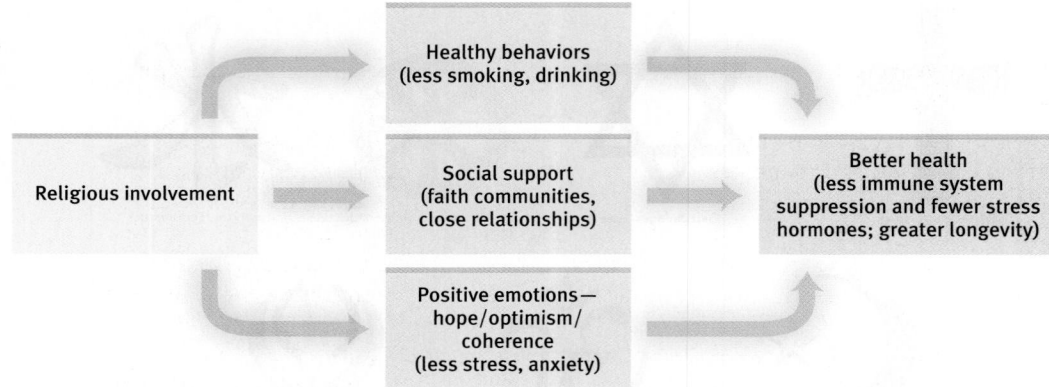

These correlational findings do not indicate that nonattenders can suddenly add 8 years of life if they start attending services and change nothing else. Nevertheless, the findings do indicate that religious involvement, like nonsmoking and exercise, is a *predictor* of health and longevity. Research points to three possible explanations for the religiosity-longevity correlation (**FIGURE 34.5**):

- *Healthy behaviors* Religion promotes self-control (DeWall et al., 2014; McCullough & Willoughby, 2009). And that helps explain why religiously active people tend to smoke and drink much less and to have healthier lifestyles (Islam & Johnson, 2003; Koenig & Vaillant, 2009; Masters & Hooker, 2013; Park, 2007). In one Gallup survey of 550,000 Americans, 15 percent of the very religious were smokers, as were 28 percent of the nonreligious (Newport et al., 2010). But such lifestyle differences are not great enough to explain the dramatically reduced mortality in the Israeli religious settlements. In American studies, too, about 75 percent of the longevity difference remained when researchers controlled for unhealthy behaviors, such as inactivity and smoking (Musick et al., 1999).

- *Social support* Could social support explain the faith factor (Ai et al., 2007; Kim-Yeary et al., 2012)? Faith is often a communal experience. To belong to a faith community is to participate in a support network. Religiously active people are there for one another when misfortune strikes. In the 20-year nurses study, social support was the biggest contributor to the religiosity factor—explaining a fourth of its effect. Moreover, religion encourages marriage, another predictor of health and longevity. In the Israeli religious settlements, for example, divorce was almost nonexistent.

- *Positive emotions* Even after controlling for social support, gender, unhealthy behaviors, and preexisting health problems, the mortality studies have found that religiously engaged people tend to live longer (Chida et al., 2009). Researchers speculate that religiously active people may benefit from a stable, coherent world-view, a sense of hope for the long-term future, feelings of ultimate acceptance, and the relaxed meditation of prayer or other religious observances. These intervening variables may also help to explain why the religiously active seem to have healthier immune functioning, fewer hospital admissions, and, for people with AIDS, fewer stress hormones and longer survival (Ironson et al., 2002; Koenig & Larson, 1998; Lutgendorf et al., 2004).

ASK YOURSELF

What strategies have you used to cope with stress in your life? How well have they worked? What other strategies could you try?

 **LaunchPad** To check your understanding of the best ways to handle stress, engage online with **Concept Practice: Methods of Managing Stress.**

🔒 **RETRIEVE IT** • • •   *ANSWERS IN APPENDIX E*

RI-2 What are some of the tactics we can use to successfully manage the stress we cannot avoid?

HAPPINESS

LOQ 34-9 What is the *feel-good, do-good phenomenon*, and what is the focus of positive psychology research?

People aspire to, and wish one another, health and happiness. And for good reason. Our state of happiness or unhappiness colors everything. Happy people perceive the world as safer. Their eyes are drawn toward emotionally positive information (Raila et al., 2015). They are more confident and decisive, and they cooperate more easily. They rate job applicants more favorably, savor their positive past experiences without dwelling on the negative, and are more socially connected. They live healthier and more energized and satisfied lives (Boehm et al., 2015; De Neve et al., 2013; Stellar et al., 2015). And they are more generous (Boenigk & Mayr, 2016). The simple conclusion: *Moods matter.* When your mood is gloomy, life as a whole seems depressing and meaningless—and you think more skeptically and attend more critically to your surroundings. Let your mood brighten and your thinking broadens, becoming more playful and creative (Baas et al., 2008; Forgas, 2008; Fredrickson, 2013).

Young adults' happiness helps predict their future life course. One study showed that the happiest 20-year-olds were later more likely to marry and less likely to divorce (Stutzer & Frey, 2006). In another study, which surveyed thousands of U.S. college students in 1976 and restudied them at age 37, happy students had gone on to earn significantly more money than their less-happy-than-average peers (Diener et al., 2002). When we are happy, our relationships, self-image, and hopes for the future also seem more promising.

Moreover—and this is one of psychology's most consistent findings—happiness doesn't just feel good, it *does* good. In study after study, a mood-boosting experience such as recalling a happy event has made people more likely to give money, pick up someone's dropped papers, volunteer time, and do other good deeds. Psychologists call it the **feel-good, do-good phenomenon** (Salovey, 1990).

The reverse is also true: Doing good also promotes good feeling. One survey of more than 200,000 people in 136 countries found that, nearly everywhere, people report feeling happier after spending money on others rather than on themselves (Aknin et al., 2013; Dunn et al., 2014). Kidney donation leaves donors feeling good (Brethel-Haurwitz & Marsh, 2014). Young children also show more positive emotion when they give, rather than receive, gifts (Aknin et al., 2015). Why does doing good feel so good? One reason is that it strengthens our social relationships (Aknin & Human, 2015; Yamaguchi et al., 2015). Some happiness coaches harness this *do-good, feel-good phenomenon* as they assign people to perform a daily "random act of kindness" and to record the results.

Positive Psychology

William James was writing about the importance of happiness ("the secret motive for all [we] do") as early as 1902. By the 1960s, the *humanistic psychologists* were interested in advancing human fulfillment. In the twenty-first century, under the leadership of American Psychological Association past-president Martin Seligman, **positive psychology** is using scientific methods to study human flourishing. This young subfield includes studies of **subjective well-being**—our feelings of happiness (sometimes defined as a high ratio of positive to negative feelings) or our sense of satisfaction with life.

Taken together, satisfaction with the past, happiness with the present, and optimism about the future define the positive psychology movement's first pillar: *positive well-being.*

Positive psychology is about building not just a pleasant life, says Seligman, but also a good life that engages one's skills, and a meaningful life that points beyond oneself. Thus, the second pillar, *positive traits*, focuses on exploring and enhancing creativity, courage, compassion, integrity, self-control, leadership, wisdom, and spirituality. Seligman views happiness as a by-product of a pleasant, engaged, and meaningful life.

ENGAGE · 💡 📗 **LaunchPad** To assess your own well-being and consider ways to improve it, engage online with **Immersive Learning: Assess Your Strengths—How Satisfied Are You With Your Life, and How Could You Be More Satisfied?**

---

feel-good, do-good phenomenon people's tendency to be helpful when in a good mood.

positive psychology the scientific study of human flourishing, with the goals of discovering and promoting strengths and virtues that help individuals and communities to thrive.

subjective well-being self-perceived happiness or satisfaction with life. Used along with measures of objective well-being (for example, physical and economic indicators) to evaluate people's quality of life.

Courtesy of Martin Seligman

MARTIN E. P. SELIGMAN "The main purpose of a positive psychology is to measure, understand, and then build the human strengths and the civic virtues."

The third pillar, *positive groups, communities, and cultures,* seeks to foster a positive social ecology. This includes healthy families, communal neighborhoods, effective schools, socially responsible media, and civil dialogue.

"Positive psychology," Seligman and colleagues have said (2005), "is an umbrella term for the study of positive emotions, positive character traits, and enabling institutions." Its focus differs from psychology's traditional interests in understanding and alleviating negative states—abuse and anxiety, depression and disease, prejudice and poverty. Indeed, psychology articles published since 1887 on depression have outnumbered those related to happiness by 15 to 1.

In ages past, times of relative peace and prosperity have enabled cultures to turn their attention from repairing weakness and damage to promoting what Seligman (2002) has called "the highest qualities of life." Prosperous fifth-century Athens nurtured philosophy and democracy. Flourishing fifteenth-century Florence nurtured great art. Victorian England, flush with the bounty of the British Empire, nurtured honor, discipline, and duty. In this millennium, Seligman believes, thriving Western cultures have a parallel opportunity to create, as a "humane, scientific monument," a more positive psychology, concerned not only with weakness and damage but also with strength and virtue. Thanks to his leadership, and to more than $200 million in funding, the movement has gained strength, with supporters in 77 countries (IPPA, 2017; Seligman, 2016).

What Affects Our Well-Being?

LOQ 34-10 How do time, wealth, adaptation, and comparison affect our happiness levels?

THE SHORT LIFE OF EMOTIONAL UPS AND DOWNS Are some days of the week happier than others? In what may be psychology's biggest-ever data sample, social psychologist Adam Kramer (at my [DM's] request and in cooperation with Facebook) did a naturalistic observation of emotion words in *billions* of status updates. After eliminating exceptional days, such as holidays, he tracked the frequency of positive and negative emotion words by day of the week. The days with the most positive moods? Friday and Saturday (**FIGURE 34.6**). Similar analyses of questionnaire responses and 59 million Twitter messages found Friday to Sunday the week's happiest days (Golder & Macy, 2011; Helliwell & Wang, 2015; Young & Lim, 2014). For you, too?

LaunchPad See the **Video: Naturalistic Observation** for a helpful tutorial animation about this type of research design.

FIGURE 34.6

USING WEB SCIENCE TO TRACK HAPPY DAYS Adam Kramer (2010) tracked positive and negative emotion words in many "billions" (the exact number is proprietary information) of status updates of U.S. Facebook users between September 7, 2007, and November 17, 2010.

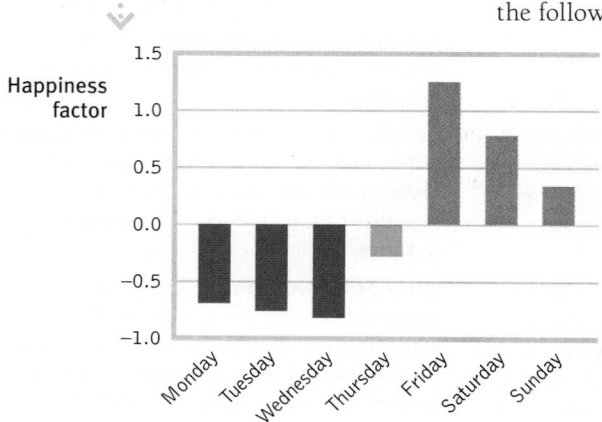

Over the long run, our emotional ups and downs tend to balance out, even over the course of the day. Positive emotion rises over the early to middle part of most days and then drops off (Kahneman et al., 2004; Watson, 2000). A stressful event—an argument, a sick child, a car problem—can trigger a bad mood. No surprise there. But by the next day, the gloom nearly always lifts (Affleck et al., 1994; Bolger et al., 1989; Stone & Neale, 1984). Our overall judgments of our lives often show lingering effects of good or bad events, but our daily moods typically rebound (Luhmann et al., 2012). If anything, people tend to bounce back from a bad day to a *better*-than-usual good mood the following day.

Worse events—the loss of a spouse or a job—can drag us down for longer periods (Infurna & Luthar, 2016a). But eventually, our bad mood usually ends. A romantic breakup feels devastating, but in time the wound heals. In one study, faculty members up for tenure expected their lives would be deflated by a negative decision. Actually, 5 to 10 years later, their happiness level was about the same as for those who received tenure (Gilbert et al., 1998).

Grief over the loss of a loved one or anxiety after a severe trauma (such as child abuse, rape, or the terrors of war) can linger. But usually, even tragedy is not permanently depressing. People who become blind or paralyzed may not completely recover their previous well-being, but those with an agreeable personality usually recover near-normal levels of day-to-day happiness (Boyce & Wood, 2011; Hall et al., 1999). So do those who count their blessings and remain optimistic in the wake of a school shooting or terrorist bombing (Birkeland et al., 2016; Vieselmeyer et al., 2017). Even if you lose the use of all four limbs, explained Daniel Kahneman (2005a), "you will gradually start thinking of other things, and the more time you spend thinking of other things the less miserable you are going to be." Contrary to what many people believe, even most patients "locked-in" a motionless body report a mostly positive outlook and no wish to die (Bruno et al., 2008, 2011; Chaudhary et al., 2017; Nizzi et al., 2012).

The surprising reality: *We overestimate the duration of our emotions and underestimate our resiliency.*

WEALTH AND WELL-BEING Would you be happier if you made more money? In a 2006 Gallup poll, 73 percent of Americans thought they would be. How important is "being very well off financially"? "Very important" or "essential," say 82 percent of entering U.S. college students (Eagen et al., 2016).

Money does buy happiness, up to a point, especially for people during their midlife working years (Cheung & Lucas, 2015). Moreover, people in rich countries are happier than those in poor countries (Diener & Tay, 2015). Having enough money to buy your way out of hunger, to have a sense of control over your life, and to treat yourself to something special predicts greater happiness (Fischer & Boer, 2011; Ruberton et al., 2016). As Australian data confirm, the power of more money to increase happiness is strongest at low incomes (Cummins, 2006). A 10 percent wage increase does a lot more for someone making $10,000 per year than for someone making $100,000. Raising low incomes will increase happiness more than will raising high incomes.

Once we have enough money for comfort and security, piling up more and more matters less and less. Experiencing luxury diminishes our savoring of life's simpler pleasures (Cooney et al., 2014; Quoidbach et al., 2010). If you ski the Alps once, your neighborhood sledding hill pales. If you ski the Alps every winter, it becomes an ordinary part of life rather than an experience to treasure (Quoidbach et al., 2015).

And consider this: During the last half-century, the average U.S. citizen's buying power almost tripled—enabling larger homes and twice as many cars per person, not to mention tablets and smart phones. Did it also buy more happiness? As **FIGURE 34.7** shows, Americans have become no happier. In 1957, some 35 percent said they were "very happy," as did slightly fewer—33 percent—in 2014. Much the same has been true of

"Weeping may tarry for the night, but joy comes with the morning."
—Psalm 30:5

"But on the positive side, money can't buy happiness—so who cares?"

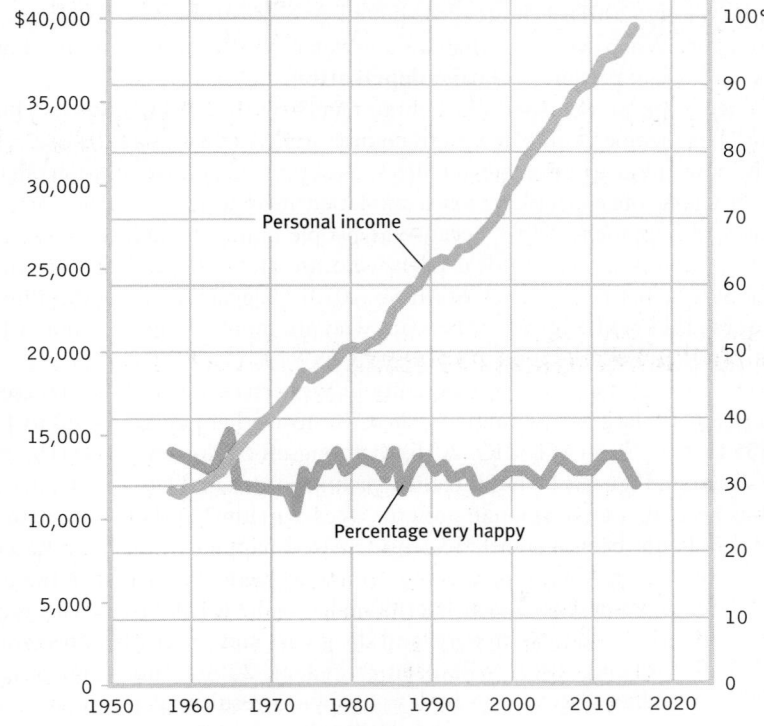

FIGURE 34.7

DOES MONEY BUY HAPPINESS? It surely helps us to avoid certain types of pain. Yet, though average buying power has nearly tripled since the 1950s, Americans' reported happiness has remained almost unchanged. (Happiness data from National Opinion Research Center surveys; income data from *Historical Statistics of the United States* and *Economic Indicators*.)

"Researchers say I'm not happier for being richer, but do you know how much researchers make?"

"Continued pleasures wear off. . . . Pleasure is always contingent upon change and disappears with continuous satisfaction." —Dutch psychologist Nico Frijda (1988)

"I have a 'fortune cookie maxim' that I'm very proud of: Nothing in life is quite as important as you think it is while you are thinking about it. So, nothing will ever make you as happy as you think it will." —Nobel laureate psychologist Daniel Kahneman, Gallup interview, "What Were They Thinking?" 2005

The effect of comparison with others helps explain why students tend to have a higher academic self-concept if they attend a school where most other students are not exceptionally able (Marsh & Parker, 1984; Rogers & Feller, 2016; Salchegger, 2016). If you were near the top of your graduating class, you might feel inferior or discouraged upon entering a college or university where all students were near the top of their class.

Europe, Canada, Australia, and Japan, where increasing real incomes have *not* produced increasing happiness (Australian Unity, 2008; Diener & Biswas-Diener, 2008; Di Tella & MacCulloch, 2010; Zuzanek, 2013). Ditto China, where living standards have risen but life satisfaction has not (Davey & Rato, 2012; Easterlin et al., 2012). These findings lob a bombshell at modern materialism: *Economic growth in affluent countries has provided no apparent boost to people's morale or social well-being.*

HAPPINESS IS RELATIVE: ADAPTATION AND COMPARISON Two psychological principles explain why, for those who are not poor, more money buys little more than temporary happiness and why our emotions seem attached to elastic bands that pull us back from highs or lows. In its own way, each principle suggests that happiness is relative.

HAPPINESS IS RELATIVE TO OUR OWN EXPERIENCE The **adaptation-level phenomenon** describes our tendency to judge various stimuli in comparison with our past experiences. As psychologist Harry Helson (1898–1977) explained, we adjust our *neutral* levels—the points at which sounds seem neither loud nor soft, temperatures neither hot nor cold, events neither pleasant nor unpleasant—based on our experience. We then notice and react to variations up or down from these levels. Thus, after an initial surge of pleasure, improvements become our "new normal," and we then require something even better to give us a boost of happiness.

So, could we ever create a permanent social paradise? Probably not (Campbell, 1975; Di Tella et al., 2010). People who have experienced a recent windfall—from a lottery, an inheritance, or a surging economy—typically feel elated (Diener & Oishi, 2000; Gardner & Oswald, 2007). So would you, if you woke up tomorrow to your utopia—perhaps a world with no bills, no ills, and perfect exam scores. But eventually, your utopia would become your new normal. Before long, you would again sometimes feel gratified (when events exceed your expectations) and sometimes feel deprived (when they fall below). *The point to remember:* Feelings of satisfaction and dissatisfaction, success and failure are judgments we make based partly on expectations formed by our recent experience (Rutledge et al., 2014). Satisfaction, as Richard Ryan (1999) said, "has a short half-life." Ditto disappointment, which means that you may bounce back from a setback or from your team's defeat sooner than you expect.

HAPPINESS IS RELATIVE TO OTHERS' SUCCESS We are always comparing ourselves with others. And whether we feel good or bad depends on who those others are (Lyubomirsky, 2001). We are slow-witted or clumsy only when others are smarter or more agile. When we sense that we are worse off than others with whom we compare ourselves, we experience **relative deprivation.**

When expectations soar above attainments, we feel disappointed. Thus, the middle- and upper-income people in a given country, who can compare themselves with the relatively poor, tend to have greater life satisfaction than their less-fortunate compatriots. Nevertheless, once people reach a moderate income level, further increases buy little additional happiness. Why? Because as people climb the ladder of success they mostly compare themselves with local peers who are at or above their current level (Gruder, 1977; Suls & Tesch, 1978; Zell & Alicke, 2010). "Beggars do not envy millionaires, though of course they will envy other beggars who are more successful," noted British philosopher Bertrand Russell (1930/1985, p. 90).

Over the last half-century, inequality in Western countries has increased. For CEOs at America's 500 largest corporations, the CEO-to-worker pay ratio—20 to 1 in 1965—rose to 335 to 1 in 2015 (AFL-CIO, 2016; Kiatpongsan & Norton, 2014). The rising economic tide shown in Figure 34.7 has lifted the yachts more than the rowboats. Increasing inequality has accompanied economic growth. Does it matter? Does this explain why economic growth has not been associated with increased happiness (Oishi & Kesebir, 2015)? *Yes.* Brain scans reveal that experiencing economic inequality activates the amygdala, leading to greater depression a year later (Tanaka et al., 2017). Places with greater inequality have more crime, obesity, anxiety, and drug use, and lower life expectancy (Burkhauser et al., 2016; Ratcliff, 2013; Wilkinson & Pickett, 2009). Times and places with greater income inequality also tend to be less happy—a result that people's social comparisons help explain (Cheung & Lucas, 2016; Helliwell et al., 2013; Roth et al., 2016).

Just as comparing ourselves with those who are better off creates envy, so counting our blessings as we compare ourselves with those worse off boosts our contentment. In one study, university women considered others' deprivation and suffering (Dermer et al., 1979). They viewed vivid depictions of how grim city life could be in 1900. They imagined and then wrote about various personal tragedies, such as being burned and disfigured. Later, the women expressed greater satisfaction with their own lives. Similarly, when mildly depressed people have read about someone who was even more depressed, they felt somewhat better (Gibbons, 1986). "I cried because I had no shoes," states a Persian saying, "until I met a man who had no feet."

What Predicts Our Happiness Levels?

LOQ 34-11 What predicts happiness, and how can we be happier?

Happy people share many characteristics (**TABLE 34.1**). But why are some people normally so joyful and others so somber? Here, as in so many other areas, the answer is found in the interplay between nature and nurture.

Genes matter. In one analysis of over 55,000 identical and fraternal twins, 36 percent of the differences among people's happiness ratings was heritable—attributable to genes (Bartels, 2015). Even identical twins raised apart are often similarly happy. Moreover, researchers are now drilling down to identify how specific genes influence our happiness (De Neve et al., 2012; Fredrickson et al., 2013).

But our personal history and our culture matter, too. On the personal level, as we have seen, our emotions tend to balance around a level defined by our experience. On the cultural level, groups vary in the traits they value. Self-esteem and achievement matter more in Western cultures, which value individualism. Social acceptance and harmony matter more in communal cultures such as Japan, which stress family and community (Diener et al., 2003; Fulmer et al., 2010; Uchida & Kitayama, 2009).

Depending on our genes, our outlook, and our recent experiences, our happiness seems to fluctuate around a "happiness set point," which disposes some people to be ever upbeat and others more negative. Even so, after following thousands of lives over two decades, researchers have determined that our satisfaction with life can change (Lucas & Donnellan, 2007). Happiness rises and falls, and can be influenced by factors that are under our control (Layous & Lyubomirsky, 2014; Nes et al., 2010). See **TABLE 34.2** for research-based suggestions for improving your mood and increasing your satisfaction with life.

"Comparison is the thief of joy."
—Attributed to Theodore Roosevelt

LaunchPad For a 6.5-minute examination of historical and modern views of happiness, see the **Video: The Search for Happiness.**

"I could cry when I think of the years I wasted accumulating money, only to learn that my cheerful disposition is genetic."

TABLE 34.1

Happiness Is . . .

Researchers Have Found That Happy People Tend to	However, Happiness Seems Not Much Related to Other Factors, Such as
Have high self-esteem (in individualist countries).	Age.
Be optimistic, outgoing, and agreeable.	Gender (women are more often depressed, but also more often joyful).
Have close, positive, and lasting relationships.	Physical attractiveness.
Have work and leisure that engage their skills.	
Have an active religious faith (especially in more religious cultures).	
Sleep well and exercise.	

Information from De Neve & Cooper (1998); Diener et al. (2003, 2011); Headey et al. (2010); Lucas et al. (2004); Myers (1993, 2000); Myers & Diener (1995, 1996); Steel et al. (2008). Veenhoven (2014, 2015) offers a database of 13,000+ correlates of happiness at WorldDatabaseofHappiness.eur.nl.

adaptation-level phenomenon our tendency to form judgments (of sounds, of lights, of income) relative to a neutral level defined by our prior experience.

relative deprivation the perception that one is worse off relative to those with whom one compares oneself.

RubberBall Selects/Alamy

 TABLE 34.2

Evidence-Based Suggestions for a Happier Life

- **Take control of your time.** Happy people feel in control of their lives: Set goals and divide them into daily aims. We all tend to overestimate how much we will accomplish in any given day, but the good news is that we generally *underestimate* how much we can accomplish in a year, given just a little daily progress.

- **Act happy.** Research shows that people who are manipulated into a smiling expression feel better. So put on a happy face. Talk *as if* you feel positive self-esteem, are optimistic, and are outgoing. We can often act our way into a happier state of mind.

- **Seek work and leisure that engage your skills.** Happy people often are in a zone called *flow*—absorbed in tasks that challenge but don't overwhelm them. Passive forms of leisure (watching TV) often provide less flow experience than exercising, socializing, or expressing artistic interests.

- **Buy shared experiences rather than things.** Money buys more happiness when spent on experiences, especially socially shared experiences, that you look forward to, enjoy, remember, and talk about (Caprariello & Reis, 2013; Carter & Gilovich, 2010; Kumar & Gilovich, 2013, 2015). As pundit Art Buchwald said, "The best things in life aren't things."

- **Join the "movement" movement.** Aerobic exercise can relieve mild depression and anxiety as it promotes health and energy. Sound minds reside in sound bodies.

- **Give your body the sleep it wants.** Happy people live active lives yet reserve time for renewing sleep. Sleep debt results in fatigue, diminished alertness, and gloomy moods. If you sleep now, you'll smile later.

- **Give priority to close relationships.** Compared with unhappy people, happy people engage in less superficial small talk and more meaningful conversations (Mehl et al., 2010). Resolve to nurture your closest relationships by *not* taking your loved ones for granted: Give them the sort of kindness and affirmation you give others. Relationships matter.

- **Focus and find meaning beyond self.** Reach out to those in need. Perform acts of kindness. Happiness increases helpfulness, but doing good also makes us feel good. We feel happier when our life has meaning and purpose.

- **Challenge your negative thinking.** Reframe "I failed" to "I can learn from this." Remind yourself that stuff happens, and that in a month or a year, this bad experience may not seem like that big a deal.

- **Count your blessings and record your gratitude.** Keeping a gratitude journal heightens well-being (Davis et al., 2016). Take time to savor positive experiences and achievements, and to appreciate why they occurred (Sheldon & Lyubomirsky, 2012). Express your gratitude to others.

- **Nurture your spiritual self.** Meditation helps us stay steady, emotionally. And for many people, faith provides a support community, a reason to focus beyond self, and a sense of purpose and hope. That helps explain why people active in faith communities report greater-than-average happiness and often cope well with crises.

If we can enhance our happiness on an *individual* level, could we use happiness research to refocus our *national* priorities more on the pursuit of happiness? Many psychologists believe we could. Ed Diener (2006, 2009, 2013), supported by 52 colleagues, has proposed ways in which nations might measure national well-being. Happiness research offers new ways to assess the impacts of various public policies, argue Diener and his colleagues (Diener et al., 2015). Happy societies are not only prosperous, but also places where people trust one another, feel free, and enjoy close relationships (Helliwell et al., 2013; Oishi & Schimmack, 2010a). Thus, in debates about the minimum wage, economic inequality, tax rates, divorce laws, health care, and city planning, people's psychological well-being can be a consideration. Many political leaders agree: 43 nations have begun measuring their citizens' well-being (Diener et al., 2015). Britain's Annual Population Survey, for example, asks its citizens how satisfied they are with their lives, how worthwhile they judge their lives, and how happy and how anxious they felt yesterday (ONS, 2015).

 (ASK YOURSELF)

Were you surprised by any of the findings related to happiness? What things might you change in your life to increase your happiness?

🔒 **RETRIEVE IT** • • •   *ANSWERS IN APPENDIX E*

RI-3 Which of the following factors does NOT predict self-reported happiness?

a. Age

b. Personality traits

c. Sleep and exercise

d. Active religious faith

🔒 **REVIEW** **HEALTH AND HAPPINESS**

⏵ Learning Objectives

TEST YOURSELF Answer these repeated Learning Objective Questions on your own (before checking the answers in Appendix D) to improve your retention of the concepts (McDaniel et al., 2009, 2015).

34-1 In what two ways do people try to alleviate stress?

34-2 How does a perceived lack of control affect health?

34-3 Why is self-control important, and can our self-control be depleted?

34-4 How does an optimistic outlook affect health and longevity?

34-5 How does social support promote good health?

34-6 How effective is aerobic exercise as a way to manage stress and improve well-being?

34-7 In what ways might relaxation and meditation influence stress and health?

34-8 What is the *faith factor*, and what are some possible explanations for the link between faith and health?

34-9 What is the *feel-good, do-good phenomenon*, and what is the focus of positive psychology research?

34-10 How do time, wealth, adaptation, and comparison affect our happiness levels?

34-11 What predicts happiness, and how can we be happier?

⏵ Terms and Concepts to Remember

TEST YOURSELF Write down the definition yourself, then check your answer on the referenced page.

coping, **p. 395**

problem-focused coping, **p. 395**

emotion-focused coping, **p. 395**

personal control, **p. 396**

learned helplessness, **p. 396**

external locus of control, **p. 396**

internal locus of control, **p. 396**

self-control, **p. 398**

aerobic exercise, **p. 401**

mindfulness meditation, **p. 404**

feel-good, do-good phenomenon, **p. 407**

positive psychology, **p. 407**

subjective well-being, **p. 407**

adaptation-level phenomenon, **p. 411**

relative deprivation, **p. 411**

⏵ Experience the Testing Effect

TEST YOURSELF Answer the following questions on your own first, then check your answers in Appendix E.

1. When faced with a situation over which you feel you have little control, you are more likely to turn to _____ (emotion/problem)-focused coping.

2. Seligman's research showed that a dog will respond with learned helplessness if it has received repeated shocks and has had

   a. the opportunity to escape.

   b. no control over the shocks.

   c. pain or discomfort.

   d. no food or water prior to the shocks.

3. When elderly patients take an active part in managing their own care and surroundings, their morale and health tend to improve. Such findings indicate that people do better when they experience an _____ (internal/external) locus of control.

4. People who have close relationships are less likely to die prematurely than those who do not, supporting the idea that

   a. social ties can be a source of stress.

   b. gender influences longevity.

   c. Type A behavior is responsible for many premature deaths.

   d. social support has a beneficial effect on health.

5. Because it triggers the release of mood-boosting neurotransmitters such as norepinephrine, serotonin, and the endorphins, _____ exercise raises energy levels and helps alleviate depression and anxiety.

6. Research on the faith factor has found that
   a. pessimists tend to be healthier than optimists.
   b. our expectations influence our feelings of stress.
   c. religiously active people tend to outlive those who are not religiously active.
   d. religious engagement promotes social isolation and repression.

7. One of the most consistent findings of psychological research is that happy people are also
   a. more likely to express anger.
   b. generally luckier than others.
   c. concentrated in the wealthier nations.
   d. more likely to help others.

8. _____ psychology is a scientific field of study focused on how humans thrive and flourish.

9. After moving to a new apartment, you find the street noise irritatingly loud, but after a while it no longer bothers you. This reaction illustrates the
   a. relative deprivation principle.
   b. adaptation-level phenomenon.
   c. feel-good, do-good phenomenon.
   d. catharsis principle.

10. A philosopher observed that we cannot escape envy, because there will always be someone more successful, more accomplished, or richer with whom to compare ourselves. In psychology, this observation is embodied in the _____ _____ principle.

Continue testing yourself with **LearningCurve** or **Achieve Read & Practice** to learn and remember most effectively.

Social Psychology

MODULES 35–37

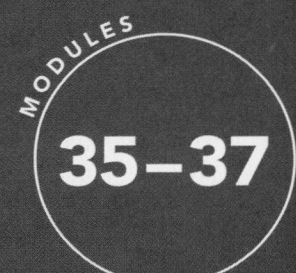

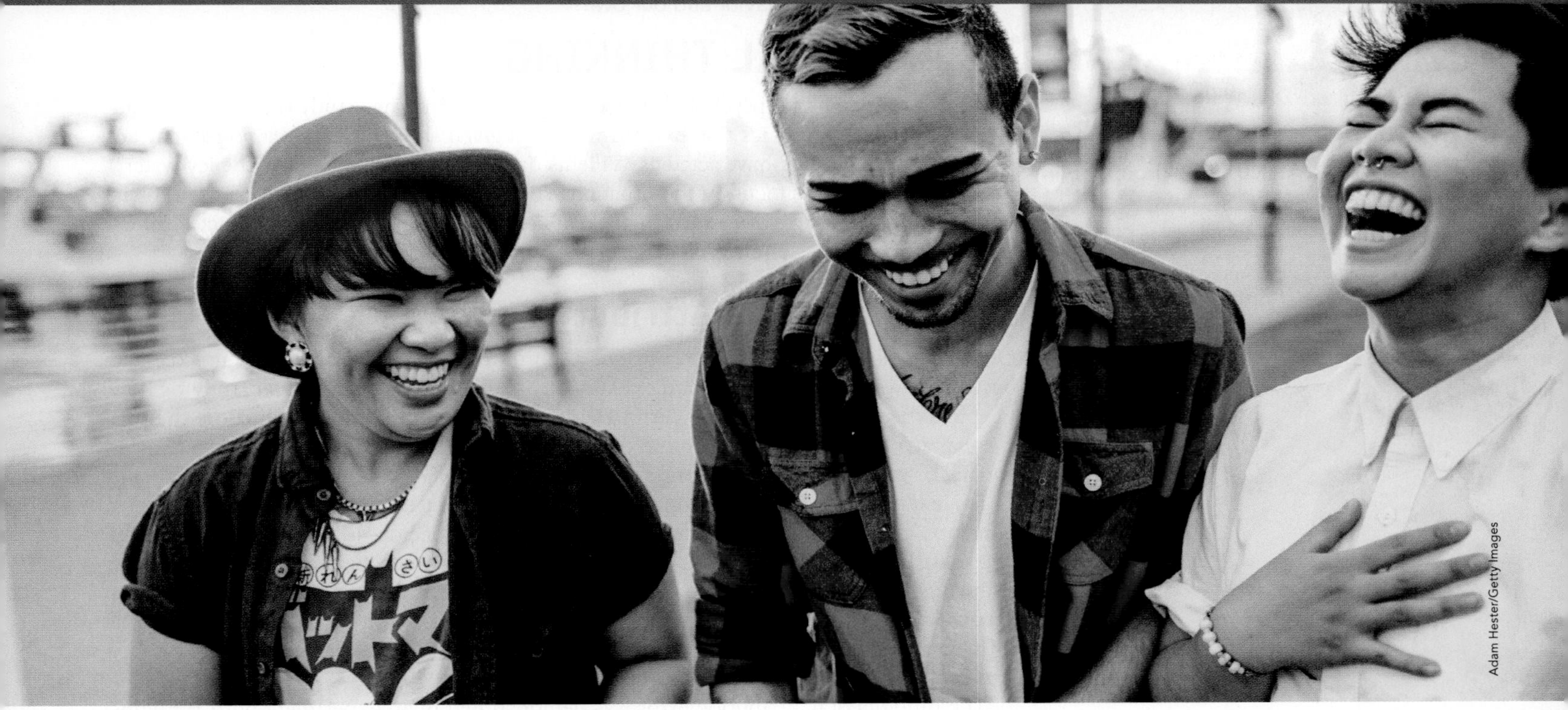

Adam Hester/Getty Images

Dirk Willems faced a moment of decision in 1569. Threatened with torture and death as a member of a persecuted religious minority, he escaped from his Asperen, Holland, prison and fled across an ice-covered pond. His stronger and heavier jailer pursued him but fell through the ice and, unable to climb out, pleaded for help.

With his freedom in front of him, Willems acted with ultimate selflessness. He turned back and rescued his pursuer, who, under orders, took him back to captivity. A few weeks later Willems was condemned to be "executed with fire, until death ensues." For his martyrdom, present-day Asperen has named a street in honor of its folk hero (Toews, 2004).

What drives people to feel contempt for minority-group members, such as Dirk Willems, and to act so spitefully? What motivates people, such as his jailer, to carry out unfair orders? And what inspired the selflessness of Willems' response, and of so many who have died trying to save others? Indeed, what motivates any of us who volunteer kindness and generosity?

As such examples demonstrate, we are social animals. We cannot live for ourselves alone. Your life is connected by "a thousand fibres" through which "run your actions as causes, and return to you as effects" (Melvill, 1855). *Social psychologists* explore these connections by scientifically studying how we *think about* and *influence* others (Module 35), and also how we *relate to* one another (Modules 36 and 37). ▶

OVERVIEW OF MODULES

AN ETCHING OF DIRK WILLEMS BY DUTCH ARTIST JAN LUYKEN (from *The Martyrs Mirror*, 1685)

Unlike sociology, which studies societies and social groupings, social psychologists focus more on how *individuals* view and affect one another.

(35) Social Thinking and Social Influence

LEARNING OBJECTIVE QUESTION (LOQ)

35-1 What do social psychologists study? How do we tend to explain others' behavior and our own?

SOCIAL THINKING

Personality psychologists focus on the person. They study the personal traits and dynamics that explain why, in a given situation, *different people* may act differently. (Would you have acted as Willems did, helping his jailer out of the icy water?) **Social psychologists** focus on the situation. They study the social influences that explain why *the same person* acts differently in *different situations*. (Might the jailer have acted differently—opting not to march Willems back to jail—under other circumstances?)

The Fundamental Attribution Error

Our social behavior arises from our social thinking. Especially when the unexpected occurs, we want to understand and explain why people act as they do. After studying how people explain others' behavior, Fritz Heider (1958) proposed an **attribution theory:** We can attribute the behavior to the person's stable, enduring traits (a *dispositional attribution*), or we can attribute it to the situation (a *situational attribution*).

For example, in class, we notice that Juliette seldom talks. Over coffee, Jack talks nonstop. That must be the sort of people they are, we decide. Juliette must be shy and Jack outgoing. Such attributions—to their dispositions—can be valid. People do have enduring personality traits. But sometimes we fall prey to the **fundamental attribution error** (Ross, 1977): We overestimate the influence of personality and underestimate the influence of situations. In class, Jack may be as quiet as Juliette. Catch Juliette at a party and you may hardly recognize your quiet classmate.

The fundamental attribution error was demonstrated in an experiment with Williams College students (Napolitan & Goethals, 1979). Students talked, one at a time, with a woman who acted either cold and critical or warm and friendly. Before the conversations, the researchers told half the students that the woman's behavior would be spontaneous. They told the other half the truth—that they had instructed her to *act* friendly or unfriendly.

Did hearing the truth affect students' impressions of the woman? Not at all! If the woman acted friendly, both groups decided she really was a warm person. If she acted unfriendly, both decided she really was a cold person. They attributed her behavior to her personal disposition *even when told that her behavior was situational*—that she was merely acting that way for the purposes of the experiment.

We all commit the fundamental attribution error. Outside their assigned roles, professors seem less professorial, presidents less presidential, managers less managerial.

WHAT FACTORS AFFECT OUR ATTRIBUTIONS? One factor is culture. Westerners more often attribute behavior to people's personal traits. People in East Asian cultures are somewhat more sensitive to the power of the situation (Kitayama et al., 2009; Riemer et al., 2014). In experiments that asked people to view scenes, such as a big fish swimming, Americans focused more on the attributes of the individual fish. Japanese viewers focused more on the scene—the situation (Chua et al., 2005; Nisbett, 2003).

Another factor is *whose* behavior. When we explain *our own* behavior, we are sensitive to how behavior changes with the situation (Idson & Mischel, 2001). We also are

social psychology the scientific study of how we think about, influence, and relate to one another.

attribution theory the theory that we explain someone's behavior by crediting either the situation or the person's disposition.

fundamental attribution error the tendency for observers, when analyzing others' behavior, to underestimate the impact of the situation and to overestimate the impact of personal disposition.

sensitive to the power of the situation when we explain the behavior of people we have seen in many different contexts. We more often commit the fundamental attribution error when a stranger acts badly. Having only seen that enraged fan screaming at the referee in the heat of competition, we may assume he is an angry person. But outside the stadium he may be a good neighbor and a great parent.

Would taking an observer's viewpoint make us more aware of our own personal style? Researchers tested this idea by using separate cameras to film two people interacting. When they showed each person a replay of the interaction—filmed from the other person's perspective—participants credited their own behavior more to their disposition, much as an observer typically would (Lassiter & Irvine, 1986; Storms, 1973).

Two important exceptions to our usual view of our own actions: Our deliberate and *admirable* actions we often attribute to our own good reasons, not to the situation (Malle, 2006; Malle et al., 2007). And as we age, we tend to attribute our younger selves' behavior mostly to our traits (Pronin & Ross, 2006). In five or ten years, your current self may seem like another person.

HOW DO OUR ATTRIBUTIONS MATTER? The way we explain others' actions, attributing them to the person or the situation, can have important real-life effects (Fincham & Bradbury, 1993; Fletcher et al., 1990). Does a warm greeting reflect romantic interest or social courtesy? Does a manager's tart-tongued remark reflect a job threat or a bad day? Was a shooting malicious or an act of self-defense? In one study, 181 U.S. state judges gave lighter sentences to a violent offender who a scientist testified had a gene that altered brain areas related to aggressiveness (Aspinwall et al., 2012). Attributions matter.

Do you attribute poverty or unemployment to social circumstances, or to personal traits and bad choices? In Britain, India, Australia, and the United States, political conservatives have tended to attribute responsibility to the personal dispositions of the poor and unemployed (Furnham, 1982; Pandey et al., 1982; Wagstaff, 1982; Zucker & Weiner, 1993). "People generally get what they deserve. Those who take initiative can choose to get ahead." In experiments, those who reflect on the power of choice—either by recalling their own choices or taking note of another's choices—become more likely to think that people get what they deserve (Savani & Rattan, 2012). Political liberals, and those not primed to consider the power of choice, are more likely to blame past and present situations: "If you or I had to live with the same poor education, lack of opportunity, and discrimination, would we be any better off?"

The point to remember: Our attributions—to a person's disposition or to the situation—have real consequences.

Some 7 in 10 college women report having experienced a man misattributing her friendliness as a sexual come-on (Jacques-Tiura et al., 2007).

"If the King destroys a man, that's proof to the King it must have been a bad man." —Thomas Cromwell, in Robert Bolt's *A Man for All Seasons*, 1960

LaunchPad For a quick interactive tutorial, engage online with **Concept Practice: Making Attributions.**

DISPOSITIONAL VERSUS SITUATIONAL ATTRIBUTIONS Should the 2015 slaughter of nine African-Americans attending a church Bible study in Charleston, West Virginia, be attributed to the shooter's disposition? (Nikki Haley, then South Carolina governor: "There is one person to blame here. A person filled with hate.") To America's gun culture? (U.S. President Barack Obama: "At some point, we as a country will have to reckon with the fact that this type of mass violence does not happen in other advanced countries . . . with this kind of frequency.") Or to both?

attitude feelings, often influenced by our beliefs, that predispose us to respond in a particular way to objects, people, and events.

peripheral route persuasion occurs when people are influenced by incidental cues, such as a speaker's attractiveness.

central route persuasion occurs when interested people focus on the arguments and respond with favorable thoughts.

foot-in-the-door phenomenon the tendency for people who have first agreed to a small request to comply later with a larger request.

role a set of expectations (*norms*) about a social position, defining how those in the position ought to behave.

Attitudes and Actions

LOQ 35-2 How do attitudes and actions interact?

Attitudes are feelings, often influenced by our beliefs, that predispose our reactions to objects, people, and events. If we *believe* someone is threatening us, we may *feel* fear and anger toward the person and *act* defensively. The traffic between our attitudes and our actions is two-way. Our attitudes affect our actions. And our actions affect our attitudes (much as our emotional expressions can affect our emotions).

ATTITUDES AFFECT ACTIONS In any debate, people on both sides aim to persuade. These efforts to *persuade* generally take two forms:

- **Peripheral route persuasion** uses attention-getting cues to trigger emotion-based snap judgments. One experiment gave some people information that debunked the vaccines-cause-autism myth; others were shown photos of children suffering mumps, measles, or rubella, along with a parent's description of measles. Only those given the vivid disease depictions became more supportive of vaccines (Horne et al., 2015). Endorsements by beautiful or famous people also can influence people's attitudes, whether the judgment is about choosing a political candidate or buying the latest tech gadget. When environmental activist and actor Leonardo DiCaprio urges action to counter climate change, or when Pope Francis (2015) states that "Climate change is a global problem with grave implications," they hope to harness their appeal for peripheral route persuasion. The same is true of heart-tugging ads for greeting cards, pet adoption, or support for the starving.

- **Central route persuasion** offers evidence and arguments that aim to trigger careful thinking. To persuade buyers to purchase a new gadget, an ad might itemize all the latest features. To marshal support for climate change intervention, effective arguments have focused on the accumulating greenhouse gases, melting Arctic ice, rising world temperatures and seas, and increasing extreme weather (van der Linden et al., 2015). Central route persuasion works well for people who are naturally analytical or involved in an issue. And because it is more thoughtful and less superficial, it is more durable.

Persuaders try to influence our behavior by changing our attitudes. But situational factors, such as strong social pressures, can override the attitude-behavior connection (Wallace et al., 2005). Politicians may vote as their supporters demand, despite privately disagreeing (Nagourney, 2002).

Attitudes are especially likely to affect behavior when external influences are minimal, and when the attitude is stable, specific to the behavior, and easily recalled (Glasman & Albarracín, 2006). One experiment used vivid, easily recalled information to persuade White sun-tanning college students that repetitive tanning put them at risk for future skin cancer. One month later, 72 percent of the participants, and only 16 percent of those in a waitlist control group, had lighter skin (McClendon & Prentice-Dunn, 2001). Persuasion changed attitudes (about skin cancer risk), which changed behavior (less tanning).

FIGURE 35.1

ATTITUDES FOLLOW BEHAVIOR Cooperative actions, such as those performed by people on sports teams (including Germany, shown here celebrating a World Cup victory), feed mutual liking. Such attitudes, in turn, promote positive behavior.

Actions

Matthias Hangst/Getty Images

Attitudes

ACTIONS AFFECT ATTITUDES Now consider a more surprising principle: Not only will we stand up for what we believe, but we also will more strongly believe in what we have stood up for. Many streams of evidence confirm that *attitudes follow behavior* (**FIGURE 35.1**).

THE FOOT-IN-THE-DOOR PHENOMENON How do you think you would react if someone induced you to act against your beliefs? In many cases, people adjust their attitudes. During the Korean war, many U.S. prisoners were held in Chinese communist war camps. The captors secured prisoners' collaboration in various activities, ranging from simple tasks (running errands to gain privileges) to more serious actions (false confessions, informing on other prisoners, and divulging military information). After doing so, the prisoners sometimes adjusted their beliefs to be more consistent with their public acts (Lifton, 1961). When the war ended, 21 prisoners chose to stay with the communists. Some others returned home convinced that communism was a good thing for Asia (though not literally "brainwashed," as has often been said).

The Chinese captors succeeded in part thanks to the **foot-in-the-door phenomenon:** They knew that people who agree to a small request will find it easier to comply later with a larger one. The captors began with harmless requests, such as copying a trivial statement, but gradually escalated their demands (Schein, 1956). The next statement to be copied might list flaws of capitalism. Then, to gain privileges, the prisoners would move up to participating in group discussions, writing self-criticisms, and finally uttering public confessions. The point is simple: To get people to agree to something big, start small and build (Cialdini, 1993). A trivial act makes the next act easier. Telling a small lie paves the way to telling a bigger lie. Succumb to a temptation and the next temptation becomes harder to resist.

In dozens of experiments, researchers have coaxed people into acting against their attitudes or violating their moral standards, with the same result: Doing becomes believing. After giving in to an order to harm an innocent victim—by making nasty comments or delivering presumed electric shocks—people begin to look down on their victim. After speaking or writing on behalf of a position they have qualms about, they begin to believe their own words.

Fortunately, the attitudes-follow-behavior principle works with good deeds as well. In one classic experiment, researchers sought permission to place a large "Drive Carefully" sign in people's front yards (Freedman & Fraser, 1966). The 17 percent rate of agreement soared to 76 percent among those who first did a small favor—placing a 3-inch-high "Be a Safe Driver" sign in their window.

The foot-in-the-door tactic has helped boost charitable contributions, blood donations, and U.S. school desegregation. With the passage of the Civil Rights Act of 1964, school desegregation became law. In the years that followed, White Americans expressed diminishing racial prejudice. And as Americans in different regions came to act more alike—thanks to more uniform national standards against discrimination—they began to think more alike.

ROLE PLAYING AFFECTS ATTITUDES When you adopt a new **role**—when you become a college student, marry, or begin a new job—you strive to follow the social prescriptions. At first, your behaviors may feel phony, because you are *acting* a role. Soldiers may at first feel they are playing war games. Newlyweds may feel they are "playing house." Before long, however, what began as playacting in the theater of life becomes *you*. As *Mad Men's* Bobbie Barrett advised, "Pick a job and then become the person [who] does it."

Role playing was dramatized in one famous, controversial study in which male college students volunteered to spend time in a simulated prison. Stanford psychologist Philip Zimbardo (1972) randomly assigned some volunteers to be guards. He gave them uniforms, clubs, and whistles and instructed them to enforce rules. Others became prisoners, locked in barren cells and forced to wear humiliating outfits. For a day or two, the volunteers self-consciously played their roles. But then, reports Zimbardo, most guards developed disparaging attitudes and "became tyrannical," devising cruel and degrading routines. One by one, the prisoners broke down, rebelled, or became passively resigned. After only six days, Zimbardo called off the study.

Critics question the reliability of Zimbardo's results (Griggs, 2014; Reicher & Haslam, 2006). Others argue that Zimbardo stage-managed the experiment to get his predicted results, and that volunteers for a "prison experiment" would have had above-average levels of aggressiveness and authoritarianism (Bartels et al., 2016; McFarland & Carnahan, 2009). But this much seems true: There is power in the situation. In the real world, role playing has even been used to train people to become torturers (Staub, 1989). In the early 1970s, the Greek military government eased men into their roles. First, a trainee stood guard outside an interrogation cell. After this foot-in-the-door step, he stood guard inside. Only then was he ready to become actively involved in the questioning and torture. In one study of German men, military training toughened their personalities, leaving them less agreeable even five years later, after leaving the military (Jackson et al., 2012). Every time we act like the people around us, we slightly change ourselves to be more like them, and less like who we used to be.

Yet people differ. In real-life atrocity-producing situations, some people have succumbed to the situation and others have not (Haslam & Reicher, 2007, 2012; Mastroianni & Reed, 2006; Zimbardo, 2007). Person and situation interact.

ENGAGE  Experiments also reveal a *door-in-the-face* effect: Approach someone with an unreasonable request ("Could you volunteer every day for the next two weeks?"). After you get turned down (the door in the face), a follow-up moderate request becomes more acceptable ("Could you volunteer for the next 30 minutes?").

ENGAGE (ASK YOURSELF)

Do you have an attitude or tendency you would like to change? Using the attitudes-follow-behavior principle, how might you go about changing that attitude?

"Fake it until you make it." —Alcoholics Anonymous saying

NEW NURSE Pulling on scrubs for the first time can feel like playing dress-up. But over time that role defines the player, as she jumps in to the day-to-day work and follows the social cues in her new environment.

Paul Burns/Blend Images/Alamy

COGNITIVE DISSONANCE: RELIEF FROM TENSION So far, we have seen that actions can affect attitudes, sometimes turning prisoners into collaborators, and doubters into believers. But why? One explanation is that when we become aware that our attitudes and actions don't coincide, we experience tension, or *cognitive dissonance*. Indeed, the brain regions that become active when people experience other forms of mental tension and negative arousal also become active when people experience cognitive dissonance (Harmon-Jones et al., 2015; Kitayama et al., 2013). To relieve this mental tension, according to Leon Festinger's (1957) **cognitive dissonance theory,** we often bring our attitudes into line with our actions.

RETAIN 🔒 📺 **LaunchPad** To check your understanding of cognitive dissonance, engage online with **Concept Practice: Cognitive Dissonance.**

ENGAGE 💡 Dozens of experiments have tested the cognitive dissonance theory. Many have made people feel responsible for behavior that clashed with their attitudes and had foreseeable consequences. As a participant in one of these experiments, you might agree for a measly $2 to help a researcher by writing an essay supporting something you don't believe in (perhaps a tuition increase). Feeling responsible for the statements (which are inconsistent with your attitudes), you would probably feel dissonance, especially if you thought your essay might influence an administrator. To reduce the uncomfortable tension, you might start believing your phony words. It's as if we rationalize, "If I chose to do it (or say it), I must believe in it." The less coerced and more responsible we feel for a troubling act, the more dissonance we feel. The more dissonance we feel, the more motivated we are to find and project consistency, such as changing our attitudes to help justify the act.

The attitudes-follow-behavior principle has a heartening implication: We cannot directly control all our feelings, but we can influence them by altering our behavior. If we are depressed, we can alter our attributions and explain events in more positive terms, with more self-acceptance and fewer self-put-downs (Rubenstein et al., 2016). If we are unloving, we can become more loving by behaving *as if* we were—by doing thoughtful things, expressing affection, giving affirmation. "Each time you ask yourself, 'How should I act?'" observes Robert Levine (2016), "you are also asking, 'Who is the person I want to become?'" That helps explain why teens' doing volunteer work promotes a compassionate identity. Pretense can become reality. Conduct sculpts character. What we do we become.

The point to remember: We can act ourselves into a way of thinking about as easily as we can think ourselves into a way of acting.

"Sit all day in a moping posture, sigh, and reply to everything with a dismal voice, and your melancholy lingers. . . . If we wish to conquer undesirable emotional tendencies in ourselves, we must . . . go through the outward movements of those contrary dispositions which we prefer to cultivate." —William James, *Principles of Psychology* (1890)

🔒 **RETRIEVE IT • • •**   *ANSWERS IN APPENDIX E*

RI-1 Driving to school one snowy day, Marco narrowly misses a car that slides through a red light. "Slow down! What a terrible driver," he thinks to himself. Moments later, Marco himself slips through an intersection and yelps, "Wow! These roads are awful. The city plows need to get out here." What social psychology principle has Marco just demonstrated? Explain.

RI-2 How do our attitudes and our actions affect each other?

RI-3 When people act in a way that is not in keeping with their attitudes, and then change their attitudes to match those actions, _____ _____ theory attempts to explain why.

SOCIAL INFLUENCE

Social psychology's great lesson is the enormous power of social influence. This influence stems in part from social **norms**—rules for expected and accepted behavior. On campus, jeans are the norm; on New York's Wall Street or London's Bond Street, business attire is expected. When we know how to act, how to groom, how to talk, life functions smoothly.

But sometimes social pressure moves people in dreadful directions. Isolated with others who share their grievances, dissenters may gradually become rebels, and rebels may become terrorists. Shootings, suicides, bomb threats, and airplane hijackings all have a curious tendency to come in clusters. After a mass killing (of four or more people), the probability of another such attack increases for the ensuing 13 days (Towers et al., 2015). Let's start by considering the nature of our cultural influences. Then we will examine the pull of our social strings. How strong are they? How do they operate? When do we break them?

Cultural Influences

LOQ 35-3   How does culture affect our behavior?

Compared with the narrow path taken by flies, fish, and foxes, the road along which environment drives us is wider. The mark of our species—nature's great gift to us—is our ability to learn and adapt. We come equipped with a huge cerebral hard drive ready to receive cultural software.

Culture is the behaviors, ideas, attitudes, values, and traditions shared by a group of people and transmitted from one generation to the next (Brislin, 1988; Cohen, 2009). Human nature, noted Roy Baumeister (2005), seems designed for culture. We are social animals, but more. Wolves are social animals; they live and hunt in packs. Ants are incessantly social, never alone. But "culture is a better way of being social," observed Baumeister. Wolves function pretty much as they did 10,000 years ago. We enjoy electricity, indoor plumbing, antibiotics, and the internet—things unknown to most of our ancestors.

We can thank our culture's mastery of language for this *preservation of innovation*. The *division of labor* also helps. Although two lucky people get their names on this book (which transmits accumulated cultural wisdom), the product actually results from the coordination and commitment of a team of gifted people, no one of whom could produce it alone.

Across cultures, we differ in our language, money, sports, religion, and customs. But beneath these differences lies our great similarity—our capacity for culture. Culture works. It transmits the customs and beliefs that enable us to communicate, to exchange money for things, to play, to eat, and to drive with agreed-upon rules and without crashing into one another.

VARIATION ACROSS CULTURES   We see our adaptability in cultural variations among our beliefs and our values, in how we nurture our children and bury our dead, and in what we wear (or whether we wear anything at all). We are ever mindful that the worldwide readers of this book are culturally diverse. You and your ancestors reach from Australia to Africa and from Singapore to Sweden.

"Have you ever noticed how one example—good or bad—can prompt others to follow? How one illegally parked car can give permission for others to do likewise? How one racial joke can fuel another?" —Marian Wright Edelman, *The Measure of Our Success*, 1992

cognitive dissonance theory the theory that we act to reduce the discomfort (dissonance) we feel when two of our thoughts (cognitions) are inconsistent. For example, when we become aware that our attitudes and our actions clash, we can reduce the resulting dissonance by changing our attitudes.

norms understood rules for accepted and expected behavior. Norms prescribe "proper" behavior.

culture the enduring behaviors, ideas, attitudes, values, and traditions shared by a group of people and transmitted from one generation to the next.

Riding along with a unified culture is like biking with the wind: As it carries us along, we hardly notice it. When we try biking *against* the wind, we feel its force. Face-to-face with a different culture, we become aware of the cultural winds. Stationed in Iraq, Afghanistan, and Kuwait, American and European soldiers were reminded how liberal their home cultures were. Each cultural group evolves its own norms. The British have a norm for orderly waiting in line. Many South Asians use only the right hand for eating. Sometimes social expectations seem oppressive: "Why should it matter what I wear?" Yet, norms—how to greet, how to eat—grease the social machinery.

When cultures collide, their differing norms often befuddle. Should we greet people by shaking hands, bowing, or kissing one or both cheeks? Knowing what sorts of gestures and compliments are culturally appropriate helps us avoid accidental insults and embarrassment.

VARIATION OVER TIME Like biological creatures, cultures vary and compete for resources, and thus evolve over time (Mesoudi, 2009). Consider how rapidly cultures may change. English poet Geoffrey Chaucer (1342–1400) is separated from a modern Briton by only 25 generations, but the two would have difficulty communicating. At the beginning of the last century, your ancestors lived in a world without cars, radio broadcasting, or electric lighting. And in the thin slice of history since 1960, most Western cultures have changed with astonishing speed. People enjoy expanded human rights. Middle-class people enjoy the convenience of air-conditioned housing, online shopping, anywhere-anytime electronic communication, and—enriched by doubled per-person real income—eating out more than twice as often as did their grandparents.

But some changes seem not so wonderfully positive. Had you fallen asleep in the United States in 1960 and awakened today, you would open your eyes to a culture with more depression and more economic inequality. You would also find North Americans—like their counterparts in Britain, Australia, and New Zealand—spending more hours at work, fewer hours with friends and family, and fewer hours asleep (BLS, 2011; Putnam, 2000).

Whether we love or loathe these changes, we cannot fail to be impressed by their breathtaking speed. And we cannot explain them by changes in the human gene pool, which evolves far too slowly to account for high-speed cultural transformations. Cultures vary. Cultures change. And cultures shape our lives.

Conformity: Complying With Social Pressures

LOQ 35-4 How is social contagion a form of conformity, and how do conformity experiments reveal the power of social influence?

"Most people are other people. Their thoughts are someone else's opinions, their lives a mimicry." —Irish dramatist Oscar Wilde "The Soul of Man Under Socialism," 1895

SOCIAL CONTAGION Fish swim in schools. Birds fly in flocks. And humans, too, tend to go with their group, to do what it does and think what it thinks. Behavior is contagious. If one of us yawns, laughs, coughs, scratches, stares at the sky, or checks our phone, others in our group will often do the same (Holle et al., 2012). Even just reading about yawning increases people's yawning (Provine, 2012), as perhaps you have noticed? Yawn mimicry also occurs in other species—among chimpanzees, for example (Anderson et al., 2004)—and even across species: Dogs more often yawn after observing their owners' yawn (Silva et al., 2012).

Tanya Chartrand and John Bargh (1999) call this social contagion the *chameleon effect,* likening it to chameleon lizards' ability to take on the color of their surroundings. They captured it by having students work in a room alongside another person (actually a "confederate" working for the experimenters). Sometimes the confederates rubbed their own face. Sometimes they shook their foot. Sure enough, students tended to rub their face with the face-rubbing person and shake their foot with the foot-shaking person.

Social contagion is not confined to behavior. We human chameleons also take on the emotional tones of those around us—their expressions, postures, and voice tones—and even their grammar (Ireland & Pennebaker, 2010). Just hearing someone reading a neutral text in either a happy- or sad-sounding voice creates *mood contagion* in listeners (Neumann & Strack, 2000).

This natural mimicry enables us to *empathize*—to feel what others are feeling. This helps explain why we feel happier around happy people than around depressed people. It also helps explain why studies of groups of British workers have revealed *mood linkage*—or the sharing of moods (Totterdell et al., 1998). Empathic mimicking fosters fondness (Chartrand & van Baaren, 2009; Lakin et al., 2008). Perhaps you've noticed that when someone nods their head as you do and echoes your words, you feel a certain rapport and liking?

Suggestibility and mimicry sometimes lead to tragedy. In the eight days following the 1999 shooting rampage at Colorado's Columbine High School, every U.S. state except Vermont experienced threats of violence. Pennsylvania alone recorded 60 such threats (Cooper, 1999). Spikes in suicide rates sometimes follow a highly publicized suicide (Phillips et al., 1985, 1989).

What causes behavior clusters? Do people act similarly because of their influence on one another? Or because they are simultaneously exposed to the same events and conditions? Seeking answers to such questions, social psychologists have conducted experiments on conformity.

THAT CONTAGIOUS LAUGH
Laughter, like yawns, is infectious. That's what "Chewbacca Mom's" (Candace Payne's) viewers discovered after her spontaneous hilarity became, with 164 million views, Facebook Live's most watched 2016 video (tinyurl.com/ThatLaugh).

"When I see synchrony and mimicry—whether it concerns yawning, laughing, dancing, or aping—I see social connection and bonding."
—Primatologist Frans de Waal "The Empathy Instinct," 2009

NON SEQUITUR   by WILEY

BANKING on the YOUTH MARKET...

TATTOO & PIERCING

BE LIKE ALL YOUR FRIENDS AND EXPRESS YOUR INDIVIDUALITY   OPEN

CONFORMITY AND SOCIAL NORMS Suggestibility and mimicry are subtle types of **conformity**—adjusting our behavior or thinking toward some group standard. To study conformity, Solomon Asch (1955) devised a simple test. Imagine yourself a participant in a supposed study of visual perception. You arrive in time to take a seat at a table with five other people. The experimenter asks the group to state, one by one, which of three comparison lines is identical to a standard line. You see clearly that the answer is Line 2, and you wait your turn to say so. Your boredom begins to show when the next set of lines proves equally easy.

Now comes the third trial, and the correct answer seems just as clear-cut (**FIGURE 35.2**). But the first person gives what strikes you as a wrong answer: "Line 3." When the second person and then the third and fourth give the same wrong answer, you sit up straight and squint. When the fifth person agrees with the first four, you feel your heart begin to pound. The experimenter then looks to you for your answer. Torn between the unanimity voiced by the five others and the evidence of your own eyes, you feel tense and suddenly unsure. You hesitate before answering, wondering whether you should suffer the discomfort of being the oddball. What answer do you give?

In Asch's experiments, college students, answering questions alone, erred less than 1 percent of the time. But what happened when several others—confederates—answered incorrectly? Although most people told the truth even when others did not, Asch was disturbed by his result: More than one-third of the time, these "intelligent and well-meaning" college students were "willing to call white black" by going along with the group.

"I love the little ways you're identical to everyone else."

conformity adjusting our behavior or thinking to coincide with a group standard.

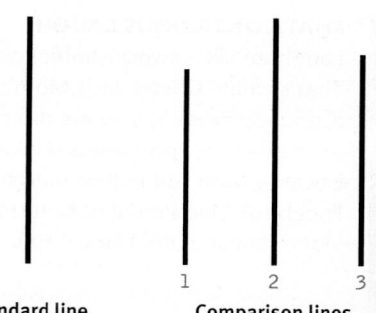

Standard line   Comparison lines

 FIGURE 35.2

ASCH'S CONFORMITY EXPERIMENTS
Which of the three comparison lines is equal to the standard line? What do you suppose most people would say after hearing five others say, "Line 3"? In this photo from one of Asch's experiments, the student in the center shows the severe discomfort that comes from disagreeing with the responses of other group members (in this case, accomplices of the experimenter).

Later investigations have not always found as much conformity as Asch found, but they have revealed that we are more likely to conform when we

- are made to feel incompetent or insecure.
- are in a group with at least three people.
- are in a group in which everyone else agrees. (If just one other person disagrees, the odds of our disagreeing greatly increase.)
- admire the group's status and attractiveness.
- have not made a prior commitment to any response.
- know that others in the group will observe our behavior.
- are from a culture that strongly encourages respect for social standards.

Why do we so often do as others do and think as they think? Why, when asked controversial questions, are students' answers more similar when they raise their hands and more diverse when they use anonymous electronic clickers (Stowell et al., 2010)? Why do we clap when others clap, eat as others eat, believe what others believe, say what others say, even see what others see?

Frequently, we conform to avoid rejection or to gain social approval (Williams & Sommer, 1997). In such cases, we are responding to **normative social influence.** We are sensitive to social norms because the price we pay for being different can be severe. We need to belong. At other times, we conform because we want to be accurate. Groups provide information, and only an uncommonly stubborn person will never listen to others. When we accept others' opinions about reality, as when reading online movie and restaurant reviews, we are responding to **informational social influence.** Sometimes it pays to assume others are right and to follow their lead. One Welsh driver set a record for the longest distance driven on the wrong side of a British divided highway—30 miles, with only one minor

TATTOOS: YESTERDAY'S NONCON-FORMITY, TODAY'S CONFORMITY?
As tattoos become perceived as fashion conformity, their popularity may wane.

normative social influence influence resulting from a person's desire to gain approval or avoid disapproval.

informational social influence influence resulting from a person's willingness to accept others' opinions about reality.

sideswipe, before the motorway ran out and police were able to puncture her tires. The driver, who was intoxicated, later explained that she thought the hundreds of other drivers coming at her were all on the wrong side of the road (Woolcock, 2004).

Is conformity good or bad? Conformity can be bad—leading people to agree with falsehoods or go along with bullying. Or it can be good—leading people to give more generously after observing others' generosity (Nook et al., 2016). The answer also depends partly on our culturally influenced values. People in many Asian, African, and Latin American countries place a higher value on *collectivism* (emphasizing group standards). Western Europeans and people in most English-speaking countries tend to prize *individualism* (emphasizing an independent self). Experiments across 17 countries have found lower conformity rates in individualist cultures (Bond & Smith, 1996).

RETAIN 🔒 📺 **LaunchPad** To review the classic conformity studies and experience a simulated experiment, visit **Topic Tutorial: PsychSim6, Everybody's Doing It!**

> 🔒 **RETRIEVE IT** • • •   *ANSWERS IN APPENDIX E*
>
> **RI-4** What is *culture,* and how does its transmission distinguish us from other social animals?
>
> **RI-5** Which of the following strengthens conformity to a group?
>
> a. Finding the group attractive
>
> b. Feeling secure
>
> c. Coming from an individualist culture
>
> d. Having made a prior commitment
>
> **RI-6** Despite her mother's pleas to use a more ergonomic backpack, Antonia insists on trying to carry all of her books to school in an oversized purse the way her fashionable friends all seem to do. Antonia is affected by what type of social influence?

Obedience: Following Orders

LOQ 35-5 What did Milgram's obedience experiments teach us about the power of social influence?

Social psychologist Stanley Milgram (1963, 1974), a high school classmate of Philip Zimbardo and later a student of Solomon Asch, knew that people often give in to social pressures. But what about outright commands? Would they respond as did those who carried out Holocaust atrocities? (Some of Milgram's family members had survived Nazi concentration camps.) To find out, he undertook what have become social psychology's most famous and controversial experiments (Benjamin & Simpson, 2009).

ENGAGE 💡 Imagine yourself as one of the nearly 1000 people who took part in Milgram's 20 experiments. You respond to an ad for participants in a Yale University psychology study of the effect of punishment on learning. Professor Milgram's assistant asks you and another person to draw slips from a hat to see who will be the "teacher" and who will be the "learner." You draw a "teacher" slip (unknown to you, both slips say "teacher"). The supposed learner, a mild and submissive-seeming man, is led to an adjoining room and strapped into a chair. From the chair, wires run through the wall to a shock machine. You sit down in front of the machine and are given your task: Teach and then test the learner on a list of word pairs. If the learner gives a wrong answer, you are to flip a switch to deliver a brief electric shock. For the first wrong answer, you will flip the switch labeled "15 Volts—Slight Shock." With each succeeding error, you will move to the next higher voltage. With each flip of a switch, lights flash and electronic switches buzz.

"Those who never retract their opinions love themselves more than they love truth." —French essayist Joseph Joubert (1754–1824)

Like humans, migrating and herding animals conform for both informational and normative reasons (Claidière & Whiten, 2012). Following others is informative; compared with solo geese, a flock of geese migrate more accurately. (There is wisdom in the crowd.) And staying with the herd also sustains group membership.

ENGAGE 💡 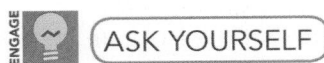 (ASK YOURSELF)

How have you found yourself conforming, or perhaps "conforming to nonconformity"? In what ways have you seen others identifying themselves with those of the same culture or subculture?

📺 **LaunchPad** See the **Video: Research Ethics** for a helpful tutorial animation.

The experiment begins, and you deliver the shocks after the first and second wrong answers. If you continue, you hear the learner grunt when you flick the third, fourth, and fifth switches. After you activate the eighth switch ("120 Volts—Moderate Shock"), the learner cries out that the shocks are painful. After the tenth switch ("150 Volts—Strong Shock"), he begins shouting: "Get me out of here! I won't be in the experiment anymore! I refuse to go on!" You draw back, but the stern experimenter prods you: "Please continue—the experiment requires that you continue." You resist, but the experimenter insists, "It is absolutely essential that you continue," or "You have no other choice, you *must* go on."

If you obey, you hear the learner shriek in apparent agony as you continue to raise the shock level after each new error. After the 330-volt level, the learner refuses to answer and falls silent. Still, the experimenter pushes you toward the final, 450-volt switch. "Ask the question," he says, "and if no correct answer is given, administer the next shock level."

Would you follow the experimenter's commands to shock someone? At what level would you refuse to obey? Before undertaking the experiments, Milgram asked nonparticipants what they would do. Most were sure they would stop soon after the learner first indicated pain, certainly before he shrieked in agony. Forty psychiatrists agreed with that prediction. Were the predictions accurate? Not even close. When Milgram conducted the experiment with other men aged 20 to 50, he was astonished. More than 60 percent complied fully—right up to the last switch. When he ran a new study, with 40 new "teachers" and a learner who complained of a "slight heart condition," the results were similar. A full 65 percent of the new teachers obeyed the experimenter right up to 450 volts (**FIGURE 35.3**). In 10 later studies, women obeyed at rates similar to men's (Blass, 1999).

Were Milgram's results a product of the 1960s American mindset? *No.* In a more recent replication, 70 percent of the participants complied up to the 150-volt point (only a modest reduction from Milgram's 83 percent at that level) (Burger, 2009). A Polish research team found 90 percent compliance to the same level (Doliński et al., 2017). And in a French reality TV show replication, 81 percent of teachers, egged on by a cheering audience, obeyed and tortured a screaming victim (Beauvois et al., 2012).

Did Milgram's teachers figure out the hoax—that no real shock was being delivered and the learner was in fact a confederate pretending to feel pain? Did they realize the experiment was really testing their willingness to comply with commands to inflict punishment? *No.* The teachers typically displayed genuine distress: They perspired, trembled, laughed nervously, and bit their lips.

Milgram's use of deception and stress triggered a debate over his research ethics. In his own defense, Milgram pointed out that, after the participants learned of the deception and actual research purposes, virtually none regretted taking part (though perhaps by then the participants had reduced their cognitive dissonance—the discomfort they

FIGURE 35.3

MILGRAM'S FOLLOW-UP OBEDIENCE EXPERIMENT In a repeat of the earlier experiment, 65 percent of the adult male "teachers" fully obeyed the experimenter's commands to continue. They did so despite the "learner's" earlier mention of a heart condition and despite hearing cries of protest after they administered what they thought were 150 volts and agonized protests after 330 volts. (Data from Milgram, 1974.)

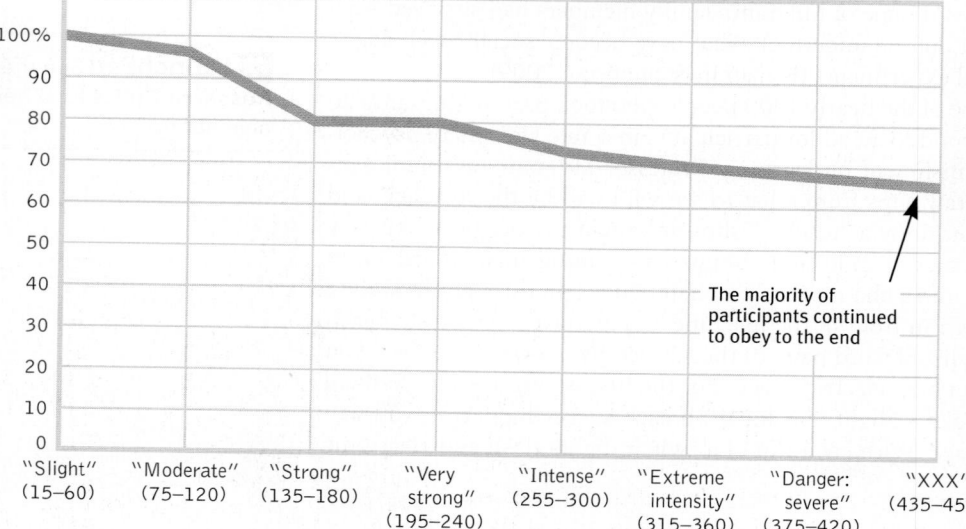

The majority of participants continued to obey to the end

Stanley Milgram, from the film "Obedience." Rights held by Alexandra Milgram

felt when their actions conflicted with their attitudes). When 40 of the teachers who had agonized most were later interviewed by a psychiatrist, none appeared to be suffering emotional aftereffects. All in all, said Milgram, the experiments provoked less enduring stress than university students experience when facing and failing big exams (Blass, 1996). Other scholars, however, after delving into Milgram's archives, report that his debriefing was less extensive and his participants' distress greater than he had suggested (Nicholson, 2011; Perry, 2013). Critics have also speculated that participants may have been identifying with the researcher and his scientific goals rather than simply being blindly obedient (Haslam et al., 2014, 2016).

In later experiments, Milgram discovered some conditions that influence people's behavior. When he varied the situation, full obedience ranged from 0 to 93 percent. Obedience was highest when

- *the person giving the orders was close at hand and was perceived to be a legitimate authority figure.* This was the case in 2005 when Temple University's basketball coach sent a 250-pound bench player, Nehemiah Ingram, into a game with instructions to commit "hard fouls." Following orders, Ingram fouled out in four minutes after breaking an opposing player's right arm.

- *the authority figure was supported by a powerful or prestigious institution.* Compliance was somewhat lower when Milgram dissociated his experiments from Yale University. People have wondered: Why, during the 1994 Rwandan Genocide, did so many Hutu citizens slaughter their Tutsi neighbors? It was partly because they were part of "a culture in which orders from above, even if evil," were understood as having the force of law (Kamatali, 2014).

- *the victim was depersonalized or at a distance, even in another room.* Similarly, many soldiers in combat either have not fired their rifles at an enemy they could see, or have not aimed them properly. Such refusals to kill are rarer among soldiers operating long-distance artillery or aircraft weapons (Padgett, 1989). Those who kill from a distance—by operating remotely piloted drones—also suffer stress, though much less posttraumatic stress than do veterans of on-the-ground conflict in Afghanistan and Iraq (Miller, 2012).

- *there were no role models for defiance.* "Teachers" did not see any other participant disobey the experimenter.

The power of legitimate, close-at-hand authorities was apparent among those who followed orders to carry out the Nazis' Holocaust atrocities. Obedience alone does not explain the Holocaust—anti-Semitic ideology produced eager killers as well (Fenigstein, 2015; Mastroianni, 2015). But obedience was a factor. In the summer of 1942, nearly 500 middle-aged German reserve police officers were dispatched to German-occupied Jozefow, Poland. On July 13, the group's visibly upset commander informed his recruits, mostly family men, of their orders. They were to round up the village's Jews, who were said to be aiding the enemy. Able-bodied men would be sent to work camps, and the rest would be shot on the spot.

The commander gave the recruits a chance to refuse to participate in the executions. Only about a dozen immediately refused. Within 17 hours, the remaining 485 officers killed 1500 helpless citizens, including women, children, and the elderly, shooting them in the back of the head as they lay face down. Hearing the victims' pleas, and seeing the gruesome results, some 20 percent of the officers did eventually dissent, managing either to miss their victims or to slip away and hide until the slaughter was over (Browning, 1992). In real life, as in Milgram's experiments, those who resisted were a minority.

A different story played out in the French village of Le Chambon. There, villagers openly defied orders to cooperate with the "New Order": They sheltered French Jews destined for deportation to Germany, and they sometimes helped them escape across the Swiss border. The villagers' Protestant ancestors had themselves been persecuted, and their pastors taught them to "resist whenever our adversaries will demand of us obedience contrary

STANDING UP FOR DEMOCRACY
Some individuals—roughly one in three in Milgram's experiments—resist social coercion, as did this unarmed man in Beijing, by single-handedly challenging an advancing line of tanks the day after the 1989 Tiananmen Square student uprising was suppressed.

Jeff Widener/AP Photo

to the orders of the Gospel" (Rochat, 1993). Ordered by police to give a list of sheltered Jews, the head pastor modeled defiance: "I don't know of Jews, I only know of human beings." At great personal risk, the people of Le Chambon made an initial commitment to resist. Throughout the long, terrible war, they suffered poverty and were punished for their disobedience. Still, supported by their beliefs, their role models, their interactions with one another, and their own initial acts, they remained defiant to the war's end.

LESSONS FROM THE CONFORMITY AND OBEDIENCE STUDIES

LOQ 35-6 What do the social influence studies teach us about ourselves? How much power do we have as individuals?

How do the laboratory experiments on social influence relate to real life? How does judging the length of a line or flicking a shock switch relate to everyday social behavior? Psychological experiments aim not to re-create the actual, complex behaviors of everyday life but to capture and explore the underlying processes that shape those behaviors. Solomon Asch and Stanley Milgram devised experiments that forced a familiar choice: Do I adhere to my own standards, even when they conflict with the expectations of others?

In Milgram's experiments and their modern replications, participants were torn. Should they respond to the pleas of the victim or the orders of the experimenter? Their moral sense warned them not to harm another, yet it also prompted them to obey the experimenter and to be a good research participant. With kindness and obedience on a collision course, obedience usually won.

These experiments demonstrated that strong social influences induce many people to conform to falsehoods or capitulate to cruelty. Milgram saw this as the fundamental lesson of this work: "Ordinary people, simply doing their jobs, and without any particular hostility on their part, can become agents in a terrible destructive process" (1974, p. 6).

Focusing on the end point—450 volts, or someone's real-life violence—we can hardly comprehend the inhumanity. But Milgram did not entrap his teachers by asking them first to zap learners with enough electricity to make their hair stand on end. Using the foot-in-the-door technique, he instead began with a little tickle of electricity and escalated step by step. In the minds of those throwing the switches, the small action became justified, making the next act tolerable. So it happens when people succumb, gradually, to evil.

In any society, great evils often grow out of people's compliance with lesser evils. The Nazi leaders suspected that most German civil servants would resist shooting or gassing Jews directly, but they found them willing to handle the paperwork of the Holocaust (Silver & Geller, 1978). Milgram found a similar reaction in his experiments. When he asked 40 men to administer the learning test while someone else did the shocking, 93 percent complied. Cruelty does not require devilish villains. All it takes is ordinary people corrupted by an evil situation. Ordinary students may follow orders to haze initiates into their group. Ordinary employees may follow orders to produce and market harmful products. Ordinary soldiers may follow orders to punish and torture prisoners (Lankford, 2009).

In Jozefow and Le Chambon, as in Milgram's experiments, those who resisted usually did so early. After the first acts of compliance or resistance, attitudes began to follow and justify behavior.

What have social psychologists learned about the power of the individual? *Social control* (the power of the situation) and *personal control* (the power of the individual) interact. Much as water dissolves salt but not sand, so rotten situations turn some people into bad apples while others resist (Johnson, 2007).

When feeling pressured, some people react by doing the opposite of what is expected (Brehm & Brehm, 1981). The power of one or two individuals to sway majorities is *minority influence* (Moscovici, 1985). One research finding repeatedly stands out. When you are the minority, you are far more likely to sway the majority if you hold firmly to your position and don't waffle. This tactic won't make you popular, but it may make you influential, especially if your self-confidence stimulates others to consider why you react as you do. Even when a minority's influence is not yet visible, people may privately develop sympathy for the minority position and rethink their views (Wood et al., 1994).

"I was only following orders." —Adolf Eichmann, director of Nazi deportation of Jews to concentration camps

"All evil begins with 15 volts." —Philip Zimbardo, Stanford lecture, 2010

Sueddeutsche Zeitung Photo/Alamy

The powers of social influence are enormous, but so are the powers of the committed individual. Were this not so, communism would have remained an obscure theory, Christianity would be a small Middle Eastern sect, and Rosa Parks' refusal to sit at the back of the bus would not have ignited the U.S. civil rights movement. Social forces matter. But individuals matter, too.

🔒 **RETRIEVE IT • • •**　　　　　　　　　　　*ANSWERS IN APPENDIX E*

RI-7 Psychology's most famous obedience experiments, in which most participants obeyed an authority figure's demands to inflict presumed painful, dangerous shocks on an innocent participant, were conducted by social psychologist
_____ _____.

RI-8 Which situations have researchers found to be most likely to encourage obedience in participants?

Group Behavior

LOQ 35-7 How does the presence of others influence our actions, via social facilitation, social loafing, and deindividuation?

Imagine standing in a room holding a fishing pole. Your task is to wind the reel as fast as you can. On some occasions you wind in the presence of another participant, who is also winding as fast as possible. Will the other's presence affect your own performance?

In one of social psychology's first experiments, Norman Triplett (1898) reported that adolescents would wind a fishing reel faster in the presence of someone doing the same thing. Although a modern reanalysis revealed that the difference was modest (Stroebe, 2012), Triplett inspired later social psychologists to study how others' presence affects our behavior. Group influences operate both in simple groups—one person in the presence of another—and in more complex groups.

SOCIAL FACILITATION Triplett's claim—of strengthened performance in others' presence—is called **social facilitation.** But studies revealed that the truth is more complicated: The presence of others strengthens our most *likely* response—the correct one on an easy task, an incorrect one on a difficult task (Guerin, 1986; Zajonc, 1965). Why? Because when others observe us, we become aroused, and this arousal amplifies our reactions. Thus, expert pool players who made 71 percent of their shots when alone made 80 percent when four people came to watch them (Michaels et al., 1982). Poor shooters, who made 36 percent of their shots when alone, made only 25 percent when watched.

The energizing effect of an enthusiastic audience probably contributes to the home advantage that has shown up in studies of more than a quarter-million college and professional athletic events in various countries (Allen & Jones, 2014; Jamieson, 2010). Home teams win about 6 in 10 games for most sports.

A MINORITY OF ONE To be August Landmesser, standing defiantly with arms folded as everyone else salutes their allegiance to the Nazi Party and Adolph Hitler, requires extraordinary courage. But sometimes such individuals have inspired others, demonstrating the power of minority influence.

JEFF KOWALSKY/Getty Images

THE POWER OF ONE After former gymnast Rachel Denhollander went public with her report of childhood sexual molestation by U.S. Gymnastics doctor Lawrence Nassar, she suffered six months of public shaming, later noting, "I was left alone and isolated . . . My sexual assault was wielded like a weapon against me . . . I was subjected to lies and attacks on my character." But eventually more than 300 other women stepped forward to publicly testify to similar abuse, and Nassar was jailed for life (Correa & Louttit, 2018). After Denhollander concluded the testimonies given at one of Nassar's criminal sentence hearings, Judge Rosemarie Aquilina said, "You made this happen. You are the bravest person I've ever had in my courtroom" (Macur, 2018).

social facilitation improved performance on simple or well-learned tasks in the presence of others.

SOCIAL FACILITATION Skilled athletes often find they are "on" before an audience. What they do well, they do even better when people are watching.

ASK YOURSELF

What could you do to discourage social loafing in a group project assigned for a class?

DEINDIVIDUATION In the excitement that followed the Philadelphia Eagles winning their first NFL Super Bowl (2018), some fans, disinhibited by social arousal and the anonymity provided by their "underdog" masks, became destructive.

The point to remember: What you do well, you are likely to do even better in front of an audience, especially a friendly audience. What you normally find difficult may seem all but impossible when you are being watched.

Social facilitation also helps explain a funny effect of crowding. Comedians know that a "good house" is a full one. What they may not know is that crowding triggers arousal. Comedy routines that are mildly amusing in an uncrowded room seem funnier in a densely packed room (Aiello et al., 1983; Freedman & Perlick, 1979). When seated close to one another, people like a friendly person even more and an unfriendly person even less (Schiffenbauer & Schiavo, 1976; Storms & Thomas, 1977). So, to increase the chances of lively interaction at your next event, choose a room or set up seating that will just barely accommodate everyone.

SOCIAL LOAFING Social facilitation experiments test the effect of others' presence on the performance of an individual task, such as shooting pool. But what happens when people perform as a group—say, in a team tug-of-war? Would you exert more, less, or the same effort as you would exert in a one-on-one match?

To find out, a University of Massachusetts research team asked blindfolded students "to pull as hard as [they] can" on a rope. When they fooled the students into believing three others were also pulling behind them, students exerted only 82 percent as much effort as when they knew they were pulling alone (Ingham et al., 1974). And consider what happened when blindfolded people seated in a group clapped or shouted as loudly as they could while hearing (through headphones) other people clapping or shouting loudly (Latané, 1981). When they thought they were part of a group effort, the participants produced about one-third less noise than when clapping or shouting "alone."

This diminished effort is called **social loafing** (Jackson & Williams, 1988; Latané, 1981). Experiments in the United States, India, Thailand, Japan, China, and Taiwan have found social loafing on various tasks, though it was especially common among men in individualist cultures (Karau & Williams, 1993). What causes social loafing? When people act as part of a group, they may

- *feel less accountable* and therefore worry less about what others think.

- *view individual contributions as dispensable* (Harkins & Szymanski, 1989; Kerr & Bruun, 1983).

- *overestimate their own contributions,* downplaying others' efforts (Schroeder et al., 2016).

- *free ride on others' efforts.* Unless highly motivated and strongly identified with the group, people may slack off (as you perhaps have observed on group assignments), especially when they share equally in the benefits, regardless of how much they contribute.

DEINDIVIDUATION We've seen that the presence of others can arouse people (social facilitation), or it can diminish their feelings of responsibility (social loafing). But sometimes the presence of others does both. The uninhibited behavior that results can range from a food fight to vandalism or rioting. This process of losing self-awareness and self-restraint, called **deindividuation,** often occurs when group participation makes people both *aroused* and *anonymous.* Compared with identifiable women in a control group, New York University women dressed in depersonalizing Ku Klux Klan–style hoods delivered twice as much presumed electric shock to a victim (Zimbardo, 1970).

Deindividuation thrives, for better or for worse, in many settings. Online anonymity can unleash mocking or cruel words; cyber-trolls report enjoyment from verbally abusing others (Buckels et al., 2014; Sest & March, 2017). They might never say "you're disgusting" to someone's face, but can hide behind their anonymity online. Tribal warriors who depersonalize themselves with face paints or masks are more likely than those with exposed faces to kill, torture, or mutilate captured enemies (Watson, 1973). When we shed self-awareness and self-restraint—whether in a mob, at a concert, at a ball game, or at worship—we become more responsive to the group experience, bad or good. For a comparison of social facilitation, social loafing, and deindividuation, see **TABLE 35.1.**

* * *

TABLE 35.1

Behavior in the Presence of Others: Three Phenomena

Phenomenon	Social context	Psychological effect of others' presence	Behavioral effect
Social facilitation	Individual being observed	Increased arousal	Amplified dominant behavior, such as doing better what one does well (or doing worse what is difficult)
Social loafing	Group projects	Diminished feelings of responsibility when not individually accountable	Decreased effort
Deindividuation	Group setting that fosters arousal and anonymity	Reduced self-awareness	Lowered self-restraint

social loafing the tendency for people in a group to exert less effort when pooling their efforts toward attaining a common goal than when individually accountable.

deindividuation the loss of self-awareness and self-restraint occurring in group situations that foster arousal and anonymity.

group polarization the enhancement of a group's prevailing inclinations through discussion within the group.

We have examined the conditions under which the *presence* of others can motivate people to exert themselves or tempt them to free ride on the efforts of others, make easy tasks easier or difficult tasks harder, and enhance humor or fuel mob violence. Research also shows that *interacting* with others can similarly have both bad and good effects.

Group Polarization

LOQ 35-8 How can group interaction enable group polarization?

We live in an increasingly polarized world. The Middle East is torn by warring factions. The European Union is struggling with nationalist divisions. In 1990, a one-minute speech in the U.S. Congress would enable you to guess the speaker's party just 55 percent of the time; by 2009, partisanship was evident 83 percent of the time (Gentzkow et al., 2016). In 2016, for the first time in survey history, most U.S. Republicans and Democrats reported having "*very* unfavorable" views of the other party (Doherty & Kiley, 2016). And a record 77 percent of Americans perceived their nation as divided (Jones, 2016).

A powerful principle helps us understand this increasing polarization: The beliefs and attitudes we bring to a group grow stronger as we discuss them with like-minded others. This process, called **group polarization,** can have beneficial results, as when low-prejudice students become even more accepting while discussing racial issues. As George Bishop and I [DM] discovered, it can also be socially toxic, as when high-prejudice students who discuss racial issues together become *more* prejudiced (Myers & Bishop, 1970) (**FIGURE 35.4**). Our repeated finding: Like minds polarize.

Analyses of terrorist organizations around the world reveal that the terrorist mentality emerges slowly among those who share a grievance (McCauley, 2002; McCauley & Segal, 1987; Merari, 2002). As susceptible individuals interact in isolation (sometimes with other "brothers" and "sisters" in camps or in prisons), their views grow more and more extreme. Increasingly, they categorize the world as "us" against "them" (Chulov, 2014; Moghaddam, 2005). Knowing that group polarization occurs when like-minded people segregate, a 2006 U.S. National Intelligence estimate speculated "that the operational threat from self-radicalized cells will grow."

The internet offers us a connected global world, yet also provides an easily accessible medium for group polarization. When I [DM] got my start in social psychology with experiments on group polarization, I never imagined the potential power of polarization in *virtual* groups. Progressives friend progressives and share links

FIGURE 35.4

GROUP POLARIZATION If a group is like-minded, discussion strengthens its prevailing opinions. Talking over racial issues increased prejudice in a high-prejudice group of high school students and decreased it in a low-prejudice group. (Data from Myers & Bishop, 1970.)

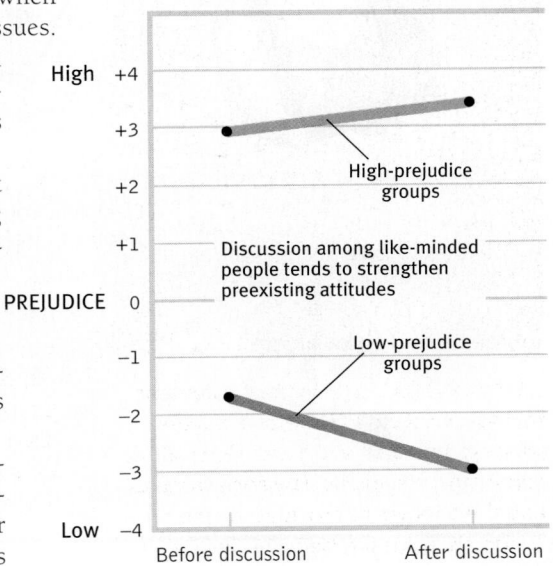

"Dear Satan, thank you for having my Internet news feeds tailored especially for ME!" —Comedian Steve Martin, 2016 tweet

to sites that affirm their shared views. Conservatives connect with conservatives and likewise share conservative perspectives. With news feeds and retweets, we fuel one another with information—and misinformation—and click on content we agree with (Bakshy et al., 2015; Barberá et al., 2015). Thus, within the internet's echo chamber of the like-minded, views become more extreme. Suspicion becomes conviction. Disagreements with the other tribe can escalate to demonization. Mindful of the viral false news phenomenon, Facebook and Google are working on ways to promote media literacy. For more on the internet's role in group polarization—toward ends that are good as well as bad—see Thinking Critically About: The Internet as Social Amplifier.

THINKING CRITICALLY ABOUT:

The Internet as Social Amplifier

LOQ 35-9 What role does the internet play in group polarization?

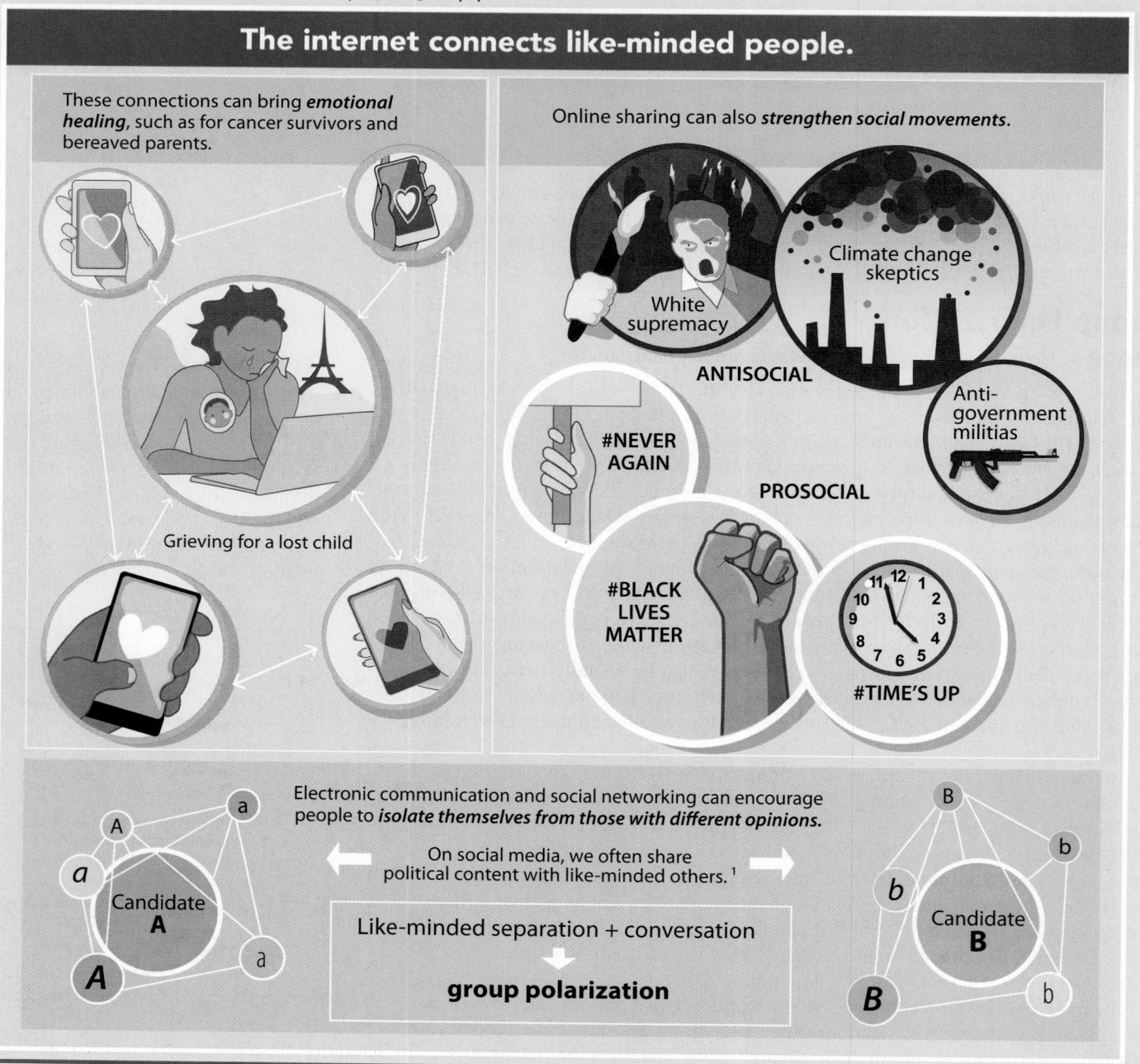

The internet connects like-minded people.

These connections can bring *emotional healing*, such as for cancer survivors and bereaved parents.

Grieving for a lost child

Online sharing can also *strengthen social movements*.

White supremacy

Climate change skeptics

ANTISOCIAL

Anti-government militias

#NEVER AGAIN

PROSOCIAL

#BLACK LIVES MATTER

#TIME'S UP

Electronic communication and social networking can encourage people to *isolate themselves from those with different opinions.*

On social media, we often share political content with like-minded others. [1]

Candidate **A**

Candidate **B**

Like-minded separation + conversation

⬇

group polarization

1. Bakshy et al., 2015; Barberá et al., 2015.

Groupthink

LOQ 35-10 How can group interaction enable groupthink?

Does group influence ever distort important national decisions? Consider the Bay of Pigs fiasco. In 1961, U.S. President John F. Kennedy and his advisers decided to invade Cuba with 1400 CIA-trained Cuban exiles. When the invaders were easily captured and quickly linked to the U.S. government, Kennedy wondered aloud, "How could I have been so stupid?"

Social psychologist Irving Janis (1982) studied the decision-making process leading to the ill-fated invasion. He discovered that the soaring morale of the recently elected president and his advisers fostered undue confidence. To preserve the good feeling, group members suppressed or self-censored their dissenting views, especially after President Kennedy voiced his enthusiasm for the scheme. Since no one spoke strongly against the idea, everyone assumed the support was unanimous. To describe this harmonious but unrealistic group thinking, Janis coined the term **groupthink.**

Later studies showed that groupthink—fed by overconfidence, conformity, self-justification, and group polarization—contributed to other fiascos as well. Among them were the failure to anticipate the 1941 Japanese attack on Pearl Harbor; the escalation of the Vietnam war; the U.S. Watergate cover-up; the Chernobyl nuclear reactor accident (Reason, 1987); the U.S. space shuttle *Challenger* explosion (Esser & Lindoerfer, 1989); and the Iraq war, launched on the false idea that Iraq had weapons of mass destruction (U.S. Senate Intelligence Committee, 2004).

Despite the dangers of groupthink, two heads are often better than one. Knowing this, Janis also studied instances in which U.S. presidents and their advisers collectively made good decisions, such as when the Truman administration formulated the Marshall Plan, which offered assistance to Europe after World War II, and when the Kennedy administration successfully prevented the Soviets from installing missiles in Cuba. His conclusion? Groupthink is prevented when a leader—whether in government or in business—welcomes various opinions, invites experts' critiques of developing plans, and assigns people to identify possible problems. Just as the suppression of dissent bends a group toward bad decisions, open debate often shapes good ones. This is especially the case with diverse groups, whose varied perspectives often enable creative or superior outcomes (Nemeth & Ormiston, 2007; Page, 2007). None of us is as smart as all of us.

groupthink the mode of thinking that occurs when the desire for harmony in a decision-making group overrides a realistic appraisal of alternatives.

"One of the dangers in the White House, based on my reading of history, is that you get wrapped up in groupthink and everybody agrees with everything, and there's no discussion and there are no dissenting views."
—Barack Obama, December 1, 2008, press conference

"If you have an apple and I have an apple and we exchange apples then you and I will still each have one apple. But if you have an idea and I have an idea and we exchange these ideas, then each of us will have two ideas."
—Attributed to dramatist George Bernard Shaw (1856–1950)

"If evil is contagious, so is goodness."
—Pope Francis tweet, 2017

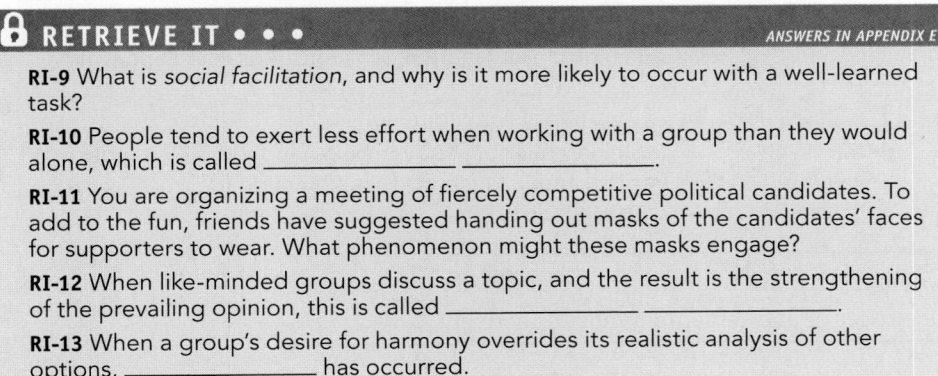

🔒 RETRIEVE IT • • •   *ANSWERS IN APPENDIX E*

RI-9 What is *social facilitation*, and why is it more likely to occur with a well-learned task?

RI-10 People tend to exert less effort when working with a group than they would alone, which is called _____ _____.

RI-11 You are organizing a meeting of fiercely competitive political candidates. To add to the fun, friends have suggested handing out masks of the candidates' faces for supporters to wear. What phenomenon might these masks engage?

RI-12 When like-minded groups discuss a topic, and the result is the strengthening of the prevailing opinion, this is called _____ _____.

RI-13 When a group's desire for harmony overrides its realistic analysis of other options, _____ has occurred.

 **ENGAGE** (ASK YOURSELF)

How have you been influenced by group polarization in your online activities?

🔒 REVIEW SOCIAL THINKING AND SOCIAL INFLUENCE

⟫ Learning Objectives

TEST YOURSELF Answer these repeated Learning Objective Questions on your own (before checking the answers in Appendix D) to improve your retention of the concepts (McDaniel et al., 2009, 2015).

35-1 What do social psychologists study? How do we tend to explain others' behavior and our own?

35-2 How do attitudes and actions interact?

35-3 How does culture affect our behavior?

35-4 How is social contagion a form of conformity, and how do conformity experiments reveal the power of social influence?

35-5 What did Milgram's obedience experiments teach us about the power of social influence?

35-6 What do the social influence studies teach us about ourselves? How much power do we have as individuals?

35-7 How does the presence of others influence our actions, via social facilitation, social loafing, and deindividuation?

35-8 How can group interaction enable group polarization?

35-9 What role does the internet play in group polarization?

35-10 How can group interaction enable groupthink?

⟐ Terms and Concepts to Remember

TEST YOURSELF Write down the definition yourself, then check your answer on the referenced page.

social psychology, **p. 416**

attribution theory, **p. 416**

fundamental attribution error, **p. 416**

attitude, **p. 418**

peripheral route persuasion, **p. 418**

central route persuasion, **p. 418**

foot-in-the-door phenomenon, **p. 418**

role, **p. 418**

cognitive dissonance theory, **p. 421**

norms, **p. 421**

culture, **p. 421**

conformity, **p. 423**

normative social influence, **p. 424**

informational social influence, **p. 424**

social facilitation, **p. 429**

social loafing, **p. 431**

deindividuation, **p. 431**

group polarization, **p. 431**

groupthink, **p. 433**

⟐ Experience the Testing Effect

TEST YOURSELF Answer the following questions on your own first, then check your answers in Appendix E.

1. If we encounter a person who appears to be high on drugs, and we make the fundamental attribution error, we will probably attribute the person's behavior to
   a. moral weakness or an addictive personality.
   b. peer pressure.
   c. the easy availability of drugs on city streets.
   d. society's acceptance of drug use.

2. Celebrity endorsements in advertising often lead consumers to purchase products through _____ (central/peripheral) route persuasion.

3. We tend to agree to a larger request more readily if we have already agreed to a small request. This tendency is called the _____-_____-_____-_____ phenomenon.

4. Jamal's therapist has suggested that Jamal should "act as if" he is confident, even though he feels insecure and shy. Which social psychological theory would best support this suggestion, and what might the therapist be hoping to achieve?

5. Researchers have found that a person is most likely to conform to a group if
   a. the group members have diverse opinions.
   b. the person feels competent and secure.
   c. the person admires the group's status.
   d. no one else will observe the person's behavior.

6. In Milgram's experiments, the rate of compliance was highest when
   a. the "learner" was at a distance from the "teacher."
   b. the "learner" was close at hand.
   c. other "teachers" refused to go along with the experimenter.
   d. the "teacher" disliked the "learner."

7. Dr. Huang, a popular music professor, delivers fascinating lectures on music history but gets nervous and makes mistakes when describing exam statistics in front of the class. Why does his performance vary by task?

8. In a group situation that fosters arousal and anonymity, a person sometimes loses self-consciousness and self-control. This phenomenon is called _____.

9. Sharing our opinions with like-minded others tends to strengthen our views, a phenomenon referred to as _____ _____.

Continue testing yourself with ⬕ **LearningCurve** or ⬕ **Achieve Read & Practice** to learn and remember most effectively.

㊱ Antisocial Relations

Social psychology studies how we think about and influence one another, and also how we *relate* to one another. What are the roots of prejudice? What causes people sometimes to hate and harm, and other times to love and help? And when destructive conflicts arise, how can we move toward a just peace? In this section we ponder insights into *antisocial* relations gleaned by researchers who have studied prejudice and aggression.

PREJUDICE

LOQ 36-1 What is *prejudice?* How do explicit and implicit prejudice differ?

Prejudice means "prejudgment." It is an unjustifiable and usually negative *attitude* toward a group and its members—who often are people of a particular racial or ethnic group, gender, sexual orientation, or belief system. You may recall that attitudes are feelings, influenced by beliefs, that predispose us to act in certain ways. The ingredients in prejudice's three-part mixture are

- *negative emotions,* such as hostility or fear.
- **stereotypes**, which are generalized beliefs about a group of people. Our stereotypes sometimes reflect reality. If you presume that young men tend to drive faster than elderly women, you may be right. But stereotypes often overgeneralize or exaggerate—as when liberals and conservatives overestimate the extremity of each other's views, or Christians and atheists misperceive each other's values (Graham et al., 2012; Simpson & Rios, 2016).
- a predisposition to **discriminate**—to act in negative and unjustifiable ways toward members of the group. Sometimes prejudice is blatant. Other times it is more subtle, taking the form of *microaggressions,* such as race-related traffic stops, a reluctance to choose a train seat next to someone of a different race, or longer Uber wait times and less Airbnb acceptance for people with African-American names (Edelman et al., 2017; Ge et al., 2016; Wang et al., 2011).

To believe that obese people are gluttonous, and to feel dislike for an obese person, is to be prejudiced. To pass over obese people on a dating site, or to reject an obese job candidate, is to discriminate.

Explicit and Implicit Prejudice

Again and again, we have seen that our brain processes thoughts, memories, and attitudes on two different tracks. Sometimes that processing is *explicit*—on the radar screen of our awareness. More often, it is *implicit*—an unthinking knee-jerk response operating below the radar, leaving us unaware of how our attitudes are influencing our behavior. In 2015, the U.S. Supreme Court, in upholding the Fair Housing Act, recognized implicit bias research, noting that "unconscious prejudices" can cause discrimination even when people do not consciously intend to discriminate.

 Psychologists study implicit prejudice by

- *testing for unconscious group associations.* Tests in which people quickly pair a person's image with a trait demonstrate that even people who deny any racial prejudice may harbor negative associations (Banaji & Greenwald, 2013). Millions of people have taken the Implicit Association Test (as you can, too, at Implicit.Harvard.edu). Critics question the test's reliability and caution against using it to assess or label individuals (Oswald et al., 2013, 2015). But defenders counter that implicit biases predict behaviors ranging from simple acts of friendliness to the evaluation of work quality (Greenwald et al., 2015).
- *considering unconscious patronization.* In one experiment, White university women assessed flawed student essays they believed had been written by either a White or a Black student. The women gave low evaluations, often with harsh comments, to the essays supposedly written by a White student. When the same essay was attributed to a Black student, their assessment was more positive (Harber, 1998). In real-world evaluations, such low expectations and the resulting "inflated praise and insufficient criticism" could hinder minority student achievement, the researcher noted, which is one reason why many teachers read essays while "blind" to their authors' race.
- *monitoring reflexive bodily responses.* Even people who consciously express little prejudice may give off telltale signals as their body responds selectively to an image of a person from another ethnic group. Neuroscientists can detect signals of implicit prejudice in the viewer's facial-muscle responses and in the activation of the emotion-processing amygdala (Cunningham et al., 2004; Eberhardt, 2005; Stanley et al., 2008).

"But who can detect their errors? Clear me from hidden faults."
—Psalm 19:12

prejudice an unjustifiable and usually negative attitude toward a group and its members. Prejudice generally involves negative emotions, stereotyped beliefs, and a predisposition to discriminatory action.

stereotype a generalized (sometimes accurate but often overgeneralized) belief about a group of people.

discrimination unjustifiable negative behavior toward a group or its members.

RESPONDING TO AN AMERICAN TRAGEDY Does implicit bias research—now being integrated into police and corporate diversity training programs in the United States and beyond—help us understand the 2013 death of Trayvon Martin (shown here 7 months before he was killed)? As he walked alone to his father's fiancée's house in a gated Florida neighborhood, a suspicious resident started following him. A confrontation led to the unarmed Martin being shot. Martin's death sparked public outrage related to racism, gun control, and social justice. Commentators wondered: Had Martin been an unarmed White teen, would he have been perceived and treated the same way?

"If we can't help our latent biases, we can help our behavior in response to those instinctive reactions, which is why we work to design systems and processes that overcome that very human part of us all." —U.S. FBI Director James B. Comey, "Hard Truths: Law Enforcement and Race," 2015

Targets of Prejudice

LOQ 36-2 What groups are frequent targets of prejudice?

RACIAL AND ETHNIC PREJUDICE Americans' expressed racial attitudes have changed dramatically in the last half-century. "Marriage between Blacks and Whites" was approved by 4 percent of Americans in 1958 and 87 percent in 2013 (Newport, 2013a). Six in ten Americans—double the number in most European countries—now agree that "an increasing number of people of many different races, ethnic groups, and nationalities in our country makes it a better place to live" (Drake & Poushter, 2016).

Yet as overt interracial prejudice wanes, *subtle* prejudice lingers. People with darker skin tones experience greater criticism and accusations of immoral behavior (Alter et al., 2016). And although many people *say* they would feel upset with someone making racist (or homophobic) slurs, they respond indifferently when they actually hear prejudice-laden language (Kawakami et al., 2009).

As noted, prejudice is not just subtle, but often unconscious (implicit). An Implicit Association Test found 9 in 10 White respondents taking longer to identify pleasant words (such as *peace* and *paradise*) as "good" when presented with Black-sounding names (such as *Latisha* and *Darnell*) than they did with White-sounding names (such as *Katie* and *Ian*). Moreover, people who more quickly associate good things with White names or faces also are the quickest to perceive anger and apparent threat in Black faces (Hugenberg & Bodenhausen, 2003). A greater association of pleasant words with European-American than African-American names has also been observed in more than 800 billion internet words (Caliskan et al., 2017). In the 2008 U.S. presidential election, those demonstrating explicit *or* implicit prejudice were less likely to vote for candidate Barack Obama. His election, however, reduced implicit prejudice (Bernstein et al., 2010; Payne et al., 2010; Stephens-Davidowitz, 2014).

Our perceptions can also reflect implicit bias. In 1999, Amadou Diallo was accosted as he approached his doorway by police officers looking for a rapist. When he pulled out his wallet, the officers, perceiving a gun, riddled his body with 19 bullets from 41 shots. In one analysis of 59 unarmed suspect shootings in Philadelphia over seven years, 49 involved the misidentification of an object (such as a phone) or movement (such as pants tugging). Black suspects were more than twice as likely to be misperceived as threatening, even by Black officers (Blow, 2015). Across the United States, nearly 40 percent of the unarmed people shot and killed by police during 2015 and 2016 were Black (*Washington Post,* 2017). One research team, drawing on responses from more than 2 million Americans, found that a region's implicit bias toward African-Americans predicted its number of African-Americans killed by police, even after accounting for other factors such as income and population density (Hehman et al., 2018).

To better understand such tragic shootings, researchers have also simulated the situation (Correll et al., 2007, 2015; Plant & Peruche, 2005; Sadler et al., 2012b). They asked viewers to press buttons quickly to "shoot" or not shoot men who suddenly appeared on screen. Some of the on-screen men held a gun. Others held a harmless object, such as a flashlight or bottle. People (both Blacks and Whites, including police officers) more often shot Black men holding the harmless object. Priming people with a flashed Black face rather than a White face also made them more likely to misperceive a flashed tool as a gun (**FIGURE 36.1**). Fatigue, which diminishes one's conscious control and increases automatic reactions, amplifies racial bias in decisions to shoot (Ma et al., 2013).

FIGURE 36.1

RACE PRIMES PERCEPTIONS In experiments by Keith Payne (2006), people viewed (a) a White or Black face, instantly followed by (b) a flashed gun or hand tool, which was then followed by (c) a masking screen. Participants were more likely to misperceive a tool as a gun when it was preceded by a Black rather than White face.

(a)

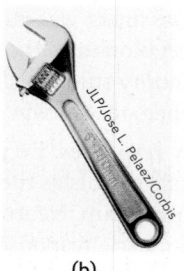
(b)

(c)

GENDER PREJUDICE Overt gender prejudice has also declined sharply. The one-third of Americans who in 1937 told Gallup pollsters that they would vote for a qualified woman whom their party nominated for president soared to 95 percent in 2012 (Jones, 2012; Newport, 1999). Although women worldwide still represent nearly two-thirds of illiterate adults, and 30 percent have experienced intimate partner violence, 65 percent of all people now say it is very important that women have the same rights as men (UN, 2015b; WHO, 2016b; Zainulbhai, 2016).

Nevertheless, both implicit and explicit gender prejudice and discrimination persist. In Western countries, we pay more to those (usually men) who care for our streets than to those (usually women) who care for our children. From 2007 through 2016, male directors of 1000 popular films (the top 100 for each year) outnumbered female directors by 24 to 1 (Smith et al., 2017). Gender bias even applies to beliefs about intelligence: Despite equality between the sexes in intelligence test scores, people tend to perceive their fathers as more intelligent than their mothers and their sons as brighter than their daughters (Furnham, 2016).

Unwanted female infants are no longer left out on a hillside to die of exposure, as was the practice in ancient Greece. Yet the normal male-to-female newborn ratio (105-to-100) doesn't explain the world's estimated 163 million (say that number slowly) "missing women" (Hvistendahl, 2011). In many places, sons are valued more than daughters. In India, there are 3.5 times more Google searches asking how to conceive a boy than how to conceive a girl (Stephens-Davidowitz, 2014). With scientific testing that enables sex-selective abortions, some countries are experiencing a shortfall in female births. India's newborn sex ratio was recently 112 boys for every 100 girls. China's has been 111 to 100, despite China's declaring sex-selective abortions—gender genocide—a criminal offense (CIA, 2014). With under-age-20 males exceeding females by 32 million, many Chinese bachelors will be unable to find mates (Zhu et al., 2009). A shortage of women also contributes to increased crime, violence, prostitution, and trafficking of women (Brooks, 2012).

LGBTQ PREJUDICE In most of the world, gay, lesbian, and transgender people cannot openly and comfortably disclose who they are and whom they love (Katz-Wise & Hyde, 2012; UN, 2011). Although by 2018 two dozen countries had allowed same-sex marriage, dozens more had laws criminalizing same-sex relationships. Cultural variation is enormous—ranging from the 98 percent in Ghana to the 6 percent in Spain for whom "homosexuality is morally unacceptable" (Pew, 2014b). Worldwide, anti-gay attitudes are most common among men, older adults, and those who are unhappy, unemployed, and less educated (Haney, 2016; Jäckle & Wenzelburger, 2015).

Explicit anti-LGBTQ prejudice persists, even in countries with legal protections in place. When U.S. and U.K. experimenters sent thousands of responses to employment ads, those whose resumes included "Treasurer, Progressive and Socialist Alliance" received more replies than did those for resumes that specified "Treasurer, Gay and Lesbian Alliance" (Agerström et al., 2012; Bertrand & Mullainathan, 2003; Drydakis, 2009, 2015). Other evidence has appeared in national surveys of LGBTQ Americans:

- 39 percent reported having been "rejected by a friend or family member" because of their sexual orientation or gender identity (Pew, 2013b).
- 58 percent reported being "subject to slurs or jokes" (Pew, 2013b).
- 54 percent reported having been harassed at school and at work (Grant et al., 2011; James et al., 2016).

Do attitudes and practices that label, disparage, and discriminate against gay, lesbian, and transgender people increase their risk of psychological disorder and ill health? In U.S. states without protections against LGBTQ hate crime and discrimination, gay and lesbian people experience substantially higher rates of depression and related disorders, even after controlling for income and education differences. In communities where anti-gay prejudice is high, so are gay and lesbian suicide and cardiovascular deaths. In 16 states that banned same-sex marriage between 2001 and 2005, gays and lesbians (but not heterosexuals) experienced a 37 percent increase in depressive disorder rates, a 42 percent increase in alcohol use disorder, and a 248 percent increase in generalized anxiety disorder. Meanwhile, gays and lesbians in other states did not experience increased psychiatric disorders (Hatzenbuehler, 2014).

"Until I was a man, I had no idea how good men had it at work. . . . The first time I spoke up in a meeting in my newly low, quiet voice and noticed that sudden, focused attention, I was so uncomfortable that I found myself unable to finish my sentence." —Thomas Page McBee, 2016, after transitioning from female to male

just-world phenomenon the tendency for people to believe the world is just and that people therefore get what they deserve and deserve what they get.

ingroup "us"—people with whom we share a common identity.

outgroup "them"—those perceived as different or apart from our ingroup.

ingroup bias the tendency to favor our own group.

scapegoat theory the theory that prejudice offers an outlet for anger by providing someone to blame.

other-race effect the tendency to recall faces of one's own race more accurately than faces of other races. (Also called the *cross-race effect* and the *own-race bias*.)

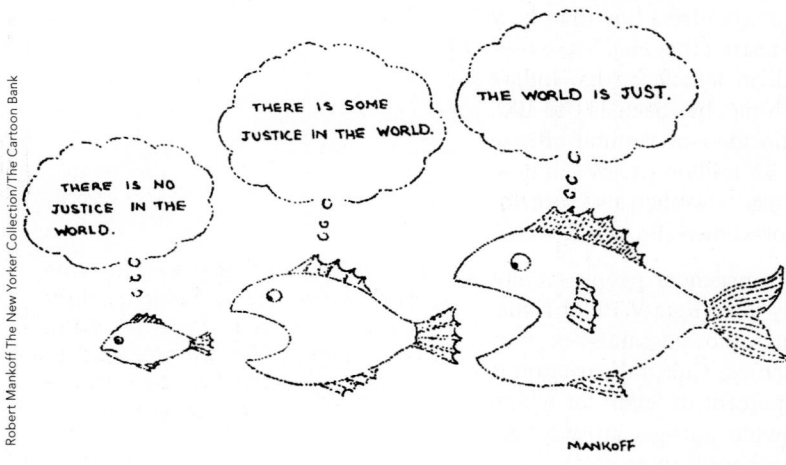

BELIEF SYSTEMS PREJUDICE In the aftermath of the 9/11 terrorist attacks, the Iraq and Afghanistan wars, and the brutal scare tactics of violent extremist groups, many Americans have developed irrational fear and anger toward *all* Muslims (and those they *think* might be Muslim). (The reality since 2001: U.S. attacks by homegrown White supremacists and other non-Muslim extremists were nearly twice as likely [Shane, 2015].) As a result, nearly half of Muslim Americans have reported personally experiencing discrimination in the last year—more than double the average among U.S. Jews, Catholics, and Protestants (Gallup, 2017).

Roots of Prejudice

LOQ 36-3 What are some social, emotional, and cognitive roots of prejudice, and what are some ways to eliminate prejudice?

Prejudice springs from a culture's divisions, the heart's passions, and the mind's natural workings.

SOCIAL INEQUALITIES AND DIVISIONS When some people have money, power, and prestige and others do not, the "haves" usually develop attitudes that justify things as they are. The **just-world phenomenon** reflects an idea we commonly teach our children—that good is rewarded and evil is punished. From this it is but a short and sometimes automatic leap to assume that those who succeed must be good and those who suffer must be bad. Such reasoning enables the rich to see both their own wealth and the poor's misfortune as justly deserved. When slavery existed in the United States, slaveholders perceived slaves as innately lazy, ignorant, and irresponsible—as having the very traits that justified enslaving them. Stereotypes rationalize inequalities.

Victims of discrimination may react with either self-blame or anger (Allport, 1954). Either reaction can feed others' prejudice through the classic *blame-the-victim* dynamic. Do the circumstances of poverty breed a higher crime rate? If so, that higher crime rate can be used to justify discrimination against those who live in poverty.

Dividing the world into "us" and "them" can entail conflict, racism, and war, but it also provides the benefits of communal solidarity. Thus, we cheer for our groups, kill for them, die for them. Indeed, we define who we are—our *social identity*—partly in terms of our groups (Greenaway et al., 2016; Hogg, 1996, 2006; Turner, 1987, 2007). When Ian identifies himself as a man, an Aussie, a University of Sydney student, a Catholic, and a MacGregor, he knows who he is, and so do we. Mentally drawing a circle defines "us," the **ingroup.** But the social definition of who we are also states who we are not. People outside that circle are "them," the **outgroup. An ingroup bias**—a favoring of our own group—soon follows. In experiments, people have favored their own group (arbitrarily created by a simple coin toss) when dividing rewards (Tajfel, 1982; Wilder, 1981). Across 17 countries, ingroup bias appears more as ingroup favoritism than as harm to the outgroup (Romano et al., 2017). Discrimination is triggered less by outgroup hostility than by ingroup networking and mutual support—such as hiring a friend's child at the expense of other candidates (Greenwald & Pettigrew, 2014).

We have inherited our Stone Age ancestors' need to belong, to live and love in groups. There was safety in solidarity: Whether hunting, defending, or attacking, 10 hands were better than 2. Evolution prepared us, when encountering strangers, to make instant judgments: friend or foe? This urge to distinguish enemies from friends, and to "otherize" as different those not like us, predisposes prejudice against strangers (Whitley, 1999). To Greeks of the classical era, all non-Greeks were "barbarians." In our own era, most children believe their school is better than all other schools in town. Many high school students form cliques—jocks, preps, nerds—and disparage those outside their own

IMPRESSIVE RESUME...

ASK YOURSELF

What are some examples of ingroup bias in your community?

THE INGROUP Scotland's famed "Tartan Army" soccer fans, shown here during a match against archrival England, share a social identity that defines "us" (the Scottish ingroup) and "them" (the English outgroup).

group. Even chimpanzees have been seen to wipe clean the spot where they were touched by a chimpanzee from another group (Goodall, 1986). They also display ingroup empathy by yawning more after seeing ingroup (rather than outgroup) members yawn (Campbell & de Waal, 2011). Although an ideal world might prioritize justice and love for all, in our real world, ingroup love often outranks universal justice.

NEGATIVE EMOTIONS Negative emotions nourish prejudice. When facing death, fearing threats, or experiencing frustration, people cling more tightly to their ingroup. As fears of terrorism heighten patriotism, they also produce loathing and aggression toward those who appear to threaten our world (Pyszczynski et al., 2002, 2008). **Scapegoat theory** notes that when things go wrong, finding someone to blame can provide a target for our negative emotions. After anti-immigrant sentiments flared in 2016 during the Brexit referendum in Britain and the contentious presidential election in the United States, reports of harassment, bullying, and hate crime rose (Crandall & White, 2016; Hassan, 2016; Kenyon, 2016; North, 2016). "Fear and anger create aggression, and aggression against citizens of different ethnicity or race creates racism and, in turn, new forms of terrorism," noted Philip Zimbardo (2001).

Evidence for the scapegoat theory of prejudice comes in two forms: (1) Economically frustrated people tend to express heightened prejudice. (2) Experiments that create temporary frustration intensify prejudice. Students who experience failure or are made to feel insecure often restore their self-esteem by disparaging a rival school or another person (Cialdini & Richardson, 1980; Crocker et al., 1987). Denigrating others may boost our own sense of status, which explains why a rival's misfortune sometimes provides a twinge of pleasure. (The German language has a word—*Schadenfreude*—for this secret joy that we sometimes take in another's failure.) By contrast, those made to feel loved and supported become more open to and accepting of others who differ (Mikulincer & Shaver, 2001).

COGNITIVE SHORTCUTS Stereotyped beliefs are in part a by-product of how we cognitively simplify the world. To help understand the world around us, we sometimes form categories. Chemists categorize molecules as organic and inorganic. Therapists categorize psychological disorders. We all categorize people by gender, ethnicity, race, age, and many other characteristics. But when we categorize people into groups, we often stereotype. We recognize how greatly *we* differ from other individuals in *our* groups. But we overestimate the extent to which members of other groups are alike (Bothwell et al., 1989). We perceive *outgroup homogeneity*—uniformity of attitudes, personality, and appearance. Our greater recognition for individual own-race faces—called the **other-race effect** (or *cross-race effect* or *own-race bias*)—emerges during infancy, between 3 and 9 months of age (Anzures et al., 2013; Telzer et al., 2013). (We also have an *own-age bias*—better recognition memory for faces of our own age group [Rhodes & Anastasi, 2012]).

Sometimes, however, people don't fit easily into our racial categories. If so, they are often assigned to their minority identity. Researchers believe this happens because,

"If the Tiber reaches the walls, if the Nile does not rise to the fields, if the sky doesn't move or the Earth does, if there is famine, if there is plague, the cry is at once: 'The Christians to the lion!'" —Tertullian, *Apologeticus*, 197 C.E.

"The misfortunes of others are the taste of honey." —Japanese saying

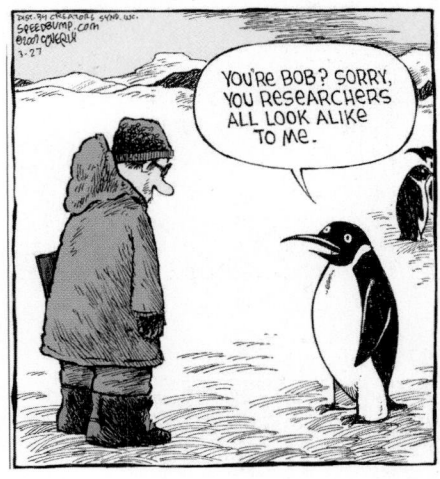

| 100% Chinese | 80% Chinese 20% Caucasian | 60% Chinese 40% Caucasian | 40% Chinese 60% Caucasian | 20% Chinese 80% Caucasian | 100% Caucasian |

Dr. Jamin Halberstadt

FIGURE 36.2

CATEGORIZING MIXED-RACE PEOPLE When New Zealanders quickly classified 104 photos by race, those of European descent more often than those of Chinese descent classified the ambiguous middle two as Chinese (Halberstadt et al., 2011).

after learning the features of a familiar racial group, the observer's *selective attention* is drawn to the distinctive features of the less-familiar minority. Jamin Halberstadt and his colleagues (2011) illustrated this learned-association effect by showing New Zealanders blended Chinese-Caucasian faces. Compared with participants of Chinese descent, European-descent New Zealanders more readily classified ambiguous faces as Chinese (see **FIGURE 36.2**). With effort and with experience, people get better at recognizing individual faces from another group (Hugenberg et al., 2010; Young et al., 2012).

REMEMBERING VIVID CASES We also simplify our world by employing *heuristics—* mental shortcuts that enable snap judgments. The *availability heuristic* is the tendency to estimate the frequency of an event by how readily it comes to mind. Vivid cases are memorable and they come to mind easily, so it's no surprise that they feed our stereotypes. In a classic experiment, researchers showed two groups of University of Oregon students lists containing information about 50 men (Rothbart et al., 1978). The first group's list included 10 men arrested for *nonviolent* crimes, such as forgery. The second group's list included 10 men arrested for *violent* crimes, such as assault. Later, both groups were asked how many men on their list had committed *any* sort of crime. The second group overestimated the number. Violent crimes form vivid memories (**FIGURE 36.3**).

FIGURE 36.3

VIVID CASES FEED STEREOTYPES Global terrorism has created, in many minds, an exaggerated stereotype of Muslims as terrorism-prone. Actually, reported a U.S. National Research Council panel on terrorism, when offering this inexact illustration, most terrorists are not Muslim and "the vast majority of Islamic people have no connection with and do not sympathize with terrorism" (Smelser & Mitchell, 2002).

Muslims   Terrorism

RETAIN 🔒 📶 **LaunchPad** To experience a simulation of how stereotypes form, visit **Topic Tutorial: PsychSim6, Not My Type**. And for a 6.5-minute synopsis of the cognitive and social psychology of prejudice, see the **Video: Prejudice**.

VICTIM BLAMING As we noted earlier, people often justify their prejudices by blaming victims. If the world is just, they assume, people must get what they deserve. As one German civilian is said to have remarked when visiting the Bergen-Belsen concentration camp shortly after World War II, "What terrible criminals these prisoners must have been to receive such treatment."

Hindsight bias amplifies victim blaming (Carli & Leonard, 1989). Have you ever heard people say that rape victims, abused spouses, or people with AIDS got what they deserved? In some countries, such as Pakistan, rape victims have been sentenced to severe punishment for violating adultery prohibitions (Mydans, 2002). In one experiment, two groups were given a detailed account of a date (Janoff-Bulman et al., 1985). The first group's account reported that the date ended with the woman being raped. Members of that group perceived the woman's behavior as at least partly to blame, and in hindsight, they thought, "She should have known better." The second group, given the same account with the rape ending deleted, did not perceive the woman's behavior as inviting rape. Hindsight bias promoted a blame-the-victim mentality among members of the first group. Blaming the victim also serves to reassure people that it couldn't happen to them.

People also have a basic tendency to justify their culture's social systems (Jost et al., 2009; Kay et al., 2009). We're inclined to see the way things are as the way they ought to be and deserve to be: If people are rich, they must be smart (Hussak & Cimpian, 2015). This natural conservatism makes it difficult to legislate major social changes, such as health care improvements or climate change policies. Once such policies are in place, our "system justification" tends to preserve them.

RI-1 When prejudiced judgment causes us to blame an undeserving person for a problem, that person is called a _____.

* * *

If your own gut-check reveals you sometimes have feelings you would rather not have about other people, remember this: It is what we *do* with our feelings that matters. By monitoring our feelings and actions, and by replacing old habits with new ones based on new friendships, we can work to free ourselves from prejudice.

AGGRESSION

LOQ 36-4 How does psychology's definition of *aggression* differ from everyday usage? What biological factors make us more prone to hurt one another?

Prejudice hurts, but aggression sometimes hurts more. In psychology, **aggression** is any physical or verbal behavior intended to harm someone, whether done out of hostility or as a calculated means to an end. The assertive, persistent salesperson is not aggressive. Nor is the dentist who makes you wince with pain. But the gossip who passes along a vicious rumor about you, the bully who torments you in person or online, and the attacker who robs you are aggressive.

Aggressive behavior emerges from the interaction of biology and experience. For a gun to fire, the trigger must be pulled; with some people, as with hair-trigger guns, it doesn't take much to trip an explosion. Let's look first at some biological factors that influence our thresholds for aggressive behavior, then at the psychological factors that pull the trigger.

The Biology of Aggression

Aggression varies too widely from culture to culture, era to era, and person to person to be considered an unlearned instinct. But biology does *influence* aggression. We can look for biological influences at three levels—genetic, neural, and biochemical.

GENETIC INFLUENCES Genes influence aggression. Animals have been bred for aggressiveness—sometimes for sport, sometimes for research. The effect of genes also appears in human *twin studies* (Miles & Carey, 1997; Rowe et al., 1999). If one identical twin admits to "having a violent temper," the other twin will often independently admit the same. Fraternal twins are much less likely to respond similarly.

Researchers continue to search for genetic markers in those who commit violent acts. One is already well known and is carried by half the human race: the Y chromosome. Another such marker is the *monoamine oxidase A (MAOA) gene,* which helps break down neurotransmitters such as dopamine and serotonin. Sometimes called the "warrior gene," people who have low *MAOA* gene expression tend to behave aggressively when provoked. In one experiment, low (compared with high) *MAOA* gene carriers gave more unpleasant hot sauce to someone who provoked them (McDermott et al., 2009; Tiihonen et al., 2015).

aggression any physical or verbal behavior intended to harm someone physically or emotionally.

Gilbert Laurie/Getty Images

DO GUNS IN THE HOME SAVE OR TAKE MORE LIVES? "Personal safety/ protection" is the number one reason U.S. gun owners give for firearm ownership (Swift, 2013). Yet in the last 40 years, well over one million Americans have suffered nonwar firearm deaths—more than all American war deaths. Compared with people of the same sex, race, age, and neighborhood, those who keep a gun in the home have been twice as likely to be murdered and three times as likely to die by suicide (Anglemyer et al., 2014; Stroebe, 2013). States and countries with high gun ownership rates also tend to have high gun death rates (VPC, 2016).

Donald Reilly The New Yorker Collection/The Cartoon Bank
"It's a guy thing."

NEURAL INFLUENCES There is no one spot in the brain that controls aggression. Aggression is a complex behavior, and it occurs in particular contexts. But animal and human brains have neural systems that, given provocation, will either inhibit or facilitate aggression (Falkner et al., 2016; Moyer, 1983; Wilkowski et al., 2011). Consider:

- Researchers implanted a radio-controlled electrode in the brain of the domineering leader of a caged monkey colony. The electrode was in an area that, when stimulated, inhibits aggression. When researchers placed the control button for the electrode in the colony's cage, one small monkey learned to push it every time the boss became threatening.

- A neurosurgeon, seeking to diagnose a disorder, implanted an electrode in the amygdala of a mild-mannered woman. Because the brain has no sensory receptors, she was unable to feel the stimulation. But at the flick of a switch she snarled, "Take my blood pressure. Take it now," then stood up and began to strike the doctor.

- Studies of violent criminals have revealed diminished activity in the frontal lobes, which play an important role in controlling impulses. If the frontal lobes are damaged, inactive, disconnected, or not yet fully mature, aggression may be more likely (Amen et al., 1996; Davidson et al., 2000; Raine, 2013).

BIOCHEMICAL INFLUENCES Our genes engineer our individual nervous systems, which operate electrochemically. The hormone testosterone, for example, circulates in the bloodstream and influences the neural systems that control aggression. A raging bull becomes a gentle giant when castration reduces its testosterone level. Conversely, when injected with testosterone, gentle, castrated mice once again become aggressive.

Humans are less sensitive to hormonal changes. But as men's testosterone levels diminish with age, hormonally charged, aggressive 17-year-olds mature into quieter and gentler 70-year-olds. Drugs that sharply reduce testosterone levels also subdue men's aggressive tendencies.

Another drug that sometimes circulates in the bloodstream—alcohol—*unleashes* aggressive responses to frustration. Across police data, prison surveys, and experiments, aggression-prone people are more likely to drink, and to become violent when intoxicated (White et al., 1993). Alcohol is a disinhibitor—it slows the brain activity that controls judgment and inhibitions. Under its influence, people may interpret ambiguous acts (such as being bumped in a crowd) as provocations and react aggressively (Bègue et al., 2010; Giancola & Gorman, 2007). Alcohol has been a factor in 73 percent of homicides in Russia and 57 percent in the United States (Landberg & Norström, 2011).

Just *thinking* you've imbibed alcohol can increase aggression (Bègue et al., 2009). But so, too, does unknowingly ingesting alcohol slipped into a drink. Thus, alcohol affects aggression both biologically and psychologically (Bushman, 1993; Ito et al., 1996; Taylor & Chermack, 1993).

"We could avoid two-thirds of all crime simply by putting all able-bodied young men in cryogenic sleep from the age of 12 through 28." —David T. Lykken, *The Antisocial Personalities,* 1995

Chris Courteau/AGE Fotostock

A LEAN, MEAN FIGHTING MACHINE— THE TESTOSTERONE-LADEN FEMALE HYENA The hyena's unusual embryology pumps testosterone into female fetuses. The result is revved-up young female hyenas who seem born to fight.

Psychological and Social-Cultural Factors in Aggression

LOQ 36-5 What psychological and social-cultural factors may trigger aggressive behavior?

Biological factors influence how easily aggression is triggered. But what psychological and social-cultural factors pull the trigger?

AVERSIVE EVENTS Suffering sometimes builds character. In laboratory experiments, however, those made miserable have often made others miserable (Berkowitz, 1983, 1989). Aversive stimuli—hot temperatures, physical pain, personal insults, foul odors, cigarette smoke, crowding, and a host of others—can evoke hostility. Even hunger can feed anger—making people "hangry" (Bushman et al., 2014). A prime example of this phenomenon is the **frustration-aggression principle:** Frustration creates anger, which can spark aggression.

The frustration-aggression link was illustrated in an analysis of 27,667 hit-by-pitch Major League Baseball incidents between 1960 and 2004 (Timmerman, 2007). Pitchers were most likely to hit batters when they had been frustrated by one of three events: the previous batter had hit a home run, the current batter had hit a home run the last time at bat, or the pitcher's teammate had been hit by a pitch in the previous half-inning. A separate study found a similar link between rising temperatures and the number of hit batters (Reifman et al., 1991; see **FIGURE 36.4**).

In the wider world, violent crime and spousal abuse rates have been higher during hotter years, seasons, months, and days (Anderson et al., 1997). Studies from other social science fields converge in finding that throughout history, higher temperatures have predicted increased individual violence, wars, and revolutions (Hsiang et al., 2013). Craig Anderson and his colleagues (2000, 2011) have projected that, other things being equal, global warming of 4 degrees Fahrenheit (about 2 degrees Celsius) could induce tens of thousands of additional assaults and murders—and that's before the added violence inducement from climate change–related drought, poverty, food insecurity, and migration. When overheated, we think, feel, and act more aggressively.

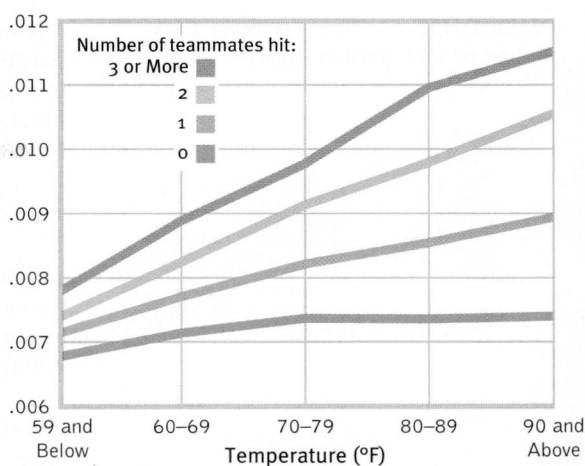

LaunchPad How have researchers studied these concepts? Play the role of a researcher by designing one of these studies in **Immersive Learning: How Would You Know If Hot Temperatures Cause Aggression?**

REINFORCEMENT AND MODELING Aggression may naturally follow aversive events, but learning can alter natural reactions. We learn when our behavior is reinforced, and we learn by watching others.

In situations where experience has taught us that aggression pays, we are likely to act aggressively again. Children whose aggression has successfully intimidated other children may become bullies. Animals that have successfully fought to get food or mates become increasingly ferocious. To foster a kinder, gentler world we had best model and reward sensitivity and cooperation from an early age, perhaps by training parents to discipline without modeling violence. Parent-training programs often advise parents to avoid modeling violence by not screaming and hitting. Instead, parents should reinforce desirable behaviors and frame statements positively. ("When you finish loading the dishwasher you can go play," rather than "If you don't load the dishwasher, you'd better watch out.").

Different cultures model, reinforce, and evoke different tendencies toward violence. For example, crime rates have been higher and average happiness lower in times and places marked by a great disparity between rich and poor (Messias et al., 2011; Oishi et al., 2011; Wilkinson & Pickett, 2009). And fathers matter (Triandis, 1994). Even after controlling for parental education, race, income, and teen motherhood, American male youths from father-absent homes are incarcerated at twice the rate of their peers (Harper & McLanahan, 2004).

Violence can vary by culture within a country. Richard Nisbett and Dov Cohen (1996) analyzed violence among White Americans in southern towns settled by Scots-Irish herders whose tradition emphasized "manly honor," the use of arms to protect one's flock, and a history of coercive slavery. Compared with their White counterparts in New England towns settled by the more traditionally peaceful Puritan, Quaker, and Dutch farmer-artisans, the cultural descendants of those herders had triple the homicide rates and were more supportive of physically punishing children, of warfare initiatives, and of uncontrolled gun ownership. "Culture of honor" states also have had higher rates of students bringing weapons to school and of school shootings (Brown et al., 2009).

MEDIA MODELS FOR VIOLENCE Parents are hardly the only aggression models. Television, films, video games, and the internet offer supersized portions of violence. An adolescent boy faced with a real-life challenge may "act like a man"—at least an action-film man—by

FIGURE 36.4

TEMPERATURE AND RETALIATION Researchers looked for occurrences of batters hit by pitches during 4,566,468 pitcher-batter matchups across 57,293 Major League Baseball games since 1952 (Larrick et al., 2011). The probability of a hit batter increased if one or more of the pitcher's teammates had been hit, and also with temperature.

frustration-aggression principle the principle that frustration—the blocking of an attempt to achieve some goal—creates anger, which can generate aggression.

social script a culturally modeled guide for how to act in various situations.

intimidating or eliminating the threat. Violent video game playing tends to make us less sensitive to cruelty (Arriaga et al., 2015). It also primes us to respond aggressively when provoked. And media violence teaches us **social scripts**—culturally provided mental files for how to act in certain situations. As more than 100 studies confirm, we sometimes imitate what we've viewed. Watching risk-glorifying behaviors (dangerous driving, extreme sports, unprotected sex) increases real-life risk taking (Fischer et al., 2011). Watching violent behaviors (murder, robbery) can increase real-life aggressiveness (Anderson et al., 2017).

Music lyrics also write social scripts. German university men who listened to woman-hating song lyrics administered the most hot chili sauce to a woman. Listening to man-hating song lyrics had a similar effect upon women (Fischer & Greitemeyer, 2006).

How does repeatedly watching pornographic films affect viewers? As pornography has become readily available, rates of reported sexual violence have decreased in the United States (though not in Canada, Australia, and Europe). Nevertheless, just as repeated viewing of on-screen violence helps immunize us to aggression, repeated viewing of pornography—even nonviolent pornography—makes sexual aggression seem less serious (Harris, 1994). In one experiment, undergraduates viewed six brief films each week for six weeks (Zillmann & Bryant, 1984). Some viewed sexually explicit films; others viewed films with no sexual content. Three weeks later, both groups, after reading a newspaper report about a man convicted of raping a female hitchhiker, suggested an appropriate prison term. Compared with sentences recommended by the control group, the sex film viewers recommended terms that were half as long. In other studies that explored pornography's effects on aggression toward relationship partners, pornography consumption predicted both self-reported aggression and participants' willingness to administer laboratory noise blasts to their partner (Lambert et al., 2011; Peter & Valkenburg, 2016).

Pornography with violent sexual content can increase men's readiness to behave aggressively toward women. A statement by 21 social scientists noted, "Pornography that portrays sexual aggression as pleasurable for the victim increases the acceptance of the use of coercion in sexual relations" (Surgeon General, 1986). Contrary to much popular opinion, viewing such depictions does not provide an outlet for bottled-up impulses. Rather, "in laboratory studies measuring short-term effects, exposure to violent pornography increases punitive behavior toward women."

COINCIDENCE OR CAUSE? In 2011, Norwegian Anders Behring Breivik bombed government buildings in Oslo, and then went to a youth camp where he shot and killed 69 people, mostly teens. As a player of first-person shooter games, Breivik stirred debate when he commented that "I see MW2 [*Modern Warfare 2*] more as a part of my training-simulation than anything else." Did his violent game playing—and that of the 2012 mass murderer of Newtown, Connecticut's first-grade children—contribute to the violence, or was it a merely coincidental association? To explore such questions, psychologists experiment.

AFP/Getty Images

DO VIOLENT VIDEO GAMES TEACH SOCIAL SCRIPTS FOR VIOLENCE? Experiments worldwide indicate that playing positive games produces positive effects (Greitemeyer & Mügge, 2014; Prot et al., 2014). For example, playing the classic video game *Lemmings*, where a goal was to help others, increased real-life helping. So, might a parallel effect occur after playing games that enact violence? Violent video games became an issue for public debate after teenagers in more than a dozen places seemed to mimic the carnage in the shooter games they had so often played (Anderson, 2004, 2013).

In 2002, three young men in Michigan spent part of a night drinking beer and playing *Grand Theft Auto III*. Using simulated cars, they ran down pedestrians, then beat them with fists, leaving a bloody body behind (Kolker, 2002). These same young men then went out for a real drive. Spotting a 38-year-old man on a bicycle, they ran him down with their car, got out, stomped and punched him, and returned home to play the game some more. (The victim, a father of three, died six days later.)

This is but one anecdote, and, as we social scientists say, "The plural of anecdote is not evidence." Yet such incidents of violent mimicry make us wonder: What are the effects of actively role-playing aggression? Does it cause people to become less sensitive to violence and more open to violent acts? Nearly 400 studies of 130,000 people offer some answers (Anderson et al., 2010; Calvert et al., 2017). Video games can prime aggressive thoughts, decrease empathy, and increase aggression. University men who spent the most hours playing violent video games have also tended to be the most physically aggressive (Anderson & Dill, 2000). For example, they more often acknowledged having hit or attacked someone else. And people randomly assigned to play a game involving bloody murders with groaning victims (rather than to play nonviolent *Myst*) became more hostile. On a follow-up task, they were more likely to blast intense noise at a fellow student.

Studies of young adolescents reveal that those who play a lot of violent video games become more aggressive and see the world as more hostile (Bushman, 2016; Exelmans et al., 2015; Gentile, 2009). Compared with nongaming kids, they get into more arguments and fights and earn poorer grades.

Ah, but is this merely because naturally hostile kids are drawn to such games? Apparently not. Comparisons of gamers and nongamers who scored low on hostility measures revealed a difference in the number of fights reported. Almost 4 in 10 violent-game players had been in fights, compared with only 4 in 100 of the nongaming kids (Anderson, 2004). Some researchers believe that, due partly to the more active participation and rewarded violence of game play, violent video games have even greater effects on aggressive behavior and cognition than do violent TV shows and movies (Anderson & Warburton, 2012).

Other researchers are unimpressed by such findings (Ferguson, 2013b, 2014, 2015). They note that from 1996 to 2006, video game sales increased yet youth violence declined. They argue that other factors—depression, family violence, peer influence—better predict aggression. The focused fun of game playing can also satisfy basic needs for a sense of competence, control, and social connection (Granic et al., 2014).

* * *

To sum up, research reveals biological, psychological, and social-cultural influences on aggressive behavior. Complex behaviors, including violence, have many causes, making any single explanation an oversimplification. Asking what causes violence is therefore like asking what causes cancer. Those who study the effects of asbestos exposure on cancer rates may remind us that asbestos is indeed a cancer cause, but it is only one among many. Like so much else, aggression is a biopsychosocial phenomenon (**FIGURE 36.5**).

A happy concluding note: Historical trends suggest that the world is becoming less violent over time (Pinker, 2011). That people vary across time and place reminds us that environments differ. Yesterday's plundering Vikings have become today's peace-promoting Scandinavians. Like all behavior, aggression arises from the interaction of persons and situations.

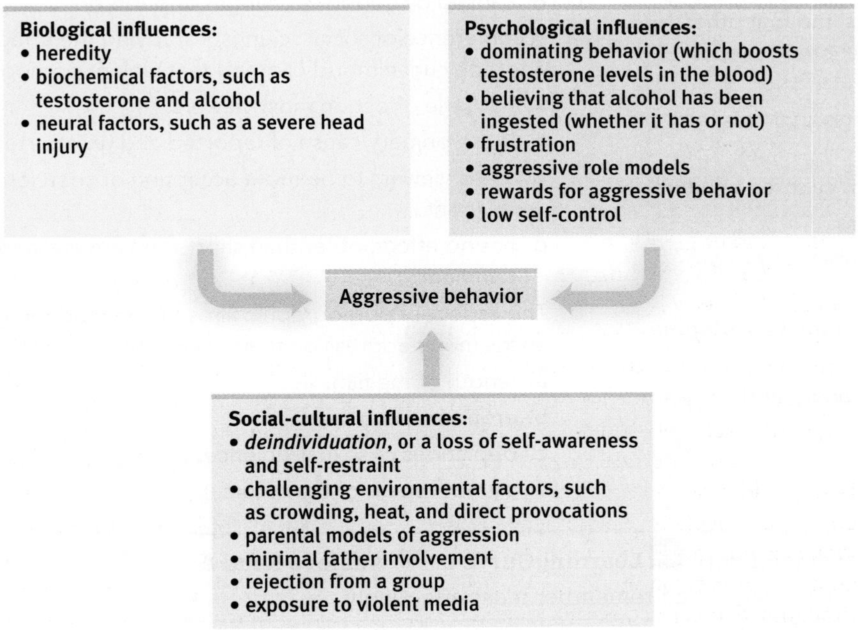

"Study finds exposure to violent children causes increased aggression in video game characters." —*The* [satirical] *Onion*, March 6, 2017

"Research demonstrates a consistent relation between violent video game use and increases in aggressive behavior, aggressive cognitions and aggressive affect, and decreases in prosocial behavior, empathy and sensitivity to aggression." —American Psychological Association Task Force on Violent Media, 2015

 (ASK YOURSELF)

In what ways have you been affected by social scripts for aggression? How have shows, movies, and video games contributed such scripts?

Biological influences:
• heredity
• biochemical factors, such as testosterone and alcohol
• neural factors, such as a severe head injury

Psychological influences:
• dominating behavior (which boosts testosterone levels in the blood)
• believing that alcohol has been ingested (whether it has or not)
• frustration
• aggressive role models
• rewards for aggressive behavior
• low self-control

Aggressive behavior

Social-cultural influences:
• *deindividuation*, or a loss of self-awareness and self-restraint
• challenging environmental factors, such as crowding, heat, and direct provocations
• parental models of aggression
• minimal father involvement
• rejection from a group
• exposure to violent media

 FIGURE 36.5

BIOPSYCHOSOCIAL UNDERSTANDING OF AGGRESSION Because many factors contribute to aggressive behavior, there are many ways to change such behavior, including learning anger management and communication skills, and avoiding violent media and video games.

 **RETRIEVE IT** • • •   *ANSWERS IN APPENDIX E*

RI-2 What biological, psychological, and social-cultural influences interact to produce aggressive behaviors?

🔒 REVIEW ANTISOCIAL RELATIONS

⤳ Learning Objectives

TEST YOURSELF Answer these repeated Learning Objective Questions on your own (before checking the answers in Appendix D) to improve your retention of the concepts (McDaniel et al., 2009, 2015).

36-1 What is *prejudice*? How do explicit and implicit prejudice differ?

36-2 What groups are frequent targets of prejudice?

36-3 What are some social, emotional, and cognitive roots of prejudice, and what are some ways to eliminate prejudice?

36-4 How does psychology's definition of *aggression* differ from everyday usage? What biological factors make us more prone to hurt one another?

36-5 What psychological and social-cultural factors may trigger aggressive behavior?

⤳ Terms and Concepts to Remember

TEST YOURSELF Write down the definition yourself, then check your answer on the referenced page.

prejudice, **p. 435**

stereotype, **p. 435**

discrimination, **p. 435**

just-world phenomenon, **p. 438**

ingroup, **p. 438**

outgroup, **p. 438**

ingroup bias, **p. 438**

scapegoat theory, **p. 438**

other-race effect, **p. 438**

aggression, **p. 441**

frustration-aggression principle, **p. 443**

social script, **p. 444**

⤳ Experience the Testing Effect

TEST YOURSELF Answer the following questions on your own first, then check your answers in Appendix E.

1. Prejudice toward a group involves negative feelings, a tendency to discriminate, and overly generalized beliefs referred to as _____.

2. If several well-publicized murders are committed by members of a particular group, we may tend to react with fear and suspicion toward all members of that group. What psychological principle can help explain this reaction?

3. The other-race effect occurs when we assume that other groups are _____ (more/less) homogeneous than our own group.

4. Evidence of a biochemical influence on aggression is the finding that
   a. aggressive behavior varies widely from culture to culture.
   b. animals can be bred for aggressiveness.
   c. stimulation of an area of the brain's limbic system produces aggressive behavior.
   d. a higher-than-average level of the hormone testosterone is associated with violent behavior in males.

5. When those who feel frustrated become angry and aggressive, this is referred to as the _____-_____ _____.

6. Studies show that parents of delinquent young people tend to use physical force to enforce discipline. This suggests that aggression can be
   a. learned through direct rewards.
   b. triggered by exposure to violent media.
   c. learned through observation of aggressive models.
   d. caused by hormone changes at puberty.

7. A conference of social scientists studying the effects of pornography unanimously agreed that violent pornography
   a. has little effect on most viewers.
   b. is the primary cause of reported and unreported rapes.
   c. leads viewers to be more accepting of coercion in sexual relations.
   d. has no effect, other than short-term arousal and entertainment.

8. The aspect of pornographic films that most directly influences men's aggression toward women seems to be the
   a. length of the film.
   b. eroticism portrayed.
   c. depictions of sexual violence.
   d. attractiveness of the actors.

Continue testing yourself with 📖 **LearningCurve** or ≈ **Achieve Read & Practice** to learn and remember most effectively.

37 Prosocial Relations

mere exposure effect the phenomenon that repeated exposure to novel stimuli increases liking of them.

As social animals—as people who need people—we often approach others not with closed fists, but with open arms. Social psychologists focus not only on the dark side of social relationships, but also on the bright side, by studying *prosocial* behavior—behavior that intends to help or benefit someone. Our positive behaviors toward others are evident from explorations of attraction, altruism, and peacemaking.

ATTRACTION

ENGAGE Pause a moment and think about your relationships with two people—a close friend and someone who has stirred your romantic feelings. What psychological chemistry binds us together in friendship or love? Social psychology suggests some answers.

The Psychology of Attraction

LOQ 37-1 Why do we befriend or fall in love with some people but not others?

We endlessly wonder how we can win others' affection and what makes our own affections flourish or fade. Does familiarity breed contempt, or does it amplify affection? Do birds of a feather flock together, or do opposites attract? Is it what's inside that counts, or does physical attractiveness matter, too? To explore these questions, let's consider three ingredients of our liking for one another: proximity, attractiveness, and similarity.

PROXIMITY Before friendships become close, they must begin. *Proximity*—geographic nearness—is friendship's most powerful predictor. Proximity can provide opportunities for aggression. But much more often it breeds liking (and sometimes even marriage) among those who live in the same neighborhood, sit nearby in class, work in the same office, share the same parking lot, or eat in the same dining hall. Look around. Mating starts with meeting.

Proximity breeds liking partly because of the **mere exposure effect.** Repeated exposure to novel visual stimuli increases our liking for them. By age 3 months, infants prefer photos of the race they most often see—usually their own race (Kelly et al., 2007). Familiarity with a face also makes it look happier (Carr et al., 2017). Mere exposure increases our liking not only for familiar faces, but also for familiar nonsense syllables, geometric figures, and Chinese characters, and for the letters of our own name (Moreland & Zajonc, 1982; Nuttin, 1987; Zajonc, 2001). So, within certain limits (after which the effect wears off), familiarity feeds fondness (Bornstein, 1989, 1999; Montoya et al., 2017). This would come as no surprise to the young Taiwanese man who wrote more than 700 letters to his girlfriend, urging her to marry him. She did marry—the mail carrier (Steinberg, 1993).

No face is more familiar than your own. And that helps explain an interesting finding by Lisa DeBruine (2002, 2004): We like other people when their faces incorporate some

(a)   (b)

Jeffrey Mayer/Getty Images

ENGAGE **WHICH IS THE REAL SOFÍA VERGARA?** The mere exposure effect applies even to ourselves. Because the human face is not perfectly symmetrical, the face we see in the mirror is not the same face our friends see. Most of us prefer the familiar mirror image, while our friends like the reverse (Mita et al., 1977). The person actress Sofía Vergara sees in the mirror each morning is shown in (b), and that's the photo she would probably prefer.

morphed features of our own. When McMaster University students played a game with a supposed other player, they were more trusting and cooperative when the other person's image had some of their own facial features morphed into it. In me I trust.

MODERN MATCHMAKING Those who have not found a romantic partner in their immediate proximity may cast a wider net by joining an online dating service. Millions search for love on one of 8000 dating sites (Hatfield, 2016). In 2015, 27 percent of 18- to 24-year-old Americans tried an online dating service or mobile dating app (Smith, 2016).

Online matchmaking definitely expands the pool of potential mates (Finkel et al., 2012a,b). But how effective is the matchmaking? Compared with those formed in person, internet-formed friendships and romantic relationships are, on average, slightly more likely to last and be satisfying (Bargh & McKenna, 2004; Bargh et al., 2002; Cacioppo et al., 2013). In one study, people disclosed more, with less posturing, to those whom they met online (McKenna et al., 2002). When conversing online with someone for 20 minutes, they felt more liking for that person than they did for someone they had met and talked with face-to-face. This was true even when (unknown to them) it was the same person! Internet friendships often feel as real and important as in-person relationships.

Small wonder that a survey found a leading online matchmaker enabling more than 500 U.S. marriages a day (Harris Interactive, 2010). By one estimate, online dating is now responsible for about a fifth of U.S. marriages (Crosier et al., 2012). And in a national survey of straight and gay/lesbian couples, nearly a quarter of heterosexual couples and some two-thirds of same-sex couples met online (Rosenfeld & Thomas, 2012; see **FIGURE 37.1**).

Speed dating pushes the search for romance into high gear. In a process pioneered by a matchmaking Jewish rabbi, people meet a succession of prospective partners, either in person or via webcam (Bower, 2009). After a 3- to 8-minute conversation, people move on to the next prospect. (In an in-person heterosexual meeting, one group—usually the women—remains seated while the other group circulates.) Those who want to meet again can arrange for future contact. For many participants, 4 minutes is enough time to form a feeling about a conversational partner and to register whether the partner likes them (Eastwick & Finkel, 2008a,b).

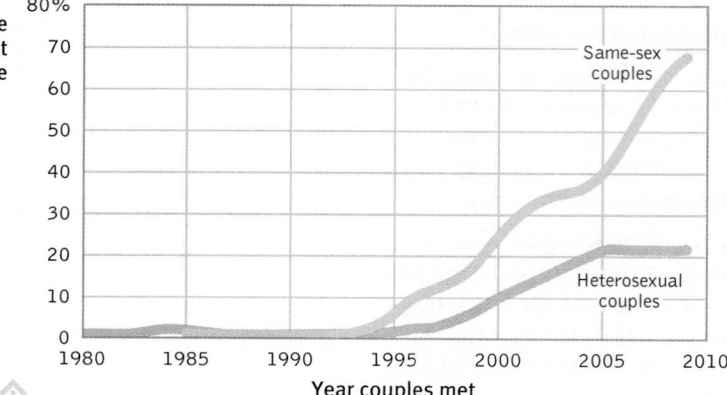

FIGURE 37.1

PERCENTAGE OF HETEROSEXUAL AND SAME-SEX COUPLES WHO MET ONLINE (Data from Rosenfeld & Thomas, 2012.)

For researchers, speed dating offers a unique opportunity for studying influences on our first impressions of potential romantic partners. Some recent findings:

- **People who fear rejection often elicit it.** After a 3-minute speed date, those who most feared rejection were least often selected for a follow-up date (McClure & Lydon, 2014).

- **Given more options, people make more superficial choices.** When people meet lots of potential partners, they focus on more easily assessed characteristics, such as height and weight (Lenton & Francesconi, 2010).

- **Men wish for future contact with more of their speed dates; women tend to be choosier.** But this difference disappears if the conventional roles are reversed, so that men stay seated while women circulate (Finkel & Eastwick, 2009).

PHYSICAL ATTRACTIVENESS Once proximity affords us contact, what most affects our first impressions? The person's sincerity? Intelligence? Personality? Hundreds of experiments (all in a heterosexual context) reveal that it is something more superficial: physical appearance. This finding is unnerving for those of us taught that "beauty is only skin deep" and "appearances can be deceiving."

In one early study, researchers randomly matched new University of Minnesota students for a Welcome Week dance (Walster et al., 1966). Before the dance, the researchers gave each student a battery of personality and aptitude tests, and they rated each student's physical attractiveness. During the blind date, the couples danced and talked for more than two hours and then took a brief intermission to rate their dates.

"I'd like to meet the algorithm that thought we'd be a good match."

What predicted whether they liked each other? Only one thing: appearance. Both the men and the women liked good-looking dates best. Women are more likely than men to say that another's looks don't affect them (Lippa, 2007). But studies show that a man's looks do affect women's behavior (Eastwick et al., 2014a,b). In speed-dating experiments, as in Tinder swipes, attractiveness influences first impressions for both sexes (Belot & Francesconi, 2006; Finkel & Eastwick, 2008).

Physical attractiveness also predicts how often people date and how popular they feel. And it affects initial impressions of people's personalities. We don't assume that attractive people are more compassionate, but we do perceive them as healthier, happier, more sensitive, more successful, and more socially skilled (Eagly et al., 1991; Feingold, 1992; Hatfield & Sprecher, 1986).

For those who find the importance of looks unfair and unenlightened, three other findings may be reassuring.

- People's attractiveness is surprisingly unrelated to their self-esteem and happiness (Diener et al., 1995; Major et al., 1984). Unless we have just compared ourselves with superattractive people, few of us (thanks, perhaps, to the mere exposure effect) view ourselves as unattractive (Thornton & Moore, 1993).

- Strikingly attractive people are sometimes suspicious that praise for their work may simply be a reaction to their looks. Less attractive people have been more likely to accept praise as sincere (Berscheid, 1981).

- For couples who were friends before lovers—who became romantically involved long after first meeting—looks matter less (Hunt et al., 2015). With slow-cooked love, shared values and interests matter more.

Beauty is also in the eye of the culture. Hoping to look attractive, people across the globe have pierced and tattooed their bodies, lengthened their necks, bound their feet, dyed their hair, and artificially lightened or darkened their skin and hair. They have gorged themselves to achieve a full figure or liposuctioned fat to achieve a slim one, applied chemicals hoping to rid themselves of unwanted hair or to regrow wanted hair, strapped on leather garments to make their breasts seem smaller or relied on push-up bras and surgery to make them look bigger. Cultural ideals change over time. For women in North America, the ultrathin ideal of the Roaring Twenties gave way to the soft, voluptuous Marilyn Monroe ideal of the 1950s, only to be replaced by today's lean yet busty ideal.

Some aspects of heterosexual attractiveness, however, do cross place and time (Cunningham et al., 2005; Langlois et al., 2000). By providing reproductive clues, bodies influence sexual attraction. As evolutionary psychologists explain, men in many cultures, from Australia to Zambia, judge women as more attractive if they have a youthful, fertile appearance, suggested by a low waist-to-hip ratio (Karremans et al., 2010; Perilloux et al., 2010; Platek & Singh, 2010). Women feel attracted to healthy-looking men, but especially to those who seem mature, dominant, masculine, and affluent (Gallup & Frederick, 2010; Gangestad et al., 2010). But faces matter, too. When people rate opposite-sex faces and bodies separately, the face tends to be the better predictor of overall physical attractiveness (Currie & Little, 2009; Peters et al., 2007).

"Personal beauty is a greater recommendation than any letter of introduction." —Aristotle, *Apothegms*, 330 B.C.E.

Sean Caffrey/Getty Images

Blend Images/Alamy

svetikd/Getty Images

IN THE EYE OF THE BEHOLDER
Conceptions of attractiveness vary by culture and over time. Yet some adult physical features, such as a healthy appearance and a relatively symmetrical face, seem attractive everywhere.

EXTREME MAKEOVER In affluent, beauty-conscious cultures, increasing numbers of people, such as reality TV star Kylie Jenner, have turned to cosmetic procedures to change their looks.

Our feelings also influence our attractiveness judgments. Imagine two people: One is honest, humorous, and polite. The other is rude, unfair, and abusive. Which one is more attractive? Most people perceive the person with the appealing traits as more physically attractive (Lewandowski et al., 2007). Or imagine being paired with a stranger of the sex you find attractive, who listens intently to your self-disclosures. Might you feel a twinge of sexual attraction toward that empathic person? Student volunteers did, in several experiments (Birnbaum & Reis, 2012). Our feelings influence our perceptions. Those we like we find attractive.

In a Rodgers and Hammerstein musical of the fairy tale, Prince Charming asks Cinderella, "Do I love you because you're beautiful, or are you beautiful because I love you?" Chances are it's both. As we see our loved ones again and again, their physical imperfections grow less noticeable and their attractiveness grows more apparent (Beaman & Klentz, 1983; Gross & Crofton, 1977). Shakespeare said it in *A Midsummer Night's Dream*: "Love looks not with the eyes, but with the mind." Come to love someone and watch beauty grow. Love sees loveliness.

SIMILARITY So proximity has brought you into contact with someone, and your appearance has made an acceptable first impression. What influences whether you will become friends? As you get to know each other, will the chemistry be better if you are opposites or if you are alike?

It makes a good story—extremely different types liking or loving each other: Rat, Mole, and Badger in *The Wind in the Willows,* the Beauty and the Beast, Frog and Toad in Arnold Lobel's books. These stories delight us by expressing what we seldom experience. In real life, opposites retract (Rosenbaum, 1986; Montoya & Horton, 2013). Compared with randomly paired people, friends and couples are far more likely to share common attitudes, beliefs, and interests (and, for that matter, age, religion, race, education, intelligence, smoking behavior, and economic status). Moreover, the more alike people are, the more their liking endures (Byrne, 1971). Journalist Walter Lippmann was right to suppose that love lasts "when the lovers love many things together, and not merely each other." Similarity breeds content.

Proximity, attractiveness, and similarity are not the only determinants of attraction. We also like those who like us. This is especially true when our self-image is low. When we believe someone likes us, we feel good and respond to them warmly, which leads them to like us even more (Curtis & Miller, 1986). To be liked is powerfully rewarding.

Indeed, all the findings we have considered so far can be explained by a simple *reward theory of attraction:* We will like those whose behavior is rewarding to us, including those who are both able and willing to help us achieve our goals (Montoya & Horton, 2014). When people live or work in close proximity to us, it requires less time and effort to develop the friendship and enjoy its benefits. When people are attractive, they are aesthetically pleasing, and associating with them can be socially rewarding. When people share our views, they reward us by validating our beliefs.

Similarity attracts; perceived dissimilarity does not.

"I like the Pope unless the Pope doesn't like me. Then I don't like the Pope." —Donald Trump, February 18, 2016

ASK YOURSELF

To what extent have your closest relationships been affected by proximity, physical attractiveness, and similarity?

 LaunchPad Test your own ability to improve your relationships by engaging online with **Immersive Learning: Assess Your Strengths—Are You a "Skilled Opener," and How Does This Affect Your Relationships?**

passionate love an aroused state of intense positive absorption in another, usually present at the beginning of a romantic relationship.

companionate love the deep affectionate attachment we feel for those with whom our lives are intertwined.

Romantic Love

LOQ 37-2 How does romantic love typically change as time passes?

Sometimes people move quickly from initial impressions to friendship to the more intense, complex, and mysterious state of romantic love. If love endures, temporary *passionate love* will mellow into a lingering *companionate love* (Hatfield, 1988).

PASSIONATE LOVE **Passionate love** mixes something new with something positive (Aron et al., 2000; Coulter & Malouff, 2013). We intensely desire to be with our partner, and seeing our partner stimulates blood flow to a brain region linked to craving and obsession (Acevedo et al., 2012; Hatfield et al., 2015).

The *two-factor theory of emotion* can help us understand the intense positive absorption of passionate love (Hatfield, 1988). That theory assumes that

• emotions have two ingredients—*physical arousal* plus *cognitive appraisal*.

• arousal from any source can enhance one emotion or another, depending on how we interpret and label the arousal.

In one classic experiment, researchers studied men crossing two bridges above British Columbia's rocky Capilano River (Dutton & Aron, 1974, 1989). One, a swaying footbridge, was 230 feet (70 meters) above the rocks; the other was low and solid. As the men came off each bridge, an attractive young woman working for the researchers intercepted them and asked them to fill out a short questionnaire. She then offered her phone number in case they wanted to hear more about her project. Far more of the men who had just crossed the high bridge—which left their hearts pounding—accepted the number and later called the woman.

To be revved up and to associate some of that arousal with a desirable person is to feel the pull of passion. Adrenaline makes the heart grow fonder. Sexual desire + a growing attachment = passionate love (Berscheid, 2010).

COMPANIONATE LOVE Although the desire and attachment of romantic love often endure, the intense absorption in the other, the thrill of the romance, the giddy "floating on a cloud" feelings typically fade. Does this mean the French are correct in saying that "love makes the time pass and time makes love pass"? Or can friendship and commitment keep a relationship going after the passion cools?

As love matures, it typically becomes a steadier **companionate love**—a deep, affectionate attachment (Hatfield, 1988). Like a passing storm, the flood of passion-facilitating hormones (testosterone, dopamine, adrenaline) subsides. But another hormone, *oxytocin,* remains, supporting feelings of trust, calmness, and bonding with the mate. This shift from passion to attachment may have adaptive value (Reis & Aron, 2008). Passionate love often produces children, whose survival is aided by the parents' waning obsession with each another.

In the most satisfying of marriages, attraction and sexual desire endure, minus the obsession of early stage romance (Acevedo & Aron, 2009). Indeed, failure to appreciate passionate love's limited half-life can doom a relationship (Berscheid et al., 1984). Recognizing the short duration of obsessive passionate love, some societies deem such feelings an irrational reason for marrying. Better, they say, to search for (or have someone search for you) a partner with a compatible background and interests. Non-Western cultures, where people often rate love as less important for marriage, do have lower divorce rates (Levine et al., 1995).

Snapshots at jasonlove.com

Bill looked at Susan, Susan at Bill. Suddenly death didn't seem like an option. This was love at first sight.

HI & LOIS

"When two people are under the influence of the most violent, most insane, most delusive, and most transient of passions, they are required to swear that they will remain in that excited, abnormal, and exhausting condition continuously until death do them part." —George Bernard Shaw, "Getting Married," 1908

One key to a gratifying and enduring relationship is **equity.** When equity exists—when both partners receive in proportion to what they give—the chances for sustained and satisfying companionate love have been good (Gray-Little & Burks, 1983; Van Yperen & Buunk, 1990). In one national survey, "sharing household chores" ranked third, after "faithfulness" and a "happy sexual relationship," on a list of nine things people associated with successful marriages. As the Pew Research Center (2007) summarized, "I like hugs. I like kisses. But what I really love is help with the dishes."

Equity's importance extends beyond marriage. Mutually sharing one's self and possessions, making decisions together, giving and getting emotional support, promoting and caring about each other's welfare—all of these acts are at the core of every type of loving relationship (Sternberg & Grajek, 1984). It's true for lovers, for parent and child, and for close friends.

Sharing includes **self-disclosure,** revealing intimate details about ourselves—our likes and dislikes, our dreams and worries, our proud and shameful moments. "When I am with my friend," noted the Roman statesman Seneca, "methinks I am alone, and as much at liberty to speak anything as to think it." Self-disclosure breeds liking, and liking breeds self-disclosure (Collins & Miller, 1994). As one person reveals a little, the other reciprocates, the first then reveals more, and on and on, as friends or lovers move to deeper intimacy (Baumeister & Bratslavsky, 1999).

One experiment marched some student pairs through 45 minutes of increasingly self-disclosing conversation—from "What is the greatest accomplishment of your life?" to "When did you last cry in front of another person? By yourself?" Other pairs spent the time with small-talk questions, such as "What was your high school like?" (Aron et al., 1997). By the experiment's end, those experiencing the escalating intimacy felt much closer to their conversation partner than did the small-talkers. Likewise, after dating couples spent 45 minutes answering such questions, they felt increased love (Welker et al., 2014).

In addition to equity and self-disclosure, a third key to enduring love is *positive support.* Relationship conflicts are inevitable, but hurtful communications are not. Do we more often express sarcasm or support, scorn or sympathy, sneers or smiles? For unhappy couples, disagreements, criticisms, and put-downs are routine. For happy couples in enduring relationships, positive interactions (compliments, touches, laughing) outnumber negative interactions (sarcasm, disapproval, insults) by at least 5 to 1 (Gottman, 2007; see also Sullivan et al., 2010).

In the mathematics of love, self-disclosing intimacy + mutually supportive equity = enduring companionate love.

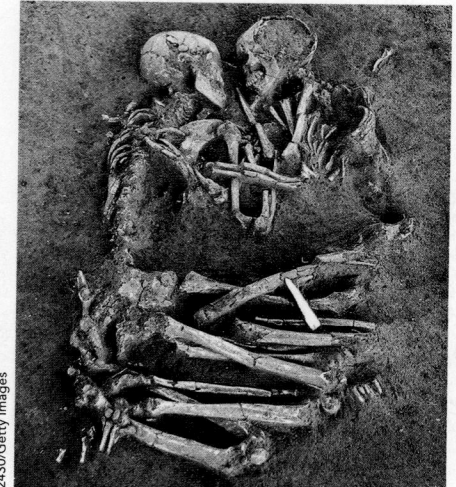

LOVE IS AN ANCIENT THING This 5000- to 6000-year-old "Romeo and Juliet" young couple was unearthed locked in embrace, near Rome.

2430/Getty Images

> 🔒 **RETRIEVE IT • • •**   *ANSWERS IN APPENDIX E*
>
> **RI-3** How does the two-factor theory of emotion help explain *passionate love?*
>
> **RI-4** Two vital components for maintaining *companionate love* are _____ and _____-_____.

ALTRUISM

LOQ 37-3 What is *altruism?* When are people most—and least—likely to help?

Altruism is an unselfish concern for the welfare of others. In rescuing his trapped jailer, rather than continuing his escape, Dirk Willems exemplified altruism. Willems fits the definition of a *hero*—moral, courageous, and protective of those in need (Kinsella et al., 2015). Carl Wilkens and Paul Rusesabagina displayed another heroic example of altruism in Kigali, Rwanda. Wilkens, a Seventh-day Adventist missionary, was living there in 1994 with his family when militia from the Hutu ethnic group began to slaughter members of a minority ethnic group, the Tutsis. The U.S. government, church leaders, and friends all implored Wilkens to leave. He refused. After evacuating his family, and even after every other American had left Kigali, he alone stayed and contested the 800,000-person genocide. When the militia came to kill him and his Tutsi servants, Wilkens' Hutu neighbors deterred them. Despite repeated death threats, he spent his days running roadblocks to take food and water to orphanages and to negotiate, plead, and bully his way through the bloodshed, saving lives time and again. "It just seemed the right thing to do," he later explained (Kristof, 2004).

Elsewhere in Kigali, Rusesabagina, a Hutu married to a Tutsi and the acting manager of a luxury hotel, was sheltering more than 1200 terrified Tutsis and moderate Hutus. When most international peacekeepers abandoned the city and hostile militia threatened his guests in the "Hotel Rwanda" (as it came to be called in a 2004 movie), the courageous Rusesabagina began cashing in past favors. He bribed the militia and telephoned influential people abroad to exert pressure on local authorities, thereby sparing the lives of the hotel's occupants, despite the surrounding chaos. Both Wilkens and Rusesabagina were displaying altruism.

Altruism became a major concern of social psychologists after an especially vile act. On March 13, 1964, a stalker repeatedly stabbed Kitty Genovese, then raped her as she lay dying outside her Queens, New York, apartment at 3:30 A.M. "Oh, my God, he stabbed me!" Genovese screamed into the early morning stillness. "Please help me!" Windows opened and lights went on as some neighbors heard her screams. Her attacker fled and then returned to stab and rape her again. Until it was too late, no one called police or came to her aid.

Bystander Intervention

Reflecting on initial reports of the Genovese murder and other such tragedies, most commentators were outraged by the bystanders' apparent "apathy" and "indifference." Rather than blaming the onlookers, social psychologists John Darley and Bibb Latané (1968b) attributed their inaction to an important situational factor—the presence of others. Given certain circumstances, they suspected, most of us might behave similarly. To paraphrase the French writer Voltaire, we all are guilty of the good we did not do.

After staging emergencies under various conditions, Darley and Latané assembled their findings into a decision scheme: We will help only if the situation enables us first to *notice* the incident, then to *interpret* it as an emergency, and finally to *assume responsibility* for helping (**FIGURE 37.2**). At each step, the presence of others can turn us away from the path that leads to helping.

One of Darley and Latané's experiments staged a fake emergency as students in separate laboratory rooms took turns talking over an intercom. Only the person whose microphone was switched on could be heard. When his turn came, one student (an accomplice of the experimenters) pretended to have an epileptic seizure, and he called for help (Darley & Latané, 1968a).

How did the others react? As **FIGURE 37.3** shows, those who believed only they could hear the victim—and therefore thought they alone were responsible for helping him—usually went to his aid. Students who thought others could also hear the victim's cries were more likely to do nothing. When more people shared responsibility for helping—when there was a *diffusion of responsibility*—any single listener was less likely to help. Indeed, inattention and diffused responsibility contribute to the "global bystander nonintervention" as millions of far-away people die of hunger, disease, and genocide (Pittinsky & Diamante, 2015).

FIGURE 37.2

THE DECISION-MAKING PROCESS FOR BYSTANDER INTERVENTION Before helping, one must first notice an emergency, then correctly interpret it, and then feel responsible. (Data from Darley & Latané, 1968b.)

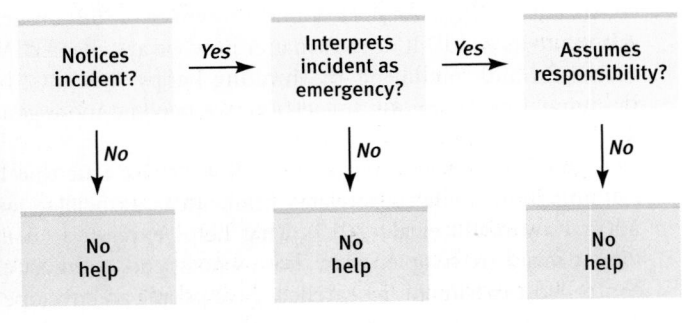

FIGURE 37.3

RESPONSES TO A SIMULATED EMERGENCY When people thought they alone heard the calls for help from a person they believed to be having an epileptic seizure, they usually helped. But when they thought four others were also hearing the calls, fewer than one-third responded. (Data from Darley & Latané, 1968a.)

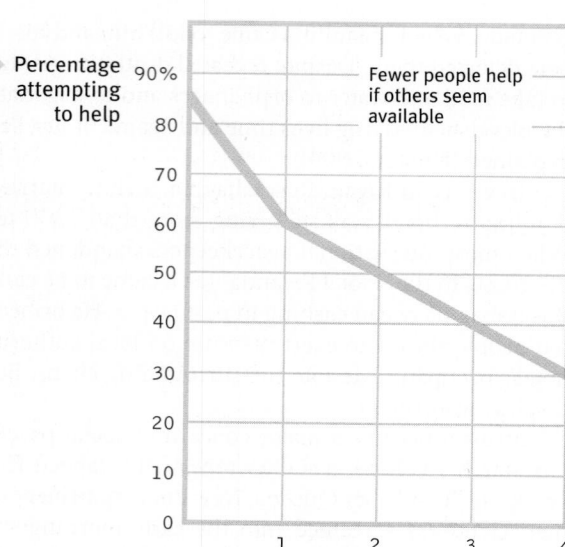

Percentage attempting to help

Fewer people help if others seem available

Number of others presumed available to help

LaunchPad To test your understanding of emergency helping, engage online with **Concept Practice: When Will People Help Others?**

© 2006 Nick Downe

PLEASE GIVE TO ALTRUISM RESEARCH

Hundreds of additional experiments have confirmed this **bystander effect.** For example, researchers and their assistants took 1497 elevator rides in three cities and "accidentally" dropped coins or pencils in front of 4813 fellow passengers (Latané & Dabbs, 1975). When alone with the person in need, 40 percent helped; in the presence of 5 other bystanders, only 20 percent helped. Ironically, Kitty Genovese's killer, Winston Moseley, was captured thanks to the intervention of a single bystander who confronted him as he later burgled a home. Disbelieving Moseley's explanation that he was helping the owners move, the bystander called another neighbor, who called police, and then pulled wires to disable Moseley's car (Kassin, 2017).

Observations of behavior in thousands of these situations—relaying an emergency phone call, aiding a stranded motorist, donating blood, picking up dropped books, contributing money, giving time—show that the odds of our helping someone depend on the characteristics of the person, the situation, and our own internal state. The odds of helping are highest when

- the person appears to need and deserve help.
- the person is in some way similar to us.
- the person is a woman.
- we have just observed someone else being helpful.
- we are not in a hurry.
- we are in a small town or rural area.
- we are feeling guilty.
- we are focused on others and not preoccupied.
- we are in a good mood.

This last result, that happy people are helpful people, is one of psychology's most consistent findings. As poet Robert Browning (1868) observed, "Oh, make us happy and you make us good!" It doesn't matter how we are cheered. Whether by being made to feel successful and intelligent, by thinking happy thoughts, by finding money, or even by receiving a posthypnotic suggestion, we become more generous and more eager to help (Carlson et al., 1988).

So happiness breeds helpfulness. But it's also true that helpfulness breeds happiness. Helping those in need activates brain areas associated with reward (Harbaugh et al., 2007; Kawamichi et al., 2015). That helps explain a curious finding: People who give money away are happier than those who spend it almost entirely on themselves. In one controlled experiment, researchers gave people an envelope with cash and instructed one group to spend it on themselves and another to spend it on others (Dunn et al., 2008;

ASK YOURSELF

Imagine being a newcomer needing directions at a busy bus terminal. What could you do to increase the odds that someone would assist you, and what sort of person would be most likely to help?

Dunn & Norton, 2013). Which group was happiest at the day's end? It was, indeed, those assigned to the spend-it-on-others condition. And in a survey of more than 200,000 people worldwide, people in both rich and poor countries were happier with their lives if they had donated to a charity in the last month. Just reflecting on an instance of spending money on others provides most people with a mood boost (Aknin et al., 2013).

🔒 **RETRIEVE IT** • • •   *ANSWERS IN APPENDIX E*

RI-5 Why didn't anybody help Kitty Genovese? What social psychology principle did this incident illustrate?

Helping: Self-Interest or Socialization?

LOQ 37-4 How do social exchange theory and social norms explain helping behavior?

Why do we help? One widely held view is that self-interest underlies all human interactions, that our constant goal is to maximize rewards and minimize costs. Accountants call it *cost-benefit analysis.* Philosophers call it *utilitarianism.* Social psychologists call it **social exchange theory.** If you are considering donating blood, you may weigh the costs of doing so (time, discomfort, anxiety) against the benefits (reduced guilt, social approval, good feelings). If the rewards exceed the costs, you will help.

Others believe we help because we have been socialized to do so, through norms that prescribe how we *ought* to behave. (Everett et al., 2015). Two such norms are the *reciprocity norm* and the *social-responsibility norm.*

The **reciprocity norm** is the expectation that we should return help, not harm, to those who have helped us. In our relations with others of similar status, this norm compels us to give (in favors, gifts, or social invitations) about as much as we receive. Sometimes this means "paying it forward," as happened in one experiment, when people who were treated generously became more likely to be generous to a stranger (Tsvetkova & Macy, 2014). Returning favors feels good, making the norm of reciprocity a pleasant strategy to help others (Hein et al., 2016).

The reciprocity norm kicked in after Dave Tally, a Tempe, Arizona, homeless man, found $3300 in a backpack that an Arizona State University student had misplaced on his way to buy a used car (Lacey, 2010). Instead of using the cash for much-needed bike repairs, food, and shelter, Tally turned the backpack in to the social service agency where he volunteered. To reciprocate Tally's help, the backpack's owner thanked him with a monetary reward. Hearing about Tally's self-giving deeds, dozens of others also sent him money and job offers.

The **social-responsibility norm** is the expectation that we should help those who need our help—young children and others who cannot give as much as they receive—even if the costs outweigh the benefits. Europeans are most welcoming of asylum seekers who are most vulnerable—those, for example, who have been tortured or have no surviving family (Bansak et al., 2016). Many world religions encourage their followers to practice the social-responsibility norm, and sometimes this leads to prosocial behavior. Between 2006 and 2008, Gallup polls sampled more than 300,000 people across 140 countries, comparing the "highly religious" (who said religion was important to them and who had attended a religious service in the prior week) to the less religious. The highly religious, despite being poorer, were about 50 percent more likely to report having "donated money to a charity in the last month" and to have volunteered time to an organization (Pelham & Crabtree, 2008).

FROM CONFLICT TO PEACE

Positive social norms encourage generosity and enable group living. But conflicts often divide us. One response to recent conflict- and scarcity-driven mass migrations has been increasing nationalism and nativism. Moreover, *every day* the world continues to spend almost $5 billion for arms and armies—money that could be used for needed housing, nutrition, education, and health care. Knowing that wars begin in human minds, psychologists have wondered: What in the human mind causes destructive conflict? How might the perceived threats of social diversity be replaced by a spirit of cooperation?

bystander effect the tendency for any given bystander to be less likely to give aid if other bystanders are present.

social exchange theory the theory that our social behavior is an exchange process, the aim of which is to maximize benefits and minimize costs.

reciprocity norm an expectation that people will help, not hurt, those who have helped them.

social-responsibility norm an expectation that people will help those needing their help.

Jeff J. Mitchell/Getty Images

NOT IN MY OCEAN! Many people support alternative energy sources, including wind turbines. But proposals to construct wind farms in real-world places elicit less support. Wind turbines in the Highlands and off the coast of Scotland have produced heated debate over the benefits of clean energy versus the costs of altering treasured scenic views.

Elements of Conflict

LOQ 37-5 How do social traps and mirror-image perceptions fuel social conflict?

To a social psychologist, a **conflict** is a perceived incompatibility of actions, goals, or ideas. The elements of conflict are much the same, whether partners sparring, political groups feuding, or nations at war. In each situation, conflict may seed positive change, or be a destructive process that can produce unwanted results. Among the destructive processes are *social traps* and *distorted perceptions*.

SOCIAL TRAPS In some situations, pursuing our personal interests also supports our collective well-being. As capitalist Adam Smith wrote in *The Wealth of Nations* (1776), "It is not from the benevolence of the butcher, the brewer, or the baker that we expect our dinner, but from their regard to their own interest." In other situations, we *harm* our collective well-being by pursuing our personal interests. Such situations are **social traps.**

Researchers have created mini social traps in laboratory games that require two participants to choose between pursuing their immediate self-interest, at others' expense, versus cooperating for mutual benefit. Many real-life situations similarly pit our individual interests against our communal well-being. Individual car owners reason, "Electric cars are more expensive. Besides, the fuel that I burn in my one car doesn't noticeably add to the greenhouse gases." When enough people reason similarly, the collective result risks disaster—climate change with rising seas and more extreme weather. In 2018, as Cape Town faced the prospect of "Day Zero"—when their water reservoir was predicted to be depleted after three years of drought—the city pleaded for voluntary water conservation. Alas, with nearly 4 million residents, it was easy for any individual to think that "my washing my hair or flushing the toilet won't noticeably affect the remaining water." The result: Businesses and residents conserved less than hoped for, hastening the reservoir depletion (Maxmen, 2018).

Social traps challenge us to reconcile our right to pursue our personal well-being with our responsibility for the well-being of all. Psychologists have therefore explored ways to convince people to cooperate for their mutual betterment—through agreed-upon *regulations,* through better *communication,* and through promoting *awareness* of our responsibilities toward community, nation, and the whole of humanity (Dawes, 1980; Linder, 1982; Sato, 1987). Given effective regulations, communication, and awareness, people more often cooperate, whether playing a laboratory game or the real game of life.

ENEMY PERCEPTIONS Psychologists have noted that those in conflict have a curious tendency to form diabolical images of one another. These distorted images are, ironically, so similar that we call them **mirror-image perceptions:** As we see "them"—as untrustworthy, with evil intentions—so "they" see us. Each demonizes the other. My political party has benevolent motives; the other party is malevolent (Waytz et al., 2014).

Mirror-image perceptions can often feed a vicious cycle of hostility. If Juan believes Maria is annoyed with him, he may snub her, causing her to act in ways that justify his perception. As with individuals, so with countries. Perceptions can become **self-fulfilling prophecies**—beliefs that confirm themselves by influencing the other country to react in ways that seem to justify them.

Individuals and nations alike tend to see their own actions as responses to provocation, not as the causes of what happens next. Perceiving themselves as returning tit for tat, they often hit back harder, as University College London volunteers did in one experiment (Shergill et al., 2003). After feeling pressure on their own finger, they were to use a mechanical device to press on another volunteer's finger. Although told to reciprocate with the same amount of pressure, they typically responded with about 40 percent more force than they had just experienced. Despite seeking only to respond in kind, their touches soon escalated to hard presses, much as when each child after a fight claims that "I just poked him, but he hit me harder."

Mirror-image perceptions feed similar cycles of hostility on the world stage. To most people, torture seems more justified when done by "us" rather than "them" (Tarrant et al., 2012). In some American media reports, Muslims who kill have been portrayed as fanatical, hateful terrorists, while an American who allegedly killed 16 Afghans was portrayed as stressed out from marriage problems, four tours of duty, and a friend's having had his leg blown off (Greenwald, 2012).

conflict a perceived incompatibility of actions, goals, or ideas.

social trap a situation in which the conflicting parties, by each pursuing their self-interest rather than the good of the group, become caught in mutually destructive behavior.

mirror-image perceptions mutual views often held by conflicting people, as when each side sees itself as ethical and peaceful and views the other side as evil and aggressive.

self-fulfilling prophecy a belief that leads to its own fulfillment.

The point is not that truth must lie midway between two such views (one may be more accurate). The point is that enemy perceptions often form mirror images. Moreover, as enemies change, so do perceptions. In American minds and media, the "bloodthirsty, cruel, treacherous" Japanese of World War II later became our "intelligent, hardworking, self-disciplined, resourceful allies" (Gallup, 1972).

🔒 **RETRIEVE IT** • • •   *ANSWERS IN APPENDIX E*

RI-6 Why do sports fans tend to feel a sense of satisfaction when their archrival team loses? Do such feelings, in other settings, make conflict resolution more challenging?

Promoting Peace

LOQ 37-6 What can we do to promote peace?

How can we make peace? Can contact, cooperation, communication, and conciliation transform the antagonisms fed by prejudice and conflict into attitudes that promote peace? Research indicates that, in some cases, they can.

CONTACT Does it help to put two conflicting parties into close contact? It depends. Negative contact increases *disliking* (Graf et al., 2014; Paolini et al., 2014). But positive contact—especially noncompetitive contact between parties of equal status, such as fellow store clerks—typically helps. Initially prejudiced co-workers of different races have, in such circumstances, usually come to accept one another. This finding is confirmed by a statistical digest of more than 500 studies of face-to-face contact between majority people and outgroups (such as ethnic minorities, older and LGBTQ people, and those with disabilities). Among the quarter-million people studied across 38 nations, contact has correlated with (and in experiments has led to) more positive attitudes (Al Ramiah & Hewstone, 2013; Lemmer & Wagner, 2015; Pettigrew & Tropp, 2011). Some examples:

- With cross-racial contact, South Africans' interracial attitudes have moved "into closer alignment" (Dixon et al., 2007; Finchilescu & Tredoux, 2010; Swart et al., 2011).

- Heterosexuals' attitudes toward gay people are influenced not only by *what* they know but also by *whom* they know (Collier et al., 2012; Smith et al., 2009). In surveys, the reason people most often give for becoming more supportive of same-sex marriage is "having friends, family, or acquaintances who are gay or lesbian" (Pew, 2013a). And in the United States, where attitudes toward gays have become more positive, 87 percent of people now say they know someone who is gay (Pew, 2016).

- Friendly interracial contact, say between Blacks and Whites as roommates, improves attitudes toward others of the different race, and even toward other racial groups (Gaither & Sommers, 2013; Tausch et al., 2010).

However, contact is not always enough. In many schools, ethnic groups segregate themselves in lunchrooms, in classrooms, and elsewhere on school grounds (Alexander & Tredoux, 2010; Clack et al., 2005; Schofield, 1986). People in each group often think that they would welcome more contact with the other group, but they assume the other group does not reciprocate the wish (Richeson & Shelton, 2007). "I don't reach out to them, because I don't want to be rebuffed; they don't reach out to me, because they're just not interested." When such mirror-image misperceptions are corrected, friendships may form and prejudices melt.

COOPERATION To see if enemies could overcome their differences, researcher Muzafer Sherif (1966) set a conflict in motion at a boys' summer camp. He separated 22 Oklahoma City boys into two separate camp areas. Then he had the two groups compete for prizes in a series of activities. Before long, each group became intensely proud of itself and hostile to the other group's "sneaky," "smart-alecky stinkers." Food wars broke out. Cabins were ransacked. Fistfights had to be broken up by camp counselors. Brought together, the two groups avoided each other, except to taunt and threaten. Little did they know that within a few days, they would be friends.

Rosiland Beckton

STRANGERS COMING TOGETHER
When a family got stuck in a Florida rip current, no less than 80 of their fellow beachgoers formed a human chain, rescuing them. Said one of the witnesses, Rosalind Beckton: "All races & ages join[ed] together to save lives" (AP, 2017).

"Me against my brother, my brothers and me against my cousins, then my cousins and me against strangers."
—Bedouin proverb

"Most of us have overlapping identities which unite us with very different groups. We *can* love what we are, without hating what—and who—we are *not*. We can thrive in our own tradition, even as we learn from others." —Nobel Peace Prize lecture, UN Secretary-General Kofi Annan, 2001

SUPERORDINATE GOALS OVERRIDE DIFFERENCES Cooperative efforts to achieve shared goals are an effective way to break down social barriers.

Grant Hindsley/AP Photo

Sherif accomplished this by giving them **superordinate goals**—shared goals that could be achieved only through cooperation. When he arranged for the camp water supply to "fail," all 22 boys had to work together to restore the water. To rent a movie in those pre-Netflix days, they all had to pool their resources. To move a stalled truck, the boys needed to combine their strength, pulling and pushing together. Having used isolation and competition to make strangers into enemies, Sherif used shared predicaments and goals to turn enemies into friends. What reduced conflict was not mere contact, but *cooperative* contact.

Critics suggest that Sherif's research team encouraged the conflict, in hopes the study would illustrate their expectations about socially toxic competition and socially beneficial cooperation (Perry, 2018). Yet shared predicaments have had powerfully unifying effects on other groups as well. Minority-group members facing rejection or discrimination develop strong ingroup identification (Bauer et al., 2014; Ramos et al., 2012). Children and youth exposed to war or conflict also develop strong social identities. Israeli children growing up in conflict areas often develop conflict-supportive perceptions, beliefs, and emotions regarding their shared adversary (Nasie et al., 2016). Such interpretations build ingroup solidarity but also insensitivity to the pain experienced by those in the outgroup (Levy et al., 2016).

In the aftermath of a divisive U.S. primary election, party members will usually eventually reunify when facing their shared threat—the opposition party candidate. At such times, cooperation can lead people to define a new, inclusive group that dissolves their former subgroups (Dovidio & Gaertner, 1999). If this were a social psychology experiment, you might seat members of two groups not on opposite sides, but alternately around a table. Give them a new, shared name. Have them work together. Then watch "us" and "them" become "we." After the 9/11 terrorist attacks, one 18-year-old New Jersey man described this shift in his own social identity: "I just thought of myself as Black. But now I feel like I'm an American, more than ever" (Sengupta, 2001). In an actual experiment, White Americans who read a newspaper article about a terrorist threat against all Americans subsequently expressed reduced prejudice against Black Americans (Dovidio et al., 2004).

If cooperative contact between rival group members encourages positive attitudes, might this principle bring diverse students together? Could cooperative learning in classrooms create interracial friendships, while also enhancing student achievement? Experiments with adolescents from 11 countries confirm that, in each case, the answer is *Yes* (Roseth et al., 2008). In the classroom as in the sports arena, members of multi-ethnic groups who work together on projects typically come to feel friendly toward one another. Knowing this, thousands of teachers have made multiethnic cooperative learning part of their classroom experience.

The power of cooperative activity to make friends of former enemies has led psychologists to urge increased international exchange and cooperation. Some experiments have found that just imagining the shared threat of global climate change reduces international hostilities (Pyszczynski et al., 2012). From adjacent Brazilian tribes to European countries, formerly conflicting groups have managed to build interconnections, interdependence, and a shared social identity as they seek common goals (Fry, 2012). As we engage in mutually beneficial trade, as we work to protect our common destiny on this fragile planet, and as we become more aware that our hopes and fears are shared, we can transform misperceptions that feed conflict into feelings of solidarity based on common interests.

COMMUNICATION When real-life conflicts become intense, a third-party mediator—a marriage counselor, labor mediator, diplomat, community volunteer—may facilitate much-needed communication (Rubin et al., 1994). Mediators help each party voice its viewpoint and understand the other's needs and goals. If successful, mediators can replace a competitive *win-lose* orientation with a cooperative *win-win* orientation that leads to a mutually beneficial resolution. A classic example: Two friends, after quarreling over an orange, agreed to split it. One squeezed his half for juice. The other used the peel from her half to flavor a cake. If only the two had communicated their motives to one another, they could have hit on the win-win solution of one having all the juice, the other all the peel.

CONCILIATION Understanding and cooperative resolution are most needed, yet least likely, in times of anger or crisis (Bodenhausen et al., 1994; Tetlock, 1988). When conflicts intensify, images become more stereotyped, judgments more rigid, and communication more difficult, or even impossible. Each party is likely to threaten, coerce, or retaliate. In the weeks before the 1990 Gulf War, U.S. President George H. W. Bush threatened, in the full glare of publicity, to "kick Saddam's ass." Iraqi President Saddam Hussein communicated in kind, threatening to make Americans "swim in their own blood." In 2017, U.S. President Donald Trump insulted North Korean leader Kim Jong-un as "Little Rocket Man" and threatened North Korea with "fire and fury like the world has never seen," to which Kim replied, "I will surely and definitely tame the mentally deranged U.S. dotard with fire (Glasser, 2017)."

Under such conditions, is there an alternative to war or surrender? Social psychologist Charles Osgood (1962, 1980) advocated a strategy of *Graduated and Reciprocated Initiatives in Tension-Reduction,* nicknamed **GRIT.** In applying GRIT, one side first announces its recognition of mutual interests and its intent to reduce tensions. It then initiates one or more small, conciliatory acts. Without weakening one's retaliatory capability, this modest beginning opens the door for reciprocity by the other party. Should the enemy respond with hostility, one reciprocates in kind. But so, too, with any conciliatory response.

In laboratory experiments, small conciliatory gestures—a smile, a touch, a word of apology—have allowed both parties to begin edging down the tension ladder to a safer rung where communication and mutual understanding can begin (Lindskold, 1978; Lindskold & Han, 1988). In a real-world international conflict, U.S. President John F. Kennedy's gesture of stopping atmospheric nuclear tests began a series of reciprocated conciliatory acts that culminated in the 1963 atmospheric test-ban treaty. (At the time of this writing, even Trump and Kim were negotiating.)

As working toward shared goals reminds us, we are more alike than different. Civilization advances not by conflict and cultural isolation, but by tapping the knowledge, the skills, and the arts that are each culture's legacy to the whole human race. Open societies are enriched by cultural sharing (Sowell, 1991). We have China to thank for paper and printing and for the magnetic compass that enabled the great explorations. We have Egypt to thank for trigonometry. We have the Islamic world and India's Hindus to thank for our Arabic numerals. While celebrating and claiming these diverse cultural legacies, we can also welcome the continuing enrichment of today's cultural diversity. We can view ourselves as instruments in a human orchestra. And we can therefore affirm our own culture's heritage while building bridges of communication, understanding, and cooperation across our cultural traditions.

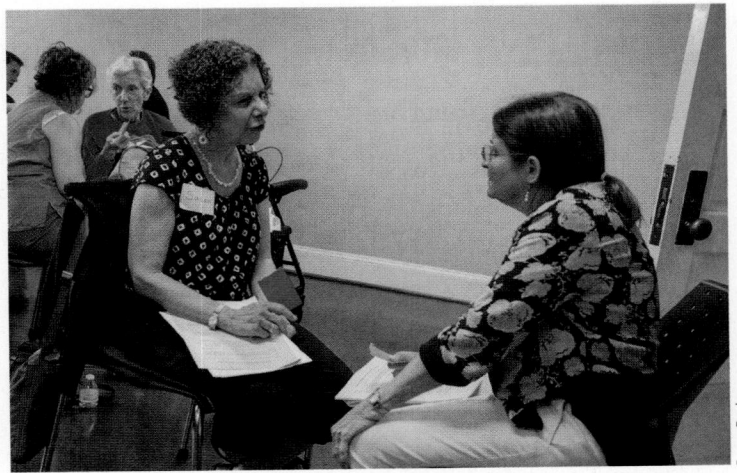

POLARIZED AMERICANS FINDING COMMON GROUND In local communities across the United States, mediators are helping "red" (conservative) and "blue" (liberal) citizens discover their common ground and form friendships (see Better-Angels.org).

 ASK YOURSELF

Do you regret not getting along with some friend or family member? How might you resolve the conflict using concepts you have just learned?

superordinate goals shared goals that override differences among people and require their cooperation.

GRIT Graduated and Reciprocated Initiatives in Tension-Reduction—a strategy designed to decrease international tensions.

 **RETRIEVE IT** • • •   *ANSWERS IN APPENDIX E*

RI-7 What are some ways to reconcile conflicts and promote peace?

🔒 REVIEW PROSOCIAL RELATIONS

⟩ Learning Objectives

TEST YOURSELF Answer these repeated Learning Objective Questions on your own (before checking the answers in Appendix D) to improve your retention of the concepts (McDaniel et al., 2009, 2015).

37-1 Why do we befriend or fall in love with some people but not others?

37-2 How does romantic love typically change as time passes?

37-3 What is *altruism*? When are people most—and least—likely to help?

37-4 How do social exchange theory and social norms explain helping behavior?

37-5 How do social traps and mirror-image perceptions fuel social conflict?

37-6 What can we do to promote peace?

⟩ Terms and Concepts to Remember

TEST YOURSELF Write down the definition yourself, then check your answer on the referenced page.

mere exposure effect, **p. 447**

passionate love, **p. 451**

companionate love, **p. 451**

equity, **p. 453**

self-disclosure, **p. 453**

altruism, **p. 453**

bystander effect, **p. 455**

social exchange theory, **p. 455**

reciprocity norm, **p. 455**

social-responsibility norm, **p. 455**

conflict, **p. 456**

social trap, **p. 456**

mirror-image perceptions, **p. 456**

self-fulfilling prophecy, **p. 456**

superordinate goals, **p. 459**

GRIT, **p. 459**

⟩ Experience the Testing Effect

TEST YOURSELF Answer the following questions on your own first, then check your answers in Appendix E.

1. The more familiar a stimulus becomes, the more we tend to like it. This exemplifies the _____ _____ effect.

2. A happy couple celebrating their fiftieth wedding anniversary is likely to experience deep _____ love, even though their _____ love has probably decreased over the years.

3. After vigorous exercise, you meet an attractive person, and you are suddenly seized by romantic feelings for that person. This response supports the two-factor theory of emotion, which assumes that emotions, such as passionate love, consist of physical arousal plus

   a. a reward.

   b. proximity.

   c. companionate love.

   d. our interpretation of that arousal.

4. The bystander effect states that a particular bystander is less likely to give aid if

   a. the victim is similar to the bystander in appearance.

   b. no one else is present.

   c. other people are present.

   d. the incident occurs in a deserted or rural area.

5. Our enemies often have many of the same negative impressions of us as we have of them. This exemplifies the concept of _____-_____ perceptions.

6. One way of resolving conflicts and fostering cooperation is by giving rival groups shared goals that help them override their differences. These are called _____ goals.

Continue testing yourself with 📘 **LearningCurve** or 📗 **Achieve Read & Practice** to learn and remember most effectively.

Personality

PeopleImages/Getty Images

L ady Gaga dazzles millions with her unique musical arrangements, tantalizing outfits, and provocative performances. In shows worldwide, Lady Gaga's most predictable feature is her unpredictability. She has worn a meat dress to an award show, sported 16-inch heels to meet with U.S. President Barack Obama (who later described the interaction as "a little intimidating"), and inspired Super Bowl viewers with her halftime musical performance.

Yet even unpredictable Lady Gaga exhibits distinctive and enduring ways of thinking, feeling, and behaving. Her fans and critics alike can depend on her openness to new experiences and the energy she gets from the spotlight. And they can also rely on her painstaking dedication to her music and performances. She describes her high school self as "very dedicated, very studious, and very disciplined." Now, in adulthood, she shows similar self-discipline: "I'm very detailed—every minute of the show has got to be perfect." Modules 38 and 39 focus on the ways we all demonstrate unique and persistent patterns of thinking, feeling, and behaving—our *personality*.

Much of this book deals with personality. Other modules consider biological influences on personality; personality development across the life span; how personality relates to learning, motivation, emotion, and health; social influences on personality; and disorders of personality. These modules focus on personality itself—what it is and how researchers study it.

We begin with two historically important theories of personality that have become part of Western culture: Sigmund Freud's *psychoanalytic theory* and the *humanistic theories*

personality an individual's characteristic pattern of thinking, feeling, and acting.

psychodynamic theories theories that view personality with a focus on the unconscious and the importance of childhood experiences.

psychoanalysis Freud's theory of personality that attributes thoughts and actions to unconscious motives and conflicts; the techniques used in treating psychological disorders by seeking to expose and interpret unconscious tensions.

(Module 38). These sweeping perspectives on human nature laid the foundation for later personality theorists and for what Module 39 presents: newer scientific explorations of personality.

Today's personality researchers study the basic dimensions of personality, and the interaction of persons and environments. They also study self-esteem, self-serving bias, and cultural influences on our concept of self—that sense of "Who I am." And they study the unconscious mind—with findings that probably would have surprised even Freud. ▶

38 Classic Perspectives on Personality

WHAT IS PERSONALITY?

LEARNING OBJECTIVE QUESTION (LOQ)

38-1 What is *personality,* and what theories inform our understanding of personality?

Psychologists have varied ways to view and study **personality**—our characteristic pattern of thinking, feeling, and acting. Sigmund Freud's *psychoanalytic theory* proposed that childhood sexuality and unconscious motivations influence personality. The *humanistic theories* focused on our inner capacities for growth and self-fulfillment. Later theorists built upon these two broad perspectives. *Trait theories* examine characteristic patterns of behavior (*traits*). *Social-cognitive theories* explore the interaction between people's traits (including their thinking) and their social context. Let's begin with Freud's work, and its modern-day descendant, *psychodynamic theories.*

PSYCHODYNAMIC THEORIES

Psychodynamic theories of personality view human behavior as a dynamic interaction between the conscious mind and unconscious mind, including associated motives and conflicts. These theories are descended from Freud's **psychoanalysis**—his theory of personality and the associated treatment techniques. Freud was the first to focus clinical attention on our unconscious mind.

Freud's Psychoanalytic Perspective: Exploring the Unconscious

LOQ 38-2 How did Sigmund Freud's treatment of psychological disorders lead to his view of the unconscious mind?

Ask 100 people on the street to name a notable deceased psychologist, suggested Keith Stanovich (1996, p. 1), and "Freud would be the winner hands down." In the popular mind, he is to psychology what Elvis Presley is to rock music. Freud's influence lingers not only in psychiatry and clinical psychology, but also in literary and film interpretation. Almost 9 in 10 American college courses that reference psychoanalysis have been outside of psychology departments (Cohen, 2007). Freud's early twentieth-century concepts penetrate our twenty-first-century language. Without realizing their source, we may speak of *ego, repression, projection, sibling rivalry, Freudian slips,* and *fixation.* So, who was Freud, and what did he teach?

Like all of us, Sigmund Freud was a product of his times. His late 1800s Victorian era was a time of tremendous discovery and scientific advancement, but also of sexual suppression and male dominance. Men's and women's roles were clearly defined, with male superiority assumed and only male sexuality generally acknowledged (discreetly).

SIGMUND FREUD (1856–1939) "I was the only worker in a new field."

These assumptions influenced Freud's thinking about personality. He believed that psychological troubles resulted from men's and women's unresolved conflicts with their expected roles.

Long before entering the University of Vienna in 1873, young Freud showed signs of independence and brilliance. He so loved reading plays, poetry, and philosophy that he once ran up a bookstore debt beyond his means. As a teen he often took his evening meal in his tiny bedroom in order to lose no time from his studies. After medical school he set up a private practice specializing in nervous disorders. Before long, however, he faced patients whose disorders made no neurological sense. A patient might have lost all feeling in a hand—yet there is no sensory nerve that, if damaged, would numb the entire hand and nothing else. Freud's search for a cause for such disorders set his mind running in a direction destined to change human self-understanding.

Do some neurological disorders have psychological causes? Observing patients led Freud to his "discovery" of the **unconscious.** He speculated that lost feeling in one's hand might be caused by a fear of touching one's genitals; that unexplained blindness or deafness might be caused by not wanting to see or hear something that aroused intense anxiety. How might such disorders be treated? After some early unsuccessful trials with hypnosis, Freud turned to **free association,** in which he told the patient to relax and say whatever came to mind, no matter how embarrassing or trivial. He assumed that a line of mental dominoes had fallen from his patients' distant past to their troubled present, and that the chain of thought revealed by free association would allow him to retrace that line into his patients' unconscious. There, painful memories, often from childhood, could then be retrieved, reviewed, and released.

Basic to Freud's theory was his belief that the mind is mostly hidden (**FIGURE 38.1**). Our *conscious* awareness is like the part of an iceberg that floats above the surface. Beneath this awareness is the larger *unconscious* mind, with its thoughts, wishes, feelings, and memories. Some of these thoughts we store temporarily in a *preconscious* area, from which we can retrieve them into conscious awareness. Of greater interest to Freud was the mass of unacceptable passions and thoughts that he believed we *repress,* or forcibly block from our consciousness because they would be too unsettling to acknowledge. Freud believed that without our awareness, these troublesome feelings and ideas powerfully influence us. Such feelings, he said, sometimes surface in disguised forms—the work we choose, the beliefs we hold, our daily habits, our upsetting symptoms.

> "The female . . . acknowledges the fact of her castration, and with it, too, the superiority of the male and her own inferiority; but she rebels against this unwelcome state of affairs." —Sigmund Freud, *Female Sexuality*, 1931

FIGURE 38.1

FREUD'S IDEA OF THE MIND'S STRUCTURE Psychologists have used an iceberg image to illustrate Freud's idea that the mind is mostly hidden beneath the conscious surface. Note that the *id* is totally unconscious, but *ego* and *superego* operate both consciously and unconsciously. Unlike the parts of a frozen iceberg, however, the id, ego, and superego interact.

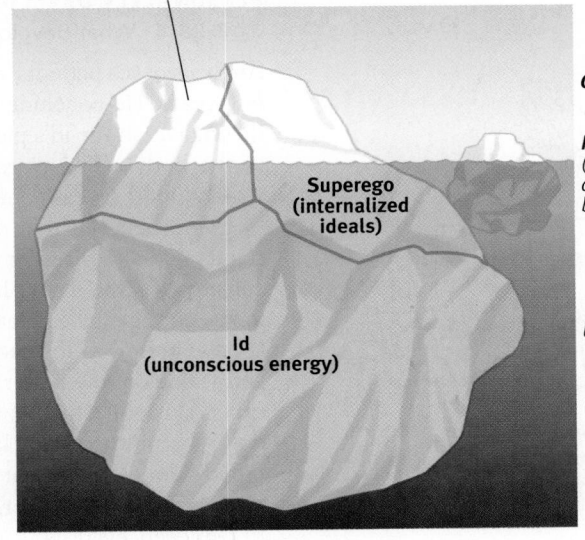

Ego
(mostly conscious; makes peace between the id and the superego)

Superego
(internalized ideals)

Id
(unconscious energy)

Conscious mind

Preconscious
(outside awareness but accessible)

Unconscious mind

PERSONALITY STRUCTURE

LOQ 38-3 What was Freud's view of personality?

Freud believed that human personality, including its emotions and strivings, arises from a conflict between impulse and restraint—between our aggressive, pleasure-seeking biological urges and our internalized social controls over these urges. Freud believed personality arises from our efforts to resolve this basic conflict—to express these impulses in ways that bring satisfaction without also bringing guilt or punishment. To understand the mind's dynamics during this conflict, Freud proposed three interacting systems: the *id, ego,* and *superego* (Figure 38.1).

The **id's** unconscious psychic energy constantly strives to satisfy basic drives to survive, reproduce, and aggress. The id operates on the *pleasure principle:* It seeks immediate gratification. To understand the id's power, think of a newborn infant crying out for satisfaction, caring nothing for the outside world's conditions and demands. Or think of people with a present rather than future time perspective—those who abuse tobacco, alcohol, and other drugs, and would sooner party now than sacrifice today's temporary pleasure for future success and happiness (Fernie et al., 2013; Friedel et al., 2014; Keough et al., 1999).

unconscious according to Freud, a reservoir of mostly unacceptable thoughts, wishes, feelings, and memories. According to contemporary psychologists, information processing of which we are unaware.

free association in psychoanalysis, a method of exploring the unconscious in which the person relaxes and says whatever comes to mind, no matter how trivial or embarrassing.

id a reservoir of unconscious psychic energy that, according to Freud, strives to satisfy basic sexual and aggressive drives. The id operates on the *pleasure principle,* demanding immediate gratification.

"Fifty is plenty."   "Hundred and fifty."

THE EGO STRUGGLES TO RECONCILE THE DEMANDS OF SUPEREGO AND ID, SAID FREUD.

"I heard that as soon as we become aware of our sexual impulses, whatever they are, we'll have to hide them."

"Oh, for goodness' sake! Smoke!"

As the **ego** develops, the young child responds to the real world. The ego, operating on the *reality principle,* seeks to gratify the id's impulses in realistic ways that will bring long-term pleasure. (Imagine what would happen if, lacking an ego, we acted on our unrestrained sexual or aggressive impulses.) The ego contains our partly conscious perceptions, thoughts, judgments, and memories.

Around age 4 or 5, Freud theorized, a child's ego recognizes the demands of the newly emerging **superego,** the voice of our moral compass (conscience) that forces the ego to consider not only the real but also the *ideal.* The superego focuses on how we *ought* to behave. It strives for perfection, judging actions and producing positive feelings of pride or negative feelings of guilt. Someone with an exceptionally strong superego may be virtuous yet guilt ridden; another with a weak superego may be outrageously self-indulgent and remorseless.

Because the superego's demands often oppose the id's, the ego struggles to reconcile the two. The ego is the personality "executive," mediating among the impulsive demands of the id, the restraining demands of the superego, and the real-life demands of the external world. If chaste Conner feels sexually attracted to Tatiana, his ego may satisfy both his id and superego by joining a volunteer organization that Tatiana attends regularly.

RETAIN **LaunchPad** To review Freud's components of personality, take advantage of the online **Concept Practice: Freud's Personality Structure.**

PERSONALITY DEVELOPMENT

LOQ 38-4 What developmental stages did Freud propose?

Analysis of his patients' histories convinced Freud that personality forms during life's first few years. He concluded that children pass through a series of **psychosexual stages,** during which the id's pleasure-seeking energies focus on distinct pleasure-sensitive areas of the body called *erogenous zones* (**TABLE 38.1**). Each stage offers its own challenges, which Freud saw as conflicting tendencies.

Freud believed that during the *phallic stage,* for example, boys develop both unconscious sexual desires for their mother and jealousy and hatred for their father, whom they consider a rival. These feelings, he thought, lead boys to feel guilty and to fear punishment, perhaps by castration, from their father. Such was Freud's (1897) own experience: "I have found, in my own case too, [the phenomenon of] being in love with my mother and jealous of my father, and I now consider it a universal event in early childhood." He called this collection of feelings the **Oedipus complex** after the Greek legend of Oedipus, who unknowingly killed his father and married his mother. Some psychoanalysts in Freud's era believed that girls experience a parallel *Electra complex* (named after a mythological plotting daughter).

Children eventually cope with the threatening feelings, said Freud, by repressing them and by trying to become like the rival parent. It's as though something inside the

TABLE 38.1

Freud's Psychosexual Stages

Stage	Focus
Oral (0–18 months)	Pleasure centers on the mouth—sucking, biting, chewing
Anal (18–36 months)	Pleasure focuses on bowel and bladder elimination; coping with demands for control
Phallic (3–6 years)	Pleasure zone is the genitals; coping with incestuous sexual feelings
Latency (6 years to puberty)	A phase of dormant sexual feelings
Genital (puberty on)	Maturation of sexual interests

child decides, "If you can't beat 'em [the same-sex parent], join 'em." Through this **identification** process, children's superegos gain strength as they incorporate many of their parents' values. Freud believed that identification with the same-sex parent provides what psychologists now call our *gender identity*—our sense of being male, female, or some combination of the two. Freud presumed that our early childhood relations—especially with our parents and other caregivers—influence our developing identity, personality, and frailties.

In Freud's view, conflicts unresolved during earlier psychosexual stages could surface as maladaptive behavior in the adult years. At any point in the oral, anal, or phallic stages, strong conflict could lock, or **fixate,** the person's pleasure-seeking energies in that stage. A person who had been either orally overindulged or deprived (perhaps by abrupt, early weaning) might fixate at the oral stage. This orally fixated adult could exhibit either passive dependence (like that of a nursing infant) or an exaggerated denial of this dependence (by acting tough or uttering biting sarcasm). Or the person might continue to seek oral gratification by smoking or excessive eating. In such ways, Freud suggested, the twig of personality is bent at an early age.

DEFENSE MECHANISMS

LOQ 38-5 How did Freud think people defended themselves against anxiety?

Anxiety, said Freud, is the price we pay for civilization. As members of social groups, we must control our sexual and aggressive impulses, not act them out. But sometimes the ego fears losing control of this inner id-superego war. The presumed result is a dark cloud of unfocused anxiety that leaves us feeling unsettled but unsure why.

Freud proposed that the ego protects itself with **defense mechanisms**—tactics that reduce or redirect anxiety by distorting reality (**TABLE 38.2**). For Freud, *all defense mechanisms function indirectly and unconsciously.* Just as the body unconsciously defends itself against disease, so also does the ego unconsciously defend itself against anxiety. For example, **repression** banishes anxiety-arousing wishes and feelings from consciousness. According to Freud, *repression underlies all the other defense mechanisms.* However, because repression is often incomplete, repressed urges may appear as symbols in dreams or as slips of the tongue in casual conversation.

> "I remember your name perfectly but I just can't think of your face." —Oxford professor W. A. Spooner (1844–1930) famous for his linguistic flip-flops (spoonerisms). Spooner rebuked one student for "fighting a liar in the quadrangle" and another who "hissed my mystery lecture," adding "You have tasted two worms."

ego the largely conscious, "executive" part of personality that, according to Freud, mediates among the demands of the id, the superego, and reality. The ego operates on the *reality principle,* satisfying the id's desires in ways that will realistically bring pleasure rather than pain.

superego the part of personality that, according to Freud, represents internalized ideals and provides standards for judgment (the conscience) and for future aspirations.

psychosexual stages the childhood stages of development (oral, anal, phallic, latency, genital) during which, according to Freud, the id's pleasure-seeking energies focus on distinct erogenous zones.

Oedipus [ED-uh-puss] complex according to Freud, a boy's sexual desires toward his mother and feelings of jealousy and hatred for the rival father.

identification the process by which, according to Freud, children incorporate their parents' values into their developing superegos.

fixation in personality theory, according to Freud, a lingering focus of pleasure-seeking energies at an earlier psychosexual stage, in which conflicts were unresolved.

defense mechanisms in psychoanalytic theory, the ego's protective methods of reducing anxiety by unconsciously distorting reality.

repression in psychoanalytic theory, the basic defense mechanism that banishes from consciousness anxiety-arousing thoughts, feelings, and memories.

TABLE 38.2

Six Defense Mechanisms

Freud believed that *repression*, the basic mechanism that banishes anxiety-arousing impulses, enables other defense mechanisms, six of which are listed here.

Defense mechanism	Unconscious Process Employed to Avoid Anxiety-Arousing Thoughts or Feelings	Example
Regression	Retreating to an earlier psychosexual stage, where some psychic energy remains fixated	A little boy reverts to the oral comfort of thumb sucking in the car on the way to his first day of school.
Reaction formation	Switching unacceptable impulses into their opposites	Repressing angry feelings, a person displays exaggerated friendliness.
Projection	Disguising one's own threatening impulses by attributing them to others	"The thief thinks everyone else is a thief" (an El Salvadoran saying).
Rationalization	Offering self-justifying explanations in place of the real, more threatening unconscious reasons for one's actions	A habitual drinker says she drinks with her friends "just to be sociable."
Displacement	Shifting sexual or aggressive impulses toward a more acceptable or less threatening object or person	A little girl kicks the family dog after her mother puts her in a time-out.
Denial	Refusing to believe or even perceive painful realities	A partner denies evidence of his loved one's affair.

"Good morning, beheaded—uh, I mean beloved."

REGRESSION Faced with a mild stressor, children and young orangutans seek protection and comfort from their care-givers. Freud might have interpreted these behaviors as regression, a retreat to an earlier developmental stage.

collective unconscious Carl Jung's con-cept of a shared, inherited reservoir of mem-ory traces from our species' history.

Thematic Apperception Test (TAT) a projective test in which people express their inner feelings and interests through the sto-ries they make up about ambiguous scenes.

projective test a personality test, such as the Rorschach or TAT, that provides ambiguous images designed to trigger pro-jection of one's inner dynamics.

Rorschach inkblot test the most widely used projective test; a set of 10 inkblots, designed by Hermann Rorschach; seeks to identify people's inner feelings by analyzing their interpretations of the blots.

Freud believed he could glimpse the unconscious seeping through when a financially stressed patient, not wanting any large pills, said, "Please do not give me any bills, because I cannot swallow them." (Today we call these "Freudian slips.") Freud also viewed jokes as expressions of repressed sexual and aggressive tendencies, and dreams as the "royal road to the unconscious." The remembered content of dreams (their *manifest content*) he believed to be a censored expression of the dreamer's unconscious wishes (the dream's *latent content*). In his dream analyses, Freud searched for patients' inner conflicts.

🔒 **RETRIEVE IT • • •**   *ANSWERS IN APPENDIX E*

RI-1 According to Freud's ideas about the three-part personality structure, the _____ operates on the *reality principle* and tries to balance demands in a way that produces long-term pleasure rather than pain; the _____ operates on the *pleasure principle* and seeks immediate gratification; and the _____ represents the voice of our internalized ideals (our *conscience*).

RI-2 In the psychoanalytic view, conflicts unresolved during one of the psychosex-ual stages may lead to _____ at that stage.

RI-3 Freud believed that our defense mechanisms operate _____ (consciously/unconsciously) and defend us against _____.

The Neo-Freudian and Later Psychodynamic Theorists

LOQ 38-6 Which of Freud's ideas did his followers accept or reject?

In a historical period when people rarely talked about sex, and certainly not unconscious desires for sex with one's parent, Freud's writings sparked intense debate. "In the Middle Ages, they would have burned me," observed Freud to a friend. "Now they are content with burning my books" (Jones, 1957). Despite the controversy, Freud attracted follow-ers. Several young, ambitious physicians formed an inner circle around their strong-minded leader. These pioneering psychoanalysts, whom we often call *neo-Freudians*, adopted Freud's interviewing techniques and accepted his basic ideas: the personality structures of id, ego, and superego; the importance of the unconscious; the childhood roots of personality; and the dynamics of anxiety and the defense mechanisms. But they broke away from Freud in two important ways. First, they placed more emphasis on the conscious mind's role in interpreting experience and in coping with the environment. And second, they doubted that sex and aggression were all-consuming motivations. Instead, they tended to emphasize loftier motives and social interactions.

Alfred Adler and Karen Horney [HORN-eye], for example, agreed with Freud that childhood is important. But they believed that childhood *social*, not sexual, tensions are crucial for personality formation (Ferguson, 2003, 2015). Adler (who gave us the still popular *inferiority complex* idea) had struggled to overcome childhood illnesses and acci-dents. He believed that much of our behavior is driven by efforts to conquer childhood inferiority feelings that trigger our strivings for superiority and power. Horney said child-hood anxiety triggers our desire for love and security. She also opposed Freud's assump-tions that women have weak superegos and suffer "penis envy," and she attempted to balance his masculine bias.

Carl Jung [Yoong], Freud's disciple-turned-dissenter, placed less emphasis on social factors and agreed with Freud that the unconscious exerts a powerful influence. But to Jung, the unconscious contains more than our repressed thoughts and feelings. He believed we also have a **collective unconscious,** a common reservoir of images, or *archetypes,* derived from our species' universal experiences. Jung said that the collective unconscious explains why, for many people, spiritual concerns are deeply rooted and why people in different cultures share certain myths and images. Most of today's psychol-ogists discount the idea of inherited experiences. But they do believe that our shared evolutionary history shaped some universal dispositions, and that experience can leave *epigenetic* marks affecting gene expression.

Freud died in 1939. Since then, some of his ideas have been incorporated into the diverse perspectives that make up modern psychodynamic theory. "Most contemporary

ALFRED ADLER (1870–1937) "The individual feels at home in life and feels his existence to be worthwhile just so far as he is useful to others and is overcoming feelings of inferiority" (*Problems of Neurosis*, 1964).

KAREN HORNEY (1885–1952) "The view that women are infantile and emotional creatures, and as such, incapable of responsibility and independence is the work of the masculine tendency to lower women's self-respect" (*Feminine Psychology*, 1932).

CARL JUNG (1875–1961) "From the living fountain of instinct flows everything that is creative; hence the unconscious is the very source of the creative impulse" (*The Structure and Dynamics of the Psyche*, 1960).

[psychodynamic] theorists and therapists are not wedded to the idea that sex is the basis of personality," noted Drew Westen (1996). They "do not talk about ids and egos, and do not go around classifying their patients as oral, anal, or phallic characters." What they do assume, with Freud and with much support from today's psychological science, is that much of our mental life is unconscious. With Freud, they also assume that we often struggle with inner conflicts among our wishes, fears, and values, and that childhood shapes our personality and ways of becoming attached to others.

Assessing Unconscious Processes

LOQ 38-7 What are *projective tests*, how are they used, and what are some criticisms of them?

Personality tests reflect the basic ideas of particular personality theories. So, what might be the assessment tool of choice for someone working in the Freudian tradition? It would need to provide some sort of road into the unconscious—to unearth the residue of early childhood experiences, move beneath surface thoughts, and reveal hidden conflicts and impulses. Objective assessment tools, such as agree-disagree or true-false questionnaires, would be inadequate because they would merely tap the conscious surface.

Henry Murray (1933) demonstrated a possible basis for such a test at a party hosted by his 11-year-old daughter. Murray engaged the children in a frightening game called "Murder." When shown some photographs after the game, the children perceived the photos as more malicious than they had before the game. These children, it seemed to Murray, had *projected* their inner feelings into the pictures.

A few years later, Murray introduced the **Thematic Apperception Test (TAT)**—a **projective test** in which people view ambiguous pictures and make up stories about them. Shown a daydreaming boy, those who imagine he is fantasizing about an achievement are presumed to be projecting their own goals. "As a rule," said Murray, "the subject leaves the test happily unaware that he has presented the psychologist with what amounts to an X-ray of his inner self" (quoted by Talbot, 1999).

Numerous studies suggest that Murray was right: The TAT provides a valid and reliable map of people's implicit motives (Jenkins, 2017). For example, such storytelling has been used to assess *achievement* and *affiliation motivation* (Drescher & Schultheiss, 2016; Schultheiss et al., 2014). TAT responses also show consistency over time (Lundy, 1985; Schultheiss & Pang, 2007). Show people a picture today, and they'll imagine a story similar to one they will tell when, a month later, they see the same picture.

Swiss psychiatrist Hermann Rorschach [ROAR-shock; 1884–1922] created the most widely used projective test. He based his famous **Rorschach inkblot test,** in which people describe what they see in a series of inkblots (**FIGURE 38.2**), on a childhood game.

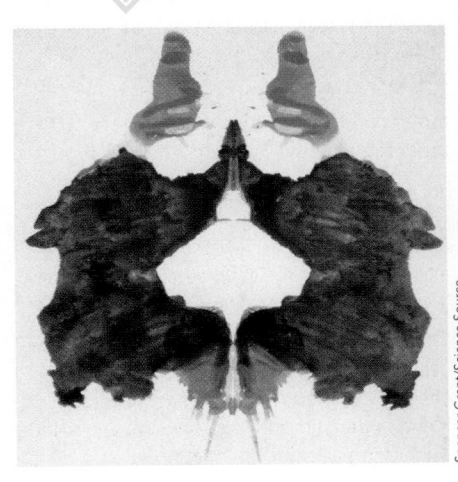

📺 **LaunchPad** For a helpful 9-minute overview, view the **Video: Psychodynamic Theories of Personality.**

FIGURE 38.2

THE RORSCHACH TEST In this projective test, people tell what they see in a series of symmetrical inkblots. Some who use this test are confident that the interpretation of ambiguous images will reveal unconscious aspects of the test-taker's personality.

Spencer Grant/Science Source

"We don't see things as they are; we see things as we are." —The Talmud

"The Rorschach [inkblot test] has the dubious distinction of being, simultaneously, the most cherished and the most reviled of all psychological assessment tools." —John Hunsley and J. Michael Bailey (1999)

"Many aspects of Freudian theory are indeed out of date, and they should be: Freud died in 1939, and he has been slow to undertake further revisions." —Psychologist Drew Westen (1998)

He and his friends would drip ink on a paper, fold it, and then say what they saw in the resulting blot (Sdorow, 2005). Do you see predatory animals or weapons? Perhaps you have aggressive tendencies. But is this a reasonable assumption? The answer varies.

Some clinicians cherish the Rorschach test, even offering Rorschach-based assessments of criminals' violence potential. Others view the test as a source of suggestive leads, an icebreaker, or a revealing interview technique.

Critics of the Rorschach insist the test is no emotional MRI. They argue that only a few of the many Rorschach-derived scores, such as those for cognitive impairment and thought disorder, have demonstrated reliability and validity (Mihura et al., 2013, 2015; Wood et al., 2015). And inkblot assessments have inaccurately diagnosed many healthy adults as pathological (Wood, 2003; Wood et al., 2006).

Evaluating Freud's Psychoanalytic Perspective and Modern Views of the Unconscious

LOQ 38-8   How do contemporary psychologists view Freud's psychoanalysis?

MODERN RESEARCH CONTRADICTS MANY OF FREUD'S IDEAS   We critique Freud from a twenty-first-century perspective. Freud did not have access to neurotransmitter or DNA studies, or to all that we have since learned about human development, thinking, and emotion. To criticize his theory by comparing it with today's thinking is like criticizing Henry Ford's Model T by comparing it with Elon Musk's Tesla Model S. How tempting it always is to judge the past from the perspective of our present.

Nevertheless, both Freud's devotees and his detractors agree that recent research contradicts many of his specific ideas. Today's developmental psychologists see our development as lifelong, not fixed in childhood. They doubt that infants' neural networks are mature enough to sustain as much emotional trauma as Freud assumed. Some think Freud overestimated parental influence and underestimated peer influence. They also doubt that conscience and gender identity form as the child resolves the Oedipus complex at age 5 or 6. We gain our gender identity earlier, and those who become strongly masculine or feminine do so even without a same-sex parent present. And they note that Freud's ideas about childhood sexuality arose from stories of childhood sexual abuse told by his female patients—stories that some scholars believe Freud doubted, and attributed to his patients' own childhood sexual wishes and conflicts (Esterson, 2001; Powell & Boer, 1994). Today, we know that *childhood sexual abuse happens,* and we also understand how Freud's questioning might have created false memories of abuse.

Modern dream research disputes Freud's belief that dreams disguise and fulfill wishes. And slips of the tongue can be explained as competition between similar verbal choices in our memory network. Someone who says "I don't want to do that—it's a lot of brothel" may simply be blending *bother* and *trouble* (Foss & Hakes, 1978). Searching the more than 250,000 emails I [DM] have received since 2000, I see that (among other such hilarities) friends have written me about their experience on "Wisconsin Pubic Radio," about accessibility in "pubic venues," and about their work as an organization's "Director of Pubic Policy." Such mistakes are likely mere random typos, concludes one big data analysis of typing errors (Stephens-Davidowitz, 2017).

Researchers find little support for Freud's idea that defense mechanisms disguise sexual and aggressive impulses (though our cognitive gymnastics do indeed work to protect our self-esteem). History also has failed to support another of Freud's ideas—that suppressed sexuality causes psychological disorders. From Freud's time to ours, sexual inhibition has diminished; psychological disorders have not.

Psychologists further criticize Freud's theory for its scientific shortcomings. It's important to remember that good scientific theories explain observations and offer testable hypotheses. Freud's theory rests on few objective observations, and parts of it offer few testable hypotheses. For Freud, his own recollections and interpretations of patients' free associations, dreams, and slips—sometimes selected to support his theory—were evidence enough.

What is the most serious problem with Freud's theory? It offers after-the-fact explanations of any characteristic (of one person's smoking, another's fear of horses, another's sexual orientation), yet fails to *predict* such behaviors and traits. If you feel angry at your mother's death, you illustrate Freud's theory because "your unresolved childhood dependency needs are threatened." If you do not feel angry, you again illustrate his theory because "you are repressing your anger." That "is like betting on a horse after the race has been run" (Hall & Lindzey, 1978, p. 68). A good theory makes testable predictions.

So, should psychology post an "Allow Natural Death" order on this old theory? Freud's supporters object. To criticize Freudian theory for not making testable predictions is, they say, like criticizing baseball for not being an aerobic exercise—something it was never intended to be. Freud never claimed that psychoanalysis was predictive science. He merely claimed that, looking back, psychoanalysts could find meaning in our state of mind (Rieff, 1979).

Freud's supporters also note that some of his ideas *are* enduring. It was Freud who drew our attention to the unconscious and the irrational, at a time when such ideas were not popular. Today, many researchers study our irrationality (Ariely, 2010; Thaler, 2015). Psychologist Daniel Kahneman (in 2002) and behavioral economist Richard Thaler (in 2017) each won Nobel Prizes for their studies of our faulty decision making. Freud also drew our attention to the importance of human sexuality, and to the tension between our biological impulses and our social well-being. It was Freud who challenged our self-righteousness, exposed our self-protective defenses, and reminded us of our potential for evil.

MODERN RESEARCH CHALLENGES THE IDEA OF REPRESSION Psychoanalytic theory hinges on the assumption that our mind often *represses* offending wishes, banishing them into the unconscious until they resurface, like long-lost books in a dusty attic. Recover and resolve childhood's conflicted wishes, and emotional healing should follow. Repression became a widely accepted concept, used to explain hypnotic phenomena and psychological disorders. Some psychodynamic followers extended repression to explain apparently lost and recovered memories of childhood traumas (Boag, 2006; Cheit, 1998; Erdelyi, 2006). In one survey, 88 percent of university students believed that painful experiences commonly get pushed out of awareness and into the unconscious (Garry et al., 1994).

Today's researchers agree that we sometimes preserve our self-esteem by neglecting threatening information (Green et al., 2008). Yet many contend that repression, if it ever occurs, is a rare mental response to terrible trauma. Even those who have witnessed a parent's murder or survived Nazi death camps have retained their unrepressed memories of the horror (Helmreich, 1992, 1994; Malmquist, 1986; Pennebaker, 1990). "Dozens of formal studies have yielded not a single convincing case of repression in the entire literature on trauma," concluded personality researcher John Kihlstrom (2006).

Some researchers do believe that extreme, prolonged stress, such as the stress some severely abused children experience, might disrupt memory by damaging the hippocampus, which is important for processing conscious memories (Schacter, 1996). But the far more common reality is that high stress and associated stress hormones *enhance* memory. Indeed, rape, torture, and other traumatic events haunt survivors, who experience unwanted flashbacks. They are seared onto the soul. "You see the babies," said Holocaust survivor Sally H. (1979). "You see the screaming mothers. You see hanging people. You sit and you see that face there. It's something you don't forget."

🎬 **LaunchPad** For a helpful 13-minute exploration, see the **Video: Repression— Reality or Myth?**

THE MODERN UNCONSCIOUS MIND

LOQ 38-9 How has modern research developed our understanding of the unconscious?

Freud was right about a big idea that underlies today's psychodynamic thinking: We have limited access to all that goes on in our mind (Erdelyi, 1985, 1988, 2006; Norman, 2010). Our two-track mind has a vast out-of-sight realm. Some researchers even argue that "most of a person's everyday life is determined by unconscious thought processes" (Bargh & Chartrand, 1999). (Perhaps, for example, you can recall being sad or mad without consciously knowing why.)

"We are arguing like a man who should say, 'If there were an invisible cat in that chair, the chair would look empty; but the chair does look empty; therefore there is an invisible cat in it'." —C. S. Lewis, *Four Loves*, 1958

"Although [Freud] clearly made a number of mistakes in the formulation of his ideas, his understanding of unconscious mental processes was pretty much on target. In fact, it is very consistent with modern neuroscientists' belief that most mental processes are unconscious." —Nobel Prize–winning neuroscientist Eric Kandel (2012)

"During the Holocaust, many children . . . were forced to endure the unendurable. For those who continue to suffer [the] pain is still present, many years later, as real as it was on the day it occurred." —Eric Zillmer, Molly Harrower, Barry Ritzler, and Robert Archer, *The Quest for the Nazi Personality*, 1995

humanistic theories theories that view personality with a focus on the potential for healthy personal growth.

hierarchy of needs Maslow's pyramid of human needs, beginning at the base with physiological needs that must first be satisfied before people can fulfill their higher-level safety needs and then psychological needs.

self-actualization according to Maslow, one of the ultimate psychological needs that arises after basic physical and psychological needs are met and self-esteem is achieved; the motivation to fulfill one's potential.

self-transcendence according to Maslow, the striving for identity, meaning, and purpose beyond the self.

unconditional positive regard a caring, accepting, nonjudgmental attitude, which Carl Rogers believed would help people develop self-awareness and self-acceptance.

Yet many research psychologists now think of the unconscious not as seething passions and repressive censoring but as cooler information processing that occurs without our awareness. To these researchers, the unconscious also involves

- the *schemas* that automatically control our perceptions and interpretations.
- the *priming* by stimuli to which we have not consciously attended.
- the right-hemisphere activity that enables the *split-brain* patient's left hand to carry out an instruction the patient cannot verbalize.
- the *implicit memories* that operate without conscious recall, even among those with amnesia.
- the *emotions* that activate instantly, before conscious analysis.
- the *stereotypes* and *implicit prejudice* that automatically and unconsciously influence how we process information about others.

More than we realize, we fly on autopilot. Our lives are guided by off-screen, out-of-sight, unconscious information processing. The unconscious mind is huge. However, our current understanding of unconscious information processing is more like the pre-Freudian view of an underground, unattended stream of thought from which spontaneous behavior and creative ideas surface (Bargh & Morsella, 2008).

Research also supports two of Freud's defense mechanisms. One study demonstrated *reaction formation* (trading unacceptable impulses for their opposite) in men who reported strong anti-gay attitudes. Compared with those who did not report such attitudes, these anti-gay men experienced greater physiological arousal (assessed with a device that measured blood flow to the penis) when watching videos of homosexual men having sex, even though they said the films did not make them sexually aroused (Adams et al., 1996). Likewise, some evidence suggests that people who unconsciously identify as homosexual—but who consciously identify as straight—report more negative attitudes toward gays (Weinstein et al., 2012).

Freud's *projection* (attributing our own threatening impulses to others) has also been confirmed. People do tend to see their traits, attitudes, and goals in others (Baumeister et al., 1998b; Maner et al., 2005). Today's researchers call this the *false consensus effect*—the tendency to overestimate the extent to which others share our beliefs and behaviors. People who binge-drink or break speed limits tend to think many others do the same. However, neuroscience research shows that projection seems motivated less by suppressing our sexual and aggressive undercurrents, as Freud imagined, than by our need to maintain a positive self-image (Welborn et al., 2017).

ENGAGE (**ASK YOURSELF**)

What understandings and impressions of Freud did you bring to this course? Are you surprised to find that some of his ideas (especially the big idea of our unconscious mind) had merit?

🔒 **RETRIEVE IT** • • •   *ANSWERS IN APPENDIX E*

RI-4 What are three big ideas that have survived from Freud's psychoanalytic theory? What are three ways in which Freud's theory has been criticized?

RI-5 Which elements of traditional psychoanalysis have modern-day *psychodynamic* theorists and therapists retained, and which elements have they mostly left behind?

HUMANISTIC THEORIES

LOQ 38-10 How did humanistic psychologists view personality, and what was their goal in studying personality?

By the 1960s, some personality psychologists had become discontented with the sometimes bleak focus on drives and conflicts in psychodynamic theory, and the mechanistic psychology of B. F. Skinner's *behaviorism.* Two pioneering theorists—Abraham Maslow (1908–1970) and Carl Rogers (1902–1987)—offered a *third-force perspective* that emphasized our potential for healthy personal growth. In contrast to Freud's emphasis on disorders born out of dark conflicts, these **humanistic theorists** emphasized the ways people strive for self-determination and self-realization. In contrast to behaviorism's scientific objectivity, they studied people through their own self-reported experiences and feelings.

Abraham Maslow's Self-Actualizing Person

Maslow proposed that we are motivated by a **hierarchy of needs**. If our physiological needs are met, we become concerned with personal safety. If we achieve a sense of security, we then seek to love, to be loved, and to love ourselves. With our love needs satisfied, we seek self-esteem. Having achieved self-esteem, we ultimately seek **self-actualization** (the process of fulfilling our potential) and **self-transcendence** (meaning, purpose, and identity beyond the self).

Maslow (1970) developed his ideas by studying healthy, creative people rather than troubled clinical cases. He based his description of self-actualization on a study of people, such as Abraham Lincoln, who seemed notable for their meaningful and productive lives. Maslow reported that such people shared certain characteristics: They were self-aware and self-accepting, open and spontaneous, loving and caring, and not paralyzed by others' opinions. Secure in their sense of who they were, their interests were problem-centered rather than self-centered. They focused their energies on a particular task, one they often regarded as their mission in life. Most enjoyed a few deep relationships rather than many superficial ones. Many had been moved by spiritual or personal *peak experiences* that surpassed ordinary consciousness.

These, said Maslow, are mature adult qualities found in those who have learned enough about life to be compassionate, to have outgrown their mixed feelings toward their parents, to have found their calling, to have "acquired enough courage to be unpopular, to be unashamed about being openly virtuous."

Carl Rogers' Person-Centered Perspective

Fellow humanistic psychologist Carl Rogers agreed with much of Maslow's thinking. Rogers' *person-centered perspective* held that people are basically good and are, as Maslow said, endowed with self-actualizing tendencies. Unless thwarted by a growth-inhibiting environment, each of us is like an acorn, primed for growth and fulfillment. Rogers (1980) believed that a growth-promoting social climate provides:

- *Acceptance.* When people are *accepting,* they offer **unconditional positive regard,** an attitude of grace that values us even knowing our failings. It is a profound relief to drop our pretenses, confess our worst feelings, and discover that we are still accepted. In a good marriage, a close family, or an intimate friendship, we are free to be spontaneous without fearing the loss of others' esteem.

- *Genuineness.* When people are *genuine,* they are open with their own feelings, drop their facades, and are transparent and self-disclosing.

- *Empathy.* When people are *empathic,* they share and mirror other's feelings and reflect their meanings. "Rarely do we listen with real understanding, true empathy," said Rogers. "Yet listening, of this very special kind, is one of the most potent forces for change that I know."

ABRAHAM MASLOW (1908–1970) "Any theory of motivation that is worthy of attention must deal with the highest capacities of the healthy and strong person as well as with the defensive maneuvers of crippled spirits" (*Motivation and Personality,* 1970, p. 33).

A FATHER *NOT* OFFERING UNCONDITIONAL POSITIVE REGARD:

"Just remember, son, it doesn't matter whether you win or lose—unless you want Daddy's love."

 ASK YOURSELF

Think back to a conversation you had when you knew someone was just waiting for their turn to speak instead of listening to you. Now consider the last time someone heard you with empathy. How did those two experiences differ?

THE PICTURE OF EMPATHY Being open and sharing confidences is easier when the listener shows real understanding. Within such relationships we can relax and fully express our true selves.

CARL ROGERS (1902–1987) "The curious paradox is that when I accept myself just as I am, then I can change." (*On Becoming a Person*, 1961).

LaunchPad To consider how this theory applies to your own life, try the online **Immersive Learning: Assess Your Strengths —What Is Your Self-Concept?**

So, some things get better with *age*: acceptance, genuineness, and empathy. These are, Rogers believed, the water, sun, and nutrients that enable people to grow like vigorous oak trees. For "as persons are accepted and prized, they tend to develop a more caring attitude toward themselves" (Rogers, 1980, p. 116). As persons are empathically heard, "it becomes possible for them to listen more accurately to the flow of inner experiencings."

Writer Calvin Trillin (2006) recalled an example of parental acceptance and genuineness at a camp for children with severe disorders, where his wife, Alice, worked. L., a "magical child," had genetic diseases that meant she had to be tube-fed and could walk only with difficulty. Alice wondered "what this child's parents could have done . . . to make her the most optimistic, most enthusiastic, most hopeful human being I had ever encountered." One day Alice spotted a note that L. received from her mom, which read, "If God had given us all of the children in the world to choose from, L., we would only have chosen you." Inspired, Alice approached a co-worker. "Quick. Read this," she whispered. "It's the secret of life."

Maslow and Rogers would have smiled knowingly. For them, a central feature of personality is one's **self-concept**—all the thoughts and feelings we have in response to the question, "Who am I?" If our self-concept is positive, we tend to act and perceive the world positively. If it is negative—if in our own eyes we fall far short of our *ideal self*—said Rogers, we feel dissatisfied and unhappy. A worthwhile goal for therapists, parents, teachers, and friends is therefore, he said, to help others know, accept, and be true to themselves.

Assessing the Self

LOQ 38-11 How did humanistic psychologists assess a person's sense of self?

Humanistic psychologists sometimes assessed personality by asking people to fill out questionnaires that would evaluate their self-concept. One questionnaire, inspired by Carl Rogers, asked people to describe themselves both as they would *ideally* like to be and as they *actually* are. When the ideal and the actual self are nearly alike, said Rogers, the self-concept is positive. Assessing his clients' personal growth during therapy, he looked for successively closer ratings of actual and ideal selves.

Some humanistic psychologists believed that any standardized assessment of personality, even a questionnaire, is depersonalizing. Rather than forcing the person to respond to narrow categories, these humanistic psychologists presumed that interviews and intimate conversation would provide a better understanding of each person's unique experiences. Some researchers believe our identity may be revealed using the *life story approach*—collecting a rich narrative detailing each person's unique life history (Adler et al., 2016; McAdams & Guo, 2015). A lifetime of stories can show more of a person's complete identity than can the responses to a few questions.

Evaluating Humanistic Theories

LOQ 38-12 How have humanistic theories influenced psychology? What criticisms have they faced?

One thing said of Freud can also be said of the humanistic psychologists: Their impact has been pervasive. Maslow's and Rogers' ideas have influenced counseling, education, child raising, and management. And they laid the groundwork for today's scientific *positive psychology* subfield.

These theorists have also influenced—sometimes in unintended ways—much of today's popular psychology. Is a positive self-concept the key to happiness and success? Do acceptance and empathy nurture positive feelings about ourselves? Are people basically good and capable of self-improvement? Many people answer *Yes, Yes,* and *Yes*. In 2006, U.S. high school students reported notably higher self-esteem and greater expectations of future career success than did students living in 1975 (Twenge & Campbell, 2008). Given a choice, today's North American college students mostly say they'd rather get a self-esteem boost, such as a compliment or good grade on a paper, than enjoy a favorite food or sexual activity (Bushman et al., 2011). Humanistic psychology's message has been heard.

self-concept all our thoughts and feelings about ourselves, in answer to the question, "Who am I?"

But the prominence of the humanistic perspective set off a backlash of criticism. First, said the critics, its concepts are vague and subjective. Consider Maslow's description of self-actualizing people as open, spontaneous, loving, self-accepting, and productive. Is this a scientific description? Or is it merely a description of the theorist's own values and ideals? Maslow, noted M. Brewster Smith (1978), offered impressions of his own personal heroes. Imagine another theorist who began with a different set of heroes—perhaps Napoleon, John D. Rockefeller, Sr., and U.S. President Donald Trump. This theorist might describe self-actualizing people as "undeterred by others' opinions," "motivated to achieve," and "comfortable with power."

Critics also objected to the idea that, as Rogers (1985) put it, "The only question which matters is, 'Am I living in a way which is deeply satisfying to me, and which truly expresses me?'" This emphasis on *individualism*—trusting and acting on one's feelings, being true to oneself, fulfilling oneself—could lead to self-indulgence, selfishness, and an erosion of moral restraint (Campbell & Specht, 1985; Wallach & Wallach, 1983). Imagine working on a group project with people who refuse to complete any task that is not deeply satisfying or does not truly express their identity.

Humanistic psychologists have replied that a secure, nondefensive self-acceptance is actually the first step toward loving others. Indeed, people who feel intrinsically liked and accepted—for who they are, not just for their achievements—exhibit less defensive attitudes (Schimel et al., 2001). Those feeling liked and accepted by a romantic partner report being happier in their relationships and acting more kindly toward their partner (Gordon & Chen, 2010).

A final critique has been that humanistic psychology is naive—that it fails to appreciate the reality of our human capacity for evil (May, 1982). Faced with climate change, overpopulation, terrorism, and the spread of nuclear weapons, we may become apathetic from either of two rationalizations. One is a starry-eyed optimism that denies the threat ("People are basically good; everything will work out"). The other is a dark despair ("It's hopeless; why try?"). Action requires enough realism to fuel concern and enough optimism to provide hope.

"We do pretty well when you stop to think that people are basically good."

🔒 RETRIEVE IT • • •   *ANSWERS IN APPENDIX E*

RI-6 How did the *humanistic theories* provide a fresh perspective?

RI-7 What does it mean to be *empathic*? How about *self-actualized*? Which humanistic psychologists used these terms?

🔒 REVIEW   CLASSIC PERSPECTIVES ON PERSONALITY

⟨⟩ Learning Objectives

TEST YOURSELF Answer these repeated Learning Objective Questions on your own (before checking the answers in Appendix D) to improve your retention of the concepts (McDaniel et al., 2009, 2015).

38-1 What is *personality*, and what theories inform our understanding of personality?

38-2 How did Sigmund Freud's treatment of psychological disorders lead to his view of the unconscious mind?

38-3 What was Freud's view of personality?

38-4 What developmental stages did Freud propose?

38-5 How did Freud think people defended themselves against anxiety?

38-6 Which of Freud's ideas did his followers accept or reject?

38-7 What are *projective tests*, how are they used, and what are some criticisms of them?

38-8 How do contemporary psychologists view Freud's psychoanalysis?

38-9 How has modern research developed our understanding of the unconscious?

38-10 How did humanistic psychologists view personality, and what was their goal in studying personality?

38-11 How did humanistic psychologists assess a person's sense of self?

38-12 How have humanistic theories influenced psychology? What criticisms have they faced?

Terms and Concepts to Remember

TEST YOURSELF Write down the definition yourself, then check your answer on the referenced page.

personality, **p. 462**

psychodynamic theories, **p. 462**

psychoanalysis, **p. 462**

unconscious, **p. 463**

free association, **p. 463**

id, **p. 463**

ego, **p. 465**

superego, **p. 465**

psychosexual stages, **p. 465**

Oedipus [ED-uh-puss] complex, **p. 465**

identification, **p. 465**

fixation, **p. 465**

defense mechanisms, **p. 465**

repression, **p. 465**

collective unconscious, **p. 466**

Thematic Apperception Test (TAT), **p. 466**

projective test, **p. 466**

Rorschach inkblot test, **p. 466**

humanistic theories, **p. 470**

hierarchy of needs, **p. 470**

self-actualization, **p. 470**

self-transcendence, **p. 470**

unconditional positive regard, **p. 470**

self-concept, **p. 472**

Experience the Testing Effect

TEST YOURSELF Answer the following questions on your own first, then check your answers in Appendix E.

1. Freud believed that we may block painful or unacceptable thoughts, wishes, feelings, or memories from consciousness through an unconscious process called _____.

2. According to Freud's view of personality structure, the "executive" system, the _____, seeks to gratify the impulses of the _____ in more acceptable ways.

   a. id; ego

   b. ego; superego

   c. ego; id

   d. id; superego

3. Freud proposed that the development of the "voice of our moral compass" is related to the _____, which internalizes ideals and provides standards for judgments.

4. According to the psychoanalytic view of development, we all pass through a series of psychosexual stages, including the oral, anal, and phallic stages. Conflicts unresolved at any of these stages may lead to

   a. dormant sexual feelings.

   b. fixation at that stage.

   c. preconscious blocking of impulses.

   d. a distorted gender identity.

5. Freud believed that defense mechanisms are unconscious attempts to distort or disguise reality, all in an effort to reduce our _____.

6. _____ tests ask test-takers to respond to an ambiguous image by describing it or telling a story about it.

7. In general, neo-Freudians such as Adler and Horney accepted many of Freud's views but placed more emphasis than he did on

   a. development throughout the life span.

   b. the collective unconscious.

   c. the role of the id.

   d. social interactions.

8. Modern-day psychodynamic theorists and therapists agree with Freud about

   a. the existence of unconscious mental processes.

   b. the Oedipus complex.

   c. the predictive value of Freudian theory.

   d. the superego's role as the executive part of personality.

9. Which of the following is NOT part of the contemporary view of the unconscious?

   a. Repressed memories of anxiety-provoking events

   b. Schemas that influence our perceptions and interpretations

   c. Stereotypes that affect our information processing

   d. Instantly activated emotions and implicit memories of learned skills

10. Maslow's hierarchy of needs proposes that we must satisfy basic physiological and safety needs before we seek ultimate psychological needs, such as self-actualization. Maslow based his ideas on

    a. Freudian theory.

    b. his experiences with patients.

    c. a series of laboratory experiments.

    d. his study of healthy, creative people.

11. How might Rogers explain how environment influences the development of a criminal?

12. The total acceptance Rogers advocated as part of a growth-promoting environment is called _____ _____ _____.

Continue testing yourself with 📖 **LearningCurve** or 📖 **Achieve Read & Practice** to learn and remember most effectively.

③⑨ Contemporary Perspectives on Personality

trait a characteristic pattern of behavior or a disposition to feel and act in certain ways, as assessed by self-report inventories and peer reports.

TRAIT THEORIES

LOQ 39-1 How do psychologists use traits to describe personality?

Rather than focusing on unconscious forces and thwarted growth opportunities, some researchers attempt to define personality in terms of stable and enduring behavior patterns, such as Lady Gaga's self-discipline and openness to new experiences. This perspective can be traced in part to a remarkable meeting in 1919, when Gordon Allport, a curious 22-year-old psychology student, interviewed Sigmund Freud in Vienna. Allport soon discovered just how preoccupied the founder of psychoanalysis was with finding hidden motives, even in Allport's own behavior during the interview. That experience ultimately led Allport to do what Freud did not do: to describe personality in terms of fundamental **traits**, or people's characteristic behaviors and conscious motives (such as the curiosity that actually motivated Allport to see Freud). Meeting Freud, said Allport, "taught me that [psychoanalysis], for all its merits, may plunge too deep, and that psychologists would do well to give full recognition to manifest motives before probing the unconscious." Allport came to define personality in terms of identifiable behavior patterns. He was concerned less with *explaining* individual traits than with *describing* them.

Exploring Traits

We are each a unique complex of multiple traits. So how can we describe our personalities in a way that captures our individuality? We might describe an apple by placing it along several trait dimensions—relatively large or small, red or green, sweet or tart. By placing people on several trait dimensions simultaneously, psychologists can describe countless individual personality variations, just as variations on only three color dimensions—*hue, saturation,* and *brightness*—create many thousands of colors.

What trait dimensions describe personality? If you were looking at profiles on a dating site or app, what personality traits would give you the best sense for each person? Allport and his associate H. S. Odbert (1936) counted all the words in an unabridged dictionary with which one could describe people. There were almost 18,000! How, then, could psychologists condense the list to a manageable number of basic traits?

FACTOR ANALYSIS One technique is *factor analysis,* a statistical procedure that identifies clusters (factors) of test items that tap basic components of a trait (McCabe & Fleeson, 2016). Imagine that people who describe themselves as outgoing also tend to say that they like excitement and practical jokes and dislike quiet reading. Such a statistically correlated cluster of behaviors reflects a basic factor, or trait—in this case, *extraversion.*

British psychologists Hans Eysenck and Sybil Eysenck [EYE-zink] believed that we can reduce many of our normal individual variations to two dimensions: *extraversion–introversion* and *emotional stability–instability* (**FIGURE 39.1**). People in 35 countries around the world, from China to Uganda to Russia, have taken the *Eysenck Personality Questionnaire.* When their answers were analyzed, the extraversion and emotionality factors inevitably emerged as basic personality dimensions (Eysenck, 1990, 1992). The Eysencks believed, and research confirms, that these factors are genetically influenced.

BIOLOGY AND PERSONALITY Brain-activity scans of extraverts add to the growing list of traits and mental states now being explored with brain-imaging procedures. Such studies indicate that extraverts seek stimulation because their normal *brain arousal* is

"Russ is the sort of person who never wants to be alone with his thoughts."

476

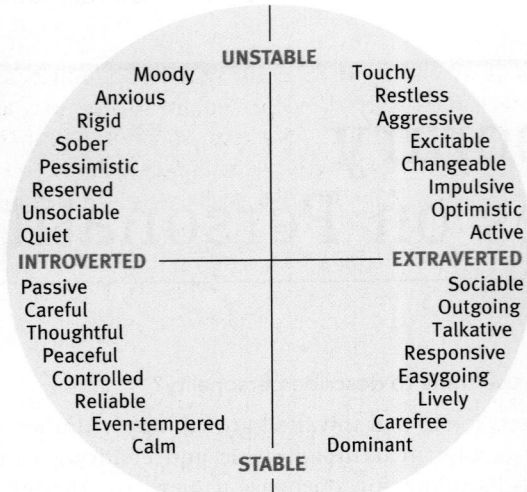

UNSTABLE

INTROVERTED	EXTRAVERTED
Moody	Touchy
Anxious	Restless
Rigid	Aggressive
Sober	Excitable
Pessimistic	Changeable
Reserved	Impulsive
Unsociable	Optimistic
Quiet	Active
Passive	Sociable
Careful	Outgoing
Thoughtful	Talkative
Peaceful	Responsive
Controlled	Easygoing
Reliable	Lively
Even-tempered	Carefree
Calm	Dominant

STABLE

FIGURE 39.1

TWO PERSONALITY DIMENSIONS

Mapmakers can tell us a lot by using two axes (north–south and east–west). Two primary personality factors (extraversion–introversion and stability–instability) are similarly useful as axes for describing personality variation. Varying combinations define other, more specific traits (Eysenck & Eysenck, 1963). Successful comedians, including Stephen Colbert, are often natural extraverts who love constant social engagement and spontaneity. However, many accomplished actors, such as Emma Watson, are introverts—particularly capable of solitary study to become each character they portray.

relatively low. For example, PET scans have shown that a frontal lobe area involved in behavior inhibition is less active in extraverts than in introverts (Johnson et al., 1999). Dopamine and dopamine-related neural activity tend to be higher in extraverts (Kim et al., 2008; Wacker et al., 2006).

Our biology influences our personality in other ways as well. As we know from twin and adoption studies, our genes have much to say about the *temperament* and behavioral style that shape our personality. Jerome Kagan (2010), for example, has explained differences in children's shyness and inhibition as a function of their autonomic nervous system reactivity (see Thinking Critically About: The Stigma of Introversion). Those with a reactive autonomic nervous system respond to stress with greater anxiety and inhibition. The fearless, curious child may become the rock-climbing or fast-driving adult.

THINKING CRITICALLY ABOUT:

The Stigma of Introversion

LOQ 39-2 What are some common misunderstandings about introversion?

Western cultures are hard on introverts:

Superheroes tend to be extraverted. Black Panther unites five tribes of people with his engaging strength of character. Take-charge Elastigirl saves the day in *The Incredibles*.

What do job interviewers want in their employees? Extraversion outranks most other personality traits.[1]

87% of Westerners want to be more extraverted.[2]

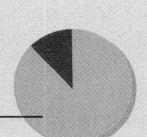
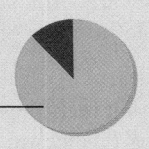

Being introverted seems to imply that we don't have the "right stuff."[3]

Attractive, successful people are presumed to be extraverts.

What is introversion?

Introverts tend to gain energy from time alone, and may find social interactions exhausting. Extraverts, by contrast, tend to draw energy from time spent with others.

Introverts are not "shy." (Shy people remain quiet because they fear others will evaluate them negatively.)

Introverted people seek low levels of stimulation from their environment because they're *sensitive.* For example, when given lemon juice, introverted people salivated more than extraverted people.[4]

Introversion has many benefits:

• Introverted leaders outperform extraverted leaders in some contexts, such as when their employees voice new ideas and challenge existing norms.[5]

• Introverts handle conflict well. In response, they seek solitude rather than revenge.[6]

• Many introverts flourish, including Bill Gates, Mother Teresa, and Jeff Bezos. Faced with the decision to start Amazon, Bezos spent days alone thinking about it. "I went away," he said.[7]

1. Kluemper et al., 2015; Salgado & Moscoso, 2002. 2. Hudson & Roberts, 2014. 3. Cain, 2012. 4. Corcoran, 1964. 5. Grant et al., 2011. 6. Ren et al., 2016. 7. Mejia, 2017.

Personality differences among dogs (in energy, affection, reactivity, and curious intelligence) are as evident, and as consistently judged, as personality differences among humans (Gosling et al., 2003; Jones & Gosling, 2005). Monkeys, bonobos, chimpanzees, orangutans, sea lions, and even birds and fish also have distinct and stable personalities (Ciardelli et al., 2017; Latzman et al., 2015; Pennisi, 2016; Weiss et al., 2017). Among the Great tit (a European relative of the American chickadee), bold birds more quickly inspect new objects and explore trees (Groothuis & Carere, 2005; Verbeek et al., 1994). Through selective breeding, researchers can produce bold or shy birds. Both have their place in natural history: In lean years, bold birds are more likely to find food; in abundant years, shy birds feed with less risk.

PUPS HAVE PERSONALITY

🔒 RETRIEVE IT • • •
ANSWERS IN APPENDIX E

RI-1 Which two primary dimensions did Hans Eysenck and Sybil Eysenck propose for describing personality variation?

Assessing Traits

LOQ 39-3 What are *personality inventories,* and what are their strengths and weaknesses as trait-assessment tools?

If stable and enduring traits guide our actions, can we devise valid and reliable tests of them? Several trait-assessment techniques exist—some more valid than others. Some provide quick assessments of a single trait, such as extraversion, anxiety, or self-esteem. **Personality inventories**—longer questionnaires covering a wide range of feelings and behaviors—assess several traits at once.

The classic personality inventory is the **Minnesota Multiphasic Personality Inventory (MMPI).** Although the MMPI was originally developed to identify emotional disorders, it also assesses people's personality traits. One of its creators, Starke Hathaway (1960), compared his effort with that of Alfred Binet. Binet developed the first intelligence test by selecting items that identified children who would probably have trouble progressing normally in French schools. Like Binet's items, the MMPI items were **empirically derived:** From a large pool of items, Hathaway and his colleagues selected those on which particular diagnostic groups differed. "My hands and feet are usually warm enough" may seem superficial, but it just so happened that anxious people were more likely to answer *False*. The researchers grouped the questions into 10 clinical scales, including scales that assess depressive tendencies, masculinity–femininity, and introversion–extraversion. Today's MMPI-2 has additional scales that assess work attitudes, family problems, and anger.

Whereas most projective tests (such as the Rorschach) are scored subjectively, personality inventories are scored objectively. (Software can administer and score these tests, and can also provide descriptions of people who previously responded similarly.) Objectivity does not, however, guarantee validity. Individuals taking the MMPI for employment purposes can give socially desirable answers to create a good impression. But in so doing they may also score high on a *lie scale* that assesses faking (as when people respond *False* to a universally true statement, such as "I get angry sometimes"). In other cases, the MMPI can be used to identify people pretending to have a disorder in order to avoid their work or other responsibilities (Chmielewski et al., 2017). The objectivity of the MMPI has contributed to its popularity and its translation into more than 100 languages.

The Big Five Factors

LOQ 39-4 Which traits seem to provide the most useful information about personality variation?

Today's trait researchers believe that simple trait factors, such as the Eysencks' introversion–extraversion and stability–instability dimensions, are important, but they do not tell the whole story. A slightly expanded set of factors—dubbed the *Big Five*—does a better job (Costa & McCrae, 2011; Soto & John, 2017). If a test specifies where you are on the five

---

LaunchPad Might astrology hold the secret to our personality traits? Play the role of a researcher testing this question by engaging online with **Immersive Learning: How Would You Know If Astrologers Can Describe People's Personality?**

People have had fun spoofing the MMPI with their own mock items: "Weeping brings tears to my eyes," "Frantic screams make me nervous," and "I stay in the bathtub until I look like a raisin" (Frankel et al., 1983).

personality inventory a questionnaire (often with *true-false* or *agree-disagree* items) on which people respond to items designed to gauge a wide range of feelings and behaviors; used to assess selected personality traits.

Minnesota Multiphasic Personality Inventory (MMPI) the most widely researched and clinically used of all personality tests. Originally developed to identify emotional disorders (still considered its most appropriate use), this test is now used for many other screening purposes.

empirically derived test a test (such as the MMPI) created by selecting from a pool of items those that discriminate between groups.

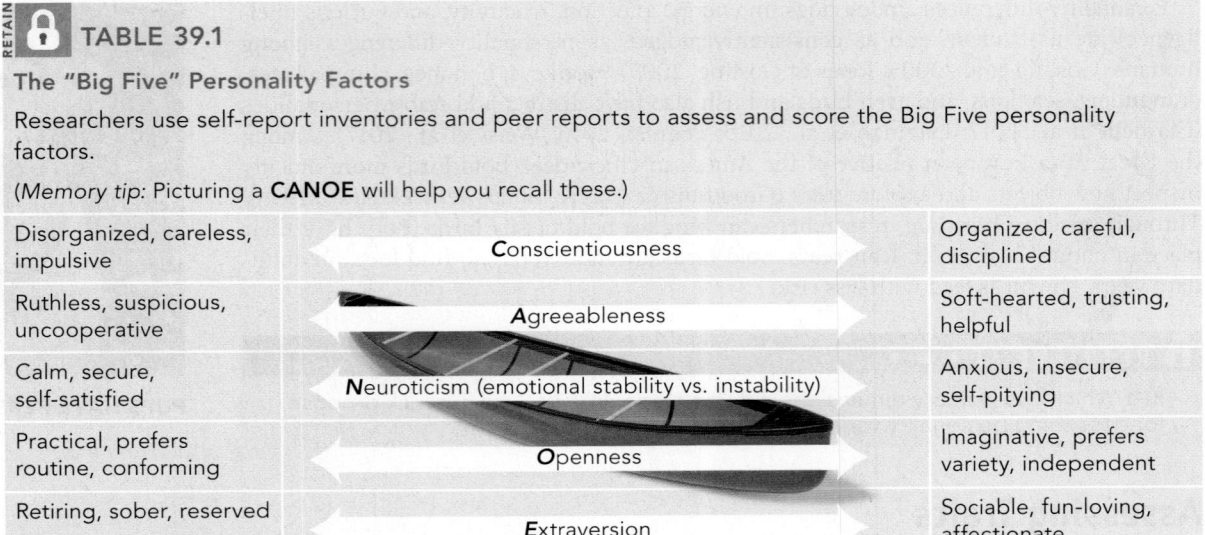

RETAIN 🔒 **TABLE 39.1**

The "Big Five" Personality Factors

Researchers use self-report inventories and peer reports to assess and score the Big Five personality factors.

(*Memory tip:* Picturing a **CANOE** will help you recall these.)

Disorganized, careless, impulsive	← **C**onscientiousness →	Organized, careful, disciplined
Ruthless, suspicious, uncooperative	← **A**greeableness →	Soft-hearted, trusting, helpful
Calm, secure, self-satisfied	← **N**euroticism (emotional stability vs. instability) →	Anxious, insecure, self-pitying
Practical, prefers routine, conforming	← **O**penness →	Imaginative, prefers variety, independent
Retiring, sober, reserved	← **E**xtraversion →	Sociable, fun-loving, affectionate

Information from McCrae & Costa (1986, 2008).

Steve Wisbauer/Getty Images

dimensions (conscientiousness, agreeableness, neuroticism, openness, and extraversion; see **TABLE 39.1**), it has said much of what there is to say about your personality. Some clinical psychologists have begun to use the Big Five to understand personality disorders, schizophrenia, and other types of dysfunction (Ohi et al., 2016; Widiger et al., 2016).

Around the world—across 56 nations and 29 languages in one study (Schmitt et al., 2007)—people describe others in terms roughly consistent with this list. The Big Five— today's "common currency for personality psychology" (Funder, 2001)—has been the most active personality research topic since the early 1990s and is currently our best approximation of the basic trait dimensions.

Big Five research has explored various questions:

- **How stable are these traits?** One research team analyzed 1.25 million participants ages 10 to 65. They learned that personality continues to develop and change through late childhood and adolescence. Up to age 40, we show signs of a *maturity principle:* We become more conscientious and agreeable and less neurotic (emotionally unstable) (Milojev & Sibley, 2017; Rohrer et al., 2018). Great apes show similar personality maturation (Weiss & King, 2015). After age 40, our traits further stabilize.

- **How heritable are these traits?** Heritability (the extent to which individual differences are attributable to genes) generally runs about 40 percent for each dimension (Vukasović & Bratko, 2015). Many genes, each having small effects, combine to influence our traits (McCrae et al., 2010; van den Berg et al., 2016).

- **Do these traits reflect differing brain structure?** The size and thickness of brain tissue correlates with several Big Five traits (DeYoung et al., 2010; Grodin & White, 2015; Riccelli et al., 2017). For example, those who score high on conscientiousness tend to have a larger frontal lobe area that aids in planning and controlling behavior. Brain connections also influence the Big Five traits (Adelstein et al., 2011). People high in neuroticism have brains that are wired to experience stress intensely (Shackman et al., 2016; Xu & Potenza, 2012).

- **Do these traits reflect birth order?** After controlling for other variables such as family size, are first-born children, for example, more conscientious and agreeable? Contrary to popular opinion, several massive studies failed to find any association between birth order and personality (Damian & Roberts, 2015; Harris, 2009; Rohrer et al., 2015).

- **How well do these traits apply to various cultures?** The Big Five dimensions describe personality in various cultures reasonably well (Fetvadjiev et al., 2017; Schmitt et al., 2007; Vazsonyi et al., 2015). After studying people from 50 cultures, Robert McCrae and 79 co-researchers concluded that "features of personality traits are common to all human groups" (2005).

- *Do the Big Five traits predict our actual behaviors?* Yes. Conscientiousness and agreeableness predict workplace success (Sackett & Walmsley, 2014). Agreeable people tend to help others, whereas people high in neuroticism are often unhelpful (Habashi et al., 2016; McCann, 2017). Traits also characterize certain career paths. For example, U.S. politicians tend to have "big" personalities, outscoring the general public on extraversion, agreeableness, conscientiousness, and emotional stability (low neuroticism) (Hanania, 2017). Our traits also appear in our language patterns. In text messaging, extraversion predicts use of personal pronouns. Neuroticism predicts negative-emotion words (Holtgraves, 2011).

By exploring such questions, Big Five research has sustained trait psychology and renewed appreciation for the importance of personality. (To describe your personality, try the brief self-assessment in **FIGURE 39.2**.) Traits matter. In the next section, we will see that situations matter, too.

HOW DO YOU VOTE? LET ME COUNT THE LIKES Researchers can use your Facebook likes to predict your Big Five traits, your opinions, and your political attitudes (Youyou et al., 2015). Companies gather these "big data" for advertisers (who then personalize the ads you see). They do the same for political candidates, who can target you with persuasive messages (Matz et al., 2017). In the 2016 U.S. presidential campaign, "both sides were certainly using big data . . . to win over voters," says researcher Michal Kosinski (Zakaria, 2017).

 (ASK YOURSELF)

Before trying the self-assessment in Figure 39.2, where would you have placed yourself on the Big Five personality dimensions? Where might your family and friends place you? Did the actual results surprise you, and do you think these results would surprise them?

 FIGURE 39.2

THE BIG FIVE SELF-ASSESSMENT

How Do You Describe Yourself?

Describe yourself as you generally are now, not as you wish to be in the future. Describe yourself as you honestly see yourself, in relation to other people you know of the same sex and roughly the same age. Use the scale below to enter a number for each statement. Then, use the scoring guide at the bottom to see where you fall on the spectrum for each of the Big Five traits.

1	2	3	4	5
Very Inaccurate	Moderately Inaccurate	Neither Accurate Nor Inaccurate	Moderately Accurate	Very Accurate

1. ___Am the life of the party

2. ___Sympathize with others' feelings

3. ___Get stressed out easily

4. ___Am always prepared

5. ___Am full of ideas

6. ___Start conversations

7. ___Take time out for others

8. ___Follow a schedule

9. ___Worry about things

10. ___Have a vivid imagination

SCORING GUIDE SORTED BY BIG FIVE PERSONALITY TRAITS

Conscientiousness: statements 4, 8

Agreeableness: statements 2, 7

Neuroticism: statements 3, 9

Openness: statements 5, 10

Extraversion: statements 1, 6

How to score:
Separate your responses by each Big Five personality trait, as noted at left, and divide by two to obtain your score for each trait. So, for example, for the "Agreeableness" trait let's say you scored 3 for statement 2 ("Sympathize with others' feelings") and 4 for statement 7 ("Take time out for others"). That means on a scale from 1 to 5, your overall score for the "Agreeableness" trait is 3 + 4 = 7 ÷ 2 = 3.5.

Scale data from Goldberg, L. R. (1992). The development of markers for the Big-Five factor structure. *Psychological Assessment, 4*, 26–42.

RETAIN 🔒 **LaunchPad** For a review of the Big Five, engage online with **Concept Practice: The Big Five Personality Traits.**

"I'm going to France—I'm a different person in France."

Victoria Roberts The New Yorker Collection/ The Cartoon Bank

"There is as much difference between us and ourselves, as between us and others." —Michel de Montaigne, *Essays*, 1588

RETAIN 🔒 Roughly speaking, the temporary, external influences on behavior are the focus of *social psychology*, and the enduring, inner influences are the focus of *personality psychology*. In actuality, behavior always depends on the interaction of persons with situations.

🔒 **RETRIEVE IT • • •**   ANSWERS IN APPENDIX E

RI-2 What are the *Big Five* personality factors, and why are they scientifically useful?

Evaluating Trait Theories

LOQ 39-5 Does research support the consistency of personality traits over time and across situations?

Are our personality traits stable and enduring? Or does our behavior depend on where and with whom we find ourselves? In some ways, our personality seems stable. Cheerful, friendly children tend to become cheerful, friendly adults. At a college reunion, I [DM] was amazed to find that my jovial former classmates were still jovial, the shy ones still shy, the happy-seeming people still smiling and laughing *50 years later*. But it's also true that a fun-loving jokester can suddenly turn serious and respectful at a job interview. New situations and major life events can shift the personality traits we express. Becoming unemployed, for example, may make us less agreeable and open-minded (Boyce et al., 2015).

THE PERSON-SITUATION CONTROVERSY Our behavior is influenced by the interaction of our inner disposition with our environment. Still, the question lingers: Which is more important? When we explore this *person-situation controversy*, we look for genuine personality traits that persist over time *and* across situations. Are some people dependably conscientious and others unreliable? Some cheerful and others dour? Some friendly and outgoing and others shy? If we are to consider friendliness a trait, friendly people must act friendly at different times and places. Do they?

In considering research that has followed lives through time, some scholars (especially those who study infants) are impressed with personality change; others are struck by personality stability during adulthood. As **FIGURE 39.3** illustrates, data from 152 long-term *(longitudinal)* studies reveal that personality trait scores are positively correlated with scores obtained seven years later, and that as people grow older, their personality stabilizes. Interests may change—the avid tropical-fish collector may become an avid gardener. Careers may change—the determined salesperson may become a determined social worker. Relationships may change—the hostile spouse may start over and antagonize a new partner. But most people recognize just who they are, as Robert McCrae and Paul Costa noted (1994), "and it is well that they do. A person's recognition of the inevitability of his or her one and only personality is . . . the culminating wisdom of a lifetime."

So most people—including most psychologists—would probably presume the stability of personality traits. Moreover, our traits are socially significant. They influence our health, our thinking, and our job choices and performance (Hogan, 1998; Jackson et al., 2012; Sutin et al., 2011). Studies that follow thousands of people through time show that personality traits rival socioeconomic status and cognitive ability as predictors of mortality, divorce, and occupational attainment (Graham et al., 2017; Roberts et al., 2007).

FIGURE 39.3

PERSONALITY STABILITY With age, personality traits become more stable, as reflected in the stronger correlation of trait scores with follow-up scores 7 years later. (Data from Roberts & DelVecchio, 2000.)

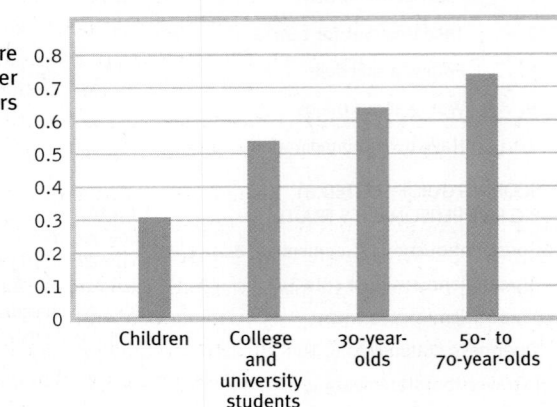

Although our personality *traits* may be both stable and potent, the consistency of our specific *behaviors* from one situation to the next is another matter. What relationship would you expect to find between being conscientious in one situation (say, showing up for class on time) and being conscientious in another (say, avoiding unhealthy foods)? If you've noticed how outgoing you are in some situations and how reserved you are in others, perhaps you said, "Very little." That's what researchers have found—only a small correlation (Mischel, 1968; Sherman et al., 2015). This inconsistency in behaviors also makes personality test scores weak predictors of behaviors. People's scores on an extraversion test, for example, do not neatly predict how sociable they actually will be on any given occasion.

If we remember such results, we will be more cautious about labeling and pigeonholing individuals (Mischel, 1968). Years in advance, science can tell us the phase of the Moon for any given date. A day in advance, meteorologists can often predict the weather. But we are much further from being able to predict how *you* will feel and act tomorrow. However, people's *average* outgoingness, happiness, or carelessness over many situations is predictable (Epstein, 1983a,b). This tendency toward trait-consistent actions occurs across cultures, from the United States to Venezuela to Japan (Locke et al., 2017). People who know someone well, therefore, generally agree when rating that person's shyness or agreeableness (Jackson et al., 2015; Kenrick & Funder, 1988). By collecting snippets of people's daily experience via body-worn recording devices, researchers confirmed that extraverts really do talk more (Mehl et al., 2006). (I [DM] have repeatedly vowed to cut back on my jabbering and joking during my noontime pickup basketball games with friends. Alas, moments later, the irrepressible chatterbox inevitably reoccupies my body. And I [ND] have a similar experience whenever I buy groceries. Somehow, I always end up chatting with the cashier!) As our best friends can verify, we do have persistent, genetically influenced personality traits. And our personality traits get expressed in our

- *music preferences.* Your playlist reveals something of your personality. Classical, jazz, blues, and folk music lovers tend to be open to experience and verbally intelligent. Extraverts tend to prefer upbeat and energetic music. Country, pop, and religious music lovers tend to be cheerful, outgoing, and conscientious (Langmeyer et al., 2012; Rentfrow & Gosling, 2003, 2006).

- *written communications.* If you have ever felt you could detect someone's personality from their writing voice, you are right!! What a cool finding!!! ☺ People's writings—even their brief tweets and Facebook posts—often express their extraversion, self-esteem, and agreeableness (Orehek & Human, 2017; Park et al., 2015; Pennebaker, 2011). "Off to meet a friend. Woohoo!!!" posted one Facebook user who had scored high on extraversion (Kern et al., 2014). Extraverts also use more adjectives.

- *online and personal spaces.* Are online profiles, websites, and avatars also a canvas for self-expression? Or are they an opportunity for people to present themselves in false or misleading ways? It's more the former (Back et al., 2010; Gosling et al., 2007; Marcus et al., 2006). People who seemed most likable on their Facebook or Twitter pages also seemed most likable in person (Qiu et al., 2012; Weisbuch et al., 2009). Even mere photos, with their associated clothes, expressions, and postures, can give clues to personality and how people act in person (Gunyadin et al., 2017; Naumann et al., 2009). Our living and working spaces also help us express our identity. They all offer clues to our extraversion, agreeableness, conscientiousness, and openness (Back et al., 2010; Fong & Mar, 2015; Gosling, 2008).

In unfamiliar, formal situations—perhaps as a guest in the home of a person from another culture—our traits remain hidden as we carefully attend to social cues. In familiar, informal situations—just hanging out with friends—we feel less constrained, allowing our traits to emerge (Buss, 1989). In these informal situations, our expressive styles—our animation, manner of speaking, and gestures—are impressively consistent. Viewing "thin slices" of someone's behavior—such as seeing a photo for a mere fraction of a second, or seeing several 2-second clips of a teacher in action—can tell us a lot about the person's basic personality traits (Ambady, 2010; Tackett et al., 2016).

my hair over time

childhood

teens and twenties - experimentation

thirties and up   *Mitra Farmand*

IT'S NOT JUST PERSONALITY THAT STABILIZES WITH AGE.

Change and consistency can coexist. If all people were to become somewhat less shy with age, there would be personality change, but also relative stability and predictability.

 ASK YOURSELF

How do you think your own personality traits shine through in your music preferences, communication style, and online and personal spaces?

ROOM WITH A CUE Even at "zero acquaintance," people can catch a glimpse of others' personality from looking at their online and personal spaces. So, what's your read on this person?

Gary Houlder/Getty Images

To sum up, we can say that at any moment the immediate situation powerfully influences a person's behavior. Social psychologists have learned that this is especially so when a "strong situation" makes clear demands (Cooper & Withey, 2009). We can better predict drivers' behavior at traffic lights from knowing the color of the lights than from knowing the drivers' personalities. Averaging our behavior across many occasions does, however, reveal distinct personality traits. Traits exist. We differ. And our differences matter.

LaunchPad For a demonstration of trait research, view the 8-minute **Video: Trait Theories of Personality.**

🔒 **RETRIEVE IT • • •**   *ANSWERS IN APPENDIX E*

RI-3 How well do personality test scores predict our behavior? Explain.

SOCIAL-COGNITIVE THEORIES

LOQ 39-6   How do social-cognitive theorists view personality development, and how do they explore behavior?

The **social-cognitive perspective** on personality, proposed by Albert Bandura (1986, 2006, 2008), emphasizes the interaction of our traits with our situations. Much as nature and nurture always work together, so do individuals and their situations.

Social-cognitive theorists believe we learn many of our behaviors either through conditioning or by observing and imitating others. (That's the "social" part.) They also emphasize the importance of mental processes: What we *think* about a situation affects our behavior in that situation. (That's the "cognitive" part.) Instead of focusing solely on how our environment *controls* us (behaviorism), social-cognitive theorists focus on how we and our environment *interact:* How do we interpret and respond to external events? How do our schemas, our memories, and our expectations influence our behavior patterns?

Reciprocal Influences

Bandura (1986, 2006) views the person-environment interaction as **reciprocal determinism.** "Behavior, internal personal factors, and environmental influences," he said, "all operate as interlocking determinants of each other" (**FIGURE 39.4**). We can see this interaction in people's relationships. For example, Rosa's past romantic experiences (her behaviors) influence her romantic attitudes (internal factor), which affect how she now responds to Ryan (environmental factor).

Consider three specific ways in which individuals and environments interact:

1. *Different people choose different environments.* The schools we attend, the reading we do, the careers we pursue, the music we listen to, the social media we use, the friends we associate with—all are part of an environment we have chosen, based

social-cognitive perspective a view of behavior as influenced by the interaction between people's traits (including their thinking) and their social context.

reciprocal determinism the interacting influences of behavior, internal cognition, and environment.

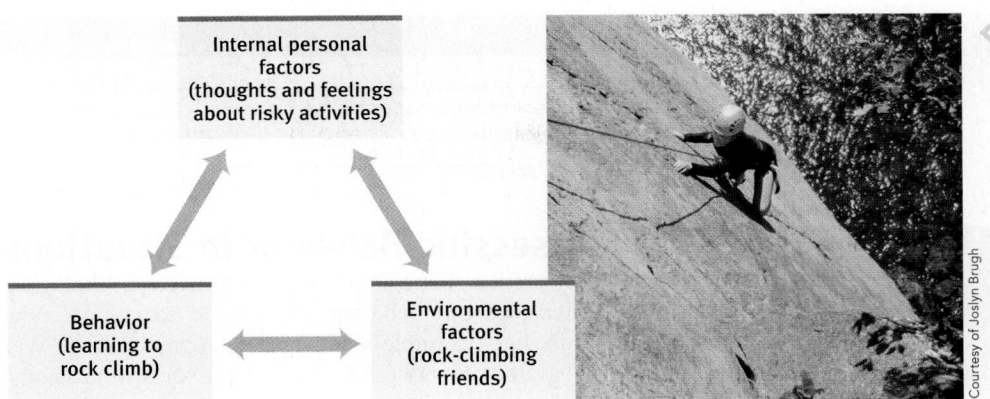

Internal personal factors (thoughts and feelings about risky activities)

Behavior (learning to rock climb)

Environmental factors (rock-climbing friends)

Courtesy of Joslyn Brugh

FIGURE 39.4
RECIPROCAL DETERMINISM

partly on our dispositions (Denissen et al., 2018; Funder, 2009). And the environments we choose then shape us. People with inflated self-esteem post frequent selfies in online environments, for example, where they can receive the public attention and praise they crave. This leads to even greater self-love (Halpern et al., 2016).

2. *Our personalities shape how we interpret and react to events.* Anxious people tend to attend and react strongly to relationship threats (Campbell & Marshall, 2011). If we perceive the world as threatening, we will watch for threats and be prepared to defend ourselves.

3. *Our personalities help create situations to which we react.* How we view and treat people influences how they then treat us. If we expect that others will not like us, our bragging and other efforts to seek their approval might actually cause them to reject us (Scopelliti et al., 2015).

In addition to the interaction of internal personal factors, the environment, and our behaviors, we also experience *gene-environment interaction.* Our genetically influenced traits evoke certain responses from others, which may nudge us in one direction or another. In one well-replicated classic study, those with the interacting factors of (1) having a specific gene associated with aggression, and (2) being raised in a difficult environment were most likely to demonstrate adult antisocial behavior (Byrd & Manuck, 2014; Caspi et al., 2002).

In such ways, we are both the products and the architects of our environments: *Behavior emerges from the interplay of external and internal influences.* Boiling water turns an egg hard and a potato soft. A threatening environment turns one person into a hero, another into a scoundrel. Extraverts enjoy greater well-being in an extraverted culture than in an introverted one (Fulmer et al., 2010). *At every moment,* our behavior is influenced by our biology, our social and cultural experiences, and our cognition and dispositions (**FIGURE 39.5**).

ENGAGE **ASK YOURSELF**

How have your experiences shaped your personality? How has your personality helped shape your environment?

LaunchPad To explore the influence of the person-environment interaction on behavior, engage online with **Concept Practice: Reciprocal Determinism.**

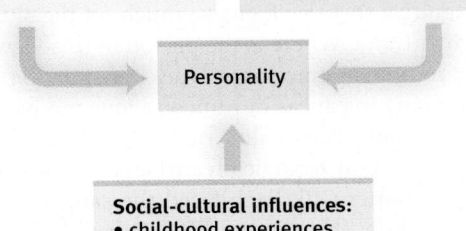

Biological influences:
• genetically determined temperament
• autonomic nervous system reactivity
• brain activity

Psychological influences:
• learned responses
• unconscious thought processes
• expectations and interpretations

Personality

Social-cultural influences:
• childhood experiences
• situational factors
• cultural expectations
• social support

RETAIN **FIGURE 39.5**

THE BIOPSYCHOSOCIAL APPROACH TO THE STUDY OF PERSONALITY As with other psychological phenomena, personality is fruitfully studied at multiple levels.

🔒 RETRIEVE IT • • •   *ANSWERS IN APPENDIX E*

RI-4 Albert Bandura proposed the _____ - _____ perspective on personality, which emphasizes the interaction of people with their environment. To describe the interacting influences of behavior, thoughts, and environment, he used the term _____ _____.

IF YOU CAN'T STAND THE HEAT . . . On the Food Network's *Chopped,* contestants are pitted against one another in stressful situations. The entertaining episodes illustrate a valid point: A chef's behavior in such job-relevant situations can help predict job performance.

Gustavo Caballero/Getty Images

Assessing Behavior in Situations

To predict behavior, social-cognitive psychologists often observe behavior in realistic situations. One ambitious example was the U.S. Army's World War II strategy for assessing candidates for spy missions. Rather than using paper-and-pencil tests, Army psychologists subjected the candidates to simulated undercover conditions. They tested their ability to handle stress, solve problems, maintain leadership, and withstand intense interrogation without blowing their cover. Although time-consuming and expensive, this assessment of behavior in a realistic situation helped predict later success on actual spy missions (OSS Assessment Staff, 1948).

Military and educational organizations and many Fortune 500 companies have adopted similar strategies, known as the *assessment center* approach (Bray & Byham, 1991, 1997; Eurich et al., 2009). AT&T has observed prospective managers doing simulated managerial work. Many colleges assess nursing students' potential by observing their clinical work, and they assess potential faculty members' teaching abilities by observing them teach. Most American cities with populations of 50,000 or more have used assessment centers in evaluating police officers and firefighters (Lowry, 1997).

These procedures exploit the principle that the best means of predicting future behavior is neither a personality test nor an interviewer's intuition; rather, it is *the person's past behavior patterns in similar situations* (Lyons et al., 2011; Mischel, 1981; Schmidt & Hunter, 1998). As long as the situation and the person remain much the same, the best predictor of future job performance is past job performance; the best predictor of future grades is past grades; the best predictor of future aggressiveness is past aggressiveness. If you can't check the person's past behavior, the next best thing is to create an assessment situation that simulates the task so you can see how the person handles it (Lievens et al., 2009; Meriac et al., 2008).

"What's past is prologue." —William Shakespeare, *The Tempest,* 1611

Evaluating Social-Cognitive Theories

LOQ 39-7   What criticisms have social-cognitive theorists faced?

Social-cognitive theories of personality sensitize researchers to how situations affect, and are affected by, individuals. More than other personality theories (see **TABLE 39.2**), they build from psychological research on learning and cognition.

Critics charge that social-cognitive theories focus so much on the situation that they fail to appreciate the person's inner traits. Where is the person in this view of personality, ask the dissenters, and where are human emotions? True, the situation does guide our behavior. But, say the critics, in many instances our unconscious motives, our emotions, and our pervasive traits shine through. Personality traits have been shown to predict behavior at work, in love, and at play. Our biologically influenced traits really do matter. Consider Percy Ray Pridgen and Charles Gill. Each faced the same situation: They had jointly won a $90 million lottery jackpot (Harriston, 1993). When Pridgen learned of the winning numbers, he began trembling uncontrollably, huddled with a friend behind a bathroom door while confirming the win, and then sobbed. When Gill heard the news, he told his wife and then went to sleep.

RETAIN

TABLE 39.2

Comparing the Major Personality Theories

Personality Theory	Key Proponents	Assumptions	View of Personality	Personality Assessment Methods
Psychoanalytic	Freud	Emotional disorders spring from unconscious dynamics, such as unresolved sexual and other childhood conflicts, and fixation at various developmental stages. Defense mechanisms fend off anxiety.	Personality consists of pleasure-seeking impulses (the id), a reality-oriented executive (the ego), and an internalized set of ideals (the superego).	Free association, projective tests, dream analysis
Psychodynamic	Adler, Horney, Jung	The unconscious and conscious minds interact. Childhood experiences and defense mechanisms are important.	The dynamic interplay of conscious and unconscious motives and conflicts shapes our personality.	Projective tests, therapy sessions
Humanistic	Rogers, Maslow	Rather than examining the struggles of sick people, it's better to focus on the ways healthy people may strive for self-realization.	If our basic human needs are met, we will strive toward self-actualization. In a climate of unconditional positive regard, we can develop self-awareness and a more realistic and positive self-concept.	Questionnaires, therapy sessions
Trait	Allport, H. Eysenck, S. Eysenck, McCrae, Costa	We have certain stable and enduring characteristics, influenced by genetic predispositions.	Scientific study of traits has isolated important dimensions of personality, such as the Big Five traits (conscientiousness, agreeableness, neuroticism, openness, and extraversion).	Personality inventories
Social-Cognitive	Bandura	Our traits interact with the social context to produce our behaviors.	Conditioning and observational learning interact with cognition to create behavior patterns. Our behavior in one situation is best predicted by considering our past behavior in similar situations.	Observing behavior in realistic situations

RETRIEVE IT • • • *ANSWERS IN APPENDIX E*

RI-5 What is the best way to predict a person's future behavior?

RETAIN **LaunchPad** To review the perspectives and methods of personality psychology, engage online with **Concept Practice: Comparing Personality Theories.**

EXPLORING THE SELF

LOQ 39-8 Why has psychology generated so much research on the self? How important is self-esteem to our well-being?

Our personality feeds our sense of self. Asked to consider "Who I am," people draw on their distinctive and enduring ways of thinking, feeling, and acting. Psychology's concern with our sense of self dates back at least to William James, who devoted more than 100 pages of his 1890 *Principles of Psychology* to the topic. By 1943, Gordon Allport lamented that the self had become "lost to view." Although humanistic psychology's later emphasis on the self did not instigate much scientific research, it did help renew the concept of self and keep it alive. Now, more than a century after James, the self is one of Western psychology's most vigorously researched topics. Every year, new studies galore appear on self-esteem, self-disclosure, self-awareness, self-schemas, self-monitoring, and more. Even neuroscientists have searched for the self, by identifying a central frontal lobe region that activates when people respond to self-reflective questions about their traits and dispositions (Damasio, 2010; Mitchell, 2009; Pauly et al., 2013). The **self,** as organizer of our thoughts, feelings, and actions, occupies the center of personality.

One example of thinking about self is the concept of *possible selves* (Markus & Nurius, 1986; Rathbone et al., 2016). Your possible selves include your visions of the self you dream of becoming—the rich self, the successful self, the loved and admired self. Your possible selves also include the self you fear becoming—the unemployed self, the academically failed self, the lonely and unpopular self. Possible selves motivate us to lay out specific goals that direct our energy effectively and efficiently (Landau et al., 2014). Middle school students whose families struggle financially are more likely to earn high grades if they have a clear vision of themselves succeeding in school (Duckworth et al., 2013). Dreams do often give birth to achievements.

Our self-focused perspective may motivate us, but it can also lead us to presume too readily that others are noticing and evaluating us. Most of them aren't. Thomas Gilovich (1996) has demonstrated this **spotlight effect** by having students don T-shirts featuring 1970s soft-rock icon Barry Manilow before entering a room with other students. Feeling self-conscious, the T-shirt wearers guessed that nearly half their peers would take note of the shirt as they walked in. How many actually noticed? Only 23 percent. The point to remember: *We stand out less than we imagine,* even with dorky clothes, bad hair, nervousness, or irritation (Gilovich & Savitsky, 1999). Even after a blunder (setting off a library alarm, showing up in the wrong clothes), we stick out like a sore thumb less than we imagine (Savitsky et al., 2001).

To turn down the spotlight's brightness, we can use two strategies. The first is simply to know and remember the spotlight effect. Public speakers perform better if they understand that their natural nervousness is hardly noticeable (Savitsky & Gilovich, 2003). The second is to take the audience's perspective. When we imagine audience members empathizing with our situation, we tend to expect we will not be judged as harshly (Epley et al., 2002).

Trinity Mirror/Mirrorpix/Alamy;
Tim Large/Shutterstock

The Benefits of Self-Esteem

Self-esteem—our feelings of high or low self-worth—matters. So does **self-efficacy,** our sense of competence on a task (Bandura, 1977). (A student might feel high self-efficacy in a math course yet low overall self-esteem.) People who feel good about themselves (who strongly agree with self-affirming questionnaire statements, such as "I am fun to be with") have fewer sleepless nights. They succumb less to pressures to conform. They make more positive Facebook posts, causing others to like them more (Forest & Wood, 2012). They are more persistent at difficult tasks. They feel less shy, anxious, and lonely, and are just plain happier (Greenberg, 2008; Orth & Robins, 2014; Swann et al., 2007). Our self-esteem grows from venturesome experiences and achievement, and therefore changes as we age (Hutteman et al., 2015). In one study of nearly 1 million people across 48 nations, self-esteem increased from adolescence to middle adulthood (Bleidorn et al., 2016).

But is high self-esteem the horse or the cart? Is it really "the armor that protects kids" from life's problems (McKay, 2000)? Some psychologists have their doubts (Baumeister, 2006; Dawes, 1994; Leary, 1999; Seligman, 1994, 2002). Children's academic self-efficacy—their confidence that they can do well in a subject—predicts school achievement. But general self-image does not (Marsh & Craven, 2006; Swann et al., 2007; Trautwein et al., 2006). Maybe self-esteem simply reflects reality. Maybe it's a side effect of meeting challenges and surmounting difficulties. Maybe self-esteem is a gauge that reports the state of our relationships with others (Reitz et al., 2016). If so, isn't pushing the gauge artificially

---

"The first step to better times is to imagine them." —Chinese fortune cookie

 ENGAGE **ASK YOURSELF**

What possible selves do you dream of—or fear—becoming? To what extent do these imagined selves motivate you now?

---

self in contemporary psychology, assumed to be the center of personality, the organizer of our thoughts, feelings, and actions.

spotlight effect overestimating others' noticing and evaluating our appearance, performance, and blunders (as if we presume a spotlight shines on us).

self-esteem one's feelings of high or low self-worth.

self-efficacy one's sense of competence and effectiveness.

self-serving bias a readiness to perceive oneself favorably.

higher with empty compliments much like forcing a car's low fuel gauge to display "full"?

If feeling good *follows* doing well, then giving praise in the absence of good performance may actually harm people. After receiving weekly self-esteem-boosting messages, struggling students earned *lower*-than-expected grades (Forsyth et al., 2007). Other research showed that giving people random rewards hurt their productivity. Martin Seligman (2012) reported that "when good things occurred that weren't earned, like nickels coming out of slot machines, it did not increase people's well-being. It produced helplessness. People gave up and became passive."

There is, however, an important *effect* of low self-esteem. When researchers temporarily deflated participants' self-image (by telling them they did poorly on an aptitude test or by disparaging their personality), those participants became more likely to disparage others or to express heightened racial prejudice (vanDellen et al., 2011; van Dijk et al., 2011; Ybarra, 1999). Self-image threat even increases unconscious racial bias (Allen & Sherman, 2011). Those who are negative about themselves have also tended to be oversensitive and judgmental (Baumgardner et al., 1989; Pelham, 1993). Self-esteem threats also lead people to spend more time with their online profiles—safe havens in which to rebuild their self-worth (Toma & Hancock, 2013). Such findings are consistent with humanistic psychology's ideas about the benefits of a healthy self-image. Accept yourself and you'll find it easier to accept others. Disparage yourself and you will be prone to the floccinaucinihilipilification[1] of others. Said more simply, some "love their neighbors as themselves"; others loathe their neighbors as themselves. People who are down on themselves tend to be down on others.

Self-Serving Bias

LOQ 39-9   What evidence reveals self-serving bias, and how do defensive and secure self-esteem differ?

Imagine dashing to class, hoping not to miss the first few minutes. But you arrive five minutes late, huffing and puffing. As you sink into your seat, what sorts of thoughts go through your mind? Do you go through a negative door, thinking "I'm so stupid" and "I always ruin things"? Or do you go through a positive door, telling yourself, "At least I made it to class" and "I really tried to get here on time"?

Personality psychologists have found that most people choose the second door, which leads to positive self-thoughts. We have a good reputation with ourselves. We show a **self-serving bias**—a readiness to perceive ourselves favorably (Myers, 2010). Consider:

People accept more responsibility for good deeds than for bad, and for successes than for failures. Athletes often privately credit their victories to their own prowess, and their losses to bad breaks, lousy officiating, or the other team's exceptional performance. Most students who receive poor exam grades criticize the exam or the instructor, not themselves. Drivers filling out insurance forms explain their accidents in such words as "As I reached an intersection, a hedge sprang up, obscuring my vision, and I did not see the other car" and "A pedestrian hit me and went under my car." The question "What have I done to deserve this?" is one we usually ask of our troubles, not our successes. Although a self-serving bias can lead us to avoid uncomfortable truths, it can also motivate us to approach difficult tasks with confidence instead of despair (Tomaka et al., 1992; von Hippel & Trivers, 2011).

Most people see themselves as better than average. Compared with most other people, how moral are you? How easy to get along with? Where would you rank yourself, from the 1st to the 99th percentile? Most people put themselves well above the 50th percentile. This better-than-average effect appears for nearly any subjectively assessed and socially desirable behavior. Some examples:

- In U.S. surveys, most business executives say they are more ethical than their average counterpart. In several studies, 90 percent of business managers and more than 90 percent of college professors also rated their performance as superior to that of their average peer.

---

1. We couldn't resist throwing that in. But don't worry, you won't be tested on floccinaucinihilipilification, which is the act of estimating something as worthless (and was the longest nontechnical word in the first edition of the *Oxford English Dictionary*).

"When kids increase in self-control, their grades go up later. But when kids increase their self-esteem, there is no effect on their grades." —Angela Duckworth, *In Character* interview, 2009

"The enthusiastic claims of the self-esteem movement mostly range from fantasy to hogwash. The effects of self-esteem are small, limited, and not all good." —Roy Baumeister (1996)

Dear diary. Sorry to bother you again.

LOW SELF-ESTEEM

Mike Twohy The New Yorker Collection/ The Cartoon Bank

"I never blame myself when I'm not hitting. I just blame the bat and if it keeps up, I change bats." —Baseball great Yogi Berra (1925–2015)

"If you are like most people, then like most people, you don't know you're like most people. Science has given us a lot of facts about the average person, and one of the most reliable of these facts is the average person doesn't see herself as average." —Daniel Gilbert, *Stumbling on Happiness*, 2006

BLINDNESS TO ONE'S OWN INCOMPETENCE Ironically, people often are most overconfident when most incompetent. That, say Justin Kruger and David Dunning (1999), is because it often takes competence to recognize competence. Our ignorance of what we don't know sustains our self-confidence, leading us to make the same mistakes (Williams et al., 2013).

"The [self-]portraits that we actually believe, when we are given freedom to voice them, are dramatically more positive than reality can sustain."
—Shelley Taylor, *Positive Illusions*, 1989

- In Australia, 86 percent of people rate their job performance as above average, and only 1 percent as below average.

- In the U.S. National Survey of Families and Households, 49 percent of men said they provided half or more of the child care, though only 31 percent of their wives or partners saw things that way (Galinsky et al., 2008).

Self-serving bias reflects both an overestimation of the self and a desire to maintain a positive self-view (Brown, 2012; Epley & Dunning, 2000). This motivation to see ourselves positively is weaker in Asia, where people tend to value modesty (Church et al., 2014; Falk et al., 2009). Yet self-serving biases have been observed worldwide: In every one of 53 countries surveyed, people expressed self-esteem above the midpoint of the most widely used scale (Schmitt & Allik, 2005).

Finding their self-esteem threatened, people with large egos may react violently. Researchers Brad Bushman and Roy Baumeister (1998; Bushman et al., 2009) had undergraduate volunteers write a brief essay, in response to which another supposed student gave them either praise ("Great essay!") or stinging criticism ("One of the worst essays I have read!"). The essay writers were then allowed to lash out at their evaluators by blasting them with unpleasant noise. Can you anticipate the result? After criticism, those with inflated self-esteem were "exceptionally aggressive." They delivered three times the auditory torture than did those with normal self-esteem. Over 80 studies have replicated the dangerous effect of **narcissism** (excessive self-love and self-focus) on aggression (Rasmussen, 2016). Researchers have concluded that "conceited, self-important individuals turn nasty toward those who puncture their bubbles of self-love" (Baumeister, 2001).

After tracking self-importance across several decades, psychologist Jean Twenge (2006; Twenge & Foster, 2010) reported that what she called *Generation Me*—born in the 1980s and early 1990s—expressed more narcissism (by agreeing more often with statements such as, "If I ruled the world, it would be a better place," or "I think I am a special person"). Why does a rise in narcissism matter? Narcissists tend to be materialistic, desire fame, have inflated expectations, hook up more often without commitment, and gamble and cheat more—all of which have been increasing as narcissism has increased.

Narcissistic people (more often men) forgive others less, take a game-playing approach to their romantic relationships, and engage in sexually forceful behavior (Blinkhorn et al., 2015; Bushman et al., 2003; Grijalva et al., 2015). They crave adulation, are active on social media, and often become enraged when criticized (Geukes et al., 2016; Krizan

PEANUTS

narcissism excessive self-love and self-absorption.

& Johar, 2015; McCain & Campbell, 2016). Many had parents who told them they were superior to others (Brummelman et al., 2015). They typically make good first impressions, which wane over time as their arrogance and bragging gets old (Czarna et al., 2016; Leckelt et al., 2015). Reality TV stars are often narcissistic (Rubinstein, 2016; Young & Pinsky, 2006).

Some critics of the concept of self-serving bias claim that it overlooks those who feel worthless and unlovable: If self-serving bias prevails, why do so many people disparage themselves? For four reasons: (1) Self-directed put-downs can be *subtly strategic*—they elicit reassuring strokes. Saying "No one likes me" may at least elicit "But not everyone has met you!" (2) Before an important event, such as a game or an exam, self-disparaging comments *prepare us for possible failure*. The coach who extols the superior strength of the upcoming opponent makes a loss understandable, a victory noteworthy. (3) A self-disparaging "How could I have been so stupid!" can help us *learn from our mistakes*. (4) Self-disparagement frequently *pertains to one's old self*. Asked to remember their really bad behaviors, people recall things from long ago; good behaviors more easily come to mind from their recent past (Escobedo & Adolphs, 2010). Even when they have not changed, people are much more critical of their distant past selves than of their current selves (Wilson & Ross, 2001). "At 18, I was a jerk; today I'm more sensitive." In their own eyes, chumps yesterday, champs today.

Even so, all of us some of the time (and some of us much of the time) do feel inferior. This is especially true when we compare ourselves with those who are a step or two higher on the ladder of status, looks, income, or ability. Olympians who win silver medals, barely missing gold, show greater sadness on the awards podium compared with the bronze medal winners (Medvec et al., 1995). The deeper and more frequently we have such feelings, the more unhappy or even depressed we become. But for most people, thinking has a naturally positive bias.

> "If you compare yourself with others, you may become vain and bitter; for always there will be greater and lesser persons than yourself." —Max Ehrmann, "Desiderata," 1927

While recognizing the dark side of self-serving bias and self-esteem, some researchers identify two types of self-esteem—defensive and secure (Kernis, 2003; Lambird & Mann, 2006; Ryan & Deci, 2004). *Defensive self-esteem* is fragile. It focuses on sustaining itself, which makes failure and criticism feel threatening. Defensive people may respond to such perceived threats with anger or aggression (Crocker & Park, 2004; Donnellan et al., 2005).

Secure self-esteem is less fragile, because it is less contingent on external evaluations. Feeling accepted for who we are, and not for our looks, wealth, or acclaim, relieves pressures to succeed and enables us to focus beyond ourselves. By losing ourselves in relationships and purposes larger than ourselves, we may achieve a more secure self-esteem, satisfying relationships, and greater quality of life (Crocker & Park, 2004). Authentic pride, rooted in actual achievement, supports self-confidence and leadership (Tracy et al., 2009; Weidman et al., 2016; Williams & DeSteno, 2009).

> "True humility is not thinking less of yourself; it is thinking of yourself less." —C. S. Lewis, *Mere Christianity*, 1952

🔒 RETRIEVE IT • • •

ANSWERS IN APPENDIX E

RI-6 What are the positive and negative effects of high self-esteem?

RI-7 The tendency to accept responsibility for success and blame circumstances or bad luck for failure is called _____ - _____ _____.

RI-8 _____ (Secure/Defensive) self-esteem is linked to angry and aggressive behavior. _____ (Secure/Defensive) self-esteem is a healthier self-image that allows us to focus beyond ourselves and enjoy a higher quality of life.

Culture and the Self

LOQ 39-10 How do individualist and collectivist cultures differ in their values and goals?

Our consideration of personality—of people's characteristic ways of thinking, feeling, and acting—concludes with a look at cultural variations. Imagine that someone ripped away your social connections, making you a solitary refugee in a foreign land. How much of your identity would remain intact?

Kyodo/Reuters/Newscom

CONSIDERATE COLLECTIVISTS
Japan's collectivist values, including duty to others and social harmony, were on display after the devastating 2011 earthquake and tsunami. Virtually no looting was reported, and residents remained calm and orderly, as shown here while waiting for drinking water.

Sam Harrel/Fairbanks/JAK/U.S./ZUMA Press/Newscom

COLLECTIVIST CULTURE Although the United States is largely individualist, many cultural subgroups remain collectivist. This is true for Alaska Natives, who demonstrate respect for tribal elders, and whose identity springs largely from their group affiliations.

"One needs to cultivate the spirit of sacrificing the *little me* to achieve the benefits of the *big me*." —Chinese saying

" I'D LiKE a DeCAFFACiNNO FRAPPA CHAPPA DAPPA DiNGO ICE BLeNDED LAST oF THe MOCCA-HiCANS VANiLLA ICE ICE BeTTeR LATTe' THAN NeVeR SMOOTHie WiTH a SHOT oF SeLF-eXPReSSo. "

The tolerance of a Starbucks barista is severely tested.

Cartoon by Buddy Hickerson

If you are an **individualist,** a great deal. You would have an independent sense of "me," and an awareness of your unique personal convictions and values. Individualists prioritize personal goals. They define their identity mostly in terms of personal traits. They strive for personal control and individual achievement.

Individualists do share the human need to belong. They join groups. But they are less focused on group harmony and doing their duty to the group (Brewer & Chen, 2007). Being more self-contained, individualists move in and out of social groups more easily. They feel relatively free to switch places of worship, change jobs, or even leave their extended families and migrate to a new place. Marriage is often for as long as they both shall love.

If set adrift in a foreign land as a **collectivist,** you might experience a greater loss of identity. Cut off from family, groups, and loyal friends, you would lose the connections that have defined who you are. *Group identifications* provide a sense of belonging, a set of values, and an assurance of security. Collectivists have deep attachments to their groups—their family, clan, company, or country. Elders receive respect. For example, Chinese law states that parents aged 60 or above can sue their sons and daughters if they fail to provide "for the elderly, taking care of them and comforting them, and cater[ing] to their special needs."

Collectivists are like athletes who take more pleasure in their team's victory than in their own performance. They find satisfaction in advancing their groups' interests, even at the expense of personal needs. They preserve group spirit by avoiding direct confrontation, blunt honesty, and uncomfortable topics. They value humility, not self-importance (Bond et al., 2012). Instead of dominating conversations, collectivists hold back and display shyness when meeting strangers (Cheek & Melchior, 1990). Given the priority on "we," not "me," that super-customized latte that feels so soothing to a North American might sound selfishly demanding in Seoul (Kim & Markus, 1999).

A question: What do you think of people who willingly change their behavior to suit different people and situations? People in individualist countries (the United States and Brazil) typically describe them as "dishonest," "untrustworthy," and "insincere" (Levine, 2016). In traditionally collectivist countries (China, India, and Nepal), people more often describe them as "mature," "honest," "trustworthy," and "sincere."

Within many countries, there are also distinct subcultures related to one's religion, economic status, and region (Cohen, 2009). In China, greater collectivist thinking occurs in provinces that have produced rice, a difficult-to-grow crop that involves cooperation to sustain irrigation (Talhelm et al., 2014). In collectivist Japan, a spirit of individualism marks the "northern frontier" island of Hokkaido (Kitayama et al., 2006). And even in the most individualist countries, people have some collectivist values. But in general, people (especially men) in competitive, individualist cultures have more personal freedom, are less geographically bound to their families, enjoy more privacy, and take more pride in personal achievements (**TABLE 39.3**).

Individualists even prefer unusual names, as Jean Twenge noticed while seeking a name for her first child. When she and her colleagues (2010a, 2016a) analyzed the first names of 358 million American babies born between 1880 and 2015, they discovered

TABLE 39.3

Value Contrasts Between Individualism and Collectivism

Concept	Individualism	Collectivism
Self	Independent (identity from individual traits)	Interdependent (identity from belonging to groups)
Life task	Discover and express one's uniqueness	Maintain connections, fit in, perform role
What matters	Me—personal achievement and fulfillment; rights and liberties; self-esteem	Us—group goals and solidarity; social responsibilities and relationships; family duty
Coping method	Change reality	Accommodate to reality
Morality	Defined by the individual (self-based)	Defined by social networks (duty-based)
Relationships	Many, often temporary or casual; confrontation acceptable	Few, close, and enduring; harmony is valued
Attributing behavior	Behavior reflects the individual's personality and attitudes	Behavior reflects social norms and roles

Information from Thomas Schoeneman (1994) and Harry Triandis (1994).

individualism giving priority to one's own goals over group goals and defining one's identity in terms of personal attributes rather than group identifications.

collectivism giving priority to the goals of one's group (often one's extended family or work group) and defining one's identity accordingly.

that the most common baby names had become less common. As **FIGURE 39.6** illustrates, the percentage of boys and girls given one of the 10 most common names for their birth year has plunged. Collectivist Japan provides a contrast: Half of Japanese baby names are among the country's 10 most common names (Ogihara et al., 2015).

Individualists demand romance and personal fulfillment in marriage (Dion & Dion, 1993). In one survey, "keeping romance alive" was rated as important to a good marriage by 78 percent of U.S. women but only 29 percent of Japanese women (*American Enterprise*, 1992). In China, love songs have often expressed enduring commitment and friendship (Rothbaum & Tsang, 1998): "We will be together from now on . . . I will never change from now to forever."

What predicts change in one culture over time, or differences between cultures? Social history matters. Individualism and independence have been fostered by voluntary emigration, a capitalist economy, and a sparsely populated, challenging environment (Kitayama et al., 2009, 2010; Varnum et al., 2010). In Western cultures over the last century and now in all but the poorest countries, individualism has increased, following closely on the heels of increasing affluence (Grossmann & Varnum, 2015; Santos et al., 2017). Might biology also play a role? One study comparing collectivists' and individualists' brain activity suggested that collectivists experienced greater emotional pain when they viewed others in distress (Cheon et al., 2013). As we have seen in personality and beyond, we are biopsychosocial creatures.

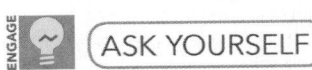

ASK YOURSELF

Do you consider yourself to be more of a collectivist or an individualist? How do you think this sense of self has influenced your behavior, emotions, and thoughts?

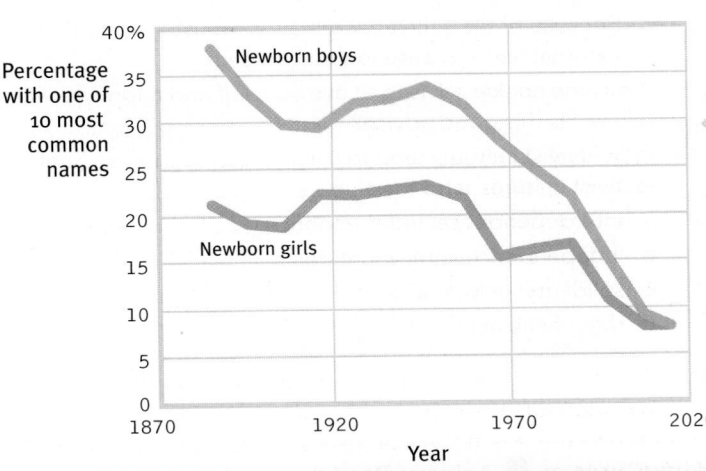

FIGURE 39.6

A CHILD LIKE NO OTHER Americans' individualist tendencies are reflected in their choices of names for their babies. In recent years, the percentage of American babies receiving one of that year's 10 most common names has plunged. (Data from Twenge et al., 2010a, 2016a.)

RETRIEVE IT • • •

ANSWERS IN APPENDIX E

RI-9 How do people in individualist and collectivist cultures differ?

⟫ Learning Objectives

TEST YOURSELF Answer these repeated Learning Objective Questions on your own (before checking the answers in Appendix D) to improve your retention of the concepts (McDaniel et al., 2009, 2015).

39-1 How do psychologists use traits to describe personality?

39-2 What are some common misunderstandings about introversion?

39-3 What are *personality inventories,* and what are their strengths and weaknesses as trait-assessment tools?

39-4 Which traits seem to provide the most useful information about personality variation?

39-5 Does research support the consistency of personality traits over time and across situations?

39-6 How do social-cognitive theorists view personality development, and how do they explore behavior?

39-7 What criticisms have social-cognitive theorists faced?

39-8 Why has psychology generated so much research on the self? How important is self-esteem to our well-being?

39-9 What evidence reveals self-serving bias, and how do defensive and secure self-esteem differ?

39-10 How do individualist and collectivist cultures differ in their values and goals?

⟫ Terms and Concepts to Remember

TEST YOURSELF Write down the definition yourself, then check your answer on the referenced page.

trait, **p. 475**

personality inventory, **p. 477**

Minnesota Multiphasic Personality Inventory (MMPI), **p. 477**

empirically derived test, **p. 477**

social-cognitive perspective, **p. 482**

reciprocal determinism, **p. 482**

self, **p. 486**

spotlight effect, **p. 486**

self-esteem, **p. 486**

self-efficacy, **p. 486**

self-serving bias, **p. 486**

narcissism, **p. 488**

individualism, **p. 491**

collectivism, **p. 491**

⟫ Experience the Testing Effect

TEST YOURSELF Answer the following questions on your own first, then check your answers in Appendix E.

1. _____ theories of personality focus on describing characteristic behavior patterns, such as agreeableness or extraversion.

2. The most widely used personality inventory is the
   a. Extraversion–Introversion Scale.
   b. Person–Situation Inventory.
   c. MMPI.
   d. Rorschach.

3. Which of the following is NOT one of the Big Five personality factors?
   a. Conscientiousness
   b. Anxiety
   c. Extraversion
   d. Agreeableness

4. Our scores on personality tests best predict
   a. our behavior on a specific occasion.
   b. our average behavior across many situations.
   c. behavior involving a single trait, such as conscientiousness.
   d. behavior that depends on the situation or context.

5. The social-cognitive perspective proposes that our personality is shaped by a process called reciprocal determinism, as internal factors, environmental factors, and behaviors interact. An example of an environmental factor is
   a. the presence of books in a home.
   b. a preference for outdoor play.
   c. the ability to read at a fourth-grade level.
   d. the fear of violent action on television.

6. Critics say that _____-_____ personality theory is very sensitive to an individual's interactions with particular situations, but that it gives too little attention to the person's enduring traits.

7. The tendency to overestimate others' attention to and evaluation of our appearance, performance, and blunders is called the _____ _____.

8. Researchers have found that low self-esteem tends to be linked with life problems. How should this link be interpreted?
   a. Life problems cause low self-esteem.
   b. The answer isn't clear because the link is correlational and does not indicate cause and effect.
   c. Low self-esteem leads to life problems.
   d. Because of the self-serving bias, we must assume that external factors cause low self-esteem.

9. A fortune cookie advises, "Love yourself and happiness will follow." Is this good advice?

10. Individualist cultures tend to value _____; collectivist cultures tend to value _____.
   a. interdependence; independence
   b. independence; interdependence
   c. solidarity; uniqueness
   d. duty; fulfillment

Continue testing yourself with 📚 **LearningCurve** or 📖 **Achieve Read & Practice** to learn and remember most effectively.

Psychological Disorders

I felt the need to clean my room . . . and would spend four to five hours at it. I would take every book out of the bookcase, dust and put it back . . . I couldn't stop.

Marc, diagnosed with obsessive-compulsive disorder (from Summers, 1996)

Whenever I get depressed it's because I've lost a sense of self. I can't find reasons to like myself. I think I'm ugly. I think no one likes me.

Greta, diagnosed with depression (from Thorne, 1993, p. 21)

Voices, like the roar of a crowd, came. I felt like Jesus; I was being crucified.

Stuart, diagnosed with schizophrenia (from Emmons et al., 1997)

Now and then, all of us feel, think, or act in ways that may resemble a psychological disorder. We feel anxious, depressed, withdrawn, or suspicious. So it's no wonder that we sometimes see ourselves in the mental illnesses we study. Personally or through friends or family, many of us will know the confusion and pain of unexplained physical symptoms, irrational fears, or a feeling that life is not worth living. Among American college students, 1 in 3 report an apparent mental health problem (Eisenberg et al., 2011).

Worldwide, more than half a billion people live with mental or behavioral disorders (WHO, 2017c). Modules 40 through 43 examine these disorders. The Therapy modules consider their *treatment.* ▶

Peopleimages/Getty Images

493

psychological disorder a syndrome marked by a clinically significant disturbance in an individual's cognition, emotion regulation, or behavior.

"Who in the rainbow can draw the line where the violet tint ends and the orange tint begins? Distinctly we see the difference of the colors, but where exactly does the one first blendingly enter into the other? So with sanity and insanity." —Herman Melville, *Billy Budd, Sailor*, 1924

40 Basic Concepts of Psychological Disorders

MODULE

LEARNING OBJECTIVE QUESTION (LOQ)

40-1 How should we draw the line between normality and disorder?

Most of us would agree that someone who is depressed and stays mostly in bed for three months has a psychological disorder. But what about a grieving father who can't resume his usual social activities three months after his child has died? Where do we draw the line between understandable grief and clinical depression? Between fear and a phobia? Between normality and abnormality? In their search for answers, theorists and clinicians ask:

- How should we define psychological disorders?

- How should we understand disorders? How do underlying biological factors contribute to disorder? How do troubling environments influence our well-being? And how do these effects of nature and nurture interact?

- How should we classify psychological disorders? And can we do so in a way that allows us to help people without stigmatizing or labeling them?

- Are those with psychological disorders at risk of doing harm to themselves or others?

- What do we know about rates of psychological disorders? How many people have them? Who is vulnerable, and when?

A **psychological disorder** is a syndrome (a symptom collection) marked by a "clinically significant disturbance in an individual's cognition, emotion regulation, or behavior" (American Psychiatric Association, 2013). Such thoughts, emotions, or behaviors are *dysfunctional* or *maladaptive*—they interfere with normal day-to-day life. Believing your home must be thoroughly cleaned every weekend is not a disorder. But if cleaning rituals interfere with work and leisure, as Marc's uncontrollable rituals did, they may be signs of a disorder. Occasional sad moods that persist and become disabling may likewise signal a psychological disorder.

Distress often accompanies such dysfunction. Marc, Greta, and Stuart were all distressed by their thoughts, emotions, or behaviors.

Over time, definitions of what makes for a "significant disturbance" have varied. In 1973, the American Psychiatric Association dropped homosexuality as a disorder after mental health workers came to consider same-sex attraction as not inherently dysfunctional or distressing. In the twenty-first century, controversies swirl over other new or altered diagnoses in the most recent edition of a common classification tool for describing disorders.

CULTURE AND NORMALITY Young American men may plan elaborate invitations for big events, as did this student (a) who appealed (successfully) to his date for prom. Young men of the West African Wodaabe tribe (b) traditionally put on decorative makeup and costumes to attract women. Each culture may view the other's behavior as abnormal.

(a)

(b)

Francois Dubourdeau/Skydive East Tennessee

Carol Beckwith

UNDERSTANDING PSYCHOLOGICAL DISORDERS

LOQ 40-2 How do the medical model and the biopsychosocial approach influence our understanding of psychological disorders?

The way we view a problem influences how we try to solve it. In earlier times, people often thought that strange behaviors were evidence of strange forces—the movements of the stars, godlike powers, or evil spirits—at work. Had you lived during the Middle Ages, you might have said, "The devil made him do it." To drive out demons, people considered "mad" were sometimes caged or given "therapies" such as genital mutilation, beatings, removal of teeth or lengths of intestines, or transfusions of animal blood (Farina, 1982).

Reformers, such as Philippe Pinel (1745–1826) in France, opposed such brutal treatments. Madness is not demonic possession, he insisted, but a sickness of the mind caused by severe stress and inhumane conditions. Curing the illness, he said, requires *moral treatment,* including boosting patients' spirits by unchaining them and talking with them. He and others worked to replace brutality with gentleness, isolation with activity, and filth with clean air and sunshine.

In some places, cruel treatments for mental illness—including chaining people to beds or confining them in spaces with wild animals—linger even today. The World Health Organization has launched a reform that aims to transform hospitals "into patient-friendly and humane places with minimum restraints" (WHO, 2014a).

The Medical Model

A medical breakthrough around 1900 prompted further reforms. Researchers discovered that syphilis, a sexually transmitted infection, invades the brain and distorts the mind. This discovery triggered an eager search for physical causes of other mental disorders, and for treatments that would cure them. Hospitals replaced asylums, and the **medical model** of mental disorders was born. This model is reflected in words we still use today. We speak of the mental *health* movement. A mental *illness* (also called a psycho*pathology*) needs to be *diagnosed* on the basis of its *symptoms*. It needs to be *treated* through *therapy,* which may include treatment in a psychiatric *hospital*. The medical perspective has been energized by more recent discoveries that genetically influenced abnormalities in brain structure and biochemistry contribute to many disorders (Insel & Cuthbert, 2015). A growing number of clinical psychologists now work in medical hospitals, where they collaborate with physicians to determine how the mind and body operate together.

The Biopsychosocial Approach

To call psychological disorders "sicknesses" tilts research heavily toward the influence of biology and away from the influence of our personal histories and social and cultural surroundings. But as we have seen throughout this text, biological, psychological, and social-cultural influences together weave the fabric of our thoughts, feelings, and behaviors. As individuals, we differ in the amount of stress we experience and in the ways we cope with stressors. Cultures also differ in the sources of stress they produce and in their traditional ways of coping. We are physically embodied and socially embedded.

Two disorders—major depressive disorder and schizophrenia—occur worldwide. From Asia to Africa and across the Americas, schizophrenia's symptoms often include irrational and incoherent speech. Other disorders tend to be associated with specific cultures.

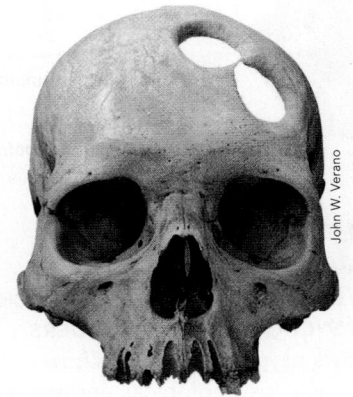

John W. Verano

YESTERDAY'S "THERAPY" Through the ages, psychologically disordered people have received brutal treatments, including the trephination evident in this Stone Age patient's skull. Drilling skull holes like these may have been an attempt to release evil spirits and cure those with mental disorders. Did this patient survive the "cure"?

medical model the concept that diseases, in this case psychological disorders, have physical causes that can be *diagnosed, treated,* and, in most cases, *cured,* often through treatment in a *hospital*.

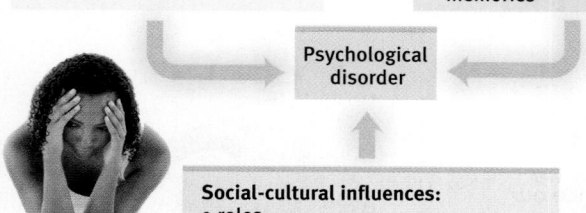

Biological influences:	Psychological influences:
• evolution	• stress
• individual genes	• trauma
• brain structure and chemistry	• learned helplessness
	• mood-related perceptions and memories

Psychological disorder

Wavebreakmedia Ltd/ Getty Images

Social-cultural influences:
• roles
• expectations
• definitions of *normality* and *disorder*

RETAIN 🔒 **FIGURE 40.1**

THE BIOPSYCHOSOCIAL APPROACH TO PSYCHOLOGICAL DISORDERS
Today's psychology studies how biological, psychological, and social-cultural factors interact to produce specific psychological disorders.

Latin America lays claim to *susto,* a condition marked by severe anxiety, restlessness, and a fear of black magic. In Japanese culture, people may experience *taijin kyofusho*—social anxiety about physical appearance, combined with a readiness to blush and a fear of eye contact. The eating disorders *anorexia nervosa* and *bulimia nervosa* occur mostly in food-abundant Western cultures. Such disorders may share an underlying dynamic (such as anxiety) while differing in the symptoms (an eating problem or a type of fear) manifested in a particular culture. Even disordered aggression may have varying explanations in different cultures. In Malaysia, *amok* describes a sudden outburst of violent behavior (as in the English phrase "run amok").

Disorders reflect genetic predispositions and physiological states, inner psychological dynamics, and social and cultural circumstances. The biopsychosocial approach emphasizes that mind and body are inseparable (**FIGURE 40.1**). Negative emotions can contribute to physical illness, and physical abnormalities can likewise contribute to negative emotions. The biopsychosocial approach gave rise to the *vulnerability-stress model,* which argues that individual characteristics combine with environmental stressors to increase or decrease the likelihood of developing a psychological disorder (Monroe & Simons, 1991; Zuckerman, 1999). Research on **epigenetics** (literally, "in addition to genetics") supports the vulnerability-stress model by showing how our DNA and our environment interact. In one environment, a gene will be *expressed,* but in another it may lie dormant. For some, that will be the difference between developing a disorder or not developing it.

🔒 **RETRIEVE IT • • •**   *ANSWERS IN APPENDIX E*

RI-2 Are psychological disorders universal or culture-specific? Explain with examples.

RI-3 What is the biopsychosocial approach, and why is it important in our understanding of psychological disorders?

CLASSIFYING DISORDERS—AND LABELING PEOPLE

LOQ 40-3 How and why do clinicians classify psychological disorders, and why do some psychologists criticize the use of diagnostic labels?

In biology, classification creates order. To classify an animal as a "mammal" says a great deal—that it is likely to be warm-blooded, have hair or fur, and produce milk to feed its young. In psychiatry and psychology, too, classification aims to order and describe symptoms. To classify a person's disorder as "schizophrenia" suggests that the person talks incoherently, has bizarre beliefs, shows either little emotion or inappropriate emotion, or is socially withdrawn. "Schizophrenia" is a quick way of describing a complex disorder.

But diagnostic classification gives more than a thumbnail sketch of a person's disordered behavior, thoughts, or feelings. In psychiatry and psychology, classification also aims to *predict* a disorder's future course, *suggest* appropriate treatment, and *prompt research* into its causes. To study a disorder, we must first name and describe it.

In the United States and many other countries, the most common tool for describing disorders and estimating how often they occur is the American Psychiatric Association's *Diagnostic and Statistical Manual of Mental Disorders,* now in its fifth edition (**DSM-5**). Physicians and mental health workers use the detailed "diagnostic criteria and codes" in the DSM-5 to guide medical diagnoses and treatment. For example, a person may be diagnosed with and treated for *insomnia disorder* if he or she meets *all* of the criteria in **TABLE 40.1**. The DSM-5's diagnostic criteria and codes closely resemble those in the World Health Organization's *International Classification of Diseases* (ICD), making it easy to track worldwide trends in psychological disorders.

Sidney Harris

"I'm always like this, and my family was wondering if you could prescribe a mild depressant."

TABLE 40.1
Insomnia Disorder

- Feeling unsatisfied with amount or quality of sleep (trouble falling asleep, staying asleep, or returning to sleep)

- Sleep disruption causes distress or diminished everyday functioning

- Happens three or more nights each week

- Occurs during at least three consecutive months

- Happens even with sufficient sleep opportunities

- Independent from other sleep disorders (such as narcolepsy)

- Independent from substance use or abuse

- Independent from other mental disorders or medical conditions

Information from: American Psychiatric Association, 2013.

In the DSM-5, some diagnostic labels changed. The conditions formerly called "autism" and "Asperger's syndrome" were combined under the label *autism spectrum disorder.* "Mental retardation" became *intellectual disability.* New disorders, such as *hoarding disorder* and *binge-eating disorder,* were added.

In real-world tests (*field trials*) assessing the reliability of the new DSM-5 categories, some diagnoses have fared well and others have fared poorly (Freedman et al., 2013). Clinician agreement on adult *posttraumatic stress disorder* and childhood autism spectrum disorder, for example, was near 70 percent. (If one psychiatrist or psychologist diagnosed someone with one of these disorders, there was a 70 percent chance that another mental health worker would independently give the same diagnosis.) But for *antisocial personality disorder* and *generalized anxiety disorder,* agreement was closer to 20 percent.

Critics have long faulted the DSM for casting too wide a net, and for bringing "almost any kind of behavior within the compass of psychiatry" (Eysenck et al., 1983). Some now worry that the DSM-5's even wider net will extend the pathologizing of everyday life. For example, the DSM has broadened the diagnostic criteria for **attention-deficit/hyperactivity disorder (ADHD).** For those who experience these challenging symptoms, diagnosis and treatment can be a relief and bring improved functioning (Kupfer, 2012; Maciejewski et al., 2016). However, critics suggest that the criteria are now too broad and may turn normal, childish rambunctiousness into a disorder (Frances, 2013, 2014). (See Thinking Critically About: ADHD—Normal High Energy or Disordered Behavior?) The DSM also now classifies severe grief following the death of a loved one as a possible *depressive disorder.* Critics suggest that such grief could instead simply be considered a normal reaction to tragic life events.

Seeking a new but complementary approach to classification, the U.S. National Institute of Mental Health has established the Research Domain Criteria (RDoC) project (Insel et al., 2010; NIMH, 2017). The RDoC aims to bring "the power of modern research approaches in genetics, neuroscience, and behavioral science" to the study of psychological disorders (Insel & Lieberman, 2013). This framework helps organize disorders according to behaviors and brain activity.

Other critics of classification register a more basic complaint—that diagnostic labels can be subjective, or even value judgments masquerading as science. Once we label a person, we view that person differently (Bathje & Pryor, 2011; Farina, 1982; Sadler et al., 2012a). Labels can change reality by putting us on alert for evidence that confirms our view. If we hear that a new co-worker is mean-spirited, we may treat her suspiciously. She may in turn react to us as a mean-spirited person would. Teachers who were told certain students were "gifted" then acted in ways that brought out the creative behaviors they expected (Snyder, 1984). Labels can be self-fulfilling, and, if negative, can be stigmatizing.

The biasing power of labels was clear in a classic, controversial study. David Rosenhan (1973) and seven others went to hospital admissions offices, complaining

A book of case illustrations accompanying a previous DSM edition provided several examples for these Psychological Disorders modules.

epigenetics "above" or "in addition to" *(epi)* genetics; the study of the molecular mechanisms by which environments can influence genetic expression (without a DNA change).

DSM-5 the American Psychiatric Association's *Diagnostic and Statistical Manual of Mental Disorders,* Fifth Edition; a widely used system for classifying psychological disorders.

attention-deficit/hyperactivity disorder (ADHD) a psychological disorder marked by extreme inattention and/or hyperactivity and impulsivity.

THINKING CRITICALLY ABOUT:

ADHD—Normal High Energy or Disordered Behavior?

LOQ 40-4 Why is there controversy over attention-deficit/hyperactivity disorder?

Diagnosis in the U.S.

Twice as often in BOYS as in girls

 11%[1] 4- to 17-year-olds

2.5%[2] adults

Symptoms

- inattention and distractibility [3]
- hyperactivity [4]
- impulsivity

SKEPTICS note:

Energetic child + boring school = ADHD overdiagnosis

- Children are not designed to sit for hours in chairs inside.
- The youngest children in a class tend to be more fidgety—and more often diagnosed. [5]
- Older students may seek out stimulant ADHD prescription drugs–"good-grade pills." [6]
- What are the long-term effects of drug treatment?
- Why the increased diagnoses worldwide? [7]

SUPPORTERS note:

- More diagnoses reflect increased awareness.
- "ADHD is a real neurobiological disorder whose existence should no longer be debated." [8]
- ADHD is associated with abnormal brain structure, abnormal brain activity patterns, and future risky or antisocial behavior. [9]

Causes?

- May co-exist with a learning disorder or with defiant and temper-prone behavior.
- May be genetic. [10]

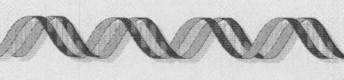

Treatment

- Stimulant drugs (Ritalin and Adderall) calm hyperactivity, and increase ability to sit and focus.[11] So do behavior therapy and aerobic exercise. [12]
- Psychological therapies help with the distress of ADHD. [13]

The bottom line:

Extreme inattention, hyperactivity, and impulsivity can derail social, academic, and work achievements. These symptoms can be treated with medication and other therapies. But the debate continues over whether normal high energy is too often diagnosed as a psychiatric disorder, and whether there is a cost to the long-term use of stimulant drugs in treating ADHD.

1. Schwarz & Cohen, 2013. 2. Simon et al., 2009. 3. Martel et al., 2016. 4. Kofler et al., 2016. 5. Chen et al., 2016. 6. Schwarz, 2012. 7. Ellison, 2015. 8. World Federation for Mental Health, 2005. 9. Barkley et al., 2002; Hoogman et al., 2017. 10. Nikolas & Burt, 2010; Poelmans et al., 2011; Volkow et al., 2009; Williams et al., 2010. 11. Barbaresi et al., 2007. 12. Cerrillo-Urbina et al., 2015; Pelham et al., 2016. 13. Fabiano et al., 2008.

(falsely) of "hearing voices" saying *empty, hollow,* and *thud*. Apart from this complaint and giving false names and occupations, they answered questions truthfully. All eight healthy people were misdiagnosed with disorders.

Should we be surprised? Surely not. As one psychiatrist noted, if someone swallowed blood, went to an emergency room, and spat it up, we wouldn't blame a doctor for diagnosing a bleeding ulcer. But what followed the diagnoses was startling. Until being released an average of 19 days later, these eight "patients" showed no other symptoms. Yet after analyzing their (quite normal) life histories, clinicians were able to "discover" the causes of their disorders, such as having mixed emotions about a parent.

Labels matter. In another study, people watched recorded interviews. If told the interviewees were job applicants, the viewers perceived them as normal (Langer & Abelson, 1974; Langer & Imber, 1980). Other viewers who were told they were watching cancer or psychiatric patients perceived the same interviewees as "different from most people." Therapists who thought they were watching an interview of a psychiatric patient perceived him as "frightened of his own aggressive impulses," a "passive, dependent type," and so forth. Labels also have power outside the laboratory. Getting a job or finding a place to rent can be a challenge for people recently released from a psychiatric hospital. Label someone as "mentally ill" and people may fear them as potentially violent. That reaction is fading as people come to better understand that psychological disorders are not failures of character. The more contact we have with people with disorders, the more accepting our attitudes become (Corrigan et al., 2014). Public figures have helped foster this understanding by speaking openly about their own struggles with disorders such as depression and substance abuse—and how beneficial it was to seek help, receive diagnosis, and get better through treatment.

Despite their risks, diagnostic labels have benefits. They help mental health professionals communicate about their cases and study the causes and treatments of disorders. Clients are often relieved to learn that their suffering has a name, and that they are not alone in experiencing their symptoms.

 LaunchPad To test your own ability to form diagnoses, try **Topic Tutorial: PsychSim6, Classifying Disorders.**

STRUGGLES AND RECOVERY During his campaign, Boston Mayor Martin Walsh spoke openly about his past struggles with alcohol. His story of recovery helped him win in 2014—the closest Boston mayoral election in decades—and again in 2017.

"What's the use of their having names," the Gnat said, "if they won't answer to them?"
"No use to *them*," said Alice; "but it's useful to the people that name them, I suppose." —Lewis Carroll, *Through the Looking-Glass*, 1871

 (ASK YOURSELF)

Do you know someone (could be you) who has been diagnosed with a psychological disorder? How do you think a diagnostic label might help or hurt this person?

BETTER PORTRAYALS Old stereotypes are slowly being replaced in media portrayals of psychological disorders. Modern films offer fairly realistic depictions. *Iron Man 3* (2013) portrayed a main character, shown here, with posttraumatic stress disorder. *Black Swan* (2010) dramatized a lead character suffering a delusional disorder. *A Single Man* (2009) depicted depression.

 **RETRIEVE IT** • • •   *ANSWERS IN APPENDIX E*

RI-4 What is the value, and what are the dangers, of labeling individuals with disorders?

RISK OF HARM TO SELF AND OTHERS

People with psychological disorders are more likely to harm themselves. Are they also more likely to harm others?

Understanding Suicide

LOQ 40-5 What factors increase the risk of suicide, and what do we know about non-suicidal self-injury?

Each year over 800,000 despairing people worldwide will elect a permanent solution to what might have been a temporary problem (WHO, 2014c). A death by suicide will likely occur in the 40 seconds or so that it takes you to read this paragraph. For those who have been anxious, the risk of suicide is tripled, and for those who have been depressed, the risk is quintupled (Bostwick & Pankratz, 2000; Kanwar et al., 2013). People seldom die by suicide while in the depths of depression, when energy and initiative are lacking. The risk increases when they begin to rebound and become capable of following through (Chu et al., 2016).

Comparing the suicide rates of different groups, researchers have found

- *national differences:* In Britain, Italy, and Spain, suicide rates have been little more than half those of Canada, Australia, and the United States. Austria's and Finland's are about double (WHO, 2011). Within Europe, people in the most suicide-prone country (Belarus) have been 16 times more likely to die by suicide than those in the least suicide-prone country (Georgia).

- *racial differences:* Within the United States, Whites and Native Americans die by suicide twice as often as Blacks, Hispanics, and Asians (CDC, 2012).

- *gender differences:* Women are much more likely than men to attempt suicide (WHO, 2011). But men are two to four times more likely (depending on the country) to actually end their lives. Men use more lethal methods, such as firing a bullet into the head, the method of choice in 6 of 10 U.S. suicides.

- *trait differences:* Among Swedes, those with obsessive-compulsive disorder are at higher risk of depression, thereby increasing their risk of suicide (de la Cruz et al., 2017). So, too, are self-critical, perfectionist people, especially when feeling like they have failed to meet others' expectations (Smith et al., 2018).

- *age differences and trends:* In late adulthood, rates increase, with the highest rate among 45- to 64-year-olds and the second-highest among those 85 and older (AFSP, 2015). In the last half of the twentieth century, the global rate of annual suicide deaths nearly doubled (WHO, 2008). In the U.S., teen depression and suicide rates have jumped about a third since 2010, in tandem with increased cell phone use and decreased time spent face-to-face with friends (Twenge et al., 2018). Studies indicate that, over time, increasing social media use predicts increased unhappiness, while unhappiness does not lead to more social media use.

- *other group differences:* Suicide rates have been much higher among the rich, the nonreligious, and those single, widowed, or divorced (Hoyer & Lund, 1993; Norko et al., 2017; Okada & Samreth, 2013; VanderWeele et al., 2016, 2017). Witnessing physical pain and trauma can increase the risk of suicide, which may help explain veterans' and physicians' elevated suicide rates (Bender et al., 2012; Cornette et al., 2009). Gay, transgender, and gender-nonconforming youth facing an unsupportive environment, including family or peer rejection, are also at increased risk of attempting suicide (Goldfried, 2001; Haas et al., 2011; Hatzenbuehler, 2011; Testa et al., 2017). Among people with alcohol use disorder, 3 percent die by suicide. This rate is roughly 37 times greater for those who have just been heavily drinking (Borges et al., 2017).

- *day-of-the-week and seasonal differences:* Negative emotion tends to go up mid-week, which can have tragic consequences (Watson, 2000). A surprising 25 percent of U.S. suicides occur on Wednesdays (Kposowa & D'Auria, 2009). Suicide rates are highest in April and May, and not (as commonly believed) over the winter holidays (Nock, 2016).

Social suggestion may trigger suicide. Following highly publicized suicides and TV programs featuring suicide, known suicides sometimes increase. So do fatal auto and private airplane "accidents." One six-year study tracked suicide cases among all 1.2 million people who lived in metropolitan Stockholm at any time during the 1990s

"But life, being weary of these worldly bars,
Never lacks power to dismiss itself."
—William Shakespeare, *Julius Caesar*, 1599

(Hedström et al., 2008). Men exposed to a family suicide were 8 times more likely to die by suicide than were nonexposed men. That phenomenon may be partly attributable to family genes. But shared genetic predispositions cannot explain why men exposed to a co-worker's suicide were 3.5 times more likely to also take their own lives, compared with nonexposed men.

Suicide is not generally an act of hostility or revenge. People—especially older adults—may choose death as an alternative to current or future suffering, a way to switch off unendurable pain and relieve a perceived burden on family members. Suicidal urges typically arise when people feel disconnected from others and a burden to them, or when they feel defeated and trapped by an inescapable situation (Joiner, 2010; Taylor et al., 2011). Thus, suicide rates increase with unemployment during economic recessions (DeFina & Hannon, 2015; Reeves et al., 2014). Suicidal thoughts also may increase when people are driven to reach a goal or standard—to become thin or straight or rich—and find it unattainable (Chatard & Selimbegović, 2011).

In hindsight, families and friends may recall signs they believe should have forewarned them—verbal hints, giving possessions away, a sudden mood change, or withdrawal and preoccupation with death (Bagge et al., 2017). To judge from surveys of 84,850 people across 17 nations, about 9 percent of people at some point in their lives have thought seriously of suicide. About 3 in 10 of those who think about it will actually attempt suicide (Nock et al., 2008). Only 3 percent of Americans die in that attempt (Han et al., 2016). In one study that followed people for up to 25 years after a first suicide attempt, some 5 percent died by suicide (Bostwick et al., 2016). One group of clinical psychologists summarized 50 years of research on suicide's unpredictability: "The vast majority of people who possess a specific risk factor [for suicide] will never engage in suicidal behavior" (Franklin et al., 2017, p. 217). But researchers continue to try to solve the suicide puzzle. Although most suicide attempts fail, the risk of eventual death by suicide is seven times greater among those who have previously attempted suicide (Al-Sayegh et al., 2015).

Each year, about 40,000 Americans will die by suicide—about two-thirds using guns. (Drug overdoses account for about 80 percent of suicide attempts, but only 14 percent of suicide fatalities.) States with high gun ownership are states with high suicide rates, even after controlling for poverty and urbanization (Miller et al., 2002, 2016; Tavernise, 2013). After Missouri repealed its tough handgun law, its suicide rate went up 15 percent; when Connecticut enacted such a law, its suicide rate dropped 16 percent (Crifasi et al., 2015). Thus, although U.S. gun owners often keep a gun to feel safer, having a gun in the home makes one less safe, because it substantially increases the odds of a family member dying by suicide or homicide (Kposowa et al., 2016; VPC, 2015; Vyse, 2016).

How can we be helpful to someone who is talking suicide—who says, for example, "I wish I could just end it all" or "I hate my life; I can't go on"? If people write such things online, you can anonymously contact various social media safety teams (including on Facebook, Twitter, Instagram, YouTube, and Tumblr). If a friend or family member talks suicide, you can

1. *listen* and empathize;
2. *connect* the person with your campus counseling center; with (in the United States) the National Suicide Prevention Lifeline (1-800-273-8255[TALK]) or Crisis Text Line (by texting HOME to 74174); or with their counterparts in other countries (such as the LifeLine App in Canada); and
3. *protect* someone who appears at immediate risk by seeking help from a doctor, the nearest hospital emergency room, or 911. Better to share a secret than to attend a funeral.

Nonsuicidal Self-Injury

Self-harm takes many forms. Some people may engage in *nonsuicidal self-injury (NSSI)*, which is more common in adolescence and among females (CDC, 2009) (**FIGURE 40.2**). Such behavior, though painful, is not fatal. Those who engage in NSSI may cut or burn their skin, hit themselves, insert objects under their nails or skin, or self-administer tattoos. People who engage in NSSI tend to experience bullying, harassment, and other life

"People desire death when two fundamental needs are frustrated to the point of extinction: The need to belong with or connect to others, and the need to feel effective with or to influence others."
—Thomas Joiner (2006, p. 47)

FIGURE 40.2

RATES OF NONFATAL SELF-INJURY IN THE UNITED STATES Self-injury rates peak higher for females than for males. (Data from CDC, 2009.)

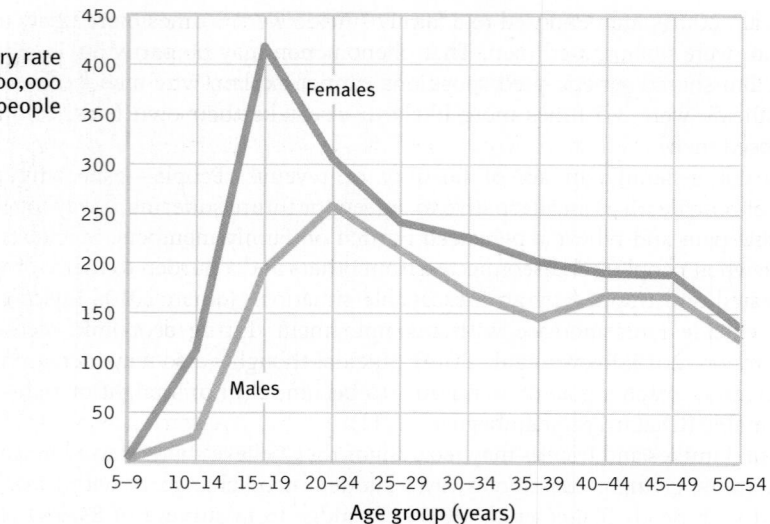

stress (Liu et al., 2016; van Geel et al., 2015). They are generally less able to tolerate and regulate emotional distress (Hamza et al., 2015). They are often extremely self-critical, and struggle to communicate, solve problems, and perform academically (Kiekens et al., 2016; Nock, 2010; You et al., 2015). Why do they hurt themselves? Reinforcement processes are at work (Bentley et al., 2014). Through NSSI they may

- find relief from intense negative thoughts through the distraction of pain.
- attract attention and possibly get help.
- relieve guilt by punishing themselves.
- get others to change their negative behavior (bullying, criticism).
- fit in with a peer group.

Does NSSI lead to suicide? Usually not. Those who engage in NSSI are typically suicide gesturers, not suicide attempters (Nock & Kessler, 2006). Nevertheless, NSSI is a risk factor for suicidal thoughts and future suicide attempts, especially when coexisting with bipolar disorder (Runeson et al., 2016; Willoughby et al., 2015). If people do not find help, their nonsuicidal behavior may escalate to suicidal thoughts and, finally, to suicide attempts.

Does Disorder Equal Danger?

LOQ 40-6 Do psychological disorders predict violent behavior?

September 16, 2013, started like any other Monday at the Navy Yard in Washington, DC, with people arriving early to begin work. Then government contractor Aaron Alexis entered the building and began shooting. An hour later, 13 people were dead, including the shooter. Reports later confirmed that Alexis had a history of mental illness, and had stated that an "ultra low frequency attack is what I've been subject to for the last three months. And to be perfectly honest, that is what has driven me to this." This devastating mass shooting, like the one in a Connecticut elementary school in 2012 and many others since then, reinforced public perceptions that people with psychological disorders pose a threat (Barry et al., 2013; Jorm et al., 2012). "People with mental illness are getting guns and committing these mass shootings," said U.S. Speaker of the House Paul Ryan (2015). In one survey, 84 percent of Americans agreed that "increased government spending on mental health screening and treatment" would be a "somewhat" or "very" effective "approach to preventing mass shootings at schools" (Newport, 2012). That was U.S. President Donald Trump's assumption, in the aftermath of a 2018 Florida school massacre. He proposed opening more mental hospitals that could house would-be mass murderers: "When you have some person like this, you can bring them into a mental institution."

Do disorders actually increase risk of violence? And can clinicians predict who is likely to do harm? *No* and *no*. Most violent criminals are not mentally ill, and most mentally ill people are not violent (Fazel & Grann, 2006; Skeem et al., 2016). Moreover, clinical prediction of violence is unreliable. The few people with disorders who commit violent acts tend to be either those, like the Navy Yard shooter, who experience threatening delusions and hallucinated voices that command them to act, who have suffered a financial crisis or lost relationship, or who abuse substances (Douglas et al., 2009; Elbogen et al., 2016; Fazel et al., 2009, 2010). In seeking some form of explanation for terrible acts, we may look for mental disorders to be involved. Yet the offenders are often "ordinary" people with no obvious mental disorder, such as the California couple arrested in 2018 who had imprisoned, starved, and assaulted their children for decades.

People with disorders are more likely to be *victims* than perpetrators of violence (Marley & Bulia, 2001). According to the U.S. Surgeon General's Office (1999, p. 7), "there is very little risk of violence or harm to a stranger from casual contact with an individual who has a mental disorder." *The bottom line:* Psychological disorders only rarely lead to violent acts, and focusing gun restrictions only on mentally ill people will likely not reduce gun violence (Friedman, 2012). Better predictors of violence are use of alcohol or drugs, previous violence, gun availability, and—as in the case of the repeatedly head-injured and ultimately homicidal National Football League player Aaron Hernandez—brain damage (Belson, 2017). The mass-killing shooters have one more thing in common: They tend to be young males.

Whether people with mental disorders who turn violent should be held responsible for their behavior remains controversial. U.S. President Ronald Reagan's near-assassin, John Hinckley, was sent to a hospital rather than to prison. The public was outraged. They were outraged again in 2011, when Jared Lee Loughner killed six people and injured several others, including U.S. Representative Gabrielle Giffords. Loughner was diagnosed with schizophrenia but nevertheless sentenced to life in prison without parole.

Which decision—hospital or prison—was correct? As we come to better understand the biological and environmental bases for human behavior, from generosity to murder, we may better determine when and how to hold people accountable for their actions.

MENTAL HEALTH AND MASS SHOOTINGS Following the 2012 Newtown, Connecticut, slaughter of 26 schoolchildren and adults, and again following the 2018 Parkland, Florida, massacre of 17 youth and adults, people wondered if such tragedies couldn't be prevented through mental health screenings. Could people with psychological disorders who are violence-prone (a tiny percentage) be identified in advance by mental health workers and prevented from gun ownership? Even if this kind of prediction could be done with complete accuracy (it can't), it turns out that in 85 percent of U.S. mass killings between 1982 and 2017, the killer had no known prior contact with mental health professionals. Most homicide "is committed by healthy people in the grip of everyday emotions using guns" (Friedman, 2017).

RATES OF PSYCHOLOGICAL DISORDERS

LOQ 40-7 How many people have, or have had, a psychological disorder? What are some of the risk factors?

Who is most vulnerable to psychological disorders? At what times of life? To answer such questions, many countries have conducted lengthy, structured interviews with representative samples of thousands of their citizens. After asking hundreds of questions that probe for symptoms—"Has there ever been a period of two weeks or more when you felt like you wanted to die?"—the researchers have estimated the current, prior-year, and lifetime prevalence of various disorders.

How many people have, or have had, a psychological disorder? More than most of us suppose.

- A World Health Organization study—based on 90-minute interviews with thousands of people who were representative of their country's population—estimated the number of prior-year mental disorders in 28 countries (Kessler et al., 2009). Cultures vary, and as **FIGURE 40.3** illustrates, the lowest rate of reported mental disorders was in Nigeria, the highest rate in the United States. Moreover, immigrants to the United States from Mexico, Africa, and Asia averaged better mental health than their U.S.-born counterparts with the same ethnic heritage (Breslau et al., 2007; Maldonado-Molina et al., 2011). For example, compared with Mexican-Americans born in the United States, Mexican-Americans who have recently immigrated are less at risk of mental disorder—a phenomenon known as the *immigrant paradox* (Schwartz et al., 2010).

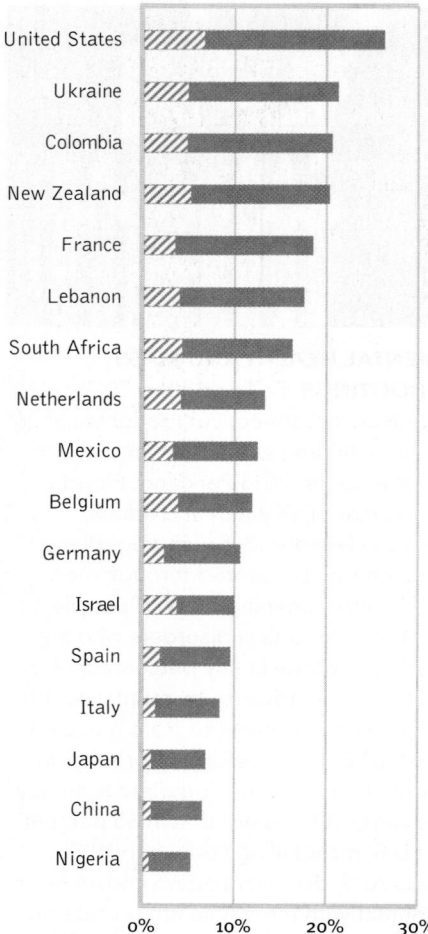

■ Percentage with any mental disorder
▨ Proportion of those disorders considered "serious"

FIGURE 40.3

PRIOR-YEAR PREVALENCE OF DISORDERS IN SELECTED AREAS
From interviews in 28 countries. (Data from Kessler et al., 2009).

TABLE 40.2

Percentage of Americans Reporting Selected Psychological Disorders in the Past Year

Psychological Disorder	Percentage
Depressive disorders or bipolar disorder	9.3
Phobia of specific object or situation	8.7
Social anxiety disorder	6.8
Attention-deficit/hyperactivity disorder (ADHD)	4.1
Posttraumatic stress disorder (PTSD)	3.5
Generalized anxiety disorder	3.1
Schizophrenia	1.1
Obsessive-compulsive disorder	1.0

Data from: National Institute of Mental Health, 2015.

- The U.S. National Institute of Mental Health (2015) has estimated that just under 1 in 5 adult Americans currently have a "mental, behavioral, or emotional disorder (excluding developmental and substance use disorders)" or have had one within the past year (**TABLE 40.2**).

What increases vulnerability to mental disorders? As **TABLE 40.3** indicates, there is a wide range of risk and protective factors for mental disorders. But one predictor of mental disorders—poverty—crosses ethnic and gender lines. The incidence of serious psychological disorders is 2.5 times higher among those below the poverty line (CDC, 2014a).

TABLE 40.3

Risk and Protective Factors for Mental Disorders

Risk Factors	Protective Factors
Academic failure	Aerobic exercise
Birth complications	Community offering empowerment, opportunity, and security
Caring for those who are chronically ill or who have a neurocognitive disorder	Economic independence
Child abuse and neglect	Effective parenting
Chronic insomnia	Feelings of mastery and control
Chronic pain	Feelings of security
Family disorganization or conflict	High self-esteem
Low birth weight	Literacy
Low socioeconomic status	Positive attachment and early bonding
Medical illness	Positive parent-child relationships
Neurochemical imbalance	Problem-solving skills
Parental mental illness	Resilient coping with stress and adversity
Parental substance abuse	Social and work skills
Personal loss and bereavement	Social support from family and friends
Poor work skills and habits	
Reading disabilities	
Sensory disabilities	
Social incompetence	
Stressful life events	
Substance abuse	
Trauma experiences	

Research from: World Health Organization (WHO, 2004a, b).

This *correlation*, like so many others, raises further questions: Does poverty cause disorders? Or do disorders cause poverty? It is both, though the answer varies with the disorder. Schizophrenia understandably leads to poverty. Yet the stresses and demoralization of poverty can also breed disorders, especially depression in women and substance abuse in men (Dohrenwend et al., 1992). In one natural experiment investigating the poverty-pathology link, researchers tracked rates of behavior problems in North Carolina Native American children as economic development enabled a dramatic reduction in their community's poverty rate. As the study began, children of poverty exhibited more deviant and aggressive behaviors. After four years, children whose families had moved above the poverty line exhibited a 40 percent decrease in behavior problems. Those who maintained their previous positions below or above the poverty line exhibited no change (Costello et al., 2003).

At what times of life do disorders strike? Usually by early adulthood. "Over 75 percent of our sample with any disorder had experienced [their] first symptoms by age 24," reported Lee Robins and Darrel Regier (1991, p. 331). Among the earliest to appear are the symptoms of antisocial personality disorder (median age 8) and of phobias (median age 10). Alcohol use disorder, obsessive-compulsive disorder, bipolar disorder, and schizophrenia symptoms appear at a median age near 20. Major depressive disorder often hits somewhat later, at a median age of 25.

LaunchPad See the **Video: Correlational Studies** for a helpful tutorial about this research design. For a summary of disorder rates, engage online with **Concept Practice: Risks and Rates of Disorders.**

RETRIEVE IT • • •   ANSWERS IN APPENDIX E

RI-5 What is the relationship between poverty and psychological disorders?

REVIEW BASIC CONCEPTS OF PSYCHOLOGICAL DISORDERS

Learning Objectives

TEST YOURSELF Answer these repeated Learning Objective Questions on your own (before checking the answers in Appendix D) to improve your retention of the concepts (McDaniel et al., 2009, 2015).

40-1 How should we draw the line between normality and disorder?

40-2 How do the medical model and the biopsychosocial approach influence our understanding of psychological disorders?

40-3 How and why do clinicians classify psychological disorders, and why do some psychologists criticize the use of diagnostic labels?

40-4 Why is there controversy over attention-deficit/hyperactivity disorder?

40-5 What factors increase the risk of suicide, and what do we know about nonsuicidal self-injury?

40-6 Do psychological disorders predict violent behavior?

40-7 How many people have, or have had, a psychological disorder? What are some of the risk factors?

Terms and Concepts to Remember

TEST YOURSELF Write down the definition yourself, then check your answer on the referenced page.

psychological disorder, **p. 494**

medical model, **p. 495**

epigenetics, **p. 497**

DSM-5, **p. 497**

attention-deficit/hyperactivity disorder (ADHD), **p. 497**

Experience the Testing Effect

TEST YOURSELF Answer the following questions on your own first, then check your answers in Appendix E.

1. Two major disorders that are found worldwide are schizophrenia and _____ _____ _____.

2. Anna is embarrassed that it takes her several minutes to parallel park her car. She usually gets out of the car once or twice to inspect her distance both from the curb and from the nearby cars. Should she worry about having a psychological disorder?

3. What is *susto*, and is this a culture-specific or universal psychological disorder?

4. A therapist says that psychological disorders are sicknesses, and people with these disorders should be treated as patients in a hospital. This therapist's belief reflects the _____ model.

5. Many psychologists reject the disorders-as-illness view and instead contend that other factors may also be involved—for example, the person's level of stress and ways of coping with it. This view represents the _____ approach.
   a. medical
   b. epigenetics
   c. biopsychosocial
   d. diagnostic

6. Why is the DSM, and the DSM-5 in particular, considered controversial?

7. One predictor of psychiatric disorders that crosses ethnic and gender lines is _____.

8. The symptoms of _____ appear around age 10; _____ tend[s] to appear later, around age 25.
   a. schizophrenia; bipolar disorder
   b. bipolar disorder; schizophrenia
   c. major depressive disorder; phobias
   d. phobias; major depressive disorder

Continue testing yourself with 📖 **LearningCurve** or 📖 **Achieve Read & Practice** to learn and remember most effectively.

---

41 Anxiety Disorders, OCD, and PTSD

Anxiety is part of life. Speaking in front of a class, peering down from a ladder, or waiting to learn the results of a final exam might make any one of us feel nervous. Anxiety may even cause us to avoid talking or making eye contact—"shyness," we call it. Fortunately for most of us, our uneasiness is not intense and persistent. Some, however, are more prone to fear the unknown and to notice and remember perceived threats (Gorka et al., 2017; Mitte, 2008). When the brain's danger-detection system becomes hyperactive, we are at greater risk for an *anxiety disorder,* and for two other disorders that involve anxiety: *obsessive-compulsive disorder (OCD)* and *posttraumatic stress disorder (PTSD).*[1]

ANXIETY DISORDERS

LOQ 41-1 How do generalized anxiety disorder, panic disorder, and phobias differ?

The **anxiety disorders** are marked by distressing, persistent anxiety or by dysfunctional anxiety-reducing behaviors. For example, people with *social anxiety disorder* become extremely anxious in social settings where others might judge them, such as parties, class presentations, or even eating in public. One university student experienced palpitations, tremors, blushing, and sweating when giving a presentation, taking an exam, or meeting an authority figure, and also feared that he would embarrass himself. He therefore avoided parties, phone calls, and other social contacts. By staying home he avoided the anxious feelings, but it was maladaptive: This prevented him from learning to cope with the world and left him feeling lonely (Leichsenring & Leweke, 2017).

Let's take a closer look at three other anxiety disorders:

- *generalized anxiety disorder,* in which a person is, for no obvious reason, continually tense and uneasy;

- *panic disorder,* in which a person experiences *panic attacks*—sudden episodes of intense dread—and fears the next episode's unpredictable onset; and

- *phobias,* in which a person is intensely and irrationally afraid of something.

anxiety disorders psychological disorders characterized by distressing, persistent anxiety or maladaptive behaviors that reduce anxiety.

---

1. OCD and PTSD were formerly classified as anxiety disorders, but the DSM-5 now classifies them separately.

Generalized Anxiety Disorder

For two years, Tom, a 27-year-old electrician, was bothered by dizziness, sweating palms, and irregular heartbeat. He felt on edge and sometimes found himself shaking. Tom was fairly successful in hiding his symptoms from his family and co-workers. But he allowed himself few other social contacts, and occasionally he had to leave work. Neither his family doctor nor a neurologist was able to find any physical problem.

Tom's unfocused, out-of-control, agitated feelings suggest **generalized anxiety disorder,** which is marked by excessive and uncontrollable worry that persists for six months or more. People with this condition (two-thirds women) worry continually, and they are often jittery, on edge, and sleep-deprived (McLean & Anderson, 2009). They become fixated on potential threats (Pergamin-Hight et al., 2015). Concentration suffers as everyday worries demand continual attention. Their *autonomic nervous system* arousal may leak out through furrowed brows, twitching eyelids, trembling, perspiration, or fidgeting.

Those affected usually cannot identify, relieve, or avoid their anxiety; to use Sigmund Freud's term, the anxiety is *free-floating* (not linked to a specific stressor or threat). Generalized anxiety disorder and depression often go hand in hand, but even without depression, this disorder tends to be disabling (Hunt et al., 2004; Moffitt et al., 2007). Moreover, it may lead to physical problems, such as high blood pressure.

Panic Disorder

Many people can experience an intense anxiety that escalates into a terrifying panic attack—a minutes-long episode of intense fear that something horrible is about to happen. Irregular heartbeat, chest pains, shortness of breath, choking, trembling, or dizziness may accompany the panic. One woman recalled suddenly feeling

> hot and as though I couldn't breathe. My heart was racing and I started to sweat and tremble and I was sure I was going to faint. Then my fingers started to feel numb and tingly and things seemed unreal. It was so bad I wondered if I was dying and asked my husband to take me to the emergency room. By the time we got there (about 10 minutes) the worst of the attack was over and I just felt washed out (Greist et al., 1986).

For the 3 percent of people with **panic disorder,** panic attacks are recurrent. These anxiety tornados strike suddenly, wreak havoc, and disappear, but are not forgotten. Ironically, worries about anxiety—perhaps fearing another panic attack, or fearing anxiety-related symptoms in public—can amplify anxiety symptoms (Olatunji & Wolitzky-Taylor, 2009). After several panic attacks, people may come to fear the fear itself. This may trigger *agoraphobia*—fear or avoidance of public situations from which escape might be difficult. People with agoraphobia may avoid being outside the home, in a crowd, or in an elevator. Smokers have at least a doubled risk of panic disorder and greater symptoms when they do have an attack (Knuts et al., 2010; Zvolensky & Bernstein, 2005). Because nicotine is a stimulant, lighting up doesn't lighten us up.

generalized anxiety disorder an anxiety disorder in which a person is continually tense, apprehensive, and in a state of autonomic nervous system arousal.

panic disorder an anxiety disorder marked by unpredictable, minutes-long episodes of intense dread in which a person may experience terror and accompanying chest pain, choking, or other frightening sensations; often followed by worry over a possible next attack.

PANIC ON THE COURSE Golfer Charlie Beljan experienced what he later learned were panic attacks during an important tournament. His thumping heartbeat and shortness of breath led him to think he was having a heart attack. But hospital tests revealed that his symptoms were not related to a physical illness. He recovered, went on to win $846,000, and has become an inspiration to others.

phobia an anxiety disorder marked by a persistent, irrational fear and avoidance of a specific object, activity, or situation.

Charles Darwin began suffering from panic disorder at age 28, after spending five years sailing the world. He moved to the country, avoided social gatherings, and traveled only in his wife's company. But the relative seclusion did free him to further develop his evolutionary theory. "Even ill health," he reflected, "has saved me from the distraction of society and its amusements" (quoted in Ma, 1997).

Phobias

We all live with some fears. But people with **phobias** are consumed by a persistent, irrational fear and avoidance of some object, activity, or situation. *Specific phobias* may focus on particular animals, insects, heights, blood, or closed spaces (**FIGURE 41.1**). Many people avoid the triggers, such as high places, that arouse their fear. Marilyn, an otherwise healthy and happy 28-year-old, so feared thunderstorms that she felt anxious as soon as a weather forecaster mentioned possible storms later in the week. If her husband was away and a storm was forecast, she often stayed with a close relative. During a storm, she hid from windows and buried her head to avoid seeing the lightning.

Martin Harvey/Getty Images

FIGURE 41.1

SOME COMMON SPECIFIC FEARS Researchers surveyed Dutch people to identify the most common events or objects they feared. A strong fear becomes a phobia if it provokes a compelling but irrational desire to avoid the dreaded object or situation. (Data from Depla et al., 2008.)

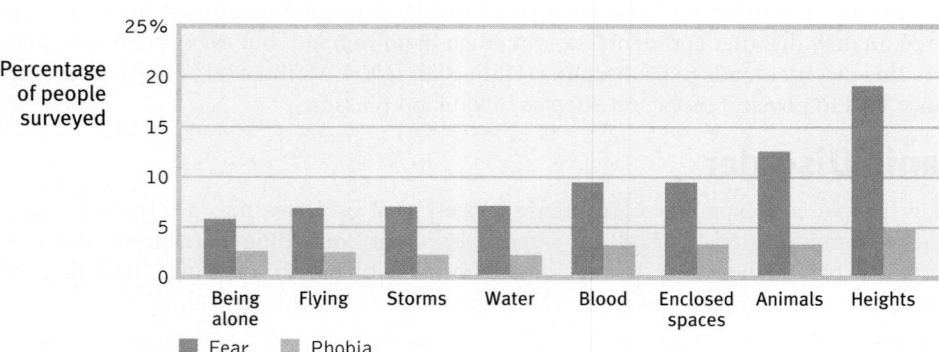

Percentage of people surveyed

- Fear
- Phobia

Being alone | Flying | Storms | Water | Blood | Enclosed spaces | Animals | Heights

🔒 RETRIEVE IT • • •   *ANSWERS IN APPENDIX E*

RI-1 Unfocused tension, apprehension, and arousal are symptoms of _____ _____ disorder.

RI-2 Those who experience unpredictable periods of terror and intense dread, accompanied by frightening physical sensations, may be diagnosed with a _____ disorder.

RI-3 If a person is focusing anxiety on specific feared objects or situations, that person may have a _____.

THRIVING WITH OCD Music star Justin Timberlake says support from his family and a sense of humor have helped him cope with the challenges of obsessive-compulsive disorder.

Michael Campanella/WireImage/Getty Images

OBSESSIVE-COMPULSIVE DISORDER (OCD)

LOQ 41-2 What is *OCD*?

As with the anxiety disorders, we can see aspects of our own behavior in **obsessive-compulsive disorder (OCD)**. *Obsessive thoughts* are unwanted and seemingly unending. *Compulsive behaviors* are responses to those thoughts.

We all are at times obsessed with thoughts and we may behave compulsively. Have you ever felt a bit anxious about how your place will appear to others and found yourself compulsively cleaning one last time before your guests arrived? Or, perhaps worried about an upcoming exam, you caught yourself lining up your study materials "just so" before studying? Our lives are full of little rehearsals and fussy behaviors. They cross the fine line between normality and disorder when they *persistently interfere* with everyday life and cause us distress. Checking that you locked the door is normal; checking 10 times is not. Washing your hands is normal; washing so often that your skin becomes raw is not. (**TABLE 41.1** offers more examples.) At some time during their lives, often during their late teens or early adulthood, about 2 percent of people cross that line from normal preoccupations and fussy behaviors to debilitating disorder (Kessler et al., 2012). Although people know their anxiety-fueled obsessive thoughts are irrational, the

TABLE 41.1

Common Obsessions and Compulsions Among Children and Adolescents With Obsessive-Compulsive Disorder

Thought or Behavior	Percentage Reporting Symptom
Obsessions (repetitive *thoughts*)	
Concern with dirt, germs, or toxins	40
Something terrible happening (fire, death, illness)	24
Symmetry, order, or exactness	17
Compulsions (repetitive *behaviors*)	
Excessive hand washing, bathing, toothbrushing, or grooming	85
Repeating rituals (in/out of a door, up/down from a chair)	51
Checking doors, locks, appliances, car brakes, homework	46

Data from: Rapoport, 1989.

thoughts can become so haunting, and the compulsive rituals so senselessly time consuming, that effective functioning becomes impossible.

OCD is more common among teens and young adults than among older people (Nestadt & Samuels, 1997). A 40-year follow-up study of 144 Swedes diagnosed with the disorder found that, for most, the obsessions and compulsions had gradually lessened, though only 1 in 5 had completely recovered (Skoog & Skoog, 1999).

Some people experience other OCD-related disorders, such as *hoarding disorder* (cluttering one's space with acquired possessions one can't let go), *body dysmorphic disorder* (preoccupation with perceived body defects), or—new words to impress your friends—*trichotillomania* (hair pulling) or *excoriation disorder* (excessive skin-picking).

POSTTRAUMATIC STRESS DISORDER (PTSD)

LOQ 41-3 What is *PTSD*?

While serving overseas, one soldier, Jesse, observed the killing "of children and women. It was just horrible for anyone to experience." Back home, he suffered "real bad flashbacks" (Welch, 2005).

Jesse is not alone. In one study of 103,788 veterans returning from Iraq and Afghanistan, 25 percent were diagnosed with a psychological disorder (Seal et al., 2007). Some had *traumatic brain injuries (TBI)*, but the most frequent diagnosis was **posttraumatic stress disorder (PTSD).** Survivors of accidents, disasters, war-related refugee displacement, and violent and sexual assaults (including an estimated two-thirds of prostitutes) have also experienced PTSD symptoms (Brewin et al., 1999; Guo et al., 2017; Reebs et al., 2017). Typical symptoms include recurring haunting memories and nightmares, laser-focused attention to and avoidance of possible threats, social withdrawal, jumpy anxiety, and trouble sleeping (Germain, 2013; Hoge et al., 2007; Yuval et al., 2017).

The greater one's emotional distress during a trauma, the higher the risk for posttraumatic symptoms (Ozer et al., 2003).

Many of us will experience a traumatic event. And many people will display *survivor resiliency*—by recovering after severe stress (Bonanno, 2004, 2005; Infurna & Luthar, 2016b). Although philosopher Friedrich Nietzsche's (1889) idea that "what does not kill me makes me stronger" is not true for all, some will even experience *posttraumatic growth* (positive psychological changes as a result of struggling with extreme challenges). Why do some 5 to 10 percent of people develop PTSD after a traumatic event while others do not (Bonanno et al., 2011)? One factor seems to be the amount of trauma-related emotional distress: The higher the distress (such as the level of physical torture suffered by prisoners of war), the greater the risk for posttraumatic symptoms (King et al., 2015; Ozer et al., 2003). Among American military

obsessive-compulsive disorder (OCD) a disorder characterized by unwanted repetitive thoughts (obsessions), actions (compulsions), or both.

posttraumatic stress disorder (PTSD) a disorder characterized by haunting memories, nightmares, hypervigilance, avoidance of trauma-related stimuli, social withdrawal, jumpy anxiety, numbness of feeling, and/or insomnia that lingers for four weeks or more after a traumatic experience.

ENGAGE 🔲 **LaunchPad** For an eye-opening, 7-minute snapshot of one person's challenges with compulsive rituals, see the **Video: Obsessive-Compulsive Disorder—A Young Mother's Struggle.**

PTSD FROM PARKLAND In the 2018 Parkland, FL school shooting, Samantha Fuentes (at right) witnessed friends dying. Shrapnel struck her face and legs. She later reported PTSD symptoms, including a fear of returning to the school and jumping at the sound of a slammed door.

Chip Somodevilla/Getty Images

personnel in Afghanistan, 7.6 percent of combatants and 1.4 percent of noncombatants developed PTSD (McNally, 2012). Among survivors of the 9/11 terrorist attack on New York's World Trade Center, the rates of subsequent PTSD diagnoses for those who had been inside were double the rates of those who had been outside (Bonanno et al., 2006).

What else can influence PTSD development? Some people may have a more sensitive emotion-processing limbic system that floods their bodies with stress hormones, which explains why PTSD may coexist with another disorder (Duncan et al., 2017; Kosslyn, 2005; Ozer & Weiss, 2004). The odds of experiencing PTSD after a traumatic event are also higher for women than for men (Olff et al., 2007; Ozer & Weiss, 2004).

Some psychologists believe that PTSD has been overdiagnosed (Dobbs, 2009; McNally, 2003). Too often, say critics, PTSD gets stretched to include normal stress-related bad memories and dreams. And some well-intentioned procedures—such as "debriefing" people by asking them to revisit the experience and vent their emotions—may worsen normal stress reactions (Bonanno et al., 2010; Wakefield & Spitzer, 2002). Other research shows that reliving traumas (such as the 2013 Boston Marathon bombing) through media coverage sustains the stress response (Holman et al., 2014). Nevertheless, people diagnosed with PTSD can benefit from other therapies.

🔒 **RETRIEVE IT • • •**   *ANSWERS IN APPENDIX E*

RI-4 Those who express anxiety through unwanted repetitive thoughts or actions may have a(n) _____-_____ disorder.

RI-5 Those with symptoms of recurring memories and nightmares, hypervigilance, avoidance, social withdrawal, jumpy anxiety, numbness of feeling, and/or insomnia for weeks after a traumatic event may be diagnosed with _____ _____ disorder.

UNDERSTANDING ANXIETY DISORDERS, OCD, AND PTSD

LOQ 41-4 How do conditioning, cognition, and biology contribute to the feelings and thoughts that mark anxiety disorders, OCD, and PTSD?

Anxiety is both a feeling and a cognition—a doubt-laden self-appraisal. How do these anxious feelings and cognitions arise? Few psychologists now interpret anxiety the way Sigmund Freud did. His psychoanalytic theory proposed that, beginning in childhood, people *repress* intolerable impulses, ideas, and feelings. Freud believed that this submerged mental energy sometimes leaks out in odd symptoms, such as anxious hand washing. Most of today's psychologists believe that three modern perspectives—conditioning, cognition, and biology—are more helpful.

Conditioning

Through *classical conditioning*, our fear responses can become linked with formerly neutral objects and events. Researchers have created anxious animals by giving rats unpredictable electric shocks (Schwartz, 1984). The rats, like assault victims who report feeling anxious when returning to the scene of the crime, learned to become uneasy in their lab environment. The lab became a cue for fear.

Such research helps explain how anxious or traumatized people learn to associate their anxiety with certain cues, and why anxious people are hyperattentive to possible threats (Bar-Haim et al., 2007; Duits et al., 2015). In one survey, 58 percent of those with social anxiety disorder said their disorder began after a traumatic event (Ost & Hugdahl, 1981). Anxiety or an anxiety-related disorder is more likely to develop when bad events happen unpredictably and uncontrollably (Field, 2006; Mineka & Oehlberg, 2008). Even a single painful and frightening event may trigger a full-blown phobia, thanks to two conditioning processes: classical conditioning's *stimulus generalization* and operant conditioning's *reinforcement*.

Stimulus generalization occurs when a person experiences a fearful event and later develops a fear of similar events. My [DM's] car was once struck by another whose driver missed a stop sign. For months afterward, I felt a twinge of unease when any car approached from a side street. Likewise, I [ND] was watching a terrifying movie about spiders, *Arachnophobia,* when a severe thunderstorm struck and the theater lost power. For months, I experienced anxiety at the sight of spiders or cobwebs. Those fears eventually disappeared, but sometimes fears linger and grow. Marilyn's thunderstorm phobia may have similarly generalized after a terrifying or painful experience during a thunderstorm.

Reinforcement helps maintain learned fears and anxieties. Anything that enables us to avoid or escape a feared situation can reinforce maladaptive behaviors. Fearing a panic attack, we may decide not to leave the house. Reinforced by feeling calmer, we are likely to repeat that behavior in the future (Antony et al., 1992). So, too, with compulsive behaviors. If washing our hands relieves our feelings of anxiety, we may wash our hands again when those feelings return.

Cognition

Conditioning influences our feelings of anxiety, but so does cognition—our thoughts, memories, interpretations, and expectations. We learn some fears by observing others. Nearly all monkeys raised in the wild fear snakes, yet lab-raised monkeys do not. Surely, most wild monkeys do not actually suffer snake bites. Do they learn their fear through observation? To find out, Susan Mineka (1985, 2002) experimented with six monkeys raised in the wild (all strongly fearful of snakes) and their lab-raised offspring (virtually none of which feared snakes). After repeatedly observing their parents or peers refusing to reach for food in the presence of a snake, the younger monkeys developed a similar strong fear of snakes. When the monkeys were retested three months later, their learned fear persisted. We humans similarly learn many of our own fears by observing others (Helsen et al., 2011; Olsson et al., 2007).

Hemera Technologies/
PhotoObjects.net/360/Getty

Our interpretations and expectations also shape our reactions. Whether we interpret the creaky sound simply as the wind or as a possible knife-wielding attacker determines whether we panic. People with anxiety disorders tend to be *hypervigilant.* They *attend* more to threatening stimuli. They more often *interpret* stimuli as threatening: A pounding heart signals a heart attack, a lone spider near the bed indicates an infestation, and an everyday disagreement with a friend or a boss spells doom for the relationship. And they more readily *remember* threatening events (Van Bockstaele et al., 2014). Anxiety is especially common when people cannot switch off such intrusive thoughts and perceive a loss of control and a sense of helplessness (Franklin & Foa, 2011).

Biology

Some aspects of anxiety disorders, OCD, and PTSD are not easily understandable in terms of conditioning and cognitive processes alone. Why do some of us develop lasting phobias after suffering traumas, but others do not? Why do we all learn some fears more readily than others? The answers lie in part in our biology.

GENES Among monkeys, fearfulness runs in families. A monkey reacts more strongly to stress if its close biological relatives have sensitive, high-strung temperaments (Suomi, 1986). So, too, with people. Although twins in general are not at higher risk for any disorder, if one identical twin has an anxiety disorder, the other is also at risk (Polderman et al., 2015). Even when raised separately, identical twins may develop similar phobias (Carey, 1990; Eckert et al., 1981). One pair of separated identical twins independently became so afraid of water that each would wade into the ocean backward and only up to her knees.

Given the genetic contribution to anxiety disorders, researchers are now sleuthing the culprit genes. Among their findings are 17 gene variations associated with typical anxiety disorder symptoms (Hovatta et al., 2005), and others that are associated specifically with OCD (Mattheisen et al., 2015; Taylor, 2013).

ENGAGE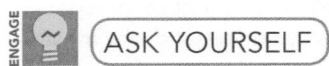

Can you recall a fear that you have learned? How were conditioning or cognition involved?

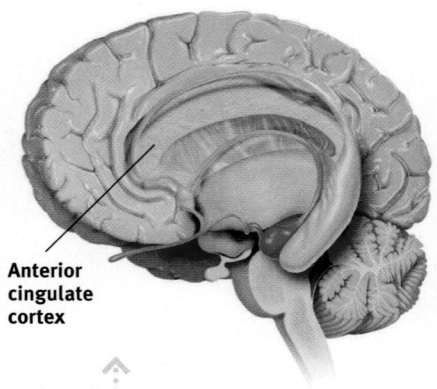

Anterior cingulate cortex

FIGURE 41.2

AN OBSESSIVE-COMPULSIVE BRAIN When people engaged in a challenging cognitive task, those with OCD showed the most activity in the anterior cingulate cortex in the brain's frontal area (Maltby et al., 2005).

Some genes can influence anxiety disorders by regulating brain levels of neurotransmitters. These include *serotonin,* which influences sleep, mood, and attending to threats (Canli, 2008; Pergamin-Hight et al., 2012), and *glutamate,* which heightens activity in the brain's alarm centers (Lafleur et al., 2006; Welch et al., 2007).

So genes matter. Some of us have genes that make us like orchids—fragile, yet capable of beauty under favorable circumstances. Others of us are like dandelions—hardy, and able to thrive in varied circumstances (Ellis & Boyce, 2008; Pluess & Belsky, 2013).

But experience affects gene expression. Among those with PTSD, a history of child abuse leaves long-term *epigenetic marks,* which are often organic molecules. These molecular tags attach to our chromosomes and turn certain genes on or off. Thus, experiences such as abuse can increase the likelihood that a genetic vulnerability to a disorder will be expressed (Mehta et al., 2013; Zannas et al., 2015). People who die by suicide show a similar epigenetic effect (Lockwood et al., 2015; McGowan et al., 2009).

THE BRAIN Our experiences change our brain, paving new pathways. Traumatic fear-learning experiences can leave tracks in the brain, creating fear circuits within the amygdala (Etkin & Wager, 2007; Herringa et al., 2013; Kolassa & Elbert, 2007). These fear pathways create easy inroads for more fear experiences (Armony et al., 1998). Some antidepressant drugs dampen this fear-circuit activity and associated obsessive-compulsive behaviors.

Generalized anxiety disorder, panic attacks, phobias, OCD, and PTSD express themselves biologically as overarousal of brain areas involved in impulse control and habitual behaviors. These disorders reflect a brain danger-detection system gone hyperactive—producing anxiety when no danger exists. In OCD, for example, when the brain detects that something is amiss, it seems to generate a mental hiccup of repeating thoughts (obsessions) or actions (compulsions) (Gehring et al., 2000). Brain scans reveal elevated activity in specific brain areas during behaviors such as compulsive hand washing, checking, ordering, or hoarding (Insel, 2010; Mataix-Cols et al., 2004, 2005). The *anterior cingulate cortex,* a brain region that monitors our actions and checks for errors, is often especially hyperactive (Maltby et al., 2005) **(FIGURE 41.2)**.

NATURAL SELECTION We seem biologically prepared to fear the threats our ancestors faced—spiders and snakes, enclosed spaces and heights, storms and darkness. Those who did not fear these threats were less likely to survive and leave descendants. Even in Britain, which has only one poisonous snake species, people often fear snakes. Nine-month-old infants attend more to sounds signaling ancient threats (hisses, thunder) than they do to sounds representing modern dangers (a bomb exploding, breaking glass) (Erlich et al., 2013). It is easy to condition and hard to extinguish fears of such "evolutionarily relevant" stimuli (Coelho & Purkis, 2009; Davey, 1995; Öhman, 2009). Some of our modern fears may also have an evolutionary explanation. A fear of flying may be rooted in our biological predisposition to fear confinement and heights.

Compare our easy-to-learn fears with those we *do not* easily learn. World War II air raids, for example, produced remarkably few lasting phobias. As the air strikes continued, the British, Japanese, and German populations did not become more and more panicked. Rather, they grew increasingly indifferent to planes outside their immediate neighborhoods (Mineka & Zinbarg, 1996). Evolution has not prepared us to fear bombs dropping from the sky.

Our phobias focus on dangers our ancestors faced. Our compulsive acts typically exaggerate behaviors that helped them survive. Grooming had survival value. Gone wild, it becomes compulsive hair pulling. So, too, with washing up, which becomes ritual hand washing. And checking territorial boundaries becomes checking and rechecking already locked doors (Rapoport, 1989). Although natural selection shaped our behaviors, when taken to an extreme, these behaviors can interfere with daily life.

FEARLESS The biological perspective helps us understand why most people are more fearful of heights than Alex Honnold, shown here in 2017 becoming the first person to free-solo climb (no safety ropes) Yosemite National Park's massive El Capitan granite wall.

Peter Bohler/Redux

🔒 REVIEW ANXIETY DISORDERS, OCD, AND PTSD

⟳ Learning Objectives

TEST YOURSELF Answer these repeated Learning Objective Questions on your own (before checking the answers in Appendix D) to improve your retention of the concepts (McDaniel et al., 2009, 2015).

41-1 How do generalized anxiety disorder, panic disorder, and phobias differ?

41-2 What is *OCD*?

41-3 What is *PTSD*?

41-4 How do conditioning, cognition, and biology contribute to the feelings and thoughts that mark anxiety disorders, OCD, and PTSD?

⟳ Terms and Concepts to Remember

TEST YOURSELF Write down the definition yourself, then check your answer on the referenced page.

anxiety disorders, **p. 506**

generalized anxiety disorder, **p. 507**

panic disorder, **p. 507**

phobia, **p. 508**

obsessive-compulsive disorder (OCD), **p. 509**

posttraumatic stress disorder (PTSD), **p. 509**

⟳ Experience the Testing Effect

TEST YOURSELF Answer the following questions on your own first, then check your answers in Appendix E.

1. An episode of intense dread that can be accompanied by chest pains, choking, or other frightening sensations is called
   a. an obsession.
   b. a compulsion.
   c. a panic attack.
   d. a specific phobia.

2. Anxiety that takes the form of an irrational and maladaptive fear of a specific object, activity, or situation is called a _____.

3. Marina became consumed with the need to clean the entire house and refused to participate in any other activities. Her family consulted a therapist, who diagnosed her as having _____-_____ disorder.

4. When a person with an anxiety disorder eases anxiety by avoiding or escaping a situation that inspires fear, this is called
   a. free-floating anxiety.
   b. reinforcement.
   c. an epigenetic mark.
   d. hypervigilance.

5. The learning perspective proposes that phobias are
   a. the result of individual genetic makeup.
   b. a way of repressing unacceptable impulses.
   c. conditioned fears.
   d. a symptom of having been abused as a child.

Continue testing yourself with 📖 **LearningCurve** or 📖 **Achieve Read & Practice** to learn and remember most effectively.

42 Major Depressive Disorder and Bipolar Disorder

LOQ 42-1 How do major depressive disorder and bipolar disorder differ?

In the past year, have you at some time "felt so depressed that it was difficult to function"? If so, you were not alone. In one national survey, 31 percent of American college students answered *Yes* (ACHA, 2009). You may feel deeply discouraged about

"My life had come to a sudden stop. I was able to breathe, to eat, to drink, to sleep. I could not, indeed, help doing so; but there was no real life in me."
—Leo Tolstoy, *My Confession*, 1887

MINDING THE GUT Digestive system bacteria produce neurotransmitters that influence human emotions and social interactions. Healthy, diverse gut microbes can reduce the risk of anxiety, depression, and PTSD (Hemmings et al., 2017; Nowakowski et al., 2016).

"If someone offered you a pill that would make you permanently happy, you would be well advised to run fast and run far. Emotion is a compass that tells us what to do, and a compass that is perpetually stuck on NORTH is worthless." —Daniel Gilbert, "The Science of Happiness," 2006

 (ASK YOURSELF)

Can you think of a time when feeling temporarily depressed actually helped you in some way? Did your rumination enable you to re-evaluate your situation or make new plans?

"Depression is a silent, slow motion tsunami of dark breaking over me. I can't swim away from it." —Effy Redman, "Waiting for Depression to Lift," 2017

Brad Wenner/Getty Images

the future, dissatisfied with your life, or socially isolated. You may lack the energy to get things done, to see people, or even to force yourself out of bed. You may be unable to concentrate, eat, or sleep normally. You might even wonder if you would be better off dead. Perhaps academic success came easily to you before, but now you find that disappointing grades jeopardize your goals. Perhaps social stresses, such as loneliness, feeling you are the target of prejudice, or experiencing a romantic breakup, have plunged you into despair. And perhaps low self-esteem increases your brooding, worsening your self-torment (Orth et al., 2016). Likely you think you are more alone in having such negative feelings than you really are (Jordan et al., 2011). Most of us will have some direct or indirect experience with depression. Misery has more company than most suppose.

Anxiety is a response to the threat of future loss. Depression is often a response to past and current loss. To feel bad in reaction to profoundly sad events (such as the death of a loved one) is to be in touch with reality. In such times, depression is like a car's low-fuel light—a signal that warns us to stop and take appropriate measures. People with *major depressive disorder* experience hopelessness and lethargy lasting several weeks or months. Those with *bipolar disorder* (formerly called *manic-depressive disorder*) alternate between depression and overexcited hyperactivity.

Biologically speaking, life's purpose is survival and reproduction, not happiness. Coughing, vomiting, and various sorts of pain protect our body from dangerous toxins and stimuli. Depression similarly protects us, sending us into a sort of psychic hibernation. It slows us down, prompting us, when losing a relationship or blocked from a goal, to conserve energy (Beck & Bredemeier, 2016; Gershon et al., 2016). When we grind temporarily to a halt and reassess our life, as depressed people do, we can redirect our energy in more promising ways (Watkins, 2008). There is sense to suffering. Even mild sadness helps people process and recall faces more accurately (Hills et al., 2011). They also tend to pay more attention to details, think more critically (with less gullibility), and make better decisions (Forgas, 2009, 2013, 2017). Bad moods can serve good purposes. But sometimes depression becomes seriously maladaptive. How do we recognize the fine line between a blue mood and disabling depression?

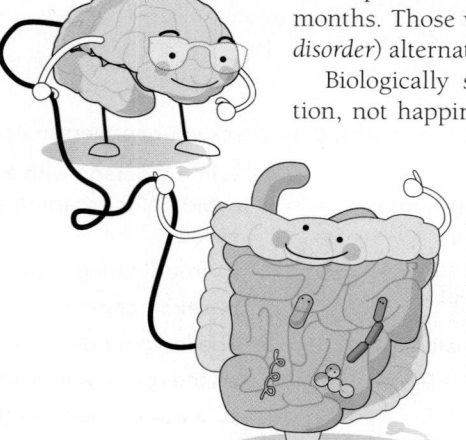

MAJOR DEPRESSIVE DISORDER

Joy, contentment, sadness, and despair exist at different points on a continuum, points at which any of us may find ourselves at any given moment. The difference between a blue mood after bad news and **major depressive disorder** is like the difference between breathing heavily after a hard run and being chronically exhausted. Major depressive disorder occurs when at least five signs of depression (including either depressed mood or loss of interest or pleasure) last two or more weeks (**TABLE 42.1**). To sense what major depressive disorder feels like, imagine combining the anguish of grief with the exhaustion you would feel after pulling an all-nighter.

Depression is the number-one reason people seek mental health services. Indeed, the World Health Organization declared depression "the leading cause of disability worldwide" (WHO, 2017a). In one survey conducted in 21 countries, 4.6 percent of people interviewed were experiencing moderate or severe depression (Thornicroft et al., 2017).

For some people, depressive symptoms may have a *seasonal pattern,* returning each winter. When asked, "Have you cried today?" Americans in one survey answered *Yes* doubly often in the winter (*Time/CNN*, 1994). But some researchers report that people in

TABLE 42.1

Diagnosing Major Depressive Disorder

The DSM-5 classifies major depressive disorder as the presence of at least five of the following symptoms over a 2-week period of time (minimally including depressed mood or reduced interest) (American Psychiatric Association, 2013).

- Depressed mood most of the time
- Dramatically reduced interest or enjoyment in most activities most of the time
- Significant challenges regulating appetite and weight
- Significant challenges regulating sleep
- Physical agitation or lethargy
- Feeling listless or with much less energy
- Feeling worthless, or feeling unwarranted guilt
- Problems in thinking, concentrating, or making decisions
- Thinking repetitively of death and suicide

major depressive disorder a disorder in which a person experiences, in the absence of drugs or another medical condition, two or more weeks with five or more symptoms, at least one of which must be either (1) depressed mood or (2) loss of interest or pleasure.

bipolar disorder a disorder in which a person alternates between the hopelessness and lethargy of depression and the overexcited state of mania. (Formerly called *manic-depressive disorder.*)

mania a hyperactive, wildly optimistic state in which dangerously poor judgment is common.

northerly or cloudier places do *not* experience more wintertime depression. Thus, they now question how often seasonal depression occurs (LoBello, 2017; Traffanstedt et al., 2016). So, stay tuned.

BIPOLAR DISORDER

Our genes dispose some of us, more than others, to respond emotionally to good and bad events (Whisman et al., 2014). In **bipolar disorder,** people bounce from one emotional extreme to the other (week to week, rather than day to day or moment to moment). When a depressive episode ends, a euphoric, overly talkative, and excessively optimistic state called **mania** follows. But before long, the elated mood either returns to normal or plunges again into depression.

If depression is living in slow motion, mania is fast forward. During the manic phase, people with bipolar disorder typically have little need for sleep. They show fewer sexual inhibitions. Their positive emotions persist abnormally (Gruber, 2011; Gruber et al., 2013). Their speech is loud, flighty, and hard to interrupt. They find advice irritating. Yet they need protection from their own poor judgment, which may lead to reckless spending or unsafe sex. Thinking fast feels good, but it also increases risk taking (Chandler & Pronin, 2012; Pronin, 2013).

Clusters of genes associated with creativity increase the likelihood of having bipolar disorder, and risk factors for developing bipolar disorder predict greater creativity (Baas et al., 2016; Power et al., 2015; Taylor, 2017). George Frideric Handel (1685–1759), who

BIPOLAR DISORDER Artist Abigail Southworth illustrated her experience of bipolar disorder.

CREATIVITY AND BIPOLAR DISORDER There have been many creative artists, composers, writers, and musical performers with bipolar disorder. Some, like Russell Brand, developed a substance abuse disorder as well. Others, like Virginia Woolf, turned to suicide.

Actor Russell Brand   Writer Virginia Woolf

many believe suffered from a mild form of bipolar disorder, composed his nearly four-hour-long *Messiah* during three weeks of intense, creative energy in 1742 (Keynes, 1980). Bipolar disorder strikes more often among those who rely on emotional expression and vivid imagery, such as poets and artists, and less often among those who rely on precision and logic, such as architects, designers, and journalists (Jamison, 1993, 1995; Kaufman & Baer, 2002; Ludwig, 1995). Indeed, one analysis of over a million individuals showed that the only psychiatric condition linked to working in a creative profession was bipolar disorder (Kyaga et al., 2013).

Bipolar disorder is much less common than major depressive disorder, but it is often more dysfunctional. It is also a potent predictor of suicide (Schaffer et al., 2015). Unlike major depressive disorder, for which women are at highest risk, bipolar disorder afflicts as many men as women. The diagnosis has risen among adolescents, whose mood swings, sometimes prolonged, may vary from raging to bubbly. In the decade between 1994 and 2003, bipolar diagnoses in under-20 Americans showed an astonishing 40-fold increase—from an estimated 20,000 to 800,000 (Carey, 2007; Flora & Bobby, 2008; Moreno et al., 2007). Americans are twice as likely as people elsewhere to have ever had a bipolar disorder diagnosis (Merikangas et al., 2011). The new DSM-5 classifications have, however, begun to reduce the number of child and adolescent bipolar diagnoses: Some of those who are persistently irritable and who have frequent and recurring behavior outbursts are now instead diagnosed with *disruptive mood dysregulation disorder* (Faheem et al., 2017).

UNDERSTANDING MAJOR DEPRESSIVE DISORDER AND BIPOLAR DISORDER

LOQ 42-2 How can the biological and social-cognitive perspectives help us understand major depressive disorder and bipolar disorder?

From thousands of studies of the causes, treatment, and prevention of major depressive disorder and bipolar disorder, researchers have pulled out some common threads. Here, we focus primarily on major depressive disorder. Any theory of depression must explain at least the following (Lewinsohn et al., 1985, 1998, 2003):

- *Behaviors and thoughts change with depression.* People trapped in a depressed mood become inactive and feel alone, empty, and without a bright or meaningful future (Bullock & Murray, 2014; Khazanov & Ruscio, 2016; Smith & Rhodes, 2014). They avoid positive information and attend selectively to negative events (Peckham et al., 2010; Winer & Salem, 2016). They more often recall negative information. And they expect negative outcomes (my team will lose, my grades will fall, my love will fail). When the depression lifts, these behaviors and thoughts disappear. Nearly half the time, people with depression also have symptoms of another disorder, such as anxiety or substance abuse.

- *Depression is widespread.* Worldwide, 350 million people have major depressive disorder and 60 million people have bipolar disorder (WHO, 2017c). At some point during their lifetime, depression has plagued 11 percent of Canadian 15- to 24-year-olds (Findlay, 2017). Depression's commonality suggests that its causes must also be common.

LIFE AFTER DEPRESSION Author J. K. Rowling reported suffering acute depression—a "dark time," with suicidal thoughts—between ages 25 and 28. It was a "terrible place," she said, but it formed a foundation that allowed her "to come back stronger" (McLaughlin, 2010).

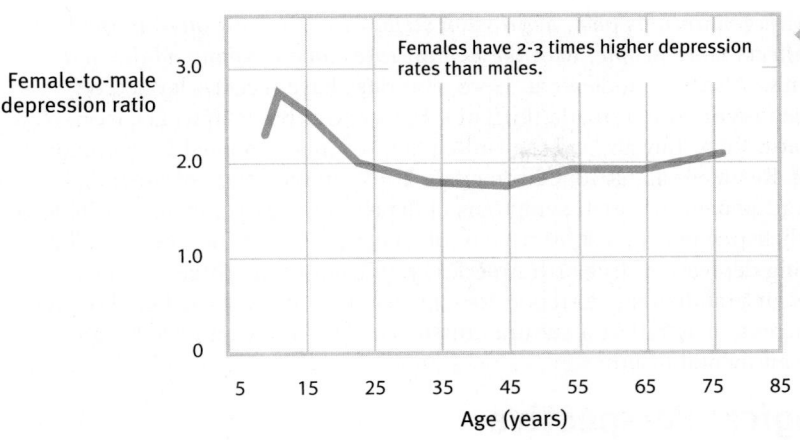

Female-to-male depression ratio

Females have 2-3 times higher depression rates than males.

Age (years)

FIGURE 42.1

FEMALE-TO-MALE DEPRESSION RATIO, WORLDWIDE Researchers Rachel Salk, Janet Hyde, and Lyn Abramson (2017) found that, compared with males, females have twice the risk of depression, and a nearly tripled rate during early adolescence. For many girls, being 13 to 15 years old is a tough time of life.

- **Women's risk of major depressive disorder is roughly double men's.** In 2009, when Gallup pollsters asked more than a quarter-million Americans if they had ever been diagnosed with depression, 13 percent of men and 22 percent of women said *Yes* (Pelham, 2009). When Gallup asked Americans if they had experienced sadness "during a lot of the day yesterday," 17 percent of men and 28 percent of women answered *Yes* (Mendes & McGeeney, 2012). A recent analysis of nearly 2 million people in 90 countries found that the depression gender gap is worldwide, and that it begins at puberty and peaks in early adolescence (Kuehner, 2017; see also **FIGURE 42.1**).

  The depression gender gap fits a bigger pattern: Women are generally more vulnerable to disorders involving internalized states, such as depression, anxiety, and inhibited sexual desire. Women experience more situations that increase their risk for depression, such as receiving less pay for equal work, juggling multiple roles, and caring for children and elderly family members (Freeman & Freeman, 2013). Men's disorders tend to be more external—alcohol use disorder, and disorders related to antisocial conduct and lack of impulse control. When women get sad, they often get sadder than men do. When men get mad, they often get madder than women do.

- **Most major depressive episodes end on their own.** Therapy often helps and tends to speed recovery. But even without professional help, most people recover from depression and return to normal. The black cloud of depression comes and, after sustained struggle, it often goes. For about half of those people, however, the dark cloud eventually returns (Curry et al., 2011; Klein & Kotov, 2016). The condition will be chronic for about 20 percent (Klein, 2010). On average, a person with major depressive disorder today will spend about three-fourths of the next decade in a normal, nondepressed state (Furukawa et al., 2009). In one study of over 20,000 Canadians, an enduring recovery was more likely if the first episode struck later in life, there was no prior history of depression, people experienced minimal physical or psychological stress, and they had ample social support (Fuller-Thomson et al., 2016).

- **Work, marriage, and relationship stresses often precede depression.** Experiencing childhood abuse doubles a person's risk of adult depression (Nelson et al., 2017). About 1 person in 4 diagnosed with depression has been brought down by a significant loss or trauma, such as a loved one's death, a ruptured marriage, a physical assault, or a lost job (Kendler et al., 2008; Monroe & Reid, 2009; Orth et al., 2009; Wakefield et al., 2007). Moving to a new culture also increases risk for depression, especially among younger people who have not yet formed their identities (Zhang et al., 2013). One long-term study tracked rates of depression in 2000 people (Kendler, 1998). Among those who had experienced no stressful life event in the preceding month, the risk of depression was less than 1 percent. Among those who had experienced three such events in that month, the risk was 24 percent. For some, grappling with life's minor daily stressors can also negatively affect mental health. People who overreacted to minor stressors, such as a broken appliance, were more often depressed 10 years later (Charles et al., 2013).

- *Compared with generations past, depression strikes earlier (now often in the late teens) and affects more people, with the highest rates among young adults in developed countries.* Although adolescent depression rates have recently leveled off, this trend has been reported in Canada, England, France, Germany, Italy, Lebanon, New Zealand, Puerto Rico, Taiwan, and the United States (Cross-National Collaborative Group, 1992; Kessler et al., 2010; Olfson et al., 2015). In one study of Australian adolescents, 12 percent reported symptoms of depression (Sawyer et al., 2000). Most hid it from their parents, almost 90 percent of whom perceived their depressed teen as *not* suffering depression. In North America, young adults are three times more likely than their grandparents to report having recently—or ever—suffered depression. This increase may reflect a cultural difference of today's young adults' greater openness about mental health.

The Biological Perspective

Depression is a whole-body disorder. It involves genetic predispositions, brain connectivity issues, and biochemical imbalances, as well as negative thoughts and a gloomy mood.

GENES AND DEPRESSION Major depressive disorder and bipolar disorder run in families. The risk of being diagnosed with one of these disorders increases if your parent or sibling has the disorder (Sullivan et al., 2000; Weissman et al., 2016). If one identical twin is diagnosed with major depressive disorder, the chances are about 1 in 2 that at some time the other twin will be, too. If one identical twin has bipolar disorder, the chances of a similar diagnosis for the co-twin are even higher—7 in 10—even for twins raised apart (DiLalla et al., 1996). Summarizing the major twin studies, one research team estimated the heritability of major depressive disorder—the extent to which individual differences are attributable to genes—at 40 percent (Polderman et al., 2015; see also **FIGURE 42.2** for another study's heritability findings for this and other disorders).

Emotions are "postcards from our genes" (Plotkin, 1994). To tease out the genes that put people at risk for depression, researchers may use *linkage analysis*. First, geneticists find families in which the disorder appears across several generations. Next, the researchers look for differences in DNA from affected and unaffected family members. Linkage analysis points them to a chromosome neighborhood; "A house-to-house search is then needed to find the culprit gene" (Plomin & McGuffin, 2003). But depression is a complex condition. Many genes work together, producing a mosaic of small effects that interact with other factors to put some people at greater risk. Researchers continue to identify culprit gene variations that may open the door to more effective drug therapy (Hyde et al., 2016; Power et al., 2017; Ripke et al., 2013).

THE DEPRESSED BRAIN Scanning devices let us eavesdrop on the brain's activity during depressed and manic states. During depression, brain activity slows; during mania, it increases (**FIGURE 42.3**). The left frontal lobe and an adjacent brain reward center become more active during positive emotions (Davidson et al., 2002; Heller et al., 2009; Robinson et al., 2012).

LaunchPad For a 9-minute story about one young man's struggle with depression, see the **Video: Depression.**

FIGURE 42.2

THE HERITABILITY OF VARIOUS PSYCHOLOGICAL DISORDERS Using aggregated data from studies of identical and fraternal twins, researchers estimated the heritability of bipolar disorder, schizophrenia, anorexia nervosa, major depressive disorder, and generalized anxiety disorder (Bienvenu et al., 2011). (Heritability was calculated by a formula that compares the extent of similarity among identical versus fraternal twins.)

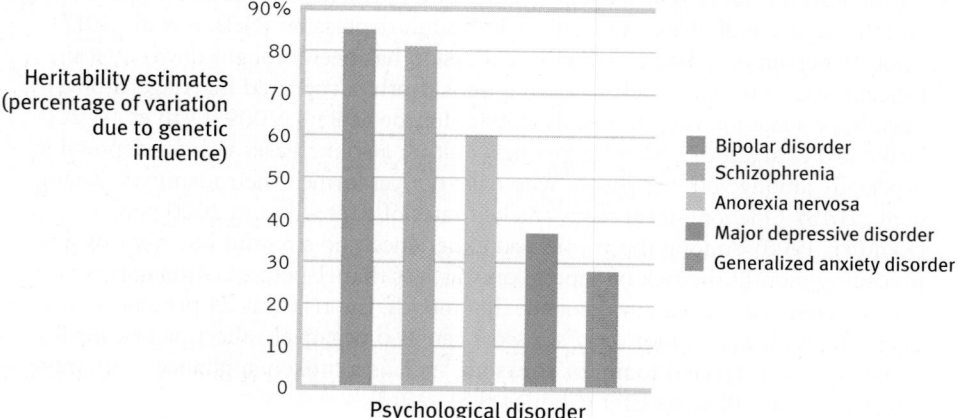

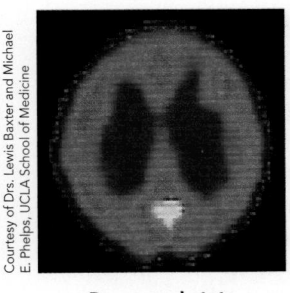
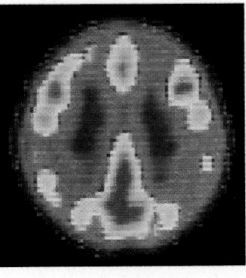
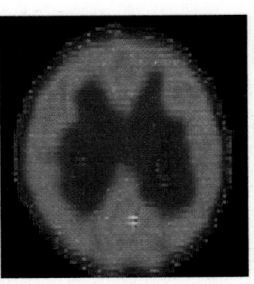

Depressed state
(May 17)

Manic state
(May 18)

Depressed state
(May 27)

FIGURE 42.3

THE UPS AND DOWNS OF BIPOLAR DISORDER These top-facing PET scans show that brain energy consumption rises and falls with the patient's emotional switches. Red areas are where the brain rapidly consumes *glucose*, an important energy source.

Analyses of *functional connectivity* help scientists understand how different brain regions work together, and can underlie psychological disorders. People with major depressive disorder tend to show low connectivity between brain regions involved in experiencing (a) emotion and (b) emotion regulation; these two types of brain regions don't "talk" to each other well (Kaiser et al., 2015). This poor neural communication may help explain why people with depression often struggle to regulate their emotions (Etkin et al., 2015; Miller et al., 2015).

At least two neurotransmitter systems are at work during the periods of brain inactivity and hyperactivity that accompany major depressive disorder and bipolar disorder. *Norepinephrine,* which increases arousal and boosts mood, is scarce during depression and over-abundant during mania. Drugs that decrease mania reduce norepinephrine.

Serotonin is also scarce or inactive during depression (Carver et al., 2008). Drugs that relieve depression tend to increase serotonin or norepinephrine supplies by blocking either their reuptake (as Prozac, Zoloft, and Paxil do with serotonin) or their chemical breakdown. Repetitive physical exercise, such as jogging, reduces depression in part because it increases serotonin (Airan et al., 2007; Harvey et al., 2018; Ilardi, 2009). In one study, running for two hours increased brain activation in regions associated with euphoria (Boecker et al., 2008). To get away from a bad mood, some people have used their own two feet.

NUTRITIONAL EFFECTS What's good for the heart is also good for the brain and mind. People who eat a heart-healthy "Mediterranean diet" (heavy on vegetables, fish, and olive oil) have a comparatively low risk of developing heart disease, stroke, late-life cognitive decline, and depression—all of which are associated with inflammation in the body (Kaplan et al., 2015; Psaltopoulou et al., 2013; Rechenberg, 2016). Excessive alcohol use also correlates with depression, partly because depression can increase alcohol use but mostly because alcohol misuse *leads to* depression (Fergusson et al., 2009).

The Social-Cognitive Perspective

Biological influences contribute to depression, but in the nature–nurture dance, our life experiences also play a part. Diet, drugs, stress, and other environmental influences lay down *epigenetic marks,* molecular genetic tags that can turn certain genes on or off. Animal studies suggested that long-lasting epigenetic influences may play a role in depression (Nestler, 2011).

Thinking matters, too. The *social-cognitive perspective* explores how people's assumptions and expectations influence what they perceive. Many depressed people see life through the dark glasses of low self-esteem (Orth et al., 2016). They have intensely negative views of themselves, their situation, and their future. Listen to Norman, a Canadian university professor, recalling his depression:

> I [despaired] of ever being human again. I honestly felt subhuman, lower than the lowest vermin. Furthermore, I . . . could not understand why anyone would want to associate with me, let alone love me. . . . I was positive that I was a fraud and a phony and that I didn't deserve my Ph.D. . . . I didn't deserve the research grants I had been awarded; I couldn't understand how I had written books and journal articles. . . . I must have conned a lot of people. (Endler, 1982, pp. 45–49)

Expecting the worst, depressed people magnify bad experiences and minimize good ones (Wenze et al., 2012). Their *self-defeating beliefs* and *negative explanatory style* feed their depression.

"I think I, like a lot of people, have that type of brain where I find it interesting or fulfilling to worry about something."
—Comedian Maria Bamford

RUMINATION RUNS WILD It's normal to think about our flaws. But dwelling constantly on negative thoughts—particularly negative thoughts about ourselves—makes it difficult to believe in ourselves and solve problems. People sometimes seek therapy to reduce their rumination.

NEGATIVE THOUGHTS, NEGATIVE MOODS, AND GENDER Why are women nearly twice as vulnerable as men to depression, and twice as likely to take antidepressant drugs (Pratt et al., 2017)? Women may respond more strongly to stress (Hankin & Abramson, 2001; Mazure et al., 2002; Nolen-Hoeksema, 2001, 2003). Do you agree or disagree that you "at least occasionally feel overwhelmed by all I have to do"? In a survey of women and men, 38 percent of women, but only 17 percent of men, agreed (Pryor et al., 2006). Relationship stresses also affect teen girls more than boys (Hamilton et al., 2015).

Susan Nolen-Hoeksema (2003) related women's higher risk of depression to what she described as their tendency to ruminate or *overthink*. Staying focused on a problem—thanks to the continuous activation of an attention-sustaining frontal lobe area—can be adaptive (Altamirano et al., 2010; Andrews & Thomson, 2009a,b). But relentless, self-focused **rumination** can distract us, increase negative emotions, and disrupt daily activities (Johnson et al., 2016; Leary, 2018; Yang et al., 2017). Comparisons can also feed misery. While Josh is happily playing video games, lonely Lauren scrolls through her social media feed and sees Maria having a blast at a party, Angelique enjoying a family vacation, and Tyra looking super in a swimsuit. In response, Lauren broods: "My life is terrible."

Even so, why do life's unavoidable failures lead only some people to become depressed? The answer lies partly in their *explanatory style*—who or what they blame for their failures. Think of how you might feel if you failed a test. If you can blame someone else ("What an unfair test!"), you are more likely to feel angry. If you blame yourself, you probably will feel stupid and depressed.

Depression-prone people respond to bad events in an especially self-focused, self-blaming way (Huang, 2015; Mor & Winquist, 2002; Wood et al., 1990a,b). As **FIGURE 42.4** illustrates, they explain bad events in terms that are *stable* ("I'll never get over this"), *global* ("I can't do anything right"), and *internal* ("It's all my fault").

Self-defeating beliefs may arise from *learned helplessness,* the hopelessness and passive resignation humans and other animals learn when they experience uncontrollable painful events (Maier & Seligman, 2016). Pessimistic, overgeneralized, self-blaming attributions may create a depressing sense of hopelessness (Abramson et al., 1989; Groß et al., 2017). As Martin Seligman has noted, "A recipe for severe depression is preexisting pessimism encountering failure" (1991, p. 78). What, then, might we expect of new college students who exhibit a pessimistic explanatory style? Lauren Alloy and her colleagues (1999) monitored several hundred students every 6 weeks for 2.5 years. Among those identified as having a pessimistic thinking style, 17 percent had a first episode of major depression, as did only 1 percent of those who began college with an optimistic thinking style.

FIGURE 42.4

EXPLANATORY STYLE AND DEPRESSION After a negative experience, a depression-prone person may respond with a negative explanatory style.

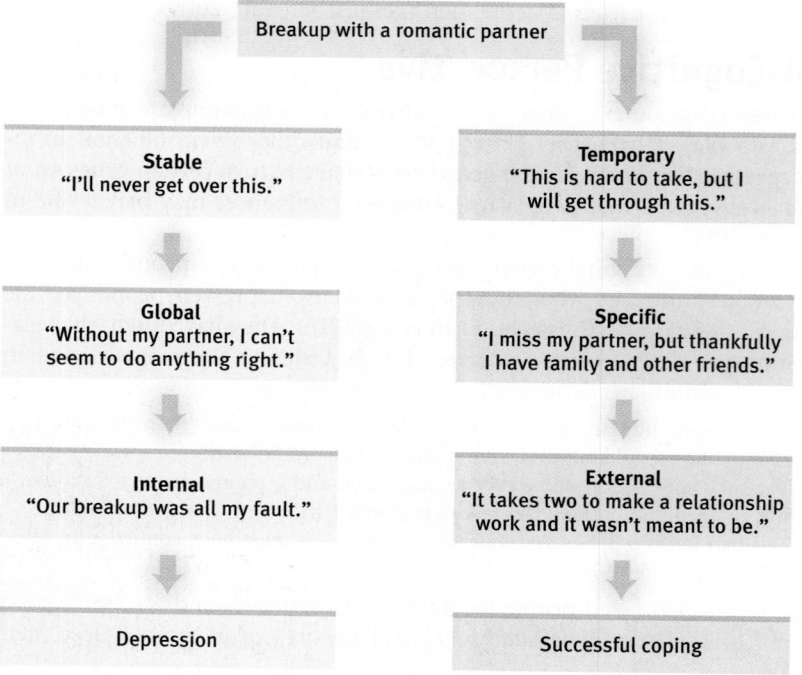

LaunchPad To explore your own thinking style, engage online with **Immersive Learning: Assess Your Strengths—How Hopeful Are You? Why Is This Important?**

rumination compulsive fretting; *over-thinking* our problems and their causes.

Critics note a chicken-and-egg problem nesting in the social-cognitive explanation of depression. Which comes first? The pessimistic explanatory style, or the depressed mood? The negative explanations *coincide* with a depressed mood, and they are *indicators* of depression. (Before or after being depressed, people's thoughts are less negative.) But do negative thoughts *cause* depression, any more than a speedometer's reading causes a car's speed? Perhaps a depressed mood triggers negative thoughts. If you temporarily put people in a bad or sad mood, their memories, judgments, and expectations suddenly become more pessimistic—a phenomenon that memory researchers call *state-dependent memory.*

Cultural forces may also nudge people toward or away from depression. Why is depression so common among young Westerners? Seligman (1991, 1995) has pointed to the rise of individualism and the decline of commitment to religion and family. In non-Western cultures, where close-knit relationships and cooperation are the norm, major depressive disorder is less common and less tied to self-blame over personal failure (Ferrari et al., 2013). In Japan, for example, depressed people instead tend to report feeling shame over letting others down (Draguns, 1990).

DEPRESSION'S VICIOUS CYCLE No matter which comes first, rejection and depression feed each other. Depression is both a cause and an effect of stressful experiences that disrupt our sense of who we are and why we are worthy. Such disruptions can lead to brooding, which is rich soil for growing negative feelings. And that negativity—being withdrawn, self-focused, and complaining—can by itself cause others to reject us (Furr & Funder, 1998; Gotlib & Hammen, 1992). Indeed, people deep in depression are at high risk for divorce, job loss, and other stressful life events. Weary of the person's fatigue, hopeless attitude, and negativity, a spouse may threaten to leave, or a boss may begin to question the person's competence. New losses and stress then plunge the already-depressed person into even deeper misery. Misery may love another's company, but company does not love another's misery.

We can now assemble pieces of the depression puzzle (**FIGURE 42.5**): (1) Stressful experiences interpreted through (2) a brooding, negative explanatory style create (3) a hopeless, depressed state that (4) hampers the way the person thinks and acts. These thoughts and actions, in turn, fuel (1) further stressful experiences such as rejection. Depression is a snake that bites its own tail.

It is a cycle we can all recognize. When we feel down, we think negatively and remember bad experiences. Britain's Prime Minister Winston Churchill called depression a "black dog" that periodically hounded him. Abraham Lincoln was so withdrawn and brooding as a young man that his friends feared he might take his own life (Kline, 1974). Olympic swimming gold medalists Michael Phelps and Grant Hackett have both battled anxiety and depression (Crouse, 2017). As their lives remind us, people can and do struggle through depression. Most regain their capacity to love, to work, and even to succeed at the highest levels.

"You should never engage in unsupervised introspection."

1
Stressful experiences

4
Cognitive and behavioral changes

2
Negative explanatory style

3
Depressed mood

FIGURE 42.5

THE VICIOUS CYCLE OF DEPRESSED THINKING Therapists recognize this cycle, and they work to help depressed people break out of it by changing their negative thinking, turning their attention outward, and engaging them in more pleasant and competent behavior.

🔒 **RETRIEVE IT • • •**

ANSWERS IN APPENDIX E

RI-1 What does it mean to say that "depression is a whole-body disorder"?

🔒 **REVIEW** MAJOR DEPRESSIVE DISORDER AND BIPOLAR DISORDER

⤜⟩ Learning Objectives

TEST YOURSELF Answer these repeated Learning Objective Questions on your own (before checking the answers in Appendix D) to improve your retention of the concepts (McDaniel et al., 2009, 2015).

42-1 How do major depressive disorder and bipolar disorder differ?

42-2 How can the biological and social-cognitive perspectives help us understand major depressive disorder and bipolar disorder?

⤜⟩ Terms and Concepts to Remember

TEST YOURSELF Write down the definition yourself, then check your answer on the referenced page.

major depressive disorder, **p. 515**

mania, **p. 515**

bipolar disorder, **p. 515**

rumination, **p. 521**

⤜⟩ Experience the Testing Effect

TEST YOURSELF Answer the following questions on your own first, then check your answers in Appendix E.

1. The gender gap in depression refers to the finding that _____ (men's/women's) risk of depression is roughly double that of _____ (men's/women's).

2. Rates of bipolar disorder in the United States rose dramatically in the decade between 1994 and 2003, especially among
   a. middle-aged women.
   b. middle-aged men.
   c. people 20 and over.
   d. people 20 and under.

3. Treatment for depression often includes drugs that increase supplies of the neurotransmitters _____ and _____.

4. Psychologists who emphasize the importance of negative perceptions, beliefs, and thoughts in depression are working within the _____-_____ perspective.

Continue testing yourself with 📖 **LearningCurve** or 📖 **Achieve Read & Practice** to learn and remember most effectively.

⒋⒊ Schizophrenia and Other Disorders

SCHIZOPHRENIA

schizophrenia a disorder characterized by delusions, hallucinations, disorganized speech, and/or diminished, inappropriate emotional expression.

psychotic disorders a group of disorders marked by irrational ideas, distorted perceptions, and a loss of contact with reality.

During their most severe periods, people with **schizophrenia** live in a private inner world, preoccupied with the strange ideas and images that haunt them. The word itself means "split" (*schizo*) "mind" (*phrenia*). It refers *not* to a multiple personality split but rather to the mind's split from reality, as shown in disturbed perceptions and beliefs, disorganized speech, and diminished, inappropriate emotions. Schizophrenia is the chief example of a **psychotic disorder,** a group of disorders marked by irrationality, distorted perceptions, and lost contact with reality.

As you can imagine, these characteristics profoundly disrupt relationships and work. Given a supportive environment and medication, over 40 percent of people with schizophrenia will have periods of a year or more of normal life experience (Jobe & Harrow, 2010). But only 1 in 7 experience a full and enduring recovery (Jääskeläinen et al., 2013).

Symptoms of Schizophrenia

LOQ 43-1 What patterns of perceiving, thinking, and feeling characterize schizophrenia?

Schizophrenia comes in varied forms. People with schizophrenia display symptoms that are *positive* (*inappropriate* behaviors are *present*) or negative (*appropriate* behaviors are *absent*). Those with positive symptoms may experience disturbed perceptions, talk in disorganized and deluded ways, or exhibit inappropriate laughter, tears, or rage. Those with negative symptoms may exhibit an absence of emotion in their voices, expressionless faces, or unmoving—mute and rigid—bodies.

DISTURBED PERCEPTIONS AND BELIEFS People with schizophrenia sometimes *hallucinate*—they see, hear, feel, taste, or smell things that exist only in their minds. Most often, the hallucinations are voices, which sometimes make insulting remarks or give orders. The voices may tell the person that she is bad or that she must burn herself with a cigarette lighter. Imagine your own reaction if a dream broke into your waking consciousness, making it hard to separate your experience from your imagination. When the unreal seems real, the resulting perceptions are at best bizarre, at worst terrifying.

Hallucinations are false *perceptions*. People with schizophrenia also have disorganized, fragmented thinking, often distorted by false *beliefs* called **delusions.** If they have *paranoid* tendencies, they may believe they are being threatened or pursued.

One cause of disorganized thinking may be a breakdown in *selective attention*. Normally, we have a remarkable capacity for giving our undivided attention to one set of sensory stimuli while filtering out others. People with schizophrenia are easily distracted by tiny unrelated stimuli, such as the grooves on a brick or the tones in a voice. This selective-attention difficulty is but one of dozens of cognitive differences associated with schizophrenia (Reichenberg & Harvey, 2007).

DISORGANIZED SPEECH Maxine, a young woman with schizophrenia, believed she was Mary Poppins. Communicating with Maxine was difficult because her thoughts spilled out in no logical order. Her biographer, Susan Sheehan (1982, p. 25), observed her saying aloud to no one in particular, "This morning, when I was at Hillside [Hospital], I was making a movie. I was surrounded by movie stars. . . . I'm Mary Poppins. Is this room painted blue to get me upset? My grandmother died four weeks after my eighteenth birthday."

Jumbled ideas may make no sense even within sentences, forming what is known as *word salad*. One young man begged for "a little more allegro in the treatment," and suggested that "liberationary movement with a view to the widening of the horizon" will "ergo extort some wit in lectures."

DIMINISHED AND INAPPROPRIATE EMOTIONS The expressed emotions of schizophrenia are often utterly inappropriate, split off from reality (Kring & Caponigro, 2010). Maxine laughed after recalling her grandmother's death. On other occasions, she cried when others laughed, or became angry for no apparent reason. Others with schizophrenia lapse into an emotionless *flat affect* state of no apparent feeling. For example, monetary perks fail to provide the normal brain reward center activation (Radua et al., 2015). Most also have an *impaired theory of mind*—they have difficulty reading other people's facial expressions and state of mind (Green & Horan, 2010; Kohler et al., 2010). Unable to understand others' mental states, those with schizophrenia struggle to feel sympathy and compassion (Bonfils et al., 2016). These emotional deficiencies occur early in the illness and have a genetic basis (Bora & Pantelis, 2013). *Motor behavior* may also be inappropriate and disruptive. Those with schizophrenia may experience *catatonia*, characterized by motor behaviors ranging from a physical stupor—remaining motionless for hours—to senseless, compulsive actions, such as continually rocking or rubbing an arm, to severe and dangerous agitation.

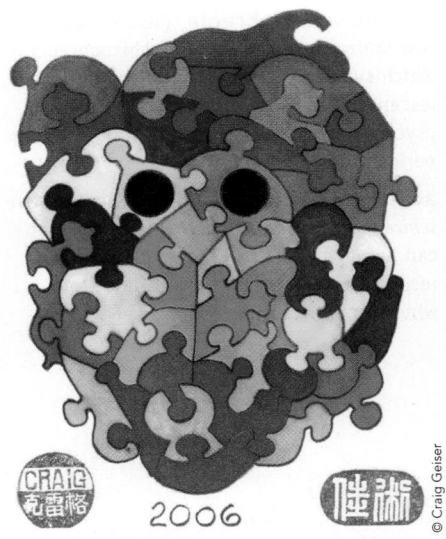

© Craig Geiser

ART BY SOMEONE DIAGNOSED WITH SCHIZOPHRENIA Commenting on the kind of artwork shown here (from Craig Geiser's 2010 art exhibit in Michigan), poet and art critic John Ashbery (1927–2017) wrote: "The lure of the work is strong, but so is the terror of the unanswerable riddles it proposes."

"Now consider this: The regulator that funnels certain information to you and filters out other information suddenly shuts off. Immediately, every sight, every sound, every smell coming at you carries equal weight; every thought, feeling, memory, and idea presents itself to you with an equally strong and demanding intensity." —Elyn R. Saks, *The Center Cannot Hold*, 2007

delusion a false belief, often of persecution or grandeur, that may accompany psychotic disorders.

chronic schizophrenia (also called *process schizophrenia*) a form of schizophrenia in which symptoms usually appear by late adolescence or early adulthood. As people age, psychotic episodes last longer and recovery periods shorten.

acute schizophrenia (also called *reactive schizophrenia*) a form of schizophrenia that can begin at any age, frequently occurs in response to a traumatic event, and from which recovery is much more likely.

Onset and Development of Schizophrenia

LOQ 43-2 How do *chronic schizophrenia* and *acute schizophrenia* differ?

This year, 1 in 100 people will join an estimated 21 million others worldwide who have schizophrenia (WHO, 2017c). This disorder knows no national boundaries and typically strikes as young people are maturing into adulthood. Men tend to be struck earlier, more severely, and more often (Aleman et al., 2003; Eranti et al., 2013; Picchioni & Murray, 2007).

When schizophrenia is a slow-developing process, called **chronic schizophrenia,** recovery is doubtful (Harrison et al., 2001; Jääskeläinen et al., 2013). This was the case with Maxine, whose schizophrenia took a slow course, emerging from a long history of social inadequacy and poor school performance (MacCabe et al., 2008). Social withdrawal, a negative symptom, is often found among those with chronic schizophrenia (Kirkpatrick et al., 2006). Men, whose schizophrenia develops on average four years earlier than women's, more often exhibit negative symptoms and chronic schizophrenia (Räsänen et al., 2000).

When previously well-adjusted people develop schizophrenia rapidly following particular life stresses, this is called **acute schizophrenia,** and recovery is much more likely. They more often have positive symptoms that respond to drug therapy (Fenton & McGlashan, 1991, 1994; Fowles, 1992).

Understanding Schizophrenia

Schizophrenia is one of the most heavily researched psychological disorders. Most studies now link it with abnormal brain tissue and genetic predispositions. Schizophrenia is a disease of the brain manifested in symptoms of the mind.

BRAIN ABNORMALITIES

LOQ 43-3 What brain abnormalities are associated with schizophrenia?

Might chemical imbalances in the brain explain schizophrenia? Scientists have long known that strange behavior can have strange chemical causes. Have you ever heard the saying "as mad as a hatter"? That phrase is often thought to refer to the psychological deterioration of British hat makers whose brains, it was later discovered, were slowly poisoned by the mercury-laden felt material (Smith, 1983). Could schizophrenia symptoms have a similar biochemical key? Scientists are searching for blood proteins that might predict schizophrenia onset (Chan et al., 2015). And they are tracking the mechanisms by which chemicals produce hallucinations and other symptoms.

DOPAMINE OVERACTIVITY One possible answer emerged when researchers examined schizophrenia patients' brains after death. They found an excess number of *dopamine* receptors, including a sixfold excess for the dopamine receptor D4 (Seeman et al., 1993; Wong et al., 1986). The resulting hyper-responsive dopamine system could intensify brain signals, creating positive symptoms such as hallucinations and paranoia (Maia & Frank, 2017). Drugs that block dopamine receptors often lessen these symptoms. Drugs that increase dopamine levels, such as nicotine, amphetamines, and cocaine, sometimes intensify them (Basu & Basu, 2015; Farnia et al., 2014).

ABNORMAL BRAIN ACTIVITY AND ANATOMY Abnormal brain activity and brain structures accompany schizophrenia. Some people diagnosed with schizophrenia have abnormally low brain activity in the brain's frontal lobes, which help us reason, plan, and solve problems (Morey et al., 2005; Pettegrew et al., 1993; Resnick, 1992). The brain waves that reflect synchronized neural firing in the frontal lobes decline noticeably (Spencer et al., 2004; Symond et al., 2005).

One study took PET scans of brain activity while people with schizophrenia were hallucinating (Silbersweig et al., 1995). When participants heard a voice or saw something, their brain became vigorously active in several core regions. One was the thalamus, the structure that filters incoming sensory signals and transmits them to the brain's cortex. Another PET scan study of people with paranoia found increased activity in the amygdala, a fear-processing center (Epstein et al., 1998).

Most people with schizophrenia smoke, which stimulates brain activity that helps focus their attention. But their smoking contributes to people with schizophrenia having a 14.5 year shorter-than-average life expectancy (Hjorthøj et al., 2017; Zhuo et al., 2017).

Many studies have also found enlarged, fluid-filled ventricles and a corresponding shrinkage and thinning of cerebral tissue (Goldman et al., 2009; van Haren et al., 2016). People often inherit these brain differences. If one affected identical twin shows brain abnormalities, the odds are at least 1 in 2 that the other twin's brain will have them (van Haren et al., 2012). Some studies have even found these abnormalities in people who *later* developed the disorder (Karlsgodt et al., 2010). The greater the brain shrinkage, the more severe the thought disorder (Collinson et al., 2003; Nelson et al., 1998; Shenton, 1992).

Smaller-than-normal areas may include the cortex, the hippocampus, and the corpus callosum connecting the brain's two hemispheres (Arnone et al., 2008; Bois et al., 2016). Often, the thalamus is also smaller than normal, which may explain why filtering sensory input and focusing attention can be difficult for people with schizophrenia (Andreasen et al., 1994; Ellison-Wright et al., 2008). Schizophrenia also tends to involve a loss of neural connections across the brain network (Bohlken et al., 2016; Kambeitz et al., 2016). *The bottom line:* Schizophrenia involves not one isolated brain abnormality but problems with several brain regions and their interconnections (Andreasen, 1997, 2001; Arnedo et al., 2015).

PRENATAL ENVIRONMENT AND RISK

LOQ 43-4 What prenatal events are associated with increased risk of developing schizophrenia?

What causes these brain abnormalities seen in people with schizophrenia? Some scientists point to mishaps during prenatal development or delivery (Fatemi & Folsom, 2009; Walker et al., 2010). Risk factors include low birth weight, maternal diabetes, older paternal age, and oxygen deprivation during delivery (King et al., 2010). Famine may also increase risks. People conceived during the peak of World War II's Dutch famine later developed schizophrenia at twice the normal rate. Those conceived during the famine of 1959 to 1961 in eastern China also displayed this doubled rate (St. Clair et al., 2005; Susser et al., 1996).

Let's consider another possible culprit. Might a midpregnancy viral infection impair fetal brain development (Brown & Patterson, 2011)? To test this fetal-virus idea, scientists have asked these questions:

- *Are people at increased risk of schizophrenia if, during the middle of their fetal development, their country experienced a flu epidemic?* The repeated answer has been *Yes* (Mednick et al., 1994; Murray et al., 1992; Wright et al., 1995).

- *Are people born in densely populated areas, where viral diseases spread more readily, at greater risk for schizophrenia?* The answer, confirmed in a study of 1.75 million Danes, has again been *Yes* (Jablensky, 1999; Mortensen, 1999).

- *Are people born during the winter and spring months—those who were in utero during the fall-winter flu season—also at increased risk?* The answer is again *Yes* (Fox, 2010; Schwartz, 2011; Torrey & Miller, 2002; Torrey et al., 1997).

- *In the Southern Hemisphere, where the seasons are the reverse of the Northern Hemisphere, are the months of above-average pre-schizophrenia births similarly reversed?* Again, the answer has been *Yes*. In Australia, people born between August and October are at greater risk. But people born in the Northern Hemisphere who later moved to Australia still have a greater risk if they were born between January and March (McGrath et al., 1995; McGrath & Welham, 1999).

- *Are mothers who report being sick with influenza during pregnancy more likely to bear children who develop schizophrenia?* In one study of nearly 8000 women, the answer was *Yes*. The schizophrenia risk increased from the customary 1 percent to about 2 percent—but only when infections occurred during the second trimester (Brown et al., 2000). Maternal influenza infection during pregnancy affects brain development in monkeys as well (Short et al., 2010).

- *Does blood drawn from pregnant women whose offspring develop schizophrenia show higher-than-normal levels of antibodies that suggest a viral infection?* In several studies, the answer has again been *Yes* (Brown et al., 2004; Buka et al., 2001; Canetta et al., 2014).

STUDYING THE NEUROPHYSIOLOGY OF SCHIZOPHRENIA Psychiatrist E. Fuller Torrey has collected the brains of hundreds of people who died as young adults and suffered disorders such as schizophrenia and bipolar disorder.

These converging lines of evidence suggest that fetal-virus infections contribute to the development of schizophrenia. This finding strengthens the U.S. government recommendation that "pregnant women need a flu shot" (CDC, 2014b).

GENETIC INFLUENCES

LOQ 43-5   How do genes influence schizophrenia?

Fetal-virus infections may increase the odds that a child will develop schizophrenia. But many women get the flu during their second trimester of pregnancy, and only 2 percent of them bear children who develop schizophrenia. Why does prenatal exposure to the flu virus put some children at risk but not others? Might some people be more genetically vulnerable to schizophrenia? *Yes.* The 1-in-100 odds of any one person being diagnosed with schizophrenia become about 1 in 10 among those who have a sibling or parent with the disorder. If the affected sibling is an identical twin, the odds increase to nearly 1 in 2 (**FIGURE 43.1**). Those odds are unchanged even when the twins are reared apart (Plomin et al., 1997). (Only about a dozen such cases are on record.)

Remember, though, that identical twins share more than their genes. They also share a prenatal environment. About two-thirds also share a placenta and the blood it supplies; the other third have separate placentas. Shared placentas matter. If the co-twin of an identical twin with schizophrenia shared the placenta, the chances of developing the disorder are 6 in 10. If the identical twins had separate placentas, the co-twin's chances of developing schizophrenia drop to 1 in 10 (Davis et al., 1995; Davis & Phelps, 1995; Phelps et al., 1997). Twins who share a placenta are more likely to share the same prenatal viruses. So perhaps shared germs as well as shared genes produce identical twin similarities.

Adoption studies help untangle genetic and environmental influences. Children adopted by someone who develops schizophrenia do not "catch" the disorder. Rather, adopted children have a higher risk if a *biological* parent has schizophrenia (Gottesman, 1991). Genes matter.

The search is on for specific genes that, in some combination, predispose schizophrenia-inducing brain abnormalities (**FIGURE 43.2**). (It is not our genes but our brains that directly control our behavior.) In the biggest-ever study of the genetics of psychiatric disorder, scientists from 35 countries pooled data from the genomes of 37,000 people with schizophrenia and 113,000 people without (Balter, 2017; Schizophrenia Working Group, 2014). They found 103 genome locations linked with the disorder. Some of these genes influence the activity of dopamine and other brain neurotransmitters. Others affect the production of *myelin,* a fatty substance that coats the axons of nerve cells and lets impulses travel at high speed through neural networks.

Although genes matter, the genetic formula is not as straightforward as the inheritance of eye color. Schizophrenia is a group of disorders influenced by many genes, each with very small effects (Arnedo et al., 2015; Darby et al., 2016; International Schizophrenia Consortium, 2009). As we have seen in so many different contexts, nature and nurture interact. Recall that *epigenetic* factors influence whether genes will be expressed. Like hot water activating a tea bag, environmental factors such as viral infections, nutritional deprivation, and maternal stress can "turn on" the genes that put some of us at higher risk for this disorder. Identical twins' differing histories in the womb and beyond explain why they may show differing gene expressions (Dempster et al., 2013; Walker et al., 2010). Our heredity and our life experiences work together. Neither hand claps alone.

LaunchPad See the **Video: Twin Studies** for a helpful tutorial animation about this type of research design.

FIGURE 43.1

RISK OF DEVELOPING SCHIZOPHRENIA   The lifetime risk of developing schizophrenia varies with one's genetic relatedness to someone having this disorder. Across countries, barely more than 1 in 10 fraternal twins, but some 5 in 10 identical twins, share a schizophrenia diagnosis. (Data from Gottesman, 2001.)

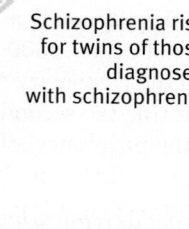

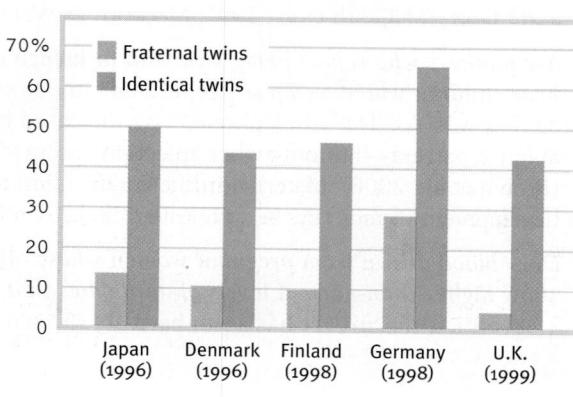

Schizophrenia risk for twins of those diagnosed with schizophrenia

- Fraternal twins
- Identical twins

Japan (1996)   Denmark (1996)   Finland (1998)   Germany (1998)   U.K. (1999)

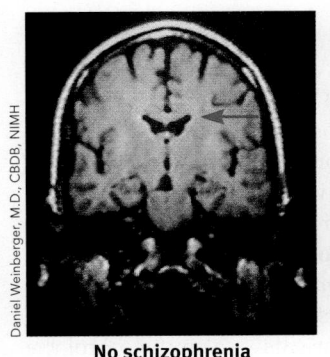 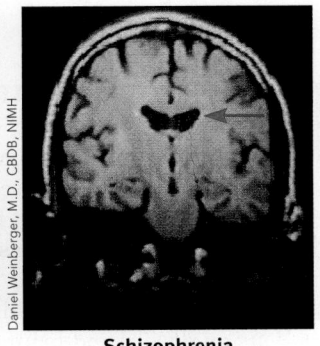

No schizophrenia
(a)

Schizophrenia
(b)

FIGURE 43.2

SCHIZOPHRENIA IN IDENTICAL TWINS When twins differ, only the one afflicted with schizophrenia typically has enlarged, fluid-filled cranial cavities (b) (Suddath et al., 1990). The difference between the twins implies some nongenetic factor, such as a virus, is also at work.

Thanks to our expanding understanding of genetic and brain influences on maladies such as schizophrenia, the general public increasingly recognizes the potency of biological factors in psychiatric disorders (Pescosolido et al., 2010).

LaunchPad Take the role of a researcher studying these issues by engaging online with **Immersive Learning: How Would You Know If Schizophrenia Is Inherited?**

* * *

Few of us can relate to the strange thoughts, perceptions, and behaviors of schizophrenia. Sometimes our thoughts jump around, but we rarely talk nonsensically. Occasionally we feel unjustly suspicious of someone, but we do not believe the world is plotting against us. Often our perceptions err, but rarely do we see or hear things that are not there. We feel regret after laughing at someone's misfortune, but we rarely giggle in response to our own bad news. At times we just want to be alone, but we do not retreat into fantasy worlds. However, millions of people around the world do talk strangely, suffer delusions, hear nonexistent voices, see things that are not there, laugh or cry at inappropriate times, or withdraw into private imaginary worlds. The quest to solve the cruel puzzle of schizophrenia continues, more vigorously than ever.

LaunchPad For an 8-minute description of how clinicians define and treat schizophrenia, see the **Video: Schizophrenia—New Definitions, New Therapies.**

🔒 **RETRIEVE IT • • •**   *ANSWERS IN APPENDIX E*

RI-1 A person with schizophrenia who has _____ (positive/negative) symptoms may have an expressionless face and toneless voice. These symptoms are most common with _____ (chronic/acute) schizophrenia and are not likely to respond to drug therapy. Those with _____ (positive/negative) symptoms are likely to experience delusions and to be diagnosed with _____ (chronic/acute) schizophrenia, which is much more likely to respond to drug therapy.

RI-2 What factors contribute to the onset and development of schizophrenia?

OTHER DISORDERS

Dissociative Disorders

LOQ 43-6 What are *dissociative disorders*, and why are they controversial?

Among the most bewildering disorders are the rare **dissociative disorders,** in which a person's conscious awareness *dissociates* (separates) from painful memories, thoughts, and feelings. The result may be a *fugue state,* a sudden loss of memory or change in identity, often in response to an overwhelmingly stressful situation (Harrison et al., 2017). Such was the case for one Vietnam veteran who was haunted by his comrades' deaths, and who had left his World Trade Center office shortly before the 9/11 terrorist attack. Later, he disappeared. Six months later, when he was discovered in a Chicago homeless shelter, he reported no memory of his identity or family (Stone, 2006).

ASK YOURSELF

Can you recall a time when you heard something or someone casually described as "schizophrenic"? Now that you know more about this disorder, how might you correct such descriptions?

dissociative disorders controversial, rare disorders in which conscious awareness becomes separated (dissociated) from previous memories, thoughts, and feelings.

MULTIPLE IDENTITIES IN THE MOVIES Chris Sizemore's story, told in the book and movie *The Three Faces of Eve*, gave early visibility to what is now called dissociative identity disorder. This controversial disorder continues to influence modern media, as in the 2017 movie *Split*, where "Kevin" (James McAvoy), pictured here, displays 24 different personalities.

DISSOCIATIVE IDENTITY DISORDER Dissociation itself is not so rare. Any one of us may have a fleeting sense of being unreal, of being separated from our body, of watching ourselves as if in a movie. A massive dissociation of self from ordinary consciousness is said to occur in **dissociative identity disorder** (**DID**—formerly called *multiple personality disorder*), in which two or more distinct identities—each with its own voice and mannerisms—seem to control the person's behavior. Thus, the person may be prim and proper one moment, loud and flirtatious the next. Typically, the original identity denies any awareness of the other(s).

People diagnosed with DID are rarely violent. But cases have been reported of dissociations into a "good" and a "bad" (or aggressive) identity—a modest version of the Dr. Jekyll–Mr. Hyde split immortalized in Robert Louis Stevenson's story. One unusual case involved Kenneth Bianchi, accused in the "Hillside Strangler" rapes and murders of 10 California women. During a hypnosis session, Bianchi's psychologist "called forth" a hidden identity: "I've talked a bit to Ken, but I think that perhaps there might be another part of Ken that . . . maybe feels somewhat differently from the part that I've talked to. . . . Would you talk with me, Part, by saying, 'I'm here'?" Bianchi answered "Yes" and then claimed to be "Steve" (Watkins, 1984).

Speaking as Steve, Bianchi stated that he hated Ken because Ken was nice and that he (Steve), aided by a cousin, had murdered women. He also claimed Ken knew nothing about Steve's existence and was innocent of the murders. Was Bianchi's second identity a trick, simply a way of disavowing responsibility for his actions? Indeed, Bianchi—a practiced liar who had read about this disorder in psychology books—was later convicted.

UNDERSTANDING DISSOCIATIVE IDENTITY DISORDER Skeptics question DID. They find it suspicious that the disorder has such a short and localized history. Between 1930 and 1960, the number of North American DID diagnoses averaged 2 per decade. By the 1980s, when the American Psychiatric Association's *Diagnostic and Statistical Manual of Mental Disorders* (DSM) contained the first formal code for this disorder, the number had exploded to more than 20,000 (McHugh, 1995). The average number of displayed identities also mushroomed—from 3 to 12 per patient (Goff & Simms, 1993). And although diagnoses have been increasing in countries where DID has been publicized, the disorder is much less prevalent outside North America (Lilienfeld, 2017).

Skeptics have also asked if DID could be an extension of our normal capacity for identity shifts. Nicholas Spanos (1986, 1994, 1996) asked college students to pretend they were accused murderers being examined by a psychiatrist. Given the same hypnotic treatment Bianchi received, most spontaneously expressed a second identity. This discovery made Spanos wonder: Perhaps dissociative identities are simply a more extreme version of the varied "selves" we normally present—to our friends, say, versus our grandparents. Are clinicians who discover multiple identities merely triggering role playing by fantasy-prone people in a particular social context (Giesbrecht et al., 2008, 2010; Lynn et al., 2014; Merskey, 1992)? After all, clients do not enter therapy saying, "Allow me to introduce myselves." Rather, charge the critics, some therapists go fishing for multiple identities: *"Have you ever felt like another part of you does things you can't control?" "Does this part of you have a name?" "Can I talk to the angry part of you?"* Once clients permit a therapist to talk, by name, "to the part of you that says those angry things," they begin acting out the fantasy. Like actors who lose themselves in their roles, vulnerable patients may "become" the parts they are acting out. The result may be the experience of another self.

Other researchers and clinicians believe DID is a real disorder. They cite findings of distinct body and brain states associated with differing identities (Putnam, 1991). Abnormal brain anatomy and activity can also accompany DID. Brain scans show shrinkage in areas that aid memory and detection of threat (Vermetten et al., 2006). Heightened activity appears in brain areas linked with the control and inhibition of traumatic memories

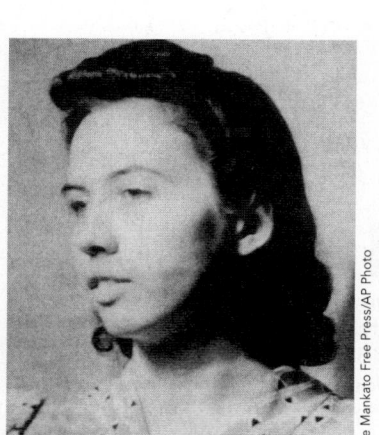

WIDESPREAD DISSOCIATION Shirley Mason was a psychiatric patient diagnosed with dissociative identity disorder. Her life formed the basis of the bestselling book, *Sybil* (Schreiber, 1973), and of two movies. The book and movies' popularity likely fueled the dramatic rise in diagnoses of DID in North America. A 2011 book complicated matters by revealing Mason's claim, in 1958, that she did not have the disorder (Nathan, 2011).

"Pretense may become reality."
—Chinese proverb

(Elzinga et al., 2007). Both the psychodynamic and learning perspectives have interpreted DID symptoms as ways of coping with anxiety. Some psychodynamic theorists see them as defenses against the anxiety caused by unacceptable impulses. In this view, a second identity could allow the discharge of forbidden impulses. Learning theorists see dissociative disorders as behaviors reinforced by anxiety reduction.

Some clinicians include dissociative disorders under the umbrella of posttraumatic stress disorder—a natural, protective response to traumatic experiences during childhood (Brand et al., 2016; Spiegel, 2008). Many people being treated for DID recall being physically, sexually, or emotionally abused as children (Gleaves, 1996; Lilienfeld et al., 1999). In one study of 12 murderers diagnosed with DID, 11 had suffered severe abuse, even torture, in childhood (Lewis et al., 1997). One had been set afire by his parents. Another had been used in child pornography and was scarred from being made to sit on a stove burner. Critics wonder, however, whether vivid imagination or therapist suggestion contributed to such recollections (Kihlstrom, 2005). So the scientific debate continues. Stay tuned.

> ## 🔒 RETRIEVE IT • • •
> ANSWERS IN APPENDIX E
>
> **RI-3** The psychodynamic and learning perspectives agree that dissociative identity disorder symptoms are ways of dealing with anxiety. How do their explanations differ?

Personality Disorders

LOQ 43-7 What are the three clusters of personality disorders? What behaviors and brain activity characterize the antisocial personality?

The inflexible and enduring behavior patterns of **personality disorders** interfere with social functioning. These ten disorders in DSM-5 tend to form three clusters, characterized by

- *anxiety,* such as a fearful sensitivity to rejection that predisposes the withdrawn *avoidant personality disorder.*

- *eccentric or odd behaviors,* such as actions prompted by the magical thinking of *schizotypal personality disorder.*

- *dramatic or impulsive behaviors,* such as the unstable, attention-getting *borderline personality disorder,* the self-focused and self-inflating *narcissistic personality disorder,* and—what we next discuss as an in-depth example—the callous, and often dangerous, *antisocial personality disorder.*

ANTISOCIAL PERSONALITY DISORDER   People with **antisocial personality disorder,** usually male, can display symptoms by age 8. Their lack of conscience becomes plain before age 15, as they begin to lie, steal, fight, or display unrestrained sexual behavior (Cale & Lilienfeld, 2002). Not all children with these traits become antisocial adults. (Note that *antisocial* means disruptive, not merely unsociable.) Those who do—about half—will generally act in violent or otherwise criminal ways, be unable to keep a job, and behave irresponsibly toward family members (Farrington, 1991). But criminality is not an essential component of antisocial behavior (Skeem & Cooke, 2010). Moreover, many criminals do not fit the description of antisocial personality disorder. Why? Because they are not impulsively antisocial (Geurts et al., 2016). Rather, they show responsible concern for their friends and family members. People with antisocial personality disorder (sometimes called *sociopaths* or *psychopaths*) may show lower *emotional intelligence*—the ability to understand, manage, and perceive emotions (Ermer et al., 2012b).

Antisocial personalities behave impulsively, and then feel and fear little (Fowles & Dindo, 2009). Their impulsivity can have horrific consequences (Camp et al., 2013). Consider the case of Henry Lee Lucas. He killed his first victim when he was 13. He felt little regret then or later. During his years of crime, he brutally murdered 157 women, men, and children. For the last six years of his reign of terror, Lucas teamed with Ottis Elwood Toole, who reportedly slaughtered people he "didn't think was worth living anyhow" (Darrach & Norris, 1984).

"Though this be madness, yet there is method in 't." —William Shakespeare, *Hamlet,* 1600

 ASK YOURSELF

Do you ever flip between displays of different aspects of your personality, depending on your surroundings? How is your experience similar to and different from the described symptoms of dissociative identity disorder?

"Would it be possible to speak with the personality that pays the bills?"

Leo Cullum The New Yorker Collection/ The Cartoon Bank

dissociative identity disorder (DID) a rare dissociative disorder in which a person exhibits two or more distinct and alternating identities. (Formerly called *multiple personality disorder.*)

personality disorders inflexible and enduring behavior patterns that impair social functioning.

antisocial personality disorder a personality disorder in which a person (usually a man) exhibits a lack of conscience for wrongdoing, even toward friends and family members; may be aggressive and ruthless or a clever con artist.

NO REMORSE Dennis Rader, known as the "BTK killer" in Kansas, was convicted in 2005 of killing 10 people over a 30-year span. Rader exhibited the extreme lack of conscience that marks antisocial personality disorder.

"Thursday is out. I have jury duty."

Many criminals, like this one, display a sense of conscience and responsibility in other areas of their life, and thus do not exhibit antisocial personality disorder.

Does a full Moon trigger "madness" in some people? Researchers examined data from 37 studies that related lunar phase to crime (including homicides specifically), crisis calls, and psychiatric hospital admissions (Rotton & Kelley, 1985). Their conclusion: There is virtually no evidence of "Moon madness." Nor does lunar phase correlate with suicides, assaults, emergency room visits, or traffic disasters (Martin et al., 1992; Raison et al., 1999).

UNDERSTANDING ANTISOCIAL PERSONALITY DISORDER Antisocial personality disorder is woven of both biological and psychological strands. Twin and adoption studies reveal that biological relatives of people with antisocial and unemotional tendencies are at increased risk for antisocial behavior (Frisell et al., 2012; Kendler et al., 2015b). No single gene codes for a complex behavior such as crime. Molecular geneticists have identified some specific genes that are more common in those with antisocial personality disorder (Gunter et al., 2010; Tielbeek et al., 2017). There may be a genetic predisposition toward a fearless and uninhibited life. The genes that put people at risk for antisocial behavior also increase the risk for substance use disorder, which helps explain why these disorders often appear together (Dick, 2007).

Genetic influences, often in combination with negative environmental factors such as childhood abuse, family instability, or poverty, help wire the brain (Dodge, 2009). This is true even in chimpanzees, which, like humans, vary in antisocial tendencies (Latzman et al., 2017). In people with antisocial criminal tendencies, the emotion-controlling amygdala is smaller (Pardini et al., 2014). The genetic vulnerability of people with antisocial and unemotional tendencies appears as low arousal in response to threats. Awaiting events that most people would find unnerving, such as electric shocks or loud noises, they show little autonomic nervous system arousal (Hare, 1975; Hoppenbrouwers et al., 2016). Long-term studies show that their stress hormone levels were lower than average as teens, before committing any crime (**FIGURE 43.3**). And those who were slow to develop conditioned fears at age 3 were also more likely to commit a crime later in life (Gao et al., 2010). Other studies have found that preschool boys who later became aggressive or antisocial adolescents tended to be impulsive, uninhibited, unconcerned with social rewards, and low in anxiety (Caspi et al., 1996; Tremblay et al., 1994).

Traits such as fearlessness and dominance can be adaptive. If channeled in more productive directions, fearlessness may lead to athletic stardom, adventurism, or courageous heroism (Smith et al., 2013). Indeed, 42 American presidents scored higher than the general population on such traits as fearlessness and dominance (Lilienfeld et al., 2012, 2016). Patient S. M., a 49-year-old woman with amygdala damage, showed fearlessness and impulsivity but also heroism: She gave a man in need her only coat and scarf, and donated her hair to the Locks of Love charity after befriending a child with cancer (Lilienfeld et al., 2017). Lacking a sense of social responsibility, the same disposition may produce a cool con artist or killer (Lykken, 1995).

With antisocial behavior, as with so much else, nature and nurture interact: The biopsychosocial perspective helps us understand the whole story. To further explore the neural basis of antisocial personality disorder, scientists are trying to identify brain

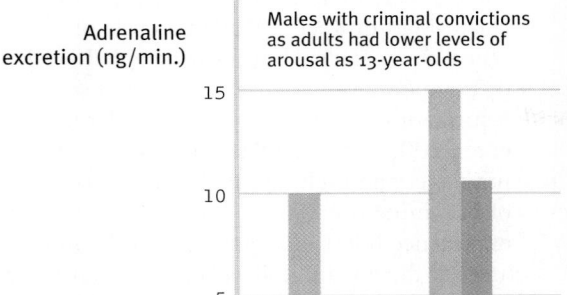

Adrenaline excretion (ng/min.)

Males with criminal convictions as adults had lower levels of arousal as 13-year-olds

■ No criminal conviction
■ Criminal conviction

FIGURE 43.3

COLD-BLOODED AROUSABILITY AND RISK OF CRIME Levels of the stress hormone adrenaline were measured in two groups of 13-year-old Swedish boys. In both stressful and nonstressful situations, those who would later be convicted of a crime as 18- to 26-year-olds showed relatively low arousal. (Data from Magnusson, 1990.)

activity differences in antisocial criminals. Shown emotionally evocative photographs, such as a man holding a knife to a woman's throat, criminals with antisocial personality disorder display blunted heart rate and perspiration responses, and less activity in brain areas that typically respond to emotional stimuli (Harenski et al., 2010; Kiehl & Buckholtz, 2010). They also have a larger and hyper-reactive dopamine reward system, which predisposes their impulsive drive to do something rewarding despite the consequences (Buckholtz et al., 2010; Glenn et al., 2010). One study compared PET scans of 41 murderers' brains with those from people of similar age and sex. The murderers' frontal lobes, an area that helps control impulses, displayed reduced activity (Raine, 1999, 2005; **FIGURE 43.4**). The reduced activation was especially apparent in those who murdered impulsively. In a follow-up study, researchers found that violent repeat offenders had 11 percent less frontal lobe tissue than normal (Raine et al., 2000). This helps explain another finding: People with antisocial personality disorder fall far below normal in aspects of thinking such as planning, organization, and inhibition, which are all frontal lobe functions (Morgan & Lilienfeld, 2000). Such data remind us: Everything psychological is also biological.

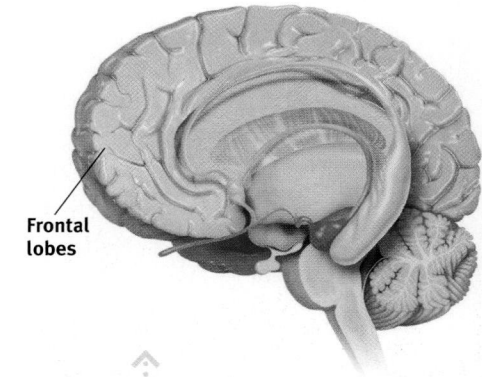

Frontal lobes

FIGURE 43.4

MURDEROUS MINDS Researchers have found reduced activation in a murderer's frontal lobes. This brain area (shown in a left-facing brain) helps brake impulsive, aggressive behavior (Raine, 1999).

🔒 **RETRIEVE IT • • •**   *ANSWERS IN APPENDIX E*

RI-4 How do biological and psychological factors contribute to antisocial personality disorder?

Eating Disorders

LOQ 43-8 What are the three main eating disorders, and how do biological, psychological, and social-cultural influences make people more vulnerable to them?

Our bodies are naturally disposed to maintain a steady weight, including storing energy for times when food becomes unavailable. But sometimes psychological influences overwhelm biological wisdom. This becomes painfully clear in three eating disorders:

- **Anorexia nervosa** typically begins as a weight-loss diet. People with anorexia—usually female adolescents, but some women, men, and boys as well—drop significantly below normal weight. Yet they feel fat, fear being fat, diet obsessively, and sometimes exercise excessively.

- **Bulimia nervosa,** unlike anorexia, is marked by weight fluctuations within or above normal ranges, making the condition easier to hide. Bulimia may also be triggered by a weight-loss diet that is broken by gorging on forbidden foods. People with this disorder—mostly women in their late teens or early twenties (but also some men)—eat in spurts, sometimes influenced by negative emotion or by

anorexia nervosa an eating disorder in which a person (usually an adolescent female) maintains a starvation diet despite being significantly underweight; sometimes accompanied by excessive exercise.

bulimia nervosa an eating disorder in which a person's binge eating (usually of high-calorie foods) is followed by inappropriate weight-loss promoting behavior, such as vomiting, laxative use, fasting, or excessive exercise.

SIBLING RIVALRY GONE AWRY Twins Maria and Katy Campbell have anorexia nervosa. As children they competed to see who could be thinner. Now, says Maria, her anorexia nervosa is "like a ball and chain around my ankle that I can't throw off" (Foster, 2011).

© Nick Holt Photography

friends who are bingeing (Crandall, 1988; Haedt-Matt & Keel, 2011). In a cycle of repeating episodes, binge eating is followed by compensatory vomiting, laxative use, fasting, or excessive exercise (Wonderlich et al., 2007). Preoccupied with food (craving sweet and high-fat foods), and fearful of becoming overweight, binge-purge eaters experience bouts of depression, guilt, and anxiety during and following binges (Hinz & Williamson, 1987; Johnson et al., 2002).

• Those with **binge-eating disorder** engage in significant bouts of bingeing, followed by remorse. But they do not purge, fast, or exercise excessively.

A U.S. National Institute of Mental Health–funded study reported that, at some point during their lifetime, 0.6 percent of Americans met the criteria for anorexia, 1 percent for bulimia, and 2.8 percent for binge-eating disorder (Hudson et al., 2007). Anorexia and bulimia can be deadly. They harm the body and mind, resulting in shorter life expectancy and greater risk of suicide and nonsuicidal self-injury (Cucchi et al., 2016; Fichter & Quadflieg, 2016; Smith et al., 2016).

UNDERSTANDING EATING DISORDERS Eating disorders are *not* (as some have speculated) a telltale sign of childhood sexual abuse (Smolak & Murnen, 2002; Stice, 2002). The family environment may influence eating disorders in other ways, however. For example, families of those with anorexia tend to be competitive, high achieving, and protective (Ahrén et al., 2013; Berg et al., 2014; Yates, 1989, 1990). Those with eating disorders often have low self-evaluations, set perfectionist standards, fret about falling short of expectations, and are intensely concerned with how others perceive them (Culbert et al., 2015; Farstad et al., 2016; Yiend et al., 2014). Some of these factors also predict teen boys' pursuit of unrealistic muscularity (Karazsia et al., 2017; Ricciardelli & McCabe, 2004).

A DISTORTED BODY IMAGE UNDERLIES ANOREXIA NERVOSA.

artbyjulie/Getty Images

📺 **LaunchPad** For an inside look at one man's experience with eating disorders, see the **Video: Overcoming Anorexia Nervosa.**

Heredity also matters. Identical twins share these disorders more often than fraternal twins do (Culbert et al., 2009; Klump et al., 2009; Root et al., 2010). Scientists are now searching for culprit genes. Data from 15 studies indicate that having a gene that reduces available serotonin adds 30 percent to a person's risk of anorexia or bulimia (Calati et al., 2011). A comparison of the genomes of nearly 3500 anorexia patients with 11,000 others identified a gene difference on chromosome 12 (Duncan et al., 2017).

But eating disorders also have cultural and gender components. Ideal shapes vary across culture and time. Plump may mean prosperity and thin may signal poverty or illness in countries with high poverty rates (Knickmeyer, 2001; Swami et al., 2010). Bigger less often seems better in wealthy Western cultures. In one analysis of 222 studies, the rise in eating disorders in the last half of the twentieth century coincided with a dramatic increase in Western women having a poor body image (Feingold & Mazzella, 1998).

Those most vulnerable to eating disorders are also those (usually women or gay men) who most idealize thinness and have the greatest body dissatisfaction (Feldman & Meyer, 2010; Kane, 2010; Stice et al., 2010). Should it surprise us, then, that women who view real and doctored images of unnaturally thin models and celebrities often feel ashamed, depressed, and dissatisfied with their own bodies—the very attitudes that predispose eating disorders (Grabe et al., 2008; Myers & Crowther, 2009; Tiggeman & Miller, 2010)?

Eric Stice and his colleagues (2001) tested this modeling idea by giving some adolescent girls (but not others) a 15-month subscription to an American teen-fashion magazine. Compared with those who had not received the magazine, vulnerable girls—defined as those who were already dissatisfied, idealizing thinness, and lacking social support—exhibited increased body dissatisfaction and eating disorder tendencies. Even ultra-thin models do not reflect the impossible standard of the original Barbie doll, who had, when adjusted to a height of 5 feet 7 inches, a 32–16–29 figure (in centimeters, 82–41–73) (Norton et al., 1996).

There is, however, more to body dissatisfaction and anorexia than media effects (Ferguson et al., 2011). Peer influences, such as teasing and harassment, also matter. Nevertheless, the sickness of today's eating disorders stems in part from today's weight-obsessed culture—a culture that says "fat is bad" in countless ways, that motivates millions of women to diet constantly, and that invites eating binges by pressuring women to live in a constant state of semistarvation. One former model recalled walking into a meeting with her agent, starving and with her organs failing due to anorexia (Caroll, 2013). Her agent's greeting: "Whatever you are doing, keep doing it."

Most people diagnosed with an eating disorder do improve. In one 22-year study, 2 in 3 women with anorexia nervosa or bulimia nervosa had recovered (Eddy et al., 2017). Prevention is also possible. Interactive programs that teach people (especially girls over age 15) to accept their bodies reduce the likelihood of an eating disorder (Beintner et al., 2012; Melioli et al., 2016; Vocks et al., 2010). By combating cultural learning, those at risk may instead live long and healthy lives.

"Up until that point, Bernice had never once had a problem with low self-esteem."

binge-eating disorder significant binge-eating episodes, followed by distress, disgust, or guilt, but without the compensatory behavior that marks bulimia nervosa.

"Why do women have such low self-esteem? There are many complex psychological and societal reasons, by which I mean Barbie." —Humorist Dave Barry, 1999

TOO THIN Many worry that superthin models make self-starvation seem fashionable. Concerned about promoting an unhealthy body image, British advertising regulators banned this advertisement because the female model appeared "unhealthily thin."

* * *

The bewilderment, fear, and sorrow caused by psychological disorders are real. But as our next topic—therapy—shows, hope, too, is real.

ANSWERS IN APPENDIX E

🔒 RETRIEVE IT • • •

RI-5 People with _____ _____ (anorexia nervosa/bulimia nervosa) continue to want to lose weight even when they are underweight. Those with _____ _____ (anorexia nervosa/bulimia nervosa) tend to have weight that fluctuates within or above normal ranges.

🔒 REVIEW SCHIZOPHRENIA AND OTHER DISORDERS

⟩ Learning Objectives

TEST YOURSELF Answer these repeated Learning Objective Questions on your own (before checking the answers in Appendix D) to improve your retention of the concepts (McDaniel et al., 2009, 2015).

43-1 What patterns of perceiving, thinking, and feeling characterize schizophrenia?

43-2 How do *chronic schizophrenia* and *acute schizophrenia* differ?

43-3 What brain abnormalities are associated with schizophrenia?

43-4 What prenatal events are associated with increased risk of developing schizophrenia?

43-5 How do genes influence schizophrenia?

43-6 What are *dissociative disorders*, and why are they controversial?

43-7 What are the three clusters of personality disorders? What behaviors and brain activity characterize the antisocial personality?

43-8 What are the three main eating disorders, and how do biological, psychological, and social-cultural influences make people more vulnerable to them?

⟩ Terms and Concepts to Remember

TEST YOURSELF Write down the definition yourself, then check your answer on the referenced page.

schizophrenia, **p. 522**

psychotic disorders, **p. 522**

delusion, **p. 523**

chronic schizophrenia, **p. 524**

acute schizophrenia, **p. 524**

dissociative disorders, **p. 527**

dissociative identity disorder (DID), **p. 529**

personality disorders, **p. 529**

antisocial personality disorder, **p. 529**

anorexia nervosa, **p. 531**

bulimia nervosa, **p. 531**

binge-eating disorder, **p. 533**

⟩ Experience the Testing Effect

TEST YOURSELF Answer the following questions on your own first, then check your answers in Appendix E.

1. Victor exclaimed, "The weather has been so schizophrenic lately: It's hot one day and freezing the next!" In addition to being insensitive to those with schizophrenia, this comparison is inaccurate. Explain.

2. A person with positive symptoms of schizophrenia is most likely to experience
   a. catatonia.
   b. delusions.
   c. withdrawal.
   d. flat emotion.

3. People with schizophrenia may hear voices urging self-destruction, an example of a(n) _____.

4. Chances for recovery from schizophrenia are best when
   a. onset is sudden, in response to stress.
   b. deterioration occurs gradually, during childhood.
   c. no environmental causes can be identified.
   d. there is a detectable brain abnormality.

5. Dissociative identity disorder is controversial because
   a. dissociation is quite rare.
   b. it was reported frequently in the 1920s but rarely today.
   c. it is almost never reported outside North America.
   d. its symptoms are nearly identical to those of obsessive-compulsive disorder.

6. A personality disorder, such as antisocial personality, is characterized by
   a. depression.
   b. hallucinations.
   c. inflexible and enduring behavior patterns that impair social functioning.
   d. an elevated level of autonomic nervous system arousal.

7. PET scans of murderers' brains have revealed
   a. higher-than-normal activation in the frontal lobes.
   b. lower-than-normal activation in the frontal lobes.
   c. more frontal lobe tissue than normal.
   d. no differences in brain structures or activity.

8. Which of the following statements is true of bulimia nervosa?
   a. People with bulimia continue to want to lose weight even when they are underweight.
   b. Bulimia is marked by weight fluctuations within or above normal ranges.
   c. Those with bulimia are equally likely to be male or female.
   d. If one twin is diagnosed with bulimia, the chances of the other twin's sharing the disorder are greater if they are fraternal rather than identical twins.

Continue testing yourself with 📘 **LearningCurve** or 📘 **Achieve Read & Practice** to learn and remember most effectively.

Therapy

Kay Redfield Jamison is both an award-winning clinical psychologist and a world expert on the emotional extremes of bipolar disorder. She knows her subject firsthand: "For as long as I can remember," she recalled in her memoir *An Unquiet Mind,* "I was frighteningly, although often wonderfully, beholden to moods. Intensely emotional as a child, mercurial as a young girl, first severely depressed as an adolescent, and then unrelentingly caught up in the cycles of manic-depressive illness [now known as bipolar disorder] by the time I began my professional life, I became, both by necessity and intellectual inclination, a student of moods" (1995, pp. 4–5). Jamison's life was blessed with times of intense sensitivity and passionate energy. But like her father's, it was also sometimes plagued by reckless spending, racing conversation, and sleeplessness, alternating with swings into "the blackest caves of the mind."

Then, "in the midst of utter confusion," she made a life-changing decision. Risking professional embarrassment, she made an appointment with a therapist, a psychiatrist she would visit weekly for years to come:

> He kept me alive a thousand times over. He saw me through madness, despair, wonderful and terrible love affairs, disillusionments and triumphs, recurrences of illness, an almost fatal suicide attempt, the death of a man I greatly loved, and the enormous pleasures and aggravations of my professional life. . . . He was very tough, as well as very kind, and even though he understood more than anyone how much I felt I was losing—in energy, vivacity, and originality—by taking medication, he never [lost] sight of the overall perspective of how costly, damaging, and life threatening my illness was. . . . Although I went to him to be treated for an illness, he taught me . . . the total beholdenness of brain to mind and mind to brain (pp. 87–88).

DOROTHEA DIX "I . . . call your attention to the state of the Insane Persons confined within this Commonwealth, in cages." (*Memorial to the Legislature of Massachusetts*, 1843)

THE HISTORY OF TREATMENT Visitors to eighteenth-century mental hospitals paid to gawk at patients, as though they were viewing zoo animals. William Hogarth's (1697–1764) painting captured one of these visits to London's St. Mary of Bethlehem hospital (commonly called Bedlam).

"Psychotherapy heals," Jamison reports. "It makes some sense of the confusion, reins in the terrifying thoughts and feelings, returns some control and hope and possibility from it all."

These modules explore some of the healing options available to therapists and the people who seek their help. We begin by exploring and evaluating *psychotherapies* (Modules 44 and 45), and then focus on *biomedical therapies* and preventing disorders (Module 46). ▶

44 Introduction to Therapy and the Psychological Therapies

The long history of efforts to treat psychological disorders has included a bewildering mix of harsh and gentle methods. Would-be healers have cut holes in people's heads and restrained, bled, or "beat the devil" out of them. But they also have given warm baths and massages and placed people in sunny, serene environments. They have given them drugs. And they have talked with them about childhood experiences, current feelings, and maladaptive thoughts and behaviors.

Reformers Philippe Pinel (1745–1826) and Dorothea Dix (1802–1887) pushed for gentler, more humane treatments and for constructing mental hospitals. Their efforts largely paid off. Since the 1950s, the introduction of effective drug therapies and community-based treatment programs has emptied most of those hospitals.

TREATING PSYCHOLOGICAL DISORDERS

LEARNING OBJECTIVE QUESTION (LOQ)

44-1 How do *psychotherapy* and the *biomedical therapies* differ?

Modern Western therapies can be classified into two main categories.

- In **psychotherapy,** a trained therapist uses psychological techniques to assist someone seeking to overcome difficulties and achieve personal growth. The therapist may explore a client's early relationships, encourage the client to adopt new ways of thinking, or coach the client in replacing old behaviors with new ones.

- **Biomedical therapy** offers medication or other biological treatments. For example, a person with severe depression may receive antidepressants, electroconvulsive shock therapy (ECT), or deep brain stimulation.

The care provider's training and expertise, as well as the disorder itself, influence the choice of treatment. Psychotherapy and medication are often combined. Kay Redfield Jamison received psychotherapy in her meetings with her psychiatrist, and she took medications to control her wild mood swings.

Let's look first at some influential psychotherapy options for those treated with "talk therapies." Each is built on one or more of psychology's major theories: psychodynamic, humanistic, behavioral, and cognitive. Most of these techniques can be used one-on-one or in groups. Some therapists combine techniques. Indeed, many psychotherapists describe their approach as **eclectic,** using a blend of therapies.

PSYCHOANALYSIS AND PSYCHODYNAMIC THERAPIES

LOQ 44-2 What are the goals and techniques of psychoanalysis, and how have they been adapted in psychodynamic therapy?

The first major psychological therapy was Sigmund Freud's **psychoanalysis.** Although few clinicians today practice therapy as Freud did, his work deserves discussion. It helped form the foundation for treating psychological disorders, and it continues to influence modern therapists working from the *psychodynamic* perspective.

The Goals of Psychoanalysis

Freud believed that in therapy, people could achieve healthier, less anxious living by releasing the energy they had previously devoted to *id-ego-superego* conflicts. Freud assumed that we do not fully know ourselves. He believed that there are threatening things we *repress*—things we do not want to know, so we disavow or deny them. Psychoanalysis was Freud's method of helping people to bring these repressed feelings into conscious awareness. By helping them reclaim their unconscious thoughts and feelings, and by giving them *insight* into the origins of their disorders, the therapist (*analyst*) could help them reduce growth-impeding inner conflicts.

The Techniques of Psychoanalysis

Psychoanalytic theory emphasizes the power of childhood experiences to mold the adult. Thus, psychoanalysis is historical reconstruction. It aims to unearth the past in the hope of loosening its bonds on the present. After discarding hypnosis as an unreliable excavator, Freud turned to *free association.*

ENGAGE Imagine yourself as a patient using free association. You begin by relaxing, perhaps by lying on a couch. The psychoanalyst, who sits out of your line of vision, asks you to say aloud whatever comes to mind. At one moment, you're relating a childhood memory. At another, you're describing a dream or recent experience. It sounds easy, but soon you notice how often you edit your thoughts as you speak. You pause for a second before uttering an embarrassing thought. You omit what seems trivial, irrelevant, or shameful. Sometimes your mind goes blank or you clutch up, unable to remember important details. You may joke or change the subject to something less threatening.

To the analyst, these mental blocks indicate **resistance.** They hint that anxiety lurks and you are defending against sensitive material. The analyst will note your resistance and then provide insight into its meaning. If offered at the right moment, this **interpretation**—of, say, your not wanting to discuss, text, or message your mother—may illuminate the underlying wishes, feelings, and conflicts you are avoiding. The analyst may also offer an explanation of how this resistance fits with other pieces of your psychological puzzle, including those based on analysis of your dream content.

Over many such sessions, your relationship patterns surface in your interaction with your therapist. You may find yourself experiencing strong positive or negative feelings for your analyst. The analyst may suggest you are **transferring** feelings, such as dependency or mingled love and anger, that you experienced in earlier relationships with family members or other important people. By exposing such feelings, you may gain insight into your current relationships.

Relatively few North American therapists now offer traditional psychoanalysis. Much of its underlying theory is not supported by scientific research. Analysts' interpretations cannot be proven or disproven. And psychoanalysis takes considerable time and money, often years of several expensive sessions per week. Some of these problems have been addressed in the modern *psychodynamic perspective* that has evolved from psychoanalysis.

psychotherapy treatment involving psychological techniques; consists of interactions between a trained therapist and someone seeking to overcome psychological difficulties or achieve personal growth.

biomedical therapy prescribed medications or procedures that act directly on the person's physiology.

eclectic approach an approach to psychotherapy that uses techniques from various forms of therapy.

psychoanalysis Sigmund Freud's therapeutic technique. Freud believed the patient's free associations, resistances, dreams, and transferences—and the analyst's interpretations of them—released previously repressed feelings, allowing the patient to gain self-insight.

resistance in psychoanalysis, the blocking from consciousness of anxiety-laden material.

interpretation in psychoanalysis, the analyst's noting of supposed dream meanings, resistances, and other significant behaviors and events in order to promote insight.

transference in psychoanalysis, the patient's transfer to the analyst of emotions linked with other relationships (such as love or hatred for a parent).

Paul Noth/The New Yorker Collection/The Cartoon Bank

"I'm more interested in hearing about the eggs you're hiding from yourself."

Psychodynamic Therapy

Although influenced by Freud's ideas, **psychodynamic therapists** don't talk much about id-ego-superego conflicts. Instead, they try to help people understand their current symptoms by focusing on important relationships, including childhood experiences and the therapist-client relationship. "We can have loving feelings and hateful feelings toward the same person," observed psychodynamic therapist Jonathan Shedler (2009), and "we can desire something and also fear it." Client-therapist meetings take place once or twice a week (rather than several times weekly), and often for only a few weeks or months. Rather than lying on a couch, out of the therapist's line of vision, clients meet with their therapist face-to-face and gain perspective by exploring defended-against thoughts and feelings.

Therapist David Shapiro (1999, p. 8) illustrated this with the case of a young man who had told women that he loved them, when he knew that he didn't. The client's explanation: They expected it, so he said it. But later, with his wife, who wished he would say that he loved her, he found he *couldn't* do that—"I don't know why, but I can't."

Therapist: Do you mean, then, that if you could, you would like to?

Patient: Well, I don't know. . . . Maybe I can't say it because I'm not sure it's true. Maybe I don't love her.

Further interactions revealed that the client could not express real love because it would feel "mushy" and "soft" and therefore unmanly. He was "in conflict with himself, and . . . cut off from the nature of that conflict." Shapiro noted that with such patients, who are estranged from themselves, therapists using psychodynamic techniques "are in a position to introduce them to themselves. We can restore their awareness of their own wishes and feelings, and their awareness, as well, of their reactions against those wishes and feelings."

Exploring past relationship troubles may help clients understand the origin of their current difficulties. Shedler (2010a) recalled "Jeffrey's" complaints of difficulty getting along with his colleagues and wife, who saw him as hypercritical. Jeffrey then "began responding to me as if I were an unpredictable, angry adversary." Shedler seized this opportunity to help Jeffrey recognize the relationship pattern and its roots in the attacks and humiliation he had experienced from his alcohol-abusing father. Jeffrey was then able to work through and let go of this defensive style of responding to people. Thus, without embracing all of Freud's theory, psychodynamic therapists aim to help people gain insight into unconscious dynamics that arise from their life experience.

HUMANISTIC THERAPIES

LOQ 44-3 What are the basic themes of humanistic therapy? What are the specific goals and techniques of Rogers' client-centered approach?

The *humanistic* perspective emphasizes people's innate potential for self-fulfillment. Not surprisingly, humanistic therapies attempt to reduce the inner conflicts that interfere with natural development and growth. To achieve this goal, humanistic therapists try to give clients new insights. Indeed, because they share this goal, the psychodynamic and humanistic therapies are often referred to as **insight therapies.** But humanistic therapies differ from psychodynamic therapies in many other ways:

- Humanistic therapists aim to boost people's self-fulfillment by helping them grow in self-awareness and self-acceptance.

- Promoting this growth, not curing illness, is the therapy focus. Thus, those in therapy have become "clients" or just "persons" rather than "patients" (a change many other therapists have adopted).

psychodynamic therapy therapy deriving from the psychoanalytic tradition; views individuals as responding to unconscious forces and childhood experiences, and seeks to enhance self-insight.

insight therapies therapies that aim to improve psychological functioning by increasing a person's awareness of underlying motives and defenses.

- The path to growth is taking immediate responsibility for one's feelings and actions, rather than uncovering hidden causes.

- Conscious thoughts are more important than the unconscious.

- The present and future are more important than the past. Therapy thus focuses on exploring feelings as they occur, rather than on achieving insight into the childhood origins of those feelings.

All these themes are present in the widely used humanistic technique that Carl Rogers (1902–1987) developed and called **client-centered therapy.** In this *nondirective therapy,* the client leads the discussion. The therapist listens, without judging or interpreting, and refrains from directing the client toward certain insights.

Believing that most people possess the resources for growth, Rogers (1961, 1980) encouraged therapists to foster that growth by exhibiting *acceptance, genuineness,* and *empathy.* By being *accepting,* therapists may help clients feel freer and more open to change. By being *genuine,* therapists hope to encourage clients to likewise express their true feelings. By being *empathic,* therapists try to sense and reflect their clients' feelings, helping clients experience a deeper self-understanding and self-acceptance (Hill & Nakayama, 2000). As Rogers (1980, p. 10) explained:

> Hearing has consequences. When I truly hear a person and the meanings that are important to him at that moment, hearing not simply his words, but him, and when I let him know that I have heard his own private personal meanings, many things happen. There is first of all a grateful look. He feels released. He wants to tell me more about his world. He surges forth in a new sense of freedom. He becomes more open to the process of change.
>
> I have often noticed that the more deeply I hear the meanings of the person, the more there is that happens. Almost always, when a person realizes he has been deeply heard, his eyes moisten. I think in some real sense he is weeping for joy. It is as though he were saying, "Thank God, somebody heard me. Someone knows what it's like to be me."

To Rogers, "hearing" was **active listening.** The therapist echoes, restates, and seeks clarification of what the client expresses (verbally or nonverbally). The therapist also acknowledges those expressed feelings. Active listening is now an accepted part of counseling practices in many schools, colleges, and clinics. Counselors listen attentively. They interrupt only to restate and confirm feelings, to accept what was said, or to check their understanding of something. In the following brief excerpt, note how Rogers tried to provide a psychological mirror that would help the client see himself more clearly (Meador & Rogers, 1984, p. 167):

Rogers: Feeling that now, hm? That you're just no good to yourself, no good to anybody. Never will be any good to anybody. Just that you're completely worthless, huh?—Those really are lousy feelings. Just feel that you're no good at all, hm?

Client: Yeah. (Muttering in low, discouraged voice) *That's what this guy I went to town with just the other day told me.*

Rogers: This guy that you went to town with really told you that you were no good? Is that what you're saying? Did I get that right?

Client: M-hm.

Rogers: I guess the meaning of that if I get it right is that here's somebody that meant something to you and what does he think of you? Why, he's told you that he thinks you're no good at all. And that just really knocks the props out from under you. (Client weeps quietly.) *It just brings the tears.* (Silence of 20 seconds)

Client: (Rather defiantly) *I don't care though.*

Rogers: You tell yourself you don't care at all, but somehow I guess some part of you cares because some part of you weeps over it.

Can a therapist be a perfect mirror, without selecting and interpreting what is reflected? Rogers conceded that no one can be *totally* nondirective. Nevertheless, he

client-centered therapy a humanistic therapy, developed by Carl Rogers, in which the therapist uses techniques such as *active listening* within an accepting, genuine, empathic environment to facilitate clients' growth. (Also called *person-centered therapy.*)

active listening empathic listening in which the listener echoes, restates, and clarifies. A feature of Rogers' client-centered therapy.

"We have two ears and one mouth that we may listen the more and talk the less." —Zeno, 335–263 B.C.E., *Diogenes Laertius*

ACTIVE LISTENING Carl Rogers (right) empathized with a client during this group therapy session.

Michael Rougier/Getty Images

said, the therapist's most important contribution is to accept and understand the client. Given a nonjudgmental, grace-filled environment that provides **unconditional positive regard,** people may accept even their worst traits and feel valued and whole.

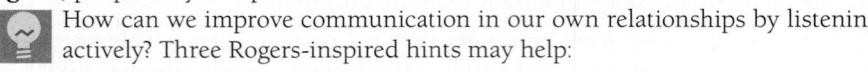 How can we improve communication in our own relationships by listening more actively? Three Rogers-inspired hints may help:

1. *Paraphrase.* Check your understanding by summarizing the person's words out loud, in your own words.

2. *Invite clarification.* "What might be an example of that?" may encourage the person to say more.

3. *Reflect feelings.* "It sounds frustrating" might mirror what you're sensing from the person's body language and intensity.

> **LaunchPad** To learn more about how therapists may use these approaches, see the **Video: Psychodynamic and Humanistic Therapies.**

BEHAVIOR THERAPIES

LOQ 44-4 How does the basic assumption of behavior therapy differ from the assumptions of psychodynamic and humanistic therapies? What techniques are used in exposure therapies and aversive conditioning?

The insight therapies assume that self-awareness and psychological well-being go hand in hand. Psychodynamic therapists expect people's problems to diminish as they gain insight into their unresolved and unconscious tensions. Humanistic therapists expect problems to diminish as people get in touch with their feelings. **Behavior therapists,** however, doubt the healing power of self-awareness. Rather than delving deeply below the surface looking for inner causes, behavior therapists assume that problem behaviors *are* the problems. (You can become aware of why you are highly anxious during exams and still be anxious.) If phobias, sexual dysfunctions, or other maladaptive symptoms are learned behaviors, why not replace them with new, constructive behaviors?

Classical Conditioning Techniques

One cluster of behavior therapies derives from principles developed in Ivan Pavlov's early twentieth-century conditioning experiments. As Pavlov and others showed, we learn various behaviors and emotions through *classical conditioning.* If we're attacked by a dog, we may thereafter have a conditioned fear response when other dogs approach. (Our fear generalizes, and all dogs become conditioned stimuli.)

Could maladaptive symptoms be examples of conditioned responses? If so, might reconditioning be a solution? Learning theorist O. H. Mowrer thought so. He developed a successful conditioning therapy for chronic bed-wetters, using a liquid-sensitive pad connected to an alarm. If the sleeping child wets the bed pad, moisture triggers the alarm, waking the child. After a number of trials, the child associates bladder relaxation with waking. In three out of four cases, the treatment has been effective and the success boosted the child's self-image (Christophersen & Edwards, 1992; Houts et al., 1994).

Can we unlearn fear responses, such as to public speaking or flying, through new conditioning? Many people have. An example: The fear of riding in an elevator is often a learned aversion to being in a confined space. **Counterconditioning,** such as with *exposure therapy,* pairs the trigger stimulus (in this case, the enclosed space of the elevator) with a new response (relaxation) that is incompatible with fear.

ASK YOURSELF

Think of your closest friends. Do they tend to express more empathy than those you don't feel as close to? How have your own active-listening skills changed as you've gotten older?

unconditional positive regard a caring, accepting, nonjudgmental attitude, which Carl Rogers believed would help clients develop self-awareness and self-acceptance.

behavior therapy therapy that applies learning principles to the elimination of unwanted behaviors.

counterconditioning behavior therapy procedures that use classical conditioning to evoke new responses to stimuli that are triggering unwanted behaviors; include *exposure therapies* and *aversive conditioning.*

exposure therapies behavioral techniques, such as *systematic desensitization* and *virtual reality exposure therapy,* that treat anxieties by exposing people (in imaginary or actual situations) to the things they fear and avoid.

> **RETRIEVE IT • • •**   *ANSWERS IN APPENDIX E*
>
> **RI-2** What might a psychodynamic therapist say about Mowrer's therapy for bed-wetting? How might a behavior therapist defend it?

EXPOSURE THERAPIES Picture this scene: Behavioral psychologist Mary Cover Jones is working with 3-year-old Peter, who is petrified of rabbits and other furry objects. To rid Peter of his fear, Jones plans to associate the fear-evoking rabbit with the pleasurable, relaxed response associated with eating. As Peter begins his midafternoon snack, she introduces a caged rabbit on the other side of the huge room. Peter, eagerly munching away on his crackers and drinking his milk, hardly notices. On succeeding days, she gradually moves the rabbit closer and closer. Within two months, Peter is holding the rabbit in his lap, even stroking it while he eats. Moreover, his fear of other furry objects subsides as well, having been *countered,* or replaced, by a relaxed state that cannot coexist with fear (Fisher, 1984; Jones, 1924).

Unfortunately for many who might have been helped by Jones' counterconditioning procedures, her story of Peter and the rabbit did not enter psychology's lore when it was reported in 1924. It was more than 30 years before psychiatrist Joseph Wolpe (1958; Wolpe & Plaud, 1997) refined Jones' counterconditioning technique into the **exposure therapies** used today. These therapies, in a variety of ways, try to change people's reactions by repeatedly exposing them to stimuli that trigger unwanted reactions. With repeated exposure to what they normally avoid or escape, people adapt. We all experience this process in everyday life. A person moving to a new apartment may be annoyed by nearby loud traffic noise, but only for a while. The person adapts. So, too, with people who have fear reactions to specific events. Exposed repeatedly to the situation that once petrified them, they can learn to react less anxiously (Barrera et al., 2013; Foa & McLean, 2016; Langkaas et al., 2017).

One exposure therapy widely used to treat phobias is **systematic desensitization.** You cannot simultaneously be anxious and relaxed. Therefore, if you can repeatedly relax when facing anxiety-provoking stimuli, you can gradually eliminate your anxiety. The trick is to proceed gradually. If you fear public speaking, a behavior therapist might first help you construct a hierarchy of anxiety-triggering speaking situations. Yours might range from mildly anxiety-provoking situations (perhaps speaking up in a small group of friends) to panic-provoking situations (having to address a large audience).

Next, the therapist would train you in *progressive relaxation.* You would learn to release tension in one muscle group after another, until you achieve a comfortable, complete relaxation. Then the therapist might ask you to imagine, with your eyes closed, a mildly anxiety-arousing situation: You are having coffee with a group of friends and are trying to decide whether to speak up. If imagining the scene causes you to feel any anxiety, you will signal by raising your finger. Seeing the signal, the therapist will instruct you to switch off the mental image and go back to deep relaxation. This imagined scene is repeatedly paired with relaxation until you feel no trace of anxiety.

The therapist will then move to the next item in your anxiety hierarchy, again using relaxation techniques to desensitize you to each imagined situation. After several sessions, you move to actual situations and practice what you had only *imagined* before, beginning with relatively easy tasks and gradually moving to more anxiety-filled ones. Conquering your anxiety in an actual situation, not just in your imagination, will increase your self-confidence (Foa & Kozak, 1986; Williams, 1987). Eventually, you may even become a confident public speaker. Often people fear not just a situation, such as public speaking, but also being incapacitated by their own fear response. As their fear subsides, so also does their fear of the fear.

Some anxiety-arousing situations (such as fears of flying, heights, particular animals, and public performances) may be too expensive, difficult, or embarrassing to re-create. In such cases, the therapist may recommend **virtual reality exposure therapy,** in which you don a head-mounted display unit that projects a lifelike three-dimensional virtual world tailored to your particular fear. If you fear flying, for example, you could peer out a virtual window of a simulated plane, feel the engine's vibrations, and hear it roar as the plane taxis down the runway and takes off. If you fear social interactions, you could experience simulated stressful situations, such as entering a roomful of people. In controlled studies, people participating in virtual reality exposure therapy have experienced significant relief from real-life fear and social anxiety (Anderson et al., 2017; Parsons & Rizzo, 2008; Turner & Casey, 2014).

systematic desensitization a type of exposure therapy that associates a pleasant relaxed state with gradually increasing anxiety-triggering stimuli. Commonly used to treat phobias.

virtual reality exposure therapy a counterconditioning technique that treats anxiety through creative electronic simulations in which people can safely face their greatest fears, such as airplane flying, spiders, or public speaking.

Jack Kearse/Emory University

William Britten/E+/Getty Images

VIRTUAL REALITY EXPOSURE THERAPY Within the confines of a room, virtual reality technology exposes people to vivid simulations of feared stimuli, such as walking across a rickety bridge high off the ground.

"The only thing we have to fear is fear itself." —U.S. President Franklin D. Roosevelt, First Inaugural Address, 1933

FIGURE 44.1

AVERSION THERAPY FOR ALCOHOL USE DISORDER After repeatedly imbibing an alcoholic drink mixed with a drug that produces severe nausea, some people with a history of alcohol use disorder develop at least a temporary conditioned aversion to alcohol. (Remember: US is unconditioned stimulus, UR is unconditioned response, NS is neutral stimulus, CS is conditioned stimulus, and CR is conditioned response.)

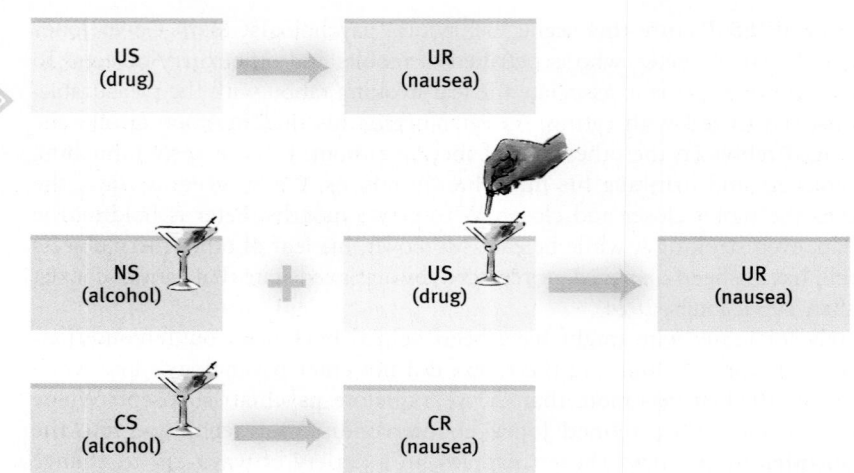

AVERSIVE CONDITIONING

AVERSIVE CONDITIONING An exposure therapy enables a more relaxed, positive response to an upsetting *harmless* stimulus. It helps you accept what you *should* do. **Aversive conditioning** creates a negative (aversive) response to a *harmful* stimulus (such as alcohol). It helps you to learn what you *should not* do. The aversive conditioning procedure is simple: It associates the unwanted behavior with unpleasant feelings. To treat nail biting, the therapist may suggest painting the fingernails with a nasty-tasting nail polish (Baskind, 1997). To treat alcohol use disorder, the therapist may offer the client appealing drinks laced with a drug that produces severe nausea. If that therapy links alcohol with violent nausea, the person's reaction to alcohol may change from positive to negative (**FIGURE 44.1**).

Taste aversion learning has been a successful alternative to killing predators in some animal protection programs (Dingfelder, 2010; Garcia & Gustavson, 1997). After being sickened by eating a tainted sheep, wolves may avoid sheep. Does aversive conditioning also transform humans' reactions to alcohol? In the short run it may. In one classic study, 685 hospital patients with alcohol use disorder completed an aversion therapy program (Wiens & Menustik, 1983). Over the next year, they returned for several booster treatments that paired alcohol with sickness. At the end of that year, 63 percent were not drinking alcohol. But after three years, only 33 percent were alcohol free.

In therapy, as in research, cognition influences conditioning. People know that outside the therapist's office they can drink without fear of nausea. This ability to discriminate between the therapy situation and all others can limit aversive conditioning's effectiveness. Thus, therapists often combine aversive conditioning with other treatments.

Operant Conditioning Techniques

LOQ 44-5 What is the main premise of therapy based on operant conditioning principles, and what are the views of its proponents and critics?

If you have learned to swim, you learned how to put your head under water without suffocating, how to pull your body through the water, and perhaps even how to dive safely. Operant conditioning shaped your swimming. You were reinforced for safe, effective behaviors. And you were naturally punished, as when you swallowed water, for improper swimming behaviors.

Consequences strongly influence our voluntary behaviors. Knowing this basic principle of operant conditioning, behavior therapists can practice *behavior modification*. They reinforce behaviors they consider desirable, and they fail to reinforce—or sometimes punish—behaviors they consider undesirable.

Using operant conditioning to solve specific behavior problems has raised hopes for some seemingly hopeless cases. Children with intellectual disabilities have been taught to care for themselves. Socially withdrawn children with autism spectrum disorder (ASD) have learned to interact. People with schizophrenia have been helped to behave more rationally in their hospital ward. In such cases, therapists used positive reinforcers to *shape* behavior. In a step-by-step manner, they rewarded closer and closer approximations of the desired behavior.

In extreme cases, treatment must be intensive. One study worked with 19 withdrawn, uncommunicative 3-year-olds with ASD. For two years, 40 hours each week, the children's parents attempted to shape their behavior (Lovaas, 1987). They positively reinforced desired behaviors and ignored or punished aggressive and self-abusive behaviors. The combination worked wonders for some children. By first grade, 9 of the 19 were functioning successfully in school and exhibiting normal intelligence. In a group of 40 comparable children not undergoing this effortful treatment, only one showed similar improvement. Later studies focused on positive reinforcement—the effective aspect of this early intensive behavioral intervention (Reichow, 2012).

Rewards used to modify behavior vary. For some people, the reinforcing power of attention or praise is sufficient. Others require concrete rewards, such as food. In institutional settings, therapists may create a **token economy.** When people display a desired behavior, such as getting out of bed, washing, dressing, eating, talking meaningfully, cleaning their rooms, or playing cooperatively, they receive a token or plastic coin. Later, they can exchange a number of these tokens for rewards, such as candy, TV time, day trips, or better living quarters. Token economies have been used successfully in homes, classrooms, and correctional institutions, and among people with various disabilities (Matson & Boisjoli, 2009).

Behavior modification critics express two concerns.

- *How durable are the behaviors?* Will people become so dependent on extrinsic rewards that the desired behaviors will stop when the reinforcers stop? Behavior modification advocates believe the behaviors will endure if therapists wean people from the tokens by shifting them toward other, real-life rewards, such as social approval. As people become more socially competent, the intrinsic satisfactions of social interaction may sustain the behaviors.

- *Is it right for one human to control another's behavior?* Those who set up token economies deprive people of something they desire and decide which behaviors to reinforce. To critics, this whole process feels too authoritarian. Advocates reply that control already exists: People's destructive behavior patterns are being maintained and perpetuated by natural reinforcers and punishers in their environments. Isn't using positive rewards to reinforce adaptive behavior more humane than institutionalizing or punishing people? Advocates also argue that the right to effective treatment and an improved life justifies temporary deprivation.

aversive conditioning associates an unpleasant state (such as nausea) with an unwanted behavior (such as drinking alcohol).

token economy an operant conditioning procedure in which people earn a token for exhibiting a desired behavior and can later exchange the tokens for privileges or treats.

ENGAGE (ASK YOURSELF)

What is your judgment of behavior modification techniques, such as those used in token economies? Do you agree or disagree with this approach?

🔒 **RETRIEVE IT • • •**   *ANSWERS IN APPENDIX E*

RI-3 What are the *insight therapies,* and how do they differ from *behavior therapies?*

RI-4 Some maladaptive behaviors are learned. What hope does this fact provide?

RI-5 Exposure therapies and aversive conditioning are applications of _____ conditioning. Token economies are an application of _____ conditioning.

COGNITIVE THERAPIES

LOQ 44-6 What are the goals and techniques of the cognitive therapies and of cognitive-behavioral therapy?

People with specific fears and problem behaviors may respond to behavior therapy. But how might behavior therapists modify the wide assortment of behaviors that accompany depressive disorders? Or treat people with generalized anxiety disorder, where unfocused anxiety doesn't lend itself to a neat list of anxiety-triggering situations? The *cognitive revolution* that has profoundly changed other areas of psychology during the last half-century has influenced therapy as well.

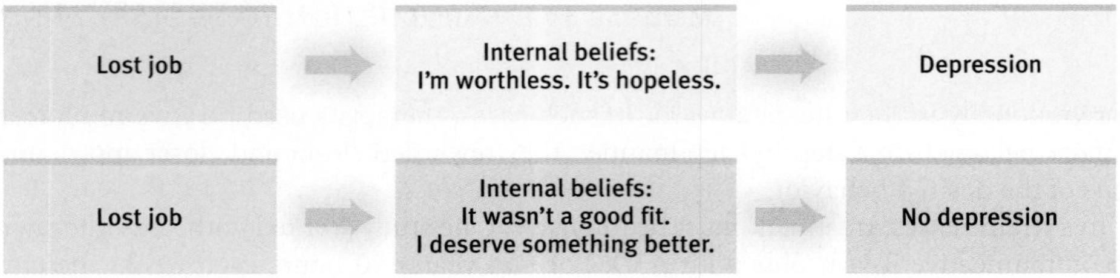

FIGURE 44.2

A COGNITIVE PERSPECTIVE ON PSYCHOLOGICAL DISORDERS The person's emotional reactions are produced not directly by the event, but by the person's thoughts in response to the event.

"Life does not consist mainly, or even largely, of facts and happenings. It consists mainly of the storm of thoughts that are forever blowing through one's mind." —Mark Twain, 1835–1910

The **cognitive therapies** assume that our thinking colors our feelings (**FIGURE 44.2**). Between an event and our response lies the mind. Anxiety, for example, can arise from an "attention bias to threat" (MacLeod & Clarke, 2015). Self-blaming and overgeneralized explanations of bad events feed depression. If depressed, we may interpret a suggestion as criticism, disagreement as dislike, praise as flattery, friendliness as pity. Dwelling on such thoughts sustains negative thinking. Cognitive therapies aim to help people change their mind with new, more constructive ways of perceiving and interpreting events (Kazdin, 2015). Let's look more closely at classic cognitive therapy, which is based on the premise that changing people's thinking can change the way they function.

Beck's Therapy for Depression

In the late 1960s, a woman left a party early. Things had not gone well. She felt disconnected from the other party-goers and assumed no one cared for her. A few days later, she visited therapist Aaron Beck. Rather than go down the traditional path to her childhood, Beck challenged her thinking. After she then listed a dozen people who *did* care for her, Beck realized that challenging people's automatic negative thoughts could be therapeutic. And thus was born his cognitive therapy (Spiegel, 2015).

Depressed people, Beck found, often reported dreams with negative themes of loss, rejection, and abandonment. These thoughts extended into their waking thoughts, and even into therapy, as clients recalled and rehearsed their failings and worst impulses (Kelly, 2000). With cognitive therapy, Beck and his colleagues (1979) sought to reverse clients' negativity about themselves, their situations, and their futures. With this technique, gentle questioning seeks to reveal irrational thinking, and then to persuade people to remove the dark glasses through which they view life (Beck et al., 1979, pp. 145–146):

Client: I agree with the descriptions of me but I guess I don't agree that the way I think makes me depressed.

Beck: How do you understand it?

Client: I get depressed when things go wrong. Like when I fail a test.

Beck: How can failing a test make you depressed?

Client: Well, if I fail I'll never get into law school.

Beck: So failing the test means a lot to you. But if failing a test could drive people into clinical depression, wouldn't you expect everyone who failed the test to have a depression? . . . Did everyone who failed get depressed enough to require treatment?

Client: No, but it depends on how important the test was to the person.

Beck: Right, and who decides the importance?

Client: I do.

Beck: And so, what we have to examine is your way of viewing the test (or the way that you think about the test) and how it affects your chances of getting into law school. Do you agree?

Client: Right.

Beck: Do you agree that the way you interpret the results of the test will affect you? You might feel depressed, you might have trouble sleeping, not feel like eating, and you might even wonder if you should drop out of the course.

Client: I have been thinking that I wasn't going to make it. Yes, I agree.

Beck: Now what did failing mean?

Client: (tearful) That I couldn't get into law school.

Beck: And what does that mean to you?

cognitive therapy therapy that teaches people new, more adaptive ways of thinking; based on the assumption that thoughts intervene between events and our emotional reactions.

Client: *That I'm just not smart enough.*

Beck: *Anything else?*

Client: *That I can never be happy.*

Beck: *And how do these thoughts make you feel?*

Client: *Very unhappy.*

Beck: *So it is the meaning of failing a test that makes you very unhappy. In fact, believing that you can never be happy is a powerful factor in producing unhappiness. So, you get yourself into a trap—by definition, failure to get into law school equals "I can never be happy."*

We often think in words. Therefore, getting people to change what they say to themselves is an effective way to change their thinking. Perhaps you can identify with the anxious students who, before an exam, make matters worse with self-defeating thoughts: "This exam's probably going to be impossible. All these other students seem so relaxed and confident. I wish I were better prepared. I'm so nervous I'll forget everything." Psychologists call this sort of relentless, overgeneralized, self-blaming behavior *catastrophizing.*

To change such negative self-talk, therapists have offered *stress inoculation training:* teaching people to restructure their thinking in stressful situations (Meichenbaum, 1977, 1985). Sometimes it may be enough simply to say more positive things to yourself: "Relax. The exam may be hard, but it will be hard for everyone else, too. I studied harder than most people. Besides, I don't need a perfect score to get a good grade." After learning to "talk back" to negative thoughts, depression-prone children, teens, and college students have shown a greatly reduced rate of future depression (Reivich et al., 2013; Seligman et al., 2009). To a large extent, it is the thought that counts. For a sampling of commonly used cognitive therapy techniques, see **TABLE 44.1.**)

PEANUTS

 TABLE 44.1

Selected Cognitive Therapy Techniques

Aim of Technique	Technique	Therapists' Directives
Reveal beliefs	Question your interpretations	Explore your beliefs, revealing faulty assumptions such as "I need to be liked by everyone."
	Rank thoughts and emotions	Gain perspective by ranking your thoughts and emotions from mildly to extremely upsetting.
Test beliefs	Examine consequences	Explore difficult situations, assessing possible consequences and challenging faulty reasoning.
	Decatastrophize thinking	Work through the actual worst-case consequences of the situation you face (it is often not as bad as imagined). Then determine how to cope with the real situation you face.
Change beliefs	Take appropriate responsibility	Challenge total self-blame and negative thinking, noting aspects for which you may be truly responsible, as well as aspects that aren't your responsibility.
	Resist extremes	Develop new ways of thinking and feeling to replace maladaptive habits. For example, change from thinking "I am a total failure" to "I got a failing grade on that paper, and I can make these changes to succeed next time."

cognitive-behavioral therapy (CBT) a popular integrative therapy that combines cognitive therapy (changing self-defeating thinking) with behavior therapy (changing behavior).

ASK YOURSELF

Have you ever struggled to reach a goal at school or work because of your own self-defeating thoughts? How could you challenge those thoughts?

LaunchPad To learn more about how cognitive therapy can be used to help those with anxiety, see the **Video: Cognitive Therapies.**

COGNITIVE-BEHAVIORAL THERAPY FOR EATING DISORDERS AIDED BY JOURNALING Cognitive-behavioral therapists guide people with eating disorders toward new ways of explaining their good and bad food-related experiences (Linardon et al., 2017). By recording positive events and how she has enabled them, this woman may become more mindful of her self-control and more optimistic.

It's not just depressed people who can benefit from positive self-talk. We all talk to ourselves (thinking "I wish I hadn't said that" can protect us from repeating the blunder). The findings of nearly three dozen sport psychology studies show that self-talk interventions can enhance the learning of athletic skills (Hatzigeorgiadis et al., 2011). For example, novice basketball players may be trained to think "focus" and "follow through," swimmers to think "high elbow," and tennis players to think "look at the ball." People anxious about public speaking have grown in confidence if asked to recall a speaking success, and then to "Explain WHY you were able to achieve such a successful performance" (Zunick et al., 2015).

Cognitive-Behavioral Therapy

"The trouble with most therapy," said therapist Albert Ellis (1913–2007), "is that it helps you to feel better. But you don't get better. You have to back it up with action, action, action." **Cognitive-behavioral therapy (CBT)** takes a combined approach to depression and other disorders. This widely practiced *integrative* therapy aims to alter not only the way people *think* but also the way they *act*. Like other cognitive therapies, CBT seeks to make people aware of their irrational negative thinking and to replace it with new ways of thinking. And like other behavior therapies, it trains people to *practice* the more positive approach in everyday settings.

Anxiety, depressive disorders, and bipolar disorder share a common problem: emotion regulation (Aldao & Nolen-Hoeksema, 2010; Szkodny et al., 2014). An effective CBT program for these emotional disorders trains people both to replace their catastrophizing thinking with more realistic appraisals and, as homework, to practice behaviors that are incompatible with their problem (Kazantzis & Dattilio, 2010; Kazantzis et al., 2010; Moses & Barlow, 2006). A person might keep a log of daily situations associated with negative and positive emotions and engage more in activities that lead to feeling good. Those who fear social situations might learn to restrain the negative thoughts surrounding their social anxiety and practice approaching people.

CBT effectively treats people with obsessive-compulsive disorder (Öst et al., 2015). In one classic study, people learned to prevent their compulsive behaviors by relabeling their obsessive thoughts (Schwartz et al., 1996). Feeling the urge to wash their hands again, they would tell themselves, "I'm having a compulsive urge." They would explain to themselves that the hand-washing urge was a result of their brain's abnormal activity, which they had previously viewed in PET scans. Then, instead of giving in, they would spend 15 minutes in an enjoyable, alternative behavior—practicing an instrument, taking a walk, gardening. This helped "unstick" the brain by shifting attention and engaging other brain areas. For two or three months, the weekly therapy sessions continued, with relabeling and refocusing practice at home. By the study's end, most participants' symptoms had diminished, and their PET scans revealed normalized brain activity. Many other studies confirm CBT's effectiveness for treating anxiety, depression, eating disorders, and ADHD (Cristea et al., 2015; Knouse et al., 2017; Linardon et al., 2017; Milrod et al., 2015). Even online or app-guided CBT quizzes and exercises—therapy without a face-to-face therapist—have helped alleviate insomnia, depression, and anxiety (Andersson, 2016; Christensen et al., 2016; Kampmann et al., 2016; Vigerland et al., 2016). By offering flexible, affordable, and effective treatments, online CBT can reach members of disadvantaged groups who may struggle to attend face-to-face therapy sessions (Sheeber et al., 2017).

A newer CBT variation, *dialectical behavior therapy (DBT),* helps change harmful and even suicidal behavior patterns (Linehan et al., 2015; Mehlum et al., 2016; Valentine et al., 2015). *Dialectical* means "opposing," and this therapy attempts to make peace between two opposing forces—acceptance and change. Therapists create an accepting and encouraging environment, helping clients feel they have an ally who will offer them constructive feedback and guidance. In individual sessions, clients learn new ways of thinking that help them tolerate distress and regulate their emotions. They also receive training in social skills and in mindfulness meditation, which helps alleviate depression (Gu et al., 2015; Kuyken et al., 2016). Group training sessions offer additional opportunities to practice new skills in a social context, with further practice as homework.

off the mark.com   by Mark Parisi

> THE WORLD IS GETTING SO IMPERSONAL...
>
> TELL ME MORE...

©2005 MARK PARISI DIST. BY UFS INC.   offthemark.com

Mark Parisi/Atlantic Feature Syndicate/Off the Mark

> ### 🔒 RETRIEVE IT • • •
>
> ANSWERS IN APPENDIX E
>
> **RI-6** How do the humanistic and cognitive therapies differ?
>
> **RI-7** A critical attribute of the _____ _____ developed by Aaron Beck focuses on the belief that changing people's thinking can change their functioning.
>
> **RI-8** What is cognitive-behavioral therapy, and what sorts of problems does this therapy best address?

GROUP AND FAMILY THERAPIES

LOQ 44-7   What are the aims and benefits of group and family therapies?

Group Therapy

Except for traditional psychoanalysis, most therapies may also occur in small groups. **Group therapy** does not provide the same degree of therapist involvement with each client. However, it offers other benefits:

- *It saves therapists' time and clients' money* and often is no less effective than individual therapy (Burlingame et al., 2016).

- *It offers a social laboratory for exploring social behaviors and developing social skills.* Therapists frequently suggest group therapy for people experiencing frequent conflicts or whose behavior distresses others. The therapist guides people's interactions as they discuss issues and try out new behaviors.

- *It enables people to see that others share their problems.* It can be a relief to discover that others, despite their composure, experience some of the same troublesome feelings and behaviors (Ooi et al., 2016).

- *It provides feedback as clients try out new ways of behaving.* Hearing that you look poised, even though you feel anxious and self-conscious, can be very reassuring.

group therapy therapy conducted with groups rather than individuals, providing benefits from group interaction.

family therapy therapy that treats people in the context of their family system. Views an individual's unwanted behaviors as influenced by, or directed at, other family members.

Family Therapy

One special type of group interaction, **family therapy,** assumes that no person is an island. We live and grow in relation to others, especially our families. We struggle to differentiate ourselves from our families, but we also need to connect with them emotionally. These two opposing tendencies can create stress for both the individual and the family.

Family therapists tend to view families as systems, in which each person's actions trigger reactions from others. A child's rebellion, for example, affects and is affected by other family tensions. Therapists are often successful in helping family members identify their roles within the family's social system, improve communication, and discover new ways of preventing or resolving conflicts (Hazelrigg et al., 1987; Shadish et al., 1993).

John Moore/Getty Images

FAMILY THERAPY This type of therapy often acts as a preventive mental health strategy and may include marriage therapy, as shown here at a retreat for U.S. military families. The therapist helps family members understand how their ways of relating to one another create problems. The treatment's emphasis is not on changing the individuals, but on changing their relationships and interactions.

Self-Help Groups

More than 100 million Americans have belonged to small religious, interest, or support groups that meet regularly—with 9 in 10 reporting that group members "support each other emotionally" (Gallup, 1994). One analysis of more than 14,000 self-help groups reported that most focus on stigmatized or hard-to-discuss illnesses (Davison et al., 2000). AIDS patients were 250 times more likely than hypertension patients to be in support groups. People with anorexia and alcohol use disorder often join groups; those with migraines and ulcers usually do not.

The grandparent of support groups, Alcoholics Anonymous (AA), reports having 2.1 million members in 118,000 groups worldwide. Its famous 12-step program, emulated by many other self-help groups, asks members to admit their powerlessness, to seek help from a higher power and from one another, and (the twelfth step) to take the message to others in need of it (Galanter, 2016). Studies of 12-step programs such as AA have found that they help reduce alcohol use disorder at rates comparable to other treatment interventions (Ferri et al., 2006; Moos & Moos, 2005). An eight-year, $27 million investigation found that AA participants reduced their drinking sharply, as did those assigned to CBT or an alternative therapy (Project Match, 1997). Another study of 2300 veterans who sought treatment for alcohol use disorder found that a high level of AA involvement was followed by diminished alcohol problems (McKellar et al., 2003). The more meetings AA members attend, the greater their alcohol abstinence (Moos & Moos, 2006). Those whose personal stories include a "redemptive narrative"—who see something good as having come from their struggles—more often sustain sobriety (Dunlop & Tracy, 2013).

In an individualist age, with more and more people living alone or feeling isolated, the popularity of support groups—for the addicted, the bereaved, the divorced, or simply those seeking fellowship and growth—may reflect a longing for community and connectedness.

* * *

For a synopsis of these modern psychotherapies, see **TABLE 44.2**.

With more than 2 million members worldwide, AA is said to be "the largest organization on Earth that nobody wanted to join" (Finlay, 2000).

RETAIN 🔒 ☁ **LaunchPad** To study and remember the aims and techniques of different psychotherapies, review **Concept Practice: Types of Therapies and Therapists**. Assess your ability to recognize excerpts from each type with **Topic Tutorial: PsychSim6, Mystery Therapist**.

RETAIN 🔒 **TABLE 44.2**

Comparing Modern Psychotherapies

Therapy	Presumed Problem	Therapy Aim	Therapy Technique
Psychodynamic	Unconscious conflicts from childhood experiences	Reduce anxiety through self-insight.	Interpret clients' memories and feelings.
Client-centered	Barriers to self-understanding and self-acceptance	Enable growth via unconditional positive regard, acceptance, genuineness, and empathy.	Listen actively and reflect clients' feelings.
Behavior	Dysfunctional behaviors	Learn adaptive behaviors; extinguish problem ones.	Use classical conditioning (via exposure or aversion therapy) or operant conditioning (as in token economies).
Cognitive	Negative, self-defeating thinking	Promote healthier thinking and self-talk.	Train people to dispute negative thoughts and attributions.
Cognitive-behavioral	Self-harmful thoughts and behaviors	Promote healthier thinking and adaptive behaviors.	Train people to counter self-harmful thoughts and to act out their new ways of thinking.
Group and family	Stressful relationships	Heal relationships.	Develop an understanding of family and other social systems, explore roles, and improve communication.

🔒 REVIEW INTRODUCTION TO THERAPY AND THE PSYCHOLOGICAL THERAPIES

⟩ Learning Objectives

TEST YOURSELF Answer these repeated Learning Objective Questions on your own (before checking the answers in Appendix D) to improve your retention of the concepts (McDaniel et al., 2009, 2015).

44-1 How do *psychotherapy* and the *biomedical therapies* differ?

44-2 What are the goals and techniques of psychoanalysis, and how have they been adapted in psychodynamic therapy?

44-3 What are the basic themes of humanistic therapy? What are the specific goals and techniques of Rogers' client-centered approach?

44-4 How does the basic assumption of behavior therapy differ from the assumptions of psychodynamic and

humanistic therapies? What techniques are used in exposure therapies and aversive conditioning?

44-5 What is the main premise of therapy based on operant conditioning principles, and what are the views of its proponents and critics?

44-6 What are the goals and techniques of the cognitive therapies and of cognitive-behavioral therapy?

44-7 What are the aims and benefits of group and family therapies?

⟩ Terms and Concepts to Remember

TEST YOURSELF Write down the definition yourself, then check your answer on the referenced page.

psychotherapy, **p. 537**

biomedical therapy, **p. 537**

eclectic approach, **p. 537**

psychoanalysis, **p. 537**

resistance, **p. 537**

interpretation, **p. 537**

transference, **p. 537**

psychodynamic therapy, **p. 538**

insight therapies, **p. 538**

client-centered therapy, **p. 539**

active listening, **p. 539**

unconditional positive regard, **p. 540**

behavior therapy, **p. 540**

counterconditioning, **p. 540**

exposure therapies, **p. 540**

systematic desensitization, **p. 541**

virtual reality exposure therapy, **p. 541**

aversive conditioning, **p. 543**

token economy, **p. 543**

cognitive therapy, **p. 544**

cognitive-behavioral therapy (CBT), **p. 546**

group therapy, **p. 547**

family therapy, **p. 547**

⟩ Experience the Testing Effect

TEST YOURSELF Answer the following questions on your own first, then check your answers in Appendix E.

1. A therapist who helps patients search for the unconscious roots of their problem and offers interpretations of their behaviors, feelings, and dreams is drawing from
   a. psychoanalysis.
   b. humanistic therapies.
   c. client-centered therapy.
   d. behavior therapy.

2. _____ therapies are designed to help individuals discover the thoughts and feelings that guide their motivation and behavior.

3. Compared with psychoanalysts, humanistic therapists are more likely to emphasize
   a. hidden or repressed feelings.
   b. childhood experiences.
   c. psychological disorders.
   d. self-fulfillment and growth.

4. A therapist who restates and clarifies the client's statements is practicing the technique of _____ _____.

5. The goal of behavior therapy is to
   a. identify and treat the underlying causes of the problem.
   b. improve learning and insight.
   c. eliminate the unwanted behavior.
   d. improve communication and social sensitivity.

6. Behavior therapies often use _____ techniques, such as systematic desensitization and aversive conditioning to encourage clients to produce new responses to old stimuli.

7. The technique of _____ _____ teaches people to relax in the presence of progressively more anxiety-provoking stimuli.

8. After a near-fatal car accident, Rico developed such an intense fear of driving on the freeway that he takes lengthy alternative routes to work each day. Which psychological therapy might best help Rico overcome his phobia, and why?

9. At a treatment center, people who display a desired behavior receive coins that they can later exchange for other rewards. This is an example of a(n) _____.

10. Cognitive therapy has been especially effective in treating
    a. nail biting.
    b. phobias.
    c. alcohol use disorder.
    d. depression.

11. _____-_____ therapy helps people to change their self-defeating ways of thinking and to act out those changes in their daily behavior.

12. In family therapy, the therapist assumes that
    a. only one family member needs to change.
    b. each person's actions trigger reactions from other family members.
    c. dysfunctional family behaviors are based largely on genetic factors.
    d. therapy is most effective when clients are treated apart from the family unit.

Continue testing yourself with 📘 **LearningCurve** or 📖 **Achieve Read & Practice** to learn and remember most effectively.

ED WAS IN THERAPY FOR BELIEVING HE WAS A THERAPIST.

Jon Carter/Cartoonstock

45 Evaluating Psychotherapies

Many Americans have great confidence in psychotherapy's effectiveness. "Seek counseling" or "Ask your mate to find a therapist," advice columnists often urge. Before 1950, psychiatrists were the primary providers of mental health care. Today's providers include clinical and counseling psychologists; clinical social workers; pastoral, marital, abuse, and school counselors; and psychiatric nurses. With such an enormous outlay of time as well as money and effort, it is important to ask: Are the millions of people worldwide justified in placing their hopes in psychotherapy?

IS PSYCHOTHERAPY EFFECTIVE?

LOQ 45-1   Does psychotherapy work? How can we know?

The question, though simply put, is not simply answered. If an infection quickly clears, we may assume an antibiotic has been effective. But how can we assess psychotherapy's effectiveness? By how we feel about our progress? By how our therapist feels about it? By how our friends and family feel about it? By how our behavior has changed?

Clients' Perceptions

If clients' testimonials were the only measuring stick, we could strongly affirm psychotherapy's effectiveness. Consider the 2900 *Consumer Reports* readers who related their experiences with mental health professionals (1995; Kotkin et al., 1996; Seligman, 1995). How many were at least "fairly well satisfied"? Almost 90 percent. Among those who recalled feeling *fair* or *very poor* when beginning therapy, 9 in 10 now were feeling *very good, good,* or at least *so-so.* We have their word for it—and who should know better?

We should not dismiss these testimonials. But critics note reasons for skepticism:

• **People often enter therapy in crisis.** When, with the normal ebb and flow of events, the crisis passes, people may attribute their improvement to the therapy. Depressed people often get better no matter what they do.

• **Clients believe that treatment will be effective.** The *placebo effect* is the healing power of positive expectations.

- *Clients generally speak kindly of their therapists.* Even if the problems remain, clients "work hard to find something positive to say. The therapist had been very understanding, the client had gained a new perspective, he learned to communicate better, his mind was eased, anything at all so as not to have to say treatment was a failure" (Zilbergeld, 1983, p. 117).

- *Clients want to believe the therapy was worth the effort.* To admit investing time and money in something ineffective is like admitting to repeatedly hiring a mechanic who never fixes your car.

Clinicians' Perceptions

If clinicians' perceptions were proof of therapy's effectiveness, we would have even more reason to celebrate. Case studies of successful treatment abound. The problem is that clients justify entering psychotherapy by emphasizing their unhappiness, and justify leaving by emphasizing their well-being. Therapists treasure compliments from clients as they say good-bye or later express their gratitude. But they hear little from clients who experience only temporary relief and seek out new therapists for their recurring problems. Thus, therapists are most aware of the failures of *other* therapists. The same person, with the same recurring anxieties, depression, or marital difficulty, may be a "success" story in several therapists' files. Moreover, therapists, like the rest of us, are vulnerable to cognitive errors, such as *confirmation bias* and *illusory correlation* (Lilienfeld et al., 2015).

Outcome Research

How, then, can we objectively measure the effectiveness of psychotherapy? What *outcomes* can we expect—what types of people and problems are helped, and by what type of psychotherapy?

In search of answers, psychologists have turned to the well-traveled path of controlled research. Similar research in the 1800s transformed the field of medicine when skeptical physicians began to realize that many patients were dying despite receiving fashionable treatments (bleeding, purging), and many others were getting better on their own. Sorting fact from superstition required observing patients and recording outcomes with and without a particular treatment. Typhoid fever patients, for example, often improved after being bled, convincing most physicians that the treatment worked. Then came the shock. A control group was given mere bed rest, and after five weeks of fever, 70 percent improved, showing that the bleeding was worthless (Thomas, 1992).

A similar shock—and a spirited debate—followed in the twentieth century, when British psychologist Hans Eysenck (1952) summarized 24 studies of psychotherapy outcomes. He found that two-thirds of those receiving psychotherapy for disorders not involving hallucinations or delusions improved markedly. To this day, no one disputes that optimistic estimate. But there was a catch: Eysenck also reported similar improvement among people who were *untreated,* such as those on treatment waiting lists. With or without psychotherapy, he said, roughly two-thirds improved noticeably. Time was a great healer.

Later research revealed shortcomings in Eysenck's analyses. His sample was small—only 24 outcome studies in 1952, compared with hundreds available today. The best of these are *randomized clinical trials,* in which researchers randomly assign people on a waiting list to therapy or to no therapy. Later, they evaluate everyone and compare outcomes, with tests and assessments by others who don't know whether therapy was given.

A glimpse of psychotherapy's overall effectiveness can then be provided by means of a **meta-analysis**, a statistical procedure that combines the conclusions of a large number of different studies. Simply said, a meta-analysis summarizes the bottom-line results of lots of studies. Therapists welcomed the first meta-analysis of some 475 psychotherapy outcome studies (Smith et al., 1980). It showed that the average therapy client ends up better off than 80 percent of the untreated individuals on waiting lists (**FIGURE 45.1**). The claim is modest—by definition, about 50 percent of untreated people also are better off than the average untreated person. Nevertheless, Mary Lee Smith and her colleagues exulted that "psychotherapy benefits people of all ages as reliably as schooling educates them, medicine cures them, or business turns a profit" (p. 183).

LaunchPad To consider the impact of clients' belief in the treatment, see **Video: Therapeutic Effectiveness—The Placebo Effect.**

meta-analysis a statistical procedure for analyzing the results of multiple studies to reach an overall conclusion.

FIGURE 45.1

TREATMENT VERSUS NO TREATMENT These two normal distribution curves based on data from 475 studies show the improvement of untreated people and psychotherapy clients. The outcome for the average therapy client surpassed the outcome for 80 percent of the untreated people. (Data from Smith et al., 1980.)

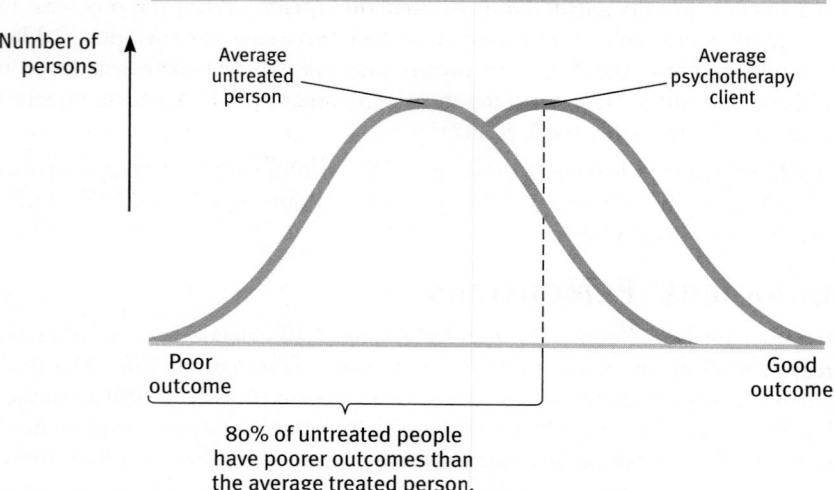

Number of persons

Average untreated person

Average psychotherapy client

Poor outcome

Good outcome

80% of untreated people have poorer outcomes than the average treated person.

TRAUMA These women were mourning the tragic loss of lives and homes in the 2010 earthquake in China. Those who suffer through such trauma may benefit from counseling, though many people recover on their own or with the help of supportive relationships with family and friends. "Life itself still remains a very effective therapist," noted psychodynamic therapist Karen Horney (*Our Inner Conflicts*, 1945).

Feng Li/Getty Images

Dozens of subsequent summaries have now examined psychotherapy's effectiveness. Their verdict echoes earlier results: *Those not undergoing therapy often improve, but those undergoing therapy are more likely to improve—and to improve more quickly and with less risk of relapse* (Kolovos et al., 2017; Weisz et al., 2017). (One qualification: Compared with studies that find no therapy benefit, those that do find a positive therapy effect are more likely to get published [Driessen et al., 2015].) Even so, many people exhibit a more stable, patient, and outgoing personality after therapy (Roberts et al., 2017). And some people experience sudden symptom reductions between their treatment sessions for depression or anxiety. Those "sudden gains" bode well for long-term improvement (Aderka et al., 2012; Wucherpfennig et al., 2017).

Psychotherapy also can be cost-effective. Studies show that when people seek psychological treatment, their search for other medical treatment drops—by 16 percent in one digest of 91 studies (Chiles et al., 1999). Psychological disorders and substance abuse exert a staggering cost on society, including crime, accidents, lost work, and treatment. By one estimate, the U.S. opioid epidemic cost the nation $95 billion in 2016 (Center for Value in Health Care, 2017). Given these enormous costs, psychotherapy is a good investment, much like money spent on prenatal and well-baby care (Chisholm et al., 2016; Ising et al., 2015). Both *reduce* long-term costs. Boosting employees' psychological well-being can lower medical costs, improve work efficiency, and diminish absenteeism.

But note that the claim—that psychotherapy, *on average*, is somewhat effective—refers to no one therapy in particular. It is like reassuring lung-cancer patients that "on average," medical treatment of health problems is effective. What people want to know is whether a *particular* treatment is effective for their specific problem.

🔒 **RETRIEVE IT** • • •   *ANSWERS IN APPENDIX E*

RI-1 How might the *placebo effect* bias clients' and clinicians' appraisals of the effectiveness of psychotherapies?

WHICH PSYCHOTHERAPIES WORK BEST?

LOQ 45-2 Are some psychotherapies more effective than others for specific disorders?

The early statistical summaries and surveys did not find that any one type of psychotherapy is generally better than others (Smith & Glass, 1977; Smith et al., 1980). Later studies have similarly found that clients can benefit from psychotherapy regardless of their clinicians' experience, training, supervision, and licensing (Cuijpers, 2017; Kivlighan et al., 2015; Wampold et al., 2017). A *Consumer Reports* survey confirmed this result (Seligman, 1995). Were clients treated by a psychiatrist, psychologist, or social worker? Were they seen in a group or individual context? Did the therapist have extensive or relatively limited training and experience? It didn't matter. Clients seemed equally satisfied.

So, was the dodo bird in *Alice in Wonderland* right: "Everyone has won and all must have prizes"? Not quite. One general finding emerges from the studies: The more specific the problem, the greater the hope that psychotherapy might solve it (Singer, 1981; Westen & Morrison, 2001). Those who experience phobias or panic, who are unassertive, or who are frustrated by sexual performance problems can hope for improvement. Those with less-focused problems, such as depression and anxiety, usually benefit in the short term but often relapse later. There often is also an overlapping or *comorbidity* of disorders.

Nevertheless, some forms of therapy do get prizes for effectively treating *particular* problems:

RETAIN 🔒

- *Cognitive and cognitive-behavioral therapies*—anxiety, posttraumatic stress disorder, insomnia, and depression (Qaseem et al., 2016; Scaini et al., 2016; Tolin, 2010).

- *Behavioral conditioning therapies*—specific behavior problems, such as bed-wetting, phobias, compulsions, marital problems, and sexual dysfunctions (Baker et al., 2008; Hunsley & DiGiulio, 2002; Shadish & Baldwin, 2005).

- *Psychodynamic therapy*—depression and anxiety (Driessen et al., 2010; Leichsenring & Rabung, 2008; Shedler, 2010b). Indeed, some analyses suggest that psychodynamic therapy is as effective as cognitive-behavioral therapy in reducing depression (Driessen et al., 2017; Steinert et al., 2017).

- *Nondirective (client-centered) counseling*—mild to moderate depression (Cuijpers et al., 2012).

The evaluation question—which therapies get prizes and which do not?—lies at the heart of what some call psychology's civil war. To what extent should science guide both clinical practice and the willingness of health care providers and insurers to pay for psychotherapy? On one side are research psychologists using scientific methods to extend the list of well-defined and validated therapies for various disorders. They decry clinicians who "give more weight to their personal experience than to science" (Baker et al., 2008). On the other side are nonscientist therapists who view their practice as more art than science: People are too complex and psychotherapy is too intuitive to describe in a manual or test in an experiment. Between these two factions stand the science-oriented clinicians calling for **evidence-based practice,** which has been endorsed by the American Psychological Association (APA) and others (2006; Lilienfeld et al., 2013). Therapists using this approach integrate the best available research with clinical expertise and with patient preferences and characteristics (**FIGURE 45.2**). After rigorous evaluation, clinicians apply therapies suited to their own skills and their patients' unique situations. Increasingly, insurer and government support for mental health services requires evidence-based practice.

"Different sores have different salves."
—English proverb

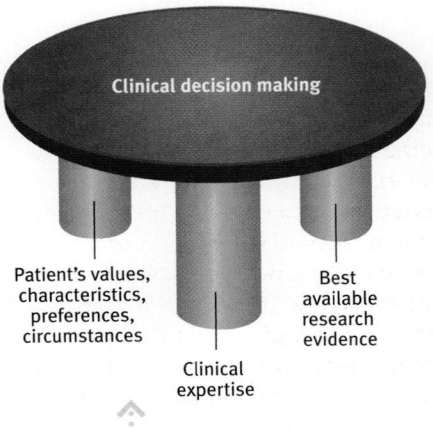

FIGURE 45.2

EVIDENCE-BASED CLINICAL DECISION MAKING The ideal clinical decision making can be visualized as a three-legged stool, upheld by research evidence, clinical expertise, and knowledge of the client.

Clinical decision making

Patient's values, characteristics, preferences, circumstances

Clinical expertise

Best available research evidence

🔒 **RETRIEVE IT • • •**   *ANSWERS IN APPENDIX E*

RI-2 Therapy is most likely to be helpful for those with problems that _____ (are/are not) well-defined.

RI-3 What is evidence-based clinical decision making?

EVALUATING ALTERNATIVE THERAPIES

LOQ 45-3 How do alternative therapies fare under scientific scrutiny?

The tendency of many abnormal states of mind to return to normal, combined with the placebo effect (the healing power of mere belief in a treatment), creates fertile soil for pseudotherapies. Bolstered by anecdotes, boosted by the media, and broadcast on the internet, alternative therapies—newer, nontraditional therapies, which often claim healing powers for various ailments—can spread like wildfire. In one national survey, 57 percent of those with a history of anxiety attacks and 54 percent of those with a history of depression had used alternative treatments, such as herbal medicine and spiritual healing (Kessler et al., 2001).

Proponents of alternative therapies often feel that their personal testimonials are evidence enough. But how well do these therapies stand up to scientific scrutiny? There

evidence-based practice clinical decision making that integrates the best available research with clinical expertise and patient characteristics and preferences.

is little evidence for or against most of them. Some, however, have been the subject of controlled research. No prizes—and no scientific support—go to certain alternative therapies (Arkowitz & Lilienfeld, 2006; Lilienfeld et al., 2015). We would all be wise to avoid *energy therapies* that propose to manipulate the client's invisible "energy fields"; *recovered-memory therapies* that aim to unearth "repressed memories" of early child abuse; and *rebirthing therapies* that reenact the supposed trauma of a client's birth.

As with some medical treatments, some psychological treatments are not only ineffective but also harmful (Barlow, 2010; Castonguay et al., 2010; Dimidjian & Hollon, 2010). The National Science and Technology Council has cited the Scared Straight program (seeking to deter children and youth from crime by having them visit with adult inmates) as an example of one such well-intentioned but ineffective program. The American Psychiatric Association and British Psychological Society have warned against "conversion therapy" for those with same-sex attractions. Conversion therapies, including "reparative therapy," aim to "repair" "something that is not a mental illness and therefore does not require therapy," declared APA president Barry Anton (2015). "There is insufficient scientific evidence that they work, and they have the potential to harm the client."

Let's look more closely at two other alternative therapies. As we do, remember that sifting sense from nonsense requires the scientific attitude: being skeptical but not cynical, open to surprises but not gullible.

Eye Movement Desensitization and Reprocessing (EMDR)

EMDR (eye movement desensitization and reprocessing) is a therapy adored by thousands and dismissed by thousands more as a sham. Psychologist Francine Shapiro (1989, 2007, 2012) developed EMDR while walking in a park and observing that anxious thoughts vanished as her eyes spontaneously darted about. Back in the clinic, she had people imagine traumatic scenes while she triggered eye movements by waving her finger in front of their eyes, supposedly enabling them to unlock and reprocess previously frozen memories. Thousands of mental health professionals from more than 75 countries have since undergone training (EMDR, 2011).

Does EMDR work? Shapiro (1999, 2002) believes it does, and she cites four studies in which it worked for 84 to 100 percent of single-trauma victims. Other studies have confirmed its benefits with trauma survivors and people with major depressive disorder (Chen et al., 2015; Littel et al., 2017; Wood et al., 2018). Why, wonder skeptics, would rapidly moving one's eyes while recalling traumas be therapeutic? Some argue that the eye movements relax or distract patients, thus allowing memory-associated emotions to extinguish (Gunter & Bodner, 2008). (Part of therapeutic change is calling up old memories and associating them with new emotions [Lane et al., 2015].) Others believe the eye movements themselves are *not* the therapeutic ingredient (nor is watching high-speed Ping-Pong therapeutic). Trials in which people imagined traumatic scenes and tapped a finger, or just stared straight ahead while the therapist's finger wagged, have also produced therapeutic results (Devilly, 2003).

Skeptics acknowledge that EMDR does work better than doing nothing (Lilienfeld & Arkowitz, 2007). But they suspect that what is therapeutic is the combination of exposure therapy—repeatedly calling up traumatic memories and reconsolidating them in a safe and reassuring context—and perhaps some placebo effect.

Light Exposure Therapy

ENGAGE Have you ever found yourself oversleeping, gaining weight, and feeling lethargic, perhaps during the dark mornings and overcast days of winter? Slowing down and conserving energy during the cold, barren winters likely gave our distant ancestors a survival advantage. To counteract lethargy, National Institute of Mental Health researchers in the early 1980s had an idea: Give people a timed daily dose of intense light. Sure enough, people reported feeling better.

Was light exposure a bright idea, or another dim-witted example of the placebo effect? Research illuminates the issue. One study exposed some people with a seasonal pattern in

"Studies indicate that EMDR is just as effective with fixed eyes. If that conclusion is right, what's useful in the therapy (chiefly behavioral desensitization) is not new, and what's new is superfluous." —Harvard Mental Health Letter, 2002

SEASONAL FUND-RAISING FOR THE *YOUNG ENTREPRENEUR*

GOT WINTER BLUES? LIGHT Therapy 5¢

their depression symptoms to 90 minutes of bright light and others to a sham placebo treatment—a hissing "negative ion generator" about which the staff expressed similar enthusiasm (but which was actually just producing white noise). After four weeks, 61 percent of those exposed to morning light had greatly improved, as had 50 percent of those exposed to evening light and 32 percent of those exposed to the placebo (Eastman et al., 1998).

Some studies have cast a shadow on light therapy. Nevertheless, others have found that 30 minutes of morning exposure of up to 10,000-lux white fluorescent light produces relief for most people with major depressive disorder and bipolar disorder. Moreover, it does so as effectively as taking antidepressant drugs or undergoing cognitive-behavioral therapy (Lam et al., 2006, 2016; Rohan et al., 2007, 2015; Sit et al., 2018). Brain scans help explain the benefit: Light therapy sparks activity in a brain region that influences the body's arousal and hormone levels (Ishida et al., 2005).

Christine Brune

LIGHT THERAPY To counter-act winter depression, some people spend time each morning exposed to intense light that mimics natural outdoor light. Light boxes are available from health supply and lighting stores.

🔒 **RETRIEVE IT • • •**   *ANSWERS IN APPENDIX E*

RI-4 What does the evidence suggest about the effectiveness of EMDR and light therapy?

HOW DO PSYCHOTHERAPIES HELP PEOPLE?

LOQ 45-4   What three elements are shared by all forms of psychotherapy?

Why have studies found little correlation between therapists' training and experience and clients' outcomes? The answer seems to be that all psychotherapies offer three basic benefits (Frank, 1982; Wampold, 2007).

- *Hope for demoralized people* People seeking therapy typically feel anxious, depressed, self-disapproving, and incapable of turning things around. What any psychotherapy offers is the expectation that, with commitment from the therapy seeker, things can and will get better. This belief, apart from any therapy technique, may improve morale, create feelings of self-efficacy, and diminish symptoms (Corrigan, 2014; Meyerhoff & Rohan, 2016).

- *A new perspective* Every psychotherapy offers people a plausible explanation of their symptoms. Armed with a believable fresh perspective, they may approach life with a new attitude, open to making changes in their behaviors and their views of themselves.

- *An empathic, trusting, caring relationship* To say that psychotherapy outcome is unrelated to training and experience is not to say that all *therapists* are equally effective. No matter what technique they use, effective therapists are empathic. They seek to understand the client's experience. They communicate care and concern, and they earn trust through respectful listening, reassurance, and guidance. These qualities were clear in recorded therapy sessions from 36 recognized master therapists (Goldfried et al., 1998). Some took a cognitive-behavioral approach. Others used psychodynamic principles. Although the master therapists used different approaches, they showed some striking behavioral *similarities*. At key moments, the empathic therapists of both persuasions would help clients evaluate themselves, link one aspect of their life with another, and gain insight into their interactions with others. The emotional bond between therapist and client—the **therapeutic alliance**—helps explain why empathic, caring therapists are especially effective (Klein et al., 2003; Wampold, 2001). A therapeutic alliance may even save lives. In one analysis of a dozen studies, a strong therapeutic alliance predicted less frequent suicidal thoughts, self-harming behaviors, and suicide attempts (Dunster-Page et al., 2017).

therapeutic alliance a bond of trust and mutual understanding between a therapist and client, who work together constructively to overcome the client's problem.

"The thing is, you have to really want to change."

ENGAGE 【ASK YOURSELF】

Based on what you've read, would you seek therapy if you were experiencing a problem? Why or why not? If you've already undergone therapy, how does what you've learned alter your feelings about the experience?

These three common elements—hope, a fresh perspective, and an empathic, caring relationship—help us understand why *paraprofessionals* (briefly trained caregivers) can assist many troubled people so effectively (Bryan & Arkowitz, 2015; Christensen & Jacobson, 1994). They also are part of what the growing numbers of self-help and support groups offer their members. And they are part of what traditional healers have offered (Jackson, 1992). Healers everywhere—special people to whom others disclose their suffering, whether psychiatrists or shamans—have listened in order to understand and to empathize, reassure, advise, console, interpret, or explain (Torrey, 1986). Such qualities may explain why people who feel supported by close relationships—who enjoy the fellowship and friendship of caring people—have been less likely to seek therapy (Frank, 1982; O'Connor & Brown, 1984).

* * *

To recap, people who seek help usually improve. So do many of those who do not undergo psychotherapy, and that is a tribute to our human resourcefulness and our capacity to care for one another. Nevertheless, though the therapist's orientation and experience appear not to matter much, people who receive some psychotherapy usually improve more than those who do not. People with clear-cut, specific problems tend to improve the most.

🔒 **RETRIEVE IT • • •**   ANSWERS IN APPENDIX E

RI-5 Those who undergo psychotherapy are _____ (more/less) likely to show improvement than those who do not undergo psychotherapy.

CULTURE AND VALUES IN PSYCHOTHERAPY

LOQ 45-5   How do culture and values influence the therapist-client relationship?

All psychotherapies offer hope. Nearly all psychotherapists attempt to enhance their clients' sensitivity, openness, personal responsibility, and sense of purpose (Jensen & Bergin, 1988). But in matters of culture and values, psychotherapists also differ from one another and may differ from their clients (Delaney et al., 2007; Kelly, 1990).

These differences can create a mismatch when a therapist from one culture interacts with a client from another. In North America, Europe, and Australia, for example, most psychotherapists reflect their culture's *individualism,* which often gives priority to personal desires and identity. Clients with a *collectivist* perspective, as with many from Asian cultures, may assume people will be more mindful of social and family responsibilities, harmony, and group goals. These clients may have trouble relating to therapies that require them to think only of their own well-being (Markus & Kitayama, 1991).

Cultural differences help explain some groups' reluctance to use mental health services. People living in "cultures of honor" prize being strong and tough. They may feel that seeking mental health care is an admission of weakness rather than an opportunity for growth (Brown et al., 2014). And some minority groups tend to be both reluctant to seek therapy and quick to leave it (Chen et al., 2009; Sue et al., 2009). In one experiment, Asian-American clients matched with counselors who shared their cultural values (rather than mismatched with those who did not) perceived more counselor empathy and felt a stronger alliance with the counselor (Kim et al., 2005).

Client-therapist mismatches may also stem from religious values. Highly religious people may prefer and benefit from religiously similar therapists and may have trouble forming an emotional bond with one who does not share their values (Masters, 2010; Pearce et al., 2015).

ENGAGE 【💡】 # FINDING A MENTAL HEALTH PROFESSIONAL

LOQ 45-6   What should a person look for when selecting a therapist?

Life for everyone is marked by a mix of serenity and stress, blessing and bereavement, good moods and bad. So, when should we seek a mental health professional's help?

The APA offers these common trouble signals:

- Feelings of hopelessness
- Deep and lasting depression
- Self-destructive behavior, such as substance abuse
- Disruptive fears
- Sudden mood shifts
- Thoughts of suicide
- Compulsive rituals, such as hand washing
- Sexual difficulties
- Hearing voices or seeing things that others don't experience

In looking for a therapist, you may want to have a preliminary consultation with two or three. College health centers are generally good starting points, and may offer some free services. You can describe your problem and learn each therapist's treatment approach. You can ask questions about the therapist's values, credentials (**TABLE 45.1**), and fees. And you can assess your own feelings about each of them. The emotional bond between therapist and client is perhaps the most important factor in effective therapy.

The APA recognizes the importance of a strong therapeutic alliance and it welcomes diverse therapists who can relate well to diverse clients. It accredits programs that provide training in cultural sensitivity (for example, differing values, communication styles, and language) and that recruit underrepresented cultural groups.

TABLE 45.1

Therapists and Their Training

Type	Therapy Description
Clinical psychologists	Most are psychologists with a Ph.D. (includes research training) or Psy.D. (focuses on therapy) supplemented by a supervised internship and, often, post-doctoral training. About half work in agencies and institutions, half in private practice.
Psychiatrists	Psychiatrists are physicians who specialize in the treatment of psychological disorders. Not all psychiatrists have had extensive training in psychotherapy, but as M.D.s or D.O.s they can prescribe medications. Thus, they tend to see those with the most serious problems. Many have their own private practice.
Clinical or psychiatric social workers	A two-year master of social work graduate program plus postgraduate supervision prepares some social workers to offer psychotherapy, mostly to people with everyday personal and family problems. About half have earned the National Association of Social Workers' designation of clinical social worker.
Counselors	Marriage and family counselors specialize in problems arising from family relations. Clergy provide counseling to countless people. Abuse counselors work with substance abusers and with spouse and child abusers and their victims. Mental health and other counselors may be required to have a two-year master's degree.

REVIEW EVALUATING PSYCHOTHERAPIES

Learning Objectives

TEST YOURSELF Answer these repeated Learning Objective Questions on your own (before checking the answers in Appendix D) to improve your retention of the concepts (McDaniel et al., 2009, 2015).

45-1 Does psychotherapy work? How can we know?

45-2 Are some psychotherapies more effective than others for specific disorders?

45-3 How do alternative therapies fare under scientific scrutiny?

45-4 What three elements are shared by all forms of psychotherapy?

45-5 How do culture and values influence the therapist-client relationship?

45-6 What should a person look for when selecting a therapist?

⦿ Terms and Concepts to Remember

TEST YOURSELF Write down the definition yourself, then check your answer on the referenced page.

meta-analysis, **p. 551**   evidence-based practice, **p. 553**   therapeutic alliance, **p. 555**

⦿ Experience the Testing Effect

TEST YOURSELF Answer the following questions on your own first, then check your answers in Appendix E.

1. The most enthusiastic or optimistic view of the effectiveness of psychotherapy comes from
   a. outcome research.
   b. randomized clinical trials.
   c. reports of clinicians and clients.
   d. a government study of treatment for depression.

2. Studies show that _____ therapy is the most effective treatment for most psychological disorders.
   a. behavior
   b. humanistic
   c. psychodynamic
   d. no one type of

3. What are the three components of evidence-based practice?

4. How does the placebo effect bias patients' attitudes about the effectiveness of various therapies?

Continue testing yourself with 📘 **LearningCurve** or 📖 **Achieve Read & Practice** to learn and remember most effectively.

ⓜ 46 The Biomedical Therapies and Preventing Psychological Disorders

"No twisted thought without a twisted molecule." —Attributed to psychologist Ralph Gerard

biomedical therapy prescribed medications or procedures that act directly on the person's physiology.

Psychotherapy is one way to treat psychological disorders. The other is **biomedical therapy**. Biomedical treatments can change the brain's chemistry with drugs; affect its circuitry with electrical stimulation, magnetic impulses, or psychosurgery; or influence its responses with lifestyle changes.

Are you surprised to find *lifestyle changes* in this list? We find it convenient to talk of separate psychological and biological influences, but everything psychological is also biological. Thus, our lifestyle—our exercise, nutrition, relationships, recreation, service to others, relaxation, and religious or spiritual engagement—affects our mental health (Schuch et al., 2016b; Walsh, 2011). (See Thinking Critically About: Therapeutic Lifestyle Change.)

Every thought and feeling depends on the functioning brain. Every creative idea, every moment of joy or anger, every period of depression emerges from the electrochemical activity of the living brain. Anxiety disorders, obsessive-compulsive disorder, posttraumatic stress disorder, major depressive disorder, bipolar disorder, and schizophrenia are all biological events. Some psychologists consider even psychotherapy to be a biological treatment, because changing the way we think and behave is a brain-changing experience (Kandel, 2013). When psychotherapy relieves behaviors associated with obsessive-compulsive disorder or schizophrenia, PET scans reveal a calmer brain (Habel et al., 2010; Schwartz et al., 1996). As we have seen over and over, *a human being is an integrated biopsychosocial system.*

THINKING CRITICALLY ABOUT:

Therapeutic Lifestyle Change

LOQ 46-1 Why is therapeutic lifestyle change considered an effective biomedical therapy, and how does it work?

LIFESTYLE (exercise, nutrition, relationships, recreation, service to others, relaxation, and religious or spiritual engagement) →	**influences our BRAIN AND BODY** →	**affects our MENTAL HEALTH** [1]

Our shared history has prepared us to be physically active and socially engaged.

Our ancestors hunted, gathered, and built in groups.

Modern researchers have found that outdoor activity in a natural environment reduces stress and promotes health. [2]

APPLICATION TO THERAPY

Training seminars promote therapeutic lifestyle change. [3] Small groups of people with depression undergo a 12-week training program with the following goals:

Aerobic exercise, 30 minutes a day, at least three times weekly (increases fitness and vitality, stimulates endorphins)

Regular aerobic exercise rivals the healing power of antidepressant drugs. [4]

Light exposure, 15 to 30 minutes each morning with a light box (amplifies arousal, influences hormones)

Reducing rumination, by identifying and redirecting negative thoughts (enhances positive thinking)

Adequate sleep, with a goal of 7 to 8 hours per night.

A complete night's sleep boosts immunity and increases energy, alertness, and mood. [5]

ZZZZZZZZZZZZZZZZZZZZZZ

Social connection, with less alone time and at least two meaningful social engagements weekly (helps satisfy the human need to belong)

Nutritional supplements, including a daily fish oil supplement with omega-3 fatty acids (aids in healthy brain functioning)

Initial small study (74 participants)[6]

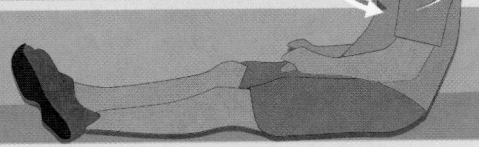

77% of those who completed the program experienced relief from depressive symptoms.

Only 19% of those assigned to a treatment-as-usual control group showed similar results.

Future research will try to identify which parts of the treatment produce the therapeutic effect.

The biomedical therapies assume that mind and body are a unit: Affect one and you will affect the other.

1. Sánchez-Villegas et al., 2015; Walsh, 2011. 2. MacKerron & Mourato, 2013; NEEF, 2015; Phillips, 2011. 3. Ilardi, 2009. 4. Babyak et al., 2000; Salmon, 2001; Schuch et al., 2016b. 5. Gregory et al., 2009; Walker & van der Helm, 2009. 6. Ilardi, 2009, 2016.

🔒 **RETRIEVE IT** • • •   *ANSWERS IN APPENDIX E*

RI-1 What are some examples of lifestyle changes people can make to enhance their mental health?

ENGAGE

ASK YOURSELF

Which lifestyle changes are most important for *you* to make to improve your mental health?

DRUG THERAPIES

LOQ 46-2 What are the drug therapies? How do double-blind studies help researchers evaluate a drug's effectiveness?

By far the most widely used biomedical treatments today are the drug therapies. Most drugs for anxiety and depression are prescribed by primary care providers, followed by psychiatrists and, in some states, psychologists.

Since the 1950s, discoveries in **psychopharmacology** (the study of drug effects on mind and behavior) have revolutionized the treatment of people with severe disorders, liberating hundreds of thousands from hospital confinement. Thanks to drug therapy and local community mental health programs, the resident population of U.S. state and county mental hospitals is now a small fraction of what it was in the mid-twentieth century. For some who are unable to care for themselves, however, release from hospitals has meant homelessness, not liberation.

Almost any new treatment, including drug therapy, is greeted by an initial wave of enthusiasm as many people apparently improve. But that enthusiasm often diminishes on closer examination. To evaluate the effectiveness of any new drug, researchers also need to know normal recovery rates.

- How many people recover without treatment, and how quickly?

- Is recovery due to the drug or to the *placebo effect?* When patients or mental health workers expect positive results, they may see what they expect, not what really happened. Even mere exposure to advertising about a drug's supposed effectiveness can increase its effect (Kamenica et al., 2013).

To control for these influences, drug researchers give half the patients the drug, and the other half a similar-appearing placebo. Because neither the staff nor the patients know who gets which, this is called a *double-blind procedure.* The good news: In double-blind studies, several types of drugs effectively treat psychological disorders.

Antipsychotic Drugs

An accidental discovery launched a treatment revolution for people with *psychosis.* The discovery: Certain drugs, used for other medical purposes, calmed the hallucinations or delusions that are part of these patients' split from reality. First-generation **antipsychotic drugs,** such as chlorpromazine (sold as Thorazine), dampened responsiveness to irrelevant stimuli. Thus, they provided the most help to patients experiencing positive (actively inappropriate) symptoms of schizophrenia, such as auditory hallucinations and paranoia (Leucht et al., 2017). (Antipsychotic drugs are less effective in changing negative symptoms such as apathy and withdrawal.)

The molecules of most conventional antipsychotic drugs are similar enough to molecules of the neurotransmitter dopamine to occupy its receptor sites and block its activity. This finding reinforces the idea that an overactive dopamine system contributes to schizophrenia.

Antipsychotics also have powerful side effects. Some produce sluggishness, tremors, and twitches similar to those of Parkinson's disease (Kaplan & Saddock, 1989). Long-term use of antipsychotics can produce *tardive dyskinesia,* with involuntary movements of the facial muscles (such as grimacing), tongue, and limbs. Although not more effective in controlling schizophrenia symptoms, many of the newer-generation antipsychotics, such as risperidone (Risperdal) and olanzapine (Zyprexa), work best for those with severe symptoms and have fewer of these effects (Furukawa et al., 2015). These drugs may, however, increase the risk of obesity and diabetes (Buchanan et al., 2010; Tiihonen et al., 2009).

Antipsychotics, combined with life-skills programs and family support, have given new hope to many people with schizophrenia (Goff et al., 2017; Guo, 2010). Hundreds of thousands of patients have left the wards of mental hospitals and returned to work and to near-normal lives (Leucht et al., 2003). Elyn Saks (2007), a University of Southern California law professor, knows what it means to live with schizophrenia. Thanks to her

"Our psychopharmacologist is a genius."

Perhaps you can guess an occasional side effect of L-dopa, a drug that raises dopamine levels for Parkinson's patients: hallucinations.

psychopharmacology the study of the effects of drugs on mind and behavior.

antipsychotic drugs drugs used to treat schizophrenia and other forms of severe thought disorder.

treatment, which combines an antipsychotic drug and psychotherapy, she noted, "Now I'm mostly well. I'm mostly thinking clearly. I do have episodes, but it's not like I'm struggling all of the time to stay on the right side of the line."

Antianxiety Drugs

Like alcohol, **antianxiety drugs,** such as Xanax or Ativan, depress central nervous system activity (and so should not be used in combination with alcohol). Some antianxiety drugs have been successfully used in combination with psychological therapy to enhance exposure therapy's extinction of learned fears and to help relieve the symptoms of posttraumatic stress disorder and obsessive-compulsive disorder (Davis, 2005; Kushner et al., 2007).

Some critics fear that antianxiety drugs may reduce symptoms without resolving underlying problems, especially when used as an ongoing treatment. "Popping a Xanax" at the first sign of tension can create a learned response: The immediate relief reinforces a person's tendency to take drugs when anxious. Antianxiety drugs can also be addictive. Regular users who stop taking these drugs may experience increased anxiety, insomnia, and other withdrawal symptoms.

Antidepressant Drugs

The **antidepressant drugs** were named for their ability to lift people up from a state of depression, and this was their main use until recently. The label is a bit of a misnomer now that these drugs are increasingly used to treat anxiety disorders, obsessive-compulsive disorder, and posttraumatic stress disorder (Wetherell et al., 2013). Many work by increasing the availability of neurotransmitters, such as norepinephrine or serotonin, which elevate arousal and mood and are scarce when a person experiences feelings of depression or anxiety. The most commonly prescribed drugs in this group, including Prozac and its cousins Zoloft and Paxil, work by blocking the normal reuptake process (**FIGURE 46.1**). Given their use in treating disorders other than depression—from anxiety to strokes—these drugs are most often called *SSRIs—selective serotonin reuptake inhibitors* (rather than antidepressants) (Kramer, 2011).

Some of the older antidepressant drugs work by blocking the reabsorption or breakdown of both norepinephrine and serotonin. Though effective, these dual-action drugs have more potential side effects, such as dry mouth, weight gain, hypertension, or dizzy spells (Anderson, 2000; Mulrow, 1999). Administering them by means of a patch, which bypasses the intestines and liver, helps reduce such side effects (Bodkin & Amsterdam, 2002). Some professionals prefer the SSRIs over other antidepressants (Jakubovski et al., 2015; Kramer, 2011).

antianxiety drugs drugs used to control anxiety and agitation.

antidepressant drugs drugs used to treat depression, anxiety disorders, obsessive-compulsive disorder, and posttraumatic stress disorder. (Several widely used antidepressant drugs are *selective serotonin reuptake inhibitors—SSRIs.*)

**FIGURE 46.1
BIOLOGY OF ANTIDEPRESSANTS** Shown here is the action of Prozac, which partially blocks the reuptake of serotonin.

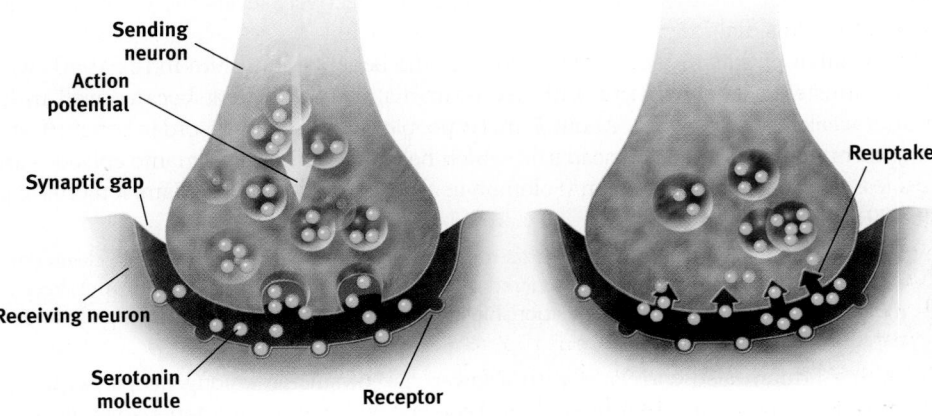
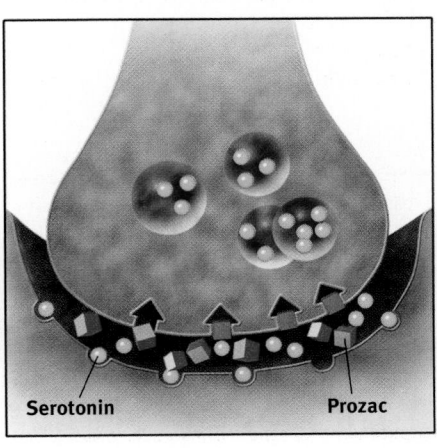

Message is sent across synaptic gap.

Message is received; excess serotonin molecules are reabsorbed by sending neuron.

Prozac partially blocks normal reuptake of the neurotransmitter serotonin; excess serotonin in synapse enhances its mood-lifting effect.

Sending neuron
Action potential
Synaptic gap
Receiving neuron
Serotonin molecule
Receptor

Reuptake

Serotonin   Prozac

(a)   (b)   (c)

But be advised: Patients with depression who begin taking antidepressants do not wake up the next morning singing "It's a beautiful day!" SSRIs begin to influence neurotransmission within hours, but their full psychological effect may take four weeks (and may involve a side effect of diminished sexual desire). One possible reason for the delay is that increased serotonin promotes new synapses plus *neurogenesis*—the birth of new brain cells, perhaps reversing stress-induced loss of neurons (Launay et al., 2011). Researchers are also exploring the possibility of quicker-acting antidepressants. One, ketamine, which is also an anesthetic and a risky, psychedelic party drug, blocks hyperactive receptors for glutamate, a neurotransmitter, and causes a burst of new synapses. It can provide relief from depression within hours of an infusion, often after transient hallucinations (Sanacora et al., 2017). Some drug companies are hoping to develop a ketamine-like, fast-acting drug without its side effects (Kirby, 2015).

Antidepressant drugs are not the only way to give the body a lift. Aerobic exercise can calm people who feel anxious, energize those who feel depressed, and offer other positive side effects. Cognitive therapy, by helping people reverse their habitual negative thinking style, can boost drug-aided relief from depression and reduce posttreatment relapses (Amick et al., 2015). Some clinicians attack depression (and anxiety) from both below and above (Cuijpers et al., 2010; Hollon et al., 2014; Kennard et al., 2014). They use antidepressant drugs (which work, bottom-up, on the emotion-forming limbic system) in conjunction with cognitive-behavioral therapy (which works, top-down, to alter frontal lobe activity and change thought processes).

Researchers generally agree that people with depression often improve after a month on antidepressant drugs. But after allowing for natural recovery and the placebo effect, how big is the drug effect? Not big, report some researchers (Kirsch et al., 1998, 2014, 2016). In double-blind clinical trials, placebos produced improvement comparable to about 75 percent of the active drug's effect. For those with severe depression, the placebo effect is less and the added drug benefit somewhat greater (Fournier et al., 2010; Kirsch et al., 2008; Olfson & Marcus, 2009). Given that antidepressants often have unwanted side effects, and that aerobic exercise and cognitive-behavioral therapy are also effective antidotes to mild or moderate depression, Irving Kirsch (2016) recommends more limited antidepressant use: "If they are to be used at all, it should be as a last resort." *The bottom line:* If you're concerned about your mental health, consult with a mental health professional to determine the best treatment for you.

"If this doesn't help you don't worry, it's a placebo."

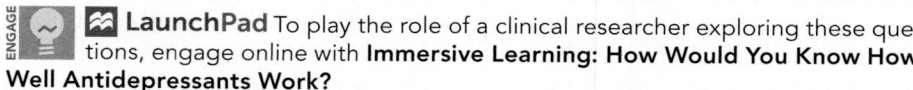

ENGAGE 🔆 📚 **LaunchPad** To play the role of a clinical researcher exploring these questions, engage online with **Immersive Learning: How Would You Know How Well Antidepressants Work?**

Mood-Stabilizing Medications

In addition to antipsychotic, antianxiety, and antidepressant drugs, psychiatrists have *mood-stabilizing drugs* in their arsenal. One of them, Depakote, was originally used to treat epilepsy. It was also found effective in controlling the manic episodes associated with bipolar disorder. Another, the simple salt *lithium,* effectively levels the emotional highs and lows of this disorder.

Australian physician John Cade discovered the benefits of lithium in the 1940s when he administered it to a patient with severe mania and the patient became well in less than a week (Snyder, 1986). About 7 in 10 people with bipolar disorder benefit from a long-term daily dose of this cheap salt, which helps prevent or ease manic episodes and, to a lesser extent, lifts depression (Solomon et al., 1995). Kay Redfield Jamison (1995, pp. 88–89) described the effect:

> Lithium prevents my seductive but disastrous highs, diminishes my depressions, clears out the wool and webbing from my disordered thinking, slows me down, gentles me out, keeps me from ruining my career and relationships, keeps me out of a hospital, alive, and makes psychotherapy possible.

Taking lithium also correlates with a lower risk of suicide among people with bipolar disorder—about one-sixth the risk of those not taking lithium (Oquendo et al., 2011). Naturally occurring lithium in drinking water has also correlated with lower suicide rates (across 18 Japanese cities and towns) and lower crime rates (across 27 Texas counties) (Ohgami et al., 2009; Schrauzer & Shrestha, 1990, 2010; Terao et al., 2010). Lithium works.

"First of all I think you should know that last quarter's sales figures are interfering with my mood-stabilizing drugs."

563

BRAIN STIMULATION

LOQ 46-3 How are brain stimulation and psychosurgery used in treating specific disorders?

Electroconvulsive Therapy

Another biomedical treatment, **electroconvulsive therapy (ECT),** manipulates the brain by shocking it. When ECT was first introduced in 1938, the wide-awake patient was strapped to a table and jolted with electricity to the brain. The procedure, which produced convulsions and brief unconsciousness, gained a barbaric image. Although that image lingers, today's ECT is much kinder and gentler, and no longer "convulsive." The patient receives a general anesthetic and a muscle relaxant (to prevent bodily convulsions). A psychiatrist then delivers a brief pulse of electrical current, sometimes only to the brain's right side, which triggers a 30- to 60-second seizure. Within 30 minutes, the patient awakens and remembers nothing of the treatment or of the preceding hours.

Study after study confirms that ECT can effectively treat severe depression in "treatment-resistant" patients who have not responded to drug therapy (Bailine et al., 2010; Fink, 2009; Lima et al., 2013; Medda et al., 2015). After three such sessions each week for two to four weeks, 70 percent or more of those receiving today's ECT improve markedly, without discernible brain damage and with less memory loss than with earlier versions of ECT (HMHL, 2007). ECT also reduces suicidal thoughts and has been credited with saving many from suicide (Kellner et al., 2006). A *Journal of the American Medical Association* editorial concluded that "the results of ECT in treating severe depression are among the most positive treatment effects in all of medicine" (Glass, 2001).

How does ECT relieve severe depression? After more than 70 years, no one knows for sure. One patient likened ECT to the smallpox vaccine, which was saving lives before we knew how it worked. Perhaps the brief electric current calms neural centers where overactivity produces depression. Some research indicates that ECT stimulates neurogenesis (new neurons) and new synaptic connections (Joshi et al., 2016; Rotheneichner et al., 2014; Wang et al., 2017b).

No matter how impressive the results, the idea of electrically shocking a person's brain still strikes many as barbaric, especially given our ignorance about why ECT works. Moreover, the mood boost may not last long. Many ECT-treated patients eventually relapse back into depression, although relapses are somewhat fewer for those who also receive antidepressant drugs or who do aerobic exercise (Rosenquist et al., 2016; Salehi et al., 2016). *The bottom line:* In the minds of many psychiatrists and patients, ECT is a lesser evil than severe depression's misery, anguish, and risk of suicide. As research psychologist Norman Endler (1982) reported after ECT alleviated his deep depression, "A miracle had happened in two weeks."

Alternative Neurostimulation Therapies

Three other neural stimulation techniques—mild cranial electrical stimulation, magnetic stimulation, and deep brain stimulation—also aim to treat the depressed brain (**FIGURE 46.2**).

TRANSCRANIAL ELECTRICAL STIMULATION In contrast to ECT, which produces a brain seizure with about 800 milliamps of electricity, *transcranial direct current stimulation (tDCS)* administers a weak 1- to 2-milliamp current to the scalp. The current is so mild that some people have attempted to use the tDCS machines to stimulate their own cognitive abilities, though skeptics argue that such a current is too weak to penetrate to the brain and that studies do not confirm cognitive benefits (Horvath et al., 2015; Underwood, 2016). After reviewing recent studies, two European expert panels did, however, report "probable efficacy" of tDCS as a depression treatment (Brunoni et al., 2016; Lefaucheur et al., 2017).

The medical use of electricity is an ancient practice. Physicians treated the Roman Emperor Claudius (10 B.C.E.–54 C.E.) for headaches by pressing electric eels to his temples. Today, about 17 people per 100,000—people whose depression has not responded to other treatments—have received ECT (Lesage et al., 2016).

"I used to . . . be unable to shake the dread even when I was feeling good, because I knew the bad feelings would return. ECT has wiped away that foreboding. It has given me a sense of control, of hope." —Kitty Dukakis, 2006

 **LaunchPad** To witness the powerful effects of ECT, see the **Video: Electroconvulsive Therapy.**

electroconvulsive therapy (ECT) a biomedical therapy for severely depressed patients in which a brief electric current is sent through the brain of an anesthetized patient.

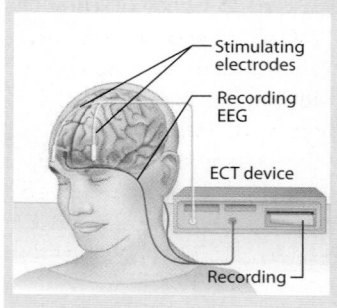

Electroconvulsive therapy (ECT)
Psychiatrist administers a strong current, which triggers a seizure in the anesthetized patient.

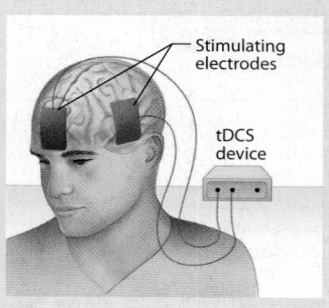

Transcranial direct current stimulation (tDCS)
Psychiatrist applies a weak current to the scalp.

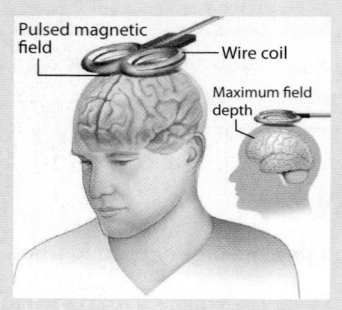

Repetitive transcranial magnetic stimulation (rTMS)
Psychiatrist sends a painless magnetic field through the skull to the surface of the cortex to alter brain activity.

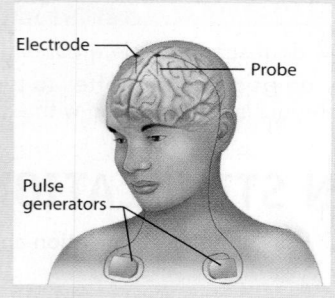

Deep brain stimulation (DBS)
Psychiatrist stimulates electrodes implanted in "sadness centers" to calm those areas.

FIGURE 46.2

A STIMULATING EXPERIENCE
Today's neurostimulation therapies apply strong or mild electricity, or magnetic energy, either to the skull's surface or directly to brain neurons.

A meta-analysis of 17 clinical experiments found that one other stimulation procedure alleviates depression: massage therapy (Hou et al., 2010).

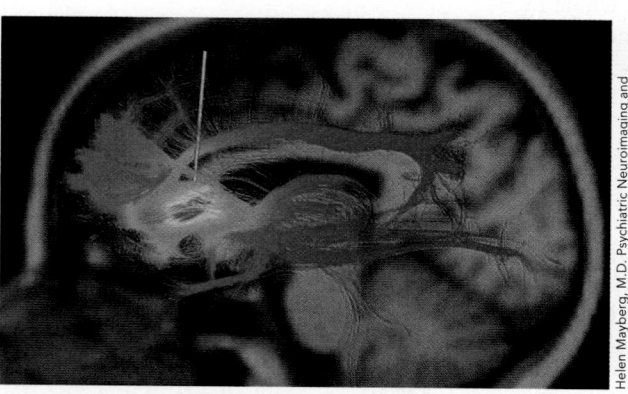

A DEPRESSION SWITCH? By comparing the brains of patients with and without depression, researcher Helen Mayberg identified a brain area (highlighted in red) that appears active in people who are depressed or sad, and whose activity may be calmed by deep brain stimulation.

Helen Mayberg, M.D. Psychiatric Neuroimaging and Therapeutics, The Mayberg Lab at Emory University, Atlanta, GA/V. J. Wedeen and L. L. Wald/Athinoula A. Martinos Center For Biomedical Imaging and The Human Connectome Project, Boston, MA

MAGNETIC STIMULATION Depressed moods also sometimes improve when a painless procedure—called **repetitive transcranial magnetic stimulation (rTMS)**—is performed on wide-awake patients over several weeks. Repeated pulses surging through a magnetic coil held close to the skull can stimulate or suppress activity in areas of the cortex. Like tDCS (and unlike ECT), the rTMS procedure produces no memory loss or other serious side effects, aside from possible headaches.

Some studies have found that, for 30 to 40 percent of people with depression, rTMS works (Becker et al., 2016; Brunoni et al., 2017; Taylor et al., 2017). How it works is unclear. One possible explanation is that the stimulation energizes the brain's left frontal lobe, which is relatively inactive during depression (Helmuth, 2001). Repeated stimulation may cause nerve cells to form new functioning circuits through the process of *long-term potentiation*.

DEEP BRAIN STIMULATION Other patients whose depression has resisted both drugs and ECT have benefited from an experimental treatment pinpointing a neural hub that bridges the thinking frontal lobes to the limbic system (Becker et al., 2016; Brunoni et al., 2017; Ryder & Holtzheimer, 2016). This area, which is overactive in the brain of a depressed or temporarily sad person, calms when treated by ECT or antidepressants. To experimentally activate neurons that inhibit this negative activity, neuroscientist Helen Mayberg drew upon the *deep brain stimulation* (DBS) technology, sometimes used to treat Parkinson's tremors. Since 2003, she and her colleagues have used DBS to treat some 200 depressed patients with implanted electrodes in a brain area that functions as the neural "sadness center" (Lozano & Mayberg, 2015). About one-third reportedly have responded "extremely well" and another 30 percent have modestly improved (Underwood, 2013). Some felt suddenly more aware and became more talkative and engaged; others improved only slightly, if at all. Other studies have found little benefit when DBS is compared with "sham" (placebo) electrode treatments (Witter & Ward, 2016). With 15 new National Institutes of Health–funded studies of DBS under way in 2017, we will soon have a better understanding of its efficacy (Underwood, 2017).

PSYCHOSURGERY

Because its effects are irreversible, **psychosurgery**—surgery that removes or destroys brain tissue—is the most drastic and least-used biomedical intervention for changing behavior. In the 1930s, Portuguese physician Egas Moniz developed what would become the best-known psychosurgical operation: the **lobotomy.** Moniz found that cutting the nerves connecting the frontal lobes with the emotion-controlling centers of the inner brain calmed uncontrollably emotional and violent patients. In what would later become, in others' hands, a crude but quick and easy procedure, a neurosurgeon would shock the patient into a coma, hammer an icepick-like instrument through each eye socket into the brain, and then wiggle it to sever connections running up to the frontal lobes. Between 1936 and 1954, tens of thousands of severely disturbed people were "lobotomized" (Valenstein, 1986).

Although the intention was simply to disconnect emotion from thought, the effect was often more drastic. A lobotomy usually decreased the person's misery or tension, but it also produced a permanently lethargic, immature, uncreative person. During the 1950s, after some 35,000 people had been lobotomized in the United States alone, calming drugs became available and psychosurgery became scorned—as in the saying sometimes attributed to W. C. Fields that "I'd rather have a bottle in front of me than a frontal lobotomy."

Today, lobotomies are history. More precise, microscale psychosurgery is sometimes used in extreme cases. For example, if a patient suffers uncontrollable seizures, surgeons can deactivate the specific nerve clusters that cause or transmit the convulsions. MRI-guided precision surgery is also occasionally done to cut the circuits involved in severe major depressive disorder and obsessive-compulsive disorder (Carey, 2009, 2011; Kim et al., 2018; Sachdev & Sachdev, 1997). Because these procedures are irreversible, neurosurgeons perform them only as a last resort.

New York Times Co./Getty Images

FAILED LOBOTOMY This 1940 photo shows Rosemary Kennedy (center) at age 22 with brother (and future U.S. president) John and sister Jean. A year later her father, on medical advice, approved a lobotomy that was promised to control her reportedly violent mood swings. The procedure left her confined to a hospital with an infantile mentality until her death in 2005 at age 86.

ENGAGE

ASK YOURSELF

What were your impressions of biomedical therapies before reading this section? Are any of your views different now? Why or why not?

* * *

TABLE 46.1 summarizes some aspects of the biomedical therapies we've discussed.

RETAIN

🔒 TABLE 46.1

Comparing Biomedical Therapies

Therapy	Presumed Problem	Therapy Aim	Therapy Technique
Therapeutic lifestyle change	Stress and unhealthy lifestyle	Restore healthy biological state.	Alter lifestyle through adequate exercise, sleep, nutrition, and other changes.
Drug therapies	Neurotransmitter malfunction	Control symptoms of psychological disorders.	Alter brain chemistry through drugs.
Brain stimulation	Depression (ECT is used only for severe, treatment-resistant depression.)	Alleviate depression, especially when it is unresponsive to drugs or other forms of therapy.	Stimulate brain through electroconvulsive shock, mild electrical stimulation, magnetic impulses, or deep brain stimulation.
Psychosurgery	Brain malfunction	Relieve severe disorders.	Remove or destroy brain tissue.

repetitive transcranial magnetic stimulation (rTMS) the application of repeated pulses of magnetic energy to the brain; used to stimulate or suppress brain activity.

psychosurgery surgery that removes or destroys brain tissue in an effort to change behavior.

lobotomy a psychosurgical procedure once used to calm uncontrollably emotional or violent patients. The procedure cut the nerves connecting the frontal lobes to the emotion-controlling centers of the inner brain.

🔒 RETRIEVE IT • • •

ANSWERS IN APPENDIX E

RI-4 Severe depression that has not responded to other therapy may be treated with _____ _____, which can cause brain seizures and memory loss. More moderate neural stimulation techniques designed to help alleviate depression include _____ direct current stimulation, _____ _____ magnetic stimulation, and _____ _____ stimulation.

THIS ANTI-DEPRESSANT WORKS BEST IF YOU TAKE IT WITH WATER LAPPING NEAR YOUR HAMMOCK ON A CARIBBEAN BEACH.

Dave Coverly/Speed Bump

PREVENTING PSYCHOLOGICAL DISORDERS AND BUILDING RESILIENCE

LOQ 46-4   What is the rationale for preventive mental health programs, and why is it important to develop resilience?

Psychotherapies and biomedical therapies tend to locate the cause of psychological disorders within the person. We infer that people who act cruelly must be cruel and that people who act "crazy" must be "sick." We attach labels to such people, thereby distinguishing them from "normal" folks. It follows, then, that we try to treat "abnormal" people by giving them insight into their problems, by changing their thinking, by helping them gain control with drugs.

There is an alternative viewpoint: We could interpret many psychological disorders as understandable responses to a disturbing and stressful society. According to this view, it is not just the person who needs treatment, but also the person's social context. Better to prevent a problem by reforming an unhealthy situation and by developing people's coping competencies than to wait for and treat problems.

Preventive Mental Health

A story about the rescue of a drowning person from a rushing river illustrates this viewpoint: Having successfully administered first aid to the first victim, the rescuer spots another struggling person and pulls her out, too. After a half-dozen repetitions, the rescuer suddenly turns and starts running away while the river sweeps yet another floundering person into view. "Aren't you going to rescue that fellow?" asks a bystander. "Heck no," the rescuer replies. "I'm going upstream to find out what's pushing all these people in."

Preventive mental health is upstream work. It seeks to prevent psychological casualties by identifying and alleviating the conditions that cause them. As George Albee (1986, 2006) pointed out, there is abundant evidence that poverty, meaningless work, constant criticism, unemployment, racism, and sexism undermine people's sense of competence, personal control, and self-esteem. Such stresses increase their risk of depression, alcohol use disorder, and suicide.

To prevent psychological casualties we should, Albee contended, support programs that alleviate these demoralizing situations. We eliminated smallpox not by treating the afflicted but by inoculating the unafflicted. We conquered yellow fever by controlling mosquitoes. Better to drain the swamps than swat the mosquitoes.

Preventing psychological problems means empowering those who have learned an attitude of helplessness and changing environments that breed loneliness. It means renewing fragile family ties and boosting parents' and teachers' skills at nurturing children's competence and belief in their abilities. It means harnessing positive psychology interventions to enhance human flourishing. One intervention taught adolescents that personality isn't fixed—people can change—and reduced their incidence of future depression by 40 percent (Miu & Yeager, 2015). In short, "everything aimed at improving the human condition, at making life more fulfilling and meaningful, may be considered part of primary prevention of mental or emotional disturbance" (Kessler & Albee, 1975, p. 557). Prevention can sometimes provide a double payoff. People with a strong sense of life's meaning are more engaging socially (Stillman et al., 2011). If we can strengthen people's sense of meaning in life, we may also lessen their loneliness as they grow into more engaging companions.

Among the upstream prevention workers are *community psychologists*. Mindful of how people interact with their environment, they focus on creating environments that support psychological health. Through their research and social action, community psychologists aim to empower people and to enhance their competence, health, and well-being.

Building Resilience

Preventive mental health includes efforts to build individuals' **resilience**—the ability to cope with stress and recover from adversity.

"It is better to prevent than to cure."
—Peruvian folk wisdom

"Mental disorders arise from physical ones, and likewise physical disorders arise from mental ones." —The Mahabharata, 200 B.C.E.

Horst Faas/AP Images

Nancy Kaszerman/ZUMA Press/Newscom

RESILIENT GROWTH FROM PRISONER TO POLITICIAN Before becoming a U.S. senator, John McCain (1936–2018) spent more than five years as a Vietnam War prisoner. He was regularly beaten and tortured, which left him permanently unable to lift his arms above his head. Yet he found strength in reflecting positively on his experience. "I put the war behind me when I left," he said. "The memories I have are of the wonderful people I had the privilege of serving with" (Myre, 2000). When diagnosed with brain cancer in 2017, his daughter Meghan tweeted that "The one of us who is most confident and calm is my father."

Faced with unforeseen trauma, most adults exhibit resilience. This was true of New Yorkers in the aftermath of the September 11 terror attacks, especially for those who enjoyed supportive close relationships and who had not recently experienced other stressful events (Bonanno et al., 2007). More than 9 in 10 New Yorkers, although stunned and grief-stricken by 9/11, did *not* have a dysfunctional stress reaction. Among those who did, the stress symptoms were mostly gone by the following January (Person et al., 2006). Even most combat-stressed veterans, most political rebels who have survived torture, and most people with spinal cord injuries do not later exhibit posttraumatic stress disorder (Bonanno et al., 2012; Mineka & Zinbarg, 1996).

Struggling with challenging crises can even lead to **posttraumatic growth.** Many cancer survivors have reported a greater appreciation for life, more meaningful relationships, increased personal strength, changed priorities, and a richer spiritual life (Tedeschi & Calhoun, 2004). Out of even our worst experiences, some good can come, especially when we can imagine new possibilities (Roepke, 2015; Roepke & Seligman, 2015). Suffering can beget new sensitivity and strength.

🔒 **RETRIEVE IT • • •**   *ANSWERS IN APPENDIX E*

RI-5 What is the difference between preventive mental health and the psychological and biomedical therapies?

LaunchPad Consider ways to build your own resilience by engaging with **Immersive Learning: Assess Your Strengths—How Resilient Are You, and Why Should You Build More Resilience?**

* * *

ENGAGE

If you just finished reading this book, your introduction to psychological science is completed. Our tour of psychological science has taught us much—and you, too?—about our moods and memories, about the reach of our unconscious, about how we flourish and struggle, about how we perceive our physical and social worlds, and about how our biology and culture shape us. Our hope, as your guides on this tour, is that you have shared some of our fascination, grown in your understanding and compassion, and sharpened your critical thinking. And we hope you enjoyed the ride.

With every good wish in your future endeavors,

David G. Myers
DavidMyers.org

Nathan DeWall
NathanDeWall.com

resilience the personal strength that helps most people cope with stress and recover from adversity and even trauma.

posttraumatic growth positive psychological changes as a result of struggling with extremely challenging circumstances and life crises.

🔒 REVIEW THE BIOMEDICAL THERAPIES AND PREVENTING PSYCHOLOGICAL DISORDERS

⟩⟩ Learning Objectives

TEST YOURSELF Answer these repeated Learning Objective Questions on your own (before checking the answers in Appendix D) to improve your retention of the concepts (McDaniel et al., 2009, 2015).

46-1 Why is therapeutic lifestyle change considered an effective biomedical therapy, and how does it work?

46-2 What are the drug therapies? How do double-blind studies help researchers evaluate a drug's effectiveness?

46-3 How are brain stimulation and psychosurgery used in treating specific disorders?

46-4 What is the rationale for preventive mental health programs, and why is it important to develop resilience?

⟩⟩ Terms and Concepts to Remember

TEST YOURSELF Write down the definition yourself, then check your answer on the referenced page.

biomedical therapy, **p. 558**

psychopharmacology, **p. 560**

antipsychotic drugs, **p. 560**

antianxiety drugs, **p. 561**

antidepressant drugs, **p. 561**

electroconvulsive therapy (ECT), **p. 563**

repetitive transcranial magnetic stimulation (rTMS), **p. 565**

psychosurgery, **p. 565**

lobotomy, **p. 565**

resilience, **p. 567**

posttraumatic growth, **p. 567**

⟩⟩ Experience the Testing Effect

TEST YOURSELF Answer the following questions on your own first, then check your answers in Appendix E.

1. Some antipsychotic drugs, used to calm people with schizophrenia, can have unpleasant side effects, most notably
   a. hyperactivity.
   b. convulsions and momentary memory loss.
   c. sluggishness, tremors, and twitches.
   d. paranoia.

2. Drugs such as Xanax and Ativan, which depress central nervous system activity, can become addictive when used as ongoing treatment. These drugs are referred to as _____ drugs.

3. A simple salt that often brings relief to patients suffering the highs and lows of bipolar disorder is _____.

4. When drug therapies have not been effective, electroconvulsive therapy (ECT) may be used as treatment, largely for people with
   a. severe obsessive-compulsive disorder.
   b. severe depression.
   c. schizophrenia.
   d. anxiety disorders.

5. An approach that seeks to identify and alleviate conditions that put people at high risk for developing psychological disorders is called
   a. deep brain stimulation.
   b. the mood-stabilizing perspective.
   c. spontaneous recovery.
   d. preventive mental health.

Continue testing yourself with 📚 **LearningCurve** or ≈ **Achieve Read & Practice** to learn and remember most effectively.

Statistical Reasoning in Everyday Life

Statistics are important tools in psychological research. But statistics also benefit us all, by helping us see what the unaided eye might miss. To be an educated person today is to be able to apply simple statistical principles to everyday reasoning. We needn't memorize complicated formulas to think more clearly and critically about data.

Off-the-top-of-the-head estimates often misread reality and mislead the public. Someone throws out a big, round number. Others echo it, and before long the big, round number becomes public misinformation. Two examples:

- ***Ten percent of people are gay or lesbian.*** Or is it 2 to 4 percent, as suggested by various national surveys (Module 15)?

- ***We ordinarily use only 10 percent of our brain.*** Or is it closer to 100 percent (Module 5)?

ENGAGE If you see an attention-grabbing headline presented without evidence—that nationally there are one million teen pregnancies, two million homeless seniors, or three million alcohol-related car accidents—you can be pretty sure that someone is guessing. If they want to emphasize the problem, they will be motivated to guess big. If they want to minimize the problem, they will guess small. *The point to remember:* Use critical thinking when presented with big, round, undocumented numbers.

Statistical illiteracy also feeds needless health scares (Gigerenzer, 2010). In the 1990s, the British press reported a study showing that women taking a particular contraceptive pill had a 100 percent increased risk of blood clots that could produce strokes. The story went viral, causing thousands of women to stop taking the pill. What happened as a result? A wave of unwanted pregnancies and an estimated 13,000 additional abortions (which also are associated with increased blood clot risk). Distracted by big, round numbers, few people focused on the study's actual findings: A 100 percent increased risk, indeed—but only from 1 in 7000 to 2 in 7000. Such false alarms underscore the need to think critically, to teach statistical reasoning, and to present statistical information more transparently.

> ⟶ **Describing Data**
> **Measures of Central Tendency**
> **Measures of Variation**
> **Correlation: A Measure of Relationships**
>
> ⟶ **Significant Differences**
> **When Is an Observed Difference Reliable?**
> **When Is an Observed Difference Significant?**

When setting goals, we love big, round numbers. We're far more likely to want to lose 20 pounds than 19 or 21 pounds (or an even 10 kilograms rather than 9.07 kilograms). And by modifying their behavior, batters are nearly four times more likely to finish the season with a .300 average than with a .299 average (Pope & Simonsohn, 2011).

"Figures can be misleading—so I've written a song which I think expresses the real story of the firm's performance this quarter."

Patrick Hardin/Cartoonstock.com

⟶ Describing Data

LEARNING OBJECTIVE QUESTION (LOQ)

A-1 How do we describe data using three measures of central tendency, and what is the relative usefulness of the two measures of variation?

Once researchers have gathered their data, they may organize that data using *descriptive statistics.* One way to do this is to show the data in a simple *bar graph,* as in **FIGURE A.1**, which displays a distribution of different brands of trucks still on the road after a decade. When reading statistical graphs such as this one, take care. It's easy to design a graph to make a

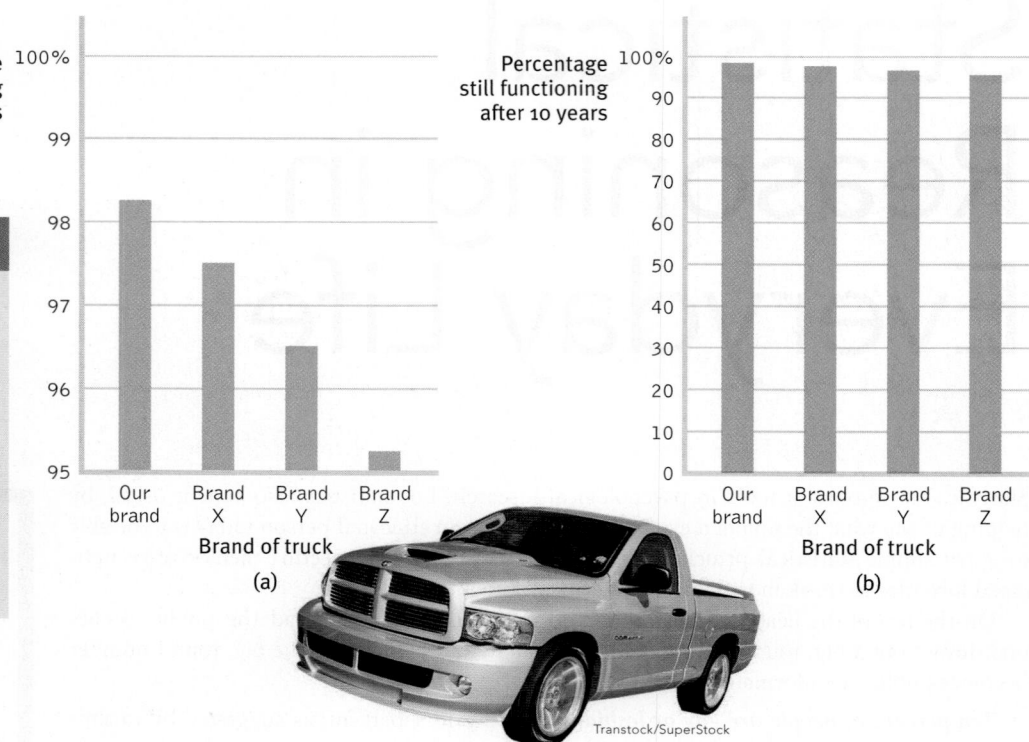

(a)

(b)

Transtock/SuperStock

FIGURE A.1

READ THE SCALE LABELS

RI-1 An American truck manufacturer offered graph (a)—with actual brand names included—to suggest the much greater durability of its trucks. What does graph (b) make clear about the varying durability, and how is this accomplished? *(See Appendix E for answers.)*

ENGAGE 💡 (**ASK YOURSELF**)

Find a graph in your social media news feed. How does the article's author use (or abuse) statistics to make a point?

The average person has one ovary and one testicle.

mode the most frequently occurring score(s) in a distribution.

mean the arithmetic average of a distribution, obtained by adding the scores and then dividing by the number of scores.

median the middle score in a distribution; half the scores are above it and half are below it.

difference look big (Figure A.1a) or small (Figure A.1b). The secret lies in how you label the vertical scale (the *y-axis*).

The point to remember: Think smart. When viewing graphs, read the scale labels and note their *range*.

Measures of Central Tendency

The next step is to summarize the data using some *measure of central tendency,* a single score that represents a whole set of scores. The simplest measure is the **mode,** the most frequently occurring score or scores. The most familiar is the **mean,** or arithmetic average—the total sum of all the scores divided by the number of scores. The midpoint—the 50th percentile—is the **median.** On a divided highway, the median is the middle. So, too, with data: If you arrange all the scores in order from the highest to the lowest, half will be above the median and half will be below it.

Measures of central tendency neatly summarize data. But consider what happens to the mean when a distribution is lopsided, when it's *skewed* by a few way-out scores. With income data, for example, the mode, median, and mean often tell very different stories (**FIGURE A.2**). This happens because the mean is biased by a few extreme incomes. When Amazon founder Jeff Bezos sits down in a small café, its average (mean) customer instantly becomes a billionaire. But median customer wealth remains unchanged. Understanding this, you can see why, according to the 2010 U.S. Census, nearly 65 percent of U.S. households have "below average" income. The bottom half of earners receive much less than half of the total national income. So, most Americans make less than the mean. Mean and median tell different true stories.

The point to remember: Always note which measure of central tendency is reported. If it is a mean, consider whether a few atypical scores could be distorting it.

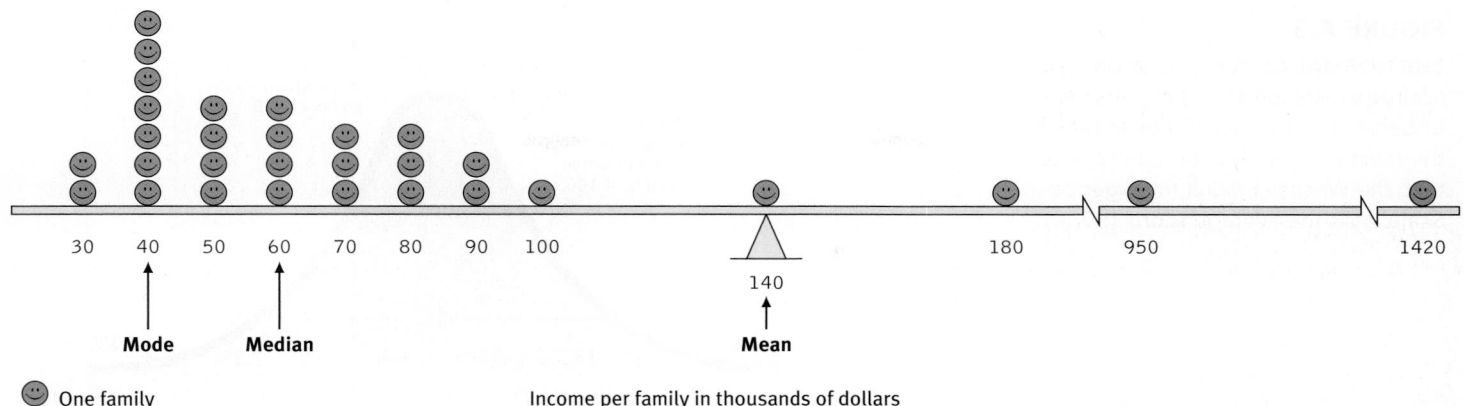

30   40   50   60   70   80   90   100   140   180   950   1420

Mode   **Median**   **Mean**

One family   Income per family in thousands of dollars

Measures of Variation

Knowing the value of an appropriate measure of central tendency can tell us a great deal. But the single number omits other information. It helps to know something about the amount of *variation* in the data—how similar or diverse the scores are. Averages derived from scores with low variability are more reliable than averages based on scores with high variability. Consider a basketball player who scored between 13 and 17 points in each of the season's first 10 games. Knowing this, we would be more confident that she would score near 15 points in her next game than if her scores had varied from 5 to 25 points.

The **range** of scores—the gap between the lowest and highest—provides only a crude estimate of variation. In an otherwise similar group, a couple of extreme scores, such as the $950,000 and $1,420,000 incomes in Figure A.2, will create a deceptively large range.

The more useful standard for measuring how much scores deviate from one another is the **standard deviation.** It better gauges whether scores are packed together or dispersed, because it uses information from each score. The computation[1] assembles information about how much individual scores differ from the mean, which can be very telling. Let's say test scores from Class A and Class B both have the same mean (75 percent correct) but very different standard deviations (5.0 for Class A and 15.0 for Class B). Have you ever had test experiences like that—where two-thirds of your classmates in one course score in the 70 to 80 percent range, with scores in another course more spread out (two-thirds between 60 and 90 percent)? The standard deviation, as well as the mean score, tell us about how each class is faring.

You can grasp the meaning of the standard deviation if you consider how scores naturally tend to be distributed. Large numbers of data—heights, intelligence scores, life expectancy (though not incomes)—often form a symmetrical, *bell-shaped* distribution. Most cases fall near the mean, and fewer cases fall near either extreme. This *bell-shaped* distribution is so typical that we call the curve it forms the **normal curve.**

As **FIGURE A.3** shows, a useful property of the normal curve is that roughly 68 percent of the cases fall within one standard deviation on either side of the mean. About 95 percent of cases fall within two standard deviations. Thus, about 68 percent of people taking an intelligence test will score within ±15 points of 100. About 95 percent will score within ±30 points.

LaunchPad For an interactive review of these statistical concepts, visit **Topic Tutorial: PsychSim6, Descriptive Statistics.**

FIGURE A.2

A SKEWED DISTRIBUTION This graphic representation of the distribution of a village's incomes illustrates the three measures of central tendency—mode, median, and mean. Note how just a few high incomes make the mean—the fulcrum point that balances the incomes above and below—deceptively high.

range the difference between the highest and lowest scores in a distribution.

standard deviation a computed measure of how much scores vary around the mean score.

normal curve a symmetrical, bell-shaped curve that describes the distribution of many types of data; most scores fall near the mean (about 68 percent fall within one standard deviation of it) and fewer and fewer near the extremes. (Also called a *normal distribution*.)

---

1. The actual standard deviation formula is: $\sqrt{\dfrac{Sum\ of\ (deviations\ from\ mean)^2}{Number\ of\ scores - 1}}$

FIGURE A.3

THE NORMAL CURVE Scores on aptitude tests tend to form a normal, or bell-shaped, curve. For example, the most commonly used intelligence test, the Wechsler Adult Intelligence Scale, calls the average score 100.

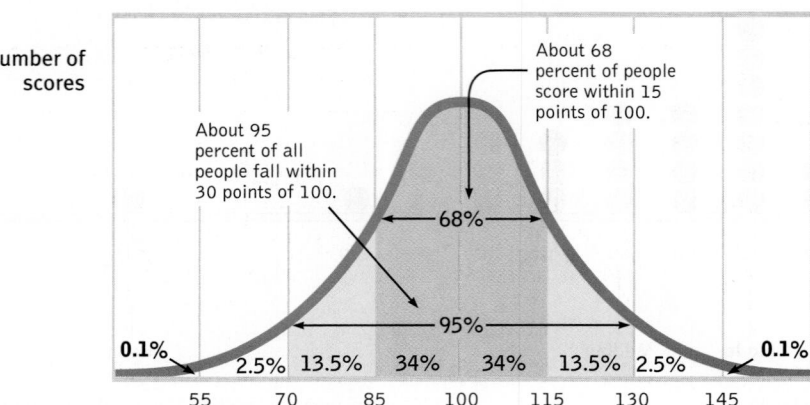

RETRIEVE IT • • •   *SEE APPENDIX E FOR ANSWERS*

RI-2 The average of a distribution of scores is the _____. The score that shows up most often is the _____. The score right in the middle of a distribution (half the scores above it; half below) is the _____. We determine how much scores vary around the average in a way that includes information about the _____ of scores (difference between highest and lowest) by using the _____ _____ formula.

variable anything that can vary and is feasible and ethical to measure.

correlation coefficient a statistical index of the relationship between two things (from −1.00 to +1.00).

scatterplot a graphed cluster of dots, each of which represents the values of two variables. The slope of the points suggests the direction of the relationship between the two variables. The amount of scatter suggests the strength of the correlation (little scatter indicates high correlation).

FIGURE A.4

SCATTERPLOTS, SHOWING PATTERNS OF CORRELATION Correlations—abbreviated *r*—can range from +1.00 (scores for one variable increase in direct proportion to scores for another), to 0.00 (no relationship), to −1.00 (scores for one variable decrease precisely as scores rise for the other).

Correlation: A Measure of Relationships

LOQ A-2   How do correlations measure relationships between variables?

Throughout this book, we often ask how strongly two **variables** are related: For example, how closely related are the personality test scores of identical twins? How well do intelligence test scores predict career achievement? How closely is stress related to disease?

Describing behavior is a first step toward predicting it. When naturalistic observation and surveys reveal that one trait or behavior accompanies another, we say the two *correlate*. A **correlation coefficient** is a statistical measure of relationship. In such cases, **scatterplots** can be very revealing.

Each dot in a scatterplot represents the values of two variables. The three scatterplots in **FIGURE A.4** illustrate the range of possible correlations from a perfect positive to a perfect negative. (Perfect correlations rarely occur in the real world.) A correlation is positive if two sets of scores, such as for height and weight, tend to rise or fall together.

Saying that a correlation is "negative" says nothing about its strength. A correlation is negative if two sets of scores relate inversely, one set going up as the other goes down. The correlation between people's height and the distance from their head to the ceiling is strongly (perfectly, in fact) negative.

Statistics can help us see what the naked eye sometimes misses. To demonstrate this for yourself, try an imaginary project. You wonder if tall men are more or less easygoing, so you collect two sets of scores: men's heights and men's anxiety. You measure the

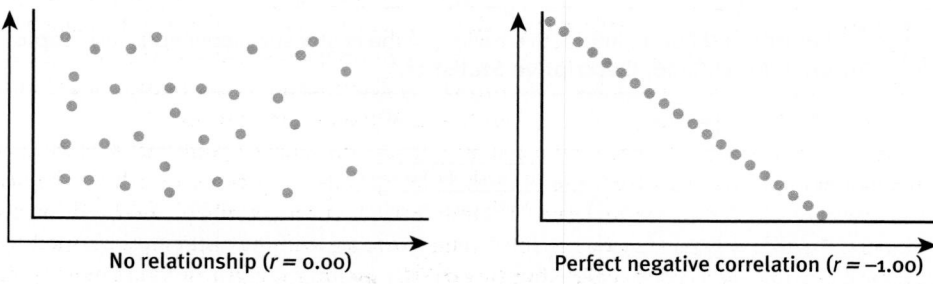

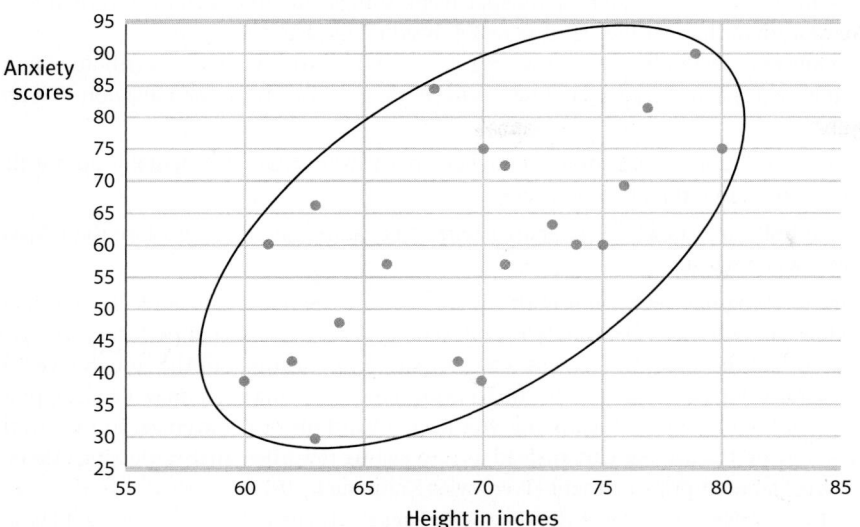

FIGURE A.5

SCATTERPLOT FOR HEIGHT AND ANXIETY This display of data from 20 imagined people (each represented by a data point) reveals an upward slope, indicating a positive correlation. The considerable scatter of the data indicates the correlation is much lower than +1.00.

TABLE A.1
Height and Anxiety Scores of 20 Men

Person	Height in Inches	Anxiety Score
1	80	75
2	63	66
3	61	60
4	79	90
5	74	60
6	69	42
7	62	42
8	75	60
9	77	81
10	60	39
11	64	48
12	76	69
13	71	72
14	66	57
15	73	63
16	70	75
17	63	30
18	71	57
19	68	84
20	70	39

heights of 20 men, and you have them complete an anxiety test, with scores ranging from 0 (*extremely calm*) to 100 (*highly anxious*).

With all the relevant data right in front of you (**TABLE A.1**), can you tell whether the correlation between height and anxiety is positive, negative, or close to zero?

Comparing the columns in Table A.1, most people detect very little relationship between height and anxiety. In fact, the correlation in this imaginary example is positive (*r* = +0.63), as we can see if we display the data as a scatterplot (**FIGURE A.5**).

If we fail to see a relationship when data are presented as systematically as in Table A.1, how much less likely are we to notice them in everyday life? To see what is right in front of us, we sometimes need statistical illumination. We can easily see evidence of gender discrimination when given statistically summarized information about job level, seniority, performance, gender, and salary. But we often see no discrimination when the same information dribbles in, case by case (Twiss et al., 1989).

The point to remember: Correlation coefficients tell us nothing about cause and effect, but they can help us see the world more clearly by revealing the extent to which two things relate.

LaunchPad For an animated tutorial on correlations, engage online with **Concept Practice: Positive and Negative Correlations.** See also the **Video: Correlational Studies** for another helpful tutorial animation.

Illusory Correlations and Regression Toward the Mean

LOQ A-3 What are *illusory correlations*, and what is *regression toward the mean*?

Correlations not only make visible the relationships we might otherwise miss, they also restrain our "seeing" nonexistent relationships. When we believe there is a relationship between two things, we are likely to notice and recall instances that confirm our belief. If we believe that dreams forecast actual events, we may notice and recall confirming instances more than disconfirming instances. The result is an **illusory correlation.**

Illusory correlations can feed an illusion of control—that chance events are subject to our personal control. Gamblers, remembering their lucky rolls, may come to believe they can influence the roll of the dice by again throwing gently for low numbers and hard for high numbers. The illusion that uncontrollable events correlate with our actions is also fed by a statistical phenomenon called **regression toward the mean.** Average results are more typical

illusory correlation perceiving a relationship where none exists, or perceiving a stronger-than-actual relationship.

regression toward the mean the tendency for extreme or unusual scores or events to fall back (regress) toward the average.

than extreme results. Thus, after an unusual event, things tend to return toward their average level; extraordinary happenings tend to be followed by more ordinary ones.

The point may seem obvious, yet we regularly miss it: We sometimes attribute what may be a normal regression (the expected return to normal) to something we have done. Consider two examples:

- Students who score much lower or higher on an exam than they usually do are likely, when retested, to return to their average.
- Unusual ESP subjects who defy chance when first tested nearly always lose their "psychic powers" when retested.

Failure to recognize regression is the source of many superstitions and of some ineffective practices as well. After berating an employee for poorer-than-usual performance, a manager may—when the employee regresses to normal—feel rewarded for the "tough love." After lavishing praise for an exceptionally fine performance, the manager may be disappointed when the employee's behavior again migrates back toward his or her average. Ironically, then, regression toward the average can mislead us into feeling rewarded after criticizing others and feeling punished after praising them (Tversky & Kahneman, 1974).

The point to remember: When a fluctuating behavior returns to normal, fancy explanations for why it does so are probably wrong. Regression toward the mean is probably at work.

"Once you become sensitized to it, you see regression everywhere."
—Psychologist Daniel Kahneman (1985)

🔒 **RETRIEVE IT • • •**   *SEE APPENDIX E FOR ANSWERS*

RI-3 You hear the school basketball coach telling her friend that she rescued her team's winning streak by yelling at the players after an unusually bad first half. What is another explanation of why the team's performance improved?

⟶ Significant Differences

LOQ A-4   How do we know whether an observed difference can be generalized to other populations?

Data are "noisy." The average score in one group could conceivably differ from the average score in another group not because of any real difference but merely because of chance fluctuations in the people sampled. How confidently, then, can we *infer* that an observed difference is not just a fluke—a chance result from the research sample? For guidance, we can ask whether the observed difference between the two groups is reliable and statistically significant. These *inferential statistics* help us determine if results describe a larger population (all those in a group being studied).

When Is an Observed Difference Reliable?

In deciding when it is safe to generalize from a sample, we should keep three principles in mind:

1. *Representative samples are better than biased (unrepresentative) samples.* The best basis for generalizing is from a representative sample of cases, not from the exceptional and memorable cases one finds at the extremes. Research never randomly samples the whole human population. Thus, it pays to keep in mind what population a study has sampled.

2. *Less-variable observations are more reliable than those that are more variable.* As we noted earlier in the example of the basketball player whose game-to-game points were consistent, an average is more reliable when it comes from scores with low variability.

3. *More cases are better than fewer cases.* An eager prospective student visits two universities campuses, each for a day. At the first, the student randomly attends two classes and discovers both instructors to be witty and engaging. At the next campus, the two sampled instructors seem dull and uninspiring. Returning home, the student (discounting the small sample size of only two teachers at each institution) tells friends about the "great teachers" at the first school and the "bores" at the second. Again, we know it but we ignore it: *Averages based on many cases are more reliable* (less variable) than averages based on only a few cases. After noticing that small schools were overrepresented among the most successful schools, several foundations invested in splitting larger schools into smaller ones—without realizing that small schools were also overrepresented among the *least* successful, because schools with fewer students have more variable outcomes (Nisbett, 2015). Again, more cases make for a more reliable average.

The point to remember: Smart thinkers are not overly impressed by a few anecdotes. Generalizations based on a few unrepresentative cases are unreliable.

When Is an Observed Difference Significant?

Let's say you compared men's and women's scores on a laboratory test of aggression and found a gender difference. But individuals differ. How likely is it that the difference you observed was just a fluke? Statistical testing can estimate the probability of the result occurring by chance.

Here is the underlying logic: When averages from two samples are each reliable measures of their respective populations (as when each is based on many observations that have small variability), then their *difference* is probably reliable as well. (Example: The less the variability in women's and in men's aggression scores, the more confidence we would have that any observed gender difference is reliable.) And when the difference between the sample averages is *large,* we have even more confidence that the difference between them reflects a real difference in their populations.

In short, when sample averages are reliable, and when the difference between them is relatively large, we say the difference has **statistical significance.** This means that the observed difference is probably not due to chance variation between the samples.

In judging statistical significance, psychologists are conservative. They are like juries who must presume innocence until guilt is proven. For most psychologists, proof beyond a reasonable doubt means not making much of a finding unless the probability (p) of it occurring by chance, if no real effect exists, is less than 5 percent ($p < .05$). Some researchers, wanting to make sure that only the most reliable findings are published, suggest that psychologists might consider making more conservative statistical significance judgments (Benjamin et al., 2018). For now, psychologists will continue to use $p < .05$, but stay tuned.

When reading about research, you should remember that, given large enough or homogeneous enough samples, a difference between them may be "statistically significant" yet have little *practical* significance. In one controversial study of nearly 700,000 Facebook users, researchers exposed people to status updates with more or with less positive words. Given

"The poor are getting poorer, but with the rich getting richer it all averages out in the long run."

statistical significance a statistical statement of how likely it is that an obtained result occurred by chance.

 ASK YOURSELF

Can you think of a situation where you were fooled by a writer or speaker's attempts to persuade you with statistics? What have you learned in this appendix that will be most helpful in the future to avoid being misled?

PEANUTS

📺 **LaunchPad** For a 9.5-minute synopsis of psychology's scientific research strategies, see the **Video: Research Methods.**

the supersized sample's "statistical power," the tweaking produced a "statistically significant" but trivial effect. For example, those who received fewer posts with positive words responded with 0.1 percent fewer positive words themselves—a "statistically significant" effect (it was not due to chance), though one too tiny to have real-world meaning (Morin, 2014). Comparisons of intelligence test scores among hundreds of thousands of first-born and later-born individuals indicate a highly significant tendency for first-born individuals to have higher average scores than their later-born siblings (Rohrer et al., 2015; Zajonc & Markus, 1975). But because the scores differ only slightly, the "significant" difference has little practical importance.

The point to remember: Statistical significance indicates the *likelihood* that a result could have happened by chance. But this does not say anything about the *importance* of the result.

🔒 RETRIEVE IT • • •

SEE APPENDIX E FOR ANSWERS

RI-4 Can you solve this puzzle?

The registrar's office at the University of Michigan has found that usually about 100 students in Arts and Sciences have perfect marks at the end of their first term at the university. However, only about 10 to 15 students graduate with perfect marks. What do you think is the most likely explanation for the fact that there are more perfect marks after one term than at graduation (Jepson et al., 1983)?

RI-5 _____ statistics summarize data, while _____ statistics determine if data can be generalized to other populations.

🔒 REVIEW STATISTICAL REASONING IN EVERYDAY LIFE

⟩⟩ Learning Objectives

TEST YOURSELF Answer these repeated Learning Objective Questions on your own (before checking the answers in Appendix D) to improve your retention of the concepts (McDaniel et al., 2009, 2015).

A-1 How do we describe data using three measures of central tendency, and what is the relative usefulness of the two measures of variation?

A-2 How do correlations measure relationships between variables?

A-3 What are *illusory correlations*, and what is *regression toward the mean*?

A-4 How do we know whether an observed difference can be generalized to other populations?

⟩⟩ Terms and Concepts to Remember

TEST YOURSELF Write down the definition yourself, then check your answer on the referenced page.

mode, **p. A-2**	standard deviation, **p. A-3**	scatterplot, **p. A-4**
mean, **p. A-2**	normal curve, **p. A-3**	illusory correlation, **p. A-5**
median, **p. A-2**	variable, **p. A-4**	regression toward the mean, **p. A-5**
range, **p. A-3**	correlation coefficient, **p. A-4**	statistical significance, **p. A-7**

⟩⟩ Experience the Testing Effect

TEST YOURSELF Answer the following questions on your own first, then check your answers in Appendix E.

1. Which of the three measures of central tendency is most easily distorted by a few very large or very small scores?
   a. The mode
   b. The mean
   c. The median
   d. They are all equally vulnerable to distortion from atypical scores.

2. The standard deviation is the most useful measure of variation in a set of data because it tells us
   a. the difference between the highest and lowest scores in the set.
   b. the extent to which the sample being used deviates from the bigger population it represents.
   c. how much individual scores differ from the mode.
   d. how much individual scores differ from the mean.

3. Another name for a bell-shaped distribution, in which most scores fall near the middle and fewer scores fall at each extreme, is a _____ _____.

4. In a _____ correlation, the scores rise and fall together; in a(n) _____ correlation, one score falls as the other rises.
   a. positive; negative
   b. positive; illusory
   c. negative; weak
   d. strong; weak

5. If a study revealed that tall people were less anxious than short people, this would suggest that the correlation between height and anxiety is _____ (positive/negative).

6. A _____ provides a visual representation of the direction and the strength of a relationship between two variables.

7. What is regression toward the mean, and how can it influence our interpretation of events?

8. When sample averages are _____ and the difference between them is _____, we can say the difference has statistical significance.
   a. reliable; large
   b. reliable; small
   c. due to chance; large
   d. due to chance; small

Find answers to these questions in Appendix E.

Continue testing yourself with ⧉ **LearningCurve** or ≈ **Achieve Read & Practice** to learn and remember most effectively.

Psychology at Work

For most people, to live is to work. Work is life's biggest waking activity. Work helps satisfy multiple needs. Work supports us, enabling food, water, and shelter. Work connects us, meeting our social needs. Work helps define us. Meeting someone for the first time and wondering about their identity, we may ask, "So, what do you do?"

We vary in our job satisfaction. On the day we leave the workforce, some of us will sadly bid our former employer farewell; others will bid our former employer good riddance. What factors influence our perceptions of work as an activity marked by frustration versus *flow*, as a necessary chore versus a meaningful calling, or as an opportunity to do the bare minimum versus maximize our potential?

⊙ Work and Life Satisfaction

Flow at Work

LEARNING OBJECTIVE QUESTION (LOQ)

B-1 What is *flow*?

Individuals across various occupations vary in their attitudes toward their work. Some view their work as a *job*, an unfulfilling but necessary way to make money. Others view their work as a *career*, an opportunity to advance from one position to a better position. The rest—those who view their work as a *calling*, a fulfilling and socially useful activity—report the highest satisfaction with their work and with their lives (Dik & Duffy, 2012; Wrzesniewski & Dutton, 2001). For example, physicians who find meaning in their work tend to avoid burnout and enjoy their careers (Levin et al., 2017).

This finding would not surprise Mihaly Csikszentmihalyi [chick-SENT-me-hi] (1990, 1999). He observed that our quality of life increases when we are purposefully engaged. Between the anxiety of being overwhelmed and stressed, and the apathy of being underwhelmed and bored, lies a zone in which we experience **flow.** When was the last time you experienced flow? Perhaps you can recall being in a zoned-out flow state while texting or playing a video game. If so, then perhaps you can sympathize with the two Northwest Airlines pilots who in 2009 were so focused on their laptops that they missed their control tower's messages. The pilots flew 150 miles past their Minneapolis destination—and lost their jobs.

Csikszentmihalyi formulated the flow concept after studying artists who spent hour after hour painting or sculpting with focused concentration. Immersed in a project, they worked as if nothing else mattered, and then, when finished, they promptly moved on. The artists seemed driven less by external rewards—money, praise, promotion—than by the intrinsic rewards of creating their art. Nearly 200 other studies confirm that *intrinsic motivation enhances performance* (Cerasoli et al., 2014).

The jobs people do: Columnist Gene Weingarten (2002) noted that sometimes a humorist knows "when to just get out of the way." Here are some sample job titles from the U.S. Department of Labor *Dictionary of Occupational Titles:* animal impersonator, human projectile, banana ripening-room supervisor, impregnator, impregnator helper, dope sprayer, finger waver, rug scratcher, egg smeller, bottom buffer, cookie breaker, brain picker, hand pouncer, bosom presser, and mother repairer.

Have you ever noticed that when you are immersed in an activity, time flies? And that when you are watching the clock, it seems to move more slowly? French researchers have confirmed that the more we attend to an event's duration, the longer it seems to last (Coull et al., 2004).

flow a completely involved, focused state, with diminished awareness of self and time; results from full engagement of our skills.

LIFE DISRUPTED Playing and socializing online are ever-present sources of distraction. It takes energy to resist checking our phones, and time to refocus mental concentration after each disruption. Such frequent interruptions disrupt flow, so it's a good idea to instead schedule regular breaks for checking our devices.

Jacob Ammentorp Lund/Getty Images

Csikszentmihalyi studied dancers, chess players, surgeons, writers, parents, mountain climbers, sailors, and farmers. His research included Australians, North Americans, Koreans, Japanese, and Italians. Participants ranged in age from the teen years to the golden years. A clear principle emerged: It's exhilarating to flow with an activity that fully engages our skills (Fong et al., 2015). Flow experiences boost our sense of self-esteem, competence, and well-being. Idleness may sound like bliss, but purposeful work enriches our lives. Busy people are happier (Hsee et al., 2010; Robinson & Martin, 2008). One research team interrupted people on about a quarter-million occasions (using a phone app), and found people's minds wandering 47 percent of the time. They were, on average, happier when their mind was *not* wandering (Killingsworth & Gilbert, 2010). A focused mind is a happy mind.

⊗ Finding Your Own Flow, and Matching Interests to Work

ENGAGE

"Find a job you love, and you'll never work another day of your life."
—Facebook hiring video, 2016

Want to identify your own path to flow? You can start by pinpointing your strengths and the types of work that may prove satisfying and successful. Marcus Buckingham and Donald Clifton (2001) suggested asking yourself four questions.

- What activities give me pleasure? Bringing order out of chaos? Playing host? Helping others? Challenging sloppy thinking?
- What activities leave me wondering, "When can I do this again?" rather than, "When will this be over?"
- What sorts of challenges do I relish? And which do I dread?
- What sorts of tasks do I learn easily? And which do I struggle with?

You may find your skills engaged and time flying when teaching or selling or writing or cleaning or consoling or creating or repairing. If an activity feels good, if it comes easily, if you look forward to it, then look deeper. You'll see your strengths at work (Buckingham, 2007). For a free (requires registration) assessment of your own strengths, take the "Brief Strengths Test" at www.AuthenticHappiness.sas.upenn.edu.

The U.S. Department of Labor also offers a career interest questionnaire through its Occupational Information Network (O*NET). At MyNextMove.org/explore/ip you will need about 10 minutes to respond to 60 items, indicating how much you would like or dislike activities ranging from building kitchen cabinets to playing a musical instrument. You will then receive feedback on how strongly your responses reflect six interest types (Holland, 1996):

- *Realistic* (hands-on doers)
- *Investigative* (thinkers)
- *Artistic* (creators)
- *Social* (helpers, teachers)
- *Enterprising* (persuaders, deciders)
- *Conventional* (organizers)

Finally, depending on how much training you are willing to complete, you will be shown occupations that fit your interest pattern (selected from a national database of 900+ occupations).

Do what you love and you will love what you do. A career counseling science aims, first, to assess people's differing values, personalities, and, especially, *interests,* which are remarkably stable and predictive of future life choices and outcomes (Dik & Rottinghaus, 2013; Stoll et al., 2017). (Your job may change, but your interests today will likely still be your interests in 10 years.) Second, it aims to alert people to well-matched vocations—vocations with a good *person-environment fit.* It pays to have a personality that fits your job. People high in openness earn more if they hold jobs that demand openness (actors), whereas people high in conscientiousness earn more if they work in jobs that require conscientiousness (financial managers) (Denissen et al., 2017).

Another study assessed 400,000 high school students' interests and then followed them over time. The take-home finding: "Interests uniquely predict academic and career success over and above cognitive ability and personality" (Rounds & Su, 2014). Sixty other studies confirm the point both for students in school and workers on the job: Interests predict both performance and persistence (Nye et al., 2012). Lack of job fit can fuel frustration, resulting in unproductive and even hostile work behavior (Harold et al., 2016). One fee-based online service, jobzology.com, was developed by industrial-organizational psychologists to implement career counseling science. First, it assesses people's interests, values, personalities, and workplace culture preferences. It then suggests occupations and connects them to job listings.

ENGAGE

ASK YOURSELF

What have you learned about your own strengths and about the kind of career you might see yourself pursuing?

⟶ Industrial-Organizational Psychology

LOQ B-2   What are three key areas of study related to industrial-organizational psychology?

In developed nations work has expanded, from farming to manufacturing to *knowledge work.* More and more work is *outsourced* to temporary employees and consultants, or to workers telecommuting from off-site workplaces (Allen, T. D., et al., 2015). (This book and its teaching package are developed and produced by a team of women and men in a dozen cities, from Alberta to Florida.) As work has changed, have our attitudes toward our work also changed? Has our satisfaction with work increased or decreased? Has the *psychological contract*—the sense of mutual obligations between workers and employers—become more or less trusting and secure? These are among the questions that fascinate **industrial-organizational (I/O) psychologists** as they apply psychology's principles to the workplace (**TABLE B.1**).

industrial-organizational (I/O) psychology the application of psychological concepts and methods to optimizing human behavior in workplaces.

TABLE B.1

I/O Psychology and Human Factors Psychology at Work

RETAIN

As scientists, consultants, and management professionals, industrial-organizational (I/O) psychologists may be found helping organizations to resolve work-family conflicts, build employee retention, address organizational climate, or promote teamwork. Human factors psychologists contribute to human safety and improved designs.

Personnel Psychology: Maximizing Human Potential	Organizational Psychology: Building Better Organizations
Developing training programs to increase job seekers' success	**Developing organizations**
Selecting and placing employees	• Analyzing organizational structures
• Developing and testing assessment tools for selecting, placing, and promoting workers	• Maximizing worker satisfaction and productivity
• Analyzing job content	• Facilitating organizational change
• Optimizing worker placement	**Enhancing quality of work life**
Training and developing employees	• Expanding individual productivity
• Identifying needs	• Identifying elements of satisfaction
• Designing training programs	• Redesigning jobs
• Evaluating training programs	• Balancing work and nonwork life in an era of social media, smartphones, and other technologies
Appraising performance	**Human Factors Psychology**
• Developing guidelines	• Designing optimum work environments
• Measuring individual performance	• Optimizing person-machine interactions
• Measuring organizational performance	• Developing systems technologies

Information from the Society of Industrial and Organizational Psychology. For more information about I/O psychology and related job opportunities, visit siop.org.

Left to right: Hope College; Lorie Hailey; Danielle Slevens; Kathryn Brownson; Trish Morgan; Don Probert; Anna Munroe; Stephanie Ellis; Jeff Brune; Laura Burden.

THE MODERN WORKFORCE The editorial team that guides, edits, and assesses this text and its resources works both in-house and from far-flung places. In column 1: Nancy Fleming in Massachusetts, Kathryn Brownson in Michigan, and Anna Munroe in New York. In column 2: Lorie Hailey in Kentucky, Trish Morgan in Alberta, Carlise Stembridge in Minnesota, and Laura Burden in New York. In column 3: Danielle Slevens in Massachusetts, Betty Probert in Florida, and Christine Brune in Washington, DC.

• The I/O psychology subfield of **personnel psychology** applies psychology's methods and principles to selecting, placing, training, and evaluating workers. Personnel psychologists match people with jobs by identifying and placing well-suited candidates. The **organizational psychology** subfield considers how work environments and management styles influence worker motivation, satisfaction, and productivity. It focuses on modifying jobs and supervision in ways that boost morale and productivity.

• **Human factors psychology,** now a distinct field allied with I/O psychology, explores how machines and environments can be optimally designed to fit human abilities. Human factors psychologists study people's natural perceptions and inclinations, using this research to create user-friendly machines and work settings.

RETRIEVE IT • • •

ANSWERS IN APPENDIX E

RI-1 What is the value of finding flow in our work?

Personnel Psychology

LOQ B-3 How do personnel psychologists facilitate job seeking, employee selection, work placement, and performance appraisal?

Psychologists assist organizations at various stages of selecting and assessing employees. They may help identify needed job skills, develop effective selection methods, recruit and evaluate diverse applicants, introduce and train new employees, appraise performance, and facilitate team building among people with differing cultural backgrounds. They also help job seekers. Across four dozen studies, training programs (which teach job-search skills, improve self-presentation, boost self-confidence, promote goal setting, and enlist support) have nearly tripled job-seekers' success (Liu et al., 2014).

Using Strengths for Successful Selection

As a new AT&T human resources executive, psychologist Mary Tenopyr (1997) was assigned to solve a problem: Customer-service representatives were failing at a high rate. After concluding that many of the hires were ill-matched to the demands of their new job, Tenopyr developed a new selection instrument:

1. She asked new applicants to respond to various test questions (without as yet making any use of their responses).

2. She followed up later to assess which of the applicants excelled on the job.

3. She identified the earlier test questions that best predicted success.

The happy result of her data-driven work was a new test that enabled AT&T to identify likely-to-succeed representatives. Personnel selection techniques such as this one aim to recruit people with the kind of strengths that will enable them and their organization to flourish. Marry the strengths of people with the tasks of organizations and the result is often prosperity and profit.

Do Interviews Predict Performance?

Employee selection usually includes an interview. And many interviewers feel confident of their ability to predict long-term job performance from a get-acquainted (*unstructured*) interview. What's therefore shocking is how error-prone interviewers' predictions may be when predicting job or graduate school success. Informal interviews are less informative than aptitude tests, work samples, job knowledge tests, and past job performance. After studying thousands of informal interviews and later job success, Google found "zero relationship. It's a complete random mess" (Bock, 2013). *Structured interviews,* however, can produce more accurate predictions.

Unstructured Interviews and the Interviewer Illusion

Traditional, *unstructured interviews* can provide a sense of someone's personality—their expressiveness, warmth, and verbal ability, for example. But these informal interviews also give interviewees considerable power to control the impression they are making in the interview situation (Barrick et al., 2009). Why, then, do many interviewers have such faith in their ability to discern interviewees' fitness for a job? "I have excellent interviewing skills," I/O psychology consultants often hear, "so I don't need reference checking as much as someone who doesn't have my ability to read people." Overrating one's ability to predict people's futures is called the *interviewer illusion* (Dana et al., 2013; Nisbett, 1987). Five factors explain interviewers' overconfidence:

- *Interviewers presume that people are what they seem to be in the interview situation.* An unstructured interview may create a false impression of a person's behavior toward others in different situations. Some interviewees may feign desired attitudes; others may be nervous. As personality psychologists explain, when meeting others, we discount the enormous influence of varying situations and mistakenly presume that what we see is what we will get. But research on everything from chattiness to conscientiousness reveals that how we behave reflects not only our enduring traits, but also the details of the particular situation (such as wanting to impress in a job interview).

- *Interviewers' preconceptions and moods color how they perceive interviewees' responses* (Cable & Gilovich, 1998; Macan & Dipboye, 1994). If interviewers instantly like a person who is similar to themselves (opening the door to unintended racial bias), they may interpret the person's assertiveness as indicating "confidence" rather than "arrogance." If told certain applicants have been prescreened, interviewers are disposed to judge them more favorably. Such interviewers are showing *confirmation bias:* They search for

personnel psychology an I/O psychology subfield that helps with job seeking, and with employee recruitment, selection, placement, training, appraisal, and development.

organizational psychology an I/O psychology subfield that examines organizational influences on worker satisfaction and productivity and facilitates organizational change.

human factors psychology a field of psychology allied with I/O psychology that explores how people and machines interact and how machines and physical environments can be made safe and easy to use.

information that supports their preconceptions about a job candidate and ignore or distort contradictory evidence (Skov & Sherman, 1986).

- *Interviewers judge people relative to those interviewed just before and after them* (Simonsohn & Gino, 2013). If you are being interviewed for a job or graduate program, hope for a day when the other interviewees have been weak.
- *Interviewers more often follow the successful careers of those they have hired than the successful careers of those they have rejected.* This missing feedback prevents interviewers from getting a reality check on their hiring ability.
- *Interviews disclose the interviewee's good intentions, which are less revealing than habitual behaviors* (Ouellette & Wood, 1998). Intentions matter. People can change. But the best predictor of the person we will be is the person we have been. Educational attainments predict job performance partly because people who make a habit of showing up for school each day and staying on task also tend to show up for work and stay on task (Ng & Feldman, 2009). Wherever we go, we take ourselves along.

"Between the idea / And the reality . . . / Falls the Shadow." —T. S. Eliot, *The Hollow Men*, 1925

Hoping to improve prediction and selection, personnel psychologists have put people in simulated work situations, sought information on past performance, aggregated evaluations from multiple interviews, administered tests, and developed job-specific interviews.

Structured Interviews

Unlike casual conversation aimed at getting a feel for someone, **structured interviews** offer a disciplined method of collecting information. A personnel psychologist may analyze a job, script questions, and train interviewers. The interviewers then ask all applicants the same questions, in the same order, and rate each applicant on established scales.

In an unstructured interview, someone might ask, "How organized are you?" "How well do you get along with people?" or "How do you handle stress?" Street-smart applicants know how to score high: "Although I sometimes drive myself too hard, I handle stress by prioritizing and delegating, and leaving time for sleep and exercise."

By contrast, structured interviews pinpoint strengths (attitudes, behaviors, knowledge, and skills) that distinguish high performers in a particular line of work. The process includes outlining job-specific situations and asking candidates to explain how they would handle them, and how they handled similar situations in their prior employment. "Tell me about a time when you were caught between conflicting demands, without time to accomplish both. How did you handle that?" In its interviews, Google has asked, "Give me an example of a time when you solved an analytically difficult problem."

To reduce memory distortions and bias, the interviewer takes notes and makes ratings as the interview proceeds and avoids irrelevant and follow-up questions. The structured interview therefore feels less warm, but that can be explained to the applicant: "This conversation won't typify how we relate to each other in this organization."

A review of 150 findings revealed that structured interviews had double the predictive accuracy of unstructured interviews (Schmidt & Hunter, 1998; Wiesner & Cronshaw, 1988). Structured interviews also reduce bias, such as against overweight applicants (Kutcher & Bragger, 2004).

If, instead, we let our intuitions bias the hiring process, noted writer Malcolm Gladwell (2000, p. 86), then "all we will have done is replace the old-boy network, where you hired your nephew, with the new-boy network, where you hire whoever impressed you most when you shook his hand. Social progress, unless we're careful, can merely be the means by which we replace the obviously arbitrary with the not so obviously arbitrary."

To recap, personnel psychologists help train job seekers, and they assist organizations in analyzing jobs, recruiting well-suited applicants, and selecting and placing employees. They also appraise employees' performance (**FIGURE B.1**)—our next topic.

Appraising Performance

structured interview an interview process that asks the same job-relevant questions of all applicants, each of whom is rated on established scales.

Performance appraisal serves organizational purposes: It helps decide who to keep on staff, how to appropriately reward and pay people, and how to better harness employee strengths, sometimes with job shifts or promotions. Performance appraisal also serves individual purposes: Feedback affirms workers' strengths and helps motivate needed improvement.

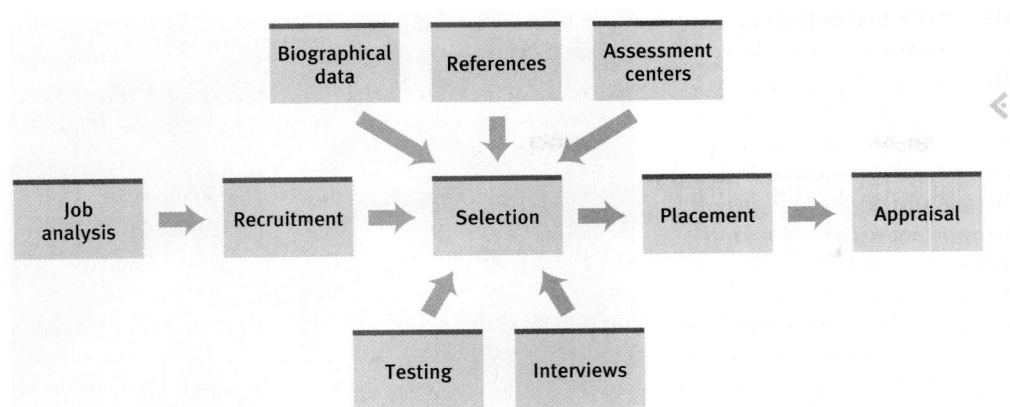

PERSONNEL PSYCHOLOGISTS AT WORK Personnel psychologists consult in human resources activities, from job definition to recruitment to employee appraisal. The assessment center approach may be used to evaluate potential and existing employees.

Performance appraisal methods include

- *checklists* on which supervisors simply check specific behaviors that describe the worker ("always attends to customers' needs"; "takes long breaks").
- *graphic rating scales* on which a supervisor checks, perhaps on a five-point scale, how often a worker is dependable, productive, and so forth.
- *behavior rating scales* on which a supervisor checks scaled behaviors that describe a worker's performance. If rating the extent to which a worker "follows procedures," the supervisor might mark the employee somewhere between "often takes shortcuts" and "always follows established procedures" (Levy, 2003).

In some organizations, performance feedback comes not only from supervisors but also from all organizational levels. If you join an organization that practices *360-degree feedback* (**FIGURE B.2**), you will rate yourself, your manager, and your other colleagues, and you will be rated by your manager, other colleagues, and customers (Green, 2002). The net result is often more open communication and more complete appraisal.

Performance appraisal, like other social judgments, is vulnerable to bias (Murphy & Cleveland, 1995). *Halo errors* occur when one's overall evaluation of an employee, or of a personal trait such as their friendliness, biases ratings of their specific work-related behaviors, such as their reliability. *Leniency* and *severity errors* reflect evaluators' tendencies to be either too easy or too harsh on everyone. *Recency errors* occur when raters focus only on easily remembered recent behavior. By using multiple raters and developing objective, job-relevant performance measures, personnel psychologists seek to support their organizations while also helping employees perceive the appraisal process as fair.

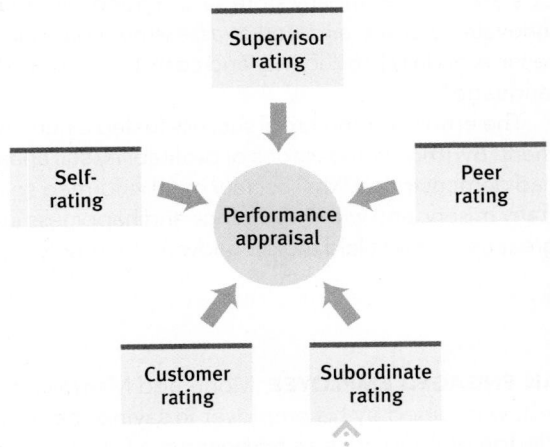

360-DEGREE FEEDBACK With multisource 360-degree feedback, our knowledge, skills, and behaviors are rated by ourselves and surrounding others. Professors, for example, may be rated by their department chairs, their students, and their colleagues. After receiving all these ratings, professors discuss the 360-degree feedback with their department chair.

🔒 **RETRIEVE IT • • •**   *ANSWERS IN APPENDIX E*

RI-2 A human resources director explains to you that "I don't bother with tests or references. It's all about the interview." Based on I/O psychology research, what concerns does this raise?

⟶ Organizational Psychology

LOQ B-4   What is the role of organizational psychologists?

Recruiting, hiring, training, and appraising capable and diverse workers matters, but so does employee motivation and morale. Organizational psychologists assist with efforts to motivate and engage employees.

DOING WELL WHILE DOING GOOD—"THE GREAT EXPERIMENT"
At the end of the 1700s, the New Lanark, Scotland, cotton mill had more than 1000 workers. Many were children drawn from Glasgow's poorhouses. They worked 13-hour days and lived in grim conditions.

On a visit to Glasgow, Welsh-born Robert Owen—an idealistic young cotton-mill manager—chanced to meet and marry the mill owner's daughter. Owen and some partners purchased the mill and on the first day of the 1800s began what he called "the most important experiment for the happiness of the human race that had yet been instituted at any time in any part of the world" (Owen, 1814). The exploitation of child and adult labor was, he observed, producing unhappy and inefficient workers. Owen showed *transformational leadership* when he undertook numerous innovations: a nursery for preschool children, education for older children (with encouragement rather than corporal punishment), Sundays off, health care, paid sick days, unemployment pay for days when the mill could not operate, and a company store selling goods at reduced prices. He also innovated a goals- and worker-assessment program that included detailed records of daily productivity and costs but with "no beating, no abusive language."

Courtesy of New Lanark Trust

The ensuing commercial success fueled a humanitarian reform movement. By 1816, with decades of profitability still ahead, Owen believed he had demonstrated "that society may be formed so as to exist without crime, without poverty, with health greatly improved, with little if any misery, and with intelligence and happiness increased a hundredfold." Although his utopian vision has not been fulfilled, Owen's great experiment laid the groundwork for employment practices that have today become accepted in much of the world.

Satisfaction and Engagement at Work

AN ENGAGED EMPLOYEE Mohamed Mamow, left, was joined by his employer in saying the Pledge of Allegiance as he became a U.S. citizen. Mamow and his wife met in a Somali refugee camp and have five children, whom he has supported by working as a machine operator. Mindful of his responsibility—"I don't like to lose my job. I have a responsibility for my children and my family"—he would arrive for work a half hour early and tend to every detail on his shift. "He is an extremely hard-working employee," noted his employer, and "a reminder to all of us that we are really blessed" (Roelofs, 2010).

MLive/Advance/Barcroft Media

I/O psychologists have found that satisfaction with work, and with work-life balance, feeds overall satisfaction with life (Bowling et al., 2010). Married people with supportive spouses often enjoy a healthy balance between work and home life, with success in both arenas (Solomon & Jackson, 2014). Moreover, as health psychologists tell us, lower job stress, sometimes supported by telecommuting, feeds better health (Allen, T. D., et al., 2015).

Satisfied employees also contribute to successful organizations. Positive moods at work enhance creativity, persistence, and helpfulness (Ford et al., 2011; Jeffrey et al., 2014; Shockley et al., 2012). Are engaged, happy workers also less often absent? Less likely to quit? Less prone to theft? More punctual? More productive? Statistical digests of prior research have found a modest positive correlation between individual job satisfaction and performance (Judge et al., 2001; Ng et al., 2009; Parker et al., 2003). In one analysis of 4500 employees at 42 British manufacturing companies, the most productive workers were those who found their work environment satisfying (Patterson et al., 2004).

Some organizations seem to have a knack for cultivating more engaged and productive employees. In the United States, *Fortune's* "100 Best Companies to Work For" have also produced markedly higher-than-average returns for their investors (Fulmer et al., 2003). And consider a study of more than 198,000 employees in nearly 8000 business units of 36 large companies (including some 1100 bank branches, 1200 stores, and 4200 teams or departments). James Harter, Frank Schmidt, and Theodore Hayes (2002) explored correlations between various measures of organizational success and *employee engagement*—the extent of workers' involvement, enthusiasm, and identification with their organizations (**TABLE B.2**). They found that engaged workers (compared with disengaged workers who are just putting in their time) knew what was expected of them, had what they needed to do their work, felt fulfilled in their work, had regular opportunities to do what they do best, perceived that they were part of something significant, and had opportunities to learn and develop. They also found that business units with engaged employees had more loyal customers, lower turnover rates, higher productivity, and greater profits.

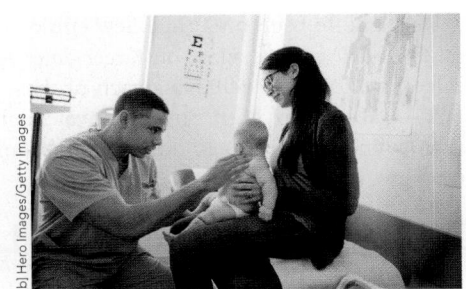

TASK SIGNIFICANCE People find their work meaningful and engaging when it has "task significance"—when they view their work as benefiting others (Allan, 2017).

TABLE B.2
Three Types of Employees

Engaged: working with passion and feeling a profound connection to their company or organization.

Not engaged: putting in the time but investing little passion or energy in their work.

Actively disengaged: unhappy workers undermining what their colleagues accomplish.

Information from Gallup via Crabtree, 2005.

But what causal arrows explain this correlation between business success and employee morale and engagement? Does success boost morale, or does high morale boost success? In a follow-up longitudinal study of 142,000 workers, researchers found that, over time, employee attitudes predicted *future* business success (more than the other way around) (Harter et al., 2010). Many other studies confirm that happy workers tend to be good workers (Ford et al., 2011; Seibert et al., 2011; Shockley et al., 2012). One analysis compared companies with top-quartile versus below-average employee engagement levels. Over a three-year period, earnings grew 2.6 times faster for the companies with highly engaged workers (Ott, 2007). It pays to have employees engaged.

Effective Leadership

LOQ B-5   How can leaders be most effective?

Great managers support employees' well-being, articulate goals clearly, and lead in ways that suit the situation and consider the cultural context.

Setting Specific, Challenging Goals

Measurable objectives, such as "finish gathering the history paper information by Friday," focus our attention and stimulate us to persist and to be creative. Goals motivate achievement, especially when combined with progress reports (Harkin et al., 2016). For many people, a landmark in time—a special birthday, the new year or new school term, graduation, a new job—spurs personal goal setting (Dai et al., 2014). Action plans that break large goals into smaller steps (*subgoals*) and that specify *implementation intentions*—when, where, and how to achieve those steps—increase the chances of completing a project on time (Fishbach et al., 2006; Gollwitzer & Sheeran, 2006). Through a task's ups and downs, we best sustain our mood and motivation when we focus on immediate goals (such as daily study) rather than distant goals (such as a course grade). Better to have our nose to the grindstone than our eye on the ultimate prize (Houser-Marko & Sheldon, 2008).

THE POWER OF POSITIVE COACHING Football coach Pete Carroll, who led the University of Southern California to two national championships and the Seattle Seahawks to a Super Bowl championship, combined positive enthusiasm and fun workouts with "a commitment to a nurturing environment that allows people to be themselves while still being accountable to the team" (Trotter, 2014). "It shows you can win with positivity," noted Seahawks star defensive player Richard Sherman. "It's literally all positive reinforcement," said teammate Jimmy Graham (Belson, 2015).

leadership an individual's ability to motivate and influence others to contribute to their group's success.

task leadership goal-oriented leadership that sets standards, organizes work, and focuses attention on goals.

social leadership group-oriented leadership that builds teamwork, mediates conflict, and offers support.

Thus, before beginning each new edition of this book, our author-editor-staff team *manages by objectives*—we agree on target dates for the completion and editing of each module draft. If we focus on achieving each of these short-term goals, then the prize—an on-time book—takes care of itself. So, to motivate high productivity, effective leaders work with people to define explicit goals, subgoals, and implementation plans, and then provide feedback on progress.

Choosing an Appropriate Leadership Style

Effective leaders of laboratory groups, work teams, and large corporations often exude *charisma* (Goethals & Allison, 2014; House & Singh, 1987; Shamir et al., 1993). People with charisma have the capacity to inspire others' loyalty and to focus their enthusiasm (Grabo & van Vugt, 2016).

Charismatic leaders' ability to inspire can bolster **leadership**—the ability to motivate and influence people to enable their group's success. Leadership styles vary, depending both on the leader and the situation. In some situations (think of a commander leading troops into battle), a *directive* style may be needed (Fiedler, 1981). In other situations—developing a comedy show, for example—a leader might get better results using a *democratic* style that welcomes team member creativity.

Leaders differ in the personal qualities they bring to the job. Some excel at **task leadership**—by setting standards, organizing work, and focusing attention on goals. To keep the group centered on its mission, task leaders typically use a directive style, which can work well if the leader gives good directions (Fiedler, 1987).

Other managers excel at **social leadership.** They explain decisions, help group members solve their conflicts, and build teams that work well together (Evans & Dion, 1991; Pfaff et al., 2013). Social leaders, many of whom are women, often have a democratic style. They share authority and welcome team members' opinions. Social leadership and team-building increases morale and productivity (Shuffler et al., 2011, 2013). We usually feel more satisfied and motivated, and perform better, when we can participate in decision making (Cawley et al., 1998; Pereira & Osburn, 2007). Moreover, when members are sensitive to one another and participate equally, groups solve problems with greater "collective intelligence" (Woolley et al., 2010).

In one study of 50 Dutch companies, the firms with the highest morale had chief executives who most inspired their colleagues "to transcend their own self-interests for the sake of the collective" (de Hoogh et al., 2004). *Transformational leadership* of this kind motivates others to identify with and commit themselves to the group's mission. Transformational leaders, many of whom are natural extraverts, articulate high standards, inspire people to share their vision, and offer personal attention (Bono & Judge, 2004). The frequent result is more engaged, trusting, and effective workers (Turner et al., 2002). Women more than men tend to exhibit transformational leadership qualities. Alice Eagly (2007, 2013) believes this helps explain why companies with female top managers have tended to enjoy superior financial results, even after controlling for such variables as company size.

Studies in India, Taiwan, and Iran suggest that effective managers—whether in coal mines, banks, or government offices—often exhibit a high degree of *both* task and social leadership

"Good leaders don't ask more than their constituents can give, but they often ask—and get—more than their constituents intended to give or thought it was possible to give."
—John W. Gardner, *Excellence*, 1984

(Smith & Tayeb, 1989). As achievement-minded people, effective managers certainly care about how well work is done, yet they are sensitive to their subordinates' needs. Workers in family-friendly organizations that offer flexible hours report feeling greater job satisfaction and loyalty to their employers (Butts et al., 2013; Roehling et al., 2001). Over time, U.S. senators who practice common virtues (humility, wisdom, courage) become more influential in leadership roles than do those who practice manipulation and intimidation (ten Brinke et al., 2016). Social virtues work.

POSITIVE REINFORCEMENT Effective leadership often builds on a basic principle of *operant conditioning*: To teach a behavior, catch a person doing something right and reinforce it. It sounds simple, but many managers are like parents who, when a child brings home a near-perfect school report card, focus on the one low grade in a troublesome biology class and ignore the rest. "Sixty-five percent of Americans received NO praise or recognition in the workplace last year," reported the Gallup organization (2004).

FULFILLING THE NEED TO BELONG A work environment that satisfies employees' need to belong is energizing. Employees who enjoy high-quality colleague relationships engage their work with more vigor (Carmeli et al., 2009). Gallup researchers have asked more than 15 million employees worldwide if they have a "best friend at work." The 30 percent who do "are *seven times* as likely to be engaged in their jobs" as those who don't, researchers report (Rath & Harter, 2010). And, as we noted earlier, positive, engaged employees are a mark of thriving organizations.

PARTICIPATIVE MANAGEMENT Employee participation in decision making is common in Sweden, Japan, the United States, and elsewhere (Cawley et al., 1998; Sundstrom et al., 1990). Workers given a chance to voice their opinion and be part of the decision-making process have responded more positively to the final decision (van den Bos & Spruijt, 2002). They also feel more empowered, and are likely, therefore, to be more creative and committed (Hennessey & Amabile, 2010; Seibert et al., 2011).

The ultimate in employee participation is the employee-owned company. One such company in my [DM's] town is the Fleetwood Group—a thriving 165-employee manufacturer of educational furniture and wireless electronic clickers. Every employee owns part of the company, and as a group they own 100 percent. The more years employees work, the more they own, yet no one owns more than 5 percent. Like every corporate president, Fleetwood's president works for his stockholders—who also just happen to be his employees.

As a company that endorses faith-inspired "respect and care for each team member-owner," Fleetwood is free to place people above profits. Thus, when orders lagged during a recession, the employee-owners decided that job security meant more to them than profits. So the company paid otherwise idle workers to do community service, such as answering phones at nonprofit agencies and building Habitat for Humanity houses. Employee ownership attracts and retains talented people, which for Fleetwood has meant company success.

Cultural Influences on Leadership Styles

LOQ B-6   What cultural influences need to be considered when choosing an effective leadership style?

I/O psychology sprang from North American roots. So, how well do its leadership principles apply to cultures worldwide?

Investigators worldwide have undertaken Project GLOBE (Global Leadership and Organizational Behavior Effectiveness) to study cultural variations in leadership expectations (House et al., 2001). Some cultures, for example, encourage collective sharing of resources and rewards; others are more individualist. Some cultures minimize and others accentuate traditional gender roles. Some cultures prioritize being friendly, caring, and kind, and others encourage aggressiveness. The program's first research phase studied 17,300 leaders of 950 organizations in 61 countries (Brodbeck et al., 2008; Dorfman et al., 2012). One finding: Leaders who fulfill expectations, such as by being directive in some cultures or participative in others, tend to be successful. Cultures shape leadership and what makes for leadership success.

Nevertheless, some leader behaviors are universally effective. From its massive study of nearly 50,000 business units in 45 countries, the Gallup Organization observed that thriving companies tend to focus on identifying and enhancing employee *strengths* (rather than punishing their deficiencies). Doing so predicts increased employee engagement, customer satisfaction, and profitability (Rigoni & Asplund, 2016a,b). "Strengths-based" leadership pays dividends, supporting happier, more creative, more productive workers with less absenteeism and turnover (Amabile & Kramer, 2011; De Neve et al., 2013). Moreover, the same principles affect student satisfaction, retention, and future success (Larkin et al., 2013; Ray & Kafka, 2014). Students who feel supported by caring friends and mentors, and engaged in their campus life, tend to persist and ultimately succeed during school and after graduation.

* * *

We have considered *personnel psychology* (the I/O psychology subfield that focuses on training job seekers and assisting with employee selection, placement, appraisal, and development). And we have considered *organizational psychology* (the I/O psychology subfield that focuses on worker satisfaction and productivity, and on organizational change). Finally, we turn to *human factors psychology*, which explores the human-machine interface.

ENGAGE
ASK YOURSELF

In what type of leadership role do you think you would most excel? How could you grow to become a more effective leader?

🔒 **RETRIEVE IT** • • •   *ANSWERS IN APPENDIX E*

RI-3 What characteristics are important for *transformational leaders*?

⟶ Human Factors Psychology

LOQ B-7   How do human factors psychologists work to create user-friendly machines and work settings?

Designs sometimes neglect the human factor. Cognitive scientist Donald Norman (2001) bemoaned the complexity of assembling his new HDTV, related components, and seven remotes into a usable home theater system: "I was VP of Advanced Technology at Apple. I can program dozens of computers in dozens of languages. I understand television, really, I do. . . . It doesn't matter: I am overwhelmed."

Human factors psychologists work with designers and engineers to tailor appliances, machines, and work settings to our natural perceptions and inclinations. Bank ATM machines are internally more complex than remote controls ever were, yet thanks to human factors engineering, ATMs are easier to operate. Digital recorders have solved the TV recording problem with a simple select-and-click menu system ("record that one"). Apple similarly engineered easy usability with the iPhone and iPad. Handheld and wearable technologies are increasingly making use of *haptic* (touch-based) feedback—opening a phone with a thumbprint, sharing your heartbeat via a smartwatch, or having GPS directional instructions ("turn left" arrow) "drawn" on your skin with other wrist-worn devices.

Norman hosts a website (jnd.org) that illustrates good designs that fit people (**FIGURE B.3**). Human factors psychologists also help design efficient environments. An ideal kitchen layout, researchers have found, puts needed items close to their usage point and near eye level. It locates work areas to enable doing tasks in order, such as placing the refrigerator, stove, and sink in a triangle. It creates counters that enable hands to work at or slightly below elbow height (Boehm-Davis, 2005).

Understanding human factors can help prevent accidents. By studying the human factor in driving accidents, psychologists seek to devise ways to reduce the distractions, fatigue, and inattention that contribute to 1.25 million annual worldwide traffic fatalities (WHO, 2016a). At least two-thirds of commercial air accidents have been caused by human error (Shappell et al., 2007). After beginning commercial flights in the 1960s, the Boeing 727 was involved in several landing accidents caused by pilot error. Psychologist Conrad Kraft (1978) noted a common context for these

FIGURE B.3

DESIGNING PRODUCTS THAT FIT PEOPLE Human factors expert Donald Norman offers these and other examples of effectively designed products. The Ride On Carry On foldable chair attachment, "designed by a flight attendant mom," enables a small suitcase to double as a stroller. The OXO measuring cup allows the user to see the quantity from above.

Ride On Carry On

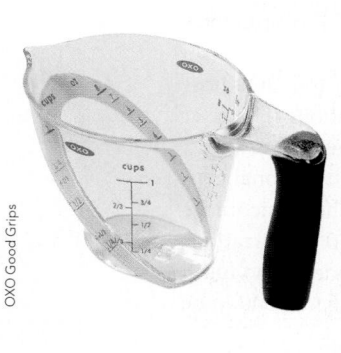

OXO Good Grips

accidents: All took place at night, and all involved landing short of the runway after crossing a dark stretch of water or unilluminated ground. Kraft reasoned that, on rising terrain, city lights beyond the runway would project a larger retinal image, making the ground seem farther away than it was. By re-creating these conditions in flight simulations, Kraft discovered that pilots were deceived into thinking they were flying higher than their actual altitudes (**FIGURE B.4**). Aided by Kraft's finding, airlines began requiring the co-pilot to monitor the altimeter—calling out altitudes during the descent—and the accidents diminished.

Human factors psychologists can also help us to function in other settings. Consider the available *assistive listening* technologies in various theaters, auditoriums, and places of worship. One technology, commonly available in the United States, requires a headset attached to a pocket-sized receiver. The well-meaning people who provide these systems correctly understand that the technology puts sound directly into the user's ears. Alas, few people with hearing loss elect the hassle and embarrassment of locating, requesting, wearing, and returning a conspicuous headset. Most such units therefore sit in closets. Britain, the Scandinavian countries, Australia, and now many parts of the United States have instead installed *loop systems* (see HearingLoop.org) that broadcast customized sound directly through a person's own hearing aid. When suitably equipped, a hearing aid can be transformed by a discreet touch of a switch into a customized in-the-ear speaker. When offered convenient, inconspicuous, personalized sound, many more people elect to use assistive listening.

Designs that enable safe, easy, and effective interactions between people and technology often seem obvious after the fact. Why, then, aren't they more common? Technology developers, like all of us, sometimes mistakenly assume that others share their expertise—that what's clear to them will similarly be clear to others (Camerer et al., 1989; Nickerson, 1999). When people rap their knuckles on a table to convey a familiar tune (try this with a friend), they often expect their listener to recognize it. But for the listener, this is a near-impossible task (Newton, 1991). When you know a thing, it's hard to mentally simulate what it's like not to know, and that is called the *curse of knowledge*.

The point to remember: Everyone benefits when designers and engineers tailor machines, technologies, and environments to fit human abilities and behaviors, when they user-test their work before production and distribution, and when they remain mindful of the curse of knowledge.

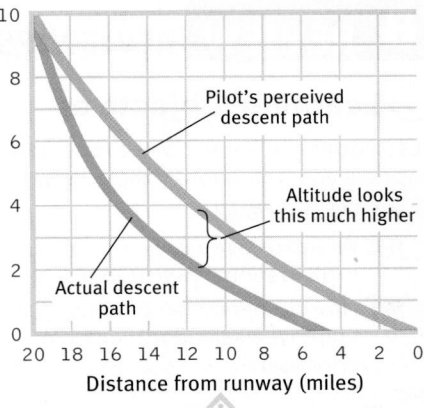

FIGURE B.4

THE HUMAN FACTOR IN ACCIDENTS Lacking distance cues when approaching a runway from over a dark surface, pilots simulating a night landing tended to fly too low. (Data from Kraft, 1978.)

"The better you know something, the less you remember about how hard it was to learn." —Psychologist Steven Pinker, *The Sense of Style,* 2014

 ASK YOURSELF

What situations have you experienced (using new technology, visiting buildings, using transportation) in which the design did not work well? What situations have you experienced in which planners did a particularly good job matching machines and physical environments to our abilities and expectations?

THE HUMAN FACTOR IN SAFE LANDINGS Advanced cockpit design and rehearsed emergency procedures aided pilot Chesley "Sully" Sullenberger, a U.S. Air Force Academy graduate who earned a Master's degree in industrial psychology. In 2009, Sullenberger's instantaneous decisions safely guided his disabled airplane onto New York City's Hudson River, where all 155 of the passengers and crew were safely evacuated.

🔒 **RETRIEVE IT** • • •   *ANSWERS IN APPENDIX E*

RI-4 What is the *curse of knowledge,* and what does it have to do with the work of human factors psychologists?

🔒 REVIEW REVIEW PSYCHOLOGY AT WORK

⟫ Learning Objectives

TEST YOURSELF Answer these repeated Learning Objective Questions on your own (before checking the answers in Appendix D) to improve your retention of the concepts (McDaniel et al., 2009, 2015).

B-1 What is *flow*?

B-2 What are three key areas of study related to industrial-organizational psychology?

B-3 How do personnel psychologists facilitate job seeking, employee selection, work placement, and performance appraisal?

B-4 What is the role of organizational psychologists?

B-5 How can leaders be most effective?

B-6 What cultural influences need to be considered when choosing an effective leadership style?

B-7 How do human factors psychologists work to create user-friendly machines and work settings?

⟫ Terms and Concepts to Remember

TEST YOURSELF Write down the definition yourself, then check your answer on the referenced page.

flow, p. B-1

industrial-organizational (I/O) psychology, p. B-3

personnel psychology, p. B-5

organizational psychology, p. B-5

human factors psychology, p. B-5

structured interview, p. B-6

leadership, p. B-10

task leadership, p. B-10

social leadership, p. B-10

⟫ Experience the Testing Effect

TEST YOURSELF Answer the following questions on your own first, then check your answers in Appendix E.

1. People who view their work as a calling often experience _____, a focused state of consciousness, with diminished awareness of themselves and of time.

2. _____ psychologists assist with job seeking, and the recruitment, selection, placement, training, appraisal, and development of employees; _____ _____ psychologists focus on how people and machines interact, and on optimizing devices and work environments.

3. A personnel psychologist scripted a set of questions to ask all applicants for a job opening. She then trained the firm's interviewers to ask only those questions, to take notes, and to rate applicants' responses. This technique is known as a(n)
   a. structured interview.
   b. unstructured interview.
   c. performance appraisal checklist.
   d. behavior rating scale.

4. In your job, you rate your own performance, your manager's, and your peers'. Your manager, your peers, and your customers also rate your performance. Your organization is using a form of performance appraisal called
   a. flow procedure.   c. structured interviews.
   b. graphic feedback.   d. 360-degree feedback

5. What type of goals will best help you stay focused and motivated to do your finest work in this class?

6. Research indicates that women are often social leaders. They are also more likely than men to have a _____ leadership style.

7. Effective managers often exhibit
   a. only task leadership.
   b. only social leadership.
   c. both task and social leadership, depending on the situation and the person.
   d. task leadership for building teams and social leadership for setting standards.

8. Human factors psychologists focus primarily on
   a. training and developing employees.
   b. appraising employee performance.
   c. maximizing worker satisfaction.
   d. improving the design of machines and environments.

Continue testing yourself with 📚 **LearningCurve** or 📖 **Achieve Read & Practice** to learn and remember most effectively.

Career Fields in Psychology

Jennifer Zwolinski
University of San Diego

What can you do with a degree in psychology? Lots!

As a psychology major, you will graduate with a scientific mindset and an awareness of basic principles of human behavior (biological mechanisms, nature–nurture interactions, life-span development, cognition, psychological disorders, social interaction). This background will prepare you for success in many areas, including business, the helping professions, health services, marketing, law, sales, and teaching. You may even go on to graduate school for specialized training to become a psychology professional. This appendix provides an overview of some of psychology's key career fields.[1] For more detailed information, see *Pursuing a Psychology Career* in LaunchPad (LaunchPadWorks.com), where you can learn more about the many interesting options available to those with bachelor's, master's, and doctoral degrees in psychology.

If you are like most psychology students, you may be unaware of the wide variety of specialties and work settings available in psychology (Terre & Stoddart, 2000). To date, the American Psychological Association (APA) has 54 divisions (**TABLE C.1**) that represent the popular subfields and interest groups of APA members. APA Division 2 (Society for the Teaching of Psychology) offers an excellent career exploration resource for those interested in learning about the hundreds of career options available for students with an undergraduate degree in psychology.

The following paragraphs (arranged alphabetically) describe some of psychology's main career fields, most of which require a graduate degree in psychology.

CLINICAL PSYCHOLOGISTS promote psychological health in individuals, groups, and organizations. Some clinical psychologists specialize in specific psychological disorders. Others treat a range of disorders, from adjustment difficulties to severe psychopathology. Clinical psychologists often provide therapy but may also engage in research, teaching, assessment, and consultation. Clinical psychologists work in a variety of settings, including private practice, mental health service organizations, schools, universities, industries, legal systems, medical systems, counseling centers, government agencies, correctional facilities, nonprofit organizations, and military services.

To become a clinical psychologist, you will need to earn a doctorate from a clinical psychology program. The APA sets the standards for clinical psychology graduate programs, offering accreditation (official recognition) to those who meet their standards. In all U.S. states, clinical psychologists working in independent practice must obtain a license to offer services such as therapy and testing.

COGNITIVE PSYCHOLOGISTS study thought processes and focus on such topics as perception, language, attention, problem solving, memory, judgment and decision making, forgetting, and intelligence. Research interests include designing computer-based models of thought processes and identifying biological correlates of cognition. As a cognitive psychologist, you might work as a professor, industrial consultant, or human factors specialist in an educational or business setting.

COMMUNITY PSYCHOLOGISTS move beyond focusing on specific individuals or families and deal with broad problems of mental health in community settings. These psychologists believe that human behavior is powerfully influenced by the interaction between people and their physical, social, political, and economic environments.

COGNITIVE CONSULTING Cognitive psychologists may advise businesses on how to operate more effectively by understanding the human factors involved.

---

1. Although this text covers the world of psychology for students in many countries, this appendix draws primarily from available U.S. data. Its descriptions of psychology's career fields are, however, also applicable in many other countries.

TABLE C.1

APA Divisions by Number and Name

1. Society for General Psychology	29. Society for the Advancement of Psychotherapy
2. Society for the Teaching of Psychology	30. Society of Psychological Hypnosis
3. Society for Experimental Psychology and Cognitive Science	31. State, Provincial, and Territorial Psychological Association Affairs
4. *There is no active Division 4.*	32. Society for Humanistic Psychology
5. Quantitative and Qualitative Methods	33. Intellectual and Developmental Disabilities/Autism Spectrum Disorder
6. Society for Behavioral Neuroscience and Comparative Psychology	34. Society for Environmental, Population, and Conservation Psychology
7. Developmental Psychology	35. Society for the Psychology of Women
8. Society for Personality and Social Psychology	36. Society for the Psychology of Religion and Spirituality
9. Society for the Psychological Study of Social Issues (SPSSI)	37. Society for Child and Family Policy and Practice
10. Society for the Psychology of Aesthetics, Creativity, and the Arts	38. Society for Health Psychology
11. *There is no active Division 11.*	39. Psychoanalysis
12. Society of Clinical Psychology	40. Society for Clinical Neuropsychology
13. Society of Consulting Psychology	41. American Psychology-Law Society
14. Society for Industrial and Organizational Psychology	42. Psychologists in Independent Practice
15. Educational Psychology	43. Society for Couple and Family Psychology
16. School Psychology	44. Society for the Psychology of Sexual Orientation and Gender Diversity
17. Society of Counseling Psychology	45. Society for the Psychological Study of Culture, Ethnicity, and Race
18. Psychologists in Public Service	46. Society for Media Psychology and Technology
19. Society for Military Psychology	47. Society for Sport, Exercise, and Performance Psychology
20. Adult Development and Aging	48. Society for the Study of Peace, Conflict, and Violence: Peace Psychology Division
21. Applied Experimental and Engineering Psychology	49. Society of Group Psychology and Group Psychotherapy
22. Rehabilitation Psychology	50. Society of Addiction Psychology
23. Society for Consumer Psychology	51. Society for the Psychological Study of Men and Masculinity
24. Society for Theoretical and Philosophical Psychology	52. International Psychology
25. Behavior Analysis	53. Society of Clinical Child and Adolescent Psychology
26. Society for the History of Psychology	54. Society of Pediatric Psychology
27. Society for Community Research and Action: Division of Community Psychology	55. American Society for the Advancement of Pharmacotherapy
28. Psychopharmacology and Substance Abuse	56. Trauma Psychology

Source: American Psychological Association

They seek to promote psychological health by enhancing environmental settings—focusing on preventive measures and crisis intervention, with special attention to the problems of underserved groups and ethnic minorities. Some community psychologists collaborate with professionals in other areas, such as public health, with a shared emphasis on prevention. As a community psychologist, your work settings could include federal, state, and local departments of mental health, corrections, and welfare. You might conduct research or help evaluate research in health service settings, serve as an independent consultant for a private or government agency, or teach and consult as a college or university faculty member.

COUNSELING PSYCHOLOGISTS help people adjust to life transitions or make lifestyle changes. Although similar to clinical psychologists, counseling psychologists typically help people with adjustment problems rather than severe psychopathology. Like clinical psychologists, counseling psychologists conduct therapy and provide assessments to individuals and groups. As a counseling psychologist, you would likely emphasize your clients' strengths, helping them to use their own skills, interests, and abilities to cope during transitions. You might find yourself working in an academic setting as a faculty member or administrator or in a university counseling center, community mental health center, business, or

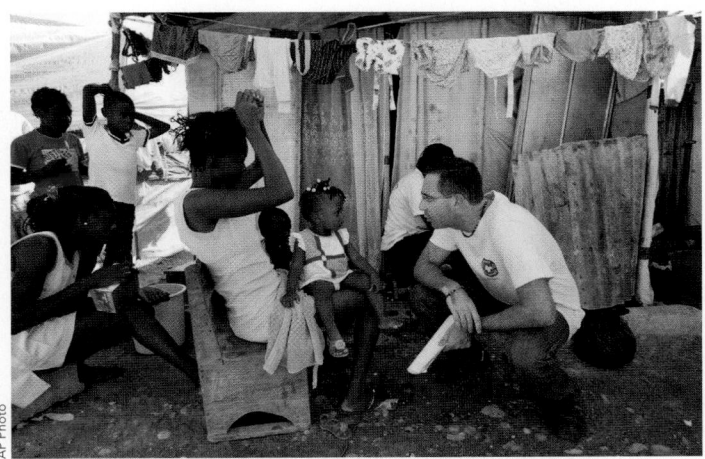

COMMUNITY CARE Community psychologists in Haiti have helped residents work through the ongoing emotional challenges that followed the devastating 2010 earthquake and the widely destructive 2016 hurricane.

private practice. As with clinical psychology, if you plan to work in independent practice you will need to obtain a state license to provide counseling services to the public.

DEVELOPMENTAL PSYCHOLOGISTS conduct research on age-related behavioral changes and apply their scientific knowledge to educational, child-care, policy, and related settings. As a developmental psychologist, you would investigate change across a broad range of topics, including the biological, psychological, cognitive, and social aspects of development. Developmental psychology informs a number of applied fields, including educational psychology, school psychology, child psychopathology, and gerontology. The field also informs public policy in areas such as education and child-care reform, maternal and child health, and attachment and adoption. You would probably specialize in a specific stage of the life span, such as infancy, childhood, adolescence, or middle or late adulthood. Your work setting could be an educational institution, day-care center, youth group program, or senior center.

EDUCATIONAL PSYCHOLOGISTS are interested in the psychological processes involved in learning. They study the relationship between learning and the physical and social environments, and they develop strategies for enhancing the learning process. As an educational psychologist, working in a university psychology department or school of education, you might conduct basic research on topics related to learning, or develop innovative methods of teaching to enhance the learning process. You might design effective tests, including measures of aptitude and achievement. You might be employed by a school or government agency or charged with designing and implementing effective employee-training programs in a business setting.

ENVIRONMENTAL PSYCHOLOGISTS study the interaction of individuals with their natural and built (urban) environments. They are interested in how we influence and are affected by these environments. As an environmental psychologist, you might study wildlife conservation, the impact of urbanization on health, or cognitive factors involved in sustainable lifestyle choices. Environmental psychologists tend to address these kinds of questions by working with other professionals as part of an interdisciplinary team. As an environmental psychologist, you might work in a consulting firm, an academic setting, the nonprofit sector, or the government.

EXPERIMENTAL PSYCHOLOGISTS are a diverse group of scientists who investigate a variety of basic behavioral processes in humans and other animals. Prominent areas of experimental research include comparative methods of science, motivation, learning, thought, attention, memory, perception, and language. Most experimental psychologists identify with a particular subfield, such as cognitive psychology, depending on their interests and training. Experimental research methods are not limited to the field of experimental psychology; many other subfields rely on experimental methodology to conduct studies. As an experimental psychologist, you would most likely work in an academic setting, teaching courses and supervising students' research in addition to conducting your own research. Or you might be employed by a research institution, zoo, business, or government agency.

FORENSIC PSYCHOLOGISTS apply psychological principles to legal issues. They conduct research on the interface of law and psychology, help to create public policies related to mental health, help law-enforcement agencies in criminal investigations, or consult on jury selection and deliberation processes. They also provide assessment to assist the legal community. Although most forensic psychologists are clinical psychologists, many have expertise in other areas of psychology, such as social or cognitive psychology. Some also hold law degrees. As a forensic psychologist, you might

CRIMINAL INVESTIGATION Forensic psychologists may be called on to assist police officers who are investigating a crime scene, as seen here after a shooting in Florida. Most forensic work, however, occurs in the lab and for the judicial system.

work in a university psychology department, law school, research organization, community mental health agency, law-enforcement agency, court, or correctional setting.

HEALTH PSYCHOLOGISTS are researchers and practitioners concerned with psychology's contribution to promoting health and preventing disease. As applied psychologists or clinicians, they may help individuals lead healthier lives by designing, conducting, and evaluating programs to stop smoking, lose weight, improve sleep, manage pain, prevent the spread of sexually transmitted infections, or treat psychosocial problems associated with chronic and terminal illnesses. As researchers and clinicians, they identify conditions and practices associated with health and illness to help create effective interventions. In public service, health psychologists study and work to improve government policies and health care systems. As a health psychologist, you could be employed in a hospital, medical school, rehabilitation center, public health agency, college or university, or, if you are also a clinical psychologist, in private practice.

INDUSTRIAL-ORGANIZATIONAL (I/O) PSYCHOLOGISTS study the relationship between people and their working environments. They may develop new ways to increase productivity, improve personnel selection, or promote job satisfaction in an organizational setting. Their interests include organizational structure and change, consumer behavior, and personnel selection and training. As an I/O psychologist, you might conduct workplace training or provide organizational analysis and development. You may find yourself working in business, industry, the government, or a college or university. Or you may be self-employed as a consultant or work for a management consulting firm. (For more on I/O psychology, see Appendix B, Psychology at Work.)

NEUROPSYCHOLOGISTS investigate the relationship between neurological processes (structure and function of the brain) and behavior. As a neuropsychologist you might assess, diagnose, or treat central nervous system disorders, such as Alzheimer's disease or stroke. You might also evaluate individuals for evidence of head injuries; learning and developmental disabilities, such as autism spectrum disorder; and other psychiatric disorders, such as attention-deficit hyperactivity disorder (ADHD). If you are a *clinical neuropsychologist,* you might work in a hospital's neurology, neurosurgery, or psychiatric unit. Neuropsychologists also work in academic settings, where they conduct research and teach.

PSYCHOMETRIC AND QUANTITATIVE PSYCHOLOGISTS study the methods and techniques used to acquire psychological knowledge. A psychometric psychologist may update existing neurocognitive or personality tests or devise new tests for use in clinical and school settings or in business and industry. These psychologists also administer, score, and interpret such tests. Quantitative psychologists collaborate with researchers to design, analyze, and interpret the results of research programs. As a psychometric or quantitative psychologist, you will need to be well trained in research methods, statistics, and computer technology. You will most likely be employed by a university or college, a testing company, a private research firm, or a government agency.

REHABILITATION PSYCHOLOGISTS are researchers and practitioners who work with people who have lost optimal functioning

ASSESSING AND SUPPORTING CHILDREN School psychologists may find themselves working with children individually or in groups. They receive interdisciplinary training in mental health assessment and behavior analysis, research methods and design, and special needs education. They work primarily in schools, but also in a range of other settings, including pediatric hospitals, mental health centers, and correctional facilities.

after an accident, illness, or other event. As a rehabilitation psychologist, you would probably work in a medical rehabilitation institution or hospital. You might also work in a medical school, university, state or federal vocational rehabilitation agency, or in private practice serving people with physical disabilities.

SCHOOL PSYCHOLOGISTS are involved in the assessment of and intervention for children in educational settings. They diagnose and treat cognitive, social, and emotional problems that may negatively influence children's learning or overall functioning at school. As a school psychologist, you would collaborate with teachers, parents, and administrators, making recommendations to improve student learning. You would work in an academic setting, a federal or state government agency, a child guidance center, or a behavioral research laboratory.

SOCIAL PSYCHOLOGISTS are interested in our interactions with others. Social psychologists study how our beliefs, feelings, and behaviors are affected by and influence other people. They study topics such as attitudes, aggression, prejudice, interpersonal attraction, group behavior, and leadership. As a social psychologist, you would probably be a college or university faculty member. You might also work in organizational consultation, market research, or an applied psychology field, such as social neuroscience. Some social psychologists work for hospitals, federal agencies, social networking sites, or businesses performing applied research.

SPORT PSYCHOLOGISTS study the psychological factors that influence, and are influenced by, participation in sports and other physical activities. Their professional activities include coach

Phil Walter/Getty Images

CRICKET CURES Sport psychologists often work directly with athletes to help them improve their performance. Here a sport psychologist consults with Brendon McCullum, a record-breaking athlete who played international cricket for New Zealand.

education and athlete preparation, as well as research and teaching. Sport psychologists who also have a clinical or counseling degree can apply those skills to working with individuals with psychological problems, such as anxiety or substance abuse, that might interfere with optimal performance. As a sport psychologist, if you were not working in an academic or research setting, you would most likely work as part of a team or an organization or in a private capacity.

* * *

So, the next time someone asks you what you will do with your psychology degree, tell them you have a lot of options. You might use your acquired skills and understanding to get a job and succeed in any number of fields, or you might pursue graduate school and then career opportunities in associated professions. In any case, what you have learned about behavior and mental processes will surely enrich your life (Hammer, 2003).

Complete Module Reviews

Thinking Critically With Psychological Science

MODULE 1 The History and Scope of Psychology

1-1 How is psychology a science?

Psychology's findings, based on an *empirical approach,* are the result of careful observation and testing. Sifting sense from nonsense requires a scientific attitude.

1-2 What are the three key elements of the scientific attitude, and how do they support scientific inquiry?

The scientific attitude equips us to be curious, skeptical, and humble in scrutinizing competing ideas or our own observations. Curiosity triggers new ideas, skepticism encourages attention to the facts, and humility helps us discard predictions that can't be verified by research. Together, these three key elements make modern science possible.

1-3 How does critical thinking feed a scientific attitude, and smarter thinking for everyday life?

Critical thinking puts ideas to the test by examining assumptions, appraising the source, discerning hidden biases, evaluating evidence, and assessing conclusions.

1-4 What were some important milestones in psychology's early development?

Wilhelm Wundt established the first psychological laboratory in 1879 in Germany. Two early schools of thought in psychology were *structuralism* and *functionalism.* Mary Whiton Calkins and Margaret Floy Washburn were two of the first women in the field.

1-5 How did behaviorism, Freudian psychology, and humanistic psychology further the development of psychological science?

Early researchers defined *psychology* as "the science of mental life." In the 1920s, under the influence of John B. Watson and the behaviorists, the field's focus changed to the "scientific study of observable behavior." *Behaviorism* became one of psychology's two major forces well into the 1960s. However, the second major force of Freudian psychology, along with the influence of *humanistic psychology,* revived interest in the study of mental processes.

1-6 How has contemporary psychology focused on cognition, on biology and experience, on culture and gender, and on human flourishing?

The *cognitive* revolution in the 1960s led psychology back to its early interest in the mind, and to its current definition as the science of behavior and mental processes. The field of *cognitive neuroscience* now examines the brain activity underlying mental activity. Our growing understanding of biology and experience has fed psychology's most enduring debate. The *nature–nurture issue* centers on the relative contributions of genes and experience, and their interaction in specific environments. Charles Darwin's view that *natural selection* shapes behaviors as well as bodies led to *evolutionary psychology's* study of our similarities because of our common biology and evolutionary history, and *behavior genetics'* focus on the relative power and limits of genetic and environmental influences on behavior. Cross-cultural and gender studies have diversified psychology's assumptions while also reminding us of our similarities. Attitudes and behaviors may vary somewhat by gender or across *cultures,* but because of our shared human kinship, the underlying processes and principles are more similar than different. Psychology's traditional focus on understanding and treating troubles has expanded with *positive psychology's* call for more research on human flourishing and its attempt to discover and promote traits that help people to thrive.

1-7 What are psychology's levels of analysis and related perspectives?

The *biopsychosocial approach* integrates information from three differing but complementary *levels of analysis:* biological, psychological, and social-cultural. This approach offers a more complete understanding than could usually be reached by relying on only one of psychology's current theoretical perspectives (neuroscience, evolutionary, behavior genetics, psychodynamic, behavioral, cognitive, and social-cultural).

1-8 What are psychology's main subfields?

Within the science of psychology, researchers may conduct *basic research* to increase the field's knowledge base (often in biological, developmental, cognitive, personality, and social psychology) or *applied research* to solve practical problems (in industrial-organizational psychology and other areas). Those who engage in psychology as a helping profession may assist people as *counseling psychologists,* helping people with challenges and crises (including academic, vocational, and relationship issues) and to improve their personal and social functioning, or as *clinical psychologists,* assessing and treating people with mental, emotional, and behavior disorders. (*Psychiatrists* also assess and treat people with disorders, but as medical doctors, they may prescribe drugs in addition to psychotherapy.) *Community psychologists* work to create healthy social and physical environments (in schools, for example).

MODULE 2 Research Strategies: How Psychologists Ask and Answer Questions

2-1   How does our everyday thinking sometimes lead us to a wrong conclusion?

Our everyday thinking can lead us astray because of three phenomena. *Hindsight bias* (the "I-knew-it-all-along phenomenon") is the tendency to believe, after learning an outcome, that we would have foreseen it. Overconfidence is often the result of our readiness to be more confident than correct. These tendencies, along with our eagerness to perceive patterns in random events, lead us to overestimate the weight of commonsense thinking. Although limited by the testable questions it can address, scientific inquiry can help us overcome such biases and shortcomings.

2-2   Why are we so vulnerable to believing untruths?

In our modern "post-truth" culture, our emotions, beliefs, and group affiliations may color our judgments, prevent our acknowledgement of objective facts, and prompt us to accept only the information that confirms our views. Misinformation may spread as a result of repetition and memorable examples, contributing to the post-truth culture. Critical evaluation of information and a scientific mindset can help to combat our biases and distorted thinking.

2-3   How do theories advance psychological science?

Psychological *theories* apply an integrated set of principles to organize observations and to generate *hypotheses.* By testing their hypotheses, researchers can confirm, reject, or revise their theories. To enable other researchers to *replicate* the studies, researchers report them using precise *operational definitions* of their procedures and concepts. If others achieve similar results, confidence in the conclusion will be greater. By combining the results of many studies, *meta-analysis* helps increase researchers' confidence in their results by avoiding the problem of small sample sizes.

2-4   How do psychologists use case studies, naturalistic observations, and surveys to observe and describe behavior, and why is random sampling important?

Descriptive methods, which include *case studies* (in-depth analyses of individuals or groups), *naturalistic observations* (recording many individuals' natural behavior), and *surveys* (asking people questions), show us what can happen, and they may offer ideas for further study. The best basis for generalizing about a *population* is a representative sample; in a *random sample,* every person in the entire population being studied has an equal chance of participating. Descriptive methods describe but do not *explain* behavior; they cannot show cause and effect because researchers cannot control variables.

2-5   What does it mean when we say two things are correlated, and what are positive and negative correlations?

Correlation is the degree to which two variables are related, and how well one predicts the other. In a positive correlation, two *variables* increase or decrease together; in a negative correlation, one variable increases as the other decreases. The strength and direction of their relationship is expressed as a *correlation coefficient,* which ranges from +1.00 (a perfect positive correlation) through 0 (no correlation) to −1.00 (a perfect negative correlation).

2-6   Why do correlations enable prediction but not cause-effect explanation?

Correlations enable prediction because they show how two factors are related—either positively or negatively. A correlation can indicate the possibility of a cause-effect relationship, but it does not prove the direction of the influence, or whether an underlying third factor may explain the correlation.

2-7   What are the characteristics of experimentation that make it possible to isolate cause and effect?

To discover cause-effect relationships, psychologists conduct *experiments,* manipulating one or more variables of interest and controlling other variables. Using *random assignment,* they can minimize *confounding variables,* such as preexisting differences between the *experimental group* (exposed to the treatment) and the *control group* (not given the treatment). The *independent variable* is the factor the experimenter manipulates to study its effect; the *dependent variable* is the factor the experimenter measures to discover any changes occurring in response to the manipulation of the independent variable. Studies may use a *double-blind procedure* to avoid the *placebo effect* and researcher bias.

2-8   How would you know which research design to use?

Psychological scientists design studies and choose research methods that will best provide meaningful results. Researchers generate testable questions, and then carefully consider the best design to use in studying those questions (experimental, correlational, case study, naturalistic observation, twin study, longitudinal, or cross-sectional). Next, psychologists measure the variables they are studying, and finally they interpret their results, keeping possible confounding variables in mind. (The online Immersive Learning "How Would You Know?" research activities allow you to play the role of the researcher, making choices about the best ways to test interesting questions.)

2-9   How can simplified laboratory conditions illuminate everyday life?

Researchers intentionally create a controlled, artificial environment in the laboratory to test general theoretical principles. It is the general principles—not the specific findings—that help explain everyday behaviors.

2-10 Why do psychologists study animals, and what ethical guidelines safeguard human and animal research participants? How do psychologists' values influence psychology?

Some psychologists are primarily interested in animal behavior; others want to better understand the physiological and psychological processes shared by humans and other species. Government agencies have established standards for animal care and housing. Professional associations and funding agencies also have guidelines for protecting animals' well-being. The ethics codes of the American Psychological Association (APA) and the British Psychological Society (BPS) outline standards for safeguarding human participants' well-being, including obtaining their *informed consent* and *debriefing* them later. Psychologists' values influence their choice of research topics, their theories and observations, their labels for behavior, and their professional advice. Applications of psychology's principles have been used mainly in the service of humanity.

2-11 How can psychological principles help you learn, remember, and thrive?

The *testing effect* shows that learning and memory are enhanced by actively retrieving, rather than simply rereading, previously studied material. The *SQ3R* study method—survey, question, read, retrieve, and review—applies principles derived from memory research and can help you learn and remember material. Four additional tips are (1) distribute your study time; (2) learn to think critically; (3) process class information actively; and (4) overlearn. Psychological research has shown that people who live happy, thriving lives manage their time to get a full night's sleep; make space for exercise; set long-term goals, with daily aims; have a growth mindset; and prioritize relationships.

The Biology of Behavior

MODULE ③ Neural and Hormonal Systems

3-1 Why are psychologists concerned with human biology?

Psychologists working from a *biological* perspective study the links between biological processes and psychological processes. We are biopsychosocial systems, in which biological, psychological, and social-cultural factors interact to influence behavior.

3-2 How do biology and experience interact in neural plasticity?

Plasticity enables our brain to adjust to new experiences, thereby being sculpted by both genes and life. While this is a lifelong ability, plasticity is greatest in childhood. With practice, our brain develops unique patterns that reflect our life experiences.

3-3 What are *neurons*, and how do they transmit information?

Neurons are the elementary components of the nervous system, the body's speedy electrochemical information system. A neuron (a *cell body* and its branching fibers) receives signals through its often bushy, branching *dendrites* and sends signals through its *axons*. Some axons are encased in a *myelin sheath*, which enables faster transmission. *Glial cells* support, nourish, and protect neurons and also play a role in learning, thinking, and memory. If the combined signals received by a neuron exceed a minimum *threshold*, the neuron fires, transmitting an electrical impulse (the *action potential*) down its axon by means of a chemistry-to-electricity process. Neurons need a short rest called the *refractory period*, after which they can fire again. The neuron's reaction is an *all-or-none response*.

3-4 How do nerve cells communicate with other nerve cells?

When action potentials reach the end of an axon (the axon terminals), they stimulate the release of *neurotransmitters*. These chemical messengers carry a message from the sending neuron across a *synapse* to receptor sites on a receiving neuron. The sending neuron, in a process called *reuptake*, then normally reabsorbs the excess neurotransmitter molecules in the synaptic gap. If incoming signals are strong enough, the receiving neuron generates its own action potential and relays the message to other cells.

3-5 How do neurotransmitters influence behavior, and how do drugs and other chemicals affect neurotransmission?

Neurotransmitters travel designated pathways in the brain and may influence specific behaviors and emotions. Acetylcholine (ACh) enables muscle action, learning, and memory. *Endorphins* are natural opiates released in response to pain and exercise. Drugs and other chemicals affect brain chemistry at synapses. *Agonists* increase a neurotransmitter's action, and may do so in various ways. *Antagonists* decrease a neurotransmitter's action by blocking production or release.

3-6 What are the functions of the nervous system's main divisions, and what are the three main types of neurons?

The *central nervous system (CNS)*—the brain and the spinal cord—is the *nervous system's* decision maker. The *peripheral nervous system (PNS)*, which connects the CNS to the rest of the body by means of *nerves*, gathers information and transmits CNS decisions to the rest of the body. The two main PNS divisions are the *somatic nervous system* (which enables voluntary control of the skeletal muscles) and the *autonomic nervous system* (which controls involuntary muscles and glands by means of its *sympathetic* and *parasympathetic* divisions). The three types of neurons cluster into working networks: (1) *Sensory (afferent) neurons* carry incoming information from the body's tissues and sensory receptors to the brain and spinal cord. (2) *Motor (efferent) neurons* carry outgoing information from the brain and spinal cord to the muscles and glands. (3) *Interneurons* communicate within the brain and spinal cord and process information between the sensory inputs and motor outputs.

3-7 How does the endocrine system transmit information and interact with the nervous system?

The *endocrine system* secretes *hormones* into the bloodstream, where they travel through the body and affect other tissues, including the brain. The endocrine system's master gland, the *pituitary*, influences hormone release by other glands, including the *adrenal glands*.

In an intricate feedback system, the brain's hypothalamus influences the pituitary gland, which influences other glands, which release hormones, which in turn influence the brain.

MODULE 4 Tools of Discovery, Older Brain Structures, and the Limbic System

4-1   How do neuroscientists study the brain's connections to behavior and mind?

Clinical observations and *lesioning* reveal the general effects of brain damage. Electrical, chemical, or magnetic stimulation can also reveal aspects of information processing in the brain. *MRI* scans show anatomy. *EEG, MEG, PET,* and *fMRI (functional MRI)* recordings reveal brain function.

4-2   What structures make up the brainstem, and what are the functions of the brainstem, thalamus, reticular formation, and cerebellum?

The *brainstem,* the oldest part of the brain, is responsible for automatic survival functions. It includes the *medulla* (which controls heartbeat and breathing), the *pons* (which helps coordinate movements and control sleep), and the *reticular formation* (which filters incoming stimuli, relays information to other brain areas, and affects arousal). The *thalamus,* sitting above the brainstem, acts as the brain's sensory control center. The *cerebellum,* attached to the rear of the brainstem, coordinates muscle movement and balance and enables nonverbal learning and memory.

4-3   What are the limbic system's structures and functions?

The *limbic system* is linked to emotions, memory, and drives. Its neural centers include the *amygdala* (involved in responses of aggression and fear); the *hypothalamus* (directs various bodily maintenance functions, helps govern the endocrine system, and is linked to emotion and reward); and the *hippocampus* (helps process explicit, conscious memories). The hypothalamus controls the pituitary (the "master gland") by stimulating it to trigger the release of hormones.

MODULE 5 The Cerebral Cortex

5-1   What four lobes make up the cerebral cortex, and what are the functions of the motor cortex, somatosensory cortex, and association areas?

The *cerebral cortex* has two hemispheres, and each hemisphere has four lobes: the *frontal, parietal, occipital,* and *temporal.* Each lobe performs many functions and interacts with other areas of the cortex. The *motor cortex,* at the rear of the frontal lobes, controls voluntary movements. The *somatosensory cortex,* at the front of the parietal lobes, registers and processes body touch and movement sensations. Body parts requiring precise control (in the motor cortex) or those that are especially sensitive (in the somatosensory cortex) occupy the greatest amount of space. Most of the brain's cortex—the major portion of each of the four lobes—is devoted to uncommitted *association areas,* which integrate information involved in higher mental functions such as learning, remembering, thinking, and speaking. Our mental experiences arise from coordinated brain activity.

5-2   Do we really use only 10 percent of our brain?

The unresponsiveness of our association areas to electrical probing led to the false claim that we only use 10 percent of our brain. But these vast areas of the brain are responsible for interpreting, integrating, and acting on sensory information and linking it with stored memories. Evidence from brain damage shows that the neurons in association areas are busy with higher mental functions; a bullet would not land in an "unused" area.

5-3   To what extent can a damaged brain reorganize itself, and what is neurogenesis?

While brain and spinal cord neurons usually do not regenerate, some neural tissue can reorganize in response to damage. The damaged brain may demonstrate plasticity, especially in young children, as new pathways are built and functions migrate to other brain regions. Reassignment of functions to different areas of the brain may also occur in blindness and deafness, or as a result of damage and disease. The brain sometimes mends itself by forming new neurons, a process known as *neurogenesis.*

5-4   What do split brains reveal about the functions of our two brain hemispheres?

Split-brain research (experiments on people with a severed *corpus callosum*) has confirmed that in most people, the left hemisphere is the more verbal. The right hemisphere excels in visual perception and making inferences, and helps us modulate our speech and orchestrate our self-awareness. Studies of healthy people with intact brains confirm that each hemisphere makes unique contributions to the integrated functioning of the whole brain.

MODULE 6 Genetics, Evolutionary Psychology, and Behavior

6-1   What are *chromosomes, DNA, genes,* and the human *genome*? How do behavior geneticists explain our individual differences?

Genes are the biochemical units of heredity that make up *chromosomes,* the threadlike coils of *DNA.* When genes are expressed, they provide the code for creating the proteins that form our body's building blocks. Most human traits are influenced by many genes acting together. The human *genome* is the shared genetic profile that distinguishes humans from other species, consisting at an individual level of all the genetic material in an organism's chromosomes. *Behavior geneticists* study the relative power and limits of genetic and *environmental* influences on behavior. Most of our differing traits are influenced by many genes, and by the interaction of our individual environments with these genetic predispositions.

6-2   How do twin and adoption studies help us understand the effects and interactions of nature and nurture?

Studies of *identical (monozygotic) twins* versus *fraternal (dizygotic) twins,* separated twins, and biological versus adoptive relatives allow researchers to consider the effects of shared environment and shared genes, which sheds light on how nature and nurture influence our traits. Shared family environments have surprisingly little effect on personality, though parenting does influence other factors.

6-3   How do heredity and environment work together?

Our genetic predispositions and our specific environments *interact*. Environments can trigger or block genetic expression, and genetically influenced traits can influence the experiences we seek and the responses we evoke from others. The field of *epigenetics* studies the influences on gene expression that occur without changes in DNA.

6-4   How do evolutionary psychologists use natural selection to explain behavior tendencies?

Evolutionary psychologists seek to understand how our traits and behavior tendencies are shaped by *natural selection*. Genetic variations that increase the odds of reproducing and surviving in a particular environment are most likely to be passed on to future generations. Some variations arise from *mutations,* others from new gene combinations at conception. Humans share a genetic legacy and are predisposed to behaviors that promoted our ancestors' survival and reproduction. Charles Darwin's theory of evolution is one of biology's fundamental organizing principles. He anticipated today's application of evolutionary principles in psychology.

Consciousness and the Two-Track Mind

MODULE 7 Consciousness: Some Basic Concepts

7-1   What is the place of consciousness in psychology's history?

After initially claiming consciousness as their area of study in the nineteenth century, psychologists abandoned it in the first half of the twentieth century, turning instead to the study of observable behavior because they believed consciousness was too difficult to study scientifically. Since 1960, under the influence of cognitive psychology, neuroscience, and *cognitive neuroscience,* our awareness of ourselves and our environment—our *consciousness*—has reclaimed its place as an important area of research.

7-2   How does selective attention direct our perceptions?

We *selectively attend* to, and process, a very limited portion of incoming information, blocking out much and often shifting the spotlight of our attention from one thing to another. Focused intently on one task, we often display *inattentional blindness* to other events, including *change blindness* to changes around us.

7-3   What is the *dual processing* being revealed by today's cognitive neuroscience?

Scientists studying the brain mechanisms underlying consciousness and cognition have discovered that the mind processes information on two separate tracks, one operating at a conscious level (*sequential processing*) and the other at an unconscious level (*parallel processing*). Parallel processing takes care of the routine business, while sequential processing is best for solving new problems that require our attention. Together, this *dual processing*—conscious and unconscious—affects our perception, memory, attitudes, and other cognitions.

MODULE 8 Sleep and Dreams

8-1   What is *sleep*?

Sleep is the periodic, natural loss of normal consciousness—as distinct from unconsciousness resulting from a coma, general anesthesia, or hibernation.

8-2   How do our biological rhythms influence our daily functioning?

Our bodies have an internal biological clock, roughly synchronized with the 24-hour cycle of night and day. This *circadian rhythm* appears in our daily patterns of body temperature, arousal, sleeping, and waking. Age and experience can alter these patterns, resetting our biological clock.

8-3   What is the biological rhythm of our sleeping and dreaming stages?

Younger adults cycle through four distinct sleep stages about every 90 minutes. (The sleep cycle repeats more frequently for older adults.) Leaving the *alpha waves* of the awake, relaxed stage, we descend into the irregular brain waves of non-REM stage 1 (NREM-1 or N1) sleep, often with *hallucinations*. NREM-2 (N2) sleep (in which we spend about half our sleep time) follows, lasting about 20 minutes, with its characteristic sleep spindles. We then enter NREM-3 (N3) sleep, lasting about 30 minutes, with large, slow *delta waves*. About an hour after falling asleep, we ascend from our initial sleep dive and begin periods of *REM* (rapid eye movement or *R*) sleep. REM sleep is described as a paradoxical sleep stage because of internal arousal but external calm (near paralysis). It includes most dreaming, and lengthens as the night goes on. During a normal night's sleep, N3 sleep shortens and REM and N2 sleep lengthens.

8-4   How do biology and environment interact in our sleep patterns?

Our biology—our circadian rhythm as well as our age and our body's production of melatonin (influenced by the brain's *suprachiasmatic nucleus*)—interacts with cultural expectations and individual behaviors to determine our sleeping and waking patterns. Being bathed in (or deprived of) light disrupts our 24-hour biological clock; night-shift workers may experience chronic desynchronization.

8-5   What are sleep's functions?

Sleep may have played a protective role in human evolution by keeping people safe during potentially dangerous periods. Sleep also helps restore and repair damaged neurons. Sleep consolidates our memories by replaying recent learning and strengthening neural connections. Sleep promotes creative problem solving the next day. During slow-wave sleep, the pituitary gland secretes a growth hormone necessary for muscle development.

8-6   How does sleep loss affect us, and what are the major sleep disorders?

Sleep deprivation causes fatigue and irritability, and it impairs concentration, productivity, and memory consolidation. It can also lead to depression, obesity, joint inflammation, a suppressed immune system, and slowed performance (with greater vulnerability to accidents). Sleep disorders include *insomnia* (recurring problems in falling or staying asleep); *narcolepsy* (sudden uncontrollable sleepiness, sometimes lapsing directly into REM sleep); *sleep apnea* (the repeated stopping of breathing while asleep; associated with obesity, especially in men); *night terrors* (high arousal and the appearance of being terrified; NREM-3 disorder found mainly in children); sleepwalking; and sleeptalking.

8-7   What do we dream, and what functions have theorists proposed for dreams?

We usually *dream* of ordinary events and everyday experiences, most involving some anxiety or misfortune. Fewer than 10 percent of dreams among men (and fewer still among women) have any sexual content. Most dreams occur during REM sleep; those that happen during NREM sleep tend to be vague fleeting images. There are five major views of the function of dreams. (1) Freud's wish-fulfillment: Dreams provide a psychic "safety valve," with *manifest content* (story line) acting as a censored version of *latent content* (underlying meaning that gratifies our unconscious wishes). (2) Information-processing: Dreams help us sort out the day's events and consolidate them in memory. (3) Physiological function: Regular brain stimulation may help develop and preserve neural pathways in the brain. (4) Neural activation: The brain attempts to make sense of neural static by weaving it into a story line. (5) Cognitive development: Dreams reflect the dreamers' level of development—their knowledge and understanding. Most sleep theorists agree that REM sleep and its associated dreams serve an important function, as shown by the *REM rebound* that occurs following REM deprivation in humans and other species.

MODULE 9 Drugs and Consciousness

9-1   What are *substance use disorders*?

Those with a *substance use disorder* experience continued substance craving and use despite significant life disruption and/or physical risk. *Psychoactive drugs* alter perceptions and moods.

9-2   What roles do tolerance and addiction play in substance use disorders, and how has the concept of *addiction* changed?

Psychoactive drugs may produce *tolerance*—requiring larger doses to achieve the desired effect—and *withdrawal*—significant discomfort, due to strong addictive cravings, accompanying attempts to quit. Addiction prompts users to crave the drug and to continue use despite known adverse consequences. Therapy or group support may help; it helps to believe that addictions are controllable and that people can change. Although psychologists try to avoid overuse of the term "addiction" to label driven, excessive behaviors, there are some behavior addictions (such as gambling disorder) in which behaviors become compulsive and dysfunctional.

9-3   What are *depressants*, and what are their effects?

Depressants, such as alcohol, *barbiturates,* and the *opiates,* reduce neural activity and slow body functions. Alcohol disinhibits, increasing the likelihood that we will act on our impulses, whether harmful or helpful. It also impairs judgment by slowing neural processing, disrupts memory processes by suppressing REM sleep, and reduces self-awareness and self-control. User expectations strongly influence alcohol's behavioral effects. Alcohol can shrink the brain in those with *alcohol use disorder* (marked by tolerance, withdrawal if use is suspended, and a drive to continue problematic use).

9-4   What are *stimulants*, and what are their effects?

Stimulants—including caffeine, nicotine, cocaine, the amphetamines, methamphetamine, and Ecstasy—excite neural activity and speed up body functions, triggering energy and mood changes. All are highly addictive. *Nicotine's* effects make tobacco product use a difficult habit to kick, yet repeated attempts to quit seem to pay off. *Cocaine* gives users a fast high, followed shortly by a crash. Its risks include cardiac arrest, respiratory failure, and emotional disturbances. *Amphetamines* stimulate neural activity, leading to heightened energy and mood. *Methamphetamine* use may permanently reduce dopamine production. *Ecstasy (MDMA)* is a combined stimulant and mild hallucinogen that produces euphoria and feelings of intimacy. Its users risk immune system suppression, permanent damage to mood and memory, and (if taken during physical activity) dehydration and escalating body temperatures.

9-5   What are *hallucinogens*, and what are their effects?

Hallucinogens, such as *LSD* and marijuana, distort perceptions and evoke hallucinations. The user's mood and expectations influence the effects of LSD, but common experiences are hallucinations and emotions varying from euphoria to panic. Marijuana's main ingredient, *THC,* may trigger feelings of disinhibition, euphoria, relaxation, relief from pain, and intense sensitivity to sensory stimuli, but may increase the risk of psychological disorders and lead to impaired learning and memory.

9-6   Why do some people become regular users of consciousness-altering drugs?

Some people may be biologically vulnerable to particular drugs. Psychological factors (such as stress, depression, and hopelessness) and social factors (such as peer pressure) combine to lead many people to experiment with—and sometimes become addicted to—drugs. Cultural and ethnic groups have differing rates of drug use. Each type of influence—biological, psychological, and social-cultural—offers a possible path for drug misuse prevention and treatment programs.

Developing Through the Life Span

MODULE 10 Developmental Issues, Prenatal Development, and the Newborn

---

10-1   What three issues have engaged developmental psychologists?

Developmental psychologists study physical, cognitive, and social changes throughout the life span. They focus on three issues: nature and nurture (the interaction between our genetic inheritance and our experiences); continuity and stages (which aspects of development are gradual and continuous and which change relatively abruptly); and stability and change (whether our traits endure or change as we age).

10-2 What is the course of prenatal development, and how do *teratogens* affect that development?

The life cycle begins at conception, when one sperm cell unites with an egg to form a *zygote*. The zygote's inner cells become the *embryo,* and the outer cells become the placenta. In the next 6 weeks, body organs begin to form and function, and by 9 weeks, the *fetus* is recognizably human. *Teratogens* are potentially harmful agents that can pass through the placenta and harm the developing embryo or fetus, as happens with *fetal alcohol syndrome.*

10-3 What are some newborn abilities, and how do researchers explore infants' mental abilities?

Babies are born with sensory equipment and reflexes that facilitate their survival and their social interactions with adults. For example, they quickly learn to discriminate their mother's smell, and they prefer the sound of human voices. Researchers use techniques that test *habituation,* such as the novelty-preference procedure, to explore infants' abilities.

MODULE 11 Infancy and Childhood

11-1 During infancy and childhood, how do the brain and motor skills develop?

The brain's nerve cells are sculpted by heredity and experience. As a child's brain develops, neural connections grow more numerous and complex. Experiences then trigger a pruning process, in which unused connections weaken and heavily used ones strengthen. Early childhood is an important period for shaping the brain, but thanks to its plasticity, our brain modifies itself in response to our learning throughout life. In childhood, complex motor skills—sitting, standing, walking—develop in a predictable sequence, though the timing of that sequence is a function of individual *maturation* and culture. For some skills, we seem to have a *critical period.* We have few or no conscious memories of events occurring before about age 4. This infantile amnesia occurs in part because major brain areas have not yet matured.

11-2 From the perspectives of Piaget, Vygotsky, and today's researchers, how does a child's mind develop?

In his theory of *cognitive* development, Jean Piaget proposed that children actively construct and modify their understanding of the world through the processes of *assimilation* and *accommodation.* They form *schemas* that help them organize their experiences. Progressing from the simplicity of the *sensorimotor stage* of the first two years, in which they develop *object permanence,* children move to more complex ways of thinking. In the *preoperational stage* (about age 2 to about 6 or 7), they develop a *theory of mind.* In the preoperational stage, children are *egocentric* and unable to perform simple logical operations. By about age 7, they enter the *concrete operational stage* and are able to comprehend the principle of *conservation.* By age 12, children enter the *formal operational stage* and can reason systematically. Research supports the sequence Piaget proposed, but it also shows that young children are more capable, and their

development more continuous, than he believed. Lev Vygotsky's studies of child development focused on the ways a child's mind grows by interacting with the social environment. In his view, parents and caretakers provide temporary *scaffolds* enabling children to step to higher levels of thinking.

11-3 What is *autism spectrum disorder?*

Autism spectrum disorder (ASD) is a disorder marked by social deficiencies and repetitive behaviors, with differing levels of severity. Children with ASD have an impaired theory of mind. By age eight, 1 in 68 U.S. children now gets diagnosed with ASD (though the reported rates vary by place). The increase in diagnoses has been offset by a decrease in the number of children with a "cognitive disability" or "learning disability." Genetic influences, abnormal brain development, and the prenatal environment—especially when altered by infection, drugs, or hormones—likely contribute to ASD.

11-4 How do parent-infant attachment bonds form?

At about 8 months, soon after object permanence develops, children separated from their caregivers display *stranger anxiety.* Infants form *attachments* with caregivers who gratify biological needs but, more importantly, who are comfortable, familiar, and responsive. Many birds and other animals have a more rigid attachment process, called *imprinting,* that occurs during a critical period.

11-5 How have psychologists studied attachment differences, and what have they learned?

Attachment has been studied in strange situation experiments, which show that some children are securely attached and others are insecurely (anxiously or avoidantly) attached. Infants' differing attachment styles reflect both their individual *temperament* and the responsiveness of their parents and child-care providers. Adult relationships seem to reflect the attachment styles of early childhood, lending support to Erik Erikson's idea that *basic trust* is formed in infancy by our experiences with responsive caregivers.

11-6 How does childhood neglect or abuse affect children's attachments?

Most children are resilient, but those who are abused or severely neglected by their caregivers, or otherwise prevented from forming attachments at an early age, may be at risk for attachment problems. Extreme trauma in childhood may alter the brain, affecting our stress responses or leaving epigenetic marks.

11-7 What are the four main parenting styles?

The main parenting styles are authoritarian (coercive), permissive (unrestraining), negligent (uninvolved), and authoritative (confrontive).

11-8 What outcomes are associated with each parenting style?

Authoritative parenting is associated with greater self-esteem, self-reliance, self-regulation, and social competence; authoritarian parenting with lower self-esteem, less social skill, and a brain that overreacts to mistakes; permissive parenting with greater aggression and immaturity; and negligent parenting with poor academic and social outcomes. However, correlation does not equal causation (it's possible that children with positive characteristics are more likely to bring out positive parenting methods).

MODULE **12** Adolescence

12-1 How is *adolescence* defined, and how do physical changes affect developing teens?

Adolescence is the transition period from childhood to adulthood, extending from *puberty* to social independence. Boys seem to benefit (though with risks) from "early" maturation, whereas girls tend to experience greater risk from early maturation. The brain's frontal lobes mature and myelin growth increases during adolescence and the early twenties, enabling improved judgment, impulse control, and long-term planning.

12-2 How did Piaget, Kohlberg, and later researchers describe adolescent cognitive and moral development?

Piaget theorized that adolescents develop a capacity for formal operations and that this development is the foundation for moral judgment. Lawrence Kohlberg proposed a stage theory of moral reasoning, from a preconventional morality of self-interest, to a conventional morality concerned with upholding laws and social rules, to (in some people) a postconventional morality of universal ethical principles. Other researchers believe that morality lies in moral intuition and moral action as well as thinking. Kohlberg's critics note that the postconventional level is culturally limited, representing morality only from the perspective of an individualist society.

12-3 What are the social tasks and challenges of adolescence?

Erik Erikson proposed eight stages of psychosocial development across the life span. He believed we need to achieve: trust, autonomy, initiative, competency, *identity* (in adolescence), *intimacy* (in young adulthood), generativity, and integrity. Each life stage has its own psychosocial task. Solidifying one's sense of self in adolescence means trying out a number of different roles. *Social identity* is the part of the self-concept that comes from a person's group memberships.

12-4 How do parents and peers influence adolescents?

During adolescence, parental influence diminishes and peer influence increases, in part because of the selection effect—the tendency to choose similar others. Adolescents adopt their peers' ways of dressing, acting, and communicating. Parents do have an influence on teens' behaviors and attitudes, but personalities and temperaments are shaped more by nature than by parental nurture.

12-5 What is emerging adulthood?

Due to earlier sexual maturity and later independence, the transition from adolescence to adulthood is taking longer than it once did. *Emerging adulthood* is the period from age 18 to the mid-twenties, when many young people are not yet fully independent. This stage is found mostly in today's Western cultures.

MODULE **13** Adulthood

13-1 What physical changes occur during middle and late adulthood?

Muscular strength, reaction time, sensory abilities, and cardiac output begin to almost imperceptibly decline in the mid-twenties; this downward trajectory accelerates through middle and late adulthood. Women's period of fertility ends with *menopause* around age 50; men experience a more gradual decline. In late adulthood, the immune system weakens, increasing susceptibility to life-threatening illnesses. But longevity-supporting genes, low stress, and healthful habits may enable good health even in late life.

13-2 How does memory change with age?

Recall begins to decline, especially for meaningless information, but recognition memory remains strong. Developmental researchers study age-related changes such as in memory with *cross-sectional studies* (comparing people of different ages at one point in time) and *longitudinal studies* (retesting the same people over a period of years). "Terminal decline" describes the cognitive decline in the final few years of life.

13-3 What themes and influences mark our social journey from early adulthood to death?

Adults do not progress through an orderly sequence of age-related social stages. Chance events can determine life choices. The *social clock* is a culture's preferred timing for events such as marriage, parenthood, and retirement. Adulthood's dominant themes are love and work (Erikson's intimacy and generativity).

13-4 How does our well-being change across the life span?

Surveys show that life satisfaction is unrelated to age until the terminal decline phase. Positive emotions increase after midlife and negative ones decrease; with age come fewer extremes of emotion and mood.

13-5 A loved one's death triggers what range of reactions?

People do not grieve in predictable stages, as was once supposed, and bereavement therapy is not significantly more effective than grieving without such aid. Life can be affirmed even at death, especially for those who experience what Erikson called a sense of integrity—a feeling that one's life has been meaningful.

Sex, Gender, and Sexuality

MODULE **14** Gender Development

14-1 How does the meaning of *gender* differ from the meaning of *sex*?

In psychology, *gender* refers to the socially and culturally constructed expectations about what it means to be a boy, girl, man, or woman. *Sex* refers to our biological status as male or female, defined by our chromosomes and anatomy. We might say that our body defines our sex, while our mind defines our gender.

14-2 What are some ways in which males and females tend to be alike and to differ?

We are more alike than different, thanks to our similar genetic makeup—we see, learn, and remember similarly, with comparable creativity, intelligence, and emotions. Males and females do differ in age of onset of puberty, life expectancy, and vulnerability to certain disorders. Men admit to more *aggression* than women do, and they are more likely to be physically (rather than *relationally*) aggressive. Women focus more on social connectedness; they are more interdependent, and they "tend and befriend."

14-3 What factors contribute to gender bias in the workplace?

Differences in male-female perceptions, compensation, and family responsibility both influence and reflect workplace gender bias. In most societies, men have more social power, and their leadership style tends to be directive, whereas women's tends to be more democratic. In their everyday behaviors and interactions, men tend to act more assertive and opinionated; women tend to act more supportive and apologetic.

14-4 How do sex hormones influence prenatal and adolescent sexual development, and what is an *intersex* condition?

Both sex chromosomes and sex hormones influence development. About seven weeks after conception, a gene on the *Y chromosome* from the father—who can contribute either this or an *X chromosome* (the mother always contributes the latter)—triggers the production of *testosterone*. This promotes male sex organ development. During the fourth and fifth prenatal months, sex hormones bathe the fetal brain, with different patterns developing due to the male's greater testosterone and the female's ovarian hormones. Prenatal exposure of females to unusually high levels of male hormones can later dispose them to more male-typical interests. Another flood of hormones occurs in *puberty,* triggering a growth spurt, the development of *primary* and *secondary sex characteristics,* and the landmark events of *menarche* and *spermarche.* Individuals with *intersex* conditions are born with unusual combinations of male and female chromosomes, hormones, and anatomy.

14-5 How do gender roles and gender identity differ?

Gender roles, the behaviors a culture expects from its men and women, vary across place and time. *Social learning theory* proposes that we learn *gender identity*—our personal sense of being male, female, or some combination of the two—as we learn other things: through reinforcement, punishment, and observation. Critics argue that cognition also plays a role, as *gender typing* varies among children. We seem to conform in ways that feel comfortable to us, whether that means taking on a male role, female role, or blend of the two (*androgyny*). *Transgender* people's gender identity or expression differs from the behaviors or traits considered typical for their birth-designated sex. Their sexual orientation may be heterosexual, homosexual, bisexual, or asexual.

14-6 What are the effects of sexual aggression? How have cultural views changed, and how can we reduce sexual aggression?

Sexual aggression, which includes sexual harassment and sexual assault, can cause anxiety and depression, increase victims' risk for posttraumatic stress disorder and borderline personality disorder, disrupt sleep and health, and make it difficult to trust new relationship partners. Cultural views of sexual aggression differ across time and place, with some cultures continuing to blame victims, but changes in the U.S. over the last half-century have made victim-blaming less acceptable. Therapy for sexual aggressors has not proven effective, but we may reduce sexual aggression by empowering victims, encouraging people to report and share their experiences, and educating communities about preventive bystander intervention strategies.

MODULE 15 Human Sexuality

15-1 How do hormones influence human sexual motivation?

For all but those few of us considered *asexual,* dating and mating become a high priority from puberty on. The female *estrogen* and male *testosterone* hormones influence human sexual behavior less directly than they influence sexual behavior in other species. Women's sexuality is more responsive to testosterone level than to estrogen level. Short-term shifts in testosterone level are normal in men, partly in response to stimulation.

15-2 What is the human *sexual response cycle,* and how do sexual dysfunctions and paraphilias differ?

William Masters and Virginia Johnson described four stages in the human *sexual response cycle:* excitement, plateau, orgasm, and resolution. During resolution there is a *refractory period* in which renewed arousal and orgasm are impossible. *Sexual dysfunctions* are problems that consistently impair sexual arousal or functioning. They include *erectile disorder* and *female orgasmic disorder,* and can often be successfully treated by behaviorally oriented therapy or drug therapy. *Paraphilias* are considered disordered if a person experiences distress from an unusual sexual interest or if it entails harm or risk of harm to others.

15-3 How can sexually transmitted infections be prevented?

Safe-sex practices help prevent sexually transmitted infections (STIs). Condoms are especially effective in preventing transmission of HIV, the virus that causes *AIDS.* Knowing one's STI status, and sharing it with one's sexual partner, is an important first step in STI prevention.

15-4 How do external and imagined stimuli contribute to sexual arousal?

External stimuli can trigger sexual arousal in both men and women. Sexually explicit material may lead people to perceive their partners as comparatively less appealing and to devalue their relationships. Viewing sexually coercive material can lead to increased acceptance of violence toward women. Extensive online pornography exposure may desensitize young men to normal sexuality, leading to erectile problems and lowered sexual desire in real life. Imagined stimuli (dreams and fantasies) also influence sexual arousal.

15-5 What factors influence teenagers' sexual behaviors and use of contraceptives?

Teen sexuality varies from culture to culture and era to era. Factors contributing to these variations include communication about birth control; impulsivity; alcohol use; and mass media. High intelligence, religious engagement, father presence, and service learning participation predict teen sexual restraint.

15-6 What has research taught us about sexual orientation?

Sexual orientation is an enduring sexual attraction toward members of one's own sex, the other sex, or both sexes. About 3 or 4 percent of men and 2 percent of women in Europe and the United States identify as exclusively homosexual. There is no evidence that environmental influences determine sexual orientation. Evidence for biological influences includes same-sex attraction in other species; gay-straight trait and brain differences; genetic influences; and prenatal influences.

15-7 How might an evolutionary psychologist explain male-female differences in sexuality and mating preferences?

Women tend to be more selective than men when choosing sexual partners. Evolutionary psychologists reason that men's attraction to multiple healthy, fertile-appearing partners increases their chances of spreading their genes widely. Because women incubate and nurse babies, they increase their own and their children's chances of survival by searching for mates with the potential for long-term investment in their joint offspring.

15-8 What are the key criticisms of evolutionary explanations of human sexuality, and how do evolutionary psychologists respond?

Critics argue that evolutionary psychologists start with an effect and work backward to an explanation, minimize contemporary social and cultural influences (including learned *social scripts*), and relieve people from taking responsibility for their sexual behavior. Evolutionary psychologists respond that they recognize the importance of social and cultural influences, but note the value in testable predictions based on evolutionary principles: Understanding our predispositions can help us overcome them.

15-9 What role do social factors play in our sexuality?

Scientific research on sexual motivation does not attempt to define the personal meaning of sex in our lives, which is influenced by many social factors. Sex is a socially significant act and is an expression of our profoundly social nature. Sex at its human best is life uniting and love renewing.

15-10 How do nature, nurture, and our own choices influence gender roles?

Individual development results from the interaction of biological, psychological, and social-cultural influences. Biological influences include our shared human genome; individual variations; prenatal environment; and sex-related genes, hormones, and physiology. Psychological influences include gene-environment interactions; the effect of early experiences on neural networks; responses evoked by our own characteristics, such as gender and temperament; and personal beliefs, feelings, and expectations. Social-cultural influences include parental and peer influences; cultural traditions and values; and cultural gender norms. And our individual choices affect the way all of these influences interact.

Sensation and Perception

MODULE **16** Basic Concepts of Sensation and Perception

16-1 What are *sensation* and *perception*? What do we mean by *bottom-up processing* and *top-down processing*?

Sensation is the process by which our *sensory receptors* and nervous system receive and represent stimulus energies from our environment. *Perception* is the process of organizing and interpreting this

information, enabling recognition of meaningful events. Sensation and perception are one continuous process. *Bottom-up processing* is sensory analysis that begins at the entry level, with information flowing from the sensory receptors to the brain. *Top-down processing* is information processing guided by high-level mental processes, as when we construct perceptions by filtering information through our experience and expectations.

16-2 What three steps are basic to all our sensory systems?

Our senses (1) receive sensory stimulation (often using specialized receptor cells); (2) transform that stimulation into neural impulses; and (3) deliver the neural information to the brain. *Transduction* is the process of converting one form of energy into another.

16-3 How do *absolute thresholds* and *difference thresholds* differ?

Our *absolute threshold* for any stimulus is the minimum stimulation necessary for us to be consciously aware of it 50 percent of the time. *Signal detection theory* predicts how and when we will detect a faint stimulus amid background noise. Individual absolute thresholds vary, depending on the strength of the signal and also on our experience, expectations, motivation, and alertness. Our *difference threshold* (also called the *just noticeable difference,* or *jnd*) is the difference we can discern between two stimuli 50 percent of the time. *Weber's law* states that two stimuli must differ by a constant minimum percentage (not a constant amount) to be perceived as different.

16-4 How are we affected by subliminal stimuli?

We do sense some stimuli *subliminally*—less than 50 percent of the time—and can be affected by these sensations. But although we can be *primed,* subliminal sensations have no powerful, enduring influence.

16-5 What is the function of sensory adaptation?

Sensory adaptation (our diminished sensitivity to constant or routine odors, sounds, and touches) focuses our attention on informative changes in our environment.

16-6 How do our expectations, contexts, motivation, and emotions influence our perceptions?

Perceptual set is a mental predisposition that functions as a lens through which we perceive the world. Our learned concepts (schemas) prime us to organize and interpret ambiguous stimuli in certain ways. Our motivation, as well as our physical and emotional context, can create expectations and color our interpretation of events and behaviors.

MODULE **17** Vision: Sensory and Perceptual Processing

17-1 What are the characteristics of the energy that we see as visible light? What structures in the eye help focus that energy?

What we see as light is only a thin slice of the broad spectrum of electromagnetic energy. The portion visible to humans extends from the blue-violet to the red light wavelengths. After entering the eye through the cornea, passing through the pupil and iris, and being focused by a *lens,* light energy particles strike the eye's inner surface, the *retina.* The *hue* we perceive in a light depends on its *wavelength,* and its brightness depends on its *intensity.*

17-2 How do the rods and cones process information, and what is the path information travels from the eye to the brain?

Light entering the eye triggers chemical changes that convert light energy into neural impulses. *Cones* and *rods* at the back of the retina each provide a special sensitivity—cones to detail and color, rods to faint light and peripheral motion. After processing by bipolar and ganglion cells, neural impulses travel from the retina through the *optic nerve* to the thalamus, and on to the visual cortex.

17-3 How do we perceive color in the world around us?

According to the *Young-Helmholtz trichromatic (three-color) theory,* the retina contains three types of color receptors. Contemporary research has found three types of cones, each most sensitive to the wavelengths of one of the three primary colors of light (red, green, or blue). According to Hering's *opponent-process theory,* there are three additional color processes (red-versus-green, blue-versus-yellow, black-versus-white). Research has confirmed that, en route to the brain, neurons in the retina and the thalamus code the color-related information from the cones into pairs of opponent colors. These two theories, and the research supporting them, show that color processing occurs in two stages.

17-4 Where are feature detectors located, and what do they do?

Feature detectors, specialized nerve cells in the visual cortex, respond to specific features of the visual stimulus, such as shape, angle, or movement. Feature detectors pass information on to other cortical areas, where supercell clusters respond to more complex patterns.

17-5 How does the brain use parallel processing to construct visual perceptions?

Through *parallel processing,* the brain handles many aspects of vision (color, movement, form, and depth) simultaneously. Other neural teams integrate the results, comparing them with stored information and enabling perceptions.

17-6 How did the Gestalt psychologists understand perceptual organization, and how do figure-ground and grouping principles contribute to our perceptions?

Gestalt psychologists searched for rules by which the brain organizes fragments of sensory data into *gestalts,* or meaningful forms. In pointing out that the whole may exceed the sum of its parts, they noted that we filter sensory information and construct our perceptions. To recognize an object, we must first perceive it (see it as a *figure*) as distinct from its surroundings (the *ground*). We bring order and form to stimuli by organizing them into meaningful *groups,* following such rules as proximity, continuity, and closure.

17-7 How do we use binocular and monocular cues to see the world in three dimensions?

Depth perception is our ability to see objects in three dimensions and judge distance. The *visual cliff* and other research demonstrate that many species perceive the world in three dimensions at, or very soon after, birth. *Binocular cues,* such as *retinal disparity,* are depth cues that rely on information from both eyes. *Monocular cues* (such as relative height, relative size, interposition, relative motion, linear perspective, and light and shadow) let us judge depth using information transmitted by only one eye. As objects move, we assume that shrinking objects are retreating and enlarging objects are approaching. The brain computes motion imperfectly, with young children especially at risk of incorrectly perceiving approaching hazards such as vehicles. A quick succession of images on the retina can create an illusion of movement, as in stroboscopic movement or the *phi phenomenon.*

17-8 How do perceptual constancies help us construct meaningful perceptions?

Perceptual constancies, such as in color, brightness (or lightness), shape, or size, enable us to perceive objects as stable despite the changing image they cast on our retinas. Our brain constructs our experience of an object's color or brightness through comparisons with other surrounding objects. Knowing an object's size gives us clues to its distance; knowing its distance gives clues about its size, but we sometimes misread monocular distance cues and reach the wrong conclusions, as in the Moon illusion.

17-9 What does research on restored vision, sensory restriction, and perceptual adaptation reveal about the effects of experience on perception?

Experience guides our perceptual interpretations. People blind from birth who gained sight after surgery lack the experience to visually recognize shapes and forms. Sensory restriction research indicates that there is a critical period for some aspects of sensory and perceptual development. Without early stimulation, the brain's neural organization does not develop normally. People given glasses that shift the world slightly to the left or right, or even upside down, experience *perceptual adaptation.* They are initially disoriented, but they manage to adapt to their new context.

MODULE 18 The Nonvisual Senses

18-1 What are the characteristics of air pressure waves that we hear as sound?

Sound waves are bands of compressed and expanded air. Our ears detect these changes in air pressure and transform them into neural impulses, which the brain decodes as sound. Sound waves vary in amplitude, which we perceive as differing loudness, and in *frequency,* which we experience as differing *pitch.*

18-2 How does the ear transform sound energy into neural messages?

The *middle ear* is the chamber between the eardrum and *cochlea;* the *inner ear* consists of the cochlea, semicircular canals, and vestibular sacs. Sound waves traveling through the auditory canal cause tiny vibrations in the eardrum. The bones of the middle ear amplify the vibrations and relay them to the fluid-filled cochlea. Rippling of the basilar membrane, caused by pressure changes in the cochlear fluid, causes movement of the tiny hair cells, triggering neural messages to be sent (via the thalamus) to the auditory cortex in the brain. *Sensorineural hearing loss* (or nerve deafness) results from damage to the cochlea's hair cells or their associated nerves. *Conduction hearing loss* results from damage to the mechanical system that transmits sound waves to the cochlea. *Cochlear implants* can restore hearing for some people.

18-3 How do we detect loudness, discriminate pitch, and locate sounds?

Loudness is not related to the intensity of a hair cell's response, but rather to the number of activated hair cells. *Place theory* explains how we hear high-pitched sounds, and *frequency theory* explains how we hear low-pitched sounds. A combination of the two theories explains how we hear pitches in the middle range. Sound waves strike one ear sooner and more intensely than the other. To locate sounds, the brain analyzes the minute differences in the sounds received by the two ears and computes the sound's source.

18-4 How do we sense touch?

Our sense of touch is actually several senses—pressure, warmth, cold, and pain—that combine to produce other sensations, such as "itchy" or "wet."

18-5 What biological, psychological, and social-cultural influences affect our experience of pain? How do placebos, distraction, and hypnosis help control pain?

The biopsychosocial perspective views our perception of pain as the sum of biological, psychological, and social-cultural influences. Pain reflects bottom-up sensations and top-down processes. One theory of pain is that a *"gate"* in the spinal cord either opens to permit pain signals traveling up small nerve fibers to reach the brain, or closes to prevent their passage. Pain treatments often combine physical and psychological elements. Combining a placebo with distraction, and amplifying the effect with *hypnosis* (which increases our response to suggestions), can help relieve pain. *Posthypnotic suggestion* is used by some clinicians to control undesired symptoms and behavior.

18-6 In what ways are our senses of taste and smell similar, and how do they differ?

Taste and smell are both chemical senses. Taste is a composite of five basic sensations—sweet, sour, salty, bitter, and umami—and of the aromas that interact with information from the taste receptor cells of the taste buds. There are no basic sensations for smell (*olfaction*). We smell something when airborne molecules reach a tiny cluster of 20 million receptor cells at the top of each nasal cavity. Odor molecules trigger combinations of receptors, in patterns that the olfactory cortex interprets. The receptor cells send messages to the brain's olfactory bulb, then to the temporal lobe, and to parts of the limbic system.

18-7 How do we sense our body's position and movement?

Through *kinesthesia,* we sense the position and movement of our body parts. We monitor our head's (and thus our body's) position and movement, and maintain our balance, with our *vestibular sense,* which relies on the semicircular canals and vestibular sacs to sense the tilt or rotation of our head.

18-8 How does *sensory interaction* influence our perceptions, and what is *embodied cognition*?

Our senses influence one another. This *sensory interaction* occurs, for example, when the smell of a favorite food amplifies its taste. *Embodied cognition* is the influence of bodily sensations, gestures, and other states on cognitive preferences and judgments.

18-9 What are the claims of *ESP*, and what have most research psychologists concluded after putting these claims to the test?

Parapsychology is the study of paranormal phenomena, including *extrasensory perception (ESP)* and psychokinesis. The three most testable forms of ESP are telepathy (mind-to-mind communication), clairvoyance (perceiving remote events), and precognition (perceiving future events). To believe in ESP is to believe the brain is capable of perceiving without sensory input; researchers have been unable to replicate ESP phenomena under controlled conditions.

Learning

MODULE 19 Basic Learning Concepts and Classical Conditioning

19-1 How do we define *learning,* and what are some basic forms of learning?

Learning is the process of acquiring through experience new information or behaviors. In *associative learning,* we learn that certain events occur together. In classical conditioning, we learn to associate two or more *stimuli.* Automatically responding to stimuli we do not control is called *respondent behavior.* In operant conditioning, we learn to associate a response and its consequence. These associations produce *operant behaviors.* Through *cognitive learning,* we acquire mental information that guides our behavior. For example, in observational learning, we learn new behaviors by observing events and watching others.

19-2 What is behaviorism's view of learning?

Ivan Pavlov's work on classical conditioning laid the foundation for *behaviorism,* the view that psychology should be an objective science that studies behavior without reference to mental processes. The behaviorists believed that the basic laws of learning are the same for all species, including humans.

19-3 Who was Pavlov, and what are the basic components of classical conditioning?

Ivan Pavlov, a Russian physiologist, created novel experiments on learning. His early twentieth-century research over the last three decades of his life demonstrated that classical conditioning is a basic form of learning. *Classical conditioning* is a type of learning in which an organism comes to associate stimuli and anticipate events. A *UR* is an event that occurs naturally (such as salivation), in response to some stimulus. A *US* is something that naturally and automatically (without learning) triggers the unlearned response (as food in the mouth triggers salivation). A *CS* is originally an *NS* (neutral stimulus, such as a tone) that, after association with a US (such as food) comes to trigger a CR. A *CR* is the learned response (salivating) to the originally neutral (but now conditioned) stimulus.

19-4   In classical conditioning, what are the processes of *acquisition, extinction, spontaneous recovery, generalization,* and *discrimination*?

In classical conditioning, the first stage is *acquisition,* associating an NS with the US so that the NS begins triggering the CR. Acquisition occurs most readily when the NS is presented just before (ideally, about a half-second before) a US, preparing the organism for the upcoming event. This finding supports the view that classical conditioning is biologically adaptive. *Extinction* is diminished responding, which occurs if the CS appears repeatedly by itself without the US. *Spontaneous recovery* is the appearance of a formerly extinguished conditioned response, following a rest period. *Generalization* is the tendency to respond to stimuli that are similar to a CS. *Discrimination* is the learned ability to distinguish between a CS and other irrelevant stimuli.

19-5   Why does Pavlov's work remain so important?

Pavlov taught us that significant psychological phenomena can be studied objectively, and that classical conditioning is a basic form of learning that applies to all species.

19-6   What have been some applications of Pavlov's work to human health and well-being? How did Watson apply Pavlov's principles to learned fears?

Classical conditioning techniques are used to improve human health and well-being in many areas, including behavioral therapy for some types of psychological disorders. The body's immune system may also respond to classical conditioning. Pavlov's work also provided a basis for Watson's idea that human emotions and behaviors, though biologically influenced, are mainly a bundle of conditioned responses. Watson applied classical conditioning principles in his studies of "Little Albert" to demonstrate how specific fears might be conditioned.

MODULE 20 Operant Conditioning

20-1   What is *operant conditioning*?

Operant conditioning is a type of learning in which behavior is strengthened if followed by a reinforcer or diminished if followed by a punisher.

20-2   Who was Skinner, and how is operant behavior reinforced and shaped?

B. F. Skinner was a college English major and aspiring writer who later entered psychology graduate school. He became modern behaviorism's most influential and controversial figure. Expanding on Edward Thorndike's *law of effect,* Skinner and others found that the behavior of rats or pigeons placed in an *operant chamber* (Skinner box) can be *shaped* by using reinforcers to guide successive approximations of the desired behavior.

20-3   How do positive and negative reinforcement differ, and what are the basic types of reinforcers?

Reinforcement is any consequence that strengthens behavior. *Positive reinforcement* adds a desirable stimulus to increase the frequency of a behavior. *Negative reinforcement* reduces or removes an aversive stimulus to increase the frequency of a behavior. *Primary reinforcers* (such as receiving food when hungry or having nausea end during an illness) are innately satisfying—no learning is required. *Conditioned* (or secondary) *reinforcers* (such as cash) are satisfying because we have learned to associate them with more basic rewards (such as the food or medicine we buy with them). Immediate reinforcers (such as a purchased treat) offer immediate payback; delayed reinforcers (such as a paycheck) require the ability to delay gratification.

20-4   How do different reinforcement schedules affect behavior?

A *reinforcement schedule* defines how often a response will be reinforced. In *continuous reinforcement* (reinforcing desired responses every time they occur), learning is rapid, but so is extinction if rewards cease. In *partial (intermittent) reinforcement* (reinforcing responses only sometimes), initial learning is slower, but the behavior is much more resistant to extinction. *Fixed-ratio schedules* reinforce behaviors after a set number of responses; *variable-ratio schedules,* after an unpredictable number. *Fixed-interval schedules* reinforce behaviors after set time periods; *variable-interval schedules,* after unpredictable time periods.

20-5   How does punishment differ from negative reinforcement, and how does punishment affect behavior?

Punishment administers an undesirable consequence (such as spanking) or withdraws something desirable (such as taking away a favorite toy) to decrease the frequency of a behavior (a child's disobedience). Negative reinforcement (taking an aspirin) removes an aversive stimulus (a headache). This desired consequence (freedom from pain) increases the likelihood that the behavior (taking aspirin to end pain) will be repeated. Punishment can have undesirable side effects, such as suppressing rather than changing unwanted behaviors, encouraging discrimination (so that the undesirable behavior appears when the punisher is not present), creating fear, and teaching aggression.

20-6   Why did Skinner's ideas provoke controversy, and how might his operant conditioning principles be applied at school, in sports, at work, in parenting, and for self-improvement?

Critics of Skinner's principles believed the approach dehumanized people by neglecting their personal freedom and seeking to control their actions. Skinner replied that people's actions are already controlled by external consequences, and that reinforcement is more humane than punishment as a means for controlling behavior. Teachers can use shaping techniques to guide students' behaviors, and use interactive media such as online adaptive quizzing to provide immediate feedback. (The LaunchPad LearningCurve and

Achieve Read & Practice systems available with this text provide such feedback, and allow students to direct the pace of their own learning.) Coaches can build players' skills and self-confidence by rewarding small improvements. Managers can boost productivity and morale by rewarding well-defined and achievable behaviors. Parents can reward desired behaviors but not undesirable ones. We can shape our own behaviors by stating realistic goals, planning how to work toward those goals, monitoring the frequency of desired behaviors, reinforcing desired behaviors, and gradually reducing rewards as behaviors become habitual.

20-7   How does operant conditioning differ from classical conditioning?

In operant conditioning, an organism learns associations between its own behavior and resulting events; this form of conditioning involves operant behavior (behavior that operates on the environment, producing rewarding or punishing consequences). In classical conditioning, the organism forms associations between stimuli—events it does not control; this form of conditioning involves respondent behavior (automatic responses to some stimulus).

MODULE 21 Biology, Cognition, and Learning

21-1   How do biological constraints affect classical and operant conditioning?

An animal's capacity for conditioning is limited by biological constraints, so some associations are easier to learn. Each species learns behaviors that aid its survival—a phenomenon called *preparedness*. Those who readily learned taste aversions were unlikely to eat the same toxic food again and were more likely to survive and leave descendants. Nature constrains each species' capacity for both classical conditioning and operant conditioning. Our preparedness to associate a CS with a US that follows predictably and immediately is often (but not always) adaptive. During operant training, animals may display *instinctive drift* by reverting to biologically predisposed patterns.

21-2   How do cognitive processes affect classical and operant conditioning?

In classical conditioning, animals may learn when to expect a US and may be aware of the link between stimuli and responses. In operant conditioning, *cognitive mapping* and *latent learning* research demonstrate the importance of cognitive processes in learning.

21-3   What is *observational learning*?

Observational learning (also called social learning) involves learning by watching and imitating, rather than through direct experience.

21-4   How may observational learning be enabled by neural mirroring?

Our brain's frontal lobes have a demonstrated ability to mirror the activity of another's brain, which may enable imitation and observational learning. Some scientists argue that *mirror neurons* are responsible for this ability, while others attribute it to distributed brain networks.

21-5   What is the impact of prosocial modeling and of antisocial modeling?

Children tend to imitate what a model does and says, whether the behavior being *modeled* is *prosocial* (positive, constructive, and helpful) or antisocial. If a model's actions and words are inconsistent, children may imitate the hypocrisy they observe.

21-6   What is the violence-viewing effect?

Media violence can contribute to aggression. This violence-viewing effect may be prompted by imitation and desensitization. Correlation does not equal causation, but study participants have reacted more cruelly when they have viewed violence (instead of entertaining nonviolence).

Memory

MODULE 22 Studying and Encoding Memories

22-1   What is *memory*, and how is it measured?

Memory is learning that has persisted over time, through the encoding, storage, and retrieval of information. Evidence of memory may be seen in an ability to *recall* information, *recognize* it, or *relearn* it more easily on a later attempt.

22-2   How do psychologists describe the human memory system?

Psychologists use memory models to think and communicate about memory. Information-processing models involve three processes: *encoding, storage,* and *retrieval.* Our agile brain processes many things simultaneously by means of *parallel processing.* The connectionism information-processing model focuses on this multitrack processing, viewing memories as products of interconnected neural networks. The three processing stages in the Atkinson-Shiffrin model are *sensory memory, short-term memory,* and *long-term memory.* This model has since been updated to include two important concepts: (1) *working memory,* to stress the active processing occurring in the second memory stage; and (2) *automatic processing,* to address the processing of information outside of conscious awareness.

22-3   How do explicit and implicit memories differ?

The human brain processes information on dual tracks, consciously and unconsciously. *Explicit* (declarative) *memories*—our conscious memories of facts and experiences—form through *effortful processing,* which requires conscious effort and attention. *Implicit* (nondeclarative) *memories*—of skills and classically conditioned associations—happen without our awareness, through *automatic processing.*

22-4   What information do we process automatically?

In addition to skills and classically conditioned associations, we automatically process incidental information about space, time, and frequency.

22-5 How does sensory memory work?

Sensory memory feeds some information into working memory for active processing there. An *iconic memory* is a very brief (a few tenths of a second) sensory memory of visual stimuli; an *echoic memory* is a three- or four-second sensory memory of auditory stimuli.

22-6 What is our short-term memory capacity?

Short-term memory capacity is about seven items, plus or minus two, but this information disappears from memory quickly without rehearsal. Our working memory capacity for active processing varies, depending on age and other factors.

22-7 What are some effortful processing strategies that can help us remember new information?

Effective effortful processing strategies include *chunking, mnemonics,* hierarchies, and distributed practice sessions (the *spacing effect*). The *testing effect* is the finding that consciously retrieving, rather than simply rereading, information enhances memory.

22-8 What are the levels of processing, and how do they affect encoding?

Depth of processing affects long-term retention. In *shallow processing,* we encode words based on their structure or appearance. Retention is best when we use *deep processing,* encoding words based on their meaning. We also more easily remember material that is personally meaningful—the self-reference effect.

MODULE 23 Storing and Retrieving Memories

23-1 What is the capacity of long-term memory? Are our long-term memories processed and stored in specific locations?

Our long-term memory capacity is essentially unlimited. Memories are not stored intact in the brain in single spots. Many parts of the brain interact as we encode, store, and retrieve memories.

23-2 What roles do the frontal lobes and hippocampus play in memory processing?

The frontal lobes and *hippocampus* are parts of the brain network dedicated to explicit memory formation. Many brain regions send information to the frontal lobes for processing. The hippocampus, with the help of surrounding areas of cortex, registers and temporarily holds elements of explicit memories (which are either *semantic* or *episodic*) before moving them to other brain regions for long-term storage. The neural storage of long-term memories is called *memory consolidation.*

23-3 What roles do the cerebellum and basal ganglia play in memory processing?

The cerebellum and basal ganglia are parts of the brain network dedicated to implicit memory formation. The cerebellum is important for storing classically conditioned memories. The basal ganglia are involved in motor movement and help form procedural memories for skills. Many reactions and skills learned during our first four years continue into our adult lives, though we cannot consciously remember learning these associations and skills (infantile amnesia).

23-4 How do emotions affect our memory processing?

Emotional arousal causes an outpouring of stress hormones, which lead to activity in the brain's memory-forming areas. Significantly stressful events can trigger very clear *flashbulb memories.*

23-5 How do changes at the synapse level affect our memory processing?

Long-term potentiation (LTP) is the neural basis of learning. In LTP, neurons become more efficient at releasing and sensing the presence of neurotransmitters, and more connections develop between neurons.

23-6 How do external cues, internal emotions, and order of appearance influence memory retrieval?

External cues activate associations that help us retrieve memories; this process may occur without our awareness, as it does in *priming.* The *encoding specificity principle* is the idea that cues and contexts specific to a particular memory will be most effective in helping us recall it. Returning to the same physical context or emotional state (*mood congruency*) in which we formed a memory can help us retrieve it. The *serial position effect* accounts for our tendency to recall best the last items (which may still be in working memory) and the first items (which we've spent more time rehearsing) in a list.

MODULE 24 Forgetting, Memory Construction, and Improving Memory

24-1 Why do we forget?

Anterograde amnesia is an inability to form new memories. *Retrograde amnesia* is an inability to retrieve old memories. Normal forgetting can happen because we have never encoded information (encoding failure); because the physical trace has decayed (storage decay); or because we cannot retrieve what we have encoded and stored (retrieval failure). Retrieval problems may result from *proactive* (forward-acting) *interference,* as prior learning interferes with recall of new information, or from *retroactive* (backward-acting) *interference,* as new learning disrupts recall of old information. Motivated forgetting occurs, but researchers have found little evidence of *repression.*

24-2 How do misinformation, imagination, and source amnesia influence our memory construction? How do we decide whether a memory is real or false?

Memories can be continually revised when retrieved, a process memory researchers call *reconsolidation.* In experiments demonstrating the *misinformation effect,* people have formed false memories, incorporating misleading details, after receiving wrong information after an event, or after repeatedly imagining and rehearsing something that never happened. When we reassemble a memory during retrieval, we may attribute it to the wrong source (*source amnesia*). Source amnesia may help explain *déjà vu.* False memories feel like real memories and can be persistent but are usually limited to the gist of the event.

24-3 Why have reports of repressed and recovered memories been so hotly debated?

The debate focuses on whether memories of early childhood abuse are repressed and can be recovered during therapy. Unless the victim was a child too young to remember, such traumas are usually remembered vividly, not repressed. Psychologists agree that childhood sexual abuse happens; injustice happens; forgetting happens; recovered memories are common; memories of events that happened before age 4 are unreliable; memories "recovered" under hypnosis are especially unreliable; and memories, whether real or false, can be emotionally upsetting.

24-4 How reliable are young children's eyewitness descriptions?

Children's eyewitness descriptions are subject to the same memory influences that distort adult reports. If questioned soon after an event in neutral words they understand, children can accurately recall events and people involved in them.

24-5 How can you use memory research findings to do better in this and other courses?

Memory research findings suggest the following strategies for improving memory: Rehearse repeatedly, make the material meaningful, activate retrieval cues, use mnemonic devices, minimize proactive and retroactive interference, sleep more, and test yourself to be sure you can retrieve, as well as recognize, material.

Thinking, Language, and Intelligence

MODULE 25 Thinking

25-1 What is cognition, and what are the functions of concepts?

Cognition refers to all the mental activities associated with thinking, knowing, remembering, and communicating. We use *concepts,* mental groupings of similar objects, events, ideas, or people, to simplify and order the world around us. We form most concepts around *prototypes,* or best examples of a category.

25-2 What cognitive strategies assist our problem solving, and what obstacles hinder it?

An *algorithm* is a methodical, logical rule or procedure (such as a step-by-step description for evacuating a building during a fire) that guarantees a solution to a problem. A *heuristic* is a simpler strategy (such as running for an exit if you smell smoke) that is usually speedier than an algorithm but is also more error prone. *Insight* is not a strategy-based solution, but rather a sudden flash of inspiration that solves a problem. Obstacles to problem solving include *confirmation bias,* which predisposes us to verify rather than challenge our hypotheses, and *fixation,* such as *mental set,* which may prevent us from taking the fresh perspective that would lead to a solution.

25-3 What is intuition, and how can the availability and representativeness heuristics influence our decisions and judgments?

Intuition is the effortless, immediate, automatic feelings or thoughts we often use instead of systematic reasoning. Heuristics, such as

the *representativeness heuristic,* enable snap judgments. Using the *availability heuristic,* we judge the likelihood of things based on how readily they come to mind.

25-4 What factors exaggerate our fear of unlikely events?

We tend to be afraid of what our ancestral history has prepared us to fear, what we cannot control, what is immediate, and what is most readily available. We fear too little the ongoing threats that claim lives one by one, such as traffic accidents and diseases.

25-5 How are our decisions and judgments affected by overconfidence, belief perseverance, and framing?

Overconfidence can lead us to overestimate the accuracy of our beliefs. When a belief we have formed and explained has been discredited, *belief perseverance* may cause us to cling to that belief. A remedy for belief perseverance is to consider how we might have explained an opposite result. *Framing* is the way a question or statement is presented. Subtle differences in presentation can dramatically alter our responses.

25-6 How do smart thinkers use intuition?

Smart thinkers welcome their intuitions (which are usually adaptive), but also know when to override them. When making complex decisions we may benefit from gathering as much information as possible and then taking time to let our two-track mind process it.

25-7 What is creativity, and what fosters it?

Creativity, the ability to produce novel and valuable ideas, correlates somewhat with aptitude, but is more than school smarts. Aptitude tests require *convergent thinking,* but creativity requires *divergent thinking.* Robert Sternberg has proposed that creativity involves expertise; imaginative thinking skills; a venturesome personality; intrinsic motivation; and a creative environment that sparks, supports, and refines creative ideas.

25-8 What do we know about thinking in other species?

Researchers make inferences about other species' consciousness and intelligence based on behavior. Evidence from studies of various species shows that many other animals use concepts, numbers, and tools and that they transmit learning from one generation to the next (cultural transmission). And, like humans, some other species show insight, self-awareness, altruism, cooperation, and grief.

MODULE 26 Language and Thought

26-1 What are the structural components of a language?

Phonemes are a *language's* basic units of sound. *Morphemes* are the elementary units of meaning. *Grammar*—the system of rules that enables us to communicate—includes semantics (rules for deriving meaning) and syntax (rules for ordering words into sentences).

26-2 How do we acquire language, and what is universal grammar?

As our biology and experience interact, we readily learn the specific grammar and vocabulary of the language we experience as children. Linguist Noam Chomsky has proposed that all human languages share a universal grammar—the basic building blocks of language—and that humans are born with a predisposition to learn language. Human languages do share some commonalities, but other researchers note that children learn grammar as they discern language patterns.

26-3 What are the milestones in language development, and when is the critical period for acquiring language?

Language development's timing varies, but all children follow the same sequence. Receptive language (the ability to understand what is said to or about you) develops before productive language (the ability to produce words). At about 4 months of age, infants *babble,* making sounds found in languages from all over the world, which by about 10 months includes only the sounds found in their household language. Around 12 months of age, children begin to speak in single words. This *one-word stage* evolves into *two-word (telegraphic)* utterances before their second birthday, after which they begin speaking in full sentences. Childhood is a critical period for learning language. A delay in exposure until age 2 or 3 produces a rush of language. But children not exposed to either a spoken or a signed language until age 7 will never master any language. The importance of early language experiences is often evident in deaf children born to hearing-nonsigning parents.

26-4 What brain areas are involved in language processing and speech?

Aphasia is an impairment of language, usually caused by left-hemisphere damage. Two important language- and speech-processing areas are *Broca's area,* a region of the left frontal lobe that controls language expression, and *Wernicke's area,* a region in the left temporal lobe that controls language reception. Language processing is spread across other brain areas as well, with different neural networks handling specific linguistic subtasks.

26-5 What do we know about other species' capacity for language?

Chimpanzees and bonobos have learned to communicate with humans by signing or by pushing buttons. Some have developed vocabularies of nearly 400 words, communicated by stringing these words together, and have demonstrated some understanding of syntax. While only humans communicate in complex sentences, other animals' impressive abilities to think and communicate challenge humans to consider what this means about the moral rights of other species.

26-6 What is the relationship between thinking and language, and what is the value of thinking in images?

Although Benjamin Lee Whorf's *linguistic determinism* hypothesis suggested that language determines thought, it is more accurate to say that language influences thought (*linguistic relativism*). Different languages embody different ways of thinking, and immersion in bilingual education can enhance thinking. We often think in images when we use implicit (nondeclarative, procedural) memory—our automatic memory system for motor and cognitive skills and classically conditioned associations. Thinking in images can increase our skills when we mentally practice upcoming events. Process simulation (focusing on the steps needed to reach a goal) is effective, but outcome simulation (fantasizing about having achieved the goal) does little.

MODULE 27 Intelligence and Its Assessment

27-1 How do psychologists define *intelligence*, and what are the arguments for *g*?

Intelligence is the ability to learn from experience, solve problems, and use knowledge to adapt to new situations. Charles Spearman proposed that we have one *general intelligence* (*g*) underlying all mental abilities. Through his work with factor analysis, a statistical procedure that identifies clusters of related abilities, he noted that those who score high in one area typically score higher than average in other areas.

27-2 How do Gardner's and Sternberg's theories of multiple intelligences differ, and what criticisms have they faced?

Howard Gardner proposed eight independent intelligences (linguistic, logical-mathematical, musical, spatial, bodily-kinesthetic, intrapersonal, interpersonal, and naturalist), as well as a possible ninth (existential intelligence). The different intelligences of people with *savant syndrome,* autism spectrum disorder (ASD), and certain kinds of brain damage seem to support his view. Robert Sternberg's triarchic theory proposes three intelligence areas that predict real-world skills: analytical (academic problem solving), creative (innovative smarts), and practical (street smarts). Critics note research that has confirmed a general intelligence factor, which widely predicts performance. But highly successful people also tend to be conscientious, well-connected, and doggedly energetic; their achievements arise from both ability *and* motivation.

27-3 What are the four components of emotional intelligence?

Emotional intelligence, which is an aspect of social intelligence, includes the abilities to perceive, understand, manage, and use emotions. Emotionally intelligent people tend to be happy, healthy, and more successful personally and professionally. Some critics question whether calling these abilities "intelligence" stretches that concept too far.

27-4 What is an *intelligence test*, and how do achievement and aptitude tests differ?

An *intelligence test* assesses an individual's mental aptitudes and compares them with those of others, using numerical scores. *Aptitude tests* measure the ability to learn, while *achievement tests* measure what we have already learned.

27-5 When and why were intelligence tests created, and how do today's tests differ from early intelligence tests?

Alfred Binet, who tended toward an environmental explanation of intelligence differences, started the modern intelligence-testing movement in France in the early 1900s, when he developed questions to help predict children's future progress in the Paris school system. Binet hoped his test would improve children's education but feared it might be used to label them. During the early twentieth century, Lewis Terman of Stanford University revised Binet's work for use in the United States. Terman thought his *Stanford-Binet* could help guide people toward appropriate opportunities, but his belief in an intelligence that was fixed at birth and differed among ethnic groups realized Binet's fear that intelligence tests would be used to limit children's opportunities. William Stern contributed the concept of the *IQ (intelligence quotient)*. The most widely used intelligence tests today are the *Wechsler Adult Intelligence Scale (WAIS)* and Wechsler's tests for children. These tests differ from their predecessors in the way they offer an overall intelligence score as well as scores for verbal comprehension, perceptual organization, working memory, and processing speed.

27-6   What is a *normal curve,* and what does it mean to say that a test has been standardized and is reliable and valid?

The distribution of test scores often forms a *normal* (bell-shaped) *curve* around the central average score, with fewer and fewer scores at the extremes. *Standardization* establishes a basis for meaningful score comparisons by giving a test to a representative sample of future test-takers. *Reliability* is the extent to which a test yields consistent results (on two halves of the test, on alternative forms of the test, or upon retesting). *Validity* is the extent to which a test measures or predicts what it is supposed to. A test has *predictive validity* if it predicts a behavior it was designed to predict. (Aptitude tests have predictive validity if they can predict future achievements; their predictive power is best for the early school years.)

27-7   What are the traits of those at the low and high intelligence extremes?

An intelligence test score of or below 70 is one diagnostic criterion for the diagnosis of *intellectual disability;* other criteria are limited conceptual, social, and practical skills. People at the high intelligence extreme tend to be healthy and well-adjusted, as well as unusually successful academically.

27-8   What are cross-sectional studies and longitudinal studies, and why is it important to know which method was used?

The differing intelligence findings of cross-sectional and longitudinal studies—that mental ability declines with age or that it remains stable (or even increases)—illustrate the fact that *cross-sectional studies* compare people of different eras and life circumstances. This can provide an excellent snapshot of a particular point in time, but *longitudinal studies* are superior for tracing the evolution of traits over a longer period.

27-9   How stable are intelligence test scores over the life span?

The stability of intelligence test scores increases with age. At age 4, scores begin to predict adolescent and adult scores. By age 11, scores are very stable and predictive.

27-10   How does aging affect crystallized and fluid intelligence?

Cross-sectional and longitudinal studies have shown that *fluid intelligence* declines in older adults, in part because neural processing slows. However, *crystallized intelligence* tends to increase.

MODULE 28 Genetic and Environmental Influences on Intelligence

28-1   What is *heritability,* and what do twin and adoption studies tell us about the nature and nurture of intelligence?

Studies of twins, family members, and adoptive parents and siblings indicate a significant hereditary contribution to intelligence scores. Intelligence is polygenetic. *Heritability* is the proportion of variation among individuals in a group that can be attributed to genes.

28-2   How can environmental influences affect cognitive development?

Studies of children raised in impoverished environments with minimal social interaction indicate that life experiences significantly influence cognitive development. No evidence supports the idea that normal, healthy children can be molded into geniuses by growing up in an exceptionally enriched environment.

28-3   How and why do the genders differ in mental ability scores?

Males and females have the same average intelligence test scores, but they tend to differ in some specific abilities. Girls, on average, are better spellers, more verbally fluent, better at locating objects, better at detecting emotions, and more sensitive to touch, taste, and color. Boys outperform girls at spatial ability and complex mathematics, though boys and girls hardly differ in math computation and overall math performance. Boys also outnumber girls at the low and high extremes of mental abilities. Evolutionary and cultural explanations have been proposed for these gender differences.

28-4   How and why do racial and ethnic groups differ in mental ability scores?

Racial and ethnic groups differ in their average intelligence test scores. Evidence suggests that environmental differences are responsible for these group differences.

28-5   Are intelligence tests biased or unfair? What is *stereotype threat,* and how does it affect test-takers' performance?

The scientific meaning of bias hinges on a test's ability to predict future behavior for all test-takers, not just for some. In this sense, most experts consider the major aptitude tests unbiased. However, if we consider bias to mean that a test may be influenced by the test-taker's cultural experience, then intelligence tests, by that definition, may be considered unfair. *Stereotype threat,* a self-confirming concern that one will be evaluated based on a negative stereotype, affects performance on all kinds of tests.

Motivation and Emotion

MODULE 29 Basic Motivational Concepts, Affiliation, and Achievement

29-1 How do psychologists define *motivation*? From what perspectives do they view motivated behavior?

Motivation is a need or desire that energizes and directs behavior. The *instinct*/evolutionary perspective explores genetic influences on complex behaviors. *Drive-reduction theory* explores how *physiological needs* create aroused tension states (drives) that direct us to satisfy those needs. Environmental *incentives* can intensify drives. Drive-reduction's goal is *homeostasis,* maintaining a steady internal state. Arousal theory proposes that some behaviors (such as those driven by curiosity) do not reduce physiological needs but rather are prompted by a search for an optimum level of arousal. The *Yerkes-Dodson law* describes the relationship between arousal and performance. Abraham Maslow's *hierarchy of needs* proposes a pyramid of human needs, from basic needs up to higher-level needs.

29-2 What evidence points to our human affiliation need—our need to belong?

Our *affiliation need*—to feel connected and identified with others—had survival value for our ancestors, which may explain why humans in every society live in groups. According to *self-determination theory,* we strive to satisfy our needs for competence, autonomy, and relatedness. Social bonds help us to be healthier and happier, and feeling loved activates brain regions associated with reward and safety systems. *Ostracism* is the deliberate exclusion of individuals or groups. Social isolation can put us at risk mentally and physically.

29-3 How does social networking influence us?

We connect with others through social networking, strengthening our relationships with those we already know and meeting new friends or romantic partners. When networking, people tend toward increased self-disclosure. People with high *narcissism* are especially active on social networking sites. Working out strategies for self-control and disciplined usage can help people maintain a healthy balance between their real-world and online time.

29-4 What is *achievement motivation*, and what are some ways to encourage achievement?

Achievement motivation is a desire for significant accomplishment, for mastery of skills or ideas, for control, and for attaining a high standard. High achievement motivation leads to greater success, especially when combined with determined, persistent *grit.* Research shows that excessive rewards (driving *extrinsic motivation*) can undermine *intrinsic motivation.*

MODULE 30 Hunger

30-1 What physiological factors produce hunger?

Hunger pangs correspond to stomach contractions, but hunger also has other causes. Neural areas in the brain, some within the hypothalamus, monitor blood chemistry (including level of *glucose*) and incoming information about the body's state. Appetite hormones include ghrelin (secreted by an empty stomach); insulin (controls blood glucose); leptin (secreted by fat cells); orexin (secreted by the hypothalamus); and PYY (secreted by the digestive tract). *Basal metabolic rate* is the body's resting rate of energy expenditure. The body may have a *set point* (a biologically fixed tendency to maintain an optimum weight) or a looser settling point (also influenced by the environment).

30-2 What cultural and situational factors influence hunger?

Hunger reflects our memory of when we last ate and our expectation of when we should eat again. Humans as a species prefer certain tastes (such as sweet and salty), but our individual preferences are also influenced by conditioning, culture, and situation. Some taste preferences have survival value. Situations, such as the presence of others, serving size, and the variety of foods offered, can also influence what and how much we eat.

30-3 How does obesity affect physical and psychological health, and what factors are involved in weight management?

Obesity, defined by a body mass index (BMI) of 30 or above, is associated with increased depression (especially among women) and bullying, and with many physical health risks. Genes and environment interact to produce obesity. Storing fat was adaptive to our ancestors, and fat requires less food intake to maintain than it did to gain. Set point and metabolism matter. Twin and adoption studies indicate that body weight is also genetically influenced. Environmental influences include sleep loss, social influence, and food and activity levels. Those wishing to lose weight are advised to make a lifelong change in habits: Begin only if you feel motivated and self-disciplined; exercise and get enough sleep; minimize exposure to tempting food cues; limit variety and eat healthy foods; reduce portion sizes; space meals throughout the day; beware of the binge; plan ahead to control eating during social events; forgive the occasional lapse; publicly chart your progress; and connect to a support group.

MODULE 31 Theories and Physiology of Emotion

31-1 How do arousal, expressive behavior, and cognition interact in emotion?

Emotions are responses of the whole organism, involving physiological arousal, expressive behaviors, and conscious experience. Theories of emotion generally address two major questions: (1) Does physiological arousal come before or after emotional feelings? and (2) how do feeling and cognition interact? The *James-Lange theory* maintains that emotional feelings follow our body's response to emotion-inducing stimuli (we observe our heart pounding and feel fear). The *Cannon-Bard theory* proposes that our physiological response to an emotion-inducing stimulus occurs at the same time as our subjective feeling of the emotion (one does not cause the other).

31-2   To experience emotions, must we consciously interpret and label them?

The Schachter-Singer *two-factor theory* holds that our emotions have two ingredients, physical arousal and a cognitive label; the cognitive labels we put on our states of arousal are an essential ingredient of emotion. Lazarus agreed that many important emotions arise from our interpretations or inferences. But Zajonc and LeDoux have contended that some simple emotional responses occur instantly, not only outside our conscious awareness, but before any cognitive processing occurs. This interplay between emotion and cognition illustrates our two-track mind.

31-3   What are some of the basic emotions?

Carroll Izard's 10 basic emotions are joy, interest-excitement, surprise, sadness, anger, disgust, contempt, fear, shame, and guilt.

31-4   What is the link between emotional arousal and the autonomic nervous system?

The arousal component of emotion is regulated by the autonomic nervous system's sympathetic (arousing) and parasympathetic (calming) divisions. In a crisis, the fight-or-flight response automatically mobilizes your body for action.

31-5   Do different emotions activate different physiological and brain-pattern responses?

The large-scale body changes that accompany fear, anger, and sexual arousal are very similar (increased perspiration, breathing, and heart rate), though they feel different. Emotions may be similarly arousing, but some subtle physiological responses, such as facial muscle movements, distinguish them. More meaningful differences have been found in activity in some brain pathways and cortical areas.

31-6   How effective are polygraphs in using body states to detect lies?

Polygraphs (lie detectors) attempt to measure several physiological indicators of emotion, but are not accurate enough to justify widespread use in business and law enforcement. Using the Concealed Information Test may produce better indications of lying.

MODULE 32 Expressing and Experiencing Emotion

32-1   How do we communicate nonverbally?

Much of our communication is through body movements, facial expressions, and voice tones. Even seconds-long filmed slices of behavior can reveal feelings.

32-2   How do the genders differ in their ability to communicate nonverbally?

Women tend to read emotional cues more easily and to be more empathic. They also express more emotion.

32-3   How are gestures and facial expressions understood within and across cultures?

The meaning of gestures varies with culture, but facial expressions, such as those of happiness and sadness, are common the world over. Cultures also differ in the amount of emotion they express.

32-4   How do our facial expressions influence our feelings?

Research on the *facial feedback effect* shows that our facial expressions can trigger emotional feelings and signal our body to respond accordingly. We also mimic others' expressions, which helps us empathize. A similar *behavior feedback effect* is the tendency of behavior to influence our own and others' thoughts, feelings, and actions.

Stress, Health, and Human Flourishing

MODULE 33 Stress and Illness

33-1   How does our appraisal of an event affect our stress reaction, and what are the three main types of stressors?

Stress is the process by which we appraise and respond to stressors that challenge or threaten us. If we appraise an event as challenging, we will be aroused and focused in preparation for success; if we appraise it as a threat, we will experience a stress reaction, and our health may suffer. The three main types of stressors are catastrophes, significant life changes, and daily hassles and social stress.

33-2   How do we respond and adapt to stress?

Walter Cannon viewed the stress response as a fight-or-flight system. Hans Selye proposed a general three-phase (alarm, resistance, exhaustion) *general adaptation syndrome (GAS)*. Facing stress, women may have a *tend-and-befriend* response; men may withdraw socially, turn to alcohol, or become emotionally insensitive.

33-3   How does stress make us more vulnerable to disease?

Psychoneuroimmunology is the study of how psychological, neural, and endocrine processes together affect the immune system and resulting health. Stress diverts energy from the immune system, inhibiting the activities of its B and T lymphocytes, macrophages, and NK cells. Stress does not cause illness, but by altering our immune functioning it may make us more vulnerable to diseases and influence their progression.

33-4   Why are some of us more prone than others to coronary heart disease?

Coronary heart disease has been linked with the reactive, anger-prone *Type A* personality. Compared with relaxed, easygoing *Type B* personalities, who are less likely to experience heart disease, Type A people secrete more stress hormones. Chronic stress also contributes to persistent inflammation, which is associated with heart and other health problems, including depression.

33-5 So, does stress *cause* illness?

Stress may not directly cause illness, but it does make us more vulnerable, by influencing our behaviors and our physiology.

33-6 What are the causes and consequences of anger?

Facing a threat or a challenge may trigger anger, and our culture can influence how we express that anger. Chronic hostility is a key negative emotion linked to heart disease. Emotional *catharsis* may be temporarily calming, but it does not reduce anger; expressing anger can make us angrier. Experts suggest reducing the level of physiological arousal of anger by waiting, finding a healthy distraction or support, and trying to move away from the situation mentally. Controlled assertions of feelings may resolve conflicts, and forgiveness may rid us of angry feelings.

MODULE **34** Health and Happiness

34-1 In what two ways do people try to alleviate stress?

We use *problem-focused coping* to change the stressor or the way we interact with it. We use *emotion-focused coping* to avoid or ignore stressors and attend to emotional needs related to stress reactions.

34-2 How does a perceived lack of control affect health?

A perceived lack of *personal control* provokes an outpouring of hormones that put people's health at risk. Being unable to avoid repeated aversive events can lead to *learned helplessness*. People who perceive an *internal locus of control* achieve more, enjoy better health, and are happier than those who perceive an *external locus of control*.

34-3 Why is self-control important, and can our self-control be depleted?

Self-control requires attention and energy, but predicts good health, higher income, and better school performance; it does better than an intelligence test score in predicting future academic and life success. Self-control varies over time. Researchers disagree about the factors influencing self-control, but strengthening it can lead to a healthier, happier, and more successful life.

34-4 How does an optimistic outlook affect health and longevity?

Studies of people with an optimistic outlook show that their immune system is stronger, their blood pressure does not increase as sharply in response to stress, their recovery from heart bypass surgery is faster, and their life expectancy is longer, compared with their pessimistic counterparts.

34-5 How does social support promote good health?

Social support promotes health by calming us, by reducing blood pressure and stress hormones, and by fostering stronger immune functioning. We can significantly reduce our stress and increase our health by building and maintaining relationships, and by confiding rather than suppressing painful feelings.

34-6 How effective is aerobic exercise as a way to manage stress and improve well-being?

Aerobic exercise is sustained, oxygen-consuming activity that increases heart and lung fitness. It increases arousal, leads to muscle relaxation and sounder sleep, triggers the production of neurotransmitters, and enhances self-image. It can relieve depression and, in later life, is associated with better cognitive functioning and longer life.

34-7 In what ways might relaxation and meditation influence stress and health?

Relaxation and meditation have been shown to lower stress, improve immune functioning, and lessen anxiety and depression. *Mindfulness meditation* is a reflective practice of attending to current experiences in a nonjudgmental and accepting manner. Massage therapy also relaxes muscles and reduces depression.

34-8 What is the *faith factor,* and what are some possible explanations for the link between faith and health?

The faith factor is the finding that religiously active people tend to live longer than those who are not religiously active. Possible explanations may include intervening variables such as the healthy behaviors, social support, or positive emotions often found among people who regularly attend religious services.

34-9 What is the *feel-good, do-good phenomenon,* and what is the focus of positive psychology research?

Happy people tend to be healthy, energized, and satisfied with life, making them more willing to help others (the *feel-good, do-good phenomenon*). *Positive psychologists* use scientific methods to study human flourishing, aiming to discover and promote strengths and virtues that help individuals and communities to thrive.

34-10 How do time, wealth, adaptation, and comparison affect our happiness levels?

The moods triggered by good or bad events seldom last beyond that day. Even significant good events, such as sudden wealth, seldom increase happiness for long. Happiness is relative to our own experiences (the *adaptation-level phenomenon*) and to others' success (the *relative deprivation* principle).

34-11 What predicts happiness, and how can we be happier?

Some individuals, because of their genetic predispositions and personal histories, are happier than others. Cultures, which vary in the traits they value and the behaviors they expect and reward, also influence personal levels of happiness. Tips for increasing happiness levels: take charge of your schedule, act happy, seek meaningful work and leisure, buy shared experiences rather than things, exercise, sleep enough, foster friendships, focus beyond the self, challenge negative thinking, and nurture gratitude and spirituality.

Social Psychology

MODULE **35** Social Thinking and Social Influence

35-1 What do social psychologists study? How do we tend to explain others' behavior and our own?

Social psychologists use scientific methods to study how people think about, influence, and relate to one another. They study the social influences that explain why the same person will act differently in different situations. When explaining others' behavior, we may—especially if we come from an individualist Western culture—commit the *fundamental attribution error,* by underestimating the influence of the situation and overestimating the effects of stable, enduring traits. When explaining our own behavior, we more readily attribute it to the influence of the situation.

35-2 How do attitudes and actions interact?

Peripheral route persuasion uses incidental cues (such as celebrity endorsement) to try to produce fast but relatively thoughtless changes in attitudes. *Central route persuasion* offers evidence and arguments to trigger thoughtful responses. When other influences are minimal, attitudes that are stable, specific, and easily recalled can affect our actions. Actions can modify attitudes, as in the *foot-in-the-door phenomenon* and *role* playing. When our attitudes don't fit with our actions, *cognitive dissonance theory* suggests that we will reduce tension by changing our attitudes to match our actions.

35-3 How does culture affect our behavior?

A *culture* is an enduring set of behaviors, ideas, attitudes, values, and traditions shared by a group and transmitted from one generation to the next. Cultural *norms* are understood rules that inform members of a culture about accepted and expected behaviors. Cultures differ across time and space.

35-4 How is social contagion a form of conformity, and how do conformity experiments reveal the power of social influence?

Social contagion (the chameleon effect)—our tendency to unconsciously imitate others' behavior, expressions, postures, voice tones, and moods—is a form of *conformity.* Solomon Asch and others found that we are most likely to adjust our behavior or thinking to coincide with a group standard when we feel incompetent or insecure, our group has at least three people, everyone else agrees, we admire the group's status and attractiveness, we have not already committed to another response, we know we are being observed, and our culture encourages respect for social standards. We may conform to gain approval (*normative social influence*) or because we are willing to accept others' opinions as new information (*informational social influence*).

35-5 What did Milgram's obedience experiments teach us about the power of social influence?

Stanley Milgram's experiments—in which people obeyed orders even when they thought they were harming another person—demonstrated that strong social influences can make ordinary people conform to falsehoods or capitulate to cruelty. Obedience was highest when the person giving orders was nearby and was perceived as a legitimate authority figure, the research was supported by a prestigious institution, the victim was depersonalized or at a distance, and there were no role models for defiance.

35-6 What do the social influence studies teach us about ourselves? How much power do we have as individuals?

These experiments have demonstrated that strong social influences can influence behavior. The power of the individual (personal control) and the power of the situation (social control) interact. A small minority that consistently expresses its views may sway the majority, as may even a single committed individual.

35-7 How does the presence of others influence our actions, via social facilitation, social loafing, and deindividuation?

In *social facilitation,* the mere presence of others arouses us, improving our performance on easy or well-learned tasks but decreasing it on difficult ones. In *social loafing,* group work makes us feel less responsible, and we may free ride on others' efforts. When the presence of others both arouses us and makes us feel anonymous, we may experience *deindividuation*—loss of self-awareness and self-restraint.

35-8 How can group interaction enable group polarization?

In *group polarization,* group discussions with like-minded others strengthen members' prevailing beliefs and attitudes.

35-9 What role does the internet play in group polarization?

Internet communication magnifies the effect of connecting like-minded people, for better and for worse. People find support, which strengthens their ideas, but also often isolation from those with different opinions. Separation plus conversation may thus lead to group polarization.

35-10 How can group interaction enable groupthink?

Groupthink is driven by a desire for harmony within a decision-making group, overriding realistic appraisal of alternatives. Group leaders can harness the benefits of group interaction by assigning people to identify possible problems, and by welcoming various opinions and expert critique.

MODULE 36 Antisocial Relations

36-1 What is *prejudice?* How do explicit and implicit prejudice differ?

Prejudice is an unjustifiable, usually negative attitude toward a group and its members. Prejudice's three components are beliefs (often *stereotypes*), emotions, and predispositions to action (*discrimination*). Prejudice may be explicit (overt), or it may be implicit—an unthinking knee-jerk response operating below conscious awareness. Implicit prejudice can cause discrimination even when people do not consciously intend to discriminate.

36-2 What groups are frequent targets of prejudice?

Prejudice involves explicit and implicit negative attitudes toward people of a particular racial or ethnic group, gender identity, sexual orientation, or belief system. In the United States, frequently targeted groups include Black Americans, women, Muslim Americans, and gay, lesbian, and transgender people.

36-3 What are some social, emotional, and cognitive roots of prejudice, and what are some ways to eliminate prejudice?

The social roots of prejudice include social inequalities and divisions. Higher-status groups often justify their privileged position with the *just-world phenomenon.* We tend to favor our own group (*ingroup bias*) as we divide ourselves into "us" (the *ingroup*) and "them" (the *outgroup*). Prejudice can also be a tool for protecting our emotional well-being, as when we focus our anger by blaming events on a *scapegoat*. The cognitive roots of prejudice grow from our natural ways of processing information: forming categories, remembering vivid cases, and believing that the world is just (and that our own and our group's ways of doing things are the right ways). Monitoring our feelings and actions, as well as developing new friendships, can help us free ourselves from prejudice.

36-4 How does psychology's definition of *aggression* differ from everyday usage? What biological factors make us more prone to hurt one another?

In psychology's more specific meaning, *aggression* is any act intended to harm someone physically or emotionally. Biology influences our threshold for aggressive behaviors at three levels: genetic (inherited traits), neural (activity in key brain areas), and biochemical (such as alcohol or excess testosterone in the bloodstream). Aggression is a complex behavior resulting from the interaction of biology and experience.

36-5 What psychological and social-cultural factors may trigger aggressive behavior?

Frustration (the *frustration-aggression principle*), previous reinforcement for aggressive behavior, observing aggressive role models, and poor self-control all contribute to aggression. Media violence provides *social scripts* that children learn to follow. Viewing sexual violence contributes to greater aggression toward women. Playing violent video games can increase aggressive thoughts, emotions, and behaviors.

MODULE 37 Prosocial Relations

37-1 Why do we befriend or fall in love with some people but not others?

Proximity (geographical nearness) increases liking, in part because of the *mere exposure effect*—exposure to novel stimuli increases liking of those stimuli. Physical attractiveness increases social opportunities and improves the way we are perceived. Similarity of attitudes and interests greatly increases liking, especially as relationships develop. We also like those who like us.

37-2 How does romantic love typically change as time passes?

Intimate love relationships start with *passionate love*—an intensely aroused state. Over time, the strong affection of *companionate love* may develop, especially if enhanced by an *equitable* relationship, intimate *self-disclosure,* and positive support.

37-3 What is *altruism*? When are people most—and least—likely to help?

Altruism is unselfish regard for the well-being of others. We are most likely to help when we notice an incident, interpret it as an emergency, and assume responsibility for helping. Other factors, including our mood and our similarity to the victim, also affect our willingness to help. We are least likely to help if other bystanders are present (the *bystander effect*).

37-4 How do social exchange theory and social norms explain helping behavior?

Social exchange theory is the view that we help others because it is in our own self-interest; in this view, the goal of social behavior is maximizing personal benefits and minimizing costs. Others believe that helping results from socialization, in which we are taught guidelines for expected behaviors in social situations, such as the *reciprocity norm* and the *social-responsibility norm.*

37-5 How do social traps and mirror-image perceptions fuel social conflict?

Social traps are situations in which people in conflict pursue their own individual self-interest, harming the collective well-being. Individuals and cultures in conflict also tend to form *mirror-image perceptions:* Each party views the opponent as untrustworthy and evil-intentioned, and itself as an ethical, peaceful victim. Perceptions can become *self-fulfilling prophecies.*

37-6 What can we do to promote peace?

Peace can result when individuals or groups work together to achieve *superordinate* (shared) goals. Research indicates that contact, cooperation, communication, and conciliation—such as the Graduated and Reciprocated Initiatives in Tension-Reduction (GRIT) strategy—help promote peace.

Personality

MODULE 38 Classic Perspectives on Personality

38-1 What is *personality,* and what theories inform our understanding of personality?

Personality is an individual's characteristic pattern of thinking, feeling, and acting. Psychoanalytic (and later psychodynamic) theory and humanistic theory have become part of our cultural legacy. They also laid the foundation for later theories, such as trait and social-cognitive theories of personality.

38-2 How did Sigmund Freud's treatment of psychological disorders lead to his view of the unconscious mind?

Psychodynamic theories view personality from the perspective that behavior is a dynamic interaction between the conscious and unconscious mind. These theories trace their origin to Sigmund Freud's theory of *psychoanalysis.* In treating patients whose disorders had no clear physical explanation, Freud concluded that these problems reflected unacceptable thoughts and feelings, hidden away in the *unconscious* mind. To explore this hidden part of a patient's mind, Freud used *free association* and dream analysis.

38-3 What was Freud's view of personality?

Freud believed that personality results from conflict arising from the interaction among the mind's three systems: the *id* (pleasure-seeking impulses), *ego* (reality-oriented executive), and *superego* (internalized set of ideals, or conscience).

38-4 What developmental stages did Freud propose?

He believed children pass through five *psychosexual stages* (oral, anal, phallic, latency, and genital). According to this view, unresolved conflicts at any stage can leave a person's pleasure-seeking impulses *fixated* (stalled) at that stage.

38-5 How did Freud think people defended themselves against anxiety?

For Freud, anxiety was the product of tensions between the demands of the id and superego. The ego copes by using unconscious *defense mechanisms,* such as *repression,* which he viewed as the basic mechanism underlying and enabling all the others.

38-6 Which of Freud's ideas did his followers accept or reject?

Freud's early followers, the neo-Freudians, accepted many of his ideas. They differed in placing more emphasis on the conscious mind and in stressing social motives more than sex or aggression. Most contemporary psychodynamic theorists and therapists reject Freud's emphasis on sexual motivation. They stress, with support from modern research findings, the view that much of our mental life is unconscious, and they believe that our childhood experiences influence our adult personality and attachment patterns. Many also believe that our species' shared evolutionary history shaped some universal predispositions.

38-7 What are *projective tests,* how are they used, and what are some criticisms of them?

Projective tests attempt to assess personality by showing people stimuli open to many possible interpretations and treating their answers as revelations of unconscious motives. The *Thematic Apperception Test (TAT)* and the *Rorschach inkblot test* are two such tests. The TAT provides a valid and reliable map of people's implicit motives that is consistent over time. The Rorschach has low reliability and validity, but some clinicians value it as a source of suggestive leads, an icebreaker, or a revealing interview technique.

38-8 How do contemporary psychologists view Freud's psychoanalysis?

They give Freud credit for drawing attention to the vast unconscious, to the struggle to cope with anxiety and sexuality, to the conflict between biological impulses and social restraints, and for some forms of defense mechanisms. But his concept of repression, and his view of the unconscious as a collection of repressed and unacceptable thoughts, wishes, feelings, and memories, cannot survive scientific scrutiny. Freud offered after-the-fact explanations, which are hard to test scientifically. Research does not support many of Freud's specific ideas, such as the view that development is fixed in childhood. (We now know it is lifelong.)

38-9 How has modern research developed our understanding of the unconscious?

Research confirms that we do not have full access to all that goes on in our mind, though today's science views the unconscious as a separate and parallel track of information processing that occurs outside our awareness. This processing includes schemas that control our perceptions, priming, implicit memories of learned skills, instantly activated emotions, and stereotypes that filter our information processing of others' traits and characteristics. Research also supports reaction formation and projection (the false consensus effect).

38-10 How did humanistic psychologists view personality, and what was their goal in studying personality?

The *humanistic* psychologists' view of personality focused on the potential for healthy personal growth and people's striving for self-determination and self-realization. Abraham Maslow proposed that human motivations form a *hierarchy of needs;* if basic needs are fulfilled, people will strive toward *self-actualization* and *self-transcendence.* Carl Rogers believed that the ingredients of a growth-promoting environment are acceptance (including *unconditional positive regard*), genuineness, and empathy. *Self-concept* was a central feature of personality for both Maslow and Rogers.

38-11 How did humanistic psychologists assess a person's sense of self?

Some rejected any standardized assessments and relied on interviews and conversations. Rogers sometimes used questionnaires in which people described their ideal and actual selves, which he later used to judge progress during therapy.

38-12 How have humanistic theories influenced psychology? What criticisms have they faced?

Humanistic psychology helped renew interest in the concept of self, and also laid the groundwork for today's scientific subfield of positive psychology. Critics have said that humanistic psychology's concepts are vague and subjective, its values self-centered, and its assumptions naively optimistic.

MODULE 39 Contemporary Perspectives on Personality

39-1 How do psychologists use traits to describe personality?

Trait theorists see personality as a stable and enduring pattern of behavior. They have been more interested in trying to describe our differences than in explaining them. Using factor analysis, they identify clusters of behavior tendencies that occur together. Genetic predispositions influence many traits.

39-2 What are some common misunderstandings about introversion?

Western cultures prize extraversion, but introverts have different, equally important skills. Introversion does not equal shyness, and extraverts don't always outperform introverts as leaders or in sales success. Introverts often experience great achievement; many introverts prosper.

39-3 What are *personality inventories,* and what are their strengths and weaknesses as trait-assessment tools?

Personality inventories (such as the *MMPI*) are questionnaires on which people respond to items designed to gauge a wide range of feelings and behaviors. Test items are *empirically derived,* and the tests are objectively scored. Objectivity does not guarantee validity; people can fake their answers to create a good impression (but may then score high on a lie scale that assesses faking).

39-4 Which traits seem to provide the most useful information about personality variation?

The Big Five personality factors—conscientiousness, agreeableness, neuroticism, openness, and extraversion (CANOE)—currently offer our best approximation of the basic trait dimensions. These factors are quite stable and appear to be found in all cultures. Many genes, each having small effects, combine to influence our traits, and heritability generally runs about 40 percent for each dimension.

39-5 Does research support the consistency of personality traits over time and across situations?

A person's average traits persist over time and are predictable over many different situations. But traits cannot predict behavior in any one situation.

39-6 How do social-cognitive theorists view personality development, and how do they explore behavior?

Albert Bandura first proposed the *social-cognitive perspective,* which emphasizes the interaction of our traits with our situations. Social-cognitive researchers apply principles of learning, cognition, and social behavior to personality. *Reciprocal determinism* describes the interaction and mutual influence of behavior, internal cognition, and environment. Assessment situations involving simulated conditions exploit the principle that the best predictor of future behavior is a person's actions in similar situations.

39-7 What criticisms have social-cognitive theorists faced?

Social-cognitive theorists build on well-established concepts of learning and cognition, sensitizing researchers to the ways situations affect, and are affected by, individuals. They have been faulted for underemphasizing the importance of unconscious motives, emotions, and biologically influenced traits.

39-8 Why has psychology generated so much research on the self? How important is self-esteem to our well-being?

The *self* is the center of personality, organizing our thoughts, feelings, and actions. Considering possible selves helps motivate us toward positive development, but focusing too intensely on ourselves can lead to the *spotlight effect.* High *self-esteem* correlates with less pressure to conform, with persistence at difficult tasks, and with happiness. But the direction of the correlation is unclear. Rather than unrealistically promoting self-worth, it's better to reward children's achievements, thus promoting feelings of competence.

39-9 What evidence reveals self-serving bias, and how do defensive and secure self-esteem differ?

Self-serving bias is our tendency to perceive ourselves favorably, as when viewing ourselves as better than average or when accepting credit for our successes but not blame for our failures. Defensive self-esteem is fragile, focuses on sustaining itself, and views failure or criticism as a threat. Secure self-esteem enables us to feel accepted for who we are.

39-10 How do individualist and collectivist cultures differ in their values and goals?

Although individuals vary, different cultures tend to emphasize either individualism or collectivism. Cultures based on self-reliant *individualism* tend to value personal independence and individual achievement. They define identity in terms of self-esteem, personal goals and attributes, and personal rights and liberties. Cultures based on socially connected *collectivism* tend to value group goals, social identity, and commitments. They define identity in terms of interdependence, tradition, and harmony.

Psychological Disorders

MODULE **40** Basic Concepts of Psychological Disorders

40-1 How should we draw the line between normality and disorder?

According to psychologists and psychiatrists, *psychological disorders* are marked by a clinically significant disturbance in an individual's cognition, emotion regulation, or behavior. Such dysfunctional or maladaptive thoughts, emotions, or behaviors interfere with daily life, and thus are disordered.

40-2 How do the medical model and the biopsychosocial approach influence our understanding of psychological disorders?

The *medical model* assumes that psychological disorders have physical causes that can be diagnosed, treated, and often cured through therapy, sometimes in a hospital. The biopsychosocial perspective assumes that disordered behavior comes from the interaction of biological characteristics, psychological dynamics, and social-cultural circumstances. This approach has given rise to the vulnerability-stress model, in which individual characteristics and environmental stressors combine to increase or decrease the likelihood of developing a psychological disorder, a model supported by *epigenetics* research.

40-3 How and why do clinicians classify psychological disorders, and why do some psychologists criticize the use of diagnostic labels?

The American Psychiatric Association's *DSM-5* (*Diagnostic and Statistical Manual of Mental Disorders,* Fifth Edition) contains diagnostic labels and descriptions that provide a common language and shared concepts for communication and research. Critics of the DSM say it casts too wide a net, pathologizing normal behaviors. A complementary approach to classification is the U.S. National Institute of Mental Health's Research Domain Criteria (RDoC) project, a framework that organizes disorders according to behaviors and brain activity along several dimensions. Any classification attempt produces diagnostic labels that may create preconceptions, which bias perceptions of the labeled person's past and present behavior.

40-4 Why is there controversy over attention-deficit/hyperactivity disorder?

A child (or, less commonly, an adult) who displays extreme inattention and/or hyperactivity and impulsivity may be diagnosed with *attention-deficit/hyperactivity disorder (ADHD)*. Controversies center on whether the growing number of ADHD cases reflect overdiagnosis or increased awareness of the disorder, and on the long-term effects of stimulant-drug treatment.

40-5　What factors increase the risk of suicide, and what do we know about nonsuicidal self-injury?

Suicide rates differ by nation, race, gender, age group, income, religious involvement, marital status, and other factors. Those lacking social support, such as many gay, transgender, and gender non-conforming youth, are at increased risk, as are people who have been anxious or depressed. Forewarnings of suicide may include verbal hints, giving away possessions, withdrawal, and preoccupation with death. People who talk about suicide should be taken seriously: listen and empathize, connect them to help, and protect those who appear at immediate risk. Nonsuicidal self-injury (NSSI) does not usually lead to suicide but may escalate to suicidal thoughts and acts if untreated. People who engage in NSSI do not tolerate stress well and tend to be self-critical, with poor communication and problem-solving skills.

40-6　Do psychological disorders predict violent behavior?

Mental disorders seldom lead to violence, but when they do, they raise moral and ethical questions about whether society should hold people with disorders responsible for their violent actions. Most people with disorders are nonviolent and are more likely to be victims than attackers.

40-7　How many people have, or have had, a psychological disorder? What are some of the risk factors?

Psychological disorder rates vary, depending on the time and place of the survey. In one multinational survey, the lowest rate of reported mental disorders was in Nigeria (6 percent), the highest rate in the United States (27 percent). Poverty is a risk factor. But some disorders, such as schizophrenia, can also drive people into poverty. Immigrants to the United States may average better mental health than their U.S. counterparts with the same ethnic heritage (a phenomenon known as the immigrant paradox).

MODULE 41　Anxiety Disorders, OCD, and PTSD

41-1　How do generalized anxiety disorder, panic disorder, and phobias differ?

Anxiety disorders are psychological disorders characterized by distressing, persistent anxiety or maladaptive behaviors that reduce anxiety. People with *generalized anxiety disorder* feel persistently and uncontrollably tense and apprehensive, for no apparent reason. In the more extreme *panic disorder,* anxiety escalates into periodic episodes of intense dread. Those with a *phobia* may be irrationally afraid of a specific object, activity, or situation.

41-2　What is OCD?

Persistent and repetitive thoughts (obsessions), actions (compulsions), or both characterize *obsessive-compulsive disorder (OCD).*

41-3　What is PTSD?

Symptoms of *posttraumatic stress disorder (PTSD)* include four or more weeks of haunting memories, nightmares, hypervigilance, avoidance of trauma-related stimuli, social withdrawal, jumpy anxiety, numbness of feeling, and/or sleep problems following some traumatic experience.

41-4　How do conditioning, cognition, and biology contribute to the feelings and thoughts that mark anxiety disorders, OCD, and PTSD?

The learning perspective views anxiety disorders, OCD, and PTSD as products of fear conditioning, stimulus generalization, fearful-behavior reinforcement, and observational learning of others' fears and cognitions. The biological perspective considers genetic predispositions for high levels of emotional reactivity and neurotransmitter production; abnormal responses in the brain's fear circuits; and the role that fears of life-threatening dangers played in natural selection and evolution.

MODULE 42　Major Depressive Disorder and Bipolar Disorder

42-1　How do major depressive disorder and bipolar disorder differ?

A person with *major depressive disorder* experiences at least five symptoms of depression (including either depressed mood or loss of interest or pleasure) for two or more weeks. A person with the less common condition of *bipolar disorder* experiences not only depression but also *mania*—episodes of hyperactive and wildly optimistic, impulsive behavior.

42-2　How can the biological and social-cognitive perspectives help us understand major depressive disorder and bipolar disorder?

The biological perspective on depressive disorders and bipolar disorder focuses on genetic predispositions, abnormalities in brain structures and function (including those found in neurotransmitter systems), and nutritional (and drug) effects. The social-cognitive perspective views depression as an ongoing cycle of stressful experiences (interpreted through negative beliefs, attributions, and memories, often with relentless *rumination*) leading to negative moods, thoughts, and actions, thereby fueling new stressful experiences.

MODULE 43　Schizophrenia and Other Disorders

43-1　What patterns of perceiving, thinking, and feeling characterize schizophrenia?

Schizophrenia is a *psychotic disorder* characterized by delusions, hallucinations, disorganized speech, and/or diminished, inappropriate emotional expression. Hallucinations are sensory experiences without sensory stimulation; *delusions* are false beliefs. Schizophrenia symptoms may be positive (the presence of inappropriate behaviors) or negative (the absence of appropriate behaviors).

43-2　How do chronic schizophrenia and acute schizophrenia differ?

Schizophrenia typically strikes during late adolescence, affects males slightly more often, and occurs in all cultures. In *chronic* (or process) *schizophrenia,* development is gradual and recovery is doubtful. In *acute* (or reactive) *schizophrenia,* onset is sudden—in reaction to stress—and prospects for recovery are brighter.

43-3 What brain abnormalities are associated with schizophrenia?

People with schizophrenia have an excess number of dopamine receptors, which may intensify brain signals, creating positive symptoms such as hallucinations and paranoia. Brain scans have revealed abnormal activity in the frontal lobes, thalamus, and amygdala, as well as a loss of neural connections across the brain network. Brain abnormalities associated with schizophrenia include enlarged, fluid-filled areas and corresponding shrinkage and thinning of cerebral tissue.

43-4 What prenatal events are associated with increased risk of developing schizophrenia?

Possible contributing factors include maternal diabetes, older paternal age, viral infections or famine conditions during the mother's pregnancy, and low weight or oxygen deprivation at birth.

43-5 How do genes influence schizophrenia?

Twin and adoption studies indicate that the predisposition to schizophrenia is inherited. Multiple genes interact to produce schizophrenia. No environmental causes invariably produce schizophrenia, but environmental events (such as prenatal viruses or maternal stress) may "turn on" genes in those who are predisposed to this disorder.

43-6 What are *dissociative disorders,* and why are they controversial?

Dissociative disorders are controversial, rare conditions in which conscious awareness seems to become separated from previous memories, thoughts, and feelings. Skeptics note that *dissociative identity disorder (DID)* increased dramatically in the late twentieth century; is rarely found outside North America; and may reflect role playing by people vulnerable to therapists' suggestions. Others view DID as a manifestation of feelings of anxiety, or as a response learned when behaviors are reinforced by anxiety-reduction.

43-7 What are the three clusters of personality disorders? What behaviors and brain activity characterize the antisocial personality?

Personality disorders are inflexible and enduring behavior patterns that impair social functioning. The ten DSM-5 disorders tend to form three clusters, characterized by (1) anxiety, (2) eccentric or odd behaviors, and (3) dramatic or impulsive behaviors. *Antisocial personality disorder* (one of those in the third cluster) is characterized by a lack of conscience and, sometimes, by aggressive and fearless behavior. The amygdala is smaller and the frontal lobes less active in people with this disorder, leading to impaired frontal lobe cognitive functions and decreased responsiveness to others' distress. Genetic predispositions may interact with the environment to produce these characteristics.

43-8 What are the three main eating disorders, and how do biological, psychological, and social-cultural influences make people more vulnerable to them?

In those with eating disorders (most often women or gay men), psychological factors overwhelm the body's tendency to maintain a normal weight. Despite being significantly underweight, people with *anorexia nervosa* (usually adolescent females) continue to diet and sometimes exercise excessively because they view themselves as fat. Those with *bulimia nervosa* (usually women in their late teens and early twenties) secretly binge and then compensate by purging, fasting, or excessively exercising. Those with *binge-eating disorder* binge but do not follow with purging, fasting, and exercising. Cultural pressures, low self-esteem, and negative emotions interact with stressful life experiences and genetics to produce eating disorders.

Therapy

MODULE 44 Introduction to Therapy and the Psychological Therapies

44-1 How do *psychotherapy* and the *biomedical therapies* differ?

Psychotherapy is treatment involving psychological techniques that consists of interactions between a trained therapist and someone seeking to overcome psychological difficulties or achieve personal growth. The major psychotherapies derive from psychology's psychodynamic, humanistic, behavioral, and cognitive perspectives. *Biomedical therapy* treats psychological disorders with medications or procedures that act directly on a patient's physiology. An *eclectic approach* combines techniques from various forms of therapy.

44-2 What are the goals and techniques of psychoanalysis, and how have they been adapted in psychodynamic therapy?

Through *psychoanalysis,* Sigmund Freud tried to give people self-insight and relief from their disorders by bringing anxiety-laden feelings and thoughts into conscious awareness. Psychoanalytic techniques included using free association and *interpretation* of instances of *resistance* and *transference. Psychodynamic therapy* has been influenced by traditional psychoanalysis but differs from it in many ways, including the lack of belief in id, ego, and superego. This contemporary therapy is briefer, less expensive, and more focused on helping the client find relief from current symptoms. Psychodynamic therapists help clients understand how past relationships create themes that may be acted out in present relationships.

44-3 What are the basic themes of humanistic therapy? What are the specific goals and techniques of Rogers' client-centered approach?

Both psychodynamic and humanistic therapies are *insight therapies*—they attempt to improve functioning by increasing clients' awareness of motives and defenses. Humanistic therapy's goals include helping clients grow in self-awareness and self-acceptance; promoting personal growth rather than curing illness; helping clients take responsibility for their own growth; focusing on conscious thoughts rather than unconscious motivations; and seeing the present and future as more important than the past. Carl Rogers' *client-centered therapy* proposed that therapists' most important contributions are to function as a psychological mirror through *active listening* and to provide a growth-fostering environment of *unconditional positive regard.*

44-4 How does the basic assumption of behavior therapy differ from the assumptions of psychodynamic and humanistic therapies? What techniques are used in exposure therapies and aversive conditioning?

Behavior therapies are not insight therapies, and instead assume that problem behaviors *are* the problem. Their goal is to apply learning principles to modify these problem behaviors. Classical conditioning techniques, including *exposure therapies* (such as *systematic desensitization* or *virtual reality exposure therapy*) and *aversive conditioning*, attempt to change behaviors through *counterconditioning*—evoking new responses to old stimuli that trigger unwanted behaviors.

44-5 What is the main premise of therapy based on operant conditioning principles, and what are the views of its proponents and critics?

Operant conditioning operates under the premise that voluntary behaviors are strongly influenced by their consequences. Therapy based on operant conditioning principles therefore uses behavior modification techniques to change unwanted behaviors by positively reinforcing desired behaviors and ignoring or punishing undesirable behaviors. Critics maintain that (1) techniques such as those used in *token economies* may produce behavior changes that disappear when rewards end, and (2) deciding which behaviors should change is authoritarian and unethical. Proponents argue that treatment with positive rewards is more humane than punishing people or institutionalizing them for undesired behaviors.

44-6 What are the goals and techniques of the cognitive therapies and of cognitive-behavioral therapy?

The *cognitive therapies,* such as Aaron Beck's cognitive therapy for depression, assume that our thinking influences our feelings, and that the therapist's role is to change clients' self-defeating thinking by training them to perceive and interpret events in more constructive ways. The widely researched and practiced *cognitive-behavioral therapy (CBT)* combines cognitive therapy and behavior therapy by helping clients regularly try out their new ways of thinking and behaving in their everyday life. A newer CBT variation, dialectical behavior therapy (DBT), teaches clients cognitive tactics for tolerating distress and regulating emotions, and trains them in social skills and mindfulness meditation.

44-7 What are the aims and benefits of group and family therapies?

Group therapy sessions can help more people with less cost than individual therapy. Clients may benefit from exploring feelings and developing social skills in a group situation, from learning that others have similar problems, and from getting feedback on new ways of behaving. *Family therapy* views a family as an interactive system. It attempts to help members discover the roles they play and learn to communicate more openly and directly.

MODULE 45 Evaluating Psychotherapies

45-1 Does psychotherapy work? How can we know?

Clients' and therapists' positive testimonials cannot prove that psychotherapy is effective, and the placebo effect makes it difficult to

judge whether improvement occurred because of the treatment. Using *meta-analyses* to statistically combine the results of hundreds of randomized psychotherapy outcome studies, researchers have found that those not undergoing treatment often improve, but those undergoing psychotherapy are more likely to improve—and to improve more quickly and with less risk of relapse.

45-2 Are some psychotherapies more effective than others for specific disorders?

No one type of psychotherapy is generally superior to all others. Therapy is most effective for those with clear-cut, specific problems. Some therapies—such as behavior conditioning for treating phobias and compulsions—are more effective for specific disorders. Cognitive and cognitive-behavioral therapies have been effective in coping with anxiety, posttraumatic stress disorder, insomnia, and depression; behavioral conditioning therapies with specific behavior problems; psychodynamic therapy for depression and anxiety; and nondirective (client-centered) counseling for mild to moderate depression. *Evidence-based practice* integrates the best available research with clinicians' expertise and patients' characteristics and preferences.

45-3 How do alternative therapies fare under scientific scrutiny?

Abnormal states tend to return to normal on their own, and the placebo effect can create the impression that a treatment has been effective. These two tendencies complicate assessments of nontraditional therapies that claim to cure certain ailments. Eye movement desensitization and reprocessing (EMDR) has shown some effectiveness—but not from the eye movement (rather from the exposure therapy nature of the treatments). Light exposure therapy does seem to help those with a seasonal pattern in depression symptoms by activating a brain region that influences arousal and hormones.

45-4 What three elements are shared by all forms of psychotherapy?

All psychotherapies offer new hope for demoralized people; a fresh perspective; and (if the therapist is effective) an empathic, trusting, and caring relationship. The emotional bond of trust and understanding between therapist and client—the *therapeutic alliance*—is an important element in effective therapy.

45-5 How do culture and values influence the client-therapist relationship?

Therapists differ in the values that influence their goals in therapy and their views of progress. These differences may create problems if therapists and clients differ in their cultural or religious perspectives.

45-6 What should a person look for when selecting a therapist?

Campus health centers are generally good starting points for counseling options, and they may offer some free services. A person seeking therapy may want to ask about the therapist's treatment approach, values, credentials, and fees. An important consideration is whether the therapy seeker feels comfortable and able to establish a bond with the therapist. Recognizing the importance of a strong therapeutic alliance, the American Psychological Association accredits programs that provide training in cultural sensitivity and that recruit underrepresented cultural groups.

MODULE 46 The Biomedical Therapies and Preventing Psychological Disorders

46-1 Why is therapeutic lifestyle change considered an effective biomedical therapy, and how does it work?

Therapeutic lifestyle change is considered a biomedical therapy because it influences the way the brain responds. Mind and body are a unit; affect one and you will affect the other. Our exercise, nutrition, relationships, recreation, relaxation, and religious or spiritual engagement affect our mental health. People who undergo a program of aerobic exercise, adequate sleep, light exposure, social engagement, rumination reduction, and better nutrition have gained relief from depressive symptoms.

46-2 What are the drug therapies? How do double-blind studies help researchers evaluate a drug's effectiveness?

Psychopharmacology has helped make drug therapy the most widely used biomedical therapy. *Antipsychotic drugs* are used in treating schizophrenia; some block dopamine activity. Side effects may include tardive dyskinesia (involuntary movements of facial muscles, tongue, and limbs) or increased risk of obesity and diabetes. *Antianxiety drugs,* which depress central nervous system activity, are used to treat anxiety disorders, obsessive-compulsive disorder, and posttraumatic stress disorder, and can be addictive. *Antidepressant drugs,* which often increase the availability of serotonin and norepinephrine, are used to treat depression, anxiety disorders, obsessive-compulsive disorder, and posttraumatic stress disorder with modest effectiveness. Given their widening use (from depression to anxiety to strokes), some professionals prefer the term SSRIs (selective serotonin reuptake inhibitors) rather than antidepressants. Lithium and Depakote are mood stabilizers prescribed for those with bipolar disorder. Studies may use a double-blind procedure to avoid the placebo effect and researcher bias.

46-3 How are brain stimulation and psychosurgery used in treating specific disorders?

Electroconvulsive therapy (ECT), in which a brief electric current is sent through the brain of an anesthetized patient, is an effective, last-resort treatment for people with severe depression who have not responded to other therapy. Newer alternative treatments for depression include transcranial direct current stimulation (tDCS; also used for scientifically unproven cognitive benefits), *repetitive transcranial magnetic stimulation (rTMS),* and deep-brain stimulation (DBS; said to work by calming an overactive brain region linked with negative emotions, and has shown benefit in some patients). *Psychosurgery* removes or destroys brain tissue in hopes of modifying behavior. Radical psychosurgical procedures such as *lobotomy* are no longer performed. Today's microscale psychosurgery and MRI-guided precision brain surgery are rare, last-resort treatments because the effects are irreversible.

46-4 What is the rationale for preventive mental health programs, and why is it important to develop resilience?

Preventive mental health programs are based on the idea that many psychological disorders could be prevented by changing oppressive, esteem-destroying environments into more benevolent, nurturing environments that foster growth, self-confidence, and *resilience.* Struggling with challenges can lead to *posttraumatic growth.* Community psychologists work to prevent psychological disorders by turning destructive environments into more nurturing places that foster competence, health, and well-being.

APPENDIX A

Statistical Reasoning in Everyday Life

A-1 How do we describe data using three measures of central tendency, and what is the relative usefulness of the two measures of variation?

Researchers use descriptive statistics to measure and describe characteristics of groups under study. A measure of central tendency is a single score that represents a whole set of scores. Three such measures that we use to describe data are the *mode* (the most frequently occurring score), the *mean* (the arithmetic average), and the *median* (the middle score in a group of data). Measures of central tendency neatly summarize data; measures of variation tell us how diverse data are. Two measures of variation are the *range* (which describes the gap between the highest and lowest scores) and the *standard deviation* (which states how much scores vary around the mean, or average, score). Scores often form a *normal* (or bell-shaped) *curve.*

A-2 How do correlations measure relationships between variables?

Correlation is the degree to which two variables are related, and how well one predicts the other. In a positive correlation, two *variables* increase or decrease together; in a negative correlation, one variable increases as the other decreases. The strength and direction of their relationship is expressed as a *correlation coefficient,* which ranges from +1.00 (a perfect positive correlation) through 0 (no correlation) to −1.00 (a perfect negative correlation). The relationship may be displayed in a *scatterplot,* in which each dot represents a value for the two variables.

A-3 What are *illusory correlations,* and what is *regression toward the mean?*

Illusory correlations are random events that we notice and falsely assume are related. *Regression toward the mean* is the tendency for extreme or unusual scores to fall back (regress) toward their average.

A-4 How do we know whether an observed difference can be generalized to other populations?

Researchers use inferential statistics (which include ways of determining the reliability and significance of an observed difference between the results for different groups) to determine if results can be generalized to a larger population. Reliable differences are based on samples that are representative of the larger population being studied; that demonstrate low variability, on average; and that consist of many cases. We can say that an observed difference has *statistical significance* if the sample averages are reliable, and when the difference between them is large.

Psychology at Work

B-1   What is *flow*?

Flow is a completely involved, focused state of consciousness with diminished awareness of self and time. It results from fully engaging one's skills. Interests predict both performance and persistence, so people should find vocations with a strong person-environment fit.

B-2   What are three key areas of study related to industrial-organizational psychology?

Three key areas of study related to *industrial-organizational (I/O) psychology* are *personnel, organizational,* and *human factors psychology.* Each uses psychological principles to study and benefit the wide range of today's workers, workplaces, and work activities.

B-3   How do personnel psychologists facilitate job seeking, employee selection, work placement, and performance appraisal?

Personnel psychologists work to provide training programs for job seekers; devise selection methods for new employees; recruit and evaluate diverse applicants; design and evaluate training programs; identify people's interests and strengths; analyze job content; and appraise individual and organizational performance. Unstructured, subjective interviews foster the interviewer illusion; *structured interviews* pinpoint job-relevant strengths and are better predictors of performance. Checklists, graphic rating scales, and behavior rating scales are useful performance appraisal methods.

B-4   What is the role of organizational psychologists?

Organizational psychologists examine influences on worker satisfaction and productivity and facilitate organizational change. Employee satisfaction and engagement tend to correlate with organizational success; in fact, employee attitudes predict future business success.

B-5   How can leaders be most effective?

Effective leaders set specific, challenging goals and choose an appropriate *leadership* style. Leadership style may be goal-oriented (*task leadership*), group-oriented (*social leadership*), or some combination of the two. Effective management often involves positive reinforcement, fulfilling the need to belong, and participative management.

B-6   What cultural influences need to be considered when choosing an effective leadership style?

Project GLOBE studies cultural variations in leadership expectations. Leaders who fulfill expectations (being directive in some cultures or participative in others) tend to be successful. But thriving companies worldwide tend to focus on identifying and enhancing employee strengths; strengths-based leadership pays dividends everywhere.

B-7   How do human factors psychologists work to create user-friendly machines and work settings?

Human factors psychologists contribute to human safety and improved design by encouraging developers and designers to consider human abilities and behaviors, to user-test their work before production and distribution, and to remain mindful of the curse of knowledge.

Answers to the *Retrieve It* and *Experience the Testing Effect* Questions

Thinking Critically With Psychological Science

MODULE **1** The History and Scope of Psychology

Retrieve It Answers

RI-1 Evaluating evidence, appraising the source, assessing conclusions, and examining our own assumptions are essential parts of critical thinking. **RI-2** Scientific psychology began in Germany in 1879 when Wilhelm Wundt opened the first psychology laboratory. **RI-3** People's self-reports varied, depending on the experience and the person's intelligence and verbal ability. **RI-4** structuralism; functionalism. **RI-5** behaviorism; Freudian. **RI-6** It recaptured the field's early interest in mental processes and made them legitimate topics for scientific study. **RI-7** This is the process by which nature selects from chance variations the traits that best enable an organism to survive and reproduce in a particular environment. **RI-8** Psychological events often stem from the interaction of nature and nurture, rather than from either of them acting alone. **RI-9** By incorporating three different levels of analysis, the biopsychosocial approach can provide a more complete view than any one perspective could offer. **RI-10** social-cultural; behavioral. **RI-11** I. b, II. c, III. a.

Experience the Testing Effect Answers

1. d. **2.** Critical thinking is smart thinking. When evaluating media claims (even about topics you might not know much about), look for empirical evidence. Ask the following questions in your analysis: Are the claims based on scientific findings? Have several studies replicated the findings and confirmed them? Are any experts cited? If so, are they affiliated with a credible institution? Have they conducted or written about scientific research? What agenda might they have? What alternative explanations are possible? **3.** Wilhelm Wundt. **4.** a. **5.** a. **6.** b. **7.** The environment (nurture) has an influence on us, but that influence is constrained by our biology (nature). Nature and nurture interact. People predisposed to be very tall (nature), for example, are unlikely to become Olympic gymnasts, no matter how hard they work (nurture). **8.** b **9.** positive psychology. **10.** d. **11.** psychiatrist. **12.** c.

MODULE **2** Research Strategies: How Psychologists Ask and Answer Questions

Retrieve It Answers

RI-1 We often suffer from hindsight bias—after we've learned a situation's outcome, that outcome seems familiar and therefore obvious. **RI-2** A good theory *organizes* observed facts and implies hypotheses that offer testable *predictions* and, sometimes, practical applications. It also often stimulates further research. **RI-3** When other investigators are able to replicate an experiment with the same (or stronger) results, scientists can confirm the result and become more confident of its reliability. **RI-4** Case studies involve only one individual or group, so we can't know for sure whether the principles observed would apply to a larger population. **RI-5** These researchers were able to carefully observe and record naturally occurring behaviors outside the artificiality of a laboratory. However, outside the lab they were not able to control for all the factors that may have influenced the everyday interactions they were recording. **RI-6** An unrepresentative sample is a group that does not represent the population being studied. *Random sampling* helps researchers form a representative sample, because each member of the population has an equal chance of being included. **RI-7** a. negative, b. positive, c. positive, d. negative. **RI-8** In this case, as in many others, a third factor can explain the correlation: Golden anniversaries and baldness both accompany aging. **RI-9** Research designed to prevent the placebo effect randomly assigns participants to an *experimental group* (which receives the real treatment) or to a *control group* (which receives a placebo). A double-blind procedure prevents people's beliefs and hopes from affecting the results, because neither the participants nor those collecting the data know who receives the placebo. A comparison of the results will demonstrate whether the real treatment produces better results than *belief* in that treatment. **RI-10** confounding variables. **RI-11** I. c, II. a, III. b. **RI-12** We learn more about the drug's effectiveness when we can compare the results of those who took the drug (the experimental group) with the results of those who did not (the control group). If we gave the drug to all 1000 participants, we would have no way of knowing whether the drug is serving as a placebo or is actually medically effective. **RI-13** Animal protection legislation, laboratory regulation and inspection, and local and university ethics committees (which screen research proposals) attempt to safeguard animal welfare. International psychological organizations urge researchers involving human participants to obtain *informed consent,* protect them from greater-than-usual harm and discomfort, treat their personal information confidentially, and *debrief* them fully at the end of the experiment. **RI-14** testing effect. **RI-15** *Survey, Question, Read, Retrieve, Review.*

Experience the Testing Effect Answers

1. Hindsight bias. 2. hypotheses. 3. c. 4. representative. 5. negative. 6. a. 7. (a) *Alcohol use is associated with violence. (One interpretation: Drinking triggers or unleashes aggressive behavior.)* Perhaps anger triggers drinking, or perhaps the same genes or child-raising practices are predisposing both drinking and aggression. (Here researchers have learned that drinking does indeed trigger aggressive behavior.) (b) *Educated people live longer, on average, than less-educated people. (One interpretation: Education lengthens life and enhances health.)* Perhaps richer people can afford more education and better health care. (Research supports this conclusion.) (c) *Teens engaged in team sports are less likely to use drugs, smoke, have sex, carry weapons, and eat junk food than are teens who do not engage in team sports. (One interpretation: Team sports encourage healthy living.)* Perhaps some third factor explains this correlation—teens who use drugs, smoke, have sex, carry weapons, and eat junk food may be "loners" who do not enjoy playing on any team. (d) *Adolescents who frequently see smoking in movies are more likely to smoke. (One interpretation: Movie stars' behavior influences impressionable teens.)* Perhaps adolescents who smoke and attend movies frequently have less parental supervision and more access to spending money than other adolescents. 8. experiments. 9. placebo. 10. c. 11. independent variable. 12. b. 13. d.

The Biology of Behavior

MODULE ③ Neural and Hormonal Systems

Retrieve It Answers

RI-1 They share a focus on the links between the brain and behavior. Phrenology faded because it had no scientific basis—skull bumps don't reveal mental traits and abilities. **RI-2** dendrites, cell body, axon. **RI-3** Stronger stimuli (the slap) cause more neurons to fire and to fire more frequently than happens with weaker stimuli (the tap). **RI-4** Neurons send neurotransmitters (chemical messengers) across this tiny space between one neuron's terminal branch and the next neuron's dendrite or cell body. **RI-5** Reuptake occurs when excess neurotransmitters are reabsorbed by the sending neuron. Neurotransmitters can also drift away or be broken down

by enzymes. **RI-6** Morphine is an agonist; curare is an antagonist. **RI-7** neurotransmitters. **RI-8** I. c, II. a, III. b. **RI-9** The sympathetic division of the autonomic nervous system would have directed arousal (accelerated heartbeat, inhibited digestion, etc.), and the parasympathetic division would have directed calming. **RI-10** Responding to signals from the hypothalamus, the pituitary releases hormones that trigger other endocrine glands to secrete hormones, which in turn influence brain and behavior. **RI-11** Both of these communication systems produce chemical molecules that act on the body's receptors to influence our behavior and emotions. The endocrine system, which secretes hormones into the bloodstream, delivers its messages much more slowly than the speedy nervous system, and the effects of the endocrine system's messages tend to linger much longer than those of the nervous system.

Experience the Testing Effect Answers

1. The human brain is uniquely designed to be flexible; it can reorganize after damage and it can build new pathways based on experience. This plasticity enables us to adapt to our changing world. 2. axon. 3. c. 4. a. 5. neurotransmitters. 6. b. 7. c. 8. autonomic. 9. central. 10. a. 11. adrenal glands.

MODULE ④ Tools of Discovery, Older Brain Structures, and the Limbic System

Retrieve It Answers

RI-1 I. b, II. a, III. c. **RI-2** brainstem. **RI-3** (a) cerebellum, (b) thalamus, (c) reticular formation, (d) medulla. **RI-4** The sympathetic nervous system. **RI-5** (1) The *amygdala* is involved in aggression and fear responses. (2) The *hypothalamus* is involved in bodily maintenance, pleasurable rewards, and control of the hormonal systems. (3) The *hippocampus* processes memories of facts and events.

Experience the Testing Effect Answers

1. b. 2. d. 3. c. 4. cerebellum. 5. b. 6. amygdala. 7. b. 8. hypothalamus.

MODULE ⑤ The Cerebral Cortex

Retrieve It Answers

RI-1 the brainstem; the cerebral cortex. **RI-2** a. The right limbs' opposed activities interfere with each other because both are controlled by the same (left) side of your brain. b. Opposite sides of your brain control your left and right limbs, so the reversed motion causes less interference. **RI-3** somatosensory; motor. **RI-4** Association areas are involved in higher mental functions—interpreting, integrating, and acting on information processed in other areas. **RI-5** (1) yes, (2) no, (3) green.

Experience the Testing Effect Answers

1. d. 2. The visual cortex is a neural network of sensory neurons connected via interneurons to other neural networks, including auditory networks. This allows you to integrate visual and auditory information to respond when a friend you recognize greets you at a party. 3. c. 4. frontal. 5. association areas. 6. c. 7. ON; HER. 8. a. 9. b.

MODULE 6 Genetics, Evolutionary Psychology, and Behavior

Retrieve It Answers

RI-1 gene, chromosome, nucleus. RI-2 Researchers use twin and adoption studies to understand how much variation among individuals is due to genetic makeup and how much is due to environmental factors. Some studies compare the traits and behaviors of identical twins (same genes) and fraternal twins (different genes, as in any two siblings). They also compare adopted children with their adoptive and biological parents. Some studies compare traits and behaviors of twins raised together or separately. RI-3 I. b, II. a. RI-4 Over multiple generations, Belyaev and Trut selected and bred foxes that exhibited a trait they desired: tameness. This process is similar to naturally occurring selection, but it differs in that natural selection is much slower, and normally favors traits (including those arising from mutations) that contribute to reproduction and survival.

Experience the Testing Effect Answers

1. chromosomes. 2. gene. 3. b. 4. c. 5. Identical. 6. b. 7. environments. 8. differences; commonalities. 9. c.

Consciousness and the Two-Track Mind

MODULE 7 Consciousness: Some Basic Concepts

Retrieve It Answers

RI-1 cognitive neuroscience. RI-2 Our *selective attention* allows us to focus on only a limited portion of our surroundings. *Inattentional blindness* explains why we don't perceive some things when we are distracted. *Change blindness,* for example, happens when we fail to notice a relatively unimportant change in our environment. These principles help magicians fool us, as they direct our attention elsewhere to perform their tricks. RI-3 Our mind simultaneously processes information on a conscious track and an unconscious track (dual processing) as we organize and interpret information.

Experience the Testing Effect Answers

1. inattentional blindness. 2. unconscious; conscious. 3. selective.

MODULE 8 Sleep and Dreams

Retrieve It Answers

RI-1 With each soldier cycling through the sleep stages independently, at any given time at least one likely will be in an easily awakened stage. RI-2 REM (R), NREM-1 (N1), NREM-2 (N2), NREM-3 (N3); normally we move through N1, then N2, then N3, then back up through N2 before we experience REM sleep. RI-3 I. b, II. c, III. a. RI-4 suprachiasmatic; circadian. RI-5 (1) Sleep has survival value. (2) Sleep helps us restore the immune system and repair brain tissue. (3) During sleep we consolidate memories. (4) Sleep fuels creativity. (5) Sleep plays a role in the growth process. RI-6 quick reaction times; gain weight. RI-7 (1) Freud's wish-fulfillment (dreams as a psychic safety valve), (2) information-processing (dreams sort the day's events and consolidate memories), (3) physiological function (dreams pave neural pathways), (4) activation-synthesis (REM sleep triggers random neural activity that the mind weaves into stories), and (5) cognitive development (dreams reflect the dreamer's developmental stage).

Experience the Testing Effect Answers

1. circadian rhythm. 2. b. 3. N3. 4. It increases in duration. 5. c. 6. With narcolepsy, the person periodically falls directly into REM sleep, with no warning; with sleep apnea, the person repeatedly awakens during the night. 7. d. 8. The activation-synthesis theory suggests that dreams are the brain's attempt to synthesize random neural activity. 9. The information-processing explanation of dreaming proposes that brain activity during REM sleep enables us to sift through the daily events and activities we have been thinking about (*what one has dwelt on by day*). 10. REM rebound.

MODULE 9 Drugs and Consciousness

Retrieve It Answers

RI-1 With repeated exposure to a psychoactive drug, the user's brain chemistry adapts and the drug's effect lessens. Thus, it takes bigger doses to get the desired effect. RI-2 Unless it becomes compulsive or dysfunctional, simply having a strong interest in shopping is not the same as having a physical addiction to a drug. It typically does not involve obsessive craving in spite of known negative consequences. RI-3 depressants. RI-4 Nicotine-withdrawal symptoms include strong cravings, insomnia, anxiety, irritability, distractibility, and difficulty concentrating. However, if your friend sticks with it, the craving and withdrawal symptoms will gradually dissipate over about 6 months. RI-5 Psychoactive drugs create pleasure by altering brain chemistry. With repeated use of the drug, the user develops tolerance and needs more of the drug to achieve the desired effect. (Marijuana is an exception.) Discontinuing use of the substance then produces painful or psychologically unpleasant withdrawal symptoms. RI-6 Nicotine is powerfully addictive, and those who start paving the neural pathways when young may find it very hard to stop using it. As a result, tobacco companies may have lifelong customers. Moreover, evidence suggests that if cigarette manufacturers haven't hooked customers by early adulthood, they most likely won't. RI-7 Possible explanations include (a) biological factors (a person could have a biological predisposition to both early use and later abuse, or alcohol use could modify a person's neural pathways); (b) psychological factors (early use could establish taste preferences for alcohol); and (c) social-cultural factors (early use could influence enduring habits, attitudes, activities, or peer relationships that could foster alcohol use disorder).

Experience the Testing Effect Answers

1. tolerance. 2. a. 3. Alcohol is a disinhibitor—it makes us more likely to do what we would have done when sober, whether that is being helpful or being aggressive. 4. d. 5. hallucinogenic. 6. a. 7. b.

Developing Through the Life Span

MODULE 10 Developmental Issues, Prenatal Development, and the Newborn

Retrieve It Answers

RI-1 nature; nurture. **RI-2** continuity; stages. **RI-3** (1) Stage theory is supported by the work of Piaget (cognitive development), Kohlberg (moral development), and Erikson (psychosocial development). (2) Some traits, such as temperament, exhibit remarkable stability across many years. **RI-4** zygote; fetus; embryo. **RI-5** habituation.

Experience the Testing Effect Answers

1. continuity/stages. 2. b. 3. c. 4. teratogens.

MODULE 11 Infancy and Childhood

Retrieve It Answers

RI-1 maturation. **RI-2** Object permanence for the sensorimotor stage, pretend play for the preoperational stage, conservation for the concrete operational stage, and abstract logic for the formal operational stage. **RI-3** I. d, II. b, III. c, IV. c, V. a, VI. b. **RI-4** Theory of mind focuses on our ability to understand our own and others' mental states. Those with autism spectrum disorder struggle with this ability. **RI-5** Attachment is the normal process by which we form emotional ties with important others. Imprinting occurs only in certain animals that have a critical period very early in their development during which they must form their attachments, and they do so in an inflexible manner. **RI-6** The authoritarian style would be described as too hard, the permissive style too soft, the negligent style too uncaring, and the authoritative style just right. Parents using the authoritative style tend to have children with high self-esteem, self-reliance, self-regulation, and social competence.

Experience the Testing Effect Answers

1. a. 2. frontal. 3. b. 4. We consciously recall little from before age 4, in part because major brain areas have not yet matured. 5. Infants in Piaget's *sensorimotor stage* tend to be focused only on their own perceptions of the world and may, for example, be unaware that objects continue to exist when unseen. A child in the *preoperational stage* is still egocentric and incapable of appreciating simple logic, such as the reversibility of operations. A preteen in the *concrete operational stage* is beginning to think logically about concrete events but not about abstract concepts. 6. a. 7. stranger anxiety. 8. Before these studies, many psychologists believed that infants simply became attached to those who nourished them.

MODULE 12 Adolescence

Retrieve It Answers

RI-1 preconventional; postconventional; conventional. **RI-2** Kohlberg's work reflected an individualist worldview, so his theory is less culturally universal than he supposed. **RI-3** Adolescents tend to *select* similar others and to sort themselves into like-minded groups. For an athletic teen, this could lead to finding other athletic teens and joining school teams together. **RI-4** I. g, II. h, III. c, IV. f, V. e, VI. d, VII. a, VIII. b.

Experience the Testing Effect Answers

1. b. 2. formal operational. 3. b. 4. emerging adulthood.

MODULE 13 Adulthood

Retrieve It Answers

RI-1 love; work. **RI-2** Challenges: decline of muscular strength, reaction times, stamina, sensory keenness, cardiac output, and immune system functioning. Risk of cognitive decline increases. Rewards: positive feelings tend to grow; negative emotions subside; and anger, stress, worry, and social-relationship problems decrease.

Experience the Testing Effect Answers

1. a. 2. Cross-sectional studies compare people of different ages at one point in time. Longitudinal studies restudy and retest the same people over a long period of time. 3. generativity. 4. c.

Sex, Gender, and Sexuality

MODULE 14 Gender Development

Retrieve It Answers

RI-1 Women; men. **RI-2** seven; puberty. **RI-3** *Gender roles* are social rules or norms for accepted and expected behavior for females and males. The norms associated with various roles, including gender roles, vary widely in different cultural contexts, which is proof that we are able to learn and adapt to the social demands of different environments.

Experience the Testing Effect Answers

1. sex; gender. 2. c. 3. Y. 4. d. 5. 11; 12. 6. intersex. 7. b. 8. gender identity.

MODULE 15 Human Sexuality

Retrieve It Answers

RI-1 testosterone; estrogens. **RI-2** sexual dysfunction; paraphilia. **RI-3** Influences include biological factors such as sexual maturity and sex hormones, psychological factors such as environmental stimuli and fantasies, and social-cultural factors such as the values and expectations absorbed from family and the surrounding culture. **RI-4** a, c, d. **RI-5** b, c, e. **RI-6** Evolutionary psychologists theorize that females have inherited their ancestors' tendencies to be more cautious sexually because of the challenges associated with incubating and nurturing offspring. Males have inherited a tendency to be more casual about sex, because their act of fathering requires a smaller investment. **RI-7** (1) It starts with an effect and works backward to propose an explanation. (2) This explanation may overlook the effects of cultural expectations and socialization. (3) Men could use such explanations to rationalize irresponsible behavior toward women.

Experience the Testing Effect Answers

1. b. 2. b. 3. Sexual dysfunctions are problems that consistently impair sexual arousal or sexual function. Paraphilias are conditions,

which may be classified as psychological disorders, in which sexual arousal is associated with nonhuman objects, the suffering of self or others, and/or nonconsenting persons. **4.** does; doesn't. **5.** c. **6.** Researchers have found no evidence that any environmental factor (parental relationships, childhood experiences, peer relationships, or dating experiences) influences the development of our sexual orientation. **7.** Natural selection favors traits and behaviors that enable survival and reproduction. Evolutionary psychologists argue that women are choosier about their mates because of the investment required to conceive, protect, birth, and nurse children. Heterosexual women tend to prefer men who seem capable of supporting and protecting their joint offspring. Men, who have less at stake, tend to be more casual about sex, and heterosexual men tend to prefer women whose traits convey health and fertility.

Sensation and Perception

MODULE 16 Basic Concepts of Sensation and Perception

Retrieve It Answers

RI-1 *Sensation* is the bottom-up process by which your sensory receptors and your nervous system receive and represent stimuli. *Perception* is the top-down process by which your brain creates meaning by organizing and interpreting what your senses detect. **RI-2** *Absolute threshold* is the minimum stimulation needed to detect a particular sound (such as an approaching bike on the sidewalk behind you) 50 percent of the time. *Subliminal stimulation* happens when, without your awareness, your sensory system processes a sound that is below your absolute threshold. A *difference threshold* is the minimum difference needed to distinguish between two stimuli (such as between the sound of a bike and the sound of a runner coming up behind you) 50 percent of the time. **RI-3** The shoes provide constant stimulation. Thanks to *sensory adaptation,* we tend to focus primarily on changing stimuli. **RI-4** It involves top-down processing, because it draws on your experiences, assumptions, and expectations when interpreting stimuli.

Experience the Testing Effect Answers

1. b. **2.** perception. **3.** d. **4.** just noticeable difference. **5.** b. **6.** d. **7.** a.

MODULE 17 Vision: Sensory and Perceptual Processing

Retrieve It Answers

RI-1 Your blind spot is on the nose side of each retina, which means that objects to your right may fall onto the right eye's blind spot. Objects to your left may fall on the left eye's blind spot. The blind spot does not normally impair your vision, because your eyes are moving and because one eye catches what the other misses. Moreover, even with only one eye open, your brain gives you a perception without a hole in it. **RI-2** rods; cones; color. **RI-3** pupils. **RI-4** The *Young-Helmholtz trichromatic theory* shows that the retina contains color receptors for red, green, and blue. The *opponent-process theory* shows that we have opponent-process cells in the retina and thalamus for red-green, blue-yellow, and white-black. These theories are complementary and outline the two stages of color

vision: (1) The retina's receptors for red, green, and blue respond to different color stimuli. (2) The receptors' signals are then processed by the opponent-process cells on their way to the visual cortex in the brain. **RI-5** Light waves reflect off the person and travel into your eyes. Receptor cells in your retina convert the light waves' energy into neural impulses sent to your brain. Your brain detector cells and work teams process the subdimensions of this visual input—including color, movement, form, and depth—separately but simultaneously. Your brain interprets this information, based on previously stored information and your expectations, and forms a conscious perception of your friend. **RI-6** figure; ground. **RI-7** Gestalt psychologists used this saying to describe our perceptual tendency to organize clusters of sensations into meaningful forms or coherent groups. **RI-8** We are normally able to perceive depth thanks to (1) binocular cues (such as retinal disparity), and (2) monocular cues (which include relative height, relative size, interposition, linear perspective, light and shadow, and relative motion).

Experience the Testing Effect Answers

1. wavelength. **2.** a. **3.** c. **4.** c. **5.** d. **6.** Your brain constructs this perception of color in two stages. In the first stage, the lemon reflects light energy into your eyes, where it is transformed into neural messages. Three sets of cones, each sensitive to a different light frequency (red, blue, and green) process color. In this case, the light energy stimulates both red-sensitive and green-sensitive cones. In the second stage, opponent-process cells sensitive to paired opposites of color (red/green, yellow/blue, and black/white) evaluate the incoming neural messages as they pass through your optic nerve to the thalamus and visual cortex. When the yellow-sensitive opponent-process cells are stimulated, you identify the lemon as yellow. **7.** feature detectors. **8.** parallel processing. **9.** a. **10.** d. **11.** b. **12.** c. **13.** monocular. **14.** b. **15.** b. **16.** perceptual adaptation.

MODULE 18 The Nonvisual Senses

Retrieve It Answers

RI-1 loudness. **RI-2** lower; lower. **RI-3** place theory; frequency theory. **RI-4** c. **RI-5** We have four basic touch senses and five basic taste sensations. But we have no specific smell receptors. Instead, different combinations of odor receptors send messages to the brain, enabling us to recognize some 1 trillion different smells. **RI-6** Kinesthetic receptors are located in our joints, tendons, and muscles. Vestibular sense receptors are located in our inner ear. **RI-7** The ESP event would need to be reproduced in other scientific studies.

Experience the Testing Effect Answers

1. cochlea. **2.** The outer ear collects sound waves, which are translated into mechanical waves by the *middle ear* and turned into fluid waves in the *inner ear*. The *auditory nerve* then translates the energy into electrical waves and sends them to the brain, which perceives and interprets the sound. **3.** Place; frequency; volley. **4.** nociceptors. **5.** c. **6.** Our experience of pain is influenced by biological factors (such as genetic differences in endorphin production), psychological factors (such as our attention), and social-cultural factors (such as the presence of others). **7.** We have specialized receptors for detecting sweet, salty, sour, bitter, and umami tastes. Being able to detect pleasurable tastes enabled our ancestors to seek out energy- or protein-rich foods. Detecting aversive tastes deterred them from eating toxic substances, increasing their chances of survival. **8.** Kinesthesia; vestibular sense. **9.** Your vestibular sense regulates balance and body positioning through kinesthetic receptors triggered by fluid in your inner ear. Wobbly legs and a spinning world are signs that these receptors are still responding to the ride's turbulence. As your vestibular sense adjusts to solid ground, your balance will be restored. **10.** d. **11.** d.

Learning

MODULE 19 Basic Learning Concepts and Classical Conditioning

Retrieve It Answers

RI-1 Habits form when we repeat behaviors in a given context and, as a result, learn associations—often without our awareness. For example, we may have eaten a sweet pastry with a cup of coffee often enough to associate the flavor of the coffee with the treat, so that the cup of coffee alone just doesn't seem right anymore! **RI-2** NS = tone before conditioning; US = air puff; UR = blink to air puff; CS = tone after conditioning; CR = blink to tone. **RI-3** The cake (including its taste) is the US. The associated aroma is the CS. Salivation to the aroma is the CR. **RI-4** acquisition; extinction. **RI-5** generalization. **RI-6** If viewing an attractive nude or seminude woman (a US) elicits sexual arousal (a UR), then pairing the US with a new NS (violence) could turn the violence into a conditioned stimulus (CS) that also becomes sexually arousing, a conditioned response (CR). **RI-7** The US was the loud noise; the UR was the fear response to the noise; the NS was the rat before it was paired with the noise; the CS was the rat after pairing; the CR was fear of the rat.

Experience the Testing Effect Answers

1. information; behaviors. **2.** c. **3.** conditioned. **4.** discrimination. **5.** b. **6.** A sexual image is a US that triggers a UR of interest or arousal. Before the ad pairs a product with a sexual image, the product is an NS. Over time the product can become a CS that triggers the CR of interest or arousal.

MODULE 20 Operant Conditioning

Retrieve It Answers

RI-1 do not; resulting. **RI-2** The baby negatively reinforces her parents' behavior when she stops crying once they grant her wish. Her parents positively reinforce her cries by letting her sleep with them. **RI-3** Spammers are reinforced on a variable-ratio schedule (after sending a varying number of emails). Cookie checkers are reinforced on a fixed-interval schedule. Donut rewards programs use a fixed-ratio schedule. **RI-4** 1. PR (positive reinforcement); 2. NP (negative punishment); 3. PP (positive punishment); 4. NR

(negative reinforcement). **RI-5** If Ethan is seeking attention, the teacher's scolding may be reinforcing rather than punishing. To change Ethan's behavior, his teacher could offer reinforcement (such as praise) each time he behaves well. The teacher might encourage Ethan toward increasingly appropriate behavior through shaping, or by rephrasing rules as rewards instead of punishments. ("You can use the blocks if you play nicely with the other children" [reward] rather than "You may not use the blocks if you misbehave!" [punishment].) **RI-6** respondent; operant.

Experience the Testing Effect Answers

1. Skinner. **2.** shaping. **3.** b. **4.** Your instructor could reinforce your attentive behavior by taking away something you dislike. For example, your instructor could offer to shorten the length of an assigned paper or replace standard lecture time with an interesting in-class activity. In both cases, the instructor would remove something aversive in order to negatively reinforce your focused attention. **5.** partial (intermittent). **6.** a. **7.** variable-interval. **8.** c.

MODULE 21 Biology, Cognition, and Learning

Retrieve It Answers

RI-1 Garcia and Koelling demonstrated that rats may learn an aversion to tastes, on which their survival depends, but not to sights or sounds. **RI-2** The success of operant conditioning is affected not just by environmental cues, but also by biological and cognitive factors. **RI-3** Jason may be more likely to speed. Observational learning studies suggest that children tend to do as others do and say what they say. **RI-4** I. c, II. d, III. a, IV. e, V. b.

Experience the Testing Effect Answers

1. taste-aversion. **2.** This finding supports Darwin's principle that natural selection favors traits that aid survival. **3.** cognitive map. **4.** latent learning. **5.** observational learning. **6.** vicarious; vicarious. **7.** a. **8.** mirror. **9.** c.

Memory

MODULE 22 Studying and Encoding Memories

Retrieve It Answers

RI-1 recognition; recall. **RI-2** It would be better to test your memory with *recall* (such as with short-answer or fill-in-the-blank self-test questions) rather than *recognition* (such as with multiple-choice questions). Recalling information is harder than recognizing it. So if you can recall it, that means your retention of the material is better than if you could only recognize it. Your chances of test success are therefore greater. **RI-3** The newer idea of a *working memory* emphasizes the active processing that we now know takes place in Atkinson-Shiffrin's short-term memory stage. While the Atkinson-Shiffrin model viewed short-term memory as a temporary holding space, working memory plays a key role in processing new information and connecting it to previously stored information.

RI-4 (1) Active processing of incoming visual and auditory information, and (2) focusing our spotlight of attention. **RI-5** *Automatic* processing occurs unconsciously (automatically) for such things as the sequence and frequency of a day's events, and reading and comprehending words in our own language(s). *Effortful* processing requires attentive awareness and happens, for example, when we work hard to learn new material in class, or new lines for a play. **RI-6** sensory memory. **RI-7** Although cramming and rereading may lead to short-term gains in knowledge, distributed practice and repeated self-testing will result in the greatest long-term retention. **RI-8** Making material personally meaningful involves processing at a deep level, because you are processing *semantically*—based on the meaning of the words. Deep processing leads to greater retention.

Experience the Testing Effect Answers

1. recall. 2. encoding; storage; retrieval. 3. a. 4. iconic; echoic.
5. seven. 6. mnemonics.

MODULE 23 Storing and Retrieving Memories

Retrieve It Answers

RI-1 The cerebellum and basal ganglia are important for *implicit* memory processing, and the frontal lobes and hippocampus are key to *explicit* memory formation. **RI-2** Our *explicit* conscious memories of facts and episodes differ from our *implicit* memories of skills (such as tying shoelaces) and classically conditioned responses. The parts of the brain involved in explicit memory processing (the frontal lobes and hippocampus) may have sustained damage in the accident, while the parts involved in implicit memory processing (the cerebellum and basal ganglia) appear to have escaped harm. **RI-3** the amygdala. **RI-4** long-term potentiation. **RI-5** *Priming* is the activation (often without our awareness) of associations. Seeing a gun, for example, might temporarily predispose someone to interpret an ambiguous face as threatening or to recall a boss as nasty. **RI-6** serial position.

Experience the Testing Effect Answers

1. a. 2. implicit. 3. c. 4. retrieval cues. 5. Memories are stored within a web of many associations, one of which is mood. When you recall happy moments from your past, you activate these positive links. You may then experience mood-congruent memory and recall other happy moments, which could improve your mood and brighten your interpretation of current events. 6. a.

MODULE 24 Forgetting, Memory Construction, and Improving Memory

Retrieve It Answers

RI-1 (1) *Encoding failure:* Unattended information never entered our memory system. (2) *Storage decay:* Information fades from our memory. (3) *Retrieval failure:* We cannot access stored information accurately, sometimes due to interference or motivated forgetting. **RI-2** retroactive. **RI-3** repress. **RI-4** Real experiences would be confused with those we dreamed. When seeing someone we know, we might therefore be unsure whether we were reacting to something they previously did or to something we dreamed they did. **RI-5** It will be important to remember the key points agreed upon by most researchers and professional associations: Sexual abuse, injustice, forgetting, and memory construction all happen; recovered memories are common; memories from before age 4 are unreliable; memories claimed to be recovered through hypnosis are especially unreliable; and memories, whether real or false, can be emotionally upsetting. **RI-6** Spend more time rehearsing or actively thinking about the material to boost long-term recall. Schedule spaced (not crammed) study times. Make the material personally meaningful, with well-organized and vivid associations. Refresh your memory by returning to contexts and moods to activate retrieval cues. Use mnemonic devices. Minimize proactive and retroactive interference. Plan ahead to ensure a complete night's sleep. Test yourself repeatedly—retrieval practice is a proven retention strategy.

Experience the Testing Effect Answers

1. d. 2. d. 3. retroactive. 4. repression. 5. b. 6. Eliza's immature hippocampus and minimal verbal skills would have prevented her from encoding an explicit memory of the wedding reception at the age of two. It's more likely that Eliza learned information (from hearing the story repeatedly) that she eventually constructed into a memory that feels very real. 7. source amnesia. 8. déjà vu. 9. b.
10. b.

Thinking, Language, and Intelligence

MODULE 25 Thinking

Retrieve It Answers

RI-1 If a tragic event such as a plane crash makes the news, it is noteworthy and unusual, unlike much more common bad events, such as traffic accidents. Knowing this, we can worry less about unlikely events and think more about improving the safety of our everyday activities. (For example, we can wear a seat belt when in a vehicle and use the crosswalk when walking.) **RI-2** I. b, II. c, III. e, IV. d, V. a, VI. f, VII. h, VIII. j, IX. i, X. g.

Experience the Testing Effect Answers

1. concept. 2. algorithm. 3. Oscar will need to guard against *confirmation bias* (searching for support for his own views and ignoring contradictory evidence) as he seeks out opposing viewpoints. Even if Oscar encounters new information that disproves his beliefs, *belief perseverance* may lead him to cling to these views anyway. It will take more compelling evidence to change his political beliefs than it took to create them. 4. c. 5. availability.
6. framing. 7. b. 8. neural networks.

MODULE 26 Language and Thought

Retrieve It Answers

RI-1 Two morphemes—*cat* and *s*, and four phonemes—*c, a, t,* and *s.*
RI-2 Chomsky maintained that humans are biologically predisposed to learn the grammar rules of language. **RI-3** Infants normally start

developing receptive language skills (ability to understand what is said to and about them) around 4 months of age. Then, starting with babbling at 4 months and beyond, infants normally start building productive language skills (ability to produce sounds and eventually words). **RI-4** Our brain's *critical period* for language learning is in childhood, when we can absorb language structure almost effortlessly. As we move past that stage in our brain's development, our ability to learn a new language diminishes dramatically. **RI-5** Broca's area; Wernicke's area. **RI-6** These are definitely communications. But if language consists of words and the grammatical rules we use to combine them to communicate meaning, few scientists would label a dog's barking and yipping as language. **RI-7** linguistic determinism. **RI-8** Mental practice uses visual imagery to mentally rehearse future behaviors, activating some of the same brain areas used during the actual behaviors. Visualizing the details of the process is more effective than visualizing only your end goal.

Experience the Testing Effect Answers

1. c. **2.** phonemes; morphemes; grammar. **3.** telegraphic speech.
4. universal grammar. **5.** a.

MODULE 27 Intelligence and Its Assessment

Retrieve It Answers

RI-1 People with savant syndrome have limited mental ability overall but possess one or more exceptional skills. According to Howard Gardner, this suggests that our abilities come in separate packages rather than being fully expressed by one general intelligence that encompasses all of our talents. **RI-2** Binet hoped that determining the child's mental age (the age that typically corresponds to a certain level of performance) would help identify appropriate school placements. **RI-3** 125 (5 ÷ 4 × 100 = 125). **RI-4** aptitude; achievement. **RI-5** A psychological test must be *standardized* (pretested on a representative sample of people), *reliable* (yielding consistent results), and *valid* (measuring and predicting what it is supposed to). **RI-6** disagreement; down; zero; agreement; up. **RI-7** An intelligence test score is only one measure of a person's ability to function. Other important factors to consider in an overall assessment include conceptual skills, social skills, and practical skills. **RI-8** Researcher A should develop a *longitudinal study* to examine how intelligence changes in the same people over the life span. Researcher B should develop a *cross-sectional study* to examine the intelligence of people now at various life stages.

Experience the Testing Effect Answers

1. general intelligence (*g*). **2.** c. **3.** analytical; creative; practical.
4. d. **5.** d. **6.** c. **7.** reliability. **8.** Writers' work relies more on crystallized intelligence, or accumulated knowledge, which increases with age. For top performance, scientists doing research may need more fluid intelligence (speedy and abstract reasoning), which tends to decrease with age. **9.** c.

MODULE 28 Genetic and Environmental Influences on Intelligence

Retrieve It Answers

RI-1 a. (Heritability—variation explained by genetic influences—will increase as environmental variation decreases.) **RI-2** Perfectly equal opportunity would create 100 percent heritability, because genes alone would account for any human differences. **RI-3** A test may be *culturally* "biased" (unfair) if higher scores are achieved by those with certain cultural experiences. That same test is not scientifically biased as long as it has *predictive validity*—if it predicts what it is supposed to predict. For example, the SAT may favor those with experience in the U.S. school system, but it does still accurately predict U.S. college success. **RI-4** stereotype threat.

Experience the Testing Effect Answers

1. c. **2.** a. **3.** c. **4.** Stereotype threat.

Motivation and Emotion

MODULE 29 Basic Motivational Concepts, Affiliation, and Achievement

Retrieve It Answers

RI-1 (1) Well-practiced runners tend to excel when aroused by competition. (2) High anxiety about a difficult exam may disrupt test-takers' performance. **RI-2** According to Maslow, our drive to meet the physiological needs of hunger and thirst takes priority over our safety needs, prompting us to take risks at times. **RI-3** They engaged in more self-defeating behaviors and displayed more disparaging and aggressive behavior. These students' basic *need to belong* seems to have been disrupted. **RI-4** strengthen; increase. **RI-5** self-discipline (*grit*).

Experience the Testing Effect Answers

1. b. **2.** a. **3.** incentive. **4.** Arousal. **5.** b. **6.** a. **7.** c. **8.** Monitor our time spent online, as well as our feelings about that time. Hide distracting online friends when necessary. Check your phone and email less often. Get outside and away from technology regularly.
9. should; should

MODULE 30 Hunger

Retrieve It Answers

RI-1 low; high. **RI-2** You have learned to respond to the sight and aroma that signal the food about to enter your mouth. Both *physiological* cues (low blood sugar) and *psychological* cues (anticipation of the tasty meal) heighten your experienced hunger. **RI-3** Genetically influenced set/settling points, metabolism, and other factors (such as adequate sleep) influence the way our bodies burn calories.

Experience the Testing Effect Answers

1. Maslow's hierarchy of needs supports this statement because it addresses the primacy of some motives over others. Once our basic physiological needs are met, safety concerns are addressed next, followed by belongingness and love needs (such as the desire to kiss). **2.** set point. **3.** c. **4.** low. **5.** basal metabolic. **6.** d. **7.** Sanjay's plan is problematic. After he gains weight, the extra fat will require less energy to maintain than it did to gain in the first place. Sanjay may have a hard time getting rid of it later, when his metabolism slows down in an effort to retain his body weight.

MODULE **31** Theories and Physiology of Emotion

Retrieve It Answers

RI-1 simultaneously; sequentially (first the physiological response, and then the experienced emotion). **RI-2** cognitive. **RI-3** Zajonc and LeDoux suggested that we experience some emotions without any conscious, cognitive appraisal. Lazarus, Schachter, and Singer emphasized the importance of appraisal and cognitive labeling in our experience of emotion. **RI-4** The *sympathetic division* of the ANS arouses us for more intense experiences of emotion, pumping out the stress hormones epinephrine and norepinephrine to prepare our body for fight or flight. The *parasympathetic division* of the ANS takes over when a crisis passes, restoring our body to a calm physiological and emotional state.

Experience the Testing Effect Answers

1. James-Lange. **2.** b. **3.** c. **4.** A polygraph measures emotion-linked physiological changes, such as in perspiration, heart rate, and breathing. But the measure cannot distinguish between emotions with similar physiology (such as anxiety and guilt).

MODULE **32** Expressing and Experiencing Emotion

Retrieve It Answers

RI-1 Women. **RI-2** gestures. **RI-3** (1) Most students report feeling more happy than sad when their cheeks are raised upward. (2) Most students report feeling more sad than happy when their cheeks are pulled downward.

Experience the Testing Effect Answers

1. facial feedback. **2.** Aiden's droopy posture could negatively affect his mood thanks to the behavior feedback effect, which tends to make us feel the way we act.

Stress, Health, and Human Flourishing

MODULE **33** Stress and Illness

Retrieve It Answers

RI-1 sympathetic; increase; muscles; fight-or-flight. **RI-2** psycho-neuroimmunology. **RI-3** Stress tends to reduce our immune system's ability to function properly, so that higher stress generally leads to greater risk of physical illness. **RI-4** Feeling angry and negative much of the time. **RI-5** b.

Experience the Testing Effect Answers

1. resistance; exhaustion. **2.** tend; befriend. **3.** b. **4.** d. **5.** lympho-cytes. **6.** c. **7.** Type A individuals frequently experience negative emotions (anger, impatience), during which the sympathetic nervous system diverts blood away from the liver. This leaves fat and cholesterol circulating in the bloodstream for deposit near the heart and other organs, increasing the risk of heart disease and other health problems. Thus, Type A individuals actually harm themselves by directing anger at others.

MODULE **34** Health and Happiness

Retrieve It Answers

RI-1 problem; emotion. **RI-2** Aerobic exercise, relaxation procedures, mindfulness meditation, and religious engagement. **RI-3** a. Age does NOT effectively predict happiness levels. Better predictors are personality traits, sleep and exercise, and religious faith.

Experience the Testing Effect Answers

1. emotion. **2.** b. **3.** internal. **4.** d. **5.** aerobic. **6.** c. **7.** d. **8.** Positive. **9.** b. **10.** relative deprivation.

Social Psychology

MODULE **35** Social Thinking and Social Influence

Retrieve It Answers

RI-1 By attributing the other person's behavior to the person ("What a terrible driver") and his own to the situation ("These roads are awful"), Marco has exhibited the fundamental attribution error. **RI-2** Our attitudes often influence our actions as we behave in ways consistent with our beliefs. However, our actions also influence our attitudes; we come to believe in what we have done. **RI-3** cognitive dissonance. **RI-4** Culture represents our shared behaviors, ideas, attitudes, values, and traditions, which we transmit across generations by way of our language ability. Culture, with its language and efficient division of labor, allows us to preserve innovation. **RI-5** a. **RI-6** normative social influence. **RI-7** Stanley Milgram. **RI-8** The Milgram studies showed that people were most likely to follow orders when the experimenter was nearby and was perceived to be a legitimate authority figure, the authority figure was supported by a powerful or prestigious institution, the victim was depersonalized or at a distance, and there were no models for defiance. **RI-9** This improved performance in the presence of others is most likely to occur with a well-learned task, because the added arousal caused by an audience tends to strengthen the most likely response. This also predicts poorer performance on a difficult task in others' presence. **RI-10** social loafing. **RI-11** The anonymity provided by the masks, combined with the arousal of the contentious setting, might create deindividuation (lessened self-awareness and self-restraint). **RI-12** group polarization. **RI-13** groupthink.

Experience the Testing Effect Answers

1. a. **2.** peripheral. **3.** foot-in-the-door. **4.** Cognitive dissonance theory best supports this suggestion. If Jamal acts confident, his behavior will contradict his negative self-thoughts, creating cognitive dissonance. To relieve the tension, Jamal may realign his attitudes with his actions by viewing himself as more outgoing and confident. **5.** c. **6.** a. **7.** The presence of a large audience generates arousal and strengthens Dr. Huang's most likely response: enhanced performance on a task he has mastered (teaching music history) and impaired performance on a task he finds difficult (statistics). **8.** deindividuation. **9.** group polarization.

MODULE 36 Antisocial Relations

Retrieve It Answers

RI-1 scapegoat.   **RI-2** Our biology (our genes, neural systems, and bio-chemistry—including testosterone and alcohol levels) influences our aggressive tendencies. Psychological factors (such as frustration, previous rewards for aggressive acts, and observation of others' aggression) can trigger any aggressive tendencies we may have. Social influences, such as exposure to violent media or being personally insulted, and cultural influences, such as whether we've grown up in a "culture of honor" or a father-absent home, can also affect our aggressive responses.

Experience the Testing Effect Answers

1. stereotypes.   2. This reaction could occur because we tend to overgeneralize from vivid, memorable cases.   3. more.   4. d. 5. frustration-aggression principle.   6. c.   7. c.   8. c.

MODULE 37 Prosocial Relations

Retrieve It Answers

RI-1 mere exposure effect.   **RI-2** Being physically attractive tends to elicit positive first impressions. People tend to assume that attractive people are healthier, happier, more sensitive, more successful, and more socially skilled than others are.   **RI-3** Emotions consist of (1) physical arousal and (2) our interpretation of that arousal. Researchers have found that any source of arousal may be interpreted as passion in the presence of a desirable person.   **RI-4** equity; self-disclosure. **RI-5** In the presence of others, an individual is less likely to notice a situation, correctly interpret it as an emergency, and take responsibility for offering help. The Kitty Genovese case demonstrated this bystander effect, as each witness assumed many others were also aware of the event.   **RI-6** Sports fans may feel they are a part of an ingroup that sets itself apart from an outgroup (fans of the archrival team). Ingroup bias tends to develop, leading to prejudice and the view that the outgroup "deserves" misfortune. So, the archrival team's loss may seem justified. In conflicts, this kind of thinking is problematic, especially when each side in the conflict develops mirror-image perceptions of the other (distorted, negative images that are ironically similar).   **RI-7** Peacemakers should encourage equal-status contact, cooperation to achieve superordinate goals (shared goals that override differences), understanding through communication, and recipro-cated conciliatory gestures (each side gives a little).

Experience the Testing Effect Answers

1. mere exposure.   2. companionate; passionate.   3. d.   4. c. 5. mirror-image.   6. superordinate.

Personality

MODULE 38 Classic Perspectives on Personality

Retrieve It Answers

RI-1 ego; id; superego.   **RI-2** fixation.   **RI-3** unconsciously; anxiety.   **RI-4** Freud is credited with first drawing attention to (1) the importance of childhood experiences, (2) the existence of the unconscious mind, and (3) our self-protective defense mechanisms. Freud's theory has been criticized as (1) not scientifically testable and offering after-the-fact explanations, (2) focusing too much on sexual conflicts in childhood, and (3) being based on the idea of repression, which has not been supported by modern research. **RI-5** Today's psychodynamic theorists and therapists still rely on the interviewing techniques that Freud used, and they still tend to focus on childhood experiences and attachments, unresolved conflicts, and unconscious influences. However, they are not likely to dwell on fixation at any psychosexual stage, or the idea that sexual issues are the basis of our personality.   **RI-6** The humanistic theories sought to turn psychology's attention away from drives and conflicts and toward our growth potential. This movement's focus on the way people strive for self-determination and self-realization was in contrast to Freudian theory and strict behaviorism.   **RI-7** To be *empathic* is to share and mirror another person's feelings. Carl Rogers believed that people nurture growth in others by being empathic. Abraham Maslow proposed that *self-actualization* is the motivation to fulfill one's potential, and one of the ultimate psychological needs (the other is self-transcendence).

Experience the Testing Effect Answers

1. repression.   2. c.   3. superego.   4. b.   5. anxiety.   6. Projective. 7. d.   8. a.   9. a.   10. d.   11. Rogers might assert that the criminal was raised in an environment lacking genuineness, acceptance (unconditional positive regard), and empathy, which inhibited psychological growth and led to a negative self-concept.   12. unconditional positive regard.

MODULE 39 Contemporary Perspectives on Personality

Retrieve It Answers

RI-1 extraversion–introversion and emotional stability–instability. **RI-2** The Big Five personality factors are *c*onscientiousness, *a*greeableness, *n*euroticism (emotional stability vs. instability), *o*penness, and *e*xtraversion: CANOE. These factors may be objectively measured, they are relatively stable over the life span, and they apply to all cultures in which they have been studied.   **RI-3** Our scores on personality tests predict our *average* behavior across many situations much better than they predict our specific behavior in any given situation.   **RI-4** social-cognitive; reciprocal determinism. **RI-5** Examine the person's past behavior patterns in similar situations.   **RI-6** People who feel confident in their abilities are often happier, have greater motivation, and are less susceptible to depression. Inflated self-esteem can lead to self-serving bias, greater aggression, and narcissism.   **RI-7** self-serving bias.   **RI-8** Defensive; Secure.   **RI-9** Individualists give priority to personal goals over group goals and tend to define their identity in terms of their own personal attributes. Collectivists give priority to group goals over individual goals and tend to define their identity in terms of group identifications.

Experience the Testing Effect Answers

1. Trait.   2. c.   3. b.   4. b.   5. a.   6. social-cognitive.   7. spotlight effect.   8. b.   9. Yes, if that self-love is of the *secure* type. Secure self-esteem promotes a focus beyond the self and a higher quality

of life. Excessive self-love may promote artificially high or defensive self-esteem, which is fragile; perceived threats may be met with anger or aggression. **10.** b.

Psychological Disorders

MODULE 40 Basic Concepts of Psychological Disorders

Retrieve It Answers

RI-1 dysfunctional or maladaptive. **RI-2** Some psychological disorders are culture-specific. For example, anorexia nervosa occurs mostly in Western cultures, and *taijin kyofusho* appears largely in Japan. Other disorders, such as major depressive disorder and schizophrenia, are universal—they occur in all cultures. **RI-3** Biological, psychological, and social-cultural influences combine to produce psychological disorders. This approach helps us understand that our well-being is affected by our genes, brain functioning, inner thoughts and feelings, and the influences of our social and cultural environment. **RI-4** Therapists and others apply disorder labels to communicate with one another using a common language, and to share concepts during research. Clients may benefit from knowing that they are not the only ones with these symptoms. The dangers of labeling people are that (1) overly broad classifications may pathologize normal behavior, and (2) the labels can trigger assumptions that will change people's behavior toward those labeled. **RI-5** Poverty-related stresses can help trigger disorders, but disabling disorders can also contribute to poverty. Thus, poverty and disorder are often a chicken-and-egg situation; it's hard to know which came first.

Experience the Testing Effect Answers

1. depression. **2.** No. Anna's behavior is unusual, causes her distress, and may make her a few minutes late on occasion, but it does not appear to significantly disrupt her ability to function. Like most of us, Anna demonstrates some unusual behaviors. Since they are not disabling or dysfunctional, they do not suggest a psychological disorder. **3.** *Susto* is a condition marked by severe anxiety, restlessness, and a fear of black magic. It is culture-specific to Latin America. **4.** medical. **5.** c. **6.** Critics have expressed concerns about the negative effects of labeling by the DSM and other classification systems. Labels have the potential to be both subjective and stigmatizing. Further, critics suggest that the DSM-5 casts too wide a net on disorders, pathologizing normal behavior. **7.** poverty. **8.** d.

MODULE 41 Anxiety Disorders, OCD, and PTSD

Retrieve It Answers

RI-1 generalized anxiety. **RI-2** panic. **RI-3** phobia. **RI-4** obsessive-compulsive. **RI-5** posttraumatic stress. **RI-6** Biological factors include inherited temperament differences and other gene variations; experience-altered brain pathways; and outdated, inherited responses that had survival value for our distant ancestors.

Experience the Testing Effect Answers

1. phobia. **2.** c. **3.** obsessive-compulsive. **4.** b. **5.** c.

MODULE 42 Major Depressive Disorder and Bipolar Disorder

Retrieve It Answers

RI-1 Many factors contribute to depression, including the biological influences of genetics and brain function. Social-cognitive factors also matter, including the interaction of explanatory style, mood, our responses to stressful experiences, changes in our patterns of thinking and behaving, and cultural influences. Depression involves the whole body and may disrupt sleep, energy levels, and concentration.

Experience the Testing Effect Answers

1. women's; men's. **2.** d. **3.** norepinephrine; serotonin. **4.** social-cognitive.

MODULE 43 Schizophrenia and Other Disorders

Retrieve It Answers

RI-1 negative; chronic; positive; acute. **RI-2** Biological factors include abnormalities in brain structure and function and a genetic predisposition to the disorder. Environmental factors such as nutritional deprivation, exposure to virus, and maternal stress contribute to activating the genes that increase risk. **RI-3** The psychodynamic explanation of DID symptoms is that they are defenses against anxiety generated by unacceptable urges. The learning perspective attempts to explain these symptoms as behaviors that have been reinforced by relieving anxiety. **RI-4** Twin and adoption studies show that biological relatives of people with this disorder are at increased risk for antisocial behavior. Researchers have also observed differences in the brain activity and structure of antisocial criminals. Negative environmental factors, such as poverty or childhood abuse, may channel genetic traits such as fearlessness in more dangerous directions—toward aggression and away from social responsibility. **RI-5** anorexia nervosa; bulimia nervosa.

Experience the Testing Effect Answers

1. Schizophrenia involves the altered perceptions, emotions, and behaviors of a mind split from reality. It does not involve the rapid changes in mood or identity suggested by this comparison. **2.** b. **3.** hallucination. **4.** a. **5.** c. **6.** c. **7.** b. **8.** b.

Therapy

MODULE 44 Introduction to Therapy and the Psychological Therapies

Retrieve It Answers

RI-1 transference; resistance; interpretation. **RI-2** A psychodynamic therapist might be more interested in helping the child develop insight about the underlying problems that have caused the bed-wetting response. A behavior therapist would be more likely to agree with Mowrer that the bed-wetting symptom *is* the problem, and that counterconditioning the unwanted behavior would indeed bring emotional relief. **RI-3** The *insight therapies*—psychodynamic and humanistic therapies—seek to relieve problems by providing an understanding of their origins. *Behavior therapies* assume the problem behavior *is* the problem and treat it directly, paying less attention to its origins. **RI-4** If a behavior can be learned, it can be *unlearned* and replaced by other more adaptive responses. **RI-5** classical; operant. **RI-6** By reflecting clients' feelings in a nondirective setting, the *humanistic therapies* attempt to foster personal growth by helping clients become more self-aware and self-accepting. By making clients aware of self-defeating patterns of thinking, *cognitive therapies* guide people toward more adaptive ways of thinking about themselves and their world. **RI-7** cognitive therapy. **RI-8** This integrative therapy helps people change self-defeating thinking and behavior. It has been shown to be effective for those with anxiety disorders, obsessive-compulsive disorder, depressive disorders, bipolar disorder, and eating disorders.

Experience the Testing Effect Answers

1. a. **2.** Insight. **3.** d. **4.** active listening. **5.** c. **6.** counterconditioning. **7.** systematic desensitization. **8.** Behavior therapies are often the best choice for treating phobias. Viewing Rico's fear of the freeway as a learned response, a behavior therapist might help Rico learn to replace his anxious response to freeway driving with a relaxation response. **9.** token economy. **10.** d. **11.** Cognitive-behavioral. **12.** b.

MODULE 45 Evaluating Psychotherapies

Retrieve It Answers

RI-1 The *placebo effect* is the healing power of *belief* in a treatment. Patients and therapists who expect a treatment to be effective may believe it was. **RI-2** are. **RI-3** Using this approach, therapists make decisions about treatment based on research evidence, clinical expertise, and knowledge of the client. **RI-4** EMDR has shown some effectiveness with trauma survivors and people with major depressive disorder. Skeptics acknowledge that EMDR works better than doing nothing, though they believe exposure therapy and the placebo effect, and not eye movements, are responsible for the treatment's successes. Light exposure therapy, while still somewhat controversial, has been shown to benefit those with a seasonal pattern in depression symptoms, as well as those with major depressive disorder and bipolar disorder. **RI-5** more.

Experience the Testing Effect Answers

1. c. **2.** d. **3.** research evidence, clinical expertise, and knowledge of the patient. **4.** The placebo effect is the healing power of belief in a treatment. When patients expect a treatment to be effective, they may believe it was.

MODULE 46 The Biomedical Therapies and Preventing Psychological Disorders

Retrieve It Answers

RI-1 Exercise regularly, get enough sleep, get more exposure to light (get outside or use a light box), nurture important relationships, redirect negative thinking, and eat a diet rich in omega-3 fatty acids. **RI-2** Researchers assign people to treatment and no-treatment conditions to see if those who receive the drug therapy improve more than those who don't. Double-blind controlled studies are most effective. If neither the therapist nor the client knows which participants have received the drug treatment, then any difference between the treated and untreated groups will reflect the drug treatment's actual effect. **RI-3** antidepressants; antipsychotic. **RI-4** electroconvulsive therapy; transcranial; repetitive transcranial; deep brain. **RI-5** Psychological and biomedical therapies attempt to relieve people's suffering from psychological disorders. Preventive mental health attempts to prevent suffering by identifying and eliminating the conditions that cause disorders, as well as by building resilience.

Experience the Testing Effect Answers

1. c. **2.** antianxiety. **3.** lithium. **4.** b. **5.** d.

APPENDIX A

Statistical Reasoning in Everyday Life

Retrieve It Answers

RI-1 Note how the *y*-axis of each graph is labeled. The range for the *y*-axis label in graph (a) is only from 95 to 100. The range for graph (b) is from 0 to 100. All the trucks rank as 95 percent and up, so almost all are still functioning after 10 years, which graph (b) makes clear. **RI-2** mean; mode; median; range; standard deviation. **RI-3** The team's poor performance was not their typical behavior. The return to their normal—their winning streak—may just have been a case of regression toward the mean. **RI-4** Averages based on fewer courses are more variable, which guarantees a greater number of extremely low and high marks at the end of the first term. **RI-5** Descriptive; inferential.

Experience the Testing Effect Answers

1. b. **2.** d. **3.** normal curve. **4.** a. **5.** negative. **6.** scatterplot. **7.** Regression toward the mean is a statistical phenomenon describing the tendency of extreme scores or outcomes to return to normal after an unusual event. Without knowing this, we may inaccurately decide the return to normal was a result of our own behavior. **8.** a.

APPENDIX B

Psychology at Work

Retrieve It Answers

RI-1 We become more likely to view our work as fulfilling and socially useful, and we experience higher self-esteem, feelings of competence, and overall well-being. **RI-2** (1) Interviewers may presume people are what they seem to be in interviews. (2) Interviewers' preconceptions and moods color how they perceive interviewees' responses. (3) Interviewers judge people relative to other recent interviewees. (4) Interviewers tend to track the successful careers of those they hire, not the successful careers of those they reject. (5) Interviews tend to disclose prospective workers' good intentions, not their habitual behaviors. **RI-3** *Transformational leaders* are able to inspire others to share a vision and commit themselves to a group's mission. They tend to be naturally extraverted and set high standards. **RI-4** To develop safer machines and work environments, human factors psychologists stay mindful of the curse of knowledge—the tendency for experts to mistakenly assume that others share their knowledge.

Experience the Testing Effect Answers

1. flow. **2.** Personnel; human factors. **3.** a. **4.** d. **5.** Focusing on specific, short-term goals, such as maintaining a regular study schedule, will be more helpful than focusing on more distant general goals, such as earning a good grade in this class. **6.** transformational. **7.** c. **8.** d.

Glossary

absolute threshold the minimum stimulus energy needed to detect a particular stimulus 50 percent of the time. (p. 191)

accommodation (1) in developmental psychology, adapting our current understandings (schemas) to incorporate new information. (2) in sensation and perception, the process by which the eye's lens changes shape to focus near or far objects on the retina. (pp. 125, 201)

achievement motivation a desire for significant accomplishment, for mastery of skills or ideas, for control, and for attaining a high standard. (p. 357)

achievement test a test designed to assess what a person has learned. (p. 327)

acquisition in classical conditioning, the initial stage, when one links a neutral stimulus and an unconditioned stimulus so that the neutral stimulus begins triggering the conditioned response. In operant conditioning, the strengthening of a reinforced response. (p. 238)

action potential a neural impulse; a brief electrical charge that travels down an axon. (p. 40)

active listening empathic listening in which the listener echoes, restates, and clarifies. A feature of Rogers' client-centered therapy. (p. 539)

acute schizophrenia (also called *reactive schizophrenia*) a form of schizophrenia that can begin at any age, frequently occurs in response to a traumatic event, and from which recovery is much more likely. (p. 524)

adaptation-level phenomenon our tendency to form judgments (of sounds, of lights, of income) relative to a neutral level defined by our prior experience. (p. 411)

adolescence the transition period from childhood to adulthood, extending from puberty to independence. (p. 141)

adrenal [ah-DREEN-el] **glands** a pair of endocrine glands that sit just above the kidneys and secrete hormones (epinephrine and norepinephrine) that help arouse the body in times of stress. (p. 48)

aerobic exercise sustained exercise that increases heart and lung fitness; also helps alleviate depression and anxiety. (p. 401)

affiliation need the need to build relationships and to feel part of a group. (p. 353)

aggression any physical or verbal behavior intended to harm someone physically or emotionally. (pp. 162, 441)

agonist a molecule that increases a neurotransmitter's action. (p. 43)

AIDS (acquired immune deficiency syndrome) a life-threatening, sexually transmitted infection caused by the *human immunodeficiency virus (HIV)*. AIDS depletes the immune system, leaving the person vulnerable to infections. (p. 175)

alcohol use disorder (popularly known as *alcoholism*) alcohol use marked by tolerance, withdrawal, and a drive to continue problematic use. (p. 103)

algorithm a methodical, logical rule or procedure that guarantees solving a particular problem. Contrasts with the usually speedier—but also more error-prone—use of *heuristics*. (p. 299)

all-or-none response a neuron's reaction of either firing (with a full-strength response) or not firing. (p. 41)

alpha waves the relatively slow brain waves of a relaxed, awake state. (p. 86)

altruism unselfish regard for the welfare of others. (p. 453)

amphetamines drugs (such as methamphetamine) that stimulate neural activity, causing accelerated body functions and associated energy and mood changes. (p. 104)

amygdala [uh-MIG-duh-la] two lima-bean-sized neural clusters in the limbic system; linked to emotion. (p. 55)

androgyny displaying both traditional masculine and feminine psychological characteristics. (p. 169)

anorexia nervosa an eating disorder in which a person (usually an adolescent female) maintains a starvation diet despite being significantly underweight; sometimes accompanied by excessive exercise. (p. 531)

antagonist a molecule that inhibits or blocks a neurotransmitter's action. (p. 43)

anterograde amnesia an inability to form new memories. (p. 285)

antianxiety drugs drugs used to control anxiety and agitation. (p. 561)

antidepressant drugs drugs used to treat depression, anxiety disorders, obsessive- compulsive disorder, and posttraumatic stress disorder. (Several widely used antidepressant drugs are *selective serotonin reuptake inhibitors—SSRIs*.) (p. 561)

antipsychotic drugs drugs used to treat schizophrenia and other forms of severe thought disorder. (p. 560)

antisocial personality disorder a personality disorder in which a person (usually a man) exhibits a lack of conscience for wrongdoing, even toward friends and family members; may be aggressive and ruthless or a clever con artist. (p. 529)

anxiety disorders psychological disorders characterized by distressing, persistent anxiety or maladaptive behaviors that reduce anxiety. (p. 506)

aphasia impairment of language, usually caused by left hemisphere damage either to Broca's area (impairing speaking) or to Wernicke's area (impairing understanding). (p. 316)

applied research a scientific study that aims to solve practical problems. (p. 13)

aptitude test a test designed to predict a person's future performance; *aptitude* is the capacity to learn. (p. 327)

asexual having no sexual attraction toward others. (p. 173)

assimilation interpreting our new experiences in terms of our existing schemas. (p. 125)

association areas areas of the cerebral cortex that are not involved in primary motor or sensory functions; rather, they are involved in higher mental functions such as learning, remembering, thinking, and speaking. (p. 62)

associative learning learning that certain events occur together. The events may be two stimuli (as in classical conditioning) or a response and its consequence (as in operant conditioning). (pp. 234, 243)

attachment an emotional tie with another person; shown in young children by their seeking closeness to their caregiver and showing distress on separation. (p. 133)

attention-deficit/hyperactivity disorder (ADHD) a psychological disorder marked by extreme inattention and/or hyperactivity and impulsivity. (p. 497)

attitude feelings, often influenced by our beliefs, that predispose us to respond in a particular way to objects, people, and events. (p. 418)

attribution theory the theory that we explain someone's behavior by crediting either the situation or the person's disposition. (p. 416)

audition the sense or act of hearing. (p. 216)

autism spectrum disorder (ASD) a disorder that appears in childhood and is marked by significant deficiencies in communication and social interaction, and by rigidly fixated interests and repetitive behaviors. (p. 130)

automatic processing unconscious encoding of incidental information, such as space, time, and frequency, and of well-earned information, such as word meanings. (p. 269)

autonomic [aw-tuh-NAHM-ik] **nervous system (ANS)** the part of the peripheral nervous system that controls the glands and the muscles of the internal organs (such as the heart). Its sympathetic division arouses; its parasympathetic division calms. (p. 45)

availability heuristic estimating the likelihood of events based on their availability in memory; if instances come readily to mind (perhaps because of their vividness), we presume such events are common. (p. 301)

aversive conditioning associates an unpleasant state (such as nausea) with an unwanted behavior (such as drinking alcohol). (p. 543)

axon the neuron extension that passes messages through its branches to other neurons or to muscles or glands. (p. 39)

babbling stage beginning around 4 months, the stage of speech development in which an infant spontaneously utters various sounds at first unrelated to the household language. (p. 315)

barbiturates drugs that depress central nervous system activity, reducing anxiety but impairing memory and judgment. (p. 104)

basal metabolic rate the body's resting rate of energy output. (p. 363)

basic research pure science that aims to increase the scientific knowledge base. (p. 13)

basic trust according to Erik Erikson, a sense that the world is predictable and trustworthy; said to be formed during infancy by appropriate experiences with responsive caregivers. (p. 137)

behavior feedback effect the tendency of behavior to influence our own and others' thoughts, feelings, and actions. (p. 381)

behavior genetics the study of the relative power and limits of genetic and environmental influences on behavior. (pp. 8, 69)

behavior therapy therapy that applies learning principles to the elimination of unwanted behaviors. (p. 540)

behaviorism the view that psychology (1) should be an objective science that (2) studies behavior without reference to mental processes. Most psychologists today agree with (1) but not with (2). (pp. 7, 236)

belief perseverance clinging to one's initial conceptions after the basis on which they were formed has been discredited. (p. 304)

binge-eating disorder significant binge-eating episodes, followed by distress, disgust, or guilt, but without the compensatory behavior that marks bulimia nervosa. (p. 533)

binocular cue a depth cue, such as retinal disparity, that depends on the use of two eyes. (p. 208)

biological psychology the scientific study of the links between biological (genetic, neural, hormonal) and psychological processes. Some biological psychologists call themselves *behavioral neuroscientists, neuropsychologists, behavior geneticists, physiological psychologists,* or *biopsychologists.* (p. 39)

biomedical therapy prescribed medications or procedures that act directly on the person's physiology. (p. 558)

biopsychosocial approach an integrated approach that incorporates biological, psychological, and social-cultural levels of analysis. (p. 11)

bipolar disorder a disorder in which a person alternates between the hopelessness and lethargy of depression and the overexcited state of mania. (Formerly called *manic- depressive disorder.*) (p. 515)

blind spot the point at which the optic nerve leaves the eye, creating a "blind" spot because no receptor cells are located there. (p. 201)

blindsight a condition in which a person can respond to a visual stimulus without consciously experiencing it. (p. 85)

bottom-up processing analysis that begins with the sensory receptors and works up to the brain's integration of sensory information. (p. 190)

brainstem the oldest part and central core of the brain, beginning where the spinal cord swells as it enters the skull; the brainstem is responsible for automatic survival functions. (p. 53)

Broca's area helps control language expression—an area of the frontal lobe, usually in the left hemisphere, that directs the muscle movements involved in speech. (p. 316)

bulimia nervosa an eating disorder in which a person's binge eating (usually of high-calorie foods) is followed by inappropriate weight-loss promoting behavior, such as vomiting, laxative use, fasting, or excessive exercise. (p. 531)

bystander effect the tendency for any given bystander to be less likely to give aid if other bystanders are present. (p. 455)

Cannon-Bard theory the theory that an emotion-arousing stimulus simultaneously triggers (1) physiological responses and (2) the subjective experience of emotion. (p. 369)

case study a descriptive technique in which one individual or group is studied in depth in the hope of revealing universal principles. (p. 20)

catharsis in psychology, the idea that "releasing" aggressive energy (through action or fantasy) relieves aggressive urges. (p. 393)

cell body the part of a neuron that contains the nucleus; the cell's life-support center. (p. 39)

central nervous system (CNS) the brain and spinal cord. (p. 45)

central route persuasion occurs when interested people focus on the arguments and respond with favorable thoughts. (p. 418)

cerebellum [sehr-uh-BELL-um] the "little brain" at the rear of the brainstem; functions include processing sensory input, coordinating movement output and balance, and enabling nonverbal learning and memory. (p. 54)

cerebral [seh-REE-bruhl] **cortex** the intricate fabric of interconnected neural cells covering the cerebral hemispheres; the body's ultimate control and information-processing center. (p. 59)

change blindness failing to notice changes in the environment; a form of *inattentional blindness.* (p. 82)

chromosomes threadlike structures made of DNA molecules that contain the genes. (p. 69)

chronic schizophrenia (also called *process schizophrenia*) a form of schizophrenia in which symptoms usually appear by late adolescence or early adulthood. As people age, psychotic episodes last longer and recovery periods shorten. (p. 524)

chunking organizing items into familiar, manageable units; often occurs automatically. (p. 270)

circadian [ser-KAY-dee-an] **rhythm** our biological clock; regular bodily rhythms (for example, of temperature and wakefulness) that occur on a 24-hour cycle. (p. 86)

classical conditioning a type of learning in which we link two or more stimuli; as a result, to illustrate with Pavlov's classic experiment, the first stimulus (a tone) comes to elicit behavior (drooling) in anticipation of the second stimulus (food). (p. 236)

client-centered therapy a humanistic therapy, developed by Carl Rogers, in which the therapist uses techniques such as *active listening* within an accepting, genuine, empathic environment to facilitate clients' growth. (Also called *person-centered therapy*.) (p. 539)

clinical psychology a branch of psychology that studies, assesses, and treats people with psychological disorders. (p. 13)

cocaine a powerful and addictive stimulant derived from the coca plant; produces temporarily increased alertness and euphoria. (p. 106)

cochlea [KOHK-lee-uh] a coiled, bony, fluid- filled tube in the inner ear; sound waves traveling through the cochlear fluid trigger nerve impulses. (p. 216)

cochlear implant a device for converting sounds into electrical signals and stimulating the auditory nerve through electrodes threaded into the cochlea. (p. 219)

cognition all the mental activities associated with thinking, knowing, remembering, and communicating. (pp. 125, 299)

cognitive dissonance theory the theory that we act to reduce the discomfort (dissonance) we feel when two of our thoughts (cognitions) are inconsistent. For example, when we become aware that our attitudes and our actions clash, we can reduce the resulting dissonance by changing our attitudes. (p. 421)

cognitive learning the acquisition of mental information, whether by observing events, by watching others, or through language. (p. 236)

cognitive map a mental representation of the layout of one's environment. For example, after exploring a maze, rats act as if they have learned a cognitive map of it. (p. 257)

cognitive neuroscience the interdisciplinary study of the brain activity linked with cognition (including perception, thinking, memory, and language). (pp. 8, 81)

cognitive psychology the study of mental processes, such as occur when we perceive, learn, remember, think, communicate, and solve problems. (p. 8)

cognitive therapy therapy that teaches people new, more adaptive ways of thinking; based on the assumption that thoughts intervene between events and our emotional reactions. (p. 544)

cognitive-behavioral therapy (CBT) a popular integrative therapy that combines cognitive therapy (changing self-defeating thinking) with behavior therapy (changing behavior). (p. 546)

cohort a group of people sharing a common characteristic, such as being from a given time period. (p. 333)

collective unconscious Carl Jung's concept of a shared, inherited reservoir of memory traces from our species' history. (p. 466)

collectivism giving priority to the goals of one's group (often one's extended family or work group) and defining one's identity accordingly. (p. 491)

community psychology a branch of psychology that studies how people interact with their social environments and how social institutions affect individuals and groups. (p. 13)

companionate love the deep affectionate attachment we feel for those with whom our lives are intertwined. (p. 451)

concept a mental grouping of similar objects, events, ideas, or people. (p. 299)

concrete operational stage in Piaget's theory, the stage of cognitive development (from about 7 to 11 years of age) during which children gain the mental operations that enable them to think logically about concrete events. (p. 128)

conditioned reinforcer a stimulus that gains its reinforcing power through its association with a primary reinforcer; also known as a *secondary reinforcer*. (p. 246)

conditioned response (CR) in classical conditioning, a learned response to a previously neutral (but now conditioned) stimulus (CS). (p. 238)

conditioned stimulus (CS) in classical conditioning, an originally neutral stimulus that, after association with an unconditioned stimulus (US), comes to trigger a conditioned response (CR). (p. 238)

conduction hearing loss a less common form of hearing loss, caused by damage to the mechanical system that conducts sound waves to the cochlea. (p. 219)

cones retinal receptors that are concentrated near the center of the retina and that function in daylight or in well-lit conditions. Cones detect fine detail and give rise to color sensations. (p. 201)

confirmation bias a tendency to search for information that supports our preconceptions and to ignore or distort contradictory evidence. (p. 299)

conflict a perceived incompatibility of actions, goals, or ideas. (p. 456)

conformity adjusting our behavior or thinking to coincide with a group standard. (p. 423)

confounding variable in an experiment, a factor other than the factor being studied that might influence a study's results. (p. 28)

consciousness our subjective awareness of ourselves and our environment. (p. 81)

conservation the principle (which Piaget believed to be a part of concrete operational reasoning) that properties such as mass, volume, and number remain the same despite changes in the forms of objects. (p. 127)

continuous reinforcement schedule reinforcing the desired response every time it occurs. (p. 246)

control group in an experiment, the group *not* exposed to the treatment; contrasts with the experimental group and serves as a comparison for evaluating the effect of the treatment. (p. 25)

convergent thinking narrowing the available problem solutions to determine the single best solution. (p. 307)

coping alleviating stress using emotional, cognitive, or behavioral methods. (p. 395)

coronary heart disease the clogging of the vessels that nourish the heart muscle; the leading cause of death in many developed countries. (p. 391)

corpus callosum [KOR-pus kah-LOW-sum] the large band of neural fibers connecting the two brain hemispheres and carrying messages between them. (p. 64)

correlation a measure of the extent to which two factors vary together, and thus of how well either factor predicts the other. (p. 24)

correlation coefficient a statistical index of the relationship between two things (from −1.00 to +1.00). (pp. 24, A-4)

counseling psychology a branch of psychology that assists people with problems in living (often related to school, work, or marriage) and in achieving greater well-being. (p. 13)

counterconditioning behavior therapy procedures that use classical conditioning to evoke new responses to stimuli that are triggering unwanted behaviors; include *exposure therapies* and *aversive conditioning*. (p. 540)

creativity the ability to produce new and valuable ideas. (p. 307)

critical period an optimal period early in the life of an organism when exposure to certain stimuli or experiences produces normal development. (p. 122)

critical thinking thinking that does not blindly accept arguments and conclusions. Rather, it examines assumptions, appraises the source, discerns hidden biases, evaluates evidence, and assesses conclusions. (p. 2)

cross-sectional study research that compares people of different ages at the same point in time. (pp. 154, 333)

crystallized intelligence our accumulated knowledge and verbal skills; tends to increase with age. (p. 333)

culture the enduring behaviors, ideas, attitudes, values, and traditions shared by a group of people and transmitted from one generation to the next. (pp. 8, 421)

debriefing the postexperimental explanation of a study, including its purpose and any deceptions, to its participants. (p. 31)

deep processing encoding semantically, based on the meaning of the words; tends to yield the best retention. (p. 273)

defense mechanisms in psychoanalytic theory, the ego's protective methods of reducing anxiety by unconsciously distorting reality. (p. 465)

deindividuation the loss of self-awareness and self-restraint occurring in group situations that foster arousal and anonymity. (p. 431)

déjà vu that eerie sense that "I've experienced this before." Cues from the current situation may unconsciously trigger retrieval of an earlier experience. (p. 291)

delta waves the large, slow brain waves associated with deep sleep. (p. 88)

delusion a false belief, often of persecution or grandeur, that may accompany psychotic disorders. (p. 523)

dendrites a neuron's often bushy, branching extensions that receive and integrate messages, conducting impulses toward the cell body. (p. 39)

dependent variable in an experiment, the outcome that is measured; the variable that may change when the independent variable is manipulated. (p. 28)

depressants drugs (such as alcohol, barbiturates, and opiates) that reduce neural activity and slow body functions. (p. 103)

depth perception the ability to see objects in three dimensions although the images that strike the retina are two-dimensional; allows us to judge distance. (p. 208)

developmental psychology a branch of psychology that studies physical, cognitive, and social change throughout the life span. (p. 116)

difference threshold the minimum difference between two stimuli required for detection 50 percent of the time. We experience the difference threshold as a *just noticeable difference* (or *jnd*). (p. 192)

discrimination (1) in classical conditioning, the learned ability to distinguish between a conditioned stimulus and similar stimuli that do not signal an unconditioned stimulus; in operant conditioning, the ability to distinguish responses that are reinforced from similar responses that are not reinforced. (2) in social psychology, unjustifiable negative behavior toward a group or its members. (pp. 241, 435)

dissociation a split in consciousness, which allows some thoughts and behaviors to occur simultaneously with others. (p. 225)

dissociative disorders controversial, rare disorders in which conscious awareness becomes separated (dissociated) from previous memories, thoughts, and feelings. (p. 527)

dissociative identity disorder (DID) a rare dissociative disorder in which a person exhibits two or more distinct and alternating identities. (Formerly called *multiple personality disorder*.) (p. 529)

divergent thinking expanding the number of possible problem solutions; creative thinking that diverges in different directions. (p. 307)

DNA (deoxyribonucleic acid) a complex molecule containing the genetic information that makes up the chromosomes. (p. 69)

double-blind procedure an experimental procedure in which both the research participants and the research staff are ignorant (blind) about whether the research participants have received the treatment or a placebo. Commonly used in drug-evaluation studies. (p. 27)

dream a sequence of images, emotions, and thoughts passing through a sleeping person's mind. (p. 97)

drive-reduction theory the idea that a physiological need creates an aroused state (a drive) that motivates an organism to satisfy the need. (p. 349)

DSM-5 the American Psychiatric Association's *Diagnostic and Statistical Manual of Mental Disorders*, Fifth Edition; a widely used system for classifying psychological disorders. (p. 497)

dual processing the principle that information is often simultaneously processed on separate conscious and unconscious tracks. (p. 85)

echoic memory a momentary sensory memory of auditory stimuli; if attention is elsewhere, sounds and words can still be recalled within 3 or 4 seconds. (p. 270)

eclectic approach an approach to psychotherapy that uses techniques from various forms of therapy. (p. 537)

Ecstasy (MDMA) a synthetic stimulant and mild hallucinogen. Produces euphoria and social intimacy, but with short-term health risks and longer-term harm to serotonin- producing neurons and to mood and cognition. (p. 106)

EEG (electroencephalogram) an amplified recording of the waves of electrical activity sweeping across the brain's surface. These waves are measured by electrodes placed on the scalp. (p. 51)

effortful processing encoding that requires attention and conscious effort. (p. 269)

ego the largely conscious, "executive" part of personality that, according to Freud, mediates among the demands of the id, the superego, and reality. The ego operates on the *reality principle*, satisfying the id's desires in ways that will realistically bring pleasure rather than pain. (p. 465)

egocentrism in Piaget's theory, the preoperational child's difficulty taking another's point of view. (p. 128)

electroconvulsive therapy (ECT) a biomedical therapy for severely depressed patients in which a brief electric current is sent through the brain of an anesthetized patient. (p. 563)

embodied cognition the influence of bodily sensations, gestures, and other states on cognitive preferences and judgments. (p. 228)

embryo the developing human organism from about 2 weeks after fertilization through the second month. (p. 119)

emerging adulthood a period from about age 18 to the mid-twenties, when many in Western cultures are no longer adolescents but have not yet achieved full independence as adults. (p. 149)

emotion a response of the whole organism, involving (1) physiological arousal, (2) expressive behaviors, and (3) conscious experience. (p. 369)

emotional intelligence the ability to perceive, understand, manage, and use emotions. (p. 327)

emotion-focused coping attempting to alleviate stress by avoiding or ignoring a stressor and attending to emotional needs related to our stress reaction. (p. 395)

empirical approach an evidence-based method that draws on observation and experimentation. (p. 2)

empirically derived test a test (such as the MMPI) created by selecting from a pool of items those that discriminate between groups. (p. 477)

encoding the process of getting information into the memory system—for example, by extracting meaning. (p. 268)

encoding specificity principle the idea that cues and contexts specific to a particular memory will be most effective in helping us recall it. (p. 280)

endocrine [EN-duh-krin] **system** the body's "slow" chemical communication system; a set of glands that secrete hormones into the bloodstream. (p. 48)

endorphins [en-DOR-fins] "morphine within"— natural, opiate-like neurotransmitters linked to pain control and to pleasure. (p. 43)

environment every nongenetic influence, from prenatal nutrition to the people and things around us. (p. 69)

epigenetics "above" or "in addition to" (*epi*) genetics; the study of the molecular mechanisms by which environments can influence genetic expression (without a DNA change). (pp. 75, 497)

episodic memory explicit memory of personally experienced events; one of our two conscious memory systems (the other is *semantic memory*). (p. 276)

equity a condition in which people receive from a relationship in proportion to what they give to it. (p. 453)

erectile disorder inability to develop or maintain an erection due to insufficient blood flow to the penis. (p. 175)

estrogens sex hormones, such as estradiol, that contribute to female sex characteristics and are secreted in greater amounts by females than by males. Estrogen levels peak during ovulation. In nonhuman mammals, this promotes sexual receptivity. (p. 173)

evidence-based practice clinical decision making that integrates the best available research with clinical expertise and patient characteristics and preferences. (p. 553)

evolutionary psychology the study of the evolution of behavior and the mind, using principles of natural selection. (pp. 8, 75)

experiment a research method in which an investigator manipulates one or more factors (independent variables) to observe the effect on some behavior or mental process (the dependent variable). By *random assignment* of participants, the experimenter aims to control other relevant factors. (p. 25)

experimental group in an experiment, the group exposed to the treatment, that is, to one version of the independent variable. (p. 25)

explicit memory retention of facts and experiences that we can consciously know and "declare." (Also called *declarative memory.*) (p. 269)

exposure therapies behavioral techniques, such as *systematic desensitization* and *virtual reality exposure therapy*, that treat anxieties by exposing people (in imaginary or actual situations) to the things they fear and avoid. (p. 540)

external locus of control the perception that chance or outside forces beyond our personal control determine our fate. (p. 396)

extinction the diminishing of a conditioned response; occurs in classical conditioning when an unconditioned stimulus (US) does not follow a conditioned stimulus (CS); occurs in operant conditioning when a response is no longer reinforced. (p. 238)

extrasensory perception (ESP) the controversial claim that perception can occur apart from sensory input; includes telepathy, clairvoyance, and precognition. (p. 228)

extrinsic motivation the desire to perform a behavior to receive promised rewards or avoid threatened punishment. (p. 358)

facial feedback effect the tendency of facial muscle states to trigger corresponding feelings such as fear, anger, or happiness. (p. 381)

family therapy therapy that treats people in the context of their family system. Views an individual's unwanted behaviors as influenced by, or directed at, other family members. (p. 547)

feature detectors nerve cells in the brain's visual cortex that respond to specific features of the stimulus, such as shape, angle, or movement. (p. 204)

feel-good, do-good phenomenon people's tendency to be helpful when in a good mood. (p. 407)

female orgasmic disorder distress due to infrequently or never experiencing orgasm. (p. 175)

fetal alcohol syndrome (FAS) physical and cognitive abnormalities in children caused by a pregnant woman's heavy drinking. In severe cases, signs include a small, out-of-proportion head and abnormal facial features. (p. 120)

fetus the developing human organism from 9 weeks after conception to birth. (p. 119)

figure-ground the organization of the visual field into objects (the *figures*) that stand out from their surroundings (the *ground*). (p. 207)

fixation (1) in thinking, the inability to see a problem from a new perspective; an obstacle to problem solving. (2) in personality theory, according to Freud, a lingering focus of pleasure-seeking energies at an earlier psychosexual stage, in which conflicts were unresolved. (pp. 301, 465)

fixed-interval schedule in operant conditioning, a reinforcement schedule that reinforces a response only after a specified time has elapsed. (p. 246)

fixed-ratio schedule in operant conditioning, a reinforcement schedule that reinforces a response only after a specified number of responses. (p. 246)

flashbulb memory a clear memory of an emotionally significant moment or event. (p. 278)

flow a completely involved, focused state, with diminished awareness of self and time; results from full engagement of our skills. (p. B-1)

fluid intelligence our ability to reason speedily and abstractly; tends to decrease with age, especially during late adulthood. (p. 333)

fMRI (functional MRI) a technique for revealing blood flow and, therefore, brain activity by comparing successive MRI scans. fMRI scans show brain function as well as structure. (p. 53)

foot-in-the-door phenomenon the tendency for people who have first agreed to a small request to comply later with a larger request. (p. 418)

formal operational stage in Piaget's theory, the stage of cognitive development (normally beginning about age 12) during which people begin to think logically about abstract concepts. (p. 129)

fovea the central focal point in the retina, around which the eye's cones cluster. (p. 203)

framing the way an issue is posed; how an issue is worded can significantly affect decisions and judgments. (p. 304)

fraternal (dizygotic) twins individuals that develop from separate fertilized eggs. They are genetically no closer than ordinary siblings, but they share a prenatal environment. (p. 70)

free association in psychoanalysis, a method of exploring the unconscious in which the person relaxes and says whatever comes to mind, no matter how trivial or embarrassing. (p. 463)

frequency the number of complete wavelengths that pass a point in a given time (for example, per second). (p. 216)

frequency theory in hearing, the theory that the rate of nerve impulses traveling up the auditory nerve matches the frequency of a tone, thus enabling us to sense its pitch. (Also called *temporal theory.*) (p. 220)

frontal lobes the portion of the cerebral cortex lying just behind the forehead; involved in speaking and muscle movements and in making plans and judgments. (p. 59)

frustration-aggression principle the principle that frustration—the blocking of an attempt to achieve some goal—creates anger, which can generate aggression. (p. 443)

functionalism an early school of thought promoted by James and influenced by Darwin; explored how mental and behavioral processes function—how they enable the organism to adapt, survive, and flourish. (p. 5)

fundamental attribution error the tendency for observers, when analyzing others' behavior, to underestimate the impact of the situation and to overestimate the impact of personal disposition. (p. 416)

gate-control theory the theory that the spinal cord contains a neurological "gate" that blocks pain signals or allows them to pass on to the brain. The "gate" is opened by the activity of pain signals traveling up small nerve fibers and is closed by activity in larger fibers or by information coming from the brain. (p. 222)

gender identity our sense of being male, female, or some combination of the two. (p. 169)

gender in psychology, the socially influenced characteristics by which people define *boy, girl, man*, and *woman*. (p. 162)

gender role a set of expected behaviors, attitudes, and traits for males or for females. (p. 169)

gender typing the acquisition of a traditional masculine or feminine role. (p. 169)

general adaptation syndrome (GAS) Selye's concept of the body's adaptive response to stress in three phases—alarm, resistance, exhaustion. (p. 386)

general intelligence (g) according to Spearman and others, underlies all mental abilities and is therefore measured by every task on an intelligence test. (p. 323)

generalization the tendency, once a response has been conditioned, for stimuli similar to the conditioned stimulus to elicit similar responses. (In operant conditioning, generalization occurs when responses learned in one situation occur in other, similar situations.) (p. 238)

generalized anxiety disorder an anxiety disorder in which a person is continually tense, apprehensive, and in a state of autonomic nervous system arousal. (p. 507)

genes the biochemical units of heredity that make up the chromosomes; segments of DNA capable of synthesizing proteins. (p. 69)

genome the complete instructions for making an organism, consisting of all the genetic material in that organism's chromosomes. (p. 69)

gestalt an organized whole. Gestalt psychologists emphasized our tendency to integrate pieces of information into meaningful wholes. (p. 207)

glial cells (glia) cells in the nervous system that support, nourish, and protect neurons; they may also play a role in learning, thinking, and memory. (p. 40)

glucose the form of sugar that circulates in the blood and provides the major source of energy for body tissues. When its level is low, we feel hunger. (p. 363)

grammar in a language, a system of rules that enables us to communicate with and understand others. *Semantics* is the language's set of rules for deriving meaning from sounds, and *syntax* is its set of rules for combining words into grammatically sensible sentences. (p. 312)

GRIT Graduated and Reciprocated Initiatives in Tension-Reduction—a strategy designed to decrease international tensions. (p. 459)

grit in psychology, passion and perseverance in the pursuit of long-term goals. (p. 358)

group polarization the enhancement of a group's prevailing inclinations through discussion within the group. (p. 431)

group therapy therapy conducted with groups rather than individuals, providing benefits from group interaction. (p. 547)

grouping the perceptual tendency to organize stimuli into coherent groups. (p. 208)

groupthink the mode of thinking that occurs when the desire for harmony in a decision-making group overrides a realistic appraisal of alternatives. (p. 433)

habituation decreasing responsiveness with repeated stimulation. As infants gain familiarity with repeated exposure to a stimulus, their interest wanes and they look away sooner. (p. 121)

hallucinations false sensory experiences, such as seeing something in the absence of an external visual stimulus. (p. 88)

hallucinogens psychedelic ("mind-manifesting") drugs, such as LSD, that distort perceptions and evoke sensory images in the absence of sensory input. (p. 109)

health psychology a subfield of psychology that provides psychology's contribution to behavioral medicine. (p. 389)

heredity the genetic transfer of characteristics from parents to offspring. (p. 69)

heritability the proportion of variation among individuals in a group that we can attribute to genes. The heritability of a trait may vary, depending on the range of populations and environments studied. (p. 336)

heuristic a simple thinking strategy that often allows us to make judgments and solve problems efficiently; usually speedier but also more error-prone than an *algorithm*. (p. 299)

hierarchy of needs Maslow's pyramid of human needs, beginning at the base with physiological needs that must first be satisfied before people can fulfill their higher- level safety needs and then psychological needs. (pp. 351, 470)

hindsight bias the tendency to believe, after learning an outcome, that one would have foreseen it. (Also known as the *I-knewit- all-along phenomenon*.) (p. 16)

hippocampus a neural center located in the limbic system; helps process explicit (conscious) memories—of facts and events—for storage. (pp. 57, 276)

homeostasis a tendency to maintain a balanced or constant internal state; the regulation of any aspect of body chemistry, such as blood glucose, around a particular level. (p. 349)

hormones chemical messengers that are manufactured by the endocrine glands, travel through the bloodstream, and affect other tissues. (p. 48)

hue the dimension of color that is determined by the wavelength of light; what we know as the color names *blue, green*, and so forth. (p. 199)

human factors psychology a field of psychology allied with I/O psychology that explores how people and machines interact and how machines and physical environments can be made safe and easy to use. (p. B-5)

humanistic psychology a historically significant perspective that emphasized human growth potential. (p. 8)

humanistic theories theories that view personality with a focus on the potential for healthy personal growth. (p. 470)

hypnosis a social interaction in which one person (the hypnotist) suggests to another (the subject) that certain perceptions, feelings, thoughts, or behaviors will spontaneously occur. (p. 225)

hypothalamus [hi-po-THAL-uh-muss] a neural structure lying below (*hypo*) the thalamus; it directs several maintenance activities (eating, drinking, body temperature), helps govern the endocrine system via the pituitary gland, and is linked to emotion and reward. (p. 57)

hypothesis a testable prediction, often implied by a theory. (p. 19)

iconic memory a momentary sensory memory of visual stimuli; a photographic or picture-image memory lasting no more than a few tenths of a second. (p. 270)

id a reservoir of unconscious psychic energy that, according to Freud, strives to satisfy basic sexual and aggressive drives. The id operates on the *pleasure principle*, demanding immediate gratification. (p. 463)

identical (monozygotic) twins individuals that develop from a single fertilized egg that splits in two, creating two genetically identical organisms. (p. 70)

identification the process by which, according to Freud, children incorporate their parents' values into their developing superegos. (p. 465)

identity our sense of self; according to Erikson, the adolescent's task is to solidify a sense of self by testing and integrating various roles. (p. 147)

illusory correlation perceiving a relationship where none exists, or perceiving a stronger- than-actual relationship. (p. A-5)

implicit memory retention of learned skills or classically conditioned associations independent of conscious recollection. (Also called *nondeclarative memory*.) (p. 269)

imprinting the process by which certain animals form strong attachments during early life. (p. 135)

inattentional blindness failing to see visible objects when our attention is directed elsewhere. (p. 82)

incentive a positive or negative environmental stimulus that motivates behavior. (p. 349)

independent variable in an experiment, the factor that is manipulated; the variable whose effect is being studied. (p. 28)

individualism giving priority to one's own goals over group goals and defining one's identity in terms of personal attributes rather than group identifications. (p. 491)

industrial-organizational (I/O) psychology the application of psychological concepts and methods to optimizing human behavior in workplaces. (p. B-3)

informational social influence influence resulting from a person's willingness to accept others' opinions about reality. (p. 424)

informed consent giving potential participants enough information about a study to enable them to choose whether they wish to participate. (p. 31)

ingroup "us"—people with whom we share a common identity. (p. 438)

ingroup bias the tendency to favor our own group. (p. 438)

inner ear the innermost part of the ear, containing the cochlea, semicircular canals, and vestibular sacs. (p. 216)

insight a sudden realization of a problem's solution; contrasts with strategy-based solutions. (p. 299)

insight therapies therapies that aim to improve psychological functioning by increasing a person's awareness of underlying motives and defenses. (p. 538)

insomnia recurring problems in falling or staying asleep. (p. 95)

instinct a complex behavior that is rigidly patterned throughout a species and is unlearned. (p. 349)

instinctive drift the tendency of learned behavior to gradually revert to biologically predisposed patterns. (p. 257)

intellectual disability a condition of limited mental ability, indicated by an intelligence test score of 70 or below and difficulty adapting to the demands of life. (Formerly referred to as *mental retardation*.) (p. 331)

intelligence the ability to learn from experience, solve problems, and use knowledge to adapt to new situations. (p. 323)

intelligence quotient (IQ) defined originally as the ratio of mental age (*ma*) to chronological age (*ca*) multiplied by 100 (thus, IQ = *ma/ca* × 100). On contemporary intelligence tests, the average performance for a given age is assigned a score of 100. (p. 329)

intelligence test a method for assessing an individual's mental aptitudes and comparing them with those of others, using numerical scores. (p. 327)

intensity the amount of energy in a light wave or sound wave, which influences what we perceive as brightness or loudness. Intensity is determined by the wave's amplitude (height). (p. 199)

interaction the interplay that occurs when the effect of one factor (such as environment) depends on another factor (such as heredity). (p. 75)

internal locus of control the perception that we control our own fate. (p. 396)

interneurons neurons within the brain and spinal cord; they communicate internally and process information between the sensory inputs and motor outputs. (p. 45)

interpretation in psychoanalysis, the analyst's noting of supposed dream meanings, resistances, and other significant behaviors and events in order to promote insight. (p. 537)

intersex a condition present at birth due to unusual combinations of male and female chromosomes, hormones, and anatomy; possessing biological sexual characteristics of both sexes. (p. 167)

intimacy in Erikson's theory, the ability to form close, loving relationships; a primary developmental task in young adulthood. (p. 147)

intrinsic motivation the desire to perform a behavior effectively for its own sake. (p. 358)

intuition an effortless, immediate, automatic feeling or thought, as contrasted with explicit, conscious reasoning. (p. 301)

James-Lange theory the theory that our experience of emotion is our awareness of our physiological responses to an emotion- arousing stimulus. (p. 369)

just-world phenomenon the tendency for people to believe the world is just and that people therefore get what they deserve and deserve what they get. (p. 438)

kinesthesia [kin-ehs-THEE-zhuh] our movement sense—our system for sensing the position and movement of individual body parts. (p. 227)

language our spoken, written, or signed words and the ways we combine them to communicate meaning. (p. 311)

latent content according to Freud, the underlying meaning of a dream (as distinct from its manifest content). (p. 97)

latent learning learning that occurs but is not apparent until there is an incentive to demonstrate it. (p. 257)

law of effect Thorndike's principle that behaviors followed by favorable consequences become more likely, and that behaviors followed by unfavorable consequences become less likely. (p. 244)

leadership an individual's ability to motivate and influence others to contribute to their group's success. (p. B-10)

learned helplessness the hopelessness and passive resignation an animal or person learns when unable to avoid repeated aversive events. (p. 396)

learning the process of acquiring through experience new and relatively enduring information or behaviors. (pp. 234, 243)

lesion [LEE-zhuhn] tissue destruction. A brain lesion is a naturally or experimentally caused destruction of brain tissue. (p. 51)

levels of analysis the differing complementary views, from biological to psychological to social-cultural, for analyzing any given phenomenon. (p. 11)

limbic system neural system (including the *amygdala, hypothalamus,* and *hippocampus*) located below the cerebral hemispheres; associated with emotions and drives. (p. 55)

linguistic determinism Whorf's hypothesis that language determines the way we think. (p. 319)

linguistic relativism the idea that language has an influence on the way we think. (p. 319)

lobotomy a psychosurgical procedure once used to calm uncontrollably emotional or violent patients. The procedure cut the nerves connecting the frontal lobes to the emotion-controlling centers of the inner brain. (p. 565)

longitudinal study research that follows and retests the same people over time. (pp. 154, 333)

long-term memory the relatively permanent and limitless storehouse of the memory system. Includes knowledge, skills, and experiences. (p. 268)

long-term potentiation (LTP) an increase in a cell's firing potential after brief, rapid stimulation; a neural basis for learning and memory. (p. 278)

LSD (*lysergic acid diethylamide*) a powerful hallucinogenic drug; also known as *acid*. (p. 109)

major depressive disorder a disorder in which a person experiences, in the absence of drugs or another medical condition, two or more weeks with five or more symptoms, at least one of which must be either (1) depressed mood or (2) loss of interest or pleasure. (p. 515)

mania a hyperactive, wildly optimistic state in which dangerously poor judgment is common. (p. 515)

manifest content according to Freud, the symbolic, remembered story line of a dream (as distinct from its latent, or hidden, content). (p. 97)

maturation biological growth processes that enable orderly changes in behavior, relatively uninfluenced by experience. (p. 122)

mean the arithmetic average of a distribution, obtained by adding the scores and then dividing by the number of scores. (p. A-2)

median the middle score in a distribution; half the scores are above it and half are below it. (p. A-2)

medical model the concept that diseases, in this case psychological *disorders*, have physical causes that can be diagnosed, treated, and, in most cases, *cured*, often through treatment in a *hospital*. (p. 495)

medulla [muh-DUL-uh] the base of the brainstem; controls heartbeat and breathing. (p. 53)

MEG (magnetoencephalography) a brain-imaging technique that measures magnetic fields from the brain's natural electrical activity. (p. 51)

memory the persistence of learning over time through the encoding, storage, and retrieval of information. (p. 267)

memory consolidation the neural storage of a long-term memory. (p. 276)

menarche [meh-NAR-key] the first menstrual period. (p. 166)

menopause the time of natural cessation of menstruation; also refers to the biological changes a woman experiences as her ability to reproduce declines. (p. 151)

mental age a measure of intelligence test performance devised by Binet; the level of performance typically associated with children of a certain chronological age. Thus, a child who does as well as an average 8-yearold is said to have a mental age of 8. (p. 329)

mental set a tendency to approach a problem in one particular way, often a way that has been successful in the past. (p. 301)

mere exposure effect the phenomenon that repeated exposure to novel stimuli increases liking of them. (p. 447)

meta-analysis a statistical procedure for analyzing the results of multiple studies to reach an overall conclusion. (pp. 20, 551)

methamphetamine a powerfully addictive drug that stimulates the central nervous system, with accelerated body functions and associated energy and mood changes; over time, appears to reduce baseline dopamine levels. (p. 106)

middle ear the chamber between the eardrum and cochlea containing three tiny bones (malleus, incus, and stapes) that concentrate the vibrations of the eardrum on the cochlea's oval window. (p. 216)

mindfulness meditation a reflective practice in which people attend to current experiences in a nonjudgmental and accepting manner. (p. 404)

Minnesota Multiphasic Personality Inventory (MMPI) the most widely researched and clinically used of all personality tests. Originally developed to identify emotional disorders (still considered its most appropriate use), this test is now used for many other screening purposes. (p. 477)

mirror neurons frontal lobe neurons that some scientists believe fire when we perform certain actions or observe another doing so. The brain's mirroring of another's action may enable imitation and empathy. (p. 259)

mirror-image perceptions mutual views often held by conflicting people, as when each side sees itself as ethical and peaceful and views the other side as evil and aggressive. (p. 456)

misinformation effect occurs when misleading information has corrupted one's memory of an event. (p. 291)

mnemonics [nih-MON-iks] memory aids, especially those techniques that use vivid imagery and organizational devices. (p. 273)

mode the most frequently occurring score(s) in a distribution. (p. A-2)

modeling the process of observing and imitating a specific behavior. (p. 259)

monocular cue a depth cue, such as interposition or linear perspective, available to either eye alone. (p. 210)

mood-congruent memory the tendency to recall experiences that are consistent with one's current good or bad mood. (p. 280)

morpheme in a language, the smallest unit that carries meaning; may be a word or a part of a word (such as a prefix). (p. 312)

motivation a need or desire that energizes and directs behavior. (p. 349)

motor (efferent) neurons neurons that carry outgoing information from the brain and spinal cord to the muscles and glands. (p. 45)

motor cortex an area at the rear of the frontal lobes that controls voluntary movements. (p. 61)

MRI (magnetic resonance imaging) a technique that uses magnetic fields and radio waves to produce computer-generated images of soft tissue. MRI scans show brain anatomy. (p. 51)

mutation a random error in gene replication that leads to a change. (p. 76)

myelin [MY-uh-lin] **sheath** a fatty tissue layer segmentally encasing the axons of some neurons; enables vastly greater transmission speed as neural impulses hop from one node to the next. (p. 40)

narcissism excessive self-love and self-absorption. (pp. 356, 488)

narcolepsy a sleep disorder characterized by uncontrollable sleep attacks. The sufferer may lapse directly into REM sleep, often at inopportune times. (p. 95)

natural selection the principle that inherited traits that better enable an organism to survive and reproduce in a particular environment will (in competition with other trait variations) most likely be passed on to succeeding generations. (pp. 8, 75)

naturalistic observation a descriptive technique of observing and recording behavior in naturally occurring situations without trying to manipulate and control the situation. (p. 23)

nature–nurture issue the longstanding controversy over the relative contributions that genes and experience make to the development of psychological traits and behaviors. Today's science sees traits and behaviors arising from the interaction of nature and nurture. (p. 8)

near-death experience an altered state of consciousness reported after a close brush with death (such as cardiac arrest); often similar to drug-induced hallucinations. (p. 109)

negative reinforcement increasing behaviors by stopping or reducing aversive stimuli. A negative reinforcer is any stimulus that, when *removed* after a response, strengthens the response. (*Note:* Negative reinforcement is not punishment.) (p. 245)

nerves bundled axons that form neural cables connecting the central nervous system with muscles, glands, and sense organs. (p. 45)

nervous system the body's speedy, electrochemical communication network, consisting of all the nerve cells of the peripheral and central nervous systems. (p. 45)

neurogenesis the formation of new neurons. (p. 64)

neuron a nerve cell; the basic building block of the nervous system. (p. 39)

neurotransmitters chemical messengers that cross the synaptic gap between neurons. When released by the sending neuron, neurotransmitters travel across the synapse and bind to receptor sites on the receiving neuron, thereby influencing whether that neuron will generate a neural impulse. (p. 42)

neutral stimulus (NS) in classical conditioning, a stimulus that elicits no response before conditioning. (p. 236)

nicotine a stimulating and highly addictive psychoactive drug in tobacco. (p. 104)

night terrors a sleep disorder characterized by high arousal and an appearance of being terrified; unlike nightmares, night terrors occur during N3 sleep, within two or three hours of falling asleep, and are seldom remembered. (p. 95)

normal curve a symmetrical, bell-shaped curve that describes the distribution of many types of data; most scores fall near the mean (about 68 percent fall within one standard deviation of it) and fewer and fewer near the extremes. (Also called a *normal distribution*.) (pp. 331, A-3)

normative social influence influence resulting from a person's desire to gain approval or avoid disapproval. (p. 424)

norms understood rules for accepted and expected behavior. Norms prescribe "proper" behavior. (p. 421)

nudge a framing of choices by which governments and companies can, without coercion or altered incentives, encourage people to make choices that support their health, retirement savings, and well-being. (p. 304)

obesity defined as a body mass index (BMI) measurement of 30 or higher, which is calculated from our weight-to-height ratio. (Overweight individuals have a BMI of 25 or higher.) (p. 365)

object permanence the awareness that things continue to exist even when not perceived. (p. 126)

observational learning learning by observing others. (p. 259)

obsessive-compulsive disorder (OCD) a disorder characterized by unwanted repetitive thoughts (obsessions), actions (compulsions), or both. (p. 509)

occipital [ahk-SIP-uh-tuhl] **lobes** the portion of the cerebral cortex lying at the back of the head; includes areas that receive information from the visual fields. (p. 59)

Oedipus [ED-uh-puss] **complex** according to Freud, a boy's sexual desires toward his mother and feelings of jealousy and hatred for the rival father. (p. 465)

olfaction our sense of smell. (p. 225)

one-word stage the stage in speech development, from about age 1 to 2, during which a child speaks mostly in single words. (p. 315)

operant behavior behavior that operates on the environment, producing a consequence. (pp. 234, 243)

operant chamber in operant conditioning research, a chamber (also known as a *Skinner box*) containing a bar or key that an animal can manipulate to obtain a food or water reinforcer; attached devices record the animal's rate of bar pressing or key pecking. (p. 244)

operant conditioning a type of learning in which a behavior becomes more likely to recur if followed by a reinforcer or less likely to recur if followed by a punisher. (p. 243)

operational definition a carefully worded statement of the exact procedures (operations) used in a research study. For example, *human intelligence* may be operationally defined as what an intelligence test measures. (p. 20)

opiates opium and its derivatives, such as morphine and heroin; depress neural activity, temporarily lessening pain and anxiety. (p. 104)

opponent-process theory the theory that opposing retinal processes (red-green, blue-yellow, white-black) enable color vision. For example, some cells are stimulated by green and inhibited by red; others are stimulated by red and inhibited by green. (p. 204)

optic nerve the nerve that carries neural impulses from the eye to the brain. (p. 201)

organizational psychology an I/O psychology subfield that examines organizational influences on worker satisfaction and productivity and facilitates organizational change. (p. B-5)

ostracism deliberate social exclusion of individuals or groups. (p. 355)

other-race effect the tendency to recall faces of one's own race more accurately than faces of other races. (Also called the *crossrace effect* and the *own-race bias*.) (p. 438)

outgroup "them"—those perceived as different or apart from our ingroup. (p. 438)

overconfidence the tendency to be more confident than correct—to overestimate the accuracy of our beliefs and judgments. (p. 303)

panic disorder an anxiety disorder marked by unpredictable, minutes-long episodes of intense dread in which a person may experience terror and accompanying chest pain, choking, or other frightening sensations; often followed by worry over a possible next attack. (p. 507)

parallel processing processing many aspects of a stimulus or problem at once. (pp. 85, 207, 268)

paraphilias sexual arousal from fantasies, behaviors, or urges involving nonhuman objects, the suffering of self or others, and/or nonconsenting persons. (p. 175)

parapsychology the study of paranormal phenomena, including ESP and psychokinesis (also called *telekinesis*). (p. 230)

parasympathetic nervous system the division of the autonomic nervous system that calms the body, conserving its energy. (p. 46)

parietal [puh-RYE-uh-tuhl] **lobes** the portion of the cerebral cortex lying at the top of the head and toward the rear; receives sensory input for touch and body position. (p. 59)

partial (intermittent) reinforcement schedule reinforcing a response only part of the time; results in slower acquisition of a response but much greater resistance to extinction than does continuous reinforcement. (p. 246)

passionate love an aroused state of intense positive absorption in another, usually present at the beginning of a romantic relationship. (p. 451)

perception the process of organizing and interpreting sensory information, enabling us to recognize meaningful objects and events. (p. 190)

perceptual adaptation the ability to adjust to changed sensory input, including an artificially displaced or even inverted visual field. (p. 213)

perceptual constancy perceiving objects as unchanging (having consistent color, brightness, shape, and size) even as illumination and retinal images change. (p. 211)

perceptual set a mental predisposition to perceive one thing and not another. (p. 194)

peripheral nervous system (PNS) the sensory and motor neurons that connect the central nervous system (CNS) to the rest of the body. (p. 45)

peripheral route persuasion occurs when people are influenced by incidental cues, such as a speaker's attractiveness. (p. 418)

personal control our sense of controlling our environment rather than feeling helpless. (p. 396)

personality an individual's characteristic pattern of thinking, feeling, and acting. (p. 462)

personality disorders inflexible and enduring behavior patterns that impair social functioning. (p. 529)

personality inventory a questionnaire (often with *true-false* or *agree-disagree* items) on which people respond to items designed to gauge a wide range of feelings and behaviors; used to assess selected personality traits. (p. 477)

personnel psychology an I/O psychology subfield that helps with job seeking, and with employee recruitment, selection, placement, training, appraisal, and development. (p. B-5)

PET (positron emission tomography) scan a visual display of brain activity that detects where a radioactive form of glucose goes while the brain performs a given task. (p. 51)

phi phenomenon an illusion of movement created when two or more adjacent lights blink on and off in quick succession. (p. 211)

phobia an anxiety disorder marked by a persistent, irrational fear and avoidance of a specific object, activity, or situation. (p. 508)

phoneme in a language, the smallest distinctive sound unit. (p. 312)

physiological need a basic bodily requirement. (p. 349)

pitch a tone's experienced highness or lowness; depends on frequency. (p. 216)

pituitary gland the endocrine system's most influential gland. Under the influence of the hypothalamus, the pituitary regulates growth and controls other endocrine glands. (p. 48)

place theory in hearing, the theory that links the pitch we hear with the place where the cochlea's membrane is stimulated. (p. 219)

placebo [pluh-SEE-bo; Latin for "I shall please"] **effect** experimental results caused by expectations alone; any effect on behavior caused by the administration of an inert substance or condition, which the recipient assumes is an active agent. (p. 27)

plasticity the brain's ability to change, especially during childhood, by reorganizing after damage or by building new pathways based on experience. (pp. 39, 64)

polygraph a machine used in attempts to detect lies that measures emotion-linked changes in perspiration, heart rate, and breathing. (p. 374)

population all those in a group being studied, from which samples may be drawn. (*Note:* Except for national studies, this does not refer to a country's whole population.) (p. 24)

positive psychology the scientific study of human flourishing, with the goals of discovering and promoting strengths and virtues that help individuals and communities to thrive. (pp. 11, 407)

positive reinforcement increasing behaviors by presenting positive reinforcers. A positive reinforcer is any stimulus that, when *presented* after a response, strengthens the response. (p. 245)

posthypnotic suggestion a suggestion, made during a hypnosis session, to be carried out after the subject is no longer hypnotized; used by some clinicians to help control undesired symptoms and behaviors. (p. 225)

posttraumatic growth positive psychological changes as a result of struggling with extremely challenging circumstances and life crises. (p. 567)

posttraumatic stress disorder (PTSD) a disorder characterized by haunting memories, nightmares, hypervigilance, avoidance of trauma-related stimuli, social withdrawal, jumpy anxiety, numbness of feeling, and/or insomnia that lingers for four weeks or more after a traumatic experience. (p. 509)

predictive validity the success with which a test predicts the behavior it is designed to predict; it is assessed by computing the correlation between test scores and the criterion behavior. (Also called *criterion- related validity*.) (p. 331)

prejudice an unjustifiable and usually negative attitude toward a group and its members. Prejudice generally involves negative emotions, stereotyped beliefs, and a predisposition to discriminatory action. (p. 435)

preoperational stage in Piaget's theory, the stage (from about 2 to 6 or 7 years of age) during which a child learns to use language but does not yet comprehend the mental operations of concrete logic. (p. 127)

preparedness a biological predisposition to learn associations, such as between taste and nausea, that have survival value. (p. 254)

primary reinforcer an innately reinforcing stimulus, such as one that satisfies a biological need. (p. 246)

primary sex characteristics the body structures (ovaries, testes, and external genitalia) that make sexual reproduction possible. (p. 166)

priming the activation, often unconsciously, of certain associations, thus predisposing one's perception, memory, or response. (pp. 193, 280)

proactive interference the forwardacting disruptive effect of older learning on the recall of *new* information. (p. 287)

problem-focused coping attempting to alleviate stress directly—by changing the stressor or the way we interact with that stressor. (p. 395)

projective test a personality test, such as the Rorschach or TAT, that provides ambiguous images designed to trigger projection of one's inner dynamics. (p. 466)

prosocial behavior positive, constructive, helpful behavior. The opposite of antisocial behavior. (p. 261)

prototype a mental image or best example of a category. Matching new items to a prototype provides a quick and easy method for sorting items into categories (as when comparing feathered creatures to a prototypical bird, such as a crow). (p. 299)

psychiatry a branch of medicine dealing with psychological disorders; practiced by physicians who sometimes provide medical (for example, drug) treatments as well as psychological therapy. (p. 13)

psychoactive drug a chemical substance that alters perceptions and moods. (p. 101)

psychoanalysis (1) Freud's theory of personality that attributes thoughts and actions to unconscious motives and conflicts. (2) Freud's therapeutic technique used in treating psychological disorders. Freud believed the patient's free associations, resistances, dreams, and transferences—and the analyst's interpretations of them—released previously repressed feelings, allowing the patient to gain self-insight. (pp. 462, 537)

psychodynamic theories theories that view personality with a focus on the unconscious and the importance of childhood experiences. (p. 462)

psychodynamic therapy therapy deriving from the psychoanalytic tradition; views individuals as responding to unconscious forces and childhood experiences, and seeks to enhance self-insight. (p. 538)

psychological disorder a syndrome marked by a clinically significant disturbance in an individual's cognition, emotion regulation, or behavior. (p. 494)

psychology the science of behavior and mental processes. (p. 8)

psychoneuroimmunology the study of how psychological, neural, and endocrine processes together affect the immune system and resulting health. (p. 389)

psychopharmacology the study of the effects of drugs on mind and behavior. (p. 560)

psychosexual stages the childhood stages of development (oral, anal, phallic, latency, genital) during which, according to Freud, the id's pleasure-seeking energies focus on distinct erogenous zones. (p. 465)

psychosurgery surgery that removes or destroys brain tissue in an effort to change behavior. (p. 565)

psychotherapy treatment involving psychological techniques; consists of interactions between a trained therapist and someone seeking to overcome psychological difficulties or achieve personal growth. (p. 537)

psychotic disorders a group of disorders marked by irrational ideas, distorted perceptions, and a loss of contact with reality. (p. 522)

puberty the period of sexual maturation, during which a person becomes capable of reproducing. (pp. 141, 166)

punishment an event that tends to *decrease* the behavior that it follows. (p. 248)

random assignment assigning participants to experimental and control groups by chance, thus minimizing preexisting differences between the different groups. (p. 25)

random sample a sample that fairly represents a population because each member has an equal chance of inclusion. (p. 24)

range the difference between the highest and lowest scores in a distribution. (p. A-3)

recall a measure of memory in which the person must retrieve information learned earlier, as on a fill-in-the-blank test. (p. 267)

reciprocal determinism the interacting influences of behavior, internal cognition, and environment. (p. 482)

reciprocity norm an expectation that people will help, not hurt, those who have helped them. (p. 455)

recognition a measure of memory in which the person identifies items previously learned, as on a multiple-choice test. (p. 267)

reconsolidation a process in which previously stored memories, when retrieved, are potentially altered before being stored again. (p. 289)

reflex a simple, automatic response to a sensory stimulus, such as the knee-jerk response. (p. 47)

refractory period (1) in neural processing, a brief resting pause that occurs after a neuron has fired; subsequent action potentials cannot occur until the axon returns to its resting state. (2) in human sexuality, a resting period that occurs after orgasm, during which a person cannot achieve another orgasm. (pp. 41, 175)

regression toward the mean the tendency for extreme or unusual scores or events to fall back (regress) toward the average. (p. A-5)

reinforcement in operant conditioning, any event that *strengthens* the behavior it follows. (p. 244)

reinforcement schedule a pattern that defines how often a desired response will be reinforced. (p. 246)

relational aggression an act of aggression (physical or verbal) intended to harm a person's relationship or social standing. (p. 162)

relative deprivation the perception that one is worse off relative to those with whom one compares oneself. (p. 411)

relearning a measure of memory that assesses the amount of time saved when learning material again. (p. 267)

reliability the extent to which a test yields consistent results, as assessed by the consistency of scores on two halves of the test, on alternative forms of the test, or on retesting. (p. 331)

REM (R) sleep rapid eye movement sleep; a recurring sleep stage during which vivid dreams commonly occur. Also known as *paradoxical sleep*, because the muscles are relaxed (except for minor twitches) but other body systems are active. (p. 86)

REM rebound the tendency for REM sleep to increase following REM sleep deprivation. (p. 99)

repetitive transcranial magnetic stimulation (rTMS) the application of repeated pulses of magnetic energy to the brain; used to stimulate or suppress brain activity. (p. 565)

replication repeating the essence of a research study, usually with different participants in different situations, to see whether the basic finding can be reproduced. (p. 20)

representativeness heuristic estimating the likelihood of events in terms of how well they seem to represent, or match, particular prototypes; may lead us to ignore other relevant information. (p. 301)

repression in psychoanalytic theory, the basic defense mechanism that banishes from consciousness anxiety-arousing thoughts, feelings, and memories. (pp. 289, 465)

resilience the personal strength that helps most people cope with stress and recover from adversity and even trauma. (p. 567)

resistance in psychoanalysis, the blocking from consciousness of anxiety-laden material. (p. 537)

respondent behavior behavior that occurs as an automatic response to some stimulus. (pp. 234, 243)

reticular formation a nerve network that travels through the brainstem into the thalamus and plays an important role in controlling arousal. (p. 54)

retina the light-sensitive inner surface of the eye, containing the receptor rods and cones plus layers of neurons that begin the processing of visual information. (p. 201)

retinal disparity a binocular cue for perceiving depth. By comparing retinal images from the two eyes, the brain computes distance— the greater the disparity (difference) between the two images, the closer the object. (p. 208)

retrieval the process of getting information out of memory storage. (p. 268)

retroactive interference the backward- acting disruptive effect of newer learning on the recall of *old* information. (p. 287)

retrograde amnesia an inability to retrieve information from one's past. (p. 285)

reuptake a neurotransmitter's reabsorption by the sending neuron. (p. 42)

rods retinal receptors that detect black, white, and gray, and are sensitive to movement; necessary for peripheral and twilight vision, when cones don't respond. (p. 201)

role a set of expectations (norms) about a social position, defining how those in the position ought to behave. (pp. 169, 418)

Rorschach inkblot test the most widely used projective test; a set of 10 inkblots, designed by Hermann Rorschach; seeks to identify people's inner feelings by analyzing their interpretations of the blots. (p. 466)

rumination compulsive fretting; *overthinking* our problems and their causes. (p. 521)

savant syndrome a condition in which a person otherwise limited in mental ability has an exceptional specific skill, such as in computation or drawing. (p. 324)

scaffold a framework that offers children temporary support as they develop higher levels of thinking. (p. 129)

scapegoat theory the theory that prejudice offers an outlet for anger by providing someone to blame. (p. 438)

scatterplot a graphed cluster of dots, each of which represents the values of two variables. The slope of the points suggests the direction of the relationship between the two variables. The amount of scatter suggests the strength of the correlation (little scatter indicates high correlation). (p. A-4)

schema a concept or framework that organizes and interprets information. (p. 125)

schizophrenia a disorder characterized by delusions, hallucinations, disorganized speech, and/or diminished, inappropriate emotional expression. (p. 522)

secondary sex characteristics nonreproductive sexual traits, such as female breasts and hips, male voice quality, and body hair. (p. 166)

selective attention the focusing of conscious awareness on a particular stimulus. (p. 81)

self in contemporary psychology, assumed to be the center of personality, the organizer of our thoughts, feelings, and actions. (p. 486)

self-actualization according to Maslow, one of the ultimate psychological needs that arises after basic physical and psychological needs are met and self-esteem is achieved; the motivation to fulfill one's potential. (p. 470)

self-concept all our thoughts and feelings about ourselves, in answer to the question, "Who am I?" (p. 472)

self-control the ability to control impulses and delay short-term gratification for greater long-term rewards. (p. 398)

self-determination theory the theory that we feel motivated to satisfy our needs for competence, autonomy, and relatedness. (p. 353)

self-disclosure the act of revealing intimate aspects of ourselves to others. (p. 453)

self-efficacy one's sense of competence and effectiveness. (p. 486)

self-esteem one's feelings of high or low self-worth. (p. 486)

self-fulfilling prophecy a belief that leads to its own fulfillment. (p. 456)

self-serving bias a readiness to perceive oneself favorably. (p. 486)

self-transcendence according to Maslow, the striving for identity, meaning, and purpose beyond the self. (p. 470)

semantic memory explicit memory of facts and general knowledge; one of our two conscious memory systems (the other is *episodic memory*). (p. 276)

sensation the process by which our sensory receptors and nervous system receive and represent stimulus energies from our environment. (p. 190)

sensorimotor stage in Piaget's theory, the stage (from birth to nearly 2 years of age) during which infants know the world mostly in terms of their sensory impressions and motor activities. (p. 126)

sensorineural hearing loss hearing loss caused by damage to the cochlea's receptor cells or to the auditory nerves; the most common form of hearing loss, also called *nerve deafness*. (p. 219)

sensory adaptation diminished sensitivity as a consequence of constant stimulation. (p. 194)

sensory interaction the principle that one sense may influence another, as when the smell of food influences its taste. (p. 228)

sensory memory the immediate, very brief recording of sensory information in the memory system. (p. 268)

sensory (afferent) neurons neurons that carry incoming information from the body's tissues and sensory receptors to the brain and spinal cord. (p. 45)

sensory receptors sensory nerve endings that respond to stimuli. (p. 190)

sequential processing processing one aspect of a stimulus or problem at a time; generally used to process new information or to solve difficult problems. (p. 85)

serial position effect our tendency to recall best the last (*recency effect*) and first (*primacy effect*) items in a list. (p. 282)

set point the point at which your "weight thermostat" may be set. When your body falls below this weight, increased hunger and a lowered metabolic rate may combine to restore lost weight. (p. 363)

sex in psychology, the biologically influenced characteristics by which people define *male* and *female*. (p. 162)

sexual aggression any physical or verbal behavior of a sexual nature that is intended to harm someone physically or emotionally. Can be expressed as either *sexual harassment* or *sexual assault*. (p. 169)

sexual dysfunction a problem that consistently impairs sexual arousal or functioning at any point in the sexual response cycle. (p. 175)

sexual orientation an enduring sexual attraction toward members of one's own sex (*homosexual* orientation), the other sex (*heterosexual* orientation), or both sexes (*bisexual* orientation). (p. 178)

sexual response cycle the four stages of sexual responding described by Masters and Johnson—excitement, plateau, orgasm, and resolution. (p. 175)

shallow processing encoding on a basic level, based on the structure or appearance of words. (p. 273)

shaping an operant conditioning procedure in which reinforcers guide behavior toward closer and closer approximations of the desired behavior. (p. 244)

short-term memory activated memory that holds a few items briefly, such as digits of a phone number while calling, before the information is stored or forgotten. (p. 268)

signal detection theory a theory predicting how and when we detect the presence of a faint stimulus (*signal*) amid background stimulation (*noise*). Assumes there is no single absolute threshold and that detection depends partly on a person's experience, expectations, motivation, and alertness. (p. 191)

sleep a periodic, natural loss of consciousness— as distinct from unconsciousness resulting from a coma, general anesthesia, or hibernation. (Adapted from Dement, 1999.) (p. 86)

sleep apnea a sleep disorder characterized by temporary cessations of breathing during sleep and repeated momentary awakenings. (p. 95)

social clock the culturally preferred timing of social events such as marriage, parenthood, and retirement. (p. 154)

social exchange theory the theory that our social behavior is an exchange process, the aim of which is to maximize benefits and minimize costs. (p. 455)

social facilitation improved performance on simple or well-learned tasks in the presence of others. (p. 429)

social identity the "we" aspect of our self-concept; the part of our answer to "Who am I?" that comes from our group memberships. (p. 147)

social leadership group-oriented leadership that builds teamwork, mediates conflict, and offers support. (p. B-10)

social learning theory the theory that we learn social behavior by observing and imitating and by being rewarded or punished. (p. 169)

social loafing the tendency for people in a group to exert less effort when pooling their efforts toward attaining a common goal than when individually accountable. (p. 431)

social psychology the scientific study of how we think about, influence, and relate to one another. (p. 416)

social script a culturally modeled guide for how to act in various situations. (pp. 176, 444)

social trap a situation in which the conflicting parties, by each pursuing their self-interest rather than the good of the group, become caught in mutually destructive behavior. (p. 456)

social-cognitive perspective a view of behavior as influenced by the interaction between people's traits (including their thinking) and their social context. (p. 482)

social-responsibility norm an expectation that people will help those needing their help. (p. 455)

somatic nervous system the division of the peripheral nervous system that controls the body's skeletal muscles. Also called the *skeletal nervous system.* (p. 45)

somatosensory cortex an area at the front of the parietal lobes that registers and processes body touch and movement sensations. (p. 61)

source amnesia faulty memory for how, when, or where information was learned or imagined. (Also called *source misattribution.*) Source amnesia, along with the misinformation effect, is at the heart of many false memories. (p. 291)

spacing effect the tendency for distributed study or practice to yield better long-term retention than is achieved through massed study or practice. (p. 273)

spermarche [sper-MAR-key] the first ejaculation. (p. 166)

split brain a condition resulting from surgery that isolates the brain's two hemispheres by cutting the fibers (mainly those of the corpus callosum) connecting them. (p. 64)

spontaneous recovery the reappearance, after a pause, of an extinguished conditioned response. (p. 238)

spotlight effect overestimating others' noticing and evaluating our appearance, performance, and blunders (as if we presume a spotlight shines on us). (p. 486)

SQ3R a study method incorporating five steps: *Survey, Question, Read, Retrieve, Review.* (p. 33)

standard deviation a computed measure of how much scores vary around the mean score. (p. A-3)

standardization defining uniform testing procedures and meaningful scores by comparison with the performance of a pretested group. (p. 329)

Stanford-Binet the widely used American revision (by Terman at Stanford University) of Binet's original intelligence test. (p. 329)

statistical significance a statistical statement of how likely it is that an obtained result occurred by chance. (p. A-7)

stereotype a generalized (sometimes accurate but often overgeneralized) belief about a group of people. (p. 435)

stereotype threat a self-confirming concern that one will be evaluated based on a negative stereotype (p. 344)

stimulants drugs (such as caffeine, nicotine, and the more powerful cocaine, amphetamines, methamphetamine, and Ecstasy) that excite neural activity and speed up body functions. (p. 104)

stimulus any event or situation that evokes a response. (pp. 234, 243)

storage the process of retaining encoded information over time. (p. 268)

stranger anxiety the fear of strangers that infants commonly display, beginning by about 8 months of age. (p. 133)

stress the process by which we perceive and respond to certain events, called *stressors,* that we appraise as threatening or challenging. (p. 385)

structuralism an early school of thought promoted by Wundt and Titchener; used introspection to reveal the structure of the human mind. (p. 5)

structured interview an interview process that asks the same job-relevant questions of all applicants, each of whom is rated on established scales. (p. B-6)

subjective well-being self-perceived happiness or satisfaction with life. Used along with measures of objective well-being (for example, physical and economic indicators) to evaluate people's quality of life. (p. 407)

subliminal below one's absolute threshold for conscious awareness. (p. 192)

substance use disorder a disorder characterized by continued substance craving and use despite significant life disruption and/or physical risk. (p. 101)

superego the part of personality that, according to Freud, represents internalized ideals and provides standards for judgment (the conscience) and for future aspirations. (p. 465)

superordinate goals shared goals that override differences among people and require their cooperation. (p. 459)

suprachiasmatic nucleus (SCN) a pair of cell clusters in the hypothalamus that controls circadian rhythm. In response to light, the SCN causes the pineal gland to adjust melatonin production, thus modifying our feelings of sleepiness. (p. 90)

survey a descriptive technique for obtaining the self-reported attitudes or behaviors of a particular group, usually by questioning a representative, *random sample* of the group. (p. 23)

sympathetic nervous system the division of the autonomic nervous system that arouses the body, mobilizing its energy. (p. 46)

synapse [SIN-aps] the junction between the axon tip of the sending neuron and the dendrite or cell body of the receiving neuron. The tiny gap at this junction is called the *synaptic gap* or *synaptic cleft.* (p. 42)

systematic desensitization a type of exposure therapy that associates a pleasant relaxed state with gradually increasing anxiety-triggering stimuli. Commonly used to treat phobias. (p. 541)

task leadership goal-oriented leadership that sets standards, organizes work, and focuses attention on goals. (p. B-10)

telegraphic speech the early speech stage in which a child speaks like a telegram—"go car"—using mostly nouns and verbs. (p. 315)

temperament a person's characteristic emotional reactivity and intensity. (p. 135)

temporal lobes the portion of the cerebral cortex lying roughly above the ears; includes the auditory areas, each receiving information primarily from the opposite ear. (p. 59)

tend-and-befriend response under stress, people (especially women) often provide support to others (tend) and bond with and seek support from others (befriend). (p. 389)

teratogens (literally, "monster makers") agents, such as chemicals and viruses, that can reach the embryo or fetus during prenatal development and cause harm. (p. 120)

testing effect enhanced memory after retrieving, rather than simply rereading, information. Also referred to as a *retrieval practice effect* or *test-enhanced learning.* (pp. 33, 273)

testosterone the most important male sex hormone. Both males and females have it, but the additional testosterone in males stimulates the growth of the male sex organs during the fetal period, and the development of the male sex characteristics during puberty. (p. 173)

thalamus [THAL-uh-muss] the brain's sensory control center, located on top of the brainstem; it directs messages to the sensory receiving areas in the cortex and transmits replies to the cerebellum and medulla. (p. 54)

THC the major active ingredient in marijuana; triggers a variety of effects, including mild hallucinations. (p. 109)

Thematic Apperception Test (TAT) a projective test in which people express their inner feelings and interests through the stories they make up about ambiguous scenes. (p. 466)

theory an explanation using an integrated set of principles that organizes observations and predicts behaviors or events. (p. 19)

theory of mind people's ideas about their own and others' mental states— about their feelings, perceptions, and thoughts, and the behaviors these might predict. (p. 128)

therapeutic alliance a bond of trust and mutual understanding between a therapist and client, who work together constructively to overcome the client's problem. (p. 555)

threshold the level of stimulation required to trigger a neural impulse. (p. 41)

token economy an operant conditioning procedure in which people earn a token for exhibiting a desired behavior and can later exchange the tokens for privileges or treats. (p. 543)

tolerance the diminishing effect with regular use of the same dose of a drug, requiring the user to take larger and larger doses before experiencing the drug's effect. (p. 102)

top-down processing information processing guided by higher-level mental processes, as when we construct perceptions drawing on our experience and expectations. (p. 190)

trait a characteristic pattern of behavior or a disposition to feel and act in certain ways, as assessed by self-report inventories and peer reports. (p. 475)

transduction conversion of one form of energy into another. In sensation, the transforming of stimulus energies, such as sights, sounds, and smells, into neural impulses our brain can interpret. (p. 199)

transference in psychoanalysis, the patient's transfer to the analyst of emotions linked with other relationships (such as love or hatred for a parent). (p. 537)

transgender an umbrella term describing people whose gender identity or expression differs from that associated with their birth-designated sex. (p. 170)

two-factor theory the Schachter-Singer theory that to experience emotion one must (1) be physically aroused and (2) cognitively label the arousal. (p. 369)

two-word stage beginning about age 2, the stage in speech development during which a child speaks mostly in two-word statements. (p. 315)

Type A Friedman and Rosenman's term for competitive, hard-driving, impatient, verbally aggressive, and anger-prone people. (p. 391)

Type B Friedman and Rosenman's term for easygoing, relaxed people. (p. 391)

unconditional positive regard a caring, accepting, nonjudgmental attitude, which Carl Rogers believed would help people develop self-awareness and self-acceptance. (pp. 470, 540)

unconditioned response (UR) in classical conditioning, an unlearned, naturally occurring response (such as salivation) to an unconditioned stimulus (US) (such as food in the mouth). (p. 236)

unconditioned stimulus (US) in classical conditioning, a stimulus that unconditionally— naturally and automatically— triggers an unconditioned response (UR). (p. 236)

unconscious according to Freud, a reservoir of mostly unacceptable thoughts, wishes, feelings, and memories. According to contemporary psychologists, information processing of which we are unaware. (p. 463)

validity the extent to which a test measures or predicts what it is supposed to. (See also *predictive validity*.) (p. 331)

variable anything that can vary and is feasible and ethical to measure. (p. A-4)

variable-interval schedule in operant conditioning, a reinforcement schedule that reinforces a response at unpredictable time intervals. (p. 248)

variable-ratio schedule in operant conditioning, a reinforcement schedule that reinforces a response after an unpredictable number of responses. (p. 246)

vestibular sense our sense of balance— our sense of body movement and position that enables our sense of balance. (p. 227)

virtual reality exposure therapy a counterconditioning technique that treats anxiety through creative electronic simulations in which people can safely face their greatest fears, such as airplane flying, spiders, or public speaking. (p. 541)

visual cliff a laboratory device for testing depth perception in infants and young animals. (p. 208)

wavelength the distance from the peak of one light wave or sound wave to the peak of the next. Electromagnetic wavelengths vary from the short gamma waves to the long pulses of radio transmission. (p. 199)

Weber's law the principle that, to be perceived as different, two stimuli must differ by a constant minimum percentage (rather than a constant amount). (p. 193)

Wechsler Adult Intelligence Scale (WAIS) the WAIS and its companion versions for children are the most widely used intelligence tests; they contain verbal and performance (nonverbal) subtests. (p. 329)

Wernicke's area a brain area involved in language comprehension and expression; usually in the left temporal lobe. (p. 316)

withdrawal the discomfort and distress that follow discontinuing an addictive drug or behavior. (p. 102)

working memory a newer understanding of short-term memory that adds conscious, active processing of incoming sensory information, and of information retrieved from long-term memory. (p. 269)

X chromosome the sex chromosome found in both males and females. Females typically have two X chromosomes; males typically have one. An X chromosome from each parent produces a female child. (p. 166)

Y chromosome the sex chromosome typically found only in males. When paired with an X chromosome from the mother, it produces a male child. (p. 166)

Yerkes-Dodson law the principle that performance increases with arousal only up to a point, beyond which performance decreases. (p. 351)

Young-Helmholtz trichromatic (three-color) theory the theory that the retina contains three different types of color receptors—one most sensitive to red, one to green, one to blue—which, when stimulated in combination, can produce the perception of any color. (p. 203)

zygote the fertilized egg; it enters a 2-week period of rapid cell division and develops into an embryo. (p. 119)

References

AAA. (2010). *Asleep at the wheel: The prevalence and impact of drowsy driving.* AAA Foundation for Traffic Safety (aaafoundation.org/pdf/2010DrowsyDrivingReport.pdf). (p. 94)

AAA. (2015). *Teen driver safety: Environmental factors and driver behaviors in teen driver crashes.* AAA Foundation for Traffic Safety (aaafoundation.org/sites/default/files/2015TeenCrashCausationFS.pdf). (p. 82)

AAMC. (2014). *Medical students, selected years, 1965–2013.* Association of American Medical Colleges (aamc.org). (pp. 164, 187)

AAMC. (2016). *Total enrollment by U.S. medical school and sex, 2011–2012 through 2015–2016.* Association of American Medical Colleges (aamc.org). (p. 187)

Aarts, H., & Custers, R. (2012). Unconscious goal pursuit: Nonconscious goal regulation and motivation. In R. M. Ryan (Ed.), *The Oxford handbook of human motivation* (pp. 232–247). New York: Oxford University Press. (p. 394)

Abrams, D. B., & Wilson, G. T. (1983). Alcohol, sexual arousal, and self-control. *Journal of Personality and Social Psychology, 45,* 188–198. (p. 104)

Abrams, L. (2008). Tip-of-the-tongue states yield language insights. *American Scientist, 96,* 234–239. (p. 287)

Abrams, M. (2002, June). Sight unseen—Restoring a blind man's vision is now a real possibility through stem-cell surgery. But even perfect eyes cannot see unless the brain has been taught to use them. *Discover, 23,* 54–60. (p. 213)

Abramson, L. Y., Metalsky, G. I., & Alloy, L. B. (1989). Hopelessness depression: A theory-based subtype. *Psychological Review, 96,* 358–372. (p. 396, 520)

Abramson, L. Y., Seligman, M. E. P., & Teasdale, J. D. (1978). Learned helplessness in humans: Critique and reformulation. *Journal of Abnormal Psychology, 87,* 49–74. (p. 396)

Abuhamdeh, S., Csikszentmihalyi, M., & Jalal, B. (2015). Enjoying the possibility of defeat: Outcome uncertainty, suspense, and intrinsic motivation. *Motivation and Emotion, 39,* 1–10. (p. 385)

Academy of Science of South Africa. (2015). *Diversity in human sexuality: Implications for policy in Africa.* Retrieved from assaf.co.za/wp-content/uploads/2015/06/8-June-Diversity-in-human-sexuality1.pdf (p. 178)

Acevedo, B. P., & Aron, A. (2009). Does a long-term relationship kill romantic love? *Review of General Psychology, 13,* 59–65. (p. 451)

Acevedo, B. P., Aron, A., Fisher, H. E., & Brown, L. L. (2012). Neural correlates of long-term intense romantic love. *Social Cognitive and Affective Neuroscience, 7,* 145–159. (p. 451)

ACHA. (2009). *American College Health Association-National College Health Assessment II: Reference group executive summary Fall 2008.* Baltimore: American College Health Association. (p. 513)

Ackerman, D. (2004). *An alchemy of mind: The marvel and mystery of the brain.* New York: Scribner. (p. 42)

ACMD. (2009). *MDMA ('Ecstasy'): A review of its harms and classification under the Misuse of Drugs Act 1971.* London: Home Office & Advisory Council on the Misuse of Drugs. (pp. 107, 108)

Adachi, T., Fujino, H., Nakae, A., Mashimo, T., & Sasaki, J. (2014). A meta-analysis of hypnosis for chronic pain problems: A comparison between hypnosis, standard care, and other psychological interventions. *International Journal of Clinical and Experimental Hypnosis, 62,* 1–28. (p. 224)

Adams, H. E., Wright, L. W., Jr., & Lohr, B. A. (1996). Is homophobia associated with homosexual arousal? *Journal of Abnormal Psychology, 105,* 440–446. (p. 470)

Adelmann, P. K., Antonucci, T. C., Crohan, S. F., & Coleman, L. M. (1989). Empty nest, cohort, and employment in the well-being of midlife women. *Sex Roles, 20,* 173–189. (p. 157)

Adelstein, J. S., Shehzad, Z., Mennes, M., DeYoung, C. G., Zuo, X.-N., Kelly, C., . . . Milham, M. P. (2011). Personality is reflected in the brain's intrinsic functional architecture. *PLoS ONE, 6,* e27633. (p. 478)

Ader, R., & Cohen, N. (1985). CNS-immune system interactions: Conditioning phenomena. *Behavioral and Brain Sciences, 8,* 379–394. (p. 241)

Aderka, I. M., Nickerson, A., Bøe, H. J., & Hofmann, S. G. (2012). Sudden gains during psychological treatments of anxiety and depression: A meta-analysis. *Journal of Consulting and Clinical Psychology, 80,* 93–101. (p. 552)

Adler, J. (2012). Erasing painful memories. *Scientific American, 306,* 56–61. (p. 279)

Adler, J. M., Lodi-Smith, J., Philippe, F. L., & Houle, I. (2016). The incremental validity of narrative identity in predicting well-being: A review of the field and recommendations for the future. *Personality and Social Psychology Review, 20,* 142–175. (p. 472)

Adolph, K. E., Kretch, K. S., & LoBue, V. (2014). Fear of heights in infants? *Current Directions in Psychological Science, 23,* 60–66. (p. 209)

Affleck, G., Tennen, H., Urrows, S., & Higgins, P. (1994). Person and contextual features of daily stress reactivity: Individual differences in relations of undesirable daily events with mood disturbance and chronic pain intensity. *Journal of Personality and Social Psychology, 66,* 329–340. (p. 408)

AFL-CIO. (2016). Executive pay. American Federation of Labor and Congress of Industrial Organizations (aflcio.org/Corporate-Watch/Paywatch-2016). (p. 410)

AFSP. (2015). *Facts and figures.* American Foundation for Suicide Prevention (afsp.org/understanding-suicide/facts-and-figures). (p. 500)

Agerström, J., Björklund, F., Carlsson, R., & Rooth, D.-O. (2012). Warm and competent Hassan = cold and incompetent Eric: A harsh equation of real-life hiring discrimination. *Basic and Applied Social Psychology, 34,* 359–366. (p. 437)

Agrillo, C. (2011). Near-death experience: Out-of-body and out-of-brain? *Review of General Psychology, 15,* 1–10. (p. 108)

Agudelo, L. Z., Femenía, T., Orhan, F., Porsmyr-Palmertz, M., Goiny, M., Martinez-Redondo, V., . . . Ruas, J. L. (2014). Skeletal muscle PGC-1α1 modulates kynurenine metabolism and mediates resilience to stress-induced depression. *Cell, 159,* 33–45. (p. 402)

Ahrén, J. C., Chiesa, F., Koupil, I., Magnusson, C., Dalman, C., & Goodman, A. (2013). We are family—parents, siblings, and eating disorders in a prospective total-population study of 250,000 Swedish males and females. *International Journal of Eating Disorders, 46,* 693–700. (p. 532)

Ai, A. L., Park, C. L., Huang, B., Rodgers, W., & Tice, T. N. (2007). Psychosocial mediation of religious coping styles: A study of short-term psychological distress following cardiac surgery. *Personality and Social Psychology Bulletin, 33,* 867–882. (p. 406)

Aichele, S., Rabbitt, P., & Ghisletta, P. (2016). Think fast, feel fine, live long: A 29-year study of cognition, health, and survival in middle-aged and older adults. *Psychological Science, 27,* 518–529. (p. 152)

Aiello, J. R., Thompson, D. D., & Brodzinsky, D. M. (1983). How funny is crowding anyway? Effects of room size, group size, and the introduction of humor. *Basic and Applied Social Psychology, 4,* 193–207. (p. 430)

Aimone, J. B., Jessberger, S., & Gage, F. H. (2010). Adult neurogenesis. *Scholarpedia, 2*(2), 2100. Retrieved from http://www.scholarpedia.org/article/Adult_neurogenesis (p. 64)

Ainsworth, M. D. S. (1973). The development of infant-mother attachment. In B. Caldwell & H. Ricciuti (Eds.), *Review of child development research* (Vol. 3). Chicago: University of Chicago Press. (p. 134)

Ainsworth, M. D. S. (1979). Infant-mother attachment. *American Psychologist, 34,* 932–937. (p. 134)

Ainsworth, M. D. S. (1989). Attachments beyond infancy. *American Psychologist, 44,* 709–716. (p. 134)

Airan, R. D., Meltzer, L. A., Roy, M., Gong, Y., Chen, H., & Deisseroth, K. (2007). High-speed imaging reveals neurophysiological links to behavior in an animal model of depression. *Science, 317,* 819–823. (p. 519)

Akbarian, S., Liu, C., Knowles, J. A., Vaccarino, F. M., Farnham, P. J., Crawford, G. E., . . . Mill, J. (2015). The PsychENCODE project. *Nature Neuroscience, 18,* 1707–1712. (p. 53)

Åkerlund, D., Golsteyn, B. H., Grönqvist, H., & Lindahl, L. (2016). Time discounting and criminal behavior. *PNAS, 113,* 6160–6165. (p. 247)

Akers, K. G., Martinez-Canabal, A., Restivo, L., Yiu, A. P., De Cristofara, A., Hsiang, H.-L., . . . Frankland, P. W. (2014). Hippocampal neurogenesis regulates forgetting during adulthood and infancy. *Science, 344,* 598–602. (pp. 124, 277)

Akiyama, M., Okada, Y., Kanai, M., Takahashi, A., Momozawa, Y., Ikeda, M., . . . Iwasaki, M. (2017). Genome-wide association study identifies 112 new loci for body mass index in the Japanese population. *Nature Genetics, 49,* 1458–1467. (p. 365)

Aknin, L. B., Barrington-Leigh, C., Dunn, E. W., Helliwell, J. F., Burns, J., Biswas-Diener, R., . . . Norton, M. I. (2013). Prosocial spending and well-being: Cross-cultural evidence for a psychological universal. *Journal of Personality and Social Psychology, 104,* 635–652. (pp. 407, 455)

Aknin, L. B., Broesch, T., Kiley Hamlin, J., & Van de Vondervoort, J. W. (2015). Pro-social behavior leads to happiness in a small-scale rural society. *Journal of Experimental Psychology: General, 144,* 788–795. (p. 407)

Aknin, L. B., & Human, L. J. (2015). Give a piece of you: Gifts that reflect givers promote closeness. *Journal of Experimental Social Psychology, 60,* 8–16. (p. 407)

Akpinar, E., & Berger, J. (2015). Drivers of cultural success: The case of sensory metaphors. *Journal of Personality and Social Psychology, 109,* 20–34. (p. 272)

Alanko, K., Santtila, P., Harlaar, N., Witting, K., Varjonen, M., Jern, P., . . . Sandnabba, N. K. (2010). Common genetic effects of gender atypical behavior in childhood and sexual orientation in adulthood: A study of Finnish twins. *Archives of Sexual Behavior, 39,* 81–92. (p. 181)

al-Asaadi, M. (2016). "We sleep afraid, we wake up afraid": A child's life in Yemen. *The New York Times* (nytimes.com). (p. 388)

Albee, G. W. (1986). Toward a just society: Lessons from observations on the primary prevention of psychopathology. *American Psychologist, 41,* 891–898. (p. 566)

Albee, G. W. (2006). Historical overview of primary prevention of psychopathology: Address to the 3rd world conference on the promotion of mental health and prevention of mental and behavioral disorders. September 15–17, 2004, Auckland, New Zealand. *The Journal of Primary Prevention, 27,* 449–456. (p. 566)

Albert, D., Chein, J., & Steinberg, L. (2013). Peer influences on adolescent decision making. *Current Directions in Psychological Science, 22,* 80–86. (p. 147)

Alcock, J. E. (2011, March/April). Back from the future: Parapsychology and the Bem affair. *Skeptical Inquirer,* pp. 31–39. (p. 231)

Aldao, A., & Nolen-Hoeksema, S. (2010). Emotion-regulation strategies across psychopathology: A meta-analytic review. *Clinical Psychology Review, 30,* 217–237. (p. 546)

Aleman, A., Kahn, R. S., & Selten, J.-P. (2003). Sex differences in the risk of schizophrenia: Evidence from meta-analysis. *Archives of General Psychiatry, 60,* 565–571. (p. 524)

Alexander, L., & Tredoux, C. (2010). The spaces between us: A spatial analysis of informal segregation. *Journal of Social Issues, 66,* 367–386. (p. 457)

Al Ibraheem, B., Kira, I. A., Aljakoub, J., & Al Ibraheem, A. (2017). The health effect of the Syrian conflict on IDPs and refugees. *Peace and Conflict: Journal of Peace Psychology, 23,* 140–152. (p. 388)

Allan, B. A. (2017). Task significance and meaningful work: A longitudinal study. *Journal of Vocational Behavior, 102,* 174–182. (p. B-9)

Allard, F., & Burnett, N. (1985). Skill in sport. *Canadian Journal of Psychology, 39,* 294–312. (p. 271)

Allen, J. P., Uchino, B. N., & Hafen, C. A. (2015). Running with the pack: Teen peer-relationship qualities as predictors of adult physical health. *Psychological Science, 26,* 1574–1583. (p. 352)

Allen, J., Weinrich, M., Hoppitt, W., & Rendell, L. (2013). Network-based diffusion analysis reveals cultural transmission of lobtail feeding in humpback whales. *Science, 340,* 485–488. (p. 259)

Allen, K. (2003). Are pets a healthy pleasure? The influence of pets on blood pressure. *Current Directions in Psychological Science, 12,* 236–239. (p. 401)

Allen, M. S., & Jones, M. V. (2014). The "home advantage" in athletic competitions. *Current Directions in Psychological Science, 23,* 48–53. (p. 429)

Allen, M., D'Alessio, D., & Emmers-Sommer, T. M. (2000). Reactions of criminal sexual offenders to pornography: A meta-analytic summary. In M. Roloff (Ed.), *Communication Yearbook 22* (pp. 139–169). Thousand Oaks, CA: Sage. (p. 176)

Allen, M., Emmers, T. M., Gebhardt, L., & Giery, M. (1995). Pornography and rape myth acceptance. *Journal of Communication, 45,* 5–26. (p. 176)

Allen, M. W., Gupta, R., & Monnier, A. (2008). The interactive effect of cultural symbols and human values on taste evaluation. *Journal of Consumer Research, 35,* 294–308. (p. 225)

Allen, T., & Sherman, J. (2011). Ego threat and intergroup bias: A test of motivated-activation versus self-regulatory accounts. *Psychological Science, 22,* 331–333. (p. 487)

Allen, T. D., Golden, T. D., & Shockley, K. M. (2015). How effective is telecommuting? Assessing the status of our scientific findings. *Psychological Science in the Public Interest, 16,* 40–68. (pp. B-3, B-8)

Allesøe, K., Hundrup, V. A., Thomsen, J. F., & Osler, M. (2010). Psychosocial work environment and risk of ischaemic heart disease in women: The Danish Nurse Cohort Study. *Occupational and Environmental Medicine, 67,* 318–322. (p. 392)

Alloy, L. B., Abramson, L. Y., Whitehouse, W. G., Hogan, M. E., Tashman, N. A., Steinberg, D. L., . . . Donovan, P. (1999). Depressogenic cognitive styles: Predictive validity, information processing and personality characteristics, and developmental origins. *Behaviour Research and Therapy, 37,* 503–531. (p. 520)

Alloy, L. B., Hamilton, J. L., Hamlat, E. J., & Abramson, L. Y. (2016). Pubertal development, emotion regulatory styles, and the emergence of sex differences in internalizing disorders and symptoms in adolescence. *Clinical Psychological Science, 4,* 867–881. (p. 142)

Allport, G. W. (1954). *The nature of prejudice.* New York: Addison-Wesley. (pp. 21, 438)

Allport, G. W., & Odbert, H. S. (1936). Trait-names: A psycho-lexical study. *Psychological Monographs, 47.* (p. 475)

Ally, B. A., Hussey, E. P., & Donahue, M. J. (2013). A case of hyperthymesia: Rethinking the role of the amygdala in autobiographical memory. *Neurocase, 19,* 166–181. (p. 284)

Almas, A. N., Degnan, K. A., Nelson, C. A., Zeanah, C. H., & Fox, N. A. (2017). IQ at age 12 following a history of institutional care: Findings from the Bucharest Early Intervention Project. *Developmental Psychology, 52,* 1858–1866. (p. 337)

Almås, I., Cappelen, A. W., Sørensen, E. Ø., & Tungodden, B. (2010). Fairness and the development of inequality acceptance. *Science, 328,* 1176–1178. (p. 143)

Al Ramiah, A., & Hewstone, M. (2013). Intergroup contact as a tool for reducing, resolving, and preventing intergroup conflict: Evidence, limitations, and potential. *American Psychologist, 68,* 527–542. (p. 457)

Al-Sayegh, H., Lowry, J., Polur, R. N., Hines, R. B., Liu, F., & Zhang, J. (2015). Suicide history and mortality: A follow-up of a national cohort in the United States. *Archives of Suicide Research, 19,* 35–47. (p. 501)

Altamirano, L. J., Miyake, A., & Whitmer, A. J. (2010). When mental inflexibility facilitates executive control: Beneficial side effects of ruminative tendencies on goal maintenance. *Psychological Science, 21,* 1377–1382. (p. 520)

Alter, A. (2017). *Irresistible: The rise of addictive technology and the business of keeping us hooked.* New York: Penguin. (p. 195)

Alter, A. L., Stern, C., Granot, Y., & Balcetis, E. (2016). The "bad is black" effect: Why people believe evildoers have darker skin than do-gooders. *Personality & Social Psychology Bulletin, 42,* 1653–1665. (p. 436)

Alvarez, L., & Schwartz, J. (2014, May 30). On death row with low I.Q., and new hope for a reprieve. *The New York Times* (nytimes.com). (p. 331)

Alving, C. R. (2011, March 2). "I was swimming in a pool of liposomes." Podcast, *Science* (membercentral.aas.org). (p. 92)

Alwin, D. F. (1990). Historical changes in parental orientations to children. In N. Mandell (Ed.), *Sociological studies of child development* (Vol. 3, pp. 65–86). Greenwich, CT: JAI Press. (p. 138)

Amabile, T. M., & Hennessey, B. A. (1992). The motivation for creativity in children. In A. K. Boggiano & T. S. Pittman (Eds.), *Achievement and motivation: A social-developmental perspective.* New York: Cambridge University Press. (p. 307)

Amabile, T. M., & Kramer, S. J. (2011). *The progress principle: Using small wins to ignite joy, engagement, and creativity at work.* Cambridge, MA: Harvard Business Review Press. (p. B-12)

Ambady, N. (2010). The perils of pondering: Intuition and thin slice judgments. *Psychological Inquiry, 21,* 271–278. (p. 481)

Ambady, N., Hallahan, M., & Rosenthal, R. (1995). On judging and being judged accurately in zero-acquaintance situations. *Journal of Personality and Social Psychology, 69,* 518–529. (p. 376)

Ambrose, C. T. (2010). The widening gyrus. *American Scientist, 98,* 270–274. (p. 124)

Amedi, A., Merabet, L. B., Bermpohl, F., & Pascual-Leone, A. (2005). The occipital cortex in the blind: Lessons about plasticity and vision. *Current Directions in Psychological Science, 14,* 306–311. (p. 64)

Amen, D. G., Stubblefield, M., Carmichael, B., & Thisted, R. (1996). Brain SPECT findings and aggressiveness. *Annals of Clinical Psychiatry, 8,* 129–137. (p. 442)

American Academy of Pediatrics. (2009). Policy statement—media violence. *Pediatrics, 124,* 1495–1503. (p. 263)

American Academy of Pediatrics. (2013). *Promoting the well-being of children whose parents are gay or lesbian.* Retrieved from pediatrics.aapublications.org (p. 135)

American Academy of Pediatrics. (2014). Policy statement: School start times for adolescents. *Pediatrics, 134,* 642–649. (p. 93)

American Enterprise. (1992, January/February). Women, men, marriages and ministers. *The American Enterprise,* p. 106. (p. 491)

American Psychiatric Association. (2013). *Diagnostic and statistical manual of mental disorders* (Fifth ed.). Arlington, VA: American Psychiatric Publishing. (pp. 101, 102, 175, 494, 497, 515)

American Sociological Association. (2013, February 28). Brief of *Amicus Curiae* American Sociological Association in support of respondent Kristin M. Perry and Respondent Edith Schlain Windsor. Supreme Court of the United States, Nos. 12–144, 12–307. (p. 135)

Amick, H. R., Gartlehner, G., Gaynes, B. N., Forneris, C., Asher, G. N., Morgan, L. C., . . . Lohr, K. N. (2015). Comparative benefits and harms of second generation antidepressants and cognitive behavioral therapies in initial treatment of major depressive disorder: Systematic review and meta-analysis. *BMJ, 351,* h6019. (p. 562)

Ammori, B. (2013, January 4). Viewpoint: Benefits of bariatric surgery. *GP* (gponline.com). (p. 362)

Andersen, R. A., Hwang, E. J., & Mulliken, G. H. (2010). Cognitive neural prosthetics. *Annual Review of Psychology, 61*, 169–190. (p. 61)

Andersen, S. M. (1998, September). *Service learning: A national strategy for youth development.* Washington, DC: Institute for Communitarian Policy Studies, George Washington University. (p. 145)

Anderson, B. L. (2002). Biobehavioral outcomes following psychological interventions for cancer patients. *Journal of Consulting and Clinical Psychology, 70*, 590–610. (p. 391)

Anderson, C., Hildreth, J. A. D., & Howland, L. (2015). Is the desire for status a fundamental human motive? A review of the empirical literature. *Psychological Bulletin, 141*, 574–601. (p. 351)

Anderson, C. A. (2004). An update on the effects of playing violent video games. *Journal of Adolescence, 27*, 113–122. (pp. 318, 444, 445)

Anderson, C. A. (2013, June). Guns, games, and mass shootings in the U.S. *Bulletin of the International Society for Research on Aggression*, pp. 14–19. (p. 444)

Anderson, C. A., Anderson, K. B., Dorr, N., DeNeve, K. M., & Flanagan, M. (2000). Temperature and aggression. In M. P. Zanna (Ed.), *Advances in experimental social psychology.* San Diego: Academic Press. (p. 443)

Anderson, C. A., Brion, S., Moore, D. A., & Kennedy, J. A. (2012). A status-enhancement account of overconfidence. *Journal of Personality and Social Psychology, 103*, 718–735. (pp. 198, 304)

Anderson, C. A., Bushman, B. J., & Groom, R. W. (1997). Hot years and serious and deadly assault: Empirical tests of the heat hypothesis. *Journal of Personality and Social Psychology, 73*, 1213–1223. (p. 443)

Anderson, C. A., & Delisi, M. (2011). Implications of global climate change for violence in developed and developing countries. In J. Forgas, A. Kruglanski., & K. Williams (Eds.), *The psychology of social conflict and aggression* (pp. 249–265). New York: Psychology Press. (p. 443)

Anderson, C. A., & Dill, K. E. (2000). Video games and aggressive thoughts, feelings, and behavior in the laboratory and in life. *Journal of Personality and Social Psychology, 78*, 772–790. (p. 444)

Anderson, C. A., Shibuya, A., Ihori, N., Swing, E. L., Bushman, B. J., Sakamoto, A., . . . Saleem, M. (2010). Violent video game effects on aggression, empathy, and prosocial behavior in Eastern and Western countries: A meta-analytic review. *Psychological Bulletin, 136*, 151–173. (p. 310, 444)

Anderson, C. A., Suzuki, K., Swing, E. L., Groves, C. L., Gentile, D. A., Prot, S., . . . Jelic, M. (2017). Media violence and other aggression risk factors in seven nations. *Personality and Social Psychology Bulletin, 43*, 986–998. (p. 444)

Anderson, C. A., & Warburton, W. A. (2012). The impact of violent video games: An overview. In W. Warburton & D. Braunstein (Eds.), *Growing up fast and furious.* Annandale, NSW, Australia: The Federation Press. (p. 445)

Anderson, I. M. (2000). Selective serotonin reuptake inhibitors versus tricyclic antidepressants: A meta-analysis of efficacy and tolerability. *Journal of Affective Disorders, 58*, 19–36. (p. 561)

Anderson, J. R., Myowa-Yamakoshi, M., & Matsuzawa, T. (2004). Contagious yawning in chimpanzees. *Biology Letters, 271*, S468–S470. (p. 422)

Anderson, P. L., Edwards, S. M., & Goodnight, J. R. (2017). Virtual reality and exposure group therapy for social anxiety disorder: Results from a 4-6 year follow-up. *Cognitive Therapy and Research, 41*, 230–236. (p. 541)

Anderson, R. C., Pichert, J. W., Goetz, E. T., Schallert, D. L., Stevens, K. V., & Trollip, S. R. (1976). Instantiation of general terms. *Journal of Verbal Learning and Verbal Behavior, 15*, 667–679. (p. 287)

Anderson, S. E., Dallal, G. E., & Must, A. (2003). Relative weight and race influence average age at menarche: Results from two nationally representative surveys of U.S. girls studied 25 years apart. *Pediatrics, 111*, 844–850. (p. 167)

Andersson, G. (2016). Internet-delivered psychological treatments. *Annual Review of Clinical Psychology, 12*, 157–179. (p. 546)

Andics, A., Gábor, A., Gácsi, M., Faragó, T., Szabó, D., & Miklósi, Á. (2016). Neural mechanisms for lexical processing in dogs. *Science, 353*, 1030–1032. (p. 67)

Andreasen, N. C. (1997). Linking mind and brain in the study of mental illnesses: A project for a scientific psychopathology. *Science, 275*, 1586–1593. (p. 525)

Andreasen, N. C. (2001). *Brave new brain: Conquering mental illness in the era of the genome.* New York: Oxford University Press. (p. 525)

Andreasen, N. C., Arndt, S., Swayze, V., II, Cizadlo, T., & Flaum, M. (1994). Thalamic abnormalities in schizophrenia visualized through magnetic resonance image averaging. *Science, 266*, 294–298. (p. 525)

Andrews, P. W., & Thomson, J. A., Jr. (2009a). The bright side of being blue: Depression as an adaptation for analyzing complex problems. *Psychological Review, 116*, 620–654. (p. 520)

Andrews, P. W., & Thomson, J. A., Jr. (2009b). Depression's evolutionary roots. *Scientific American Mind, 20*, 56–61. (p. 520)

Andrillon, T., Nir, Y., Cirelli, C., Tononi, G., & Fried, I. (2015). Single-neuron activity and eye movements during human REM sleep and awake vision. *Nature Communications, 6*, Article 7884. doi:10.1038/ncomms8884 (p. 89)

Anglemyer, A., Horvath, T., & Rutherford, G. (2014). The accessibility of firearms and risk for suicide and homicide victimization among household members. *Annals of Internal Medicine, 160*, 101–112. (p. 441)

Annese, J., Schenker-Ahmed, N. M., Bartsch, H., Maechler, P., Sheh, C., Thomas, N., . . . Corkin, S. (2014). Postmortem examination of patient H. M.'s brain based on histological sectioning and digital 3D reconstruction. *Nature Communications, 5*, Article 3122. doi:10.1038/ncomms4122 (p. 284)

Ansari, A., Purtell, K., & Gershoff, E. (2015). Classroom age composition and the school readiness of 3- and 4-year-olds in the Head Start program. *Psychological Science, 27*, 53–63. (p. 315)

Anton, B. S. (2015, June). Quoted in, "APA applauds President Obama's call to end use of therapies intended to change sexual orientation." *Monitor, 46*, p. 10. (p. 554)

Antonaccio, O., Botchkovar, E. V., & Tittle, C. R. (2011). Attracted to crime: Exploration of criminal motivation among respondents in three European cities. *Criminal Justice and Behavior, 38*, 1200–1221. (p. 163)

Antony, M. M., Brown, T. A., & Barlow, D. H. (1992). Current perspectives on panic and panic disorder. *Current Directions in Psychological Science, 1*, 79–82. (p. 511)

Antrobus, J. (1991). Dreaming: Cognitive processes during cortical activation and high afferent thresholds. *Psychological Review, 98*, 96–121. (p. 98)

Anzures, G., Quinn, P. C., Pascalis, O., Slater, A. M., Tanaka, J. W., & Lee, K. (2013). Developmental origins of the other-race effect. *Current Directions in Psychological Science, 22*, 173–178. (p. 439)

AP. (2007). AP-Ipsos poll of 1,013 U.S. adults taken October 16–18, 2007 and distributed via Associated Press. (p. 229)

AP. (2009, May 9). *AP-mtvU AP 2009 Economy, College Stress and Mental Health Poll.* Associated Press (surveys.ap.org). (p. 93)

AP. (2017). Strangers on beach form 80-link human chain, rescue family from rip current. CBC. Retrieved from cbc.ca/news/world/human-chain-saves-family-in-water-1.4199181 (p. 458)

APA. (2006). Evidence-based practice in psychology (from APA Presidential Task Force on Evidence-Based Practice). *American Psychologist, 61*, 271–285. (p. 553)

APA. (2007). *Report of the task force on the sexualization of girls.* Washington, DC: American Psychological Association (apa.org). (p. 177)

APA. (2009). *Report of the APA task force on appropriate therapeutic responses to sexual orientation.* American Psychological Association (apa.org). (p. 179)

APA. (2010). *Answers to your questions about transgender individuals and gender identity.* American Psychological Association (apa.org). (p. 170)

APA. (2012). *Guidelines for ethical conduct in the care and use of nonhuman animals in research.* Washington, DC: American Psychological Association. (p. 31)

APA. (2017). Stress in America: Coping with change. Washington, DC: American Psychological Association. (p. 386)

APA Task Force on Violent Media. (2015). *Technical report on the review of the violent video game literature.* American Psychological Association (apa.org/pi/families/review-video-games.pdf). (p. 263)

Archer, J. (2000). Sex differences in aggression between heterosexual partners: A meta-analytic review. *Psychological Bulletin, 126*, 651–680. (p. 163)

Archer, J. (2004). Sex differences in aggression in real-world settings: A meta-analytic review. *Review of General Psychology, 8*, 291–322. (p. 163)

Archer, J. (2007). A cross-cultural perspective on physical aggression between partners. *Issues in Forensic Psychology, 6*, 125–131. (p. 163)

Archer, J. (2009). Does sexual selection explain human sex differences in aggression? *Behavioral and Brain Sciences, 32*, 249–311. (p. 163)

Arendt, H. (1963). *Eichmann in Jerusalem: A report on the banality of evil.* New York: Viking. (p. 145)

Ariel, R., & Karpicke, J. D. (2017). Improved self-regulated learning with a retrieval practice intervention. *Journal of Experimental Psychology: Applied.* Advance online publication. doi:10.1037/xap0000133 (p. 33)

Ariely, D. (2009). *Predictably irrational: The hidden forces that shape our decisions.* New York: HarperCollins. (p. 281)

Ariely, D. (2010). *Predictably irrational, revised and expanded edition: The hidden forces that shape our decisions.* New York: Harper Perennial. (p. 469)

Ariely, D., & Loewenstein, G. (2006). The heat of the moment: The effect of sexual arousal on sexual decision making. *Journal of Behavioral Decision Making, 19*, 87–98. (p. 177)

Aries, E. (1987). Gender and communication. In P. Shaver & C. Henrick (Eds.), *Review of Personality and Social Psychology, 7*, 149–176. (p. 164)

Arkowitz, H., & Lilienfeld, S. O. (2006, April/May). Psychotherapy on trial. *Scientific American: Mind*, pp. 42–49. (p. 554)

Armony, J. L., Quirk, G. J., & LeDoux, J. E. (1998). Differential effects of amygdala lesions on early and late plastic components of auditory cortex spike trains during fear conditioning. *Journal of Neuroscience, 18,* 2592–2601. (p. 512)

Armstrong, E. A., England, P., & Fogarty, A. C. K. (2012). Accounting for women's orgasm and sexual enjoyment in college hookups and relationships. *American Sociological Review, 77,* 435–462. (p. 186)

Arnedo, J., Mamah, D., Baranger, D. A., Harms, M. P., Barch, D. M., Svrakic, D. M., . . . Zwir, I. (2015). Decomposition of brain diffusion imaging data uncovers latent schizophrenias with distinct patterns of white matter anisotropy. *NeuroImage, 120,* 43–54. (pp. 525, 526)

Arnett, J. J. (1999). Adolescent storm and stress, reconsidered. *American Psychologist, 54,* 317–326. (p. 141)

Arnett, J. J. (2006). Emerging adulthood: Understanding the new way of coming of age. In J. J. Arnett & J. L. Tanner (Eds.), *Emerging adults in America: Coming of age in the 21st century* (pp. 3–19). Washington, DC: American Psychological Association. (p. 149)

Arnett, J. J. (2007). Socialization in emerging adulthood: From the family to the wider world, from socialization to self-socialization. In J. E. Grusec & P. D. Hastings (Eds.), *Handbook of socialization: Theory and research* (pp. 208–230). New York: Guilford Press. (p. 149)

Arnold, K. M., Umanath, S., Thio, K., Reilly, W. B., McDaniel, M. A., & Marsh, E. J. (2017). Understanding the cognitive processes involved in writing to learn. *Journal of Experimental Psychology: Applied, 23,* 115–127. (p. 34)

Arnone, D., McIntosh, A. M., Tan, G. M. Y., & Ebmeier, K. P. (2008). Meta-analysis of magnetic resonance imaging studies of the corpus callosum in schizophrenia. *Schizophrenia Research, 101,* 124–132. (p. 525)

Aron, A. P., Melinat, E., Aron, E. N., Vallone, R. D., & Bator, R. J. (1997). The experimental generation of interpersonal closeness: A procedure and some preliminary findings. *Personality and Social Psychology Bulletin, 23,* 363–377. (p. 452)

Aron, A., Norman, C. C., Aron, E. N., McKenna, C., & Heyman, R. E. (2000). Couples' shared participation in novel and arousing activities and experienced relationship quality. *Journal of Personality and Social Psychology, 78,* 273–284. (p. 451)

Aronson, E. (2001, April 13). *Newsworthy violence.* [E-mail to Society for Personality and Social Psychology discussion list, drawing from *Nobody left to hate: Teaching compassion after Columbine.* (2000). New York: Freeman]. (p. 148)

Arriaga, P., Adrião, J., Madeira, F., Cavaleiro, I., Maia e Silva, A., Barahona, I., & Esteves, F. (2015). A "dry eye" for victims of violence: Effects of playing a violent video game on pupillary dilation to victims and on aggressive behavior. *Psychology of Violence, 5,* 199–208. (p. 444)

Artiga, A. I., Viana, J. B., Maldonado, C. R., Chandler-Laney, P. C., Oswald, K. D., & Boggiano, M. M. (2007). Body composition and endocrine status of long-term stress-induced binge-eating rats. *Physiology and Behavior, 91,* 424–431. (p. 363)

Arzi, A., Shedlesky, L., Ben-Shaul, M., Nasser, K., Oksenberg, A., Hairston, I. S., & Sobel, N. (2012). Humans can learn new information during sleep. *Nature Neuroscience, 15,* 1460–1465. (p. 97)

Ascády, L., & Harris, K. D. (2017). Synaptic scaling in sleep. *Science, 355,* 457. (p. 91)

Asch, S. E. (1955). Opinions and social pressure. *Scientific American, 193,* 31–35. (p. 423)

Aserinsky, E. (1988, January 17). Personal communication. (p. 87)

Ashton, K., Bellis, M., Davies, A., Hardcastle, K., & Hughes, K. (2016). *Adverse childhood experiences and their association with chronic disease and health service use in the Welsh adult population.* Welsh Adverse Childhood Experiences (ACE) Study, NHS Wales Public Trust. Retrieved from wales.nhs.uk/ (p. 386)

Askay, S. W., & Patterson, D. R. (2007). Hypnotic analgesia. *Expert Review of Neurotherapeutics, 7,* 1675–1683. (p. 224)

Aspinwall, L. G., Brown, T. R., & Tabery, J. (2012). The double-edged sword: Does biomechanism increase or decrease judges' sentencing of psychopaths? *Science, 337,* 846–849. (p. 417)

Aspinwall, L. G., & Tedeschi, R. G. (2010). The value of positive psychology for health psychology: Progress and pitfalls in examining the relation of positive phenomena to health. *Annals of Behavioral Medicine, 39,* 4–15. (p. 398)

Aspy, C. B., Vesely, S. K., Oman, R. F., Rodine, S., Marshall, L., & McLeroy, K. (2007). Parental communication and youth sexual behaviour. *Journal of Adolescence, 30,* 449–466. (p. 177)

Assanand, S., Pinel, J. P. J., & Lehman, D. R. (1998). Personal theories of hunger and eating. *Journal of Applied Social Psychology, 28,* 998–1015. (p. 363)

Astin, A. W., Astin, H. S., & Lindholm, J. A. (2004). *Spirituality in higher education: A national study of college students' search for meaning and purpose.* Los Angeles: Higher Education Research Institute, University of California, Los Angeles. (p. 146)

Atkinson, R. C., & Shiffrin, R. M. (1968). Human memory: A control system and its control processes. In K. Spence (Ed.), *The psychology of learning and motivation* (Vol. 2). New York: Academic Press. (p. 268)

Atkinson, R. C., & Shiffrin, R. M. (2016). Human memory: A proposed system and its control processes. In R. J. Sternberg, S. T. Fiske, & D. J. Foss (Eds.), *Scientists making a difference: One hundred eminent behavioral and brain scientists talk about their most important contributions.* New York: Cambridge University Press. (p. 268)

Atlas, D. (2016, January 29). Autism's first-ever patient, now 82, "has continued to grow his whole life." *People* (people.com/article/donald-triplett-first-ever-autism-case). (p. 131)

Austin, E. J., Deary, I. J., Whiteman, M. C., Fowkes, F. G. R., Pedersen, N. L., Rabbitt, P., . . . McInnes, L. (2002). Relationships between ability and personality: Does intelligence contribute positively to personal and social adjustment? *Personality and Individual Differences, 32,* 1391–1411. (p. 331)

Australian Unity. (2008). *What makes us happy? The Australian Unity Wellbeing Index.* South Melbourne: Australian Unity. (p. 410)

Averill, J. R. (1993). William James's other theory of emotion. In M. E. Donnelly (Ed.), *Reinterpreting the legacy of William James.* Washington, DC: American Psychological Association. (p. 369)

Aviezer, H., Hassin, R. R., Ryan, J., Grady, C., Susskind, J., Anderson, A., . . . Bentin, S. (2008). Angry, disgusted, or afraid? Studies on the malleability of emotion perception. *Psychological Science, 19,* 724–732. (p. 380)

Ayan, S. (2009). Laughing matters. *Scientific American Mind, 20,* 24–31. (p. 399)

Aydin, N., Fischer, P., & Frey, D. (2010). Turning to God in the face of ostracism: Effects of social exclusion on religiousness. *Personality and Social Psychology Bulletin, 36,* 742–753. (p. 354)

Azar, B. (1998, June). Why can't this man feel whether or not he's standing up? *APA Monitor* (apa.org/monitor/jun98/touch.html). (p. 227)

Azevedo, F. A., Carvalho, L. R., Grinberg, L. T., Farfel, J. M., Ferretti, R. E., Leite, R. E., . . . Herculano-Houzel, S. (2009). Equal numbers of neuronal and nonneuronal cells make the human brain an isometrically scaled-up primate brain. *Journal of Comparative Neurology, 513,* 532–541. (p. 47)

Baas, M., De Dreu, C. K. W., & Nijstad, B. A. (2008). A meta-analysis of 25 years of mood-creativity research: Hedonic tone, activation, or regulatory focus? *Psychological Bulletin, 134,* 779–806. (p. 407)

Baas, M., Nijstad, B. A., Boot, N. C., & De Dreu, C. K. (2016). Mad genius revisited: Vulnerability to psychopathology, biobehavioral approach-avoidance, and creativity. *Psychological Bulletin, 142,* 668–692. (p. 515)

Babyak, M., Blumenthal, J. A., Herman, S., Khatri, P., Doraiswamy, M., Moore, K., . . . Krishnan, K. R. (2000). Exercise treatment for major depression: Maintenance of therapeutic benefit at ten months. *Psychosomatic Medicine, 62,* 633–638. (p. 559)

Bachman, J., O'Malley, P. M., Schulenberg, J. E., Johnston, L. D., Freedman-Doan, P., & Messersmith, E. E. (2007). *The education–drug use connection: How successes and failures in school relate to adolescent smoking, drinking, drug use, and delinquency.* Mahwah, NJ: Erlbaum. (p. 112)

Back, M. D., Stopfer, J. M., Vazire, S., Gaddis, S., Schmukle, S. C., Egloff, B., & Gosling, S. D. (2010). Facebook profiles reflect actual personality, not self-idealization. *Psychological Science, 21,* 372–374. (p. 481)

Backman, L., & MacDonald, S. W. S. (2006). Death and cognition: Synthesis and outlook. *European Psychologist, 11,* 224–235. (p. 155)

Baddeley, A. D. (1982). *Your memory: A user's guide.* New York: Macmillan. (pp. 267, 268)

Baddeley, A. D. (2002, June). Is working memory still working? *European Psychologist, 7,* 85–97. (p. 269)

Baddeley, A. D., Thomson, N., & Buchanan, M. (1975). Word length and the structure of short-term memory. *Journal of Verbal Learning and Verbal Behavior, 14,* 575–589. (p. 271)

Baddeley, J. L., & Singer, J. A. (2009). A social interactional model of bereavement narrative disclosure. *Review of General Psychology, 13,* 202–218. (p. 160)

Bagemihl, B. (1999). *Biological exuberance: Animal homosexuality and natural diversity.* New York: St. Martin's Press. (p. 180)

Bagge, C. L., Littlefield, A. K., & Glenn, C. R. (2017). Trajectories of affective response as warning signs for suicide attempts: An examination of the 48 hours prior to a recent suicide attempt. *Clinical Psychological Science, 5,* 259–271. (p. 501)

Baglioni, C., Nanovska, S., Regen, W., Spiegelhalder, K., Feige, B., Nissen, C., . . . Riemann, D. (2016). Sleep and mental disorders: A meta-analysis of polysomnographic research. *Psychological Bulletin, 142,* 969–990. (pp. 93, 96)

Bahrick, H. P. (1984). Semantic memory content in permastore: Fifty years of memory for Spanish learned in school. *Journal of Experimental Psychology: General, 111,* 1–29. (p. 286)

Bahrick, H. P., Bahrick, P. O., & Wittlinger, R. P. (1975). Fifty years of memory for names and faces: A cross-sectional approach. *Journal of Experimental Psychology: General, 104,* 54–75. (p. 267)

Bailey, J. M., Gaulin, S., Agyei, Y., & Gladue, B. A. (1994). Effects of gender and sexual orientation on evolutionary relevant aspects of human mating psychology. *Journal of Personality and Social Psychology, 66,* 1081–1093. (p. 183)

Bailey, J. M., Kirk, K. M., Zhu, G., Dunne, M. P., & Martin, N. G. (2000). Do individual differences in sociosexuality represent genetic or environmentally contingent strategies? Evidence from the Australian twin registry. *Journal of Personality and Social Psychology, 78,* 537–545. (p. 184)

Bailey, J. M., Vasey, P. L., Diamond, L. M., Breedlove, S. M., Vilain, E., & Epprecht, M. (2016). Sexual orientation, controversy, and science. *Psychological Science in the Public Interest, 17,* 45–101. (pp. 181, 182)

Bailey, R. E., & Gillaspy, J. A., Jr. (2005). Operant psychology goes to the fair: Marian and Keller Breland in the popular press, 1947–1966. *The Behavior Analyst, 28,* 143–159. (p. 233)

Bailine, S., Fink, M., Knapp, R., Petrides, G., Husain, M. M., Rasmussen, K., . . . Kellner, C. H. (2010). Electroconvulsive therapy is equally effective in unipolar and bipolar depression. *Acta Psychiatrica Scandinavica, 121,* 431–436. (p. 563)

Baillargeon, R. (2008). Innate ideas revisited: For a principle of persistence in infants' physical reasoning. *Perspectives in Psychological Science, 3,* 2–13. (p. 127)

Baillargeon, R., Scott, R. M., & Bian, L. (2016). Psychological reasoning in infancy. *Annual Review of Psychology, 67,* 159–186. (p. 127)

Bak, T. H., Nissan, J. J., Allerhand, M. M., & Deary, I. J. (2014, June). Does bilingualism influence cognitive aging? *Annals of Neurology, 75,* 959–963. (p. 320)

Baker, T. B., McFall, R. M., & Shoham, V. (2008). Current status and future prospects of clinical psychology: Toward a scientifically principled approach to mental and behavioral health care. *Psychological Science in the Public Interest, 9,* 67–103. (p. 553)

Baker, T. B., Piper, M. E., McCarthy, D. E., Majeskie, M. R., & Fiore, M. C. (2004). Addiction motivation reformulated: An affective processing model of negative reinforcement. *Psychological Review, 111,* 33–51. (p. 246)

Bakermans-Kranenburg, M. J., van IJzendoorn, M. H., & Juffer, F. (2003). Less is more: Meta-analyses of sensitivity and attachment interventions in early childhood. *Psychological Bulletin, 129,* 195–215. (p. 135)

Bakshy, E., Messing, S., & Adamic, L. A. (2015). Exposure to ideologically diverse news and opinion on Facebook. *Science, 348,* 1130–1132. (p. 432)

Balcetis, E., & Dunning, D. (2010). Wishful seeing: More desire objects are seen as closer. *Psychological Science, 21,* 147–152. (p. 197)

Ball, G., Adamson, C., Beare, R., & Seal, M. L. (2017). Modelling neuroanatomical variation due to age and sex during childhood and adolescence. Unpublished manuscript: biorxiv.org/content/early/2017/07/16/126441 (p. 340)

Balodis, I. M., & Potenza, M. N. (2015). Anticipatory reward processing in addicted populations: A focus on the monetary incentive delay task. *Biological Psychiatry, 77,* 434–444. (p. 56)

Balodis, I. M., Wynne-Edwards, K. E., & Olmstead, M. C. (2010). The other side of the curve: Examining the relationship between pre-stressor physiological responses and stress reactivity. *Psychoneuroendocrinology, 35,* 1363–1373. (p. 386)

Balsam, K. F., Beauchaine, T. P., Rothblum, E. S., & Solomon, S. E. (2008). Three-year follow-up of same-sex couples who had civil unions in Vermont, same-sex couples not in civil unions, and heterosexual married couples. *Developmental Psychology, 44,* 102–116. (p. 156)

Balter, M. (2010). Animal communication helps reveal roots of language. *Science, 328,* 969–970. (p. 317)

Balter, M. (2014). Science misused to justify Ugandan antigay law. *Science, 343,* 956. (p. 182)

Balter, M. (2015). Can epigenetics explain homosexuality puzzle? *Science, 350,* 148. (p. 181)

Balter, M. (2017, May). Schizophrenia's unyielding mysteries. *Scientific American,* pp. 55–61. (p. 526)

Bambico, F. R., Nguyen N.-T., Katz, N., & Gobbi, G. (2010). Chronic exposure to cannabinoids during adolescence but not during adulthood impairs emotional behaviour and monoaminergic neurotransmission. *Neurobiology of Disease, 37,* 641–655. (p. 109)

Banaji, M. R., & Greenwald, A. G. (2013). *Blindspot: Hidden biases of good people.* New York: Delacorte Press. (p. 435)

Bancroft, J., Loftus, J., & Long, J. S. (2003). Distress about sex: A national survey of women in heterosexual relationships. *Archives of Sexual Behavior, 32,* 193–208. (p. 175)

Bandura, A. (1977). Self-efficacy: Toward a unifying theory of behavior. *Psychological Review, 84,* 191–215. (p. 486)

Bandura, A. (1982). The psychology of chance encounters and life paths. *American Psychologist, 37,* 747–755. (p. 155)

Bandura, A. (1986). *Social foundations of thought and action: A social-cognitive theory.* Englewood Cliffs, NJ: Prentice-Hall. (p. 482)

Bandura, A. (2005). The evolution of social cognitive theory. In K. G. Smith & M. A. Hitt (Eds.), *Great minds in management: The process of theory development* (pp. 9–35). Oxford: Oxford University Press. (pp. 155, 258)

Bandura, A. (2006). Toward a psychology of human agency. *Perspectives on Psychological Science, 1,* 164–180. (p. 482)

Bandura, A. (2008). An agentic perspective on positive psychology. In S. J. Lopez (Ed.), *The science of human flourishing.* Westport, CT: Praeger. (p. 482)

Bandura, A. (2016). The power of observational learning through social modeling. In R. J. Sternberg, S. T. Fiske, & D. J. Foss (Eds.), *Scientists making a difference: One hundred eminent behavioral and brain scientists talk about their most important contributions.* New York: Cambridge University Press, pp. 235–239. (p. 259)

Bandura, A., Ross, D., & Ross, S. A. (1961). Transmission of aggression through imitation of aggressive models. *Journal of Abnormal and Social Psychology, 63,* 575–582. (p. 258)

Bansak, K., Hainmueller, J., & Hangartner, D. (2016). How economic, humanitarian, and religious concerns shape European attitudes toward asylum seekers. *Science, 354,* 217–222. (p. 455)

Banville, J. (2012, April). APA weighs in on the constitutionality of life without parole for juvenile offenders. *Monitor on Psychology,* p. 12. (p. 142)

Barash, D. P. (2006, July 14). I am, therefore I think. *The Chronicle of Higher Education,* pp. B9, B10. (p. 81)

Barash, D. P. (2012). *Homo mysterius: Evolutionary puzzles of human nature.* New York: Oxford University Press. (p. 186)

Barbaresi, W. J., Katusic, S. K., Colligan, R. C., Weaver, A. L., & Jacobsen, S. J. (2007). Modifiers of long-term school outcomes for children with attention deficit/hyperactivity disorder: Does treatment with stimulant medication make a difference? Results from a population-based study. *Journal of Developmental and Behavioral Pediatrics, 28,* 274–287. (p 498)

Barberá, P., Jost, J. T., Nagler, J., Tucker, J. A., & Bonneau, R. (2015). Tweeting from left to right: Is online political communication more than an echo chamber? *Psychological Science, 26,* 1531–1542. (p. 432)

Bargh, J. A., & Chartrand, T. L. (1999). The unbearable automaticity of being. *American Psychologist, 54,* 462–479. (pp. 84, 469)

Bargh, J. A., & McKenna, K. Y. A. (2004). The internet and social life. *Annual Review of Psychology, 55,* 573–590. (p. 448)

Bargh, J. A., McKenna, K. Y. A., & Fitzsimons, G. M. (2002). Can you see the real me? Activation and expression of the "true self" on the internet. *Journal of Social Issues, 58,* 33–48. (p. 448)

Bargh, J. A., & Morsella, E. (2008). The unconscious mind. *Perspectives on Psychological Science, 3,* 73–79. (p. 470)

Bar-Haim, Y., Lamy, D., Pergamin, L., Bakermans-Kranenburg, M. J., & van IJzendoorn, M. H. (2007). Threat-related attentional bias in anxious and nonanxious individuals: A meta-analytic study. *Psychological Bulletin, 133,* 1–24. (p. 510)

Barinaga, M. B. (1992). The brain remaps its own contours. *Science, 258,* 216–218. (p. 64)

Barinaga, M. B. (1997). How exercise works its magic. *Science, 276,* 1325. (p. 401)

Barker, D. J. P. (2012). Developmental origins of chronic disease. *Public Health, 126,* 185–189. (p. 120)

Barkley, R. A., et al. (2002). International consensus statement (January 2002). *Clinical Child and Family Psychology Review, 5*(2), 89–111. (p. 498)

Barkley-Levenson, E., & Galván, A. (2014). Neural representation of expected value in the adolescent brain. *PNAS, 111,* 1646–1651. (p. 142)

Barlow, D. H. (2010). Negative effects from psychological treatments: A perspective. *American Psychologist, 65,* 13–20. (p. 554)

Barlow, M., Woodman, T., & Hardy, L. (2013). Great expectations: Different high-risk activities satisfy different motives. *Journal of Personality and Social Psychology, 105,* 458–475. (p. 349)

Barnier, A. J., & McConkey, K. M. (2004). Defining and identifying the highly hypnotizable person. In M. Heap, R. J. Brown, & D. A. Oakley (Eds.), *The highly hypnotizable person: Theoretical, experimental and clinical issues* (pp. 30–60). London: Brunner-Routledge. (p. 224)

Baron, C. E., Smith, T. W., Uchino, B. N., Baucom, B. R., & Birmingham, W. C. (2016). Getting along and getting ahead: Affiliation and dominance predict ambulatory blood pressure. *Health Psychology, 35,* 253–261. (p. 400)

Baron-Cohen, S. (2010). Autism and the empathizing-systemizing (E-S) theory. In P. D. Zelazo, M. Chandler & E. Crone (Eds.), *Developmental social cognitive neuroscience.* New York: Psychology Press, pp. 125–138. (p. 131)

Baron-Cohen, S. (2017). The eyes as window to the mind. *American Journal of Psychiatry, 174,* 1–2. (p. 131)

Baron-Cohen, S., Bowen, D. C., Rosemary, J. H., Allison, C., Auyeung, B., Lombardo, M. V., & Lai, M.-C. (2015). The "reading the mind in the eyes" test: Complete absence of typical difference in ~400 men and women with autism. *PLoS ONE, 10,* e0136521. (p. 131)

Baron-Cohen, S., Golan, O., Chapman, E., & Granader, Y. (2007). Transported to a world of emotion. *The Psychologist, 20,* 76–77. (p. 132)

Barrera, T. L., Mott, J. M., Hofstein, R. F., & Teng, E. J. (2013). A meta-analytic review of exposure in group cognitive behavioral therapy for posttraumatic stress disorder. *Clinical Psychology Review, 33*, 24–32. (p. 541)

Barrett, D. (2011). Answers in your dreams. *Scientific American Mind, 22*, 26–33. (p. 92)

Barrett, H. C., Bolyanatz, A., Crittenden, A. N., Fessler, D. M., Fitzpatrick, S., Gurven, M., . . . Scelza, B. A. (2016). Small-scale societies exhibit fundamental variation in the role of intentions in moral judgment. *PNAS, 113*, 4688–4693. (p. 144)

Barrett, L. F. (2006). Are emotions natural kinds? *Perspectives on Psychological Science, 1*, 28–58. (pp. 369, 373)

Barrett, L. F. (2012). Emotions are real. *Emotion, 12*, 413–429. (p. 368)

Barrett, L. F. (2013). Quoted by Fischer, S. About face: Emotional and facial expressions may not be directly related. *Boston Magazine*. (p. 368)

Barrett, L. F., & Bliss-Moreau, E. (2009). She's emotional. He's having a bad day: Attributional explanations for emotion stereotypes. *Emotion, 9*, 649–658. (p. 378)

Barrett, L. F., Lane, R. D., Sechrest, L., & Schwartz, G. E. (2000). Sex differences in emotional awareness. *Personality and Social Psychology Bulletin, 26*, 1027–1035. (p. 377)

Barretto, R. P., Gillis-Smith, S., Chandrashekar, J., Yarmolinsky, D. A., Schnitzer, M. J., Ryba, N. J., & Zuker, C. S. (2015). The neural representation of taste quality at the periphery. *Nature, 517*, 373–376. (p. 225)

Barrick, M. R., Shaffer, J. A., & DeGrassi, S. W. (2009). What you see may not be what you get: Relationships among self-presentation tactics and ratings of interview and job performance. *Journal of Applied Psychology, 94*, 1304–1411. (p. B-5)

Barrington-Trimis, J. L., Berhane, K., Unger, J. B., Cruz, T. B., Urman, R., Chou, C. P., . . . Huh, J. (2016). The e-cigarette social environment, e-cigarette use, and susceptibility to cigarette smoking. *Journal of Adolescent Health, 59*, 75–80. (p. 105)

Barrouillet, P., Portrat, S., & Camos, V. (2011). On the law relating processing to storage in working memory. *Psychological Review, 118*, 175–192. (p. 269)

Barry, C. L., McGinty, E. E., Vernick, J. S., & Webster, D. W. (2013). After Newtown—Public opinion on gun policy and mental illness. *New England Journal of Medicine, 368*, 1077–1081. (p. 502)

Barry, D. (1995, September 17). Teen smokers, too, get cool, toxic, waste-blackened lungs. *The Asbury Park Press*, p. D3. (p. 106)

Bartels, J. M., Milovich, M. M., & Moussier, S. (2016). Coverage of the Stanford prison experiment in introductory psychology courses: A survey of introductory psychology instructors. *Teaching of Psychology, 43*, 136–141. (p. 419)

Bartels, M. (2015). Genetics of wellbeing and its components with life, happiness, and quality of life: A review of meta-analysis of heritability studies. *Behavior Genetics, 45*, 137–156. (p. 411)

Bashore, T. R., Ridderinkhof, K. R., & van der Molen, M. W. (1997). The decline of cognitive processing speed in old age. *Current Directions in Psychological Science, 6*, 163–169. (p. 152)

Baskind, D. E. (1997, December 14). Personal communication, from Delta College. (p. 542)

Basu, S., & Basu, D. (2015). The relationship between psychoactive drugs, the brain and psychosis. *International Archives of Addiction Research and Medicine, 1*(003). (p. 524)

Bates, T. C. (2015). The glass is half full and half empty: A population-representative twin study testing if optimism and pessimism are distinct systems. *Journal of Positive Psychology, 10*, 533–542. (p. 399)

Bathje, G. J., & Pryor, J. B. (2011). The relationships of public and self-stigma to seeking mental health services. *Journal of Mental Health Counseling, 33*, 161–177. (p. 497)

Batsell, W. R., Perry, J. L., Hanley, E., & Hostetter, A. B. (2017). Ecological validity of the testing effect: The use of daily quizzes in introductory psychology. *Teaching of Psychology, 44*, 18–23. (p. 273)

Bauer, M., Cassar, A., Chytilová, J., & Henrich, J. (2014). War's enduring effects on the development of egalitarian motivations and in-group biases. *Psychological Science, 25*, 47–57. (p. 458)

Bauer, P. J., Burch, M. M., Scholin, S. E., & Güler, O. E. (2007). Using cue words to investigate the distribution of autobiographical memories in childhood. *Psychological Science, 18*, 910–916. (p. 277)

Bauer, P. J., & Larkina, M. (2014). The onset of childhood amnesia in childhood: A prospective investigation of the course and determinants of forgetting of early-life events. *Memory, 22*, 907–924. (p. 124)

Baumann, J., & DeSteno, D. (2010). Emotion guided threat detection: Expecting guns where there are none. *Journal of Personality and Social Psychology, 99*, 595–610. (p. 198)

Baumeister, R. F. (1996). Should schools try to boost self-esteem? Beware the dark side. *American Educator, 20*, 43. (p. 489)

Baumeister, R. F. (2000). Gender differences in erotic plasticity: The female sex drive as socially flexible and responsive. *Psychological Bulletin, 126*, 347–374. (p. 179)

Baumeister, R. F. (2001). Violent pride: Do people turn violent because of self-hate, or self-love? *Scientific American, 17*, 96–101. (p. 488)

Baumeister, R. F. (2005). *The cultural animal: Human nature, meaning, and social life.* New York: Oxford University Press. (p. 421)

Baumeister, R. F. (2006). Violent pride. *Scientific American Mind, 17*, 54–59. (p. 486)

Baumeister, R. F. (2010). *Is there anything good about men?: How cultures flourish by exploiting men.* New York: Oxford University Press. (p. 163)

Baumeister, R. F. (2015). Toward a general theory of motivation: Problems, challenges, opportunities, and the big picture. *Motivation and Emotion, 40*, 1–10. (p. 349)

Baumeister, R. F., & Bratslavsky, E. (1999). Passion, intimacy, and time: Passionate love as a function of change in intimacy. *Personality and Social Psychology Review, 3*, 49–67. (p. 452)

Baumeister, R. F., Bratslavsky, E., Muraven, M., & Tice, D. M. (1998a). Ego depletion: Is the active self a limited resource? *Journal of Personality and Social Psychology, 74*, 1252–1265. (p. 398)

Baumeister, R. F., Catanese, K. R., & Vohs, K. D. (2001). Is there a gender difference in strength of sex drive? Theoretical views, conceptual distinctions, and a review of relevant evidence. *Personality and Social Psychology Review, 5*, 242–273. (p. 183)

Baumeister, R. F., Dale, K., & Sommer, K. L. (1998b). Freudian defense mechanisms and empirical findings in modern personality and social psychology: Reaction formation, projection, displacement, undoing, isolation, sublimation, and denial. *Journal of Personality, 66*, 1081–1125. (p. 470)

Baumeister, R. F., & Leary, M. R. (1995). The need to belong: Desire for interpersonal attachments as a fundamental human motivation. *Psychological Bulletin, 117*, 497–529. (p. 352)

Baumeister, R. F., & Tice, D. M. (1986). How adolescence became the struggle for self: A historical transformation of psychological development. In J. Suls & A. G. Greenwald (Eds.), *Psychological perspectives on the self* (Vol. 3, pp. 183–201). Hillsdale, NJ: Erlbaum. (p. 149)

Baumeister, R. F., & Vohs, K. D. (2016). Strength model of self-regulation as limited resource: Assessment, controversies, update. *Advances in Experimental Social Psychology, 54*, 67–127. (p. 398)

Baumgardner, A. H., Kaufman, C. M., & Levy, P. E. (1989). Regulating affect interpersonally: When low esteem leads to greater enhancement. *Journal of Personality and Social Psychology, 56*, 907–921. (p. 487)

Baumrind, D. (1966). Effects of authoritative parental control on child behavior. *Child Development*, 887–907. (pp. 138, 139)

Baumrind, D. (1967). Child care practices anteceding three patterns of preschool behavior. *Genetic Psychology Monographs, 75*, 43–88. (p. 138)

Baumrind, D. (1996). The discipline controversy revisited. *Family Relations, 45*, 405–414.

Baumrind, D. (2013). Is a pejorative view of power assertion in the socialization process justified? *Review of General Psychology, 17*, 420–427. (p. 139)

Baumrind, D., Larzelere, R. E., & Cowan, P. A. (2002). Ordinary physical punishment: Is it harmful? Comment on Gershoff (2002). *Psychological Bulletin, 128*, 602–611. (p. 250)

Baur, E., Forsman, M., Santtila, P., Johansson, A., Sandnabba, K., & Långström, N. (2016). Paraphilic sexual interests and sexually coercive behavior: A population-based twin study. *Archives of Sexual Behavior, 45*, 1163–1172. (p. 175)

Bavelier, D., Newport, E. L., & Supalla, T. (2003). Children need natural languages, signed or spoken. *Cerebrum, 5*, 19–32. (p. 313)

Bavelier, D., Tomann, A., Hutton, C., Mitchell, T., Corina, D., Liu, G., & Neville, H. (2000). Visual attention to the periphery is enhanced in congenitally deaf individuals. *Journal of Neuroscience, 20*, 1–6. (p. 39)

Baxter, M. G., & Burwell, R. D. (2017). Promoting transparency and reproducibility in *Behavioral Neuroscience*: Publishing replications, registered reports, and null results. *Behavioral Neuroscience, 131*, 275–276. (p. 20)

Beam, C. R., Emery, R. E., Reynolds, C. A., Gatz, M., Turkheimer, R., & Pedersen, N. L. (2016). Widowhood and the stability of late life depressive symptomatology in the Swedish Adoption Twin Study of Aging. *Behavior Genetics, 46*, 100–113. (p. 353)

Beaman, A. L., & Klentz, B. (1983). The supposed physical attractiveness bias against supporters of the women's movement: A meta-analysis. *Personality and Social Psychology Bulletin, 9*, 544–550. (p. 450)

Beames, J. R., Schofield, T. P., & Denson, T. F. (2017). A meta-analysis of improving self-control with practice. In D. T. D. de Ridder, M. A. Adriaanse, & K. Fujita (Eds.), *Handbook of self-control in health and well-being.* New York: Routledge. (p. 398)

Bearzi, M., & Stanford, C. (2010). A bigger, better brain. *American Scientist, 98*, 402–409. (p. 310)

Beauchamp, G. K. (1987). The human preference for excess salt. *American Scientist, 75*, 27–33. (p. 363)

Beauvois, J.-L., Courbet, D., & Oberlé, D. (2012). The prescriptive power of the television host: A transposition of Milgram's obedience paradigm to the context of TV game show. *European Review of Applied Psychology/Revue Européenne De Psychologie Appliquée, 62*, 111–119. (p. 426)

Beck, A. T., & Bredemeier, K. (2016). A unified model of depression: Integrating clinical, cognitive, biological, and evolutionary perspectives. *Clinical Psychological Science, 4,* 596–619. (p. 514)

Beck, A. T., Rush, A. J., Shaw, B. F., & Emery, G. (1979). *Cognitive therapy of depression.* New York: Guilford Press. (p. 544)

Becker, D. V., Kenrick, D. T., Neuberg, S. L., Blackwell, K. C., & Smith, D. M. (2007). The confounded nature of angry men and happy women. *Journal of Personality and Social Psychology, 92,* 179–190. (p. 377)

Becker, J. E., Maley, C., Shultz, E., & Taylor, W. D. (2016). Update on transcranial magnetic stimulation for depression and other neuropsychiatric illnesses. *Psychiatric Annals, 46,* 637–641. (p. 564)

Becker, M., Cortina, K. S., Tsai, Y., & Eccles, J. S. (2014). Sexual orientation, psychological well-being, and mental health: A longitudinal analysis from adolescence to young adulthood. *Psychology of Sexual Orientation and Gender Diversity, 1,* 132–145. (p. 179)

Becklen, R., & Cervone, D. (1983). Selective looking and the noticing of unexpected events. *Memory and Cognition, 11,* 601–608. (p. 82)

Beeman, M. J., & Chiarello, C. (1998). Complementary right- and left-hemisphere language comprehension. *Current Directions in Psychological Science, 7,* 2–8. (p. 67)

Bègue, L., Bushman, B. J., Giancola, P. R., Subra, B., & Rosset, E. (2010). "There is no such thing as an accident," especially when people are drunk. *Personality and Social Psychology Bulletin, 36,* 1301–1304. (p. 442)

Bègue, L., Subra, B., Arvers, P., Muller, D., Bricout, V., & Zorman, M. (2009). A message in a bottle: Extrapharmacological effects of alcohol on aggression. *Journal of Experimental Social Psychology, 45,* 137–142. (p. 442)

Beilin, H. (1992). Piaget's enduring contribution to developmental psychology. *Developmental Psychology, 28,* 191–204. (p. 130)

Beilock, S. (2010). *Choke: What the secrets of the brain reveal about getting it right when you have to.* New York: Free Press. (p. 305)

Beintner, I., Jacobi, C., & Taylor, C. B. (2012). Effects of an internet-based prevention programme for eating disorders in the USA and Germany: A meta-analytic review. *European Eating Disorders Review, 20,* 1–8. (p. 533)

Bell, A. P., Weinberg, M. S., & Hammersmith, S. K. (1981). *Sexual preference: Its development in men and women.* Bloomington: Indiana University Press. (p. 180)

Belluck, P. (2013, February 5). People with mental illness more likely to be smokers, study finds. *The New York Times* (nytimes.com). (p. 26)

Belot, M., & Francesconi, M. (2006, November). *Can anyone be "the one"? Evidence on mate selection from speed dating.* London: Centre for Economic Policy Research (cepr.org). (p. 449)

Belsky, D. W., Moffitt, T. E., Corcoran, D. L., Domingue, B., Harrington, H., Hogan, S., . . . Poulton, R. (2016). The genetics of success: How single-nucleotide polymorphisms associated with educational attainment relate to life-course development. *Psychological Science, 27,* 957–972. (p. 336)

Belson, K. (2015, September 6). No foul mouths on this field: Football with a New Age twist. *The New York Times* (nytimes.com). (p. B-9)

Belson, K. (2017, September 21). Aaron Hernandez had severe C.T.E. when he died at age 27. *The New York Times* (nytimes.com). (p. 503)

Bem, D., Tressoldi, P. E., Rabeyron, T., & Duggan, M. (2014, April 11). *Feeling the future: A meta-analysis of 90 experiments on the anomalous anticipation of random future events.* Retrieved from papers.ssrn.com/sol3/papers.cfm?abstract_id=2423692 (p. 231)

Bem, D. J. (1984). Quoted in *The Skeptical Inquirer, 8,* 194. (p. 231)

Bem, D. J. (2011). Feeling the future: Experimental evidence for anomalous retroactive influences on cognition and affect. *Journal of Personality and Social Psychology, 100,* 407–425. (p. 231)

Bem, S. L. (1987). Masculinity and femininity exist only in the mind of the perceiver. In J. M. Reinisch, L. A. Rosenblum, & S. A. Sanders (Eds.), *Masculinity/femininity: Basic perspectives* (pp. 304–311). New York: Oxford University Press. (p. 169)

Bem, S. L. (1993). *The lenses of gender: Transforming the debate on sexual inequality.* New Haven, CT: Yale University Press. (p. 169)

Benartzi, S., Beshears, J., Milkman, K. L., Sunstein, C. R., Thaler, R. H., Shankar, M., . . . Galing, S. (2017). Should governments invest more in nudging? *Psychological Science, 28,* 1041–1055. (p. 304)

Bench, S. W., Rivera, G. N., Schlegel, R. J., Hicks, J. A., & Lench, H. C. (2017). Does expertise matter in replication? An examination of the reproducibility project. *Journal of Experimental Social Psychology, 68,* 181–184. (p. 20)

Bender, T. W., Anestis, M. D., Anestis, J. C., Gordon, K. H., & Joiner, T. E. (2012). Affective and behavioral paths toward the acquired capacity for suicide. *Journal of Social and Clinical Psychology, 31,* 81–100. (p. 500)

Benedict, C., Brooks, S. J., O'Daly, O. G., Almen, M. S., Morell, A., Aberg, K., . . . Schiöth, H. B. (2012). Acute sleep deprivation enhances the brain's response to hedonic food stimuli: An fMRI study. *Journal of Clinical Endocrinology and Metabolism, 97,* 2011–2759. (p. 93)

Benjamin, D. J., Bergerg, J. O., Johannesson, M., Nosek, B. A., Wagenmakers, E.-J., Berk, R., . . . Johnson, V. E. (2018). Redefine statistical significance. *Nature Human Behaviour, 2,* 6–10. (p. A-7)

Benjamin, L. T., Jr., & Simpson, J. A. (2009). The power of the situation: The impact of Milgram's obedience studies on personality and social psychology. *American Psychologist, 64,* 12–19. (p. 425)

Benjamins, M. R., Ellison, C. G., & Rogers, R. G. (2010). Religious involvement and mortality risk among pre-retirement aged U.S. adults. In C. E. Ellison & R. A. Hummer (Eds.), *Religion, families, and health: Population-based research in the United States.* New Brunswick, NJ: Rutgers University Press. (p. 405)

Bennett, W. I. (1995). Beyond overeating. *New England Journal of Medicine, 332,* 673–674. (p. 366)

Ben-Shakhar, G., & Elaad, E. (2003). The validity of psychophysiological detection of information with the guilty knowledge test: A meta-analytic review. *Journal of Applied Psychology, 88,* 131–151. (p. 374)

Bensley, D. A., Lilienfeld, S. O., & Powell, L. A. (2014). A new measure of psychological misconceptions: Relations with academic background, critical thinking, and acceptance of paranormal and pseudoscientific claims. *Learning and Individual Differences, 36,* 9–18. (p. 3)

Bentley, K. H., Nock, M. K., & Barlow, D. H. (2014). The four-function model of nonsuicidal self-injury: Key directions for future research. *Clinical Psychological Science, 2,* 638–656. (p. 502)

Berg, J. M., Wall, M., Larson, N., Eisenberg, M. E., Loth, K. A., & Neumark-Sztainer, D. (2014). The unique and additive associations of family functioning and parenting practices with disordered eating behaviors in diverse adolescents. *Journal of Behavioral Medicine, 37,* 205–217. (p. 532)

Bergelson, E., & Swingley, D. (2012). At 6–9 months, human infants know the meanings of many common nouns. *PNAS, 109,* 3253–3258. (p. 314)

Bergelson, E., & Swingley, D. (2013). The acquisition of abstract words by young infants. *Cognition, 127,* 391–397. (p. 314)

Bergen, B. K. (2014). Universal grammar. Response to 2014 Edge question: What scientific idea is ready for retirement? *The Edge* (edge.org). (p. 313)

Berk, L. E. (1994, November). Why children talk to themselves. *Scientific American,* pp. 78–83. (p. 130)

Berk, L. S., Felten, D. L., Tan, S. A., Bittman, B. B., & Westengard, J. (2001). Modulation of neuroimmune parameters during the eustress of humor-associated mirthful laughter. *Alternative Therapies, 7,* 62–76. (p. 399)

Berken, J. A., Gracco, V. L., Chen, J., Soles, J., Watkins, K. E., Baum, S., . . . Klein, D. (2015). Neural activation in speech production and reading aloud in native and non-native languages. *NeuroImage, 112,* 208–217. (p. 317)

Berkman, E. T., Hutcherson, C. A., Livingston, J. L., Kahn, L. E., & Inzlicht, M. (2017). Self-control as a value-based choice. *Current Directions in Psychological Science.* Advance online publication. doi:10.17605/OSFIO/N4YY2 (p. 145)

Berkovich-Ohana, A., Glickson, J., & Goldstein, A. (2014). Studying the default mode and its mindfulness-induced changes using EEF functional connectivity. *Social Cognitive and Affective Neuroscience, 9,* 1616–1624. (p. 404)

Berkowitz, L. (1983). Aversively stimulated aggression: Some parallels and differences in research with animals and humans. *American Psychologist, 38,* 1135–1144. (p. 442)

Berkowitz, L. (1989). Frustration-aggression hypothesis: Examination and reformulation. *Psychological Bulletin, 106,* 59–73. (p. 442)

Berman, M. G., Jonides, J., & Kaplan, S. (2008). The cognitive benefits of interacting with nature. *Psychological Science, 19,* 1207–1212. (p. 357)

Bernieri, F., Davis, J., Rosenthal, R., & Knee, C. (1994). Interactional synchrony and rapport: Measuring synchrony in displays devoid of sound and facial affect. *Personality and Social Psychology Bulletin, 20,* 303–311. (p. 260)

Bernstein, D. M., & Loftus, E. F. (2009a). The consequences of false memories for food preferences and choices. *Perspectives on Psychological Science, 4,* 135–139. (p. 290)

Bernstein, D. M., & Loftus, E. F. (2009b). How to tell if a particular memory is true or false. *Perspectives on Psychological Science, 4,* 370–374. (p. 289)

Bernstein, M. J., Young, S. G., & Claypool, H. M. (2010). Is Obama's win a gain for Blacks? Changes in implicit racial prejudice following the 2008 election. *Social Psychology, 41,* 147–151. (p. 436)

Berntson, G. G., Norman, G. J., Bechara, A., Bruss, J., Tranel, D., & Cacioppo, J. T. (2011). The insula and evaluative processes. *Psychological Science, 22,* 80–86. (p. 55)

Berridge, K. C., Robinson, T. E., & Aldridge, J. W. (2009). Dissecting components of reward: "liking", "wanting", and learning. *Current Opinion in Pharmacology, 9,* 65–73. (p. 102)

Berry, C. M., & Zhao, P. (2015). Addressing criticisms of existing predictive bias research: Cognitive ability test scores still overpredict African Americans' job performance. *Journal of Applied Psychology, 100,* 162–179. (p. 343)

Berscheid, E. (1981). An overview of the psychological effects of physical attractiveness and some comments upon the psychological effects of knowledge of the effects of physical attractiveness. In G. W. Lucker, K. Ribbens, & J. A. McNamara (Eds.), *Psychological aspects of facial form* (Craniofacial Facial Growth Series). Ann Arbor: Center for Human Growth and Development, University of Michigan. (p. 449)

Berscheid, E. (1985). Interpersonal attraction. In G. Lindzey & E. Aronson (Eds.), *The handbook of social psychology.* New York: Random House. (p. 352)

Berscheid, E. (2010). Love in the fourth dimension. *Annual Review of Psychology, 61,* 1–25. (p. 451)

Berscheid, E., Gangestad, S. W., & Kulakowski, D. (1984). Emotion in close relationships: Implications for relationship counseling. In S. D. Brown & R. W. Lent (Eds.), *Handbook of counseling psychology.* New York: Wiley. (p. 451)

Berti, A., Cottini, G., Gandola, M., Pia, L., Smania, N., Stracciari, A., . . . Paulesu, E. (2005). Shared cortical anatomy for motor awareness and motor control. *Science, 309,* 488–491. (p. 67)

Bértolo, H. (2005). Visual imagery without visual perception? *Psicológica, 26,* 173–188. (p. 97)

Bertrand, M., & Mullainathan, S. (2003). *Are Emily and Greg more employable than Lakisha and Jamal? A field experiment on labor market discrimination.* Massachusetts Institute of Technology, Department of Economics, Working Paper 03–22. (p. 437)

Bhatt, R. S., Wasserman, E. A., Reynolds, W. F., Jr., & Knauss, K. S. (1988). Conceptual behavior in pigeons: Categorization of both familiar and novel examples from four classes of natural and artificial stimuli. *Journal of Experimental Psychology: Animal Behavior Processes, 14,* 219–234. (p. 245)

Bialystok, E. (2017). The bilingual adaptation: How minds accommodate experience. *Psychological Bulletin, 143,* 233–262. (p. 320)

Bialystok, E., Kroll, J. F., Green, D. W., MacWhinney, B., & Craik, F. I. M. (2015). Publication bias and the validity of evidence: What's the connection? *Psychological Science, 26,* 944–946. (p. 320)

Bianconi, E., Piovesan, A., Facchin, F., Beraudi, A., Casadei, R., Frabetti, F., . . . Canaider, S. (2013). An estimation of the number of cells in the human body. *Annals of Human Biology, 40,* 463–471. (p. 119)

Bick, J., Fox, N., Zeanah, C., & Nelson, C. A. (2015). Early deprivation, atypical brain development, and internalizing symptoms in late childhood. *Neuroscience.* Advance online publication. doi:10.1016/j.neuroscience.2015.09.026 (p. 137)

Bienvenu, O. J., Davydow, D. S., & Kendler, K. S. (2011). Psychiatric "diseases" versus behavioral disorders and degree of genetic influence. *Psychological Medicine, 41,* 33–40. (p. 518)

Bilefsky, D. (2009, March 10). Europeans debate castration of sex offenders. *The New York Times* (nytimes.com). (p. 174)

Billock, V. A., & Tsou, B. H. (2012). Elementary visual hallucinations and their relationships to neural pattern-forming mechanisms. *Psychological Bulletin, 138,* 744–774. (p. 108)

Binet, A. (1909). Les idées modernes sur les enfants [Modern ideas about children]. Paris: Flammarion. Quoted in A. Clarke & A. Clarke (2006), Born to be bright. *The Psychologist, 19,* 409. (p. 328)

Bird, C. D., & Emery, N. J. (2009). Rooks use stones to raise the water level to reach a floating worm. *Current Biology, 19,* 1410–1414. (p. 309)

Birkeland, M. S., Blix, I., Solberg, Ø., & Heir, T. (2016). Does optimism act as a buffer against posttraumatic stress over time? A longitudinal study of the protective role of optimism after the 2011 Oslo bombing. *Psychological Trauma.* Advance online publication. dx.doi.org/10.1037/tra0000188 (p. 409)

Birnbaum, G. E., & Reis, H. T. (2012). When does responsiveness pique sexual interest? Attachment and sexual desire in initial acquaintanceships. *Personality and Social Psychology Bulletin, 38,* 946–958. (p. 450)

Birnbaum, G. E., Reis, H. T., Mikulincer, M., Gillath, O., & Orpaz, A. (2006). When sex is more than just sex: Attachment orientations, sexual experience, and relationship quality. *Journal of Personality and Social Psychology, 91,* 929–943. (p. 136)

Biro, D., Humle, T., Koops, K., Sousa, C., Hayashi, M., & Matsuzawa, T. (2010). Chimpanzee mothers at Bossou, Guinea carry the mummified remains of their dead infants. *Current Biology, 20,* R351–R352. (p. 310)

Biro, F. M., Galvez, M. P., Greenspan, L. C., Succop, P. A., Vangeepuram, N., Pinney, S. M., . . . Wolff, M. S. (2010). Pubertal assessment method and baseline characteristics in a mixed longitudinal study of girls. *Pediatrics, 126,* e583–e590. doi:10.1542/peds.2009-3079. (p. 167)

Biro, F. M., Greenspan, L. C., & Galvez, M. P. (2012). Puberty in girls of the 21st century. *Journal of Pediatric and Adolescent Gynecology, 25,* 289–294. (p. 167)

Bishop, D. I., Weisgram, E. S., Holleque, K. M., Lund, K. E., & Wheeler, J. R. (2005). Identity development and alcohol consumption: Current and retrospective self-reports by college students. *Journal of Adolescence, 28,* 523–533. (p. 147)

Bishop, G. D. (1991). Understanding the understanding of illness: Lay disease representations. In J. A. Skelton & R. T. Croyle (Eds.), *Mental representation in health and illness.* New York: Springer-Verlag. (p. 298)

Bjork, E. L., & Bjork, R. (2011). Making things hard on yourself, but in a good way: Creating desirable difficulties to enhance learning. In M. A. Gernsbacher, M. A. Pew, L. M. Hough, & J. R. Pomerantz (Eds.), *Psychology and the real world* (pp. 55–64). New York: Worth. (p. 35)

Bjork, R. (2011, January 20). Quoted by P. Belluck, To really learn, quit studying and take a test. *The New York Times* (nytimes.com). (p. 273)

Bjorklund, D. F., & Green, B. L. (1992). The adaptive nature of cognitive immaturity. *American Psychologist, 47,* 46–54. (p. 130)

BJS. (2017). *Data collection: National Crime Victimization Survey (NCVS).* Retrieved from Bureau of Justice Statistics (bjs.gov/index.cfm?ty=dcdetail&iid=245). (p. 18)

Black, M. C., Basile, K. C., Breiding, M. J., Smith, S. G., Walters, M. L., Merrick, M. T., . . . Stevens, M. R. (2011). *The National Intimate Partner and Sexual Violence Survey (NISVS): 2010 summary report.* Atlanta, GA: National Center for Injury Prevention and Control, Centers for Disease Control and Prevention. (p. 170)

Blackhart, G. C., Nelson, B. C., Knowles, M. L., & Baumeister, R. F. (2009). Rejection elicits emotional reactions but neither causes immediate distress nor lowers self-esteem: A meta-analytic review of 192 studies on social exclusion. *Personality and Social Psychology Bulletin, 13,* 269–309. (p. 353)

Blake, A., Nazarian, M., & Castel, A. (2015). The Apple of the mind's eye: Everyday attention, metamemory, and reconstructive memory for the Apple logo. *Quarterly Journal of Experimental Psychology, 68,* 858–865. (p. 285)

Blake, W. (2013, March). Voices from solitary: A sentence worse than death. Essay published at *Solitary Watch, News from a Nation in Lockdown* (solitarywatch.com). (p. 354)

Blakemore, S.-J. (2008). Development of the social brain during adolescence. *Quarterly Journal of Experimental Psychology, 61,* 40–49. (p. 142)

Blakemore, S.-J., Wolpert, D. M., & Frith, C. D. (1998). Central cancellation of self-produced tickle sensation. *Nature Neuroscience, 1,* 635–640. (. 221)

Blakeslee, S. (2006, January 10). Cells that read minds. *The New York Times* (nytimes.com). (p. 259)

Blanchard, R. (2004). Quantitative and theoretical analyses of the relation between older brothers and homosexuality in men. *Journal of Theoretical Biology, 230,* 173–187. (p. 181)

Blanchard, R. (2008a). Review and theory of handedness, birth order, and homosexuality in men. *Laterality, 13,* 51–70. (p. 181)

Blanchard, R. (2008b). Sex ratio of older siblings in heterosexual and homosexual, right-handed and non-right-handed men. *Archives of Sexual Behavior, 37,* 977–981. (p. 181)

Blanchard, R. (2014). Detecting and correcting for family size differences in the study of sexual orientation and fraternal birth order. *Archives of Sexual Behavior, 43,* 845–852. (p. 181)

Blanchard-Fields, F. (2007). Everyday problem solving and emotion: An adult developmental perspective. *Current Directions in Psychological Science, 16,* 26–31. (p. 334)

Blanke, O. (2012). Multisensory brain mechanisms of bodily self-consciousness. *Nature Reviews Neuroscience, 13,* 556–571. (p. 81)

Blascovich, J., & Mendes, W. B. (2010). Social psychophysiology and embodiment. In S. T. Fiske, D. T. Gilbert, & G. Lindzey (Eds.), *The handbook of social psychology,* 5th ed. (pp. 194–227). New York: Wiley. (p. 385)

Blasi, D. E., Wichmann, S., Hammarström, H., Stadler, P. F., & Christiansen, M. H. (2016). Sound-meaning association biases evidenced across thousands of languages. *PNAS, 113,* 10818–10823. (p. 313)

Blass, T. (1996). Stanley Milgram: A life of inventiveness and controversy. In G. A. Kimble, C. A. Boneau, & M. Wertheimer (Eds.), *Portraits of pioneers in psychology* (Vol. II). Washington, DC, and Mahwah, NJ: American Psychological Association and Lawrence Erlbaum. (p. 427)

Blass, T. (1999). The Milgram paradigm after 35 years: Some things we now know about obedience to authority. *Journal of Applied Social Psychology, 29,* 955–978. (p. 426)

Blease, C. R. (2015). Too many "friends," too few "likes"? Evolutionary psychology and "Facebook depression." *Review of General Psychology, 19,* 1–13. (p. 355)

Blechert, J., Testa, G., Georgii, C., Klimesch, W., & Wilhelm, F. H. (2016). The Pavlovian craver: Neural and experiential correlates of single trial naturalistic food conditioning in humans. *Physiology & Behavior, 158,* 18–25. (p. 241)

Bleidorn, W., Arslan, R. C., Denissen, J. J. A., Rentfrow, P. J., Gebauer, J. E., Potter, J., & Gosling, S. D. (2016). Age and gender differences in self-esteem—a cross-cultural window. *Journal of Personality and Social Psychology, 111,* 396–410. (p. 486)

Blinkhorn, V., Lyons, M., & Almond, L. (2015). The ultimate femme fatale? Narcissism predicts serious and aggressive sexually coercive behavior in females. *Personality and Individual Differences, 87,* 219–223. (p. 488)

Bloom, B. C. (Ed.). (1985). *Developing talent in young people.* New York: Ballantine. (p. 357)

Bloom, P. (2000). *How children learn the meanings of words.* Cambridge, MA: MIT Press. (p. 313)

Blow, C. M. (2015, March 26). Officers' race matters less than you think. *The New York Times* (nytimes.com). (p. 436)

BLS. (2011, June 22). *American time use survey summary.* Bureau of Labor Statistics (bls.gov). (p. 422)

BLS. (2017). *Labor force statistics from the Current Population Survey.* Retrieved from Bureau of Labor Statistics (data.bls.gov/timeseries/LNS14000000). (p. 18)

Blum, D. (2011). Love at Goon Park: Harry Harlow and the science of affection (2nd edition). New York: Perseus. (p. 134)

Blum, K., Cull, J. G., Braverman, E. R., & Comings, D. E. (1996). Reward deficiency syndrome. *American Scientist, 84,* 132–145. (p. 56)

Blumenstein, B., & Orbach, I. (2012). *Mental practice in sport: Twenty case studies.* New York: Novinka/Nova Science. (p. 321)

Boag, S. (2006). Freudian repression, the common view, and pathological science. *Review of General Psychology, 10,* 74–86. (p. 469)

Boccardi, M., Frisoni, G. B., Hare, R. D., Cavedo, E., Najt, P., Pievani, M., . . . Tiihonen, J. (2011). Cortex and amygdala morphology in psychopathy. *Psychiatry Research: Neuroimaging, 193,* 85–92. (p. 55)

Bock, L. (2013, June 19). Interview by Adam Bryant, "In head-hunting, big data may not be such a big deal." *The New York Times* (nytimes.com). (p. B-5)

Bocklandt, S., Horvath, S., Vilain, E., & Hamer, D. H. (2006). Extreme skewing of X chromosome inactivation in mothers of homosexual men. *Human Genetics, 118,* 691–694. (p. 181)

Bockting, W. O. (2014). Transgender identity development. In D. L. Tolman & L. M. Diamond (Eds.), *APA handbook of sexuality and psychology: Vol. 1. Person-based approaches* (pp. 739–758). Washington, DC: American Psychological Association. (p. 170)

Bodenhausen, G. V., Sheppard, L. A., & Kramer, G. P. (1994). Negative affect and social judgment: The differential impact of anger and sadness. *European Journal of Social Psychology, 24,* 45–62. (p. 459)

Bodenmann, G., Meuwly, N., Germann, J., Nussbeck, F. W., Heinrichs, M., & Bradbury, T. N. (2015). Effects of stress on the social support provided by men and women in intimate relationships. *Psychological Science, 26,* 1584–1594. (p. 388)

Bodkin, J. A., & Amsterdam, J. D. (2002). Transdermal selegiline in major depression: A double-blind, placebo-controlled, parallel-group study in outpatients. *American Journal of Psychiatry, 159,* 1869–1875. (p. 561)

Boecker, H., Sprenger, T., Spilker, M. E., Henriksen, G., Koppenhoefer, M., Wagner, K. J., . . . Tolle, T. R. (2008). The runner's high: Opioidergic mechanisms in the human brain. *Cerebral Cortex, 18,* 2523–2531. (pp. 43, 519)

Boehm, J. K., & Kubzansky, L. D. (2012). The heart's content: The association between positive psychological well-being and cardiovascular health. *Psychological Bulletin, 138,* 655–691. (p. 398)

Boehm, J. K., Trudel-Fitzgerald, C., Kivimaki, M., & Kubzansky, L. D. (2015). The prospective association between positive psychological well-being and diabetes. *Health Psychology, 34,* 1013–1021. (p. 407)

Boehm-Davis, D. A. (2005). Improving product safety and effectiveness in the home. In R. S. Nickerson (Ed.), *Reviews of human factors and ergonomics.* Volume 1. Santa Monica, CA: Human Factors and Ergonomics Society, pp. 219–253. (p. B-12)

Boenigk, S., & Mayr, M. L. (2016). The happiness of giving: Evidence from the German socioeconomic panel that happier people are more generous. *Journal of Happiness Studies, 17,* 1825–1846. (p. 407)

Boesch-Achermann, H., & Boesch, C. (1993). Tool use in wild chimpanzees: New light from dark forests. *Current Directions in Psychological Science, 2,* 18–21. (p. 309)

Bogaert, A. F. (2003). Number of older brothers and sexual orientation: New texts and the attraction/behavior distinction in two national probability samples. *Journal of Personality and Social Psychology, 84,* 644–652. (p. 181)

Bogaert, A. F. (2004). Asexuality: Prevalence and associated factors in a national probability sample. *Journal of Sex Research, 41,* 279–287. (p. 172)

Bogaert, A. F. (2006). Biological versus nonbiological older brothers and men's sexual orientation. *PNAS, 103,* 10771–10774. (p. 182)

Bogaert, A. F. (2015). Asexuality: What it is and why it matters. *Journal of Sex Research, 52,* 362–379. (p. 172)

Boggiano, A. K., Harackiewicz, J. M., Bessette, M. M., & Main, D. S. (1985). Increasing children's interest through performance-contingent reward. *Social Cognition, 3,* 400–411. (p. 358)

Bohannon, J. (2016). Government "nudges" prove their worth. *Science, 352,* 1042. (p. 304)

Bohlken, M. M., Brouwer, R. M., Mandl, R. C. W., Van, d. H., Hedman, A. M., De Hert, M., . . . Hulshoff Pol, H. E. (2016). Structural brain connectivity as a genetic marker for schizophrenia. *JAMA Psychiatry, 73,* 11–19. (p. 525)

Bohman, M., & Sigvardsson, S. (1990). Outcome in adoption: Lessons from longitudinal studies. In D. Brodzinsky & M. Schechter (Eds.), *The psychology of adoption* (pp. 93–106). New York: Oxford University Press. (p. 73)

Bois, C., Levita, L., Ripp, I., Owens, D. C. G., Johnstone, E. C., Whalley, H. C., & Lawrie, S. M. (2016). Longitudinal changes in hippocampal volume in the Edinburgh High Risk Study of Schizophrenia. *Schizophrenia Research, 173,* 146–151. (p. 525)

Bolger, N., DeLongis, A., Kessler, R. C., & Schilling, E. A. (1989). Effects of daily stress on negative mood. *Journal of Personality and Social Psychology, 57,* 808–818. (p. 408)

Bolmont, M., Cacioppo, J. T., & Cacioppo, S. (2014). Love is in the gaze: An eyetracking study of love and sexual desire. *Psychological Science, 25,* 1748–1756. (p. 375)

Boly, M., Garrido, M. I., Gosseries, O., Bruno, M.-A., Boveroux, P., Schnakers, C., . . . Friston, K. (2011). Preserved feed-forward but impaired top-down processes in the vegetative state. *Science, 332,* 858–862. (p. 81)

Bonanno, G. A. (2004). Loss, trauma, and human resilience: Have we underestimated the human capacity to thrive after extremely aversive events? *American Psychologist, 59,* 20–28. (pp. 160, 509)

Bonanno, G. A. (2005). Adult resilience to potential trauma. *Current Directions in Psychological Science, 14,* 135–137. (p. 509)

Bonanno, G. A., Brewin, C. R., Kaniasty, K., & La Greca, A. M. (2010). Weighing the costs of disaster: Consequences, risks, and resilience in individuals, families, and communities. *Psychological Science in the Public Interest, 11,* 1–49. (p. 510)

Bonanno, G. A., Galea, S., Bucciarelli, A., & Vlahov, D. (2006). Psychological resilience after disaster. *Psychological Science, 17,* 181–186. (p. 510)

Bonanno, G. A., Galea, S., Bucciarelli, A., & Vlahov, D. (2007). What predicts psychological resilience after disaster? The role of demographics, resources, and life stress. *Journal of Consulting and Clinical Psychology, 75,* 671–682. (p. 567)

Bonanno, G. A., & Kaltman, S. (1999). Toward an integrative perspective on bereavement. *Psychological Bulletin, 125,* 760–777. (p. 159)

Bonanno, G. A., Kennedy, P., Galatzer-Levy, I. R., Lude, P., & Elfström, M. L. (2012). Trajectories of resilience, depression, and anxiety following spinal cord injury. *Rehabilitation Psychology, 57,* 236–247. (p. 567)

Bonanno, G. A., Westphal, M., & Mancini, A. D. (2011). Resilience to loss and potential trauma. *Annual Review of Clinical Psychology, 11,* 511–535. (p. 509)

Bond, C. F., Jr., & DePaulo, B. M. (2006). Accuracy of deception judgments. *Personality and Social Psychology Review, 10,* 214–234. (p. 376)

Bond, M. H., Lun, V. M.-C., Chan, J., Chan, W. W.-Y., & Wong, D. (2012). Enacting modesty in Chinese culture: The joint contribution of personal characteristics and contextual features. *Asian Journal of Social Psychology, 15,* 14–25. (p. 490)

Bond, R., & Smith, P. B. (1996). Culture and conformity: A meta-analysis of studies using Asch's (1952b, 1956) line judgment task. *Psychological Bulletin, 119,* 111–137. (p. 425)

Bonezzi, A., Brendl, C. M., & DeAngelis, M. (2011). Stuck in the middle: The psychophysics of goal pursuit. *Psychological Science, 22,* 607–612. (p. 357)

Bonfils, K. A., Lysaker, P. H., Minor, K. S., & Salyers, M. P. (2016). Affective empathy in schizophrenia: A meta-analysis. *Schizophrenia Research, 175,* 109–117. (p. 523)

Bono, J. E., & Judge, T. A. (2004). Personality and transformational and transactional leadership: A meta-analysis. *Journal of Applied Psychology, 89,* 901–910. (p. B-10)

Bonos, L. (2018, March 8). A legislator has a bill to ban *The Bachelor's* Arie Luyendyk Jr. from Minnesota. *The Washington Post* (washingtonpost.com). (p. 31)

Boone, A. P., & Hegarty, M. (2017). Sex differences in mental rotation tasks: Not just in the mental rotation process! *Journal of Experimental Psychology: Learning, Memory, and Cognition, 43,* 1005–1019. (p. 182)

Bora, E., & Pantelis, C. (2013). Theory of mind impairments in first-episode psychosis, individuals at ultra-high risk for psychosis and in first-degree relatives of schizophrenia: Systematic review and meta-analysis. *Schizophrenia Research, 144,* 31–36. (p. 523)

Borges, G., Bagge, C. L., Cherpitel, C. J., Conner, K. R., Orozco, R., & Rossow, I. (2017). A meta-analysis of acute use of alcohol and the risk of suicide attempt. *Psychological Medicine, 47,* 949–957. (p. 500)

Boring, E. G. (1930). A new ambiguous figure. *American Journal of Psychology, 42,* 444–445. (p. 195)

Bornstein, M. H., Cote, L. R., Maital, S., Painter, K., Park, S.-Y., Pascual, L., . . . Vyt, A. (2004). Cross-linguistic analysis of vocabulary in young children: Spanish, Dutch, French, Hebrew, Italian, Korean, and American English. *Child Development, 75,* 1115–1139. (p. 313)

Bornstein, M. H., Tal, J., Rahn, C., Galperin, C. Z., Pecheux, M.-G., Lamour, M., . . . Tamis-LeMonda, C. S. (1992a). Functional analysis of the contents of maternal speech to infants of 5 and 13 months in four cultures: Argentina, France, Japan, and the United States. *Developmental Psychology, 28,* 593–603. (p. 117)

Bornstein, M. H., Tamis-LeMonda, C. S., Tal, J., Ludemann, P., Toda, S., Rahn, C. W., . . . Vardi, D. (1992b). Maternal responsiveness to infants in three societies: The United States, France, and Japan. *Child Development, 63*, 808–821. (p. 117)

Bornstein, R. F. (1989). Exposure and affect: Overview and meta-analysis of research, 1968–1987. *Psychological Bulletin, 106*, 265–289. (pp. 133, 447)

Bornstein, R. F. (1999). Source amnesia, misattribution, and the power of unconscious perceptions and memories. *Psychoanalytic Psychology, 16*, 155–178. (p. 447)

Bornstein, R. F., Galley, D. J., Leone, D. R., & Kale, A. R. (1991). The temporal stability of ratings of parents: Test-retest reliability and influence of parental contact. *Journal of Social Behavior and Personality, 6*, 641–649. (p. 281)

Boroditsky, L. (2009, June 12). How does our language shape the way we think? *The Edge* (edge.org). (pp. 312, 320)

Boroditsky, L. (2011, February). How language shapes thought. *Scientific American*, pp. 63–65. (p. 319)

Bos, H. M. W., Knox, J. R., van Rijn-van Gelderen, L., & Gartrell, N. K. (2016). Same-sex and different-sex parent households and child health outcomes: Findings from the national survey of children's health. *Journal of Developmental and Behavioral Pediatrics, 37*, 179–187. (p. 180)

Bosma, H., Marmot, M. G., Hemingway, H., Nicolson, A. C., Brunner, E., & Stansfeld, S. A. (1997). Low job control and risk of coronary heart disease in Whitehall II (prospective cohort) study. *British Medical Journal, 314*, 558–565. (p. 396)

Bosma, H., Peter, R., Siegrist, J., & Marmot, M. (1998). Two alternative job stress models and the risk of coronary heart disease. *American Journal of Public Health, 88*, 68–74. (p. 396)

Bostean, G., & Gillespie, B. J. (2017). Acculturation, acculturative stressors, and family relationships among Latina/o immigrants. *Cultural Diversity and Ethnic Minority Psychology*. Advance online publication. http://dx.doi.org/10.1037/cdp0000169 (p. 385)

Bostwick, J. M., Pabbati, C., Geske, J. R., & McKean, A. J. (2016). Suicide attempt as a risk factor for completed suicide: Even more lethal than we knew. *The American Journal of Psychiatry, 173*, 1094–1100. (p. 501)

Bostwick, J. M., & Pankratz, V. S. (2000). Affective disorders and suicide risk: A re-examination. *American Journal of Psychiatry, 157*, 1925–1932. (p. 500)

Bosworth, R. G., & Dobkins, K. R. (1999). Left-hemisphere dominance for motion processing in deaf signers. *Psychological Science, 10*, 256–262. (p. 64)

Bothwell, R. K., Brigham, J. C., & Malpass, R. S. (1989). Cross-racial identification. *Personality and Social Psychology Bulletin, 15*, 19–25. (p. 439)

Bouchard, T. J., Jr. (2009). Genetic influences on human intelligence (Spearman's g): How much? *Annals of Human Biology, 36*, 527–544. (p. 72)

Boucher, J., Mayes, A., & Bigham, S. (2012). Memory in autistic spectrum disorder. *Psychological Bulletin, 138*, 458–496. (p. 131)

Bowden, E. M., & Beeman, M. J. (1998). Getting the right idea: Semantic activation in the right hemisphere may help solve insight problems. *Psychological Science, 9*, 435–440. (p. 67)

Bower, B. (2009, February 14). The dating go round. *Science News*, pp. 22–25. (p. 448)

Bower, G. H. (1986). Prime time in cognitive psychology. In P. Eelen (Ed.), *Cognitive research and behavior therapy: Beyond the conditioning paradigm*. Amsterdam: North Holland Publishers. (p. 280)

Bower, G. H., Clark, M. C., Lesgold, A. M., & Winzenz, D. (1969). Hierarchical retrieval schemes in recall of categorized word lists. *Journal of Verbal Learning and Verbal Behavior, 8*, 323–343. (p. 272)

Bower, G. H., & Morrow, D. G. (1990). Mental models in narrative comprehension. *Science, 247*, 44–48. (p. 274)

Bower, J. M., & Parsons, L. M. (2003, August). Rethinking the "lesser brain." *Scientific American*, pp. 50–57. (p. 55)

Bowers, J. S. (2009). On the biological plausibility of grandmother cells: Implications for neural network theories in psychology and neuroscience. *Psychological Review, 116*, 220–251. (p. 206)

Bowers, J. S. (2016). The practical and principled problems with educational neuroscience. *Psychological Review*. Advance online publication. dx.doi.org/10.1037/rev0000025. (p. 52)

Bowers, J. S., Mattys, S. L., & Gage, S. H. (2009). Preserved implicit knowledge of a forgotten childhood language. *Psychological Science, 20*, 1064–1069. (p. 125)

Bowker, E., & Dorstyn, D. (2016). Hypnotherapy for disability-related pain: A meta-analysis. *Journal of Health Psychology, 21*, 526–539. (p. 224)

Bowling, N. A., Eschleman, K. J., & Wang, Q. (2010). A meta-analytic examination of the relationship between job satisfaction and subjective well-being. *Journal of Occupational and Organizational Psychology, 83*, 915–934. (p. B-8)

Boxer, P., Huesmann, L. R., Bushman, B. J., O'Brien, M., & Moceri, D. (2009). The role of violent media preference in cumulative developmental risk for violence and general aggression. *Journal of Youth and Adolescence, 38*, 417–428. (p. 263)

Boyatzis, C. J. (2012). Spiritual development during childhood and adolescence. In L. J. Miller (Ed.), *The Oxford handbook of psychology and spirituality* (pp. 151–164). New York: Oxford University Press. (p. 143)

Boyatzis, C. J., Matillo, G. M., & Nesbitt, K. M. (1995). Effects of the "Mighty Morphin Power Rangers" on children's aggression with peers. *Child Study Journal, 25*, 45–55. (p. 263)

Boyce, C. J., & Wood, A. M. (2011). Personality prior to disability determines adaptation: Agreeable individuals recover lost life satisfaction faster and more completely. *Psychological Science, 22*, 1397–1402. (p. 408)

Boyce, C. J., Wood, A. M., Daly, M., & Sedikides, C. (2015). Personality change following unemployment. *Journal of Applied Psychology, 100*, 991–1011. (p. 480)

Boyce, R., Glasgow, S. D., Williams, S., & Adamantidis, A. (2016). Causal evidence for the role of REM sleep theta rhythm in contextual memory consolidation. *Science, 352*, 812–816. (p. 92)

Boynton, R. M. (1979). *Human color vision*. New York: Holt, Rinehart & Winston. (p. 204)

Braden, J. P. (1994). *Deafness, deprivation, and IQ*. New York: Plenum. (p. 342)

Bradley, D. R., Dumais, S. T., & Petry, H. M. (1976). Reply to Cavonius. *Nature, 261*, 78. (p. 207)

Bradley, R. B., Binder, E. B., Epstein, M. P., Tang, Y., Nair, H. P., Liu, W., . . . Ressler, K. J. (2008). Influence of child abuse on adult depression: Moderation by the corticotropin-releasing hormone receptor gene. *Archives of General Psychiatry, 65*, 190–200. (p. 138)

Bradshaw, C., Sawyer, A., & O'Brennan, L. (2009). A social disorganization perspective on bullying-related attitudes and behaviors: The influence of school context. *American Journal of Community Psychology, 43*, 204–220. (p. 13)

Brady, W. J., Wills, J. A., Jost, J. T., Tucker, J. A., & Van Bavel, J. J. (2017). Emotion shapes the diffusion of moralized content in social networks. *PNAS, 114*, 7313–7318. (p. 19)

Braiker, B. (2005, October 18). A quiet revolt against the rules on SIDS. *The New York Times* (nytimes.com). (p. 124)

Brainerd, C. J. (1996). Piaget: A centennial celebration. *Psychological Science, 7*, 191–195. (p. 125)

Brand, B. L., Sar, V., Stavropoulos, P., Krüger, C., Korzekwa, M., Martínez-Taboas, A., & Middleton, W. (2016). Separating fact from fiction: An empirical examination of six myths about dissociative identity disorder. *Harvard Review of Psychiatry, 24*, 257–270. (p. 529)

Brandon, S., Boakes, J., Glaser, D., & Green, R. (1998). Recovered memories of childhood sexual abuse: Implications for clinical practice. *British Journal of Psychiatry, 172*, 294–307. (p. 293)

Brang, D., Edwards, L., Ramachandran, V. S., & Coulson, S. (2008). Is the sky 2? Contextual priming in grapheme-color synaesthesia. *Psychological Science, 19*, 421–428. (p. 229)

Brannan, D., Biswas-Diener, R., Mohr, C., Mortazavi, S., & Stein, N. (2013). Friends and family: A cross-cultural investigation of social support and subjective well-being among college students. *Journal of Positive Psychology, 8*, 65–75. (p. 399)

Bransford, J. D., & Johnson, M. K. (1972). Contextual prerequisites for understanding: Some investigations of comprehension and recall. *Journal of Verbal Learning and Verbal Behavior, 11*, 717–726. (p. 273)

Brasel, S. A., & Gips, J. (2011). Media multitasking behavior: Concurrent television and computer usage. *Cyberpsychology, Behavior, and Social Networking, 14*, 527–534. (p. 82)

Braun, S. (1996). New experiments underscore warnings on maternal drinking. *Science, 273*, 738–739. (p. 120)

Braun, S. (2001, April). Seeking insight by prescription. *Cerebrum*, pp. 10–21. (p. 107)

Braunstein, G. D., Sundwall, D. A., Katz, M., Shifren, J. L., Buster, J. E., Simon, J. A., . . . Watts, N. B. (2005). Safety and efficacy of a testosterone patch for the treatment of hypoactive sexual desire disorder in surgically menopausal women: A randomized, placebo-controlled trial. *Archives of Internal Medicine, 165*, 1582–1589. (p. 173)

Bray, D. W., & Byham, W. C. (1991, Winter). Assessment centers and their derivatives. *Journal of Continuing Higher Education*, pp. 8–11. (p. 484)

Bray, D. W., & Byham, W. C., interviewed by Mayes, B. T. (1997). Insights into the history and future of assessment centers: An interview with Dr. Douglas W. Bray and Dr. William Byham. *Journal of Social Behavior and Personality, 12*, 3–12. (p. 484)

Brayne, C., Spiegelhalter, D. J., Dufouil, C., Chi, L.-Y., Dening, T. R., Paykel, E. S., . . . Huppert, F. A. (1999). Estimating the true extent of cognitive decline in the old old. *Journal of the American Geriatrics Society, 47*, 1283–1288. (p. 332)

Breedlove, S. M. (1997). Sex on the brain. *Nature, 389*, 801. (p. 180)

Brehm, S., & Brehm, J. W. (1981). *Psychological reactance: A theory of freedom and control*. New York: Academic Press. (p. 428)

Brennan, Z. (2010, April 8). The Goering who saved Jews: While Hermann masterminded the Final Solution his brother Albert rescued Gestapo victims. *Daily Mail* (dailymail.co.uk). (p. 73)

Breslau, J., Aguilar-Gaxiola, S., Borges, G., Kendler, K. S., Su, M., & Kessler, R. C. (2007). Risk for psychiatric disorder among immigrants and their US-born descendants. *Journal of Nervous and Mental Disease, 195,* 189–195. (p. 503)

Breslin, C. W., & Safer, M. A. (2011). Effects of event valence on long-term memory for two baseball championship games. *Psychological Science, 22,* 1408–1412. (p. 278)

Brethel-Haurwitz, K. M., & Marsh, A. A. (2014, March). Geographical differences in subjective well-being predict extraordinary altruism. *Psychological Science, 25,* 762–771. (p. 407)

Brewer, C. L. (1996). Personal communication. (p. 10)

Brewer, M. B., & Chen, Y.-R. (2007). Where (who) are collectives in collectivism? Toward conceptual clarification of individualism and collectivism. *Psychological Review, 114,* 133–151. (p. 490)

Brewer, W. F. (1977). Memory for the pragmatic implications of sentences. *Memory & Cognition, 5,* 673–678. (p. 274)

Brewin, C. R., & Andrews, B. (2017). Creating memories for false autobiographical events in childhood: A systematic review. *Applied Cognitive Psychology, 31,* 2–23. (pp. 290, 294)

Brewin, C. R., Andrews, B., Rose, S., & Kirk, M. (1999). Acute stress disorder and posttraumatic stress disorder in victims of violent crime. *American Journal of Psychiatry, 156,* 360–366. (p. 509)

Brewin, C. R., Kleiner, J. S., Vasterling, J. J., & Field, A. P. (2007). Memory for emotionally neutral information in posttraumatic stress disorder: A meta-analytic investigation. *Journal of Abnormal Psychology, 116,* 448–463. (p. 277)

Briscoe, D. (1997, February 16). Women lawmakers still not in charge. *The Grand Rapids Press,* p. A23. (p. 168)

Brislin, R. W. (1988). Increasing awareness of class, ethnicity, culture, and race by expanding on students' own experiences. In I. Cohen (Ed.), *The G. Stanley Hall lecture series.* Washington, DC: American Psychological Association. (p. 421)

Broadbent, E., Kakokehr, A., Booth, R. J., Thomas, J., Windsor, J. A., Buchanan, C. M., . . . Hill, A. G. (2012). A brief relaxation intervention reduces stress and improves surgical wound healing response: A randomized trial. *Brain, Behavior, and Immunity, 26,* 212–217. (p. 404)

Brodbeck, F. C., Chhokar, J. S., & House, R. J. (2008). Culture and leadership in 25 societies: Integration, conclusions, and future directions. In J. S. Chhokar, F. C. Brodbeck & R. J. House (Eds.), *Culture and leadership across the world: The GLOBE book of in-depth studies of 25 societies,* pp. 1023–1099. Mahwah, NJ: Lawrence Erlbaum, Mahwah, NJ. (p. B-12)

Brody, S., & Tillmann, H. C. (2006). The post-orgasmic prolactin increase following intercourse is greater than following masturbation and suggests greater satiety. *Biological Psychology, 71,* 312–315. (p. 185)

Brooks, R. (2012). "Asia's missing women" as a problem in applied evolutionary psychology? *Evolutionary Psychology, 12,* 910–925. (p. 437)

Brooks, S. (2015). Does personal social media usage affect efficiency and well-being? *Computers in Human Behavior, 46,* 26–37. (p. 356)

Brown, A. S., Begg, M. D., Gravenstein, S., Schaefer, C. A., Wyatt, R. J., Bresnahan, M., . . . Susser, E. S. (2004). Serologic evidence of prenatal influenza in the etiology of schizophrenia. *Archives of General Psychiatry, 61,* 774–780. (p. 525)

Brown, A. S., & Marsh, E. (2009). Creating illusions of past encounter through brief exposure. *Psychological Science, 20,* 534–538. (p. 291)

Brown, A. S., & Patterson, P. H. (2011). Maternal infection and schizophrenia: Implications for prevention. *Schizophrenia Bulletin, 37,* 284–290. (p. 525)

Brown, A. S., Schaefer, C. A., Wyatt, R. J., Goetz, R., Begg, M. D., Gorman, J. M., & Susser, E. S. (2000). Maternal exposure to respiratory infections and adult schizophrenia spectrum disorders: A prospective birth cohort study. *Schizophrenia Bulletin, 26,* 287–295. (p. 525)

Brown, E. L., & Deffenbacher, K. (1979). *Perception and the senses.* New York: Oxford University Press. (p. 220)

Brown, J. A. (1958). Some tests of the decay theory of immediate memory. *Quarterly Journal of Experimental Psychology, 10,* 12–21. (p. 271)

Brown, J. D. (2012). Understanding the better than average effect: Motives (still) matter. *Personality and Social Psychology Bulletin, 38,* 209–219. (p. 488)

Brown, K. W., Goodman, R. J., & Inzlicht, M. (2013). Dispositional mindfulness and the attenuation of neural responses to emotional stimuli. *Social Cognitive and Affective Neuroscience, 8,* 93–99. (p. 404)

Brown, P. C., Roediger, H. L., III, & McDaniel, M. A. (2014). *Make it stick: The science of successful learning.* Cambridge, MA: Harvard University Press. (pp. 272, 556)

Brown, R. (1986). Linguistic relativity. In S. H. Hulse & B. F. Green, Jr. (Eds.), *One hundred years of psychological research in America.* Baltimore: Johns Hopkins University Press. (p. 319)

Brown, R. P., Osterman, L. L., & Barnes, C. D. (2009). School violence and the culture of honor. *Psychological Science, 20,* 1400–1405. (p. 443)

Brown, S. L., Brown, R. M., House, J. S., & Smith, D. M. (2008). Coping with spousal loss: Potential buffering effects of self-reported helping behavior. *Personality and Social Psychology Bulletin, 34,* 849–861. (p. 160)

Brown, S. L., Stykes, J. B., & Manning, W. D. (2016). Trends in children's family instability, 1995–2010. *Journal of Marriage and Family, 78,* 1173–1183. (pp. 136, 404)

Browning, C. (1992). *Ordinary men: Reserve Police Battalion 101 and the final solution in Poland.* New York: HarperCollins. (p. 427)

Browning, R. (1868). *The ring and the book. IV—Tertium quid.* New York: Thomas Y. Crowell. (p. 454)

Bruck, M., & Ceci, S. J. (1999). The suggestibility of children's memory. *Annual Review of Psychology, 50,* 419–439. (p. 292)

Bruck, M., & Ceci, S. J. (2004). Forensic developmental psychology: Unveiling four common misconceptions. *Current Directions in Psychological Science, 15,* 229–232. (p. 292)

Bruer, J. T. (1999). *The myth of the first three years: A new understanding of early brain development and lifelong learning.* New York: Free Press. (p. 339)

Brummelman, E., Thomaes, S., Nelemans, S. A., Orobio de Castro, B., Overbeek, G., & Bushman, B. J. (2015). Origins of narcissism in children. *PNAS, 112,* 3659–3662. (pp. 138, 489)

Brunner, M., Gogol, K. M., Sonnleitner, P., Keller, U., Krauss, S., & Preckel, F. (2013). Gender differences in the mean level, variability, and profile shape of student achievement: Results from 41 countries. *Intelligence, 41,* 378–395. (p. 340)

Bruno, M.-A., Bernheim, J. L., Ledoux, D., Pellas, F., Demertzi, A., & Laureys, S. (2011). A survey on self-assessed well-being in a cohort of chronic locked-in syndrome patients: Happy majority, miserable minority. *BMJ Open, 1,* e000039. (p. 409)

Bruno, M.-A., Pellas, F., & Laureys, S. (2008). Quality of life in locked-in syndrome survivors. In J. L. Vincent (Ed.), *2008 yearbook of intensive care and emergency medicine.* New York: Springer. (p. 409)

Brunoni, A. R., Chaimani, A., Moffa, A. H., Razza, L. B., Gattaz, W. F., Daskalakis, Z. J., & Carvalho, A. F. (2017). Repetitive transcranial magnetic stimulation for the acute treatment of major depressive episodes: A systematic review with network meta-analysis. *JAMA Psychiatry, 74,* 143–152. (p. 564)

Brunoni, A. R., Moffa, A. H., Fregni, F., Palm, U., Padberg, F., Blumberger, D. M., . . . Loo, C. K. (2016). Transcranial direct current stimulation for acute major depressive episodes: Meta-analysis of individual patient data. *The British Journal of Psychiatry, 208,* 522–531. (p. 563)

Bryan, A. D., Gillman, A. S., & Hansen, N. S. (2016). Changing the context is important and necessary, but not sufficient, for reducing adolescent risky sexual behavior: A reply to Steinberg (2015). *Perspectives on Psychological Science, 11,* 535–538. (p. 178)

Bryan, A. E. B., & Arkowitz, H. (2015). Meta-analysis of the effects of peer-administered psychosocial interventions on symptoms of depression. *American Journal of Community Psychology, 55,* 455–471. (p. 556)

Bryant, A. N., & Astin, H. A. (2008). The correlates of spiritual struggle during the college years. *Journal of Higher Education, 79,* 1–27. (p. 146)

Bub, K. L., Robinson, L. E., & Curtis, D. S. (2016). Longitudinal associations between self-regulation and health across childhood and adolescence. *Health Psychology, 35,* 1235–1245. (p. 398)

Buchanan, R. W., Kreyenbuhl, J., Kelly, D. L., Noel, J. M., Boggs, D. L., Fischer, B. A., . . . Keller, W. (2010). The 2009 schizophrenia PORT psychopharmacological treatment recommendations and summary statements. *Schizophrenia Bulletin, 36,* 71–93. (p. 560)

Buchanan, T. W. (2007). Retrieval of emotional memories. *Psychological Bulletin, 133,* 761–779. (p. 277)

Buck, L. B., & Axel, R. (1991). A novel multigene family may encode odorant receptors: A molecular basis for odor recognition. *Cell, 65,* 175–187. (p. 226)

Buckels, E. E., Trapnell, P. D., & Paulhus, D. L. (2014). Trolls just want to have fun. *Personality and Individual Differences, 67,* 97–102. (p. 430)

Buckholtz, J. W., Treadway, M. T., Cowan, R. L., Woodward, N. D., Benning, S. D., Li, R., . . . Zald, D. H. (2010). Mesolimbic dopamine reward system hypersensitivity in individuals with psychopathic traits. *Nature Neuroscience, 13,* 419–421. (p. 531)

Buckingham, M. (2007). *Go put your strengths to work: 6 powerful steps to achieve outstanding performance.* New York: Free Press. (p. B-2)

Buckingham, M., & Clifton, D. O. (2001). *Now, discover your strengths.* New York: Free Press. (p. B-2)

Buehler, R., Griffin, D., & Ross, M. (1994). Exploring the "planning fallacy": Why people underestimate their task completion times. *Journal of Personality and Social Psychology, 67,* 366–381. (p. 303)

Buehler, R., Griffin, D., & Ross, M. (2002). Inside the planning fallacy: The causes and consequences of optimistic time predictions. In T. Gilovich, D. Griffin, & D. Kahneman (Eds.), *Heuristics and biases: The psychology of intuitive judgment.* Cambridge: Cambridge University Press. (p. 303)

Buffardi, L. E., & Campbell, W. K. (2008). Narcissism and social networking web sites. *Personality and Social Psychology Bulletin, 34,* 1303–1314. (p. 356)

Bugental, D. B. (1986). Unmasking the "polite smile": Situational and personal determinants of managed affect in adult-child interaction. *Personality and Social Psychology Bulletin, 12,* 7–16. (p. 376)

Buhle, J. T., Silvers, J. A., Wager, T. D., Lopez, R., Onyemekwu, C., Kober, H., . . . Ochsner, K. N. (2014). Cognitive reappraisal of emotion: A meta-analysis of human neuroimaging studies. *Cerebral Cortex, 24,* 2981–2990. (p. 371)

Buhle, J. T., Stevens, B. L., Friedman, J. J., & Wager, T. D. (2012). Distraction and placebo: Two separate routes to pain control. *Psychological Science, 23,* 246–253. (p. 224)

Buka, S. L., Tsuang, M. T., Torrey, E. F., Klebanoff, M. A., Wagner, R. L., & Yolken, R. H. (2001). Maternal infections and subsequent psychosis among offspring. *Archives of General Psychiatry, 58,* 1032–1037. (p. 525)

Bullock, B., & Murray, G. (2014). Reduced amplitude of the 24-hour activity rhythm: A biomarker of vulnerability to bipolar disorder? *Clinical Psychological Science, 2,* 86–96. (p. 516)

Bunde, J., & Suls, J. (2006). A quantitative analysis of the relationship between the Cook-Medley Hostility Scale and traditional coronary artery disease risk factors. *Health Psychology, 25,* 493–500. (p. 391)

Buquet, R. (1988). Le rêve et les déficients visuels [Dreams and the visually impaired]. *Psychanalyse-a-l'Universite, 13,* 319–327. (p. 97)

Burger, J. M. (2009). Replicating Milgram: Would people still obey today? *American Psychologist, 64,* 1–11. (p. 426)

Burger, J. M., Bender, T. J., Day, L., DeBolt, J. A., Guthridge, L., How, H. W., . . . Taylor, S. (2015). The power of one: The relative influence of helpful and selfish models. *Social Influence, 10,* 77–84. (p. 261)

Buri, J. R., Louiselle, P. A., Misukanis, T. M., & Mueller, R. A. (1988). Effects of parental authoritarianism and authoritativeness on self-esteem. *Personality and Social Psychology Bulletin, 14,* 271–282. (p. 139)

Burish, T. G., & Carey, M. P. (1986). Conditioned aversive responses in cancer chemotherapy patients: Theoretical and developmental analysis. *Journal of Counseling and Clinical Psychology, 54,* 593–600. (p. 255)

Burk, W. J., Denissen, J., Van Doorn, M. D., Branje, S. J. T., & Laursen, B. (2009). The vicissitudes of conflict measurement: Stability and reliability in the frequency of disagreements. *European Psychologist, 14,* 153–159. (p. 147)

Burke, D. M., & Shafto, M. A. (2004). Aging and language production. *Current Directions in Psychological Science, 13,* 21–24. (p. 154)

Burkhauser, R. V., De Neve, J.-E., & Powdthavee, N. (2016, January). *Top incomes and human well-being around the world.* London School of Economic and Political Science: Centre for Economic Performance, CEP Discussion Paper No. 1400. (p. 410)

Burlingame, G. M., Seebeck, J. D., Janis, R. A., Whitcomb, K. E., Barkowski, S., Rosendahl, J., & Strauss, B. (2016). Outcome differences between individual and group formats when identical and nonidentical treatments, patients, and doses are compared: A 25-year meta-analytic perspective. *Psychotherapy, 53,* 446–461. (p. 547)

Burns, B. C. (2004). The effects of speed on skilled chess performance. *Psychological Science, 15,* 442–447. (p. 305)

Burrell, B. D. (2015). Genius in a jar: The bizarre journey of Einstein's brain illustrates the pitfalls in science's search for the origins of brilliance. *Scientific American, 313,* 82–87. (p. 63)

Burris, C. T., & Branscombe, N. R. (2005). Distorted distance estimation induced by a self-relevant national boundary. *Journal of Experimental Social Psychology, 41,* 305–312. (p. 320)

Burrow, A. L., Hill, P. L., & Sumner, R. (2016). Leveling mountains: Purpose attenuates links between perceptions of effort and steepness. *Personality and Social Psychology Bulletin, 42,* 94–103. (p. 197)

Burt, M. R. (1980). Cultural myths and supports for rape. *Journal of Personality and Social Psychology, 38,* 217–230. (p. 170)

Burton, C. M., & King, L. A. (2008). Effects of (very) brief writing on health: The two-minute miracle. *British Journal of Health Psychology, 13,* 9–14. (p. 401)

Busby, D. M., Carroll, J. S., & Willoughby, B. J. (2010). Compatibility or restraint? The effects of sexual timing on marriage relationships. *Journal of Family Psychology, 24,* 766–774. (p. 186)

Bushdid, C., Magnasco, M. O., Vosshall, L. B., & Keller, A. (2014). Humans can discriminate more than 1 trillion olfactory stimuli. *Science, 343,* 1370–1372. (p. 226)

Bushman, B. J. (1993). Human aggression while under the influence of alcohol and other drugs: An integrative research review. *Current Directions in Psychological Science, 2,* 148–152. (p. 442)

Bushman, B. J. (2002). Does venting anger feed or extinguish the flame? Catharsis, rumination, distraction, anger, and aggressive responding. *Personality and Social Psychology Bulletin, 28,* 724–731. (p. 393)

Bushman, B. J. (2016). Violent media and hostile appraisals: A meta-analytic review. *Aggressive Behavior, 42,* 605–613. (p. 445)

Bushman, B. J., & Anderson, C. A. (2009). Comfortably numb: Desensitizing effects of violent media on helping others. *Psychological Science, 20,* 273–277. (p. 263)

Bushman, B. J., & Baumeister, R. F. (1998). Threatened egotism, narcissism, self-esteem, and direct and displaced aggression: Does self-love or self-hate lead to violence? *Journal of Personality and Social Psychology, 75,* 219–229. (p. 488)

Bushman, B. J., Baumeister, R. F., Thomaes, S., Ryu, E., Begeer, S., & West, S. G. (2009). Looking again, and harder, for a link between low self-esteem and aggression. *Journal of Personality, 77,* 427–446. (p. 488)

Bushman, B. J., Bonacci, A. M., van Dijk, M., & Baumeister, R. F. (2003). Narcissism, sexual refusal, and aggression: Testing a narcissistic reactance model of sexual coercion. *Journal of Personality and Social Psychology, 84,* 1027–1040. (p. 488)

Bushman, B. J., DeWall, C. N., Pond, R. S., Jr., & Hanus, M. D. (2014). Low glucose relates to greater aggression in married couples. *PNAS, 111,* 6254–6257. (p. 442)

Bushman, B. J., Gollwitzer, M., & Cruz, C. (2015). There is broad consensus: Media researchers agree that violent media increase aggression in children, and pediatricians and parents concur. *Psychology of Popular Media Culture, 4,* 200–214. (p. 262)

Bushman, B. J., & Huesmann, L. R. (2010). Aggression. In S. T. Fiske, D. T. Gilbert, & G. Lindzey (Eds.), *Handbook of social psychology* (5th ed., pp. 833–863). New York: Wiley. (p. 163)

Bushman, B. J., Moeller, S. J., & Crocker, J. (2011). Sweets, sex, or self-esteem? Comparing the value of self-esteem boosts with other pleasant rewards. *Journal of Personality, 79,* 993–1012. (p. 472)

Bushman, B. J., Ridge, R. D., Das, E., Key, C. W., & Busath, G. L. (2007). When God sanctions killing: Effects of scriptural violence on aggression. *Psychological Science, 18,* 204–207. (p. 163)

Buss, A. H. (1989). Personality as traits. *American Psychologist, 44,* 1378–1388. (p. 481)

Buss, D. M. (1994). The strategies of human mating: People worldwide are attracted to the same qualities in the opposite sex. *American Scientist, 82,* 238–249. (p. 184)

Buss, D. M. (1995). Evolutionary psychology: A new paradigm for psychological science. *Psychological Inquiry, 6,* 1–30. (p. 184)

Buss, D. M. (2008). *Female sexual psychology.* Retrieved from edge.org/q2008/q08_12.html#buss (p. 176)

Buster, J. E., Kingsberg, S. A., Aguirre, O., Brown, C., Breaux, J. G., Buch, A., . . . Casson, P. (2005). Testosterone patch for low sexual desire in surgically menopausal women: A randomized trial. *Obstetrics and Gynecology, 105,* 944–952. (p. 173)

Butler, A., Oruc, I., Fox, C. J., & Barton, J. J. S. (2008). Factors contributing to the adaptation aftereffects of facial expression. *Brain Research, 1191,* 116–126. (p. 195)

Butler, R. A. (1954, February). Curiosity in monkeys. *Scientific American,* pp. 70–75. (p. 349)

Butts, M. M., Casper, W. J., & Yang, T. S. (2013). How important are work-family support policies? A meta-analytic investigation of their effects on employee outcomes. *Journal of Applied Psychology, 98,* 1–25. (p. B-11)

Buxton, O. M., Cain, S. W., O'Connor, S. P., Porter, J. H., Duffy, J. F., Wang, W., . . . Shea, S. A. (2012). Adverse metabolic consequences in humans of prolonged sleep restriction combined with circadian disruption. *Science Translational Medicine, 4,* 129–143. (p. 93)

Byck, R., & Van Dyke, C. (1982, March). Cocaine. *Scientific American,* pp. 128–141. (p. 107)

Byers-Heinlein, K., Burns, T. C., & Werker, J. F. (2010). The roots of bilingualism in newborns. *Psychological Science, 21,* 343–348. (p. 120)

Byrc, K., Durand, E. Y., Macpherson, J. M., Reich, D., & Mountain, J. L. (2015). The genetic ancestry of African Americans, Latinos, and European Americans across the United States. *American Journal of Human Genetics 96,* 37–53. (p. 342)

Byrd, A. L., & Manuck, S. B. (2014). MAOA, childhood maltreatment, and antisocial behavior: Meta-analysis of a gene-environment interaction. *Biological Psychiatry, 75,* 9–17. (p. 483)

Byrne, D. (1971). *The attraction paradigm.* New York: Academic Press. (p. 450)

Byrne, D. (1982). Predicting human sexual behavior. In A. G. Kraut (Ed.), *The G. Stanley Hall Lecture Series* (Vol. 2, pp. 211–254). Washington, DC: American Psychological Association. (pp. 173, 238)

Byrne, R. W. (1991, May/June). Brute intellect. *The Sciences,* pp. 42–47. (p. 317)

Byrne, R. W., Bates, L. A., & Moss, C. J. (2009). Elephant cognition in primate perspective. *Comparative Cognition & Behavior Reviews, 4,* 1–15. (p. 310)

Byrne, R. W., & Whiten, A. (1988). Toward the next generation in data quality: A new survey of primate tactical deception. *Behavioral and Brain Sciences, 11,* 267–273. (p. 22)

Byron, K., & Khazanchi, S. (2011). A meta-analytic investigation of the relationship of state and trait anxiety to performance on figural and verbal creative tasks. *Personality and Social Psychology Bulletin, 37,* 269–283. (p. 307)

Cable, D. M., & Gilovich, T. (1998). Looked over or overlooked? Prescreening decisions and post-interview evaluations. *Journal of Personality and Social Psychology, 83*, 501–508. (p. B-5)

Cacioppo, J. T., Cacioppo, S., Capitanio, J. P., & Cole, S. W. (2015). The neuroendocrinology of social isolation. *Annual Review of Psychology, 66*, 733–767. (p. 353)

Cacioppo, J. T., Cacioppo, S., Gonzaga, G. C., Ogburn, E. L., & VanderWeele, T. J. (2013). Marital satisfaction and break-ups differ across on-line and off-line meeting venues. *PNAS, 110*, 10135–10140. (p. 448)

Cacioppo, S., Bianchi-Demicheli, F., Frum, C., Pfaus, J. G., & Lewis, J.W. (2012). The common neural bases between sexual desire and love: A multilevel kernel density fMRI analysis. *Journal of Sexual Medicine, 12*, 1048–1054. (p. 186)

Cacioppo, S., Capitanio, J. P., & Cacioppo, J. T. (2014). Toward a neurology of loneliness. *Psychological Bulletin, 140*, 1464–1504. (p. 399)

Caddick, A., & Porter, L. E. (2012). Exploring a model of professionalism in multiple perpetrator violent crime in the UK. *Criminological and Criminal Justice, 12*, 61–82. (p. 163)

Cain, S. (2012). *Quiet: The power of introverts in a world that can't stop talking.* New York: Crown. (p. 476)

Calati, R., De Ronchi, D., Bellini, M., & Serretti, A. (2011). The 5-HTTLPR polymorphism and eating disorders: A meta-analysis. *International Journal of Eating Disorders, 44*, 191–199. (p. 532)

Caldwell, J. A. (2012). Crew schedules, sleep deprivation, and aviation performance. *Current Directions in Psychological Science, 21*, 85–89. (p. 93)

Cale, E. M., & Lilienfeld, S. O. (2002). Sex differences in psychopathy and antisocial personality disorder: A review and integration. *Clinical Psychology Review, 22*, 1179–1207. (p. 530)

Caliskan, A., Bryson, J. J., & Narayanan, A. (2017). Semantics derived automatically from language corpora contain human-like biases. *Science, 356*, 183–186. (p. 436)

Callaghan, T., Rochat, P., Lillard, A., Claux, M. L., Odden, H., Itakura, S., . . . Singh, S. (2005). Synchrony in the onset of mental-state reasoning. *Psychological Science, 16*, 378–384. (p. 128)

Callan, M. J., Shead, N. W., & Olson, J. M. (2011). Personal relative deprivation, delay discounting, and gambling. *Journal of Personality and Social Psychology, 101*, 955–973. (p. 145)

Calvert, S. L., Appelbaum, M., Dodge, K. A., Graham, S., Nagayama Hall, G. C., Hamby, S., . . . Hedges, L. V. (2017). The American Psychological Association Task Force assessment of violent video games: Science in the service of public interest. *American Psychologist, 72*, 126–143. (p. 444)

Calvin, C. M., Batty, G. D., Der, G., Brett, C. E., Taylor, A., Pattie, A., . . . Deary, I. J. (2017). Childhood intelligence in relation to major causes of death in 68 year follow-up: Prospective population study. *BMJ: British Medical Journal, 357*, 13 (j2708). (p. 333)

Calvo-Merino, B., Glaser, D. E., Grèzes, J., Passingham, R. E., & Haggard, P. (2004). Action observation and acquired motor skills: An fMRI study with expert dancers. *Cerebral Cortex, 15*, 1243–1249. (p. 321)

Camerer, C. F., Loewenstein, G., & Weber, M. (1989). The curse of knowledge in economic settings: An experimental analysis. *Journal of Political Economy, 97*, 1232–1254. (p. B-13)

Camp, J. P., Skeem, J. L., Barchard, K., Lilienfeld, S. O., & Poythress, N. G. (2013). Psychopathic predators? Getting specific about the relation between psychopathy and violence. *Journal of Consulting and Clinical Psychology, 81*, 467–480. (p. 530)

Campbell, A. (2010). Oxytocin and human social behavior. *Personality and Social Psychology Review, 14*, 281–205. (p. 399)

Campbell, D. T. (1975). On the conflicts between biological and social evolution and between psychology and moral tradition. *American Psychologist, 30*, 1103–1126. (p. 410)

Campbell, D. T., & Specht, J. C. (1985). Altruism: Biology, culture, and religion. *Journal of Social and Clinical Psychology, 3*, 33–42. (p. 473)

Campbell, L., & Marshall, T. (2011). Anxious attachment and relationship processes: An interactionist perspective. *Journal of Personality, 79*, 1219–1249. (p. 483)

Campbell, M. W., & de Waal, F. B. M. (2011). Ingroup-outgroup bias in contagious yawning by chimpanzees supports link to empathy. *PLoS ONE, 6*, e18283. (p. 438)

Campbell, S. (1986). *The Loch Ness Monster: The evidence.* Wellingborough, England: Aquarian Press. (p. 196)

Camperio-Ciani, A., Corna, F., & Capiluppi, C. (2004). Evidence for maternally inherited factors favouring male homosexuality and promoting female fecundity. *Proceedings of the Royal Society of London B, 271*, 2217–2221. (p. 181)

Camperio-Ciani, A., Lemmola, F., & Blecher, S. R. (2009). Genetic factors increase fecundity in female maternal relatives of bisexual men as in homosexuals. *Journal of Sexual Medicine, 6*, 449–455. (p. 181)

Camperio-Ciani, A., & Pellizzari, E. (2012). Fecundity of paternal and maternal non-parental female relatives of homosexual and heterosexual men. *PLoS ONE, 7*, e51088. (p. 181)

Campitelli, G., & Gobet, F. (2011). Deliberate practice: Necessary but not sufficient. *Current Directions in Psychological Science, 20*, 280–285. (p. 326)

Campos, J. J., Bertenthal, B. I., & Kermoian, R. (1992). Early experience and emotional development: The emergence of wariness and heights. *Psychological Science, 3*, 61–64. (p. 209)

Canavello, A., & Crocker, J. (2017). Compassionate goals and affect in social situations. *Motivation and Emotion, 41*, 158–179. (p. 352)

Canetta, S., Sourander, A., Surcel, H., Hinkka-Yli-Salomäki, S., Leiviskä, J., Kellendonk, C., . . . Brown, A. S. (2014). Elevated maternal C-reactive protein and increased risk of schizophrenia in a national birth cohort. *American Journal of Psychiatry, 171*, 960–968. (p. 525)

Canli, T. (2008). The character code. *Scientific American Mind, 19*, 52–57. (p. 512)

Canli, T., Desmond, J. E., Zhao, Z., & Gabrieli, J. D. E. (2002). Sex differences in the neural basis of emotional memories. *PNAS, 99*, 10789–10794. (p. 378)

Cannon, W. B. (1929). *Bodily changes in pain, hunger, fear, and rage.* New York: Branford. (pp. 361, 386)

Cannon, W. B., & Washburn, A. L. (1912). An explanation of hunger. *American Journal of Physiology, 29*, 441–454. (p. 361)

Cantor, N., & Kihlstrom, J. F. (1987). *Personality and social intelligence.* Englewood Cliffs, NJ: Prentice-Hall. (p. 326)

Caplan, N., Choy, M. H., & Whitmore, J. K. (1992, February). Indochinese refugee families and academic achievement. *Scientific American*, pp. 36–42. (p. 148)

Caprariello, P. A., & Reis, H. T. (2013). To do, to have, or to share? Valuing experiences over material possessions depends on the involvement of others. *Journal of Personality and Social Psychology, 104*, 199–215. (p. 412)

Carey, B. (2007, September 4). Bipolar illness soars as a diagnosis for the young. *The New York Times* (nytimes.com). (p. 516)

Carey, B. (2009, November 27). Surgery for mental ills offers both hope and risk. *The New York Times* (nytimes.com). (p. 565)

Carey, B. (2010). Seeking emotional clues without facial cues. *The New York Times* (nytimes.com). (p. 382)

Carey, B. (2011, February 14). Wariness on surgery of the mind. *The New York Times* (nytimes.com).

Carey, B. (2016, December 29). Did Debbie Reynolds die of a broken heart? *The New York Times* (nytimes.com). (p. 392)

Carey, G. (1990). Genes, fears, phobias, and phobic disorders. *Journal of Counseling and Development, 68*, 628–632. (p. 511)

Carhart-Harris, R. L., Muthukumaraswamy, S., Roseman, L., Kaelen, M., Droog, W., Murphy, K., . . . Leech, R. (2016). Neural correlates of the LSD experience revealed by multimodal neuroimaging. *PNAS, 113*, 4853–4858. (p. 108)

Carli, L. L., & Leonard, J. B. (1989). The effect of hindsight on victim derogation. *Journal of Social and Clinical Psychology, 8*, 331–343. (p. 440)

Carlson, M., Charlin, V., & Miller, N. (1988). Positive mood and helping behavior: A test of six hypotheses. *Journal of Personality and Social Psychology, 55*, 211–229. (p. 454)

Carmeli, A., Ben-Hador, B., Waldman, D. A., & Rupp, D. E. (2009). How leaders cultivate social capital and nurture employee vigor: Implications for job performance. *Journal of Applied Psychology, 94*, 1553–1561. (p. B-11)

Carney, D. R., Cuddy, A. J. C., & Yap, A. J. (2015). Review and summary of research on the embodied effects of expansive (vs. contractive) nonverbal displays. *Psychological Science, 26*, 657–663. (p. 381)

Caroll, H. (2013, October). Teen fashion model Georgina got so thin her organs were failing. But fashion designers still queued up to book her. Now she's telling her story to shame the whole industry. *The Daily Mail* (dailymail.co.uk). (p. 533)

Carpusor, A., & Loges, W. E. (2006). Rental discrimination and ethnicity in names. *Journal of Applied Social Psychology, 36*, 934–952. (p. 28)

Carr, E. W., Brady, T. F., & Winkielman, P. (2017). Are you smiling, or have I seen you before? Familiarity makes faces look happier. *Psychological Science, 28*, 1087–1102. (p. 447)

Carragan, R. C., & Dweck, C. S. (2014). Rethinking natural altruism: Simple reciprocal interactions trigger children's benevolence. *PNAS, 111*, 17051–17074. (p. 144)

Carroll, D., Davey Smith, G., & Bennett, P. (1994, March). Health and socioeconomic status. *The Psychologist*, pp. 122–125. (p. 396)

Carroll, E. L., & Bright, P. (2016). Involvement of Spearman's g in conceptualization versus execution of complex tasks. *Acta Psychologica, 170*, 112–126. (p. 324)

Carroll, J. M., & Russell, J. A. (1996). Do facial expressions signal specific emotions? Judging emotion from the face in context. *Journal of Personality and Social Psychology, 70*, 205–218. (p. 379)

Carskadon, M. (2002). *Adolescent sleep patterns: Biological, social, and psychological influences.* New York: Cambridge University Press. (p. 93)

Carstensen, L. L. (2011). *A long bright future: Happiness, health and financial security in an age of increased longevity.* New York: PublicAffairs. (p. 155)

Carstensen, L. L., & Mikels, J. A. (2005). At the intersection of emotion and cognition: Aging and the positivity effect. *Current Directions in Psychological Science, 14*, 117–121. (p. 334)

Carstensen, L. L., Turan, B., Scheibe, S., Ram, N., Ersner-Hershfield, H., Samanez-Larkin, G. R., . . . Nesselroade, J. R. (2011). Emotional experience improves with age: Evidence based on over 10 years of experience sampling. *Psychology and Aging, 26*, 21–33. (p. 158)

Carter, C. S., Bearden, C. E., Bullmore, E. T., Geschwind, D. H., Glahn, D. C., Gur, R. E., . . . Weinberger, D. R. (2017). Enhancing the informativeness and replicability of imaging genomics studies. *Biological Psychiatry, 82*, 157–164. (p. 20)

Carter, T. J., & Gilovich, T. (2010). The relative relativity of material and experiential purchases. *Journal of Personality and Social Psychology, 98*, 146–159. (p. 412)

Carver, C. S., Johnson, S. L., & Joormann, J. (2008). Serotonergic function, two-mode models of self-regulation, and vulnerability to depression: What depression has in common with impulsive aggression. *Psychological Bulletin, 134*, 912–943. (p. 519)

Carver, C. S., Scheier, M. F., & Segerstrom, S. C. (2010). Optimism. *Clinical Psychology Review, 30*, 879–889. (p. 398)

CASA. (2003). *The formative years: Pathways to substance abuse among girls and young women ages 8–22.* National Center on Addiction and Substance Use at Columbia University (casacolumbia.org/addiction-research/reports/formative-years-pathways-substance-abuse-among-girls-and-young-women-ages). (pp. 103, 111)

Casey, B. J., & Caudle, K. (2013). The teenage brain: Self-control. *Current Directions in Psychological Science, 22*, 82–87. (p. 142)

Casey, B. J., Getz, S., & Galvan, A. (2008). The adolescent brain. *Developmental Review, 28*, 62–77. (p. 142)

Casey, B. J., Somerville, L. H., Gotlib, I. H., Ayduk, O., Franklin, N. T., Askren, M. K., . . . Shoda, Y. (2011). Behavioral and neural correlates of delay of gratification 40 years later. *PNAS, 108*, 14998–15003. (p. 145)

Caspi, A., Houts, R. M., Belsky, D. W., Harrington, H., Hogan, S., Ramrakha, S., . . . Moffitt, T. E. (2016). Childhood forecasting of a small segment of the population with large economic burden. *Nature Human Behavior, 1*, article 0005. (p. 135)

Caspi, A., McClay, J., Moffitt, T., Mill, J., Martin, J., Craig, I. W., . . . Poulton, R. (2002). Role of genotype in the cycle of violence in maltreated children. *Science, 297*, 851–854. (p. 483)

Caspi, A., Moffitt, T. E., Newman, D. L., & Silva, P. A. (1996). Behavioral observations at age 3 years predict adult psychiatric disorders: Longitudinal evidence from a birth cohort. *Archives of General Psychiatry, 53*, 1033–1039. (p. 530)

Cassidy, J., & Shaver, P. R. (1999). *Handbook of attachment: Theory, research, and clinical applications.* New York: Guilford Press. (p. 133)

Castillo-Gualda, R., Cabello, R., Herrero, M., Rodríguez-Carvajal, R., & Fernández-Berrocal, P. (2017). A three-year emotional intelligence intervention to reduce adolescent aggression: The mediating role of unpleasant affectivity. *Journal of Research on Adolescence.* Advance online publication. doi:10.1111/jora.12325 (p. 326)

Castonguay, L. G., Boswell, J. F., Constantino, M. J., Goldfried, M. R., & Hill, C. E. (2010). Training implications of harmful effects of psychological treatments. *American Psychologist, 65*, 34–49. (p. 554)

Catalan-Matamoros, D., Gomez-Conesa, A., Stubbs, B., & Vancampfort, D. (2016). Exercise improves depressive symptoms in older adults: An umbrella review of systematic reviews and meta-analyses. *Psychiatry Research, 244*, 202–209. (p. 402)

CATO Institute. (2017). Criminal immigrants: Their numbers, demographics, and countries of origin. Retrieved from object.cato.org/sites/cato.org/files/pubs/pdf/immigration_brief-1.pdf (p. 18)

Cattell, R. B. (1963). Theory of fluid and crystallized intelligence: A critical experiment. *Journal of Educational Psychology, 54*, 1–22. (p. 333)

Cavalli-Sforza, L., Menozzi, P., & Piazza, A. (1994). *The history and geography of human genes.* Princeton, NJ: Princeton University Press. (p. 342)

Cawley, B. D., Keeping, L. M., & Levy, P. E. (1998). Participation in the performance appraisal process and employee reactions: A meta-analytic review of field investigations. *Journal of Applied Psychology, 83*, 615–633. (pp. B-10, B-11)

CBC News. (2014, March 19). *Distracted driving laws across Canada.* CBC News (cbc.ca). (p. 82)

CCSA. (2017, August). Canadian drug use summary: Cannabis. Canadian Centre on Substance Use and Addiction (ccsa.ca). (p. 110)

CDC. (2009). *Self-harm, all injury causes, nonfatal injuries and rates per 100,000.* National Center for Injury Prevention and Control. Retrieved from webappa.cdc.gov/cgi-bin/broker.exe (pp. 501, 502)

CDC. (2011, February). *HIV surveillance report: Vol. 21. Diagnoses of HIV infection and AIDS in the United States and dependent areas, 2009.* Centers for Disease Control and Prevention (cdc.gov/hiv/pdf/statistics_2009_hiv_surveillance_report_vol_21.pdf). (p. 113)

CDC. (2012, May 11). *Suicide rates among persons ages 10 years and older, by race/ethnicity and sex, United States, 2005–2009.* National Suicide Statistics at a Glance, Centers for Disease Control and Prevention (cdc.gov). (p. 500)

CDC. (2013). *Diagnoses of HIV infection in the United States and dependent areas, 2013.* HIV Surveillance Report, Volume 25. Washington, DC: Centers for Disease Control and Prevention. (p. 175)

CDC. (2014a, December). *Depression in the U.S. household population, 2009–2012* (NCHS Data Brief No. 172). Centers for Disease Control and Prevention (cdc.gov). (p. 504)

CDC. (2014b). *Pregnant women need a flu shot.* Centers for Disease Control and Prevention. Retrieved from cdc.gov/flu/pdf/freeresources/pregnant/flushot_pregnant_factsheet.pdf (p. 526)

CDC. (2014c, March 28). Prevalence of autism spectrum disorder among children aged 8 years—Autism and developmental disabilities monitoring network, 11 sites. United States, 2010. *Morbidity and Mortality Weekly Report (MMWR), 63*(SS02), 1–21. (p. 131)

CDC. (2016a). Heart disease facts. Centers for Disease Control and Prevention. Retrieved from cdc.gov/heartdisease/facts.htm (p. 391)

CDC. (2016b, accessed January 21). *Reproductive health: Teen pregnancy.* Centers for Disease Control and Prevention. Retrieved from cdc.gov/teenpregnancy (pp. 175, 177)

CDC. (2017). Drugs involved in U.S. overdose deaths, 2000 to 2016. Centers for Disease Control and Prevention. Retrieved from https://www.drugabuse.gov/related-topics/trends-statistics/overdose-death-rates. (p. 104)

CEA. (2014). *Nine facts about American families and work.* Office of the President of the United States: Council of Economic Advisers. (p. 164)

Ceci, S. J. (1993). *Cognitive and social factors in children's testimony.* Master lecture presented at the Annual Convention of the American Psychological Association. (pp. 292, 294)

Ceci, S. J., & Bruck, M. (1993). Child witnesses: Translating research into policy. *Social Policy Report (Society for Research in Child Development), 7*, 1–30. (p. 292)

Ceci, S. J., & Bruck, M. (1995). *Jeopardy in the courtroom: A scientific analysis of children's testimony.* Washington, DC: American Psychological Association. (p. 292)

Ceci, S. J., Ginther, D. K., Kahn, S., & Williams, W. M. (2014). Women in academic science: A changing landscape. *Psychological Science in the Public Interest, 15*, 75–141. (p. 168)

Ceci, S. J., Huffman, M. L. C., Smith, E., & Loftus, E. F. (1994). Repeatedly thinking about a non-event: Source misattributions among preschoolers. *Consciousness and Cognition, 3*, 388–407. (p. 294)

Ceci, S. J., & Williams, W. M. (1997). Schooling, intelligence, and income. *American Psychologist, 52*, 1051–1058. (p. 339)

Ceci, S. J., & Williams, W. M. (2009). *The mathematics of sex: How biology and society conspire to limit talented women and girls.* New York: Oxford University Press. (p. 339)

Census Bureau. (2014). Industry and occupation. Table 1: Full-time, year-round workers and median earnings in the past 12 months by sex and detailed occupation. Washington, DC: Bureau of the Census. (p. 164)

Center for Value in Health Care. (2017). The potential societal benefit of eliminating opioid overdoses, deaths, and substance use disorders exceeds $95 billion per year. Retrieved from https://altarum.org/about/news-and-events/burden-of-opioid-crisis-reached-95-billion-in-2016-private-sector-hit-hardest (p. 552)

Centerwall, B. S. (1989). Exposure to television as a risk factor for violence. *American Journal of Epidemiology, 129*, 643–652. (p. 263)

Cepeda, N. J., Pashler, H., Vul, E., Wixted, J. T., & Rohrer, D. (2006). Distributed practice in verbal recall tasks: A review and quantitative synthesis. *Psychological Bulletin, 132*, 354–380. (p. 272)

Cepeda, N. J., Vul, E., Rohrer, D., Wixed, J. T., & Pashler, H. (2008). Spacing effects in learning: A temporal ridgeline of optimal retention. *Psychological Science, 19*, 1095–1102. (p. 272)

Cerasoli, C. P., Nicklin, J. M., & Ford, M. T. (2014). Intrinsic motivation and extrinsic incentives jointly predict performance: A 40-year meta-analysis. *Psychological Bulletin, 140*, 980–1008. (p. B-1)

Cerasoli, C. P., Nicklin, J. M., & Nassrelgrgawi, A. S. (2016). Performance, incentives, and needs for autonomy, competence, and relatedness: A meta-analysis. *Motivation and Emotion, 40*, 781–813. (p. 353)

Cerrillo-Urbina, A. J., García-Hermoso, A., Sánchez-López, M., Pardo-Guijarro, M. J., Santos Gómez, J. L., & Martínez-Vizcaíno, V. (2015). The effects of physical exercise in children with attention deficit hyperactivity disorder: A systematic review and meta-analysis of randomized control trials. *Child: Care, Health and Development, 41*, 779–788. (p. 498)

CFI. (2003, July). *International developments. Report.* Amherst, NY: Center for Inquiry International. (p. 231)

Chabris, C. (2015, February 9). Quoted by Parker-Pope, T. Was Brian Williams a victim of false memory? *The New York Times* (nytimes.com). (p. 291)

Chabris, C. F., & Simons, D. (2010). *The invisible gorilla: And other ways our intuitions deceive us.* New York: Crown. (p. 83)

Chajut, E., Caspi, A., Chen, R., Hod, M., & Ariely, D. (2014). In pain thou shalt bring forth children: The peak-and-end rule in recall of labor pain. *Psychological Science, 25*, 2266–2271. (p. 223)

Chamove, A. S. (1980). Nongenetic induction of acquired levels of aggression. *Journal of Abnormal Psychology, 89,* 469–488. (p. 262)

Champagne, F. A. (2010). Early adversity and developmental outcomes: Interaction between genetics, epigenetics, and social experiences across the life span. *Perspectives on Psychological Science, 5,* 564–574. (p. 74)

Champagne, F. A., Francis, D. D., Mar, A, & Meaney, M. J. (2003). Variations in maternal care in the rat as a mediating influence for the effects of environment on development. *Physiology & Behavior, 79,* 359–371. (p. 74)

Champagne, F. A., & Mashoodh, R. (2009). Genes in context: Gene–environment interplay and the origins of individual differences in behavior. *Current Directions in Psychological Science, 18,* 127–131. (p. 74)

Chan, M. K., Krebs, M. O., Cox, D., Guest, P. C., Yolken, R. H., Rahmoune, H., . . . Bahn, S. (2015, July 14). Development of a blood-based molecular biomarker test for identification of schizophrenia before disease onset. *Translational Psychiatry, 5,* e601. (p. 524)

Chance News. (1997, 25 November). More on the frequency of letters in texts. Dart. Chance@Dartmouth.edu. (p. 24)

Chandler, J. J., & Pronin, E. (2012). Fast thought speed induces risk taking. *Psychological Science, 23,* 370–374. (p. 515)

Chandra, A., Mosher, W. D., & Copen, C. (2011, March 3). *Sexual behavior, sexual attraction, and sexual identity in the United States: Data from the 2006–2008 National Survey of Family Growth* (National Health Statistics Report No. 36). Retrieved from cdc.gov/nchs/data/nhsr/nhsr036.pdf (pp. 178, 179)

Chang, A.-M., Aeschbach, D., Duggy, J. F., & Czeisler, C. A. (2015). Evening use of light-emitting eReaders negatively affects sleep, circadian timing, and next-morning alertness. *PNAS, 112,* 1232–1237. (p. 90)

Chang, Y.-T., Chen, Y.-C., Hayter, M., & Lin, M.-L. (2009). Menstrual and menarche experience among pubescent female students in Taiwan: Implications for health education and promotion service. *Journal of Clinical Nursing, 18,* 2040–2048. (p. 167)

Chaplin, T. M. (2015). Gender and emotion expression: A developmental contextual perspective. *Emotion Review, 7,* 14–21. (p. 165)

Chaplin, T. M., & Aldao, A. (2013). Gender differences in emotion expression in children: A meta-analytic review. *Psychological Bulletin, 139,* 735–765. (p. 377)

Chaplin, W. F., Phillips, J. B., Brown, J. D., Clanton, N. R., & Stein, J. L. (2000). Handshaking, gender, personality, and first impressions. *Journal of Personality and Social Psychology, 79,* 110–117. (p. 375)

Charles, S. T., Piazza, J. R., Mogle, J., Sliwinski, M. J., & Almeida, D. M. (2013). The wear and tear of daily stressors on mental health. *Psychological Science, 24,* 733–741. (p. 517)

Charness, N., & Boot, W. R. (2009). Aging and information technology use. *Current Directions in Psychological Science, 18,* 253–258. (p. 334)

Charpak, G., & Broch, H. (2004). *Debunked! ESP, telekinesis, and other pseudoscience.* Baltimore, MD: Johns Hopkins University Press. (p. 230)

Chartrand, T. L., & Bargh, J. A. (1999). The chameleon effect: The perception-behavior link and social interaction. *Journal of Personality and Social Psychology, 76,* 893–910. (p. 422)

Chartrand, T. L., & Lakin, J. (2013). The antecedents and consequences of human behavioral mimicry. *Annual Review of Psychology, 64,* 285–308. (p. 260)

Chartrand, T. L., & van Baaren, R. (2009). Human mimicry. In M. P. Zanna (Ed.), *Advances in experimental social psychology* (pp. 219–274). San Diego, CA: Elsevier Academic Press. (p. 423)

Chassin, M. R. L., & MacKinnon, D. P. (2015). Role transitions and young adult maturing out of heavy drinking: Evidence for larger effects of marriage among more severe premarriage problem drinkers. *Alcoholism: Clinical and Experimental Research, 39,* 1064–1074. (p. 113)

Chassy, P., & Gobet, F. (2011). A hypothesis about the biological basis of expert intuition. *Review of General Psychology, 15,* 198–212. (p. 305)

Chatard, A., & Selimbegović, L. (2011). When self-destructive thoughts flash through the mind: Failure to meet standards affects the accessibility of suicide-related thoughts. *Journal of Personality and Social Psychology, 100,* 587–605. (p. 501)

Chater, N., Reali, F., & Christiansen, M. H. (2009). Restrictions on biological adaptation in language evolution. *PNAS, 106,* 1015–1020. (p. 315)

Chatterjee, R. (2015, October 3). Out of the darkness. *Science, 350,* 372–375. (p. 213)

Chaudhary, U., Xia, B., Silvoni, S., Cohen, L. G., & Birbaumer, N. (2017). Brain–computer interface–based communication in the completely locked-in state. *PLoS Biology, 15,* 25. (p. 409)

Cheek, J. M., & Melchior, L. A. (1990). Shyness, self-esteem, and self-consciousness. In H. Leitenberg (Ed.), *Handbook of social and evaluation anxiety* (pp. 47–82). New York: Plenum Press. (p. 490)

Chein, J., Albert, D., O'Brien, L., Uckert, K., & Steinberg, L. (2011). Peers increase adolescent risk taking by enhancing activity in the brain's reward circuitry. *Developmental Science, 14,* F1–F10. (p. 147)

Chein, J. M., & Schneider, W. (2012). The brain's learning and control architecture. *Current Directions in Psychological Science, 21,* 78–84. (p. 63)

Cheit, R. E. (1998). Consider this, skeptics of recovered memory. *Ethics & Behavior, 8,* 141–160. (p. 469)

Chen, A. W., Kazanjian, A., & Wong, H. (2009). Why do Chinese Canadians not consult mental health services: Health status, language or culture? *Transcultural Psychiatry, 46,* 623–640. (p. 556)

Chen, E., Turiano, N. A., Mroczek, D. K., & Miller, G. E. (2016). Association of reports of childhood abuse and all-cause mortality rates in women. *JAMA Psychiatry, 73,* 920–927. (p. 138)

Chen, L., Zhang, G., Hu, M., & Liang, X. (2015). Eye movement desensitization and reprocessing versus cognitive-behavioral therapy for adult posttraumatic stress disorder: Systematic review and meta-analysis. *Journal of Nervous and Mental Disease, 203,* 443–451. (p. 554)

Chen, M.-H., Lan, W.-H., Bai, Y.-M., Huang, K.-L., Su, T.-P., Tsai, S.-J., . . . Hsu, J.-W. (2016). Influence of relative age on diagnosis and treatment of attention-deficit hyperactivity disorder in Taiwanese children. *Journal of Pediatrics, 172,* 162–167. (p. 498)

Chen, S. H., Kennedy, M., & Zhou, Q. (2012). Parents' expression and discussion of emotion in the multilingual family: Does language matter? *Perspectives on Psychological Science, 7,* 365–383. (p. 319)

Chen, S. X., & Bond, M. H. (2010). Two languages, two personalities? Examining language effects on the expression of personality in a bilingual context. *Personality and Social Psychology Bulletin, 36,* 1514–1528. (p. 319)

Cheng, C., & Li, A. Y.-I. (2014). Internet addiction prevalence and quality of (real) life: A meta-analysis of 31 nations across seven world regions. *Cyberpsychology, Behavior, and Social Networking, 17,* 755–760. (p. 102)

Chennu, S., Pinoia, P., Kamau, E. Allanson, J., Williams, G. B., Monti, M. M., . . . Bekinschtein, T. A. (2014). Spectral signatures of reorganised brain network in disorders of consciousness. *PLoS Computational Biology, 10:*e1003887. (p. 81)

Cheon, B. K., Im, D.-M., Harada, T., Kim, J.-S., Mathur, V. A., Scimeca, J. M., . . . Chiao, J. Y. (2013). Cultural modulation of the neural correlates of emotional pain perception: The role of other-focusedness. *Neuropsychologia, 51,* 1177–1186. (p. 491)

Cherniss, C. (2010a). Emotional intelligence: New insights and further clarifications. *Industrial and Organizational Psychology, 3,* 183–191. (p. 326)

Cherniss, C. (2010b). Emotional intelligence: Toward clarification of a concept. *Industrial and Organizational Psychology, 3,* 110–126. (p. 326)

Chess, S., & Thomas, A. (1987). *Know your child: An authoritative guide for today's parents.* New York: Basic Books. (p. 135)

Chester, D. S., & DeWall, C. N. (2016). The pleasure of revenge: Retaliatory aggression arises from a neural imbalance toward reward. *Social Cognitive and Affective Neuroscience, 11,* 1173–1182. (p. 144)

Cheung, B. Y., Chudek, M., & Heine, S. J. (2011). Evidence for a sensitive period for acculturation: Younger immigrants report acculturating at a faster rate. *Psychological Science, 22,* 147–152. (p. 315)

Cheung, F., & Lucas, R. E. (2015). When does money matter most? Examining the association between income and life satisfaction over the life course. *Psychology and Aging, 30,* 120–135. (p. 409)

Cheung, F., & Lucas, R. E. (2016). Income inequality is associated with stronger social comparison effects: The effect of relative income on life satisfaction. *Journal of Personality and Social Psychology, 110,* 332–341. (p. 410)

Chida, Y., & Hamer, M. (2008). Chronic psychosocial factors and acute physiological responses to laboratory-induced stress in healthy populations: A quantitative review of 30 years of investigations. *Psychological Bulletin, 134,* 829–885. (p. 391)

Chida, Y., Hamer, M., Wardle, J., & Steptoe, A. (2008). Do stress-related psychosocial factors contribute to cancer incidence and survival? *Nature Reviews: Clinical Oncology, 5,* 466–475. (p. 390)

Chida, Y., & Steptoe, A. (2009). The association of anger and hostility with future coronary heart disease: A meta-analytic review of prospective evidence. *Journal of the American College of Cardiology, 17,* 936–946. (p. 391)

Chida, Y., Steptoe, A., & Powell, L. H. (2009). Religiosity/spirituality and mortality. *Psychotherapy and Psychosomatics, 78,* 81–90. (p. 406)

Chida, Y., & Vedhara, K. (2009). Adverse psychosocial factors predict poorer prognosis in HIV disease: A meta-analytic review of prospective investigations. *Brain, Behavior, and Immunity, 23,* 434–445. (p. 390)

Chiles, J. A., Lambert, M. J., & Hatch, A. L. (1999). The impact of psychological interventions on medical cost offset: A meta-analytic review. *Clinical Psychology: Science and Practice, 6,* 204–220. (p. 552)

Chisholm, D., Sweeny, K., Sheehan, P., Rasmussen, B., Smit, F., Cuijpers, P., & Saxena, S. (2016). Scaling-up treatment of depression and anxiety: A global return on investment analysis. *The Lancet Psychiatry, 3,* 415–424. (p. 552)

Chivers, M. L., Seto, M. C., Lalumière, M. L., Laan, E., & Grimbos, T. (2010). Agreement of self-reported and genital measures of sexual arousal in men and women: A meta-analysis. *Archives of Sexual Behavior, 39,* 5–56. (p. 176)

Chmielewski, M., Zhu, J., Burchett, D., Bury, A. S., & Bagby, R. M. (2017). The comparative capacity of the Minnesota Multiphasic Personality Inventory–2 (MMPI–2) and MMPI–2 Restructured Form (MMPI-2-RF) validity scales to detect suspected malingering in a disability claimant sample. *Psychological Assessment, 29,* 199–208. (p. 477)

Cho, K. W., Neely, J. H., Crocco, S., & Vitrano, D. (2017). Testing enhances both encoding and retrieval for both tested and untested items. *The Quarterly Journal of Experimental Psychology, 70,* 1211–1235. (p. 33)

Choi, C. Q. (2008, March). Do you need only half your brain? *Scientific American.* Retrieved from scientificamerican.com/article/do-you-need-only-half-your-brain/ (p. 64)

Choi, J., Broersma, M., & Cutler, A. (2017). Early phonology revealed by international adoptees' birth language retention. *PNAS, 114,* 7307–7312. (p. 315)

Chomsky, N. (1972). *Language and mind.* New York: Harcourt Brace. (p. 317)

Chopik, W., & O'Brien, E. (2017). Happy you, healthy me? Having a happy partner is independently associated with better health in oneself. *Health Psychology, 36,* 21–30. (p. 392)

Chopik, W. J., Edelstein, R. S., & Fraley, R. C. (2013). From the cradle to the grave: Age differences in attachment from early adulthood to old age. *Journal of Personality, 81,* 171–183. (p. 158)

Choudhary, E., Smith, M., & Bossarte, R. M. (2012). Depression, anxiety, and symptom profiles among female and male victims of sexual violence. *American Journal of Men's Health, 6,* 28–36. (p. 170)

Christakis, D. A., Garrison, M. M., Herrenkohl, T., Haggerty, K., Rivara, K. P., Zhou, C., & Liekweg, K. (2013). Modifying media content for preschool children: A randomized control trial. *Pediatrics, 131,* 431–438. (p. 263)

Christakis, N. A., & Fowler, J. H. (2007). The spread of obesity in a large social network over 32 years. *New England Journal of Medicine, 357,* 370–379. (p. 365)

Christakis, N. A., & Fowler, J. H. (2008). The collective dynamics of smoking in a large social network. *New England Journal of Medicine, 358,* 2249–2258. (p. 113)

Christensen, A., & Jacobson, N. S. (1994). Who (or what) can do psychotherapy: The status and challenge of nonprofessional therapies. *Psychological Science, 5,* 8–14. (p. 556)

Christensen, H., Batterham, P. J., Gosling, J. A., Ritterband, L. M., Griffiths, K. M., Thorndike, F. P., . . . Mackinnon, A. J. (2016). Effectiveness of an online insomnia program (SHUTi) for prevention of depressive episodes (the GoodNight study): A randomised controlled trial: Correction. *The Lancet Psychiatry, 3,* 331–341. (p. 546)

Christiansen, P., Jennings, E., & Rose, A. K. (2016). Anticipated effects of alcohol stimulate craving and impair inhibitory control. *Psychology of Addictive Behaviors, 30,* 383–388. (p. 104)

Christophersen, E. R., & Edwards, K. J. (1992). Treatment of elimination disorders: State of the art 1991. *Applied & Preventive Psychology, 1,* 15–22. (p. 540)

Chu, C., Podlogar, M. C., Hagan, C. R., Buchman-Schmitt, J. M., Silva, C., Chiurliza, B., . . . Joiner, T. E. (2016). The interactive effects of the capability for suicide and major depressive episodes on suicidal behavior in a military sample. *Cognitive Therapy and Research, 40,* 22–30. (p. 500)

Chua, H. F., Boland, J. E., & Nisbett, R. E. (2005). Cultural variation in eye movements during scene perception. *PNAS, 102,* 12629–12633. (p. 416)

Chugani, H. T., & Phelps, M. E. (1986). Maturational changes in cerebral function in infants determined by 18FDG positron emission tomography. *Science, 231,* 840–843. (p. 123)

Chulov, M. (2014, December 11). ISIS: The inside story. *The Guardian* (theguardian.com). (p. 431)

Church, A. T., Katigbak, M. S., Mazuera Arias, R., Rincon, B. C., Vargas-Flores, J., Ibáñez-Reyes, J., . . . Ortiz, F. A. (2014). A four-culture study of self-enhancement and adjustment using the social relations model: Do alternative conceptualizations and indices make a difference? *Journal of Personality and Social Psychology, 106,* 997–1014. (p. 488)

Churchland, P. S. (2013). *Touching a nerve: The self as brain.* New York: Norton. (p. 108)

CIA. (2014, accessed April 23). Sex ratio. *The world fact book* (cia.gov). (p. 437)

Cialdini, R. B. (1993). *Influence: Science and practice* (3rd ed.). New York: HarperCollins. (p. 419)

Cialdini, R. B., & Richardson, K. D. (1980). Two indirect tactics of image management: Basking and blasting. *Journal of Personality and Social Psychology, 39,* 406–415. (p. 439)

Ciardelli, L. E., Weiss, A., Powell, D. M., & Reiss, D. (2017). Personality dimensions of the captive California sea lion (*Zalophus californianus*). *Journal of Comparative Psychology, 131,* 50–58. (p. 477)

Cin, S. D., Gibson, B., Zanna, M. P., Shumate, R., & Fong, G. T. (2007). Smoking in movies, implicit associations of smoking with the self, and intentions to smoke. *Psychological Science, 18,* 559–563. (p. 111)

Clack, B., Dixon, J., & Tredoux, C. (2005). Eating together apart: Patterns of segregation in a multi-ethnic cafeteria. *Journal of Community and Applied Social Psychology, 15,* 1–16. (p. 457)

Claidière, N., & Whiten, A. (2012). Integrating the study of conformity and culture in humans and nonhuman animals. *Psychological Bulletin, 138,* 126–145. (pp. 310, 425)

Clancy, S. A. (2005). *Abducted: How people come to believe they were kidnapped by aliens.* Cambridge, MA: Harvard University Press. (p. 88)

Clancy, S. A. (2010). *The trauma myth: The truth about the sexual abuse of children—and its aftermath.* New York: Basic Books. (p. 137)

Clark, A., Seidler, A., & Miller, M. (2001). Inverse association between sense of humor and coronary heart disease. *International Journal of Cardiology, 80,* 87–88. (p. 399)

Clark, C. J., Luguri, J. B., Ditto, P. H., Knobe, J., Shariff, A. F., & Baumeister, R. F. (2014). Free to punish: A motivated account of free will belief. *Journal of Personality and Social Psychology, 106,* 501–513. (p. 397)

Clark, I. A., & Maguire, E. A. (2016). Remembering preservation in hippocampal amnesia. *Annual Review of Psychology, 67,* 51–82. (p. 56)

Clark, K. B., & Clark, M. P. (1947). Racial identification and preference in Negro children. In T. M. Newcomb & E. L. Hartley (Eds.), *Readings in social psychology.* New York: Holt. (p. 32)

Clark, R. D., III, & Hatfield, E. (1989). Gender differences in willingness to engage in casual sex. *Journal of Psychology and Human Sexuality, 2,* 39–55. (p. 185)

Clarke, E., Reichard, U. H., & Zuberbuehler, K. (2015). Context-specific close-range "hoo" calls in wild gibbons (Hylobates lar). *BMC Evolutionary Biology, 15,* 56. (p. 317)

Clausen, J., Fetz, E., Donoghue, J., Ushiba, J., Spöhase, J., Birbaummer, N., & Soekadar, S. R. (2017). Help, hope, and hype: Ethical dimensions of neuroprosthetics. *Science, 356,* 1338–1339. (p. 61)

Claxton, S. E., DeLuca, H. K., & van Dulmen, M. H. (2015). The association between alcohol use and engagement in casual sexual relationships and experiences: A meta-analytic review of non-experimental studies. *Archives of Sexual Behavior, 44,* 837–856. (p. 103)

Cleary, A. M. (2008). Recognition memory, familiarity, and déjà vu experiences. *Current Directions in Psychological Science, 17,* 353–357. (p. 291)

Clynes, T. (2016). How to raise a genius. *Nature, 537,* 152–155. (p. 332)

Coan, J. A., Schaefer, H. S., & Davidson, R. J. (2006). Lending a hand: Social regulation of the neural response to threat. *Psychological Science, 17,* 1032–1039. (p. 400)

Coelho, C. M., & Purkis, H. (2009). The origins of specific phobias: Influential theories and current perspectives. *Review of General Psychology, 13,* 335–348. (p. 512)

Cohen, A. B. (2009). Many forms of culture. *American Psychologist, 64,* 194–204. (pp. 421, 490)

Cohen, A. O., Breiner, K., Steinberg, L., Bonnie, R. J., Scott, E. S., Taylor-Thompson, K. A., . . . Silverman, M. R. (2016). When is an adolescent an adult? Assessing cognitive control in emotional and nonemotional contexts. *Psychological Science, 27,* 549–562. (pp. 142, 385)

Cohen, G. L., & Sherman, D. K. (2014). The psychology of change: Self-affirmation and social psychological intervention. *Annual Review of Psychology, 65,* 333–371. (p. 344)

Cohen, P. (2007, November 15). Freud is widely taught at universities, except in the psychology department. *The New York Times* (nytimes.com). (p. 462)

Cohen, P. (2010, June 11). Long road to adulthood is growing even longer. *The New York Times* (nytimes.com). (p. 150)

Cohen, S. (2004). Social relationships and health. *American Psychologist, 59,* 676–684. (p. 400)

Cohen, S., Alper, C. M., Doyle, W. J., Treanor, J. J., & Turner, R. B. (2006). Positive emotional style predicts resistance to illness after experimental exposure to rhinovirus or influenza A virus. *Psychosomatic Medicine, 68,* 809–815. (p. 390)

Cohen, S., Doyle, W. J., Skoner, D. P., Rabin, B. S., & Gwaltney, J. M., Jr. (1997). Social ties and susceptibility to the common cold. *Journal of the American Medical Association, 277,* 1940–1944. (pp. 397, 400)

Cohen, S., Doyle, W. J., Turner, R., Alper, C. M., & Skoner, D. P. (2003). Sociability and susceptibility to the common cold. *Psychological Science, 14,* 389–395. (p. 390)

Cohen, S., Janicki-Deverts, D., Turner, R. B., & Doyle, W. J. (2015). Does hugging provide stress-buffering social support? A study of susceptibility to upper respiratory infection and illness. *Psychological Science, 26,* 135–147. (p. 400)

Cohen, S., Kaplan, J. R., Cunnick, J. E., Manuck, S. B., & Rabin, B. S. (1992). Chronic social stress, affiliation, and cellular immune response in nonhuman primates. *Psychological Science, 3,* 301–304. (p. 389)

Cohen, S., & Pressman, S. D. (2006). Positive affect and health. *Current Directions in Psychological Science, 15,* 122–125. (p. 390)

Cohen, S., Tyrrell, D. A. J., & Smith, A. P. (1991). Psychological stress and susceptibility to the common cold. *New England Journal of Medicine, 325,* 606–612. (p. 390)

Cohn, D. (2013, February 13). *Love and marriage.* Retrieved from pewsocialtrends.org/2013/02/13/love-and-marriage/ (p. 156)

Coker, A. L., Bush, H. M., Cook-Craig, P. G., DeGue, S. A., Clear, E. R., Brancato, C. J., . . . Recktenwald, E. A. (2017). RCT testing bystander effectiveness to reduce violence. *American Journal of Preventative Medicine, 52,* 566–578. (p. 170)

Colapinto, J. (2000). *As nature made him: The boy who was raised as a girl.* New York: HarperCollins. (p. 168)

Colarelli, S. M., Spranger, J. L., & Hechanova, M. R. (2006). Women, power, and sex composition in small groups: An evolutionary perspective. *Journal of Organizational Behavior, 27,* 163–184. (p. 154)

Cole, K. C. (1998). *The universe and the teacup: The mathematics of truth and beauty.* New York: Harcourt Brace. (p. 105)

Cole, M. W., Ito, T., & Braver, T. S. (2015). Lateral prefrontal cortex contributes to fluid intelligence through multinetwork connectivity. *Brain Connectivity, 5,* 497–504. (p. 324)

Colen, C. G., & Ramey, D. M. (2014). Is breast truly best? Estimating the effects of breastfeeding on long-term child health and well-being in the United States using sibling comparisons. *Social Science & Medicine, 109,* 55–65. (p. 25)

Coley, R. L., Medeiros, B. L., & Schindler, H. (2008). Using sibling differences to estimate effects of parenting on adolescent sexual risk behaviors. *Journal of Adolescent Health, 43,* 133–140. (p. 178)

Collier, K. L., Bos, H. M. W., & Sandfort, T. G. M. (2012). Intergroup contact, attitudes toward homosexuality, and the role of acceptance of gender non-conformity in young adolescents. *Journal of Adolescence, 35,* 899–907. (p. 457)

Collins, F. (2006). *The language of God.* New York: Free Press. (p. 77)

Collins, G. (2009, March 4). The rant list. *The New York Times* (nytimes.com). (p. 31)

Collins, N. L., & Miller, L. C. (1994). Self-disclosure and liking: A meta-analytic review. *Psychological Bulletin, 116,* 457–475. (p. 452)

Collins, R. L., Elliott, M. N., Berry, S. H., Danouse, D. E., Kunkel, D., Hunter, S. B., & Miu, A. (2004). Watching sex on television predicts adolescent initiation of sexual behavior. *Pediatrics, 114,* 280–289. (p. 25)

Collins, W. A., Welsh, D. P., & Furman, W. (2009). Adolescent romantic relationships. *Annual Review of Psychology, 60,* 631–652. (p. 147)

Collinson, S. L., MacKay, C. E., James, A. C., Quested, D. J., Phillips, T., Roberts, N., & Crow, T. J. (2003). Brain volume, asymmetry and intellectual impairment in relation to sex in early-onset schizophrenia. *British Journal of Psychiatry, 183,* 114–120. (p. 525)

Colombo, J. (1982). The critical period concept: Research, methodology, and theoretical issues. *Psychological Bulletin, 91,* 260–275. (p. 134)

Colvert, E., Beata, T., McEwen, F., Stewart, C., Curran, S. R., Woodhouse, E., . . . Bolton, P. (2015). Heritability of autism spectrum disorder in a UK population-based twin sample. *JAMA Psychiatry, 72,* 415–423. (p. 131)

Comfort, A. (2002). *The joy of sex: Fully revised & completely updated for the 21st century.* New York: Crown. (p. 151)

Confer, J. C., Easton, J. A., Fleischman, D. S., Goetz, C. D., Lewis, D. M. G., Perilloux, C., & Buss, D. M. (2010). Evolutionary psychology: Controversies, questions, prospects, and limitations. *American Psychologist, 65,* 110–126. (pp. 185, 186)

Conley, C. S., & Rudolph, K. D. (2009). The emerging sex difference in adolescent depression: Interacting contributions of puberty and peer stress. *Development and Psychopathology, 21,* 593–620. (p. 142)

Conley, T. D. (2011). Perceived proposer personality characteristics and gender differences in acceptance of casual sex offers. *Journal of Personality and Social Psychology, 100,* 309–329. (p. 185)

Connor, C. E. (2010). A new viewpoint on faces. *Science, 330,* 764–765. (p. 205)

Connor-Smith, J. K., & Flachsbart, C. (2007). Relations between personality and coping: A meta-analysis. *Journal of Personality and Social Psychology, 93,* 1080–1107. (p. 396)

Conroy-Beam, D., Buss, D. M., Pham, M. N., & Shackelford, T. K. (2015). How sexually dimorphic are human mate preferences? *Personality and Social Psychology Bulletin, 41,* 1082–1093. (p. 184)

Consumer Reports. (1995, November). Does therapy help? pp. 734–739. (p. 550)

Conway, A. R. A., Skitka, L. J., Hemmerich, J. A., & Kershaw, T. C. (2009). Flashbulb memory for 11 September 2001. *Applied Cognitive Psychology, 23,* 605–623. (p. 278)

Conway, M. A., Wang, Q., Hanyu, K., & Haque, S. (2005). A cross-cultural investigation of autobiographical memory. On the universality and cultural variation of the reminiscence bump. *Journal of Cross-Cultural Psychology, 36,* 739–749. (p. 153)

Cook, S., Kokmotou, K., Soto, V., Fallon, N., Tyson-Carr, J., Thomas, A., . . . Stancak, A. (2017). Pleasant and unpleasant odour-face combinations influence face and odour perception: An event-related potential study. *Behavioural Brain Research, 333,* 304–313. (p. 226)

Cooke, L. J., Wardle, J., & Gibson, E. L. (2003). Relationship between parental report of food neophobia and everyday food consumption in 2–6-year-old children. *Appetite, 41,* 205–206. (p. 225)

Cooney, G., Gilbert, D. T., & Wilson, T. D. (2014). The unforeseen costs of extraordinary experience. *Psychological Science, 25,* 2259–2265. (p. 409)

Cooper, K. J. (1999, May 1). This time, copycat wave is broader. *The Washington Post.* Retrieved from washingtonpost.com/wp-srv/national/longterm/juvmurders/stories/copycat050199.htm (p. 423)

Cooper, W. H., & Withey, M. J. (2009). The strong situation hypothesis. *Personality and Social Psychology Review, 13,* 62–72. (p. 482)

Coopersmith, S. (1967). *The antecedents of self-esteem.* San Francisco: Freeman. (p. 139)

Copeland, W., Shanahan, L., Miller, S., Costello, E. J., Angold, A., & Maughan, B. (2010). Outcomes of early pubertal timing in young women: A prospective population-based study. *American Journal of Psychiatry, 167,* 1218–1225. (p. 142)

Copen, C. E., Chandra, A., & Febo-Vazquez, I. (2016, January 7). Sexual behavior, sexual attraction, and sexual orientation among adults aged 18–44 in the United States: Data from the 2011–2013 National Survey of Family Growth. Centers for Disease Control and Prevention, *National Health Statistics Reports,* Number 88. (p. 179)

Corballis, M. C. (2002). *From hand to mouth: The origins of language.* Princeton, NJ: Princeton University Press. (p. 317)

Corballis, M. C. (2003). From mouth to hand: Gesture, speech, and the evolution of right-handedness. *Behavioral and Brain Sciences, 26,* 199–260. (p. 317)

Corcoran, D. W. J. (1964). The relation between introversion and salivation. *The American Journal of Psychology, 77,* 298–300. (p. 476)

Coren, S. (1996). *Sleep thieves: An eye-opening exploration into the science and mysteries of sleep.* New York: Free Press. (p. 92, 94)

Corey, D. P., García-Añoveros, J., Holt, J. R., Kwan, K. Y., Lin, S.-Y., Vollrath, M. A., . . . Zhang, D.-S. (2004). TRPA1 is a candidate for the mechanosensitive transduction channel of vertebrate hair cells. *Nature, 432,* 723–730. (p. 218)

Corina, D. P. (1998). The processing of sign language: Evidence from aphasia. In B. Stemmer & H. A. Whittaker (Eds.), *Handbook of neurolinguistics* (pp. 313–329). San Diego, CA: Academic Press. (p. 67)

Corina, D. P., Vaid, J., & Bellugi, U. (1992). The linguistic basis of left hemisphere specialization. *Science, 255,* 1258–1260. (p. 67)

Corkin, S. (2013). *Permanent present tense: The unforgettable life of the amnesic patient.* New York: Basic Books. (p. 284)

Corkin, S., quoted by R. Adelson. (2005, September). Lessons from H. M. *Monitor on Psychology,* p. 59. (p. 284)

Cormier, Z. (2016). Brain scans reveal how LSD affects consciousness. *Nature* (nature.com). (p. 61)

Corneille, O., Huart, J., Becquart, E., & Brédart, S. (2004). When memory shifts toward more typical category exemplars: Accentuation effects in the recollection of ethnically ambiguous faces. *Journal of Personality and Social Psychology, 86,* 236–250. (p. 298)

Cornette, M. M., deRoom-Cassini, T. A., Fosco, G. M., Holloway, R. L., Clark, D. C., & Joiner, T. E. (2009). Application of an interpersonal-psychological model of suicidal behavior to physicians and medical trainees. *Archives of Suicide Research, 13,* 1–14. (p. 500)

Cornier, M.-A. (2011). Is your brain to blame for weight regain? *Physiology & Behavior, 104,* 608–612. (p. 362)

Cornil, Y., & Chandon, P. (2013). From fan to fat? Vicarious losing increases unhealthy eating, but self-affirmation is an effective remedy. *Psychological Science, 24,* 1936–1946. (p. 363)

Coronado-Montoya, S., Levis, A. W., Kwakkenbos, L., Steele, R. J., Turner, E. H., & Thombs, B. D. (2016). Reporting of positive results in randomized controlled trials of mindfulness-based mental health interventions. *PLoS ONE, 11,* 18. (p. 404)

Correa, C., & Louttit, M. (2018, January 24). More than 160 women say Larry Nassar sexually abused them. Here are his accusers in their own words. *The New York Times* (nytimes.com). (p. 429)

Correll, J., Park, B., Judd, C. M., Wittenbrink, B., Sadler, M. S., & Keesee, T. (2007). Across the thin blue line: Police officers and racial bias in the decision to shoot. *Journal of Personality and Social Psychology, 92,* 1006–1023. (p. 436)

Correll, J., Wittenbrink, B., Crawford, M. T., & Sadler, M. S. (2015). Stereotypic vision: How stereotypes disambiguate visual stimuli. *Journal of Personality and Social Psychology, 108,* 219–233. (p. 436)

Corrigan, P. W. (2014). Can there be false hope in recovery? *British Journal of Psychiatry, 205,* 423–424. (p. 555)

Corrigan, P. W., Druss, B. G., & Perlick, D. A. (2014). The impact of mental illness stigma on seeking and participating in mental health care. *Psychological Science in the Public Interest, 15,* 37–70. (p. 499)

Costa, A., Foucart, A., Hayakawa, S., Aparici, M., Apesteguia, J., Heafner, J., & Keysar, B. (2014). Your morals depend on language. *PLoS ONE, 9,* e94842. doi:10.1371/journal.pone.0094842 (p. 319)

Costa, P. T., Jr., & McCrae, R. R. (2011). The five-factor model, five factor theory, and interpersonal psychology. In L. M. Horowitz & S. Strack (Eds.), *Handbook of interpersonal psychology: Theory, research, assessment, and therapeutic interventions* (pp. 91–104). Hoboken, NJ: Wiley. (p. 477)

Costa, P. T., Jr., Terracciano, A., & McCrae, R. R. (2001). Gender differences in personality traits across cultures: Robust and surprising findings. *Journal of Personality and Social Psychology, 81,* 322–331. (p. 377)

Costello, E. J., Compton, S. N., Keeler, G., & Angold, A. (2003). Relationships between poverty and psychopathology: A natural experiment. *Journal of the American Medical Association, 290,* 2023–2029. (pp. 25, 505)

Coughlin, J. F., Mohyde, M., D'Ambrosio, L. A., & Gilbert, J. (2004). *Who drives older driver decisions?* Cambridge, MA: MIT Age Lab. (p. 152)

Couli, J. T., Vidal, F., Nazarian, B., & Macar, F. (2004). Functional anatomy of the attentional modulation of time estimation. *Science, 303,* 1506–1508. (p. B-1)

Coulter, K. C., & Malouff, J. M. (2013). Effects of an intervention designed to enhance romantic relationship excitement: A randomized-control trial. *Couple and Family Psychology: Research and Practice, 2,* 34–44. (p. 451)

Courtney, J. G., Longnecker, M. P., Theorell, T., & de Verdier, M. G. (1993). Stressful life events and the risk of colorectal cancer. *Epidemiology, 4,* 407–414. (p. 390)

Cowan, N. (1988). Evolving conceptions of memory storage, selective attention, and their mutual constraints within the human information-processing system. *Psychological Bulletin, 104,* 163–191. (p. 270)

Cowan, N. (2010). The magical mystery four: How is working memory capacity limited, and why? *Current Directions in Psychological Science, 19,* 51–57. (p. 269)

Cowan, N. (2015). George Miller's magical number of immediate memory in retrospect: Observations on the faltering progression of science. *Psychological Review, 122,* 536–541. (p. 271)

Cowan, N. (2016). Working memory maturation: Can we get at the essence of cognitive growth? *Perspectives on Psychological Science, 11,* 239–264. (p. 269)

Cowart, B. J. (1981). Development of taste perception in humans: Sensitivity and preference throughout the life span. *Psychological Bulletin, 90,* 43–73. (p. 225)

Cowart, B. J. (2005). Taste, our body's gustatory gatekeeper. *Cerebrum, 7,* 7–22. (p. 225)

Cowell, J. M., & Decety, J. (2015). Precursors to morality in development as a complex interplay between neural, socioenvironmental, and behavioral facets. *PNAS, 112,* 12657–12662. (p. 144)

Cox, J. J., Reimann, F., Nicholas, A. K., Thornton, G., Robert, E., Springell, K., . . . Woods, C. G. (2006). An SCN9A channelopathy causes congenital inability to experience pain. *Nature, 444,* 894–898. (p. 223)

Coye, C., Ouattara, K., Zuberbühler, K., & Lemasson, A. (2015). Suffixation influences receivers' behaviour in non-human primates. *Proceedings of the Royal Society B, 282,* 1807. (p. 317)

Coyne, J. C., Ranchor, A. V., & Palmer, S. C. (2010). Meta-analysis of stress-related factors in cancer. *Nature Reviews: Clinical Oncology, 7.* doi:10.1038/ncponc1134-c1 (p. 390)

Coyne, J. C., Stefanek, M., & Palmer, S. C. (2007). Psychotherapy and survival in cancer: The conflict between hope and evidence. *Psychological Bulletin, 133,* 367–394. (p. 391)

Coyne, J. C., & Tennen, H. (2010). Positive psychology in cancer care: Bad science, exaggerated claims, and unproven medicine. *Annals of Behavioral Medicine, 39,* 16–26. (p. 391)

Coyne, J. C., Thombs, B. C., Stefanek, M., & Palmer, S. C. (2009). Time to let go of the illusion that psychotherapy extends the survival of cancer patients: Reply to Kraemer, Kuchler, and Spiegel (2009). *Psychological Bulletin, 135,* 179–182. (p. 391)

Crabbe, J. C. (2002). Genetic contributions to addiction. *Annual Review of Psychology, 53,* 435–462. (p. 110)

Crabtree, S. (2005, January 13). Engagement keeps the doctor away. *Gallup Management Journal* (gmj.gallup.com). (p. B-9)

Crabtree, S. (2011, December 12). *U.S. seniors maintain happiness highs with less social time.* Gallup poll (gallup.com). (p. 158)

Craik, F. I. M., & Tulving, E. (1975). Depth of processing and the retention of words in episodic memory. *Journal of Experimental Psychology: General, 104,* 268–294. (p. 273)

Crandall, C. S. (1988). Social contagion of binge eating. *Journal of Personality and Social Psychology, 55,* 588–598. (p. 532)

Crandall, C. S., & White, M. H., II. (2016, November 17). Trump and the social psychology of prejudice. *Undark.* Retrieved from undark.org/article/trump-social-psychology-prejudice-unleashed (p. 439)

Crawford, M., Chaffin, R., & Fitton, L. (1995). Cognition in social context. Learning and individual differences, special issue: Psychological and psychobiological perspectives on sex differences in cognition: 1. *Theory and Research, 7,* 341–362. (p. 341)

Credé, M., & Kuncel, N. R. (2008). Study habits, skills, and attitudes: The third pillar supporting collegiate academic performance. *Perspectives on Psychological Science, 3,* 425–453. (p. 339)

Creswell, J. D., Bursley, J. K., & Satpute, A. B. (2013). Neural reactivation links unconscious thought to decision making performance. *Social Cognitive and Affective Neuroscience, 8,* 863–869. (p. 305)

Creswell, J. D., Way, B. M., Eisenberger, N. I., & Lieberman, M. D. (2007). Neural correlates of dispositional mindfulness during affect labeling. *Psychosomatic Medicine, 69,* 560–565. (p. 404)

Creswell, K. G., Chung, T., Clark, D., & Martin, C. (2014). Solitary alcohol use in teens is associated with drinking in response to negative affect and predicts alcohol problems in young adulthood. *Clinical Psychological Science, 2,* 602–610. (p. 104)

Crews, F. T., He, J., & Hodge, C. (2007). Adolescent cortical development: A critical period of vulnerability for addiction. *Pharmacology Biochemistry and Behavior, 86,* 189–199. (pp. 103, 142)

Crews, F. T., Mdzinarishvili, A., Kim, D., He, J., & Nixon, K. (2006). Neurogenesis in adolescent brain is potently inhibited by ethanol. *Neuroscience, 137,* 437–445. (p. 103)

Crifasi, C. K., Meyers, J. S., Vernick, J. S., & Webster, D. W. (2015). Effects of changes in permit-to-purchase handgun laws in Connecticut and Missouri on suicide rates. *Preventive Medicine: An International Journal Devoted to Practice and Theory, 79,* 43–49. (p. 501)

Cristea, I. A., Huibers, M. J., David, D., Hollon, S. D., Andersson, G., & Cuijpers, P. (2015). The effects of cognitive behavior therapy for adult depression on dysfunctional thinking: A meta-analysis. *Clinical Psychology Review, 42,* 62–71. (p. 546)

Crivelli, C., Jarillo, S., Russell, J. A., & Fernández-Dols, J. M. (2016a). Reading emotions from faces in two indigenous societies. *Journal of Experimental Psychology: General, 145,* 830–843. (p. 378)

Crivelli, C., Russell, J. A., Jarillo, S., & Fernández-Dols, J. M. (2016b). The fear gasping face as a threat display in a Melanesian society. *PNAS, 113,* 12403–12407. (p. 378)

Crocker, J., & Park, L. E. (2004). The costly pursuit of self-esteem. *Psychological Bulletin, 130,* 392–414. (p. 489)

Crocker, J., Thompson, L. L., McGraw, K. M., & Ingerman, C. (1987). Downward comparison, prejudice, and evaluation of others: Effects of self-esteem and threat. *Journal of Personality and Social Psychology, 52,* 907–916. (p. 439)

Crockett, M. J., Kurth-Nelson, Z., Siegel, J. Z., Dayan, P., & Dolan, R. J. (2014). Harm to others outweighs harm to self in moral decision making. *PNAS, 111,* 17320–17325. (p. 144)

Croft, A., Schmader, T., Block, K., & Baron, A. S. (2014). The second shift reflected in the second generation: Do parents' gender roles at home predict children's aspirations? *Psychological Science, 25,* 1418–1428. (p. 169)

Croft, R. J., Klugman, A., Baldeweg, T., & Gruzelier, J. H. (2001). Electrophysiological evidence of serotonergic impairment in long-term MDMA ("Ecstasy") users. *American Journal of Psychiatry, 158,* 1687–1692. (p. 108)

Crook, T. H., & West, R. L. (1990). Name recall performance across the adult life-span. *British Journal of Psychology, 81,* 335–340. (pp. 153, 154)

Crosier, B. S., Webster, G. D., & Dillon, H. M. (2012). Wired to connect: Evolutionary psychology and social networks. *Review of General Psychology, 16,* 230–239. (p. 448)

Cross-National Collaborative Group. (1992). The changing rate of major depression. *Journal of the American Medical Association, 268,* 3098–3105. (p. 518)

Crouse, K. (2017, September 21). Michael Phelps: A golden shoulder to lean on. *The New York Times* (nytimes.com). (p. 521)

Crowell, J. A., & Waters, E. (1994). Bowlby's theory grown up: The role of attachment in adult love relationships. *Psychological Inquiry, 5,* 1–22. (p. 133)

Croy, I., Bojanowski, V., & Hummel, T. (2013). Men without a sense of smell exhibit a strongly reduced number of sexual relationships, women exhibit reduced partnership security: A reanalysis of previously published data. *Biological Psychology, 92,* 292–294. (p. 225)

Croy, I., Negoias, S., Novakova, L., Landis, B. N., & Hummel, T. (2012). Learning about the functions of the olfactory system from people without a sense of smell. *PLoS ONE 7,* e33365. doi:10.1371/journal.pone.0033365 (p. 225)

Csikszentmihalyi, M. (1990). *Flow: The psychology of optimal experience.* New York: Harper & Row. (p. B-1)

Csikszentmihalyi, M. (1999). If we are so rich, why aren't we happy? *American Psychologist, 54,* 821–827. (p. B-1)

Csikszentmihalyi, M., & Hunter, J. (2003). Happiness in everyday life: The uses of experience sampling. *Journal of Happiness Studies, 4,* 185–199. (p. 147)

Cucchi, A., Ryan, D., Konstantakopoulos, G., Stroumpa, S., Kaçar, A. Ş., Renshaw, S., . . . Kravariti, E. (2016). Lifetime prevalence of non-suicidal self-injury in patients with eating disorders: A systematic review and meta-analysis. *Psychological Medicine, 46,* 1345–1358. (p. 532)

Cuijpers, P. (2017). Four decades of outcome research on psychotherapies for adult depression: An overview of a series of meta-analyses. *Canadian Psychology/Psychologie Canadienne, 58,* 7–19. (p. 552)

Cuijpers, P., Driessen, E., Hollon, S. D., van Oppen, P., Barth, J., & Andersson, G. (2012). The efficacy of non-directive supportive therapy for adult depression: A meta-analysis. *Clinical Psychology Review, 32,* 280–291. (p. 553)

Cuijpers, P., van Straten, A., Schuurmans, J., van Oppen, P., Hollon, S. D., & Andersson, G. (2010). Psychotherapy for chronic major depression and dysthymia: A meta-analysis. *Clinical Psychology Review, 30,* 51–62. (p. 562)

Culbert, K. M., Burt, S. A., McGue, M., Iacono, W. G., & Klump, K. L. (2009). Puberty and the genetic diathesis of disordered eating attitudes and behaviors. *Journal of Abnormal Psychology, 118,* 788–796. (p. 532)

Culbert, K. M., Racine, S. E., & Klump, K. L. (2015). Research review: What we have learned about the causes of eating disorders—a synthesis of sociocultural, psychological, and biological research. *Journal of Child Psychology and Psychiatry, 56,* 1141–1164. (p. 532)

Cummins, R. A. (2006, April 4). *Australian Unity Wellbeing Index: Survey 14.1.* Melbourne, Victoria, Australia: Australian Centre on Quality of Life, Deakin University. (p. 409)

Cunningham, G. B., Ferreira, M., & Fink, J. S. (2009). Reactions to prejudicial statements: The influence of statement content and characteristics of the commenter. *Group Dynamics: Theory, Research, and Practice, 13,* 59–73. (p. 299)

Cunningham, M. R., Roberts, A., Barbee, A. P., Druen, P. B., & Wu, C.-H. (2005). "Their ideas of beauty are, on the whole, the same as ours": Consistency and variability in the cross-cultural perception of female physical attractiveness. *Journal of Personality and Social Psychology, 68,* 261–279. (p. 449)

Cunningham, W. A., Johnson, M. K., Raye, C. L., Gatenby, J. C., Gore, J. C., & Banaji, M. R. (2004). Separable neural components in the processing of Black and White faces. *Psychological Science, 15,* 806–813. (p. 435)

Curci, A., Lanciano, T., Mastandrea, S., & Sartori, G. (2015). Flashbulb memories of the Pope's resignation: Explicit and implicit measure across different religious groups. *Memory, 23,* 529–544. (p. 278)

Currie, T. E., & Little, A. C. (2009). The relative importance of the face and body in judgments of human physical attractiveness. *Evolution and Human Behavior, 30,* 409–416. (p. 449)

Curry, J., Silva, S., Rohde, P., Ginsburg, G., Kratochvil, C., Simons, A., . . . March, J. (2011). Recovery and recurrence following treatment for adolescent major depression. *Archives of General Psychiatry, 68,* 263–269. (p. 517)

Curtis, R. C., & Miller, K. (1986). Believing another likes or dislikes you: Behaviors making the beliefs come true. *Journal of Personality and Social Psychology, 51,* 284–290. (p. 450)

Custers, R., & Aarts, H. (2010). The unconscious will: How the pursuit of goals operates outside of conscious awareness. *Science, 329,* 47–50. (p. 305)

Cyders, M. A., & Smith, G. T. (2008). Emotion-based dispositions to rash action: Positive and negative urgency. *Psychological Bulletin, 134,* 807–828. (p. 368)

Czarna, A. Z., Leifeld, P., Śmieja, M., Dufner, M., & Salovey, P. (2016). Do narcissism and emotional intelligence win us friends? Modeling dynamics of peer popularity using inferential network analysis. *Personality and Social Psychology Bulletin, 42,* 1588–1599. (pp. 326, 489)

Czeisler, C. A., Allan, J. S., Strogatz, S. H., Ronda, J. M., Sanchez, R., Rios, C. D., . . . Kronauer, R. E. (1986). Bright light resets the human circadian pacemaker independent of the timing of the sleep-wake cycle. *Science, 233,* 667–671. (p. 91)

Czeisler, C. A., Duffy, J. F., Shanahan, T. L., Brown, E. N., Mitchell, J. F., Rimmer, D. W., . . . Kronauer, R. E. (1999). Stability, precision, and near-24-hour period of the human circadian pacemaker. *Science, 284,* 2177–2181. (p. 90)

Czeisler, C. A., Kronauer, R. E., Allan, J. S., & Duffy, J. F. (1989). Bright light induction of strong (Type 0) resetting of the human circadian pacemaker. *Science, 244,* 1328–1333. (p. 91)

da Cunha-Bang, S., Fisher, P. M., Hjordt, L. V., Perfalk, E., Persson Skibsted, A., Bock, C., . . . Knudsen, G. M. (2017). Violent offenders respond to provocations with high amygdala and striatal reactivity. *Social Cognitive and Affective Neuroscience, 12,* 802–810. (p. 55)

Dai, H., Milkman, K. L., & Riis, J. (2014). The fresh start effect: Temporal landmarks motivate aspirational behavior. *Management Science, 60,* 2563–2582. (p. B-9)

Daley, J. (2011, July/August). What you don't know can kill you. *Discover* (discovermagazine.com). (p. 302)

Daly, M., Delaney, L., Egan, R. F., & Baumeister, R. F. (2015). Childhood self-control and unemployment throughout the life span: Evidence from two British cohort studies. *Psychological Science, 26,* 709–723. (p. 145)

Damasio, A. R. (2003). *Looking for Spinoza: Joy, sorrow, and the feeling brain.* New York: Harcourt. (p. 369)

Damasio, A. R. (2010). *Self comes to mind: Constructing the conscious brain.* New York: Pantheon. (p. 486)

Damian, R. I., & Roberts, B. W. (2015). The associations of birth order with personality and intelligence in a representative sample of U.S. high school students. *Journal of Research in Personality, 58,* 96–105. (p. 478)

Damon, W., Menon, J., & Bronk, K. (2003). The development of purpose during adolescence. *Applied Developmental Science, 7,* 119–128. (p. 147)

Dana, J., Dawes, R., & Peterson, N. (2013). Belief in the unstructured interview: The persistence of an illusion. *Judgment and Decision Making, 8,* 512–520. (p. B-5)

Danelli, L., Cossu, G., Berlingeri, M., Bottini, G., Sberna, M., & Paulesu, E. (2013). Is a lone right hemisphere enough? Neurolinguistic architecture in a case with a very early left hemispherectomy. *Neurocase, 19,* 209–231. (p. 64)

Daniel, T. A., & Katz, J. S. (2017). Primacy and recency effects for taste. *Journal of Experimental Psychology: Learning, Memory, and Cognition.* Advance online publication. http://dx.doi.org/10.1037/xlm0000437 (p. 282)

Danner, D. D., Snowdon, D. A., & Friesen, W. V. (2001). Positive emotions in early life and longevity: Findings from the Nun Study. *Journal of Personality and Social Psychology, 80,* 804–813. (p. 399)

Danso, H., & Esses, V. (2001). Black experimenters and the intellectual test performance of White participants: The tables are turned. *Journal of Experimental Social Psychology, 37,* 158–165. (p. 344)

Danziger, S., & Ward, R. (2010). Language changes implicit associations between ethnic groups and evaluation in bilinguals. *Psychological Science, 21,* 799–800. (p. 319)

Darby, M. M., Yolken, R. H., & Sabunciyan, S. (2016). Consistently altered expression of gene sets in postmortem brains of individuals with major psychiatric disorders. *Translational Psychiatry, 6,* e890. (p. 526)

Darley, J. M. (2009). Morality in the law: The psychological foundations of citizens' desires to punish transgressions. *Annual Review of Law and Social Science, 5,* 1–23. (p. 144)

Darley, J. M., & Alter, A. (2013). Behavioral issues of punishment, retribution, and deterrence. In E. Shafir (Ed.), *The behavioral foundations of public policy* (pp. 181–194). Princeton, NJ: Princeton University Press. (p. 249)

Darley, J. M., & Latané, B. (1968a). Bystander intervention in emergencies: Diffusion of responsibility. *Journal of Personality and Social Psychology, 8,* 377–383. (pp. 453, 454)

Darley, J. M., & Latané, B. (1968b, December). When will people help in a crisis? *Psychology Today,* pp. 54–57, 70–71. (p. 453)

Darrach, B., & Norris, J. (1984, August). An American tragedy. *Life,* pp. 58–74. (p. 530)

Darwin, C. (1859). *On the origin of species by means of natural selection.* London: John Murray. (p. 76)

Darwin, C. (1872). *The expression of the emotions in man and animals.* London: John Murray. (p. 380)

Das, S., Tonelli, M., & Ziedonis, D. (2016). Update on smoking cessation: E-cigarettes, emerging tobacco products trends, and new technology-based interventions. *Current Psychiatry Reports, 18*(5), 51. (p. 105)

Daum, I., & Schugens, M. M. (1996). On the cerebellum and classical conditioning. *Psychological Science, 5,* 58–61. (p. 277)

Davey, G., & Rato, R. (2012). Subjective well-being in China: A review. *Journal of Happiness Studies, 13,* 333–346. (p. 410)

Davey, G. C. L. (1992). Classical conditioning and the acquisition of human fears and phobias: A review and synthesis of the literature. *Advances in Behavior Research and Therapy, 14,* 29–66. (p. 255)

Davey, G. C. L. (1995). Preparedness and phobias: Specific evolved associations or a generalized expectancy bias? *Behavioral and Brain Sciences, 18,* 289–297. (p. 512)

Davidoff, J. (2004). Coloured thinking. *The Psychologist, 17,* 570–572. (p. 319)

Davidson, R. J. (2000). Affective style, psychopathology, and resilience: Brain mechanisms and plasticity. *American Psychologist, 55,* 1196–1209. (p. 374)

Davidson, R. J., & Begley, S. (2012). *The emotional life of your brain: How its unique patterns affect the way you think, feel, and live—and how you can change them.* New York: Hudson Street Press. (p. 369)

Davidson, R. J., Kabat-Zinn, J., Schumacher, J., Rosenkranz, M., Muller, D., Santorelli, S. F., . . . Sheridan, J. F. (2003). Alterations in brain and immune function produced by mindfulness meditation. *Psychosomatic Medicine, 65,* 564–570. (p. 404)

Davidson, R. J., Pizzagalli, D., Nitschke, J. B., & Putnam, K. (2002). Depression: Perspectives from affective neuroscience. *Annual Review of Psychology, 53,* 545–574. (p. 518)

Davidson, R. J., Putnam, K. M., & Larson, C. L. (2000). Dysfunction in the neural circuitry of emotion regulation—a possible prelude to violence. *Science, 289,* 591–594. (p. 442)

Davidson, T. L., & Riley, A. L. (2015). Taste, sickness, and learning. *American Scientist, 103,* 204–211. (p. 255)

Davies, P. (2007). *Cosmic jackpot: Why our universe is just right for life.* Boston: Houghton Mifflin. (p. 77)

Davis, B. E., Moon, R. Y., Sachs, H. C., & Ottolini, M. C. (1998). Effects of sleep position on infant motor development. *Pediatrics, 102,* 1135–1140. (p. 124)

Davis, D. E., Choe, E., Meyers, J., Wade, N., Varias, K., Gifford, A., . . . Worthington, E. L. (2016). Thankful for the little things: A meta-analysis of gratitude interventions. *Journal of Counseling Psychology, 63,* 20–31. (p. 412)

Davis, E. P., Stout, S. A., Molet, J., Vegetabile, B., Glynn, L. M., Sandman, C. A., . . . Baram, T. Z. (2017). Exposure to unpredictable maternal sensory signals influences cognitive development across species. *PNAS, 114,* 10390–10395. (p. 133)

Davis, J. O., & Phelps, J. A. (1995). Twins with schizophrenia: Genes or germs? *Schizophrenia Bulletin, 21,* 13–18. (p. 526)

Davis, J. O., Phelps, J. A., & Bracha, H. S. (1995). Prenatal development of monozygotic twins and concordance for schizophrenia. *Schizophrenia Bulletin, 21,* 357–366. (p. 526)

Davis, J. P., Lander, K., & Jansari, A. (2013). I never forget a face. *The Psychologist, 26,* 726–729. (p. 266)

Davis, K., Christodoulou, J., Seider, S., & Gardner, H. (2011). The theory of multiple intelligences. In R. J. Sternberg & S. B. Kaufman (Eds.), *Cambridge handbook of intelligence.* Cambridge, UK; New York: Cambridge University Press. (p. 324)

Davis, M. (2005). Searching for a drug to extinguish fear. *Cerebrum, 7,* 47–58. (p. 561)

Davison, K. P., Pennebaker, J. W., & Dickerson, S. S. (2000). Who talks? The social psychology of illness support groups. *American Psychologist, 55,* 205–217. (p. 548)

Davison, S. L., & Davis, S. R. (2011). Androgenic hormones and aging—the link with female sexual function. *Hormones and Behavior, 59,* 745–753. (p. 173)

Dawes, R. M. (1980). Social dilemmas. *Annual Review of Psychology, 31,* 169–193. (p. 456)

Dawes, R. M. (1994). *House of cards: Psychology and psychotherapy built on myth.* New York: Free Press. (p. 486)

Dawkins, L., Shahzad, F.-Z., Ahmed, S. S., & Edmonds, C. J. (2011). Expectation of having consumed caffeine can improve performance and moods. *Appetite, 57,* 597–600. (p. 27)

Dawkins, R. (1998). *Unweaving the rainbow: Science, delusion and the appetite for wonder.* Boston: Houghton Mifflin. (p. 77)

Day, F. R., Thompson, D. J., Helgason, H., Chasman, D. I., Finucane, H., Sulem, P., . . . Altmaier, E. (2017). Genomic analyses identify hundreds of variants associated with age at menarche and support a role for puberty timing in cancer risk. *Nature Genetics, 49,* 834–841. (p. 167)

de Boysson-Bardies, B., Halle, P., Sagart, L., & Durand, C. (1989). A cross linguistic investigation of vowel formats in babbling. *Journal of Child Language, 16,* 1–17. (p. 314)

de Bruin, A., Barbara, T., & Della Sala, S. (2015a). Cognitive advantage in bilingualism: An example of publication bias? *Psychological Science, 26,* 99–107. (p. 320)

de Bruin, A., Treccani, B., & Della Sala, S. (2015b). The connection is in the data: We should consider them all. *Psychological Science, 26,* 947–949. (p. 320)

de Chastelaine, M., Mattson, J. T., Wang, T. H., Donley, B. E., & Rugg, M. D. (2016). The neural correlates of recollection and retrieval monitoring: Relationships with age and recollection performance. *NeuroImage, 138,* 164–175. (p. 276)

de Courten-Myers, G. M. (2005, February 4). Personal communication. (p. 59)

De Dreu, C. K. W., Greer, L. L., Handgraaf, M. J. J., Shalvi, S., Van Kleef, G. A., Baas, M., . . . Feith, S. W. W. (2010). The neuropeptide oxytocin regulated parochial altruism in intergroup conflict among humans. *Science, 328,* 1409–1411. (p. 49)

De Dreu, C. K. W., Nijstad, B. A., Baas, M., Wolsink, I., & Roskes, M. (2012). Working memory benefits creative insight, musical improvisation, and original ideation through maintained task-focused attention. *Personality and Social Psychology Bulletin, 38,* 656–669. (p. 271)

de Gee, J., Knapen, T., & Donner, T. H. (2014). Decision-related pupil dilation reflects upcoming choice and individual bias. *PNAS, 111,* E618–E625. (p. 201)

de Gelder, B. (2010, May). Uncanny sight in the blind. *Scientific American,* pp. 60–65. (p. 84)

de Hoogh, A. H. B., den Hartog, D. N., Koopman, P. L., Thierry, H., van den Berg, P. T., van der Weide, J. G., & Wilderom, C. P. M. (2004). Charismatic leadership, environmental dynamism, and performance. *European Journal of Work and Organisational Psychology, 13,* 447–471. (p. B-10)

de la Cruz, L. F., Rydell, M., Runeson, B., D'Onofrio, B. M., Brander, G., Rück, C., . . . Matai-Cols, D. (2017). Suicide in obsessive-compulsive disorder: A population-based study of 36788 Swedish patients. *Molecular Psychiatry, 22,* 1626–1632. (p. 500)

de Lange, M., Debets, L., Ruitenberg, K., & Holland, R. (2012). Making less of a mess: Scent exposure as a tool for behavioral change. *Social Influence, 7,* 90–97. (p. 227)

de Lau, L. M., & Breteler, M. M. (2006). Epidemiology of Parkinson's disease. *The Lancet Neurology, 5,* 525–535.

de la Vega, A., Chang, L. J., Banich, M. T., Wager, T. D., & Yarkoni, T. (2016). Large-scale meta-analysis of human medial frontal cortex reveals tripartite functional organization. *The Journal of Neuroscience, 36,* 6553–6562. (p. 62)

De Neve, J., Christakis, N. A., Fowler, J. H., & Frey, B. S. (2012). Genes, economics, and happiness. *Journal of Neuroscience, Psychology, and Economics, 5,* 193–211. (p. 411)

De Neve, J.-E., Diener, E., Tay, L., & Xuereb, C. (2013). The objective benefits of subjective well-being. In J. F. Helliwell, R. Layard, & J. Sachs (Eds.), *World happiness report 2013.* Volume 2. (pp. 54–79). New York: UN Sustainable Network Development Solutions Network. (pp. 407, B-12)

De Neve, K. M., & Cooper, H. (1998). The happy personality: A meta-analysis of 137 personality traits and subjective well-being. *Psychological Bulletin, 124,* 197–229. (p. 411)

de Waal, F. (2016). *Are we smart enough to know how smart animals are?* New York: Norton. (p. 309)

de Wit, L., Luppino, F., van Straten, A., Penninx, B., Zitman, F., & Cuijpers, P. (2010). Depression and obesity: A meta-analysis of community-based studies. *Psychiatry Research, 178,* 230–235. (p. 365)

De Wolff, M. S., & van IJzendoorn, M. H. (1997). Sensitivity and attachment: A meta-analysis on parental antecedents of infant attachment. *Child Development, 68,* 571–591. (p. 134)

Deal, G. (2011, January 14). Chinese parenting: Thanks, I'll pass. *The Wall Street Journal.* Retrieved from http://blogs.wsj.com/wsjam/2011/01/14/chinese-parenting-thanks-ill-pass/ (p. 149)

Dean, G. (2012, November/December). Phrenology and the grand delusion of experience. *Skeptical Inquirer,* pp. 31–38. (p. 38)

Deary, I. J. (2008). Why do intelligent people live longer? *Nature, 456,* 175–176. (p. 333)

Deary, I. J. (2016, February). Intelligence over time. Quoted in APS Award Address. Association for Psychological Science *Observer,* p. 15. (p. 333)

Deary, I. J., Johnson, W., & Houlihan, L. M. (2009a). Genetic foundations of human intelligence. *Human Genetics, 126,* 215–232. (pp. 336, 338)

Deary, I. J., Pattie, A., & Starr, J. M. (2013). The stability of intelligence from age 11 to age 90 years: The Lothian birth cohort of 1921. *Psychological Science, 24,* 2361–2368. (pp. 332, 333)

Deary, I. J., & Ritchie, S. J. (2016). Processing speed differences between 70- and 83-year-olds matched on childhood IQ. *Intelligence, 55,* 28–33. (p. 333)

Deary, I. J., Thorpe, G., Wilson, V., Starr, J. M., & Whalley, L. J. (2003). Population sex differences in IQ at age 11: The Scottish mental survey 1932. *Intelligence, 31,* 533–541. (p. 340)

Deary, I. J., Whalley, L. J., & Starr, J. M. (2009b). *A lifetime of intelligence: Follow-up studies of the Scottish Mental Surveys of 1932 and 1947.* Washington, DC: American Psychological Association. (p. 332)

Deary, I. J., Whiteman, M. C., Starr, J. M., Whalley, L. J., & Fox, H. C. (2004). The impact of childhood intelligence on later life: Following up the Scottish mental surveys of 1932 and 1947. *Journal of Personality and Social Psychology, 86,* 130–147. (pp. 332, 333)

Deary, I. J., Yang, J., Davies, G., Harris, S. E., Tenesa, A., Liewald, D., . . . Visscher, P. M. (2012). Genetic contributions to stability and change in intelligence from childhood to old age. *Nature, 481,* 212–215. (p. 338)

DeBruine, L. M. (2002). Facial resemblance enhances trust. *Proceedings of the Royal Society of London, 269,* 1307–1312. (p. 447)

DeBruine, L. M. (2004). Facial resemblance increases the attractiveness of same-sex faces more than other-sex faces. *Proceedings of the Royal Society of London B, 271,* 2085–2090. (p. 447)

DeCasper, A. J., Lecanuet, J.-P., Busnel, M.-C., Granier-Deferre, C., & Maugeais, R. (1994). Fetal reactions to recurrent maternal speech. *Infant Behavior and Development, 17,* 159–164. (p. 119)

DeCasper, A. J., & Spence, M. J. (1986). Prenatal maternal speech influences newborns' perception of speech sounds. *Infant Behavior and Development, 9,* 133–150. (p. 119)

Dechêne, A., Stahl, C., Hansen, J., & Wänke, M. (2010). The truth about the truth: A meta-analytic review of the truth effect. *Personality and Social Psychology Review, 14,* 238–257. (pp. 16, 18)

Dechesne, M., Pyszczynski, T., Arndt, J., Ransom, S., Sheldon, K. M., van Knippenberg, A., & Janssen, J. (2003). Literal and symbolic immortality: The effect of evidence of literal immortality on self-esteem striving in response to mortality salience. *Journal of Personality and Social Psychology, 84,* 722–737. (p. 29)

Deci, E. L., Koestner, R., & Ryan, R. M. (1999, November). A meta-analytic review of experiments examining the effects of extrinsic rewards on intrinsic motivation. *Psychological Bulletin, 125,* 627–668. (p. 358)

Deci, E. L., & Ryan, R. M. (2009). Self-determination theory: A consideration of human motivational universals. In P. J. Corr & G. Matthews (Eds.), *The Cambridge handbook of personality psychology.* New York: Cambridge University Press. (p. 353)

Deci, E. L., & Ryan, R. M. (2012). Motivation, personality, and development within embedded social contexts: An overview of self-determination theory. In R. M. Ryan (Ed.), *Oxford handbook of human motivation* (pp. 85–107). Oxford: Oxford University Press. (p. 352)

DeFina, R., & Hannon, L. (2015). The changing relationship between unemployment and suicide. *Suicide and Life-Threatening Behavior, 45,* 217–229. (p. 501)

Dehne, K. L., & Riedner, G. (2005). *Sexually transmitted infections among adolescents: The need for adequate health services.* Geneva, Switzerland: World Health Organization. (p. 175)

DeLamater, J. (2012). Sexual expression in later life: A review and synthesis. *Journal of Sex Research, 49,* 125–141. (p. 151)

DeLamater, J. D., & Sill, M. (2005). Sexual desire in later life. *Journal of Sex Research, 42,* 138–149. (p. 151)

Delaney, H. D., Miller, W. R., & Bisonó, A. M. (2007). Religiosity and spirituality among psychologists: A survey of clinician members of the American Psychological Association. *Professional Psychology: Research and Practice, 38,* 538–546. (p. 556)

Delaunay-El Allam, M., Soussignan, R., Patris, B., Marlier, L., & Schaal, B. (2010). Long-lasting memory for an odor acquired at the mother's breast. *Developmental Science, 13,* 849–863. (p. 121)

Delgado, J. M. R. (1969). *Physical control of the mind: Toward a psychocivilized society.* New York: Harper & Row. (p. 60)

DeLoache, J. S. (1987). Rapid change in the symbolic functioning of very young children. *Science, 238,* 1556–1557. (p. 127)

DeLoache, J. S., Chiong, C., Sherman, K., Islam, N., Vanderborght, M., Troseth, G. L., . . . O'Doherty, K. (2010). Do babies learn from baby media? *Psychological Science, 21,* 1570–1574. (p. 339)

DeLongis, A., Coyne, J. C., Dakof, G., Folkman, S., & Lazarus, R. S. (1982). Relationship of daily hassles, uplifts, and major life events to health status. *Health Psychology, 1,* 119–136. (p. 386)

DeLongis, A., Folkman, S., & Lazarus, R. S. (1988). The impact of daily stress on health and mood: Psychological and social resources as mediators. *Journal of Personality and Social Psychology, 54,* 486–495. (p. 386)

DelPriore, D. J., Schlomer, G. L., & Ellis, B. J. (2017). Impact of fathers on parental monitoring of daughters and their affiliation with sexually promiscuous peers: A genetically and environmentally controlled sibling study. *Developmental Psychology, 53,* 1330–1343. (p. 135)

Dement, W. C. (1978). *Some must watch while some must sleep.* New York: Norton. (p. 87)

Dement, W. C. (1999). *The promise of sleep.* New York: Delacorte Press. (pp. 88, 90, 92, 93)

Dement, W. C., & Wolpert, E. A. (1958). The relation of eye movements, body mobility, and external stimuli to dream content. *Journal of Experimental Psychology, 55,* 543–553. (p. 97)

Demir, E., & Dickson, B. J. (2005). *fruitless* splicing specifies male courtship behavior in *Drosophila. Cell, 121,* 785–794. (p. 181)

Dempster, E., Viana, J., Pidsley, R., & Mill, J. (2013). Epigenetic studies of schizophrenia: Progress, predicaments, and promises for the future. *Schizophrenia Bulletin, 39,* 11–16. (p. 526)

Denissen, J. J. A., Bleidorn, W., Hennecke, M., Luhmann, M., Orth, U., Specht, J., & Zimmermann, J. (2017). Uncovering the power of personality to shape income. *Psychological Science, 29,* 3–13. (p. B-3)

Denissen, J. J. A., Bleidorn, W., Hennecke, M., Luhmann, M., Orth, U., Specht, J., & Zimmermann, J. (2018). Uncovering the power of personality to shape income. *Psychological Science.* Advance online publication. doi:10.1177/0956797617724435 (p. 483)

Dennehy, T. C., & Dasgupta, N. (2017). Female peer mentors early in college increase women's positive academic experiences and retention in engineering. *PNAS, 114,* 5964–5969. (p. 168)

Denny, B. T., Inhoff, M. C., Zerubavel, N., Davachi, L., & Ochsner, K. N. (2015). Getting over it: Long-lasting effects of emotion regulation on amygdala response. *Psychological Science, 26,* 1377–1388. (p. 371)

Denton, K., & Krebs, D. (1990). From the scene to the crime: The effect of alcohol and social context on moral judgment. *Journal of Personality and Social Psychology, 59,* 242–248. (p. 103)

Depla, M. F. I. A., ten Have, M. L., van Balkom, A. J. L. M., & de Graaf, R. (2008). Specific fears and phobias in the general population: Results from the Netherlands Mental Health Survey and Incidence Study (NEMESIS). *Social Psychiatry and Psychiatric Epidemiology, 43,* 200–208. (p. 508)

Dermer, M., Cohen, S. J., Jacobsen, E., & Anderson, E. A. (1979). Evaluative judgments of aspects of life as a function of vicarious exposure to hedonic extremes. *Journal of Personality and Social Psychology, 37,* 247–260. (p. 411)

Desikan, R. S., Cabral, H. J., Hess, C. P., Dillon, W. P., Glastonbury, C. M., Weiner, M. W., & Fischl, B. (2009). Automated MRI measures identify individuals with mild cognitive impairment and Alzheimer's disease. *Brain, 132,* 2048–2057. (p. 266)

DeSteno, D., Petty, R. E., Wegener, D. T., & Rucker, D. D. (2000). Beyond valence in the perception of likelihood: The role of emotion specificity. *Journal of Personality and Social Psychology, 78,* 397–416. (p. 281)

Dettman, S. J., Pinder, D., Briggs, R. J. S., Dowell, R. C., & Leigh, J. R. (2007). Communication development in children who receive the cochlear implant younger than 12 months: Risk versus benefits. *Ear and Hearing, 28*(2, Suppl.), 11S–18S. (p. 218)

Deutsch, J. A. (1972, July). Brain reward: ESP and ecstasy. *Psychology Today,* 46–48. (p. 56)

DeValois, R. L., & DeValois, K. K. (1975). Neural coding of color. In E. C. Carterette & M. P. Friedman (Eds.), *Handbook of perception: Vol. 5. Seeing* (pp. 117–166). New York: Academic Press. (p. 204)

Devilly, G. J. (2003). Eye movement desensitization and reprocessing: A chronology of its development and scientific standing. *Scientific Review of Mental Health Practice, 1,* 113–118. (p. 554)

Dew, M. A., Hoch, C. C., Buysse, D. J., Monk, T. H., Begley, A. E., Houck, P. R., . . . Reynolds, C. F., III. (2003). Healthy older adults' sleep predicts all-cause mortality at 4 to 19 years of follow-up. *Psychosomatic Medicine, 65,* 63–73. (p. 93)

DeWall, C. N., MacDonald, G., Webster, G. D., Masten, C. L., Baumeister, R. F., Powell, C., . . . Eisenberger, N. I. (2010). Acetaminophen reduces social pain: Behavioral and neural evidence. *Psychological Science, 21,* 931–937. (p. 354)

DeWall, C. N., & Pond, R. S., Jr. (2011). Loneliness and smoking: The costs of the desire to reconnect. *Self and Identity, 10,* 375–385. (p. 111)

DeWall, C. N., Pond, R. S., Jr., Campbell, W. K., & Twenge, J. M. (2011). Tuning in to psychological change: Linguistic markers of psychological traits and emotions over time in popular U.S. song lyrics. *Psychology of Aesthetics, Creativity, and the Arts, 5,* 200–207. (p. 136)

DeWall, C. N., Pond, R. S., Jr., Carter, E. C., McCullough, M. E., Lambert, N. M., Fincham, F. D., & Nezlek, J. B. (2014). Explaining the relationship between religiousness and substance use: Self-control matters. *Journal of Personality and Social Psychology, 107,* 339–351. (pp. 112, 406)

Dewar, M., Alber, J., Butler, C., Cowan, N., & Sala, S. D. (2012). Brief wakeful resting boosts new memories over the long term. *Psychological Science, 23,* 955–960. (p. 295)

DeYoung, C. G., Hirsch, J. B., Shane, M. S., Papademetris, X., Rajeevan, N., & Gray, J. R. (2010). Testing predictions from personality neuroscience: Brain structure and the Big Five. *Psychological Science, 21,* 820–828. (p. 478)

Di Tella, R., Haisken-De New, J., & MacCulloch, R. (2010). Happiness adaptation to income and to status in an individual panel. *Journal of Economic Behavior & Organization, 76,* 834–852. (p. 410)

Di Tella, R., & MacCulloch, R. (2010). Happiness adaptation to income beyond "basic needs." In E. Diener, J. Helliwell, & D. Kahneman (Eds.), *International differences in well-being,* pp. 217–247. New York: Oxford University Press. (p. 410)

Diaconis, P. (2002, August 11). Quoted by L. Belkin, The odds of that. *The New York Times* (nytimes.com). (p. 17)

Diaconis, P., & Mosteller, F. (1989). Methods for studying coincidences. *Journal of the American Statistical Association, 84,* 853–861. (p. 17)

Dick, D. M. (2007). Identification of genes influencing a spectrum of externalizing psychopathology. *Current Directions in Psychological Science, 16,* 331–335. (p. 530)

Dickens, W. T., & Flynn, J. R. (2006). Black Americans reduce the racial IQ gap: Evidence from standardization samples. *Psychological Science, 17,* 913–920. (p. 342)

Dickerson, S. S., & Kemeny, M. E. (2004). Acute stressors and cortisol responses: A theoretical integration and synthesis of laboratory research. *Psychological Bulletin, 130,* 355–391. (pp. 386, 396)

Dickson, B. J. (2005, June 3). Quoted in E. Rosenthal, For fruit flies, gene shift tilts sex orientation. *The New York Times* (nytimes.com). (p. 181)

Dickson, N., van Roode, T., Cameron, C., & Paul, C. (2013). Stability and change in same-sex attraction, experience, and identity by sex and age in a New Zealand birth cohort. *Archives of Sexual Behavior, 42,* 753–763. (p. 179)

Diener, E. (2006). Guidelines of national indicators of subjective well-being and ill-being. *Journal of Happiness Studies, 7,* 397–404. (p. 412)

Diener, E. (2013). The remarkable changes in the science of well-being. *Perspectives on Psychological Science, 8,* 663–666. (p. 412)

Diener, E., & Biswas-Diener, R. (2008). *Happiness: Unlocking the mysteries of psychological wealth.* Malden, MA: Blackwell. (p. 410)

Diener, E., Nickerson, C., Lucas, R. E., & Sandvik, E. (2002). Dispositional affect and job outcomes. *Social Indicators Research, 59,* 229–259. (p. 407)

Diener, E., & Oishi, S. (2000). Money and happiness: Income and subjective well-being across nations. In E. Diener & E. M. Suh (Eds.), *Subjective well-being across cultures.* Cambridge, MA: MIT Press. (p. 410)

Diener, E., Oishi, S., & Lucas, R. E. (2003). Personality, culture, and subjective well-being: Emotional and cognitive evaluations of life. *Annual Review of Psychology, 54,* 403–425. (p. 411)

Diener, E., Oishi, S., & Lucas, R. E. (2009). Subjective well-being: The science of happiness and life satisfaction. In S. J. Lopez & C. R. Snyder (Eds.), *The Oxford handbook of positive psychology* (2nd ed., pp. 187–194). New York: Oxford University Press. (p. 412)

Diener, E., Oishi, S., & Lucas, R. E. (2015). National accounts of subjective well-being. *American Psychologist, 70,* 234–242. (p. 412)

Diener, E., Oishi, S., & Park, J. Y. (2014). An incomplete list of eminent psychologists of the modern era. *Archives of Scientific Psychology, 21,* 20–31. (p. 258)

Diener, E., Pressman, S. D., Hunter, J., & Delgadillo-Chase, D. (2017). If, why, and when subjective well-being influences health, and future needed research. *Applied Psychology: Health and Well-Being, 9*(2), 133–167. (p. 392)

Diener, E., & Seligman, M. E. P. (2002). Very happy people. *Psychological Science, 13,* 81–84. (p. 352)

Diener, E., & Tay, L. (2015). Subjective well-being and human welfare around the world as reflected in the Gallup world poll. *International Journal of Psychology, 50,* 135–149. (p. 409)

Diener, E., Tay, L., & Myers, D. G. (2011). The religion paradox: If religion makes people happy, why are so many dropping out? *Journal of Personality and Social Psychology, 101,* 1278–1290. (pp. 23, 411)

Diener, E., Wolsic, B., & Fujita, F. (1995). Physical attractiveness and subjective well-being. *Journal of Personality and Social Psychology, 69,* 120–129. (p. 449)

DiFranza, J. R. (2008, May). Hooked from the first cigarette. *Scientific American,* pp. 82–87. (p. 105)

Dijksterhuis, A., & Aarts, H. (2003). On wildebeests and humans: The preferential detection of negative stimuli. *Psychological Science, 14*, 14–18. (p. 376)

Dijksterhuis, A., & Strick, M. (2016). A case for thinking without consciousness. *Perspectives on Psychological Science, 11*, 117–132. (p. 305)

Dik, B. J., & Duffy, R. D. (2012). *Make your job a calling: How the psychology of vocation can change your life at work.* Conshohocken, PA: Templeton Press. (p. B-1)

Dik, B. J., & Rottinghaus, P. J. (2013). Assessments of interests. In K. F. Geisinger & six others (Eds.). *APA handbook of testing and assessment in psychology, Vol. 2.* Washington, DC: APA. (p. B-3)

DiLalla, D. L., Carey, G., Gottesman, I. I., & Bouchard, T. J., Jr. (1996). Heritability of MMPI personality indicators of psychopathology in twins reared apart. *Journal of Abnormal Psychology, 105*, 491–499. (p. 518)

Dimberg, U., Thunberg, M., & Elmehed, K. (2000). Unconscious facial reactions to emotional facial expressions. *Psychological Science, 11*, 86–89. (pp. 370, 382)

Dimidjian, S., & Hollon, S. D. (2010). How would we know if psychotherapy were harmful? *American Psychologist, 65*, 21–33. (p. 554)

Ding, F., O'Donnell, J., Xu, Q., Kang, N., Goldman, N., & Nedergaard, M. (2016). Changes in the composition of brain interstitial ions control the sleep-wake cycle. *Science, 352*, 550–555. (p. 91)

Dinges, C. W., Varnon, C. A., Cota, L. D., Slykerman, S., & Abramson, C. I. (2017). Studies of learned helplessness in honey bees (*Apis mellifera ligustica*). *Journal of Experimental Psychology: Animal Learning and Cognition, 43*, 147–158. (p. 31)

Dinges, N. G., & Hull, P. (1992). Personality, culture, and international studies. In D. Lieberman (Ed.), *Revealing the world: An interdisciplinary reader for international studies.* Dubuque, IA: Kendall-Hunt. (p. 319)

Dingfelder, S. F. (2010, November). A second chance for the Mexican wolf. *Monitor on Psychology*, pp. 20–21. (pp. 255, 542)

Dion, K. K., & Dion, K. L. (1993). Individualistic and collectivistic perspectives on gender and the cultural context of love and intimacy. *Journal of Social Issues, 49*, 53–69. (p. 491)

Dirix, C. E. H., Nijhuis, J. G., Jongsma, H. W., & Hornstra, G. (2009). Aspects of fetal learning and memory. *Child Development, 80*, 1251–1258. (p. 120)

DiSantis, K. I., Birch, L. L., Davey, A., Serrano, E. L., Zhang, J., Bruton, Y., & Fisher, J. O. (2013). Plate size and children's appetite: Effects of larger dishware on self-served portions and intake. *Pediatrics, 131*, e1451–e1458. (p. 364)

Discover. (1996, May). A fistful of risks, pp. 82–83. (p. 105)

Ditre, J. W., Brandon, T. H., Zale, E. L., & Meagher, M. M. (2011). Pain, nicotine, and smoking: Research findings and mechanistic considerations. *Psychological Bulletin, 137*, 1065–1093. (p. 105)

Ditto, P., Wojcik, S., Chen, E., Grady, R., & Ringel, M. (2015). Political bias is tenacious. *Behavioral and Brain Sciences, 38.* doi:10.1017/S0140525X14001186 (p. 18)

Dixon, J., Durrheim, K., & Tredoux, C. (2007). Intergroup contact and attitudes toward the principle and practice of racial equality. *Psychological Science, 18*, 867–872. (p. 457)

Dobbs, D. (2009). The post-traumatic stress trap. *Scientific American, 300*, 64–69. (p. 510)

Dodge, K. A. (2009). Mechanisms of gene-environment interaction effects in the development of conduct disorder. *Perspectives on Psychological Science, 4*, 408–414. (p. 530)

Dodge, K. A., Bai, Y., Ladd, H. F., & Muschkin, C. G. (2017). Impact of North Carolina's early childhood programs and policies on educational outcomes in elementary school. *Child Development, 88*(3), 996–1014. (p. 339)

Doherty, C., & Kiley, J. (2016, June 22). Key facts about partisanship and political animosity in America. Pew Research (pewresearch.org). (p. 431)

Doherty, E. W., & Doherty, W. J. (1998). Smoke gets in your eyes: Cigarette smoking and divorce in a national sample of American adults. *Families, Systems, and Health, 16*, 393–400. (p. 106)

Dohrenwend, B. P., Levav, I., Shrout, P. E., Schwartz, S., Naveh, G., Link, B. G., Skodol, A., . . . Stueve, A. (1992). Socioeconomic status and psychiatric disorders: The causation-selection issue. *Science, 255*, 946–952. (p. 505)

Dohrenwend, B. P., Pearlin, L., Clayton, P., Hamburg, B., Dohrenwend, B. P., Riley, M., & Rose, R. (1982). Report on stress and life events. In G. R. Elliott & C. Eisdorfer (Eds.), *Stress and human health: Analysis and implications of research* (A study by the Institute of Medicine/National Academy of Sciences). New York: Springer. (p. 385)

DOL. (2015). *Women in labor force.* U.S. Department of Labor. Retrieved from dol.gov/wb/stats/facts_over_time.htm (p. 168)

Dolezal, H. (1982). *Living in a world transformed.* New York: Academic Press. (p. 214)

Dolinoy, D. C., Huang, D., & Jirtle, R. L. (2007). Maternal nutrient supplementation counteracts bisphenol A-induced DNA hypomethylation in early development. *Proceedings of the National Academic of Sciences of the United States of America, 104*, 13056–13061. (p. 74)

Doliński, D., Grzyb, T., Folwarczny, M., Grzybała, P., Krzyszycha, K., Martynowska, K., & Trojanowski, J. (2017). Would you deliver an electric shock in 2015? Obedience in the experimental paradigm developed by Stanley Milgram in the 50 years following the original studies. *Social Psychological and Personality Science, 8.* doi:10.1177/1948550617693060 (p. 426)

Dollfus, S., Lecardeur, L., Morello, R., & Etard, O. (2016). Placebo response in repetitive transcranial magnetic stimulation trials of auditory hallucinations in schizophrenia: A meta-analysis. *Schizophrenia Bulletin, 42*, 301–308. (p. 27)

Domhoff, G. W. (1996). *Finding meaning in dreams: A quantitative approach.* New York: Plenum. (p. 96)

Domhoff, G. W. (2003). *The scientific study of dreams: Neural networks, cognitive development, and content analysis.* Washington, DC: American Psychological Association. (pp. 97, 99)

Domhoff, G. W. (2007). Realistic simulations and bizarreness in dream content: Past findings and suggestions for future research. In D. Barrett & P. McNamara (Eds.), *The new science of dreaming: Content, recall, and personality characteristics* (Vol. 2, pp. 1–27). Westport, CT: Praeger. (p. 96)

Domhoff, G. W. (2010). *The case for a cognitive theory of dreams.* Retrieved from http://www2.ucsc.edu/dreams/Library/domhoff_2010a.html (p. 99)

Domhoff, G. W. (2011). The neural substrate for dreaming: Is it a subsystem of the default network? *Consciousness and Cognition, 20*, 1163–1174. (p. 99)

Domjan, M. (1992). Adult learning and mate choice: Possibilities and experimental evidence. *American Zoologist, 32*, 48–61. (p. 238)

Domjan, M. (1994). Formulation of a behavior system for sexual conditioning. *Psychonomic Bulletin & Review, 1*, 421–428. (p. 238)

Domjan, M. (2005). Pavlovian conditioning: A functional perspective. *Annual Review of Psychology, 56*, 179–206. (p. 238)

Donnellan, M. B., Trzesniewski, K. H., Robins, R. W., Moffitt, T. E., & Caspi, A. (2005). Low self-esteem is related to aggression, antisocial behavior, and delinquency. *Psychological Science, 16*, 328–335. (p. 489)

Donnerstein, E. (1998). *Why do we have those new ratings on television?* Invited address to the National Institute on the Teaching of Psychology. (p. 262)

Donnerstein, E. (2011). The media and aggression: From TV to the internet. In J. Forgas, A. Kruglanski, & K. Williams (Eds.), *The psychology of social conflict and aggression.* New York: Psychology Press. (p. 262)

Dorfman, P., Javidan, M., Hanges, P., Dastmalchian, A., & House, R. (2012). GLOBE: A twenty year journey into the intriguing world of culture and leadership. *Journal of World Business, 47*, 504–518. (p. B-12)

Doss, B. D., Rhoades, G. K., Stanley, S. M., & Markman, H. J. (2009). The effect of the transition to parenthood on relationship quality: An 8-year prospective study. *Journal of Personality and Social Psychology, 96*, 601–619. (p. 157)

Dotan-Eliaz, O., Sommer, K. L., & Rubin, S. (2009). Multilingual groups: Effects of linguistic ostracism on felt rejection and anger, coworker attraction, perceived team potency, and creative performance. *Basic and Applied Social Psychology, 31*, 363–375. (p. 354)

Doty, R. L. (2001). Olfaction. *Annual Review of Psychology, 52*, 423–452. (p. 227)

Douglas, K. S., Guy, L. S., & Hart, S. D. (2009). Psychosis as a risk factor for violence to others: A meta-analysis. *Psychological Bulletin, 135*, 679–706. (p. 502)

Dovidio, J. F., & Gaertner, S. L. (1999). Reducing prejudice: Combating intergroup biases. *Current Directions in Psychological Science, 8*, 101–105. (p. 458)

Dovidio, J. F., ten Vergert, M., Stewart, T. L., Gaertner, S. L., Johnson, J. D., Esses, V. M., . . . Pearson, A. R. (2004). Perspective and prejudice: Antecedents and mediating mechanisms. *Personality and Social Psychology Bulletin, 30*, 1537–1549. (p. 458)

Downing, P. E., Jiang, Y., & Shuman, M. (2001). A cortical area selective for visual processing of the human body. *Science, 293*, 2470–2473. (p. 205)

Downs, E., & Smith, S. L. (2010). Keeping abreast of hypersexuality: A video game character content analysis. *Sex Roles, 62*, 721–733. (p. 177)

Doyle, R. (2005, March). Gay and lesbian census. *Scientific American*, p. 28. (p. 183)

Draganski, B., Gaser, C., Busch, V., Schuierer, G., Bogdahn, U., & May, A. (2004). Neuroplasticity: Changes in grey matter induced by training. *Nature, 427*, 311–312. (p. 39)

Draguns, J. G. (1990). Normal and abnormal behavior in cross-cultural perspective: Specifying the nature of their relationship. *Nebraska Symposium on Motivation 1989, 37*, 235–277. (p. 521)

Drake, B., & Poushter, J. (2016, July 12). In views of diversity, many Europeans are less positive than Americans. Pew Research Center (pewresearch.org). (p. 436)

Drescher, A., & Schultheiss, O. C. (2016). Meta-analytic evidence for higher implicit affiliation and intimacy motivation scores in women, compared to men. *Journal of Research in Personality, 64*, 1–10. (p. 467)

Drew, T., Võ, M. L.-H., & Wolfe, J. M. (2013). The invisible gorilla strikes again: Sustained inattentional blindness in expert observers. *Psychological Science, 24*, 1848–1853. (pp. 82, 83)

Drewelies, J., Wagner, J., Tesch-Römer, C., Heckhausen, J., & Gerstorf, D. (2017). Perceived control across the second half of life: The role of physical health and social integration. *Psychology and Aging, 32*, 76–92. (p. 396)

Driessen, E., Cuijpers, P., de Maat, S. C. M., Abbas, A. A., de Jonghe, F., & Dekker, J. J. M. (2010). The efficacy of short-term psychodynamic psychotherapy for depression: A meta-analysis. *Clinical Psychology Review, 30*, 25–36. (p. 553)

Driessen, E., Hollon, S. D., Bockting, C. L. H., Cuijpers, P., & Turner, E. H. (2015, September 30). Does publican bias inflate the apparent efficacy of psychological treatment for major depressive disorder? A systematic review and meta-analysis of U.S. National Institutes of Health-funded trials. *PLoS ONE 10*, e0137864. (p. 552)

Driessen, E., Van, H. L., Peen, J., Don, F. J., Twisk, J. W. R., Cuijpers, P., & Dekker, J. J. M. (2017). Cognitive-behavioral versus psychodynamic therapy for major depression: Secondary outcomes of a randomized clinical trial. *Journal of Consulting and Clinical Psychology, 85*, 653–663. (p. 553)

Drummond, S. (2010). *Relationship between changes in sleep and memory in older adults.* Presentation at AAAS 2010 Annual Meeting, University of California, San Diego, CA. (p. 92)

Drydakis, N. (2009). Sexual orientation discrimination in the labour market. *Labour Economics, 16*, 364–372. (p. 437)

Drydakis, N. (2015). Sexual orientation discrimination in the United Kingdom's labour market: A field experiment. *Human Relations, 68*, 1769–1796. (p. 437)

Duckworth, A. (2016). *Grit: The power of passion and perseverance.* New York: Scribner. (p. 358)

Duckworth, A. L., Gendler, T. S., & Gross, J. J. (2016). Situational strategies for self-control. *Perspectives on Psychological Science, 11*, 35–55. (p. 359)

Duckworth, A. L., Quinn, P. D., Lynam, D. R., Loeber, R., & Stouthamer-Loeber, M. (2011). Role of test motivation in intelligence testing. *PNAS, 108*, 7716–7720. (p. 339)

Duckworth, A. L., & Seligman, M. E. P. (2005). Discipline outdoes talent: Self-discipline predicts academic performance in adolescents. *Psychological Science, 12*, 939–944. (pp. 357, 398)

Duckworth, A. L., & Seligman, M. E. P. (2006). Self-discipline gives girls the edge: Gender in self-discipline, grades, and achievement tests. *Journal of Educational Psychology, 98*, 198–208. (p. 357)

Duckworth, A. L., Tsukayama, E., & Kirby, T. A. (2013). Is it really self-control? Examining the predictive power of the delay of gratification task. *Personality and Social Psychology Bulletin, 39*, 843–855. (p. 486)

Duclos, S. E., Laird, J. D., Sexter, M., Stern, L., & Van Lighten, O. (1989). Emotion-specific effects of facial expressions and postures on emotional experience. *Journal of Personality and Social Psychology, 57*, 100–108. (p. 381)

Dugan, A. (2015, June 19). *Men, women differ on morals of sex, relationships.* Gallup Poll (gallup.com). (p. 184)

Duggan, J. P., & Booth, D. A. (1986). Obesity, overeating, and rapid gastric emptying in rats with ventromedial hypothalamic lesions. *Science, 231*, 609–611. (p. 362)

Duits, P., Cath, D. C., Lissek, S., Hox, J. J., Hamm, A. O., Engelhard, I. M., . . . Baas, J. M. P. (2015). Updated meta-analysis of classical fear conditioning in the anxiety disorders. *Depression and Anxiety, 32*, 239–253. (p. 510)

Dumont, K. A., Widom, C. S., & Czaja, S. J. (2007). Predictors of resilience in abused and neglected children grown-up: The role of individual and neighborhood characteristics. *Child Abuse & Neglect, 31*, 255–274. (p. 137)

Dunbar, R. I. M., Baron, R., Frangou, A., Pearce, E., van Leeuwin, E. J. C., Stow, J., . . . van Vugt, M. (2011). Social laughter is correlated with an elevated pain threshold. *Proceedings of the Royal Society B, 279*, 1161–1167. (p. 399)

Duncan, L., Yilmaz, Z., Gaspar, H., Walters, R., Goldstein, J., Anttila, V., . . . Bulik, C. M. (2017). Significant locus and metabolic genetic correlations revealed in genome-wide association study of anorexia nervosa. *The American Journal of Psychiatry, 174*, 850–858. (pp. 510, 532)

Dunlop, W. L., & Tracy, J. L. (2013). Sobering stories: Narratives of self-redemption predict behavioral change and improved health among recovering alcoholics. *Journal of Personality and Social Psychology, 104*, 576–590. (p.548)

Dunn, E., & Norton, M. (2013). *Happy money: The science of smarter spending.* New York: Simon & Schuster. (p. 454)

Dunn, E. W., Aknin, L. B., & Norton, M. I. (2008). Spending money on others promotes happiness. *Science, 319*, 1687–1688. (p. 454)

Dunn, E. W., Aknin, L. B., & Norton, M. I. (2014). Pro-social spending and happiness: Using money to benefit others pays off. *Current Directions in Psychological Science, 13*, 347–355. (p. 407)

Dunn, M., & Searle, R. (2010). Effect of manipulated prestige-car ownership on both sex attractiveness ratings. *British Journal of Psychology, 101*, 69–80. (p. 184)

Dunsmoor, J. E., Murty, V. P., Davachi, L., & Phelps, E. A. (2015). Emotional learning selectively and retroactively strengthens memories for related events. *Nature, 520*, 345–348. (p. 278)

Dunson, D. B., Colombo, B., & Baird, D. D. (2002). Changes with age in the level and duration of fertility in the menstrual cycle. *Human Reproduction, 17*, 1399–1403. (p. 151)

Dunster-Page, C., Haddock, G., Wainwright, L., & Berry, K. (2017). The relationship between therapeutic alliance and patient's suicidal thoughts, self-harming behaviours and suicide attempts: A systematic review. *Journal of Affective Disorders, 223*, 165–174. (p. 555)

Dutton, D. G., & Aron, A. P. (1974). Some evidence for heightened sexual attraction under conditions of high anxiety. *Journal of Personality and Social Psychology, 30*, 510–517. (p. 451)

Dutton, D. G., & Aron, A. P. (1989). Romantic attraction and generalized liking for others who are sources of conflict-based arousal. *Canadian Journal of Behavioural Sciences, 21*, 246–257. (p. 451)

Dweck, C. S. (2012a). Implicit theories. In P. A. M. Van Lange, A. Kruglanski, & E. T. Higgins (Eds.), *Handbook of theories of social psychology* (Vol. 2, pp. 43–61). Thousand Oaks, CA: Sage. (p. 339)

Dweck, C. S. (2012b). Mindsets and human nature: Promoting change in the Middle East, the schoolyard, the racial divide, and willpower. *American Psychologist, 67*, 614–622. (p. 339)

Dweck, C. S. (2015, January 1). The secret to raising smart kids. *Scientific American.* Retrieved from scientificamerican.com/article/the-secret-to-raising-smart-kids1/ (p. 339)

Dyrdal, G. M., & Lucas, R. E. (2011). *Reaction and adaptation to the birth of a child: A couple level analysis.* Unpublished manuscript, Michigan State University, East Lansing, MI. (p. 155)

Eagen, K., Stolzenberg, E. B., Bates, A. K., Aragon, M. C. Suchard, M. R., & Rios-Aguilar, C. R. (2016). *The American freshman: National norms 2015.* Los Angeles, Higher Education Research Institute, UCLA. (p. 409)

Eagan, K., Stolzenberg, E. B., Ramirez, J. J., Aragon, M. C., Suchard, M. R., & Hurtado, S. (2014). *The American freshman: National norms fall 2014.* Los Angeles: UCLA Higher Education Research Institute. (p. 355)

Eagleman, D. (2011, September). Secret life of the mind. *Discover*, pp. 50–53. (p. 84)

Eagly, A. H. (2007). Female leadership advantage and disadvantage: Resolving the contradictions. *Psychology of Women Quarterly, 31*, 1–12. (p. B-10)

Eagly, A. H. (2009). The his and hers of prosocial behavior: An examination of the social psychology of gender. *American Psychologist, 64*, 644–658. (p. 185)

Eagly, A. H. (2013, March 20). Hybrid style works, and women are best at it. *The New York Times* (nytimes.com). (p. B-10)

Eagly, A. H., Ashmore, R. D., Makhijani, M. G., & Kennedy, L. C. (1991). What is beautiful is good, but . . .: A meta-analytic review of research on the physical attractiveness stereotype. *Psychological Bulletin, 110*, 109–128. (p. 449)

Eagly, A. H., & Carli, L. (2007). *Through the labyrinth: The truth about how women become leaders.* Cambridge, MA: Harvard University Press. (p. 164)

Eagly, A. H., & Wood, W. (1999). The origins of sex differences in human behavior: Evolved dispositions versus social roles. *American Psychologist, 54*, 408–423. (p. 185)

Eagly, A. H., & Wood, W. (2013). The nature–nurture debates: 25 years of challenges in understanding the psychology of gender. *Perspectives on Psychological Science, 8*, 340–357. (p. 162)

Easterlin, R. A., Morgan, R., Switek, M., & Wang, F. (2012). China's life satisfaction, 1990–2010. *PNAS, 109*, 9670–9671. (p. 410)

Eastman, C. L., Boulos, Z., Terman, M., Campbell, S. S., Dijk, D.-J., & Lewy, A. J. (1995). Light treatment for sleep disorders: Consensus report. VI. Shift work. *Journal of Biological Rhythms, 10*, 157–164. (p. 91)

Eastman, C. L., Young, M. A., Fogg, L. F., Liu, L., & Meaden, P. M. (1998). Bright light treatment of winter depression: A placebo-controlled trial. *Archives of General Psychiatry, 55*, 883–889. (p. 555)

Eastwick, P. W., & Finkel, E. J. (2008a). Speed-dating as a methodological innovation. *The Psychologist, 21*, 402–403. (p. 448)

Eastwick, P. W., & Finkel, E. J. (2008b). Sex differences in mate preferences revisited: Do people know what they initially desire in a romantic partner? *Journal of Personality and Social Psychology, 94*, 245–264. (p. 448)

Eastwick, P. W., Luchies, L. B., Finkel, E. J., & Hunt, L. L. (2014a). The many voices of Darwin's descendants: Reply to Schmitt (2014). *Psychological Bulletin, 140*, 673–681. (p. 449)

Eastwick, P. W., Luchies, L. B., Finkel, E. J., & Hunt, L. L. (2014b). The predictive validity of ideal partner preferences: A review and meta-analysis. *Psychological Bulletin, 140*, 623–665. (p. 449)

Ebbinghaus, H. (1885/1964). *Memory: A contribution to experimental psychology* (H. A. Ruger & C. E. Bussenius, Trans.). New York: Dover. (pp. 272, 286)

Eberhardt, J. L. (2005). Imaging race. *American Psychologist, 60*, 181–190. (p. 435)

Eccles, J. S., Jacobs, J. E., & Harold, R. D. (1990). Gender role stereotypes, expectancy effects, and parents' socialization of gender differences. *Journal of Social Issues, 46*, 183–201. (p. 341)

Eckensberger, L. H. (1994). Moral development and its measurement across cultures. In W. J. Lonner & R. Malpass (Eds.), *Psychology and culture* (pp. 71–78). Boston: Allyn & Bacon. (p. 144)

Eckert, E. D., Heston, L. L., & Bouchard, T. J., Jr. (1981). MZ twins reared apart: Preliminary findings of psychiatric disturbances and traits. In L. Gedda, P. Paris, & W. D. Nance (Eds.), *Twin research: Vol. 3. Pt. B. Intelligence, personality, and development.* New York: Alan Liss. (p. 511)

Eckholm, E. (2010, September 21). Woman on death row runs out of appeals. *The New York Times* (nytimes.com). (p. 331)

Ecklund-Flores, L. (1992, August). *The infant as a model for the teaching of introductory psychology.* Paper presented at the 100th Annual Convention of the American Psychological Association, Washington, DC. (p. 119)

Economist. (2001, December 20). An anthropology of happiness. *The Economist* (economist.com/world/asia). (p. 353)

Eddy, K. T., Tabri, N., Thomas, J. J., Murray, H. B., Keshaviah, A., Hastings, E., . . . Franko, D. L. (2017). Recovery from anorexia nervosa and bulimia nervosa at 22-year follow-up. *Journal of Clinical Psychiatry, 78,* 184–189. (p. 533)

Edelman, B., Luca, M., & Svirsky, D. (2017). Racial discrimination in the sharing economy: Evidence from a field experiment. *American Economic Journal: Applied Economics, 9,* 1–22. (p. 435)

Edwards, A. C., & Kendler, K. S. (2012). A twin study of depression and nicotine dependence: Shared liability or causal relationship? *Journal of Affective Disorders, 142,* 90–97. (p. 106)

Edwards, L. A. (2014). A meta-analysis of imitation abilities in individuals with autism spectrum disorders. *Autism Research, 7,* 363–380. (p. 132)

Edwards, R. R., Campbell, C., Jamison, R. N., & Wiech, K. (2009). The neurobiological underpinnings of coping with pain. *Current Directions in Psychological Science, 18,* 237–241. (p. 223)

Egan, P. J., & Mullin, M. (2012). Turning personal experience into political attitudes: The effects of local weather on Americans' perceptions about global warming. *Journal of Politics, 74,* 796–809. (p. 303)

Egeland, M., Zunszain, P. A., & Pariante, C. M. (2015). Molecular mechanisms in the regulation of adult neurogenesis during stress. *Nature Reviews Neuroscience, 16,* 189–200. (p. 64)

Eibl-Eibesfeldt, I. (1971). *Love and hate: The natural history of behavior patterns.* New York: Holt, Rinehart & Winston. (p. 378)

Eich, E. (1990). Learning during sleep. In R. B. Bootzin, J. F. Kihlstrom, & D. L. Schacter (Eds.), *Sleep and cognition* (pp. 88–108). Washington, DC: American Psychological Association. (p. 97)

Eichstaedt, J. C., Schwartz, H. A., Kern, M. L., Park, G., Labarthe, D. R., Merchant, R. M., ... Seligman, M. E. P. (2015). Psychological language on Twitter predicts county-level heart disease mortality. *Psychological Science, 26,* 159–169. (p. 22)

Ein-Dor, T., Mikulincer, M., Doron, G., & Shaver, P. R. (2010). The attachment paradox: How can so many of us (the insecure ones) have no adaptive advantages? *Perspectives on Psychological Science, 5,* 123–141. (p. 136)

Eippert, F., Finsterbush, J., Bingel, U., & Büchel, C. (2009). Direct evidence for spinal cord involvement in placebo analgesia. *Science, 326,* 404. (p. 223)

Eisenberg, D., Hunt, Speer, & Zivin, K. (2011). Mental health service utilization among college students in the United States. *The Journal of Nervous and Mental Disease, 199,* 301–308. (p. 493)

Eisenberg, N., & Lennon, R. (1983). Sex differences in empathy and related capacities. *Psychological Bulletin, 94,* 100–131. (p. 378)

Eisenberger, N. I., Master, S. L., Inagaki, T. K., Taylor, S. E., Shirinyan, D., Lieberman, M. D., & Naliboff, B. D. (2011). Attachment figures activate a safety signal-related neural region and reduce pain experience. *PNAS, 108,* 11721–11726. (p. 353)

Eisenberger, R., & Aselage, J. (2009). Incremental effects of reward on experienced performance pressure: Positive outcomes for intrinsic interest and creativity. *Journal of Organizational Behavior, 30,* 95–117. (p. 358)

Eklund, A., Nichols, T. E., & Knutsson, H. (2016). Cluster failure: Why fMRI inferences for spatial extent have inflated false-positive rates. *PNAS, 113,* 7900–7905. (p. 20)

Ekman, P. (1994). Strong evidence for universals in facial expressions: A reply to Russell's mistaken critique. *Psychological Bulletin, 115,* 268–287. (p. 378)

Ekman, P. (2016). What scientists who study emotion agree about. *Perspectives on Psychological Science, 11,* 31–34. (pp. 372, 378)

Ekman, P., & Friesen, W. V. (1971). Constants across cultures in the face and emotion. *Journal of Personality and Social Psychology, 17,* 124–129. (p. 379)

Elbogen, E. B., Dennis, P. A., & Johnson, S. C. (2016). Beyond mental illness: Targeting stronger and more direct pathways to violence. *Clinical Psychological Science, 4,* 747–759. (p. 503)

Elfenbein, H. A., & Ambady, N. (2002). On the universality and cultural specificity of emotion recognition: A meta-analysis. *Psychological Bulletin, 128,* 203–235. (p. 378)

Elias, S., Lozano, J., & Bentley, J. (2016). *How executive functioning, anxiety, and technology use impact university students' course performance.* Paper presented at the Western Psychological Association Convention. (p. 355)

Elkind, D. (1970). The origins of religion in the child. *Review of Religious Research, 12,* 35–42. (p. 143)

Elkind, D. (1978). *The child's reality: Three developmental themes.* Hillsdale, NJ: Erlbaum. (p. 143)

Elkins, G., Johnson, A., & Fisher, W. (2012). Cognitive hypnotherapy for pain management. *American Journal of Clinical Hypnosis, 54,* 294–310. (p. 224)

Ellenbogen, J. M., Hu, P. T., Payne, J. D., Titone, D., & Walker, M. P. (2007). Human relational memory requires time and sleep. *PNAS, 104,* 7723–7728. (p. 92)

Ellis, A., & Becker, I. M. (1982). *A guide to personal happiness.* North Hollywood, CA: Wilshire. (p. 242)

Ellis, B. J., Bates, J. E., Dodge, K. A., Fergusson, D. M., John, H. L., Pettit, G. S., & Woodward, L. (2003). Does father absence place daughters at special risk for early sexual activity and teenage pregnancy? *Child Development, 74,* 801–821. (p. 178)

Ellis, B. J., & Boyce, W. T. (2008). Biological sensitivity to context. *Current Directions in Psychological Science, 17,* 183–187. (p. 512)

Ellis, B. J., Schlomer, G. L., Tilley, E. H., & Butler, E. A. (2012). Impact of fathers on risky sexual behavior in daughters: A genetically and environmentally controlled sibling study. *Development and Psychopathology, 24,* 317–332. (p. 167)

Ellis, L., & Ames, M. A. (1987). Neurohormonal functioning and sexual orientation: A theory of homosexuality–heterosexuality. *Psychological Bulletin, 101,* 233–258. (p. 181)

Ellison, K. (2015, November 9). A.D.H.D. rates rise around globe, but sympathy often lags. *The New York Times* (nytimes.com). (p. 498)

Ellison-Wright, I., Glahn, D. C., Laird, A. R., Thelen, S. M., & Bullmore, E. (2008). The anatomy of first-episode and chronic schizophrenia: An anatomical likelihood estimation meta-analysis. *American Journal of Psychiatry, 165,* 1015–1023. (p. 525)

Else-Quest, N. M., Hyde, J. S., & Linn, M. C. (2010). Cross-national patterns of gender differences in mathematics: A meta-analysis. *Psychological Bulletin, 136,* 103–127. (p. 340)

Elzinga, B. M., Ardon, A. M., Heijnis, M. K., De Ruiter, M. B., Van Dyck, R., & Veltman, D. J. (2007). Neural correlates of enhanced working-memory performance in dissociative disorder: A functional MRI study. *Psychological Medicine, 37,* 235–245. (p. 529)

EMDR. (2011, February 18). E-mail correspondence from Robbie Dunton, EMDR Institute (emdr.org). (p. 554)

Emmons, S., Geisler, C., Kaplan, K. J., & Harrow, M. (1997). *Living with schizophrenia.* Muncie, IN: Taylor and Francis (Accelerated Development). (p. 493)

Empson, J. A. C., & Clarke, P. R. F. (1970). Rapid eye movements and remembering. *Nature, 227,* 287–288. (p. 97)

Endendijk, J. J., Beltz, A. M., McHale, S. M., Bryk, K., & Berenbaum, S. A. (2016). Linking prenatal androgens to gender-related attitudes, identity, and activities: Evidence from girls with congenital adrenal hyperplasia. *Archives of Sexual Behavior, 45,* 1807–1815. (p. 166)

Endler, N. S. (1982). *Holiday of darkness: A psychologist's personal journey out of his depression.* New York: Wiley. (pp. 519, 563)

Engen, T. (1987). Remembering odors and their names. *American Scientist, 75,* 497–503. (p. 227)

Engle, R. W. (2002). Working memory capacity as executive attention. *Current Directions in Psychological Science, 11,* 19–23. (p. 269)

English, T., Davis, J., Wei, M., & Gross, J. J. (2017). Homesickness and adjustment across the first year of college: A longitudinal study. *Emotion, 17,* 1–5. (p. 353)

Epley, N., & Dunning, D. (2000). Feeling "holier than thou": Are self-serving assessments produced by errors in self- or social prediction? *Journal of Personality and Social Psychology, 79,* 861–875. (p. 488)

Epley, N., Keysar, B., Van Boven, L., & Gilovich, T. (2004). Perspective taking as egocentric anchoring and adjustment. *Journal of Personality and Social Psychology, 87,* 327–339. (p. 128)

Epley, N., Savitsky, K., & Gilovich, T. (2002). Empathy neglect: Reconciling the spotlight effect and the correspondence bias. *Journal of Personality and Social Psychology, 83,* 300–312. (p. 486)

Epstein, J., Stern, E., & Silbersweig, D. (1998). Mesolimbic activity associated with psychosis in schizophrenia: Symptom-specific PET studies. In J. F McGinty (Ed.), *Advancing from the ventral striatum to the extended amygdala: Implications for neuropsychiatry and drug use: In honor of Lennart Heimer. Annals of the New York Academy of Sciences, 877,* 562–574. (p. 524)

Epstein, S. (1983a). Aggregation and beyond: Some basic issues on the prediction of behavior. *Journal of Personality, 51,* 360–392. (p. 481)

Epstein, S. (1983b). The stability of behavior across time and situations. In R. Zucker, J. Aronoff, & A. I. Rabin (Eds.), *Personality and the prediction of behavior.* San Diego: Academic Press. (p. 481)

Eranti, S. V., MacCabe, J. H., Bundy, H., & Murray, R. M. (2013). Gender difference in age at onset of schizophrenia: A meta-analysis. *Psychological Medicine, 43,* 155–167. (p. 524)

Erdelyi, M. H. (1985). *Psychoanalysis: Freud's cognitive psychology.* New York: Freeman. (p. 469)

Erdelyi, M. H. (1988). Repression, reconstruction, and defense: History and integration of the psychoanalytic and experimental frameworks. In J. Singer (Ed.), *Repression: Defense mechanism and cognitive style.* Chicago: University of Chicago Press. (p. 469)

Erdelyi, M. H. (2006). The unified theory of repression. *Behavioral and Brain Sciences, 29,* 499–551. (p. 469)

Erel, O., & Burman, B. (1995). Interrelatedness of marital relations and parent–child relations: A meta-analytic review. *Psychological Bulletin, 118,* 108–132. (p. 157)

Erickson, K. I. (2009). Aerobic fitness is associated with hippocampal volume in elderly humans. *Hippocampus, 19,* 1030–1039. (p. 153)

Erickson, K. I., Banducci, S. E., Weinstein, A. M., MacDonald, A. W., III, Ferrell, R. E., Halder, I., . . . Manuck, S. B. (2013). The brain-derived neurotrophic factor Val66Met polymorphism moderates an effect of physical activity on working memory performance. *Psychological Science, 24,* 1770–1779. (p. 153)

Erickson, M. F., & Aird, E. G. (2005). *The motherhood study: Fresh insights on mothers' attitudes and concerns.* New York: The Motherhood Project, Institute for American Values. (p. 157)

Ericsson, K. A. (2001). Attaining excellence through deliberate practice: Insights from the study of expert performance. In M. Ferrari (Ed.), *The pursuit of excellence in education.* Hillsdale, NJ: Erlbaum. (p. 357)

Ericsson, K. A. (2002). Attaining excellence through deliberate practice: Insights from the study of expert performance. In C. Desforges & R. Fox (Eds.), *Teaching and learning: The essential readings* (pp. 4–37). Malden, MA: Blackwell. (p. 325)

Ericsson, K. A. (2006). The influence of experience and deliberate practice on the development of superior expert performance. In K. A. Ericsson, N. Charness, P. J. Feltovich, & R. R. Hoffman (Eds.), *The Cambridge handbook of expertise and expert performance.* Cambridge: Cambridge University Press. (p. 357)

Ericsson, K. A. (2007). Deliberate practice and the modifiability of body and mind: Toward a science of the structure and acquisition of expert and elite performance. *International Journal of Sport Psychology, 38,* 4–34. (p. 357)

Ericsson, K. A., Cheng, X., Pan, Y., Ku, Y., Ge, Y., & Hu, Y. (2017). Memory skills mediating superior memory in a world-class memorist. *Memory, 25,* 1294–1302. (p. 266)

Ericsson, K. A., & Pool, R. (2016). *PEAK: Secrets from the New Science of Expertise.* Boston: Houghton Mifflin. (p. 325)

Ericsson, K. A., Roring, R. W., & Nandagopal, K. (2007). Giftedness and evidence for reproducibly superior performance: An account based on the expert performance framework. *High Ability Studies, 18,* 3–56. (p. 339)

Erikson, E. H. (1963). *Childhood and society.* New York: Norton. (p. 145)

Erikson, E. H. (1983, June). A conversation with Erikson (by E. Hall). *Psychology Today,* pp. 22–30. (p. 137)

Erlich, N., Lipp, O. V., & Slaughter, V. (2013). Of hissing snakes and angry voices: Human infants are differentially responsive to evolutionary fear-relevant sounds. *Developmental Science, 16,* 894–904. (p. 512)

Ermer, E., Cope, L. M., Nyalakanti, P. K., Calhoun, V. D., & Kiehl, K. A. (2012a). Aberrant paralimbic gray matter in criminal psychopathy. *Journal of Abnormal Psychology, 121,* 649–658. (p. 55)

Ermer, E., Kahn, R. E., Salovey, P., & Kiehl, K. A. (2012b). Emotional intelligence in incarcerated men with psychopathic traits. *Journal of Personality and Social Psychology, 103,* 194–204. (p. 530)

Ert, E., Yechiam, E., & Arshavsky, O. (2013). Smokers' decision making: More than mere risk taking. *PLoS ONE, 8*(7), e68064. doi:10.1371/journal.pone.0068064 (p. 145)

Ertmer, D. J., Young, N. M., & Nathani, S. (2007). Profiles of focal development in young cochlear implant recipients. *Journal of Speech, Language, and Hearing Research, 50,* 393–407. (p. 315)

Escasa, M. J., Casey, J. F., & Gray, P. B. (2011). Salivary testosterone levels in men at a U.S. sex club. *Archives of Sexual Behavior, 40,* 921–926. (p. 173)

Escobar-Chaves, S. L., Tortolero, S. R., Markham, C. M., Low, B. J., Eitel, P., & Thickstun, P. (2005). Impact of the media on adolescent sexual attitudes and behaviors. *Pediatrics, 116,* 303–326. (p. 177)

Escobedo, J. R., & Adolphs, R. (2010). Becoming a better person: Temporal remoteness biases autobiographical memories for moral events. *Emotion, 10,* 511–518. (p. 489)

Esposito, G., Yoshida, S., Ohnishi, R., Tsuneoka, Y., Rostagno, M., Yokoto, S., . . . Kuroda, K. O. (2013). Infant calming responses during maternal carrying in humans and mice. *Current Biology, 23,* 739–745. (p. 352)

Esser, J. K., & Lindoerfer, J. S. (1989). Groupthink and the space shuttle *Challenger* accident: Toward a quantitative case analysis. *Journal of Behavioral Decision Making, 2,* 167–177. (p. 433)

Esterson, A. (2001). The mythologizing of psychoanalytic history: Deception and self-deception in Freud's accounts of the seduction theory episode. *History of Psychiatry, 12,* 329–352. (p. 468)

Etkin, A., Büchel, C., & Gross, J. J. (2015). The neural bases of emotion regulation. *Nature Reviews Neuroscience, 16,* 693–700. (p. 519)

Etkin, A., & Wager, T. D. (2007). Functional neuroimaging of anxiety: A meta-analysis of emotional processing in PTSD, social anxiety disorder, and specific phobia. *American Journal of Psychiatry, 164,* 1476–1488. (p. 512)

Eurich, T. L., Krause, D. E., Cigularov, K., & Thornton, G. C., III. (2009). Assessment centers: Current practices in the United States. *Journal of Business Psychology, 24,* 387–407. (p. 484)

Euston, D. R., Tatsuno, M., & McNaughton, B. L. (2007). Fast-forward playback of recent memory sequences in prefrontal cortex during sleep. *Science, 318,* 1147–1150. (p. 277)

Evans, C. R., & Dion, K. L. (1991). Group cohesion and performance: A meta-analysis. *Small Group Research, 22,* 175–186. (p. B-10)

Evans, G. W., Palsane, M. N., & Carrere, S. (1987). Type A behavior and occupational stress: A cross-cultural study of blue-collar workers. *Journal of Personality and Social Psychology, 52,* 1002–1007. (p. 391)

Evans, J. St. B. T., & Stanovich, K. E. (2013). Dual-process theories of higher cognition: Advancing the debate. *Perspectives on Psychological Science, 8,* 223–241. (p. 84)

Evenson, K. R., Wen, F., & Herring, A. H. (2016). Associations of accelerometry-assessed and self-reported physical activity and sedentary behavior with all-cause and cardiovascular mortality among U.S. adults. *American Journal of Epidemiology, 184,* 621–632. (p. 401)

Everett, J. A. C., Caviola, L., Kahane, G., Savulescu, J., & Faber, N. S. (2015). Doing good by doing nothing? The role of social norms in explaining default effects in altruistic contexts. *European Journal of Social Psychology, 45,* 230–241. (p. 455)

Evers, A., Muñiz, J., Bartram, D., Boben, D., Egeland, J., Fernández-Hermida, J. R., . . . Urbánek, T. (2012). Testing practices in the 21st century: Developments and European psychologists' opinions. *European Psychologist, 17,* 300–319. (p. 329)

Everson, S. A., Goldberg, D. E., Kaplan, G. A., Cohen, R. D., Pukkala, E., Tuomilehto, J., & Salonen, J. T. (1996). Hopelessness and risk of mortality and incidence of myocardial infarction and cancer. *Psychosomatic Medicine, 58,* 113–121. (p. 399)

Exelmans, L., Custers, K., & Van den Bulck, J. (2015). Violent video games and delinquent behavior in adolescents: A risk factor perspective. *Aggressive Behavior, 41,* 267–279. (p. 445)

Eysenck, H. J. (1952). The effects of psychotherapy: An evaluation. *Journal of Consulting Psychology, 16,* 319–324. (p. 551)

Eysenck, H. J. (1990, April 30). An improvement on personality inventory. *Current Contents: Social and Behavioral Sciences, 22,* 20. (p. 475)

Eysenck, H. J. (1992). Four ways five factors are *not* basic. *Personality and Individual Differences, 13,* 667–673. (p. 475)

Eysenck, H. J., & Grossarth-Maticek, R. (1991). Creative novation behaviour therapy as a prophylactic treatment for cancer and coronary heart disease: Part II—Effects of treatment. *Behaviour Research and Therapy, 29,* 17–31. (p. 403)

Eysenck, H. J., Wakefield, J. A., Jr., & Friedman, A. F. (1983). Diagnosis and clinical assessment: The DSM-III. *Annual Review of Psychology, 34,* 167–193. (p. 497)

Eysenck, S. B. G., & Eysenck, H. J. (1963). The validity of questionnaire and rating assessments of extraversion and neuroticism, and their factorial stability. *British Journal of Psychology, 54,* 51–62. (p. 476)

Fabiano, G. A., Pelham, W. E., Jr., Coles, E. K., Gnagy, E. M., Chronis-Tuscano, A., & O'Connor, B. C. (2008). A meta-analysis of behavioral treatments for attention-deficit/hyperactivity disorder. *Clinical Psychology Review, 29,* 129–140. (p. 498)

Fabiansson, E. C., Denson, T. F., Moulds, M. L., Grisham, J. R., & Schira, M. M. (2012). Don't look back in anger: Neural correlates of reappraisal, analytical rumination, and angry rumination during a recall of an anger-inducing autobiographical memory. *NeuroImage, 59,* 2974–2981. (p. 394)

Fagan, J. F., & Holland, C. R. (2007). Racial equality in intelligence: Predictions from a theory of intelligence as processing. *Intelligence, 35,* 319–334. (p. 344)

Fagan, J. F., & Holland, C. R. (2009). Culture-fair prediction of academic achievement. *Intelligence, 37,* 62–67. (p. 344)

Fagundes, C. P., & Way, B. (2014). Early-life stress and adult inflammation. *Current Directions in Psychological Science, 23,* 277–283. (p. 137)

Faheem, S., Petti, V., & Mellos, G. (2017). Disruptive mood dysregulation disorder and its effect on bipolar disorder. *Annals of Clinical Psychiatry, 29*(1), e1–e8. (p. 516)

Fairbairn, C. E., & Sayette, M. A. (2014). A social-attributional analysis of alcohol response. *Psychological Bulletin, 140,* 1361–1382. (pp. 103, 104)

Fairfield, H. (2012, February 4). Girls lead in science exam, but NOT in the United States. *The New York Times* (nytimes.com). (p. 341)

Fales, M. R., Frederick, D. A., Garcia, J. R., Gildersleeve, K. A., Haselton, M. G., & Fisher, H. E. (2016). Mating markets and bargaining hands: Mate preferences for attractiveness and resources in two national US studies. *Personality and Individual Differences, 88,* 78–87. (p. 184)

Falk, C. F., Heine, S. J., Yuki, M., & Takemura, K. (2009). Why do Westerners self-enhance more than East Asians? *European Journal of Personality, 23,* 183–203. (pp. 17, 488)

Falkner, A. L., Grosenick, L., Davidson, T. J., Deisseroth, K., & Lin, D. (2016). Hypothalamic control of male aggression-seeking behavior. *Nature Neuroscience, 19,* 596–604. (p. 442)

Fan, S. P., Liberman, Z., Keysar, B., & Kinzler, K. D. (2015). The exposure advantage: Early exposure to a multilingual environment promotes effective communication. *Psychological Science, 26,* 1090–1097. (p. 320)

Fang, Z., Spaeth, A. M., Ma, N., Zhu, S., Hu, S., Goel, N., . . . Rao, H. (2015). Altered salience network connectivity predicts macronutrient intake after sleep deprivation. *Scientific Reports, 5,* Article 8215. doi:10.1038/srep08215 (p. 93)

Fanti, K. A., Vanman, E., Henrich, C. C., & Avraamides, M. N. (2009). Desensitization to media violence over a short period of time. *Aggressive Behavior, 35,* 179–187. (p. 263)

Farah, M. J., Rabinowitz, C., Quinn, G. E., & Liu, G. T. (2000). Early commitment of neural substrates for face recognition. *Cognitive Neuropsychology, 17,* 117–124. (p. 64)

Farb, N. A. S., Anderson, A. K., Mayberg, H., Bean, J., McKeon, D., & Segal, Z. V. (2010). Minding one's emotions: Mindfulness training alters the neural expression of sadness. *Emotion, 10,* 25–33. (p. 404)

Farina, A. (1982). The stigma of mental disorders. In A. G. Miller (Ed.), *In the eye of the beholder.* New York: Praeger. (pp. 495, 497)

Farnia, V., Shakeri, J., Tatari, F., Juibari, T. A., Yazdchi, K., Bajoghli, H., . . . Aghaei, A. (2014). Randomized controlled trial of aripiprazole versus risperidone for the treatment of amphetamine-induced psychosis. *The American Journal of Drug and Alcohol Abuse, 40,* 10–15. (p. 524)

Farr, R. H. (2017). Does parental sexual orientation matter? A longitudinal follow-up of adoptive families with school-age children. *Developmental Psychology, 53,* 252–264. (p. 180)

Farrington, D. P. (1991). Antisocial personality from childhood to adulthood. *The Psychologist: Bulletin of the British Psychological Society, 4,* 389–394. (p. 530)

Farsalinos, K. E., Kistler, K. A., Gillman, G., & Voudris, V. (2014). Evaluation of electronic cigarette liquids and aerosol for the presence of selected inhalation toxins. *Nicotine and Tobacco Research, 17,* 168–174. (p. 105)

Farstad, S. M., McGeown, L. M., & von Ranson, K. M. (2016). Eating disorders and personality, 2004–2016: A systematic review and meta-analysis. *Clinical Psychology Review, 46,* 91–105. (p. 532)

Fatemi, S. H., & Folsom, T. D. (2009). The neurodevelopmental hypothesis of schizophrenia, revisted. *Schizophrenia Bulletin, 35,* 528–548. (p. 525)

Fattore, L. (2016). Synthetic cannabinoids—further evidence supporting the relationship between cannabinoids and psychosis. *Biological Psychiatry, 79,* 539–548. (p. 108)

Fazel, S., & Grann, M. (2006). The population impact of severe mental illness on violent crime. *American Journal of Psychiatry, 163,* 1397–1403. (p. 503)

Fazel, S., Langstrom, N., Hjern, A., Grann, M., & Lichtenstein, P. (2009). Schizophrenia, substance abuse, and violent crime. *Journal of the American Medical Association, 301,* 2016–2023. (p. 503)

Fazel, S., Lichtenstein, P., Grann, M., Goodwin, G. M., & Långström, N. (2010). Bipolar disorder and violent crime: New evidence from population-based longitudinal studies and systematic review. *Archives of General Psychiatry, 67,* 931–938. (p. 503)

Fazio, L. K., Brashier, N. M., Payne, B. K., & Marsh, E. J. (2015). Knowledge does not protect against illusory truth. *Journal of Experimental Psychology: General, 144,* 993–1002. (pp. 16, 18)

Fedorenko, E., Scott, T. L., Brunner, P., Coon, W. G., Pritchett, B., Schalk, G., & Kanwisher, N. (2016). Neural correlate of the construction of sentence meaning. *PNAS, 113,* E6256–E6262. (p. 317)

Feeney, D. M. (1987). Human rights and animal welfare. *American Psychologist, 42,* 593–599. (p. 31)

Feigenson, L., Carey, S., & Spelke, E. (2002). Infants' discrimination of number vs. continuous extent. *Cognitive Psychology, 44,* 33–66. (p. 127)

Feinberg, M., Willer, R., Antonenko, O., & John, O. P. (2012). Liberating reason from the passions: Overriding intuitionist moral judgments through emotion reappraisal. *Psychological Science, 23,* 788–795. (p. 145)

Feinberg, M., Willer, R., & Schultz, M. (2014). Gossip and ostracism promote cooperation in groups. *Psychological Science, 25,* 656–664. (p. 352)

Feinberg, T. E., & Mallatt, J. (2016). The nature of primary consciousness: A new synthesis. *Consciousness and Cognition, 43,* 113–127. (p. 80)

Feingold, A. (1992). Good-looking people are not what we think. *Psychological Bulletin, 111,* 304–341. (p. 449)

Feingold, A., & Mazzella, R. (1998). Gender differences in body image are increasing. *Psychological Science, 9,* 190–195. (p. 532)

Feinstein, J. S., Buzza, C., Hurlemann, R., Follmer, R. L., Dahdaleh, N. S., Coryell, W. H., . . . Wemmie, J. A. (2013). Fear and panic in humans with bilateral amygdala damage. *Nature Neuroscience, 16,* 270–272. (p. 55)

Feldman, M. B., & Meyer, I. H. (2010). Comorbidity and age of onset of eating disorders in gay men, lesbians, and bisexuals. *Psychiatry Research, 180,* 126–131. (p. 532)

Feldman, R., Rosenthal, Z., & Eidelman, A. I. (2014). Maternal-preterm skin-to-skin contact enhances child physiologic organization and cognitive control across the first 10 years of life. *Biological Psychiatry, 75,* 56–64. (pp. 123, 397)

Fenigstein, A. (2015). Milgram's shock experiments and the Nazi perpetrators: A contrarian perspective on the role of obedience pressures during the Holocaust. *Theory and Psychology, 25,* 581–598. (p. 427)

Fenn, K. M., & Hambrick, D. Z. (2012). Individual differences in working memory capacity predict sleep-dependent memory consolidation. *Journal of Experimental Psychology: General, 141,* 404–410. (p. 271)

Fenton, W. S., & McGlashan, T. H. (1991). Natural history of schizophrenia subtypes: II. Positive and negative symptoms and long-term course. *Archives of General Psychiatry, 48,* 978–986. (p. 524)

Fenton, W. S., & McGlashan, T. H. (1994). Antecedents, symptom progression, and long-term outcome of the deficit syndrome in schizophrenia. *American Journal of Psychiatry, 151,* 351–356. (p. 524)

Ferguson, C. (2009, June 14). Not every child is secretly a genius. *The Chronicle Review* (chronicle.com). (p. 325)

Ferguson, C. J. (2013a). Spanking, corporal punishment and negative long-term outcomes: A meta-analytic review of longitudinal studies. *Clinical Psychology Review, 33,* 196–208. (p. 249)

Ferguson, C. J. (2013b). Violent video games and the Supreme Court: Lessons for the scientific community in the wake of *Brown v. Entertainment Merchants Association. American Psychologist, 68,* 57–74. (p. 445)

Ferguson, C. J. (2014). Is video game violence bad? *Psychologist, 27,* 324–327. (p. 445)

Ferguson, C. J. (2015). Do angry birds make for angry children? A meta-analysis of video game influences on children's and adolescents' aggression, mental health, prosocial behavior, and academic performance. *Perspectives on Psychological Science, 10,* 646–666. (pp. 445, 466)

Ferguson, C. J., Winegard, B., & Winegard, B. M. (2011). Who is the fairest one of all? How evolution guides peer and media influences on female body dissatisfaction. *Review of General Psychology, 15,* 11–28. (p. 533)

Ferguson, E. D. (1989). Adler's motivational theory: An historical perspective on belonging and the fundamental human striving. *Individual Psychology, 45,* 354–361. (p. 352)

Ferguson, E. D. (2001). Adler and Dreikurs: Cognitive-social dynamic innovators. *Journal of Individual Psychology, 57,* 324–341. (p. 352)

Ferguson, E. D. (2003). Social processes, personal goals, and their intertwining: Their importance in Adlerian theory and practice. *Journal of Individual Psychology, 59,* 136–144. (p. 466)

Ferguson, E. D. (2010). Editor's notes: Adler's innovative contributions regarding the need to belong. *Journal of Individual Psychology, 66,* 1–7. (p. 352)

Ferguson, M. J., & Zayas, V. (2009). Automatic evaluation. *Current Directions in Psychological Science, 18,* 362–366. (pp. 192, 193)

Fergusson, D. M., Boden, J. M., & Horwood, L. J. (2009). Tests of causal links between alcohol abuse or dependence and major depression. *Archives of General Psychiatry, 66,* 260–266. (p. 519)

Fernández-Dols, J.-M., & Ruiz-Belda, M.-A. (1995). Are smiles a sign of happiness? Gold medal winners at the Olympic Games. *Journal of Personality and Social Psychology, 69,* 1113–1119. (p. 379)

Fernandez-Duque, E., Evans, J., Christian, C., & Hodges, S. D. (2015). Superfluous neuroscience information makes explanations of psychological phenomena more appealing *Journal of Cognitive Neuroscience, 27,* 926–944. (p. 52)

Fernbach, P. M., Rogers, T., Fox, C. R., & Sloman, S. A. (2013). Political extremism is supported by an illusion of understanding. *Psychological Science, 24,* 939–946. (p. 304)

Fernie, G., Peeters, M., Gullo, M. J., Christianson, P., Cole, J. C., Sumnall, H., & Field, M. (2013). Multiple behavioral impulsivity tasks predict prospective alcohol involvement in adolescents. *Addiction, 108,* 1916–1923. (p. 463)

Fernyhough, C. (2008). Getting Vygotskian about theory of mind: Mediation, dialogue, and the development of social understanding. *Developmental Review, 28,* 225–262. (p. 129)

Ferrari, A. J., Charlson, F. J., Norman, R. E., Patten, S. B., Freedman, G., Murray, C. J. L., . . . Whiteford, H. A. (2013). Burden of depressive disorders by country, sex, age, and year: Findings from the Global Burden of Disease Study 2010. *PLOS Medicine, 10,* e1001547. (p. 521)

Ferri, M., Amato, L., & Davoli, M. (2006). Alcoholics Anonymous and other 12-step programmes for alcohol dependence. *Cochrane Database of Systematic Reviews,* Issue 3. Art. No. CD005032. (p. 548)

Ferriman, K., Lubinski, D., & Benbow, C. P. (2009). Work preferences, life values, and personal views of top math/science graduate students and the profoundly gifted: Developmental changes and gender differences during emerging adulthood and parenthood. *Journal of Personality and Social Psychology, 97,* 517–522. (p. 165)

Ferris, C. F. (1996, March). The rage of innocents. *The Sciences*, pp. 22–26. (p. 137)

Festinger, L. (1957). *A theory of cognitive dissonance.* Stanford: Stanford University Press. (p. 420)

Fetvadjiev, V. H., Meiring, D., van de Vijver, F. J., Nel, J. A., Sekaja, L., & Laher, S. (2017). Personality and behavior prediction and consistency across cultures: A multimethod study of blacks and whites in South Africa. *Journal of Personality and Social Psychology.* Advance online publication. doi:10.1037/pspp0000129 (p. 478)

Fichter, M. M., & Quadflieg, N. (2016). Mortality in eating disorders—results of a large prospective clinical longitudinal study. *International Journal of Eating Disorders, 49*, 391–401. (p. 532)

Fiedler, F. E. (1981). Leadership effectiveness. *American Behavioral Scientist, 24*, 619–632. (p. B-10)

Fiedler, F. E. (1987, September). When to lead, when to stand back. *Psychology Today*, pp. 26–27. (p. B-10)

Field, A. P. (2006). Is conditioning a useful framework for understanding the development and treatment of phobias? *Clinical Psychology Review, 26*, 857–875. (p. 510)

Field, T., Diego, M., & Hernandez-Reif, M. (2007). Massage therapy research. *Developmental Review, 27*, 75–89. (p. 123)

Field, T., Hernandez-Reif, M., Feijo, L., & Freedman, J. (2006). Prenatal, perinatal and neonatal stimulation: A survey of neonatal nurseries. *Infant Behavior & Development, 29*, 24–31. (p. 220)

Fielder, R. L., Walsh, J. L., Carey, K. B., & Carey, M. P. (2013). Predictors of sexual hookups: A theory-based, prospective study of first-year college women. *Archives of Sexual Behavior, 42*, 1425–1441. (pp. 26, 177)

Fields, R. D. (2004, April). The other half of the brain. *Scientific American*, pp. 54–61. (p. 40)

Fields, R. D. (2008, March). White matter matters. *Scientific American*, pp. 54–61. (p. 40)

Fields, R. D. (2011, May/June). The hidden brain. *Scientific American*, pp. 53–59. (p. 40)

Fields, R. D. (2013). Neuroscience: Map the other brain. *Nature, 501*, 25–27. (p. 40)

Fincham, F. D., & Bradbury, T. N. (1993). Marital satisfaction, depression, and attributions: A longitudinal analysis. *Journal of Personality and Social Psychology, 64*, 442–452. (p. 417)

Finchilescu, G., & Tredoux, C. (Eds.) (2010). Intergroup relations in post apartheid South Africa: Change, and obstacles to change. *Journal of Social Issues, 66*, 223–236. (p. 457)

Findlay, L. (2017, January 18). *Depression and suicidal ideation among Canadians aged 15 to 24.* Statistics Canada (statcan.gc.ca/pub/82-003-x/2017001/article/14697-eng.htm). (p. 516)

Fine, C. (2010). From scanner to sound bite: Issues in interpreting and reporting sex differences in the brain. *Current Directions in Psychological Science, 19*, 280–283. (p. 52)

Finer, L. B., & Philbin, J. M. (2014). Trends in ages at key reproductive transitions in the United States, 1951–2010. *Women's Health Issues, 24*, e271–279. (p. 149)

Fingelkurts, A. A., & Fingelkurts, A. A. (2009). Is our brain hardwired to produce God, or is our brain hardwired to perceive God? A systematic review on the role of the brain in mediating religious experience. *Cognitive Processes, 10*, 293–326. (p. 63)

Fingerman, K. L., & Charles, S. T. (2010). It takes two to tango: Why older people have the best relationships. *Current Directions in Psychological Science, 19*, 172–176. (p. 158)

Fink, M. (2009). *Electroconvulsive therapy: A guide for professionals and their patients.* New York: Oxford University Press. (p. 563)

Finkel, E. J. (2017). *The all-or-nothing marriage.* New York: Dutton. (p. 156)

Finkel, E. J., DeWall, C. N., Slotter, E. B., McNulty, J. K., Pond, R. S., Jr., & Atkins, D. C. (2012a). Using I3 theory to clarify when dispositional aggressiveness predicts intimate partner violence perpetration. *Journal of Personality and Social Psychology, 102*, 533–549. (p. 448)

Finkel, E. J., & Eastwick, P. W. (2008). Speed-dating. *Current Directions in Psychological Science, 17*, 193–197. (p. 449)

Finkel, E. J., & Eastwick, P. W. (2009). Arbitrary social norms influence sex differences in romantic selectivity. *Psychological Science, 20*, 1290–1295. (p. 448)

Finkel, E. J., Eastwick, P. W., Karney, B. R., Reis, H. T., & Sprecher, S. (2012b, September/October). Dating in a digital world. *Scientific American Mind*, pp. 26–33. (p. 448)

Finkenauer, C., Buyukcan-Tetik, A., Baumeister, R. F., Schoemaker, K., Bartels, M., & Vohs, K. D. (2015). Out of control: Identifying the role of self-control strength in family violence. *Current Directions in Psychological Science, 24*, 261–266. (p. 249)

Finlay, S. W. (2000). Influence of Carl Jung and William James on the origin of alcoholics anonymous. *Review of General Psychology, 4*, 3–12. (p. 548)

Fiore, M. C., Jaén, C. R., Baker, T. B., Bailey, W. C., Benowitz, N. L., Curry, S. J., . . . Wewers, M. E. (2008, May). *Treating tobacco use and dependence: 2008 update.* Rockville, MD: U.S. Department of Health and Human Services, Public Health Service. (p. 106)

Fischer, A., & LaFrance, M. (2015). What drives the smile and the tear: Why women are more emotionally expressive than men. *Emotion Review, 7*, 22–29. (pp. 162, 377)

Fischer, P., & Greitemeyer, T. (2006). Music and aggression: The impact of sexual-aggressive song lyrics on aggression-related thoughts, emotions, and behavior toward the same and the opposite sex. *Personality and Social Psychology Bulletin, 32*, 1165–1176. (p. 444)

Fischer, P., Greitemeyer, T., Kastenmüller, A., Vogrincic, C., & Sauer, A. (2011). The effects of risk-glorifying media exposure on risk-positive cognitions, emotions, and behaviors: A meta-analytic review. *Psychological Bulletin, 137*, 367–390. (p. 444)

Fischer, R., & Boer, D. (2011). What is more important for national well-being: Money or autonomy? A meta-analysis of well-being, burnout, and anxiety across 63 societies. *Journal of Personality and Social Psychology, 101*, 164–184. (p. 409)

Fischhoff, B. (1982). Debiasing. In D. Kahneman, P. Slovic, & A. Tversky (Eds.), *Judgment under uncertainty: Heuristics and biases.* New York: Cambridge University Press. (p. 304)

Fischhoff, B., Slovic, P., & Lichtenstein, S. (1977). Knowing with certainty: The appropriateness of extreme confidence. *Journal of Experimental Psychology: Human Perception and Performance, 3*, 552–564. (p. 303)

Fishbach, A., Dhar, R., & Zhang, Y. (2006). Subgoals as substitutes or complements: The role of goal accessibility. *Journal of Personality and Social Psychology, 91*, 232–242. (p. B-9)

Fisher, G., & Rangel, A. (2014). Symmetry in cold-to-hot and hot-to-cold valuation gaps. *Psychological Science, 25*, 120–127. (p. 361)

Fisher, H. E. (1993, March/April). After all, maybe it's biology. *Psychology Today*, pp. 40–45. (p. 156)

Fisher, H. T. (1984). Little Albert and Little Peter. *Bulletin of the British Psychological Society, 37*, 269. (p. 541)

Fitzgerald, R. J., & Price, H. L. (2015). Eyewitness identification across the life span: A meta-analysis of age differences. *Psychological Bulletin, 141*, 1228–1265. (p. 294)

Flack, W. F. (2006). Peripheral feedback effects of facial expressions, bodily postures, and vocal expressions on emotional feelings. *Cognition and Emotion, 20*, 177–195. (pp. 381, 393)

Flaherty, D. K. (2011). The vaccine-autism connection: A public health crisis caused by unethical medical practices and fraudulent science. *Annals of Pharmacotherapy, 45*, 1302–1304. (p. 131)

Flegal, K. M., Carroll, M. D., Kit, B. K., & Ogden, C. L. (2012). Prevalence of obesity and trends in the distribution of body mass index among US adults, 1999–2010. *JAMA, 307.* (p. 365)

Flegal, K. M., Carroll, M. D., Ogden, C. L., & Curtin, L. R. (2010). Prevalence and trends in obesity among US adults, 1999–2008. *JAMA, 303*, 235–241. (p. 365)

Flegal, K. M., Kruszon-Moran, D., Carroll, M. D., Fryar, C. D., & Ogden, C. L. (2016). Trends in obesity among adults in the United States, 2005 to 2014. *JAMA, 315*, 2284–2291. (p. 365)

Fleischman, D. A., Yang, J., Arfanakis, K., Avanitakis, Z., Leurgans, S. E., Turner, A. D., . . . Buchman, A. S. (2015). Physical activity, motor function, and white matter hyperintensity burden in healthy older adults. *Neurology, 84*, 1294–1300. (p. 153)

Fleming, I., Baum, A., & Weiss, L. (1987). Social density and perceived control as mediator of crowding stress in high-density residential neighborhoods. *Journal of Personality and Social Psychology, 52*, 899–906. (p. 397)

Fleming, J. H., & Scott, B. A. (1991). The costs of confession: The Persian Gulf War POW tapes in historical and theoretical perspective. *Contemporary Social Psychology, 15*, 127–138. (p. 378)

Fletcher, G. J. O., Fitness, J., & Blampied, N. M. (1990). The link between attributions and happiness in close relationships: The roles of depression and explanatory style. *Journal of Social and Clinical Psychology, 9*, 243–255. (p. 417)

Flinker, A., Korzeniewska, A., Shestyuk, A. Y., Franaszczuk, P. J., Dronkers, N. F., Knight, R. T., & Crone, N. E. (2015). Redefining the role of Broca's area in speech. *PNAS, 112*, 2871–2875. (p. 317)

Flora, S. R. (2004). *The power of reinforcement.* Albany, NY: SUNY Press. (p. 250)

Flora, S. R., & Bobby, S. E. (2008, September/October). The bipolar bamboozle. *Skeptical Inquirer*, pp. 41–45. (p. 516)

Flores, A. R., Herman, J. L., Gates, G. J., & Brown, T. N. T. (2016, June). *How many adults identify as transgender in the United States?* Los Angeles: Williams Institute. (p. 171)

Flouri, E., & Buchanan, A. (2004). Early father's and mother's involvement and child's later educational outcomes. *British Journal of Educational Psychology, 74*, 141–153. (p. 135)

Flueckiger, L., Lieb, R., Meyer, A., Witthauer, C., & Mata, J. (2016). The importance of physical activity and sleep for affect on stressful days: Two intensive longitudinal studies. *Emotion, 16*, 488–497. (p. 401)

Flynn, J. R. (2012). *Are we getting smarter? Rising IQ in the twenty-first century.* Cambridge: Cambridge University Press. (p. 342)

Foa, E. B., & Kozak, M. J. (1986). Emotional processing of fear: Exposure to corrective information. *Psychological Bulletin, 99*, 20–35. (p. 541)

Foa, E. B., & McLean, C. P. (2016). The efficacy of exposure therapy for anxiety-related disorders and its underlying mechanisms: The case of OCD and PTSD. *Annual Review of Clinical Psychology, 12*, 1–28. (p. 541)

Foer, J. (2011). *Moonwalking with Einstein: The art and science of remembering everything.* New York: Penguin. (p. 272)

Foley, M. A. (2015). Setting the records straight: Impossible memories and the persistence of their phenomenological qualities. *Review of General Psychology, 19,* 230–248. (p. 291)

Foley, R. T., Whitwell, R. L., & Goodale, M. A. (2015). The two-visual-systems hypothesis and the perspectival features of visual experience. *Consciousness and Cognition, 35,* 225–233. (p. 84)

Fong, C. J., Zaleski, D. J., & Leach, J. K. (2015). The challenge–skill balance and antecedents of flow: A meta-analytic investigation. *Journal of Positive Psychology, 10,* 425–446. (p. B-2)

Fong, K., & Mar, R. A. (2015). What does my avatar say about me? Inferring personality from avatars. *Personality and Social Psychology Bulletin, 41,* 237–249. (p. 481)

Ford, E. S. (2002). Does exercise reduce inflammation? Physical activity and B-reactive protein among U.S. adults. *Epidemiology, 13,* 561–569. (p. 401)

Ford, M. T., Cerasoli, C. P., Higgins, J. A., & Deccesare, A. L. (2011). Relationships between psychological, physical, and behavioural health and work performance: A review and meta-analysis. *Work & Stress, 25,* 185–204. (p. B-8, B-9)

Foree, D. D., & LoLordo, V. M. (1973). Attention in the pigeon: Differential effects of food-getting versus shock-avoidance procedures. *Journal of Comparative and Physiological Psychology, 85,* 551–558. (p. 256)

Forest, A., & Wood, J. (2012). When social networking is not working: Individuals with low self-esteem recognize but do not reap the benefits of self-disclosure on Facebook. *Psychological Science, 23,* 295–302. (p. 486)

Forest, A. L., Kille, D. R, Wood, J. V., & Stehouwer, L. R. (2015). Turbulent times, rocky relationships: Relational consequences of experiencing physical instability. *Psychological Science, 26,* 1261–1271. (p. 229)

Forgas, J. (2017, May 14). Why bad moods are good for you: The surprising benefits of sadness. *The Conversation* (theconversation.com). (p. 514)

Forgas, J. P. (2008). Affect and cognition. *Perspectives on Psychological Science, 3,* 94–101. (p. 407)

Forgas, J. P. (2009, November/December). Think negative! *Australian Science,* pp. 14–17. (p. 514)

Forgas, J. P. (2013). Don't worry, be sad! On the cognitive, motivational, and interpersonal benefits of negative mood. *Current Directions in Psychological Science, 22,* 225–232. (p. 514)

Forgas, J. P., Bower, G. H., & Krantz, S. E. (1984). The influence of mood on perceptions of social interactions. *Journal of Experimental Social Psychology, 20,* 497–513. (p. 281)

Forman, D. R., Aksan, N., & Kochanska, G. (2004). Toddlers' responsive imitation predicts preschool-age conscience. *Psychological Science, 15,* 699–704. (p. 261)

Forsyth, D. R., Lawrence, N. K., Burnette, J. L., & Baumeister, R. F. (2007). Attempting to improve academic performance of struggling college students by bolstering their self-esteem: An intervention that backfired. *Journal of Social and Clinical Psychology, 26,* 447–459. (p. 487)

Foss, D. J., & Hakes, D. T. (1978). *Psycholinguistics: An introduction to the psychology of language.* Englewood Cliffs, NJ: Prentice-Hall. (p. 468)

Foss, D. J., & Pirozzolo, J. W. (2017). Four semesters investigating frequency of testing, the testing effect, and transfer of training. *Journal of Educational Psychology.* Advance online publication. doi:10.1037/edu0000197 (p. 33)

Foster, E., Wildner, H., Tudeau, L., Haueter, S., Ralvenius, W., Jegen, M., . . . Zeilhofer, H. (2015). Targeted ablation, silencing, and activation establish glycinergic dorsal horn neurons as key components of a spinal gate for pain and itch. *Neuron, 85,* 1289–1304.

Foster, J. (2011). Our deadly anorexic pact. *The Daily Mail* (dailymail.co.uk). (p. 532)

Fothergill, E., Guo, J., Howard, L., Kerns, J. C., Knuth, J. D., Brychta, R., . . . Hall, K. D. K. (2016). Persistent metabolic adaptation 6 years after "The Biggest Loser" competition. *Obesity, 24,* 1612–1619. (p. 365)

Foubert, J. D., Brosi, M. W., & Bannon, R. S. (2011). Pornography viewing among fraternity men: Effects on bystander intervention, rape myth acceptance, and behavioral intent to commit sexual assault. *Sexual Addiction & Compulsivity, 18,* 212–231. (p. 176)

Foulkes, D. (1999). *Children's dreaming and the development of consciousness.* Cambridge, MA: Harvard University Press. (p. 99)

Fournier, J. C., DeRubeis, R. J., Hollon, S. D., Dimidjian, S., Amsterdam, J. D., Shelton, R. C., & Fawcett, J. (2010). Antidepressant drug effects and depression severity: A patient-level meta-analysis. *Journal of the American Medical Association, 303,* 47–53. (p. 562)

Fowles, D. C. (1992). Schizophrenia: Diathesis-stress revisited. *Annual Review of Psychology, 43,* 303–336. (p. 524)

Fowles, D. C., & Dindo, L. (2009). Temperament and psychopathy: A dual-pathway model. *Current Directions in Psychological Science, 18,* 179–183. (p. 530)

Fox, A. S., Oler, J. A., Shackman, A. J., Shelton, S. E., Raveendran, M., McKay, D. R., . . . Rogers, J. (2015). Intergenerational neural mediators of early-life anxious temperament. *PNAS, 112,* 9118–9122. (p. 52)

Fox, D. (2010, June). The insanity virus. *Discover,* pp. 58–64. (p. 525)

Fox, K. C. R., Nijeboer, S., Solomonova, E., Domhoff, G. W., & Christoff, K. (2013). Dreaming as mind wandering: Evidence from functional neuroimaging and first-person content reports. *Frontiers in Human Neuroscience, 7,* Article 412. http://dx.doi.org/10.3389/fnhum.2013.00412 (p. 99)

Fox, M. L., Dwyer, D. J., & Ganster, D. C. (1993). Effects of stressful job demands and control on physiological and attitudinal outcomes in a hospital setting. *Academy of Management Journal, 36,* 289–318. (p. 397)

Fox, N. A., Bakermans-Kranenburg, M., Yoo, K. H., Bowman, L. C., Cannon, E. N., Vanderwert, R. E., . . . van IJzendoorn, M. H. (2016). Assessing human mirror activity with EEG mu rhythm: A meta-analysis. *Psychological Bulletin, 142,* 291–313. (p. 260)

Fozard, J. L., & Popkin, S. J. (1978). Optimizing adult development: Ends and means of an applied psychology of aging. *American Psychologist, 33,* 975–989. (p. 152)

Fragaszy, D. M., Eshchar, Y., Visalberghi, E., Resende, B., Laity, K., & Izar, P. (2017). Synchronized practice helps bearded capuchin monkeys learn to extend attention while learning a tradition. *PNAS, 114,* 7798–7805. (p. 259)

Fraley, R. C., Roisman, G. I., Booth-LaForce, C., Owen, M. T., & Holland, A. S. (2013). Interpersonal and genetic origins of adult attachment styles: A longitudinal study from infancy to early adulthood. *Journal of Personality and Social Psychology, 104,* 817–838. (p. 136)

Fraley, R. C., & Tancredy, C. M. (2012). Twin and sibling attachment in a nationally representative sample. *Personality and Social Psychology Bulletin, 38,* 308–316. (p. 135)

Fraley, R. C., Vicary, A. M., Brumbaugh, C. C., & Roisman, G. I. (2011). Patterns of stability in adult attachment: An empirical test of two models of continuity and change. *Journal of Personality and Social Psychology, 101,* 974–992. (p. 136)

Frances, A. J. (2013). *Saving normal: An insider's revolt against out-of-control psychiatric diagnosis, DSM-5, big pharma, and the medicalization of ordinary life.* New York: HarperCollins. (p. 497)

Frances, A. J. (2014, September/October). No child left undiagnosed. *Psychology Today,* pp. 49–50. (p. 497)

Frank, J. D. (1982). Therapeutic components shared by all psychotherapies. In J. H. Harvey & M. M. Parks (Eds.), *The Master Lecture Series: Vol. 1. Psychotherapy research and behavior change.* Washington, DC: American Psychological Association. (pp. 555, 556)

Frankel, A., Strange, D. R., & Schoonover, R. (1983). CRAP: Consumer rated assessment procedure. In G. H. Scherr & R. Liebmann-Smith (Eds.), *The best of The Journal of Irreproducible Results.* New York: Workman. (p. 477)

Frankenburg, W., Dodds, J., Archer, P., Shapiro, H., & Bresnick, B. (1992). The Denver II: A major revision and restandardization of the Denver Developmental Screening Test. *Pediatrics, 89,* 91–97. (p. 124)

Frankl, V. E. (1962). *Man's search for meaning: An introduction to logotherapy.* Boston: Beacon Press. (p. 350)

Franklin, J. C., Ribeiro, J. D., Fox, K. R., Bentley, K. H., Kleiman, E. M., Huang, X., . . . Nock, M. K. (2017). Risk factors for suicidal thoughts and behaviors: A meta-analysis of 50 years of research. *Psychological Bulletin, 143,* 187–232. (p. 501)

Franklin, M., & Foa, E. B. (2011). Treatment of obsessive-compulsive disorder. *Annual Review of Clinical Psychology, 7,* 229–243. (p. 511)

Franz, E. A., Waldie, K. E., & Smith, M. J. (2000). The effect of callosotomy on novel versus familiar bimanual actions: A neural dissociation between controlled and automatic processes? *Psychological Science, 11,* 82–85. (p. 66)

Fraser, M. A., Shaw, M. E., & Cherubin, N. (2015). A systematic review and meta-analysis of longitudinal hippocampal atrophy in healthy human ageing. *NeuroImage, 112,* 364–374. (p. 152)

Frassanito, P., & Pettorini, B. (2008). Pink and blue: The color of gender. *Child's Nervous System, 24,* 881–882. (p. 162)

Frasure-Smith, N., & Lesperance, F. (2005). Depression and coronary heart disease: Complex synergism of mind, body, and environment. *Current Directions in Psychological Science, 14,* 39–43. (p. 392)

Frattaroli, J. (2006). Experimental disclosure and its moderators: A meta-analysis. *Psychological Bulletin, 132,* 823–865. (p. 400)

Frederick, S. (2005). Cognitive reflection and decision making. *Journal of Economic Perspectives, 4,* 25–42. (p. 306)

Fredrickson, B. L. (2013). Positive emotions broaden and build. In E. Ashby Plant & P.G. Devine (Eds.), *Advances on Experimental Social Psychology, 47,* 1–3. Burlington, MA: Academic Press. (p. 407)

Fredrickson, B. L., Grewen, K. M., Coffey, K. A., Algoe, S. B., Firestine, A. M., Arevalo, J. M. G., . . . Cole, S. W. (2013). A functional genomic perspective on human well-being. *PNAS, 110,* 13684–13689. (p. 411)

Freedman, D. H. (2011, February). How to fix the obesity crisis. *Scientific American,* pp. 40–47. (p. 366)

Freedman, D. J., Riesenhuber, M., Poggio, T., & Miller, E. K. (2001). Categorical representation of visual stimuli in the primate prefrontal cortex. *Science, 291,* 312–316. (p. 309)

Freedman, J. L., & Fraser, S. C. (1966). Compliance without pressure: The foot-in-the-door technique. *Journal of Personality and Social Psychology, 4,* 195–202. (p. 419)

Freedman, J. L., & Perlick, D. (1979). Crowding, contagion, and laughter. *Journal of Experimental Social Psychology, 15,* 295–303. (p. 430)

Freedman, R., Lewis, D. A., Michels, R., Pine, D. S., Scultz, S. K., Tamminga, C. A., . . . Yager, J. (2013). The initial field trials of DSM-5: New blooms and old thorns. *American Journal of Psychiatry, 170,* 1–5. (p. 497)

Freeman, D., & Freeman, J. (2013). *The stressed sex: Uncovering the truth about men, women, and mental health.* Oxford: Oxford University Press. (p. 517)

Freeman, E. C., & Twenge, J. M. (2010, January). *Using MySpace increases the endorsement of narcissistic personality traits.* Poster presented at the annual conference of the Society for Personality and Social Psychology, Las Vegas, NV. (p. 356)

Freeman, S., Eddy, S. L., McDonough, M., Smith, M. K., Okoroafor, N., Jordt, H., & Wenderoth, M. P. (2014). Active learning increases student performance in science, engineering, and mathematics. *PNAS, 111,* 8410–8415. (p. 33)

Freeman, W. J. (1991, February). The physiology of perception. *Scientific American,* pp. 78–85. (p. 216)

Frenda, S. J., Patihis, L., Loftus, E. F., Lewis, H. C., & Fenn, K. M. (2014). Sleep deprivation and false memories. *Clinical Psychological Science, 25,* 1674–1681. (p. 295)

Freud, S. (1897, October 15). Letter of Freud to Fliess. In J. M. Masson (Ed.) (1985), *The complete letters of Sigmund Freud to Wilhelm Fleiss, 1887–1904.* Cambridge, MA: Harvard University Press. (p. 464)

Freud, S. (1935: reprinted 1960). *A general introduction to psychoanalysis.* New York: Washington Square Press. (p. 156)

Freyd, J. J., DePrince, A. P., & Gleaves, D. H. (2007). The state of betrayal trauma theory: Reply to McNally—Conceptual issues and future directions. *Memory, 15,* 295–311. (p. 293)

Friedel, J. E., DeHart, W. B., Madden, G. J., & Odum, A. L. (2014). Impulsivity and cigarette smoking: Discounting of monetary and consumable outcomes in current and non-smokers. *Psychopharmacology, 231,* 4517–4526. (p. 463)

Friedman, H. S., & Martin, L. R. (2012). *The longevity project.* New York: Penguin (Plume). (p. 331)

Friedman, M., & Ulmer, D. (1984). *Treating Type A behavior—and your heart.* New York: Knopf. (p. 391, 403)

Friedman, R., & James, J. W. (2008). The myth of the stages of dying, death and grief. *Skeptic, 14*(2), 37–41. (p. 159)

Friedman, R. A. (2012, December 17). In gun debate, a misguided focus on mental illness. *The New York Times* (nytimes.com). (p. 503)

Friedman, R. A. (2017, October 11). Psychiatrists can't stop mass killers. *The New York Times* (nytimes.com). (p. 503)

Friedrich, M., Wilhelhm, I., Born, J., & Friederici, A. D. (2015). Generalization of word meanings during infant sleep. *Nature Communications, 6,* Article 6004. doi:10.1038/ncomms7004 (p. 91)

Friend, T. (2004). *Animal talk: Breaking the codes of animal language.* New York: Free Press. (p. 318)

Friesen, J. P., Campbell, T. H., & Kay, A. C. (2015). The psychological advantage of unfalsifiability: The appeal of untestable religious and political ideologies. *Journal of Personality and Social Psychology, 108,* 515–529. (p. 304)

Frijda, N. H. (1988). The laws of emotion. *American Psychologist, 43,* 349–358. (p. 410)

Frisell, T., Pawitan, Y., Långström, N., & Lichtenstein, P. (2012). Heritability, assortative mating and gender differences in violent crime: Results from a total population sample using twin, adoption, and sibling models. *Behavior Genetics, 42,* 3–18. (pp. 163, 530)

Frith, U., & Frith, C. (2001). The biological basis of social interaction. *Current Directions in Psychological Science, 10,* 151–155. (p. 131)

Fritz, C., Curtin, J., Poitevineau, J., & Tao, F.-C. (2017). Listener evaluations of new and old Italian violins. *PNAS, 114,* 5395–5400. (p. 198)

Fromkin, V., & Rodman, R. (1983). An introduction to language (3rd ed.). New York: Holt, Rinehart & Winston. (p. 314)

Frühauf, S., Gerger, H., Schmidt, H. M., Munder, T., & Barth, J. (2013). Efficacy of psychological interventions for sexual dysfunction: A systematic review and meta-analysis. *Archives of Sexual Behavior, 42,* 915–933. (p. 175)

Fry, A. F., & Hale, S. (1996). Processing speed, working memory, and fluid intelligence: Evidence for a developmental cascade. *Psychological Science, 7,* 237–241. (p. 152)

Fry, D. P. (2012). Life without war. *Science, 336,* 879–884. (p. 458)

Fry, R. (2017, May 5). It's becoming more common for young adults to live at home—and for longer stretches. Pew Research Center (pewresearch.org). (p. 149)

FTC. (2016, January 5). *Lumosity to pay $2 million to settle FTC deceptive advertising charges for its "brain training" program.* Press release. Federal Trade Commission (ftc.gov/news-events/press-releases/2016/01/lumosity-pay-2-million-settle-ftc-deceptive-advertising-charges). (p. 155)

Fu, A., & Markus, H. R. (2014). My mother and me: Why tiger mothers motivate Asian Americans but not European Americans. *Personality and Social Psychology Bulletin, 40,* 739–749. (p. 149)

Fuhrmann, D., Knoll, L. J., & Blakemore, S. J. (2015). Adolescence as a sensitive period of brain development. *Trends in Cognitive Sciences, 19*(10), 558–566. (p. 142)

Fuller, M. J., & Downs, A. C. (1990, June). Spermarche is a salient biological marker in men's development. Poster session presented at the Second Annual Convention of the American Psychological Society, Dallas, TX. (p. 167)

Fuller-Thomson, E., Agbeyaka, S., LaFond, D. M., & Bern-Klug, M. (2016). Flourishing after depression: Factors associated with achieving complete mental health among those with a history of depression. *Psychiatry Research, 242,* 111–120. (p. 517)

Fulmer, C. A., Gelfand, M. J., Kruglanski, A. W., Kim-Prieto, C., Diener, E., Pierro, A., & Higgins, E. T. (2010). On "feeling right" in cultural contexts: How person-culture match affects self-esteem and subjective well-being. *Psychological Science, 21,* 1563–1569. (pp. 411, 483)

Fulmer, I. S., Gerhart, B., & Scott, K. S. (2003). Are the 100 best better? An empirical investigation of the relationship between being a "great place to work" and firm performance. *Personnel Psychology, 56,* 965–993. (p. B-8)

Funder, D. C. (2001). Personality. *Annual Review of Psychology, 52,* 197–221. (p. 478)

Funder, D. C. (2009). Persons, behaviors and situations: An agenda for personality psychology in the postwar era. *Journal of Research in Personality, 43,* 155–162. (p. 483)

Funder, D. C., & Block, J. (1989). The role of ego-control, ego-resiliency, and IQ in delay of gratification in adolescence. *Journal of Personality and Social Psychology, 57,* 1041–1050. (p. 145)

Furnham, A. (1982). Explanations for unemployment in Britain. *European Journal of Social Psychology, 12,* 335–352. (p. 417)

Furnham, A. (2016). Whether you think you can, or you think you can't—you're right. In R. J. Sternberg, S. T. Fiske, & D. J. Foss (Eds.), *Scientists making a difference: One hundred eminent behavioral and brain scientists talk about their most important contributions.* New York: Cambridge University Press. (p. 437)

Furnham, A., & Baguma, P. (1994). Cross-cultural differences in the evaluation of male and female body shapes. *International Journal of Eating Disorders, 15,* 81–89. (p. 365)

Furr, R. M., & Funder, D. C. (1998). A multimodal analysis of personal negativity. *Journal of Personality and Social Psychology, 74,* 1580–1591. (p. 521)

Furukawa, T. A., Levine, S. Z., Tanaka, S., Goldberg, Y., Samara, M., Davis, J. M., . . . Leucht, S. (2015). Initial severity of schizophrenia and efficacy of antipsychotics: Participant-level meta-analysis of 6 placebo-controlled studies. *JAMA Psychiatry, 72,* 14–21. (p. 560)

Furukawa, T. A., Yoshimura, R., Harai, H., Imaizumi, T., Takeuchi, H., Kitamua, T., & Takahashi, K. (2009). How many well vs. unwell days can you expect over 10 years, once you become depressed? *Acta Psychiatrica Scandinavica, 119,* 290–297. (p. 517)

Fuss, J., Steinle, J., Bindila, L., Auer, M. K., Kirchherr, H., Lutz, B., & Gass, P. (2015). A runner's high depends on cannabinoid receptors in mice. *PNAS, 112,* 13105–13108. (p. 43)

Futrell, R., Mahowald, K., & Gibson, E. (2015). Large-scale evidence of dependency length minimization in 37 languages. *PNAS, 112,* 10336–10341. (p. 313)

Gable, S. L., Gonzaga, G. C., & Strachman, A. (2006). Will you be there for me when things go right? Supportive responses to positive event disclosures. *Journal of Personality and Social Psychology, 91,* 904–917. (p. 157)

Gable, S. L., Gosnell, C. L., Maisel, N. C., & Strachman, A. (2012). Safely testing the alarm: Close others' responses to personal positive events. *Journal of Personality and Social Psychology, 103,* 963–981. (p. 399)

Gaddy, M. A., & Ingram, R. E. (2014). A meta-analytic review of mood-congruent implicit memory in depressed mood. *Clinical Psychology Review, 34,* 402–416. (p. 281)

Gaertner, L., Iuzzini, J., & O'Mara, E. M. (2008). When rejection by one fosters aggression against many: Multiple-victim aggression as a consequence of social rejection and perceived groupness. *Journal of Experimental Social Psychology, 44,* 958–970. (p. 355)

Gaissmaier, W., & Gigerenzer, G. (2012). 9/11, Act II: A fine-grained analysis of regional variations in traffic fatalities in the aftermath of the terrorist attacks. *Psychological Science, 23,* 1449–1454. (p. 302)

Gaither, S. E., & Sommers, S. R. (2013). Living with another-race roommate shapes whites' behavior in subsequent diverse settings. *Journal of Experimental Social Psychology, 49,* 272–276. (p. 457)

Galak, J., Leboeuf, R. A., Nelson, L. D., & Simmons, J. P. (2012). Correcting the past: Failures to replicate psi. *Journal of Personality and Social Psychology, 103,* 933–948. (p. 231)

Galambos, N. L. (1992). Parent–adolescent relations. *Current Directions in Psychological Science, 1,* 146–149. (p. 148)

Galanter, E. (1962). Contemporary psychophysics. In R. Brown, E. Galanter, E. H. Hess, & G. Mandler (Eds.), *New directions in psychology* (pp. 87–156). New York: Holt, Rinehart & Winston. (p. 190)

Galanter, M. (2016). *What is Alcoholics Anonymous?* New York: Oxford University Press. (p. 548)

Galati, D., Scherer, K. R., & Ricci-Bitti, P. E. (1997). Voluntary facial expression of emotion: Comparing congenitally blind with normally sighted encoders. *Journal of Personality and Social Psychology, 73*, 1363–1379. (p. 378)

Gale, C. R., Batty, G. D., & Deary, I. J. (2008). Locus of control at age 10 years and health outcomes and behaviors at age 30 years: The 1970 British Cohort Study. *Psychosomatic Medicine, 70*, 397–403. (p. 397)

Galinsky, A. D., Magee, J. C., Inesi, M. E., & Gruenfeld, D. H. (2006). Power and perspectives not taken. *Psychological Science, 17*, 1068–1074. (p. 128)

Galinsky, A. M., & Sonenstein, F. L. (2013). Relationship commitment, perceived equity, and sexual enjoyment among young adults in the United States. *Archives of Sexual Behavior, 42*, 93–104. (p. 186)

Galinsky, E., Aumann, K., & Bond, J. T. (2008). *Times are changing: Gender and generation at work and at home.* Work and Families Institute. Retrieved from familiesandwork.org (p. 488)

Galla, B. M., & Duckworth, A. L. (2015). More than resisting temptation: Beneficial habits mediate the relationship between self-control and positive life outcomes. *Journal of Personality and Social Psychology, 109*, 508–525. (pp. 234, 359)

Gallace, A. (2012). Living with touch. *Psychologist, 25*, 896–899. (p. 83)

Gallace, A., & Spence, C. (2011). To what extent do Gestalt grouping principles influence tactile perception? *Psychological Bulletin, 137*, 538–561. (p. 108)

Gallese, V., Gernsbacher, M. A., Heyes, C., Hickok, G., & Iacoboni, M. (2011). Mirror neuron forum. *Perspectives on Psychological Science, 6*, 369–407. (pp. 132, 259, 260)

Gallo, W. T., Teng, H. M., Falba, T. A., Kasl, S. V., Krumholz, H. M., & Bradley, E. H. (2006). The impact of late career job loss on myocardial infarction and stroke: A 10-year follow up using the health and retirement survey. *Occupational and Environmental Medicine, 63*, 683–687. (p. 392)

Gallup. (2004, August 16). 65% of Americans receive NO praise or recognition in the workplace. E-mail from Tom Rath: bucketbook@gallup.com. (p. B-11)

Gallup. (2017, February 10). Islamophobia: Understanding anti-Muslim sentiment in the West. (p. 438)

Gallup, G. G., Jr., & Frederick, D. A. (2010). The science of sex appeal: An evolutionary perspective. *Review of General Psychology, 14*, 240–250. (p. 449)

Gallup, G. H. (1972). *The Gallup poll: Public opinion 1935–1971* (Vol. 3). New York: Random House. (p. 457)

Gallup, G. H., Jr. (1994, October). Millions finding care and support in small groups. *Emerging Trends*, pp. 2–5. (p. 548)

Gana, K., Broc, G., Saada, Y., Amieva, H., & Quintard, B. (2016). Subjective wellbeing and longevity: Findings from a 22-year cohort study. *Journal of Psychosomatic Research, 85*, 28–34. (p. 392)

Gandhi, A. V., Mosser, E. A., Oikonomou, G., & Prober, D. A. (2015). Melatonin is required for the circadian regulation of sleep. *Neuron, 85*, 1193–1199. (p. 90)

Gandhi, T. K., Ganesh, S., & Sinha, P. (2014). Improvement in spatial imagery following sight onset late in childhood. *Psychological Science, 25*, 693–701. (p. 213)

Gandhi, T. K., Singh, A. K., Swami, P., Ganesh, S., & Sinha, P. (2017). Emergence of categorical face perception after extended early-onset blindness. *PNAS, 114*, 6139–6143. (p. 213)

Gangestad, S. W., Thornhill, R., & Garver-Apgar, C. E. (2010). Men's facial masculinity predicts changes in their female partners' sexual interests across the ovulatory cycle, whereas men's intelligence does not. *Evolution and Human Behavior, 31*, 412–424. (p. 449)

Gangwisch, J. E., Babiss, L. A., Malaspina, D., Turner, J. B., Zammit, G. K., & Posner, K. (2010). Earlier parental set bedtimes as a protective factor against depression and suicidal ideation. *Sleep, 33*, 97–106. (p. 93)

Gao, Y., Raine, A., Venables, P. H., Dawson, M. E., & Mednick, S. A. (2010). Association of poor child fear conditioning and adult crime. *American Journal of Psychiatry, 167*, 56–60. (p. 530)

Garcia, J., & Gustavson, A. R. (1997, January). Carl R. Gustavson (1946–1996): Pioneering wildlife psychologist. *APS Observer*, pp. 34–35. (pp. 255, 542)

Garcia, J., & Koelling, R. A. (1966). Relation of cue to consequence in avoidance learning. *Psychonomic Science, 4*, 123–124. (p. 254)

Garcia, J. L., Heckman, J. J., Leaf, D. E., & Prados, M. J. (2016, December). The life-cycle benefits of an influential early childhood program. Working paper 2015-35, Human Capital and Economic Opportunity Global Working Group (hceeconomics.org), University of Chicago. (p. 339)

Garcia, J. R., Reiber, C., Massey, S. G., & Merriwether, A. M. (2012). Sexual hookup culture: A review. *Review of General Psychology, 16*, 161–176. (p. 186)

Garcia, J. R., Reiber, C., Massey, S. G., & Merriwether, A. M. (2013, February). Sexual hook-up culture. *Monitor on Psychology*, pp. 60–66. (pp. 177, 186)

Garcia-Falgueras, A., & Swaab, D. F. (2010). Sexual hormones and the brain: An essential alliance for sexual identity and sexual orientation. *Endocrine Development, 17*, 22–35. (p. 181)

Gardner, H. (1983). *Frames of mind: The theory of multiple intelligences.* New York: Basic Books. (p. 324)

Gardner, H. (1998, March 19). An intelligent way to progress. *The Independent* (London), p. E4. (p. 324)

Gardner, H. (1999a). *Multiple views of multiple intelligence.* New York: Basic Books. (p. 324)

Gardner, H. (1999b, February). Who owns intelligence? *Atlantic Monthly*, pp. 67–76. (p. 327)

Gardner, H. (2006). *The development and education of the mind: The selected works of Howard Gardner.* New York: Routledge/Taylor & Francis. (p. 324)

Gardner, H. (2011). *The theory of multiple intelligences: As psychology, as education, as social science.* Address on the receipt of an honorary degree from José Cela University in Madrid and the Prince of Asturias Prize for Social Science. (p. 324)

Gardner, J., & Oswald, A. J. (2007). Money and mental well-being: A longitudinal study of medium-sized lottery wins. *Journal of Health Economics, 6*, 49–60. (p. 410)

Gardner, R. A., & Gardner, B. I. (1969). Teaching sign language to a chimpanzee. *Science, 165*, 664–672. (p. 317)

Garfield, C. (1986). *Peak performers: The new heroes of American business.* New York: Morrow. (p. 321)

Garon, N., Bryson, S. E., & Smith, I. M. (2008). Executive function in preschoolers: A review using an integrative framework. *Psychological Bulletin, 134*, 31–60. (p. 123)

Garry, M., Loftus, E. F., & Brown, S. W. (1994). Memory: A river runs through it. *Consciousness and Cognition, 3*, 438–451. (p. 469)

Gartrell, N., & Bos, H. (2010). US National Longitudinal Lesbian Family Study: Psychological adjustment of 17-year-old adolescents. *Pediatrics, 126*, 28–36. (p. 180)

Gasiorowska, A., Chaplin, L. N., Zaleskiewicz, T., Wygrab, S., & Vohs, K. D. (2016). Money cues increase agency and decrease prosociality among children: Early signs of market-mode behaviors. *Psychological Science, 27*, 331–344. (p. 281)

Gatchel, R. J., Peng, Y. B., Peters, M. L., Fuchs, P. N., & Turk, D. C. (2007). The biopsychosocial approach to chronic pain: Scientific advances and future directions. *Psychological Bulletin, 133*, 581–624. (pp. 222, 223)

Gates, W. (1998, July 20). Charity begins when I'm ready (interview). *Fortune.* Retrieved from pathfinder.com/fortune/1998/980720/bil7.html (p. 326)

Gavin, K. (2004, November 9). *U-M team reports evidence that smoking affects human brain's natural "feel good" chemical system* [Press release]. Retrieved from http://www.med.umich.edu/ (p. 105)

Gawande, A. (1998, September 21). The pain perplex. *The New Yorker*, pp. 86–94. (p. 223)

Gawin, F. H. (1991). Cocaine addiction: Psychology and neurophysiology. *Science, 251*, 1580–1586. (p. 107)

Gawronski, B., & Quinn, K. (2013). Guilty by mere similarity: Assimilative effects of facial resemblance on automatic evaluation. *Journal of Experimental Social Psychology, 49*, 120–125. (p. 240)

Gazzaniga, M. (2006). *The ethical brain: The science of our moral dilemmas.* New York: HarperPerennial. (p. 66)

Gazzaniga, M. S. (1967, August). The split brain in man. *Scientific American*, pp. 24–29. (p. 65)

Gazzaniga, M. S. (1983). Right hemisphere language following brain bisection: A 20-year perspective. *American Psychologist, 38*, 525–537. (p. 66)

Gazzola, V., Spezio, M. L., Etzel, J. A., Catelli, F., Adolphs, R., & Keysers, C. (2012). Primary somatosensory cortex discriminates affective significance in social touch. *PNAS, 109*, E1657–E1666. (p. 221)

GBD 2015 Obesity Collaborators. (2017). Health effects of overweight and obesity in 195 countries over 25 years. *New England Journal of Medicine, 377*, 13–27. (p. 365)

GBD. (2017). Smoking prevalence and attributable disease burden in 195 countries and territories, 1990–2015: A systematic analysis from the Global Burden of Disease Study 2015. *The Lancet, 389*, 1885–1906. (p. 106)

Ge, X., & Natsuaki, M. N. (2009). In search of explanations for early pubertal timing effects on developmental psychopathology. *Current Directions in Psychological Science, 18*, 327–441. (p. 142)

Ge, Y., Knittel, C. R., MacKenzie, D., & Zoepf, S. (2016, October). Racial and gender discrimination in transportation network companies. NBER Working Paper No. 22776. Retrieved from nber.org/papers/w2276 (p. 435)

Geary, D. C. (2010). *Male, female: The evolution of human sex differences* (2nd ed.). Washington, DC: American Psychological Association. (p. 165)

Geary, D. C., Salthouse, T. A., Chen, G.-P., & Fan, L. (1996). Are East Asian versus American differences in arithmetical ability a recent phenomenon? *Developmental Psychology, 32*, 254–262. (p. 342)

Geen, R. G., & Quanty, M. B. (1977). The catharsis of aggression: An evaluation of a hypothesis. In L. Berkowitz (Ed.), *Advances in experimental social psychology* (Vol. 10). New York: Academic Press. (p. 393)

Gehring, W. J., Wimke, J., & Nisenson, L. G. (2000). Action monitoring dysfunction in obsessive-compulsive disorder. *Psychological Science, 11,* 1–6. (p. 512)

Geier, A. B., Rozin, P., & Doros, G. (2006). Unit bias: A new heuristic that helps explain the effects of portion size on food intake. *Psychological Science, 17,* 521–525. (p. 364)

Gellis, L. A., Arigo, D., & Elliott, J. C. (2013). Cognitive refocusing treatment for insomnia: A randomized controlled trial in university students. *Behavior Therapy, 44,* 100–110. (p. 95)

Gelman, A. (2009, April 16). Red and blue economies? *FiveThirtyEight.* Retrieved from fivethirtyeight.com/features/red-andblue-economies (p. 18)

Gelman, D. (1989, May 15). Voyages to the unknown. *Newsweek,* pp. 66–69. (p. 379)

Genesee, F., & Gándara, P. (1999). Bilingual education programs: A cross-national perspective. *Journal of Social Issues, 55,* 665–685. (p. 320)

Gentile, D. A. (2009). Pathological video-game use among youth ages 8 to 18: A national study. *Psychological Science, 20,* 594–602. (pp. 102, 445)

Gentile, D. A., & Bushman, B. J. (2012). Reassessing media violence effects using a risk and resilience approach to understanding aggression. *Psychology of Popular Media Culture, 1,* 138–151. (p. 263)

Gentile, D. A., Coyne, S., & Walsh, D. A. (2011). Media violence, physical aggression and relational aggression in school age children: A short-term longitudinal study. *Aggressive Behavior, 37,* 193–206. (p. 263)

Gentner, D. (2016). Language as cognitive tool kit: How language supports relational thought. *American Psychologist, 71,* 650–657. (p. 319)

Gentzkow, M., Shapiro, J. M., & Taddy, M. (2016, July). Measuring polarization in high-dimensional data: Method and application to congressional speech. NBER Working Paper 22423. Retrieved from nber.org/papers/w22423 (p. 431)

Geraerts, E., Bernstein, D. M., Merckelbach, H., Linders, C., Raymaekers, L., & Loftus, E. F. (2008). Lasting false beliefs and their behavioral consequences. *Psychological Science, 19,* 749–753. (p. 290)

Geraerts, E., Schooler, J. W., Merckelbach, H., Jelicic, M., Hauer, B. J. A., & Ambadar, Z. (2007). The reality of recovered memories: Corroborating continuous and discontinuous memories of childhood sexual abuse. *Psychological Science, 18,* 564–568. (p. 293)

Germain, A. (2013). Sleep disturbances as the hallmark of PTSD: Where are we now? *Archives of Journal of Psychiatry, 170,* 372–382. (p. 509)

Gernsbacher, M. A., Dawson, M., & Goldsmith, H. H. (2005). Three reasons not to believe in an autism epidemic. *Current Directions in Psychological Science, 14,* 55–58. (p. 131)

Gershenson, S., Holt, S. B., & Papageorge, N. W. (2016). Who believes in me? The effect of student-teacher demographic match on teacher expectations. *Economics of Education Review, 52,* 209–224. (p. 344)

Gershoff, E. T. (2002). Parental corporal punishment and associated child behaviors and experiences: A meta-analytic and theoretical review. *Psychological Bulletin, 128,* 539–579. (p. 249)

Gershoff, E. T., & Grogan-Kaylor, A. (2016). Spanking and child outcomes: Old controversies and new meta-analyses. *Journal of Family Psychology, 30,* 453–469. (p. 249)

Gershoff, E. T., Grogan-Kaylor, A., Lansford, J. E., Chang, L., Zelli, A., Deater-Deckard, K., & Dodge, K. A. (2010). Parent discipline practices in an international sample: Associations with child behaviors and moderation by perceived normativeness. *Child Development, 81,* 487–502. (p. 249)

Gershon, A., Ram, N., Johnson, S. L., Harvey, A. G., & Zeitzer, J. M. (2016). Daily actigraphy profiles distinguish depressive and interepisode states in bipolar disorder. *Clinical Psychological Science, 4,* 641–650. (p. 514)

Gerst-Emerson, K., & Jayawardhana, J. (2015). Loneliness as a public health issue: The impact of loneliness on health care utilization among older adults. *American Journal of Public Health, 105,* 1013–1019. (p. 353)

Geschwind, N. (1979, September). Specializations of the human brain. *Scientific American, 241,* 180–199. (p. 316)

Geukes, K., Nestler, S., Hutteman, R., Dufner, M., Küfner, A. C., Egloff, B., . . . Back, M. D. (2016). Puffed-up but shaky selves: State self-esteem level and variability in narcissists. *Journal of Personality and Social Psychology.* Advance online publication. doi:10.1037/pspp0000093 (p. 488)

Geurts, D. E., Von Borries, K., Volman, I., Bulten, B. H., Cools, R., & Verkes, R. J. (2016). Neural connectivity during reward expectation dissociates psychopathic criminals from non-criminal individuals with high impulsive/antisocial psychopathic traits. *Social Cognitive and Affective Neuroscience, 11,* 1326–1334. (p. 530)

Giampietro, M., & Cavallera, G. M. (2007). Morning and evening types and creative thinking. *Personality and Individual Differences, 42,* 453–463. (p. 87)

Giancola, P. R., & Corman, M. D. (2007). Alcohol and aggression: A test of the attention-allocation model. *Psychological Science, 18,* 649–655. (p. 442)

Giancola, P. R., Josephs, R. A., Parrott, D. J., & Duke, A. A. (2010). Alcohol myopia revisited: Clarifying aggression and other acts of disinhibition through a distorted lens. *Perspectives on Psychological Science, 5,* 265–278. (p. 104)

Gibbons, F. X. (1986). Social comparison and depression: Company's effect on misery. *Journal of Personality and Social Psychology, 51,* 140–148. (p. 411)

Gibbs, W. W. (1996). Mind readings. *Scientific American, 274,* 34–36. (p. 60)

Gibson, E. J., & Walk, R. D. (1960, April). The "visual cliff." *Scientific American,* pp. 64–71. (p. 208)

Giedd, J. N. (2015, June). The amazing teen brain. *Scientific American,* pp. 33–37. (p. 142)

Giesbrecht, T., Lynn, S. J., Lilienfeld, S. O., & Merckelbach, H. (2008). Cognitive processes in dissociation: An analysis of core theoretical assumptions. *Psychological Bulletin, 134,* 617–647. (p. 528)

Giesbrecht, T., Lynn, S. J., Lilienfeld, S. O., & Merckelbach, H. (2010). Cognitive processes, trauma, and dissociation—Misconceptions and misrepresentations: Reply to Bremner (2010). *Psychological Bulletin, 136,* 7–11. (p. 528)

Gigerenzer, G. (2004). Dread risk, September 11, and fatal traffic accidents. *Psychological Science, 15,* 286–287. (p. 302)

Gigerenzer, G. (2006). Out of the frying pan into the fire: Behavioral reactions to terrorist attacks. *Risk Analysis, 26,* 347–351. (p. 302)

Gigerenzer, G. (2010). *Rationality for mortals: How people cope with uncertainty.* New York: Oxford University Press. (p. A-1)

Gigerenzer, G. (2015). *Simply rational: Decision making in the real world.* New York: Oxford University Press. (p. 300)

Gilbert, D. T. (2006). *Stumbling on happiness.* New York: Knopf. (pp. 157, 369)

Gilbert, D. T., King, G., Pettigrew, S., & Wilson, T. D. (2016). Comment on "Estimating the reproducibility of psychological science." *Science, 351,* 1037. (p. 20)

Gilbert, D. T., Pinel, E. C., Wilson, T. D., Blumberg, S. J., & Wheatley, T. P. (1998). Immune neglect: A source of durability bias in affective forecasting. *Journal of Personality and Social Psychology, 75,* 617–638. (p. 408)

Gildersleeve, K., Haselton, M., & Fales, M. R. (2014). Do women's mate preferences change across the menstrual cycle? A meta-analytic review. *Psychological Bulletin, 140,* 1205–1259. (p. 173)

Gillen-O'Neel, C., Huynh, V. W., & Fuligni, A. J. (2013). To study or to sleep? The academic costs of extra studying at the expense of sleep. *Child Development, 84,* 133–142. (p. 98)

Gilmore, R. O., & Adolph, K. E. (2017). Video can make behavioural science more reproducible. *Nature Human Behaviour, 1,* s41562–017. (p. 20)

Gilovich, T. (1991). *How we know what isn't so: The fallibility of human reason in everyday life.* New York: Free Press. (p. 18)

Gilovich, T. D. (1996). *The spotlight effect: Exaggerated impressions of the self as a social stimulus.* Unpublished manuscript, Cornell University. (p. 486)

Gilovich, T. D., & Medvec, V. H. (1995). The experience of regret: What, when, and why. *Psychological Review, 102,* 379–395. (p. 158)

Gilovich, T. D., & Savitsky, K. (1999). The spotlight effect and the illusion of transparency: Egocentric assessments of how we are seen by others. *Current Directions in Psychological Science, 8,* 165–168. (p. 486)

Gingerich, O. (1999, February 6). *Is there a role for natural theology today?* Retrieved from http://www.origins.org/real/n9501/natural.html (p. 77)

Gino, G., Wilmuth, C. A., & Brooks, A. W. (2015). Compared to men, women view professional advancement as equally attainable, but less desirable. *PNAS, 112,* 12354–12359. (p. 164)

Giuliano, T. A., Barnes, L. C., Fiala, S. E., & Davis, D. M. (1998). *An empirical investigation of male answer syndrome.* Paper presented at the Southwestern Psychological Association convention. (p. 163)

Gladwell, M. (2000, May 9). The new-boy network: What do job interviews really tell us? *The New Yorker,* pp. 68–86. (p. B-6)

Glasman, L. R., & Albarracín, D. (2006). Forming attitudes that predict future behavior: A meta-analysis of the attitude-behavior relation. *Psychological Bulletin, 132,* 778–822. (p. 418)

Glass, R. M. (2001). Electroconvulsive therapy: Time to bring it out of the shadows. *Journal of the American Medical Association, 285,* 1346–1348. (p. 563)

Glasser, M. F., Coalson, T. S., Robinson, E. C., Hacker, C. D., Harwell, J., Yacoub, E., . . . Van Essen, D. C. (2016). A multi-modal parcellation of human cerebral cortex. *Nature, 536,* 171–178. (p. 53)

Glasser, S. B. (2017, November 13). "They want to know if Trump's crazy." *Politico* (politico.com). (p. 459)

Gleaves, D. H. (1996). The sociocognitive model of dissociative identity disorder: A reexamination of the evidence. *Psychological Bulletin, 120,* 42–59. (p. 529)

Glenn, A. L., & Raine, A. (2014). Neurocriminology: Implications for the punishment, prediction and prevention of criminal behavior. *Nature Reviews Neuroscience, 15,* 54–63. (p. 52)

Glenn, A. L., Raine, A., Yaralian, P. S., & Yang, Y. (2010). Increased volume of the striatum in psychopathic individuals. *Biological Psychiatry, 67,* 52–58. (p. 531)

Gliklich, E., Guo, R., & Bergmark, R. W. (2016). Texting while driving: A study of 1211 US adults with the Distracted Driving Survey. *Preventive Medicine Reports, 4,* 486–489. (p. 82)

Global Burden of Disease Study, 2013 collaborators. (2015). Global, regional, and national incidence, prevalence, and years lived with disability for 301 acute and chronic diseases and injuries in 188 countries, 1990–2013: A systematic analysis for the Global Burden of Disease Study 2013. *The Lancet, 386,* 743–800. (p. 218)

GLSEN. (2012). *The 2011 national school climate survey.* New York: Gay, Lesbian & Straight Education Network (glsen.org). (p. 170)

Glynn, L. M., & Sandman, C. A. (2011). Prenatal origins of neurological development: A critical period for fetus and mothers. *Current Directions in Psychological Science, 20,* 384–389. (p. 120)

Glynn, T. R., Gamarel, K. E., Kahler, C. W., Iwamoto, M., Operario, D., & Nemoto, T. (2017). The role of gender affirmation in psychological well-being among transgender women. *Psychology of Sexual Orientation and Gender Diversity, 3,* 336–344. (p. 171)

Godden, D. R., & Baddeley, A. D. (1975). Context-dependent memory in two natural environments: On land and underwater. *British Journal of Psychology, 66,* 325–331. (p. 281)

Goethals, G. R., & Allison, S. T. (2014). Kings and charisma, Lincoln and leadership: An evolutionary perspective. In G. R. Goethals, S. T. Allison, R. M. Kramer, & D. M. Messick (Eds.), *Conceptions of leadership: Enduring ideas and emerging insights* (pp. 111–124). New York: Palgrave Macmillan. (p. B-10)

Goetz, S. M. M., Tang, L., Thomason, M. E., Diamond, M. P., Hariri, A. R., & Carré, J. (2014). Testosterone rapidly increases neural reactivity to threat in healthy men: A novel two-step pharmacological challenge paradigm. *Biological Psychiatry, 76,* 324–331. (p. 49)

Goff, D. C., Falkai, P., Fleischhacker, W. W., Girgis, R. R., Kahn, R. M., Uchida, H., . . . Lieberman, J. A. (2017). The long-term effects of antipsychotic medication on clinical course in schizophrenia. *The American Journal of Psychiatry, 174,* 840–849. (p. 560)

Goff, D. C., & Simms, C. A. (1993). Has multiple personality disorder remained consistent over time? *Journal of Nervous and Mental Disease, 181,* 595–600. (p. 528)

Golan, O., Ashwin, E., Granader, Y., McClintock, S., Day, K., Leggett, V., & Baron-Cohen, S. (2010). Enhancing emotion recognition in children with autism spectrum conditions: An intervention using animated vehicles with real emotional faces. *Journal of Autism Development and Disorders, 40,* 269–279. (p. 132)

Gold, M., & Yanof, D. S. (1985). Mothers, daughters, and girlfriends. *Journal of Personality and Social Psychology, 49,* 654–659. (p. 148)

Goldberg, J. (2007). *Quivering bundles that let us hear.* Retrieved from hhmi.org/senses/c120. html (p. 218)

Golder, S. A., & Macy, M. W. (2011). Diurnal and seasonal mood vary with work, sleep, and day-length across diverse cultures. *Science, 333,* 1878–1881. (pp. 22, 408)

Goldfried, M. R. (2001). Integrating gay, lesbian, and bisexual issues into mainstream psychology. *American Psychologist, 56,* 977–988. (p. 500)

Goldfried, M. R., Raue, P. J., & Castonguay, L. G. (1998). The therapeutic focus in significant sessions of master therapists: A comparison of cognitive–behavioral and psychodynamic–interpersonal interventions. *Journal of Consulting and Clinical Psychology, 66,* 803–810. (p. 555)

Goldinger, S. D., & Papesh, M. H. (2012). Pupil dilation reflects the creation and retrieval of memories. *Current Directions in Psychological Science, 21,* 90–95. (p. 201)

Goldman, A. L., Pezawas, L., Mattay, V. S., Fischl, B., Verchinski, B. A., Chen, Q., . . . Meyer-Lindenberg, A. (2009). Widespread reductions of cortical thickness in schizophrenia and spectrum disorders and evidence of heritability. *Archives of General Psychiatry, 66,* 467–477. (p. 525)

Goldstein, I., Lue, T. F., Padma-Nathan, H., Rosen, R. C., Steers, W. D., & Wicker, P. A. (1998). Oral sildenafil in the treatment of erectile dysfunction. *New England Journal of Medicine, 338,* 1397–1404. (p. 28)

Goleman, D. (1980, February). 1,528 little geniuses and how they grew. *Psychology Today,* pp. 28–53. (p. 357)

Goleman, D. (2006). *Social intelligence.* New York: Bantam Books. (p. 326)

Golkar, A., Selbing, I., Flygare, O., Öhman, A., & Olsson, A. (2013). Other people as means to a safe end: Vicarious extinction blocks the return of learned fear. *Psychological Science, 24,* 2182–2190. (p. 259)

Gollwitzer, P. M., & Oettingen, G. (2012). Goal pursuit. In P. M. Gollwitzer & G. Oettingen (Eds.), *The Oxford handbook of human motivation,* pp. 208–231. New York: Oxford University Press. (pp. 251, 359)

Gollwitzer, P. M., & Sheeran, P. (2006). Implementation intentions and goal achievement: A meta-analysis of effects and processes. *Advances in Experimental Social Psychology, 38,* 69–119. (p. B-9)

Gómez-Robles, A., Hopkins, W. D., Schapiro, S. J., & Sherwood, C. C. (2015). Relaxed genetic control of cortical organization in humans brains compared with chimpanzees. *PNAS, 112,* 14799–14804. (p. 39)

Gong, H., Liu, Y.-Z., Zhang, Y., Su, W.-J., Lian, Y.-J., Peng, W., & Jiang, C.-L. (2016). Mindfulness meditation for insomnia: A meta-analysis of randomized controlled trials. *Journal of Psychosomatic Research, 89,* 1–6. (p. 404)

Gongola, J., Scurich, N., & Quas, J. A. (2017). Detecting deception in children: A meta-analysis. *Law and Human Behavior, 41,* 44–54. (p. 376)

Gonsalkorale, K., & Williams, K. D. (2006). The KKK would not let me play: Ostracism even by a despised outgroup hurts. *European Journal of Social Psychology, 36,* 1–11. (p. 354)

Goodale, M. A., & Milner, D. A. (2004). *Sight unseen: An exploration of conscious and unconscious vision.* Oxford: Oxford University Press. (p. 84)

Goodall, J. (1986). *The chimpanzees of Gombe: Patterns of behavior.* Cambridge, MA: Harvard University Press. (p. 439)

Goodall, J. (1998). Learning from the chimpanzees: A message humans can understand. *Science, 282,* 2184–2185. (p. 23)

Goode, E. (1999, April 13). If things taste bad, "phantoms" may be at work. *The New York Times* (nytimes.com). (p. 222)

Goodman, G. S. (2006). Children's eyewitness memory: A modern history and contemporary commentary. *Journal of Social Issues, 62,* 811–832. (p. 294)

Goodman, G. S., Ghetti, S., Quas, J. A., Edelstein, R. S., Alexander, K. W., Redlich, A. D., . . . Jones, D. P. H. (2003). A prospective study of memory for child sexual abuse: New findings relevant to the repressed-memory controversy. *Psychological Science, 14,* 113–118. (p. 293)

Goodwin, P. Y., Mosher, W. D., & Chandra, A. (2010, February). *Marriage and cohabitation in the United States: A statistical portrait based on Cycle 6 (2002) of the National Survey of Family Growth* (Vital Health Statistics Series 23, No. 28). Washington, DC: U.S. Department of Health and Human Service, Centers for Disease Control and Prevention, National Center for Health Statistics. (p. 156)

Gopnik, A., Griffiths, T. L., & Lucas, C. G. (2015). When younger learners can be better (or at least more open-minded) than older ones. *Current Directions in Psychological Science, 24,* 87–92. (p. 127)

Gopnik, A., & Meltzoff, A. N. (1986). Relations between semantic and cognitive development in the one-word stage: The specificity hypothesis. *Child Development, 57,* 1040–1053. (p. 320)

Goranson, A., Ritter, R. S., Waytz, A., Norton, M. I., & Gray, K. (2017). Dying is unexpectedly positive. *Psychological Science, 28,* 988–999. (p. 160)

Goranson, R. E. (1978). *The hindsight effect in problem solving.* Unpublished manuscript cited in G. Wood (1984), Research methodology: A decision-making perspective. In A. M. Rogers & C. J. Scheirer (Eds.), *The G. Stanley Hall Lecture Series* (Vol. 4, pp. 193–217). Washington, DC: American Psychological Association. (p. 17)

Gorchoff, S. M., John, O. P., & Helson, R. (2008). Contextualizing change in marital satisfaction during middle age. *Psychological Science, 19,* 1194–1200. (p. 157)

Gordon, A. M., & Chen, S. (2010). When you accept me for me: The relational benefits of intrinsic affirmations from one's relationship partner. *Personality and Social Psychology Bulletin, 36,* 1439–1453. (p. 473)

Gordon, A. M., & Chen, S. (2014). The role of sleep in interpersonal conflict: Do sleepless nights mean worse fights? *Social Psychological and Personality Science, 5,* 168–175. (pp. 93)

Gordon, I., Vander Wyk, B. C., Bennett, R. H., Cordeaux, C., Lucas, M. V., Eilbott, J. A., . . . Pelphrey, K. A. (2013). Oxytocin enhances brain function in children with autism. *PNAS, 110,* 20953–20958. (p. 132)

Gordon, P. (2004). Numerical cognition without words: Evidence from Amazonia. *Science, 306,* 496–499. (p. 319)

Gore-Felton, C., Koopman, C., Thoresen, C., Arnow, B., Bridges, E., & Spiegel, D. (2000). Psychologists' beliefs and clinical characteristics: Judging the veracity of childhood sexual abuse memories. *Professional Psychology: Research and Practice, 31,* 372–377. (p. 293)

Gore, J., & Sadler-Smith, E. (2011). Unpacking intuition: A process and outcome framework. *Review of General Psychology, 15,* 304–316. (p. 305)

Gorka, S. M., Lieberman, L., Shankman, S. A., & Phan, K. L. (2017). Startle potentiation to uncertain threat as a psychophysiological indicator of fear-based psychopathology: An examination across multiple internalizing disorders. *Journal of Abnormal Psychology, 126,* 8. (p. 506)

Gorlick, A. (2010, January 13). Stanford scientists link brain development to chances of recovering vision after blindness. *Stanford Report* (news.stanford.edu). (p. 213)

Gorman, J. (2014, January 6). The brain, in exquisite detail. *The New York Times* (nytimes.com). (p. 53)

Gorrese, A., & Ruggieri, R. (2012). Peer attachment: A meta-analytic review of gender and age differences and associations with parent attachment. *Journal of Youth and Adolescence, 41,* 650–672. (p. 136)

Gosling, S. D. (2008). *Snoop: What your stuff says about you.* New York: Basic Books. (p. 481)

Gosling, S. D., Gladdis, S., & Vazire, S. (2007). *Personality impressions based on Facebook profiles.* Paper presented to the Society for Personality and Social Psychology meeting. (p. 481)

Gosling, S. D., Kwan, V. S. Y., & John, O. P. (2003). A dog's got personality: A cross-species comparative approach to personality judgments in dogs and humans. *Journal of Personality and Social Psychology, 85,* 1161–1169. (p. 477)

Gotink, R. A., Meijboom, R., Vernooij, M. W., Smits, M., & Hunink, M. G. M. (2016). 8-week mindfulness based stress reduction induces brain changes similar to traditional long-term meditation practice—A systematic review. *Brain and Cognition, 108,* 32–41. (p. 404)

Gotlib, I. H., & Hammen, C. L. (1992). *Psychological aspects of depression: Toward a cognitive-interpersonal integration.* New York: Wiley. (p. 521)

Gottesman, I. I. (1991). *Schizophrenia genesis: The origins of madness.* New York: Freeman. (p. 526)

Gottesman, I. I. (2001). Psychopathology through a life span—genetic prism. *American Psychologist, 56,* 867–881. (p. 526)

Gottfredson, L. S. (2002a). Where and why g matters: Not a mystery. *Human Performance, 15,* 25–46. (p. 325)

Gottfredson, L. S. (2002b). g: Highly general and highly practical. In R. J. Sternberg & E. L. Grigorenko (Eds.), *The general factor of intelligence: How general is it?* Mahwah, NJ: Erlbaum. (p. 325)

Gottfredson, L. S. (2003a). Dissecting practical intelligence theory: Its claims and evidence. *Intelligence, 31,* 343–397. (p. 325)

Gottfredson, L. S. (2003b). On Sternberg's "Reply to Gottfredson." *Intelligence, 31,* 415–424. (p. 325)

Gottfried, J. A., O'Doherty, J., & Dolan, R. J. (2003). Encoding predictive reward value in human amygdala and orbitofrontal cortex. *Science, 301,* 1104–1108. (p. 237)

Gottman, J. (1994). *Why marriages succeed or fail: And how you can make yours last.* New York: Simon & Schuster. (p. 157)

Gottman, J. (2007). *Why marriages succeed or fail.* London: Bloomsbury. (p. 452)

Gould, E. (2007). How widespread is adult neurogenesis in mammals? *Nature Neuroscience, 8,* 481–488. (p. 64)

Gould, S. J. (1981). *The mismeasure of man.* New York: Norton. (p. 328)

Gow, A. J., Bastin, M. E., Maniega, S. M., Hernández, M. C. V., Morris, Z., Murray, C., . . . Wardlaw, J. M. (2012). Neuroprotective lifestyles and the aging brain: Activity, atrophy, and white matter integrity. *Neurology, 79,* 1802–1808. (p. 153)

Goyal, M., Singh, S., Sibinga, E. S., Gould, N. F., Rowland-Seymour, A., Sharma, R., . . . Haythornthwaite, J. A. (2014). Meditation programs for psychological stress and well-being: A systematic review and meta-analysis. *JAMA Internal Medicine, 174,* 357–368. (p. 404)

Goyer, J. P., Garcia, J., Purdie-Vaughns, V., Binning, K. R., Cook, J. E., Reeves, S. L., . . . Cohen, G. L. (2017). Self-affirmation facilitates minority middle schoolers' progress along college trajectories. *PNAS, 114*(29), 7594–7599. (p. 344)

Grabe, S., Ward, L. M., & Hyde, J. S. (2008). The role of the media in body image concerns among women: A meta-analysis of experimental and correlational studies. *Psychological Bulletin, 134,* 460–476. (p. 532)

Grabo, A., & van Vugt, M. (2016). Charismatic leadership and the evolution of cooperation. *Evolution and Human Behavior, 37,* 399–406. (p. B-10)

Grady, C. L., McIntosh, A. R., Horwitz, B., Maisog, J. M., Ungeleider, L. G., Mentis, M. J., . . . Haxby, J. V. (1995). Age-related reductions in human recognition memory due to impaired encoding. *Science, 269,* 218–221. (p. 285)

Graf, S., Paolini, S., & Rubin, M. (2014). Negative intergroup contact is more influential, but positive intergroup contact is more common: Assessing contact prominence and contact prevalence in five central European countries. *European Journal of Social Psychology, 44,* 536–547. (p. 457)

Graham, A. M., Fisher, P. A., & Pfeifer, J. H. (2013). What sleeping babies hear: A functional MRI study of interparental conflict and infants' emotion processing. *Psychological Science, 24,* 782–789. (p. 137)

Graham, E. K., Rutsohn, J. P., Turiano, N. A., Bendayan, R., Batterham, P. J., Gerstorf, D., . . . Bastarache, E. D. (2017). Personality predicts mortality risk: An integrative data analysis of 15 international longitudinal studies. *Journal of Research in Personality, 70,* 174–186. (p. 480)

Graham, J., Nosek, B. A., & Haidt, J. (2012, December 12). The moral stereotypes of liberals and conservatives: Exaggeration of differences across the political spectrum. *PLoS ONE 7,* e50092. (p. 435)

Grand, J. A. (2016). Brain drain? An examination of stereotype threat effects during training on knowledge acquisition and organizational effectiveness. *Journal of Applied Psychology.* Advance online publication. doi:10.1037/apl0000171 (p. 344)

Granic, I., Lobel, A., & Engels, R. C. M. E. (2014). The benefits of playing video games. *American Psychologist, 69,* 66–78. (p. 445)

Granqvist, P., Mikulincer, M., & Shaver, P. R. (2010). Religion as attachment: Normative processes and individual differences. *Personality and Social Psychology Review, 14,* 49–59. (p. 136)

Grant, A. M., Gino, F., & Hofmann, D. A. (2011). Reversing the extraverted leadership advantage: The role of employee proactivity. *Academy of Management Journal, 54,* 528–550. (p. 476)

Grant, J. M., Mottet, L. A., Tanis, J., Herman, J. L., Harrison, J., & Keisling, M. (2011). National transgender discrimination survey report on health and health care. National Center for Transgender Equality and National Gay and Lesbian Task Force. (p. 437)

Grant, N., Wardle, J., & Steptoe, A. (2009). The relationship between life satisfaction and health behavior: A cross-cultural analysis of young adults. *International Journal of Behavioral Medicine, 16,* 259–268. (p. 401)

Gray-Little, B., & Burks, N. (1983). Power and satisfaction in marriage: A review and critique. *Psychological Bulletin, 93,* 513–538. (p. 452)

Graybiel, A. M., & Smith, K. S. (2014, June). Good habits, bad habits. *Scientific American, 310,* 38–43. (p. 234)

Green, B. (2002). Listening to leaders: Feedback on 360-degree feedback one year later. *Organizational Development Journal, 20,* 8–16. (p. B-7)

Green, J. D., Sedikides, C., & Gregg, A. P. (2008). Forgotten but not gone: The recall and recognition of self-threatening memories. *Journal of Experimental Social Psychology, 44,* 547–561. (p. 469)

Green, J. T., & Woodruff-Pak, D. S. (2000). Eyeblink classical conditioning: Hippocampal formation is for neutral stimulus associations as cerebellum is for association-response. *Psychological Bulletin, 126,* 138–158. (p. 277)

Green, M. F., & Horan, W. P. (2010). Social cognition in schizophrenia. *Current Directions in Psychological Science, 19,* 243–248. (p. 523)

Greenaway, K. H., Cruwys, T., Haslam, S. A., & Jetten, J. (2016). Social identities promote well-being because they satisfy global psychological needs. *European Journal of Social Psychology, 46,* 294–307. (pp. 352, 438)

Greenaway, K. H., Haslam, S. A., Cruwys, T., Branscombe, N. R., Ysseldyk, R., & Heldreth, C. (2015). From "we" to "me": Group identification enhances perceived personal control with consequences for health and well-being. *Journal of Personality and Social Psychology, 109,* 53–74. (p. 352)

Greenberg, J. (2008). Understanding the vital human quest for self-esteem. *Perspectives on Psychological Science, 3,* 48–55. (p. 486)

Greene, J. (2010). Remarks to an Edge conference: The new science of morality. *The Edge* (edge.org). (p. 145)

Greene, J. D., Sommerville, R. B., Nystrom, L. E., Darley, J. M., & Cohen, J. D. (2001). An fMRI investigation of emotional engagement in moral judgment. *Science, 293,* 2105–2108. (p. 145)

Greenwald, A. G. (1992). *Subliminal semantic activation and subliminal snake oil.* Paper presented to the American Psychological Association Convention, Washington, DC. (p. 193)

Greenwald, A. G., Banaji, M. R., & Nosek, B. A. (2015). Statistically small effects of the implicit association test can have societally large effects. *Journal of Personality and Social Psychology, 108,* 553–561. (p. 435)

Greenwald, A. G., & Pettigrew, T. F. (2014, March). With malice toward none and charity for some: Ingroup favoritism enables discrimination. *American Psychologist, 69,* 645–655. (p. 438)

Greenwald, A. G., Spangenberg, E. R., Pratkanis, A. R., & Eskenazi, J. (1991). Double-blind tests of subliminal self-help audiotapes. *Psychological Science, 2,* 119–122. (p. 193)

Greenwald, G. (2012, March 19). Discussing the motives of the Afghan shooter. *Salon* (salon.com). (p. 456)

Greer, S. G., Goldstein, A. N., & Walker, M. P. (2013). The impact of sleep deprivation on food desire in the human brain. *Nature Communications, 4,* Article 2259. doi:10.1038/ncomms3259 (p. 93)

Gregory, A. M., Rijksdijk, F. V., Lau, J. Y., Dahl, R. E., & Eley, T. C. (2009). The direction of longitudinal associations between sleep problems and depression symptoms: A study of twins aged 8 and 10 years. *Sleep, 32,* 189–199. (pp. 93, 559)

Gregory, R. L. (1978). *Eye and brain: The psychology of seeing* (3rd ed.). New York: McGraw-Hill. (pp. 206, 213)

Gregory, R. L., & Gombrich, E. H. (Eds.). (1973). *Illusion in nature and art.* New York: Charles Scribner's Sons. (p. 197)

Greist, J. H., Jefferson, J. W., & Marks, I. M. (1986). *Anxiety and its treatment: Help is available.* Washington, DC: American Psychiatric Press. (p. 507)

Greitemeyer, T., & Mügge, D. O. (2014). Video games do affect social outcomes: A meta-analytic review of the effects of violent and prosocial video game play. *Personality and Social Psychology Bulletin, 40,* 578–589. (p. 444)

Greyson, B. (2010). Implications of near-death experiences for a postmaterialist psychology. *Review of Religion and Spirituality, 2,* 37–45. (p. 108)

Grèzes, J., & Decety, J. (2001). Function anatomy of execution, mental simulation, observation, and verb generation of actions: A meta-analysis. *Human Brain Mapping, 12,* 1–19. (p. 321)

Griffiths, M. (2001). Sex on the internet: Observations and implications for internet sex addiction. *Journal of Sex Research, 38,* 333–342. (p. 102)

Griggs, R. (2014). Coverage of the Stanford Prison Experiment in introductory psychology textbooks. *Teaching of Psychology, 41,* 195–203. (p. 419)

Grijalva, E., Newman, D. A., Tay, L., Donnellan, M. B., Harms, P. D., Robins, R. W., & Yan, T. (2015). Gender differences in narcissism: A meta-analytic review. *Psychological Bulletin, 141,* 261–310. (p. 488)

Grillon, C., Quispe-Escudero, D., Mathur, A., & Ernst, M. (2015). Mental fatigue impairs emotion regulation. *Emotion, 15,* 383–389. (p. 398)

Grilo, C. M., & Pogue-Geile, M. F. (1991). The nature of environmental influences on weight and obesity: A behavior genetic analysis. *Psychological Bulletin, 110,* 520–537. (p. 365)

Grinker, R. R. (2007). *Unstrange minds: Remapping the world of autism.* New York: Basic Books. (p. 131)

Grobstein, C. (1979, June). External human fertilization. *Scientific American,* pp. 57–67. (p. 119)

Grodin, E. N., & White, T. L. (2015). The neuroanatomical delineation of agentic and affiliative extraversion. *Cognitive, Affective, and Behavioral Neuroscience, 15,* 321–334. (p. 478)

Grønnerød, C., Grønnerød, J. S., & Grøndahl, P. (2015). Psychological treatment of sexual offenders against children: A meta-analytic review of treatment outcome studies. *Trauma, Violence, & Abuse, 16,* 280–290. (p. 170)

Groothuis, T. G. G., & Carere, C. (2005). Avian personalities: Characterization and epigenesis. *Neuroscience and Biobehavioral Reviews, 29,* 137–150. (p. 477)

Gross, A. E., & Crofton, C. (1977). What is good is beautiful. *Sociometry, 40,* 85–90. (p. 450)

Gross, J. J. (2013). Emotion regulation: Taking stock and moving forward. *Emotion, 13,* 359–365. (p. 371)

Grossberg, S. (1995). The attentive brain. *American Scientist, 83,* 438–449. (p. 197)

Grossmann, I., Na, J., Varnum, M. E. W., Park, D. C., Kitayama, S., & Nisbett, R. E. (2010). Reasoning about social conflicts improves into old age. *PNAS, 107,* 7246–7250. (p. 334)

Grossmann, I., & Varnum, M. E. W. (2015). Social structure, infectious diseases, disasters, secularism, and cultural change in America. *Psychological Science, 26,* 311–324. (p. 491)

Groß, J., Blank, H., & Bayen U. J. (2017). Hindsight bias in depression. *Clinical Psychological Science, 5,* 771–788. (p. 520)

Grover, S. & Helliwell, J. F. (2014, December). *How's life at home? New evidence on marriage and the set point for happiness* (NBER Working Paper No. 20794). Retrieved from nber.org/papers/w20794 (p. 353)

Gruber, J. (2011). Can feeling too good be bad? Positive emotion persistence (PEP) in bipolar disorder. *Current Directions in Psychological Science, 20,* 217–221. (p. 515)

Gruber, J., Gilbert, K. E., Youngstrom, E., Kogos Youngstrom, J., Feeny, N. C., & Findling, R. L. (2013). Reward dysregulation and mood symptoms in an adolescent outpatient sample. *Journal of Abnormal Child Psychology, 41,* 1053–1065. (p. 525)

Gruder, C. L. (1977). Choice of comparison persons in evaluating oneself. In J. M. Suls & R. L. Miller (Eds.), *Social comparison processes.* New York: Hemisphere. (p. 410)

Gu, J., Strauss, C., Bond, R., & Cavanagh, K. (2015). How do mindfulness-based cognitive therapy and mindfulness-based stress reduction improve mental health and wellbeing? A systematic review and meta-analysis of mediation studies. *Clinical Psychology Review, 37,* 1–12. (p. 547)

Gu, X., Lohrenz, T., Salas, R., Baldwin, P. R., Soltani, A., Kirk, U., . . . Montague, P. R. (2015). Belief about nicotine selectively modulates value and reward prediction error signals in smokers. *PNAS, 112,* 2539–2544. (p. 101)

Guardino, C. M., Schetter, C. D., Saxbe, D. E., Adam, E. K., Ramey, S. L., & Shalowitz, M. U. (2016). Diurnal salivary cortisol patterns prior to pregnancy predict infant birth weight. *Health Psychology, 35,* 625–633. (p. 385)

Guéguen, N. (2011). Effects of solicitor sex and attractiveness on receptivity to sexual offers: A field study. *Archives of Sexual Behavior, 40,* 915–919. (p. 185)

Guerin, B. (1986). Mere presence effects in humans: A review. *Journal of Personality and Social Psychology, 22,* 38–77. (p. 429)

Guerin, B. (2003). Language use as social strategy: A review and an analytic framework for the social sciences. *Review of General Psychology, 7,* 251–298. (p. 311)

Guertin, C., Pelletier, L. G., Émond, C., & Lalande, G. (2017). Change in physical and psychological health over time in patients with cardiovascular disease: On the benefits of being self-determined, physically active, and eating well. *Motivation and Emotion,* 1–14. (p. 353)

Guiso, L., Monte, F., Sapienza, P., & Zingales, L. (2008). Culture, gender, and math. *Science, 320,* 1164–1165. (p. 341)

Gunderson, E. A., Gripshover, S. J., Romero, C., Dweck, C. S., Goldin-Meadow, S., & Levine, S. C. (2013). Parent praise to 1- to 3-year-olds predicts children's motivational frameworks 5 years later. *Child Development, 84,* 1526–1541. (p. 339)

Gunnery, S. D., & Ruben, M. A. (2016). Perceptions of Duchenne and non-Duchenne smiles: A meta-analysis. *Cognition and Emotion, 30,* 501–515. (p. 376)

Gunter, R. W., & Bodner, G. E. (2008). How eye movements affect unpleasant memories: Support for a working-memory account. *Behaviour Research and Therapy, 46,* 913–931. (p. 554)

Gunter, T. D., Vaughn, M. G., & Philibert, R. A. (2010). Behavioral genetics in antisocial spectrum disorders and psychopathy: A review of the recent literature. *Behavioral Sciences and the Law, 28,* 148–173. (p. 530)

Gunyadin, G., Selcuk, E., & Zayas, V. (2017). Impressions based on a portrait predict, 1-month later, impressions following a live interaction. *Social Psychological and Personality Science, 8,* 36–44. (p. 481)

Guo, J., He, H., Qu, Z., Wang, X., & Liu, C. (2017). Post-traumatic stress disorder and depression among adult survivors 8 years after the 2008 Wenchuan earthquake in China. *Journal of Affective Disorders, 210,* 27–34. (p. 509)

Guo, X., Zhai, J., Liu, Z., Fang, M., Wang, B., Wang, C., . . . Zhao, J. (2010). Effect of antipsychotic medication alone vs combined with psychosocial intervention on outcomes of early-stage schizophrenia. *Archives of General Psychiatry, 67,* 895–904. (p. 560)

Gustavson, C. R., Garcia, J., Hankins, W. G., & Rusiniak, K. W. (1974). Coyote predation control by aversive conditioning. *Science, 184,* 581–583. (p. 255)

Gustavson, C. R., Kelly, D. J., & Sweeney, M. (1976). Prey-lithium aversions I: Coyotes and wolves. *Behavioral Biology, 17,* 61–72. (p. 255)

Gutchess, A. (2014). Plasticity in the aging brain: New directions in cognitive neuroscience. *Science, 346,* 579–582. (pp. 39, 154)

Guttmacher Institute. (1994). *Sex and America's teenagers.* New York: Alan Guttmacher Institute. (pp. 149, 175)

H., Sally. (1979, August). Videotape recording number T–3, Fortunoff Video Archive of Holocaust Testimonies. New Haven, CT: Yale University Library. (p. 469)

Haaker, J., Yi, J., Petrovic, P., & Olsson, A. (2017). Endogenous opioids regulate social threat learning in humans. *Nature Communications, 8,* 15495. (p. 260)

Haapakoski, R., Mathieu, J., Ebmeier, K. P., Alenius, H., & Kivimäki, M. (2015). Cumulative meta-analysis of interleukins 6 and 1ß, tumour necrosis factor a and C-reactive protein in patients with major depressive disorder. *Brain, Behavior, and Immunity, 49,* 206–215. (p. 391)

Haas, A. P., Eliason, M., Mays, V. M., Mathy, R. M., Cochran, S. D., D'Augelli, A. R., . . . Clayton, P. J. (2011). Suicide and suicide risk in lesbian, gay, bisexual, and transgender populations: Review and recommendations. *Journal of Homosexuality, 58,* 10–51. (p. 500)

Habashi, M. M., Graziano, W. G., & Hoover, A. E. (2016). Searching for the prosocial personality: A big five approach to linking personality and prosocial behavior. *Personality and Social Psychology Bulletin, 42,* 1177–1192. (p. 479)

Habel, U., Koch, K., Kellerman, T., Reske, M., Frommann, N., Wolwer, W., . . . Schneider, F. (2010). Training of affect recognition in schizophrenia: Neurobiological correlates. *Social Neuroscience, 5,* 92–104. (p. 558)

Haber, R. N. (1970). How we remember what we see. *Scientific American,* pp. 104–112. (p. 266)

Hadjistavropoulos, T., Craig, K. D., Duck, S. Cano, A., Goubert, L., Jackson, P. L., . . . Fitzgerald, T. D. (2011). A biopsychosocial formulation of pain communication. *Psychological Bulletin, 137,* 910–939. (p. 221)

Haedt-Matt, A. A., & Keel, P. K. (2011). Revisiting the affect regulation model of binge eating: A meta-analysis of studies using ecological momentary assessment. *Psychological Bulletin, 137,* 660–681. (p. 532)

Hafenbrack, A. C., Kinias, Z., & Barsade, S. G. (2014). Debiasing the mind through meditation: Mindfulness and the sunk-cost bias. *Psychological Science, 25,* 369–376. (p. 404)

Hagger, M. S., Chatzisarantis, N. L. D., Alberts, H., Anggono, C. O., Birt, A., Brand, R., . . . Cannon, T. (2016). A multi-lab pre-registered replication of the ego-depletion effect. *Perspectives on Psychological Science, 11,* 546–573. (p. 398)

Hahn, A., Kranz, G., Sladky, R., Kaufmann, U., Ganger, S., Hummer, A., . . . Lanzenberger, R. (2016). Testosterone affects language areas of the adult human brain. *Human Brain Mapping, 37,* 1738–1748. (p. 340)

Haidt, J. (2000). The positive emotion of elevation. *Prevention and Treatment, 3,* article 3. Retrieved from journals.apa.org/prevention/volume3 (p. 144)

Haidt, J. (2002). The moral emotions. In R. J. Davidson, K. Scherer, & H. H. Goldsmith (Eds.), *Handbook of affective sciences.* New York: Oxford University Press. (p. 144)

Haidt, J. (2012). *The righteous mind: Why good people are divided by politics and religion.* New York: Pantheon. (p. 144)

Hajhosseini, B., Stewart, B., Tan, J. C., Busque, S., & Melcher, M. L. (2013). Evaluating deceased donor registries: Identifying predictive factors of donor designation. *American Surgeon, 79,* 235–241. (p. 305)

Hakuta, K., Bialystok, E., & Wiley, E. (2003). Critical evidence: A test of the critical-period hypothesis for second-language acquisition. *Psychological Science, 14,* 31–38. (p. 315)

Halberstadt, J. B., Niedenthal, P. M., & Kushner, J. (1995). Resolution of lexical ambiguity by emotional state. *Psychological Science, 6,* 278–281. (p. 197)

Halberstadt, J., Sherman, S. J., & Sherman, J. W. (2011). Why Barack Obama is Black. *Psychological Science, 22,* 29–33. (p. 440)

Haldeman, D. C. (1994). The practice and ethics of sexual orientation conversion therapy. *Journal of Consulting and Clinical Psychology, 62,* 221–227. (p. 179)

Haldeman, D. C. (2002). Gay rights, patient rights: The implications of sexual orientation conversion therapy. *Professional Psychology: Research and Practice, 33,* 260–264. (p. 179)

Hales, A. H., Kassner, M. P., Williams, K. D., & Graziano, W. G. (2016). Disagreeableness as a cause and consequence of ostracism. *Personality and Social Psychology Review, 42,* 782–797. (p. 354)

Hall, C. S., & Lindzey, G. (1978). *Theories of personality* (2nd ed.). New York: Wiley. (p. 469)

Hall, C. S., Dornhoff, W., Blick, K. A., & Weesner, K. E. (1982). The dreams of college men and women in 1950 and 1980: A comparison of dream contents and sex differences. *Sleep, 5,* 188–194. (p. 96)

Hall, G. (1997). Context aversion, Pavlovian conditioning, and the psychological side effects of chemotherapy. *European Psychologist, 2,* 118–124. (p. 255)

Hall, G. S. (1904). *Adolescence: Its psychology and its relations to physiology, anthropology, sex, crime, religion and education* (Vol. 1). New York: Appleton-Century-Crofts. (p. 141)

Hall, J. A., Gunnery, S. D., & Horgan, T. G. (2016). Gender differences in interpersonal accuracy. In J. A. Hall, M. S. Mast & T. V. West (Eds.), *The social psychology of perceiving others accurately* (pp. 309–327). New York: Cambridge University Press. (p. 377)

Hall, K. M., Knudson, S. T., Wright, J., Charlifue, S. W., Graves, D. E., & Warner, P. (1999). Follow-up study of individuals with high tetraplegia (C1-C4) 14 to 24 years postinjury. *Archives of Physical Medicine and Rehabilitation, 80,* 1507–1513. (p. 408)

Hall, P. A. (2016). Executive-control processes in high-calorie food consumption. *Current Directions in Psychological Science, 25,* 91–98. (p. 365)

Hall, S. S. (2004, May). The good egg. *Discover,* pp. 30–39. (p. 119)

Hall, S., S., Knox, D., & Shapiro, K. (2017). "I have," "I would," "I won't": Hooking up among sexually diverse groups of college students. *Psychology of Sexual Orientation and Gender Diversity, 4,* 233–240. (p. 183)

Hallal, P. C., Andersen, L. B., Bull, F. C., Guthold, R., Haskell, W., & Ekelund, U. (2012). Global physical activity levels: Surveillance progress, pitfalls, and prospects. *The Lancet, 380,* 247–257. (p. 365)

Haller, R., Rummel, C., Henneberg, S., Pollmer, U., & Köster, E. P. (1999). The influence of early experience with vanillin on food preference later in life. *Chemical Senses, 24,* 465–467. (p. 225)

Halmburger, A., Baumert, A., & Schmitt, M. (2015). Anger as driving factor of moral courage in comparison with guilt and global mood: A multimethod approach. *European Journal of Social Psychology, 45,* 39–51. (p. 394)

Halpern, D. (2015). The rise of psychology in policy: The UK's de facto council of psychological science advisers. *Perspectives on Psychological Science, 10,* 768–771. (p. 304)

Halpern, D., Valenzuela, S., & Katz, J. E. (2016). "Selfie-ists" or "Narci-selfiers"?: A cross-lagged panel analysis of selfie taking and narcissism. *Personality and Individual Differences, 97,* 98–101. (p. 483)

Halpern, D. F., Benbow, C. P., Geary, D. C., Gur, R. C., Hyde, J. S., & Gernsbacher, M. A. (2007). The science of sex differences in science and mathematics. *Psychological Science in the Public Interest, 8,* 1–51. (p. 340)

Hambrick, D. Z. (2014, December 2). Brain training doesn't make you smarter. *Scientific American* (scientificamerican.com/article/brain-training-doesn-t-make-you-smarter/). (p. 154)

Hambrick, D. Z., Altmann, E. M., Oswald, F. L., Meinz, E. J., Gobet, F., & Campitelli, G. (2014a). Accounting for expert performance: The devil is in the details. *Intelligence, 45,* 112–114. (p. 357)

Hambrick, D. Z., & Meinz, E. J. (2011). Limits on the predictive power of domain-specific experience and knowledge in skilled performance. *Current Directions in Psychological Science, 20,* 275–279. (p. 357)

Hambrick, D. Z., Oswald, F. L., Altmann, E. M., Meinz, E. J., Gobet, F., & Campitelli, G. (2014b). Deliberate practice: Is that all it takes to become an expert? *Intelligence, 45,* 34–45. (p. 357)

Hamid, A. A., Pettibone, J. R., Mabrouk, O. S., Hetrick, V. L., Schmidt, R., Vander Weele, C. M., . . . Berke, J. D. (2016). Mesolimbic dopamine signals the value of work. *Nature Neuroscience, 19,* 117–126. (pp. 56, 349)

Hamilton, J. L., Stange, J. P., Abramson, L. Y., & Alloy, L. B. (2015). Stress and the development of cognitive vulnerabilities to depression explain sex differences in depressive symptoms during adolescence. *Clinical Psychological Science, 3,* 702–714. (p. 520)

Hammack, P. L. (2005). The life course development of human sexual orientation: An integrative paradigm. *Human Development, 48,* 267–290. (p. 179)

Hammer, E. (2003). How lucky you are to be a psychology major. *Eye on Psi Chi,* 4–5. (p. C-5)

Hammersmith, S. K. (1982, August). *Sexual preference: An empirical study from the Alfred C. Kinsey Institute for Sex Research.* Paper presented at the 90th Annual Convention of the American Psychological Association, Washington, DC. (p. 180)

Hammond, D. C. (2008). Hypnosis as sole anesthesia for major surgeries: Historical and contemporary perspectives. *American Journal of Clinical Hypnosis, 51,* 101–121. (p. 224)

Hampshire, A., Highfield, R. R., Parkin, B. L., & Owen, A. M. (2012). Fractionating human intelligence. *Neuron, 76,* 1225–1237. (p. 324)

Hamza, C. A., Willoughby, T., & Heffer, T. (2015). Impulsivity and nonsuicidal self-injury: A review and meta-analysis. *Clinical Psychology Review, 38,* 13–24. (p. 502)

Han, B., Kott, P. S., Hughes, A., McKeon, R., Blanco, C., & Compton, W. M. (2016). Estimating the rates of deaths by suicide among adults who attempt suicide in the United States. *Journal of Psychiatric Research, 77,* 125–133. (p. 501)

Hanania, R. (2017). The personalities of politicians: A big five survey of American legislators. *Personality and Individual Differences, 108,* 164–167. (p. 479)

Haney, J. L. (2016). Predictors of homonegativity in the United States and the Netherlands using the fifth wave of the World Values Survey. *Journal of Homosexuality, 63,* 1355–1377. (p. 437)

Hänggi, J., Koeneke, S., Bezzola, L., & Jäncke, L. (2010). Structural neuroplasticity in the sensorimotor network of professional female ballet dancers. *Human Brain Mapping, 31,* 1196–1206. (p. 39)

Hankin, B. L., & Abramson, L. Y. (2001). Development of gender differences in depression: An elaborated cognitive vulnerability-transactional stress theory. *Psychological Bulletin, 127,* 773–796. (p. 520)

Hanlon, E. C., Tasali, E., Leproult, R., Stuhr, K. L., Doncheck, E., de Wit, H., . . . Van Cauter, E. (2016). Sleep restriction enhances the daily rhythm of circulating levels of Endocannabinoid 2-Arachidonoylglycerol. *Sleep, 39,* 653–664. (p. 93)

Hannikainen, I., Cabral, G., Machery, E., & Struchiner, N. (2016). A deterministic worldview promotes approval of state paternalism. *Journal of Experimental Social Psychology 70,* 251–259. (p. 397)

Harackiewicz, J. M., Canning, E. A., Tibbetts, Y., Giffen, C. J., Blair, S. S., Rouse, D. I., & Hyde, J. S. (2014). Closing the social class achievement gap for first-generation students in undergraduate biology. *Journal of Educational Psychology, 106,* 375–389. (p. 344)

Harackiewicz, J. M., Canning, E. A., Tibbetts, Y., Priniski, S. J., & Hyde, J. S. (2016). Closing achievement gaps with a utility-value intervention: Disentangling race and social class. *Journal of Personality and Social Psychology, 111,* 745–765. (p. 344)

Harari, G. M., Lane, N. D., Wang, R., Crosier, B. S., Campbell, A. T., & Gosling, S. D. (2016). Using smartphones to collect behavioral data in psychological science: Opportunities, practical considerations, and challenges. *Perspectives on Psychological Science, 11,* 838–854. (p. 22)

Harbaugh, W. T., Mayr, U., & Burghart, D. R. (2007). Neural responses to taxation and voluntary giving reveal motives for charitable donations. *Science, 316,* 1622–1625. (p. 454)

Harber, K. D. (1998). Feedback to minorities: Evidence of a positive bias. *Journal of Personality and Social Psychology, 74,* 622–628. (p. 435)

Harden, K. P. (2012). True love waits? A sibling-comparison study of age at first sexual intercourse and romantic relationships in young adulthood. *Psychological Science, 23,* 1324–1336. (p. 186)

Harden, K. P., & Mendle, J. (2011). Why don't smart teens have sex? A behavioral genetic approach. *Child Development, 82,* 1327–1344. (p. 178)

Hardt, O., Einarsson, E. O., & Nader, K. (2010). A bridge over troubled water: Reconsolidation as a link between cognitive and neuroscientific memory research traditions. *Annual Review of Psychology, 61,* 141–167. (p. 289)

Hare, R. D. (1975). Psychophysiological studies of psychopathy. In D. C. Fowles (Ed.), *Clinical applications of psychophysiology* (pp. 77–105). New York: Columbia University Press. (p. 530)

Harenski, C. L., Harenski, K. A., Shane, M. W., & Kiehl, K. A. (2010). Aberrant neural processing of moral violations in criminal psychopaths. *Journal of Abnormal Psychology, 119,* 863–874. (p. 531)

Harkin, B., Webb, T. L., Chang, B. P. I., Prestwich, A., Conner, M., Kellar, I., . . . Sheeran, P. (2016). Does monitoring goal progress promote goal attainment? A meta-analysis of the experimental evidence. *Psychological Bulletin, 142,* 198–229. (pp. 358, 359, 366, B-9)

Harkins, S. G., & Szymanski, K. (1989). Social loafing and group evaluation. *Journal of Personality and Social Psychology, 56,* 934–941. (p. 430)

Harlow, H. F., Harlow, M. K., & Suomi, S. J. (1971). From thought to therapy: Lessons from a primate laboratory. *American Scientist, 59,* 538–549. (p. 133)

Harmon-Jones, E., Abramson, L. Y., Sigelman, J., Bohlig, A., Hogan, M. E., & Harmon-Jones, C. (2002). Proneness to hypomania/mania symptoms or depression symptoms and asymmetrical frontal cortical responses to an anger-evoking event. *Journal of Personality and Social Psychology, 82,* 610–618. (p. 374)

Harmon-Jones, E., Harmon-Jones, C., & Levy, N. (2015). An action-based model of cognitive-dissonance processes. *Current Directions in Psychological Science, 24,* 184–189. (p. 420)

Harnett, N. G., Shumen, J. R., Wagle, P. A., Wood, K. H., Wheelock, M. D., Baños, J. H., & Knight, D. C. (2016). Neural mechanisms of human temporal fear conditioning. *Neurobiology of Learning and Memory, 136,* 97–104. (p. 240)

Harold, C. M., Oh, I.-S., Holtz, B. C., Han, S., & Giacalone, R. A. (2016). Fit and frustration as drivers of targeted counterproductive work behaviors: A multifoci perspective. *Journal of Applied Psychology, 101,* 1513–1535. (p. B-3)

Harper, C., & McLanahan, S. (2004). Father absence and youth incarceration. *Journal of Research on Adolescence, 14,* 369–397. (p. 443)

Harris, B. (1979). Whatever happened to Little Albert? *American Psychologist, 34,* 151–160. (p. 241)

Harris Interactive. (2010). *2009 eHarmony® marriage metrics study: Methodological notes.* eHarmony. Retrieved from eharmony.com/press-release/31/ (p. 448)

Harris, J. R. (1998). *The nurture assumption: Why children turn out the way they do.* New York: Free Press. (pp. 135, 147)

Harris, J. R. (2002). Beyond the nurture assumption: Testing hypotheses about the child's environment. In J. G. Borkowski, S. L. Ramey, & M. Bristol-Power (Eds.), *Parenting and the child's world: Influences on academic, intellectual, and social-emotional development* (pp. 3–20). Mahwah, NJ: Erlbaum. (p. 147)

Harris, J. R. (2006). *No two are alike: Human nature and human individuality.* New York: Norton. (p. 72)

Harris, J. R. (2009). *The nurture assumption: Why children turn out the way they do, revised and updated.* New York: Free Press. (p. 478)

Harris, M. A., Brett, C. E., Johnson, W., & Deary, I. J. (2016). Personality stability from age 14 to age 77 years. *Psychology and Aging, 31,* 862–874. (p. 118)

Harris, R. J. (1994). The impact of sexually explicit media. In J. Brant & D. Zillmann (Eds.), *Media effects: Advances in theory and research.* Hillsdale, NJ: Erlbaum. (p. 444)

Harrison, G., Hopper, K. I. M., Craig, T., Laska, E., Siegel, C., Wanderling, J., . . . Holmberg, S. K. (2001). Recovery from psychotic illness: A 15-and 25-year international follow-up study. *The British Journal of Psychiatry, 178,* 506–517. (p. 524)

Harrison, L. A., Hurlemann, R., & Adolphs, R. (2015). An enhanced default approach bias following amygdala lesions in humans. *Psychological Science, 26,* 1543–1555. (p. 55)

Harrison, N. A., Johnston, K., Corno, F., Casey, S. J., Friedner, K., Humphreys, K., . . . Kopelman, M. D. (2017). Psychogenic amnesia: Syndromes, outcome, and patterns of retrograde amnesia. *Brain: A Journal of Neurology, 140,* 2498–2510. (p. 527)

Harriston, K. A. (1993, December 24). 1 shakes, 1 snoozes: Both win $45 million. *Washington Post* release (in Tacoma News Tribune, pp. A1, A2). (p. 484)

Harter, J. K., Schmidt, F. L., Asplund, J. W., Killham, E. A., & Agrawal, S. (2010). Causal impact of employee work perceptions on the bottom line of organizations. *Perspectives on Psychological Science, 5,* 378–389. (p. B-9)

Harter, J. K., Schmidt, F. L., & Hayes, T. L. (2002). Business-unit-level relationship between employee satisfaction, employee engagement, and business outcomes: A meta-analysis. *Journal of Applied Psychology, 87,* 268–279. (p. B-8)

Hartl, A. C., Laursen, B., & Cillessen, A. H. (2015). A survival analysis of adolescent friendships: The downside of dissimilarity. *Psychological Science, 26,* 1304–1315. (p. 141)

Hartwig, M., & Bond, C. F., Jr. (2011). Why do lie-catchers fail? A lens model meta-analysis of human lie judgments. *Psychological Bulletin, 137,* 643–659. (p. 376)

Harvey, A. G., & Tang, N. K. Y. (2012). (Mis)perception of sleep in insomnia: A puzzle and a resolution. *Psychological Bulletin, 138,* 77–101. (p. 96)

Harvey, S. B., Øverland, S., Hatch, S. L., Wessely, S., Mykletun, A., & Hotopf, M. (2018). Exercise and the prevention of depression: Results of the HUNT Cohort Study. *American Journal of Psychiatry, 175,* 28–36. (pp. 402, 519)

Harward, S. C., Hedrick, N. G., Hall, C. E., Parra-Bueno, P., Milner, T. A., Pan, E., . . . McNamara, J. O. (2016). Autocrine BDNF–TrkB signalling within a single dendritic spine. *Nature, 538,* 99–103. (p. 279)

Haselton, M. G., & Gildersleeve, K. (2011). Can men detect ovulation? *Current Directions in Psychological Science, 20,* 87–92. (p. 173)

Haselton, M. G., & Gildersleeve, K. (2016). Human ovulation cues. *Current Opinion in Psychology, 7,* 120–125. (p. 173)

Haslam, S. A., & Reicher, S. D. (2007). Beyond the banality of evil: Three dynamics of an interactionist social psychology of tyranny. *Personality and Social Psychology Bulletin, 33,* 615–622. (p. 419)

Haslam, S. A., & Reicher, S. D. (2012). Contesting the "nature" of conformity: What Milgram and Zimbardo's studies really show. *PLoS Biology, 10,* e1001426. (p. 419)

Haslam, S. A., Reicher, S. D., & Birney, M. E. (2014). Nothing by mere authority: Evidence that in an experimental analogue of the Milgram paradigm participants are motivated not by orders but by appeals to science. *Journal of Social Issues, 70,* 473–488. (p. 427)

Haslam, S. A., Reicher, S. D., & Birney, M. E. (2016). Questioning authority: New perspectives on Milgram's "obedience" research and its implications for intergroup relations. *Current Opinion in Psychology, 11,* 6–9. (p. 427)

Hassan, B., & Rahman, Q. (2007). Selective sexual orientation–related differences in object location memory. *Behavioral Neuroscience, 121,* 625–633. (p. 182)

Hassan, J. (2016, October 12). Homophobic attacks in the U.K. have risen 147% since Brexit, report says. *The Washington Post* (washingtonpost.com). (p. 439)

Hassin, R. R. (2013). Yes it can: On the functional abilities of the human unconscious. *Perspectives on Psychological Science, 8,* 195–207. (p. 305)

Hatfield, E. (1988). Passionate and companionate love. In R. J. Sternberg & M. L. Barnes (Eds.), *The psychology of love.* New Haven, CT: Yale University Press. (p. 451)

Hatfield, E. (2016). Love and sex in the marketplace. In R. J. Sternberg, S. T. Fiske, & D. J. Foss (Eds.), *Scientists making a difference: One hundred eminent behavioral and brain scientists talk about their most important contributions.* New York: Cambridge University Press. (p. 448)

Hatfield, E., Mo, Y., & Rapson, R. L. (2015). Love, sex, and marriage across cultures. *Oxford Handbooks Online* (oxfordhandbooks.com). (p. 451)

Hatfield, E., & Sprecher, S. (1986). *Mirror, mirror . . . The importance of looks in everyday life.* Albany: State University of New York Press. (p. 449)

Hathaway, S. R. (1960). *An MMPI Handbook* (Vol. 1, Foreword). Minneapolis: University of Minnesota Press (rev. ed.), 1972. (p. 477)

Hatzenbuehler, M. L. (2011). The social environment and suicide attempts in lesbian, gay, and bisexual youth. *Pediatrics, 127,* 896–903. (p. 500)

Hatzenbuehler, M. L. (2014). Structural stigma and the health of lesbian, gay, and bisexual populations. *Current Directions in Psychological Science, 23,* 127–132. (p. 437)

Hatzigeorgiadis, A., Zourbanos, N., Galanis, E., & Theodorakis, Y. (2011). Self-talk and sports performance: A meta-analysis. *Perspectives on Psychological Science, 6,* 348–356. (p. 546)

Haun, D. B. M., Rekers, Y., & Tomasello, M. (2014). Children conform to the behavior of peers; other great apes stick with what they know. *Psychological Science, 25,* 2160–2167. (p. 144)

Havas, D. A., Glenberg, A. M., Gutowski, K. A., Lucarelli, M. J., & Davidson, R. J. (2010). Cosmetic use of Botulinum Toxin-A affects processing of emotional language. *Psychological Science, 21,* 895–900. (p. 381)

Hawkley, L. C., Hughes, M. E., Waite, L. J., Masi, C. M., Thisted, R. A., & Cacioppo, J. T. (2008). From social structure factors to perceptions of relationship quality and loneliness: The Chicago Health, Aging, and Social Relations Study. *Journal of Gerontology: Series B, 63,* S375–S384. (p. 399)

Haworth, C. M. A., Wright, M. J., Luciano, M., Martin, N. G., de Geus, E. J., van Beijsterveldt, C. E., . . . Plomin, R. (2010). The heritability of general cognitive ability increases linearly from childhood to young adulthood. *Molecular Psychiatry, 15,* 1112–1120. (p. 338)

Haworth, C. M. A., Wright, M. J., Martin, N. W., Martin, N. G., Boomsma, D. I., Bartels, M., . . . Plomin, R. (2009). A twin study of the genetics of high cognitive ability selected from 11,000 twin pairs in six studies from four countries. *Behavior Genetics, 39,* 359–370. (p. 336)

Haxby, J. V. (2001, July 7). Quoted in B. Bower, Faces of perception. Science News, pp. 10–12. See also J. V. Haxby, M. I. Gobbini, M. L. Furey, A. Ishai, J. L. Schouten & P. Pietrini (2001), Distributed and overlapping representations of faces and objects in ventral temporal cortex. *Science, 293,* 2425–2430. (p. 205)

Hayashi, Y., Kashiwagi, M., Yasuda, K., Ando, R., Kanuka, M., Sakai, K., & Itohara, S. (2015). Cells of a common developmental origin regulate REM/non-REM sleep and wakefulness in mice. *Science, 350,* 957–961. (p. 90)

Hays, C., & Carver, L. J. (2014). Follow the liar: The effects of adult lies on children's honesty. *Developmental Science, 17,* 977–983. (p. 262)

Hazan, C., & Shaver, P. R. (1994). Attachment as an organizational framework for research on close relationships. *Psychological Inquiry, 5,* 1–22. (p. 138)

Hazelrigg, M. D., Cooper, H. M., & Borduin, C. M. (1987). Evaluating the effectiveness of family therapies: An integrative review and analysis. *Psychological Bulletin, 101,* 428–442. (p. 547)

HBVA. (2018, accessed February 20). *Honour killings by region, South and Central Asia.* Honour Based Violence Awareness Network. Retrieved from hbv-awareness.com (p. 170)

He, Z., & Jin, Y. (2016). Intrinsic control of axon regeneration. *Neuron, 90,* 437–451. (p. 64)

Headey, B., Muffels, R., & Wagner, G. G. (2010). Long-running German panel survey shows that personal and economic choices, not just genes, matter for happiness. *PNAS, 107,* 17922–17926. (p. 411)

Healy, A. F., Jones, M., Lalchandani, L. A., & Tack, L. A. (2017). Timing of quizzes during learning: Effects on motivation and retention. *Journal of Experimental Psychology: Applied, 23,* 128–137. (p. 246)

Heavey, C. L., & Hurlburt, R. T. (2008). The phenomena of inner experience. *Consciousness and Cognition, 17,* 798–810. (p. 319)

Heberle, A. E., & Carter, A. S. (2015). Cognitive aspects of young children's experience of economic disadvantage. *Psychological Bulletin, 141,* 723–746. (p. 339)

Hedström, P., Liu, K.-Y., & Nordvik, M. K. (2008). Interaction domains and suicides: A population-based panel study of suicides in the Stockholm metropolitan area, 1991–1999. *Social Forces, 2,* 713–740. (p. 501)

Hehman, E., Flake, J. K., & Calanchini, J. (2018). Disproportionate use of lethal force in policing is associated with regional racial biases of residents. *Social Psychological Personality Science,* in press. (p. 426)

Heider, F. (1958). *The psychology of interpersonal relations.* New York: Wiley. (p. 416)

Heiman, J. R. (1975, April). The physiology of erotica: Women's sexual arousal. *Psychology Today,* pp. 90–94. (p. 176)

Hein, G., Morishima, Y., Leiberg, S., Sul, S., & Fehr, E. (2016). The brain's functional network architecture reveals human motives. *Science, 351,* 1074–1078. (p. 455)

Heine, S. J., Proulx, T., & Vohs, K. D. (2006). Meaning maintenance model: On the coherence of human motivations. *Personality and Social Psychology Review, 10,* 88–110. (p. 350)

Hejmadi, A., Davidson, R. J., & Rozin, P. (2000). Exploring Hindu Indian emotion expressions: Evidence for accurate recognition by Americans and Indians. *Psychological Science, 11,* 183–187. (p. 376)

Helfand, D. (2011, January 7). An assault on rationality. *The New York Times* (nytimes.com). (p. 231)

Helleberg, M., Afzal, S., Kronborg, G., Larsen, C. S., Pedersen, G., Pedersen, C., . . . Obel, N. (2013). Mortality attributable to smoking among HIV-1-infected individuals: A nationwide, population-based cohort study. *Clinical Infectious Diseases, 56,* 727–734. (p. 105)

Heller, A. S., Johnstone, T., Schackman, A. J., Light, S. N., Peterson, M. J., Kolden, G. G., . . . Davidson, R. J. (2009). Reduced capacity to sustain positive emotion in major depression reflects diminished maintenance of fronto-striatal brain activation. *PNAS, 106,* 22445–22450. (p. 518)

Heller, S. B. (2014). Summer jobs reduce violence among disadvantaged youth. *Science, 346,* 1219–1222. (p. 145)

Heller, W. (1990, May/June). Of one mind: Second thoughts about the brain's dual nature. *The Sciences,* pp. 38–44. (p. 67)

Helliwell, J., Layard, R., & Sachs, J. (Eds.) (2013). *World happiness report.* New York: The Earth Institute, Columbia University. (pp. 410, 412)

Helliwell, J. F., & Wang, S. (2015). How was the weekend? How the social context underlies weekend effects in happiness and other emotions for U.S. workers. *PLoS ONE, 10,* e0145123. (p. 408)

Helmreich, W. B. (1992). *Against all odds: Holocaust survivors and the successful lives they made in America.* New York: Simon & Schuster. (pp. 137, 469)

Helmreich, W. B. (1994). Personal correspondence. Department of Sociology, City University of New York. (p. 469)

Helms, J. E., Jernigan, M., & Mascher, J. (2005). The meaning of race in psychology and how to change it: A methodological perspective. *American Psychologist, 60,* 27–36. (p. 342)

Helmuth, L. (2001). Boosting brain activity from the outside in. *Science, 292,* 1284–1286. (p. 564)

Helsen, K., Goubert, L., Peters, M. L., & Vlaeyen, J. W. S. (2011). Observational learning and pain-related fear: An experimental study with colored cold pressor tasks. *The Journal of Pain, 12,* 1230–1239. (p. 511)

Hembree, R. (1988). Correlates, causes, effects, and treatment of test anxiety. *Review of Educational Research, 58,* 47–77. (p. 350)

Hemmings, S. M. J., Malan-Müller, S., van den Heuvel, L. L., Demmitt, B. A., Stanislawski, M. A., Smith, D. G., . . . Lowry, C. A. (2017). The microbiome in posttraumatic stress disorder and trauma-exposed controls: An exploratory study. *Psychosomatic Medicine, 79,* 936–946. (p. 514)

Henderlong, J., & Lepper, M. R. (2002). The effects of praise on children's intrinsic motivation: A review and synthesis. *Psychological Bulletin, 128,* 774–795. (p. 358)

Henderson, J. M. (2007). Regarding scenes. *Current Directions in Psychological Science, 16,* 219–222. (p. 194)

Henig, R. M. (2010, August 18). What is it about 20-somethings? *The New York Times Magazine* (nytimes.com). (p. 149)

Henley, N. M. (1989). Molehill or mountain? What we know and don't know about sex bias in language. In M. Crawford & M. Gentry (Eds.), *Gender and thought: Psychological perspectives* (pp. 59–78). New York: Springer-Verlag. (p. 320)

Hennenlotter, A., Dresel, C., Castrop, F., Ceballos Baumann, A., Wohschlager, A., & Haslinger, B. (2008). The link between facial feedback and neural activity within central circuitries of emotion: New insights from Botulinum Toxin-induced denervation of frown muscles. *Cerebral Cortex, 19,* 537–542. (p. 381)

Hennessey, B. A., & Amabile, T. M. (2010). Creativity. *Annual Review of Psychology, 61,* 569–598. (pp. 306, B-11)

Henrich, J., Heine, S. J., & Norenzayan, A. (2010). The weirdest people in the world? *Behavioral and Brain Sciences, 33,* 61–135. (p. 9)

Hensley, C., Browne, J. A., & Trentham, C. E. (2018). Exploring the social and emotional context of childhood animal cruelty and its potential link to adult human violence. *Psychology, Crime & Law, 24*(5). (p. 118)

Hepper, P. (2005). Unravelling our beginnings. *The Psychologist, 18,* 474–477. (p. 119)

Herbenick, D., Reece, M., Schick, V., & Sanders, S. A. (2014). Erect penile length and circumference dimensions of 1,661 sexually active men in the United States. *Journal of Sexual Medicine, 11,* 93–101. (p. 174)

Herbenick, D., Reece, M., Schick, V., Sanders, S. A., Dodge, B., & Fortenberry, J. D. (2010). Sexual behavior in the United States: Results from a national probability sample of men and women ages 14–94. *Journal of Sexual Medicine, 7*(Suppl. 5), 255–265. (p. 178)

Herculano-Houzel, S. (2012). The remarkable, yet not extraordinary, human brain as a scaled-up primate brain and its associated cost. *PNAS, 109*(suppl 1), 10661–10668. (p. 47)

Herholz, S. C., & Zatorre, R. J. (2012). Musical training as a framework for brain plasticity: Behavior, function, and structure. *Neuron, 76,* 486–502. (p. 39)

Herman, C. P., & Polivy, J. (1980). Restrained eating. In A. J. Stunkard (Ed.), *Obesity.* Philadelphia: Saunders. (p. 366)

Herman, C. P., Polivy, J., Pliner, P., & Vartanian, L. R. (2015). Mechanisms underlying the portion-size effect. *Physiology & Behavior, 144,* 129–136. (p. 364)

Herman, C. P., Roth, D. A., & Polivy, J. (2003). Effects of the presence of others on food intake: A normative interpretation. *Psychological Bulletin, 129,* 873–886. (p. 364)

Herman-Giddens, M. E. (2013). The enigmatic pursuit of puberty in girls. *Pediatrics, 132,* 1125–1126. (p. 167)

Herman-Giddens, M. E., Steffes, J., Harris, D., Slora, E., Hussey, M., Dowshen, S. A., . . . Reiter, E. O. (2012). Secondary sexual characteristics in boys: Data from the pediatric research in office settings network. *Pediatrics, 130,* 1058–1068. (p. 166)

Hernandez, A. E., & Li, P. (2007). Age of acquisition: Its neural and computational mechanisms. *Psychological Bulletin, 133,* 638–650. (p. 315)

Hernandez, R., Kershaw, K. N., Siddique, J., Boehm, J. K., Kubzansky, L. D., Diez-Roux, A., . . . Lloyd-Jones, D. M. (2015). Optimism and cardiovascular health: Multi-ethnic study of atherosclerosis (MESA). *Health Behavior and Policy Review, 2,* 62–73. (p. 398)

Herring, D. R., White, K. R., Jabeen, L. N., Hinojos, M., & Terrazas, G. (2013). On the automatic activation of attitudes: A quarter century of evaluative priming research. *Psychological Bulletin, 132,* 1062–1089. (pp. 192, 281)

Herringa, R. J., Phillips, M. L., Fournier, J. C., Kronhaus, D. M., & Germain, A. (2013). Childhood and adult trauma both correlate with dorsal anterior cingulate activation to threat in combat veterans. *Psychological Medicine, 43,* 1533–1542. (p. 512)

Herrmann, E., Call, J., Hernández-Lloreda, M. V., Hare, B., & Tomasello, M. (2007). Humans have evolved specialized skills of social cognition: The cultural intelligence hypothesis. *Science, 317,* 1360–1365. (p. 260)

Herrnstein, R. J., & Loveland, D. H. (1964). Complex visual concept in the pigeon. *Science, 146,* 549–551. (p. 245)

Hershenson, M. (1989). *The moon illusion.* Hillsdale, NJ: Erlbaum. (p. 212)

Hertenstein, M. (2009). *The tell: The little cues that reveal big truths about who we are.* New York: Basic Books. (pp. 118, 392)

Hertenstein, M. J., Hansel, C., Butts, S., Hile, S. (2009). Smile intensity in photographs predicts divorce later in life. *Motivation & Emotion, 33,* 99–105. (p. 118)

Hertenstein, M. J., Keltner, D., App, B., Bulleit, B., & Jaskolka, A. (2006). Touch communicates distinct emotions. *Emotion, 6,* 528–533. (p. 133)

Herz, R. (2007). *The scent of desire: Discovering our enigmatic sense of smell.* New York: Morrow/HarperCollins. (p. 226)

Herz, R. (2012, January 28). You eat that? *The Wall Street Journal* (online.wsj.com). (p. 363)

Herz, R. S. (2001). Ah sweet skunk! Why we like or dislike what we smell. *Cerebrum, 3,* 31–47. (p. 226)

Herz, R. S., Beland, S. L., & Hellerstein, M. (2004). Changing odor hedonic perception through emotional associations in humans. *International Journal of Comparative Psychology, 17,* 315–339. (p. 226)

Hess, E. H. (1956, July). Space perception in the chick. *Scientific American,* pp. 71–80. (p. 213)

Hess, U., & Thibault, P. (2009). Darwin and emotion expression. *American Psychologist, 64,* 120–128. (p. 379)

Hetherington, M. M., Anderson, A. S., Norton, G. N. M., & Newson, L. (2006). Situational effects on meal intake: A comparison of eating alone and eating with others. *Physiology and Behavior, 88,* 498–505. (p. 364)

Hewett, R., & Conway, N. (2015). The undermining effect revisited: The salience of everyday verbal rewards and self-determined motivation. *Journal of Organizational Behavior, 37*, 436–455. (p. 358)

Hickok, G. (2014). *The myth of mirror neurons: The real neuroscience of communication and cognition.* New York: Norton. (pp. 259, 260)

Hickok, G., Bellugi, U., & Klima, E. S. (2001, June). Sign language in the brain. *Scientific American*, pp. 58–65. (p. 67)

Hilgard, E. R. (1986). *Divided consciousness: Multiple controls in human thought and action.* New York: Wiley. (p. 224)

Hilgard, E. R. (1992). Dissociation and theories of hypnosis. In E. Fromm & M. R. Nash (Eds.), *Contemporary hypnosis research.* New York: Guilford. (p. 224)

Hill, A. J. (2007). The psychology of food craving. *Proceedings of the Nutrition Society, 66*, 277–285. (p. 241)

Hill, C. E., & Nakayama, E. Y. (2000). Client-centered therapy: Where has it been and where is it going? A comment on Hathaway. *Journal of Clinical Psychology, 56*, 961–875. (p. 539)

Hills, P. J., Werno, M. A., & Lewis, M. B. (2011). Sad people are more accurate at face recognition than happy people. *Consciousness and Cognition, 20*, 1502–1517. (p. 514)

Hines, M. (2004). *Brain gender.* New York: Oxford University Press. (p. 166)

Hingson, R. W., Heeren, T., & Winter, M. R. (2006). Age at drinking onset and alcohol dependence. *Archives of Pediatrics & Adolescent Medicine, 160*, 739–746. (p. 112)

Hintzman, D. L. (1978). *The psychology of learning and memory.* San Francisco: Freeman. (p. 271)

Hinz, L. D., & Williamson, D. A. (1987). Bulimia and depression: A review of the affective variant hypothesis. *Psychological Bulletin, 102*, 150–158. (p. 532)

Hirsh-Pasek, K., Adamson, L. B., Bakeman, R., Owen, M. T., Golinkoff, R. M., Pace, A., . . . Suma, K. (2015). The contribution of early communication quality to low-income children's language success. *Psychological Science, 26*, 1071–1083. (p. 315)

Hirst, W., & Phelps, E. A. (2016). Flashbulb memories. *Current Directions in Psychological Science, 25*, 36–41. (p. 278)

Hirst, W., Phelps, E. A., Buckner, R. L., Budson, A. E., Cuc, A., Gabrieli, J. D. E., . . . Vaidya, C. J. (2009). Long-term memory for the terrorist attack of September 11: Flashbulb memories, event memories, and the factors that influence their retention. *Journal of Experimental Psychology: General, 138*, 161–176. (p. 278)

Hjelmborg, J. V. B., Fagnani, C., Silventoinen, K., McGue, M., Korkeila, M., Christensen, K., . . . Kaprio, J. (2008). Genetic influences on growth traits of BMI: A longitudinal study of adult twins. *Obesity, 16*, 847–852. (p. 365)

Hjorthøj, C., Stürup, A. E., McGrath, J. J., & Nordentoft, M. (2017). Years of potential life lost and life expectancy in schizophrenia: A systematic review and meta-analysis. *The Lancet Psychiatry, 4*, 295–301. (p. 524)

HMHL. (2002, January). Disaster and trauma. *Harvard Mental Health Letter*, pp. 1–5. (p. 385)

HMHL. (2007, February). Electroconvulsive therapy. *Harvard Mental Health Letter*, Harvard Medical School, pp. 1–4. (p. 563)

Hoang, T. D., Reis, J., Zhu, N., Jacobs, D. R., Jr., Launer, L. J., Whitmer, R. A., . . . Yaffe, K. (2016). Effect of early adult patterns of physical activity and television viewing on midlife cognitive function. *JAMA Psychiatry, 73*, 73–79. (p. 153)

Hobaiter, C., Poisot, T., Zuberbühler, K., Hoppitt, W., & Gruber, T. (2014). Social network analysis shows direct evidence for social transmission of tool use in wild chimpanzees. *PLoS Biology, 12*, e1001960. (p. 310)

Hobbs, W. R., Burke, M., Christakis, N. A., & Fowler, J. H. (2016). Online social integration is association with reduced mortality risk. *PNAS, 113*, 12980–12984. (p. 356)

Hobson, J. A. (1995, September). Quoted in G. H. Colt, The power of dreams. *Life*, pp. 36–49. (p. 97)

Hobson, J. A. (2003). *Dreaming: An introduction to the science of sleep.* New York: Oxford University Press. (p. 98)

Hobson, J. A. (2004). *13 dreams Freud never had: The new mind science.* New York: Pi Press. (p. 98)

Hobson, J. A. (2009). REM sleep and dreaming: Towards a theory of protoconsciousness. *Nature Reviews Neuroscience, 10*, 803–814. (p. 98)

Hochberg, L. R., Serruya, M. D., Friehs, G. M., Mukand, J. A., Saleh, M., Caplan, A. H., . . . Donoghue, J. P. (2006). Neuronal ensemble control of prosthetic devices by a human with tetraplegia. *Nature, 442*, 164–171. (p. 61)

Hochmair, I. (2013, September). *Cochlear implants: The size of the task concerning children born deaf.* Retrieved from www.medel.com/cochlear-implants-facts. (p. 218)

Hoebel, B. G., & Teitelbaum, P. (1966). Effects of forcefeeding and starvation on food intake and body weight in a rat with ventromedial hypothalamic lesions. *Journal of Comparative and Physiological Psychology, 61*, 189–193. (p. 362)

Hoeft, F., Watson, C. L., Kesler, S. R., Bettinger, K. E., & Reiss, A. L. (2008). Gender differences in the mesocorticolimbic system during computer game-play. *Journal of Psychiatric Research, 42*, 253–258. (p. 102)

Hoffman, B. M., Babyak, M. A., Craighead, W. E., Sherwood, A., Doraiswamy, P. M., Coons, M. J., & Blumenthal, J. A. (2011). Exercise and pharmacotherapy in patients with major depression: One-year follow-up of the SMILE study. *Psychosomatic Medicine, 73*, 127–133. (p. 402)

Hoffman, D. D. (1998). *Visual intelligence: How we create what we see.* New York: Norton. (p. 206)

Hoffman, H. (2012). Considering the role of conditioning in sexual orientation. *Archives of Sexual Behavior, 41*, 63–71. (p. 238)

Hoffman, H. G. (2004, August). Virtual-reality therapy. *Scientific American*, pp. 58–65. (p. 224)

Hoffman, Y. S. G., Shrira, A., Cohen-Fridel, S., Grossman, E. S., & Bodner, E. (2016). The effect of exposure to missile attacks on posttraumatic stress disorder symptoms as a function of perceived media control and locus of control. *Psychiatry Research, 244*, 51–56. (p. 397)

Hofmann, W., De Houwer, J., Perugini, M., Baeyens, F., & Crombez, G. (2010). Evaluative conditioning in humans: A meta-analysis. *Psychological Bulletin, 136*, 390–421. (p. 404)

Hogan, C. L., Catalino, L. I., Mata, J., & Fredrickson, B. L. (2015). Beyond emotional benefits: Physical activity and sedentary behavior affect psychosocial resources through emotions. *Psychology & Health, 30*, 354–369. (p. 401)

Hogan, R. (1998). Reinventing personality. *Journal of Social and Clinical Psychology, 17*, 1–10. (p. 480)

Hoge, C. W., Terhakopian, A., Castro, C. A., Messer, S. C., & Engel, C. C. (2007). Association of posttraumatic stress disorder with somatic symptoms, health care visits, and absenteeism among Iraq War veterans. *American Journal of Psychiatry, 164*, 150–153. (p. 509)

Hogg, M. A. (1996). Intragroup processes, group structure and social identity. In W. P. Robinson (Ed.), *Social groups and identities: Developing the legacy of Henri Tajfel.* Oxford: Butterworth Heinemann. (p. 438)

Hogg, M. A. (2006). Social identity theory. In P. J. Burke (Ed.), *Contemporary social psychological theories.* Stanford, CA: Stanford University Press. (p. 438)

Hohmann, G. W. (1966). Some effects of spinal cord lesions on experienced emotional feelings. *Psychophysiology, 3*, 143–156. (p. 368)

Hokanson, J. E., & Edelman, R. (1966). Effects of three social responses on vascular processes. *Journal of Personality and Social Psychology, 3*, 442–447. (p. 393)

Holahan, C. K., & Sears, R. R. (1995). *The gifted group in later maturity.* Stanford, CA: Stanford University Press. (p. 331)

Holden, G. W., & Miller, P. C. (1999). Enduring and different: A meta-analysis of the similarity in parents' child rearing. *Psychological Bulletin, 125*, 223–254. (p. 139)

Holland, D., Chang, L., Ernst, T. M., Curran, M., Buchthal, S. D., Alicata, D., . . . Dale, A. M. (2014). Structural growth trajectories and rates of change in the first 3 months of infant brain development. *JAMA Neurology, 71*, 1266–1274. (p. 123)

Holland, J. L. (1996). Exploring careers with a typology: What we have learned and some new directions. *American Psychologist, 51*, 397–406. (p. B-3)

Holle, H., Warne, K., Seth, A. K., Critchley, H. D., & Ward, J. (2012). Neural basis of contagious itch and why some people are more prone to it. *PNAS, 109*, 19816–19821. (p. 422)

Holliday, R. E., & Albon, A. J. (2004). Minimizing misinformation effects in young children with cognitive interview mnemonics. *Applied Cognitive Psychology, 18*, 263–281. (p. 294)

Hollis, K. L. (1997). Contemporary research on Pavlovian conditioning: A "new" functional analysis. *American Psychologist, 52*, 956–965. (p. 238)

Hollon, S. D., DeRubeis, R. J., Fawcett, J., Amsterdam, J. D., Shelton, R. C., Zajecka, J., . . . Gallop, R. (2014). Effect of cognitive therapy with antidepressant medications vs. antidepressants alone on the rate of recovery in major depressive disorder. *JAMA Psychiatry, 71*, 1157–1164. (p. 562)

Holman, E. A., Garfin, D. R., & Silver, R. C. (2014). Media's role in broadcasting acute stress following the Boston marathon bombings. *PNAS, 111*, 93–98. (p. 510)

Holstege, G., Georgiadis, J. R., Paans, A. M. J., Meiners, L. C., van der Graaf, F. H. C. E., & Reinders, A. A. T. S. (2003a). Brain activation during male ejaculation. *Journal of Neuroscience, 23*, 9185–9193. (p. 174)

Holstege, G., Reinders, A. A. T., Paans, A. M. J., Meiners, L. C., Pruim, J., & Georgiadis, J. R. (2003b). *Brain activation during female sexual orgasm* (Annual Conference Abstract Viewer/Itinerary Planner Program No. 727.7). Washington, DC: Society for Neuroscience. (p. 174)

Holt-Lunstad, J., Robles, T. F., & Sbarra, D. A. (2017). Advancing social connection as a public health priority in the United States. *American Psychologist, 72*, 517–530. (p. 399)

Holt-Lunstad, J., Smith, T. B., Baker, M., Harris, T., & Stephenson, D. (2015). Loneliness and social isolation as risk factors for mortality: A meta-analytic review. *Perspectives on Psychological Science, 10,* 227–237. (p. 399)

Holt-Lunstad, J., Smith, T. B., & Layton, J. B. (2010). Social relationships and mortality risk: A meta-analytic review. *PLoS Medicine, 7,* e1000316. (pp. 353, 399)

Holtgraves, T. (2011). Text messaging, personality, and the social context. *Journal of Research in Personality, 45,* 92–99. (p. 479)

Holwerda, T. J., Deeg, D. J., Beekman, A. T., van Tilburg, T. G., Stek, M. L., Jonker, C., & Schoevers, R. A. (2014). Feelings of loneliness, but not social isolation, predict dementia onset: Results from the Amsterdam Study of the Elderly (AMSTEL). *Journal of Neurology, Neurosurgery, and Psychiatry, 85,* 135–142. (p. 353)

Homer, B. D., Solomon, T. M., Moeller, R. W., Mascia, A., DeRaleau, L., & Halkitis, P. N. (2008). Methamphetamine abuse and impairment of social functioning: A review of the underlying neurophysiological causes and behavioral implications. *Psychological Bulletin, 134,* 301–310. (p. 107)

Hoogman, M., Bralten, J., Hibar, D. P., Mennes, M., Zwiers, M. P., Schweren, L. S., . . . de Zeeuw, P. (2017). Subcortical brain volume differences in participants with attention deficit hyperactivity disorder in children and adults: A cross-sectional mega-analysis. *The Lancet Psychiatry, 4,* 310–319. (p. 498)

Hooper, J., & Teresi, D. (1986). *The three-pound universe.* New York: Macmillan. (p. 56)

Hopkins, E. D., & Cantalupo, C. (2008). Theoretical speculations on the evolutionary origins of hemispheric specialization. *Current Directions in Psychological Science, 17,* 233–237. (p. 67)

Hoppenbrouwers, S. S., Bulten, B. H., & Brazil, I. A. (2016). Parsing fear: A reassessment of the evidence for fear deficits in psychopathy. *Psychological Bulletin, 142,* 573–600.(p. 530)

Hopper, L. M., Lambeth, S. P., Schapiro, S. J., & Whiten, A. (2008). Observational learning in chimpanzees and children studied through "ghost" conditions. *Proceedings of the Royal Society, 275,* 835–840. (p. 259)

Horne, J. (2011). The end of sleep: "Sleep debt" versus biological adaptation of human sleep to waking needs. *Biological Psychology, 87,* 1–14. (p. 90)

Horne, Z., Powell, D., Hummel, J. E., & Holyoak, K. J. (2015). Countering antivaccination attitudes. *PNAS, 112,* 10321–10324. (p. 418)

Horowitz, S. S. (2012, November 9). The science and art of listening. *The New York Times* (nytimes.com). (p. 216)

Horta, L., de Mola, C. L., & Victora, C. G. (2015). Breastfeeding and intelligence: Systematic review and meta-analysis. *Acta Paediatrica, 104,* 14–19. (p. 25)

Horvath, J. C., Forte, J. D., & Carter, O. (2015). Quantitative review finds no evidence of cognitive effects in healthy populations from single-session transcranial direct current stimulation (tDCS). *Brain Stimulation, 8,* 535–550. (p. 563)

Horváth, K., Hannon, B., Ujma, P. P., Gombos, F., & Plunkett, K. (2017). Memory in 3-month-old infants benefits from a short nap. *Developmental Science, 21*(1), e12587. (p. 92)

Horwood, L. J., & Fergusson, D. M. (1998). Breastfeeding and later cognitive and academic outcomes. *Pediatrics, 101,* E9. (p. 25)

Hostetter, A. B. (2011). When do gestures communicate? A meta-analysis. *Psychological Bulletin, 137,* 297–315. (p. 317)

Hostinar, C. E., Sullivan, R., & Gunnar, M. R. (2014). Psychobiological mechanisms underlying the social buffering of the hypothalamic-pituitary-adrenocortical axis: A review of animal models and human studies across development. *Psychological Bulletin, 140,* 256–282. (p. 400)

Hou, W.-H., Chiang, P.-T., Hsu, T.-Y., Chiu, S.-Y., & Yen, Y.-C. (2010). Treatment effects of massage therapy in depressed people: A meta-analysis. *Journal of Clinical Psychiatry, 71,* 894–901. (pp. 404, 564)

House, R., Javidan, M., & Dorfman, P. (2001). Project GLOBE: An introduction. *Applied Psychology: An International Review, 50,* 489–505. (p. B-11)

House, R. J., & Singh, J. V. (1987). Organizational behavior: Some new directions for I/O psychology. *Annual Review of Psychology, 38,* 669–718. (p. B-10)

Houser-Marko, L., & Sheldon, K. M. (2008). Eyes on the prize or nose to the grindstone? The effects of level of goal evaluation on mood and motivation. *Personality and Social Psychology Bulletin, 34,* 1556–1569. (p. B-9)

Houts, A. C., Berman, J. S., & Abramson, H. (1994). Effectiveness of psychological and pharmacological treatments for nocturnal enuresis. *Journal of Consulting and Clinical Psychology, 62,* 737–745. (p. 540)

Hovatta, I., Tennant, R. S., Helton, R., Marr, R. A., Singer, O., Redwine, J. M., . . . Barlow, C. (2005). Glyoxalase 1 and glutathione reductase 1 regulate anxiety in mice. *Nature, 438,* 662–666. (p. 511)

Hoyer, G., & Lund, E. (1993). Suicide among women related to number of children in marriage. *Archives of General Psychiatry, 50,* 134–137. (p. 500)

Hsee, C. K., & Ruan, B. (2016). The Pandora effect: The power and peril of curiosity. *Psychological Science, 27,* 659–666. (p. 349)

Hsee, C. K., Yang, A. X., & Wang, L. (2010). Idleness aversion and the need for justifiable busyness. *Psychological Science, 21,* 926–930. (p. B-2)

Hsiang, S. M., Burke, M., & Miguel, E. (2013). Quantifying the influence of climate on human conflict. *Science, 341,* 1212. (p. 443)

Huang, C. (2015). Relation between attributional style and subsequent depressive symptoms: A systematic review and meta-analysis of longitudinal studies. *Cognitive Therapy and Research, 39,* 721–735. (p. 520)

Huang, J., Chaloupka, F. J., & Fong, G. T. (2013). Cigarette graphic warning labels and smoking prevalence in Canada: A critical examination and reformulation of the FDA regulatory impact analysis. *Tobacco Control* (tobaccocontrol.bmj.com/content/early/2013/11/11/tobaccocontrol-2013-051170.full.pdf+html). (p. 303)

Huart, J., Corneille, O., & Becquart, E. (2005). Face-based categorization, context-based categorization, and distortions in the recollection of gender ambiguous faces. *Journal of Experimental Social Psychology, 41,* 598–608. (p. 298)

Hubbard, E. M., Arman, A. C., Ramachandran, V. S., & Boynton, G. M. (2005). Individual differences among grapheme-color synesthetes: Brain-behavior correlations. *Neuron, 45,* 975–985. (p. 229)

Hubel, D. H. (1979, September). The brain. *Scientific American,* pp. 45–53. (p. 194)

Hubel, D. H., & Wiesel, T. N. (1979, September). Brian mechanisms of vision. *Scientific American,* pp. 150–162. (p. 205)

Huber, E., Webster, J. M., Brewer, A. A., MacLeod, D. I. A., Wandell, B. A., Boynton, G. M., . . . Fine, I. (2015). A lack of experience-dependent plasticity after more than a decade of recovered sight. *Psychological Science, 26,* 393–401. (p. 213)

Hucker, S. J., & Bain, J. (1990). Androgenic hormones and sexual assault. In W. L. Marshall, D. R. Laws, & H. E. Barbaree (Eds.), *Handbook of sexual assault: Issues, theories, and treatment of the offender* (pp. 209–229). New York: Plenum Press. (p. 174)

Hudson, J. I., Hiripi, E., Pope, H. G., & Kessler, R. C. (2007). The prevalence and correlates of eating disorders in the National Comorbidity Survey Replication. *Biological Psychiatry, 61,* 348–358. (p. 532)

Hudson, N. W., & Roberts, B. W. (2014). Goals to change personality traits: Concurrent links between personality traits, daily behavior, and goals to change oneself. *Journal of Research in Personality, 53,* 68–83. (p. 476)

Huey, E. D., Krueger, F., & Grafman, J. (2006). Representations in the human prefrontal cortex. *Current Directions in Psychological Science, 15,* 167–171. (p. 62)

Hugenberg, K., & Bodenhausen, G. V. (2003). Facing prejudice: Implicit prejudice and the perception of facial threat. *Psychological Science, 14,* 640–643. (p. 436)

Hugenberg, K., Young, S. G., Bernstein, M. J., & Sacco, D. F. (2010). The categorization–individuation model: An integrative account of the other-race recognition deficit. *Psychological Review, 117,* 1168–1187. (p. 440)

Hughes, J. R. (2010). Craving among long-abstinent smokers: An internet survey. *Nicotine & Tobacco Research, 12,* 459–462. (p. 106)

Hughes, M. L., Geraci, L., & De Forrest, R. L. (2013). Aging 5 years in 5 minutes: The effect of taking a memory test on older adults' subjective age. *Psychological Science, 24,* 2481–2488. (p. 152)

Hulbert, A. (2005, November 20). The prodigy puzzle. *New York Times Magazine* (nytimes.com). (p. 331)

Hull, H. R., Morrow, M. L., Dinger, M. K., Han, J. L., & Fields, D. A. (2007, November 20). Characterization of body weight and composition changes during the sophomore year of college. *BMC Women's Health, 7,* Article 21. Retrieved from http://www.biomedcentral.com/1472-6874/7/21 (p. 93)

Hull, J. G., & Bond, C. F., Jr. (1986). Social and behavioral consequences of alcohol consumption and expectancy: A meta-analysis. *Psychological Bulletin, 99,* 347–360. (p. 104)

Hull, J. M. (1990). *Touching the rock: An experience of blindness.* New York: Vintage Books. (p. 280)

Hull, S. J., Hennessy, M., Bleakley, A., Fishbein, M., & Jordan, A. (2011). Identifying the causal pathways from religiosity to delayed adolescent sexual behavior. *Journal of Sex Research, 48,* 543–553. (p. 178)

Hülsheger, U. R., Anderson, N., & Salgado, J. F. (2009). Team-level predictors of innovation at work: A comprehensive meta-analysis spanning three decades of research. *Journal of Applied Psychology, 94,* 1128–1145. (p. 307)

Human Connectome Project. (2013). The Human Connectome Project (humanconnectome.org). (p. 53)

Hummer, R. A., Rogers, R. G., Nam, C. B., & Ellison, C. G. (1999). Religious involvement and U.S. adult mortality. *Demography, 36,* 273–285. (p. 405)

Humphrey, S. E., Nahrgang, J. D., & Morgeson, F. P. (2007). Integrating motivational, social, and contextual work design features: A meta-analytic summary and theoretical extension of the work design literature. *Journal of Applied Psychology, 92,* 1332–1356. (p. 396)

Humphreys, L. G., & Davey, T. C. (1988). Continuity in intellectual growth from 12 months to 9 years. *Intelligence, 12,* 183–197. (p. 332)

Hunsberger, J. G., Newton, S. S., Bennett, A. H., Duman, C. H., Russell, D. S., Salton, S. R., & Duman, R. S. (2007). Antidepressant actions of the exercise-regulated gene VGF. *Nature Medicine, 13,* 1476–1482. (p. 402)

Hunsley, J., & Bailey, J. M. (1999). The clinical utility of the Rorschach: Unfulfilled promises and an uncertain future. *Psychological Assessment, 11,* 266–277. (p. 468)

Hunsley, J., & Di Giulio, G. (2002). Dodo bird, phoenix, or urban legend? The question of psychotherapy equivalence. *Scientific Review of Mental Health Practice, 1,* 11–22. (p. 553)

Hunt, C., Slade, T., & Andrews, G. (2004). Generalized anxiety disorder and major depressive disorder comorbidity in the National Survey of Mental Health and Well-Being. *Depression and Anxiety, 20,* 23–31. (p. 507)

Hunt, J. M. (1982). Toward equalizing the developmental opportunities of infants and preschool children. *Journal of Social Issues, 38,* 163–191. (p. 338)

Hunt, L. L., Eastwick, P. W., & Finkel, E. J. (2015). Leveling the playing field: Longer acquaintance predicts reduced assortative mating on attractiveness. *Psychological Science, 26,* 1046–1053. (p. 449)

Hunt, M. (1993). *The story of psychology.* New York: Doubleday. (pp. 4, 8, 38, 242, 332)

Hunter, S., & Sundel, M. (Eds.). (1989). *Midlife myths: Issues, findings, and practice implications.* Newbury Park, CA: Sage. (p. 155)

Hurd, Y. L., Michaelides, M., Miller, M. L., & Jutras-Aswad, D. (2013). Trajectory of adolescent cannabis use on addiction vulnerability. *Neuropharmacology, 76,* 416–424. (p. 109)

Hurlburt, R. T., Heavey, C. L., & Kelsey, J. M. (2013). Toward a phenomenology of inner speaking. *Consciousness and Cognition: An International Journal, 22,* 1477–1494. (p. 319)

Hussak, L. J., & Cimpian, A. (2015). An early-emerging explanatory heuristic promotes support for the status quo. *Journal of Personality and Social Psychology, 109,* 739–752. (p. 441)

Hutchinson, R. (2006). *Calum's road.* Edinburgh, Scotland: Burlinn Limited. (p. 358)

Hutchison, K. A., Smith, J. L., & Ferris, A. (2013). Goals can be threatened to extinction using the Stroop task to clarify working memory depletion under stereotype threat. *Social and Personality Psychological Science, 4,* 74–81. (p. 344)

Hutteman, R., Nestler, S., Wagner, J., Egloff, B., & Back, M. D. (2015). Wherever I may roam: Processes of self-esteem development from adolescence to emerging adulthood in the context of international student exchange. *Journal of Personality and Social Psychology, 108,* 767–783. (p. 486)

Hvistendahl, M. (2011). China's population growing slowly, changing fast. *Science, 332,* 650–651. (p. 437)

Hyde, C. L., Nagle, M. W., Tian, C., Chen, X., Paciga, C. A., Wendland, J. R., . . . Winslow, A. R. (2016). Identification of 15 genetic loci associated with risk of major depression in individuals of European descent. *Nature Genetics, 48,* 1031–1036. (p. 518)

Hyde, J. S. (2005). The gender similarities hypothesis. *American Psychologist, 60,* 581–592. (pp. 163, 183)

Hyde, J. S. (2014). Gender similarities and differences. *Annual Review of Psychology, 65,* 373–398. (p. 162)

Hyde, J. S., & Mertz, J. E. (2009). Gender, culture, and mathematics performance. *PNAS, 106,* 8801–8807. (p. 340)

Hymowitz, K., Carroll, J. S., Wilcox, W. B., & Kaye, K. (2013). *Knot yet: The benefits and costs of delayed marriage in America.* Charlottesville: National Marriage Project, University of Virginia. (p. 135)

Iacoboni, M. (2008). *Mirroring people: The new science of how we connect with others.* New York: Farrar, Straus & Giroux. (pp. 259, 260)

Iacoboni, M. (2009). Imitation, empathy, and mirror neurons. *Annual Review of Psychology, 60,* 653–670. (pp. 259, 260)

Ibbotson, P., & Tomasello, M. (2016, November). Language in a new key. *Scientific American,* pp. 71–75. (p. 313)

Ibos, G., & Freedman, D. J. (2014). Dynamic integration of task-relevant visual features in posterior parietal cortex. *Neuron, 83,* 1468–1480. (p. 63)

Idson, L. C., & Mischel, W. (2001). The personality of familiar and significant people: The lay perceiver as a social–cognitive theorist. *Journal of Personality and Social Psychology, 80,* 585–596. (p. 416)

IJzerman, H., & Semin, G. R. (2009). The thermometer of social relations: Mapping social proximity on temperature. *Psychological Science, 20,* 1214–1220. (p. 229)

Ikizer, E. G., & Blanton, H. (2016). Media coverage of "wise" interventions can reduce concern for the disadvantaged. *Journal of Experimental Psychology: Applied, 22,* 135–147. (p. 340)

Ilardi, S. (2016, accessed May 2). *Therapeutic lifestyle change (TLC).* University of Kansas (tlc.ku.edu). (p. 559)

Ilardi, S. S. (2009). *The depression cure: The six-step program to beat depression without drugs.* Cambridge, MA: De Capo Lifelong Books. (pp. 519, 559)

Ilieva, I. P., Hook, C. J., & Farah, M. J. (2015). Prescription stimulants' effects on healthy inhibitory control, working memory, and episodic memory: A meta-analysis. *Journal of Cognitive Neuroscience, 27,* 1069–1089. (p. 105)

Imuta, K., Henry, J. D., Slaughter, V., Selcuk, B., & Ruffman, T. (2016). Theory of mind and prosocial behavior in childhood: A meta-analytic review. *Developmental Psychology, 52,* 1192–1205. (p. 128)

Inagaki, T., & Eisenberger, N. (2013). Shared neural mechanisms underlying social warmth and physical warmth. *Psychological Science, 24,* 2272–2280. (p. 352)

Inbar, Y., Cone, J., & Gilovich, T. (2010). People's intuitions about intuitive insight and intuitive choice. *Journal of Personality and Social Psychology, 99,* 232–247. (p. 305)

Inbar, Y., Pizarro, D., & Bloom, P. (2011). *Disgusting smells cause decreased liking of gay men.* Unpublished manuscript, Tillburg University. (p. 227)

Infurna, F. J., & Luthar, S. S. (2016a). The multidimensional nature of resilience to spousal loss. *Journal of Personality and Social Psychology.* http://dx.doi.org/10.1037/pspp0000095 (pp. 159, 408)

Infurna, F. J., & Luthar, S. S. (2016b). Resilience to major life stressors is not as common as thought. *Perspectives on Psychological Science, 11,* 175–194. (p. 509)

Ingalhalikar, M., Smith, A., Parker, D., Satterthwaite, T. D., Elliott, M. A., Ruparel, K., . . . Verma, R. (2013). Sex differences in the structural connectome of the human brain. *PNAS, 111,* 823–828. (p. 164)

Ingham, A. G., Levinger, G., Graves, J., & Peckham, V. (1974). The Ringelmann effect: Studies of group size and group performance. *Journal of Experimental Social Psychology, 10,* 371–384. (p. 430)

Inglehart, R. (1990). *Culture shift in advanced industrial society.* Princeton, NJ: Princeton University Press. (p. 353)

Ingraham, C. (2016, May 1). Toddlers have shot at least 23 people this year. *The Washington Post* (washingtonpost.com). (p. 302)

Inman, M. L., & Baron, R. S. (1996). Influence of prototypes on perceptions of prejudice. *Journal of Personality and Social Psychology, 70,* 727–739. (p. 299)

Innocence Project. (2015). Eyewitness misidentification. Retrieved from innocenceproject.org/understand/Eyewitness-Misidentification.php (p. 292)

Insel, T., Cuthbert, B., Garvey, M., Heinssen, R., Pine, D. S., Quinn, K., . . . Wang, P. (2010). Research Domain Criteria (RDoC): Toward a new classification framework for research on mental disorders. *American Journal of Psychiatry, 167,* 748–751. (p. 497)

Insel, T. R. (2010). Faulty circuits. *Scientific American, 302,* 44–51. (p. 512)

Insel, T. R., & Cuthbert, B. N. (2015). Brain disorders? Precisely. *Science, 348,* 499–500. (p. 495)

Insel, T. R., & Lieberman, J. A. (2013, May 13). DSM-5 and RDoC: Shared interests. National Institute of Mental Health. [Press release.] Retrieved from nimh.nih.gov/news/science-news/2013/dsm-5-and-rdoc-shared-interests.shtml (p. 497)

International Schizophrenia Consortium. (2009). Common polygenic variation contributes to risk of schizophrenia and bipolar disorder. *Nature, 460,* 748–752. (p. 526)

Inzlicht, M., & Ben-Zeev, T. (2000). A threatening intellectual environment: Why females are susceptible to experiencing problem-solving deficits in the presence of males. *Psychological Science, 11,* 365–371. (p. 344)

Inzlicht, M., & Kang, S. K. (2010). Stereotype threat spillover: How coping with threats to social identity affects aggression, eating, decision making, and attention. *Journal of Personality and Social Psychology, 99,* 467–481. (p. 344)

IPPA. (2017, January 27). Communication from International Positive Psychology Association. (p. 408)

Ipsos. (2010, April 8). *One in five (20%) global citizens believe that alien beings have come down to earth and walk amongst us in our communities disguised as humans.* Retrieved from ipsos.com/en-us/one-five-20-global-citizens-believe-alien-beings-have-come-down-earth-and-walk-amongst-us-our (p. 23)

IPU. (2018). *Women in parliament in 2017: The year in review.* Geneva: Inter-Parliamentary Union (ipu.org). (pp. 164, 169)

Ireland, M. E., & Pennebaker, J. W. (2010). Language style matching in writing: Synchrony in essays, correspondence, and poetry. *Journal of Personality and Social Psychology, 99,* 549–571. (pp. 260, 422)

Ironson, G., Solomon, G. F., Balbin, E. G., O'Cleirigh, C., George, A., Kumar, M., . . . Woods, T. E. (2002). The Ironson-Woods spiritual/religiousness index is associated with long survival, health behaviors, less distress, and low cortisol in people with HIV/AIDS. *Annals of Behavioral Medicine, 24,* 34–48. (p. 406)

Irwin, M. R., Cole, J. C., & Nicassio, P. M. (2006). Comparative meta-analysis of behavioral interventions for insomnia and their efficacy in middle-aged adults and in older adults 55+ years of age. *Health Psychology, 25,* 3–14. (p. 96)

Isaacowitz, D. M. (2012). Mood regulation in real time: Age differences in the role of looking. *Current Directions in Psychological Science, 21,* 237–242. (p. 158)

Ishida, A., Mutoh, T., Ueyama, T., Brando, H., Masubuchi, S., Nakahara, D., . . . Okamura, H. (2005). Light activates the adrenal gland: Timing of gene expression and glucocorticoid release. *Cell Metabolism, 2,* 297–307. (p. 555)

Ishiyama, S., & Brecht, M. (2017). Neural correlates of ticklishness in the rat somatosensory cortex. *Science, 354,* 757–760. (p. 51)

Ising, H. K., Smit, F., Veling, W., Rietdijk, J., Dragt, S., Klaassen, R. M. C., . . . van der Gaag, M. (2015). Cost-effectiveness of preventing first-episode psychosis in ultra-high-risk subjects: Multi-centre randomized controlled trial. *Psychological Medicine, 45,* 1435–1446. (p. 552)

Islam, S. S., & Johnson, C. (2003). Correlates of smoking behavior among Muslim Arab-American adolescents. *Ethnicity & Health, 8,* 319–337. (p. 406)

Iso, H., Simoda, S., & Matsuyama, T. (2007). Environmental change during postnatal development alters behaviour. *Behavioural Brain Research, 179,* 90–98. (p. 64)

Iso-Markku, P., Waller, K., Vuoksimaa, E., Heikkilä, K., Rinne, J., Kaprio, J., & Kujala, U. M. (2016). Midlife physical activity and cognition later in life: A prospective twin study. *Journal of Alzheimer's Disease,* Preprint, 1–15. (p. 153)

Ito, T. A., Miller, N., & Pollock, V. E. (1996). Alcohol and aggression: A meta-analysis on the moderating effects of inhibitory cues, triggering events, and self-focused attention. *Psychological Bulletin, 120,* 60–82. (p. 442)

ITU. (2016, accessed December 26). *ICT facts and figures 2016.* International Telecommunications Union (itu.int/en/ITU-D/Statistics/Documents/facts/ICTFactsFigures2016.pdf). (p. 355)

Ives-Deliperi, V. L., Solms, M., & Meintjes, E. M. (2011). The neural substrates of mindfulness: An fMRI investigation. *Social Neuroscience, 6,* 231–242. (p. 404)

Iyengar, S., & Westwood, S. J. (2015). Fear and loathing across party lines: New evidence on group polarization. *American Journal of Political Science, 59,* 690–707. (p. 18)

Izard, C. E. (1977). *Human emotions.* New York: Plenum Press. (pp. 372, 378)

Izard, C. E. (1994). Innate and universal facial expressions: Evidence from developmental and cross-cultural research. *Psychological Bulletin, 114,* 288–299. (p. 378)

Izawa, S., Matsudaira, K., Miki, K., Arisaka, M., & Tsuchiya, M. (2017). Psychosocial correlates of cortisol levels in fingernails among middle-aged workers. *The International Journal on the Biology of Stress, 20,* 386–389. (p. 391)

Jääskeläinen, E., Juola, P., Hirvonen, N., McGrath, J. J., Saha, S., Isohanni, M., . . . Miettunen, J. (2013). A systematic review and meta-analysis of recovery in schizophrenia. *Schizophrenia Bulletin, 39,* 1296–1306. (pp. 523, 524)

Jablensky, A. (1999). Schizophrenia: Epidemiology. *Current Opinion in Psychiatry, 12,* 19–28. (p. 525)

Jack, R. E., Garrod, O. G. B., Yu, H., Caldara, R., & Schyns, P. G. (2012). Facial expressions of emotion are not culturally universal. *PNAS, 109,* 7241–7244. (p. 378)

Jäckle, S., & Wenzelburger, G. (2015). Religion, religiosity, and the attitudes toward homosexuality—A multilevel analysis of 79 countries. *Journal of Homosexuality, 62,* 207–241. (p. 437)

Jackson, G. (2009). Sexual response in cardiovascular disease. *Journal of Sex Research, 46,* 233–236. (p. 173)

Jackson, J. J., Connolly, J. J., Garrison, S. M., Leveille, M. M., & Connolly, S. L. (2015). Your friends know how long you will live: A 75-year study of peer-rated personality traits. *Psychological Science, 26,* 335–340. (p. 481)

Jackson, J. J., Thoemmes, F., Jonkmann, K., Lüdtke, O., & Trautwein, U. (2012). Military training and personality trait development: Does the military make the man, or does the man make the military? *Psychological Science, 23,* 270–277. (pp. 419, 480)

Jackson, J. M., & Williams, K. D. (1988). *Social loafing: A review and theoretical analysis.* Unpublished manuscript, Fordham University. (p. 430)

Jackson, S. W. (1992). The listening healer in the history of psychological healing. *American Journal Psychiatry, 149,* 1623–1632. (p. 556)

Jacobs, B. L. (1994). Serotonin, motor activity, and depression-related disorders. *American Scientist, 82,* 456–463. (p. 402)

Jacoby, L. L., Bishara, A. J., Hessels, S., & Toth, J. P. (2005). Aging, subjective experience, and cognitive control: Dramatic false remembering by older adults. *Journal of Experimental Psychology: General, 154,* 131–148. (p. 294)

Jacoby, L. L., & Rhodes, M. G. (2006). False remembering in the aged. *Current Directions in Psychological Science, 15,* 49–53. (p. 294)

Jacques, C., & Rossion, B. (2006). The speed of individual face categorization. *Psychological Science, 17,* 485–492. (p. 189)

Jacques-Tiura, A. J., Abbey, A., Parkhill, M. R., & Zawacki, T. (2007). Why do some men misperceive women's sexual intentions more frequently than others do? An application of the confluence model. *Personality and Social Psychology Bulletin, 33,* 1467–1480. (p. 417)

Jaffe, E. (2004, October). Peace in the Middle East may be impossible: Lee D. Ross on naive realism and conflict resolution. *APS Observer,* pp. 9–11. (p. 197)

Jakubovski, E., Varigonda, A. L., Freemantle, N., Taylor, M. J., & Bloch, M. H. (2015). Systematic review and meta-analysis: Dose-response relationship of selective serotonin reuptake inhibitors in major depressive disorder. *American Journal of Psychiatry, 173,* 174–183. (p. 561)

James, K. (1986). Priming and social categorizational factors: Impact on awareness of emergency situations. *Personality and Social Psychology Bulletin, 12,* 462–467. (p. 281)

James, S. E., Herman, J. L., Rankin, S., Keisling, M., Mottet, L., & Anafi, M. (2016). *The report of the 2015 U.S. Transgender Survey.* Washington, DC: National Center for Transgender Equality. (pp. 171, 437)

James, W. (1890). *The principles of psychology* (Vol. 2). New York: Holt. (pp. 6, 221, 283, 295, 368, 380, 420, 485)

Jameson, D. (1985). Opponent-colors theory in light of physiological findings. In D. Ottoson & S. Zeki (Eds.), *Central and peripheral mechanisms of color vision* (pp. 83–102). New York: Macmillan. (p. 211)

Jamieson, J. P. (2010). The home field advantage in athletics: A meta-analysis. *Journal of Applied Social Psychology, 40,* 1819–1848. (p. 429)

Jamieson, J. P., Peters, B. J., Greenwood, E. J., & Altose, A. J. (2016). Reappraising stress arousal improves performance and reduces evaluation anxiety in classroom exam situations. *Social Psychological and Personality Science, 7,* 579–587. (p. 371)

Jamison, K. R. (1993). *Touched with fire: Manic-depressive illness and the artistic temperament.* New York: Free Press. (p. 516)

Jamison, K. R. (1995). *An unquiet mind.* New York: Knopf. (pp. 516, 535, 562)

Janis, I. L. (1982). *Groupthink: Psychological studies of policy decisions and fiascoes.* Boston: Houghton Mifflin. (p. 433)

Janis, I. L. (1986). Problems of international crisis management in the nuclear age. *Journal of Social Issues, 42,* 201–220. (p. 300)

Janoff-Bulman, R., Timko, C., & Carli, L. L. (1985). Cognitive biases in blaming the victim. *Journal of Experimental Social Psychology, 21,* 161–177. (p. 440)

Janssen, S. M. J., Rubin, D. C., & Conway, M. A. (2012). The reminiscence bump in the temporal distribution of the best football players of all time: Pelé, Cruijff or Maradona? *Quarterly Journal of Experimental Psychology, 65,* 165–178. (p. 153)

Jarbo, K., & Verstynen, T. D. (2015). Converging structural and functional connectivity of orbitofrontal, dorsolateral prefrontal, and posterior parietal cortex in the human striatum. *Journal of Neuroscience, 35,* 3865–3878. (p. 53)

Jayakar, R., King, T. Z., Morris, R., & Na, S. (2015). Hippocampal volume and auditory attention on a verbal memory task with adult survivors of pediatric brain tumor. *Neuropsychology, 29,* 303–319. (p. 56)

Jedrychowski, W., Perera, F., Jankowski, J., Butscher, M., Mroz, E., Flak, E., . . . Sowa, A. (2012). Effect of exclusive breastfeeding on the development of children's cognitive function in the Krakow prospective birth cohort study. *European Journal of Pediatrics, 171,* 151–158. (p. 25)

Jeffrey, K., Mahoney, S., Michaelson, J., & Abdallah, S. (2014). Well-being at work: A review of the literature. Retrieved from neweconomics.org/publications/entry/well-being-at-work (p. B-8)

Jenkins, J. G., & Dallenbach, K. M. (1924). Obliviscence during sleep and waking. *American Journal of Psychology, 35,* 605–612. (p. 287)

Jenkins, J. M., & Astington, J. W. (1996). Cognitive factors and family structure associated with theory of mind development in young children. *Developmental Psychology, 32,* 70–78. (p. 128)

Jenkins, S. R. (2017). Not your same old story: New rules for Thematic Apperceptive Techniques (TATs). *Journal of Personality Assessment, 99,* 238–253. (p. 467)

Jensen, J. P., & Bergin, A. E. (1988). Mental health values of professional therapists: A national interdisciplinary survey. *Professional Psychology: Research and Practice, 19,* 290–297. (p. 556)

Jensen, M. P. (2008). The neurophysiology of pain perception and hypnotic analgesia: Implications for clinical practice. *American Journal of Clinical Hypnosis, 51,* 123–147. (p. 224)

Jepson, C., Krantz, D. H., & Nisbett, R. E. (1983). Inductive reasoning: Competence or skill. *The Behavioral and Brain Sciences, 3,* 494–501. (p. A-7)

Jessberger, S., Aimone, J. B., & Gage, F. H. (2008). Neurogenesis. In J. H. Byrne (Ed.), *Learning and memory: A comprehensive reference: Vol. 4. Molecular mechanisms of memory* (pp. 839–858). Oxford: Elsevier. (p. 64)

Jha, P., Ramasundarahettige, C., Landsman, V., Rostron, B., Thun, M. D., Anderson, R. N., . . . Peto, R. (2013). 21st-century hazards of smoking and benefits of cessation in the United States. *New England Journal of Medicine, 368,* 341–350. (p. 105)

Jiang, H., White, M. P., Greicius, M. D., Waelde, L. C., & Spiegel, D. (2016). Brain activity and functional connectivity associated with hypnosis. *Cerebral Cortex.* doi:10.1093/cercor/bhw220 (p. 224)

Jiang, Y., Costello, P., Fang, F., Huang, M., & He, S. (2006). A gender- and sexual orientation-dependent spatial attentional effect of invisible things. *PNAS, 103,* 17048–17052. (p. 192)

Job, V., Dweck, C. S., & Walton, G. M. (2010). Ego depletion—Is it all in your head?: Implicit theories about willpower affect self-regulation. *Psychological Science, 21,* 1686–1693. (pp. 145, 397)

Jobe, T. H., & Harrow, M. (2010). Schizophrenia course, long-term outcome, recovery, and prognosis. *Current Directions in Psychological Science, 19,* 220–225. (p. 523)

Joel, D., Berman, Z., Tavor, I., Wexler, N., Gaber, O., Stein, Y., . . . Assaf, Y. (2015, December). Sex beyond the genitalia: The human brain mosaic. *PNAS, 112,* 15468–15473. (p. 164)

Joel, S., Eastwick, P. W., & Finkel, E. J. (2017). Is romantic desire predictable? Machine learning applied to initial romantic attraction. *Psychological Science, 28,* 1478–1489. (p. 355)

Johnson, D. F. (1997, Winter). Margaret Floy Washburn. *Psychology of Women Newsletter,* pp. 17, 22. (p. 7)

Johnson, D. L., Wiebe, J. S., Gold, S. M., Andreasen, N. C., Hichwa, R. D., Watkins, G. L., & Ponto, L. L. B. (1999). Cerebral blood flow and personality: A positron emission tomography study. *American Journal of Psychiatry, 156,* 252–257. (p. 476)

Johnson, D. P., Rhee, S. H., Friedman, N. P., Corley, R. P., Munn-Chernoff, M., Hewitt, J. K., & Whisman, M. A. (2016). A twin study examining rumination as a transdiagnostic correlate of psychopathology. *Clinical Psychological Science, 4,* 971–987. (p. 520)

Johnson, E. J., & Goldstein, D. (2003). Do defaults save lives? *Science, 302,* 1338–1339. (p. 305)

Johnson, J. A. (2007, June 26). Not so situational. Commentary on the SPSP listserv (spsp-discuss@stolaf.edu). (p. 428)

Johnson, J. G., Cohen, P., Kotler, L., Kasen, S., & Brook, J. S. (2002). Psychiatric disorders associated with risk for the development of eating disorders during adolescence and early adulthood. *Journal of Consulting and Clinical Psychology, 70,* 1119–1128. (p. 532)

Johnson, J. S., & Newport, E. L. (1991). Critical period affects on universal properties of language: The status of subjacency in the acquisition of a second language. *Cognition, 39,* 215–258. (pp. 315, 316)

Johnson, K. (2008, January 29). For many of USA's inmates, crime runs in the family. *USA Today,* pp. 1A, 2A. (p. 163)

Johnson, M. D., & Chen, J. (2015). Blame it on the alcohol: The influence of alcohol consumption during adolescence, the transition to adulthood, and young adulthood on one-time sexual hookups. *Journal of Sex Research, 52,* 570–579. (pp. 103, 177)

Johnson, M. H. (1992). Imprinting and the development of face recognition: From chick to man. *Current Directions in Psychological Science, 1,* 52–55. (p. 134)

Johnson, M. H., & Morton, J. (1991). *Biology and cognitive development: The case of face recognition.* Oxford: Blackwell. (p. 121)

Johnson, R. (2017, August 12). The mystery of S., the man with an impossible memory. *The New Yorker* (newyorker.com). (p. 289)

Johnson, W. (2010). Understanding the genetics of intelligence: Can height help? Can corn oil? *Current Directions in Psychological Science, 19,* 177–182. (p. 337)

Johnson, W., Carothers, A., & Deary, I. J. (2008). Sex differences in variability in general intelligence: A new look at the old question. *Perspectives on Psychological Science, 3,* 518–531. (p. 325)

Johnson, W., Gow, A. J., Corley, J., Starr, J. M., & Deary, I. J. (2010). Location in cognitive and residential space at age 70 reflects a lifelong trait over parental and environmental circumstances: The Lothian Birth Cohort 1936. *Intelligence, 38,* 403–411. (p. 333)

Johnston, L. D., O'Malley, P. M., Bachman, J. G., & Schulenberg, J. E. (2007, May). *Monitoring the Future national results on adolescent drug use: Overview of key findings, 2006.* Bethesda, MD: National Institute on Drug Abuse. (p. 112)

Johnston, L. D., O'Malley, P. M., Miech, R. A., Bachman, J. G., & Schulenberg, J. E. (2018). Monitoring the Future national results on adolescent drug use: Overview of key findings, 2017. Ann Arbor, MI: Institute for Social Research, the University of Michigan. (pp. 106, 107, 110)

Joiner, T. E., Jr. (2006). *Why people die by suicide.* Cambridge, MA: Harvard University Press. (p. 501)

Joiner, T. E., Jr. (2010). *Myths about suicide.* Cambridge, MA: Harvard University Press. (p. 501)

Jokela, M., Elovainio, M., Archana, S.-M., & Kivimäki, M. (2009). IQ, socioeconomic status, and early death: The U.S. National Longitudinal Survey of Youth. *Psychosomatic Medicine, 71,* 322–328. (p. 396)

Jolly, A. (2007). The social origin of mind. *Science, 317,* 1326. (p. 310)

Jones, A. C., & Gosling, S. D. (2005). Temperament and personality in dogs (*Canis familiaris*): A review and evaluation of past research. *Applied Animal Behaviour Science, 95,* 1–53. (p. 477)

Jones, B., Reedy, E. J., & Weinberg, B. A. (2014, January). Age and scientific genius. NBER Working Paper Series. Retrieved from nber.org/papers/w19866 (p. 334)

Jones, E. (1957). *Sigmund Freud: Life and Work,* Vol. 3, Pt. 1., Ch. 4. New York: Basic Books. (p. 466)

Jones, J. M. (2012, June 21). Atheists, Muslims see most bias as presidential candidates. Retrieved from gallup.com/poll/155285/atheistsmuslims-bias-presidential-candidates.aspx (p. 437)

Jones, J. M. (2016, November 21). Record-high 77% of Americans perceive nation as divided. Gallup Poll (gallup.com). (p. 431)

Jones, M. C. (1924). A laboratory study of fear: The case of Peter. *Journal of Genetic Psychology, 31,* 308–315. (p. 541)

Jones, S. S. (2007). Imitation in infancy: The development of mimicry. *Psychological Science, 18,* 593–599. (p. 260)

Jones, W. H., Carpenter, B. N., & Quintana, D. (1985). Personality and interpersonal predictors of loneliness in two cultures. *Journal of Personality and Social Psychology, 48,* 1503–1511. (p. 10)

Jordan, A. H., Monin, B., Dweck, C. S., Lovett, B. J., John, O. P., & Gross, J. J. (2011). Misery has more company than people think: Underestimating the prevalence of others' negative emotions. *Personality and Social Psychology Bulletin, 37,* 120–135. (p. 514)

Jordan, G., Deeb, S. S., Bosten, J. M., & Mollon, J. D. (2010). The dimensionality of color vision in carriers of anomalous trichromacy. *Journal of Vision, 10,* ArtID: 12. (p. 204)

Jorm, A. F., Reavley, N. J., & Ross, A. M. (2012). Belief in the dangerousness of people with mental disorders: A review. *Australian and New Zealand Journal of Psychiatry, 46,* 1029–1045. (p. 502)

Jose, A., O'Leary, D., & Moyer, A. (2010). Does premarital cohabitation predict subsequent marital stability and marital quality? A meta-analysis. *Journal of Marriage and Family, 72,* 105–116. (p. 156)

Joseph, J. (2001). Separated twins and the genetics of personality differences: A critique. *American Journal of Psychology, 114,* 1–30. (p. 72)

Joshi, S. H., Espinoza, R. T., Pirnia, T., Shi, J., Wang, Y., Ayers, B., . . . Narr, K. L. (2016). Structural plasticity of the hippocampus and amygdala induced by electroconvulsive therapy in major depression. *Biological Psychiatry, 79,* 282–292. (p. 563)

Jost, J. T., Kay, A. C., & Thorisdottir, H. (Eds.). (2009). *Social and psychological bases of ideology and system justification.* New York: Oxford University Press. (p. 441)

Jovanovic, T., Blanding, N. Q., Norrholm, S. D., Duncan, E., Bradley, B., & Ressler, K. J. (2009). Childhood abuse is associated with increased startle reactivity in adulthood. *Depression and Anxiety, 26,* 1018–1026. (p. 137)

Judge, T. A., Thoresen, C. J., Bono, J. E., & Patton, G. K. (2001). The job satisfaction/job performance relationship: A qualitative and quantitative review. *Psychological Bulletin, 127,* 376–407. (p. B-8)

Jung, R. E., & Haier, R. J. (2013). Creativity and intelligence: Brain networks that link and differentiate the expression of genius. In O. Vartanian, A. S. Bristol, & J. C. Kaufman (Eds.), *Neuroscience of creativity.* Cambridge, MA: MIT Press. (p. 306)

Jung-Beeman, M., Bowden, E. M., Haberman, J., Frymiare, J. L., Arambel-Liu, S., Greenblatt, R., . . . Kounios, J. (2004). Neural activity when people solve verbal problems with insight. *PLoS Biology, 2,* e111. (p. 299)

Just, M. A., Keller, T. A., & Cynkar, J. (2008). A decrease in brain activation associated with driving when listening to someone speak. *Brain Research, 1205,* 70–80. (p. 82)

Kabadayi, C., & Osvath, M. (2017). Ravens parallel great apes in flexible planning for tool-use and bartering. *Science, 357,* 202–203. (p. 309)

Kabat-Zinn, J. (2001). Mindfulness-based interventions in context: Past, present, and future. *Clinical Psychology: Science and Practice, 10,* 144–156. (p. 404)

Kadohisa, M. (2013). Effects of odor on emotion, with implications. *Frontiers in Systems Neuroscience, 7,* 6. (p. 227)

Kagan, J. (1976). Emergent themes in human development. *American Scientist, 64,* 186–196. (p. 136)

Kagan, J. (1984). *The nature of the child.* New York: Basic Books. (p. 133)

Kagan, J. (1995). On attachment. *Harvard Review of Psychiatry, 3,* 104–106. (p. 134)

Kagan, J. (2010). *The temperamental thread: How genes, culture, time, and luck make us who we are.* Washington, DC: Dana Press. (p. 476)

Kagan, J., & Snidman, N. (2004). *The long shadow of temperament.* Cambridge, MA: Belknap Press. (p. 135)

Kahan, D. M. (2015). What is the "science of science communication"? *Journal of Science Communication, 14,* 1–10. (p. 18)

Kahneman, D. (1985, June). Quoted by K. McKean, Decisions, decisions. *Discover,* pp. 22–31. (p. A-6)

Kahneman, D. (1999). Assessments of objective happiness: A bottom-up approach. In D. Kahneman, E. Diener, & N. Schwartz (Eds.), *Understanding well-being: Scientific perspectives on enjoyment and suffering.* New York: Russell Sage Foundation. (p. 223)

Kahneman, D. (2005a, February 10). Are you happy now? *Gallup Management Journal* interview (gmj.gallup.com). (p. 409)

Kahneman, D. (2005b, January 13). What were they thinking? Q&A with Daniel Kahneman. *Gallup Management Journal* (gmj.gallup.com). (p. 301)

Kahneman, D. (2011). *Thinking, fast and slow.* New York: Farrar, Straus and Giroux. (p. 84)

Kahneman, D. (2015, July 18). Quoted by D. Shariatmadari, "Daniel Kahneman: 'What would I eliminate if I had a magic wand? Overconfidence.'" *The Guardian* (theguardian.com). (p. 303)

Kahneman, D., Fredrickson, B. L., Schreiber, C. A., & Redelmeier, D. A. (1993). When more pain is preferred to less: Adding a better end. *Psychological Science, 4,* 401–405. (p. 223)

Kahneman, D., Krueger, A. B., Schkade, D. A., Schwarz, N., & Stone, A. A. (2004). A survey method for characterizing daily life experience: The day reconstruction method. *Science, 306,* 1776–1780. (p. 408)

Kail, R. (1991). Developmental change in speed of processing during childhood and adolescence. *Psychological Bulletin, 109,* 490–501. (p. 152)

Kail, R., & Hall, L. K. (2001). Distinguishing short-term memory from working memory. *Memory & Cognition, 29,* 1–9. (p. 269)

Kaiser, R. H., Andrews-Hanna, J. R., Wager, T. D., & Pizzagalli, D. A. (2015). Large-scale network dysfunction in major depressive disorder: a meta-analysis of resting-state functional connectivity. *JAMA Psychiatry, 72,* 603–611. (p. 519)

Kaiser Family Foundation. (2010, January). *Generation M2: Media in the lives of 8- to 18-year-olds* (by V. J. Rideout, U. G. Foeher, & D. F. Roberts). Menlo Park, CA: Henry J. Kaiser Family Foundation. (p. 356)

Kakinami, L., Barnett, T. A., Séguin, L., & Paradis, G. (2015). Parenting style and obesity risk in children. *Preventive Medicine, 75,* 18–22. (pp. 138, 139)

Kállay, É. (2015). Physical and psychological benefits of written emotional expression: Review of meta-analyses and recommendations. *European Psychologist, 20,* 242–251. (p. 401)

Kamatali, J.-M. (2014, April 4). Following orders in Rwanda. *The New York Times* (nytimes.com). (p. 427)

Kambeitz, J., Kambelitz-Hankovic, L., Cabral, C., Dwyer, D. B., Calhoun, V. C., van den Heuvel, M. P., . . . Malchow, B. (2016). Aberrant functional whole-brain network architecture in patients with schizophrenia: A meta-analysis. *Schizophrenia Bulletin, 42,* Suppl. no. 1, S13–S21. (p. 525)

Kamel, N. S., & Gammack, J. K. (2006). Insomnia in the elderly: Cause, approach, and treatment. *American Journal of Medicine, 119,* 463–469. (p. 89)

Kamenica, E., Naclerio, R., & Malani, A. (2013). Advertisements impact the physiological efficacy of a branded drug. *PNAS, 110,* 12931–12935. (p. 560)

Kamil, A. C., & Cheng, K. (2001). Way-finding and landmarks: The multiple-bearings hypothesis. *Journal of Experimental Biology, 204,* 103–113. (p. 276)

Kaminski, J., Cali, J., & Fischer, J. (2004). Word learning in a domestic dog: Evidence for "fast mapping." *Science, 304,* 1682–1683. (p. 318)

Kampmann, I. L., Emmelkamp, P. M. G., & Morina, N. (2016). Meta-analysis of technology-assisted interventions for social anxiety disorder. *Journal of Anxiety Disorders, 42,* 71–84. (p. 546)

Kandel, D. B., & Raveis, V. H. (1989). Cessation of illicit drug use in young adulthood. *Archives of General Psychiatry, 46,* 109–116. (p. 113)

Kandel, E. (2008, October/November). Quoted in S. Avan, Speaking of memory. *Scientific American Mind,* pp. 16–17. (p. 84)

Kandel, E. (2012, March 5). Interview by Claudia Dreifus: A quest to understand how memory works. *The New York Times* (nytimes.com). (pp. 278, 469)

Kandel, E. (2013, September 6). The new science of mind. *The New York Times* (nytimes.com). (p. 558)

Kandel, E. R., & Schwartz, J. H. (1982). Molecular biology of learning: Modulation of transmitter release. *Science, 218,* 433–443. (p. 278)

Kandler, C., Bleidorn, W., Riemann, R., Angleitner, A., & Spinath, F. M. (2011). The genetic links between the Big Five personality traits and general interest domains. *Personality and Social Psychology Bulletin, 37,* 1633–1643. (p. 71)

Kandler, C., Bleidorn, W., Riemann, R., Angleitner, A., & Spinath, F. M. (2012). Life events as environmental states and genetic traits and the role of personality: A longitudinal twin study. *Behavior Genetics, 42,* 57–72. (p. 74)

Kandler, C., & Riemann, R. (2013). Genetic and environmental sources of individual religiousness: The roles of individual personality traits and perceived environmental religiousness. *Behavior Genetics, 43,* 297–313. (p. 72)

Kandler, C., Riemann, R., & Angleitner, A. (2013). Patterns and sources of continuity and change of energetic and temporal aspects of temperament in adulthood: A longitudinal twin study of self- and peer reports. *Developmental Psychology, 49,* 1739–1753. (p. 135)

Kane, G. D. (2010). Revisiting gay men's body image issues: Exposing the fault lines. *Review of General Psychology, 14,* 311–317. (p. 532)

Kane, J. M., & Mertz, J. E. (2012). Debunking myths about gender and mathematics performance. *Notices of the American Mathematical Society, 59,* 10–21. (p. 341)

Kanwar, A., Malik, S., Prokop, L. J., Sim, L. A., Feldstein, D., Wang, Z., & Murad, M. H. (2013). The association between anxiety disorders and suicidal behaviors: A systematic review and meta-analysis. *Depression and Anxiety, 30,* 917–929. (p. 500)

Kaplan, B. J., Rucklidge, J. J., Romijn, A., & McLeod, K. (2015). The emerging field of nutritional mental health: Inflammation, the microbiome, oxidative stress, and mitochondrial function. *Clinical Psychological Science, 3,* 964–980. (p. 519)

Kaplan, H. I., & Saddock, B. J. (Eds.). (1989). *Comprehensive textbook of psychiatry, V.* Baltimore, MD: Williams and Wilkins. (p. 560)

Kaprio, J., Koskenvuo, M., & Rita, H. (1987). Mortality after bereavement: A prospective study of 95,647 widowed persons. *American Journal of Public Health, 77,* 283–287. (p. 385)

Karacan, I., Aslan, C., & Hirshkowitz, M. (1983). Erectile mechanisms in man. *Science, 220,* 1080–1082. (p. 89)

Karacan, I., Goodenough, D. R., Shapiro, A., & Starker, S. (1966). Erection cycle during sleep in relation to dream anxiety. *Archives of General Psychiatry, 15,* 183–189. (p. 89)

Karasik, L. B., Adolph, K. E., Tamis-LeMonda, C. S., & Bornstein, M. H. (2010). WEIRD walking: Cross-cultural research on motor development. *Behavioral and Brain Sciences, 33,* 95–96. (p. 124)

Karau, S. J., & Williams, K. D. (1993). Social loafing: A meta-analytic review and theoretical integration. *Journal of Personality and Social Psychology, 65,* 681–706. (p. 430)

Karazsia, B. T., Murnen, S. K., & Tylka, T. L. (2017). Is body dissatisfaction changing across time? A cross-temporal meta-analysis. *Psychological Bulletin, 143,* 293–320. (p. 532)

Kark, J. D., Shemi, G., Friedlander, Y., Martin, O., Manor, O., & Blondheim, S. H. (1996). Does religious observance promote health? Mortality in secular vs. religious kibbutzim in Israel. *American Journal of Public Health, 86,* 341–346. (p. 405)

Karlén, J., Ludvigsson, J., Hedmark, M., Faresjö, Å., Theodorsson, E., & Faresjö, T. (2015). Early psychosocial exposures, hair cortisol levels, and disease risk. *Pediatrics, 135,* e1450–e1457. (p. 391)

Karlsgodt, K. H., Sun, D., & Cannon, T. D. (2010). Structural and functional brain abnormalities in schizophrenia. *Current Directions in Psychological Science, 19,* 226–231. (p. 525)

Karni, A., & Sagi, D. (1994). Dependence on REM sleep for overnight improvement of perceptual skills. *Science, 265,* 679–682. (p. 97)

Karpicke, J. D. (2012). Retrieval-based learning: Active retrieval promotes meaningful learning. *Current Directions in Psychological Science, 21,* 157–163. (p. 34)

Karremans, J. C., Frankenhis, W. E., & Arons, S. (2010). Blind men prefer a low waist-to-hip ratio. *Evolution and Human Behavior, 31,* 182–186. (pp. 184, 449)

Kasen, S., Chen, H., Sneed, J., Crawford, T., & Cohen, P. (2006). Social role and birth cohort influences on gender-linked personality traits in women: A 20-year longitudinal analysis. *Journal of Personality and Social Psychology, 91,* 944–958. (p. 165)

Kassin, S. M. (2017). The killing of Kitty Genovese: What else does this case tell us? *Perspectives on Psychological Science, 12,* 374–381. (p. 454)

Katz-Wise, S. L., & Hyde, J. S. (2012). Victimization experiences of lesbian, gay, and bisexual individuals: A meta-analysis. *Journal of Sex Research, 49,* 142–167. (p. 437)

Katz-Wise, S. L., Priess, H. A., & Hyde, J. S. (2010). Gender-role attitudes and behavior across the transition to parenthood. *Developmental Psychology, 46,* 18–28. (p. 165)

Kaufman, J. C., & Baer, J. (2002). I bask in dreams of suicide: Mental illness, poetry, and women. *Review of General Psychology, 6,* 271–286. (p. 516)

Kaufman, J., & Zigler, E. (1987). Do abused children become abusive parents? *American Journal of Orthopsychiatry, 57,* 186–192. (p. 137)

Kaufman, L., & Kaufman, J. H. (2000). Explaining the moon illusion. *PNAS, 97,* 500–505. (p. 212)

Kaufmann, R. K., Mann, M. L., Gopal, S., Liederman, J. A., Howe, P. D., Pretis, F., . . . Gilmore, M. (2017). Spatial heterogeneity of climate change as an experiential basis for skepticism. *PNAS, 114*(1), 67–71. (p. 303)

Kaunitz, L. N., Rowe, E. G., & Tsuchiya, N. (2016). Large capacity of conscious access for incidental memories in natural scenes. *Psychological Science, 27,* 1266–1277. (p. 266)

Kawakami, K., Dunn, E., Karmali, F., & Dovidio, J. F. (2009). Mispredicting affective and behavioral responses to racism. *Science, 323,* 276–278. (p. 436)

Kawamichi, H., Yoshihara, K., Sugawara, S. K., Matsunaga, M., Makita, K., Hamano, Y. H., . . . Sadato, N. (2015). Helping behavior induced by empathic concern attenuates anterior cingulate activation in response to others' distress. *Social Neuroscience, 11,* 109–122. doi:10.1080/17470919.2015.1049709 (p. 454)

Kay, A. C., Baucher, D., Peach, J. M., Laurin, K., Friesen, J., Zanna, M. P., & Spencer, S. J. (2009). Inequality, discrimination, and the power of the status quo: Direct evidence for a motivation to see the way things are as the way they should be. *Journal of Personality and Social Psychology, 97,* 421–434. (p. 441)

Kayser, C. (2007, April/May). Listening with your eyes. *Scientific American Mind,* pp. 24–29. (p. 228)

Kazantzis, N., & Dattilio, F. M. (2010). Definitions of homework, types of homework and ratings of the importance of homework among psychologists with cognitive behavior therapy and psychoanalytic theoretical orientations. *Journal of Clinical Psychology, 66,* 758–773. (p. 546)

Kazantzis, N., Whittington, C., & Dattilio, F. M. (2010). Meta-analysis of homework effects in cognitive and behavioral therapy: A replication and extension. *Clinical Psychology: Science and Practice, 17,* 144–156. (p. 546)

Kazdin, A. E. (2015). Editor's introduction to the special series: Targeted training of cognitive processes for behavioral and emotional disorders. *Clinical Psychological Science, 3,* 38. (p. 544)

Kean, S. (2016, September). The audacious plan to save this man's life by transplanting his head. *The Atlantic* (theatlantic.com). (p. 37)

Kearns, M. C., Ressler, K. J., Zatzick, D., & Rothbaum, B. O. (2012). Early interventions for PTSD: A review. *Depression and Anxiety, 29,* 833–842. (p. 279)

Keesey, R. E., & Corbett, S. W. (1984). Metabolic defense of the body weight set-point. In A. J. Stunkard & E. Stellar (Eds.), *Eating and its disorders.* New York: Raven Press. (p. 363)

Keiser, H. N., Sackett, P. R., Kuncel, N. R., & Brothen, T. (2016). Why women perform better in college than admission scores would predict: Exploring the roles of conscientiousness and course-taking patterns. *Journal of Applied Psychology, 101,* 569–581. (pp. 168, 343)

Keith, S. W., Redden, D. T., Katzmarzyk, P. T., Boggiano, M. M., Hanlon, E. C., Benca, R. M., . . . Allison, D. B. (2006). Putative contributors to the secular increase in obesity: Exploring the roads less traveled. *International Journal of Obesity, 30,* 1585–1594. (p. 365)

Kell, H. J., Lubinski, D., & Benbow, C. P. (2013). Who rises to the top? Early indicators. *Psychological Science, 24,* 648–659. (p. 331)

Keller, C., Hartmann, C., & Siegrist, M. (2016). The association between dispositional self-control and longitudinal changes in eating behaviors, diet quality, and BMI. *Psychology & Health, 31,* 1311–1327. (p. 398)

Kellerman, J., Lewis, J., & Laird, J. D. (1989). Looking and loving: The effects of mutual gaze on feelings of romantic love. *Journal of Research in Personality, 23,* 145–161. (p. 376)

Kelling, S. T., & Halpern, B. P. (1983). Taste flashes: Reaction times, intensity, and quality. *Science, 219,* 412–414. (p. 225)

Kellner, C. H., Knapp, R. G., Petrides, G., Rummans, T. A., Husain, M. M., Rasmussen, K., . . . Fink, M. (2006). Continuation electroconvulsive therapy vs. pharmacotherapy for relapse prevention in major depression: A multisite study from the Consortium for Research in Electroconvulsive Therapy (CORE). *Archives of General Psychiatry, 63,* 1337–1344. (p. 563)

Kelly, A. E. (2000). Helping construct desirable identities: A self-presentational view of psychotherapy. *Psychological Bulletin, 126,* 475–494. (p. 544)

Kelly, D. J., Quinn, P. C., Slater, A. M., Lee, K., Ge, L., & Pascalis, O. (2007). The other-race effect develops during infancy: Evidence of perceptual narrowing. *Psychological Science, 18,* 1084–1089. (p. 447)

Kelly, S. D., Özyürek, A., & Maris, E. (2010). Two sides of the same coin: Speech and gesture mutually interact to enhance comprehension. *Psychological Science, 21,* 260–267. (p. 317)

Kelly, T. A. (1990). The role of values in psychotherapy: A critical review of process and outcome effects. *Clinical Psychology Review, 10,* 171–186. (p. 556)

Kempe, R. S., & Kempe, C. C. (1978). *Child abuse.* Cambridge, MA: Harvard University Press. (p. 137)

Kendall-Tackett, K. A., Williams, L. M., & Finkelhor, D. (1993). Impact of sexual abuse on children: A review and synthesis of recent empirical studies. *Psychological Bulletin, 113,* 164–180. (p. 293)

Kendler, K. S. (1996). Parenting: A genetic-epidemiologic perspective. *The American Journal of Psychiatry, 153,* 11–20. (p. 139)

Kendler, K. S. (1998, January). Major depression and the environment: A psychiatric genetic perspective. *Pharmacopsychiatry, 31*(1), 5–9. (p. 517)

Kendler, K. S., Maes, H. H., Lönn, S. L., Morris, N. A., Lichtenstein, P., Sundquist, J., & Sundquist, K. (2015a). A Swedish national twin study of criminal behavior and its violent, white-collar and property subtypes. *Psychological Medicine, 45,* 2253–2262. (p. 337)

Kendler, K. S., Myers, J., & Zisook, S. (2008). Does bereavement-related major depression differ from major depression associated with other stressful life events? *American Journal of Psychiatry, 165,* 1449–1455. (p. 517)

Kendler, K. S., Neale, M. C., Kessler, R. C., Heath, A. C., & Eaves, L. J. (1994). Parent treatment and the equal environment assumption in twin studies of psychiatric illness. *Psychological Medicine, 24,* 579–590. (p. 71)

Kendler, K. S., Neale, M. C., Thornton, L. M., Aggen, S. H., Gilman, S. E., & Kessler, R. C. (2002). Cannabis use in the last year in a U.S. national sample of twin and sibling pairs. *Psychological Medicine, 32,* 551–554. (p. 110)

Kendler, K. S., Ohlsson, H., Sundquist, J., & Sundquist, K. (2016). Alcohol use disorder and mortality across the lifespan: A longitudinal cohort and co-relative analysis. *JAMA Psychiatry, 73,* 575–581. (p. 103)

Kendler, K. S., Sundquist, K., Ohlsson, H., Palmer, K., Maes, H., Winkleby, M. A., & Sundquist, J. (2012). Genetic and familiar environmental influences on the risk for drug abuse: A Swedish adoption study. *Archives of General Psychiatry, 69,* 690–697. (p. 111)

Kendler, K. S., Turkheimer, E., Ohlsson, H., Sundquist, J., & Sundquist, K. (2015b). Family environment and the malleability of cognitive ability: A Swedish national home-reared and adopted-away cosibling control study. *PNAS, 112,* 4612–4617. (pp. 73, 530)

Kendrick, K. M., & Feng, J. (2011). Neural encoding principles in face perception revealed using non-primate models. In G. Rhodes, A. Calder, M. Johnson, & J. V. Haxby (Eds.), *The Oxford handbook of face perception.* Oxford: Oxford University Press. (p. 266)

Kennard, B. D., Emslie, G. J., Mayes, T. L., Nakonezny, P. A., Jones, J. M., Foxwell, A. A., & King, J. (2014). Sequential treatment of fluoxetine and relapse-prevention CBT to improve outcomes in pediatric depression. *American Journal of Psychiatry, 171,* 1083–1090. (p. 562)

Kennedy, M., Kreppner, J., Knights, N., Kumsta, R., Maughan, B., Golm, D., . . . Sonuga-Barke, E. J. (2016). Early severe institutional deprivation is associated with a persistent variant of adult attention-deficit/hyperactivity disorder: Clinical presentation, developmental continuities and life circumstances in the English and Romanian Adoptees study. *Journal of Child Psychology and Psychiatry, 57,* 1113–1125. (p. 137)

Kenrick, D. T., & Funder, D. C. (1988). Profiting from controversy: Lessons from the person-situation debate. *American Psychologist, 43,* 23–34. (p. 481)

Kenrick, D. T., Griskevicious, V., Neuberg, S. L., & Schaller, M. (2010). Renovating the pyramid of needs: Contemporary extensions build upon ancient foundations. *Perspectives on Psychological Science, 5,* 292–314. (p. 351)

Kenrick, D. T., & Gutierres, S. E. (1980). Contrast effects and judgments of physical attractiveness: When beauty becomes a social problem. *Journal of Personality and Social Psychology, 38,* 131–140. (p. 176)

Kenrick, D. T., Nieuweboer, S., & Buunk, A. P. (2009). Universal mechanisms and cultural diversity: Replacing the blank slate with a coloring book. In M. Schaller, A. Norenzayan, S. Heine, A. Norenzayan, T. Yamagishi, & T. Kameda (Eds.), *Evolution, culture, and the human mind* (pp. 257–271). Mahwah, NJ: Erlbaum. (pp. 123, 184)

Kensinger, E. A. (2007). Negative emotion enhances memory accuracy: Behavioral and neuroimaging evidence. *Current Directions in Psychological Science, 16,* 213–218. (p. 277)

Kenyon, P. (2016, June 29). After Brexit vote, U.K. sees a wave of hate crimes and racist abuse. National Public Radio (npr.org). (p. 439)

Keough, K. A., Zimbardo, P. G., & Boyd, J. N. (1999). Who's smoking, drinking, and using drugs? Time perspective as a predictor of substance use. *Basic and Applied Social Psychology, 2,* 149–164. (p. 463)

Keramati, M., Durand, A., Girardeau, P., Gutkin, B., & Ahmed, S. H. (2017). Cocaine addiction as a homeostatic reinforcement learning disorder. *Psychological Review, 124,* 130–153. (p. 107)

Keresztes, A., Bender, A. R., Bodammer, N. C., Lindenberger, U., Shing, Y. L., & Werkle-Bergner, M. (2017). Hippocampal maturity promotes memory distinctiveness in childhood and adolescence. *PNAS, 114,* 9212–9217. (p. 276)

Kern, M. L., Eichstaedt, J. C., Schwartz, H. A., Dziurzynski, L., Ungar, L. H., Stillwell, D. J., . . . Seligman, M. E. P. (2014). The online social self: An open vocabulary approach to personality. *Assessment, 21,* 158–169. (p. 481)

Kernis, M. H. (2003). Toward a conceptualization of optimal self-esteem. *Psychological Inquiry, 14,* 1–26. (p. 489)

Kerns, J. C., Guo, J., Fothergill, E., Howard, L., Knuth, N. D., Brychta, R., . . . Hall, K. D. (2017). Increased physical activity associated with less weight regain six years after "The Biggest Loser" competition. *Obesity, 25,* 1838–1843. (p. 366)

Kerr, N. L., & Bruun, S. E. (1983). Dispensability of member effort and group motivation losses: Free-rider effects. *Journal of Personality and Social Psychology, 44,* 78–94. (p. 430)

Kessler, M., & Albee, G. (1975). Primary prevention. *Annual Review of Psychology, 26,* 557–591. (p. 566)

Kessler, R. C., Aguilar-Gaxiola, S., Alonso, J., Chatterji, S., Lee, S., Ormel, J., . . . Wang, P. S. (2009). The global burden of mental disorders: An update from the WHO World Mental Health (WMH) Surveys. *Epidemiology and Psychiatric Services, 18,* 23–33. (pp. 503, 504)

Kessler, R. C., Birnbaum, H. G., Shahly, V., Bromet, E., Hwang, I., McLaughlin, K. A., . . . Stein, D. J. (2010). Age differences in the prevalence and co-morbidity of DSM-IV major depressive episodes: Results from the WHO World Mental Health Survey Initiative. *Depression and Anxiety, 27,* 351–364. (pp. 298, 518)

Kessler, R. C., Petukhova, M., Sampson, N. A., Zaslavsky, A. M., & Wittchen, H.-A. (2012). Twelve-month and lifetime morbid risk of anxiety and mood disorders in the United States. *International Journal of Methods in Psychiatric Research, 21,* 169–184. (p. 508)

Kessler, R. C., Soukup, J., Davis, R. B., Foster, D. F., Wilkey, S. A., Van Rompay, M. I., & Eisenberg, D. M. (2001). The use of complementary and alternative therapies to treat anxiety and depression in the United States. *American Journal of Psychiatry, 158*, 289–294. (p. 553)

Keyes, K. M., Maslowsky, J., Hamilton, A., & Schulenberg, J. (2015). The great sleep recession: Changes in sleep duration among U.S. adolescents, 1991–2012. *Pediatrics, 135*, 460–468. (p. 92)

Keynes, M. (1980, December 20/27). Handel's illnesses. *The Lancet*, pp. 1354–1355. (p. 516)

Keys, A., Brozek, J., Henschel, A., Mickelsen, O., & Taylor, H. L. (1950). *The biology of human starvation*. Minneapolis: University of Minnesota Press. (p. 360)

Khanna, S., & Greyson, B. (2014). Daily spiritual experiences before and after near-death experiences. *Psychology of Religion and Spirituality, 6*, 302–309. (p. 108)

Khanna, S., & Greyson, B. (2015). Near-death experiences and posttraumatic growth. *Journal of Nervous and Mental Disease, 203*, 749–755. (p. 108)

Khazanoy, G. K., & Ruscio, A. M. (2016). Is low positive emotionality a specific risk factor for depression? A meta-analysis of longitudinal studies. *Psychological Bulletin, 142*, 991–1015. (p. 516)

Khera, M., Bhattacharya, R. K., Blick, G., Kushner, H., Nguyen, D., & Miner, M. M. (2011). Improved sexual function with testosterone replacement therapy in hypogonadal men: Real-world data from the Testim Registry in the United States (TriUS). *Journal of Sexual Medicine, 8*, 3204–3213. (p. 173)

Kiatpongsan, S., & Norton, M. I. (2014). How much (more) should CEOs make? A universal desire for more equal pay. *Perspectives on Psychological Science, 9*, 587–593. (p. 410)

Kiecolt-Glaser, J. K. (2009). Psychoneuroimmunology: Psychology's gateway to the biomedical future. *Perspectives on Psychological Science, 4*, 367–369. (p. 388)

Kiecolt-Glaser, J. K., Loving, T. J., Stowell, J. R., Malarkey, W. B., Lemeshow, S., Dickinson, S. L., & Glaser, R. (2005). Hostile marital interactions, proinflammatory cytokine production, and wound healing. *Archives of General Psychiatry, 62*, 1377–1384. (p. 389)

Kiecolt-Glaser, J. K., Page, G. G., Marucha, P. T., MacCallum, R. C., & Glaser, R. (1998). Psychological influences on surgical recovery: Perspectives from psychoneuroimmunology. *American Psychologist, 53*, 1209–1218. (p. 389)

Kiehl, K. A., & Buckholtz, J. W. (2010). Inside the mind of a psychopath. *Scientific American Mind, 21*, 22–29. (p. 531)

Kiekens, G., Claes, L., Demyttenaere, K., Auerbach, R. P., Green, J. G., Kessler, R. C., . . . Bruffaerts, R. (2016). Lifetime and 12-month nonsuicidal self-injury and academic performance in college freshmen. *Suicide and Life-Threatening Behavior, 46*, 563–576. (p. 502)

Kihlstrom, J. F. (2005). Dissociative disorders. *Annual Review of Clinical Psychology, 1*, 227–253. (p. 529)

Kihlstrom, J. F. (2006). Repression: A unified theory of a will-o'-the-wisp. *Behavioral and Brain Sciences, 29*, 523. (p. 469)

Kilgore, A. (2017, November 9). Aaron Hernandez suffered from most severe CTE ever found in a person his age. *The Washington Post* (washingtonpost.com). (p. 57)

Kille, D. R., Forest, A. L., & Wood, J. V. (2013). Tall, dark, and stable: Embodiment motivates mate selection preferences. *Psychological Science, 24*, 112–114. (p. 229)

Killingsworth, M. A., & Gilbert, D. T. (2010). A wandering mind is an unhappy mind. *Science, 330*, 932. (p. B-2)

Kilpatrick, L. A., Suyenobu, B. Y., Smith, S. R., Bueller, J. A., Goodman, T., Creswell, J. D., . . . Naliboff, B. D. (2011). Impact of mindfulness-based stress reduction training on intrinsic brain activity. *NeuroImage, 56*, 290–298. (p. 404)

Kim, B. S. K., Ng, G. F., & Ahn, A. J. (2005). Effects of client expectation for counseling success, client-counselor worldview match, and client adherence to Asian and European American cultural values on counseling process with Asian Americans. *Journal of Counseling Psychology, 52*, 67–76. (p. 556)

Kim, E. S., Hagan, K. A., Grodstein, F., DeMeo, D. L., De Vivo, I., & Kubzansky, L. D. (2017). Optimism and cause-specific mortality: A prospective cohort study. *American Journal of Epidemiology, 185*, 21–29. (p. 399)

Kim, H., & Markus, H. R. (1999). Deviance or uniqueness, harmony or conformity? A cultural analysis. *Journal of Personality and Social Psychology, 77*, 785–800. (p. 490)

Kim, J., Suh, W., Kim, S., & Gopalan, H. (2012). Coping strategies to manage acculturative stress: Meaningful activity participation, social support, and positive emotion among Korean immigrant adolescents in the USA. *International Journal of Qualitative Studies on Health and Well-Being, 7*, 1–10. (p. 385)

Kim, J. L., & Ward, L. M. (2012). Striving for pleasure without fear: Short-term effects of reading a women's magazine on women's sexual attitudes. *Psychology of Women Quarterly, 36*, 326–336. (p. 177)

Kim, M., Kim, C.-H., Jung, H. H., Kim, S. J., & Chang, J. W. (2018). Treatment of major depressive disorder via magnetic resonance-guided focused ultrasound surgery. *Biological Psychiatry, 83*, e17-e18. (p. 565)

Kim, S. H., Hwang, J. H., Park, H. S., & Kim, S. E. (2008). Resting brain metabolic correlates of neuroticism and extraversion in young men. *NeuroReport, 19*, 883–886. (p. 476)

Kim, S. H., Vincent, L. C., & Goncalo, J. A. (2013). Outside advantage: Can social rejection fuel creative thought? *Journal of Experimental Psychology: General, 142*, 605–611. (p. 307)

Kim, S. Y., Liu, L., & Cao, F. (2017). How does first language (L1) influence second language (L2) reading in the brain? Evidence from Korean-English and Chinese-English bilinguals. *Brain and Language, 171*, 1–13. (p. 317)

Kim, Y. S., Leventhal, B. L., Koh, Y., Fombonne, E., Laska, E., Lim, E., . . . Grinker, R. R. (2011). Prevalence of autism spectrum disorders in a total population sample. *American Journal of Psychiatry, 168*, 904–912. (p. 131)

Kimata, H. (2001). Effect of humor on allergen-induced wheal reactions. *Journal of the American Medical Association, 285*, 737. (p. 399)

Kimble, G. A. (1956). *Principles of general psychology*. New York: Ronald Press. (p. 254)

Kimble, G. A. (1981). *Biological and cognitive constraints on learning*. Washington, DC: American Psychological Association. (p. 254)

Kim-Yeary, K. H., Ounpraseuth, S., Moore, P., Bursac, Z., & Greene, P. (2012). Religion, social capital, and health. *Review of Religious Research, 54*, 331–347. (p. 406)

King, D. W., King, L. A., Park, C. L., Lee, L. O., Pless Kaiser, A., Spiro, A., . . . Keane, T. M. (2015). Positive adjustment among American repatriated prisoners of the Vietnam War: Modeling the long-term effects of captivity. *Clinical Psychological Science, 3*, 861–876. (p. 509)

King, L. A., Heintzelman, S. J., & Ward, S. J. (2016). Beyond the search for meaning: A contemporary science of the experience of meaning in life. *Current Directions in Psychological Science, 25*, 211–216. (p. 350)

King, S., St-Hilaire, A., & Heidkamp, D. (2010). Prenatal factors in schizophrenia. *Current Directions in Psychological Science, 19*, 209–213. (p. 525)

Kinnier, R. T., & Metha, A. T. (1989). Regrets and priorities at three stages of life. *Counseling and Values, 33*, 182–193. (p. 158)

Kinsella, E. L., Ritchie, T. D., & Igou, E. R. (2015). Zeroing in on heroes: A prototype analysis of hero features. *Journal of Personality and Social Psychology, 108*, 114–127. (p. 452)

Kinsey, A. C., Pomeroy, W. B., & Martin, C. E. (1948). *Sexual behavior in the human male*. Bloomington: Indiana University Press. (p. 172)

Kinsey, A. C., Pomeroy, W. B., Martin, C. E., & Gebhard, P. H. (1953). *Sexual behavior in the human female*. Philadelphia: W. B. Saunders. (p. 172)

Kirby, D. (2002). Effective approaches to reducing adolescent unprotected sex, pregnancy, and childbearing. *Journal of Sex Research, 39*, 51–57. (p. 178)

Kirby, T. (2015, September). Ketamine for depression: The highs and lows. *The Lancet Psychiatry, 2*, 783–784. (p. 562)

Kirkpatrick, B., Fenton, W. S., Carpenter, W. T., Jr., & Marder, S. R. (2006). The NIMH-MATRICS consensus statement on negative symptoms. *Schizophrenia Bulletin, 32*, 214–219. (p. 524)

Kirkpatrick, L. (1999). Attachment and religious representations and behavior. In J. Cassidy & P. R. Shaver (Eds.), *Handbook of attachment*. New York: Guilford. (p. 136)

Kirsch, I. (2010). *The emperor's new drugs: Exploding the antidepressant myth*. New York: Basic Books. (p. 27)

Kirsch, I. (2016). The emperor's new drugs: Medication and placebo in the treatment of depression. In *Behind and beyond the brain*. Symposium conducted by the Bial Foundation, March 30–April 2 (www.bial.com/imagem/Programa_e%20_Resumos-Program_and_Abstracts.pdf). (p. 562)

Kirsch, I., Deacon, B. J., Huedo-Medina, T. B., Scoboria, A., Moore, T. J., & Johnson, B. T. (2008). Initial severity and antidepressant benefits: A meta-analysis of data submitted to the Food and Drug Administration. *Public Library of Science Medicine, 5*, e45. (p. 562)

Kirsch, I., Kong, J., Sadler, P., Spaeth, R., Cook, A., Kaptchuk, T. J., & Gollub, R. (2014). Expectancy and conditioning in placebo analgesia: Separate or connected processes? *Psychology of Consciousness; Theory, Research, and Practice, 1*, 51–59. (p. 562)

Kirsch, I., & Sapirstein, G. (1998). Listening to Prozac but hearing placebo: A meta-analysis of antidepressant medication. *Prevention and Treatment, 1*, posted June 26 at (journals.apa.org/prevention/volume1). (p. 562)

Kirsch, I., Wampold, B., & Kelley, J. M. (2016). Controlling for the placebo effect in psychotherapy: Noble quest or tilting at windmills? *Psychology of Consciousness: Theory, Research, and Practice, 3*, 121–131. (p. 562)

Kisley, M. A., Wood, S., & Burrows, C. L. (2007). Looking at the sunny side of life: Age-related change in an event-related potential measure of the negativity bias. *Psychological Science, 18*, 838–843. (p. 158)

Kitahara, C. M., Flint, A. J., de Gonzalez, A. B., Bernstein, L., Brotzman, M., MacInnis, R. J., . . . Hartge, P. (2014, July 8). Association between class III obesity (BMI of 40–59 kg/m2) and mortality: A pooled analysis of 20 prospective studies. *PLoS Medicine*. doi:10.1371/journal.pmed.1001673 (p. 365)

Kitaoka, A. (2016, September 11). Facebook post. Retrieved from facebook.com/photo.php?fbid=10207806660899237&set=a.2215289656523.118366.1076035621&type=3&theater (p. 202)

Kitayama, S., Chua, H. F., Tompson, S., & Han, S. (2013). Neural mechanisms of dissonance: An fMRI investigation of choice justification. *NeuroImage, 69*, 206–212. (p. 420)

Kitayama, S., Conway, L. G., III, Pietromonaci, P. R., Park, H., & Plaut, V. C. (2010). Ethos of independence across regions in the United States: The production–adoption model of cultural change. *American Psychologist, 65*, 559–574. (p. 491)

Kitayama, S., Ishii, K., Imada, T., Takemura, K., & Ramaswamy, J. (2006). Voluntary settlement and the spirit of independence: Evidence from Japan's "northern frontier." *Journal of Personality and Social Psychology, 91*, 369–384. (p. 490)

Kitayama, S., Park, H., Sevincer, A. T., Karasawa, M., & Uskul, A. K. (2009). A cultural task analysis of implicit independence: Comparing North America, Western Europe, and East Asia. *Journal of Personality and Social Psychology, 97*, 236–255. (pp. 416, 491)

Kitayama, S., Park, J., Boylan, J. M., Miyamoto, Y., Levine, C. S., Markus, H. R., . . . Ryff, C. D. (2015). Expression of anger and ill health in two cultures: An examination of inflammation and cardiovascular risk. *Psychological Science, 26*, 211–220. (p. 392)

Kivimaki, M., Leino-Arjas, P., Luukkonen, R., Rihimaki, H., & Kirjonen, J. (2002). Work stress and risk of cardiovascular mortality: Prospective cohort study of industrial employees. *British Medical Journal, 325*, 857. (p. 396)

Kivipelto, M., & Håkansson, K. (2017, April). A rare success against Alzheimer's. *Scientific American*, pp. 33–37. (p. 153)

Kivlighan, D. M., Goldberg, S. B., Abbas, M., Pace, B. T., Yulish, N. E., Thomas, J. G., . . . Wampold, B. E. (2015). The enduring effects of psychodynamic treatments vis-à-vis alternative treatments: A multilevel longitudinal meta-analysis. *Clinical Psychology Review, 40*, 1–14. (p. 552)

Klahr, A. M., & Burt, S. A. (2014). Elucidating the etiology of individual differences in parenting: A meta-analysis of behavioral genetic research. *Psychological Bulletin, 140*, 544–586. (p. 139)

Klayman, J., & Ha, Y.-W. (1987). Confirmation, disconfirmation, and information in hypothesis testing. *Psychological Review, 94*, 211–228. (p. 300)

Klein, D. N. (2010). Chronic depression: Diagnosis and classification. *Current Directions in Psychological Science, 19*, 96–100. (p. 517)

Klein, D. N., & Kotov, R. (2016). Course of depression in a 10-year prospective study: Evidence for qualitatively distinct subgroups. *Journal of Abnormal Psychology, 125*, 337–348. (p. 517)

Klein, D. N., Schwartz, J. E., Santiago, N. J., Vivian, D., Vocisano, C., Castonguay, L. G., . . . Keller, M. B. (2003). Therapeutic alliance in depression treatment: Controlling for prior change and patient characteristics. *Journal of Consulting and Clinical Psychology, 71*, 997–1006. (p. 555)

Klein, R. A., Ratliff, K. A., Vianello, M., Adams, R. B., Jr., Bahník, Š., Bernstein, M. J., . . . Nosek, B. A. (2014). Investigating variation in replicability: A "many labs" replication project. *Social Psychology, 45*, 142–152. (p. 20)

Kleinke, C. L. (1986). Gaze and eye contact: A research review. *Psychological Bulletin, 1000*, 78–100. (p. 375)

Kleinman, D., & Gollan, T. H. (2016). Speaking two languages for the price of one: Bypassing language control mechanisms via accessibility-driven switches. *Psychological Science, 27*, 700–714. (p. 320)

Kleinmuntz, B., & Szucko, J. J. (1984). A field study of the fallibility of polygraph lie detection. *Nature, 308*, 449–450. (p. 374)

Kleitman, N. (1960, November). Patterns of dreaming. *Scientific American*, pp. 82–88. (p. 87)

Klemm, W. R. (1990). Historical and introductory perspectives on brainstem-mediated behaviors. In W. R. Klemm & R. P. Vertes (Eds.), *Brainstem mechanisms of behavior* (pp. 3–32). New York: Wiley. (p. 54)

Klimstra, T. A., Hale, W. W., III, Raaijmakers, Q. A. W., Branje, S. J. T., & Meeus, W. H. J. (2009). Maturation of personality in adolescence. *Journal of Personality and Social Psychology, 96*, 898–912. (p. 147)

Klimstra, T. A., Kuppens, P., Luyckx, K., Branje, S., Hale, W. W., Oosterwegel, A., . . . Meeus, W. H. J. (2015). Daily dynamics of adolescent mood and identity. *Journal of Research on Adolescence*. Advance online publication. doi:10.1111/jora.12205 (p. 146)

Kline, D., & Schieber, F. (1985). Vision and aging. In J. E. Birren & K. W. Schaie (Eds.), *Handbook of the psychology of aging* (2nd ed., pp. 296–331). New York: Van Nostrand Reinhold. (p. 152)

Kline, N. S. (1974). *From sad to glad.* New York: Ballantine Books. (p. 521)

Klinke, R., Kral, A., Heid, S., Tillein, J., & Hartmann, R. (1999). Recruitment of the auditory cortex in congenitally deaf cats by long-term cochlear electrostimulation. *Science, 285*, 1729–1733. (p. 218)

Kluemper, D. H., McLarty, B. D., Bishop, T. R., & Sen, A. (2015). Interviewee selection test and evaluator assessments of general mental ability, emotional intelligence and extraversion: Relationships with structured behavioral and situational interview performance. *Journal of Business and Psychology, 30*, 543–563. (p. 476)

Klump, K. L., Suisman, J. L., Burt, S. A., McGue, M., & Iacono, W. G. (2009). Genetic and environmental influences on disordered eating: An adoption study. *Journal of Abnormal Psychology, 118*, 797–805. (p. 532)

Knapp, S., & VandeCreek, L. (2000). Recovered memories of childhood abuse: Is there an underlying professional consensus? *Professional Psychology: Research and Practice, 31*, 365–371. (p. 293)

Knickmeyer, E. (2001, August 7). In Africa, big is definitely better. *Seattle Times*, p. A7. (p. 532)

Knight, R. T. (2007). Neural networks debunk phrenology. *Science, 316*, 1578–1579. (p. 63)

Knight, W. (2004, August 2). Animated face helps deaf with phone chat. *NewScientist.com*. (p. 228)

Knoblich, G., & Oellinger, M. (2006, October/November). The Eureka moment. *Scientific American Mind*, pp. 38–43. (p. 299)

Knouse, L. E., Teller, J., & Brooks, M. A. (2017). Meta-analysis of cognitive–behavioral treatments for adult ADHD. *Journal of Consulting and Clinical Psychology, 85*, 737–750. (p. 546)

Knuts, I. J. E., Cosci, F., Esquivel, G., Goossens, L., van Duinen, M., Bareman, M., . . . Schruers, K. R. J. (2010). Cigarette smoking and 35% CO_2 induced panic in panic disorder patients. *Journal of Affective Disorders, 124*, 215–218. (p. 507)

Knutsen, J., Mandell, D. S., & Frye, D. (2015). Children with autism are impaired in the understanding of teaching. *Developmental Science*. doi:10.1111/desc.12368 (p. 131)

Knutsson, A., & Bøggild, H. (2010). Gastrointestinal disorders among shift workers. *Scandinavian Journal of Work, Environment & Health*, 85–95. (p. 90)

Ko, C.-K., Yen, J.-Y., Chen, C.-C., Chen, S.-H., & Yen, C.-F. (2005). Proposed diagnostic criteria of internet addiction for adolescents. *Journal of Nervous and Mental Disease, 193*, 728–733. (p. 102)

Koch, C. (2015, January/February). The face as entryway to the self. *Scientific American Mind*, pp. 26–29. (p. 205)

Koenen, K. C., Moffitt, T. E., Roberts, A. L., Martin, L. T., Kubzansky, L., Harrington, H., . . . Caspi, A. (2009). Childhood IQ and adult mental disorders: A test of the cognitive reserve hypothesis. *American Journal of Psychiatry, 166*, 50–57. (p. 331)

Koenig, H. G., King, D. E., & Carson, V. B. (2012). *Handbook of religion and health* (2nd ed.). New York: Oxford University Press. (p. 404)

Koenig, H. G., & Larson, D. B. (1998). Use of hospital services, religious attendance, and religious affiliation. *Southern Medical Journal, 91*, 925–932. (p. 406)

Koenig, L. B., & Vaillant, G. E. (2009). A prospective study of church attendance and health over the lifespan. *Health Psychology, 28*, 117–124. (p. 406)

Koenigs, M., Young, L., Adolphs, R., Tranel, D., Cushman, F., Hauser, M., & Damasio, A. (2007). Damage to the prefrontal cortex increases utilitarian moral judgements. *Nature, 446*, 908–911. (p. 63)

Kofler, M. J., Raiker, J. S., Sarver, D. E., Wells, E. L., & Soto, E. F. (2016). Is hyperactivity ubiquitous in ADHD or dependent on environmental demands? Evidence from meta-analysis. *Clinical Psychology Review, 46*, 12–24. (p. 498)

Kohlberg, L. (1981). *The philosophy of moral development: Essays on moral development* (Vol. 1). San Francisco: Harper & Row. (p. 143)

Kohlberg, L. (1984). *The psychology of moral development: Essays on moral development* (Vol. 2). San Francisco: Harper & Row. (p. 143)

Kohler, C. G., Walker, J. B., Martin, E. A., Healey, K. M., & Moberg, P. J. (2010). Facial emotion perception in schizophrenia: A meta-analytic review. *Schizophrenia Bulletin, 36*, 1009–1019. (p. 523)

Kohler, I. (1962, May). Experiments with goggles. *Scientific American*, pp. 62–72. (p. 214)

Köhler, W. (1925; reprinted 1957). *The mentality of apes.* London: Pelican. (p. 309)

Kolassa, I.-T., & Elbert, T. (2007). Structural and functional neuroplasticity in relation to traumatic stress. *Current Directions in Psychological Science, 16*, 321–325. (p. 512)

Kolb, B. (1989). Brain development, plasticity, and behavior. *American Psychologist, 44*, 1203–1212. (p. 64)

Kolb, B., & Whishaw, I. Q. (1998). Brain plasticity and behavior. *Annual Review of Psychology, 49*, 43–64. (p. 123)

Kolb, B., & Whishaw, I. Q. (2006). An introduction to brain and behavior (2nd ed.) New York: Worth. (p. 306)

Kolker, K. (2002, December 8). Video violence disturbs some: Others scoff at influence. *The Grand Rapids Press*, pp. A1, A12. (p. 444)

Kolovos, S., van Tulder, M. W., Cuijpers, P., Prigent, A., Chevreul, K., Riper, H., & Bosmans, J. E. (2017). The effect of treatment as usual on major depressive disorder: A meta-analysis. *Journal of Affective Disorders, 210*, 72–81. (p. 552)

Koltko-Rivera, M. E. (2006). Rediscovering the later version of Maslow's hierarchy of needs: Self-transcendence and opportunities for theory, research, and unification. *Review of General Psychology, 10*, 302–317. (p. 350)

Komisaruk, B. R., & Whipple, B. (2011). Non-genital orgasms. *Sexual and Relationship Therapy, 26,* 356–372. (p. 177)

Kondoh, K., Lu, Z., Olson, D. P., Lowell, B. B., & Buck, L. B. (2016). A specific area of olfactory cortex involved in stress hormone responses to predator odours. *Nature, 532,* 103–106. (p. 226)

Konkle, T., Brady, T. F., Alvarez, G. A., & Oliva, A. (2010). Conceptual distinctiveness supports detailed visual long-term memory for real-world objects. *Journal of Experimental Psychology: General, 139,* 558–578. (p. 266)

Kontula, O., & Haavio-Mannila, E. (2009). The impact of aging on human sexual activity and sexual desire. *Journal of Sex Research, 46,* 46–56. (p. 151)

Kornell, N., & Bjork, R. A. (2008). Learning concepts and categories: Is spacing the "enemy of induction"? *Psychological Science, 19,* 585–592. (p. 34)

Kosslyn, S. M. (2005). Reflective thinking and mental imagery: A perspective on the development of posttraumatic stress disorder. *Development and Psychopathology, 17,* 851–863. (p. 510)

Kosslyn, S. M. (2008). The world in the brain. In 2008: What have you changed your mind about? Why? *The Edge* (edge.org). (p. 315)

Kosslyn, S. M., & Koenig, O. (1992). *Wet mind: The new cognitive neuroscience.* New York: Free Press. (p. 47)

Kotchick, B. A., Shaffer, A., & Forehand, R. (2001). Adolescent sexual risk behavior: A multi-system perspective. *Clinical Psychology Review, 21,* 493–519. (p. 177)

Koten, J. W., Jr., Wood, G., Hagoort, P., Goebel, R., Propping, P., Willmes, K., & Boomsma, D. I. (2009). Genetic contribution to variation in cognitive function: An fMRI study in twins. *Science, 323,* 1737–1740. (p. 336)

Kotkin, M., Daviet, C., & Gurin, J. (1996). The *Consumer Reports* mental health survey. *American Psychologist, 51,* 1080–1082. (p. 550)

Kounios, J., & Beeman, M. (2014). The cognitive neuroscience of insight. *Annual Review of Psychology, 65,* 71–93. (p. 299)

Kovelman, I., Shalinsky, M. H., Berens, M. S., & Petitto, L. (2014). Words in the bilingual brain: An fNIRS brain imaging investigation of lexical processing in sign-speech bimodal bilinguals. *Frontiers in Human Neuroscience, 8,* article 606. (p. 317)

Kposowa, A., Hamilton, D., & Wang, K. (2016). Impact of firearm availability and gun regulation on state suicide rates. *Suicide and Life-Threating Behavior, 46,* 678–696. (p. 501)

Kposowa, A. J., & D'Auria, S. (2009). Association of temporal factors and suicides in the United States, 2000–2004. *Social Psychiatry and Psychiatric Epidemiology, 45,* 433–445. (p. 500)

Kraft, C. (1978). A psychophysical approach to air safety: Simulator studies of visual illusions in night approaches. In H. L. Pick, H. W. Leibowitz, J. E. Singer, A. Steinschneider, & H. W. Stevenson (Eds.), *Psychology: From research to practice.* New York: Plenum Press. (p. B-13)

Kraft, T., & Pressman, S. (2012). Grin and bear it: The influence of the manipulated facial expression on the stress response. *Psychological Science, 23,* 137–1378. (p. 381)

Krahé, B., & Berger, A. (2017). Longitudinal pathways of sexual victimization, sexual self-esteem, and depression in women and men. *Psychological Trauma: Theory, Research, Practice, and Policy, 9,* 147–155. (p. 170)

Krakow, B., Germain, A., Warner, T. D., Schrader, R., Koss, M. P., Hollifield, M., . . . Johnston, L. (2001). The relationship of sleep quality and posttraumatic stress to potential sleep disorders in sexual assault survivors with nightmares, insomnia, and PTSD. *Journal of Traumatic Stress, 14,* 647–665. (p. 170)

Krakow, B., Schrader, R., Tandberg, D., Hollifield, M., Koss, M. P., Yau, C. L., & Cheng, D. T. (2002). Nightmare frequency in sexual assault survivors with PTSD. *Journal of Anxiety Disorders, 16,* 175–190. (p. 170)

Kramer, A. (2010). Personal communication. (p. 408)

Kramer, A. D. I. (2012). The spread of emotion via Facebook. *Proceedings of the SIGCHI Conference on Human Factors in Computing Systems.* ACM (Association for Computing Machinery), New York, 767–770. (p. 382)

Kramer, A. F., & Erickson, K. I. (2007). Capitalizing on cortical plasticity: Influence of physical activity on cognition and brain function. *Trends in Cognitive Sciences, 11,* 342–348. (p. 401)

Kramer, M. S., Aboud, F., Mironova, E., Vanilovich, I., Platt, R. W., Matush, L., . . . Promotion of Breastfeeding Intervention Trial (PROBIT) Study Group. (2008). Breastfeeding and child cognitive development: New evidence from a large randomized trial. *Archives of General Psychiatry, 65,* 578–584. (p. 27)

Kramer, P. D. (2011, July 9). In defense of antidepressants. *The New York Times* (nytimes.com). (p. 561)

Kranz, F., & Ishai, A. (2006). Face perception is modulated by sexual preference. *Current Biology, 16,* 63–68. (p. 181)

Kranz, G. S., Hahn, A., Kaufmann, U., Küblböck, M., Hummer, A., Ganger, S., . . . Lanzenberger, R. (2014). White matter microstructure in transsexuals and controls investigated by diffusion tensor imaging. *The Journal of Neuroscience, 34,* 15466–15475. (p. 170)

Kraul, C. (2010, October 12). Chief engineer knew it would take a miracle. *The Los Angeles Times* (latimes.com). (p. 230)

Kring, A. M., & Caponigro, J. M. (2010). Emotion in schizophrenia: Where feeling meets thinking. *Current Directions in Psychological Science, 19,* 255–259. (p. 523)

Kring, A. M., & Gordon, A. H. (1998). Sex differences in emotion: Expression, experience, and physiology. *Journal of Personality and Social Psychology, 74,* 686–703. (p. 378)

Kringelbach, M. L., & Berridge, K. C. (2012, August). The joyful mind. *Scientific American,* pp. 40–45. (p. 56)

Krishnan, A., Zhang, R., Yao, V., Theesfeld, C. L., Wong, A. K., Tadych, A., . . . Troyanskaya, O. G. (2016). Genome-wide prediction and functional characterization of the genetic basis of autism spectrum disorder. *Nature Neuroscience.* Advance online publication. doi:10.1038/nn.4353 (p. 131)

Kristof, N. (2017, February 11). Husbands are deadlier than terrorists. *The New York Times* (nytimes.com). (p. 18)

Kristof, N. D. (2004, July 21). Saying no to killers. *The New York Times* (nytimes.com). (p. 453)

Krizan, Z., & Johar, O. (2015). Narcissistic rage revisited. *Journal of Personality and Social Psychology, 108,* 784–801. (p. 488)

Kroes, M. C. W., Tendolkar, I., van Wingen, G. A., van Waarde, J. A., Strange, B. A., & Fernández, G. (2014). An electroconvulsive therapy procedure impairs reconsolidation of episodic memories in humans. *Nature Neuroscience, 17,* 204–206. (p. 289)

Kroll, J. F., Bobb, S. C., & Hoshino, N. (2014). Two languages in mind: Bilingualism as a tool to investigate language, cognition, and the brain. *Current Directions in Psychological Science, 23,* 159–163. (p. 320)

Krosnick, J. A., & Alwin, D. F. (1989). Aging and susceptibility to attitude change. *Journal of Personality and Social Psychology, 57,* 416–425. (p. 118)

Krosnick, J. A., Betz, A. L., Jussim, L. J., & Lynn, A. R. (1992). Subliminal conditioning of attitudes. *Personality and Social Psychology Bulletin, 18,* 152–162. (p. 193)

Kross, E., & Ayduk, O. (2011). Making meaning out of negative experiences by self-distancing. *Current Directions in Psychological Science, 20,* 187–191. (p. 394)

Kross, E., Berman, M., Mischel, W., Smith, E. E., & Wager, T. (2011). Social rejection shares somatosensory representations with physical pain. *PNAS, 108,* 6270–6275. (p. 354)

Kross, E., Bruehlman-Senecal, E., Park, J., Burson, A., Dougherty, A., Shablack, H., . . . Ayduk, O. (2014). Self-talk as a regulatory mechanism: How you do it matters. *Journal of Personality and Social Psychology, 106,* 304–324. (p. 130)

Kruger, J., & Dunning, D. (1999). Unskilled and unaware of it: How difficulties in recognizing one's own incompetence lead to inflated self-assessments. *Journal of Personality and Social Psychology, 77,* 1121–1134. (p. 488)

Kruger, J., Epley, N., Parker, J., & Ng, Z.-W. (2005). Egocentrism over e-mail: Can we communicate as well as we think? *Journal of Personality and Social Psychology, 89,* 925–936. (pp. 128, 377)

Krumhansl, C. L. (2010). Plink: "Thin slices" of music. *Music Perception, 27,* 337–354. (p. 266)

Krupenye, C., Kano, F., Hirata, S., Call, J., & Tomasello, M. (2016). Great apes anticipate that other individuals will act according to false beliefs. *Science, 354,* 110–113. (p. 309)

Krützen, M., Mann, J., Heithaus, M. R., Connor, R. C., Bejder, L., & Sherwin, W. B. (2005). Cultural transmission of tool use in bottlenose dolphins. *PNAS, 102,* 8939–8943. (p. 310)

Kubzansky, L. D., Koenen, K. C., Jones, C., & Eaton, W. W. (2009). A prospective study of posttraumatic stress disorder symptoms and coronary heart disease in women. *Health Psychology, 28,* 125–130. (p. 392)

Kubzansky, L. D., Sparrow, D., Vokanas, P., & Kawachi, I. (2001). Is the glass half empty or half full? A prospective study of optimism and coronary heart disease in the normative aging study. *Psychosomatic Medicine, 63,* 910–916. (p. 392)

Kuehner, C. (2017). Why is depression more common among women than among men? *The Lancet Psychiatry, 4,* 146–158. (p. 517)

Kuhl, P. K., & Meltzoff, A. N. (1982). The bimodal perception of speech in infancy. *Science, 218,* 1138–1141. (p. 314)

Kuhl, P. K., Ramírez, R. R., Bosseler, A., Lin, J. L., & Imada, T. (2014). Infants' brain responses to speech suggest analysis by synthesis. *PNAS, 111,* 11238–11245. (p. 314)

Kühn, S., & Gallinat, J. (2014). Brain structure and functional connectivity associated with pornography consumption. *Journal of the American Medical Association Psychiatry, 71,* 827–834. (p. 176)

Kumar, A., & Gilovich, T. (2013). Talking about what you did and what you have: The differential story utility of experiential and material purchases. *Advances in Consumer Research, 41.* (p. 412)

Kumar, A., & Gilovich, T. (2015). Some "thing" to talk about? Differential story utility from experiential and material purchases. *Personality and Social Psychology Bulletin, 41,* 1320–1331. (p. 412)

Kuncel, N. R., & Hezlett, S. A. (2010). Fact and fiction in cognitive ability testing for admissions and hiring decisions. *Current Directions in Psychological Science, 19*, 339–345. (p. 325)

Kunst-Wilson, W. & Zajonc, R. (*1980*). Affective discrimination of stimuli that cannot be recognized. *Science, 207*, 557–558. (p. 370)

Kupfer, D. J. (2012, June 1). Dr. Kupfer defends DSM-5. *Medscape* (medscape.com). (p. 497)

Kupper, N., & Denollet, J. (2007). Type D personality as a prognostic factor in heart disease: Assessment and mediating mechanisms. *Journal of Personality Assessment, 89*, 265–276. (p. 392)

Kurtycz, L. M. (2015). Choice and control for animals in captivity. *The Psychologist, 28*, 892–893. (p. 31)

Kushlev, K., & Dunn, E. W. (2015). Checking email less frequently reduces stress. *Computers in Human Behavior, 43*, 220–228. (p. 350)

Kushner, M. G., Kim, S. W., Conahue, C., Thuras, P., Adson, D., Kotlyar, M., . . . Foa, E. B. (2007). D-cycloserine augmented exposure therapy for obsessive-compulsive disorder. *Biological Psychiatry, 62*, 835–838. (p. 561)

Kutas, M. (1990). Event-related brain potential (ERP) studies of cognition during sleep: Is it more than a dream? In R. R. Bootzin, J. F. Kihlstrom, & D. Schacter (Eds.), *Sleep and cognition* (pp. 43–57). Washington, DC: American Psychological Association. (p. 86)

Kutcher, E. J., & Bragger, J. D. (2004). Selection interviews of overweight job applicants: Can structure reduce the bias? *Journal of Applied Social Psychology, 34*, 1993–2022. (p. B-6)

Kuttler, A. F., La Greca, A. M., & Prinstein, M. J. (1999). Friendship qualities and social–emotional functioning of adolescents with close, cross-sex friendships. *Journal of Research on Adolescence, 9*, 339–366. (p. 165)

Kuyken, W., Warren, F. C., Taylor, R. S., Whalley, B., Crane, C., Bondolfi, G., . . . Dalgleish, T. (2016). Efficacy of mindfulness-based cognitive therapy in prevention of depressive relapse: An individual patient data meta-analysis from randomized trials. *JAMA Psychiatry, 73*, 565–574. (p. 547)

Kuzawa, C. W., Chugani, H. T., Grossman, L. I., Lipovich, L., Muzik, O., Hof, P. R., . . . Lange, N. (2014). Metabolic costs and evolutionary implications of human brain development. *PNAS, 111*, 13010–13015. (p. 123)

Kvam, S., Kleppe, C. L., Nordhus, I. H., & Hovland, A. (2016). Exercise as a treatment for depression: A meta-analysis. *Journal of Affective Disorders, 202*, 67–86. (p. 402)

Kyaga, S., Landén, M., Boman, M., Hultman, C. M., Långström, N., & Lichtenstein, P. (2013). Mental illness, suicide, and creativity: 40-year prospective total population study. *Journal of Psychiatric Research, 47*, 83–90. (p. 516)

La Londe, K. B., Mahoney, A., Edwards, T. L., Cox, C., Weetjens, B., Durgin, A., & Poling, A. (2015). Training pouched rats to find people. *Journal of Applied Behavior Analysis, 48*, 1–10. (p. 245)

LaCapria, K. (2015, December 17). Kindergarten, stop. Snopes.com. (p. 302)

Laceulle, O. M., Ormel, J., Aggen, S. H., Neale, N. C., & Kendler, K. S. (2011). Genetic and environmental influences on the longitudinal structure of neuroticism: A trait-state approach. *Psychological Science, 24*, 1780–1790. (p. 71)

Lacey, M. (2010, December 11). He found bag of cash, but did the unexpected. *The New York Times* (nytimes.com). (p. 455)

Lachman, M. E. (2004). Development in midlife. *Annual Review of Psychology, 55*, 305–331. (p. 155)

Ladd, G. T. (1887). *Elements of physiological psychology.* New York: Scribner's. (p. 80)

Laeng, B., & Sulutvedt, U. (2014). The eye pupil adjusts to imaginary light. *Psychological Science, 25*, 188–197. (p. 201)

Lafleur, D. L., Pittenger, C., Kelmendi, B., Gardner, T., Wasylink, S., Malison, R. T., . . . Coric, V. (2006). N-acetylcysteine augmentation in serotonin reuptake inhibitor refractory obsessive-compulsive disorder. *Psychopharmacology, 184*, 254–256. (p. 512)

Laird, J. D. (1974). Self-attribution of emotion: The effects of expressive behavior on the quality of emotional experience. *Journal of Personality and Social Psychology, 29*, 475–486. (p. 380)

Laird, J. D. (1984). The real role of facial response in the experience of emotion: A reply to Tourangeau and Ellsworth, and others. *Journal of Personality and Social Psychology, 47*, 909–917. (p. 380)

Laird, J. D., & Lacasse, K. (2014). Bodily influences on emotional feelings: Accumulating evidence and extensions of William James's theory of emotion. *Emotion Review, 6*, 27–34. (p. 380)

Lakin, J. L., Chartrand, T. L., & Arkin, R. M. (2008). I am too just like you: Nonconscious mimicry as an automatic behavioral response to social exclusion. *Psychological Science, 19*, 816–822. (p. 423)

Lally, P., Van Jaarsveld, C. H. M., Potts, H. W. W., & Wardle, J. (2010). How are habits formed: Modelling habit formation in the real world. *European Journal of Social Psychology, 40*, 998–1009. (p. 234)

Lam, C. B., & McBride-Chang, C. A. (2007). Resilience in young adulthood: The moderating influences of gender-related personality traits and coping flexibility. *Sex Roles, 56*, 159–172. (p. 169)

Lam, R. W., Levitt, A. J., Levitan, R. D., Enns, M. W., Morehouse, R., Michalak, E. E., & Tam, E. M. (2006). The Can-SAD study: A randomized controlled trial of the effectiveness of light therapy and fluoxetine in patients with winter seasonal affective disorder. *American Journal of Psychiatry, 163*, 805–812. (p. 555)

Lam, R. W., Levitt, A. J., Levitan, R. D., Michalak, E. E., Cheung, A. H., Morehouse, R., . . . Tam, E. M. (2016). Efficacy of bright light treatment, fluoxetine, and the combination in patients with nonseasonal major depressive disorder: A randomized clinical trial. *JAMA Psychiatry, 73*, 56–63. (p. 555)

Lambert, N. M., DeWall, C. N., Bushman, B. J., Tillman, T. F., Fincham, F. D., Pond, R. S., Jr., & Gwinn, A. M. (2011). *Lashing out in lust: Effect of pornography on nonsexual, physical aggression against relationship partners.* Paper presentation at the Society for Personality and Social Psychology convention. (p. 444)

Lambert, N. M., Negash, S., Stillman, T. F., Olmstead, S. B., & Fincham, F. D. (2012). A love that doesn't last: Pornography consumption and weakened commitment to a romantic partner. *Journal of Social and Clinical Psychology, 31*, 410–438. (p. 176)

Lambert, W. E. (1992). Challenging established views on social issues: The power and limitations of research. *American Psychologist, 47*, 533–542. (p. 320)

Lambert, W. E., Genesee, F., Holobow, N., & Chartrand, L. (1993). Bilingual education for majority English-speaking children. *European Journal of Psychology of Education, 8*, 3–22. (p. 320)

Lambird, K. H., & Mann, T. (2006). When do ego threats lead to self-regulation failure? Negative consequences of defensive high self-esteem. *Personality and Social Psychology Bulletin, 32*, 1177–1187. (p. 489)

Lamm, B., Keller, H., Teiser, J., Gudi, H., Yovsi, R. D., Freitag, C., . . . Vöhringer, I. (2017). Waiting for the second treat: Developing culture-specific modes of self-regulation. *Child Development.* Advance online publication. doi:10.1111/cdev.12847 (p. 145)

Landau, E., Verjee, Z., & Mortensen, A. (2014, February 24). Uganda president: Homosexuals are "disgusting." CNN (cnn.com). (pp. 182, 486)

Landauer, T. (2001, September). Quoted by R. Herbert, You must remember this. *APS Observer,* p. 11. (p. 294)

Landberg, J., & Norström, T. (2011). Alcohol and homicide in Russia and the United States: A comparative analysis. *Journal of Studies on Alcohol and Drugs, 72*, 723–730. (p. 442)

Landry, M. J. (2002). MDMA: A review of epidemiologic data. *Journal of Psychoactive Drugs, 34*, 163–169. (p. 108)

Lane, R. D., Ryan, L., Nadel, L., & Greenberg, L. (2015). Memory reconsolidation, emotional arousal, and the process of change in psychotherapy: New insights from brain science. *Behavioral and Brain Sciences, 38*, e28. (p. 554)

Lange, N., & McDougle, C. J. (2013, October). Help for the child with autism. *Scientific American,* pp. 72–77. (p. 132)

Langer, E. J. (1983). *The psychology of control.* Beverly Hills, CA: Sage. (p. 396)

Langer, E. J., & Abelson, R. P. (1974). A patient by any other name . . .: Clinician group differences in labeling bias. *Journal of Consulting and Clinical Psychology, 42*, 4–9. (p. 499)

Langer, E. J., & Imber, L. (1980). The role of mindlessness in the perception of deviance. *Journal of Personality and Social Psychology, 39*, 360–367. (p. 499)

Langkaas, T. F., Hoffart, A., Øktedalen, T., Ulvenes, P., Hembree, E. A., & Smucker, M. (2017). Exposure to non-fear emotions: A randomized controlled study of exposure-based and rescripting-based imagery in PTSD treatment. *Behavior Research Therapy, 97*, 33–42. (p. 541)

Langlois, J. H., Kalakanis, L., Rubenstein, A. J., Larson, A., Hallam, M., & Smoot, M. (2000). Maxims or myths of beauty? A meta-analytic and theoretical review. *Psychological Bulletin, 126*, 390–423. (p. 449)

Langmeyer, A., Guglhör-Rudan, A., & Tarnai, C. (2012). What do music preferences reveal about personality? A cross-cultural replication using self-ratings and ratings of music samples. *Journal of Individual Differences, 33*, 119–130. (p. 481)

Långström, N. H., Rahman, Q., Carlström, E., & Lichtenstein, P. (2010). Genetic and environmental effects on same-sex sexual behavior: A population study of twins in Sweden. *Archives of Sexual Behavior, 39*, 75–80. (p. 181)

Lankford, A. (2009). Promoting aggression and violence at Abu Ghraib: The U.S. military's transformation of ordinary people into torturers. *Aggression and Violent Behavior, 14*, 388–395. (p. 428)

Larkin, J. E., Brasel, A. M., & Pines, H. A. (2013). Cross-disciplinary applications of I/O psychology concepts: Predicting student retention and employee turnover. *Review of General Psychology, 17*, 82–92. (p. B-12)

Larkin, K., Resko, J. A., Stormshak, F., Stellflug, J. N., & Roselli, C. E. (2002, November). *Neuroanatomical correlates of sex and sexual partner preference in sheep.* Paper presented at the annual meeting of the Society for Neuroscience, Orlando, FL. (p. 181)

Larrick, R. P., Timmerman, T. A., & Carton, A. M., & Abrevaya, J. (2011). Temper, temperature, and temptation: Heat-related retaliation in baseball. *Psychological Science, 22*, 423–428. (p. 443)

Larsen, R. J., & Diener, E. (1987). Affect intensity as an individual difference characteristic: A review. *Journal of Research in Personality, 21,* 1–39. (p. 135)

Larson, R. W., & Verma, S. (1999). How children and adolescents spend time across the world: Work, play, and developmental opportunities. *Psychological Bulletin, 125,* 701–736. (p. 342)

Larzelere, R. E. (2000). Child outcomes of non-abusive and customary physical punishment by parents: An updated literature review. *Clinical Child and Family Psychology Review, 3,* 199–221. (p. 249)

Larzelere, R. E., & Kuhn, B. R. (2005). Comparing child outcomes of physical punishment and alternative disciplinary tactics: A meta-analysis. *Clinical Child and Family Psychology Review, 8,* 1–37. (p. 250)

Larzelere, R. E., Kuhn, B. R., & Johnson, B. (2004). The intervention selection bias: An underrecognized confound in intervention research. *Psychological Bulletin, 130,* 289–303. (p. 249)

Lashley, K. S. (1950). In search of the engram. In J. F. Danielli & R. Brown (Eds.), *Symposia of the Society for Experimental Biology: Vol. 4. Physiological mechanisms in animal behaviour* (pp. 454–482). New York: Cambridge University Press. (p. 276)

Lassiter, G. D., & Irvine, A. A. (1986). Video-taped confessions: The impact of camera point of view on judgments of coercion. *Journal of Personality and Social Psychology, 16,* 268–276. (p. 417)

Latané, B. (1981). The psychology of social impact. *American Psychologist, 36,* 343–356. (p. 430)

Latané, B., & Dabbs, J. M., Jr. (1975). Sex, group size and helping in three cities. *Sociometry, 38,* 180–194. (p. 454)

Latzman, R. D., Freeman, H. D., Schapiro, S. J., & Hopkins, W. D. (2015). The contribution of genetics and early rearing experiences to hierarchical personality dimensions in chimpanzees (Pan troglodytes). *Journal of Personality and Social Psychology, 109,* 889–900. (p. 477)

Latzman, R. D., Patrick, C. J., Freeman, H. D., Schapiro, S. J., & Hopkins, W. D. (2017). Etiology of triarchic psychopathy dimensions in chimpanzees (Pan troglodytes). *Clinical Psychological Science, 5,* 341–354. (p. 530)

Laudenslager, M. L., & Reite, M. L. (1984). Losses and separations: Immunological consequences and health implications. *Review of Personality and Social Psychology, 5,* 285–312. (p. 396)

Laukka, P., Elfenbein, H. A., Thingujam, N. S., Rockstuhl, T., Iraki, F. K., Chui, W., & Althoff, J. (2016). The expression and recognition of emotions in the voice across five nations: A lens model analysis based on acoustic features. *Journal of Personality and Social Psychology, 111,* 686–705. (p. 378)

Laumann, E. O., Gagnon, J. H., Michael, R. T., & Michaels, S. (1994). *The social organization of sexuality: Sexual practices in the United States.* Chicago: University of Chicago Press. (p. 184)

Launay, J. M., Mouillet-Richard, S., Baudry, A., Pietri, M., & Kellermann, O. (2011). Raphe-mediated signals control the hippocampal response to SRI antidepressants via miR-16. *Translational Psychiatry, 1,* e56. (p. 562)

Laws, K. R., & Kokkalis, J. (2007). Ecstasy (MDMA) and memory function: A meta-analytic update. *Human Psychopharmacology: Clinical and Experimental, 22,* 381–388. (p. 108)

Layous, K., & Lyubomirsky, S. (2014). The how, who, what, when, and why of happiness: Mechanisms underlying the success of positive activity interventions. In J. Gruber & J. T. Moskowitz (Eds.), *Positive emotions: Integrating the light and dark sides* (pp. 473–495). New York: Oxford University Press. (p. 411)

Lazaruk, W. (2007). Linguistic, academic, and cognitive benefits of French immersion. *Canadian Modern Language Review, 63,* 605–628. (p. 320)

Lazarus, R. S. (1990). Theory-based stress measurement. *Psychological Inquiry, 1,* 3–13. (p. 386)

Lazarus, R. S. (1991). Progress on a cognitive-motivational-relational theory of emotion. *American Psychologist, 46,* 352–367. (p. 371)

Lazarus, R. S. (1998). *Fifty years of the research and theory of R. S. Lazarus: An analysis of historical and perennial issues.* Mahwah, NJ: Erlbaum. (pp. 371, 384)

Lea, S. E. G. (2000). Towards an ethical use of animals. *The Psychologist, 13,* 556–557. (p. 31)

Leaper, C., & Ayres, M. M. (2007). A meta-analytic review of gender variations in adults' language use: Talkativeness, affiliative speech, and assertive speech. *Personality and Social Psychology Review, 11,* 328–363. (p. 164)

Leary, M. R. (1999). The social and psychological importance of self-esteem. In R. M. Kowalski & M. R. Leary (Eds.), *The social psychology of emotional and behavioral problems.* Washington, DC: APA Books. (p. 486)

Leary, M. R. (2012). Sociometer theory. In L. Van Lange, A. W. Kruglanski, & E. T. Higgins (Eds.), *Handbook of theories of social psychology* (Vol. 2, pp. 141–159). Los Angeles: Sage Publications. (p. 353)

Leary, M. R. (2018). Self-awareness, hypo-egoicism, and psychological well-being. In J. E. Maddux (Ed.), *Subjective well-being and life satisfaction.* New York: Routledge. (p. 520)

Lebedev, A. V., Lövdén, M., Rosenthal, G., Feilding, A., Nutt, D. J., & Carhart-Harris, R. L. (2015). Finding the self by losing the self: Neural correlates of ego-dissolution under psilocybin. *Human Brain Mapping, 36,* 3137–3153. (p. 108)

Leckelt, M., Küfner, A. C. P., Nestler, S., & Back, M. D. (2015). Behavioral processes underlying the decline of narcissists' popularity over time. *Journal of Personality and Social Psychology, 109,* 856–871. (p. 489)

LeDoux, J. (1996). *The emotional brain: The mysterious underpinnings of emotional life.* New York: Simon & Schuster. (p. 277)

LeDoux, J. (2002). *The synaptic self.* London: Macmillan. (p. 370)

LeDoux, J. (2009, July/August). Quoted by K. McGowan, Out of the past. *Discover,* pp. 28–37. (p. 289)

LeDoux, J. (2015). *Anxious: Using the brain to understand and treat fear and anxiety.* New York: Viking. (p. 370)

LeDoux, J. E., & Armony, J. (1999). Can neurobiology tell us anything about human feelings? In D. Kahneman, E. Diener, & N. Schwartz (Eds.), *Well-being: The foundations of hedonic psychology.* New York: Sage. (p. 370)

LeDoux, J. E., & Brown, R. (2017). A higher-order theory of emotional consciousness. *PNAS, 114,* E2016–E2025. (p. 370)

Lee, C. A., Derefinko, K. J., Milich, R., Lynam, D. R., & DeWall, C. N. (2017). Longitudinal and reciprocal relations between delay discounting and crime. *Personality and Individual Differences, 111,* 193–198. (pp. 145, 401)

Lee, C. S., Therriault, D. J., & Linderholm, T. (2012). On the cognitive benefits of cultural experience: Exploring the relationship between studying abroad and creative thinking. *Applied Cognitive Psychology, 26,* 768–778. (p. 307)

Lee, D. S., Kim, E., & Schwartz, N. (2015). Something smells fishy: Olfactory suspicion cues improve performance on the Moses illusion and Wason rule discovery task. *Journal of Experimental Social Psychology, 59,* 47–50. (p. 227)

Lee, G. Y., & Kisilevsky, B. S. (2014). Fetuses respond to father's voice but prefer mother's voice after birth. *Developmental Psychobiology, 56,* 1–11. (p. 119)

Lee, G., Ojha, A., Kang, J.-S., & Lee, M. (2015). Modulation of resource allocation by intelligent individuals in linguistic, mathematical, and visuo-spatial tasks. *International Journal of Psychophysiology, 97,* 14–22. (p. 324)

Lee, L., Frederick, S., & Ariely, D. (2006). Try it, you'll like it: The influence of expectation, consumption, and revelation on preferences for beer. *Psychological Science, 17,* 1054–1058. (p. 196)

Lefaucheur, J.-P., Antal, A., Ayache, S. S., Benninger, D. H., Brunelin, J., Cogiamanian, F., . . . Paulus, W. (2017). Evidence-based guidelines on the therapeutic use of transcranial direct current stimulation (tDCS). *Clinical Neuropsychology, 128,* 56–92. (p. 563)

Lefcourt, H. M. (1982). *Locus of control: Current trends in theory and research.* Hillsdale, NJ: Erlbaum. (p. 397)

Lehman, D. R., Wortman, C. B., & Williams, A. F. (1987). Long-term effects of losing a spouse or child in a motor vehicle crash. *Journal of Personality and Social Psychology, 52,* 218–231. (p. 159)

Leichsenring, F., & Leweke, F. (2017). Social anxiety disorder. *The New England Journal of Medicine, 376,* 2255–2264. (p. 506)

Leichsenring, F., & Rabung, S. (2008). Effectiveness of long-term psychodynamic psychotherapy: A meta-analysis. *JAMA, 300,* 1551–1565. (p. 553)

Leitenberg, H., & Henning, K. (1995). Sexual fantasy. *Psychological Bulletin, 117,* 469–496. (pp. 174, 177)

Lemmer, G., & Wagner, U. (2015). Can we really reduce ethnic prejudice outside the lab? A meta-analysis of direct and indirect contact interventions. *European Journal of Social Psychology, 45,* 152–168. (p. 457)

Lemonick, M. D. (2002, June 3). Lean and hungrier. *Time,* p. 54. (p. 362)

Lenhart, A. (2015a, April 9). *Mobile access shifts social media use and other online activities.* Pew Research Center (pewresearch.org). (p. 165)

Lenhart, A. (2015b, April 9). *Teens, social media & technology overview 2015.* Pew Internet & Research Center (pewinternet.org). (pp. 148, 355)

Lenneberg, E. H. (1967). *Biological foundations of language.* New York: Wiley. (p. 315)

Lennox, B. R., Bert, S., Park, G., Jones, P. B., & Morris, P. G. (1999). Spatial and temporal mapping of neural activity associated with auditory hallucinations. *The Lancet, 353,* 644. (p. 61)

Lenton, A. P., & Francesconi, M. (2010). How humans cognitively manage an abundance of mate options. *Psychological Science, 21,* 528–533. (p. 448)

LePort, A. K. R., Mattfeld, A. T., Dickinson-Anson, H., Fallon, J. H., Stark, C. E. L., Kruggel, F., . . . McGaugh, J. L. (2012). Behavioral and neuroanatomical investigation of highly superior autobiographical memory (HSAM). *Neurobiology of Learning and Memory, 98,* 78–92. (p. 284)

Lepp, A., Barkley, J. E., & Karpinski, A. C. (2014). The relationship between cell phone use, academic performance, anxiety, and satisfaction with life in college students. *Computers in Human Behavior, 31,* 343–350. (p. 356)

Lereya, S. T., Copeland, W. E., Costello, E. J., & Wolke, D. (2015). Adult mental health consequences of peer bullying and maltreatment in childhood: Two cohorts in two countries. *Lancet Psychiatry, 2,* 524–531. (p. 138)

Lesage, A., Lemasson, M., Medina, K., Tsopmo, J., Sebti, N., Potvin, S., & Patry, S. (2016). The prevalence of electroconvulsive therapy use since 1973: A meta-analysis. *Journal of ECT, 32,* 236–242. (p. 563)

Leucht, S., Barnes, T. R. E., Kissling, W., Engel, R. R., Correll, C., & Kane, J. M. (2003). Relapse prevention in schizophrenia with new-generation antipsychotics: A systematic review and exploratory meta-analysis of randomized, controlled trials. *American Journal of Psychiatry, 160,* 1209–1222. (p. 560)

Leucht, S., Leucht, C., Huhn, M., Chaimani, A., Mavridis, D., Helfer, B., . . . Geddes, J. R. (2017). Sixty years of placebo-controlled antipsychotic drug trials in acute schizophrenia: Systematic review, Bayesian meta-analysis, and meta-regression of efficacy predictors. *American Journal of Psychiatry, 174,* 927–942. (p. 5600)

LeVay, S. (1991). A difference in hypothalamic structure between heterosexual and homosexual men. *Science, 253,* 1034–1037. (p. 180)

LeVay, S. (1994, March). Quoted in D. Nimmons, Sex and the brain. *Discover,* pp. 64–71. (p. 180)

LeVay, S. (2011). *Gay, straight, and the reason why: The science of sexual orientation.* New York: Oxford University Press. (pp. 181, 182)

Levenson, R. M., Krupinski, E. A., Navarro, V. M., & Wasserman, E. A. (2015, November 18). Pigeons (*Columba livia*) as trainable observers of pathology and radiology breast cancer images. *PLoS ONE, 10,* e0141357. (p. 245)

Levin, K. H., Shanafelt, T. D., Keran, C. M., Busis, N. A., Foster, L. A., Molano, J. R. V., . . . Cascino, T. L. (2017). Burnout, career satisfaction, and well-being among US neurology residents and fellows in 2016. *Neurology, 89,* 492–501. (p. B-1)

Levin, R., & Nielsen, T. A. (2007). Disturbed dreaming, posttraumatic stress disorder, and affect distress: A review and neurocognitive model. *Psychological Bulletin, 133,* 482–528. (p. 96)

Levin, R., & Nielsen, T. A. (2009). Nightmares, bad dreams, and emotion dysregulation. *Current Directions in Psychological Science, 18,* 84–87. (p. 96)

Levine, J. A., Lanningham-Foster, L. M., McCrady, S. K., Krizan, A. C., Olson, L. R., Kane, P. H., . . . Clark, M. M. (2005). Interindividual variation in posture allocation: Possible role in human obesity. *Science, 307,* 584–586. (p. 365)

Levine, R. (2016). *Stranger in the mirror: The scientific search for self.* Princeton, NJ: Princeton University Press. (pp. 420, 490)

Levine, R., Sato, S., Hashimoto, T., & Verma, J. (1995). Love and marriage in eleven cultures. *Journal of Cross-Cultural Psychology, 26,* 554–571. (p. 451)

Levine, R. V., & Norenzayan, A. (1999). The pace of life in 31 countries. *Journal of Cross-Cultural Psychology, 30,* 178–205. (p. 23)

Levy, D. J., Heissel, J. A., Richeson, J. A., & Adam, E. K. (2016). Psychological and biological responses to race-based social stress as pathways to disparities in educational outcomes. *American Psychologist, 71,* 455–473. (pp. 386, 458)

Levy, P. E. (2003). *Industrial/organizational psychology: Understanding the workplace.* Boston: Houghton Mifflin. (p. B-7)

Lewandowski, G. W., Jr., Aron, A., & Gee, J. (2007). Personality goes a long way: The malleability of opposite-sex physical attractiveness. *Personality Relationships, 14,* 571–585. (p. 450)

Lewinsohn, P. M., Hoberman, H., Teri, L., & Hautziner, M. (1985). An integrative theory of depression. In S. Reiss & R. Bootzin (Eds.), *Theoretical issues in behavior therapy.* Orlando, FL: Academic Press. (p. 516)

Lewinsohn, P. M., Petit, J., Joiner, T. E., Jr., & Seeley, J. R. (2003). The symptomatic expression of major depressive disorder in adolescents and young adults. *Journal of Abnormal Psychology, 112,* 244–252. (p. 516)

Lewinsohn, P. M., Rohde, P., & Seeley, J. R. (1998). Major depressive disorder in older adolescents: Prevalence, risk factors, and clinical implications. *Clinical Psychology Review, 18,* 765–794. (p. 516)

Lewis, C. S. (1960). *Mere Christianity.* New York: Macmillan. (p. 7)

Lewis, C. S. (1967). *Christian reflections.* Grand Rapids, MI: Eerdmans. (p. 285)

Lewis, D. M. G., Al-Shawaf, L., Conroy-Beam, D., Asao, K., & Buss, D. M. (2017). Evolutionary psychology: A how-to guide. *American Psychologist, 72,* 353–373. (p. 186)

Lewis, D. M. G., Russell, E. M., Al-Shawaf, L., & Buss, D. M. (2015). Lumbar curvature: A previously undiscovered standard of attractiveness. *Evolution and Human Behavior, 36,* 345–350. (p. 184)

Lewis, D. O., Pincus, J. H., Bard, B., Richardson, E., Prichep, L. S., Feldman, M., & Yeager, C. (1988). Neuropsychiatric, psychoeducational, and family characteristics of 14 juveniles condemned to death in the United States. *American Journal of Psychiatry, 145,* 584–589. (p. 137)

Lewis, D. O., Yeager, C. A., Swica, Y., Pincus, J. H., & Lewis, M. (1997). Objective documentation of child abuse and dissociation in 12 murderers with dissociative identity disorder. *American Journal of Psychiatry, 154,* 1703–1710. (p. 529)

Li, C.-M., Zhang, X., Hoffman, H. J., Cotch, M. F., Themann, C. L., & Wilson, M. R. (2014). Hearing impairment associated with depression in US adults, National Health and Nutrition Examination Survey 2005–2010. *Otolaryngology—Head & Neck Surgery, 140,* 293–302. (p. 216)

Li, J., Laursen, T. M., Precht, D. H., Olsen, J., & Mortensen, P. B. (2005). Hospitalization for mental illness among parents after the death of a child. *New England Journal of Medicine, 352,* 1190–1196. (p. 159)

Li, L., Abutalebi, J., Emmorey, K., Gong, G., Yan, X., Feng, X., . . . Ding, G. (2017). How bilingualism protects the brain from aging: Insights from bimodal bilinguals. *Human Brain Mapping, 38,* 4109–4124. (p. 320)

Li, N., & DiCarlo, J. J. (2008). Unsupervised natural experience rapidly alters invariant object representation in visual cortex. *Science, 321,* 1502–1506. (p. 212)

Li, N. P., & Kanazawa, S. (2016). Country roads, take me home . . . to my friends: How intelligence, population density, and friendship affect modern happiness. *British Journal of Psychology, 107,* 675–697. (p. 353)

Li, S., Stampfer, M. J., Williams, D. R., & VanderWeele, T. J. (2016). Association of religious service attendance with mortality among women. *JAMA Internal Medicine, 176,* 777–785. (p. 405)

Li, W., Ma, L., Yang, G., & Gan, W.-B. (2017). REM sleep selectively prunes and maintains new synapses in development and learning. *Nature Neuroscience, 20,* 427–437. (p. 91)

Li, Y., Johnson, E. J., & Zaval, L. (2011). Local warming: Daily temperature change influences belief in global warming. *Psychological Science, 22,* 454–459. (p. 303)

Li, Z. H., Jiang, D., Pepler, D., & Craig, W. (2010). Adolescent romantic relationships in China and Canada: A cross-national comparison. *Internal Journal of Behavioral Development, 34,* 113–120. (p. 147)

Liberman, M. C. (2015, August). Hidden hearing loss. *Scientific American,* pp. 49–53. (p. 218)

Libertus, M. E., & Brannon, E. M. (2009). Behavioral and neural basis of number sense in infancy. *Current Directions in Psychological Science, 18,* 346–351. (p. 127)

Licata, A., Taylor, S., Berman, M., & Cranston, J. (1993). Effects of cocaine on human aggression. *Pharmacology Biochemistry and Behavior, 45,* 549–552. (p. 107)

Lichtenstein, E., Zhu, S.-H., & Tedeschi, G. J. (2010). Smoking cessation quitlines: An underrecognized intervention success story. *American Psychologist, 65,* 252–261. (p. 106)

Lick, D. J., Durso, L. E., & Johnson, K. L. (2013). Minority stress and physical health among sexual minorities. *Perspectives on Psychological Science, 8,* 521–548. (p. 386)

Liddle, J. R., Shackelford, T. K., & Weekes-Shackelford, V. W. (2012). Why can't we all just get along? Evolutionary perspectives on violence, homicide, and war. *Review of General Psychology, 16,* 24–36. (p. 163)

Lieberman, M. D., & Eisenberger, N. I. (2015). The dorsal anterior cingulate is selective for pain: Results from large-scale fMRI reverse inference. *PNAS, 112,* 15250–15255. (p. 354)

Lieberman, M. D., Eisenberger, N. L., Crockett, M. J., Tom, S. M., Pfeifer, J. H., & Way, B. M. (2007). Putting feelings into words: Affect labeling disrupts amygdala activity in response to affective stimuli. *Psychological Science, 18,* 421–428. (p. 400)

Lieberman, P. (2013). Synapses, language, and being human. *Science, 342,* 944–945. (p. 318)

Lievens, F., Dilchert, S., & Ones, D. S. (2009). The importance of exercise and dimension factors in assessment centers: Simultaneous examinations of construct-related and criterion-related validity. *Human Performance, 22,* 375–390. (p. 484)

Lifton, R. J. (1961). *Thought reform and the psychology of totalism: A study of "brainwashing" in China.* New York: Norton. (p. 418)

Lilienfeld, S. O. (2009, Winter). Tips for spotting psychological pseudoscience: A student-friendly guide. *Eye of Psi Chi,* pp. 23–26. (p. 230)

Lilienfeld, S. O. (2017). Clinical psychological science: Then and now. *Clinical Psychological Science, 5,* 3–13. (p. 528)

Lilienfeld, S. O., & Arkowitz, H. (2007, December, 2006/January, 2007). Taking a closer look: Can moving your eyes back and forth help to ease anxiety? *Scientific American Mind,* pp. 80–81. (p. 554)

Lilienfeld, S. O., Lynn, S. J., Kirsch, I., Chaves, J. F., Sarbin, T. R., Ganaway, G. K., & Powell, R. A. (1999). Dissociative identity disorder and the sociocognitive model: Recalling the lessons of the past. *Psychological Bulletin, 125,* 507–523. (p. 529)

Lilienfeld, S. O., Marshall, J., Todd, J. T., & Shane, H. C. (2015). The persistence of fad interventions in the face of negative scientific evidence: Facilitated communication for autism as a case example. *Evidence-Based Communication Assessment and Intervention, 8,* 62–101. (pp. 551, 554)

Lilienfeld, S. O., Ritschel, L. A., Lynn, S. J., Cautin, R. L., & Latzman, R. D. (2013). Why many clinical psychologists are resistant to evidence-based practice: Root causes and constructive remedies. *Clinical Psychology Review, 33,* 883–900. (p. 553)

Lilienfeld, S. O., Sauvigné, K. C., Reber, J., Watts, A. L., Hamann, S., Smith, S. F., . . . Tranel, D. (2017). Potential effects of severe bilateral amygdala damage on psychopathic features: A case report. *Personality Disorders: Theory, Research, and Treatment*. Advance online publication. doi:10.1037/per0000230 (p. 530)

Lilienfeld, S. O., Smith, S. F., & Watts, A. L. (2016). Fearless dominance and its implications for psychopathy: Are the right stuff and the wrong stuff flip sides of the same coin? In V. Zeigler-Hill, & D. K. Marcus (Eds.), *The dark side of personality: Science and practice in social, personality, and clinical psychology*. Washington, DC: American Psychological Association, pp. 65–86. (p. 530)

Lilienfeld, S. O., Waldman, I. D., Landfield, K., Watts, A. L., Rubenzer, S., & Fashingbauer, T. R. (2012). Fearless dominance and the U.S. presidency: Implications of psychopathic personality traits for successful and unsuccessful political leadership. *Journal of Personality and Social Psychology, 103*, 489–505. (p. 530)

Lim, D., & DeSteno, D. (2016). Suffering and compassion: The links among adverse life experiences, empathy, compassion, and prosocial behavior. *Emotion, 16*, 175–182. (p. 388)

Lim, J., & Dinges, D. F. (2010). A meta-analysis of the impact of short-term sleep deprivation on cognitive variables. *Psychological Bulletin, 136*, 375–389. (p. 93)

Lima, N., Nascimento, V., Peixoto, J. A. C., Moreira, M. M., Neto, M. L. R., Almeida, J. C., . . . Reis, A. O. A. (2013). Electroconvulsive therapy use in adolescents: A systematic review. *Annals of General Psychiatry, 12*, 17. doi:10.1186/1744-859X-12-17. (p. 563)

Lin, P. (2016). Risky behaviors: Integrating adolescent egocentrism with the theory of planned behavior. *Review of General Psychology, 20*, 392–398. (p. 128)

Lin, X., Chen, W., Wei, F., Ying, M., Wei, W., & Xie, X. (2015). Night-shift work increases morbidity of breast cancer and all-cause mortality: A meta-analysis of 16 prospective cohort studies. *Sleep Medicine, 16*, 1381–1387. (p. 90)

Lin, Z., & Murray, S. O. (2015). More power to the unconscious: Conscious, but not unconscious, exogenous attention requires location variation. *Psychological Science, 26*, 221–230. (p. 305)

Linardon, J., Wade, T. D., de la Piedad Garcia, X., & Brennan, L. (2017). The efficacy of cognitive-behavioral therapy for eating disorders: A systematic review and meta-analysis. *Journal of Consulting and Clinical Psychology, 85*, 1080–1094. (p. 546)

Lind, A., Hall, L., Breidegard, B., Balkenius, C., & Johansson, P. (2014). Speakers' acceptance of real-time speech exchange indicates that we use auditory feedback to specify the meaning of what we say. *Psychological Science, 25*, 1198–1205. (p. 196)

Lindberg, S. M., Hyde, J. S., Linn, M. C., & Petersen, J. L. (2010). New trends in gender and mathematics performance: A meta-analysis. *Psychological Bulletin, 136*, 1125–1135. (p. 340)

Linder, D. (1982). Social trap analogs: The tragedy of the commons in the laboratory. In V. J. Derlega & J. Grzelak (Eds.), *Cooperative and helping behavior: Theories and research*. New York: Academic Press. (p. 456)

Lindner, I., Echterhoff, G., Davidson, P. S. R., & Brand, M. (2010). Observation inflation: Your actions become mine. *Psychological Science, 21*, 1291–1299. (p. 260)

Lindskold, S. (1978). Trust development, the GRIT proposal, and the effects of conciliatory acts on conflict and cooperation. *Psychological Bulletin, 85*, 772–793. (p. 459)

Lindskold, S., & Han, G. (1988). GRIT as a foundation for integrative bargaining. *Personality and Social Psychology Bulletin, 14*, 335–345. (p. 459)

Lindson-Hawley, N., Banting, M., West, R., Michie, S., Shinkins, B., & Aveyard, P. (2016). Gradual versus abrupt smoking cessation: A randomized, controlled noninferiority trial. *Annals of Internal Medicine, 164*, 585–592. (p. 106)

Linehan, M. M., Korslund, K. E., Harned, M. S., Gallop, R. J., Lungu, A., Neacsiu, A. D., . . . Murray-Gregory, A. M. (2015). Dialectical behavior therapy for high suicide risk in individuals with borderline personality disorder: A randomized clinical trial and component analysis. *JAMA Psychiatry, 72*, 475–482. (p. 546)

Lippa, R. A. (2007). The relation between sex drive and sexual attraction to men and women: A cross-national study of heterosexual, bisexual, and homosexual men and women. *Archives of Sexual Behavior, 36*, 209–222. (p. 449)

Lippa, R. A. (2008). Sex differences and sexual orientation differences in personality: Findings from the BBC Internet survey. *Archives of Sexual Behavior, 37*, 173–187. (p. 183)

Lippa, R. A. (2009). Sex differences in sex drive, sociosexuality, and height across 53 nations: Testing evolutionary and social structural theories. *Archives of Sexual Behavior, 38*, 631–651. (p. 183)

Lipsitt, L. P. (2003). Crib death: A biobehavioral phenomenon? *Current Directions in Psychological Science, 12*, 164–170. (p. 124)

Littel, M., Remijn, M., Tinga, A. M., Engelhard, I. M., & van den Hout, M. A. (2017). Stress enhances the memory-degrading effects of eye movements on emotionally neutral memories. *Clinical Psychological Science, 5*, 316–324. (p. 554)

Liu, D., & Baumeister, R. F. (2016). Social networking online and personality of self-worth: A meta-analysis. *Journal of Research in Personality, 64*, 79–89. (p. 356)

Liu, R. T., Cheek, S. M., & Nestor, B. A. (2016). Non-suicidal self-injury and life stress: A systematic meta-analysis and theoretical elaboration. *Clinical Psychology Review, 47*, 1–14. (pp. 92, 502)

Liu, S., Huang, J. L., & Wang, M. (2014). Effectiveness of job search interventions: A meta-analytic review. *Psychological Bulletin, 140*, 1009–1041. (p. B-5)

Liu, Y., Balaraman, Y., Wang, G., Nephew, K. P., & Zhou, F. C. (2009). Alcohol exposure alters DNA methylation profiles in mouse embryos at early neurulation. *Epigenetics, 4*, 500–511. (p. 120)

Livingston, G., & Parker, K. (2011). A tale of two fathers: More are active, but more are absent. Pew Research Center (pewresearch.org). (p. 135)

Livingstone, M., & Hubel, D. (1988). Segregation of form, color, movement, and depth: Anatomy, physiology, and perception. *Science, 240*, 740–749. (p. 206)

Lo, J. C., Chong, P. L., Ganesan, S., Leong, R. L., & Chee, M. W. (2016). Sleep deprivation increases formation of false memory. *Journal of Sleep Research*. Advance online publication. doi:10.1111/jsr.12436 (p. 295)

LoBello, S. G. (2017). The validity of major depression with seasonal pattern: Reply to young. *Clinical Psychological Science, 5*, 755–757. (p. 515)

Locke, K. D., Church, A. T., Mastor, K. A., Curtis, G. J., Sadler, P., McDonald, K., . . . Cabrera, H. F. (2017). Cross-situational self-consistency in nine cultures: The importance of separating influences of social norms and distinctive dispositions. *Personality and Social Psychology Bulletin, 43*, 1033–1049. (p. 481)

Lockwood, L. E., Su, S., & Youssef, N. A. (2015). The role of epigenetics in depression and suicide: A platform for gene-environment interactions. *Psychiatry Research, 228*, 235–242. (p. 512)

Loehlin, J. C. (2012). The differential heritability of personality item clusters. *Behavior Genetics, 42*, 500–507. (p. 71)

Loehlin, J. C. (2016). What can an adoption study tell us about the effect of prenatal environment on a trait. *Behavior Genetics, 46*, 329–333. (p. 338)

Loehlin, J. C., Horn, J. M., & Ernst, J. L. (2007). Genetic and environmental influences on adult life outcomes: Evidence from the Texas Adoption Project. *Behavior Genetics, 37*, 463–476. (p. 73)

Loehlin, J. C., & Nichols, R. C. (1976). *Heredity, environment, and personality*. Austin: University of Texas Press. (p. 71)

Loewenstein, G., Krishnamurti, T., Kopsic, J., & McDonald, D. (2015). Does increased sexual frequency enhance happiness? *Journal of Economic Behavior & Organization, 116*, 206–218. (p. 186)

Loftus, E. F. (2012, July). *Manufacturing memories*. Invited address to the International Congress of Psychology, Cape Town. (p. 289)

Loftus, E. F., & Ketcham, K. (1994). *The myth of repressed memory: False memories and allegations of sexual abuse*. New York: St. Martin's Press. (p. 96)

Loftus, E. F., Levidow, B., & Duensing, S. (1992). Who remembers best? Individual differences in memory for events that occurred in a science museum. *Applied Cognitive Psychology, 6*, 93–107. (p. 290)

Loftus, E. F., & Loftus, G. R. (1980). On the permanence of stored information in the human brain. *American Psychologist, 35*, 409–420. (p. 276)

Loftus, E. F., & Palmer, J. C. (October, 1974). Reconstruction of automobile destruction: An example of the interaction between language and memory. *Journal of Verbal Learning & Verbal Behavior, 13*, 585–589. (p. 290)

Logan, T. K., Walker, R., Cole, J., & Leukefeld, C. (2002). Victimization and substance abuse among women: Contributing factors, interventions, and implications. *Review of General Psychology, 6*, 325–397. (p. 111)

Logue, A. W. (1998a). Laboratory research on self-control: Applications to administration. *Review of General Psychology, 2*, 221–238. (p. 247)

Logue, A. W. (1998b). Self-control. In W. T. O'Donohue (Ed.), *Learning and behavior therapy*. Boston: Allyn & Bacon. (p. 247)

London, P. (1970). The rescuers: Motivational hypotheses about Christians who saved Jews from the Nazis. In J. Macaulay & L. Berkowitz (Eds.), *Altruism and helping behavior*. New York: Academic Press. (p. 261)

Lonergan, M. H., Olivera-Figueroa, L., Pitman, R. K., & Brunet, A. (2013). Propranolol's effects on the consolidation and reconsolidation of long-term emotional memory in healthy participants: A meta-analysis. *Journal of Psychiatry & Neuroscience, 38*, 222–231. (p. 289)

Lonsway, K.A., & Fitzgerald, L.F. (1994). Rape myths: In review. *Psychology of Women Quarterly, 18*, 133–164. (p. 111)

Loomes, R., Hull, L., & Mandy, W. P. L. (2017). What is the male-to-female ratio in autism spectrum disorder? A systematic review and meta-analysis. *Journal of the American Academy of Child & Adolescent Psychiatry, 56*, 466–474. (p. 131)

Lopez, D. J. (2002, January/February). Snaring the fowler: Mark Twain debunks phrenology. *Skeptical Inquirer* (csicop.org). (p. 38)

Lopez-Quintero, C., de los Cobos, P., Hasin, D. S., Okuda, M., Wang, S., Grant, B. F., & Blanco, C. (2011). Probability and predictors of transition from first use to dependence on nicotine, alcohol, cannabis, and cocaine: Results of the national epidemiologic survey on alcohol and related conditions (NESARC). *Drug and Alcohol Dependence, 115,* 120–130. (p. 102)

Loprinzi, P. D., Loenneke, J. P., & Blackburn, E. H. (2015). Movement-based behaviors and leukocyte telomere length among US adults. *Medical Science and Sports Exercise, 47,* 2347–2352. (p. 153)

Lord, C. G., Lepper, M. R., & Preston, E. (1984). Considering the opposite: A corrective strategy for social judgment. *Journal of Personality and Social Psychology, 47,* 1231–1247. (p. 304)

Lord, C. G., Ross, L., & Lepper, M. (1979). Biased assimilation and attitude polarization: The effects of prior theories on subsequently considered evidence. *Journal of Personality and Social Psychology, 37,* 2098–2109. (p. 304)

Lorenz, K. (1937). The companion in the bird's world. *Auk, 54,* 245–273. (p. 134)

Louie, K., & Wilson, M. A. (2001). Temporally structured replay of awake hippocampal ensemble activity during rapid eye movement sleep. *Neuron, 29,* 145–156. (p. 98)

Lourenco, O., & Machado, A. (1996). In defense of Piaget's theory: A reply to 10 common criticisms. *Psychological Review, 103,* 143–164. (p. 130)

Lovaas, O. I. (1987). Behavioral treatment and normal educational and intellectual functioning in young autistic children. *Journal of Consulting and Clinical Psychology, 55,* 3–9. (p. 543)

Low, P. (2012). *The Cambridge declaration on consciousness.* Publicly proclaimed in Cambridge, UK, on July 7, 2012, at the Francis Crick Memorial Conference on Consciousness in Human and Non-Human Animals (fcmconference.org/img/CambridgeDeclarationOnConsciousness. pdf). (p. 309)

Lowry, P. E. (1997). The assessment center process: New directions. *Journal of Social Behavior and Personality, 12,* 53–62. (p. 484)

Lozano, A. M., & Mayberg, H. S. (2015, February). Treating depression at the source. *Scientific American,* pp. 68–73. (p. 564)

Lu, J., Zhong, X., Liu, H., Hao, L., Huang, C. T. L., Sherafat, M. A., . . . Zhang, S. C. (2016). Generation of serotonin neurons from human pluripotent stem cells. *Nature Biotechnology, 34,* 89–94. (p. 64)

Lu, Z.-L., Williamson, S. J., & Kaufman, L. (1992). Behavioral lifetime of human auditory sensory memory predicted by physiological measures. *Science, 258,* 1668–1670. (p. 270)

Lubinski, D. (2009). Cognitive epidemiology: With emphasis on untangling cognitive ability and socioeconomic status. *Intelligence, 37,* 625–633. (p. 331)

Lubinski, D. (2016). From Terman to today: A century of findings on intellectual precocity. *Review of Educational Research, 86,* 900–944. (pp. 331, 332)

Lubinski, D., Benbow, C. P., & Kell, H. J. (2014). Life paths and accomplishments of mathematically precocious males and females four decades later. *Psychological Science, 25,* 2217–2232. (p. 331)

Luby, J. L., Belden, A., Harms, M. P., Tillman, R., & Barch, D. M. (2016). Preschool is a sensitive period for the influence of maternal support on the trajectory of hippocampal development. *PNAS, 113,* 5742–5747. (p. 124)

Lucas, A., Morley, R., Cole, T. J., Lister, G., & Leeson-Payne, C. (1992). Breast milk and subsequent intelligence quotient in children born preterm. *The Lancet, 339,* 261–264. (p. 27)

Lucas, R. E., Clark, A. E., Georgellis, Y., & Diener, E. (2004). Unemployment alters the set point for life satisfaction. *Psychological Science, 15,* 8–13. (p. 411)

Lucas, R. E., & Donnellan, M. B. (2007). How stable is happiness? Using the STARTS model to estimate the stability of life satisfaction. *Journal of Research in Personality, 41,* 1091–1098. (p. 411)

Lucas, R. E., & Donnellan, M. B. (2009). Age differences in personality: Evidence from a nationally representative Australian sample. *Developmental Psychology, 45,* 1353–1363. (p. 118)

Ludwig, A. M. (1995). *The price of greatness: Resolving the creativity and madness controversy.* New York: Guilford Press. (p. 516)

Ludwig, D. S., & Friedman, M. I. (2014). Increasing adiposity: Consequence or cause of overeating? *JAMA, 311,* 2167–2168. (p. 363)

Luethi, M. S., Friese, M., Binder, J., Boesiger, P., Luechinger, R., & Rasch, B. (2016). Motivational incentives lead to a strong increase in lateral prefrontal activity after self-control exertion. *Social Cognitive and Affective Neuroscience, 10,* 1618–1626. (p. 398)

Luhmann, M., & Hawkley, L. C. (2016). Age differences in loneliness from late adolescence to oldest old age. *Developmental Psychology, 52,* 943–959. (p. 158)

Luhmann, M., Hofmann, W., Eid, M., & Lucas, R. E. (2012). Subjective well-being and adaptation to life events: A meta-analysis. *Journal of Personality and Social Psychology, 102,* 592–615. (p. 408)

Lukaszewski, A. W., Simmons, Z. L., Anderson, C., & Roney, J. R. (2016). The role of physical formidability in human social status allocation. *Journal of Personality and Social Psychology, 110,* 385–406. (p. 184)

Lund, T. J., & Dearing, E. (2012). Is growing up affluent risky for adolescents or is the problem growing up in an affluent neighborhood? *Journal of Research on Adolescence, 23,* 274–282. (p. 137)

Lundy, A. C. (1985). The reliability of the Thematic Apperception Test. *Journal of Personality Assessment, 49,* 141–145. (p. 467)

Luppino, F. S., de Wit, L. M., Bouvy, P. F., Stijnen, T., Cuijpers, P., Penninx, W. J. H., & Zitman, F. G. (2010). Overweight, obesity, and depression. *Archives of General Psychiatry, 67,* 220–229. (p. 365)

Luria, A. M. (1968). In L. Solotaroff (Trans.), *The mind of a mnemonist.* New York: Basic Books. (p. 284)

Lustig, C., & Buckner, R. L. (2004). Preserved neural correlates of priming in old age and dementia. *Neuron, 42,* 865–875. (p. 285)

Lutfey, K. E., Link, C. L., Rosen, R. C., Wiegel, M., & McKinlay, J. B. (2009). Prevalence and correlates of sexual activity and function in women: Results from the Boston Area Community Health (BACH) Survey. *Archives of Sexual Behavior, 38,* 514–527. (p. 175)

Lutgendorf, S. K., & Andersen, B. L. (2015). Biobehavioral approaches to cancer progression and survival. *American Psychologist, 70,* 186–197. (p. 390)

Lutgendorf, S. K., Lamkin, D. M., Jennings, N. B., Arevalo, J. M. G., Penedo, F., DeGeest, K., . . . Sood, A. K. (2008). Biobehavioral influences on matrix metalloproteinase expression in ovarian carcinoma. *Clinical Cancer Research, 14,* 6839–6846. (p. 390)

Lutgendorf, S. K., Russell, D., Ullrich, P., Harris, T. B., & Wallace, R. (2004). Religious participation, interleukin-6, and mortality in older adults. *Health Psychology, 23,* 465–475. (p. 406)

Luthar, S. S., Barkin, S. H., & Crossman, E. J. (2013). "I can, therefore I must": Fragility in the upper-middle classes. *Development and Psychopathology, 25,* 1529–1549. (p. 137)

Lutz, P. E., Gross, J. A., Dhir, S. K., Maussion, G., Yang, J., Bramoullé, A., . . . Turecki, G. (2017). Epigenetic regulation of the kappa opioid receptor by child abuse. *Biological Psychiatry.* Advance online publication. doi:10.1016/j.biopsych.2017.07.012 (p. 137)

Luyckx, K., Tildesley, E. A., Soenens, B., Andrews, J. A., Hampson, S. E., Peterson, M., & Duriez, B. (2011). Parenting and trajectories of children's maladaptive behaviors: A 12-year prospective community study. *Journal of Clinical Child and Adolescent Psychology, 40,* 468–478. (p. 139)

Lyall, S. (2005, November 29). What's the buzz? Rowdy teenagers don't want to hear it. *The New York Times* (nytimes.com). (p. 152)

Lykes, V. A., & Kemmelmeier, M. (2014). What predicts loneliness? Cultural difference between individualistic and collectivistic societies in Europe. *Journal of Cross-Cultural Psychology, 45,* 468–490. (p. 10)

Lykken, D. T. (1991). *Science, lies, and controversy: An epitaph for the polygraph.* Invited address upon receipt of the Senior Career Award for Distinguished Contribution to Psychology in the Public Interest, American Psychological Association convention. (p. 374)

Lykken, D. T. (2006). The mechanism of emergenesis. *Genes, Brain & Behavior, 5,* 306–310. (p. 336)

Lynch, G. (2002). Memory enhancement: The search for mechanism-based drugs. *Nature Neuroscience, 5* (suppl.), 1035–1038. (p. 278)

Lynch, G., & Staubli, U. (1991). Possible contributions of long-term potentiation to the encoding and organization of memory. *Brain Research Reviews, 16,* 204–206. (p. 279)

Lynn, M. (1988). The effects of alcohol consumption on restaurant tipping. *Personality and Social Psychology Bulletin, 14,* 87–91. (p. 103)

Lynn, R., Cheng, H., & Wang, M. (2016). Differences in the intelligence of children across thirty-one provinces and municipalities of China and their economic and social correlates. *Intelligence, 58,* 10–13. (p. 342)

Lynn, R., Sakar, C., & Cheng, H. (2015). Regional differences in intelligence, income and other socio-economic variables in Turkey. *Intelligence, 50,* 144–149. (p. 342)

Lynn, R., & Vanhanen, T. (2012). *Intelligence: A unifying construct for the social sciences.* London: Ulster Institute for Social Research. (p. 342)

Lynn, S. J., Laurence, J., & Kirsch, I. (2015). Hypnosis, suggestion, and suggestibility: An integrative model. *American Journal of Clinical Hypnosis, 57,* 314–329. (p. 224)

Lynn, S. J., Lilienfeld, S. O., Merckelbach, H., Giesbrecht, T., McNally, R. J., Loftus, E. F., . . . Malaktaris, A. (2014). The trauma model of dissociation: Inconvenient truths and stubborn fictions. Comment on Dalenberg et al. (2012). *Psychological Bulletin, 140,* 896–910. (p. 528)

Lynn, S. J., Rhue, J. W., & Weekes, J. R. (1990). Hypnotic involuntariness: A social cognitive analysis. *Psychological Review, 97,* 169–184. (p. 224)

Lynne, S. D., Graber, J. A., Nichols, T. R., Brooks-Gunn, J., & Botvin, G. J. (2007). Links between pubertal timing, peer influences, and externalizing behaviors among urban students followed through middle school. *Journal of Adolescent Health, 40,* 181.e7–181.e13. doi:10.1016/j.jadohealth.2006.09.008 (p. 142)

Lyons, A. (2015). Resilience in lesbians and gay men: A review and key findings from a nationwide Australian survey. *International Review of Psychiatry, 27,* 435–443. (p. 179)

Lyons, B. D., Hoffman, B. J., Michel, J. W., & Williams, K. J. (2011). On the predictive efficiency of past performance and physical ability: The case of the National Football League. *Human Performance, 24,* 158–172. (p. 484)

Lyons, D. E., Young, A. G., & Keil, F. C. (2007). The hidden structure of overimitation. *PNAS, 104,* 19751–19756. (p. 260)

Lyons, H. A., Manning, W. D., Longmore, M. A., & Giordano, P. C. (2015). Gender and casual sexual activity from adolescence to emerging adulthood: Social and life course correlates. *Journal of Sex Research, 52,* 543–557. (p. 177)

Lyons, L. (2004, February 3). *Growing up lonely: Examining teen alienation.* Retrieved from gallup.com/poll/10465/growing-lonely-examining-teen-alienation.aspx (p. 146)

Lyons, M. J., Panizzon, M. S., Liu, W., McKenzie, R., Bluestone, N. J., Grant, M. D., . . . Xian, H. (2017). A longitudinal twin study of general cognitive ability over four decades. *Developmental Psychology, 53,* 1170–1177. (p. 330)

Lyubomirsky, S. (2001). Why are some people happier than others? The role of cognitive and motivational processes in well-being. *American Psychologist, 56,* 239–249. (p. 410)

Lyubomirsky, S. (2008). *The how of happiness.* New York: Penguin. (p. 398)

Lyubomirsky, S., Sousa, L., & Dickerhoof, R. (2006). The costs and benefits of writing, talking, and thinking about life's triumphs and defeats. *Journal of Personality and Social Psychology, 90,* 690–708. (p. 401)

Ma, A., Landau, M. J., Narayanan, J., & Kay, A. C. (2017). Thought-control difficulty motivates structure seeking. *Journal of Experimental Psychology: General.* Advance online publication. doi:10.1037/xge0000282 (p. 17)

Ma, D. S., Correll, J., Wittenbrink, B., Bar-Anan, Y., Sriram, N., & Nosek, B. A. (2013). When fatigue turns deadly: The association between fatigue and racial bias in the decision to shoot. *Basic and Applied Social Psychology, 35,* 515–524. (p. 436)

Ma, L. (1997, September). On the origin of Darwin's ills. *Discover,* p. 27. (p. 508)

Maas, J. B. (1999). *Power sleep: The revolutionary program that prepares your mind and body for peak performance.* New York: HarperCollins. (p. 94)

Maas, J. B., & Robbins, R. S. (2010). *Sleep for success: Everything you must know about sleep but are too tired to ask.* Bloomington, IN: Author House. (p. 92)

Maass, A., D'Ettole, C., & Cadinu, M. (2008). Checkmate? The role of gender stereotypes in the ultimate intellectual sport. *European Journal of Social Psychology, 38,* 231–245. (p. 344)

Macan, T. H., & Dipboye, R. L. (1994). The effects of the application on processing of information from the employment interview. *Journal of Applied Social Psychology, 24,* 1291. (p. B-5)

MacCabe, J. H., Lambe, M. P., Cnattingius, S., Torrång, A., Björk, C., Sham, P. C., . . . Hultman, C. M. (2008). Scholastic achievement at age 16 and risk of schizophrenia and other psychoses: A national cohort study. *Psychological Medicine, 38,* 1133–1140. (p. 524)

Maccoby, E. E. (1990). Gender and relationships: A developmental account. *American Psychologist, 45,* 513–520. (p. 164)

Maccoby, E. E. (1998). *The two sexes: Growing up apart, coming together.* Cambridge, MA: Belknap Press. (p. 165)

Maccoby, E. E. (2002). Gender and group process: A developmental perspective. *Current Directions in Psychological Science, 11,* 54–58. (p. 165)

MacCormack, J. K., & Lindquist, K. A. (2016). Bodily contribution to emotion: Schachter's legacy for a psychological constructionist view on emotion. *Emotion Review, 9,* 36–45. (p. 369)

MacDonald, G., & Leary, M. R. (2005). Why does social exclusion hurt? The relationship between social and physical pain. *Psychological Bulletin, 131,* 202–223. (p. 354)

MacDonald, T. K., & Hynie, M. (2008). Ambivalence and unprotected sex: Failure to predict sexual activity and decreased condom use. *Journal of Applied Social Psychology, 38,* 1092–1107. (p. 177)

MacDonald, T. K., Zanna, M. P., & Fong, G. T. (1995). Decision making in altered states: Effects of alcohol on attitudes toward drinking and driving. *Journal of Personality and Social Psychology, 68,* 973–985. (p. 103)

MacFarlane, A. (1978, February). What a baby knows. *Human Nature,* pp. 74–81. (p. 121)

Macfarlane, J. W. (1964). Perspectives on personality consistency and change from the guidance study. *Vita Humana, 7,* 115–126. (p. 141)

Maciejewski, P. K., Maercker, A., Boelen, P. A., & Prigerson, H. G. (2016). "Prolonged grief disorder" and "persistent complex bereavement disorder," but not "complicated grief," are one and the same diagnostic entity: An analysis of data from the Yale Bereavement Study. *World Psychiatry, 15,* 266–275. (p. 497)

MacInnis, C. C., & Hodson, G. (2015). Do American states with more religious or conservative populations search more for sexual content on Google? *Archives of Sexual Behavior, 44,* 137–147. (p. 179)

Mack, A., & Rock, I. (2000). *Inattentional blindness.* Cambridge, MA: MIT Press. (p. 82)

Mackenzie, A. K., & Harris, J. M. (2017). A link between attentional function, effective eye movements, and driving ability. *Journal of Experimental Psychology: Human Perception and Performance, 43,* 381–394. (p. 82)

Mackenzie, J. L., Aggen, S. H., Kirkpatrick, R. M., Kendler, K. S., & Amstadter, A. B. (2015). A longitudinal twin study of insomnia symptoms in adults. *Sleep, 38,* 1423–1430. (p. 90)

MacKenzie, M. J., Nicklas, E., Waldfogel, J., & Brooks-Gunn, J. (2013). Spanking and child development across the first decade of life. *Pediatrics, 132,* e1118–1125. (p. 249)

MacKerron, G., & Mourato, S. (2013). Happiness is greater in natural environments. *Global Environmental Change, 23,* 992–1000. (p. 559)

MacLean, E. L., Hare, B., Nunn, C. L., Addessi, E., Amici, F., Anderson, R. C., . . . Boogert, N. J. (2014). The evolution of self-control. *PNAS, 111,* E2140–E2148. (p. 145)

MacLeod, C., & Clarke, P. J. F. (2015). The attentional bias modification approach to anxiety intervention. *Clinical Psychological Science, 3,* 58–78. (p. 544)

MacLeod, C. M., & Bodner, G. E. (2017). The production effect in memory. *Current Directions in Psychological Science, 26,* 390–395. (p. 295)

Macmillan, M., & Lena, M. L. (2010). Rehabilitating Phineas Gage. *Neuropsychological Rehabilitation, 17,* 1–18. (p. 63)

Macnamara, B. N., Hambrick, D. Z., & Oswald, F. L. (2014). Deliberate practice and performance in music, games, sports, education, and professions: A meta-analysis. *Psychological Science, 25,* 1608–1618. (p. 326) (p. 357)

Macnamara, B. N., Moreau, D., & Hambrick, D. Z. (2016). The relationship between deliberate practice and performance in sports: A meta-analysis. *Perspectives on Psychological Science, 11,* 333–350. (pp. 326, 357)

MacNeilage, P. F., & Davis, B. L. (2000). On the origin of internal structure of word forms. *Science, 288,* 527–531. (p. 314)

MacNeilage, P. F., Rogers, L. J., & Vallortigara, G. (2009). Origins of the left and right brain. *Scientific American, 301,* 60–67. (p. 67)

MacPherson, S. E., Turner, M. S., Bozzali, M., Cipolotti, L., & Shallice, T. (2016). The Doors and People Test: The effect of frontal lobe lesions on recall and recognition memory performance. *Neuropsychology, 30,* 332–337. (p. 62)

Macur, J. (2018, January 24). In Larry Nassar's case, a single voice eventually raised an army. *The New York Times* (nytimes.com). (p. 429)

Madison, G., Mosling, M. A., Verweij, K. J. H., Pedersen, N. L., & Ullen, F. (2016). Common genetic influences on intelligence and auditory simple reaction time in a large Swedish sample. *Intelligence, 59,* 157–162. (p. 336)

Maeda, Y., & Yoon, S. Y. (2013). A meta-analysis on gender differences in mental rotation ability measured by the Purdue spatial visualization tests: Visualization of rotations (PSVT:R). *Educational Psychology Review, 25,* 69–94. (p. 340)

Maes, H. H., Neale, M. C., Ohlsson, H., Zahery, M., Lichtenstein, P., Sundquist, K., . . . Kendler, K. S. (2016). A bivariate genetic analysis of drug abuse ascertained through medical and criminal registries in Swedish twins, siblings and half-siblings. *Behavior Genetics, 46,* 735–741. (p. 111)

Maes, H. H. M., Neale, M. C., & Eaves, L. J. (1997). Genetic and environmental factors in relative body weight and human adiposity. *Behavior Genetics, 27,* 325–351. (p. 365)

Maestripieri, D. (2003). Similarities in affiliation and aggression between cross-fostered rhesus macaque females and their biological mothers. *Developmental Psychobiology, 43,* 321–327. (p. 72)

Maestripieri, D. (2005). Early experience affects the intergenerational transmission of infant abuse in rhesus monkeys. *PNAS, 102,* 9726–9729. (p. 137)

Magnusson, D. (1990). Personality research—challenges for the future. *European Journal of Personality, 4,* 1–17. (p. 531)

Maguire, E. A., Gadian, D. G., Johnsrude, I. S., Good, C. D., Ashburner, J., Frackowiak, R. S. J., & Frith, C. D. (2000). Navigation-related structural change in the hippocampi of taxi drivers. *PNAS, 97,* 4398–4403. (pp. 39, 124)

Maguire, E. A., Spiers, H. J., Good, C. D., Hartley, T., Frackowiak, R. S. J., & Burgess, N. (2003a). Navigation expertise and the human hippocampus: A structural brain imaging analysis. *Hippocampus, 13,* 250–259. (p. 276)

Maguire, E. A., Valentine, E. R., Wilding, J. M., & Kapur, N. (2003b). Routes to remembering: The brains behind superior memory. *Nature Neuroscience, 6,* 90–95. (p. 272)

Maguire, E. A., Woollett, K., & Spiers, H. J. (2006). London taxi drivers and bus drivers: A structural MRI and neuropsychological analysis. *Hippocampus, 16,* 1091–1101. (p. 39)

Maher, S., Ekstrom, T., & Chen, Y. (2014). Greater perceptual sensitivity to happy facial expression. *Perception, 43,* 1353–1364. (p. 376)

Maia, T. V., & Frank, M. J. (2017). An integrative perspective on the role of dopamine in schizophrenia. *Biological Psychiatry, 81,* 52–66. (p. 524)

Maier, S. F., & Seligman, M. E. P. (2016). Learned helplessness at fifty: Insights from neuroscience. *Psychological Review, 123,* 349–367. (p. 520)

Maier, S. F., Watkins, L. R., & Fleshner, M. (1994). Psychoneuroimmunology: The interface between behavior, brain, and immunity. *American Psychologist, 49,* 1004–1017. (p. 389)

Major, B., Carrington, P. I., & Carnevale, P. J. D. (1984). Physical attractiveness and self-esteem: Attribution for praise from an other-sex evaluator. *Personality and Social Psychology Bulletin, 10,* 43–50. (p. 449)

Major, B., Schmidlin, A. M., & Williams, L. (1990). Gender patterns in social touch: The impact of setting and age. *Journal of Personality and Social Psychology, 58,* 634–643. (p. 164)

Makel, M. C., Kell, H. J., Lubinski, D., Putallaz, M., & Benbow, C. P. (2016). When lightning strikes twice: Profoundly gifted, profoundly accomplished. *Psychological Science, 27,* 1004–1018. (p. 331)

Makel, M. C., Wai, J., Peairs, K., & Putallaz, M. (2016). Sex differences in the right tail of cognitive abilities: An update and cross cultural extension. *Intelligence, 59,* 8–15. (p. 341)

Makin, S. (2015). What really causes autism. *Scientific American, 26,* 56–63. (p. 131)

Maldonado-Molina, M. M., Reingle, J. M., Jennings, W. G., & Prado, G. (2011). Drinking and driving among immigrant and US-born Hispanic young adults: Results from a longitudinal and nationally representative study. *Addictive Behaviors, 36,* 381–388. (p. 503)

Malkiel, B. G. (2016). *A random walk down Wall Street: The time-tested strategy for successful investing* (11th Edition). New York: Norton. (p. 303)

Malle, B. F. (2006). The actor–observer asymmetry in attribution: A (surprising) meta-analysis. *Psychological Bulletin, 132,* 895–919. (p. 417)

Malle, B. F., Knobe, J. M., & Nelson, S. E. (2007). Actor–observer asymmetries in explanations of behavior: New answers to an old question. *Journal of Personality and Social Psychology, 93,* 491–514. (p. 417)

Malmquist, C. P. (1986). Children who witness parental murder: Post-traumatic aspects. *Journal of the American Academy of Child Psychiatry, 25,* 320–325. (p. 469)

Maltby, N., Tolin, D. F., Worhunsky, P., O'Keefe, T. M., & Kiehl, K. A. (2005). Dysfunctional action monitoring hyperactivates frontal-striatal circuits in obsessive-compulsive disorder: An event-related fMRI study. *NeuroImage, 24,* 495–503. (p. 512)

Mampe, B., Friederici, A. D., Christophe, A., & Wermke, K. (2009). Newborns' cry melody is shaped by their native language. *Current Biology, 19,* 1–4. (p. 120)

Maner, J. K., DeWall, C. N, Baumeister, R. F., & Schaller, M. (2007). Does social exclusion motivate interpersonal reconnection? Resolving the "porcupine problem." *Journal of Personality and Social Psychology, 92,* 42–55. (p. 354)

Maner, J. K., Kenrick, D. T., Neuberg, S. L., Becker, D. V., Robertson, T., Hofer, B., . . . Schaller, M. (2005). Functional projection: How fundamental social motives can bias interpersonal perception. *Journal of Personality and Social Psychology, 88,* 63–78. (p. 470)

Mani, A., Mullainathan, S., Shafir, E., & Zhao, J. (2013). Poverty impedes cognitive function. *Science, 341,* 976–980. (p. 339)

Mann, T., Tomiyama, A. J., & Ward, A. (2015). Promoting public health in the context of the "obesity epidemic": False starts and promising new directions. *Perspectives on Psychological Science, 10,* 706–710. (p. 365)

Manning, W., & Cohen, J. A. (2012). Premarital cohabitation and marital dissolution: An examination of recent marriages. *Journal of Marriage and Family 74,* 377–387. (p. 156)

Manson, J. E. (2002). Walking compared with vigorous exercise for the prevention of cardiovascular events in women. *New England Journal of Medicine, 347,* 716–725. (p. 401)

Maquet, P. (2001). The role of sleep in learning and memory. *Science, 294,* 1048–1052. (p. 98)

Maquet, P., Peters, J.-M., Aerts, J., Delfiore, G., Degueldre, C., Luxen, A., & Franck, G. (1996). Functional neuroanatomy of human rapid-eye-movement sleep and dreaming. *Nature, 383,* 163–166. (p. 99)

Mar, R. A., & Oatley, K. (2008). The function of fiction is the abstraction and simulation of social experience. *Perspectives on Psychological Science, 3,* 173–192. (p. 260)

Mar, R. A., Oatley, K., & Peterson, J. B. (2009). Exploring the link between reading fiction and empathy: Ruling out individual differences and examining outcomes. *Communications: The European Journal of Communication, 34,* 407–428. (p. 378)

Marangolo, P., Fiori, V., Sabatini, U., De Pasquale, G., Razzano, C., Caltagirone, C., & Gili, T. (2016). Bilateral transcranial direct current stimulation language treatment enhances functional connectivity in the left hemisphere: Preliminary data from aphasia. *Journal of Cognitive Neuroscience, 28,* 724–738. (p. 317)

Marcus, B., Machilek, F., & Schütz, A. (2006). Personality in cyberspace: Personal web sites as media for personality expressions and impressions. *Journal of Personality and Social Psychology, 90,* 1014–1031. (p. 481)

Margolis, M. L. (2000). Brahms' lullaby revisited: Did the composer have obstructive sleep apnea? *Chest, 118,* 210–213. (p. 95)

Mariani, J., Simonini, M. V., Palejev, D., Tomasini, L., Coppola, G., Szekely, A. M., . . . Vaccarino, F. M. (2012). Modeling human cortical development in vitro using induced pluripotent stem cells. *PNAS, 109,* 12779–12775. (p. 64)

Marinak, B. A., & Gambrell, L. B. (2008). Intrinsic motivation and rewards: What sustains young children's engagement with text? *Literacy Research and Instruction, 47,* 9–26. (p. 358)

Marjonen, H., Sierra, A., Nyman, A., Rogojin, V., Gröhn, O., Linden, A.-M., . . . Kaminen-Ahola, N. (2015). Early maternal alcohol consumption alters hippocampal DNA methylation, gene expression and volume in a mouse model. *PLoS ONE, 10*(5), e0124931. doi:10.1371/journal.pone.0124931 (p. 120)

Markovizky, G., & Samid, Y. (2008). The process of immigrant adjustment: The role of time in determining psychological adjustment. *Journal of Cross-Cultural Psychology, 39,* 782–798. (p. 385)

Marks, A. K., Patton, F., & Coll, C. G. (2011). Being bicultural: A mixed-methods study of adolescents' implicitly and explicitly measured multiethnic identities. *Developmental Psychology, 47,* 270–288. (p. 146)

Markus, G. B. (1986). Stability and change in political attitudes: Observe, recall, and "explain." *Political Behavior, 8,* 21–44. (p. 292)

Markus, H. R., & Kitayama, S. (1991). Culture and the self: Implications for cognition, emotion, and motivation. *Psychological Review, 98,* 224–253. (pp. 319, 393, 556)

Markus, H. R., & Nurius, P. (1986). Possible selves. *American Psychologist, 41,* 954–969. (p. 486)

Marley, J., & Bulia, S. (2001). Crimes against people with mental illness: Types, perpetrators and influencing factors. *Social Work, 46,* 115–124. (p. 503)

Marmot, M. G., Bosma, H., Hemingway, H., Brunner, E., & Stansfeld, S. (1997). Contribution to job control and other risk factors to social variations in coronary heart disease incidents. *The Lancet, 350,* 235–239. (p. 396)

Marsh, A. A., Elfenbein, H. A., & Ambady, N. (2003). Nonverbal "accents": Cultural differences in facial expressions of emotion. *Psychological Science, 14,* 373–376. (p. 378)

Marsh, H. W., & Craven, R. G. (2006). Reciprocal effects of self-concept and performance from a multidimensional perspective: Beyond seductive pleasure and unidimensional perspectives. *Perspectives on Psychological Science, 1,* 133–163. (p. 486)

Marsh, H. W., & Parker, J. W. (1984). Determinants of student self-concept: Is it better to be a relatively large fish in a small pond even if you don't learn to swim as well? *Journal of Personality and Social Psychology, 47,* 213–231. (p. 410)

Marsh, N., Scheele, D., Gerhardt, H., Strang, S., Enax, L., Weber, B., . . . Hurlemann, R. (2017). The neuropeptide oxytocin induces a social altruism bias. *Journal of Neuroscience, 35,* 15696–15701. (p. 49)

Marshall, M. J. (2002). *Why spanking doesn't work.* Springville, UT: Bonneville Books. (p. 249)

Marshall, P. J., & Meltzoff, A. N. (2014). Neural mirroring mechanisms and imitation in human infants. *Philosophical Transactions of the Royal Society: Series B, 369.* doi:10.1098/rstb.2013.0620 (p. 260)

Marteau, T. M. (1989). Framing of information: Its influences upon decisions of doctors and patients. *British Journal of Social Psychology, 28,* 89–94. (p. 305)

Martel, M. M., Levinson, C. A., Langer, J. K., & Nigg, J. T. (2016). A network analysis of developmental change in ADHD symptom structure from preschool to adulthood. *Clinical Psychological Science, 4,* 988–1001. (p. 498)

Martela, F., & Steger, M. F. (2016). The three meanings of meaning in life: Distinguishing coherence, purpose, and significance. *The Journal of Positive Psychology, 11,* 531–545. (p. 350)

Martin, C. K., Anton, S. D., Walden, H., Arnett, C., Greenway, F. L., & Williamson, D. A. (2007). Slower eating rate reduces the food intake of men, but not women: Implications for behavioural weight control. *Behaviour Research and Therapy, 45,* 2349–2359. (p. 366)

Martin, C. L., & Ruble, D. (2004). Children's search for gender cues. *Current Directions in Psychological Science, 13,* 67–70. (p. 169)

Martin, C. L., Ruble, D. N., & Szkrybalo, J. (2002). Cognitive theories of early gender development. *Psychological Bulletin, 128,* 903–933. (p. 169)

Martín, R., Bajo-Grañeras, R., Moratalla, R., Perea, G., & Araque, A. (2015). Circuit-specific signaling in astrocyte-neuron networks in basal ganglia pathways. *Science, 349,* 730–734. (p. 40)

Martin, S. J., Kelly, I. W., & Saklofske, D. H. (1992). Suicide and lunar cycles: A critical review over 28 years. *Psychological Reports, 71,* 787–795. (p. 530)

Martín-María, N., Miret, M., Caballero, F. F., Rico-Uribe, L., Steptoe, A., Chatterji, S., & Ayuso-Mateos, J. (2017). The impact of subjective well-being on mortality: A meta-analysis of longitudinal studies in the general population. *Psychosomatic Medicine, 79,* 565–575. (p. 392)

Martins, Y., Preti, G., Crabtree, C. R., & Wysocki, C. J. (2005). Preference for human body odors is influenced by gender and sexual orientation. *Psychological Science, 16,* 694–701. (p. 181)

Marzoli, D., Custodero, M., Pagliara, A., & Tommasi, L. (2013). Sun-induced frowning fosters aggressive feelings. *Cognition and Emotion, 27,* 1513–1521. (p. 381)

Maslow, A. H. (1970). *Motivation and personality* (2nd ed.). New York: Harper & Row. (pp. 350, 471)

Maslow, A. H. (1971). *The farther reaches of human nature.* New York: Viking Press. (p. 350)

Mason, A. E., Sbarra, D. A., & Mehl, M. R. (2010). Thin-slicing divorce: Thirty seconds of information predict changes in psychological adjustment over 90 days. *Psychological Science, 21,* 1420–1422. (p. 377)

Mason, C., & Kandel, E. R. (1991). Central visual pathways. In E. R. Kandel, J. H. Schwartz, & T. M. Jessell (Eds.), *Principles of neural science* (3rd ed.). New York: Elsevier. (p. 45)

Mason, H. (2003, March 25). *Wake up, sleepy teen.* Retrieved from gallup.com/poll/8059/wake-up-sleepy-teen.aspx (p. 93)

Mason, H. (2005, January 25). *Who dreams, perchance to sleep?* Retrieved from gallup.com/poll/14716/who-dreams-perchance-sleep.aspx (p. 93)

Mason, M. F., & Morris, M. W. (2010). Culture, attribution and automaticity: A social cognitive neuroscience view. *Social Cognitive and Affective Neuroscience, 5,* 292–306. (p. 378)

Mason, R. A., & Just, M. A. (2004). How the brain processes causal inferences in text. *Psychological Science, 15,* 1–7. (p. 67)

Massimini, M., Ferrarelli, F., Huber, R., Esser, S. K., Singh, H., & Tononi, G. (2005). Breakdown of cortical effective connectivity during sleep. *Science, 309,* 2228–2232. (p. 87)

Masten, A. S. (2001). Ordinary magic: Resilience processes in development. *American Psychologist, 56,* 227–238. (p. 137)

Masters, K. S. (2010). The role of religion in therapy: Time for psychologists to have a little faith? *Cognitive and Behavioral Practice, 17,* 393–400. (p. 556)

Masters, K. S., & Hooker, S. A. (2013). Religiousness/spirituality, cardiovascular disease, and cancer: Cultural integration for health research and intervention. *Journal of Consulting and Clinical Psychology, 81,* 206–216. (p. 406)

Masters, W. H., & Johnson, V. E. (1966). *Human sexual response.* Boston: Little, Brown. (p. 174)

Mastroianni, G. R. (2015). Obedience in perspective: Psychology and the Holocaust. *Theory and Psychology, 25,* 657–669. (p. 427)

Mastroianni, G. R., & Reed, G. (2006). Apples, barrels, and Abu Ghraib. *Sociological Focus, 39,* 239–250. (p. 419)

Masuda, T., Ellsworth, P. C., Mesquita, B., Leu, J., Tanida, S., & Van de Veerdonk, E. (2008). Placing the face in context: Cultural differences in the perception of facial emotion. *Journal of Personality and Social Psychology, 94,* 365–381. (p. 379)

Mata, A., Ferreira, M. B., & Sherman, S. J. (2013). The metacognitive advantage of deliberative thinkers: A dual-process perspective on overconfidence. *Journal of Personality and Social Psychology, 105,* 353–373. (p. 306)

Mata, R., Josef, A. K., & Hertwig, R. (2016). Propensity for risk taking across the life span and around the globe. *Psychological Science, 27,* 231–243. (p. 118)

Mataix-Cols, D., Rosario-Campos, M. C., & Leckman, J. F. (2005). A multidimensional model of obsessive-compulsive disorder. *American Journal of Psychiatry, 162,* 228–238. (p. 512)

Mataix-Cols, D., Wooderson, S., Lawrence, N., Brammer, M. J., Speckens, A., & Phillips, M. L. (2004). Distinct neural correlates of washing, checking, and hoarding symptom dimensions in obsessive-compulsive disorder. *Archives of General Psychiatry, 61,* 564–576. (p. 512)

Mather, M. (2016). The affective neuroscience of aging. *Annual Review of Psychology, 67,* 213–238. (p. 158)

Mather, M., Cacioppo, J. T., & Kanwisher, N. (2013). How fMRI can inform cognitive theories. *Perspectives on Psychological Science, 8,* 108–113. (p. 53)

Mather, M., Canli, T., English, T., Whitfield, S., Wais, P., Ochsner, K., . . . Carstensen, L. L. (2004). Amygdala responses to emotionally valenced stimuli in older and younger adults. *Psychological Science, 15,* 259–263. (p. 158)

Mather, M., & Sutherland, M. (2012, February). The selective effects of emotional arousal on memory. *APA Science Brief* (apa.org). (p. 278)

Matson, J. L., & Boisjoli, J. A. (2009). The token economy for children with intellectual disability and/or autism: A review. *Research on Developmental Disabilities, 30,* 240–248. (p. 543)

Matsumoto, D. (1994). *People: Psychology from a cultural perspective.* Pacific Grove, CA: Brooks/Cole. (p. 319)

Matsumoto, D., & Ekman, P. (1989). American-Japanese cultural differences in intensity ratings of facial expressions of emotion. *Motivation and Emotion, 13,* 143–157. (p. 379)

Matsumoto, D., Frank, M. G., & Hwang, H. C. (2015). The role of intergroup emotions on political violence. *Current Directions in Psychological Science, 24,* 369–373. (p. 261)

Matsumoto, D., Willingham, B., & Olide, A. (2009). Sequential dynamics of culturally moderated facial expressions of emotion. *Psychological Science, 20,* 1269–1275. (p. 379)

Mattanah, J. F., Lopez, F. G., & Govern, J. M. (2011). The contributions of parental attachment bonds to college student development and adjustment: A meta-analytic review. *Journal of Counseling Psychology, 58,* 565–596. (p. 136)

Mattheisen, M., Samuels, J. F., Wang, Y., Greenberg, B. D., Fyer, A. J., McCracken, J. T., . . . Riddle, M. A. (2015). Genome-wide association study in obsessive-compulsive disorder: Results from OCGAS. *Molecular Psychiatry, 20,* 337–344. (p. 511)

Matthews, R. N., Domjan, M., Ramsey, M., & Crews, D. (2007). Learning effects on sperm competition and reproductive fitness. *Psychological Science, 18,* 758–762. (p. 238)

Matz, S. C., Kosinski, M., Nave, G., & Stillwell, D. J. (2017). Psychological targeting as an effective approach to digital mass persuasion. *PNAS, 114,* 12714–12719. (p. 479)

Maurer, D., & Maurer, C. (1988). *The world of the newborn.* New York: Basic Books. (p. 121)

Mautz, B., Wong, B., Peters, R., & Jennions, M. (2013). Penis size interacts with body shape and height to influence male attractiveness. *PNAS, 110,* 6925–6693. (p. 184)

Maxmen, A. (2018, January 24). As Cape Town water crisis deepens, scientists prepare for 'Day Zero.' *Nature* (nature.com/articles/d41586-018-01134-x). (p. 456)

Maxwell, S. E., Lau, M. Y., & Howard, G. S. (2015). Is psychology suffering from a replication crisis? What does "failure to replicate" really mean? *American Psychologist, 70,* 487–498. (p. 20)

May, C., & Hasher, L. (1998). Synchrony effects in inhibitory control over thought and action. *Journal of Experimental Psychology: Human Perception and Performance, 24,* 363–380. (p. 86)

May, P. A., Baete, J., Russo, A. J., Elliott, J., Blankenship, J., Kalberg, W. O., . . . Hoyme, H. E. (2014). Prevalence and characteristics of fetal alcohol spectrum disorders. *Pediatrics, 134,* 855–866. (p. 120)

May, R. (1982). The problem of evil: An open letter to Carl Rogers. *Journal of Humanistic Psychology, 22,* 10–21. (p. 473)

Mayberry, R. I., Lock, E., & Kazmi, H. (2002). Linguistic ability and early language exposure. *Nature, 417,* 38. (p. 316)

Mayer, J. D., Caruso, D. R., & Salovey, P. (2016). The ability model of emotional intelligence: Principles and updates. *Emotion Review, 8,* 290–300. (p. 326)

Mayer, J. D., Salovey, P., & Caruso, D. R. (2002). *The Mayer-Salovey-Caruso emotional intelligence test (MSCEIT).* Toronto: Multi-Health Systems. (p. 326)

Mayer, J. D., Salovey, P., & Caruso, D. R. (2012). The validity of the MSCEIT: Additional analyses and evidence. *Emotion Review, 4,* 403–408. (p. 326)

Mazure, C., Keita, G., & Blehar, M. (2002). *Summit on women and depression: Proceedings and recommendations.* Washington, DC: American Psychological Association (apa.org/pi/wpo/women&depression.pdf). (p. 520)

Mazza, S., Gerbier, E., Gustin, M. P., Kasikci, Z., Koenig, O., Toppino, T. C., & Magnin, M. (2016). Relearn faster and retain longer: Along with practice, sleep makes perfect. *Psychological Science, 27,* 1321–1330. (p. 276)

Mazzoni, G., Scoboria, A., & Harvey, L. (2010). Nonbelieved memories. *Psychological Science, 21,* 1334–1340. (p. 291)

Mazzoni, G., & Vannucci, M. (2007). Hindsight bias, the misinformation effect, and false autobiographical memories. *Social Cognition, 25,* 203–220. (p. 292)

McAdams, D. P., & Guo, J. (2015). Narrating the generative life. *Psychological Science, 26,* 475–483. (p. 472)

McAleer, P., Todorov, A., & Belin, P. (2014). How do you say "hello"? Personality impressions from brief novel voices. *PLoS ONE, 9,* 9. (p. 377)

McBurney, D. H. (1996). *How to think like a psychologist: Critical thinking in psychology.* Upper Saddle River, NJ: Prentice-Hall. (p. 62)

McBurney, D. H., & Collings, V. B. (1984). *Introduction to sensation and perception* (2nd ed.). Englewood Cliffs, NJ: Prentice-Hall. (p. 212)

McBurney, D. H., & Gent, J. F. (1979). On the nature of taste qualities. *Psychological Bulletin, 86,* 151–167. (p. 225)

McCabe, K. O., & Fleeson, W. (2016). Are traits useful? Explaining trait manifestations as tools in the pursuit of goals. *Journal of Personality and Social Psychology, 110,* 287–301. (p. 475)

McCain, J. (2017, February 17). Munich speech, reported by *The Guardian* (February 18, 2017), McCain attacks Trump administration and inability to "separate truth from lies." *The Guardian* (theguardian.com). (p. 18)

McCain, J. L., & Campbell, W. K. (2016). Narcissism and social media use: A meta-analytic review. *Psychology of Popular Media Culture.* Advance online publication. doi:10.1037/ppm0000137 (p. 489)

McCann, I. L., & Holmes, D. S. (1984). Influence of aerobic exercise on depression. *Journal of Personality and Social Psychology, 46,* 1142–1147. (p. 402)

McCann, S. J. H. (2017). Higher USA state resident neuroticism is associated with lower state volunteering rates. *Psychological Science, 43,* 1659–1674. (p. 479)

McCann, U. D., Eligulashvili, V., & Ricaurte, G. A. (2000). (±)3,4-Methylenedioxymethamphetamine ("Ecstasy")-induced serotonin neurotoxicity: Clinical studies. *Neuropsychobiology, 42,* 11–16. (p. 108)

McCarthy, J. (2016, August 8). *One in eight U.S. adults say they smoke marijuana.* Gallup Poll (gallup.com). (p. 109)

McCarthy, P. (1986, July). Scent: The tie that binds? *Psychology Today,* pp. 6, 10. (p. 226)

McCauley, C. R. (2002). Psychological issues in understanding terrorism and the response to terrorism. In C. E. Stout (Ed.), *The psychology of terrorism* (Vol. 3). Westport, CT: Praeger/Greenwood. (p. 431)

McCauley, C. R., & Segal, M. E. (1987). Social psychology of terrorist groups. In C. Hendrick (Ed.), *Group processes and intergroup relations*. Beverly Hills, CA: Sage. (p. 431)

McClendon, B. T., & Prentice-Dunn, S. (2001). Reducing skin cancer risk: An intervention based on protection motivation theory. *Journal of Health Psychology, 6*, 321–328. (p. 418)

McClintock, M. K., & Herdt, G. (1996). Rethinking puberty: The development of sexual attraction. *Current Directions in Psychological Science, 5*, 178–183. (p. 166)

McClung, M., & Collins, D. (2007). "Because I know it will!": Placebo effects of an ergogenic aid on athletic performance. *Journal of Sport & Exercise Psychology, 29*, 382–394. (p. 27)

McClure, E. B. (2000). A meta-analytic review of sex differences in facial expression processing and their development in infants, children, and adolescents. *Psychological Bulletin, 126*, 424–453. (p. 377)

McClure, M. J., & Lydon, J. E. (2014). Anxiety doesn't become you: How attachment compromises relational opportunities. *Journal of Personality and Social Psychology, 106*, 89–111. (p. 448)

McConnell, A. R., Brown, C. M., Shoda, T. M., Stayton, L. E., & Martin, C. E. (2011). Friends with benefits: On the positive consequences of pet ownership. *Journal of Personality and Social Psychology, 101*, 1239–1252. (p. 401)

McCrae, R. R., & Costa, P. T., Jr. (1986). Clinical assessment can benefit from recent advances in personality psychology. *American Psychologist, 41*, 1001–1003. (p. 478)

McCrae, R. R., & Costa, P. T., Jr. (1990). *Personality in adulthood.* New York: Guilford Press. (p. 155)

McCrae, R. R., & Costa, P. T., Jr. (1994). The stability of personality: Observations and evaluations. *Current Directions in Psychological Science, 3*, 173–175. (p. 480)

McCrae, R. R., & Costa, P. T., Jr. (2008). The Five-Factor Theory of personality. In O. P. John, R. W., Robins, & L. A. Pervin (Eds.), *Handbook of personality: Theory and research* (3rd ed.). New York: Guilford. (p. 478)

McCrae, R. R., Scally, M., Terraccioani, A., Abecasis, G. R., & Costa, P. T., Jr. (2010). An alternative to the search for single polymorphisms: Toward molecular personality scales for the Five-Factor Model. *Journal of Personality and Social Psychology, 99*, 1014–1024. (p. 478)

McCrae, R. R., Terracciano, A., & 78 members of the Personality Profiles and Cultures Project. (2005). Universal features of personality traits from the observer's perspective: Data from 50 cultures. *Journal of Personality and Social Psychology, 88*, 547–561. (p. 478)

McCrink, K., & Wynn, K. (2004). Large-number addition and subtraction by 9-month-old infants. *Psychological Science, 15*, 776–781. (p. 127)

McCrory, E. J., De Brito, S. A., Sebastian, C. L., Mechelli, A., Bird, G., Kelly, P. A., & Viding, E. (2011). Heightened neural reactivity to threat in child victims of family violence. *Current Biology, 21*, R947–948. (p. 137)

McCullough, M. E., Hoyt, W. T., Larson, D. B., Koenig, H. G., & Thoresen, C. (2000). Religious involvement and mortality: A meta-analytic review. *Health Psychology, 19*, 211–222. (p. 405)

McCullough, M. E., & Laurenceau, J.-P. (2005). Religiousness and the trajectory of self-rated health across adulthood. *Personality and Social Psychology Bulletin, 31*, 560–573. (p. 405)

McCullough, M. E., & Willoughby, B. L. B. (2009). Religion, self-regulation, and self-control: Associations, explanations, and implications. *Psychological Bulletin, 135*, 69–93. (p. 406)

McDaniel, M. A., Bugg, J. M., Liu, Y., & Brick, J. (2015). When does the test-study-test sequence optimize learning and retention? *Journal of Experimental Psychology: Applied, 21*, 370–382. (pp. 14, 35, 49, 58, 68, 78, 85, 100, 114, 122, 140, 150, 160, 171, 187, 198, 214, 232, 242, 253, 264, 274, 282, 295, 310, 322, 334, 345, 359, 366, 375, 382, 394, 413, 433, 446, 460, 473, 492, 505, 513, 522, 534, 549, 557, 568, A-8, B-14)

McDaniel, M. A., Howard, D. C., & Einstein, G. O. (2009). The read-recite-review study strategy: Effective and portable. *Psychological Science, 20*, 516–522. (pp. 14, 33, 35, 49, 58, 68, 78, 85, 100, 114, 122, 140, 150, 160, 171, 187, 198, 214, 232, 242, 253, 264, 274, 282, 295, 310, 322, 334, 345, 359, 366, 375, 382, 394, 413, 433, 446, 460, 473, 492, 505, 513, 522, 534, 549, 557, 568, A-8, B-14)

McDermott, R., Tingley, D., Cowden, J., Frazzetto, G., & Johnson, D. D. P. (2009). Monoamine oxidase A gene (MAOA) predicts behavioral aggression following provocation. *PNAS, 106*, 2118–2123. (p. 441)

McDonald, P. (2012). Workplace sexual harassment 30 years on: A review of the literature. *International Journal of Management Reviews, 14*, 1–17. (p. 169)

McDuff, D., Kodra, E., el Kallouby, R., & LaFrance, M. (2017). A large-scale analysis of sex differences in facial expressions. *PLoS ONE, 12*(4), e0173942. (p. 377)

McEvoy, S. P., Stevenson, M. R., McCartt, A. T., Woodward, M., Hawroth, C., Palamara, P., & Ceracelli, R. (2005). Role of mobile phones in motor vehicle crashes resulting in hospital attendance: A case-crossover study. *British Medical Journal, 331*, 428. http://dx.doi.org/10.1136/bmj.38537.397512.55 (p. 82)

McEvoy, S. P., Stevenson, M. R., & Woodward, M. (2007). The contribution of passengers versus mobile phone use to motor vehicle crashes resulting in hospital attendance by the driver. *Accident Analysis and Prevention, 39*, 1170–1176. (p. 82)

McFarland, C., & Ross, M. (1987). The relation between current impressions and memories of self and dating partners. *Psychological Bulletin, 13*, 228–238. (p. 292)

McFarland, S., & Carnahan, T. (2009). A situation's first powers are attracting volunteers and selecting participants: A reply to Haney and Zimbardo (2009). *Personality and Social Psychology Bulletin, 35*, 815–818. (p. 419)

McGaugh, J. L. (1994). Quoted by B. Bower, Stress hormones hike emotional memories. *Science News, 146*, 262. (p. 278)

McGaugh, J. L. (2003). *Memory and emotion: The making of lasting memories.* New York: Columbia University Press. (p. 278)

McGaugh, J. L. (2015). Consolidating memories. *Annual Review of Psychology, 66*, 1–24. (p. 277)

McGaugh, J. L., & LePort, A. (2014). Remembrance of all things past. *Scientific American, 310*, 40–45. (p. 284)

McGhee, P. E. (June, 1976). Children's appreciation of humor: A test of the cognitive congruency principle. *Child Development, 47*, 420–426. (p. 128)

McGowan, P. O., Sasaki, A., D'Alessio, A. C., Dymov, S., Labonté, B., Szyl, M., . . . Meaney, M. J. (2009). Epigenetic regulation of the glucocorticoid receptor in human brain associates with childhood abuse. *Nature Neuroscience, 12*, 342–348. (p. 512)

McGrath, J. J., & Welham, J. L. (1999). Season of birth and schizophrenia: A systematic review and meta-analysis of data from the Southern hemisphere. *Schizophrenia Research, 35*, 237–242. (p. 525)

McGrath, J. J., Welham, J., & Pemberton, M. (1995). Month of birth, hemisphere of birth and schizophrenia. *British Journal of Psychiatry, 167*, 783–785. (p. 525)

McGue, M. (2010). The end of behavioral genetics? *Behavioral Genetics, 40*, 284–296. (p. 75)

McGue, M., & Bouchard, T. J., Jr. (1998). Genetic and environmental influences on human behavioral differences. *Annual Review of Neuroscience, 21*, 1–24. (p. 72)

McGue, M., Bouchard, T. J., Jr., Iacono, W. G., & Lykken, D. T. (1993). Behavioral genetics of cognitive ability: A life-span perspective. In R. Plomin & G. E. McClearn (Eds.), *Nature, nurture and psychology.* Washington, DC: American Psychological Association. (pp. 337, 338)

McGurk, H., & MacDonald, J. (1976). Hearing lips and seeing voices. *Nature, 264*, 746–748. (p. 228)

McHugh, P. R. (1995). Resolved: Multiple personality disorder is an individually and socially created artifact. *Journal of the American Academy of Child and Adolescent Psychiatry, 34*, 957–959. (p. 528)

McKay, J. (2000). Building self-esteem in children. In M. McKay & P. Fanning (Eds.), *Self-esteem.* New York: New Harbinger/St. Martins. (p. 486)

McKellar, J., Stewart, E., & Humphreys, K. (2003). Alcoholics Anonymous involvement and positive alcohol-related outcomes: Cause, consequence, or just a correlate? A prospective 2-year study of 2,319 alcohol-dependent men. *Journal of Consulting and Clinical Psychology, 71*, 302–308. (p. 548)

McKenna, K. Y. A., Green, A. S., & Gleason, M. E. J. (2002). What's the big attraction? Relationship formation on the internet. *Journal of Social Issues, 58*, 9–31. (p. 448)

McKinnon, M. C., Palombo, D. J., Nazarov, A., Kumar, N., Khuu, W., & Levine, B. (2015). Threat of death and autobiographical memory: A study of passengers from flight AT236. *Clinical Psychological Science, 3*, 487–502. (p. 289)

McKone, E., Kanwisher, N., & Duchaine, B. C. (2007). Can generic expertise explain special processing for faces? *Trends in Cognitive Sciences, 11*, 8–15. (p. 205)

McLaughlin, K. A., Sheridan, M. A., Tibu, F., Fox, N. A., Zeanah, C. H., & Nelson, C. A. (2015). Causal effects of the early caregiving environment on development of stress response systems in children. *PNAS, 112*, 5637–5642. (p. 137)

McLaughlin, M. (2010, October 2). J. K. Rowling: Depression, the "terrible place that allowed me to come back stronger." *The Scotsman* (scotsman.com). (p. 516)

McLean, C. P., & Anderson, E. R. (2009). Brave men and timid women? A review of the gender differences in fear and anxiety. *Clinical Psychology Review, 29*, 496–505. (p. 507)

McMurray, B. (2007). Defusing the childhood vocabulary explosion. *Science, 317*, 631. (p. 313)

McNally, R. J. (2003). *Remembering trauma.* Cambridge, MA: Harvard University Press. (pp. 293, 510)

McNally, R. J. (2007). Betrayal trauma theory: A critical appraisal. *Memory, 15*, 280–294. (p. 293)

McNally, R. J. (2012). Are we winning the war against posttraumatic stress disorder? *Science, 336*, 872–874. (pp. 88, 510)

McNally, R. J., & Geraerts, E. (2009). A new solution to the recovered memory debate. *Perspectives on Psychological Science, 4*, 126–134. (p. 293)

McNeil, B. J., Pauker, S. G., & Tversky, A. (1988). On the framing of medical decisions. In D. E. Bell, H. Raiffa, & A. Tversky (Eds.), *Decision making: Descriptive, normative, and prescriptive interactions* (pp. 562–568). New York: Cambridge University Press. (p. 305)

McNulty, J. K., Olson, M. A., Meltzer, A. L., & Shaffer, M. J. (2013). Though they may be unaware, newlyweds implicitly know whether their marriage will be satisfying. *Science, 342,* 1119–1120. (p. 305)

Meador, B. D., & Rogers, C. R. (1984). Person-centered therapy. In R. J. Corsini (Ed.), *Current psychotherapies* (3rd ed.). Itasca, IL: Peacock. (p. 539)

Medda, P., Toni, C., Mariani, M. G., De Simone, L., Mauri, M., & Perugi, G. (2015). Electroconvulsive therapy in 197 patients with a severe, drug-resistant bipolar mixed state: Treatment outcome and predictors of response. *The Journal of Clinical Psychiatry, 76,* 1168–1173. (p. 563)

Mednick, S. A., Huttunen, M. O., & Machon, R. A. (1994). Prenatal influenza infections and adult schizophrenia. *Schizophrenia Bulletin, 20,* 263–267. (p. 525)

Medvec, V. H., Madey, S. F., & Gilovich, T. (1995). When less is more: Counterfactual thinking and satisfaction among Olympic medalists. *Journal of Personality and Social Psychology, 69,* 603–610. (p. 489)

Mehl, M., Gosling, S. D., & Pennebaker, J. W. (2006). Personality in its natural habitat: Manifestations and implicit folk theories of personality in daily life. *Journal of Personality and Social Psychology, 90,* 862–877. (p. 481)

Mehl, M. R., Vazire, S., Holleran, S. E., & Clark, C. S. (2010). Eavesdropping on happiness: Well-being is related to having less small talk and more substantive conversations. *Psychological Science, 21,* 539–541. (p. 412)

Mehlum, L., Ramberg, M., Tørmoen, A. J., Haga, E., Diep, L. M., Stanley, B. H., . . . Grøholt, B. (2016). Dialectical behavior therapy compared with enhanced usual care for adolescents with repeated suicidal and self-harming behavior: Outcomes over a one-year follow-up. *Journal of the American Academy of Child & Adolescent Psychiatry, 55,* 295–300. (p. 546)

Mehta, D., Klengel, T., Conneely, K. N., Smith, A. K., Altmann, A., Pace, T. W., . . . Binder, E. B. (2013). Childhood maltreatment is associated with distinct genomic and epigenetic profiles in posttraumatic stress disorder. *PNAS, 110,* 8302–8307. (p. 512)

Mehta, M. R. (2007). Cortico-hippocampal interaction during up-down states and memory consolidation. *Nature Neuroscience, 10,* 13–15. (p. 277)

Meichenbaum, D. (1977). *Cognitive-behavior modification: An integrative approach.* New York: Plenum Press. (p. 545)

Meichenbaum, D. (1985). *Stress inoculation training.* New York: Pergamon. (p. 545)

Mejia, Z. (2017, November 17). What billionaire Amazon founder Jeff Bezos did at 30 to avoid living with regret. CNBC. Retrieved from cnbc.com/2017/11/17/what-amazons-jeff-bezos-did-at-30-to-avoid-living-with-regret.html (p. 476)

Melby-Lervåg, M., Redick, T. S., & Hulme, C. (2016). Working memory training does not improve performance on measures of intelligence or other measures of "far transfer": Evidence from a meta-analytic review. *Perspectives on Psychological Science, 11,* 512–534. (p. 154)

Melioli, T., Bauer, S., Franko, D. L., Moessner, M., Ozer, F., Chabrol, H., & Rodgers, R. F. (2016). Reducing eating disorder symptoms and risk factors using the internet: A meta-analytic review. *International Journal of Eating Disorders, 49,* 19–31. (p. 533)

Mellers, B., Stone, E., Atanasov, P., Rohrbaugh, N., Metz, S. E., Ungar, L., . . . Tetlock, P. (2015). The psychology of intelligence analysis: Drivers of prediction accuracy in world politics. *Journal of Experimental Psychology: Applied, 21,* 1–14. (p. 303)

Meltzoff, A. N. (1988). Infant imitation after a 1-week delay: Long-term memory for novel acts and multiple stimuli. *Developmental Psychology, 24,* 470–476. (p. 260)

Meltzoff, A. N., Kuhl, P. K., Movellan, J., & Sejnowski, T. J. (2009). Foundations for a new science of learning. *Science, 325,* 284–288. (pp. 260, 314)

Meltzoff, A. N., & Moore, M. K. (1989). Imitation in newborn infants: Exploring the range of gestures imitated and the underlying mechanisms. *Developmental Psychology, 25,* 954–962. (p. 260)

Meltzoff, A. N., & Moore, M. K. (1997). Explaining facial imitation: A theoretical model. *Early Development and Parenting, 6,* 179–192. (p. 260)

Melvill, H. (1855). Partaking in other men's sins. Sermon at St. Margaret's Church, Lothbury, England. No. 2,365 in the "Penny Pulpit" series. Reprinted in *The golden lecture: Forty-five sermons delivered at St. Margaret's Church, Lothbury.* London: James Paul. (p. 415)

Melzack, R. (1992, April). Quoted in Phantom limbs. *Scientific American,* pp. 120–126. (p. 222)

Melzack, R. (1998, February). Quoted in Phantom limbs. *Discover,* p. 20. (p. 222)

Melzack, R. (2005). Evolution of the neuromatrix theory of pain. *Pain Practice, 5,* 85–94. (p. 222)

Melzack, R., & Katz, J. (2013). Pain. *Wiley Interdisciplinary Reviews: Cognitive Science, 4,* 1–15. (p. 222)

Melzack, R., & Wall, P. D. (1965). Pain mechanisms: A new theory. *Science, 150,* 971–979. (p. 222)

Melzack, R., & Wall, P. D. (1983). *The challenge of pain.* New York: Basic Books. (p. 222)

Mendelson, J. L., Gates, J. A., & Lerner, M. D. (2016). Friendship in school-age boys with autism spectrum disorders: A meta-analytic summary and developmental, process-based model. *Psychological Bulletin, 142,* 601–622. (p. 131)

Mendes, E. (2010, June 2). *U.S. exercise levels up, but demographic differences remain.* Gallup poll (gallup.com). (p. 402)

Mendes, E., & McGeeney, K. (2012, July 9). Women's health trails men's most in former Soviet Union. Gallup (gallup.com). (p. 517)

Mendle, J., Turkheimer, E., & Emery, R. E. (2007). Detrimental psychological outcomes associated with early pubertal timing in adolescent girls. *Developmental Review, 27,* 151–171. (p. 142)

Mendolia, M., & Kleck, R. E. (1993). Effects of talking about a stressful event on arousal: Does what we talk about make a difference? *Journal of Personality and Social Psychology, 64,* 283–292. (p. 400)

Merari, A. (2002). *Explaining suicidal terrorism: Theories versus empirical evidence.* Invited address to the American Psychological Association. (p. 431)

Mercer, T. (2015). Wakeful rest alleviates interference-based forgetting. *Memory, 23,* 127–137. (p. 287)

Meriac, J. P., Hoffman, B. J., Woehr, D. J., & Fleisher, M. S. (2008). Further evidence for the validity of assessment center dimensions: A meta-analysis of the incremental criterion-related validity of dimension ratings. *Journal of Applied Psychology, 93,* 1042–1052. (p. 484)

Merikangas, K. R., Jin, R., He, J. P., Kessler, R. C., Lee, S., Sampson, N. A., . . . Zarkov, Z. (2011). Prevalence and correlates of bipolar spectrum disorder in the world mental health survey initiative. *Archives of General Psychiatry, 68,* 241–251. (p. 516)

Merskey, H. (1992). The manufacture of personalities: The production of multiple personality disorder. *British Journal of Psychiatry, 160,* 327–340.(p. 528)

Merzenich, M. (2007). Quoted in the Posit Science Brain Fitness Program. Retrieved from positscience.com/ (p. 154)

Mesman, J., van Ijzendoorn, M., Behrens, K., Carbonell, O. A., Cárcamo, R., Cohen-Paraira, I., . . . Kondo-Ikemura, K. (2015). Is the ideal mother a sensitive mother? Beliefs about early childhood parenting in mothers across the globe. *International Journal of Behavioral Development, 40,* 385–397. (p. 133)

Mesoudi, A. (2009). How cultural evolutionary theory can inform social psychology and vice versa. *Psychological Review, 116,* 929–952. (p. 422)

Messerli, F. H. (2012). Chocolate consumption, cognitive function, and Nobel laureates. *The New England Journal of Medicine, 367,* 1562–1564. (p. 23)

Messias, E., Eaton, W. W., & Grooms, A. N. (2011). Economic grand rounds: Income inequality and depression prevalence across the United States: An ecological study. *Psychiatric Services, 62,* 710–712. (p. 443)

Meston, C. M., & Buss, D. M. (2007). Why humans have sex. *Archives of Sexual Behavior, 36,* 477–507. (p. 176)

Metcalfe, J. (1986). Premonitions of insight predict impending error. *Journal of Experimental Psychology: Learning, Memory, and Cognition, 12,* 623–634. (p. 299)

Metcalfe, J. (1998). Cognitive optimism: Self-deception or memory-based processing heuristics. *Personality and Social Psychology Review, 2,* 100–110. (p. 303)

Metzler, D. (2011, Spring). Vocabulary growth in adult cross-fostered chimpanzees. *Friends of Washoe, 32,* 11–13. (p. 317)

Meyer, A., Proudfit, G. H., Bufferd, S. J., Kujawa, A. J., Laptook, R. S., Torpey, D. C., & Klein, D. N. (2015). Self-reported and observed punitive parenting prospectively predicts increased error-related brain activity in six-year-old children. *Journal of Abnormal Child Psychology, 43,* 821–829. (p. 139)

Meyer-Bahlburg, H. F. L. (1995). Psychoneuroendocrinology and sexual pleasure: The aspect of sexual orientation. In P. R. Abramson & S. D. Pinkerton (Eds.), *Sexual nature/sexual culture* (pp. 135–153). Chicago: University of Chicago Press. (p. 181)

Meyerhoff, J., & Rohan, K. J. (2016). Treatment expectations for cognitive-behavioral therapy and light therapy for seasonal affective disorder: Change across treatment and relation to outcome. *Journal of Consulting and Clinical Psychology, 84,* 898–906. (p. 555)

Mez, J., Daneshvar, D. H., Kiernan, P. T., Abdolmohammadi, B., Alvarez, V. E., Huber, B. R., . . . Cormier, K. A. (2017). Clinicopathological evaluation of chronic traumatic encephalopathy in players of American football. *Journal of the American Medical Association, 318,* 360–370. (p. 57)

Miao, C., Humphrey, R. H., & Qian, S. (2016). Leader emotional intelligence and subordinate job satisfaction: A meta-analysis of main, mediator, and moderator effects. *Personality and Individual Differences, 102,* 13–24. (p. 326)

Michael, R. B., Garry, M., & Kirsch, I. (2012). Suggestion, cognition, and behavior. *Current Directions in Psychological Science, 21,* 151–156. (p. 27)

Michaels, J. W., Bloomel, J. M., Brocato, R. M., Linkous, R. A., & Rowe, J. S. (1982). Social facilitation and inhibition in a natural setting. *Replications in Social Psychology, 2,* 21–24. (p. 429)

Michalka, S. W., Kong, L., Rosen, M. L., Shinn-Cunningham, B., & Somers, D. C. (2015). Short-term memory for space and time flexibly recruit complementary sensory-biased frontal lobe attention networks. *Neuron, 87*, 882–892. (p. 276)

Middlebrooks, J. C., & Green, D. M. (1991). Sound localization by human listeners. *Annual Review of Psychology, 42*, 135–159. (p. 220)

Miech, R. A., Johnston, L. D., O'Malley, P. M., Bachman, J. G., & Schulenberg, J. E. (2016). *Monitoring the Future national survey results on drug use, 1975–2015: Volume I, Secondary school students.* Ann Arbor: Institute for Social Research, The University of Michigan. (p. 110)

Miers, R. (2009, Spring). Calum's road. *Scottish Life*, pp. 36–39, 75. (p. 358)

Mihura, J. L., Meyer, G. J., Bombel, G., & Dumitrascu, N. (2015). Standards, accuracy, and questions of bias in Rorschach meta-analyses: Reply to Wood, Garb, Nezworski, Lilienfeld, and Duke (2015). *Psychological Bulletin, 141*, 250–260. (p. 468)

Mihura, J. L., Meyer, G. J., Dumitrascu, N., & Bombel, G. (2013). The validity of individual Rorschach variables: Systematic reviews and meta-analyses of the comprehensive system. *Psychological Bulletin, 139*, 548–605. (p. 468)

Mikulincer, M., & Shaver, P. R. (2001). Attachment theory and intergroup bias: Evidence that priming the secure base schema attenuates negative reactions to out-groups. *Journal of Personality and Social Psychology, 81*, 97–115. (p. 439)

Milan, R. J., Jr., & Kilmann, P. R. (1987). Interpersonal factors in premarital contraception. *Journal of Sex Research, 23*, 289–321. (p. 187)

Miles, D. R., & Carey, G. (1997). Genetic and environmental architecture of human aggression. *Journal of Personality and Social Psychology, 72*, 207–217. (p. 441)

Milgram, S. (1963). Behavioral study of obedience. *Journal of Abnormal and Social Psychology, 67*, 371–378. (p. 425)

Milgram, S. (1974). *Obedience to authority.* New York: Harper & Row. (pp. 425, 426, 428)

Miller, B. G., Kors, S., & Macfie, J. (2017). No differences? Meta-analytic comparisons of psychological adjustment in children of gay fathers and heterosexual parents. *Psychology of Sexual Orientation and Gender Diversity, 4*, 14–22. (p. 180)

Miller, C. H., Hamilton, J. P., Sacchet, M. D., & Gotlib, I. H. (2015). Meta-analysis of functional neuroimaging of major depressive disorder in youth. *JAMA Psychiatry, 72*, 1045–1053. (p. 519)

Miller, G. (2004). Axel, Buck share award for deciphering how the nose knows. *Science, 306*, 207. (p. 226)

Miller, G. (2008). Tackling alcoholism with drugs. *Science, 320*, 168–170. (p. 111)

Miller, G. (2012). Drone wars: Are remotely piloted aircraft changing the nature of war? *Science, 336*, 842–843. (pp. 276, 427)

Miller, G. A. (1956). The magical number seven, plus or minus two: Some limits on our capacity for processing information. *Psychological Review, 63*, 81–97. (p. 271)

Miller, G. E., & Blackwell, E. (2006). Turning up the heat: Inflammation as a mechanism linking chronic stress, depression, and heart disease. *Current Directions in Psychological Science, 15*, 269–272. (p. 392)

Miller, J. F., Neufang, M., Solway, A., Brandt, A., Trippel, M., Mader, I., . . . Schulze-Bonhage, A. (2013). Neural activity in human hippocampal formation reveals the spatial context of retrieved memories. *Science, 342*, 1111–1114. (p. 276)

Miller, J. G., & Bersoff, D. M. (1995). Development in the context of everyday family relationships: Culture, interpersonal morality and adaptation. In M. Killen & D. Hart (Eds.), *Morality in everyday life: A developmental perspective* (pp. 259–282). New York: Cambridge University Press. (p. 144)

Miller, L. K. (1999). The savant syndrome: Intellectual impairment and exceptional skill. *Psychological Bulletin, 125*, 31–46. (p. 325)

Miller, M., Azrael, D., & Hemenway, D. (2002). Household firearm ownership levels and suicide across U.S. regions and states, 1988–1997. *Epidemiology, 13*, 517–524. (p. 501)

Miller, M., Swanson, S. A., & Azrael, D. (2016). Are we missing something pertinent? A bias analysis of unmeasured confounding in the firearm-suicide literature. *Epidemiologic Reviews, 38*, 62–69. (p. 501)

Miller, N. E. (1985, February). Rx: Biofeedback. *Psychology Today*, pp. 54–59. (p. 403)

Miller, P. (2012, January). A thing or two about twins. *National Geographic*, pp. 38–65. (p. 71)

Miller, P. J. O., Aoki, K., Rendell, L. E., & Amano, M. (2008). Stereotypical resting behavior of the sperm whale. *Current Biology, 18*, R21–R23. (p. 87)

Milner, A. D., & Goodale, M. A. (2008). Two visual systems reviewed. *Neuropsychologia, 46*, 774–785. (p. 84)

Milojev, P., & Sibley, C. G. (2017). Normative personality trait development in adulthood: A 6-year cohort-sequential growth model. *Journal of Personality and Social Psychology, 112*, 510–526. (p. 478)

Milrod, B., Chambless, D. L., Gallop, R., Busch, F. N., Schwalberg, M., McCarthy, K. S., . . . Barber, J. P. (2015, June 9). Psychotherapies for panic disorder: A tale of two sites. *Journal of Clinical Psychiatry, 77*, 927–935. (p. 546)

Mineka, S. (1985). The frightful complexity of the origins of fears. In F. R. Brush & J. B. Overmier (Eds.), *Affect, conditioning and cognition: Essays on the determinants of behavior.* Hillsdale, NJ: Erlbaum. (p. 511)

Mineka, S. (2002). Animal models of clinical psychology. In N. Smelser & P. Baltes (Eds.), *International encyclopedia of the social and behavioral sciences.* Oxford: Elsevier Science. (p. 511)

Mineka, S., & Oehlberg, K. (2008). The relevance of recent developments in classical conditioning to understanding the etiology and maintenance of anxiety disorders. *Acta Psychologica, 127*, 567–580. (p. 510)

Mineka, S., & Zinbarg, R. (1996). Conditioning and ethological models of anxiety disorders: Stress-in-dynamic-context anxiety models. In D. Hope (Ed.), *Perspectives on anxiety, panic, and fear* (Nebraska Symposium on Motivation). Lincoln: University of Nebraska Press. (pp. 512, 567)

Minsky, M. (1986). *The society of mind.* New York: Simon & Schuster. (p. 81)

Mischel, W. (1968). *Personality and assessment.* New York: Wiley. (p. 481)

Mischel, W. (1981). Current issues and challenges in personality. In L. T. Benjamin, Jr. (Ed.), *The G. Stanley Hall Lecture Series* (Vol. 1). Washington, DC: American Psychological Association. (p. 484)

Mischel, W. (2014). *The marshmallow test: Mastering self-control.* Boston: Little, Brown. (pp. 145, 247)

Mischkowski, D., Kross, E., & Bushman, B. (2012). Flies on the wall are less aggressive: Self-distancing "in the heat of the moment" reduces aggressive thoughts, angry feelings and aggressive behavior. *Journal of Experimental Social Psychology, 48*, 1187–1191. (p. 394)

Miserandino, M. (1991). Memory and the seven dwarfs. *Teaching of Psychology, 18*, 169–171. (p. 267)

Mishkin, M. (1982). A memory system in the monkey. *Philosophical Transactions of the Royal Society of London: Biological Sciences, 298*, 83–95. (p. 277)

Mishkin, M., Suzuki, W. A., Gadian, D. G., & Vargha-Khadem, F. (1997). Hierarchical organization of cognitive memory. *Philosophical Transactions of the Royal Society of London: Biological Sciences, 352*, 1461–1467. (p. 277)

Mishra, A., & Mishra, H. (2010). Border bias: The belief that state borders can protect against disasters. *Psychological Science, 21*, 1582–1586. (p. 320)

Mita, T. H., Dermer, M., & Knight, J. (1977). Reversed facial images and the mere-exposure hypothesis. *Journal of Personality and Social Psychology, 35*, 597–601. (p. 447)

Mitani, J. C., Watts, D. P., & Amsler, S. J. (2010). Lethal intergroup aggression leads to territorial expansion in wild chimpanzees. *Current Biology, 20*, R507–R509. (p. 310)

Mitchell, G. (2012). Revisiting truth or triviality: The external validity of research in the psychological laboratory. *Perspectives on Psychological Science, 7*, 109–117. (p. 30)

Mitchell, J. P. (2009). Social psychology as a natural kind. *Cell, 13*, 246–251. (p. 486)

Mitte, K. (2008). Memory bias for threatening information in anxiety and anxiety disorders: A meta-analytic review. *Psychological Bulletin, 134*, 886–911. (p. 506)

Miu, A. S., & Yeager, D. S. (2015). Preventing symptoms of depression by teaching adolescents that people can change: Effects of a brief incremental theory of personality intervention at 9-month follow-up. *Clinical Psychological Science, 3*, 726–743. (p. 566)

Mobbs, D., Yu, R., Meyer, M., Passamonti, L., Seymour, B., Calder, A. J., . . . Dalgeish, T. (2009). A key role for similarity in vicarious reward. *Science, 324*, 900. (p. 259)

Moffitt, T. E., Arsenault, L., Belsky, D., Dickson, N., Hancox, R. J., Harrington, H., . . . Caspi, A. (2011). A gradient of childhood self-control predicts health, wealth, and public safety. *PNAS, 108*, 2693–2698. (p. 398)

Moffitt, T. E., Caspi, A., Harrington, H., & Milne, B. J. (2002). Males on the life-course-persistent and adolescence-limited antisocial pathways: Follow-up at age 26 years. *Development and Psychopathology, 14*, 179–207. (p. 118)

Moffitt, T. E., Harrington, H., Caspi, A., Kim-Cohen, J., Goldberg, D., Gregory, A. M., & Poulton, R. (2007). Depression and generalized anxiety disorder: Cumulative and sequential comorbidity in a birth cohort followed prospectively to age 32 years. *Archives of General Psychiatry, 64*, 651–660. (p. 507)

Moffitt, T. E., Poulton, R., & Caspi, A. (2013). Lifelong impact of early self-control. *American Scientist, 101*, 352–359. (p. 118)

Moghaddam, F. M. (2005). The staircase to terrorism: A psychological exploration. *American Psychologist, 60*, 161–169. (p. 431)

Molenberghs, P., Ogilivie, C., Louis, W. R., Decety, J., Bagnall, J., & Bain, P. G. (2015). The neural correlates of justified and unjustified killing: An fMRI study. *Social Cognitive and Affective Neuroscience, 10*, 1397–1404. (p. 63)

Möller-Levet, C. S., Archer, S. N., Bucca, G., Laing, E. E., Slak, A., Kabiljo, R., . . . Dijk, D.-J. (2013). Effects of insufficient sleep on circadian rhythmicity and expression amplitude of the human blood transcriptome. *PNAS, 110*, E1132–E1141. (p. 93)

Mommersteeg, P. M. C., Schoemaker, R. G., Naudé, P. J., Eisel, U. L., Garrelds, I. M., Schalkwijk, C. G., . . . Denollet, J. (2016). Depression and markers of inflammation as predictors of all-cause mortality in heart failure. *Brain, Behavior, and Immunity, 57*, 144–150. (p. 392)

Mondloch, C. J., Lewis, T. L., Budreau, D. R., Maurer, D., Dannemiller, J. L., Stephens, B. R., & Kleiner-Gathercoal, K. A. (1999). Face perception during early infancy. *Psychological Science, 10*, 419–422. (p. 121)

Money, J. (1987). Sin, sickness, or status? Homosexual gender identity and psychoneuroendocrinology. *American Psychologist, 42*, 384–399. (pp. 179, 181)

Money, J., Berlin, F. S., Falck, A., & Stein, M. (1983). *Antiandrogenic and counseling treatment of sex offenders.* Baltimore: Johns Hopkins University School of Medicine, Department of Psychiatry and Behavioral Sciences. (p. 174)

Monroe, S. M., & Reid, M. W. (2009). Life stress and major depression. *Current Directions in Psychological Science, 18*, 68–72. (p. 517)

Monroe, S. M., & Simons, A. D. (1991). Diathesis-stress theories in the context of life stress research: Implications for the depressive disorders. *Psychological Bulletin, 110*, 406–425. (p. 496)

Montagne, A., Barnes, S. R., Sweeney, M. D., Halliday, M. R., Sagare, A. P., Zhao, Z., . . . Zlokovic, B. V. (2015). Blood-brain barrier breakdown in the aging human hippocampus. *Neuron, 85*, 296–302. (p. 152)

Montoya, R. M., & Horton, R. S. (2013). A meta-analytic investigation of the processes underlying the similarity-attraction effect. *Journal of Social and Personal Relationships, 30*, 64–94. (p. 450)

Montoya, R. M., & Horton, R. S. (2014). A two-dimensional model for the study of interpersonal attraction. *Personality and Social Psychology Review, 18*, 59–86. (p. 450)

Montoya, R. M., Horton, R. S., Vevea, J. L., Citkowicz, M., & Lauber, E. A. (2017). A re-examination of the mere exposure effect: The influence of repeated exposure on recognition, familiarity, and liking. *Psychological Bulletin, 143*, 459–498. (p. 447)

Mook, D. G. (1983). In defense of external invalidity. *American Psychologist, 38*, 379–387. (p. 30)

Moon, C., Lagercrantz, H., & Kuhl, P. K. (2013). Language experienced in utero affects vowel perception after birth: A two-country study. *Acta Paediatrica, 102*, 156–160. (p. 119)

Moorcroft, W. H. (2003). *Understanding sleep and dreaming.* New York: Kluwer Academic/Plenum Press. (pp. 87, 99)

Moore, D. W. (2004, December 17). Sweet dreams go with a good night's sleep. *Gallup News Service* (gallup.com). (p. 90)

Moore, D. W. (2005, June 16). Three in four Americans believe in paranormal. *Gallup News Service* (gallup.com). (p. 229)

Moore, S. C., Lee, I., Weiderpass, E., Campbell, P. T., Sampson, J. N., Kitahara, C. M., . . . Patel, A. V. (2016). Association of leisure-time physical activity with risk of 26 types of cancer in 1.44 million adults. *JAMA Internal Medicine, 176*, 816–825. (p. 103)

Moore, S. C., Patel, A. V., Matthews, C. E., Berrington de Gonzalez, A., Park, Y., Katki, H. A., . . . Lee, I.-M. (2012). Leisure time physical activity of moderate to vigorous intensity and mortality: A large pooled cohort analysis. *PLoS Medicine, 9*, e1001335. (p. 401)

Moos, R. H., & Moos, B. S. (2005). Sixteen-year changes and stable remission among treated and untreated individuals with alcohol use disorders. *Drug and Alcohol Dependence, 80*, 337–347. (p. 548)

Moos, R. H., & Moos, B. S. (2006). Participation in treatment and Alcoholics Anonymous: A 16-year follow-up of initially untreated individuals. *Journal of Clinical Psychology, 62*, 735–750. (p. 548)

Mor, N., & Winquist, J. (2002). Self-focused attention and negative affect: A meta-analysis. *Psychological Bulletin, 128*, 638–662. (p. 520)

More, H. L., Hutchinson, J. R., Collins, D. F., Weber, D. J., Aung, S. K. H., & Donelan, J. M. (2010). Scaling of sensorimotor control in terrestrial mammals. *Proceedings of the Royal Society: Series B, 277*, 3563–3568. (p. 40)

Moreira, M. T., Smith, L. A., & Foxcroft, D. (2009). Social norms interventions to reduce alcohol misuse in university or college students. *Cochrane Database of Systematic Reviews 2009*, Issue 3, Article CD006748. doi:10.1002/14651858.CD006748.pub2 (p. 112)

Moreland, R. L., & Zajonc, R. B. (1982). Exposure effects in person perception: Familiarity, similarity, and attraction. *Journal of Experimental Social Psychology, 18*, 395–415. (p. 447)

Morelli, G. A., Rogoff, B., Oppenheim, D., & Goldsmith, D. (1992). Cultural variation in infants' sleeping arrangements: Questions of independence. *Developmental Psychology, 26*, 604–613. (p. 139)

Moreno, C., Laje, G., Blanco, C., Jiang, H., Schmidt, A. B., & Olfson, M. (2007). National trends in the outpatient diagnosis and treatment of bipolar disorder in youth. *Archives of General Psychiatry, 64*, 1032–1039. (p. 516)

Morey, R. A., Inan, S., Mitchell, T. V., Perkins, D. O., Lieberman, J. A., & Belger, A. (2005). Imaging frontostriatal function in ultra-high-risk, early, and chronic schizophrenia during executive processing. *Archives of General Psychiatry, 62*, 254–262. (p. 524)

Morgan, A. B., & Lilienfeld, S. O. (2000). A meta-analytic review of the relation between antisocial behavior and neuropsychological measures of executive function. *Clinical Psychology Review, 20*, 113–136. (p. 531)

Morgenthaler, T. I., Hashmi, S., Croft, J. B., Dort, L., Heald, J. L., & Mullington, J. (2016). High school start times and the impact on high school students: What we know, and what we hope to learn. *Journal of Clinical Sleep Medicine, 12*, 1681–1689. (p. 93)

Mori, K., & Mori, H. (2009). Another test of the passive facial feedback hypothesis: When you face smiles, you feel happy. *Perceptual and Motor Skills, 109*, 1–3. (p. 381)

Morin, R. (2014, July 2). Facebook's experiment causes a lot of fuss for little result. Pew Research Center (pewresearch.org). (p. A-8)

Moriuchi, J. M., Klin, A., & Jones, W. (2017). Mechanisms of diminished attention to eyes in autism. *American Journal of Psychiatry, 174*, 26–35. (p. 131)

Morris, G., Baker-Ward, L., & Bauer, P. J. (2010). What remains of that day: The survival of children's autobiographical memories across time. *Applied Cognitive Psychology, 24*, 527–544. (p. 124)

Morris, M. (2015, September 18). Damaging labels do transgender people a disservice. *Edmonton Journal* (edmontonjournal.com). (p. 171)

Morrison, A. R. (2003, July). The brain on night shift. *Cerebrum*, pp. 23–36. (p. 89)

Morrison, M., Tay, L., & Diener, E. (2014). *Subjective well-being across the lifespan worldwide.* Paper presented at the Society for Personality and Social Psychology convention, Austin, Texas. (p. 158)

Mortensen, P. B. (1999). Effects of family history and place and season of birth on the risk of schizophrenia. *New England Journal of Medicine, 340*, 603–608. (p. 525)

Moruzzi, G., & Magoun, H. W. (1949). Brain stem reticular formation and activation of the EEG. *Electroencephalography and Clinical Neurophysiology, 1*, 455–473. (p. 54)

Moscovici, S. (1985). Social influence and conformity. In G. Lindzey & E. Aronson (Eds.), *The handbook of social psychology* (3rd ed.). Hillsdale, N.J.: Erlbaum. (p. 428)

Moses, E. B., & Barlow, D. H. (2006). A new unified treatment approach for emotional disorders based on emotion science. *Current Directions in Psychological Science, 15*, 146–150. (p. 546)

Mosher, C. E., & Danoff-Burg, S. (2008). Agentic and communal personality traits: Relations to disordered eating behavior, body shape concern, and depressive symptoms. *Eating Behaviors, 9*, 497–500. (p. 169)

Mosher, W. D., Chandra, A., & Jones, J. (2005, September 15). *Sexual behavior and selected health measures: Men and women 15–44 years of age, United States, 2002* (Advance Data from Vital and Health Statistics No. 362). Hyattsville, MD: National Center for Health Statistics. (p. 179)

Mosing, M. A., Zietsch, B. P., Shekar, S. N., Wright, M. J., & Martin, N. G. (2009). Genetic and environmental influences on optimism and its relationship to mental and self-rated health: A study of aging twins. *Behavior Genetics, 39*, 597–604. (p. 399)

Mosnier, I., Bebear, J.-P., Marx, M., Fraysse, B., Truy, E., Lina-Granade, G., . . . Sterkers, O. (2015). Improvement of cognitive function after cochlear implantation in elderly patients. *JAMA Otolaryngology—Head & Neck Surgery, 141*, 442–450. (p. 218)

Moss, A. C., & Albery, I. P. (2009). A dual-process model of the alcohol–behavior link for social drinking. *Psychological Bulletin, 135*, 516–530. (p. 104)

Moss, A. J., Allen, K. F., Giovino, G. A., & Mills, S. L. (1992, December 2). Recent trends in adolescent smoking, smoking-update correlates, and expectations about the future. *Advance Data No. 221* (from Vital and Health Statistics of the Centers for Disease Control and Prevention). (p. 112)

Motivala, S. J., & Irwin, M. R. (2007). Sleep and immunity: Cytokine pathways linking sleep and health outcomes. *Current Directions in Psychological Science, 16*, 21–25. (p. 93)

Moulin, S., Waldfogel, J., & Washbrook, E. (2014). Baby bonds: Parenting, attachment, and a secure base for children. *Sutton Trust*, 1–42. (p. 134)

Moxley, J. H., Ericsson, K. A., Charness, N., & Krampe, R. T. (2012). The role of intuition and deliberative thinking in experts' superior tactical decision-making. *Cognition, 124*, 72–78. (p. 306)

Moyer, K. E. (1983). The physiology of motivation: Aggression as a model. In C. J. Scheier & A. M. Rogers (Eds.), *The G. Stanley Hall Lecture Series* (Vol. 3, pp. 123–139). Washington, DC: American Psychological Association. (p. 441)

Mrkva, K. (2017). Giving, fast and slow: Reflection increases costly (but not uncostly) charitable giving. *Journal of Behavioral Decision Making.* Advance online publication. doi:10.1002/bdm.2023. (p. 81)

Mroczek, D. K., & Kolarz, D. M. (1998). The effect of age on positive and negative affect: A developmental perspective on happiness. *Journal of Personality and Social Psychology, 75*, 1333–1349. (p. 155)

Mueller, P. A., & Oppenheimer, D. M. (2014). The pen is mightier than the keyboard: Advantages of longhand over laptop note-taking. *Psychological Science, 25*, 1159–1168. (pp. 34, 295)

Muhlnickel, W. (1998). Reorganization of auditory cortex in tinnitus. *PNAS, 95*, 10340–10343. (p. 61)

Mulcahy, N. J., & Call, J. (2006). Apes save tools for future use. *Science, 312,* 1038–1040. (p. 309)

Muldoon, S., Taylor, S. C., & Norma, C. (2016). The survivor master narrative in sexual assault. *Violence Against Women, 22,* 565–587. (p. 170)

Muller, J. E., Mittleman, M. A., Maclure, M., Sherwood, J. B., & Tofler, G. H. (1996). Triggering myocardial infarction by sexual activity. *Journal of the American Medical Association, 275,* 1405–1409. (p. 174)

Muller, J. E., & Verrier, R. L. (1996). Triggering of sudden death—Lessons from an earthquake. *New England Journal of Medicine, 334,* 461. (pp. 173, 385)

Mullin, C. R., & Linz, D. (1995). Desensitization and resensitization to violence against women: Effects of exposure to sexually violent films on judgments of domestic violence victims. *Journal of Personality and Social Psychology, 69,* 449–459. (p. 263)

Mulrow, C. D. (1999, March). Treatment of depression—newer pharmacotherapies, summary. *Evidence Report/Technology Assessment, 7.* Agency for Health Care Policy and Research, Rockville, MD. Retrieved from ahrq.gov/clinic/deprsumm.htm (p. 561)

Murayama, K., Pekrun, R., Lichtenfeld, S., & vom Hofe, R. (2013). Predicting long-term growth in students' mathematics achievement: The unique contributions of motivation and cognitive strategies. *Child Development, 84,* 1475–1490. (p. 339)

Murdik, L., Breska, A., Lamy, D., & Deouell, L. Y. (2011). Integration without awareness: Expanding the limits of unconscious processing. *Psychological Science, 22,* 764–770. (p. 81)

Murphy, K. R., & Cleveland, J. N. (1995). *Understanding performance appraisal: Social, organizational, and goal-based perspectives.* Thousand Oaks, CA: Sage. (p. B-7)

Murphy, S. T., Monahan, J. L., & Zajonc, R. B. (1995). Additivity of nonconscious affect: Combined effects of priming and exposure. *Journal of Personality and Social Psychology, 69,* 589–602. (p. 370)

Murray, H. (1938). *Explorations in personality.* New York: Oxford University Press. (p. 357)

Murray, H. A. (1933). The effect of fear upon estimates of the maliciousness of other personalities. *Journal of Social Psychology, 4,* 310–329. (p. 467)

Murray, H. A., & Wheeler, D. R. (1937). A note on the possible clairvoyance of dreams. *Journal of Psychology, 3,* 309–313. (pp. 21, 230)

Murray, R., Jones, P., O'Callaghan, E., Takei, N., & Sham, P. (1992). Genes, viruses, and neurodevelopmental schizophrenia. *Journal of Psychiatric Research, 26,* 225–235. (p. 525)

Murray, S. L., Bellavia, G. M., Rose, P., & Griffin, D. W. (2003). Once hurt, twice hurtful: How perceived regard regulates daily marital interactions. *Journal of Personality and Social Psychology, 84,* 126–147. (p. 198)

Murty, V. P., Calabro, F., & Luna, B. (2016). The role of experience in adolescent cognitive development: Integration of executive, memory, and mesolimbic systems. *Neuroscience & Biobehavioral Reviews.* Advance online publication. doi:10.1016/j.neubiorev.2016.07.034 (p. 124)

Musick, M. A., Herzog, A. R., & House, J. S. (1999). Volunteering and mortality among older adults: Findings from a national sample. *Journals of Gerontology, 54B,* 173–180. (p. 406)

Muusses, L. D., Kerkhof, P., & Finkenauer, C. (2015). Internet pornography and relationship quality: A longitudinal study of within and between partner effects of adjustment, sexual satisfaction and sexually explicit internet material among newly-weds. *Computers in Human Behavior, 45,* 77–84. (p. 25)

Mydans, S. (2002, May 17). In Pakistan, rape victims are the 'criminals.' *The New York Times.* Retrieved from nytimes.com/2002/05/17/world/in-pakistan-rape-victims-are-the-criminals.html (p. 440)

Myers, D. G. (1992). *The pursuit of happiness.* New York: William Morrow. (p. xx)

Myers, D. G. (1993). *The pursuit of happiness.* New York: Harper. (pp. xx, 411)

Myers, D. G. (2000). *The American paradox: Spiritual hunger in an age of plenty.* New Haven, CT: Yale University Press. (p. 411)

Myers, D. G. (2010). *Social psychology* (10th ed.). New York: McGraw-Hill. (p. 487)

Myers, D. G., & Bishop, G. D. (1970). Discussion effects on racial attitudes. *Science, 169,* 78–779. (p. 431)

Myers, D. G., & Diener, E. (1995). Who is happy? *Psychological Science, 6,* 10–19. (p. 411)

Myers, D. G., & Diener, E. (1996, May). The pursuit of happiness. *Scientific American* (scientificamerican.com/article/the-pursuit-of-happiness/). (p. 411)

Myers, D. G., & Scanzoni, L. D. (2005). *What God has joined together?* San Francisco: Harper. (pp. 157, 179)

Myers, T. A., & Crowther, J. H. (2009). Social comparison as a predictor of body dissatisfaction: A meta-analytic review. *Journal of Abnormal Psychology, 118,* 683–698. (p. 532)

Myre, G. (2000, April 27). McCain still can't forgive guards at "Hanoi Hilton." *The Washington Post.* Retrieved from washingtonpost.com/wp-dyn/content/article/2008/08/13/AR2008081302644.html (p. 567)

Nagourney, A. (2002, September 25). For remarks on Iraq, Gore gets praise and scorn. *The New York Times* (nytimes.com). (p. 418)

Nagourney, A., Sanger, D. E., & Barr, J. (2018, January 13). Hawaii panics after alert about incoming missile is sent in error. *The New York Times* (nytimes.com). (p. 47)

Napolitan, D. A., & Goethals, G. R. (1979). The attribution of friendliness. *Journal of Experimental Social Psychology, 15,* 105–113. (p. 416)

NAS. (2011). *Statistics: How many people have autism spectrum disorders.* National Autistic Society (autism.org.uk). (p. 131)

Nasie, M., Diamond, A. H., & Bar-Tal, D. (2016). Young children in intractable conflicts: The Israeli case. *Personality and Social Psychology Review, 20,* 365–392. (p. 458)

Nathan, D. (2011). *Sybil exposed: The extraordinary story behind the famous multiple personality case.* Simon and Schuster. (p. 528)

Nathanson, L., Rivers, S. E., Flynn, L. M., & Brackett, M. A. (2016). Creating emotionally intelligent schools with RULER. *Emotion Review, 8,* 1–6. (p. 326)

National Academies of Sciences, Engineering, and Medicine. (2017). *The health effects of cannabis and cannabinoids: The current state of evidence and recommendations for research.* Washington, DC: National Academies Press. (p. 109)

National Academy of Sciences. (2001). *Exploring the biological contributions to human health: Does sex matter?* Washington, DC: National Academy Press. (p. 168)

National Academy of Sciences. (2002). *The polygraph and lie detection.* Washington, DC: National Academies Press. (p. 374)

National Center for Health Statistics. (1990). *Health, United States, 1989.* Washington, DC: U.S. Department of Health and Human Services. (p. 152)

National Research Council. (1990). *Human factors research needs for an aging population.* Washington, DC: National Academy Press. (p. 153)

National Safety Council. (2017). *Injury Facts®, 2017 Edition,* pp. 156–157. Itasca, IL: National Safety Council. (p. 302)

Naumann, L. P., Vazire, S., Rentfrow, P. J., & Gosling, S. D. (2009). Personality judgments based on physical appearance. *Personality and Social Psychology Bulletin, 35,* 1661–1671. (p. 481)

Nausheen, B., Carr, N. J., Peveler, R. C., Moss-Morris, R., Verrill, C., Robbins, E., . . . Gidron, Y. (2010). Relationship between loneliness and proangiogenic cytokines in newly diagnosed tumors of colon and rectum. *Psychosomatic Medicine, 72,* 912–916. (p. 390)

NCASA. (2007). *Wasting the best and the brightest: Substance abuse at America's colleges and universities.* New York: National Center on Addiction and Drug Abuse, Columbia University. (p. 112)

NCD Risk Factor Collaboration. (2016). Trends in adult body-mass index in 200 countries from 1975 to 2014: A pooled analysis of 1698 population-based measurement studies with 19.2 million participants. *The Lancet, 387,* 1377–1396. (p. 365)

Neal, D. T., Wood, W., & Drolet, A. (2013). How do people adhere to goals when willpower is low? The profits (and pitfalls) of strong habits. *Journal of Personality and Social Psychology, 104,* 959–975. (p. 234)

Nedeltcheva, A. V., Kilkus, J. M., Imperial, J., Schoeller, D. A., & Penev, P. D. (2010). Insufficient sleep undermines dietary efforts to reduce adiposity. *Annals of Internal Medicine, 153,* 435–441. (p. 365)

NEEF. (2015). Fact sheet: Children's health and nature. National Environmental Education Foundation. Retrieved from neefusa.org/resource/children%E2%80%99s-health-and-nature-fact-sheet (p. 559)

Neese, R. M. (1991, November/December). What good is feeling bad? The evolutionary benefits of psychic pain. *The Sciences,* pp. 30–37. (pp. 221, 255)

Neimeyer, R. A., & Currier, J. M. (2009). Grief therapy: Evidence of efficacy and emerging directions. *Current Directions in Psychological Science, 18,* 352–356. (p. 160)

Neisser, U. (1979). The control of information pickup in selective looking. In A. D. Pick (Ed.), *Perception and its development: A tribute to Eleanor J. Gibson* (pp. 209–219). Hillsdale, NJ: Erlbaum. (pp. 82, 83)

Neisser, U., Boodoo, G., Bouchard, T. J., Jr., Boykin, A. W., Brody, N., Ceci, S. J., . . . Urbina, S. (1996). Intelligence: Knowns and unknowns. *American Psychologist, 51,* 77–101. (p. 343)

Neisser, U., Winograd, E., & Weldon, M. S. (1991). Remembering the earthquake: "What I experienced" vs. "How I heard the news." Paper presented to the Psychonomic Society convention. (p. 278)

Neitz, J., Carroll, J., & Neitz, M. (2001). Color vision: Almost reason enough for having eyes. *Optics & Photonics News, 12,* 26–33. (p. 204)

Neitz, J., Geist, T., & Jacobs, G. H. (1989). Color vision in the dog. *Visual Neuroscience, 3,* 119–125. (p. 204)

Nelson, C. A., III, Fox, N. A., & Zeanah, C. H., Jr. (2013). Anguish of the abandoned child. *Scientific American, 308,* 62–67. (p. 157)

Nelson, C. A., III, Fox, N. A., & Zeanah, C. H., Jr. (2014). *Romania's abandoned children.* Cambridge, MA: Harvard University Press. (pp. 137, 338)

Nelson, C. A., III, Furtado, E. Z., Fox, N. A., & Zeanah, C. H., Jr. (2009). The deprived human brain. *American Scientist, 97,* 222–229. (p. 338)

Nelson, J., Klumparendt, A., Doebler, P., & Ehring, T. (2017). Childhood maltreatment and characteristics of adult depression: A meta-analysis. *The British Journal of Psychiatry, 210,* 96–104. (p. 517)

Nelson, M. D., Saykin, A. J., Flashman, L. A., & Riordan, H. J. (1998). Hippocampal volume reduction in schizophrenia as assessed by magnetic resonance imaging. *Archives of General Psychiatry, 55,* 433–440. (p. 525)

Nelson, S. K., Kushlev, K., English, T., Dunn, E. W., & Lyubomirsky, S. (2013). In defense of parenthood: Children are associated with more joy than misery. *Psychological Science, 24,* 3–10. (pp. 157, 338)

Nemeth, C. J., & Ormiston, M. (2007). Creative idea generation: Harmony versus stimulation. *European Journal of Social Psychology, 37,* 524–535. (p. 433)

Nemmi, F., Nymberg, C., Helander, E., & Klingberg, T. (2016). Grit is associated with structure of nucleus accumbens and gains in cognitive training. *Journal of Cognitive Neuroscience, 28,* 1688–1699. (p. 358)

Nes, R. B., Czajkowski, N., & Tambs, K. (2010). Family matters: Happiness in nuclear families and twins. *Behavior Genetics, 40,* 577–590. (p. 411)

Ness, E. (2016, January/February). FDA OKs sex drug for women. *Discover,* p. 45. (p. 28)

Nestadt, G., & Samuels, J. (1997). Epidemiology and genetics of obsessive-compulsive disorder. *International Review of Psychiatry, 9,* 61–71. (p. 509)

Nestler, E. J. (2011). Hidden switches in the mind. *Scientific American, 305,* 76–83. (p. 519)

Nestoriuc, Y., Rief, W., & Martin, A. (2008). Meta-analysis of biofeedback for tension-type headache: Efficacy, specificity, and treatment moderators. *Journal of Consulting and Clinical Psychology, 76,* 379–396. (p. 403)

Nettle, D., Andrews, C., & Bateson, M. (2017). Food insecurity as a driver of obesity in humans: The insurance hypothesis. *Behavioral and Brain Sciences, 40,* e105. (p. 365)

Neubauer, D. N. (1999). Sleep problems in the elderly. *American Family Physician, 59,* 2551–2558. (p. 89)

Neumann, R., & Strack, F. (2000). "Mood contagion": The automatic transfer of mood between persons. *Journal of Personality and Social Psychology, 79,* 211–223. (pp. 382, 422)

Newcomb, M. D., & Harlow, L. L. (1986). Life events and substance use among adolescents: Mediating effects of perceived loss of control and meaninglessness in life. *Journal of Personality and Social Psychology, 51,* 564–577. (p. 111)

Newell, B. R. (2015). "Wait! Just let me not think about that for a minute": What role do implicit processes play in higher-level cognition? *Current Directions in Psychological Science, 24,* 65–70. (p. 306)

Newport, C., Wallis, G., Reshitnyk, Y., & Siebeck, U. E. (2016). Discrimination of human faces by archerfish (*Toxotes chatareus*). *Scientific Reports, 6,* 27523. (p. 266)

Newport, E. L. (1990). Maturational constraints on language learning. *Cognitive Science, 14,* 11–28. (p. 316)

Newport, F. (1999, accessed April 28, 2016). Americans today much more accepting of a woman, black, Catholic, or Jew as president. Gallup Poll (gallup.com). (p. 437)

Newport, F. (2001, February). Americans see women as emotional and affectionate, men as more aggressive. *The Gallup Poll Monthly,* pp. 34–38. (p. 377)

Newport, F. (2012, December 19). *To stop shootings, Americans focus on police, mental health.* Gallup (gallup.com). (p. 502)

Newport, F. (2013a, July 25). In U.S. 87% approve of Black-White marriage, vs. 4% in 1958. *Gallup Poll* (gallup.com). (p. 436)

Newport, F. (2013b, July 31). *Former smokers say best way to quit is just to stop "cold turkey."* Gallup Poll (gallup.com). (pp. 102, 106)

Newport, F. (2014, June 2). *In U.S., 42% believe creationist view of human origins.* Gallup. Gallup Poll (gallup.com). (p. 77)

Newport, F. (2015, July 9). *Most U.S. smartphone owners check phone at least hourly.* Gallup Poll (gallup.com). (p. 355)

Newport, F., Argrawal, S., & Witters, D. (2010, December 23). *Very religious Americans lead healthier lives.* Gallup poll (gallup.com). (p. 406)

Newport, F., & Pelham, B. (2009, December 14). *Don't worry, be 80: Worry and stress decline with age.* Gallup Poll (gallup.com). (p. 385)

Newport, F., & Wilke, J. (2013, August 2). *Most in U.S. want marriage, but its importance has dropped.* Gallup Poll (gallup.com). (p. 156)

Newton, E. L. (1991). The rocky road from actions to intentions. *Dissertation Abstracts International, 51,* 4105. (p. B-13)

Newton, I. (1704). *Opticks: Or, a treatise of the reflexions, refractions, inflexions and colours of light.* London: Royal Society. (p. 203)

Ng, J. Y. Y., Ntoumanis, N., Thøgersen-Ntoumani, C., Deci, E. L., Ryan, R. M., Duda, J. L., & Williams, G. C. (2012). Self-determination theory applied to health contexts: A meta-analysis. *Perspectives on Psychological Science, 7,* 325–340. (p. 396)

Ng, S. H. (1990). Androcentric coding of man and his in memory by language users. *Journal of Experimental Social Psychology, 26,* 455–464. (p. 320)

Ng, T. W. H., & Feldman, D. C. (2009). How broadly does education contribute to job performance. *Personnel Psychology, 62,* 89–134. (p. B-6)

Ng, T. W. H., Sorensen, K. L., & Yim, F. H. K. (2009). Does the job satisfaction–job performance relationship vary across cultures? *Journal of Cross-Cultural Psychology, 40,* 761–796. (p. B-8)

Ng, W. W. H., Sorensen, K. L., & Eby, L. T. (2006). Locus of control at work: A meta-analysis. *Journal of Organizational Behavior, 27,* 1057–1087. (p. 397)

Nguyen, H.-H. D., & Ryan, A. M. (2008). Does stereotype threat affect test performance of minorities and women? A meta-analysis of experimental evidence. *Journal of Applied Psychology, 93,* 1314–1334. (p. 344)

NHTSA. (2000). *Traffic safety facts 1999: Older population.* Washington, DC: National Highway Traffic Safety Administration (ntl.bts.gov). (p. 152)

Nicholson, I. (2011). "Torture at Yale": Experimental subjects, laboratory torment and the "rehabilitation" of Milgram's "Obedience to Authority." *Theory and Psychology, 21,* 737–761. (p. 427)

Nickell, J. (Ed.). (1994). *Psychic sleuths: ESP and sensational cases.* Buffalo, NY: Prometheus Books. (p. 230)

Nickell, J. (2005, July/August). The case of the psychic detectives. *Skeptical Inquirer.* Retrieved from skeptically.org/skepticism/id10.html (p. 230)

Nickerson, R. S. (1999). How we know—and sometimes misjudge—what others know: Imputing one's own knowledge to others. *Psychological Bulletin, 125,* 737–759. (p. B-13)

Nickerson, R. S. (2002). The production and perception of randomness. *Psychological Review, 109,* 330–357. (p. 17)

Nickerson, R. S. (2005). Bertrand's chord, Buffon's needles, and the concept of randomness. *Thinking & Reasoning, 11,* 67–96. (p. 17)

Nicolas, S., & Levine, Z. (2012). Beyond intelligence testing: Remembering Alfred Binet after a century. *European Psychologist, 17,* 320–325. (p. 328)

Nicolaus, L. K., Cassel, J. F., Carlson, R. B., & Gustavson, C. R. (1983). Taste-aversion conditioning of crows to control predation on eggs. *Science, 220,* 212–214. (p. 255)

NIDA. (2002). *NIDA Research Report Series: Methamphetamine abuse and addiction* (NIH Publication No. 02-4210). Bethesda, MD: National Institute on Drug Abuse. (p. 107)

NIDA. (2005, May). *DrugFacts: Methamphetamine.* Bethesda, MD: National Institute on Drug Abuse. (p. 107)

Nielsen, K. M., Faergeman, O., Larsen, M. L., & Foldspang, A. (2006). Danish singles have a twofold risk of acute coronary syndrome: Data from a cohort of 138,290 persons. *Journal of Epidemiology and Community Health, 60,* 721–728. (p. 400)

Nielsen, M., & Tomaselli, K. (2010). Overimitation in Kalahari Bushman children and the origins of human cultural cognition. *Psychological Science, 21,* 729–736. (p. 260)

Nietzsche, F. (1889/1990). *Twilight of the idols and the Anti-Christ: Or how to philosophize with a hammer* (R. J. Hollindale, translator). New York: Penguin Classics. (p. 509)

Nieuwenstein, M. R., Wierenga, T., Morey, R. D., Wicherts, J. M., Blom, T. N., Wagenmakers, E., & van Rijn, H. (2015). On making the right choice: A meta-analysis and large-scale replication attempt of the unconscious thought advantage. *Judgment and Decision Making, 10,* 1–17. (p. 306)

NIH. (2001, July 20). *Workshop summary: Scientific evidence on condom effectiveness for sexually transmitted disease (STD) prevention.* Bethesda, MD: National Institute of Allergy and Infectious Diseases, National Institutes of Health. (p. 175)

NIH. (2010). *Teacher's guide: Information about sleep.* National Institutes of Health (nih.gov). (p. 92)

NIH. (2013, January 24). *Prenatal inflammation linked to autism risk.* National Institutes of Health (nih.gov). (p. 131)

NIH. (2015, December). *College drinking.* Bethesda, MD: National Institute of Alcohol Abuse and Alcoholism, National Institutes of Health. (p. 103)

NIH. (2016). *NIH Senior Health.* National Institutes of Health. Retrieved from nihseniorhealth.gov/parkinsonsdisease/whatcausesparkinsonsdisease/01.html (p. 44)

Nikles, M., Stiefel, F., & Bourquin, C. (2017). What medical students dream of: A standardized and data-driven approach. *Dreaming.* Advance online publication. doi:10.1037/drm0000057 (p. 96)

Nikolas, M. A., & Burt, A. (2010). Genetic and environmental influences on ADHD symptom dimensions of inattention and hyperactivity: A meta-analysis. *Journal of Abnormal Psychology, 119,* 1–17. (p. 498)

Nikolova, H., & Lamberton, C. (2016). Men and the middle: Gender differences in dyadic compromise effects. *Journal of Consumer Research.* Advance online publication. doi:10.1093/jcr/ucw035 (p. 154)

Niles, A. N., Craske, M. G., Lieberman, M. D., & Hur, C. (2015). Affect labeling enhances exposure effectiveness for public speaking anxiety. *Behavior Research and Therapy, 68,* 27–36. (p. 400)

NIMH. (2015). *Any mental illness (AMI) among U.S. adults.* National Institute of Mental Health (nimh.nih.gov/health/statistics/prevalence/any-mental-illness-ami-among-us-adults.shtml). (p. 504)

NIMH. (2017, accessed February 27). *Research Domain Criteria (RDoC)*. National Institute of Mental Health (nimh.nih.gov/research-priorities/rdoc). (p. 497)

Ninio, J., & Stevens, K. A. (2000) Variations on the Hermann grid: An extinction illusion. *Perception, 29,* 1209–1217. (p. 202)

Nir, Y., & Tononi, G. (2010). Dreaming and the brain: From phenomenology to neurophysiology. *Trends in Cognitive Sciences, 14,* 88–100. (p. 99)

Nisbett, R. (2015). *Mindware: Tools for smart thinking.* New York: Farrar, Straus and Giroux. (p. A-7)

Nisbett, R. E. (1987). Lay personality theory: Its nature, origin, and utility. In N. E. Grunberg, R. E. Nisbett et al. (Eds.), *A distinctive approach to psychological research: The influence of Stanley Schachter.* Hillsdale, NJ: Erlbaum. (p. B-5)

Nisbett, R. E. (2003). The geography of thought: How Asians and Westerners think differently . . . and why. New York: Free Press. (p. 416)

Nisbett, R. E. (2009). *Intelligence and how to get it: Why schools and culture count.* New York: Norton. (p. 342)

Nisbett, R. E., Aronson, J., Blair, C., Dickens, W., Flynn, J., Halpern, D. F., & Turkheimer, E. (2012). Intelligence: New findings and theoretical developments. *American Psychologist, 67,* 130–159. (pp. 337, 341, 342)

Nisbett, R. E., & Cohen, D. (1996). *Culture of honor: The psychology of violence in the South.* Boulder, CO: Westview Press. (p. 443)

Nisbett, R. E., & Ross, L. (1980). *Human inference: Strategies and shortcomings of social judgment.* Englewood Cliffs, NJ: Prentice-Hall. (p. 301)

Nizzi, M. C., Demertzi, A., Gosseries, O., Bruno, M. A., Jouen, F., & Laureys, S. (2012). From armchair to wheelchair: How patients with a locked-in syndrome integrate bodily changes in experienced identity. *Consciousness and Cognition, 21,* 431–437. (p. 409)

Nock, M. (2016, May 6). Five myths about suicide. *The Washington Post* (washingtonpost. com). (p. 500)

Nock, M. K. (2010). Self-injury. *Annual Review of Clinical Psychology, 6,* 339–363. (p. 502)

Nock, M. K., Borges, G., Bromet, E. J., Alonso, J., Angermeyer, M., Beautrais, A., . . . Williams, D. (2008). Cross-national prevalence and risk factors for suicidal ideation, plans, and attempts. *British Journal of Psychiatry, 192,* 98–105. (p. 501)

Nock, M. K., & Kessler, R. C. (2006). Prevalence of and risk factors for suicide attempts versus suicide gestures: Analysis of the National Comorbidity Survey. *Journal of Abnormal Psychology, 115,* 616–623. (p. 502)

Noel, J. G., Forsyth, D. R., & Kelley, K. N. (1987). Improving the performance of failing students by overcoming their self-serving attributional biases. *Basic and Applied Social Psychology, 8,* 151–162. (p. 398)

Noice, H., & Noice, T. (2006). What studies of actors and acting can tell us about memory and cognitive functioning. *Current Directions in Psychological Science, 15,* 14–18. (p. 274)

Nolen-Hoeksema, S. (2001). Gender differences in depression. *Current Directions in Psychological Science, 10,* 173–176. (p. 520)

Nolen-Hoeksema, S. (2003). *Women who think too much: How to break free of overthinking and reclaim your life.* New York: Holt. (p. 520)

Nolen-Hoeksema, S., & Larson, J. (1999). *Coping with loss.* Mahwah, NJ: Erlbaum. (p. 159)

Nook, E. C., Ong, D. C., Morelli, S. A., Mitchell, J. P., & Zaki, J. (2016). Prosocial conformity: Prosocial norms generalize across behavior and empathy. *Personality and Social Psychology Bulletin, 42,* 1045–1062. (p. 425)

Nørby, S. (2015). Why forget? On the adaptive value of memory loss. *Perspectives on Psychological Science, 10,* 551–578. (p. 283)

NORC. (2016a). National Opinion Research Center (University of Chicago) General Social Survey data, 1972 through 2014, accessed via sda.berkeley.edu. (p. 353)

NORC. (2016b). *New insights into Americans' perceptions and misperceptions of obesity treatments, and the struggles many face.* Chicago: National Opinion Research Center and the American Society for Metabolic and Bariatric Surgery (norc.org). (p. 365)

Nordgren, L. F., McDonnell, M.-H. M., & Loewenstein, G. (2011). What constitutes torture? Psychological impediments to an objective evaluation of enhanced interrogation tactics. *Psychological Science, 22,* 689–694. (p. 198)

Nordgren, L. F., van der Pligt, J., & van Harreveld, F. (2006). Visceral drives in retrospect: Explanations about the inaccessible past. *Psychological Science, 17,* 635–640. (p. 361)

Nordgren, L. F., van der Pligt, J., & van Harreveld, F. (2007). Evaluating Eve: Visceral states influence the evaluation of impulsive behavior. *Journal of Personality and Social Psychology, 93,* 75–84. (p. 361)

Norko, M. A., Freeman, D., Phillips, J., Hunter, W., Lewis, R., & Viswanathan, R. (2017). Can religion protect against suicide? *Journal of Nervous and Mental Disease, 205,* 9–14. (p. 500)

Norman, D. A. (2001). *The perils of home theater.* Retrieved from jnd.org/dn.mss/ ProblemsOfHomeTheater.html (p. B-12)

Norman, E. (2010). "The unconscious" in current psychology. *European Psychologist, 15,* 193–201. (p. 469)

Norris, A. L., Marcus, D. K., & Green, B. A. (2015). Homosexuality as a discrete class. *Psychological Science, 26,* 1843–1853. (p. 179)

North, A. (2016, November 8). A wave of harassment after Trump's victory. *The New York Times* (nytimes.com). (p. 439)

Norton, K. L., Olds, T. S., Olive, S., & Dank, S. (1996). Ken and Barbie at life size. *Sex Roles, 34,* 287–294. (p. 533)

Nosek, B. A., Alter, G., Banks, G. C., Borsboom, D., Bowman, S. D., Breckler, S. J., . . . Yarkoni, T. (2015). Promoting an open research culture: Author guidelines for journals could help to promote transparency, openness, and reproducibility. *Science, 348,* 1422–1425. (p. 20)

Nowakowski, M. E., McCabe, R., Rowa, K., Pellizzari, J., Surette, M., Moayyedi, P., & Anglin, R. (2016). The gut microbiome: Potential innovations for the understanding and treatment of psychopathology. *Canadian Psychology/Psychologie Canadienne, 57,* 67–75. (p. 514)

NSC. (2010). Transportation mode comparisons. In *Injury facts 2010 edition.* National Safety Council (nsc.org). (p. 82)

NSF. (2001, October 24). *Public bounces back after Sept. 11 attacks, national study shows.* National Science Foundation. Retrieved from nsf.gov/od/lpa/news/press/ol/pr0185.htm (p. 385)

NSF. (2006, August 16). *The ABCs of back-to-school sleep schedules: The consequences of insufficient sleep* [Press release]. National Sleep Foundation (sleepfoundation.org). (p. 93)

NSF. (2013). *2013 International Bedroom Poll: Summary of findings.* National Sleep Foundation (sleepfoundation.org). (p. 90)

NSF. (2016, accessed November 29). *Sleepwalking.* National Sleep Foundation (sleepfoundation.org). (p. 95)

Nugent, N. R., Goldberg, A., & Uddin, M. (2016). Topical review: The emerging field of epigenetics: Informing models of pediatric trauma and physical health. *Journal of Pediatric Psychology, 41,* 55–64. (p. 74)

Nurmikko, A. V., Donoghue, J. P., Hochberg, L. R., Patterson, W. R., Song, Y.-K., Bull, C. W., . . . Aceros, J. (2010). Listening to brain microcircuits for interfacing with external world—Progress in wireless implantable microelectronic neuroengineering devices. *Proceedings of the IEEE, 98,* 375–388. (p. 61)

Nussinovitch, U., & Shoenfeld, Y. (2012). The role of gender and organ specific autoimmunity. *Autoimmunity Reviews, 11,* A377–A385. (p. 389)

Nuttin, J. M., Jr. (1987). Affective consequences of mere ownership: The name letter effect in twelve European languages. *European Journal of Social Psychology, 17,* 381–402. (p. 447)

Nye, C. D., Su, R., Rounds, J., & Drasgow, F. (2012). Vocational interests and performance: A quantitative summary of over 60 years of research. *Perspectives on Psychological Science, 7,* 384–403. (p. B-3)

O'Brien, E., & Ellsworth, P. C. (2012). Saving the last for best: A positivity bias for end experiences. *Psychological Science, 23,* 163–165. (p. 223)

O'Brien, F., Bible, J., Liu, D., & Simons-Morton, B. (2017). Do young drivers become safer after being involved in a collision? *Psychological Science, 28(4),* 407–413. (p. 239)

O'Brien, L., Albert, D., Chein, J., & Steinberg, L. (2011). Adolescents prefer more immediate rewards when in the presence of their peers. *Journal of Research on Adolescence, 21,* 747–753. (p. 148)

O'Connor, P., & Brown, G. W. (1984). Supportive relationships: Fact or fancy? *Journal of Social and Personal Relationships, 1,* 159–175. (p. 556)

O'Donnell, L., Stueve, A., O'Donnell, C., Duran, R., San Doval, A., Wilson, R. F., . . . Pleck, J. H. (2002). Long-term reduction in sexual initiation and sexual activity among urban middle schoolers in the reach for health service learning program. *Journal of Adolescent Health, 31,* 93–100. (p. 178)

O'Donovan, A., Neylan, T. C., Metzler, T., & Cohen, B. E. (2012). Lifetime exposure to traumatic psychological stress is associated with elevated inflammation in the heart and soul study. *Brain, Behavior, and Immunity, 26,* 642–649. (p. 391)

O'Hara, R. E., Gibbons, F. X., Gerrard, M., Li, Z., & Sargent, J. D. (2012). Greater exposure to sexual content in popular movies predicts earlier sexual debut and increased sexual risk taking. *Psychological Science, 23,* 984–993. (p. 177)

O'Leary, T., Williams, A. H., Franci, A., & Marder, E. (2014). Cell types, network homeostasis, and pathological compensation from a biologically plausible ion channel expression model. *Neuron, 82,* 809–821. (p. 39)

O'Neill, M. J. (1993). *The relationship between privacy, control, and stress responses in office workers.* Paper presented at the Human Factors and Ergonomics Society convention. (p. 396)

O'Sullivan, M., Frank, M. G., Hurley, C. M., & Tiwana, J. (2009). Police lie detection accuracy: The effect of lie scenario. *Law and Human Behavior, 33,* 530–538. (p. 376)

Oakley, D. A., & Halligan, P. W. (2013). Hypnotic suggestion: Opportunities for cognitive neuroscience. *Nature Reviews Neuroscience, 14,* 565–576. (p. 224)

Obama, B. (2017, January 10). President Obama's farewell address. *The New York Times* (nytimes.com). (p. 18)

Oberman, L. M., & Ramachandran, V. S. (2007). The simulating social mind: The role of the mirror neuron system and simulation in the social and communicative deficits of autism spectrum disorders. *Psychological Bulletin, 133,* 310–327. (p. 132)

Ochsner, K. N., Ray, R. R., Hughes, B., McRae, K., Cooper, J. C., Weber, J., . . . Gross, J. J. (2009). Bottom-up and top-down processes in emotion generation: Common and distinct neural mechanisms. *Psychological Science, 20,* 1322–1331. (p. 370)

Odgers, C. L., Caspi, A., Nagin, D. S., Piquero, A. R., Slutske, W. S., Milne, B. J., . . . Moffitt, T. E. (2008). Is it important to prevent early exposure to drugs and alcohol among adolescents? *Psychological Science, 19,* 1037–1044. (p. 112)

Oelschläger, M., Pfannmöller, J., Langer, I., & Lotze, M. (2014). Using of the middle finger shapes reorganization of the primary somatosensory cortex in patients with index finger. *Restorative Neurology and Neuroscience, 32,* 507–515. (p. 64)

Oettingen, G., & Mayer, D. (2002). The motivating function of thinking about the future: Expectations versus fantasies. *Journal of Personality and Social Psychology, 83,* 1198–1212. (p. 399)

Offer, D., Ostrov, E., Howard, K. I., & Atkinson, R. (1988). *The teenage world: Adolescents' self-image in ten countries.* New York: Plenum Press. (p. 148)

Ogden, J. (2012, January 16). HM, the man with no memory. *Psychology Today* (psychologytoday.com). (p. 284)

Ogihara, Y., Fujita, H., Tominaga, H., Ishigaki, S., Kashimoto, T., Takahashi, A., . . . Uchida, Y. (2015). Are common names becoming less common? The rise in uniqueness and individualism in Japan. *Frontiers in Psychology, 6,* article 1490. (p. 491)

Ogunnaike, O., Dunham, Y., & Banaji, M. R. (2010). The language of implicit preferences. *Journal of Experimental Social Psychology, 46,* 999–1003. (p. 319)

Ohgami, H., Terao, T., Shiotsuki, I., Ishii, N., & Iwata, N. (2009). Lithium levels in drinking water and risk of suicide. *British Journal of Psychiatry, 194,* 464–465. (p. 562)

Ohi, K., Shimada, T., Nitta, Y., Kihara, H., Okubo, H., Uehara, T., & Kawasaki, Y. (2016). The five-factor model personality traits in schizophrenia: A meta-analysis. *Psychiatry Research, 240,* 34–41. (p. 478)

Öhman, A. (2009). Of snakes and faces: An evolutionary perspective on the psychology of fear. *Scandinavian Journal of Psychology, 50,* 543–552. (p. 512)

Oishi, S., & Diener, E. (2014). Can and should happiness be a policy goal? *Policy Insights from Behavioral and Brain Sciences, 1,* 195–203. (p. 350)

Oishi, S., Diener, E. F., Lucas, R. E., & Suh, E. M. (1999). Cross-cultural variations in predictors of life satisfaction: Perspectives from needs and values. *Personality and Social Psychology Bulletin, 25,* 980–990. (p. 351)

Oishi, S., & Kesebir, S. (2015). Income inequality explains why economic growth does not always translate to an increase in happiness. *Psychological Science, 26,* 1630–1638. (p. 410)

Oishi, S., Kesebir, S., & Diener, E. (2011). Income inequality and happiness. *Psychological Science, 22,* 1095–1100. (p. 443)

Oishi, S., Kesebir, S., Miao, F., Talhelm, T., Endo, U., Uchida, Y., . . . Norasakkunkit, V. (2013). Residential mobility increases motivation to expand social network. But why? *Journal of Experimental Social Psychology, 49,* 217–223. (p. 353)

Oishi, S., Schiller, J., & Blair, E. G. (2013). Felt understanding and misunderstanding affect the perception of pain, slant, and distance. *Social Psychological and Personality Science, 4,* 259–266. (p. 197)

Oishi, S., & Schimmack, U. (2010a). Culture and well-being: A new inquiry into the psychological wealth of nations. *Perspectives in Psychological Science, 5,* 463–471. (p. 412)

Oishi, S., & Schimmack, U. (2010b). Residential mobility, well-being, and mortality. *Journal of Personality and Social Psychology, 98,* 980–994. (p. 353)

Okada, K., & Samreth, S. (2013). A study on the socio-economic determinants of suicide: Evidence from 13 European OECD countries. *Journal of Behavioral Economics, 45,* 78–85. (p. 500)

Okbay, A., Beauchamp, J. P., Fontana, M. A., Lee, J. J., Pers, T. H., Rietveld, C. A., . . . Oskarsson, S. (2016). Genome-wide association study identifies 74 loci associated with educational attainment. *Nature, 533,* 539–542. (p. 70)

Okimoto, T. G., & Brescoll, V. L. (2010). The price of power: Power seeking and backlash against female politicians. *Personality and Social Psychology Bulletin, 36,* 923–936. (p. 164)

Okuyama, T., Kitamura, T., Roy, D. S., Itohara, S., & Tonegawa, S. (2016). Ventral CA1 neurons store social memory. *Science, 353,* 1536–1541. (p. 276)

Olatunji, B. O., & Wolitzky-Taylor, K. B. (2009). Anxiety sensitivity and the anxiety disorders: A meta-analytic review and synthesis. *Psychological Bulletin, 135,* 974–999. (p. 507)

Olds, J. (1975). Mapping the mind onto the brain. In F. G. Worden, J. P. Swazey, & G. Adelman (Eds.), *The neurosciences: Paths of discovery* (pp. 375–400). Cambridge, MA: MIT Press. (p. 56)

Olds, J., & Milner, P. (1954). Positive reinforcement produced by electrical stimulation of the septal area and other regions of rat brain. *Journal of Comparative and Physiological Psychology, 47,* 419–427. (p. 56)

Olff, M., Langeland, W., Draijer, N., & Gersons, B. P. R. (2007). Gender differences in posttraumatic stress disorder. *Psychological Bulletin, 135,* 183–204. (p. 510)

Olfson, M., Gerhard, T., Huang, C., Crystal, S., & Stroup, T. S. (2015). Premature mortality among adults with schizophrenia in the United States. *JAMA Psychiatry, 72,* 1172–1181. (p. 518)

Olfson, M., & Marcus, S. C. (2009). National patterns in antidepressant medication treatment. *Archives of General Psychiatry, 66,* 848–856. (p. 562)

Oliner, S. P., & Oliner, P. M. (1988). *The altruistic personality: Rescuers of Jews in Nazi Europe.* New York: Free Press. (p. 261)

Olivé, I., Templemann, C., Berthoz, A., & Heinze, H.-J. (2015). Increased functional connectivity between superior colliculus and brain regions implicated in bodily self-consciousness during the rubber band illusion. *Human Brain Mapping, 36,* 717–730. (p. 81)

Olivola, C. Y., & Todorov, A. (2010). Elected in 100 milliseconds: Appearance-based trait inferences and voting. *Journal of Nonverbal Behavior, 54,* 83–110. (p. 376)

Olshansky, S. J. (2011). Aging of U.S. Presidents. *Journal of the American Medical Association, 306,* 2328–2329. (p. 396)

Olson, K. R., Key, A. C., & Eaton, N. R. (2015). Gender cognition in transgender children. *Psychological Science, 26,* 467–474. (pp. 85, 170)

Olson, R. L., Hanowski, R. J., Hickman, J. S., & Bocanegra, J. (2009, September). *Driver distraction in commercial vehicle operations.* Washington, DC: U.S. Department of Transportation, Federal Motor Carrier Safety Administration. (p. 82)

Olsson, A., Nearing, K. I., & Phelps, E. A. (2007). Learning fears by observing others: The neural systems of social fear transmission. *Social Cognitive and Affective Neuroscience, 2,* 3–11. (p. 511)

Oman, D., Kurata, J. H., Strawbridge, W. J., & Cohen, R. D. (2002). Religious attendance and cause of death over 31 years. *International Journal of Psychiatry in Medicine, 32,* 69–89. (p. 405)

ONS. (2015, September 23). *Personal well-being in the UK, 2014/2015.* Office for National Statistics (ons.gov.uk/). (p. 412)

Ooi, J., Dodd, H. F., Stuijfzand, B. G., Walsh, J., & Broeren, S. (2016). Do you think I should be scared? The effect of peer discussion on children's fears. *Behaviour Research and Therapy, 87,* 23–33. (p. 547)

Open Science Collaboration. (2015). Estimating the reproducibility of psychological science. *Science, 349,* 943. (p. 20)

Open Science Collaboration. (2017). Maximizing the reproducibility of your research. In S. O. Lilienfeld & I. D. Waldman (Eds.), *Psychological science under scrutiny: Recent challenges and proposed solutions.* New York: Wiley. (p. 20)

Opp, M. R., & Krueger, J. M. (2015). Sleep and immunity: A growing field with clinical impact. *Brain, Behavior, and Immunity, 47,* 1–3. (p. 93)

Oquendo, M. A., Galfalvy, H. C., Currier, D., Grunebaum, M. F., Sher, L., Sullivan, G. M., . . . Mann, J. J. (2011). Treatment of suicide attempters with bipolar disorder: A randomized clinical trial comparing lithium and valproate in the prevention of suicidal behavior. *The American Journal of Psychiatry, 168,* 1050–1056. (p. 562)

Orehek, E., & Human, L. J. (2017). Self-expression on social media: Do tweets present accurate and positive portraits of impulsivity, self-esteem, and attachment style? *Personality and Social Psychology Bulletin, 43,* 60–70. (p. 481)

Oren, D. A., & Terman, M. (1998). Tweaking the human circadian clock with light. *Science, 279,* 333–334. (p. 90)

Orth, U., & Robins, R. W. (2014). The development of self-esteem. *Current Directions in Psychological Science, 23,* 381–387. (p. 486)

Orth, U., Robins, R. W., Meier, L. L., & Conger, R. D. (2016). Refining the vulnerability model of low self-esteem and depression: Disentangling the effects of genuine self-esteem and narcissism. *Journal of Personality and Social Psychology, 110,* 133–149. (pp. 514, 519)

Orth, U., Robins, R. W., Trzesniewski, K. H., Maes, J., & Schmitt, M. (2009). Low self-esteem is a risk factor for depressive symptoms from young adulthood to old age. *Journal of Abnormal Psychology, 118,* 472–478. (p. 517)

Osborne, L. (1999, October 27). A linguistic big bang. *The New York Times Magazine* (nytimes.com). (p. 313)

Osgood, C. E. (1962). *An alternative to war or surrender.* Urbana: University of Illinois Press. (p. 459)

Osgood, C. E. (1980). *GRIT: A strategy for survival in mankind's nuclear age?* Paper presented at the Pugwash Conference on New Directions in Disarmament. (p. 459)

Oskarsson, A. T., Van Voven, L., McClelland, G. H., & Hastie, R. (2009). What's next? Judging sequences of binary events. *Psychological Bulletin, 135,* 262–285. (p. 17)

OSS Assessment Staff. (1948). *The assessment of men.* New York: Rinehart. (p. 484)

Ossher, L., Flegal, K. E., & Lustig, C. (2012). Everyday memory errors in older adults. *Aging, Neuropsychology, and Cognition, 20,* 220–242. (p. 154)

Ossola, A. (2014). This woman sees 100 times more colors than the average person. *Popular Science*. Retrieved from popsci.com/article/science/woman-sees-100-times-more-colors-average-person (p. 204)

Öst, L. -G., Havnen, A., Hansen, B., & Kvale, G. (2015). Cognitive behavioral treatments of obsessive–compulsive disorder. A systematic review and meta-analysis of studies published 1993–2014. *Clinical Psychology Review, 40*, 156–169. (p. 546)

Öst, L. -G., & Hugdahl, K. (1981). Acquisition of phobias and anxiety response patterns in clinical patients. *Behaviour Research and Therapy, 16*, 439–447. (p. 510)

Österman, K., Björkqvist, K., & Wahlbeck, K. (2014). Twenty-eight years after the complete ban on the physical punishment of children in Finland: Trends and psychosocial concomitants. *Aggressive Behavior, 40*, 568–581. (p. 249)

Ostfeld, A. M., Kasl, S. V., D'Atri, D. A., & Fitzgerald, E. F. (1987). *Stress, crowding, and blood pressure in prison*. Hillsdale, NJ: Erlbaum. (p. 397)

Osvath, M., & Karvonen, E. (2012). Spontaneous innovation for future deception in a male chimpanzee. *PLoS ONE, 7*, e36782. (p. 309)

Oswald, F. L., Mitchell, G., Blanton, H., Jaccard, J., & Tetlock, P. E. (2013). Predicting ethnic and racial discrimination: A meta-analysis of IAT criterion studies. *Journal of Personality and Social Psychology, 105*, 171–192. (p. 435)

Oswald, F. L., Mitchell, G., Blanton, H., Jaccard, J., & Tetlock, P. E. (2015). Using the IAT to predict ethnic and racial discrimination: Small effect sizes of unknown societal significance. *Journal of Personality and Social Psychology, 108*, 562–571. (p. 435)

Otgaar, H., & Baker, A. (2018). When lying changes memory for the truth. *Memory, 1*, 2–14. (p. 290)

Ott, B. (2007, June 14). Investors, take note: Engagement boosts earnings. *Gallup Management Journal* (gmj.gallup.com). (p. B-9)

Ott, C. H., Lueger, R. J., Kelber, S. T., & Prigerson, H. G. (2007). Spousal bereavement in older adults: Common, resilient, and chronic grief with defining characteristics. *Journal of Nervous and Mental Disease, 195*, 332–341. (p. 159)

Ouellette, J. A., & Wood, W. (1998). Habit and intention in everyday life: The multiple processes by which past behavior predicts future behavior. *Psychological Bulletin, 124*, 54–74. (p. B-6)

Overall, N. C., Fletcher, G. J. O., Simpson, J. A., & Fillo, J. (2015). Attachment insecurity, biased perceptions of romantic partners' negative emotions, and hostile relationship behavior. *Journal of Personality and Social Psychology, 108*, 730–749. (p. 136)

Owen, A. M. (2014). Disorders of consciousness: Diagnostic accuracy of brain imaging in the vegetative state. *Nature Review: Neurology, 10*, 370–371. (p. 81)

Owen, A. M., Coleman, M. R., Boly, M., Davis, M. H., Laureys, S., & Pickard, J. D. (2006). Detecting awareness in the vegetative state. *Science, 313*, 1402. (p. 81)

Owen, R. (1814). First essay in *New view of society or the formation of character*. Quoted in *The story of New Lamark*. New Lamark Mills, Lamark, Scotland: New Lamark Conservation Trust, 1993. (p. B-8)

Oxfam. (2005, March 26). *Three months on: New figures show tsunami may have killed up to four times as many women as men*. [Oxfam press release] (oxfam.org.uk). (p. 168)

Özçaliskan, S., Lucero, C., & Goldin-Meadow, S. (2016). Is *seeing gesture* necessary to *gesture* like a native speaker? *Psychological Science, 27*, 737–747. (p. 317)

Ozer, E. J., Best, S. R., Lipsey, T. L., & Weiss, D. S. (2003). Predictors of posttraumatic stress disorder and symptoms in adults: A meta-analysis. *Psychological Bulletin, 1*, 52–73. (p. 509)

Ozer, E. J., & Weiss, D. S. (2004). Who develops posttraumatic stress disorder? *Current Directions in Psychological Science, 13*, 169–172. (p. 510)

Özgen, E. (2004). Language, learning, and color perception. *Current Directions in Psychological Science, 13*, 95–98. (p. 320)

Pace-Schott, E. F., Germain, A., & Milad, M. R. (2015). Effects of sleep on memory for conditioned fear and fear extinction. *Psychological Bulletin, 141*, 835–857. (p. 91)

Pace-Schott, E. P., & Spencer, R. M. C. (2011). Age-related changes in the cognitive function of sleep. *Progress in Brain Research, 191*, 75–89. (p. 92)

Padgett, V. R. (1989). *Predicting organizational violence: An application of 11 powerful principles of obedience*. Paper presented to the American Psychological Association convention. (p. 427)

Page, S. E. (2007). The difference: How the power of diversity creates better groups, firms, schools, and societies. Princeton, NJ: Princeton University Press. (p. 433)

Palejwala, M. H., & Fine, J. G. (2015). Gender differences in latent cognitive abilities in children aged 2 to 7. *Intelligence, 48*, 96–108. (p. 340)

Palladino, J. J., & Carducci, B. J. (1983). *"Things that go bump in the night"*: Students' knowledge of sleep and dreams. Paper presented at the meeting of the Southeastern Psychological Association. (p. 86)

Pallier, C., Colomé, A., & Sebastián-Gallés, N. (2001). The influence of native-language phonology on lexical access: Exemplar-based versus abstract lexical entries. *Psychological Science, 12*, 445–448. (p. 314)

Palmer, D. C. (1989). A behavioral interpretation of memory. In L. J. Hayes (Ed.), *Dialogues on verbal behavior: The first international institute on verbal relations* (pp. 261–279). Reno, NV: Context Press. (p. 281)

Palmer, S., Schreiber, C., & Box, C. (1991). *Remembering the earthquake: "Flashbulb" memory for experienced vs. reported events*. Paper presented to the Psychonomic Society convention. (p. 278)

Palomar-García, M. Á., Bueichekú, E., Ávila, C., Sanjuán, A., Strijkers, K., Ventura-Campos, N., & Costa, A. (2015). Do bilinguals show neural differences with monolinguals when processing their native language? *Brain and Language, 142*, 36–44. (p. 320)

Palombo, D. J., McKinnon, M. C., McIntosh, A. R., Anderson, A. K., Todd, R. M., & Levine, B. (2015). The neural correlates of memory for a life-threatening event: An fMRI study of passengers from Flight AT236. *Clinical Psychological Science*. https://doi.org/10.1177/2167702615589308. (p. 52)

Pan, S. C., Pashler, H., Potter, Z. E., & Rickard, T. C. (2015). Testing enhances learning across a range of episodic memory abilities. *Journal of Memory and Language, 83*, 53–61. (p. 272)

Pandey, J., Sinha, Y., Prakash, A., & Tripathi, R. C. (1982). Right-left political ideologies and attribution of the causes of poverty. *European Journal of Social Psychology, 12*, 327–331. (p. 417)

Pänkäläinen, M., Kerola, T., Kampman, O., Kauppi, M., & Hintikka, J. (2016). Pessimism and risk of death from coronary heart disease among middle-aged and older Finns: An eleven-year follow-up study. *BMC Public Health, 16*, 1124. (p. 392)

Panksepp, J. (2007). Neurologizing the psychology of affects: How appraisal-based constructivism and basic emotion theory can coexist. *Perspectives on Psychological Science, 2*, 281–295. (p. 374)

Pantev, C., Oostenveld, R., Engelien, A., Ross, B., Roberts, L. R., & Hoke, M. (1998). Increased auditory cortical representation in musicians. *Nature, 392*, 811–814. (p. 39)

Paolini, S., Harwood, J., Rubin, M., Husnu, S., Joyce, N., & Hewstone, M. (2014). Positive and extensive intergroup contact in the past buffers against the disproportionate impact of negative contact in the present. *European Journal of Social Psychology, 44*, 548–562. (p. 457)

Pardini, D. A., Raine, A., Erickson, K., & Loeber, R. (2014). Lower amygdala volume in men is associated with childhood aggression, early psychopathic traits, and future violence. *Biological Psychiatry, 75*, 73–80. (p. 530)

Park, C. L. (2007). Religiousness/spirituality and health: A meaning systems perspective. *Journal of Behavioral Medicine, 30*, 319–328. (p. 406)

Park, D. C., & McDonough, I. M. (2013). The dynamic aging mind: Revelations from functional neuroimaging research. *Perspectives on Psychological Science, 8*, 62–67. (p. 153)

Park, G., Lubinski, D., & Benbow, C. P. (2008). Ability differences among people who have commensurate degrees matter for scientific creativity. *Psychological Science, 19*, 957–961. (p. 306)

Park, G., Schwartz, H. A., Eichstaedt, J. C., Kern, M. L., Kosinski, M., Stillwell, D. J., . . . Seligman, M. E. P. (2015). Automatic personality assessment through social media language. *Journal of Personality and Social Psychology, 108*, 934–952. (p. 481)

Park, G., Yaden, D. R., Schwartz, H. A., Kern, M. L., Eichstaedt, J. C., Kosinski, M., . . . Seligman, M. E. P. (2016). Women are warmer but no less assertive than men: Gender and language on Facebook. *PLoS ONE*. doi:10.1371/journal.pone.0155885 (p. 165)

Parker, C. P., Baltes, B. B., Young, S. A., Huff, J. W., Altmann, R. A., LaCost, H. A., & Roberts, J. E. (2003). Relationships between psychological climate perceptions and work outcomes: A meta-analytic review. *Journal of Organizational Behavior, 24*, 389–416. (p. B-8)

Parker, E. S., Cahill, L., & McGaugh, J. L. (2006). A case of unusual autobiographical remembering. *Neurocase, 12*, 35–49. (p. 284)

Parker, K., & Wang, W. (2013. March 14). *Modern parenthood: Roles of moms and dads converge as they balance work and family*. Retrieved from pewsocialtrends.org/2013/03/14/modern-parenthood-roles-of-moms-and-dads-converge-as-they-balance-work-and-family/ (pp. 164, 187)

Parkes, A., Wight, D., Hunt, K., Henderson, M., & Sargent, J. (2013). Are sexual media exposure, parental restrictions on media use and co-viewing TV and DVDs with parents and friends associated with teenagers' early sexual behaviour? *Journal of Adolescence, 36*, 1121–1133. (p. 177)

Parkinson's Foundation. (2018). Statistics. Parkinson's Foundation. Retrieved from http://parkinson.org/Understanding-Parkinsons/Causes-and-Statistics/Statistics (p. 44)

Parnia, S., Spearpoint, K., de Vos, G., Fenwick, P., Goldberg, D., Yang, J., . . . Wood, M. (2014). AWARE—AWAreness during REsuscitation—A prospective study. *Resuscitation, 85*, 1799–1805. (p. 108)

Parsaik, A. K., Mascarenhas, S. S., Hashmi, A., Prokop, L. J., John, V., Okusaga, O., & Singh, B. (2016). Role of botulinum toxin in depression. *Journal of Psychiatric Practice, 22*, 99–110. (p. 381)

Parsons, T. D., & Rizzo, A. A. (2008). Affective outcomes of virtual reality exposure therapy for anxiety and specific phobias: A meta-analysis. *Journal of Behavior Therapy and Experimental Psychiatry, 39*, 250–261. (p. 541)

Partanen, E., Kujala, T., Näätänen, R., Liitola, A., Sambeth, A., & Huotilainen, M. (2013). Learning-induced neural plasticity of speech processing before birth. *PNAS, 110*, 15145–15150. (p. 119)

Parthasarathy, S., Vasquez, M. M., Halonen, M., Bootzin, R., Quan, S. F., Martinez, F. D., & Guerra, S. (2015). Persistent insomnia is associated with mortality risk. *American Journal of Medicine, 128*, 268–275. (p. 93)

Paşca, A. M., Sloan, S. A., Clarke, L. E., Tian, Y., Makinson, C. D., Huber, N., . . . Smith, S. J. (2015). Functional cortical neurons and astrocytes from human pluripotent stem cells in 3D culture. *Nature Methods, 12*, 671–678. (p. 64)

Pascoe, E. A., & Richman, L. S. (2009). Perceived discrimination and health: A meta-analytic review. *Psychological Bulletin, 135*, 531–554. (p. 386)

Passell, P. (1993, March 9). Like a new drug, social programs are put to the test. *The New York Times*, pp. C1, C10. (p. 28)

Patihis, L. (2016). Individual differences and correlates of highly superior autobiographical memory. *Memory, 24*, 961–978. (p. 284)

Patihis, L., Frenda, S. J., LePort, A. K., Petersen, N., Nichols, R. M., Stark, C. E., . . . Loftus, E. F. (2013). False memories in highly superior autobiographical memory individuals. *PNAS, 110*, 20947–20952. (p. 289)

Patihis, L., Ho, L. Y., Tingen, I. W., Lilienfeld, S. O., & Loftus, E. F. (2014a). Are the "memory wars" over? A scientist-practitioner gap in beliefs about repressed memory. *Psychological Science, 25*, 519–530. (pp. 288, 293)

Patihis, L., Lilienfeld, S. O., Ho, L. Y., & Loftus, E. F. (2014b). Unconscious repressed memory is scientifically questionable. *Psychological Science, 25*, 1967–1968. (p. 288)

Patterson, F. (1978, October). Conversations with a gorilla. *National Geographic*, pp. 438–465. (p. 317)

Patterson, G. R., Chamberlain, P., & Reid, J. B. (1982). A comparative evaluation of parent training procedures. *Behavior Therapy, 13*, 638–650. (p. 250)

Patterson, M., Warr, P., & West, M. (2004). Organizational climate and company productivity: The role of employee affect and employee level. *Journal of Occupational and Organizational Psychology, 77*, 193–216. (p. B-8)

Pauker, K., Weisbuch, M., Ambady, N., Sommers, S. R., Adams, R. B., Jr., & Ivcevic, Z. (2009). Not so Black and White: Memory for ambiguous group members. *Journal of Personality and Social Psychology, 96*, 795–810. (p. 342)

Paulesu, E., Demonet, J.-F., Fazio, F., McCrory, E., Chanoine, V., Brunswick, N., . . . Frith, U. (2001). Dyslexia: Cultural diversity and biological unity. *Science, 291*, 2165–2167. (p. 10)

Pauletti, R. E., Menon, M., Cooper, P. J., Aults, C. D., & Perry, D. G. (2017). Psychological androgyny and children's mental health: A new look with new measures. *Sex Roles, 76*, 705–718. (p. 169)

Pauly, K., Finkelmeyer, A., Schneider, F., & Habel, U. (2013). The neural correlates of positive self-evaluation and self-related memory. *Social Cognitive and Affective Neuroscience, 8*, 878–886. (p. 486)

Paunesku, D., Walton, G. M., Romero, C., Smith, E. N., Yeager, D. S., & Dweck, C. S. (2015). Mind-set interventions are a scalable treatment for academic underachievement. *Psychological Science, 26*, 784–793. (p. 339)

Paus, T., Zijdenbos, A., Worsley, K., Collins, D. L., Blumenthal, J., Giedd, J. N., . . . Evans, A. C. (1999). Structural maturation of neural pathways in children and adolescents: In vivo study. *Science, 283*, 1908–1911. (p. 123)

Pavlenko, A. (2014). *The bilingual mind and what it tells us about language and thought.* New York: Cambridge University Press. (p. 319)

Pavlov, I. (1927). *Conditioned reflexes: An investigation of the physiological activity of the cerebral cortex.* Oxford: Oxford University Press. (pp. 236, 240)

Payne, B. K. (2006). Weapon bias: Split-second decisions and unintended stereotyping. *Current Directions in Psychological Science, 15*, 287–291. (p. 436)

Payne, B. K., & Corrigan, E. (2007). Emotional constraints on intentional forgetting. *Journal of Experimental Social Psychology, 43*, 780–786. (p. 288)

Payne, B. K., Krosnick, J. A., Pasek, J., Lelkes, Y., Akhtar, O., & Tompson, T. (2010). Implicit and explicit prejudice in the 2008 American presidential election. *Journal of Experimental Social Psychology, 46*, 367–374. (p. 436)

Pearce, M. J., Koenig, H. G., Robins, C. J., Nelson, B., Shaw, S. F., Cohen, H. J., & King, M. B. (2015). Religiously integrated cognitive behavioral therapy: A new method of treatment for major depression in patients with chronic medical illness. *Psychotherapy, 52*, 56–66. (p. 556)

Peck, E. (2015, April 29). Harvard Business School launches new effort to attract women. *Huffington Post* (huffingtonpost.com). (p. 164)

Peckham, A. D., McHugh, R. K., & Otto, M. W. (2010). A meta-analysis of the magnitude of biased attention in depression. *Depression and Anxiety, 27*, 1135–1142. (p. 516)

Pedersen, A., Zachariae, R., & Bovbjerg, D. H. (2010). Influence of psychological stress on upper respiratory infection—A meta-analysis of prospective studies. *Psychosomatic Medicine, 72*, 823–832. (p. 390)

Peigneux, P., Laureys, S., Fuchs, S., Collette, F., Perrin, F., Reggers, J., . . . Maquet, P. (2004). Are spatial memories strengthened in the human hippocampus during slow wave sleep? *Neuron, 44*, 535–545. (p. 277)

Pelham, B., & Crabtree, S. (2008, October 8). *Worldwide, highly religious more likely to help others.* Gallup Poll (gallup.com). (p. 455)

Pelham, B. W. (1993). On highly positive thoughts of the highly depressed. In R. F. Baumeister (Ed.), *Self-esteem: The puzzle of low self-regard.* New York: Plenum. (p. 487)

Pelham, B. W. (2009, October 22). About one in six Americans report history of depression. *Gallup* (gallup.com). (p. 517)

Pelham, W. E., Jr., Fabiano, G. A., Waxmonsky, J. G., Greiner, A. R., Gnagy, E. M., Pelham, W. E., . . . Murphy, S. A. (2016). Treatment sequencing for childhood ADHD: A multiple-randomization study of adaptive medication and behavioral interventions. *Journal of Clinical Child and Adolescent Psychology, 45*, 396–415. (p. 498)

Pennebaker, J. (1990). *Opening up: The healing power of confiding in others.* New York: William Morrow. (pp. 401, 469)

Pennebaker, J. W. (1985). Traumatic experience and psychosomatic disease: Exploring the roles of behavioral inhibition, obsession, and confiding. *Canadian Psychology, 26*, 82–95. (p. 400)

Pennebaker, J. W. (2011). *The secret life of pronouns: What our words say about us.* New York: Bloomsbury Press. (p. 481)

Pennebaker, J. W., Barger, S. D., & Tiebout, J. (1989). Disclosure of traumas and health among Holocaust survivors. *Psychosomatic Medicine, 51*, 577–589. (p. 400)

Pennebaker, J. W., Gosling, S. D., & Ferrell, J. D. (2013). Daily online testing in large classes: Boosting college performance while reducing achievement gaps. *PLoS ONE, 8*, e79774. (p. 273)

Pennebaker, J. W., & O'Heeron, R. C. (1984). Confiding in others and illness rate among spouses of suicide and accidental death victims. *Journal of Abnormal Psychology, 93*, 473–476. (p. 400)

Pennisi, E. (2016). The power of personality. *Science, 352*, 644–647. (p. 477)

Peplau, L. A., & Fingerhut, A. W. (2007). The close relationships of lesbians and gay men. *Annual Review of Psychology, 58*, 405–424. (pp. 157, 183)

Pepperberg, I. M. (2009). *Alex & me: How a scientist and a parrot discovered a hidden world of animal intelligence—and formed a deep bond in the process.* New York: Harper. (p. 309)

Pepperberg, I. M. (2012). Further evidence for addition and numerical competence by a grey parrot (Psittacus erithacus). *Animal Cognition, 15*, 711–717. (p. 309)

Pepperberg, I. M. (2013). Abstract concepts: Data from a grey parrot. *Behavioural Processes, 93*, 82–90. (p. 309)

Pereg, D., Gow, R., Mosseri, M., Lishner, M., Rieder, M., Van Uum, S., & Koren, G. (2011). Hair cortisol and the risk for acute myocardial infarction in adult men. *Stress, 14*, 73–81. (p. 391)

Pereira, A. C., Huddleston, D. E., Brickman, A. M., Sosunov, A. A., Hen, R., McKhann, G. M., . . . Small, S. A. (2007). An *in vivo* correlate of exercise-induced neurogenesis in the adult dentate gyrus. *PNAS, 104*, 5638–5643. (pp. 64, 153)

Pereira, G. M., & Osburn, H. G. (2007). Effects of participation in decision making on performance and employee attitudes: A quality circles meta-analysis. *Journal of Business Psychology, 22*, 145–153. (p. B-10)

Pergamin-Hight, L., Bakermans-Kranenburg, M. J., van IJzendoorn, M. H., & Bar-Haim, Y. (2012). Variations in the promoter region of the serotonin transporter gene and biased attention for emotional information: A meta-analysis. *Biological Psychiatry, 71*, 373–379. (p. 512)

Pergamin-Hight, L., Naim, R., Bakermans-Kranenburg, M. J., van IJzendoorn, M. H., & Bar-Haim, Y. (2015). Content specificity of attention bias to threat in anxiety disorders: A meta-analysis. *Clinical Psychology Review, 35*, 10–18. (p. 507)

Perilloux, H. K., Webster, G. D., & Gaulin, S. J. (2010). Signals of genetic quality and maternal investment capacity: The dynamic effects of fluctuating asymmetry and waist-to-hip ratio on men's ratings of women's attractiveness. *Social Psychology and Personality Science, 1*, 34–42. (pp. 184, 449)

Perkins, A., & Fitzgerald, J. A. (1997). Sexual orientation in domestic rams: Some biological and social correlates. In L. Ellis & L. Ebertz (Eds.), *Sexual orientation: Toward biological understanding* (p. 107–128). Westport, CT: Praeger. (p. 180)

Perkins, A. M., Inchley-Mort, S. L., Pickering, A. D., Corr, P. J., & Burgess, A. P. (2012). A facial expression for anxiety. *Journal of Personality and Social Psychology, 102*, 910–924. (p. 375)

Perrachione, T. K., Del Tufo, S. N., & Gabrieli, J. D. E. (2011). Human voice recognition depends on language ability. *Science, 333*, 595. (p. 317)

Perrett, D. I., Harries, M., Mistlin, A. J., & Chitty, A. J. (1990). Three stages in the classification of body movements by visual neurons. In H. Barlow, C. Blakemore, & M. Weston-Smith (Eds.), *Images and understanding* (pp. 94–108). Cambridge, England: Cambridge University Press. (p. 205)

Perrett, D. I., Hietanen, J. K., Oram, M. W., & Benson, P. J. (1992). Organization and functions of cells responsive to faces in the temporal cortex. *Philosophical Transactions of the Royal Society of London: Series B, 335*, 23–30. (p. 205)

Perrett, D. I., May, K. A., & Yoshikawa, S. (1994). Facial shape and judgments of female attractiveness. *Nature, 368*, 239–242. (p. 205)

Perry, G. (2013). Behind the shock machine: The untold story of the notorious Milgram psychology experiments. New York: New Press. (p. 427)

Perry, G. (2018). *The lost boys: Inside Muzafer Sherif's Robbers Cave experiment.* Melbourne/London: Scribe. (p. 458)

Person, C., Tracy, M., & Galea, S. (2006). Risk factors for depression after a disaster. *Journal of Nervous and Mental Disease, 194*, 659–666. (p. 567)

Pert, C. B. (1986). Quoted in J. Hooper & D. Teresi, *The three-pound universe.* New York: Macmillan. (p. 56)

Pert, C. B., & Snyder, S. H. (1973). Opiate receptor: Demonstration in nervous tissue. *Science, 179*, 1011–1014. (p. 43)

Perugini, E. M., Kirsch, I., Allen, S. T., Coldwell, E., Meredith, J., Montgomery, G. H., & Sheehan, J. (1998). Surreptitious observation of responses to hypnotically suggested hallucinations: A test of the compliance hypothesis. *International Journal of Clinical and Experimental Hypnosis, 46*, 191–203. (p. 224)

Peschel, E. R., & Peschel, R. E. (1987). Medical insights into the castrati in opera. *American Scientist, 75*, 578–583. (p. 173)

Pescosolido, B. A., Martin, J. K., Long, J. S., Medina, T. R., Phelan, J. C., & Link, B. G. (2010). "A disease like any other"? A decade of change in public reactions to schizophrenia, depression, and alcohol dependence. *American Journal of Psychiatry, 167*, 1321–1330. (p. 527)

Pesko, M. F. (2014). Stress and smoking: Associations with terrorism and causal impact. *Contemporary Economic Policy, 32*, 351–371. (p. 105)

Peter, C. J., Fischer, L. K., Kundakovic, M., Garg, P., Jakovcevski, M., Dincer, A., . . . Akbarian, S. (2016). DNA methylation signatures of early childhood malnutrition associated with impairments in attention and cognition. *Biological Psychiatry, 80*, 765–774. (p. 74)

Peter, J., & Valkenburg, P. M. (2016). Adolescents and pornography: A review of 20 years of research. *Journal of Sex Research, 53*, 509–531. (p. 444)

Peters, K., & Kashima, Y. (2015). A multimodal theory of affect diffusion. *Psychological Bulletin, 141*, 966–992. (p. 382)

Peters, M., Rhodes, G., & Simmons, L. W. (2007). Contributions of the face and body to overall attractiveness. *Animal Behaviour, 73*, 937–942. (p. 449)

Peters, T. J., & Waterman, R. H., Jr. (1982). *In search of excellence: Lessons from America's best-run companies.* New York: Harper & Row. (p. 251)

Petersen, J. L., & Hyde, J. S. (2010). A meta-analytic review of research on gender differences in sexuality, 1993–2007. *Psychological Bulletin, 136*, 21–38. (p. 183)

Petersen, J. L., & Hyde, J. S. (2011). Gender differences in sexual attitudes and behaviors: A review of meta-analytic results and large datasets. *Journal of Sex Research, 48*, 149–165. (p. 173)

Peterson, C., & Barrett, L. C. (1987). Explanatory style and academic performance among university freshmen. *Journal of Personality and Social Psychology, 53*, 603–607. (p. 398)

Peterson, C., Peterson, J., & Skevington, S. (1986). Heated argument and adolescent development. *Journal of Social and Personal Relationships, 3*, 229–240. (p. 143)

Peterson, L. R., & Peterson, M. J. (1959). Short-term retention of individual verbal items. *Journal of Experimental Psychology, 58*, 193–198. (p. 271)

Petitto, L. A., & Marentette, P. F. (1991). Babbling in the manual mode: Evidence for the ontogeny of language. *Science, 251*, 1493–1496. (p. 314)

Pettegrew, J. W., Keshavan, M. S., & Minshew, N. J. (1993). 31P nuclear magnetic resonance spectroscopy: Neurodevelopment and schizophrenia. *Schizophrenia Bulletin, 19*, 35–53. (p. 524)

Petticrew, M., Bell, R., & Hunter, D. (2002). Influence of psychological coping on survival and recurrence in people with cancer: Systematic review. *British Medical Journal, 325*, 1066. (p. 390)

Petticrew, M., Fraser, J. M., & Regan, M. F. (1999). Adverse life events and risk of breast cancer: A meta-analysis. *British Journal of Health Psychology, 4*, 1–17. (p. 390)

Pettigrew, T. F., & Tropp, L. R. (2011). *When groups meet: The dynamics of intergroup contact.* New York: Psychology Press. (p. 457)

Pew. (2006). Remembering 9/11. Pew Research Center (pewresearch.org). (p. 278)

Pew. (2007, July 18). Modern marriage: "I like hugs. I like kisses. But what I really love is help with the dishes." Pew Research Center (pewresearch.org). (p. 452)

Pew. (2009, November 4). *Social isolation and new technology: How the internet and mobile phones impact Americans' social networks.* Pew Research Center (pewresearch.org). (p. 356)

Pew. (2010, July 1). *Gender equality universally embraced, but inequalities acknowledged: Men's lives often seen as better.* Pew Research Center (pewglobal.org). (p. 169)

Pew. (2011, December 15). *17% and 61%—Texting, talking on the phone and driving.* Pew Research Center (pewresearch.org). (p. 82)

Pew. (2013a, June 4). *The global divide on homosexuality.* Pew Research Center, Global Attitudes Project (pewglobal.org). (p. 178)

Pew. (2013b, June 13). *A survey of LGBT Americans.* Pew Research Center (SDT_LGBT-Americans_06-2013.pdf). (p. 437)

Pew. (2014a, January 27). Climate change: Key data points from Pew Research. Pew Research Center (pewresearch.org). (p. 303)

Pew. (2014b). *Global views of morality.* Pew Research Center, Global Attitudes Project (pewglobal.org). (pp. 177, 437)

Pew. (2015, November 4). *Raising kids and running a household: How working parents share the load.* Pew Research Center (pewsocialtrends.org). (p. 154)

Pew. (2016, September 28). *Where the public stands on religious liberty vs. nondiscrimination.* Pew Forum (pewforum.org). (p. 457)

Pew. (2017). Internet/broadband technology fact sheet. Pew Research Center. Retrieved from pewinternet.org/fact-sheet/internet-broadband/ (p. 334)

Pfaff, L. A., Boatwright, K. J., Potthoff, A. L., Finan, C., Ulrey, L. A., & Huber, D. M. (2013). Perceptions of women and men leaders following 360-degree feedback evaluations. *Performance Improvement Quarterly, 26*, 35–56. (p. B-10)

Pfundmair, M., Zwarg, C., Paulus, M., & Rimpel, A. (2017). Oxytocin promotes attention to social cues regardless of group membership. *Hormones and Behavior, 90*, 136–140. (p. 49)

Phelps, J. A., Davis J. O., & Schartz, K. M. (1997). Nature, nurture, and twin research strategies. *Current Directions in Psychological Science, 6*, 117–120. (p. 526)

Philbeck, J. W., & Witt, J. K. (2015). Action-specific influences on perception and postperceptual processes: Present controversies and future directions. *Psychological Bulletin, 141*, 1120–1144. (p. 197)

Philip Morris. (2003). Philip Morris USA youth smoking prevention. Teenage attitudes and behavior study, 2002. In *Raising kids who don't smoke*, Vol. 1(2). (p. 112)

Phillips, A. C., Batty, G. D., Gale, C. R., Deary, I. J., Osborn, D., MacIntyre, K., & Carroll, D. (2009). Generalized anxiety disorder, major depressive disorder, and their comorbidity as predictors of all-cause and cardiovascular mortality: The Vietnam Experience Study. *Psychosomatic Medicine, 71*, 395–403. (p. 399)

Phillips, A. L. (2011). A walk in the woods. *American Scientist, 69*, 301–302. (p. 559)

Phillips, D. P. (1985). Natural experiments on the effects of mass media violence on fatal aggression: Strengths and weaknesses of a new approach. In L. Berkowitz (Ed.), *Advances in experimental social psychology* (Vol. 19, pp. 207–250). Orlando, FL: Academic Press. (p. 423)

Phillips, D. P., Carstensen, L. L., & Paight, D. J. (1989). Effects of mass media news stories on suicide, with new evidence on the role of story content. In C. R. Pfeffer (Ed.), *Suicide among youth: Perspectives on risk and prevention* (pp. 101–116). Washington, DC: American Psychiatric Press. (p. 423)

Phillips, J. L. (1969). *Origins of intellect: Piaget's theory.* San Francisco: Freeman. (p. 128)

Phillips, W. J., Fletcher, J. M., Marks, A. D. G., & Hine, D. W. (2016). Thinking styles and decision making: A meta-analysis. *Psychological Bulletin, 142*, 260–290. (p. 306)

Piaget, J. (1930). *The child's conception of physical causality.* London: Routledge & Kegan Paul. (p. 125)

Piaget, J. (1932). *The moral judgment of the child* (M. Gabain, Trans.). New York: Harcourt, Brace & World. (p. 143)

Piazza, J. R., Charles, S. T., Silwinski, M. J., Mogle, J., & Almeida, D. M. (2013). Affective reactivity to daily stressors and long-term risk of reporting a chronic health condition. *Annals of Behavioral Medicine, 45*, 110–120. (p. 386)

Picardi, A., Fagnani, C., Nisticò, L., & Stazi, M. A. (2011). A twin study of attachment style in young adults. *Journal of Personality, 79*, 965–992. (p. 134)

Picchioni, M. M., & Murray, R. M. (2007). Schizophrenia. *British Medical Journal, 335*, 91–95. (p. 524)

Picci, G., Gotts, S. J., & Scherf, K. S. (2016). A theoretical rut: Revisiting and critically evaluating the generalized under/over-connectivity hypothesis of autism. *Developmental Science, 19*, 524–549. (p. 131)

Picci, G., & Scherf, K. S. (2016). From caregivers to peers: Puberty shapes human face perception. *Psychological Science, 27*, 1461–1473. (p. 147)

Piekarski, D. J., Routman, D. M., Schoomer, E. E., Driscoll, J. R., Park, J. H., Butler, M. P., & Zucker, I. (2009). Infrequent low dose testosterone treatment maintains male sexual behavior in Syrian hamsters. *Hormones and Behavior, 55*, 182–189. (p. 173)

Pierce, L. J., Klein, D., Chen, J., Delcenserie, A., & Genesee, F. (2014). Mapping the unconscious maintenance of a lost first language. *PNAS, 111,* 17314–17319. (p. 125)

Pietschnig, J., & Voracek, M. (2015). One century of global IQ gains: A formal meta-analysis of the Flynn effect (1909–2013). *Perspectives on Psychological Science, 10,* 282–306. (p. 342)

Piliavin, J. A. (2003). Doing well by doing good: Benefits for the benefactor. In C.L.M. Keyes & J. Haidt (Eds.), *Flourishing: Positive psychology and the life well-lived* (pp. 227–247). Washington, DC: American Psychological Association. (p. 145)

Pillemer, D. B. (1998). *Momentous events, vivid memories.* Cambridge, MA: Harvard University Press. (p. 153)

Pillemer, D. B., Ivcevic, Z., Gooze, R. A., & Collins, K. A. (2007). Self-esteem memories: Feeling good about achievement success, feeling bad about relationship distress. *Personality and Social Psychology Bulletin, 33,* 1292–1305. (p. 354)

Pilley, J. W. (2013). *Chaser: Unlocking the genius of the dog who knows a thousand words.* Boston: Houghton Mifflin. (p. 318)

Pinker, S. (1990, September-October). Quoted by J. de Cuevas, "No, she holded them loosely." *Harvard Magazine,* pp. 60–67. (p. 312)

Pinker, S. (1995). The language instinct. *The General Psychologist, 31,* 63–65. (p. 318)

Pinker, S. (1998). Words and rules. *Lingua, 106,* 219–242. (p. 311)

Pinker, S. (2005, April 22). The science of gender and science: A conversation with Elizabeth Spelke. Harvard University. *The Edge* (edge.org). (p. 340)

Pinker, S. (2008). *The sexual paradox: Men, women, and the real gender gap.* New York: Scribner. (p. 164)

Pinker, S. (2010, June 10). Mind over mass media. *The New York Times,* A31. (p. 357)

Pinker, S. (2011, September 27). A history of violence. *The Edge* (edge.org). (p. 445)

Pinker, S. (2014). *The village effect: Why face-to-face contact matters.* Toronto: Random House Canada. (p. 356)

Pinker, S. (2015, June 8). The trauma of residential schools is passed down through the generations. *The Globe and Mail* (globeandmail.com). (p. 75)

Pinkham, A. E., Griffin, M., Baron, R., Sasson, N. J., & Gur, R. C. (2010). The face in the crowd effect: Anger superiority when using real faces and multiple identities. *Emotion, 10,* 141–146. (p. 376)

Pinquart, M. (2015). Associations of parenting styles and dimensions with academic achievement in children and adolescents: A meta-analysis. *Educational Psychology Review,* 1–19. doi:10.1007/s10648-015-9338-y (p. 139)

Pipe, M.-E., Lamb, M. E., Orbach, Y., & Esplin, P. W. (2004). Recent research on children's testimony about experienced and witnessed events. *Developmental Review, 24,* 440–468. (p. 294)

Pipher, M. (2002). *The middle of everywhere: The world's refugees come to our town.* New York: Harcourt Brace. (pp. 353, 385)

Pitcher, D., Walsh, V., Yovel, G., & Duchaine, B. (2007). TMS evidence for the involvement of the right occipital face area in early face processing. *Current Biology, 17,* 1568–1573. (p. 205)

Pitman, R. K., & Delahanty, D. L. (2005). Conceptually driven pharmacologic approaches to acute trauma. *CNS Spectrums, 10,* 99–106. (p. 279)

Pitman, R. K., Sanders, K. M., Zusman, R. M., Healy, A. R., Cheema, F., Lasko, N. B., . . . Orr, S. P. (2002). Pilot study of secondary prevention of posttraumatic stress disorder with propranolol. *Biological Psychiatry, 51,* 189–192. (p. 279)

Pittinsky, T. L., & Diamante, N. (2015). Global bystander nonintervention. *Peace and Conflict: Journal of Peace Psychology, 21,* 226–247. (p. 453)

Place, S. S., Todd, P. M., Penke, L., & Asendorph, J. B. (2009). The ability to judge the romantic interest of others. *Psychological Science, 20,* 22–26. (p. 376)

Plant, E. A., & Peruche, B. M. (2005). The consequences of race for police officers' responses to criminal suspects. *Psychological Science, 16,* 180–183. (p. 436)

Plassmann, H., O'Doherty, J., Shiv, B., & Rangel, A. (2008). Marketing actions can modulate neural representations of experienced pleasantness. *PNAS, 105,* 1050–1054. (p. 225)

Platek, S. M., & Singh, D. (2010) Optimal waist-to-hip ratios in women activate neural reward centers in men. *PLoS ONE, 5,* e9042. doi:10.1371/journal.pone.0009042. (p. 449)

Pliner, P. (1982). The effects of mere exposure on liking for edible substances. *Appetite: Journal for Intake Research, 3,* 283–290. (p. 364)

Pliner, P., Pelchat, M., & Grabski, M. (1993). Reduction of neophobia in humans by exposure to novel foods. *Appetite, 20,* 111–123. (p. 364)

Plomin, R. (1999). Genetics and general cognitive ability. *Nature, 402,* C25–C29. (p. 323)

Plomin, R. (2011). Why are children in the same family so different? Nonshared environment three decades later. *International Journal of Epidemiology, 40,* 582–592. (pp. 72, 149)

Plomin, R., & Bergeman, C. S. (1991). The nature of nurture: Genetic influence on "environmental" measures. *Behavioral and Brain Sciences, 14,* 373–427. (p. 74)

Plomin, R., & Daniels, D. (1987). Why are children in the same family so different from one another? *Behavioral and Brain Sciences, 10,* 1–60. (p. 149)

Plomin, R., & DeFries, J. C. (1998). The genetics of cognitive abilities and disabilities. *Scientific American, 278,* 62–69. (p. 338)

Plomin, R., DeFries, J. C., Knopik, V. S., & Neiderhiser, J. M. (2016). Top 10 replicated findings from behavioral genetics. *Perspectives on Psychological Science, 11,* 3–23. (pp. 70, 336)

Plomin, R., DeFries, J. C., McClearn, G. E., & Rutter, M. (1997). *Behavioral genetics.* New York: Freeman. (pp. 365, 526)

Plomin, R., McClearn, G. E., Pedersen, N. L., Nesselroade, J. R., & Bergeman, C. S. (1988). Genetic influence on childhood family environment perceived retrospectively from the last half of the life span. *Developmental Psychology, 24,* 37–45. (p. 74)

Plomin, R., & McGuffin, P. (2003). Psychopathology in the postgenomic era. *Annual Review of Psychology, 54,* 205–228. (p. 518)

Plomin, R., Reiss, D., Hetherington, E. M., & Howe, G. W. (January, 1994). Nature and nurture: Genetic contributions to measures of the family environment. *Developmental Psychology, 30,* 32–43. (p. 74)

Plotkin, H. (1994). *Darwin machines and the nature of knowledge.* Cambridge, MA: Harvard University Press. (p. 518)

Plous, S., & Herzog, H. A. (2000). Poll shows researchers favor lab animal protection. *Science, 290,* 711. (p. 31)

Pluess, M., & Belsky, J. (2013). Vantage sensitivity: Individual differences in response to positive experiences. *Psychological Bulletin, 139,* 901–916. (p. 512)

Poelmans, G., Pauls, D. L., Buitelaar, J. K., & Franke, B. (2011). Integrated genomewide association study findings: Identification of a neurodevelopmental network for attention deficit hyperactivity disorder. *American Journal of Psychiatry, 168,* 365–377. (p. 498)

Polanin, J. R., Espelage, D. L., & Pigott, T. D. (2012). A meta-analysis of school-based bully prevention programs' effects on bystander intervention behavior. *School Psychology Review, 41,* 47–65. (p. 13)

Polderman, T. J. C., Benyamin, B., de Leeuw, C. A., Sullivan, P. F., van Bochoven, A., Visscher, P. M., & Posthuma, D. (2015). Meta-analysis of the heritability of human traits based on fifty years of twin studies. *Nature Genetics, 47,* 702–709. (pp. 70, 511, 518)

Poldrack, R. A., Halchenko, Y. O., & Hanson, S. J. (2009). Decoding the large-scale structure of brain function by classifying mental states across individuals. *Psychological Science, 20,* 1364–1372. (p. 52)

Polivy, J., Herman, C. P., & Coelho, J. S. (2008). Caloric restriction in the presence of attractive food cues: External cues, eating, and weight. *Physiology and Behavior, 94,* 729–733. (p. 364)

Pollak, S., Cicchetti, D., & Klorman, R. (1998). Stress, memory, and emotion: Developmental considerations from the study of child maltreatment. *Developmental Psychopathology, 10,* 811–828. (p. 240)

Pollak, S. D., & Kistler, D. J. (2002). Early experience is associated with the development of categorical representations for facial expressions of emotion. *PNAS, 99,* 9072–9076. (p. 376)

Pollak, S. D., & Tolley-Schell, S. A. (2003). Selective attention to facial emotion in physically abused children. *Journal of Abnormal Psychology, 112,* 323–328. (p. 376)

Pollard, R. (1992). *100 years in psychology and deafness: A centennial retrospective.* Invited address to the American Psychological Association convention, Washington, DC. (p. 317)

Pollatsek, A., Romoser, M. R. E., & Fisher, D. L. (2012). Identifying and remediating failures of selective attention in older drivers. *Current Directions in Psychological Science, 21,* 3–7. (p. 152)

Pollick, A. S., & de Waal, F. B. M. (2007). Ape gestures and language evolution. *PNAS, 104,* 8184–8189. (p. 317)

Poole, D. A., & Lindsay, D. S. (1995). Interviewing preschoolers: Effects of nonsuggestive techniques, parental coaching and leading questions on reports of nonexperienced events. *Journal of Experimental Child Psychology, 60,* 129–154. (p. 291)

Poole, D. A., & Lindsay, D. S. (2001). Children's eyewitness reports after exposure to misinformation from parents. *Journal of Experimental Psychology: Applied, 7,* 27–50. (p. 291)

Pope, D., & Simonsohn, U. (2011). Round numbers as goals: Evidence from baseball, SAT takers, and the lab. *Psychological Science, 22,* 71–79. (p. A-1)

Pope Francis. (2015). *Encyclical Letter Laudato Si' of the Holy Father Francis on care for our common home (official English-language text of encyclical). Retrieved from* w2.vatican.va (pp. 77, 418)

Poropat, A. E. (2014). Other-rated personality and academic performance: Evidence and implications. *Learning and Individual Differences, 34,* 24–32. (p. 342)

Porter, D., & Neuringer, A. (1984). Music discriminations by pigeons. *Journal of Experimental Psychology: Animal Behavior Processes, 10,* 138–148. (p. 245)

Porter, S., & Peace, K. A. (2007). The scars of memory: A prospective, longitudinal investigation of the consistency of traumatic and positive emotional memories in adulthood. *Psychological Science, 18,* 435–441. (p. 293)

Poulton, R., Moffitt, T. E., & Silva, P. A. (2015). The Dunedin multidisciplinary health and development study: Overview of the first 40 years, with an eye to the future. *Social Psychiatry and Psychiatric Epidemiology, 50,* 679–693. (p. 398)

Poundstone, W. (2014). *How to predict the unpredictable. The art of outsmarting almost everyone.* London: OneWorld. (p. 17)

Poushter, J. (2016, February 22). *Smartphone ownership and internet usage continues to climb in emerging economies.* Pew Research Center (pewglobal.org). (p. 355)

Powell, R., Digdon, N. A., Harris, B., & Smithson, C. (2014). Correcting the record on Watson, Rayner and Little Albert: Albert Barger as "Psychology's Lost Boy." *American Psychologist, 69,* 600–611. (p. 241)

Powell, R. A., & Boer, D. P. (1994). Did Freud mislead patients to confabulate memories of abuse? *Psychological Reports, 74,* 1283–1298. (p. 468)

Powell, R. A., & Schmaltz, R. M. (2017, July). Did Little Albert actually acquire a conditioned fear of animals? What the film evidence tells us. Paper presented at the Vancouver International Conference on the Teaching of Psychology. (p. 241)

Power, R. A., Steinberg, S., Bjornsdottir, G., Rietveld, C. A., Abdellaoui, A., Nivard, M. M., . . . Stefansson, K. (2015). Polygenic risk scores for schizophrenia and bipolar disorder predict creativity. *Nature Neuroscience, 18,* 953–955. (p. 515)

Power, R. A., Tansey, K. E., Buttenschøn, H. N., Cohen-Woods, S., Bigdeli, T., Hall, L. S., . . . Teumer, A. (2017). Genome-wide association for major depression through age at onset stratification: Major depressive disorder working group of the psychiatric genomics consortium. *Biological Psychiatry, 81,* 325–335. (p. 518)

PPP. (2016, December 9). Trump remains unpopular; voters prefer Obama on SCOTUS pick. Public Policy Polling. Retrieved from http://www.publicpolicypolling.com/wp-content/uploads/2017/09/PPP_Release_National_120916.pdf (p. 18)

Prather, A. A., Janicki-Deverts, D., Hall, M. H., & Cohen, S. (2015). Behaviorally assessed sleep and susceptibility to the common cold. *Sleep, 38,* 1353–1359. (p. 93)

Pratt, L. A., Brody, D. J., & Gu, Q. (2017, August). Antidepressant use among persons aged 12 and over: United States, 2011–2014. *NCHS Data Brief, 283,* 1–8. (p. 520)

Preckel, F., Lipnevich, A., Boehme, K., Branderner, L., Georgi, K., Könen, T., . . . Roberts, R. (2013). Morningness–eveningness and educational outcomes: The lark has an advantage over the owl at high school. *British Journal of Educational Psychology, 83,* 114–134. (p. 87)

Premack, D. G., & Woodruff, G. (1978). Does the chimpanzee have a theory of mind? *Behavioral and Brain Sciences, 1,* 515–526. (p. 128)

Prentice, D. A., & Miller, D. T. (1993). Pluralistic ignorance and alcohol use on campus: Some consequences of misperceiving the social norm. *Journal of Personality and Social Psychology, 64,* 243–256. (p. 112)

Primack, B. A., Shensa, A., Escobar-Viera, C. G., Barrett, E. L., Sidani, J. E., Colditz, J. B., & James, A. E. (2016). Use of multiple social media platforms and symptoms of depression and anxiety: A nationally-representative study among U.S. young adults. *Computers in Human Behavior, 69,* 1–9. (p. 356)

Profet, M. (1992). Pregnancy sickness as adaptation: A deterrent to maternal ingestion of teratogens. In J. H. Barkow, L. Cosmides, & J. Tooby (Eds.), *The adapted mind: Evolutionary psychology and the generation of culture* (pp. 327–366). New York: Oxford University Press. (p. 76)

Proffitt, D. R. (2006a). Distance perception. *Current Directions in Psychological Research, 15,* 131–135. (p. 197)

Proffitt, D. R. (2006b). Embodied perception and the economy of action. *Perspectives on Psychological Science, 1,* 110–122. (p. 197)

Project Match Research Group. (1997). Matching alcoholism treatments to client heterogeneity: Project MATCH posttreatment drinking outcomes. *Journal of Studies on Alcohol, 58,* 7–29. (p. 548)

Pronin, E. (2013). When the mind races: Effects of thought speed on feeling and action. *Current Directions in Psychological Science, 22,* 283–288. (p. 515)

Pronin, E., & Ross, L. (2006). Temporal differences in trait self-ascription: When the self is seen as another. *Journal of Personality and Social Psychology, 90,* 197–209. (p. 417)

Propper, R. E., Stickgold, R., Keeley, R., & Christman, S. D. (2007). Is television traumatic? Dreams, stress, and media exposure in the aftermath of September 11, 2001. *Psychological Science, 18,* 334–340. (p. 96)

Prot, S., Gentile, D. A., Anderson, C. A., Suzuki, K., Horiuchi, Y., Jelic, M., . . . Lam, B. C. P. (2014). Long-term relations among prosocial-media use, empathy, and prosocial behavior. *Psychological Science, 25,* 358–368. (pp. 261, 444)

Protzko, J., Aronson, J., & Blair, C. (2013). How to make a young child smarter: Evidence from the database of raising intelligence. *Perspectives on Psychological Science, 8,* 25–40. (p. 339)

Provine, R. R. (2001). *Laughter: A scientific investigation.* New York: Penguin. (p. 23)

Provine, R. R. (2012). *Curious behavior: Yawning, laughing, hiccupping, and beyond.* Cambridge, MA: Harvard University Press. (pp. 22, 422)

Provine, R. R., Krosnowski, K. A., & Brocato, N. W. (2009). Tearing: Breakthrough in human emotional signaling. *Evolutionary Psychology, 7,* 52–56. (p. 380)

Pryor, J. H., Hurtado, S., DeAngelo, L., Blake, L. P., & Tran, S. (2011). *The American freshman: National norms fall 2010.* Los Angeles: UCLA Higher Education Research Institute. (p. 165)

Pryor, J. H., Hurtado, S., Saenz, V. B., Korn, J. S., Santos, J. L., & Korn, W. S. (2006). *The American freshman: National norms for Fall 2006.* Los Angeles: UCLA Higher Education Research Institute. (p. 520)

Pryor, J. H., Hurtado, S., Saenz, V. B., Lindholm, J. A., Korn, W. S., & Mahoney, K. M. (2005). *The American freshman: National norms for Fall 2005.* Los Angeles: UCLA Higher Education Research Institute. (p. 184)

Pryor, J. H., Hurtado, S., Sharkness, J., & Korn, W. S. (2007). *The American freshman: National norms for fall 2007.* Los Angeles: UCLA Higher Education Research Institute. (p. 165)

Psaltopoulou, T., Sergentanis, T. N., Panagiotakos, D. B., Sergentanis, I. N., Kosti, R., & Scarmeas, N. (2013). Mediterranean diet, stroke, cognitive impairment, and depression: A meta-analysis. *Annals of Neurology, 74,* 580–591. (p. 519)

Psychologist. (2003). Who's the greatest? *The Psychologist, 16,* 170–175. (p. 130)

PTC. (2007, January 10). Dying to entertain: Violence on prime time broadcast TV, 1998 to 2006. Parents Television Council (parentstv.org). (p. 262)

Puhl, R. M., Latner, J. D., O'Brien, K., Luedicke, J., Forhan, M., & Danielsdottir, S. (2015). Cross-national perspectives about weigh-based bullying in youth: Nature, extent and remedies. *Pediatric Obesity, 11,* 241–250. (p. 365)

Punamäki, R. L., & Joustie, M. (1998). The role of culture, violence, and personal factors affecting dream content. *Journal of Cross-Cultural Psychology, 29,* 320–342. (p. 96)

Putnam, F. W. (1991). Recent research on multiple personality disorder. *Psychiatric Clinics of North America, 14,* 489–502. (p. 528)

Putnam, R. (2000). *Bowling alone.* New York: Simon and Schuster. (p. 422)

Puttonen, S., Kivimäki, M., Elovainio, M., Pulkki-Råback, L., Hintsanen, M., Vahtera, J., . . . Keltikangas-Järvinen, L. (2009). Shift work in young adults and carotid artery intima–media thickness: The Cardiovascular Risk in Young Finns study. *Atherosclerosis, 205,* 608–613. (p. 90)

Pyszczynski, T. A., Motyl, M., Vail, K. E., III, Hirschberger, G., Arndt, J., & Kesebir, P. (2012). Drawing attention to global climate change decreases support for war. *Peace and Conflict: Journal of Peace Psychology, 18,* 354–368. (p. 458)

Pyszczynski, T. A., Rothschild, Z., & Abdollahi, A. (2008). Terrorism, violence, and hope for peace: A terror management perspective. *Current Directions in Psychological Science, 17,* 318–322. (p. 439)

Pyszczynski, T. A., Solomon, S., & Greenberg, J. (2002). *In the wake of 9/11: The psychology of terror.* Washington, DC: American Psychological Association. (p. 439)

Qaseem, A., Kansagara, D., Forciea, M. A., Cooke, M., & Denberg, T. D., for the Clinical Guidelines Committee of the American College of Physicians. (2016). Management of chronic insomnia disorder in adults: A clinical practice guideline from the American College of Physicians. *Annals of Internal Medicine, 165,* 125–133. (p. 553)

Qin, H.-F., & Piao, T.-J. (2011). Dispositional optimism and life satisfaction of Chinese and Japanese college students: Examining the mediating effects of affects and coping efficacy. *Chinese Journal of Clinical Psychology, 19,* 259–261. (p. 399)

Qiu, L., Lin, H., Ramsay, J., & Yang, F. (2012). You are what you tweet: Personality expression and perception on Twitter. *Journal of Research in Personality, 46,* 710–718. (p. 481)

Quaedflieg, C. W. E. M., & Schwabe, L. (2017). Memory dynamics under stress. *Memory.* Advance online publication. http://dx.doi.org/10.1080/09658211.2017.1338299 (p. 288)

Quasha, S. (1980). *Albert Einstein: An intimate portrait.* New York: Forest. (p. 332)

Quinn, P. C., Bhatt, R. S., Brush, D., Grimes, A., & Sharpnack, H. (2002). Development of form similarity as a Gestalt grouping principle in infancy. *Psychological Science, 13,* 320–328. (p. 208)

Quiroga, R. Q., Fried, I., & Koch, C. (2013, February). Brain cells for grandmother. *Scientific American,* pp. 30–35. (p. 206)

Quoidbach, J., Dunn, E. W., Hansenne, M., & Bustin, G. (2015). The price of abundance: How a wealth of experiences impoverishes savoring. *Personality and Social Psychology Bulletin, 41,* 393–404. (p. 409)

Quoidbach, J., Dunn, E. W., Petrides, K. V., & Mikolajczak, M. (2010). Money giveth, money taketh away: The dual effect of wealth on happiness. *Psychological Science, 21,* 759–763. (p. 409)

Rabbitt, P. (2006). Tales of the unexpected: 25 years of cognitive gerontology. *The Psychologist, 19,* 674–676. (p. 154)

Raby, K. L., Cicchetti, D., Carlson, E. A., Cutuli, J. J., Englund, M. M., & Egeland, B. (2012). Genetic and care-giving-based contributions to infant attachment: Unique associations with distress reactivity and attachment security. *Psychological Science, 23,* 1016–1023. (p. 134)

Raby, K. L., Roisman, G. I., Fraley, R. C., & Simpson, J. A. (2014). The enduring predictive significance of early maternal sensitivity: Social and academic competence through age 32 years. *Child Development, 86,* 695–708. (p. 136)

Racsmány, M., Conway, M. A., & Demeter, G. (2010). Consolidation of episodic memories during sleep: Long-term effects of retrieval practice. *Psychological Science, 21,* 80–85. (p. 91)

Radford, B. (2010, March 5). Missing persons and abductions reveal psychics' failures. Retrieved from seeker.com/missing-persons-and-abductions-reveal-psychics-failures-1765030268.html (p. 230)

Radford, B. (2013, May 8). Psychic claimed Amanda Berry was dead. Retrieved from seeker.com/psychic-claimed-amanda-berry-was-dead-1767492815.html (p. 230)

Radua, J., Schmidt, A., Borgwardt, S., Heinz, A., Schlagenhauf, F., McGuire, P., & Fusar-Poli, P. (2015). Ventral striatal activation during reward processing in psychosis: A neurofunctional meta-analysis. *JAMA Psychiatry, 72,* 1243–1251.

Rahl, H. A., Lindsay, E. K., Pacilio, L. E., Brown, K. W., & Creswell, J. D. (2016). Brief mindfulness meditation training reduces mind wandering: The critical role of acceptance. *Emotion.* Advance online publication. dx.doi.org/10.1037/emo0000250 (p. 404)

Rahman, Q. (2015, July 24). "Gay genes": Science is on the right track, we're born this way. Let's deal with it. *The Guardian* (theguardian.com). (p. 181)

Rahman, Q., & Koerting, J. (2008). Sexual orientation-related differences in allocentric spatial memory tasks. *Hippocampus, 18,* 55–63. (p. 182)

Rahman, Q., & Wilson, G. D. (2003). Born gay? The psychobiology of human sexual orientation. *Personality and Individual Differences, 34,* 1337–1382. (p. 181)

Rahman, Q., Wilson, G. D., & Abrahams, S. (2004). Biosocial factors, sexual orientation and neurocognitive functioning. *Psychoneuroendocrinology, 29,* 867–881. (pp. 182, 183)

Raichle, M. (2010, March). The brain's dark energy. *Scientific American,* pp. 44–49. (p. 85)

Raila, H., Scholl, B. J., & Gruber, J. (2015). Seeing the world through rose-colored glasses: People who are happy and satisfied with life preferentially attend to positive stimuli. *Emotion, 15,* 449–462. (p. 407)

Raine, A. (1999). Murderous minds: Can we see the mark of Cain? *Cerebrum: The Dana Forum on Brain Science 1*(1), 15–29. (p. 531)

Raine, A. (2005). The interaction of biological and social measures in the explanation of antisocial and violent behavior. In D. M. Stoff & E. J. Susman (Eds.) *Developmental psychobiology of aggression.* New York: Cambridge University Press. (p. 531)

Raine, A. (2013). *The anatomy of violence: The biological roots of crime.* New York: Pantheon. (p. 442)

Raine, A., Lencz, T., Bihrle, S., LaCasse, L., & Colletti, P. (2000). Reduced prefrontal gray matter volume and reduced autonomic activity in antisocial personality disorder. *Archives of General Psychiatry, 57,* 119–127. (p. 531)

Rainie, L., Purcell, K., Goulet, L. S., & Hampton, K. H. (2011, June 16). *Social networking sites and our lives.* Pew Research Center (pewresearch.org). (p. 356)

Rainville, P., Duncan, G. H., Price, D. D., Carrier, B., & Bushnell, M. C. (1997). Pain affect encoded in human anterior cingulate but not somatosensory cortex. *Science, 277,* 968–971. (p. 224)

Raison, C. L., Klein, H. M., & Steckler, M. (1999). The moon and madness reconsidered. *Journal of Affective Disorders, 53,* 99–106. (p. 530)

Rajendran, G., & Mitchell, P. (2007). Cognitive theories of autism. *Developmental Review, 27,* 224–260. (p. 131)

Raji, C. A., Merrill, D. A., Eyre, H., Mallam, S., Torosyan, N., Erickson, K.I. . . . Kuller, L. H. (2016). Longitudinal relationships between caloric expenditure and gray matter in the cardiovascular health study. *Journal of Alzheimer's Disease, 52,* 719–729. (p. 153)

Ramachandran, V. S., & Blakeslee, S. (1998). *Phantoms in the brain: Probing the mysteries of the human mind.* New York: Morrow. (pp. 64, 222)

Ramírez-Esparza, N., Gosling, S. D., Benet-Martínez, V., Potter, J. P., & Pennebaker, J. W. (2006). Do bilinguals have two personalities? A special case of cultural frame switching. *Journal of Research in Personality, 40,* 99–120. (p. 319)

Ramos, M. R., Cassidy, C., Reicher, S., & Haslam, S. A. (2012). A longitudinal investigation of the rejection-identification hypothesis. *British Journal of Social Psychology, 51,* 642–660. (p. 458)

Randall, D. K. (2012, September 22). Rethinking sleep. *The New York Times* (nytimes.com). (p. 90)

Randi, J. (1999, February 4). 2000 club mailing list e-mail letter. (p. 231)

Randler, C. (2008). Morningness–eveningness and satisfaction with life. *Social Indicators Research, 86,* 297–302. (p. 87)

Randler, C. (2009). Proactive people are morning people. *Journal of Applied Social Psychology, 39,* 2787–2797. (p. 87)

Rapoport, J. L. (1989). The biology of obsessions and compulsions. *Scientific American, 260,* 83–89. (pp. 509, 512)

Räsänen, S., Pakaslahti, A., Syvalahti, E., Jones, P. B., & Isohanni, M. (2000). Sex differences in schizophrenia: A review. *Nordic Journal of Psychiatry, 54,* 37–45. (p. 524)

Rasmussen, H. N., Scheier, M. F., & Greenhouse, J. B. (2009). Optimism and physical health: A meta-analytic review. *Annals of Behavioral Medicine, 37,* 239–256. (p. 398)

Rasmussen, K. (2016). Entitled vengeance: A meta-analysis relating narcissism to provoked aggression. *Aggressive Behavior.* Advance online publication. doi:10.1002/ab.21632 (p. 488)

Ratcliff, K. S. (2013). The power of poverty: Individual agency and structural constraints. In K. M. Fitzpatrick (Ed.), *Poverty and health: A crisis among America's most vulnerable* (vol. 1), pp. 5–30. Santa Barbara, CA: Praeger. (p. 410)

Rath, T., & Harter, J. K. (2010, August 19). Your friends and your social well-being: Close friendships are vital to health, happiness, and even workplace productivity. *Gallup Management Journal* (gmj.gallup.com). (p. B-11)

Rathbone, C. J., Salgado, S., Akan, M., Havelka, J., & Berntsen, D. (2016). Imagining the future: A cross-cultural perspective on possible selves. *Consciousness and Cognition, 42,* 113–124. (p. 486)

Rattan, A., Savani, K., Naidu, N. V. R., & Dweck, C. S. (2012). Can everyone become highly intelligent? Cultural differences in and societal consequences of beliefs about the universal potential for intelligence. *Journal of Personality and Social Psychology, 103,* 787–803. (p. 340)

Ravizza, S. M., Uitvlught, M. G., & Fenn, K. M. (2017). Logged in and zoned out. *Psychological Science, 28,* 171–180. (p. 295)

Ray, J., & Kafka, S. (2014, May 6). *Life in college matters for life after college.* Gallup (gallup.com/poll). (p. B-12)

Ray, O., & Ksir, C. (1990). Drugs, society, and human behavior (5th ed.). St. Louis: Times Mirror/Mosby. (p. 107)

Raynor, H. A., & Epstein, L. H. (2001). Dietary variety, energy regulation, and obesity. *Psychological Bulletin, 127,* 325–341. (p. 363)

Reason, J. (1987). The Chernobyl errors. *Bulletin of the British Psychological Society, 40,* 201–206. (p. 433)

Reason, J., & Mycielska, K. (1982). *Absent-minded? The psychology of mental lapses and everyday errors.* Englewood Cliffs, NJ: Prentice-Hall. (p. 196)

Rebar, A. L., Stanton, R., Geard, D., Short, C., Duncan, M. J., & Vandelanotte, C. (2015). A meta-meta-analysis of the effect of physical activity on depression and anxiety in non-clinical adult populations. *Health Psychology Review, 9,* 366–378. (p. 401)

Rechenberg, K. (2016). Nutritional interventions in clinical depression. *Clinical Psychological Science, 4*(1), 144–162. (p. 519)

Redden, J. P., Mann, T., Vickers, Z., Mykerezi, E., Reicks, M., & Elsbernd, E. (2015). Serving first in isolation increases vegetable intake among elementary schoolchildren. *PLoS ONE, 10,* e0121283. (p. 364)

Reebs, A., Yuval, K., & Bernstein, A. (2017). Remembering and responding to distressing autobiographical memories: Exploring risk and intervention targets for posttraumatic stress in traumatized refugees. *Clinical Psychological Science, 5,* 789–797. (p. 509)

Reed, D. (2011, January). Quoted in P. Miller, A thing or two about twins. *National Geographic,* pp. 39–65. (p. 74)

Reed, P. (2000). Serial position effects in recognition memory for odors. *Journal of Experimental Psychology: Learning, Memory, and Cognition, 26,* 411–422. (p. 282)

Rees, M. (1999). *Just six numbers: The deep forces that shape the universe.* New York: Basic Books. (p. 77)

Reeves, A., McKee, M., & Stuckler, D. (2014). Economic suicides in the Great Recession in Europe and North America. *British Journal of Psychiatry, 205,* 246–247. (p. 501)

Regan, P. C., & Atkins, L. (2007). Sex differences and similarities in frequency and intensity of sexual desire. *Social Behavior and Personality, 34,* 95–102. (p. 183)

Reichenberg, A., Cederlöf, M., McMillan, A., Trzaskowski, M., Kapara, O., Fruchter, E., . . . Plomin, R. (2016). Discontinuity in the genetic and environmental causes of the intellectual disability spectrum. *PNAS, 113,* 1098–1103. (p. 331)

Reichenberg, A., & Harvey, P. D. (2007). Neuropsychological impairments in schizophrenia: Integration of performance-based and brain imaging findings. *Psychological Bulletin, 133,* 833–858. (p. 523)

Reichert, R. A., Robb, M. B., Fender, J. G., & Wartella, E. (2010). Word learning from baby videos. *Archives of Pediatrics & Adolescent Medicine, 164,* 432–437. (p. 339)

Reicher, S., & Haslam, S. A. (2006). Rethinking the psychology of tyranny: The BBC prison study. *British Journal of Social Psychology, 45,* 1–40. (p. 419)

Reichow, B. (2012). Overview of meta-analyses on early intensive behavioral intervention for young children with autism spectrum disorders. *Journal of Autism and Developmental Disorders, 42,* 512–520. (p. 543)

Reid, V. M., Dunn, K., Young, R. J., Amu, J., Donovan, T., & Reissland, N. (2017). The human fetus preferentially engages with face-like visual stimuli. *Current Biology, 27,* 1825–1828. (p. 121)

Reifman, A. S., Larrick, R. P., & Fein, S. (1991). Temper and temperature on the diamond: The heat-aggression relationship in major league baseball. *Personality and Social Psychology Bulletin, 17,* 580–585. (p. 443)

Reimann, F., Cox, J. J., Belfer, I., Diatchenko, L., Zaykin, D. V., McHale, D. P., . . . Woods, C. G. (2010). Pain perception is altered by a nucleotide polymorphism in SCN9A. *PNAS, 107,* 5148–5153. (pp. 222, 223)

Reimão, R. N., & Lefévre, A. B. (1980). Prevalence of sleep-talking in childhood. *Brain and Development, 2,* 353–357. (p. 95)

Reiner, W. G., & Gearhart, J. P. (2004). Discordant sexual identity in some genetic males with cloacal exstrophy assigned to female sex at birth. *New England Journal of Medicine, 350,* 333–341. (p. 167)

Reinhart, R. J. (2017, June 20). Terrorism fears drive more in US to avoid crowds. Gallup poll (gallup.com). (p. 301)

Reis, H. T., & Aron, A. (2008). Love: What is it, why does it matter, and how does it operate? *Perspectives on Psychological Science, 3,* 80–86. (p. 451)

Reis, H. T., Smith, S. M., Carmichael, C. L., Caprariello, P. A., Tsa, F.-F., Rodrigues, A., & Maniaci, M. R. (2010). Are you happy for me? How sharing positive events with others provides personal and interpersonal benefits. *Journal of Personality and Social Psychology, 99,* 311–329. (p. 352)

Reis, M., Ramiro, L., Camacho, I., Tomé, G., Brito, C., & Gaspar de Matos, G. (2017). Does having a pet make a difference? Highlights from the HBSC Portuguese study. *European Journal of Developmental Psychology.* (p. 401)

Reis, S. M. (2001). Toward a theory of creativity in diverse creative women. In M. Bloom & T. Gullotta (Eds.), *Promoting creativity across the life span* (pp. 231–275). Washington, DC: CWLA Press. (p. 306)

Reisenzein, R. (1983). The Schachter theory of emotion: Two decades later. *Psychological Bulletin, 94,* 239–264. (p. 369)

Reiser, M. (1982). *Police psychology.* Los Angeles: LEHI. (p. 230)

Reitz, A. K., Motti-Stefanidi, F., & Asendorpf, J. B. (2016). Me, us, and them: Testing sociometer theory in a socially diverse real-life context. *Journal of Personality and Social Psychology, 110,* 908–920. (p. 486)

Reitzle, M. (2006). The connections between adulthood transitions and the self-perception of being adult in the changing contexts of East and West Germany. *European Psychologist, 11,* 25–38. (p. 149)

Reivich, K., Gillham, J. E., Chaplin, T. M., & Seligman, M. E. P. (2013). *From helplessness to optimism: The role of resilience in treating and preventing depression in youth.* New York: Springer Science & Business Media. (p. 545)

Rekker, R., Keijsers, L., Branje, S., & Meeus, W. (2015). Political attitudes in adolescence and emerging adulthood: Developmental changes in mean level, polarization, rank-order stability, and correlates. *Journal of Adolescence, 41,* 136–147. (p. 118)

Remick, A. K., Polivy, J., & Pliner, P. (2009). Internal and external moderators of the effect of variety on food intake. *Psychological Bulletin, 135,* 434–451. (p. 364)

Remington, A., Swettenham, J., Campbell, R., & Coleman, M. (2009). Selective attention and perceptual load in autism spectrum disorder. *Psychological Science, 20,* 1388–1393. (p. 131)

Remley, A. (1988, October). From obedience to independence. *Psychology Today,* pp. 56–59. (p. 138)

Ren, D., Wesselmann, E., & Williams, K. D. (2016). Evidence for another response to ostracism: Solitude seeking. *Social Psychological and Personality Science, 7*(3), 204–212. (p. 476)

Renner, M. J., & Renner, C. H. (1993). Expert and novice intuitive judgments about animal behavior. *Bulletin of the Psychonomic Society, 31,* 551–552. (p. 123)

Renninger, K. A., & Granott, N. (2005). The process of scaffolding in learning and development. *New Ideas in Psychology, 23,* 111–114. (p. 129)

Rentfrow, P. J., & Gosling, S. D. (2003). The do re mi's of everyday life: The structure and personality correlates of music preferences. *Journal of Personality and Social Psychology, 84,* 1236–1256. (p. 481)

Rentfrow, P. J., & Gosling, S. D. (2006). Message in a ballad: The role of music preferences in interpersonal perception. *Psychological Science, 17,* 236–242. (p. 481)

Repacholi, B. M., Meltzoff, A. N., Toub, T. S., & Ruba, A. L. (2016). Infants' generalizations about other people's emotions: Foundations for trait-like attributions. *Developmental Psychology, 52,* 364. (p. 128)

Rescorla, R. A., & Wagner, A. R. (1972). A theory of Pavlovian conditioning: Variations in the effectiveness of reinforcement and nonreinforcement. In A. H. Black & W. F. Perokasy (Eds.), *Classical conditioning II: Current theory.* New York: Appleton-Century-Crofts. (p. 256)

Resnick, M. D., Bearman, P. S., Blum, R. W., Bauman, K. E., Harris, K. M., Jones, J., . . . Udry, J. R. (1997). Protecting adolescents from harm: Findings from the National Longitudinal Study on Adolescent Health. *Journal of the American Medical Association, 278,* 823–832. (pp. 26, 83, 148)

Resnick, S. M. (1992). Positron emission tomography in psychiatric illness. *Current Directions in Psychological Science, 1,* 92–98. (p. 524)

Reuters. (2000, July 5). *Many teens regret decision to have sex (National Campaign to Prevent Teen Pregnancy survey).* Retrieved from washingtonpost.com (p. 177)

Reuters. (2015, November 25). *Most important problem facing the U.S. today.* Reuters Polling. Retrieved from polling.reuters.com/#!poll/SC8/type/smallest/dates/20150901-20151125/collapsed/true/spotlight/1 (p. 301)

Reyna, V. F., Chick, C. F., Corbin, J. C., & Hsia, A. N. (2014). Developmental reversals in risky decision making: Intelligence agents show larger decision biases than college students. *Psychological Science, 25,* 76–84. (p. 305)

Reyna, V. F., & Farley, F. (2006). Risk and rationality in adolescent decision making: Implications for theory, practice, and public policy. *Psychological Science in the Public Interest, 7,* 1–44. (p. 142)

Reynolds, G. (2009, November 18). Phys ed: Why exercise makes you less anxious. *The New York Times blog.* Retrieved from well.blogs.nytimes.com (p. 402)

Rhodes, E. (2017, August). Back to academia . . . and elephants. *The Psychologist,* pp. 12–13. (p. 240)

Rhodes, M. G., & Anastasi, J. S. (2012). The own-age bias in face recognition: A meta-analytic and theoretical review. *Psychological Bulletin, 138,* 146–174. (p. 439)

Riccelli, R., Toschi, N., Nigro, S., Terracciano, A., & Passamonti, L. (2017). Surface-based morphometry reveals the neuroanatomical basis of the five-factor model of personality. *Social Cognitive and Affective Neuroscience, 12,* 671–684. (p. 478)

Ricciardelli, L. A., & McCabe, M. P. (2004). A biopsychosocial model of disordered eating and the pursuit of muscularity in adolescent boys. *Psychological Bulletin, 130,* 179–205. (p. 532)

Rice, M. E., & Grusec, J. E. (1975). Saying and doing: Effects on observer performance. *Journal of Personality and Social Psychology, 32,* 584–593. (p. 262)

Richardson, J. T. E., & Zucco, G. M. (1989). Cognition and olfaction: A review. *Psychological Bulletin, 105,* 352–360. (p. 227)

Richardson, M., Abraham, C., & Bond, R. (2012). Psychological correlates of university students' academic performance: A systematic review and meta-analysis. *Psychological Bulletin, 138,* 353–387. (p. 339)

Richeson, J. A., & Shelton, J. N. (2007). Negotiating interracial interactions. *Current Directions in Psychological Science, 16,* 316–320. (p. 457)

Rickard, I. J., Frankenhuis, W. E., & Nettle, D. (2014). Why are childhood family factors associated with timing of maturation? A role for internal prediction. *Perspectives on Psychological Science, 9,* 3–15. (p. 167)

Rieff, P. (1979). *Freud: The mind of a moralist* (3rd ed.). Chicago: University of Chicago Press. (p. 469)

Rieger, G., Savin-Williams, R., Chivers, M. L., & Bailey, J. M. (2016). Sexual arousal and masculinity-femininity of women. *Journal of Personality and Social Psychology, 111,* 265–283. (p. 182)

Riemer, H., Shavitt, S., Koo, M., & Markus, H. R. (2014). Preferences don't have to be personal: Expanding attitude theorizing with a cross-cultural perspective. *Psychological Review, 121,* 619–648. (p. 416)

Rietveld, C. A., Conley, D., Eriksson, N., Esko, T., Medland, S. E., Vinkhuyzen, A. A. E., . . . Koellinger, P. D. (2014). Replicability and robustness of genome-wide-association studies for behavioral traits. *Psychological Science, 25,* 1975–1986. (p. 336)

Rietveld, C. A., Medland, S. E., Derringer, J., Yang, J., Esko, T., Martin, N. W., . . . Koellinger, P. D. (2013). GWAS of 126,559 individuals identifies genetic variants associated with educational attainment. *Science, 340,* 1467–1471. (p. 336)

Rigoni, J. B., & Asplund, J. (2016a, July 7). *Strengths-based development: The business results.* The Gallup Organization (gallup.com). (p. B-12)

Rigoni, J. B., & Asplund, J. (2016b, July 12). *Global study: ROI for strengths-based development.* The Gallup Organization (gallup.com). (p. B-12)

Riley, L. D., & Bowen, C. (2005). The sandwich generation: Challenges and coping strategies of multigenerational families. *The Family Journal, 13,* 52–58. (p. 155)

Rimfeld, K., Kovas, Y., Dale, P. S., & Plomin, R. (2016). True grit and genetics: Predicting academic achievement from personality. *Journal of Personality and Social Psychology, 111,* 780–789. (p. 358)

Rindermann, H., & Ceci, S. J. (2009). Educational policy and country outcomes in international cognitive competence studies. *Perspectives on Psychological Science, 4,* 551–577. (p. 342)

Riordan, M. (2013, March 19). *Tobacco warning labels: Evidence of effectiveness.* Washington, DC: The Campaign for Tobacco-Free Kids (tobaccofreekids.org). (p. 303)

Ripke, S., Wray, N. R., Lewis, C. M., Hamilton, S. P., Weissman, M. M., Breen, G., . . . Heath, A. C. (2013). A mega-analysis of genome-wide association studies for major depressive disorder. *Molecular Psychiatry, 18,* 497–511. (p. 518)

Ritchie, S. J., Dickie, D. A., Cox, S. R., Hernandez, M. del C. V., Corley, J., Royle, N. A., . . . Deary, I. J. (2015). Brain volumetric changes and cognitive ageing during the eighth decade of life. *Human Brain Mapping, 36,* 4910–4925. (p. 152)

Ritchie, S. J., Wiseman, R., & French, C. C. (2012). Failing the future: Three unsuccessful attempts to replicate Bem's "retroactive facilitation of recall" effect. *PLoS ONE, 7,* e33r23 (plosone.org). (p. 231)

Ritter, S. M., Damian, R. I., Simonton, D. K., van Baaren, R. B., Strick, M., Derks, J., & Dijksterhuis, A. (2012). Diversifying experiences enhance cognitive flexibility. *Journal of Experimental Social Psychology, 48,* 961–964. (p. 307)

Rizzolatti, G., Fadiga, L., Fogassi, L., & Gallese, V. (2002). From mirror neurons to imitation: Facts and speculations. In A. N. Meltzoff & W. Prinz (Eds.), *The imitative mind: Development, evolution, and brain bases.* Cambridge, England: Cambridge University Press. (p. 259)

Rizzolatti, G., Fogassi, L., & Gallese, V. (2006, November). Mirrors in the mind. *Scientific American, 295,* 54–61. (p. 259)

Roberson, D., Davidoff, J., Davies, I. R. L., & Shapiro, L. R. (2004). The development of color categories in two languages: A longitudinal study. *Journal of Experimental Psychology: General, 133,* 554–571. (p. 319)

Roberson, D., Davies, I. R. L., Corbett, G. G., & Vandervyver, M. (2005). Free-sorting of colors across cultures: Are there universal grounds for grouping? *Journal of Cognition and Culture, 5,* 349–386. (p. 319)

Roberti, J. W., Storch, E. A., & Bravata, E. A. (2004). Sensation seeking, exposure to psychosocial stressors, and body modifications in a college population. *Personality and Individual Differences, 37,* 1167–1177. (p. 349)

Roberts, A. L., Glymour, M. M., & Koenen, K. C. (2013). Does maltreatment in childhood affect sexual orientation in adulthood? *Archives of Sexual Behavior, 42,* 161–171. (pp. 118, 180)

Roberts, B. W., & DelVecchio, W. F. (2000). The rank-order consistency of personality traits from childhood to old age: A quantitative review of longitudinal studies. *Psychological Bulletin, 126,* 3–25. (p. 480)

Roberts, B. W., Kuncel, N. R., Shiner, R., Caspi, A., & Goldberg, L. R. (2007). The power of personality: The comparative validity of personality traits, socioeconomic status, and cognitive ability for predicting important life outcomes. *Perspectives on Psychological Science, 2,* 313–345. (p. 480)

Roberts, B. W., Luo, J., Briley, D. A., Chow, P. I., Su, R., & Hill, P. L. (2017). A systematic review of personality trait change through intervention. *Psychological Bulletin, 143,* 117–141. (p. 552)

Roberts, L. (1988). Beyond Noah's ark: What do we need to know? *Science, 242,* 1247. (p. 397)

Roberts, T.-A. (1991). Determinants of gender differences in responsiveness to others' evaluations. *Dissertation Abstracts International, 51*(08–B). (p. 164)

Robertson, K. F., Smeets, S., Lubinski, D., & Benbow, C. P. (2010). Beyond the threshold hypothesis: Even among the gifted and top math/science graduate students, cognitive abilities, vocational interests, and lifestyle preferences matter for career choice, performance, and persistence. *Current Directions in Psychological Science, 19,* 346–351. (p. 306)

Robins, L. N., Davis, D. H., & Goodwin, D. W. (1974). Drug use by U.S. Army enlisted men in Vietnam: A follow-up on their return home. *American Journal of Epidemiology, 99,* 235–249. (p. 113)

Robins, L., & Regier, D. (Eds.). (1991). *Psychiatric disorders in America.* New York: Free Press. (p. 505)

Robinson, F. P. (1970). *Effective study.* New York: Harper & Row. (p. 33)

Robinson, J. P., & Martin, S. (2008). What do happy people do? *Social Indicators Research, 89,* 565–571. (p. B-2)

Robinson, J. P., & Martin, S. (2009). Changes in American daily life: 1965–2005. *Social Indicators Research, 93,* 47–56. (p. 262)

Robinson, O. J., Cools, R., Carlisi, C. O., & Drevets, W. C. (2012). Ventral striatum response during reward and punishment reversal learning in unmedicated major depressive disorder. *American Journal of Psychiatry, 169,* 152–159. (p. 518)

Robinson, T. E., & Berridge, K. C. (2003). Addiction. *Annual Review of Psychology, 54,* 25–53. (p. 102)

Robinson, T. N., Borzekowski, D. L. G., Matheson, D. M., & Kraemer, H. C. (2007). Effects of fast food branding on young children's taste preferences. *Archives of Pediatric and Adolescent Medicine, 161,* 792–797. (p. 196)

Robinson, V. M. (1983). Humor and health. In P. E. McGhee & J. H. Goldstein (Eds.), *Handbook of humor research: Vol. II.* Applied studies. New York: Springer-Verlag. (p. 399)

Robles, T. F. (2015). Marital quality and health: Implications for marriage in the 21st century. *Current Directions in Psychological Science, 23,* 427–432. (p. 400)

Rochat, F. (1993). *How did they resist authority? Protecting refugees in Le Chambon during World War II.* Paper presented at the American Psychological Association convention. (p. 428)

Rock, I., & Palmer, S. (1990, December). The legacy of Gestalt psychology. *Scientific American,* pp. 84–90. (p. 208)

Rodin, J. (1986). Aging and health: Effects of the sense of control. *Science, 233,* 1271–1276. (pp. 396, 397)

Roediger, H. L. (1980). Memory metaphors in cognitive psychology. *Memory & Cognition, 8,* 231–246. (p. 268)

Roediger, H. L., III. (2013). Applying cognitive psychology to education: Translational educational science. *Psychological Science in the Public Interest, 14,* 1–3. (pp. 272, 273)

Roediger, H. L., III., & DeSoto, K. A. (2016). Was Alexander Hamilton president? *Psychological Science, 27,* 644–650. (p. 290)

Roediger, H. L., III., & Finn, B. (2010, March/April). The pluses of getting it wrong. *Scientific American Mind,* pp. 39–41. (p. 33)

Roediger, H. L., III. & Geraci, L. (2007). Aging and the misinformation effect: A neuropsychological analysis. *Journal of Experimental Psychology, 33,* 321–334. (p. 294)

Roediger, H. L., III., & Karpicke, J. D. (2006). Test-enhanced learning: Taking memory tests improves long-term retention. *Psychological Science, 17,* 249–255. (pp. 33, 272)

Roediger, H. L., III., & McDaniel, M. A. (2007). Illusory recollection in older adults: Testing Mark Twain's conjecture. In M. Garry H. Hayne (Ed.), *Do justice and let the sky fall: Elizabeth F. Loftus and her contributions to science, law, and academic freedom.* Mahwah, NJ: Erlbaum. (p. 294)

Roediger, H. L., III., & McDermott, K. B. (1995). Creating false memories: Remembering words not presented in lists. *Journal of Experimental Psychology: Learning, Memory, and Cognition, 21,* 803–814. (p. 292)

Roediger, H. L., III., Meade, M. L., & Bergman, E. T. (2001). Social contagion of memory. *Psychonomic Bulletin & Review, 8,* 365–371. (p. 292)

Roediger, H. L., III., Wheeler, M. A., & Rajaram, S. (1993). Remembering, knowing, and reconstructing the past. In D. L. Medin (Ed.), *The psychology of learning and motivation: Advances in research and theory* (Vol. 30). Orlando, FL: Academic Press. (p. 292)

Roehling, P. V., Roehling, M. V., & Moen, P. (2001). The relationship between work-life policies and practices and employee loyalty: A life course perspective. *Journal of Family and Economic Issues, 22,* 141–170. (p. B-11)

Roelofs, T. (2010, September 22). Somali refugee takes oath of U.S. citizenship year after his brother. *The Grand Rapids Press* (mlive.com). (p. B-8)

Roenneberg, T., Kuehnle, T., Pramstaller, P. P., Ricken, J., Havel, M., Guth, A., & Merrow, M. (2004). A marker for the end of adolescence. *Current Biology, 14,* R1038–R1039. (p. 87)

Roepke, A. M. (2015). Psychosocial interventions and posttraumatic growth: A meta-analysis. *Journal of Consulting and Clinical Psychology, 83,* 129. (p. 567)

Roepke, A. M., & Seligman, M. E. P. (2015). Doors opening: A mechanism for growth after adversity. *Journal of Positive Psychology, 10,* 107–115. (p. 567)

Roese, N. J., & Summerville, A. (2005). What we regret most . . . and why. *Personality and Social Psychology Bulletin, 31,* 1273–1285. (p. 158)

Roese, N. J., & Vohs, K. D. (2012). Hindsight bias. *Perspectives on Psychological Science, 7,* 411–426. (p. 16)

Roesser, R. (1998). *What you should know about hearing conservation.* Retrieved from betterhearing.org/ (p. 218)

Rogers, C. R. (1961). *On becoming a person: A therapist's view of psychotherapy.* Boston: Houghton Mifflin. (pp. 472, 539)

Rogers, C. R. (1980). *A way of being.* Boston: Houghton Mifflin. (pp. 471, 472, 539)

Rogers, C. R. (1985, February). Quoted by M. L. Wallach & L. Wallach, How psychology sanctions the cult of the self. *Washington Monthly,* pp. 46–56. (p. 473)

Rogers, T., & Feller, A. (2016). Discouraged by peer excellence: Exposure to exemplary peer performance causes quitting. *Psychological Science, 27,* 365–374. (p. 410)

Rogers, T., & Milkman, K. L. (2016). Reminders through association. *Psychological Science, 27,* 973–986. (p. 280)

Rohan, K. J., Mahon, J. N., Evans, M., Ho, S., Meyerhoff, J., Postolache, T. T., & Vacek, P. M. (2015). Randomized trial of cognitive-behavioral therapy versus light therapy for seasonal affective disorder: Acute outcomes. *The American Journal of Psychiatry, 172,* 862–869. (p. 555)

Rohan, K. J., Roecklein, K. A., Lindsey, K. T., Johnson, L. G., Lippy, R. D., Lacy, T. J., & Barton, F. B. (2007). A randomized controlled trial of cognitive-behavioral therapy, light therapy, and their combination for seasonal affective disorder. *Journal of Consulting and Clinical Psychology, 75,* 489–500. (p. 555)

Rohner, R. P., & Veneziano, R. A. (2001). The importance of father love: History and contemporary evidence. *Review of General Psychology, 5,* 382–405. (p. 135)

Rohrer, J. M., Egloff, B., Kosinski, M., Stillwell, D., & Schmukle, S. C. (2018). In your eyes only? Discrepancies and agreement between self- and other-reports of personality from age 14 to 29. *Journal of Personality and Social Psychology,* in press. (p. 478)

Rohrer, J. M., Egloff, B., & Schmukle, S. C. (2015). Examining the effects of birth order on personality. *PNAS, 112,* 14224–14229. (pp. 478, A-8)

Roiser, J. P., Cook, L. J., Cooper, J. D., Rubinsztein, D. C., & Sahakian, B. J. (2005). Association of a functional polymorphism in the serotonin transporter gene with abnormal emotional processing in Ecstasy users. *American Journal of Psychiatry, 162,* 609–612. (p. 108)

Rokach, A., Orzeck, T., Moya, M., & Expósito, F. (2002). Causes of loneliness in North America and Spain. *European Psychologist, 7,* 70–79. (p. 10)

Romano, A., Balliet, D., Yamagishi, T., & Liu, J. H. (2017). Parochial trust and cooperation across 17 societies. *PNAS, 114,* 12702–12707. (p. 438)

Romelsjö, A., Danielsson, A., Wennberg, P., & Hibell, B. (2014). Cannabis use and drug related problems among adolescents in 27 European countries: The utility of the prevention paradox. *Nordic Studies on Alcohol and Drugs, 31,* 359–369. (p. 112)

Romens, S. E., McDonald, J., Svaren, J., & Pollak, S. D. (2015). Associations between early life stress and gene methylation in children. *Child Development, 86,* 303–309. (p. 137)

Ronald, A., & Hoekstra, R. A. (2011). Autism spectrum disorders and autistic traits: A decade of new twin studies. *American Journal of Medical Genetics Part B, 156,* 255–274. (p. 70)

Ronay, R., & von Hippel, W. (2010). The presence of an attractive woman elevates testosterone and physical risk taking in young men. *Social Psychology and Personality Science, 1,* 57–64. (p. 173)

Root, T. L., Thornton, L. M., Lindroos, A. K., Stunkard, A. J., Lichtenstein, P., Pedersen, N. L., . . . Bulik, C. M. (2010). Shared and unique genetic and environmental influences on binge eating and night eating: A Swedish twin study. *Eating Behaviors, 11,* 92–98. (p. 532)

Roper, K. R. (2016, July 19). Public Facebook post. Retrieved from facebook.com/kate.riffleroper/posts/1746348308987959 (p. 301)

Roper, S. D., & Chaudhari, N. (2017). Taste buds: Cells, signals, and synapses. *Nature Reviews Neuroscience, 18,* 485–497. (p. 225)

Roque, L., Verissimo, M., Oliveira, T. F., & Oliveira, R. F. (2012). Attachment security and HPA axis reactivity to positive and challenging emotional situations in child–mother dyads in naturalistic settings. *Developmental Psychobiology, 54,* 401–411. (p. 135)

Rosch, E. (1978). Principles of categorization. In E. Rosch & B. L. Lloyd (Eds.), *Cognition and categorization.* Hillsdale, NJ: Erlbaum. (p. 298)

Rose, A. J., & Rudolph, K. D. (2006). A review of sex differences in peer relationship processes: Potential trade-offs for the emotional and behavioral development of girls and boys. *Psychological Bulletin, 132,* 98–131. (p. 163)

Rose, H., & Rose, S. (2016). *Can neuroscience change our minds?* Cambridge, UK: Polity. (p. 52)

Rose, J. S., Chassin, L., Presson, C. C., & Sherman, S. J. (1999). Peer influences on adolescent cigarette smoking: A prospective sibling analysis. *Merrill-Palmer Quarterly, 45,* 62–84. (pp. 112, 147)

Rose, R. J., Viken, R. J., Dick, D. M., Bates, J. E., Pulkkinen, L., & Kaprio, J. (2003). It *does* take a village: Nonfamiliar environments and children's behavior. *Psychological Science, 14,* 273–277. (p. 147)

Roselli, C. E., Larkin, K., Schrunk, J. M., & Stormshak, F. (2004). Sexual partner preference, hypothalamic morphology and aromatase in rams. *Physiology and Behavior, 83,* 233–245. (p. 181)

Roselli, C. E., Resko, J. A., & Stormshak, F. (2002). Hormonal influences on sexual partner preference in rams. *Archives of Sexual Behavior, 31,* 43–49. (p. 181)

Rosenbaum, M. (1986). The repulsion hypothesis: On the nondevelopment of relationships. *Journal of Personality and Social Psychology, 51,* 1156–1166. (p. 450)

Rosenberg, E. L., Zanesco, A. P., King, B. G., Aichele, S. R., Jacobs, R. L., Bridwell, D. A., . . . Saron, C. D. (2015). Intensive meditation training influences emotional responses to suffering. *Emotion, 15,* 775–790. (p. 404)

Rosenberg, N. A., Pritchard, J. K., Weber, J. L., Cann, H. M., Kidd, K. K., Zhivotosky, L. A., & Feldman, M. W. (2002). Genetic structure of human populations. *Science, 298,* 2381–2385. (p. 342)

Rosenberg, T. (2010, November 1). The opt-out solution. *The New York Times.* Retrieved from http://opinionator.blogs.nytimes.com/2010/11/01/the-opt-out-solution/ (p. 304)

Rosenblum, L. D. (2013, January). A confederacy of senses. *Scientific American,* pp. 73–78. (p. 228)

Rosenfeld, M. J. (2013, August 26). Personal communication. (p. 156)

Rosenfeld, M. J. (2014). Couple longevity in the era of same-sex marriage in the United States. *Journal of Marriage and Family, 76,* 905–911. (p. 156)

Rosenfeld, M. J., & Thomas, R. J. (2012). Searching for a mate: The rise of the internet as a social intermediary. *American Sociological Review, 77,* 523–547. (pp. 156, 448)

Rosenhan, D. L. (1973). On being sane in insane places. *Science, 179,* 250–258. (p. 497)

Rosenkranz, M. A., Davidson, R. J., Maccoon, D. G., Sheridan, J. F., Kalin, N. H., & Lutz, A. (2013). A comparison of mindfulness-based stress reduction and an active control in modulation of neurogenic inflammation. *Brain, Behavior, and Immunity, 27,* 174–184. (p. 404)

Rosenquist, P. B., McCall, W. V., & Youssef, N. (2016). Charting the course of electroconvulsive therapy: Where have we been and where are we headed? *Psychiatric Annals, 46,* 647–651. (p. 563)

Rosenthal, E. (2009, November 2). When texting kills, Britain offers path of prison. *The New York Times* (nytimes.com). (p. 82)

Rosenthal, R., Hall, J. A., Archer, D., DiMatteo, M. R., & Rogers, P. L. (1979). The PONS test: Measuring sensitivity to nonverbal cues. In S. Weitz (Ed.), *Nonverbal communication* (2nd ed.). New York: Oxford University Press. (p. 376)

Rosenzweig, M. R., Krech, D., Bennett, E. L., & Diamond, M. C. (1962). Effects of environmental complexity and training on brain chemistry and anatomy: A replication and extension. *Journal of Comparative and Physiological Psychology, 55,* 429–437. (p. 123)

Roseth, C. J., Johnson, D. W., & Johnson, R. T. (2008). Promoting early adolescents' achievement and peer relationships: The effects of cooperative, competitive, and individualistic goal structures. *Psychological Bulletin, 134,* 223–246. (p. 458)

Ross, J. (2006, December). Sleep on a problem . . . it works like a dream. *The Psychologist, 19,* 738–740. (p. 92)

Ross, L. (1977). The intuitive psychologist and his shortcomings: Distortions in the attribution process. In L. Berkowitz (Ed.) *Advances in experimental social psychology* (Vol. 10). New York: Academic Press. (p. 416)

Ross, M., McFarland, C., & Fletcher, G. J. O. (1981). The effect of attitude on the recall of personal histories. *Journal of Personality and Social Psychology, 40,* 627–634. (p. 288)

Ross, M., Xun, W. Q. E., & Wilson, A. E. (2002). Language and the bicultural self. *Personality and Social Psychology Bulletin, 28,* 1040–1050. (p. 319)

Rossi, P. J. (1968). Adaptation and negative aftereffect to lateral optical displacement in newly hatched chicks. *Science, 160,* 430–432. (p. 213)

Rossion, B., & Boremanse, A. (2011). Robust sensitivity to facial identity in the right human occipito-temporal cortex as revealed by steady-state visual-evoked potentials. *Journal of Vision, 11*(2), Article 16. doi:10.1167/11.2.16 (p. 189)

Rotge, J.-Y., Lemogne, C., Hinfray, S., Huguet, P., Grynszpan, O., Tartour, E., . . . Fossati, P. (2015). A meta-analysis of the anterior cingulate contribution to social pain. *Social Cognitive and Affective Neuroscience, 10,* 19–27. (p. 354)

Roth, B., Becker, N., Romeyke, S., Schäfer, S., Domnick, F., & Spinath, F. M. (2015). Intelligence and school grades: A meta-analysis. *Intelligence, 53,* 118–137. (p. 330)

Roth, B., Hahn, E., & Spinath, F. M. (2016). Income inequality, life satisfaction, and economic worries. *Social Psychological and Personality Science.* Advance online publication. doi:10.1177/1948550616664955 (p. 410)

Roth, T., Roehrs, T., Zwyghuizen-Doorenbos, A., Stpeanski, E., & Witting, R. (1988). Sleep and memory. In I. Hindmarch & H. Ott (Eds.), *Benzodiazepine receptor ligands, memory and information processing* (pp. 140–145). Berlin, Germany: Springer-Verlag. (p. 97)

Rothbart, M., Fulero, S., Jensen, C., Howard, J., & Birrell, P. (1978). From individual to group impressions: Availability heuristics in stereotype formation. *Journal of Experimental Social Psychology, 14,* 237–255. (p. 440)

Rothbaum, F., & Tsang, B. Y.-P. (1998). Lovesongs in the United States and China: On the nature of romantic love. *Journal of Cross-Cultural Psychology, 29,* 306–319. (p. 491)

Rotheneichner, P., Lange, S., O'Sullivan, A., Marschallinger, J., Zaunmair, P., Geretsegger, C., . . . Couillard-Despres, S. (2014). Hippocampal neurogenesis and antidepressive therapy: Shocking relations. *Neural Plasticity, 2014,* 723915. (p. 563)

Rothman, A. J., & Salovey, P. (1997). Shaping perceptions to motivate healthy behavior: The role of message framing. *Psychological Bulletin, 121,* 3–19. (p. 305)

Rottensteiner, M., Leskinen, T., Niskanen, E., Aaltonen, S., Mutikainen, S., Wikgren, J., . . . Kujala, U. M. (2015). Physical activity, fitness, glucose homeostasis, and brain morphology in twins. *Medicine and Science in Sports and Exercise, 47,* 509–518. (p. 153)

Rotton, J., & Kelly, I. W. (1985). Much ado about the full moon: A meta-analysis of lunar-lunacy research. *Psychological Bulletin, 97,* 286–306. (p. 530)

Rounds, J., & Su, R. (2014). The nature and power of interests. *Current Directions in Psychological Science, 23,* 98–103. (p. B-3)

Rovee-Collier, C. (1989). The joy of kicking: Memories, motives, and mobiles. In P. R. Solomon, G. R. Goethals, C. M. Kelley, & B. R. Stephens (Eds.), *Memory: Interdisciplinary approaches* (pp. 151–179). New York: Springer-Verlag. (p. 125)

Rovee-Collier, C. (1993). The capacity for long-term memory in infancy. *Current Directions in Psychological Science, 2,* 130–135. (p. 281)

Rovee-Collier, C. (1997). Dissociations in infant memory: Rethinking the development of implicit and explicit memory. *Psychological Review, 104,* 467–498. (p. 125)

Rovee-Collier, C. (1999). The development of infant memory. *Current Directions in Psychological Science, 8,* 80–85. (p. 125)

Rowe, D. C. (1990). As the twig is bent? The myth of child-rearing influences on personality development. *Journal of Counseling and Development, 68,* 606–611. (p. 72)

Rowe, D. C., Almeida, D. M., & Jacobson, K. C. (1999). School context and genetic influences on aggression in adolescence. *Psychological Science, 10,* 277–280. (p. 441)

Roy, J., & Forest, G. (2017). Greater circadian disadvantage during evening games for the National Basketball Association (NBA), National Hockey League (NHL) and National Football League (NFL) teams travelling westward. *Journal of Sleep Research*. Advance online publication. doi:10.1111/jsr.12565 (p. 91)

Rozin, P., Dow, S., Mosovitch, M., & Rajaram, S. (1998). What causes humans to begin and end a meal? A role for memory for what has been eaten, as evidenced by a study of multiple meal eating in amnesic patients. *Psychological Science, 9*, 392–396. (p. 363)

Rozin, P., Haddad, B., Nemeroff, C., & Slovic, P. (2015). Psychological aspects of the rejection of recycled water: Contamination, purification and disgust. *Judgment and Decision Making, 10*, 50–63. (p. 240)

Rozin, P., Millman, L., & Nemeroff, C. (1986). Operation of the laws of sympathetic magic in disgust and other domains. *Journal of Personality and Social Psychology, 50*, 703–712. (p. 240)

Ruau, D., Liu, L. Y., Clark, J. D., Angst, M. S., & Butte, A. J. (2012). Sex differences in reported pain across 11,000 patients captured in electronic medical records. *Journal of Pain, 13*, 228–234. (p. 222)

Ruback, R. B., Carr, T. S., & Hopper, C. H. (1986). Perceived control in prison: Its relation to reported crowding, stress, and symptoms. *Journal of Applied Social Psychology, 16*, 375–386. (p. 396)

Rubenstein, J. S., Meyer, D. E., & Evans, J. E. (2001). Executive control of cognitive processes in task switching. *Journal of Experimental Psychology: Human Perception and Performance, 27*, 763–797. (p. 82)

Rubenstein, L. M., Freed, R. D., Shapero, B. G., Fauber, R. L., & Alloy, L. B. (2016, June). Cognitive attributions in depression: Bridging the gap between research and clinical practice. *Journal of Psychotherapy Integration, 26*, 103–115. (p. 420)

Ruberton, P. M., Gladstone, J., & Lyubomirsky, S. (2016). How your bank balance buys happiness. *Emotion, 16*, 575–580. (p. 409)

Rubin, D. C., Rahhal, T. A., & Poon, L. W. (1998). Things learned in early adulthood are remembered best. *Memory and Cognition, 26*, 3–19. (p. 153)

Rubin, J. Z., Pruitt, D. G., & Kim, S. H. (1994). *Social conflict: Escalation, stalemate, and settlement*. New York: McGraw-Hill. (p. 459)

Rubin, L. B. (1985). *Just friends: The role of friendship in our lives*. New York: Harper & Row. (p. 165)

Rubin, Z. (1970). Measurement of romantic love. *Journal of Personality and Social Psychology, 16*, 265–273. (p. 375)

Rubinstein, G. (2016). Modesty doesn't become me: Narcissism and the Big Five among male and female candidates for the *Big Brother* TV show. *Journal of Individual Differences, 37*, 223–230. (p. 489)

Rubio-Fernández, P., & Geurts, B. (2013). How to pass the false-belief task before your fourth birthday. *Psychological Science, 24*, 27–33. (p. 128)

Ruchlis, H. (1990). *Clear thinking: A practical introduction*. Buffalo, NY: Prometheus Books. (p. 299)

Rueckert, L., Doan, T., & Branch, B. (2010). *Emotion and relationship effects on gender differences in empathy*. Presented at the annual meeting of the Association for Psychological Science, Boston, MA. (p. 378)

Rueger, S. Y., Malecki, C. K., Pyun, Y., Aycock, C., & Coyle, S. (2016). A meta-analytic review of the association between perceived social support and depression in childhood and adolescence. *Psychological Bulletin, 142*, 1017–1067. (p. 399)

Ruffin, C. L. (1993). Stress and health—little hassles vs. major life events. *Australian Psychologist, 28*, 201–208. (p. 386)

Rule, B. G., & Ferguson, T. J. (1986). The effects of media violence on attitudes, emotions, and cognitions. *Journal of Social Issues, 42*, 29–50. (p. 263)

Rumbaugh, D. M. (1977). *Language learning by a chimpanzee: The Lana project*. New York: Academic Press. (p. 317)

Rumbaugh, D. M., & Washburn, D. A. (2003). *Intelligence of apes and other rational beings*. New Haven, CT: Yale University Press. (p. 318)

Runeson, B., Haglund, A., Lichtenstein, P., & Tidemalm, C. (2016). Suicide risk after nonfatal self-harm: A national cohort study, 2000–2008. *Journal of Clinical Psychiatry, 77*, 240–256. (p. 502)

Ruotsalainen, H., Kyngäs, H., Tammelin, T., & Kääriäinen, M. (2015). Systematic review of physical activity and exercise interventions on body mass indices, subsequent physical activity and psychological symptoms in overweight and obese adolescents. *Journal of Advanced Nursing, 71*, 2461–2477. (p. 366)

Rushton, J. P. (1975). Generosity in children: Immediate and long-term effects of modeling, preaching, and moral judgment. *Journal of Personality and Social Psychology, 31*, 459–466. (p. 262)

Russell, B. (1930/1985). *The conquest of happiness*. London: Unwin Paperbacks. (p. 410)

Ruthsatz, J., & Urbach, J. B. (2012). Child prodigy: A novel cognitive profile places elevated general intelligence, exceptional working memory and attention to detail at the root of prodigiousness. *Intelligence, 40*, 419–426. (p. 357)

Rutledge, R. B., Skandali, N., Dayan, P., & Dolan, R. J. (2014). A computational and neural model of momentary subjective well-being. *PNAS, 111*, 12252–12257. (p. 410)

Rutz, C., Klump, B. C., Komarczyk, L., Leighton, R., Kramer, R., Wischnewski, S., . . . Masuda, B. M. (2016). Discovery of species-wide tool use in the Hawaiian crow. *Nature, 537*, 403–407. (p. 309)

Ryan, B. (2016, March 8). *Women's life ratings get better with full-time jobs*. Gallup World Poll (gallup.com). (p. 165)

Ryan, P. (2015, December 15). Quoted by Editorial Board of *The New York Times*. Don't blame mental illness for gun violence. *The New York Times* (nytimes.com). (p. 502)

Ryan, R. (1999, February 2). Quoted by Alfie Kohn, In pursuit of affluence, at a high price. *The New York Times* (nytimes.com). (p. 410)

Ryan, R. M., & Deci, E. L. (2000). Self-determination theory and the facilitation of intrinsic motivation, social development, and well-being. *American Psychologist, 55*, 68–78. (p. 352)

Ryan, R. M., & Deci, E. L. (2004). Avoiding death or engaging life as accounts of meaning and culture: Comment on Pyszczynski et al. (2004). *Psychological Bulletin, 130*, 473–477. (p. 489)

Rydell, R. J., Rydell, M. T., & Boucher, K. L. (2010). The effect of negative performance stereotypes on learning. *Journal of Personality and Social Psychology, 99*, 883–896. (p. 344)

Ryder, J. G., & Holtzheimer, P. E. (2016). Deep brain stimulation for depression: An update. *Current Behavioral Neuroscience Reports, 3*, 102–108. (p. 564)

Saad, L. (2002, November 21). *Most smokers wish they could quit*. Retrieved from gallup.com/poll/7270/most-smokers-wish-they-could-quit.aspx (p. 106)

Saad, L. (2015, July 13). Nearly half of smartphone users can't imagine life without it. Gallup (gallup.com). (p. 355)

Sabbagh, M. A., Xu, F., Carlson, S. M., Moses, L. J., & Lee, K. (2006). The development of executive functioning and theory of mind: A comparison of Chinese and U.S. preschoolers. *Psychological Science, 17*, 74–81. (p. 128)

Sabesan, R., Schmidt, B. P., Tuten, W. S., & Roorda, A. (2016). The elementary representation of spatial and color vision in the human retina. *Science Advances, 2*, e1600797. (p. 202)

Sachdev, P., & Sachdev, J. (1997). Sixty years of psychosurgery: Its present status and its future. *Australian and New Zealand Journal of Psychiatry, 31*, 457–464. (p. 565)

Sackett, P. R., & Walmsley, P. T. (2014). Which personality attributes are most important in the workplace? *Perspectives on Psychological Science, 9*, 538–551. (p. 479)

Sacks, O. (1985). *The man who mistook his wife for a hat*. New York: Summit Books. (pp. 227, 284)

Sadato, N., Pascual-Leone, A., Grafman, J., Ibanez, V., Deiber, M.-P., Dold, G., & Hallett, M. (1996). Activation of the primary visual cortex by Braille reading in blind subjects. *Nature, 380*, 526–528. (p. 64)

Sadler, M. S., Correll, J., Park, B., & Judd, C. M. (2012b). The world is not Black and White: Racial bias in the decision to shoot in a multiethnic context. *Journal of Social Issues, 68*, 286–313. (p. 436)

Sadler, M. S., Meagor, E. L., & Kaye, M. E. (2012a). Stereotypes of mental disorders differ in competence and warmth. *Social Science and Medicine, 74*, 915–922. (p. 497)

Sagan, C. (1977). *The dragons of Eden: Speculations on the evolution of human intelligence*. New York: Ballantine. (p. 190)

Sagan, C. (1987, February 1). The fine art of baloney detection. *Parade*. (p. 231)

Saint Louis, C. (2017, February 2). Pregnant women turn to marijuana, perhaps harming infants. *The New York Times* (nyti.ms/2k6F9wc). (p. 120)

Saks, E. (2007, August 27). A memoir of schizophrenia. *Time* (time.com). (p. 560)

Salas-Wright, C. P., Vaughn, M. G., Hodge, D. R., & Perron, B. E. (2012). Religiosity profiles of American youth in relation to substance use, violence, and delinquency. *Journal of Youth and Adolescence, 41*, 1560–1575. (p. 112)

Salchegger, S. (2016). Selective school systems and academic self-concept: How explicit and implicit school-level tracking relate to the big-fish–little-pond effect across cultures. *Journal of Educational Psychology, 108*, 405–423. (p. 410)

Salehi, I., Hosseini, S. M., Haghighi, M., Jahangard, L., Bajoghli, H., Gerber, M., . . . Brand, S. (2016). Electroconvulsive therapy (ECT) and aerobic exercise training (AET) increased plasma BDNF and ameliorated depressive symptoms in patients suffering from major depressive disorder. *Journal of Psychiatric Research, 76*, 1–8. (p. 563)

Salgado, J. F., & Moscoso, S. (2002). Comprehensive meta-analysis of the construct validity of the employment interview. *European Journal of Work and Organizational Psychology, 11*, 299–326. (p. 476)

Salk, R. H., Hyde, J. S., & Abramson, L. Y. (2017). Gender differences in depression in representative national samples: Meta-analyses of diagnoses and symptoms. *Psychological Bulletin, 143*, 783–822. (p. 502)

Salmon, P. (2001). Effects of physical exercise on anxiety, depression, and sensitivity to stress: A unifying theory. *Clinical Psychology Review, 21*, 33–61. (pp. 402, 559)

Salovey, P. (1990, January/February). Interview. *American Scientist*, pp. 25–29. (p. 407)

Salthouse, T. A. (2009). When does age-related cognitive decline begin? *Neurobiology of Aging, 30,* 507–514. (p. 333)

Salthouse, T. A. (2010). Selective review of cognitive aging. *Journal of the International Neuropsychological Society, 16,* 754–760. (pp. 332, 334)

Salthouse, T. A. (2013). Within-cohort age-related differences in cognitive functioning. *Psychological Science, 24,* 123–130. (p. 333)

Salthouse, T. A. (2014). Why are there different age relations in cross-sectional and longitudinal comparisons of cognitive functioning? *Current Directions in Psychological Science, 23,* 252–256. (p. 332)

Salthouse, T. A., & Mandell, A. R. (2013). Do age-related increases in tip-of-the-tongue experiences signify episodic memory impairments? *Psychological Science, 24,* 2489–2497. (p. 287)

Samson, D. R., Crittenden, A. N., Mabulla, I. A., Mabulla, A. Z. P., & Nunn, C. L. (2017). Chronotype variation drives night-time sentinel-like behaviour in hunter-gatherers. *Processing of the Royal Society B, 284*(1858), 20170967. doi:10.5061/dryad.jd651/2 (p. 86)

Sanacora, G., Frye, M. A., McDonald, W., Mathew, S. J., Turner, M. S., Schatzberg, A. F., . . . Nemeroff, C. B. (2017). A consensus statement on the use of ketamine in the treatment of mood disorders. *JAMA Psychiatry, 74,* 399–405. (p. 562)

Sánchez-Álvarez, N., Extremera, N., & Fernández-Berrocal, P. (2016). The relation between emotional intelligence and subjective well-being: A meta-analytic investigation. *Journal of Positive Psychology, 11,* 276–285. (p. 326)

Sánchez-Villegas, A., Henríquez-Sánchez, P., Ruiz-Canela, M., Lahortiga, F., Molero, P., Toledo, E., & Martínez-González, M. A. (2015). A longitudinal analysis of diet quality scores and the risk of incident depression in the SUN Project. *BMC Medicine, 13,* 1. ([p. 559)

Sanders, A. R., Martin, E. R., Beecham, G. W., Guo, S., Dawood, K., Rieger, G., . . . Bailey, J. M. (2015). Genome-wide scan demonstrates significant linkage for male sexual orientation. *Psychological Medicine, 45,* 1379–1388. (p. 181)

Sandler, W., Meir, I., Padden, C., & Aronoff, M. (2005). The emergence of grammar: Systematic structure in a new language. *PNAS, 102,* 2261–2265. (p. 313)

Sandoval, M., Leclerc, J. A., & Gómez, R. L. (2017). Words to sleep on: Naps facilitate verb generalization in habitually and nonhabitually napping preschoolers. *Child Development, 88*(5), 1615–1626. (p. 92)

Sandstrom, A. (2015, December 2). *Religious groups' policies on transgender members vary widely.* Pew Research Center (pewresearch.org). (p. 171)

Santos, H. C., Varnum, M. E. W., & Grossmann, I. (2017). Global increases in individualism. *Psychological Science, 28,* 1228–1239. (p. 491)

Sanz, C., Blicher, A., Dalke, K., Gratton-Fabri, L., McClure-Richards, T., & Fouts, R. (1998, Winter-Spring). Enrichment object use: Five chimpanzees' use of temporary and semi-permanent enrichment objects. *Friends of Washoe, 19,* 9–14. (p. 317)

Sanz, C., Morgan, D., & Gulick, S. (2004). New insights into chimpanzees, tools, and termites from the Congo Basin. *American Naturalist, 164,* 567–581. (p. 310)

Sapadin, L. A. (1988). Friendship and gender: Perspectives of professional men and women. *Journal of Social and Personal Relationships, 5,* 387–403. (p. 165)

Saphire-Bernstein, S., Way, B. M., Kim, H. S, Sherman, D. K., & Taylor, S. E. (2011). Oxytocin receptor gene (OXTR) is related to psychological resources. *PNAS, 108,* 15118–15122. (p. 399)

Sapolsky, R. (2005). The influence of social hierarchy on primate health. *Science, 308,* 648–652. (pp. 396, 397)

Sapolsky, R. (2010, November 14). This is your brain on metaphors. *The New York Times* (nytimes.com). (p. 373)

Sapolsky, R. (2015, September 3). Caitlyn Jenner and our cognitive dissonance. *Nautilus.* Retrieved from nautil.us/issue/28/2050/caitlyn-jenner-and-our-cognitive-dissonance (p. 171)

Sarro, E. C., Wilson, D. A., & Sullivan, R. M. (2014). Maternal regulation of infant brain state. *Current Biology, 24,* 1664–1669. (p. 123)

Satel, S., & Lilienfeld, S. G. (2013). *Brainwashed: The seductive appeal of mindless neuroscience.* New York: Basic Books. (p. 52)

Sato, K. (1987). Distribution of the cost of maintaining common resources. *Journal of Experimental Social Psychology, 23,* 19–31. (p. 456)

Saulny, S. (2006, June 21). A legacy of the storm: Depression and suicide. *The New York Times* (nytimes.com). (p. 385)

Saurat, M., Agbakou, M., Attigui, P., Golmard, J., & Arnulf, I. (2011). Walking dreams in congenital and acquired paraplegia. *Consciousness and Cognition, 20,* 1425–1432. (p. 97)

Savage-Rumbaugh, E. S., Murphy, J., Sevcik, R. A., Brakke, K. E., Williams, S. L., & Rumbaugh, D. M., with commentary by Bates, E. (1993). Language comprehension in ape and child. *Monographs of the Society for Research in Child Development, 58,* 1–254. (p. 318)

Savage-Rumbaugh, E. S., Rumbaugh, D., & Fields, W. M. (2009). Empirical Kanzi: The ape language controversy revisited. *Skeptic, 15,* 25–33. (p. 318)

Savani, K., & Rattan, A. (2012). A choice mind-set increases the acceptance and maintenance of wealth inequality. *Psychological Science, 23,* 796–804. (p. 417)

Savelieva, K., Pulkki-Råback, L., Jokela, M., Kubzansky, L. D., Elovainio, M., Mikkilä, V., . . . Keltikangas-Järvinen, L. (2016). Intergenerational transmission of socioeconomic position and ideal cardiovascular health: 32-year follow-up study. *Health Psychology.* Advance online publication. doi:10.1037/hea0000441 (p. 397)

Savic, I., Berglund, H., & Lindstrom, P. (2005). Brain response to putative pheromones in homosexual men. *PNAS, 102,* 7356–7361. (p. 181)

Savin-Williams, R., Joyner, K., & Rieger, G. (2012). Prevalence and stability of self-reported sexual orientation identity during young adulthood. *Archives of Sexual Behavior, 41,* 103–110. (p. 178)

Savitsky, K., Epley, N., & Gilovich, T. D. (2001). Do others judge us as harshly as we think? Overestimating the impact of our failures, shortcomings, and mishaps. *Journal of Personality and Social Psychology, 81,* 44–56. (p. 486)

Savitsky, K., & Gilovich, T. D. (2003). The illusion of transparency and the alleviation of speech anxiety. *Journal of Experimental Social Psychology, 39,* 618–625. (p. 486)

Savoy, C., & Beitel, P. (1996). Mental imagery for basketball. *International Journal of Sport Psychology, 27,* 454–462. (p. 321)

Sawyer, A. C. P., Miller-Lewis, L. R., Searle, A. K., & Sawyer, M. G. (2015). Is greater improvement in early self-regulation associated with fewer behavioral problems later in childhood? *Developmental Psychology, 51,* 1740–1755. (p. 145)

Sawyer, M. G., Arney, F. M., Baghurst, P. A., Clark, J. J., Graetz, B. W., Kosky, R. J., . . . Zubrick, S. R. (2000). *The mental health of young people in Australia.* Canberra: Mental Health and Special Programs Branch, Commonwealth Department of Health and Aged Care. (p. 518)

Sayer, L. C. (2016). Trends in women's and men's time use, 1965–2012: Back to the future? In S. M. McHale, V. King, J. Van Hook, and A. Booth (Eds.), *Gender and couple relationships.* Cham, Switzerland: Springer International. (p. 187)

Sayette, M. A., Loewenstein, G., Griffin, K. M., & Black, J. J. (2008). Exploring the cold-to-hot empathy gap in smokers. *Psychological Science, 19,* 926–932. (p. 105)

Sayette, M. A., Reichle, E. D., & Schooler, J. W. (2009). Lost in the sauce: The effects of alcohol on mind wandering. *Psychological Science, 20,* 747–752. (p. 104)

Sayette, M. A., Schooler, J. W., & Reichle, E. D. (2010). Out for a smoke: The impact of cigarette craving on zoning out during reading. *Psychological Science, 21,* 26–30. (p. 105)

Sbarra, D. A., Hasselmo, K., & Bourassa, K. J. (2015). Divorce and health: Beyond individual differences. *Current Directions in Psychological Science, 24,* 109–113. (p. 385)

Scaini, S., Belotti, R., Ogliari, A., & Battaglia, M. (2016). A comprehensive meta-analysis of cognitive-behavioral interventions for social anxiety disorder in children and adolescents. *Journal of Anxiety Disorders, 42,* 105–112. (p. 553)

Scarborough, E., & Furumoto, L. (1987). *Untold lives: The first generation of American women psychologists.* New York: Columbia University Press. (p. 6)

Scarf, D., Boy, K., Reinert, A. U., Devine, J., Güntürkün, O., & Colombo, M. (2016). Orthographic processing in pigeons (*Columba livia*). *PNAS, 113,* 11272–11276. (p. 317)

Scarr, S. (1984, May). What's a parent to do? A conversation with E. Hall. *Psychology Today,* pp. 58–63. (p. 339)

Scarr, S. (1989). Protecting general intelligence: Constructs and consequences for interventions. In R. J. Linn (Ed.), *Intelligence: Measurement, theory, and public policy.* Champaign: University of Illinois Press. (p. 325)

Scarr, S. (1990). Back cover comments on J. Dunn & R. Plomin, *Separate lives: Why siblings are so different.* New York: Basic Books. (p. 74)

Scarr, S. (1993, May/June). Quoted in Nature's thumbprint: So long, superparents. *Psychology Today,* p. 16. (p. 149)

Schab, F. R. (1991). Odor memory: Taking stock. *Psychological Bulletin, 109,* 242–251. (p. 227)

Schachter, S., & Singer, J. E. (1962). Cognitive, social and physiological determinants of emotional state. *Psychological Review, 69,* 379–399. (p. 369)

Schacter, D. L. (1992). Understanding implicit memory: A cognitive neuroscience approach. *American Psychologist, 47,* 559–569. (p. 285)

Schacter, D. L. (1996). *Searching for memory: The brain, the mind, and the past.* New York: Basic Books. (pp. 276, 285, 469)

Schafer, G. (2005). Infants can learn decontextualized words before their first birthday. *Child Development, 76,* 87–96. (p. 314)

Schaffer, A., Isometsä, E. T., Tondo, L., Moreno, D., Turecki, G., Reis, C., . . . Ha, K. (2015). International society for bipolar disorders task force on suicide: Meta-analyses and meta-regression of correlates of suicide attempts and suicide deaths in bipolar disorder. *Bipolar Disorders, 17,* 1–16. (p. 516)

Schaie, K. W., & Geiwitz, J. (1982). *Adult development and aging.* Boston: Little, Brown. (p. 332)

Schalock, R. L., Borthwick-Duffy, S., Bradley, V. J., Buntinx, W. H. E., Coulter, D. L., & Craig, E. M. (2010). *Intellectual disability: Definition, classification, and systems of supports* (11th ed.). Washington, DC: American Association on Intellectual and Developmental Disabilities. (p. 331)

Schein, E. H. (1956). The Chinese indoctrination program for prisoners of war: A study of attempted brainwashing. *Psychiatry, 19*, 149–172. (p. 419)

Schetter, C. D., Schafer, P., Lanzi, R. G., Clark-Kauffman, E., Raju., T. N. K., & Hillemeier, M. M. (2013). Shedding light on the mechanisms underlying health disparities through community participatory methods: The stress pathway. *Perspectives on Psychological Science, 8*, 613–633. (p. 386)

Schiavi, R. C., & Schreiner-Engel, P. (1988). Nocturnal penile tumescence in healthy aging men. *Journal of Gerontology: Medical Sciences, 43*, M146–M150. (p. 89)

Schick, V., Herbenick, D., Reece, M., Sanders, S. A., Dodge, B., Middlestadt, S. E., & Fortenberry, J. D. (2010). Sexual behaviors, condom use, and sexual health of Americans over 50: Implications for sexual health promotion for older adults. *Journal of Sexual Medicine, 7*(Suppl. 5), 315–329. (p. 151)

Schiffenbauer, A., & Schiavo, R. S. (1976). Physical distance and attraction: An intensification effect. *Journal of Experimental Social Psychology, 12*, 274–282. (p. 430)

Schilt, T., de Win, M. M. L, Koeter, M., Jager, G., Korf, D. J., van den Brink, W., & Schmand, B. (2007). Cognition in novice Ecstasy users with minimal exposure to other drugs. *Archives of General Psychiatry, 64*, 728–736. (p. 108)

Schimel, J., Arndt, J., Pyszczynski, T., & Greenberg, J. (2001). Being accepted for who we are: Evidence that social validation of the intrinsic self reduces general defensiveness. *Journal of Personality and Social Psychology, 80*, 35–52. (p. 473)

Schink, T., Kreutz, G., Busch, V., Pigeot, I., & Ahrens, W. (2014). Incidence and relative risk of hearing disorders in professional musicians. *Occupational and Environmental Medicine, 71*, 472–476. (p. 218)

Schizophrenia Working Group of the Psychiatric Genomics Consortium. (2014). Biological insights from 108 schizophrenia-associated genetic loci. *Nature, 511*, 421–427. (p. 526)

Schlaug, G., Jancke, L., Huang, Y., & Steinmetz, H. (1995). In vivo evidence of structural brain asymmetry in musicians. *Science, 267*, 699–701. (p. 52)

Schlomer, G. L., Del Giudice, M., & Ellis, B. J. (2011). Parent–offspring conflict theory: An evolutionary framework for understanding conflict within human families. *Psychological Review, 118*, 496–521. (p. 148)

Schmidt, F. L., & Hunter, J. E. (1998). The validity and utility of selection methods in personnel psychology: Practical and theoretical implications of 85 years of research findings. *Psychological Bulletin, 124*, 262–274. (pp. 484, B-6)

Schmidt, M. F. H., & Tomasello, M. (2012). Young children enforce social norms. *Current Directions in Psychological Science, 21*, 232–236. (p. 144)

Schmitt, D. P. (2003). Universal sex differences in the desire for sexual variety; tests from 52 nations, 6 continents, and 13 islands. *Journal of Personality and Social Psychology, 85*, 85–104. (p. 183)

Schmitt, D. P. (2007). Sexual strategies across sexual orientations: How personality traits and culture relate to sociosexuality among gays, lesbians, bisexuals, and heterosexuals. *Journal of Psychology and Human Sexuality, 18*, 183–214. (p. 183)

Schmitt, D. P., & Allik, J. (2005). Simultaneous administration of the Rosenberg Self-Esteem Scale in 53 nations: Exploring the universal and culture-specific features of global self-esteem. *Journal of Personality and Social Psychology, 89*, 623–642. (p. 488)

Schmitt, D. P., Allik, J., McCrae, R. R., & Benet-Martínez, V., Reips, U.-D. (2007). The geographic distribution of Big Five personality traits: Patterns and profiles of human self-description across 56 nations. *Journal of Cross-Cultural Psychology, 38*, 173–212. (p. 478)

Schmitt, D. P., & Fuller, R. C. (2015). On the varieties of sexual experience: Cross-cultural links between religiosity and human mating strategies. *Psychology of Religion and Spirituality, 7*, 314–326. (p. 178)

Schmitt, D. P., Jonason, P. K., Byerley, G. J., Flores, S. D., Illbeck, B. E., O'Leary, K. N., & Qudrat, A. (2012). A reexamination of sex differences in sexuality: New studies reveal old truths. *Current Directions in Psychological Science, 21*, 135–139. (p. 177)

Schmitt, D. P., & Pilcher, J. J. (2004). Evaluating evidence of psychological adaptation: How do we know one when we see one? *Psychological Science, 15*, 643–649. (p. 76)

Schmitt, E. (2017, September 27). Navy returns to compasses and pencils to help avoid collisions at sea. *The New York Times* (nytimes.com). (p. 93)

Schnall, E., Wassertheil-Smoller, S., Swencionis, C., Zemon, V., Tinker, L., O'Sullivan., M. J., . . . Goodwin, M. (2010). The relationship between religion and cardiovascular outcomes and all-cause mortality in the women's health initiative observational study. *Psychology and Health, 25*, 249–263. (p. 405)

Schnall, S., Haidt, J., Clore, G. L., & Jordan, A. (2008). Disgust as embodied moral judgment. *Personality and Social Psychology Bulletin, 34*, 1096–1109. (p. 227)

Schneider, M., and Preckel, F. (2017, March 23). Variables associated with achievement in higher education: A systematic review. *Psychological Bulletin.* (p. xxiv)

Schneider, W. J., & McGrew, K. S. (2012). The Cattell-Horn-Carroll model of intelligence In In Flanagan D. P., Harrison P. L. (Eds.), *Contemporary intellectual assessment: Theories, tests, and issues* (3rd ed.). New York: Guilford Press. (p. 324)

Schneier, B. (2007, May 17). Virginia Tech lesson: Rare risks breed irrational responses. *Wired* (wired.com). (p. 302)

Schoen, R., & Canudas-Romo, V. (2006). Timing effects on divorce: 20th century experience in the United States. *Journal of Marriage and Family, 68*, 749–758.

Schoeneman, T. J. (1994). Individualism. In V. S. Ramachandran (Ed.), *Encyclopedia of human behavior* (Vol. 2, pp. 631–643). San Diego: Academic Press. (p. 491)

Schofield, J. W. (1986). Black-White contact in desegregated schools. In M. Hewstone & R. Brown (Eds.), *Contact and conflict in intergroup encounters*. Oxford: Basil Blackwell. (p. 457)

Scholtz, S., Miras, A. D., Chhina, N., Prechtl, C. G., Sleeth, M. L., Daud, N. M., . . . Vincent, R. P. (2013). Obese patients after gastric bypass surgery have lower brain-hedonic responses to food than after gastric banding. *Gut, 63*, 891–902. (p. 362)

Schonfield, D., & Robertson, B. A. (1966). Memory storage and aging. *Canadian Journal of Psychology, 20*, 228–236. (p. 154)

Schooler, J. W., Gerhard, D., & Loftus, E. F. (1986). Qualities of the unreal. *Journal of Experimental Psychology: Learning, Memory, and Cognition, 12*, 171–181. (p. 292)

Schorr, E. A., Fox, N. A., van Wassenhove, V., & Knudsen, E. I. (2005). Auditory–visual fusion in speech perception in children with cochlear implants. *PNAS, 102*, 18748–18750. (p. 218)

Schrauzer, G. N., & Shrestha, K. P. (1990). Lithium in drinking water and the incidences of crimes, suicides, and arrests related to drug addictions. *Biological Trace Element Research, 25*, 105–113. (p. 562)

Schrauzer, G. N., & Shrestha, K. P. (2010). Lithium in drinking water. *British Journal of Psychiatry, 196*, 159.

Schreiber, F. R. (1973). *Sybil*. Chicago: Regnery. (p. 528)

Schroeder, J., Caruso, E. M., & Epley, N. (2016). Many hands make overlooked work: Over-claiming of responsibility increases with group size. *Journal of Experimental Psychology: Applied, 22*, 238–246. (p. 430)

Schroeder, J., & Epley, N. (2015). The sound of intellect: Speech reveals a thoughtful mind, increasing a job candidate's appeal. *Psychological Science, 26*, 877–891. (p. 216)

Schroeder, J., & Epley, N. (2016). Mistaking minds and machines: How speech affects dehumanization and anthropomorphism. *Journal of Experimental Psychology: General, 145*, 1427–1437. (p. 216)

Schuch, F. B., Vancampfort, D., Richards, J., Rosenbaum, S., Ward, P. B., & Stubbs, B. (2016a). Exercise as a treatment for depression: A meta-analysis adjusting for publication bias. *Journal of Psychiatric Research, 77*, 42–51. (p. 402)

Schuch, F. B., Vancampfort, D., Rosenbaum, S., Richards, J., Ward, P. B., & Stubbs, B. (2016b). Exercise improves physical and psychological quality of life in people with depression: A meta-analysis including the evaluation of control group response. *Psychiatry Research, 241*, 47–54. (pp. 558, 559)

Schultheiss, O. C., & Pang, J. S. (2007). Measuring implicit motives. In R. W. Robins, R. C. Fraley, & R. F. Krueger (Eds.), *Handbook of research methods in personality psychology* (pp. 322–345). New York: Guilford Press. (p. 467)

Schultheiss, O., Wiemers, U., & Wolf, O. (2014). Implicit need for achievement predicts attenuated cortisol responses to difficult tasks. *Journal of Research in Personality, 48*, 84–92. (p. 467)

Schuman, H., & Scott, J. (1989). Generations and collective memories. *American Sociological Review, 54*, 359–381. (p. 153)

Schumann, K., & Ross, M. (2010). Why women apologize more than men: Gender differences in thresholds for perceiving offensive behavior. *Psychological Science, 21*, 1649–1655. (p. 164)

Schutte, N. S., Malouff, J. M., Thorsteinsson, E. B., Bhullar, N., & Rooke, S. E. (2007). A meta-analytic investigation of the relationship between emotional intelligence and health. *Personality and Individual Differences, 42*, 921–933. (p. 326)

Schutte, N. S., Palanisamy, S. K. A., & McFarlane, J. R. (2016). The relationship between positive characteristics and longer telomeres. *Psychology & Health, 31*, 1466–1480. (p. 326)

Schuyler, A. C., Kintzle, S., Lucas, C. L., Moore, H., & Castro, C. A. (2017). Military sexual assault (MSA) among veterans in Southern California: Associations with physical health, psychological health, and risk behaviors. *Traumatology, 23*, 223–234. (p. 170)

Schwartz, B. (1984). *Psychology of learning and behavior* (2nd ed.). New York: Norton. (pp. 241, 510)

Schwartz, H. A., Eichstaedt, J. C., Kern, M. L., Dziurzynski, L., Ramones, S. M., Agrawal, M., . . . Ungar, L. H. (2013). Personality, gender, and age in the language of social media: The open-vocabulary approach. *PLoS ONE, 8*(9), e73791. doi:10.1371/journal.pone.0073791 (pp. 162, 165)

Schwartz, J. M., Stoessel, P. W., Baxter, L. R., Jr., Martin, K. M., & Phelps, M. E. (1996). Systematic changes in cerebral glucose metabolic rate after successful behavior modification treatment of obsessive-compulsive disorder. *Archives of General Psychiatry, 53,* 109–113. (pp. 546, 558)

Schwartz, P. J. (2011). Season of birth in schizophrenia: A maternal-fetal chronobiological hypothesis. *Medical Hypotheses, 76,* 785–793. (p. 525)

Schwartz, S. (2012). Dreams, emotions and brain plasticity. In *Aquém e além do cérebro* [Behind and beyond the brain]. Bial: Fundação Bial Institution of Public Utility. (p. 98)

Schwartz, S. H., & Rubel-Lifschitz, T. (2009). Cross-national variation in the size of sex differences in values: Effects of gender equality. *Journal of Personality and Social Psychology, 97,* 171–185. (p. 164)

Schwartz, S. J., Lilienfeld, S. O., Meca, A., & Sauvigné, K. C. (2016). The role of neuroscience within psychology: A call for inclusiveness over exclusiveness. *American Psychologist, 71,* 52–70. (p. 52)

Schwartz, S. J., Unger, J. B., Zamboanga, B. L., & Szapocznik, J. (2010). Rethinking the concept of acculturation: Implications for theory and research. *American Psychologist, 65,* 237–251. (p. 503)

Schwartzman-Morris, J., & Putterman, C. (2012). Gender differences in the pathogenesis and outcome of lupus and of lupus nephritis. *Clinical and Developmental Immunology,* 604892. (p. 389)

Schwarz, A. (2012, June 9). Risky rise of the good-grade pill. *The New York Times* (nytimes.com). (p. 498)

Schwarz, A., & Cohen, S. (2013, March 31). A.D.H.D. seen in 11% of U.S. children as diagnoses rise. *The New York Times* (nytimes.com). (p. 498)

Schwarz, N., Strack, F., Kommer, D., & Wagner, D. (1987). Soccer, rooms, and the quality of your life: Mood effects on judgments of satisfaction with life in general and with specific domains. *European Journal of Social Psychology, 17,* 69–79. (p. 281)

Sclafani, A. (1995). How food preferences are learned: Laboratory animal models. *PNAS, 54,* 419–427. (p. 364)

Scoboria, A., Wade, K. A., Lindsay, D. S., Azad, T., Strange, D., Ost, J., & Hyman, I. E. (2017). A mega-analysis of memory reports from eight peer-reviewed false memory implantation studies. *Memory, 25,* 146–163. (p. 290)

Scopelliti, I., Loewenstein, G., & Vosgerau, J. (2015). You call it "self-exuberance"; I call it "bragging": Miscalibrated predictions of emotional responses to self-promotion. *Psychological Science, 26,* 903–914. (p. 483)

Scott, D. J., Stohler, C. S., Egnatuk, C. M., Wang, H., Koeppe, R. A., & Zubieta, J.-K. (2007). Individual differences in reward responding explain placebo-induced expectations and effects. *Neuron, 55,* 325–336. (p. 223)

Scott, K. M., Wells, J. E., Angermeyer, M., Brugha, T. S., Bromet, E., Demyttenaere, K., . . . Kessler, R. C. (2010). Gender and the relationship between marital status and first onset of mood, anxiety and substance use disorders. *Psychological Medicine, 40,* 1495–1505. (p. 156)

Scott-Sheldon, L. A. J., Carey, K. B., Elliott, J. C., Garey, L., & Carey, M. P. (2014). Efficacy of alcohol interventions for first-year college students: A meta-analytic review of randomized controlled trials. *Journal of Consulting and Clinical Psychology, 82,* 177–188. (p. 104)

Scullin, M. K., & Bliwise, D. L. (2015). Sleep, cognition, and normal aging: Integrating a half century of multidisciplinary research. *Perspectives on Psychological Science, 10,* 97–137. (p. 93)

Scullin, M. K., & McDaniel, M. A. (2010). Remembering to execute a goal: Sleep on it! *Psychological Science, 21,* 1028–1035. (p. 288)

Sdorow, L. M. (2005). The people behind psychology. In B. Perlman, L. McCann, & W. Buskist (Eds.), *Voices of experience: Memorable talks from the National Institute on the Teaching of Psychology.* Washington, DC: American Psychological Society. (p. 468)

Seal, K. H., Bertenthal, D., Miner, C. R., Sen, S., & Marmar, C. (2007). Bringing the war back home: Mental health disorders among 103,788 U.S. veterans returning from Iraq and Afghanistan seen at Department of Veterans Affairs facilities. *Archives of Internal Medicine, 167,* 467–482. (p. 509)

Sedley, W., Gander, P. E., Kumar, S., Oya, H., Kovach, C. K., Nourski, K. V., . . . Griffiths, T. D. (2015). Intracranial mapping of a cortical tinnitus system using residual inhibition. *Current Biology, 25,* 1208–1214. (p. 222)

Sedlmeier, P., Eberth, J., Schwarz, M., Zimmermann, D., Haarig, F., Jaeger, S., & Kunze, S. (2012). The psychological effects of meditation: A meta-analysis. *Psychological Bulletin, 138,* 1139–1171. (p. 404)

Seehagen, S., Konrad, C., Herbert, J. S., & Schneider, S. (2015). Timely sleep facilitates declarative memory consolidation in infants. *PNAS, 112,* 1625–1629. (p. 92)

Seeman, P., Guan, H.-C., & Van Tol, H. H. M. (1993). Dopamine D4 receptors elevated in schizophrenia. *Nature, 365,* 441–445. (p. 524)

Seery, M. D. (2011). Resilience: A silver lining to experiencing adverse life events. *Current Directions in Psychological Science, 20,* 390–394. (pp. 137, 385)

Segal, N. L. (2005). *Indivisible by two: Lives of extraordinary twins.* Cambridge: Harvard University Press. (p. 73)

Segal, N. L. (2013). Personality similarity in unrelated look-alike pairs: Addressing a twin study challenge. *Personality and Individual Differences, 54,* 23–28. (p. 71)

Segal, N. L., Graham, J. L., & Ettinger, U. (2013). Unrelated look-alikes: Replicated study of personality similarity and qualitative findings on social relatedness. *Personality and Individual Differences, 55,* 169–174. (p. 71)

Segal, N. L., McGuire, S. A., & Stohs, J. H. (2012). What virtual twins reveal about general intelligence and other behaviors. *Personality and Individual Differences, 53,* 405–410. (p. 337)

Segall, M. H., Dasen, P. R., Berry, J. W., & Poortinga, Y. H. (1990). *Human behavior in global perspective: An introduction to cross-cultural psychology.* New York: Pergamon Press. (pp. 130, 168)

Sege, R., Nykiel-Bub, L., & Selk, S. (2015). Sex differences in institutional support for junior biomedical researchers. *Journal of American Medical Association, 314,* 1175–1177. (p. 168)

Segerstrom, S. C. (2007). Stress, energy, and immunity. *Current Directions in Psychological Science, 16,* 326–330. (p. 384)

Segerstrom, S. C., Taylor, S. E., Kemeny, M. E., & Fahey, J. L. (1998). Optimism is associated with mood, coping, and immune change in response to stress. *Journal of Personality and Social Psychology, 74,* 1646–1655. (p. 398)

Seibert, S. E., Wang, G., & Courtright, S. H. (2011). Antecedents and consequences of psychological and team empowerment in organizations: A meta-analytic review. *Journal of Applied Psychology, 96,* 981–1003. (pp. B-9, B-11)

Sejnowski, T. (2016, January 20). Quoted in "Memory capacity of brain is 10 times more than previously thought." *KurzweilAI Accelerating Intelligence News* (kurzweilai.net). (p. 275)

Self, C. E. (1994). *Moral culture and victimization in residence halls.* Unpublished master's thesis, Bowling Green State University, Bowling Green, OH. (p. 112)

Seli, P., Risko, E. F., Smilek, D., & Schacter, D. L. (2016). Mind-wandering with and without intention. *Trends in Cognitive Sciences, 20,* 605–617. (p. 104)

Seligman, M. (2016). How positive psychology happened and where it is going. In R. J. Sternberg, S. T. Fiske & D. J. Foss (Eds.), *Scientists making a difference: One hundred eminent behavioral and brain scientists talk about their most important contributions.* New York: Cambridge University Press, pp. 478–480. (p. 408)

Seligman, M. E. P. (1975). *Helplessness: On depression, development and death.* San Francisco: Freeman. (p. 396)

Seligman, M. E. P. (1991). *Learned optimism: How to change your mind and your life.* New York: Knopf. (pp. 80, 520, 521)

Seligman, M. E. P. (1994). *What you can change and what you can't.* New York: Knopf. (p. 486)

Seligman, M. E. P. (1995). The effectiveness of psychotherapy: The *Consumer Reports* study. *American Psychologist, 50,* 965–974. (pp. 521, 550, 552)

Seligman, M. E. P. (2002). *Authentic happiness: Using the new positive psychology to realize your potential for lasting fulfillment.* New York: Free Press. (pp. 10, 408, 486)

Seligman, M. E. P. (2011). *Flourish: A visionary new understanding of happiness and well-being.* New York: Free Press. (p. 10)

Seligman, M. E. P. (2012, May 8). Quoted in A. C. Brooks, America and the value of "earned success." *The Wall Street Journal* (wsj.com). (p. 487)

Seligman, M. E. P., Ernst, R. M., Gillham, J., Reivich, K., & Linkins, M. (2009). Positive education: Positive psychology and classroom interventions. *Oxford Review of Education, 35,* 293–311. (p. 545)

Seligman, M. E. P., & Maier, S. F. (1967). Failure to escape traumatic shock. *Journal of Experimental Psychology, 74,* 1–9. (p. 396)

Seligman, M. E. P., Steen, T. A., Park, N., & Peterson, C. (2005). Positive psychology progress: Empirical validation of interventions. *American Psychologist, 60,* 410–421. (pp. 10, 408)

Seligman, M. E. P., & Yellen, A. (1987). What is a dream? *Behavior Research and Therapy, 25,* 1–24. (p. 87)

Selimbeyoglu, A., & Parvizi, J. (2010). Electrical stimulation of the human brain: Perceptual and behavioral phenomena reported in the old and new literature. *Frontiers in Human Neuroscience, 4,* 1–11. (p. 51)

Sellers, H. (2010). *You don't look like anyone I know.* New York: Riverhead Books. (p. 189)

Selye, H. (1936). A syndrome produced by diverse nocuous agents. *Nature, 138,* 32. (p. 386)

Selye, H. (1976). *The stress of life.* New York: McGraw-Hill. (p. 386)

Selzam, S., Krapohl, E., von Stumm, S., O'Reilly, P. F., Rimfeld, K., Kovas, Y., . . . Plomin, R. (2016). Predicting educational achievement from DNA. *Molecular Psychiatry, 22,* 267–272. (p. 337)

Senghas, A., & Coppola, M. (2001). Children creating language: How Nicaraguan Sign Language acquired a spatial grammar. *Psychological Science, 12,* 323–328. (p. 313)

Sengupta, S. (2001, October 10). Sept. 11 attack narrows the racial divide. *The New York Times* (nytimes.com). (p. 458)

Senju, A., Southgate, V., White, S., & Frith, U. (2009). Mindblind eyes: An absence of spontaneous theory of mind in Asperger syndrome. *Science, 325*, 883–885. (p. 131)

Sergeant, S., & Mongrain, M. (2014). An online optimism intervention reduces depression in pessimistic individuals. *Journal of Consulting and Clinical Psychology, 82*, 263–274. (p. 399)

Service, R. F. (1994). Will a new type of drug make memory-making easier? *Science, 266*, 218–219. (p. 279)

Sest, N., & March, E. (2017). Constructing the cyber-troll: Psychopathy, sadism, and empathy. *Personality and Individual Differences, 119*, 69–72. (p. 430)

Sexton, C. E., Betts, J. F., Demnitz, N., Dawes, H., Ebmeier, K. P., & Johansen-Berg, H. (2016). A systematic review of MRI studies examining the relationship between physical fitness and activity and the white matter of the ageing brain. *NeuroImage, 131*, 81–90. (p. 64)

Shackman, A. J., Tromp, D. P., Stockbridge, M. D., Kaplan, C. M., Tillman, R. M., & Fox, A. S. (2016). Dispositional negativity: An integrative psychological and neurobiological perspective. *Psychological Bulletin, 142*, 1275–1314. (p. 478)

Shadish, W. R., & Baldwin, S. A. (2005). Effects of behavioral marital therapy: A meta-analysis of randomized controlled trials. *Journal of Consulting and Clinical Psychology, 73*, 6–14. (p. 553)

Shadish, W. R., Montgomery, L. M., Wilson, P., Wilson, M. R., Bright, I., & Okwumabua, T. (1993). Effects of family and marital psychotherapies: A meta-analysis. *Journal of Consulting and Clinical Psychology, 61*, 992–1002. (p. 547)

Shaffer, R. (2013, September–October). The psychic: Years later, Sylvia Browne's accuracy remains dismal. *Skeptical Inquirer*, pp. 30–35. (p. 230)

Shafir, E. (Ed.). (2013). *The behavioral foundations of public policy.* Princeton, NJ: Princeton University Press. (p. 4)

Shafir, E., & LeBoeuf, R. A. (2002). Rationality. *Annual Review of Psychology, 53*, 491–517. (p. 305)

Shaki, S. (2013). What's in a kiss? Spatial experience shapes directional bias during kissing. *Journal of Nonverbal Behavior, 37*, 43–50. (p. 10)

Shallcross, A. J., Ford, B. Q., Floerke, V. A., & Mauss, I. B. (2013). Getting better with age: The relationship between age, acceptance, and negative affect. *Journal of Personality and Social Psychology, 104*, 734–749. (p. 158)

Shamir, B., House, R. J., & Arthur, M. B. (1993). The motivational effects of charismatic leadership: A self-concept based theory. *Organizational Science, 4*, 577–594. (p. B-10)

Shanahan, L., McHale, S. M., Osgood, D. W., & Crouter, A. C. (2007). Conflict frequency with mothers and fathers from middle childhood to late adolescence: Within- and between-families comparisons. *Developmental Psychology, 43*, 539–550. (p. 147)

Shane, S. (2015, June 24). Homegrown extremists tied to deadlier toll than jihadis in U.S. since 9/11. *The New York Times* (nytimes.com). (p. 438)

Shankar, S. (2016, June 1). Is the spelling bee success of Indian-Americans a legacy of British colonialism? *The Conversation* (theconversation.com). (p. 340)

Shannon, B. J., Raichle, M. E., Snyder, A. Z., Fair, D. A., Mills, K. L., Zhanga, D., . . . Kiehl, K. A. (2011). Premotor functional connectivity predicts impulsivity in juvenile offenders. *PNAS, 108*, 11241–11245. (p. 142)

Shapin, S. (2013, October 15). The man who forgot everything. *The New Yorker* (newyorker.com). (p. 285)

Shapiro, D. (1999). *Psychotherapy of neurotic character.* New York: Basic Books. (p. 538)

Shapiro, F. (1989). Efficacy of the eye movement desensitization procedure in the treatment of traumatic memories. *Journal of Traumatic Stress, 2*, 199–223. (p. 554)

Shapiro, F. (1999). Eye movement desensitization and reprocessing (EMDR) and the anxiety disorders: Clinical and research implications of an integrated psychotherapy treatment. *Journal of Anxiety Disorders, 13*, 35–67. (p. 554)

Shapiro, F. (Ed.). (2002). *EMDR as an integrative psychotherapy approach: Experts of diverse orientations explore the paradigm prism.* Washington, DC: APA Books. (p. 554)

Shapiro, F. (2007). EMDR and case conceptualization from an adaptive information processing perspective. In F. Shapiro, F. W. Kaslow, & L. Maxfield (Eds.), *Handbook of EMDR and family therapy processes.* Hoboken, NJ: Wiley. (p. 554)

Shapiro, F. (2012, March 2). The evidence on E.M.D.R. *The New York Times* (nytimes.com). (p. 554)

Shapiro, K. A., Moo, L. R., & Caramazza, A. (2006). Cortical signatures of noun and verb production. *Proceedings of the National Academic of Sciences, 103*, 1644–1649. (p. 317)

Shappell, S., Detweiler, C., Holcomb, K., Hackworth, C., Boquet, A., & Wiegmann, D. A. (2007). Human error and commercial aviation accidents: An analysis using the human factors analysis and classification system. *Human Factors, 49*, 227–242. (p. B-13)

Shargorodsky, J., Curhan, S. G., Curhan, G. C., & Eavey, R. (2010). Changes of prevalence of hearing loss in US adolescents. *JAMA, 304*, 772–778. (p. 218)

Shariff, A. F., Greene, J. D., Karremans, J. C., Luguri, J. B., Clark, C. J., Schooler, J. W., . . . Vohs, K. D. (2014). Free will and punishment: A mechanistic view of human nature reduces retribution. *Psychological Science, 25*, 1563–1570. (p. 29)

Sharma, A. R., McGue, M. K., & Benson, P. L. (1998). The psychological adjustment of United States adopted adolescents and their nonadopted siblings. *Child Development, 69*, 791–802. (p. 73)

Shattuck, P. T. (2006). The contribution of diagnostic substitution to the growing administrative prevalence of autism in US special education. *Pediatrics, 117*, 1028–1037. (p. 131)

Shaver, P. R., Morgan, H. J., & Wu, S. (1996). Is love a basic emotion? *Personal Relationships, 3*, 81–96. (p. 372)

Shaw, B. A., Liang, J., & Krause, N. (2010). Age and race differences in the trajectories of self-esteem. *Psychology and Aging, 25*, 84–94. (p. 118)

Shaw, J., & Porter, S. (2015). Constructing rich false memories of committing crime. *Psychological Science, 26*, 291–301. (p. 290)

Shedler, J. (2009, March 23). *That was then, this is now: Psychoanalytic psychotherapy for the rest of us.* Unpublished manuscript, Department of Psychiatry, University of Colorado Health Sciences Center, Aurora, CO. (p. 538)

Shedler, J. (2010a, November/December). Getting to know me. *Scientific American Mind*, pp. 53–57. (p. 538)

Shedler, J. (2010b). The efficacy of psychodynamic psychotherapy. *American Psychologist, 65*, 98–109. (p. 553)

Sheeber, L. B., Feil, E. G., Seeley, J. R., Leve, C., Gau, J. M., Davis, B., . . . Allan, S. (2017). Mom-net: Evaluation of an internet-facilitated cognitive behavioral intervention for low-income depressed mothers. *Journal of Consulting and Clinical Psychology, 85*, 355–366. (p. 546)

Sheehan, S. (1982). *Is there no place on earth for me?* Boston: Houghton Mifflin. (p. 523)

Sheikh, S., & Janoff-Bulman, R. (2013). Paradoxical consequences of prohibitions. *Journal of Personality and Social Psychology, 105*, 301–315. (p. 250)

Sheldon, K. M., Elliot, A. J., Kim, Y., & Kasser, T. (2001). What is satisfying about satisfying events? Testing 10 candidate psychological needs. *Journal of Personality and Social Psychology, 80*, 325–339. (p. 352)

Sheldon, K. M., & Lyubomirsky, S. (2012). The challenge of staying happier: Testing the hedonic adaptation prevention model. *Personality and Social Psychology Bulletin, 38*, 670–680. (p. 412)

Sheltzer, J. M., & Smith, J. C. (2014). Elite male faculty in the life sciences employ fewer females. *PNAS, 111*, 10107–10112. (p. 168)

Shen, L., Fishbach, A., & Hsee, C. K. (2015, February). The motivating-uncertainty effect: Uncertainty increases resource investment in the process of reward pursuit. *Journal of Consumer Research, 41*, 1301–1315. (p. 349)

Shen, W., Yuan, Y., Liu, C., & Luo, J. (2017). The roles of the temporal lobe in creative insight: An integrated review. *Thinking & Reasoning, 23*, 321–375. (p. 306)

Shenton, M. E. (1992). Abnormalities of the left temporal lobe and thought disorder in schizophrenia: A quantitative magnetic resonance imaging study. *New England Journal of Medicine, 327*, 604–612. (p. 525)

Shepard, R. N. (1990). *Mind sights: Original visual illusions, ambiguities, and other anomalies.* New York: Freeman. (p. 32)

Shepherd, C. (1997, April). News of the weird. *Funny Times*, p. 15. (p. 71)

Shergill, S. S., Bays, P. M., Frith, C. D., & Wolpert, D. M. (2003). Two eyes for an eye: The neuroscience of force escalation. *Science, 301*, 187. (p. 456)

Sherif, M. (1966). *In common predicament: Social psychology of intergroup conflict and cooperation.* Boston: Houghton Mifflin. (p. 457)

Sherif, M., Radhakrishnan, R., D'Souza, D. C., & Ranganathan, M. (2016). Human laboratory studies on cannabinoids and psychosis. *Biological Psychiatry, 79*, 526–538. (p. 108)

Sherman, G. D., Lee, J. J., Cuddy, A. J. C., Renshon, J., Oveis, C., Gross, J. J., & Lerner, J. S. (2012). Leadership is associated with lower levels of stress. *PNAS, 109*, 17903–17907. (p. 397)

Sherman, L. E., Payton, A. A., Hernandez, L. M., Greenfield, P. M., & Dapretto, M. (2016). The power of the like in adolescence: Effects of peer influence on neural and behavioral responses to social media. *Psychological Science, 27*, 1027–1035. (pp. 148, 355)

Sherman, P. W., & Flaxman, S. M. (2001). Protecting ourselves from food. *American Scientist, 89*, 142–151. (p. 364)

Sherman, R. A., Rauthmann, J. F., Brown, N. A., Serfass, D. S., & Jones, A. B. (2015). The independent effects of personality and situations on real-time expressions of behavior and emotion. *Journal of Personality and Social Psychology, 109*, 872–888. (p. 481)

Sherry, D., & Vaccarino, A. L. (1989). Hippocampus and memory for food caches in black-capped chickadees. *Behavioral Neuroscience, 103*, 308–318. (p. 276)

Shettleworth, S. J. (1973). Food reinforcement and the organization of behavior in golden hamsters. In R. A. Hinde & J. Stevenson-Hinde (Eds.), *Constraints on learning.* London: Academic Press. (p. 256)

Shettleworth, S. J. (1993). Where is the comparison in comparative cognition? Alternative research programs. *Psychological Science, 4,* 179–184. (p. 276)

Shiell, M. M., Champoux, F., & Zatorre, R. (2014). Enhancement of visual motion detection thresholds in early deaf people. *PLOS ONE, 9*(2), e90498. doi:10.1371/journal.pone.0090498 (p. 64)

Shifren, J. L., Monz, B. U., Russo, P. A., Segreti, A., & Johannes, C. B. (2008). Sexual problems and distress in United States women: Prevalence and correlates. *Obstetrics & Gynecology, 112,* 970–978. (p. 175)

Shilsky, J. D., Hartman, T. J., Kris-Etherton, P. M., Rogers, C. J., Sharkey, N. A., & Nickols-Richardson, S. M. (2012). Partial sleep deprivation and energy balance in adults: An emerging issue for consideration by dietetics practitioners. *Journal of the Academy of Nutrition and Dietetics, 112,* 1785–1797. (p. 93)

Shiromani, P. J., Horvath, T., Redline, S., & Van Cauter E. (Eds.) (2012). *Sleep loss and obesity: Intersecting epidemics.* New York: Springer Science. (p. 93)

Shockley, K. M., Ispas, D., Rossi, M. E., & Levine, E. L. (2012). A meta-analytic investigation of the relationship between state affect, discrete emotions, and job performance. *Human Performance, 25,* 377–411. (pp. B-8, B-9)

Shor, E., Roelfs, D. J., Bugyi, P., & Schwartz, J. E. (2012). Meta-analysis of marital dissolution and mortality: Reevaluating the intersection of gender and age. *Social Science & Medicine, 75,* 46–59. (pp. 353, 400)

Shor, E., Roelfs, D. J., & Yogev, T. (2013). The strength of family ties: A meta-analysis and meta-regression of self-reported social support and mortality. *Social Networks, 35,* 626–638. (p. 399)

Shors, T. J. (2014). The adult brain makes new neurons, and effortful learning keeps them alive. *Current Directions in Psychological Science, 23,* 311–318. (p. 39)

Short, M., Gradisar, M., Wright, H., Dewald, J., Wolfson, A., & Carskadon, M. (2013). A cross-cultural comparison of sleep duration between U.S. and Australian adolescents: The effect of school start time, parent-set bedtimes, and extra-curricular load. *Health Education Behavior, 40,* 323–330. (p. 90)

Short, S. J., Lubach, G. R., Karasin, A. I., Olsen, C. W., Styner, M., Knickmeyer, R. C., . . . Coe, C. L. (2010). Maternal influenza infection during pregnancy impacts postnatal brain development in the rhesus monkey. *Biological Psychiatry, 67,* 965–973. (p. 525)

Shrestha, A., Nohr, E. A., Bech, B. H., Ramlau-Hansen, C. H., & Olsen, J. (2011). Smoking and alcohol during pregnancy and age of menarche in daughters. *Human Reproduction, 26,* 259–265. (p. 167)

Shuffler, M. L., Burke, C. S., Kramer, W. S., & Salas, E. (2013). Leading teams: Past, present, and future perspectives. In M. G. Rumsey (Ed.), *The Oxford handbook of leadership.* New York: Oxford University Press. (p. B-10)

Shuffler, M. L., DiazGranados, D., & Salas, E. (2011). There's a science for that: Team development interventions in organizations. *Current Directions in Psychological Science, 20,* 365–372. (p. B-10)

Shuwairi, S. M., & Johnson, S. P. (2013). Oculomotor exploration of impossible figures in early infancy. *Infancy, 18,* 221–232. (p. 127)

Sicarli, F., Baird, B., Perogamvros, L., Bernardi, G., LaRocque, J. J., Riedner, B., . . . Tononi, G. (2017). The neural correlates of dreaming. *Nature Neuroscience, 20,* 872–878. (p. 90)

Siegel, J. M. (1982, October). Quoted in J. Hooper, Mind tripping. *Omni,* pp. 72–82, 159–160. (p. 108)

Siegel, J. M. (2009). Sleep viewed as a state of adaptive inactivity. *Nature Reviews Neuroscience, 10,* 747–753. (p. 91)

Siegel, J. M. (2012). Suppression of sleep for mating. *Science, 337,* 1610–1611. (p. 91)

Siegel, R. K. (1977, October). Hallucinations. *Scientific American,* pp. 132–140. (p. 108)

Siegel, R. K. (1980). The psychology of life after death. *American Psychologist, 35,* 911–931. (p. 108)

Siegel, R. K. (1984, March 15). Personal communication. (p. 108)

Siegel, R. K. (1990). *Intoxication: Life in pursuit of artificial paradise.* New York: Pocket Books. (pp. 109, 400)

Siegel, S. (2005). Drug tolerance, drug addiction, and drug anticipation. *Current Directions in Psychological Science, 14,* 296–300. (p. 241)

Silber, M. H., Ancoli-Israel, S., Bonnet, M. H., Chokroverty, S., Grigg-Damberger, M. M., Hirshkowitz, M., . . . Iber, C. (2007). The visual scoring of sleep in adults. *Journal of Clinical Sleep Medicine, 3,* 121–131. (p. 87)

Silbersweig, D. A., Stern, E., Frith, C., Cahill, C., Holmes, A., Grootoonk, S., . . . Frackowiak, R. S. J. (1995). A functional neuroanatomy of hallucinations in schizophrenia. *Nature, 378,* 176–179. (p. 524)

Silva, C. E., & Kirsch, I. (1992). Interpretive sets, expectancy, fantasy proneness, and dissociation as predictors of hypnotic response. *Journal of Personality and Social Psychology, 63,* 847–856. (p. 224)

Silva, K., Bessa, J., & de Sousa, L. (2012). Auditory contagious yawning in domestic dogs (*Canis familiaris*): First evidence for social modulation. *Animal Cognition, 15,* 721–724. (p. 422)

Silver, M., & Geller, D. (1978). On the irrelevance of evil: The organization and individual action. *Journal of Social Issues, 34,* 125–136. (p. 428)

Silver, N. (2012). *The signal and the noise: Why so many predictions fail—but some don't.* New York: Penguin. (p. 151)

Silver, R. C., Holman, E. A., Anderson, J. P., Poulin, M., McIntosh, D. N., & Gil-Rivas, V. (2013). Mental- and physical-health effects of acute exposure to media images of the September 11, 2001 attacks and Iraq War. *Psychological Science, 24,* 1623–1634. (p. 385)

Silver, R. C., Holman, E. A., McIntosh, D. N., Poulin, M., & Gil-Rivas, V. (2002). Nationwide longitudinal study of psychological responses to September 11. *Journal of the American Medical Association, 288,* 1235–1244. (p. 385)

Silverman, K., Evans, S. M., Strain, E. C., & Griffiths, R. R. (1992). Withdrawal syndrome after the double-blind cessation of caffeine consumption. *New England Journal of Medicine, 327,* 1109–1114. (p. 105)

Silverman, L. (2015, April 12). Ranulph Fiennes: Marathon des Sables was hell on Earth. *The Telegraph.* Retrieved from http://www.telegraph.co.uk/goodlife/11529641/Ranulph-Fiennes-Marathon-des-Sables-was-hell-on-Earth.html (p. 383)

Silverstein, B. H., Snodgrass, M., Shevrin, H., & Kushwaha, R. (2015). P3b, consciousness, and complex unconscious processing. *Cortex, 73,* 216–227. (p. 81)

Silwa, J., & Frehwald, W. A. (2017). A dedicated network for social interaction processing in the primate brain. *Science, 356,* 745–749. (p. 62)

Simek, T. C., & O'Brien, R. M. (1981). *Total golf: A behavioral approach to lowering your score and getting more out of your game.* Huntington, NY: B-MOD Associates. (p. 251)

Simek, T. C., & O'Brien, R. M. (1988). A chaining-mastery, discrimination training program to teach Little Leaguers to hit a baseball. *Human Performance, 1,* 73–84. (p. 251)

Simon, H. A., & Chase, W. G. (1973). Skill in chess. *American Scientist, 61,* 394–403. (p. 325)

Simon, V., Czobor, P., Bálint, S., Mésáros, A., & Bitter, I. (2009). Prevalence and correlates of adult attention-deficit hyperactivity disorder: Meta-analysis. *British Journal of Psychiatry, 194,* 204–211. (p. 498)

Simons, D. J., Boot, W. R., Charness, N., Gathercole, S. E., Chabris, C. F., Hambrick, D. Z., & Stine-Morrow, E. A. L. (2016). Do "brain-training" programs work? *Psychological Science in the Public Interest, 17,* 103–186. (p. 154)

Simons, D. J., & Chabris, C. F. (1999). Gorillas in our midst: Sustained inattentional blindness for dynamic events. *Perception, 28,* 1059–1074. (p. 82)

Simons, D. J., & Chabris, C. F. (2011). What people believe about how memory works: A representative survey of the U.S. population. *PLoS ONE, 6,* e22757. (p. 289)

Simons, D. J., & Levin, D. T. (1998). Failure to detect changes to people during a real-world interaction. *Psychonomic Bulletin & Review, 5,* 644–649. (p. 83)

Simonsohn, U., & Gino, F. (2013). Daily horizons: Evidence of narrow bracketing in judgment from 10 years of M.B.A. admissions interviews. *Psychological Science, 24,* 219–224. (p. B-6)

Simonton, D. K. (1988). Age and outstanding achievement: What do we know after a century of research? *Psychological Bulletin, 104,* 251–267. (p. 334)

Simonton, D. K. (1990). Creativity in the later years: Optimistic prospects for achievement. *The Gerontologist, 30,* 626–631. (p. 334)

Simonton, D. K. (1992). The social context of career success and course for 2,026 scientists and inventors. *Personality and Social Psychology Bulletin, 18,* 452–463. (p. 307)

Simonton, D. K. (2000). Methodological and theoretical orientation and the long-term disciplinary impact of 54 eminent psychologists. *Review of General Psychology, 4,* 13–24. (p. 263)

Simonton, D. K. (2012a). Teaching creativity: Current findings, trends, and controversies in the psychology of creativity. *Teaching of Psychology, 39,* 217–222. (p. 307)

Simonton, D. K. (2012b, November–December). The science of genius. *Scientific American Mind,* pp. 35–41. (p. 307)

Simpson, A., & Rios, K. (2016). How do U.S. Christians and atheists stereotype one another's moral values? *International Journal for the Psychology of Religion, 26,* 320–336. (p. 435)

Sin, N. L., Graham-Engeland, J. E., Ong, A. D., & Almeida, D. M. (2015). Affective reactivity to daily stressors is associated with elevated inflammation. *Health Psychology, 34,* 154–1165. (p. 386)

Sinclair, R. C., Hoffman, C., Mark, M. M., Martin, L. L., & Pickering, T. L. (1994). Construct accessibility and the misattribution of arousal: Schachter and Singer revisited. *Psychological Science, 5,* 15–18. (p. 369)

Singer, J. L. (1981). Clinical intervention: New developments in methods and evaluation. In L. T. Benjamin, Jr. (Ed.), *The G. Stanley Hall Lecture Series* (Vol. 1). Washington, DC: American Psychological Association. (p. 553)

Singer, T., Seymour, B., O'Doherty, J., Kaube, H., Dolan, R. J., & Frith, C. (2004). Empathy for pain involves the affective but not sensory components of pain. *Science, 303*, 1157–1162. (pp. 223, 260)

Singh, D. (1993). Adaptive significance of female physical attractiveness: Role of waist-to-hip ratio. *Journal of Personality and Social Psychology, 65*, 293–307. (p. 185)

Singh, D., & Randall, P. K. (2007). Beauty is in the eye of the plastic surgeon: Waist–hip ratio (WHR) and women's attractiveness. *Personality and Individual Differences, 43*, 329–340. (p. 185)

Singh, S. (1997). *Fermat's enigma: The epic quest to solve the world's greatest mathematical problem.* New York: Bantam Books. (p. 306)

Singh, S., & Riber, K. A. (1997, November). Fermat's last stand. *Scientific American*, pp. 68–73. (p. 307)

Sio, U. N., Monahan, P., & Ormerod, T. (2013). Sleep on it, but only if it is difficult: Effects of sleep on problem solving. *Memory and Cognition, 41*, 159–166. (p. 92)

Sireteanu, R. (1999). Switching on the infant brain. *Science, 286*, 59–61. (p. 218)

Sit, D. K., McGowan, J., Wiltrout, C., Diler, R. S., Dills, J., Luther, J., . . . Terman, M. (2018). Adjunctive bright light therapy for bipolar depression: A randomized double-blind placebo-controlled trial. *American Journal of Psychiatry, 175*(2), 131–139. (p. 555)

Sixtus, E., Fischer, M. H., & Lindemann, O. (2017). Finger posing primes number comprehension. *Cognitive Processing, 18*, 237–248. (p. 229)

Skeem, J., Kennealy, P., Monahan, J., Peterson, J., & Appelbaum, P. (2016). Psychosis uncommonly and inconsistently precedes violence among high-risk individuals. *Clinical Psychological Science, 4*, 40–49. (p. 502)

Skeem, J. L., & Cooke, D. J. (2010). Is criminal behavior a central component of psychopathy? Conceptual directions for resolving the debate. *Psychological Assessment, 22*, 433–445. (p. 530)

Skinner, B. F. (1953). *Science and human behavior.* New York: Macmillan. (p. 247)

Skinner, B. F. (1956). A case history in scientific method. *American Psychologist, 11*, 221–233. (p. 248)

Skinner, B. F. (1961, November). Teaching machines. *Scientific American, 205*, 90–112. (pp. 247, 248)

Skinner, B. F. (1966). *The behavior of organisms: An experimental analysis.* New York: Appleton-Century-Crofs. (Original work published 1938.) (p. 250)

Skinner, B. F. (1983, September). Origins of a behaviorist. *Psychology Today*, pp. 22–33. (p. 250)

Skinner, B. F. (1989). Teaching machines. *Science, 243*, 1535. (p. 251)

Sklar, L. S., & Anisman, H. (1981). Stress and cancer. *Psychological Bulletin, 89*, 369–406. (p. 390)

Skoog, G., & Skoog, I. (1999). A 40-year follow-up of patients with obsessive-compulsive disorder. *Archives of General Psychiatry, 56*, 121–127. (p. 509)

Skov, R. B., & Sherman, S. J. (1986). Information-gathering processes: Diagnosticity, hypothesis-confirmatory strategies, and perceived hypothesis confirmation. *Journal of Experimental Social Psychology, 22*, 93–121. (pp. 300, B-6)

Slagt, M., Dubas, J. S., Dekovi☒, M., & van Aken, M. A. (2016). Differences in sensitivity to parenting depending on child temperament: A meta-analysis. *Psychological Bulletin, 142*, 1068–1110. (p. 135)

Slatcher, R. B., Selcuk, E., & Ong, A. (2015). Perceived partner responsiveness predicts diurnal cortisol profiles 10 years later. *Psychological Science, 26*, 972–982. (p. 400)

Slaughter, V., Imuta, K., Peterson, C. C., & Henry, J. D. (2015). Meta-analysis of theory of mind and peer popularity in the preschool and early school years. *Child Development, 86*, 1159–1174. (p. 128)

Sloan, R. P. (2005). *Field analysis of the literature on religion, spirituality, and health.* Columbia University. Retrieved from metanexus.net/tarp (p. 405)

Sloan, R. P., & Bagiella, E. (2002). Claims about religious involvement and health outcomes. *Annals of Behavioral Medicine, 24*, 14–21. (p. 405)

Sloan, R. P., Bagiella, E., & Powell, T. (1999). Religion, spirituality, and medicine. *The Lancet, 353*, 664–667. (p. 405)

Sloan, R. P., Bagiella, E., VandeCreek, L., & Poulos, P. (2000). Should physicians prescribe religious activities? *New England Journal of Medicine, 342*, 1913–1917. (p. 405)

Slopen, N., Glynn, R. J., Buring, J., & Albert, M. A. (2010, November 23). Job strain, job insecurity, and incident cardiovascular disease in the Women's Health Study. *Circulation, 122*(21, Suppl.), Abstract A18520. (p. 392)

Slovic, P. (2007). "If I look at the mass I will never act": Psychic numbing and genocide. *Judgment and Decision Making, 2*, 79–95. (p. 303)

Slovic, P., Västfjälla, D., Erlandsson, A., & Gregory, R. (2017). Iconic photographs and the ebb and flow of empathic response to humanitarian disasters. *PNAS, 114*, 640–644. (p. 303)

Slutske, W. S., Moffitt, T. E., Poulton, R., & Caspi, A. (2012). Undercontrolled temperament at age 3 predicts disordered gambling at age 32: A longitudinal study of a complete birth cohort. *Psychological Science, 23*, 510–516. (p. 118)

Smalarz, L., & Wells, G. L. (2015). Contamination of eyewitness self-reports and the mistaken identification problem. *Current Directions in Psychological Science, 24*, 120–124. (p. 292)

Small, M. F. (1997). Making connections. *American Scientist, 85*, 502–504. (p. 140)

Smedley, A., & Smedley, B. D. (2005). Race as biology is fiction, racism as a social problem is real: Anthropological and historical perspectives on the social construction of race. *American Psychologist, 60*, 16–26. (p. 342)

Smelser, N. J., & Mitchell, F. (Eds.). (2002). *Terrorism: Perspectives from the behavioral and social sciences.* Washington, DC: National Research Council, National Academies Press. (p. 440)

Smith, A. (1776). An inquiry into the nature and causes of the wealth of nations. London: W. Strahan and T. Cadell. (p. 456)

Smith, A. (1983). Personal correspondence. (p. 524)

Smith, A. M., Floerke, V. A., & Thomas, A. K. (2016). Retrieval practice protects memory against acute stress. *Science, 354*, 1046–1048. (p. 272)

Smith, A. R., Dodd, D. R., Forrest, L. N., Witte, T. K., Bodell, L., Ribeiro, J. D., . . . Bartlett, M. (2016). Does the interpersonal-psychological theory of suicide provide a useful framework for understanding suicide risk among eating disorder patients? A test of the validity of the IPTS. *International Journal of Eating Disorders, 49*, 1082–1086. (p. 532)

Smith, B. C. (2011, January 16). The senses and the multi-sensory. *World Question Center* (edge.org). (p. 228)

Smith, C. (2006, January 7). Nearly 100, LSD's father ponders his "problem child." *The New York Times* (nytimes.com). (p. 108)

Smith, G. E. (2016). Healthy cognitive aging and dementia prevention. *American Psychologist, 71*, 268–275. (pp. 153, 448)

Smith, J. A., & Rhodes, J. E. (2014). Being depleted and being shaken: An interpretative phenomenological analysis of the experiential features of a first episode of depression. *Psychology and Psychotherapy: Theory, Research and Practice, 88*, 197–209. (p. 516)

Smith, J. C., Nielson, K. A., Woodard, J. L., Seidenberg, M., Durgerian, S., Hazlett, K. E., . . . Rao, S. M. (2014, April 23). Physical activity reduces hippocampal atrophy in elders at genetic risk for Alzheimer's disease. *Frontiers in Aging Neuroscience, 6*, 61. (p. 153)

Smith, M. B. (1978). Psychology and values. *Journal of Social Issues, 34*, 181–199. (p. 473)

Smith, M. L., & Glass, G. V. (1977). Meta-analysis of psychotherapy outcome studies. *American Psychologist, 32*, 752–760. (p. 552)

Smith, M. L., Glass, G. V., & Miller, R. L. (1980). *The benefits of psychotherapy.* Baltimore: Johns Hopkins Press. (pp. 551, 552)

Smith, M. M., Sherry, S. B., Chen, S., Saklofske, D. H., Mushquash, C., Flett, G. L., & Hewitt, P. L. (2018). The perniciousness of perfectionism: A meta-analytic review of the perfectionism-suicide relationship. *Journal of Personality, 86*(3), 522–542. (p. 500)

Smith, P. B., & Tayeb, M. (1989). Organizational structure and processes. In M. Bond (Ed.), *The cross-cultural challenge to social psychology.* Newbury Park, CA: Sage. (p. B-11)

Smith, S. F., Lilienfeld, S. O., Coffey, K., & Dabbs, J. M. (2013). Are psychopaths and heroes twigs off the same branch? Evidence from college, community, and presidential samples. *Journal of Research in Personality, 47*, 634–646. (p. 530)

Smith, S. J., Axelton, A. M., & Saucier, D. A. (2009). The effects of contact on sexual prejudice: A meta-analysis. *Sex Roles, 61*, 178–191. (p. 457)

Smith, S. L., Pieper, K., & Choueiti, M. (2017, February). Inclusion in the director's chair? Gender, race, & age of film directors across 1,000 films from 2007–2016. Media, Diversity, & Social Change Initiative, University of Southern California Annenberg School for Communications and Journalism. (p. 437)

Smith, S. M., Nichols, T. E., Vidaurre, D., Winkler, A. M., Behrens, T. E., Glasser, M. F., . . . Miller, K. L. (2015). A positive-negative mode of population covariation links brain connectivity, demographics, and behavior. *Nature Neuroscience, 18*, 1565–1567. (p. 53)

Smith, T. W., & Baucom, B. R. W. (2017). Intimate relationships, individual adjustment, and coronary heart disease: Implications of overlapping associations in psychosocial risk. *American Psychologist, 72*, 578–589. (p. 400)

Smith, T. W., Marsden, P. V., & Hout, M. (2017). *General social surveys, 1972–2016 cumulative file* (ICPSR31521-v1). Chicago: National Opinion Research Center. Ann Arbor, MI: Inter-university Consortium for Political and Social Research. doi:10.3886/ICPSR31521.v1 (p. 249)

Smits, I. A. M., Dolan, C. V., Vorst, H. C. M., Wicherts, J. M., & Timmerman, M. E. (2011). Cohort differences in big five personality traits over a period of 25 years. *Journal of Personality and Social Psychology, 100*, 1124–1138. (p. 401)

Smolak, L., & Murnen, S. K. (2002). A meta-analytic examination of the relationship between child sexual abuse and eating disorders. *International Journal of Eating Disorders, 31,* 136–150.(p. 532)

Snedeker, J., Geren, J., & Shafto, C. L. (2007). Starting over: International adoption as a natural experiment in language development. *Psychological Science, 18,* 79–86. (p. 315)

Sniekers, S., Stringer, S., Watanabe, K., Jansen, P. R., Coleman, J. R. I., Krapohl, E., . . . Posthuma, D. (2017). Genome-wide association meta-analysis of 78,308 individuals identifies new loci and genes influencing human intelligence. *Nature Genetics, 49,* 1107–1112. (p. 337)

Snipes, D. J., Calton, J. M., Green, B. A., Perrin, P. B., & Benotsch, E. G. (2017). Rape and posttraumatic stress disorder (PTSD): Examining the mediating role of explicit sex-power beliefs for men versus women. *Journal of Interpersonal Violence, 32,* 2453–2470. (p. 170)

Snippe, E., Simons, C. J., Hartmann, J. A., Menne-Lothmann, C., Kramer, I., Booij, S. H., . . . Wichers, M. (2016). Change in daily life behaviors and depression: Within-person and between-person associations. *Health Psychology, 35,* 433–441. (p. 402)

Snodgrass, S. E., Higgins, J. G., & Todisco, L. (1986). *The effects of walking behavior on mood.* Paper presented at the American Psychological Association convention. (p. 393)

Snyder, F., & Scott, J. (1972). The psychophysiology of sleep. In N. S. Greenfield & R. A. Sterbach (Eds.), *Handbook of psychophysiology* (pp. 645–708). New York: Holt, Rinehart & Winston. (p. 98)

Snyder, S. H. (1984). Neurosciences: An integrative discipline. *Science, 225,* 1255–1257. (p. 497)

Snyder, S. H. (1986). *Drugs and the brain.* New York: Scientific American Library. (p. 562)

Soderstrom, N. C., Kerr, T. K., & Bjork, R. A. (2016). The critical importance of retrieval—and spacing—for learning. *Psychological Science, 27,* 223–230. (p. 272)

Solomon, B. C., & Jackson, J. J. (2014). The long reach of one's spouse: Spouses' personality influences occupational success. *Psychological Science, 25,* 2189–2198. (p. B-8)

Solomon, D. A., Keitner, G. I., Miller, I. W., Shea, M. T., & Keller, M. B. (1995). Course of illness and maintenance treatments for patients with bipolar disorder. *Journal of Clinical Psychiatry, 56,* 5–13. (p. 562)

Solomon, Z., Greene, T., Ein-Dor, T., Zerach, G., Benyamini, Y., & Ohry, A. (2014). The long-term implications of war captivity for mortality and health. *Journal of Behavioral Medicine, 37,* 849–859. (p. 388)

Solomon, Z., Tsur, N., Levin, Y., Uziel, O., Lahav, M., & Ohry, A. (2017). The implications of war captivity and long-term psychopathology trajectories for telomere length. *Psychoneuroendocrinology, 81,* 122–128. (p. 388)

Somerville, L. H., Jones, R. M., Ruberry, E. J., Dyke, J. P., Glover, G., & Casey, B. J. (2013). The medial prefrontal cortex and the emergence of self-conscious emotion in adolescence. *Psychological Science, 24,* 1554–1562. (p. 142)

Song, S. (2006, March 27). Mind over medicine. *Time,* p. 47. (p. 224)

Sontag, S. (1978). *Illness as metaphor.* New York: Farrar, Straus, & Giroux. (p. 390)

Sood, A. K., Armaiz-Pena, G. N., Halder, J., Nick, A. M., Stone, R. L., Hu, W., . . . Lutgendorf, S. K. (2010). Adrenergic modulation of focal adhesion kinase protects human ovarian cancer cells from anoikis. *Journal of Clinical Investigation, 120,* 1515–1523. (p. 390)

Soto, C. J., & John, O. P. (2017). The next big five inventory (BFI-2): Developing and assessing a hierarchical model with 15 facets to enhance bandwidth, fidelity, and predictive power. *Journal of Personality and Social Psychology, 113,* 117–143. (p. 477)

Soussignan, R. (2001). Duchenne smile, emotional experience, and autonomic reactivity: A test of the facial feedback hypothesis. *Emotion, 2,* 52–74. (p. 381)

South, S. C., Krueger, R. F., Johnson, W., & Iacono, W. G. (2008). Adolescent personality moderates genetic and environmental influences on relationships with parents. *Journal of Personality and Social Psychology, 94,* 899–912. (p. 139)

Sowell, T. (1991, May/June). Cultural diversity: A world view. *American Enterprise,* pp. 44–55. (p. 459)

Spanos, N. P. (1986). Hypnosis, nonvolitional responding, and multiple personality: A social psychological perspective. *Progress in Experimental Personality Research, 14,* 1–62. (p. 528)

Spanos, N. P. (1994). Multiple identity enactments and multiple personality disorder: A sociocognitive perspective. *Psychological Bulletin, 116,* 143–165. (p. 528)

Spanos, N. P. (1996). *Multiple identities and false memories: A sociocognitive perspective.* Washington, DC: American Psychological Association Books. (p. 528)

Spanos, N. P., & Coe, W. C. (1992). A social-psychological approach to hypnosis. In E. Fromm & M. R. Nash (Eds.), *Contemporary hypnosis research* (pp. 102–130). New York: Guilford Press. (p. 224)

Sparks, S., Cunningham, S. J., & Kritikos, A. (2016). Culture modulates implicit ownership-induced self-bias in memory. *Cognition, 153,* 89–98. (p. 274)

Sparrow, B., Liu, J., & Wegner, D. M. (2011). Google effects on memory: Cognitive consequences of having information at our fingertips. *Science, 333,* 776–778. (p. 269)

Spaulding, S. (2013). Mirror neurons and social cognition. *Mind and Language, 28,* 233–257. (p. 260)

Spearman, C. (1904). "General intelligence," objectively determined and measured. *American Journal of Psychology, 15,* 201–292. (p. 323)

Spector, T. (2012). *Identically different: Why you can change your genes.* London: Weidenfeld & Nicolson. (p. 74)

Speer, N. K., Reynolds, J. R., Swallow, K. M., & Zacks, J. M. (2009). Reading stories activates neural representations of visual and motor experiences. *Psychological Science, 20,* 989–999. (pp. 260, 317)

Spelke, E. S., Bernier, E. P., & Skerry, A. E. (2013). Core social cognition. In M. R. Banaji & S. A. Gelman (Eds.), *Navigating the social world: What infants, children, and other species can teach us* (pp. 11–16). New York: Oxford University Press. (p. 127)

Spencer, K. M., Nestor, P. G., Perlmutter, R., Niznikiewicz, M. A., Klump, M. C., Frumin, M., . . . McCarley, R. W. (2004). Neural synchrony indexes disordered perception and cognition in schizophrenia. *PNAS, 101,* 17288–17293. (p. 524)

Spencer, S. J., Logel, C., & Davies, P. G. (2016). Stereotype threat. *Annual Review of Psychology, 67,* 415–437. (p. 344)

Spencer, S. J., Steele, C. M., & Quinn, D. M. (1997). *Stereotype threat and women's math performance.* Unpublished manuscript, Hope College. (p. 344)

Sperling, G. (1960). The information available in brief visual presentations. *Psychological Monographs, 74* (Whole No. 498). (p. 270)

Sperry, R. W. (1964). *Problems outstanding in the evolution of brain function.* The James Arthur Lecture, delivered at the American Museum of Natural History, New York, NY. Cited in R. Ornstein (1977), *The psychology of consciousness* (2nd ed.). New York: Harcourt Brace Jovanovich. (p. 66)

Sperry, R. W. (1985). Changed concepts of brain and consciousness: Some value implications. *Zygon, 20,* 41–57. (p. 206)

Spiegel, A. (2015, January 8). Dark thoughts. From "Invisibilia," National Public Radio (npr.org). (p. 544)

Spiegel, D. (2007). The mind prepared: Hypnosis in surgery. *Journal of the National Cancer Institute, 99,* 1280–1281. (p. 224)

Spiegel, D. (2008, January 31). *Coming apart: Trauma and the fragmentation of the self.* Dana Foundation (dana.org). (p. 529)

Spielberger, C., & London, P. (1982). Rage boomerangs. *American Health, 1,* 52–56. (p. 392)

Sprecher, S., Treger, S., & Sakaluk, J. K. (2013). Premarital sexual standards and sociosexuality: Gender, ethnicity, and cohort differences. *Archives of Sexual Behavior, 42,* 1395–1405. (p. 183)

Spring, B., Pingitore, R., Bourgeois, M., Kessler, K. H., & Bruckner, E. (1992). *The effects and non-effects of skipping breakfast: Results of three studies.* Paper presented at the American Psychological Association convention. (p. 366)

Sproesser, G., Schupp, H. T., & Renner, B. (2014). The bright side of stress-induced eating: Eating more when stressed but less when pleased. *Psychological Science, 25,* 58–65. (pp. 354, 363)

Squire, L. R., & Zola-Morgan, S. (1991, September 20). The medial temporal lobe memory system. *Science, 253,* 1380–1386. (p. 277)

Srivastava, S., McGonigal, K. M., Richards, J. M., Butler, E. A., & Gross, J. J. (2006). Optimism in close relationships: How seeing things in a positive light makes them so. *Journal of Personality and Social Psychology, 91,* 143–153. (p. 399)

St-Onge, M.-P., McReynolds, A., Trivedi, Z. B., Roberts, A. L., Sy, M., & Hirsch, J. (2012). Sleep restriction leads to increased activation of brain regions sensitive to food stimuli. *American Journal of Clinical Nutrition, 95,* 818–824. (p. 93)

St. Clair, D., Xu, M., Wang, P., Yu, Y., Fang, Y., Zhang, F., . . . He, L. (2005). Rates of adult schizophrenia following prenatal exposure to the Chinese famine of 1959–1961. *Journal of the American Medical Association, 294,* 557–562. (p. 525)

Stacey, D., Bilbao, A., Maroteaux, M., Jia, T., Easton, A. E., Longueville, S., . . . the IMAGEN Consortium. (2012). *RASGRF2* regulates alcohol-induced reinforcement by influencing mesolimbic dopamine neuron activity and dopamine release. *PNAS, 109,* 21128–21133. (p. 111)

Stafford, T., & Dewar, M. (2014). Tracing the trajectory of skill learning with a very large sample of online game players. *Psychological Science, 25,* 511–518. (p. 272)

Stager, C. L., & Werker, J. F. (1997). Infants listen for more phonetic detail in speech perception than in word-learning tasks. *Nature, 388,* 381–382. (p. 314)

Stahl, A. E., & Feigenson, L. (2015). Observing the unexpected enhances infants' learning and exploration. *Science, 348,* 91–94. (p. 127)

Stanley, D., Phelps, E., & Banaji, M. (2008). The neural basis of implicit attitudes. *Current Directions in Psychological Science, 17,* 164–170. (p. 435)

Stanley, S., & Rhoades, G. (2016a, July 19). Testing a relationship is probably the worst reason to cohabit. *Family Studies* (family-studies.org). (p. 156)

Stanley, S., & Rhoades, G. (2016b, July/August). The perils of sowing your wild oats. *Psychology Today*, pp. 40–42. (p. 156)

Stanley, S. M., Rhoades, G. K., Amato, P. R., Markman, H. J., & Johnson, C. A. (2010). The timing of cohabitation and engagement: Impact on first and second marriages. *Journal of Marriage and Family, 72*, 906–918. (p. 156)

Stanovich, K. (1996). *How to think straight about psychology*. New York: HarperCollins. (p. 462)

Stanovich, K. E., & West, R. F. (2014a). The assessment of rational thinking: IQ ≠ RQ. *Teaching of Psychology, 41*, 265–271. (p. 345)

Stanovich, K. E., & West, R. F. (2014b). What intelligence tests miss. *Psychologist, 27*, 80–83. (p. 345)

Stanovich, K. E., West, R. F., & Toplak, M. E. (2013). My side bias, rational thinking, and intelligence. *Current Directions in Psychological Science, 22*, 259–264. (pp. 305, 345)

Starcke, K., & Brand, M. (2016). Effects of stress on decisions under uncertainty: A meta-analysis. *Psychological Bulletin, 142*, 909–933. (p. 385)

Stark, R. (2003a). For the glory of God: How monotheism led to reformations, science, witch-hunts, and the end of slavery. Princeton, NJ: Princeton University Press. (p. 3)

Stark, R. (2003b, October-November). False conflict: Christianity is not only compatible with science—it created it. *American Enterprise*, pp. 27–33. (p. 3)

Starzynski, L. L., Ullman, S. E., & Vasquez, A. L. (2017). Sexual assault survivors' experiences with mental health professionals: A qualitative study. *Women & Therapy, 40*, 228–246. (p. 170)

Statista. (2017). *Reported violent crime in the United States from 1990 to 2015*. Retrieved from statista.com/statistics/191219/reported-violent-crime-rate-in-the-usa-since-1990 (p. 18)

Statistics Canada. (1999, September). *Statistical report on the health of Canadians*. Prepared by the Federal, Provincial and Territorial Advisory Committee on Population Health for the Meeting of Ministers of Health, Charlottetown, P. E. I. (p. 385)

Statistics Canada. (2011). *Marital status: Overview, 2011*. Table 2: Divorces and crude divorce rates, Canada, provinces and territories, 1981 to 2008. Retrieved from statcan.gc.ca/pub/91-209-x/2013001/article/11788/tbl/tbl2-eng.htm (p. 156)

Statistics Canada. (2013). Table A.5.1. Second language immersion program enrolments in public elementary and secondary schools, Canada, provinces and territories, 2005/2006 to 2009/2010. Retrieved from statcan.gc.ca/pub/81-595-m/2011095/tbl/tbla.5.1-eng.htm (p. 320)

Staub, E. (1989). The roots of evil: The psychological and cultural sources of genocide. New York: Cambridge University Press. (p. 419)

Stavrinos, D., Pope, C. N., Shen, J., & Schwebel, D. C. (2017). Distracted walking, bicycling, and driving: Systematic review and meta-analysis of mobile technology and youth crash risk. *Child Development*. Advance online publication. doi:10.1111/cdev.12827 (p. 82)

Steel, P., Schmidt, J., & Schultz, J. (2008). Refining the relationship between personality and subject well-being. *Psychological Bulletin, 134*, 138–161. (p. 411)

Steele, C. M. (1990, May). A conversation with Claude Steele. *APS Observer*, pp. 11–17. (p. 342)

Steele, C. M. (1995, August 31). Black students live down to expectations. *The New York Times* (nytimes.com). (p. 344)

Steele, C. M. (2010). *Whistling Vivaldi: And other clues to how stereotypes affect us*. New York: Norton. (p. 344)

Steele, C. M., & Josephs, R. A. (1990). Alcohol myopia: Its prized and dangerous effects. *American Psychologist, 45*, 921–933. (p. 104)

Steele, C. M., Spencer, S. J., & Aronson, J. (2002). Contending with group image: The psychology of stereotype and social identity threat. *Advances in Experimental Social Psychology, 34*, 379–440. (p. 344)

Steinberg, L. (1987, September). Bound to bicker. *Psychology Today*, pp. 36–39. (p. 148)

Steinberg, L. (2001). We know some things: Parent–adolescent relationships in retrospect and prospect. *Journal of Research on Adolescence, 11*, 1–19. (p. 138)

Steinberg, L. (2007). Risk taking in adolescence: New perspectives from brain and behavioral science. *Current Directions in Psychological Science, 16*, 55–59. (p. 142)

Steinberg, L. (2010, March). Analyzing adolescence (Interview by Sara Martin). *Monitor on Psychology*, pp. 26–29. (p. 142)

Steinberg, L. (2012, Spring). Should the science of adolescent brain development inform public policy? *Issues in Science and Technology*, pp. 67–78. (p. 142)

Steinberg, L. (2013). The influence of neuroscience on U.S. Supreme Court decisions involving adolescents' criminal culpability. *Nature Reviews Neuroscience, 14*, 513–518. (p. 142)

Steinberg, L. (2015). How to improve the health of American adolescents. *Perspectives on Psychological Science, 10*, 711–715. (p. 178)

Steinberg, L., Cauffman, E., Woolard, J., Graham, S., & Banich, M. (2009). Are adolescents less mature than adults? Minors' access to abortion, the juvenile death penalty, and the alleged APA "flip-flop." *American Psychologist, 64*, 583–594. (p. 142)

Steinberg, L., Lamborn, S. D., Darling, N., Mounts, N. S., & Dornbusch, S. M. (1994). Overtime changes in adjustment and competence among adolescents from authoritative, authoritarian, indulgent, and neglectful families. *Child Development, 65*, 754–770. (p. 139)

Steinberg, L., & Morris, A. S. (2001). Adolescent development. *Annual Review of Psychology, 52*, 83–110. (p. 147)

Steinberg, L., & Scott, E. S. (2003). Less guilty by reason of adolescence: Developmental immaturity, diminished responsibility, and the juvenile death penalty. *American Psychologist, 58*, 1009–1018. (p. 142)

Steinberg, N. (1993, February). Astonishing love stories (from an earlier United Press International report). *Games*, p. 47. (p. 447)

Steiner, J. L., Murphy, E. A., McClellan, J. L., Carmichael, M. D., & Davis, J. M. (2011). Exercise training increases mitochondrial biogenesis in the brain. *Journal of Applied Physiology, 111*, 1066–1071. (p. 153)

Steinert, C., Munder, T., Rabung, S., Hoyer, J., & Leichsenring, F. (2017). Psychodynamic therapy: As efficacious as other empirically supported treatments? A meta-analysis testing equivalence of outcomes. *American Journal of Psychiatry, 174*, 943–953. (p. 553)

Stellar, J. E., John-Henderson, N., Anderson, C. L., Gordon, A. M., McNeil, G. D., & Keltner, D. (2015). Positive affect and markers of inflammation: Discrete positive emotions predict lower levels of inflammatory cytokines. *Emotion, 15*, 129–133. (p. 407)

Stender, J., Gosseries, O., Bruno, M.-A., Charland-Verville, V., Vanhaudenhuyse, A., Demertzi, A., . . . Laurey, S. (2014). Diagnostic precision of PET imaging and functional MRI in disorders of consciousness: A clinical validation study. *The Lancet, 384*, 514–522. (p. 81)

Stephens-Davidowitz, S. (2013, December 7). How many American men are gay? *The New York Times* (nytimes.com). (p. 179)

Stephens-Davidowitz, S. (2014). The effects of racial animus on a black candidate: Evidence using Google search data. *Journal of Public Economics, 118*, 26–40. (pp. 436, 437)

Stephens-Davidowitz, S. (2017). *Everybody lies: Big data, new data, and what the internet can tell us about who we really are*. New York: Dey St. (Morrow). (pp. 22, 97, 468)

Steptoe, A., Chida, Y., Hamer, M., & Wardle, J. (2010). Author reply: Meta-analysis of stress-related factors in cancer. *Nature Reviews: Clinical Oncology, 7*. doi:10.1038/ncponc1134-c2 (p. 390)

Steptoe, A., & Wardle, J. (2011). Positive affect measured using ecological momentary assessment and survival in older men and woman. *PNAS, 108*, 18244–18248. (p. 392)

Steptoe, A., & Wardle, J. (2017). Life skills, wealth, health, and wellbeing later in life. *PNAS, 114*, 4354–4359. (p. 357)

Stern, M., & Karraker, K. H. (1989). Sex stereotyping of infants: A review of gender labeling studies. *Sex Roles, 20*, 501–522. (p. 196)

Sternberg, E. M. (2009). *Healing spaces: The science of place and well-being*. Cambridge, MA: Harvard University Press. (p. 389)

Sternberg, R. J. (1985). *Beyond IQ: A triarchic theory of human intelligence*. New York: Cambridge University Press. (p. 325)

Sternberg, R. J. (1988). Applying cognitive theory to the testing and teaching of intelligence. *Applied Cognitive Psychology, 2*, 231–255. (p. 306)

Sternberg, R. J. (2003). Our research program validating the triarchic theory of successful intelligence: Reply to Gottfredson. *Intelligence, 31*, 399–413. (p. 306)

Sternberg, R. J. (2006). The Rainbow Project: Enhance the SAT through assessments of analytical, practical, and creative skills. *Intelligence, 34*, 321–350. (p. 307)

Sternberg, R. J. (2011). The theory of successful intelligence. In R. J. Sternberg & S. B. Kaufman (Eds.), *The Cambridge handbook of intelligence*. New York: Cambridge University Press. (p. 325)

Sternberg, R. J., & Grajek, S. (1984). The nature of love. *Journal of Personality and Social Psychology, 47*, 312–329. (p. 452)

Sternberg, R. J., & Kaufman, J. C. (1998). Human abilities. *Annual Review of Psychology, 49*, 479–502. (p. 323)

Sternberg, R. J., & Lubart, T. I. (1991). An investment theory of creativity and its development. *Human Development, 34*, 1–31. (p. 306)

Sternberg, R. J., & Lubart, T. I. (1992). Buy low and sell high: An investment approach to creativity. *Psychological Science, 1*, 1–5. (p. 306)

Sterzing, P. R., Shattuck, P. T., Narendorf, S. C., Wagner, M., & Cooper, B. P. (2012). Bullying involvement and autism spectrum disorders: Prevalence and correlates of bullying involvement among adolescents with an autism spectrum disorder. *Archives of Pediatric and Adolescent Medicine, 166*, 1058–1064. (p. 131)

Stetter, F., & Kupper, S. (2002). Autogenic training: A meta-analysis of clinical outcome studies. *Applied Psychophysiology and Biofeedback, 27*, 45–98. (p. 403)

Stevenson, H. W. (1992). Learning from Asian schools. *Scientific American, 267*, 70–76. (p. 342)

Stevenson, R. J. (2014). Flavor binding: Its nature and cause. *Psychological Bulletin, 140,* 487–510. (p. 228)

Stice, E. (2002). Risk and maintenance factors for eating pathology: A meta-analytic review. *Psychological Bulletin, 128,* 825–848. (p. 532)

Stice, E., Ng, J., & Shaw, H. (2010). Risk factors and prodromal eating pathology. *Journal of Child Psychology and Psychiatry, 51,* 518–525. (p. 532)

Stice, E., Spangler, D., & Agras, W. S. (2001). Exposure to media-portrayed thin-ideal images adversely affects vulnerable girls: A longitudinal experiment. *Journal of Social and Clinical Psychology, 20,* 270–288. (p. 533)

Stickgold, R. (2000, March 7). Quoted in S. Blakeslee, For better learning, researchers endorse "sleep on it" adage. *The New York Times,* p. F2. (p. 98)

Stickgold, R. (2012). Sleep, memory and dreams: Putting it all together. In *Aquém e além do cérebro* [Behind and beyond the brain]. Bial: Fundação Bial Institution of Public Utility. (p. 97)

Stillman, T. F., Baumeister, R. F., Vohs, K. D., Lambert, N. M., Fincham, F. D., & Brewer, L. E. (2010). Personal philosophy and personnel achievement: Belief in free will predicts better job performance. *Social Psychological and Personality Science, 1,* 43–50. (p. 397)

Stillman, T. F., Lambet, N. M., Fincham, F. D., & Baumeister, R. F. (2011). Meaning as magnetic force: Evidence that meaning in life promotes interpersonal appeal. *Social Psychological and Personality Science, 2,* 13–20. (p. 566)

Stinson, D. A., Logel, C., Zanna, M. P., Holmes, J. G., Camerson, J. J., Wood, J. V., & Spencer, S. J. (2008). The cost of lower self-esteem: Testing a self- and social-bonds model of health. *Journal of Personality and Social Psychology, 94,* 412–428. (p. 401)

Stith, S. M., Rosen, K. H., Middleton, K. A., Busch, A. L., Lunderberg, K., & Carlton, R. P. (2000). The intergenerational transmission of spouse abuse: A meta-analysis. *Journal of Marriage and the Family, 62,* 640–654. (p. 262)

Stockton, M. C., & Murnen, S. K. (1992, June). *Gender and sexual arousal in response to sexual stimuli: A meta-analytic review.* Paper presented at the Fourth Annual Convention of the American Psychological Society, San Diego, CA. (p. 176)

Stoll, G., Rieger, S., Lüdtke, O., Nagengast, B., Trautwein, U., & Roberts, B. W. (2017). Vocational interests assessed at the end of high school predict life outcomes assessed 10 years later over and above IQ and big five personality traits. *Journal of Personality and Social Psychology, 113,* 167–184. (p. B-3)

Stone, A. A., & Neale, J. M. (1984). Effects of severe daily events on mood. *Journal of Personality and Social Psychology, 46,* 137–144. (p. 408)

Stone, A. A., Schwartz, J. E., Broderick, J. E., & Deaton, A. (2010). A snapshot of the age distribution of psychological well-being in the United States. *PNAS, 107,* 9985–9990. (p. 158)

Stone, A. A., Schwartz, J. E., Broderick, J. E., & Shiffman, S. S. (2005). Variability of momentary pain predicts recall of weekly pain: A consequences of the peak (or salience) memory heuristic. *Personality and Social Psychology Bulletin, 31,* 1340–1346. (p. 223)

Stone, G. (2006, February 17). Homeless man discovered to be lawyer with amnesia. *ABC News* (abcnews.go.com). (p. 527)

Stop Street Harrassment. (2018). *The facts behind the #metoo movement: A national study on sexual harassment and assault.* Reston, Virginia. (p. 170)

Storbeck, J., Robinson, M. D., & McCourt, M. E. (2006). Semantic processing precedes affect retrieval: The neurological case for cognitive primary in visual processing. *Review of General Psychology, 10,* 41–55. (p. 371)

Storm, B. C., & Jobe, T. A. (2012). Retrieval-induced forgetting predicts failure to recall negative autobiographical memories. *Psychological Science, 23,* 1356–1363. (p. 278)

Storm, L., Tressoldi, P. E., & Di Risio, L. (2010a). Meta-analysis of free-response studies, 1992–2008: Assessing the noise reduction model in parapsychology. *Psychological Bulletin, 136,* 471–485. (p. 230)

Storm, L., Tressoldi, P. E., & Di Risio, L. (2010b). A meta-analysis with nothing to hide: Reply to Hyman (2010). *Psychological Bulletin, 136,* 491–494. (p. 230)

Storms, M. D. (1973). Videotape and the attribution process: Reversing actors' and observers' points of view. *Journal of Personality and Social Psychology, 27,* 165–175. (p. 417)

Storms, M. D. (1983). *Development of sexual orientation.* Washington, DC: Office of Social and Ethical Responsibility, American Psychological Association. (p. 180)

Storms, M. D., & Thomas, G. C. (1977). Reactions to physical closeness. *Journal of Personality and Social Psychology, 35,* 412–418. (p. 430)

Stothart, C., Mitchum, A., & Yehnert, C. (2015). The attentional cost of receiving a cell phone notification. *Journal of Experimental Psychology: Human Perception and Performance, 41,* 893–897. (p. 195)

Stowell, J. R., Oldham, T., & Bennett, D. (2010). Using student response systems ("clickers") to combat conformity and shyness. *Teaching of Psychology, 37,* 135–140. (p. 424)

Strack, F. (2016). Reflection on the smiling preregistered replication report. *Perspectives on Psychological Science, 11,* 929–930. (p. 381)

Strain, J. F., Womack, K. B., Didenbani, N., Spence, J. S., Conover, H., Hart, J., Jr., . . . Cullum, C. M. (2015). Imaging correlates of memory and concussion history in retired National Football League athletes. *JAMA Neurology, 72,* 773–780. (p. 56)

Strand, L. B., Mukamal, K. J., Halasz, J., Vatten, L. J., & Janszky, I. (2016). Short-term public health impact of the July 22, 2011, terrorist attacks in Norway: A nationwide register-based study. *Psychosomatic Medicine, 78,* 525–531. (p. 385)

Strang, S., Utikal, V., Fischbacher, U., Weber, B., & Falk, A. (2014). Neural correlates of receiving an apology and active forgiveness: An fMRI study. *PLoS ONE, 9,* e87654. (p. 394)

Strange, D., Hayne, H., & Garry, M. (2008). A photo, a suggestion, a false memory. *Applied Cognitive Psychology, 22,* 587–603. (p. 291)

Strasburger, V. C., Jordan, A. B., & Donnerstein, E. (2010). Health effects of media on children and adolescents. *Pediatrics, 125,* 756–767. (p. 262)

Stratton, G. M. (1896). Some preliminary experiments on vision without inversion of the retinal image. *Psychological Review, 3,* 611–617. (p. 214)

Straub, R. O., Seidenberg, M. S., Bever, T. G., & Terrace, H. S. (1979). Serial learning in the pigeon. *Journal of the Experimental Analysis of Behavior, 32,* 137–148. (p. 318)

Straus, M. A., & Gelles, R. J. (1980). *Behind closed doors: Violence in the American family.* New York: Anchor/Doubleday. (p. 249)

Straus, M. A., Sugarman, D. B., & Giles-Sims, J. (1997). Spanking by parents and subsequent antisocial behavior of children. *Archives of Pediatric Adolescent Medicine, 151,* 761–767. (p. 249)

Strawbridge, W. J. (1999). *Mortality and religious involvement: A review and critique of the results, the methods, and the measures.* Paper presented at a Harvard University conference on religion and health, sponsored by the National Institute for Health Research and the John Templeton Foundation. (p. 405)

Strawbridge, W. J., Cohen, R. D., & Shema, S. J. (1997). Frequent attendance at religious services and mortality over 28 years. *American Journal of Public Health, 87,* 957–961. (p. 405)

Strick, M., Dijksterhuis, A., Bos, M. W., Sjoerdsma, A., & van Baaren, R. B. (2011). A meta-analysis on unconscious thought effects. *Social Cognition, 29,* 738–762. (p. 305)

Strick, M., Dijksterhuis, A., & van Baaren, R. B. (2010). Unconscious-thought effects take place off-line, not on-line. *Psychological Science, 21,* 484–488. (p. 305)

Stroebe, M., Finenauer, C., Wijngaards-de Meij, L., Schut, H., van den Bout, J., & Stroebe, W. (2013). Partner-oriented self-regulation among bereaved parents: The costs of holding in grief for the partner's sake. *Psychological Science, 24,* 395–402. (p. 159)

Stroebe, W. (2012). The truth about Triplett (1898), but nobody seems to care. *Perspectives on Psychological Science, 7,* 54–57. (p. 429)

Stroebe, W. (2013). Firearm possession and violent death: A critical review. *Aggression and Violent Behavior, 18,* 709–721. (p. 441)

Stroebe, W., Schut, H., & Stroebe, M. S. (2005). Grief work, disclosure and counseling: Do they help the bereaved? *Clinical Psychology Review, 25,* 395–414. (p. 160)

Stroud, L. R., Panadonatos, G. D., Rodriguez, D., McCallum, M., Salisbury, A. L., Phipps, M. G., . . . Marsit, C. J. (2014). Maternal smoking during pregnancy and infant stress response: Test of a prenatal programming hypothesis. *Psychoneuroendocrinology, 48,* 29–40. (p. 120)

Strully, K. W. (2009). Job loss and health in the U.S. labor market. *Demography, 46,* 221–246. (p. 385)

Stuart, G. J., & Spruston, N. (2015). Dendritic integration: 60 years of progress. *Nature Neuroscience, 18,* 1713–1721. (p. 39)

Stubbs, B., Vancampfort, D., Rosenbaum, S., Firth, J., Cosco, T., Veronese, N., . . . Schuch, F. B. (2017). An examination of the anxiolytic effects of exercise for people with anxiety and stress-related disorders: A meta-analysis. *Psychiatry Research, 249,* 102–108. (p. 402)

Studte, S., Bridger, E., & Mecklinger, A. (2017). Sleep spindles during a nap correlate with post sleep memory performance for highly rewarded word-pairs. *Brain and Language, 167,* 28–35. (p. 88)

Štulhofer, A., Šoh, D., Jelaska, N., Baćak, V., & Landripet, I. (2011). Religiosity and sexual risk behavior among Croatian college students, 1998–2008. *Journal of Sex Research, 48,* 360–371. (p. 178)

Stutzer, A., & Frey, B. S. (2006). Does marriage make people happy, or do happy people get married? *Journal of Socio-Economics, 35,* 326–347. (p. 407)

Subrahmanyam, K., & Greenfield, P. (2008). Online communication and adolescent relationships. *The Future of Children, 18,* 119–146. (p. 148)

Suddath, R. L., Christison, G. W., Torrey, E. F., Casanova, M. F., & Weinberger, D. R. (1990). Anatomical abnormalities in the brains of monozygotic twins discordant for schizophrenia. *New England Journal of Medicine, 322,* 789–794. (p. 527)

Sue, S., Zane, N., Hall, G. C. N., & Berger, L. K. (2009). The case for cultural competency in psychotherapeutic interventions. *Annual Review of Psychology, 60,* 525–548. (p. 556)

Suedfeld, P., & Mocellin, J. S. P. (1987). The "sensed presence" in unusual environments. *Environment and Behavior, 19,* 33–52. (p. 108)

Sugaya, L., Hasin, D. S., Olfson, M., Lin, K.-H., Grant, B. F., & Blanco, C. (2012). Child physical abuse and adult mental health: A national study. *Journal of Traumatic Stress, 25,* 384–392. (p. 138)

Suglia, S. F., Kara, S., & Robinson, W. R. (2014). Sleep duration and obesity among adolescents transitioning to adulthood: Do results differ by sex? *The Journal of Pediatrics, 165,* 750–754. (p. 93)

Sulik, M. J., Blair, C., Mills-Koonce, R., Berry, D., Greenberg, M., & Family Life Project Investigators. (2015). Early parenting and the development of externalizing behavior problems: Longitudinal mediation through children's executive function. *Child Development, 86,* 1588–1603. (p. 139)

Sullivan, K. T., Pasch, L. A., Johnson, M. D., & Bradbury, T. N. (2010). Social support, problem solving, and the longitudinal course of newlywed marriage. *Journal of Personality and Social Psychology, 98,* 631–644. (p. 452)

Sullivan, P. F., Neale, M. C., & Kendler, K. S. (2000). Genetic epidemiology of major depression: Review and meta-analysis. *American Journal of Psychiatry, 157,* 1552–1562. (p. 518)

Suls, J. M., & Tesch, F. (1978). Students' preferences for information about their test performance: A social comparison study. *Journal of Experimental Social Psychology, 8,* 189–197. (p. 410)

Summers, M. (1996, December 9). Mister Clean. *People Weekly,* pp. 139–142. (p. 493)

Sun, G. J., Zhou, Y., Ito, S., Bonaguidi, M. A., Stein-O'Brien, G., Kawasaki, N. K., . . . Song, H. (2015). Latent tri-lineage potential of adult hippocampal neural stem cells revealed by Nf1 inactivation. *Nature Neuroscience, 18,* 1722–1724. (p. 64)

Sundstrom, E., De Meuse, K. P., & Futrell, D. (1990). Work teams: Applications and effectiveness. *American Psychologist, 45,* 120–133. (p. B-11)

Sung, S., Simpson, J. A., Griskevicius, V., Sally, I., Kuo, C., Schlomer, G. L., & Belsky, J. (2016). Secure infant-mother attachment buffers the effect of early-life stress on age of menarche. *Psychological Science, 27,* 667–674. (p. 167)

Sunstein, C. R., Bobadilla-Suarez, S., Lazzaro, S. C., & Sharot, T. (2016). How people update beliefs about climate change: Good news and bad news. Social Science Research Network (ssrn.com). (p. 304)

Suomi, S. J. (1986). Anxiety-like disorders in young nonhuman primates. In R. Gettleman (Ed.), *Anxiety disorders of childhood.* New York: Guilford Press. (p. 511)

Suomi, S. J., Collins, M. L., Harlow, H. F., & Ruppenthal, G. C. (1976). Effects of maternal and peer separations on young monkeys. *Journal of Child Psychology and Psychiatry, 17,* 101–112. (p. 220)

Suppes, P. (1982). Quoted in R. H. Ennis, Children's ability to handle Piaget's propositional logic: A conceptual critique. In S. Modgil & C. Modgil (Eds.), *Jean Piaget: Consensus and controversy* (pp. 101–130). New York: Praeger. (p. 129)

Surgeon General. (1986). *The Surgeon General's workshop on pornography and public health,* June 22–24. Report prepared by E. P. Mulvey & J. L. Haugaard and released by Office of the Surgeon General on August 4, 1986. (p. 444)

Surgeon General. (2012). *Preventing tobacco use among youth and young adults: A report of the Surgeon General.* Rockville, MD: Department of Health and Human Services, Office of the Surgeon General. (p. 112)

Surgeon General's Office. (1999). *Mental health: A report of the surgeon general.* Rockville, MD: U.S. Department of Health and Human Services. (p. 503)

Susser, E. S., Neugenbauer, R., Hoek, H. W., Brown, A. S., Lin, S., Labovitz, D., & Gorman, J. M. (1996). Schizophrenia after prenatal famine. *Archives of General Psychiatry, 53*(1), 25–31. (p. 525)

Sutcliffe, J. S. (2008). Insights into the pathogenesis of autism. *Science, 321,* 208–209. (p. 131)

Sutin, A. R., Ferrucci, L., Zonderman, A. B., & Terracciano, A. (2011). Personality and obesity across the adult life span. *Journal of Personality and Social Psychology, 101,* 579–592. (p. 480)

Swami, V. (2015). Cultural influences on body size ideals: Unpacking the impact of Westernization and modernization. *European Psychologist, 20,* 44–51. (p. 365)

Swami, V., Frederick, D. A., Aavik, T., Alcalay, L., Allik, J., Anderson, D., . . . Zivcic-Becirevic, I. (2010). The attractive female body weight and female body dissatisfaction in 26 countries across 10 world regions: Results of the International Body Project I. *Personality and Social Psychology Bulletin, 36,* 309–325. (p. 532)

Swann, W. B., Jr., Chang-Schneider, C., & McClarty, K. L. (2007). Do people's self-views matter? Self-concept and self-esteem in everyday life. *American Psychologist, 62,* 84–94. (p. 486)

Swart, H., Hewstone, M., Christ, O., & Voci, A. (2011). Affective mediators of intergroup contact: A three-wave longitudinal study in South Africa. *Journal of Personality and Social Psychology, 101,* 1221–1238. (p. 457)

Swartz, J. R., Hariri, A. R., & Williamson, D. E. (2016). An epigenetic mechanism links socioeconomic status to changes in depression-related brain function in high-risk adolescents. *Molecular Psychiatry, 22,* 209–214. (p. 74)

Swift, A. (2013, October 28). *Personal safety top reason Americans own guns today.* Gallup (gallup.com). (p. 441)

Swift, A. (2016, November 9). Americans' perception of US crime problem are steady. *Gallup.* Retrieved from gallup.com/poll/197318/americans-perceptions-crime-problem-steady.aspx (p. 18)

Symbaluk, D. G., Heth, C. D., Cameron, J., & Pierce, W. D. (1997). Social modeling, monetary incentives, and pain endurance: The role of self-efficacy and pain perception. *Personality and Social Psychology Bulletin, 23,* 258–269. (p. 223)

Symond, M. B., Harris, A. W. F., Gordon, E., & Williams, L. M. (2005). "Gamma synchrony" in first-episode schizophrenia: A disorder of temporal connectivity? *American Journal of Psychiatry, 162,* 459–465. (p. 524)

Symons, C. S., & Johnson, B. T. (1997). The self-reference effect in memory: A meta-analysis. *Psychological Bulletin, 121,* 371–394. (p. 274)

Szkodny, L. E., Newman, M. G., & Goldfried, M. R. (2014). Clinical experiences in conducting empirically supported treatments for generalized anxiety disorder. *Behavior Therapy, 45,* 7–20. (p. 546)

Tackett, J. L., Herzhoff, K., Kushner, S. C., & Rule, N. (2016). Thin slices of child personality: Perceptual, situational, and behavioral contributions. *Journal of Personality and Social Psychology, 110,* 150–166. (p. 481)

Tadmor, C. T., Galinsky, A. D., & Maddux, W. W. (2012). Getting the most out of living abroad: Biculturalism and integrative complexity as key drivers of creative and professional success. *Journal of Personality and Social Psychology, 103,* 520–542. (p. 307)

Taha, F. A. (1972). A comparative study of how sighted and blind perceive the manifest content of dreams. *National Review of Social Sciences, 9*(3), 28. (p. 97)

Taheri, S. (2004, December 20). Does the lack of sleep make you fat? *University of Bristol Research News* (bristol.ac.uk). (p. 365)

Taheri, S., Lin, L., Austin, D., Young, T., & Mignot, E. (2004). Short sleep duration is associated with reduced leptin, elevated ghrelin, and increased body mass index. *PLoS Medicine, 1,* e62. (p. 365)

Tajfel, H. (Ed.). (1982). *Social identity and intergroup relations.* New York: Cambridge University Press. (p. 438)

Takizawa, R., Maughan, B., & Arseneault, L. (2014). Adult health outcomes of childhood bullying victimization: Evidence from a five-decade longitudinal British birth cohort. *American Journal of Psychiatry, 171,* 777–784. (p. 148)

Talarico, J. M., & Moore, K. M. (2012). Memories of "the rivalry": Differences in how fans of the winning and losing teams remember the same game. *Applied Cognitive Psychology, 26,* 746–756. (p. 278)

Talbot, M. (1999, October). The Rorschach chronicles. *The New York Times* (nytimes.com). (p. 466)

Talhelm, T., Zhang, X., Oishi, S., Shimin, C., Duan, D., Lan, X., & Kitayama, S. (2014). Large-scale psychological differences within China explained by rice versus wheat agriculture. *Science, 344,* 603–608. (p. 490)

Tamres, L. K., Janicki, D., & Helgeson, V. S. (2002). Sex differences in coping behavior: A meta-analytic review and an examination of relative coping. *Personality and Social Psychology Review, 6,* 2–30. (p. 165)

Tanaka, T., Yamamoto, T., & Haruno, M. (2017). Brain response patterns to economic inequity predict present and future depression indices. *Nature Human Behavior, 1,* 748–756. (p. 410)

Tang, S.-H., & Hall, V. C. (1995). The overjustification effect: A meta-analysis. *Applied Cognitive Psychology, 9,* 365–404. (p. 358)

Tang, Y. Y., Ma, Y., Wang, J., Fan, Y., Feng, S., Lu, Q., . . . Posner, M. I. (2007). Short-term meditation training improves attention and self-regulation. *PNAS, 104,* 17152–17156. (p. 404)

Tannen, D. (1990). *You just don't understand: Women and men in conversation.* New York: Morrow. (p. 163)

Tannen, D. (2001). *You just don't understand: Women and men in conversation.* New York: HarperCollins. (p. 10)

Tanner, J. M. (1978). *Fetus into man: Physical growth from conception to maturity.* Cambridge, MA: Harvard University Press. (p. 165)

Tardif, T., Fletcher, P., Liang, W., Zhang, Z., Kaciroti, N., & Marchman, V. A. (2008). Baby's first 10 words. *Developmental Psychology, 44,* 929–938. (p. 314)

Tarrant, M., Branscombe, N. R., Warner, R. H., & Weston, D. (2012). Social identity and perceptions of torture: It's moral when we do it. *Journal of Experimental Social Psychology, 48,* 513–518. (p. 456)

Tasbihsazan, R., Nettelbeck, T., & Kirby, N. (2003). Predictive validity of the Fagan test of infant intelligence. *British Journal of Developmental Psychology, 21,* 585–597. (p. 332)

Tatlow, D. K. (2016, June 11). Doctor's plan for full-body transplants raises doubts even in daring China. *The New York Times* (nytimes.com). (p. 37)

Taubes, G. (2001). The soft science of dietary fat. *Science, 291,* 2536–2545. (p. 366)

Taubes, G. (2002, July 7). What if it's all been a big fat lie? *The New York Times* (nytimes.com). (p. 366)

Tausch, N., Hewstone, M., Kenworthy, J. B., Psaltis, C., Schmid, K., Popan, J. R., . . . Hughes, J. (2010). Secondary transfer effects of intergroup contact: Alternative accounts and underlying processes. *Journal of Personality and Social Psychology, 99,* 282–302. (p. 457)

Tavernier, R., & Willoughby, T. (2014). Bidirectional associations between sleep (quality and duration) and psychosocial functioning across the university years. *Developmental Psychology, 50,* 674–682. (p. 93)

Tavernise, S. (2013, February 13). To reduce suicide rates, new focus turns to guns. *The New York Times* (nytimes.com). (p. 501)

Tavernise, S. (2016, February 29). "Female Viagra" only modestly increases sexual satisfaction, study finds. *The New York Times* (nytimes.com). (p. 28)

Tavris, C. (1982, November). Anger defused. *Psychology Today,* pp. 25–35. (p. 393)

Tavris, C., & Aronson, E. (2007). *Mistakes were made (but not by me).* Orlando, FL: Harcourt. (p. 288)

Tay, L., & Diener, E. (2011). Needs and subjective well-being around the world. *Journal of Personality and Social Psychology, 101,* 354–365. (p. 351)

Taylor-Covill, G. A., & Eves, F. F. (2016). Carrying a biological "backpack": Quasi-experimental effects of weight status and body fat change on perceived steepness. *Journal of Experimental Psychology: Human Perception and Performance, 42,* 331–338. (p. 197)

Taylor, C. (2017). Creativity and mood disorder: A systematic review and meta-analysis. *Perspectives on Psychological Science, 12,* 1040-1076. (p. 515)

Taylor, C. A., Manganello, J. A., Lee, S. J., & Rice, J. C. (2010). Mothers' spanking of 3-year-old children and subsequent risk of children's aggressive behavior. *Pediatrics, 125,* 1057–1065. (p. 250)

Taylor, K., & Rohrer, D. (2010). The effects of interleaved practice. *Applied Cognitive Psychology, 24,* 837–848. (p. 34)

Taylor, L. E., Swerdfeger, A. L., & Eslick, G. D. (2014). Vaccines are not associated with autism: An evidence-based meta-analysis of case-control and cohort studies. *Vaccine, 32,* 3623–3629. (p. 131)

Taylor, P. (2014). *The next America: Boomers, millennials, and the looming generational showdown.* New York: Public Affairs. (p. 135)

Taylor, P. J., Gooding, P., Wood, A. M., & Tarrier, N. (2011). The role of defeat and entrapment in depression, anxiety, and suicide. *Psychological Bulletin, 137,* 391–420. (p. 501)

Taylor, P. J., Russ-Eft, D. F., & Chan, D. W. L. (2005). A meta-analytic review of behavior modeling training. *Journal of Applied Psychology, 90,* 692–709. (p. 261)

Taylor, S. (2013). Molecular genetics of obsessive-compulsive disorder: A comprehensive meta-analysis of genetic association studies. *Molecular Psychiatry, 18,* 799–805. (p. 511)

Taylor, S., Kuch, K., Koch, W. J., Crockett, D. J., & Passey, G. (1998). The structure of posttraumatic stress symptoms. *Journal of Abnormal Psychology, 107,* 154–160. (p. 321)

Taylor, S. E. (2002). *The tending instinct: How nurturing is essential to who we are and how we live.* New York: Times Books. (p. 165)

Taylor, S. E. (2006). Tend and befriend: Biobehavioral bases of affiliation under stress. *Current Directions in Psychological Science, 15,* 273–277. (p. 388)

Taylor, S. E., Cousino, L. K., Lewis, B. P., Gruenewald, T. L., Gurung, R. A. R., & Updegraff, J. A. (2000). Biobehavioral responses to stress in females: Tend-and-befriend, not fight-or-flight. *Psychological Review, 107,* 411–430. (p. 388)

Taylor, S. F., Bhati, M. T., Dubin, M. J., Hawkins, J. M., Lisanby, S. H., Morales, O., . . . Watcharotone, K. (2017). A naturalistic, multi-site study of repetitive transcranial magnetic stimulation therapy for depression. *Journal of Affective Disorders, 208,* 284–290. (p. 564)

Taylor, S. P., & Chermack, S. T. (1993). Alcohol, drugs and human physical aggression. *Journal of Studies on Alcohol, Supplement 11,* 78–88. (p. 442)

Taylor, V. J., & Walton, G. M. (2011). Stereotype threat undermines academic learning. *Personality and Social Psychology Bulletin, 37,* 1055–1067. (p. 344)

Tedeschi, R. G., & Calhoun, L. G. (2004). Posttraumatic growth: Conceptual foundations and empirical evidence. *Psychological Inquiry, 15,* 1–18. (p. 567)

Teghtsoonian, R. (1971). On the exponents in Stevens' law and the constant in Ekinan's law. *Psychological Review, 78,* 71–80. (p. 193)

Teicher, M. H., & Samson, J. A. (2016). Annual research review: Enduring neurobiological effects of childhood abuse and neglect. *Journal of Child Psychology and Psychiatry, 57,* 241–266. (p. 137)

Teller. (2009, April 20). Quoted by J. Lehrer, Magic and the brain: Teller reveals the neuroscience of illusion. *Wired Magazine* (wired.com). (p. 83)

Telzer, E. H., Flannery, J., Shapiro, M., Humphreys, K. L., Goff, B., Gabard-Durman, . . . Tottenham, N. (2013). Early experience shapes amygdala sensitivity to race: An international adoption design. *The Journal of Neuroscience, 33,* 13484–13488. (p. 439)

ten Brinke, L., Liu, C. C., Keltner, D., & Srivastava, S. B. (2016a). Virtues, vices, and political influence in the U.S. Senate. *Psychological Science, 27,* 85–93. (p. B-11)

ten Brinke, L., Vohs, K. D., & Carney. D. (2016b). Can ordinary people detect deception after all? *Trends in Cognitive Sciences, 20,* 579–588. (p. 376)

Tenenbaum, H. R., & Leaper, C. (2002). Are parents' gender schemas related to their children's gender-related cognitions? A meta-analysis. *Developmental Psychology, 38,* 615–630. (p. 169)

Tenopyr, M. L. (1997). Improving the workplace: Industrial/organizational psychology as a career. In R. J. Sternberg (Ed.), *Career paths in psychology: Where your degree can take you.* Washington, DC: American Psychological Association. (p. B-5)

Tepper, S. J. (2000). Fiction reading in America: Explaining the gender gap. *Poetics, 27,* 255–275. (p. 378)

Terada, S., Sakurai, Y., Nakahara, H., & Fujisawa, S. (2017). Temporal and rate coding for discrete event sequences in the hippocampus. *Neuron, 94,* 1248–1262. (p. 276)

Terao, T., Ohgami, H., Shlotsuki, I., Ishil, N., & Iwata, N. (2010). Author's reply. *British Journal of Psychiatry, 196,* 160. (p. 562)

Terrace, H. S. (1979, November). How Nim Chimpsky changed my mind. *Psychology Today,* pp. 65–76. (p. 318)

Terre, L., & Stoddart, R. (2000). Cutting edge specialties for graduate study in psychology. *Eye on Psi Chi, 23–26.* (p. C-1)

Terrell, J., Kofink, A., Middleton, J., Rainear, C., Murphy-Hill, E., Parnin, C., & Stallings, J. (2017). Gender differences and bias in open source: Pull request acceptance of women versus men. *PeerJ Computer Science, 3,* e111. (p. 168)

Tesser, A., Forehand, R., Brody, G., & Long, N. (1989). Conflict: The role of calm and angry parent-child discussion in adolescent development. *Journal of Social and Clinical Psychology, 8,* 317–330. (p. 147)

Testa, R. J., Michaels, M. S., Bliss, W., Rogers, M. L., Balsam, K. F., & Joiner, T. (2017). Suicidal ideation in transgender people: Gender minority stress and interpersonal factors. *Journal of Abnormal Psychology, 126,* 125–136. (p. 500)

Tetlock, P. E. (1988). Monitoring the integrative complexity of American and Soviet policy rhetoric: What can be learned? *Journal of Social Issues, 44,* 101–131. (p. 459)

Tetlock, P. E. (1998). Close-call counterfactuals and belief-system defenses: I was not almost wrong but I was almost right. *Journal of Personality and Social Psychology, 75,* 639–652. (p. 17)

Tetlock, P. E. (2005). *Expert political judgement: How good is it? How can we know?* Princeton, NJ: Princeton University Press. (p. 17)

Tetlock, P. E., & Gardner, D. (2016). *Superforecasting: The art and science of prediction.* New York: Broadway Books. (p. 17)

Thaler, L., Arnott, S. R., & Goodale, M. A. (2011). Neural correlates of natural human echolocation in early and late blind echolocation experts. *PLoS ONE, 6,* e20162. (p. 39)

Thaler, L., Milne, J. L., Arnott, S. R., Kish, D., & Goodale, M. A. (2014). Neural correlates of motion processing through echolocation, source hearing, and vision in blind echolocation experts and sighted echolocation novices. *Journal of Neurophysiology, 111,* 112–127. (p. 39)

Thaler, R. H. (2015, May 8). Unless you are Spock, irrelevant things matter in economic behavior. *The New York Times* (nytimes.com). (p. 469)

Thaler, R. H., & Sunstein, C. R. (2008). *Nudge: Improving decisions about health, wealth, and happiness.* New Haven, CT: Yale University Press. (p. 304)

Thatcher, R. W., Walker, R. A., & Giudice, S. (1987). Human cerebral hemispheres develop at different rates and ages. *Science, 236,* 1110–1113. (pp. 117, 123)

Thayer, R. E. (1987). Energy, tiredness, and tension effects of a sugar snack versus moderate exercise. *Journal of Personality and Social Psychology, 52,* 119–125. (p. 402)

Thayer, R. E. (1993). Mood and behavior (smoking and sugar snacking) following moderate exercise: A partial test of self-regulation theory. *Personality and Individual Differences, 14,* 97–104. (p. 402)

The Guardian. (2014, August 12). Maryam Mirzakhani: "The more I spent time on maths, the more excited I got." *The Guardian* (theguardian.com). (p. 341)

Théoret, H., Halligan, H., Kobayashi, M., Fregni, F., Tager-Flusberg, H., & Pascual-Leone, A. (2005). Impaired motor facilitation during action observation in individuals with autism spectrum disorder. *Current Biology, 15,* R84–R85. (p. 132)

Thernstrom, M. (2006, May 14). My pain, my brain. *The New York Times* (nytimes.com). (p. 223)

Thibodeau, R., Jorgensen, R. S., & Kim, S. (2006). Depression, anxiety, and resting frontal EEG asymmetry: A meta-analytic review. *Journal of Abnormal Psychology, 115,* 715–729. (p. 52)

Thiel, A., Hadedank, B., Herholz, K., Kessler, J., Winhuisen, L., Haupt, W. F., & Heiss, W.-D. (2006). From the left to the right: How the brain compensates progressive loss of language function. *Brain and Language, 98,* 57–65. (p. 64)

Thomas, A., & Chess, S. (1986). The New York Longitudinal Study: From infancy to early adult life. In R. Plomin & J. Dunn (Eds.), *The study of temperament: Changes, continuities, and challenges* (pp. 39–52). Hillsdale, NJ: Erlbaum. (p. 118)

Thomas, L. (1992). *The fragile species.* New York: Scribner's. (pp. 77, 551)

Thompson, G. (2010). The $1 million dollar challenge. *Skeptic Magazine, 15*, 8–9. (p. 231)

Thompson, J. K., Jarvie, G. J., Lahey, B. B., & Cureton, K. J. (1982). Exercise and obesity: Etiology, physiology, and intervention. *Psychological Bulletin, 91*, 55–79. (p. 366)

Thompson, P. M., Cannon, T. D., Narr, K. L., van Erp, T., Poutanen, V.-P., Huttunen, M., . . . Toga, A. W. (2001). Genetic influences on brain structure. *Nature Neuroscience, 4*, 1253–1258. (p. 336)

Thompson, P. M., Giedd, J. N., Woods, R. P., MacDonald, D., Evans, A. C., & Toga, A. W. (2000). Growth patterns in the developing brain detected by using continuum mechanical tensor maps. *Nature, 404*, 190–193. (p. 123)

Thompson, R., Emmorey, K., & Gollan, T. H. (2005). "Tip of the fingers" experiences by Deaf signers. *Psychological Science, 16*, 856–860. (p. 287)

Thompson-Schill, S. L., Ramscar, M., & Chrysikou, E. G. (2009). Cognition without control: When a little frontal lobe goes a long way. *Current Directions in Psychological Science, 18*, 259–263. (p. 123)

Thomson, K. S., & Oppenheimer, D. M. (2016). Investigating an alternate form of the cognitive reflection test. *Judgment and Decision Making, 11*, 99–113. (p. 306)

Thorndike, E. L. (1898). Animal intelligence: An experimental study of the associative processes in animals. *Psychological Review Monograph Supplement, 2*, 4–160. (p. 244)

Thorne, J., with Larry Rothstein. (1993). *You are not alone: Words of experience and hope for the journey through depression.* New York: HarperPerennial. (p. 493)

Thornicroft, G., Chatterji, S., Evans-Lacko, S., Gruber, M., Sampson, N., Aguilar-Gaxiola, S., . . . Bruffaerts, R. (2017). Undertreatment of people with major depressive disorder in 21 countries. *British Journal of Psychiatry, 210*, 119–124. (p. 514)

Thornton, B., & Moore, S. (1993). Physical attractiveness contrast effect: Implications for self-esteem and evaluations of the social self. *Personality and Social Psychology Bulletin, 19*, 474–480. (p. 449)

Thorpe, W. H. (1974). *Animal nature and human nature.* London: Metheun. (p. 318)

Tibbetts, Y., Harackiewicz, J. M., Canning, E. A., Boston, J. S., Priniski, S. J., & Hyde, J. S. (2016). Affirming independence: Exploring mechanisms underlying a values affirmation intervention for first-generation students. *Journal of Personality and Social Psychology, 110*, 635–659. (p. 344)

Tick, B., Bolton, P., Happé, F., Rutter, M., & Rijsdijk, F. (2015). Heritability of autism spectrum disorders: A meta-analysis of twin studies. *Journal of Child Psychology and Psychiatry, 57*, 585–595. (p. 131)

Tickle, J. J., Hull, J. G., Sargent, J. D., Dalton, M. A., & Heatherton, T. F. (2006). A structural equation model of social influences and exposure to media smoking on adolescent smoking. *Basic and Applied Social Psychology, 28*, 117–129. (p. 111)

Tiedens, L. Z. (2001). Anger and advancement versus sadness and subjugation: The effect of negative emotion expressions on social status conferral. *Journal of Personality and Social Psychology, 80*, 86–94. (p. 394)

Tielbeek, J. J., Johansson, A., Polderman, T. J., Rautiainen, M. R., Jansen, P., Taylor, M., . . . Viding, E. (2017). Genome-wide association studies of a broad spectrum of antisocial behavior. *JAMA Psychiatry, 74*, 1242–1250. (p. 530)

Tigbe, W. W., Granat, M. H., Sattar, N., & Lean, M. E. J. (2017). Time spent in sedentary posture is associated with waist circumference and cardiovascular risk. *International Journal of Obesity, 41*, 689–696. (p. 401)

Tiggemann, M., & Miller, J. (2010). The internet and adolescent girls' weight satisfaction and drive for thinness. *Sex Roles, 63*, 79–90. (p. 532)

Tiihonen, J., Lönnqvist, J., Wahlbeck, K., Klaukka, T., Niskanen, L., Tanskanen, A., & Haukka, J. (2009). 11-year follow-up of mortality in patients with schizophrenia: A population-based cohort study (FIN11 study). *The Lancet, 374*, 260–267. (p. 560)

Tiihonen, J., Rautiainen, M. R., Ollila, H. M., Repo-Tiihonen, E., Virkkunen, M., Palotie, A., . . . Paunio, T. (2015). Genetic background of extreme violent behavior. *Molecular Psychiatry, 20*, 786–792. (p. 441)

Time/CNN Survey. (1994, December 19). Vox pop: Happy holidays, *Time*. (p. 514)

Timmerman, T. A. (2007). "It was a thought pitch": Personal, situational, and target influences on hit-by-pitch events across time. *Journal of Applied Psychology, 92*, 876–884. (p. 443)

Tinbergen, N. (1951). *The study of instinct.* Oxford: Clarendon. (p. 348)

Tirrell, M. E. (1990). Personal communication. (p. 239)

Tobin, D. D., Menon, M., Menon, M., Spatta, B. C., Hodges, E. V. E., & Perry, D. G. (2010). The intrapsychics of gender: A model of self-socialization. *Psychological Review, 117*, 601–622. (p. 169)

Todd, R. M., MacDonald, M. J., Sedge, P., Robertson, A., Jetly, R., Taylor, M. J., & Pang, E. W. (2015). Soldiers with posttraumatic stress disorder see a world full of threat: Magnetoencephalography reveals enhanced tuning to combat-related cues. *Biological Psychiatry, 78*, 821–829. (p. 52)

Todes, D. P. (2014). *Ivan Pavlov: A Russian life in science.* New York: Oxford University Press. (p. 236)

Toews, P. (2004, December 30). *Dirk Willems: A heart undivided.* Mennonite Brethren Historical Commission (mbhistory.org/profiles/dirk.en.html). (p. 415)

Tolin, D. F. (2010). Is cognitive-behavioral therapy more effective than other therapies? A meta-analytic review. *Clinical Psychology Review, 30*, 710–720. (p. 553)

Tolman, E. C., & Honzik, C. H. (1930). Introduction and removal of reward, and maze performance in rats. *University of California Publications in Psychology, 4*, 257–275. (p. 257)

Toma, C., & Hancock, J. (2013). Self-affirmation underlies Facebook use. *Personality and Social Psychology Bulletin, 369*, 321–331. (p. 487)

Tomaka, J., Blascovich, J., & Kelsey, R. M. (1992). Effects of self-deception, social desirability, and repressive coping on psychophysiological reactivity to stress. *Personality and Social Psychology Bulletin, 18*, 616–624. (p. 487)

Toni, N., Buchs, P.-A., Nikonenko, I., Bron, C. R., & Muller, D. (1999). LTP promotes formation of multiple spine synapses between a single axon terminal and a dendrite. *Nature, 402*, 421–442. (p. 279)

Topolinski, S., & Reber, R. (2010). Gaining insight into the "aha" experience. *Current Directions in Psychological Science, 19*, 401–405. (p. 299)

Torrey, E. F. (1986). *Witchdoctors and psychiatrists.* New York: Harper & Row. (p. 556)

Torrey, E. F., & Miller, J. (2002). *The invisible plague: The rise of mental illness from 1750 to the present.* New Brunswick, NJ: Rutgers University Press. (p. 525)

Torrey, E. F., Miller, J., Rawlings, R., & Yolken, R. H. (1997). Seasonality of births in schizophrenia and bipolar disorder: A review of the literature. *Schizophrenia Research, 28*, 1–38. (p. 525)

Totterdell, P., Kellett, S., Briner, R. B., & Teuchmann, K. (1998). Evidence of mood linkage in work groups. *Journal of Personality and Social Psychology, 74*, 1504–1515. (p. 423)

Towers, S., Gomez-Lievano, A., Khan, M., Mubayi, A., & Castillo-Chavez, C. (2015) Contagion in mass killings and school shootings. *PLoS ONE 10*, e0117259. (p. 421)

Tracy, J. L., Cheng, J. T., Robins, R. W., & Trzesniewski, K. H. (2009). Authentic and hubristic pride: The affective core of self-esteem and narcissism. *Self and Identity, 8*, 196–213. (p. 489)

Tracy, J. L., & Robins, R. W. (2004). Show your pride: Evidence for a discrete emotion expression. *Psychological Science, 15*, 194–197. (p. 372)

Tracy, J. L., Shariff, A. F., Zhao, W., & Henrich, J. (2013). Cross-cultural evidence that the nonverbal expression of pride is an automatic status signal. *Journal of Experimental Psychology: General, 142*, 163–180. (p. 375)

Traffanstedt, M. K., Mehta, S., & LoBello, S. G. (2016). Major depression with seasonal variation: Is it a valid construct? *Clinical Psychological Science, 4*, 825–834. (p. 515)

Trahan, L. H., Stuebing, K. K., Fletcher, J. M., & Hiscock, M. (2014). The Flynn effect: A meta-analysis. *Psychological Bulletin, 140*, 1332–1360. (p. 342)

Trautwein, U., Lüdtke, O., Köller, O., & Baumert, J. (2006). Self-esteem, academic self-concept, and achievement: How the learning environment moderates the dynamics of self-concept. *Journal of Personality and Social Psychology, 90*, 334–349. (p. 486)

Treanor, M., Brown, L. A., Rissman, J., & Craske, M. G. (2017). Can memories of traumatic experiences or addiction be erased or modified? A critical review of research on the disruption of memory reconsolidation and its applications. *Perspectives on Psychological Science, 12*, 290–305. (p. 289)

Treffert, D. A. (2010). *Islands of genius: The beautiful mind of the autistic, acquired, and sudden savant.* Philadelphia: Jessica Kinsley. (p. 324)

Treffert, D. A., & Christensen, D. D. (2005). Inside the mind of a savant. *Scientific American, 293*, 108–113. (p. 325)

Treisman, A. (1987). Properties, parts, and objects. In K. R. Boff, L. Kaufman, & J. P. Thomas (Eds.), *Handbook of perception and human performance* (pp. 159–198). New York: Wiley. (p. 208)

Tremblay, P., & Dick, A. S. (2016). Broca and Wernicke are dead, or moving past the classic model of language neurobiology. *Brain and Language, 162*, 60–71. (p. 317)

Tremblay, R. E., Pihl, R. O., Vitaro, F., & Dobkin, P. L. (1994). Predicting early onset of male antisocial behavior from preschool behavior. *Archives of General Psychiatry, 51*, 732–739. (p. 530)

Triandis, H. C. (1994). *Culture and social behavior.* New York: McGraw-Hill. (pp. 443, 491)

Trickett, E. (2009). Community psychology: Individuals and interventions in community context. *Annual Review of Psychology, 60*, 395–419. (p. 13)

Trillin, C. (2006, March 27). Alice off the page. *The New Yorker*, p. 44. (p. 472)

Triplett, N. (1898). The dynamogenic factors in pacemaking and competition. *American Journal of Psychology, 9*, 507–533. (p. 429)

Trotter, J. (2014). The power of positive coaching. *Sports Illustrated* (mmqb.si.com). (p. B-9)

Trumbo, M. C., Leiting, K. A., McDaniel, M. A., & Hodge, G. K. (2016). Effects of reinforcement on test-enhanced learning in a large, diverse introductory college psychology course. *Journal of Experimental Psychology: Applied, 22*, 148–160. (pp. 33, 272)

Trump, D. J. (2017, August 8). Tweet from @realDonaldTrump. (p. 104)

Trut, L. N. (1999). Early canid domestication: The farm-fox experiment. *American Scientist, 87,* 160–169. (p. 75)

Tsai, J. L., Ang, J. Y. Z., Blevins, E., Goernandt, J., Fung, H. H., Jiang, D., . . . Haddouk, L. (2016). Leaders' smiles reflect cultural differences in ideal affect. *Emotion, 16,* 183–195. (p. 379)

Tsai, J. L., & Chentsova-Dutton, Y. (2003). Variation among European Americans in emotional facial expression. *Journal of Cross-Cultural Psychology, 34,* 650–657. (p. 380)

Tsai, J. L., Knutson, B., & Fung, H. H. (2006). Cultural variation in affect valuation. *Journal of Personality and Social Psychology, 90,* 288–307. (p. 379)

Tsai, J. L., Miao, F. F., Seppala, E., Fung, H. H., & Yeung, D. Y. (2007). Influence and adjustment goals: Sources of cultural differences in ideal affect. *Journal of Personality and Social Psychology, 92,* 1102–1117. (p. 379)

Tsang, Y. C. (1938). Hunger motivation in gastrectomized rats. *Journal of Comparative Psychology, 26,* 1–17. (p. 361)

Tsvetkova, M., & Macy, M. W. (2014). The social contagion of generosity. *PLoS ONE, 9,* e87275. (p. 455)

Tuber, D. S., Miller, D. D., Caris, K. A., Halter, R., Linden, F., & Hennessy, M. B. (1999). Dogs in animal shelters: Problems, suggestions, and needed expertise. *Psychological Science, 10,* 379–386. (p. 31)

Tucker-Drob, E. (2012). Preschools reduce early academic-achievement gaps: A longitudinal twin approach. *Psychological Science, 23,* 310–319. (p. 339)

Tucker-Drob, E. M., & Bates, T. C. (2016). Large cross-national differences in gene x socioeconomic status interaction on intelligence. *Psychological Science, 27,* 138–149. (p. 339)

Tucker-Drob, E., & Briley, D. A. (2014). Continuity of genetic and environmental influences on cognition across the life span: A meta-analysis of longitudinal twin and adoption studies. *Psychological Bulletin, 140,* 949–979. (p. 332)

Tuerk, P. W. (2005). Research in the high-stakes era: Achievement, resources, and No Child Left Behind. *Psychological Science, 16,* 419–425. (p. 339)

Tuk, M. A., Zhang, K., & Sweldens, S. (2015). The propagation of self-control: Self-control in one domain simultaneously improves self-control in other domains. *Journal of Experimental Psychology: General, 144,* 639–654. (p. 398)

Tullett, A. M., Kay, A. C., & Inzlicht, M. (2015). Randomness increases self-reported anxiety and neurophysiological correlates of performance monitoring. *Social Cognitive and Affective Neuroscience, 10,* 628–635. (p. 17)

Tully, T. (2003). Reply: The myth of a myth. *Current Biology, 13,* R426. (p. 237)

Turner, J. C. (1987). Rediscovering the social group: A self-categorization theory. New York: Basil Blackwell. (p. 438)

Turner, J. C. (2007) Self-categorization theory. In R. Baumeister & K. Vohs (Eds.), *Encyclopedia of social psychology.* Thousand Oaks, CA: Sage. (p. 438)

Turner, N., Barling, J., & Zacharatos, A. (2002). Positive psychology at work. In C. R. Snyder & S. J. Lopez (Eds.), *The handbook of positive psychology.* New York: Oxford University Press. (p. B-10)

Turner, W. A., & Casey, L. M. (2014). Outcomes associated with virtual reality in psychological interventions: Where are we now? *Clinical Psychology Review, 34,* 634–644. (p. 541)

Turpin, A. (2005, April 3). The science of psi. *FT Weekend,* pp. W1, W2. (p. 230)

Tversky, A. (1985, June). Quoted in K. McKean, Decisions, decisions. *Discover,* pp. 22–31. (p. 301)

Tversky, A., & Kahneman, D. (1974). Judgment under uncertainty: Heuristics and biases. *Science, 185,* 1124–1131. (p. 300)

Twenge, J. M. (2006). *Generation me.* New York: Free Press. (p. 488)

Twenge, J. M., Abebe, E. M., & Campbell, W. K. (2010a). Fitting in or standing out: Trends in American parents' choices for children's names, 1880–2007. *Social Psychology and Personality Science, 1,* 19–25. (pp. 490, 491)

Twenge, J. M., Baumeister, R. F., Tice, D. M., & Stucke, T. S. (2001). If you can't join them, beat them: Effects of social exclusion on aggressive behavior. *Journal of Personality and Social Psychology, 81,* 1058–1069. (p. 355)

Twenge, J. M., & Campbell, W. K. (2008). Increases in positive self-views among high school students: Birth-cohort changes in anticipated performance, self-satisfaction, self-liking, and self-competence. *Psychological Science, 19,* 1082–1086. (p. 472)

Twenge, J. M., Dawson, L., & Campbell, W. K. (2016a). Still standing out: Children's names in the United States during the Great Recession and correlations with economic indicators. *Journal of Applied Social Psychology, 46,* 663–670. (pp. 490, 491)

Twenge, J. M., & Foster, J. D. (2010). Birth cohort increases in narcissistic personality traits among American college students, 1982–2009. *Social Psychological and Personality Science, 1,* 99–106. (p. 488)

Twenge, J. M., Gentile, B., DeWall, C. N., Ma, D., Lacefield, K., & Schurtz, D. R. (2010b). Birth cohort increases in psychopathology among young Americans, 1938–2007:

A cross-temporal meta-analysis of the MMPI. *Clinical Psychology Review, 30,* 145–154. (pp. 177, 397)

Twenge, J. M., Joiner, T. E., Rogers, M. L., & Martin, G. N. (2018). Increases in depressive symptoms, suicide-related outcomes, and suicide rates among U.S. adolescents after 2010 and links to increased new media screen time. *Clinical Psychological Science,6(1),* 3–17. (p. 500)

Twenge, J. M., Sherman, R. A., & Wells, B. E. (2016b). Sexual inactivity during young adulthood is more common among US millennials and iGen: Age, period, and cohort effects on having no sexual partners after age 18. *Archives of Sexual Behavior, 6,* 1–8. (p. 177)

Twenge, J. M., Sherman, R. A., & Wells, B. E. (2017). Declines in sexual frequency among American adults, 1989–2014. *Archives of Sexual Behavior, 46,* 2389–2401. (p. 23)

Twenge, J. M., Zhang, L., & Im, C. (2004). It's beyond my control: A cross-temporal meta-analysis of increasing externality in locus of control, 1960–2002. *Personality and Social Psychology Review, 8,* 308–319. (p. 397)

Twiss, C., Tabb, S., & Crosby, F. (1989). Affirmative action and aggregate data: The importance of patterns in the perception of discrimination. In F. Blanchard & F. Crosby (Eds.), *Affirmative action: Social psychological perspectives.* New York: Springer-Verlag. (p. A-5)

U.S. Department of Justice. (2018, accessed February 20). Sexual assault. United States Department of Justice. Retrieved from justice.gov (p. 170)

U.S. Equal Employment Opportunity Commission. (2018, accessed February 20). *Sexual harassment.* Equal Employment Opportunity Commission (eeoc.gov). (p. 170)

U.S. Senate Intelligence Committee. (2004, July 9). *Report of the Select Committee on Intelligence on the U.S. intelligence community's prewar intelligence assessments on Iraq.* Washington, DC: Author. (p. 433)

Uchida, Y., & Kitayama, S. (2009). Happiness and unhappiness in East and West: Themes and variations. *Emotion, 9,* 441–456. (p. 411)

Uchino, B. N., Cacioppo, J. T., & Kiecolt-Glaser, J. K. (1996). The relationship between social support and physiological processes: A review with emphasis on underlying mechanisms and implications for health. *Psychological Bulletin, 119,* 488–531. (p. 400)

Uchino, B. N., & Way, B. M. (2017). Integrative pathways linking close family ties to health: A neurochemical perspective. *American Psychologist, 72,* 590–600. (p. 400)

Udry, J. R. (2000). Biological limits of gender construction. *American Sociological Review, 65,* 443–457. (p. 166)

Uga, V., Lemut, M. C., Zampi, C., Zilli, I., & Salzarulo, P. (2006). Music in dreams. *Consciousness and Cognition, 15,* 351–357. (p. 96)

Ullén, F., Hambrick, D. Z., & Mosing, M. A. (2016). Rethinking expertise: A multifactorial gene–environment interaction model of expert performance. *Psychological Bulletin, 142,* 427–446. (p. 357)

UN. (2011, November 17). Discriminatory laws and practices and acts of violence against individuals based on their sexual orientation and gender identity. Report of the United Nations High Commissioner for Human Rights. (p. 437)

UN. (2015a). *Human development report 2015.* New York: United Nations Development Programme. (p. 169)

UN. (2015b). *The world's women: Trends and statistics.* United Nations Statistics Division. (p. 437)

UNAIDS. (2013). *Global report: UNAIDS report on the global AIDS epidemic 2013.* Joint United Nations Programme on HIV/AIDS (unaids.org). (p. 175)

Underwood, E. (2013). Short-circuiting depression. *Science, 342,* 548–551. (p. 564)

Underwood, E. (2016). Cadaver study challenges brain stimulation methods. *Science, 352,* 397. (p. 563)

Underwood, E. (2017). Brain implant trials spur ethical discussions. *Science, 358,* 710. (p. 564)

Ungar, L. (2014). Quiz: How long will you live? *Time Magazine.* Retrieved from http://time.com/3485579/when-will-i-die-life-expectancy-calculator/?xid=time_socialflow_twitter&utm_campaign=time&utm_source=twitter.com&utm_medium=social (p. 353)

Ungerleider, S. (2005). *Mental training for peak performance, revised & updated edition.* New York: Rodale. (p. 321)

Urbain, C., De Tiège, X., De Beeck, M. O., Bourguignon, M., Wens, V., Verheulpen, D., . . . Peigneux, P. (2016). Sleep in children triggers rapid reorganization of memory-related brain processes. *NeuroImage, 134,* 213–222. (p. 91)

Urry, H. L., & Gross, J. J. (2010). Emotion regulation in older age. *Current Directions in Psychological Science, 19,* 352–357. (p. 158)

Urry, H. L., Nitschke, J. B., Dolski, I., Jackson, D. C., Dalton, K. M., Mueller, C. J., . . . Davidson, R. J. (2004). Making a life worth living: Neural correlates of well-being. *Psychological Science, 15,* 367–372. (p. 374)

Vaillant, G. (2013, May). What makes us happy, revisited? *The Atlantic* (theatlantic.com/magazine/archive/2013/05/thanks-mom/309287/). (p. 355)

Vaillant, G. E. (1977). *Adaptation to life.* New York: Little, Brown. (p. 292)

Vaillant, G. E. (2002). *Aging well: Surprising guideposts to a happier life from the landmark Harvard study of adult development.* Boston: Little, Brown. (p. 400)

Valenstein, E. S. (1986). *Great and desperate cures: The rise and decline of psychosurgery.* New York: Basic Books. (p. 565)

Valentine, S. E., Bankoff, S. M., Poulin, R. M., Reidler, E. B., & Pantalone, D. W. (2015). The use of dialectical behavior therapy skills training as standalone treatment: A systematic review of the treatment outcome literature. *Journal of Clinical Psychology, 71,* 1–20. (p. 546)

Valkenburg, P. M., & Peter, J. (2009). Social consequences of the internet for adolescents: A decade of research. *Current Directions in Psychological Science, 18,* 1–5. (pp. 148, 356)

van Anders, S. M. (2012). Testosterone and sexual desire in healthy women and men. *Archives of Sexual Behavior, 41,* 1471–1484. (p. 173)

Van Bavel, J. J., Mende-Siedlecki, P., Brady, W. J., & Reinero, D. A. (2016). Contextual sensitivity in scientific reproducibility. *PNAS, 23,* 6454–6459. (p. 20)

Van Bockstaele, B., Verschuere, B., Tibboel, H., De Houwer, J., Crombez, G., & Koster, E. H. W. (2014). A review of current evidence for the causal impact of attentional bias on fear and anxiety. *Psychological Bulletin, 140,* 682–721. (p. 511)

Van Dam, N. T., van Vugt, M. K., Vago, D. R., Schmalzl, L., Saron, C. D., Olendzki, A., . . . Meyer, D. E. (2018). Mind the hype: A critical evaluation and prescriptive agenda for research on mindfulness and meditation. *Perspectives on Psychological Science, 13,* 36–61. (p. 404)

van de Bongardt, D., Reitz, E., Sandfort, T., & Deković, M. (2015). A meta-analysis of the relations between three types of peer norms and adolescent sexual behavior. *Personality and Social Psychology Review, 19,* 203–234. (p. 177)

van de Waal, E., Borgeaud, C., & Whiten, A. (2013). Potent social learning and conformity shape a wild primate's foraging decisions. *Science, 340,* 483–485. (p. 259)

Van den Akker, A. L., Asscher, J., & Prinzie, P. (2014). Mean-level personality development across childhood and adolescence: A temporary defiance of the maturity principle and bidirectional associations with parenting. *Journal of Personality and Social Psychology, 107,* 736–750. (p. 118)

van den Berg, S. M., de Moor, M. H., Verweij, K. J., Krueger, R. F., Luciano, M., Vasquez, A. A., . . . Gordon, S. D. (2016). Meta-analysis of genome-wide association studies for extraversion: Findings from the genetics of personality consortium. *Behavior Genetics, 46,* 170–182. (p. 478)

van den Bos, K., & Spruijt, N. (2002). Appropriateness of decisions as a moderator of the psychology of voice. *European Journal of Social Psychology, 32,* 57–72. (p. B-11)

Van den Bulck, J., Çetin, Y., Terzi, Ö., & Bushman, B. J. (2016). Violence, sex, and dreams: Violent and sexual media content infiltrate our dreams at night. *Dreaming, 26,* 271–279. (p. 97)

Van den Bussche, E., Van Den Noortgate, W., & Reynvoet, B. (2009). Mechanisms of masked priming: A meta-analysis. *Psychological Bulletin, 135,* 452–477. (p. 192)

van der Lee, R., & Ellemers, N. (2015). Gender contributes to personal research funding success in The Netherlands. *PNAS, 112,* 12349–12353. (p. 164)

van der Linden, S. L., Leiserowitz, A. A., Feinberg, G. D, & Maibach, E. W. (2015). The scientific consensus on climate change as a gateway belief: Experimental evidence. *PLoS ONE 10,* e0118489. (p. 418)

van Dijk, W. W., Van Koningsbruggen, G. M., Ouwerkerk, J. W., & Wesseling, Y. M. (2011). Self-esteem, self-affirmation, and schadenfreude. *Emotion, 11,* 1445–1449. (p. 487)

van Emmerik, A. A. P., Reijntjes, A., & Kamphuis, J. H. (2013). Writing therapy for posttraumatic stress: A meta-analysis. *Psychotherapy and Psychosomatics, 82,* 82–88. (p. 401)

van Engen, M. L., & Willemsen, T. M. (2004). Sex and leadership styles: A meta-analysis of research published in the 1990s. *Psychological Reports, 94,* 3–18. (p. 164)

van Geel, M., Goemans, A., & Vedder, P. (2015). A meta-analysis on the relation between peer victimization and adolescent non-suicidal self-injury. *Psychiatry Research, 230,* 364–368. (p. 502)

van Haren, N. E., Schnack, H. G., Koevoets, M. G., Cahn, W., Pol, H. E. H., & Kahn, R. S. (2016). Trajectories of subcortical volume change in schizophrenia: A 5-year follow-up. *Schizophrenia Research, 173,* 140–145. (p. 525)

Van Haren, N. M., Rijsdijk, F., Schnack, H. G., Picchioni, M. M., Toulopoulou, T., Weisbrod, M., . . . Kahn, R. S. (2012). The genetic and environmental determinants of the association between brain abnormalities and schizophrenia: The schizophrenia twins and relatives consortium. *Biological Psychiatry, 71,* 915–921. (p. 525)

van Hemert, D. A., Poortinga, Y. H., & van de Vijver, F. J. R. (2007). Emotion and culture: A meta-analysis. *Cognition and Emotion, 21,* 913–943. (p. 379)

van Honk, J., Schutter, D. J., Bos, P. A., Kruijt, A.-W., Lentje, E. G., & Baron-Cohen, S. (2011). Testosterone administration impairs cognitive empathy in women depending on second-to-fourth digit ratio. *PNAS, 108,* 3448–3452. (p. 131)

Van Horn, J., Irimia, A., Torgerson, C., Chambers, M., Kikinis, R., & Toga, A. (2012). Mapping connectivity damage in the case of Phineas Gage. *PLOS ONE, 7*(5), e37454. doi:10.1371/journal.pone.0037454 (p. 63)

van IJzendoorn, M. H., Fearon, P., & Bakermans-Kranenburg, M. (2017). Attachment—public and scientific. *The Psychologist, 30,* 6-9. (p. 137)

van IJzendoorn, M. H., & Juffer, F. (2006). The Emanual Miller Memorial Lecture 2006: Adoption as intervention. Meta-analytic evidence for massive catch-up and plasticity in physical, socio-emotional, and cognitive development. *Journal of Child Psychology and Psychiatry, 47,* 1228–1245. (p. 73)

van Ijzendoorn, M. H., Juffer, F., & Poelhuis, C. W. K. (2005). Adoption and cognitive development: A meta-analytic comparison of adopted and nonadopted children's IQ and school performance. *Psychological Bulletin, 131,* 301–316. (p. 73)

van IJzendoorn, M. H., & Kroonenberg, P. M. (1988). Cross-cultural patterns of attachment: A meta-analysis of the strange situation. *Child Development, 59,* 147–156. (p. 134)

van IJzendoorn, M. H., Luijk, M. P. C. M., & Juffer, F. (2008). IQ of children growing up in children's homes: A meta-analysis on IQ delays in orphanages. *Merrill-Palmer Quarterly, 54,* 341–366. (pp. 137, 338)

Van Kesteren, P. J. M., Asscheman, H., Megens, J. A. J., & Gooren, L. J. G. (1997). Mortality and morbidity in transsexual subjects treated with cross-sex hormones. *Clinical Endocrinology, 47,* 337–342. (p. 171)

Van Leeuwen, M. S. (1978). A cross-cultural examination of psychological differentiation in males and females. *International Journal of Psychology, 13,* 87–122. (p. 168)

van Praag, H. (2009). Exercise and the brain: Something to chew on. *Trends in Neuroscience, 32,* 283–290. (p. 402)

Van Tongeren, D. R., DeWall, C. N., Green, J. D., Cairo, A. H., Davis, D. E., & Hook, J. N. (2018). Self-regulation facilitates meaning in life. *Review of General Psychology.* Advance online publication. http://dx.doi.org/10.1037/gpr0000121 (p. 350)

Van Yperen, N. W., & Buunk, B. P. (1990). A longitudinal study of equity and satisfaction in intimate relationships. *European Journal of Social Psychology, 20,* 287–309. (p. 452)

Van Zeijl, J., Mesman, J., van IJzendoorn, M. H., Bakermans-Kranenburg, M. J., Juffer, F., Stolk, M. N., . . . Alink, L. R. A. (2006). Attachment-based intervention for enhancing sensitive discipline in mothers of 1- to 3-year-old children at risk for externalizing behavior problems: A randomized controlled trial. *Journal of Consulting and Clinical Psychology, 74,* 994–1005. (p. 135)

van Zuiden, M., Geuze, E., Willemen, H. L., Vermetten, E., Maas, M., Amarouchi, K., . . . Heijnen, C. J. (2012). Glucocorticoid receptor pathway components predict posttraumatic stress disorder symptom development: A prospective study. *Biological Psychiatry, 71,* 309–316. (p. 137)

Vance, E. B., & Wagner, N. N. (1976). Written descriptions of orgasm: A study of sex differences. *Archives of Sexual Behavior, 5,* 87–98. (p. 174)

vanDellen, M. R., Campbell, W. K., Hoyle, R. H., & Bradfield, E. K. (2011). Compensating, resisting, and breaking: A meta-analytic examination of reactions to self-esteem threat. *Personality and Social Psychological Review, 15,* 51–74. (p. 487)

VanderLaan, D. P., Forrester, D. L., Petterson, L. J., & Vasey, P. L. (2012). Offspring production among the extended relatives of Samoan men and Fa'afafi ne. *PloS ONE, 7,* e36088. (p. 181)

VanderLaan, D. P., & Vasey, P. L. (2011). Male sexual orientation in Independent Samoa: Evidence for fraternal birth order and maternal fecundity effects. *Archives of Sexual Behavior, 40,* 495–503. (p. 181)

VanderWeele, T. J., Li, S., & Kawachi, I. (2017). Religious service attendance and suicide rates—reply. *JAMA Psychiatry, 74,* 197–198. (p. 500)

VanderWeele, T. J., Li, S., Tsai, A. C., & Kawachi, I. (2016). Association between religious service attendance and lower suicide rates among U.S. women. *Journal of American Medication Association Psychiatry, 73,* 845–851. (p. 500)

Vanhalst, J., Soenens, B., Luyckx, K., Van Petegem, S., Weeks, M. S., & Asher, S. R. (2015). Why do the lonely stay lonely? Chronically lonely adolescents' attributions and emotions in situations of social inclusion and exclusion. *Journal of Personality and Social Psychology, 109,* 932–948. (p. 354)

Vardi, N. (2017, January 17). Inside the Obama stock market's 235% return. *Forbes* (forbes.com). (p. 18)

Varnum, M. E. W., Grossmann, I., Kitayama, S., & Nisbett, R. E. (2010). The origin of cultural differences in cognition: The social orientation hypothesis. *Current Directions in Psychological Science, 19,* 9–13. (p. 491)

Vaughn, K. B., & Lanzetta, J. T. (1981). The effect of modification of expressive displays on vicarious emotional arousal. *Journal of Experimental Social Psychology, 17,* 16–30. (p. 381)

Vazsonyi, A., Ksinan, A., Mikuška, J., & Jiskrova, G. (2015). The Big Five and adolescent adjustment: An empirical test across six cultures. *Personality and Individual Differences, 83,* 234–244. (p. 478)

Vecera, S. P., Vogel, E. K., & Woodman, G. F. (2002). Lower region: A new cue for figure-ground assignment. *Journal of Experimental Psychology: General, 13,* 194–205. (p. 210)

Veenhoven, R. (2014, accessed March 17). World database of happiness. Retrieved from worlddatabaseofhappiness.eur.nl (p. 411)

Veenhoven, R. (2015). Informed pursuit of happiness: What we should know, do know and can get to know. *Journal of Happiness Studies, 16,* 1035–1071. (p. 411)

Vekassy, L. (1977). Dreams of the blind. *Magyar Pszichologiai Szemle, 34,* 478–491. (p. 97)

Verbeek, M. E. M., Drent, P. J., & Wiepkema, P. R. (1994). Consistent individual differences in early exploratory behaviour of male great tits. *Animal Behaviour, 48,* 1113–1121. (p. 477)

Verduyn, P., Ybarra, O., Résibois, M., Jonides, J., & Kross, E. (2017). Do social network sites enhance or undermine subjective well-being? A critical review. *Social Issues and Policy Review, 11,* 274–302. (p. 355)

Verhaeghen, P., & Salthouse, T. A. (1997). Meta-analyses of age–cognition relations in adulthood: Estimates of linear and nonlinear age effects and structural models. *Psychological Bulletin, 122,* 231–249. (p. 152)

Vermetten, E., Schmahl, C., Lindner, S., Loewenstein, R. J., & Bremner, J. D. (2006). Hippocampal and amygdalar volumes in dissociative identity disorder. *American Journal of Psychiatry, 163,* 630–636. (p. 528)

Verschuere, B., & Meijer, E. H. (2014). What's on your mind? Recent advances in memory detection using the concealed information test. *European Psychologist, 19,* 162–171. (p. 374)

Vezzali, L., Stathi, S., Giovannini, D., Capozza, D., & Trifiletti, E. (2015). The greatest magic of Harry Potter: Reducing prejudice. *Journal of Applied Social Psychology, 45,* 105–121. (p. 260)

Victora, C. G., Horta, B. L., de Mola, C. L., Quevedo, L., Pinheiro, R. T., Gigante, D. P., . . . Barros, F. C. (2015). Association between breastfeeding and intelligence, educational attainment, and income at 30 years of age: A prospective birth cohort study from Brazil. *Lancet Global Health, 3,* e199–205 (thelancet.com/lancetgh). (p. 25)

Vieselmeyer, J., Holguin, J., & Mezulis, A. (2017). The role of resilience and gratitude in posttraumatic stress and growth following a campus shooting. *Psychological Trauma: Theory, Research, Practice, and Policy, 9,* 62–69. (p. 408)

Vigerland, S., Lenhard, F., Bonnert, M., Lalouni, M., Hedman, E., Ahlen, J., . . . Ljótsson, B. (2016). Internet-delivered cognitive behavior therapy for children and adolescents: A systematic review and meta-analysis. *Clinical Psychology Review, 50,* 1–10. (p. 546)

Vigliocco, G., & Hartsuiker, R. J. (2002). The interplay of meaning, sound, and syntax in sentence production. *Psychological Bulletin, 128,* 442–472. (p. 312)

Vining, E. P. G., Freeman, J. M., Pillas, D. J., Uematsu, S., Carson, B. S., Brandt, J., . . . Zukerberg, A. (1997). Why would you remove half a brain? The outcome of 58 children after hemispherectomy—The Johns Hopkins Experience: 1968 to 1996. *Pediatrics, 100,* 163–171. (p. 64)

Visich, P. S., & Fletcher, E. (2009). Myocardial infarction. In J. K. Ehrman, P. M., Gordon, P. S. Visich, & S. J. Keleyian (Eds.). *Clinical exercise physiology,* 2nd ed. Champaign, IL: Human Kinetics. (p. 401)

Visser, B. A., Ashton, M. C., & Vernon, P. A. (2006). Beyond g: Putting multiple intelligences theory to the test. *Intelligence, 34,* 487–502. (p. 327)

Vita, A. J., Terry, R. B., Hubert, H. B., & Fries, J. F. (1998). Aging, health risks, and cumulative disability. *New England Journal of Medicine, 338,* 1035–1041. (p. 106)

Vitello, P. (2012, August 1). George A. Miller. A pioneer in cognitive psychology, is dead at 92. *The New York Times* (nytimes.com). (p. 271)

Vitiello, M. V. (2009). Recent advances in understanding sleep and sleep disturbances in older adults: Growing older does not mean sleeping poorly. *Current Directions in Psychological Science, 18,* 316–320. (p. 96)

Vitória, P. D., Salgueiro, M. F., Silva, S. A., & De Vries, H. (2009). The impact of social influence on adolescent intention to smoke: Combining types and referents of influence. *British Journal of Health Psychology, 14,* 681–699. (p. 112)

Vliegenthart, J., Noppe, G., van Rossum, E. F. C., Koper, J. W., Raat, H., & van den Akker, E. L. T. (2016). Socioeconomic status in children is associated with hair cortisol levels as a biological measure of chronic stress. *Psychoneuroendocrinology, 65,* 9–14. (p. 391)

Vocks, S., Tuschen-Caffier, B., Pietrowsky, R., Rustenbach, S. J., Kersting, A., & Herpertz, S. (2010). Meta-analysis of the effectiveness of psychological and pharmacological treatments for binge eating disorder. *International Journal of Eating Disorders, 43,* 205–217. (p. 533)

Vogel, G. (2010). Long-fought compromise reached on European animal rules. *Science, 329,* 1588–1589. (p. 31)

Vogel, N., Schilling, O. K., Wahl, H.-W., Beekman, A. T. F., & Penninx, B. W. J. H. (2013). Time-to-death-related change in positive and negative affect among older adults approaching the end of life. *Psychology and Aging, 28,* 128–141. (p. 155)

Vohs, K. D., Baumeister, R. F., & Schmeichel, B. J. (2012). Motivation, personal beliefs, and limited resources all contribute to self-control. *Journal of Experimental Social Psychology, 48,* 943–947. (p. 398)

Vohs, K. D., Mead, N. L., & Goode, M. R. (2006). The psychological consequences of money. *Science, 314,* 1154–1156. (p. 281)

Volkow, N. D., Swanson, J. M., Evins, A. E., DeLisi, L. E., Meier, M. H., Gonzalez, R., . . . Baler, R. (2016). Effects of cannabis use on human behavior, including cognition, motivation, and psychosis: a review. *JAMA Psychiatry, 73,* 292–297. (p. 109)

Volkow, N. D., Wang, G. J., Kollins, S. H., Wigal, T. L., Newcorn, J. H., Telang, F., . . . Swanson, J. M. (2009). Evaluating dopamine reward pathway in ADHD: Clinical implications. *Journal of the American Medical Association, 302,* 1084–1091. (p. 498)

von Békésy, G. (1957, August). The ear. *Scientific American,* pp. 66–78. (p. 219)

von Hippel, W. (2007). Aging, executive functioning, and social control. *Current Directions in Psychological Science, 16,* 240–244. (p. 153)

von Hippel, W. (2015, July 17). Do people become more prejudiced as they grow older? *BBC News Magazine* (bbc.com/news/magazine-33523313). (p. 153)

von Hippel, W., & Trivers, R. (2011). The evolution and psychology of self-deception. *Behavioral and Brain Sciences, 34,* 1–56. (p. 487)

von Senden, M. (1932). *The perception of space and shape in the congenitally blind before and after operation.* Glencoe, IL: Free Press. (p. 213)

von Stumm, S., Hell, B., & Chamorro-Premuzic, T. (2011). The hungry mind: Intellectual curiosity is the third pillar of academic performance. *Perspectives on Psychological Science, 6,* 574–588. (p. 340)

von Stumm, S., & Plomin, R. (2015). Breastfeeding and IQ growth from toddlerhood through adolescence. *PLoS ONE, 10,* e0138676. (p. 25)

Vonk, J., Jett, S. E., & Mosteller, K. W. (2012). Concept formation in American black bears, *Ursus americanus. Animal Behaviour, 84,* 953–964. (p. 309)

Vorona, R. D., Szklo-Coxe, M., Wu, A., Dubik, M., Zhao, Y., & Ware, J. C. (2011). Dissimilar teen crash rates in two neighboring Southeastern Virginia cities with different high school start times. *Journal of Clinical Sleep Medicine, 7,* 145–151. (p. 94)

Vosoughi, S., Roy, D., & Aral, S. (2018). The spread of true and false news online. *Science, 359,* 1146–1151. (p. 18)

Voss, U., Tuin, I., Schermelleh-Engel, K., & Hobson, A. (2011). Waking and dreaming: Related but structurally independent. Dream reports of congenitally paraplegic and deaf-mute persons. *Consciousness and Cognition, 20,* 673–687. (p. 97)

Voyer, D., & Voyer, S. D. (2014). Gender differences in scholastic achievement: A meta-analysis. *Psychological Bulletin, 140,* 1174–1204. (p. 340)

VPC. (2015, June). *Firearm justifiable homicides and non-fatal self-defense gun use: An analysis of Federal Bureau of Investigation and National Crime Victimization Survey Data.* Washington, DC: Violence Policy Center (vpc.org). (p. 501)

VPC. (2016, January 4). States with weak gun laws and higher gun ownership lead nation in gun deaths, new data for 2014 confirms. Violence Policy Center (vpc.org). (p. 441)

Vrij, A., & Fisher, R. P. (2016). Which lie detection tools are ready for use in the criminal justice system? *Journal of Applied Research in Memory and Cognition, 5,* 302–307. (p. 374)

Vukasović, T., & Bratko, D. (2015). Heritability of personality: A meta-analysis of behavior genetic studies. *Psychological Bulletin, 141,* 769–785. (p. 478)

Vyse, S. (2016, March/April). Guns: Feeling safe ≠ being safe. *Skeptical Inquirer,* pp. 27–30. (p. 501)

Waber, R. L., Shiv, B., Carmon, Z. & Ariely, D. (2008). Commercial features of placebo and therapeutic efficacy. *Journal of the American Medical Association, 299,* 1016–1017. (p. 27)

Wacker, J., Chavanon, M.-L., & Stemmler, G. (2006). Investigating the dopaminergic basis of extraversion in humans: A multilevel approach. *Journal of Personality and Social Psychology, 91,* 177–187. (p. 476)

Wade, K. A., Garry, M., Read, J. D., & Lindsay, D. S. (2002). A picture is worth a thousand lies: Using false photographs to create false childhood memories. *Psychonomic Bulletin & Review, 9,* 597–603. (p. 291)

Wadley, J., & Lee, J. (2016, September 23). Compared with Europe, American teens have high rates of illicit drug use. Michigan News (University of Michigan). (p. 110)

Wagar, B. M., & Cohen, D. (2003). Culture, memory, and the self: An analysis of the personal and collective self in long-term memory. *Journal of Experimental Social Psychology, 39,* 458–475. (p. 274)

Wagemans, J., Elder, J. H., Kubovy, M., Palmer, S. E., Peterson, M. A., Singh, M., & von der Heydt, R. (2012a). A century of Gestalt psychology in visual perception: I. Perceptual grouping and figure–ground organization. *Psychological Bulletin, 138,* 1172–1217. (p. 207)

Wagemans, J., Feldman, J., Gepshtein, S., Kimchi, R., Pomerantz, J. R, van der Helm, P., & van Leeuwen, C. (2012b). A century of Gestalt psychology in visual perception: II. Conceptual and theoretical foundations. *Psychological Bulletin, 138,* 1218–1252. (p. 207)

Wagenmakers, E.-J. (2014, June 25). *Bem is back: A skeptic's review of a meta-analysis on psi.* Retrieved from centerforopenscience.github.io/osc/2014/06/25/a-skeptics-review (p. 231)

Wagenmakers E.-J., Beek T., Dijkhoff L., Gronau Q. F., Acosta A., Adams R. B., Jr., . . . Zwaan R. A. (2016). Registered replication report: Strack, Martin, & Stepper (1988). *Perspectives on Psychological Science, 11,* 917–928. (p. 381)

Wagenmakers, E.-J., Wetzels, R., Borsboom, D., & van der Maas, H. (2011). Why psychologists must change the way they analyze their data: The case of psi. *Journal of Personality and Social Psychology, 100,* 1–12. (p. 231)

Wager, R. D., & Atlas, L. Y. (2013). How is pain influenced by cognition? Neuroimaging weighs in. *Perspectives on Psychological Science, 8,* 91–97. (p. 223)

Wagner, D., Becker, B., Koester, P., Gouzoulis-Mayfrank, E., & Daumann, J. (2012). A prospective study of learning, memory, and executive function in new MDMA users. *Addiction, 108,* 136–145. (p. 108)

Wagner, J., Gerstorf, D., Hoppmann, C., & Luszcz, M. A. (2013). The nature and correlates of self-esteem trajectories in late life. *Journal of Personality and Social Psychology, 105,* 139–153. (p. 158)

Wagner, J., Ram, N., Smith, J., & Gerstorf, D. (2016). Personality trait development at the end of life: Antecedents and correlates of mean-level trajectories. *Journal of Personality and Social Psychology, 111,* 411–429. (p. 158)

Wagner, K., & Dobkins, K. R. (2011). Synaesthetic associations decrease during infancy. *Psychological Science, 22,* 1067–1072. (p. 229)

Wagstaff, G. (1982). Attitudes to rape: The "just world" strikes again? *Bulletin of the British Psychological Society, 13,* 275–283. (p. 417)

Wakefield, J. C., Schmitz, M. F., First, M. B., & Horwitz, A. V. (2007). Extending the bereavement exclusion for major depression to other losses: Evidence from the National Comorbidity Survey. *Archives of General Psychiatry, 64,* 433–440. (p. 517)

Wakefield, J. C., & Spitzer, R. L. (2002). Lowered estimates—but of what? *Archives of General Psychiatry, 59,* 129–130. (p. 510)

Walfisch, A., Sermer, C., Cressman, A., & Koren, G. (2014). Breast milk and cognitive development—the role of confounders: A systematic review. *BMJ Open, 3,* e003259. (p. 25)

Walker, E., Shapiro, D., Esterberg, M., & Trotman, H. (2010). Neurodevelopment and schizophrenia: Broadening the focus. *Current Directions in Psychological Science, 19,* 204–208. (pp. 525, 526)

Walker, M. P., & van der Helm, E. (2009). Overnight therapy? The role of sleep in emotional brain processing. *Psychological Bulletin, 135,* 731–748. (pp. 93, 559)

Walker, W. R., Skowronski, J. J., & Thompson, C. P. (2003). Life is pleasant—and memory helps to keep it that way! *Review of General Psychology, 7,* 203–210. (p. 158)

Wall, P. D. (2000). *Pain: The science of suffering.* New York: Columbia University Press. (p. 222)

Wallace, D. S., Paulson, R. M., Lord, C. G., & Bond, C. F., Jr. (2005). Which behaviors do attitudes predict? Meta-analyzing the effects of social pressure and perceived difficulty. *Review of General Psychology, 9,* 214–227. (p. 418)

Wallach, M. A., & Wallach, L. (1983). *Psychology's sanction for selfishness: The error of egoism in theory and therapy.* New York: Freeman. (p. 473)

Walsh, J. L., Fielder, R. L., Carey, K. B., & Carey, M. P. (2013). Female college students' media use and academic outcomes: Results from a longitudinal cohort study. *Emerging Adulthood, 1,* 219–232. (p. 356)

Walsh, R. (2011). Lifestyle and mental health. *American Psychologist, 66,* 579–592. (pp. 558, 559)

Walster (Hatfield), E., Aronson, V., Abrahams, D., & Rottman, L. (1966). Importance of physical attractiveness in dating behavior. *Journal of Personality and Social Psychology, 4,* 508–516. (p. 448)

Walton, G. M., & Spencer S. J. (2009). Latent ability: Grades and test scores systematically underestimate the intellectual ability of negatively stereotyped students. *Psychological Science, 20,* 1132–1139. (p. 344)

Wampold, B. E. (2001). *The great psychotherapy debate: Models, methods, and findings.* Mahwah, NJ: Erlbaum. (p. 555)

Wampold, B. E. (2007). Psychotherapy: The humanistic (and effective) treatment. *American Psychologist, 62,* 857–873. (p. 555)

Wampold, B. E., Flückiger, C., Del Re, A. C., Yulish, N. E., Frost, N. D., Pace, B. T., . . . Hilsenroth, M. J. (2017). In pursuit of truth: A critical examination of meta-analyses of cognitive behavior therapy. *Psychotherapy Research, 27,* 14–32. (p. 552)

Wang, F., DesMeules, M., Luo, W., Dai, S., Lagace, C. & Morrison, H. (2011). Leisure-time physical activity and marital status in relation to depression between men and women: A prospective study. *Health Psychology, 30,* 204–211. (p. 402, 435)

Wang, J., Häusermann, M., Wydler, H., Mohler-Kuo, M., & Weiss, M. G. (2012). Suicidality and sexual orientation among men in Switzerland: Findings from 3 probability surveys. *Journal of Psychiatric Research, 46,* 980–986. (p. 179)

Wang, J., He, L., Liping, J., Tian, J., & Benson, V. (2015a). The "positive effect" is present in older Chinese adults: Evidence from an eye tracking study. *PLoS ONE, 10,* e0121372. doi:10.1371/journal.pone.0121372 (pp. 158, 385)

Wang, J., Plöderl, M., Häusermann, M., & Weiss, M. G. (2015b). Understanding suicide attempts among gay men from their self-perceived causes. *Journal of Nervous and Mental Disease, 203,* 499–506. (p. 179)

Wang, J., Rao, Y., & Houser, D. E. (2017a). An experimental analysis of acquired impulse control among adult humans intolerant to alcohol. *PNAS, 114,* 1299–1304. (p. 398)

Wang, J., Wei, Q., Bai, T., Zhou, X., Sun, H., Becker, B., . . . Kendrick, K. (2017b). Electroconvulsive therapy selectively enhanced feedforward connectivity from fusiform face area to amygdala in major depressive disorder. *Social Cognitive and Affective Neuroscience 2,* 1983–1992. (p. 563)

Wang, J. X., Rogers, L. M., Gross, E. Z., Ryals, A. J., Dokucu, M. E., Brandstatt, K. L., . . . Voss, J. L. (2014). Targeted enhancement of cortical-hippocampal brain networks and associative memory. *Science, 345,* 1054–1057. (p. 276)

Wang, S. (2014, March 29). How to think about the risk of autism. *The New York Times* (nytimes.com). (p. 131)

Wang, S.-H., Baillargeon, R., & Brueckner, L. (2004). Young infants' reasoning about hidden objects: Evidence from violation-of-expectation tasks with test trials only. *Cognition, 93,* 167–198. (p. 126)

Wang, Y., Highhouse, S., Lake, C. J., Petersen, N. L., & Rada, T. B. (2017). Meta-analytic investigations of the relation between intuition and analysis. *Journal of Behavioral Decision Making, 30,* 15–25. (pp. 84, 145)

Wang, Z., Lukowski, S. L., Hart, S. A., Lyons, I. M., Thompson, L. A., Kovas, Y., . . . Petrill, S. A. (2015). Is math anxiety always bad for math learning? The role of math motivation. *Psychological Science, 26,* 1863–1876. (p. 350)

Ward, A., & Mann, T. (2000). Don't mind if I do: Disinhibited eating under cognitive load. *Journal of Personality and Social Psychology, 78,* 753–763. (p. 366)

Ward, B. W., Dahlhamer, J. M., Galinsky, A. M., & Joestl, S. S. (2014, July 15). *Sexual orientation and health among U.S. adults: National Health Interview Survey, 2013* (National Health Statistics Reports No. 77). Retrieved from cdc.gov/nchs/data/nhsr/nhsr077.pdf (p. 178)

Ward, C. (1994). Culture and altered states of consciousness. In W. J. Lonner & R. Malpass (Eds.), *Psychology and culture* (pp. 59–64). Boston: Allyn & Bacon. (p. 101)

Ward, J. (2003). State of the art synaesthesia. *The Psychologist, 16,* 196–199. (p. 229)

Ward, K. D., Klesges, R. C., & Halpern, M. T. (1997). Predictors of smoking cessation and state-of-the-art smoking interventions. *Journal of Social Issues, 53,* 129–145. (p. 106)

Wardle, J., Cooke, L. J., Gibson, L., Sapochnik, M., Sheiham, A., & Lawson, M. (2003). Increasing children's acceptance of vegetables: A randomized trial of parent-led exposure. *Appetite, 40,* 155–162. (p. 225)

Wargo, E. (2007, December). Understanding the have-knots. *APS Observer,* pp. 18–21. (p. 403)

Washburn, M. F. (1908). *The animal mind: A textbook of comparative psychology.* New York: The Macmillan Company. (pp. 6, 309)

Washington Post. (2017). Fatal force. Retrieved from washingtonpost.com/graphics/national/police-shootings-2016/?tid=a_inl and washingtonpost.com/graphics/national/police-shootings/ (p. 436)

Wason, P. C. (1960). On the failure to eliminate hypotheses in a conceptual task. *Quarterly Journal of Experimental Psychology, 12,* 129–140. (p. 300)

Wason, P. C. (1981). The importance of cognitive illusions. *The Behavioral and Brain Sciences, 4,* 356. (p. 300)

Wasserman, E. A. (1993). Comparative cognition: Toward a general understanding of cognition in behavior. *Psychological Science, 4,* 156–161. (p. 245)

Wasserman, E. A. (1995). The conceptual abilities of pigeons. *American Scientist, 83,* 246–255. (p. 309)

Wastell, C. A. (2002). Exposure to trauma: The long-term effects of suppressing emotional reactions. *Journal of Nervous and Mental Disorders, 190,* 839–845. (p. 401)

Waterman, A. S. (1988). Identity status theory and Erikson's theory: Commonalities and differences. *Developmental Review, 8,* 185–208. (p. 147)

Watkins, E. R. (2008). Constructive and unconstructive repetitive thought. *Psychological Bulletin, 134,* 163–206. (p. 514)

Watkins, J. G. (1984). The Bianchi (L. A. Hillside Strangler) case: Sociopath or multiple personality? *International Journal of Clinical and Experimental Hypnosis, 32,* 67–101. (p. 528)

Watson, D. (2000). *Mood and temperament.* New York: Guilford Press. (pp. 402, 408, 500)

Watson, J. B. (1913). Psychology as the behaviorist views it. *Psychological Review, 20,* 158–177. (pp. 80, 236, 241)

Watson, J. B. (1924). The unverbalized in human behavior. *Psychological Review, 31,* 339–347. (p. 241)

Watson, J. B., & Rayner, R. (1920). Conditioned emotional reactions. *Journal of Experimental Psychology, 3,* 1–14. (p. 241)

Watson, R. I., Jr. (1973). Investigation into deindividuation using a cross-cultural survey technique. *Journal of Personality and Social Psychology, 25,* 342–345. (p. 430)

Watts, T. W., Dundan, G. J., & Quan, H. (2018, May). Revisiting the marshmallow test: A conceptual replication investigating links between early delay of gratification and later outcomes. *Psychological Science,* 1–19. (p. 145)

Way, B. M., Creswell, J. D., Eisenberger, N. I., & Lieberman, M. D. (2010). Dispositional mindfulness and depressive symptomatology: Correlations with limbic and self-referential neural activity during rest. *Emotion, 10,* 12–24. (p. 404)

Wayment, H. A., & Peplau, L. A. (1995). Social support and well-being among lesbian and heterosexual women: A structural modeling approach. *Personality and Social Psychology Bulletin, 21,* 1189–1199. (p. 157)

Waytz, A., Young, L. L., & Ginges, J. (2014). Motive attribution asymmetry for love vs. hate drives intractable conflict. *PNAS, 111,* 15687–15692. (p. 456)

Weber, A., Fernald, A., & Diop, Y. (2017). When cultural norms discourage talking to babies: Effectiveness of a parenting program in rural Senegal. *Child Development, 88,* 1513–1526. (p. 140)

Webster, G. D., DeWall, C. N., Pond, R. S., Jr., Deckman, T., Jonason, P. K., Le, B. M., . . . Bator, R. J. (2014). The Brief Aggression Questionnaire: Psychometric and behavioral evidence for an efficient measure of trait aggression. *Aggressive Behavior, 40,* 120–139. (p. 29)

Wechsler, D. (1972). "Hold" and "Don't Hold" tests. In S. M. Chown (Ed.), *Human aging.* New York: Penguin. (p. 332)

Wegner, D. M., & Ward, A. F. (2013). How Google is changing your brain. *Scientific American, 309,* 58–61. (p. 269)

Wei, W., Lu, H., Zhao, H., Chen, C., Dong, Q., & Zhou, X. (2012). Gender differences in children's arithmetic performance are accounted for by gender differences in language abilities. *Psychological Science, 23,* 320–330. (p. 137)

Weidman, A. C., Tracy, J. L., & Elliot, A. J. (2016). The benefits of following your pride: Authentic pride promotes achievement. *Journal of Personality, 84,* 607–622. (p. 489)

Weingarden, H., & Renshaw, K. D. (2012). Early and late perceived pubertal timing as risk factors for anxiety disorders in adult women. *Journal of Psychiatric Research, 46,* 1524–1529. (p. 142)

Weingarten, G. (2002, March 10). Below the beltway. *The Washington Post,* p. WO3. (p. B-1)

Weinstein, N. D., Ryan, W. S., DeHaan, C. R., Przbylski, A. K., Legate, N., & Ryan, R. M. (2012). Parental autonomy support and discrepancies between implicit and explicit sexual identities: Dynamics of self-acceptance and defense. *Journal of Personality and Social Psychology, 102,* 815–832. (p. 470)

Weir, K. (2013, May). Captive audience. *Monitor on Psychology,* pp. 44–49. (p. 31)

Weisbuch, M., Ivcevic, Z., & Ambady, N. (2009). On being liked on the web and in the "real world": Consistency in first impressions across personal webpages and spontaneous behavior. *Journal of Experimental Social Psychology, 45,* 573–576. (p. 481)

Weiser, E. B. (2015). #Me: Narcissism and its facets as predictors of selfie-posting frequency. *Personality and Individual Differences, 86,* 477–481. (p. 356)

Weiskrantz, L. (2009). *Blindsight: A case study spanning 35 years and new developments.* Oxford: Oxford University Press. (p. 84)

Weiskrantz, L. (2010). Looking back: Blindsight in hindsight. *The Psychologist, 23,* 356–358. (p. 84)

Weiss, A., & King, J. E. (2015). Great ape origins of personality maturation and sex differences: A study of orangutans and chimpanzees. *Journal of Personality and Social Psychology, 108,* 648–664. (p. 478)

Weiss, A., Wilson, M. L., Collins, D. A., Mhungu, D., Kamenya, S., Foerster, S., & Pusey, A. E. (2017). Personality in the chimpanzees of Gombe National Park. *Nature: Scientific Data, 4,* #170146. (p. 477)

Weissman, M. M., Wickramaratne, P., Gameroff, M. J., Warner, V., Pilowsky, D., Kohad, R. G., . . . Talati, A. (2016). Offspring of depressed parents: 30 years later. *American Journal of Psychiatry, 173,* 1024–1032. (p. 518)

Weisz, J. R., Kuppens, S., Ng, M. Y., Eckshtain, D., Ugueto, A. M., Vaughn-Coaxum, R., . . . Weersing, V. R. (2017). What five decades of research tells us about the effects of youth psychological therapy: A multilevel meta-analysis and implications for science and practice. *American Psychologist, 72,* 79–117. (p. 552)

Welborn, B. L., Gunter, B. C., Vesich, I. S., & Lieberman, M. D. (2017). Neural correlates of the false consensus effect: Evidence for motivated projection and regulatory restraint. *Journal of Cognitive Neuroscience, 29,* 708–717. (p. 470)

Welch, J. M., Lu, J., Rodriquiz, R. M., Trotta, N. C., Peca, J., Ding, J.-D., . . . Feng, G. (2007). Cortico-striatal synaptic defects and OCD-like behaviours in *Sapap3*-mutant mice. *Nature, 448,* 894–900. (p. 512)

Welch, W. W. (2005, February 28). Trauma of Iraq war haunting thousands returning home. *USA Today* (usatoday.com). (p. 509)

Welker, K. M., Baker, L., Padilla, A., Holmes, H., Aron, A., & Slatcher, R. B. (2014). Effects of self-disclosure and responsiveness between couples on passionate love within couples. *Personal Relationships, 21,* 692–708. (p. 452)

Weller, S. C., & Davis-Beaty, K. (2002). Condom effectiveness in reducing heterosexual HIV transmission. *Cochrane Database of Systematic Reviews,* Issue 1, Article CD003255. doi:10.1002/14651858.CD003255 (p. 175)

Wells, D. L. (2009). The effects of animals on human health and well-being. *Journal of Social Issues, 65,* 523–543. (p. 401)

Wells, G. L. (1981). Lay analyses of causal forces on behavior. In J. Harvey (Ed.), *Cognition, social behavior and the environment.* Hillsdale, NJ: Erlbaum. (p. 234)

Wenze, S. J., Gunthert, K. C., & German, R. E. (2012). Biases in affective forecasting and recall in individuals with depression and anxiety symptoms. *Personality and Social Psychology Bulletin, 38,* 895–906. (p. 519)

Werner, L., Geisler, J., & Randler, C. (2015). Morningness as a personality predictor of punctuality. *Current Psychology, 34,* 130–139. (p. 87)

Westen, D. (1996). *Is Freud really dead? Teaching psychodynamic theory to introductory psychology.* Presentation to the Annual Institute on the Teaching of Psychology, St. Petersburg Beach, FL. (p. 467)

Westen, D. (1998). The scientific legacy of Sigmund Freud: Toward a psychodynamically informed psychological science. *Psychological Bulletin, 124,* 333–371. (p. 468)

Westen, D. (2007). *The political brain: The role of emotion in deciding the fate of the nation.* New York: PublicAffairs. (p. 371)

Westen, D., & Morrison, K. (2001). A multidimensional meta-analysis of treatments for depression, panic, and generalized anxiety disorder: An empirical examination of the status of empirically supported therapies. *Journal of Consulting and Clinical Psychology, 69,* 875–899. (p. 553)

Wetherell, J. L., Petkus, A. J., White, K. S., Nguyen, H., Kornblith, S., Andreescu, . . . Lenze, E. J. (2013). Antidepressant medication augmented with cognitive-behavioral therapy for generalized anxiety disorder in older adults. *American Journal of Psychiatry, 170,* 782–789. (p. 561)

Whalen, P. J., Shin, L. M., McInerney, S. C., Fisher, H., Wright, C. I., & Rauch, S. L. (2001). A functional MRI study of human amygdala responses to facial expressions of fear versus anger. *Emotion, 1,* 70–83. (p. 374)

Whelan, R., Conrod, P. J., Poline, J.-B., Lourdusamy, A., Banaschewski, T., Barker, G. J., . . . Garavan, H. (2012). Adolescent impulsivity phenotypes characterized by distinct brain networks. *Nature Neuroscience, 15,* 920–925. (p. 142)

Whisman, M. A., Johnson, D. P., & Rhee, S. H. (2014). A behavior genetic analysis of pleasant events, depressive symptoms, and their covariation. *Clinical Psychological Science, 2,* 535–544. (p. 515)

Whitaker, K. J., Vértes, P. E., Romero-Garcia, R., Váša, F., Moutoussis, M., Prabhu, G., . . . Tait, R. (2016). Adolescence is associated with genomically patterned consolidation of the hubs of the human brain connectome. *PNAS, 113,* 9105–9110. (p. 142)

White, H. R., Brick, J., & Hansell, S. (1993). A longitudinal investigation of alcohol use and aggression in adolescence. *Journal of Studies on Alcohol, Supplement 11,* 62–77. (p. 442)

White, L., & Edwards, J. (1990). Emptying the nest and parental well-being: An analysis of national panel data. *American Sociological Review, 55,* 235–242. (p. 157)

White, R. A. (1998). Intuition, heart knowledge, and parapsychology. *Journal of the American Society for Psychical Research, 92,* 158–171. (p. 231)

White, R. E., Kross, E., & Duckworth, A. L. (2015). Spontaneous self-distancing and adaptive self-reflection across adolescence. *Child Development, 86,* 1272–1281. (p. 394)

Whitehurst, L. N., Cellini, N., McDevitt, E. A., Duggan, K. A., & Mednick, S. C. (2016). Autonomic activity during sleep predicts memory consolidation in humans. *PNAS, 113,* 7272–7277. (pp. 92, 277)

Whitelock, C. F., Lamb, M. E., & Rentfrow, P. J. (2013). Overcoming trauma: Psychological and demographic characteristics of child sexual abuse survivors in adulthood. *Clinical Psychological Science, 1,* 351–362. (p. 138)

Whiten, A., & Boesch, C. (2001, January). Cultures of chimpanzees. *Scientific American,* pp. 60–67. (p. 310)

Whiten, A., & Byrne, R. W. (1988). Tactical deception in primates. *Behavioral and Brain Sciences, 11,* 233–244. (p. 22)

Whiten, A., Spiteri, A., Horner, V., Bonnie, K. E., Lambeth, S. P., Schapiro, S. J., & de Waal, F. B. M. (2007). Transmission of multiple traditions within and between chimpanzee groups. *Current Biology, 17,* 1038–1043. (p. 259)

Whiting, B. B., & Edwards, C. P. (1988). *Children of different worlds: The formation of social behavior.* Cambridge, MA: Harvard University Press. (p. 139)

Whitley, B. E., Jr. (1999). Right-wing authoritarianism, social dominance orientation, and prejudice. *Journal of Personality and Social Psychology, 77,* 126–134. (p. 438)

Whitlock, J. R., Heynen, A. L., Shuler, M. G., & Bear, M. F. (2006). Learning induces long-term potentiation in the hippocampus. *Science, 313,* 1093–1097. (p. 278)

WHO. (2000). *Effectiveness of male latex condoms in protecting against pregnancy and sexually transmitted infections.* World Health Organization (who.int). (p. 175)

WHO. (2003). *The male latex condom: Specification and guidelines for condom procurement.* Department of Reproductive Health and Research, Family and Community Health, World Health Organization. Retrieved from who.int/iris/bitstream/10665/42873/1/9241591277.pdf (p. 175)

WHO. (2004a). *Prevention of mental disorders: Effective interventions and policy options. Summary report.* Geneva: World Health Organization, Department of Mental Health and Substance Abuse. (pp. 495, 504)

WHO. (2004b). *Promoting mental health: Concepts, emerging evidence, practice. Summary report.* Geneva: World Health Organization, Department of Mental Health and Substance Abuse. (p. 504)

WHO. (2008). *Mental health (nearly 1 million annual suicide deaths).* Geneva: World Health Organization. Retrieved from who.int/mental_health/en (p. 500)

WHO. (2011). Country reports and charts available. Geneva: World Health Organization. Retrieved from int/mental_health/prevention/suicide/country_reports/en/index.html (p. 500)

WHO. (2012). *WHO global estimates on prevalence of hearing loss: Mortality and burden of diseases and prevention of blindness and deafness.* World Health Organization (who.int/pbd/deafness/WHO_GE_HL.pdf). (p. 105)

WHO. (2013, November). *Sexually transmitted infections (STIs)* (Fact Sheet No. 110). World Health Organization. Retrieved from who.int/mediacentre/factsheets/fs110/en/ (p. 175)

WHO. (2014a, accessed September 20). Chain-free initiative. Geneva: World Health Organization. Retrieved from emro.who.int/mental-health/chain-free-initiative (p. 495)

WHO. (2014b). *Global status report on alcohol and health 2014.* World Health Organization (who.int/substance_abuse/publications/global_alcohol_report/msb_gsr_2014_1.pdf). (p. 102)

WHO. (2014c, October). *Mental disorders.* World Health Organization. Retrieved from who.int/mediacentre/factsheets/fs396/en/ (p. 500)

WHO. (2016a). Global status on road safety 2015. World Health Organization (who.int/violence_injury_prevention/road_safety_status/2015/en/). (p. B-13)

WHO. (2016b, November). *Violence against women. Intimate partner and sexual violence against women.* Fact Sheet. World Health Organization (who.int/mediacentre/factsheets/fs239/en/). (p. 437)

WHO. (2017b). *The determinants of health.* World Health Organization. Retrieved from http://www.who.int/hia/evidence/doh/en/ (p. 353)

WHO. (2017c). *Mental disorders.* World Health Organization. Retrieved from who.int/mediacentre/factsheets/fs396/en (pp. 493, 516, 524)

WHO. (2017a). *Depression.* World Health Organization. Retrieved from who.int/mediacentre/factsheets/fs369/en (p. 514)

Whooley, M. A., de Jonge, P., Vittinghoff, E., Otte, C., Noos, R., Carney, R. M., . . . Browner, W. S. (2008). Depressive symptoms, health behaviors, and risk of cardiovascular events in patients with coronary heart disease. *JAMA, 300,* 2379–2388. (p. 392)

Whorf, B. L. (1956). Science and linguistics. In J. B. Carroll (Ed.), *Language, thought, and reality: Selected writings of Benjamin Lee Whorf.* Cambridge, MA: MIT Press. (p. 319)

Wicherts, J. M., Dolan, C. V., Carlson, J. S., & van der Maas, H. L. J. (2010). Raven's test performance of sub-Saharan Africans: Mean level, psychometric properties, and the Flynn effect. *Learning and Individual Differences, 20,* 135–151. (p. 342)

Wickelgren, I. (2009, September/October). I do not feel your pain. *Scientific American Mind,* pp. 51–57. (pp. 222, 227)

Wickelgren, W. A. (1977). *Learning and memory.* Englewood Cliffs, NJ: Prentice-Hall. (p. 274)

Widiger, T. A., Gore, W. L., Crego, C., Rojas, S. L., & Oltmanns, J. R. (2016). Five-factor model and personality disorder. In T. A. Widiger (Ed.), *The Oxford handbook of the five factor model of personality.* New York: Oxford University Press. (p. 478)

Wiens, A. N., & Menustik, C. E. (1983). Treatment outcome and patient characteristics in an aversion therapy program for alcoholism. *American Psychologist, 38,* 1089–1096. (p. 542)

Wierson, M., & Forehand, R. (1994). Parent behavioral training for child noncompliance: Rationale, concepts, and effectiveness. *Current Directions in Psychological Science, 3,* 146–149. (p. 251)

Wierzbicki, M. (1993). Psychological adjustment of adoptees: A meta-analysis. *Journal of Clinical Child Psychology, 22,* 447–454. (p. 73)

Wiesel, T. N. (1982). Postnatal development of the visual cortex and the influence of environment. *Nature, 299,* 583–591. (pp. 124, 213)

Wiesner, W. H., & Cronshaw, S. P. (1988). A meta-analytic investigation of the impact of interview format and degree of structure on the validity of the employment interview. *Journal of Occupational Psychology, 61,* 275–290. (p. B-6)

Wigdor, A. K., & Garner, W. R. (1982). *Ability testing: Uses, consequences, and controversies.* Washington, DC: National Academy Press. (p. 343)

Wilcox, W. B., & DeRose, L. (2017, March 27). In Europe, cohabitation is stable . . . right? Brookings Institution (www.brookings.edu). (p. 136)

Wilcox, W. B., & Marquardt, E. (2011, December). *When baby makes three: How parenthood makes life meaningful and how marriage makes parenthood bearable.* Charlottesville, VA: National Marriage Project, University of Virginia. (p. 135)

Wilder, D. A. (1981). Perceiving persons as a group: Categorization and intergroup relations. In D. L. Hamilton (Ed.), *Cognitive processes in stereotyping and intergroup behavior.* Hillsdale, NJ: Erlbaum. (p. 438)

Wiley, J., & Jarosz, A. F. (2012). Working memory capacity, attentional focus, and problem solving. *Current Directions in Psychological Science, 21,* 258–262. (p. 271)

Wilford, J. N. (1999, February 9). New findings help balance the cosmological books. *The New York Times* (nytimes.com). (p. 77)

Wilkinson, R., & Pickett, K. (2009). The *spirit level: Why greater equality makes societies stronger.* London: Bloomsbury Press. (pp. 410, 443)

Wilkowski, B. M., Robinson, M. D., & Troop-Gordon, W. (2011). How does cognitive control reduce anger and aggression? The role of conflict monitoring and forgiveness processes. *Journal of Personality and Social Psychology, 98,* 830–840. (p. 442)

Willett, L. L., Halvorsen, A. J., McDonald, F. S., Chaudhry, S. I., & Arora, V. M. (2015). Gender differences in salary of internal medicine residency directors: A national survey. *The American Journal of Medicine, 128,* 659–665. (p. 164)

Williams, C. L., & Berry, J. W. (1991). Primary prevention of acculturative stress among refugees. *American Psychologist, 46,* 632–641. (p. 385)

Williams, E. F., Dunning, D., & Kruger, J. (2013). The hobgoblin of consistency: Algorithmic judgment strategies underlie inflated self-assessments of performance. *Journal of Personality and Social Psychology, 104,* 976–994. (p. 488)

Williams, J. E., & Best, D. L. (1990). *Measuring sex stereotypes: A multination study.* Newbury Park, CA: Sage. (pp. 163, 164)

Williams, K. D. (2007). Ostracism. *Annual Review of Psychology, 58,* 425–452. (pp. 354, 355)

Williams, K. D. (2009). Ostracism: A temporal need-threat model. *Advances in Experimental Social Psychology, 41,* 275–313. (p. 354)

Williams, K. D., & Sommer, K. L. (1997). Social ostracism by coworkers: Does rejection lead to loafing or compensation? *Personality and Social Psychology Bulletin, 23,* 693–706. (p. 424)

Williams, L. A., & Bartlett, M. Y. (2015). Warm thanks: Gratitude expression facilitates social affiliation in new relationships via perceived warmth. *Emotion, 15,* 1–5. (p. 352)

Williams, L. A., & DeSteno, D. (2009). Adaptive social emotion or seventh sin? *Psychological Science, 20,* 284–288. (p. 489)

Williams, L. E., & Bargh, J. A. (2008). Experiencing physical warmth promotes interpersonal warmth. *Science, 322,* 606–607. (p. 229)

Williams, N. M., Zaharieva, I., Martin, A., Langley, K., Mantripragada, K., Fossdal, R., . . . Thapar, A. (2010). Rare chromosomal deletions and duplications in attention-deficit hyperactivity disorder: A genome-wide analysis. *The Lancet, 376,* 1401–1408. (p. 498)

Williams, S. L. (1987, August). *Self-efficacy and mastery-oriented treatment for severe phobias.* Paper presented at the 95th Annual Convention of the American Psychological Association, New York, NY. (p. 541)

Williams, T. (2015, March 17). Missouri executes killer who had brain injury. *The New York Times* (nytimes.com). (p. 63)

Williams, W. W., & Ceci, S. J. (2015). National hiring experiments reveal 2:1 faculty preference for women on STEM tenure track. *PNAS, 112,* 5360–5365. (p. 168)

Willingham, D. T. (2010, Summer). Have technology and multitasking rewired how students learn? *American Educator, 34,* 23–28, 42. (pp. 271, 357)

Willis, J., & Todorov, A. (2006). First impressions: Making up your mind after a 100-ms. exposure to a face. *Psychological Science, 17,* 592–598. (pp. 371, 376)

Willmuth, M. E. (1987). Sexuality after spinal cord injury: A critical review. *Clinical Psychology Review, 7,* 389–412. (p. 177)

Willoughby, B. J., Carroll, J. S., & Busby, D. M. (2014). Differing relationship outcomes when sex happens before, on, or after first dates. *Journal of Sex Research, 51,* 52–61. (p. 26)

Willoughby, T., Heffer, T., & Hamza, C. A. (2015). The link between nonsuicidal self-injury and acquired capability for suicide: A longitudinal study. *Journal of Abnormal Psychology, 124,* 1110–1115. (p. 502)

Wilson, A. E., & Ross, M. (2001). From chump to champ: People's appraisals of their earlier and present selves. *Journal of Personality and Social Psychology, 80,* 572–584. (p. 489)

Wilson, B., Smith, K., & Petkov, C. I. (2015). Mixed-complexity artificial grammar learning in humans and macaque monkeys: Evaluating learning strategies. *European Journal of Neuroscience, 41,* 568–578. (p. 318)

Wilson, R. E., Gosling, S. D., & Graham, L. T. (2012). A review of Facebook research in the social sciences. *Perspectives on Psychological Science, 7,* 203–220. (p. 148)

Wilson, R. S. (1979). Analysis of longitudinal twin data: Basic model and applications to physical growth measures. *Acta Geneticae Medicae et Gemellologiae, 28,* 93–105. (p. 124)

Wilson, R. S., Arnold, S. E., Schneider, J. A., Tang, Y., & Bennett, D. A. (2007). The relationship between cerebral Alzheimer's disease pathology and odour identification in old age. *Journal of Neurology, Neurosurgery, and Psychiatry, 78,* 30–35. (p. 155)

Wilson, R. S., & Matheny, A. P., Jr. (1986). Behavior genetics research in infant temperament: The Louisville Twin Study. In R. Plomin & J. Dunn (Eds.), *The study of temperament: Changes, continuities, and challenges* (pp. 81–97). Hillsdale, NJ: Erlbaum. (p. 135)

Wilson, T. D. (2002). *Strangers to ourselves: Discovering the adaptive unconscious.* Cambridge, MA: Harvard University Press. (p. 81)

Wilson, T. D., Reinhard, D. A., Westgate, E. C., Gilbert, D. T., Ellerbeck, N., Hahn, C., . . . Shaked, A. (2014). Just think: The challenges of the disengaged mind. *Science, 345,* 75–77. (p. 349)

Wilson, W. A., & Kuhn, C. M. (2005, April). How addiction hijacks our reward system. *Cerebrum,* pp. 53–66. (p. 111)

Wimber, M., Alink, A., Charest, I., Kriegeskorte, N., & Anderson, M. C. (2015). Retrieval induces adaptive forgetting of competing memories via cortical pattern suppression. *Nature Neuroscience, 18,* 582–589. (p. 287)

Wimmer, R. D., Schmitt, L. I., Davidson, T. J., Nakajima, M., Deisseroth, K., & Halassa, M. M. (2015). Thalamic control of sensory selection in divided attention. *Nature, 526,* 705–709. (p. 54)

Windholz, G. (1989, April-June). The discovery of the principles of reinforcement, extinction, generalization, and differentiation of conditional reflexes in Pavlov's laboratories. *Pavlovian Journal of Biological Science, 26,* 64–74. (p. 239)

Windholz, G. (1997). Ivan P. Pavlov: An overview of his life and psychological work. *American Psychologist, 52,* 941–946. (p. 238)

Winer, E. S., & Salem, T. (2016). Reward devaluation: Dot-probe meta-analytic evidence of avoidance of positive information in depressed persons. *Psychological Bulletin, 142,* 18–78. (p. 516)

Winkler, A., Dörsing, B., Rief, W., Shen, Y., & Glombiewski, J. A. (2013). Treatment of internet addiction: A meta-analysis. *Clinical Psychology Review, 33,* 317–329. (p. 102)

Winner, E. (2000). The origins and ends of giftedness. *American Psychologist, 55,* 159–169. (p. 332)

Winsler, A., Deutsch, A., Vorona, R. D., Payne, P. A., & Szklo-Coxe, M. (2015). Sleepless in Fairfax: The difference one more hour of sleep can make for teen hopelessness, suicidal ideation, and substance use. *Journal of Youth and Adolescence, 44,* 362–378. (p. 93)

Winter, W. C., Hammond, W. R., Green, N. H., Zhang, Z., & Bilwise, D. L. (2009). Measuring circadian advantage in Major League Baseball: A 10-year retrospective study. *International Journal of Sports Physiology and Performance, 4,* 394–401. (p. 91)

Wirth, J. H., Sacco, D. F., Hugenberg, K., & Williams, K. D. (2010). Eye gaze as relational evaluation: Averted eye gaze leads to feelings of ostracism and relational devaluation. *Personality and Social Psychology Bulletin, 36,* 869–882. (p. 354)

Wiseman, R., & Greening, E. (2002). The Mind Machine: A mass participation experiment into the possible existence of extra-sensory perception. *British Journal of Psychology, 93,* 487–499. (p. 231)

Witt, J. K., & Brockmole, J. R. (2012). Action alters object identification: Wielding a gun increases the bias to see guns. *Journal of Experimental Psychology: Human Perception and Performance, 38,* 1159–1167. (p. 197)

Witt, J. K., Linkenauger, S. A., & Proffitt, D. R. (2012). Get me out of this slump! Visual illusions improve sports performance. *Psychological Science, 23,* 397–399. (p. 197)

Witt, J. K., & Proffitt, D. R. (2005). See the ball, hit the ball: Apparent ball size is correlated with batting average. *Psychological Science, 16,* 937–938. (p. 197)

Wittek, C. T., Finserås, T. R., Pallesen, S., Mentzoni, R. A., Hanss, D., Griffiths, M. D., & Molde, H. (2016). Prevalence and predictors of video game addiction: A study based on a national representative sample of gamers. *International Journal of Mental Health and Addiction, 14,* 672-686. (p. 102)

Witter, D. P., & Ward, H. E. (2016). Overview of the current use of deep brain stimulation in psychiatric disorders. *Psychiatric Annals, 46,* 631–636. (p. 564)

Witters, D. (2014, October 20). *U.S. adults with children at home have greater joy, stress.* Gallup (gallup.com/poll/178631/adults-childrenhome-greaterjoy-stress.aspx). (p. 157)

Witters, D., & Wood, J. (2015, January 14). *Heart attacks and depression closely linked.* Gallup (gallup.com). (p. 392)

Wittgenstein, L. (1922). *Tractatus logico-philosophicus* (C. K. Ogden, Trans.). New York: Harcourt, Brace. (p. 77)

Witvliet, C. V. O., & Vrana, S. R. (1995). Psychophysiological responses as indices of affective dimensions. *Psychophysiology, 32,* 436–443. (p. 374)

Wixted, J. T., & Ebbesen, E. B. (1991). On the form of forgetting. *Psychological Science, 2,* 409–415. (p. 286)

WKYT. (2017). Kentucky fans set crowd roar world record. Retrieved from wkyt.com/content/news/Kentucky-fans-set-crowd-roar-world-record-412059133.html (p. 217)

Wölfer, R., & Hewstone, M. (2015, August). Intra-versus intersex aggression. Testing theories of sex differences using aggression networks. *Psychological Science, 26,* 1285–1294. (p. 163)

Wolfinger, N. H. (2015). *Want to avoid divorce? Wait to get married, but not too long.* Institute for Family Studies (family-studies.org/want-to-avoid-divorce-wait-toget-married-but-not-too-long/). (p. 156)

Wolfson, A. R., & Carskadon, M. A. (1998). Sleep schedules and daytime functioning in adolescents. *Child Development, 69,* 875–887. (p. 98)

Wolke, D., Copeland, W. E., Angold, A., & Costello, E. J. (2013). Impact of bullying in childhood on adult health, wealth, crime, and social outcomes. *Psychological Science, 24,* 1958–1970. (p. 138)

Wolpe, J. (1958). *Psychotherapy by reciprocal inhibition.* Stanford, CA: Stanford University Press. (p. 541)

Wolpe, J., & Plaud, J. J. (1997). Pavlov's contributions to behavior therapy: The obvious and the not so obvious. *American Psychologist, 52,* 966–972. (p. 541)

Wonderlich, S. A., Joiner, T. E., Jr., Keel, P. K., Williamson, D. A., & Crosby, R. D. (2007). Eating disorder diagnoses: Empirical approaches to classification. *American Psychologist, 62,* 167–180. (p. 532)

Wondra, J. D., & Ellsworth, P. C. (2015). An appraisal theory of empathy and other vicarious emotional experiences. *Psychological Review, 122,* 411–428. (p. 378)

Wong, D. F., Wagner, H. N., Tune, L. E., Dannals, R. F., Pearlson, G. D., Links, J. M., . . . Gjedde, A. (1986). Positron emission tomography reveals elevated D_2 dopamine receptors in drug-naive schizophrenics. *Science, 234,* 1588–1593. (p. 524)

Wong, M. M., & Csikszentmihalyi, M. (1991). Affiliation motivation and daily experience: Some issues on gender differences. *Journal of Personality and Social Psychology, 60,* 154–164. (p. 164)

Wood, D., Bruner, J., & Ross, G. (1976). The role of tutoring in problem solving. *Journal of Child Psychology and Child Psychiatry, 17,* 89–100. (p. 189)

Wood, E., Ricketts, T., & Perry, G. (2018). EMDR as a treatment for long-term depression: A feasibility study. *Psychology and Psychotherapy,* in press. (p. 554)

Wood, J. M. (2003, May 19). Quoted in R. Mestel, Rorschach tested: Blot out the famous method? Some experts say it has no place in psychiatry. *The Los Angeles Times.* Retrieved from articles.latimes.com/2003/may/19/health/he-rorschach19 (p. 468)

Wood, J. M., Bootzin, R. R., Kihlstrom, J. F., & Schacter, D. L. (1992). Implicit and explicit memory for verbal information presented during sleep. *Psychological Science, 3,* 236–239. (p. 288)

Wood, J. M., Garb, H. N., Nezworski, M. T., Lilienfeld, S. O., & Duke, M. C. (2015). A second look at the validity of widely used Rorschach indices: Comment on Mihura, Meyer, Dumitrascu, and Bombel (2013). *Psychological Bulletin, 141,* 236–249. (p. 468)

Wood, J. M., Nezworski, M. T., Garb, H. N., & Lilienfeld, S. O. (2006). The controversy over the Exner Comprehensive System and the Society for Personality Assessment's white paper on the Rorschach. *Independent Practitioner, 26.* (p. 468)

Wood, J. V., Saltzberg, J. A., & Goldsamt, L. A. (1990a). Does affect induce self-focused attention? *Journal of Personality and Social Psychology, 58,* 899–908. (p. 520)

Wood, J. V., Saltzberg, J. A., Neale, J. M., Stone, A. A., & Rachmiel, T. B. (1990b). Self-focused attention, coping responses, and distressed mood in everyday life. *Journal of Personality and Social Psychology, 58,* 1027–1036. (p. 520)

Wood, W. (1987). Meta-analytic review of sex differences in group performance. *Psychological Bulletin, 102,* 53–71. (p. 164)

Wood, W., & Eagly, A. H. (2002). A cross-cultural analysis of the behavior of women and men: Implications for the origins of sex differences. *Psychological Bulletin, 128,* 699–727. (p. 163)

Wood, W., & Eagly, A. H. (2007). Social structural origins of sex differences in human mating. In S. W. Gagestad & J. A. Simpson (Eds.), *The evolution of mind: Fundamental questions and controversies* (pp. 383–390). New York: Guilford Press. (p. 163)

Wood, W., Kressel, L., Joshi, P. D., & Louie, B. (2014a). Meta-analysis of menstrual cycle effects on women's mate preferences. *Emotion Review, 6,* 229–249. (p. 173)

Wood, W., Labrecque, J. S., Lin, P.-T., & Rúnger, D. (2014b). Habits in dual process models. In J. Sherman, B. Gawronski, & Y. Trope (Eds.), *Dual process theories of the social mind.* New York: Guilford Press. (p. 234)

Wood, W., Lundgren, S., Ouellette, J. A., Busceme, S., & Blackstone, T. (1994). Minority influence: A meta-analytic review of social influence processes. *Psychological Bulletin, 115,* 323–345. (p. 428)

Woolcock, N. (2004, September 3). Driver thought everyone else was on wrong side. *The Times,* p. 22. (p. 425)

Woolett, K., & Maguire, E. A. (2011). Acquiring "the knowledge" of London's layout drives structural brain changes. *Current Biology, 21,* 2109–2114. (p. 276)

Woolley, A. W., Chabris, C. F., Pentland, A., Hasmi, N., & Malone, T. W. (2010). Evidence for a collective intelligence factor in the performance of human groups. *Science, 330,* 686–688. (p. B-10)

Woolley, K., & Fishbach, A. (2017). Immediate rewards predict adherence to long-term goals. *Personality and Social Psychology Bulletin, 43,* 151–162. (pp. 252, 359)

World Federation for Mental Health. (2005). ADHD: The hope behind the hype. World Federation for Mental Health (wfmh.org). (p. 498)

Worldwatch Institute (2017). Meat production continues to rise. Retrieved July 24, 2017, from worldwatch.org/node/5443 (p. 31)

Worobey, J., & Blajda, V. M. (1989). Temperament ratings at 2 weeks, 2 months, and 1 year: Differential stability of activity and emotionality. *Developmental Psychology, 25,* 257–263. (p. 135)

Wortman, C. B., & Silver, R. C. (1989). The myths of coping with loss. *Journal of Consulting and Clinical Psychology, 57,* 349–357. (p. 159)

Wren, C. S. (1999, April 8). Drug survey of children finds middle school a pivotal time. *The New York Times* (nytimes.com). (p. 112)

Wright, J. (2006, March 16). *Boomers in the bedroom: Sexual attitudes and behaviours in the boomer generation.* Retrieved from ipsos-na.com/news-polls/pressrelease.aspx?id=3011 (p. 151)

Wright, P., Takei, N., Rifkin, L., & Murray, R. M. (1995). Maternal influenza, obstetric complications, and schizophrenia. *American Journal of Psychiatry, 152,* 1714–1720. (p. 525)

Wright, P. H. (1989). Gender differences in adults' same- and cross-gender friendships. In R. G. Adams & R. Blieszner (Eds.), *Older adult friendships: Structure and process.* Newbury Park, CA: Sage. (p. 163)

Wrzesniewski, A., & Dutton, J. E. (2001). Crafting a job: Revisioning employees as active crafters of their work. *Academy of Management Review.* (p. B-1)

Wrzesniewski, A., Schwartz, B., Cong, X., Kane, M., Omar, A., & Kolditz, T. (2014). Multiple types of motives don't multiply the motivation of West Point cadets. *PNAS, 111,* 10990–10995. (p. 358)

Wu, H. Y., Kung, F. Y., Chen, H. C., & Kim, Y. H. (2016). Academic success of "Tiger Cubs": Self-control (not IQ) predicts academic growth and explains girls' edge in Taiwan. *Social Psychological and Personality Science.* Advanced online publication. doi:10.1177/1948550616675667 (p. 398)

Wu, S., Wu, F., Ding, Y., Hou, J., Bi, J., & Zhang, Z. (2017). Advanced parental age and autism risk in children: A systematic review and meta-analysis. *Acta Psychiatrica Scandinavica, 135,* 29–41. (p. 131)

Wu, X., Zhang, Z., Zhao, F., Wang, W., Li, Y., Bi, L., . . . Sun, Y. (2016). Prevalence of internet addiction and its association with social support and other related factors among adolescents in china. *Journal of Adolescence, 52,* 103–111. (p. 102)

Wucherpfennig, F., Rubel, J. A., Hofmann, S. G., & Lutz, W. (2017). Processes of change after a sudden gain and relation to treatment outcome—Evidence for an upward spiral. *Journal of Consulting and Clinical Psychology, 85,* 1199–1210. (p. 552)

Wulsin, L. R., Vaillant, G. E., & Wells, V. E. (1999). A systematic review of the mortality of depression. *Psychosomatic Medicine, 61,* 6–17. (p. 392)

Wyatt, J. K., & Bootzin, R. R. (1994). Cognitive processing and sleep: Implications for enhancing job performance. *Human Performance, 7,* 119–139. (pp. 97, 288)

Wynn, K. (1992). Addition and subtraction by human infants. *Nature, 358,* 749–759. (p. 127)

Wynn, K. (2000). Findings of addition and subtraction in infants are robust and consistent: Reply to Wakeley, Rivera, and Langer. *Child Development, 71,* 1535–1536. (p. 127)

Wynn, K. (2008). Some innate foundations of social and moral cognition. In K. Wynn (Ed.), *The innate mind: Vol. 3. Foundations and the future* (pp. 330–347). New York: Oxford University Press.

Wynne, C. D. L. (2004). *Do animals think?* Princeton, NJ: Princeton University Press. (p. 318)

Wynne, C. D. L. (2008). Aping language: A skeptical analysis of the evidence for nonhuman primate language. *Skeptic, 13,* 10–13. (pp. 127, 318)

Wysocki, C. J., & Gilbert, A. N. (1989). National Geographic Smell Survey: Effects of age are heterogeneous. *Annals of the New York Academy of Sciences, 561,* 12–28. (p. 227)

Xie, L., Kang, H., Xu, Q., Chen, M. J., Liao, Y., Thiyagarajan, M., . . . Nedergaard, M. (2013). Sleep drives metabolite clearance from the adult brain. *Science, 342,* 373–377. (p. 91)

Xu, J., Murphy, S. L., Kochanek, K. D., & Bastian B. A. (2016, February 16). Deaths: Final data for 2013. *National Vital Statistics Report, 64*(2). Centers for Disease Control and Prevention (cdc.gov). (p. 302)

Xu, J., & Potenza, M. N. (2012). White matter integrity and five-factor personality measures in healthy adults. *NeuroImage, 59,* 800–807. (p. 478)

Xu, Y., & Corkin, S. (2001). H.M. revisits the Tower of Hanoi puzzle. *Neuropsychology, 15,* 69–79. (p. 285)

Yamaguchi, M., Masuchi, A., Nakanishi, D., Suga, S., Konishi, N., Yu, Y. Y., & Ohtsubo, Y. (2015). Experiential purchases and prosocial spending promote happiness by enhancing social relationships. *The Journal of Positive Psychology,* 1–9. (p. 407)

Yang, G., Lai, G. S. W., Cichon, J., Ma, L., Li, W., & Gan, W.-B. (2014). Sleep promotes branch-specific formation of dendritic spines after learning. *Science, 344,* 1173–1178. (p. 91)

Yang, J., & Hofmann, J. (2015). Action observation and imitation in autism spectrum disorders: an ALE meta-analysis of fMRI studies. *Brain Imaging and Behavior,* 1–10. (p. 132)

Yang, Y., Cao, S., Shields, G. S., Teng, Z., & Liu, Y. (2017). The relationships between rumination and core executive functions: A meta-analysis. *Depression and Anxiety, 34,* 37–50. (p. 520)

Yang, Y., & Raine, A. (2009). Prefrontal structural and functional brain imaging findings in antisocial, violent, and psychopathic individuals: A meta-analysis. *Psychiatry Research: Neuroimaging, 174,* 81–88. (p. 63)

Yang, Y. C., Boen, C., Gerken, K., Li, T., Schorpp, K., & Harris, K. M. (2016). Social relationships and physiological determinants of longevity across the human life span. *PNAS, 113,* 578–583. (p. 353)

Yankelovich Partners. (1995, May/June). Growing old. *American Enterprise,* p. 108. (p. 151)

Yarnell, P. R., & Lynch, S. (1970, April 25). Retrograde memory immediately after concussion. *The Lancet,* pp. 863–865. (p. 279)

Yates, A. (1989). Current perspectives on the eating disorders: I. History, psychological and biological aspects. *Journal of the American Academy of Child and Adolescent Psychiatry, 28,* 813–828. (p. 532)

Yates, A. (1990). Current perspectives on the eating disorders: II. Treatment, outcome, and research directions. *Journal of the American Academy of Child and Adolescent Psychiatry, 29,* 1–9. (p. 532)

Ybarra, O. (1999). Misanthropic person memory when the need to self-enhance is absent. *Personality and Social Psychology Bulletin, 25,* 261–269. (p. 487)

Yeager, D. S., Johnson, R., Spitzer, B. J., Trzesniewski, K. H., Powers, J., & Dweck, C. S. (2014). The far-reaching effects of believing people can change: Implicit theories of personality shape stress, health, and achievement during adolescence. *Journal of Personality and Social Psychology, 106,* 867–884. (p. 339)

Yeager, D. S., Lee, H. Y., & Jamieson, J. P. (2016a). How to improve adolescent stress responses: Insights from integrating implicit theories of personality and biopsychosocial models. *Psychological Science, 27,* 1078–1091. (p. 339)

Yeager, D. S., Miu, A. S., Powers, J., & Dweck, C. S. (2013). Implicit theories of personality and attributions of hostile intent: A meta-analysis, an experiment, and a longitudinal intervention. *Child Development, 84,* 1651–1667. (p. 339)

Yeager, D. S., Walton, G. M., Brady, S. T., Akcinar, E. N., Paunesku, D., Keane, L., . . . Gomez, E. M. (2016b). Teaching a lay theory before college narrows achievement gaps at scale. *PNAS, 113,* E3341–E3348. (p. 344)

Yehuda, R., Daskalakis, N. P., Bierer, L. M., Bader, H. N., Klengel, T., Holsboer, F., & Binder, E. B. (2016). Holocaust exposure induced intergenerational effects on FKBP5 methylation. *Biological Psychiatry, 80,* 372–380. (p. 74)

Yerkes, R. M., & Dodson, J. D. (1908). The relation of strength of stimulus to rapidity of habit-formation. *Journal of Comparative Neurology and Psychology, 18,* 459–482. (p. 350)

Yiend, J., Parnes, C., Shepherd, K., Roche, M.-K., & Cooper, M. J. (2014). Negative self-beliefs in eating disorders: A cognitive-bias-modification study. *Clinical Psychological Science, 2,* 756–766. (p. 532)

YOU. (2009, September 10). Wow, look at Caster now! *YOU* (you.co.za/). (p. 168)

You, J., Lin, M., & Leung, F. (2015). A longitudinal moderated mediation model of nonsuicidal self-injury among adolescents. *Journal of Abnormal Child Psychology, 43,* 381–390. (p. 502)

Young, C., & Lim, C. (2014). Time as a network good: Evidence from unemployment and the standard workweek. *Sociological Science, 1,* 10–27. (p. 408)

Young, S. G., Hugenberg, K., Bernstein, M. J., & Sacco, D. F. (2012). Perception and motivation in face recognition: A critical review of theories of the cross-race effect. *Personality and Social Psychology Review, 16,* 116–142. (p. 440)

Young, S. M., & Pinsky, D. (2006). Narcissism and celebrity. *Journal of Personality, 40,* 463–471. (p. 489)

Youngentob, S. L., & Glendinning, J. I. (2009). Fetal ethanol exposure increases ethanol intake by making it smell and taste better. *PNAS, 106,* 5359. (p. 120)

Youngentob, S. L., Kent, P. F., Scheehe, P. R., Molina, J. C., Spear, N. E., & Youngentob, L. M. (2007). Experience-induced fetal plasticity: The effect of gestational ethanol exposure on the behavioral and neurophysiologic olfactory response to ethanol odor in early postnatal and adult rats. *Behavioral Neuroscience, 121,* 1293–1305. (p. 120)

Younger, J., Aron, A., Parke, S., Chatterjee, N., & Mackey, S. (2010) Viewing pictures of a romantic partner reduces experimental pain: Involvement of neural reward systems. *PLoS ONE, 5,* e13309. (p. 353)

Yount, K. M., James-Hawkins, L., Cheong, Y. F., & Naved, R. T. (2017). Men's perpetration of partner violence in Bangladesh: Community gender norms and violence in childhood. *Psychology of Men & Masculinity.* Advance online publication. http://dx.doi.org/10.1037/men0000069 (p. 163)

Youyou, W., Kosinski, M., & Stillwell, D. (2015). Computer-based personality judgments are more accurate than those made by humans. *PNAS, 112,* 1036–1040. (p. 479)

Yuen, R. K., Merico, D., Cao, H., Pellecchia, G., Alipanahi, B., Thiruvahindrapuram, B., . . . Wu, X. (2016). Genome-wide characteristics of de novo mutations in autism. *NPJ Genomic Medicine, 1.* (p. 131)

Yuki, M., Maddux, W. W., & Masuda. T. (2007). Are the windows to the soul the same in the East and West? Cultural differences in using the eyes and mouth as cues to recognize emotions in Japan and the United States. *Journal of Experimental Social Psychology, 43,* 303–311. (p. 379)

Yuval, K., Zvielli, A., & Bernstein, A. (2017). Attentional bias dynamics and posttraumatic stress in survivors of violent conflict and atrocities: New directions in clinical psychological science of refugee mental health. *Clinical Psychological Science, 5,* 64–73. (p. 509)

Zagorsky, J. L. (2007). Do you have to be smart to be rich? The impact of IQ on wealth, income and financial distress. *Intelligence, 35,* 489–501. (p. 326)

Zahrt, O. H., & Crum, A. J. (2017). Perceived physical activity and mortality: Evidence from three nationally representative U.S. samples. *Health Psychology, 36,* 1017–1025. (p. 401)

Zainulbhai, H. (2016, March 8). Strong global support for gender equality, especially among women. Pew Research Center (pewresearch.org). (p. 437)

Zajonc, R. B. (1965). Social facilitation. *Science, 149,* 269–274. (p. 429)

Zajonc, R. B. (1980). Feeling and thinking: Preferences need no inferences. *American Psychologist, 35,* 151–175. (p. 370)

Zajonc, R. B. (1984a). On the primacy of affect. *American Psychologist, 39,* 117–123. (p. 370)

Zajonc, R. B. (1984b, July 22). Quoted by D. Goleman, Rethinking IQ tests and their value. *The New York Times,* p. D22. (p. 328)

Zajonc, R. B. (2001). Mere exposure: A gateway to the subliminal. *Current Directions in Psychological Science, 10,* 224–228. (p. 447)

Zajonc, R. B., & Markus, G. B. (1975). Birth order and intellectual development. *Psychological Review, 82,* 74–88. (p. A-8)

Zakaria, F. (2017). How big data can reveal your political views. CNN interview with researcher Michal Kosinski. Retrieved from cnn.com/videos/tv/2017/03/05/exp-gps-michal-kosinski-big-data-election-trump.cnn (p. 479)

Zanarini, M. C., Williams, A. A., Lewis, R. E., Reich, R. B., Vera, S. C., Marino, M. F., . . . Frankenburg, R. F. (1997). Reported pathological childhood experiences associated with the development of borderline personality disorder. *American Journal of Psychiatry, 154,* 1101–1106. (p. 170)

Zannas, A. S., Provençal, N., & Binder, E. B. (2015). Epigenetics of posttraumatic stress disorder: current evidence, challenges, and future directions. *Biological Psychiatry, 78,* 327–335. (p. 512)

Zaslavsky, O., Palgi, Y., Rillamas-Sun, E., LaCroix, A. Z., Schnall, E., Woods, N. F., . . . Shrira, A. (2015). Dispositional optimism and terminal decline in global quality of life. *Developmental Psychology, 51,* 856–863. (p. 399)

Zauberman, G., & Lynch, J. G., Jr. (2005). Resource slack and propensity to discount delayed investments of time versus money. *Journal of Experimental Psychology: General, 134,* 23–37. (p. 303)

Zaval, L., Keenan, E. A., Johnson, E. J., & Weber, E. U. (2014). How warm days increase belief in global warming. *Nature Climate Change, 4,* 143–147. (p. 303)

Zeelenberg, R., Wagenmakers, E.-J., & Rotteveel, M. (2006). The impact of emotion on perception. *Psychological Science, 17,* 287–291. (p. 370)

Zeidner, M. (1990). Perceptions of ethnic group modal intelligence: Reflections of cultural stereotypes or intelligence test scores? *Journal of Cross-Cultural Psychology, 21,* 214–231. (p. 342)

Zeineh, M. M., Engel, S. A., Thompson, P. M., & Bookheimer, S. Y. (2003). Dynamics of the hippocampus during encoding and retrieval of face-name pairs. *Science, 299,* 577–580. (p. 276)

Zelenski, J. M., & Nisbet, E. K. (2014). Happiness and feeling connected: The distinct role of nature relatedness. *Environmental Behavior, 46,* 3–23. (p. 357)

Zell, E., & Alicke, M. D. (2010). The local dominance effect in self-evaluation: Evidence and explanations. *Personality and Social Psychology Review, 14,* 368–384. (p. 410)

Zell, E., Krizan, Z., & Teeter, S. R. (2015). Evaluating gender similarities and differences using metasynthesis. *American Psychologist, 70,* 10–20. (p. 162)

Zentner, M., & Eagly, A. H. (2015). A sociocultural framework for understanding partner preferences of women and men: Integration of concepts and evidence. *European Journal of Social Psychology, 26,* 328–373. (p. 168)

Zhang, J., Fang, L., Yow-Wu, B. W., & Wieczorek, W. F. (2013). Depression, anxiety, and suicidal ideation among Chinese Americans: A study of immigration-related factors. *The Journal of Nervous and Mental Disease, 201,* 17–22. (p. 517)

Zhang, W., Jiao, B., Zhou, M., Zhou, T., & Shen, L. (2016). Modeling Alzheimer's disease with induced pluripotent stem cells: Current challenges and future concerns. *Stem Cells International, 2016,* 7828049. (p. 64)

Zhong, C.-B., Dijksterhuis, A., & Galinsky, A. D. (2008). The merits of unconscious thought in creativity. *Psychological Science, 19,* 912–918. (p. 307)

Zhu, W. X., Lu, L., & Hesketh, T. (2009). China's excess males, sex selective abortion, and one child policy: Analysis of data from 2005 national intercensus survey. *British Medical Journal (BMJ), 338,* b1211. (p. 437)

Zhuo, C., Tao, R., Jiang, R., Lin, X., & Shao, M. (2017). Cancer mortality in patients with schizophrenia: Systematic review and meta-analysis. *The British Journal of Psychiatry, 211,* 7–13. (p. 524)

Zilbergeld, B. (1983). *The shrinking of America: Myths of psychological change.* Boston: Little, Brown. (p. 551)

Zill, N., & Wilcox, W. B. (2017, June 8). What happens at home doesn't stay there: It goes to school. Institute for Family Studies (ifstudies.org). (p. 136)

Zillmann, D. (1989). Effects of prolonged consumption of pornography. In D. Zillmann & J. Bryant (Eds.), *Pornography: Research advances and policy considerations* (pp. 127–157). Hillsdale, NJ: Erlbaum. (p. 176)

Zillmann, D., & Bryant, J. (1984). Effects of massive exposure to pornography. In N. Malamuth & E. Donnerstein (Eds.), *Pornography and sexual aggression.* Orlando, FL: Academic Press. (p. 444)

Zimbardo, P., Wilson, G., & Coulombe, N. (2016). How porn is messing with your manhood. *Skeptic.* Retrieved from skeptic.com/reading_room/how-porn-is-messing-with-your-manhood (p. 176)

Zimbardo, P. G. (1970). The human choice: Individuation, reason, and order versus deindividuation, impulse, and chaos. In W. J. Arnold & D. Levine (Eds.), *Nebraska Symposium on Motivation, 1969.* Lincoln, NE: University of Nebraska Press. (p. 430)

Zimbardo, P. G. (1972, April). Pathology of imprisonment. *Transaction/Society,* pp. 4–8. (p. 419)

Zimbardo, P. G. (2001, September 16). *Fighting terrorism by understanding man's capacity for evil.* Op-ed essay distributed by spsp-discuss@stolaf.edu. (p. 439)

Zimbardo, P. G. (2004, May 25). Journalist interview re: Abu Ghraib prison abuses: Eleven answers to eleven questions. Unpublished manuscript, Stanford University.

Zimbardo, P. G. (2007, September). Person x situation x system dynamics. *The Observer* (Association for Psychological Science), p. 43. (p. 419)

Zinzow, H. M., Amstadter, A. B., McCauley, J. L., Ruggiero, K. J., Resnick, H. S., & Kilpatrick, D. G. (2011). Self-rated health in relation to rape and mental health disorders in a national sample of college women. *Journal of American College Health, 59,* 588–594. (p. 170)

Zogby, J. (2006, March). *Survey of teens and adults about the use of personal electronic devices and head phones.* Utica, NY: Zogby International. (p. 218)

Zoma, M., & Gielen, U. P. (2015). How many psychologists are there in the world? *International Psychology Bulletin, 19,* 47–50. (p. 8)

Zou, L. Q., van Hartevelt, T. J., Kringelbach, M. L., Cheung, E. F., & Chan, R. C. (2016). The neural mechanism of hedonic processing and judgment of pleasant odors: An activation likelihood estimation meta-analysis. *Neuropsychology, 30,* 970–979. (p. 226)

Zubieta, J.-K., Bueller, J. A., Jackson, L. R., Scott, D. J., Xu, Y., Koeppe, R. A., . . . Stohler, C. S. (2005). Placebo effects mediated by endogenous opioid activity on μ-opioid receptors. *Journal of Neuroscience, 25,* 7754–7762. (p. 223)

Zubieta, J.-K., Heitzeg, M. M., Smith, Y. R., Bueller, J. A., Xu, K., Xu, Y., . . . Goldman, D. (2003). COMT val158met genotype affects μ-opioid neurotransmitter responses to a pain stressor. *Science, 299,* 1240–1243. (p. 223)

Zucco, G. M. (2003). Anomalies in cognition: Olfactory memory. *European Psychologist, 8,* 77–86. (p. 227)

Zucker, G. S., & Weiner, B. (1993). Conservatism and perceptions of poverty: An attributional analysis. *Journal of Applied Social Psychology, 23,* 925–943. (p. 417)

Zuckerberg, M. (2012, February 1). Letter to potential investors. Quoted by S. Sengupta & C. C. Miller, "Social mission" vision meets Wall Street. *The New York Times* (nytimes.com). (p. 352)

Zuckerman, M. (1979). *Sensation seeking: Beyond the optimal level of arousal.* Hillsdale, NJ: Erlbaum. (p. 349)

Zuckerman, M. (1999). *Vulnerability to psychopathology: A biosocial model.* Washington, DC: American Psychological Association. (p. 496)

Zuckerman, M. (2009). Sensation seeking. In M. Zuckerman (Ed.), *Handbook of individual differences in social behavior.* New York: Guilford Press. (p. 349)

Zuckerman, M., Li, C., & Hall, J. A. (2016). When men and women differ in self-esteem and when they don't: A meta-analysis. *Journal of Research in Personality, 64,* 34–51. (p. 147)

Zunick, P. V., Fazio, R. H., & Vasey, M. W. (2015). Directed abstraction: Encouraging broad, personal generalizations following a success experience. *Journal of Personality and Social Psychology, 109,* 1–19. (p. 545)

Zuzanek, J. (2013). Does being well-off make us happier? Problems of measurement. *Journal of Happiness Studies, 14,* 795–815. (p. 410)

Zvolensky, M. J., & Bernstein, A. (2005). Cigarette smoking and panic psychopathology. *Current Directions in Psychological Science, 14,* 301–305. (p. 507)

Zvolensky, M. J., Bakhshaie, J., Sheffer, C., Perez, A., & Goodwin, R. D. (2015). Major depressive disorder and smoking relapse among adults in the United States: A 10-year, prospective investigation. *Psychiatry Research, 226,* 73–77. (p. 105)

Name Index

Subject Index

The Story of Psychology: A Timeline *(continued from front of book)*

1949 — In *The Organization of Behavior: A Neuropsychological Theory*, Canadian psychologist Donald O. Hebb outlines a new and influential conceptualization of how the nervous system functions.

1950 — Solomon Asch publishes studies of effects of conformity on judgments of line length.

— In *Childhood and Society*, Erik Erikson outlines his stages of psychosocial development.

1951 — Carl Rogers publishes *Client-Centered Therapy*.

1952 — The American Psychiatric Association publishes the *Diagnostic and Statistical Manual of Mental Disorders*, an influential book that will be updated periodically.

1953 — Eugene Aserinski and Nathaniel Kleitman describe rapid eye movements (REM) that occur during sleep.

— Janet Taylor's Manifest Anxiety Scale appears in the *Journal of Abnormal Psychology*.

1954 — In *Motivation and Personality*, Abraham Maslow proposes a hierarchy of motives ranging from physiological needs to self-actualization. (Maslow later updates the hierarchy to include self-transcendence needs.)

— James Olds and Peter Milner, McGill University neuropsychologists, describe the rewarding effects of electrical stimulation of the hypothalamus in rats.

— Gordon Allport publishes *The Nature of Prejudice*.

1956 — In his *Psychological Review* article titled "The Magical Number Seven, Plus or Minus Two: Some Limits on Our Capacity for Processing Information," George Miller coins the term *chunk* for memory researchers.

1957 — Robert Sears, Eleanor Maccoby, and Harry Levin publish *Patterns of Child Rearing*.

— Charles Ferster and B. F. Skinner publish *Schedules of Reinforcement*.

1958 — Harry Harlow outlines "The Nature of Love," his work on attachment in monkeys.

1959 — Noam Chomsky's critical review of B. F. Skinner's *Verbal Behavior* appears in the journal *Language*.

— Eleanor Gibson and Richard Walk report their research on infants' depth perception in "The Visual Cliff."

— Lloyd Peterson and Margaret Peterson in the *Journal of Experimental Psychology* article, "Short-Term Retention of Individual Verbal Items," highlight the importance of rehearsal in memory.

— John Thibaut and Harold Kelley publish *The Social Psychology of Groups*.

1960 — George Sperling publishes "The Information Available in Brief Visual Presentations."

1961 — Georg von Békésy receives a Nobel Prize for research on the physiology of hearing.

— David McClelland publishes *The Achieving Society*.

1962 — Jerome Kagan and Howard Moss publish *Birth to Maturity*.

— Stanley Schachter and Jerome Singer publish findings that support the two-factor theory of emotion.

— Albert Ellis' *Reason and Emotion in Psychotherapy* appears; it is a milestone in the development of rational-emotive therapy (RET).

1963 — Raymond B. Cattell distinguishes between *fluid* and *crystallized* intelligence.

— Stanley Milgram's "Behavioral Study of Obedience" appears in the *Journal of Abnormal and Social Psychology*.

1965 — Canadian researcher Ronald Melzack and British researcher Patrick Wall propose the gate-control theory of pain.

— Robert Zajonc's "Social Facilitation" is published in *Science*.

— The Archives of the History of American Psychology is founded at the University of Akron.

1966 — Nancy Bayley becomes the first woman to receive the APA's Distinguished Scientific Contribution Award.

— Jerome Bruner and colleagues at Harvard University's Center for Cognitive Studies publish *Studies in Cognitive Growth*.

— William Masters and Virginia Johnson publish results of their research in *Human Sexual Responses*.

— Allen Gardner and Beatrix Gardner begin training a chimpanzee (Washoe) in American Sign Language at the University of Nevada, Reno. Washoe dies in 2007.

— John Garcia and Robert Koelling publish a study on taste aversion in rats.

— David M. Green and John A. Swets publish *Signal Detection Theory and Psychophysics*.

— Julian Rotter publishes research on locus of control.

1967 — Ulric Neisser's *Cognitive Psychology* helps to steer psychology away from behaviorism and toward cognitive processes.

— Martin Seligman and Steven Maier publish the results of their research with "learned helplessness" in dogs.

1968 — Richard Atkinson and Richard Shiffrin's influential three-stage memory model appears in *The Psychology of Learning and Motivation*.

— Neal E. Miller's article in *Science*, describing instrumental conditioning of autonomic responses, stimulates research on biofeedback.

1969 — Albert Bandura publishes *Principles of Behavior Modification*.

— In his APA presidential address, "Psychology as a Means of Promoting Human Welfare," George Miller emphasizes the importance of "giving psychology away."

1971 — Kenneth B. Clark becomes the first African-American president of the American Psychological Association.

— Albert Bandura publishes *Social Learning Theory*.

— Allan Paivio publishes *Imagery and Verbal Processes*.

— B. F. Skinner publishes *Beyond Freedom and Dignity*.